Winter 2019 Volume 28, Number 1

Federal Regional
YELLOW BOOK

who's who in
the federal government's
departments, agencies,
diplomatic missions,
military installations and
service academies outside
of Washington, DC

LEADERSHIP DIRECTORIES, INC.

www.leadershipconnect.io
info@leadershipconnect.io

New York Office
1407 Broadway Suite 318
New York, NY 10018
(212) 627-4140
Fax (212) 645-0931

Washington, DC Office
1667 K Street, NW, Suite 801
Washington, DC 20006
(202) 347-7757
Fax (202) 628-3430

Congressional
YELLOW BOOK
who's who in congress,
including committees and key staff

Federal
YELLOW BOOK
who's who in federal departments and agencies

State
YELLOW BOOK
who's who in the executive and legislative branches
of the 50 state governments

Municipal
YELLOW BOOK
who's who in the leading city and county governments
and local authorities

Federal Regional
YELLOW BOOK
who's who in the federal government's departments,
agencies, diplomatic missions, military installations
and service academies outside of Washington, DC

Judicial
YELLOW BOOK
who's who in federal and state courts

Corporate
YELLOW BOOK
who's who at the leading U.S. companies

News Media
YELLOW BOOK
who's who among reporters, writers, editors
and producers in the leading national news media

Associations
YELLOW BOOK
who's who at the leading U.S.
trade and professional associations

Law Firms
YELLOW BOOK
who's who in the management
of the leading U.S. law firms

Government Affairs
YELLOW BOOK
who's who in government affairs

The Leadership Library®
who's who in the leadership of the United States

Leadership Directories, Inc.
FEDERAL REGIONAL YELLOW BOOK

Winter 2019, Volume 28, Number 1

Frank Poppe, *Team Leader and Content Manager*
Daniel Hafner, *Content Manager*
Zayn Hasan, Assistant *Content Manager*
Justin Jon, Assistant *Content Manager*
Sydney King, *Content Manager*
John Lee, Assistant *Content Manager*
Andrew Ramos-Flynn, *Content Manager*
NickTschida, *Content Manager*

ISBN: 978-0-87289-718-2

Printed in the United States of America.

The *Federal Regional Yellow Book* (ISSN 1061-3153) is published semiannually by Leadership Directories, Inc., 1407 Broadway, Suite 318, NewYork, NY 10018. Annual subscription: $485. Additional subscriptions delivered to the same individual and address: $364. For air mail postage: Canada and Mexico add $75 per subscription. Outside North America add $100 per subscription.

POSTMASTER: Send address changes to *Federal Regional Yellow Book*, Leadership Directories, Inc., 1407 Broadway, Suite 318, NewYork, NY 10018.

For additional information, including details about other Leadership Directories, Inc. publications, please call (212) 627-4140.

Federal Regional
YELLOW BOOK

Winter 2019

Table of Contents

(continued on next page)

Regional REVIEW

By Frank Poppe
Team Leader and Content Manager, *Federal Regional Yellow Book* November 14, 2018

The Winter 2019 edition of the *Federal Regional Yellow Book* features current listings for the regional offices and installations of the federal government's departments and independent agencies.

In addition, the *Federal Regional Yellow Book* features updated listings for United States Embassies, Consulates, and Diplomatic Missions currently operating throughout the world. Below are some highlighted personnel changes that have occurred since the publication of the Summer 2018 edition.

Confirmations

The Senate has confirmed the following individuals to their positions:

Name	Position	Agency
Dallas L. Carlson	U.S. Marshal for the District of North Dakota	Department of Justice
Sonya K. Chavez	U.S. Marshal for the District of New Mexico	Department of Justice
Jason R. Dunn	U.S. Attorney for the District of Colorado	Department of Justice
Charles L. Goodwin	U.S. Marshal for the District of Hawaii	Department of Justice
Scott Patrick Illing	U.S. Marshal for the Eastern District of Louisiana	Department of Justice
John D. Jordan	U.S. Marshal for the Eastern District of Missouri	Department of Justice
Scott E. Kracl	U.S. Marshal for the District of Nebraska	Department of Justice
R. Don Ladler, Jr.	U.S. Marshal for the Northern District of Florida	Department of Justice
Mara Chapa Lopez	U.S. Attorney for the Middle District of Florida	Department of Justice
Cheryl A. Lydon	U.S. Attorney for the District of South Carolina	Department of Justice
Erica H. MacDonald	U.S. Attorney for the District of Minnesota	Department of Justice
Ariana Fajardo Orshan	U.S. Attorney for the Southern District of Florida	Department of Justice
Susan Lewellyn Pamerleau	U.S. Marshal for the Western District of Texas	Department of Justice

(continued on next page)

Confirmations–continued

Name	Position	Agency
J.C. Rafferty	U.S. Marshal for the Northern District of West Virginia	Department of Justice
Gadyaces S. Serralta	U.S. Marshal for the Southern District of Florida	Department of Justice
Mark F. Sloke	U.S. Marshal for the Southern District of Alabama	Department of Justice
Peter G. Strasser	U.S. Attorney for the Eastern District of Louisiana	Department of Justice
Richard E. Taylor Jr.	U.S. Marshal for the Northern District of Texas	Department of Justice
G. Zachary Terwilliger	U.S. Attorney for the Eastern District of Virginia	Department of Justice
Nick Willard	U.S. Marshal for the District of New Hampshire	Department of Justice
Robin S. Bernstein	Ambassador to the Dominican Republic	Department of State
Randy W. Berry	Ambassador to Nepal	Department of State
David B. Cornstein	Ambassador to Hungary	Department of State
James Randolph Evans	Ambassador to Luxembourg	Department of State
Ronald Gidwitz	Ambassador to Belgium	Department of State
Michael A. Hammer	Ambassador to the Democratic Republic of the Congo	Department of State
Harry B. Harris Jr.	Ambassador to South Korea	Department of State
Dereck J. Hogan	Ambassador to Moldova	Department of State
Philip S. Kosnett	Ambassador to Kosovo	Department of State
Donald Lu	Ambassador to Kyrgyz Republic	Department of State
Earl Robert Miller	Ambassador to Bangladesh	Department of State
Joseph N. Mondello	Ambassador to Trinidad and Tobago	Department of State
Georgette Mosbacher	Ambassador to Poland	Department of State
Brian A. Nichols	Ambassador to Zimbabwe	Department of State
Judy Rising Reinke	Ambassador to Montenegro	Department of State
Gordon D. Sondland	U.S. Representative to the European Union	Department of State
Kevin K. Sullivan	Ambassador to Nicaragua	Department of State
Stephanie Sanders Sullivan	Ambassador to Ghana	Department of State
Alaina Teplitz	Ambassador to Sri Lanka and Maldives	Department of State

Confirmations–continued

Name	Position	Agency
Karen L. Williams	Ambassador to Suriname	Department of State
Jackie Wolcott	U.S. Representative to the International Atomic Energy Agency and the Vienna Office of the United Nations	Department of State
Donald Y. Yamamoto	Ambassador to Somalia	Department of State

The Summer 2019 edition of the *Federal Regional Yellow Book* will be published in June 2019. As always, the editors of the *Federal Regional Yellow Book* extend our sincere thanks to the hundreds of government employees who have consistently taken time out of their busy schedules to provide us with accurate and timely information, enabling the *Federal Regional Yellow Book* to remain as current as possible. We always welcome your comments and suggestions on improving the *Federal Regional Yellow Book*. We can be reached by phone at (202) 347-7757 and by email at info@leadershipconnect.io

User's Guide

The *Federal Regional Yellow Book* gives you direct access to more than 44,000 top people in the regional offices of the Federal Government. The *Federal Regional Yellow Book* is divided into the following sections: Maps, Departments, and Independent Agencies.

1 Each **Listing** begins with the name of the department/agency, followed by a description of the department/agency's function.

2 Useful **Telephone Numbers** and Internet home pages for the department/agency are provided.

3 Offices are listed according to hierarchy and include the mailing address, telephone number, fax number, Internet home page and e-mail addresses, where applicable. The geographical area covered by the office is provided, where applicable.

4 Individuals are listed hierarchically by title and/or rank. Features here include direct-dial telephone numbers, fax numbers and e-mail addresses.

If an individual works at a location different from the address provided beneath the office title, that individual's work address is indicated beneath his/her name and job title. Numbers that appear following an individual's name are office room numbers.

Educational Data is provided for senior personnel, where available.

5 Coded Symbols are located at the bottom of the page with an explanatory key to better locate appointed officials.

Agriculture—Office of the Secretary

1

United States Department of Agriculture (USDA)

Description: The Department of Agriculture is responsible for the improvement and maintenance of farm income. Departmental activities include the development and expansion of international markets for agricultural projects, implementation of rural development projects, the oversight of credit and conservation programs, and agricultural research on crop production. The department also oversees the Forest Service and the Natural Resources Conservation Service, which serve to protect the nation's soil, water, forests and natural resources. Through inspection and grading services, the department safeguards and ensures standards of quality in the food supply.

2

1400 Independence Avenue, SW, Washington, DC 20250
Tel: (202) 720-3202 (Procurement Information)
Tel: (202) 720-2791 (Public Information)
Tel: (202) 720-8164 (Freedom of Information/Privacy Act)
Tel: (202) 690-1622 (Fraud, Waste and Abuse Hotline - DC Metropolitan Area)
Tel: (800) 424-9121 (Fraud, Waste and Abuse Hotline - Continental US)
Tel: (202) 690-1533 (Rural Development Center)
Tel: (202) 720-8732 (Personnel Locator)
Tel: (202) 720-4623 (Media Inquiries)
E-mail: open@usda.gov (Open Government Directive Email)
E-mail: press@oc.usda.gov (Media Inquiries) Internet: www.usda.gov
Internet: www.usda.gov/open (Open Government Directive Website)
Internet: www.usa.gov (Official US Government Website)

3

Office of the Secretary

Jamie L. Whitten Federal Building, 1400 Independence Avenue, SW, Room 200-A, Washington, DC 20250
Tel: (202) 720-3631 Fax: (202) 720-2166

OFFICE OF THE DEPUTY SECRETARY (ODS)

Jamie L. Whitten Federal Building, 1400 Independence Avenue, SW, Room 200-A, Washington, DC 20250
Fax: (202) 720-6314

Departmental Management (DM)

Jamie L. Whitten Federal Building, 1400 Independence Avenue, SW, Room 240-W, Washington, DC 20250
Tel: (202) 720-3291 Fax: (202) 720-2191 Internet: www.dm.usda.gov

Office of the Chief Information Officer (OCIO)

South Agriculture Building, 1400 Independence Avenue, SW, Washington, DC 20250
Tel: (202) 720-8833 Fax: (202) 690-1915 E-mail: open@usda.gov
Internet: www.ocio.usda.gov Internet: www.usda.gov/open

National Information Technology Center (NITC)

8930 Ward Parkway, Kansas City, MO 64114-3302
Fax: (816) 926-6080 E-mail: nitcservicedesk@ocio.usda.gov

4

● Associate Chief Information Officer for Data Center Operations and Director (Acting) **Victoria K. Turley** .... (816) 823-1468
South Agriculture Building, 1400 Independence Avenue, SW, Washington, DC 20250
E-mail: Victoria.Turley@ocio.usda.gov
Education: Auburn 1983 BS; George Mason 1989 MS
Executive Assistant **(Vacant)** .... (202) 690-0048

Principal Deputy Associate Chief Information Officer for Enterprise Data Center Operations and Application Development (Acting) **Victoria K. Turley** .... (816) 823-1468
E-mail: Victoria.Turley@ocio.usda.gov
Education: Auburn 1983 BS; George Mason 1989 MS

Deputy Associate Chief Information Officer, Business, Finance and Security **(Vacant)** .... (816) 926-6606

National Information Technology Center *(continued)*

Deputy Associate Chief Information Officer, Operations **(Vacant)** .... (816) 926-6503
Deputy Associate Chief Information Officer, Security Operations **(Vacant)** .... (816) 926-2356

Architecture and Systems Integration Division (ASID)

8930 Ward Parkway, Kansas City, MO 64114

Division Director **Charles T. Gowans** .... (816) 926-2345
E-mail: chuck.gowans@ocio.usda.gov
Enterprise Architecture Branch Chief **(Vacant)** .... (816) 926-6516
Network Architect **(Vacant)** .... (816) 926-6516
Service Portfolio Branch Chief **(Vacant)** .... (816) 926-6516
Systems Integration Branch Chief **Brian L. Fields** .... (970) 295-5167
Building A, 2150 Centre Avenue, Fort Collins, CO 80526
E-mail: brian.fields@ocio.usda.gov

Business Division

8930 Ward Parkway, Kansas City, MO 64114

Director **Chad N. Bixby** .... (202) 720-8833

Data Center Consolidation Office

Data Center Consolidation Office Director **Bryan Dixon** .... (202) 720-8232
E-mail: bryan.dixon@ocio.usda.gov

Information Services Division

8930 Ward Parkway, Kansas City, MO 64114-3302
Fax: (816) 926-6754

Division Director **Greta R. Nash** .... (816) 926-2377
E-mail: greta.nash@usda.gov
Education: Missouri (Kansas City) 1982 BBA
Database Management Branch Chief **Scott A. Middendorf** .... (816) 926-6082
E-mail: scott.middendorf@usda.gov
Education: Washburn BBA
Network Services Branch Chief **Randal "Scott" Clark** .... (816) 926-6082
E-mail: randal.clark@usda.gov
Storage Management Branch Chief **Rachel A. Mecham** .... (816) 926-6082

Infrastructure Operations Division

8930 Ward Parkway, Kansas City, MO 64114-3302
Fax: (816) 926-6754

Director **Scott P. O'Hare** .... (816) 926-2139
Education: Excelsior BA
IT Service Management Branch Chief **Kim Hull** .... (816) 926-2139
Service Operations and Support Branch Chief **Robert J. Boucher** .... (816) 926-2139
Systems Network Control Center Chief **Rickey N. Smith** .... (816) 926-2139
Executive Assistant **Jessica Her** .... (816) 926-2139

Process Engineering Office

Process Engineering Office Director **Steven Larry "Steve" Sanders** .... (816) 926-6516
E-mail: steve.sanders@ocio.usda.gov
Education: Ohio State 1983 BS

5

★ Presidential Appointment Requiring Senate Confirmation ☆ Presidential Appointment ◦ Schedule C Appointment ◦ Career Senior Foreign Service Appointment
● Career Senior Executive Service (SES) Appointment ◦ Non-Career Senior Executive Service (SES) Appointment ■ Postal Career Executive Service

Winter 2019 © Leadership Directories, Inc. *Federal Regional Yellow Book*

Tables of Contents

The *Federal Regional Yellow Book* contains the following tables:

- ▶Master Table of Contents (pages iii and iv)
- ▶Section Tables (at the beginning of each section)
- ▶Departmental Tables (at the beginning of each department). The departmental tables use a system of indents to represent the hierarchical structure of the departments.

Major Categories of Federal Government Employment

Special coded symbols preceding an individual's title are used to identify positions or individuals in the largest categories of federal employment outside the regular civil service.

▶ Presidential Appointment

A bold star [★] preceding an individual's title indicates that the position is subject to Senate confirmation. An open-faced star [☆] preceding an individual's title indicates that the incumbent in the position is appointed by the President and does not require Senate confirmation.

▶ Senior Executive Service

The Senior Executive Service (SES) is a personnel system covering top-level executive, policy-making, managerial and supervisory positions. SES appointees do not require Senate confirmation, but their selection is regulated by the Office of Personnel Management. In the hierarchy of the federal government, SES members rank just below the top presidential appointees who head the departments and agencies. Positions may be specified as general (to be filled by either career or noncareer SES members) or career reserved.

A bold dot [●] indicates that the SES member is a career employee. This means that the individual is filling a position in either the career reserved or general categories of SES employment. Career reserved positions must be filled by career appointees in order to ensure the public's confidence in the impartiality of the government. Tax, law enforcement, and contract administration positions are examples. Career appointment to a position in the general category of the SES is identical to that in the career reserved category. There are limitations to ensure that most of the general positions are filled by career appointees at any given time.

An open-faced dot [○] indicates that the SES member is a noncareer employee. Noncareer SES appointees receive noncompetitive appointments to SES positions that normally involve advocating, formulating and directing the policies and programs of the administration in power or require maintenance of a relationship of trust and confidentiality with the agency's top executives.

▶ Career Senior Foreign Service Appointment

An open-faced diamond [◇] preceding an individual's title indicates that the incumbent is a Career Senior Foreign Service member. Members of the Senior Foreign Service comprise the corps of senior leaders and experts for the management of the Foreign Service and the performance of its functions. Senior career members are appointed by the President, with the advice and consent of the Senate, usually through the promotion of career members of the Foreign Service.

▶ Schedule C Appointment

An open-faced square [□] preceding an individual's title indicates that the incumbent in the position is appointed under Schedule C of the civil service rules. These regulations allow the Office of Personnel Management to exempt from the competitive civil service positions of a policy-making role or positions that require a close, confidential working relationship with the agency head or other key officials of the agency. Schedule C appointees serve at the pleasure of the agency head.

▶ **Postal Career Executive Service**

A bold square [■] preceding an individual's name indicates that the individual is a member of the Postal Career Executive Service (PCES). The PCES is an internal staffing category of the United States Postal Service. The PCES develops and maintains a group of employees for key management positions. There are two levels in PCES: Level I includes district, area, and headquarters executives, and Level II consists of U.S. Postal Service officers, including vice presidents.

Maps

A map displaying the Ten Standard Federal regions is located on page xi. The remaining maps detail regions with irregular boundaries.

Indexes

Three indexes have been prepared to assist readers in locating specific information quickly and easily.

▶ The **Geographical Index** has been provided to assist you in locating listings in a given area. A parent department or agency is identified under the city heading, which appears under its state or territory heading.

▶ The **Name Index** has been provided to assist you in locating an individual who is listed in the *Federal Regional Yellow Book*, even if you do not know for which department or agency he or she works.

▶ The **Organizational Index** has been provided to assist you in locating sub-offices that appear within the departments and independent agencies.

Dialing International Telephone and Fax Numbers

With the exception of Canada and the Caribbean Islands, all international long distance calls from the United States begin with 011.

Maps

Contents

Maps

Departments and Independent Agencies that conform to the Ten Standard Federal Regions:

Education
Secretary's Regional Representatives

Environmental Protection Agency

Homeland Security
Federal Emergency Management Agency

Health and Human Services
HHS Regional Directors
Administration for Children and Families
Administration on Aging
Centers for Medicare and Medicaid Services
Office of Public Health and Science

Justice
Community Relations Service

Labor
Employment Standards Administration/
Office of Workers' Compensation Programs
Employment and Training Administration
Occupational Safety and Health Administration
Veterans' Employment and Training Service
Women's Bureau

Small Business Administration

Social Security Administration

Transportation
Federal Transit Administration
National Highway Traffic Safety Administration

The Ten Standard Federal Regions

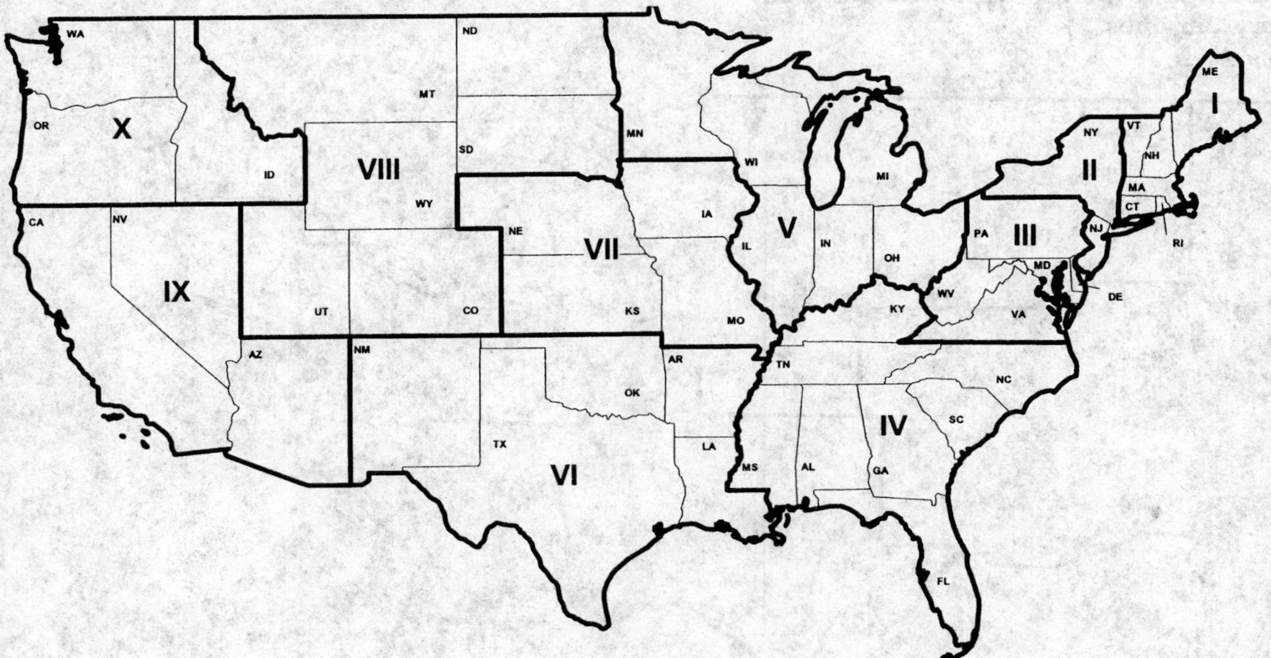

Note: Alaska is included in Region X; Hawaii, Guam, and the Trust Territory of the Pacific Islands are included in Region IX; Puerto Rico and the Virgin Islands are included in Region II.

MAPS

Department of Agriculture

Agricultural Research Service

Area Boundaries

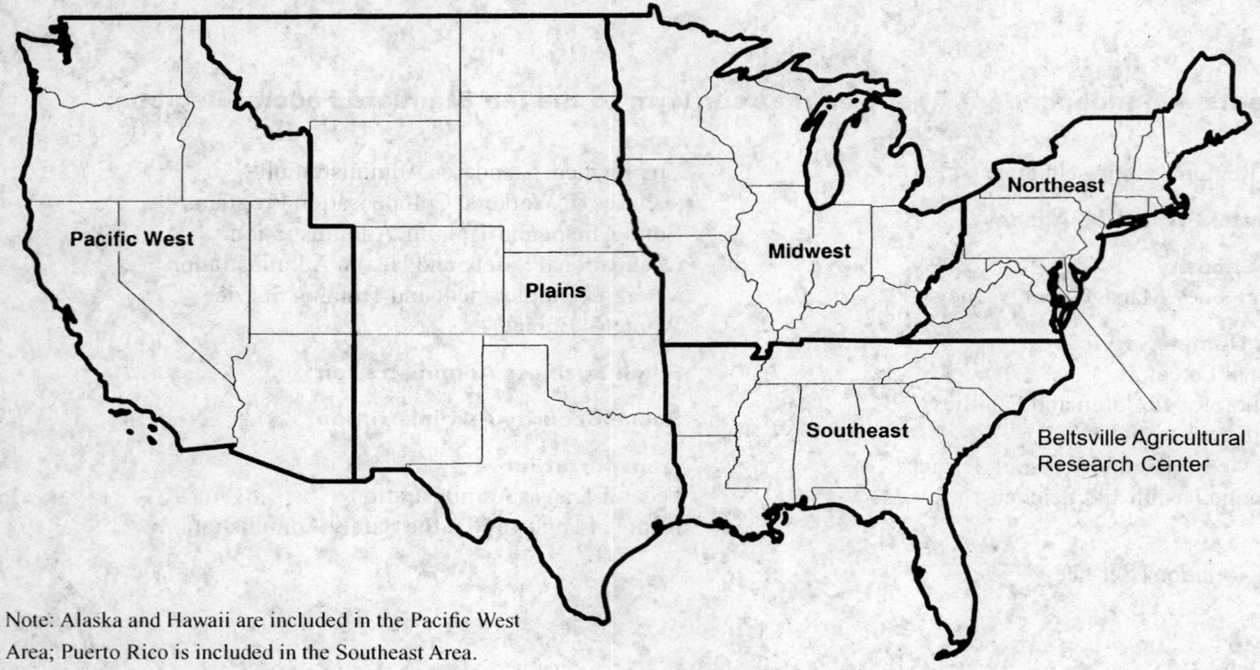

Note: Alaska and Hawaii are included in the Pacific West Area; Puerto Rico is included in the Southeast Area.

Department of Agriculture

Animal and Plant Health Inspection Service
Veterinary Services

District Boundaries

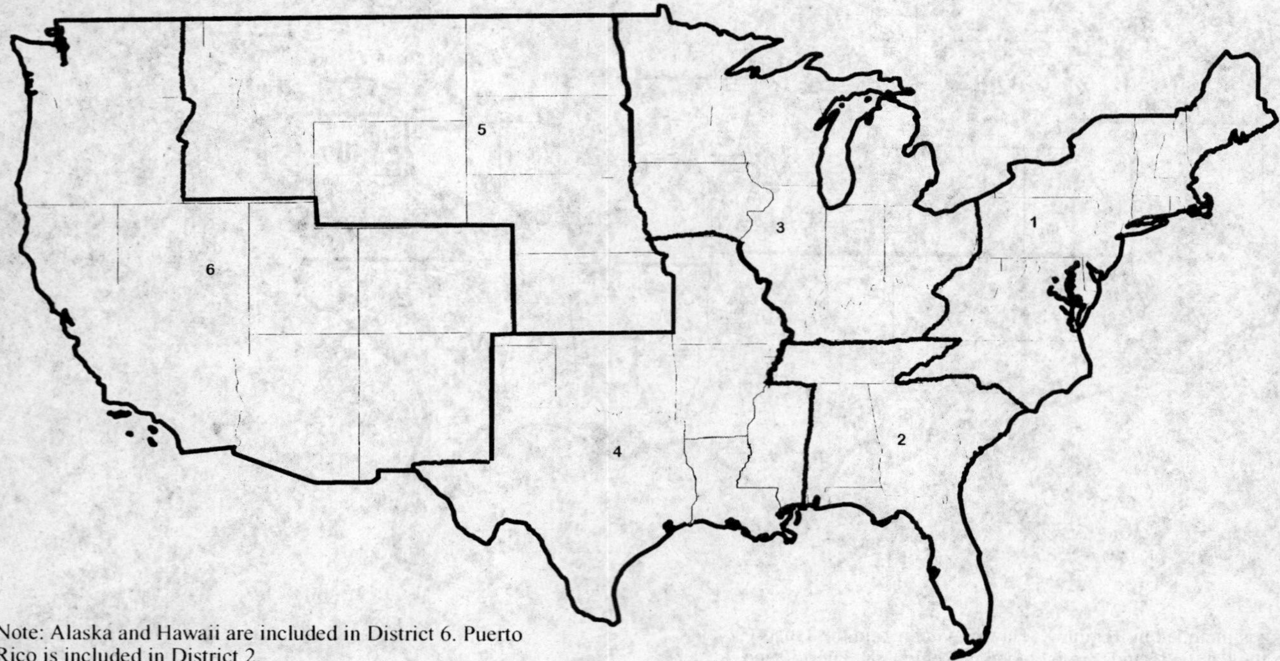

Note: Alaska and Hawaii are included in District 6. Puerto Rico is included in District 2.

Department of Agriculture

Food and Nutrition Service

Region Boundaries

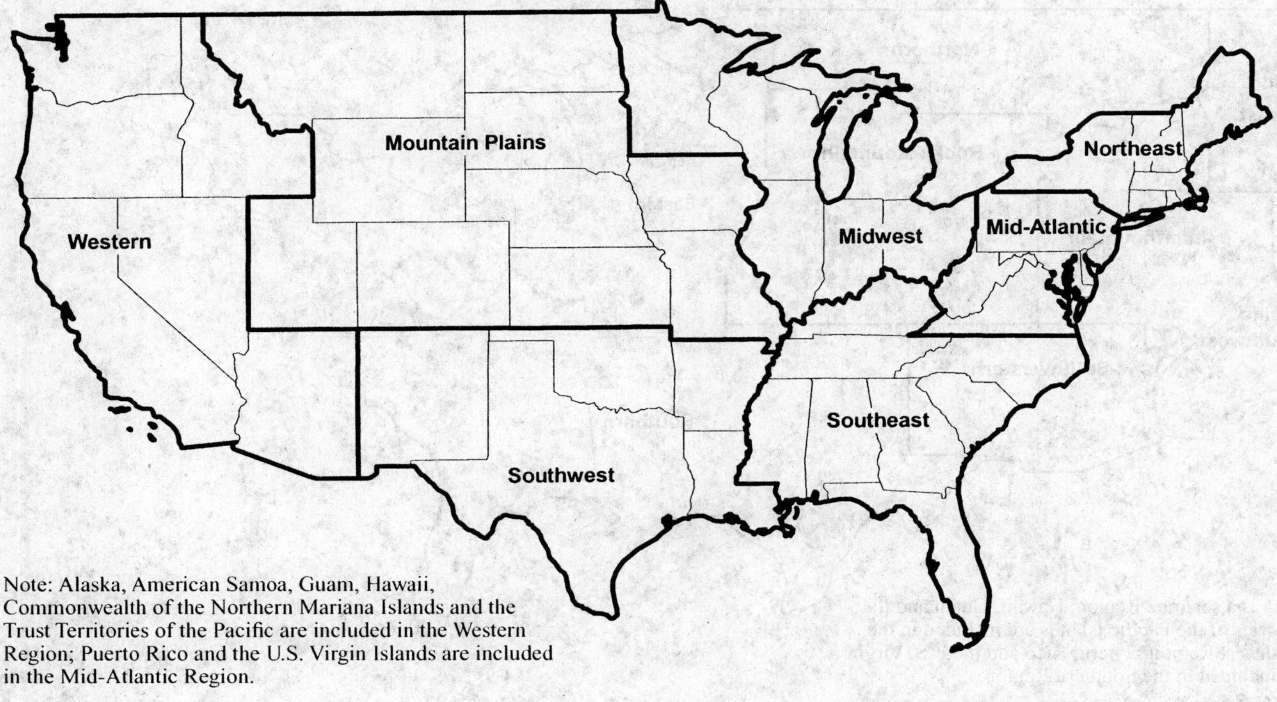

Note: Alaska, American Samoa, Guam, Hawaii, Commonwealth of the Northern Mariana Islands and the Trust Territories of the Pacific are included in the Western Region; Puerto Rico and the U.S. Virgin Islands are included in the Mid-Atlantic Region.

Department of Agriculture

Food Safety and Inspection Service

District Office Boundaries

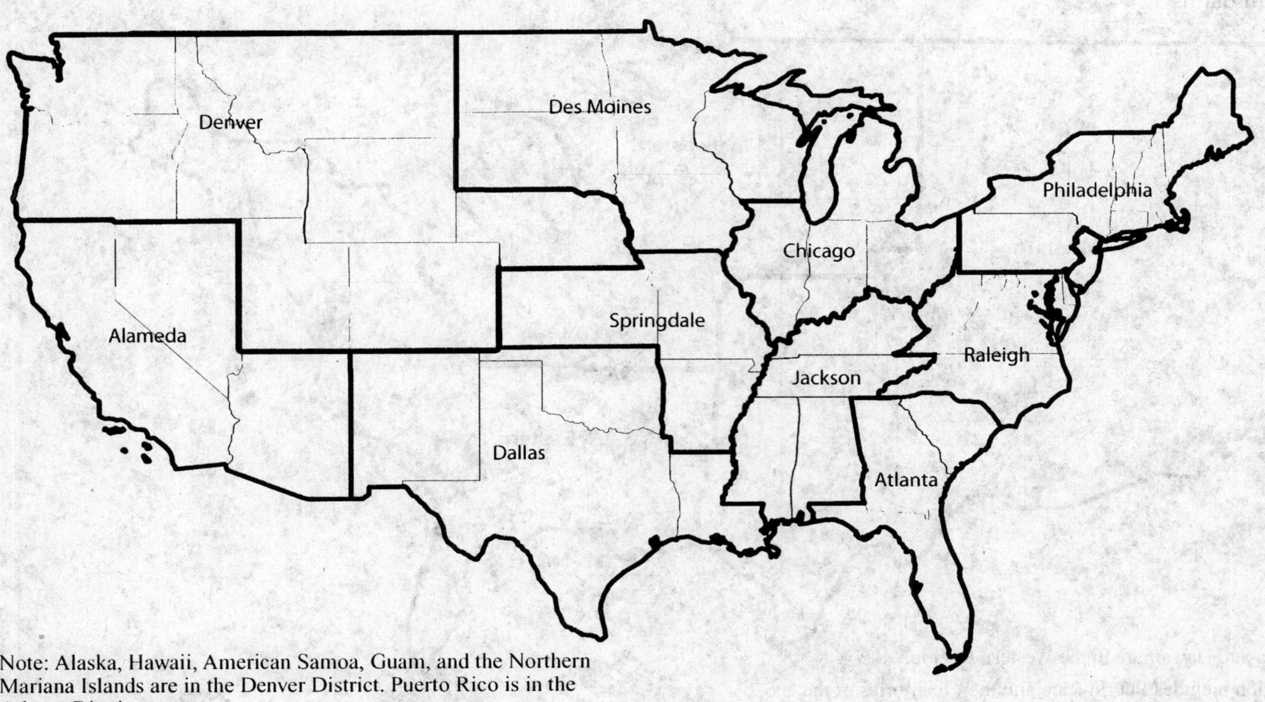

Note: Alaska, Hawaii, American Samoa, Guam, and the Northern Mariana Islands are in the Denver District. Puerto Rico is in the Atlanta District.

MAPS

Department of Agriculture

Forest Service

Region Boundaries

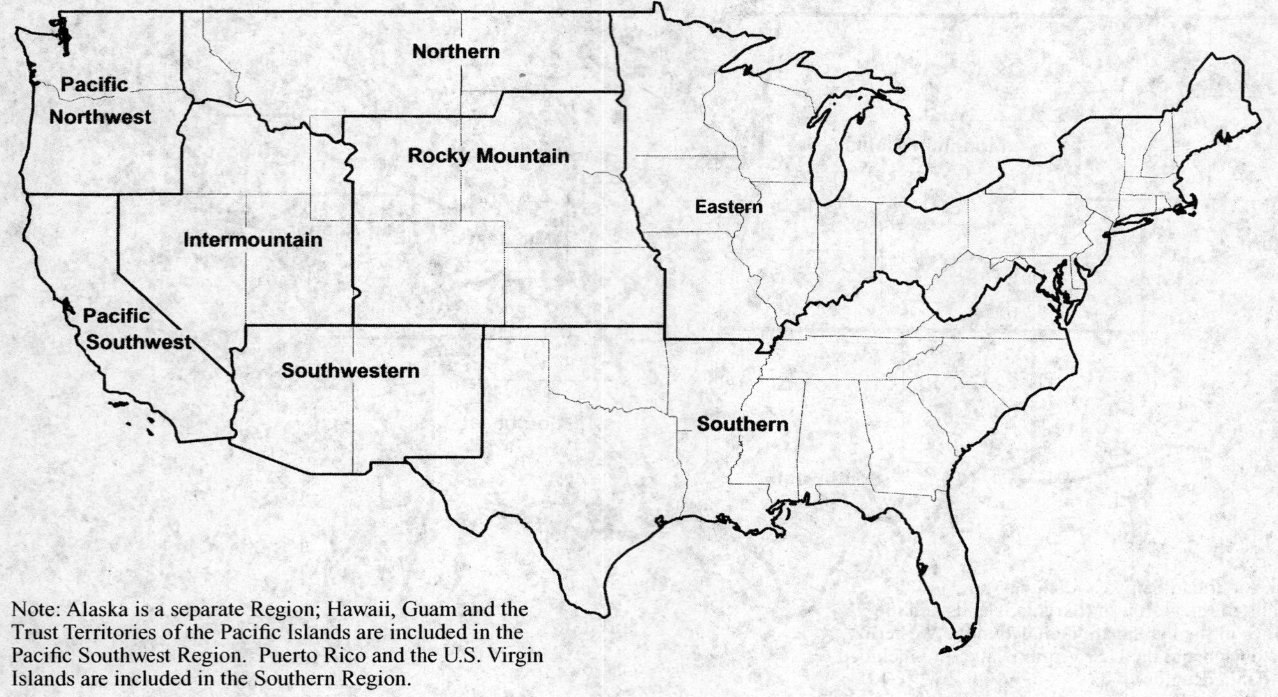

Note: Alaska is a separate Region; Hawaii, Guam and the Trust Territories of the Pacific Islands are included in the Pacific Southwest Region. Puerto Rico and the U.S. Virgin Islands are included in the Southern Region.

Department of Agriculture

Agricultural Marketing Service
Packers and Stockyards Division

Region Boundaries

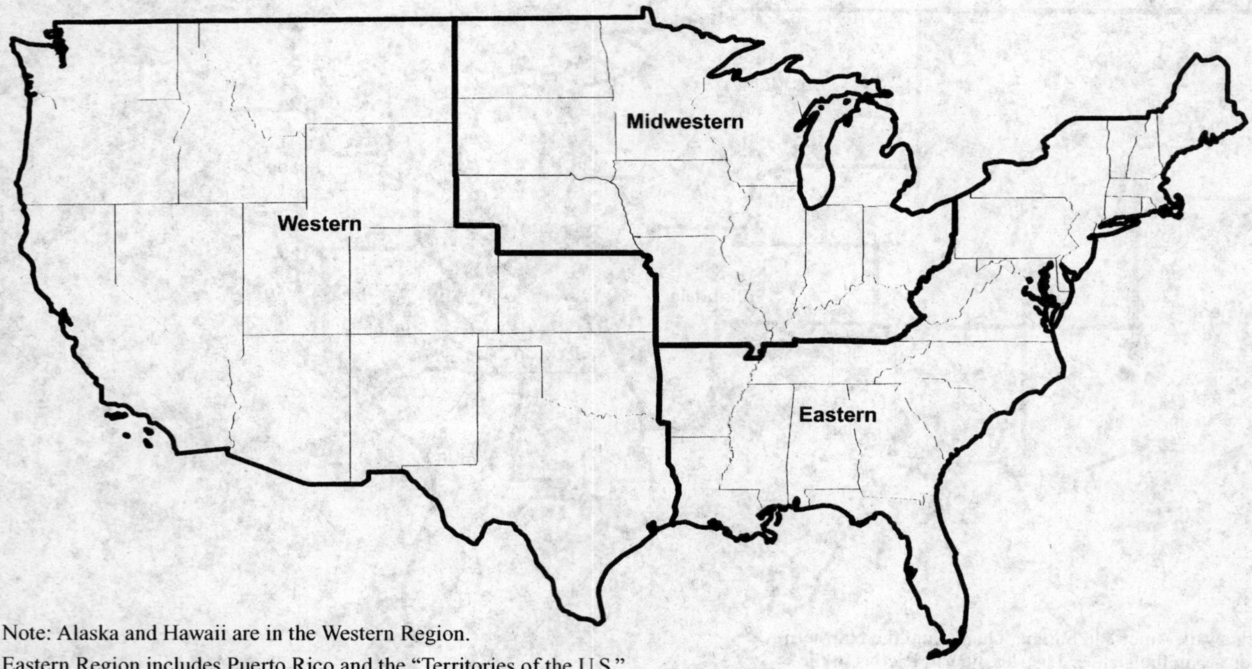

Note: Alaska and Hawaii are in the Western Region.

Eastern Region includes Puerto Rico and the "Territories of the U.S."

Department of Agriculture

Natural Resources Conservation Service

Region Boundaries

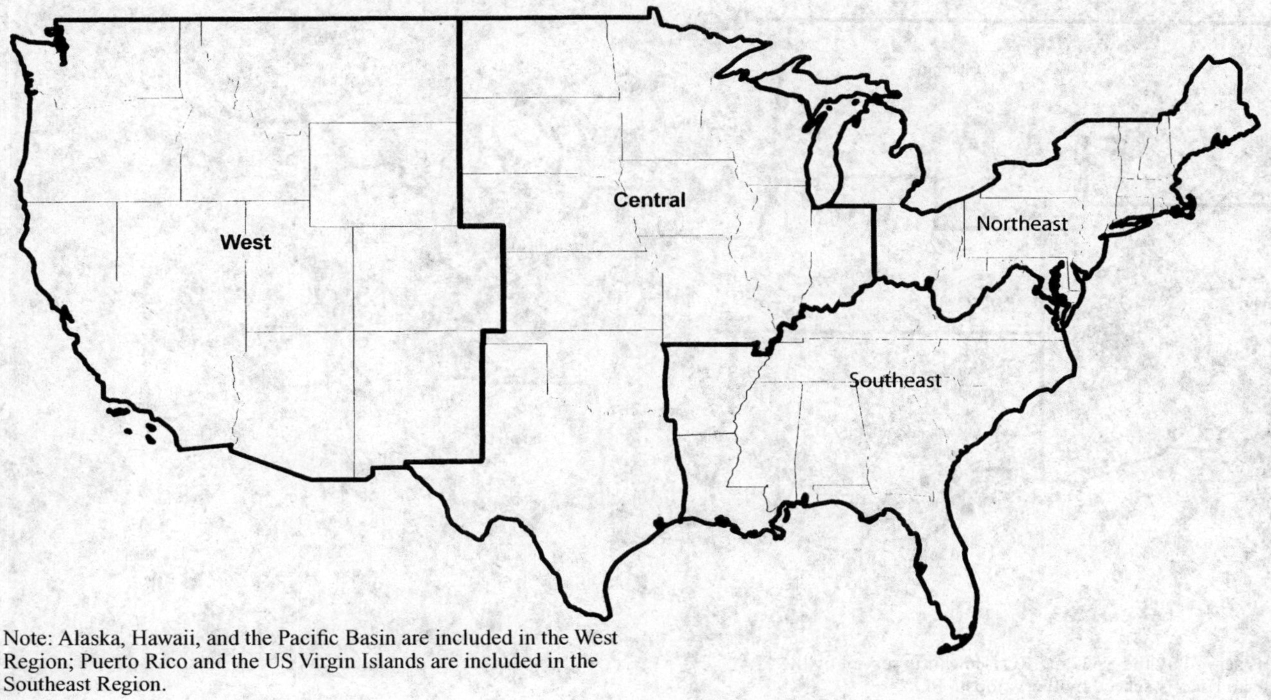

Note: Alaska, Hawaii, and the Pacific Basin are included in the West Region; Puerto Rico and the US Virgin Islands are included in the Southeast Region.

Department of Agriculture

Risk Management Agency Compliance

Regional Office Boundaries

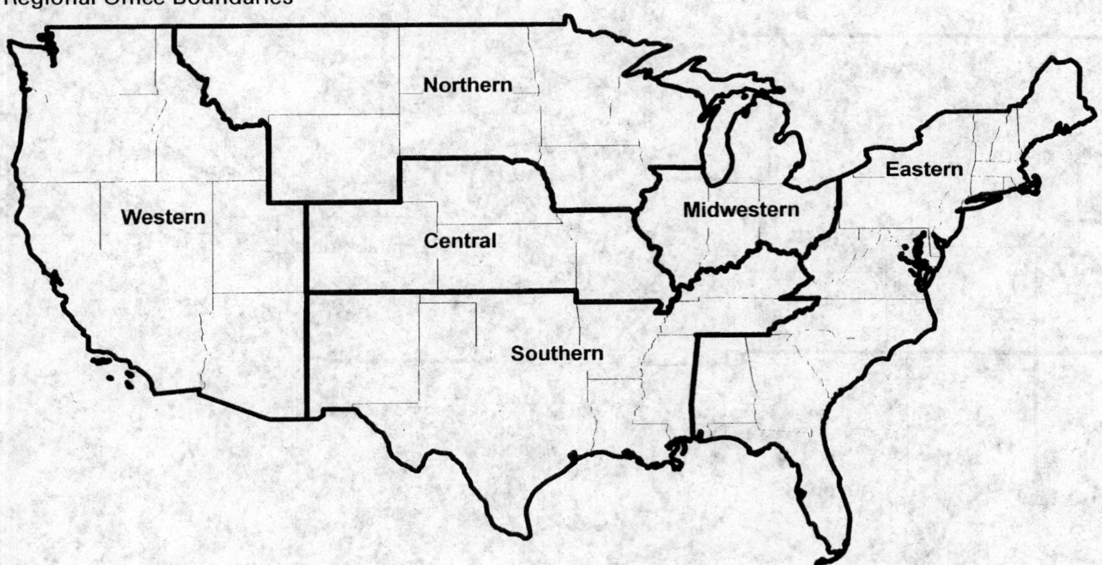

Note: Alaska and Hawaii are included in the Western Region; Puerto Rico and the U.S. Virgin Islands are included in the Eastern Region.

MAPS

Department of Agriculture

Risk Management Agency
Insurance Services

Regional Office Boundaries

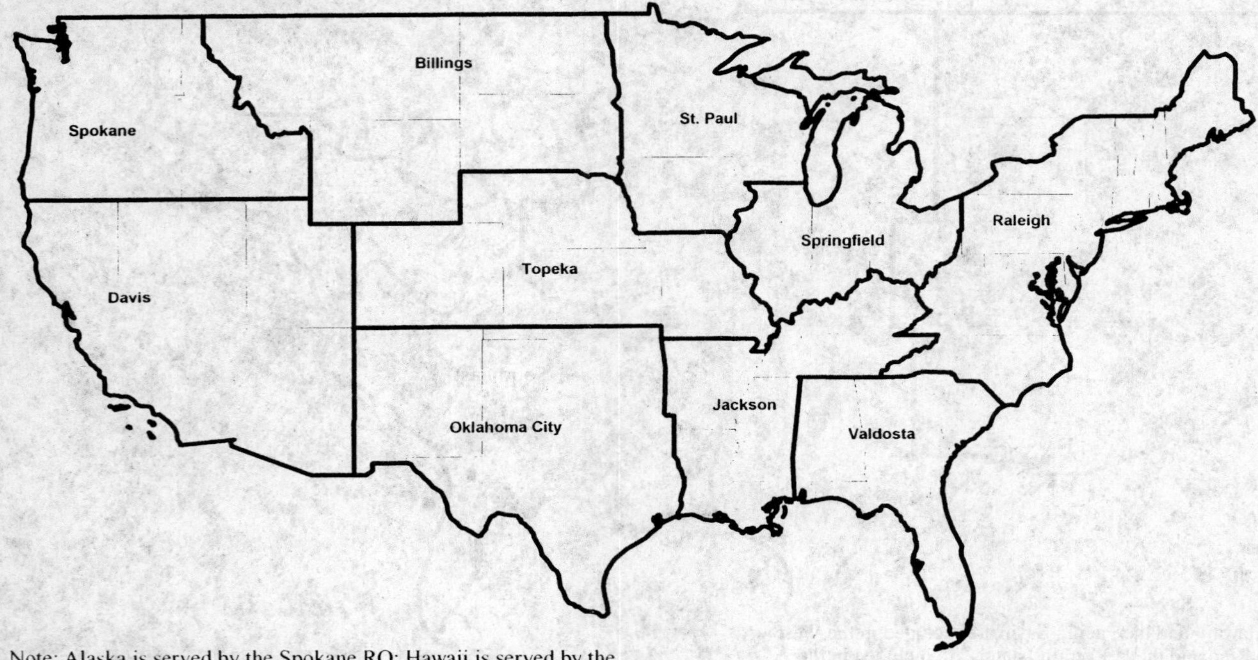

Note: Alaska is served by the Spokane RO; Hawaii is served by the Davis RO; Puerto Rico is served by the Valdosta RO.

Department of Commerce

Economic Development Administration

Region Boundaries

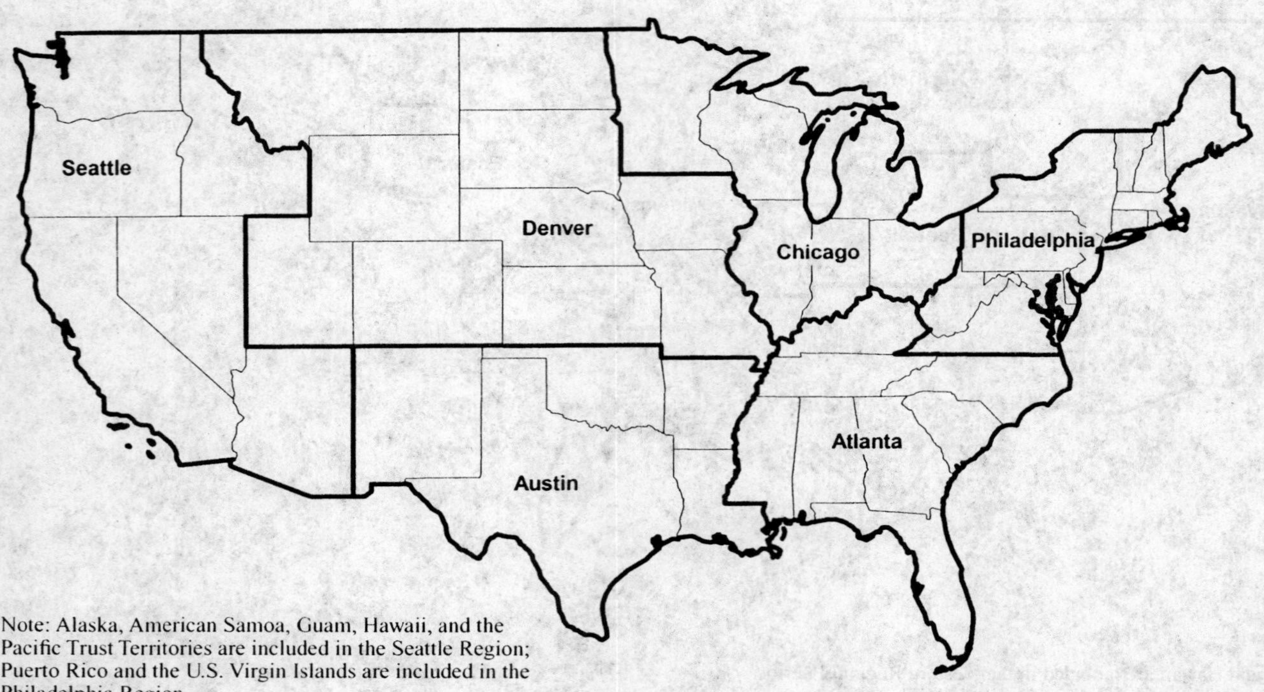

Note: Alaska, American Samoa, Guam, Hawaii, and the Pacific Trust Territories are included in the Seattle Region; Puerto Rico and the U.S. Virgin Islands are included in the Philadelphia Region.

Department of Commerce

Economic and Statistics Administration
Bureau of the Census

Region Boundaries

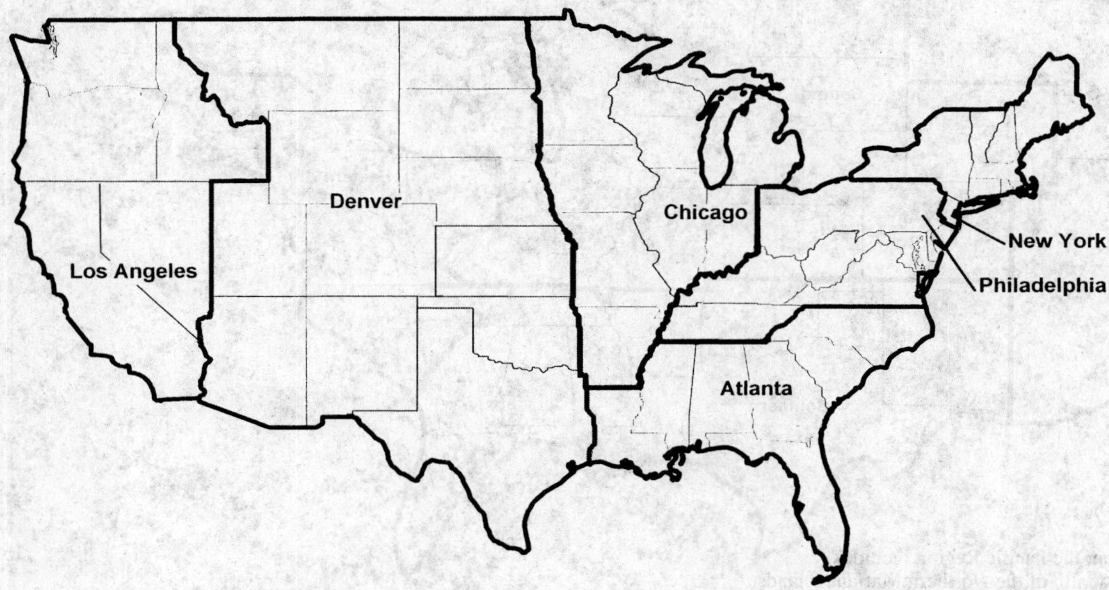

Note: Alaska and Hawaii are in the Los Angeles Region.
Puerto Rico and the U.S. Virgin Islands are in the New York Region.

Department of Commerce

National Oceanic and Atmospheric Administration
NOAA Fisheries

Region Boundaries

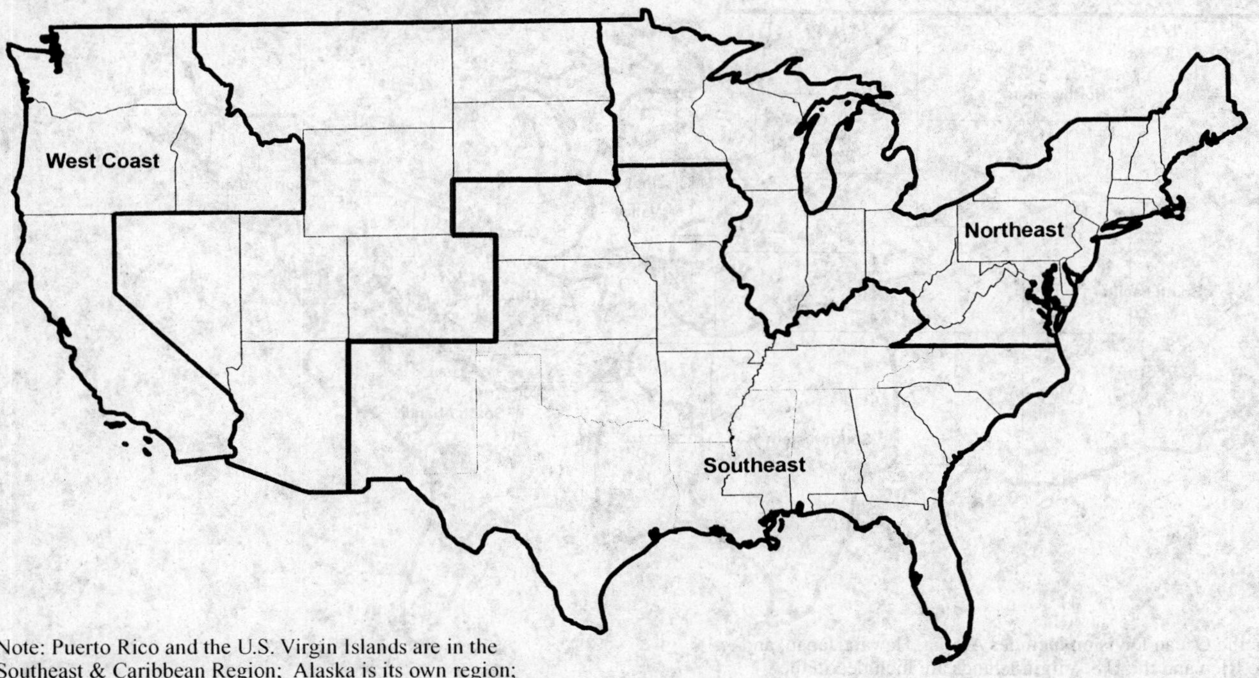

Note: Puerto Rico and the U.S. Virgin Islands are in the Southeast & Caribbean Region; Alaska is its own region; American Samoa, Guam, and Hawaii are in the Pacific Islands Region.

MAPS

Department of Commerce

National Oceanic and Atmospheric Administration
National Weather Service

Region Boundaries

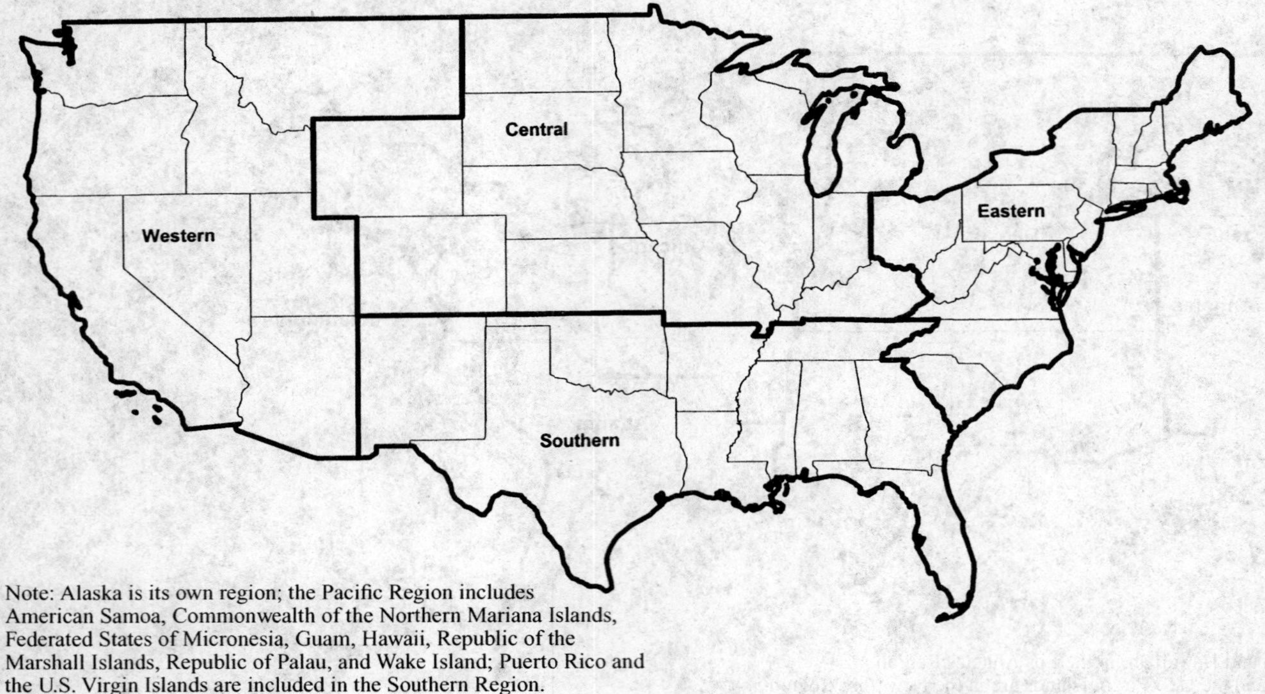

Note: Alaska is its own region; the Pacific Region includes American Samoa, Commonwealth of the Northern Mariana Islands, Federated States of Micronesia, Guam, Hawaii, Republic of the Marshall Islands, Republic of Palau, and Wake Island; Puerto Rico and the U.S. Virgin Islands are included in the Southern Region.

Department of Defense

U.S. Army Corps of Engineers

Civil Works

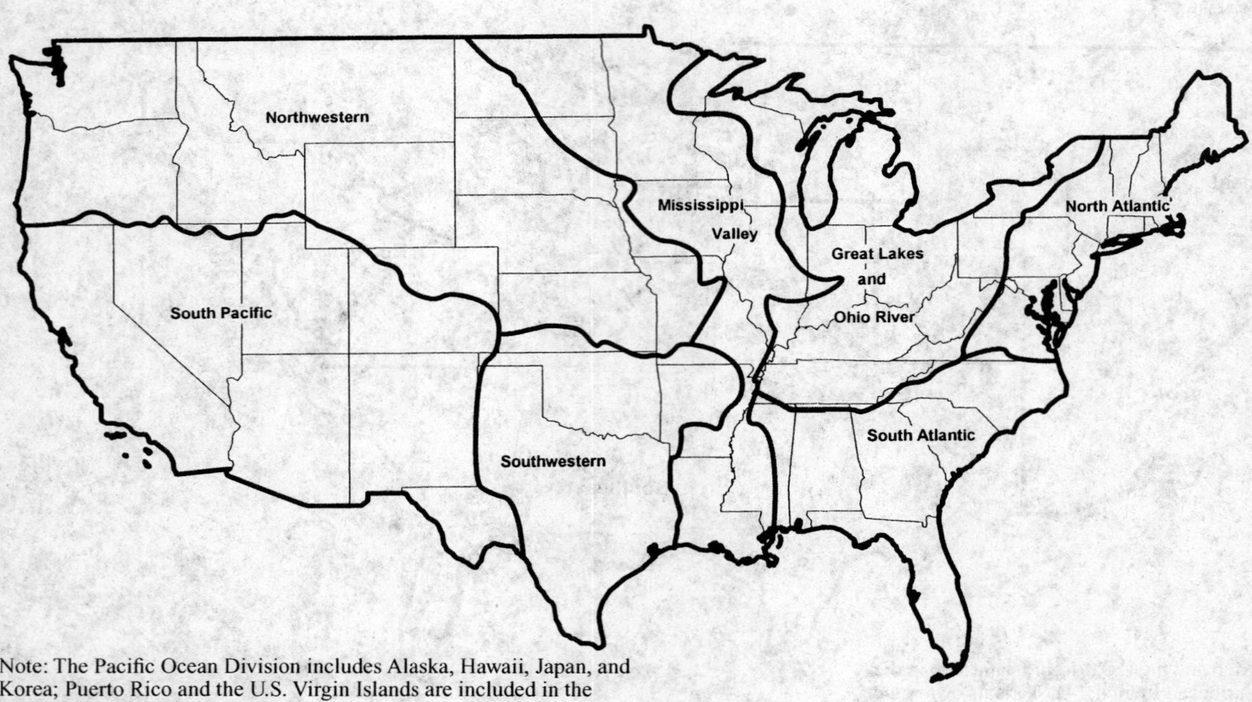

Note: The Pacific Ocean Division includes Alaska, Hawaii, Japan, and Korea; Puerto Rico and the U.S. Virgin Islands are included in the South Atlantic Division.

Department of Energy

Federal Energy Regulatory Commission

Region Boundaries

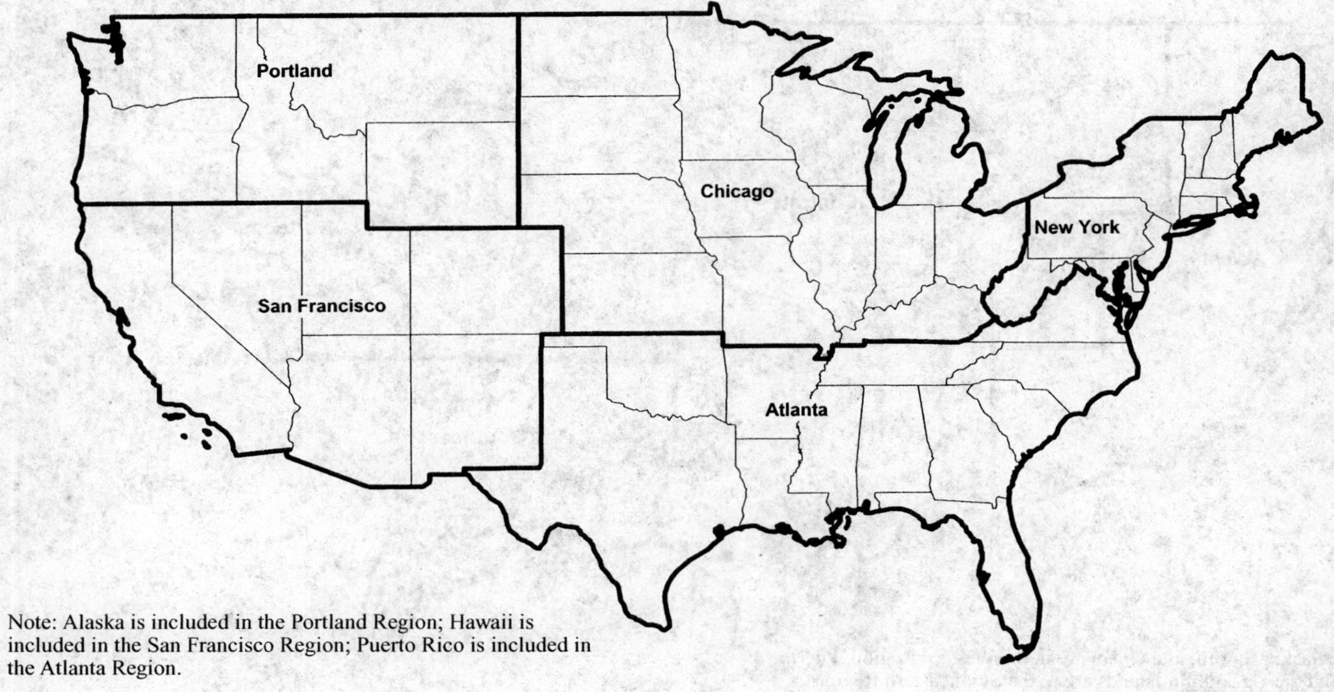

Note: Alaska is included in the Portland Region; Hawaii is included in the San Francisco Region; Puerto Rico is included in the Atlanta Region.

Department of Health and Human Services

Indian Health Service

Area Boundaries

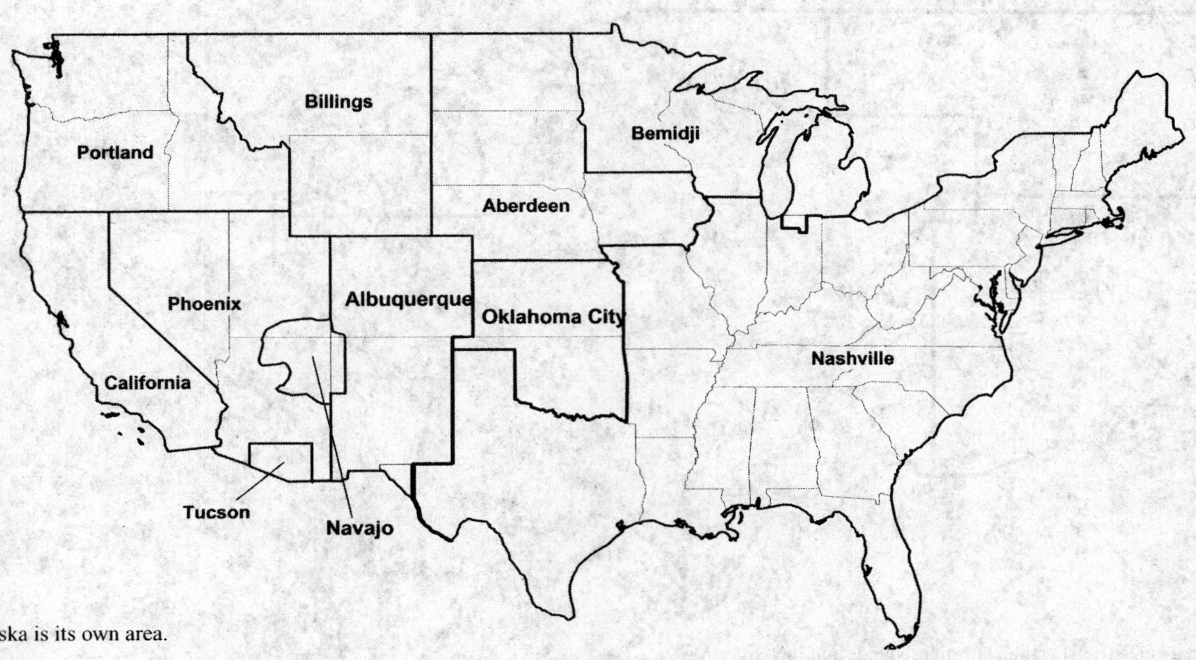

Note: Alaska is its own area.

Department of Homeland Security

U.S. Citizenship and Immigration Services

Region Boundaries

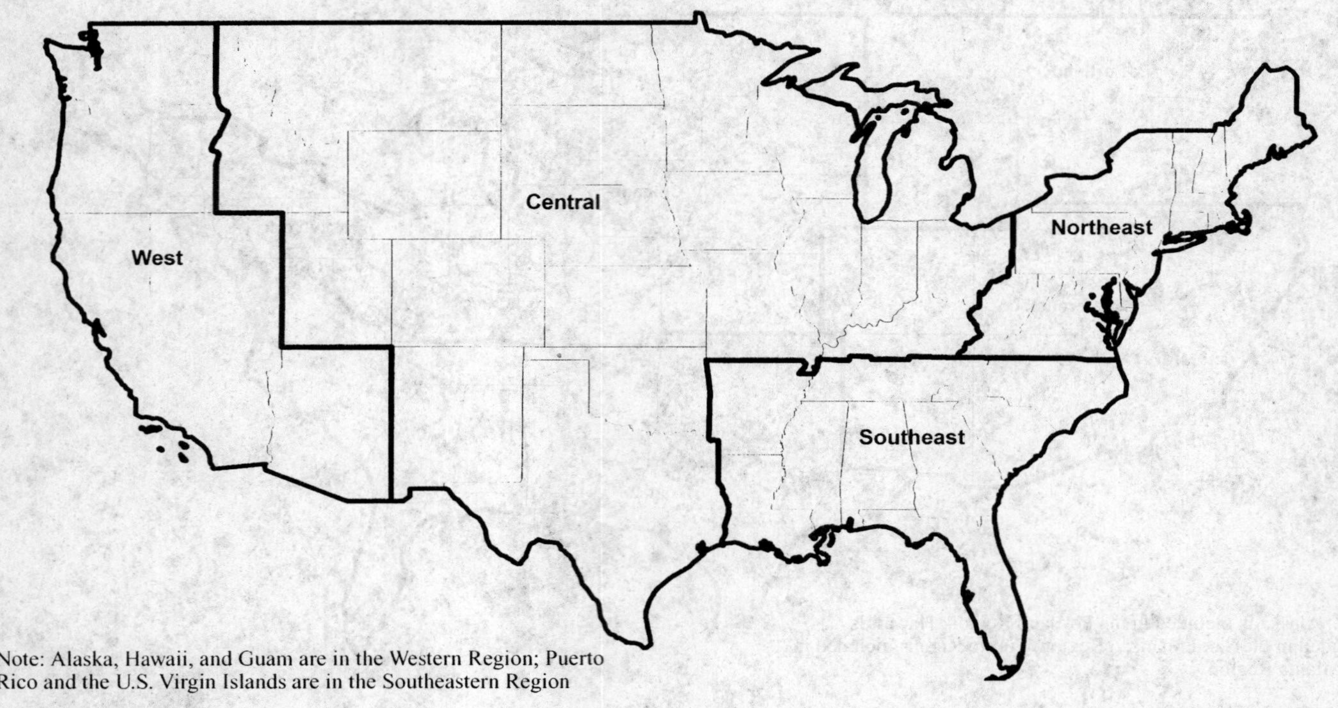

Note: Alaska, Hawaii, and Guam are in the Western Region; Puerto Rico and the U.S. Virgin Islands are in the Southeastern Region

Department of Homeland Security

U.S. Coast Guard

District Boundaries

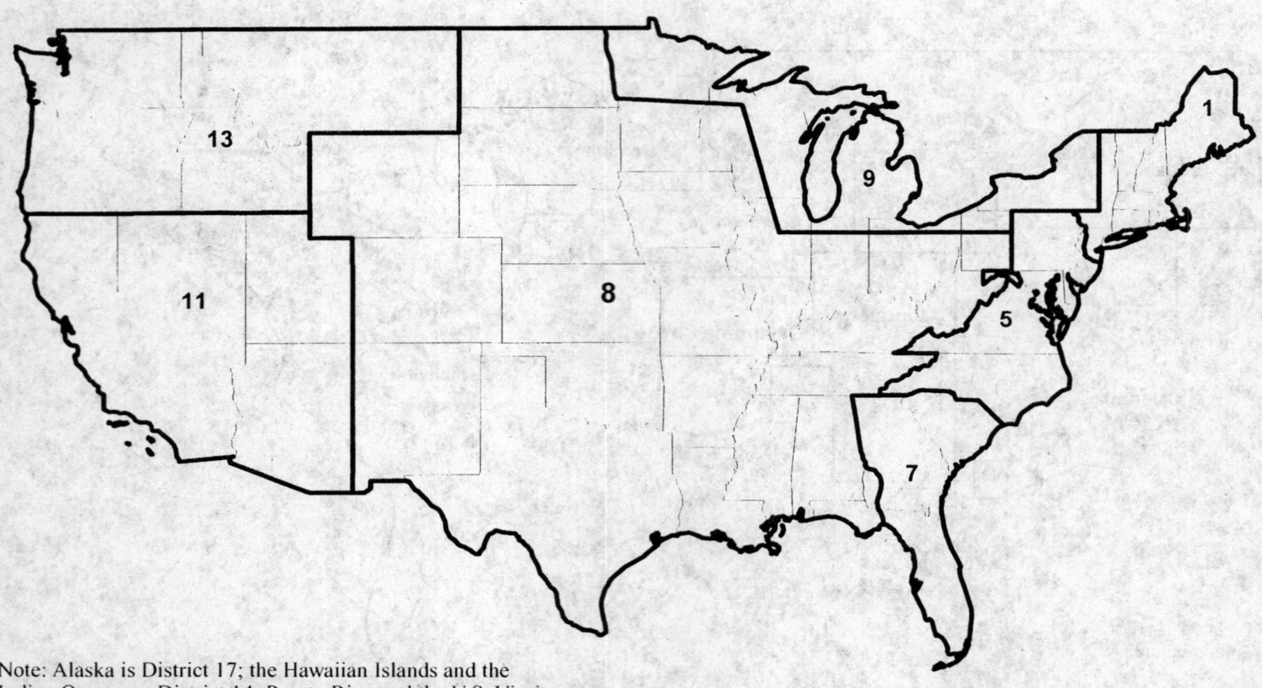

Note: Alaska is District 17; the Hawaiian Islands and the Indian Ocean are District 14; Puerto Rico and the U.S. Virgin Islands are included in District 7.

Department of Homeland Security

U.S. Customs and Border Protection

Field Operations Boundaries

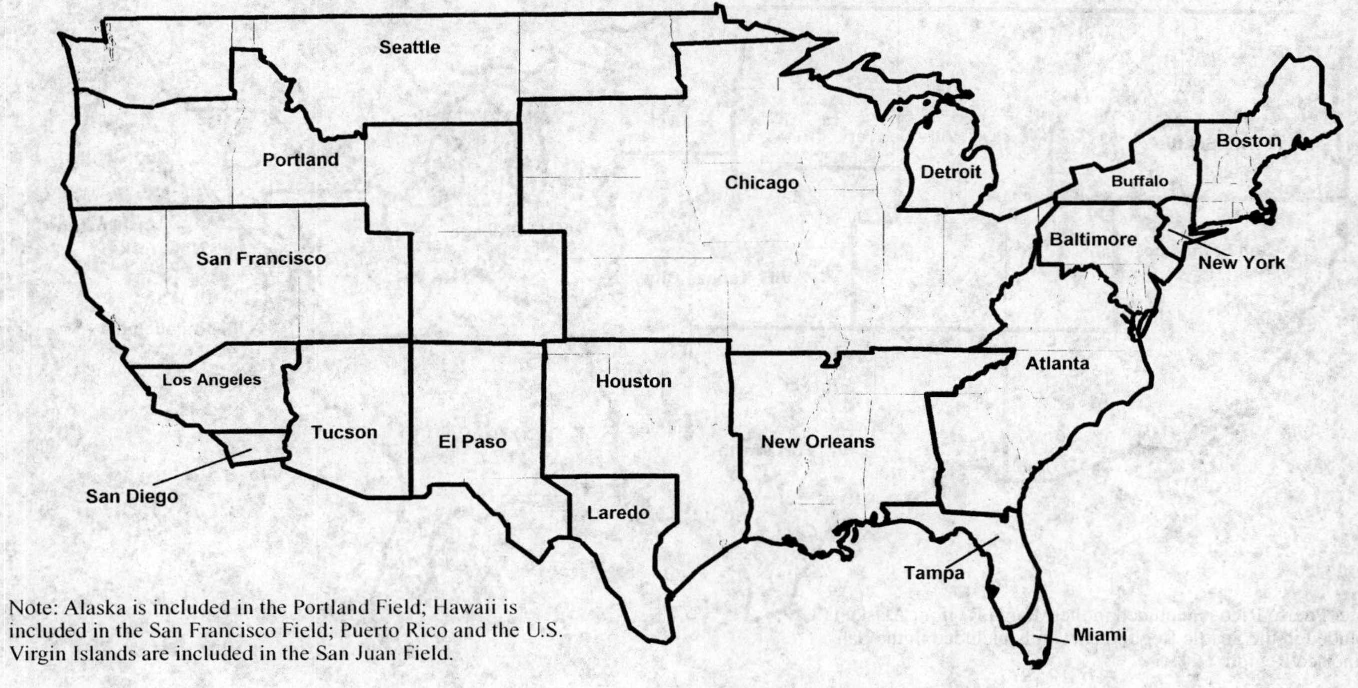

Note: Alaska is included in the Portland Field; Hawaii is included in the San Francisco Field; Puerto Rico and the U.S. Virgin Islands are included in the San Juan Field.

Department of Homeland Security

U.S. Customs and Border Protection

U.S. Border Patrol Sectors

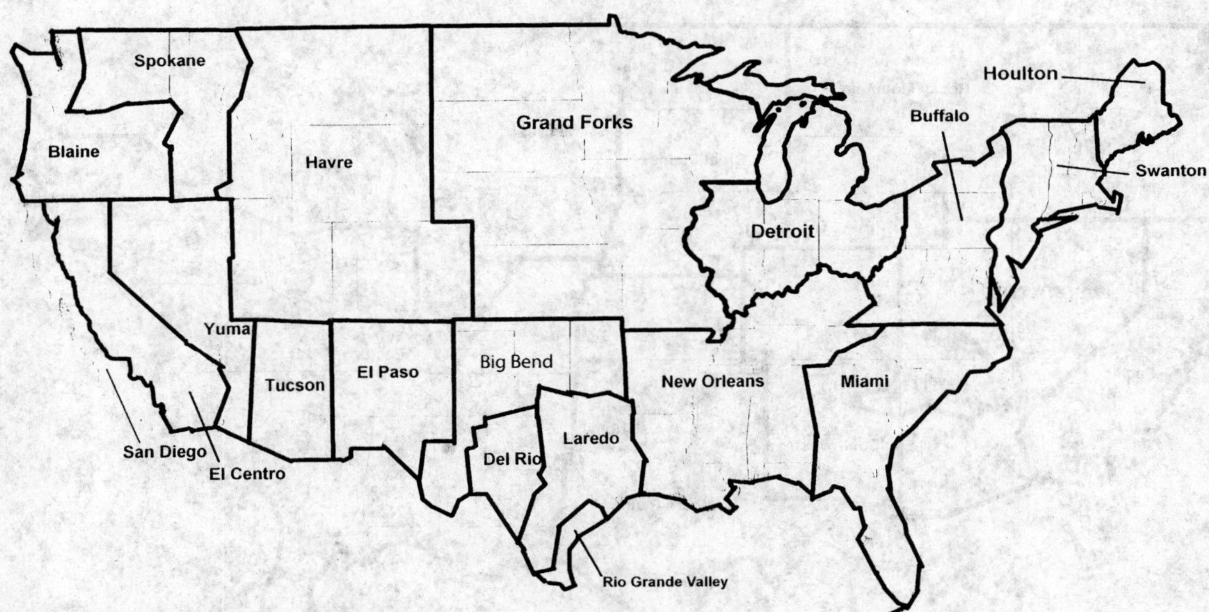

Note: Alaska is included in the Blaine Sector; Puerto Rico and the U.S. Virgin Islands are included in the Ramey Sector; Hawaii is included in the San Diego Sector.

Department of Housing and Urban Development

Field Boundaries

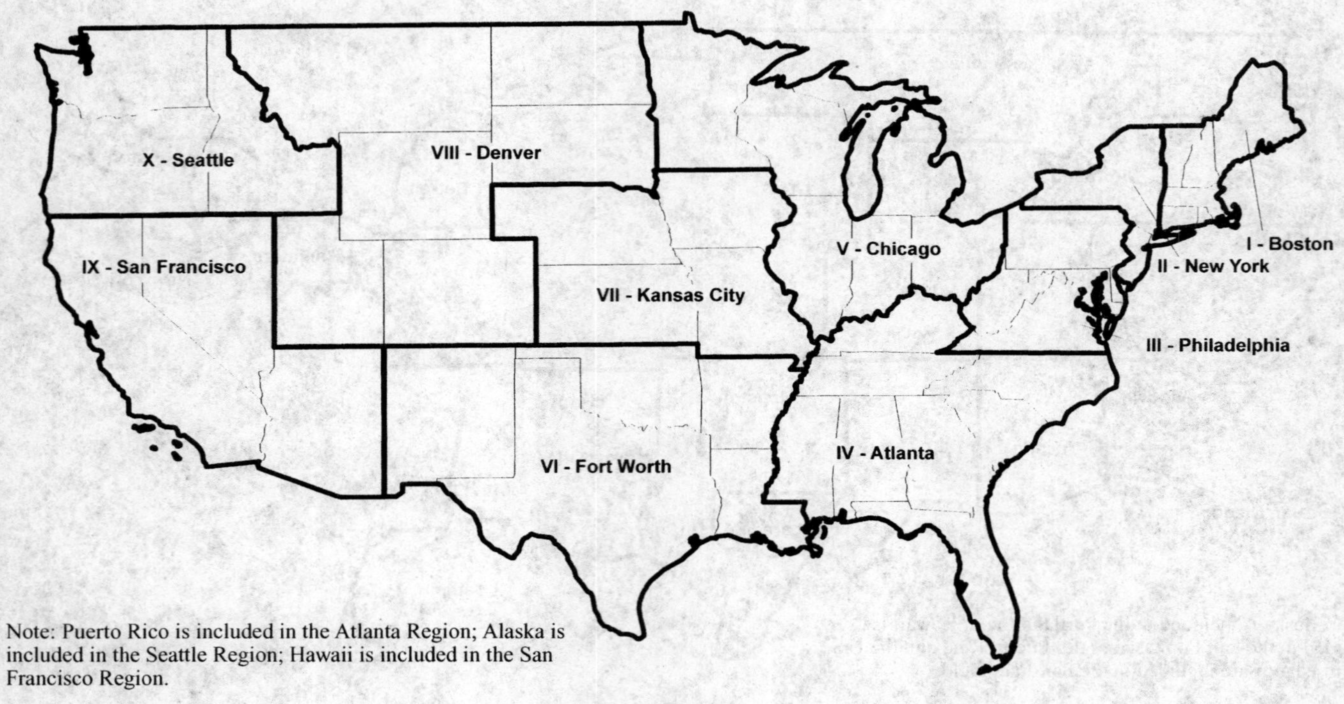

Note: Puerto Rico is included in the Atlanta Region; Alaska is included in the Seattle Region; Hawaii is included in the San Francisco Region.

Department of the Interior

Bureau of Indian Affairs

Region Boundaries

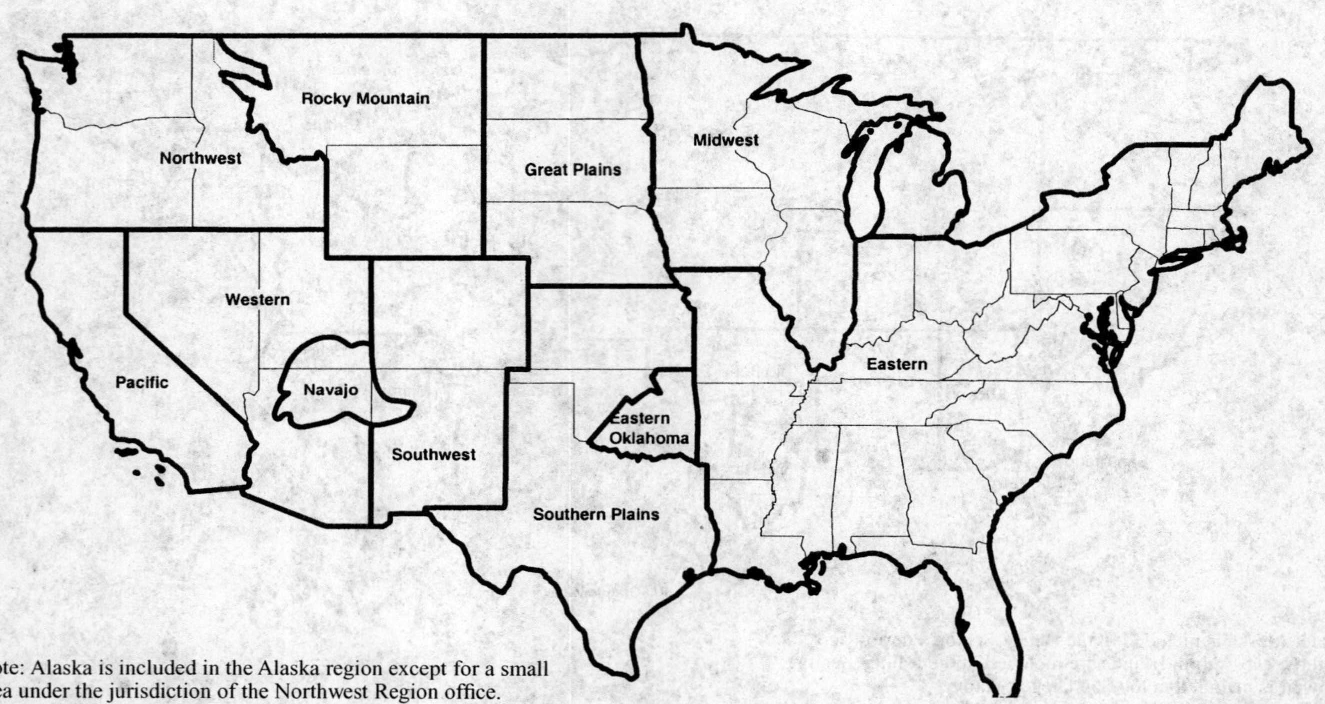

Note: Alaska is included in the Alaska region except for a small area under the jurisdiction of the Northwest Region office.

Department of the Interior

Bureau of Land Management

State Office Boundaries

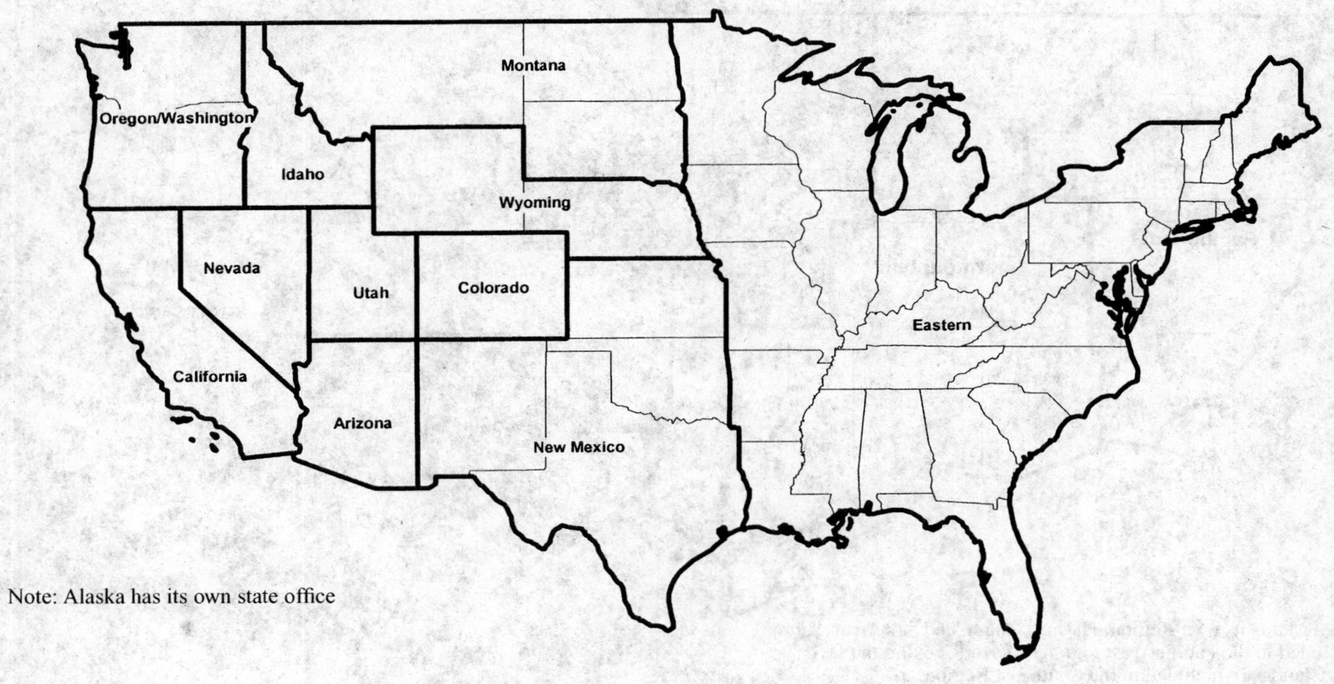

Note: Alaska has its own state office

Department of the Interior

Bureau of Reclamation

Region Boundaries

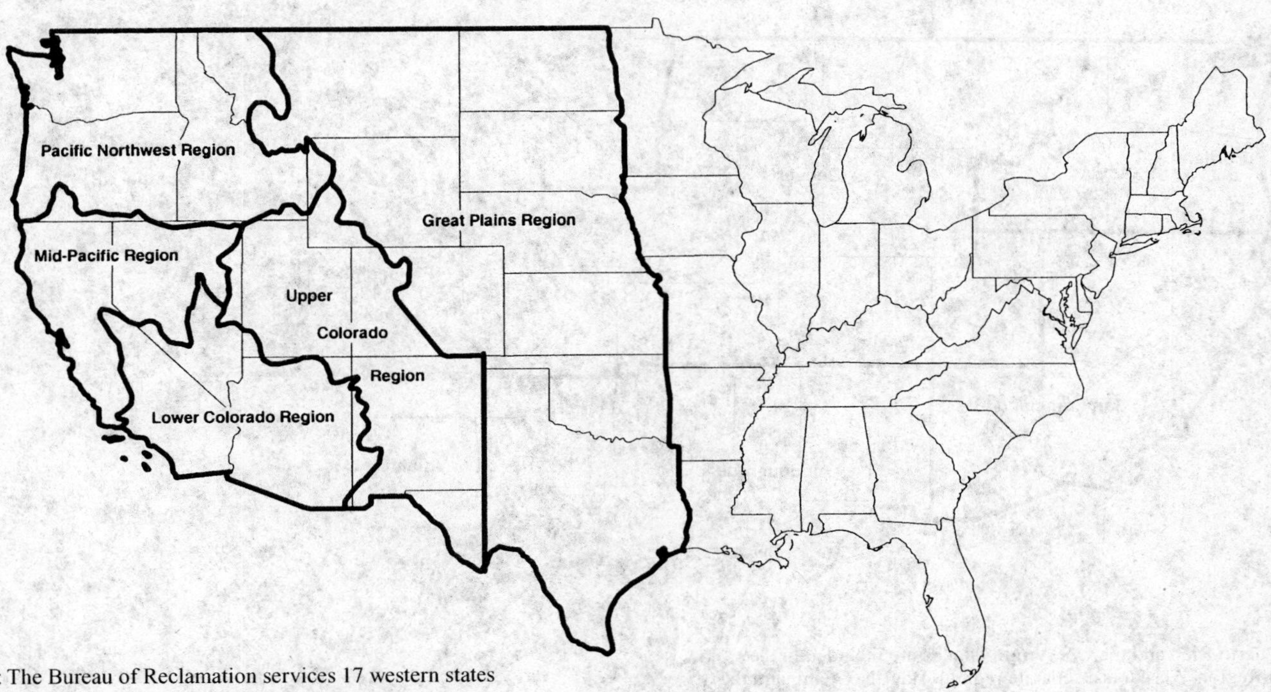

Note: The Bureau of Reclamation services 17 western states

MAPS

Department of the Interior

National Park Service

Region Boundaries

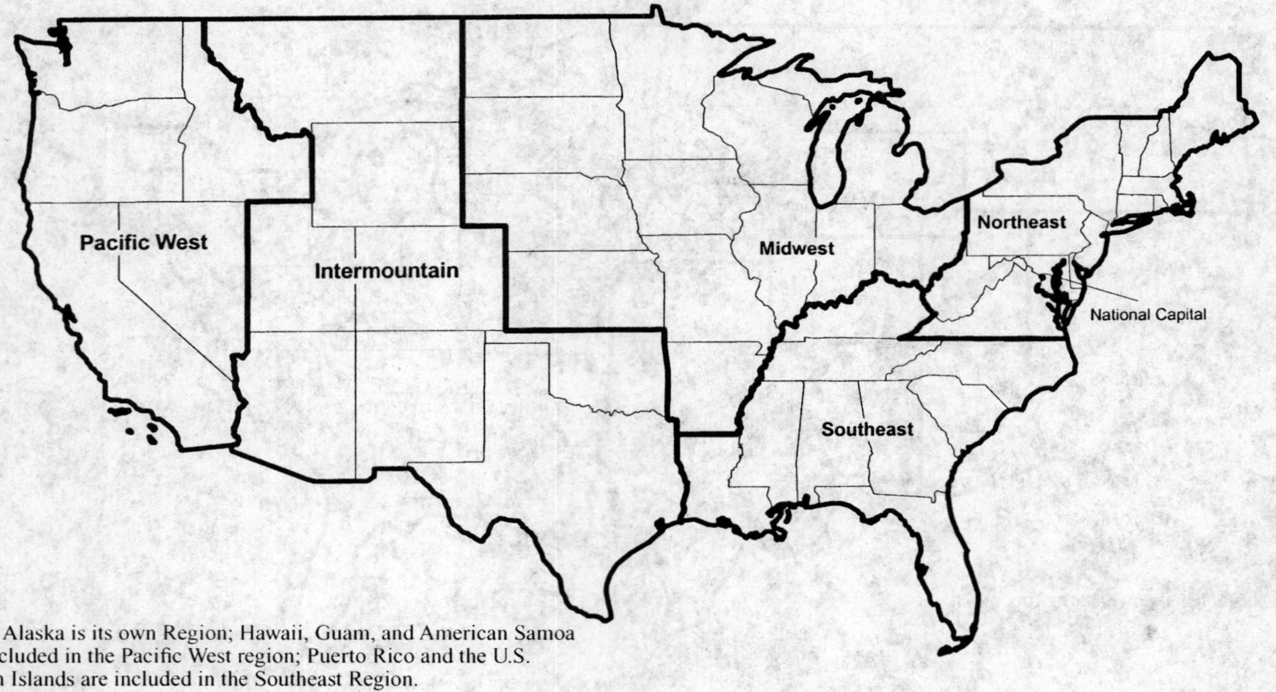

Note: Alaska is its own Region; Hawaii, Guam, and American Samoa are included in the Pacific West region; Puerto Rico and the U.S. Virgin Islands are included in the Southeast Region.

Department of the Interior

Office of Environmental Policy and Compliance

Region Boundaries

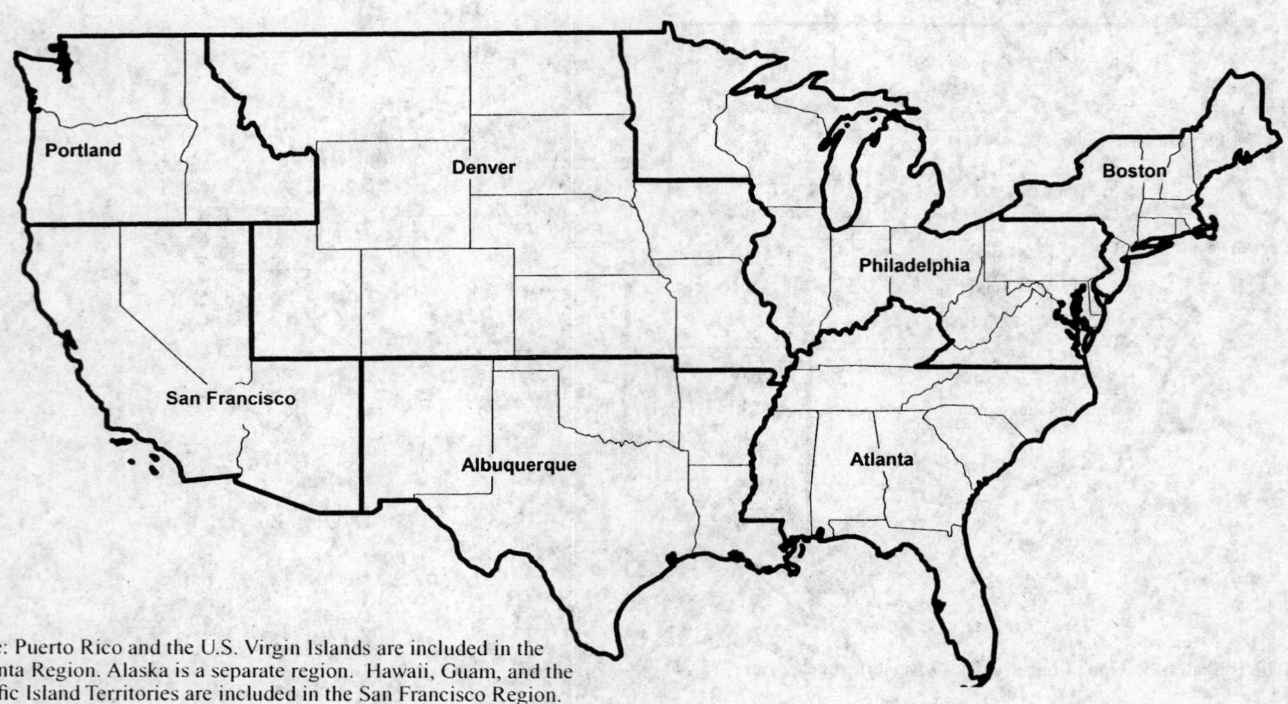

Note: Puerto Rico and the U.S. Virgin Islands are included in the Atlanta Region. Alaska is a separate region. Hawaii, Guam, and the Pacific Island Territories are included in the San Francisco Region.

Department of the Interior

Office of Surface Mining Reclamation and Enforcement

Region Boundaries

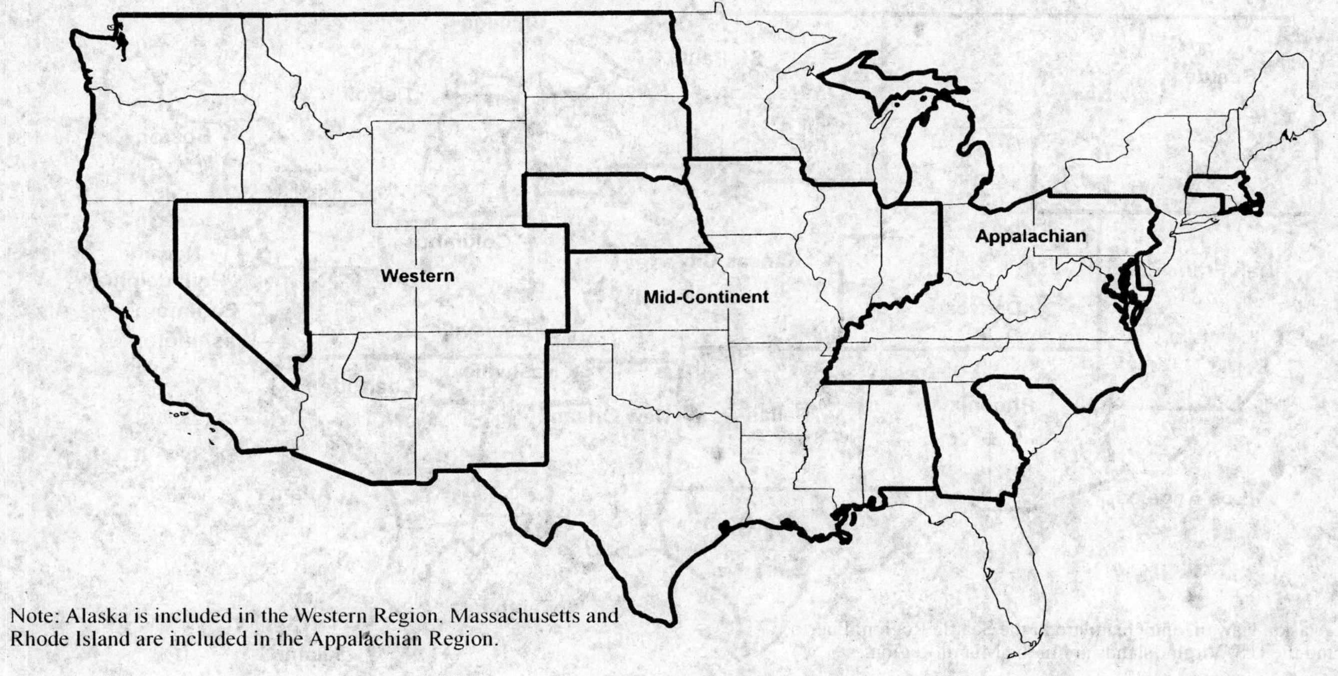

Note: Alaska is included in the Western Region. Massachusetts and Rhode Island are included in the Appalachian Region.

Department of the Interior

U.S. Geological Survey

Region Boundaries

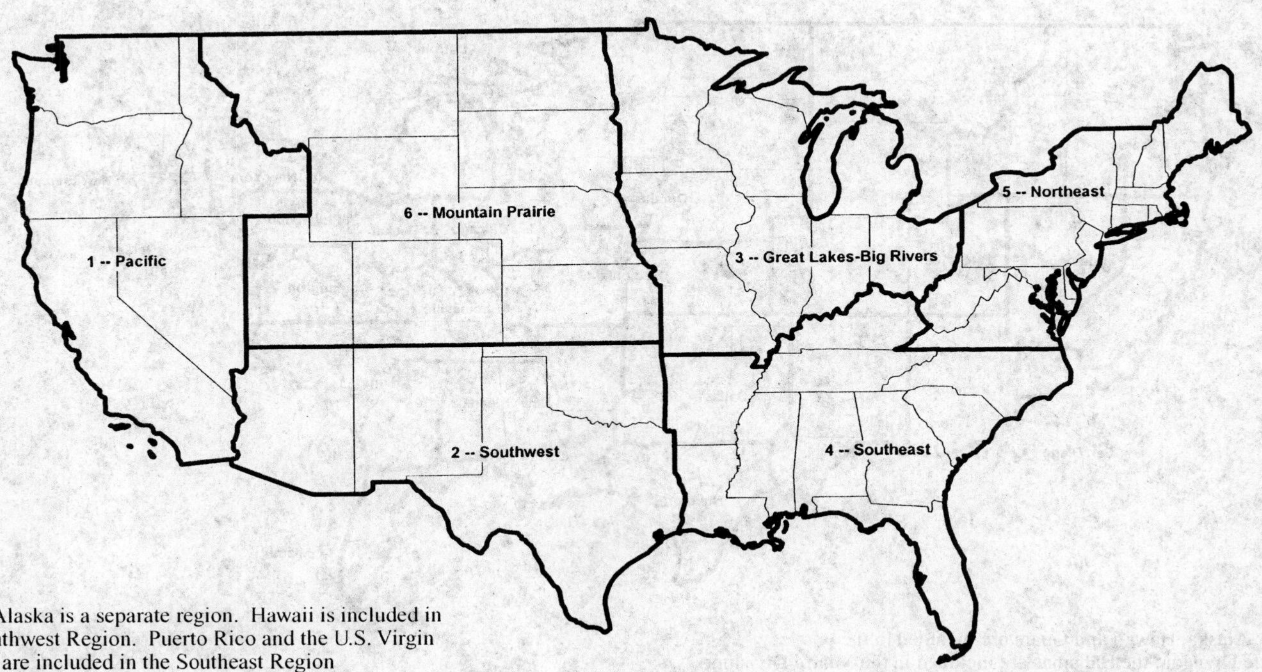

Note: Alaska is a separate region. Hawaii is included in the Southwest Region. Puerto Rico and the U.S. Virgin islands are included in the Southeast Region

MAPS

Department of Justice

Bureau of Alcohol, Tobacco, Firearms and Explosives

Field Divisions

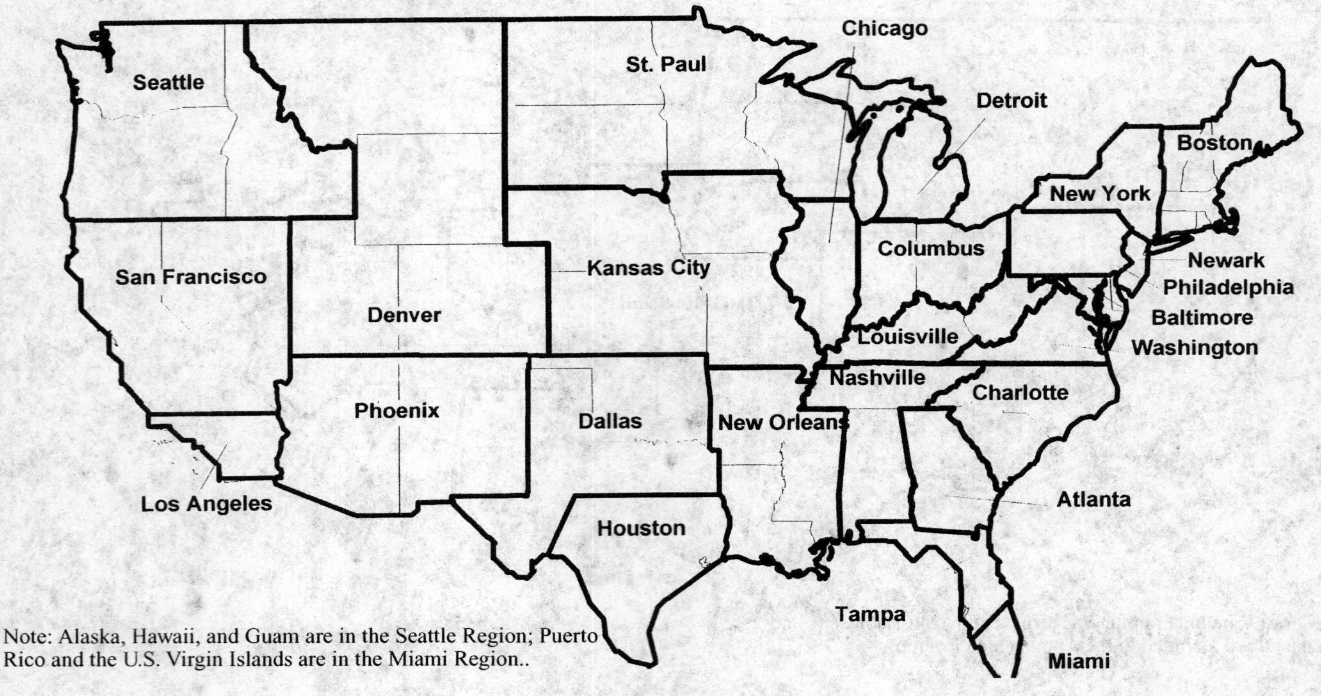

Note: Alaska, Hawaii, and Guam are in the Seattle Region; Puerto Rico and the U.S. Virgin Islands are in the Miami Region..

Department of Justice

Drug Enforcement Administration

Division Boundaries

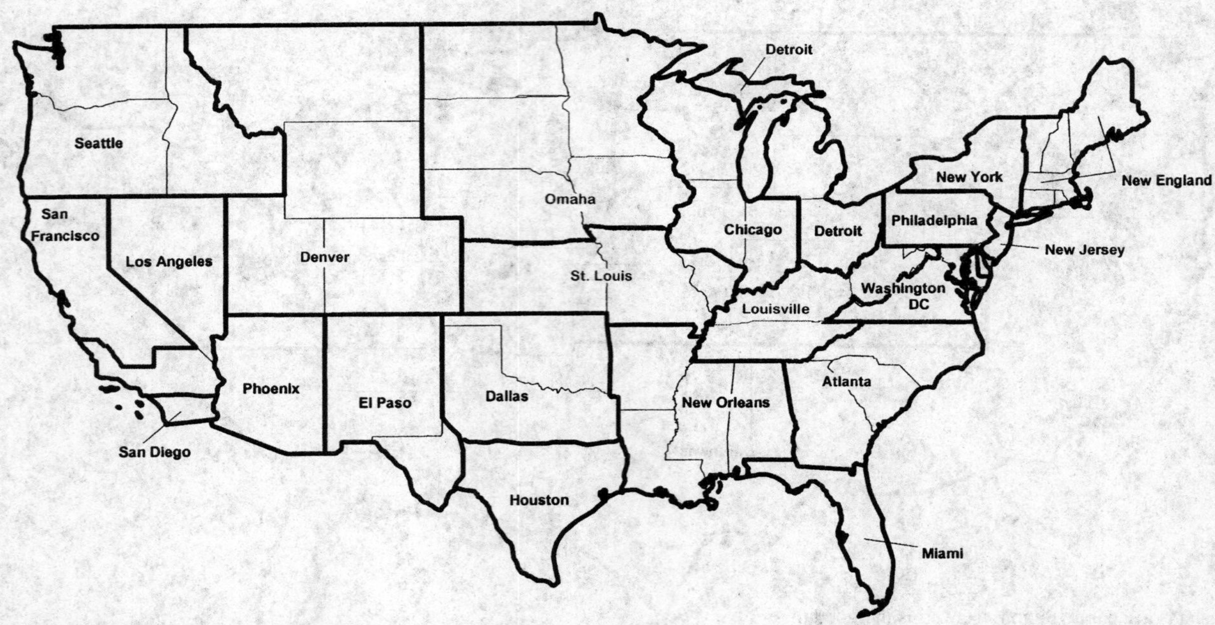

Note: Alaska, Hawaii and Guam are included in the Seattle Division; the Bahamas are included in the Miami Division; Hawaii is part of the Los Angeles Division; Puerto Rico and the U.S. Virgin Islands are included in the Caribbean Division.

Department of Justice

Federal Bureau of Prisons

Region Boundaries

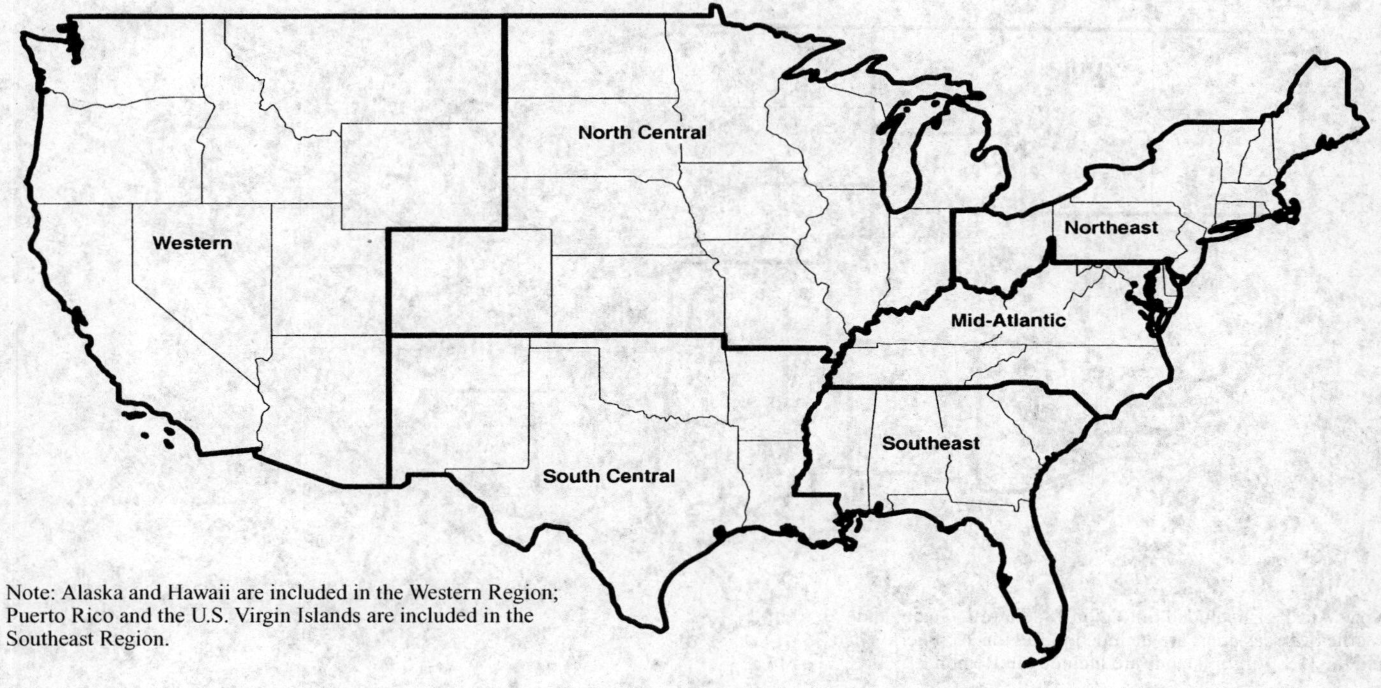

Note: Alaska and Hawaii are included in the Western Region; Puerto Rico and the U.S. Virgin Islands are included in the Southeast Region.

Department of Justice

Federal Judicial Districts
U.S. Attorneys and U.S. Marshals Service

District Office Boundaries

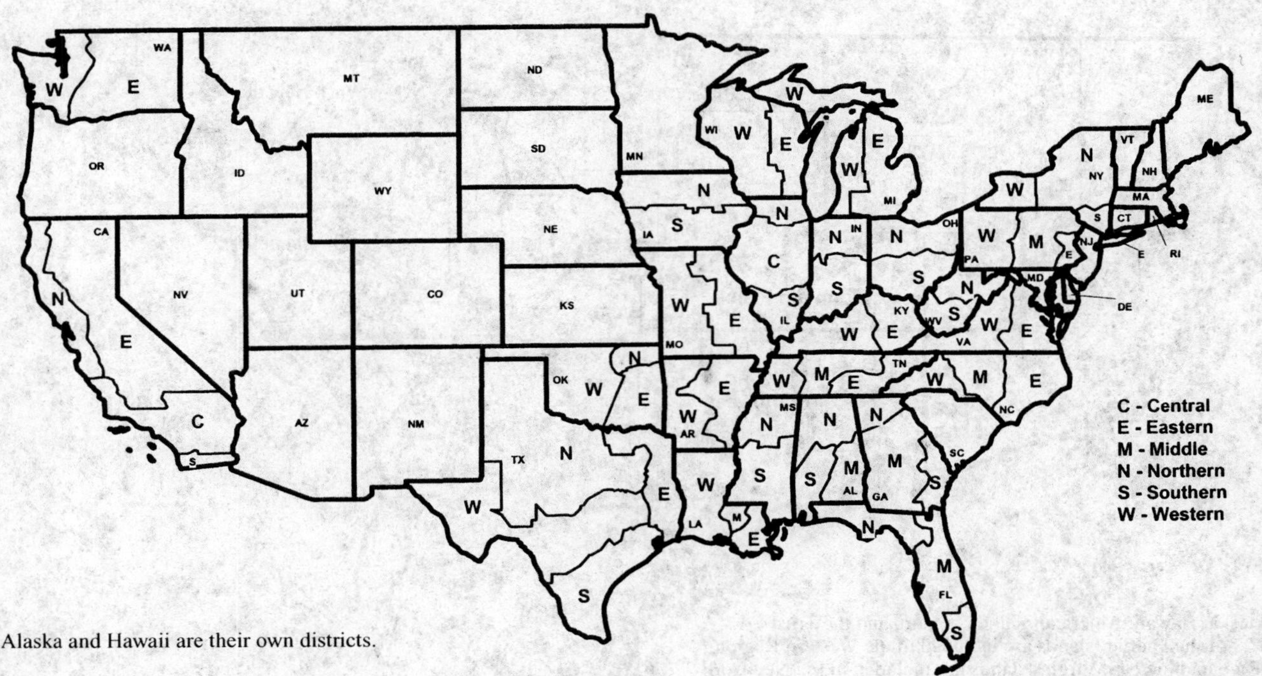

Note: Alaska and Hawaii are their own districts.

Department of Justice

U.S. Trustee Circuits

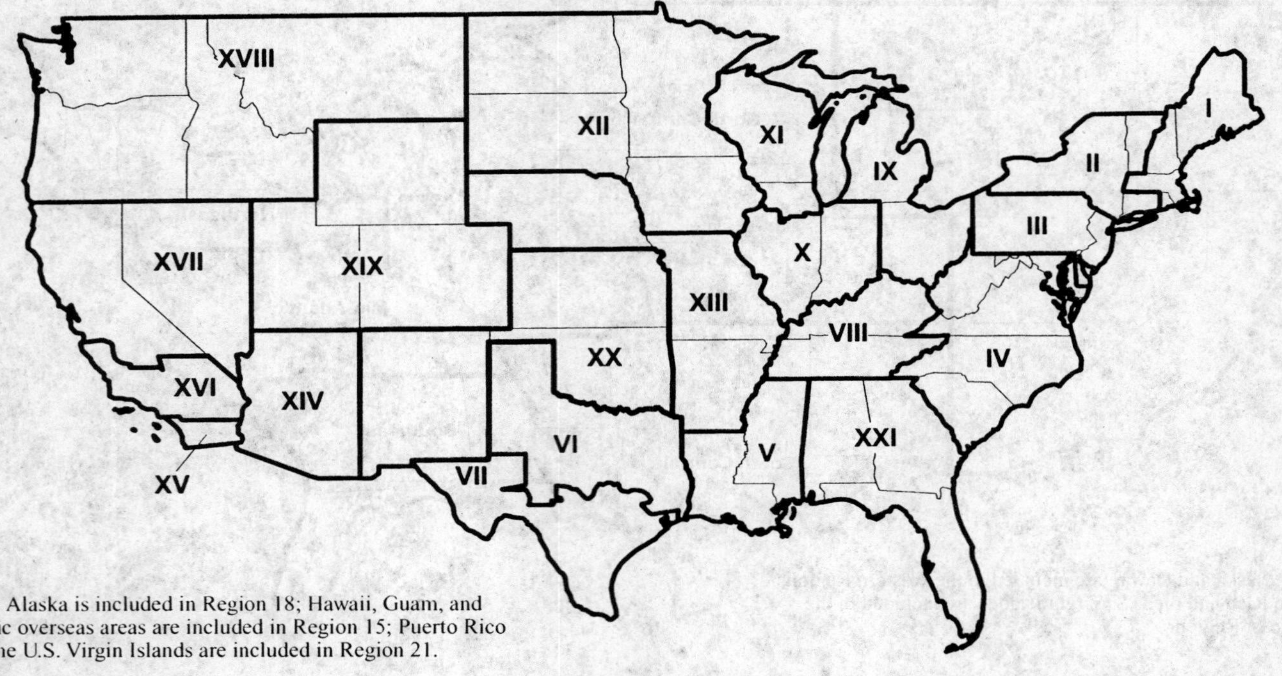

Note: Alaska is included in Region 18; Hawaii, Guam, and Pacific overseas areas are included in Region 15; Puerto Rico and the U.S. Virgin Islands are included in Region 21.

Department of Labor

Bureau of Labor Statistics

Region Boundaries

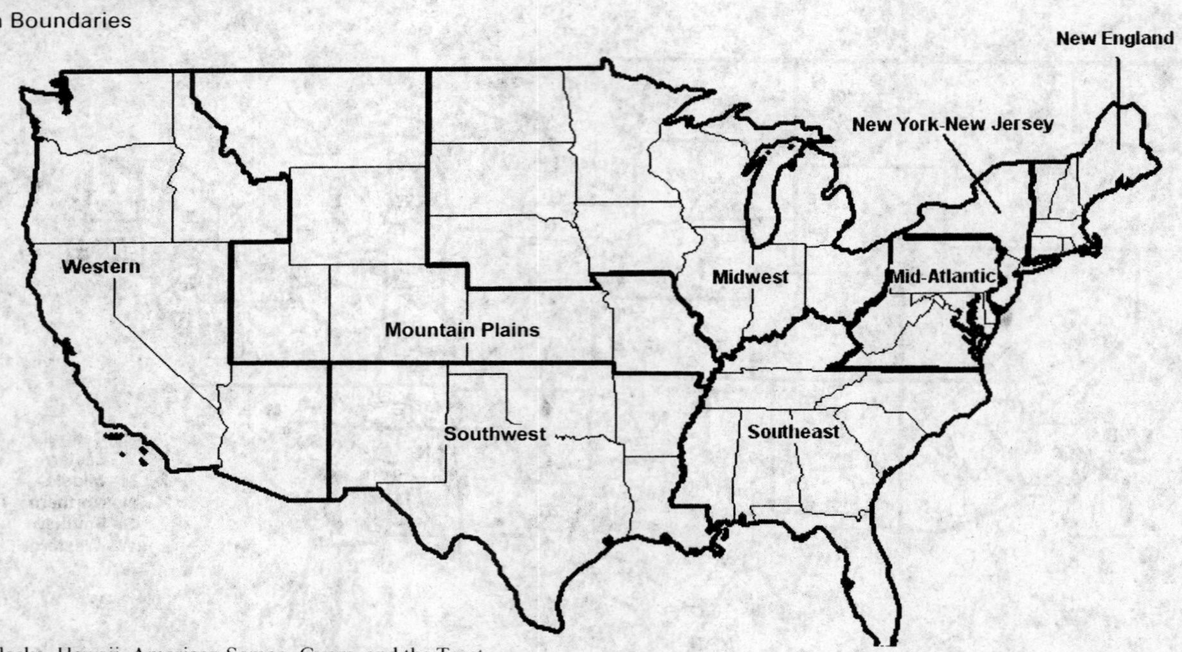

Note: Alaska, Hawaii, American Samoa, Guam, and the Trust Territories of the Pacific Islands are included in the Western Region; Puerto Rico and the U.S. Virgin Islands are included in the New York-New Jersey Region.

Department of Labor

Employee Benefits Security Administration

Region Boundaries

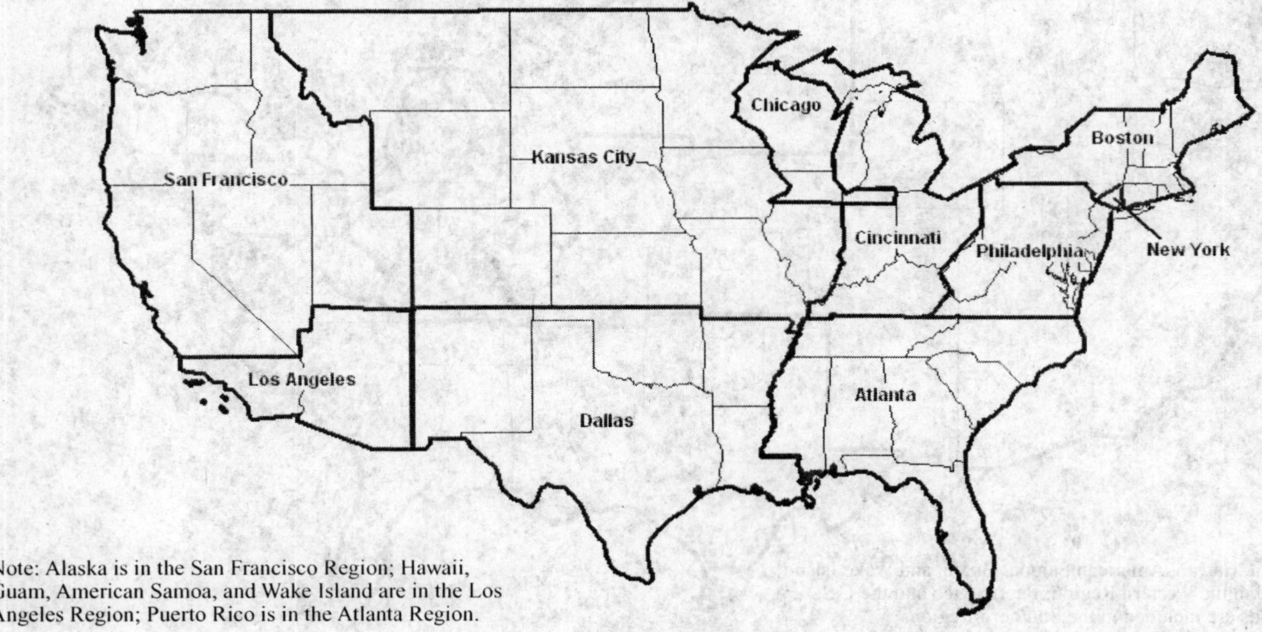

Note: Alaska is in the San Francisco Region; Hawaii, Guam, American Samoa, and Wake Island are in the Los Angeles Region; Puerto Rico is in the Atlanta Region.

Department of Labor

Employment Standards Administration
Office of Federal Contract Compliance Programs

Region Boundaries

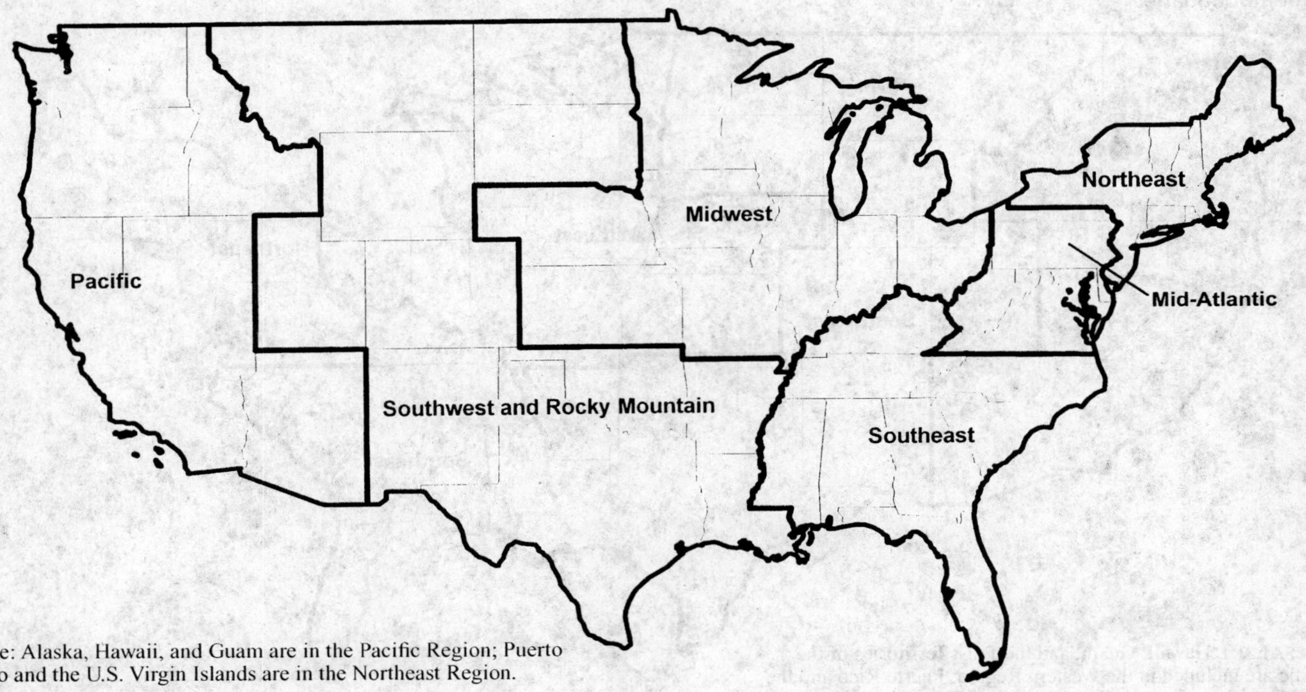

Note: Alaska, Hawaii, and Guam are in the Pacific Region; Puerto Rico and the U.S. Virgin Islands are in the Northeast Region.

Department of Labor

Office of Labor-Management Standards

Region Boundaries

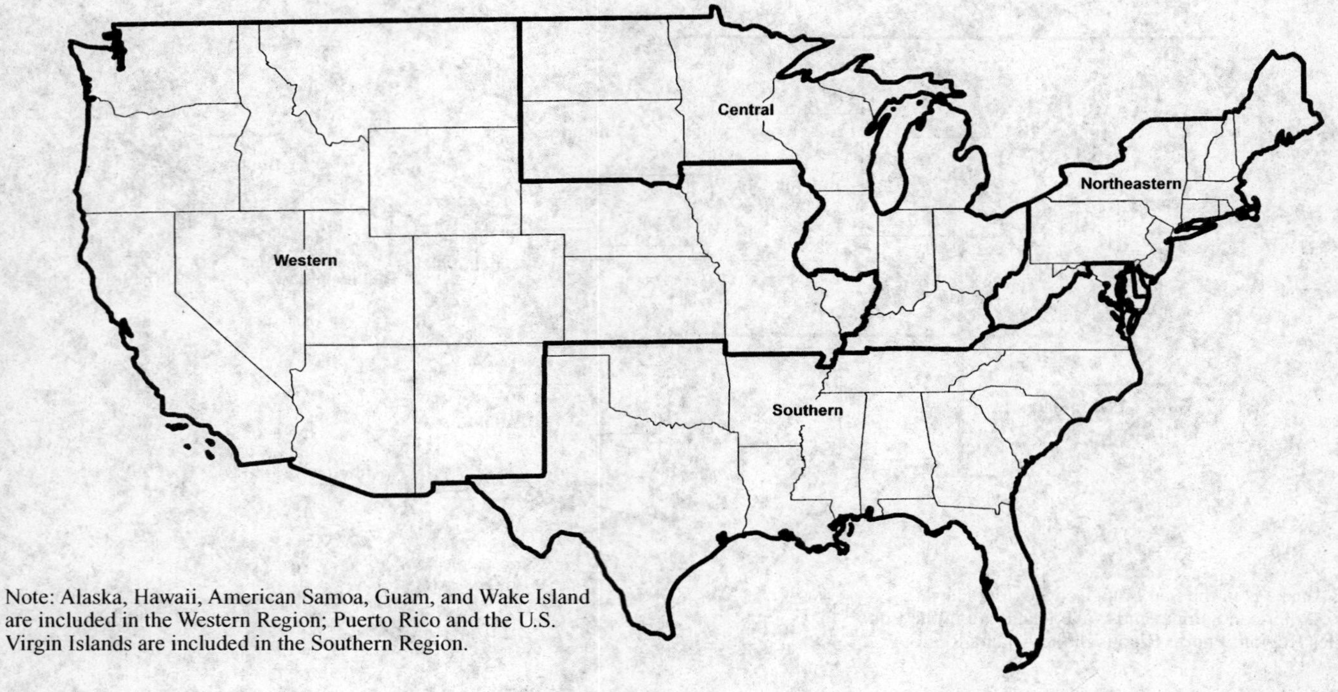

Note: Alaska, Hawaii, American Samoa, Guam, and Wake Island are included in the Western Region; Puerto Rico and the U.S. Virgin Islands are included in the Southern Region.

Department of Labor

Employment Standards Administration
Wage and Hour Division

Region Boundaries

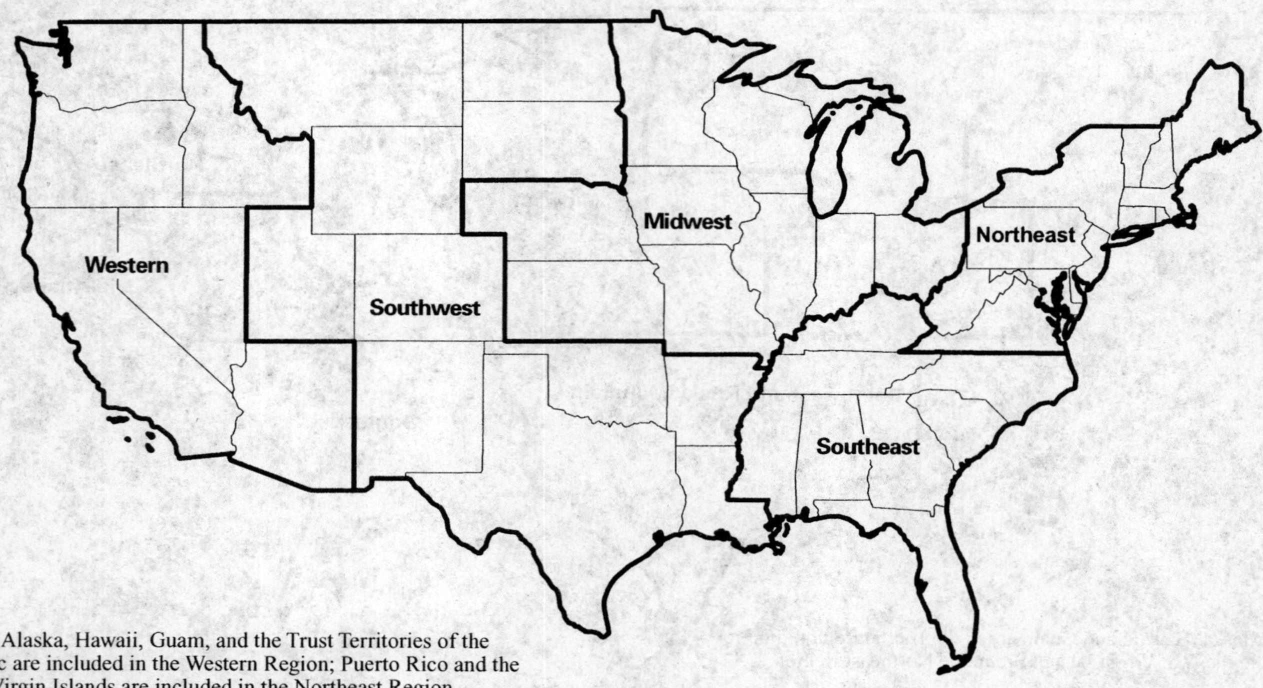

Note: Alaska, Hawaii, Guam, and the Trust Territories of the Pacific are included in the Western Region; Puerto Rico and the U.S. Virgin Islands are included in the Northeast Region.

Department of Labor

Mine Safety and Health Administration
Coal Mine Safety and Health

District Boundaries

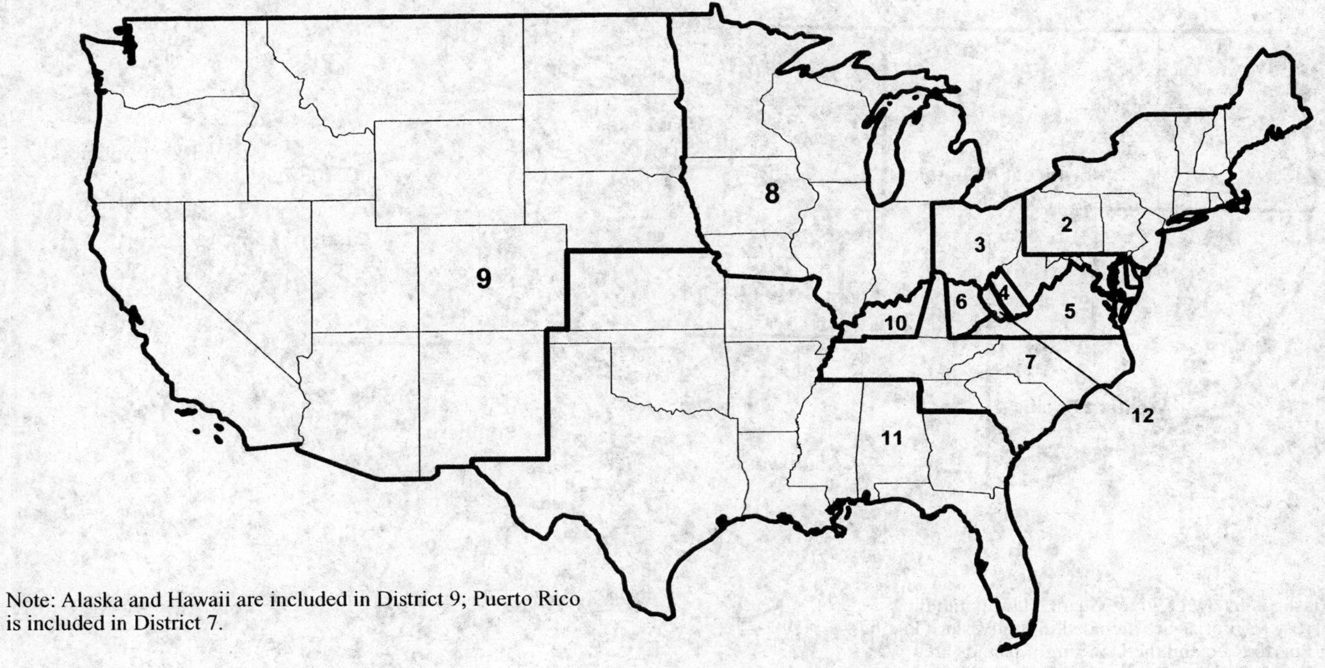

Note: Alaska and Hawaii are included in District 9; Puerto Rico is included in District 7.

Department of Labor

Mine Safety and Health Administration
Metal and Nonmetal Mine Safety and Health

District Boundaries

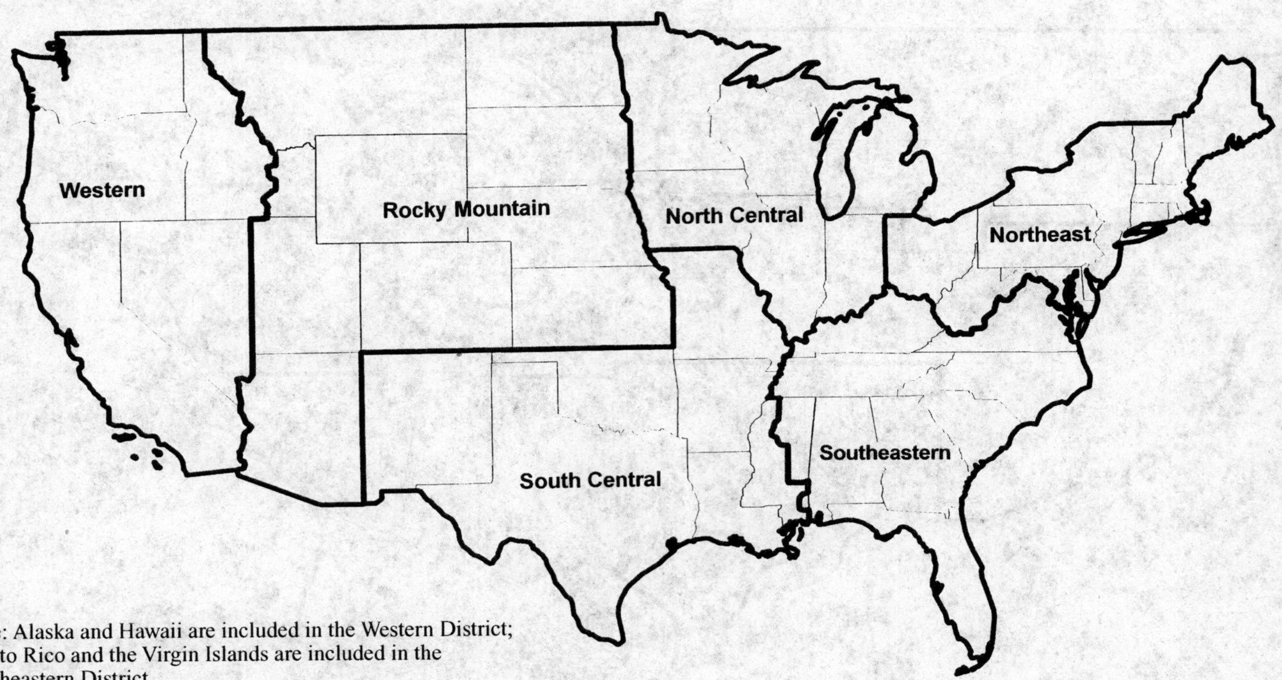

Note: Alaska and Hawaii are included in the Western District; Puerto Rico and the Virgin Islands are included in the Southeastern District..

MAPS

Department of Transportation

Federal Aviation Administration

Region Boundaries

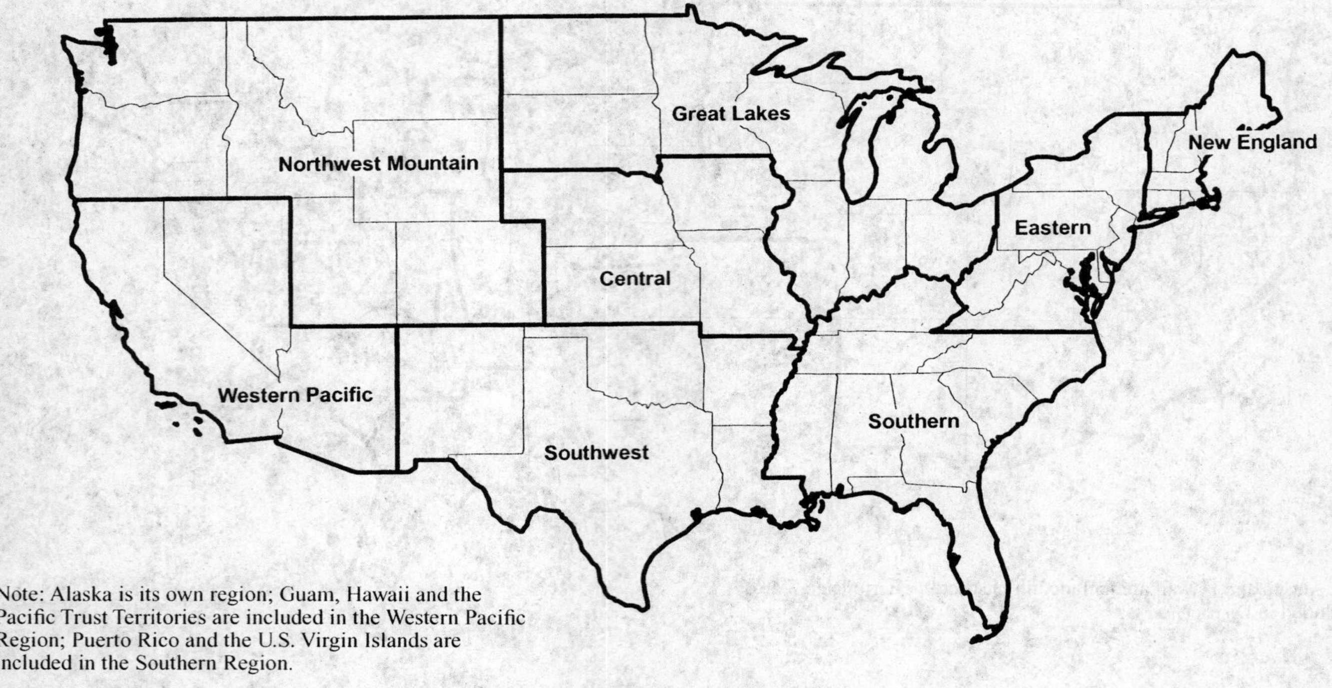

Note: Alaska is its own region; Guam, Hawaii and the Pacific Trust Territories are included in the Western Pacific Region; Puerto Rico and the U.S. Virgin Islands are included in the Southern Region.

Department of Transportation

Federal Railroad Administration

Region Boundaries

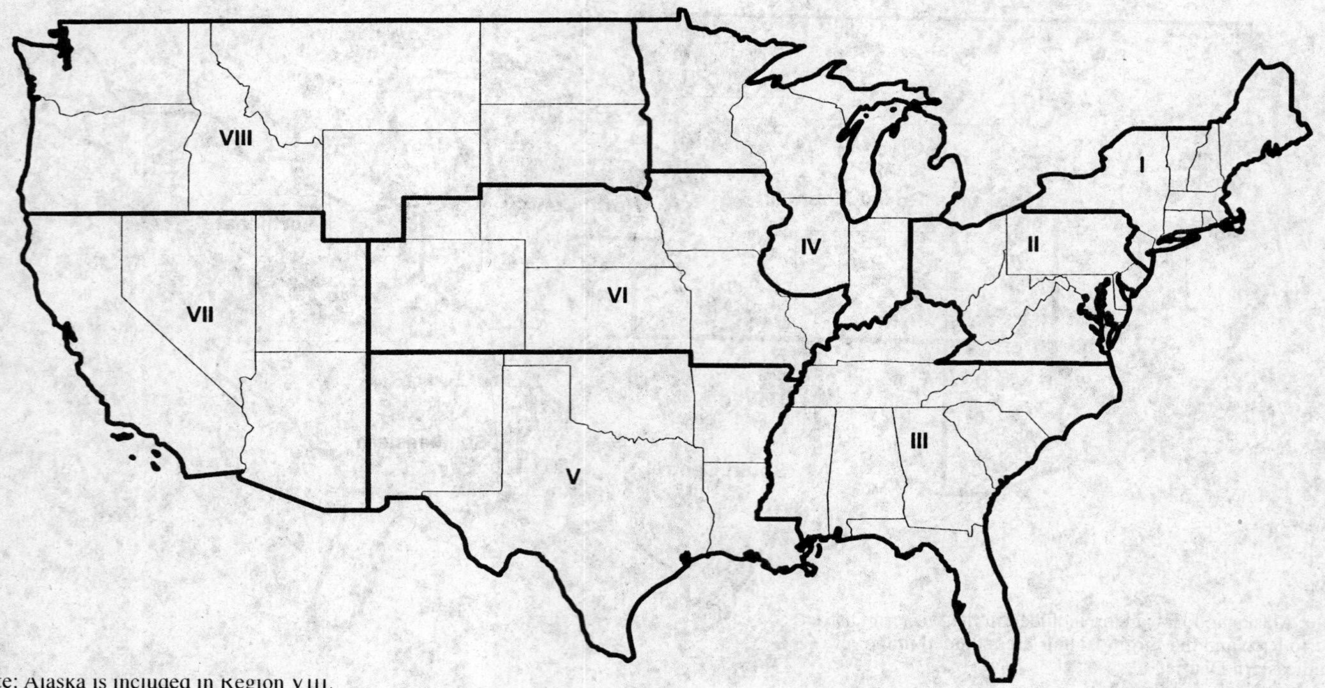

Note: Alaska is included in Region VIII.

Department of Transportation

Maritime Administration

Region Boundaries

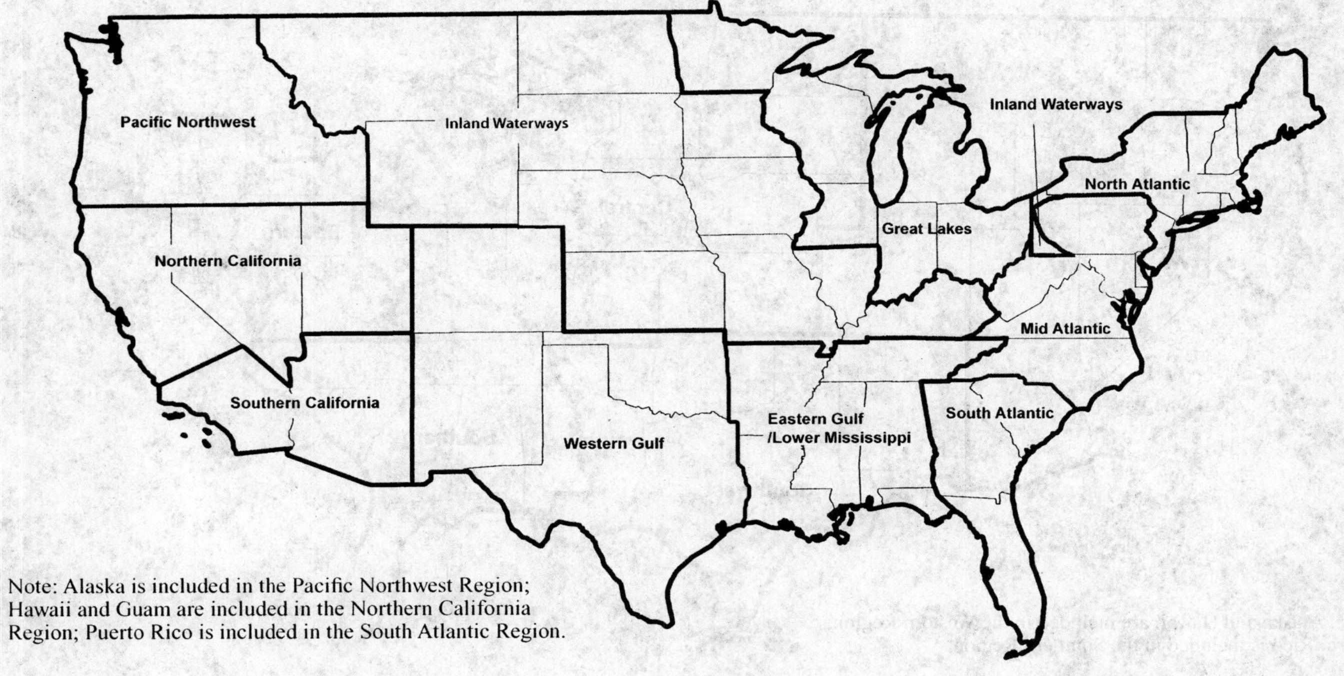

Note: Alaska is included in the Pacific Northwest Region; Hawaii and Guam are included in the Northern California Region; Puerto Rico is included in the South Atlantic Region.

Department of Transportation

Pipeline and Hazardous Materials Safety Administration
Office of Hazardous Materials Safety

Region Boundaries

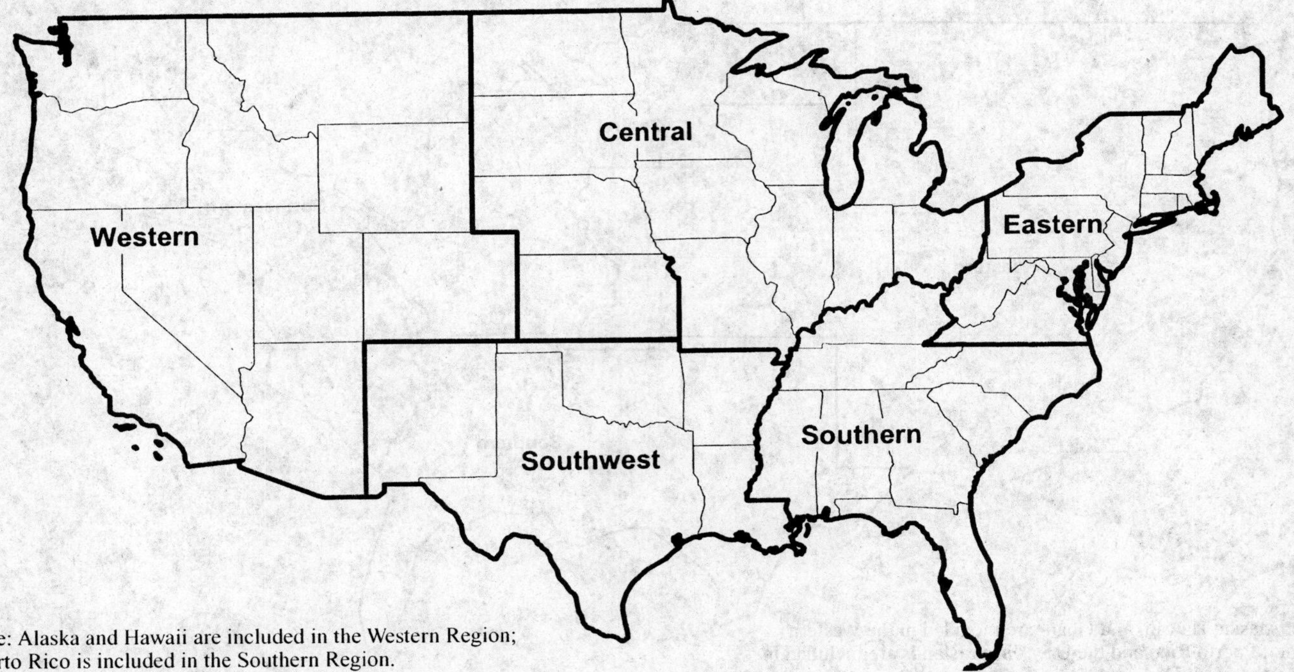

Note: Alaska and Hawaii are included in the Western Region; Puerto Rico is included in the Southern Region.

Department of Transportation

Pipeline and Hazardous Materials Safety Administration
Office of Pipeline Safety

Region Boundaries

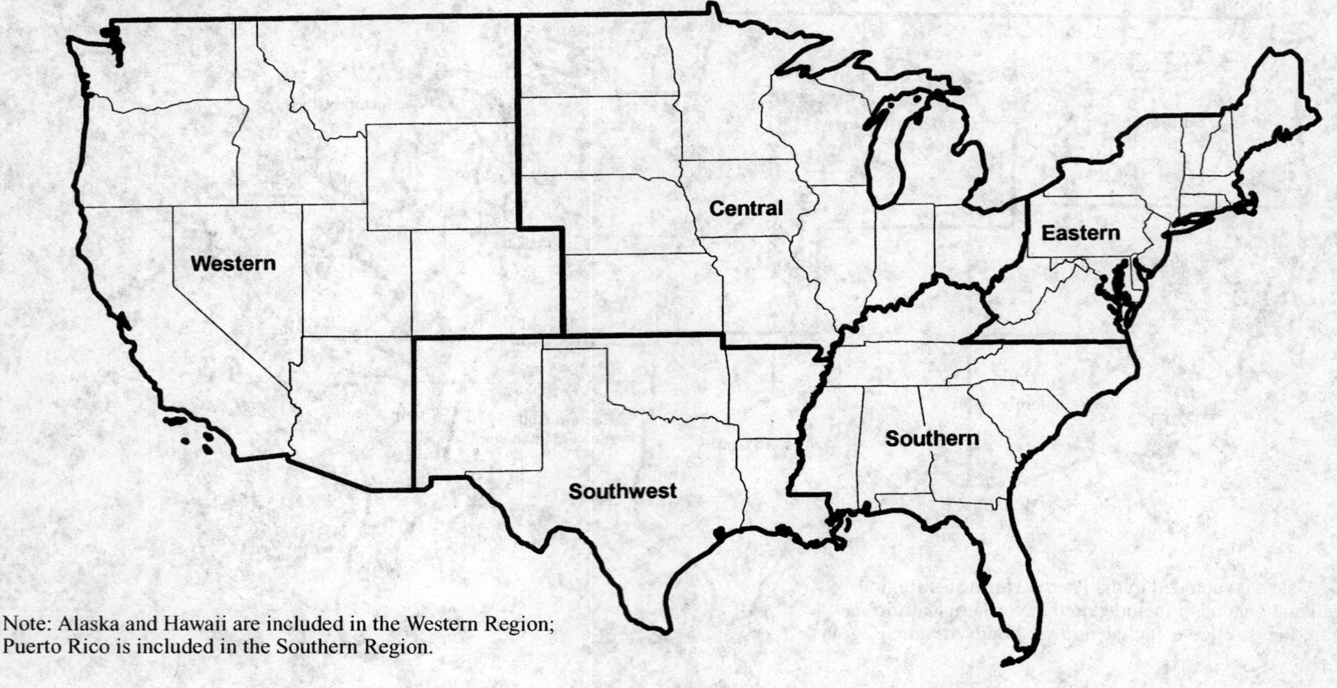

Note: Alaska and Hawaii are included in the Western Region; Puerto Rico is included in the Southern Region.

Department of the Treasury

Comptroller of the Currency

District Boundaries

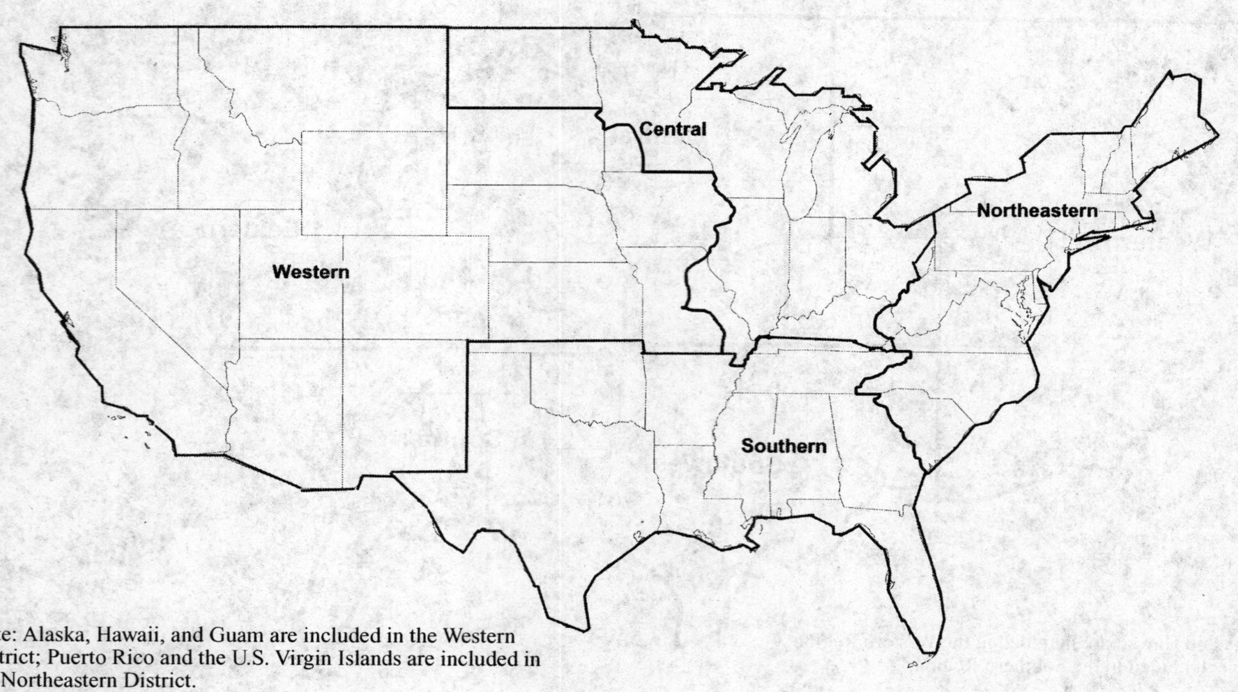

Note: Alaska, Hawaii, and Guam are included in the Western District; Puerto Rico and the U.S. Virgin Islands are included in the Northeastern District.

Department of Veterans Affairs

Veterans Benefits Administration

Area Boundaries

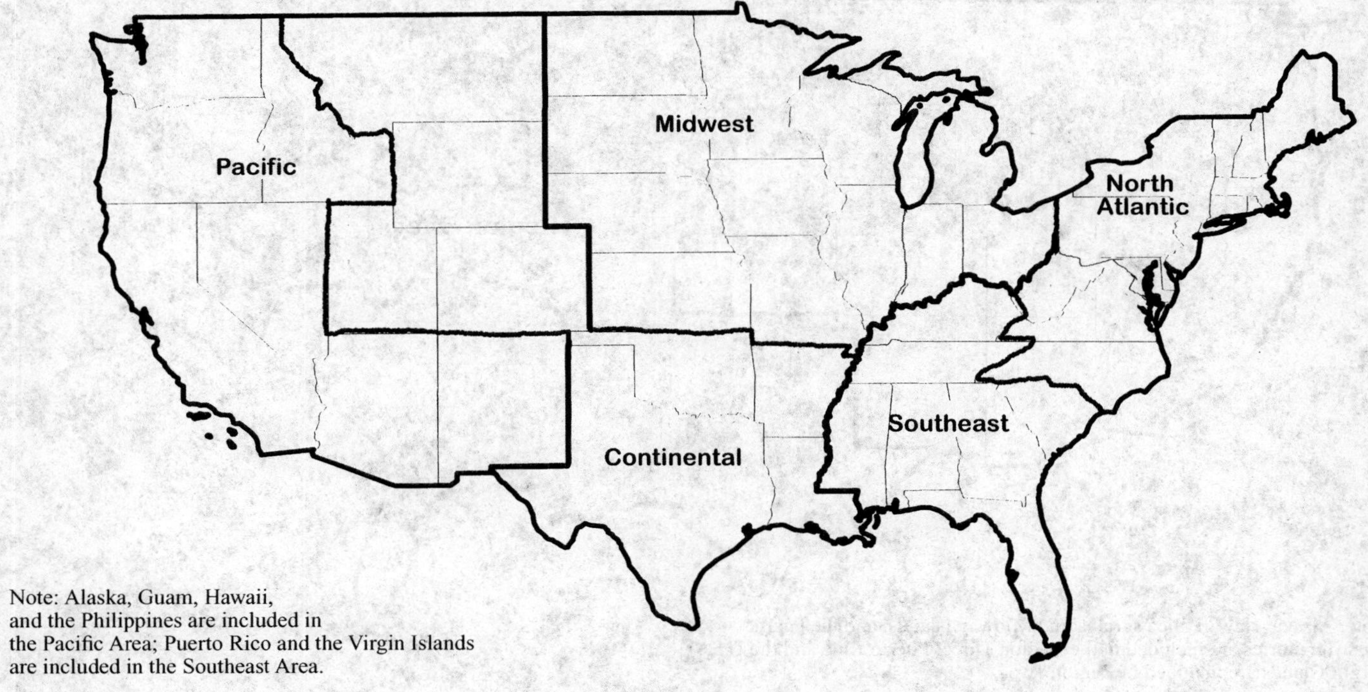

Note: Alaska, Guam, Hawaii, and the Philippines are included in the Pacific Area; Puerto Rico and the Virgin Islands are included in the Southeast Area.

Commission on Civil Rights

Region Boundaries

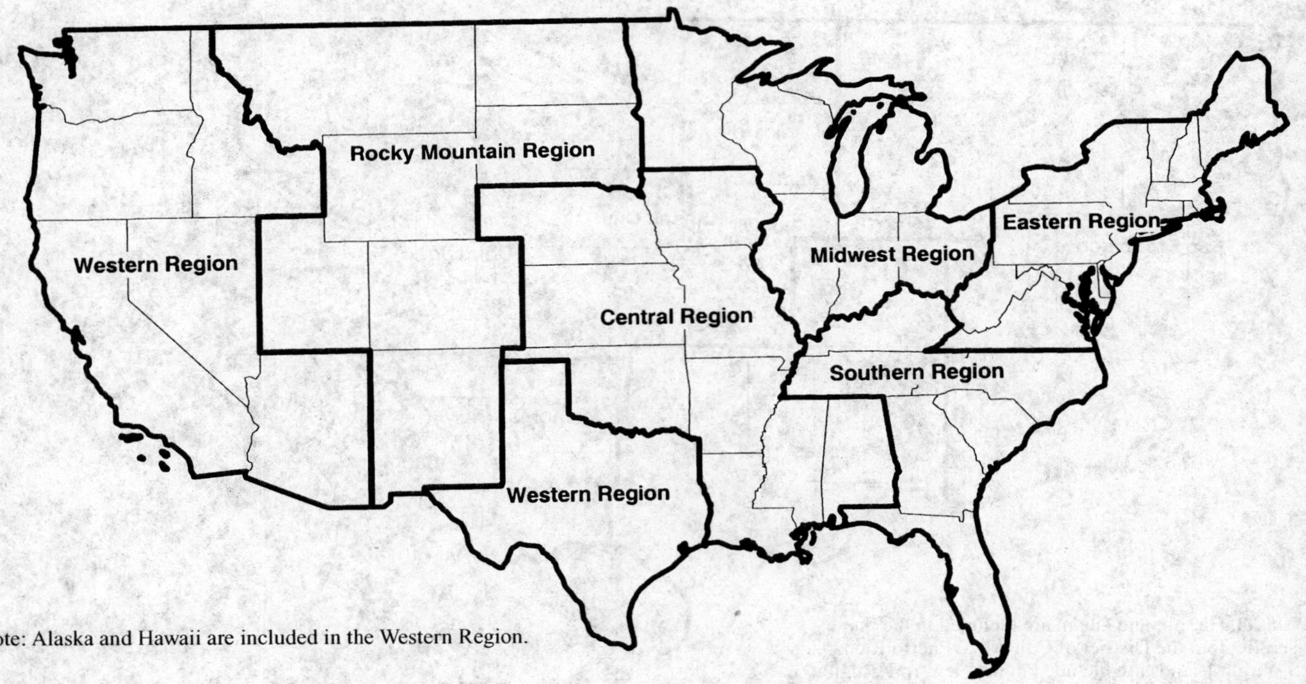

Note: Alaska and Hawaii are included in the Western Region.

Federal Communications Commission

Enforcement Bureau

Region Boundaries

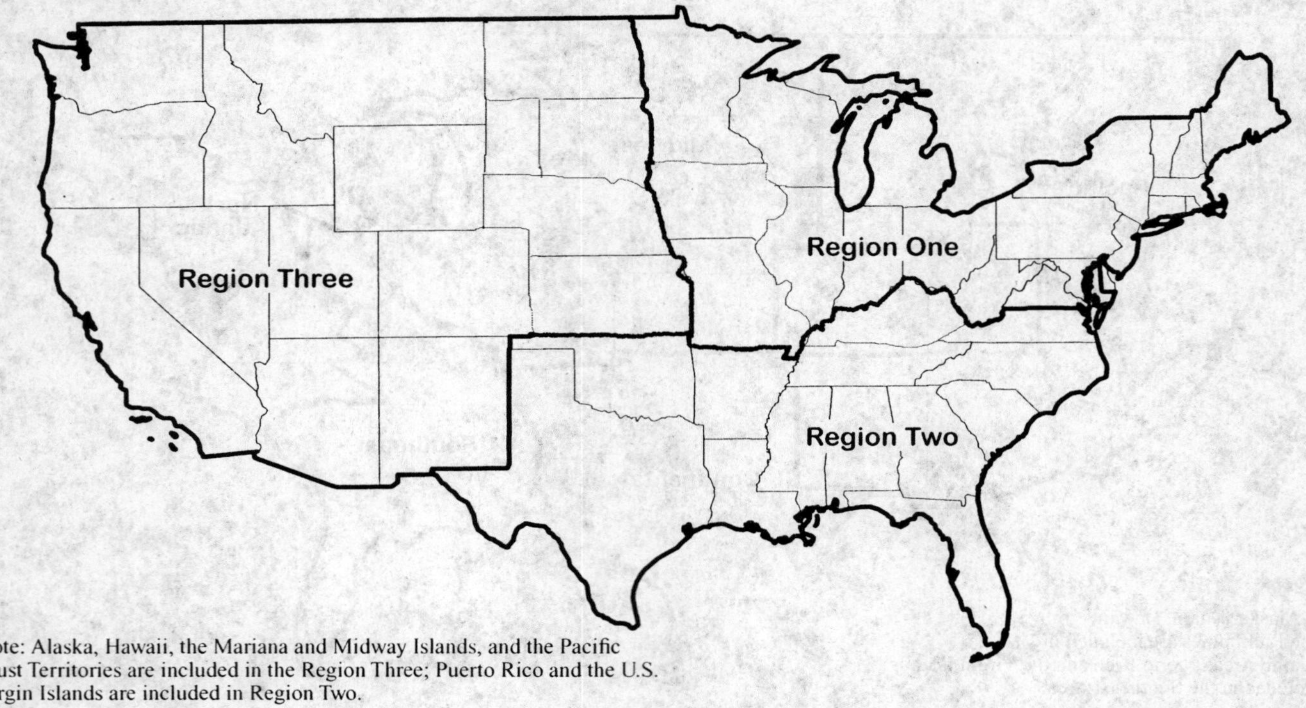

Note: Alaska, Hawaii, the Mariana and Midway Islands, and the Pacific Trust Territories are included in the Region Three; Puerto Rico and the U.S. Virgin Islands are included in Region Two.

Federal Deposit Insurance Corporation

Division of Supervision and Consumer Protection

Office Boundaries

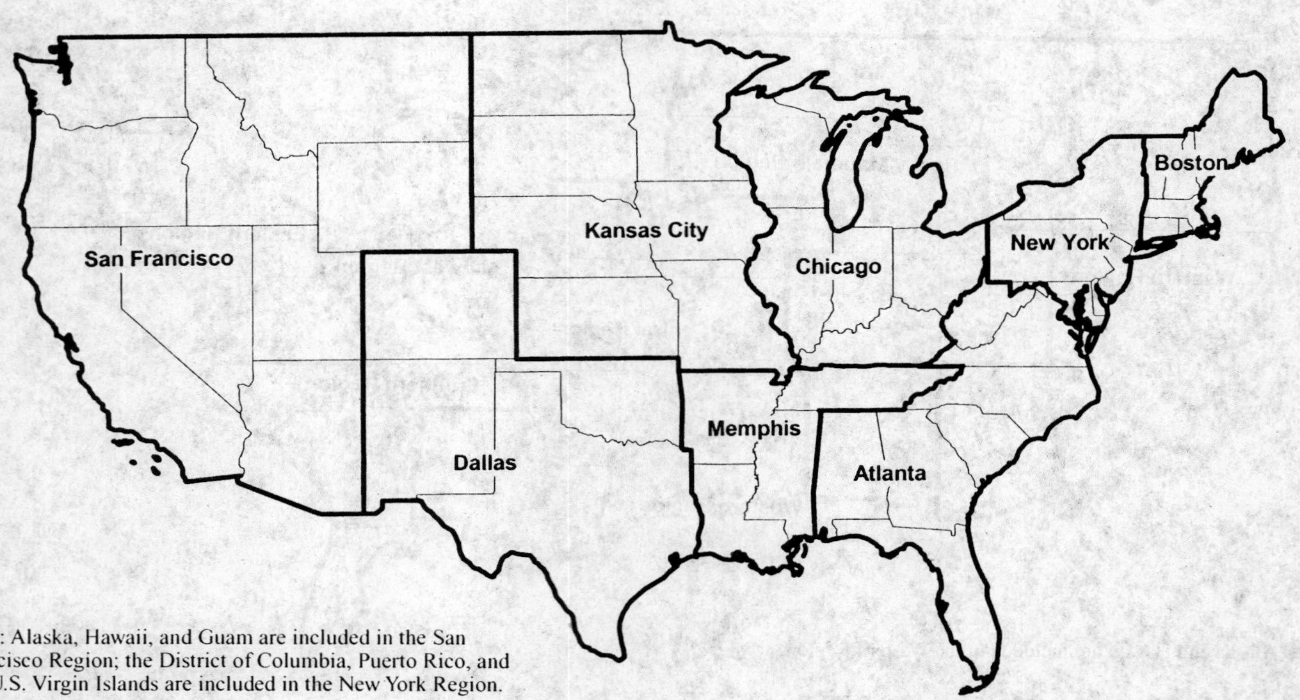

Note: Alaska, Hawaii, and Guam are included in the San Francisco Region; the District of Columbia, Puerto Rico, and the U.S. Virgin Islands are included in the New York Region.

Federal Reserve System

District Boundaries

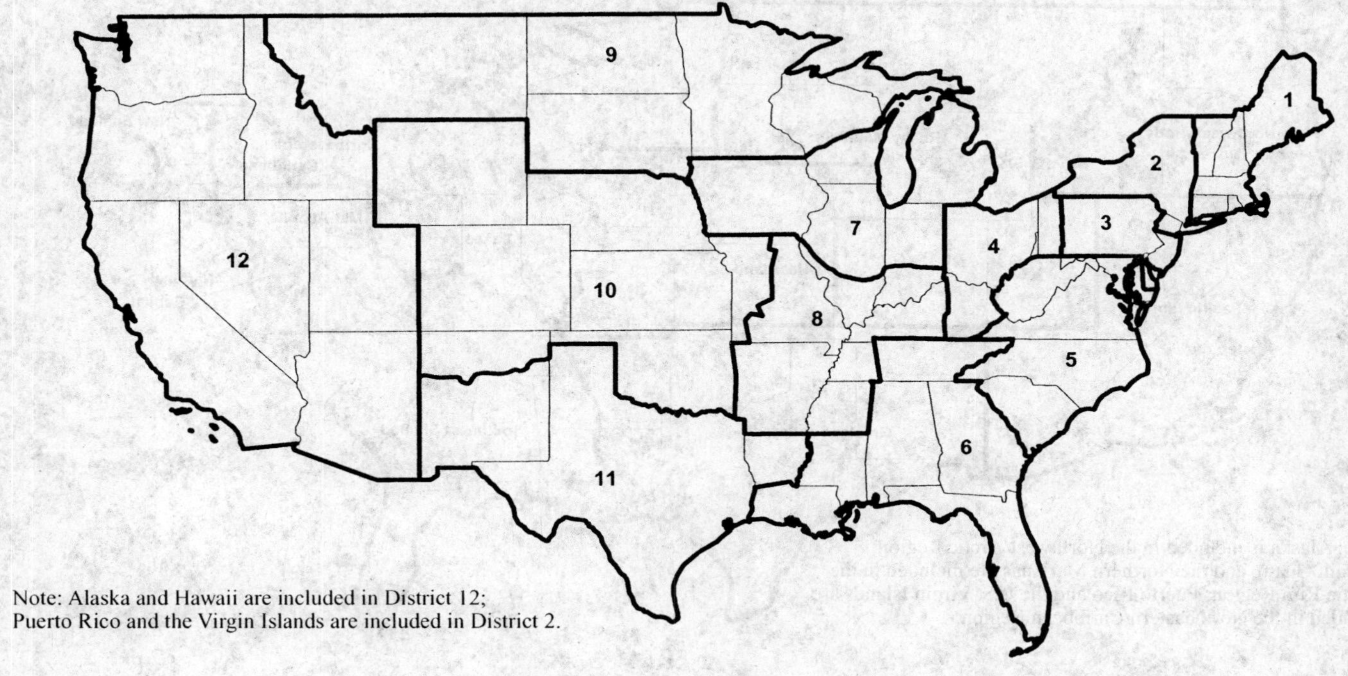

Note: Alaska and Hawaii are included in District 12; Puerto Rico and the Virgin Islands are included in District 2.

Federal Trade Commission

Region Boundaries

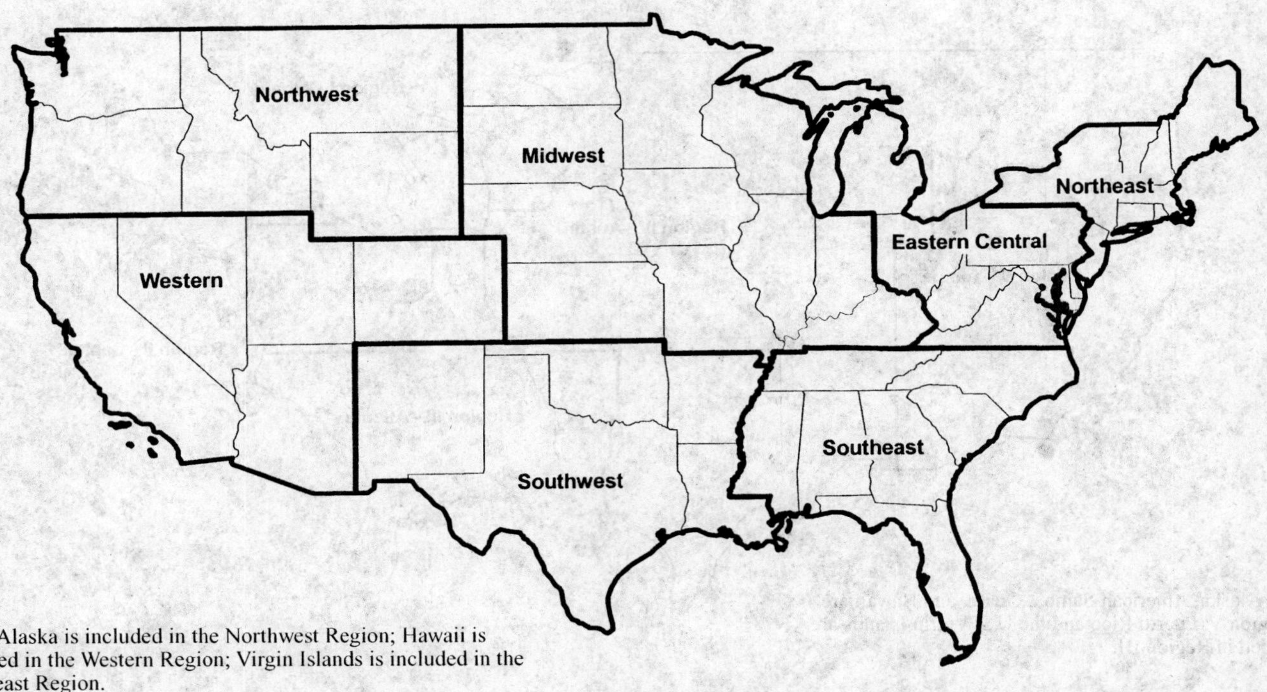

Note: Alaska is included in the Northwest Region; Hawaii is included in the Western Region; Virgin Islands is included in the Northeast Region.

General Services Administration

Region Boundaries

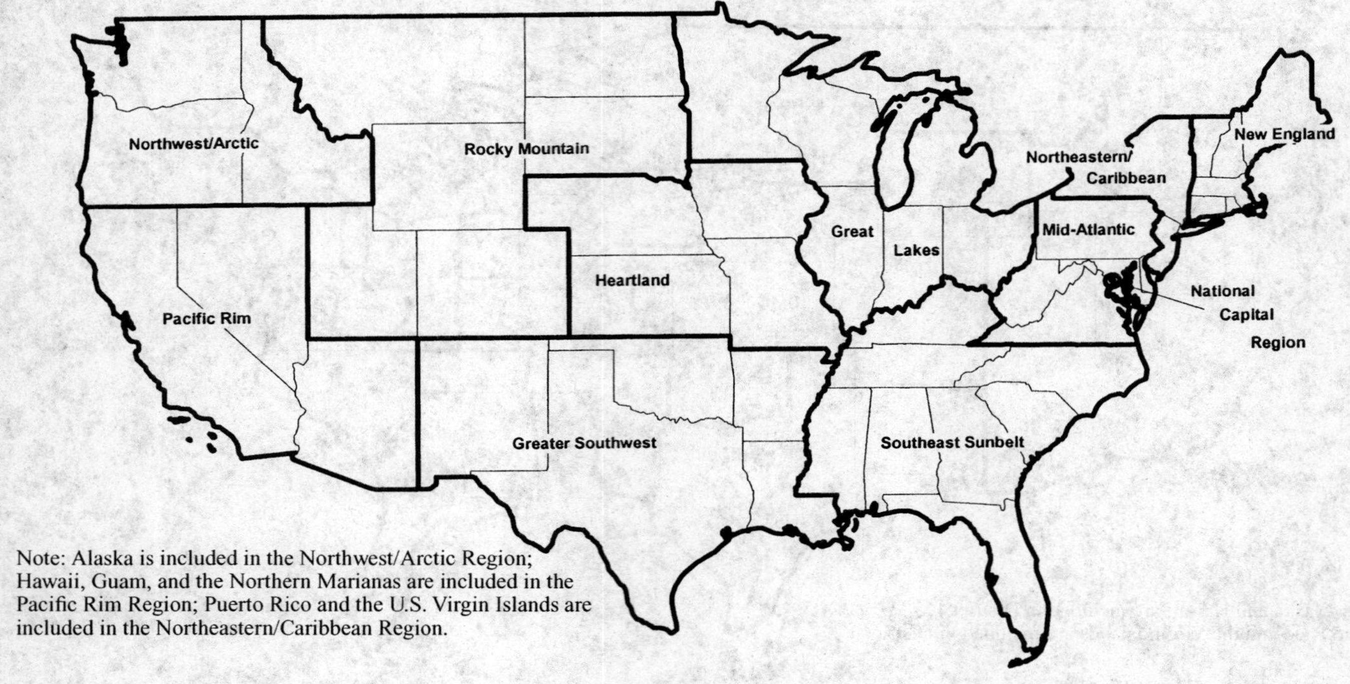

Note: Alaska is included in the Northwest/Arctic Region; Hawaii, Guam, and the Northern Marianas are included in the Pacific Rim Region; Puerto Rico and the U.S. Virgin Islands are included in the Northeastern/Caribbean Region.

National Credit Union Administration

Region Boundaries

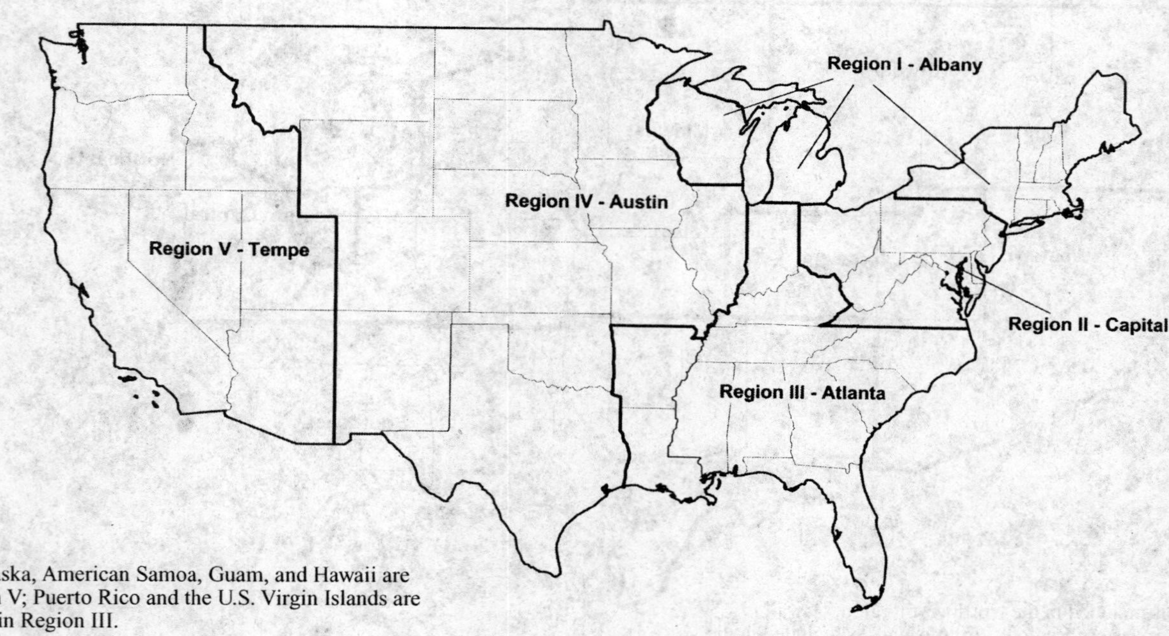

Note: Alaska, American Samoa, Guam, and Hawaii are in Region V; Puerto Rico and the U.S. Virgin Islands are included in Region III.

National Labor Relations Board

Region Boundaries

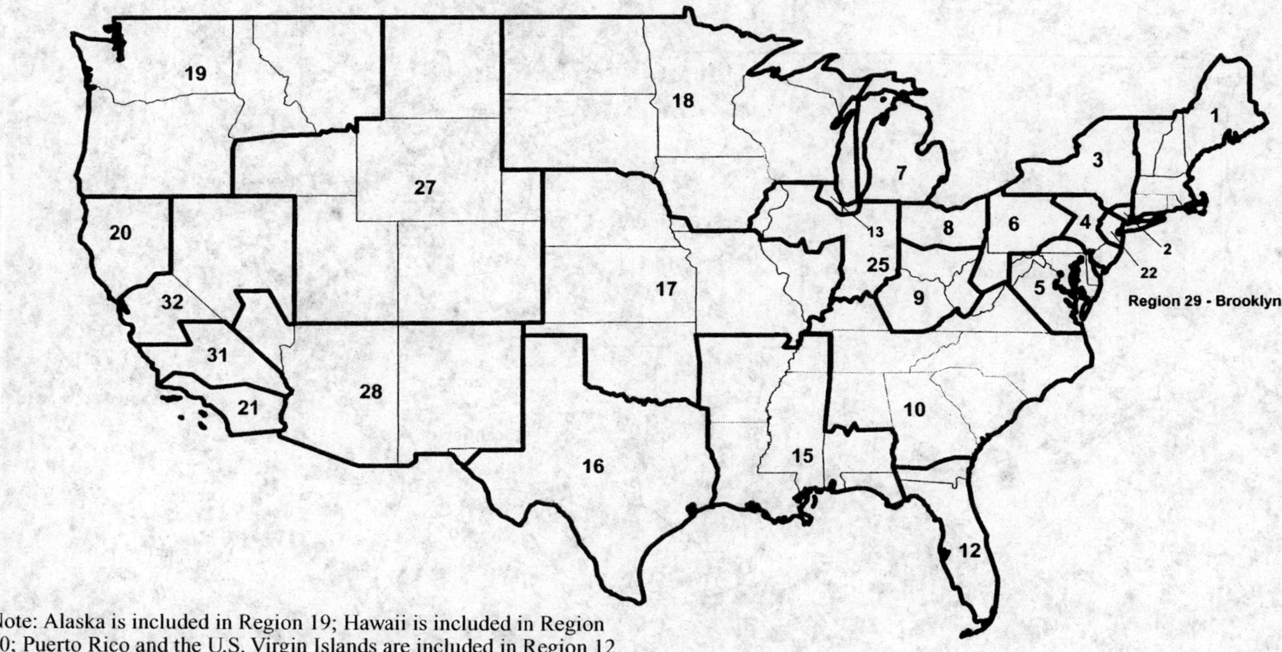

Note: Alaska is included in Region 19; Hawaii is included in Region 20; Puerto Rico and the U.S. Virgin Islands are included in Region 12.

National Transportation Safety Board

Office of Aviation Safety

Region Boundaries

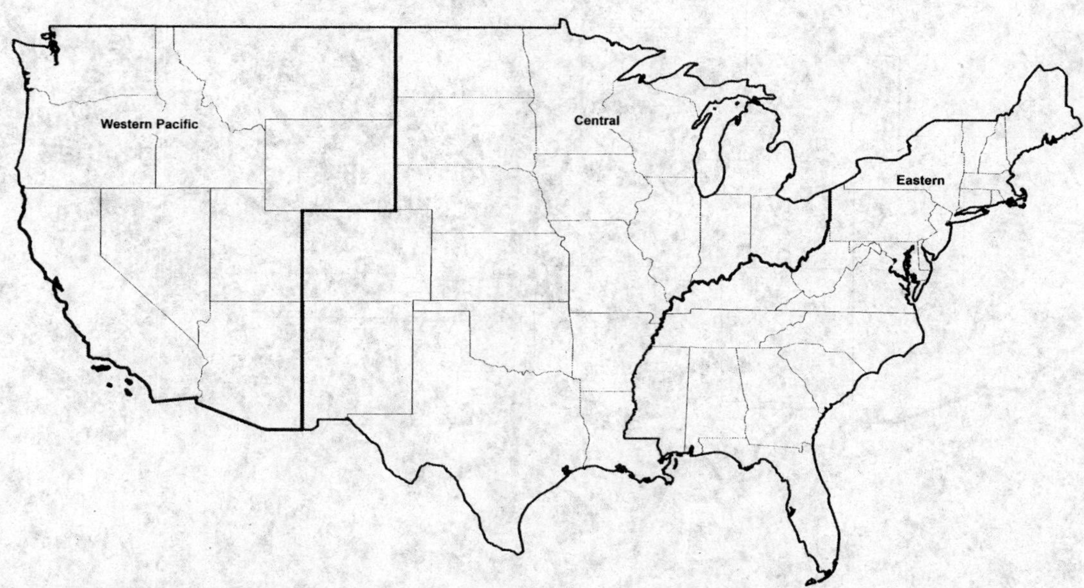

Note: Alaska is its own Region; American Samoa, Guam and Hawaii are in the Western Region; Puerto Rico and the U.S. Virgin Islands are in the Eastern Region.

Neighborhood Reinvestment Corporation

Regional Boundaries

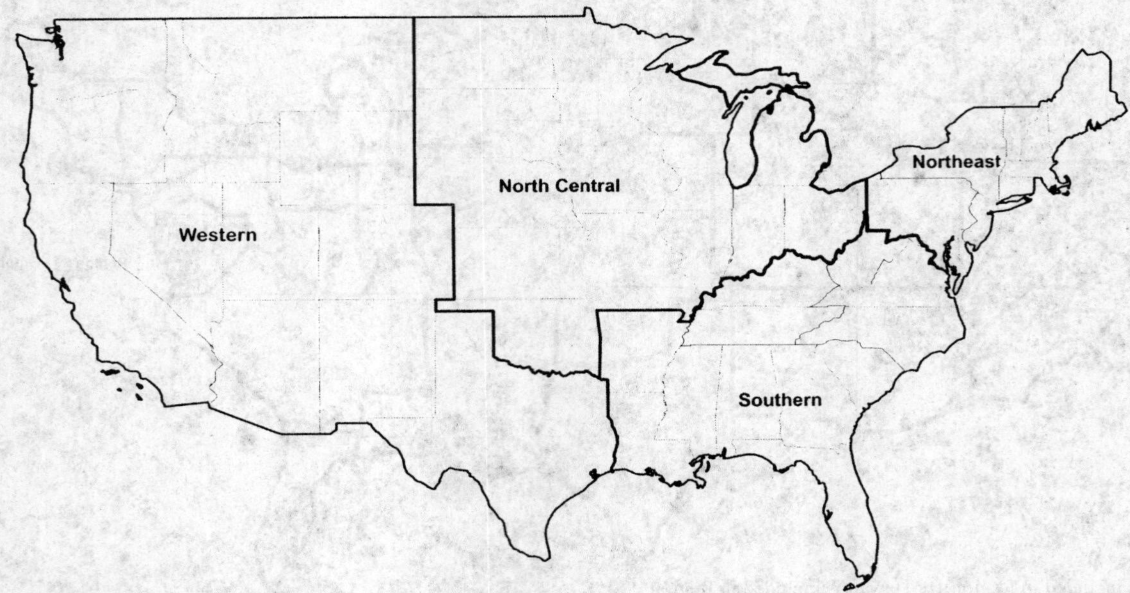

Note: Alaska and Hawaii are included in the Western Region; Puerto Rico and the U.S. Virgin Islands are in the Northeast Region.

Nuclear Regulatory Commission

Region Boundaries

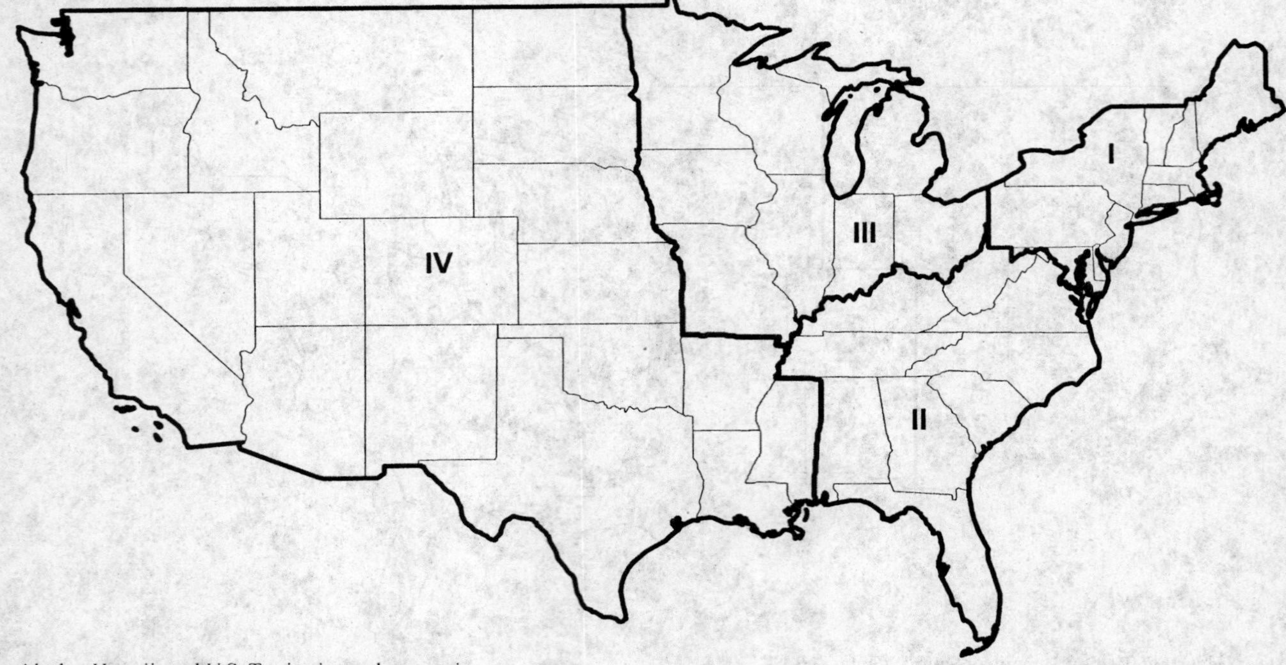

Note: Alaska, Hawaii, and U.S. Territories and possessions in the Pacific are included in Region IV; the District of Columbia is included in Region I; Puerto Rico and the U.S. Virgin Islands are included in Region II.

United States Postal Service

Area Boundaries

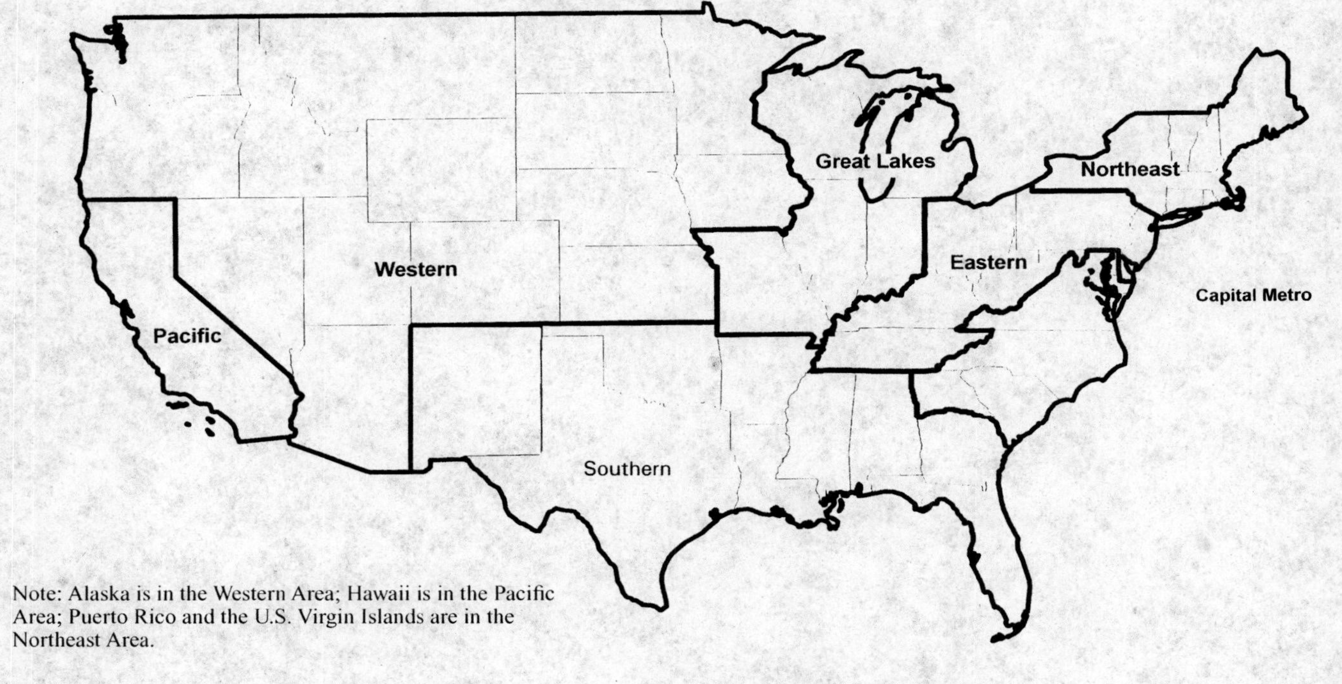

Note: Alaska is in the Western Area; Hawaii is in the Pacific Area; Puerto Rico and the U.S. Virgin Islands are in the Northeast Area.

Securities and Exchange Commission

Regional Boundaries

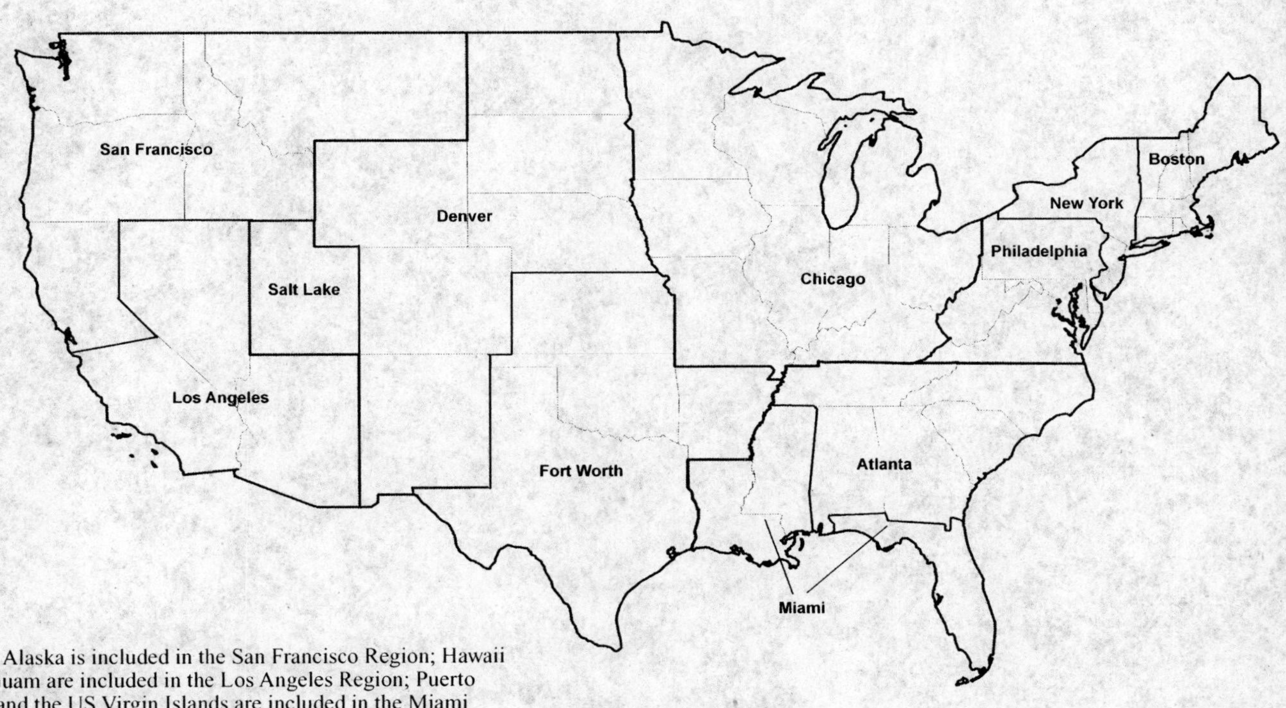

Note: Alaska is included in the San Francisco Region; Hawaii and Guam are included in the Los Angeles Region; Puerto Rico and the US Virgin Islands are included in the Miami Region.

Departments

DEPARTMENTS

Table of Contents

United States Department of Agriculture

DEPARTMENTS

Contents

DEPARTMENTS

United States Department of Agriculture (USDA)

Description: The Department of Agriculture is responsible for the improvement and maintenance of farm income. Departmental activities include the development and expansion of international markets for agricultural products, implementation of rural development projects, the oversight of credit and conservation programs, and agricultural research on crop production. The department also oversees the Forest Service and the Natural Resources Conservation Service, which serve to protect the nation's soil, water, forests, and natural resources. Through inspection and grading services, the department safeguards and ensures standards of quality in the food supply.

1400 Independence Avenue, SW, Washington, DC 20250
Tel: (202) 720-3202 (Procurement Information)
Tel: (202) 720-2791 (Public Information)
Tel: (202) 720-8164 (Freedom of Information/Privacy Act)
Tel: (202) 690-1622 (Fraud, Waste and Abuse Hotline - DC Metropolitan Area)
Tel: (800) 424-9121 (Fraud, Waste and Abuse Hotline - Continental US)
Tel: (202) 690-1533 (Rural Development Center)
Tel: (202) 720-8732 (Personnel Locator)
Tel: (202) 720-4623 (Media Inquiries)
E-mail: open@usda.gov (Open Government Directive Email)
E-mail: press@oc.usda.gov (Media Inquiries) Internet: www.usda.gov
Internet: www.usda.gov/open (Open Government Directive Website)
Internet: www.usa.gov (Official US Government Website)

Office of the Secretary

Jamie L. Whitten Federal Building, 1400 Independence Avenue, SW, Room 200-A, Washington, DC 20250
Tel: (202) 720-3631 Fax: (202) 720-2166

OFFICE OF THE DEPUTY SECRETARY (ODS)

Jamie L. Whitten Federal Building, 1400 Independence Avenue, SW, Room 200-A, Washington, DC 20250
Fax: (202) 720-6314

Departmental Management (DM)

Jamie L. Whitten Federal Building, 1400 Independence Avenue, SW, Room 240-W, Washington, DC 20250
Tel: (202) 720-3291 Fax: (202) 720-2191 Internet: www.dm.usda.gov

Office of the Chief Information Officer (OCIO)

South Agriculture Building, 1400 Independence Avenue, SW, Washington, DC 20250
Tel: (202) 720-8833 Fax: (202) 690-1915 E-mail: open@usda.gov
Internet: www.ocio.usda.gov Internet: www.usda.gov/open

National Information Technology Center (NITC)

8930 Ward Parkway, Kansas City, MO 64114-3302
Fax: (816) 926-6080 E-mail: nitcservicedesk@ocio.usda.gov

● Associate Chief Information Officer for Data Center Operations and Director (Acting) **Victoria K. Turley** .... (816) 823-1468
South Agriculture Building, 1400 Independence Avenue, SW, Washington, DC 20250
E-mail: Victoria.Turley@ocio.usda.gov
Education: Auburn 1983 BS; George Mason 1989 MS
Executive Assistant **(Vacant)** .... (202) 690-0048

Principal Deputy Associate Chief Information Officer for Enterprise Data Center Operations and Application Development (Acting) **Victoria K. Turley** ... (816) 823-1468
E-mail: Victoria.Turley@ocio.usda.gov
Education: Auburn 1983 BS; George Mason 1989 MS

Deputy Associate Chief Information Officer, Business, Finance and Security **(Vacant)** .... (816) 926-6606

National Information Technology Center *(continued)*

Deputy Associate Chief Information Officer, Operations **(Vacant)** .... (816) 926-6503

Deputy Associate Chief Information Officer, Security Operations **(Vacant)** .... (816) 926-2356

Architecture and Systems Integration Division (ASID)

8930 Ward Parkway, Kansas City, MO 64114

Division Director **Charles T. Gowans** .... (816) 926-2345
E-mail: chuck.gowans@ocio.usda.gov

Enterprise Architecture Branch Chief **(Vacant)** .... (816) 926-6516
Network Architect **(Vacant)** .... (816) 926-6516

Service Portfolio Branch Chief **(Vacant)** .... (816) 926-6516

Systems Integration Branch Chief **Brian L. Fields** .... (970) 295-5167
Building A, 2150 Centre Avenue, Fort Collins, CO 80526
E-mail: brian.fields@ocio.usda.gov

Business Division

8930 Ward Parkway, Kansas City, MO 64114

Director **Chad N. Bixby** .... (202) 720-8833

Data Center Consolidation Office

Data Center Consolidation Office Director **Bryan Dixon** .... (202) 720-8232
E-mail: bryan.dixon@ocio.usda.gov

Information Services Division

8930 Ward Parkway, Kansas City, MO 64114-3302
Fax: (816) 926-6754

Division Director **Greta R. Nash** .... (816) 926-2377
E-mail: greta.nash@usda.gov
Education: Missouri (Kansas City) 1982 BBA

Database Management Branch Chief **Scott A. Middendorf** .... (816) 926-6082
E-mail: scott.middendorf@usda.gov
Education: Washburn BBA

Network Services Branch Chief **Randal "Scott" Clark** ... (816) 926-6082
E-mail: randal.clark@usda.gov

Storage Management Branch Chief **Rachel A. Mecham** .... (816) 926-6082

Infrastructure Operations Division

8930 Ward Parkway, Kansas City, MO 64114-3302
Fax: (816) 926-6754

Director **Scott P. O'Hare** .... (816) 926-2139
Education: Excelsior BA

IT Service Management Branch Chief **Kim Hull** .... (816) 926-2139

Service Operations and Support Branch Chief **Robert J. Boucher** .... (816) 926-2139

Systems Network Control Center Chief **Rickey N. Smith** .... (816) 926-2139
Executive Assistant **Jessica Her** .... (816) 926-2139

Process Engineering Office

Process Engineering Office Director **Steven Larry "Steve" Sanders** .... (816) 926-6516
E-mail: steve.sanders@ocio.usda.gov
Education: Ohio State 1983 BS

★ Presidential Appointment Requiring Senate Confirmation ☆ Presidential Appointment □ Schedule C Appointment ◇ Career Senior Foreign Service Appointment
● Career Senior Executive Service (SES) Appointment ○ Non-Career Senior Executive Service (SES) Appointment ■ Postal Career Executive Service

Resource Management Division
8930 Ward Parkway, Kansas City, MO 64114

Director **Pamela A. "Pam" Yancey** .... (816) 926-6516
E-mail: pamela.yancey@usda.gov

Account and Project Management Branch Chief **Wesley L. Manning** .... (816) 926-6516
E-mail: wesley.manning@kcc.usda.gov

Budget Management Branch Chief **David A. "Dave" Gatliff** .... (816) 926-6516
E-mail: david.gatliff@usda.gov
Education: Missouri State U 1985 BS; Kansas 1993 MBA

Financial Management Branch Chief **Charles D. "Chuck" Koelsch** .... (816) 926-6516
E-mail: charles.koelsch@usda.gov

Systems Engineering Division
8930 Ward Parkway, Kansas City, MO 64114
Tel: (816) 926-6516

Director **Jeff R. Claunch** .... (816) 926-6516
E-mail: jeff.claunch@mo.usda.gov
Education: Emporia State 1999 BS

Data Center Floor Manager **Danial "Dan" McCord** ...... (816) 926-6516

Mainframe Systems Branch Chief **Danial "Dan" McCord** .... (816) 926-6516
E-mail: danial.mccord@mo.usda.gov

Open Systems Branch Chief **(Vacant)** .... (816) 926-6516

Windows Systems Branch Chief **Fernando Jimenez** ..... (816) 926-6516

Office of Hearings and Appeals (OHA)

Park Office Center, 3101 Park Center Drive,
Suite 1100, Alexandria, VA 22302
Tel: (703) 305-1166 Fax: (703) 305-2825 Internet: www.nad.usda.gov

Eastern Region
P.O. Box 68806, Indianapolis, IN 46268
Tel: (317) 875-9648 Tel: (800) 541-0457 TTY: (800) 791-3222
Fax: (317) 875-9674
Areas Covered: CT, DE, IA, IL, IN, KY, MA, MD, ME, MI, MN, MO, NH, NJ, NY, OH, PA, RI, VA, VT, WI, WV,

Regional Director **Duane Sinclair** .... (317) 875-9648
E-mail: duane.sinclair@usda.gov

Southern Region
57 Germantown Court, Suite 203, Memphis, TN 38018
P.O. Box 1508, Cordova, TN 38088
Tel: (901) 544-0359 Tel: (800) 552-5377 TTY: (800) 627-8332
Fax: (901) 544-0363
Areas Covered: AL, AR, FL, GA, LA, MS, NC, PR, SC, TN

Regional Assistant Director **Mark G. Kooker** ...... (901) 544-0359 ext. 2
E-mail: mark.kooker@usda.gov

Western Region
755 Parfet Street, Suite 494, Lakewood, CO 80215-5506
Tel: (303) 236-2862 Tel: (800) 541-0483 TTY: (800) 497-0253
Fax: (303) 236-2820
Areas Covered: AK, AZ, CA, CO, HI, ID, KS, MT, ND, NE, NM, NV, OK, OR, SD, TX, UT, WA, WY,

Regional Director **Patricia A. Leslie** .... (303) 236-2828
E-mail: patricia.leslie@nad.usda.gov

Deputy Regional Director **Michael Buchanan** .... (303) 236-2973
E-mail: michael.buchanan@nad.usda.gov

Deputy Assistant Director **Joli Liebrock** .... (303) 236-2974
E-mail: joli.liebrock@nad.usda.gov

Office of the General Counsel (OGC)

Jamie L. Whitten Federal Building, 1400 Independence Avenue, SW, Room 107-W, Washington, DC 20250
Tel: (202) 720-3351 (General Information) Fax: (202) 720-8666

Regional Offices

Central Region
Beacon Facility, 2312 East Bannister Road,
Mail Stop 1401, Kansas City, MO 64131-3011
Mail: P.O. Box 419205, Kansas City, MO 64141-6205
Tel: (816) 823-4646 Fax: (816) 823-4688

● Regional Attorney **John P. Vos** .... (816) 823-4646
E-mail: john.vos@ogc.usda.gov

Deputy Regional Attorney **David Schaaf** .... (816) 823-4646

Administrative Officer **Venessa Cobbs** .... (816) 823-4681
E-mail: venessa.cobbs@ogc.usda.gov Fax: (816) 823-4688

Little Rock (AR) Field Office
3201 Federal Building, 700 West Capitol Street,
Little Rock, AR 72201-3225
Tel: (501) 324-5246 Fax: (501) 324-5482

Senior Counsel (Acting) **Danny Woodyard** .... (501) 324-4246
Education: Arkansas (Little Rock) BA; Arkansas 1979 JD

Temple (TX) Field Office
101 South Main Street, Suite 351, Temple, TX 76501-7686
Tel: (254) 743-6636 Fax: (254) 298-1209

Associate Regional Attorney **Daniel A. "Dan" Bowen** ... (254) 743-6636
E-mail: daniel.bowen@ogc.usda.gov

Eastern Region
1718 Peachtree Street, NW, Suite 576, Atlanta, GA 30309-2409
Tel: (404) 347-1060 Fax: (404) 347-1065

● Regional Attorney **Andrea L. Foster** .... (404) 347-1060
E-mail: andrea.foster@ogc.usda.gov

Deputy Regional Attorney **Jay McWhirter** .... (404) 347-1060
E-mail: jay.mcwhirter@ogc.usda.gov

Administrative Officer **Avarel M. Rivera-Allen** .... (404) 347-1060
E-mail: avarel.rivera@ogc.usda.gov
Education: U Phoenix BS

Paralegal Specialist **Renee Tyler** .... (404) 347-1060

Paralegal Specialist, Atlanta Field Office **Marie Roman** .... (404) 347-1074
Fax: (404) 347-1065

Harrisburg (PA) Field Office
470 Federal Building, 228 Walnut Street, Harrisburg, PA 17108-1134
Mail: P.O. Box 1134, Harrisburg, PA 17108-1134
Tel: (717) 221-3713 Fax: (717) 221-3443

Associate Regional Attorney **Julie Quirk** .... (717) 221-3713
E-mail: julie.quirk@ogc.usda.gov

Milwaukee (WI) Field Office
Gas Light Building, 626 East Wisconsin Avenue,
Suite 601, Milwaukee, WI 53202-4616
Tel: (414) 297-3774 Fax: (844) 288-3359

Associate Regional Attorney **Vincent "Vince" Vukelich** .... (414) 297-3786
E-mail: vincent.vukelich@ogc.usda.gov

Attorney **Conrado Almario** .... (414) 297-3774
E-mail: conrado.almario@ogc.usda.gov

Attorney **Peter "Pete" Jurgeleit** .... (414) 297-1891

Attorney **Isabel Rosa** .... (414) 297-3613

Attorney **Jessica Schmitt** .... (414) 297-3776
E-mail: jessica.schmitt@ogc.usda.gov

Senior Counsel **John Vandlik** .... (414) 297-3774

Legal Instruments Examiner **Kathy Gohr** .... (414) 297-3775
E-mail: kathy.gohr@ogc.usda.gov

★ Presidential Appointment Requiring Senate Confirmation ☆ Presidential Appointment ☐ Schedule C Appointment ◇ Career Senior Foreign Service Appointment
● Career Senior Executive Service (SES) Appointment ○ Non-Career Senior Executive Service (SES) Appointment ■ Postal Career Executive Service

Mountain Region
Building 17, 1617 Cole Boulevard, Lakewood, CO 80401-3305
Tel: (303) 275-5555

● Regional Attorney (Acting) **Kenneth D. "Ken" Paur** .... (303) 275-5536
E-mail: kenneth.paur@dm.usda.gov
Deputy Regional Attorney **Kenneth D. "Ken" Paur** ..... (303) 275-5548
E-mail: kenneth.paur@dm.usda.gov
Senior Counsel **Randall "Randy" Bramer** .... (303) 275-5537
E-mail: randy.bramer@ogc.usda.gov
Senior Counsel **Kenneth Capps** .... (303) 275-5538
E-mail: kenneth.capps@ogc.usda.gov
Senior Counsel **Daniel Rosenbluth** .... (303) 275-5540
E-mail: daniel.rosenbluth@ogc.usda.gov
Senior Counsel **Lois Witte** .... (303) 275-5535
E-mail: lois.witte@ogc.usda.gov
Regional Administrative Officer **Millicent Haupt** .... (303) 275-5543
E-mail: millicent.haupt@ogc.usda.gov
Attorney **Diane "M." Connolly** .... (303) 275-5551
E-mail: diane.connolly@ogc.usda.gov
Attorney **Heather Hinton** .... (303) 275-5543
E-mail: heather.hinton@ogc.usda.gov
Attorney **Michael Hope** .... (303) 275-5545
E-mail: michael.hope@ogc.usda.gov
General Attorney **Thomas Japhet** .... (303) 275-5552
E-mail: thomas.japhet@ogc.usda.gov
Attorney **Helena Jones-Siddle** .... (303) 275-5550
E-mail: helena.jones-siddle@ogc.usda.gov
Attorney **Kirk Minckler** .... (303) 275-5549
E-mail: kirk.minckler@ogc.usda.gov
Attorney **(Vacant)** .... (303) 275-5538
Paralegal Specialist **Denise Belanger** .... (303) 275-5542
Education: Hilbert 2001
Paralegal Specialist **(Vacant)** .... (303) 275-5555

Albuquerque (NM) Field Office
500 Gold Avenue, SW, Suite 11016, Albuquerque, NM 87103-0586
Mail: P.O. Box 586, Albuquerque, NM 87103-0586
Tel: (505) 248-6010 Fax: (505) 248-6013

Assistant Regional Attorney **Cassandra Carrie** .... (505) 248-6010
Legal Instrument Examiner **Susan C. Sanchez** .... (505) 248-6010
E-mail: susan.sanchez@usda.gov
Legal Technician **Angela McGuire-Pike** .... (505) 248-6010
E-mail: angela.mcguire-pike@ogc.usda.gov
Attorney **(Vacant)** .... (505) 248-6010
Attorney **Dawn Dickman** .... (505) 248-6010
E-mail: dawn.dickman@ogc.usda.gov
Attorney **(Vacant)** .... (505) 248-6010
Attorney **Nicholas Pino** .... (505) 248-6010
Attorney **M'Leah Woodard** .... (505) 248-6002

Missoula (MT) Field Office
Federal Building, 340 North Pattee Street,
Room 205, Missoula, MT 59807-7669
Mail: P.O. Box 7669, Missoula, MT 59807
Tel: (406) 329-3061 Fax: (406) 329-3064

Associate Regional Attorney **(Vacant)** .... (406) 329-3073
Attorney Advisor **Alan J. Campbell** .... (406) 329-3072
Attorney Advisor **Nicholas Peno** .... (406) 329-3074
Attorney Advisor **Elise Foster** .... (406) 329-3068
Attorney Advisor **Jody M. Miller** .... (406) 329-3069
Attorney Advisor **Jennifer T. Newbold** .... (406) 329-3065
Attorney Advisor **Babak Rastgoufard** .... (406) 329-3075
Support Staff **Kim Luebke** .... (406) 329-3061

Pacific Region
33 New Montgomery Street, 17th Floor, San Francisco, CA 94105-1924
Tel: (415) 744-3011 Fax: (415) 744-3170

● Regional Attorney **Jeff Moulton** .... (415) 744-3166
E-mail: jeff.moulton@ogc.usda.gov
Deputy Regional Attorney **John Eichard** .... (415) 744-3011
Administrative Officer **(Vacant)** .... (415) 744-3168

Juneau (AK) Field Office
Federal Building, 709 West Ninth Street,
Room 913, Juneau, AK 99802
Mail: P.O. Box 21628, Juneau, AK 99802
Tel: (907) 586-8826 Fax: (907) 586-7251

Assistant Regional Attorney
James J. "Jim" Ustasiewski .... (907) 586-8826
E-mail: jim.ustasiewski@ogc.usda.gov
Administrative Support Assistant **Julia D. Daws** .... (907) 586-8826
E-mail: julia.daws@ogc.usda.gov

Portland (OR) Field Office
1220 SW Third Avenue, Suite 310, Portland, OR 97204-2825
Tel: (503) 808-5962 Fax: (503) 808-5977

Associate Regional Attorney **Beverly F. Li** .... (503) 326-7265
Education: U Washington 1998 BABA; Cornell 2002 JD
Deputy Associate Regional Attorney **(Vacant)** .... (503) 326-7261

Office of the Inspector General (OIG)

Jamie L. Whitten Federal Building, 1400 Independence Avenue, SW,
Room 117-W, Washington, DC 20250
Tel: (202) 720-8001 Fax: (202) 690-1278 Internet: www.usda.gov/oig

Audit

Jamie Whitten Building, 1400 Independence Avenue, SW,
Room 117-W, Washington, DC 20250-1599
Fax: (202) 720-0319

Regional Offices

Eastern Region - Audit
111 North Canal Street, Suite 325, Chicago, IL 60606
Tel: (312) 353-1352 Fax: (312) 353-3017
Areas Covered: IL, IN, MI, MN, OH, WI

Director **Paul Keating** .... (312) 353-1352
E-mail: paul.keating@oig.usda.gov
Assistant Director **Dennis Boedigheimer** .... (312) 353-1352
E-mail: dennis.boedigheimer@oig.usda.gov
Administrative Officer **Vernessa Barnes** .... (312) 353-3903
E-mail: vernessa.barnes@oig.usda.gov

Midwestern Region - Audit
8930 Ward Parkway, Suite 3016, Kansas City, MO 64114
Fax: (816) 926-7676
Areas Covered: CO, IA, KS, MO, MT, NE, ND, SD, UT, WY

Regional Director **Carlin Walker** .... (816) 926-7367
E-mail: carlin.walker@oig.usda.gov
Assistant Director **Larry Ellis** .... (816) 926-7667
E-mail: larry.ellis@oig.usda.gov
Assistant Director **Doug Larson** .... (816) 926-7667
Administrative Officer **Greg Raney** .... (816) 926-8232
E-mail: greg.raney@oig.usda.gov

Midwestern Region - Financial Audit Operations
8930 Ward Parkway, Suite 3016, Kansas City, MO 64114
Tel: (816) 823-3949
Areas Covered: Fort Collins Computer Center, Ft. Collins, CO; OCFO National Finance Center, New Orleans, LA; Rural Development Finance Office, St. Louis, MO; FSA Kansas City Operations and National Information Technology Center, Kansas City, MO

Regional Director **Marlene F. Parnacott** .... (816) 823-3860
Assistant Director **Stephen "Steve" Boozell** .... (816) 823-3860
Assistant Director **Luana Young** .... (816) 823-3860
Assistant Director **Denise Baldridge** .... (816) 823-3860
Administrative Officer **Greg Raney** .... (816) 926-8232
E-mail: greg.raney@oig.usda.gov

★ Presidential Appointment Requiring Senate Confirmation ☆ Presidential Appointment ☐ Schedule C Appointment ◇ Career Senior Foreign Service Appointment
● Career Senior Executive Service (SES) Appointment ○ Non-Career Senior Executive Service (SES) Appointment ■ Postal Career Executive Service

DEPARTMENTS

Midwestern Region - Temple Field Office
101 South Main Street, Suite 324, Temple, TX 76501-7686
Tel: (254) 743-6565 Fax: (254) 298-1373
Areas Covered: AR, LA, MS, NM, OK, TX

Regional Director **Kimberly Bretz** .... (254) 743-6565
E-mail: kimberly.bretz@oig.usda.gov
Assistant Director **Amy M. McCormack** .... (254) 743-6566
E-mail: amy.mccormack@usda.gov
Assistant Director **Scott Oakes** .... (254) 743-6568
E-mail: scott.oakes@oig.usda.gov
Assistant Director **Melinda S. Wenzl** .... (254) 743-6570
E-mail: melinda.wenzl@usda.gov
Administrative Officer **Cindy Bailey** Suite 309 .... (254) 743-6500
Fax: (254) 298-1357

Northeast Region - Audit
5601 Sunnyside Avenue, Suite 2-2230, Stop 5300,
Beltsville, MD 20705-5000
Tel: (301) 504-2100 Fax: (301) 504-2437
Areas Covered: CT, DE, DC, ME, MD, MA, NH, NJ, NY, PA, PR, VT, VI, VA, WV

Regional Director (Acting) **Kimberly Bretz** .... (301) 504-2101
E-mail: kimberly.bretz@oig.usda.gov
Assistant Director **Belinda Davis** .... (301) 504-2101
E-mail: belinda.davis2@usda.gov
Assistant Director **(Vacant)** .... (301) 504-2101
Administrative Officer **Kecia Cooper** .... (301) 504-2074
E-mail: klcooper@oig.usda.gov

Southeast Region - Audit
Peachtree Summit Federal Building, 401 West Peachtree Street, NW,
Room 2328, Atlanta, GA 30308
Tel: (404) 730-3210 Fax: (404) 730-3221
Areas Covered: AL, FL, GA, KY, MS, NC, PR, SC, TN

Regional Director **Michael K. Yarbrough** .... (404) 730-3210
E-mail: michael.yarbrough@usda.gov
Assistant Director **Steven Dula** .... (404) 730-3217
Assistant Director **Kevin Gunnells** .... (404) 730-3214
Assistant Director **Tiffany Hooper** .... (404) 730-3217
E-mail: tiffany.conn@usda.gov
Assistant Director **(Vacant)** .... (404) 730-3212
Administrative Officer **(Vacant)** Room 2334 .... (404) 730-3200

Western Region - Audit
1333 Broadway, Suite 400, Oakland, CA 94612
Tel: (510) 208-6800 Fax: (510) 208-3735
Areas Covered: AK, AZ, CA, HI, ID, NV, OR, WA

Regional Director **Patricia Van Duzer** .... (510) 208-6800
Assistant Director **Robert Brown** .... (510) 208-6800
Assistant Director **Jowdy L. Johnson** .... (510) 208-6800
E-mail: jljohnson@oig.usda.gov
Assistant Director **Larry Gee** .... (510) 208-6800
E-mail: larry.gee@usda.gov
Senior Auditor **Gary Morin** .... (510) 208-6800
E-mail: gary.morin@usda.gov
Senior Auditor **Donna Smith** .... (503) 326-2737
100 SW Main Street, Suite 625, Portland, OR 97204
E-mail: donna.smith@usda.gov
Administrative Officer **Thomas "Tom" Taylor** .... (510) 208-6852
E-mail: thomas.taylor@oig.usda.gov

Investigations
1400 Independence Avenue, SW, Room 146-W,
Washington, DC 20250-1567
Fax: (202) 720-4683

Regional Offices

Midwest Region - Investigations
111 North Canal Street, Suite 325, Chicago, IL 60606-7213
Tel: (312) 353-1358 Fax: (312) 353-0135
Areas Covered: IL, IN, MI, OH, WI

Special Agent-in-Charge **Anthony Mohatt** .... (312) 353-1358
E-mail: anthony.mohatt@usda.gov
Assistant Special Agent-in-Charge **Salvador Gonzalez** ... (312) 353-1358
Administrative Officer **Vernessa Barnes** .... (312) 353-3903
E-mail: vernessa.barnes@oig.usda.gov

Northeast Region - Investigations
26 Federal Plaza, Room 1409, New York, NY 10278-0004
Tel: (212) 264-8400 Fax: (301) 504-2025
Areas Covered: CT, DC, DE, MA, MD, ME, NH, NJ, NY, PA, RI, VA, VT, WV

Special Agent-in-Charge **Bethanne Dinkins** .... (212) 264-8400
Assistant Special Agent-in-Charge
Beth Dinkens .... (212) 264-8400 ext. 318
E-mail: beth.dinkens@usda.gov
Assistant Special Agent-in-Charge **(Vacant)** .... (301) 504-2005
Assistant Special Agent-in-Charge **(Vacant)** ..... (212) 264-8400 ext. 317
Administrative Officer **Kecia Cooper** .... (301) 504-2074
E-mail: klcooper@oig.usda.gov

Southeast Region - Investigations
Peachtree Summit Federal Building, 401 West Peachtree Street, NW,
Room 2329, Atlanta, GA 30308
Tel: (404) 730-3170 Fax: (404) 730-3181
Areas Covered: AL, FL, GA, KY, MS, NC, SC, TN

Special Agent-in-Charge **Dr. Karen Citizen-Wilcox** ...... (404) 730-3170
Assistant Special Agent-in-Charge **Shedrick Sublett** ..... (404) 730-3170
Administrative Officer **Robin Anderson** .... (404) 730-3200

Southwest Region - Investigations
101 South Main, Suite 311, Temple, TX 76501
Tel: (254) 743-6535 Fax: (254) 298-1358
Areas Covered: AR, LA, MS, NM, OK, TX

Special Agent-in-Charge **Dax Roberson** .... (254) 743-6535
E-mail: dax.roberson@usda.gov
Assistant Special Agent-in-Charge **Patrick Munday** ...... (214) 767-4604
Assistant Special Agent-in-Charge
Gregory "Greg" Henderson .... (601) 965-4503
Administrative Officer **Cindy Bailey** Suite 309 .... (254) 743-6500
E-mail: cindy.bailey@usda.gov Fax: (254) 298-1357

Western Region - Investigations
1333 Broadway, Suite 400, Oakland, CA 94612
Tel: (510) 208-6860 Tel: (877) 509-5805 (Pager for On-Call Duty Agent)
Fax: (510) 208-3751
Areas Covered: AK, AZ, CA, CO, HI, ID, MT, NV, OR, UT, WA, WY, Guam, Trust Territories of the Pacific

Special Agent-in-Charge **Lori Chan** .... (510) 208-6860 ext. 301
Assistant Special Agent-in-Charge **(Vacant)** .... (510) 208-6860

★ Presidential Appointment Requiring Senate Confirmation ☆ Presidential Appointment ☐ Schedule C Appointment ◇ Career Senior Foreign Service Appointment
● Career Senior Executive Service (SES) Appointment ○ Non-Career Senior Executive Service (SES) Appointment ■ Postal Career Executive Service

Farm Production and Conservation (FPAC)

OFFICE OF THE UNDER SECRETARY
1400 Independence Avenue, SW, Washington, DC 20250-1567

Farm Service Agency (FSA)
South Agriculture Building, 1400 Independence Avenue, SW,
Mail Stop 0506, Washington, DC 20250
Fax: (202) 720-9105 Internet: www.fsa.usda.gov

Note: On September 7, 2017, Secretary of Agriculture Sonny Perdue announced that the Farm Service Agency will be merged into the Agricultural Marketing Service.

Deputy Administrator for Commodity Operations
South Agriculture Building, 1400 Independence Avenue, SW,
Washington, DC 20250
Fax: (202) 720-8055 Internet: www.fsa.usda.gov/daco

Kansas City Commodity Office
6501 Beacon Drive, Kansas City, MO 64131
Mail: P.O. Box 419205, Kansas City, MO 64141-6205
Tel: (816) 926-6843 Fax: (816) 823-4034

● Director (Acting) **Patrick M. Dardis** .... (816) 926-1432
E-mail: pmdardis@kcc.usda.gov
Deputy Director **Patrick M. Dardis** .... (816) 926-1432
E-mail: pmdardis@kcc.usda.gov
Business Operations Support Division Chief
Penny Carlson .... (816) 926-6843
E-mail: penny.carlson@kcc.usda.gov
Contract Reconciliation Division Chief **Greg Borchert** ... (816) 926-6525
E-mail: greg.borchert@kcc.usda.gov
Commodity Procurement Support Branch Chief
Sandra Dukes .... (816) 926-3501
International Procurement Division Chief **Todd Shuck** ... (816) 823-1114
Warehouse License and Examination Division Chief
Tim Mehl .... (816) 926-6843
Agricultural Data Specialist **(Vacant)** .... (816) 926-2851
Fax: (816) 926-1648
Section 508 Coordinator [Section 508 Coordinator]
Steve Meacham .... (816) 926-1942
E-mail: steve.meacham@kcc.usda.gov

Commodity Operations Division
1400 Independence Avenue, SW, Washington, DC 20250-1567
Director **(Vacant)** .... (202) 690-2534

Deputy Administrator for Farm Programs
South Agriculture Building, 1400 Independence Avenue, SW,
Washington, DC 20250
Tel: (202) 720-3175 Fax: (202) 720-4726

Aerial Photography Field Office
2222 West 2300 South, Salt Lake City, UT 84119-2020
Tel: (801) 844-2900 Fax: (801) 956-3652
Director **Denny Allen Skiles** .... (801) 844-2903
Customer Service Supervisor **David L. Parry** .... (801) 844-2923
E-mail: david.parry@slc.usda.gov
Geospatial Service Branch Chief **Zachary Adkins** .... (801) 844-2930
Information Technology Services Branch Chief
(Vacant) .... (801) 844-2970
Business Management Officer **Lori Uhlhorn** .... (801) 844-2923
Photography Services Branch Chief **John Stadelman** .... (801) 844-2940
Quality Assurance Branch Chief **(Vacant)** .... (801) 844-2912

Deputy Administrator for Field Operations
South Agriculture Building, 1400 Independence Avenue, SW,
Washington, DC 20250
Fax: (202) 690-3309

State Offices

Alabama State Office
4121 Carmichael Road, Suite 600, Montgomery, AL 36106-2872
Tel: (334) 279-3501 Fax: (334) 279-3550 Internet: www.fsa.usda.gov/al
□ State Executive Director **David C. McCurdy** .... (334) 567-2264
E-mail: david.mccurdy@al.usda.gov
Public Affairs Specialist **Cassondra Searight** .... (334) 279-3502
E-mail: cassondra.searight@al.usda.gov

Alaska State Office
800 West Evergreen, Suite 216, Palmer, AK 99645-6539
Tel: (907) 761-7738 Fax: (907) 761-7795 Internet: www.fsa.usda.gov/ak
□ State Executive Director **Bryan J. Scoresby** .... (907) 761-7750
E-mail: bryan.scoresby@ak.usda.gov

Arizona State Office
230 North First Avenue, Suite 506, Phoenix, AZ 85003
Tel: (602) 285-6300 Fax: (855) 220-1760 Internet: www.fsa.usda.gov/az
□ State Executive Director **James Mago** .... (870) 895-3357
E-mail: James.Mago@az.usda.gov
Education: South Carolina BBA; Columbia Col (SC) MBA
District Director **Mark W. Grubbs** .... (602) 640-5200 ext. 229
E-mail: mark.grubbs@az.usda.gov
Supervisory Loan Specialist, Agriculture
Sharon D. Kinnison .... (602) 285-6319
Loan Specialist **Fred Sannicolas** .... (602) 285-6300
Supervisory Program Specialist/Administrative
Officer **Grace M. Lamas** .... (602) 640-6322 ext. 229
E-mail: grace.lamas@az.usda.gov
Administrative Specialist **Alicia Martinez** .... (602) 285-6322
E-mail: alicia.martinez@az.usda.gov
Program Specialist **Carla Hill** .... (602) 285-6314
Program Specialist **Ryan Hunt** .... (602) 285-6309

Arkansas State Office
Federal Building, 700 West Capitol Avenue,
Room 3416, Little Rock, AR 72201
Tel: (501) 301-3000 Fax: (501) 301-3085 Internet: www.fsa.usda.gov/ar
□ State Executive Director **David Glen Curtis** .... (501) 301-3000
E-mail: David.Curtis@ar.usda.gov
Chief Administrative Officer **Sharon Baker** .... (501) 301-3014
E-mail: sharon.baker@ar.usda.gov Fax: (501) 301-3086

California State Office
430 G Street, Suite 4161, Davis, CA 95616-4161
Tel: (530) 792-5520 Fax: (530) 792-5555 Internet: www.fsa.usda.gov/ca
□ State Executive Director **Aubrey Bettencourt** .... (530) 792-5538
E-mail: Aubrey.Bettencourt@ca.usda.gov
Education: Westmont 2008 BA
Administrative Officer **Jacque Johnson** .... (530) 792-5520
E-mail: jacque.johnson@ca.usda.gov

Colorado State Office
Denver Federal Center, Building 56, Room 2760, Denver, CO 80225
Mail: P.O. Box 25426, Denver, CO 80225
Tel: (720) 544-2874 Fax: (844) 860-8238 Internet: www.fsa.usda.gov/co
□ State Executive Director
Clarice Yvette Navarro-Ratzlaff .... (720) 544-2875
E-mail: clarice.navarro@co.usda.gov Fax: (844) 860-8228
Education: National American U BBA
Executive Officer (Acting) **Jenny Lynn Peterson** .... (720) 544-2895
E-mail: jenny.peterson@co.usda.gov
Agricultural Loan Specialist **Scott Miller** .... (720) 544-2897
Agricultural Loan Specialist **Casey Toyne** .... (720) 544-2874
Agricultural Program Specialist
Tamra K. "Tammy" Cook .... (720) 544-2881
Agricultural Program Specialist **Diane Kay Pierson** ..... (970) 356-8097
Agricultural Program Specialist **Tomika E. Sales** .... (229) 649-4495

(continued on next page)

★ Presidential Appointment Requiring Senate Confirmation ☆ Presidential Appointment □ Schedule C Appointment ◇ Career Senior Foreign Service Appointment
● Career Senior Executive Service (SES) Appointment ○ Non-Career Senior Executive Service (SES) Appointment ■ Postal Career Executive Service

DEPARTMENTS

Colorado State Office *(continued)*

Agricultural Program Specialist
Cindy Vukasin . . . . (406) 487-5366 ext. 102
Agricultural Program Technology Specialist
Corey L. Pelton . . . . (303) 659-0525
E-mail: Corey.Pelton@co.usda.gov

Connecticut State Office
344 Merrow Road, Suite B, Tolland, CT 06084-3917
Tel: (860) 871-4090 Fax: (855) 934-2463 Internet: www.fsa.usda.gov/ct

□ State Executive Director **Clark Jay Chapin** . . . . (860) 887-9941
E-mail: clark.chapin@ct.usda.gov
Education: Rhode Island BS; Iowa State MS
Administrative Officer **Doris G. Ostrowski** . . . . (860) 871-4090 ext. 196
E-mail: doris.ostrowski@ct.usda.gov
Administrative Specialist **Rebecca Palmer** . . . . (860) 871-4090 ext. 190
E-mail: rebecca.palmer@ks.usda.gov
Communications Coordinator
Dawn S. Pindell . . . . (860) 779-0557 ext. 109
E-mail: dawn.pindell@ct.usda.gov
Program Specialist **Devon B. Marsden** . . . . (860) 871-4090
District Director **(Vacant)** . . . . (860) 871-4090
Farm Loan Chief **Julie Kolodji** . . . . (413) 253-4510
445 West Street, Amherst, MA 01002-2994
Web Manager **(Vacant)** . . . . (860) 871-4090 ext. 190

Delaware State Office
1221 College Park Drive, Suite 201, Dover, DE 19904
Tel: (302) 678-4250 Fax: (855) 389-2246 Internet: www.fsa.usda.gov/de

□ State Executive Director **Sean McKeon** . . . . (302) 678-4258
E-mail: sean.mckeon@de.usda.gov
Administrative Officer **(Vacant)** . . . . (302) 678-4250

Florida State Office
4440 NW 25th Place, Suite 1, Gainesville, FL 32606
Mail: P.O. Box 141030, Gainesville, FL 32614-1030
Tel: (352) 379-4500 Fax: (352) 379-4580 Internet: www.fsa.usda.gov/fl

□ State Executive Director **Justin Teuton** . . . . (352) 379-4542

Georgia State Office
Federal Building, 355 East Hancock Avenue,
Room 102, Mail Stop 100, Athens, GA 30601-2775
Tel: (706) 546-2266 Fax: (855) 409-5735 Internet: www.fsa.usda.gov/ga

□ State Executive Director
Talmadge A. "Tas" Smith, Sr. . . . . (706) 546-2266
E-mail: tas.smith@ga.usda.gov
Education: Valdosta State U 2003 BA
Chief Administrative Officer
Dianne R. Westmoreland . . . . (706) 546-2269
E-mail: dianne.westmoreland@ga.usda.gov

Hawaii State and Pacific Basin Office
300 Ala Moana Boulevard, Room 5-108, Honolulu, HI 96850
Tel: (808) 541-2600 ext. 2 Fax: (855) 356-9492
Internet: www.fsa.usda.gov/hi

□ State Executive Director
COL Allen "AL" Frenzel USA (Ret) . . . . (808) 600-2927 ext. 123
E-mail: Allen.Frenzel@hi.usda.gov
Education: Central Texas Col 1982 BSBA; Boston U 1984 MSBA
Administrative Officer **Shirley Nakamura** . . . . (808) 600-2952 ext. 148
E-mail: shirley.nakamura@hi.usda.gov

Idaho State Office
9173 West Barnes Drive, Suite B, Boise, ID 83709-1555
Tel: (208) 378-5650 Fax: (855) 516-8875 Internet: www.fsa.usda.gov/id

□ State Executive Director **Evan Frasure** . . . . (208) 378-5651
E-mail: Evan.Frasure@id.usda.gov
Administrative Officer **Brandi Mitchell** . . . . (208) 378-5661
E-mail: brandi.mitchell@id.usda.gov

Illinois State Office
3500 Wabash Avenue, Springfield, IL 62711-8287
Tel: (217) 241-6600 ext. 2 Fax: (855) 800-1760
Internet: www.fsa.usda.gov/il

□ State Executive Director **William J. Graff** . . . . (217) 241-6600 ext. 2

Indiana State Office
5981 Lakeside Boulevard, Indianapolis, IN 46278-1996
Tel: (317) 290-3030 Fax: (855) 374-4066 Internet: www.fsa.usda.gov/in

□ State Executive Director **Steven Edward Brown** . . . . (317) 290-3030
E-mail: steven.brown2@in.usda.gov
Administrative Officer **Pauletta Dusterberg** . . . . (317) 295-5902
E-mail: pauletta.dusterberg@in.usda.gov
Secretary **Emily Willis** . . . . (317) 290-3030

Iowa State Office
10500 Buena Vista Court, Des Moines, IA 50322
Tel: (515) 254-1540 Fax: (855) 218-8672 Internet: www.fsa.usda.gov/ia

□ State Executive Director **Amanda R. De Jong** . . . . (515) 331-8480
E-mail: Amanda.DeJong@ia.usda.gov
Education: Iowa State 2002 BS; Iowa 2005 JD
Administrative Officer **Bob Wegand** . . . . (515) 331-8420

Kansas State Office
3600 Anderson Avenue, Manhattan, KS 66503
Tel: (785) 539-3531 Fax: (855) 782-9609 Internet: www.fsa.usda.gov/ks

□ State Executive Director **David Kelly Schemm** . . . . (785) 539-3531
E-mail: David.Schemm@ks.usda.gov
E-mail: KS-fsa-webmaster@one.usda.gov
Administrative Officer **Dawna Ford** . . . . (785) 539-3531
E-mail: dawna.ford@ks.usda.gov
Executive Officer **Jack R. Salava** . . . . (785) 539-0113
E-mail: jack.salava@ks.usda.gov

Kentucky State Office
771 Corporate Drive, Suite 205, Lexington, KY 40503-5478
Tel: (859) 224-7601 Fax: (855) 768-4254 Internet: www.fsa.usda.gov/ky

□ State Executive Director **Brian Douglas Lacefield** . . . . (859) 224-7601
E-mail: brian.lacefield@ky.usda.gov
Administrative Officer **Debbie Wakefield** . . . . (859) 224-7622
E-mail: debbie.wakefield@ky.usda.gov
Executive Officer **Robert W. "Bob" Finch** . . . . (859) 224-7696
Management Information Systems Coordinator
Walena "Winnie" Breeding . . . . (859) 224-7624
E-mail: winnie.breeding@ky.usda.gov
Division Chief, Farm Programs **(Vacant)** . . . . (859) 224-7637
Farm Loan Chief **Michael "Mike" Hoyt** . . . . (859) 224-7440
E-mail: mike.hoyt@ky.usda.gov

Louisiana State Office
3737 Government Street, Alexandria, LA 71302-3395
Tel: (318) 473-7721 Fax: (844) 325-6942 Internet: www.fsa.usda.gov/la

□ State Executive Director **Craig A. McCain** . . . . (318) 473-7950
Education: Northeast Louisiana 1986 BS
Administrative Programs Chief **T. Christine Normand** . . . (318) 473-7650
E-mail: christine.normand@la.usda.gov
Farm Loans Chief **Thomas Chachere** . . . . (318) 473-7797
Production Adjustment Chief **DeWanna Pitman** . . . . (318) 473-7717
Conservation Program Specialist **Matt Springer** . . . . (318) 473-7716
Price Support Program Specialist **Rose Bordelon** . . . . (318) 473-7726

Maine State Office
967 Illinois Avenue, Suite 2, Bangor, ME 04401
Tel: (207) 990-9140 Tel: (207) 990-9100 ext. 2 Fax: (207) 990-9168
Internet: www.fsa.usda.gov/me

□ State Executive Director **David R. Lavway** . . . . (207) 990-9140
E-mail: David.Lavway@me.usda.gov
Education: Maine BS
Administrative Officer **Ken Gustin** . . . . (207) 990-9100 ext. 2
E-mail: ken.gustin@me.usda.gov

★ Presidential Appointment Requiring Senate Confirmation ☆ Presidential Appointment □ Schedule C Appointment ◇ Career Senior Foreign Service Appointment
● Career Senior Executive Service (SES) Appointment ○ Non-Career Senior Executive Service (SES) Appointment ■ Postal Career Executive Service

Maryland State Office
339 Busch's Frontage Road, Suite 104, Annapolis, MD 21409
Tel: (443) 482-2760 Fax: (855) 401-6638 Internet: www.fsa.usda.gov/md

□ State Executive Director **James P. "Jim" Eichhorst** . . . . . (443) 482-2764
E-mail: James.Eichhorst@md.usda.gov
Executive Officer **Vicky Coppage** . . . . . (443) 482-2771
E-mail: vicky.coppage@md.usda.gov
Farm Loan Chief **Cheryl Walker** . . . . . (443) 482-2767
Agricultural Program Chief/Program Specialist
Robert Wevodav . . . . . (443) 482-2770

Massachusetts State Office
445 West Street, Amherst, MA 01002-2994
Tel: (413) 253-4500 Fax: (855) 596-7665 Internet: www.fsa.usda.gov/ma

□ State Executive Director **Edward Davidian** . . . . . (413) 253-4501
Executive Officer **Lori Carver** . . . . . (413) 253-4503
E-mail: lori.carver@usda.gov
District Director **Daniel Smiarowski** . . . . . (413) 253-4511
E-mail: daniel.smiarowski@ma.usda.gov
Farm Loan Program Chief **Julie Kolodji** . . . . . (413) 253-4510
GIS Program Specialist **John Devine** . . . . . (413) 253-4502

Michigan State Office
700 South Main Street, Suite 120-C, Lapeer, MI 48446-3088
Tel: (810) 664-0895 Fax: (855) 647-0827 Internet: www.fsa.usda.gov/mi

□ State Executive Director **Joel Clay Johnson** . . . . . (517) 324-5110
E-mail: joel.c.johnson@mi.usda.gov
Education: Michigan State 1978 BA

Minnesota State Office
375 Jackson Street, Room 400, St. Paul, MN 55101-1852
Tel: (651) 602-7700 Fax: (651) 602-7743 Internet: www.fsa.usda.gov/mn

□ State Executive Director
Joseph Patrick "Joe" Martin . . . . . (651) 602-7700
E-mail: Joe.Martin@mn.usda.gov
Education: Minnesota 1997 BA

Mississippi State Office
6311 Ridgewood Road, Jackson, MS 39211
Tel: (601) 965-4300 Fax: (601) 965-4184 Internet: www.fsa.usda.gov/ms

□ State Executive Director
Robert Alexander "Bobby" Carson, Jr. . . . . . (601) 965-6670 ext. 102
Administrative Officer **Aaron C. Robinson** . . . . . (601) 965-6672 ext. 107
E-mail: aaron.robinson@ms.usda.gov
Conservation and Compliance Division
Program Specialist **Patty W. Roberts** . . . . . (601) 965-6684 ext. 127
Farm Loan Division Chief **Bart Miller** . . . . . (601) 965-6678 ext. 122
Price Support Division Program Specialist
Ricky M. Carnegie III . . . . . (601) 965-6680 ext. 124
Production Adjustment Division Program
Specialist **Kristi B. Gill** . . . . . (601) 965-6681 ext. 128

Missouri State Office
Parkade Center, 601 Business Loop 70 West,
Suite 225, Columbia, MO 65203
Tel: (573) 876-0925 Fax: (855) 830-0680 Internet: www.fsa.usda.gov/mo

□ State Executive Director **Brent Hampy** . . . . . (573) 876-0925
Education: Missouri BS; Texas Tech MS
Secretary **(Vacant)** . . . . . (573) 876-0925
Administrative Officer **Kimberly Viers** . . . . . (573) 876-0926
E-mail: kim.viers@mo.usda.gov
Management Information System Coordinator
Steven G. Niemeyer . . . . . (573) 876-0933
E-mail: steven.niemeyer@mo.usda.gov

Montana State Office
10 East Babcock, Room 557, Bozeman, MT 59715
Mail: P.O. Box 670, Bozeman, MT 59771-0670
Tel: (406) 587-6872 Fax: (406) 587-6887 Internet: www.fsa.usda.gov/mt

□ State Executive Director **Mike Foster** . . . . . (406) 587-6872
E-mail: Michael.Foster@mt.usda.gov
Education: Montana (Western) BA; Carroll Col (MT) BA;
Montana MPA

Montana State Office *(continued)*

Administrative Officer **Jennifer Cole** . . . . . (406) 587-6883
E-mail: jennifer.cole@mt.usda.gov

Nebraska State Office
7131 A Street, Lincoln, NE 68510-4202
Tel: (402) 437-5581 Fax: (402) 437-5280 Internet: www.fsa.usda.gov/ne

□ State Executive Director **Nancy Johner** . . . . . (402) 437-5581
E-mail: Nancy.Johner@ne.usda.gov
Education: Nebraska (Kearney) 1994 BS; Doane 2017 MM
Contracting Specialist **Julie Zimmerman** . . . . . (402) 437-5049
E-mail: julie.zimmerman@ne.usda.gov
Administrative Officer **Mike Sander** . . . . . (402) 437-5286

Nevada State Office
1365 Corporate Boulevard, Suite 200, Reno, NV 89502
Tel: (775) 857-8500 Fax: (855) 816-0896 Internet: www.fsa.usda.gov/nv

□ State Executive Director **Janice Kolvet** . . . . . (775) 857-8500 ext. 128
E-mail: janice.kolvet@nv.usda.gov
Administrative Specialist **Daniel G. Rybicki** . . . . . (775) 857-8500 ext. 112
E-mail: daniel.rybicki@nv.usda.gov
Farm Loan Chief **(Vacant)** . . . . . (775) 857-8500
District Director **Gus Wegren** . . . . . (775) 857-8500 ext. 143
Program Specialist **Debbie Goin** . . . . . (775) 857-8500 ext. 126

New Hampshire State Office
JC Cleveland Federal Building, 53 Pleasant Street,
Room 1601, Concord, NH 03301
Tel: (603) 224-7941 Fax: (855) 428-0330 Internet: www.fsa.usda.gov/nh

□ State Executive Director
Jeffrey Andrew "Jeff" Holmes . . . . . (603) 224-7941
E-mail: Jeffrey.Holmes2@nh.usda.gov
Executive Officer **Marilyn Mile** . . . . . (603) 224-7941 ext. 11

New Jersey State Office
300 Clocktower Drive, Hamilton Square, NJ 08690
Tel: (609) 587-0104 Fax: (609) 587-0904 Internet: www.fsa.usda.gov/nj

Executive Officer **Henri Ann Olsen** . . . . . (609) 587-0104
E-mail: henri.olsen@nj.usda.gov
Education: West Virginia 1975 MA

New Mexico State Office
6200 Jefferson Street, NE, Suite 211, Albuquerque, NM 87109
Tel: (800) 410-2067 Tel: (505) 761-4900 Fax: (877) 450-0860
Internet: www.fsa.usda.gov/nm

□ State Executive Director **Michael Steven White** . . . . . (505) 761-4900
E-mail: Michael.White4@nm.usda.gov
Executive Officer **Brenda Archuleta** . . . . . (505) 761-4921
E-mail: brenda.archuleta@nm.usda.gov

New York State Office
The Galleries, 441 South Salina Street,
5th Floor, Room 536, Syracuse, NY 13202-2455
Tel: (315) 477-6303 Fax: (315) 477-6300 Internet: www.fsa.usda.gov/ny

□ State Executive Director **Clark Putman** . . . . . (315) 477-6303
Executive Officer **Mark Dennis** . . . . . (315) 477-6303
E-mail: mark.dennis@ny.usda.gov

North Carolina State Office
4407 Bland Road, Suite 175, Raleigh, NC 27609-6296
Tel: (919) 875-4800 Fax: (919) 875-4825 Internet: www.fsa.usda.gov/nc

□ State Executive Director
Lindsay William "Len" McBride . . . . . (919) 875-4802
E-mail: len.mcbride@nc.usda.gov
Education: North Carolina Wilmington BA
Executive Officer **(Vacant)** . . . . . (919) 875-4809
Administrative Officer **(Vacant)** . . . . . (919) 875-4810
Information Management Specialist
Alicia Best Bridges . . . . . (919) 875-4803
E-mail: alicia.bridges@nc.usda.gov Fax: (919) 875-4828
Farm Loan Chief **Paula Nicholls** . . . . . (919) 875-4854
E-mail: paula.nicholls@nc.usda.gov

★ Presidential Appointment Requiring Senate Confirmation ☆ Presidential Appointment □ Schedule C Appointment ◇ Career Senior Foreign Service Appointment
● Career Senior Executive Service (SES) Appointment ○ Non-Career Senior Executive Service (SES) Appointment ■ Postal Career Executive Service

North Dakota State Office
1025 - 28th Street, S, Fargo, ND 58103
Tel: (701) 239-5224 Fax: (855) 813-6644 Internet: www.fsa.usda.gov/nd

□ State Executive Director **Brad Thykeson** . . . . (701) 239-5224
E-mail: Brad.Thykeson@nd.usda.gov
Administrative Officer **Russell L. Bubach** . . . . (701) 893-2204
E-mail: russell.bubach@nd.usda.gov

Ohio State Office
Bricker Federal Building, 200 North High Street,
Room 540, Columbus, OH 43215-2495
Tel: (614) 255-2441 Fax: (855) 832-5100 Internet: www.fsa.usda.gov/oh

□ State Executive Director **Leonard J. Hubert** . . . . (614) 255-2441
Education: Alabama A&M BS, MS
Administrative Officer **Mary "Mimi" Garringer** . . . . (614) 255-2519
E-mail: mimi.garringer@oh.usda.gov

Oklahoma State Office
100 USDA, Suite 102, Stillwater, OK 74074-2653
Tel: (405) 742-1130 Fax: (855) 416-9557 Internet: www.fsa.usda.gov/ok

□ State Executive Director **Scott R. Biggs** . . . . (405) 742-1130
E-mail: Scott.Biggs@ok.usda.gov
Education: Oklahoma State 2001 BA; Oklahoma 2006 JD
Administrative Specialist **Jan Courtright** . . . . (405) 742-1142

Oregon State Office
7620 SW Mohawk Street, Tualatin, OR 97062-8121
Tel: (503) 692-6830 Fax: (855) 824-6185 Internet: www.fsa.usda.gov/or

□ State Executive Director **(Vacant)** . . . . (503) 692-6830
Administrative Officer **Dan LoFaro** . . . . (503) 692-6830 ext. 238
E-mail: dan.lofaro@or.usda.gov
Chief Information Officer **(Vacant)** . . . . (503) 692-6830 ext. 232
Purchasing/Procurement Officer **Tim Hines** . . . . . (503) 692-6830 ext. 245
Communications Coordinator
Taylor B. Murray . . . . (503) 692-6830 ext. 228
E-mail: taylor.murray@or.usda.gov

Pennsylvania State Office
One Credit Union Place, Suite 320, Harrisburg, PA 17110-2994
Tel: (717) 237-2113 Fax: (717) 237-2149 Internet: www.fsa.usda.gov/pa

□ State Executive Director **Gary Harvey Groves** . . . . (717) 237-2115
E-mail: Gary.Groves@pa.usda.gov
Education: Purdue

Puerto Rico State Office
654 Muñoz Rivera Avenue, Suite 829, San Juan, PR 00918
Tel: (787) 294-1613 Fax: (787) 294-1607 Internet: www.fsa.usda.gov/pr

● State Executive Director **Wanda J. Perez** . . . . (787) 294-1613 ext. 103
E-mail: wanda.perez@pr.usda.gov
Executive Officer **(Vacant)** . . . . (787) 294-1610 ext. 105
Fax: (787) 294-1609

Rhode Island State Office
60 Quaker Lane, Room 62, Warwick, RI 02886
Tel: (401) 828-8232 Fax: (855) 924-2345

□ State Executive Director **Michael Sullivan** . . . . (401) 828-8232
Education: Rhode Island BA; Vermont MA; Nebraska Ph.D. Fax: (855) 924-2345
Administrative Officer **Alison Rose** . . . . (401) 828-8232
E-mail: alison.rose@ri.usda.gov

South Carolina State Office
1927 Thurmond Mall, Suite 100, Columbia, SC 29201-2375
Tel: (803) 534-2409 ext. 110 Fax: (855) 563-9305
Internet: www.fsa.usda.gov/sc

□ State Executive Director
Boone Solomon Peeler . . . . (803) 534-2409 ext. 110
E-mail: Boone.Peeler@sc.usda.gov
Administrative Officer **Toni G. Turner** . . . . (803) 534-2409 ext. 110
E-mail: toni.turner@sc.usda.gov

South Dakota State Office
200 Fourth Street, SW, Room 308, Huron, SD 57350
Tel: (605) 352-1160 Fax: (855) 243-6003 Internet: www.fsa.usda.gov/sd

□ State Executive Director **Paul Eric Shubeck** . . . . (605) 352-1160
E-mail: Paul.Shubeck@sd.usda.gov
Executive Officer **James Patrick "Jamie" White** . . . . (605) 352-1181
200 Fourth Street SW, Huron, SD 57350
E-mail: jamie.white@sd.usda.gov
Secretary **Deb Olerud** . . . . (605) 352-1161
E-mail: deb.olerud@sd.usda.gov

Tennessee State Office
Federal Building, 801 Broadway, Room 579, Nashville, TN 37203-3883
Tel: (615) 277-2600 Fax: (615) 277-2659 Internet: www.fsa.usda.gov/tn

□ State Executive Director **Dennis Houston Beavers** . . . . . . (615) 277-2600
E-mail: Dennis.Beavers@tn.usda.gov
Administrative Officer **Tyeisha Smith-Samples** . . . . (615) 277-2608
E-mail: tyeisha.smith@tn.usda.gov
Farm Programs Director **Patty Taylor** . . . . (615) 277-2616
Farm Loan Programs Chief **James Welborn** . . . . (615) 277-2627

Texas State Office
Compass Bank Building, 2405 Texas Avenue South,
College Station, TX 77840
Tel: (979) 680-5151 Fax: (844) 496-7880 Internet: www.fsa.usda.gov/tx

□ State Executive Director **Gary L. Six** . . . . (979) 680-5796
E-mail: gary.six@tx.usda.gov
Executive Officer **Erasmo "Eddie" Trevino** . . . . (979) 680-5196
Administrative Officer **(Vacant)** . . . . (979) 680-5192

Utah State Office
Federal Building, 125 South State Street,
Room 3202, Salt Lake City, UT 84138-1189
Tel: (801) 524-4530 Fax: (801) 524-5244 Internet: www.fsa.usda.gov/ut

□ State Executive Director **Bruce J. Richeson** . . . . (801) 524-4537
E-mail: Bruce.Richeson@ut.usda.gov
Education: Weber State 1985 BA
Executive Secretary **Kelli Coplin** . . . . (801) 524-4530
Program Specialist **Heidi K. Brooks** . . . . (435) 257-5402
Administrative Officer **Jeanine H. Cook** . . . . (801) 524-4541
E-mail: jeanine.cook@ut.usda.gov

Vermont State Office
356 Mountain View Drive, Suite 104, Colchester, VT 05446
Tel: (802) 658-2803 Fax: (802) 794-3676 Internet: www.fsa.usda.gov/vt

□ State Executive Director **Wendy L. Wilton** . . . . (802) 658-2803
E-mail: wendy.wilton@vt.usda.gov
Farm Loan Chief **Patrick K. Freeman** . . . . (802) 658-2803

Virginia State Office
1606 Santa Rosa Road, Suite 138, Richmond, VA 23229
Tel: (804) 287-1503 Fax: (855) 616-1657 Internet: www.fsa.usda.gov/va

□ State Executive Director **Nivin A. Elgohary** . . . . (804) 287-1503
E-mail: nivin.elgohary@va.usda.gov
Education: Old Dominion BA
Administrative Officer **Connie Washburn-Marsh** . . . . (804) 287-1514
E-mail: connie.washburn-marsh@va.usda.gov
Agricultural Program Technology Specialist
Daniel J. "Dan" Mertz . . . . (804) 287-1548
E-mail: dan.mertz@va.usda.gov
Public Affairs Specialist **Diane Lenoir Giles** . . . . (804) 537-1537
E-mail: diane.lenoir-giles@va.usda.gov

Washington State Office
Rock Pointe Tower, 316 West Boone Avenue,
Suite 568, Spokane, WA 99201-2350
Tel: (509) 323-3000 Fax: (855) 843-6123 Internet: www.fsa.usda.gov/wa

□ State Executive Director **Brian Dansel** . . . . (509) 323-3003
E-mail: brian.dansel@osec.usda.gov
Administrative Chief **Mike Mandere** . . . . (509) 323-3005
E-mail: mike.mandere@wa.usda.gov

West Virginia State Office
1550 Earl Core Road, Suite 102, Morgantown, WV 26505
Tel: (304) 284-4800 Fax: (855) 854-3074 Internet: www.fsa.usda.gov/wv

□ State Executive Director **Roger Dahmer** . . . . (304) 284-4800
E-mail: roger.dahmer@wv.usda.gov
Executive Officer **John C. Pettit** . . . . (304) 284-4803
E-mail: john.pettit@wv.usda.gov
Education: West Virginia BS, MS
Supervisory Agricultural Program Specialist **Kevin Hinkle** . . . . (304) 284-4805
Agricultural Program Specialist **Leanne Taylor** . . . . (304) 284-4807
Communication and Outreach Specialist **Travis L. Wilfong** . . . . (304) 284-4800
E-mail: travis.wilfong@wv.usda.gov Fax: (304) 252-5809
GIS Specialist **April L. Savage** . . . . (304) 284-4800
E-mail: april.enlow@wv.usda.gov
Education: West Virginia BS
Farm Loan Chief **(Vacant)** . . . . (304) 284-4811
Farm Loan Program Specialist **Tom Landis** . . . . (304) 284-4812
Education: West Virginia BS
Farm Loan Program Specialist **Thomas "Thom" Loughry** . . . . (304) 284-4814
Management Analyst **(Vacant)** . . . . (304) 284-4800
District Director **Douglas Cyphers** . . . . (304) 284-4820
E-mail: douglas.cyphers@wv.usda.gov
Education: West Virginia BS
District Director **Joshua Lewis** . . . . (304) 636-6703
District Director **Mike Taylor** . . . . (304) 257-4702
E-mail: michael.w.taylor@wv.usda.gov

Wisconsin State Office
8030 Excelsior Drive, Suite 100, Madison, WI 53717-2906
Tel: (608) 662-4422 Fax: (855) 758-0755 Internet: www.fsa.usda.gov/wi

□ State Executive Director **Sandra "Sandy" Chalmers** . . . . (608) 662-4422 ext. 100
E-mail: sandra.chalmers@wi.usda.gov
Education: Wisconsin BA; Nebraska MM
Executive Officer **Russell Raeder** . . . . (608) 662-4422 ext. 127
E-mail: russell.raeder@usda.gov
Administrative Officer **Warren Hanson** . . . . (608) 662-4422 ext. 130
E-mail: warren.hanson@wi.usda.gov
IT Specialist **James D "Jim" Zamzow** . . . . (608) 662-4422 ext. 123
E-mail: jim.zamzow@wi.usda.gov

Wyoming State Office
951 Werner Court, Suite 130, Casper, WY 82601-1307
Tel: (307) 261-5231 Fax: (855) 415-3427 Internet: www.fsa.usda.gov/wy

□ State Executive Director **Lois Ann Van Mark** . . . . (307) 261-5230
E-mail: lois.vanmark@wy.usda.gov
State Outreach Officer **Rob Weppner** . . . . (307) 682-8843
E-mail: rob.weppner@wy.usda.gov
Administrative Officer **Stephen C. Swieter** . . . . (307) 261-5232
E-mail: steve.swieter@wy.usda.gov
Communication Coordinator **Carry Martin** . . . . (307) 261-5231
E-mail: carry.martin@wy.usda.gov

Deputy Administrator for Management (DAM)
South Agriculture Building, 1400 Independence Avenue, SW, Washington, DC 20250

Kansas City Management Office (KSMO)
6501 Beacon Drive, Kansas City, MO 64133

Director **Ralph Garcia, Jr.** . . . . (816) 926-6095
E-mail: ralph.garcia@kcc.usda.gov
DC Number: (202) 690-2501

Risk Management Agency (RMA)
South Agriculture Building, 1400 Independence Avenue, SW, Room 6092-S, Washington, DC 20250
Tel: (202) 690-2803 Fax: (202) 690-2818 E-mail: rma.cco@rma.usda.gov
E-mail: rma.media.requests@rma.usda.gov (Public Affairs email)
Internet: www.rma.usda.gov

Insurance Services
South Agriculture Building, 1400 Independence Avenue, SW, Room 6709-S, MS 0805, Washington, DC 20250
Tel: (202) 690-4494 Fax: (202) 690-2095

Billings (MT) Regional Office
3490 Gabel Road, Suite 100, Billings, MT 59102-7302
Tel: (406) 657-6447 Fax: (406) 657-6573
Areas Covered: MT, ND, SD, WY

Director **Eric Bashore** . . . . (406) 657-6447
Deputy Director **Cynthia Cruea** . . . . (406) 657-6447
Risk Management Analyst **Karen Korenko** . . . . (406) 657-6447

Davis (CA) Regional Office
430 G Street, Room 4168, Davis, CA 95616-4168
Tel: (530) 792-5870 Fax: (530) 792-5893
Areas Covered: AZ, CA, HI, NV, UT

Director **Jeff Yasui** . . . . (530) 792-5870
Deputy Director **Ruben Saavedra** . . . . (530) 792-5870
Senior Risk Management Specialist **Laura Hernandez** . . . (530) 792-5870
Senior Risk Management Specialist **Robert Smith** . . . . . . (530) 792-5870
Risk Management Specialist **Ski Allender** . . . . (530) 792-5870
Information Technology Analyst **Renette Carrillo** . . . . (530) 792-5870
E-mail: renette.carrillo@rma.usda.gov

Jackson (MS) Regional Office
803 Liberty Road, Flowood, MS 39232-9000
Tel: (601) 965-4771 Fax: (601) 965-4517 E-mail: rsoms@rma.usda.gov
Internet: www.rma.usda.gov/aboutrma/fields/ms_rso
Areas Covered: AR, KY, LA, MS, TN

Director **Roddric L. Bell** . . . . (601) 965-4771
Deputy Director **Cody Adkins** . . . . (601) 965-4771
Webmaster **(Vacant)** . . . . (601) 965-4771

Oklahoma City (OK) Regional Office
205 NW 63rd Street, Suite 170, Oklahoma City, OK 73116
Tel: (405) 879-2700 Fax: (405) 879-2741
Areas Covered: NM, OK, TX

Director **James Bellmon** . . . . (405) 605-6216 ext. 110
Deputy Director **Grant James** . . . . (405) 605-6216 ext. 115

Raleigh (NC) Regional Office
4405 Bland Road, Suite 160, Raleigh, NC 27609
Tel: (919) 875-4880 Fax: (919) 875-4915 E-mail: rsonc@rma.usda.gov
Areas Covered: CT, DE, ME, MD, MA, NH, NJ, NY, NC, PA, RI, VA, VT, WV

Director **Alexander Sereno** . . . . (919) 875-4880

Saint Paul (MN) Regional Office
30 Seventh Street East, Suite 1890, St. Paul, MN 55101-4901
Tel: (651) 290-3304 Fax: (651) 290-4139 E-mail: rsomn@rma.usda.gov
Areas Covered: IA, MN, WI

Director **Duane A. Voy PMP** . . . . (651) 290-3304 ext. 233
Education: Iowa State 1998 BSAg; Bethel Sem 1992; Regent U 1996

Spokane (WA) Regional Office
11707 East Sprague Avenue, Suite 201, Spokane Valley, WA 99206
Tel: (509) 228-6320 Fax: (509) 228-6321 E-mail: rsowa@rma.usda.gov
Areas Covered: AK, ID, OR, WA

Director **Benjamin "Ben" Thiel** . . . . (509) 228-6320
Education: Idaho State BA
Administrative Assistant **Mark Slingerland** . . . . (509) 228-6320
Deputy Director **Cara McNab** . . . . (509) 228-6320
Education: Arkansas LLM

(continued on next page)

DEPARTMENTS

★ Presidential Appointment Requiring Senate Confirmation ☆ Presidential Appointment □ Schedule C Appointment ◇ Career Senior Foreign Service Appointment
● Career Senior Executive Service (SES) Appointment ○ Non-Career Senior Executive Service (SES) Appointment ■ Postal Career Executive Service

Spokane (WA) Regional Office *(continued)*

Senior Risk Management Specialist
Jonquil Henderson . . . . (509) 228-6320
Senior Risk Management Specialist **Rick Williams** . . . . (509) 228-6320
Outreach Coordinator **Jo Lynne Seufer** . . . . (509) 228-6320
Computer Specialist **Donald "Don" Kaufman** . . . . (509) 228-6320

Springfield (IL) Regional Office
3500 Wabash Avenue, Springfield, IL 62711
Tel: (217) 241-6600 Fax: (217) 241-6618 E-mail: rsoil@rma.usda.gov
Areas Covered: IL, IN, MI, OH

Director **Brian D. Frieden** . . . . (217) 241-6600 ext. 113

Topeka (KS) Regional Office
2641 SW Wanamaker Road, Suite 201, Topeka, KS 66614
Tel: (785) 228-5512 Fax: (785) 228-1456 E-mail: rsoks@rma.usda.gov
Areas Covered: CO, KS, MO, NE

Director **Rebecca Davis** . . . . (785) 228-5512
Webmaster **Jeffrey "Jeff" Darrow** . . . . (816) 926-7841
6501 Beacon Drive, Fax: (816) 823-4699
Kansas City, MO 64133-0833

Valdosta (GA) Regional Office
106 South Patterson Street, Suite 250, Valdosta, GA 31601-5609
Tel: (229) 219-2200 Fax: (229) 242-3566 E-mail: rsoga@rma.usda.gov
Areas Covered: AL, FL, GA, PR, SC

Director **Davina Lee** . . . . (229) 219-2200
Fax: (229) 244-6103

Product Management
6501 Beacon Drive, Room 403, Kansas City, MO 64133-4676
Tel: (816) 926-7394 Fax: (816) 926-1803

● Deputy Administrator **Richard Flournoy** . . . . (816) 926-7394
E-mail: richard.flournoy@rma.usda.gov
Associate Deputy Administrator **John Underwood** . . . . (816) 926-7394
E-mail: john.w.underwood@rma.usda.gov
Actuarial and Product Design Division Director
(Acting) **Jason Albright** . . . . (816) 926-7394
Product Administration and Standards Division
Director **Francie Kucera Tolle** . . . . (816) 926-7387
Fax: (816) 926-1841
Product Analysis and Accounting Division Director
Jason Albright . . . . (816) 926-6530
Fax: (816) 926-1857

Risk Compliance (RC)
South Agriculture Building, 1400 Independence Avenue, SW,
Room 6604, Washington, DC 20250
Tel: (202) 720-0642 Fax: (202) 690-3602

Central Regional Compliance Office (CRCO)
P.O. Box 419205, Kansas City, MO 64141-6205
Tel: (816) 926-7963 Fax: (816) 823-1830 E-mail: cfomo@rma.usda.gov
Areas Covered: CO, KS, MO, NE

Field Director **Alvin A. Gilmore** . . . . (816) 926-7963

Eastern Regional Compliance Office (ERCO)
4405 Bland Road, Suite 165, Raleigh, NC 27609
Tel: (919) 875-4930 Fax: (919) 875-4929
Areas Covered: AL, CT, DE, FL, GA, ME, MD, MA, NH, NJ, NY, NC, PA, PR, RI, SC, VT, VA, VI, WV

Director **Jessica Dedrick** . . . . (919) 875-4945

Midwest Regional Compliance Office (MRCO)
6045 Lakeside Boulevard, Indianapolis, IN 46278
Tel: (317) 290-3050 Fax: (317) 290-3065
E-mail: cfoin@rma.usda.gov (CFOIN@rma.usda.gov)
Internet: www.rma.usda.gov/aboutrma/fields/in_cfo.html
Areas Covered: IL, IN, MI, OH

Director **Ronie C. Griffin** . . . . (317) 290-3050
Deputy Director **Joshua "Josh" Engelking** . . . . (317) 290-3050
Senior Investigator **Stacey Shell** . . . . (317) 290-3050

Midwest Regional Compliance Office *(continued)*

Senior Investigator **Stacy L. Shell** . . . . (317) 290-3050
Administrative and Program Assistant
Victoria Stewart . . . . (317) 290-3050
E-mail: victoria.stewart@rma.usda.gov

Northern Regional Compliance Office (NRCO)
3440 Federal Drive, Suite 200, Eagan, MN 55122-1301
Tel: (651) 452-1688 Fax: (651) 452-1689 E-mail: cfomn@rma.usda.gov
Areas Covered: IA, MN, MT, ND, SD, WI, WY

Director **Scott Tincher** . . . . (651) 452-1688 ext. 222
Administrative and Program Assistant
Susan Angell . . . . (651) 452-1688 ext. 221
E-mail: susan.angell@rma.usda.gov

Southern Regional Compliance Office (SRCO)
1111 West Mockingbird Lane, Suite 280, Dallas, TX 75247
Tel: (214) 767-7700 Fax: (214) 767-7721 E-mail: cfotx@rma.usda.gov
Areas Covered: AR, KY, LA, MS, NM, OK, TN, TX

Regional Director **Mariano Lerma** . . . . (214) 767-7700

Western Regional Compliance Office (WRCO)
430 G Street, Agency 4167, Davis, CA 95616-4167
Tel: (530) 792-5850 Fax: (530) 792-5865 E-mail: cfoca@rma.usda.gov
Areas Covered: AK, AZ, CA, HI, ID, NV, OR, UT, WA

Director **Sandy Sanchez** . . . . (530) 792-5850 ext. 5851

Food, Nutrition and Consumer Services (FNCS)

Jamie L. Whitten Federal Building, 1400 Independence Avenue, SW, Washington, DC 20250

OFFICE OF THE UNDER SECRETARY

Jamie L. Whitten Building, 1400 Independence Avenue, SW, Room 216-E, Washington, DC 20250-0106
Fax: (202) 690-3100

Food and Nutrition Service (FNS)

Park Office Center, 3101 Park Center Drive, Alexandria, VA 22302
Tel: (703) 305-2060 Fax: (703) 305-2908 Internet: www.fns.usda.gov

Note: On September 7, 2017, Secretary of Agriculture Sonny Perdue announced that the Center for Nutrition Policy and Promotion would be merged into the Food and Nutrition Service.

Office of the Associate Administrator for Regional Operations and Support

Park Office Center, 3101 Park Center Drive,
Room 906, Alexandria, VA 22302

Regional Offices

Mid-Atlantic Region
Mercer Corporate Park, 300 Corporate Boulevard,
Robbinsville, NJ 08691-1598
Tel: (609) 259-5085 Fax: (609) 259-5185
Areas Covered: DE, DC, MD, NJ, PA, PR, VA, VI, WV

● Regional Administrator **Patricia "Pat" Dombroski** . . . . (609) 259-5025
E-mail: patricia.dombroski@fns.usda.gov Fax: (609) 259-5185
Deputy Regional Administrator **Diana Limbacher** . . . . (609) 259-5086
E-mail: diana.limbacher@fns.usda.gov
Civil Rights Director **Michele Sazo** . . . . (609) 259-5061
E-mail: michele.sazo@fns.usda.gov Fax: (609) 259-5027
Grants Management and Administrative Services
Director **Debbie Mansfield** . . . . (609) 259-5140
Public Affairs Director (Acting)
Christopher Chris Kelly . . . . (609) 259-5026
Outreach Strategist Coordinator **Kirk Wilborne** . . . . (410) 296-1697
515 East Joppa Road, Towson, MD 21286-5418
E-mail: kirk.wilborne@fns.usda.gov

★ Presidential Appointment Requiring Senate Confirmation ☆ Presidential Appointment □ Schedule C Appointment ◇ Career Senior Foreign Service Appointment
● Career Senior Executive Service (SES) Appointment ○ Non-Career Senior Executive Service (SES) Appointment ■ Postal Career Executive Service

Mid-Atlantic Region *(continued)*

SNAP Director **Eric Ratchford** ....(609) 259-5088
Special Nutrition Programs Director **(Vacant)** ....(609) 259-5021
Disaster Assistance Director **David Gagliardi** ....(609) 259-5028

Midwest Region

77 West Jackson Boulevard, 20th Floor, Chicago, IL 60604-3507
Tel: (312) 353-6664 Fax: (312) 886-6598
Areas Covered: IL, IN, MI, MN, OH, WI

● Regional Administrator **Tim English** ....(312) 353-6664
E-mail: tim.english@fns.usda.gov
Deputy Regional Administrator **Patricia "Trish" Solis** ....(312) 353-6663
E-mail: patricia.solis@fns.usda.gov
SNAP Director **Susan Holzer** ....(312) 353-1478
Special Nutrition Programs Director **Julie Mikkelson** ....(312) 353-1901
Grants Management and Administrative Services
Director **Michael Chambers** ....(312) 886-2276
E-mail: michael.chambers@fns.usda.gov
Public Affairs Director **Alan Shannon** ....(312) 353-1045
E-mail: alan.shannon@fns.usda.gov
Civil Rights Director **Tamara Earley** ....(312) 353-6657
E-mail: tamara.earley@fns.usda.gov
Disaster Assistance Coordinator **Sandra MacMartin** .....(312) 353-1666

Mountain Plains Region

Cesar E. Chavez Federal Building, 3101 Park Center Drive,
Room 903, Alexandria, VA 22302
Tel: (303) 844-0300 Fax: (303) 844-6203
Areas Covered: CO, IA, KS, MO, MT, NE, ND, SD, UT, WY

● Regional Administrator (Acting) **Cheryl Kennedy** ....(303) 844-0300
E-mail: cheryl.kennedy@fns.usda.gov
Deputy Regional Administrator **Kathie Ferguson** ....(303) 844-0300
E-mail: kathie.ferguson@fns.usda.gov
Education: Lyndon State BA, BS
Assistant to the Regional Administrator
Bart Bushman ....(303) 844-0310
E-mail: bart.bushman@fns.usda.gov Fax: (303) 844-6203
Civil Rights Director **Sharon Dafondanouto** ....(303) 844-0371
Grants Management and Administrative Services
Director **Cynthia "Cindy" Archuleta** ....(303) 844-0328
E-mail: cynthia.archuleta@fns.usda.gov
SNAP Program Director **Joe Casey** ....(303) 844-0306
Information Technology Director **Ralph King** ....(303) 844-0182
E-mail: ralph.king@fns.usda.gov
Public Affairs Director **David Van Behren** ....(303) 844-0314
Regional Nutrition Director **Stella Nash** ....(303) 844-0308
Special Nutrition Programs Director **Jane Brand** ....(303) 844-0363
Supplemental Food Program (WIC) Director
Sandy A. Clark ....(303) 844-0335
Regional Human Resources Liaison **Debra Visser** ....(303) 844-0311
Administrative Officer **Michael "Mike" Todd** ....(303) 844-5244
E-mail: michael.todd@fns.usda.gov
Disaster Assistance Coordinator **Philip Fraley** ....(303) 844-0341

Northeast Region

Thomas P. O'Neill Federal Building, 10 Causeway Street,
Room 501, Boston, MA 02222-1071
Tel: (617) 565-6370 Fax: (617) 565-6473
Areas Covered: CT, ME, MA, NH, NY, RI, VT

● Regional Administrator **Kurt Messner** ....(617) 565-6370
E-mail: kurt.messner@fns.usda.gov
Executive Secretary **Meredith Baker** ....(617) 565-6370
Deputy Regional Administrator **Nancy Ann Bodell** ......(617) 565-6370
Field Operations Director **(Vacant)** ....(617) 565-6371
Assistant Director, Field Operations, Upstate New
York and New England **Peter Conti** ....(617) 565-6370
E-mail: peter.conti@fns.usda.gov
Grants Management and Administrative Services
Director **Kirk Hassel** ....(617) 565-6370
E-mail: kirk.hassel@fns.usda.gov
SNAP Director **Bonnie Brathwaite** ....(617) 565-6397
E-mail: bonnie.brathwaite@fns.usda.gov

Northeast Region *(continued)*

Branch Chief **Kenneth Sierra** ....(617) 565-6418
E-mail: kenneth.sierra@fns.usda.gov
Special Nutrition Programs Director **Candice Stoiber** ....(617) 565-6370
E-mail: candice.stoiber@fns.usda.gov
Civil Rights Director **Stephen Miliano** ....(617) 565-6424
E-mail: stephen.miliano@fns.usda.gov
Public Affairs Director **Cindy Packett** ....(617) 565-6418
Disaster Assistance Coordinator **Jason McGrath** ....(617) 565-4211

Southeast Region

Atlanta Federal Center, 61 Forsyth Street, SW,
Suite 8T36, Atlanta, GA 30303-3415
Tel: (404) 562-1800 Fax: (404) 562-1807
Areas Covered: AL, FL, GA, KY, MS, NC, SC, TN

● Regional Administrator **(Vacant)** ....(404) 562-1801
Deputy Regional Administrator **Erin Swanson-Hall** ......(404) 562-1804
E-mail: erin.swan-hall@fns.usda.gov
Field Operations Regional Director **Yameche Madre** .....(404) 562-1912
Civil Rights Director **Gail A. Hoffman** ....(404) 562-7033
Grants Management and Administrative Services
Director **Izra Brown** ....(404) 562-1825
SNAP Director **Peggy Fouts** ....(404) 562-7099
E-mail: peggy.fouts@fns.usda.gov
Disaster Assistance Coordinator **Eugene Malveaux** ......(678) 704-2021
E-mail: eugene.malveaux@fns.usda.gov
Public Affairs Director **Aaron Wiley** ....(404) 562-1811
Special Nutrition Programs Director **Lily Bouie** ....(404) 562-7072
Supplemental Food Programs Director
Sandra "Sandy" Benton-Davis ....(404) 562-7111
E-mail: sandy.benton-davis@fns.usda.gov
Management Analyst **Angela Gregg** ....(404) 562-1888
Human Resources Officer **(Vacant)** ....(404) 562-1800

Southwest Region

Earle Cabell Federal Building, 1100 Commerce Street,
Room 522, Dallas, TX 75242-1005
Tel: (214) 290-9800 Fax: (214) 767-0271
Areas Covered: AR, LA, NM, OK, TX

● Regional Administrator **William E. "Bill" Ludwig** ....(214) 290-9800
E-mail: william.ludwig@fns.usda.gov
Public Affairs Director **Leslie Lankster** ....(214) 290-9834
Deputy Regional Administrator **Karen Twitty** ....(214) 290-9800
E-mail: karen.twitty@fns.usda.gov
Civil Rights Director **Kamar Pelee** ....(214) 290-9837
1100 Commerce Street, Fax: (214) 767-9600
Room 522, Dallas, TX 75242-9800
Grants Management and Administrative Services
Director **Jeff Wingate** ....(214) 290-9831
SNAP Director **Dwight Crudup** ....(214) 290-9820
Special Nutrition Programs Director **Eddie Longoria** .....(214) 290-9908
Disaster Assistance Director **Catrina Kamau** ....(214) 290-9929

Western Region

90 Seventh St., Suite 10-100, San Francisco, CA 94103
Tel: (415) 705-1310 Fax: (415) 705-1364
Areas Covered: AK, AZ, CA, GU, HI, ID, NV, OR, WA, American Samoa, Guam, Northern Mariana Islands.

● Regional Administrator **Jesus Mendoza, Jr.** ....(415) 705-1310
E-mail: jesus.mendoza@fns.usda.gov
Secretary **Jason Levondski** ....(415) 705-1310
E-mail: jason.levondski@fns.usda.gov
Deputy Regional Administrator **Terry Gunnell** ....(415) 705-1310
Education: West Georgia 1985 BS
Grants Management and Administrative Services
Director **Edward Fortenberry** ....(415) 645-1916
Regional Civil Rights Director (Acting) **Tamara Earley** ...(415) 705-1330
Fax: (415) 705-1353
Public Affairs Director (Acting) **Jesus Mendoza, Jr.** ....(415) 705-1337
E-mail: jesus.mendoza@fns.usda.gov
Personnel Liaison **Mike Dickison** ....(415) 705-1314
Fax: (415) 705-1353

(continued on next page)

★ Presidential Appointment Requiring Senate Confirmation ☆ Presidential Appointment ☐ Schedule C Appointment ◇ Career Senior Foreign Service Appointment
● Career Senior Executive Service (SES) Appointment ○ Non-Career Senior Executive Service (SES) Appointment ■ Postal Career Executive Service

Western Region *(continued)*

SNAP Division Director (Acting)
Rebecca "Becky" Hobbs .... (415) 705-1341
Education: George Mason MPA
Special Nutrition Programs Division Director
Marisa Cheung .... (415) 437-8804
Disaster Assistance Coordinator **Maribelle Balbes** .... (415) 437-8802

Food Safety (FS)

South Agriculture Building, 1400 Independence Avenue, SW,
Washington, DC 20250
Internet: www.fsis.usda.gov

OFFICE OF THE UNDER SECRETARY

Jamie L. Whitten Federal Building, 1400 Independence Avenue, SW,
Room 227-E, Washington, DC 20250
Tel: (202) 720-0350
Tel: (202) 720-3333 (Meat and Poultry Hotline - DC Metropolitan Area)
Tel: (800) 535-4555 (Meat and Poultry Hotline - Continental US)
TTY: (800) 256-7072 (Meat and Poultry Hotline) Fax: (202) 690-0820

Food Safety and Inspection Service (FSIS)

Jamie L. Whitten Federal Building, 1400 Independence Avenue, SW,
Room 331-E, Washington, DC 20250
Tel: (202) 720-9113 (Media Inquiries) Fax: (202) 720-5704
Internet: www.fsis.usda.gov

Office of Field Operations (OFO)

Administration Building, 1400 Independence Avenue, SW,
Room 344-E, Washington, DC 20250
Fax: (202) 720-5439

Regulatory Operations

District Offices

Alameda (CA) District Office
800 Buchanan St, Albany, CA 94710
Tel: (510) 769-5712 Fax: (510) 337-5081
Areas Covered: AZ, CA, NV

District Manager **Dr. Yudhbir Sharma** .... (510) 769-5712
E-mail: yudhbir.sharma@fsis.usda.gov
Deputy District Manager **Abdalla Amin** .... (510) 769-5712
Deputy District Manager **Sheryl Beckett** .... (510) 769-5712
Deputy District Manager **Virginia Felix** .... (510) 769-5712
Deputy District Manager **Frank Gillis** .... (510) 769-5712

Atlanta (GA) District Office
1924 Building, 100 Alabama Street, SW,
Suite 3R90, Atlanta, GA 30303-3104
Tel: (404) 562-5900 Fax: (404) 652-5877
Areas Covered: FL, GA, PR, SC, Virgin Islands

District Manager **Dr. Phyllis Adams** .... (404) 562-5900

Dallas (TX) District Office
1100 Commerce Street, Room 516, Dallas, TX 75242-9800
Tel: (214) 767-9116 Fax: (844) 706-9296
Areas Covered: TX

District Manager **Dr. Jennifer Beasley-McKean** .... (214) 767-1253
Deputy District Manager **Dr. Gary Davis** .... (214) 767-1257
Deputy District Manager **Sam Dragoi** .... (214) 767-1256
Deputy District Manager **Dr. Ronald "Ron" Nida** .... (214) 767-1275
District Case Specialist **Johnny McAdams** .... (214) 767-1261
Regional Investigation Manager **(Vacant)** .... (214) 767-2783
Resource Manager **Marc Coudriet** .... (214) 767-1271

Denver (CO) District Office
1 Denver Federal Center, Building 45, Door S3, Denver, CO 80225
P.O. Box 25387, Denver, CO 80225
Tel: (303) 236-9800 Fax: (303) 236-9794
Areas Covered: AK, AZ, CO, HI, ID, NE, NM, OR, UT, WA, WY, American Samoa, Guam, Northern Mariana Islands

District Manager **(Vacant)** .... (303) 236-9793
Deputy District Manager **Scott Hoffman** .... (303) 236-9860
Deputy District Manager **Dr. Maria Esteras** .... (303) 236-9804
Deputy District Manager **Dr. Robert Reeder** .... (303) 236-9788
Administrative Officer **Latoya Younger** .... (303) 236-9787

Des Moines (IA) District Office
210 Walnut Street, Room 985, Des Moines, IA 50309-2123
Tel: (515) 727-8960 Fax: (515) 727-8991
Areas Covered: IA, MN, ND, SD, WI

District Manager **Dawn Sprouls** .... (515) 727-8960
E-mail: dawn.sprouls@fsis.usda.gov
Deputy District Manager **Dr. Todd Gerwig** .... (515) 727-8984
Deputy District Manager **Dr. Khalid Masood** .... (515) 343-4499
Deputy District Manager **Tom Beck** .... (515) 727-8978
Administrative Support **Paul Palmer** .... (515) 727-8976
E-mail: paul.palmer@fsis.usda.gov

Chicago (IL) District Office
1919 South Highland Avenue, Lombard, IL 60148
Tel: (630) 620-7474 Fax: (630) 620-7599
Areas Covered: IL, IN, MI, OH

District Manager **Paul Wolseley** .... (630) 620-9772
Deputy District Manager **Dr. Tamara Mayberry-Davis** ... (630) 620-9764
E-mail: tamara.mayberry@fsis.usda.gov
Deputy District Manager **Karnail Mudahar** .... (630) 620-0697
E-mail: karnail.mudahar@fsis.usda.gov
Deputy District Manager **Dr. Mounira Naguib** .... (630) 620-0135
E-mail: mounira.naguib@fsis.usda.gov

Jackson (MS) District Office
713 South Pear Orchard Road, Suite 402, Ridgeland, MS 39157
Tel: (601) 965-4312 Fax: (601) 965-5901
Areas Covered: AL, KY, MS, TN

District Manager **Larry Davis** .... (601) 927-9901
E-mail: larry.davis4@fsis.usda.gov
Deputy District Manager
Dr. Gregory "Greg" Brookhouser DVM .... (769) 231-4027
Education: Iowa State 1985 DVM
Deputy District Manager **William Griffin** .... (601) 398-5642
Deputy District Manager **Dr. David Thompson** .... (601) 965-4312
E-mail: david.thompson4@fsis.usda.gov

Philadelphia (PA) District Office
Mellon Independence Center, 701 Market Street,
Suite 4100-A, Philadelphia, PA 19106
Tel: (800) 637-6222 Fax: (215) 597-4217
Areas Covered: CT, MA, ME, NH, NY, PA, RI, VT

District Manager **Susan Scarcia** .... (215) 430-6302
Deputy District Manager **Salah Ibrahim** .... (215) 430-6312
Deputy District Manager **Michael Osisat** .... (215) 430-6218
Deputy District Manager **Joseph Schein** .... (215) 430-6219
Deputy District Manager **Lynda Lilyestrom** .... (215) 430-6304

Raleigh (NC) District Office
6020 Six Forks Road, Raleigh, NC 27609
Tel: (919) 844-8400 Fax: (919) 844-8411
Areas Covered: DC, DE, MD, NC, NJ, VA, WV

District Manager **Todd M. Furey** .... (919) 208-2945
E-mail: Todd.Furey2@fsis.usda.gov
Deputy District Manager **Dr. Beth Cunningham** .... (919) 208-2934
Deputy District Manager **Roger Murphy** .... (919) 208-2947
Deputy District Manager **Mark Roling** .... (919) 208-2935
Resource Management Analyst **(Vacant)** .... (919) 208-2931
Resource Management Assistant **(Vacant)** .... (919) 208-2937

★ Presidential Appointment Requiring Senate Confirmation ☆ Presidential Appointment ☐ Schedule C Appointment ◇ Career Senior Foreign Service Appointment
● Career Senior Executive Service (SES) Appointment ○ Non-Career Senior Executive Service (SES) Appointment ■ Postal Career Executive Service

Springdale (AR) District Office
Building B, 4700 South Thompson, Suite B201, Springdale, AR 72764
Tel: (479) 751-8412 Fax: (479) 751-9049
Areas Covered: AR, KS, MO

District Manager **Robert Bane** .... (479) 770-0982
Deputy District Manager **Dr. Julie Cornett DVM** .... (479) 770-0912
Building B, Country Club Center, 4700 South Thompson, Suite 201, Springdale, AR 72764
Deputy District Manager **Evan Sumner** .... (479) 751-8412
Building B, Country Club Center, 4700 South Thompson, Suite 201, Springdale, AR 72764
Deputy District Manager **Don Dowdle** .... (479) 751-8412
Country Club Center, 4700 South Thompson, Springdale, AR 72764

Office of Management (OM)
South Agriculture Building, 1400 Independence Avenue, SW, Room 347-E, Washington, DC 20250
Fax: (202) 690-1742

● Assistant Administrator (Acting) **CAPT Frank Mays USN (Ret)** .... (202) 720-4425
● Deputy Assistant Administrator (Acting) **Cara LeConte** .... (301) 344-0725
E-mail: cara.leconte@fsis.usda.gov

Office of Human Resources
South Agriculture Building, 1400 Independence Avenue, SW, Room 3149, Washington, DC 20250-1567
Fax: (202) 401-1760

Human Resources Operations
Butler Square West, 100 North Sixth Street, Suite 420C, Minneapolis, MN 55403-1564
Tel: (800) 370-3747 Fax: (612) 370-2005

Assistant Director **Laura Frantes** .... (301) 659-8591
Branch Chief **Shannon Montgomery** .... (800) 370-3747
E-mail: shannon.montgomery@fsis.usda.gov

Office of Public Health Science (OPHS)
Jamie L. Whitten Federal Building, 1400 Independence Avenue, SW, Room 341-E, Room 341 East, Washington, DC 20250
Fax: (202) 690-2980

Food Emergency Response Network Staff (FERN)
950 College Station Road, Suite 104-C, Athens, GA 30605-2720
Tel: (706) 546-3572 Fax: (706) 546-3656

Director **Randal C. Layton DVM** .... (706) 546-2376
Fax: (706) 546-3656

Laboratory Quality Assurance Staff
Russell Research Center, 950 College Station Road, Suite PB-4, Athens, GA 30605-2720
Tel: (706) 546-3559 Fax: (706) 546-3453

Director (Acting) **Dr. Michael Day** .... (706) 546-3559
Secretary **Tracey Hardy** .... (706) 546-3559
E-mail: tracey.hardy@fsis.usda.gov

Eastern Laboratory
Russell Research Center, Room 205, Athens, GA 30605
Mail: P.O. Box 6085, Athens, GA 30604
Tel: (706) 546-3576 Fax: (706) 546-3383

Director **Frankie Beacorn** .... (706) 546-3589
Secretary **Shirley Thurmond** .... (706) 546-3576
E-mail: shirley.thurmond@fsis.usda.gov

Midwestern Laboratory
Building 105D, Federal Center, 4300 Goodfellow Boulevard, Room 344, St. Louis, MO 63120-0005
P.O. Box 200005, St. Louis, MO 63120-0005
Tel: (314) 263-2680 Fax: (314) 263-2679

Director **Terry Dutko** .... (314) 263-2686 ext. 344
Secretary **Arneather Thompson** .... (314) 263-2680 ext. 301
E-mail: arneather.thompson@fsis.usda.gov

Western Laboratory
Building 2A, 620 Central Avenue, Alameda, CA 94501
Tel: (510) 814-3000 Fax: (510) 814-3090

Director (Acting) **John Jarosh** .... (510) 982-4957
Western Laboratory, 800 Buchanan St, Room 41, Albany, CA 94710 Fax: (510) 982-4957
Deputy Director **John Jarosh** .... (510) 982-4957
Fax: (510) 980-4998

Office of the Chief Financial Officer
South Agriculture Building, 1400 Independence Avenue, SW, Room 3165, Washington, DC 20250
Tel: (202) 720-8700

Financial Management Division
George Washington Carver Center, 5601 Sunnyside Avenue, Mail Drop 5262, Beltsville, MD 20705-5000
Fax: (301) 504-5910

Urbandale Financial Services Center
4520 114th Street, Urbandale, IA 50322-5410
Tel: (515) 334-2000 Fax: (515) 334-2059

Branch Chief **Julie Hove** .... (515) 334-2004

Marketing and Regulatory Programs (MRP)
Jamie L. Whitten Federal Building, 1400 Independence Avenue, SW, Washington, DC 20250

OFFICE OF THE UNDER SECRETARY
Jamie L. Whitten Federal Building, 1400 Independence Avenue, SW, Room 228-W, Washington, DC 20250
Tel: (202) 720-4256 Fax: (202) 720-5775

Agricultural Marketing Service (AMS)
South Agriculture Building, 1400 Independence Avenue, SW, Mail Stop 0201, Washington, DC 20250
Fax: (202) 205-5772 Internet: www.ams.usda.gov

Note: On September 7, 2017, Secretary of Agriculture Sonny Perdue announced that the Farm Service Agency and the Grain Inspection, Packers, and Stockyards Administration will be merged into the Agricultural Marketing Service.

Cotton and Tobacco Programs
3275 Appling Road, Room 11, Memphis, TN 38133
Tel: (901) 384-3193 Fax: (901) 384-3021
Internet: www.ams.usda.gov/cotton

Tobacco Field Operations
1306 Annapolis Drive, Raleigh, NC 27608-2136
Tel: (919) 856-4584 Fax: (919) 856-4208

Field Operations Deputy Director **Kenneth E. "Ken" Wall** .... (919) 856-4584 ext. 100
Field Operations Supervisor **Gilbert L. Todd, Sr.** .... (919) 856-4584 ext. 105

Grading Division (GD)
3275 Appling Road, Memphis, TN 38133
Fax: (901) 384-3038

Director **Robert L. "Robbie" Seals, Jr.** .... (901) 384-3010

Abilene (TX) Classing Office
24 Windmill Circle, Abilene, TX 79606
Tel: (325) 690-9378 Fax: (325) 690-1659

Area Director **Kenneth D. Day** .... (325) 690-9378
E-mail: kenneth.day@ams.usda.gov

★ Presidential Appointment Requiring Senate Confirmation ☆ Presidential Appointment ☐ Schedule C Appointment ◇ Career Senior Foreign Service Appointment
● Career Senior Executive Service (SES) Appointment ○ Non-Career Senior Executive Service (SES) Appointment ■ Postal Career Executive Service

DEPARTMENTS

Dumas (AR) Classing Office
996 Highway 65 South, Dumas, AR 71639
Tel: (870) 382-5328 Fax: (870) 382-5347
Areas Covered: Portions of MS and Southeastern AR

Area Director **Keith Maloney** .... (870) 382-5328
E-mail: keith.maloney@ams.usda.gov

Florence (SC) Classing Office
1725 Otis Way, Florence, SC 29501
Tel: (843) 667-4381 Fax: (843) 669-4247

Area Director **Charles "Chuck" Dubose** .... (843) 667-4381
E-mail: charles.dubose@ams.usda.gov Fax: (843) 669-4247

Lamesa (TX) Classing Office
906 North Elgin, Lamesa, TX 79331
Tel: (806) 872-8870 Fax: (806) 872-6369

Area Director **Ralph S. Cummings** .... (806) 872-8870
E-mail: ralph.cummings@ams.usda.gov

Lubbock (TX) Classing Office
4316 Ironton, Lubbock, TX 79407
Tel: (806) 472-7620 Fax: (806) 472-7629

Area Director **Daniel "Danny" Martinez** .... (806) 472-7620
E-mail: danny.martinez@ams.usda.gov

Macon (GA) Classing Office
1100 Parkway Drive, Macon, GA 31220
Tel: (478) 474-2831 Fax: (478) 474-9917

Area Director **Noah F. Bell, Jr.** .... (478) 474-2831
E-mail: noah.bell@ams.usda.gov

Memphis (TN) Classing Office
3275 Appling Road, Memphis, TN 38133
Tel: (901) 384-3025 Fax: (901) 384-3037

Area Director **Byron Cole** Room 6 .... (901) 384-3025
E-mail: byron.cole@ams.usda.gov

Rayville (LA) Classing Office
161 Industrial Loop, Rayville, LA 71269-8698
Tel: (318) 728-6418 Fax: (318) 728-6547

Area Director **Terry D. Sims** .... (318) 728-6418
E-mail: terry.sims@ams.usda.gov

Visalia (CA) Classing Office
7100 West Sunnyview Avenue, Visalia, CA 93291
Tel: (559) 651-3015 Fax: (559) 651-0752

Area Director **Greg R. Townsend** .... (559) 651-3015
E-mail: greg.townsend@ams.usda.gov

Market News Division (MND)
3275 Appling Road, Memphis, TN 38133
Fax: (901) 384-3036

Director **Barbara Meredith** .... (901) 384-3016

Quality Assurance Division (QAD)
3275 Appling Road, Memphis, TN 38133
Fax: (901) 384-3034

Director **Kevin L. Letbetter** .... (901) 384-3020

Standardization and Engineering Division (SED)
3275 Appling Road, Memphis, TN 38133
Tel: (901) 384-3030 Fax: (901) 384-3032

Director **James Knowlton** .... (901) 384-3030

Dairy Program (DP)
South Agriculture Building, 1400 Independence Avenue, SW, Washington, DC 20250
Fax: (202) 690-3410

Grading and Standardization Division
South Agriculture Building, 355 E St NW, Room 2746, Washington, DC 20250-1597
Tel: (202) 720-3171

Dairy Grading and Inspections National Field Office
2150 Western Court, Suite 100, Lisle, IL 60532-1973
Tel: (630) 810-9999 Fax: (630) 437-5060
Internet: www.ams.usda.gov/dairy

Branch Chief **Terrance Jackson** .... (630) 437-5037
E-mail: Terrance.Jackson@ams.usda.gov
National Field Director **Bao Tcheng** .... (630) 297-4740
E-mail: bao.tcheng@ams.usda.gov
Assistant National Field Director **Darrell DeMont** .... (630) 297-5030
National Program Coordinator, Surveys and Equipment Reviews **(Vacant)** .... (630) 437-5024
LAN Administrator **Steven Foust** .... (630) 437-5038
E-mail: steven.foust@ams.usda.gov
Computer Specialist **(Vacant)** .... (630) 437-5032
Administrative Officer **Michael Eichorst** .... (630) 437-5073
E-mail: michael.eichorst@ams.usda.gov
Education: Western Illinois 2012 BS
Staff Assistant **(Vacant)** .... (630) 437-5045
Program Support Assistant **Desiree Pitts** .... (630) 437-5054
E-mail: desiree.pitts@ams.usda.gov
Program Support Assistant **Gloria Brenski** .... (630) 810-9999
Education: Northern Illinois 2011 BA

Market News Branch (MNB)
355 E St NW, Room 2977, Washington, DC 20250-1597
Fax: (202) 720-4844

Dairy Market News Office
4600 American Parkway, Suite 106, Madison, WI 53718-8334
Tel: (608) 422-8587
Internet: https://www.ams.usda.gov/market-news/dairy
Fax: (608) 240-6689

National Supervisor (Acting) **Janet Linder** .... (608) 422-8588
Organic/International Reports **Daniel Johnson** .... (608) 422-8590
E-mail: daniel.johnson@ams.usda.gov
Central Region **Israel Weber** .... (608) 422-8601
Eastern Region **Jessica Mueller** .... (608) 422-8589
Eastern Region **Jessica Mueller** .... (608) 422-8605
Northwest/Mountain Region **Mike Bandli** .... (608) 422-8592
Southwest Region **Angel Teran** .... (608) 422-8593

Milk Market Administrators (MMA)

Appalachian Marketing Area
10301 Village Boulevard, Louisville, KY 40291
Mail: P.O. Box 18030, Louisville, KY 40261-0030
Tel: (502) 499-0040 Fax: (502) 499-8749
Internet: www.malouisville.com

Market Administrator **Harold Friedly, Jr.** .... (502) 499-0040 ext. 219
E-mail: friedly@malouisville.com
Assistant Market Administrator **Jeff Gooch** ..... (502) 499-0040 ext. 207
E-mail: gooch@malouisville.com
Agricultural Economist **Jason Nierman** .... (502) 499-0040 ext. 222
E-mail: nierman@malouisville.com
Information Technology **Karen Cecil** .... (502) 499-0040 ext. 205
E-mail: cecil@malouisville.com
Marketing Service **Kelly Wedding** .... (502) 499-0040 ext. 216
Personnel **Jackie Anderson** .... (502) 499-0040 ext. 213
E-mail: anderson@malouisville.com

★ Presidential Appointment Requiring Senate Confirmation ☆ Presidential Appointment □ Schedule C Appointment ◇ Career Senior Foreign Service Appointment
● Career Senior Executive Service (SES) Appointment ○ Non-Career Senior Executive Service (SES) Appointment ■ Postal Career Executive Service

Central Marketing Area
10801 Renner Boulevard, Lenexa, KS 66219-9608
Mail: P.O. Box 14650, Shawnee Mission, KS 66285-4650
Tel: (913) 495-9300 Fax: (913) 888-9207
E-mail: market.administrator@fmmacentral.com
Internet: www.fmmacentral.com

Market Administrator **Todd D. Wilson** .... (913) 495-9326 ext. 326
E-mail: todd.wilson@ams.usda.gov
Assistant Market Administrator **Tim Hjorth** ..... (913) 495-9334 ext. 323
Administrative Officer **Barry Crudup** .... (913) 495-9318 ext. 336
E-mail: barry.crudup@fmmacentral.com
Financial Officer **Michael "Mike" Root** .... (913) 495-9331 ext. 331
E-mail: mroot@fmmacentral.com
Webmaster **Ali Lotia** .... (913) 495-9317 ext. 317
E-mail: alotia@fmmacentral.com

Mideast Marketing Area
1325 Industrial Parkway North, Brunswick, OH 44212
Tel: (888) 751-3220 Tel: (330) 225-4758 Fax: (330) 220-6675
E-mail: clevelandma1@sprynet.com Internet: www.fmmaclev.com

Market Administrator **Sharon R. Uther** .... (888) 751-3220
E-mail: suther@fmmaclev.com
Assistant Market Administrator **Alan L. Christian** .... (888) 751-3220
E-mail: achristian@fmmaclev.com
Assistant Market Administrator **William L. Farquhar** .... (888) 751-3220
E-mail: william.farquhar@ams.usda.gov
Audit Manager **David A. Hoedt** .... (888) 751-3220
E-mail: dhoedt@fmmaclev.com
Audit Manager **James M. Burch, Jr.** .... (888) 751-3220
E-mail: jburch@fmmaclev.com
Administrative Officer **Michele D. Crowe** .... (888) 751-3220
E-mail: mcrowe@fmmaclev.com

Northeast Marketing Area
89 South Street, Suite 301, Boston, MA 02111
Tel: (617) 737-7199 Fax: (617) 737-8002
E-mail: maboston@fedmilk1.com Internet: www.fmmone.com

Market Administrator **(Vacant)** .... (617) 737-7199
Associate Market Administrator (Marketing Service) **(Vacant)** .... (617) 737-7199 ext. 3537
Assistant Market Administrator (EDP/Information Systems) **Shawn Boockoff** .... (617) 737-7199 ext. 3553
E-mail: sboockoff@fedmilk1.com
Administrative/Personnel Officer **John F. Poole** .... (518) 452-4410 ext. 1616
302A Washington Avenue Extention, Albany, NY 12203
Internal Accounting Officer **Kimberley Pietrowski** .... (617) 737-7199 ext. 3580

Pacific Northwest and Arizona Marketing Areas
Building J, 1930 - 220th Street, SE, Suite 102, Bothell, WA 98021-8471
Tel: (425) 487-6009 (Washington office)
Tel: (602) 547-2909 (Arizona office)
Fax: (425) 487-2775 (Washington office)
Fax: (602) 547-2906 (Arizona office)
E-mail: fmmaseattle@fmmaseattle.com Internet: www.fmmaseattle.com

Market Administrator **William A. Wise** .... (425) 487-6009
E-mail: wisew@fmmaseattle.com
Assistant Market Administrator/Accounting **Lisa Wyatt** ... (602) 547-2909
4835 East Cactus Road, Suite 365, Scottsdale, AZ 85254
E-mail: wyattl@fmmaseattle.com
Auditing **Michael Enos** .... (425) 487-6009
E-mail: menos@fmmaseattle.com
Data Processing **Mark L. Taber** .... (425) 487-6009
E-mail: mtaber@fmmaseattle.com
Marketing Specialist **Lori Espe** .... (425) 487-6009
Agricultural Economist **John L. Mykrantz** .... (425) 487-6009
Assistant Market Administrator/Pooling **Alyce L. Owen** .... (425) 487-6009

Southeast and Florida Marketing Area
2763 Meadow Church Road, Suite 100, Duluth, GA 30097
Tel: (770) 682-2501 Fax: (770) 545-8850 Fax: (770) 545-8852
E-mail: FMMA6&7@fmmatlanta.com Internet: www.fmmatlanta.com
Areas Covered: AL, AR, FL, GA, LA, MS, Southern MO, TN

Market Administrator **(Vacant)** .... (770) 682-2536
Assistant Market Administrator **(Vacant)** .... (770) 682-2501
Associate Market Administrator for Audit and Pool Oversight **Rick Mills** .... (770) 682-2501
Associate Market Administrator for Computer and Technology Oversight **Sheila J. Sabb** .... (770) 682-2501
E-mail: ssabb@fmmatlanta.com
Associate Market Administrator for Marketing Service Oversight **(Vacant)** .... (770) 682-2526

Southwest Milk Marketing Area
1404 Carroll Street, Carrollton, TX 75006
Mail: P.O. Box 110939, Carrollton, TX 75011-0939
Tel: (972) 245-6060 Fax: (972) 245-3211 Internet: www.dallasma.com

Market Administrator **Cary J. Hunter** .... (972) 245-6060
E-mail: cary.hunter@dallasma.com
Assistant Market Administrator, Market Analysis/Statistics **Michael R. Johnson** .... (972) 245-6060
E-mail: michael.johnson@ams.usda.gov
Administrative Officer and Personnel **Vicki Smithey** ..... (972) 245-6060
E-mail: vicki.smithey@dallasma.com
Associate Market Administrator **Frank Sheckarski, Sr.** ... (972) 245-6060
E-mail: frank.sheckarski@dallasma.com
Laboratory Manager **Cecilia "Ann" Bauer** .... (972) 245-6060
E-mail: ann.bauer@dallasma.com
Information Technology Specialist **Mark Johnson** .... (972) 245-6060
E-mail: mark.johnson@dallasma.com
Information Technology Specialist **Larry Robertson** ..... (972) 245-6060
E-mail: larry.robertson@dallasma.com
Audit Manager **Delaina Dries** .... (972) 245-6060
E-mail: delaina.dries@dallasma.com
Audit Manager **Bradley Vierra** .... (972) 245-6060
E-mail: bradley.vierra@ams.usda.gov

Upper Midwest Marketing Area
1600 Weest 82nd Street, Suite 200, Minneapolis, MN 55431
Tel: (952) 831-5292 Fax: (952) 881-6900 E-mail: fo30@fmma30.com
Internet: www.fmma30.com

Market Administrator **Victor J. Halverson** ...... (952) 831-5292 ext. 207
Assistant Market Administrator **Glen A. Rieck** ... (952) 831-5292 ext. 211
Assistant Market Administrator **Shirley I. Willis** .... (952) 277-2332
Assistant Market Administrator **(Vacant)** .... (952) 831-5292 ext. 207
Communications/Computers Coordinator **Dave Etter** .... (952) 831-5292 ext. 233
E-mail: dave.etter@ams.usda.gov
Market Information **Harold J. Ferguson** .... (952) 831-5292 ext. 231
Order Formulation and Market Analysis **(Vacant)** .... (952) 831-5292 ext. 208
Pool and Producer Data **Craig M. Miller** .... (952) 831-5292 ext. 209

Livestock and Poultry Program (L&P)
355 E St NW, STOP 0249, Washington, DC 20250-1597
E-mail: AskLPS@ams.usda.gov

● Deputy Administrator **Jennifer Porter** .... (202) 720-5705
South Agriculture Building, 1400 Independence Avenue, SW, Room 2092, Washington, DC 20250
E-mail: AskLPS@ams.usda.gov
Associate Deputy Administrator **Dr. Melissa R. Bailey PhD** .... (202) 205-9356
1400 Independence Avenue, SW, Room 2092, Washington, DC 20250
E-mail: melissa.bailey@ams.usda.gov
Education: Northeastern 1998 BS; Tufts 2003 MS, 2010 PhD
Chief of Staff (Acting) **Alexandria Smith** .... (202) 720-8054
E-mail: AlexandriaP.Smith@ams.usda.gov

DEPARTMENTS

★ Presidential Appointment Requiring Senate Confirmation ☆ Presidential Appointment ☐ Schedule C Appointment ◇ Career Senior Foreign Service Appointment
● Career Senior Executive Service (SES) Appointment ○ Non-Career Senior Executive Service (SES) Appointment ■ Postal Career Executive Service

Quality Assessment Division
1400 Independence Avenue, SW, 39325, Washington, DC 20250

Business Operations Branch
Branch Chief **Julie Hartley** .... (501) 224-9201
10809 Executive Center Drive, Little Rock, AR 72211-6022
Assistant Branch Chief **Keith Reisma** .... (501) 224-9201
10809 Executive Center Drive, Little Rock, AR 72211-6022

National Billing Office
10809 Executive Center Drive, Suite 318, Little Rock, AR 72211-6022
Tel: (501) 312-2962 Fax: (844) 345-3575
Supervisory Financial Specialist **Debra Stutts** .... (501) 312-2962

Grading and Auditing Services Branch
Grading and Auditing Branch Chief
Jeffrey H. "Jeff" Waite .... (202) 720-4411

Poultry and Egg Grading Division
South Agricultural Building, 355 E St NW,
Room 2092, Washington, DC 20250-1597
Fax: (202) 690-2746 Fax: (202) 690-3165

Central Region
10809 Executive Center Drive, Suite 318, Little Rock, AR 72211-6022
Tel: (501) 224-9201 Fax: (501) 227-4114
Areas Covered: IA, MN, ND, NE, SD, WI, IL, KY, MO, AL, MS, TN, AR, LA, OK, TX, KS
Regional Director **Gerald D. Laird** .... (501) 224-9201
Assistant Regional Director **(Vacant)** .... (501) 224-9201
Assistant Regional Director- Red Meat **Mark Hanson** .... (501) 224-9201

Buda (TX) Field Office
5025 FM 2001, Suite C, Buda, TX 78610
Tel: (512) 295-5851 Fax: (512) 295-5853
Areas Covered: OK, TX, KS
Federal-State Supervisor **Christoper Swodick** .... (512) 295-5851

Marion (IL) Field Office
1107 West DeYoung, Suite 72, Marion, IL 62959
Tel: (618) 997-6820 Fax: (618) 993-3507
Areas Covered: IL, KY, MO, AL, MS, TN
Federal-State Supervisor **Randy Harmon** .... (618) 997-6820

St. Paul (MN) Field Office
3550 Lexington Avenue, North, Suite 200, St. Paul, MN 55126
Tel: (651) 482-0781 Tel: (651) 482-0821
Areas Covered: IA, MN, ND, NE, SD, WI
Federal-State Supervisor **Scott Throp** .... (651) 482-0781

Eastern Region
100 Riverside Parkway, Suite 101, Fredericksburg, VA 22406
Tel: (704) 860-1372 Fax: (540) 310-4942
Areas Covered: CT, DE, FL, GA, MA, MD, ME, NC, NH, NJ, NY, PA, PR, RI, SC, VA, VI, VT, WV
Regional Director **Ben A. Cockfield** .... (704) 860-1372
Assistant Regional Director **Eric Saxton** .... (704) 685-3322

Gainesville (GA) Field Office
P.O. Box 7609, Gainesville, GA 30504-7609
Tel: (770) 535-5770 Fax: (770) 535-5763
Areas Covered: FL, GA, VI, PR
Federal-State Supervisor **Eric Saxton** .... (770) 535-5704

Raleigh (NC) Field Office
P.O. Box 27686, Raleigh, NC 27611-7686
Tel: (919) 733-7576 Tel: (919) 707-3104 Fax: (919) 733-9724
Areas Covered: NC, SC
Federal-State Supervisor **James "Jim" Delmaine** .... (919) 270-4385

Western Region
313 Banner Court, Suite B, Modesto, CA 95356
Tel: (209) 522-5251 Fax: (209) 522-7260
Areas Covered: AK, AZ, CA, CO, HI, ID, MT, NM, NV, OR, UT, WA, WY
Regional Director **(Vacant)** .... (209) 522-5251
Assistant Regional Director **(Vacant)** .... (209) 522-5251

Modesto (CA) Field Office
313 Banner Court, Modesto, CA 95356
Tel: (209) 522-5253 Fax: (209) 522-7260
Areas Covered: Northern CA
Federal-State Supervisor **Ron Nicholas** .... (209) 522-5253
Assistant Federal-State Supervisor **Ray Vazquez** .... (209) 522-5253

Olympia (WA) Field Office
1017 Fourth Avenue East, Suite 2, Olympia, WA 98506
Tel: (360) 705-0330 Fax: (360) 750-1159
Areas Covered: AK, ID, MT, OR, WA
Federal-State Supervisor **Jacob Bechtold** .... (360) 705-0330

Riverside (CA) Field Office
4504 Allstate Drive, Suite 220, Riverside, CA 92501
Tel: (951) 369-0110 Fax: (951) 369-0123
Areas Covered: Southern CA, HI, NV
Federal-State Supervisor **Mario Ramirez** .... (951) 276-0483

Thornton (CO) Field Office
9324 Bellaire Street, Thornton, CO 80229-4010
Tel: (303) 288-2451 Fax: (303) 289-4490
Areas Covered: AZ, CO, NM, UT, WY
Federal-State Supervisor **Kellie Anderson** .... (303) 288-2451

Federal Grain Inspection Service (FGIS)
1400 Independence Avenue, SW, Stop 3614, Washington, DC 20250-3601
Tel: (202) 720-9170 Fax: (202) 481-5719

Field Management Division (FMD)
South Agriculture Building, 1400 Independence Avenue, SW,
Room 2409-S, Mailstop 3630, Washington, DC 20250
Fax: (202) 720-1015

Grand Forks (ND) Field Office
Bringewatt Building, 2625 - 24th Avenue South,
Suite C, Grand Forks, ND 58201-6180
Mail: P.O. Box 13427, Grand Forks, ND 58208-3427
Tel: (800) 793-7244 Tel: (701) 772-3371 Fax: (701) 772-0362
Areas Covered: Portions of MN, Portions of MT, ND, Portions of SD
Field Office Manager
Edward R. "Ed" Stallman .... (701) 772-3371 ext. 202
Administrative Support Assistant **(Vacant)** ...... (701) 772-3371 ext. 201
Shift Supervisor, CDSHO **Valerie J. Hills** .... (701) 772-3371 ext. 208
Checktesting, Equipment **Andrew Otto** .... (701) 772-3371 ext. 209
Certification, Safety **(Vacant)** .... (701) 772-3371 ext. 208
Quality Assurance **(Vacant)** .... (701) 772-3371 ext. 211

League City (TX) Field Office
1025 East Main Street, Suite 104, League City, TX 77573-2483
Tel: (281) 338-2787 Fax: (281) 338-2788
Areas Covered: Portions of TX
Manager **Alan Wadyko** .... (281) 338-2787 ext. 24
Assistant Manager **Jorge Vazquez** .... (281) 338-2787 ext. 32
Administrative Officer **Deborah A. Edwards** ..... (281) 338-2787 ext. 42
Computer Specialist **Adel S. Ibrahim** .... (281) 338-2787 ext. 33
E-mail: adel.s.ibrahim@usda.gov

★ Presidential Appointment Requiring Senate Confirmation ☆ Presidential Appointment ☐ Schedule C Appointment ◇ Career Senior Foreign Service Appointment
● Career Senior Executive Service (SES) Appointment ○ Non-Career Senior Executive Service (SES) Appointment ■ Postal Career Executive Service

New Orleans (LA) Field Office
104 Campus Drive East, Suite 200, Destrehan, LA 70047-5207
P.O. Box 640, Destrehan, LA 70047-0640
Tel: (985) 764-2324 Fax: (985) 764-0732
Areas Covered: AL, portions of FL, GA, LA, SC

Field Office Manager **Kenneth W. DeWert** ...... (985) 764-2324 ext. 50
E-mail: Kenneth.W.DeWert@usda.gov
Assistant Field Office Manager
George D. Banks, Jr. .... (985) 764-2324 ext. 42
E-mail: george.d.banks@usda.gov
Assistant Field Office Manager **(Vacant)** .... (985) 764-2324 ext. 88
Administrative Officer **(Vacant)** .... (985) 764-2324 ext. 46
Computer Specialist **Phillip W. Thomas** .... (985) 764-2324 ext. 57
E-mail: phillip.w.thomas@usda.gov

Portland (OR) Field Office
1100 NW Naito Parkway, Portland, OR 97209-2818
Tel: (503) 326-7887 Fax: (503) 326-7896

Manager **Andy Ping** .... (503) 326-7887 ext. 2
Quality Assurance Specialist **Kim H. Harper** ...... (503) 326-7887 ext. 7
Supervisory Certification Assistant
Heather R. Schlecht .... (503) 326-7887 ext. 13
E-mail: heather.r.schlecht@usda.gov
Training Officer **(Vacant)** .... (503) 326-7887 ext. 16

Stuttgart (AR) Field Office
211 South Leslie Street, Stuttgart, AR 72160-0137
Tel: (870) 673-2508 Fax: (870) 673-2500
Areas Covered: AR, CA, TN, portions of IL, IN, KY, MO, MS, TX

Field Office Manager **Sandra A. Metheny** .... (870) 678-2508 ext. 28
Assistant Field Office Manager **(Vacant)** .... (870) 673-2508
Supervisory Certification Assistant
Tina M. Crane .... (870) 673-2508 ext. 21
E-mail: tina.m.crane@usda.gov
Quality Assurance Specialist
Jimmie W. Nesselroad .... (870) 673-2508 ext. 31
Shift Supervisor **Albert G. Snelson** .... (870) 673-2508 ext. 29

Toledo (OH) Field Office
1910 Indian Wood Circle, Suite 401, Maumee, OH 43537
Tel: (419) 893-3076 Fax: (419) 893-2861 E-mail: fmtol@usda.gov
Areas Covered: CT, DE, DC, portions of IL, portions of IN, portions of KY, ME, MD, MA, MI, NH, NJ, NY, NC, OH, PA, RI, VT, VA, WV

Field Office Manager **Lynn E. Thomas** .... (419) 893-3076
Assistant Manager **Ronald E. Bundy** .... (419) 893-3076

Washington Federal - State Office
3939 Cleveland Avenue, SE, Olympia, WA 98501-4079
Tel: (360) 664-8952 Fax: (360) 586-5257 E-mail: fmwas@usda.gov
Areas Covered: AK, WA

Federal/State Manager **Randall R. Deike** .... (360) 664-8952
Assistant Federal Manager and Quality Assurance
Specialist **Scott J. Cooley** .... (360) 753-9072
Administrative Assistant **Reola C. Loomis** .... (360) 664-8952
E-mail: rloomis@agr.wa.gov

Technology and Sciences Division (TSD)
10383 North Ambassador Drive, Kansas City, MO 64153-1394
Mail: P.O. Box 20285, Kansas City, MO 64195
Fax: (816) 891-8070

Director **(Vacant)** .... (816) 891-0463
Assistant to the Director **Charles W. "Bill" Burden** .... (816) 891-0437
E-mail: charles.w.burden@usda.gov
Deputy Director (Acting) **Timothy D. "Tim" Norden** .... (816) 891-0470
Fax: (816) 891-7314
Secretary **Barbara Benedict** .... (816) 891-0401
E-mail: barbara.l.benedict@usda.gov
Administrative Assistant **Martha T. "Terri" Liberty** ...... (816) 891-0457
E-mail: martha.t.liberty@usda.gov
Board of Appeals and Review Chairman
Brian C. Adam .... (816) 891-0421
E-mail: brian.c.adam@usda.gov Fax: (816) 891-7314

Technology and Sciences Division *(continued)*

Analytical Chemistry Branch Chief
Thomas A. "Tom" Weber .... (816) 891-0449
Biotechnology and Analytical Services Branch Chief
Tandace A. "Tandy" Bell .... (816) 891-0459
Inspection Instrumentation Branch Chief
Cathleen A. Brenner .... (816) 891-0486
Program Assistant **Sara K. Dobbins** .... (816) 891-0464
E-mail: sara.k.dobbins@usda.gov

Fair Trade Practices Program
1400 Independence Avenue, SW, Washington, DC 20250-3601
Tel: (202) 720-0219 Fax: (202) 205-9237

Packers and Stockyards Division (PSD)
South Agriculture Building, 1400 Independence Avenue, SW, Room 2055-S, Stop 3601, Washington, DC 20250-3601
Tel: (202) 720-7051 Fax: (202) 205-9237

Regional Operations Division

Eastern Regional Office
75 Spring Street, Suite 230, Atlanta, GA 30303
Tel: (404) 562-5840 Fax: (404) 562-5848
E-mail: PSPAtlantaGA.GIPSA@usda.gov
Areas Covered: AL, AR, CT, DC, DE, FL, GA, LA, MA, MD, ME, MS, NC, NH, NJ, NY, PA, RI, SC, TN, VA, VT, WV

Regional Supervisor **Elkin W. Parker** .... (404) 562-5400
E-mail: elkin.w.parker@ams.usda.gov
Administrative Officer **Pamela L. Lake** .... (404) 562-5410
E-mail: pamela.l.lake@usda.gov

Western Regional Office
One Gateway Center, 3950 Lewiston, Suite 200, Aurora, CO 80011
Tel: (303) 375-4240 Fax: (303) 371-4609
E-mail: PSPDenverCO.GIPSA@usda.gov
Areas Covered: AK, AZ, CA, CO, HI, ID, KS, MT, NV, NM, OK, OR, TX, UT, WA, WY

Regional Director **Kraig Roesch** .... (303) 375-4250
E-mail: kraig.j.roesch@usda.gov
Administrative Officer **Tim F. Johnson** .... (303) 375-4242
E-mail: tim.f.johnson@usda.gov

Midwestern Regional Office
Federal Building, 210 Walnut Street, Room 317, Des Moines, IA 50309
Tel: (515) 323-2579 Fax: (515) 323-2590
E-mail: pspdesmoinesia.gipsa@usda.gov
Areas Covered: IA, IL, IN, KY, OH, MI, MO, MN, ND, NE, SD, WI

Regional Director **Stuart D. Frank** .... (515) 323-2579
E-mail: stuart.frank@usda.gov

Perishable Agricultural Commodities Act Division (PACA Division)
355 E St NW, Room 1518, Washington, DC 20250-1597
Fax: (202) 690-4413 Internet: www.ams.usda.gov/rules-regulations/paca

Central Regional Office
819 Taylor Street, Suite 8B02, Fort Worth, TX 76102
Tel: (817) 978-0777 Fax: (817) 978-0786
Areas Covered: AL, AR, FL, IL, IN, KY, LA, MI, MS, OK, TN, TX, WI

Regional Director **Jeffrey K. Spradlin** .... (817) 978-0777
E-mail: jeffrey.spradlin@ams.usda.gov
Assistant Regional Director **Dean K. Johnson** .... (817) 978-0784
E-mail: dean.johnson2@ams.usda.gov

Eastern Regional Office
100 Riverside Parkway, Suite 101, Fredericksburg, VA 22406
Tel: (800) 495-7222 ext. 3 Tel: (540) 376-6022 Fax: (540) 373-2690
Areas Covered: CT, DE, DC, GA, GU, ME, MD, MA, NH, NJ, NY, NC, OH, PA, PR, RI, SC, VI, VA, VT, WV

Regional Director **Basil W. Coale** .... (540) 376-6022
E-mail: basil.coale@ams.usda.gov

(continued on next page)

★ Presidential Appointment Requiring Senate Confirmation ☆ Presidential Appointment ☐ Schedule C Appointment ◇ Career Senior Foreign Service Appointment
● Career Senior Executive Service (SES) Appointment ○ Non-Career Senior Executive Service (SES) Appointment ■ Postal Career Executive Service

Eastern Regional Office *(continued)*

Assistant Regional Director **(Vacant)** .... (540) 376-6022

Western Regional Office
Federal Building, 300 West Congress Street Box FB30,
Room 7T, Tucson, AZ 85701-1319
Tel: (800) 495-7222 Tel: (520) 879-4361 Fax: (520) 670-4798
Areas Covered: AZ, AK, CA, CO, HI, ID, IA, KS, MN, MO, MT, NE, NV, NM, ND, OR, SD, UT, WA, WY

Regional Director **Patrick P. Romero** .... (520) 879-4361
E-mail: patrick.romero@ams.usda.gov

Science and Technology Program (S&T)
South Agriculture Building, 1400 Independence Avenue, SW,
STOP 0272, Washington, DC 20250
Fax: (202) 720-6496 Fax: (202) 205-7397 (Alternate)

Associate Deputy Administrator for Science
South Agricultural Building, 355 E St NW,
Room 3549, Washington, DC 20250-1597
Fax: (202) 720-6496

National Science Laboratory (NSL)
801 Summit Crossing Place, Suite B, Gastonia, NC 28054-3441
Tel: (704) 867-3873 Fax: (855) 296-1230

Laboratory Chief **Roger Simonds** .... (704) 867-3873

Specialty Crops Program
South Agriculture Building, 1400 Independence Avenue, SW,
Room 2077-S, Washington, DC 20250-0235
Fax: (202) 720-0016

Marketing Order and Agreement Division
South Agriculture Building, 355 E St NW,
Room 1406, Washington, DC 20250-1597
Fax: (202) 720-5698

California Marketing Field Office
2202 Monterey Street, Suite 102B, Fresno, CA 93721-9868
Tel: (559) 487-5901 Fax: (559) 487-5906

Regional Manager **Jeffrey "Jeff" Smutny** .... (559) 487-5901 ext. 11
Assistant Regional Manager **(Vacant)** .... (559) 487-5901 ext. 34
Program Assistant **Jeffery M. Ryman** .... (559) 487-5901 ext. 10
Marketing Assistant **(Vacant)** .... (559) 487-5901

Northwest Marketing Field Office
1220 SW Third Avenue, Portland, OR 97204
Tel: (503) 326-2724 Fax: (503) 326-7440

Regional Director **Gary D. Olson** .... (503) 326-2724

Southeast Marketing Field Office
1124 First Street South, Winter Haven, FL 33880
Tel: (863) 324-3375 Fax: (863) 325-8793

Regional Director **Christian D. Nissen** .... (863) 324-3375

Specialty Crops Inspection Division
South Agricultural Building, 355 E St NW,
Room 1536, STOP 0240, Washington, DC 20250-1597
Fax: (202) 720-5870

California (Los Angeles) Inspection Office
6055 East Washington Boulevard, Suite 390, Commerce, CA 90040
Tel: (323) 725-0442 Fax: (323) 725-7853
Areas Covered: Los Angeles, CA; HI

Officer-in-Charge/Federal Supervisor **Bruce Copeland** .... (323) 725-0442
Assistant Federal Supervisor **(Vacant)** .... (323) 725-0442

Illinois (Chicago) Inspection Office
2404 South Wolcott Avenue, Unit 5, Chicago, IL 60608
Tel: (773) 376-8441 Fax: (773) 376-8503

Federal Supervisor **Philip E. "Phil" Brickner** .... (773) 376-8441

Indiana Inspection Office
7202 North Shadeland Avenue, Suite 121, Indianapolis, IN 46250
Tel: (574) 287-5407 Fax: (574) 287-5456

Officer-in-Charge **Gary L. Peterson** .... (574) 287-5407

Louisiana Inspection Office
47076 North Morrison Boulevard, Hammond, LA 70401-7308
Fax: (225) 923-4877
Areas Covered: LA

Program Manager **Jim Jenkins** .... (225) 925-3773

Michigan Inspection Office
7445 Allen Road, Suite 108, Allen Park, MI 48101
Tel: (313) 928-1150 Fax: (313) 928-0283

Officer-in-Charge **Colleen Bess** .... (313) 928-1150

Oklahoma Inspection Office
218 Southwest First Street, Anadarko, OK 73005
Tel: (405) 247-2040 Fax: (405) 783-4269
Areas Covered: AR, KS, MO, OK

Federal Commodities Inspector **Stephen L. Mueller** ..... (405) 247-2040
Tel: (405) 783-4339

Puerto Rico Inspection Office
GSA Center, 651 Federal Drive, Suite 103-05, Guaynabo, PR 00965
Tel: (787) 783-2230 Fax: (787) 722-3447

Officer-in-Charge **(Vacant)** .... (787) 977-6330

Fresh Products Branch Internal Quality Management System (BIQMS)

Central Office
Islander Building, 1511 NE Parvin Road,
Suite 1511B, Kansas City, MO 64116
Tel: (816) 453-4926 Fax: (816) 453-4914
Areas Covered: AR, CO, IA, KS, MN, MO, NE, NM, ND, SD, TX, WI, WY

Central BIQMS Program Manager **Harley Olinske** .... (816) 453-4926
Central BIQMS Program Manager **Edgar Ed Rippee** ..... (816) 453-4926

Mid-Atlantic – Northeastern Office
8610 Washington Boulevard, Suite 212, Jessup, MD 20794
Tel: (301) 317-5365 Fax: (301) 317-5438
Areas Covered: CT, DE, KY, ME, MD, MA, NH, NJ, NY, NC, PA, RI, SC, TN, VT, VA, WV

BIQMS Program Manager **Gary Crane** .... (301) 317-5365
BIQMS Program Manager **Alan Novakowski** .... (301) 317-5365

Northwestern Office
410 North King's Road, Suite 118, Nampa, ID 83687
Tel: (208) 467-6187 Fax: (208) 467-6258
Areas Covered: AK, ID, MT, OR, WA

Federal Program Manager **Todd Mattos** .... (208) 467-6187
Federal Program Manager **Greg McNair** .... (208) 467-6187

Southeast Office
98 Third Street, SW, Winter Haven, FL 33880-2905
Tel: (863) 299-7132 Fax: (844) 598-2533
Areas Covered: AL, FL, GA, LA, MS, PR

BIQMS Program Manager **Richard Marowski** .... (863) 299-7132
BIQMS Program Manager **William Shoulders** .... (863) 299-7132

Western Office
5635 Stratford Circle, Suite A11, Stockton, CA 95207-5055
Tel: (209) 477-0124 Fax: (209) 476-8919
Areas Covered: AZ, CA, HI, NV, UT

Federal Program Manager **Nathan "Nate" O'Connor** .... (916) 332-4758

★ Presidential Appointment Requiring Senate Confirmation ☆ Presidential Appointment ☐ Schedule C Appointment ◇ Career Senior Foreign Service Appointment
● Career Senior Executive Service (SES) Appointment ○ Non-Career Senior Executive Service (SES) Appointment ■ Postal Career Executive Service

Western Office *(continued)*

Federal Program Manager
Alexander Alex Wladyszewski .... (916) 332-4758

Central Operations Branch
Building A, 800 Roosevelt Road, Suite 380, Glen Ellyn, IL 60137-7688
Tel: (630) 790-6937 Fax: (630) 469-5162

Branch Chief **(Vacant)** .... (630) 790-6939
Assistant Branch Chief **Philip E. "Phil" Brickner** .... (630) 790-6936

College Park (GA) Inspection Office
Phoenix Center Office Park, 1651 Phoenix Bouldevard,
Suite 1, College Park, GA 30349-5552
Tel: (770) 909-6780 Fax: (770) 909-7540

Officer-in-Charge **Anthony Georgiana** .... (770) 909-6780

Hunt Valley (MD) Inspection Office
Hunt Valley Professional Building, Nine Schilling Road,
Suite 213, Hunt Valley, MD 21031-8604
Tel: (410) 584-9008 Fax: (410) 527-0402

Officer-in-Charge **(Vacant)** .... (410) 584-9008

North Brunswick (NJ) Inspection Office
Park Plaza Building, 622 Georges Road,
Suite 304, North Brunswick, NJ 08902-3377
Tel: (732) 545-0939 Fax: (732) 545-1909

Officer-in-Charge **Thomasene Reed** .... (732) 545-0939

Richmond (VA) Inspection Office
600 North 5th Street, Room B38, Richmond, VA 23219
Tel: (804) 786-2422 Fax: (804) 786-7130

Officer-in-Charge **Shari Harris** .... (804) 786-2422

Oshkosh Inspection Office
2490 Enterprise Drive, Oshkosh, WI 54904-6321
Tel: (920) 232-0295 Fax: (920) 232-0341

Officer-in-Charge **Andrew Hankes** .... (920) 232-0295

South Bend (IN) Inspection Office
4318 North Technology Drive, South Bend, IN 46628
Tel: (574) 287-5407 Fax: (574) 287-5456

Officer-in-Charge **Anthony Chartrand** .... (574) 287-5407

San Antonio (TX) Inspection Office
3453 IH 35 North, Suite 103, San Antonio, TX 78219
Tel: (210) 228-9626 Fax: (210) 224-0729

Officer-in-Charge **Dwain Parrish** .... (210) 228-9625

San Juan (PR) Inspection Office
P.O. Box 10163, San Juan, PR 00908-1163
Tel: (787) 977-6330 Fax: (787) 722-3447

Officer-in-Charge **Jose Cruz-Medina** .... (787) 977-6330

Winter Haven (FL) Inspection Office
98 Third Street, SW, Winter Haven, FL 33880-2905
Tel: (863) 294-7416 Fax: (863) 294-4219

Officer-in-Charge **Jessica Brower** .... (863) 294-7416

Western Operations Branch
2202 Monterey Street, Suite 102-C, Fresno, CA 93721-3129
Tel: (559) 487-5891 Fax: (559) 487-5900
Areas Covered: AK, AZ, CA, CO, HI, ID, MT, NV, NM, OR, UT, WA, WY

Branch Chief **Michael Harutinian** .... (559) 487-5891
Program Specialist **Phyllis Thrailkill** .... (559) 487-5891
Assistant Branch Chief **(Vacant)** .... (559) 487-5891
Administrative Officer **Stephen J. Spenst** .... (559) 487-5893
E-mail: stephen.spenst@ams.usda.gov

Covina (CA) Inspection Office
740 East Arrow Highway, Suite A, Covina, CA 91722-2103
Tel: (626) 967-9790 Fax: (626) 967-6267

Officer-in-Charge **Bruce Copeland** .... (626) 967-9790
Assistant Officer-in-Charge **(Vacant)** .... (626) 967-9790
Administrative Support Assistant **Barbara Dominguez** ... (626) 967-9790

Fresno (CA) Inspection Office
2202 Monterey Street, Suite 102-A, Fresno, CA 93721-3175
Tel: (559) 487-5210 Fax: (559) 485-5914

Officer-in-Charge **Ryan Wilson** .... (559) 487-5210
Assistant Officer-in-Charge **(Vacant)** .... (559) 487-5210
Administrative Support Assistant **(Vacant)** .... (559) 487-5210

Honolulu (HI) Inspection Office
State of Hawaii Department of Agriculture,
1851 Auiki Street, Honolulu, HI 96819-3100
Tel: (808) 832-0709 Fax: (808) 832-0683

Federal/State Supervisor **Keith H. Otsuka** .... (808) 832-0709

Stockton (CA) Inspection Office
5635 Stratford Circle, Suite 11, Stockton, CA 95207-5055
Tel: (209) 946-6301 Fax: (209) 476-8919

Officer-in-Charge **Daniel A. "Dan" Casares** .... (209) 946-6301
Assistant Officer-in-Charge **Raymon Stuart** .... (209) 946-6301
Administrative Support Assistant **(Vacant)** .... (209) 946-6301

Yakima (WA) Inspection Office
108 South 6th Avenue, Yakima, WA 98902
Tel: (509) 575-5869 Fax: (509) 575-5881

Officer-in-Charge **Douglas M. Augspurg** .... (509) 575-5869
Assistant Officer-in-Charge **Ronald Evans** .... (509) 575-5869
Administrative Support Assistant **Joan Riese** .... (509) 575-5869

Animal and Plant Health Inspection Service (APHIS)
Jamie L. Whitten Federal Building, 1400 Independence Avenue, SW,
Room 312E, Washington, DC 20250
Tel: (202) 799-7000 Fax: (301) 734-5157 Fax: (202) 720-3054
Internet: www.aphis.usda.gov

● Administrator **Kevin A. Shea** .... (202) 799-7017
E-mail: kevin.a.shea@aphis.usda.gov
Education: Maryland 1976 BA; Baltimore 1991 JD

Legislative and Public Affairs (LPA)
USDA Riverside, 4700 River Road, Unit 50, Riverdale, MD 20737
Tel: (202) 799-7030 Fax: (301) 734-5387

● Deputy Administrator **Bethany X. Jones** .... (202) 799-7037
South Agriculture Building, Fax: (202) 720-3982
1400 Independence Avenue, SW,
Room 1147, Washington, DC 20250
E-mail: bethany.x.jones@usda.gov
Education: Randolph-Macon Woman's 1990 BA

Associate Deputy Administrator **James Ivy** .... (202) 799-7026
South Agriculture Building, 1400 Independence Avenue, SW,
Room 1147, Washington, DC 20250
E-mail: james.ivy@usda.gov

Director for Executive Communications
Christina J. Myers Unit 49 .... (301) 734-8297
E-mail: christina.j.myers@aphis.usda.gov
Education: Wisconsin 1993 MA

Director for Freedom of Information **Tonya Woods** ...... (301) 851-4076
E-mail: tonya.woods@usda.gov Fax: (301) 734-5941
E-mail: foia.officer@aphis.usda.gov

Director for Public Affairs
Ed C. Curlett Room Unit 51 .... (301) 851-4052
E-mail: ed.c.curlett@aphis.usda.gov Fax: (301) 734-5221
Education: Maryland 1990 BS

Public Affairs Specialist **Abbey Powell** .... (301) 851-4054

Governmental Affairs Specialist **Tanika Whittington** ..... (301) 851-4071
E-mail: tanika.c.whittington@aphis.usda.gov

(continued on next page)

★ Presidential Appointment Requiring Senate Confirmation ☆ Presidential Appointment ☐ Schedule C Appointment ◇ Career Senior Foreign Service Appointment
● Career Senior Executive Service (SES) Appointment ○ Non-Career Senior Executive Service (SES) Appointment ■ Postal Career Executive Service

DEPARTMENTS

Legislative and Public Affairs *(continued)*

Legislative Director **Christopher M. Needham** .... (202) 799-7027
E-mail: christopher.m.needham@aphis.usda.gov

Colorado Field Office
Building B, 2150 Centre Avenue, Cube 2E16, Mail Stop 2E6,
Fort Collins, CO 80526-8119
Tel: (970) 494-7410 Fax: (970) 494-7414

Public Affairs Specialist **Lyndsay M. Cole** .... (970) 494-7410
E-mail: lyndsay.m.cole@usda.gov

Animal Care (AC)

APHIS Animal Care, 4700 River Road,
Unit 84, Riverdale, MD 20737
Tel: (301) 734-3751 (General Information) Fax: (301) 734-4978
E-mail: ace@usda.gov Internet: www.aphis.usda.gov/animal_welfare

Eastern Region
920 Main Campus Drive, Suite 200, Raleigh, NC 27606
Tel: (919) 855-7100 Fax: (919) 855-7123

Eastern Regional Director **(Vacant)** .... (919) 855-7096
Administrative Support Assistant **Linda E. Cooley** ..... (919) 855-7115
Administrative Support Assistant **(Vacant)** .... (919) 855-7099
Assistant Regional Director **William Stokes** .... (919) 855-7097
Inspection and Licensing Assistant **Amy Benson** .... (919) 855-7108
Inspection and Licensing Assistant **Sophia Branson** ..... (919) 855-7113
Inspection and Licensing Assistant
Vicky J. McCollough .... (919) 855-7100
E-mail: vicky.j.mccollough@aphis.usda.gov
Inspection and Licensing Assistant **Ama-Sei Nkromah** ... (919) 855-7102
Inspection and Licensing Assistant **RaNeshia Smith** ..... (919) 855-7103
Fax: (919) 855-7124
CEA **Teany Gurkin** .... (919) 855-7116
Supervisory Animal Care Specialist
Dr. Ellen J. Magid .... (919) 855-7111
E-mail: ellen.j.magid@aphis.usda.gov
Regional Animal Care Specialist **Nicolette Petervary** .... (919) 855-7100
E-mail: nicolette.petervary@aphis.usda.gov
Information Technology Specialist Customer Support
Jonathan Peach .... (919) 855-7107
Program Manager **(Vacant)** .... (919) 855-7106
Administrative Officer **Charlene H. Mayo** .... (919) 855-7109
E-mail: charlene.h.mayo@aphis.usda.gov
Program Specialist **Teany Garkin** .... (919) 855-7104

Western Region
Building B, 2150 Centre Avenue, Mail Stop 3W11,
Fort Collins, CO 80526
Tel: (970) 494-7478 Fax: (970) 472-9558
Internet: www.aphis.usda.gov/animal_welfare/index.shtml

Regional Director **Dr. Robert M. Gibbens** .... (970) 494-7478
E-mail: robert.m.gibbens@aphis.usda.gov
Education: Oklahoma State 1980 BS, 1984 DVM
Assistant Regional Director **Dr. Elizabeth C. Meek** ...... (970) 494-7478
Animal Care Specialist **Dr. V. Wensley Koch** .... (970) 494-7476
Program Specialist **Craig Nowakowski** .... (970) 494-7479
Program Assistant **(Vacant)** .... (970) 494-7468
Administrative Support Assistant **Paula D. Bovee** .... (970) 494-7480
Administrative Support Assistant **Marcia C. Graham** .... (970) 494-7475
E-mail: marcia.c.graham@aphis.usda.gov
Compliance and Enforcement Assistant
Karen L. March .... (970) 494-7481
E-mail: karen.l.march@aphis.usda.gov
Compliance and Enforcement Assistant **(Vacant)** .... (970) 494-4458
Computer Specialist **Emil J. Ewing** .... (970) 494-7465
E-mail: emil.j.ewing@aphis.usda.gov
Emergency Program Manager **Kevin M. Dennison** ...... (970) 494-7433
Inspection and Licensing Assistant **Lauren Atkinson** .... (970) 494-7457
Inspection and Licensing Assistant **Evelyn M. Celli** ...... (970) 494-7467
E-mail: evelyn.m.celli@aphis.usda.gov
Inspection and Licensing Assistant **Emily Fausch** .... (970) 494-7469
E-mail: emily.r.fausch@aphis.usda.gov
Inspection and Licensing Assistant **Linda L. Kovar** ...... (970) 494-7463

Western Region *(continued)*

Inspection and Licensing Assistant
Katie M. Whisenton .... (970) 494-7587
E-mail: katie.m.green@aphis.usda.gov
Inspection and Licensing Assistant
Dean W. Wonsbeck .... (970) 494-7472
E-mail: dean.w.wonsbeck@aphis.usda.gov
Inspection and Licensing Assistant **(Vacant)** .... (970) 494-7454
Travel and Transportation Specialist **(Vacant)** .... (970) 494-7411

Marketing and Regulatory Programs-Business Services (MRPBS)

1400 Independence Avenue, SW, Room 308-E, Washington, DC 20250
Tel: (301) 851-2873 Fax: (202) 690-0686

Investigative and Enforcement Services (IES)

4700 River Road, Unit 85, Riverdale, MD 20737
Tel: (301) 851-2948 Fax: (301) 734-4328 E-mail: ies@aphis.usda.gov

Eastern Region
920 Main Campus Drive, Suite 200, Raleigh, NC 27606-5213
Tel: (919) 855-7080 Fax: (919) 855-7090

Eastern Regional Director **(Vacant)** .... (919) 855-7078
Eastern Deputy Regional Director **(Vacant)** .... (919) 855-7078

Western Region
Building B-3W10, 2150 Centre Avenue, Fort Collins, CO 80526-8117
Tel: (970) 494-7485 Fax: (970) 494-7487

● Western Regional Director **Timothy R. Fordahl** .... (970) 494-7485
E-mail: timothy.r.fordahl@aphis.usda.gov
● Deputy Regional Director **Eric S. Nickerson** .... (970) 494-7491
E-mail: eric.s.nickerson@aphis.usda.gov

Plant Protection and Quarantine (PPQ)

Jamie L. Whitten Federal Building, 1400 Independence Avenue,
SW, Washington, DC 20250
Tel: (800) 877-3835 (Antismuggling Hotline) Fax: (202) 690-0472

Center for Plant Health Science and Technology (CPHST)

1730 Varsity Drive, Suite 400, Raleigh, NC 27606

● Associate Deputy Administrator **Ron Sequeira** .... (301) 851-2090
4700 River Road, Riverdale, MD 20737
E-mail: ron.sequeira@aphis.usda.gov
● Executive Director **Philip H. Berger** .... (919) 855-7400
E-mail: philip.h.berger@usda.gov
Associate Executive Director **Wendy Jin** .... (919) 855-7400
National Science Director **Russ Bulluck** .... (919) 855-7400
E-mail: russ.bulluck@aphis.usda.gov
National Science Director
Michael "Mike" Hennessey .... (919) 855-7400
E-mail: michael.hennessey@aphis.usda.gov
National Science Director **Charla Hollingsworth** .... (919) 855-7400
E-mail: charla.hollingsworth@aphis.usda.gov
Staff Assistant **Davis A. Abner** .... (919) 855-7400

National Plant Germplasm and Biotechnology Laboratory (NPGBL)

Building 580, BARC-East, Beltsville, MD 20705-2325
Tel: (301) 504-7100 Fax: (301) 504-8539

Director **Mark K. Nakhla** .... (301) 504-7100
E-mail: mark.k.nakhla@aphis.usda.gov

Pest Detection, Diagnostic and Management Laboratory (PDDML)

USDA APHIS PPQ CPHST PDDML Plant Protection Laboratory,
22675 North Moorfield Road, Building 6414,
Moore Air Base, Edinburg, TX 78541-5033
Tel: (956) 205-7668 Fax: (956) 205-7680

Laboratory Director **Matt A. Ciomperlik** .... (956) 205-7667
E-mail: matt.a.ciomperlik@aphis.usda.gov

★ Presidential Appointment Requiring Senate Confirmation ☆ Presidential Appointment ☐ Schedule C Appointment ◇ Career Senior Foreign Service Appointment
● Career Senior Executive Service (SES) Appointment ○ Non-Career Senior Executive Service (SES) Appointment ■ Postal Career Executive Service

Pest Survey Detection and Exclusion Laboratory
1398 West Truck Road, Buzzards Bay, MA 02542
Tel: (508) 563-9303 Fax: (508) 564-4398
Director **Scott Pfister** .... (508) 563-0900

Plant Epidemiology and Risk Analysis Laboratory (PERAL)
1730 Varsity Drive, Suite 300, Raleigh, NC 27606
Fax: (919) 855-7599
Director **Wendy Jin** .... (919) 855-7500

Treatment Quality Assurance Unit (TQAU)
1730 Varsity Drive, Suite 400, Raleigh, NC 27606
Fax: (919) 855-7493
Coordinator **Woodward Bailey** .... (919) 855-7475

Field Operations
920 Main Campus Drive, Raleigh, NC 27606-5202
Tel: (919) 855-7300 Fax: (919) 855-7393
● Associate Deputy Administrator **Matthew H. Royer** ..... (919) 855-7300
E-mail: matthew.royer@aphis.usda.gov
Associate Executive Director **Craig Southwick** .... (970) 494-7541
2150 Centre Avenue, Fort Collins, CO 80526-8119
Administrative Support Assistant
Elizabeth "Liz" Bickel .... (970) 494-7417
2150 Centre Avenue, Fort Collins, CO 80526-8119
E-mail: elizabeth.bickel@aphis.usda.gov
● Executive Director **Carlos F. Martinez** .... (970) 494-7503
2150 Centre Avenue, Fort Collins, CO 80526-8119
E-mail: carlos.f.martinez@aphis.usda.gov
Executive Secretary **(Vacant)** .... (919) 855-7316
Associate Executive Director **Diana L. Hoffman** .... (919) 855-7398
E-mail: diana.l.hoffman@aphis.usda.gov
Associate Executive Director (Acting) **Katie Hough** ..... (919) 855-7300
Associate Executive Director **Clint McFarland** .... (919) 855-7300
Associate Executive Director (Acting)
Scott M. Sanner .... (919) 855-7300
Associate Executive Director **Calvin H. Shuler** .... (919) 855-7300
Senior Program Manager **(Vacant)** .... (970) 494-7500
2150 Centre Avenue, Fort Collins, CO 80526-8119
Senior Program Manager - Domestic **(Vacant)** .... (919) 855-7326
Senior Program Manager - Risk Management
Adam Brookbank .... (919) 855-7326
Outreach Coordinator **Camille E. Morris** .... (919) 855-7340
E-mail: camille.e.morris@aphis.usda.gov
Administrative Officer **Robert Hostetter** .... (970) 494-7540
2150 Centre Avenue, Fort Collins, CO 80526-8119

Boll Weevil Eradication Program
4700 River Road, Unit 26, Riverdale, MD 20737
Tel: (919) 855-7300 Fax: (205) 752-1338
Areas Covered: AL, GA, FL, MS, MO, NC, SC, TN, VA
Program Coordinator **William "Bill" Newton** .... (301) 851-3128

Alabama State Office
1836 Glynwood Drive, Prattville, AL 36066
Tel: (334) 358-4920
State Plant Health Director **Jeffrey L. Head** .... (662) 270-4412
505 Russell Street, Starkville, MS 39759
E-mail: jeffrey.l.head@aphis.usda.gov
Office Manager **Dorraine Burney** .... (662) 270-4415
E-mail: dorraine.burney@aphis.usda.gov

Alaska State Office
Building B, 1700 East Bogard Road, Suite 101, Wasilla, AK 99654
Tel: (907) 357-9542 Fax: (907) 357-9548
Plant Health Director **Timothy "Tim" St. Germain** ..... (253) 944-2040
33400 9th Avenue S., Fax: (253) 874-1109
Suite 200, Federal Way, WA 98003
E-mail: timothy.stgermain@aphis.usda.gov

Arizona State Office
3658 East Chipman Road, Phoenix, AZ 85040
Tel: (602) 431-3200 Fax: (602) 414-9870
Plant Health Director **Jerald L. Levitt** .... (602) 431-3200
E-mail: jerald.l.levitt@aphis.usda.gov
Administrative Officer **Karla Kahealani Kekela** .... (602) 431-3200
E-mail: karla.kekela@ams.usda.gov

Arkansas State Office
1200 Cherry Brook Drive, Suite 100, Little Rock, AR 72211
Tel: (501) 324-5258 Fax: (501) 324-5230
State Plant Health Director **Joel W. Bard** .... (501) 324-5258
E-mail: joel.w.bard@aphis.usda.gov
Export Certification Specialist **Brannen V. Hardy** .... (501) 324-5258
Fax: (501) 324-5230

California State Office
650 Capitol Mall, Suite 6-400, Sacramento, CA 95814
Tel: (916) 930-5500 Fax: (916) 930-5518
Plant Health Director **Helene R. Wright** .... (916) 930-5500
E-mail: helene.r.wright@aphis.usda.gov
Office Manager **Kathi P. Johnson** .... (916) 930-5500
Administrative Support Assistant **Terry D. Williams** .... (916) 930-5500
Administrative Support Assistant **(Vacant)** .... (916) 930-5500

Colorado State Office
3950 North Lewiston, Suite 330, Aurora, CO 80011
Tel: (303) 371-3355 Fax: (303) 371-4774
Plant Health Director **Patrick W. McPherren** .... (303) 371-3355
E-mail: patrick.w.mcpherren@aphis.usda.gov
Office Manager **Becky L. Roberts** .... (303) 373-6640

Connecticut and Rhode Island State Office
900 Northrup Road, Suite C, Wallingford, CT 06492-1900
Tel: (203) 741-5656 Fax: (203) 741-5660
State Plant Health Director **Kate Aitkenhead** .... (203) 741-5641
E-mail: kate.r.aitkenhead@aphis.usda.gov
Office Manager **Sindey Y. Parker** .... (203) 741-5642

Delaware State Office
500 W Loockerman St, Suite 310, Dover, DE 19904-6726
Tel: (302) 744-1800 Fax: (302) 734-7814
State Plant Health Director **Darryl C. Moore** .... (302) 744-1800
E-mail: Darryl.C.Moore@aphis.usda.gov Fax: (302) 734-7814
Office Manager **Donna Johnston** .... (302) 744-1800

Florida State Office
8100 NW 15th Place, Gainesville, FL 32606
Fax: (352) 313-3041
State Plant Health Director **Richard Miranda** .... (352) 313-3040
Office Manager **Dorothea Jacobs** .... (352) 313-3040

Georgia State Office
1506 Klondike Road, Suite 306, Conyers, GA 30094
Tel: (770) 860-4020 Fax: (770) 860-4050
State Plant Health Director
William C. "Bill" Kauffman .... (770) 860-4020
E-mail: william.c.kauffmann@aphis.usda.gov
Office Manager **Fonda Tanner** .... (770) 860-4020

Hawaii State Office
Prince Jonah Kuhio Kalanianaole Federal Building,
300 Ala Moana Boulevard, Room 8-120, Honolulu, HI 96850
P.O. Box 50002, Honolulu, HI 96850
Tel: (808) 838-2781 Fax: (808) 541-1978
State Plant Health Director **Vernon Harrington** .... (808) 541-2780
E-mail: vernon.harrington@aphis.usda.gov
Administration Support Assistant
Yvonne R. Mediros .... (808) 838-2781
E-mail: yvonne.r.medeiros@aphis.usda.gov
Office Manager **Betty Ann Singh** .... (808) 838-2781

(continued on next page)

★ Presidential Appointment Requiring Senate Confirmation ☆ Presidential Appointment ☐ Schedule C Appointment ◇ Career Senior Foreign Service Appointment
● Career Senior Executive Service (SES) Appointment ○ Non-Career Senior Executive Service (SES) Appointment ■ Postal Career Executive Service

Hawaii State Office *(continued)*

State Operations Support Officer **Yolisha C. Ishibashi** . . . . (808) 541-2780

Idaho State Office
9134 West Blackeagle Drive, Boise, ID 83709
Tel: (208) 373-1600 Fax: (208) 378-5794

Plant Health Director **Brian L. Marschman** . . . . (208) 373-1600
E-mail: brian.l.marschman@aphis.usda.gov
Office Manager **Crystal Svervesten** . . . . (208) 373-1600

Illinois State Office
2300 East Devon, Suite 210, Des Plaines, IL 60018-4617
Fax: (847) 699-2430

State Plant Health Director **Greg J. Rentschler** . . . . (847) 699-2422
E-mail: greg.j.rentschler@aphis.usda.gov
Office Manager **Julie M. Kaiser** . . . . (847) 699-2414

Indiana State Office
1305 Cumberland Avenue, Suite 102, West Lafayette, IN 47906
Fax: (765) 446-8274

State Plant Health Director **Gary W. Simon** . . . . (765) 497-2879
E-mail: gary.w.simon@aphis.usda.gov
Office Manager **Lauren Julie Shepherd** . . . . (765) 497-2847

Iowa State Office
11213 Aurora Avenue, Urbandale, IA 50322
Tel: (515) 251-4083 Fax: (515) 251-4093

State Plant Health Director (Acting) **Mark G. Hollister** . . . (515) 251-4083
E-mail: mark.g.hollister@aphis.usda.gov
Office Manager **Regina L. Moriarty** . . . . (515) 251-4083

Kansas State Office
431 Northwest Independence Boulevard, Topeka, KS 66608
Tel: (785) 228-6550 Fax: (402) 434-2330

State Plant Health Director (Acting)
Shayne P. Galford . . . . (402) 434-2346
E-mail: Shayne.P.Galford@aphis.usda.gov
Export Certification Specialist **(Vacant)** . . . . (785) 228-6550
Office Manager **Allison L. Matthews** . . . . (785) 228-6550
Fax: (785) 228-6558

Kentucky State Office
1973 Burlington Pike, Burlington, KY 41005
Fax: (502) 543-1609

State Plant Health Director (Acting) **Harold Hempfing** . . . (502) 439-7043
E-mail: harold.hempfling@aphis.usda.gov
Office Manager **Kelly M. Smith** . . . . (502) 439-7043

Louisiana State Office
4354 South Sherwood Forest Boulevard,
Room 150, Baton Rouge, LA 70816
Tel: (225) 298-5410 Fax: (225) 298-5415

State Plant Health Director **Tad N. Hardy** . . . . (225) 298-5410
E-mail: tad.n.hardy@aphis.usda.gov
Education: Fort Hays State 1979 BS; Iowa State 1981 MS

Maine State Office
15 Iron Road, Suite 1, Bangor, ME 04401
Tel: (207) 848-0000 Fax: (207) 848-2537

State Plant Health Director **Terry L. Bourgoin** . . . . (207) 848-0000
E-mail: terry.bourgoin@aphis.usda.gov
Office Manager **Carol L. Murphy** . . . . (207) 848-0003

Maryland State Office
2200 Broening Highway, Suite 102, Baltimore, MD 21224
Fax: (410) 288-5542

State Plant Health Director **Matthew A. Travis** . . . . (410) 288-5540
E-mail: matthew.a.travis@aphis.usda.gov
Office Manager **John Young** . . . . (410) 631-0073 ext. 16

Massachusetts State Office
Thomas P. O'Neill Building, 10 Causeway Street,
Room 516, Boston, MA 02222-1088
Tel: (617) 565-7030 Fax: (617) 565-6933

State Plant Health Director **Kate Aitkenhead** . . . . (203) 741-5641
97 Barnes Road, Unit 200, Wallingford, CT 06492
E-mail: kate.r.aitkenhead@aphis.usda.gov
Office Manager **Sindey Y. Parker** . . . . (203) 741-5642

Michigan State Office
11200 Metro Airport Center Drive, Room 140, Romulus, MI 48174
Tel: (734) 942-9005 Fax: (734) 942-7691

State Plant Health Director **Craig Kellogg** . . . . (734) 942-9005
E-mail: craig.kellogg@aphis.usda.gov
Office Manager **Jill A. Hand** . . . . (734) 229-1651

Minnesota State Office
900 American Boulevard, Suite 101, Bloomington, MN 55420
Tel: (952) 814-1071 Fax: (952) 814-1073

State Plant Health Director **Erin N. Stiers** . . . . (952) 814-1071
E-mail: erin.n.stiers@aphis.usda.gov Fax: (952) 814-1073
Office Manager **(Vacant)** . . . . (952) 814-1072

Mississippi State Office
505 Russell Street, Starkville, MS 39759
Fax: (662) 323-8827

State Plant Health Director **Jeffrey L. Head** . . . . (662) 270-4412
Office Manager **Dorraine Burney** . . . . (662) 270-4415

Missouri State Office
1715 Southridge Drive, Suite 2, Jefferson City, MO 65109
Tel: (573) 893-6833 Fax: (573) 893-6751

State Plant Health Director **Michael E. Brown** . . . . (573) 893-6833
E-mail: michael.e.brown@aphis.usda.gov
Office Manager **(Vacant)** . . . . (573) 893-6833

Montana State Office
1220 Cole Avenue, Helena, MT 59601
Tel: (406) 449-5210 Fax: (406) 449-5212

Plant Health Director **Gary D. Adams** . . . . (406) 449-5210
E-mail: gary.d.adams@aphis.usda.gov
Office Manager **Ryan Richter** . . . . (406) 449-5210

Nebraska State Office
5940 South 58th Street, Lincoln, NE 68516
Mail: P.O. Box 81866, Lincoln, NE 68501
Tel: (402) 434-2346 Fax: (402) 434-2330

State Plant Health Director **Shayne P. Galford** . . . . (402) 434-2346
E-mail: shayne.p.galford@aphis.usda.gov
Office Manager **(Vacant)** . . . . (402) 434-2346
Plant Health Safeguarding Specialist **(Vacant)** . . . . (402) 434-2333

Nevada State Office
8775 Technology Way, Reno, NV 89521
Tel: (775) 851-8818 Fax: (775) 851-8828

Plant Health Director **Alana Wild** . . . . (775) 851-8818
E-mail: alana.l.wild@aphis.usda.gov Fax: (775) 851-8828
Program Support Assistant **Claudia S. Roberts** . . . . (775) 851-8818
E-mail: claudia.s.roberts@aphis.usda.gov
Domestic Program Coordinator **(Vacant)** . . . . (775) 851-4812

New Hampshire and Vermont State Office
617 Comstock Road, Suite 3, Berlin, VT 05602-8927
Fax: (802) 828-4591

State Plant Health Director **Stephen Lavallee** . . . . (802) 224-1402
E-mail: stephen.g.lavallee@aphis.usda.gov
Office Manager **Carol L. Murphy** . . . . (207) 848-0003

New Jersey State Office
350 Corporate Boulevard, Mercer Corporate Park, West,
Robbinsville, NJ 08691
Fax: (609) 259-5243

State Plant Health Director **George J. Nelson** .... (609) 259-5242
E-mail: george.j.nelson@aphis.usda.gov
Office Manager **Melissa Rehl** .... (609) 259-5240

New Mexico State Office
6200 Jefferson Street NE, Suite 130, Albuquerque, NM 87109-3434
Tel: (505) 761-3189 Fax: (505) 761-3197

Plant Health Director **Waleska V. Ramirez** .... (505) 761-3189
E-mail: waleska.v.ramirez@aphis.usda.gov
Office Manager **Karla Kahealani Kekela** .... (505) 761-3191

New York State Office
500 New Karner Road, Second Floor, Albany, NY 12205-1121
Tel: (518) 218-7510 Fax: (518) 218-7518

State Plant Health Director **Eddie Chen** .... (518) 218-7510
Office Manager **Karen Greenwood** .... (518) 218-7510

North Carolina State Office
920 Main Campus Drive, Suite 150, Raleigh, NC 27606-5202
Tel: (919) 855-7600 Fax: (919) 855-7611

State Plant Health Director **Joe Beckwith** .... (919) 855-7600
Education: Florida 1986 BS
Office Manager **Seantoya Hinton** .... (919) 855-7606

North Dakota State Office
3509 Miriam Avenue, Suite A, Bismarck, ND 58501
Tel: (701) 250-4473 Fax: (701) 250-4640

State Plant Health Director **David C. Hirsch** .... (701) 250-4473
E-mail: david.c.hirsch@aphis.usda.gov
Office Manager **Donald G. Anderson** .... (701) 250-4473

Ohio State Office
8995 East Main Street, Room 202, Reynoldsburg, OH 43068
Tel: (614) 322-4700 Fax: (614) 322-4704

State Plant Health Director **John M. Burch** .... (614) 322-4700
E-mail: john.m.burch@aphis.usda.gov
Office Manager **Sandie Lehberger** .... (614) 322-4700

Oklahoma State Office
301 NW Sixth Street, Suite 101, Oklahoma City, OK 73102
Tel: (405) 609-8840 Fax: (405) 609-8841

State Plant Health Director **Blaine Powell** .... (405) 609-8840
E-mail: blaine.powell@aphis.usda.gov
Office Manager **Toni Grant** .... (405) 609-8840

Oregon State Office
Airport Business Center, 6135 NE 80th Avenue,
Suite A-5, Portland, OR 97218-4033
Tel: (503) 326-2814 Fax: (503) 326-2969

Plant Health Director **(Vacant)** .... (503) 326-2814 ext. 233
Office Manager **Cynthia C. Ross** .... (503) 326-2814 ext. 237

Pennsylvania State Office
401 East Louther Street, Suite 102, Carlisle, PA 17013
Tel: (717) 241-0140 Fax: (717) 241-0718

State Plant Health Director **Timothy E. Newcamp** .... (717) 241-0140
E-mail: timothy.e.newcamp@aphis.usda.gov Fax: (717) 241-0718
Office Manager **Pamela Williams** .... (717) 241-2465

Puerto Rico and U.S. Virgin Islands Office
654 Muñoz Rivera Avenue, Suite 700, Hato Rey, PR 00918
Tel: (787) 771-3611 Fax: (787) 771-3613

State Plant Health Director **Leyinska Wiscovitch** .... (787) 919-0585
E-mail: leyinska.wiscovitch@aphis.usda.gov
Office Manager **Janice Simmons** .... (787) 771-4007

South Carolina State Office
4600 Goer Drive, Suite 104, Charleston, SC 29406
Fax: (843) 746-2954

State Plant Health Director **Carl W. Lightfoot** .... (843) 480-4334
E-mail: carl.w.lightfoot@aphis.usda.gov Fax: (843) 746-2954
Office Manager **Kim P. Williams** .... (843) 480-4334

South Dakota State Office
314 South Henry Street, Suite 200, Pierre, SD 57501
Mail: P.O. Box 250, Pierre, SD 57501
Tel: (605) 224-1713 Fax: (605) 224-0172

State Plant Health Director (Acting) **David C. Hirsch** .... (701) 250-4473
3509 Miriam Avenue, Bismarck, ND 58501-7902
E-mail: david.c.hirsch@aphis.usda.gov
Office Manager **(Vacant)** .... (605) 224-1713

Tennessee State Office
1410 Kensington Square Court, Suite 101, Murfreesboro, TN 37130
Fax: (502) 543-1609

State Plant Health Director **Jason J. Watkins** .... (615) 907-3357
E-mail: jason.j.watkins@aphis.usda.gov Fax: (615) 907-8168
Office Manager **Kelly M. Smith** .... (502) 955-4041

Texas State Office
Homer Thornberry Judicial Building, 903 San Jacinto Boulevard,
Suite 270, Austin, TX 78701-2450
Tel: (512) 916-5241 Fax: (512) 916-5243

State Plant Health Director **Stuart W. Kuehn** .... (512) 916-5241
E-mail: stuart.w.kuehn@aphis.usda.gov
Office Manager **(Vacant)** .... (512) 916-5241

Utah State Office
1860 West Alexander, Suite B, West Valley City, UT 84119
Tel: (801) 975-3310 Fax: (801) 975-3313

Plant Health Director (Acting) **Alana Wild** .... (801) 975-3310
E-mail: alana.l.wild@aphis.usda.gov
Office Manager **Brittany J. Kinney** .... (801) 975-3310

Virginia State Office
5657 South Laburnum Avenue, Richmond, VA 23231-4536
Fax: (804) 226-5263

State Plant Health Director (Acting)
Karen A. Williams .... (757) 815-2064
E-mail: Karen.A.Willams@aphis.usda.gov
Office Manager **Chickeilla J. Carter** .... (804) 226-5261

Washington State Office
33400 9th Avenue S., Suite 200, Federal Way, WA 98003
Tel: (253) 944-2040 Fax: (253) 874-1109

Plant Health Director **Timothy "Tim" St. Germain** .... (253) 944-2040
E-mail: timothy.stgermain@aphis.usda.gov
Office Manager **Bertha A. Hines** .... (253) 944-2040

West Virginia State Office
275 Gus R. Douglass Lane, Charleston, WV 25312
Fax: (304) 343-8586

State Plant Health Director **Eric W. Ewing** .... (304) 343-8585
E-mail: Eric.Ewing@aphis.usda.gov Fax: (304) 343-8586
Office Manager **Cheryl D. Hersman** .... (304) 343-8585

Wisconsin State Office
One Gifford Pinchot Drive, Building 1,
Room 229, Madison, WI 53726-2366
Tel: (608) 286-3604 Fax: (608) 231-9581

State Plant Health Director (Acting)
Christopher Deegan .... (608) 286-3604 ext. 2
E-mail: Christopher.Deegan@wisconsin.gov
Education: Iowa BA; SUNY Environmental BS; Arizona MS
Office Manager **(Vacant)** .... (608) 286-3604

Wyoming State Office
5353 Yellowstone Road, Suite 208, Cheyenne, WY 82009
Tel: (307) 432-7979 Fax: (307) 432-7970

Plant Health Director **Bruce A. Shambaugh** . . . . (307) 432-7979
E-mail: bruce.a.shambaugh@aphis.usda.gov
Office Manager **Regina L. Wolf** . . . . (307) 432-7979

Veterinary Services (VS)

Administration Building, 1400 Independence Avenue SW,
Washington, DC 20250
Fax: (202) 690-4171

Regional Operations

District 1

Albany (NY) Office
500 New Korner Road, Second Floor, Albany, NY 12205
Tel: (518) 218-7540 Fax: (518) 218-7545 E-mail: vspsny@aphis.usda.gov
Areas Covered: NY

Assistant District Director **Dr. Robert Brady** . . . . (518) 218-7540

Harrisburg (PA) Office
2300 Vartan Way, Suite 250, Harrisburg, PA 17110
Tel: (717) 540-2777 Fax: (717) 782-3809
Areas Covered: PA

Assistant District Director
Dr. Michael A. Kornreich DVM . . . . (717) 540-2763

Raleigh (NC) Office
NCSU Centennial Campus, 920 Main Campus Drive,
Suite 200, Raleigh, NC 27606-5202
Tel: (919) 855-7700 Fax: (919) 855-7720 E-mail: vsnc@aphis.usda.gov
Areas Covered: NC

Assistant District Director **Barry Meade** . . . . (919) 855-7700

Richmond (VA) Office
400 North Eighth Street, Suite 726, Richmond, VA 23240-1001
Tel: (804) 343-2560 Fax: (804) 343-2599 E-mail: vspsva@aphis.usda.gov
Areas Covered: VA

Assistant District Director **Dr. Mark A. Remick DVM** . . . . (804) 343-2560

Robbinsville (NJ) Office
Mercer Corporate Park, 320 Corporate Boulevard,
Robbinsville, NJ 08691-1598
Tel: (609) 259-5260 Fax: (609) 259-2477
Areas Covered: NJ

Assistant District Director
Dr. Michael A. Kornreich DVM . . . . (609) 259-5260

Sutton (MA) Office
Sutton Square Plaza, 160 Worcester-Providence Road,
Suite 20, Sutton, MA 01590-9998
P.O. Box 787, Sutton, MA 01590
Tel: (508) 363-2290 Fax: (508) 363-2272
Areas Covered: CT, ME, MA, NH, RI, VT

District Director **Dr. Thomas S. McKenna** . . . . (508) 363-2290
Education: Lehigh 1973 BS; Alaska (Fairbanks) 1984 BS;
UC Davis PhD, DVM

New York (NY) Animal Import Center
474 International Boulevard, Rock Tavern, NY 12575
Tel: (845) 838-5500 Fax: (845) 564-1075

Assistant District Director **Michael Burke** . . . . (845) 838-5500

District 2

Columbia (SC) Office
9600 Two Notch Road, Suite 10, Columbia, SC 29223
Tel: (803) 462-2910 Fax: (803) 788-2102 E-mail: vssc@aphis.usda.gov
Areas Covered: SC

Assistant District Director
Dr. Delorias M. Lenard DVM . . . . (803) 462-2910

Conyers (GA) Office
1506 Klondike Road, Suite 300, Conyers, GA 30094
Tel: (770) 761-5420 Fax: (770) 761-5956 E-mail: vspsga@aphis.usda.gov
Areas Covered: GA

Assistant District Director **Dr. Christopher A. Young** . . . . (770) 761-5420

Gainesville (FL) Office
8100 NW 15th Place, Gainesville, FL 32606
Tel: (352) 313-3060 Fax: (352) 313-3041 E-mail: vspsfl@aphis.usda.gov
Areas Covered: FL

District Director **Dix Harrell** . . . . (352) 313-3060

Montgomery (AL) Office
Beard Office Building, 1445 Federal Drive,
Room 224, Montgomery, AL 36107
P.O. Box 70429, Montgomery, AL 36107
Tel: (334) 551-2180 Fax: (334) 223-7352
Areas Covered: AL

Assistant District Director (Acting)
Dr. K. Mark Krause DVM . . . . (334) 551-2180

Nashville (TN) Office
Animal Industries Building, Ellington Agricultural Center,
440 Hogan Road, Room 206, Nashville, TN 37220
P.O. Box 110950, Nashville, TN 37222
Tel: (615) 781-5310 Fax: (615) 781-5309
Areas Covered: TN

Assistant District Director **Dr. K. Mark Krause DVM** . . . . (615) 781-5310

San Juan (PR) Office
654 Munoz Rivera Avenue, Suite 700, Hato Rey, PR 00918
Tel: (787) 766-6050 Fax: (787) 766-5159
Areas Covered: PR, VI

Assistant District Director **Dr. Fred V. Soltero VMD** . . . . . (787) 766-6050

Miami (FL) Animal Import - Export Center
6300 NW 36th Street, Miami, FL 33122
Mail: P.O. Box 660657, Miami, FL 33266
Tel: (305) 876-2200 Fax: (305) 526-2929

Center Director **Kathleen E. Turner** . . . . (352) 313-3060

District 3

Des Moines (IA) Office
Federal Building, 210 Walnut Street, Room 891, Des Moines, IA 50309
Tel: (515) 284-4140 Fax: (515) 284-4156
Areas Covered: IA

Assistant District Director
Dr. Kevin L. Petersburg DVM . . . . (515) 284-4140

East Lansing (MI) Office
3001 Coolidge Road, Suite 325, East Lansing, MI 48823
Tel: (517) 337-4700 Fax: (517) 337-4722
E-mail: vspsmi@aphis.usda.gov
Areas Covered: MI

Assistant District Director **Dr. Jean Ray PhD, DVM** . . . . . (517) 337-4700
Education: Michigan State 1978 BS, 1983 DVM, 1992 PhD

Frankfort (KY) Office
105 Corporate Drive, Frankfort, KY 40601
P.O. Box 399, Frankfort, KY 40602
Tel: (502) 848-2040 Fax: (502) 848-2041 E-mail: vspsky@aphis.usda.gov
Areas Covered: KY

Assistant District Director **(Vacant)** . . . . (502) 848-2040

Indianapolis (IN) Office
5685 Lafayette Road, Suite 400, Indianapolis, IN 46254
Tel: (317) 347-3100 Fax: (317) 347-3311 E-mail: vspsin@aphis.usda.gov
Areas Covered: IN

Assistant District Director **Dr. Frank R. Wilson** . . . . (317) 347-3100

★ Presidential Appointment Requiring Senate Confirmation ☆ Presidential Appointment □ Schedule C Appointment ◇ Career Senior Foreign Service Appointment
● Career Senior Executive Service (SES) Appointment ○ Non-Career Senior Executive Service (SES) Appointment ■ Postal Career Executive Service

Madison (WI) Office
1111 Deming Way, Suite 100, Madison, WI 53717
Tel: (608) 662-0600 Fax: (608) 662-0601 E-mail: vspswi@aphis.usda.gov
Areas Covered: WI
Assistant District Director **(Vacant)** .... (608) 662-0600

Pickerington (OH) Office
12927 Stonecreek Drive, Pickerington, OH 43147
Tel: (614) 856-4735 Fax: (614) 866-1086 E-mail: vspsoh@aphis.usda.gov
Areas Covered: OH, WV
Assistant District Director **Dr. Susan M. Skorupski** ..... (614) 856-4735

Saint Paul (MN) Office
Bolander Building, 251 Starkey Street,
Suite 229, St. Paul, MN 55107
Tel: (651) 290-3691 Fax: (651) 228-0654 E-mail: vsmn@aphis.usda.gov
Areas Covered: MN
District Director **(Vacant)** .... (651) 290-3691

Springfield (IL) Office
3410 Hedley Road, Springfield, IL 62711
Tel: (217) 547-6030 Fax: (217) 547-6031
Areas Covered: IL
Assistant District Director **Dr. Frank R. Wilson** .... (217) 547-6030

District 4

Austin (TX) Office
Homer Thornberry Judicial Building, 903 San Jacinto Boulevard,
Room 220, Austin, TX 78701-2450
Tel: (512) 383-2400 Fax: (512) 916-5197 E-mail: vstx@aphis.usda.gov
Areas Covered: TX
District Director **(Vacant)** .... (512) 383-2400

Baton Rouge (LA) Office
5825 Florida Boulevard, Room 1140, Baton Rouge, LA 70806-9985
Tel: (601) 936-8580 Fax: (601) 965-5535
Areas Covered: LA
Assistant District Director **Kenneth L. Angel** .... (601) 936-8580
345 Keyway Drive, Flowood, MS 39232

Flowood (MS) Office
345 Keyway Drive, Flowood, MS 39232
Tel: (601) 936-8580 Fax: (601) 965-5535
Areas Covered: MS
Assistant District Director **Kenneth L. Angel** .... (601) 936-8580

Jefferson City (MO) Office
1715 Southridge Drive, Jefferson City, MO 65109
Mail: P.O. Box 104418, Jefferson City, MO 65110-4418
Tel: (573) 636-3116 Fax: (573) 636-4384
E-mail: vspsmo@aphis.usda.gov (Exports and Accreditation)
Areas Covered: MO
Assistant District Director **Thomas Easley** .... (573) 636-3116

Little Rock (AR) Office
1200 Cherry Brook Drive, Suite 300, Little Rock, AR 72211
Tel: (501) 224-9515 Fax: (501) 225-5823 E-mail: vsar@aphis.usda.gov
Areas Covered: AR
Assistant District Director **Becky L. Brewer DVM** .... (501) 224-9515

Oklahoma City (OK) Office
12304 Market Drive, Oklahoma City, OK 73114
Tel: (405) 751-1701 Fax: (405) 751-2344
Areas Covered: OK
Assistant District Director **Dr. Byron R. Schick** .... (405) 751-1701

District 5

Bismarck (ND) Office
3509 Miriam Avenue, Suite B, Bismarck, ND 58501-7902
Tel: (701) 250-4210 Fax: (701) 250-4471 E-mail: vsnd@aphis.usda.gov
E-mail: vsps_nd@aphis.usda.gov (Exports and Accreditation)
Areas Covered: ND
Assistant District Director **Dr. Lynn A. Tesar** .... (701) 250-4210

Boise (ID) Office
9158 West Blackeagle Drive, Boise, ID 83709
Tel: (208) 373-1620 Fax: (208) 378-5637 E-mail: vspsid@aphis.usda.gov
E-mail: vsps_id@aphis.usda.gov (Exports and Accreditation)
Areas Covered: ID
Assistant District Director **Dr. Cynthia M. Gaborick** ..... (208) 373-1620

Cheyenne (WY) Office
5353 Yellowstone Road, Room 209, Cheyenne, WY 82009
Tel: (307) 432-7960 Fax: (307) 772-2592 E-mail: vswy@aphis.usda.gov
E-mail: vsps_wy@aphis.usda.gov (Exports and Accreditation)
Areas Covered: WY
Assistant District Director (Acting)
Dr. Thomas F.T. Linfield DVM .... (307) 432-7960

Helena (MT) Office
208 North Montana Avenue, Suite 101, Helena, MT 59601-3837
Tel: (406) 449-2220 Fax: (406) 449-5439 E-mail: vsmt@aphis.usda.gov
E-mail: vspsmt@aphis.usda.gov (Exports and Accreditation)
Areas Covered: MT
Assistant District Director
Dr. Thomas F.T. Linfield DVM .... (406) 449-2220

Lincoln (NE) Office
5940 South 58th Street, Lincoln, NE 68516
P.O. Box 81866, Lincoln, NE 68501
Tel: (402) 434-2300 Fax: (402) 434-2330 E-mail: vsne@aphis.usda.gov
E-mail: vspsne@aphis.usda.gov (Exports and Accreditation)
Areas Covered: NE
Assistant District Director **Kimberly A. Kirkham** .... (402) 434-2300

Pierre (SD) Office
314 South Henry, Suite 100, Pierre, SD 57501-0640
P.O. Box 640, Pierre, SD 57501-0640
Tel: (605) 224-6186 Fax: (605) 224-8451 E-mail: vssd@aphis.usda.gov
E-mail: vsps_sd@aphis.usda.gov (Exports and Accreditation)
Areas Covered: SD
Assistant District Director **Dr. Lynn A. Tesar** .... (605) 224-6186

Topeka (KS) Office
1131 SW Winding Road, Suite A, Topeka, KS 66615
Tel: (785) 228-6565 Fax: (785) 228-6570
Areas Covered: KS
Assistant District Director **(Vacant)** .... (785) 228-6565

District 6

Albuquerque (NM) Office
6200 Jefferson Street NE, Suite 117, Albuquerque, NM 87109
Tel: (505) 761-3160 Fax: (505) 761-3176 E-mail: vsnm@aphis.usda.gov
E-mail: vspsnm@aphis.usda.gov (Exports and Accreditation)
Areas Covered: NM
Assistant District Director **Dr. Paul Sciglibaglio DVM** ... (505) 761-3160

Lakewood (CO) Office
755 Parfet Street, Suite 136, Lakewood, CO 80215
Tel: (303) 231-5385 Fax: (303) 231-5390
Areas Covered: CO
Assistant District Director
Dr. Donald L. "Don" Beckett DVM .... (303) 231-5385

DEPARTMENTS

Los Angeles (CA) Import Center
11850 South La Cienega Boulevard, Hawthorne, CA 90250
Tel: (310) 725-1970 Fax: (310) 725-9119
District Director **Tremon C. Bell** .... (916) 854-3950

Olympia (WA) Office
1550 Irving Street, Suite 100, Tumwater, WA 98512
Tel: (360) 753-9430 Fax: (360) 753-9585
E-mail: vspswa@aphis.usda.gov (Exports and Accreditation)
Areas Covered: AK, HI, WA
Assistant District Director **Leonard Eldrige** .... (360) 753-9430

Sacramento (CA) Office
10365 Old Placerville Road, Suite 210, Sacramento, CA 95827-2518
Tel: (916) 854-3900 Fax: (916) 363-1125 E-mail: vsca@aphis.usda.gov
Areas Covered: CA, NV
District Director **Dr. Gary L. Brickler** .... (916) 854-3950

Salt Lake City (UT) Office
176 North 2200 West, Suite 230, Salt Lake City, UT 84116
Tel: (801) 524-5010 Fax: (801) 524-6898
E-mail: vsps_ut@aphis.usda.gov (Exports and Accreditation)
Areas Covered: UT
Assistant District Director **Dr. Robert A. DeCarolis** ......(801) 524-5010

Wildlife Services (WS)

South Agriculture Building, 1400 Independence Avenue, SW,
Stop 3402, Washington, DC 20250
Fax: (202) 690-0053

Eastern Region

Venture II, Centennial Campus, 920 Main Campus Drive,
Suite 200, Raleigh, NC 27606
Tel: (919) 855-7200 Fax: (919) 855-7215
Areas Covered: AL, AR, CT, DE, DC, FL, GA, IL, IN, IA, KY, LA, ME, MD, MA, MI, MN, MS, MO, NH, NJ, NY, NC, OH, PA, PR, RI, SC, TN, VT, VA, VI, WV, WI
● Regional Director **Willie D. Harris** .... (919) 855-7200
920 Main Campus Drive, Raleigh, NC 27606-5213
E-mail: Willie.D.Harris@aphis.usda.gov
Education: Florida Memorial U BS; Strayer U MBA
Assistant Regional Director **Robert L. Hudson** .... (919) 855-7201
Assistant Regional Director **John E. McConnell** .... (919) 855-7199

Alabama - Puerto Rico - Virgin Islands State Office
School of Forestry and Wildlife, 602 Duncan Drive,
Auburn University, AL 36849
Tel: (334) 844-5670 Fax: (334) 844-5321
State Director **Kenneth S. "Ken" Gruver** .... (334) 844-5670

Arkansas State Office
1020 Lantrip, Sherwood, AR 72120
Tel: (501) 835-2318 Fax: (501) 835-2350
Areas Covered: AR
State Director **Thurman W. Booth** .... (501) 835-2318
Budget Analyst **Karen Tate** .... (501) 835-2318

Florida State Office
2820 East University Avenue, Gainesville, FL 32641
Tel: (352) 377-5556 Fax: (352) 377-5559
State Director **(Vacant)** .... (352) 377-5556

Georgia State Office
School of Forestry and Natural Resources,
University of Georgia, Athens, GA 30602
Tel: (706) 546-5637 Fax: (706) 316-9248
State Director **Steven H. "Steve" Smith** ....(706) 546-5637 ext. 203

Illinois State Office
2869 Via Verde Drive, Springfield, IL 62703-4325
Tel: (217) 241-6700 Fax: (217) 241-6702
State Director **Scott Beckerman** ....(217) 241-6700 ext. 108

Indiana State Office
Purdue University, Smith Hall, 901 West State Street,
West Lafayette, IN 47907-2089
Tel: (765) 494-6229 Fax: (765) 494-9475
State Director **Lee A. Humberg** .... (765) 494-6229
Budget Analyst **Cheryl A. Towell** .... (765) 494-6229
E-mail: cheryl.a.towell@usda.gov Fax: (765) 494-9475
Education: Purdue 1977 BS

Louisiana State Office
1780 Commercial Drive, Port Allen, LA 70767
P.O. Box 589, Port Allen, LA 70767
Tel: (225) 389-0229 Fax: (225) 389-0228
State Director **Dwight LeBlanc** .... (225) 389-0229

Maine State Office
Capital West Business Center, 79 Leighton Road,
Suite 12, Augusta, ME 04330
Tel: (207) 629-5181 Fax: (207) 629-5182
State Director **Robin A. Dyer** .... (207) 629-5181

Maryland - Delaware - DC State Office
1568 Whitehall Road, Annapolis, MD 21401
Tel: (410) 349-8055 Fax: (410) 349-8258
State Director **Kevin J. Sullivan** .... (410) 349-8055

Massachusetts - Connecticut - Rhode Island State Office
463 West Street, Amherst, MA 01002
Tel: (413) 253-2403 Fax: (413) 253-7577
State Director **Monte D. Chandler** ....(413) 253-2403 ext. 5

Michigan State Office
2803 Jolly Road, Suite 100, Okemos, MI 48864-3670
Tel: (517) 336-1928 Fax: (517) 336-1934
State Director **Anthony G. Duffiney, Jr.** .... (517) 336-1928

Minnesota State Office
644 Bayfield Street, Suite 215, St. Paul, MN 55107
Fax: (651) 224-4271
State Director **Gary Nohrenberg** .... (651) 224-6027

Mississippi State Office
Thompson Hall, 775 Stone Boulevard,
Room 200, Mississippi State, MS 39762
P.O. Drawer FW, Mississippi State, MS 39762
Tel: (662) 325-3014 Fax: (662) 325-3690
State Director **Kris Godwin** .... (662) 325-3014

Missouri - Iowa State Office
1714 Commerce Street, Suite C, Columbia, MO 65202
Tel: (573) 449-3033 Fax: (573) 449-4382
State Director **Parker T. Hall** .... (573) 449-3033

New Hampshire - Vermont State Office
59 Chenell Drive, Suite 7, Concord, NH 03301-8548
Tel: (603) 223-6832 Fax: (603) 229-1951 Fax: (603) 229-1851
State Director **David Allaben** .... (603) 223-6832
District Supervisor, NH **Carolyn Stengel** .... (603) 223-6832
District Supervisor, Vermont **Frederick Pogmore** .... (802) 223-8690
617 Comstock Road, Berlin, VT 05602
Wildlife Services National Rabies Coordinator
Richard B. Chipman .... (603) 223-9623
E-mail: richard.b.chipman@aphis.usda.gov

★ Presidential Appointment Requiring Senate Confirmation ☆ Presidential Appointment □ Schedule C Appointment ◇ Career Senior Foreign Service Appointment
● Career Senior Executive Service (SES) Appointment ○ Non-Career Senior Executive Service (SES) Appointment ■ Postal Career Executive Service

New Jersey State Office
140-C Locust Grove Road, Pittstown, NJ 08867-4049
Tel: (908) 735-5654 Fax: (908) 735-0821
Areas Covered: NJ

State Director **Aaron Guikema** . . . . (908) 735-5654 ext. 11
Program Support **Dawn Golden** . . . . (908) 735-5654 ext. 12

New York State Office
1930 Route 9, Castleton on Hudson, NY 12033-9653
Tel: (518) 477-4837 Fax: (518) 477-4899

State Director **Allen Gosser** . . . . (518) 477-4837
Assistant State Director **William "Bill" Williams** . . . . (518) 477-4837
District Supervisor **Scott Clemmons** . . . . (315) 267-2288
230 Timerman Hall, Fax: (315) 267-2241
44 Pierrepont Avenue, Potsdam, NY 13676
District Supervisor **Kenneth J. Preusser** . . . . (518) 477-4837

North Carolina State Office
6213-E Angus Dr., Raleigh, NC 27617
Tel: (919) 786-4480 Fax: (919) 782-4159

State Director **Keith P. Wehner** . . . . (919) 786-4480 ext. 228

Ohio State Office
6929 Americana Parkway, Columbus, OH 43068
Tel: (614) 993-3444 Fax: (614) 836-5597

State Director **Andrew J. Montoney** . . . . (614) 993-3444

South Carolina State Office
USDA-APHIS-WS, 400 Northeast Drive,
Suite L, Columbia, SC 29203-5182
Tel: (803) 786-9455 Fax: (803) 786-9472

State Director **Noel E. Myers** . . . . (803) 786-9455 ext. 4

Tennessee - Kentucky State Office
537 Myatt Drive, Madison, TN 37115
Tel: (615) 736-5506 Fax: (615) 736-2768

State Director **Brett G. Dunlap** . . . . (615) 736-5506 ext. 102

Virginia State Office
P.O. Box 130, Moseley, VA 23120
Tel: (804) 739-7739 Fax: (804) 739-7738

State Director **Scott C. Barras** . . . . (804) 739-7739

West Virginia State Office
730 Yokum Street, Elkins, WV 26241
Tel: (304) 636-1785 Fax: (304) 636-5397

State Director **John Forbes** . . . . (304) 636-1785 ext. 11

Wisconsin State Office
732 Lois Drive, Sun Prairie, WI 53590
Tel: (608) 837-2727 Fax: (608) 837-6754

State Director **Daniel Hirchert** . . . . (608) 837-2727
Budget Analyst **(Vacant)** . . . . (608) 837-2727

Western Region
Building B, 2150 Centre Avenue, MS 3W9, Fort Collins, CO 80526
Tel: (970) 494-7443 Fax: (970) 494-7455
Areas Covered: AK, AZ, CA, CO, GU, HI, ID, KS, MT, NE, NV, NM, ND, OK, OR, SD, TX, UT, WA, WY

● Regional Director **Jason Suckow** . . . . (970) 494-7453
E-mail: jsuckow@aphis.usda.gov

Arizona State Office
8836 North 23rd Avenue, Suite 2, Phoenix, AZ 85021
Tel: (602) 870-2081 Fax: (602) 870-2951

State Director **David L. Bergman** . . . . (602) 870-2081

California State Office
3419 A Arden Way, Sacramento, CA 95825-5348
Tel: (916) 979-2675 Fax: (916) 979-2680

State Director **Dennis L. Orthmeyer** . . . . (916) 979-2030 ext. 103

Colorado State Office
12345 West Alameda Parkway, Suite 204, Lakewood, CO 80228
Tel: (303) 236-5810 Fax: (303) 236-5821

State Director **Martin S. Lowney** . . . . (303) 236-5813

Hawaii - Guam State Office
3375 Koapaka Street, Suite H420, Honolulu, HI 96819
Tel: (808) 838-2840 Fax: (808) 838-2860
Areas Covered: GU, HI

State Director **Craig S. Clark** . . . . (808) 838-2840
Education: New Mexico BS; Ohio State MS
Administrative Officer **(Vacant)** . . . . (808) 838-2842

Idaho State Office
9134 West Blackeagle Drive, Boise, ID 83709
Tel: (208) 373-1630 Fax: (208) 378-5349

State Director **Todd K. Grimm** . . . . (208) 373-1630

Montana State Office
Logan Airport, 2441 Overlook Drive, Billings, MT 59105
P.O. Box 1938, Billings, MT 59103
Tel: (406) 657-6464 Fax: (406) 657-6110

State Director **John E. Steuber** . . . . (406) 657-6464

Nebraska State Office
5940 South 58th Street, Lincoln, NE 68516
Tel: (402) 434-2340 Fax: (402) 434-2339

State Director **Timothy B. "Tim" Veenendaal** . . . . (402) 434-2340

Nevada State Office
8775 Technology Way, Reno, NV 89521
Tel: (775) 851-4848 Fax: (775) 851-4828

State Director **Mark Jensen** . . . . (775) 851-4848
West District Supervisor **Jack Spencer** . . . . (775) 851-4848

New Mexico State Office
8441 Washington NE, Albuquerque, NM 87113
Tel: (505) 346-2640 Fax: (505) 346-2627

State Director **Alan May** . . . . (505) 346-2640
Budget Analyst **Patsy Baca** . . . . (505) 346-2640
E-mail: patsy.baca@aphis.usda.gov

North Dakota State Office
2110 Miriam Circle, Suite A, Bismarck, ND 58501-2502
Tel: (701) 355-3300 Fax: (701) 250-4408

State Director **John D. Paulson** . . . . (701) 355-3300
Office Support Assistant **(Vacant)** . . . . (701) 250-4405
District Supervisor **(Vacant)** . . . . (701) 250-4405

Oklahoma State Office
Agriculture Building, 2800 North Lincoln Boulevard,
Oklahoma City, OK 73105-4298
Tel: (405) 521-4039 Fax: (405) 525-5951

State Director **Kevin R. Grant** . . . . (405) 521-4039

Oregon State Office
6135 NE 80th, Suite A-8, Portland, OR 97218
Tel: (503) 326-2346 Fax: (503) 326-2367

State Director **David E. Williams** . . . . (503) 326-2346

South Dakota State Office
420 South Garfield, Suite 300, Pierre, SD 57501
Tel: (701) 355-3300 Fax: (701) 250-4408

State Director **John D. Paulson** . . . . (701) 355-3300
2110 Miriam Circle, Suite A, Bismarck, ND 58501-2502
District Supervisor **(Vacant)** . . . . (701) 250-4405
2110 Miriam Circle, Suite A, Bismarck, ND 58501-2502

★ Presidential Appointment Requiring Senate Confirmation ☆ Presidential Appointment ☐ Schedule C Appointment ◇ Career Senior Foreign Service Appointment
● Career Senior Executive Service (SES) Appointment ○ Non-Career Senior Executive Service (SES) Appointment ■ Postal Career Executive Service

DEPARTMENTS

Texas State Office
5730 Northwest Parkway, Suite 700, San Antonio, TX 78249
P.O. Box 690170, San Antonio, TX 78269
Tel: (210) 472-5451 Fax: (210) 561-3846

State Director **Michael J. Bodenchuk** . . . . (210) 472-5451
Assistant State Director **Bruce R. Leland** . . . . (210) 472-5451

Utah State Office
1860 West Alexander Street, Suite A, West Valley City, UT 84119
Mail: P.O. Box 26976, Salt Lake City, UT 84126-0976
Tel: (801) 975-3315 Fax: (801) 975-3320

State Director **Chad Heuser** . . . . (801) 975-3315

Washington - Alaska State Office
720 O'Leary Street, NW, Olympia, WA 98502-9593
Tel: (360) 753-9884 Fax: (360) 753-9466

State Director **Michael A. "Mike" Linnell** . . . . (360) 753-9884

Wyoming State Office
P.O. Box 59, Casper, WY 82602-0059
Tel: (307) 261-5336 Fax: (307) 261-5996

State Director **Michael "Mike" Foster** . . . . (307) 261-5336
Assistant State Director **(Vacant)** . . . . (307) 261-5336
Management Information Services Technician
Vivian J. Meek . . . . (307) 261-5336
E-mail: vivian.j.meek@aphis.usda.gov
Budget Analyst **Melissa Souza** . . . . (307) 261-5336
Budget Technician **Twila Eli** . . . . (307) 261-5336

Natural Resources and Environment (NRE)

OFFICE OF THE UNDER SECRETARY

Jamie L. Whitten Building, 1400 Independence Avenue, SW,
Room 240-E, Washington, DC 20250
Tel: (202) 720-7173 Fax: (202) 720-0632

Forest Service (FS)

Sidney R. Yates Building, 201 14th Street, SW,
4th Floor, Washington, DC 20250
Fax: (202) 205-1765 E-mail: mailroom@fs.fed.us Internet: www.fs.fed.us

Research Stations (RS)

Forest Products Laboratory (FPL)
One Gifford Pinchot Drive, Madison, WI 53726-2398
Tel: (608) 231-9200 Fax: (608) 231-9592 Internet: www.fpl.fs.fed.us

Director **Tony L. Ferguson** . . . . (610) 557-4017
11 Campus Boulevard, Fax: (608) 231-9567
Newtown Square, PA 19073
Deputy Director **Col Lon M. Yeary USMC (Ret)** . . . . (608) 231-9320
E-mail: lmyeary@fs.fed.us
Education: Naval Acad 1978 BS
Assistant Director for Business Operations **(Vacant)** . . . . (608) 231-9285
Fax: (608) 231-9567
Assistant Director for Public Affairs
Douglas "Doug" Clawson . . . . (608) 231-9325
E-mail: dclawson@fs.fed.us
Assistant Director for Wood, Fiber and Composites
Alan Rudie . . . . (608) 231-9496
Education: Wartburg Col BA; MIT PhD Fax: (608) 231-9567
Assistant Director for Wood Products Research
Michael A. Ritter . . . . (608) 231-9493
Supervisory Librarian **Julie Blankenburg** . . . . (608) 231-9491
E-mail: jblankenburg@fs.fed.us Fax: (608) 231-9311
Education: Wisconsin 1980 MALS
Public Affairs/Webmaster **Rajinder "Raj" Lal** . . . . (608) 231-9524
E-mail: rlal@fs.fed.us

International Institute of Tropical Forestry (IITP)
Jardin Botanico Sur, 1201 Calle Ceiba, San Juan, PR 00926-1119
Tel: (787) 766-5335 Fax: (787) 766-6263
Internet: https://www.fs.usda.gov/iitf

● Director **Dr. Ariel E. Lugo PhD** . . . . (787) 766-5335 ext. 7
E-mail: alugo@fs.fed.us

Northern Research Station
11 Campus Boulevard, Suite 200, Newtown Square, PA 19073
Tel: (610) 557-4017 TTY: (610) 557-4132 Fax: (610) 557-4095
Internet: www.nrs.fs.fed.us

● Director **Tony L. Ferguson** . . . . (610) 557-4017
E-mail: tferguson@fs.fed.us
Assistant Director for Research **Thomas L. Schmidt** . . . . (651) 649-5216
1992 Folwell Avenue, St. Paul, MN 55108
Information Technology Specialist **(Vacant)** . . . . (517) 884-8061
Stephen S. Nisbet Building, 1407 South Harrison Road,
Room 220, East Lansing, MI 48823
Public Affairs Web Developer
Jim Lootens-White . . . . (847) 866-9311 ext. 23
1033 University Place, Fax: (847) 866-9506
Suite 360, Evanston, IL 60201
E-mail: jlootenswhite@fs.fed.us

Pacific Northwest Research Station
Edith Greene/Wendel Wyatt, 1220 SW Third Avenue,
Portland, OR 97204-2825
P.O. Box 3890, Portland, OR 97208-3890
Tel: (503) 808-2592 Fax: (503) 808-2130 Internet: www.fs.fed.us/pnw

● Station Director (Acting) **Paul D. Anderson** . . . . (503) 808-2100
E-mail: pdanderson@fs.fed.us
Assistant Director for Administration **Lesley A. Kelly** . . . . (503) 808-2102
E-mail: lakelly@fs.fed.us
Assistant Director for Communications and
Applications **Cynthia Miner** . . . . (503) 808-2135
E-mail: clminer@fs.fed.us
Assistant Director for Program Development
Katherine L. Smith . . . . (503) 808-2104
Assistant Director for Research **(Vacant)** . . . . (503) 808-2115

Pacific Southwest Research Station
800 Buchanan Street, Albany, CA 94710
Mail: P.O. Box 245, Berkeley, CA 94701
Tel: (510) 883-8830 Fax: (510) 883-8858 Internet: www.fs.fed.us/psw

Station Director **Alexander L. Friend** . . . . (510) 883-8832
Education: Sewanee BS; North Carolina State MS; U Washington PhD
Executive Assistant **(Vacant)** . . . . (510) 559-6322
Assistant Station Director for Business Operations
Colleen Schneider . . . . (510) 883-8834
Assistant Station Director for Research (Acting)
Valerie Hipkins . . . . (510) 883-8835
Education: Humboldt State 1985 BS; Oregon State 1988 MS,
1993 PhD
Communications Director **(Vacant)** . . . . (510) 883-8862
Web Manager **Brandon Schulze** . . . . (510) 984-4691
E-mail: bschulze@fs.fed.us
Statistical Scientist **Haiganoush Preisler** . . . . (510) 883-8826
Research Planning Director **Arthur A. Duggan** . . . . (510) 883-8836

Institute of Forest Genetics
2480 Carson Road, Placerville, CA 95667
Fax: (530) 622-1225 Fax: (530) 622-2633
Internet: www.fs.fed.us/psw/locations/placerville/
Internet: www.fs.fed.us/NFGEL/

Program Manager, Conservation of Biodiversity
Patricia Manley . . . . (530) 621-6882
Fax: (530) 622-2633
Director, National Forest Genetics Laboratory
Joe Eric Davis . . . . (202) 403-8954

★ Presidential Appointment Requiring Senate Confirmation ☆ Presidential Appointment ☐ Schedule C Appointment ◇ Career Senior Foreign Service Appointment
● Career Senior Executive Service (SES) Appointment ○ Non-Career Senior Executive Service (SES) Appointment ■ Postal Career Executive Service

Institute of Pacific Islands Forestry
60 Nowelo Street, Hilo, HI 96720
Tel: (808) 933-8121 Fax: (808) 933-8120
Internet: www.fs.fed.us/psw/programs/ipif

Director (Acting) **Susan Cordell** .... (808) 854-2601

Redding Silviculture Laboratory
USDA Service Center, 3644 Avtech Parkway, Redding, CA 96002-2041
Tel: (530) 226-2530 Fax: (530) 226-5091
Internet: www.fs.fed.us/psw/locations/redding/

Forestry Technician **Bob Carlson** .... (530) 226-2533
Forestry Technician **(Vacant)** .... (530) 226-2536
Administrative Support Assistant **Rochelle E. Mullins** .... (530) 759-1773
E-mail: remullins@fs.fed.us

Redwood Sciences Laboratory
1700 Bayview Drive, Arcata, CA 95521
Fax: (707) 825-2900 Fax: (707) 825-2901
Internet: www.fs.fed.us/psw/locations/arcata/

Research Fisheries Biologist **Bret C. Harvey** .... (707) 825-2926
Research Wildlife Biologist **Karen Pope** .... (707) 825-2957

Riverside Forest Fire Laboratory
4955 Canyon Crest Drive, Riverside, CA 92507
Tel: (951) 680-1500 Fax: (951) 680-1501
Internet: www.fs.fed.us/psw/locations/riverside

Soil Scientist, Fire and Fuels **Philip J. Riggan** .... (951) 680-1534
Research Plant Physiologist, Conservation of Biodiversity Program **Pamela E. Padgett** .... (951) 680-1584
Supervisory Research Forester, Fire and Fuels Program **David Weise** .... (951) 680-1543
Education: Auburn 1984 BS, 1986 MS; UC Berkeley 1993 PhD
Plant Scientist, Fire and Fuels Program **(Vacant)** .... (951) 680-1527
Program Manager, Urban Ecosystems and Social Dynamics **Joshua Wilson** .... (951) 680-1558
Information Technology Specialist, Fire and Fuels Program **John W. Benoit** .... (951) 680-1553
E-mail: jbenoit@fs.fed.us

Davis Research Center
1731 Research Park Drive, Davis, CA 95618
Tel: (530) 759-1700 Fax: (530) 747-0241

Administrative Officer **Christine P. "Christie" Aldrete** ... (530) 759-1716
E-mail: caldrete@fs.fed.us Fax: (530) 747-0241
Invasives and Threats Team Leader, Ecosystem Function and Health Program **Chris Fettig** .... (530) 759-1708
Education: Virginia Tech 1993 BS, 1996 MS; Georgia 1999 PhD Fax: (530) 747-0241
Partnerships and Collaboration Director **(Vacant)** .... (530) 759-1703
Program Manager, Ecosystem Function and Health **(Vacant)** .... (510) 883-8839
Research Plant Geneticist **Andrew T. Groover** .... (530) 759-1738
Education: Georgia 1988 BS, 1991 MS; North Carolina 1997 PhD
Supervisory Human Resource Specialist **Rochelle Selvin** .... (510) 883-8860
E-mail: rselvin@fs.fed.us
Urban Ecosystems and Processes Research Scientist, Urban Ecosystems and Social Dynamics Program **(Vacant)** .... (530) 759-1723
Water, Air, and Soil Team Leader, Ecosystem Function and Health Program **Matt D. Busse** .... (530) 759-1721
Education: Cal Poly San Luis Obispo 1981 BS; Nebraska 1984 MS; Oregon State 1989 PhD Fax: (530) 226-5091

Forestry Sciences Laboratory
2081 E. Sierra Avenue, Fresno, CA 93710-4639
Tel: (559) 323-3200 Fax: (559) 297-3355
Internet: www.fs.fed.us/psw/locations/fresno/

Research Wildlife Biologist, Conservation of Biodiversity Program **Kathryn Purcell** .... (559) 323-3217

Rocky Mountain Research Station
240 West Prospect Road, Fort Collins, CO 80526-2098
Tel: (970) 498-1100 TTY: (970) 498-1025 Fax: (970) 498-1010
Internet: www.fs.fed.us/rmrs

● Station Director **John Phipps** .... (970) 498-1353
E-mail: jphipps@fs.fed.us
Education: U Washington 1973 BS, 1975 MA
Executive Secretary **Sara Senn** .... (970) 498-1353
Assistant Station Director for Communications **(Vacant)** .... (970) 498-1369
Assistant Station Director for Operations **Cloetta J. Schroeder** .... (970) 498-1325
Assistant Station Director for Science Applications and Integration **Jan Engert** .... (970) 498-1377
Assistant Station Director for Strategic Management Systems **Ron Archuleta** .... (970) 498-1325
Director of Civil Rights **Angela Baca** .... (970) 498-1343
E-mail: abaca@fs.fed.us
Director, National Genomics Center **Dr. Michael K. Schwartz** .... (406) 542-4161
800 East Beckwith Avenue, Missoula, MT 59801 Fax: (406) 543-2663
Education: Colby 1991 BA; American U 1996 MS; Montana 2001 PhD
Public and Legislative Affairs Specialist **Jennifer Hayes** .... (970) 498-1365
Webmaster **Sharon L. Payne** .... (208) 373-4356
322 East Front Street, Boise, ID 83702

Southern Research Station
200 W. T. Weaver Boulevard, Asheville, NC 28804
Tel: (828) 257-4300 Fax: (828) 257-4313 Internet: www.srs.fs.fed.us

● Station Director **Dr. Robert L. "Rob" Doudrick** .... (828) 257-4300
E-mail: rdoudrick@fs.fed.us Fax: (828) 257-4313
Education: Missouri BS, MS; Minnesota PhD
Executive Assistant to the Director **Jennifer Parsell** .... (828) 257-4300
Executive Assistant **(Vacant)** .... (828) 257-4300
Assistant Director for Business Operations **Gerry Jackson** .... (828) 257-4308
Assistant Director for Forest Values, Uses, and Policies **(Vacant)** .... (828) 257-4367
Assistant Director for Forest Watershed Science **(Vacant)** .... (828) 257-4303
Assistant Director for Planning and Applications **Monica Schwalbach** .... (828) 257-4305
Education: Cornell BS; South Dakota State MS
Assistant Director for Threats to Forest Health **Kier D. Klepzig** .... (828) 257-4307
Education: Wisconsin (Platteville) 1986 BS; Wisconsin 1989 MS, 1994 PhD

Forest Restoration and Management
Forest Genetics and Biological Foundations Project Leader **C. Dana Nelson** .... (228) 832-2747 ext. 201
23332 Highway 67, Saucier, MS 39574
Education: Iowa State 1982 BS; Oklahoma State 1984 MS; Minnesota 1988 PhD
Restoring Longleaf Pine Ecosystems Project Leader (Acting) **James M. "Jim" Guldin** .... (334) 826-8700
G.W. Andrews Forestry Sciences Laboratory, 521 Devall Drive, Auburn, AL 36849 Fax: (334) 821-0037
Southern Pine Ecology Project Leader **James M. "Jim" Guldin** .... (501) 623-1180 ext. 103
1270, Hot Springs, AR 71902
Upland Hardwood Ecology and Management Project Leader **Kurt Johnsen** .... (828) 667-5261 ext. 113
Bent Creek Experimental Forest, 1577 Brevard Road, Asheville, NC 28806

DEPARTMENTS

★ Presidential Appointment Requiring Senate Confirmation ☆ Presidential Appointment ☐ Schedule C Appointment ◇ Career Senior Foreign Service Appointment
● Career Senior Executive Service (SES) Appointment ○ Non-Career Senior Executive Service (SES) Appointment ■ Postal Career Executive Service

DEPARTMENTS

Regional Offices

Forest Service – Region 1 (Northern Region)

Federal Building, P.O. Box 7669, Missoula, MT 59807
Tel: (406) 329-3511 TTY: (406) 329-3510 Fax: (406) 329-3411
Internet: www.fs.usda.gov/r1
Areas Covered: Northern ID, MT, ND and Northwestern SD

● Regional Forester **Leanne M. Marten** .... (406) 329-3315
E-mail: lmarten@fs.fed.us
Executive Assistant **Carol Moore** .... (406) 329-3315
Supervisory Administrative Support Assistant
Karen M. Hardy .... (406) 329-3659
E-mail: karenhardy@fs.fed.us
Deputy Regional Forester **Jane Darnell** .... (406) 329-3317
Deputy Regional Forester **David E. "Dave" Schmid** ..... (406) 329-3311
Executive Assistant **Kelly J. Forthofer** .... (406) 329-3439
Webmaster **(Vacant)** .... (406) 329-3511

Acquisition Management
Director **Carol McCauslin** .... (406) 329-3541

Civil Rights
Director **Theresa L. Doty** .... (406) 329-3508
E-mail: tdoty@fs.fed.us

Ecosystem Assessment and Planning
Director **Karen Mollander** .... (406) 329-3453
E-mail: kmollander@fs.fed.us

Engineering
26 Fort Missoula Road, Missoula, MT 59804
Fax: (406) 329-3198
Director **Dan Hager** .... (406) 329-3173
Deputy Director **Harvey Hergett** .... (406) 329-3307

Fire, Aviation, and Air
Director **(Vacant)** .... (406) 329-3402
Deputy Director **Greg Morris** .... (406) 329-3296
Risk Management Officer **Steve Zachry** .... (406) 329-3422
Regional Aviation Officer
Margaret M. "Maggie" Doherty .... (406) 329-4903
Assistant Director for Fire Planning and Budget
Julie Shea .... (406) 329-3232
E-mail: jshea@fs.fed.us

Human Resources Management
Director, Albuquerque Service Center **Nancy Kollin** ..... (406) 329-3139
E-mail: nkollin@fs.fed.us Fax: (886) 288-4231

Law Enforcement and Investigations
Special-Agent-in-Charge **John Byas** .... (406) 329-3590
E-mail: jbyas@fs.fed.us
Assistant Special-Agent-in-Charge **(Vacant)** .... (406) 329-3648

Public and Governmental Relations
Director **David Smith** .... (406) 329-3089
Assistant Director, Legislative Affairs
Angela Harrington .... (406) 329-3028
E-mail: aharrington@fs.fed.us
Education: Whitman 1989 BA; Montana 2005 MS

Recreation, Minerals, Lands, Heritage and Wilderness
Director **Joseph G. "Joe" Alexander** .... (406) 329-3584
E-mail: jgalexander@fs.fed.us Fax: (406) 329-3536
Education: Montana 1993 BS
Deputy Director **(Vacant)** .... (406) 329-3518

Safety and Health
Regional Safety and Health Manager **David Goodin** ..... (406) 329-3237
E-mail: dgoodin@fs.fed.us

State and Private Forestry
Director **Michael "Mike" Dudley** .... (801) 625-5253
324 25th Street, Ogden, UT 84401-2310
Education: Oregon State 1986 BF

State and Private Forestry *(continued)*
Director **Timothy P. "Tim" Garcia** .... (406) 329-3797
324 25th Street, Ogden, UT 84401-2310
Deputy Director **John T. Shannon** .... (406) 329-3280
Education: North Carolina State 1977 BSF; Duke 1980 MF; Arkansas (Little Rock) 1989 JD
Coeur d'Alene Field Office Group Leader
Gina A. Davis .... (208) 765-7342
3815 Schreiber Way, Coeur d'Alene, ID 83815
Missoula Field Office Group Leader
Gregg A. DeNitto .... (406) 329-3637

Renewable Resources Management
Director **Christine Dawe** .... (406) 329-3311
Deputy Director **Jennifer "Erin" Swaider** .... (406) 329-3164
Assistant Director **Carol McKenzie** .... (406) 329-3608

National Forests – Idaho

Nez Perce-Clearwater National Forests
903 Third Street, Kamiah, ID 83536
Tel: (208) 935-2513 Fax: (208) 935-4275 TTY: (208) 476-0129
Internet: www.fs.usda.gov/nezperceclearwater
Forest Supervisor **Cheryl Probert** .... (208) 935-4265
Education: Montana 1990 BS
Deputy Forest Supervisor **Kurt Steele** .... (208) 935-4283
Executive Assistant **Joslyn P. Osborn** .... (208) 935-4253
Fax: (208) 935-4275
Ecosystem Management **Michele Windsor** .... (208) 935-4282
Public Affairs Officer **Laura Smith** .... (208) 983-5143
Technical Services and Recreation **Quentin P. Smith** .... (208) 935-4281

Idaho Panhandle National Forests
3815 Schreiber Way, Coeur d'Alene, ID 83815-8363
Tel: (208) 765-7223 Fax: (208) 765-7307 Internet: www.fs.usda.gov/ipnf
Forest Supervisor **Holly Jewkes** .... (208) 765-7223
Education: New Hampshire BS; Alaska (Fairbanks) MS
Deputy Forest Supervisor **Kim Pierson** .... (208) 765-7223
Education: Utah State 1994 BS, 1999 MS
Public Affairs Officer **Shoshana M. Cooper** .... (208) 765-7369
E-mail: smcooper@fs.fed.us
Executive Assistant **Michelle Norton** .... (208) 765-7369
E-mail: michellenorton@fs.fed.us
Bonners Ferry District Ranger **Kevin S. Knauth** .... (208) 267-5561
6286 Main Street, Bonners Ferry, ID 83805-9764
Coeur d'Alene Nursery Manager **Aram D. Eramian** ..... (208) 765-7372
3600 Nursery Way, Coeur d'Alene, ID 83815 Fax: (208) 765-7474
Coeur d'Alene River District Ranger **Dan Scaife** .... (208) 669-3001
Fernan Office, 2502 East Sherman Avenue, Coeur d'Alene, ID 83814-9764
Silver Valley Office Deputy District Ranger
Phillip A. Blundell JD .... (208) 783-2101
173 Commerce Drive, Smelterville, ID 83868
Mail: 159, Smelterville, ID 83868
Education: Central Oklahoma BBA; Oklahoma JD
Priest Lake District Ranger **Timothy C. Knight** .... (208) 443-6801
32203 Highway 57, Priest River, ID 83856-8680
Sandpoint District Ranger **Jessie Berner** .... (208) 263-5111
1602 Ontario Street, Sandpoint, ID 83864-9509 Fax: (208) 265-6670
Education: Tennessee (Martin) 1990 BS
St. Joe District Ranger **Matthew A. "Matt" Davis** ...... (208) 245-2531
Avery Office, 34 Hoyt Drive, Avery, ID 83802-9702
St. Maries Office District Ranger
Matthew A. "Matt" Davis .... (208) 245-6001
St. Maries, ID 83861-0407 Fax: (208) 245-6052

National Forests – Montana

Beaverhead-Deerlodge National Forest
420 Barrett Street, Dillon, MT 59725-3572
Tel: (406) 683-3900 Fax: (406) 683-3855 Internet: www.fs.usda.gov/bdnf
Forest Supervisor **Melany I. Glossa** .... (406) 683-3973
Deputy Forest Supervisor **Jeff Tomac** .... (406) 683-3978
Public Affairs Officer **Leona M. Rodreick** .... (406) 683-3984
E-mail: lmrodreick@fs.fed.us
Education: Eastern Montana 1987 BS

★ Presidential Appointment Requiring Senate Confirmation ☆ Presidential Appointment ☐ Schedule C Appointment ◇ Career Senior Foreign Service Appointment
● Career Senior Executive Service (SES) Appointment ○ Non-Career Senior Executive Service (SES) Appointment ■ Postal Career Executive Service

Bitterroot National Forest
1801 North First Street, Hamilton, MT 59840
Tel: (406) 363-7100 Fax: (406) 363-7159
E-mail: mailroom/r1_bitterroot@fs.fed.us
Internet: www.fs.usda.gov/bitterroot

Forest Supervisor (Acting) **Kurt Steele** .... (406) 363-7121
Public Affairs Specialist **Tod G. McKay** .... (406) 363-7122
E-mail: tgmckay@fs.fed.us
Range Management Program Leader
Gilbert B. "Gil" Gale .... (406) 821-3201

Flathead National Forest
650 Wolfpack Way, Kalispell, MT 59901
Tel: (406) 758-5204 Fax: (406) 758-5367
Internet: www.fs.usda.gov/flathead

Forest Supervisor **Chip Weber** .... (406) 758-5251
Public Affairs Officer **Janette Turk** .... (406) 758-5252
E-mail: jturk@fs.fed.us

Custer Gallatin National Forest
Federal Building, 10 East Babcock, Bozeman, MT 59715
P.O. Box 130, Bozeman, MT 59771
Tel: (406) 587-6701 Fax: (406) 587-6758

Forest Supervisor **Mary C. Erickson** .... (406) 587-6949
Deputy Forest Supervisor **(Vacant)** .... (406) 587-6776
Executive Assistant **(Vacant)** .... (406) 587-6949
Public Affairs Officer **Marna Daley** .... (406) 587-6703
E-mail: mdaley@fs.fed.us
Education: Idaho 1995 BS
Ashland District Ranger **Ronald E. Hecker** .... (406) 784-2344
2378 Highway 212, Ashland, MT 59003
Beartooth District Ranger **Ken W. Coffin** .... (406) 446-3918
6811 Hgihway 212, Red Lodge, MT 59068
Bozeman District Ranger **Corey Lewellen** .... (406) 522-2520
3710 Fallon Street, Bozeman, MT 59718
Gardiner District Ranger **Michael "Mike" Thom** .... (406) 848-7375
805 Scott Street, Gardiner, MT 59030
Hebgen Lake District Ranger **Jason D. Brey** .... (406) 823-6963
330 Gallatin Road, West Yellowstone, MT 59758
Sioux District Ranger **Kurt A. Hansen** .... (605) 797-4432
101 SE First Street, Camp Crook, SD 57724
Yellowstone District Ranger **Alex Sienkiewicz** .... (406) 222-1892
5242 Highway 89 South, Livingston, MT 59047

Helena-Lewis and Clark National Forest
2880 Skyway Drive, Helena, MT 59602
Tel: (406) 449-5201 Fax: (406) 449-5436
Internet: www.fs.usda.gov/helena

Forest Supervisor **William "Bill" Avey** .... (406) 449-5201
Deputy Forest Supervisor **Sara Mayben** .... (406) 791-7726
Education: Colorado State MS
Judith District Ranger **Ron B. Wiseman** .... (406) 566-2292
Swan Lake Ranger District, Bigfork, MT 59911 Fax: (406) 837-7522
Public Affairs Officer **Katherine "Kathy" Bushnell** .... (406) 495-3747
E-mail: kbushnell@fs.fed.us
Education: Montana 2002 BJ
Contract Specialist **Alisha D. Knaub** .... (406) 495-3860
E-mail: aknaub@fs.fed.us Fax: (406) 226-5484

Kootenai National Forest
31374 Highway 2 West, Libby, MT 59923
Tel: (406) 293-6211 Fax: (406) 283-7709 E-mail: aobst@fs.fed.us
Internet: www.fs.usda.gov/kootenai

Forest Supervisor **Christopher Savage** .... (406) 293-7763
Public Affairs Officer **Willie Sykes** .... (406) 283-7694
E-mail: wsykes@fs.fed.us

Lolo National Forest
Building 24, Fort Missoula, Missoula, MT 59804
Tel: (406) 329-3750 Fax: (406) 329-3795 E-mail: r1_lolo@fs.fed.us
Internet: www.fs.usda.gov/lolo

Forest Supervisor (Acting)
Joseph G. "Joe" Alexander .... (406) 329-3750
Note: Until January 30, 2019.
Education: Montana 1993 BS
Public Affairs Officer **Boyd C. Hartwig** .... (406) 329-1024
E-mail: bchartwig@fs.fed.us

National Grasslands - North Dakota

Dakota Prairie Grasslands
2000 Miriam Circle, Bismarck, ND 58501
Tel: (701) 989-7300 Fax: (701) 989-7299
Internet: https://www.fs.usda.gov/dpg/

Grasslands Supervisor **William P. "Bill" O'Donnell** .... (701) 989-7301
Education: Nevada (Reno) 1983 BSc

Forest Service - Region 2 (Rocky Mountain Region)

Building 17, 1617 Cole Boulevard, Lakewood, CO 80401-3305
Tel: (303) 275-5350 Fax: (303) 275-5482
Areas Covered: CO, KS, NE, SD, Eastern WY

● Regional Forester **Brian Ferebee** .... (303) 275-5350
E-mail: bferebee@fs.fed.us
Education: North Carolina State
Executive Assistant **Elayne Boyce** .... (303) 275-5451
Chief of Staff **Terri A. Gates** .... (303) 275-5427
E-mail: tgates@fs.fed.us
Deputy Regional Forester, Operations
Tammy Whittington .... (303) 275-5449
Executive Assistant **Heather Trussell** .... (303) 275-5448
Deputy Regional Forester, Resources
Jacqueline "Jacque" Buchanan .... (303) 275-5448
Executive Assistant (Acting) **Maria Beltran** .... (303) 275-5448

Acquisition Management
740 Simms Street, Golden, CO 80401-4720
Tel: (303) 275-5258 Fax: (303) 275-5453

Director (Acting) **Ron Schilz** .... (303) 275-5280
E-mail: rschilz@fs.fed.us
Education: Wisconsin (Stevens Point) 1980 BS
Deputy Director **Shane LaValley** .... (303) 275-5284
E-mail: slavalley@fs.fed.us
Education: Northern Montana 1990 ABA, 1990 BBA; Comm Col Air Force 1992 AS
Supervisory Contract Specialist, Simplified Acquisition Team **Barbara K. Darling** .... (605) 673-9355
1019 North 5th Street, Custer, SD 57730
E-mail: barbaradarling@fs.fed.us
Supervisory Contract Specialist, Southern Tier
Christina A. Schofield .... (970) 295-6635
E-mail: christinaacook@fs.fed.us
Administrative Assistant **Joellen Davis** .... (303) 275-5281

Budget Office
740 Simms Street, Golden, CO 80401-4720
Tel: (303) 275-5136 Fax: (303) 275-5299

Director (Acting) **Kathy Sutphen** .... (303) 275-5136
E-mail: ksutphen@fs.fed.us

Chief Information Office
740 Simms Street, Golden, CO 80401-4720
Tel: (303) 275-5150 Fax: (303) 275-5134

Desktop Support Supervisor (Acting)
Debra A. "Debbie" Milner .... (303) 275-5196
E-mail: debraamilner@fs.fed.us

Civil Rights
Building 17, 740 Simms Street, Golden, CO 80401-4720

Director **Ricardo M. Martinez** .... (303) 275-5340

★ Presidential Appointment Requiring Senate Confirmation ☆ Presidential Appointment ☐ Schedule C Appointment ◇ Career Senior Foreign Service Appointment
● Career Senior Executive Service (SES) Appointment ○ Non-Career Senior Executive Service (SES) Appointment ■ Postal Career Executive Service

Cooperative Forestry and Tribal Relations
740 Simms Street, Golden, CO 80401-4720
Tel: (303) 275-5745 Fax: (303) 275-5754
Director **Jason Lawhon** . . . . (303) 275-5750

Engineering
740 Simms Street, Golden, CO 80401-4720
Tel: (303) 275-5221 Fax: (303) 275-5170
Director **Mary DeAguero** . . . . (303) 275-5171

External Affairs
740 Simms Street, Golden, CO 80401-4720
Tel: (303) 275-5354 Fax: (303) 275-5336
Director **Valerie Baca** . . . . (303) 275-5118
E-mail: vbaca@fs.fed.us

Fire and Aviation Management
Director **Curtis Heaton** . . . . (303) 275-5736

Recreation, Lands and Minerals
740 Simms Street, Golden, CO 80401-4720
Tel: (303) 275-5042 Fax: (303) 275-5407
Director **E. Lynn Burkett** . . . . (303) 275-5135
Education: Texas A&M 1986 BS; Golden Gate MPA

Renewable Resources
740 Simms Street, Golden, CO 80401-4720
Tel: (303) 275-5068 Fax: (303) 275-5075
Director **Steve Lohr** . . . . (303) 275-5014

Strategic Planning
740 Simms Street, Golden, CO 80401-4720
Tel: (303) 275-5103 Fax: (303) 275-5134
Director **Bryan West** . . . . (303) 275-5161
Education: North Carolina 2005 BA; Colorado (Denver) 2017 MES

Collbran (CO) Job Corps Center
57608 Highway 330, Collbran, CO 81624-9702
Tel: (970) 487-3576 Fax: (970) 487-3823
Center Director **Gove G. Aker** . . . . (970) 487-3576 ext. 3030
Administrative Officer **Diane K. Slagle** . . . . (970) 487-3576 ext. 3001
E-mail: dkslagle@fs.fed.us
Information Technology Specialist
William M. "Bill" Ridings . . . . (970) 487-2006
E-mail: bmridings@fs.fed.us
Support Services Specialist **Tammi Bieser** . . . . . (970) 487-3576 ext. 3002
E-mail: tjbieser@fs.fed.us

Rocky Mountain Area Interagency Fire Coordination Center (RMACC)
2850 Youngfield Street, Lakewood, CO 80215
Tel: (303) 445-4300 Fax: (888) 850-2925
E-mail: rmacoordctr@gmail.com Internet: gacc.nifc.gov/rmcc
Manager **Scott Swendsen** . . . . (303) 445-4302
E-mail: sswendsen@fs.fed.us

National Forests – Colorado

Arapaho and Roosevelt National Forests and Pawnee National Grassland
Building E, 2150 Centre Avenue, Fort Collins, CO 80526-8119
Tel: (970) 295-6600 Fax: (970) 295-6695
Forest Supervisor **Monte L. Williams** . . . . (970) 295-6601
Education: Utah State BS
Deputy Forest Supervisor **(Vacant)** . . . . (970) 295-6602
Public Affairs Officer **Tammy Williams** . . . . (970) 295-6693
E-mail: tjwilliams@fs.fed.us
Boulder District Manager **(Vacant)** . . . . (303) 541-2505
2140 Yarmouth Avenue, Boulder, CO 80301 Fax: (303) 541-2515
Canyon Lakes District Ranger **Katie Donahue** . . . . (970) 295-6711
2150 Centre Avenue, Fort Collins, CO 80526
Education: American U 1999 BA; Maryland 2009 MA
Clear Creek District Ranger **Scott E. Haas** . . . . (303) 567-3001
101 Chicago Creek Road, Idaho Springs, CO 80452

Arapaho and Roosevelt National Forests and Pawnee National Grassland *(continued)*

Pawnee National Grassland District Ranger
Curtis Youngman . . . . (970) 834-9271
115 North Second Avenue, P.O. Box 386, Ault, CO 80610
Sulphur District Ranger **Jon Morrissey** . . . . (970) 887-4124
9 Ten Mile Drive, Granby, CO 80446
Education: Texas A&M BS, 1983 MS

Grand Mesa, Uncompahgre and Gunnison National Forests
2250 South Main Street, Delta, CO 81416
Tel: (970) 874-6600 Fax: (970) 874-6686
E-mail: mailroom/r2_gmug@fs.fed.us Internet: www.fs.usda.gov/gmug
Forest Supervisor **(Vacant)** . . . . (970) 874-6685
Executive Assistant **Cande Read** . . . . (970) 874-6609
Deputy Forest Supervisor **Chad Stewart** . . . . (970) 874-6674
Education: Oregon 1997 BS; Minnesota 2001 MS; Touro U International MBA
Public Affairs Officer **Kimberlee "Kim" Phillips** . . . . (970) 874-6717
E-mail: kjphillips@fs.fed.us

Pike and San Isabel National Forests - Cimarron and Comanche National Grasslands
2840 Kachina Drive, Pueblo, CO 81008-1797
Tel: (719) 553-1400 Fax: (719) 553-1440 Internet: www.fs.usda.gov/psicc
Forest and Grassland Supervisor **Erin Connelly** . . . . (719) 553-1400
Deputy Forest and Grassland Supervisor **Dave Condit** . . . . (719) 553-1412
Fax: (719) 553-1416
Public Affairs Officer **Barbara Timock** . . . . (719) 553-1415
E-mail: btimock@fs.fed.us Fax: (719) 553-1416

Rio Grande National Forest
1803 West Highway 160, Monte Vista, CO 81144
Tel: (719) 852-5941 Fax: (719) 852-6250
Internet: www.fs.usda.gov/riogrande
Forest Supervisor **Dan Dallas** . . . . (719) 852-6247
Education: Idaho BS
Deputy Forest Supervisor **Thomas "Tom" Malecek** . . . . . (719) 852-6255

San Juan National Forest
Public Lands Center, BLM/San Juan National Forest, 15 Burnett Court, Durango, CO 81301
Tel: (970) 247-4874 TTY: (970) 385-1257 Fax: (970) 385-1243
Internet: www.fs.fed.us/r2/sanjuan/
Forest Supervisor/Center Manager **Kara Chadwick** . . . . . . (970) 385-1289
Executive Assistant **(Vacant)** . . . . (970) 385-1290
Fax: (970) 375-2331
Associate Forest Supervisor/Associate Center Manager
(Vacant) . . . . (970) 385-1289

White River National Forest
900 Grand Avenue, Golden, CO 81601-3602
Mail: P.O. Box 948, Glenwood Springs, CO 81601
Tel: (970) 945-3230 Fax: (970) 945-9029 E-mail: white_river@fs.fed.us
Internet: www.fs.usda.gov/whiteriver
Forest Supervisor **Scott Fitzwilliams** . . . . (970) 945-3200
Education: Wisconsin BS; Comm Col Denver MEP Fax: (970) 945-3266
Deputy Forest Supervisor **Lisa Stoeffler** . . . . (970) 945-3242
Public Affairs Officer **(Vacant)** . . . . (970) 945-3237
Fax: (970) 495-3211

National Forests – South Dakota

Black Hills National Forest
1019 North 5th Street, Custer, SD 57730
Tel: (605) 673-9200 Fax: (605) 673-9350
E-mail: r2_blackhills_webinfo@fs.fed.us
Internet: www.fs.usda.gov/blackhills
Forest Supervisor **Mark E. Van Every** . . . . (605) 673-9203
Deputy Forest Supervisor
Dr. Jerome A. "Jerry" Krueger PhD . . . . (605) 673-9202
Education: Minnesota BS; Michigan MSc; Minnesota PhD Fax: (605) 673-9208

★ Presidential Appointment Requiring Senate Confirmation ☆ Presidential Appointment ☐ Schedule C Appointment ◇ Career Senior Foreign Service Appointment
● Career Senior Executive Service (SES) Appointment ○ Non-Career Senior Executive Service (SES) Appointment ■ Postal Career Executive Service

Black Hills National Forest *(continued)*

Public Affairs Officer and Web Coordinator
Pam Wilhelm .... (605) 673-9205
E-mail: pwilhelm@fs.fed.us

Bearlodge District Ranger **Michael Gosse** ..... (307) 283-1361 ext. 3451
101 South 21st Street, Sundance, WY 82729 Fax: (307) 283-3727
Education: Wisconsin (Stevens Point) 1986 BS

Hell Canyon District Ranger **Tracy L. Anderson** .... (605) 673-4853
Fax: (605) 673-9350

Mystic District Ranger **Ruth Esperance** .... (605) 716-2021
8221 Mt. Rushmore Road, Rapid City, SD 57702 Fax: (605) 343-7134

Northern Hills District Ranger **Steve Kozel** .... (605) 642-4622
2014 North Main Street, Spearfish, SD 57789 Fax: (605) 642-4156
Education: South Dakota State BSc; Wyoming MS

National Forests – Wyoming

Bighorn National Forest
2013 Eastside Second Street, Sheridan, WY 82801-9638
Tel: (307) 674-2600 Fax: (307) 674-2668
E-mail: mailroom_r2_bighorn@fs.fed.us
Internet: www.fs.usda.gov/bighorn

Forest Supervisor **Andrew K. Johnson** .... (307) 674-2612

Medicine Bow-Routt National Forests & Thunder Basin National Grassland
2468 Jackson Street, Laramie, WY 82070-6535
Tel: (307) 745-2300 TTY: (307) 745-2307 Fax: (307) 745-2398
Internet: www.fs.usda.gov/mbr

Forest Supervisor **Russel M. "Russ" Bacon** .... (307) 745-2400
Education: Idaho 1997 BS Fax: (307) 745-2467

Shoshone National Forest
808 Meadow Lane, Cody, WY 82414-4516
Tel: (307) 578-5100 Fax: (307) 578-5112
Internet: www.fs.usda.gov/shoshone

Forest Supervisor **Lisa A. Timchak** .... (307) 578-5187
Education: Utah State MS

Nebraska National Forests and Grasslands (NNFG)
125 North Main Street, Chadron, NE 69337-2118
Tel: (308) 432-0300 Fax: (308) 432-0309
Internet: www.fs.usda.gov/main/nebraska/home

Forest Supervisor **Jack Isaacs** .... (308) 432-0311
Education: South Dakota State BS

Deputy Forests and Grasslands Supervisor **(Vacant)** ...... (308) 432-0315

Public Affairs Specialist **Cydney D. "Cyd" Janssen** ..... (308) 432-0326
E-mail: cdjanssen@fs.fed.us

Buffalo Gap National Grassland (East Half) - Wall Ranger District
710 Main Street, Wall, SD 57790
Tel: (605) 279-2126 Fax: (605) 279-2725

District Ranger **Alex B. Grant** .... (605) 279-2125
E-mail: abgrant@fs.fed.us
Education: Tuskegee BS

Buffalo Gap National Grassland (West Half) - Fall River Ranger District
1801 Highway 19, Truck Bypass, Hot Springs, SD 57747
Tel: (605) 745-4107 Fax: (605) 745-4179

District Ranger **Mike McNeill** .... (605) 745-4107
E-mail: mmcneill@fs.fed.us

Charles E. Bessey Tree Nursery
40637 River Loop, Halsey, NE 69142
Tel: (308) 533-2257 Fax: (308) 533-2310

Manager **Richard E. Gilbert** ....(308) 533-2257 ext. 8117

Fort Pierre National Grassland
1020 North Deadwood Street, Fort Pierre, SD 57532
Tel: (605) 224-5517 Fax: (605) 224-6517

District Ranger **Dan Svingen** .... (605) 224-5517
E-mail: dsvingen@fs.fed.us

Ogala National Grassland
125 North Main Street, Chadron, NE 69337-9355
Tel: (308) 432-0300 Fax: (308) 432-0309

District Ranger **Tim Buskirk** .... (308) 432-0300
E-mail: tbuskirk@fs.fed.us

Samuel R. McKelvie National Forest - Bessey Ranger District
40637 River Loop, Halsey, NE 69142
Tel: (308) 533-2257 Fax: (308) 533-2310

District Ranger **Julie Bain** .... (308) 533-2257
E-mail: jbain@fs.fed.us

Forest Service – Region 3 (Southwestern Region)

333 Broadway Boulevard, SE, Albuquerque, NM 87102
Tel: (505) 842-3292 Fax: (505) 842-3800
E-mail: r3_visitor_info_center@fs.fed.us Internet: www.fs.usda.gov/r3
Areas Covered: AZ, NM and Oklahoma Grasslands

Regional Forester **Calvin N. "Cal" Joyner** .... (505) 842-3301

Executive Assistant to Regional Forester
Janine Daniels .... (505) 842-3301

Administrative Support Assistant **Patricia F. Mares** ..... (505) 842-3396
E-mail: pmares@fs.fed.us

Chief of Staff (Acting) **Rita Skinner** .... (505) 842-3305
E-mail: reskinner@fs.fed.us

Deputy Regional Forester **Elaine Kohrman** .... (505) 842-3306

Deputy Regional Forester **Sandra Watts** .... (505) 842-3307

Deputy Regional Forester **(Vacant)** .... (505) 842-3292

Regional Health and Safety Officer (Acting)
Shelly Pacheco .... (505) 842-3133
E-mail: spacheco@fs.fed.us

State Liaison (Acting) **Ericka Luna** .... (602) 225-5205
E-mail: elluna@fs.fed.us

State Liaison **Ericka Luna** .... (202) 205-0980
E-mail: elluna@fs.fed.us

Tribal Government Program Manager **Yolynda Begay** .... (505) 842-3424

Acquisition Management

Director **Roberta R. Zachary** .... (505) 842-3383
E-mail: rzachary@fs.fed.us

Office Manager **(Vacant)** .... (505) 842-3318

Deputy Director **(Vacant)** .... (505) 842-3340

Database Manager **(Vacant)** .... (505) 842-3348

Supervisory Contract Officer **(Vacant)** .... (505) 842-3342

FOIA Specialist **Raquel Cantu** .... (505) 842-3121
E-mail: raquelcantu@fs.fed.us

Grants and Agreements Specialist **Carmen Melendez** .... (505) 842-3199
E-mail: cmelendez@fs.fed.us

Leasing Officer **Lorrie Evans** .... (602) 225-5348

Property Management Specialist **(Vacant)** .... (505) 842-3345

Purchasing Agent **Marcella Lucero** .... (505) 842-3326
E-mail: melucero@fs.fed.us

Records and Directives Specialist **Paula Barnhill** .... (505) 842-3890
E-mail: pbarnhill@fs.fed.us

Appeals and Litigation
333 Broadway Boulevard, SE, Albuquerque, NM 87102
Fax: (505) 842-3173

Director **(Vacant)** .... (505) 842-3305

Litigation Program Manager (Acting)
Margaret Van Gilder .... (505) 842-3219
E-mail: mvangilder@fs.fed.us

Appeals Program Manager (Acting)
Roxanne A. Turley .... (505) 842-3223
E-mail: raturley@fs.fed.us

Office Clerk **(Vacant)** .... (505) 842-3218

Budget and Finance

Director **Lewis H. Carroll** .... (505) 842-3201
E-mail: lewishcarroll@fs.fed.us Fax: (505) 842-3457

Administrative Assistant **Rosa Ayala** .... (505) 842-3411

Program Analyst **(Vacant)** .... (505) 842-3369

Regional Office Budget Officer **Deena Gutowski** .... (505) 842-3430
E-mail: dgutowski@fs.fed.us

(continued on next page)

★ Presidential Appointment Requiring Senate Confirmation ☆ Presidential Appointment □ Schedule C Appointment ◇ Career Senior Foreign Service Appointment
● Career Senior Executive Service (SES) Appointment ○ Non Career Senior Executive Service (SES) Appointment ■ Postal Career Executive Service

DEPARTMENTS

Budget and Finance *(continued)*

Budget Analyst **Aurelio N. Corral** .... (505) 842-3174
E-mail: ancorral@fs.fed.us
Budget Analyst **(Vacant)** .... (505) 842-3430

Civil Rights

Director **Amy Padilla** .... (505) 842-3813
E-mail: apadilla@fs.fed.us
Administrative Assistant **Rosa Ayala** .... (505) 842-3411
Civil Rights/Equal Employment Specialist
Aurelia "Bea" Harris .... (505) 842-3422
E-mail: abharris@fs.fed.us
Civil Rights/Program Specialist **(Vacant)** .... (505) 842-3809
Outreach Coordinator **(Vacant)** .... (505) 842-3188
Fax: (505) 842-3807

Ecosystem Analysis and Planning, Watershed, and Air Management

Director **Bob Davis** .... (505) 842-3210
Deputy Director **Jennifer Ruyle** .... (505) 842-3886
Regional Analyst **(Vacant)** .... (505) 842-3217
Ecologist and Air Program Manager **Jack Triepke** .... (505) 842-3146
E-mail: jtriepke@fs.fed.us
Regional Planner **Matthew Turner** .... (505) 842-3214
Terrestrial Ecological Unit Inventory Program Manager
Wayne Robbie .... (505) 842-3253
E-mail: wrobbie@fs.fed.us
Water Resources Program Manager **Roy Jemison** .... (505) 842-3255
Watershed Improvement Program Manager
Anna Jaramillo-Scarborough .... (505) 842-3254
E-mail: ajaramillo@fs.fed.us
Regional NEPA Team Leader **Roxanne A. Turley** .... (505) 842-3178
Regional Social Scientist **Maureen Yonovitz** .... (505) 842-3144
Assistant Water Resources Program Manager
Lavonna Begay .... (505) 842-3312
Terrestrial Ecosystem Survey Project Leader (Arizona)
(Vacant) .... (602) 225-5207
Terrestrial Ecosystem Survey Project Leader (New Mexico) **Steven H. Strenger** .... (505) 842-3145
E-mail: sstrenger@fs.fed.us
Office Manager **Denise Aragon** .... (505) 842-3332

Engineering

Director **Danny R. Montoya** .... (505) 842-3370
Engineering Management and Programs Group Leader
William Medina .... (505) 842-3830
Environmental Engineering Group Leader
Maria McGaha .... (505) 842-3837
Fleet and Equipment Specialist **Valerie Gomez** .... (505) 842-3853
Facilities Engineering Group Leader **Patrick Leyba** .... (505) 842-3851
Geometronics Group Leader, Regional NRM Program Manager **Mark Jacobsen** .... (505) 842-3846
Transportation Group Leader **Marjorie Apodaca** .... (505) 842-3852
E-mail: mapodaca@fs.fed.us
Office Manager **Andrea Carter** .... (505) 842-3371

Forestry, Forest Health, and Cooperative Forestry

Director **Clifford "Cliff" Dils** .... (505) 842-3242
● Assistant Director **(Vacant)** .... (505) 842-3240
Forester, Administration **(Vacant)** .... (505) 842-3426
E-mail: dcummings@fs.fed.us
Administrative Support Assistant **(Vacant)** .... (505) 842-3243

Fire and Aviation Management

Director **Bill Van Bruggen** .... (505) 842-3206
E-mail: bvanbruggen@fs.fed.us Fax: (505) 842-3806
Deputy Director **Judith Palmer** .... (505) 842-3206
Assistant Director, Aviation **(Vacant)** .... (505) 842-3359
Assistant Director, Aviation Safety **Jami Anzalone** .... (505) 842-3351
E-mail: jamianzalone@fs.fed.us
Assistant Director, Fire Operations **Richard Nieto** .... (505) 842-3418
Assistant Director, Fire Planning, Budget and Cooperative Fire Programs **Billy Zamora** .... (505) 842-3388
E-mail: bzamora@fs.fed.us
Assistant Director, Fuels and Fire Ecology **(Vacant)** .... (505) 842-3281
Office Manager **Colleen Loretto** .... (505) 842-3460

Human Resources

Human Resources Officer **Frank D. Gomez** .... (505) 842-3421
E-mail: frankdgomez@fs.fed.us
Employee Relations Specialist **Rhonda Cortez** .... (505) 842-3489
Human Resource Liaison **Valerie V. Herrera** .... (505) 842-3185
E-mail: vvherrera@fs.fed.us
Regional Health and Safety Officer (Acting)
Shelly Pacheco .... (505) 842-3351
E-mail: spacheco@fs.fed.us
Strategic Enterprise Solutions Manager
Teresa Rodriguez .... (505) 563-9446
E-mail: trodriguez@fs.fed.us

Land and Minerals Management

Director **Tracy Parker** .... (505) 842-3270
Administrative Support Assistant **Angela Sandoval** .... (505) 842-3271
E-mail: asandoval@fs.fed.us
Regional Geologist **Mike Linden** .... (505) 842-3158
Regional Land Surveyor and Small Tracts Act Specialist **Chris Chavez** .... (505) 842-3272
Regional Appraiser **David McInnis** .... (505) 842-3379
Apprentice Appraiser **Yvonne Lovato** .... (505) 842-3156
Senior Review Appraiser **Joe R. Payne** .... (505) 842-3273
Rights-of-Way and Special Uses Group Leader
(Vacant) .... (505) 842-3445

Law Enforcement and Investigations

Special Agent-in-Charge (Acting)
Michael F. "Mike" Gardiner, Jr. .... (505) 842-3104
E-mail: mgardiner@fs.fed.us
Regional Patrol Commander **Aban Lucero** .... (505) 842-3362
E-mail: alucero@fs.fed.us
Assistant Special Agent - New Mexico
Michael F. "Mike" Gardiner, Jr. .... (505) 842-3363
E-mail: mgardiner@fs.fed.us
Program Specialist **(Vacant)** .... (505) 842-3186
Administrative Assistant **Erika C. Mascarenas** .... (505) 842-3196

Public Affairs Office

333 Broadway Boulevard, SE, Albuquerque, NM 87102
Tel: (505) 842-3497 Fax: (505) 842-3106

Director **Marie T. Sebrechts** .... (505) 842-3290
E-mail: msebrechts@fs.fed.us
Public Affairs Officer **Sheila Poole** .... (505) 842-3291
E-mail: spoole@fs.fed.us
Regional Cooperative Education Coordinator
Elise "Apple" Snider .... (505) 842-3398
Printing and Publications Specialist
Patricia E. "Pat" Johnson .... (505) 842-3295
E-mail: patriciaejohnson@fs.fed.us
Webmaster (Acting) **Linda Harms** .... (575) 434-7213
E-mail: ldharms@fs.fed.us
National Fire Plan Information (Public Affairs Officer)
Mary Zabinski .... (505) 842-3897
Arizona Media and Issues Manager **(Vacant)** .... (928) 226-4616
New Mexico Media and Issues Manager **(Vacant)** .... (505) 842-3393

Rangeland Management

333 Broadway Boulevard, SE, Albuquerque, NM 87102
Tel: (505) 842-3220

Director **Robert G. Trujillo** .... (505) 842-3224
Deputy Director **Judith Dyess** .... (505) 842-3229
Assistant Director and Grazing Permit Administration
(Vacant) .... (505) 842-3220
Invasive Species Plant Coordinator **Allen White** .... (505) 842-3280
Rangeland Data Management **Kevin Sanchez** .... (505) 842-3169
Rangeland Inventory, Assessment and Monitoring
(Vacant) .... (505) 842-3229
Office Manager **(Vacant)** .... (505) 842-3247

Recreation, Heritage, and Wilderness Resources

333 Broadway Boulevard, SE, Albuquerque, NM 87102
Fax: (505) 842-3165

Director **Francisco Valenzuela** .... (505) 842-3442
Education: Colorado State 1980 SB; Milwaukee Inst Art 1999 MFA

Recreation, Heritage, and Wilderness Resources *(continued)*

Heritage Program Assistant Director **David Johnson** ..... (505) 842-3232
Landscape Architect Assistant Director **(Vacant)** .... (505) 842-3451
Recreation Special Uses Program Manager
Elizabeth P. "Beth" Dykstra .... (505) 842-3235
Office Manager **Leo Sanchez** .... (505) 842-3446

Wildlife, Fish, and Rare Plants
Director **Robert G. Trujillo** .... (505) 842-3224
Administrative Support Assistant **(Vacant)** .... (505) 842-3435
Deputy Director **Bobbi L. Barrera** .... (505) 842-3194
Fisheries Program Manager **Yvette M. Paroz** .... (505) 842-3228
Wildlife Program Manager **Brian Dykstra** .... (505) 842-3268

Visitor Information Desk
333 Broadway Boulevard, SE, Albuquerque, NM 87102
Tel: (505) 842-3292 Fax: (505) 842-3258
Information Assistant **Melissa Dean** .... (505) 842-3898
E-mail: melissadean@fs.fed.us
Information Assistant **Wade J. Tigelaar** .... (505) 842-3193
E-mail: wtigelaar@fs.fed.us

National Forests – Arizona

Apache-Sitgreaves National Forests (ASNF)
30 South Chiricahua Drive, Springerville, AZ 85938
Mail: P.O. Box 640, Springerville, AZ 85938
Tel: (928) 333-6280 TTY: (928) 333-6292 Fax: (928) 333-5966
Internet: www.fs.usda.gov/asnf
Forest Supervisor **Stephen "Steve" Best** .... (928) 333-6301
Education: Austin State MSF, BSF
Deputy Forest Supervisor **Wendy Jo Haskins** .... (928) 333-6300
Springerville District Ranger **Rob Lever**
P.O. Box 116, Fortine, MT 59918 Fax: (928) 687-1301
E-mail: rlever@fs.fed.us
Education: Linfield BS
Public Affairs Officer **(Vacant)** .... (928) 333-6263

Coconino National Forest
1824 South Thompson Street, Flagstaff, AZ 86001
Tel: (928) 527-3600 Fax: (928) 527-3620
Internet: www.fs.usda.gov/coconino
Forest Supervisor **Laura Jo West** .... (928) 527-3501
E-mail: ljwest@fs.fed.us
Deputy Forest Supervisor (Acting) **Aaron Mayville** ...... (928) 527-3456

Coronado National Forest
Federal Building, 300 West Congress Street,
6th Floor, Tucson, AZ 85701
Tel: (520) 388-8300 Fax: (520) 388-8305
Internet: www.fs.usda.gov/coronado
Forest Supervisor **Kerwin Dewberry** .... (520) 388-8306
Deputy Forest Supervisor **John E. Waconda** .... (520) 388-8307
Public Affairs Staff Officer **Heidi Schewel** .... (520) 388-8343
E-mail: hschewel@fs.fed.us
Douglas District Ranger **Douglas T. "Doug" Ruppel** .... (520) 364-3468
1192 West Saddleview Road, Douglas, AZ 85607 Fax: (520) 364-6667
E-mail: druppel@fs.fed.us
Nogales District Ranger **James Copeland** .... (520) 281-2296
303 Old Tucson Road, Nogales, AZ 85621 Fax: (520) 281-2396
E-mail: jcopeland@fs.fed.us
Safford District Ranger **Curtis P. "Curt" Booher** .... (928) 428-4150
E-mail: curtispbooher@fs.fed.us Fax: (928) 428-2393
Santa Catalina District Ranger **Charles E. Woodard** ..... (520) 749-8700
Sabino Canyon, Fax: (520) 749-7723
5700 North Sabino Canyon Road,
Tucson, AZ 85706
E-mail: cewoodard@fs.fed.us
Education: Tuskegee BS
Sierra Vista District Ranger **Celeste "Daisy" Kinsey** .... (520) 378-0311
4070 South Avenida Saracino, Fax: (520) 378-0519
Hereford, AZ 85615
E-mail: ckinsey@fs.fed.us

Kaibab National Forest
800 South Sixth Street, Williams, AZ 86046
Tel: (928) 635-8200 TTY: (928) 635-8222 Fax: (928) 635-8208
Internet: www.fs.usda.gov/kaibab
Forest Supervisor **Heather C. Provencio** .... (928) 635-8301
Public Affairs Officer
Jacqueline C. "Jackie" Banks .... (928) 635-8314 ext. 4314
E-mail: jcbanks@fs.fed.us

Prescott National Forest
344 South Cortez Street, Prescott, AZ 86303
Tel: (928) 443-8000 TTY: (928) 443-8001 Fax: (928) 443-8008
Internet: www.fs.usda.gov/prescott
Forest Supervisor **Dale A. Deiter** .... (928) 443-8000
Education: Northern Arizona BS, MS
Public Affairs **Debbie Maneely** .... (928) 443-8130
E-mail: dmaneely@fs.fed.us
Bradshaw District Ranger **Sarah E. Tomsky** .... (928) 443-8000
Bradshaw Deputy District Ranger **Karina Gutierrez** ...... (928) 567-4121
Tel: (928) 777-2221
Chino Valley District Ranger **Sarah E. Tomsky** .... (928) 777-2200
Tel: (928) 443-8070
Chino Valley Deputy District Ranger **Karina Gutierrez** ... (928) 567-4121
Tel: (928) 777-2221
Verde District Ranger **Todd Willard** .... (928) 567-4121

Tonto National Forest
2324 East McDowell Road, Phoenix, AZ 85006
Tel: (602) 225-5200 TTY: (602) 225-5395 Fax: (602) 225-5292
Internet: www.fs.usda.gov/tonto
Forest Supervisor **Neil Bosworth** .... (602) 225-5201
Deputy Forest Supervisor **(Vacant)** .... (602) 225-5203
Public and Legislative Affairs Officer **(Vacant)** .... (602) 225-5290

National Forests – New Mexico

Carson National Forest
208 Cruz Alta Road, Taos, NM 87571
Tel: (575) 758-6200 Fax: (505) 758-6213
Internet: www.fs.usda.gov/carson/
Forest Supervisor **James D. Duran** .... (575) 758-6301
IT Specialist/Webmaster **(Vacant)** .... (575) 758-6305
Public Affairs Officer **(Vacant)** .... (575) 758-6303
Administrative Officer **Ricardo M. Martinez** .... (575) 758-6320
E-mail: rmmartinez@fs.fed.us
Administrative Assistant **Debra "Debbie" Romero** ...... (575) 758-6307

Cibola National Forest
2113 Osuna Road NE, Albuquerque, NM 87113
Tel: (505) 346-3900 Fax: (505) 346-3901
Internet: www.fs.usda.gov/cibola
Forest Supervisor
Steven L. "Steve" Hattenbach MPA, JD .... (505) 346-3804
Public Affairs Officer **Donna Nemeth** .... (505) 346-3894
E-mail: dnemeth@fs.fed.us

Gila National Forest
3005 East Camino Del Bosque, Silver City, NM 88061
Tel: (575) 388-8201 TTY: (575) 388-8489 Fax: (575) 388-8204
Internet: www.fs.usda.gov/gila
Forest Supervisor **Adam Mendonca** .... (575) 388-8304
Public Affairs Officer **Marta I. Call** .... (575) 388-8211
E-mail: martaicall@fs.fed.us
Education: Weber State 1988 BEd

Lincoln National Forest
3463 Las Palomas Road, Alamogordo, NM 88310-6992
Tel: (575) 434-7200 Fax: (575) 434-7218
Internet: www.fs.usda.gov/lincoln/
Forest Supervisor **Travis Moseley** .... (575) 434-7306
Education: Colorado State 1989 BS
Deputy Forest Supervisor **(Vacant)** .... (575) 434-7200
Public Affairs Officer **Loretta Benavidez** .... (575) 434-7290
E-mail: llbenavidez@fs.fed.us

DEPARTMENTS

★ Presidential Appointment Requiring Senate Confirmation ☆ Presidential Appointment □ Schedule C Appointment ◇ Career Senior Foreign Service Appointment
● Career Senior Executive Service (SES) Appointment ○ Non-Career Senior Executive Service (SES) Appointment ■ Postal Career Executive Service

DEPARTMENTS

Santa Fe National Forest (SFNF)
11 Forest Lane, Santa Fe, NM 87508
Mail: P.O. Box 1689, Santa Fe, NM 87504
Tel: (505) 438-5300 Fax: (505) 438-5390 Internet: www.fs.usda.gov/sfe

Forest Supervisor **James Melonas** .... (505) 438-5310
Fax: (505) 438-5391

Deputy Forest Supervisor (Acting)
Karl Malcolm .... (505) 438-5300 ext. 5311
Note: Until the end of January, 2019.
Deputy Forest Supervisor **Joe Norrell** .... (505) 438-5311
Note: Away on detail until the end of January 2019.
Public Affairs Officer **Bruce R. Hill, Jr.** .... (505) 438-5320
Education: Northwest Missouri State 1992 BS;
Air Command Col 2017 MS
Assistant Public Affairs Officer **(Vacant)** .... (505) 438-5320

Forest Service – Region 4 (Intermountain Region)
Federal Building, 324 25th Street, Ogden, UT 84401-2310
Tel: (801) 625-5605 Fax: (801) 625-5359 Internet: www.fs.usda.gov/r4
Areas Covered: Southern ID, NV, UT, Western WY

● Regional Forester **Nora Rasure** .... (801) 625-5605
E-mail: nrasure@fs.fed.us
Education: Illinois 1980 BS
Deputy Regional Forester (Acting) **Mark Bethke** .... (801) 625-5605
Deputy Regional Forester **Mary Farnsworth** .... (801) 625-5605
Deputy Regional Forester
David P. "Dave" Rosenkrance .... (801) 625-5605
Executive Assistant **Paula J. Bailey** .... (801) 625-5919
Executive Secretary **Tamara Minnock** .... (801) 625-5605
Support Services Supervisor **Janae B. Pearson** .... (801) 625-5827
EAP Coordinator **Larry Velarde** .... (801) 625-5295
E-mail: lvelarde@fs.fed.us
Regional Safety Officer **Randy Draeger** .... (801) 625-5296
E-mail: rdraeger@fs.fed.us

Acquisition Management
Federal Building, 324 25th Street, Ogden, UT 84401-2310
Tel: (801) 625-5762

Director **Melanie Russel** .... (801) 625-5137
Deputy Director **(Vacant)** .... (801) 625-5137
Supervisory Contract Specialist **Cary L. Williams** .... (801) 625-5737
E-mail: clwilliams01@fs.fed.us
Grants and Agreements Specialist **Carla Pickering** .... (801) 625-5796
Purchasing Agent **Thomas M. "Tom" Underwood** ..... (801) 625-5652
E-mail: tmunderwood@fs.fed.us

Civil Rights and Equal Employment Opportunity
324 25th Street, Ogden, UT 84401-2310
Fax: (801) 625-5722

Director **Sherry L. Neal** .... (801) 625-5416
E-mail: slneal01@fs.fed.us
Deputy Director **(Vacant)** .... (801) 625-5416
EEO Specialist **(Vacant)** .... (801) 625-5144
EEO Specialist **(Vacant)** .... (801) 625-5806
Employee Assistant Coordinator **(Vacant)** .... (801) 625-5073
Administrative Support Assistant **Cindy Simmons** ...... (801) 625-5686
E-mail: csimmons01@fs.fed.us
Tel: (801) 625-5229

Engineering
324 25th Street, Ogden, UT 84401-2310
Tel: (801) 625-5228

Director **Gina Freel** .... (801) 625-5194
Administrative Support Assistant **Farrah Chesnut** .... (801) 625-5460

Financial Resources
324 25th Street, Ogden, UT 84401-2310
Tel: (801) 625-5796

Director **Mark Bethke** .... (801) 625-5269
E-mail: mbethke@fs.fed.us
Administrative Support Assistant **Janae B. Pearson** ..... (801) 625-5827
E-mail: jbpearson@fs.fed.us
Budget Analyst **(Vacant)** .... (801) 625-5266

Financial Resources *(continued)*
Budget Analyst **(Vacant)** .... (801) 625-5140

Fire and Aviation Management
324 25th Street, Ogden, UT 84401-2310
Tel: (801) 625-5512 Fax: (801) 625-5594

Director **Susan A. Stewart** .... (801) 625-5507
E-mail: sastewart@fs.fed.us
Deputy Director **Elizabeth Lund** .... (801) 625-5513
E-mail: elund@fs.fed.us
Support Services Assistant **Janae B. Pearson** .... (801) 625-5827
E-mail: jbpearson@fs.fed.us
Regional Aviation Safety Officer **(Vacant)** .... (801) 625-5510
Air Quality Specialist **(Vacant)** .... (303) 275-5759
740 Simms Street, Golden, CO 80401-4720
Cooperative Fire Protection **(Vacant)** .... (801) 625-5264
Fire Business Management **(Vacant)** .... (801) 625-5565
Fire Planning Specialist **Barbara Knieling** .... (801) 625-5508
E-mail: bknieling@fs.fed.us
Fuels Management **Mesia Nyman** .... (801) 625-5505

Human Resources
324 25th Street, Ogden, UT 84401-2310
Tel: (801) 625-5298

Human Resources Liaison **Valerie Del Rio** .... (801) 625-5300
E-mail: vdelrio02@fs.fed.us
Human Resources Officer **Melissa A. Dittmann** .... (801) 625-5316
E-mail: madittmann@fs.fed.us

Lands and Minerals
324 25th Street, Ogden, UT 84401-2310
Tel: (801) 625-5438 Fax: (801) 625-5378

Director **Kathryn J. Conant** .... (801) 625-5150
Acquisition Management **(Vacant)** .... (801) 625-5931
Senior Review Appraiser **(Vacant)** .... (801) 625-5787
Boundary and Title Management **Belle Craig** .... (801) 625-5226
Regional Special Uses Program Manager
Melissa Hearst .... (801) 625-5141
Support Services Assistant **Alisha Murri** .... (801) 625-5438
E-mail: amurri@fs.fed.us
Regional Appraiser **Kraig Frome** .... (801) 625-5367

Law Enforcement and Investigations
324 25th Street, Ogden, UT 84401-2310
Fax: (801) 625-5225

Special Agent In Charge **Scott Harris** .... (801) 625-5324
Assistant Special Agent in Charge **Mike McKinney** ...... (801) 625-5430
Patrol Commander **Larry Hall** .... (801) 625-5582
E-mail: lhall@fs.fed.us
Program Assistant **Julie White** .... (801) 625-5230
E-mail: jwhite03@fs.fed.us
Budget Analyst **Ragan D. Hall** .... (801) 625-5780
E-mail: rdhall@fs.fed.us

Natural Resources
324 25th Street, Ogden, UT 84401-2310
Tel: (801) 625-5686

Director **Kristine M. Lee** .... (801) 625-5669
Aquatic Ecologist **Cynthia Tait** .... (801) 625-5358
Budget Officer **Dana Hoskins** .... (801) 625-5156
E-mail: dhoskins@fs.fed.us
Fisheries Program Manager **Dan Duffield** .... (801) 625-5662
Range Program Management/Appeals Coordinator
Terry Padilla .... (801) 625-5518
E-mail: tpadilla@fs.fed.us
Rangeland Data Manager **(Vacant)** .... (801) 625-5598
Regional Ecologist **David Tart** .... (801) 625-5817
Regional Hydrologist **(Vacant)** .... (801) 625-5267
Regional Silviculturist **Patrick Behrens** .... (801) 625-5220
Soils and Geology Specialist **Jeffrey Bruggink** .... (801) 625-5357
Support Services Assistant **Cindy Simmons** .... (801) 625-5686
E-mail: csimmons01@fs.fed.us Fax: (801) 625-5229

★ Presidential Appointment Requiring Senate Confirmation ☆ Presidential Appointment □ Schedule C Appointment ◇ Career Senior Foreign Service Appointment
● Career Senior Executive Service (SES) Appointment ○ Non-Career Senior Executive Service (SES) Appointment ■ Postal Career Executive Service

Natural Resources *(continued)*

T and E Program Coordinator **Lee Jacobson** . . . . (801) 625-5664
Fax: (801) 625-5483
Timber Sales Administration **Megan Timoney** . . . . (801) 625-5520
Timber Sales Preparation **Shannon Hitch** . . . . (801) 625-5600
Wildlife Ecologist **(Vacant)** . . . . (801) 625-5671
Fax: (801) 625-5756
Wildlife Program Manager **Dr. John Shivik** . . . . (801) 625-5667
Fax: (801) 625-5756

Information Planning and Appeals Management
324 25th Street, Ogden, UT 84401-2310
Tel: (801) 625-5804

Director **Deborah Oakeson** . . . . (801) 625-5777
E-mail: doakeson@fs.fed.us
Cartographer and Visual Arts Team Leader
Teresa Rhoades . . . . (801) 625-5213
Appeal and Litigation Specialist **Kris Rutledge** . . . . (801) 625-5301
E-mail: krutledge@fs.fed.us
Regional Environmental Coordinator
Georgina M. "Gina" Lampman . . . . (801) 625-5301
Regional Environmental Coordinator **Fred Noack** . . . . (801) 625-5897
E-mail: fnoack@fs.fed.us

Recreation, Heritage and Wilderness Resources Management (RHWR)
324 25th Street, Ogden, UT 84401-2310
Tel: (801) 625-5228 Fax: (801) 625-5365

Director **Chris Hartman** . . . . (801) 625-5164
Interpretive Specialist **Carol Ryan** . . . . (801) 625-5171
E-mail: caolryan@fs.fed.us
Wilderness, Rivers, Trails, and Caves **(Vacant)** . . . . (801) 625-5250
Recreation Business Management/Computer Specialist
Joanna J. Wilson . . . . (801) 625-5152
E-mail: jwilson08@fs.fed.us
Recreation Special Uses Program Leader **(Vacant)** . . . . (801) 625-5175

State and Private Forestry
324 25th Street, Ogden, UT 84401-2310
Tel: (801) 625-5827 Fax: (801) 625-5716

Director **Michael "Mike" Dudley** . . . . (801) 625-5253
Education: Oregon State 1986 BF
Director **Timothy P. "Tim" Garcia** . . . . (406) 329-3797
Deputy Director **(Vacant)** . . . . (406) 329-3280
P.O. Box 7669, Missoula, MT 59807
Pesticide Coordinator **Anne P. Hoover** . . . . (801) 625-5258
Budget, Grants **Suzanne Schutz** . . . . (801) 625-5759
E-mail: sschutz@fs.fed.us
Forest Health Monitoring **Rob Cruz** . . . . (801) 625-5162
Stewardship Forest Legacy **Janet Valle** . . . . (801) 625-5258
Community Assistance **Scott Bell** . . . . (801) 625-5259

Strategic Communications
324 25th Street, Ogden, UT 84401-2310
Tel: (801) 625-5350

Director (Acting) **Tammy Wentland** . . . . (801) 625-5347
E-mail: twentland@fs.fed.us
FOIA Coordinator **Matthew D. "Matt" Ocana** . . . . (801) 625-5354
E-mail: matthewocana@fs.fed.us

Weber Basin Job Corps Center
7400 South Cornia Drive, Ogden, UT 84405-9605
Tel: (801) 479-9806 Fax: (801) 476-5985
Internet: https://weberbasin.jobcorps.gov/

Center Director **Matthew S. "Matt" Nielsen** . . . . (801) 625-5403
E-mail: msnielsen@fs.fed.us
Administrative Officer **Laurie Villalpando** . . . . (801) 476-5933
E-mail: lmvillalpando@fs.fed.us
Webmaster **Brenda Gain** . . . . (801) 476-5935
E-mail: bkgain@fs.fed.us

National Forests – Idaho

Boise National Forest
1249 South Vinnell Way, Suite 200, Boise, ID 83709-1663
Tel: (208) 373-4100 Fax: (208) 373-4111
Internet: www.fs.fed.us/r4/boise
Areas Covered: National Forest within: Ada County, Boise County, Elmore County, Gem County, Valley County

Forest Supervisor **Cecilia Romero Seesholtz** . . . . (208) 373-4102
Education: Northern Arizona BS
Deputy Forest Supervisor **Tawnya Brummett** . . . . (208) 373-4103
Fax: (208) 373-4201
Public Affairs Officer **Venetia Gempler** . . . . (208) 373-4105
E-mail: vgempler@fs.fed.us
Public Affairs Specialist (web) **Linda Steinhaus** . . . . (208) 373-4106
E-mail: lsteinhaus@fs.fed.us

Caribou-Targhee National Forest
1405 Hollipark Drive, Idaho Falls, ID 83401
Tel: (208) 557-5900 Fax: (208) 557-5826 Internet: www.fs.usda.gov/ctnf
Areas Covered: Southeastern ID, Northwestern WY

Forest Supervisor **Mel Bolling** . . . . (208) 557-5761
Support Services Specialist **Brian Micklich** . . . . (208) 557-5762
Contracting Officer **Kellie Shaw** . . . . (208) 557-5841
E-mail: kjshaw@fs.fed.us Fax: (208) 557-5829
Public Affairs Officer (Acting) **Greg O. Burch** . . . . (208) 557-5765
E-mail: goburch@fs.fed.us Fax: (208) 557-5827
Ecosystem Management Branch Chief
Robert Mickelsen . . . . (208) 557-5764
Forest Engineer **Wes H. Stumbo** . . . . (208) 557-5767
Fax: (208) 557-5827
Forest Planner **Doug Hercog** . . . . (208) 354-6613

Payette National Forest
800 West Lakeside Avenue, McCall, ID 83638-3602
Tel: (208) 634-0700 Fax: (208) 634-0744
Internet: www.fs.usda.gov/payette

Forest Supervisor **Keith Lannom** . . . . (208) 634-0701
Law Enforcement Officer **Amy Ohme** . . . . (208) 634-0733
E-mail: ahohme@fs.fed.us
Public Affairs Officer **Brian D. Harris** . . . . (208) 634-0784
E-mail: bdharris@fs.fed.us
Council and Weiser District Ranger **Ronda M. Bishop** . . . (208) 549-4201

Salmon-Challis National Forest
Headquarters Building, 1206 South Challis, Salmon, ID 83467
Tel: (208) 756-5100 Fax: (208) 756-5151 Internet: www.fs.usda.gov/scnf
Areas Covered: Central ID, including the Frank Church River of No Return Wilderness

Forest Supervisor **Charles A. "Chuck" Mark** . . . . (208) 756-5100
Fax: (208) 756-5220
Deputy Forest Supervisor **Cheri A. Ford** . . . . (208) 756-5131
Ecosystem and Public Uses Staff Officer **Tom Ford** . . . . . . (208) 756-5290
Operations Staff Officer **Jim Tucker** . . . . (208) 756-5134
Engineering, Planning, Minerals and Administrative
Officer **Kimberly Nelson** . . . . (208) 756-5557
E-mail: kdnelson@fs.fed.us
Public Affairs Officer **Amy Baumer** . . . . (208) 756-5145
E-mail: abaumer@fs.fed.us

Sawtooth National Forest
370 American Avenue, Jerome, ID 83338
Tel: (208) 423-7500 Fax: (208) 423-7510
Internet: www.fs.usda.gov/sawtooth

Forest Supervisor **(Vacant)** . . . . (208) 423-7500
Public Affairs Officer **Julie A. Thomas** . . . . (208) 423-7500
E-mail: jathomas@fs.fed.us

National Forests – Nevada

Humboldt-Toiyabe National Forest
1200 Franklin Way, Sparks, NV 89431
Tel: (775) 355-5310 Fax: (775) 355-5399 Internet: www.fs.usda.gov/htnf

Forest Supervisor **William A. "Bill" Dunkelberger** . . . . . . (775) 355-5310
Education: Washington State BA

(continued on next page)

★ Presidential Appointment Requiring Senate Confirmation ☆ Presidential Appointment □ Schedule C Appointment ◇ Career Senior Foreign Service Appointment
● Career Senior Executive Service (SES) Appointment ○ Non-Career Senior Executive Service (SES) Appointment ■ Postal Career Executive Service

DEPARTMENTS

Humboldt-Toiyabe National Forest *(continued)*

Deputy Forest Supervisor **Teresa McClung** . . . . . (775) 355-5309
Public Affairs Officer **Erica Hupp** . . . . . (775) 355-5311
E-mail: ehupp@fs.fed.us

National Forests – Utah

Ashley National Forest

355 North Vernal Avenue, Vernal, UT 84078
Tel: (435) 789-1181 Fax: (435) 781-5142
Internet: www.fs.usda.gov/ashley

Forest Supervisor **John R. Erickson** . . . . . (435) 781-5101
Public Affairs Officer **Louis J. Haynes** . . . . . (435) 781-5105
E-mail: ljhaynes@fs.fed.us

Dixie National Forest

1789 North Wedgewood Lane, Cedar City, UT 84721
Tel: (435) 865-3700 Fax: (435) 865-3791 Internet: www.fs.usda.gov/dixie

Forest Supervisor **Angelita S. Bulletts** . . . . . (435) 865-3701
Public Affairs Officer (Acting) **Bode Mecham** . . . . . (435) 865-3773
E-mail: bmecham@fs.fed.us

Fishlake National Forest

115 East 900 North, Richfield, UT 84701
Tel: (435) 896-9233 Tel: (435) 896-1600 Fax: (435) 896-9347
Internet: www.fs.usda.gov/fishlake

Forest Supervisor **Mike Elson** . . . . . (435) 896-1001
Education: BYU BS; Northern Arizona MS

Manti-La Sal National Forest

599 West Price River Drive, Price, UT 84501
Tel: (435) 637-2817 Fax: (435) 637-4940
E-mail: Mailroom_R4_Manti_LaSal@fs.fed.us
Internet: www.fs.usda.gov/mantilasal/

Forest Supervisor **Ryan E. Nehl** . . . . . (435) 637-2817
Tel: (435) 636-3536 Fax: (435) 637-2824

Uinta-Wasatch-Cache National Forest

88 West 100 North, Provo, UT 84601
Tel: (801) 999-2103 Fax: (801) 253-8856 Fax: (801) 253-8118
Internet: www.fs.usda.gov/uwcnf

Forest Supervisor **Dave Whittekiend** . . . . . (801) 999-2108
E-mail: dwhittikiend@fs.fed.us
Education: Colorado State 1988 BS; BYU 1992 MS
Deputy Forest Supervisor **Chad E. Hudson** . . . . . (801) 999-2109
Forest Engineer **Kim J. Martin** . . . . . (801) 999-2137
Fire Management Officer **Kevin Pfister** . . . . . (801) 999-2147
8236 Federal Building, 125 South State Street, Salt Lake City, UT 84138
Recreation and Lands Group Leader **Larry C. Lucas** . . . . . (801) 999-2157
Public Affairs Officer **Loyal F. Clark** . . . . . (801) 999-2113
E-mail: lfclark@fs.fed.us
Public Service Group Leader **Larry C. Lucas** . . . . . (801) 999-2157
E-mail: lclucas@fs.fed.us
Renewable Resources Staff Officer **Paul Cowley** . . . . . (801) 999-2167
Program Specialist **Denise N. Johnson** . . . . . (801) 999-2104
E-mail: djohnson@fs.fed.us
Safety Officer **Paul B. Gauchay** . . . . . (801) 999-2110
E-mail: pgauchay@fs.fed.us

National Forests – Wyoming

Bridger-Teton National Forest

340 North Cache, Jackson, WY 83001
Mail: P. O. Box 1888, Jackson, WY 83001
Tel: (307) 739-5500 Fax: (307) 739-5010 Internet: www.fs.fed.us/r4/btnf/

Forest Supervisor **Patricia O'Connor** . . . . . (307) 739-5510
Fax: (307) 739-5442
Deputy Forest Supervisor **Derek Ibarguen** . . . . . (307) 739-5510
Fax: (307) 739-5442
Administrative Officer **Susan R. Colligan** . . . . . (307) 739-5423
E-mail: susanrcolligan@fs.fed.us
Public Affairs Officer **Mary Cernicek** . . . . . (307) 739-5564
E-mail: mcernicek@fs.fed.us

Bridger-Teton National Forest *(continued)*

Executive Assistant **Marinda Rogers-Gardner** . . . . . (307) 739-5510
E-mail: mrogergardner@fs.fed.us

Forest Service – Region 5 (Pacific Southwest Region)

1323 Club Drive, Vallejo, CA 94592
TTY: (707) 562-8737 Fax: (707) 562-9130 Internet: www.fs.usda.gov/r5
Areas Covered: CA, GU, HI, Trust Territories of the Pacific Islands

● Regional Forester **Randy Moore** . . . . . (707) 562-9000
E-mail: rmoore@fs.fed.us Fax: (707) 562-9091
Deputy Regional Forester for Operations
Jennifer Eberlien . . . . . (707) 562-9000
Fax: (707) 562-9091
Deputy Regional Forester for Natural Resources
Barnie Gyant . . . . . (707) 562-9000
Deputy Regional Forester for State and Private Forestry
(Vacant) . . . . . (707) 562-9000
Public Affairs and Communications Director
CDR Joseph S. "Joe" Navratil USN . . . . . (707) 562-8737
Regional Appeals and Objections Coordinator
Theresa I. Corless . . . . . (707) 562-8768
E-mail: tcorless@fs.fed.us
Tribal Relations Program Manager
Wade A. McMaster . . . . . (707) 562-8919
Regional Health and Safety Manager
Jeffrey W. Bradshaw . . . . . (707) 562-8748
E-mail: jeffreybradshaw@fs.fed.us Fax: (707) 562-9091
Partnership Coordinator **Lara Y. Buluc** . . . . . (707) 562-8937
E-mail: laraybuluc@fs.fed.us

Acquisition Management

1323 Club Drive, Vallejo, CA 94592
Fax: (707) 562-9056

Director **LtCol Pierce E. Tucker ANG** . . . . . (707) 562-8909
Note: Pierce Tucker is on detail to Klamath National Forest. Fax: (707) 562-9144
E-mail: piercetucker@fs.fed.us
Education: Southern Illinois 1987 BS; Lesley U 1992 MSBA
Deputy Director **Alfort Belin** . . . . . (707) 562-9107
E-mail: abelin@fs.fed.us Fax: (707) 562-9146
Grants and Agreements Program Manager (Acting)
Constance "Connie" Zipperer . . . . . (707) 562-9120
E-mail: czipperer@fs.fed.us
Procurement Manager **(Vacant)** . . . . . (707) 562-9107

Civil Rights

1323 Club Drive, Vallejo, CA 94592
Fax: (707) 562-9044

Director **Ricky Balolong** . . . . . (707) 562-8752
E-mail: rbalolong@fs.fed.us
Deputy Director **Lois Lawson** . . . . . (707) 562-9185
E-mail: lois.lawson@usda.gov
Conflict Management and Prevention Program Manager
Markette Drone . . . . . (707) 562-8993

Ecosystem Management

1323 Club Drive, Vallejo, CA 94592
Fax: (707) 562-9050

Director **John D. Exline** . . . . . (707) 562-8689
Education: Duke 1980 MSc; Lycoming 1979 BA
Deputy Director **Diana Craig** . . . . . (707) 562-8975
Fax: (707) 562-9054
Regional Ecologist **Hugh D. Safford** . . . . . (707) 562-8934
E-mail: hsafford@fs.fed.us
Education: Montana State BS; San Francisco State U MA; UC Davis PhD
Aquatic Ecologist **(Vacant)** . . . . . (707) 562-8952
Fax: (707) 562-9145
Wildlife Ecologist **(Vacant)** . . . . . (707) 562-9054
Threatened and Sensitive Species Program Manager
Diane MacFarlane . . . . . (707) 562-8931
Regional Wildlife Program Manager **Greg Schroer** . . . . . (707) 562-8930
Regional Threatened and Endangered Species Coordinator **Patricia A. "Patti" Krueger** . . . . . (707) 562-8954

★ Presidential Appointment Requiring Senate Confirmation ☆ Presidential Appointment □ Schedule C Appointment ◇ Career Senior Foreign Service Appointment
● Career Senior Executive Service (SES) Appointment ○ Non-Career Senior Executive Service (SES) Appointment ■ Postal Career Executive Service

Ecosystem Planning
1323 Club Drive, Vallejo, CA 94592
Fax: (707) 562-9229

Director **Alan D. "Al" Olson** .... (707) 562-8823
Tel: (707) 562-8957
Deputy Director **Mary Beth Hennessy** .... (707) 562-9027
Regional Appeals and Litigation Manager **(Vacant)** .... (707) 562-8945
Regional Analyst **Donald A. "Don" Yasuda** .... (707) 562-8970
Regional Environmental Coordinator **Laura Hierholzer** .... (707) 562-8949
Regional Planner **Richard "Rick" Stevens** .... (707) 562-8950

Engineering
1323 Club Drive, Vallejo, CA 94592
Fax: (707) 562-9047

Regional Engineer **Tyrone Kelley** .... (707) 562-8841
Transportation Engineer **Leslie Boak** .... (707) 562-8876

Fire and Aviation Management
1323 Club Drive, Vallejo, CA 94592
Tel: (707) 562-8737 Fax: (707) 562-9048

Director **Robert "Bob" Baird** .... (707) 562-8925
Deputy Director **Christian R. "Chris" Schow** .... (707) 562-8927
Fax: (707) 562-9048
Assistant Director and Aviation Officer **Jeff M. Power** .... (202) 205-1410
3237 Peacekeeper Way, Fax: (916) 640-1090
Building 200, McClellan, CA 95652
Fire Management Specialist (Fuels and Planning)
Jennifer R. Anderson .... (530) 841-4434
Education: Georgia State BA; Georgia MA
Assistant Director, Strategic Planning **(Vacant)** .... (707) 562-8966
Assistant Director, Workforce Development and Fire Training **Sharon D. Allenbrick** .... (916) 640-1052
Assistant Director, Cooperative Fire Program
Trudie Mahoney .... (707) 562-9184

Human Resources
1323 Club Drive, Vallejo, CA 94592
Fax: (707) 562-9211

Human Resources Officer **Nelson R. Bonilla** .... (707) 562-8736
E-mail: nbonilla@fs.fed.us
Labor Relations Officer **Janet Crowley** .... (707) 562-8802
E-mail: jcrowley@fs.fed.us
Supervisory Human Resources Specialist
Nelson R. Bonilla .... (707) 562-9200
E-mail: nbonilla@fs.fed.us
Supervisory Human Resources Specialist
Donna R. Oglethorpe .... (707) 562-8778
E-mail: donnaroglethorpe@fs.fed.us
Supervisory Human Resources Specialist
Christie M. Porter .... (707) 562-8685
E-mail: cmporter@fs.fed.us
Supervisory Human Resources Specialist
Karen Voorwinden .... (707) 562-9112
E-mail: kvoorwinden@fs.fed.us

Information Management
1323 Club Drive, Vallejo, CA 94592

Director **(Vacant)** .... (707) 562-9019
Fax: (707) 562-9052
Geospatial Services Group Leader **(Vacant)** .... (707) 562-8883
Fax: (707) 562-9056
Regional GIS Coordinator **David J. "Dave" Watkins** .... (707) 562-8933
Vegetation Inventory and Mapping Program Manager
Carlos Ramirez .... (916) 640-1275
E-mail: carlosramirez@fs.fed.us

Law Enforcement and Investigations
1323 Club Drive, Vallejo, CA 94592
Fax: (707) 562-9031

Special Agent-in-Charge **Don Hoang** .... (707) 562-8647

Public Affairs and Communications
1323 Club Drive, Vallejo, CA 94592
Fax: (707) 562-9053

Director **(Vacant)** .... (707) 562-9016
Deputy Director **(Vacant)** .... (707) 562-8995

Public Services
1323 Club Drive, Vallejo, CA 94592
Fax: (707) 562-9055

Director **James J. "Jim" Bacon** .... (707) 562-8856
Deputy Director **(Vacant)** .... (707) 562-8658

State and Private Forestry
1323 Club Drive, Vallejo, CA 94592
Fax: (707) 562-9054

Director **Sherry Hazelhurst** .... (707) 562-8920
Deputy Director **Chris Fischer** .... (707) 562-8921

National Forests – California

Angeles National Forest
701 North Santa Anita Avenue, Arcadia, CA 91006
Tel: (626) 574-1613 Fax: (626) 821-6777
Internet: www.fs.usda.gov/angeles

Forest Supervisor **Jerry Perez** .... (626) 574-1613
Executive Assistant **Lisa Lugo** .... (626) 574-5215
Deputy Forest Supervisor **Dr. Rachel C. Smith PhD** .... (626) 574-5217
Education: Whitman 2003 BA; UC Berkeley 2011 PhD
Patrol Captain **Russell Tuttle** .... (626) 574-5355
Public Affairs Officer **(Vacant)** .... (818) 899-1900
Resource Officer **Julie Uyehara** .... (626) 574-5258
Public Services Officer **Justin Seastrand** .... (626) 574-5278
Forest Engineer **Ricardo Lopez** .... (626) 574-5292
Education: Cal Poly (Pomona) BS, MEN

Cleveland National Forest
10845 Rancho Bernardo Road, Suite 200, San Diego, CA 92127-2107
Tel: (858) 674-2901
Tel: (619) 557-5262 (Emergency Communications Center)
Fax: (619) 557-6935 (Emergency Communications Center)
Fax: (858) 673-6192 Internet: www.fs.usda.gov/cleveland

Forest Supervisor **William Metz** .... (858) 674-2982
Fax: (858) 673-6192
Executive Assistant **La Sean Y. Brown** .... (858) 674-2983
Fire Management Officer **Brian Rhodes** .... (858) 674-2980
Staff Director, Infrastructure **(Vacant)** .... (858) 674-2901
Ecosystem and Planning Staff Officer
Jeffrey "Jeff" Heys .... (858) 524-0136
Lands and Special Use Program Manager
Spencer M. Bleadorn .... (858) 674-2904
Administrative Officer **(Vacant)** .... (858) 674-2917
Civil Rights Officer **Josielyn P. Gauthier** .... (858) 674-2928
E-mail: josielyngauthier@fs.fed.us
Public Affairs Officer **Olivia A. Walker** .... (858) 674-2984
E-mail: owalker@fs.fed.us Fax: (858) 674-2967

Eldorado National Forest
100 Forni Road, Placerville, CA 95667
Tel: (530) 622-5061 TTY: (530) 642-5122 Fax: (530) 621-5297
Internet: www.fs.usda.gov/eldorado

Forest Supervisor **Laurence Crabtree** .... (530) 621-5205
Fax: (530) 562-9055
Public Affairs Officer **Jennifer Chapman** .... (530) 295-5610
Webmaster and Assistant Public Affairs Officer
Kristi Schroeder .... (530) 295-5610
E-mail: kschroeder@fs.fed.us

Inyo National Forest
351 Pacu Lane, Suite 200, Bishop, CA 93514
Tel: (760) 873-2400 TTY: (760) 873-2538 Fax: (760) 873-2458
Internet: www.fs.usda.gov/inyo

Forest Supervisor
Tamera K. "Tammy" Randall-Parker .... (760) 873-2400
Education: Northern Arizona BS

(continued on next page)

★ Presidential Appointment Requiring Senate Confirmation ☆ Presidential Appointment ☐ Schedule C Appointment ◇ Career Senior Foreign Service Appointment
● Career Senior Executive Service (SES) Appointment ○ Non-Career Senior Executive Service (SES) Appointment ■ Postal Career Executive Service

DEPARTMENTS

Inyo National Forest *(continued)*

Public Affairs Officer **Debra Schweizer** . . . . (760) 873-2427
E-mail: debraaschweizer@fs.fed.us

Klamath National Forest
1711 South Main Street, Yreka, CA 96097
Tel: (530) 842-6131 Tel: (530) 841-4485 TTY: (530) 841-4573
Fax: (530) 841-4571 Internet: www.fs.usda.gov/klamath

Forest Supervisor **Patricia A. Grantham** . . . . (530) 841-4502
Deputy Forest Supervisor **LtCol Pierce E. Tucker ANG** . . . (530) 841-4501
Note: Pierce Tucker is on detail from the Forest Service's Region 5 office.
Education: Southern Illinois 1987 BS; Lesley U 1992 MSBA
Public Affairs Officer **Joshua M. "Josh" Veal** . . . . (530) 841-4485
Note: Joshua Veal is on detail from the Forest Service's Region 5 office.
E-mail: joshuaveal@fs.fed.us

Lake Tahoe Basin Management Unit
35 College Drive, South Lake Tahoe, CA 96150
Tel: (530) 543-2600 TTY: (530) 543-0956 Fax: (530) 543-2694
E-mail: mailroom_r5_lake_tahoe_basin@fs.fed.us
Internet: https://www.fs.usda.gov/ltbmu

Forest Supervisor **Jeff Marsolais** . . . . (530) 543-2640
E-mail: smarsolais@fs.fed.us
Deputy Forest Supervisor **(Vacant)** . . . . (530) 543-2641
Legislative and External Affairs Staff Officer
Heather Noel . . . . (530) 543-2608
E-mail: hmnoel@fs.fed.us
Public Affairs Specialist **Lisa A. Herron** . . . . (530) 543-2815
E-mail: laherron@fs.fed.us Fax: (530) 543-2743

Lassen National Forest
2550 Riverside Drive, Susanville, CA 96130
Tel: (530) 257-2151 Fax: (530) 252-6428
Internet: www.fs.usda.gov/lassen
Areas Covered: Butte County; Lassen County; Modoc County; Plumas County; Shasta County; Tehama County

Forest Supervisor **(Vacant)** . . . . (530) 252-6600
Public Affairs Officer **(Vacant)** . . . . (530) 252-6604
Web Manager **Jason Flaherty** . . . . (530) 580-8879
E-mail: jflaherty@fs.fed.us

Los Padres National Forest
6750 Navigator Way, Suite 150, Goleta, CA 93117
Tel: (805) 968-6640 Internet: www.fs.usda.gov/lpnf/

Forest Supervisor (Acting) **Kevin B. Elliott** . . . . (805) 961-5733
Deputy Forest Supervisor **Kenneth E. Heffner** . . . . (805) 961-5733
Fax: (805) 961-5755
Civil Rights Officer **Julissa Gonzalez** . . . . (805) 961-5748
Ecosystem Management Officer **Susan Shaw** . . . . (805) 961-5709
E-mail: sshaw@fs.fed.us
Fire Management Officer **Carolyn Landon** . . . . (805) 961-5741
Public Affairs Officer **Andrew Madsen** . . . . (805) 961-5795
E-mail: andrewmadsen@fs.fed.us
Recreation, Lands and Engineering Officer **(Vacant)** . . . . . (805) 961-5734

Mendocino National Forest
825 North Humboldt Avenue, Willows, CA 95988
Tel: (530) 934-3316 Tel: (530) 934-2350 (Recreation Information)
TTY: (530) 934-7724 Fax: (530) 934-7760
E-mail: mailroom_r5_mendocino@fs.fed.us
Internet: www.fs.usda.gov/mendocino

Forest Supervisor **Gar Abbas** . . . . (530) 934-1100
Public Affairs Officer **Sandra "Punky" Moore** . . . . (530) 934-1137
E-mail: sjmoore@fs.fed.us

Modoc National Forest
225 West 8th Street, Alturas, CA 96101
Tel: (530) 233-5811 Fax: (530) 233-8709
Internet: www.fs.usda.gov/modoc

Forest Supervisor **(Vacant)** . . . . (530) 233-8700
Fax: (530) 233-8719

Modoc National Forest *(continued)*

Public Affairs Staff Officer **Ken L. Sandusky** . . . . (530) 233-8713
E-mail: klsandusky@fs.fed.us

Plumas National Forest
159 Lawrence Street, Box 11500, Quincy, CA 95971-6025
Tel: (530) 283-2050 Fax: (530) 283-7746
E-mail: mailroom_r5_plumas@fs.fed.us Internet: www.fs.usda.gov/plumas

Forest Supervisor **Daniel A. Lovato** . . . . (530) 283-7801
Fax: (530) 283-7746
Deputy Forest Supervisor **Barbara Drake** . . . . (530) 283-7810
Beckworth District Ranger **Matt Jedra** . . . . (530) 836-2575
23 Mohawk Road, Blairsden, CA 96103 Fax: (530) 388-8305
Feather River District Ranger
David B. "Dave" Brillenz . . . . (530) 534-6500
875 Mitchell Avenue, Oroville, CA 95965 Fax: (530) 532-1210
Mount Hough District Ranger **Micki D. Smith** . . . . (530) 283-0555
39696 State Highway Seventy, Quincy, CA 95971 Fax: (530) 283-1821

San Bernardino National Forest
602 South Tippecanoe Avenue, San Bernardino, CA 92408
Tel: (909) 382-2600 Fax: (909) 383-5770 Internet: www.fs.usda.gov/sbnf

Forest Supervisor **Jody Noiron** . . . . (909) 382-2710
Fax: (909) 383-5504
Deputy Forest Supervisor **Kay Wiand** . . . . (909) 382-2603
Public Affairs Officer **Zachary T. Behrens** . . . . (909) 382-2788
E-mail: zbehrens@fs.fed.us
Deputy Public Affairs Officer **(Vacant)** . . . . (909) 382-2788
Fax: (909) 383-5770
Administrative Operations Specialist **Lawrence A. Lee** . . . (909) 382-2669
E-mail: lawrencealee@fs.fed.us Fax: (909) 383-5504

Sequoia National Forest
1839 South Newcomb Street, Porterville, CA 93257
Tel: (559) 784-1500 Fax: (559) 781-4744
E-mail: mailroom_r5_sequoia@fs.fed.us
Internet: www.fs.usda.gov/sequoia/

Forest Supervisor **Teresa Benson** . . . . (559) 784-1500 ext. 1111
Public Affairs Officer **Alicia Embrey** . . . . (559) 784-1500 ext. 1112
E-mail: aembrey@fs.fed.us

Shasta-Trinity National Forest
USDA Service Center, 3644 Avtech Parkway, Redding, CA 96002
Tel: (530) 226-2500 Fax: (530) 226-2470 Internet: www.fs.usda.gov/stnf

Forest Supervisor **Scott A. Russell** . . . . (530) 226-2520
Education: Stanford 1977 BS
Executive Assistant **Nancy C. Henderson** . . . . (530) 226-2522
E-mail: nancychenderson@fs.fed.us
Deputy Forest Supervisor **Terri Simon-Jackson** . . . . (530) 226-2521
Public Affairs Officer **Carol Underhill** . . . . (530) 226-2494
E-mail: cunderhill@fs.fed.us
Assistant Public Affairs Officer **(Vacant)** . . . . (530) 226-2595

Sierra National Forest
1600 Tollhouse Road, Clovis, CA 93611-0532
Tel: (559) 297-0706 Fax: (559) 294-4809
Internet: www.fs.usda.gov/sierra/

Forest Supervisor **Dean A. Gould** . . . . (559) 297-0706 ext. 4801
Public Affairs Officer **(Vacant)** . . . . (559) 297-0706 ext. 4804

Six Rivers National Forest
1330 Bayshore Way, Eureka, CA 95501-3834
Tel: (707) 442-1721 Fax: (707) 442-9242 Fax: (707) 441-3598
Internet: https://www.fs.usda.gov/srnf

Forest Supervisor **Ted O. McArthur** . . . . (707) 441-3531
Fax: (707) 441-3598
Deputy Forest Supervisor (Acting)
Stewart C. "Stew" Richter . . . . (707) 562-8851
Fax: (707) 441-3598
Executive Assistant **(Vacant)** . . . . (707) 441-3517
Fax: (707) 441-3598
Public Affairs Officer **Bridget M. Litten** . . . . (707) 441-3673
E-mail: bridgetmlitten@fs.fed.us Fax: (707) 442-9242

★ Presidential Appointment Requiring Senate Confirmation ☆ Presidential Appointment □ Schedule C Appointment ◇ Career Senior Foreign Service Appointment
● Career Senior Executive Service (SES) Appointment ○ Non-Career Senior Executive Service (SES) Appointment ■ Postal Career Executive Service

Stanislaus National Forest
19777 Greenley Road, Sonora, CA 95370
Tel: (209) 532-3671 Fax: (209) 533-1890
Internet: www.fs.usda.gov/stanislaus

Forest Supervisor **Jason Kuiken** .... (209) 288-6265
Fax: (209) 532-5265
Deputy Forest Supervisor **Scott Tangenberg** .... (209) 288-6265
Public Affairs Officer **Diana Fredlund** .... (209) 288-6261
E-mail: dfredlund@fs.fed.us

Tahoe National Forest
631 Coyote Street, Nevada City, CA 95959-6003
Tel: (530) 478-6100 Fax: (530) 478-6109
Internet: www.fs.usda.gov/tahoe

Forest Supervisor **Eliseo "Eli" Ilano** .... (530) 478-6200
Deputy Forest Supervisor (Acting) **Michael A. Green** .... (530) 478-6201
Public Affairs Officer **(Vacant)** .... (530) 478-6205

Northern California Service Center, Northern Operations
6101 Airport Road, Redding, CA 96002
Tel: (530) 226-8010 Fax: (530) 223-1536

Assistant Director **Paige R. Boyer** .... (530) 226-2700
GACC Manager **Anthony J. Masovero** .... (530) 226-2812
Deputy GACC Manager **Curtis "Curt" Stanley** .... (530) 226-2835
Information Technology Specialist **(Vacant)** .... (530) 226-2711
Fire Cache Manager **Mark Garland** .... (530) 226-2851
Fax: (530) 226-2854

Forest Service – Region 6 (Pacific Northwest Region)
1220 SW Third Avenue, Portland, OR 97204
Mail: P.O. Box 3623, Portland, OR 97208-3623
Tel: (503) 808-2468 Fax: (503) 808-2210 Internet: www.fs.usda.gov/r6
Areas Covered: OR, WA

• Regional Forester **Glenn Casamassa** .... (503) 808-2200
E-mail: gcasamassa@fs.fed.us
Education: Utah State BS
Executive Assistant **Monica L. Neal** .... (503) 808-2204
E-mail: monicaneal@fs.fed.us
Deputy Regional Forester **Dianne C. Guidry** .... (503) 808-2468
Education: Maryland; Oklahoma City MBA
Deputy Regional Forester (Acting) **Debbie A. Hollen** .... (503) 808-2203
Deputy Regional Forester **Lisa Northrop** .... (503) 808-2202
Education: UC Riverside BS; Tennessee MS
Executive Assistant to the Deputy Regional Foresters
Catherine A. "Cathy" Pearson .... (503) 808-2213

Acquisition Management
1220 SW Third Avenue, Portland, OR 97204-2825
Tel: (503) 808-2380 Fax: (503) 808-2365

Director **Charles Hill** .... (503) 808-2263
E-mail: chill@fs.fed.us

Budget and Financial Management
1220 SW Third Avenue, Portland, OR 97204-2825
Tel: (503) 808-2306 Fax: (503) 808-2467

Director **Debbie Boggess** .... (503) 808-2271

Engineering
1220 SW Third Avenue, Portland, OR 97204-2825
Tel: (503) 808-2500 Fax: (503) 808-2511

Director **Christy Darden** .... (503) 808-2500
Tel: (503) 808-2532
Deputy Director **Amy Thomas** .... (503) 808-2532

Fire and Aviation Management
1220 SW Third Avenue, Portland, OR 97204-2825
Tel: (503) 808-2145 Fax: (503) 808-2511

Director **John E. Giller** .... (503) 808-2145
Assistant Director for Business **Cici Chitwood** .... (503) 808-2466
Assistant Director for Fire Integrations **Craig Glazier** .... (503) 808-2145
Assistant Director Aviation Officer
Aaron L. Schoolcraft .... (503) 808-2359

Fire and Aviation Management *(continued)*

Assistant Fire Director, Operations (Acting)
Steve Rawlings .... (503) 808-2314
Deputy Director **Jeffrey L. Fedrizzi** .... (503) 808-6461
NW Coordination Center Manager **Dan O'Brien** .... (503) 808-2732
E-mail: dobrien02@fs.fed.us Fax: (503) 808-2750

Civil Rights
1220 SW Third Avenue, Portland, OR 97204-2825

Director Pacific NW CR Service Center (CRSC)
Toya L. Bligen .... (503) 808-2818
E-mail: tbligen@fs.fed.us

Data Resources Management
1220 SW Third Avenue, Portland, OR 97204-2825
Tel: (503) 808-2800 Fax: (503) 808-2586

Director **Nora Miebach** .... (503) 808-2800
E-mail: nmiebach@fs.fed.us
Assistant Director **Lisa Greber** .... (503) 808-2605
E-mail: lgreber@fs.fed.us

Natural Resources
1220 SW Third Avenue, Portland, OR 97204-2825
Tel: (503) 808-2955 Fax: (503) 808-2469

Director **Marie-Louise "M.L." Smith** .... (503) 808-2955
Education: Michigan 1989 BS; Wisconsin 1992 MS; New Hampshire 2000 PhD
Assistant Director **Eric Johnston** .... (503) 808-2922

Occupational Safety and Health Program
1220 SW Third Avenue, Portland, OR 97204-2825

Manager **Charles L. "Buddy" Byrd** .... (503) 808-2626
E-mail: clbyrd@fs.fed.us

Office of Communications and Community Engagement
1220 SW Third Avenue, Portland, OR 97204-2825
Tel: (503) 808-2240 Fax: (503) 808-2229

Director **Shoshona M. "Shoni" Pilip-Florea** .... (503) 808-2240
E-mail: smpilipflorea@fs.fed.us
Assistant Director (Acting) **Heather C. Zissler** .... (503) 808-2637
E-mail: hzissler@fs.fed.us

Recreation, Lands and Mineral Resources
1220 SW Third Avenue, Portland, OR 97204-2825
Tel: (503) 808-2966 Fax: (503) 808-2429

Director **Tracy Tophooven** .... (503) 808-2966
Assistant Director for Lands and Minerals
Karen Brand .... (503) 808-2421
Assistant Director for Recreation **Michelle Mitchell** .... (503) 808-2438

Resource Planning and Monitoring
1220 SW Third Avenue, Portland, OR 97204-2825
Fax: (503) 808-2255

Director **Julia Riber** .... (503) 808-2266

State and Private Forestry
1220 SW Third Avenue, Portland, OR 97204-2825
Tel: (503) 808-2340 Fax: (503) 808-2339

Director **Debbie A. Hollen** .... (503) 808-2340
Assistant Director **Karl R. Dalla Rosa** .... (503) 808-2913
Assistant Director Resource Planning and Monitoring
Debra R. Whitall .... (503) 808-2464
Forest Legacy & Community Forest Program Manager
Bradley Siemens .... (503) 808-3535

Support Services Group
1220 SW Third Avenue, Portland, OR 97204-2825
Fax: (503) 808-2469

Supervisory Support Services **Rosie Chaney** .... (503) 808-2460
E-mail: rmchaney@fs.fed.us
Supervisory Administrative Operations Assistant
(Vacant) .... (503) 808-2450

★ Presidential Appointment Requiring Senate Confirmation ☆ Presidential Appointment ☐ Schedule C Appointment ◇ Career Senior Foreign Service Appointment
● Career Senior Executive Service (SES) Appointment ○ Non-Career Senior Executive Service (SES) Appointment ■ Postal Career Executive Service

Columbia River Gorge National Scenic Area
902 Wasco Street, Suite 200, Hood River, OR 97031
Tel: (541) 308-1700 Fax: (541) 386-1916
Internet: www.fs.usda.gov/crgnsa

Area Manager **Lynn Burditt** .... (541) 308-1706
Lands Staff Officer **Miki Fujikawa** .... (541) 308-1714
Public Affairs Officer **Rachel Pawlitz** .... (541) 308-1744
E-mail: rpawlitz@fs.fed.us

Columbia Basin Job Corps Center
Building 2402, 6739 - 24th Street, Moses Lake, WA 98837
Tel: (509) 762-5581 Fax: (509) 793-1758

Center Director **Karl W. Lester** .... (509) 793-1625

Fort Simcoe Job Corps Center
40 Abella Lane, White Swan, WA 98952
Tel: (509) 874-2244 Fax: (509) 874-2983
Internet: https://fortsimcoe.jobcorps.gov/

Center Director **Bradley L. "Brad" Hill** .... (509) 874-8901
Education: George Washington 2010 MA

National Forests – Oregon

Deschutes National Forest
63095 Deschutes Market Road, Bend, OR 97701
Tel: (541) 383-5300 Fax: (541) 383-5531
Internet: www.fs.usda.gov/main/deschutes/home

Forest Supervisor **John P. Allen** .... (541) 383-5512
Deputy Forest Supervisor **Shanda Dekome** .... (541) 383-5709
Scenic Byways Leader and Landscape Architect
Robin Lee Gyorgyfalvy FASLA .... (541) 383-4786
Education: Dartmouth (Attended); Mount Holyoke 1973 BA; Oregon 1978

Fremont-Winema National Forests
1301 South G Street, Lakeview, OR 97630
Tel: (541) 947-2151 TTY: (541) 947-6239 Fax: (541) 947-6399
Internet: www.fs.usda.gov/fremont-winema

Forest Supervisor **Barry Imler** .... (541) 947-6201
Education: Cochise 1990 AS; Arizona 1992 ScB, 1998 ScM
Deputy Forest Supervisor (Acting)
Kathleen M. "Kathy" Johnson .... (541) 947-6205
Education: Humboldt State BS
Public Affairs Officer **Lisa Swinney** .... (541) 947-5419
E-mail: lswinney@fs.fed.us

Malheur National Forest
431 Patterson Bridge Road, John Day, OR 97845
Mail: P.O. Box 909, John Day, OR 97845
Tel: (541) 575-3000 Fax: (541) 575-3001
Internet: www.fs.fed.us/r6/malheur

Forest Supervisor **Steve Beverlin** .... (541) 575-3073
Deputy Forest Supervisor **Ryan E. Nehl** .... (541) 575-3000
Public Affairs Officer **Michael J. Stearly** .... (541) 575-3144
E-mail: mstearly@fs.fed.us

Mt. Hood National Forest
16400 Champion Way, Sandy, OR 97055
Tel: (503) 668-1700 Fax: (503) 668-1641
Internet: www.fs.usda.gov/mthood

Forest Supervisor **Richard Periman** .... (503) 668-1750
Fax: (503) 558-1794
Deputy Forest Supervisor **Jim DeMaagd** .... (503) 668-1749
Fax: (503) 668-1794
Executive Assistant **Lisa Coriell** .... (503) 668-1752

Ochoco National Forest
3160 NE Third Street, Prineville, OR 97754
Tel: (541) 416-6500 Fax: (541) 416-6695
Internet: www.fs.usda.gov/ochoco

Forest Supervisor **Shane Jeffries** .... (541) 416-6625

Rogue River - Siskiyou National Forest
3040 Biddle Road, Medford, OR 97504
Tel: (541) 618-2200 Fax: (541) 618-2144 TTY: (866) 296-3823
Internet: www.fs.usda.gov/rogue-siskiyou

Forest Supervisor **Merv L. George, Jr.** .... (541) 618-2030
Education: Humboldt State BA
Deputy Forest Supervisor **Craig P. Trulock** .... (541) 618-2032
Staff Assistant **Anna Lori Blundell** .... (541) 618-2034
Public Affairs Officer **Virginia M. Gibbons** .... (541) 618-2113
E-mail: vgibbons@fs.fed.us Fax: (541) 618-2143

Siuslaw National Forest
4077 SW Research Way, Corvallis, OR 97333
Mail: POBox 1148, Corvallis, OR 97339
Tel: (541) 750-7000 TTY: (541) 750-7006
Tel: (541) 563-8400 (Central Coast Ranger District) Tel: (541) 271-3611 (Oregon Dunes National Recreation Area Visitor Center)
Fax: (541) 750-7234 Internet: www.fs.usda.gov/siuslaw

Forest Supervisor **Robert F. Sanchez** .... (541) 750-7008
Education: Idaho BS
Webmaster **Elaine Bernat** .... (541) 225-6381
E-mail: ebernat@fs.fed.us Fax: (541) 225-6224

Umatilla National Forest
72510 Coyote Road, Pendleton, OR 97801
Tel: (541) 278-3716 Fax: (541) 278-3730
E-mail: r6_umatilla_public_inquiries@fs.fed.us
Internet: www.fs.usda.gov/umatilla

Forest Supervisor **Eric J. Watrud** .... (541) 278-3752
Education: Oregon State BS Fax: (541) 278-3920
Public Affairs Officer **Darcy Weseman** .... (541) 278-3722
E-mail: dweseman@fs.fed.us

Umpqua National Forest
2900 NW Stewart Parkway, Roseburg, OR 97471
Tel: (541) 957-3200 Fax: (541) 957-3495
Internet: www.fs.usda.gov/umpqua

Forest Supervisor **Alice B. Carlton** .... (541) 957-3203
Education: Oregon State 1979 BS
Deputy Forest Supervisor **David "Dave" Warnack** .... (541) 957-3281
Public Affairs Officer **Mark R. Turney** .... (541) 957-3200
Education: Syracuse BA

Wallowa-Whitman National Forest
1550 Dewey Avenue, Baker City, OR 97814
Mail: P.O. Box 907, Baker City, OR 97814
Tel: (541) 523-6391 Fax: (541) 523-1315
Internet: www.fs.usda.gov/wallowa-whitman

Forest Supervisor **Tom Montoya** .... (541) 523-1201
Deputy Forest Supervisor **Charles "Chuck" Oliver** .... (541) 523-1203
Public Affairs Officer **Kathryn L. "Katy" Gray** .... (541) 523-1246
E-mail: kathrynlgray@fs.fed.us

Willamette National Forest
3106 Pierce Parkway, Suite D, Springfield, OR 97477
Tel: (541) 225-6300 Fax: (541) 225-6220
Internet: fs.usda.gov/main/willamette/home

Forest Supervisor **Tracy Beck** .... (541) 225-6312
Fax: (541) 225-6222
Deputy Forest Supervisor **Holly Jewkes** .... (541) 225-6311
Education: New Hampshire BS; Alaska (Fairbanks) MS
Lead Planner **Suzanne Schindler** .... (541) 225-6436
Education: Montana (Western) 1986 BSF Fax: (541) 225-6377
Detroit District Ranger **Dave Halemeier** .... (503) 854-3366
44125 North Santiam Highway SE, Detroit, OR 97342 Fax: (503) 854-4239
McKenzie River District Ranger **Darren M. Cross** .... (541) 822-3381
576000 McKenzie Highway, Blue River, OR 97413 Fax: (541) 225-6377
Middle Fork District Ranger **Duane Bishop** .... (541) 782-2283
46375 Highway 58, Westfir, OR 97492 Fax: (541) 782-5306
Sweet Home District Ranger **Cindy Glick** .... (541) 367-3147
4431 Highway 20, Sweet Home, OR 97386 Fax: (541) 367-2367

★ Presidential Appointment Requiring Senate Confirmation ☆ Presidential Appointment ☐ Schedule C Appointment ◇ Career Senior Foreign Service Appointment
● Career Senior Executive Service (SES) Appointment ○ Non-Career Senior Executive Service (SES) Appointment ■ Postal Career Executive Service

Willamette National Forest *(continued)*

Webmaster **Elaine Bernat** .... (541) 225-6381
E-mail: ebernat@fs.fed.us Fax: (541) 225-6224

National Forests – Washington

Colville National Forest

765 South Main Street, Colville, WA 99114-2507
Tel: (509) 684-7000 Fax: (509) 684-7280 E-mail: colville@fs.fed.us
Internet: www.fs.usda.gov/colville

Forest Supervisor **Rodney D. Smoldon** .... (509) 684-7015
Education: Eastern Washington 1985
Executive Assistant **Janet B. Thrasher** .... (509) 684-7163

Gifford Pinchot National Forest

1501 East Evergreen Boulevard, Vancouver, WA 98661
Tel: (360) 891-5000 Fax: (360) 891-5045 E-mail: r6_gp_forest@fs.fed.us
Internet: www.fs.usda.gov/giffordpinchot

Forest Supervisor **Gina Owens** .... (360) 891-5100
Deputy Forest Supervisor **Angela Elam** .... (306) 891-5101
Public Affairs Officer **Sue Ripp** .... (360) 891-5222
E-mail: sripp@fs.fed.us Fax: (360) 891-5010

Mt. Baker-Snoqualmie National Forest

2930 Wetmore Avenue, Suite 3A, Everett, WA 98201
Tel: (425) 783-6000 Tel: (800) 627-0062 Fax: (425) 783-0212
E-mail: mailroom_r6_mt_baker_snoqualmie@fs.fed.us
Internet: www.fs.usda.gov/mbs/

Forest Supervisor **Jamie Kingsbury** .... (425) 783-6010
Deputy Forest Supervisor **Diane Freeman** .... (425) 783-6011
Public Affairs Officer **Tracy O'Toole** .... (425) 783-6015
E-mail: tracymotoole@fs.fed.us

Okanogan - Wenatchee National Forest

215 Melody Lane, Wenatchee, WA 98801-5933
Tel: (509) 664-9200 Fax: (509) 664-9280
Internet: www.fs.usda.gov/okawen

Forest Supervisor **Mike R. Williams** .... (509) 664-9323
Fax: (509) 664-9286
Deputy Forest Supervisor **Erick J. Walker** .... (509) 664-9200
Education: Nevada (Reno) 1992 BS

Olympic National Forest

1835 Black Lake Boulevard SW, Suite A, Olympia, WA 98512-5623
Tel: (360) 956-2402 Fax: (360) 956-2330
Internet: www.fs.fed.us/r6/olympic

Forest Supervisor **Reta Laford** .... (360) 956-2301
E-mail: rlaford@fs.fed.us
Public Affairs Officer **Susan Garner** .... (360) 956-2390
E-mail: scgarner@fs.fed.us
Administrative Assistant **Grace A. Haight** .... (360) 956-2303

Forest Service – Region 8 (Southern Region)

1720 Peachtree Road NW, Suite 760 South, Atlanta, GA 30309
Tel: (404) 347-4095 Fax: (404) 347-1781
Internet: www.fs.usda.gov/main/r8/home
Areas Covered: AL, AR, FL, GA, KY, LA, MS, NC, OK, PR, SC, TN, TX, VI, VA

● Regional Forester (Acting) **Ken S. Arney** .... (404) 347-4177
E-mail: karney@fs.fed.us
Executive Assistant **Silvia Molina** .... (404) 347-7930
Deputy Regional Forester for Natural Resources
Frank R. Beum .... (404) 347-4177

Civil Rights Unit

1720 Peachtree Road NW, Atlanta, GA 30309
Tel: (404) 347-7358 Fax: (404) 347-0563

Director **Wil Santiago** .... (404) 347-1628
E-mail: wsantiago@fs.fed.us

Law Enforcement and Investigations

1720 Peachtree Road NW, Atlanta, GA 30309
Special Agent-in-Charge
Michael E. "Mike" Donaldson .... (404) 347-3701
Assistant Special Agent-in-Charge **Courtney McCrae** .... (404) 347-2522
Assistant Special Agent-in-Charge **Brian Southard** ...... (404) 347-4182

Public Affairs Unit

1720 Peachtree Road NW, Atlanta, GA 30309
Tel: (404) 347-4192 Fax: (404) 347-1781

Director **Stephanie Neal Johnson** .... (404) 347-7226
E-mail: snjohnson@fs.fed.us
Legislative Affairs Liaison **Steve Bekkerus** .... (404) 347-7240
E-mail: sbekkerus@fs.fed.us
Webmaster **Russell L. Chaffin** .... (404) 347-3284
E-mail: rchaffin@fs.fed.us

Natural Resources Team

1720 Peachtree Road NW, Atlanta, GA 30309
Tel: (404) 347-4177 Fax: (404) 347-4821

Deputy Regional Forester **Jerome Thomas** .... (404) 347-2693
Biological and Physical Resources Director
Margrett "Gretta" Boley .... (404) 347-7397
Education: Southern U A&M BS
Forest Management Director **Jose Castro** .... (404) 347-7396

Operations, Recreation and Engineering Team

1720 Peachtree Road NW, Atlanta, GA 30309
Tel: (404) 347-4177 Fax: (404) 347-4821

Deputy Regional Forester (Acting) **Mark D. Green** ...... (404) 347-4044
Executive Assistant **Renai Artis** .... (404) 347-7248
Director, Budget and Financial Management
Sherry Reaves .... (404) 347-2692
E-mail: sreaves@fs.fed.us
Safety and Health Program Manager **Darryl M. Harley** ... (404) 347-7781
E-mail: dmharley@fs.fed.us
Lands, Minerals and Uses Director
Timothy "Tim" Abing .... (404) 347-3989
Education: Wisconsin (Platteville) 1980 BS
Planning Director **Peter T. Gaulke** .... (404) 347-3183
Director of Engineering **(Vacant)** .... (404) 347-7395
Procurement and Property Director
Anthony "Tony" Love .... (404) 347-2597
E-mail: alove@fs.fed.us
Recreation Director **Tiffany P. Williams** .... (404) 347-2479
E-mail: tiffanypwilliams@fs.fed.us

State and Private Forestry Team

1720 Peachtree Road NW, Atlanta, GA 30309
Tel: (404) 347-4177 Fax: (404) 347-4821

Deputy Regional Forester (Acting) **Jeffrey Vail** .... (404) 347-4408
Executive Assistant **Renai Artis** .... (404) 347-7248
Cooperative Forestry Director **Kay Reed** .... (404) 347-7200
Director, Forest Health Protection Unit **Donald Duerr** .... (404) 347-2719
Alexandria (LA) Field Office Representative **(Vacant)** ... (318) 473-7294
2500 Shreveport Highway, Pineville, LA 71360 Fax: (318) 473-7292
Asheville (NC) Field Office Representative
William A. "Bill" Carothers .... (828) 257-4321
200 Weaver Blvd., Asheville, NC 28804 Fax: (828) 257-4856

Southern Area Coordinator Center

1200 Ashwood Parkway, Suite 230, Atlanta, GA 30338
Tel: (678) 320-3000 Fax: (678) 320-3036

Center Manager **(Vacant)** .... (678) 320-3001

Fire and Aviation Unit

Fire and Aviation Director **Shardul Raval** .... (404) 347-3464
Fixed Wing Inspector Pilot
Timmy B. Rikard .... (770) 237-0119 ext. 1015
Briscoe Field, 460 Briscoe Boulevard,
Suite 101, Lawrenceville, GA 30045

(continued on next page)

DEPARTMENTS

★ Presidential Appointment Requiring Senate Confirmation ☆ Presidential Appointment □ Schedule C Appointment ◇ Career Senior Foreign Service Appointment
● Career Senior Executive Service (SES) Appointment ○ Non-Career Senior Executive Service (SES) Appointment ■ Postal Career Executive Service

Fire and Aviation Unit *(continued)*

Inspector Pilot **(Vacant)** .... (770) 237-0119 ext. 1004
Briscoe Field, 460 Briscoe Boulevard,
Suite 101, Lawrenceville, GA 30045

National Tree Seed Laboratory
5156 Riggins Mill Road, Dry Branch, GA 31020
Mail: USDA Forest Service, Route 1, Box 182B,
Dry Branch, GA 31020-9696
Tel: (478) 751-3551 Fax: (478) 751-3554

Laboratory Director **Robert P. Karrfalt** .... (478) 751-4134

National Forests – Alabama
2946 Chestnut Street, Montgomery, AL 36107-3010
Tel: (334) 832-4470 Fax: (334) 241-8111
Internet: www.fs.usda.gov/alabama
Areas Covered: Conecuh National Forest; Talladega National Forest; Tuskegee National Forest; William B. Bankhead National Forest

Forest Supervisor (Acting) **Gary Church** .... (334) 832-4470 ext. 165
Note: Gary Church is Acting Forest Supervisor while Carl Petrick is on detail to the Forest Service's Mississippi office. Fax: (334) 241-8111
Education: Georgia 1994 BS

Forest Supervisor **Carl Petrick** .... (334) 832-4470 ext. 165
Note: On detail to the Forest Service's Mississippi office. Fax: (334) 241-8111

Public Affairs Officer **Freeman Brown** .... (334) 241-8144
Fax: (334) 241-8177

Administrative Officer **Anthony J. Edwards** .... (334) 241-8159
E-mail: ajedwards@fs.fed.us

National Forests – Arkansas
Ouachita National Forest
Federal Building, 100 Reserve Street, 2nd Floor, Hot Springs, AR 71901
Mail: Ouachita National Forest, P.O. Box 1270, Hot Springs, AR 71902
Tel: (501) 321-5202 Fax: (501) 321-5334
Internet: www.fs.usda.gov/ouachita

Forest Supervisor **Norman L. Wagoner** .... (501) 321-5275
Deputy Forest Supervisor **Shawn Cochran** .... (501) 321-5274

Ozark and St. Francis National Forests
605 West Main, Russellville, AR 72801-3614
Tel: (479) 964-7200 Fax: (479) 964-7255
Internet: www.fs.usda.gov/osfnf/

Forest Supervisor **Reggie L. Blackwell** .... (479) 964-7200
Public Affairs Officer **Tracy P. Farley** .... (479) 964-7232
E-mail: tfarley@fs.fed.us

National Forests – Florida
National Forests in Florida, 325 John Knox Road,
Suite F-100, Tallahassee, FL 32303-4160
Tel: (850) 523-8566 Fax: (850) 523-8543 E-mail: mailroomr8fl@fs.fed.us
Internet: www.fs.usda.gov/florida
Areas Covered: Apalachicola National Forest; Ocala National Forest; Osceola National Forest

Forest Supervisor **Kelly M. Russell** .... (850) 523-8547
Fax: (850) 523-8504

Executive Assistant **Carla S. Martin** .... (850) 523-8549
E-mail: carlamartin@fs.fed.us

Deputy Forest Supervisor **(Vacant)**..................... (850) 523-8545
Fax: (850) 523-8504

Public Affairs Officer **Michelle Burnett** .... (850) 523-8568
E-mail: michelleburnett@fs.fed.us Fax: (850) 523-8505

National Forests – Georgia
Chattahoochee and Oconee National Forests
1755 Cleveland Highway, Gainesville, GA 30501
Tel: (770) 297-3000 Fax: (770) 297-3011 Internet: www.fs.usda.gov/conf

Forest Supervisor **Betty M. Jewett** .... (770) 297-3010
Fax: (770) 297-3025

Chattahoochee and Oconee National Forests *(continued)*

Public Affairs Officer **Judy Toppins** .... (770) 297-3061
E-mail: jrtoppins@fs.fed.us

National Forests – Kentucky
Daniel Boone National Forest
1700 Bypass Road, Winchester, KY 40391
Tel: (859) 745-3100 Fax: (859) 744-1568 Internet: www.fs.usda.gov/dbnf

Forest Supervisor **Dan Olsen** .... (859) 745-3100 ext. 101
Education: SUNY (Morrisville) 1980 AS

Deputy Forest Supervisor **Harvey Scott Ray** .... (859) 745-3102
Public Affairs Officer **Marie Walker** .... (859) 745-3145
E-mail: mwalker04@fs.fed.us

Webmaster **Gwen Hensley** .... (859) 745-3135
E-mail: ghensley@fs.fed.us

National Forests – Louisiana
Kisatchie National Forest
2500 Shreveport Highway, Pineville, LA 71360-2009
Tel: (318) 473-7160 Fax: (318) 473-7117
Internet: www.fs.usda.gov/kisatchie

Forest Supervisor **(Vacant)** .... (936) 639-8506
Fax: (318) 473-7066

Executive Assistant **Charlene Howell** .... (318) 473-7102
Fax: (318) 473-7066

Public Affairs Officer **James R. "Jim" Caldwell** .... (318) 473-7168
E-mail: jcaldwell@fs.fed.us

Procurement and Contracting **Donna Oliveria** .... (318) 473-7116
E-mail: doliveria@fs.fed.us Fax: (318) 473-7106

National Forests – Mississippi
200 S. Lamar St., Suite 500-N, Jackson, MS 39201
Tel: (601) 965-1600 Fax: (601) 965-1780
Internet: www.fs.usda.gov/mississippi
Areas Covered: Bienville National Forest; Chickasawhay National Forest; Delta National Forest; De Soto National Forest; Holly Springs National Forest; Homochitto National Forest; Tombigbee National Forest

Forest Supervisor (Acting) **Carl Petrick** .... (601) 965-1602
Note: On detail from the Forest Service's Alabama office..
Executive Assistant **(Vacant)** .... (601) 965-1602
Fax: (601) 965-1783

Deputy Forest Supervisor **(Vacant)**.................... (601) 965-1651
Fax: (601) 965-1783

Administrative Officer **(Vacant)** .... (601) 965-1649
Public Affairs Officer **Mario T. Rossilli** .... (601) 965-1647
E-mail: mtrossilli@fs.fed.us

Bienville District Ranger **Andy Hunter** .... (601) 384-5876
3473 Highway 35 South, Forest, MS 39074

Chickasawhay District Ranger **(Vacant)** .... (601) 428-0594
968 Highway 15 South, Laurel, MS 39443

Delta District Ranger **Valencia C. Morris** .... (662) 873-6256
68 Frontage Road, Rolling Fork, MS 39159

De Soto District Ranger **Anne Casey** .... (601) 528-6160
654 West Frontage Road, Wiggins, MS 39577
Education: Auburn BSC; Arizona MS

Holly Springs District Ranger
Caren F. Briscoe .... (662) 236-6550 ext. 241
1000 Front Street, Oxford, MS 38655

Homochitto District Ranger **Jonny Fryar** .... (601) 384-5876 ext. 156
1200 highway 184 East, Meadville, MS 39653
Education: Louisiana Tech U

Tombigbee District Ranger **Caren F. Briscoe** ..... (662) 285-3264 ext. 14
912, Ackerman, MS 39735

★ Presidential Appointment Requiring Senate Confirmation ☆ Presidential Appointment □ Schedule C Appointment ◇ Career Senior Foreign Service Appointment
● Career Senior Executive Service (SES) Appointment ○ Non-Career Senior Executive Service (SES) Appointment ■ Postal Career Executive Service

National Forests – North Carolina
160-A Zillicoa Street, Asheville, NC 28801
Tel: (828) 257-4200 Fax: (828) 257-4263
Internet: www.fs.usda.gov/nfsnc
Areas Covered: Appalachian National Forest; Cheoah National Forest; Croatan National Forest; Grandfather National Forest; Nantahala National Forest; Pisgah National Forest; Uwharrie National Forest

Forest Supervisor **Allen Nicholas** .... (828) 257-4269
Fax: (828) 259-0584
Deputy Forest Supervisor **(Vacant)** .... (828) 257-4270
Fax: (828) 259-0584
Law Enforcement Officer **(Vacant)** .... (828) 257-4267
Public Affairs Officer **Cathryn "Cathy" Dowd** .... (828) 257-4215
E-mail: cdowd@fs.fed.us

Croatan National Forest
141 East Fisher Avenue, New Bern, NC 28560

Forest Supervisor (Acting) **Kevin Knesek** .... (252) 632-5628

Nantahala National Forest
90 Sloan Road, Franklin, NC 28734

Forest Supervisor **(Vacant)** .... (828) 524-6441
Cheoah District Ranger **Andy Gaston** .... (828) 479-6431
1070 Massey Branch Road, Robbinsville, NC 28771
Nantahala District Ranger **Mike Wilkins** .... (828) 524-6441
1070 Massey Branch Road, Robbinsville, NC 28771
Tusquitee District Ranger **Andy Gaston** .... (828) 837-5152
123 Woodland Drive, Murphy, NC 28906

Pisgah National Forest
1600 Pisgah Highway, Pisgah Forest, NC 28768

Forest Supervisor **(Vacant)** .... (828) 877-3265
Appalachian District Ranger
Richard M. Thornburgh .... (828) 689-9694 ext. 101
Grandfather District Ranger **Nicholas "Nick" Larson** .... (828) 652-2144
109 Lawing Drive, Nebo, NC 28761
Pisgah District Ranger **David M. Casey** .... (828) 877-3265
Education: Tennessee Tech 2001 BS; Tennessee 2004 MS

Uwharrie National Forest
789 NC 24/27 East, Troy, NC 27371
E-mail: uwharrie@fs.fed.us

District Ranger **Michael "Mike" Spisak** .... (910) 576-6391
Education: Penn State BSF

National Forests – Puerto Rico and the Virgin Islands

El Yunque National Forest
HC-01, Box 13490, Rio Grande, PR 00745-9625
Tel: (787) 888-1880 TTY: (800) 260-2050 Fax: (787) 888-5685
Internet: www.fs.usda.gov/elyunque

Forest Supervisor **Sharon I. Wallace** .... (787) 888-5607
Fax: (787) 888-5668
Forest Ecosystem and Planning Team Leader
Pedro Ríos .... (787) 888-5655
E-mail: prios@fs.fed.us
Forest Planner and Administration Team Leader
(Vacant) .... (787) 888-5655
Fax: (787) 888-5685
Law Enforcement and Investigation Team Leader
Derek Ortiz .... (787) 888-5675
E-mail: derekortiz@fs.fed.us Fax: (787) 888-5680
Forest Engineer (Acting) **Rachael E. Thurston** .... (787) 888-5669
Fax: (787) 888-5685
Public Affairs Officer **Carolyn J. Krupp** .... (787) 888-5616
E-mail: ckrupp@fs.fed.us

National Forests – South Carolina

Francis Marion and Sumter National Forests
4931 Broad River Road, Columbia, SC 29212-3530
Tel: (803) 561-4000 TTY: (803) 561-4023 Fax: (803) 561-4004
E-mail: mailroom_r8_francis_marion@fs.fed.us
Internet: https://www.fs.usda.gov/scnfs

Forest Supervisor **Richard "Rick" Lint** .... (803) 561-4081
GIS Planning and Public Affairs Officer **(Vacant)** .... (803) 561-4091
Public Affairs Specialist
Pamela M. "Pam" Baltimore .... (803) 561-4091
E-mail: pmbaltimore@fs.fed.us
Public Affairs Specialist **Gwyn A. Ingram** .... (803) 561-4007
E-mail: gingram@fs.fed.us
Andrew Pickens District Ranger **Robbie Sitzlar** .... (864) 638-9568
112 Andrew Pickens Circle, Mountain Rest, SC 29664
Enoree District Ranger **(Vacant)** .... (803) 276-4810
20 Work Center Road, Whitmire, SC 29178 Fax: (803) 276-9303
Long Cane District Ranger
John R. "J.R." Kirkaldie .... (803) 637-5396 ext. 13
810 Buncombe Street, Edgefield, SC 29824 Fax: (803) 637-5247
Francis Marion District Ranger **Rhea Whalen** .... (843) 336-2201
2967 Steed Creek Road, Huger, SC 29450 Fax: (843) 336-2252

National Forests – Tennessee

Cherokee National Forest
2800 North Ocoee Street, Cleveland, TN 37312
Tel: (423) 476-9700 Fax: (423) 476-9754
Internet: www.fs.usda.gov/cherokee

Forest Supervisor **JaSal Morris** .... (423) 476-9703
Executive Assistant **Lisa Blackmon** .... (423) 476-9703
E-mail: lblackmon@fs.fed.us
Deputy Forest Supervisor **(Vacant)** .... (423) 476-9703
Public Affairs Officer **Terry W. McDonald** .... (423) 476-9729
E-mail: twmcdonald@fs.fed.us Fax: (423) 339-8652

National Forests and Grasslands – Texas
2221 North Raguet Street, Lufkin, TX 75904
Tel: (936) 639-8501 Fax: (936) 639-8588
E-mail: mailroom_r8_texas@fs.fed.us Internet: www.fs.usda.gov/texas
Areas Covered: Angelina National Forest; Caddo National Grassland; Davy Crockett National Forest; Lyndon Baines Johnson National Grassland; Sabine National Forest; Sam Houston National Forest

Forest Supervisor **William Eddie Taylor, Jr.** .... (936) 639-8501
Education: Texas A&M BA Fax: (936) 639-8513
Public Affairs Specialist **Ernie Murray** .... (936) 639-8562
E-mail: emurray@fs.fed.us
Patrol Captain **Chris Crain** .... (936) 639-8530
E-mail: ccrain@fs.fed.us
Administrative Officer **Tammie Mask** .... (936) 639-8596
E-mail: tmask@fs.fed.us Fax: (936) 639-8588

National Forests – Virginia

George Washington and Jefferson National Forests
5162 Valleypointe Parkway, Roanoke, VA 24019-3050
Tel: (540) 265-5100 ext. 102 Fax: (540) 265-5145
Internet: www.fs.usda.gov/gwj

Forest Supervisor **Job P. "Joby" Timm** .... (540) 265-5118
Education: North Dakota State BSLA Fax: (540) 265-5110
Deputy Forest Supervisor **Elizabeth "Beth" LeMaster** ... (540) 265-5119
Education: Clemson BSC, MS
Planning, Lands, Special Uses, Public and Legislative
Affairs Officer **JoBeth Brown** .... (540) 265-5102
E-mail: jobethbrown@fs.fed.us
Patrol Captain **Larry B. "Brian" Webb** .... (505) 842-3362
E-mail: lbwebb@fs.fed.us

Forest Service – Region 9 (Eastern Region)
626 East Wisconsin Avenue, Milwaukee, WI 53202-4616
Tel: (414) 297-3600 Fax: (414) 944-3966 E-mail: mailroomr9@fs.fed.us
Internet: https://www.fs.usda.gov/r9
Areas Covered: CT, IL, IN, IA, ME, MD, MA, MI, MN, MO, NH, NY, OH, PA, VT, WV, WI

★ Presidential Appointment Requiring Senate Confirmation ☆ Presidential Appointment ☐ Schedule C Appointment ◇ Career Senior Foreign Service Appointment
● Career Senior Executive Service (SES) Appointment ○ Non-Career Senior Executive Service (SES) Appointment ■ Postal Career Executive Service

DEPARTMENTS

Office of the Regional Forester
626 East Wisconsin Avenue, Suite 800, Milwaukee, WI 53202-4616
Fax: (414) 944-3973

● Regional Forester **Kathleen Atkinson** . . . . . (414) 297-3765
E-mail: katkinson@fs.fed.us Fax: (414) 944-3973
Education: Michigan 1981 BS; South Dakota 1988 MPA; American U 2008 (Attended)
Special Assistant **Michelle Damato** . . . . . (414) 297-3765
Education: Wisconsin (Eau Claire) 1989; Wisconsin (Milwaukee) 1994
Executive Secretary **Elizabeth "Liz" Sporcich** . . . . . (414) 297-3646
Deputy Regional Forester **Mary Beth Borst** . . . . . (414) 297-3646
Deputy Regional Forester **Robert "Bob" Lueckel** . . . . . (414) 297-1693
Deputy Regional Forester **Kathryn "Kathy" Lynn** . . . . . (414) 297-3646
Acquisition Management and Administrative Services Director **Colleen Hightower** . . . . . (414) 297-3625
E-mail: chightower@fs.fed.us Fax: (414) 297-1908
Budget and Performance Accountability Director **Darrell L. Woods** . . . . . (414) 297-3726
E-mail: dlwoods@fs.fed.us
Civil Rights and Multiculturalism Director **Sheree Johnson** . . . . . (414) 297-3264
Engineering Director **Josiah Kim** . . . . . (414) 297-1693
Fire and Aviation Management Director **Steven R. Miller** . . . . . (414) 297-1280
Education: Wisconsin (Stevens Point) 1985 BS; Florida 2016 MA
Fire and Aviation Management Deputy Director **Steve Goldman** . . . . . (414) 297-1812
Human Resources Director **Patrick "Rick" Carey** . . . . . (414) 297-1901
E-mail: pcarey@fs.fed.us
Information Management Director **Wanda Hodge** . . . . . (414) 297-3806
E-mail: whodge@fs.fed.us
Lands, Minerals, Soil, Water and Air Director **Shawn A. Olson** . . . . . (414) 297-3718
Fax: (414) 944-3964
Public and Government Relations Director **Kathryn "Katie" O'Connor** . . . . . (414) 297-3640
E-mail: kathrynoconnor@fs.fed.us
Education: Dartmouth 1999 BA; Indiana 2005 MPA
Planning, Administrative Review, Litigation and Landscape Conservation Director **Anthony E. "Tony" Erba** . . . . . (414) 297-1905
Recreation, Heritage, Wilderness Resources and Volunteer & Service Program Director **David B. Jenkins** . . . . . (414) 297-3635
Renewable Resources Director **Stephen "Steve" Kuennen** . . . . . (414) 297-3655
Fax: (414) 944-3963
Legislative Affairs Coordinator **Suzanne C. Flory** . . . . . (715) 362-1185
Program Analyst **Trish Adams** . . . . . (414) 297-1137

Law Enforcement and Investigations
626 East Wisconsin Avenue, Milwaukee, WI 53202-4616
Tel: (414) 297-3841 Fax: (414) 297-3723

Special Agent-in-Charge **Mary V. King** . . . . . (414) 297-3841
Assistant Special Agent-in-Charge/Patrol Captain **Paul Joyner** . . . . . (414) 297-1203
Administrative Support/Budget Analyst **Bernard Taylor** . . . (414) 297-3937
Staff Assistant **Carrie Stepien** . . . . . (414) 297-3346

National Forests – Illinois

Shawnee National Forest
50 Highway 145 South, Harrisburg, IL 62946
Tel: (800) 699-6637 Tel: (618) 253-7114 Fax: (618) 253-1060
Internet: www.fs.usda.gov/shawnee

Forest Supervisor **Brendan J. Cain** . . . . . (618) 253-1001
Public Affairs Officer **Tracy Fidler** . . . . . (618) 253-1031
E-mail: tfidler@fs.fed.us
Hidden Springs District Ranger **Timothy Pohlman** . . . . . (618) 658-1326
602 North First Street, Route 45 North, Vienna, IL 62995 Fax: (618) 658-1300
E-mail: tpohlman@fs.fed.us
Mississippi Bluffs District Ranger **Timothy Pohlman** . . . . (618) 658-1326
521 Main Street, Jonesboro, IL 62952 Fax: (618) 833-3693
E-mail: tpohlman@fs.fed.us

Midewin National Tallgrass Prairie
30239 S. State Route 53, Wilmington, IL 60481
Tel: (815) 423-6370 Fax: (815) 423-6376
Internet: www.fs.usda.gov/midewin

Prairie Supervisor **Wade Spang** . . . . . (815) 423-2113

National Forests – Indiana

Hoosier National Forest
811 Constitution Avenue, Bedford, IN 47421
Tel: (812) 275-5987 Fax: (812) 279-3423
Internet: www.fs.usda.gov/hoosier/

Forest Supervisor **Michael Chaveas** . . . . . (812) 276-4739
Forest Engineer **Gerald Gammon, Jr.** . . . . . (812) 276-4756
Brownstown District Ranger **Michelle Paduani** . . . . . (812) 547-5987
E-mail: mpaduani@fs.fed.us
Education: Montana 2007 BS
Tell City District Ranger **Michelle Paduani** . . . . . (812) 547-7051
E-mail: mpaduani@fs.fed.us
Education: Montana 2007 BS
Planning and Public Affairs Officer **Marion Mason** . . . . . (812) 276-4770

National Forests – Michigan

Hiawatha National Forest
820 Rains Drive, Gladstone, MI 49837
Tel: (906) 428-5800 Fax: (906) 789-3311 E-mail: hiawathanf@fs.fed.us

Forest Supervisor **Cid H. Morgan** . . . . . (906) 428-5839
Administrative Officer **Piper Desy** . . . . . (906) 428-5831
E-mail: pdesy@fs.fed.us
Public Affairs Officer **Janel M. Crooks** . . . . . (906) 428-5829
E-mail: jmcrooks@fs.fed.us
Fire, Fuels, GIS, Planning and Ecosystem Team Leader **Louise Congdon** . . . . . (906) 428-5801
Graymont Land Exchange Environmental Analysis Project Leader (Interim) **Joanne M. Sanfilippo** . . . . . (906) 428-5800
E-mail: jmsanfilippo@fs.fed.us
Lands, Engineering, Heritage, Recreation and Minerals Team Leader **Loren Everest** . . . . . (906) 428-5831

Huron-Manistee National Forests
1755 South Mitchell Street, Cadillac, MI 49601
Tel: (231) 775-2421 TTY: (231) 775-3183 Fax: (231) 775-5551
Internet: www.fs.usda.gov/hmnf

Forest Supervisor **Leslie Auriemmo** . . . . . (231) 775-2421 ext. 8710
Education: Illinois BS; Minnesota MS; John Marshall JD
Staff Assistant **Jennifer Gallagher** . . . . . (231) 775-5023 ext. 8722
Operations/Administrative Staff Officer **Shannon Rische** . . . . . (231) 775-5023 ext. 8759

Ottawa National Forest
E6248, U.S. Highway 2, Ironwood, MI 49938
Tel: (906) 285-1330 TTY: (906) 932-0301 Fax: (906) 932-0122
Internet: www.fs.usda.gov/ottawa/

Forest Supervisor **Linda Jackson** . . . . . (906) 285-6914
Administrative Officer **Lisa Klaus** . . . . . (906) 285-6904
E-mail: lklaus@fs.fed.us

National Forests – Minnesota

Chippewa National Forest
200 Ash Avenue, NW, Cass Lake, MN 56633-8929
Tel: (218) 335-8600 Fax: (218) 335-8637
E-mail: r9_chippewa_public@fs.fed.us
Internet: www.fs.usda.gov/chippewa

Forest Supervisor **Darla Lenz** . . . . . (218) 335-8631
Executive Assistant **Tyrone Clark** . . . . . (218) 335-8617
Tel: (808) 366-2045
Natural Resource Team Leader **Jim Gries** . . . . . (218) 335-8649
Public Affairs Specialist **(Vacant)** . . . . . (218) 335-8673
Forest Engineer **Jon D. Hodgson** . . . . . (218) 335-8687
Public Services Team Leader **Ann Long-Voelkner** . . . . . (218) 835-8688
E-mail: alongvoelkner@fs.fed.us
Administrative Operations Specialist **(Vacant)** . . . . . (218) 335-8646

★ Presidential Appointment Requiring Senate Confirmation ☆ Presidential Appointment ☐ Schedule C Appointment ◇ Career Senior Foreign Service Appointment
● Career Senior Executive Service (SES) Appointment ○ Non-Career Senior Executive Service (SES) Appointment ■ Postal Career Executive Service

Superior National Forest
8901 Grand Avenue Place, Duluth, MN 55808-1122
Tel: (218) 626-4300 Fax: (218) 626-4396
E-mail: r9_superior_nf@fs.fed.us Internet: www.fs.usda.gov/superior

Forest Supervisor **Constance "Connie" Cummins** ...... (218) 626-4302
Executive Assistant **(Vacant)** ...... (218) 626-4301
Fax: (218) 626-4396
Deputy Forest Supervisor (Acting)
Megan E. "Meg" Roessing ...... (218) 626-4303
Education: Bowdoin 1999 BA; Yale 2003 MEM Fax: (218) 626-4396
Administrative Officer **Stephen C. Popkowski** ...... (218) 626-4365
E-mail: spopkowski@fs.fed.us Fax: (218) 626-4396
Fire and Aviation Management Officer (Acting)
Michael D. "Mike" Burow ...... (218) 327-4568
Minnesota Interagency Fire Center, Fax: (218) 327-4527
402 - 11th Street SE, Grand Rapids, MN 55744
Natural Resources Team Leader **James D. McFarland** ... (218) 626-4317
Fax: (218) 626-4396
Public Service Team Leader **A. Dawn Laybolt** ...... (218) 626-4305
Partnership Coordinator/Tribal Liaison
Lisa Radosevich-Craig ...... (218) 626-4336
E-mail: lradosevichcraig@fs.fed.us Fax: (218) 626-4312
Forest Planner **Pooja S. Kanwar** ...... (218) 626-4383

National Forests – Missouri

Mark Twain National Forest
401 Fairgrounds Road, Rolla, MO 65401
Tel: (573) 364-4621 Fax: (573) 364-6844 Fax: (573) 341-7415
Internet: www.fs.usda.gov/mtnf

Forest Supervisor **Sherri K. Schwenke** ...... (573) 341-7413
Education: Davidson 1986 BA; Virginia Tech 1988 MA
Deputy Forest Supervisor **(Vacant)** ...... (573) 341-7413
Recreation Program Manager **Cory Roegner** ...... (573) 341-7413
Program Specialist **Cheryl Moreland** ...... (573) 341-7413

National Forests – New Hampshire and Maine

White Mountain National Forest
71 White Mountain Drive, Campton, NH 03223
Tel: (603) 536-6100 Fax: (603) 536-3673
Internet: https://www.fs.usda.gov/whitemountain

Forest Supervisor **Clare R. Mendelsohn** ...... (603) 536-6202
Education: Michigan Tech 1987 BS; Fax: (603) 536-3673
Air Force Inst Tech 1992 MS; MIT 2002 MBA
Deputy Forest Supervisor **Diane Taliaferro** ...... (603) 536-6201
Executive Secretary **Joseph Roberts** ...... (603) 536-6203
Public Services Team Leader **Tiffany Benna** ...... (603) 536-6241
E-mail: tbenna@fs.fed.us
Administrative Team Leader **Colette M. Simons** ...... (603) 536-6204
E-mail: colettesimons@fs.fed.us
Androscoggin District Ranger **Jennifer Barnhart** ...... (603) 466-2713
300 Glen Road, Gorham, NH 03581
Education: Virginia Tech 2002 BS; Minnesota 2005 MSc
Pemigewasset District Ranger **Brooke Brown** ...... (603) 536-6101
Front Desk: (603) 536-6100
TTY: (603) 536-3665
Saco District Ranger **James C. "Jim" Innes** .... (603) 447-5448 ext. 102
33 Kancamagus Highway, Conway, NH 03818
Education: New Hampshire 1998 BS, 2001 MS

National Forests – Ohio

Wayne National Forest
13700 U.S. Highway 33, Nelsonville, OH 45764-9880
Tel: (740) 753-0101 TTY: (800) 877-8339 Fax: (740) 753-0118
Fax: (740) 753-0119 E-mail: r9_wayne_website@fs.fed.us
Internet: www.fs.usda.gov/wayne

Forest Supervisor (Acting) **Jon Kazmierski** ...... (740) 753-0880
Education: Michigan 1998 BS, 2002 MS
Executive Assistant **Regina K. Martin** ...... (740) 753-0245
Operations Staff Officer **Christopher A. Dahl** ...... (740) 753-0852
Natural Resources Staff Officer
William E. "Will" Dienst ...... (740) 753-0684
Public Affairs Officer **Gary Chancey** ...... (740) 753-0862
E-mail: gchancey@fs.fed.us

Wayne National Forest *(continued)*

Patrol Captain **Joseph McGallicher** ...... (740) 753-0578
E-mail: jmcgallicher@fs.fed.us Fax: (740) 753-0118

National Forests – Pennsylvania

Allegheny National Forest
Four Farm Colony Drive, Warren, PA 16365
Tel: (814) 723-5150 TTY: (814) 726-2710
Fax: (814) 726-1465 E-mail: r9_allegheny_nf@fs.fed.us
Internet: https://www.fs.usda.gov/allegheny

Forest Supervisor **Roman L. "Ray" Torres** ...... (814) 728-6299
Executive Assistant **Kathryn L. "Kathy" Mohney** ..... (814) 728-6298
Deputy Forest Supervisor **Christopher J. Cook** ...... (814) 728-6171
Budget Officer **(Vacant)** ...... (814) 728-6119
Supervisory Contracting Specialist (NEAT) **Alan Zero** .... (814) 728-6288
E-mail: azero@fs.fed.us
Ecosystems Management **(Vacant)** ...... (814) 728-6179
Public Affairs Specialist **(Vacant)** ...... (814) 728-6115
Operations Staff Officer **James Seyler** ...... (814) 728-6239
E-mail: jseyler@fs.fed.us

National Forests – Vermont and New York

Green Mountain and Finger Lakes National Forests
231 North Main Street, Rutland, VT 05701
Tel: (802) 747-6700 Fax: (802) 747-6766
E-mail: r9_gmfl_webmaster@fs.fed.us Internet: www.fs.usda.gov/gmfl

Forest Supervisor **John A. Sinclair** ...... (802) 747-6704
Ecological Services Staff Officer **Steve Roy** ...... (802) 747-6739
Technical Services Staff Officer **Brian C. Austin** ...... (802) 747-6757
Public Services Staff Officer **Donna Grosz** ...... (802) 747-6722
Public Affairs Officer **Ethan M. Ready** ...... (802) 747-6760
E-mail: eready@fs.fed.us
Special Uses, Lands, and Recreation **(Vacant)** ...... (802) 747-6746
Recreation Team **(Vacant)** ...... (802) 747-6749

National Forests – West Virginia

Monongahela National Forest
200 Sycamore Street, Elkins, WV 26241-3962
Tel: (304) 636-1800 Fax: (304) 636-1875
E-mail: mailroom_r9_monongahela@fs.fed.us
Internet: https://www.fs.usda.gov/mnf/

Forest Supervisor **Clyde N. Thompson** ...... (304) 635-4482
Executive Assistant **Doris C. Nelson** ...... (304) 636-1800 ext. 226

National Forests – Wisconsin

Chequamegon-Nicolet National Forest
1170 Fourth Avenue, South, Park Falls, WI 54552 (Park Falls, WI Office)
500 Hanson Lake Road, Rhinelander, WI 54501 (Rhinelander, WI Office)
Tel: (715) 362-1300 (Rhinelander, WI Office) TTY: (715) 762-5701
Fax: (715) 369-8859 (Rhinelander, WI Office)
Internet: www.fs.usda.gov/cnnf/

Forest Supervisor **Paul Strong** ...... (715) 362-1323
Deputy Forest Supervisor **Jamie L. Davidson** ...... (715) 362-1324
Public Affairs Officer **(Vacant)** ...... (715) 362-1354
Public Affairs Specialist/Website Manager **(Vacant)** ...... (715) 362-1362

Forest Service – Region 10 (Alaska Region)

Federal Building, 709 West Ninth Street,
Room 549, Juneau, AK 99802
Mail: USDA Forest Service, R-10, Box 21628, Juneau, AK 99802-1628
Tel: (907) 586-8806 Fax: (907) 586-7840
E-mail: mailroom_r10@fs.fed.us Internet: www.fs.usda.gov/r10
Areas Covered: AK

Office of the Regional Forester

P.O. Box 21628, Juneau, AK 99802
Tel: (907) 586-8863 Fax: (907) 586-7840

● Regional Forester (Acting) **David E. "Dave" Schmid** .... (907) 586-8863
E-mail: dschmid@fs.fed.us

(continued on next page)

★ Presidential Appointment Requiring Senate Confirmation ☆ Presidential Appointment ☐ Schedule C Appointment ◇ Career Senior Foreign Service Appointment
● Career Senior Executive Service (SES) Appointment ○ Non-Career Senior Executive Service (SES) Appointment ■ Postal Career Executive Service

Office of the Regional Forester *(continued)*

Deputy Regional Forester **Jerry Ingersoll** .... (907) 586-8863
Education: UC Berkeley 1985 BSF, 1987 ScM
Executive Assistant **Penny A Bullingham** .... (907) 586-8775
E-mail: pennyabullingham@fs.fed.us
Special Assistant **Marilyn N. Orr** .... (907) 586-8863
E-mail: marilynorr@fs.fed.us
Transition Framework Coordinator **(Vacant)** .... (503) 802-8100

Public Affairs and Partnership Office
P.O. Box 21628, Juneau, AK 99802
Fax: (907) 586-7892

Director (Acting) **Kaari Carpenter** .... (907) 586-7945
E-mail: kaaricarpenter@fs.fed.us
Public Affairs Specialist **Dru Fenster** .... (907) 586-8892
Internal Relations Specialist **(Vacant)** .... (907) 789-6245
Visual Information Specialist **Carol Teitzel** .... (406) 498-8372
E-mail: cateitzel@fs.fed.us
Partnership Coordinator **(Vacant)** .... (907) 586-8863

Natural Resources Staffs

Ecosystem Planning and Budget
P.O. Box 21628, Juneau, AK 99802
Tel: (907) 586-8884 Fax: (907) 586-7852

Director **Chad M. VanOrmer** .... (907) 586-8887
Appeals, Litigation, FOIA Group Leader **Robin Dale** .... (907) 586-9344
E-mail: rdale@fs.fed.us
Regional Land Management Planner **(Vacant)** .... (907) 586-9323
Regional Policy Analyst **(Vacant)** .... (907) 586-8814
Regional Economist **Nicole R. Grewe** .... (907) 586-8809
E-mail: nicolergrewe@fs.fed.us
Regional Environmental Coordinator
Lauren Dalton McChesney .... (907) 586-8796

Engineering Management
P.O. Box 21628, Juneau, AK 99802
Tel: (907) 586-8866 Fax: (907) 586-7555

Director **Sam Carlson** .... (907) 586-8733
E-mail: samcarlson@fs.fed.us
Education: Oregon State 1987 BS, 1994 MSCE
Deputy Director **Christy Darden** .... (503) 808-2500
333 SW First Avenue, Portland, OR 97204-3440
E-mail: cdarden@fs.fed.us
Administrative Team Lead **Hannah V. Cross** .... (907) 586-7964
E-mail: hvcross@fs.fed.us
Budget and Program Manager **Macky A. McClung** ...... (907) 586-7904
E-mail: mmcclung@fs.fed.us
Environmental Engineer **Julie Creed** .... (503) 808-2526
3623, Portland, OR 97208
E-mail: jcreed01@fs.fed.us
Fleet Manager **(Vacant)** .... (503) 808-2892
1220 SW Third Avenue, Portland, OR 97204-2825
Structural Engineer **(Vacant)** .... (907) 586-8717
Transportation Planning, Operations and Maintenance
Engineer **Amanda L. Warner Thorpe** .... (503) 808-2512
Transportation System Engineer **(Vacant)** .... (907) 586-8834

Forest Management
P.O. Box 21628, Juneau, AK 99802
Tel: (907) 586-8871 Fax: (907) 586-7877

Director **David P. "Dave" Harris** .... (907) 586-7875
Products Group Leader **(Vacant)** .... (907) 586-7878
Administrative Support Assistant **Joanne Behrends** ..... (907) 586-7932
E-mail: jbehrends@fs.fed.us Fax: (907) 586-7877

Recreation, Lands, and Minerals
P.O. Box 21628, Juneau, AK 99802
Tel: (907) 586-8729 Fax: (907) 586-7866

Director **James G. King** .... (907) 586-8877
Regional Partnership and Outreach Program Leader
George V. Schaaf .... (907) 586-8729
Regional Appraiser **(Vacant)** .... (907) 743-9580

Recreation, Lands, and Minerals *(continued)*

Regional Geologist **Jeff DeFreest** .... (907) 586-7869
E-mail: jdefreest@fs.fed.us
Regional Landscape Architect **Eric Ouderkirk** .... (907) 586-8728

Wildlife, Fisheries, Ecology, and Watershed
P.O. Box 21628, Juneau, AK 99802
Tel: (907) 586-8752 Fax: (907) 586-7877
Fax: (907) 586-7860 (Alternate)

Director **Dr. Wayne Owen** .... (907) 586-7916
Education: UC Davis PhD
Fish and Aquatic Program Leader
Donald "Don" Martin .... (907) 586-8712
Administrative Assistant **Joanne Behrends** .... (907) 586-7932
E-mail: jbehrends@fs.fed.us
Regional Subsistence Program Leader
Thomas "Tom" Whitford .... (907) 743-9461
Fax: (907) 743-9479
Vegetation Ecologist and Invasive Species Program
Leader **Barbara Schrader** .... (907) 586-7863
Regional Watershed and Air Program Leader
John R. Lane .... (907) 586-8978

Operations Staff
P.O. Box 21628, Juneau, AK 99802
Fax: (907) 586-8879

Director **(Vacant)** .... (907) 586-8732

Acquisition Management
P.O. Box 21628, Juneau, AK 99802
Tel: (907) 586-8880 Fax: (907) 586-7090

Director **Scott Langston** .... (907) 586-8732
E-mail: slangton@fs.fed.us
Lead Contract Specialist **(Vacant)** .... (907) 586-7902
Supervisory Procurement Analyst **(Vacant)** .... (907) 586-7835
Fax: (907) 586-7740
Supervisory Contract Specialist **Della Koelling** .... (907) 586-8852
E-mail: dkoelling@fs.fed.us Fax: (907) 586-7090
Supervisory Contract Specialist **Denise A. Murphy** ...... (907) 743-9531
E-mail: denisemurphy@fs.fed.us Fax: (907) 743-9492
Supervisory Contract Specialist **Kim B. Toland** .... (907) 772-5804
E-mail: kimtoland@fs.fed.us

Human Resources
Human Resources Officer **Sandiann G. Devaney** .... (907) 586-8773
E-mail: sgdevaney@fs.fed.us
Human Resources Specialist **Julie A. Beall** .... (907) 747-4262
E-mail: julieabeall@fs.fed.us
Human Resources Specialist **Erin M. Hansen** .... (907) 747-4315
E-mail: erinmhansen@fs.fed.us
Human Resources Specialist **Ron Jablonski** .... (907) 747-4262
E-mail: rjablonski@fs.fed.us
Human Resources Specialist
Maxwell "Max" Martinez .... (505) 373-4033
E-mail: mmartinez@fs.fed.us
Human Resources Specialist **Eleyna Rosenthal** .... (505) 252-8959
E-mail: erosenthal@fs.fed.us
Employee Relations Specialist **James Kirkland** .... (907) 228-6249

Civil Rights
P.O. Box 21628, Juneau, AK 99802
Tel: (907) 586-8895 Fax: (907) 586-7892

Director (Acting) **Toya L. Bligen** .... (503) 882-8717
1220 SW Third Avenue, Portland, OR 97204-2825
E-mail: toyabligen@fs.fed.us
Equal Employment Specialist (Title VI) **Teddy Castillo** ... (907) 586-8895
E-mail: tcastillo@fs.fed.us

Information Management
P.O. Box 21628, Juneau, AK 99802
Tel: (907) 586-8860 Fax: (907) 586-8856

Director **Sam Carlson** .... (907) 586-8733
E-mail: samcarlson@fs.fed.us
Education: Oregon State 1987 BS, 1994 MSCE

★ Presidential Appointment Requiring Senate Confirmation ☆ Presidential Appointment ☐ Schedule C Appointment ◇ Career Senior Foreign Service Appointment
● Career Senior Executive Service (SES) Appointment ○ Non-Career Senior Executive Service (SES) Appointment ■ Postal Career Executive Service

Information Management *(continued)*

Data Management Specialist **Kelly J. Hall** . . . . (907) 772-3619
E-mail: kjhall@fs.fed.us Fax: (907) 772-5966
Wireless Devices and Information Technology Specialist **(Vacant)** . . . . (907) 586-7963
Fax: (907) 586-7555
Program Assistant **(Vacant)** . . . . (907) 586-7802
Cartography Program Manager **(Vacant)** . . . . (907) 586-7966
Fax: (907) 586-7555
Geospatial Data Specialist **Christal Rose Higdon** . . . . . . (907) 586-8708
E-mail: christalrhigdon@fs.fed.us
Geospatial Program Manager **Kim R. Homan** . . . . (907) 586-7957
E-mail: kimhoman@fs.fed.us
Geospatial Services Specialist **Dustin T. Wittwer** . . . . . . (907) 586-8764
E-mail: dwittwer@fs.fed.us
GIS Coordinator **Gary J. Fisher** . . . . (907) 586-7839
E-mail: gfisher@fs.fed.us Fax: (907) 586-8856

Office of Performance and Budget Accountability
P.O. Box 21628, Juneau, AK 99802
Tel: (907) 586-7841 Fax: (907) 586-7740

Program Manager/Analyst **Dawn Heutte** . . . . (907) 586-7836
Supervisory Budget Analyst **(Vacant)** . . . . (907) 586-7835
Fax: (907) 586-7740
Budget Analyst **Robin Airozo** . . . . (907) 586-8748
E-mail: rairozo@fs.fed.us
Budget Analyst **Anne L. Bergstrom** . . . . (907) 586-8731
E-mail: albergstrom@fs.fed.us
Budget Analyst **(Vacant)** . . . . (907) 586-9375

Safety and Health
Safety and Health Manager **David L. Barto** . . . . (907) 586-8322
E-mail: dlbatro@fs.fed.us

State and Private Forestry
161 East 1st Avenue, Anchorage, AK 99501
Tel: (907) 743-9455 Fax: (907) 743-9479

Director **Debbie A. Hollen** . . . . (503) 808-2340
Assistant Director **Karl Dalla Rosa** . . . . (907) 743-9451
Biological Science Technician **Garret Dubois** . . . . (907) 743-9453
Biological Science Technician **Steve W. Swenson** . . . . . . (907) 743-9456
Fire Safety and Training Officer **Gary Lehnhausen** . . . . . . (907) 743-9458
Interagency Dispatch Coordinator **(Vacant)** . . . . (907) 356-5683
Fax: (907) 356-5678
Director, Fire and Fuels Management **John E. Giller** . . . . . (503) 808-2143
1220 SW Third Avenue, Portland, OR 97204-2825
E-mail: jegiller@fs.fed.us
Budget and Administration Program Work Leader **(Vacant)** . . . . (503) 808-2323
333 SW First Avenue, Portland, OR 97204-3440

Law Enforcement and Investigations
P.O. Box 21628, Juneau, AK 99802
Tel: (907) 586-9395 Fax: (907) 586-8780

Special Agent-in-Charge **Bryan Roemeling** . . . . (907) 586-8820
Special Agent, Anchorage **(Vacant)** . . . . (907) 586-8786
Special Agent, Ketchikan **(Vacant)** . . . . (907) 586-8786
Program Specialist **Joleen B. Wheeland** . . . . (907) 586-7910

Forestry Sciences Laboratory - Juneau (AK) Office
11175 Auke Lake Way, Juneau, AK 99801
Tel: (907) 586-8811 Fax: (907) 586-7848

Assistant Station Director for Program Development **Susan J. "Sue" Alexander** . . . . (907) 586-7801

Sitka Wood Utilization Research and Development Center
901 Halibut Point Road, Sitka, AK 99835
Tel: (907) 747-4308 Fax: (907) 747-4294

Regional Forester **Allen M. Brackley** . . . . (907) 747-4308
Education: Maine 1966 BS, 1968 MS, 1989 PhD

Chugach National Forest
161 East 1st Avenue, Door 8, Anchorage, AK 99501
Tel: (907) 743-9500 Fax: (907) 743-9476
Internet: www.fs.usda.gov/chugach/

Forest Supervisor **Terri Marceron** . . . . (907) 743-9525
Education: San Diego State BA; U Washington MS Fax: (907) 743-9488
Deputy Forest Supervisor **Sharon LaBrecque-Smith** . . . . (907) 743-9516
Executive Assistant **Maile J. Zimin** . . . . (907) 743-9523
Fax: (907) 743-9488
Forest Engineer **Griffith Berg** . . . . (907) 743-9442
Fax: (907) 743-9481
Administrative Operations Specialist **Laura C. Taylor** . . . . (907) 743-9554
E-mail: lctaylor@fs.fed.us
Planning and Resources Staff Officer **Deyna Kuntzsch** . . . (907) 743-9517
Public Affairs (Acting) **Mona Spargo** . . . . (907) 743-9572
E-mail: mspargo@fs.fed.us
Public Services **Alicia F. King** . . . . (907) 743-9444
E-mail: aliciaking@fs.fed.us

Tongass National Forest
Federal Building, 648 Mission Street, Ketchikan, AK 99901-6591
Tel: (907) 228-6218 Fax: (907) 228-6215
Internet: www.fs.usda.gov/tongass

Forest Supervisor **M. E. "Earl" Stewart** . . . . (907) 225-3101
Education: Oklahoma State 1985 BS
Executive Assistant **Amy M. Manuel** . . . . (907) 228-6200
Fax: (907) 228-6292
Administrative Staff Officer **Austin "Alex" O'Brien** . . . . . . (907) 874-7575
Fax: (907) 874-7595
Public Affairs and Partnerships Staff Officer **Paul Robbins** . . . . (907) 228-6201
E-mail: paulrobbins@fs.fed.us Fax: (907) 228-6292
Education: Phoenix Col 2011 ABA; Maryland University Col 2015 BMS; George Washington 2017 MA
Webmaster **Melinda Kuharich** . . . . (907) 228-6291
E-mail: mkuharich@fs.fed.us

Natural Resources Conservation Service (NRCS)

South Agriculture Building, 1400 Independence Avenue, SW, Washington, DC 20250
Tel: (202) 720-7246 Fax: (202) 720-7690 Internet: www.nrcs.usda.gov

Associate Chief for Conservation
1400 Independence Avenue, SW, Washington, DC 20250
Tel: (202) 720-4531

• Associate Chief for Conservation (Acting) **James E. Tillman, Sr.** South Agriculture Building, Room 5103-S . . . . (202) 720-7246
E-mail: james.tillman@wdc.usda.gov
Executive Assistant **Joyce Hawkins** South Agriculture Building, Room 5104-S . . . . (202) 720-4531
Chief of Staff (Acting) **Leslie Deavers** . . . . (202) 690-4616
355 E St NW, Room 6004-S, Washington, DC 20250-1597
E-mail: leslie.deavers@wdc.usda.gov

Deputy Chief for Science and Technology
South Agriculture Building, 1400 Independence Avenue, SW, Room 5113-S, Washington, DC 20250
Tel: (202) 720-4527 Fax: (202) 720-7710

Central National Technology Support Center (CNTSC)
Building 23, 501 West Felix Street, Fort Worth, TX 76115
Mail: P.O. Box 6567, Fort Worth, TX 76115
Tel: (817) 509-3302 Fax: (817) 509-3337
Internet: www.nrcs.usda.gov/about/ntsc/central
Areas Covered: AR, IL, IA, KS, LA, MN, MO, NE, ND, OK, SD, TX, WI

Director **Rafael Guerrero** . . . . (817) 509-3570

DEPARTMENTS

★ Presidential Appointment Requiring Senate Confirmation ☆ Presidential Appointment □ Schedule C Appointment ◇ Career Senior Foreign Service Appointment
● Career Senior Executive Service (SES) Appointment ○ Non-Career Senior Executive Service (SES) Appointment ■ Postal Career Executive Service

DEPARTMENTS

Grazing Lands Team
Grazing Lands Team Leader **Dana Larsen** . . . . (817) 509-3211

Wetlands Team
Team Leader, Botanist **Dr. Norman C. Melvin III** . . . . (817) 509-3572
Education: Presbyterian Col 1973 BS; Clemson 1976 MS; Miami U (OH) 1980 PhD

Wildlife Team
Wildlife Technology Development Team Leader
(Vacant) . . . . (817) 509-3572

East National Technology Support Center (ENTSC)
2901 East Gate City Boulevard, Suite 2100, Greensboro, NC 27401-4901
Tel: (336) 370-3331 Fax: (336) 273-8132
Internet: www.nrcs.usda.gov/about/ntsc/east
Areas Covered: AL, CT, DE, FL, GA, IN, KY, ME, MD, MA, MI, MS, NH, NJ, NY, NC, OH, PA, RI, SC, TN, VT, VA, WV, Caribbean

Director **Eric B. Banks** . . . . (336) 370-3352
Fax: (336) 370-3377

National Manure Management Team
2901 East Gate City Boulevard, Greensboro, NC 27401-4901
Tel: (336) 370-3364 Fax: (336) 370-3376

National Manure Management Team Leader
Jeffrey "Jeff" Porter . . . . (336) 370-3342

National Plant Data Team
2901 East Gate City Boulevard, Greensboro, NC 27401-4901
Tel: (336) 370-3364 Fax: (336) 370-3376

National Plant Data Team Leader **Dr. Gerry Moore** . . . . . . (336) 370-3337
E-mail: gerry.moore@gnb.usda.gov

West National Technology Support Center (WNTSC)
1201 NE Lloyd Boulevard, Suite 1000, Portland, OR 97232
Tel: (503) 273-2422 Fax: (503) 273-2401
Areas Covered: AK, AZ, CA, CO, HI, ID, MT, NV, NM, OR, UT, WA, WY, Pacific Basin

Director **Shaun McKinney** . . . . (503) 273-2413
Education: Michigan State BS; Oregon State MS

Environmental Markets and Energy Team
Team Co-Leader **Adam Chambers** . . . . (503) 273-2410
E-mail: adam.chambers@por.usda.gov
Team Co-Leader **Kenneth "Kip" Pheil** . . . . (503) 273-2437
E-mail: kenneth.pheil@por.usda.gov

Air Quality and Atmospheric Change Team
Leader **Greg Johnson** . . . . (503) 273-2424

Water Quality and Quantity Team
Water Quality and Quantity Technology Development Team Leader **Karma Anderson** . . . . (503) 273-2413

Deputy Chief for Soil Science and Resource Assessment (SSRA)
5601 Sunnyside Avenue, Room 1-1289, Beltsville, MD 20705-5000
Tel: (301) 504-2302 Fax: (202) 504-3788

Soil and Plant Science Division
South Agriculture Building, 1400 Independence Avenue, SW, Room 4838-S, Washington, DC 20250
Tel: (202) 260-9233 Fax: (202) 260-9234

Major Land Resource Area Soil Survey Offices

Region 1 – Pacific Northwest Region
1201 Northeast Lloyd Boulevard, Suite 900, Portland, OR 97232-1274
800 West Evergreen, Palmer, AK 99645
Tel: (503) 414-3261 Fax: (855) 651-9082
Areas Covered: AK, ID, OR, WA

Soil Survey Regional Director (Alaska) (Acting)
Cathy E. McGuire . . . . (602) 285-6347
Tel: (503) 414-3261
Soil Survey Regional Director (Lower 48) (Acting)
Eva M. Muller . . . . (406) 587-6866
Geographic Information Services Specialist **(Vacant)** . . . . . (503) 414-3024
Regional Ecological Site Specialist **(Vacant)** . . . . . (907) 373-6492 ext. 119
1508 Bogard Road, Wasilla, AK 99645
Regional Soil Scientist **Dennis Mulligan** . . . . (907) 373-6492 ext. 120
1508 Bogard Road, Wasilla, AK 99645
Soil Data Quality Specialist **Michael P. "Mike" Regan** . . . (503) 414-3262
1508 Bogard Road, Wasilla, AK 99645
Soil Data Quality Specialist
Timothy "Tim" Riebe . . . . (907) 373-6492 ext. 121
1508 Bogard Road, Wasilla, AK 99645
Soil Data Quality Specialist **Kyle Stephens** . . . . (503) 414-3289
Editor **Susan D. "Sue" Tester** . . . . (503) 414-3207

Region 2 – Pacific Southwest Region
430 G Street, Room 4164, Davis, CA 95616-4164
Tel: (530) 792-5640 Fax: (530) 792-5794
Areas Covered: CA, ID, HI, NV, OR, and the Pacific Basin

Soil Survey Regional Director **Cynthia Stiles** . . . . (530) 792-5640
E-mail: cynthia.stiles@ca.usda.gov

Region 3 – Mid-Atlantic and Caribbean Region
4407 Bland Road, Suite 117, Raleigh, NC 27609
Tel: (919) 873-2142 Fax: (919) 873-2157
Areas Covered: AL, DE, FL, GA, MD, NC, NJ, PR, SC, VA, and US Virgin Islands

Soil Survey Regional Director
Deborah T. "Debbie" Anderson . . . . (919) 873-2139
Ecological Site Inventory Specialist
Michelle Clendenin . . . . (919) 873-2125
Ecological Data Quality Specialist **Matt Duvall** . . . . (919) 873-2119
GIS Specialist **(Vacant)** . . . . (919) 873-2137
Senior Regional Soil Scientist **Greg Taylor** . . . . (919) 873-2170
Soil Data Quality Specialist **Mark Van Lear** . . . . (540) 265-5215
Soil Data Quality Specialist **(Vacant)** . . . . (919) 873-2135
Administrative Officer **Camilla R. "Rosetta" Curtis** . . . (919) 873-2142
E-mail: rosetta.curtis@nc.usda.gov

Region 4 – Northern Rocky Mountain Region
Federal Building, 10 E. Babcock Street, Room 443, Bozeman, MT 59715-4704
Tel: (406) 587-6818 Fax: (855) 510-7028
Areas Covered: CO, ID, MT, NM, OR, UT, WA and WY

Soil Survey Regional Director **Eva M. Muller** . . . . (406) 587-6866
Webmaster **Mary Myers** . . . . (406) 587-6945
E-mail: mary.myers@mt.usda.gov
E-mail: mt-nrcs-webmaster@one.usda.gov

Region 5 – Central Great Plains Region
P.O. Box 25426, Denver, CO 80225
Tel: (720) 544-2850 Fax: (720) 544-2962
Areas Covered: CO, KS, NE, ND, OK, and SD

Soil Survey Regional Director
James C. "Chad" Remley .... (785) 823-4559
760 South Broadway, Salina, KS 67401-4642
Office Automation Assistant **Olivia Romero** .... (720) 544-2849
E-mail: olivia.romero@co.usda.gov
Senior Regional Soil Scientist **(Vacant)** .... (785) 823-4560
760 South Broadway, Salina, KS 67401-4642
Soil Data Quality Specialist **Paul Rindfleisch** .... (720) 544-2848
E-mail: paul.rindfleisch@co.usda.gov
Soil Data Quality Specialist **John Warner** .... (785) 823-4559
760 South Broadway, Salina, KS 67401-4642
E-mail: john.warner@ks.usda.gov
Geographic Information Specialist **Lucas Wiseley** .... (720) 544-2842
Administrative Support Assistant **Susan K. Picking** .... (785) 823-4555
760 South Broadway, Salina, KS 67401-4642
E-mail: susan.picking@ks.usda.gov

Region 6 – Appalachian and Interior Plateaus Region
1550 Earl Core Road, Suite 200, Morgantown, WV 26505
Tel: (304) 284-7540 Fax: (304) 284-4839
Areas Covered: AL, AR, GA, IN, KY, MO, NC, OH, OK, PA, TN, VA, and WV

Soil Survey Regional Director **David Kingsbury** .... (304) 284-7589
Fax: (304) 284-4839
Senior Regional Soil Scientist **Jeffrey R. Thomas** .... (304) 284-7594
Soil Data Quality Specialist **Michael Jones** .... (304) 284-7588
Fax: (304) 284-4839
Soil Data Quality Specialist **Alan K. Moore** ..... (304) 697-6033 ext. 118
GIS Specialist **Wendy Noll** .... (304) 284-7590

Region 7 – Southeast Coastal Plain and Lower Mississippi River Valley Region
P.O. Box 311, Auburn, AL 36830
Tel: (334) 887-4580
Areas Covered: AL, AR, FL, GA, IL, KY, LA, MS, MO, SC, TN, and TX

Soil Survey Regional Director
Deborah T. "Debbie" Anderson .... (919) 873-2139
Senior Regional Soil Scientist **Jessica Jobe** .... (334) 887-4565
Senior Regional Soil Scientist **(Vacant)** .... (334) 887-4580
Assistant State Soil Scientist **(Vacant)** .... (334) 887-4559
Soil Data Quality Specialist **Aaron K. Friend** .... (334) 887-4516
Soil Data Quality Specialist **Alison Steglich** .... (334) 887-4563
Administrative Assistant **(Vacant)** .... (334) 887-4580

Region 8 – Southwest Region
230 North First Avenue, Suite 509, Phoenix, AZ 85003-1733
Fax: (602) 280-8805
Areas Covered: AZ, CA, CO, NM, NV, TX, and UT

Soil Survey Regional Director **Cathy E. McGuire** .... (602) 285-6347
Senior Regional Soil Scientist **Nathaniel M. Starman** ... (602) 280-8837
Ecological Site Specialist **Robert "Scott" Woodall** ..... (602) 280-8789
GIS Specialist **Eric J. Wolfbrandt** .... (602) 280-8822
Administrative Assistant **(Vacant)** .... (602) 285-6353

Region 9 – Southern Great Plains Region
101 South Main Street, Temple, TX 76501-7682
Tel: (254) 742-9800 Fax: (844) 332-7989

Soil Survey Regional Director (Acting)
James C. "Chad" Remley .... (785) 823-4558
Administrative Assistant **Suzanne Root** .... (254) 742-9850

Region 10 – West Central Glaciated Region
375 Jackson Street, Suite 600, St. Paul, MN 55101-1854
Tel: (651) 602-7861 Fax: (651) 602-7914
Areas Covered: IL, IA, portions of KS, MI, MN, MO, NE, SD, WI

Soil Survey Regional Director (Acting)
Kevin Norwood .... (317) 295-5840
6013 Lakeside Boulevard, Indianapolis, IN 46278

Region 10 – West Central Glaciated Region *(continued)*

Senior Regional Soil Scientist **Daniel "Dan" Wing** ...... (651) 602-7891
Cartographic Technician **(Vacant)** .... (651) 602-7890
Cartographer **(Vacant)** .... (517) 324-5268
Ecological Site Inventory Specialist **Stacey Clark** .... (651) 602-7892
GIS Specialist **Adolfo Diaz** .... (608) 662-4422
Soil Database Specialist **Peter C. Weikle** .... (651) 602-7894
Soil Data Quality Specialist **Joseph Brennan** .... (651) 602-7925
Soil Data Quality Specialist
Jeremiah Josiah "Jo" Parsley .... (651) 602-7932
Soil Data Quality Specialist **(Vacant)** .... (651) 602-7864
Administrative Assistant **Helen M. Beeler** .... (651) 602-7878
E-mail: helen.beeler@mn.usda.gov

Region 11 – East Central Glaciated Region
6013 Lakeside Boulevard, Indianapolis, IN 46278
Tel: (317) 295-5870 Fax: (317) 290-3225
Areas Covered: Indianapolis, IN; Atlantic, Findlay, OH; Waverly, IA; Juneau, WI; Aurora, Carbondale, Springfield, IL; Clinton, Gallatin, Union, MO

MLRA Soil Survey Regional Director
Kevin Norwood .... (317) 295-5880
Administrative Assistant **Linda K. Cox** .... (317) 295-5870
E-mail: linda.cox@in.usda.gov
Senior Regional Soil Scientist **Tonie Endres** .... (317) 295-5872
Soil Data Quality Specialist **John Hammerly** .... (317) 295-5874
Soil Data Quality Specialist **Stephen Roecker** .... (317) 295-5768

Region 12 – New England Region
451 West Street, Suite 1, Amherst, MA 01002-2995
Tel: (413) 253-4350 Fax: (855) 596-7666

Soil Survey Regional Director **Luis Hernandez** .... (413) 253-4370

Regional Offices

14th and Independence Avenue, SW, Room 5204-S,
Washington, DC 20250-9338

Central Region

NRCS, 1400 Independence Avenue, SW,
Room 5204, Washington, DC 20250
Mail: P.O. Box 2890, Washington, DC 20013
Tel: (202) 690-2196
Areas Covered: IL, IA, KS, MN, MO, NE, ND, OK, SD, TX, WI

● Regional Conservationist **Kevin Wickey** .... (202) 690-2197
E-mail: kevin.wickey@wv.usda.gov
Education: Michigan Tech 1985 BS
Agricultural Engineer **Lane Johnson** .... (817) 509-3558
501 West Felix Street, Fort Worth, TX 76115-0567
Financial Administration Specialist **(Vacant)** .... (817) 509-3311
501 West Felix Street, Fort Worth, TX 76115-0567
Management Analyst **Aaron Pratt** .... (202) 720-3360
Management Analyst **Gerome Andler** .... (817) 509-3307
501 West Felix Street, Fort Worth, TX 76115-0567
Natural Resources Specialist **(Vacant)** .... (817) 509-3220
501 West Felix Street, Fort Worth, TX 76115-0567
Oversight and Evaluation Team Leader (Acting)
Kevin Stein .... (817) 509-3329
Building 24, 501 West Felix Street, Fort Worth, TX 76115-0567
Resource Conservationist **Kevin Stein** .... (817) 509-3329
501 West Felix Street, Fort Worth, TX 76115-0567
Resource Conservationist **Teresa D. Stewart** .... (817) 509-3745
501 West Felix Street, Fort Worth, TX 76115-0567
Soil Conservationist **(Vacant)** .... (817) 509-3409
501 West Felix Street, Fort Worth, TX 76115-0567

Illinois Office

2118 West Park Court, Champaign, IL 61821
Tel: (217) 353-6600 Fax: (855) 668-0602

State Conservationist **Ivan Dozier** .... (217) 353-6601
Executive Assistant **Kristi J. Einck** .... (217) 353-6604

DEPARTMENTS

Wetland and Highly Erodible Land Compliance
Assistant State Conservationist **Ron Collman** . . . . (217) 353-6621

Programs
Assistant State Conservationist for Easements
Paula Hingson . . . . (217) 353-6602
Assistant State Conservationist for Financial Assistance
Programs **Eric Gerth** . . . . (217) 353-6628

Public Affairs
State Public Affairs Specialist **Paige E. Buck** . . . . (217) 353-6606
E-mail: paige.buck@il.usda.gov

National Delivery Team
Supervisory Property Specialist **Bernita R. Clark** . . . . (217) 353-6615
E-mail: bernita.clark@il.usda.gov

Engineering
State Conservation Engineer **Ruth Book** . . . . (217) 353-6626
Fax: (855) 668-0601
Assistant State Conservation Engineer **(Vacant)** . . . . (217) 353-6633
Fax: (855) 668-0601

Ecological Sciences
State Resource Conservationist (Acting)
Gene Barickman . . . . (217) 353-6647
State Soil Scientist **Ron Collman** . . . . (217) 353-6639

Iowa Office
210 Walnut Street, Room 693, Des Moines, IA 50309-2180
Tel: (515) 284-6655 Fax: (855) 261-3544

State Conservationist **Kurt A. Simon** . . . . (515) 323-2210
Executive Assistant **Shelly Grimmius** . . . . (515) 323-2205
State Wetland Specialist **(Vacant)** . . . . (712) 276-4648

Management and Strategy
Assistant State Conservationist for Management and
Strategy **Jaia Fischer** . . . . (515) 323-2209

Programs
Assistant State Conservationist for Programs (Acting)
David Brommel . . . . (515) 323-2235
E-mail: david.brommel@ia.usda.gov

Partnerships
Assistant State Conservationist for Partnerships
Martin "Marty" Adkins . . . . (515) 323-2211

Public Affairs
State Public Affairs Specialist and Outreach
Coordinator **(Vacant)** . . . . (515) 323-2207

Ecological Sciences and Conservation Planning
State Resource Conservationist (Acting) **Jon Hubbert** . . . . (515) 323-2292

Soils
State Soil Scientist **Rick Bednarek** . . . . (515) 323-2238

Indiana Office
6013 Lakeside Boulevard, Indianapolis, IN 46278
Tel: (317) 290-3200 Fax: (317) 290-3399 Internet: www.in.nrcs.usda.gov

State Conservationist **Jerry C. Raynor** . . . . (317) 295-5801
Executive Assistant **Lisa Bolton** . . . . (317) 295-5800
E-mail: lisa.bolton@in.usda.gov

Management and Strategy
Assistant State Conservationist for Management and
Strategy **Roger Kult** . . . . (317) 295-5841

National Support Assignments
Asset Management Specialist **(Vacant)** . . . . (317) 295-5836

Programs
Assistant State Conservationist for Programs
Gerald "Jerry" Roach . . . . (317) 295-5820
E-mail: jerry.roach@in.usda.gov

Soils
State Soil Scientist **Gary Struben** . . . . (317) 295-5885

Special Projects
Assistant State Conservationist for Special Projects
Jill Reinhart . . . . (317) 295-5883
E-mail: jill.reinhart@in.usda.gov

Technology
State Resource Conservationist **Shannon Zezula** . . . . (317) 295-5888

Kansas Office
760 South Broadway, Salina, KS 67401-4604
Tel: (785) 823-4500 Fax: (855) 533-5070

State Conservationist **Karen Woodrich** . . . . (785) 823-4565
Assistant State Conservationist for Management and
Strategy **Gaye L. Benfer** . . . . (785) 823-4508
Financial Resources Specialist **Loren L. Graff** . . . . (758) 823-4521
E-mail: loren.graff@ks.usda.gov

Conservation Programs
Assistant State Conservationist for Programs (Acting)
Bruce Wells . . . . (785) 823-4569
E-mail: bruce.wells@ks.usda.gov

Engineering
State Conservation Engineer (Acting)
Shawn T. Sherraden . . . . (785) 823-4534

Resource Conservation
State Resource Conservationist **R. Dean Krehbiel** . . . . (785) 823-4547

Water Resources
Assistant State Conservationist for Water Resources
Bruce Wells . . . . (785) 823-4550

Minnesota State Office
375 Jackson Street, Suite 600, St. Paul, MN 55101-1854
Tel: (651) 602-7900 Fax: (855) 823-7656

State Conservationist (Acting) **Curtis Elke** . . . . (651) 602-7854
Fax: (855) 823-7656

Business Operations
State Administrative Officer **Rafael Fernandez** . . . . (651) 602-7887
E-mail: rafael.fernandez@mn.usda.gov

Ecological Sciences
State Resource Conservationist **Ryan Galbreath** . . . . (651) 602-7879

Engineering
State Conservation Engineer **(Vacant)** . . . . (651) 602-7880

Programs
Assistant State Conservationist (Easements)
Lanette Dietrich . . . . (651) 602-7855
Assistant State Conservationist (Financial Assistance)
(Acting) **Jeremy Bennett** . . . . (651) 602-7931

Soils
State Soil Scientist **(Vacant)** . . . . (651) 602-7895

Management and Strategy

Missouri Office
Parkade Center, 601 Business Loop 70 West,
Suite 250, Columbia, MO 65203
Tel: (573) 876-0909 Fax: (855) 830-0683

State Conservationist **Serapio "J.R." Flores, Jr.** . . . . (573) 876-0901

★ Presidential Appointment Requiring Senate Confirmation ☆ Presidential Appointment □ Schedule C Appointment ◇ Career Senior Foreign Service Appointment
● Career Senior Executive Service (SES) Appointment ○ Non-Career Senior Executive Service (SES) Appointment ■ Postal Career Executive Service

Management Strategy
Assistant State Conservationist for Operations
Joseph "Joe" Steuber . . . . . (573) 876-9424

Programs
601 Business Loop 70 West, Parkade Center,
Suite 250, Columbia, MO 65203-2546
Tel: (573) 876-0909

Assistant State Conservationist for Programs (Acting)
Lauren A. Cartwright . . . . . (573) 876-0909

Engineering Staff
State Conservation Engineer **Marty A. Comstock** . . . . . (573) 876-9410

Support Services Staff
State Administrative Officer **Joseph "Joe" Steuber** . . . . . (573) 876-9368
E-mail: joe.steuber@mo.usda.gov

Water Resources
Assistant State Conservationist for Water Resources
(Acting) **J. Christopher "Chris" Hamilton** . . . . . (573) 876-9421

Nebraska Office
Federal Building, 100 Centennial Mall, North,
Room 152, Lincoln, NE 68508-3866
Tel: (402) 437-5300 Internet: www.ne.nrcs.usda.gov

State Conservationist **Craig Derickson** . . . . . (402) 437-5300

Programs
Assistant State Conservationist for Programs
Brad Soncksen . . . . . (402) 437-4111

Management Support Staff
Assistant State Conservationist for Management and
Strategy **Julie A. Crew** . . . . . (402) 437-4131

Engineering
State Conservation Engineer **Allen Gehring** . . . . . (402) 437-4037

Ecological Sciences Staff
State Resource Conservationist **Britt Weiser** . . . . . (402) 437-4116

Soil Surveys Staff
State Soil Scientist **Neil Dominy** . . . . . (402) 437-4113

North Dakota Office
Federal Building, 220 East Rosser Avenue,
Room 270, Bismarck, ND 58502-1458
Mail: P.O. Box 1458, Bismarck, ND 58502-1458
Tel: (701) 530-2000 Fax: (855) 813-7556
Internet: www.nrcs.usda.gov/wps/portal/nrcs/site/nd/home

State Conservationist **Mary E. Podoll** . . . . . (701) 530-2003
Assistant State Conservationist (Partnership
Coordinator) **Jill S. Howard** . . . . . (701) 530-2073
State Public Affairs Specialist **Tanya J Koch** . . . . . (701) 530-2096
220 East Rosser Avenue, Room 270, Bismarck, ND 58501-1458
E-mail: tanya.koch@nd.usda.gov

Programs and Easement Staff
Assistant State Conservationist for Programs/Water
Resources **Todd Hagel** . . . . . (701) 530-2004

Management and Strategy
Assistant State Conservationist for Management and
Strategy **Lisa J. Lund** . . . . . (701) 530-2098
E-mail: lisa.lund@nd.usda.gov

Engineering Staff
State Conservation Engineer **Christi A. Fisher** . . . . . (701) 530-2091

Ecological Sciences Staff
State Resource Conservationist **Todd A. Schwagler** . . . . . (701) 530-2084

Soil Survey and Resource Assessment Staff
Federal Building, 220 East Rosser Avenue,
Room 257, Bismarck, ND 58501-1458

State Soil Scientist **Wade D. Bott** . . . . . (701) 530-2021

Oklahoma State Office
100 USDA Building, Suite 206, Stillwater, OK 74074-2655
Tel: (405) 742-1204 Fax: (405) 742-1201

State Conservationist **Gary L. O'Neill** . . . . . (405) 742-1220
Assistant State Conservationist for Outreach/Civil
Rights **Gilbert F. Guerrero** . . . . . (405) 742-1207
E-mail: gilbert.guerrero@ok.usda.gov
Assistant State Conservationist for Strategy and
Management (Acting) **James D. "Jamey" Wood II** . . . . (405) 742-1277

Administrative Staff
State Administrative Officer **(Vacant)** . . . . . (405) 742-1209

Ecological Sciences and Conservation Planning Staff
State Resources Conservationist
Steven "Steve" Glasgow . . . . . (405) 742-1235

Engineering Staff
State Conservation Engineer **Chris Stoner** . . . . . (405) 742-1260

Programs Staff
Assistant State Conservationist for Programs
Stacy M. Riley . . . . . (405) 742-1215
E-mail: stacy.riley@ok.usda.gov

Soil Sciences Staff
State Soil Scientist **Steven "Steve" Alspach** . . . . . (405) 742-1249

Water Resources Staff
Assistant State Conservationist for Water Resources
(Acting) **April Burns** . . . . . (405) 742-1284
E-mail: april.burns@ok.usda.gov

South Dakota Office
Federal Building, 200 Fourth Street SW,
Room 203, Huron, SD 57350
Tel: (605) 352-1200 Fax: (605) 352-1270 Fax: (855) 256-2565
Internet: www.nrcs.usda.gov/wps/portal/nrcs/site/sd/home

State Conservationist **Jeffrey J. Zimprich** . . . . . (605) 352-1200 ext. 1201
Assistant State Conservationist for Field Operations
Tate Latz . . . . . (605) 342-0301
Assistant State Conservationist for Management and
Strategy **Denise Gauer** . . . . . (605) 352-1243
Public Affairs Officer **Collette Kessler** . . . . . (605) 352-1228

Program Services
Assistant State Conservationist for Programs
Jeff Vander Wilt . . . . . (605) 352-1226

Ecological Sciences
State Resource Conservationist **Karl Anderson** . . . . . (605) 352-1234

Soils
State Soil Scientist **Nathan Jones** . . . . . (605) 352-1253

Engineering
State Conservation Engineer **Jay Cobb** . . . . . (605) 352-1260

Texas Office
W. R. Poage Federal Building, 101 South Main Street, Temple, TX 76501
Tel: (254) 742-9800 Fax: (254) 742-9819 Internet: www.tx.nrcs.usda.gov

● State Conservationist **Salvador Salinas** . . . . . (254) 742-9800
E-mail: salvador.salinas@tx.usda.gov
Deputy State Conservationist **(Vacant)** . . . . . (254) 742-9800
Executive Assistant **Nadine Shock** . . . . . (254) 742-9800
E-mail: nadine.shock@tx.usda.gov

★ Presidential Appointment Requiring Senate Confirmation ☆ Presidential Appointment ☐ Schedule C Appointment ◇ Career Senior Foreign Service Appointment
● Career Senior Executive Service (SES) Appointment ○ Non-Career Senior Executive Service (SES) Appointment ■ Postal Career Executive Service

Management and Strategy
Assistant State Conservationist for Operations
Drenda J. Williams . . . . (254) 742-9808

Programs Planning
Assistant State Conservationist for Programs **Lori Ziehr** . . . (254) 742-9881

Administrative Staff
State Administrative Officer (Acting)
Drenda J. Williams . . . . (254) 742-9808
E-mail: drenda.williams@tx.usda.gov

Engineering Staff
State Conservation Engineer (Acting) **Brian Wenberg** . . . . (254) 742-9911
Assistant State Conservation Engineer **Brian Wenberg** . . . (254) 742-9945

Public Affairs Staff
State Public Affairs Director **Beverly Moseley** . . . . (254) 742-9810
E-mail: beverly.moseley@tx.usda.gov

State Soil Science Staff
State Soil Scientist **Alan Stahnke** . . . . (254) 742-9857

Resource Conservation Staff
State Resource Conservationist **Kristy Oates** . . . . (254) 742-9505

Wisconsin Office
8030 Excelsior Drive, Suite 200, Madison, WI 53717
Tel: (608) 662-4422 Fax: (608) 662-9425

State Conservationist **Angela Biggs** . . . . (608) 662-4422 ext. 203
E-mail: angela.biggs@wi.usda.gov

Administrative
Assistant State Conservationist
for Management and Strategy
Deborah L. White . . . . (608) 662-4422 ext. 255
E-mail: deborah.white@wi.usda.gov

Easements
Assistant State Conservationist (Easements)
Greg Kidd . . . . (608) 662-4422 ext. 252
E-mail: greg.kidd@wi.usda.gov

Engineering
State Conservation Engineer **John Ramsden** . . . . (608) 662-4422 ext. 234

Financial Assistance
Assistant State Conservationist (Financial
Programs) **Tom Krapf** . . . . (608) 662-4422 ext. 232
E-mail: tom.krapf@wi.usda.gov

Resources
State Resource Conservationist (Acting)
Judy Derricks . . . . (608) 662-4422 ext. 258

Soils
State Soil Scientist **Jason Nemecek** . . . . (608) 662-4422 ext. 202

Northeast Region
NRCS, 1400 Independence Avenue, SW,
Room 5204, Washington, DC 20250
Mail: P.O. Box 2890, Washington, DC 20013
Tel: (202) 690-2197
Areas Covered: CT, DE, ME, MD, MA, MI, NH, NJ, NY, OH, PA, RI, VT, WV

Regional Conservationist (Acting) **Terrell Erickson** . . . . (202) 690-2196

Connecticut Office
344 Merrow Road, Suite A, Tolland, CT 06084-3917
Tel: (860) 871-4011 Fax: (855) 934-2776 Internet: www.ct.nrcs.usda.gov

State Conservationist **Thomas "Tom" Morgart** . . . . (860) 871-4011
Assistant State Conservationist (Programs)
Joyce Purcell . . . . (860) 871-4028

Connecticut Office *(continued)*

Assistant State Conservationist for Management and
Strategy **Michelle Hendricks** . . . . (860) 871-4034
E-mail: michelle.hendricks@ct.usda.gov
State Resource Conservationist **Nancy Ferlow** . . . . (860) 871-4049
State Conservation Engineer **Arthur Ramthun** . . . . (860) 871-4030
State Soil Scientist **Deborah "Debbie" Surabian** . . . . (860) 871-4042

Delaware Office
1221 College Park Drive, Suite 100, Dover, DE 19904-8713
Tel: (302) 678-4160 Fax: (855) 306-3386

State Conservationist **Kasey Taylor** . . . . (302) 678-4160
Executive Administrative Assistant **Ivy L. McBride** . . . . (302) 678-4175
Assistant State Conservationist for Management and
Strategy **Eileen Campbell** . . . . (302) 678-4161
E-mail: eileen.campbell@de.usda.gov
Assistant State Conservationist for Programs
Paul M. Petrichenko . . . . (302) 678-4180
E-mail: paul.petrichenko@de.usda.gov
Public Affairs Specialist **Dastina Wallace** . . . . (302) 678-4179
E-mail: dastina.wallace@de.usda.gov
State Resource Conservationist
Sally L. Griffith-Kepfer . . . . (302) 678-4182
State Soil Scientist **Phillip S. "Phil" King** . . . . (302) 678-4172

Maine Office
967 Illinois Avenue, Suite 3, Bangor, ME 04401
Tel: (207) 990-9100 ext. 3 Fax: (855) 589-1058

State Conservationist **Juan Hernandez** . . . . (207) 990-9585
Assistant State Conservationist for Field Operations
Daniel "Dan" Schmidt . . . . (207) 947-9570
Assistant State Conservationist for Management and
Strategy **Brian L. Vigue** . . . . (207) 990-9567
E-mail: brian.vigue@usda.gov
Assistant State Conservationist for Operations
Management **(Vacant)** . . . . (207) 990-9554
Assistant State Conservationist for Programs
Susan Arrants . . . . (207) 990-9564
E-mail: susan.arrants@usda.gov
Assistant State Conservationist for Special
Projects **Cathee Pullman** . . . . (207) 990-9100 ext. 563
State Conservation Engineer
Daniel J. "Dan" Baumert . . . . (207) 990-9555
State Soil Scientist **Anthony "Tony" Jenkins** . . . (207) 990-9100 ext. 557
Public Affairs Specialist **Thomas Kielbasa** . . . . (207) 990-9569
E-mail: thomas.kielbasa@usda.gov

Maryland Office
John Hanson Business Center, 339 Busch's Frontage Road,
Suite 301, Annapolis, MD 21409
Tel: (410) 757-0861 Fax: (855) 432-9027
Internet: www.md.nrcs.usda.gov

State Conservationist (Acting) **Robert "Rob" McAfee** . . . (410) 757-0861
Note: On detail to NRCS's Public Affairs Division in Washington, DC.
State Conservationist **Terron Hillsman** . . . . (410) 757-0861
Note: On detail to NRCS's Public Affairs Division in Washington, DC.
Executive Assistant **Nora De La Rosa** . . . . (443) 482-2907
National Plant Materials Center Manager
David Kidwell-Slak . . . . (301) 504-8176
E-mail: david.kidwellslak@md.usda.gov
Assistant State Conservationist for Management and
Strategy (Acting) **Wendy Smith** . . . . (443) 482-2938
Assistant State Conservationist for Management and
Strategy **Odessa Armstrong** . . . . (443) 482-2938
Note: Currently on leave.
Assistant State Conservationist for Field Operations
Ramon Ortiz . . . . (443) 482-2962
Note: On detail as Acting State Conservationist.

Assistant State Conservationist for Field Operations
Robert "Rob" McAfee . . . . (443) 482-2953
Note: On detail as Acting State Conservationist.

★ Presidential Appointment Requiring Senate Confirmation ☆ Presidential Appointment ☐ Schedule C Appointment ◇ Career Senior Foreign Service Appointment
● Career Senior Executive Service (SES) Appointment ○ Non-Career Senior Executive Service (SES) Appointment ■ Postal Career Executive Service

Maryland Office *(continued)*

Assistant State Conservationist for Programs
Jacqueline "Jackie" Byam . . . . (443) 482-2927
State Resource Conservationist
Patricia "Patty" Engler . . . . (443) 482-2929
State Conservation Engineer **Allan Stahl** . . . . (443) 482-2912
State Soil Scientist **Phillip S. "Phil" King** . . . . (443) 482-2931
Human Resources Assistant **Brock R. Chalmers** . . . . (443) 482-2932
E-mail: brock.chalmers@md.usda.gov Fax: (410) 757-6009
State Public Affairs Officer **Genevieve Lister** . . . . (443) 482-2911
E-mail: genevieve.lister@md.usda.gov

Massachusetts Office

451 West Street, Amherst, MA 01002-2995
Tel: (413) 253-4350 Fax: (855) 596-7666

State Conservationist **Christine S. Clarke** . . . . (413) 253-4350
Assistant State Conservationist for Field Operations
Vince Snyder . . . . (413) 253-4378
Assistant State Conservationist for Management and
Strategy **(Vacant)** . . . . (413) 253-4364
State Conservation Engineer **Deron Davis** . . . . (413) 253-4362
State Resource Conservationist **Tom Akin** . . . . (413) 253-4365
State Soil Scientist **Albert Averill, Jr.** . . . . (413) 253-4382
Public Affairs Officer **Diane Petit** . . . . (413) 253-4371
E-mail: diane.petit@ma.usda.gov
Administrative Support Assistant **Holly Nemeth** . . . . (413) 253-4373

Michigan Office

3001 Coolidge Road, Suite 250, East Lansing, MI 48823-6321
Tel: (517) 324-5270 Fax: (855) 701-4363

State Conservationist **Garry Lee** . . . . (517) 324-5277
Assistant to the State Conservationist **Lorrie Skinner** . . . (517) 324-5426
Assistant State Conservationist for Management and
Strategy **Diane Gray** . . . . (517) 324-5135
E-mail: diane.gray@mi.usda.gov
Assistant State Conservationist for Programs
Kim Wieber . . . . (517) 324-5276
E-mail: kim.wieber@mi.usda.gov
Public Affairs Specialist **Brian Buehler** . . . . (517) 324-5244
E-mail: brian.buehler@mi.usda.gov
State Conservation Engineer
Richard "Rick" Woodford . . . . (517) 324-5232
State Resource Conservationist **Betsy Dierberger** . . . . (517) 324-5265
State Soil Scientist **Martin Rosek** . . . . (517) 324-5241
Human Resources Manager **Jessica Daigle** . . . . (517) 324-5238
E-mail: jessica.daigle@mi.usda.gov

New Hampshire Office

273 Locust St, Suite 2D, Dover, NH 03820
Tel: (603) 868-7581 Fax: (855) 428-0332 Internet: www.nh.nrcs.usda.gov

State Conservationist **Richard P. "Rick" Ellsmore** . . . . (603) 868-7581
Executive Assistant **Janet D. Martin** . . . . (603) 868-9931 ext. 100
Assistant State Conservationist for
Management and Strategy **Jade Nield** . . . . (603) 868-9931 ext. 112
Assistant State Conservationist for Operations
Kimberly L. "Kim" McCracken . . . . (603) 868-9931 ext. 123
Assistant State Conservationist
for Programs/Field Operations
Deborah S. Weymouth . . . . (603) 868-9931 ext. 102
E-mail: deb.weymouth@nh.usda.gov
Biologist **Kelly Boland** . . . . (603) 868-9931 ext. 113
Human Resources Specialist **Holly R. Boyson** . . . (603) 868-9931 ext. 116
E-mail: holly.boyson@nh.usda.gov
Human Resources Specialist **Karen Goulet** . . . . . (603) 868-9931 ext. 127
E-mail: karen.goulet@nh.usda.gov
Information Technology Specialist
Rebecca E. Lee . . . . (603) 868-9931 ext. 121
E-mail: rebecca.lee@nh.usda.gov
Public Affairs Specialist **(Vacant)** . . . . (603) 868-9931 ext. 136
Concord Field Service Center/District Conservationist
Chad Cochrane . . . . (603) 223-6021
10 Ferry Street, Box 312, Concord, NH 03301-5081
Administrative Assistant **Kimberly Zaleski** . . . . (603) 868-9931 ext. 100

New Hampshire Office *(continued)*

Administrative Assistant **Laura Chandler** . . . . . (603) 868-9931 ext. 108

New Jersey Office

220 Davidson Avenue, 4th Floor, Somerset, NJ 08873
Tel: (732) 537-6040 Fax: (855) 305-7157 Internet: www.nj.nrcs.usda.gov

State Conservationist **Carrie Lindig** . . . . (732) 537-6041
Assistant State Conservationist for Management and
Strategy **Maria Collazo** . . . . (732) 537-6043
Assistant State Conservationist for Programs
Gail Bartok . . . . (732) 537-6042
Assistant State Soil Scientist **Edwin Muñiz** . . . . (732) 537-6062
National Employee/Labor Relations Specialist
Carol Parker . . . . (732) 537-6081
E-mail: carol.parker@nj.usda.gov
Public Affairs Specialist **Barbara Phillips** . . . . (732) 537-6044
E-mail: barbara.phillips@nj.usda.gov
State Conservation Engineer **David T. Lamm** . . . . (732) 537-6071
State Resource Conservationist **Christine Hall** . . . . (732) 537-6051
State Soil Scientist **Richard K. Shaw** . . . . (732) 537-6061

Cape May Plant Materials Center

1536 Route 9 North, Cape May Court House, NJ 08210
Tel: (609) 536-6352 Fax: (609) 465-9284

Manager **Christopher Miller** . . . . (609) 536-6352
Biological Lab Technician **Scott Snell** . . . . (609) 536-6354

New York Office

The Galleries of Syracuse, 441 South Salina Street,
Room 520, Suite 354, Syracuse, NY 13202-2450
Tel: (315) 477-6504 Fax: (855) 477-8518
E-mail: stc@spock.ny.nrcs.usda.gov

State Conservationist **Greg Kist** . . . . (315) 477-6504
Executive Assistant and Freedom of Information Act
Officer **Angela Van Dyke** . . . . (315) 477-6504
E-mail: angela.vandyke@ny.usda.gov
Assistant State Conservationist for Management and
Strategy **Michele DeMaio Grace** . . . . (315) 477-6509
E-mail: michele.demaio.grace@ny.usda.gov
Assistant State Conservationist for Programs
Tammy Willis . . . . (315) 477-6503
Assistant State Conservationist for Water Resources
Dennis DeWeese . . . . (315) 477-6527
Public Affairs Specialist **Jeremy Call** . . . . (315) 477-6504
E-mail: Jeremy.Call@ny.usda.gov
State Conservation Engineer **(Vacant)** . . . . (315) 736-3316
State Resource Conservationist **Edward Henry** . . . . (315) 477-6529
State Soil Scientist **Stephen Page** . . . . (315) 477-6526

Ohio Office

Federal Building, 200 North High Street, Columbus, OH 43215-2478
Tel: (614) 255-2472 Fax: (855) 854-9149

State Conservationist **Terry J. Cosby** . . . . (614) 255-2472
Assistant State Conservationist for Natural Resources
Barbara Baker . . . . (614) 255-2502
Education: Ohio State PhD Fax: (855) 854-9149
Assistant State Conservationist for Programs
John Wilson . . . . (614) 255-2480
E-mail: john.wilson@oh.usda.gov
Assistant State Conservationist for Special Projects
Patrecia Davis . . . . (614) 255-2508
State Conservation Engineer **Bruce Atherton** . . . . (614) 255-2488
Fax: (855) 867-9515
State Soil Scientist **Steven Baker** . . . . (614) 255-2483
Fax: (855) 867-9515
MLRA Project Leader **Scott Hoover** . . . . (740) 885-3315
Fax: (877) 832-0489
MLRA Project Leader **Neil Martin** . . . . (419) 581-4520
Fax: (855) 842-9051
Soil Scientist **Dan Benyei** . . . . (740) 885-3317
Fax: (877) 832-0489
Office Manager **Jane Aycock** . . . . (614) 255-2472
200 North High Street, Room 522, Columbus, OH 43215-2408

(continued on next page)

DEPARTMENTS

Ohio Office *(continued)*

Public Affairs Specialist **Christina "Chris" Coulon** . . . . . . (614) 255-2471
E-mail: chris.coulon@oh.usda.gov Fax: (855) 867-9515
Education: Michigan State 1996 MS
Management Assistant **(Vacant)** . . . . (614) 255-2490
Fax: (855) 867-9515
Budget Analyst **(Vacant)** . . . . (614) 255-2485
Natural Resource Specialist **(Vacant)** . . . . (614) 255-2565
Human Resources Officer **Shirley Yarbrough** . . . . (614) 255-2509
E-mail: shirley.yarbrough@oh.usda.gov Fax: (855) 854-9150

Management and Strategy

Assistant State Conservationist for Operations
Randy Jordan . . . . (614) 255-2493
Administrative Support Specialist **Mary Ardrey** . . . . (614) 255-2479
E-mail: mary.ardrey@oh.usda.gov
Tel: (855) 854-9149
Management Analyst **William "Bill" Dwyer** . . . . (614) 255-2501
Fax: (855) 867-9514
Natural Resource Specialist **Felicity Weatherspoon** . . . . . (614) 255-2465
Natural Resource Specialist **Carrie Cusick** . . . . (937) 856-5428
Human Resources Assistant **Alberta Owensby** . . . . (614) 255-2473
E-mail: alberta.owensby@oh.usda.gov Fax: (855) 854-9150
Human Resources Specialist **Jimmy Lewis** . . . . (614) 255-2470
E-mail: jimmy.lewis@oh.usda.gov

Public Affairs

Visual Information Assistant **Dianne Johnson** . . . . (614) 255-2463
E-mail: dianne.johnson@oh.usda.gov Fax: (855) 867-9515

Special Projects Staff

Outreach Coordinator for Special Projects
Johnnie Freeman . . . . (937) 382-2461 ext. 114
Urban Resource Conservationist **Cheryl Rice** . . . . (419) 893-1966
Fax: (855) 854-9149

State Conservation Engineer Staff

State Resource Conservationist **Mark Smith** . . . . (614) 255-2474
Fax: (855) 854-9149

Pennsylvania Office

359 East Park Drive, Suite 2, Harrisburg, PA 17111
Tel: (717) 237-2100 TTY: (717) 237-2235 Fax: (855) 813-2861

State Conservationist **Denise Coleman** . . . . (717) 237-2203
Assistant State Conservationist for Management and Strategy **Shozette L. Smith** . . . . (717) 237-2230
E-mail: shozette.smith@pa.usda.gov
Assistant State Conservationist for Operations
Susan Marquart . . . . (717) 237-2237
Assistant State Conservationist for Programs
Susan Kubo . . . . (717) 237-2216
E-mail: susan.kubo@pa.usda.gov
Public Affairs Specialist **Molly Hippensteel** . . . . (717) 237-2208
E-mail: molly.mcdonough@pa.usda.gov
State Conservation Engineer **Peter Vanderstappen** . . . . . . (717) 237-2212
State Resource Conservationist **Daniel "Dan" Dostie** . . . . (717) 237-2204
State Soil Scientist **Yuri Plowden** . . . . (717) 237-2207
Administrative Operations Assistant **Timothy Kinney** . . . . (717) 237-2221
E-mail: timothy.kinney@pa.usda.gov
Assistant State Conservationist for Operations, West Pennsylvania
Jeffrey M. "Jeff" Werner . . . . (814) 226-8160 ext. 122
Assistant State Conservationist for Operations, Northeast Pennsylvania **Nancy DiFiore** . . . . (570) 784-4401 ext. 133
Assistant State Conservationist for Operations, Southeast Pennsylvania **Charles Hanner** . . . . (717) 376-3489

Rhode Island Office

60 Quaker Lane, Suite 40, Warwick, RI 02886-0181
Tel: (401) 828-1300 ext. 1 Fax: (855) 924-4748
State Conservationist
R. Phoukham "Phou" Vongkhamdy . . . . (401) 828-1300 ext. 1

Rhode Island Office *(continued)*

Public Affairs Specialist/Webmaster
Walter J. Marshall . . . . (401) 822-8816
E-mail: walter.marshall@ri.usda.gov

Vermont Office

356 Mountain View Drive, Suite 105, Colchester, VT 05446
Tel: (802) 951-6796 Fax: (802) 951-6327 Internet: www.vt.nrcs.usda.gov/
State Conservationist **Vicky M. Drew** . . . . (802) 951-6796 ext. 242
Education: Georgia BS

West Virginia Office

1550 Earl Core Road, Suite 200, Morgantown, WV 26505
Tel: (304) 284-7540 Fax: (855) 857-6448 Internet: www.wv.nrcs.usda.gov
State Conservationist **Louis E. Aspey II** . . . . (304) 284-7540

Southeast Region

1400 Independence Avenue, SW, Room 5204, Washington, DC 20250
Tel: (202) 690-2197
Areas Covered: AL, AR, Caribbean, FL, GA, KY, LA, MS, NC, SC, TN, VA

● Regional Conservationist **(Vacant)** . . . . (202) 690-2197

Alabama Office

3381 Skyway Drive, Auburn, AL 36830
Mail: P.O. Box 311, Auburn, AL 36831
Tel: (334) 887-4500 Fax: (855) 292-1671
State Conservationist **Ben Malone** . . . . (334) 887-4500
Public Affairs Specialist **Amelia Hines Dortch** . . . . (334) 887-4581
E-mail: amelia.hines@ga.usda.gov
Assistant State Conservationist for Partnerships
(Vacant) . . . . (334) 887-4532

Technology

Assistant State Conservationist for Technology
Shannon Weaver . . . . (334) 887-4533

Administrative Services

State Administrative Officer **John Hughes** . . . . (334) 887-4568
E-mail: john.hughes@al.usda.gov

Arkansas Office

Federal Building, 700 West Capitol Avenue,
Room 3416, Little Rock, AR 72201
Tel: (501) 301-3100 Fax: (855) 681-7041 Internet: www.ar.nrcs.usda.gov
State Conservationist **Michael E. Sullivan** . . . . (501) 301-3100

Administrative Services

700 West Capitol Avenue, Suite 3416, Little Rock, AR 72201-3225
Fax: (855) 681-7042
Assistant State Conservationist for Management and Strategy **Kathy Anderson** . . . . (501) 301-3132
E-mail: kathy.anderson@ar.usda.gov

Easements and Watershed

700 West Capitol Avenue, Suite 3416, Little Rock, AR 72201-3225
Fax: (855) 681-7043
Assistant State Conservationist for Easements
Randy Childress . . . . (501) 301-3131

Ecological Sciences

700 West Capitol Avenue, Suite 3416, Little Rock, AR 72201-3225
Fax: (855) 681-7044
State Resource Conservationist **Nancy Young** . . . . (501) 301-3134

Engineering

700 West Capitol Avenue, Suite 3416, Little Rock, AR 72201-3225
Fax: (855) 681-7044
State Conservation Engineer **Walter "Walt" Delp** . . . . (501) 301-3141

★ Presidential Appointment Requiring Senate Confirmation ☆ Presidential Appointment ☐ Schedule C Appointment ◇ Career Senior Foreign Service Appointment
● Career Senior Executive Service (SES) Appointment ○ Non-Career Senior Executive Service (SES) Appointment ■ Postal Career Executive Service

Partnership Coordination
Assistant State Conservationist (Partnership Coordination) **Amanda Mathis** .... (501) 301-3162

Programs
700 West Capitol Avenue, Suite 3416, Little Rock, AR 72201-3225
Fax: (855) 681-7043
Assistant State Conservationist for Programs **Kenneth Lee** .... (501) 301-3165

Public Affairs and Earth Team
700 West Capitol Avenue, Suite 3416, Little Rock, AR 72201-3225
Fax: (855) 681-7044
State Public Affairs Specialist **Reginald L. Jackson** ..... (501) 301-3133
E-mail: reginald.jackson@ar.usda.gov

Caribbean Area Office
654 Muñoz Rivera Avenue, Suite 604, San Juan, PR 00918-4129
Tel: (787) 766-5206 Fax: (855) 415-2513
State Conservationist **Edwin Almodóvar** .... (787) 281-4836

Ecological Sciences and Planning Division
State Resource Conservationist **Jaime Valentín** .... (787) 766-5065
Biologist **(Vacant)** .... (787) 766-5132
Conservation Agronomist **Mario Rodriguez** ..... (787) 831-3101 ext. 116
Grazing Lands and Plant Minerals Specialist **Edwin G. Más** .... (787) 831-3101 ext. 106
National Resources Inventory Specialist **Ismael Matos** . . . (787) 766-6139

Engineering Division
State Conservation Engineer **Damaris Medina** .... (787) 766-5715
Hydrology Engineer **(Vacant)** .... (787) 766-5840

Programs Staff
Natural Resource Specialist **(Vacant)** .... (787) 766-5206

Florida Office
2614 NW 43rd Street, Gainesville, FL 32606-6611
Mail: P.O. Box 141510, Gainesville, FL 32614-1510
Tel: (352) 338-9500 Fax: (352) 338-9574
Areas Covered: FL
State Conservationist **Russell Morgan** .... (352) 338-9500
Assistant State Conservationist for Financial Assistance Programs **Jeffrey Woods** .... (352) 338-9515
Conservation Program Specialist **Nathan Fikkert** .... (352) 338-9545
Conservation Program Specialist **Georganne Wiltse** ..... (352) 338-9545

Administration
Assistant State Conservationist for Administration **Bruce Hawkins** .... (352) 338-9525
E-mail: bruce.hawkins@fl.usda.gov Fax: (352) 338-9575

Easements
Assistant State Conservationist for Easement Programs **Roney Gutierrez** .... (352) 338-9502

Ecological Sciences
State Resource Conservationist **Henry Burkwhat** .... (352) 338-9543

Engineering
State Conservation Engineer **Jason Strenth** .... (352) 338-9557

Management and Strategy
Assistant State Conservationist for Management and Strategy **Robert Lawson** .... (608) 662-4422 ext. 255
Tel: (352) 338-9577

Plant Materials Center
14119 Broad Street, Brooksville, FL 34601
Tel: (352) 796-9600 Fax: (352) 799-7305
Plant Materials Center Manager **Janet Grabowski** .... (352) 796-9600 ext. 3831

Public Affairs
State Public Information Officer **Dawn "Renee" Bodine** .... (352) 338-9565
E-mail: renee.bodine@fl.usda.gov

Soils
State Soil Scientist **Kevin Sullivan** .... (352) 338-9538

Georgia Office
Stephens Federal Building, 355 East Hancock Avenue, Room 200, Mail Stop 200, Athens, GA 30601-2769
Tel: (706) 546-2272 Fax: (855) 417-8490
● State Conservationist **Terrance Rudolph** .... (706) 546-2272
E-mail: terrance.rudolph@ga.usda.gov
Secretary **Kandi Hostetler** .... (706) 546-2080
E-mail: kandi.hostetler@ga.usda.gov

Management and Strategy
355 East Hancock Avenue, Athens, GA 30601-2768
Tel: (706) 546-2272 Fax: (855) 417-8490
State Administrative Officer **Sharon Gipson** .... (706) 546-2086
E-mail: sharon.gipson@ga.usda.gov

Programs
Assistant State Conservationist for Programs **Katura Wright** .... (706) 546-2083
Office Automation Clerk **Janice Lester** .... (706) 546-2420
E-mail: janice.lester@ga.usda.gov

Technical Support
355 East Hancock Avenue, Athens, GA 30601-2768
Tel: (706) 546-2114 Tel: (706) 546-2115 Fax: (855) 452-0954
State Resource Conservationist **Kristina "Tina" Jerome** .... (706) 546-2009

Public Affairs
355 East Hancock Avenue, Athens, GA 30601-2768
Tel: (706) 546-2069 Fax: (855) 452-0954
State Public Affairs Specialist **Chris Groskreutz** .... (706) 546-2069
E-mail: chris.groskreutz@ga.usda.gov

Engineering
355 East Hancock Avenue, Athens, GA 30601-2768
Tel: (706) 546-2310 Fax: (855) 452-0954
State Conservation Engineer **Diane Guthrie** .... (706) 546-2310

Soil Sciences, Geographic Information Services and National Resources Inventory
355 East Hancock Avenue, Athens, GA 30601-2768
Tel: (706) 546-2278 Fax: (855) 452-0954
State Soil Scientist **Jim Lathem** .... (706) 546-2077

Partnerships
Assistant State Conservationist for Partnerships **Tansel Hudson** .... (706) 546-2097

Kentucky Office
771 Corporate Drive, Suite 300, Lexington, KY 40503-5479
Tel: (859) 224-7350 Fax: (855) 768-4251
Internet: www.nrcs.usda.gov/wps/portal/nrcs/site/ky/home
State Conservationist **Karen Woodrich** .... (859) 224-7350
Executive Assistant **Hilda Pagan-Nunez** .... (859) 224-7350
Assistant State Conservationist for Partnerships **(Vacant)** .... (859) 224-7373

Management and Strategy
Assistant State Conservationist for Management and Strategy **Amanda Moore** .... (859) 224-7309

Programs Staff
Assistant State Conservationist for Programs **Deena Wheby** .... (859) 224-7403

★ Presidential Appointment Requiring Senate Confirmation ☆ Presidential Appointment □ Schedule C Appointment ◇ Career Senior Foreign Service Appointment
● Career Senior Executive Service (SES) Appointment ○ Non-Career Senior Executive Service (SES) Appointment ■ Postal Career Executive Service

Natural Resources Planning Staff
Assistant State Conservationist for Natural Resources Planning **Reed Cripps** .... (859) 224-7371

Ecological Sciences Staff
State Resource Conservationist, Conservation Programs **(Vacant)** .... (859) 224-7370

Engineering Staff
State Engineer **(Vacant)** .... (859) 224-7383

Soils Staff
State Soil Scientist **Steven J. Blanford** .... (859) 224-7607

Louisiana Office
3737 Government Street, Alexandria, LA 71302-3327
Tel: (318) 473-7751 Fax: (844) 325-6947
Internet: www.nrcs.usda.gov/wps/portal/nrcs/site/la/home

State Conservationist **Kevin D. Norton** .... (318) 473-7751
Assistant State Conservationist for Partnership and Initiative Coordination **(Vacant)** .... (337) 893-5664 ext. 3
Executive Secretary **Jacqueline "Jackie" Guillory** .... (318) 473-7751
E-mail: jacqueline.guillory@la.usda.gov
Secretary (Office Automation) **Christopher Byard** .... (318) 473-7751
E-mail: christopher.byard@la.usda.gov

Administrative Section
3737 Government Street, Alexandria, LA 71302-3327
Tel: (318) 473-7767

Assistant State Conservationist for Management and Strategy **(Vacant)** .... (318) 473-7767

Public Affairs Section
3737 Government Street, Alexandria, LA 71302-3327
Tel: (318) 473-7762

State Public Affairs Specialist **Amy Robertson** .... (318) 473-7762
E-mail: amy.robertson@la.usda.gov

Human Resources Section
3737 Government Street, Alexandria, LA 71302-3327
Tel: (318) 473-7769

Human Resources Manager **(Vacant)** .... (318) 473-7769

Conservation Programs Section
3737 Government Street, Alexandria, LA 71302-3327
Tel: (318) 473-7755

Assistant State Conservationist for Programs **Scott Edwards** .... (318) 473-7766

Engineering Section
3737 Government Street, Alexandria, LA 71302-3327
Tel: (318) 473-7795

State Conservation Engineer **John Jurgensen** .... (318) 473-7694

Water Resources Section
3737 Government Street, Alexandria, LA 71302-3327
Tel: (318) 473-7795

Assistant State Conservationist for Water Resources **W. Britt Paul** .... (318) 473-7756

Soils Section
3737 Government Street, Alexandria, LA 71302-3327
Tel: (318) 473-7757

State Soil Scientist **Michael Lindsey** .... (318) 473-7757
Assistant State Soil Scientist **Mitchell Mouton** .... (318) 473-7789

Ecological Sciences and Conservation Planning Section
3737 Government Street, Alexandria, LA 71302-3327
Tel: (318) 473-7774

State Resource Conservationist **John Pitre** .... (318) 473-7774

Mississippi Office
Dr. A. H. McCoy Federal Building, 100 West Capitol Street, Suite 1321, Jackson, MS 39269
Tel: (601) 863-3947 Fax: (601) 965-4940

State Conservationist **Kurt Readus** .... (601) 965-5205 ext. 140

Management and Strategy
100 West Capitol Street, Suite 1321, Jackson, MS 39269-1602
Fax: (601) 965-5178

Assistant State Conservationist **Michael Carr** .... (601) 863-3947 ext. 3939
E-mail: michael.carr@ms.usda.gov

Ecological Sciences
100 West Capitol Street, Suite 1321, Jackson, MS 39269-1602
Fax: (601) 965-5162

State Resource Conservationist **Roderick Thompson** .... (601) 863-3947 ext. 3911

Engineering Staff
100 West Capitol Street, Suite 1321, Jackson, MS 39269-1602
Tel: (601) 965-5205 Fax: (844) 265-0386

State Conservation Engineer **(Vacant)** .... (601) 965-5209 ext. 157

Programs
Assistant State Conservationist for Programs **Clarence Finley** .... (601) 965-5205 ext. 114
E-mail: clarence.finley@ms.usda.gov

Public Affairs and Communications
McCoy Federal Building, 100 West Capitol Street, Suite 1321, Jackson, MS 39269-1602
Fax: (844) 265-0386 Tel: (601) 965-5205

State Public Affairs Specialist **(Vacant)** .... (601) 965-5205 ext. 134

Soil Sciences Staff
100 West Capitol Street, Jackson, MS 39269-1602
Fax: (601) 965-5162

State Soil Scientist **Delaney B. Johnson** .... (601) 863-3947 ext. 3910

North Carolina Office
4407 Bland Road, Suite 117, Raleigh, NC 27609-6293
Tel: (919) 873-2100 Fax: (844) 325-6871 Internet: www.nc.nrcs.usda.gov

State Conservationist **Timothy A. "Tim" Beard** .... (919) 873-2101

Ecological Sciences Staff
Assistant State Conservationist for Technology **Rafael Vega** .... (919) 873-2124

Engineering Staff
State Conservation Engineer (Acting) **J'Que Jones** .... (919) 873-2129

Management and Strategy
Assistant State Conservationist for Management and Strategy **Stuart Lee** .... (919) 873-2017

Management Services Staff
State Administrative Officer **Jane D. LaBounty** .... (919) 873-2172
E-mail: jane.labounty@nc.usda.gov

Programs
Assistant State Conservationist for Easements and Water Resources **Gregory A. "Greg" Walker** .... (919) 873-2104
Assistant State Conservationist for Programs **Gregory A. "Greg" Walker** .... (919) 873-2104
E-mail: greg.walker@nc.usda.gov

Public Affairs Staff
State Public Affairs Specialist **Stuart Lee** .... (919) 873-2107
E-mail: stuart.lee@nc.usda.gov

Soils Staff
State Soil Scientist **Kent Clary** .... (919) 873-2141

South Carolina Office
Strom Thurmond Federal Building, 1835 Assembly Street, Room 950, Columbia, SC 29201
Tel: (803) 253-3935 Fax: (803) 253-3670

State Conservationist **Ann M. English** .... (803) 253-3935

Administration
Assistant State Conservationist for Management and Strategy **Jada Burrell** .... (803) 253-3974
Contract Specialist **Dorothea Martinez** .... (803) 253-3899
E-mail: dorothea.martinez@sc.usda.gov
Business Services Specialist **Curtis Hall** .... (803) 253-3265
E-mail: curtis.hall@sc.usda.gov
Financial Resources Specialist **Steven "Steve" Bourque** .... (803) 253-3898
E-mail: steven.bourque@sc.usda.gov
Management Analyst **(Vacant)** .... (803) 253-3297
Management and Program Analyst **Alford Bell** .... (803) 253-3971
E-mail: alford.bell@sc.usda.gov

Engineering
State Conservation Engineer **(Vacant)** .... (803) 765-5683
Assistant State Conservation Engineer **Stephen Henry** ... (803) 765-5350
Civil Engineering Technician **(Vacant)** .... (803) 253-3938
Geologist **Kim G. Kroeger** .... (919) 873-2128
State Civil Engineer **(Vacant)** .... (803) 253-3895

Operations Management
Assistant State Conservationist for Partnerships **Dennis Mobley** .... (803) 253-3892
Program Analyst **Lavetta Blair** .... (803) 253-3970
E-mail: lavetta.blair@sc.usda.gov

Programs
Assistant State Conservationist for Programs **Kellee Melton** .... (803) 765-5681
Program Specialist **Glenn Sandifer** .... (803) 253-3894
Program Specialist **Shaun Worley** .... (803) 253-3512
Administrative Assistant **Beverly Alexander** .... (803) 253-3977
E-mail: beverly.alexander@sc.usda.gov

Public Affairs and Outreach Staff
Public Affairs and Outreach Coordinator **Jerry R. Bynum** .... (803) 253-3314
E-mail: jerry.bynum@sc.usda.gov

Resource Conservation
State Resource Conservationist **Jerome Brown** .... (803) 765-5685
State Forester **Robert "Rob" Chambers** .... (803) 253-3229
Conservation Agronomist **Gordon Mikell** .... (803) 253-3893
Cultural Resources Specialist **Jim Errante** .... (803) 253-3937
Natural Resources Specialist **David Findley** .... (803) 765-5480
Grazing Land Specialist **Jill Epley** .... (803) 253-3930
Administrative Assistant **Angela Snell** .... (803) 765-5682
E-mail: angela.snell@sc.usda.gov

Soils
State Soil Scientist **Kamara Holmes** .... (803) 765-5685
GIS Specialist **Taylor Ammons** .... (803) 253-3976
GIS Specialist **George Sullivan** .... (803) 253-3723

Tennessee Office
675 U.S. Courthouse, 801 Broadway Street, Nashville, TN 37203
Tel: (615) 277-2531 Fax: (855) 540-3502 Internet: www.tn.nrcs.usda.gov

State Conservationist (Acting) **Robert W. Anderson** ..... (615) 277-2559
Executive Assistant **Alan Fisher** .... (615) 277-2592
E-mail: alan.fisher@tn.usda.gov

Administrative Management
State Administrative Officer (Acting) **Mary Huntington** .... (615) 277-2574
E-mail: Mary.Huntington@tn.usda.gov

Ecological Sciences and Planning
State Resource Conservationist **Matt Walker** .... (615) 277-2587

Engineering
State Conservation Engineer **Robert W. Anderson** ...... (615) 277-2559

Human Resources Staff
801 Broadway, Suite 675, Nashville, TN 37203-3883
Fax: (615) 277-2579

Human Resources Officer **Mary Huntington** .... (615) 277-2574
E-mail: mary.huntington@tn.usda.gov

Program Planning
Assistant State Conservationist for Programs **Jamie Carpenter** .... (615) 277-2595

Public Affairs
801 Broadway, Suite 675, Nashville, TN 37203-3883
Fax: (615) 452-7394

State Public Affairs Specialist **Katherine K. Burse** ...... (615) 277-2533
E-mail: katherine.burse@tn.usda.gov

Soils
State Soil Scientist **(Vacant)** .... (615) 277-2550

Virginia Office
1606 Santa Rosa Road, Suite 209, Richmond, VA 23229-5014
Tel: (804) 287-1691 Fax: (855) 627-9827 Internet: www.va.nrcs.usda.gov

State Conservationist **John A. "Jack" Bricker** .... (804) 287-1691
Assistant State Conservationist (Water Resource Operations) **David Kriz** .... (804) 287-1646
Public Affairs Assistant **(Vacant)** .... (804) 287-1681

Programs Team
1606 Santa Rosa Road, Suite 209, Richmond, VA 23229-5014
Tel: (804) 287-1638 Fax: (855) 627-9827

Assistant State Conservationist (Programs) **Julie Hawkins** .... (804) 287-1692
E-mail: julie.hawkins@va.usda.gov

West Region
NRCS, 1400 Independence Avenue, SW, Room 5204, Washington, DC 20250
Tel: (202) 690-2196
Areas Covered: AK, AZ, CA, CO, HI, ID, MT, NV, NM, OR, UT, WA, WY, Pacific Basin

● Regional Conservationist **Astor Boozer** .... (202) 690-2196
E-mail: astor.boozer@wdc.usda.gov
Education: Prairie View A&M 1987 BS
Executive Assistant **(Vacant)** .... (202) 690-2196
Program Analyst **(Vacant)** .... (202) 720-0244
1400 Independence Avenue, SW, Room 6105-S, Washington, DC 20250-3815

Alaska Office
800 West Evergreen Avenue, Suite 100, Palmer, AK 99645
Tel: (907) 761-7760 Fax: (907) 761-7790

State Conservationist **Robert N. Jones** .... (907) 761-7780
South Hub Leader **Meg Mueller** .... (907) 283-8732 ext. 100
110 Trading Bay, Suite 160, Kenai, AK 99611
Education: Bemidji State 1996 BS; Iowa State 1999 MS
North Hub Leader **Joanne Kuykendall** .... (907) 479-3159 ext. 1010
590 University Avenue, Suite B, Fairbanks, AK 99709 Fax: (855) 833-8625
Central Hub Leader **Michelle B. Jezeski** .... (907) 373-6492 ext. 101
1508 East Bogard Road, Wasilla, AK 99654 Fax: (855) 705-9788

Administrative
Assistant State Conservationist for Management and Strategy **Cassie Storms** .... (907) 761-7776
E-mail: cassie.storms@ak.usda.gov

★ Presidential Appointment Requiring Senate Confirmation ☆ Presidential Appointment □ Schedule C Appointment ◇ Career Senior Foreign Service Appointment
● Career Senior Executive Service (SES) Appointment ○ Non-Career Senior Executive Service (SES) Appointment ■ Postal Career Executive Service

DEPARTMENTS

Engineering
State Conservation Engineer **Brett Nelson** . . . . (907) 761-7717

Operations
Assistant State Conservationist for Operations **(Vacant)** . . . (907) 761-7758
Resource Conservationist **Sydney L. Thielke** . . . . (907) 761-7764

Programs
Assistant State Conservationist for Programs
Amanda Crowe . . . . (907) 761-7757

Public Affairs/Outreach
Public Affairs Specialist **(Vacant)** . . . . (907) 761-7749
800 West Evergreen, Suite 100, Palmer, AK 99645

Resource Technology
State Resource Conservationist **J. Scott Crockett** . . . . (907) 761-7758

Arizona Office
230 North First Avenue, Suite 509, Phoenix, AZ 85003-1706
Tel: (602) 280-8801 Fax: (855) 844-9178
State Conservationist **Keisha Tatem** . . . . (602) 280-8808
Assistant State Conservationist for Water Resources
David Beyman . . . . (602) 285-6351
Assistant State Conservationist/Field Office
Area 1 **Kendal B. Hicks** . . . . (928) 214-0459 ext. 119
Assistant State Conservationist/Field Office
Area 2 **Ralph Ware** . . . . (520) 670-6602 ext. 248
State Soil Scientist **D'andre Yancey** . . . . (602) 280-8817
Soil Survey Regional Director **(Vacant)** . . . . (602) 285-6347

Administrative Support
State Administrative Officer **Janice Hahn** . . . . (602) 280-8814
E-mail: janice.hahn@az.usda.gov

Engineering/Water Resources
State Conservation Engineer **David Beyman** . . . . (602) 285-6351

Management and Strategy
Assistant State Conservationist for Management and
Strategy **Becky Faught** . . . . (602) 285-6354

Partnerships
Assistant State Conservationist for Partnerships
Rebecca De La Torre . . . . (602) 280-8830
Public Affairs Specialist **Valentino Reyes** . . . . (602) 280-8780
E-mail: valentino.reyes@az.usda.gov

Programs
Assistant State Conservationist for Programs
Emily Fife . . . . (602) 280-8800
E-mail: emily.fife@az.usda.gov

Technology
State Resource Conservationist **Steve Smarik** . . . . (602) 280-8785

California Office
430 G Street, Room 4164, Davis, CA 95616-4164
Tel: (530) 792-5600 Fax: (530) 792-5790
● State Conservationist **Carlos Suarez** . . . . (530) 792-5600
E-mail: carlos.suarez@ca.usda.gov
Special Assistant to the State Conservationist
(Vacant) . . . . (530) 792-5661
Deputy State Conservationist **(Vacant)** . . . . (530) 792-5602
Assistant State Conservationist (Operations) **(Vacant)** . . . . (530) 792-5605
State Soil Scientist **George A. "Tony" Rolfes** . . . . (530) 792-5656

Administrative Management Support
State Administrative Officer **(Vacant)** . . . . (530) 792-5674

Ecological Sciences Staff
State Resource Conservationist **Thomas Tom Hedt** . . . . . . (530) 792-5667

Engineering Staff
● State Conservation Engineer
Gregory R. "Greg" Norris . . . . (530) 792-5609
E-mail: greg.norris@ca.usda.gov
Education: Cal Poly (Pomona) 1990 BS; Oklahoma State 1992 MS

Programs Staff
Assistant State Conservationist (Programs)
Alan Forkey . . . . (530) 792-5653

Public Affairs and Outreach Staff
Public Affairs Director **Anita Brown** . . . . (530) 792-5644
E-mail: anita.brown@ca.usda.gov

Colorado Office
Denver Federal Center, Building 56, West Sixth Avenue and Kipling Street, Room 2604, Denver, CO 80225
Tel: (720) 544-2810 Fax: (720) 544-2965
State Conservationist **Clinton "Clint" Evans** . . . . (720) 544-2810
Secretary to the State Conservationist
Cyndee Hjelmstad . . . . (720) 544-2809
E-mail: cyndee.hjelmstad@co.usda.gov
State Administrative Officer **(Vacant)** . . . . (720) 544-2822 ext. 2833
Grants & Agreements Specialist **(Vacant)** . . . . (720) 544-2867
Contracting Officer **(Vacant)** . . . . (720) 544-2822
MLRA Leader **(Vacant)** . . . . (720) 544-2850

Management & Services Staff
Assistant State Conservationist for Management and
Strategy (Acting) **Donna Rasmussen** . . . . (720) 544-2819

Ecological Sciences
State Resource Conservationist
Eugene "Gene" Backhaus . . . . (720) 544-2868
Fax: (720) 544-2978

Engineering
State Conservation Engineer **John E. Andrews** . . . . (720) 544-2834
Fax: (720) 544-2962

Partnerships
Assistant State Conservationist for Partnerships
Randy Randall . . . . (720) 544-2824
E-mail: randy.randall@co.usda.gov

Programs
Assistant State Conservationist for Programs
Becky Ross . . . . (720) 544-2822
E-mail: becky.ross@co.usda.gov

Public Affairs
Public Information Officer **Petra Popiel** . . . . (720) 544-2810 ext. 2808
E-mail: petra.popiel@co.usda.gov

Soil Science
State Soil Scientist **William J. "B.J." Shoup** . . . . (720) 544-2850

Snow Survey
Snow Survey Supervisor **Brian Domonkos** . . . . (720) 544-2852

Idaho Office
9173 West Barnes Drive, Suite C, Boise, ID 83709-1574
Tel: (208) 378-5700 Fax: (855) 524-1691 Internet: www.id.nrcs.usda.gov
State Conservationist **Curtis Elke** . . . . (208) 378-5701
Executive Assistant **Pamela "Pam" Dugan** . . . . (208) 378-5705

Administrative Staff
Assistant State Conservationist for Management and
Strategy **Mary Goode** . . . . (208) 378-5713
E-mail: mary.goode@id.usda.gov

Engineering Staff
State Conservation Engineer **Bruce Sandoval** . . . . (208) 378-5727

★ Presidential Appointment Requiring Senate Confirmation ☆ Presidential Appointment ☐ Schedule C Appointment ◇ Career Senior Foreign Service Appointment
● Career Senior Executive Service (SES) Appointment ○ Non-Career Senior Executive Service (SES) Appointment ■ Postal Career Executive Service

Programs Staff
Assistant State Conservationist for Programs
Morgan Bennetts . . . . . (530) 667-4247
E-mail: Morgan.Bennetts@id.usda.gov

Public Affairs Staff
Public Affairs Specialist **Mindi L. Rambo** . . . . . (208) 378-5720
E-mail: mindi.rambo@id.usda.gov

Soils Staff
State Soil Scientist **Shawn Nield** . . . . . (208) 378-5728

Technical Services Staff
Assistant State Conservationist for Technical Resources
James Eller . . . . . (208) 685-6978

Montana Office
Federal Building, 10 East Babcock Street,
Room 443, Bozeman, MT 59715
Tel: (406) 587-6811 Fax: (855) 510-7028 Internet: www.mt.nrcs.usda.gov
State Conservationist (Acting) **Kristine "Kris" Berg** . . . . . (406) 587-6811
Secretary and Freedom of Information Act Officer
Heather Higgs . . . . . (406) 587-6814
E-mail: heather.higgs@mt.usda.gov

Bridger Plant Materials Center
98 South River Road, Bridger, MT 59014
Tel: (406) 662-3579
Plant Materials Center Manager **Joseph Scianna** Bridger Plant Materials Center . . . . . (406) 662-3579 ext. 101

Easements
Assistant State Conservationist for Easements
Erik Suffridge . . . . . (406) 587-6873

Farm Production and Conservation (FPAC) Business Center (FPAC)
Human Resources Systems, Analytics, and Reporting
(Acting) **Bart Huber** . . . . . (406) 587-6811
E-mail: bart.huber@mt.usda.gov

Partnerships
Assistant State Conservationist for Partnerships
Gerald L. "Jerry" Shows . . . . . (406) 587-6967

Programs
Assistant State Conservationist for Programs (Acting)
Gerald L. "Jerry" Shows . . . . . (406) 587-6873
E-mail: jerry.shows@mt.usda.gov

Public Affairs
Public Affairs Manager/Outreach Coordinator
Lori Valadez . . . . . (406) 587-6969
E-mail: lori.valadez@mt.usda.gov
Visual Information Specialist **Mary Myers** . . . . . (406) 587-6945
E-mail: mt-nrcs-webmaster@one.usda.gov
E-mail: mary.myers@mt.usda.gov

Soils, NRI Collection, and Coordination
State Resource Inventory Coordinator **Julie Tesky** . . . . . (406) 587-6908
E-mail: julie.tesky@mt.usda.gov
State Soil Scientist (Acting) **Kale Gullett** . . . . . (406) 587-6998

Technology
State Resource Conservationist **Kale Gullett** . . . . . (406) 587-6998

Nevada Office
1365 Corporate Boulevard, Reno, NV 89502
Tel: (775) 857-8500 Fax: (855) 816-0893
State Conservationist **Ray Dotson** . . . . . (775) 857-8500 ext. 102
Human Resources Officer **(Vacant)** . . . . . (775) 857-8500

Administrative Office
Assistant State Conservationist for Management and Strategy
Dennis Workeman . . . . . (775) 857-8500 ext. 110
E-mail: dennis.workeman@nv.usda.gov

Engineering
State Conservation Engineer **Vinh Hoang** . . . . . (775) 857-8500 ext. 150
Assistant State Engineer/Civil Engineer
Carmella Irwin . . . . . (775) 857-8500
Civil Engineer **(Vacant)** . . . . . (775) 857-8500

Information Technology
Information Technology Specialist **Sam Liu** . . . . . (775) 857-8500 ext. 160
E-mail: sam.liu@nv.usda.gov

Programs Management
Assistant State Conservationist for Programs
Gary Roeder . . . . . (775) 857-8500 ext. 103

Public Affairs
State Public Affairs Officer **Heather Emmons** . . . . . (775) 861-6594
E-mail: heather.emmons@nv.usda.gov

Resource Technology
State Resource Conservationist (Acting)
Julie Malvitz . . . . . (715) 362-5941 ext. 111

Soils
State Soil Scientist **James Komar** . . . . . (775) 857-8500 ext. 122
2738 Crossroads Boulevard, Suite 104, Grand Junction, CO 81506
Senior Regional Soil Scientist **(Vacant)** . . . . . (775) 857-8500 ext. 120
Soil Conservationist **Edwin Jarrod Edmunds** . . . . . (775) 857-8500

New Mexico State Office
100 Sun Avenue NE, Suite 602, Albuquerque, NM 87109
Tel: (505) 761-4400 Fax: (855) 538-6003
Internet: www.nm.nrcs.usda.gov
State Conservationist **Juan Xavier Montoya** . . . . . (505) 761-4400
Executive Assistant **Nathaniel Duran** . . . . . (505) 761-4402
Assistant State Conservationist for Partnerships
Alicia Rodriguez . . . . . (505) 761-4421

Communications
Public Affairs Officer (Acting) **Alicia Rodriguez** . . . . . (505) 761-4421
E-mail: alicia.rodriguez@nm.usda.gov

Engineering
State Conservation Engineer **James Hewitt** . . . . . (505) 761-4490

Management and Strategy
Assistant State Conservationist for Management and Strategy **Rosabeth R. Garcia-Sais** . . . . . (505) 761-4411
E-mail: rosabeth.garciasais@nm.usda.gov
Management Information Technician **Theresa Nelson** . . . . (505) 761-4405
E-mail: theresa.nelson@nm.gov

Plant Materials Center
Plant Materials Center Manager
Bernadette Cooney . . . . . (505) 865-4684 ext. 105
1036 Miller Street, Los Lunas, NM 87031 Fax: (505) 865-5163

Programs
Assistant State Conservationist for Program
Kristin Graham Chavez . . . . . (505) 761-4404
E-mail: kristin.grahamchavez@nm.usda.gov

Resource Inventories and Assessments
State Soil Scientist **Richard "Rick" Strait** . . . . . (505) 761-4433

Resource Technology
State Resource Conservationist **Steve Kadas** . . . . . (505) 761-4422

★ Presidential Appointment Requiring Senate Confirmation ☆ Presidential Appointment □ Schedule C Appointment ◇ Career Senior Foreign Service Appointment
● Career Senior Executive Service (SES) Appointment ○ Non-Career Senior Executive Service (SES) Appointment ■ Postal Career Executive Service

DEPARTMENTS

Oregon Office
1201 Northeast Lloyd Boulevard, Suite 900, Portland, OR 97232-1274
Tel: (503) 414-3200 Fax: (855) 651-9082 Internet: www.or.nrcs.usda.gov

State Conservationist **Ronald "Ron" Alvarado** .... (503) 414-3200
Fax: (855) 651-9154
Executive Assistant **Jessica Bras** .... (503) 414-3221
Office Assistant **(Vacant)** .... (503) 414-3206
Administrative Officer **(Vacant)** .... (503) 414-3211
State Resource Conservationist **Scott Cook** .... (503) 414-3234

Partnership and Outreach
Assistant State Conservationist for Partnership Liaison
Julie A. MacSwain .... (503) 414-3250
E-mail: Julie.MacSwain@or.usda.gov
Public Affairs Specialist **Catherine "Cat" Bailey** .... (503) 414-3238
E-mail: catherine.bailey@or.usda.gov
State Public Affairs Officer **Tracy Robillard** .... (503) 414-3220
E-mail: tracy.robillard@or.usda.gov

Management and Strategy
Assistant State Conservationist for Management and Strategy **Jason Jeans** .... (503) 414-3222

Programs
1201 Northeast Lloyd Boulevard, Suite 900, Portland, OR 97232-1274
Fax: (855) 651-9154
Assistant State Conservationist, Programs
Loren Unruh .... (503) 414-3235

Technology
Leader for Technology **Tom Makowski** .... (503) 414-3202
E-mail: tom.makowski@or.usda.gov

Major Lands Resources Area Office
Soil Survey Regional Director **Ed Tallyn** .... (530) 792-5639

Office of the Chief Information Officer
Group Manager **Lynaan Stewart** .... (208) 378-5680
E-mail: lynaan.stewart@id.usda.gov

State Soil Survey
1201 Northeast Lloyd Boulevard, Suire 900, Portland, OR 97232-1274
Fax: (855) 651-9082
State Soil Scientist **Cory Owens** .... (503) 414-3261
Natural Resource Specialist **Gary Diridoni** .... (503) 414-3092
Resource Conservationist **Mary Beth Smith** .... (503) 414-3283
Cultural Resources Specialist **Dan Snyder** .... (541) 801-2677
Program Assistant **Laura Gay** .... (503) 414-3200

Engineering
State Conservation Engineer **Jeffrey Brown** .... (503) 414-3254

Pacific Islands Area State Office (PIA)
PJKK Federal Building, 300 Ala Moana Boulevard,
Room 4-118, Honolulu, HI 96850
Mail: P.O. Box 50004, Honolulu, HI 96850-0050
Tel: (808) 600-2911 Fax: (855) 838-6330
Internet: www.pia.nrcs.usda.gov
Areas Covered: American Samoa, Guam, Hawaii, Marshall Islands, Micronesia, Northern Mariana Islands, Palau

Director **Travis Thomason** .... (808) 600-2969
Executive Assistant **Cheryl Morton** .... (808) 600-2911
Office Assistant **(Vacant)** .... (808) 541-2600 ext. 165
Public Affairs Officer **Douglas Maguire** .... (808) 600-2957
E-mail: douglas.maguire@hi.usda.gov

ASTC - Strategy and Management
Assistant Director for Strategy and Management
Jason Peel .... (808) 600-2920

Ecological Sciences Staff
Assistant Director for Technology
Anthony "Tony" Ingersoll .... (808) 600-2915

Engineering Staff
State Conservation Engineer **Sherman White** .... (808) 600-2930

Programs
Assistant Director for Programs **Nicola Giardina** .... (808) 600-2959
E-mail: nicola.giardina@hi.usda.gov
Natural Resources Specialist/Program Manager
(Vacant) .... (808) 541-2600 ext. 155
Program Support Specialist **Porsha Thomas** .... (808) 600-2926

Soil Science and Natural Resource Assessments Staff
Assistant State Director for Soil Science **Amy Koch** ..... (808) 933-8351

Utah Office
Bennett Federal Building, 125 South State Street,
Room 4010, Salt Lake City, UT 84138-1100
Tel: (801) 524-4550 Fax: (844) 715-4928

State Conservationist **Timothy Wilson** .... (801) 524-4551
Administrative Assistant **(Vacant)** .... (801) 524-4588
Assistant State Conservationist for Operations **(Vacant)** ... (801) 524-4565
Assistant State Conservationist for Programs
Pedro Ramos, Jr. .... (801) 524-4552
E-mail: pedro.ramos@ut.usda.gov
State Administrative Officer **(Vacant)** .... (801) 524-4549
Executive Assistant **Gayla Pressett** .... (801) 524-4555
State Conservation Engineer **Bronson Smart** .... (801) 524-4559
State Resource Conservationist **Elise Boeke** .... (801) 524-4562
State Soil Scientist **(Vacant)** .... (801) 524-4574
State Public Affairs Specialist and Outreach
Coordinator **(Vacant)** .... (801) 524-4557

Washington Office
Rock Pointe Tower, 316 West Boone Avenue,
Suite 450, Spokane, WA 99201-2348
Tel: (509) 323-2900 Fax: (855) 847-5492

State Conservationist **Roylene Rides at the Door** .... (509) 323-2900
Tribal Liaison, Olympia Office **Nick Vira** .... (360) 704-7758
Tribal Liaison, Puyallup Office **Robin Slate** .... (360) 704-7780

Ecological Sciences Staff
State Resource Conservationist **Bonda Habets** .... (509) 323-2961
Resource Conservationist **Shelly Lassiter** .... (509) 323-2987

Engineering Staff
State Conservation Engineer **Larry A. Johnson** .... (509) 323-2955

Management and Strategy Staff
Assistant State Conservationist
Peter P. "Pete" Bautista .... (509) 323-2941
Business Services Specialist **(Vacant)** .... (509) 323-2921
Financial Resource Specialist **Troy Dixon** .... (509) 323-2927

Plant Materials Center
Plant Materials Center Team Leader **Allen Casey** .... (509) 335-6892
Conservation Agronomist **(Vacant)** .... (509) 335-6894

Program Staff
Assistant State Conservationist for Programs
Jeffrey "Jeff" Harlow .... (509) 323-2971

Public Affairs Staff
Public Affairs Officer **Gina Kerzman** .... (509) 323-2911
E-mail: gina.kerzman@wa.usda.gov

Soil Science Staff

Wyoming Office
100 East "B" Street, Room 3124, Casper, WY 82601-1911
P.O. Box 33124, Casper, WY 82602
Tel: (307) 233-6750 Fax: (855) 415-3404 Internet: www.wy.nrcs.usda.gov

State Conservationist **Astrid Martinez** .... (307) 233-6750
Administrative Assistant **Jill Binette** .... (307) 233-6750
E-mail: jill.binette@wy.usda.gov

★ Presidential Appointment Requiring Senate Confirmation ☆ Presidential Appointment ☐ Schedule C Appointment ◇ Career Senior Foreign Service Appointment
● Career Senior Executive Service (SES) Appointment ○ Non-Career Senior Executive Service (SES) Appointment ■ Postal Career Executive Service

Wyoming Office *(continued)*

State Public Affairs Specialist **Rachel Bundschuh** . . . . (307) 240-3213
E-mail: Rachel.Bundschuh@wy.usda.gov

Engineering
State Conservation Engineer **Chuck Schmitt PE** . . . . (307) 233-6748

Management and Strategy
Assistant State Conservationist for Management and Strategy **James Bauchert** . . . . (307) 233-6768

Programs
Assistant State Conservationist for Programs
Kresta Faaborg . . . . (307) 233-6757

Resource Conservation
State Resource Conservationist (Acting) **Lori Kassib** . . . . . (307) 233-6763

Soil Sciences
State Soil Scientist (Acting) **Dan Mattke** . . . . (307) 233-6784

Research, Education and Economics (REE)

1400 Independence Avenue, SW, Washington, DC 20250
Tel: (202) 720-5923 Fax: (202) 690-2842 Internet: www.ree.usda.gov

OFFICE OF THE UNDER SECRETARY

Jamie L. Whitten Federal Building, 1400 Independence Avenue, SW, Washington, DC 20250
Tel: (202) 720-5923 Fax: (202) 690-2842

Agricultural Research Service (ARS)

Jamie L. Whitten Federal Building, 1400 Independence Avenue, SW, Washington, DC 20250
Fax: (202) 720-5427 Internet: www.ars.usda.gov

Area Offices

Midwest Area

1815 North University Street, Peoria, IL 61604-3999
Tel: (309) 681-6602 Fax: (309) 681-6684
Areas Covered: IL, IN, IA, MI, MN, MO, OH, WI

● Area Director (Acting)
Dr. Julious L. "J.L." Willett Room 2004 . . . . (309) 681-6602
E-mail: JL.Willett@ars.usda.gov
Associate Area Director
Dr. Julious L. "J.L." Willett Room 2004 . . . . (309) 681-6601
Statistician General **Debra E. Palmquist** Room 3006 . . . . (309) 681-6587
Fax: (309) 681-6695
Technology Transfer Coordinator
Dr. Renee Wagner Room 3014 . . . . (309) 681-6565

Illinois

National Center for Agricultural Utilization Research (NCAUR)
1815 North University Street, Peoria, IL 61604-3999
Mail: REE-USDA-ARS-MWA-NCAUR, Peoria, IL 61604
Tel: (309) 685-4011 Fax: (309) 681-6686

● Director (Acting) **Dr. Sean X. Liu** Room 2042 . . . . (309) 681-6541
E-mail: sean.liu@ars.usda.gov Fax: (309) 681-6682
Bacterial Foodborne Pathogens and Mycology Research Leader **Dr. Todd Ward PhD** Room 2057A . . . . (309) 681-6394
Fax: (309) 681-6672
Bio-Energy Research Leader **(Vacant)** Room 2058A . . . . . (309) 681-6500
Fax: (309) 681-6427
Bio-Oils Research Leader (Acting) **Dr. Terry A. Isbell** . . . . (309) 681-6532
Fax: (309) 681-6524
Crop Bioprotection Research Leader
Alejandro P. Rooney . . . . (309) 681-6395
Fax: (309) 681-6427

National Center for Agricultural Utilization Research *(continued)*

Functional Foods Research Leader
Dr. Sean X. Liu Room 2054 . . . . (309) 681-6551
Fax: (309) 681-6685
Plant Polymer Research Leader **Veera Boddu** . . . . (309) 681-6557
Renewable Product Tech Research Leader
(Vacant) Room 2054 . . . . (309) 681-6117
Fax: (309) 681-6040

Urbana (University of Illinois) Location
Edward R. Madigan Laboratory, 1201 West Gregory Drive, Room 190, Urbana, IL 61801-3838
Tel: (217) 333-2093 Fax: (217) 244-4419
Location Coordinator **(Vacant)** . . . . (217) 333-2093

Indiana

West Lafayette (IN) – Purdue University Location
Purdue University, 275 South Russell Street, West Lafayette, IN 47907-2077
Tel: (765) 494-9726 Fax: (765) 494-1705
Location Coordinator **(Vacant)** . . . . (765) 494-4604
Administrative Officer **Sherry Egbert** . . . . (765) 494-9726
E-mail: sherry.egbert@ars.usda.gov

Iowa

Ames (IA) – Iowa State University Location

Corn Insects and Crop Genetics Research Unit
Iowa State University, Ames, IA 50011
Tel: (515) 294-3122 Fax: (515) 294-9420 (Bessey Hall)
Fax: (515) 294-2265 (Genetics Laboratory)
Fax: (515) 294-9359 (Crop Genome Informatics Laboratory)
Research Leader **Dr. Craig A. Abel** . . . . (515) 294-8614
Genetic Laboratory, Iowa State University, Room 106, Ames, IA 50011

National Animal Disease Center
P.O. Box 70, Ames, IA 50010
1920 Dayton Road, Ames, IA 50010
Tel: (515) 337-7558 Fax: (515) 663-7428
Internet: www.nadc.ars.usda.gov
Director **Dr. Marcus Kehrli** . . . . (515) 337-7201
Associate Director **Diana Whipple** . . . . (515) 337-7285
Supervisory Research Microbiologist **(Vacant)** . . . . (515) 337-7350
Fax: (515) 337-7402
Supervisory Veterinary Medical Officer, Infectious Bacterial Diseases **Dr. Steven C. Olsen** . . . . (515) 337-7230
Fax: (515) 337-7148
Supervisory Research Animal Scientist
Eduardo Casas . . . . (515) 337-6356
Fax: (515) 337-7402
Resident Veterinary Medical Officer
Susan Brockmeier . . . . (515) 337-7221
Fax: (515) 337-7149

National Laboratory for Agriculture and the Environment (NLAE)
2110 University Boulevard, Ames, IA 50011
Tel: (515) 294-5723 Fax: (515) 294-8125
Director **Dennis Todey** . . . . (515) 294-2013
Supervisory Plant Physiologist **Jerry L. Hatfield** . . . . (515) 294-5723
E-mail: jerry.hatfield@ars.usda.gov
Education: Iowa State 1975 PhD
Supervisory Chemist **Amy Morrow** . . . . (515) 294-6536
Coordinator, Cooperative Interactions and Grantsmanship **Charlene Felkley** . . . . (515) 294-0136
Agroecosystems Management Research Unit Leader
Thomas B. "Tom" Moorman . . . . (515) 294-2308
E-mail: tom.moorman@ars.usda.gov
Soil, Water, and Air Processes Research Unit Leader
Thomas "Tom" Sauer . . . . (515) 294-3416
Facilities Manager **Aaron Rosales** . . . . (515) 294-3679
Information Technology Specialist **Bob Jaquis** . . . . (515) 294-4005
E-mail: bob.jaquis@ars.usda.gov

★ Presidential Appointment Requiring Senate Confirmation ☆ Presidential Appointment □ Schedule C Appointment ◇ Career Senior Foreign Service Appointment
● Career Senior Executive Service (SES) Appointment ○ Non-Career Senior Executive Service (SES) Appointment ■ Postal Career Executive Service

Plant Introduction Research Unit
G212 Agronomy Hall, Iowa State University, Ames, IA 50011-1170
Tel: (515) 294-3255 Fax: (515) 294-4880

Research Leader **Dr. Candice A. Gardner** .... (515) 294-7967
Education: Iowa State 1975 BS; Missouri 1979 MS, PhD
Information Technology Specialist **Peter "Pete" Cyr** ..... (515) 294-3617
E-mail: pete.cyr@ars.usda.gov
Education: Iowa State 1985 BS, 1988 MS

Michigan

Avian Disease and Oncology Laboratory
4279 East Mount Hope Road, East Lansing, MI 48823-5338
Tel: (517) 337-6828 Fax: (517) 337-6776 E-mail: arsadol@msu.edu

Supervisory Veterinary Medical Officer **(Vacant)** .... (517) 337-6829

Sugarbeet and Bean Research Unit
Plant and Soil Science Building, 1066 Bogue Street,
Michigan State University, #494, East Lansing, MI 48824-1325
Tel: (517) 353-0205 Fax: (517) 337-6782

Agricultural Engineer **Renfu Lu** .... (517) 432-8062
Education: Zhejiang U BS; Cornell MS; Penn State PhD

Minnesota

North Central Soil Conservation Research Laboratory
803 Iowa Avenue, Morris, MN 56267
Tel: (320) 589-3411 Fax: (320) 589-3787
Internet: www.ars.usda.gov/mwa/ncscrl

Research Leader **Dr. Abdullah A. Jaradat** ...... (320) 589-3411 ext. 124
Program Support Assistant **Beth Burmeister** .... (320) 589-3411
E-mail: beth.burmeister@ars.usda.gov
Purchasing Agent **Shawn E. Rohloff** .... (320) 589-3411 ext. 122
E-mail: shawn.rohloff@ars.usda.gov

Saint Paul (MN) – University of Minnesota Location
1551 Lindig Street, St. Paul, MN 55108-1050
Tel: (651) 649-5046 Fax: (651) 649-5055

Location Coordinator and Research Leader
Dr. John M. Baker .... (612) 625-4249
411 Borlaug Hall, 1991 Upper Buford Circle, St. Paul, MN 55108-6026
E-mail: john.baker@ars.usda.gov
Location Administrative Officer
Pamela J. "Pam" Groth .... (651) 649-5046
E-mail: pam.groth@ars.usda.gov
Purchasing Agent **Randall W. "Randy" Kiehne** .... (651) 649-5047
E-mail: randy.kiehne@ars.usda.gov
Financial Technician **Amy A. Dolan** .... (651) 649-5048
E-mail: amy.dolan@ars.usda.gov

Cereal Disease Laboratory
University of Minnesota, Cereal Disease Laboratory,
1551 Lindig Street, St. Paul, MN 55108-1050
Tel: (612) 625-7081 Fax: (651) 649-5054

Research Leader **Shahryar Kianian** .... (612) 624-4155

Plant Science Research Unit
University of Minnesota, 411 Borlaug Hall,
1991 Upper Buford Circle, St. Paul, MN 55108-6026
Tel: (612) 624-0763 Fax: (651) 649-5048

Research Leader **Deborah Samac** .... (612) 625-1243

Soil and Water Management Research Unit
University of Minnesota, 439 Borlaug Hall,
1911 Upper Buford Circle, St. Paul, MN 55108-6024
Tel: (612) 625-9270 Fax: (651) 649-5175

Location Coordinator and Research Leader
Dr. John M. Baker .... (612) 624-4249

Missouri

Columbia (MO) Location
403 Vandiver Drive, Suite D, Columbia, MO 65202
Tel: (573) 875-5293 Fax: (573) 449-6148

Administrative Officer **Heather Lewandowski** .... (573) 882-7375
E-mail: heather.lewandowski@ars.usda.gov
Purchasing Agent **Brionna Wade** .... (573) 882-9387
E-mail: brionna.wade@ars.usda.gov

Biological Control of Insects Research Unit
1503 South Providence Road, Research Park, Columbia, MO 65211
Fax: (573) 875-5364

Research Leader **Dr. David W. Stanley** .... (573) 876-8301

Cropping Systems and Water Quality Research Unit
Ag Engineering Building, University of Missouri,
Room 269, Columbia, MO 65211
Tel: (573) 882-1114

Research Leader **Dr. E. John Sadler** .... (573) 882-1971 ext. 309

Plant Genetics Research Unit
206 Curtis Hall, University of Missouri, Columbia, MO 65211

Research Geneticist **Dr. Melvin J. "Mel" Oliver PhD** .... (573) 882-9645

Ohio

Soil Drainage Research Unit
590 Woody Hayes Drive, Columbus, OH 43210
Tel: (614) 292-9806 Fax: (614) 292-9448

Research Leader (Acting) **Kevin W. King** .... (614) 292-3550
Education: Purdue 1991 BS, 1992 MS; Texas A&M 2000 PhD

Wooster (OH) Location
1680 Madison Avenue, Wooster, OH 44691
Tel: (330) 263-3774 Fax: (330) 263-3662

Administrative Officer **James "Jim" Hampton** .... (330) 263-3774
E-mail: jim.hampton@ars.usda.gov

Application Technology Research Unit (ATRU)
1680 Madison Avenue, Room 206, Wooster, OH 44691
Tel: (330) 263-3868 Fax: (330) 263-3670

Research Leader (Acting) **James Altland** .... (330) 263-3870
E-mail: james.altland@ars.usda.gov

Corn, Soybean and Wheat Quality Research Unit
1680 Madison Avenue, Wooster, OH 44691
Fax: (330) 263-3841

Research Leader **Dr. Margaret G. "Peg" Redinbaugh** ... (330) 263-3965

Wisconsin

Madison (WI) – University of Wisconsin Location
University of Wisconsin, 1925 Linden Drive,
Room 132, Madison, WI 53706
Tel: (608) 890-0044 Fax: (608) 890-0048

Administrative Officer **Terri Gureno** .... (608) 890-0044
E-mail: terri.gureno@ars.usda.gov
Financial Technician **Julie Grogan** .... (608) 890-0101
E-mail: Julie.Grogan@ars.usda.gov
Information Technology Specialist **Joshua Nehring** ..... (608) 890-1322
E-mail: josh.nehring@ars.usda.gov
Purchasing Agent **Laura Jones** .... (608) 890-0047
E-mail: Laura.Jones@ars.usda.gov
Purchasing Agent **Dolores J. Milton** .... (608) 890-0045
E-mail: Dolores.Milton@ars.usda.gov

Cereal Crops Research Unit
502 Walnut St., Madison, WI 53726
Fax: (608) 890-0306

Research Leader **Dr. Cynthia A. Henson** .... (608) 262-0377

U.S. Dairy Forage Research Center
1925 Linden Drive, Madison, WI 53706
Tel: (608) 890-0050 Fax: (608) 890-0076

Center Director **Mark Boggess PhD** .... (608) 890-0050
Education: Cornell 1985 MS; Iowa State 2000 PhD

Vegetable Crops Research Leader
1575 Linden Drive, Room 203, Madison, WI 53706
Tel: (608) 262-1248 Fax: (608) 262-4743

Research Leader **Dr. Philipp W. Simon** .... (608) 262-1248

Kentucky

Animal Waste Management Research Unit (AWMRU)
230 Bennet Lane, Bowling Green, KY 42104
Tel: (270) 781-2260 Fax: (270) 781-7994

Research Leader **Karamat Sistani** Room 101 ... (270) 781-2260 ext. 222
Program Support Assistant **Kay Richardson** ..... (270) 781-2260 ext. 221
Administrative Officer **(Vacant)** .... (270) 781-2260 ext. 224

Forage-Animal Production Research Unit
Agricultural Science Building North, University of Kentucky Campus,
Room N-220, Lexington, KY 40546
Tel: (859) 257-1647 Fax: (859) 257-3334

Supervisory Animal Scientist/Research Leader
Glen Aiken .... (859) 257-1647
Program Support Assistant **Kelli M. Adkins** .... (859) 257-1647
E-mail: kelli.adkins@ars.usda.gov

Northeast Area

600 East Mermaid Lane, Wyndmoor, PA 19038-8551
Tel: (215) 233-6593 Fax: (215) 233-6719
Areas Covered: CT, DE, MA, ME, MD, NH, NJ, NY, PA, RI, VT, WV

● Area Director **Dr. Dariusz M. Swietlik** .... (301) 504-6078
10300 Baltimore Avenue, Beltsville, MD 20705-2350
E-mail: dariusz.swietlik@ars.usda.gov
Education: Research Inst (Poland) 1980 PhD
Secretary (Office Automation) **Gloria James** .... (301) 504-6078
10300 Baltimore Avenue, Beltsville, MD 20705-2350
E-mail: gloria.james@ars.usda.gov
Executive Assistant **(Vacant)** .... (215) 233-6668
Associate Area Director **Charles I. Onwulata** .... (301) 504-8310
10300 Baltimore Avenue, Beltsville, MD 20705-2350
Education: Alabama A&M 1984 BS, 1986 MS; Missouri 1991 PhD
Statistician General **Bryan T. Vinyard** .... (301) 504-8121
10300 Baltimore Avenue, Beltsville, MD 20705-2350
Contract Specialist **Karen Gardner** .... (814) 863-0928
E-mail: karen.gardner@ars.usda.gov
Equal Employment Specialist **Jenny Allen** .... (301) 504-6507

Delaware

Beneficial Insects Introduction Research Laboratory
501 South Chapel Street, Newark, DE 19713
Tel: (302) 731-7330 Fax: (302) 737-6780

Research Leader **Kim A. Hoelmer** .... (302) 731-7330 ext. 242
Biological Science Technician **Erin Langton** .... (302) 731-7330 ext. 226
Facilities Manager **(Vacant)** .... (302) 731-7330 ext. 230
Program Support Assistant (Office
Automation) **Brenda R. Holmes** .... (302) 731-7330 ext. 221
E-mail: brenda.holmes@ars.usda.gov

Maine

New England Plant, Soil and Water Laboratory
University of Maine, Orono, ME 04469
Tel: (207) 581-3266 Fax: (207) 866-0464

Research Leader **Brian Peterson** .... (207) 422-2713
Iowa State University, Ames, IA 50011 Fax: (207) 422-2723
Plant Pathologist **Robert "Bob" Larkin** .... (207) 581-3367

Maryland

Foreign Disease-Weed Science Research Unit
1301 Ditto Avenue, Frederick, MD 21702-5023
Tel: (301) 619-7344 Fax: (301) 619-2880

Research Leader **Reid D. Frederick** .... (301) 619-7344

Massachusetts

Jean Mayer Human Nutrition Research Center on Aging (HNRCA)
Tufts University, 711 Washington Street,
9th Floor, Boston, MA 02111
Tel: (617) 556-3000 Fax: (617) 556-3344 Internet: http://hnrca.tufts.edu/

Director (Interim) **Sarah Booth PhD** .... (617) 556-3231
Fax: (617) 556-3295
Associate Director **Sarah Booth PhD** .... (617) 556-3131
E-mail: sarah.booth@tufts.edu Fax: (617) 556-3149
Administrative Director **Mark Wesley** .... (617) 556-3391
E-mail: mark.wesley@tufts.edu Fax: (617) 556-3149
Education: Northeastern 1977 BS
Planning and Analysis Manager **Lily Yee** .... (617) 556-3308
E-mail: lily.yee@tufts.edu
Senior Human Resources Partner **Michelle Boucher** ..... (617) 627-3589
E-mail: Michelle.Boucher@tufts.edu
Communications Specialist **Deborah Dutcher** .... (617) 556-3357
E-mail: deborah.dutcher@tufts.edu
Program Analyst (ARS Onsite Representative)
Kathi R. Wilhelm .... (617) 556-3312
Fax: (617) 556-3299

New York

Robert W. Holley Center for Agriculture and Health
Tower Road, Ithaca, NY 14853-2901
Tel: (607) 255-4549 Fax: (607) 255-2459

Center Director **(Vacant)** .... (607) 255-2454
Emerging Pests and Pathogens Research Leader
Stewart M. Gray .... (607) 255-2359
Plant, Soil and Nutrition Research Leader (Acting)
Raymond Glahn Room 121 .... (607) 255-2454
Administrative Officer **Doris Hagin** .... (607) 255-5487
E-mail: doris.hagin@ars.usda.gov

Geneva (NY) Location
630 West North Street, Geneva, NY 14456

Location Coordinator **Gan-Yuan Zhong** .... (315) 787-2482
308 Sturtevant Hall, Cornell University, Geneva, NY 14456-0462
Administrative Officer **Rose Marie Nichols** .... (315) 787-2329
E-mail: rose.nichols@ars.usda.gov
Program Support Assistant **Tiffany Fisk** .... (315) 787-2307
E-mail: tiffany.fisk@ars.usda.gov

Pennsylvania

Pasture Systems and Watershed Management Research Unit
Building 3702, Curtin Road, University Park, PA 16802-3702
Tel: (814) 863-0939 Fax: (814) 863-0935

Research Leader and Soil Scientist
Dr. Peter J. Kleinman .... (814) 865-3184
Administrative Officer **Donita Gibboney** .... (814) 863-0940
E-mail: donita.gibboney@ars.usda.gov

Eastern Regional Research Center (ERRC)
600 East Mermaid Lane, Wyndmoor, PA 19038-8598
Tel: (215) 233-6400 (Information) Tel: (215) 233-6595
Fax: (215) 233-6777

● Director **Dr. Sevim Z. Erhan** .... (215) 233-6595
E-mail: sevim.erhan@ars.usda.gov
Biobased and Other Animal Co-Products Research Unit
Cheng Kung "CK" Liu .... (215) 836-6924
Fax: (215) 233-6795
Dairy and Functional Foods Research Unit
Dr. Peggy M. Tomasula .... (215) 233-6703
Fax: (215) 233-6795

(continued on next page)

DEPARTMENTS

★ Presidential Appointment Requiring Senate Confirmation ☆ Presidential Appointment ☐ Schedule C Appointment ◇ Career Senior Foreign Service Appointment
● Career Senior Executive Service (SES) Appointment ○ Non-Career Senior Executive Service (SES) Appointment ■ Postal Career Executive Service

DEPARTMENTS

Eastern Regional Research Center *(continued)*

Food Safety Intervention Technologies Research Unit
Brendan A. Niemira .... (215) 233-6583
Fax: (215) 233-6406

Molecular Characterization of Foodborne Pathogens Research Unit **Daniel Solaiman** .... (215) 233-6611
Fax: (215) 233-6581

Residue Chemistry and Predictive Microbiology Research Unit **Lihan Huang** .... (215) 233-6621
Fax: (215) 233-6406

Sustainable Biofuels and Co-Products Research Unit
Robert A. Moreau .... (215) 233-6580
Fax: (215) 233-6406

Core Technologies: Integrated Biomolecular Resources
Alberto Nunez .... (215) 233-6639
Fax: (215) 233-6581

Core Technologies: Magnetic Resonance Spectroscopy Group **Dr. Gary Strahan** .... (215) 233-6775
Fax: (215) 233-6581

Core Technologies: Research Data Systems Group
Dr. William C. Damert .... (215) 233-6616
Fax: (215) 233-6581

Core Technologies: Scientific Information Resources Group **Wendy H. Kramer** .... (215) 233-6602
E-mail: wendy.kramer@ars.usda.gov Fax: (215) 233-6606

Human Resources Assistant **Marcia Henson** .... (215) 233-6571
E-mail: marcia.henson@ars.usda.gov

West Virginia

Appalachian Fruit Research Station
2217 Wiltshire Road, Kearneysville, WV 25430
Tel: (304) 725-3451 Fax: (304) 728-2340

Director/Research Leader **Tracy C. Leskey** ...... (304) 725-3451 ext. 329
Education: Wilson Col 1990 BS; Penn State 1995 MS; UMass (Amherst) 2000 PhD

Administrative Officer **Stephanie Kreger** .... (304) 725-3451 ext. 332
E-mail: stephanie.hartsock@ars.usda.gov Fax: (304) 728-7182

Pacific West Area

800 Buchanan Street, Room 2030, Albany, CA 94710-1105
Tel: (510) 559-6060 Fax: (510) 559-5779
Areas Covered: AZ, CA, HI, ID, NV, OR, UT, WA

● Area Director **Dr. Robert "Bob" Matteri** .... (510) 559-6060
E-mail: Robert.Matteri@ars.usda.gov

Secretary to the Director **(Vacant)** .... (510) 559-6071

Executive Assistant **Billi Jean Combs** .... (510) 559-6071
E-mail: billi.combs@ars.usda.gov

Executive Assistant **Alicia Finley** .... (510) 559-6060
E-mail: alicia.finley@ars.usda.gov

Associate Director **Dr. Thomas Shanower PhD** .... (510) 559-6063
Education: Marietta 1979 BS; Illinois 1982 MS; UC Berkeley 1989 PhD

Associate Area Director **Hao C. Tran** .... (510) 559-6071
Education: Australian National U 1977 BSF; UC Berkeley 1979 BS, 1986 PhD

Area Information Technology Manager
David Nicholson .... (510) 559-5641
Fax: (510) 559-5612

Statistician General **Bruce E. Mackey** .... (510) 559-6078

● Collaborator **(Vacant)** .... (510) 559-6060

Arizona

Tucson (AZ) Research Unit
2000 East Allen Road, Tucson, AZ 85719
Tel: (520) 670-6481 Fax: (520) 670-6493

Carl Hayden Bee Research Center Leader
Dr. Gloria DeGrandi-Hoffman .... (520) 647-9187
E-mail: gloria.hoffman@ars.usda.gov
Education: Penn State 1975 BS, 1980 MS; Michigan State 1983 PhD

Program Support Assistant **(Vacant)** .... (520) 647-9107

Southwest Watershed Research Center Leader
Philip "Phil" Heilman .... (520) 647-9202

Program Support Assistant **Mary White** .... (520) 657-2856
E-mail: mary.white@ars.usda.gov Fax: (520) 670-5550

Tucson (AZ) Research Unit *(continued)*

Administrative Officer **(Vacant)** .... (520) 647-9160

Administrative Assistant **(Vacant)** .... (520) 647-9207

U.S. Arid Land Agricultural Research Center (USALARC)
21881 North Cardon Lane, Maricopa, AZ 85238
Tel: (520) 316-6300 Fax: (520) 316-6329

Director **Steven E. "Steve" Naranjo** .... (520) 316-6333
E-mail: steve.naranjo@ars.usda.gov
Education: Colorado State 1978 BS; Florida 1983 MS; Cornell 1987 PhD

Secretary **Cheryl A. Borg** .... (520) 316-6300 ext. 313
E-mail: cheryl.borg@ars.usda.gov

Administrative Officer **Joseph L. Garrett** .... (520) 316-6310
E-mail: joseph.garrett@ars.usda.gov

Safety and Occupational Health Specialist
Rodney Gaither .... (520) 316-6316
E-mail: rodney.gaither@ars.usda.gov

IT Manager **Robert LaMorte** .... (520) 316-6390
E-mail: robert.lamorte@ars.usda.gov Fax: (520) 316-6330

California

Crop Improvement and Protection Unit – U.S. Agricultural Research Station
1636 East Alisal Street, Salinas, CA 93905-3018
Tel: (831) 755-2800 Fax: (831) 755-2814

Research Leader **Dr. James D. "Jim" McCreight** .... (831) 755-2864

Program Support Assistant **Amy Liu** .... (831) 755-2897
E-mail: amy.liu@ars.usda.gov

Davis (CA) Research Units
Tel: (530) 754-5849 Fax: (530) 754-7195

Crops Pathology and Genetics Research Leader/Location Coordinator **Dr. Daniel A. Kluepfel** .... (530) 752-1137
University of California, Hutchinson Hall, Room 284, Davis, CA 95616 Fax: (530) 754-7195
Education: Missouri (St Louis) BA; Florida PhD

Secretary **Lynne M. Pearson** .... (530) 754-5849
E-mail: lmpearson@ucdavis.edu Fax: (530) 754-7195

National Clonal Germplasm Repository for Fruit and Nut Crops Research Leader **John Preece** .... (530) 752-7009
Fax: (530) 752-5974

San Joaquin Valley Agricultural Sciences Center
9611 South Riverbend Avenue, Parlier, CA 93648
Tel: (559) 596-2950 Fax: (559) 596-2951

Center Director **Dr. James E. "Jim" Throne** .... (559) 596-2702
Education: SE Massachusetts 1976 BS; Washington State 1978 MS; Cornell 1983 PhD Fax: (559) 596-2701

Secretary (Office Automation) **Satomi Hiyama** .... (559) 596-2950
E-mail: satomi.hiyama@ars.usda.gov

Administrative Officer **Ronald "Ron" Colby** .... (559) 596-2960
E-mail: ronald.colby@ars.usda.gov

Program Support Assistant **Allen Perez** .... (559) 596-2720
E-mail: allen.perez@ars.usda.gov

Research Leader, Crop Diseases, Pests and Genetic Research **Drake C. Stenger** .... (559) 596-2922
Fax: (559) 596-2921

Research Leader, Water Management Research
Dong Wang .... (559) 596-2852
Education: Idaho 1989 MS; Wisconsin 1993 PhD

Supervisory Research Plant Pathologist, Commodity Protection and Quality **Chang-Lin Xiao** .... (559) 596-2722

Plant Gene Expression Center
800 Buchanan Street, Room 1026G, Albany, CA 94710
Tel: (510) 559-5907

Director **Dr. Sarah C. Hake** .... (510) 559-5907

Lab Manager **Rebecca Haussmann** .... (510) 559-5913

★ Presidential Appointment Requiring Senate Confirmation ☆ Presidential Appointment □ Schedule C Appointment ◇ Career Senior Foreign Service Appointment
● Career Senior Executive Service (SES) Appointment ○ Non-Career Senior Executive Service (SES) Appointment ■ Postal Career Executive Service

Western Human Nutrition Research Center (WHNRC)
430 West Health Sciences Drive, Davis, CA 95616
Fax: (530) 752-5271 Internet: www.ars.usda.gov/pwa/davis/whnrc

Director **Dr. Lindsay Allen** UC Davis (WHNRC), University of California Davis . . . . . (530) 752-5268
E-mail: lindsay.allen@ars.usda.gov

Western Regional Research Center (WRRC)
800 Buchanan Street, Albany, CA 94710-1105
Tel: (510) 559-5600 Fax: (510) 559-5963
Internet: www.ars.usda.gov/pwa/wrrc

Research Leader **Dr. William J. "Bill" Orts** Room 2006 . . . . . (510) 559-5730
Research Leader **Dr. Tara McHugh** . . . . . (510) 559-5864
Secretary (Office Automation) **Christopher Allen "Chris" Carter** . . . . . (510) 559-5600
Administrative Assistant **Sylvia Abolencia** . . . . . (510) 559-6090
Administrative Officer **Gwyn Watson** . . . . . (510) 599-6029
E-mail: gwyn.watson@ars.usda.gov
Administrative Support Assistant **Dolores Gantan** . . . . . (510) 559-6030
E-mail: dolores.gantan@ars.usda.gov
Budget Analyst **Kimberly Mah** . . . . . (510) 559-6161
E-mail: kimberly.mah@ars.usda.gov
Information Technology Specialist (Customer Support) **(Vacant)** . . . . . (510) 559-5690
Purchasing Agent **(Vacant)** . . . . . (510) 559-6021
Safety and Occupational Health Manager **Megan Kennedy** . . . . . (510) 559-6059
E-mail: Megan.Kennedy@ars.usda.gov

U.S Salinity Laboratory
450 West Big Springs Road, Riverside, CA 92507-4617
Tel: (951) 369-4814 Fax: (951) 342-4960

Director **(Vacant)** . . . . . (951) 369-4815
Fax: (951) 342-4960
Secretary **Patricia Gonzalez** . . . . . (951) 369-4810
E-mail: patricia.gonzalez@ars.usda.gov
Contaminant Fate and Transport Research Unit Leader **(Vacant)** . . . . . (951) 369-4803
Fax: (951) 342-4964
Water Reuse and Remediation Research Unit Leader **(Vacant)** . . . . . (951) 369-4815
Administrative Officer **Nancy E. Knap** . . . . . (951) 369-4813
E-mail: nancy.knap@ars.usda.gov Fax: (951) 369-4818
Information Technology Specialist **Daniel Kain** . . . . . (951) 369-4827
E-mail: dainel.kain@ars.usda.gov

National Clonal Germplasm Repository for Citrus and Dates
1060 Martin Luther King Boulevard, Riverside, CA 92507-5437
Tel: (951) 827-4399 Fax: (951) 827-4398

Research Leader **MaryLou Polek** . . . . . (951) 827-4399

Hawaii

U.S. Pacific Basin Agricultural Research Center
64 Nowelo Street, Hilo, HI 96720
Mail: P.O. Box 4459, Hilo, HI 96720-4277
Tel: (808) 932-2100 Fax: (808) 959-5470

Center Director **Marisa Wall** . . . . . (808) 932-2100
E-mail: marisa.wall@ars.usda.gov
Administrative Officer **(Vacant)** . . . . . (808) 959-4305

Tropical Crop and Commodity Protection Research Unit
64 Nowelo Street, Hilo, HI 96720
Mail: P.O. Box 4459, Hilo, HI 96720
Tel: (808) 959-4340 Fax: (808) 959-5470

Research Leader **Nicholas Manoukis** . . . . . (808) 932-2118
Fax: (808) 959-5470

Tropical Plant Genetic Resource and Disease Research Unit
64 Nowelo Street, Hilo, HI 96720
Mail: P.O. Box 4459, Hilo, HI 96720
Tel: (808) 959-2110 Fax: (808) 959-5470

Research Leader **Tracie Matsumoto Brower** . . . . . (808) 959-4358

Idaho

Northwest Irrigation and Soils Research Laboratory
3793 North 3600 East, Kimberly, ID 83341-5076
Tel: (208) 423-5582 Fax: (208) 423-6555

Laboratory Director **Dr. David L. "Dave" Bjorneberg** . . . . (208) 423-6521
Education: South Dakota State 1987 BS, 1989 MSE; Iowa State 1995 PhD
Administrative Officer **Kara L. Vander Linden** . . . . . (208) 423-6566
E-mail: kara.vanderlinden@ars.usda.gov
IT Specialist **Dan Stieneke** . . . . . (208) 423-6519
E-mail: dan.stieneke@ars.usda.gov Fax: (208) 423-6555
Financial Technician **Paul G. McClintock** . . . . . (208) 423-6520

Northwest Watershed Research Center (NWRC)
Plaza IV, 800 Park Boulevard, Suite 105, Boise, ID 83712-7716
Tel: (208) 422-0700 Fax: (208) 334-1502

Research Leader **Frederick B. "Fred" Pierson, Jr.** . . . . . (208) 422-0720
Program Support Assistant **(Vacant)** . . . . . (208) 422-0700
Information Technology Specialist **Thomas Gatchell** . . . . (208) 422-0707
E-mail: thomas.gatchell@ars.usda.gov
Administrative Officer **Brooke Bowers** . . . . . (208) 422-0701
E-mail: brooke.bowers@ars.usda.gov

Small Grains and Potato Germplasm Research
1691 South 2700 West, Aberdeen, ID 83210
Tel: (208) 397-4162 Fax: (208) 397-4165

Supervisory Research Plant Pathologist **Dr. John Michael "Mike" Bonman** . . . . . (208) 397-4162 ext. 108
Administrative Officer **Glenda Rutger** . . . . . (208) 397-4162 ext. 102
E-mail: glenda.rutger@ars.usda.gov

Oregon

Columbia Plateau Conservation Research Center
48037 Tubbs Ranch Road, Adams, OR 97810
P.O. Box 370, Pendleton, OR 97801
Tel: (541) 278-4380 Fax: (541) 278-4372

Research Leader **Dr. Daniel S. "Dan" Long** . . . . . (541) 278-4391
Education: Washington State 1982 BS; Montana State 1986 MS; Cornell 1993 PhD
Administrative Officer **Jean Wise** . . . . . (541) 278-4402
E-mail: jean.wise@ars.usda.gov
Information Technology Specialist **(Vacant)** . . . . . (541) 278-4418
Purchasing Agent **Jeffery Fite** . . . . . (541) 278-4400
E-mail: jeffery.fite@ars.usda.gov

Corvallis (OR) Location
3450 SW Campus Way, Corvallis, OR 97331-8539
Tel: (541) 738-4000 Fax: (541) 738-2477

Crop Genetics Research Unit
141 Experiment Station Road, Stoneville, MS 38776
Tel: (541) 738-4125 Fax: (541) 738-4160

Research Leader **(Vacant)** . . . . . (662) 320-7414
810 Highway 12 East, Mississippi State, MS 39762

Horticultural Crops Research Unit
3420 NW Orchard Avenue, Corvallis, OR 97330-5098
Tel: (541) 738-4020 Fax: (541) 738-4025

Supervisory Research Plant Pathologist **Dr. Robert R. "Bob" Martin** . . . . . (541) 738-4041

National Clonal Germplasm Repository (Oregon)
33447 Peoria Road, Corvallis, OR 97333-2521
Tel: (541) 738-4200 Fax: (541) 738-4205

Supervisory Research Horticulturist **Dr. Kim E. Hummer** . . . . . (541) 738-4201

★ Presidential Appointment Requiring Senate Confirmation ☆ Presidential Appointment ☐ Schedule C Appointment ◇ Career Senior Foreign Service Appointment
● Career Senior Executive Service (SES) Appointment ○ Non-Career Senior Executive Service (SES) Appointment ■ Postal Career Executive Service

DEPARTMENTS

Eastern Oregon Agriculture Research Center – Burns (OR) Station (EOARC)
67826-A Highway 205, Burns, OR 97720
Tel: (541) 573-8900 Fax: (541) 573-3042
Areas Covered: ID, NV, OR, WA

Research Leader **Chad S. Boyd** . . . . (541) 573-8938
E-mail: chad.boyd@ars.usda.gov Fax: (541) 573-3042
Education: Texas Tech 1991 BS;
Utah State 1993 MS; Oklahoma State 1999 PhD
Ecologist **Roger L. Sheley** . . . . (541) 573-8938
Rangeland Ecologist **Jonathan D. "Jon" Bates** . . . . (541) 573-8932
Education: Cornell 1984 BS; Oregon State 1989 MS, 1996 PhD
Rangeland Scientist **Kirk Davies** . . . . (541) 573-4074
Education: Oregon State 2000 BS, 2005 PhD
Rangeland Scientist **(Vacant)** . . . . (541) 573-8939
Rangeland Scientist **(Vacant)** . . . . (541) 573-8936

Washington

Tree Fruit Research Laboratory
1104 North Western Avenue, Wenatchee, WA 98801
Tel: (509) 664-2280 Fax: (509) 664-2287

Research Leader
Dr. James Peter Mattheis Room 49 . . . . (509) 664-2280 ext. 249
Administrative Assistant
Michael Tonge Room 61 . . . . (509) 664-2280 ext. 261
E-mail: michael.tonge@ars.usda.gov
Research Plant Physiologist **David R. Rudell** . . . . (509) 664-2280 ext. 245

U.S. Department of Agriculture - Agricultural Research Service at Washington State University
211 Hulbert Hall, Pullman, WA 99164
Tel: (509) 335-8663 Fax: (509) 335-6669

Research Leader **Dr. Donald P. Knowles, Jr.** . . . . (509) 335-6022
Administrative Officer **Travis Frost** . . . . (509) 335-3238
E-mail: travis.frost@ars.usda.gov
Administrative Support Clerk
Deborah A. "Debbie" Parker . . . . (509) 335-8663
E-mail: debbie.parker@ars.usda.gov
Budget and Accounting Technician **Stefanie Clark** . . . . (509) 335-2507
E-mail: stefanie.clark@ars.usda.gov
Information Technology Specialist **Harold Christian** . . . . . (509) 335-8606
E-mail: harold.christian@ars.usda.gov
Safety and Occupational Health Specialist
Richard W. Partain . . . . (509) 335-7766
E-mail: richard.partain@ars.usda.gov
Office Automation Assistant **(Vacant)** . . . . (509) 335-8662

Animal Diseases Research Unit
P.O. Box 646630, Pullman, WA 99164-6630
3003 ADBF, Washington State University, Pullman, WA 99164-6630
Tel: (509) 335-6001 Fax: (509) 335-8328

Research Leader **Dr. Donald P. Knowles, Jr.** . . . . (509) 335-6022

Grain Legume Genetics Physiology Research Unit
Johnson Hall, Washington State University,
Room 303, Pullman, WA 99164-6434
Tel: (509) 335-7728 Fax: (509) 335-7692

Research Leader **George J. Vandemark** . . . . (509) 335-7728

Northwest Sustainable Agroecosystems Research
Johnson Hall, Washington State University,
Room 215, Pullman, WA 99164-6421
Tel: (509) 335-1552 Fax: (509) 335-3842

Research Leader **Brenton S. Sharratt** . . . . (509) 335-2724 ext. 146
Fax: (509) 335-7786

Plant Germplasm Introduction and Testing Research Unit – Western Regional Plant Introduction Station (WRPIS)
Johnson Hall, Washington State University,
Room 59, Pullman, WA 99164-6402
Tel: (509) 335-1502 Fax: (509) 335-6654

Research Leader/Station Coordinator **Jinguo Hu** . . . . (509) 335-3683

Plant Germplasm Introduction and Testing Research Unit – Western Regional Plant Introduction Station *(continued)*

Information Technology Specialist **Bo Gao** . . . . (509) 335-5409
E-mail: Bo.Gao@ars.usda.gov

Root Disease and Biological Control Research Unit
Johnson Hall, Washington State University,
Room 367A, Pullman, WA 99164-6430
Tel: (509) 335-1116 Fax: (509) 335-7674

Research Leader **Dr. David M. Weller** . . . . (509) 335-1116
Education: Miami U (OH) 1973 BA; Fax: (509) 335-7674
Michigan State 1975 MS, 1978 PhD

Wheat Genetics, Quality Physiology and Disease Research Unit
Johnson Hall, Washington State University,
Room 209, Pullman, WA 99164-6420
Tel: (509) 335-3632 Fax: (509) 335-2553

Research Leader **Dr. David M. Weller** . . . . (509) 335-6210
Education: Miami U (OH) 1973 BA; Michigan State 1975 MS, 1978 PhD
Supervisory Research Chemist/Western Wheat Quality
Laboratory Director **Craig F. Morris** . . . . (509) 335-4062
Food Science Building, Fax: (509) 335-8573
Washington State University,
Room E202, Pullman, WA 99164-6394
Education: Iowa State 1982 BS; Kansas State 1984 MS, 1987 PhD

Yakima Agricultural Research Laboratory (YARL)
5230 Konnowac Pass Road, Wapato, WA 98951
Tel: (509) 454-6550 Fax: (509) 454-5646

Research Leader **Dr. Peter J. Landolt** . . . . (509) 454-6551
Office Automation Assistant **Merilee Bayer** . . . . (509) 454-6550
E-mail: merilee.bayer@ars.usda.gov
Administrative Officer **Patricia Gregory** . . . . (509) 454-6562
E-mail: patti.gregory@ars.usda.gov
Webmaster **Eric A. Bruntjen** . . . . (509) 454-6562
E-mail: eric.bruntjen@ars.usda.gov

Utah

Forage and Range Research Laboratory
Utah State University, 696 North 1100 East,
Room 206, Logan, UT 84322-6300
Tel: (435) 797-2249 Fax: (435) 797-3075

Research Leader **(Vacant)** . . . . (435) 797-2249

Poisonous Plant Research Laboratory
1150 East 1400 North, Logan, UT 84341
Tel: (435) 752-2941 Fax: (435) 753-5681

Research Leader **(Vacant)** . . . . (435) 752-2941 ext. 1123

Pollinating Insect-Biology, Management Systematics Research
Utah State University, BNR-261, Logan, UT 84322-5310
Tel: (435) 797-2524 Fax: (435) 797-0461
Internet: www.ars.usda.gov/npa/beelab

Research Leader **Diana Cox-Foster** . . . . (435) 797-0530

Plains Area

1001 Holleman Drive East, College Station, TX 77840-4117
Tel: (979) 260-9346 Fax: (979) 260-9415
Areas Covered: CO, KS, MT, ND, NE, NM, OK, SD, TX, WY

Area Director **Dr. Laurence D. "Larry" Chandler** . . . . (970) 492-7057
Associate Director **Dr. Bryan Kaphammer** . . . . (970) 492-7058
Associate Director **Joseph Rich PhD** . . . . (970) 492-7056
● Associate Area Director **John McMurtry** . . . . (970) 492-7056
E-mail: john.mcmurtry@ars.usda.gov
Administrative Officer **Kimberly Plummer** . . . . (785) 776-2737
E-mail: kimberly.plummer@ars.usda.gov
Area Procurement Analyst **(Vacant)** . . . . (979) 260-9447
Equal Employment Manager **Alan Cohen** . . . . (970) 492-7098
Human Resources Assistant **(Vacant)** . . . . (979) 260-9443
Fax: (979) 260-9344
IT Specialist **(Vacant)** . . . . (979) 260-9666

★ Presidential Appointment Requiring Senate Confirmation ☆ Presidential Appointment ☐ Schedule C Appointment ◇ Career Senior Foreign Service Appointment
● Career Senior Executive Service (SES) Appointment ○ Non-Career Senior Executive Service (SES) Appointment ■ Postal Career Executive Service

Plains Area *(continued)*

Program Analyst **Reagan Heese** .... (970) 492-7006
Realty Officer **(Vacant)** .... (662) 686-5323
Secretary **Olga Lee** .... (970) 492-7050
Secretary (Office Automation) **(Vacant)** .... (402) 762-4140
Statistician **Sara Duke** .... (979) 260-9320
Technology Transfer Coordinator
Jeffrey "Jeff" Walenta .... (970) 492-7055
Technology Transfer Assistant **Tara Marostica** .... (970) 492-7059

Colorado

Central Great Plains Research Station

40335 County Road GG, Akron, CO 80720
Tel: (970) 345-2259 Fax: (970) 345-2088

Research Leader **Dr. Merle F. Vigil** .... (970) 345-0517
Administrative Officer **Sarah E. "Phelan" Bernhardt** .... (970) 345-0504
E-mail: sarah.bernhardt@ars.usda.gov
Secretary (Office Automation) **Carolyn K. Brandon** .... (970) 345-0505
E-mail: carolyn.brandon@ars.usda.gov
Secretary (Office Automation) **(Vacant)** .... (970) 345-2259

Agricultural Systems Research Unit

Building D, USDA-ARS-NPA, Natural Resources Research Center,
2150 Centre Avenue, Suite 200, Fort Collins, CO 80526-8199
Tel: (970) 492-7000 Fax: (970) 492-7310
Internet: www.ars.usda.gov/npa/ftcollins/asru

Center Director **R. Daren Harmel** .... (970) 492-7771
Education: Central Col (IA) 1992 BA; Texas Tech 1994 MS; Oklahoma State 1997 PhD
Research Agricultural Engineer **Larry Wagner** .... (970) 492-7382
E-mail: larry.wagner@ars.usda.gov
Soil Scientist **John Tatarko** .... (970) 492-7320
E-mail: john.tatarko@ars.usda.gov
Information Technology Specialist **Fred Fox, Jr.** .... (970) 492-7370
E-mail: fred.fox@ars.usda.gov

Soil Management and Sugarbeet Research

Building D, USDA-ARS-NPA, Natural Resources Research Center,
2150 Centre Avenue, Suite 100, Fort Collins, CO 80526-8199
Tel: (970) 492-7200 Fax: (970) 492-7213

Research Leader **(Vacant)** .... (970) 492-7220
Supervisory Research Geneticist (Plants) **(Vacant)** .... (970) 492-7140
Geneticist (Plants) **Ann Fenwick** .... (970) 492-7145
Research Soil Scientist **Jorge Delgado** .... (970) 492-7260
Biological Science Lab Technician **Amber Brandt** .... (970) 492-7234
Biological Science Lab Technician **Amy Nielson** .... (970) 492-7142
Secretary (Office Automation) **Stacey Wilkins** .... (970) 492-7200

Water Management and Systems Research

Building D, USDA-ARS-WMRU, Natural Resources Research Center,
2150 Centre Avenue, Suite 320, Fort Collins, CO 80526-2098
Tel: (970) 492-7400 Fax: (970) 492-7408

Research Leader **(Vacant)** .... (970) 492-7419
Program Support Assistant (Office Automation)
Kristi Downing .... (970) 492-7770
E-mail: kristi.downing@ars.usda.gov

Plant and Animal Genetic Resources Preservation (NCGRP)

1111 South Mason Street, Fort Collins, CO 80521-4500
Tel: (970) 495-3200 Fax: (970) 221-1427

Director **(Vacant)** .... (970) 495-3265

Kansas

Center for Grain and Animal Health Research (CGAHR)

1515 College Avenue, Manhattan, KS 66502
Tel: (800) 627-0388 Tel: (785) 776-2701 Fax: (785) 776-2789

Agricultural Administrator and Center Director
D. Scott McVey .... (785) 776-2702
Research Leader **(Vacant)** .... (785) 776-2717
Administrative Officer **Kimberly Plummer** .... (785) 776-2737
E-mail: Kimberly.Plummer@ars.usda.gov
Facilities Manager **(Vacant)** .... (785) 537-5579

Center for Grain and Animal Health Research *(continued)*

Information Technology Specialist **Joseph King** .... (785) 776-2722
E-mail: joseph.king@ars.usda.gov
Safety and Occupational Health Specialist **Cary Bott** ..... (785) 776-2733
E-mail: cary.bott@ars.usda.gov

Arthropod-Borne Animal Diseases Research Unit (ABADRU)

1515 College Avenue, Manhattan, KS 66502
Tel: (785) 537-5578 Fax: (785) 537-5560

Research Veterinary Medical Officer **Leela Noronha** ..... (785) 776-2705
Fax: (785) 537-5560
Secretary (Office Automation) **Nicholas Watson** .... (785) 537-5578
E-mail: nicholas.watson@ars.usda.gov

Grain Quality and Structure Research Unit (GQSRU)

1515 College Avenue, Manhattan, KS 66502
Tel: (785) 776-2757 Fax: (785) 537-5534

Center Director (Acting)
Dr. Thomas J. "Tom" Herald .... (785) 776-2703
Research Leader (Acting) **Scott Bean** .... (785) 776-2725

Hard Winter Wheat and Genetics Research Unit (HWWGRU)

4008 Throckmorton Hall, Kansas State University, Manhattan, KS 66506
Tel: (785) 532-6168 Fax: (785) 532-5692

Research Leader **Dr. Robert Bowden** .... (785) 532-2368

Stored Product Insect and Engineering Research Unit (SPIERU)

1515 College Avenue, Manhattan, KS 66502
Tel: (785) 776-2704 Fax: (785) 537-5584

Research Leader **James F. "Jim" Campbell** .... (785) 776-2717
Program Support Assistant **Dianna Halcumb** .... (785) 776-2704
E-mail: dianna.halcumb@ars.usda.gov
Secretary (Office Automation) **(Vacant)** .... (785) 776-2726

Montana

Fort Keogh Livestock and Range Research Laboratory

243 Fort Keogh Road, Miles City, MT 59301-4016
Tel: (406) 874-8200 Fax: (406) 874-8289

Research Leader **Mark Petersen** .... (406) 874-8219
Administrative Officer **Amy Bontrager** .... (406) 874-8239
E-mail: amy.bontrager@ars.usda.gov
Administrative Assistant **Travis Helm** .... (406) 874-8224
E-mail: travis.helm@ars.usda.gov
Program Support Assistant **Diona Austill** .... (406) 874-8219
E-mail: diona.austill@ars.usda.gov
Agricultural Statistician **(Vacant)** .... (406) 874-8214
Animal Scientist **Thomas W. "Tom" Geary** .... (406) 874-8215
Animal Scientist and Range Nutritionist
Richard Carl Waterman .... (406) 874-8208
Education: Colorado State 1998 BSAg; New Mexico State 2000 MNU, 2003 DScAgr
Ecologist **Kurt Reinhart** .... (406) 874-8211
E-mail: kurt.reinhart@ars.usda.gov
Ecologist **Lance Vermeire** .... (406) 874-8206
E-mail: lance.vermeire@ars.usda.gov
Information Technology Specialist **Sharon Stanton** .... (406) 874-8212
Molecular Geneticist **El Hamidi Hay** .... (406) 874-8234
Physiologist **Andrew "Andy" Roberts** .... (406) 874-8216
Rangeland Management Specialist
Matthew "Matt" Rinella .... (406) 874-8232

Northern Plains Agricultural Research Laboratory

1500 North Central, Sidney, MT 59270
Tel: (406) 433-2020 Fax: (406) 433-5038
E-mail: info@sidney.ars.usda.gov

Agricultural Systems Research Leader (Acting)
John Gaskin .... (406) 433-9444
Education: UC Santa Cruz 1996 BS; Washington U (MO) 2002 PhD
Administrative Officer **(Vacant)** .... (406) 433-9480
Fax: (406) 433-9455
IT Specialist **Kevin Dahl** .... (406) 433-9409
E-mail: kevin.dahl@ars.usda.gov

(continued on next page)

★ Presidential Appointment Requiring Senate Confirmation ☆ Presidential Appointment □ Schedule C Appointment ◇ Career Senior Foreign Service Appointment
● Career Senior Executive Service (SES) Appointment ○ Non-Career Senior Executive Service (SES) Appointment ■ Postal Career Executive Service

Northern Plains Agricultural Research Laboratory *(continued)*

Technical Information Specialist **Bethany Redlin** . . . . (406) 433-9427
E-mail: beth.redlin@ars.usda.gov
Pest Management Research Unit Leader **John Gaskin** . . . . (406) 433-9444
Education: UC Santa Cruz 1996 BS; Washington U (MO) 2002 PhD

Nebraska

Lincoln (NE) – University of Nebraska Location
East Campus, University of Nebraska, Lincoln, NE 68583-0934
Tel: (402) 472-1490 Fax: (402) 472-4020
Internet: www.ars.usda.gov/main/site_main.htm?modecode=54-40-00-00
Location Coordinator **Dr. Brian J. Wienhold** . . . . (402) 472-1484
Administrative Officer **Gary Maixner** . . . . (402) 472-9691
E-mail: gary.maixner@ars.usda.gov
Information Technology Specialist **Myron Coleman** . . . . . (402) 472-1205
E-mail: Myron.Coleman@ars.usda.gov

Wheat, Sorghum and Forage Research
251 Filley Hall, East Campus, University of Nebraska, Lincoln, NE 68583
Tel: (402) 472-1490 Fax: (402) 472-4020
Research Leader **Robert "Bob" Graybosch** . . . . (402) 472-1563

Agroecosystem Management Research
251 Filley Hall, East Campus, University of Nebraska, Lincoln, NE 68583
Tel: (402) 472-5158 Fax: (402) 472-0516
Research Leader **Dr. Brian J. Wienhold** . . . . (402) 472-1484
E-mail: brian.wienhold@ars.usda.gov

U.S. Meat Animal Research Center (USMARC)
Building 1, State Spur 18D, Clay Center, NE 68933-0166
Mail: P.O. Box 166, Clay Center, NE 68933-0166
Tel: (402) 762-4100 Fax: (402) 762-4148
● Center Director **Mark Boggess PhD** . . . . (402) 762-4109
E-mail: mark.boggess@ars.usda.gov
Education: Cornell 1985 MS; Iowa State 2000 PhD
Environmental Management Research Leader
Mindy Spiehs . . . . (402) 762-4271
Genetics, Breeding, and Animal Health Research
Leader **Dr. Gary L. Bennett** . . . . (402) 762-4254
Fax: (402) 762-4155
Meat Quality and Safety Research Leader
Dr. Tommy Wheeler . . . . (402) 762-4221
Fax: (402) 762-4149
Nutrition and Environmental Management Research
Leader **Harvey C. Freetly** . . . . (402) 762-4202
Fax: (402) 762-4209
Reproduction Research Leader **Gary Rohrer** . . . . (402) 762-4365
Fax: (402) 762-4382
Veterinary Services **Shuna A. Jones** . . . . (402) 762-4114
Fax: (402) 762-4119
General Engineer **Joseph S. "Joe" Warrick** . . . . (402) 762-4131
Administrative Officer **Bucky R. Herman** . . . . (402) 762-4141
E-mail: bucky.herman@ars.usda.gov

New Mexico

Las Cruces (NM) Location
2995 Knox Street, Las Cruces, NM 88003
Fax: (575) 646-5889
Location Coordinator
Dr. Laurence D. "Larry" Chandler . . . . (970) 492-7057
2150 Centre Avenue, Fort Collins, CO 80526
Administrative Officer **Jo Ann S. Fernandez** . . . . (575) 646-6316
E-mail: joann.chavira@ars.usda.gov

Southwestern Cotton Ginning Research Laboratory
300 East College Drive, Mesilla Park, NM 88047
P.O. Box 578, Mesilla Park, NM 88047
Tel: (575) 526-6381 Fax: (575) 525-1076
Internet: www.swcgrl.ars.usda.gov
Supervisory Agricultural Engineer **(Vacant)** . . . . (575) 526-6381

Jornada Experimental Range
P.O. Box 30003, MSC 3JER NMSU, Las Cruces, NM 88003-8003
Tel: (575) 646-4842 Fax: (575) 646-5889
Supervisory Research Specialist
Brandon Bestelmeyer . . . . (575) 646-4842
E-mail: brandon.bestelmeyer@ars.usda.gov

North Dakota

Edward T. Schafer Agricultural Research Center
1605 Albrecht Boulevard North, Fargo, ND 58102-2765
Tel: (701) 239-1370 Fax: (701) 239-1202
Center Director **Michael Grusak** . . . . (701) 239-1371
Administrative Officer **John E. Johnson** . . . . (701) 239-1203
E-mail: john.johnson@ars.usda.gov

Biosciences Research Laboratory
1605 Albrecht Boulevard North, Fargo, ND 58102-2765
Tel: (701) 239-1370 Fax: (701) 239-1202
Animal Metabolism - Agricultural Chemicals Research
Unit **Dr. David J. Smith PhD** . . . . (701) 239-1238
Fax: (701) 239-1430
Insect Genetics and Biochemistry Research Unit
(Acting) **Dr. William P. "Bill" Kemp** . . . . (701) 239-1371
Fax: (701) 239-1348
Sunflower and Plant Biology Research Unit **(Vacant)** . . . . . (701) 239-1250
Fax: (701) 239-1252

Northern Crop Science Laboratory
1307 18th Street North, Fargo, ND 58102-2765
Tel: (701) 239-1370 Fax: (701) 239-1202
Cereal Crops Research Unit **Dr. Michael C. Edwards** . . . . (701) 239-1341
Fax: (701) 239-1369
Sugarbeet and Potato Research Unit **(Vacant)** . . . . (701) 239-1257
Fax: (701) 239-1349
Sunflower and Plant Biology Research Unit
Dr. Michael E. Foley . . . . (701) 239-1322
Fax: (701) 239-1346

Potato Research Laboratory Worksite
311 Fifth Avenue, NE, East Grand Forks, MN 56721
Tel: (218) 773-2473 Fax: (218) 773-1478
Food Technologist **(Vacant)** . . . . (218) 773-2473

Northern Great Plains Research Laboratory (NGPRL)
P.O. Box 459, Mandan, ND 58554-0459
Tel: (701) 663-6445 Fax: (701) 667-3054
Research Leader **David W. Archer** . . . . (701) 667-3048
E-mail: david.archer@ars.usda.gov
Education: Rocky Mt Col (MT) 1988 BS; Iowa State 1995 PhD
Administrative Officer **(Vacant)** . . . . (701) 667-3014
Information Technology Specialist **(Vacant)** . . . . (701) 667-3029

Grand Forks (ND) Human Nutrition Research Center
2420 Second Avenue North, Grand Forks, ND 58203
Tel: (701) 795-8353 Fax: (701) 795-8395
Director **James Norman Roemmich** . . . . (701) 795-8456
E-mail: james.roemmich@ars.usda.gov
Secretary **Teri Reed** . . . . (701) 795-8456
E-mail: teri.reed@ars.usda.gov Fax: (701) 795-8240
Dietary Prevention of Obesity-Related
Disease Supervisory Research Physiologist
Dr. Matthew Picklo . . . . (701) 795-8380
Education: Delaware 1990 BS; Vanderbilt 1995 PhD
Healthy Body Weight Research Supervisory Research
Physiologist **(Vacant)** . . . . (701) 795-8272
Administrative Officer **Susan M. Sorum** . . . . (701) 795-8358
E-mail: susan.sorum@ars.usda.gov
Purchasing Agent **Peter B. Nelson** . . . . (701) 795-8354
E-mail: peter.nelson@ars.usda.gov

★ Presidential Appointment Requiring Senate Confirmation ☆ Presidential Appointment ☐ Schedule C Appointment ◇ Career Senior Foreign Service Appointment
● Career Senior Executive Service (SES) Appointment ○ Non-Career Senior Executive Service (SES) Appointment ■ Postal Career Executive Service

Oklahoma

ARS - Stillwater (OK)
1301 North Western Road, Stillwater, OK 74075-2714
Tel: (405) 624-4141 Fax: (405) 624-4142

Location Coordinator **Norman C. Elliott** .... (405) 624-4141 ext. 227
E-mail: norman.elliott@ars.usda.gov
Administrative Officer **Linda Gronewaller** ...... (405) 624-4141 ext. 247
E-mail: linda.gronewaller@ars.usda.gov

Hydraulic Engineering Research Unit
1301 North Western Road, Stillwater, OK 74075-2714
Tel: (405) 624-4135 Fax: (405) 624-4136

Research Leader/Research Hydraulic Engineer
Sherry L. Hunt .... (405) 624-4135 ext. 222
Research Hydraulic Engineer **(Vacant)** .... (405) 624-4135

Wheat, Peanut and Other Field Crops Research Unit
1301 North Western Road, Stillwater, OK 74075-2714
Tel: (405) 624-4141 Fax: (405) 624-4142

Research Leader/Supervisory Research
Biologist **Norman C. Elliott** .... (405) 624-4141 ext. 227

Grazinglands Research Laboratory
7207 West Cheyenne Street, El Reno, OK 73036
Tel: (405) 262-5291 Fax: (405) 262-0133

Director **Dr. Jean L. Steiner** .... (405) 262-5291
Director, Regional Climate Hub **David P. Brown** .... (405) 262-5291
Forage and Livestock Production Research
Leader **Prasanna H. Gowda** .... (405) 262-5291 ext. 2470
Grazinglands Research Leader **Dr. Jean L. Steiner** ...... (405) 262-5291
Administrative Officer **Eilene Gibbens** .... (405) 262-5291
E-mail: eilene.gibbens@ars.usda.gov
Information Technology Specialist
Dennis W. Wallin .... (405) 262-5291 ext. 261
E-mail: dennis.wallin@ars.usda.gov

Southern Plains Range Research Station (SPRRS)
2000 18th Street, Woodward, OK 73801
Tel: (580) 256-7449 Fax: (580) 256-1322

Research Leader **Dr. Stacey A. Gunter PhD** .... (580) 256-7449

South Dakota

North Central Agricultural Research Laboratory
2923 Medary Avenue, Brookings, SD 57006-9803
Tel: (605) 693-3241 Fax: (605) 693-5240

Research Leader **Sharon K. Papiernik** .... (605) 693-5201
Education: Minnesota 1991 BA; Nebraska 1995 PhD

Texas

Conservation and Production Research Laboratory
2300 Experiment Station Road, Bushland, TX 79012-0010
Mail: P.O. Drawer 10, Bushland, TX 79012-0010
Tel: (806) 356-5724 Fax: (806) 356-5750

Laboratory Director **(Vacant)** .... (806) 356-5748
Livestock Nutrient Management Research Leader
(Vacant) .... (806) 356-5748
Soil and Water Management Research Leader **(Vacant)** ... (806) 356-5762
Administrative Officer **James "Jim" Mills** .... (806) 356-5706
E-mail: jim.mills@ars.usda.gov
Information Technology Specialist **Kerry Jones** .... (806) 356-5757
E-mail: kerry.jones@ars.usda.gov

Cropping Systems Research Laboratory
3810 Fourth Street, Lubbock, TX 79415
Tel: (806) 749-5560 Fax: (806) 723-5272

Laboratory Director **Dr. John J. Burke** .... (806) 749-5560 ext. 5216
Cotton Production and Processing Research
Unit Leader **Dr. Gregory Alan "Greg" Holt** ... (806) 746-5353 ext. 105
1604 East FM, Fax: (806) 744-4402
Room 1294, Lubbock, TX 79403
E-mail: greg.holt@ars.usda.gov

Cropping Systems Research Laboratory *(continued)*

Livestock Issues Research Unit Leader
Dr. Jeffery Carroll .... (806) 746-5353 ext. 120
1604 East FM, Fax: (806) 744-4402
Room 1294, Lubbock, TX 79403
Plant Stress and Germplasm Development
Research Leader **Dr. John J. Burke** .... (806) 749-5560 ext. 5216
E-mail: john.burke@ars.usda.gov
Wind Erosion and Water Conservation Research Unit
Leader **Robert Lascano** .... (806) 749-5560
E-mail: robert.lascano@ars.usda.gov
Administrative Officer **Harrison Axum** .... (806) 749-5560 ext. 5213
E-mail: harrison.axum@ars.usda.gov

Grassland, Soil and Water Research Laboratory
808 East Blackland Road, Temple, TX 76502
Tel: (254) 770-6500 Fax: (254) 770-6561
Internet: www.ars.usda.gov/spa/gswrl

Supervisory Agricultural Engineer **R. Daren Harmel** ..... (254) 770-6521
Education: Central Col (IA) 1992 BA; Texas Tech 1994 MS;
Oklahoma State 1997 PhD
Agricultural Engineer
Dr. Jeffrey G. "Jeff" Arnold PhD .... (254) 770-6502
Education: Illinois 1981 BS, 1983 MS; Purdue 1992 PhD
Agricultural Engineer **Michael J. "Mike" White** .... (254) 770-6523
Agricultural Engineer **(Vacant)** .... (254) 770-6505
Administrative Officer **Janice Brown** .... (254) 770-6543
E-mail: janice.brown@ars.usda.gov
Research Microbiologist **(Vacant)** .... (509) 786-9250

Knipling-Bushland U.S. Livestock Insects Research Laboratory (KBUSLIRL)
2700 Fredricksburg Road, Kerrville, TX 78028-9184
Tel: (830) 792-0308 Fax: (830) 792-0314

Laboratory Director
Adalberto A. "Beto" Perez de Leon .... (830) 792-0304
E-mail: beto.perezdeleon@ars.usda.gov
GIS Research Scientist **(Vacant)** .... (830) 792-0338
Fax: (830) 792-0337
Administrative Officer **Thomas Hall** .... (830) 792-0303
E-mail: thomas.hall@ars.usda.gov Fax: (830) 792-0372
Administrative Support Assistant **(Vacant)** .... (830) 792-0308

Crop Germplasm Research
10200 FM 50, Somerville, TX 77879
Tel: (979) 272-1402 Fax: (979) 272-1401

Research Leader **(Vacant)** .... (979) 260-9311
Research Geneticist **Byron Burson** .... (979) 272-9300
Research Geneticist **Lori Hinze** .... (979) 272-9533
Research Geneticist **Robert "Bob" Klein** .... (979) 777-4470
Research Geneticist **John Yu** .... (979) 272-9237
Research Geneticist (Plants) **Xinwang Wang** .... (979) 272-1402
Research Horticulturist **Dr. Larry J. "L.J." Grauke** ...... (979) 272-1402

Southern Plains Agricultural Research Center (SPARC)
2881 F & B Road, College Station, TX 77845
Tel: (979) 260-9372 Fax: (979) 260-9377

Director and Location Coordinator **Dr. G. Wayne Ivie** .... (979) 260-9372
Aerial Application Technology Research Leader
Clint Hoffmann .... (979) 260-9354
Insect Control and Cotton Disease Research Leader
(Vacant) .... (979) 260-9232
Fax: (979) 260-9319
Crop Germplasm Research Leader **(Vacant)** .... (979) 260-9311
Fax: (979) 260-9333
Food and Feed Safety Research Leader
Dr. David J. "Dave" Nisbet .... (979) 260-9484
Fax: (979) 260-9332
Information Technology Specialist **Paul G. Schleider** .... (979) 260-9561
E-mail: paul.schleider@ars.usda.gov

DEPARTMENTS

★ Presidential Appointment Requiring Senate Confirmation ☆ Presidential Appointment ☐ Schedule C Appointment ◇ Career Senior Foreign Service Appointment
● Career Senior Executive Service (SES) Appointment ○ Non-Career Senior Executive Service (SES) Appointment ■ Postal Career Executive Service

Children's Nutrition Research Center
Baylor College of Medicine, 1100 Bates Street, Houston, TX 77030-2600
Tel: (713) 798-7022 Fax: (713) 798-7046 E-mail: cnrc@bcm.tmc.edu

Center Director **Dr. Dennis M. Bier MD** .... (713) 798-7046

Wyoming

High Plains Grasslands Research Station
8408 Hildreth Road, Cheyenne, WY 82009-8899
Tel: (307) 772-2433 Fax: (307) 637-6124

Research Leader **Justin D. Derner** .... (307) 772-2433 ext. 113
Education: Nebraska 1991 BS; Oklahoma State 1993 MS; Texas A&M 1996 PhD
Program Analyst (Office Automation)
Ann L. Heckart .... (307) 772-2433 ext. 100
E-mail: ann.heckart@ars.usda.gov

Southeast Area

141 Experiment Station Road, Stoneville, MS 38776
Mail: P.O. Box 225, Stoneville, MS 38776-0225
Tel: (662) 686-3000 Fax: (662) 686-5309
Areas Covered: AL, AR, FL, GA, LA, MS, NC, PR, SC

● Area Director **Archie Tucker** Room 102 .... (662) 686-5266
E-mail: archie.tucker@ars.usda.gov
Secretary **Mary Sluder** .... (662) 686-5266
Associate Director **Dr. Ellen Harris** .... (662) 686-5266
Associate Director **(Vacant)** .... (662) 686-5266
Statistician **Deborah "Debbie" Boykin** .... (662) 686-5274
Office Automation Assistant **Joan Fabick** .... (662) 686-3035
E-mail: joan.fabick@ars.usda.gov
Safety and Occupational Health Manager
David B. Daniels .... (706) 546-3311
Safety and Occupational Health Manager
Shelia Parker .... (662) 686-3745
Equal Employment Manager **Jimmy Ray McAlpine** ..... (662) 686-3634
Technology Transfer Coordinator **(Vacant)** .... (662) 686-5255
Associate Technology Transfer Coordinator
Dr. Joseph "Joe" Lipovsky .... (662) 686-5432
Technology Transfer Assistant **Annetta Ebelhar** .... (662) 686-3010
Epidemiologist **Jessica Thomson** .... (225) 892-3662
E-mail: jessica.thomson@ars.usda.gov
Management and Program Analyst **Fratesi Drusilla** ...... (662) 686-3633
Fax: (662) 686-5459
Program Analyst **Sharon Jett** .... (706) 546-3221
Program Analyst **Jessica Loggins** .... (706) 546-3614
Management Analyst **Ann McGee** .... (662) 686-5265
E-mail: ann.mcgee@ars.usda.gov

Florida

Center for Medical, Agricultural and Veterinary Entomology
1600/1700 Southwest 23rd Drive, Gainesville, FL 32608
Tel: (352) 374-5860 Fax: (352) 374-5850

Center Director **Dr. Kenneth J. "Ken" Linthicum** ...... (352) 374-5700
Education: UCLA 1972 BA, 1974 MA, 1978 PhD
Secretary **Bonnie Ebel** .... (352) 374-5901
E-mail: bonnie.ebel@ars.usda.gov
Insect Behavior and Biocontrol Research Unit Leader
Paul D. Shirk .... (352) 374-5791
Chemistry Research Unit Leader **John D. Beck** .... (352) 374-5730
Imported Fire Ant and Household Insects Research Unit Leader **Dr. Robert "Bob" Vander Meer** .... (352) 374-5855
Mosquito and Fly Research Unit Leader **(Vacant)** .... (352) 374-5910
Research Entomologist **Christopher J. "Chris" Geden** ... (352) 374-5919
Education: Boston Col 1976 BS; UMass (Amherst) 1979 MS, 1983 PhD
Information Technology Specialist
Dianne Underwood .... (352) 374-5856
E-mail: dianne.underwood@ars.usda.gov
Information Technology Specialist (Webmaster)
Eric Daniels .... (352) 374-5882
E-mail: eric.daniels@ars.usda.gov Fax: (352) 374-5818

Invasive Plant Research Laboratory
3225 College Avenue, Fort Lauderdale, FL 33314
Tel: (954) 475-0541 Fax: (954) 476-9169

Research Leader **Philip W. Tipping** .... (954) 475-6543
Administrative Officer **Donna Signa** .... (954) 475-6541
E-mail: donna.signa@ars.usda.gov
Ecologist **F. Allen Dray, Jr.** .... (954) 475-6556
Plant Physiologist **Paul T. Madeira** .... (954) 475-6553
Research Ecologist **Aaron David** .... (954) 475-6547
Research Ecologist **Melissa C. Smith** .... (954) 475-6549
Research Entomologist **Ashley Goode** .... (954) 475-6577
Fax: (954) 476-9160
Research Entomologist **Dale Halbritter** .... (954) 475-6548
Research Entomologist **Ellen C. Lake** .... (954) 475-6547
E-mail: ellen.lake@ars.usda.gov
Education: Delaware 2011 PhD
Research Entomologist **Gregory S. Wheeler** .... (954) 475-6546
E-mail: greg.wheeler@ars.usda.gov
Education: Florida 1989 PhD
Entomologist **(Vacant)** .... (352) 395-4796
Fax: (352) 955-2301
Plant Pathologist **Min Rayamajhi** .... (954) 475-6552

Subtropical Horticulture Research Station (SHRS)
13601 Old Cutler Road, Miami, FL 33158-1334
Tel: (786) 573-7094 Fax: (786) 573-7100

Research Leader **Hamed K. Abbas** .... (602) 686-5313
Administrative Officer **Mary Martinez** .... (786) 573-7059
E-mail: mary.martinez@ars.usda.gov
Research Agronomist **(Vacant)** .... (786) 573-7048
Research Entomologist **Paul Kendra** .... (786) 573-7090
E-mail: paul.kendra@ars.usda.gov
Research Entomologist **(Vacant)** .... (786) 573-7088
Research Entomologist **(Vacant)** .... (786) 573-7062
Research Geneticist (Plants) **Osman Gutierrez** .... (786) 573-7097
E-mail: osman.gutierrez@ars.usda.gov
Research Geneticist (Plants) **Alan W. Meerow** .... (786) 573-7075
E-mail: alan.meerow@ars.usda.gov
Research Molecular Biologist **David Kuhn** .... (786) 573-7087
E-mail: david.kuhn@ars.usda.gov

U.S. Horticultural Research Laboratory
2001 South Rock Road, Fort Pierce, FL 34945
Tel: (772) 462-5800 Fax: (772) 462-5986

Director **Brian T. Scully** .... (772) 462-5810
Education: Cal Poly San Luis Obispo BS; UC Davis MS; Cornell PhB
Citrus Subtropical Products Unit Research Leader
Elizabeth A. "Liz" Baldwin .... (772) 462-5979
Education: Florida PhD
Subtropical Insects and Horticulture Research Unit Leader **Dr. David Hall** .... (772) 462-5814
Subtropical Plant Pathology Research Unit Leader
Dr. Timothy R. Gottwald .... (772) 462-5883
Administrative Officer **(Vacant)** .... (772) 462-5802
Information Technology Specialist **Tom Dean** .... (772) 462-5891
E-mail: thomas.dean@ars.usda.gov
Purchasing Agent **(Vacant)** .... (772) 462-5809

U.S. Sugarcane Field Station
12990 U.S. Highway 441 North, Canal Point, FL 33438
Tel: (561) 924-5227 Fax: (561) 924-6109

Research Leader **Duli Zhao** .... (561) 924-5227
Agricultural Research Technical Supervisor
(Vacant) .... (561) 924-5227 ext. 29
Program Support Assistant **Troy Honaker** .... (561) 924-5227 ext. 13
E-mail: Troy.Honaker@ars.usda.gov
Administrative Officer **Audra Macnaught** .... (772) 462-5883
E-mail: audra.mcnaught@ars.usda.gov

★ Presidential Appointment Requiring Senate Confirmation ☆ Presidential Appointment ☐ Schedule C Appointment ◇ Career Senior Foreign Service Appointment
● Career Senior Executive Service (SES) Appointment ○ Non-Career Senior Executive Service (SES) Appointment ■ Postal Career Executive Service

Georgia

National Peanut Research Laboratory (NPRL)
1011 Forrester Drive, SE, Dawson, GA 39842
Mail: P.O. Box 509, Dawson, GA 39842-0509
Tel: (229) 995-7400 Fax: (229) 995-7416

Research Leader **Marshall C. Lamb** .... (229) 995-7417
Program Support Assistant **Beverly Hill** .... (229) 995-7400
E-mail: beverly.hill@ars.usda.gov
Research Agronomist **Ronald B. Sorensen** .... (229) 995-7411
Research Chemist **Phat M. Dang** .... (229) 995-7432
E-mail: phat.dang@ars.usda.gov
Research Chemist **Victor S. Sobolev** .... (229) 995-7446
E-mail: victor.sobolev@ars.usda.gov
Research Microbiologist **(Vacant)** .... (229) 995-7410
Research Plant Pathologist **Renee S. Arias De Ares** ..... (229) 995-7430
E-mail: renee.arias@ars.usda.gov

Plant Genetic Resources Conservation Unit (PGRCU)
Redding Building, 1109 Experiment Street,
Room 160A, Griffin, GA 30223-1797
Tel: (770) 228-7254 Fax: (770) 229-3323

Research Leader **Melanie Harrison** .... (770) 233-6198
Fax: (770) 229-3323
Supervisory Geneticist and Research Leader
John Bradley "Brad" Morris .... (770) 229-3253
Information Technology Specialist **Nicholas Stigura** ..... (770) 229-3297
E-mail: Nicholas.Stigura@ars.usda.gov Fax: (770) 229-3324
Administrative Officer
Jacqueline "Jacquie" McDonald .... (770) 228-7207
E-mail: jacquie.mcdonald@ars.usda.gov
Program Support Assistant (Office Automation)
Peggy Morgan .... (770) 228-7254
E-mail: Peggy.Tubertini@ars.usda.gov

U.S. National Poultry Research Center
950 College Station Road, Athens, GA 30605
Tel: (706) 546-3152 Fax: (706) 546-3367

Center Director **Eileen Thacker PhD** .... (706) 546-3541
Room 352, Athens, GA 30605 Fax: (706) 546-3116
Location Administrative Officer **(Vacant)** Room 106 ..... (706) 546-3029
Bacterial Epidemiology and Antimicrobial Research
Unit Leader **(Vacant)** .... (706) 546-3685
Egg Safety and Quality Research Unit Leader
Dr. Richard Gast .... (706) 546-3445
Poultry Microbiological Safety and Processing
Research Unit Leader **(Vacant)** Room 553 .... (706) 546-3549
Quality and Safety Assessment Research Unit Leader
Dr. Kurt Lawrence .... (706) 546-3527
Research Food Technologist **Dr. Deana R. Jones** ...... (706) 546-3486
Toxicology and Mycotoxin Research Unit Leader
Dr. Charles W. Bacon Room 352 .... (706) 546-3158
Fax: (706) 546-3116
Webmaster **Calvin Williams** .... (706) 546-3547
E-mail: calvin.williams@ars.usda.gov

Southeast Poultry Research Laboratory (SEPRL)
934 College Station Road, Athens, GA 30605
Tel: (706) 546-3434 Fax: (706) 546-3161

Director **Dr. David E. Swayne** .... (706) 546-3433
Endemic Poultry Viral Diseases Research Leader
Laszlo Zsak Room 14 .... (706) 546-3654
Exotic and Emerging Avian Viral Diseases Research
Leader **David L. Suarez** .... (706) 546-3479

Southeastern Fruit and Tree Nut Research Laboratory
21 Dunbar Road, Byron, GA 31008
Tel: (478) 956-6421 Fax: (478) 956-2929

Research Leader **Clive Brock** .... (912) 956-5656
E-mail: clive.brock@ars.usda.gov
Administrative Officer **Tracy George** .... (478) 956-6416
E-mail: tracy.george@ars.usda.gov
Plant Biologist **Bryan Blackburn** .... (478) 956-6404

Tifton Location
2316 Rainwater Road, Tifton, GA 31793
Tel: (229) 386-3504 Fax: (229) 386-7225

Location Coordinator
Timothy C. "Tim" Strickland PhD .... (229) 386-3664
Administrative Assistant **Amanda Cravens** .... (229) 386-3504
E-mail: Amanda.Cravens@ars.usda.gov
Administrative Officer **Deborah D. "Debbie" Padgett** ... (229) 386-3498
E-mail: debbie.padgett@ars.usda.gov
Information Technology Supervisory Specialist
Nathanael Flader .... (229) 386-3594
E-mail: nathanael.flader@ars.usda.gov
Purchasing Agent **Juan Gaytan** .... (229) 386-3496
E-mail: juan.gaytan@ars.usda.gov

Crop Protection and Management Research
USDA-ARS, CPMRU, 2747 Davis Road, Tifton, GA 31793
Tel: (229) 387-2330 Fax: (229) 387-2321

Supervisory Research Agronomist **(Vacant)** .... (229) 387-2330
Research Agronomist **Wiley C. "Carroll" Johnson** ...... (229) 387-2347
Education: Auburn BS; North Carolina State MS, PhD
Research Agronomist **(Vacant)** .... (229) 387-2343
Research Entomologist **Dawn Olson** .... (229) 387-2374
Education: Minnesota BS, PhD
Research Entomologist **Patricia G. "Glynn" Tillman** .... (229) 387-2375
Education: Augusta State BS; Georgia Southern MS; Texas A&M PhD
Research Entomologist **(Vacant)** .... (229) 387-2348
Research Geneticist **(Vacant)** .... (229) 386-3170
Research Plant Pathologist **Richard F. Davis** .... (229) 387-2341
Education: Auburn BS, MS; Illinois PhD
Research Plant Pathologist **Baozhu Guo** .... (229) 387-2334
Education: Shanxi U BS; Kentucky MS; LSU PhD
Research Plant Pathologist **Patricia Timper** .... (229) 387-2377
Education: UC Davis BS, MS, PhD
Program Support Assistant (Office Automation)
Deborah J. Osborne .... (229) 387-2330
Office Automation Clerk **(Vacant)** .... (229) 387-2332

Crop Genetics and Breeding Research
2316 Rainwater Road, Tifton, GA 31793
Tel: (229) 386-3353 Fax: (229) 391-3701

Supervisory Research Geneticist (Plants)
C. Corley Holbrook .... (229) 386-3176
E-mail: corley.holbrook@ars.usda.gov
Research Entomologist **Xinzhi Ni** .... (229) 387-2340
Research Geneticist **Karen Harris-Shultz** .... (229) 386-3906
Research Geneticist (Plants) **Joseph "Joe" Knoll** .... (229) 386-3189
E-mail: joe.knoll@ars.usda.gov
Research Geneticist (Plants)
William F. "Bill" Anderson .... (229) 386-3170
E-mail: bill.anderson@ars.usda.gov
Education: New Hampshire BS; North Carolina State MS, PhD
Program Support Assistant **Kathy W. Marchant** .... (229) 386-3176
E-mail: Kathy.Marchant@ars.usda.gov Fax: (229) 386-3437

Southeast Watershed Research
2316 Rainwater Road, Tifton, GA 31793
Tel: (229) 386-3515 Fax: (229) 386-7215

Supervisory Research Soil Scientist
Timothy C. "Tim" Strickland PhD .... (229) 386-3664
Research Chemist **Oliva Pisani** .... (229) 386-3390
Ecologist **Alisa Coffin** .... (229) 386-3665
Research Hydraulic Engineer **David D. "Dave" Bosch** ... (229) 386-3899
Research Hydraulic Engineer **Dinku Endale** .... (229) 386-3893
Biological Science Technician **Lorine Lewis** .... (229) 386-3277
Biological Science Technician **Thoris Green** .... (229) 386-3012
Office Automation Clerk **Shannon R. Giddens** .... (229) 387-2332
E-mail: Shannon.Giddens@ars.usda.gov

★ Presidential Appointment Requiring Senate Confirmation ☆ Presidential Appointment □ Schedule C Appointment ◇ Career Senior Foreign Service Appointment
● Career Senior Executive Service (SES) Appointment ○ Non-Career Senior Executive Service (SES) Appointment ■ Postal Career Executive Service

DEPARTMENTS

North Carolina

North Carolina State University Location
North Carolina State University, Box 7610, Raleigh, NC 27695-7610
Tel: (919) 515-2731 Fax: (919) 856-4712

Location Coordinator **Dr. David S. Marshall** .... (919) 515-6819
Administrative Officer **Audra Bowman** .... (919) 515-2731
E-mail: audra.bowman@ars.usda.gov

Food Science Research Unit
Box 7624, North Carolina State University, Raleigh, NC 27695-7631
Tel: (919) 513-7781 Fax: (919) 513-0180

Research Leader **Van-Den Truong** .... (919) 513-7781

Market Quality and Handling Research Unit
Box 7624, North Carolina State University, Raleigh, NC 27695-7631
Tel: (919) 515-6312 Fax: (919) 513-8023

Research Leader **(Vacant)** .... (919) 515-9108

Plant Science Research Unit
Gardner Hall, Box 7616, North Carolina State University, Raleigh, NC 27695-7616
Tel: (919) 515-6819 Fax: (919) 515-7716

Research Leader **Dr. David S. Marshall** .... (919) 515-6819
Program Support Assistant (Office Automation)
Rachel LaManna .... (919) 513-2037
E-mail: rachel.lamanna@ars.usda.gov

Soybean and Nitrogen Fixation Research Unit
3127 Ligon Street, Raleigh, NC 27607
Tel: (919) 515-2734 Fax: (919) 856-4598

Research Leader **Thomas Carter** .... (919) 513-1480

Puerto Rico

Tropical Agriculture Research Station
2200 P.A. Campos Avenue, Suite 201, Mayaguez, PR 00680-5470
Tel: (787) 831-3435 Fax: (787) 831-3386

Location Coordinator and Research Plant Physiologist
Dr. Ricardo Goenaga .... (787) 831-3435
Administrative Officer **Salvio Torres-Cardona** . . . (787) 831-3435 ext. 230
E-mail: salvio.torrescardona@ars.usda.gov
Secretary **Maribel Roldan** .... (787) 831-3435 ext. 227
E-mail: maribel.roldan@ars.usda.gov

South Carolina

Coastal Plains Soil, Water and Plant Research Center
2611 West Lucas Street, Florence, SC 29501-1242
Tel: (843) 669-5203 Fax: (843) 669-6970

Research Leader **Dr. Ariel Szogi** .... (843) 669-5203 ext. 101
Information Technology Specialist
Dean E. Evans .... (843) 669-5203 ext. 114
E-mail: dean.evans@ars.usda.gov
Research Geneticist
Benjamin Todd Campbell .... (843) 669-5203 ext. 142
Fax: (843) 662-3110
Research Soil Scientist **Gilbert C. Sigua** .... (843) 669-5203 ext. 105
Administrative Officer **James Dann** .... (843) 669-5203 ext. 103

U.S. Vegetable Laboratory
2700 Savannah Highway, Charleston, SC 29414
Tel: (843) 402-5300 Fax: (843) 573-4715

Director/Research Leader **Mark W. Farnham** .... (843) 402-5301
Administrative Officer **Shelby Good** .... (843) 402-5302
E-mail: shelby.good@ars.usda.gov
Research Plant Pathologist **Kai Ling** .... (843) 402-5313
Fax: (843) 573-4715
Plant Pathologist **William Rutter** Room 207 .... (843) 402-5317

Arkansas

Arkansas Children's Nutrition Center (ACNC)
15 Children's Way, Little Rock, AR 72202
Tel: (501) 364-2785 Fax: (501) 364-2818

Director **Sean H. Adams PhD** .... (501) 364-2785
Education: UC Santa Cruz MS

Harry K. Dupree Stuttgart National Aquaculture Research Center
2955 Highway 130 East, Stuttgart, AR 72160
Tel: (870) 672-8274 Fax: (870) 673-7710

Center Director/Research Leader **Carl D. Webster** .... (870) 672-8267
Research Fish Biologist **Miles Lange** .... (870) 673-4483
Research Fish Biologist
Bartholomew W. "Bart" Green .... (870) 672-8275
Research Fish Biologist **(Vacant)** .... (870) 673-4483 ext. 286
Fax: (870) 673-7710
Research Physiologist (Animals) **Jason Abernathy** ...... (870) 672-8278
Research Physiologist (Animals)
Steven D. "Steve" Rawles .... (870) 672-8270
Fish Biologist **Matthew E. McEntire** .... (870) 672-8268
Geneticist (Animals) **Adam Fuller** .... (870) 672-8263
Microbiologist **Bradley Farmer** .... (870) 672-8262
Research Toxicologist **David "Dave" Straus** .... (870) 672-8265

Dale Bumpers National Rice Research Center (DBNRRC)
2890 Highway 130 East, Stuttgart, AR 72160
Tel: (870) 672-9300 Fax: (870) 673-7581

Director **Dr. Anna Myers McClung PhD** .... (870) 672-6129
E-mail: anna.mcclung@ars.usda.gov
Program Support Assistant - Office Automation
Floyd "Glen" Beedle .... (870) 672-6138
E-mail: floyd.beedle@ars.usda.gov

Dale Bumpers Small Farms Research Center
6883 South State Highway 23, Booneville, AR 72927
Tel: (479) 675-3834 Fax: (479) 675-2940

Research Leader **Phillip Owens** .... (479) 675-3834

Poultry Production and Product Safety Research Unit
0-303 Poultry Science Center, University of Arkansas, Fayetteville, AR 72701-1201
Tel: (479) 575-2654 Fax: (479) 575-4202

Research Leader **Dr. Ann M. "Annie" Donoghue** .... (479) 575-2413
Education: San Diego State 1983 BS; Texas A&M 1986 MS; Uniformed Services 1991 PhD
Program Support Assistant (Office Automation)
Lara A. Baker .... (479) 575-2654
E-mail: lara.baker@ars.usda.gov

Alabama

Aquatic Animal Health Research Unit
990 Wire Road, Auburn, AL 36832
Tel: (334) 887-3741 Fax: (334) 887-2983

Research Leader **Benjamin H. Beck** .... (334) 887-3741
Fax: (334) 887-2983
Veterinarian Medical Officer/Animal Care and United States Program Manager
John Paul "Johnny" Shelley .... (334) 887-3741
E-mail: john.shelley@ars.usda.gov Fax: (334) 887-2383
Program Support Assistant
Patricia E. Hodnett .... (334) 887-3741 ext. 110
E-mail: patricia.hodnett@ars.usda.gov
Purchasing Agent **(Vacant)** .... (334) 821-1700 ext. 41

National Soil Dynamics Laboratory
411 South Donahue Drive, Auburn, AL 36832
Tel: (334) 887-8596 Fax: (334) 887-8597

Supervisory Soil Scientist **Henry A. "Allen" Torbert** ..... (334) 844-3979

★ Presidential Appointment Requiring Senate Confirmation ☆ Presidential Appointment □ Schedule C Appointment ☆ Career Senior Foreign Service Appointment
● Career Senior Executive Service (SES) Appointment ○ Non-Career Senior Executive Service (SES) Appointment ■ Postal Career Executive Service

DEPARTMENTS

Louisiana

Honey Bee Breeding Genetics and Physiology Research Unit
1157 Ben Hur Road, Baton Rouge, LA 70820-5502
Tel: (225) 767-9280 Fax: (225) 766-9212

Research Leader **(Vacant)** . . . . (225) 767-9281
Program Support Assistant
Sandra L. "Sandy" Hineman . . . . (225) 767-9280
E-mail: sandy.hineman@ars.usda.gov
Supervisory Research Entomologist
Robert G. "Bob" Danka . . . . (225) 767-9294
Research Entomologist **Lilia I. De Guzman** . . . . (225) 767-9282
Research Entomologist **Frank D. Rinkevich** . . . . (225) 767-9291
Research Entomologist **(Vacant)** . . . . (225) 767-9293
Research Molecular Biologist **Lanie Bourgeois** . . . . (225) 767-9299
Research Molecular Biologist
Michael Simone-Finstrom . . . . (225) 767-9293
Research Molecular Biologist **(Vacant)** . . . . (225) 767-9284
Biological Science Aid **Natalie Martin** . . . . (225) 767-9280
Fax: (225) 766-9212
Biological Science Aid **Frederick Ziegler** . . . . (225) 767-9280
Fax: (225) 766-9212

Sugarcane Research Unit
5883 USDA Road, Houma, LA 70360
Tel: (985) 872-5042 Fax: (985) 868-8369

Research Leader/Supervisory Research Plant
Pathologist **Michael P Grisham** . . . . (985) 853-3172 ext. 172

Southern Regional Research Center (SRRC)
1100 Robert E. Lee Boulevard, New Orleans, LA 70124
Tel: (504) 286-4200 Fax: (504) 286-4419

● Director **Deepak Bhatnagar** . . . . (504) 286-4214
Fax: (504) 286-4234
Cotton Program Coordinator
Dr. Thomas E. "Ed" Cleveland . . . . (504) 286-4214
Fax: (504) 286-4234
Supervisory General Engineer **(Vacant)** . . . . (504) 427-7217
Fax: (504) 286-4318
Administrative Officer **Janell M. Becker** . . . . (504) 286-4311
E-mail: janell.becker@ars.usda.gov Fax: (504) 286-4221
Librarian **Suhad K. Wojkowski** . . . . (504) 286-4288
E-mail: suhad.wojkowski@ars.usda.gov Fax: (504) 286-4396
Safety and Occupational Health Specialist **(Vacant)** . . . . . . (504) 286-4395
Fax: (504) 286-4416
Human Resources Assistant (Office Automation)
Jocelyn D. Mack . . . . (504) 286-4415
E-mail: jocelyn.mack@ars.usda.gov

Mississippi

Thad Cochran Southern Horticultural Laboratory
810 Highway 26 West, Poplarville, MS 39470
Mail: P.O. Box 287, Poplarville, MS 39470
Tel: (601) 403-8750 Fax: (601) 795-4965

Research Leader **Dr. John J. Adamczyk, Jr.** . . . . (601) 403-8754
Education: Wisconsin 1992 BS; Clemson 1994 MS; LSU 1998 PhD
Administrative Officer **(Vacant)** . . . . (601) 403-8755

Crop Science Research Laboratory
R. W. Harned Building, 810 Highway 12 East,
Room 106, Mississippi State, MS 39762
Mail: P.O. Box 5367, Mississippi State, MS 39762-5367
Tel: (662) 320-7387 Fax: (662) 320-7528

Director/Location Coordinator
Dr. Johnie Norton Jenkins . . . . (662) 320-7386
Secretary (Office Automation) **Stephanie S. Pitts** . . . . . (662) 325-2733
E-mail: stephanie.pitts@ars.usda.gov

Corn Host Plant Resistance Research Unit
Dorman Hall, MSU, Room 347, Mississippi State, MS 39762
Mail: P.O. Box 5367, Mississippi State, MS 39762-5367
Tel: (662) 325-2735 Fax: (662) 325-8441

Research Leader **Dr. William Paul Williams** . . . . (662) 325-2735

Genetics and Sustainable Agriculture Research Unit
R. W. Harned Building, 810 Highway 12 East,
Room 106, Mississippi State, MS 39762
Mail: P.O. Box 5367, Mississippi State, MS 39762-5367
Tel: (662) 320-7387 Fax: (662) 320-7528

Research Leader **Dr. Johnie Norton Jenkins** . . . . (662) 320-7386
Secretary (Office Automation) **Stephanie S. Pitts** . . . . . (662) 325-2733
E-mail: stephanie.pitts@ars.usda.gov

Poultry Research Unit
USDA, ARS, Poultry Research Unit, 606 Spring Street,
Starkville, MS 39759
Mail: P.O. Box 5367, Mississippi State, MS 39762-5367
Tel: (662) 320-7479 Fax: (662) 320-7589

Research Leader **Scott Branton** . . . . (662) 320-7478
Secretary **Melanie Carter** . . . . (662) 320-7501
E-mail: melanie.carter@ars.usda.gov

Jamie Whitten Delta States Research Center - Stoneville (MS) (JWDSRC)
141 Experiment Station Road, Stoneville, MS 38776
Mail: P.O. Box 225, Stoneville, MS 38776-0225
Tel: (662) 686-5326 Fax: (662) 686-9406

Location Coordinator **(Vacant)** . . . . (662) 686-5206
Administrative Officer **Caroline F. "Carlean" Horton** . . . . (662) 686-5424
E-mail: carlean.horton@ars.usda.gov
Financial Technician **Jessica Harrell** . . . . (662) 686-5303
Financial Technician **Kelly Casavechia** . . . . (662) 686-3030
Human Resources Assistant **(Vacant)** . . . . (662) 686-5239
Information Technology Specialist **Mitzi Dean** . . . . (662) 686-5305
E-mail: mitzi.dean@ars.usda.gov Fax: (662) 686-5373
Office Automation Assistant . . . . (662) 686-3000
Purchasing Agent **Jessica Pacheco** . . . . (662) 686-5296
E-mail: jessica.pacheco@ars.usda.gov
Supply Technician **Gloria Williams** . . . . (662) 686-5227

National Sedimentation Laboratory (NSL)
598 McElroy Drive, P.O. Box 1157, Oxford, MS 38655
Tel: (662) 232-2900 Fax: (662) 281-5713

Location Coordinator **Martin A. Locke PhD** . . . . (662) 232-2908
Education: Southwest Missouri State 1976 BSB, 1982 BSAg;
Missouri 1984 MS; Texas A&M 1987 PhD

Natural Products Utilization Research Unit
P.O. Box 8048, University, MS 38677
Tel: (662) 915-1036 Fax: (662) 915-1035

Research Leader **Stephen O. Duke** . . . . (662) 915-1036

Watershed Physical Processes Research Unit
598 McElroy Drive, P.O. Box 1157, Oxford, MS 38655
Tel: (662) 232-2996 Fax: (662) 281-5706

Research Leader **Dr. Seth Dabney** . . . . (662) 232-2975

Water Quality and Ecology Research Unit
598 McElroy Drive, P.O. Box 1157, Oxford, MS 38655
Tel: (662) 232-2917 Fax: (662) 232-2988

Research Leader **Martin A. Locke PhD** . . . . (662) 232-2908
Education: Southwest Missouri State 1976 BSB, 1982 BSAg;
Missouri 1984 MS; Texas A&M 1987 PhD

National Agricultural Statistics Service (NASS)

South Agriculture Building, 1400 Independence Avenue, SW,
Washington, DC 20250
Tel: (202) 720-2707
Tel: (800) 727-9540 (National Agricultural Statistics Hotline)
Fax: (202) 690-2090 (Headquarters) E-mail: nass@nass.usda.gov
Internet: www.nass.usda.gov

Eastern Field Operations
Director **Jay V. Johnson** . . . . (202) 720-3638
Education: Penn State 1989 BS; North Carolina State 1997 MS

(continued on next page)

★ Presidential Appointment Requiring Senate Confirmation ☆ Presidential Appointment ☐ Schedule C Appointment ◇ Career Senior Foreign Service Appointment
● Career Senior Executive Service (SES) Appointment ○ Non-Career Senior Executive Service (SES) Appointment ■ Postal Career Executive Service

DEPARTMENTS

Eastern Field Operations *(continued)*

Secretary **Brenda J. Edgerton** .... (202) 720-8220
E-mail: brenda.edgerton@nass.usda.gov

Delta Region
10800 Financial Centre Parkway, Suite 110, Little Rock, AR 72211
Tel: (501) 228-9926 Tel: (800) 327-2970 Fax: (855) 270-2705
E-mail: nassrfodlr@nass.usda.gov

Regional Director **Eugene Young** .... (501) 228-9926
Deputy Regional Director **Jill Bishop** .... (501) 228-9926
E-mail: jill.bishop@usda.gov
Deputy Regional Director **Michael Klamm** .... (501) 228-9926

Arkansas Field Office
10800 Financial Centre Parkway, Suite 110, Little Rock, AR 72211
Tel: (501) 228-9926 Fax: (855) 270-2705 E-mail: nass-ar@nass.usda.gov

State Statistician **(Vacant)** .... (501) 228-9926

Louisiana Field Office
5825 Florida Boulevard, Room 1179, Baton Rouge, LA 70806
Tel: (800) 256-4485 Fax: (888) 922-0744 E-mail: nass-la@nass.usda.gov

State Statistician **Kathy Broussard** .... (225) 922-1362
E-mail: kathy.broussard@nass.usda.gov

Mississippi Field Office
121 North Jefferson Street, Suite 230, Jackson, MS 39201
Mail: P.O. Box 980, Jackson, MS 39205-0980
Tel: (601) 359-1259 Fax: (601) 965-5622

State Statistician **Esmerelda Dickson** .... (601) 359-1259
E-mail: esmerelda.dickson@nass.usda.gov

Eastern Mountain Region
601 West Broadway, Louisville, KY 40202
P.O. Box 1120, Louisville, KY 40201
Tel: (800) 928-5277 Fax: (855) 270-2708
E-mail: nassrfoemr@nass.usda.gov

Regional Director **David Knopf** .... (502) 582-5260
E-mail: david.knopf@nass.usda.gov
Deputy Regional Director **Barry Adams** .... (800) 928-5277
E-mail: barry.adams@usda.gov
Deputy Regional Director **James Scott Lemmons** ...... (502) 582-5293
E-mail: scott_lemmons@nass.usda.gov

Kentucky Field Office
Gene Snyder Courthouse, 601 West Broadway,
Room 645, Louisville, KY 40202
Mail: P.O. Box 1120, Louisville, KY 40201
Tel: (502) 582-5293 Tel: (800) 928-5277 Fax: (855) 270-2708
E-mail: nassrfoemr@nass.usda.gov

State Statistician **(Vacant)** .... (502) 582-5293

North Carolina Field Office
2 West Edenton Street, Raleigh, NC 27601
Mail: P.O. Box 27767, Raleigh, NC 27611
Tel: (919) 856-4394 Fax: (919) 856-4139 E-mail: ncagstat@ncagr.gov

State Statistician **Dee Webb** .... (919) 856-4394
E-mail: dee.webb@nass.usda.gov
Administrative Technician **(Vacant)** .... (919) 856-4394

Tennessee Field Office
Holeman Office Building, Ellington Agricultural Center,
440 Hogan Road, Nashville, TN 37220-1626
Mail: P.O. Box 41505, Nashville, TN 37204-1505
Tel: (615) 781-5300 Fax: (615) 781-5303

State Statistician **Debra K. Kenerson** .... (615) 781-5300
E-mail: debra.kenerson@nass.usda.gov

Virginia Field Office
102 Governor Street, Room LL20, Richmond, VA 23219
P.O. Box 1659, Richmond, VA 23218-1659
Tel: (804) 771-2493 Fax: (804) 771-2651 E-mail: nass-va@nass.usda.gov

State Statistician **Herman Ellison** .... (804) 771-2493
E-mail: herman.ellison@nass.usda.gov

West Virginia Field Office
Building 2, 217 Gus R. Douglass Lane,
Room 203, Charleston, WV 25312
Tel: (304) 357-5123 Tel: (800) 535-7088 Fax: (855) 270-2708
E-mail: nass-wv@nass.usda.gov

State Statistician **Charmaine Wilson** .... (304) 357-5123
E-mail: charmaine.wilson@nass.usda.gov

Great Lakes Region
3001 Coolidge Road, Suite 400, East Lansing, MI 48823
Tel: (800) 453-7501 Fax: (855) 270-2709
E-mail: nassrfoglr@nass.usda.gov

Regional Director **Marlo D. Johnson** .... (800) 453-7501
E-mail: marlo.johnson@nass.usda.gov
Education: Alcorn State 1993; Mississippi State 1994 MS
Deputy Regional Director **Kiflam "Kif" Hurlbut** .... (800) 453-7501
E-mail: kiflam.hurlbut@nass.usda.gov
Deputy Regional Director **Ty Kalaus** .... (800) 453-7501
E-mail: ty.kalaus@nass.usda.gov

Ohio Field Office
8995 East Main Street, Reynoldsburg, OH 43068
Mail: P.O. Box 686, Reynoldsburg, OH 43068-0686
Tel: (614) 728-2100 Tel: (800) 858-8144 Fax: (855) 270-2709
E-mail: nass-oh@nass.usda.gov

State Statistician **Cheryl Turner** .... (614) 728-2100
E-mail: cheryl.turner@nass.usda.gov
Education: Auburn BBA

Michigan Field Office
3001 Coolidge Road, Suite 400, East Lansing, MI 48823
Tel: (517) 324-5300 Fax: (517) 324-5299 E-mail: nass-mi@nass.usda.gov

State Statistician **Marlo D. Johnson** .... (517) 324-5300
E-mail: marlo.johnson@nass.usda.gov
Education: Alcorn State 1993; Mississippi State 1994 MS

Indiana Field Office
1435 Win Hentschel Boulevard, Suite 110, West Lafayette, IN 47906-4145
Tel: (765) 494-8371 Fax: (765) 494-4315 E-mail: nass-in@nass.usda.gov
Internet: www.nass.usda.gov/in

State Statistician **Greg Matli** .... (765) 494-8371
E-mail: greg.matli@nass.usda.gov

Northeastern Region
4050 Crums Mill Road, Suite 203, Harrisburg, PA 17112
Tel: (717) 787-3904 Fax: (855) 270-2719
E-mail: nassrfoner@nass.usda.gov

Regional Director **King Whetstone** .... (717) 787-3904
E-mail: king.whetstone@nass.usda.gov
Deputy Regional Director **Robert "Bob" McEwen** ...... (717) 787-3904
E-mail: bob.mcewen@nass.usda.gov
Deputy Regional Director **Kevin Pautler** .... (717) 787-3904
E-mail: kevin_pautler@nass.usda.gov
Education: Southern Illinois BS

Delaware Field Office
Delaware Department of Agriculture Building,
2320 South DuPont Highway, Dover, DE 19901-5515
Tel: (302) 698-4537 Tel: (800) 282-8685 Fax: (302) 697-4450
E-mail: nass-de@nass.usda.gov

State Statistician **Dale Hawks** .... (410) 841-5740
E-mail: dale.hawks@nass.usda.gov

Maryland Field Office
50 Harry S. Truman Parkway, Suite 210, Annapolis, MD 21401
Tel: (410) 841-5740 Fax: (410) 841-5755
E-mail: nass-md@nass.usda.gov Internet: www.nass.usda.gov/md

State Statistician **Dale Hawks** .... (410) 841-5740
E-mail: dale.hawks@nass.usda.gov

New England Field Office
53 Pleasant Street, 2nd Floor, Concord, NH 03301
Tel: (603) 224-9639 Fax: (603) 225-1434
Internet: www.nass.usda.gov/Statistics_by_State/New_England
Areas Covered: CT, ME, MA, NH, RI, VT

Director **Gary Keough** . . . . (603) 224-9639 ext. 3129
E-mail: gary.keough@nass.usda.gov

New Jersey Field Office
Health and Agriculture Building, South Warren Street,
Room 205, Trenton, NJ 08625
P.O. Box 330, Trenton, NJ 08625-9825
Tel: (503) 308-0404 Fax: (609) 633-9231 E-mail: nass-nj@nass.usda.gov

State Statistician **Bruce Eklund** . . . . (503) 308-0404
E-mail: bruce.eklund@nass.usda.gov

New York Field Office
10B Airline Drive, Albany, NY 12235
Tel: (518) 457-5570 Tel: (800) 821-1276 Fax: (800) 591-3834
E-mail: nass-ny@nass.usda.gov

State Statistician **Blair L. Smith** . . . . (518) 457-5570
E-mail: blair.smith@nass.usda.gov

Pennsylvania Field Office
4050 Crums Mill Road, Suite 203, Harrisburg, PA 17112
Tel: (717) 787-3904 Fax: (717) 782-4011 E-mail: nass-pa@nass.usda.gov

State Statistician **King Whetstone** . . . . (717) 787-3904
E-mail: king.whetstone@nass.usda.gov

Southern Plains Region
300 East 8th Street, Austin, TX 78767-0070
Tel: (512) 501-3200 Fax: (855) 270-2725
E-mail: nassrfomtr@nass.usda.gov
Internet: www.nass.usda.gov/Statistics_by_State/Texas

Regional Director **Wilbert C. "Wil" Hundl, Jr.** . . . . (512) 501-3200
E-mail: wil.hundl@nass.usda.gov
Deputy Regional Director **Quentin Hart** . . . . (512) 501-3200
E-mail: quentin_hart@nass.usda.gov
Deputy Regional Director **Joel Moore** . . . . (512) 501-3200
E-mail: joel.moore@nass.usda.gov

Oklahoma Field Office
Agriculture Building, 2800 Lincoln Boulevard,
3rd Floor, Oklahoma City, OK 73105
Tel: (405) 415-8850 Fax: (405) 528-2296 E-mail: nass-ok@nass.usda.gov

State Statistician **Troy Marshall** . . . . (405) 415-8850

Texas Field Office
Federal Building, 300 East Eighth Street,
Room 500, Austin, TX 78701
Mail: P.O. Box 70, Austin, TX 78767-0070
Tel: (512) 501-3200 Fax: (855) 270-2725
E-mail: nassrfospr@nass.usda.gov
Internet: www.nass.usda.gov/Statistics_by_State/Texas

State Statistician **Wilbert C. "Wil" Hundl, Jr.** . . . . (512) 501-3200
E-mail: wil.hundl@nass.usda.gov

Southern Region
355 East Hancock Avenue, Suite 100, Athens, GA 30601-2768
Tel: (706) 713-5400 Tel: (800) 253-4419 Fax: (855) 271-9801

Regional Director **James "Jim" Ewing** . . . . (706) 713-5400
E-mail: jim_ewing@nass.usda.gov
Deputy Regional Director **Jacqueline Moore** . . . . (706) 713-5400
E-mail: jacqueline.moore@nass.usda.gov
Deputy Regional Director **Erika White** . . . . (706) 713-5400

Alabama Field Office
4121 Carmichael Road, Suite 200, Montgomery, AL 36106-2872
Mail: P.O. Box 240578, Montgomery, AL 36124-0578
Tel: (334) 279-3555 Fax: (334) 279-3590 E-mail: nass-al@nass.usda.gov

State Statistician **Cynthia Price** . . . . (334) 279-3555
E-mail: cynthia.price@nass.usda.gov
Survey Coordinator **Richard S. "Rick" Geesey** . . . . (334) 279-3555

Florida Field Office
2290 Lucien Way, Suite 300, Maitland, FL 32751
Tel: (407) 648-6013 Fax: (855) 271-9801 E-mail: nass-fl@nass.usda.gov
Internet: www.nass.usda.gov/fl

State Statistician **Mark E. Hudson** . . . . (407) 648-6013
E-mail: mark.hudson@nass.usda.gov

Georgia Field Office
Stephens Federal Building, 355 East Hancock Avenue,
Suite 100, Athens, GA 30601
Tel: (800) 253-4419 Tel: (706) 546-2236 Fax: (855) 271-9801
E-mail: nass-ga@nass.usda.gov

State Statistician **James "Jim" Ewing** . . . . (706) 713-5400
E-mail: jim_ewing@nass.usda.gov

South Carolina Field Office
208 Wholesale Lane, West Columbia, SC 29172
Tel: (803) 734-2506 Fax: (855) 271-9801 E-mail: nass-sc@nass.usda.gov
Internet: www.nass.usda.gov/sc

State Statistician **Edward "Eddie" Wells** . . . . (803) 734-2506
E-mail: edward.wells@nass.usda.gov
Administrative Technician **(Vacant)** . . . . (803) 765-5334

Western Field Operations
Director (Acting) **Jay V. Johnson** . . . . (202) 720-8220
Education: Penn State 1989 BS; North Carolina State 1997 MS
Secretary **Brenda Payne** . . . . (202) 720-8220
E-mail: Brenda.Payne@nass.usda.gov

Heartland Region
9700 Page Avenue, Suite 400, St. Louis, MO 63132
Tel: (314) 595-9594 Fax: (855) 270-2717
E-mail: nassrfohlr@nass.usda.gov

Regional Director **Brad Summa** . . . . (314) 595-9594
E-mail: brad.summa@nass.usda.gov
Deputy Regional Director **Bryan Durham** . . . . (314) 595-9594
Deputy Regional Director **Steven Maliszewski** . . . . (314) 595-9594

Illinois Field Office
Illinois Department of Agriculture Building, 801 Sangamon Avenue,
Room 62, Springfield, IL 62702
Tel: (217) 492-9606 Fax: (855) 270-2717
E-mail: nassrfohlr@nass.usda.gov

State Statistician **Mark Schleusener** . . . . (217) 524-9606
E-mail: mark.schleusener@nass.usda.gov Fax: (855) 270-2717

Missouri Field Office
601 Bus Loop 70 West, Suite 240, Columbia, MO 65203
Mail: Box L, Columbia, MO 65205
Tel: (573) 876-0950 Fax: (855) 270-2717
E-mail: nass-mo@nass.usda.gov

State Statistician **Robert "Bob" Garino** . . . . (573) 876-0950
E-mail: bob.garino@nass.usda.gov

Mountain Region
PO Box150969, Lakewood, CO 80215-0969
Building 67, One Denver Federal Center, Denver, CO 80225
Tel: (720) 787-3150 Fax: (866) 314-4029
E-mail: nassrfomtr@nass.usda.gov

Regional Director **William R. "Bill" Meyer** . . . . (720) 787-3150
E-mail: bill_meyer@nass.usda.gov
Deputy Regional Director **Leslee Lohrenz** . . . . (720) 787-3150
E-mail: leslee.lohrenz@nass.usda.gov
Deputy Regional Director **Rodger Ott** . . . . (720) 787-3150
E-mail: rodger.ott@nass.usda.gov

Arizona Field Office
230 North First Avenue, Suite 302-A, Phoenix, AZ 85003
Tel: (602) 280-8850 Fax: (602) 280-8897

State Statistician **Dave DeWalt** . . . . (602) 280-8860
E-mail: dave.dewalt@nass.usda.gov

DEPARTMENTS

★ Presidential Appointment Requiring Senate Confirmation ☆ Presidential Appointment □ Schedule C Appointment ◇ Career Senior Foreign Service Appointment
● Career Senior Executive Service (SES) Appointment ○ Non-Career Senior Executive Service (SES) Appointment ■ Postal Career Executive Service

Colorado Field Office
Building 67, One Denver Federal Center, Denver, CO 80225
Tel: (720) 787-3150 Fax: (866) 314-4029 E-mail: nass-co@nass.usda.gov
Internet: www.nass.usda.gov/co

State Statistician **William R. "Bill" Meyer** .... (303) 236-2300
Building 67, One Denver Federal Center,
Room 630, Denver, CO 80215
E-mail: bill_meyer@nass.usda.gov
Field Services Section Head **(Vacant)** .... (303) 236-2300

Montana Field Office
Max Baucus Federal Building, 10 West 15th Street,
Room 3100, Helena, MT 59626
Tel: (406) 441-1240 Fax: (406) 441-1250

State Statistician **Eric Sommer** .... (406) 389-3600
E-mail: eric.sommer@nass.usda.gov Fax: (406) 441-1250

New Mexico Field Office
505 South Main Street, Suite 114, Las Cruces, NM 88011
Tel: (575) 522-6023 Fax: (505) 522-7646
E-mail: nass-nm@nass.usda.gov

State Statistician **Longino Bustillos** .... (575) 522-6023
E-mail: longino.bustillos@nass.usda.gov

Utah Field Office
350 South Main Street, Room 100, Salt Lake City, UT 84101
Tel: (801) 524-5003 Fax: (801) 524-3090

State Statistician **John Hilton** .... (801) 524-5003
E-mail: john.hilton@nass.usda.gov
Tel: (800) 747-8522

Wyoming Field Office
308 West 21st Street, Suite 301, Cheyenne, WY 82001
Mail: P.O. Box 1148, Cheyenne, WY 82003
Tel: (307) 432-5600 ext. 1 Fax: (866) 314-4029
E-mail: nass-wy@nass.usda.gov

State Statistician **Rhonda Brandt** .... (307) 432-5600 ext. 1
E-mail: rhonda.brandt@nass.usda.gov

Northern Plains Region
100 Centennial Mall North, Room 263, Lincoln, NE 68508-3866
Tel: (402) 437-5541 Tel: (800) 582-6443 Fax: (855) 270-2720
E-mail: nassrfonpr@nass.usda.gov

Regional Director **Dean C. Groskurth** .... (402) 437-5541 ext. 5220
E-mail: dean_groskurth@nass.usda.gov
Deputy Regional Director **Patrick Boyle** .... (402) 437-5541 ext. 5515
E-mail: patrick.boyle@nass.usda.gov
Deputy Regional Director **Nicholas Streff** ..... (402) 437-5541 ext. 5514
E-mail: nicholas_streff@nass.usda.gov

Kansas Field Office
3705 Miller Parkway, Manhattan, KS 66503-7604
Tel: (800) 582-6443 Fax: (855) 270-2720 E-mail: nass-ks@nass.usda.gov

State Statistician **(Vacant)** .... (800) 582-6443

Nebraska Field Office
Federal Building and U.S. Courthouse, 100 Centennial Mall North,
Room 263, Lincoln, NE 68508
Tel: (402) 437-5541 Fax: (855) 270-2720

State Statistician **Dean C. Groskurth** .... (402) 437-5541
E-mail: dean_groskurth@nass.usda.gov

North Dakota Field Office
Research 2 Bldg., 1805 NDSU Research Park Dr., Fargo, ND 58102
Tel: (800) 582-6443 Fax: (855) 270-2720 E-mail: nass-nd@nass.usda.gov

State Statistician **Darin Jantzi** .... (800) 582-6443
E-mail: darin.jantzi@nass.usda.gov

South Dakota Field Office
4301 W 57th Street, Sioux Falls, SD 57108
Tel: (800) 582-6443 Fax: (855) 270-2720 E-mail: nass-sd@nass.usda.gov

State Statistician **Erik Gerlach** .... (800) 582-6443

Northwest Region
P.O. Box 609, Olympia, WA 98507-0609
Tel: (360) 709-2400 Tel: (800) 435-5883 Fax: (855) 270-2721
E-mail: nassrfonwr@nass.usda.gov

Regional Director **Christopher A. "Chris" Mertz** .... (360) 709-2400
E-mail: chris.mertz@nass.usda.gov
Deputy Regional Director **Steve Anderson** .... (360) 709-2400
E-mail: steve.anderson@nass.usda.gov
Deputy Regional Director **Dennis Koong** .... (360) 709-2400
E-mail: dennis_koong@nass.usda.gov

Alaska Field Office
1150 South Colony Way, Suite 11, Palmer, AK 99645
P.O. Box 799, Palmer, AK 99645
Tel: (907) 745-4272 Fax: (855) 270-2721

State Statistician **Suzan "Sue" Benz** .... (907) 745-4272
E-mail: suzan.benz@nass.usda.gov

Idaho Field Office
550 W Fort Street, Suite 180, Boise, ID 83724
Mail: P.O. Box 1699, Boise, ID 83701
Tel: (208) 334-1507 Fax: (208) 334-1114 E-mail: nass-id@nass.usda.gov

State Statistician **Randy Welk** .... (208) 334-1507
Tel: (800) 691-9987

Oregon Field Office
805 SW Broadway, Suite 910, Portland, OR 97205
Tel: (360) 890-3300 Fax: (503) 326-2549 E-mail: nass-or@nass.usda.gov

State Statistician **David "Dave" Losh** .... (503) 326-2131
E-mail: dave.losh@nass.usda.gov

Washington Field Office
112 Henry Street NE, Suite 201, Olympia, WA 98506
Mail: P.O. Box 609, Olympia, WA 98507-0609
Tel: (360) 709-2400 Fax: (360) 902-2091
E-mail: nass-wa@nass.usda.gov Internet: www.nass.usda.gov/wa

State Statistician **Christopher A. "Chris" Mertz** .... (360) 709-2400

Pacific Region
650 Capitol Mall, Suite 6-100, Sacramento, CA 95814
P.O. Box 1258, Sacramento, CA 95812-1258
Tel: (916) 738-6600 Tel: (800) 851-1127 Fax: (855) 270-2722
E-mail: nassrfopcr@nass.usda.gov

Regional Director (Acting) **Curt Stock** .... (916) 738-6600
Deputy Regional Director **Curt Stock** .... (916) 738-6600
Deputy Regional Director **Brenda Hill** .... (916) 738-6600

California Field Office
650 Capitol Mall, Suite 6-100, Sacramento, CA 95814
Mail: P.O. Box 1258, Sacramento, CA 95812-1258
Tel: (916) 498-5161 Fax: (916) 498-5186 E-mail: nass-ca@nass.usda.gov

State Statistician **Christina S. "Chris" Messer** .... (916) 498-5161
E-mail: chris.messer@nass.usda.gov

Hawaii Field Office
300 Ala Moana Blvd, Suite 7-118, Honolulu, HI 96850
Tel: (808) 522-8080 Fax: (844) 332-7146 E-mail: nass-hi@nass.usda.gov

State Statistician **Kathy King** .... (808) 522-8080
E-mail: kathy.king@nass.usda.gov

Nevada Field Office
5600 Fox Avenue, Reno, NV 89506-1300
P.O. Box 8880, Reno, NV 89507
Tel: (775) 353-3714 Fax: (775) 972-6002 E-mail: nass-nv@nass.usda.gov

State Statistician **Scot Rumburg** .... (775) 353-3714
E-mail: scot.rumburg@nass.usda.gov

Upper Midwest Region
833 Federal Building, 210 Walnut Street, Des Moines, IA 50309-2123
Tel: (515) 776-3400 Tel: (515) 776-3400 Fax: (855) 271-9802
E-mail: nassrfoumr@nass.usda.gov

Regional Director **Greg Thessen** .... (515) 776-3400
E-mail: greg_thessen@nass.usda.gov

★ Presidential Appointment Requiring Senate Confirmation ☆ Presidential Appointment ☐ Schedule C Appointment ◇ Career Senior Foreign Service Appointment
● Career Senior Executive Service (SES) Appointment ○ Non-Career Senior Executive Service (SES) Appointment ■ Postal Career Executive Service

Upper Midwest Region *(continued)*

Deputy Regional Director **Cynthia "Cindy" Adamson** . . . (515) 776-3400
E-mail: cindy_adamson@nass.usda.gov
Deputy Regional Director **Douglas "Doug" Hartwig** . . . . (515) 776-3400
E-mail: dhartwig@nass.usda.gov

Iowa Field Office
Federal Building, 210 Walnut Street, Room 833, Des Moines, IA 50309
Tel: (515) 776-3400 Fax: (515) 284-4342 E-mail: nass-ia@nass.usda.gov

State Statistician **Greg Thessen** . . . . (515) 776-3400
E-mail: greg_thessen@nass.usda.gov

Minnesota Field Office
375 Jackson Street, Suite 610, St. Paul, MN 55101
Tel: (651) 728-3113 Fax: (855) 271-9802
E-mail: nass-mn@nass.usda.gov
Internet: www.nass.usda.gov/Statistics_by_State/Minnesota

State Statistician **Dan Lofthus** . . . . (651) 728-3113
E-mail: dan.lofthus@nass.usda.gov

Wisconsin Field Office
2811 Agriculture Drive, Madison, WI 53718-6777
Tel: (608) 224-4848 Fax: (800) 838-6277

State Statistician **Greg Bussler** . . . . (608) 224-4848
Webmaster **Adrien Joyner** . . . . (608) 224-4850
E-mail: adrien.joyner@nass.usda.gov

Rural Development (RD)

Jaime L. Whitten Building, 1400 Independence Avenue, SW,
Washington, DC 20250
Internet: www.rd.usda.gov

OFFICE OF THE ASSISTANT TO THE SECRETARY

Jamie L. Whitten Federal Building, 1400 Independence Avenue,
SW, Washington, DC 20250
Tel: (202) 720-4581 Fax: (202) 720-2080

Rural Development State Offices

Note: Within each Rural Development State office, under the supervision of the State Director, there are three sections: Rural Business-Cooperative Service, Rural Housing Service, and Rural Utilities Service. All three services are located at the same address and utilize the same telephone and facsimile numbers. The offices are responsible for: housing programs, utility programs, business-cooperative programs, and community development programs.

Alabama Rural Development State Office
Sterling Centre, 4121 Carmichael Road,
Suite 601, Montgomery, AL 36106-3683
Tel: (334) 279-3400 Fax: (855) 304-8456

□ State Director **Chris Beeker III** . . . . (334) 279-3400
E-mail: chris.beeker@al.usda.gov
Assistant to State Director **Beverly Helton** . . . . (334) 279-3441

Alaska Rural Development State Office
800 West Evergreen, Suite 201, Palmer, AK 99645
Tel: (907) 761-7705 Fax: (907) 761-7783
Internet: https://www.rd.usda.gov/ak

□ State Director **Jerry Ward** . . . . (907) 761-7705
E-mail: Jerry.Ward2@ak.usda.gov
Administrative Programs Director **Colleen J. Dow** . . . . . . (907) 761-7704
E-mail: colleen.dow@ak.usda.gov
Business Programs Director **Renee Johnson** . . . . (907) 761-7712
E-mail: renee.johnson@ak.usda.gov
Program Director (Acting) **Colleen J. Dow** . . . . (907) 761-7704
E-mail: colleen.dow@ak.usda.gov
Multi-Family Housing Program Director
Deborah Davis . . . . (907) 761-7740
E-mail: deborah.davis@ak.usda.gov
Public Affairs Director **(Vacant)** . . . . (907) 271-2424 ext. 125

Alaska Rural Development State Office *(continued)*

Director, Community Facilities and Sanitation
Programs **Tasha Deardorff** . . . . (907) 271-2424 ext. 118
E-mail: tasha.deardorff@ak.usda.gov

Arizona Rural Development State Office
230 North First Avenue, Suite 206, Phoenix, AZ 85003
Tel: (602) 280-8701 Fax: (855) 699-8035 Internet: www.rd.usda.gov/az

□ State Director
James Christopher "J. C." Sherman III . . . . (602) 280-8701
Administrative Programs Director **LaRoy Cadiz** . . . . (602) 280-8707
E-mail: laroy.cadiz@az.usda.gov
Business and Cooperative Programs Director
Gary Mack . . . . (602) 280-8717
E-mail: gary.mack@az.usda.gov
Community Programs Director **Jeff Hays** . . . . (928) 759-9301 ext. 103
Contract Program Manager **James Sowden** . . . . (602) 280-8713
Rural Housing Program Director (Acting) **Jeff Hays** . . . . . (520) 254-8101
E-mail: Jeff.Hays@az.usda.gov

Arkansas Rural Development State Office
Federal Building, 700 West Capitol Avenue,
Room 3416, Little Rock, AR 72201-3225
Tel: (501) 301-3200 Internet: https://www.rd.usda.gov/ar

□ State Director **David L. Branscum** . . . . (501) 301-3200
Education: Arkansas

California Rural Development State Office
430 G Street, Davis, CA 95616-4169
Tel: (530) 792-5800 Fax: (530) 792-5837 Internet: www.rd.usda.gov/ca

□ State Director **Kim Dolbow Vann** . . . . (530) 792-5800

Colorado Rural Development State Office
Denver Federal Center, Building 56, Room 2300, Denver, CO 80225
P.O. Box 25426, Denver, CO 80225
Tel: (720) 544-2903 Tel: (800) 659-9656 (Colorado Relay)
Fax: (866) 587-7607 Internet: www.rd.usda.gov/co

□ State Director **Sallie Clark** . . . . (720) 544-2903
E-mail: Sallie.Clark@co.usda.gov
Administrative Programs Director **Jeanne Watt** . . . . (720) 544-2910
E-mail: jeanne.watt@co.usda.gov
Business and Cooperative Programs Director
April Dahlager . . . . (720) 544-2909
E-mail: april.dahlager@co.usda.gov
Community Programs Director **James "Jim" Maras** . . . . (720) 544-2927
Single Family Housing Programs Director
Scott A. Wilson . . . . (720) 544-2929
E-mail: scott.wilson@co.usda.gov
Multi-Family Housing Programs Director
Susan McKitrick . . . . (720) 544-2952
E-mail: susan.mckitrick@co.usda.gov

Delaware - Maryland Rural Development State Office
1221 College Park Drive, Suite 200, Dover, DE 19904
Tel: (302) 857-3580 TTY: (302) 857-3585 Fax: (855) 389-2236

□ State Director **Denise Lovelady** . . . . (302) 857-3582
Assistant to the State Director **Kathy Beisner** . . . . (302) 857-3582
E-mail: Kathy.Beisner@de.usda.gov
Business and Cooperative Program Director
Letitia Nichols . . . . (302) 857-3628
E-mail: letitia.nichols@de.usda.gov
Community Program Director **(Vacant)** . . . . (302) 857-3625
Multi-Family Housing Program Coordinator
Jeff Williams . . . . (302) 857-3615
E-mail: jeff.williams2@de.usda.gov
Single Family Housing Program Director
Brad King . . . . (302) 857-3595 ext. 5
1260 Maryland Avenue, Fax: (855) 401-6645
Suite 100, Hagerstown, MD 21740
E-mail: brad.king@md.usda.gov
Water and Environmental Program Director **(Vacant)** . . . . . (302) 857-3580

DEPARTMENTS

★ Presidential Appointment Requiring Senate Confirmation ☆ Presidential Appointment □ Schedule C Appointment ◇ Career Senior Foreign Service Appointment
● Career Senior Executive Service (SES) Appointment ○ Non-Career Senior Executive Service (SES) Appointment ■ Postal Career Executive Service

DEPARTMENTS

Florida and U.S. Virgin Islands Rural Development State Office
4440 NW 25th Place, Gainesville, FL 32614
Tel: (352) 338-3402 TTY: (352) 338-3499 Fax: (352) 338-3405
Internet: www.rd.usda.gov/fl

□ State Director **Sydney Gruters** (352) 338-3411
Administrative Programs Director (Acting)
Christine Goddard (352) 338-3441
E-mail: Christine.Goddard@fl.usda.gov Fax: (352) 338-3405
Multi-Family Housing Director **Tim G. Rogers** (352) 338-3464
E-mail: tim.rogers@fl.usda.gov Fax: (352) 338-3405
Education: Kansas State BS
Rural Business-Cooperative Service Director
Christine Goddard (352) 338-3441
E-mail: Christine.Goddard@fl.usda.gov Fax: (352) 338-3452
Rural Utilities/Community Programs Director
Michael A. Langston (352) 338-3485
E-mail: michael.langston@fl.usda.gov Fax: (352) 338-3452
Single Family Housing Director **Daryl L. Cooper** (352) 338-3436
E-mail: daryl.cooper@fl.usda.gov Fax: (352) 338-3405
Public Affairs Coordinator **Michelle Jacobs** (352) 338-3419
E-mail: michelle.m.jacobs@fl.usda.gov
State Engineer **Steve Morris** (352) 338-3448
State Architect **John R. Secleter** (352) 338-3469

Georgia Rural Development State Office
Stephens Federal Building, 355 East Hancock Avenue,
Suite 300, Athens, GA 30601-2768
Tel: (706) 546-2162 Fax: (855) 452-0956 Internet: www.rd.usda.gov/ga

□ State Director **Joyce White** (706) 546-2162
Secretary to State Director **Jacqueline Tracy** (706) 552-2583
E-mail: jacqueline.tracy@ga.usda.gov
Assistant State Director **Donnie D. Thomas** (706) 546-2162
E-mail: donnie.thomas@ga.usda.gov
Education: Georgia BA; Piedmont Col MPA
Administrative Programs Director **Donna Graves** (706) 546-2173
E-mail: donna.graves@ga.usda.gov
Business and Cooperatives Program Director
Karen L. Davis (706) 546-2154
E-mail: karen.davis@ga.usda.gov Fax: (855) 452-0958
Community Programs Director **Jack Stanek** (706) 546-2171
E-mail: jack.stanek@ga.usda.gov Fax: (855) 452-0958
Management and Program Assistant
Phillip L. "Phil" Phillips (706) 552-2588
E-mail: phil.phillips@ga.usda.gov
Multi-Family Housing Program Director **Eric Hixson** (706) 546-2164
E-mail: eric.hixson@ga.usda.gov Fax: (855) 452-0959
Single Family Housing Director
Edward E. "Ed" Peace (706) 546-2169
E-mail: ed.peace@ga.usda.gov Fax: (855) 452-0960
Public Affairs and Web Content Manager
Deborah L. Callahan (706) 552-2595
E-mail: deborah.callahan@ga.usda.gov Fax: (706) 546-2152
Civil Rights Manager **(Vacant)** (706) 552-2588
Fax: (855) 577-0880

Hawaii Rural Development State Office
Federal Building, 154 Waianuenue Avenue,
Room 311, Hilo, HI 96720-2452
Tel: (808) 933-8380 Fax: (855) 878-2460
Internet: https://www.rd.usda.gov/hi

□ State Director **Gigi Jones** (808) 600-2937
E-mail: Gigi.Jones@hi.usda.gov
Education: Alaska 1996 BS
Business Programs Director **Denise M. Oda** (808) 933-8323
E-mail: denise.oda@hi.usda.gov
Community Programs Director (Acting)
Samantha Shimizu (808) 933-8307
Human Resources Manager
John Hiduchick-Nakayama (808) 933-8315
Rural Housing Programs Director **John Antonio** (808) 933-8318
E-mail: john.antonio@hi.usda.gov

Idaho Rural Development State Office
9713 West Barnes Drive, Suite A1, Boise, ID 83709
Tel: (208) 378-5600 Fax: (855) 505-1560
Internet: https://www.rd.usda.gov/id

□ State Director **Layne Bangerter** (208) 378-5600
Business Program Director **Daryl Moser** (208) 378-5615
Fax: (855) 505-1563
Community Program Director
David A. "Dave" Flesher (208) 378-5617
Fax: (855) 505-1564
Housing Program Director **Diane Lisa Allen** (208) 378-5629
E-mail: lisa.allen@id.usda.gov Fax: (855) 505-1562
Public Affairs Specialist **Beverly J. Fish** (208) 378-5627
E-mail: beverly.fish@id.usda.gov

Illinois Rural Development State Office
2118 West Park Court, Suite A, Champaign, IL 61821
Tel: (217) 403-6200 Fax: (855) 832-8691
Internet: https://www.rd.usda.gov/il

□ State Director **Douglas Wilson** (217) 403-6200
Assistant to the State Director **Molly K. Hammond** (217) 403-6203
Administrative Programs Director **Julie Wilson** (217) 403-6204
E-mail: julie.wilson@il.usda.gov Fax: (217) 403-6208
Business and Cooperatives Programs Director
Ronald M. "Ron" Firkins (217) 403-6217
E-mail: ronald.firkins@il.usda.gov Fax: (217) 403-6215
Community Programs Director **Mike Wallace** (217) 403-6209
E-mail: michael.wallace@il.usda.gov Fax: (217) 403-6215
Public Information Coordinator, Community and Economic Development Coordinator
Katherine O'Hara (217) 403-6205
E-mail: kate.ohara@il.usda.gov
Rural Housing Program Director **(Vacant)** (217) 403-6222
Fax: (217) 403-6231

Indiana Rural Development State Office
5975 Lakeside Boulevard, Indianapolis, IN 46278-1996
Tel: (317) 290-3100 Fax: (855) 541-9018 Internet: www.rd.usda.gov/in

□ State Director **Michael Reed Dora** (317) 290-3100
● Public Information Officer **(Vacant)** (317) 295-5770
● Business Programs Director **Robert Hill** (317) 295-5780 ext. 420
E-mail: r.hill@in.usda.gov
● Community Programs Director **Rochelle Owen** (317) 295-5767
E-mail: rochelle.owen@in.usda.gov
● Housing Director **Vincent Maloney** (317) 295-5774
E-mail: vincent.maloney@in.usda.gov
● Webmaster **Darrell Mowery** (317) 295-5770
E-mail: darrell.mowery@in.usda.gov
Purchasing Agent **Cindy Martin** (317) 295-5765
E-mail: cindy.martin@in.usda.gov

Iowa Rural Development State Office
873 Federal Building, 210 Walnut Street,
Room 873, Des Moines, IA 50309-2196
Tel: (515) 284-4663 TTY: (515) 284-4858 Fax: (515) 284-4821
Internet: www.rd.usda.gov/ia

□ State Director **Grant Menke** (515) 284-4663
E-mail: grant.menke@ia.usda.gov
Secretary to State Director **Victoria Lacey** (515) 284-4663
E-mail: victoria.lacey@ia.usda.gov
Administrative Programs Director/Program Support Director **Timothy Helmbrecht** (515) 284-4470
E-mail: tim.helmbrecht@ia.usda.gov
Community Programs Director **Kate Sand** (515) 284-4459
E-mail: kate.sand@ia.usda.gov
Rural Business and Cooperative Services Programs Director **Jeff Jobe** (515) 284-4480
E-mail: jeff.jobe@ia.usda.gov
Rural Housing Program Director **Mary Beth Juergens** (515) 284-4493
Public Information Coordinator **Darin Leach** (515) 284-4747
E-mail: darin.leach@ia.usda.gov

★ Presidential Appointment Requiring Senate Confirmation ☆ Presidential Appointment □ Schedule C Appointment ◇ Career Senior Foreign Service Appointment
● Career Senior Executive Service (SES) Appointment ○ Non-Career Senior Executive Service (SES) Appointment ■ Postal Career Executive Service

Kansas Rural Development State Office
1303 SW First American Place, Suite 100, Topeka, KS 66604
Tel: (785) 271-2700 Fax: (877) 470-3801 Internet: www.rd.usda.gov/ks

□ State Director **Lynne Hinrichsen** .... (785) 271-2700
E-mail: Lynne.Hinrichsen@ks.usda.gov
Assistant to the State Director **Karissa D. Stiers** .... (785) 271-2700
Business Programs Director
Randall L. "Randy" Snider .... (785) 380-3113
Community Programs Director **Shane Hastings** .... (785) 271-2728
E-mail: shane.hastings@ks.usda.gov
Multi-Family Housing Programs Director
Wilma Marconnet .... (785) 271-2718
E-mail: wilma.marconnet@ks.usda.gov
Single-Family Housing Programs Director
Kent Colwell .... (785) 628-3081
Public Affairs Specialist **Jessica R. Bowser** .... (785) 271-2701
E-mail: jessica.bowser@ks.usda.gov

Kentucky Rural Development State Office
771 Corporate Drive, Suite 200, Lexington, KY 40503-5479
Tel: (859) 224-7300 Fax: (855) 694-4748
Internet: https://www.rd.usda.gov/ky

□ State Director **Hilda Gay Legg** .... (859) 224-7300
Education: Campbellsville Col BS; Western Kentucky MA
Administrative Program Director **Tom Kostelnik** .... (859) 224-7302
E-mail: tom.kostelnick@ky.usda.gov
Civil Rights Manager/Management Control Officer
Michele Witt .... (859) 224-7324
E-mail: michele.witt@ky.usda.gov
Multi-Family Housing Program Director **Paul Higgins** .... (859) 224-7357
E-mail: paul.higgins@ky.usda.gov Fax: (855) 661-8335
Single-Family Housing Program Director **(Vacant)** .... (859) 224-7322
Fax: (855) 661-8335
Public Information Coordinator **Katherine Belcher** ...... (859) 224-7350
E-mail: katherine.belcher@ky.usda.gov Fax: (855) 694-4748
Rural Business Program Director **Jeff Jones** .... (859) 224-7435
E-mail: jeff.jones@ky.usda.gov Fax: (859) 224-7347
Business and Cooperative Programs Director
(Vacant) .... (606) 864-2172 ext. 133
Community Facilities Director **Vernon C. Brown** .... (859) 224-7336
E-mail: vernon.brown@ky.usda.gov Fax: (855) 661-8335
Program Analyst **Traci Vaught** .... (859) 224-7300

Louisiana Rural Development State Office
3727 Government Street, Alexandria, LA 71302
Tel: (318) 473-7920 Fax: (884) 332-7476 Internet: www.rd.usda.gov/la

□ State Director **Dr. Carrie L. Castille PhD** .... (318) 473-7921
Education: Louisiana (Lafayette) 1998 BS; LSU 2003 MS, 2007 PhD
Public Affairs Specialist **Karen K. Lawson** .... (318) 473-7917
E-mail: karen.lawson@wdc.usda.gov Fax: (844) 325-6949
Administrative Programs Director **Karen G. Nardini** ..... (318) 473-7922
E-mail: karen.nardini@la.usda.gov Fax: (844) 325-6950
Community Programs Director **Reinette Foster** .... (318) 473-7940
E-mail: reinette.foster@la.usda.gov Fax: (844) 332-7476
Business and Cooperative Programs Director
Jared Hicks .... (318) 473-7960
E-mail: jared.hicks@la.usda.gov Fax: (844) 332-7476
Multi-Family Housing Program Director
Scott Pousson .... (318) 473-7962
E-mail: scott.pousson@la.usda.gov Fax: (844) 332-7476
Single-Family Housing Program Director **Brian Lewis** .... (318) 473-7916
E-mail: brian.lewis@la.usda.gov Fax: (844) 332-7476

Maine Rural Development State Office
967 Illinois Avenue, Suite 4, Bangor, ME 04401-2767
Tel: (207) 990-9160 TTY: (207) 942-7331 Fax: (855) 589-1060
Internet: https://www.rd.usda.gov/me

□ State Director **Timothy "Tim" Hobbs** .... (207) 990-9161
Secretary **Charles Jeff Bergeron** .... (207) 990-9161
E-mail: jeff.bergeron@me.usda.gov
Administrative Programs Director **(Vacant)** .... (207) 990-9103
Budget Analyst **(Vacant)** .... (207) 990-9160 ext. 101
Human Resources Manager
Anthony "Tony" Nedik .... (207) 990-9160 ext. 108
E-mail: anthony.nedik@me.usda.gov

Maine Rural Development State Office *(continued)*

Business and Cooperative Programs Director
Brian A. Wilson .... (207) 990-9168
E-mail: brian.wilson@me.usda.gov
Community Programs Director **Robert Nadeau** .... (207) 990-9121
E-mail: robert.nadeau@me.usda.gov
Housing Programs Director **Laurie A. Warzinski** .... (207) 990-9110
E-mail: laurie.warzinski@me.usda.gov
Public Information Coordinator
Emily J. Cannon .... (207) 990-9160 ext. 175
E-mail: emily.cannon@me.usda.gov

Michigan Rural Development State Office
3001 Coolidge Road, Suite 200, East Lansing, MI 48823
Tel: (517) 324-5190 TTY: (517) 324-5200 Fax: (855) 813-7741
Internet: https://www.rd.usda.gov/mi

□ State Director **Jason Edward Allen** .... (517) 324-5190
Education: Miami U (OH) BA
Assistant to the State Director **(Vacant)** .... (517) 324-5207
Public Affairs Officer **Alec Lloyd** .... (517) 324-5204

Minnesota Rural Development State Office
375 Jackson Street, Suite 410, St. Paul, MN 55101
Tel: (651) 602-7800 Fax: (855) 744-0402
Internet: https://www.rd.usda.gov/mn

□ State Director **Brad Finstad** .... (651) 602-7801
Education: Minnesota BS
Deputy State Director **(Vacant)** .... (651) 602-7805
Associate Director **Michael "Mike" Navin** .... (651) 602-7780
E-mail: michael.navin@mn.usda.gov
Community Programs Director **Terry Louwagie** .... (651) 602-7810
E-mail: terry.louwagie@mn.usda.gov
Housing Program Director **Stephanie Vergin** .... (763) 689-3354
E-mail: stephanie.vergin@mn.usda.gov
Business and Cooperative Programs Director
Cheryl Seanoa .... (651) 602-7814
E-mail: cheryl.seanoa@mn.usda.gov

Mississippi Rural Development State Office
Dr. A. H. McCoy Federal Building, 100 West Capitol Street,
Suite 831, Jackson, MS 39269-1602
Tel: (601) 965-4316 Fax: (844) 325-7035 Internet: www.rd.usda.gov/ms

□ State Director **John Walter Rounsaville** .... (601) 965-4316
Education: Mississippi State 1997 BA, 1998 MBA
Assistant to the State Director
Cynthia S. "Cindy" McKay .... (601) 965-5466
E-mail: cindy.mckay@ms.usda.gov
Administrative Programs Director **Douglas Simons** ..... (601) 965-4316
Multi-Family Housing Programs Director
Cecil Williams .... (601) 965-4326
Fax: (844) 325-7036
Rural Business-Cooperative Service Program Director
George G. "Gary" Jones .... (601) 965-5457
E-mail: george.jones@ms.usda.gov Fax: (844) 325-7036
Water Programs and Community Facilities Director
Patricia McDowell .... (601) 965-5460
Fax: (844) 325-7034
Single Family Housing Program Director
John O. Jones .... (601) 965-4325
E-mail: john.jones@ms.usda.gov Fax: (844) 325-7036
Civil Rights Manager **(Vacant)** .... (601) 965-4316
Inventory Property Coordinator **(Vacant)** .... (601) 965-4316
Program Support Division Director (Acting)
Ken Stribling .... (601) 965-4322
E-mail: ken.stribling@ms.usda.gov Fax: (844) 325-7036
Public Information Coordinator **(Vacant)** ...... (601) 965-4316 ext. 1115
Fax: (601) 965-5384

Missouri Rural Development State Office
601 Business Loop 70 West, Parkade Center,
Suite 235, Columbia, MO 65203-2546
Tel: (573) 876-0976 Fax: (855) 849-1529 Fax: (855) 830-0685
Internet: www.rd.usda.gov/mo

□ State Director **Jeffrey Dale "Jeff" Case** .... (573) 876-0976
E-mail: Jeffrey.Case2@mo.usda.gov

(continued on next page)

★ Presidential Appointment Requiring Senate Confirmation ☆ Presidential Appointment □ Schedule C Appointment ◇ Career Senior Foreign Service Appointment
● Career Senior Executive Service (SES) Appointment ○ Non-Career Senior Executive Service (SES) Appointment ■ Postal Career Executive Service

DEPARTMENTS

Missouri Rural Development State Office *(continued)*

Assistant to the State Director **Tim Rickabaugh** .... (573) 876-9328
Business Programs Director **Matthew C. Moore** .... (573) 876-9318
E-mail: matt.moore@mo.usda.gov Fax: (573) 876-9348
Community Programs Director **Clark Thomas** .... (573) 876-0995
E-mail: clark.thomas@mo.usda.gov
Housing Program Director **Pamela "Pam" Anglin** ...... (573) 876-9305
E-mail: pamela.anglin@mo.usda.gov

Montana Rural Development State Office
2229 Boot Hill Court, Bozeman, MT 59715
Tel: (406) 585-2580 Fax: (406) 585-2565
Internet: https://www.rd.usda.gov/mt

□ State Director **Frank Charles Robison** .... (406) 585-2580
E-mail: Charles.Robison@mt.usda.gov
Education: Hillsdale 2000 BA; Montana 2010 MBA, 2010 JD
Assistant to the Director **Janelle Gustafson** .... (406) 585-2508
E-mail: janelle.gustafson@wdc.usda.gov
Business and Cooperative Services Program Director
Brent Donnelly .... (406) 585-2540
Community Program Director **Steve Troendle** .... (406) 585-2520
Rural Housing Program Director **Thomas Atkins** .... (406) 585-2551
E-mail: thomas.atkins@wdc.usda.gov

Nebraska Rural Development State Office
Federal Building, 100 Centennial Mall North,
Suite 308, Lincoln, NE 68508
Tel: (402) 437-5551 Fax: (402) 437-5408 Tel: (866) 460-1257
Internet: www.rd.usda.gov/ne

□ State Director **Karl Leonard Elmshaeuser** .... (402) 437-5551
E-mail: Karl.Elmshaeuser@ne.usda.gov
Program Support Director **(Vacant)** .... (402) 437-5742
Business and Cooperative Programs Director
Joan Scheel .... (402) 437-5594
Community Programs Director **Denise Brosius-Meeks** ... (402) 437-5559
Single Family Housing Director
Michael "Mike" Buethe .... (402) 437-5574
E-mail: mike.buethe@ne.usda.gov
Multifamily Housing Director **(Vacant)** .... (308) 237-3118 ext. 1122
4009 Sixth Avenue, Fax: (308) 236-6290
Suite 1, Kearney, NE 68845
Civil Rights Manager **(Vacant)** .... (402) 437-5598
Information Officer **Vicki Schurman** .... (402) 437-5563
E-mail: vicki.schurman@ne.usda.gov
Webmaster **(Vacant)** .... (402) 437-5563

Nevada Rural Development State Office
1390 South Curry Street, Carson City, NV 89703-5146
Tel: (775) 887-1222 Fax: (855) 816-1209
Internet: https://www.rd.usda.gov/nv

□ State Director **Philip Cowee** .... (775) 887-1222 ext. 4751
E-mail: philip.cowee@nv.usda.gov
Administrative Programs Director **(Vacant)** ..... (775) 887-1222 ext. 4750
Business and Cooperative Programs Director
Herb Shedd .... (775) 887-1222 ext. 4763
E-mail: herb.shedd@nv.usda.gov Fax: (775) 887-1287
Community Programs Director
Cheryl Couch .... (775) 887-1222 ext. 4760
E-mail: cheryl.couch@nv.usda.gov Fax: (775) 885-1287
Housing Programs Director **Jeffery Glass** ..... (775) 887-1222 ext. 4755
E-mail: jeffery.glass@nv.usda.gov Fax: (775) 885-0738

New Jersey Rural Development State Office
8000 Midlantic Drive, 5th Floor North, Suite 500,
Mount Laurel, NJ 08054
Tel: (856) 787-7700 Fax: (855) 305-7343 Internet: www.rd.usda.gov/nj

□ State Director (Acting) **Kenneth C. Drewes** ...... (856) 787-7700 ext. 6
E-mail: kenneth.drewes@nj.usda.gov
Administrative Programs Director **(Vacant)** .... (856) 787-7712
Business Programs Director **Victoria M. Fekete** .... (856) 787-7752
E-mail: victoria.fekete@nj.usda.gov
Civil Rights Coordinator **(Vacant)** .... (856) 787-7773
Community Programs Director **Kenneth C. Drewes** ..... (856) 787-7753
E-mail: kenneth.drewes@nj.usda.gov

New Jersey Rural Development State Office *(continued)*

Housing Programs Director **Michael Mathews** .... (856) 787-7732
Columbus/Hackettstown/Vineland/Woodstown Area
Director **Janis L. Rega** .... (908) 441-7523
E-mail: janis.rega@nj.usda.gov

New Mexico Rural Development State Office
100 Sun Avenue NE, Suite 130, Albuquerque, NM 87109
Tel: (505) 761-4950 Fax: (855) 543-9500 Internet: www.rd.usda.gov/nm

□ State Director **Arthur A. "Art" Garcia** .... (505) 761-4950
E-mail: arthur.garcia@nm.usda.gov
Education: New Mexico State BA; Webster MS, MBA
Assistant to the State Director **Eric Vigil** .... (505) 761-4962
Community Programs Director **(Vacant)** .... (505) 761-4950
Rural Business-Cooperative Service Director
Richard Carrig .... (505) 761-4956
E-mail: richard.carrig@nm.usda.gov
Rural Housing Service Program Director **(Vacant)** .... (505) 761-4944

New York Rural Development State Office
The Galleries of Syracuse, 441 South Salina Street,
5th Floor, Suite 357, Syracuse, NY 13202-2541
Tel: (315) 477-6400 TTY: (315) 477-6447 Fax: (855) 477-8540
Internet: www.rd.usda.gov/ny

□ State Director **Richard Mayfield** .... (315) 477-6437
E-mail: richard.mayfield@ny.usda.gov
Assistant State Director **Scott R. Collins** .... (315) 477-6409
E-mail: scott.collins@ny.usda.gov
Administrative Program Director **(Vacant)** .... (315) 477-6433
Fax: (855) 477-8536
Community Program Director **Brenda L. Smith** .... (315) 870-2497
E-mail: brenda.smith@ny.usda.gov Fax: (855) 477-8536
Rural Business-Cooperative Service Program Director
Walter D. "David" Schermerhorn .... (315) 477-6425
Rural Housing Service Program Director (Multifamily)
Mike Bosak .... (315) 477-6421
E-mail: michael.bosak@ny.usda.gov Fax: (855) 477-8536
Rural Housing Service Program Director (Single
Family) **Jennifer Jackson** .... (315) 477-6417
E-mail: jennifer.jackson@ny.usda.gov Fax: (855) 477-8531

North Carolina Rural Development State Office
4405 Bland Road, Suite 260, Raleigh, NC 27609
Tel: (919) 873-2000 Fax: (844) 325-6921 Internet: www.rd.usda.gov/nc

□ State Director **Bob Dixon Chandler** .... (828) 452-0319
Assistant to the State Director **(Vacant)** .... (919) 873-2033
Administrative Programs Director
Melchior B. "Mel" Ellis .... (919) 873-2021
E-mail: mel.ellis@nc.usda.gov
Civil Rights Coordinator **Brenda B. Woolard** .... (919) 873-2012
E-mail: brenda.woolard@nc.usda.gov Fax: (919) 873-2075
Community Programs Director **Garland Burnette** .... (919) 873-2063
E-mail: garland.burnette@nc.usda.gov
Multi-Family Housing Program Director **Bryon Waters** ... (919) 873-2055
E-mail: bryon.waters@nc.usda.gov
Rural Business and Cooperative Services Director
Bruce Pleasant .... (919) 873-2031
E-mail: bruce.pleasant@nc.usda.gov
Single Family Program Director **William Kenney** .... (919) 873-2041
Public Information Chief Officer **Kim Hunt** .... (919) 873-2033
E-mail: kim.hunt@nc.usda.gov

North Dakota Rural Development State Office
Federal Building, 220 East Rosser Avenue,
Room 208, Bismarck, ND 58501-1458
P.O. Box 1737, Bismarck, ND 58502-1737
Tel: (701) 530-2037 Fax: (855) 427-8188 Internet: www.rd.usda.gov/nd

□ State Director **Clare A. Carlson** .... (701) 530-2061
E-mail: Clare.Carlson@nd.usda.gov
Education: North Dakota State BS; U Mary MM
Administrative Program Director **Myron C. Lepp** .... (701) 530-2054
E-mail: myron.lepp@nd.usda.gov
Business Cooperative Program Director **Dennis Rodin** ... (701) 530-2065
E-mail: dennis.rodin@nd.usda.gov

★ Presidential Appointment Requiring Senate Confirmation ☆ Presidential Appointment □ Schedule C Appointment ◇ Career Senior Foreign Service Appointment
● Career Senior Executive Service (SES) Appointment ○ Non-Career Senior Executive Service (SES) Appointment ■ Postal Career Executive Service

North Dakota Rural Development State Office *(continued)*

Community Program Director **Mark Wax** . . . . (701) 530-2029
E-mail: mark.wax@nd.usda.gov
Multi-Family Housing Director
Steven A. "Steve" Lervik . . . . (701) 225-9168 ext. 133
E-mail: steve.lervik@nd.usda.gov
Single Family Housing Director **William A. Schafer** . . . . . (701) 530-2045
E-mail: william.schafer@nd.usda.gov
Public Affairs Specialist **(Vacant)** . . . . (701) 893-2220

Ohio Rural Development State Office
Federal Building, 200 North High Street, Columbus, OH 43215-2408
Tel: (614) 255-2400 Fax: (614) 255-2561 Internet: www.rd.usda.gov/oh

□ State Director **David Lewis "Dave" Hall** . . . . (614) 255-2400
E-mail: David.Hall5@oh.usda.gov
Administrative Programs Director **Beth A. Huhn** . . . . (614) 255-2515
E-mail: beth.huhn@oh.usda.gov
Business and Cooperative Programs Director (Acting)
Deborah Rauch . . . . (614) 255-2425
E-mail: deborah.rausch@oh.usda.gov
Community/Water & Environmental Programs Director
David M. Douglas . . . . (614) 255-2391
E-mail: david.douglas@oh.usda.gov
Management Control Officer **Holly Doughman** . . . . (614) 255-2393
E-mail: holly.doughman@oh.usda.gov
Public Affairs Specialist **Heather Hartley** . . . . (614) 255-2394
E-mail: heather.hartley@oh.usda.gov
Community Economic Development Specialist
Vince Paumier . . . . (614) 255-2425
Rural Housing Programs Director **Gerald B. Arnott** . . . . . (614) 255-2401
E-mail: gerald.arnott@oh.usda.gov
Rural Utility Programs - Electric General Field
Representative **Patrick Sarver** . . . . (740) 920-9079
22837, Lexington, KY 40522-2837
E-mail: Patrick.Sarver@wdc.usda.gov
Rural Utility Programs - Telecommunications General
Field Representative **Anthony Tindall** . . . . (859) 533-0334
22837, Lexington, KY 40522-2837
E-mail: anthony.tindall@wdc.usda.gov

Oklahoma Rural Development State Office
100 USDA, Suite 108, Stillwater, OK 74074-2654
Tel: (405) 742-1000 Fax: (405) 742-1005 Internet: www.rd.usda.gov/ok

□ State Director **Dr. Lee Roberts Denney** . . . . (405) 742-1000
E-mail: Lee.Denney@ok.usda.gov
Education: Oklahoma State 1976 BS, 1978 DVM
Administrative Programs Director **(Vacant)** . . . . (405) 742-1011
Business and Community Programs Director (Acting)
Brian S. Wiles . . . . (405) 742-1060
E-mail: brian.wiles@ok.usda.gov
Single Family Program Director **Tommy K. Earls** . . . . (405) 742-1070
E-mail: tommy.earls@ok.usda.gov
E-mail: Oklahoma-Direct@ok.usda.gov
Webmaster **Kathleen James** . . . . (405) 742-1000 ext. 1014
E-mail: kathleen.james@ok.usda.gov

Oregon Rural Development State Office
1220 SW 3rd Avenue, Suite 1801, Portland, OR 97204
Tel: (503) 414-3306 Fax: (503) 414-3392 Internet: www.rd.usda.gov/or

□ State Director **John E. Huffman USA** . . . . (503) 414-3305
E-mail: john.huffman@or.usda.gov
Secretary **Denneva Coats** . . . . (503) 414-3306
Assistant to the State Director **Jill Rees** . . . . (503) 414-3302
Business and Cooperative Program Director
Rachel Reister . . . . (503) 414-3393
Fax: (503) 414-6181
Community Program Director **Sam Goldstein** . . . . (503) 414-3362
E-mail: sam.goldstein@or.usda.gov Fax: (855) 824-6181
Community and Economic Development Coordinator
Jill Rees . . . . (503) 414-3302
E-mail: jill.rees@or.usda.gov
Multi-Family Housing Program Director **Wes Cochran** . . . (503) 414-3310
Single-Family Housing Program Director **Drew Davis** . . . . (503) 414-3353

Pennsylvania Rural Development State Office
359 East Park Drive, Suite 4, Harrisburg, PA 17111
Tel: (717) 237-2299 TTY: (717) 237-2261 Fax: (855) 813-2864
Internet: www.rd.usda.gov/pa

□ State Director **Curt Coccodrilli** . . . . (717) 237-2262
E-mail: Curt.Coccodrilli@pa.usda.gov
Administrative Programs Director **Jeremy Wilson** . . . . (717) 237-2265
E-mail: jeremy.wilson@pa.usda.gov
Business and Cooperative Development Programs
Director **Greg Greco** . . . . (717) 237-2181
E-mail: greg.greco@pa.usda.gov
Housing Program Director **David Corwin** . . . . (717) 237-2279
E-mail: david.corwin@pa.usda.gov
Water and Environmental Program Director
Susanne Gantz . . . . (717) 237-2281
E-mail: susanne.gantz@pa.usda.gov

Puerto Rico Rural Development State Office
654 Muñoz Rivera Avenue, Suite 601, Hato Rey, PR 00918
Tel: (787) 766-5095 Fax: (787) 766-5844
Internet: https://www.rd.usda.gov/pr

□ State Director **Josue Emanuel Rivera** . . . . (787) 766-5067
E-mail: Josue.Rivera@pr.usda.gov
Assistant to the State Director **Luis R. Garcia** . . . . (787) 766-5481
E-mail: luis.garcia@pr.usda.gov
Administrative Programs Director **Pedro Gómez** . . . . (787) 766-5017
E-mail: pedro.gomez@pr.usda.gov
Community Programs Director **Nereida Rodriguez** . . . . . . (787) 766-5158
E-mail: nereida.rodriguez@pr.usda.gov
Housing Program Director **Arlene Zambrana** . . . . (787) 766-5709
E-mail: arlene.zambrana@pr.usda.gov
Rural Business Program Director **Danna Quiles** . . . . (787) 766-5346
E-mail: danna.quiles@pr.usda.gov

South Carolina Rural Development State Office
Strom Thurmond Federal Building, 1835 Assembly Street,
Suite 1007, Columbia, SC 29201
Tel: (803) 765-5163 Fax: (800) 670-6553
Internet: https://www.rd.usda.gov/sc

□ State Director **Debbie S. Turbeville** . . . . (803) 765-5163
E-mail: debbie.turbeville@sc.usda.gov
Administrative Programs Director
Martha Bright-Rivera . . . . (803) 253-3993
E-mail: martha.bright-rivera@sc.usda.gov
Chester Office (Area 1) Director
Timothy O. "Tim" Ellis . . . . (803) 581-1906 ext. 113
E-mail: TIM.ELLIS@SC.USDA.GOV
Kingstree Office (Area 2) Director
George W. Hicks, Jr. . . . . (843) 669-9686 ext. 133
Community Programs Director **Michele J. Cardwell** . . . . . (803) 253-3645
Fax: (855) 565-9482
Multi Family Housing Program Director
Dwayne White . . . . (803) 253-3655
E-mail: dwayne.white@sc.usda.gov Fax: (855) 565-9482
Single Family Housing Program Director
George H. Randolph, Jr. . . . . (803) 765-5245
E-mail: george.randolph@sc.usda.gov Fax: (855) 565-9482
Rural Business/Cooperative Program Director
Jesse T. Risher . . . . (803) 765-5881
E-mail: jesse.risher@sc.usda.gov
Business and Industry Specialist **Douglas Dunkelberg** . . . (803) 765-5533
State Civil Rights Manager **Janice R. Allen** . . . . (803) 765-5246
E-mail: janice.allen@sc.usda.gov
Human Resources Specialist **Debbie Shealy** . . . . (803) 253-3993
Special Projects Coordinator
Wieslawa Gartman . . . . (843) 549-1822 ext. 119
E-mail: wieslawa.gartman@sc.usda.gov
Public Information Coordinator **(Vacant)** . . . . (803) 253-3725
Management Control Officer **(Vacant)** . . . . (803) 253-3425

DEPARTMENTS

★ Presidential Appointment Requiring Senate Confirmation ☆ Presidential Appointment □ Schedule C Appointment ◇ Career Senior Foreign Service Appointment
● Career Senior Executive Service (SES) Appointment ○ Non-Career Senior Executive Service (SES) Appointment ■ Postal Career Executive Service

DEPARTMENTS

South Dakota Rural Development State Office
Federal Building, 200 Fourth Street SW,
Room 210, Huron, SD 57350
Tel: (605) 352-1100 Fax: (855) 262-1940 TTY: (605) 352-1147
Internet: https://www.rd.usda.gov/sd

□ State Director **Julie Gross** . . . . . . (605) 352-1100
Community Program Director **Tim Potts** . . . . . . (605) 342-0301 ext. 4
Administrative Programs Director **Kay Daugherty** . . . . . . (605) 352-1105
E-mail: kay.daugherty@sd.usda.gov
Rural Business and Cooperative Programs Director
Dana Kleinsasser . . . . . . (605) 352-1157
E-mail: dana.kleinsasser@sd.usda.gov Fax: (855) 262-1940
Multi-Family Housing Director **Trace Davids** . . . . . . (605) 352-1132
E-mail: trace.davids@sd.usda.gov Fax: (855) 262-1940
Single Family Housing Director **Janell Telin** . . . . . . (605) 352-1132
E-mail: janell.telin@sd.usda.gov Fax: (855) 262-1940

Southern New England Rural Development Office
451 West Street, Suite 2, Amherst, MA 01002-2998
Tel: (413) 253-4302 Fax: (855) 596-7673 Internet: www.rd.usda.gov/ct
Internet: www.rd.usda.gov/ma Internet: www.rd.usda.gov/ri
Areas Covered: CT, MA, RI

□ State Director **George E. Krivda, Jr.** . . . . . . (413) 253-4302
E-mail: george.krivda@ma.usda.gov
Administrative Programs Director **Mary E. Grasso** . . . . . . (413) 253-4310
E-mail: mary.grasso@ma.usda.gov
Business and Cooperative Programs Director
Jennifer Lerch . . . . . . (413) 253-4316
E-mail: jennifer.lerch@ma.usda.gov
Housing Programs Director
Michael J. Rendulic . . . . . . (413) 253-4310 ext. 141
E-mail: michael.rendulic@ct.usda.gov
Management Analyst/Civil Rights Coordinator
Cara M. Rigali . . . . . . (413) 253-4320
E-mail: cara.rigali@ma.usda.gov

Tennessee Rural Development State Office
3322 West End Avenue, Suite 300, Nashville, TN 37203-1084
Tel: (615) 783-1300 Tel: (855) 776-7057 Fax: (855) 776-7057
Internet: https://www.rd.usda.gov/tn

□ State Director **Jim D. Tracy** . . . . . . (615) 783-1312
E-mail: jim.tracy@tn.usda.gov
Education: Martin U 1978 BS
Assistant to the State Director **Dan Beasley** . . . . . . (615) 783-1321
E-mail: dan.beasley@tn.usda.gov
Administrative Programs Director **Dan Beasley** . . . . . . (615) 783-1321
E-mail: dan.beasley@tn.usda.gov
Rural Business-Cooperative Programs Director
Dan Beasley . . . . . . (615) 783-1321
E-mail: dan.beasley@tn.usda.gov
Civil Rights Coordinator **(Vacant)** . . . . . . (615) 783-1300
Rural Utilities Service and Community Facilities
Director **Terence McGhee** . . . . . . (615) 783-1348
E-mail: terence.mcghee@tn.usda.gov
Housing Programs Director
Donald L. "Don" Harris, Jr. . . . . . . (615) 783-1388
E-mail: donald.harris@tn.usda.gov
Public Information Coordinator **(Vacant)** . . . . . . (615) 783-1300

Texas Rural Development State Office
Federal Building, 101 South Main Street,
Suite 102, Temple, TX 76501
Tel: (254) 742-9700 Fax: (844) 496-8123 Internet: www.rd.usda.gov/tx

□ State Director **Edward Eugene "Edd" Hargett** . . . . . . (254) 742-9700
E-mail: Edd.Hargett@tx.usda.gov Fax: (844) 496-8123
Education: Texas A&M
Secretary **Tasha Lemon** . . . . . . (254) 742-9710
E-mail: tasha.lemon@tx.usda.gov
Administrative Programs Director **Gary Jacobs** . . . . . . (254) 742-9706
E-mail: gary.jacobs@tx.usda.gov Fax: (254) 742-9753
Business and Cooperative Programs Director
Daniel Torres . . . . . . (254) 742-9756
E-mail: daniel.torres@tx.usda.gov
Community Programs Director **Michael B. Canales** . . . . . . (254) 742-9787
E-mail: michael.canales@tx.usda.gov

Texas Rural Development State Office *(continued)*

Multi-Family Housing Program Director
Jonathan D. Bell . . . . . . (254) 742-9770
Single-Family Housing Program Director
Regina Wilcox . . . . . . (254) 742-9761
E-mail: regina.wilcox@tx.usda.gov

Utah Rural Development State Office
Federal Building, 125 South State Street,
Room 4311, Salt Lake City, UT 84138
Tel: (801) 524-4320 Fax: (801) 524-4406
Internet: https://www.rd.usda.gov/ut

□ State Director **Randy Parker** . . . . . . (801) 524-4321
E-mail: randy.parker@ut.usda.gov
Education: Utah State BS, MS
Assistant to the State Director
Debra "Debbie" Meyer . . . . . . (801) 524-4326
Business and Cooperative Programs Director
M. Perry Mathews . . . . . . (801) 524-4328
E-mail: perry.mathews@ut.usda.gov
Community Programs Director **Heath Price** . . . . . . (801) 524-4325
Housing Programs Director **Lori Silva** . . . . . . (801) 524-4323
E-mail: lori.silva@wdc.usda.gov
Multi-Family Housing Specialist **Shelly Prothero** . . . . . . (801) 524-4302
E-mail: shelly.prothero@ut.usda.gov
Mutual Self-Help Housing Manager
Debbie Cook . . . . . . (801) 377-5580 ext. 12
BOR Building, 302 East 1860 South, Provo, UT 84606
E-mail: debbie.cook@ut.usda.gov
Community and Economic Development
Director **(Vacant)** . . . . . . (435) 238-8004 ext. 106
5 South Main, Suite 202, Ephraim, UT 84627
Public Information Officer **Jamie Welch Jaro** . . . . . . (801) 524-4324
E-mail: jamie.welchjaro@ut.usda.gov
Human Resources Manager **Jonathan Tufuga** . . . . . . (801) 524-4331
E-mail: jonathan.tufuga@ut.usda.gov
State Engineer **Jeff Rich** . . . . . . (801) 524-4327

Vermont - New Hampshire Rural Development State Office
87 State Street, Suite 324, Montpelier, VT 05601
Tel: (802) 828-6080 TTY: (802) 223-6365 Fax: (855) 794-3630
Internet: www.rd.usda.gov/vt Internet: www.rd.usda.gov/nh

□ State Director **Anthony Linardos** . . . . . . (802) 828-6080
E-mail: Anthony.Linardos@nh.usda.gov Fax: (802) 828-6018
Education: Northeastern BPharm;
Plymouth State U MBA
□ Assistant State Director **Ben Doyle** . . . . . . (802) 828-6042
E-mail: benjamin.doyle@vt.usda.gov Fax: (802) 828-6018
Public Information Coordinator and Administrative
Assistant to the State Director **(Vacant)** . . . . . . (802) 828-6080
Fax: (855) 794-3680
Vermont Area Director **Jon-Michael "Jon" Muise** . . . . . . (802) 689-3026
28 Vernon Street, Suite 333, Brattleboro, VT 05301
E-mail: jon.muise@vt.usda.gov
Administrative Program Director **(Vacant)** . . . . . . (603) 447-3318 ext. 201
Program Director (Acting) **Karen E. Gagnon** . . . . . . (802) 828-6045
E-mail: karen.gagnon@vt.usda.gov
Business-Cooperative Program Director (Acting)
Cheryl Ducharme . . . . . . (802) 828-6083
E-mail: cheryl.ducharme@vt.usda.gov
Community Programs Director **Eric Law** . . . . . . (802) 828-6033
E-mail: deborah.maguire@vt.usda.gov
Rural Housing Programs Director **Seth Leonard** . . . . . . (802) 828-6068
E-mail: seth.leonard@vt.usda.gov

Virginia Rural Development State Office
1606 Santa Rosa Road, Suite 238, Richmond, VA 23229-5014
Tel: (804) 287-1615 Fax: (855) 616-1655 Internet: www.rd.usda.gov/va

□ State Director **Elizabeth Walker Green** . . . . . . (804) 287-1552
E-mail: Elizabeth.Green@va.usda.gov
Assistant to the State Director **(Vacant)** . . . . . . (804) 287-1615
Administrative Programs Director **(Vacant)** . . . . . . (804) 287-1569
Community Programs Director **Robin P. Pulkkinen** . . . . . . (804) 287-1565
Housing Programs Director **Ora Rollins** . . . . . . (804) 287-1584
E-mail: ora.rollins@va.usda.gov

★ Presidential Appointment Requiring Senate Confirmation ☆ Presidential Appointment □ Schedule C Appointment ◇ Career Senior Foreign Service Appointment
● Career Senior Executive Service (SES) Appointment ○ Non-Career Senior Executive Service (SES) Appointment ■ Postal Career Executive Service

Virginia Rural Development State Office *(continued)*

Rural Business-Cooperative Program Director
Ricardo Colon .... (804) 287-1557
E-mail: Ricardo.Colon@va.usda.gov
Executive Support Specialist **Nancy Lewis** .... (804) 287-1552

Washington Rural Development State Office
1835 Black Lake Boulevard, SW, Suite B, Olympia, WA 98512-5716
Tel: (360) 704-7740 Fax: (855) 843-6124 Internet: www.rd.usda.gov/wa

□ State Director **Kirk John Pearson** .... (360) 704-7700
E-mail: Kirk.Pearson@wa.usda.gov
Education: Wenatchee Valley 1977 BA
Secretary **(Vacant)** .... (360) 704-7700
Administrative Programs Director **Tuana Jones** .... (360) 704-7740
E-mail: tuana.jones@wa.usda.gov
Rural Business and Cooperative Programs Director
Brian Buch .... (360) 704-7707
E-mail: brian.buch@wa.usda.gov
Community Programs Director **Peter McMillin** .... (360) 704-7737
E-mail: peter.mcmillin@wa.usda.gov
Single Family Housing Programs Director **Trudy Teter** ... (360) 704-7731
E-mail: trudy.teter@wa.usda.gov
Multi-Family Housing Programs Director **Mary Traxler** ... (360) 704-7725
E-mail: mary.traxler@wdc.usda.gov
Housing Programs Director **(Vacant)** .... (360) 704-7767
State Architect **Agnieszka K. Kisza** .... (360) 704-7735
Human Resource Manager **Gerald Hancock** .... (360) 704-7701
Environmental Specialist **(Vacant)** .... (360) 704-7739

West Virginia Rural Development State Office
1550 Earl Core Road, Suite 101, Morgantown, WV 26505
Tel: (304) 284-4860 Tel: (800) 295-8228 Fax: (855) 859-1834
Internet: https://www.rd.usda.gov/wv

□ State Director **Kristian Escridge "Kris" Warner** .... (304) 284-4860
Rural Development Coordinator and Community
Development Liaison **Lisa Sharp** .... (304) 284-4871
E-mail: lisa.sharp@wv.usda.gov Fax: (304) 284-4893
Human Resources Manager **(Vacant)** .... (304) 284-4870
Public Affairs Specialist and Management
Control Officer **J. Gail Bennett** .... (304) 366-2921 ext. 214
53 Mountain Park Drive, Whitehall, WV 26554 Fax: (304) 363-7027
E-mail: gail.bennett@wv.usda.gov
Housing Programs Director **David L. Cain** .... (304) 284-4872
E-mail: david.cain@wv.usda.gov Fax: (304) 284-4893
State Civil Engineer **Harry Taylor** .... (304) 284-4887
Business Programs Director **Lisa Sharp** .... (304) 284-4871
E-mail: lisa.sharp@wv.usda.gov
Community Programs Director **Janna Lowery** .... (304) 284-4886
E-mail: janna.lowery@wv.usda.gov Fax: (304) 284-4892

Wisconsin Rural Development State Office
5417 Clem's Way, Stevens Point, WI 54482
Tel: (715) 345-7600 Fax: (855) 814-3109
E-mail: rd.stateoffice@wi.usda.gov Internet: www.rd.usda.gov/wi

□ State Director **Frank Joseph Frassetto** .... (715) 345-7668
E-mail: Frank.Frassetto@wi.usda.gov
Education: Wisconsin (Oshkosh) 1984 BS
Administrative Programs Director
Michelle Wallace .... (715) 345-7655 ext. 455
E-mail: michelle.wallace@wi.usda.gov
Business Programs Director **Jeff Hudson** .... (715) 345-7600 ext. 131
E-mail: jeff.hudson@wi.usda.gov
Community Programs Director **Brian Deaner** ...... (715) 232-2614 ext. 4
E-mail: brian.deaner@wi.usda.gov
Single-Family Housing Programs Director
David "Dave" Schwobe .... (715) 345-7611
E-mail: dave.schwobe@wi.usda.gov
Multi-Family Housing Programs Director
Donna Huebner .... (715) 340-3682
E-mail: donna.huebner@wi.usda.gov

Wyoming Rural Development State Office
Federal Building, 100 East B Street, Room 1005, Casper, WY 82601
Mail: P.O. Box 11005, Casper, WY 82602-5006
Tel: (307) 233-6700 TTY: (307) 233-6733 Fax: (855) 415-3411
Internet: https://www.rd.usda.gov/wy

□ State Director **Chad Rupe** .... (307) 233-6700
Assistant to the State Director **Janice Blare** .... (307) 233-6700
E-mail: janice.blare@wy.usda.gov
Business Programs Director **Scott Sutherland** .... (307) 233-6716
Education: Wyoming 1990 BS Fax: (855) 415-3411
Single and Multi-Family Housing Program Director
Scott Sutherland .... (307) 233-6706
Education: Wyoming 1990 BS Fax: (855) 415-3412
Community Programs Director **Lorraine Werner** .... (307) 233-6710
E-mail: lorraine.werner@wy.usda.gov

DEPARTMENTS

Rural Utilities Service (RUS)
South Agriculture Building, 1400 Independence Avenue, SW,
Room 5135, Washington, DC 20250
Tel: (202) 720-9540 Fax: (202) 720-1725

Telecommunications Program
South Agriculture Building, 1400 Independence Avenue, SW,
Room 5151, 1590, Washington, DC 20250
Fax: (202) 720-0810 Tel: (202) 720-9556

Loan Origination and Approval Division
USDA-RUS, South Agriculture Building, 355 E St NW,
Room 2808, Stop 1597, Washington, DC 20250-1597
Tel: (202) 720-0800 Fax: (202) 205-2921

Deputy Assistant Administrator (Acting)
Richard J. Anderson .... (202) 720-0800
E-mail: Richard.Anderson@wdc.usda.gov
Engineering Branch Chief **Scott Steiner** .... (202) 720-2540
Engineer **Frank Chandler** .... (202) 690-4513
Engineer **Ruhul Choudhury** .... (202) 690-3080
Engineer **Brad Shuman** .... (202) 720-0725
Secretary **(Vacant)** .... (202) 720-0806
Operations Branch Chief **Richard J. Anderson** .... (202) 720-0733
E-mail: richard.anderson@wdc.usda.gov
Secretary **Brenda K. Bell** .... (202) 720-0733
Financial and Loan Business Specialist
Jarvis Jackson .... (202) 720-4287
E-mail: jarvis.jackson@wdc.usda.gov
Financial and Loan Business Specialist
John Moorehead .... (202) 720-0733
Financial and Loan Business Specialist
Mark D. Walther .... (202) 720-0789
Supervisory General Field Representative
Jacqueline Rosier .... (202) 720-0733
E-mail: jacqueline.rosier@wdc.usda.gov
Supervisory General Field Representative **(Vacant)** ...... (202) 720-0451

Ames (IA) Field Office
809 Wheeler Street, Suite 110, Ames, IA 50010
Areas Covered: Iowa

General Field Representative **Thomas Jensen** .... (641) 231-8007
Note: Temporarily covering VT, NH, MA, CT, RI, NY and NJ.
E-mail: thomas.jensen@wdc.usda.gov

Amherst (MA) Field Office
451 West Street, Suite 2, Amherst, MA 01002-2995
Areas Covered: Massachusetts, Maine, New York (Northern), New Hampshire, Vermont, Connecticut, and Rhode Island

General Field Representative **(Vacant)** .... (413) 253-4333

Austin (TX) Field Office
P.O. Box 151630, Austin, TX 78715
Tel: (512) 288-5820
Areas Covered: Southern TX

General Field Representative **Jose P. De Leon** .... (512) 288-5820
E-mail: jose.deleon@wdc.usda.gov

★ Presidential Appointment Requiring Senate Confirmation ☆ Presidential Appointment □ Schedule C Appointment ◇ Career Senior Foreign Service Appointment
● Career Senior Executive Service (SES) Appointment ○ Non-Career Senior Executive Service (SES) Appointment ■ Postal Career Executive Service

Ball (LA) Field Office
P.O. Box 979, Ball, LA 71405-0979
Tel: (318) 640-1407
Areas Covered: AR, LA

General Field Representative **William H. Vogt** . . . . (318) 640-1407
E-mail: william.vogt@wdc.usda.gov

Bismarck (ND) Field Office
547 South Seventh Street, Room 393, Bismarck, ND 58504
Areas Covered: North Dakota

General Field Representative **Cory Herman** . . . . (701) 214-9869
E-mail: cory.herman@wdc.usda.gov

Castle Rock (CO) Field Office
P.O. Box 1895, Castle Rock, CO 80104
Tel: (303) 688-8079 Fax: (303) 514-6386
Areas Covered: CO, NM, UT

General Field Representative **Randall Dinogan** . . . . (303) 688-8079

Cedar Hill (TX) Field Office
P.O. Box 1629, Cedar Hill, TX 75106-1629
Tel: (972) 780-7832
Areas Covered: OK, Northern TX

General Field Representative **Michael L. Becker** . . . . (972) 780-7832
E-mail: michael.becker@wdc.usda.gov

Centennial (CO) Field Office
8200 S. Quebec Street, Suite A3 747, Centennial, CO 80112

General Field Representative **Randall Dinogan** . . . . (303) 514-6386
E-mail: randall.dinogan@wdc.usda.gov

Columbia (MO) Field Office
601 Business Loop 70 West, Parkade Center,
Suite 235, Columbia, MO 65203-2546
Fax: (573) 876-3920
Areas Covered: Missouri, Illinois

General Field Representative
Christopher L. "Chris" Collins . . . . (573) 445-0765
E-mail: chris.collins@wdc.usda.gov

Gallatin (TN) Field Office
P.O. Box 1915, Gallatin, TN 37066
Tel: (615) 451-9498

General Field Representative **(Vacant)** . . . . (615) 451-9498
P.O. Box 1915, Gallatin, TN 37066

Glenrock (WY) Field Office
PO Box 610, Glenrock, WY 82637-0610

General Field Representative **Timothy Brooks** . . . . (307) 532-4880
E-mail: Timothy.Brooks@wdc.usda.gov

Goodyear (AZ) Field Office
500 N. Estrella Parkway, Suite B2 454, Goodyear, AZ 85338
Areas Covered: AZ, NM

General Field Representative **Brian Smith** . . . . (623) 293-0913 (Cell)
E-mail: brian.smith@wdc.usda.gov

Hilliard (OH) Field Office
4964 Cemetary Road, PMB 386, Hilliard, OH 43026

General Field Representative **Anthony Tindall** . . . . (859) 533-0334
E-mail: anthony.tindall@wdc.usda.gov

Huntington Beach (CA) Field Office
9121 Atlanta Avenue, #758, Huntington Beach, CA 92646
Areas Covered: California, Nevada, Federated States of Micronesia, Guam, Hawaii, Northern Mariana Islands, Marshall Islands, American Samoa and Palau

General Field Representative **Rocky Chenelle** . . . . (530) 379-5032
E-mail: rocky.chenelle@wdc.usda.gov

Huron (SD) Field Office
410 Dakota Avenue South, 1323, Huron, SD 57350
Areas Covered: South Dakota

General Field Representative **Patrick "Pat" Hemen** . . . . . . (605) 352-1143
E-mail: pat.hemen@wdc.usda.gov

Lewisburg (WV) Field Office
P.O. Box 167, Lewisburg, WV 24901
Tel: (304) 645-1947
Areas Covered: VA, WV, North West NC

General Field Representative **Richard E. Jenkins** . . . . (681) 318-3236
Note: Temporarily covering PA, MD and DE.
E-mail: richard.jenkins@wdc.usda.gov

Lexington (KY) Field Office
P.O. Box 22837, Lexington, KY 40522-2837
Tel: (859) 335-5483
Areas Covered: KY, IN

General Field Representative **James E. Wilson** . . . . (859) 335-5483
E-mail: james.wilson@wdc.usda.gov

McDonough (GA) Field Office
289 Jonesboro Road, Suite 340, McDonough, GA 30253
Tel: (770) 914-8643
Areas Covered: FL, GA

General Field Representative **Andrew E. Hayes** . . . . (770) 914-8643
E-mail: andrew.hayes@wdc.usda.gov

Meridian (ID) Field Office
104 East Fairview Avenue, No. 291, Meridian, ID 83642-1733
Areas Covered: Idaho, Eastern Oregon, Eastern Washington

General Field Representative **Joe D. Bradley**
E-mail: joe.bradley@wdc.usda.gov

Merrifield (MN) Field Office
P.O. Box 190, Merrifield, MN 56465
Areas Covered: Northern Minnesota

General Field Representative **Dominic A. Henderson** . . . . (218) 765-3854
E-mail: dominic.henderson@wdc.usda.gov

Mooresville (NC) Field Office
PO Box 5347, Mooresville, NC 28117
Tel: (704) 896-8402
Areas Covered: NC, PR, SC, VI

General Field Representative **(Vacant)** . . . . (704) 896-8402

Owens Cross Road (AL) Field Office
P.O. Box 344, Owens Cross Roads, AL 35763
Tel: (256) 725-5353
Areas Covered: AL, MS

General Field Representative **Teresa C. Hunkapiller** . . . . . (256) 725-5353
P.O. Box 344, Owens Cross Roads, AL 35763
E-mail: teresa.hunkapiller@wdc.usda.gov

Tomah (WI) Field Office
P.O. Box 823, Tomah, WI 54660
Areas Covered: WI

General Field Representative **Andre M. Boening** . . . . (608) 372-2135
E-mail: andre.boening@wdc.usda.gov

Vancouver (WA) Field Office
800 NE Tenney Road, Suite 110-126, Vancouver, WA 98685
Areas Covered: Western Oregon, Western Washington

General Field Representative
Steven G. "Steve" Coyner . . . . (360) 574-9768
E-mail: steve.coyner@wdc.usda.gov

Wichita (KS) Field Office
329, Wichita, KS 67201
Areas Covered: KS, AK

General Field Representative **Shekinah Bailey** . . . . (316) 570-3249
Note: Temporarily covering ME.
E-mail: shekinah.bailey@wdc.usda.gov

★ Presidential Appointment Requiring Senate Confirmation ☆ Presidential Appointment ☐ Schedule C Appointment ◇ Career Senior Foreign Service Appointment
● Career Senior Executive Service (SES) Appointment ○ Non-Career Senior Executive Service (SES) Appointment ■ Postal Career Executive Service

United States Department of Commerce

Contents

United States Department of Commerce (DOC)

Description: The Department of Commerce supports and encourages the nation's international trade, economic growth and technological advancement. Among its programs are provisions for research and support of scientific, engineering and technological development, and assistance for domestic economic development. The department also provides statistics and analyses for business and government planners along with conducting the decennial census of the United States. The National Oceanic and Atmospheric Administration reports the weather and undertakes research into the physical environment and oceanic resources. The department also develops policies and conducts research in telecommunications, as well as granting patents and trademarks.

Herbert Clark Hoover Building, 1401 Constitution Avenue, NW, Washington, DC 20230
Tel: (202) 482-2000 (Personnel Locator)
Tel: (202) 482-6900 (Commerce Acquisitions Solutions)
Tel: (202) 482-4883 (Public Affairs)
Tel: (202) 482-3707 (Freedom of Information/Privacy Act)
Tel: (202) 482-2495 (Inspector General's Hotline - DC Metropolitan Area)
Tel: (800) 424-5197 (Inspector General's Hotline - Continental US, Alaska and Hawaii) Tel: (888) 487-2362 (Department of Commerce Hurricane Relief Call Center) Internet: www.commerce.gov
Internet: http://open.commerce.gov/ (Open Government Directive)
Internet: http://dir.commerce.gov (Person Finder)
Internet: www.usa.gov (Official US Government Website)

OFFICE OF THE SECRETARY

Herbert Clark Hoover Building, 1401 Constitution Avenue, NW, Washington, DC 20230
Tel: (202) 482-2000 Fax: (202) 482-4090

Office of the Inspector General (OIG)

Herbert Clark Hoover Building, 1401 Constitution Avenue, NW, Room 7898C, Washington, DC 20230
Tel: (202) 482-4661 Fax: (202) 482-0567 Internet: www.oig.doc.gov

Deputy Inspector General

Herbert Clark Hoover Building, 1401 Constitution Avenue, NW, Washington, DC 20230
Tel: (202) 482-4661 Fax: (202) 482-0567

Office of Financial and Intellectual Property Audits

Herbert Clark Hoover Building, 1401 Constitution Avenue NW, Room 7085, Washington, DC 20230

Atlanta (GA) Regional Office

Peachtree Summit Federal Building, 401 West Peachtree Street, NW, Suite 2742, Atlanta, GA 30308-3510
Tel: (404) 730-2780 Fax: (404) 730-2788

Regional Inspector General for Audit and Evaluation
Susan Roy .... (404) 730-2063
E-mail: sroy@oig.doc.gov

Denver (CO) Regional Office

1961 Stout Street, Suite 12-400, Denver, CO 80294
Tel: (303) 312-7674 Fax: (303) 312-7671

Regional Inspector General for Audit and Evaluation
Kenneth Stagner ....(303) 312-7674
E-mail: kstagner@oig.doc.gov

Seattle (WA) Regional Office

915 Second Avenue, Seattle, WA 98174
Tel: (206) 220-7970 Fax: (206) 220-7967

Regional Inspector General for Audit and Evaluation
David Sheppard ....(206) 220-7970
E-mail: dsheppard@oig.doc.gov
Education: Morgan State 1987 BAcc

Office of the Deputy Secretary

Herbert Clark Hoover Building, 1401 Constitution Avenue, NW, Room 5838, Washington, DC 20230
Tel: (202) 482-8376 Fax: (202) 501-1262

Bureau of Industry and Security (BIS)

Herbert Clark Hoover Building, 1401 Constitution Avenue, NW, Room 3898, Washington, DC 20230
Tel: (202) 482-2000 (Public Information) Internet: www.bis.doc.gov

OFFICE OF THE UNDER SECRETARY (OUS)

Herbert Clark Hoover Building, 1401 Constitution Avenue, NW, Washington, DC 20230
Fax: (202) 482-6216

Assistant Secretary for Export Administration

Herbert Clark Hoover Building, 1401 Constitution Avenue, NW, Washington, DC 20230
Fax: (202) 482-3911

Office of Exporter Services

Herbert Clark Hoover Building, 1401 Constitution Avenue, NW, Washington, DC 20230
Tel: (202) 482-4811 Fax: (202) 482-3322

Western Regional Office

2302 Martin Street, Suite 330, Irvine, CA 92612
Tel: (949) 660-0144 Fax: (949) 660-9347 Internet: www.bis.doc.gov

Network Director **Michael E. Hoffman**.........(949) 660-0144 ext. 112
E-mail: mhoffman@bis.doc.gov

Northern California Branch

111 North Market Street, 6th Floor, San Jose, CA 95113
Tel: (408) 998-8806 Fax: (408) 998-8677 Internet: www.bis.doc.gov
Areas Covered: AK, AZ, CA, CO, GU, HI, ID, NV, NM, OR, UT, WA

Export Licensing Counselor **Larry Sullivan** .... (408) 998-8806
E-mail: lsullivan@bis.doc.gov

★ Presidential Appointment Requiring Senate Confirmation ☆ Presidential Appointment □ Schedule C Appointment ◇ Career Senior Foreign Service Appointment
● Career Senior Executive Service (SES) Appointment ○ Non-Career Senior Executive Service (SES) Appointment ■ Postal Career Executive Service

DEPARTMENTS

Assistant Secretary for Export Enforcement
Herbert Clark Hoover Building, 1401 Constitution Avenue, NW, Room 3723, Washington, DC 20230
Tel: (202) 482-3618 Fax: (202) 482-4173

Office of Export Enforcement (OEE)
Herbert Clark Hoover Building, 1401 Constitution Avenue, NW, Washington, DC 20230
Tel: (202) 482-1208 Fax: (202) 482-5889

Boston (MA) Office
Thomas P. O'Neill, Jr. Federal Building, 10 Causeway Street., Room 253, Boston, MA 02222
Tel: (617) 565-6030 Fax: (617) 565-6039
Areas Covered: CT, MA, ME, NH, RI, VT

Special Agent-in-Charge **(Vacant)** .... (617) 565-6030
Assistant Special Agent-in-Charge **William Higgins** ..... (617) 565-6030
E-mail: william.higgins@bis.doc.gov

Chicago (IL) Office
One Oakbrook Terrace, Suite 804, Oakbrook Terrace, IL 60181
Tel: (630) 705-7010 Fax: (630) 705-0118
Areas Covered: IL, IN, IA, MI, MN, MO, NE, ND, SD, WI

Special Agent-in-Charge **Dan Clutch** .... (630) 705-7010
E-mail: dan.clutch@bis.doc.gov
Assistant Special Agent-in-Charge **(Vacant)** .... (630) 705-7010
Administrative Specialist **Maureen Entwisle** .... (630) 705-7010
E-mail: marueen.entwisle@bis.doc.gov

Dallas (TX) Office
225 East John Carpenter Freeway, Suite 820, Irving, TX 75062
Tel: (214) 296-1060 Fax: (214) 496-0647
Areas Covered: AR, KS, LA, OK, TX

Special Agent-in-Charge **Tracy Martin** .... (214) 296-1060
E-mail: tmartin@bis.doc.gov

Los Angeles (CA) Office
2601 Main Street, Suite 310, Irvine, CA 92614
Tel: (949) 251-9001 Fax: (949) 251-9103
Areas Covered: AZ, CO, HI, NM, Southern CA, Southern NV

Special Agent-in-Charge **Richard Weir** .... (949) 251-9001
Assistant Special Agent-in-Charge **Dan McGowan** ...... (949) 251-9001

Miami (FL) Office
200 East Las Olas Boulevard, Suite 1800, Fort Lauderdale, FL 33301
Tel: (954) 356-7540 Fax: (954) 356-7549

Special Agent-in-Charge **Robert Luzzi** .... (954) 356-7540
E-mail: robert.luzzi@bis.doc.gov

New York (NY) Office
1200 South Avenue, Suite 104, Staten Island, NY 10314-3420
Tel: (718) 370-0070 Fax: (718) 370-0826
Areas Covered: NJ, NY, PA

Special Agent-in-Charge **Jonathan Carson** .... (718) 370-0070
E-mail: jonathan.carson@bis.doc.gov

San Jose (CA) Office
160 West Santa Clara Street, Suite 725, San Jose, CA 95113
Tel: (408) 291-4204 Fax: (408) 291-4320

Special Agent-in-Charge **Joseph Whitehead** .... (408) 291-4215
E-mail: joseph.whitehead@bis.doc.gov
Assistant Special Agent-in-Charge **Todd Harris** .... (408) 291-4206
E-mail: todd.harris@bis.doc.gov

Washington (DC) Office
381 Elden Street, Suite 1125, Herndon, VA 20170-4817
Tel: (703) 487-9300 Fax: (703) 487-9463

Special Agent-in-Charge **Nasir Khan** .... (703) 487-9300
E-mail: nasir.khan@bis.doc.gov
Assistant Special Agent-in-Charge **Elizabeth Blanch** ..... (703) 487-9300
E-mail: elizabeth.blanch@bis.doc.gov

Washington (DC) Office *(continued)*

Administrative Specialist **Nick Crane** .... (703) 487-9300
E-mail: nick.crane@bis.doc.gov

Economic Development Administration (EDA)
Herbert Clark Hoover Building, 1401 Constitution Avenue, NW, Washington, DC 20230
Tel: (202) 482-2900 Tel: (202) 482-5271 (Human Resources)
Tel: (202) 482-5081 (Office of the Assistant Secretary)
Tel: (202) 482-4085 (Office of Public Affairs) Fax: (202) 273-4723
Internet: www.eda.gov

OFFICE OF THE ASSISTANT SECRETARY
Herbert Clark Hoover Building, 1401 Constitution Avenue, NW, Washington, DC 20230
Tel: (202) 482-5081 Fax: (202) 273-4781

Office of Regional Affairs

Atlanta (GA) Regional Office
Peachtree Summit Federal Building, 401 West Peachtree Street, NW, Suite 1820, Atlanta, GA 30308-3510
Tel: (404) 730-3002 Fax: (404) 730-3025
Areas Covered: AL, FL, GA, KY, MS, NC, SC, TN

● Regional Director **H. Phillip "Phil" Paradice, Jr.** .... (404) 730-3002
E-mail: hparadice@eda.gov
Education: Georgia Tech; Georgia State MBA
Regional Counsel **David E. Todd** .... (404) 730-3006
E-mail: dtodd@eda.gov
Area Director **Lee Mertins** .... (404) 730-3015
E-mail: lmertins@eda.gov
Administrative Director **Priscilla A. Kittles** .... (404) 730-3004
E-mail: pkittles@eda.gov
Administrative Officer **(Vacant)** .... (404) 730-3004
Economic Development Representative for Alabama **(Vacant)** .... (404) 730-3020
Economic Development Representative for Georgia **Jonathan Corso** .... (404) 730-3023
E-mail: jcorso@eda.gov
Economic Development Representative for Kentucky **Pamela Farmer** .... (404) 730-3026
E-mail: pfarmer@eda.gov
Economic Development Representative for Mississippi **Gilbert "Gil" Patterson** .... (404) 730-3032
E-mail: gpatterson2@eda.gov
Economic Development Representative for North Carolina **Hillary Sherman** .... (404) 730-3013
E-mail: hsherman@eda.gov
Economic Development Representative for Tennessee **Bertha Partin** .... (404) 730-3010
E-mail: bpartin@eda.gov
Economic Development Representative for Florida **Gregory Vaday** .... (404) 730-3009
E-mail: gvaday@eda.gov

South Carolina Office
1835 Assembly Street, Columbia, SC 29201
Tel: (803) 253-3640 Fax: (803) 253-3642

Economic Development Representative **Robin Cooley** .... (803) 253-3640
E-mail: rcooley@eda.gov

Austin (TX) Regional Office
903 San Jacinto Blvd, Suite 206, Austin, TX 78701-2858
Tel: (512) 381-8144 Fax: (512) 381-8177
Areas Covered: AR, LA, NM, OK, TX

● Regional Director **Jorge D. Ayala** .... (512) 381-8150
E-mail: jayala@eda.gov

★ Presidential Appointment Requiring Senate Confirmation ☆ Presidential Appointment □ Schedule C Appointment ◇ Career Senior Foreign Service Appointment
● Career Senior Executive Service (SES) Appointment ○ Non-Career Senior Executive Service (SES) Appointment ■ Postal Career Executive Service

Austin (TX) Regional Office *(continued)*

Economic Development Representative for Arkansas and Louisiana **Vicki Hendershot** .... (225) 964-6858
903 San Jacinto, Suite 206, Austin, TX 78701
E-mail: vhendershot@eda.gov

Economic Development Representative for South Texas **Robert Peche** .... (512) 568-7732
E-mail: rpeche1@eda.gov
Education: Trinity U BA, MURS

Economic Development Representative for New Mexico, West Texas **Trisha Korbas** .... (720) 626-1499
903 San Jacinto, Suite 206, Austin, TX 78701
E-mail: tkorbas@eda.gov

Economic Development Representative for Oklahoma and North Texas **Cornell Wesley** .... (405) 318-8588
903 San Jacinto, Suite 206, Austin, TX 78701
E-mail: cwesley@eda.gov

Chicago (IL) Regional Office

111 North Canal Street, Suite 855, Chicago, IL 60606-7204
Tel: (312) 353-8143 Fax: (312) 353-8575
Areas Covered: IL, IN, MI, MN, OH, WI

● Regional Director **Jeannette Tamayo** .... (312) 353-8143 ext. 121
E-mail: jtamayo@eda.gov
Administrative Director (Acting) **Anne Watkins** .... (312) 758-9770

Regional Counsel **Susan Brehm** .... (312) 353-8143 ext. 146
E-mail: sbrehm@eda.gov

Area Director **Dennis M. Foldenauer** .... (312) 353-8143 ext. 131
E-mail: DFoldenauer1@eda.gov

Area Director **Doggan Salley** .... (312) 353-8143 ext. 159
E-mail: dsalley@eda.gov

Economic Development Representative for Illinois and Minnesota **Darrin Fleener** .... (312) 353-7148 ext. 122
E-mail: dfleener@eda.gov

Economic Development Representative for Michigan and Wisconsin **Lee Shirey** .... (312) 353-8143 ext. 151
E-mail: lshirey@eda.gov

Economic Development Representative for Indiana and Ohio **Kyle Darton** .... (312) 789-9752
E-mail: kdarton@eda.gov

Denver (CO) Regional Office

410 17th Street, Suite 250, Denver, CO 80202
Tel: (303) 844-4715 Fax: (303) 844-3968
Areas Covered: CO, IA, KS, MO, MT, NE, ND, SD, UT, WY

● Regional Director **Angela Belden "Angie" Martinez** .... (303) 844-5360
E-mail: amartinez@eda.gov

Regional Counsel **Rachael B. Gamble** .... (303) 844-4404
E-mail: rgamble@eda.gov

Administrative Director **(Vacant)** .... (303) 844-4704

Administrative Officer **(Vacant)** .... (303) 844-4717

East Area Director **Cindy Edwards** .... (303) 844-5360
E-mail: cedwards@eda.gov

West Area Director **Mari V. Sutton** .... (303) 844-4403
E-mail: msutton@eda.gov

Economic Development Representative for Colorado **Trent Thompson** .... (303) 844-5452
E-mail: tthompson@eda.gov

Economic Development Representative for Iowa, Eastern and Central Missouri **Steven Castaner** .... (573) 590-1194
1244 Speer Boulevard, Suite 431, Denver, CO 80204
E-mail: scastaner@eda.gov

Economic Development Representative for Kansas, Nebraska, Missouri **Mark A. Werthmann** .... (913) 894-1586
1244 Speer Boulevard, Suite 431, Denver, CO 80204
E-mail: mwerthmann@eda.gov

Economic Development Representative for Montana, North Dakota, South Dakota and Wyoming **Kirk Keysor** .... (406) 599-9795
1244 Speer Boulevard, Suite 431, Denver, CO 80204
E-mail: kkeysor@eda.gov

Economic Development Representative for Utah **Trent Thompson** .... (303) 844-5452
E-mail: tthompson@eda.gov

Denver (CO) Regional Office *(continued)*

Economic Development Representative for North Dakota and South Dakota **Alex Smith** .... (303) 844-4715
1244 Speer Boulevard, Denver, CO 80204
E-mail: asmith1@eda.gov

Philadelphia (PA) Regional Office

The Curtis Center, Independence Square West, Suite 140 South, Philadelphia, PA 19106
Tel: (215) 597-4603 Fax: (215) 597-1063
Areas Covered: CT, DE, DC, ME, MD, MA, NH, NJ, NY, PA, PR, RI, VA, VI, VT, WV

● Regional Director (Acting) **Linda Cruz-Carnall** .... (215) 597-4603
E-mail: lcruz-carnall@eda.gov

Regional Counsel **(Vacant)** .... (215) 597-7896

Attorney-Advisor **William J. "Bill" O'Connor** .... (215) 597-7806
E-mail: bo'connor@eda.gov

Administrative Officer **Sanchia Gomez** .... (215) 597-4400
E-mail: sgomez@eda.gov

North Atlantic Area Director **(Vacant)** .... (215) 597-0642

South Atlantic Area Director **(Vacant)** .... (215) 597-4603

Economic Development Representative for New Jersey and New York City Metro **Edward L. Hummel** .... (215) 597-6767
E-mail: ehummel@eda.gov

Economic Development Representative for West Virginia **Tracey Rowan** .... (215) 597-1242
E-mail: trowan@eda.gov

Maine Office

34 Timberhill Road, Windham, ME 04062
Tel: (215) 316-2965

Economic Development Representative **Alan Brigham** ... (207) 347-2965
E-mail: abrigham@eda.gov

Seattle (WA) Regional Office

Jackson Federal Building, 915 Second Avenue, Room 1890, Seattle, WA 98174
Tel: (206) 220-7660 Fax: (206) 220-7669
Areas Covered: AK, American Samoa, AZ, CA, GU, HI, ID, Marshall Islands, Micronesia, NV, Northern Marianas, OR, and WA

● Regional Director **A. Leonard Smith** .... (206) 220-7660
E-mail: asmith@eda.gov

Regional Counsel **(Vacant)** .... (206) 220-7663
E-mail: KChekouras@eda.gov

Administrative Director **Cristina "CJ" Jackson** .... (206) 220-7662
E-mail: cjackson@eda.gov

Area Director **(Vacant)** .... (206) 220-7702

Environmental Protection Specialist **(Vacant)** .... (206) 220-7703

Economic Development Representative for Arizona and Washington **Jacob Macias** .... (206) 220-7666
E-mail: jmacias@eda.gov

Economic Development Representative for California (Northern and Costal) **Malinda Matson** .... (916) 235-0088
915 Second Avenue, Room 1890, Seattle, WA 98174
E-mail: mmatson@eda.gov

Alaska Office

510 L Street, Suite 444, Anchorage, AK 99501
Tel: (907) 271-2272 Fax: (907) 271-2274

Economic Development Representative **Shirley Kelly** ..... (907) 271-2272
E-mail: skelly2@eda.gov

Southern and Central California Office

5777 West Century Boulevard, Suite 1675, Los Angeles, CA 90045
Tel: (310) 348-5386 Fax: (310) 348-5387
Areas Covered: CA: Counties of Fresno, Imperial, Inyo, Kern, King, Los Angeles, Madera, Mariposa, Merced, Mono, Orange, Riverside, Sacramento, San Bernardino, San Diego, San Joaquin, San Luis Obispo, Santa Barbara, Stanislaus, Tulare, and Ventura.
Areas Covered: California (Southern and Central)

Economic Development Representative **Wilfred L. Marshall** .... (310) 348-5386
E-mail: wmarshall@eda.gov

★ Presidential Appointment Requiring Senate Confirmation ☆ Presidential Appointment ☐ Schedule C Appointment ◇ Career Senior Foreign Service Appointment
● Career Senior Executive Service (SES) Appointment ○ Non-Career Senior Executive Service (SES) Appointment ■ Postal Career Executive Service

Hawaii Office
Prince Jonah Kuhio Federal Building, 300 Ala Moana Boulevard, Room 5180, Honolulu, HI 96850
P.O. Box 50264, Honolulu, HI 96850
Tel: (808) 541-3391 Fax: (808) 541-3138
Areas Covered: Hawaii, Guam, American Samoa, Marshall Islands, Micronesia, Northern Marianas and Republic of Palau.

Economic Development Representative
Herbert Thweatt . . . . (808) 541-3391
E-mail: hthweatt@eda.gov

Oregon and Eastern Washington Office
One World Trade Center, 121 Southwest Salmon Street, Suite 244, Portland, OR 97204
Tel: (503) 326-3078 Fax: (503) 326-3160
Areas Covered: Oregon, Clark County, Washington and Eastern Washington.

Economic Development Representative for Oregon, Clark County, Idaho, Washington and Eastern WA
David Porter . . . . (503) 326-3078
E-mail: dporter@eda.gov

Economics and Statistics Administration (ESA)

1401 Constitution Avenue, NW, Room 4848, Washington, DC 20230
Fax: (202) 482-2889 Internet: www.esa.doc.gov

OFFICE OF THE UNDER SECRETARY

Herbert Clark Hoover Building, 14th Street and Constitution Avenue, NW, Room 4848, Washington, DC 20230
Tel: (202) 482-6607 Fax: (202) 482-0432

United States Bureau of the Census

4600 Silver Hill Road, Suitland, MD 20746
Mail: 4600 Silver Hill Road, Washington, DC 20233
Tel: (301) 763-4748 (General Information)
Tel: (301) 763-3342 (Procurement Information)
Tel: (301) 763-3000 (Public Information)
Tel: (301) 763-4636 (Publications Information/Customer Services)
Tel: (301) 763-3949 (Freedom of Information/Privacy Act)
Internet: www.census.gov
Internet: http://factfinder2.census.gov (American Factfinder)

Office of the Director

4600 Silver Hill Road, Room 8H006, Washington, DC 20233

Associate Director for Field Operations

4700 Silver Hill Road, Room 8H124, Washington, DC 20233-5000

Field Division

4700 Silver Hill Road, Mail Stop 5700, Washington, DC 20233-5700

Atlanta (GA) Regional Office
101 Marietta Street NW, Suite 3200, Atlanta, GA 30303-2700
Tel: (404) 730-3832 Fax: (404) 730-3835
E-mail: atlanta.regional.office@census.gov
Areas Covered: AL, FL, GA, LA, MS, NC, SC

Regional Director **George Grandy, Jr.** . . . . (404) 730-3921
E-mail: george.grandy.jr@census.gov
Assistant Regional Director **Reginald Bigham** . . . . (404) 730-3922
E-mail: reginald.bigham@census.gov
Assistant Regional Director **Peggy J. Howell-Jones** . . . . . (404) 730-3832
E-mail: peggy.j.howell-jones@census.gov
Administrative Officer **Crystal Boyett** . . . . (404) 730-3832
E-mail: crystal.n.boyett@census.gov
Data Dissemination Specialist **Gale D. Brock** . . . . (404) 865-1046
E-mail: gale.d.brock@census.gov
Data Dissemination Specialist **Monica K. Dukes** . . . . (404) 865-7236
E-mail: monica.k.dukes@census.gov

Atlanta (GA) Regional Office *(continued)*

Data Dissemination Assistant **Victoria Brooks** . . . . (404) 865-1108
E-mail: victoria.brooks@census.gov
Secretary **Angela M. Cirino** . . . . (404) 865-1119
E-mail: angela.m.cirino@census.gov
Coordinator **Margaret Bonaparte Kelly** . . . . (404) 730-3925
E-mail: margaret.bonaparte.kelly@census.gov
Coordinator **Dominic Koon** . . . . (404) 730-3924
E-mail: dominic.koon@census.gov
Coordinator **David D. Ratliff** . . . . (404) 865-1149
E-mail: david.d.ratliff@census.gov
Coordinator **Harry M. Rodriguez** . . . . (404) 865-1058
E-mail: harry.m.rodriguez@census.gov

Chicago (IL) Regional Office
1111 West 22nd Street, Suite 400, Oak Brook, IL 60523
Tel: (630) 288-9200 Fax: (630) 288-9288
E-mail: chicago.regional.office@census.gov
Internet: www.census.gov/rochi/www
Areas Covered: AR, IA, IL, IN, MI, MN, MO, WI

Regional Director **Marilyn A. Sanders** . . . . (630) 288-9201
E-mail: marilyn.a.sanders@census.gov
Assistant Regional Director
Lutricia D. "Trish" Thomas . . . . (630) 288-9206
E-mail: lutricia.d.thomas@census.gov
Assistant Regional Director **P. Andrew Cabiness** . . . . (630) 288-9200
E-mail: p.andrew.cabiness@census.gov
Education: Notre Dame 1996 BSc; Michigan State 1998 SM
Survey Coordinator **Rhonda Baksa** . . . . (630) 288-9226
E-mail: rhonda.baksa@census.gov
Survey Coordinator **Magdalena Z. Chuchra** . . . . (630) 288-9205
E-mail: magdalena.z.chuchra@census.gov
Survey Coordinator (Acting) **Debra A. Stanley** . . . . (630) 288-9200
E-mail: debra.a.stanley@census.gov
Survey Coordinator **(Vacant)** . . . . (630) 288-9206
Geographer **(Vacant)** . . . . (312) 454-2709
Data Dissemination Specialist **Jeana D. Bunn Hector** . . . . (313) 969-8571
E-mail: jeana.d.bunn.hector@census.gov
Data Dissemination Specialist
Deborah "Toni" Pitchford . . . . (312) 498-2240
E-mail: deborah.t.pitchford@census.gov
Data Dissemination Specialist **David F. Schuler** . . . . (630) 288-9269
E-mail: david.f.schuler@census.gov
Data Dissemination Specialist **Ileana C. Serrano** . . . . (630) 453-0752
E-mail: ileana.c.serrano@census.gov
Computer Specialist **(Vacant)** . . . . (630) 288-9256
Administrative Officer **Carol Reckamp** . . . . (630) 288-9303
E-mail: carol.reckamp@census.gov

Denver (CO) Regional Office
6950 West Jefferson Avenue, Suite 250, Denver, CO 80235
Tel: (720) 962-3700 Fax: (303) 969-6777
E-mail: denver_regional_office@census.gov
Areas Covered: AZ, CO, KS, MT, NE, NM, ND, OK, SD, TX, UT, WY

Regional Director **Cathy L. Lacy** . . . . (720) 962-3702
E-mail: cathy.lynn.lacy@census.gov
Education: Auburn 1986 BAM
Assistant Regional Director **Sherry D. Dowell** . . . . (720) 962-3711
Assistant Regional Director **Vicki A. McIntire** . . . . (720) 962-3703
Administrative Officer **Terry Bowman** . . . . (720) 962-3745
Information Technology Specialist **Mark Leroy Gum** . . . . (720) 962-3845
E-mail: mark.leroy.gum@census.gov
Information Technology Specialist
Pamela K. Owensby . . . . (720) 962-3834
E-mail: pamela.k.owensby@census.gov
Program Coordinator **Teresa M. Caldaro** . . . . (720) 962-3782
E-mail: teresa.m.caldaro@census.gov
Program Coordinator **Richard Gerdes** . . . . (720) 962-3712
E-mail: richard.gerdes@census.gov
Program Coordinator **Mark R. Hendrick** . . . . (720) 962-3713
E-mail: mark.r.hendrick@census.gov
Program Coordinator **Alyson R. Matti** . . . . (720) 962-3725
E-mail: alyson.r.matti@census.gov
Recruiting Officer **Leslie Jeanne Wright** . . . . (720) 962-3803

★ Presidential Appointment Requiring Senate Confirmation ☆ Presidential Appointment ☐ Schedule C Appointment ◇ Career Senior Foreign Service Appointment
● Career Senior Executive Service (SES) Appointment ○ Non-Career Senior Executive Service (SES) Appointment ■ Postal Career Executive Service

Los Angeles (CA) Regional Office
15350 Sherman Way, Suite 400, Van Nuys, CA 91406-4224
Tel: (818) 267-1700 Fax: (818) 267-1711 TTY: (818) 904-6249
E-mail: la.regional.office@census.gov
Areas Covered: AK, CA, HI, ID, NV, OR, WA

Regional Director **Julie A. Lam** . . . . (818) 267-1700
E-mail: julie.a.lam@census.gov Fax: (818) 267-1714
Assistant Regional Director **(Vacant)** . . . . (818) 267-1757
Assistant Regional Director **Thomas Kenneth Szabla** . . . (818) 267-1740
E-mail: thomas.kenneth.szabla@census.gov
Administrative Contact **Maria Isabel Cesena** . . . . . . (818) 267-1747
E-mail: maria.isabel.cesena@census.gov
Program Coordinator **Jeffrey C. Enos** . . . . (818) 267-1741
E-mail: jeffrey.c.enos@census.gov
Program Coordinator **Celeste Jimenez** . . . . (818) 267-1780
E-mail: celeste.jimenez@census.gov
Program Coordinator **Jennifer L. Marshall** . . . . . . (818) 267-1756
E-mail: jennifer.l.marshall@census.gov
Information Technology Specialist **Greg Johnson** . . . . (818) 267-1739
E-mail: gregory.johnson@census.gov
Information Technology Specialist **(Vacant)** . . . . . . (818) 267-1700
Recruiter **Yolanda Lazcano** . . . . (818) 267-1762

New York (NY) Regional Office
395 Hudson Street, Suite 800, New York, NY 10014-7451
Tel: (212) 584-3400 Fax: (212) 478-4800
E-mail: ny.regional.office@census.gov
Areas Covered: CT, ME, MA, NH, NJ, NY, PR, RI, VT

Regional Director **Jeff T. Behler** . . . . (212) 584-3491
E-mail: jeff.t.behler@census.gov
Education: Central Michigan BA
Assistant Regional Director **Jared Gerstenbluth** . . . . (212) 584-3400
E-mail: jared.gerstenbluth@census.gov
Assistant Regional Director **(Vacant)** . . . . (212) 584-3400
Program Coordinator **Lisa Moore** . . . . (212) 584-3400
E-mail: lisa.moore@census.gov
Program Coordinator **Lance W. Sanchez** . . . . (212) 584-3404
E-mail: lance.w.sanchez@census.gov
Program Coordinator **Harold Winsman** . . . . (212) 584-3439
E-mail: harold.winsman@census.gov
Program Coordinator **Joshua D. Winston** . . . . . . (212) 584-3403
E-mail: joshua.d.winston@census.gov
Information Services Assistant **Elizabeth Gaskin** . . . . (212) 584-3422
E-mail: elizabeth.gaskin@census.gov
Information Services Specialist **(Vacant)** . . . . . . (212) 584-3440

Philadelphia (PA) Regional Office
833 Chestnut Street, Suite 504, Philadelphia, PA 19107
Tel: (215) 717-1800 Fax: (215) 717-2588
E-mail: philadelphia.regional.office@census.gov
Internet: www.census.gov/rophi/www
Areas Covered: DE, DC, KY, MD, OH, PA, TN, VA, WV

Regional Director **Fernando E. Armstrong** . . . . . . (215) 717-1801
E-mail: fernando.e.armstrong@census.gov
Assistant Regional Director **Rosa M. Estrada** . . . . . (215) 717-1806
E-mail: rosa.m.estrada@census.gov
Assistant Regional Director **Mario T. Matthews** . . . . (215) 717-1802
E-mail: mario.t.matthews@census.gov
Geographic Programs and Data Services Coordinator
(Vacant) . . . . (215) 717-1062
Information Services Specialist **Joseph P. Quartullo** . . . (215) 756-5238
E-mail: joseph.p.quartullo@census.gov
Information Services Specialist **Noemi Eliasen** . . . . (215) 717-1834
E-mail: noemi.mendez@census.gov
Program Coordinator **Thomas J. Almerini** . . . . . . (215) 717-1804
E-mail: thomas.j.almerini@census.gov
Education: Temple 1983 AB, 1987 MUS
Program Coordinator **Philip M. Lutz** . . . . (215) 717-1805
E-mail: philip.m.lutz@census.gov
Program Coordinator **Terri Lyn Norris** . . . . (215) 717-1867
E-mail: terri.lyn.norris@census.gov
Program Coordinator **Maritza Laureda Padilla** . . . . . (215) 717-1803
E-mail: maritza.padilla.laureda@census.gov
Regional Recruiter **Lanette M. Swopes** . . . . (215) 717-1822

Philadelphia (PA) Regional Office *(continued)*

Administrative Officer **(Vacant)** . . . . (215) 717-1800
Administrative Assistant **Gwenn G. O'Grady** . . . . . (215) 717-1807
E-mail: gwenn.g.ogrady@census.gov

International Trade Administration (ITA)

Herbert Clark Hoover Building, 14th Street and Constitution Avenue, NW, Washington, DC 20230
Tel: (800) 872-8723 (Trade Information Center)
E-mail: tic@ita.doc.gov (Trade Information Center)
Internet: www.ita.doc.gov Internet: www.trade.gov

OFFICE OF THE UNDER SECRETARY

Herbert Clark Hoover Building, 1401 Constitution Avenue, NW, Washington, DC 20230
Tel: (202) 482-2867 Fax: (202) 482-4821

Assistant Secretary for the U.S. and Foreign Commercial Service (USFCS)

Herbert Clark Hoover Building, 14th Street and Constitution Avenue, NW, Washington, DC 20230
Tel: (202) 482-5777 Fax: (202) 482-5013 Internet: www.export.gov

Regional Offices

Great Lakes Network
600 Superior Avenue, East, Cleveland, OH 44114
Director **Michael "Mike" Miller** . . . . (216) 522-4750
E-mail: mike.miller@trade.gov

Buffalo (NY) U.S. Export Assistance Center
130 South Elmwood Avenue, Suite 530, Buffalo, NY 14202
Tel: (716) 551-4191 Fax: (716) 551-5290
Director **Rosanna Masucci** . . . . (716) 551-4191
E-mail: rosanna.masucci@trade.gov
International Trade Specialist **John Tracy** . . . . . . (315) 453-4070
445 Electronics Parkway, Suite 207, Liverpool, NY 13088
E-mail: john.tracy@trade.gov
International Trade Specialist **(Vacant)** . . . . (716) 551-4191

Cleveland (OH) U.S. Export Assistance Center
600 Superior Avenue, East, Suite 700, Cleveland, OH 44114
Tel: (216) 522-4750 Fax: (216) 522-2235
Director **Susan Whitney** . . . . (216) 522-4755
E-mail: susan.whitney@trade.gov
International Trade Specialist **Amy Freedman** . . . . . (216) 522-4732
E-mail: amy.freedman@trade.gov
International Trade Specialist **Todd Hiser** . . . . . . (216) 522-4756
E-mail: todd.hiser@trade.gov
International Trade Specialist **(Vacant)** . . . . (216) 522-4732
Regional Export Finance Manager
Patrick K. "Pat" Hayes . . . . (216) 522-4750
E-mail: pat.hayes@trade.gov

Cincinnati (OH) U.S. Export Assistance Center
36 East Seventh Street, Suite 2025, Cincinnati, OH 45202
Tel: (513) 684-2947 Fax: (513) 684-3200
E-mail: office.cincinnati@mail.doc.gov
Internet: http://export.gov/Ohio/southernohio/
Director **Marcia Brandstadt** . . . . (513) 684-3898
E-mail: marcia.brandstadt@trade.gov
Senior International Trade Specialist **Deborah Dirr** . . . . . (937) 775-4836
E-mail: deborah.dirr@trade.gov
International Trade Specialist **Christopher Simpson** . . . . (513) 684-6342
E-mail: chris.simpson@trade.gov

★ Presidential Appointment Requiring Senate Confirmation ☆ Presidential Appointment ☐ Schedule C Appointment ◇ Career Senior Foreign Service Appointment
● Career Senior Executive Service (SES) Appointment ○ Non-Career Senior Executive Service (SES) Appointment ■ Postal Career Executive Service

DEPARTMENTS

DEPARTMENTS

Detroit (MI) U.S. Export Assistance Center
8109 East Jefferson Avenue, Suite 110, Detroit, MI 48214
Tel: (313) 226-3650 Fax: (313) 226-3657
E-mail: office.detroit@mail.doc.gov

Director **Sara Coulter** .... (313) 226-3058
E-mail: sara.coulter@trade.gov
Financial Management Analyst **John O'Gara** .... (313) 226-3038

Grand Rapids (MI) U.S. Export Assistance Center
50 Front Avenue, Suite 1119, Grand Rapids, MI 49504
Tel: (616) 458-3564 Fax: (616) 458-3872

Director **Kendra Kuo** .... (616) 458-3564
E-mail: kendra.kuo@trade.gov

Lexington (KY) U.S. Export Assistance Center
333 East Vine Street, Suite 150, Lexington, KY 40507
Tel: (859) 225-7001 Fax: (859) 201-1139

Director **Sara Moreno** .... (859) 225-7001
E-mail: sara.moreno@trade.gov

Libertyville (IL) U.S. Export Assistance Center
28055 Ashley Circle, Suite 212, Libertyville, IL 60048
Tel: (847) 327-9082 Fax: (847) 247-0423 Internet: www.export.gov

Director **(Vacant)** .... (847) 327-9082

Memphis (TN) U.S. Export Assistance Center
22 North Front Street, Suite 200, Memphis, TN 38104
Tel: (901) 544-0930 Fax: (901) 543-3510
E-mail: Office.Memphis@trade.gov

Director (Acting) **Brie A. Knox** .... (615) 736-2223
E-mail: Brie.Knox@trade.gov
International Trade Specialist **Anne Gillman Cronin** ..... (615) 736-2224
E-mail: Anne.Cronin@trade.gov
International Trade Specialist **Patrick Spence** .... (615) 736-2225
E-mail: Patrick.Spence@trade.gov

Milwaukee (WI) U.S. Export Assistance Center
1235 North Milwaukee Street, Room R01, Milwaukee, WI 53202
Mail: 1025 North Broadway, Room R01, Milwaukee, WI 53202
Tel: (414) 297-3473 Fax: (414) 297-3470

Director **Koreen Grube** .... (414) 217-8333
E-mail: Koreen.Grube@trade.gov
International Trade Specialist **Rebecca Gladen** .... (414) 405-3560
E-mail: Rebecca.Gladen@trade.gov
International Trade Specialist **Elizabeth Laxague** .... (414) 297-3458
E-mail: elizabeth.laxague@trade.gov

Pontiac (MI) U.S. Export Assistance Center
Building 47 West, 1025 Campus Drive South, Waterford, MI 48328
Tel: (248) 975-9600 Fax: (248) 975-9606

Director **Richard Corson** .... (248) 975-9604
E-mail: richard.corson@trade.gov
Senior International Trade Specialist **Eve Lerman** .... (248) 975-9605
E-mail: eve.lerman@trade.gov
Senior International Trade Specialist **Jennifer Loffredo** ... (248) 452-2254
E-mail: jennifer.loffredo@trade.gov
International Trade Specialist **(Vacant)** .... (248) 975-9609
International Trade Specialist **(Vacant)** .... (248) 975-9602

Rochester (NY) U.S. Export Assistance Center
400 Andrews Street, Suite 710, Rochester, NY 14604
Tel: (585) 399-7065 Fax: (585) 399-7570

Director **Timothy McCall** .... (585) 399-7065
E-mail: timothy.mccall@trade.gov

Ypsilanti (MI) U.S. Export Assistance Center
c/o Eastern Michigan University College of Business,
300 West Michigan Avenue, Suite 306G, Ypsilanti, MI 48197
Tel: (616) 458-3564 Fax: (616) 458-3872

Director **(Vacant)** .... (616) 458-3564

Midwest Network
1000 Walnut Street, Suite 505, Kansas City, MO 64106

Director **Regina Heise** .... (816) 421-1876
E-mail: regina.heise@trade.gov

Chicago (IL) U.S. Export Assistance Center
233 North Michigan Ave, Suite 260, Chicago, IL 60601
Tel: (312) 353-8040 Fax: (312) 353-8120

Director **Hovan Asdourian** .... (312) 886-8094
E-mail: hovan.asdourian@trade.gov
Senior International Trade Specialist
Kyungsoo "Dan" Kim .... (312) 353-4798
E-mail: kyungsoo.kim@trade.gov
Senior International Trade Specialist **Haley Pitonyak** ..... (312) 353-5096
E-mail: haley.pitonyak@trade.gov
Senior International Trade Specialist **Debra Rogers** ...... (312) 353-6988
E-mail: debra.rogers@trade.gov
Senior International Trade Specialist
Richard Carpenter .... (312) 353-7711
E-mail: richard.carpenter@trade.gov
International Trade Specialist **Monica Toporkiewicz** ..... (312) 353-8059
E-mail: monica.toporkewicz@trade.gov
International Trade Specialist **(Vacant)** .... (312) 353-5097
Commercial Officer **Evan Scritchfield** .... (312) 482-3222
E-mail: evan.scritchfield@trade.gov
Foreign Officer **(Vacant)** .... (312) 353-8490

Des Moines (IA) U.S. Export Assistance Center
210 Walnut Street, Suite 749, Des Moines, IA 50309
Tel: (515) 284-4590 Fax: (515) 288-1437

Director **Patricia Cook** .... (515) 284-4590
E-mail: patricia.cook@trade.gov
International Trade Specialist **Tom Dykes** .... (515) 284-4591

Indianapolis (IN) U.S. Export Assistance Center
46 E. Ohio St., Room #508, Indianapolis, IN 46142
Tel: (317) 226-6153 Fax: (317) 221-0120

Director **Mark Cooper** .... (317) 226-6290
E-mail: mark.cooper@trade.gov
Senior International Trade Specialist
Dusan Marinkovic .... (317) 582-2300
E-mail: dusan.marinkovic@trade.gov
International Trade Specialist **Ye Hu** .... (317) 582-2300
E-mail: ye.hu@trade.gov

Kansas City (MO) U.S. Export Assistance Center
1000 Walnut Street, Suite 505, Kansas City, MO 64106
Tel: (816) 421-1876 Fax: (816) 471-7839
E-mail: office.kansascity@trade.gov

Director (Acting) **Sally Pacheco** .... (816) 421-0541
E-mail: sally.pacheco@trade.gov
International Trade Specialist **Sally Pacheco** .... (816) 421-1876
E-mail: sally.pacheco@trade.gov
International Trade Specialist **Marisa Ring** .... (816) 421-4809
E-mail: marisa.ring@trade.gov

Louisville (KY) U.S. Export Assistance Center
601 West Broadway, Room 634B, Louisville, KY 40202
Tel: (502) 582-5066 Fax: (502) 582-6573

Director **Margaret "Peggy" Pauley** .... (502) 836-1677
E-mail: peggy.pauley@trade.gov
Senior International Trade Specialist **Brian Miller** .... (502) 693-9591
E-mail: brian.miller@trade.gov
Senior International Trade Specialist **Mona Musa** .... (502) 683-8770
E-mail: mona.musa@trade.gov

Minneapolis (MN) U.S. Export Assistance Center
330 Second Avenue South, Suite 410, Minneapolis, MN 55401
Tel: (612) 348-1638 Fax: (612) 348-1650
E-mail: office.minneapolis@trade.gov

Director **Ryan Kanne** .... (612) 348-1637
E-mail: ryan.kanne@trade.gov

★ Presidential Appointment Requiring Senate Confirmation ☆ Presidential Appointment □ Schedule C Appointment ◇ Career Senior Foreign Service Appointment
● Career Senior Executive Service (SES) Appointment ○ Non-Career Senior Executive Service (SES) Appointment ■ Postal Career Executive Service

Peoria (IL) U.S. Export Assistance Center
Jobst Hall, 922 North Glenwood Avenue, Bradley University, Room 141, Peoria, IL 61606 (Deliveries)
Mail: 1501 West Bradley Avenue, Peoria, IL 61625
Tel: (309) 671-7815 Fax: (309) 671-7818

Director **Elizabeth Ahern** .... (309) 671-7815
E-mail: elizabeth.ahern@trade.gov

Oklahoma City (OK) U.S. Export Assistance Center
301 NW 63rd Street, Suite 330, Oklahoma City, OK 73116
Tel: (405) 608-5302 Fax: (405) 608-4211
E-mail: oklahomacity.office@trade.gov

Director **Marcus Verner** .... (405) 608-5302
E-mail: marcus.verner@trade.gov
International Trade Specialist **Ashley Wilson** .... (405) 608-5302
E-mail: Ashley.Wilson@trade.gov
International Trade Specialist **(Vacant)** .... (405) 608-5302

Omaha (NE) U.S. Export Assistance Center
6708 Pine Street, Room 205, Omaha, NE 68182
Tel: (402) 597-0193 Fax: (402) 554-3473
Internet: http://export.gov/nebraska/

Director **Meredith Bond** .... (402) 346-6947
E-mail: meredith.bond@trade.gov

Rockford (IL) U.S. Export Assistance Center
327 South Church Street, Rockford, IL 61101
Tel: (815) 316-2380 Fax: (888) 628-2571
E-mail: Office.Rockford@trade.gov

Director **(Vacant)** .... (815) 316-2380

Saint Louis (MO) U.S. Export Assistance Center
4300 Goodfellow Boulevard, Building 110, Suite 1100-A, St. Louis, MO 63120
Tel: (314) 432-1500 Fax: (314) 425-3381
E-mail: office.stlouis@trade.gov
Internet: www.export.gov/missouri/st.louis

Director **Cory Simek** .... (314) 260-3782
E-mail: cory.simek@trade.gov Fax: (314) 260-3793
International Trade Specialist **Warren Anderson** .... (314) 260-3785
E-mail: warren.anderson@trade.gov
International Trade Specialist **Margaret Gottlieb** .... (314) 260-3786
E-mail: margaret.gottlieb@trade.gov
International Trade Specialist **Diana Poli** .... (314) 260-3783
E-mail: diana.poli@trade.gov
International Trade Specialist **Kristi Wiggins** .... (314) 260-3787
E-mail: kristi.wiggins@trade.gov

Sioux Falls (SD) U.S. Export Assistance Center
Madsen Center, Augustana College, 2001 South Summit Avenue, Room 122, Sioux Falls, SD 57197
Tel: (605) 330-4265 Fax: (605) 330-4266

Director **Cinnamon King** .... (605) 330-4265
E-mail: cinnamon.king@trade.gov

Tulsa (OK) U.S. Export Assistance Center
700 North Greenwood Avenue, Suite 1400, Tulsa, OK 74106
Tel: (918) 581-7650 Fax: (918) 581-6263
Internet: www.export.gov/oklahoma

International Trade Specialist (Acting) **Ashley Wilson** ... (918) 581-7650
E-mail: ashley.wilson@trade.gov

Wichita (KS) U.S. Export Assistance Center
150 North Main Street, Suite 200, Wichita, KS 67202
Tel: (316) 263-4067 Fax: (316) 263-8306
Internet: www.buyusa.gov/wichita

Director **Andrew J. Anderson** .... (316) 263-4067
E-mail: andrew.anderson@trade.gov

Mid-Atlantic Network
One Penn Center, 1617 John F. Kennedy Boulevard, Suite 1580, Philadelphia, PA 19106

Regional Director **Joseph Hanley** .... (215) 597-6108
E-mail: joseph.hanley@trade.gov
Education: Scranton 1987 BS; George Washington 1990 MA

Arlington (VA) U.S. Export Assistance Center
1501 Wilson Boulevard, Suite 1225, Arlington, VA 22206
Tel: (703) 235-0100 Internet: https://www.export.gov/virginia/

Director **William Fanjoy** .... (703) 235-0100
E-mail: william.fanjoy@trade.gov
Senior International Trade Specialist **Sandra Collazo** .... (703) 235-0101
E-mail: sandra.collazo@trade.gov
Senior International Trade Specialist
Pompeya Lambrecht .... (703) 235-0102
E-mail: pompeya.Llambrecht@trade.gov
Senior International Trade Specialist **April Redmon** ..... (703) 235-0103
E-mail: april.redmon@trade.gov
Senior International Trade Specialist **(Vacant)** .... (703) 235-0104
Commercial Officer **Cody Dietrich** .... (703) 235-0064
E-mail: cody.dietrich@trade.gov
Communications Manager **(Vacant)** .... (703) 235-0100

Baltimore (MD) U.S. Export Assistance Center
300 West Pratt Street, Suite 300, Baltimore, MD 21201
Tel: (410) 962-4539 Fax: (410) 962-4529

Director **Colleen Fisher** .... (410) 962-3097
E-mail: colleen.fisher@trade.gov
Senior International Trade Specialist **Jolanta Coffey** ..... (410) 962-4578
E-mail: jolanta.coffey@trade.gov
Senior International Trade Specialist
Carey Paul Esslinger .... (410) 962-4518
E-mail: carey.esslinger@trade.gov
Senior International Trade Specialist **Aisha Jones** .... (410) 962-6896
E-mail: aisha.jones@trade.gov
Senior International Trade Specialist
Paul Matino .... (410) 962-4539 ext. 108
E-mail: paul.matino@trade.gov
Commercial Officer **Carey Arun** .... (410) 962-4576
E-mail: Carey.Arun@trade.gov

Charleston (SC) U.S. Export Assistance Center
1362 McMillan Avenue, Suite 100, North Charleston, SC 29405
Tel: (843) 746-3404 Fax: (843) 529-0305
Internet: www.export.gov/southcarolina

Director **Phil Minard** .... (843) 746-3404
E-mail: phil.minard@trade.gov

Charlotte (NC) U.S. Export Assistance Center
521 East Morehead Street, Suite 435, Charlotte, NC 28202
Tel: (704) 333-4886 Fax: (704) 332-2681
E-mail: office.charlotte@trade.gov

Office Director **Greg Sizemore** .... (704) 333-4886 ext. 229
E-mail: greg.sizemore@trade.gov
Senior International Trade Specialist
Juanita Harthun .... (704) 333-2198 ext. 224
E-mail: juanita.harthun@trade.gov
Senior International Trade Specialist
Daniel "Dan" Holt .... (704) 333-4886 ext. 226
E-mail: dan.holt@trade.gov
Senior International Trade Specialist
Crystal Mills .... (704) 333-4886 ext. 223
E-mail: Crystal.Mills@trade.gov

Commercial Service Harlem
163 West 125th Street, Suite 901, New York, NY 10027
Tel: (212) 860-6200 Fax: (212) 860-6203
E-mail: office.harlem@trade.gov
Internet: http://export.gov/newyork/harlem/

Director **K. L. Fredericks** .... (212) 860-6200
E-mail: kl.fredericks@trade.gov
Education: Montclair State Col; Rutgers MA; Baruch Col MBA

(continued on next page)

★ Presidential Appointment Requiring Senate Confirmation ☆ Presidential Appointment □ Schedule C Appointment ◇ Career Senior Foreign Service Appointment
● Career Senior Executive Service (SES) Appointment ○ Non-Career Senior Executive Service (SES) Appointment ■ Postal Career Executive Service

DEPARTMENTS

Commercial Service Harlem *(continued)*

Export Assistance Specialist **David A. Roman** .... (212) 860-6200
E-mail: david.roman@trade.gov

U.S. Commercial Service Long Island
Entrepreneurship and Technology Innovation Center,
Room 401, Old Westbury, NY 11568
Tel: (516) 427-9117 E-mail: office.longisland@trade.gov

Director **Susan Sadocha** .... (516) 427-9117
E-mail: susan.sadocha@trade.gov
International Trade Specialist **Marisel Trespalacios** ...... (516) 493-8150
E-mail: marisel.trespalacios@trade.gov

New York (NY) U.S. Export Assistance Center
The Ted Weiss Federal Building, 290 Broadway,
Suite 1312, New York, NY 10007
Tel: (212) 809-2675 Fax: (212) 809-2687
E-mail: office.newyork@trade.gov
Areas Covered: NJ, NY, Manhattan, Staten Island

Director **Carmela Mammas** .... (212) 809-2676
E-mail: carmela.mammas@trade.gov
Senior International Trade Specialist **Melissa Hill** .... (212) 471-0062
E-mail: melissa.hill@trade.gov
Senior International Trade Specialist **Peter Sexton** ...... (212) 809-2647
E-mail: peter.sexton@trade.gov
Senior International Trade Specialist
Anastasia Xenias .... (212) 809-2685
E-mail: anastasia.xenias@trade.gov
Commercial Officer **(Vacant)** .... (212) 471-0060
NY/NJ Regional Manager **(Vacant)** .... (212) 809-2645

Northern New Jersey U.S. Export Assistance Center
744 Broad Street, Suite 1505, Newark, NJ 07102
Tel: (973) 645-4682 Fax: (973) 645-4783
E-mail: office.newark@trade.gov

Director **Susan Widmer** .... (973) 645-4682 ext. 216
E-mail: susan.widmer@trade.gov
Senior International Trade Specialist
Brian Beams .... (973) 645-4682 ext. 210
E-mail: brian.beams@trade.gov
Senior International Trade Specialist
Tricia McLain .... (973) 645-4682 ext. 212
E-mail: tricia.mclain@trade.gov

Philadelphia (PA) U.S. Export Assistance Center
The Curtis Center, 1617 John F. Kennedy Boulevard,
Suite 580 West, Philadelphia, PA 19106
Tel: (215) 597-6101 Fax: (215) 597-6123
Internet: http://export.gov/pennsylvania/philadelphia/

Director **Antonio Ceballos** .... (215) 597-7141
E-mail: antonio.ceballos@trade.gov
Education: Claremont Grad 1998 MIA
Senior International Trade Specialist **Theo Hunte** .... (215) 597-6105
E-mail: theo.hunte@trade.gov
International Trade Specialist **Iris Kapo** .... (215) 597-6127
E-mail: iris.kapo@trade.gov
International Trade Specialist **Tony Pu** .... (215) 597-6120
E-mail: tony.pu@trade.gov

Pittsburgh (PA) U.S. Export Assistance Center
William S. Moorhead Federal Building, 1000 Liberty Avenue,
Suite 807, Pittsburgh, PA 15222
Tel: (412) 644-2800 Fax: (412) 644-2803
E-mail: office.pittsburgh@trade.gov
Internet: www.export.gov/pennsylvania/pittsburgh

Director **Lyn Doverspike** .... (412) 644-2820
E-mail: lyn.doverspike@trade.gov
Senior International Trade Specialist **Steven Murray** ..... (412) 644-2819
E-mail: steven.murray@trade.gov
International Trade Specialist **LeeAnne Haworth** .... (412) 644-2816
E-mail: leeanne.haworth@trade.gov
International Trade Specialist **Ryan Russell** .... (412) 644-2817
E-mail: ryan.russell@trade.gov

Richmond (VA) U.S. Export Assistance Center
800 East Leigh Street, Richmond, VA 23219
Tel: (804) 771-2246 Fax: (804) 771-2390

Director **Joshua Kaplan** .... (804) 461-9324
E-mail: joshua.kaplan@trade.gov

Trenton (NJ) U.S. Export Assistance Center
Princeton Pike Corporate Center, Lawrenceville, NJ 08648-2311
Tel: (856) 722-0958 Fax: (856) 722-0716
Areas Covered: Central and Southern NJ

Director (Acting) **Debora Sykes** .... (609) 896-2734
E-mail: debora.sykes@trade.gov
Senior International Trade Specialist
Thomas P. Mottley .... (732) 571-3641
E-mail: thomas.mottley@trade.gov
Senior International Trade Specialist **Janice Barlow** ..... (609) 896-2731
E-mail: janice.barlow@trade.gov Fax: (609) 896-4294
Commercial Officer **Janet Robertson** .... (609) 896-2734
E-mail: Janet.Robertson@trade.gov
Export Assistance Specialist **(Vacant)** .... (609) 896-2732

Westchester U.S. Export Assistance Center
707 Westchester Avenue, Suite 209, White Plains, NY 10604
Tel: (914) 682-6712 Fax: (914) 682-6698
E-mail: office.westchester@mail.doc.gov

Director **Joan G. Kanlian** .... (914) 682-6712
E-mail: joan.kanlian@trade.gov
Senior International Trade Specialist **Cathy Gibbons** ..... (914) 682-6712
E-mail: cathy.gibbons@trade.gov
Senior International Trade Specialist
Michael Grossman .... (914) 682-6712
E-mail: michael.grossman@trade.gov

Northeast Network
55 New Sudbury Street, Suite 1826A, Boston, MA 02203

Director **James Cox** .... (617) 565-4307
E-mail: james.cox@trade.gov

Boston (MA) U.S. Export Assistance Center
John F. Kennedy Federal Building, 55 New Sudbury Street,
Suite 1826A, Boston, MA 02203
Tel: (617) 565-4301 Fax: (617) 565-4313
E-mail: office.boston@mail.doc.gov

Director **James Paul** .... (617) 565-4304
E-mail: james.paul@trade.gov
Senior International Trade Specialist **Maryanne Burke** ... (617) 565-4303
E-mail: maryanne.burke@trade.gov
Senior International Trade Specialist
Michelle Ouellette .... (617) 565-4302
E-mail: michelle.ouellette@trade.gov
Foreign Commercial Officer **(Vacant)** .... (617) 565-4308
International Trade Specialist **(Vacant)** .... (617) 565-4301
Program Manager **John Joyce** .... (617) 565-4305
E-mail: john.joyce@trade.gov

Middletown (CT) U.S. Export Assistance Center
213 Court Street, Suite 903, Middletown, CT 06457-3382
Tel: (860) 638-6950 Fax: (860) 638-6970
E-mail: office.middletown@trade.gov

Director **Anne S. Evans** .... (860) 638-6953
E-mail: anne.evans@trade.gov
Senior International Trade Specialist **Melissa Grosso** .... (860) 638-6955
E-mail: melissa.grosso@trade.gov
International Trade Specialist **Anthony Sargis** .... (860) 638-6954
E-mail: Anthony.Sargis@trade.gov
Market Research Specialist **Cheryl McClellan** .... (860) 638-6951
E-mail: cheryl.mcclellan@trade.gov
New to Export Trade Specialist **(Vacant)** .... (860) 638-6952

★ Presidential Appointment Requiring Senate Confirmation ☆ Presidential Appointment ☐ Schedule C Appointment ◇ Career Senior Foreign Service Appointment
● Career Senior Executive Service (SES) Appointment ○ Non-Career Senior Executive Service (SES) Appointment ■ Postal Career Executive Service

Montpelier (VT) U.S. Export Assistance Center
87 State Street, Room 205, Montpelier, VT 05601
Tel: (802) 828-4508 Fax: (802) 828-3258

Director **Susan Murray** .... (802) 828-4508
E-mail: susan.murray@trade.gov

New Hampshire U.S. Export Assistance Center
121 Technology Drive, Suite 2, Durham, NH 03824
Tel: (603) 953-0212 Fax: (603) 953-0213

Director **Justin Oslowski** .... (603) 610-2416
E-mail: justin.oslowski@trade.gov
International Trade Specialist **Taylor Little** .... (603) 610-2417
E-mail: taylor.little@trade.gov

Portland (ME) U.S. Export Assistance Center
Maine International Trade Center, 511 Congress Street, Portland, ME 04101
Tel: (207) 780-3756 Fax: (207) 780-3761

Director **Jeffrey Porter** .... (207) 541-3756
E-mail: jeffrey.porter@trade.gov

Providence (RI) U.S. Export Assistance Center
315 Iron Horse Way, Suite 101, Providence, RI 02908
Tel: (401) 528-5104 Fax: (401) 528-5067
E-mail: office.providence@mail.doc.gov

Director **Keith Yatsuhashi** .... (401) 528-5104
E-mail: keith.yatsuhashi@trade.gov

Pacific North Network
1410 Ethan Way, Sacramento, CA 95825

Regional Director **David G. Fiscus** .... (408) 242-9770
E-mail: David.Fiscus@trade.gov

Alaska U.S. Export Assistance Center
431 West 7th Avenue, Suite 108, Anchorage, AK 99501
Tel: (907) 271-6237 Fax: (907) 278-2982
Internet: www.buyusa.gov/alaska

Director **Debra "Debbie" Franklin** .... (907) 271-6237
E-mail: debra.franklin@trade.gov

Boise (ID) U.S. Export Assistance Center
700 West State Street, 2nd Floor, Boise, ID 83720
Tel: (208) 364-7791 Fax: (208) 334-2783
E-mail: boise.office.box@mail.doc.gov

Director **Amy Benson** .... (208) 364-7791
E-mail: amy.benson@trade.gov

Fresno (CA) U.S. Export Assistance Center
801 R Street, Suite 201, Fresno, CA 93721
Tel: (559) 348-9859 Fax: (559) 278-6964
Internet: www.export.gov/fresno

Director **Glen Roberts** .... (559) 680-3378
E-mail: glen.roberts@trade.gov
Senior International Trade Specialist **Bernadette Rojas** ... (559) 341-7137
E-mail: bernadette.rojas@trade.gov

Honolulu (HI) U.S. Export Assistance Center
521 Ala Moana Boulevard, Foreign Trade Zone #9, Room 214, Honolulu, HI 96813
Tel: (808) 522-8040 Fax: (808) 522-8045

Director **John Holman** .... (808) 522-8041
E-mail: john.holman@trade.gov

Montana U.S. Export Assistance Center
Gallagher Business Building, Suite 257, Missoula, MT 59812
Tel: (406) 370-0097 Fax: (503) 326-6351

Director **Carey Hester** .... (406) 370-0097
E-mail: carey.hester@trade.gov

Monterey U.S. Export Assistance Center
411 Pacific Street, Suite 316A, Monterey, CA 93940
Tel: (408) 535-2757 ext. 108 Fax: (831) 402-9849

Director (Acting) **Joanne Vliet** .... (408) 535-2757
E-mail: Joanne.Vliet@trade.gov

North Bay U.S. Export Assistance Center
50 Acacia Avenue, San Rafael, CA 94901
Tel: (415) 485-6200 Fax: (415) 485-6219

Director **Elizabeth Krauth** .... (415) 485-6200
E-mail: elizabeth.krauth@trade.gov
International Trade Specialist **Daniel Giavina** .... (415) 485-6200
E-mail: daniel.giavina@trade.gov

Oakland (CA) U.S. Export Assistance Center
1301 Clay Street, Suite 630-N, Oakland, CA 94612
Tel: (510) 273-7350 Fax: (510) 273-7352

Office Director **Rod Hirsch** .... (510) 273-7350
E-mail: rod.hirsch@trade.gov
International Trade Specialist **Cindy Ma** .... (510) 273-7351
E-mail: cindy.ma@trade.gov

Portland (OR) U.S. Export Assistance Center
One World Trade Center, 121 SW Salmon Street, Suite 242, Portland, OR 97204
Tel: (503) 326-3001 Fax: (503) 326-6351
Internet: www.export.gov/oregon

Director **Scott Goddin** .... (503) 326-5156
E-mail: scott.goddin@trade.gov
Senior International Trade Specialist **Allan Christian** ..... (503) 326-5450
E-mail: allan.christian@trade.gov
Senior International Trade Specialist
Kellie Holloway-Jarman .... (503) 326-3002
E-mail: kellie.holloway@trade.gov
Senior International Trade Specialist **Jennifer Woods** .... (503) 326-5290
E-mail: jennifer.woods@trade.gov
International Trade Finance Specialist SBA
James "Jim" Newton .... (503) 326-5498
E-mail: jim.newton@sba.gov

Sacramento (CA) U.S. Export Assistance Center
1410 Ethan Way, Suite N-131, Sacramento, CA 95825
Tel: (916) 566-7170 Fax: (916) 566-7123
Internet: http://export.gov/california/sacramento/

Director **George Tastard** .... (916) 566-7170
E-mail: george.tastard@trade.gov
International Trade Specialist **Anthony Hill** .... (916) 566-7011
E-mail: anthony.hill@trade.gov
Trade Center Assistant **(Vacant)** .... (916) 566-7169

San Francisco (CA) U.S. Export Assistance Center
50 Fremont Street, Suite 2450, San Francisco, CA 94105
Tel: (415) 705-2300 Fax: (415) 705-2299
E-mail: office.sanfrancisco@mail.doc.gov

Director **Stephan Crawford** .... (415) 705-2301
E-mail: stephan.crawford@trade.gov
Commercial Officer **Joshua Startup** .... (415) 705-1765
E-mail: joshua.startup@trade.gov
International Trade Specialist **Ludwika Alvarez** .... (415) 705-1765
E-mail: Ludwika.Alvarez@trade.gov
Education: La Salle U BA; George Washington MA
International Trade Specialist **Jetta DeNend** .... (415) 744-7728
E-mail: jetta.denend@trade.gov
International Trade Specialist **Daniel Giavina** .... (415) 705-2281
E-mail: daniel.giavina@trade.gov

Seattle (WA) U.S. Export Assistance Center
2001 Sixth Avenue, Suite 2610, Seattle, WA 98121
Tel: (206) 553-5615 Fax: (206) 553-7253
Internet: http://export.gov/washington/Seattle/

Director **Diane Mooney** .... (206) 553-5615 ext. 236
E-mail: diane.mooney@trade.gov

(continued on next page)

★ Presidential Appointment Requiring Senate Confirmation ☆ Presidential Appointment ☐ Schedule C Appointment ◇ Career Senior Foreign Service Appointment
● Career Senior Executive Service (SES) Appointment ○ Non-Career Senior Executive Service (SES) Appointment ■ Postal Career Executive Service

Seattle (WA) U.S. Export Assistance Center *(continued)*

Senior International Trade Specialist **Young Oh** . . . . (253) 973-5386
E-mail: young.oh@trade.gov
International Trade Specialist **Janet Bauermeister** . . . . . . (509) 344-9398
E-mail: Janet.Bauermeister@trade.gov
International Trade Specialist **Bob Deane** . . . . (206) 553-5615 ext. 225
E-mail: bob.deane@trade.gov
International Trade Specialist **Sam Tsoming** . . . . (206) 553-5615 ext. 232
E-mail: sam.tsoming@trade.gov
Project Manager **Laura McCall** . . . . (206) 553-5615 ext. 226
E-mail: laura.mccall@trade.gov

Silicon Valley U.S. Export Assistance Center
55 South Market Street, Suite 1040, San Jose, CA 95113
Tel: (408) 535-2757 Fax: (408) 535-2758
E-mail: silicon.valley.office.box@mail.doc.gov

Director **Joanne Vliet** . . . . (408) 535-2747
E-mail: joanne.vliet@trade.gov
Senior International Trade Specialist **Chris Damm** . . . . (408) 535-2743
E-mail: chris.damm@trade.gov
International Trade Specialist **Shannon Fraser** . . . . (408) 535-2751
E-mail: shannon.fraser@trade.gov
International Trade Specialist **Sheryl Hitomi** . . . . (408) 535-2745
E-mail: sheryl.hitomi@trade.gov
International Trade Specialist **Cindy Ma** . . . . (408) 535-2744
E-mail: cindy.ma@trade.gov
International Trade Specialist **Gabriela Zelaya** . . . . (408) 535-2748
E-mail: gabriela.zelaya@trade.gov
Foreign Commercial Officer **(Vacant)** . . . . (408) 535-2757 ext. 102

Spokane (WA) U.S. Export Assistance Center
801 West Riverside, Suite 100, Spokane, WA 99201
Tel: (509) 344-9398 Fax: (503) 326-6351
E-mail: spokane.office.box@trade.gov

Director **Janet Bauermeister** . . . . (509) 344-9398
E-mail: janet.bauermeister@trade.gov

Pacific South Network
2302 Martin Court, Irvine, CA 92612

Director **Richard Swanson** . . . . (949) 283-1024
E-mail: richard.swanson@trade.gov

Bakersfield (CA) U.S. Export Assistance Center
2100 Chester Avenue, Suite 166, Bakersfield, CA 93301
Tel: (661) 637-0136 Fax: (661) 637-0156 Internet: www.export.gov/kern

Director **Glen Roberts** . . . . (559) 680-3378
E-mail: glen.roberts@trade.gov

Downtown Los Angeles (CA) U.S. Export Assistance Center
444 South Flower Street, 37th Floor, Los Angeles, CA 90071
Tel: (213) 894-8784 Fax: (213) 894-5432

Director **Rachid Sayouty** . . . . (213) 894-4022
E-mail: rachid.sayouty@trade.gov
Senior International Trade Specialist **Jason Sproule** . . . . . (213) 894-8785
E-mail: jason.sproule@trade.gov
International Trade Specialist **Bobby Hines** . . . . (213) 894-8784
E-mail: bobby.hines@trade.gov
International Trade Specialist **Amy Magat** . . . . (213) 894-8784
E-mail: amy.magat@trade.gov

Inland Empire U.S. Export Assistance Center
3110 East Guasti Road, Suite 465, Ontario, CA 91761
Tel: (909) 390-8283 Fax: (909) 390-5315
Internet: www.export.gov/inlandempire

Director **(Vacant)** . . . . (909) 390-8429
Senior International Trade Specialist **Tony Michalski** . . . . . (909) 390-8469
E-mail: tony.michalski@trade.gov
Senior International Trade Specialist **Eduard Roytberg** . . . (909) 390-8482
E-mail: eduard.roytberg@trade.gov
Senior International Trade Specialist **(Vacant)** . . . . (909) 390-8491

Irvine (CA) U.S. Export Assistance Center
2302 Martin Court, Suite 315, Irvine, CA 92612
Tel: (949) 660-1688 Fax: (949) 660-1338 E-mail: officeirvine@trade.gov
Internet: www.export.gov/irvine

Director **Jim Mayfield** . . . . (949) 246-1768
E-mail: jim.mayfield@trade.gov
Senior International Trade Specialist **Maryavis Bokal** . . . . (949) 660-1879
E-mail: maryavis.bokal@trade.gov
Senior International Trade Specialist **Kristin Houston** . . . . (949) 660-7103
E-mail: kristin.houston@trade.gov
Senior International Trade Specialist **(Vacant)** . . . . (949) 660-7105
Senior International Trade Specialist **(Vacant)** . . . . (949) 660-1782
International Trade Specialist **Tatyana Aguirre** . . . . (949) 660-1410
E-mail: tatyana.aguirre@trade.gov
International Trade Specialist **Jasmine Braswell** . . . . (949) 660-9545
E-mail: jasmine.braswell@trade.gov
Commercial Officer **(Vacant)** . . . . (949) 660-0672

San Diego (CA) U.S. Export Assistance Center
9449 Balboa Avenue, Suite 111, San Diego, CA 92123
Tel: (858) 467-7032 Fax: (858) 467-7043

Director **Matthew "Matt" Andersen** . . . . (858) 467-7033
E-mail: matt.andersen@trade.gov
Senior International Trade Specialist **Carrie Brooks** . . . . . . (858) 467-7034
E-mail: carrie.brooks@trade.gov
Senior International Trade Specialist **Aron Davidson** . . . . . (858) 467-7038
E-mail: aron.davidson@trade.gov
Senior International Trade Specialist **Julie Osman** . . . . (858) 467-7037
E-mail: julie.osman@trade.gov
Senior International Trade Specialist **(Vacant)** . . . . (858) 467-7038
International Trade Specialist **Kathy Bridges** . . . . (858) 467-7042
E-mail: kathy.bridges@trade.gov
Commercial Officer **Rebecca Balogh** . . . . (858) 467-7042
E-mail: kathy.bridges@trade.gov
Commercial Officer **Thomas P. "Pat" Cassidy** . . . . (858) 467-7041
E-mail: pat.cassidy@trade.gov

Ventura (CA) U.S. Export Assistance Center
333 Ponoma Street, Port Hueneme, CA 93041
Tel: (805) 488-4844 Fax: (805) 488-7801

Director **Gerald Vaughn** . . . . (805) 676-1573
E-mail: gerald.vaughn@trade.gov

West Los Angeles (CA) U.S. Export Assistance Center
11150 West Olympic Boulevard, Suite 975, Los Angeles, CA 90064
Tel: (310) 235-7104 Fax: (310) 235-7220
Internet: www.buyusa.gov/westlosangeles

Office Director **Julieanne Hennessy** . . . . (310) 235-7206
E-mail: julieanne.hennessy@trade.gov
International Trade Specialist **Leticia Arias** . . . . (310) 235-7204
E-mail: leticia.arias@trade.gov
International Trade Specialist **Terri Batch** . . . . (310) 882-1750
E-mail: terri.batch@trade.gov
International Trade Specialist **Maura Kawai** . . . . (310) 235-7207
E-mail: maura.kim@trade.gov
International Trade Specialist **Cynthia Torres** . . . . (310) 882-1043
E-mail: cynthia.torres@trade.gov
International Trade Specialist **Delia Valdivia** . . . . (310) 235-7203
E-mail: delia.valdivia@trade.gov

Southern Network
75 Fifth Street, NW, Atlanta, GA 30308

Regional Director **Thomas A. "Tom" Strauss** . . . . (404) 815-1529
E-mail: Thomas.Strauss@trade.gov Fax: (404) 347-0002

Atlanta (GA) U.S. Export Assistance Center
75 Fifth Street, NW, Suite 1060, Atlanta, GA 30308
Tel: (404) 815-1498 Fax: (404) 347-0002
E-mail: office.atlanta@mail.doc.gov
Areas Covered: AK, AL, FL, GA, MS, OK, PR

● Director **George Tracy** . . . . (404) 815-1794
E-mail: george.tracy@trade.gov

★ Presidential Appointment Requiring Senate Confirmation ☆ Presidential Appointment ☐ Schedule C Appointment ◇ Career Senior Foreign Service Appointment
● Career Senior Executive Service (SES) Appointment ○ Non-Career Senior Executive Service (SES) Appointment ■ Postal Career Executive Service

Atlanta (GA) U.S. Export Assistance Center *(continued)*

Senior International Trade Specialist **Eric Johnson** ...... (404) 815-1750
E-mail: eric.johnson@trade.gov
Senior International Trade Specialist **Dina Molaison** ..... (404) 815-1530
E-mail: dina.molaison@trade.gov
Senior International Trade Specialist **Amy Ryan** .... (404) 815-1748
E-mail: amy.ryan@trade.gov
Senior International Trade Specialist **(Vacant)** .... (404) 815-1498
Regional Communications Specialist **Amina Brock** ...... (404) 815-1567
E-mail: amina.brock@trade.gov
Commercial Officer **(Vacant)** .... (404) 815-1528

Birmingham (AL) U.S. Export Assistance Center
950 22nd Street, North, Suite 773, Birmingham, AL 35203
Tel: (205) 731-1331 Fax: (205) 731-0076

Director **Robert Stackpole** .... (205) 731-1333 ext. 222
E-mail: robert.stackpole@trade.gov
Field Support Specialist **(Vacant)** .... (205) 731-0190
Fax: (205) 731-0076
International Trade Specialist **William Toerpe** ... (205) 731-1333 ext. 223
E-mail: william.toerpe@trade.gov

Charleston (WV) U.S. Export Assistance Center
1116 Smith Street, Charleston, WV 25301
Tel: (304) 347-5123 Fax: (304) 347-5408

Director **Leslie Drake** .... (304) 347-5123
E-mail: leslie.drake@trade.gov

Columbia (SC) U.S. Export Assistance Center
USC Moorse School of Business, 1705 College Street,
Suite 600, Columbia, SC 29208
Tel: (803) 255-2623 Fax: (803) 777-2615
Internet: www.buyusa.gov/southcarolina

Director **Dorette Coetsee** .... (803) 397-4590
E-mail: dorette.coetsee@trade.gov

Fort Lauderdale (FL) U.S. Export Assistance Center
1850 Eller Drive, Suite 401, Fort Lauderdale, FL 35316
Tel: (954) 356-6640 Fax: (954) 356-6644

Director **Eduardo Torres** .... (954) 356-6643
E-mail: eduardo.torres@trade.gov
Senior International Trade Specialist **Kathryn Dye** .... (954) 356-6621
E-mail: kathryn.dye@trade.gov
Senior International Trade Specialist **Miguel Olivares** .... (954) 356-6649
E-mail: miguel.olivares@trade.gov
Senior International Trade Specialist
Leandro Solorzano .... (954) 356-6647
E-mail: leandro.solorzano@trade.gov
Commercial Officer **(Vacant)** .... (954) 356-6645

Greensboro (NC) U.S. Export Assistance Center
342 North Elm Street, 1st Floor, Greensboro, NC 27401
Tel: (336) 333-5345 Fax: (336) 333-5158
E-mail: office.greensboro@mail.doc.gov

USEAC Director **Stephanie Bethel** .... (336) 333-5345
E-mail: stephanie.bethel@trade.gov
Senior International Trade Specialist **Emily Gereffi** ...... (336) 333-5345

Greenville (SC) U.S. Export Assistance Center
Buck Mickel Center, 216 South Pleasantburg Drive,
Room 243, Greenville, SC 29607
Tel: (864) 250-8429 Fax: (864) 250-6729
Internet: www.buyusa.gov/southeast/greenville.html

Director **Shannon Christenbury** .... (864) 250-8429
E-mail: shannon.christenbury@trade.gov

Jackson (MS) U.S. Export Assistance Center
1230 Raymond Road, Jackson, MS 39204
Tel: (601) 373-0773 Fax: (601) 373-0959

Director **Carol Moore** .... (601) 373-0773
E-mail: carol.moore@trade.gov

Jackson (MS) U.S. Export Assistance Center *(continued)*

International Trade Specialist **Glenn Ferreri** .... (601) 373-0849
E-mail: glenn.ferreri@trade.gov
International Trade Specialist **(Vacant)** .... (601) 373-0784

Jacksonville (FL) U.S. Export Assistance Center
Three Independent Drive, Jacksonville, FL 32262
Tel: (904) 232-1270 Fax: (904) 232-1271

Director **Jorge Arce** .... (904) 232-1270
E-mail: jorge.arce@trade.gov

Knoxville (TN) U.S. Export Assistance Center
17 Market Square, #201, Knoxville, TN 37902
Tel: (865) 545-4637 Fax: (865) 545-4435

Director **Robert Leach** .... (865) 545-4637
E-mail: robert.leach@trade.gov

Little Rock (AR) U.S. Export Assistance Center
425 West Capitol Avenue, Suite 425, Little Rock, AR 72201
Tel: (501) 324-5794 Fax: (501) 324-7380
Internet: www.buyusa.gov/arkansas

Director **James M. "Jim" Aardappel** .... (501) 324-5797
E-mail: james.aardappel@trade.gov
Education: Santa Barbara City; Golden Gate BS
Senior International Trade Specialist **(Vacant)** .... (501) 324-5794

Miami (FL) U.S. Export Assistance Center
5835 Blue Lagoon Drive, Suite 203, Miami, FL 33301
Tel: (305) 526-7428 Fax: (305) 526-7434

Director **Edward Torres** .... (305) 954-6643
Senior International Trade Specialist
Lesa Forbes .... (305) 526-7428 ext. 28
E-mail: lesa.forbes@trade.gov
Senior International Trade Specialist
William Lawton .... (305) 526-7428 ext. 27
E-mail: william.lawton@trade.gov
International Trade Specialist
Martina Echevarria .... (305) 526-7428 ext. 26
E-mail: martina.echevarria@trade.gov
Commercial Officer **(Vacant)** .... (305) 526-7428

Nashville (TN) U.S. Export Assistance Center
312 Rosa Parks Avenue, 10th Floor, Nashville, TN 37243
Tel: (615) 736-2222 Fax: (615) 736-2226

Director **Brie A. Knox** .... (615) 736-2223
E-mail: brie.knox@trade.gov

Orlando (FL) U.S. Export Assistance Center
3201 East Colonial Drive, Suite A-20, Orlando, FL 32803
Tel: (407) 648-6170 Fax: (407) 420-4425

Director **Kenneth Mouradian** .... (407) 420-4877
E-mail: kenneth.mouradian@trade.gov

San Juan (PR) U.S. Export Assistance Center
Centro Internacional De Mercadeo Torre II,
Suite 702, Carr.165, Guaynabo, PR 00968-8058
Tel: (787) 775-1992 Fax: (787) 781-7178
E-mail: office.sanjuanpr@mail.doc.gov

Director **Jose F. Burgos** .... (787) 775-1992
E-mail: jose.burgos@trade.gov
International Trade Specialist **(Vacant)** .... (787) 775-1974

Savannah (GA) U.S. Export Assistance Center
111 East Liberty Street, Suite 202, Savannah, GA 31401
Tel: (912) 652-4204 Fax: (912) 652-4241
E-mail: office.savannah@mail.doc.gov

Director **Todd Gerken** .... (912) 652-4204
E-mail: todd.gerken@trade.gov

DEPARTMENTS

★ Presidential Appointment Requiring Senate Confirmation ☆ Presidential Appointment □ Schedule C Appointment ◇ Career Senior Foreign Service Appointment
● Career Senior Executive Service (SES) Appointment ○ Non Career Senior Executive Service (SES) Appointment ■ Postal Career Executive Service

DEPARTMENTS

Tallahassee (FL) U.S. Export Assistance Center
The Atrium Building, 325 John Knox Road,
Suite 201, Tallahassee, FL 32303
Tel: (850) 942-9635 Fax: (850) 298-6659
Note: Tallahassee is currently covered by the Jacksonville office.
Director **(Vacant)** .... (850) 942-9635

Tampa Bay U.S. Export Assistance Center
13805 58th Street North, Suite 1-200, Clearwater, FL 33760
Tel: (727) 893-3738 Fax: (727) 893-3839
Director **Sandra Campbell** .... (727) 893-3738
E-mail: sandra.campbell@trade.gov
International Trade Specialist **Dan Bjerk** .... (727) 464-7347
E-mail: dan.bjerk@trade.gov Fax: (727) 893-3839
Commercial Officer **(Vacant)** .... (727) 893-3738
Commercial Officer **(Vacant)** .... (727) 893-3128

Triangle U.S. Export Assistance Center
10900 World Trade Boulevard, Suite 110, Raleigh, NC 27617
Tel: (919) 281-2750 Fax: (919) 281-2754
Internet: www.buyusa.gov/northcarolina
Director **Frances Selema** .... (919) 281-2753
E-mail: frances.selema@trade.gov
International Trade Specialist **Shirreef Loza** .... (919) 281-2752
E-mail: shirreef.loza@trade.gov
International Trade Specialist **(Vacant)** .... (919) 281-2750

Wheeling (WV) U.S. Export Assistance Center
Wheeling Jesuit University, 316 Washington Avenue,
NTTC Building, Room 134, Wheeling, WV 26003
Tel: (304) 243-5493 Fax: (304) 243-5494
Director **Diego Gattesco** .... (304) 243-5493
E-mail: diego.gattesco@trade.gov

Southwest Network
120 North Stone Avenue, Tucson, AZ 85701
Regional Director **Eric Nielsen** .... (520) 670-5808
E-mail: eric.nielsen@trade.gov Fax: (520) 243-1910

Austin (TX) U.S. Export Assistance Center
221 East 11th Street, 4th Floor, Austin, TX 78701
P.O. Box 12428, Austin, TX 78711
Tel: (512) 916-5939 Fax: (512) 916-5940
Director **Karen Parker** .... (512) 916-5939
E-mail: karen.parker@trade.gov
International Trade Specialist **Larry Tabash** .... (512) 936-0039
E-mail: larry.tabash@trade.gov

Denver (CO) U.S. Export Assistance Center
1999 Broadway, Suite 2205, Denver, CO 80202
Tel: (303) 844-6623 Fax: (303) 844-5651
E-mail: denver.office.box@mail.doc.gov
Internet: www.export.gov/colorado
Areas Covered: CO, WY
Director **Paul G. Bergman, Jr.** .... (303) 844-6001
E-mail: paul.bergman@trade.gov
Senior International Trade Specialist **Lana Lennberg** .... (303) 844-5654
E-mail: lana.lennberg@trade.gov
Senior International Trade Specialist **Selina Marquez** .... (303) 844-2155
E-mail: selina.marquez@trade.gov
Senior International Trade Specialist **Suzette Nickle** ..... (303) 844-5655
E-mail: suzette.nickle@trade.gov
Senior International Trade Specialist **(Vacant)** .... (303) 844-3247

Houston (TX) U.S. Export Assistance Center
1919 Smith Street, Suite 10079, Houston, TX 77002
Tel: (281) 228-5650 Fax: (281) 228-5663
Director **Nyamusi Igambi** .... (281) 228-5652
E-mail: nyamusi.igambi@trade.gov
Advanced Manufacturing Team Leader
Pamela "Pam" Plagens .... (281) 228-5653

Houston (TX) U.S. Export Assistance Center *(continued)*
Global Energy Team Leader **Danielle Caltabiano** .... (281) 228-5655
Education: Dallas 2006 MA
Senior International Trade Specialist **Steven Garrett** ..... (281) 228-5657
E-mail: steven.garrett@trade.gov
Senior International Trade Specialist **Brendan Kelly** ..... (832) 431-7371
E-mail: brendan.kelly@trade.gov
Senior International Trade Specialist **Brent Klepko** ...... (281) 228-5654
E-mail: brent.klepko@trade.gov
Senior International Trade Specialist **Peter Tataris** .... (281) 228-5656
E-mail: peter.tataris@trade.gov

Las Vegas (NV) U.S. Export Assistance Center
300 South Fourth Street, Suite 400, Las Vegas, NV 89101
Tel: (702) 388-6694 Fax: (702) 388-6469
Director **Martin Herbst** .... (702) 540-0518
E-mail: Martin.Herbst@trade.gov
International Trade Specialist **Hector Rodriguez** .... (702) 388-6694
E-mail: hector.rodriguez@trade.gov
Foreign Commercial Officer **(Vacant)** .... (702) 388-6018

New Orleans (LA) U.S. Export Assistance Center
423 Canal Street, Room 419, New Orleans, LA 70130
Tel: (504) 589-6546 Fax: (504) 589-2337
E-mail: office.neworleans@trade.gov Internet: www.export.gov/louisiana
Director **Erin Butler** .... (504) 589-6530
E-mail: erin.butler@trade.gov
International Trade Specialist **John Henry Jackson** ..... (504) 589-6549
E-mail: jh.jackson@trade.gov
International Trade Specialist **(Vacant)** .... (504) 589-6703
Commercial Officer **(Vacant)** .... (504) 589-6702

North Texas U.S. Export Assistance Center
4300 Amon Carter Boulevard, Suite 114, Fort Worth, TX 76115
Tel: (817) 684-5347 Fax: (817) 684-5345
E-mail: office.northtexas@trade.gov
Office Director **Jessica Gordon** .... (817) 684-5355
E-mail: jessica.gordon@trade.gov
Senior International Trade Specialist **Matt Baker** .... (817) 684-5349
E-mail: matt.baker@trade.gov
Senior International Trade Specialist
Elizabeth Graham .... (817) 684-5350
E-mail: elizabeth.graham@trade.gov
Senior International Trade Specialist **David Royce** .... (817) 684-5354
E-mail: david.royce@trade.gov
Senior International Trade Specialist **Greg Thompson** ... (214) 712-1932
E-mail: greg.thompson@trade.gov Fax: (214) 746-6799
Senior International Trade Specialist **(Vacant)** .... (817) 684-5352
International Trade Specialist **Kenneth Haynes** .... (817) 684-5348
E-mail: kenneth.haynes@trade.gov
Senior Commercial Officer **Sheryl Pinckney Maas** ...... (817) 684-5336
E-mail: sheryl.pinckney-maas@trade.gov

Phoenix (AZ) U.S. Export Assistance Center
2828 North Central Avenue, Suite 800, Phoenix, AZ 85004
Tel: (602) 640-2513 Fax: (602) 745-7210
E-mail: Office.Phoenix@trade.gov
Director **Daniel Gaines** .... (480) 645-2171
E-mail: Daniel.Gaines@trade.gov
Senior International Trade Specialist **Anna Flaaten** ...... (480) 884-1673
E-mail: anna.flaaten@trade.gov
Senior International Trade Specialist **Molly Ho** .... (602) 640-2513
E-mail: molly.ho@trade.gov
International Trade Specialist **Fernando Jimenez** .... (602) 514-7221
E-mail: fernando.jimenez@trade.gov

Reno (NV) U.S. Export Assistance Center
808 West Nye Lane, Carson City, NV 89703
E-mail: reno.office.box@trade.gov
Director **Janis Kalnins** .... (775) 301-0037
E-mail: janis.kalnins@trade.gov
Senior Trade Specialist **(Vacant)** .... (775) 784-6018

★ Presidential Appointment Requiring Senate Confirmation ☆ Presidential Appointment ☐ Schedule C Appointment ◇ Career Senior Foreign Service Appointment
● Career Senior Executive Service (SES) Appointment ○ Non-Career Senior Executive Service (SES) Appointment ■ Postal Career Executive Service

Salt Lake City (UT) U.S. Export Assistance Center
MCPC Building, 9690 South 300 west,
Suite 201D, Sandy, UT 84070
Tel: (801) 255-1872 Fax: (801) 255-3147

Director (Acting) **Shelby Peterson** .... (801) 255-1872
E-mail: Shelby.Peterson@trade.gov

San Antonio (TX) U.S. Export Assistance Center
615 East Houston Street, Suite 207, San Antonio, TX 78205
Tel: (210) 472-4020 Fax: (210) 472-4019
E-mail: Office.SanAntonio@trade.gov

Director **Daniel G. Rodriguez** .... (210) 472-4020
E-mail: daniel.rodriguez@trade.gov
Education: Texas State (San Marcos) BA, MPA
Senior International Trade Specialist **Michael Rosales** ... (210) 472-4020
E-mail: michael.rosales@trade.gov
International Trade Specialist **Oscar Magana** .... (210) 472-4020
E-mail: Oscar.Magana@trade.gov

Tucson (AZ) U.S. Export Assistance Center
120 North Stone Avenue, Suite 200, Tucson, AZ 85701
Tel: (520) 670-5540 Fax: (520) 243-1910

Director **Eric Neilson** .... (520) 670-5540
International Trade Specialist **Christina Parisi** .... (520) 670-5809
E-mail: christina.parisi@trade.gov

National Oceanic and Atmospheric Administration (NOAA)

Silver Spring Metro Center 3, 1315 East West Highway,
Silver Spring, MD 20910
Mail: Department of Commerce (NOAA),
14th Street and Constitution Avenue, NW, Washington, DC 20230
Tel: (301) 713-4000 (Personnel Locator)
Tel: (301) 713-0820 (Procurement Information)
Tel: (202) 482-6090 (Public Information)
Tel: (202) 482-6090 (Publications Information)
Tel: (301) 713-3540 (Freedom of Information/Privacy Act)
Fax: (202) 482-3154 Internet: www.noaa.gov
Internet: www.climate.gov (NOAA Climate Service Portal)
Internet: http://www.gulfspillrestoration.noaa.gov/ (NOAA Gulf Spill Restoration) Internet: https://nsd.rdc.noaa.gov/ (Personnel Locator)

OFFICE OF THE UNDER SECRETARY AND ADMINISTRATOR

Herbert Clark Hoover Building, 14th Street and Constitution Avenue, NW, Washington, DC 20230
Fax: (202) 408-9674

Office of the General Counsel (OGC)
Herbert Clark Hoover Building, 1401 Constitution Avenue, NW,
Room A100, Washington, DC 20230
Tel: (202) 482-4080 Fax: (202) 482-4893

Alaska Section
Federal Office Building, 709 West Ninth Street,
Room 909A, Juneau, AK 99801
P.O. Box 21109, Juneau, AK 99802-1109
Tel: (907) 586-7414 Fax: (907) 586-7263

Section Chief **Maura Sullivan** .... (907) 586-7328
E-mail: Maura.Sullivan@noaa.gov
Secretary **Carol Schirmer** .... (907) 586-7415
E-mail: carol.schirmer@noaa.gov
Deputy Section Chief **Demian Schane** .... (907) 586-7027
E-mail: Demian.Schane@noaa.gov
Senior Enforcement Attorney
Brian T. McTague USCG (Ret) .... (907) 586-7205
E-mail: brian.mctague@noaa.gov
Enforcement Attorney **Alisha Falberg** .... (907) 586-7078
E-mail: alisha.falberg@noaa.gov

Alaska Section *(continued)*

Staff Attorney **Joshua Fortenbery** .... (907) 586-7047
E-mail: Joshua.Fortenbery@noaa.gov
Staff Attorney **John Lepore** .... (907) 586-7238
E-mail: john.lepore@noaa.gov
Staff Attorney **Thomas Meyer** .... (907) 586-7271
E-mail: tom.gcak.meyer@noaa.gov
Staff Attorney **Lauren Smoker** .... (907) 586-7019
E-mail: lauren.smoker@noaa.gov
Staff Attorney **Molly Watson** .... (907) 586-7342
E-mail: molly.watson@noaa.gov
Legal Assistant **Amy Kauffman** .... (907) 586-7826
E-mail: amy.kauffman@noaa.gov
Paralegal **Joseph Joe McCabe** .... (907) 586-7264
E-mail: joe.mccabe@noaa.gov

Northeast Regional Office
One Blackburn Drive, Gloucester, MA 01930-2298
Tel: (978) 281-9211 Fax: (978) 281-9389

Regional Counsel **Gene S. Martin** .... (978) 281-9242
E-mail: gene.s.martin@noaa.gov

Northwest Section
7600 Sand Point Way, NE, Seattle, WA 98115
Tel: (206) 526-6075 Fax: (206) 526-6542

Northwest Section Chief **Chris McNulty** .... (206) 526-6077
E-mail: chris.mcnulty@noaa.gov
Northwest Section Deputy Chief **Sheila Lynch** .... (206) 526-6533
E-mail: Sheila.Lynch@noaa.gov
Staff Attorney **Laurie Beale** .... (206) 526-6327
E-mail: laurie.beale@noaa.gov
Staff Attorney **Kirsten L. Erickson** .... (206) 526-4600
E-mail: kirsten.l.erickson@noaa.gov
Staff Attorney **Christopher Fontecchio** .... (206) 526-6153
E-mail: chris.fontecchio@noaa.gov
Staff Attorney **Niel Moeller** .... (206) 526-6238
E-mail: niel.moeller@noaa.gov
Staff Attorney **Maggie Smith** .... (206) 526-4418
E-mail: maggie.smith@noaa.gov
Staff Attorney **(Vacant)** .... (206) 526-6075
Staff Attorney **(Vacant)** .... (206) 526-6075
Paralegal Specialist **Brittany Pugh** .... (206) 526-6079
E-mail: brittany.pugh@noaa.gov

Southeast Regional Office
263 13th Avenue South, Suite 177, Saint Petersburg, FL 33701
Tel: (727) 824-5370 Fax: (727) 824-5376

Section Chief **B. Michael McLemore** .... (727) 824-5370
E-mail: michael.mclemore@noaa.gov
Deputy Section Chief **Monica A. Smit-Brunello** .... (727) 824-5361

Southwest Regional Office
501 West Ocean Boulevard, Suite 4470, Long Beach, CA 90802
Tel: (562) 980-4080 Fax: (562) 980-4084

Section Chief **Judson J. Feder** .... (562) 980-4067
E-mail: judson.feder@noaa.gov
Deputy Section Chief **Deanna R. Harwood** .... (562) 980-4068
E-mail: deanna.harwood@noaa.gov
Deputy Section Chief for Natural Resources
Laurie Lee .... (562) 980-4078
E-mail: laurie.lee@noaa.gov
Attorney Advisor **Dan A. Hytrek** .... (562) 980-4075
E-mail: dan.hytrek@noaa.gov
Attorney Advisor **Christopher A. Keifer** .... (562) 980-4076
E-mail: christopher.keifer@noaa.gov
Attorney Advisor **Kathryn Kempton** .... (562) 980-4091
E-mail: kathryn.kempton@noaa.gov
Attorney Advisor **(Vacant)** .... (562) 980-4071
Senior Enforcement Attorney **Paul A. Ortiz** .... (562) 980-4069
E-mail: paul.ortiz@noaa.gov
Paralegal Specialist **Julia Caracoza** .... (562) 437-5076

(continued on next page)

★ Presidential Appointment Requiring Senate Confirmation ☆ Presidential Appointment ☐ Schedule C Appointment ◇ Career Senior Foreign Service Appointment
● Career Senior Executive Service (SES) Appointment ○ Non-Career Senior Executive Service (SES) Appointment ■ Postal Career Executive Service

Southwest Regional Office *(continued)*

Senior Counsel for Natural Resources
Katherine A. Pease . . . . . (562) 980-4077
E-mail: katherine.pease@noaa.gov Fax: (562) 980-4065
Natural Resources Attorney Advisor
Ericka Hailstocke-Johnson . . . . . (562) 980-4070
E-mail: ericka.hailstocke-johnson@noaa.gov
Natural Resources Attorney Advisor
Christopher Plaisted . . . . . (562) 980-3237
E-mail: christopher.plaisted@noaa.gov
Administrative Support **Vanessa Nalle** . . . . . (562) 980-4080
E-mail: vanessa.nalle@noaa.gov

Office of the Assistant Secretary for Conservation and Management

1401 Constitution Avenue, NW, Room 51027, Washington, DC 20230
Tel: (202) 482-6255

National Marine Fisheries Service (NMFS)

Silver Spring Metro Center 3, 1315 East-West Highway,
Silver Spring, MD 20910
Tel: (301) 427-8000 Fax: (301) 713-1940 Internet: www.nmfs.noaa.gov

Regulatory Programs (RP)

Silver Spring Metro Center 3, 1315 East-West Highway,
Silver Spring, MD 20910
Fax: (301) 713-1940 Internet: www.nmfs.noaa.gov

Office of Habitat Conservation

Silver Spring Metro Center 3, 1315 East-West Hwy,
Room 14828, Silver Spring, MD 20910
Fax: (301) 713-1043 Internet: www.habitat.noaa.gov

National Oceanic and Atmospheric Administration Chesapeake Bay Office

NOAA Chesapeake Bay Office, 410 Severn Avenue,
Suite 107A, Annapolis, MD 21403
Tel: (410) 267-5660 Fax: (410) 267-5666
Internet: noaa.chesapeakebay.net Internet: habitat.noaa.gov/chesapeakebay

Director (Acting) **Sean Corson** . . . . . (410) 267-5646
E-mail: Sean.Corson@noaa.gov
Deputy Director **Sean Corson** . . . . . (410) 267-5646 ext. 646

Regional Offices

Alaska Region

Federal Office Building, 709 West Ninth Street, Juneau, AK 99801
P.O. Box 21668, Juneau, AK 99802-1668
Tel: (800) 304-4846 (Restricted Access Management)
Tel: (907) 586-7221 Fax: (907) 586-7249 Internet: www.fakr.noaa.gov

● Regional Administrator **Dr. James W. "Jim" Balsiger** . . . (907) 586-7221
E-mail: jim.balsiger@noaa.gov
Education: Michigan Tech 1966 BSF; Purdue MS; U Washington PhD
Executive Secretary **(Vacant)** . . . . . (907) 586-7601
Deputy Regional Administrator
Robert D. "Doug" Mecum . . . . . (907) 586-7221
E-mail: doug.mecum@noaa.gov
Education: Wyoming 1980 BS; Alaska (Fairbanks) 1984 MS
Assistant Regional Administrator for Habitat Conservation Division **Gretchen A. Harrington** . . . . . (907) 586-7445
E-mail: gretchen.harrington@noaa.gov
Assistant Regional Administrator for Protected Resources Division **Jon Kurland** . . . . . (907) 586-7638
E-mail: jon.kurland@noaa.gov
Assistant Regional Administrator for Sustainable Fisheries Division **Glenn Merrill** . . . . . (907) 586-7775
E-mail: glenn.merrill@noaa.gov
General Counsel **(Vacant)** . . . . . (907) 586-7198
Public Affairs Officer **Julie Speegle** . . . . . (907) 586-7032
E-mail: julie.speegle@noaa.gov
Program Administrator for Information Services
Daniel R. Rothman . . . . . (907) 586-7095
E-mail: daniel.rothman@noaa.gov

Alaska Region *(continued)*

Operations and Management Division Chief
Peter D. Jones . . . . . (907) 586-7280
E-mail: peter.d.jones@noaa.gov
Law Enforcement Special Agent-in-Charge **Will Ellis** . . . . . (907) 586-7225
E-mail: will.ellis@noaa.gov
Law Enforcement Deputy Special Agent-in-Charge
Nathan Lagerwey . . . . . (907) 271-3031
E-mail: nathan.lagerwey@noaa.gov
Chief Information Resource Officer **Greg Bledsoe** . . . . . (907) 586-7053
E-mail: greg.bledsoe@noaa.gov Fax: (907) 586-7255
Exxon Valdez Oil Spill (EVOS) Trustee Council Director **(Vacant)** . . . . . (907) 278-8012
Webmaster **(Vacant)** . . . . . (907) 586-7213
Fax: (907) 586-7255

Alaska Fisheries Science Center

7600 Sand Point Way, NE, Building 4, Seattle, WA 98115-0070
P.O. Box 15700, Seattle, WA 98115
Tel: (206) 526-4000 Fax: (206) 526-4004 Internet: www.afsc.noaa.gov

● Science and Research Director
Dr. Douglas P. DeMaster . . . . . (907) 789-6617
E-mail: douglas.demaster@noaa.gov
Education: Minnesota 1978 PhD
Deputy Science and Research Director **(Vacant)** . . . . . (206) 526-4621
Building 4, 7600 Sand Point Way, NE, Seattle, WA 98115 Fax: (206) 526-4004
Auke Bay Fisheries Laboratory Director **Phil Mundy** . . . . . (907) 789-6001
11305 Glacier Highway, Juneau, AK 99801-8626
Education: Maryland 1970 BS; Alabama 1973 MS; U Washington 1979 PhD
Fisheries Monitoring and Analysis Director
Gene Christopher "Chris" Rilling . . . . . (206) 526-4194
Fax: (206) 526-4066
Office of Fisheries Information Systems Director
Ajith Abraham . . . . . (206) 526-4055
E-mail: ajith.abraham@noaa.gov
Operations, Management, and Information Services Director **Lori Budbill** . . . . . (206) 526-4005
E-mail: lori.budbill@noaa.gov
Resource Assessment and Conservation Engineering Director **Jeffrey Napp** . . . . . (206) 526-4148
Resource Ecology and Fisheries Management Director
Ron Felthoven . . . . . (206) 526-4114
E-mail: ron.felthoven@noaa.gov
Habitat and Ecological Processes Program Leader
Michael F. Sigler . . . . . (907) 789-6037
17109 Point Lena Loop Road, Juneau, AK 99801-8344 Fax: (907) 789-6094
E-mail: mike.sigler@noaa.gov
National Marine Mammal Laboratory Director
John L. Bengtson . . . . . (206) 526-4016
Librarian **Sonja Kromann** . . . . . (206) 526-4013
E-mail: sonja.kromann@noaa.gov Fax: (206) 526-6615

Greater Atlantic Region (GARFO)

55 Great Republic Drive, Gloucester, MA 01930
Tel: (978) 281-9300 Fax: (978) 281-9207
Internet: http://www.greateratlantic.fisheries.noaa.gov/
Areas Covered: CT, DE, DC, IL, IN, ME, MD, MA, MI, MN, NH, NJ, NY, OH, PA, RI, VT, VA, WV, WI

● Regional Administrator **Michael Pentony** . . . . . (978) 281-6283
E-mail: michael.pentony@noaa.gov
Education: Duke 1987 BS, 1996 MEM
Deputy Regional Administrator (Acting)
Kimberly Damon-Randall . . . . . (978) 282-6485
E-mail: kimberly.damon-randall@noaa.gov
Assistant Regional Administrator for Habitat Conservation **Lou Chiarella** . . . . . (978) 281-6277
E-mail: lou.chiarella@noaa.gov
Assistant Regional Administrator for Operations and Budget Division **(Vacant)** . . . . . (978) 281-6221
Assistant Regional Administrator for Protected Resources (Acting) **Jennifer Anderson** . . . . . (978) 281-9226

★ Presidential Appointment Requiring Senate Confirmation ☆ Presidential Appointment ☐ Schedule C Appointment ◇ Career Senior Foreign Service Appointment
● Career Senior Executive Service (SES) Appointment ○ Non-Career Senior Executive Service (SES) Appointment ■ Postal Career Executive Service

Greater Atlantic Region *(continued)*

Assistant Regional Administrator for Stakeholder Engagement **Shannon Dionne** .... (978) 281-9243
E-mail: shannon.dionne@noaa.gov
Assistant Regional Administrator for Sustainable Fisheries (Acting) **Peter Christopher** .... (978) 281-9288
Northeast Inspection Officer **Steven Ross** .... (978) 281-6263
Secretary **(Vacant)** .... (978) 281-9300
Analysis and Program Support Division Chief **David Gouveia** .... (978) 281-6280
E-mail: david.gouveia@noaa.gov
Information Resource Management Director (Acting) **Peter Couture** .... (978) 281-6115
E-mail: peter.couture@noaa.gov
Aquaculture Coordinator **Kevin Madley** .... (978) 281-8494

Northeast Fisheries Science Center (NEFSC)
166 Water Street, Woods Hole, MA 02543-1026
Tel: (508) 495-2000 Fax: (508) 495-2258
Internet: http://www.nefsc.noaa.gov/

Science and Research Director (Acting) **Jonathan Hare** .... (401) 871-4705
Deputy Center Director (Acting) [Science and Research Director] **Susan C. Gardner** .... (508) 495-2279
Associate Director **CAPT Jack Moakley NOAA (Ret)** .... (508) 495-2235
Planning Officer **Andrew "Andy" Lipsky** .... (508) 495-2394
Operations, Management and Information Division Chief **Garth Smelser** .... (508) 495-2241
E-mail: garth.smelser@noaa.gov
Data Management Support Staff Chief (Acting) **David Gloeckner** .... (305) 361-4257
E-mail: david.gloeckner@noaa.gov
Education: Ohio State 1996 BS; East Carolina 2002 MS, 2009 PhD
Oceans and Climate Division Chief **Paula Fratantoni** .... (508) 495-2306

Ecosystems and Aquaculture Division
Chief (Acting) **Dr. Thomas Noji** .... (732) 872-3024

Ecosystems Processes Division
Chief (Acting) **Jonathan Hare** .... (401) 871-4705
215 S Ferry Rd, Narragansett, RI 02882
E-mail: jon.hare@noaa.gov

Population and Ecosystems Monitoring and Analysis
Chief **Dr. Wendy Gabriel** .... (508) 495-2213
E-mail: wendy.gabriel@noaa.gov

Resource Evaluation and Assessment Division
Chief **Michael A. Simpkins PhD** .... (508) 495-2358

Northeast Enforcement Division
Law Enforcement Special Agent-in-Charge **Timothy J. "Tim" Donovan** .... (978) 281-9156
E-mail: timothy.donovan@noaa.gov
Deputy Special Agent-in-Charge (Acting) **Jeffrey Ray** .... (732) 280-6490
E-mail: jeffrey.ray@noaa.gov
Deputy Special Agent-in-Charge **(Vacant)** .... (978) 281-9300
Compliance Assistance Liaison **Donald R. Frei** .... (978) 281-9221

Pacific Islands Region
NOAA Inouye Regional Center, 1845 Wasp Boulevard, Building 176, Honolulu, HI 96818
Tel: (808) 725-5000 Fax: (808) 725-5215
Internet: http://www.fpir.noaa.gov

● Pacific Islands Regional Administrator **Michael Tosatto** .... (808) 725-5001
E-mail: michael.tosatto@noaa.gov
Education: US Coast Guard Acad 1984 BS
Deputy Regional Administrator **Sarah Malloy** .... (808) 725-5002
Assistant Regional Administrator for Habitat and Conservation **Gerald "Gerry" Davis** .... (808) 725-5080
E-mail: gerry.davis@noaa.gov
Assistant Regional Administrator for Protected Resources **Ann M. Garrett** .... (808) 725-5130

Pacific Islands Region *(continued)*

Assistant Regional Administrator for Sustainable Fisheries **Robert "Bob" Harman** .... (808) 725-5170
E-mail: bob.harman@noaa.gov
Law Enforcement Special Agent-in-Charge **William R. "Bill" Pickering** .... (808) 725-6100
E-mail: bill.pickering@noaa.gov
Law Enforcement Deputy Special Agent-in-Charge **Martina Sagapolu** .... (808) 725-6112
E-mail: martina.sagapolu@noaa.gov
Program Manager for Fishery Observers **John D. Kelly, Jr.** .... (808) 725-5100
Program Manager For International Fisheries **Thomas R. "Tom" Graham** .... (808) 725-5032
E-mail: tom.graham@noaa.gov
Program Manager for Marine National Monuments **(Vacant)** .... (808) 725-5015
Executive Officer **James C. "Jim" Cry** .... (808) 725-5050
E-mail: jim.cry@noaa.gov
External Communications Specialist **Jolene Lau** .... (808) 725-5020
E-mail: jolene.lau@noaa.gov
Regional Aquaculture Specialist **David Nichols** .... (808) 725-5180

Pacific Islands Fisheries Science Center (PIFSC)
Daniel K. Inouye Regional Center, 1845 Wasp Boulevard, Building 176, Honolulu, HI 96818
Tel: (808) 725-5300 Fax: (808) 725-5332 Internet: http://noaa.pifsc.gov

Director **Dr. Michael P. Seki PhD** .... (808) 725-5393
Education: Oregon 1979 BS; Hawaii 2001 MSc; Hokkaido U (Japan) 2003 PhD
Deputy Director **Evan A. Howell** .... (808) 725-5306

Southeast Region
263 13th Avenue South, Saint Petersburg, FL 33701
Tel: (727) 824-5301 Fax: (727) 824-5320
Internet: http://sero.nmfs.noaa.gov
Areas Covered: AL, AR, FL, GA, IA, KS, KY, LA, MS, MO, NE, NM, NC, OK, PR, SC, TN, TX, VI

● Regional Administrator **Dr. Roy E. Crabtree** .... (727) 824-5301
E-mail: roy.crabtree@noaa.gov
Education: Furman 1976 BS; South Carolina 1978 MS; William & Mary 1984 PhD
Deputy Regional Administrator **Andy Strelcheck** .... (727) 824-5374
E-mail: andy.strelcheck@noaa.gov
National Policy Advisor for Recreational Fisheries **Russell B. Dunn** .... (727) 551-5740
Seafood Inspection Office Chief **Brian C. Vaubel** .... (727) 570-5747
9887 Fourth Street, Suite 220, Saint Petersburg, FL 33702

Habitat Conservation Division
Silver Spring Metro Center 3, 1315 East-West Hwy, 14th Floor F/HC, Silver Spring, MD 20910
Fax: (727) 824-5300

Assistant Regional Administrator **Virginia M. Fay** .... (727) 824-5317
E-mail: virginia.fay@noaa.gov

Highly Migratory Species Management Division
Silver Spring Metro Center 3, 1315 East-West Hwy, Silver Spring, MD 20910
Fax: (727) 824-5398

Branch Chief **David R. "Randy" Blankinship** .... (727) 824-5399

Management, Budget and Operations Division
Silver Spring Metro Center 3, 1315 East-West Hwy, Silver Spring, MD 20910
Fax: (727) 824-5320

Assistant Regional Administrator **Lauren B. Lugo** .... (727) 551-5703
E-mail: lauren.b.lugo@noaa.gov
Constituency Services Branch Leader **Carolyn Sramek** .... (727) 824-5326
Financial Services Branch Chief **David Moyer** .... (727) 824-5377
Information Technology Branch Leader **Shawn Puyear** .... (727) 551-5730
E-mail: shawn.puyear@noaa.gov
Computer Services Team Leader **(Vacant)** .... (727) 551-5748

(continued on next page)

★ Presidential Appointment Requiring Senate Confirmation ☆ Presidential Appointment □ Schedule C Appointment ◇ Career Senior Foreign Service Appointment
● Career Senior Executive Service (SES) Appointment ○ Non-Career Senior Executive Service (SES) Appointment ■ Postal Career Executive Service

DEPARTMENTS

Management, Budget and Operations Division *(continued)*

Information Resources Team Leader **(Vacant)** .... (727) 824-5301
Supervisory Administrative Officer (Branch Chief)
Hal Dawkins .... (727) 824-5608
E-mail: hal.dawkins@noaa.gov
State/Federal Branch Leader **Jeff Brown** .... (727) 551-5324
E-mail: jeff.brown@noaa.gov
Education: Nebraska (Omaha) 1978 BS; South Florida 1987 MS

Protected Resources Division
Silver Spring Metro Center 3, 1315 East-West Hwy,
Silver Spring, MD 20910
Fax: (727) 824-5309

Assistant Regional Administrator **David Bernhart** .... (727) 824-5312
E-mail: david.bernhart@noaa.gov

Recreational Fisheries Division
Marine Recreational Fisheries Coordinator
Kimberly B. Amendola .... (727) 551-5707

Southeast Enforcement Division
75 Virginia Beach Drive, Miami, FL 33149
Tel: (727) 824-5344 Fax: (727) 824-5321

Special Agent In Charge **Tracy Dunn** .... (727) 824-5344
E-mail: tracy.dunn@noaa.gov
Deputy Special Agent in Charge **(Vacant)** .... (727) 824-5344

Sustainable Fisheries Division
263 13th Avenue South, Saint Petersburg, FL 33701
Fax: (727) 824-5308

Assistant Regional Administrator **John McGovern** ...... (727) 824-5305
E-mail: john.mcgovern@noaa.gov
Fisheries Operations Branch Leader - Caribbean
Bill Arnold .... (727) 824-5305
Fisheries Operations Branch Leader - Gulf
Susan Gerhart .... (727) 824-5305
Fisheries Operations Branch Leader - South Atlantic
Rick Devictor .... (727) 824-5305
Fisheries Policy Branch Leader **Scott Sandorf** .... (727) 824-5305
Fisheries Social Science Branch Chief **(Vacant)** .... (727) 824-5301
LTD Access Program/Data Management Branch Leader
Dr. Jessica Stephen .... (727) 824-5305
E-mail: jessica.stephen@noaa.gov

Southeast Fisheries Science Center
75 Virginia Beach Drive, Miami, FL 33149
Tel: (305) 361-5761 Fax: (305) 361-4499 Internet: www.sefsc.noaa.gov

Science and Research Director
Clarence E. "Clay" Porch .... (305) 361-4232
Education: Miami U (OH) BS, MS, 1993 PhD
Secretary **(Vacant)** .... (305) 361-4567
Deputy Director **Dr. Theo Brainerd** .... (305) 361-4284
Operation, Management, and Information
Division Chief **Dr. Peter Thompson** .... (305) 361-4217 ext. 217
E-mail: peter.thompson@noaa.gov
Librarian **Maria J. Bello** .... (305) 361-4229
E-mail: maria.bello@noaa.gov
Science Planning and Coordination **Stacy Hargrove** .... (305) 361-4491
Information Resources Management Division Chief
(Acting) **Tyree Davis** .... (305) 361-4564
E-mail: tyree.davis@noaa.gov
Education: Kentucky State 2001 BS; Barry 2001 MBA, 2006 MS
Lead Economist (Acting) **Christopher Liese** .... (305) 365-4109
Fisheries Statistics Division Chief (Acting)
Vivian M. Matter .... (305) 361-4482 ext. 482
Tel: (305) 361-4571
Protected Resources and Biodiversity Division
Chief **Dr. James "Jim" Bohnsack** .... (305) 361-4252 ext. 252
Education: Tulane 1969 BS; Miami 1976 MS, 1979 PhD
Sustainable Fisheries Division Chief
(Acting) **Shannon Cass-Calay** .... (305) 361-4231 ext. 231
Education: Miami 1992 BS; Western State U San Diego 2000 PhD

West Coast Region (WCRO)
7600 Sand Point Way, NE,, Building 1, Seattle, WA 98115-6349
Tel: (206) 526-6150 Fax: (206) 526-6426
Internet: http://www.westcoast.fisheries.noaa.gov/
Areas Covered: CO, ID, MT, ND, OR, SD, UT, WA, WY

○ Regional Administrator (Acting) **Barry Thom** .... (503) 231-6266
E-mail: barry.thom@noaa.gov
Secretary **Joan R. Langhans** .... (206) 526-6150
Deputy Regional Administrator **Scott M. Rumsey** .... (503) 872-2791
1201 NE Lloyd Boulevard, Suite 1100, Portland, OR 97232-1274
E-mail: scott.rumsey@noaa.gov
Secretary **(Vacant)** .... (206) 526-6150
Associate Deputy Administrator (Acting)
Nicolle D. Hill .... (206) 526-4358
E-mail: nicolle.hill@noaa.gov
Law Enforcement Special Agent-in-Charge **(Vacant)** ..... (206) 526-6133
Law Enforcement Deputy Special Agent-in-Charge
Michael Killary .... (206) 526-6134
1201 NE Lloyd Boulevard, Suite 1025, Portland, OR 97232-1274
E-mail: Michael.Killary@noaa.gov

Partnerships, Communications and External Affairs Branch
Branch Chief **Ruth Howell** .... (206) 302-2474
E-mail: Ruth.Howell@noaa.gov
Senior Communications Specialist
Katherine A. Cheney .... (503) 231-6730
1201 NE Lloyd Boulevard, Portland, OR 97232-1274
E-mail: katherine.cheney@noaa.gov
Public Affairs Officer **James C. "Jim" Milbury** .... (562) 980-4006
501 West Ocean Boulevard, Long Beach, CA 90802
E-mail: jim.milbury@noaa.gov
Public Affairs Officer **Michael Milstein** .... (503) 231-6268
1201 NE Lloyd Boulevard, Portland, OR 97232-1274
E-mail: michael.milstein@noaa.gov
Communications Specialist **Merlin Alix Smith** .... (503) 231-2119
Congressional Affairs Specialist **(Vacant)** .... (916) 930-3606
Education and Outreach Specialist **Alicia Keefe** .... (206) 526-4447
E-mail: alicia.keefe@noaa.gov
Social Media Specialist **Alan Rahi** .... (503) 231-6718
Tribal Relations Specialist **Amilee Wilson** .... (206) 522-5556
1201 NE Lloyd Boulevard, Portland, OR 97232-1274
E-mail: Amilee.Wilson@noaa.gov
Clearance and Taskers Chief **Jennifer Ise** .... (562) 980-4046
Clearance and Taskers Officer **Hannah Mellman** .... (206) 526-6148
Public Affairs Specialist **(Vacant)** .... (206) 526-6150
1201 NE Lloyd Boulevard, Portland, OR 97232-1274

Operations, Management and Information Division
7600 Sand Point Way, NE, Seattle, WA 98115

Assistant Regional Administrator (Acting)
Korie Schaeffer .... (707) 575-6087
E-mail: Korie.Schaeffer@noaa.gov
Administrative and Operations Branch Chief
Patrick Garber .... (562) 980-4028
501 West Ocean Boulevard, Long Beach, CA 90802
E-mail: patrick.garber@noaa.gov
Budget, Planning and Execution Branch Chief
Stephanie Anne Coleman .... (503) 231-2337
1201 NE Lloyd Boulevard, Portland, OR 97232-1274
E-mail: stephanie.coleman@noaa.gov
Division Manager (Acting) **Eric Chavez** .... (562) 980-4064
E-mail: Eric.Chavez@noaa.gov
Information Services and Management Branch Chief
(Acting) **Rosalie Del Rosario** .... (562) 980-4085
501 West Ocean Boulevard, Long Beach, CA 90802
E-mail: Rosalie.delRosario@noaa.gov
Information Systems and Technology Branch Chief
Mike McCully .... (206) 518-2347
E-mail: Mike.McCully@noaa.gov
Webmaster **(Vacant)** .... (562) 980-4012
501 West Ocean Boulevard, Fax: (562) 980-4093
Long Beach, CA 90802

★ Presidential Appointment Requiring Senate Confirmation ☆ Presidential Appointment □ Schedule C Appointment ◇ Career Senior Foreign Service Appointment
● Career Senior Executive Service (SES) Appointment ○ Non-Career Senior Executive Service (SES) Appointment ■ Postal Career Executive Service

Protected Resources Division
501 West Ocean Boulevard, Long Beach, CA 90802

Assistant Regional Administrator
Christopher E. Yates . . . . (562) 980-4007
E-mail: chris.yates@noaa.gov Fax: (562) 980-4027

Long Beach Branch Chief **Penny Ruvelas** . . . . (562) 980-4197
E-mail: penny.ruvelas@noaa.gov

Portland Branch Chief **Robert Markle** . . . . (503) 230-5419
1201 NE Lloyd Boulevard, Suite 1100, Portland, OR 97232-1274
E-mail: Robert.Markle@noaa.gov

Seattle Branch Chief **Lynne M. Barre** . . . . (206) 526-4745
7600 Sand Point Way, NE, Seattle, WA 98115
E-mail: lynne.barre@noaa.gov

Sustainable Fisheries Division
7600 Sand Point Way, NE, Seattle, WA 98115

Assistant Regional Administrator (Acting)
Ryan J. Wulff . . . . (916) 930-3733
E-mail: ryan.wulff@noaa.gov

Anadromous Harvest Management Branch Chief
Susan Bishop . . . . (206) 526-4587
E-mail: Susan.Bishop@noaa.gov

Anadromous Production and Inland Fisheries Branch Chief **Allyson Purcell** . . . . (503) 736-4736
1201 NE Lloyd Boulevard, Portland, OR 97232-1274
E-mail: Allyson.Purcell@noaa.gov

Groundfish and Coastal Pelagic Species Branch Chief
Aja Szumylo . . . . (206) 526-4746
E-mail: Aja.Szumylo@noaa.gov

Groundfish and Coastal Pelagic Species Senior Policy Advisor **Frank D. Lockhart** . . . . (206) 526-6142
E-mail: frank.lockhart@noaa.gov

Permits and Monitoring Branch Chief (Acting)
Melissa Hooper . . . . (206) 526-4357
E-mail: melissa.hooper@noaa.gov

Highly Migratory Species Branch Chief
Heidi L. Taylor-Lindsay . . . . (562) 980-4039
501 West Ocean Boulevard, Long Beach, CA 90802
E-mail: heidi.taylor@noaa.gov

Operations and Policy Branch Chief **Kelly Ames** . . . . (503) 230-5427
501 West Ocean Boulevard, Long Beach, CA 90802
E-mail: Kelly.Ames@noaa.gov

Northwest Fisheries Science Center
2725 Montlake Boulevard, East, Seattle, WA 98112-2097
Tel: (206) 860-3200 TTY: (206) 860-3320 Fax: (206) 860-3217
Internet: www.nwfsc.noaa.gov

● Science and Research Director **Dr. Kevin Werner** . . . . (206) 860-6795
E-mail: kevin.werner@noaa.gov

Deputy Science Director **Mark S. Strom PhD** . . . . (206) 860-3356
Education: U Washington 1977 BS, 1982 MS, 1992 PhD

Director OMI **Stewart Toshach** . . . . (206) 860-3495

Program Manager (Administrative Officer)
Diane L. Tierney . . . . (206) 856-4107
E-mail: diane.tierney@noaa.gov

Program Manager (Facilities Manager)
Thanh M. Trinh . . . . (206) 860-6798

Program Manager (Information Technology)
Alicia Matter . . . . (206) 860-3367
E-mail: alicia.matter@noaa.gov

Librarian **(Vacant)** . . . . (206) 860-3210

Conservation Biology Division Director
Dr. Mike J. Ford . . . . (206) 860-3234
Education: Stanford BS; Cornell PhD

Environmental and Fisheries Science Division Director
Dr. Walton W. "Walt" Dickhoff . . . . (206) 860-3380
E-mail: walton.w.dickhoff@noaa.gov
Education: UC Berkeley 1970 ABS, 1976 PhD

Fish Ecology Division Director **Richard Zabel PhD** . . . . (206) 860-3290

Fishery Resource Analysis and Monitoring Division Director **Dr. Michelle M. Mcclure** . . . . (206) 860-3402

Southwest Fisheries Science Center
8901 La Jolla Shores Drive, La Jolla, CA 92037
Tel: (858) 546-7000 Fax: (858) 546-7003 Internet: swfsc.noaa.gov

Science and Research Director (Acting)
Kristen C. Koch . . . . (858) 546-7081

Deputy Science and Research Director (Acting)
Newell "Toby" Garfield III . . . . (858) 546-5623

Assistant Center Director for Ships and Infrastructure
Dr. Roger Hewitt . . . . (858) 546-5602

Executive Secretary **Dawn Graham** . . . . (858) 546-7081
Fax: (858) 546-5655

Librarian **Debra A. Losey** . . . . (858) 546-7196
E-mail: debra.losey@noaa.gov

Director of ITS **Heather B. Nicholas** . . . . (858) 546-7055
E-mail: heather.nicholas@noaa.gov

California Central Valley Area Office
650 Capitol Mall, Suite 8-300, Sacramento, CA 95814-4706
Tel: (916) 930-3601 Fax: (916) 930-3629

Assistant Regional Administrator **Maria C. Rea** . . . . (916) 930-3623

California Coastal Area Office
1655 Heindon Road, Arcata, CA 95521-4573
Tel: (707) 825-5163 Fax: (707) 825-4840

Assistant Regional Administrator
Alecia "Lisa" Van Atta . . . . (707) 575-6058

Interior Columbia Basin Area Office
1201 NE Lloyd Boulevard, Portland, OR 97232-1274
Tel: (503) 230-5400 Fax: (503) 231-6265

Assistant Regional Administrator
Michael "Mike" Tehan . . . . (503) 231-2224
E-mail: michael.tehan@noaa.gov

Assistant Regional Administrator for Hydropower Division **Ritchie J. Graves** . . . . (503) 231-6891
E-mail: ritchie.graves@noaa.gov Fax: (503) 231-2318

Oregon and Washington Coastal Area Office
1201 NE Lloyd Boulevard, Portland, OR 97232-1274
Tel: (503) 230-5400

Assistant Regional Administrator **Kim Kratz** . . . . (503) 231-2155

Environmental Services Branch Chief
Keith R. Kirkendall . . . . (503) 230-5431
E-mail: keith.kirkendall@noaa.gov

North Puget Sound Branch Chief **Elizabeth Babcock** . . . . (206) 526-4505
7600 Sand Point Way, NE, Seattle, WA 98115

Upper Willamette River Branch Chief
Marc C. Liverman . . . . (503) 231-2336

Aquaculture Coordinator for Oregon and Washington
Laura Hoberecht PhD . . . . (503) 230-5400
Education: UC Berkeley 1993 BS; U Washington 2001 MS, 2006 PhD

Office of the Deputy Under Secretary for Operations

Herbert Clark Hoover Building, 1401 Constitution Avenue, NW, Room 7316, Washington, DC 20230
Tel: (202) 482-4569

Office of Marine and Aviation Operations and NOAA Corps
8403 Colesville Road, Suite 500, Silver Spring, MD 20910
Fax: (301) 713-1541 Internet: www.omao.noaa.gov

Aircraft Operations Center (AOC)
Hangar 5, 7917 Hangar Loop Drive, MacDill AFB, FL 33621-5401
P.O. Box 6829, MacDill AFB, FL 33608-0829
Tel: (813) 828-3310 Fax: (813) 828-3266

Commanding Officer **Michael Silah** . . . . (301) 683-1327
E-mail: michael.silah@noaa.gov
Education: Duke 1992 BA; JFK School Govt 2009 MPA

Deputy Director **RDML Nancy Hann NOAA** . . . . (301) 713-1045
E-mail: nancy.hann@noaa.gov
Education: San Diego BS; Embry-Riddle MS; JFK School Govt MPA

(continued on next page)

★ Presidential Appointment Requiring Senate Confirmation ☆ Presidential Appointment □ Schedule C Appointment ◇ Career Senior Foreign Service Appointment
● Career Senior Executive Service (SES) Appointment ○ Non-Career Senior Executive Service (SES) Appointment ■ Postal Career Executive Service

DEPARTMENTS

Aircraft Operations Center *(continued)*

Public Affairs Coordinator and Outreach Specialist
Lori Bast .... (863) 500-3889
E-mail: lori.bast@noaa.gov

Information Technology Specialist
Jason W. McCombs .... (863) 500-3923
E-mail: jason.mccombs@noaa.gov Fax: (813) 828-5749

Deputy Assistant Administrator for Programs and Administration **Gary C. Reisner** .... (301) 713-1045
E-mail: gary.reosner@noaa.gov

Regional Support Centers

Central Regional Center

601 East 12th Street, Room 1736, Kansas City, MO 64106-2876
Fax: (816) 426-7459

Acquisitions Management Division Chief
Donita S. McCullough .... (816) 426-7286
E-mail: donita.s.mccullough@noaa.gov

Finance Division Chief **(Vacant)** .... (816) 426-7543

Project Planning and Management Division Chief
(Vacant) .... (816) 426-7811

Real Property Management Division Chief
(Acting) **Marc Rappaport** .... (301) 713-0937 ext. 112
E-mail: marc.rappaport@noaa.gov

Systems Division Chief **(Vacant)** .... (816) 426-2110

DOC Bankcard Center Chief **Michael McConnell** .... (816) 823-3851
1500 East Bannister Road, Room 1186, Kansas City, MO 64131

National Logistics Support Center Chief **(Vacant)** .... (816) 268-3133
Building 1, 1510 East Bannister Road, Kansas City, MO 64131

Workforce Management Office Director, NWS Client Services Division **Pamela Sellman** .... (301) 713-6346
E-mail: pamela.sellman@noaa.gov

Eastern Regional Center

Norfolk Federal Building, 200 Granby Street,
Room 815, Norfolk, VA 23510
Tel: (757) 441-6893 Fax: (757) 441-3846

Acquisition Management Division Chief
Jack O. Salmon, Jr. .... (757) 441-6893
E-mail: jack.o.salmon@noaa.gov

Information Technology Chief
James R. "Rob" Bruner, Jr. .... (757) 441-6871
E-mail: rob.bruner@noaa.gov

Security Office Chief **(Vacant)** .... (757) 441-6893

Workforce Management Director **(Vacant)** .... (757) 441-6549

Western Regional Center (WRC)

7600 Sand Point Way, NE, Seattle, WA 98115-0070

Acquisition Division Chief (Acting) **Chad M. Hepp** .... (303) 497-3443
E-mail: chad.m.hepp@noaa.gov

Small Business Specialist **Elizabeth Babcock** .... (206) 526-4505
325 Broadway St, Boulder, CO 80305-3328
E-mail: elizabeth.babcock@noaa.gov

Finance Division Chief **(Vacant)** .... (206) 526-6041

Operations Branch Chief **Angela Hunter** .... (206) 526-6041

Project, Planning, and Management Division Chief
(Vacant) .... (206) 526-6191

Service Delivery Division Chief
George Eric Kasahara .... (206) 526-6244
E-mail: eric.kasahara@noaa.gov

Workforce Management Office, Ecosystems Client Services Division Chief **(Vacant)** .... (206) 526-6057

National Environmental Satellite, Data and Information Service (NESDIS)

Silver Spring Metro Center 1, 1335 East-West Highway,
Silver Spring, MD 20910
Fax: (301) 713-1249 Internet: www.nesdis.noaa.gov

National Oceanographic Data Center

NOAA/NEDIS E/OC, SSMC-3, 1315 East-West Highway,
4th Floor, Silver Spring, MD 20960-3282
Tel: (301) 713-3277 Fax: (301) 713-3300 Internet: www.nodc.noaa.gov

NOAA Central Library

Silver Spring Metro Center One, 2242 W North Temple,
Room 2456, Silver Spring, MD 20910
Fax: (301) 713-4598 Tel: (301) 713-2600

NOAA Miami (FL) Regional Library

4301 Rickenbacker Causeway, Miami, FL 33149
Tel: (305) 361-4428 Fax: (305) 361-4448
Internet: www.aoml.noaa.gov/general/lib

Director **Linda L. Pikula** .... (305) 361-4429
E-mail: linda.pikula@noaa.gov

NOAA Seattle (WA) Regional Library

E/OC43, 7600 Sand Point Way, NE, Building 3, Seattle, WA 98115-6349
Tel: (206) 526-6241 E-mail: seattle.library@noaa.gov
Internet: www.wrclib.noaa.gov

Chief Librarian **Brian Voss** .... (206) 526-6242 ext. 1
E-mail: brian.voss@noaa.gov

Systems Administrator **(Vacant)** .... (206) 526-6241 ext. 3

Office of Satellite and Product Operations

4231 Suitland Road, Suitland, MD 20746
Tel: (301) 457-5184

National Ice Center (NATICE)

4231 Suitland Road, Suitland, MD 20746
Tel: (301) 817-3977 E-mail: nic.cdo@noaa.gov
Internet: www.natice.noaa.gov/

Director **CDR Ruth A. Lane USN** .... (301) 817-3977

Deputy Director **Kevin Berberich** .... (301) 817-3939

Fairbanks (AK) Command and Data Acquisition Station (FCDAS)

1300 Eisele Road, Fairbanks, AK 99712-1725
Tel: (907) 451-1200 Fax: (907) 451-1210

Station Manager **Larry L. Ledlow** .... (907) 451-1274
E-mail: larry.ledlow@noaa.gov

Senior Systems Engineer **(Vacant)** .... (907) 451-1230

Information Systems Security Officer **(Vacant)** .... (907) 451-1284

Wallops (VA) Command and Data Acquisition Station

35663 Chincoteague Road, Wallops Island, VA 23337
Tel: (757) 824-3446 Fax: (757) 824-7300

Station Manager **Albert J. McMath, Jr.** .... (757) 824-7316
E-mail: albert.j.mcmath.jr@noaa.gov

Operations Branch Chief **Albert J. McMath, Jr.** .... (757) 824-7316

Support Branch Chief **James Deck** .... (757) 824-7311

Systems Engineering Branch Manager **Bob Clark** .... (757) 824-7328
E-mail: bob.clark@noaa.gov

National Ocean Service (NOS)
Silver Spring Metro Center 4, 1305 East-West Highway,
Silver Spring, MD 20910
Tel: (301) 713-3074 Fax: (301) 713-4269 Internet: www.nos.noaa.gov

Center for Operational Oceanographic Products and Services (CO-OPS)
Silver Spring Metro Center 4, 1305 East-West Highway,
Room 6633, Silver Spring, MD 20910
Tel: (301) 713-2981 Fax: (301) 713-4019

Field Operations Division
672 Independence Parkway, Chesapeake, VA 23320
Tel: (757) 842-4400 Fax: (757) 436-9292
Internet: www.tidesandcurrents.noaa.gov

Chief **Katherine "Kate" Bosley** .... (757) 842-4406

Atlantic Operations Branch
672 Independence Parkway, Chesapeake, VA 23320
Tel: (757) 842-4400 Fax: (757) 436-9292
Internet: http://tidesandcurrents.noaa.gov

Officer-in-Charge **David Lane** .... (757) 842-4444

Pacific Operations Branch
7600 Sand Point Way, NE, Seattle, WA 98115
Tel: (206) 526-6360 Fax: (206) 526-6365
Internet: http://tidesandcurrents.noaa.gov

Officer-in-Charge **Rolin S. Meyer** .... (206) 526-6367

National Weather Service (NWS)
Silver Spring Metro Center 2, 1325 East-West Highway,
Silver Spring, MD 20910
Fax: (301) 713-0662 Internet: www.weather.gov

Office of the Chief Learning Officer

Training Division

National Weather Service Training Center
7220 NW 101st Terrace, Kansas City, MO 64153
Tel: (816) 994-3000 Fax: (816) 880-0377 Internet: www.nwstc.noaa.gov

Director **John E. Ogren** .... (816) 994-3001
E-mail: john.ogren@noaa.gov
Education: Western Illinois BS
Engineering and Electronics Training Section
James Poole .... (816) 994-3002
Meteorology, Hydrology and Management Training
Section **Jeffrey Zeltwanger** .... (816) 994-3017
Budget and Accounting Chief **(Vacant)** .... (816) 994-3004
Correspondence/Student Coordinator **Denise Lewis** ...... (816) 994-3006
E-mail: denise.lewis@noaa.gov
Webmaster **Dave Rowell** .... (816) 994-3010
E-mail: dave.rowell@noaa.gov

Office of Planning and Programming for Service Delivery

Office of Observations

Radar Operations Center
Radar Operations Center, 1200 Westheimer Drive, Norman, OK 73069
Tel: (405) 573-8803 Internet: www.roc.noaa.gov

Chief **Terrance J. "Terry" Clark** Room WSR-88D .... (405) 573-8803
Education: South Dakota State BS; Texas Tech MS
Deputy Chief **(Vacant)** .... (405) 573-8803
Applications Branch Chief (Acting)
CAPT Joseph A. Pica NOAA .... (301) 427-9778
Education: Illinois 1992 BS; Portland State 1998 MS
Engineering Branch Chief **Christina A. Horvat** .... (405) 573-3496
Fax: (405) 573-3340
Operations Branch Chief **Michael Wayne Miller** .... (405) 573-8810
Fax: (405) 573-8860
Program Branch Chief **Cheryl A. Stephenson** .... (405) 573-3317
E-mail: cheryl.a.stephenson@noaa.gov Fax: (405) 573-3480

Telecommunications Operations Center
Silver Spring Metro Center 2, 1325 East-West Highway,
Silver Spring, MD 20910

● Telecommunication Operations Center Chief (Acting)
Deirdre Reynolds Jones Room 5214 .... (301) 427-9183
E-mail: deirdre.r.jones@noaa.gov
Education: Rensselaer Poly 1983 BSEE; USC 1985 MS
Operations Support and Performance
Monitoring Branch Chief
(Vacant) Room 5348 .... (301) 713-0864 ext. 107
Telecommunications Gateway Operations
Branch Chief **(Vacant)** Room 5306 .... (301) 713-0864 ext. 171
Telecommunications Infrastructure Branch Chief
Bernard Werwinski Room 5425 .... (301) 427-9563
E-mail: bernard.werwinski@noaa.gov Fax: (301) 713-0285
Telecommunications Software Branch Chief
Robert D. Bunge Room 5146 .... (301) 683-3565
E-mail: robert.bunge@noaa.gov

National Data Buoy Center
Building 3205, Room 116, Stennis Space Center, MS 39529-6000
Tel: (228) 688-2805 Fax: (228) 688-3153 Internet: www.ndbc.noaa.gov

Director **Helmut H. Portmann** .... (228) 688-2805
E-mail: helmut.portmann@noaa.gov
Education: Georgia Tech BSEE; Johns Hopkins 1990 MSEE
Technical Assistant **Kathleen O'Neil** .... (228) 688-2823
Data Management Branch Chief **Joseph Swaykos** ...... (228) 688-4766
E-mail: joe.swaykos@noaa.gov
Operations Branch Chief **Craig A. Kohler** .... (228) 688-1421
Resources Branch Chief **Herschel Rector** .... (228) 688-2451
E-mail: herschel.rector@noaa.gov
Webmaster **Kevin J. Kern** .... (228) 688-1721
E-mail: kevin.kern@noaa.gov

Logistics Management Branch

National Reconditioning Center
National Weather Service, 1520 East Bannister Road,
Kansas City, MO 64131

Chief **Charles L. "Chuck" Maples** .... (816) 926-3217 ext. 231
Fax: (816) 926-3105
Administrative Officer
Marjorie A. "Margie" Sabbagh .... (816) 926-3217 ext. 234
E-mail: margie.sabbagh@noaa.gov
NEXRAD Repair Branch Chief **(Vacant)** .... (816) 926-3217 ext. 232
Weather Systems Repair Branch Chief
(Vacant) .... (816) 926-3217 ext. 228

Office of the Chief Operating Officer

Regional Offices

Alaska Region
James M. Fitzgerald Federal Building & U.S. Courthouse,
222 West Seventh Avenue, #23, Anchorage, AK 99513-7575
Tel: (907) 271-5136 Fax: (907) 271-3711 Internet: www.arh.noaa.gov
Areas Covered: AK

Regional Director **Carven A. Scott** .... (907) 271-5126
E-mail: carven.scott@noaa.gov
Education: Texas A&M 1974 BS, 1977 MS
Deputy Regional Director **John H. Dragomir** .... (907) 271-3442
E-mail: john.dragomir@noaa.gov
Administrative Management Division Chief (Acting)
Lisa M. Fair .... (907) 271-1248
E-mail: lisa.fair@noaa.gov
Environmental and Scientific Services Division Chief
Michael M. Mercer .... (907) 271-5131
E-mail: michael.mercer@noaa.gov
Systems Operations Division Chief **Angel M. Corona** .... (907) 271-5119
E-mail: angel.corona@noaa.gov
Regional Hydrologist **Scott Lindsey** .... (907) 266-5152

★ Presidential Appointment Requiring Senate Confirmation ☆ Presidential Appointment ☐ Schedule C Appointment ◇ Career Senior Foreign Service Appointment
● Career Senior Executive Service (SES) Appointment ○ Non-Career Senior Executive Service (SES) Appointment ■ Postal Career Executive Service

National Tsunami Warning Center
910 South Felton Street, Palmer, AK 99645
Tel: (907) 745-4212 Fax: (907) 745-6071 E-mail: wcatwc@noaa.gov
Areas Covered: Coastal AK, CA, OR, WA; British Columbia

Scientist-in-Charge (Acting)
CAPT Michael Angove USN .... (907) 745-4212
E-mail: Michael.Angove@noaa.gov

Central Region
NOAA Building, 7220 NW 101st Terrace, Kansas City, MO 64153
Tel: (816) 891-8914 Fax: (816) 891-8362 Internet: www.crh.noaa.gov
Areas Covered: CO, IL, IN, IA, KS, KY, MI, MN, MO, NE, ND, SD, WI, WY

• Regional Director (Acting) **Kenneth Harding** .... (816) 268-3131
E-mail: Kenneth.Harding@noaa.gov
Education: Iowa State 1986 BS; Colorado State 1991 MS
Deputy Director **Kenneth Harding** .... (816) 268-3131
Education: Iowa State 1986 BS; Colorado State 1991 MS
Chief Operating Officer **Scott Tessmer** .... (816) 268-3140
Administrative Management Division Chief
Whitney M. Harris .... (816) 268-3100
E-mail: whitney.harris@noaa.gov Fax: (816) 891-9028
Integrated Services Division Chief **Michael J. Hudson** ... (816) 268-3132
E-mail: Michael.Hudson@noaa.gov
Public Affairs Specialist **(Vacant)** .... (816) 268-3135
Fax: (816) 891-8362
Scientific Services Division Chief **Bruce B. Smith** ...... (816) 268-3110
E-mail: bruce.smith@noaa.gov
• Systems Operation and Facilities Division Chief
Robert L. "Bob" Brauch .... (816) 268-3150
E-mail: bob.brauch@noaa.gov

Eastern Region
Airport Corporate Center, 630 Johnson Avenue,
Suite 202, Bohemia, NY 11716-2618
Tel: (631) 244-0101 Fax: (631) 244-0109
Areas Covered: CT, DE, DC, ME, MD, MA, NH, NJ, NY, NC, OH, PA, RI, SC, VT, VA, WV

• Regional Director **Jason P. Tuell** .... (631) 244-0101
E-mail: jason.tuell@noaa.gov
Education: Worcester Polytech 1979 BS; Georgia Tech 1990 PhD
Deputy Director **Mickey J. Brown** .... (631) 244-0102
E-mail: mickey.brown@noaa.gov Fax: (631) 244-0109
Administrative Management Division Chief
Richard Cochrane .... (631) 244-0160
E-mail: richard.cochrane@noaa.gov
Meteorological Services Division Chief
John L. Guiney .... (631) 244-0121
Scientific Services Division Chief
Kenneth W. Johnson PhD .... (631) 244-0136
System Operations Division Chief **Peter J. Gabrielsen** ... (631) 244-0111
Regional Hydrologist Division Chief **(Vacant)** .... (631) 244-0113

Pacific Region
Mauka Tower, Pacific Guardian Center, 737 Bishop Street,
Suite 2200, Honolulu, HI 96813
Tel: (808) 532-6416 Fax: (808) 532-5569
E-mail: w-prh.webmaster@noaa.gov Internet: www.prh.noaa.gov/pr/hq
Areas Covered: GU, HI, American Samoa, Commonwealth of the Northern Mariana Islands, Federated States of Micronesia, Republic of the Marshall Islands, Republic of Palau

• Regional Director **Raymond M. Tanabe** .... (808) 725-6000
E-mail: raymond.tanabe@noaa.gov
Education: Hawaii MS
Deputy Regional Director
Thomas E. "Tom" Evans III .... (808) 725-6002
E-mail: tom.evans@noaa.gov
Regional Aviation Operations Meteorologist
Charles Woodrum .... (808) 725-6012
Regional Engineer **Wesley W. Lum** .... (808) 725-6040
Administrative Management Division Chief
Angela Nyul .... (808) 725-6020
E-mail: Angela.Nyul@noaa.gov
Budget Analyst **(Vacant)** .... (808) 725-6023

Pacific Region *(continued)*

Environmental and Scientific Services Division Chief
Bill D. Ward .... (808) 725-6010
E-mail: bill.ward@noaa.gov
Data Systems Manager **David B. Meek** .... (808) 725-6015
E-mail: david.meek@noaa.gov
Systems Operations Division Chief **Derek K. Ching** ..... (808) 725-6030
E-mail: derek.ching@noaa.gov

International Tsunami Information Center (ITIC)
1845 Wasp Boulevard, Building 176, Honolulu, HI 96818
Tel: (808) 725-6051 Fax: (808) 725-6055
E-mail: itic.tsunami@unesco.org
Internet: http://itic.ioc-unesco.org/index.php

Director **Dr. Laura S.L. Kong PhD** .... (808) 725-6051
Education: Brown U; MIT 1990 PhD
Associate Director **Carlos Zuniga** 56 (32) 2766671
Fax: 56 (32) 2766542
Disaster Management Specialist
Cynthia C. "Cindi" Preller .... (907) 271-3352
Information Technology Specialist **Tammy W.L. Fukuji** ... (808) 725-6054
E-mail: tammy.fukuji@noaa.gov
Technical Information Specialist **(Vacant)** .... (808) 725-6053
Administrative Assistant **Arthur Sonen** .... (808) 725-6050
E-mail: arthur.sonen@noaa.gov

Southern Region
819 Taylor Street, Room 10E09, Fort Worth, TX 76102
Tel: (817) 978-1000 Fax: (817) 978-4187 Internet: www.srh.noaa.gov
Areas Covered: AL, AR, FL, GA, LA, MS, NM, OK, PR, TN, TX

• Regional Director **Steven G. Cooper** .... (817) 978-1000 ext. 103
E-mail: steven.cooper@noaa.gov
Education: Florida State 1980 BS; New Mexico 1985 MS
Deputy Regional Director (Acting)
John Michael Coyne .... (817) 978-1000 ext. 103
E-mail: mike.coyne@noaa.gov
Chief Program Officer **Jose Garcia** .... (817) 978-1000
E-mail: Jose.Garcia@noaa.gov
Education: Texas 1982 BS; Texas A&M 1989 MPA
Administrative Management Division Chief
Michael Gallant .... (817) 978-1111
E-mail: michael.gallant@noaa.gov
Operational Support Division Chief **Jeffrey Cupo** .... (682) 703-3709
Science and Technology Services Division
Chief **Gregory R. Patrick** .... (817) 978-1300 ext. 119
E-mail: gregory.patrick@noaa.gov Fax: (817) 978-3475
Education: Oklahoma 1987 BS
Systems Operations Division Chief **John Duxbury** ...... (682) 703-3703
E-mail: john.duxbury@noaa.gov

Western Region
Federal Building, 125 South State Street,
Room 1311, Salt Lake City, UT 84138-1102
Tel: (801) 524-5122 Fax: (801) 524-5270
Areas Covered: AZ, CA, ID, MT, NV, OR, UT, WA

• Regional Director **CAPT Grant A. Cooper USN (Ret)** ... (801) 524-6295
E-mail: grant.cooper@noaa.gov
Education: San Diego State BS; Naval Postgrad MS, 2002 PhD
Deputy Director **David B. Billingsley** .... (801) 524-6295
E-mail: david.billingsley@noaa.gov
Administration Management Division Chief
Douglas Alston .... (801) 524-5125
E-mail: douglas.alston@noaa.gov
Meteorological Services Division Chief
(Vacant) .... (801) 524-4000 ext. 262
Scientific Services Division Chief
Delain "Andy" Edman .... (801) 524-5131 ext. 249
Systems Operations Division Chief
Sean P. Wink .... (801) 524-5138 ext. 275
E-mail: sean.wink@noaa.gov
Regional Hydrologist **(Vacant)** .... (801) 524-5137 ext. 230

★ Presidential Appointment Requiring Senate Confirmation ☆ Presidential Appointment ☐ Schedule C Appointment ◇ Career Senior Foreign Service Appointment
● Career Senior Executive Service (SES) Appointment ○ Non-Career Senior Executive Service (SES) Appointment ■ Postal Career Executive Service

Oceanic and Atmospheric Research (OAR)
Silver Spring Metro Center, Building 3, 1315 East-West Highway, Room 11458, Silver Spring, MD 20910
Tel: (301) 713-2458 Fax: (301) 713-0163 Internet: www.oar.noaa.gov

Labs and Cooperative Institutes
Executive Director **Candice G. Jongsma** .... (301) 734-1177

Air Resources Laboratory (ARL)
5830 University Research Court, Room 4217, College Park, MD 20740
Tel: (301) 683-1365 Fax: (301) 683-1370 Internet: www.arl.noaa.gov
• Director (Acting) **Ariel F. Stein** Room 4215 .... (301) 683-1379
E-mail: ariel.stein@noaa.gov

Atlantic Oceanographic and Meteorological Laboratory (AOML)
4301 Rickenbacker Causeway, Miami, FL 33149
Tel: (305) 361-4300 Fax: (305) 361-4449 Internet: www.aoml.noaa.gov
• Director **Dr. Robert M. Atlas** .... (305) 361-4300
E-mail: robert.atlas@noaa.gov
Education: Saint Louis U 1970 BS; NYU 1976 PhD
Deputy Director **(Vacant)** .... (305) 361-4345
Director of Outreach and Communications **Erica Rule** .... (305) 361-4541
E-mail: erica.rule@noaa.gov
Director of Computer Network and Services Division
Robert E. Kohler .... (305) 361-4307
E-mail: robert.e.kohler@noaa.gov
Associate Director for Fleet, Facilities, and Safety
Mark Blankenship .... (305) 361-4544
Administrative Assistant **Dalynne Julmiste** .... (305) 361-4310
E-mail: dalynne.julmiste@noaa.gov

Earth System Research Laboratory (ESRL)
Skaggs Building, 325 Broadway, Boulder, CO 80305
Tel: (303) 497-6005 Fax: (303) 497-6951 Internet: www.esrl.noaa.gov
• Director **Robert S. "Robin" Webb** .... (303) 497-6078
E-mail: robert.s.webb@noaa.gov
Program Analyst **Kathleen G. "Katy" Stewart** .... (303) 497-6005
Deputy Director **Jerry Janssen** .... (303) 497-6647
E-mail: Jerry.Janssen@noaa.gov
Education: New Mexico 1988 BSEE
Chief Budget and Administrative Officer **Tom Statz** ..... (303) 497-6803
E-mail: tom.statz@noaa.gov
Chief Information Technology Manager **Nick Wilde** ...... (303) 497-6175
E-mail: nicholas.wilde@noaa.gov

Geophysical Fluid Dynamics Laboratory (GFDL)
P.O. Box 308, NOAA, Forrestal Campus, Princeton University, Princeton, NJ 08540
Internet: www.gfdl.noaa.gov
• Director **Dr. Venkatachalam "Ram" Ramaswamy** ..... (609) 452-6510
E-mail: v.ramaswamy@noaa.gov
Education: U Delhi (India); SUNY (Albany) 1982 PhD
Deputy Director **Whit G. Anderson PhD** .... (609) 452-5308
201 Forrestal Road, Princeton, NJ 08540

Great Lakes Environmental Research Laboratory (GLERL)
4840 South State Road, Ann Arbor, MI 48108-9719
Tel: (734) 741-2335 Fax: (734) 741-2055 Internet: www.glerl.noaa.gov
• Director **Deborah H. "Debbie" Lee PE** .... (734) 741-2244
E-mail: deborah.lee@noaa.gov
Education: Ohio State 1984 BSCE, 1986 MSCE; Michigan 1998

National Severe Storms Laboratory (NSSL)
120 David L. Boren Boulevard, Suite 2400, Norman, OK 73069
Tel: (405) 325-3620 Fax: (405) 325-1889 Internet: www.nssl.noaa.gov
• Director **Steven E. Koch PhD** .... (405) 325-6904
E-mail: steven.koch@noaa.gov
Education: Wisconsin 1972 BS, 1974 MS; Oklahoma 1979 PhD

Pacific Marine Environmental Laboratory (PMEL)
7600 Sand Point Way, NE, Seattle, WA 98115-0070
Fax: (206) 526-6815 Fax: (206) 526-4576 (Alternate)
Internet: www.pmel.noaa.gov
• Director (Acting) **Dr. Gary C. Matlock** .... (206) 526-6800
E-mail: Gary.C.Matlock@noaa.gov
Deputy Director **James L. "Jim" Guyton** .... (206) 526-6813
E-mail: jim.guyton@noaa.gov
Associate Director for Information Technology
Eugene F. Burger .... (206) 526-4586
E-mail: Eugene.Burger@noaa.gov
Associate Director for Operations
CDR Thomas J. Peltzer NOAA .... (206) 526-4485
E-mail: thomas.peltzer@noaa.gov

DEPARTMENTS

U.S. Patent and Trademark Office (USPTO)
Madison West Building, 600 Dulany Street, Alexandria, VA 22313-1450
P.O. Box 1450, Alexandria, VA 22313-1450
Tel: (571) 272-1000 (Personnel Locator)
Tel: (571) 384-5446 (Procurement Information)
Tel: (571) 272-1000 (PTO Information Line/Patent Assistance Center)
Tel: (800) 786-9199 (PTO Information Line/Patent Assistance Center)
Tel: (571) 272-3350 (Customer Services - Assignment Recordation Status)
Tel: (571) 272-3150 (Customer Services - Certification Services Status - Orders, Status and Information - Patent and Trademark Copy Sales Information) Tel: (800) 972-6382 (Customer Services - Patent and Trademark Copy Sales Information) Internet: www.uspto.gov
Internet: portal.uspto.gov/external/portal/emlocator (Personnel Locator)

OFFICE OF THE UNDER SECRETARY
Madison West Building, 600 Dulany Street, Alexandria, VA 22313-1450
Tel: (571) 272-8600 Fax: (571) 273-0464

Dallas (TX) Regional Patent and Trademark Office
Terminal Annex Federal Building, 207 South Houston Street, Dallas, TX 75202
Director **Hope Shimabuku** .... (469) 295-9000
E-mail: hope.shimabuku@uspto.gov
Education: Texas 1996 BA; Southern Methodist 2005 JD

Denver (CO) Regional Patent and Trademark Office
1961 Stout Street, Denver, CO 80294
Tel: (303) 297-4600
Director **Mollybeth Kocialski** .... (303) 297-4700
E-mail: mollybeth.kocialski@uspto.gov
Education: New Mexico 1994 BSChE; SUNY Col (Buffalo) 1997 JD

Detroit (MI) Regional Patent Office
Elijah J. McCoy Midwest Regional Office, 300 River Place Drive, Detroit, MI 48207
Tel: (313) 446-4800
• Director **Damian Porcari** .... (313) 446-4877
E-mail: damian.porcari@uspto.gov
Education: Michigan State 1981 BS; Detroit Mercy 1984 JD
Regional Manager **(Vacant)** .... (313) 446-0735
Administrative Patent Judge **Justin Busch** .... (313) 446-4831
E-mail: justin.busch@uspto.gov
Administrative Patent Judge **Beverly Bunting** .... (313) 446-4838
E-mail: beverly.bunting@uspto.gov
Administrative Patent Judge **Jeremy J. Curcuri** .... (313) 446-4832
E-mail: jeremy.curcuri@uspto.gov
Education: GMI BS; Walsh Col MS; Wayne State U JD
Administrative Patent Judge **James Dejmek** .... (313) 446-4872
E-mail: james.dejmek@uspto.gov
Administrative Patent Judge **David McKone** .... (313) 446-4823
E-mail: david.mckone@uspto.gov
Administrative Patent Judge **Michelle Osinski** .... (313) 446-4835
E-mail: michelle.osinski@uspto.gov

(continued on next page)

★ Presidential Appointment Requiring Senate Confirmation ☆ Presidential Appointment ☐ Schedule C Appointment ◇ Career Senior Foreign Service Appointment
● Career Senior Executive Service (SES) Appointment ○ Non-Career Senior Executive Service (SES) Appointment ■ Postal Career Executive Service

DEPARTMENTS

Detroit (MI) Regional Patent Office *(continued)*

Administrative Patent Judge **Patrick R. Scanlon** . . . .(313) 446-4836
E-mail: patrick.scanlon@uspto.gov

Silicon Valley Patent and Trademark Office
345 Middlefield Rd, Building 1, Menlo Park, CA 94025
Tel: (571) 272-8100 E-mail: siliconvalley@uspto.gov

Director **John W. Cabeca** . . . . (408) 918-9700

United States Department of Defense

Contents

United States Department of Defense (DOD)

Description: The Department of Defense provides the military force necessary to deter war and to protect the security of the United States. The Secretary of each military department (Air Force, Army and Navy) is responsible to the Secretary of Defense for the operation and efficiency of his or her department.

1400 Defense Pentagon, Washington, DC 20301-1000
Tel: (703) 545-6700 (Personnel Locator - Military and Key Civilian)
Tel: (703) 695-7145 (Procurement Information)
Tel: (703) 697-5131 (Press Office) Tel: (703) 571-3343 (Public Affairs)
Tel: (703) 697-1180 (Privacy Act Information)
Tel: (202) 685-3912 (National Defense University Information)
Tel: (703) 604-8569 (Fraud, Waste and Abuse Hotline - DC Metropolitan Area) Tel: (800) 424-9098 (Fraud, Waste and Abuse Hotline - Continental US, Alaska and Hawaii)
Tel: (800) 497-6261 (Deployment Health Support Directorate Hotline)
Tel: (800) 334-3414 (Electronic Commerce Information Center Hotline)
Internet: https://www.defense.gov/
Internet: https://dodcio.defense.gov/Social-Media/ (Social Media Hub)
Internet: https://www.usa.gov/ (Official US Government Web Site)

OFFICE OF THE SECRETARY OF DEFENSE (OSD)

1000 Defense Pentagon, Washington, DC 20301-1000
Tel: (703) 692-7100 Fax: (703) 571-8951

Deputy Secretary of Defense

1010 Defense Pentagon, Washington, DC 20301-1010
Tel: (703) 692-7150 Fax: (703) 697-7374

National Guard Bureau (NGB)

111 South George Mason Drive, Arlington, VA 22204
Tel: (703) 601-6767 (Press Office) Tel: (703) 607-2584 (Public Affairs)
E-mail: ngbpa.oncall@mail.mil (Media Queries)
Internet: www.nationalguard.mil

Note: The National Guard Bureau is a joint bureau of the departments of the Army and Air Force.

Air National Guard (ANG)

3500 Fetchet Avenue,
Joint Base Andrews-Naval Air Facility Washington, MD 20762-5157
1000 Air Force Pentagon, Room 4E126, Washington, DC 20330-1000
Fax: (703) 692-9056 Internet: www.ang.af.mil

Air National Guard Readiness Center (ANGRC - Joint Base Andrews)

Joint Base Andrews-Naval Air Facility Washington, MD 20762
Fax: (301) 836-8914 Internet: http://www.angrc.ang.af.mil/

Commander **MajGen Steven S. Nordhaus ANG** .... (240) 612-8001
3500 Fetchet Avenue,
Joint Base Andrews-Naval Air Facility Washington, MD 20762-5157
Vice Commander **Col Barbra S. Buls ANG** .... (240) 612-8001
Command Chief Master Sergeant
CMSgt Lorraine F. Regan ANG .... (703) 601-6767

Army National Guard (ARNG)

Army National Guard Readiness Center,
111 South George Mason Drive, Arlington, VA 22204
Fax: (703) 614-3387

LaVern E. Weber National Guard Professional Education Center (PEC)

NGB Professional Education Center, Camp Joseph T. Robinson, North Little Rock, AR 72115-0797
Tel: (501) 212-4665 Fax: (501) 212-4699

Commandant **COL Edwin Larkin ARNG** .... (501) 212-4662
Senior Administrative Assistant **Jillian Hurst** .... (501) 212-4665
Deputy Commandant and Chief of Staff
Eugene O'Nale .... (501) 212-4663
Command Sergeant Major
CSM Matthew Billet ARNG .... (501) 212-4664
Conference Scheduler **CPT John Mitchell USA** .... (501) 212-4763
Contracting Officer **Carl E. Moore** .... (501) 212-4766
Information Management Director **Steven Burrus** .... (501) 212-4606
Operations Training Director **LTC Ricky Utley USA** ..... (501) 212-4314
Support Service Director **John Frost** .... (501) 212-4647
Logistics Training Center Chief
LTC Michael Bryant ARNG .... (501) 212-4717
Strength Maintenance Training Center Chief
MAJ Carlos Woodard ARNG .... (501) 212-4133
Physical Security Officer **(Vacant)** .... (501) 212-4698

Office of the Chief Information Officer (DOD CIO)

6000 Defense Pentagon, Room 3E1030, Washington, DC 20301-6000
Tel: (703) 695-0348 Fax: (703) 614-8060
Internet: http://dodcio.defense.gov/

Defense Information Systems Agency (DISA)

6910 Cooper Avenue, Fort George G. Meade, MD 20755
Tel: (301) 225-8100 E-mail: disa.meade.spi.mbx.disa-pao@mail.mil
Internet: www.disa.mil

Component Acquisition Executive

P.O. Box 549, Fort George G. Meade, MD 20755-0549
Tel: (301) 225-4000

Procurement Directorate

6910 Cooper Avenue, Fort George G. Meade, MD 20755

Defense Information Technology Contracting Organization (DITCO)

2300 East Drive, Scott AFB, IL 62225-5406
Tel: (618) 229-9100 Fax: (618) 229-9305

Chief **James D. McCreary** .... (618) 229-9100
E-mail: james.d.mcreary.civ@mail.mil
Deputy Chief **Brent Baxter** .... (618) 229-9100
Counsel **JoAnn W. Melesky** .... (618) 229-9100
E-mail: joann.w.melesky.civ@mail.mil
E-mail: disa.scott.ditco.mbx.legal-office@mail.mil

(continued on next page)

Defense Information Technology Contracting Organization *(continued)*

Telecommunications Contracting Division Chief
Constance "Coni" Jackson . . . . (618) 229-9560
E-mail: coni.jackson@disa.mil

Development and Business Center

Joint Interoperability Test Command (JITC)

P.O. Box 12798, Fort Huachuca, AZ 85670-2798
E-mail: disa.huachuca.jitc.mbx.command-support-team-cst@mail.mil
Tel: (520) 538-5000 Fax: (520) 538-5068 Internet: http://jitc.fhu.disa.mil

Commander **CAPT Shawn Roberts USN** . . . . (520) 538-5002
Deputy Commander **Richard Clarke** . . . . (520) 538-5001
Senior Enlisted Leader **SGM Mary Carr USA** . . . . (520) 538-5066
Chief Engineer **Randon R. Herrin** . . . . (520) 538-5151
E-mail: randon.r.herrin.civ@mail.mil
Chief Information Officer **(Vacant)** . . . . (520) 538-5061
Staff Director **(Vacant)** . . . . (520) 538-5032
Security Officer **MIke Lynch** . . . . (520) 538-5573

Operations Center

6910 Cooper Avenue, Fort George G. Meade, MD 20755

Field Offices and Commands

Defense Information Systems Agency U.S. Central Command Field Command (DISA-CENT - MacDill AFB)
7115 South Boundary Boulevard, MacDill AFB, FL 33621-5131
Tel: (813) 529-6606

Commander **(Vacant)** . . . . (813) 529-6606

Defense Information Systems Agency Global Operations Command (DISA-DGOC - Scott AFB)
Scott AFB, IL 62225
Mail: DISA, CONUS, P.O. Box 25860, Scott AFB, IL 62225-5860
Tel: (618) 220-8840 Fax: (618) 220-9888

Commander **COL Paul G. Craft USA** . . . . (618) 220-8801
Deputy Commander **Dana Rowe** . . . . (618) 220-8801
Business Management Division Chief **Ron Black** . . . . (618) 220-8810
Fax: (618) 229-8941
Defense Information Systems Network (DISN)
Engineering Division Chief **Mark Heffron** . . . . (618) 220-8656
E-mail: heffronm@scott.disa.mil Fax: (618) 220-9074
Defense Information Systems Network (DISN)
Operations Division Chief **Clayton Peters** . . . . (618) 229-8651
Fax: (618) 229-8882
Information Systems Division Chief **Bill Bruns** . . . . (618) 220-9883
Systems Integration Liaison Chief **Ron Hoff** . . . . (618) 220-9881
Fax: (618) 229-8979

Defense Information Systems Agency European Field Command (DISA-EUROPE)
Patch Barracks, Vaihingen, Stuttgart, Germany
Mail: Unit 30403, APO, AE 09131
Tel: 49 (711) 680-5905 E-mail: custsvc@eur.disa.mil

Commander **COL Joel Lindeman USA** 49 (711) 680-5905

Defense Information Systems Agency U.S. Joint Forces Command Field Office (DISA-JFCOM)
1562 Mitscher Avenue, Suite 200, Norfolk, VA 23551
Tel: (757) 836-5753 Fax: (757) 836-5146
Internet: www.disa.mil/about/offices/field/jfcom.html

Division Chief **Hugh Walsh** . . . . (757) 836-5155
E-mail: hugh.walsh@disa.mil

Defense Information Systems Agency U.S. Northern Command Field Office (DISA-NORTHCOM)
250 South Peterson Boulevard, Suite 215, Peterson AFB, CO 80914-3200
Tel: (719) 554-3800 Fax: (719) 554-9741

Commander **Col Trevor Wall USAF** . . . . (719) 554-3800

Defense Information Systems Agency Pacific Field Command (DISA-PAC)
477 Essex Street, Suite 183, Pearl Harbor, HI 96860-5815
Tel: (808) 656-2782 (24-hour Theater Network Operations Center)
Fax: (808) 472-1917

Commander **Col Joseph E. Delaney USMC** . . . . (808) 472-0051
E-mail: joseph.e.delaney.mil@mail.mil
Deputy Commander **Bruce Morgan** . . . . (808) 472-0051
E-mail: bruce.a.morgan.civ@mail.mil
Resource Management **LTC Robert Fisher USA (Ret)** . . . (808) 472-0980
Operations **(Vacant)** . . . . (808) 656-1202
Technical Advisor and DISN Support **John Coller** . . . . (808) 472-1970
Security Manager **Edward W. "Ed" Ferrick** . . . . (808) 472-0008
E-mail: edward.w.ferrick.civ@mail.mil
Plans and Engineering **(Vacant)** . . . . (808) 472-0283

Defense Information Systems Agency Special Operations Command Field Office (DISA-SOC - MacDill AFB)
7701 Tampa Point Boulevard, MacDill AFB, FL 33621-5323
Tel: (813) 826-2086

Commander **(Name Withheld)** . . . . (813) 826-2086

Defense Information Systems Agency U.S. Strategic Command Field Office (DISA-STRATCOM)
DISA Field Office, 901 SAC Boulevard,
Suite 1F14, Offutt AFB, NE 68113-6601
Tel: (402) 294-5761 Fax: (402) 294-5798

Commander **(Vacant)** . . . . (402) 294-1248

Defense Information Systems Agency U.S. Transportation Command Field Office (DISA-TRANSCOM)
Building 1961, 508 Scott Drive, Scott AFB, IL 62225-5357
Tel: (618) 220-4074 Fax: (618) 256-1591

Commander **(Vacant)** . . . . (618) 220-4074

Office of the Inspector General (DODIG)

4800 Mark Center Drive, Suite 15G27, Alexandria, VA 22350-1500
Tel: (703) 604-8300 Tel: (800) 424-9098 (Fraud Hotline)
Fax: (703) 604-8310 E-mail: public.affairs@dodig.mil
Internet: www.dodig.mil

INVESTIGATIONS

4800 Mark Center Drive, Suite 15A27, Alexandria, VA 22350-1500
Tel: (703) 604-8600

Defense Criminal Investigative Service (DCIS)

4800 Mark Center Drive, Alexandria, VA 22350-1500

Central Field Office (CFO)

1222 Spruce Street, Suite 8.308E, St. Louis, MO 63103-2811
Tel: (314) 539-2172 Fax: (314) 539-2967 E-mail: 40sl@dodig.mil

Special Agent-in-Charge **Brian Reihms** . . . . (314) 425-5759
Assistant Special Agent-in-Charge **Jeff Arsenault** . . . . (314) 425-5744
Resident Agent-in-Charge **Mitchell Berry** . . . . (314) 425-5742

Columbus (OH) Resident Agency

4449 Easton Way, Suite 375, Columbus, OH 43219
Tel: (614) 428-1712 Fax: (614) 428-5268 E-mail: 40co@dodig.mil

Resident Agent-in-Charge **Sean Clayton** . . . . (614) 414-3531

Cleveland (OH) Post of Duty

Islander Park One Building, 7550 Lucerne,
Suite 200, Middleburg Heights, OH 44130-6503
Tel: (216) 535-5380 Fax: (216) 522-7196 E-mail: 40cl@dodig.mil

Senior Agent-in-Charge **Glen Caiola** . . . . (216) 535-3820

★ Presidential Appointment Requiring Senate Confirmation ☆ Presidential Appointment □ Schedule C Appointment ◇ Career Senior Foreign Service Appointment
● Career Senior Executive Service (SES) Appointment ○ Non-Career Senior Executive Service (SES) Appointment ■ Postal Career Executive Service

Dayton (OH) Resident Agency
3055 Kettering Boulevard, Suite 205, Dayton, OH 45439
Tel: (937) 534-0100 Fax: (937) 534-0116 E-mail: 40dy@dodig.mil
Resident Agent-in-Charge **Sean Clayton** . . . . (937) 534-0109

Indianapolis (IN) Resident Agency
6666 East 75th Street, Suite 501, Indianapolis, IN 46250
Tel: (317) 708-2010 Tel: (317) 841-7703 (Automated Attendant)
E-mail: 40in@dodig.mil
Resident Agent-in-Charge **Matthew Day** . . . . (317) 708-2010

Chicago Post of Duty
701 Lee Street, Suite 810, Des Plaines, IL 60016
Tel: (847) 827-9482 Fax: (847) 827-3724 E-mail: 40ch@dodig.mil
Areas Covered: Northern and Central IL, Northern IN, Western MI, WI
Resident Agent-in-Charge **Louis B. Mitchell** . . . . (847) 459-2781
E-mail: louis.mitchell@dodig.mil

Kansas City (KS) Resident Agency
Federal Building, 500 State Avenue, Suite 565,
Kansas City, KS 66101-2433
Tel: (913) 551-1350 Fax: (913) 551-1362 E-mail: 40kc@dodig.mil
Resident Agent-in-Charge **Mitchell Berry** . . . . (913) 551-1350

Minneapolis (MN) Post of Duty
414 Galtier Plaza, 380 Jackson Street, St. Paul, MN 55101-2901
Tel: (651) 238-8401 Fax: (612) 222-8316 E-mail: 40mn@dodig.mil
Special Agent **Louis B. Mitchell** . . . . (651) 238-8401
E-mail: louis.mitchell@dodig.mil

Sioux Falls (SD) Post of Duty
230 South Phillips Street, Suite 404, Sioux Falls, SD 57104
Tel: (605) 793-4000 Fax: (605) 793-4001 E-mail: 40sx@dodig.mil
Special Agent **Louis B. Mitchell** . . . . (605) 793-4000
E-mail: louis.mitchell@dodig.mil

Wichita (KS) Post of Duty
271 West Third Street, Suite 4020, Wichita, KS 67202-1202
Tel: (316) 265-2470 Fax: (316) 265-2357 E-mail: 40wc@dodig.mil
Special Agent **Mitchell Berry** . . . . (316) 265-2470

Mid-Atlantic Field Office
4800 Mark Center Drive, Suite 10D25-04, Alexandria, VA 22350
Tel: (703) 604-8439 Fax: (703) 602-3879
Special Agent-in-Charge **Robert E. Craig, Jr.** . . . . (703) 604-8424
E-mail: robert.craig@dodig.mil
Assistant Special Agent-in-Charge **Paul Sternal** . . . . (703) 604-8411
E-mail: paul.sternal@dodig.mil
Administrative Support Assistant **(Vacant)** . . . . (703) 604-8410
Administrative Officer **Alfreda Adams** . . . . (703) 604-8969
E-mail: alfreda.adams@dodig.mil

Baltimore (MD) Resident Agency
Bank of America Building, Tower II, 100 South Charles Street,
Suite 401, Baltimore, MD 21201
Tel: (410) 347-1625 Fax: (410) 735-1595
Resident Agent-in-Charge **Charles R. "C. R." Gillum** . . . . (703) 699-5406
E-mail: charles.gillum@dodig.mil

European Post Deputy
CMR. 24310 Box 34, APO, AE 09005-4310
Assistant Special Agent in Charge **Paul Sternal** . . . . (703) 604-8411
4800 Mark Center Drive, Suite 10D25-04, Alexandria, VA 22350

Norfolk (VA) Resident Agency
Federal Building, 200 Granby Street, Room 412, Norfolk, VA 23510-1811
Tel: (757) 441-3412 Fax: (757) 626-1891
Resident Agent-in-Charge **Christine S. Marrion** . . . . (757) 963-5227
E-mail: christine.marrion@dodig.mil

Richmond (VA) Post of Duty
5309 Commonwealth Centre Parkway, Suite 403, Midlothian, VA 23112
Tel: (804) 639-8360 Fax: (804) 763-0833
Senior Resident Agent **(Vacant)** . . . . (804) 639-8361

Northeast Field Office
Building Y, Airport Business Center, 10 Industrial Highway,
Mail Stop 75, Lester, PA 19113
Tel: (610) 595-1923 Fax: (610) 595-1934 E-mail: 10pa@dodig.mil
Special Agent-in-Charge **Craig W. Rupert** . . . . (610) 537-9941
E-mail: craig.rupert@dodig.mil
Assistant Special Agent-in-Charge
Leigh-Alistair Barzey . . . . (617) 565-4410
E-mail: leigh.barzey@dodig.mil

Boston (MA) Resident Agency
JFK Federal Building, 55 New Sudbury Street,
Room 1325, Boston, MA 02203-0131
Tel: (617) 565-4445 Fax: (617) 565-4406 E-mail: 10bn@dodig.mil
Resident Agent-in-Charge **Patrick Hegarty** . . . . (617) 565-4410

New Haven (CT) Resident Agency
One Century Tower, 265 Church Street,
Suite 404, New Haven, CT 06510-7013
Tel: (203) 782-4700 Fax: (203) 782-4708 E-mail: 10hf@dodig.mil
Resident Agent-in-Charge **(Vacant)** . . . . (203) 782-4700 ext. 211

New Jersey Resident Agency
Wick Plaza One, 100 Dey Place, Suite 102, Edison, NJ 08817-3700
Tel: (732) 819-8455 Fax: (732) 819-9430 E-mail: 10sp@dodig.mil
Resident Agent-in-Charge **Richard Monticello** . . . . (732) 819-4260
E-mail: richard.monticello@dodig.mil

New York (NY) Resident Agency
One Huntington Quadrangle, Suite 2C01, Melville, NY 11747-4427
Tel: (631) 420-4302 Fax: (631) 420-4316 E-mail: 10ny@dodig.mil
Resident Agent-in-Charge **Kenneth Siegler** . . . . (631) 391-7900
E-mail: kenneth.siegler@dodig.mil

Pittsburgh (PA) Resident Agency
Morehead Federal Building, 1000 Liberty Avenue,
Suite 2101, Pittsburgh, PA 15222-4004
Tel: (412) 395-6931 Fax: (412) 395-4557 E-mail: 10pb@dodig.mil
Resident Agent-in-Charge **Matthew Dunaway** . . . . (412) 995-2047
E-mail: matthew.dunaway@dodig.mil

Southeast Field Office
1899 Powers Ferry Road, Suite 300, Atlanta, GA 30339
Tel: (770) 916-9920 Fax: (770) 916-9937 E-mail: 20at@dodig.mil
Special Agent-in-Charge **John F. Khin** . . . . (770) 916-9923
Assistant Special Agent-in-Charge **Amie R. Tanchak** . . . . . (954) 325-9643
E-mail: amie.tanchak@dodig.mil
Administrative Officer **Marla Frett** . . . . (678) 236-0163
E-mail: marla.frett@dodig.mil

Atlanta (GA) Resident Agency
1899 Powers Ferry Road, Suite 300, Atlanta, GA 30339
Resident Agent-in-Charge **Robert J. Koons** . . . . (770) 916-9924

Fort Lauderdale (FL) Resident Agency
1475 West Cypress Creek Road, Suite 200,
Fort Lauderdale, FL 33309-1953
Tel: (954) 202-9167 Fax: (954) 202-9217 E-mail: 20fl@dodig.mil
Resident Agent-in-Charge **Jeffrey "Jeff" Lysaght** . . . . (954) 229-1712

Huntsville (AL) Resident Agency (Redstone Arsenal)
Building 3421, Gray Road, Suite 8, Redstone Arsenal, AL 35898-7245
Resident Agent-in-Charge **Jeffrey Walfield** . . . . (571) 230-6563

★ Presidential Appointment Requiring Senate Confirmation ☆ Presidential Appointment □ Schedule C Appointment ◇ Career Senior Foreign Service Appointment
● Career Senior Executive Service (SES) Appointment ○ Non-Career Senior Executive Service (SES) Appointment ■ Postal Career Executive Service

New Orleans (LA) Resident Agency
109 New Camellia Boulevard, Suite 200, Covington, LA 70433
Tel: (985) 845-5020 Fax: (985) 845-4151 E-mail: 20no@dodig.mil

Resident Agent-in-Charge **Darrin Jones** . . . . (985) 845-5021
E-mail: darrin.jones@dodig.mil

Pensacola (FL) Post of Duty
One Eleventh Avenue, Suite E-1, Shalimar, FL 32579-1305
Tel: (850) 651-6377 Fax: (850) 651-6962 E-mail: 20pc@dodig.mil

Senior Resident Agent **Paul Tarnuzzer** . . . . (404) 709-1879
E-mail: paul.tarnuzzer@dodig.mil

Tampa (FL) Resident Agency
400 North Tampa Street, Room 1130, Tampa, FL 33602
Tel: (813) 275-0592 Fax: (813) 314-0293

Resident Agent-in-Charge **Brooke Harris** . . . . (813) 675-8214

Southwest Field Office
2201 North Collins, Suite 300, Arlington, TX 76011
Tel: (817) 303-6059 Fax: (817) 543-4372 E-mail: inv30da@dodig.mil

Special Agent-in-Charge **Janice M. Flores** . . . . (703) 604-8603
E-mail: janice.flores@dodig.mil
Resident Agent-in-Charge **(Vacant)** . . . . (817) 303-6059
Assistant Special Agent-in-Charge **Michael Mentavlos** . . . (817) 303-0501
E-mail: michael.mentavlos@dodig.mil Fax: (817) 543-4372

Denver (CO) Resident Agency
6430 South Fiddlers Green Circle, Suite 350,
Greenwood Village, CO 80111
Tel: (303) 799-8182 Fax: (303) 799-8615 E-mail: inv30dv@dodig.mil

Resident Agent-in-Charge **Patrick O'Toole** . . . . (303) 689-7040
E-mail: patrick.otoole@dodig.mil

Albuquerque (NM) Post of Duty
P.O. Box 6792, Albuquerque, NM 87197
Tel: (505) 450-5257 Fax: (505) 856-9750 E-mail: inv30aq@dodig.mil

Senior Resident Agent **Monique Sanchez** . . . . (505) 450-5257
E-mail: monique.sanchez@dodig.mil

Houston (TX) Resident Agency
1919 Smith Street, Suite 1000, Houston, TX 77002
Tel: (713) 227-7263 Fax: (713) 236-8487 E-mail: inv30hs@dodig.mil

Resident Agent-in-Charge **(Vacant)** . . . . (713) 427-7203

San Antonio (TX) Resident Agency
North Chase I, 10127 Morocco Drive,
Suite 250, San Antonio, TX 78216-3954
Tel: (210) 340-7210 Fax: (210) 366-4031 E-mail: inv30sa@dodig.osd.mil

Resident Agent-in-Charge **Anthony Virgilio** . . . . (210) 212-1301
E-mail: anthony.virgilio@dodig.mil

Dallas (TX) Post of Duty
Resident Agent **Joshua Hyde** . . . . (817) 303-2001

Phoenix (AZ) Resident Agency
One North Central Avenue, Suite 1020, Phoenix, AZ 85004
Tel: (602) 379-4427 Fax: (602) 258-1068 E-mail: inv30px@dodig.mil

Resident Agent-in-Charge **Darren Pear** . . . . (602) 256-4060

Tulsa (OK) Resident Agency
1603 South 101st East Avenue, Suite 131, Tulsa, OK 74128
Tel: (918) 270-5750 Fax: (918) 581-6489 E-mail: inv30tl@dodig.mil

Resident Agent-in-Charge **Charles Case** . . . . (918) 270-5751
E-mail: charles.case@dodig.mil

Western Field Office
26722 Plaza Street, Suite 130, Mission Viejo, CA 92691-6300
Tel: (949) 282-2620 Fax: (949) 367-0403 E-mail: 50la@dodig.mil

Special Agent-in-Charge **Chris D. Hendrickson** . . . . (949) 282-2621
E-mail: chris.hendrickson@dodig.mil

Western Field Office *(continued)*

Assistant Special Agent-in-Charge **Bryan Denny** . . . . (949) 282-2622
E-mail: bryan.denny@dodig.mil

Long Beach (CA) Resident Agency
501 West Ocean Boulevard, Suite 7300, Long Beach, CA 90802-4222
Tel: (562) 256-2500 Fax: (562) 980-4249 E-mail: 50es@dodig.mil

Resident Agent-in-Charge **Craig A. Adams** . . . . (562) 256-2500
E-mail: craig.adams@dodig.mil

San Diego (CA) Resident Agency
4542 Ruffner Street, Suite 360, San Diego, CA 92111-2241
Tel: (858) 397-1987 Fax: (858) 569-6401 E-mail: 50sd@dodig.mil

Resident Agent-in-Charge **John J. Noack** . . . . (858) 397-1987
E-mail: john.noack@dodig.mil

San Francisco (CA) Resident Agency
Federal Building, 1301 Clay Street, Suite 480N, Oakland, CA 94612-5217
Tel: (510) 287-3660 Fax: (510) 637-2972 E-mail: 50sf@dodig.mil

Resident Agent-in-Charge **Brian Harrison** . . . . (510) 287-3669

Seattle (WA) Resident Agency
300 Fifth Avenue, Suite 820, Seattle, WA 98104
Tel: (206) 553-0700 Fax: (206) 839-1001 E-mail: 50se@dodig.mil

Resident Agent-in-Charge **Dan Hald** . . . . (206) 913-4580
E-mail: dan.hald@dodig.mil

Hawaii Post of Duty
300 Ala Moana Boulevard, Suite 6-209, Honolulu, HI 96850
Mail: P.O. Box 50045, Honolulu, HI 96850-0001
Tel: (808) 541-2575 Fax: (808) 541-3609

Senior Agent **Michael Naito** . . . . (808) 478-8210
E-mail: michael.naito@dodig.mil

Portland (OR) Post of Duty
9109 Northeast Cascades Parkway, Portland, OR 97220
Tel: (503) 460-8273 Fax: (503) 460-8286

Special Agent **Jeffrey "Jeff" Ledbetter** . . . . (503) 969-3207

Valencia (CA) Resident Agency
25350 Magic Mountain Parkway, Suite 200, Valencia, CA 91355
Tel: (661) 253-5007 Fax: (661) 253-4969 E-mail: 50vn@dodig.mil

Resident Agent-in-Charge **Nathan A. Deschenes** . . . . (661) 414-1121
E-mail: nathan.deschenes@dodig.mil

★ Presidential Appointment Requiring Senate Confirmation ☆ Presidential Appointment ☐ Schedule C Appointment ◇ Career Senior Foreign Service Appointment
● Career Senior Executive Service (SES) Appointment ○ Non-Career Senior Executive Service (SES) Appointment ■ Postal Career Executive Service

Comptroller
1100 Defense Pentagon, Washington, DC 20301-1100

OFFICE OF THE UNDER SECRETARY OF DEFENSE (COMPTROLLER) (OUSD-C)
1100 Defense Pentagon, Washington, DC 20301-1100
Internet: http://comptroller.defense.gov/

Defense Contract Audit Agency (DCAA)
8725 John J Kingman Road, Suite 2135, Fort Belvoir, VA 22060-6219
Tel: (703) 767-3265 Tel: (703) 767-3200 (Personnel Locator)
Fax: (703) 767-3267 Internet: www.dcaa.mil

Regional Offices

Central Region
2250 West John Carpenter Freeway, Irving, TX 75063
Tel: (972) 652-3600
Areas Covered: States of Alabama, Florida, Indiana, Kentucky, Louisiana, Michigan excluding the Upper Peninsula, Mississippi, New York (excluding counties of Suffolk, Nassau, Richmond, Kings, Queens, New York, Bronx, Rockland, Westchester, Orange, Dutchess, Sullivan, Ulster, Columbia, Green, Delaware), Ohio, Pennsylvania (excluding the counties of Philadelphia, Delaware, Chester, Montgomery, Bucks), Tennessee, Texas, Vermont, West Virginia. Plus Puerto Rico.

- ● Regional Manager **Diana P. Graff** .... (972) 652-3600
  Education: Arizona State 1985 BAcc; Troy State 1995 MPA
- ● Deputy Regional Manager **Debbra M. Caw** .... (972) 652-3600
- Audit Manager **Gordon A. Eeten** .... (972) 652-3600
  E-mail: dcaa-rama-3@dcaa.mil
- Audit Manager **Angela Moomand** .... (972) 652-3600
- Audit Manager **Jody Niebruegge** .... (972) 652-3600
  E-mail: dcaa-ramc-3@dcaa.mil
- Audit Manager **Dan St. John** .... (972) 652-3600

Eastern Region
2400 Lake Park Drive, Suite 300, Smyrna, GA 30080-7644
Tel: (770) 319-4400 Fax: (770) 319-4514
Areas Covered: States of Connecticut, Delaware, Georgia, Maine, Maryland, Massachusetts, New Hampshire, New Jersey, New York (counties Suffolk, Nassau, Richmond, Kings, Queens, New York, Bronx, Rockland, Westchester, Orange, Dutchess, Sullivan, Ulster, Columbia, Green, Delaware), North Carolina, Pennsylvania (counties of Philadelphia, Delaware, Chester, Montgomery, Bucks), Rhode Island, South Carolina, Virginia, Washington D.C. Plus countries in Europe, Southwest Asia.

- ● Director **David E. Johnson** .... (770) 319-4400
  E-mail: david.johnson@dcaa.mil
- ● Deputy Director **Catherine Carrell** .... (770) 319-4400
  E-mail: catherine.carrell@dcaa.mil
- Chief, RSA - Information Systems Division **Mecia Harris** .... (770) 319-4411
  E-mail: mecia.harris@dcaa.mil Fax: (770) 319-4527
- Regional Special Programs Manager **Dave Fix** .... (770) 319-4453
  E-mail: dave.fix@dcaa.mil

Western Region
4 Centerpoint Drive, Suite 400, La Palma, CA 90623-1074
Tel: (714) 228-7002 Fax: (714) 228-7089
Areas Covered: States of Alaska, Arizona, Arkansas, California, Colorado, Hawaii, Idaho, Illinois, Iowa, Kansas, Michigan - Upper Peninsula, Minnesota, Missouri, Montana, Nebraska, Nevada, New Mexico, North Dakota, Oklahoma, Oregon, South Dakota, Utah, Washington, Wisconsin, Wyoming. Plus Countries in South East Asia.

- ● Regional Director **(Vacant)** .... (714) 228-7001
- Deputy Regional Director **C. Steven Hernandez** .... (714) 228-7003

Defense Finance and Accounting Service (DFAS)
8899 East 56th Street, Indianapolis, IN 46249-2000
Tel: (216) 522-5955 Tel: (317) 212-7528 (Corporate Communications)
Tel: (888) 332-7411 (Military Pay)
Tel: (800) 255-0574 (Reserve Pay Center)
Tel: (800) 321-1080 (Retired Military Pay Center)
Tel: (888) 898-0087 (Vendor Pay Center [Air Force])
Tel: (888) 332-7366 (Vendor Pay Center [Army])
Tel: (816) 926-7480 (Vendor Pay Center [Marine Corps])
Internet: www.dfas.mil

Operations Directorate

Regional Offices

Defense Finance and Accounting Service Cleveland (OH)
A. J. Celebrezze Federal Building, 1240 East Ninth Street, Cleveland, OH 44199-2055
Tel: (216) 522-5511 Tel: (216) 522-5620 (Public Affairs)
Tel: (216) 204-7019 (Corporate Communications) Fax: (216) 522-6055
Internet: www.dod.mil/dfas/about/locations/cl_index.htm

- ● Director **Robert A. Edwards** .... (216) 522-5707
  Education: Excelsior 2008 BS
- ● Deputy Director **Melissa Sikora** .... (216) 522-5511
- Chief of Staff **John Lucas** .... (216) 522-6336
- Chief of Staff for the Deputy Director of Strategic Business Management **(Vacant)** .... (216) 522-5511

Defense Finance and Accounting Service Columbus (OH)
3990 East Broad Street, Columbus, OH 43213
Mail: P.O. Box 182317, Columbus, OH 43218-2317
Tel: (216) 522-6998 Fax: (614) 693-2594
Fax: (216) 367-3343 (Public Affairs) E-mail: dfas.columbus@dfas.mil
Internet: http://www.dfas.mil/

- ● Director **Pamela Franceschi** .... (614) 693-6710
  Fax: (614) 693-2497
- ● Deputy Director **Jim Likes** .... (614) 696-6600
- Accounting Operations Director **Tom Joyce** .... (614) 693-7358
- Administrative Services Directorate Manager **Ronald Trego** .... (614) 693-1351
  E-mail: ronald.trego@dfas.mil
- Contract Entitlement Division **Diane L. Johnson** .... (614) 693-4855
- Corporate Communications Office **Thomas "Tom" Casasanta** .... (614) 693-5040
- Customer Service Resource Center **Monica Long** .... (614) 693-0334
  E-mail: monica.long@dfas.mil
- Departmental Reporting Office Director **Charlayne Martin** .... (614) 693-5237
- Disbursing Services Director **Tim Segebarth** .... (614) 693-6506
- Finance Director **Toni Phelps** .... (614) 693-6139

Defense Finance and Accounting Service Indianapolis (IN)
8899 East 56th Street, Indianapolis, IN 46249-2000
Tel: (317) 212-3953 (Media Relations) Fax: (317) 510-5655

- ● Director **Gregory "Greg" Schmalfeldt** .... (317) 212-3953
- Secretary to the Director **Monica Cooper** .... (317) 212-3953

Defense Finance and Accounting Service Rome (NY)
325 Brooks Road, Rome, NY 13441-4527
Tel: (315) 330-6005 Fax: (315) 709-6010

- ● Director **Cynthia B. Garcia** .... (315) 709-6005

Acquisition, Technology and Logistics
3330 Defense Pentagon, Washington, DC 20301-3010
Note: Acquisition, Technology and Logistics is currently undergoing reorganization.

DEPARTMENTS

★ Presidential Appointment Requiring Senate Confirmation ☆ Presidential Appointment ☐ Schedule C Appointment ◇ Career Senior Foreign Service Appointment
● Career Senior Executive Service (SES) Appointment ○ Non-Career Senior Executive Service (SES) Appointment ■ Postal Career Executive Service

DEPARTMENTS

OFFICE OF THE UNDER SECRETARY OF DEFENSE FOR ACQUISITION AND SUSTAINMENT (USD A&S)

3010 Defense Pentagon, Washington, DC 20301-3010
Tel: (703) 697-2525 (Front Desk)
Tel: (703) 695-4893 (Personnel Information)
Tel: (703) 697-7261 (Programs Information)
Internet: https://www.acq.osd.mil/
Internet: www.defenseinnovationmarketplace.mil/ (Defense Innovation Marketplace)

Industrial Policy

3330 Defense Pentagon, Room 3B854, Washington, DC 20301-3330
Tel: (703) 697-2321 E-mail: osd.mibp.inquiries@mail.mil
Internet: http://www.businessdefense.gov/

Office of Small Business Programs (OSBP)

4800 Mark Center Drive, Suite 15G13, Alexandria, VA 22350-1500
Tel: (571) 372-6191 Fax: (571) 372-6195 E-mail: osbpinfo@osd.mil
Internet: www.acq.osd.mil/osbp

Regional Councils for Small Business Education and Privacy

Office of the Assistant Secretary of Defense for Logistics and Materiel Readiness (ASD-L&MR)

3500 Defense Pentagon, Room 1E518, Washington, DC 20301-3500
Tel: (703) 697-1369 Fax: (703) 693-0555 Fax: (703) 767-6312
E-mail: osd.pentagon.ousd-atl.mxb.rm@mail.mil
Internet: www.acq.osd.mil/log

Defense Logistics Agency (DLA)

8725 John J. Kingman Road, Suite 2533, Fort Belvoir, VA 22060-6221
Tel: (703) 767-5200
Tel: (703) 767-4012 (Information and Staff Duty Officer)
Internet: www.dla.mil

J3 Logistics Operations

8725 John J. Kingman Road, Suite 4325, Fort Belvoir, VA 22060-6221
Fax: (703) 767-7733

DLA Distribution (Defense Distribution Center)

Building 81, 2001 Mission Drive, New Cumberland, PA 17070-5000
Tel: (717) 770-6223 Fax: (717) 770-7180 E-mail: ddc.paostaff@dla.mil
Internet: http://www.dla.mil/Distribution.aspx

Commander **(Vacant)** . . . . (717) 770-7401
Commander **RDML Kevin M. Jones USN** . . . . (717) 770-7401
E-mail: kevin.jones3@navy.mil
● Deputy Commander **Twila C. Gonzales** . . . . (717) 770-7401
E-mail: twila.gonzales@dla.mil
Chief Integration Officer
COL Perry L. Knight USA (Ret) . . . . (717) 770-2880
Education: VMI 1982 BA; Army War Col MSS

Supply Centers

DLA Aviation (Defense Supply Center Richmond)

8000 Jefferson Davis Highway, Richmond, VA 23297-5100
Tel: (804) 279-3139 (Public Affairs) Fax: (804) 279-4099
Internet: http://www.dla.mil/Aviation/

Commander **BrigGen Linda S. Hurry USAF** . . . . (804) 279-3801
● Deputy Commander **RDML Charlie Lilli USN (Ret)** . . . . . (804) 279-3803
E-mail: charles.lilli@dla.mil
Education: Muhlenberg 1980; Naval Postgrad 1992
Acquisition Executive **Catherine "Cathy" Contreras** . . . . (804) 279-3805
Chief of Staff **CAPT Steve Kinskie USN (Ret)** . . . . (804) 279-2252
E-mail: steve.kinskie@dla.mil
Equal Employment Opportunity Officer
Harold McManus . . . . (804) 279-4443
E-mail: harold.mcmanus@dla.mil

DLA Aviation *(continued)*

Human Resources Office Chief **Rocky Weaver** . . . . (804) 279-4776
E-mail: rocky.weaver@dla.mil
Public Affairs Officer **Amy T. Clement** . . . . (804) 279-3139
E-mail: amy.clement@dla.mil
Public Safety Officer **(Vacant)** . . . . (804) 279-4753
Small Business Office Chief **John H. Henley** . . . . (804) 279-6330
Counsel Chief **Stephen Davis** . . . . (804) 279-4811
Financial Operations Director (Acting) **Chuck Smith** . . . . (804) 279-6674
Information Operations Liaison Officer **Martin Steiner** . . . (804) 279-6875
Aviation Engineering Director **David Cams** . . . . (804) 279-5759
Aviation Supplier Operations Director
CAPT Robert A. Keating USN . . . . (804) 279-4885
Business Process Support Director **Kent Ennis** . . . . (804) 279-5609
DLA Installation Support at Richmond **David Gibson** . . . . (804) 279-3852
Education: Christopher Newport BSBA; Troy U MBA; Indust'l Col Armed Forces MS
Procurement Process Support Director **(Vacant)** . . . . (804) 279-3611
Planning Process Director **Teresa Kyte** . . . . (804) 279-5954

DLA Energy (Defense Energy Support Center)

8725 John J. Kingman Road, Room 4955, Fort Belvoir, VA 22060-6222
Tel: (703) 767-5042 Fax: (703) 767-9690 Internet: www.energy.dla.mil

Commander **BrigGen Albert G. Miller USAF** . . . . (703) 767-9706
Education: Air Force Acad 1992 BSCE; Webster 1999 MA
Deputy Commander (Acting)
Guy C. Beougher USA (Ret) . . . . (703) 767-9700
Chief of Staff **COL Doug Henry USA** . . . . (703) 767-8415
Director, Customer Operations
Col John D. Martin USAF . . . . (703) 767-9301
Director, Supplier Operations **Gabriella M. Earhardt** . . . . (703) 767-5042

DLA Energy Americas

2320 La Branch Street, Suite 2118, Houston, TX 77004-1091

Commander **COL Craig A. Simonsgaard USA** . . . . (713) 754-9501
E-mail: craig.a.simonsgaard.mil@mail.mil

DLA Energy Americas at Houston

2320 La Branch Street, Suite 1005, Houston, TX 77004-1091
Tel: (713) 718-3770 Fax: (713) 718-3769

Commander **LTC Chris O'Danee USA** . . . . (713) 754-9502

DLA Energy Americas at San Pedro

3171 North Gaffey Street, San Pedro, CA 90731-1099
Tel: (310) 241-2800

Commander **Maj Todd Morin USAF** . . . . (310) 241-2801
Education: East Carolina 2001
Distribution Manager **Bowdoin Swenson** . . . . (310) 241-2807
E-mail: bowdoin.swenson@dla.mil Fax: (310) 241-2835
Quality Manager **Michael J. Koury, Jr.** . . . . (310) 241-2806
E-mail: michael.koury@dla.mil

DLA Energy Europe and Africa

American Arms Office Tower, Augusta Strasse 6,
4th Floor, Room 4J9, 65189 Wiesbaden, Germany
Mail: CMR 443, Box 5000, APO, AE 09096-5000

Commander **LTC Dennis F. Williams USA** 49 631-411-2033
E-mail: dennis.f.williams.mil@mail.mil
Deputy Director **William "Bill" Brennan** Room 4J11 . . . 49 631-411-2033

DLA Energy Europe and Africa at Incirlik

Unit 1010, Box 12, APO, AE 09824
Tel: 90 (322) 316-8325 Fax: 90 (312) 417-1184

Director **David Sanders** 90 (322) 316-8325
E-mail: david.sanders@dla.mil

DLA Energy Pacific

Building 479, 1025 Quincy Avenue, Suite 2000,
Pearl Harbor, HI 96860-4512
Tel: (808) 473-4306 Fax: (808) 473-4232

Commander **CAPT Christopher S. Bower USN** . . . . (808) 473-4312
E-mail: christopher.s.bower@dla.mil

★ Presidential Appointment Requiring Senate Confirmation ☆ Presidential Appointment ☐ Schedule C Appointment Career Senior Foreign Service Appointment
● Career Senior Executive Service (SES) Appointment ○ Non-Career Senior Executive Service (SES) Appointment ■ Postal Career Executive Service

DLA Energy Pacific *(continued)*

Deputy Director **Rockne E. Krill** .... (808) 473-4292
E-mail: rockne.krill@dla.mil
Secretary **Louise Santos** .... (808) 473-4306
E-mail: louise.santos@dla.mil

DLA Energy Pacific at Alaska (Joint Base Elmendorf-Richardson)
10480 22nd Street, Room 300,
Joint Base Elmendorf-Richardson, AK 99506-2570
Tel: (907) 552-3949 Fax: (907) 753-0517

Commander **(Vacant)** .... (907) 552-3949
Deputy Director **Randy Banez** .... (907) 552-5777
E-mail: randy.banez@dla.mil
Information Technology Specialist
Sam Rodriguez-Fontanez .... (907) 552-4450
Fax: (907) 552-2857

DLA Energy Pacific at Guam (Andersen AFB)
Bldg 21000, Lower Bay 6, APO, AP 96543
Tel: (671) 366-7764 Fax: (671) 366-7767

Commander **CDR Bruce Kong USN** .... (661) 366-7764

DLA Energy Pacific at Japan (Yokota Air Base)
Yokota Air Base, Japan
Mail: Building 714, Unit 5266, Room 211/B-18, APO, AP 96328-5266
Tel: 81 311-755-2673 Fax: 81 311-755-3598

Commander **Maj Andre Bradley USAF** 81 311-755-2673
E-mail: andre.bradley@dla.mil
Administrative Specialist **Yayoi Martin** 81 311-755-2671
E-mail: yayoi.martin@dla.mil

DLA Energy Pacific at Korea (Camp Walker)
Daegu, South Korea
Mail: Unit 15105 Building S-348, Camp Walker, APO, AP 96218-0171
Tel: 82 (53) 470-5204 Fax: 82 (53) 470-5103

Commander **LTC Wheeler Manning USA** 82 (53) 470-5204

DLA Energy Middle East
PSC 451, Box DESC-ME, FPO, AE 09834-2800
Tel: 973 1785-4650 Fax: 973 1785-4655

Commander **LTC Henry Brown USA** 973 1785-4661

DLA Land and Maritime (Defense Supply Center Columbus)
P.O. Box 3990, Columbus, OH 43218-3990
Tel: (614) 692-2166 Fax: (614) 692-1902
Internet: http://www.dla.mil/LandandMaritime.aspx

Commander **RDML John T. Palmer USN** .... (614) 692-2166
E-mail: john.t.palmer@navy.mil
● Deputy Commander **Steven K. Alsup** .... (614) 692-2167
E-mail: steven.alsup@dla.mil
Chief of Staff **Griffin Warren** .... (614) 692-2165
E-mail: griffin.warren@dla.mil
Deputy Chief of Staff **Donald L. Schulze** .... (614) 692-3659
E-mail: donald..schulze@dla.mil
Executive Officer **LT Autumn Daniel USN** .... (614) 692-2169
E-mail: autumn.daniel@dla.mil
Counsel **Michael S. Gordon** .... (614) 692-3284
E-mail: michael.1.gordon@dla.mil
Administrative Officer **Janet L. Bunnell** .... (614) 692-5018
E-mail: janet.bunnell@dla.mil
Procurement Officer **Mark Brown** .... (614) 692-3514
E-mail: mark.brown@dla.mil Fax: (614) 692-3231
Public Affairs Officer **Michael L. Jones** .... (614) 692-2328
E-mail: michael.jones@dla.mil Fax: (614) 692-2307
Comptroller **Oscar Mitchell** .... (614) 692-2743
E-mail: oscar.mitchell@dla.mil Fax: (614) 692-5768
Acquisition Executive Director **(Vacant)** .... (703) 767-1470
Process Management Office Director
Barbara "Barb" Robertson .... (614) 692-1638
E-mail: barbara.robertson@dla.mil Fax: (614) 692-4531
DLA Enterprise Services Columbus Site Director
Daniel L. Bell .... (614) 692-3101
E-mail: daniel.l.bell@dla.mil Fax: (614) 692-3390

DLA Land and Maritime *(continued)*

Equal Employment Office Director **Charles Palmer** ...... (614) 692-0743
E-mail: charles.palmer@dla.mil Fax: (614) 692-4797
Internal Review Office Director **Melanie Schmechel** .... (614) 692-3273
Fax: (614) 692-2244
Land Customer Operations Director
COL Dale Farrand USA .... (614) 692-3569
E-mail: dale.farrand@dla.mil
Land Supplier Operations Director
COL Yee Hang USA .... (614) 692-4636
E-mail: yee.hang@dla.mil Fax: (614) 692-5298
Maritime Customer Operations Director
CAPT Brian Ginnane USN .... (614) 692-3121
E-mail: brian.ginnane@dla.mil
Maritime Supplier Operations Director
CAPT Jeffrey A. Schmidt USN .... (614) 692-7613
E-mail: jeffrey.schmidt@dla.mil
Operations Support Group Director **Todd Lewis** .... (614) 692-3251
Fax: (614) 692-1901
Readiness and Business Operations Office Director
Craig Linderman .... (614) 692-8686
E-mail: craig.linderman@dla.mil Fax: (614) 692-3703
Small Business Office Associate Director
Coleen McCormick .... (614) 692-3735
E-mail: coleen.mccormick@dla.mil Fax: (614) 692-4920
Strategic Programs Division Director
CAPT Justin Debord USN .... (614) 692-2191
E-mail: justin.debord@dla.mil

DLA Troop Support (Defense Supply Center Philadelphia)
700 Robbins Avenue, Philadelphia, PA 19111
Tel: (215) 737-2300 Fax: (215) 737-7263

Commander **BG Mark T. Simerly USA** .... (215) 737-2300
Deputy Commander **Richard A. Ellis** .... (215) 737-2304
E-mail: richard.a.ellis@dla.mil
Education: Jacksonville U BSBA; U Washington 1996 MBA
Chief of Staff **Robert A. Ratner** .... (215) 737-2303
E-mail: robert.ratner@dla.mil
Education: Temple BA; Central Michigan MBA
Executive Officer **Susan M. Schafer** .... (215) 737-2307
E-mail: susan.schafer@dla.mil
● Executive Director, Troop Support Contract and
Acquisition Management **William J. "Bill" Kenny** ..... (215) 737-2308
E-mail: william.kenny@dla.mil
Education: St Joseph's U BS, MSBA; Pennsylvania 1995 MS
Director, Business Process Support
Elizabeth McMaster .... (215) 737-0400
E-mail: elizabeth.mcmaster@dla.mil Fax: (215) 737-0451
Deputy Director, Business Process Support
Debra Bakeoven .... (215) 737-7936
E-mail: debra.bakeoven@dla.mil Fax: (215) 737-0451
Director, Clothing and Textiles
Col Melvin Maxwell USAF .... (215) 737-3001
Fax: (215) 737-2452
Deputy Director, Clothing and Textiles **Roy Dillard** ..... (215) 737-3220
Director, Clothing and Textiles Customer Operations
Col Patrick "Spike" Owens USAF .... (215) 737-4367
Director, Clothing and Textiles Supplier Operations
Steven Merch .... (215) 737-2300
Director, Command Support **(Vacant)** .... (215) 737-4300
Director, Comptroller **Barbara Curran** .... (215) 737-2700
Deputy Director, Comptroller **(Vacant)** .... (215) 737-2701
Director, Construction and Equipment
CAPT Gerald "Gerry" Raia USN .... (215) 737-2300
Deputy Director, Construction and Equipment
Thomas M. "Tom" Grace .... (215) 737-9151
Director, Construction and Equipment Customer
Operations **MAJ Marko Graham USA** .... (215) 737-3160
Fax: (215) 737-9155
Director, Construction and Equipment Supplier
Operations **Tom Page** .... (215) 737-7563
Director, Customer Operations
CAPT William Clakre USN .... (215) 737-9159
Fax: (215) 737-3815

(continued on next page)

★ Presidential Appointment Requiring Senate Confirmation ☆ Presidential Appointment □ Schedule C Appointment ◇ Career Senior Foreign Service Appointment
● Career Senior Executive Service (SES) Appointment ○ Non-Career Senior Executive Service (SES) Appointment ■ Postal Career Executive Service

DEPARTMENTS

DLA Troop Support *(continued)*

Deputy Director, Customer Operations **(Vacant)** .... (215) 737-4503
Fax: (215) 737-5655

Director, Equal Employment Opportunity
Ruben Filomeno .... (215) 737-7909
E-mail: ruben.filomeno@dla.mil Fax: (215) 737-2520

Director, Industrial Hardware
Col Adrian Crowley USAF .... (215) 737-4202

Deputy Director, Industrial Hardware
Tina Piotrowski .... (215) 737-3764
E-mail: tina.piotrowski@dla.mil

Director, Information Technology **Nelson Alvarez** .... (215) 737-4319

Deputy Director, Information Technology **Bob Jolly** .... (215) 737-4600

Medical Director **COL Matthew Voyles USA** .... (215) 737-2100
Fax: (215) 737-3104

Medical Deputy Director **David Johns** .... (215) 737-2101

Director, Medical Customer Operations
Nora Steigerwalt .... (215) 737-2801

Director, Medical Supplier Operations **Daniel Keefe** .... (215) 737-2606

Director, Procurement Process Support
CAPT James Clayton USN .... (215) 737-2600
Fax: (215) 737-8271

Deputy Director, Procurement Process Support
Jeffrey Horton .... (215) 737-2601
E-mail: jeffrey.horton@dla.mil Fax: (215) 737-8251

Associate Director, Small Business **Michael McCall** ..... (215) 737-2323
E-mail: michael.mccall@dla.mil Fax: (215) 737-7116

Director, Subsistence **LTC Abel E. Young USA** .... (215) 737-2900

Deputy Director, Subsistence **Richard "Rich" Faso** ..... (215) 737-2904

Director, Subsistence Customer Operations
John Sheehan .... (215) 737-2952

Director, Subsistence Supplier Operations
Gina Vasquez .... (215) 737-2902
Fax: (215) 737-7541

Director, Installation Support **Charles Stagner** .... (215) 737-7100
E-mail: charles.stagner@dla.mil Fax: (215) 737-9075

Command Security Officer **Donald Hutter** .... (215) 737-5861
Fax: (215) 737-2247

Strategic Communications **Diana Stewart** .... (215) 737-2280
E-mail: diana.stewart@dla.mil Fax: (215) 737-7113

Europe and Africa Region
Ludwig-Wolker Strasse, Building 4043, 55252 Mainz, Kastel Depot, Germany
Mail: DSCPE, CMR 444, Box 9000, APO, AE 09096
Tel: 49 6134-60-4540

Commander **LTC Shane Cuellar USA** 49 6134-60-4539
Tel: 49 6134-60-4303

Pacific Region
1025 Quincy Avenue, Suite 2000, Pearl Harbor, HI 96860-4512
Tel: (808) 474-2911 Fax: (808) 473-4235

Commander **CDR Shani S. LeBlanc SC, USN** .... (808) 473-4252

J6 Information Operations
8725 John J. Kingman Road, Suite 1318, Fort Belvoir, VA 22060-6221
E-mail: j6communications@dla.mil

Data Management Services
Building 09, 5450 Carlisle Pike, Mechanicsburg, PA 17055-0788
Mail: P.O. Box 2020, Mechanicsburg, PA 17055-0788
Tel: (866) 736-7010 Fax: (717) 605-3971

Director **(Vacant)** .... (866) 736-7010

Director of Field Offices **Richard Tebeau** .... (866) 736-7010

Director of Financial Operations
Charley L. "Chuck" McNelley, Jr. .... (866) 736-7010

Director of Information Technology **(Vacant)** .... (866) 736-7010

Director of Strategy and Development **(Vacant)** .... (866) 736-7010

Chief of Contracting
Charley L. "Chuck" McNelley, Jr. .... (866) 736-7010

Defense Logistics Information Service (DLIS)
Federal Center, 74 Washington Avenue, North, Battle Creek, MI 49017-3084
Tel: (269) 961-4000 Fax: (269) 961-7383 Internet: www.dlis.dla.mil

Director **Raymond Zingaretti** .... (269) 961-4990

Deputy Director **(Vacant)** .... (269) 961-4989

Equal Employment Opportunity Office
Abraham Poston .... (269) 961-4304

Office of Internal Review and Audit **Shyrll Brown** ...... (269) 961-4000

Directorates

Information Technology Director **Kevin Saber** .... (269) 961-4305

J7 Acquisition
8725 John J. Kingman Road, Fort Belvoir, VA 22060-6218
Tel: (703) 767-1645

DLA Strategic Materials (Fort Belvoir)
8725 John J. Kingman Road, Suite 3229, Fort Belvoir, VA 22060-6223
Tel: (703) 767-5500 Fax: (703) 767-3316

Administrator **Ronnie Favors** .... (703) 767-5500
E-mail: ronnie.favors@dla.mil

Deputy Administrator **Eric Mata** .... (703) 767-5500
E-mail: eric.mata@dla.mil

OFFICE OF THE UNDER SECRETARY OF DEFENSE FOR RESEARCH AND ENGINEERING

Office of the Deputy Under Secretary of Defense for Research and Engineering (DUSD R&E)

Assistant Secretary of Defense for Research and Engineering (ASD-R&E)
3030 Defense Pentagon, Washington, DC 20301-3030
Tel: (703) 697-5776 Internet: https://www.acq.osd.mil/chieftechnologist/

Defense Technical Information Center (DTIC)
8725 John J. Kingman Road, Fort Belvoir, VA 22060-6218
Tel: (703) 767-9100 Tel: (800) 225-3842 Fax: (703) 767-9183
Internet: www.dtic.mil

● Administrator **Christopher E. Thomas** .... (703) 767-9200
Education: Old Dominion BS; George Mason MA

Deputy Administrator **Yvette R. Jacks** .... (703) 767-9187
E-mail: yvette.r.jacks.civ@mail.mil

Chief of Staff **William A. Hicks** .... (703) 767-9100
E-mail: william.a.hicks12.civ@mail.mil

Public Affairs Officer **Michele L. Finley** .... (703) 767-8215
E-mail: michele.l.finley2.civ@mail.mil

Records Officer **Angeleque C. McDowney** .... (703) 767-9223
E-mail: angeleque.c.mcdowney.civ@mail.mil

Security Officer **Harvey R. Bullock** .... (703) 767-9106
E-mail: harvey.r.bullock.civ@mail.mil

Lead Management Analyst **Michael A. Hamilton** .... (703) 767-9204
E-mail: michael.a.hamilton88.civ@mail.mil

★ Presidential Appointment Requiring Senate Confirmation ☆ Presidential Appointment □ Schedule C Appointment ◇ Career Senior Foreign Service Appointment
● Career Senior Executive Service (SES) Appointment ○ Non-Career Senior Executive Service (SES) Appointment ■ Postal Career Executive Service

Intelligence

OFFICE OF THE UNDER SECRETARY OF DEFENSE FOR INTELLIGENCE (USD-I)
5000 Defense Pentagon, Washington, DC 20301-5000
Fax: (703) 693-5706
E-mail: osd.pentagon.ousd-intel.list.cos-execsec@mail.mil

Defense Security Service (DSS)
27130 Telegraph Road, Quantico, VA 22134-2253
Tel: (571) 305-6751 Tel: (571) 305-6562 (Public Affairs)
Tel: (703) 617-2352 (Office of Legislative Affairs)
E-mail: dss.quantico.dss.mbx.cdse-registrar-office@mail.mil
Internet: www.dss.mil

National Center for Credibility Assessment (NCCA)
7540 Pickens Avenue, Columbia, SC 29207
Tel: (803) 751-9100 Fax: (803) 751-9137 Internet: www.ncca.mil
● Director **Zach Vaughn** .... (803) 751-9103

Personnel Security Management Office for Industry (PSMO-I)
2780 Airport Drive, Suite 400, Columbus, OH 43219-2268
Director (Acting) **Heather Green** .... (614) 827-1530
Chief Information Officer **Craig Kaucher** .... (571) 305-6451
27130 Telegraph Road, Quantico, VA 22134
Education: Temple 1982 BA; Central Michigan 2000 MS
Strategic Management Officer **Daniel Allen** .... (571) 305-6125
27130 Telegraph Road, Quantico, VA 22134

Regional Offices

Capital Region
2331 Mill Road, 4th Floor, Alexandria, VA 22314
Tel: (571) 551-7900
Regional Director **(Vacant)**................(571) 551-7900 ext. 136070
Regional Operations Manager
Douglas Stone .... (571) 551-7900 ext. 197915
Office of the Designated Approving
Authority **(Vacant)**......................(571) 551-7900 ext. 56071

Northern Region
One Tech Drive, Suite 335, Andover, MA 01810
Tel: (978) 242-2400 Fax: (978) 291-2874
E-mail: dss.dss-northern.dss.isfo.mbx.northern-regional-office@mail.mil
Regional Director **Cheryl Matthew**...................(978) 242-2400

Southern Region
5800 East Campus Circle Drive, Suite 218A, Irving, TX 75063
Tel: (469) 276-2330 Fax: (972) 580-1623
Regional Director **Regina Johnson**...................(469) 276-2330
Regional Operations Manager **Matt Blakley**............(469) 276-2330

Western Region
11770 Bernardo Plaza, Suite 213, San Diego, CA 92128-2426
Tel: (858) 207-0140 Fax: (858) 451-1564
E-mail: dss.dss-western.dss-isfo.mbx.western-regional-office@mail.mil
Regional Director **David "Dave" Bauer** .... (858) 385-1100

Personnel and Readiness
The Pentagon, Washington, DC 20301-1000

OFFICE OF THE UNDER SECRETARY OF DEFENSE FOR PERSONNEL AND READINESS (USD-P&R)
The Pentagon, Room 3E986, Washington, DC 20301
Tel: (703) 697-2121 Fax: (703) 571-0847 (Correspondence Control)
Internet: https://prhome.defense.gov/

Office of the Principal Deputy Under Secretary of Defense for Personnel and Readiness (PDUSD)
The Pentagon, Washington, DC 20301

Office of the Deputy Assistant Secretary of Defense for Military Community and Family Policy
4000 Defense Pentagon, Room 5A736, Washington, DC 20301-4000
Fax: (703) 614-9303

Defense Commissary Agency (DeCA)
1300 E Avenue, Fort Lee, VA 23801-1800
Tel: (804) 734-8000 Internet: https://www.commissaries.com/

Store Operations Group (Fort Lee)

Defense Commissary Agency Central (DeCA Central)
1300 E Avenue, Fort Lee, VA 23801-1800
Tel: (804) 734-8000 Fax: (804) 734-8744
Director **Ronald R. McMasters**.............(804) 734-8000 ext. 48953
Education: Wayland Baptist 2003 BS
Administrative Assistant **Tianta Jones**.......(804) 734-8000 ext. 86069
Assistant Area Director **Jim Clark**...........(804) 734-8000 ext. 48326

Defense Commissary Agency East (DeCA East - Fort Lee)
1300 E Avenue, Fort Lee, VA 23801-1800
Tel: (804) 734-8000 Fax: (804) 734-8744
Area Director **Bonita M. Moffett** .... (804) 734-8000 ext. 485278
E-mail: bonita.moffett@deca.mil
Deputy Area Director **Jim Clark** .... (804) 734-8000 ext. 48326
Public Affairs Officer
Richard "Rick" Brink .... (804) 734-8000 ext. 48409
E-mail: richard.brink@deca.mil
Education: Oklahoma BA
Administrative Support Assistant
Tianta Jones .... (804) 734-8000 ext. 86435

Defense Commissary Agency Europe (DeCA Europe)
Kaiserslautern, Germany
Mail: Building 2780, Unit 3060, APO, AE 09021
Tel: 49 (631) 3523-101 Fax: 49 (631) 3523-104
Director **Norman E. "Norm" Brown** .... (314) 459-7538
E-mail: norman.brown@deca.mil
Deputy Director **Michael Yaksich**.................. 49 (631) 3523-050
E-mail: michael.yaksich@deca.mil
Senior Enlisted Advisor
CMSAF Wayne B. Jones USAF .... 49 (631) 3523 ext. 109
Area Safety Officer **Scott Livingston** 49 (631) 3523-034
Equal Employment Opportunity Officer
Ellen Bentley 49 (631) 3523-107
E-mail: ellen.brantley@deca.mil
Acquisition Management Division Chief
Petra Pulze 49 (631) 3523-128
E-mail: petra.pulze@deca.mil
Human Resources Division Chief **Melanie Driskell** ... 49 (631) 3523-200
Information Technology Division Chief
Evelyn Shaffer 49 (631) 3523-406
Financial Manager **Christine Frey** 49 (631) 3523-237
E-mail: christine.frey@deca.mil
Security **Ray Parcher**........................... 49 (631) 3523-133
Administrative Assistant **Mike Brahm** 49 (631) 3523-101

★ Presidential Appointment Requiring Senate Confirmation ☆ Presidential Appointment ☐ Schedule C Appointment ◇ Career Senior Foreign Service Appointment
● Career Senior Executive Service (SES) Appointment ○ Non-Career Senior Executive Service (SES) Appointment ■ Postal Career Executive Service

Defense Commissary Agency Pacific Area
Building 950, 3401 Acacia Street, McClellan, CA 95652-1028
Tel: (916) 569-4697

Pacific Area Director **David C. Carey, Jr.** . . . . (916) 569-4978
E-mail: david.carey@deca.mil
Pacific Area Deputy Director **Martin Jackson** . . . . (210) 382-4841
E-mail: martin.jackson@deca.mil

Defense Commissary Agency West Area (DeCA West)
Building 950, 3401 Acacia Street, Suite 115, McClellan, CA 95652-1028
Tel: (916) 569-4697 Fax: (916) 569-4695

West Area Director **Michelle Frost** . . . . (916) 569-4978
E-mail: michelle.frost@deca.mil
West Area Deputy Director **Martin Jackson** . . . .(916) 569-4841
E-mail: martin.jackson@deca.mil
Public Affairs Officer **Keith Debois** . . . . (804) 734-8000 ext. 48842
E-mail: keith.desbois@deca.mil

Defense Field Activities

Armed Forces Experimental Training Activity (Camp Peary)

Camp Peary, 1100 Executive Drive, Williamsburg, VA 23188-4005
Tel: (757) 229-2121 Fax: (757) 221-8616

Director **(Vacant)** . . . . (757) 229-2121

Unified Combatant Commands

U.S. AFRICA COMMAND (AFRICOM)

Unit 29951, APO, AE 09751
Tel: 49 (711) 729-4710 E-mail: africom-pao-media@mail.mil
Internet: www.africom.mil

★ Commander **Gen Thomas D. Waldhauser USMC** 49 (711) 729-4710
Education: Bemidji State; National War Col 1996
Political Advisor **Mary E. Daschbach** 49 (711) 729-4710
Education: Yale 1986 BA
Special Assistant to the Commander
MG Kenneth H. Moore, Jr. USAR . . . . 49 (711) 729 ext. 4710
◇ Deputy Commander for Civil-Military Engagement
Ambassador Alexander Mark Laskaris 49 (711) 729-4710
Education: Georgetown BS; Army War Col MA
Deputy Commander for Military Operations
LtGen James C. Vechery USAF 49 (711) 729-4710
Education: Maryland 1988 BA; Webster 1997 MA; Air Command Col 2001; Air War Col 2004
Chief of Staff **MG Todd B. McCaffrey USA** 49 (711) 729-4710
Education: West Point 1986
Inspector General **CAPT Gregg Romero USN** 49 (711) 729-2682
Command Senior Enlisted Leader
CMSgt Ramon "CZ" Colon-Lopez USAF 49 (711) 729-4710
◇ Senior Development Advisor **Kevin J. Mullally** 49 (711) 729-4710
Education: Austin State 1971 BSF; Texas 1980 MA
Chief of Public Affairs and Communication Synchronization **COL Mark R. Cheadle USA** 49 (711) 729-4710
Public Affairs Branch Chief **(Vacant)** 49 (711) 729-4710

J1 Manpower and Personnel
Unit 29951, APO, AE 09751
Fax: 49 (711) 729-3833

● Director **(Vacant)** 49 (711) 729-2884

J2 Intelligence and Knowledge Development
Unit 29951, APO, AE 09751

Director **RDML Heidi K. Berg USN** 49 (711) 421-2099
Education: Naval Acad 1991 BS

J3 Operations and Cyber
Unit 29951, APO, AE 09751

Director **MajGen Gregg P. Olson USMC** 49 (711) 729-4628
Education: Naval Acad 1985
Deputy Director **BrigGen William P. West USAF** 49 (711) 729-4628

J4 Logistics
Unit 29951, APO, AE 09751
Tel: 49 (711) 729-5633

Director **BrigGen Mark D. Camerer USAF** 49 (711) 729-5633
Education: Wyoming 1989 BS; Webster 1998 MM

J5 Strategy, Engagement, and Programs
Unit 29951, APO, AE 09751

Director **MajGen Christopher E. Craige USAF** 49 (711) 729-2423

J6 Command, Control, Communications and Computer Systems (C4S Systems)
Unit 29951, APO, AE 09751

Director **(Vacant)** 49 (711) 729-4521

J8 Resources and Assessments
Unit 29951, APO, AE 09751

Director **(Vacant)** 49 (711) 729-4728

Combined Joint Task Force - Horn of Africa (CJTF-HOA)
Camp Lemonier, Djibouti, Djibouti
Mail: Camp Lemonier, CJTF-HOA, APO, AE 09363
Tel: 253 35-89-97 E-mail: cjtfhoapublicaffairs@hoa.africom.mil

Commanding General **MG James D. Craig USA** 253 35 89 97
◇ Foreign Policy Advisor **Irvin "Irv" Hicks, Jr.** 253 358-973
Education: George Washington
Deputy Commanding General
BrigGen Howard "Phil" Purcell ANG 253 35 89 97
Deputy Commanding General - Somalia
BG Miguel A. Castellanos USA 253 35 89 97
Command Senior Enlisted Leader
CMDCM Karl W. Parsons USN 253 35 89 97
Chief of Staff **CAPT Ian Branum USN** 253 359-523

U.S. CENTRAL COMMAND (CENTCOM)

7115 South Boundary Boulevard, MacDill AFB, FL 33621-5101
Tel: (813) 529-0214 Tel: (813) 529-0220 (Public Affairs)
E-mail: centcom.macdill.centcom-hq.mbx.ccci-media-desk@mail.mil
Internet: www.centcom.mil
Areas Covered: 25 Countries from the Horn of Africa, the Middle East and Central Asia.

★ Commander **GEN Joseph Leonard Votel USA** . . . . (813) 529-0064
Education: West Point 1980 BS
Executive Officer **(Vacant)** . . . . (813) 529-0064
Foreign Policy Advisor **Catherine Hill-Herndon** . . . . (813) 529-0322
Education: Colgate 1982 BA
Deputy Commander
LtGen Thomas W. Bergeson USAF . . . . (813) 529-0214
Education: Air Force Acad 1985 BS; Embry-Riddle 1997 MAS; Air Command Col 1998
Chief of Staff **MG Michael E. "Erik" Kurilla USA** . . . . . . (813) 529-0039
Education: West Point 1988 BS; National War Col MNSSS; Regis U MBA
Command Sergeant Major
CSM William "Bill" Thetford USA . . . . (813) 529-0043
Command Surgeon **(Vacant)** . . . . (813) 529-0214
Director, Manpower and Personnel, J1 **(Vacant)** . . . . (813) 529-1001
Director, Intelligence, J2 **BG Karen H. Gibson USA** . . . . . (813) 529-0214
Deputy Director, Intelligence, J2
MAJ Gregory Lee Ryckman USAR (Ret) . . . . (813) 529-0214
Director, Operations, J3
RADM Samuel J. "Sam" Paparo, Jr. USN . . . . (813) 529-3004
Education: Villanova 1987 BA; Old Dominion 1998 MA; Naval Postgrad 2015 MS
Deputy Director, Operations, J3
BrigGen Derek C. France USAF . . . . (813) 529-3004

★ Presidential Appointment Requiring Senate Confirmation ☆ Presidential Appointment □ Schedule C Appointment ◇ Career Senior Foreign Service Appointment
● Career Senior Executive Service (SES) Appointment ○ Non-Career Senior Executive Service (SES) Appointment ■ Postal Career Executive Service

U.S. Central Command *(continued)*

Director, Logistics and Engineering, J4
MG Edward F. Dorman III USA .... (813) 529-4002
E-mail: edward.f.dorman.mil@mail.mil
Education: Tennessee Tech 1983; Middlebury MA; US Army Command
Director, Strategy, Plans and Policy, J5 **(Vacant)** .... (813) 529-5010
Deputy Director, Strategy, Plans and Policy, J5
BrigGen Eric Hill USAF .... (813) 529-5010
Deputy Director, Special Plans Working Group
(Vacant) .... (813) 529-5010
Director, Command, Control, Communications and Computer Systems, J6 **BG Mitchell L. Kilgo USA** ..... (813) 529-0220
Director, Exercises and Training, J7 **(Vacant)** .... (813) 529-7002
● Director, Resources and Analysis, J8 **(Vacant)** .... (813) 529-8005
Director, Public Affairs **(Vacant)** .... (813) 529-0214
Spokesman **MAJ Josh Jacques USA** .... (813) 529-0220
Staff Judge Advocate **(Vacant)** .... (813) 529-0282
Director, Deployment and Distribution Operations Center **BrigGen Darren Cole USAF** .... (215) 737-2300
700 Robbins Avenue, Philadelphia, PA 19111
Director, Forward Operational Contract Support
(Vacant) .... (813) 529-0214

U.S. Forces - Afghanistan (USFOR-A)

Headquarters Resolute Support - Kabul, Afghanistan, APO, AE 09356
Tel: 93 0-700-13-2114 (International Security Assistance Force Public Affairs) E-mail: pressoffice@hq.isaf.nato.int

★ Commander, U.S. Forces and Resolute Support Mission **GEN Austin Scott Miller USA** 93 0-700-13-2114
Education: West Point 1983
Deputy Commander **Maj Gen Richard Cripwell** 93 0-700-13-2114
Deputy Commander - Air
MajGen Barre R. Seguin USAF 93 0-700-13-2114
Education: SUNY (Potsdam) 1988; Embry-Riddle 1994 MAS
Chief of Staff **LTG Johann Langenegger USA** 93 0-700-13-2114
Deputy Chief of Staff, Intelligence and Deputy Director, Operations and Support
BG Anthony R. Hale USA 93 0-700-13-2114
Deputy Chief of Staff, Strategy and Policy
MG Daniel R. Walrath USA 93 0-700-13-2114
Director, Air Component Coordination Element
(Vacant) 93 0-700-13-2114
Senior Advisor to the Afghan Ministry of Defense
(Vacant) 93 0-700-13-2114
Senior Enlisted Leader **CSM David M. Clark USA** 93 0-700-13-2114
Director, Future Operations (CJ-35) **(Vacant)** 93 0-700-13-2114
Director, CJ-5 **(Vacant)** 93 0-700-13-2114
Commander, 9th Air and Space Expeditionary Task Force - Afghanistan
MajGen Barre R. Seguin USAF 93 0-700-13-2114
Education: SUNY (Potsdam) 1988; Embry-Riddle 1994 MAS

Combined Security Transition Command Afghanistan (CSTC-A - Camp Resolute Support)

APO, AE 09536
Tel: 93 (70) 007-6406 (Public Affairs) E-mail: cstc-apao@swa.army.mil

Commanding General **LTG James E. Rainey USA** 93 (70) 007-6406
Education: Eastern Kentucky 1987 BA; Troy U MPA
Deputy Commanding General
BG Patrick W. Burden USA 93 (70) 007-6406
E-mail: patrick.w.burden.mil@mail.mil
Senior Enlisted Leader **SGM John Hilton USA** 93 (70) 007-6406

U.S. Air Forces Central Command (USAFCENT)

Shaw AFB, SC 29152
Tel: (803) 895-5800 Tel: (803) 895-4953 (Public Affairs)
Internet: www.centaf.af.mil

Commander **LtGen Joseph T. Guastella, Jr. USAF** ..... (803) 895-5801
Education: Air Force Acad 1987 BS; Embry-Riddle 1997 MS; Air Command Col 2001; National War Col 2006 MS

U.S. Air Forces Central Command *(continued)*

Air National Guard Assistant to the Commander
MajGen Mark R. Kraus ANG .... (803) 895-5800
Foreign Policy Advisor **James Soriano** .... (803) 895-3128
Mobilization Assistant to the Commander
BrigGen Jose R. Monteagudo USAFR .... (803) 895-5800
Education: Florida 1988 BS; Kellogg 2011 MBA
Deputy Commander
BrigGen Gregory M. Guillot USAF .... (803) 895-2875
Education: Air Force Acad 1989 BS
Assistant Deputy Commander
Col Matthew C. Isler USAF .... (803) 895-5800
Education: Air Force Acad 1991 BS; Air Command Col 2004
Chief Master Sergeant
CMSgt Joseph A. Montgomery USAF .... (803) 895-2875

U.S. Army Central Command (USARCENT)

One Gabreski Drive, Shaw AFB, SC 29152
E-mail: usarmy.shaw.usarcent.mbx.public-affairs@mail.mil
Internet: http://www.usarcent.army.mil/

Commander **LTG Michael X. Garrett USA** .... (803) 885-8757
Executive Officer **COL Terry P. Cook USA** .... (803) 885-8794
Foreign Policy Advisor **(Vacant)** .... (803) 885-8874
Deputy Commanding General **MG David C. Hill USA** .... (803) 885-8757
E-mail: david.c.hill10.mil@mail.mil
Deputy Commanding General for Sustainment
MG Flem B. "Donnie" Walker, Jr. USA .... (803) 885-8757
E-mail: flem.b.walker.mil@mail.mil
Director, Army Reserve Engagement Cell
BG Leela J. Gray USAR .... (813) 529-0214
Chief of Staff **BG James H. Raymer USA** .... (813) 529-0214
Deputy Chief of Staff for Logistics
COL William M. Krahling USA .... (803) 885-8757
Deputy Chief of Staff for Resource Management
BG Bradley K. Dreyer USA .... (813) 529-0214
Assistant Chief of Staff for Operations **(Vacant)** .... (813) 529-0214
Command Sergeant Major
CSM Joseph Cornelison USA .... (803) 885-8774

U.S. Marine Corps Forces Central Command (MARCENT)

MacDill AFB, FL 33621
Tel: (813) 827-4297 (Public Affairs) Internet: www.marcent.marines.mil

Commander
LtGen Carl Epting "Sam" Mundy III USMC .... (813) 827-7110
Education: Auburn 1983
Aide de Camp **Capt Brent M. Ogden USMC** .... (813) 827-7110
Foreign Policy Advisor **Shannon Quinn** .... (813) 827-7011
Deputy Commander **(Vacant)** .... (813) 827-7110
Chief of Staff **Col Thomas "Tom" Pecina USMC** ...... (813) 827-7110
Assistant Chief of Staff, G4 Logistics **(Vacant)** .... (813) 827-4297
Sergeant Major **SgtMaj William T. Thurber USMC** ..... (813) 827-7110
Personnel Officer and Equal Opportunity Program Manager **GySgt Karl Fuchs USMC** .... (813) 827-7048
Public Affairs Chief **MSgt Stephen Treyhar USMC** ..... (813) 827-4297
Public Affairs Officer **Maj Bradlee J. Avots USMC** ..... (813) 827-4297
E-mail: bradlee.avots@marcent.usmc.mil

U.S. Naval Forces Central Command/Combined Maritime Forces

APO, AE 09501-6008
Tel: 973 1785-9980 Fax: 973 1785-6137 E-mail: pao@cusnc.navy.mil
Internet: www.cusnc.navy.mil

Commander **VADM Scott A. Stearney USN** 973 1785-6030
Education: Notre Dame 1982 BA
Deputy Commander **RDML Paul J. Schlise USN** 973 1785-6030
Education: Marquette 1989; National War Col 2006 MNSSS
Vice Commander
RDML Alan Douglas "Woody" Beal USNR 973 1785-6030
Education: Purdue 1986 BSE; Southern Methodist MSE; National War Col MNSSS

(continued on next page)

★ Presidential Appointment Requiring Senate Confirmation ☆ Presidential Appointment □ Schedule C Appointment ◇ Career Senior Foreign Service Appointment
● Career Senior Executive Service (SES) Appointment ○ Non-Career Senior Executive Service (SES) Appointment ■ Postal Career Executive Service

U.S. Naval Forces Central Command/Combined Maritime Forces *(continued)*

Command Master Chief, U.S. Naval Forces Central Command **CMDCM Dayna S. Winn USN** 973 1785-6030
Chief of Staff, U.S. Naval Forces Central Command **CAPT Benjamin J. Allbritton USN** 973 1785-6030
Maritime Operations Center Director **CAPT Robert D. Westendorff USN** 973 1785-6030
Education: Kansas State 1992 BB

U.S. 5th Fleet (C5F)

Note: The U.S. 5th Fleet is operated under a shared command with the U.S. Naval Forces Central Command.

Commander **VADM Scott A. Stearney USN** 973 1785-6030
Education: Notre Dame 1982 BA
Deputy Commander **RDML Paul J. Schlise USN** 973 1785-6030
Education: Marquette 1989; National War Col 2006 MNSSS
Vice Commander **RDML Alan Douglas "Woody" Beal USNR** 973 1785-6030
Education: Purdue 1986 BSE; Southern Methodist MSE; National War Col MNSSS
Command Master Chief **CMDCM Russell S. Mason USN** 973 1785-6030
Chief of Staff **CAPT Benjamin J. Allbritton USN** 973 1785-6030

U.S. Special Operations Command Central (USSOCCENT)

MacDill AFB, 7701 Tampa Point Blvd., MacDill AFB, FL 33621-5323
Tel: (813) 828-7424

Commander **RDML Hugh Wyman Howard III USN** ..... (813) 828-7424
Foreign Policy Advisor **(Vacant)** .... (813) 828-7424

U.S. CYBER COMMAND (CYBERCOM)

9800 Savage Road, Fort George G. Meade, MD 20755
Tel: (301) 677-1465 (Ft. Meade Public Affairs)

★ Commander **GEN Paul M. Nakasone USA** .... (301) 688-6524
Education: St John's U (MN); Army War Col; National Defense U; USC
Deputy Commander **LtGen Vincent R. Stewart USMC** .... (301) 688-6524
Education: Western Illinois 1981; Naval War 1994; Indust'l Col Armed Forces 2002
Deputy Commander **(Vacant)** .... (301) 688-6524
Chief of Staff **RADM Ross A. Myers USN** .... (301) 688-6524
E-mail: ross.a.myers.mil@mail.mil
Director, J2 Intelligence Directorate **BrigGen Douglas S. Coppinger USAF** .... (301) 688-6524
Education: Regents 1991 BS; National Defense Intelligence Col 1997 MS
Director, J3 Operations Directorate **MajGen Charles L. Moore, Jr. USAF** .... (301) 688-6524
Education: Air Force Acad 1989 BS; Troy State 1999 MHR; Air Command Col 2002 MMAS
Deputy Director, J3 Operations Directorate **(Vacant)** ..... (301) 688-6524
Deputy Director, J3F Future Operations **RDML Craig A. Clapperton USN** .... (301) 688-6524
Director, J5 Plans and Policy Directorate **RADM William W. "Trey" Wheeler III USN** .... (443) 654-1210
Director, J6 C4 Systems and Chief Information Officer **(Vacant)** .... (301) 688-6524
Director, J7 Exercises and Training **RDML John W. Mauger USCG** .... (301) 677-1465
Director, J8 Capability and Resource Integration **BG Karl H. Gingrich USA** .... (301) 688-6524
Commander, Cyber National Mission Force **BrigGen Timothy D. Haugh USAF** .... (301) 677-1465
Deputy Commander, Operations, Cyber National Mission Force **(Vacant)** .... (301) 677-1465
Commander, Joint Intelligence Operations Center **(Vacant)** .... (301) 677-1465
Deputy Commander, Joint Task Force ARES **(Vacant)** .... (301) 677-1465

U.S. Cyber Command *(continued)*

Command Senior Enlisted Leader **MGySgt Scott H. Stalker USMC** .... (301) 677-1465
Public Affairs Officer **Jennifer A. Downing** .... (301) 833-2012
E-mail: jennifer.a.downing.li.civ@mail.mil

U.S. Army Cyber Command (ARCYBER)

Fort Belvoir, VA 22060
Tel: (703) 706-1517 Internet: https://www.army.mil/armycyber

Commander **LTG Stephen G. Fogarty USA** .... (703) 706-1517
Education: North Georgia BA; Central Michigan MSA; Army War Col MS
Deputy Commander for Joint Force Headquarters Cyber **BG William Joseph "Joe" Hartman USA** ..... (703) 706-1517
Deputy Commander for Operations **BG Richard E. Angle USA** .... (703) 706-1517
Deputy to the Commander **Ronald W. "Ron" Pontius** ... (703) 706-1517
Chief of Current Operations **COL Alan Quattrin USA** ... (703) 706-1517
Chief of Staff **COL John Delaney USA** .... (703) 706-2390
Command Sergeant Major **SGM Sheryl D. Lyon USA** ... (703) 706-2390
Public Affairs Chief **Charles K. "Charlie" Stadtlander** .... (703) 706-1420
E-mail: charles.k.stadtlander.civ@mail.mil
Education: U Washington 2006 BA

Technical Warfare Center (TWC)

● Director and Chief Technology Officer **David T. Kim USA (Ret)** .... (703) 706-1517
Education: Arizona State; Eisenhower National Security and Resource Strategy; Central Michigan; US Army Command

U.S. Army Intelligence and Security Command (INSCOM)

8825 Beulah Street, Fort Belvoir, VA 22060
Fax: (703) 706-2909 E-mail: army.inscom.pao@mail.mil
Internet: www.inscom.army.mil

Commanding General **MG Gary W. Johnston USAR** .... (703) 706-1603
Deputy to the Commanding General **Clyde T. Harthcock** .... (703) 706-1653
Executive Officer to the Commanding General **LTC Kevin Buettner USA** .... (703) 706-1205
Deputy Commanding General **(Vacant)** .... (703) 706-1637
Command Chief Warrant Officer **CW5 Kevin G. Boughton USA** .... (703) 706-1637
Command Sergeant Major **CSM Eric M. Schmitz USA** .... (703) 706-1205
Education: Wayland Baptist BS
● Chief of Staff **Charles F. Sardo** .... (703) 706-1232
Public Affairs Office Chief **MyRon H. Young** .... (703) 428-4965
8825 Beulah Street, Fort Belvoir, VA 22060-5246
E-mail: army.inscom.pao@mail.mil

U.S. Army Network Enterprise Technology Command (NETCOM)

2133 Cushing Street, Fort Huachuca, AZ 85613-7070
E-mail: netcom.hq.pao@mail.mil

Commanding General **BG Maria B. Barrett USA** .... (520) 538-6100
Education: Tufts 1988 BA
Aide-de-Camp **CPT Katherine Haapala USA** .... (520) 538-6162
Deputy Commander - Operations **COL Scott Bird USA** .... (520) 538-6100
Deputy Commander - Support **COL Christina Bloss USA** Room 3000 .... (520) 538-6100
● Deputy to the Commander, Senior Technical Director and Chief Engineer **Dovarius L. Peoples** Room 3000 ... (520) 538-6363
Chief of Staff **COL Timothy P. Norton USA** Room 3000 .... (520) 538-6363
Command Sergeant Major **CSM Jennifer Taylor USA** ... (520) 538-6000
Public Affairs Officer **Gordon Van Vleet** Room 3211 .... (520) 538-8609
E-mail: gordon.m.vanvleet.civ@mail.mil
Education: Maryland 2000 BS; U Phoenix 2005 MS

★ Presidential Appointment Requiring Senate Confirmation ☆ Presidential Appointment ☐ Schedule C Appointment ◇ Career Senior Foreign Service Appointment
● Career Senior Executive Service (SES) Appointment ○ Non-Career Senior Executive Service (SES) Appointment ■ Postal Career Executive Service

55th Signal Company (Combat Camera)
845 Chisholm Avenue, Fort George G. Meade, MD 20755
Tel: (301) 677-5342 Fax: (301) 677-3049
E-mail: cdr55@meade-emh2.ftmeade.army.mil

Commander **MAJ Holly Glisson USA** . . . . (301) 677-5342
Operations Non-Commissioned Officer in Charge
1SG Ronald Shaw USA . . . . (301) 677-5343

U.S. Fleet Cyber Command (FLTCYBERCOM)
9800 Savage Road, Fort George G. Meade, MD 20755
Tel: (240) 373-3640 Tel: (240) 373-3359 (Public Affairs)

★ Commander **VADM Timothy J. "T.J." White USN** . . . . . . (240) 373-3359
Deputy Commander **RDML James M. Butler USNR** . . . . (240) 373-3359
Education: Naval Acad 1988 BS
Public Affairs Officer **LCDR Sean P. Riordan USN** . . . . . . (240) 373-3640
Fax: (240) 373-3232

U.S. 10th Fleet (C10F)
Note: The U.S. 10th Fleet is operated under a shared command with Fleet Cyber Command.

★ Commander **VADM Timothy J. "T.J." White USN** . . . . . . (240) 373-3359
Deputy Commander **RDML Michael A. Brookes USN** . . . (240) 373-3640
Public Affairs Officer **LCDR Sean P. Riordan USN** . . . . . . (240) 373-3640

Naval Network Warfare Command (NETWARCOM)
112 Lake View Parkway, Suffolk, VA 23435
Tel: (757) 203-0300 Fax: (757) 203-0231

Commander **CAPT Adam C. Lyons USN** . . . . (757) 203-0300
E-mail: adam.c.lyons.mil@mail.mil
Education: Naval Acad 1994; Maryland MA
Senior Enlisted Advisor **(Vacant)** . . . . (757) 203-0300
Public Affairs Officer **LT Luke Chapman USN** . . . . (757) 203-0205
Fax: (757) 203-0231

Naval Computer and Telecommunications Area Master Station Atlantic (NCTAMS-LANT)
9625 Moffett Avenue, Norfolk, VA 23511
Tel: (757) 443-9157

Commander **CAPT Jody H. Grady USN** . . . . (757) 443-9142
Education: Georgia Tech 1994 BE; Naval Postgrad MCS
Chief Staff Officer
CDR Patrick E. Lancaster, Jr. USN . . . . (757) 443-9142
Education: Southern Illinois BSEd
Command Master Chief
CMDCM Thomas K. Hayden USN . . . . (757) 443-9120
Education: Excelsior 2014 BS
Telecommunications Manager **Diana Carlson** . . . . (757) 443-9070
E-mail: diane.carlson1@navy.mil
Information Systems Security Manager
Sharon Brightwell . . . . (757) 443-9157

Naval Computer and Telecommunications Area Master Station Pacific (NCTAMSPAC)
NCTAMS PAC, 500 Center Street, Wahiawa, HI 96786-3050
Tel: (808) 653-5344 Fax: (808) 653-0080

Commander **CAPT Bryan E. Braswell USN** . . . . (808) 653-5344
Chief Staff Officer **CDR Roger L. Koopman USN** . . . . . . (808) 653-5344
Command Master Chief
CMDCM Donald O. Leppert USN . . . . (808) 653-0197
Contracting/Small Business **Dave McDonald** . . . . (808) 653-1111

Information Operations Directorate (N33)
Staff Office, 9800 Savage Road, Suite 6585,
Fort George G. Meade, MD 20755-6585
Tel: (240) 373-3613

Cryptologic Warfare Group Six (CWG6)
9800 Savage Road, Fort George G. Meade, MD 20755-6585
Tel: (301) 677-0860 (Public Affairs)

Commanding Officer **CAPT Joe J. Johnson USN** . . . . . . (301) 677-0217
E-mail: joe.j.johnson@navy.mil
Education: Naval Acad 1992 BS

Navy Information Operations Command Georgia (NIOC GA)
Building 28423, 537 Brainard Avenue, Fort Gordon, GA 30905-5810
Tel: (706) 791-2996

Commanding Officer
CAPT William J. "Bill" Kramer, Jr. USN . . . . (706) 791-9580
E-mail: usn.gordon.inscom.list.nsag-nioc-ga-xo@mail.mil

Navy Information Operations Command Pensacola (NIOC Pensacola)
475 Jones Street, Pensacola, FL 32511-5201
Tel: (850) 452-0237

Commanding Officer **CDR Eduardo Salazar USN** . . . . . . (850) 452-0237
Executive Officer **LCDR Michael Papa USN** . . . . (850) 452-0202
Command Master Chief
CMDCM Marisol Dumlao USN . . . . (850) 452-0237

Navy Information Operations Command San Diego (NIOC San Diego)
P.O. Box 357023, San Diego, CA 92135
Tel: (619) 545-9920 Fax: (619) 545-9906

Commanding Officer **CDR Robert C. Cadena USN** . . . . . (619) 545-9909
Executive Officer **LCDR Kumar Sankara USN** . . . . (619) 545-9912
Command Master Chief **ITCS Helen Allen USN** . . . . (619) 545-9920

Navy Information Operations Command Texas (NIOC TX)
NIOC-TX, 7700 Potranco Road, Arlington, TX 78251

Commanding Officer
CAPT Clarence Franklin, Jr. USN . . . . (210) 346-4546

Navy Information Operations Command Whidbey Island (NIOC Whidbey Island)
Building 2700, 1280 West Intruder Street, Oak Harbor, WA 98278-9500
Tel: (360) 257-5465 Fax: (360) 257-4016
Internet: www.nioc-whidbeyisland.navy.mil

Commanding Officer **CDR Brian Harding USN** . . . . (360) 914-7800
Executive Officer **LCDR Colin G. Larkins USN** . . . . (360) 914-7800
Command Master Chief
MCPO Albert John Ondo USN . . . . (360) 914-7800

Navy Information Operations Detachment Groton (NIOD Groton)
Box 99, NAVSUBASE New London, Groton, CT 06349-5099
Tel: (860) 625-1994 (Duty Officer)
Tel: (860) 625-1992 (Command Duty Officer)
Tel: (860) 694-1076 (Quarterdeck)

Officer in Charge **LCDR Ryan N. Haag USN** . . . . (860) 694-2440
E-mail: nwln_nwln_niodgtn_oic@navy.mil
Assistant Officer in Charge
LT Josh "Robi" Robishaw USN . . . . (860) 694-2440
E-mail: nwln_niodgtn_aoic@navy.mil
Senior Enlisted Advisor
CTRCM Duain E. Woodruff USN . . . . (860) 625-1994

Naval Information Warfare Training Group Norfolk (IWTG Norfolk)
2555 Amphibious Drive, Naval Amphibious Base,
Norfolk, VA 23521-3225
Tel: (757) 417-4006 Fax: (757) 417-4010

Commanding Officer
CAPT Christopher P. "Chris" Slattery USN . . . . (757) 417-4006
Executive Officer **CAPT Edwin Grohe USN** . . . . (757) 417-4006
E-mail: edwin.grohe@navy.mil
Education: Naval Acad 1993 BS
Command Master Chief **(Vacant)** . . . . (757) 417-4003

U.S. Marine Forces Cyberspace Command (MARFORCYBER)
7125 Columbia Gateway Drive, Suite 201, Columbia, MD 21046
Mail: 9800 Savage Road, Fort George G. Meade, MD 20755-6272

Commander **MajGen Matthew G. Glavy USMC** . . . . (443) 654-6316
Education: Naval Acad 1986
Executive Director **Gregg Kendrick** . . . . (443) 654-6316
Senior Enlisted Leader **SgtMaj Daniel Krause USMC** . . . (443) 654-6312
Chief of Staff **Col Daniel J. Haas USMC** . . . . (443) 654-6308

(continued on next page)

DEPARTMENTS

U.S. Marine Forces Cyberspace Command *(continued)*

Department Head, G1 Manpower and Personnel
Scott Kirklighter .... (443) 654-6315
Department Head, G2 Intelligence **(Vacant)** .... (443) 654-6334
Department Head, G3 Operations **(Vacant)** .... (443) 654-6343
Department Deputy, G3 Operations
Col Mark H. Bacharach USMCR .... (443) 654-6347
Education: Rochester BA; Johns Hopkins 2006 MS
Department Head, G4 Logistics **(Vacant)** .... (443) 654-7628
Department Head, G5 Civil-Military Operations
(Vacant) .... (443) 654-6362
Department Head, G6 Communications-Electronics
Michael Wahlhaupter .... (443) 654-6328
Department Head, G8 Comptroller **Jerry Burke** .... (703) 784-4686

U.S. EUROPEAN COMMAND (EUCOM)

HQ USEUCOM, Geb 2314, Patch Barracks, D-70569 Stuttgart, Germany
Mail: HQ USEUCOM (ECPA), Unit 30400, Box 1000, APO, AE 09131
Tel: 49 (711) 680-8503 (Public Affairs) Fax: 49 (711) 680-5380
Internet: http://www.eucom.mil/

★ Commander, U.S. European Command and
NATO Supreme Allied Commander Europe
GEN Curtis Michael "Mike" Scaparrotti USA 49 (711) 680-4464
Education: West Point BS; South Carolina MEd
Civilian Deputy to the Commander
and Foreign Policy Advisor
Ambassador Philip Thomas Reeker 49 (711) 680-2341
Education: Yale 1986 BA; Fax: 49 (711) 680-4298
Thunderbird International 1991 MBA
Senior Special Assistant
Col Charles E. Brown, Jr. USAF 49 (711) 680-8503
Executive Officer
RDML Frederick William "Fred" Kacher USN ... 49 (711) 680-8503
Education: Naval Acad BS; Harvard MPP
Deputy Commander **LTG Stephen M. Twitty USA** ... 49 (711) 680-4121
Education: South Carolina State 1985; Central Michigan MPA;
National Defense U MS
Senior Enlisted Leader
CMDCM Crispian D. Addington USN 49 (711) 680-4464
Senior Enlisted Leader
CMSgt Phillip L. Easton USAF, USAF 49 (711) 680-4464
Note: On October 4, 2018, the Office of the Senior Enlisted Advisor to the Chairman of the Joint Chiefs of Staff announced the assignment of CMSgt Phillip L. Easton as Senior Enlisted Leader, U.S. European Command, with an effective date to be announced.
Chief of Staff **RADM Patrick A. Piercey USN** 49 (711) 680-4450
Education: Naval Acad 1985 BS
Director, J-1 Manpower, Personnel and
Administration Directorate **(Vacant)** 49 (711) 680-6943
Fax: 49 (711) 680-6395
Director, J-2 Intelligence Directorate **(Vacant)** 49 (711) 680-8007
Fax: 49 (711) 680-6776
Director, J-3 European Command
Plans and Operations Center (EPOC)
MG Robert P. "Pat" White USA 49 (711) 680-4169
Education: Claremont McKenna 1986; Central Michigan;
Army War Col
Deputy Director, J-3 European Command Plans
and Operations Center (EPOC) **(Vacant)** 49 (711) 680-4169
Director, J-4 Logistics Directorate
RDML Paul J. Verrastro USN 49 (711) 680-4444
E-mail: paul.verrastro@navy.mil Fax: 49 (711) 680-7363
E-mail: eucom.stuttgart.ecj4.mbx.xo@mail.mil
Education: SUNY (Albany) 1986 BSBA
Director, J-5/8 Policy, Strategy,
Partnering and Capabilities Directorate
MajGen David W. Allvin USAF 49 (711) 680-5005
Tel: 49 (711) 680-7451
Education: Air Force Acad 1986 BS; Troy State 1989 MSM;
National War Col 2004 MNSSS
Deputy Director, J-5/8 Policy, Strategy,
Partnering and Capabilities Directorate
RDML Fred I. Pyle USN 49 (711) 680-5005
Tel: 49 (711) 680-7451

U.S. European Command *(continued)*

Director, J-6 C4/Cyber
COL Maria Anton Biank USA 49 (711) 680-8503
Deputy CIO Division Chief **Daniel R. Pierson** 49 (711) 680-7159
Fax: 49 (711) 680-4411
Director, J-7 Exercises and Assessments **(Vacant)** 49 (711) 680-4002
Fax: 49 (711) 680-6851
● Director, J-9 Interagency Partnering **(Vacant)** 49 (711) 680-6558
E-mail: eucom.stuttgart.ecj9.mbx.xo@mail.mil Fax: 49 (711) 680-9307
Headquarters Commandant **(Vacant)** 49 (711) 680-8481
Chaplain **CAPT Gary P. Weeden CHC, USN** 49 (711) 680-5151
E-mail: eucom.stuttgart.ecch.list.ecch-xo@mail.mil
Education: Western Sem 1987
Command Historian **Daniel O. Fitzpatrick** 49 (711) 680-7679
Command Surgeon
Col John P. Mitchell USAF, FCCP 49 (711) 680-7460
E-mail: ecj4-mraogroup@eucom.mil
Comptroller **COL Karl Krauss USA** 49 (711) 680-5985
E-mail: eucom.stuttgart.eccm.mbx.xo@mail.mil
Inspector General **COL Kristin A. "Kris" Ellis USA** ... 49 (711) 680-5556
E-mail: eucom.stuttgart.ecig.list.xo-mb-access1@mail.mil
Judge Advocate **(Vacant)** 49 (711) 680-8001
E-mail: eucom.stuttgart.ecja.mbx.xo@mail.mil Fax: 49 (711) 680-5732
Director, Mobilization and Reserve
Component Affairs Directorate
BG Jeffery E. Marshall ARNG 49 (711) 680-4496
E-mail: ecra-ex@eucom.mil Fax: 49 (711) 680-6851
Education: West Point 1981 BS;
Johns Hopkins 1990 MAS; Army War Col 2000 MSS
Director, Communication and Engagement
CAPT Daniel J. "Danny" Hernandez USN 49 (711) 680-4986
E-mail: Fax: 49 (711) 680-5380
eucom.stuttgart.ecce.list.media-ops@mail.mil
Director, Protocol **LtCol Calvin Daniels USAF** 49 (711) 680-4018

U.S. Army Europe - 7th Army (USAREUR)

Wiesbaden, Germany
Mail: HQ USAREUR and 7th Army, AEAPA, Unit 29351,
APO, AE 09014
Tel: 49 (611) 143-537-0110 E-mail: usarmyeurope.contact@mail.mil
Internet: www.eur.army.mil

Commanding General
LTG Christopher G. Cavoli USA 49 (611) 143-537-0110
Deputy Commanding General
MG Andrew M. Rohling USA 49 (611) 143-537-0800
Deputy Commanding General for Army
National Guard **MG John L. Gronski ARNG** ... 49 (611) 143-537-0800
E-mail: john.l.gronski.mil@mail.mil
Deputy Commanding General for
Mobilization and Reserve Affairs
BG Mary-Kate "Kate" Leahy USA 49 (611) 143-537-0800
Chief of Staff **BG Hartmut Renk USA** 49 (611) 143-537-0420
Deputy Chief of Staff for Operations (G3)
BG Sean C. Bernabe USA 49 (611) 143-537-3013
Senior Enlisted Advisor
CSM Robert V. Abernethy USA 49 (611) 143-537-0301

21st Theater Sustainment Command (21st TSC)

APO AE 09054, CMR 479, Germany
331 Mannheimer Street, 67657 Kaiserslautern, Alberta, Germany
Tel: 49 (631) 413-8104
E-mail: usarmy.rheinland-pfalz.21-tsc.mbx.webmaster@mail.mil

Commanding General
MG Steven A. Shapiro USA 49 (631) 413-7771
E-mail: steven.a.shapiro.mil@mail.mil
Deputy Commanding General
BG Frederick R. Maiocco USA 49 (631) 413-7781
Deputy Commanding Officer
COL William S. Galbraith USA 49 (631) 413-7758
Chief of Staff **CPT Geoffrey C. De Tingo USA** 49 (631) 413-7758
Command Sergeant Major
CSM Rocky L. Carr USA 49 (631) 413-7788
Senior Civilian Executive Assistant
Thomas C. "Tom" Nunn 49 (631) 413-7615

★ Presidential Appointment Requiring Senate Confirmation ☆ Presidential Appointment □ Schedule C Appointment ◇ Career Senior Foreign Service Appointment
● Career Senior Executive Service (SES) Appointment ○ Non-Career Senior Executive Service (SES) Appointment ■ Postal Career Executive Service

409th Contracting Support Brigade (409 CSB)
Hammonds Barracks, Geb 973, Seckenheimerhaupstrasse,
68239 Mannheim, Germany
Mail: USACCE, Unit 29331, APO, AE 09266-9331
Tel: 49 0-61-11-43-542-6400 Internet: https://www.army.mil/ecc/

Commander **COL Douglas S. Lowrey USA** 49 0-61-11-43-542-6400
E-mail: douglas.s.lowrey.mil@mail.mil

Regional Contracting Office, Bavaria
Unit 28130, APO, AE 09114
Tel: 49 (9641) 83-8710 Fax: 49 (9641) 83-7258

Commander **LTC Isaac M. Torres USA** 49 (9641) 83-8700
Senior Enlisted Advisor
SGM Angella M. Beckford USA 49 (9641) 83-8705

Regional Contracting Office, Benelux
Unit 8100, Box 15, APO, AE 09714
Tel: 32 (2) 717-9611 Fax: 32 2717-9610

Chief of Office **Tunissha I. Marshall** 32 (2) 717-9625
E-mail: tunissha.i.marshall.civ@mail.mil
Business Management Team Leader **(Vacant)** 32 (2) 717-9626

Theater Contracting Center (TCC)
Theater Contracting Center, Mannheimer Strasse 208,
67657 Kaiserslautern, Germany
Mail: Unit 23156, APO, AE 09227
Tel: 49 (611) 816-2102
Tel: 49 (611) 816-2168 (Business Management Division)
Fax: 49 (611) 816-2104

Director **Dana D. Harris** 49 483-5131
E-mail: dana.d.harris10.civ@mail.mil
Facilities Maintenance Division Chief
Brigitte F. Bryant 49 (631) 483-5190
E-mail: brigitte.f.bryant.civ@mail.mil
Installation Services Division Chief
Roger A. Martin 49 (631) 483-5159
E-mail: roger.a.martin.civ@mail.mil
Small Purchases Division Chief
Shawn O. Peynado 49 (631) 483-5196
E-mail: shawn.o.peynado.mil@mail.mil
Special Acquisition Division Chief
Latosha V. McCoy 49 (631) 483-5147
E-mail: latosha.v.mccoy.civ@mail.mil

Germany

American Forces Network Europe (AFN Europe)
HQ AFN - Europe, Viernheimer Weg, Geb. 23,
68307 Coleman Kaserne, Gelnhausen, Germany
Mail: Building 23, HQ AFN - Europe,
Coleman Barracks, CMR 418, APO, AE 09058
Internet: www.afneurope.net

Director **Douglas Smith** 49 (611) 143-537-0110
Education: South Florida 1981 BA
Command Sergeant Major **(Vacant)** 49 (611) 143-537-0110

7th Army Training Command (7th ATC)
Lager Grafenwöhr, Gebäude 621, 92655 Grafenwoehr, Germany
Mail: Unit 28130, APO, AE 09114
Tel: 49 (9641) 83-7776

Commanding General
BG Christopher C. "Chris" LaNeve USA 49 (9641) 83-7776
Chief of Staff **COL William Linder USA** 49 (9641) 83-8305
Command Sergeant Major
CSM William L. Gardner II USA 49 (9641) 83-8090

Joint Multinational Readiness Center (JMRC)
Hohenfels, Germany
Mail: Unit 28126, APO, AE 09114
Tel: 49 (9472) 83-5047
E-mail: usarmy.jmrc.jmtc.mbx.jmrc-public-affairs-office@mail.mil

Commander **COL Joseph E. Hilbert USA** 49 (9472) 83-5805

Joint Multinational Readiness Center *(continued)*

Command Sergeant Major **CSM T.J. Holland USA** ... 49 (9472) 83-5805

Italy

U.S. Army Africa (USARAF)
AESG-CG, Box 10, 36100 Vicenza, Italy
Mail: AESG-CG, Unit 31401, Box 10, APO, AE 09630
Tel: 39 (0444) 71-7618 (Public Affairs) Fax: 39 (0444) 71-7543
E-mail: setafpao@setaf.army.mil E-mail: webmaster@setaf.army.mil
Internet: http://www.usaraf.army.mil/

Commanding General
MG Roger L. Cloutier, Jr. USA 39 (0444) 71-7618
Education: San Diego State; Troy U
Deputy Commanding General and Army
Reserve Engagement Cell Director
BG Eugene J. LeBoeuf USA 39 (0444) 71-7618
Deputy Commanding General and Army
Reserve Component Integration Advisor
BG Lapthe C. Flora USAR 39 (0444) 71-7618
Chief of Staff **COL Michael M. Larsen USA** 39 (0444) 71-7618

U.S. Marine Forces Europe and Africa (MARFOREUR)
HQ US MARFOREUR, Unit 30401, APO, AE 09046
Tel: 49 (7031) 15-2380 Internet: www.marforeur.marines.mil

Commander
MajGen Russell A. C. Sanborn USMC 49 (7031) 15-2380
Deputy Commander
Col John J. Carroll, Jr. USMC 49 (7031) 15-2380
Education: North Carolina
Chief of Staff **Col Sean M. McBride USMC** 49 (7031) 15-2380
Sergeant Major **SgtMaj Michael P. Woods USMC** ... 49 (7031) 15-2380

U.S. Special Operations Command Europe (USSOCEUR)
Geb. 2302 Patch Barracks, Stuttgart, Germany 70569
Mail: Unit 30400, APO, AE 09131
Internet: http://www.socom.mil/soceur/

Commander **MajGen Kirk W. Smith USAF** 49 (711) 680-5273
Deputy Commander **CAPT Anthony Baker USN** 49 (711) 680-5273
Senior Enlisted Advisor
CMDCM Bruce W. Holmes USN 49 (711) 680-5273
Intelligence Director (J2) **COL Terry A. Guild USA** ... 49 (711) 680-8503
E-mail: terry.a.guild.mil@mail.mil
Director, Public Affairs
MAJ Michael Weisman USA 49 (711) 680-6597

U.S. INDO-PACIFIC COMMAND (USINDOPACOM)
Commander U.S. Pacific Command, USPACOM / J01PA,
Box 64031, Camp H. M. Smith, HI 96861-4031
Tel: (808) 477-1341 Fax: (808) 477-6247 Internet: www.pacom.mil

Commander **ADM Philip S. Davidson USN** .... (808) 477-1341
Education: Naval Acad 1982 BS; Fax: (808) 477-7839
Naval War 1992 MA
Aide-de-Camp **MAJ David Webb USA** .... (808) 477-7804
Executive Assistant **CPT Lance Scott USN** .... (808) 477-7811
Mobilization Assistant to the Commander
MG Suzanne P. Vares-Lum USA .... (808) 477-7820
Economic Advisor **Dr. Brooks B. Robinson** .... (808) 477-9195
Education: Wisconsin; George Mason PhD
Foreign Policy Advisor **Candy Green** .... (808) 477-7603
Education: UC Berkeley BA; Fax: (808) 477-7607
Fletcher Law & Diplomacy
Deputy Commander **MG Bryan P. Fenton USA** .... (808) 477-7622
Chief of Staff **BrigGen Kevin B. Schneider USAF** ...... (808) 477-7612
Senior Enlisted Leader
SgtMaj Anthony A. Spadaro USMC .... (808) 477-9595
Director for Manpower, Personnel, and Administration
(J1) **Col Peter Santa Ana USAF** .... (808) 477-7872
Fax: (808) 477-7877

(continued on next page)

★ Presidential Appointment Requiring Senate Confirmation ☆ Presidential Appointment ☐ Schedule C Appointment ◇ Career Senior Foreign Service Appointment
● Career Senior Executive Service (SES) Appointment ○ Non-Career Senior Executive Service (SES) Appointment ■ Postal Career Executive Service

U.S. Indo-Pacific Command *(continued)*

Director for Intelligence (J2)
MajGen Jeffrey A. Kruse USAF . . . . . . (808) 477-7323
Education: Miami U (OH) 1990 Fax: (808) 477-7359
Exercises Division Chief (J37)
COL Bryan Mullins USA . . . . . . (808) 477-8200
Director for Logistics, Engineering and Security Assistance (J4) **MG Susan A. Davidson USA** . . . . . . (808) 477-7655
Education: New Mexico State 1983 BS Fax: (808) 477-6669
Director for Strategic Planning and Policy (J5)
MajGen Joaquin F. Malavet USMC . . . . . . (808) 477-7684
Education: Penn State 1985 BSIE Fax: (808) 477-0821
Deputy Director for Strategic Planning and Policy (J5)
BG Stephen L.A. Michael USA . . . . . . (808) 477-7684
Director for Command, Control, Communications, and Cyber (J6) **BG Paul H. Fredenburgh III USA** . . . . . . (808) 477-8004
Fax: (808) 477-3120
Chief Information Officer (J6C)
Randall C. "Randy" Cieslak . . . . . . (808) 477-7466
E-mail: randall.cieslak@pacom.mil
Director for Resources Assessment (J8)
Dr. George Ka'iliwai III . . . . . . (808) 477-0775
Education: Air Force Acad 1978 BSEE; Golden Gate 1980 MBA, 1981 MPA; Caltech 1984 MS; USC 2000 DEduc
Director for Pacific Outreach (J9)
Dr. John Randolph Wood USN (Ret) . . . . . . (808) 477-9084
Chief Legislative Affairs (J93)
CAPT John J. Zerr USN . . . . . . (808) 477-6030
Command Surgeon (J07)
RDML Louis C. Tripoli USNR . . . . . . (808) 477-7885
Chief of Protocol **Thomas Burton** . . . . . . (808) 477-7721
Comptroller **(Vacant)** . . . . . . (808) 477-9050
Inspector General **COL Sean G. Barrett USA** . . . . . . (808) 477-5101
Public Affairs Office Chief
LTC Derrick W. Cheng USA . . . . . . (808) 477-1341

Special Operations Command Pacific (SOCPAC)
HQ SOCPAC / SOJ0PA, Box 64046, Camp H. M. Smith, HI 96861

Commander **BG Jonathan P. Braga USA** . . . . . . (808) 477-6180
Education: Naval War MS
Executive Officer **MAJ Kate Guttormsen USA** . . . . . . (808) 477-9947
Foreign Policy Advisor **(Vacant)** . . . . . . (808) 477-9660
Deputy Commander **COL Bob G. Bond USA** . . . . . . (808) 477-9947
Education: Texas A&M 1984 BS
Command Sergeant Major
CSM Shane W. Shorter USA . . . . . . (808) 477-9914

U.S. Forces Korea (USFK)

Camp Humphreys, APO, AP 96271
Tel: 82 (2) 7913-6029 Fax: 82 (2) 7913-3537 Internet: www.usfk.mil

★ Commanding General
GEN Robert B. "Abe" Abrams USA 82 (2) 7913-7255
Education: West Point 1982 BS; Central Michigan MS; Army War Col MSS
Deputy Commander
LtGen Kenneth S. Wilsbach USAF 82 (2) 7913-6029
Education: Florida 1985 BS; Embry-Riddle 1997 MAE; Indust'l Col Armed Forces 2003
Deputy Commander, United Nations Command
BGen Wayne D. Eyre CF 82 (2) 7913-5236
Chief of Staff, Combined Forces Command
LTG Michael A. Bills USA 82 (2) 7913-8431
Command Sergeant Major
CSM Walter A. Tagalicud USA 82 (2) 7913-5228
Public Affairs Officer **(Vacant)** 82 (2) 7913-4661
E-mail: usarmy.yongsan.usfk.mbx.usfk-web-master@mail.mil

8th U.S. Army (EUSA - Yongsan Army Garrison)
Yongsan Army Garrison, Seoul, South Korea
Mail: PSC 303, Box 42, APO, AP 96205-0010
Tel: 82 (2) 7913-4678

Commanding General **LTG Michael A. Bills USA** 82 (2) 7913-8431
Deputy Commanding General for Operations
(Vacant) 82 (2) 7913-8431

8th U.S. Army *(continued)*

Deputy Commanding General for Support
MG Arlan M. DeBlieck USA 82 (2) 7913-8431
Wartime Chief of Staff
BG Andrew J. Juknelis USA 82 (2) 7913-4678
Education: West Point 1988 BS
Command Sergeant Major
CSM Richard E. "Rick" Merritt USA 82 (2) 7913-5228
Education: Shawnee State

2nd Infantry Division (2nd ID)
APO, AP 96258
E-mail: usarmy.redcloud.2-id.list.web-2id@mail.mil
Internet: http://www.2id.korea.army.mil/

Commander **BG Dennis S. McKean USA** 82 (31) 870-6131
E-mail: dennis.s.mckean.mil@mail.mil
Deputy Commanding General (Maneuver)
BG Stephen J. "Steve" Maranian USA 82 (31) 870-6131
Deputy Commanding General (Support)
COL Michael C. "Mac" McCurry USA 82 (31) 870-6131
Chief of Staff **COL Andrew Morgado USA** 82 (31) 870-6131
Education: Lehigh 1994 BA; Norwich MA
Command Sergeant Major
CSM Phil K. Barretto USA 82 (31) 870-6131

19th Sustainment Command (Expeditionary)
Camp Henry, Daegu, South Korea
Mail: 19th ESC, Unit 15015, Box 2506, APO, AP 96218-5015
Tel: 82 (53) 470-7660 Fax: 82 (53) 470-6644

Commanding General
BG Michel M. Russell, Sr. USA 82 (53) 470-7396
Deputy Commander **COL Michael Siegl USA** 82 (53) 470-7555
Command Sergeant Major **(Vacant)** 82 (53) 470-7581

U.S. Marine Corps Forces Korea (MARFORK)
Yongsan Army Garrison, Seoul, South Korea
Internet: http://www.marfork.marines.mil/

Commander
MajGen Patrick J. Hermesmann USMCR 82 (2) 7913-6029
Education: Rutgers; Toledo JD; Army War Col MSS
Deputy Commander **LtCol Scott M. Koltick USMC** . . . 82 (2) 7913-6029
Sergeant Major
SgtMaj Michael R. Saucedo USMC 82 (2) 7913-6029

U.S. NORTHERN COMMAND (NORTHCOM)

Peterson AFB, CO 80914-3808
Tel: (719) 554-5916 E-mail: northcompa@northcom.mil
Internet: www.northcom.mil

★ Commander **Gen Terrence J. O'Shaughnessy USAF** . . . (719) 554-3001
Education: Air Force Acad 1986 BS; Embry-Riddle 1996 MS; Air Command Col 1998; Indust'l Col Armed Forces 2003 Fax: (719) 554-9779
Executive Assistant **(Vacant)** . . . . . . (719) 554-3001
Foreign Policy Advisor
Christopher J. "Chris" Sandrolini . . . . . . (719) 554-6191
Education: Chicago 1982 BA; Johns Hopkins 1984 MA Fax: (719) 554-2619
Special Assistant for Reserve Matters
BG John E. Cardwell USAR . . . . . . (719) 554-6889
Education: Tennessee; Army War Col MSS
Deputy Commander
VADM Michael J. "Mike" Dumont USNR . . . . . . (719) 554-3892
Education: Southern Maine BA; Suffolk JD; Army War Col MSS
Senior Enlisted Advisor
SgtMaj Paul G. McKenna USMC . . . . . . (719) 554-7688
Chief of Staff **MG Richard J. Gallant ARNG** . . . . . . (719) 554-6889
Command Surgeon **(Vacant)** . . . . . . (719) 554-5916
Deputy Chief of Staff for Communications and Public Affairs Officer **(Vacant)** . . . . . . (719) 554-6889
250 Vandenberg, Suite B016, Peterson AFB, CO 80914-3808
Architectures and Integration Director **(Vacant)** . . . . . . (719) 554-3001
Director, Cyberspace Operations
BrigGen Angela M. "Angie" Cadwell USAF . . . . . . (719) 554-5916

★ Presidential Appointment Requiring Senate Confirmation ☆ Presidential Appointment □ Schedule C Appointment ◇ Career Senior Foreign Service Appointment
● Career Senior Executive Service (SES) Appointment ○ Non-Career Senior Executive Service (SES) Appointment ■ Postal Career Executive Service

U.S. Northern Command *(continued)*

Director, Intelligence and Information
BrigGen Daniel L. Simpson USAF . . . . (719) 554-3001
Director, Operations
MajGen Jeffrey B. Taliaferro USAF . . . . (719) 554-3001
Education: Air Force Acad 1989 BS; George Washington 1997 MM; Air U (USAF) 1997; Air Command Col 2002; Joint Forces Staff Col 2007
Deputy Director of Operations **(Vacant)** . . . . (719) 554-3001
Strategy, Policy and Plans Director
RDML John V. Fuller USN . . . . (719) 554-6889

Alaskan Command (ALCOM)

9480 Pease Avenue, Suite 111,
Joint Base Elmendorf-Richardson, AK 99506
Tel: (907) 552-3100 Fax: (907) 552-5411

Commander **LtGen Thomas A. Bussiere USAF** . . . . (907) 552-3100
Education: Norwich 1985 BSBusMgt; Air Command Col 2000; Air U (USAF) 2000 MA, 2001 MA; Air War Col 2004; Army War Col 2007 MSS
Executive Officer **Maj Gina M. Schneider USAF** . . . . . . (907) 552-5400
Deputy Commander **(Vacant)** . . . . (907) 552-3100
Chief Master Sergeant **CMSgt Gay Veale USAF** . . . . (907) 552-2295
E-mail: gay.veale@us.af.mil
Chief of Staff **COL Cory Mendenhall USA** . . . . (907) 552-3932
Public Affairs Director
Capt Anastasia Schmidt USAF . . . . (907) 552-2341
E-mail: anastasia.wasem@us.af.mil

U.S. SOUTHERN COMMAND (SOUTHCOM)

9301 NW 33rd Street, Doral, FL 33172
Tel: (305) 437-1000 Tel: (305) 437-1213 (Public Affairs)
Fax: (305) 437-1241 Internet: www.southcom.mil

★ Commander **ADM Kurt W. Tidd USN** . . . . (305) 437-1002
Note: Until November 26, 2018.
E-mail: kurt.w.tidd.mil@mail.mil
Education: Naval Acad 1978; U Bordeaux (France) 1984 MS; Joint Forces Staff Col
Secretary to the Commander **Carol I. Maldonado** . . . . . . (305) 437-1000
E-mail: carol.i.maldonado2.civ@mail.mil
Military Deputy Commander **(Vacant)** . . . . (305) 437-1052
Fax: (305) 437-1018
Secretary to the Deputy Commander **Edisa M. Dale** . . . . (305) 437-1052
E-mail: edisa.m.dale.civ@mail.mil
◇ Civilian Deputy to the Commander and Foreign Policy Advisor **Ambassador Liliana Ayalde** . . . . (305) 437-1012
Education: American U BA; Tulane MPH Fax: (305) 437-2929
Deputy Commander for Mobilization and Reserve Affairs **MajGen Robert M. Branyon ANG** . . . . (305) 437-2673
Senior Enlisted Advisor
SgtMaj Bryan K. Zickefoose USMC . . . . (305) 437-1000
Chief of Staff **MG Patricia M. Anslow USA** . . . . (305) 437-1000
Executive Officer **Col James B. Wellons USMC** . . . . (305) 437-1009
E-mail: james.b.wellons.mil@mail.mil
Director, Manpower and Personnel (J1)
CAPT Carol M. Kushmier USN . . . . (305) 437-1101
E-mail: carol.m.kushmier2.mil@mail.mil Fax: (305) 437-1175
Director, Intelligence (J2)
RDML Michael W. "Mike" Studeman USN . . . . (305) 437-2003
E-mail: michael.studeman@navy.mil
Education: William & Mary 1988
Director, Operations (J3)
RADM Steven D. Poulin USCG . . . . (305) 437-3333
Education: US Coast Guard Acad 1984 BS; Miami 1992 JD Fax: (305) 437-3451
Deputy Director, Operations (J3) **(Vacant)** . . . . (305) 437-3331
Director, Logistics (J4) **Col David S. Gibbs USMC** . . . . . . (305) 437-2040
Director, Strategy, Policy and Plans (J5) **(Vacant)** . . . . (305) 437-1501
Director, Communications Systems (J6)
COL John J. Pugliese USA . . . . (305) 437-1601
Director, Exercises and Coalition (J7/9)
Juan Pablo Forero . . . . (305) 437-2233

U.S. Southern Command *(continued)*

Director, Resources and Assessments (J8)
James "Jim" Worm . . . . (305) 437-1801
Command Surgeon **Col Guillermo J. Tellez USAF** . . . . . . (305) 437-1327
Education: Texas 1981 BS; Texas Tech 1985 MD; Air War Col 2003
Congressional Affairs Chief **Elizabeth Gonzalez** . . . . (305) 437-1020
Inspector General **COL Bryan P. Hernandez USA** . . . . (305) 437-1000
E-mail: southcom.miami.sc-cc.mbx.uscig@mail.mil Fax: (605) 437-1074
Public Affairs Chief **COL Amanda Azubuike USA** . . . . . . (305) 437-1201
Fax: (305) 437-1241
Staff Judge Advocate **CAPT Bill Dwyer USCG** . . . . (305) 437-1304
Fax: (305) 437-1320

Joint Task Force-Bravo (JTF-B)

Soto Cano Air Base, Tegucigalpa, Honduras
Mail: PSC 42, APO, AA 34042
Tel: 504 2234-4634 ext. 4150 Internet: www.jtfb.southcom.mil

Commander **Col Keith A. McKinley USAF** . . . . 504 2234-4634 ext. 4150
Command Sergeant Major
CSM Robert M. Keith USA . . . . 504 2234-4634 ext. 4150

Joint Task Force-Guantanamo (JTF-GTMO)

Guantanamo Bay, Cuba, APO, AE 09630
Tel: 53 660-8135 Tel: 53 011-5399-8141
E-mail: osd.pentagon.pa.mbx.gtmo-press@mail.mil
Internet: www.jtfgtmo.southcom.mil

Commander **RDML John Clinton Ring USN** 53 99-99-28
Education: Arizona BA
Deputy Commander **(Vacant)** 53 99-99-28
Senior Enlisted Leader
CMSgt Zaki J. "Tico" Mazid USAF 53 99-99-28

U.S. Army South (USARSO)

1835 Army Boulevard, Suite 700, Fort Sam Houston, TX 78234-2645
Tel: (210) 221-2163 Internet: https://www.arsouth.army.mil/

Commanding General **MG Mark R. Stammer USA** . . . . . (210) 221-2163
Deputy Commanding General and Director, Army Reserve Engagement Cell **COL Ellen S. Clark USAR** . . . (210) 295-6337
Deputy Commanding General and Director, Operations and National Guard Affairs
BG James P. Wong ARNG . . . . (210) 295-6337
Command Sergeant Major
CSM William M. Rinehart USA . . . . (210) 221-2163
Foreign Policy Advisor **Drew G. Blakeney** . . . . (210) 221-2163

U.S. Marine Corps Forces, South (MARFORSOUTH)

9301 NW 33rd Street, Doral, FL 33172
Tel: (305) 437-2553 Tel: (305) 437-2554 (Public Affairs)
Internet: http://www.marforsouth.marines.mil/

Commanding General **BGen David G. Bellon USMC** . . . . (305) 437-2544
Chief of Staff **Col Michael Farrell USMC** . . . . (305) 437-2553
Sergeant Major **SgtMaj Eric D. Cook USMC** . . . . (305) 437-2552

U.S. Naval Forces Southern Command/U.S. 4th Fleet (NAVSOUTH)

P.O. Box 280003, Building 1878, Mayport Naval Station, FL 32228-0003
Tel: (904) 270-7354

Commander **RDML Sean S. Buck USN** . . . . (904) 270-7350
Education: Naval Acad 1983 BS
Deputy Commander
RDML Linda Rosa Del Wackerman USNR . . . . (904) 220-7350
Education: Metro State Col Denver BS
Maritime Operations Center Director
CAPT Daniel Gillen USN . . . . (904) 270-7354
Chief of Staff **Capt Wyatt N. Chidester USN** . . . . (904) 270-4778
Command Master Chief **(Vacant)** . . . . (904) 270-7350
Public Affairs Officer **CDR Erik Reynolds USN** . . . . (904) 270-4813

★ Presidential Appointment Requiring Senate Confirmation ☆ Presidential Appointment □ Schedule C Appointment ◇ Career Senior Foreign Service Appointment
● Career Senior Executive Service (SES) Appointment ○ Non-Career Senior Executive Service (SES) Appointment ■ Postal Career Executive Service

DEPARTMENTS

U.S. SPACE COMMAND

Note: The Pentagon is working to create a new Unified Combatant Command called U.S. Space Command to oversee national security in space, develop procedures and tactics to combat potential space threats, and improve and evolve space warfighting.

★ Commander **(Vacant)** .... (703) 692-7150

U.S. SPECIAL OPERATIONS COMMAND (USSOCOM)

MacDill AFB, 7701 Tampa Point Blvd., MacDill AFB, FL 33621-5323
Tel: (813) 826-4600 (Public Affairs) Fax: (813) 826-4035
E-mail: public.affairs@socom.mil Internet: www.socom.mil

Note: USSOCOM components: U.S. Army Special Operations Command (Fort Bragg, NC); Joint Special Operations Command (Fort Bragg, NC); Naval Special Warfare Command (Coronado, CA); Air Force Special Operations Command (Hurlbert Field, FL); Marine Corps Forces Special Operations Command (Camp LeJeune, NC)

★ Commander
GEN Raymond A. "Tony" Thomas III USA .... (813) 826-5100
Education: West Point 1980 BS; Naval War MA; Army War Col 2000 MS
Senior Foreign Policy Advisor
Ambassador Greta Christine Holtz .... (813) 826-5166
Education: Vanderbilt 1982 BS; Kentucky 1984 MA; National War Col 2004 MNSSS — Fax: (813) 826-5139
Deputy Commander **(Vacant)** .... (813) 826-5113
Fax: (813) 828-5139
Vice Commander
MajGen James C. "Jim" Slife USAF .... (813) 826-5113
Education: Auburn 1989 BS; Embry-Riddle 1995 MS
Chief of Staff **MG James B. Linder USA** .... (813) 826-5123
Education: Clemson 1983
Intelligence Director (J2) **(Vacant)** .... (813) 826-4600
Operations Director (J3) **MG James B. Jarrard USA** .... (813) 826-4600
Strategy, Plans and Policy Director (J5)
William J. "Joe" Miller .... (813) 826-4600
Education: Florida 1979 BBA
Strategy, Plans and Policy Deputy Director (J5)
(Vacant) .... (813) 826-4600
Communications Systems Director (J6) and Chief Information Officer **John A. Wilcox** .... (813) 826-4600
Director (J7/9) **MG Robert A. Karmazin USAR** .... (813) 826-4600
Force Structure Requirements, Resources and Strategic Assessments Director (J8)
MG Sean P. Swindell USA .... (813) 826-4600
Education: Citadel BSBA; US Army Command MMAS; Army War Col MSS
Chief Financial Officer **D. Mark Peterson** .... (813) 826-4600
Force Management and Development Director **(Vacant)** .... (813) 826-4600
Mobilization and Reserve Affairs Deputy Commander
(Vacant) .... (813) 826-4600
Plans and Policy for Countering Weapons of Mass Destruction Deputy Director
RDML Joseph "Joe" DiGuardo USN .... (813) 826-4600
E-mail: joseph.diguardo@navy.mil
Public Affairs Officer **LCDR Matt Allen USN** .... (813) 826-4600
E-mail: public.affairs@socom.mil
Senior Enlisted Leader
CSM Patrick L. McCauley USA .... (813) 826-5144
Small Business Programs Director
Christopher Harrington .... (813) 826-9475
E-mail: christopher.harrington@socom.mil

Joint Special Operations Command (JSOC)

Fort Bragg, NC 28307-5243
Tel: (910) 243-2400

Commander **(Vacant)** .... (910) 243-5409
Deputy Commander **MG Mark C. Schwartz USA** .... (910) 243-5409
Assistant Commanding General
BrigGen David H. Tabor USAF .... (910) 243-5409
Command Senior Enlisted Leader
CSM David J. Blake USA .... (910) 243-5409

U.S. STRATEGIC COMMAND (USSTRATCOM)

901 SAC Boulevard, Suite 2A, Offutt AFB, NE 68113-6000
Tel: (402) 294-4111 Fax: (402) 294-4114 E-mail: pa@stratcom.mil
Internet: www.stratcom.mil

★ Commander **Gen John E. Hyten USAF** .... (402) 294-4111
Education: Harvard 1981 BSE; Auburn 1985 MBA
Executive Assistant **Valerie Meyer** .... (402) 294-4111
Fax: (402) 294-4114
Executive Assistant **(Vacant)** .... (402) 294-4112
Aide **Maj Jessica C. Corea USAF** .... (402) 294-4113
Fax: (402) 294-4114
Aide **(Vacant)** .... (402) 294-4113
Fax: (402) 294-4114
Deputy Commander **VADM David M. Kriete USN** .... (402) 294-4124
Education: Naval Acad 1984 BS; Old Dominion MEM
Mobilization Assistant to the Deputy Commander
MG Michael D. Navrkal ARNG .... (402) 294-4124
Education: Nebraska 1984 BSBA; Bellevue U 2006 MS
Chief of Staff **MG Daniel L. Karbler USA** .... (402) 294-2417
Education: West Point BS; Benedictine MS; National War Col MS
Commandant and Senior Enlisted Advisor to the Chief of Staff
MGySgt Terrance L. Meekins USMC .... (402) 294-4111
Deputy Chief of Staff **Col Jeffrey A. Hagan USMC** .... (402) 294-7775
● Foreign Policy Advisor **Linda Specht** .... (402) 294-9773
Education: Fletcher Law & Diplomacy MALD; National War Col 2008 MNSSS
Command Senior Enlisted Leader
CMSgt Patrick F. McMahon USAF .... (402) 294-5881
Director, Human Capital (J1)
Col Carolyn D. Bird USMC .... (402) 294-2711
Director, Intelligence (J2)
RADM Kelly A. Aeschbach USN .... (402) 294-4959
Deputy Director, Intelligence (DJ2)
Wayne A. Ulman .... (402) 294-4959
Director, Global Operations (J3)
MajGen Stephen L. Davis USAF .... (402) 294-4111
Deputy Director, Global Operations (J3)
BG Gregory S. Bowen USA .... (402) 294-2211
Deputy Director, Joint Electromagnetic Spectrum Operations (J3E) **(Vacant)** .... (402) 294-4111
Deputy Director, Nuclear Operations (J3N) **(Vacant)** .... (402) 294-4111
Director, Logistics (J4) **CAPT Dennis Turner USN** .... (402) 294-4111
Director, Plans and Policy (J5)
RADM Richard A. Correll USN .... (402) 294-4225
Education: Rose-Hulman 1986 BSChE; Fletcher Law & Diplomacy 1997
Deputy Director, Plans and Policy (DJ5M) **(Vacant)** .... (402) 294-4225
Deputy Director, Plans and Policy (DJ5M)
RDML Ryan B. Scholl USN .... (402) 294-4225
● Deputy Director, Plans and Policy (DJ5C)
COL Robert J. Taylor USA (Ret) .... (402) 294-4225
Deputy Director, Strategic Targeting and Nuclear Mission Planning (J5N)
RDML (Sel) William J. Houston USN .... (402) 232-9793
Education: Notre Dame 1990 BSEE; William & Mary MBA
● Director, C4 Systems (J6) **(Vacant)** .... (402) 294-4130
Deputy Director, C4 Systems (J6)
RDML Linnea J. Sommer-Weddington USNR .... (402) 294-4111
Education: Slippery Rock State; Meredith 1996 MBA
● Director, Joint Exercises, Training, and Assessment (J7) **Patrick A. McVay** .... (402) 294-4111
● Director, Capability and Resource Integration (J8)
(Vacant) .... (402) 294-5691
Associate Director, Capability and Resource Integration (J8A) **(Vacant)** .... (402) 294-5691
● Director, Mission Assessment and Analysis Directorate (J9) **(Vacant)** .... (402) 294-4130
Director, Reserve Directorate (J10) and Mobilization Assistant to the Commander
MajGen Richard J. "Rick" Evans III ANG .... (402) 294-2339
Education: Nebraska (Omaha) 1984 BSBA; Air Command Col 1999; Air War Col 2003

★ Presidential Appointment Requiring Senate Confirmation ☆ Presidential Appointment □ Schedule C Appointment ◇ Career Senior Foreign Service Appointment
● Career Senior Executive Service (SES) Appointment ○ Non-Career Senior Executive Service (SES) Appointment ■ Postal Career Executive Service

U.S. Strategic Command *(continued)*

Commander, Joint Force Air Component
Gen Timothy M. Ray USAF . . . . (402) 294-4111
Education: Air Force Acad 1985 BS; Embry-Riddle 1998 MS; Air War Col 2004 MSS

Commander, Joint Functional Component Command - Integrated Missile Defense
LTG James H. Dickinson USA . . . . (703) 607-1873

Commander, Joint Functional Component Command - Intelligence, Surveillance, and Reconnaissance
LTG Robert P. Ashley USA . . . . (703) 607-1873
Education: Appalachian State BA; Military Intelligence Col MS; Army War Col MS

Deputy Commander, Joint Functional Component Command - Intelligence, Surveillance, and Reconnaissance **(Vacant)** . . . . (703) 607-1873

Commander, Joint Force Space Component
Gen John W. "Jay" Raymond USAF . . . . (402) 294-4111
Education: Clemson 1984 BS; Central Michigan 1990 MS; Air Command Col 1997; Naval War 2003 MNSSS; Joint Forces Staff Col 2007

Deputy Commander, Joint Force Space Component
MajGen Stephen N. Whiting USAF . . . . (402) 294-4111
Education: Air Force Acad 1989 BS; Air U (USAF) 1993; George Washington 1997 MAS; Air Command Col 2001 MMAS; Joint Forces Staff Col 2008

Commander, Marine Corps Forces
LtGen Robert S. Walsh USMC . . . . (402) 294-9298
Education: Naval Acad 1979; National War Col 2002 MS

Commander, Standing Joint Force Headquarters for the Elimination of Weapons of Mass Destruction
RADM Scott B. J. Jerabek USNR . . . . (703) 767-6622
8725 John J. Kingman Road, Fort Belvoir, VA 22060-6218
Education: Nebraska

Future Capabilities Branch Chief
LtCol Brian O. Crooks USAF . . . . (402) 294-4111
E-mail: brian.o.crooks.mil@mail.mil
Education: New York City Col Tech 2000 BTech

Public Affairs Officer **CAPT Pamela S. Kunze USN** . . . . . (402) 294-4130
E-mail: pa@stratcom.mil Fax: (402) 294-4892

National Airborne Operations Center (NAOC)
102 Looking Glass Avenue, Suite 19, Offutt AFB, NE 68113-3150
Tel: (402) 294-5400 Fax: (402) 294-4906

Commander **CAPT Dennis Crews USN** . . . . (402) 294-5400

U.S. TRANSPORTATION COMMAND (USTRANSCOM)

508 Scott Drive, Scott AFB, IL 62225-5357
Tel: (618) 229-3205 Tel: (618) 220-4999 (Public Affairs)
Fax: (618) 229-2811 Internet: https://www.ustranscom.mil/
Internet: https://www.move.mil/ (DOD Moving Portal)

★ Commander **LTG Stephen R. Lyons USA** . . . . (618) 220-4999
Education: RIT
Executive Officer **(Vacant)** . . . . (618) 229-3205
Mobilization Assistant to the Commander
BrigGen Steven J. Berryhill USAF . . . . (618) 220-4900

Deputy Commander
LtGen John J. Broadmeadow USMC . . . . (618) 229-2478
E-mail: john.broadmeadow@usmc.mil
Education: Norwich BS; Webster MA; Army War Col MS

Chief of Staff
MajGen John C. "Jay" Flournoy, Jr. USAFR . . . . (618) 229-4933
Education: Southern IL Edwardsville 1986 BA; National Defense U 2003 MS

Senior Enlisted Leader
CMSgt Jason L. France USAF . . . . (618) 229-3205

Commander, Joint Enabling Capabilities Command (JECC) **BrigGen Lenny J. Richoux USAF** . . . . (757) 836-5689
9712 Virginia Avenue, Norfolk, VA 23511
Education: Georgia Tech 1989 BS; George Washington 1997 MA; Air Command Col 2003; Air War Col 2005

U.S. Transportation Command *(continued)*

Vice Commander, Joint Enabling Capabilities Command (JECC)
BrigGen Udo K. "Karl" McGregor USAFR . . . . (757) 836-5689
Building X-132, 9712 Virginia Avenue, Norfolk, VA 23511
Education: Texas 1984; Webster 1990 MA; Naval War 2003 MA

Chief, Commander's Action Group
Col Greg G. Young USAF . . . . (618) 229-3205

Command Chaplain **LTC George L. Wallace USA** . . . . (618) 229-3205

Command FOIA Officer **Tammy Hickey** . . . . (618) 229-3828

Command Surgeon **Col John R. Andrus USAF, MD** . . . . . (618) 229-5298
Education: UC Irvine 1988 BS; Uniformed Services 1993 MD; UC Berkeley 2002 MPH
Deputy Command Surgeon
CAPT Garland H. Andrews USN . . . . (618) 229-5298

◇ Foreign Policy Advisor **Alan G. Misenheimer** . . . . (618) 229-1158

Inspector General **COL Chad A. Callis USA** . . . . (618) 220-6632

Joint Operations Chief
BrigGen Joel D. Jackson USAF . . . . (618) 229-3205
Education: Air Force Acad 1992 BS; U Washington 1993 MSAE; George Washington 2000 MA

Legislative Affairs Chief **Kurt LaFrance** . . . . (618) 220-4811

Protocol Chief **Rita Whited** . . . . (618) 229-4098

Public Affairs Chief **CAPT Kevin R. Stephens USN** . . . . (618) 220-4999
E-mail: transcom.scott.tcpa.mbx.director@mail.mil

Research Center Director **Dr. Robert Sligh** . . . . (618) 220-5807

Staff Judge Advocate **COL Eric Werner USA** . . . . (618) 220-3982

Deputy Director, Office of the Staff Judge Advocate
Col Matthew J. "Matt" Mulbarger USAF . . . . (618) 229-3205

Section 508 Coordinator [Section 508 Coordinator]
Matthew M. "Fritz" Mihelcic . . . . (618) 220-3982
E-mail: matthew.m.mihelcic.civ@mail.mil

Acquisition Directorate (TCAQ)
Scott AFB, IL 62225

● Director **Gail Jorgenson** . . . . (618) 220-6413
● Deputy Director **Tamara D. Thouvenot** . . . . (618) 220-6413

Manpower and Personnel (J1) (TCJ1)
508 Scott Drive, Scott AFB, IL 62225-5357
Tel: (618) 220-6700

Director **Col Wistaria J. Joseph USAF** . . . . (618) 220-6700
Deputy Director **William J. Buechel** . . . . (618) 220-6700

Intelligence (J2) (TCJ2)
508 Scott Drive, Scott AFB, IL 62225-5357
Tel: (618) 220-7846

Director **Capt Henry A. Stephenson USAF** . . . . (618) 220-7846
Deputy Director **Dalton R. Jones** . . . . (618) 220-7846
Education: Arkansas Tech 1980 BA
Senior Enlisted Advisor
CMSgt James L. Hoffman USAF . . . . (618) 220-7846

Operations and Plans (J3) (TCJ3)
508 Scott Drive, Scott AFB, IL 62225-5357
Tel: (618) 220-7000

Director **MajGen Ricky N. Rupp USAF** . . . . (618) 220-7000
Education: Southwest Texas State 1988; Embry-Riddle 1996 MASc
Deputy Director **Robert Brisson** . . . . (618) 220-7001

Strategy, Capabilities, Policy, and Logistics (J5/4) (TCJ5/4)
508 Scott Drive, Scott AFB, IL 62225-5357
Tel: (618) 229-3999

Director **RDML Peter J. Clarke USN** . . . . (618) 229-3999
Deputy Director **James R. "Rick" Marsh** . . . . (618) 229-3499

Command, Control, Communications and Cyber Systems (J6) (TCJ6)
508 Scott Drive, Scott AFB, IL 62225-5357
Tel: (618) 220-3824

Director **BrigGen Robert K. "Rob" Lyman USAF** . . . . . . (618) 220-3824
Education: Rensselaer Poly 1993 BSEE; George Washington 2001 MA

(continued on next page)

★ Presidential Appointment Requiring Senate Confirmation ☆ Presidential Appointment □ Schedule C Appointment ◇ Career Senior Foreign Service Appointment
● Career Senior Executive Service (SES) Appointment ○ Non-Career Senior Executive Service (SES) Appointment ■ Postal Career Executive Service

Command, Control, Communications and Cyber Systems (J6) *(continued)*

• Deputy Director **Elizabeth M. Durham-Ruiz** . . . . (618) 220-1296

Program Analysis and Financial Management (J8) (TCJ8)

508 Scott Drive, Scott AFB, IL 62225-5357
Tel: (618) 229-5358

• Director **Daniel F. McMillin** . . . . (618) 229-5358
Education: Western Illinois 1983 BSB; American U 1992 MPFM
Deputy Director **(Vacant)** . . . . (618) 229-5358

Joint Reserve Component Directorate (J9) (TCRA - Scott AFB)

508 Scott Drive, Scott AFB, IL 62225-5357
Tel: (618) 220-4900

Director and Commander, Joint Transportation Reserve Unit **MG Daniel R. Ammerman USAR** . . . .(618) 220-4900
Deputy Commander **COL Carl W. Koehlinger USAR** . . . . (618) 220-4875

★ Presidential Appointment Requiring Senate Confirmation ☆ Presidential Appointment □ Schedule C Appointment ◇ Career Senior Foreign Service Appointment
● Career Senior Executive Service (SES) Appointment ○ Non-Career Senior Executive Service (SES) Appointment ■ Postal Career Executive Service

United States Department of the Air Force

DEPARTMENTS

Contents

United States Department of the Air Force (USAF)

The Pentagon, Washington, DC 20330-1000
Tel: (703) 588-7003 (Contracting Information)
Tel: (703) 545-6700 (Department of Defense General Information)
Tel: (703) 695-9664 (Public Inquiries)
Tel: (800) 423-8723 (Nationwide Recruiting) Fax: (703) 696-7273
Internet: www.af.mil Internet: www.usafservices.com
Internet: www.usa.gov (Official US Government Website)

OFFICE OF THE SECRETARY OF THE AIR FORCE (SAF/OS)

1670 Air Force Pentagon, Washington, DC 20330-1670
Tel: (703) 697-7376 Fax: (703) 695-8809

Chief of Staff of the Air Force (CSAF)

The Pentagon, Washington, DC 20330

OFFICE OF THE CHIEF

1670 Air Force Pentagon, Washington, DC 20330-1670
Fax: (703) 693-9297

Safety

1670 Air Force Pentagon, Washington, DC 20330-1670 (Pentagon Office)
9700 G Avenue, SE, Kirtland AFB, NM 87117 (Air Force Safety Center)

Air Force Chief of Safety
MajGen John T. Rauch, Jr. USAF .... (505) 846-1403
Education: Colorado 1989 BS; George Washington 1997 MA
Executive Officer to the Air Force Chief of Safety
(Vacant) .... (703) 614-3389

Air Force Safety Center (AFSEC)

9700 Avenue G, SE, Suite 240, Kirtland AFB, NM 87117-5670
Tel: (505) 846-1403 Fax: (505) 853-0565
Internet: http://www.safety.af.mil/

Commander **MajGen John T. Rauch, Jr. USAF** .... (505) 846-1403
Education: Colorado 1989 BS; George Washington 1997 MA
● Executive Director **James T. Rubeor** .... (505) 846-2372
E-mail: james.rubeor@kirtland.af.mil
Education: Air Force Acad 1978 BS; Air Command Col 1987; Air War Col 1993; National War Col 1993 MS

Direct Reporting Units (DRU)

Air Force District of Washington (AFDW)

1500 West Perimeter Road, Suite 5 Room 790,
Joint Base Andrews-Naval Air Facility Washington, MD 20762-7001
Tel: (301) 981-1110 (Base Operator)

Commander **MajGen James A. Jacobson USAF** .... (240) 857-4312
Vice Commander **Col Kevin M. Eastland USAF** .... (240) 857-4312
Education: Notre Dame 1994 BS; UC Davis 1998 MBA
Director of Contracting **Col Sheri Bennington USAF** .... (301) 981-1110
Director of Financial Management and Comptroller
Maritza LoGrasso .... (301) 981-1110
Inspector General **Col Michael S. Smith USAF** .... (301) 981-1110

Air Force District of Washington *(continued)*

Chief Master Sergeant
CMSgt Melanie K. Noel USAF .... (240) 857-1611
First Sergeant **CMSgt Manny Pineiro USAF** .... (240) 857-1611
Public Affairs **(Vacant)** .... (240) 857-1931
E-mail: afdw.pa@afncr.af.mil

844th Communications Group

1500 West Perimeter Road, Suite A212,
Joint Base Andrews-Naval Air Facility Washington, MD 20762-6602
Fax: (202) 404-6216

Commander **Col Michael Sinks USAF** .... (240) 857-2379

11th Wing (11 WG - Joint Base Andrews)

1500 West Perimeter Road,
Joint Base Andrews-Naval Air Facility Washington, MD 20762-6602
Tel: (240) 612-4428 (Public Affairs) Internet: www.andrews.af.mil

Commander **Col Andrew M. Purath USAF** .... (240) 612-4428
Vice Commander
Col Jocelyn J. Schermerhorn USAF .... (240) 612-4428
Chief Master Sergeant
CMSgt Thomas C. Daniels USAF .... (240) 612-4428
Librarian **Shirley Foster** .... (202) 767-5578
Building 4439, 410 Tinker Street, Fax: (202) 404-8526
FL 4400, HQ 11, MSG-SVMG,
Bolling AFB, DC 20032-0703

Air Force Operational Test and Evaluation Center (AFOTEC)

8500 Gibson Boulevard SE, Kirtland AFB, NM 87117
Tel: (505) 846-4525 Internet: www.afotec.af.mil

Commander **MajGen Matthew H. Molloy USAF** .... (505) 846-4533
Education: Colorado 1987 BS; Air U (USAF) 1992; Embry-Riddle 1998 MS; Air Command Col 1999; Air U (USAF) 2000; Air War Col 2002; National War Col 2005 MNSSS
Commander **MajGen Michael T. Brewer USAF** .... (505) 846-4525
Education: North Carolina State 1986 BSEE; Troy State 1988 MS
● Executive Director **William C. Redmond** .... (505) 846-4533
Vice Commander **Col Thomas J. Timmerman USAF** ... (505) 846-6172
Chief Enlisted Manager
CMSgt David S. Southall II USAF .... (505) 846-5234
Chief of Public Affairs
Katherine C. "Kathy" Gandara .... (505) 846-8513

United States Air Force Academy (USAFA)

2304 Cadet Drive, Suite 3300, U.S.A.F. Academy, CO 80840-5016
Tel: (719) 333-1110 Fax: (719) 333-4146 Internet: www.usafa.af.mil

Administration

Superintendent and President
LtGen Jay B. Silveria USAF .... (719) 333-4140
Education: Air Force Acad 1985 BS; Air Command Col 1996; Syracuse 1997 MA; National War Col 1995
Mobilization Assistant to the Superintendent
(Vacant) .... (719) 333-7648
Vice Superintendent **Col David A. Harris, Jr. USAF** ..... (719) 333-4140
Command Chief Master Sergeant
CMSgt Robert A. Boyer USAF .... (719) 333-7693
Commandant of Cadets
BrigGen Kristin Goodwin USAF .... (719) 333-2263

(continued on next page)

★ Presidential Appointment Requiring Senate Confirmation ☆ Presidential Appointment ☐ Schedule C Appointment ◇ Career Senior Foreign Service Appointment
● Career Senior Executive Service (SES) Appointment ○ Non-Career Senior Executive Service (SES) Appointment ■ Postal Career Executive Service

Administration *(continued)*

Vice Commandant of Cadets
Col John F. Price, Jr. USAF . . . . (719) 333-0130
Education: Air Force Acad 1993 BS; George Washington 2002 MA
Vice Commandant of Cadets (Culture and Climate)
Col Julian Stephens USAF . . . . (719) 333-4290
Dean of the Faculty
BrigGen Andrew Armacost USAF . . . . (719) 333-4270
E-mail: andrew.armacost@usafa.edu
Education: Northwestern 1989 BS; MIT 1995 SM, 2000 PhD
Vice Dean of Faculty **Col Gary A. Packard USAF** . . . . (719) 333-2018
Associate Dean for Curriculum and Strategy
Dr. David A. Westmoreland . . . . (719) 333-4270
Chief Diversity Officer **Yvonne Roland** . . . . (719) 333-7648
Director, Academic Affairs and Registrar
Dr. Thomas Mabry . . . . (719) 333-2229
Director, Academic Computing **Larry W. Bryant** . . . . (719) 333-3994
E-mail: larry.bryant@usafa.edu
Education: UCLA MS
Director, Academy Culture, Climate and Diversity
(Acting) **Moses Stewart, Jr.** . . . . (719) 333-3870
Director, Academy Libraries **Dr. Edward A. Scott** . . . . (719) 333-2590
FL 7000, HQ USAFA/DFSEL, Fax: (719) 333-4754
2354 Fairchild Drive,
Suite 3A10, Colorado Springs, CO 80840-6214
E-mail: edward.scott@usafa.edu
Education: South Carolina PhD
Director, Admissions
Col Carolyn A. M. Benyshek USAF . . . . (719) 333-3070
Director, Communications **Kimberly "Kim" Tebrugge** . . . (719) 333-7714
Associate Director, Sports Information
Troy Garnhart . . . . (719) 333-9263 ext. 2313
E-mail: troy.garnhart@usafa.edu
Chief, Community Relations **Harry J. Lundy** . . . . (719) 333-7648
E-mail: harry.lundy@usafa.af.mil
Director, Education **Dr. Rolf C. Enger** . . . . (719) 333-2740
E-mail: rolf.enger@usafa.edu
Education: Minnesota PhD
Director, Faculty Development
LtCol Brent Morris USAF . . . . (719) 333-2549
Director, Graduate Scholarships Office **(Vacant)** . . . . (719) 333-4172
Director, Research and Chief Scientist
Dr. James P. "Jim" Solti . . . . (719) 333-4195
E-mail: james.solti@usafa.edu
Director, Staff **(Vacant)** . . . . (719) 333-0789
Director, Strategic Plans and Programs **(Vacant)** . . . . (719) 333-2250
Director, United States Air Force Institute for National Security Studies **James M. Smith** . . . . (719) 333-7144
E-mail: james.smith@usafa.edu
Education: Alabama PhD
Permanent Professor, Center for Character and Leadership Development
Col Mark C. Anarumo USAF . . . . (719) 333-1110
Faculty Advisor **(Vacant)** . . . . (719) 333-8253
Inspector General **Col David P. Kuenzli USAF** . . . . (719) 333-3490
E-mail: david.kuenzli@usafa.edu

Vice Chief of Staff (VCSAF)

1670 Air Force Pentagon, Washington, DC 20330-1670
Fax: (703) 614-2693

A1 Manpower, Personnel and Services

1040 Air Force Pentagon, Room 4D765, HQ USAF/A1, Washington, DC 20330-1040

Air Force Personnel Center (AFPC)

550 C Street West, Joint Base San Antonio, TX 78150-4703
Tel: (210) 565-2334 (Public Affairs) Fax: (210) 565-3658
Internet: www.afpc.af.mil

Commander **MajGen Andrew J. Toth USAF** . . . . (210) 565-4252
● Executive Director **Kimberly K. Toney** . . . . (210) 565-5000
Education: Louisiana Tech U 1985 BS; Webster 1993 MS

Air Force Personnel Center *(continued)*

Chief Master Sergeant
CMSgt Kenneth L. Lindsey USAF . . . . (210) 565-5000

A3 Operations

1630 Air Force Pentagon, Washington, DC 20330-1630
Fax: (703) 697-1345

Weather (AF/A3W)

1490 Air Force Pentagon, Washington, DC 20330-1490
Fax: (703) 614-0055 Internet: www.afweather.af.mil

557th Weather Wing (557th WW)

101 Nelson Drive, Offutt AFB, NE 68113
Tel: (402) 294-5749 Fax: (402) 232-8168 E-mail: afwapa@offutt.af.mil
Internet: http://www.557weatherwing.af.mil/

Commander **Col Brian D. Pukall USAF** . . . . (402) 294-5749
Vice Commander **Col Richard E. Wagner USAF** . . . . (402) 294-5749
Director, Public Affairs **Ryan Hansen** . . . . (402) 294-3663
E-mail: afwapa@offutt.af.mil
Commander, First Weather Group
Col Thomas Blazek USAF . . . . (402) 232-1105
E-mail: 1wxgcc@offutt.af.mil Fax: (402) 232-8597
Commander, Second Weather Group
Col Jason Patla USAF . . . . (402) 294-3159
E-mail: 2wxg.cc@offutt.af.mil

14th Weather Squadron

151 Patton Avenue, Room 120, Asheville, NC 28801-5002
Tel: (828) 271-4201 Tel: (828) 271-4291 (Customer Service)
Fax: (828) 271-4334

Commander **LtCol Earl Nast USAF** . . . . (828) 271-4201

Major U.S. Air Force Commands

1670 Air Force Pentagon, Washington, DC 20330-1670

Air Combat Command (ACC)

205 Dodd Boulevard, Suite 100,
Joint Base Langley-Eustis, VA 23665-2788
Tel: (757) 764-3204 Fax: (757) 764-3589 Internet: www.acc.af.mil

U.S. Air Force Warfare Center (USAFWC)

4370 North Washington Boulevard, Nellis AFB, NV 89191-7078
Tel: (702) 652-2201 Fax: (702) 652-5733 Internet: www.nellis.af.mil

Commander **MajGen Peter E. Gersten USAF** . . . . (702) 652-2201
Education: Air Force Acad 1989 BS; Embry-Riddle 1996 MS; National War Col 2004 MS
Mobilization Assistant **(Vacant)** . . . . (702) 652-2201
Vice Commander **BrigGen David W. Snoddy USAF** . . . . (702) 652-2201
Chief of Staff **Col Woody Pike USAF** . . . . (702) 652-4979
Chief Master Sergeant
CMSgt Charles R. Hoffman USAF . . . . (702) 652-2201

53rd Wing (53 WG)

203 West "D" Avenue, Suite 400, Eglin AFB, FL 32542
Tel: (850) 882-0053 Internet: www.eglin.af.mil/units/53rdwing

Commander **Col David Abba USAF** . . . . (850) 882-0053
Vice Commander **Col Eric Smith USAF** . . . . (850) 882-0053
Chief Master Sergeant
CMSgt Kathleen M. "Katie" McCool USAF . . . . (850) 882-0053
Staff Director **(Vacant)** . . . . (850) 882-0053

57th Wing (57 WG)

4430 Grissom Avenue, Nellis AFB, NV 89191-6521
Tel: (702) 652-5700 E-mail: 57wg.ccs@nellis.af.mil

Commander **BrigGen Robert G. Novotny USAF** . . . . (702) 652-5700
Vice Commander **Col Ronald E. Gilbert USAF** . . . . (702) 652-5700
Chief Master Sergeant
CMSgt Anthony Stewart USAF . . . . (702) 653-5700

★ Presidential Appointment Requiring Senate Confirmation ☆ Presidential Appointment ☐ Schedule C Appointment ◇ Career Senior Foreign Service Appointment
● Career Senior Executive Service (SES) Appointment ○ Non-Career Senior Executive Service (SES) Appointment ■ Postal Career Executive Service

99th Air Base Wing (99 ABW)
4430 Grissom Avenue, Nellis AFB, NV 89191-6520
Tel: (702) 652-9900 Fax: (702) 652-9832 Internet: www.nellis.af.mil
Commander **Col Cavan K. Craddock USAF** . . . . (702) 652-9900
Vice Commander **Col Michael T. Davis USAF** . . . . (703) 652-9900
Chief Master Sergeant
CMSgt Ronald D. "Dewayne" Beadles USAF . . . . (702) 652-9900

505th Command and Control Wing (505 CCW - Hurlburt Field)
Hurlburt Field, FL 32544-5271
Tel: (850) 884-1800 Internet: www.505ccw.acc.af.mil
Commander **Col Sean M. Choquette USAF** . . . . (850) 884-1800
Vice Commander **Col Joel O. Cook USAF** . . . . (850) 884-1800
Chief Master Sergeant
CMSgt Anthony B. Duplechain USAF . . . . (850) 884-1800

Nevada Test and Training Range (NTTR)
3770 Duffer Drive, Nellis AFB, NV 89191-7001
Fax: (702) 653-4864
Commander **Col Christopher J. Zuhlke USAF** . . . . (702) 653-4600
Vice Director **Yvonne M. Gresnick** . . . . (702) 653-4600

Air National Guard Units

102nd Intelligence Wing
Otis ANGB, 158 Reilly Street, Box 60, Buzzards Bay, MA 02542-1330
Fax: (508) 968-4665
Commander **Col Virginia I. Doonan ANG** . . . . (508) 968-1000
Vice Commander **(Vacant)** . . . . (508) 968-1000
Chief Master Sergeant **CMSgt Karen P. Cozza USAF** . . . . (508) 968-1000

103rd Airlift Wing (103 AW)
Bradley International Airport, 100 Nicholson Road,
East Granby, CT 06026-9309
Tel: (860) 292-2480 Fax: (860) 220-2725
Internet: http://www.103aw.ang.af.mil/
Commander **Col Stephen R. Gwinn USAF** . . . . (860) 292-2480
Public Affairs Officer **Maj Jefferson Heiland ANG** . . . . . (860) 292-2506
E-mail: usaf.ct.103-aw.mbx.aw-pa@mail.mil

104th Fighter Wing (104 FW)
Barnes ANG Municipal Airport, 175 Falcon Drive,
Westfield, MA 01085-1482
Tel: (413) 568-9151 Fax: (413) 572-1515 Internet: www.104fw.ang.af.mil
Commander **Col Peter T. Green III ANG** . . . (413) 568-9151 ext. 6981220
E-mail: peter.t.green.mil@mail.mil
Education: UMass (Amherst) BA
Vice Commander **LtCol David Halasikun ANG** . . . . (413) 568-9151
Chief Master Sergeant **CMSgt Maryanne Walts ANG** . . . (413) 568-9151
Contracting/Small Business Officer
SMSgt Kyle Kiepke ANG . . . . (413) 572-1593
E-mail: kyle.d.kiepke.mil@mail.mil Fax: (413) 572-1521
Public Affairs Officer
Capt Anthony Mutti ANG . . . . (413) 568-9151 ext. 6981263
E-mail: usaf.mi.110-atkw.mbx.pa-visual-information@mail.mil

110th Airlift Wing (110 AW)
W.K. Kellogg Airport, 3545 Mustang Avenue,
Battle Creek, MI 47037-5509
Tel: (269) 969-3400 Fax: (269) 969-3421 Internet: www.110aw.ang.af.mil
Commander **Col Brian Teff USAF** . . . . (269) 969-3299
Vice Commander **Col Keir Knapp ANG** . . . . (269) 969-3299
Command Chief Master Sergeant
CMSgt Trever J. Slater ANG . . . . (269) 969-3299

111th Attack Wing (111 ATKW)
Willow Grove Naval Air Station Joint Reserve Base,
1151 Fairchild Street, Willow Grove, PA 19090-5300
Internet: www.111fw.ang.af.mil
Commander **Col William "Bill" Griffin ANG** . . . . (215) 323-7412
Vice Commander **LtCol Daryl Newhart USAF** . . . . (215) 323-7412
Command Chief **CMSgt Paul G. Frisco, Jr. ANG** . . . . (215) 323-7412

113th Wing (113 WG - Joint Base Andrews)
3252 East Perimeter Road,
Joint Base Andrews-Naval Air Facility Washington, MD 20762
Tel: (240) 857-2810 Fax: (240) 857-2813
Internet: http://www.113wg.ang.af.mil/
Commander **Col Keith G. MacDonald USAF** . . . . (240) 857-2811
Vice Commander **Col Christopher Sheperd USAF** . . . . . . (240) 857-2812
Chief Master Sergeant
CMSgt Kimberly S. Turner USAF . . . . (240) 857-2811

DEPARTMENTS

114th Fighter Wing (114 FW)
Joe Foss Field Municipal Airport, 1201 West Algonquin Street,
Sioux Falls, SD 57104-0264
Tel: (605) 988-5700 Fax: (605) 988-5764 Internet: www.114fw.ang.af.mil
Commander **Col Nathan B. Alholinna ANG** . . . . (605) 988-5701
Vice Commander **Col Quenten M. Esser ANG** . . . . (605) 988-5703
Command Chief **CMSgt Zona Hornstra ANG** . . . . (605) 988-5700
Public Affairs Officer **Capt Jessica Bark USAF** . . . . (605) 988-5644
Contracting/Small Business Officer
SMSgt Kurtis C. Lunstra USAF . . . . (605) 988-5933
E-mail: kurtis.c.lunstra.mil@mail.mil

115th Fighter Wing (115 FW - Truax Field ANGB)
Truax Field, 3110 Mitchell Street, Madison, WI 53704-2591
Tel: (608) 245-4300 Fax: (608) 245-4489
Commander **Col Erik A. Peterson ANG** . . . . (608) 245-4503
Vice Commander **Col Kevin Philpot ANG** . . . . (608) 245-4503
Executive Officer
Maj Jacqueline "Jackie" Wheeler USAF . . . . (608) 245-4339
Contracting/Small Business Officer **(Vacant)** . . . . (608) 245-4548

116th Air Control Wing (116 ACW)
555 Borghese Drive, Robins AFB, GA 31098
Internet: www.116acw.acc.af.mil
Commander **Col Ato Crumbly ANG** . . . . (478) 201-2656
Vice Commander **Col John M. Verhage ANG** . . . . (478) 201-2658
Command Chief Master Sergeant **(Vacant)** . . . . (478) 201-2656

119th Wing (119 WG - Fargo ANGB)
1400 28th Avenue North, Fargo, ND 58102-1051
Tel: (701) 451-2264 (Public Affairs) Fax: (701) 451-2109
Internet: www.119wg.ang.af.mil
Commander **Col Darrin Anderson ANG** . . . . (701) 451-2102
Vice Commander **Col Mitchell R. Johnson USAF** . . . . . . (701) 451-2264
Public Affairs/Freedom of Information Act Officer
2nd Lt Jeremiah Colbert ANG . . . . (701) 451-2264
E-mail: usaf.nd.119-wg.list.pa@mail.mil
Information Systems Manager **(Vacant)** . . . . (701) 451-2584
Contracting Officer **MSgt Lee F. Gunderson USAF** . . . . . (701) 451-2331
E-mail: lee.f.gunderson.mil@mail.mil Fax: (701) 451-2371

120th Airlift Wing (120 AW)
120 FW/MT ANG, 2800 Airport Avenue B, Great Falls, MT 59404-5570
Tel: (406) 791-0285 Fax: (406) 791-0488
Internet: http://www.120thairliftwing.ang.af.mil/
Commander **Col Buel J. Dickson ANG** . . . . (406) 791-0280
Training Manager **SMSgt Tiffany Franklin USAF** . . . . (406) 791-0283

122nd Fighter Wing (122 FW)
3005 Ferguson Road, Fort Wayne International Airport,
Fort Wayne, IN 46809-0122
Tel: (260) 478-3201 Fax: (260) 478-3300 Internet: www.122fw.ang.af.mil
Commander **Col Michael D. Stohler ANG** . . . . (260) 478-3201
Vice Commander **Col Kyle J. Noel USAF** . . . . (260) 478-3279
Chief Master Sergeant **CMSgt Michael C. May ANG** . . . . (260) 478-3265

124th Fighter Wing (124 FW)
Building 411, 4474 S. DeHaviland Street, Boise, ID 83705-8103
Tel: (208) 272-5322 Fax: (208) 422-6161
Internet: http://www.124thfighterwing.ang.af.mil/
Commander **Col Timothy J. "Tim" Donnellan ANG** . . . . (208) 422-5322
Vice Commander
Col Jeffery D. "Jeff" Aebischer ANG . . . . (208) 422-5322

(continued on next page)

★ Presidential Appointment Requiring Senate Confirmation ☆ Presidential Appointment ☐ Schedule C Appointment ◇ Career Senior Foreign Service Appointment
● Career Senior Executive Service (SES) Appointment ○ Non-Career Senior Executive Service (SES) Appointment ■ Postal Career Executive Service

124th Fighter Wing *(continued)*

Chief Master Sergeant
CMSgt Tammy S. Ladley ANG .... (208) 422-5322
E-mail: tammy.s.ladley.mil@mail.mil
Maintenance Group Commander
Col Scott J. Salois ANG .... (208) 272-5322
Operations Group Commander
Col Shannon D. Smith ANG .... (208) 422-5300
Fax: (208) 422-4122
Support Group Commander
LtCol Stephanie L. Sheppard ANG .... (208) 272-5322
Public Affairs Officer
1st Lt Cassidy "Cassie" Morlock ANG .... (208) 422-5398
E-mail: cassidy.e.morlock.mil@mail.mil

125th Fighter Wing (Jacksonville ANGB)
14300 FANG Drive, Jacksonville, FL 32218-7933
Tel: (904) 741-7030 Fax: (904) 741-7099

Commander **Col Brian T. "Banzai" Bell ANG** .... (904) 741-7030
Education: Air Force Acad 1996 BS; U Phoenix 2013 MBA
Public Affairs Superintendent
MSgt Jaclyn "Jackie" Lyons ANG .... (904) 434-0506

127th Wing (127 WG - Selfridge ANGB)
Building 303, 29553 George Avenue, Selfridge ANGB, MI 48045-5248
Tel: (586) 239-4011 Tel: (586) 239-4588 (Freedom of Information Act)
Fax: (586) 239-4430 E-mail: prevailingwind@miself.ang.af.mil
Internet: www.127wg.ang.af.mil/

Commander **BrigGen John D. Slocum ANG** .... (586) 239-4888
Public Affairs Officer **Phillip "Phil" Ulmer** .... (586) 239-4888
Freedom of Information Act Officer **(Vacant)** .... (586) 239-4588
Contracting/Small Business Officer **Darryl Mitchell** ...... (586) 239-4733

131st Bomb Wing (131 BW)
10800 Lambert International Boulevard, Bridgeton, MO 63044-2371
Tel: (314) 527-8033 Fax: (314) 527-6344
Internet: www.131bw.ang.af.mil

Commander **Col Kenneth S. Eaves ANG** .... (314) 527-8033
Education: LeTourneau 1987 BS
Vice Commander **Col Matthew D. Calhoun ANG** ...... (314) 527-8033
Chief Master Sergeant **CMSgt Jessica L. Settle ANG** ... (314) 527-8033

132nd Fighter Wing (132 FW)
3100 McKinley Avenue, Des Moines, IA 50321-2799
Tel: (515) 256-8210 Fax: (515) 256-8283
Internet: http://www.132dwing.ang.af.mil/

Commander **Col Mark A. Chidley ANG** .... (515) 256-8210
Education: Iowa State 1989 BA
Executive Assistant **Nancy Jausel** .... (515) 256-8210
Vice Commander **Col Travis J. Crawmer ANG** .... (515) 256-8210
Education: Northern Iowa 1993 BA
Contracting/Small Business Officer
MSgt Patrick Olson USAF .... (515) 261-8523
E-mail: patrick.j.olson.mil@mail.mil
Freedom of Information Act Officer
MSgt Rebecca Starmer ANG .... (515) 256-8745
Public Affairs Officer **Capt Kenny Hartman ANG** ...... (515) 256-5603
Security Sergeant **CMSgt Smith USAF** .... (515) 256-8225
Webmaster/Planning and Implementation Branch Chief
Michelle R. Yost .... (515) 256-8584
Fax: (515) 256-8297

138th Fighter Wing (138 FW)
9121 East Mustang Street, Tulsa, OK 74115-5801
Tel: (918) 833-7208 Fax: (918) 833-7363
Internet: http://www.138fw.ang.af.mil/

Commander **Col Raymond H. Siegfried III ANG** .... (918) 833-7208
Education: Notre Dame 1992 BBA
Vice Commander **Col Brent Wright USAF** .... (918) 833-7208
Education: Oklahoma State 1989 BSBA
Chief Master Sergeant
CMSgt Phillip R. Kaase, Jr. USAF .... (918) 833-7208
Public Affairs Officer **1st Lt Jennifer Proctor ANG** ..... (918) 833-7389

140th Wing (140 WG)
Colorado Military and Veterans Affairs Department,
6848 South Revere Parkway, Centennial, CO 80112
Tel: (720) 250-1515 Fax: (720) 250-1509
Internet: www.140wg.ang.af.mil

Commander **Col Brian D. "Ike" Turner ANG** .... (720) 847-9555
140 South Aspen Street, Fax: (720) 847-9173
Mail Stop 37, Aurora, CO 80011
Education: Air Force Acad 1993 BS
Vice Commander **Col Timothy Conklin ANG** .... (720) 847-9557
140 South Aspen Street, Fax: (720) 847-9173
Mail Stop 37, Aurora, CO 80011
Education: Air Force Acad 1988 BS
Command Chief
CMSgt Mikael "Mack" Sundin USAF .... (720) 847-9574
Public Affairs Officer **Maj Kinder Blacke ANG** .... (720) 847-9558
18860 East Breckenridge Avenue, Fax: (720) 847-9959
Mail Stop 65, Aurora, CO 80011
E-mail: kinder.l.blacke.mil@mail.mil

142nd Fighter Wing (142 FW)
Portland International Airport, 6801 Northeast Cornfoot Road,
Portland, OR 97218-2797
Tel: (503) 335-4000 Internet: www.142fw.ang.af.mil

Commander **Col Duke A. Pirak USAF** .... (503) 335-4142
Vice Commander **Col Adam R. Sitler ANG** .... (503) 335-4035
Command Chief **CMSgt Nikese R. Swift USAF** .... (503) 335-4055
Education: Comm Col Air Force 2002 AAS; Park U 2005 BS, 2005 BS

144th Fighter Wing (144 FW)
5323 East McKinley Avenue, Fresno, CA 93727
Fax: (559) 453-5472 Internet: www.144fw.ang.af.mil

Commander **Col Daniel Kelly ANG** .... (559) 454-5154
Vice Commander **LtCol Jeremiah Cruise USAF** .... (559) 454-5154
Command Chief **CMSgt Jason Rogers USAF** .... (559) 454-5154
Maintenance Group Commander (Acting)
LtCol John Lundholm ANG .... (559) 454-5154
Medical Group Commander
LtCol John Blackburn ANG .... (559) 454-5154
Mission Support Group Commander
Col Dave Johnson ANG .... (559) 454-5154
Operations Group Commander
LtCol Victor S. Sikora ANG .... (559) 454-5154
Public Affairs Officer **Maj Jennifer M. Piggott ANG** .... (559) 454-5246
E-mail: jennifer.piggott.3@us.af.mil

147th Reconnaissance Wing (147 RW)
14657 Sneider Street, Houston, TX 77034-5586
Tel: (281) 929-2222 Fax: (281) 929-2300

Commander **Col Gary Jones ANG** .... (281) 929-2222
Executive Officer **LtCol Shaunte Cooper ANG** .... (281) 929-2327
Fax: (281) 929-2300
Executive Assistant **MSgt Promise Harris ANG** .... (281) 929-2222
Vice Commander **Col Matthew Barker ANG** .... (281) 929-2222
Contracting/Small Business Officer
SMSgt Denise Bailey USAF .... (281) 929-2743
Security Officer **Maj Kelly Bean ANG** .... (281) 929-2820
Education and Training Manager
SMSgt Shannon Lee USAF .... (281) 929-2675
Fax: (281) 929-2415

148th Fighter Wing (148 FW)
4680 Viper Street, Duluth, MN 55811-6031
Tel: (218) 788-7200 Fax: (218) 788-7504 Internet: www.148fw.ang.af.mil

Commander **Col Christopher Blomquist ANG** .... (218) 788-7200
Vice Commander **Col Troy Havener ANG** .... (218) 788-7200
Chief Master Sergeant **CMSgt Lisa K. Erikson ANG** .... (218) 788-7200

150th Special Operations Wing (150 SOW - Kirtland AFB)
Kirtland AFB, NM 87116
Tel: (505) 846-5957 Internet: http://www.150fw.ang.af.mil/

Commander **Col John P. Castillo ANG** .... (505) 846-5957

★ Presidential Appointment Requiring Senate Confirmation ☆ Presidential Appointment □ Schedule C Appointment ◇ Career Senior Foreign Service Appointment
● Career Senior Executive Service (SES) Appointment ○ Non-Career Senior Executive Service (SES) Appointment ■ Postal Career Executive Service

158th Fighter Wing (158 FW)
105 NCO Drive, South Burlington, VT 05403-5873
Tel: (802) 660-5215 Fax: (802) 660-5981 Internet: www.158fw.ang.af.mil

Commander **Col David A. Smith ANG** . . . . (802) 660-5215
Education: Vermont 1987 BS; Army War Col 2010 MSS
Vice Commander
Col Henry "Hank" Harder ANG . . . . . . (802) 660-5215 ext. 3140
Public Affairs Officer **2nd Lt Chelsea Clark ANG** . . . . (802) 660-5379
Green Mountain Armory, Camp Johnson,
789 Vermont National Guard Road, Colchester, VT 05446-3099
Chief Master Sergeant
CMSgt Brian J. Marchessault ANG . . . . (802) 660-5215
Education: Champlain 2016 BS

169th Fighter Wing (169 FW)
1325 South Carolina Road, Eastover, SC 29044-5001
Tel: (800) 432-2754 Fax: (803) 647-8225 Internet: www.169fw.ang.af.mil

Commander **Col Nicholas A. Gentile, Jr. ANG, ANG** . . . (803) 647-8200
Executive Officer **Maj David Bell ANG** . . . . (803) 647-8403
Vice Commander **Col Akshai Gandhi USAF** . . . . . . (803) 647-8200
Chief of Staff **Col Michael "Mike" Hudson ANG** . . . . (803) 647-8224
Command Chief Master Sergeant
CMSgt Stephen P. Shepherd ANG . . . . (803) 647-8200
Contracting Officer **MSgt John W. Wilkes ANG** . . . . (803) 647-8255
E-mail: john.w.wilkes.mil@mail.mil Fax: (803) 647-8487

174th Attack Wing (174 AW - Hancock Field ANGB)
6001 East Molloy Road, Syracuse, NY 13211-7099
Tel: (315) 233-2100 Tel: (315) 233-2651 (Public Affairs)
Fax: (315) 233-2145 Internet: http://www.174attackwing.ang.af.mil/

Commander **Col Michael Smith ANG** . . . . (315) 233-2599

175th Wing (175 WG)
Warfield ANG Base, 2701 Eastern Boulevard, Baltimore, MD 21220-2899
Tel: (410) 918-6464 Fax: (410) 918-6557 E-mail: pa.175wg@ang.af.mil

Commander **BrigGen Paul D. Johnson ANG** . . . . . . (410) 918-6301
Education: Maryland 1988 BS; Embry-Riddle 1995
Vice Commander **Col Jori Robinson ANG** . . . . (410) 918-6420
Education: Missouri 1999 BA; Oklahoma 2003 MA;
George Washington 2007 MA
Chief Master Sergeant
CMSgt Stanley F. Dulski USAF . . . . (410) 918-6464

177th Fighter Wing (177 FW - Atlantic City ANGB)
400 Langley Road, Egg Harbor Township, NJ 08234-9500
Tel: (609) 761-6000 Internet: www.177fw.ang.af.mil

Commander **Col Bradford R. Everman USAF** . . . . . . (609) 761-6000
Vice Commander **Col John M. Cosgrove USAF** . . . . . (609) 761-6000
Command Chief **CMSgt James F. McCloskey ANG** . . . . (609) 761-6000
Public Affairs Officer **2nd Lt Amanda Batiz USAF** . . . . (609) 761-6000
Base Contracting Officer
MSgt JoAnn Ferguson ANG . . . . (609) 645-6096
Fax: (609) 383-6377

180th Fighter Wing (180 FW - Toledo ANGB)
2660 South Eber Road, Swanton, OH 43558-9645
Tel: (419) 868-4078 Fax: (419) 868-4201 Internet: www.180fw.ang.af.mil

Commander **Col Kevin V. Doyle USAF** . . . . (419) 868-4030
Vice Commander **Col Scott Reed ANG** . . . . (419) 868-4030
Command Chief **MSgt John Deraedt ANG** . . . . (419) 868-4030
Knowledge Operations Officer
MSgt Jason P. Mims ANG . . . . (419) 868-4219
E-mail: foia@ng.army.mil
Contracting/Small Business Officer
MSgt Matt Michael ANG . . . . (419) 868-4142

181st Intelligence Wing (181 IW)
Indiana Air National Guard, Terre Haute International Airport,
Terre Haute, IN 47803-5000
Tel: (812) 877-5210 Internet: www.181iw.ang.af.mil

Commander **Col Christopher R. Alderdice USAF** . . . . (812) 877-5218
Vice Commander **Col Matthew C. Brown USAF** . . . . (812) 877-5225
Chief Master Sergeant
CMSgt Chris G. Durcholz ANG . . . . (812) 877-5218

183rd Fighter Wing (183 FW)
Abraham Lincoln Capital Airport, 3101 J. David Jones Parkway,
Springfield, IL 62707-5001
Internet: www.ilspri.ang.af.mil

Commander **Col John E. Patterson ANG** . . . . (217) 757-1219
Vice Commander **COL Jeffry A. Rice ANG** . . . . . . (217) 757-1219
Command Chief **CMSgt Wayne A. Vorreyer ANG** . . . . (217) 757-1219
E-mail: wayne.a.vorreyer.mil@mail.mil

188th Wing (188 WG)
188th Fighter Wing, 4850 Leigh Avenue, Fort Smith, AR 72903-6096
Tel: (479) 573-5100 Internet: www.188wg.ang.af.mil

Commander **Col Robert Inscoe Kinney ANG** . . . . . (479) 573-5300
Vice Commander **Col Leon Dodroe ANG** . . . . (479) 573-5300
Chief Master Sergeant
CMSgt Stephen R. Bradley ANG . . . . (479) 573-5300
Public Affairs Officer **2nd Lt Dylan Hollums ANG** . . . . (479) 573-5170
Fax: (479) 573-5837

192nd Fighter Wing (192 FW)
50 Falcon Road, Sandston, VA 23150-2524
Tel: (757) 764-1110 Fax: (757) 764-4932 Internet: www.192fw.ang.af.mil

Commander **Col Frank J. Lobash ANG** . . . . (757) 225-0192
Vice Commander **Col Jeffrey L. Ryan ANG** . . . . . . (757) 225-0192
Chief Master Sergeant
CMSgt Christopher L. "Chris" Amburn ANG . . . . (757) 225-0192

1st Air Force/Air Forces Northern (CONR-1AF/AFNORTH)
501 Illinois Avenue, Suite 11, Tyndall AFB, FL 32403-5549
Tel: (850) 283-8080 (Public Affairs) Fax: (850) 283-3376
E-mail: afnorthpa@tyndall.af.mil (Public Affairs)
Internet: www.1af.acc.af.mil

Note: The 1st Air Force is operated under a shared command with Air Forces Northern.

Commander
LtGen Robert Scott "R." Williams USAF . . . . . . (850) 283-8657
Education: Georgia Tech 1984 BS
Executive Officer **LtCol Sheldon Gardner USAF** . . . . (850) 283-2625
Air National Guard Assistant
MajGen Peter J. Byrne USAF . . . . (850) 283-8657
Air Force Reserve Command Mobilization Assistant
MajGen Donald R. Lindberg USAFR . . . . (850) 283-8657
Deputy Commander
BrigGen Sylvain Y. Menard USAF . . . . (850) 283-4272
Vice Commander
BrigGen Kenneth P. "Ken" Ekman USAF . . . . . . (850) 283-4272
Education: Air Force Acad 1991 BS; Cal State (Fresno) 1994 MS
Chief of Staff **Col Christopher A. Jarratt USAF** . . . . (850) 283-8657
Chief Master Sergeant **CMSgt Richard D. King USAF** . . . (850) 283-8657
Public Affairs Officer **Mary McHale** . . . . (850) 283-8080

9th Air Force (9AF)
504 Shaw Drive, Shaw AFB, SC 29152-5029
Tel: (803) 895-2875 (Public Affairs) Internet: http://www.9af.acc.af.mil/

Commander **MajGen Scott J. Zobrist USAF** . . . . . . (803) 895-5800
Education: USC 1986 BS
Vice Commander **Col Craig M. Hollis USAF** . . . . . . (803) 895-5801
Executive Officer **Paula Pawlowski** . . . . (803) 895-5803
Air National Guard Assistant
MajGen Steven E. Foster ANG . . . . (803) 895-3035
Command Chief Master Sergeant
CMSgt David W. Wade USAF . . . . (803) 895-3287

18th Air Support Operations Group (18 ASOG)
1414 Reilly Street, Pope AFB, NC 28308-2387

Commander **Col Dane Crawford USAF** . . . . (910) 394-4864

1st Fighter Wing (1 FW)
159 Sweeney Boulevard, Suite 200,
Joint Base Langley-Eustis, VA 23665-2292
Tel: (757) 764-5321 Fax: (757) 764-2492

Commander **Col Jason T. Hinds USAF** . . . . (757) 764-5321
Vice Commander **Col Steven Fino USAF** . . . . (757) 764-5321

(continued on next page)

1st Fighter Wing *(continued)*

Chief Master Sergeant
CMSgt Derek T. Crowder USAF .... (757) 764-2726
Maintenance Group Commander
Col David Seitz USAF .... (757) 764-4068
Operations Group Commander
Col David R. Lopez USAF .... (757) 764-5275

4th Fighter Wing (Seymour Johnson AFB)
1510 Wright Brothers Avenue, Suite 200,
Seymour Johnson AFB, NC 27531-2468
Tel: (919) 722-0027 Fax: (919) 722-0007
Internet: www.seymourjohnson.af.mil

Commander **Col Donn C. Yates USAF** .... (919) 722-0029
Vice Commander **Col R. Ryan Messer USAF** .... (919) 722-0027
Command Chief Master Sergeant
CMSgt Stephen Cornelius USAF .... (919) 722-0018
Maintenance Group Commander
Col Leah R. Fry USAF .... (919) 722-2057
Mission Support Group Commander
Col Jason L. Knight USAF .... (919) 722-0101
Operations Group Commander
Col A. Joel Meyers USAF .... (919) 722-2601

20th Fighter Wing (20 FW)
517 Lance Avenue, Shaw AFB, SC 29152-5041
Tel: (803) 895-2019 Fax: (803) 895-2028 Internet: www.shaw.af.mil

Commander **Col Derek J. O'Malley USAF** .... (803) 895-2011
E-mail: derek.j.omalley.mil@mail.mil
Vice Commander **Col Ryan J. Inman USAF** .... (803) 895-2011
Chief Master Sergeant
CMSgt Daniel L. Hoglund USAF .... (803) 895-2035
Maintenance Group Commander **Randall E. May** .... (803) 895-2734
E-mail: randall.may@shaw.af.mil
Mission Support Group Commander
LtCol John J. Thomas USAF .... (803) 895-1634
Operations Group Commander **(Vacant)** .... (803) 895-1884
Public Affairs Chief **Capt Keavy Rake USAF** .... (803) 895-2019
Contracting Officer **Maj John W. Kendall USAF** .... (803) 895-5623
E-mail: 20cons.cc@shaw.af.mil
Freedom of Information Act Officer
Jeffery "Jeff" Gordy .... (803) 895-1630
Historian **Dr. Karen Miller** .... (803) 895-1952

23rd Wing (23 WG)
Moody AFB, GA 31699
Tel: (229) 257-4210 Fax: (229) 257-4804
E-mail: 23wg.pa2@moody.af.mil Internet: www.moody.af.mil

Commander **Col Jennifer M. Short USAF** .... (229) 257-3395
Vice Commander **Col Justin D. DeMarco USAF** .... (229) 257-3395
Director of Staff **LtCol Jeffrey Barker USAF** .... (229) 257-3408
Chief Master Sergeant **CMSgt James R. Allen USAF** .... (229) 257-3395
Fighter Group Commander **(Vacant)** .... (229) 257-4210
Maintenance Group Commander
Col John W. Chastain III USAF .... (229) 257-3395
347th Rescue Group Commander
Col Jason N. Gingrich USAF .... (229) 257-3395
Education: Penn State 1997 BSCE
Mission Support Group Commander
Col Susan Riordan-Smith USAF .... (229) 257-3395
E-mail: norman.dozier@moody.af.mil
Education: Villanova 1994 BS

325th Fighter Wing (325 FW)
Tyndall AFB, FL 32403-5000
Tel: (850) 283-4500 (Public Affairs Office phone) Tel: (850) 283-1110
Fax: (850) 283-3225 E-mail: pacontacts@tyndall.af.mil
Internet: www.tyndall.af.mil

Commander **Col Brian S. Laidlaw USAF** .... (850) 283-1113
Vice Commander **Col Jefferson G. Hawkins USAFR** .... (850) 283-1113
Chief Master Sergeant
CMSgt Craig V. Williams USAF .... (850) 283-1113

633rd Air Base Wing (633 ABW)
Joint Base Langley-Eustis, VA 23665

Commander **Col Sean K. Tyler USAF** .... (757) 764-2108
Vice Commander **Col Edward M. Vedder USAF** .... (757) 764-2108
Command Chief **CMSgt Shane Wagner USAF** .... (757) 764-2108

12th Air Force (12AF)
Building 12, 5275 East Granite Street,
Suite 228, Davis Monthan AFB, AZ 85707-4930
Tel: (520) 228-6053 (Public Affairs) E-mail: 12af.pa2@dm.af.mil
Internet: www.12af.acc.af.mil

Commander **MajGen Andrew A. Croft USAF** .... (520) 228-2312
Education: UCLA 1988 BA; Embry-Riddle 1994 MBA
Executive Officer **LtCol Brian Buscher USAF** .... (520) 228-2312
Mobilization Assistant **Col Bryan P. Radliff USAF** .... (520) 228-6053
Education: Southern Illinois 1989 BS
Vice Commander **BrigGen Craig R. Baker USAF** .... (520) 228-3653
Chief Master Sergeant **(Vacant)** .... (520) 228-1110

49th Wing (Holloman AFB)
Holloman AFB, NM 88330-5000
Tel: (575) 572-5406 Fax: (575) 572-5908 Internet: www.holloman.af.mil

Commander **Col Houston R. Cantwell USAF** .... (575) 572-5571
Vice Commander **Col Brian P. Patterson ANG** .... (575) 572-5571
Chief Master Sergeant
CMSgt Barrington E. Bartlett USAF .... (575) 572-5576
Maintenance Group Commander
Col Tim W. Harbor USAF .... (575) 572-7183
Operations Group Commander
Col Jeffery S. Patton USAF .... (575) 572-7092
49th Mission Support Group Commander
Col Anthony J. Ajello USAF .... (575) 572-5541
635th Materiel Maintenance Group Commander
Col Joseph Moehlmann USAF .... (575) 572-5802
Public Affairs Director
Capt Phillip B. Davis, Jr. USAF .... (575) 572-7381

355th Fighter Wing (355 FW)
3405 South Fifth Street, Davis Monthan AFB, AZ 85707
Tel: (520) 228-3406 (Public Affairs) Fax: (520) 228-3328
Internet: www.dm.af.mil

Commander **Col Michael R. Drowley USAF** .... (520) 228-3206
Vice Commander **Col Chad A. Balettie USAF** .... (520) 228-3206
Chief Master Sergeant
CMSgt Shanece Johnson USAF .... (520) 228-3559

366th Fighter Wing (366 FW)
366 Gunfighter Avenue, Suite 331, Mountain Home AFB, ID 83648-5299
Tel: (208) 828-6800 Fax: (208) 828-4205
E-mail: 366wgpa@mountainhome.af.mil
Internet: www.mountainhome.af.mil

Commander **Col Joseph Kunkel USAF** .... (208) 828-2366
Deputy Commander for Operations
Col Kurt C. Helphinstine USAF .... (208) 828-2366
Deputy Commander for Support
Col Matthew J. Sandelier USAF .... (208) 828-2366
Chief of Staff **Col Thomas S. Palmer USAF** .... (208) 828-6800
Command Chief Master Sergeant
CMSgt Wendell J. Snider USAF .... (208) 828-2366
Public Affairs Officer **Tracey Giles** .... (208) 828-6800
Maintenance Group Commander
Col Scott A. Grover USAF .... (208) 828-6800
Mission Support Group Commander
Col John C. Blackwell USAF .... (208) 828-6800

388th Fighter Wing (388 FW)
Hill AFB, UT 84056
Tel: (801) 777-3200 Fax: (801) 777-2923 Internet: www.388fw.acc.af.mil

Commander **Col Lee E. Kloos USAF** .... (801) 777-3200
Vice Commander **Col Michael T. Ebner USAF** .... (801) 777-3200
Chief Master Sergeant **CMSgt Dan Taylor USAF** .... (801) 777-3200

24th Air Force - Air Forces Cyber (24AF)
Lackland AFB, 3515 S. General McMullen Drive,
Joint Base San Antonio, TX 78226
Tel: (210) 395-0296 (Public Affairs) Internet: www.24af.af.mil

Commander **MajGen Robert J. Skinner USAF** . . . . (210) 395-0296
Education: Park U 1989 BS; Oklahoma City 1993 MS
Mobilization Assistant to the Commander
BrigGen Jay S. "Scott" Goldstein USAFR . . . . (210) 395-0296
E-mail: jay.goldstein@us.af.mil
Education: George Mason 1989 BS, 1992 MS; USC 1997 PhD
Air National Guard Assistant to the Commander
BrigGen Timothy T. Lunderman ANG . . . . (210) 395-0296
Vice Commander
BrigGen Michelle L. Hayworth USAF . . . . (210) 395-0296
Chief Master Sergeant **(Vacant)** . . . . (210) 395-0296
Executive Director
Col Robert H. "Chipper" Cole USAF (Ret) . . . . (301) 677-1465
9800 Savage Road, Fort George G. Meade, MD 20755
Education: Texas Christian 1987 BS, 1996 MS;
Army War Col 2006 MS
Public Affairs **Jessica Turner** . . . . (210) 395-0296
E-mail: 24af.pa@us.af.mil

5th Combat Communications Group
575 10th Street, Robins AFB, GA 31098-1662

Commander
Col Jeremiah S. "Jeremy" Boenisch USAF . . . . (478) 926-3223
Education: Oregon State 1995 BS
Deputy Commander **LtCol Randolph B. Witt USAF** . . . . . (478) 926-3223
Superintendent **CMSgt Cora U. Cruz USAF** . . . . (478) 926-3223
Education: Bellevue U 2013 BS

67th Cyberspace Wing (67 CW)
467 Moore Street, Lackland AFB, TX 78243
Tel: (210) 977-6700

Commander **Col Melissa S. Cunningham USAF** . . . . (210) 977-6700
Vice Commander **Col Greg D. Whitaker USAF** . . . . (210) 997-6700
Chief Master Sergeant
CMSgt David L. Anthony USAF . . . . (210) 977-6700
Civilian Director **Theresa A. Haak** . . . . (210) 997-6700

624th Operations Center
Lackland AFB, Joint Base San Antonio, TX 78150
Tel: (210) 395-9600

Commander **Col George B. Kinney III USAF** . . . . (210) 395-0027
Superintendent **CMSgt Joshua D. Kahney USAF** . . . . (210) 395-0027

688th Cyberspace Wing (688 CW - Lackland AFB)
Lackland AFB, 102 Hall Boulevard, San Antonio, TX 78243-7009
Tel: (210) 977-2091 Tel: (210) 977-4425 (Commander's Action Group)
Fax: (210) 977-5474

Commander **Col Eric P. DeLange USAF** . . . . (210) 977-2091
Education: Air Force Acad 1993 BS; Arizona State 1994 MS;
National War Col 2013 MS
Vice Commander **(Vacant)** . . . . (210) 977-2091
Chief Master Sergeant **CMSgt Emilio J. Avila USAF** . . . . (210) 977-2623
Technical Director **J. Michael Kretzer** . . . . (210) 977-2094

25th Air Force
Lackland AFB, 102 Hall Boulevard, Suite 106,
San Antonio, TX 78243-7009
Tel: (210) 977-2166 Fax: (210) 977-3541
Internet: http://www.25af.af.mil/

Commander **MajGen Mary F. O'Brien USAF** . . . . (210) 977-2001
Mobilization Assistant to the Commander
Col Lynette J. Hebert USAF . . . . (210) 977-2001
Air National Guard Advisor to the Commander
BrigGen Larry Kip Clark ANG . . . . (210) 977-2001
Vice Commander
Col George Marty "Moose" Reynolds USAF . . . . (210) 977-2002
Director of Staff **William B. Apodaca** . . . . (210) 977-2005
Command Chief **CMSgt Stanley C.P. Cadell USAF** . . . . . (210) 977-2064
● Executive Director **Dominic F. Pohl** . . . . (210) 977-2005
Education: Columbia 1982 BA; Military Intelligence Col 1995 MS

Air Force Technical Applications Center (AFTAC)
1030 South Highway A1A, Patrick AFB, FL 32925-3002
Tel: (321) 494-7688 Fax: (321) 494-2637

Commander **Col Steven M. "Steve" Gorski USAF** . . . . . (321) 494-2334

Joint Information Operations Warfare Center (JIOWC)
102 Hall Boulevard, Suite 201, San Antonio, TX 78243-7009
Tel: (210) 977-2071 Fax: (210) 977-3539

● Director **Gregory C. Radabaugh** . . . . (210) 977-2071

National Air and Space Intelligence Center
4180 Watson Way, Wright-Patterson AFB, OH 45433-5648
Tel: (937) 656-7402 Internet: http://www.nasic.af.mil/

Commander **Col Parker H. Wright USAF** . . . . (937) 522-6600
Vice Commander **Col Jed S. Cohen USAF** . . . . (937) 522-6600
● Chief Scientist **Curtis A. Rowland** . . . . (937) 522-6600
Command Chief **CMSgt Christopher Easter USAF** . . . . . (937) 522-6600

9th Reconnaissance Wing (9 RW)
Beale AFB, CA 95903
Tel: (530) 634-3000 Internet: http://www.beale.af.mil/

Commander **Col Andrew M. Clark USAF** . . . . (530) 634-2692
Vice Commander **Col Spencer S. Thomas USAF** . . . . (530) 634-2692
Command Chief **CMSgt Jessica Bender USAF** . . . . (530) 634-3000
Maintenance Group Commander **(Vacant)** . . . . (530) 634-9353
Maintenance Group Deputy Commander
LtCol Grant Meadows USAF . . . . (530) 634-9352
Mission Support Group Commander
Col Stephen Huffman USAF . . . . (530) 634-3000
Operations Group Commander
Col Andrew Warner USAF . . . . (530) 634-3000

55th Wing (55 WG)
55th Wing Command Section, 205 Looking Glass Avenue,
Suite 121, Offutt AFB, NE 68113-3130
Tel: (402) 294-4109 Fax: (402) 294-7172 E-mail: 55wg.pa@offutt.af.mil
Internet: www.offutt.af.mil

Commander **Col Michael H. Manion USAF** . . . . (402) 294-5555
Education: Missouri 1995 BS
Vice Commander **Col David "Dave" Berg USAF** . . . . (402) 294-5555
Chief Master Sergeant
CMSgt Brian Kruzelmick USAF . . . . (402) 294-6818
Communications Group Commander
Col Corey M. Ramsby USAF . . . . (402) 294-4108
Education: Purdue 1994 BSEE; Air Command Col 2008 MMAS;
Air War Col 2015 MSS
Contracting Squadron Commander
LtCol Hayes Weidman USAF . . . . (402) 232-6358
101 Washington Square, Suite 2N3, Offutt AFB, NE 68113-2107
Small Business Specialist **Mike Hall** . . . . (402) 294-5426
E-mail: mike.hall@offutt.af.mil Fax: (402) 294-6375
Freedom of Information Act Officer
Vickie Moldenhauer . . . . (402) 294-9994

319th Air Base Wing (319 ABW)
Grand Forks AFB, ND 58205-5000
Tel: (701) 747-3000 Fax: (701) 747-5022
Internet: www.grandforks.af.mil

Commander **Col Benjamin W. Spencer USAF** . . . . (701) 747-4150
Vice Commander **Col Jeremy L. Thiel USAF** . . . . (701) 747-4150
Chief Master Sergeant **CMSgt Brian C. Thomas ANG** . . . (701) 747-4511

Air Education and Training Command (AETC)
100 H Street, Suite 4, Joint Base San Antonio, TX 78150-4331
Tel: (210) 652-6307 Internet: www.aetc.af.mil

Air Force Recruiting Service (AFRS)
550 D Street West, Suite 1, Joint Base San Antonio, TX 78150-4527
Tel: (210) 565-4678 E-mail: afrshqpa@us.af.mil
Internet: http://www.recruiting.af.mil/

Commander **BrigGen Jeannie M. Leavitt USAF** . . . . (210) 565-0600
Education: Texas 1990 BS; Stanford 1991 MS

(continued on next page)

★ Presidential Appointment Requiring Senate Confirmation ☆ Presidential Appointment ☐ Schedule C Appointment ◇ Career Senior Foreign Service Appointment
● Career Senior Executive Service (SES) Appointment ○ Non-Career Senior Executive Service (SES) Appointment ■ Postal Career Executive Service

Air Force Recruiting Service *(continued)*

Individual Mobilization Augmentee to the Commander **Col Brian E. Wish USAF** . . . . (210) 565-0600
Vice Commander **Col Robert W. Trayers, Jr. USAF** . . . . (210) 565-0600
Chief Master Sergeant **CMSgt Brian K. LaBounty USAF** . . . . (210) 565-0600
First Sergeant **MSgt Kathryn N. Bender USMC** . . . . (210) 565-0600
Public Affairs Chief **Leslie Brown** . . . . (210) 565-0600
Recruiting Service Information Chief **James Herrick** . . . . (210) 565-0483
E-mail: james.herrick@us.af.mil

Air University (AU)
55 LeMay Plaza South, Maxwell AFB, AL 36112-6335
Tel: (334) 953-2015 (Public Affairs) Fax: (334) 953-4131
Internet: http://www.airuniversity.af.mil/

Commander and President
LtGen Anthony J. Cotton USAF . . . . (334) 953-2044
Education: North Carolina State 1986 BS; Central Michigan 1991 MAdm
Senior Advisor **Michael B. Gray** . . . . (334) 953-2015
Executive Assistant **Vicki Freeman** . . . . (334) 953-2044
Air National Guard Assistant
BrigGen Dawn M. Ferrell ANG . . . . (334) 953-2046
Education: Midwestern State; North Texas
Mobilization Assistant to the Commander and President **BrigGen Jeffrey T. Pennington USAFR** . . . . (334) 953-8290
Education: Kansas State 1988 BS; American Military U 2012 MA — Fax: (334) 953-3790
Vice Commander
MajGen Michael D. Rothstein USAF . . . . (334) 953-2046
Education: Air Force Acad 1988; US Army Command 1999 MMAS; Air War Col 2006 MSS
Chief Academic Officer
Col Jeffrey W. "Jeff" Donnithorne USAF . . . . (334) 953-5613
Associate Vice President for Academic Affairs
Dr. Anthony C. "Chris" Cain . . . . (334) 953-3056
E-mail: anthony.cain@us.af.mil
Chief Information Officer **Scott A. Baker** . . . . (334) 953-2015
E-mail: scott.a.baker72.civ@mail.mil
Command Chief Master Sergeant
CMSgt Todd Simmons USAF . . . . (334) 953-6393
Director of Staff **Col Jason Delamater USAF** . . . . (334) 953-2046
Director, Education Operations and Communications
(Vacant) . . . . (334) 953-3768
Fax: (334) 953-5600
Director, Financial Management
Col Tony Douglas USAF . . . . (334) 953-7535
Director, History and Research **(Vacant)** . . . . (334) 953-5262
Director, International Affairs
Col Scott W. Rizer USAF . . . . (334) 953-6338
Education: Nebraska (Omaha) 1987 BSBA; South Dakota 1994 MBA; Air Force Inst Tech 2002 MS — Fax: (334) 953-2530
Director, Muir S. Fairchild Research Information Center **(Vacant)** . . . . (334) 953-2606
600 Chennault Circle, Maxwell AFB, AL 36112-6424 — Fax: (334) 953-6939
E-mail: aul@us.af.mil
Director, Personnel **(Vacant)** . . . . (334) 953-4011
Fax: (334) 953-3379
Director, Plans and Programs **(Vacant)** . . . . (334) 953-5156
Director, Public Affairs **(Vacant)** . . . . (334) 953-6475
Fax: (334) 953-3379
Inspector General **Col Paul Lips USAF** . . . . (334) 953-6623
Fax: (334) 953-7751
Protocol Officer **Col Bernadette Bowman USAF** . . . . (334) 953-2095
Fax: (334) 953-2225
Staff Judge Advocate **Col Eric F. Mejia USAF** . . . . (334) 953-6590
Fax: (334) 953-2787
Executive Services **Toni Wade** . . . . (334) 953-2048

42nd Air Base Wing (42 ABW - Maxwell AFB)
50 LeMay Plaza, South, Maxwell AFB, AL 36112-6335
Tel: (334) 953-4200 Fax: (334) 953-7330 Internet: www.maxwell.af.mil
Commander **(Vacant)** . . . . (334) 953-4200

42nd Air Base Wing *(continued)*

Vice Commander **Col Barry A. Dickey USAF** . . . . (334) 953-4211
Chief Master Sergeant **CMSgt Erica Shipp USAF** . . . . (334) 953-4275
Small Business Officer **Marsha Goodman** . . . . (334) 953-3541
E-mail: marsha.goodman@us.af.mil

Air Force Institute of Technology (AFIT)
2950 Hobson Way, Wright-Patterson AFB, OH 45433-7765
Tel: (937) 255-6565 Tel: (937) 255-9354 (Public Affairs Office)
Internet: www.afit.edu
Director and Chancellor
MajGen Todd I. Stewart USAF (Ret) . . . . (937) 255-2321
Education: Michigan Tech 1968 BCE — Fax: (937) 656-7600
Deputy Director and Vice Chancellor
Dr. Sivaguru S. Sritharan . . . . (937) 255-6565 ext. 3315
Education: U Washington 1979 MS; Arizona 1982 MS, 1982 Ph.D.
Air University Detachment 1 Commander/Director of Staff **Col Paul Cotellesso USAF** . . . . (937) 255-2321
Executive Officer **Maj Debra Donley USAF** . . . . (937) 255-2321

National Security Space Institute (NSSI)
236 Paine Street, Peterson AFB, CO 80914
Tel: (719) 593-8794
Commandant **Col Richard B. Van Hook USAF** . . . . (719) 556-3457
Deputy Commandant **James E. Moschgat** . . . . (719) 556-3458
Associate Dean of Academics **Joseph Scholes** . . . . (719) 556-3462
Education: Utah State 1997; Texas 2007 MA
Superintendent **MSgt Jeffrey "Jeff" Roberts USAF** . . . . (719) 556-3459
Administrative Assistant **Cleo M. Griffith** . . . . (719) 556-3456
E-mail: cleo.griffith.2@us.af.mil

Carl A. Spaatz Center for Officer Education
325 Chennault Circle, Maxwell AFB, AL 36112
Commander
BrigGen Christopher A. "Boots" Coffelt USAF . . . . (334) 953-7288
Education: Colorado 1989 BS; George Washington 1998 MA

Air Command and Staff College (Maxwell AFB)
225 Chennault Circle, Maxwell AFB, AL 36112
Tel: (334) 953-2224 Internet: http://www.airuniversity.af.mil/ACSC/
Commandant **(Vacant)** . . . . (334) 953-2295
Vice Commandant **Col Leon Perkowski USAF** . . . . (334) 953-2288

Air War College (AWC)
325 Chennault Circle, Maxwell AFB, AL 36112
Tel: (334) 953-1110 Internet: www.au.af.mil/au/awc/awchome.htm
Commandant
BrigGen Christopher A. "Boots" Coffelt USAF . . . . (334) 953-7288
Education: Colorado 1989 BS; George Washington 1998 MA
Vice Commandant **Col Michael Sierco USAF** . . . . (334) 953-7288

Center for Strategic Deterrence Studies
Building 1403, 125 Chennault Circle, Room 1101, Maxwell AFB, AL 36112
Tel: (334) 953-7538 Fax: (334) 953-7530
E-mail: CPC.ADMIN@us.af.mil
Commander **Al Mauroni** . . . . (334) 953-7538
Education: Carnegie Mellon 1985 BS; Central Michigan 1992 MSA

International Officer School (IOS - Maxwell AFB)
120 S. Mitchell Street, Maxwell AFB, AL 36112
Tel: (334) 953-6338 Fax: (334) 953-2530
E-mail: ios.student.operations@us.af.mil
Internet: www.au.af.mil/au/spaatz/ios
Commandant **Col Scott W. Rizer USAF** . . . . (334) 953-6338
Education: Nebraska (Omaha) 1987 BSBA; South Dakota 1994 MBA; Air Force Inst Tech 2002 MS

School of Advanced Air and Space Studies (SAASS)
600 Chennault Circle, Maxwell AFB, AL 36112-6424
Tel: (334) 953-5155 Fax: (334) 953-3015
Internet: www.au.af.mil/au/saass
Commandant **Col Shawn T. Cochran USAF** . . . . (334) 953-5155

★ Presidential Appointment Requiring Senate Confirmation ☆ Presidential Appointment ☐ Schedule C Appointment ◇ Career Senior Foreign Service Appointment
● Career Senior Executive Service (SES) Appointment ○ Non-Career Senior Executive Service (SES) Appointment ■ Postal Career Executive Service

Squadron Officer College (SOC - Maxwell AFB)
125 Chennault Circle, Maxwell AFB, AL 36112-6417
Internet: www.au.af.mil/au/soc
Commandant **Col Wayne W. Straw USAF** .... (334) 953-2231

Squadron Officer School (Maxwell AFB)
Building 1403, 125 Chennault Circle, Maxwell AFB, AL 36112-6417
Tel: (334) 953-6060
Commandant **(Vacant)** .... (334) 953-6060

Curtis E. LeMay Center for Doctrine Development and Education
1401 Chennault Circle, Maxwell AFB, AL 36112
Fax: (334) 953-2556 Internet: http://www.airuniversity.af.mil/LeMay/
Commander **MajGen Michael D. Rothstein USAF** ...... (334) 953-7442
E-mail: lemayctr.dd.wkflw@maxwell.af.mil
Education: Air Force Acad 1988; US Army Command 1999 MMAS; Air War Col 2006 MSS
Executive Officer **Maj Amanda Gonzales USAF** ...... (334) 953-7443
Executive Assistant **Dustin Moye** .... (334) 953-7442
Mobilization Assistant **Col Jeffery E. Elliott USAF** .... (334) 953-2015

Ira C. Eaker College for Professional Development (ECPD - Maxwell AFB)
525 Chennault Circle, Maxwell AFB, AL 36112-6335
Tel: (334) 953-2864 Fax: (334) 953-2865
E-mail: ECPDCC_Workflow@us.af.mil
Internet: http://www.airuniversity.af.mil/Eaker-Center/
Commander **Col Michael A. Grogan USAF** .... (334) 953-2864

Air Force Chaplain Corps College
525 Chennault Circle, Maxwell AFB, AL 36112
Commandant **(Vacant)** .... (803) 751-9475

USAF Personnel Professional Development School (AFPPDS)
525 Chennault Circle, Maxwell AFB, AL 36112-6335
Fax: (334) 953-3672
Director **Col Adrian Hovious USAF** .... (334) 953-2864

Commanders' Professional Development School
525 Chennault Circle, Maxwell AFB, AL 36112-6335
Tel: (334) 953-7716 Internet: www.au.af.mil/au/ecpd/cpds
Director **Leah Goerke** .... (334) 953-7716

Defense Financial Management and Comptroller School (DFMCS)
525 Chennault Circle, Maxwell AFB, AL 36112-6335
Tel: (334) 953-6656 Fax: (334) 953-5739
Director **Col Dwayne A. LaHaye USAF** .... (334) 953-6656

Jeanne M. Holm Center for Officer Accessions and Citizen Development
Building 836, 130 West Maxwell Boulevard,
Maxwell AFB, AL 36112-6106
Tel: (800) 522-0033 ext. 7087 Internet: www.afoats.af.mil
Commander
Col Christopher J. Niemi USAF .... (800) 522-0033 ext. 7087

Air Force Junior Reserve Officer Training Corps (AFJROTC)
Building 835, 60 West Maxwell Boulevard, Maxwell AFB, AL 36112
Commander **(Vacant)** .... (334) 953-7513

Air Force Reserve Officer Training Corps (AFROTC)
Building 835, 60 West Maxwell Boulevard, Maxwell AFB, AL 36112
Internet: https://www.afrotc.com/
Commander **Col Tammy M. Knierim USAF** .... (334) 953-9415
Education: John Carroll 1989 BA; Webster 1996 MA

Officer Training School (OTS)
Building 835, 60 West Maxwell Boulevard, Maxwell AFB, AL 36112
Internet: www.au.af.mil/au/holmcenter/OTS
Commandant **Col Peter G. Bailey USAF** .... (334) 953-5222 ext. 6

Thomas N. Barnes Center for Enlisted Education
50 South Turner Boulevard,
Maxwell AFB, Gunter Annex, AL 36114-3107
Internet: www.au.af.mil/au/barnes
Commander **Col James D. "Jim" Dryjanski USAF** ..... (334) 416-1470

Air Force Senior Noncommissioned Officer Academy (SNCOA - Maxwell AFB)
550 McDonald Street, Maxwell AFB, Gunter Annex, AL 36114-3107
Tel: (334) 416-4134 Internet: http://www.airuniversity.af.mil/Barnes/sncoa
Commandant **CMSgt Benjamin Caro, Jr. USAF** .... (334) 416-4134
E-mail: ben.caro@us.af.mil

Community College of the Air Force (CCAF)
100 South Turner Boulevard,
Maxwell AFB, Gunter Annex, AL 36114-3011
Tel: (334) 649-5150 Fax: (334) 416-2347
Commandant **LtCol Nathan Sherman USAF** .... (334) 649-5150

USAF First Sergeant Academy (FSA)
Building 1143, 550 McDonald Street,
Maxwell AFB, Gunter Annex, AL 36114-3107
Tel: (334) 953-2900 Fax: (334) 416-1004
Internet: www.au.af.mil/au/barnes/fsa
Commandant **CMSgt Danny R. Doucette ANG** .... (334) 416-2906

2nd Air Force (2AF - Keesler AFB)
Keesler AFB, MS 39534-5000
Commander **MajGen Timothy J. Leahy USAF** .... (228) 337-1368
Education: Citadel 1985 BS; Troy State 1995 MS; Naval War 1997 MA
Executive Officer **Capt Phillip Freeman USAF** .... (228) 337-1368

17th Training Wing (17 TW)
351 Kearney Boulevard, Goodfellow AFB, TX 76908
Tel: (325) 654-3876 Fax: (325) 654-5414
Internet: www.goodfellow.af.mil
Commander **Col Ricky L. Mills USAF** .... (325) 654-5402
Education: Texas A&M 1994 BBA; George Washington 2003 MA; Army War Col 2013 MSS
Vice Commander **Col Jeffrey A. Sorrell USAF** .... (325) 654-5405
Education: North Texas 1992 BBA; Webster 1996 MA; National Defense U 2014 MA
Chief Master Sergeant
CMSgt Bobbie J. Fillbrandt USAF .... (325) 654-5401
Education: Southwestern Col (KS) 2014 BS
Executive Officer **Capt John Pendergrass USAF** .... (325) 654-5403
Mission Support Group Commander
Col Jason Beck USAF .... (325) 654-3407
Training Group Commander
Col Alex R. Ganster USAF .... (325) 654-5512
Public Affairs Chief **Robert Martinez** .... (325) 654-3877
Freedom of Information Act Officer **Steve Chenault** .... (325) 654-3416
E-mail: steve.chenault@goodfellow.af.mil
Contracting Officer **LtCol John Travieso USAF** .... (325) 654-3812
Small Business Officer **Brenda Lauer** .... (325) 654-3812
E-mail: brenda.lauer@goodfellow.af.mil
Librarian **Cynthia L. "Cindy" Tews** .... (325) 654-3045
Fax: (915) 654-1109

37th Training Wing (37 TW)
1701 Kenly Avenue, Suite 102, Joint Base San Antonio, TX 78236-5103
Tel: (210) 671-1110 (Base Operator) Fax: (210) 671-2022
Internet: www.37trw.af.mil
Commander **Col Roy Collins USAF** .... (210) 671-3337
Vice Commander **Col Phillip G. Born USAF** .... (210) 671-3337
Chief Master Sergeant
CMSgt Philip E. Eckenrod, Jr. USAF .... (210) 671-3337
Public Affairs Director **Robert Rubio** .... (210) 671-3136

DEPARTMENTS

★ Presidential Appointment Requiring Senate Confirmation ☆ Presidential Appointment ☐ Schedule C Appointment ◇ Career Senior Foreign Service Appointment
● Career Senior Executive Service (SES) Appointment ○ Non-Career Senior Executive Service (SES) Appointment ■ Postal Career Executive Service

81st Training Wing (Keesler AFB)
Keesler AFB, MS 39534-5000
Tel: (228) 377-2783 Fax: (228) 377-3940
E-mail: 81trw.pa@keesler.af.mil Internet: www.keesler.af.mil

Commander **Col Debra A. Lovette USAF** . . . . (228) 377-2010
Education: Air Force Acad 1994 BS; Troy State 1996 MS; Air Force Inst Tech MS; National War Col 2013 MS
Vice Commander **Col Mike Smith USAF** . . . . (228) 377-2010
Chief Master Sergeant **CMSgt Kenneth Carter USAF** . . . (228) 377-2010
Mission Support Group Commander
Col Danny Davis USAF . . . . (228) 377-2783
Training Group Commander
Col Leo Lawson, Jr. USAF . . . . (228) 377-2783

82nd Training Wing (82 TW)
419 G Avenue, Suite 1, Sheppard AFB, TX 76311-2941
Tel: (940) 676-2121 Internet: www.sheppard.af.mil

Vice Commander **Col Scott Belanger USAF** . . . . (940) 676-2324
Chief Master Sergeant
CMSgt Michelle R. Jackson USAF . . . . (940) 676-2749
Director of Public Affairs **George Woodward** . . . . (940) 676-2732
E-mail: george.woodward@sheppard.af.mil
Contracting Officer **LtCol Roderick Edwards USAF** . . . . . (940) 676-2663

19th Air Force (19AF)
Randolph AFB, TX 78148

Commander **MajGen Patrick J. Doherty USAF** . . . . (210) 652-6307
Education: Iowa State 1987 BS; Embry-Riddle 1997 MS
Vice Commander **Col Travis A. Willis USAF** . . . . (210) 652-6307

Air National Guard Units

189th Airlift Wing (189 AW)
Little Rock AFB, AR 72076
Tel: (501) 987-6011 Fax: (501) 987-1049
Internet: http://www.189aw.ang.af.mil/

Commander **Col Thomas D. Crimmins USAF** . . . . (501) 987-6011
Vice Commander
Col Christopher L. "Chris" Montanaro ANG . . . . (501) 987-6011
Command Chief **CMSgt Ronaldo O. Boston ANG** . . . . . (501) 987-6011

162nd Fighter Wing (162 FW)
1650 East Perimeter Way, Tucson, AZ 85706-6052
Tel: (520) 295-6105 Fax: (520) 295-6023 Internet: www.162fw.ang.af.mil

Commander **BrigGen Andrew J. MacDonald ANG** . . . . . (520) 295-6100
Public Affairs Officer **Capt Mary Hook ANG** . . . . (520) 295-6192
Freedom of Information Act Officer
CMSgt Amy O'Neil ANG . . . . (520) 295-6013
Contracting/Small Business Officer
MSgt Keron A. Watson ANG . . . . (520) 295-6113
E-mail: keron.a.watson.mil@mail.mil Fax: (520) 295-6493

173rd Fighter Wing (173 FW)
Kingsley Field ANG Base, 211 Arnold Avenue, Suite 11, Klamath Falls, OR 97603-2111
Tel: (541) 885-6302 Fax: (541) 885-6187 Internet: www.173fw.ang.af.mil

Commander **Col Jeff S. Smith ANG** . . . . (541) 885-6173
Education: Air Force Acad 1995 BS; Oklahoma State 2012 MBA
Executive Administrative Assistant
TSgt Melissa Wohlers ANG . . . . (541) 885-6302
Executive Officer **Capt Scott Gerhart ANG** . . . . (541) 885-6302
Vice Commander **Col Jeffrey B. Edwards ANG** . . . . (541) 885-6476
Public Affairs Officer **Capt Nikki Jackson ANG** . . . . (541) 885-6308

178th Fighter Wing (178 FW)
5319 Regola Avenue, Springfield, OH 45502-8789
Tel: (937) 327-2321 Fax: (937) 327-2121
Internet: http://www.178wing.ang.af.mil/

Commander **Col Gregg J. Hesterman USAF** . . . . (937) 327-2178
Vice Commander
LtCol Kimberly A. Fitzgerald USAF . . . . (937) 327-2178
Public Affairs/Freedom of Information Act Officer
2nd Lt Lou J. Burton USAF . . . . (937) 525-2557

Air Force Global Strike Command (AFGSC)
Barksdale AFB, LA 71110-2270
Tel: (318) 456-1305 E-mail: afgsc.paworkflow@us.af.mil
Internet: www.afgsc.af.mil

8th Air Force (8AF)
Barksdale AFB, LA 71110-2270
E-mail: 2bw.pa@barksdale.af.mil Internet: www.8af.af.mil

Commander
MajGen James C. "Jim" Dawkins, Jr. USAF . . . . (318) 456-2170
E-mail: 2bwwingcommander@barksdale.af.mil
Education: Baylor 1988 BB; Embry-Riddle 2000 MS
Mobilization Assistant to the Commander
BrigGen Jonathan M. Ellis USAFR . . . . (318) 456-2170
Education: Penn State 1984 BS; Embry-Riddle 1995 MBA
Vice Commander **Col Roy P. Fatur USAF** . . . . (318) 456-2170
Chief Master Sergeant **CMSgt Alan G. Boling USAF** . . . . (318) 456-2170

2nd Bomb Wing (2 BW)
Barksdale AFB, LA 71110-2270
Tel: (318) 456-3065 Fax: (318) 456-5986 E-mail: 2bw.pa@us.af.mil
Internet: www.barksdale.af.mil

Commander **Col Michael A. Miller USAF** . . . . (318) 456-3065
Vice Commander **Col Robert H.W. Makros USAF** . . . . . . (318) 456-3065
Education: Air Force Acad 1998 BS; Central Missouri 2009
Chief Master Sergeant **CMSgt Teresa Clapper USAF** . . . . (318) 456-3065
Base Contracting Officer **Maj Jennifer McGee USAF** . . . . (318) 456-6939
E-mail: jennifer.mcgee@us.af.mil
Contracting Officer **Erin K. VanCise** . . . . (318) 456-5205
E-mail: erin.vancise@us.af.mil
Community Relations **SSgt Chad Warren USAF** . . . . . . (318) 456-5505
Small Business Officer **Brenda Russo** . . . . (318) 456-6940
E-mail: brenda.russo@barksdale.af.mil
Supervisory Librarian **Coralie Morris** . . . . (318) 456-4182
Building 4244, 744 Douhet Drive, Barksdale AFB, LA 71110-2428 Fax: (318) 456-1323

5th Bomb Wing (5 BW)
201 Summit Drive, Suite 1, Minot AFB, ND 58705-5049
Tel: (701) 723-1110 Fax: (701) 723-7395 E-mail: 5bw.pa@minot.af.mil
Internet: www.minot.af.mil

Commander **Col Bradley L. Cochran USAF** . . . . (701) 723-3115
Education: BYU 1997 BA; Central Missouri 2004 MS; Air War Col 2016 MSS
Vice Commander **Col David Ballew USAF** . . . . (701) 723-3115
E-mail: 5bw.cv@minot.af.mil
Chief Master Sergeant
CMSgt Brent S. Sheehan USAF . . . . (701) 723-3836
Contracting Squadron Commander
Maj Olga Brandt USAF . . . . (701) 723-4186
E-mail: 5cons.cc3@minot.af.mil
Public Affairs Chief **Maj Natassia Cherne USAF** . . . . (701) 723-6212
Freedom of Information **Vickie Phippins** . . . . (701) 723-3529
E-mail: vickie.phippins@minot.af.mil
Library Director **Lindsey Guderjahn** . . . . (701) 723-4554
FL 4528, 210 Missile Avenue, Suite 1, Minot AFB, ND 58705-5026 Fax: (701) 727-9850

7th Bomb Wing (7 BW)
7 Lancer Loop, Dyess AFB, TX 79607-1960
Tel: (325) 696-2863 Fax: (325) 696-2866 E-mail: 7bwpa@dyess.af.mil
Internet: www.dyess.af.mil

Commander **Col Brandon D. Parker USAF** . . . . (325) 696-2121
Education: Air Force Acad 1996 BS; Embry-Riddle 2007 MAS; Air U (USAF) 2008 MMAS
Vice Commander **Col David A. Doss USAF** . . . . (325) 696-2121
Chief Master Sergeant **CMSgt Eric Dugger USAF** . . . . . . (325) 696-2868
Contracting Officer **Maj Kenneth Smith USAF** . . . . (325) 696-2284
Public Affairs Officer **Capt Alexander Trobe USAF** . . . . . (325) 696-2863
Base Library Director **Toyya Cisneros** . . . . (325) 696-1397
349 Third Street, Dyess AFB, TX 79607-1242 Fax: (325) 696-1501

★ Presidential Appointment Requiring Senate Confirmation ☆ Presidential Appointment ☐ Schedule C Appointment ◇ Career Senior Foreign Service Appointment
● Career Senior Executive Service (SES) Appointment ○ Non-Career Senior Executive Service (SES) Appointment ■ Postal Career Executive Service

28th Bomb Wing (28 BW - Ellsworth AFB)
1958 Scott Drive, Ellsworth AFB, SD 57706
Tel: (605) 385-5056 Fax: (605) 385-4668
E-mail: 28bw.pa@ellsworth.af.mil Internet: www.ellsworth.af.mil

Commander **Col John R. Edwards USAF** .... (605) 385-2801
Education: Hawaii 1995 BS; George Washington 2003 MA; Air Command Col 2007 MMAS
Vice Commander **(Vacant)** .... (605) 385-5056
Chief Master Sergeant **CMSgt Adam J. Vizi USAF** ..... (605) 385-5056
Public Affairs **SrA Michella Stowers USAF** .... (605) 385-5056
E-mail: 28bw.pa@us.af.mil
Freedom of Information Act Officer **Steven J. Merrill** ... (605) 385-1564
E-mail: ellsworth.foia@ellsworth.af.mil Fax: (605) 385-2460
Library Director **Wanda Greene** .... (605) 385-5191
2828 SVS/SVMG FL 4690, Fax: (605) 385-4467
2650 Dolittle Drive,
Ellsworth AFB, SD 57706-4820

509th Bomb Wing (509 BW)
Building 59, 509 Spirit Boulevard, Whiteman AFB, MO 65305
Tel: (660) 687-6123 Fax: (660) 687-7948 Internet: www.whiteman.af.mil/

Commander **BrigGen John J. Nichols USAF** .... (660) 687-5090
Education: Air Force Acad 1992 BS
Vice Commander **(Vacant)** .... (660) 687-5090
Chief Master Sergeant **CMSgt James R. Lyda USAF** .... (660) 687-5090
Public Affairs Chief **Capt Kennan Kunst USAF** .... (660) 687-6124
Contracting Officer **Maj Leigh Baumbaugh USAF** ...... (660) 687-5421
Small Business Officer **Linda Walker** .... (660) 687-3641

552nd Air Control Wing
Tinker AFB, OK 73145
Tel: (405) 734-5570 Fax: (405) 734-5114
Internet: www.552acw.acc.af.mil

Commander **Col Geoffrey F. "Skippy" Weiss USAF** .... (405) 734-7313
Vice Commander **Col Gavin P. Marks USAF** .... (405) 734-7313
Command Chief **CMSgt Mark A. Hurst USAF** .... (405) 734-7313

20th Air Force (20AF)
Francis E. Warren AFB, 5305 Randall Avenue,
F.E. Warren AFB, WY 82005-2266
Tel: (307) 773-5202

Commander
MajGen Ferdinand B. "Fred" Stoss USAF .... (307) 773-5202
Education: Kansas State 1987 BA; Embry-Riddle 1993 MA; Naval War 2000 MA; Air War Col 2003; Nebraska (Omaha) 2006 MS
Mobilization Assistant
BrigGen Erich C. Novak USAF .... (804) 734-1345
Vice Commander **Col Matthew E. Dillow USAF** .... (307) 773-5202
Chief Master Sergeant
CMSgt Thomas F. Good USAF .... (307) 773-5202

90th Missile Wing (90 MW)
Francis E. Warren AFB, 5305 Randall Avenue,
F.E. Warren AFB, WY 82005-2266
Tel: (307) 773-1110 Internet: www.warren.af.mil

Commander **Col Stacy J. Huser USAF** .... (307) 773-2005
Vice Commander **Col Brian G. Young USAF** .... (307) 773-2005
Command Chief Master Sergeant
CMSgt Kristian Farve USAF .... (307) 773-3975
Director of Staff **(Vacant)** .... (307) 773-2005
Maintenance Group Commander
Col Greg D. Buckner USAF .... (307) 773-2260
Mission Support Group Commander
Col Tricia A. Van Den Top USAF .... (307) 773-3100
Operations Group Commander
Col Robert T. Ewers USAF .... (307) 773-3071
Security Forces Commander **Col John Grimm USAF** .... (307) 773-4142
Building 34, 7100 Garrison Loop, Room 129,
F.E. Warren AFB, WY 82005
Contracting Commander **Maj Bryce Fiacco USAF** .... (307) 773-3535
Historian **Michael Byrd** .... (307) 773-6062

91st Missile Wing (Minot AFB)
300 Minuteman Drive, Minot AFB, ND 58705-5049
Tel: (701) 723-3818

Commander **Col Glenn T. Harris USAF** .... (701) 723-3215
Vice Commander **Col Kelvin Townsend USAF** .... (701) 723-3215
E-mail: v391sw.cc@minot.af.mil
Command Chief Master Sergeant
CMSgt John A. Burks USAF .... (701) 723-3014
E-mail: 91sw.ccc@minot.af.mil
Missile Maintenance Group Commander
Col Earl R. Bennett USAF .... (701) 723-3215
Operations Group Commander **(Vacant)** .... (701) 723-3215
Security Forces Group Commander **(Vacant)** .... (701) 723-3215

341st Missile Wing (341 MW)
21 77th Street North, Malmstrom AFB, MT 59402-6863
Tel: (406) 731-1110 (Base Operator)
Tel: (406) 731-4016 (Contracting and Small Business)
Tel: (406) 731-4638 (Library) Fax: (406) 731-4048
Internet: www.malmstrom.af.mil

Commander **Col Jennifer Reeves USAF** .... (406) 731-3411
Vice Commander **Col Peter M. Bonetti USAF** .... (406) 731-3411
Chief Master Sergeant
CMSgt Eryn C. McElroy USAF .... (406) 731-3411

Air Force Materiel Command (AFMC)
4375 Chidlaw Road, Wright-Patterson AFB, OH 45433-5001
Tel: (937) 257-6033 Fax: (937) 257-5769 Internet: www.afmc.af.mil

309th Aerospace Maintenance and Regeneration Group (309 AMARG - Davis Monthan AFB)
4820 South Wickenburg Avenue, Davis Monthan AFB, AZ 85707-4332
Tel: (520) 228-8146 Fax: (520) 228-8513

Commander **Col Jennifer M. Barnard USAF** .... (520) 228-8146
Deputy Director
Col David "Dave" Wiesner USAF (Ret) .... (520) 228-8146
Education: Arizona State 1989; Embry-Riddle 1993
Public Affairs Officer **Teresa Pittman** .... (520) 228-8448
E-mail: 309.amarg.business.affairs.liaison@us.af.mil
Education and Training Division Chief
Theodore Schwab .... (520) 228-8091
E-mail: theodore.schwab@dm.af.mil Fax: (520) 228-8083

Air Force Installation and Mission Support Center (AFIMSC)
Joint Base San Antonio, TX 78150
Tel: (210) 395-1666 (Public Affairs)

Commander **BrigGen Bradley D. Spacy USAF** .... (210) 395-1666
Education: Cal State (Fresno) 1987 BA; Southern Mississippi 1996 MSE
Mobilization Assistant to the Commander **(Vacant)** ..... (210) 395-1666
Vice Commander **Col Gregory J. Reese USAF** .... (210) 395-1666
● Executive Director **Terry G. Edwards** .... (210) 395-1666
Education: BYU 1983 BSCE, 1984 MEM
Command Chief **CMSgt Brion P. Blais USAF** .... (210) 395-1666
● Director, Resources **Monica A. Anders** .... (937) 257-6033
Wright-Patterson AFB, OH 45433

Air Force Director of Civil Engineers (A7C)
1260 Air Force Pentagon, Washington, DC 20330-1260
Tel: (703) 693-4301 Fax: (703) 693-4893

Air Force Civil Engineer Center (AFCEC)
2261 Hughes Avenue, Suite 155, Lackland AFB, TX 78236-9853
Internet: www.afcec.af.mil

● Director **Col Edwin H. "Ed" Oshiba USAF (Ret)** .... (210) 395-8000
E-mail: edwin.p.oshiba.civ@mail.mil
Deputy Director **Col Matthew P. Benivegna USAF** ..... (210) 395-8000
Deputy Director **Col Timothy Dodge USAF** .... (850) 283-6101
Education: Notre Dame 1989 BS
Chief Financial Officer **Geoff Schurman** .... (210) 395-8802
E-mail: geoffrey.schurman.3@us.af.mil
Chief Information Officer (Acting) **Amy Love** .... (210) 395-9469

(continued on next page)

DEPARTMENTS

★ Presidential Appointment Requiring Senate Confirmation ☆ Presidential Appointment □ Schedule C Appointment ◇ Career Senior Foreign Service Appointment
● Career Senior Executive Service (SES) Appointment ○ Non-Career Senior Executive Service (SES) Appointment ■ Postal Career Executive Service

Air Force Civil Engineer Center *(continued)*

Chief Counsel **Fraser B. Jones, Jr.** .... (210) 395-8316
E-mail: fraser.jones@us.af.mil
Director of Staff **Col Tiffany Warnke USAF** .... (210) 395-8000
Staff Judge Advocate **LtCol Daniel Watson USAF** ...... (210) 395-8037
Public Affairs Chief **Mark Kinkade** .... (210) 925-0956

Air Force Life Cycle Management Center (AFLCMC)

Wright-Patterson AFB, OH 45433
Tel: (937) 255-5714 Fax: (937) 656-7088
Internet: www.wpafb.af.mil/aflcmc

Commander **LtGen Robert D. McMurry, Jr. USAF** ...... (937) 255-5714
Education: Texas 1984 BS; West Florida 1993 MS
Mobilization Assistant to the Commander
BrigGen Russell P. Reimer USAFR .... (937) 255-5714
Vice Commander **Col Teresa A. Quick USAF** .... (937) 255-5714
• Executive Director **Kathy L. Watern** .... (937) 255-5714
E-mail: kathy.watern@us.af.mil
Education: Wright State 1981 BS; Dayton 1984 MBA; Indust'l Col Armed Forces 2000 MS
Command Chief Master Sergeant
CMSgt Michelle Thorstein-Richards USAF .... (937) 255-5714
• Director of Engineering and Technical Management
(Vacant) .... (937) 255-5714
• Director of Financial Management and Comptroller
Kathryn J. Sowers .... (937) 255-5917
Education: Wright State 1984 BS, 1988 MBA
Director of Staff **Thomas M. Zerba** .... (937) 255-5714
E-mail: thomas.zerba.1@us.af.mil
Education: Southern Maine 1987 BA; Dayton 1999 JD

66th Air Base Group (66 ABG)

20 Schilling Circle, Hanscom AFB, MA 01731
Tel: (781) 225-1686

Commander **Col Chad R. Ellsworth USAF** .... (781) 225-1305
Deputy Commander **(Vacant)** .... (781) 225-1686
Chief Master Sergeant
CMSgt Henry L. Hayes, Jr. USAF .... (781) 225-1686
Communications Squadron Commander
Ann Markman .... (781) 225-1305
E-mail: ann.markman@us.af.mil

88th Air Base Wing

5135 Pearson Road, Wright-Patterson AFB, OH 45433
Tel: (937) 522-3252 (Public Affairs) Internet: http://www.wpafb.af.mil/

Commander **Col Thomas P. Sherman USAF** .... (937) 522-3252
Education: Air Force Acad 1995 BS
Vice Commander **LtCol Dave R. Anzaldúa USAF** ...... (937) 522-3252
Vice Director **Janet M. Wirth** .... (937) 522-3252
Command Chief **CMSgt Kathlina G. Racine USAF** ..... (937) 522-3252
Public Affairs Director **Laura McGowan** .... (937) 522-3252
E-mail: 88abw.pa@us.af.mil

Air Force Security Assistance and Cooperation Directorate

1822 Van Patton Drive, Wright-Patterson AFB, OH 45333
Tel: (937) 257-2552 Fax: (937) 257-7645

Director **BrigGen Gregory M. Gutterman USAF** .... (937) 257-2552
E-mail: gregory.gutterman@us.af.mil

Contracting Directorate (Wright-Patterson AFB)

• Director of Contracting **Thomas D. "Tom" Robinson** ... (937) 255-3741
E-mail: thomas.robinson.29@us.af.mil
Education: Canisius 1983 BA; Northern Michigan 1987 MPA; Air War Col 2006 MS

Air Force Nuclear Weapons Center (AFNWC)

1551 Wyoming Boulevard SE, Kirtland AFB, NM 87117-5606
Tel: (505) 846-0011 E-mail: 377abw.pa@kirtland.af.mil

Commander **MajGen Shaun Q. Morris USAF** .... (505) 846-0011
Education: Air Force Acad 1988 BS; USC 1992 MS
Vice Commander **Col George R. Farfour USAF** .... (505) 846-2368
E-mail: afnwccv@kirtland.af.mil
Education: East Carolina 1989 BS; Webster 1993 MA

Air Force Nuclear Weapons Center *(continued)*

• Executive Director **Joseph M. Oder** .... (505) 846-0887
E-mail: afnwcca@kirtland.af.mil
Chief of Staff **Thomas F. Berardinelli** .... (505) 846-6567
Education: Rutgers 1980 BA; Webster 1983 MA

Air Force Sustainment Center (AFSC)

Tinker AFB, OK 73145
Tel: (405) 739-2201 Fax: (405) 739-7155 Internet: www.afsc.af.mil

Commander
LtGen Donald E. "Gene" Kirkland USAF .... (405) 739-2201
Education: Florida 1987 BS; Central Michigan 1990 MSA
Mobilization Assistant to the Commander **(Vacant)** ..... (405) 739-2201
• Executive Director **Kevin D. Stamey** .... (405) 739-2202
Education: Texas Tech 1989 BS; Webster 1998 MA
Vice Commander **Col Brian R. Moore USAF** .... (405) 739-2202
• Engineering Director **(Vacant)** .... (405) 736-3184
Chief Master Sergeant **CMSgt Gary P. Sharp USAF** ..... (405) 739-2201
Education: Comm Col Air Force 1999 AS; Wayland Baptist 2007 BS; Colorado State 2013 MSOL

Ogden Air Logistics Complex (OO-ALC)

Building 1102, 7981 Georgia Street, Hill AFB, UT 84056
Tel: (801) 777-5201 Fax: (801) 777-4640 Internet: www.hill.af.mil
E-mail: ooalc.workflow@hill.af.mil

Commander **BrigGen Stacey T. Hawkins USAF** .... (801) 777-5076
Education: Air Force Acad 1991 BS; MIT 2011 MBA
Vice Director **Linda K. Fields** .... (801) 777-5201
Deputy Commander for Maintenance
Col Lawrence B. Havird USAF .... (801) 777-5076

Oklahoma City Air Logistics Complex (OC-ALC)

3001 Staff Drive, Suite 1AG78A, Tinker AFB, OK 73145-3010
Tel: (405) 736-2651 Fax: (405) 736-5052

Commander **BrigGen Christopher D. Hill USAF** .... (405) 736-2651
Mobilization Assistant **Col John N. Tree USAF** .... (405) 736-2651
Vice Director **Wade V. Wolfe** .... (405) 736-2651
Director, Aerospace Sustainment **Wendy Walder** .... (405) 736-7492

Warner Robins Air Logistics Complex

Robins AFB, GA 31098-1662
Tel: (478) 926-2123

Commander **BrigGen John C. Kubinec USAF** .... (478) 926-1113
Education: Air Force Acad 1992 BS; George Washington 2000 MA; Air U (USAF) 2006 MS

Air Force Test Center (AFTC)

One South Rosamond Boulevard, Edwards AFB, CA 93524-1225
Tel: (661) 277-2141 Fax: (661) 277-2732 (Public Affairs)
Internet: www.edwards.af.mil

Commander **MajGen David A. Harris USAF** .... (661) 277-2140
E-mail: david.harris@us.af.mil
Education: BYU 1986 BSME; Cal State (Fresno) 1998 MSE; Air War Col 2005 MSS
Mobilization Assistant to the Commander **(Vacant)** ..... (661) 277-2141
Executive Officer **Maj Robert Waller USAF** .... (661) 277-4648
Vice Commander **Col Angela W. Suplisson USAF** ..... (661) 277-2141
• Executive Director **David K. Robertson** .... (661) 277-4436
Education: Cal State (Fresno) 1985 BS, 1989 MS; Indust'l Col Armed Forces 2007 MS
Command Chief Master Sergeant
CMSgt Christopher M. Lantagne USAF .... (661) 277-3402
Technical Advisor **Dr. Joseph W. Nichols PhD** .... (661) 275-2074
Education: BYU 1983 BSME; Air Force Inst Tech 1987 MS; BYU 2013 PhD
Director of Contracting **(Vacant)** .... (661) 277-2006
Chief of Staff **Dr. Kathleen Thome-Diorio** .... (661) 277-5244

96th Test Wing (96 TW)

Eglin AFB, FL 32542
Internet: www.eglin.af.mil

Commander **BrigGen Evan C. Dertien USAF** .... (661) 277-2141
Vice Commander **Col Scott A. Dickson USAF** .... (850) 882-3333

★ Presidential Appointment Requiring Senate Confirmation ☆ Presidential Appointment ☐ Schedule C Appointment ◇ Career Senior Foreign Service Appointment
● Career Senior Executive Service (SES) Appointment ○ Non-Career Senior Executive Service (SES) Appointment ■ Postal Career Executive Service

96th Test Wing *(continued)*

Chief Master Sergeant **CMSgt Jamie Auger USAF** ..... (850) 882-2349

412th Test Wing
195 East Popson Avenue, Edwards AFB, CA 93524

Commander **BrigGen Ernest John Teichert III USAF** .... (661) 275-4000
Vice Commander **Col Kirk L. Reagan USAF** .... (661) 275-4000
Chief Master Sergeant
CMSgt Roosevelt Jones USAF .... (661) 275-9306
Director of Installation Support **Dr. David Smith** .... (661) 275-4000
Chief Executive Officer **Becca Schweitzer** .... (661) 277-2673
Executive Officer **Capt Brian Gilliam USAF** .... (661) 277-2673
Executive Officer **Maj Sandra Deering USAF** .... (661) 277-2673

Arnold Engineering Development Complex (AEDC)
100 Kindel Drive, Suite A303, Arnold AFB, TN 37389-1303
Tel: (931) 454-4204 Fax: (931) 454-6086
E-mail: publicaffairs@hap.arnold.af.mil Internet: www.arnold.af.mil

Commander **Col Scott A. Cain USAF** .... (931) 454-4204
Chief of Staff **Kenneth E. Jacobsen** .... (931) 454-4204
Chief Technologist **Thomas Fetterhoff** .... (931) 454-4204
Vice Director **(Vacant)** .... (931) 454-4204
Superintendent **CMSgt Robert A. Heckman USAF** ..... (931) 454-4204
Public Affairs Director **Jason Austin** .... (931) 454-4204
E-mail: jason.austin@arnold.af.mil

National Museum of the U.S. Air Force (Wright-Patterson AFB)
1100 Spaatz Street, Wright-Patterson AFB, OH 45433-7102
Tel: (937) 255-3286 E-mail: nationalmuseum.usaf@wpafb.af.mil
Internet: www.nationalmuseum.af.mil

• Director **LtGen John L. "Jack" Hudson USAF (Ret)** ... (937) 255-3286
Education: Air Force Acad 1973 BS; Purdue 1974 MS; Air Command Col 1987; Naval War 1991 MS; Salve Regina U 1993 MSM
Deputy Director and Senior Curator **Krista Strider** ...... (937) 255-3286

Air Force Reserve Command (AFRC)
155 Richard Ray Boulevard, Robins AFB, GA 31098-1635
Tel: (478) 327-1753 Tel: (478) 327-1753 (Public Affairs)
Fax: (478) 327-0082 Internet: www.afrc.af.mil

Air Reserve Personnel Center (ARPC)
Buckley AFB, Building 390, 18420 East Silver Creek Avenue, Mail Stop 68, Aurora, CO 80011
Tel: (720) 847-3000 Fax: (720) 847-3994 Internet: www.arpc.afrc.af.mil

Commander **BrigGen Ellen M. Moore USAF** .... (720) 847-3000
Vice Commander **Col Kevin Heckle USAF** .... (720) 847-3000
Mobilization Assistant to the Vice Commander
Col Constance Johnson-Cage USAFR .... (720) 847-3000
Director of Staff **Mr. Scott C. Fromm** .... (720) 847-3021
Education: Embry-Riddle 1994 BSAv; Webster 1999 MM; George Washington 2005 MA
Command Chief **CMSgt Jeanette Masters USAF** ...... (720) 847-3000
First Sergeant **MSgt Elizabeth Anschutz USAF** .... (720) 847-3018
Director of Assignments **Col Jena L. Silva USAF** .... (720) 847-3000
Director of Financial Management **Juan Limon** .... (720) 847-3000
Director of Future Operations and Integration
Col Charlan "Charlie" Poirson USAFR .... (720) 847-3000
Director of Personnel and Total Force Services
Col Ashley L. Heyen USAFR .... (720) 847-3000
Director of Public Affairs **(Vacant)** .... (720) 847-3030
E-mail: arpc.pa@arpc.denver.af.mil
Staff Judge Advocate **Col Kyle W. Green USAFR** .... (720) 847-3000

Force Generation Center (FGC)
693 Lakeside Circle, Robins AFB, GA 31098

Commander **BrigGen William R. Kountz USAFR** .... (478) 327-2233

4th Air Force (4AF)
Commander **MajGen Randall A. Ogden USAFR** .... (478) 327-1003
Education: Portland State 1983 BS; Troy U 1987 MPA
Vice Commander **(Vacant)** .... (478) 327-1003

4th Air Force *(continued)*

Chief Master Sergeant
CMSgt Timothy C. White, Jr. USAFR .... (478) 327-1003
Education: U Phoenix 2010 BS; Brandman U 2016 MA, 2017 MBA

315th Airlift Wing (315 AW)
Joint Base Charleston, SC 29404-5154
Fax: (843) 963-2019 Internet: www.315aw.afrc.af.mil

Commander **Col Gregory S. Gilmour USAFR** .... (843) 963-3338
Education: Citadel 1986 BA
Vice Commander **Col Jeanine M. McAnaney USAFR** ... (843) 963-3338
Chief Master Sergeant **CMSgt Mark Barber USAF** ...... (843) 963-3338

434th Air Refueling Wing (434 ARW)
Grissom ARB, IN 46971-5000
Tel: (800) 635-0961 Tel: (765) 688-3348 (Public Affairs)
Fax: (765) 688-3319 (Public Affairs) Internet: www.grissom.afrc.af.mil

Commander **Col Lorenza H. "Larry" Shaw III USAF** .... (765) 688-4340
E-mail: lorenza.shaw@us.af.mil
Vice Commander **Col Anne B. Noel USAFR** .... (765) 688-4340
Executive Officer **1st Lt Erica Morgan USAF** .... (765) 688-4341
Training **MSgt Darlene Cornelius USAFR** .... (765) 688-3910
E-mail: darlene.cornelius@us.af.mil Fax: (765) 688-3099
Security Forces Squadron Commander
Maj Matthew Garvelink USAF .... (765) 688-4330
E-mail: matthew.garvelink@us.af.mil Fax: (765) 688-8500
Public Affairs Chief **Abby Nelson** .... (765) 688-3348

439th Airlift Wing (439 AW)
100 Lloyd Street, East Wing, Suite 103, Chicopee, MA 01022-1825
Tel: (413) 557-1110 Tel: (413) 557-2020 (Public Affairs)
Fax: (413) 557-2011 E-mail: 439aw.pa@us.af.mil
Internet: www.westover.afrc.af.mil

Commander **Col D. Scott Durham USAF** .... (413) 557-1110
Vice Commander **Col Howard T. Clark III USAFR** ...... (413) 557-1110
Command Chief Master Sergeant **(Vacant)** .... (413) 557-1110
Maintenance Group Commander
Col David C. Post USAFR .... (413) 557-3816
Mission Support Group Commander
Col Karen L. Magnus USAFR .... (413) 557-3044
Education: Portland 1987 BBA
Operations Group Commander
Col Neil M. Hede USAF .... (413) 557-2204
Public Affairs Chief **(Vacant)** .... (413) 557-2020

512th Airlift Wing (Dover AFB)
Dover AFB, DE 19902
Tel: (302) 677-3000 Internet: www.512aw.afrc.af.mil

Commander **Col Craig C. Peters USAF** .... (302) 677-3000
Education: Anna Maria 1989 BBA
Vice Commander **Col Norman B. Shaw, Jr. USAF** ...... (302) 677-3000
Command Chief Master Sergeant
CMSgt Shirley C. Ozio USAF .... (302) 677-3000

514th Airlift Mobility Wing
Joint Base McGuire-Dix-Lakehurst, NJ 08641-5002
Internet: www.514amw.afrc.af.mil

Commander **Col Thomas O. Pemberton USAF** .... (609) 754-3487
Vice Commander **Col Adrian R. Byers USAF** .... (609) 754-3487
Command Chief Master Sergeant
CMSgt Dana L. Capaldi USAF .... (609) 754-3487
Chief, C-17 Current Operations
Maj Edward G. Yeash III USAF .... (609) 754-3907

10th Air Force (10AF)
NAS JRB Fort Worth, Fort Worth, TX 76127
Tel: (817) 782-3133 Internet: www.10af.afrc.af.mil

Commander **MajGen Ronald Bruce Miller USAFR** ..... (817) 782-3133
Education: South Carolina 1983 BSBA; Air Command Col 2002; Air War Col 2005
Vice Commander
BrigGen Damon S. Feltman USAFR .... (817) 782-3133
E-mail: damon.s.feltman.mil@mail.mil

(continued on next page)

DEPARTMENTS

★ Presidential Appointment Requiring Senate Confirmation ☆ Presidential Appointment □ Schedule C Appointment ◇ Career Senior Foreign Service Appointment
● Career Senior Executive Service (SES) Appointment ○ Non Career Senior Executive Service (SES) Appointment ■ Postal Career Executive Service

10th Air Force *(continued)*

Command Chief Master Sergeant
CMSgt James W. Loper USAFR .... (817) 782-3133
Education: Regis U 2003 BS

301st Fighter Wing (301 FW - Naval Air Station Fort Worth Joint Reserv)
NAS JRB Fort Worth, Fort Worth, TX 76127
Tel: (817) 782-7170 (Public Affairs) E-mail: 301fw.pa@us.af.mil
Internet: www.301fw.afrc.af.mil

Commander **Col Mitchell A. Hanson USAF** .... (817) 782-6872
Vice Commander **(Vacant)** .... (817) 782-6872
Chief Master Sergeant
CMSgt Robert S. Safley USAFR .... (817) 782-6874

482nd Fighter Wing (Homestead ARB)
482FW/PA, 29050 Coral Sea Boulevard, Homestead, FL 33039-1299
Tel: (786) 415-7000 Fax: (786) 415-7302
Internet: www.homestead.afrc.af.mil

Commander **Col David A. Piffarerio USAFR** .... (786) 415-7002
Public Affairs Chief **F.J. Brown** .... (786) 415-7330
E-mail: 482fw.pa@us.af.mil

944th Fighter Wing
14708 West Super Sabre Street, Luke AFB, AZ 85309-1722
Tel: (623) 856-5388 E-mail: 944FW.PA@luke.af.mil

Commander **Col Bryan E. Cook USAF** .... (623) 856-5388
Vice Commander **Col Robert R. Tofil USAFR** .... (623) 856-5388
Command Chief **CMSgt Jeremy N. Malcom USAF** ..... (623) 856-5388
Mission Support Group Commander
Col Gavin D. Tade USAF .... (623) 856-5388
Operations Group Commander
Col Korey E. Amundson USAF .... (623) 856-5388

22nd Air Force (22AF)
Dobbins Air Reserve Base, Marietta, GA 30062
Tel: (678) 655-5000 Tel: (678) 655-5467 (Public Affairs)
Internet: http://www.22af.afrc.af.mil/

Commander **MajGen Craig La Fave USAF** .... (678) 655-5000
Deputy Commander **Col Steven B. Parker USAFR** ...... (678) 655-5000
Chief of Staff **Col Michael J. Underkofler USAFR** ...... (678) 655-5000
Education: North Carolina 1984 BA; Embry-Riddle 1994 MAS; Air U (USAF) 2002 MSS
Chief Master Sergeant
CMSgt Imelda B. Johnson USAF .... (678) 655-5000

94th Airlift Wing (94 AW)
1430 First Street, Dobbins Air Reserve Base, Marietta, GA 30069-5009
Tel: (678) 655-5055 Fax: (678) 655-5056
E-mail: 94aw.pav3@dobbins.af.mil
Internet: http://www.dobbins.afrc.af.mil/Home.aspx

Commander **BrigGen Richard L. Kemble USAFR** .... (678) 655-5055

403rd Wing
Keesler AFB, MS 39534-5000
Tel: (228) 377-2056 (Public Affairs) Internet: www.403wg.afrc.af.mil

Commander **Col Jennie R. Johnson USAF** .... (228) 377-2056
Executive Officer **(Vacant)** .... (228) 377-2056
Vice Commander **Col Robert J. Stanton USAF** .... (228) 377-2056
Maintenance Group Commander
LtCol Jay D. Johnson USAF .... (228) 377-2056
Mission Support Group Commander
Col Edward "Chad" Sequra USAF .... (228) 377-2056
Operations Group Commander **Col Brian May USAF** .... (228) 377-2056
Command Chief
CMSgt Christopher L. Bamby USAF .... (228) 377-2056

910th Airlift Wing (910 AW)
910 Airlift Wing, Youngstown Air Reserve Station, 3976 King Graves Road, Vienna, OH 44473-5912
Tel: (330) 609-1000 Internet: www.youngstown.afrc.af.mil

Commander **Col Daniel J. Sarachene USAF** .... (330) 609-1243
Education: Kent State 1989; Air Command Col 2005; Air War Col 2012
Vice Commander **Col Joseph D. Janik USAF** .... (330) 609-1243
Executive Officer **Maj Wendy Strainic USAFR** .... (330) 609-1243
E-mail: wendy.strainic@us.af.mil
Chief Master Sergeant
CMSgt Robert J. Potts USAFR .... (330) 609-1150
Maintenance Group Commander **(Vacant)** .... (330) 609-1225
Mission Support Group Commander
Col Donald F. Wren USAF .... (330) 609-1354
Operations Group Commander **(Vacant)** .... (330) 609-1179
Public Affairs Officer **Maj Scott Allen USAF** .... (330) 609-1364

911th Airlift Wing (911 AW)
2475 Defense Avenue, Coraopolis, PA 15108-4403
Tel: (412) 474-8511 E-mail: 911aw.pa@us.af.mil
Internet: http://www.pittsburgh.afrc.af.mil/

Commander
Col Douglas N. "Doug" Strawbridge USAFR .... (412) 474-8511
Vice Commander **(Vacant)** .... (412) 474-8511
Command Master Sergeant
CMSgt Christopher D. Neitzel USAF .... (412) 474-8511
Mission Support Group Commander
Col Beena N. Maharaj USAF .... (412) 474-8511
Operations Group Commander
Col Joseph M. Potts USAFR .... (412) 474-8511

914th Air Refueling Wing (Niagara Falls Air Reserve Station)
Niagara Falls (NY) International Airport Air Reserve Station, 2720 Kirkbridge Drive, Niagara Falls, NY 14304-5001
Tel: (716) 236-2136 Fax: (716) 236-3268 E-mail: 914awpa@us.af.mil
Internet: http://www.niagara.afrc.af.mil/

Commander **Col Mark S. Larson USAFR** .... (716) 236-2122
E-mail: mark.s.larson.mil@mail.mil
Education: Utah State
Public Affairs Officer **MSgt Kevin Nichols USAF** ...... (716) 236-2136
Fax: (716) 236-3268

934th Airlift Wing
Minneapolis - St. Paul Int'l Airport Reserve Station, 760 Military Highway, Minneapolis, MN 55450-2100
Tel: (612) 713-1217 Fax: (612) 713-1229
Internet: www.minneapolis.afrc.af.mil

Commander **Col Anthony G. Polashek USAFR** .... (612) 713-1200
Deputy Public Affairs Officer **Paul Zadach** .... (612) 713-1217
E-mail: 934aw.pa@minneapolis.af.mil

Air Force Space Command (AFSPC)
150 Vandenberg Street, Suite 1105, Peterson AFB, CO 80914-4500
Tel: (719) 554-3731 (Public Affairs) Fax: (719) 554-6013
Internet: www.afspc.af.mil

Note: On December 3, 2017, the Air Force Space Command was designated Air Forces Strategic-Space (AFSTRAT-Space).

Air Force Network Integration Center (AFNIC)
203 West Losey Street, Room 3000, Scott AFB, IL 62225-5222
Fax: (618) 256-5126 Internet: www.afnic.af.mil

Commander **Col Douglas Dudley USAF** .... (618) 229-6571
Education: Baylor 1990 BBA
Executive Director **Markus E. Rogers** .... (618) 229-6573
Superintendent **CMSgt William Higginbotham USAF** ... (618) 229-6573
Director, Integration Services **Pamela Piazza** .... (618) 229-5330
Director, Technical Services **Tom Korte** .... (618) 229-6573

★ Presidential Appointment Requiring Senate Confirmation ☆ Presidential Appointment ☐ Schedule C Appointment ◇ Career Senior Foreign Service Appointment
● Career Senior Executive Service (SES) Appointment ○ Non-Career Senior Executive Service (SES) Appointment ■ Postal Career Executive Service

Space and Missile Systems Center (SMC)

Los Angeles AFB, 483 North Aviation Boulevard, El Segundo, CA 90245
Tel: (310) 653-0030

Commander **LtGen John F. Thompson USAF** . . . . (310) 653-1110
Education: Air Force Acad 1984 BS; St Mary's U (TX) 1988 MS
Mobilization Assistant to the Commander **(Vacant)** . . . . . (310) 653-0030
Deputy Commander
BrigGen Philip A. "Phil" Garrant USAF . . . . (310) 653-1110
E-mail: philip.garrant@losangeles.af.mil
Education: Johns Hopkins 1991 BSEE; Capitol Col 1995 MS
Command Chief Master Sergeant
CMSgt Scott A. Myers USAF . . . . (310) 653-5204
● Executive Director **Joy M. White** . . . . (310) 653-1110
E-mail: joy.white@losangeles.af.mil
Education: William & Mary 1985 BBA

14th Air Force (14AF)

HQ 14 AF/CCX, Vandenberg AFB, 747 Nebraska Avenue,
Suite A-300-8, Vandenberg AFB, CA 93437-6249
Tel: (805) 606-1400 Fax: (805) 605-8856

Commander **MajGen Stephen N. Whiting USAF** . . . . (805) 606-1400
Education: Air Force Acad 1989 BS; Air U (USAF) 1993;
George Washington 1997 MAS; Air Command Col 2001 MMAS;
Joint Forces Staff Col 2008
Vice Commander
BrigGen Matthew "Wolfe" Davidson USAF . . . . (805) 606-1400
Command Chief Master Sergeant
CMSgt Craig A. Neri USAF . . . . (805) 606-1400

21st Space Wing (21 SW)

775 Loring Avenue, Suite 219, Peterson AFB, CO 80914-1294
Tel: (719) 556-7321 Tel: (719) 554-2666 (PeakNet Webmaster)
Internet: https://www.peterson.af.mil/

Commander **Col Todd Moore USAF** . . . . (719) 556-2100
Vice Commander **Col Eric S. Dorminey USAF** . . . . (719) 556-2100
Individual Mobilization Augmentee to the Commander
Col John Doucet III USAF . . . . (719) 556-2105
Command Chief Master Sergeant
CMSgt Jacob C. Simmons USAF . . . . (719) 556-2105
Inspector General **LtCol Sacha N. Tomlinson USAF** . . . . (719) 556-2104
Internal Operations **Alethea Smock** . . . . (719) 556-8335
Public Affairs Officer **Maj Will Russell USAF** . . . . (719) 556-7321
Fax: (719) 556-7848
Media Relations Chief **Stephen Brady** . . . . (719) 556-5185
Librarian **Rebecca Perkins** . . . . (719) 556-7462
Building 1171, Fax: (719) 556-6752
201 West Stewart Avenue,
FL 2500, 21 SVS/SVMG, Peterson AFB, CO 80914-1600
Visual Information Manager **Rob Bussard** . . . . (719) 556-7192

821st Air Base Group (821 ABG)

APO, AE 09704

Commander **Col Mafwa M. Kuvibidila USAF** . . . . (719) 474-3840
Deputy Commander **LtCol Scott A. Schmunk USAF** . . . . (719) 474-3840
Senior Master Sergeant
CMSgt Frank Graziano USAF . . . . (719) 474-3840
Security Forces Squadron Commander
Maj Adam Morgan USAF . . . . (719) 474-3840

721st Mission Support Group

Cheyenne Mountain AFS, Building 101, One NORAD Road,
Suite 203, Colorado Springs, CO 80914-6099
Tel: (719) 474-2252 Fax: (719) 474-2298

Commander **Col Robert G. Moose USAF** . . . . (719) 474-2252
E-mail: robert.moose@us.af.mil

30th Space Wing (30 SW)

Vandenberg AFB, 747 Nebraska Avenue,
Suite A-200, Vandenberg AFB, CA 93437-6261
Tel: (805) 606-3595 Fax: (805) 606-8303
Internet: www.vandenberg.af.mil

Commander **Col Michael S. Hough USAF** . . . . (805) 606-3000
Education: Texas Tech 1992 BBA; U Great Falls 1996 MHR;
Naval War 2010 MS

30th Space Wing *(continued)*

Vice Commander **Col Bob A. Reeves USAF** . . . . (805) 606-3000
Executive Director **Ronald B. Cortopassi** . . . . (805) 606-3000
Chief Master Sergeant
CMSgt Diena M. Mosely USAF . . . . (805) 606-3000
Communications Squadron Commander
LtCol Matthew Hyland USAF . . . . (805) 606-5316
Mission Support Group Commander
Col Michael Hunsberger USAF . . . . (805) 606-4230
108 Colorado Ave., Fax: (805) 605-0772
Vandenberg AFB, CA 93437-6300
Public Affairs **SrA Michael Peterson USAF** . . . . (805) 606-3595

45th Space Wing (45 SW)

45SW/PA, 1201 Edward H. White II Street,
Suite C 129, Patrick AFB, FL 32925-4500
Tel: (321) 494-5933 Fax: (321) 494-7302
Internet: https://www.patrick.af.mil

Commander **BrigGen Douglas A. Schiess USAF** . . . . (321) 494-4502
Vice Commander **Col Thomas R. Ste. Marie USAF** . . . . . (321) 494-4505
Chief Master Sergeant **CMSgt Dan Delzingaro USAF** . . . (321) 494-4506
Public Affairs Chief **John Way** . . . . (321) 494-5933

50th Space Wing

210 Falcon Parkway, Suite 2102, Schriever AFB, CO 80912-2102
Tel: (719) 567-5040 Fax: (719) 567-5306
E-mail: 50swpa.workflow@schriever.af.mil Internet: www.schriever.af.mil

Commander **Col Jennifer L. Grant USAF** . . . . (719) 567-5040
Vice Commander **Col Jacob Middleton USAF** . . . . (719) 567-5040
Education: Augusta State 1991 BA; Troy U 1997 MA
Command Chief **CMSgt Boston Alexander USAF** . . . . . . (719) 567-5040
Public Affairs Chief **Jennifer Thibault** . . . . (719) 567-5448
E-mail: 50swpa.workflow@schriever.af.mil

21st Space Operations Squadron

Vandenberg AFB, CA 93437
Tel: (805) 606-8323

Commander **LtCol Phillip A. "Phil" Verroco USAF** . . . . . (805) 606-8323

460th Space Wing (460 SW)

Buckley AFB, 510 South Aspen Street,
Mail Stop 88, Aurora, CO 80011-9524
Tel: (720) 847-9011 Internet: www.buckley.af.mil

Commander **COL Troy Endicott USAF** . . . . (720) 847-9011
Vice Commander **Col Robert B. Riegel USAF** . . . . (720) 847-9011
Chief Master Sergeant **CMSgt Tamar Dennis USAF** . . . . . (720) 847-9011
Mission Support Group Commander
Col Trevor A. Wentlandt USAF . . . . (720) 847-9011
Operations Group Commander
Col Robert "Bobby" Hutt USAF . . . . (720) 847-9011

Air Force Special Operations Command (AFSOC)

Hurlburt Field, FL 32544-5271
Tel: (850) 884-5515 Fax: (850) 884-7249 Internet: www.afsoc.af.mil

Commander **LtGen Marshall B. "Brad" Webb USAF** . . . (850) 884-2323
Education: Air Force Acad 1984 BS; Troy State 1994 MS;
Air Command Col 1998; Air War Col 2003;
National War Col 2004 MS
Special Assistant to the Commander
BrigGen Vincent K. Becklund USAF . . . . (850) 884-5515
Mobilization Assistant to the Commander
MajGen James P. Scanlan USAFR . . . . (850) 884-5515
Education: Villanova 1985 BS
Deputy Commander **MajGen Michael T. Plehn USAF** . . . (850) 884-2323
E-mail: michael.t.plehn.mil@mail.mil
Education: Air Force Acad 1988 BS; Embry-Riddle 1997 MAS
● Executive Director **(Vacant)** . . . . (850) 884-5515
Command Chief Master Sergeant
CMSgt Gregory A. Smith USAF . . . . (850) 884-2323
Command Surgeon **Col Lee H. Harvis USAF** . . . . (850) 884-5515
Education: Michigan 1985 BS; Philadelphia Osteopathic 1996 DO
Contracting Director **(Vacant)** . . . . (850) 554-3990
Fax: (850) 884-2476

(continued on next page)

★ Presidential Appointment Requiring Senate Confirmation ☆ Presidential Appointment ☐ Schedule C Appointment ◇ Career Senior Foreign Service Appointment
● Career Senior Executive Service (SES) Appointment ○ Non-Career Senior Executive Service (SES) Appointment ■ Postal Career Executive Service

DEPARTMENTS

Air Force Special Operations Command *(continued)*

Installations and Mission Support Director
Col David C. Piech USAF .... (850) 884-5515
Operations Director **BrigGen Brenda Cartier USAF** ..... (850) 884-5515
Mobilization Assistant
BrigGen Jon A. Weeks USAF .... (850) 884-5515
Education: Troy U 1983 BS
Strategic Plans, Programs and Requirements Director
BrigGen Sean M. Farrell USAF .... (850) 884-2323
Mobilization Assistant
Col William W. Whittenberger, Jr. USAFR .... (850) 884-5515
Weather Director **LtCol John C. Roberts USAF** .... (850) 884-2323

18th Flight Test Squadron (Hurlburt Field)
Hurlburt Field, FL 32544-5446
Commander **LtCol Kevin D. Huebert USAF** .... (850) 884-5732

352nd Special Operations Wing (352 SOW - RAF Mildenhall)
RAF Mildenhall, Bury St. Edmunds, Suffolk, England IP28 8NF, United Kingdom
Mail: Unit 4840, Box 30, APO, AE 09459-8501
Internet: http://www.352sow.af.mil/
Commander **Col Matthew D. Smith USAF** 44 1638-544631
Vice Commander **Col Tracy L. Onufer USAF** 44 1638-544631
Education: Michigan 1995 BSChE

353rd Special Operations Group (353 SOG - Kadena AB)
Unit 5249, APO, AP 96368
Tel: 81 (98) 961-6131 Fax: 81 (98) 961-6912
Internet: http://www.353sog.af.mil/
Commander **Col Jason T. Kirby USAF** 81 (98) 961-6131

Air Force Special Operations Air Warfare Center (AFSOAWC)
Hurlburt Field, FL 32544-5271
Commander **(Vacant)** .... (850) 884-2755
Vice Commander **Col Royce Lott USAF** .... (850) 884-2755

1st Special Operations Wing (1 SOW)
131 Bartley Street, Suite 315, Hurlburt Field, FL 32544-5271
Tel: (850) 884-1110 Fax: (850) 884-2449
Commander **Col Michael E. Conley USAF** .... (850) 884-7782
Vice Commander **Col Michael D. Curry USAF** .... (850) 884-7782
Chief Master Sergeant **CMSgt David Wolfe USAF** .... (850) 884-7782
Public Affairs Chief **Amy Nicholson** .... (850) 884-7464
E-mail: amy.nicholson@hurlburt.af.mil
Contracting/Small Business **Chris Wentworth** .... (850) 884-1250
E-mail: chris.wentworth@hurlburt.af.mil
Freedom of Information Officer **Mabel Insco** .... (850) 884-2290
E-mail: mabel.insco@hurlburt.af.mil
Library Director **Vicky Stever** .... (850) 884-6947
Building 90337, 16 SVS/SVMG, Fax: (850) 884-6050
443 Cody Avenue, Hurlburt Field, FL 32544-5417

24th Special Operations Wing (24 SOW)
119 Terry Avenue, Hurlburt Field, FL 32544
Tel: (850) 884-8070 Internet: www.afsoc.af.mil/24sow
Commander **Col Claude K. Tudor, Jr. USAF** .... (850) 884-8070
Vice Commander **Col Eric D. Ray USAF** .... (850) 884-8070
E-mail: eric.ray@hurlburt.af.mil
Education: Air Force Acad 1989 BS; Troy State 2003 MS; Air U (USAF) 2011 MS
Command Chief Master Sergeant
CMSgt James E. Clark USAF .... (850) 884-8070

720th Special Tactics Group (Hurlburt Field)
Hurlburt Field, FL 32544-5271
Commander **Col Kurt W. Buller USAF** .... (850) 884-2288
E-mail: kurt.buller@hurlburt.af.mil

27th Special Operations Wing (27th SOW)
100 South DL Ingram, Suite 1, Cannon AFB, NM 88103
Tel: (575) 784-2727 Fax: (575) 784-2787 Internet: www.cannon.af.mil
Commander **Col Stewart A. Hammons USAF** .... (575) 784-2727

27th Special Operations Wing *(continued)*
Vice Commander **(Vacant)** .... (575) 784-2727
Chief Master Sergeant **CMSgt Eric Thompson USAF** ... (575) 784-2727
Contracting Squadron Commander
LtCol Anthony D. "Tony" Diaz USAF .... (575) 784-2321
Maintenance Group Commander
Col Clay Mason USAF .... (575) 784-2727
Mission Support Group Commander
Col Douglas Gilpin USAF .... (575) 784-2727
Small Business Officer **Horace Bates** .... (575) 784-2322
E-mail: horace.bates@cannon.af.mil
Public Affairs Chief **(Vacant)** .... (575) 784-4131

Air National Guard Units

106th Rescue Wing (106 RQW)
Francis S. Gabreski Airport, 150 Old Riverhead Road, Westhampton Beach, NY 11978-1201
Tel: (631) 723-7400 Internet: www.106rqw.ang.af.mil
Commander **Col Michael W. Bank ANG** .... (631) 723-7484
Education: Florida State BS
Vice Commander **(Vacant)** .... (631) 723-7484
Command Chief Master Sergeant
CMSgt Michael Hewson ANG .... (631) 723-7400
Maintenance Group Commander
LtCol Andrew J. Wineberger ANG .... (631) 723-7485
Medical Group Commander
Col Pamela Combs USAF .... (631) 723-7585
Mission Support Group Commander
Col Shawn P. Fitzgerald ANG .... (631) 723-7484
Operations Group Commander
LtCol Geoffrey Petyak ANG .... (631) 723-7422

193rd Special Operations Wing (193 SOW)
Harrisburg International Airport, 81 Constellation Court, Middletown, PA 17057-5086
Tel: (717) 948-2320 Fax: (717) 948-3299
Internet: www.193sow.ang.af.mil
Commander **Col Terrence L. Koudelka, Jr. USAF** .... (717) 948-2201
Chief Master Sergeant **William T. Yingling** .... (717) 948-2201
Public Affairs Officer **1st Lt Susan Penning USAF** ..... (717) 948-2311
E-mail: usafa.pa.193-sow.mbx.193-sow-pa@mail.mil
Freedom of Information Act Officer
MSgt Kathy Suhr USAF .... (717) 948-3140

Air Mobility Command (AMC)
402 Scott Drive, Scott AFB, IL 62225
Tel: (618) 229-3200 Tel: (618) 256-1110 (Base Locator)
Fax: (618) 229-0200 Internet: www.amc.af.mil

18th Air Force (18AF)
503 Ward Drive, Suite 214, Scott AFB, IL 62225-5335
Tel: (618) 402-0586 E-mail: 18.af.pa@us.af.mil
Internet: http://www.18af.amc.af.mil/
Commander **MajGen Sam C. Barrett USAF** .... (618) 229-7843
Education: Air Force Acad 1988 BS
Mobilization Assistant to the Commander
BrigGen Boyd C. L. Parker IV USAFR .... (618) 402-0586
Assistant to the Commander
Col Thomas J. Kennett ANG .... (618) 402-0586
Vice Commander **(Vacant)** .... (618) 229-0626
Chief Master Sergeant **CMSgt Todd S. Petzel USAF** .... (618) 229-0889
E-mail: todd.petzel@us.af.mil

Air Mobility Command Museum
Building 1301, Dover AFB, DE 19902-7219
Tel: (302) 677-5939 Fax: (302) 677-5940 Internet: www.amcmuseum.org
Director **MSgt Johnny Taylor USAF (Ret)** .... (302) 677-5939

317th Airlift Wing
110 2nd Avenue, Dyess AFB, TX 79607
Commander **Col Jeffrey Menasco USAF** .... (325) 696-0317

★ Presidential Appointment Requiring Senate Confirmation ☆ Presidential Appointment ☐ Schedule C Appointment ◇ Career Senior Foreign Service Appointment
● Career Senior Executive Service (SES) Appointment ○ Non-Career Senior Executive Service (SES) Appointment ■ Postal Career Executive Service

317th Airlift Wing *(continued)*

Maintenance Group Commander
Col William G. Maxwell, Jr. USAF (325) 696-0317
Operations Group Commander
Col James Hackbarth USAF (325) 696-0317

715th Air Mobility Operations Group (715 AMOG)
800 Scott Circle, Joint Base Pearl Harbor-Hickam, HI 96853-5328

Commander **Col Seaborn J. Whatley III USAF** (618) 402-2586

6th Air Mobility Wing (6 AMW)
6th Air Mobility Wing, 8208 Hangar Loop Drive,
Suite 1, MacDill AFB, FL 33621-5502
Tel: (813) 828-2215 Fax: (813) 828-3653
Internet: http://www.macdill.af.mil/

Commander **Col Stephen P. Snelson USAF** (813) 828-4444
Vice Commander **Col S. Troy Pananon USAF** (813) 828-4444
Chief Master Sergeant
CMSgt Sarah A. Sparks USAF (813) 828-4444
Maintenance Group Commander
Col Clifton D. "Cliff" Reed USAF (813) 828-2025
7709 Hangar Loop Drive, MacDill AFB, FL 33621-5201
Mission Support Group Commander
Col Edward P. "Eddie" Phillips USAF (813) 828-4545
2909 Nighthawk Place, MacDill AFB, FL 33621
Contracting Squadron Commander
Jeffrey Peske USAF (813) 828-4743
Operations Group Commander
Col Lisa A. Nemeth USAF (813) 828-9550
8011 Hangar Loop Drive, MacDill AFB, FL 33621
Freedom of Information Act Officer **Elizabeth Trask** (813) 828-4036
Base Historian **Stephen Ove** (813) 828-0434
Building 252, FL 4814, Fax: (813) 828-4416
8102 Condor Street,
MacDill AFB, FL 33621-5313

19th Airlift Wing (19 AW)
1250 Thomas Avenue, Little Rock AFB, AR 72099-4940
Tel: (501) 987-3434 (Public Affairs) Fax: (501) 987-3753
E-mail: 19aw.paall@littlerock.af.mil (Public Affairs)
Internet: www.littlerock.af.mil

Commander **Col Gerald A. Donohue USAF** (501) 987-1901
Education: Air Force Acad 1995 BS
Vice Commander **Col Christopher L. Lambert USAF** (501) 987-1901
Chief Master Sergeant **CMSgt David A. Morse USAF** (501) 987-1901
Communications Squadron Commander
Maj Daniel Presland USAF (501) 987-3735

22nd Air Refueling Wing (McConnell AFB)
57837 Coffeyville Street, Suite 240, McConnell AFB, KS 67221-3504
Tel: (316) 759-6100 (Base Operator)

Commander **Col Joshua M. Olson USAF** (316) 759-3100
Vice Commander **Maj Phil Heseltine USAF** (316) 759-3100
Command Chief Master Sergeant
CMSgt Leon O. Calloway USAF (316) 759-3100
Communications Squadron Commander **(Vacant)** (316) 759-4800
Public Affairs Chief **Ashley White** (316) 759-3154
Fax: (316) 759-3148
Contracting Officer **(Vacant)** (316) 759-3275
Freedom of Information Act Officer **Linda Pinkett** (316) 759-2097
E-mail: linda.pinkett@mcconnell.af.mil
Small Business Officer **Dennis Fry** (316) 759-3275
E-mail: dennis.fry@us.af.mil Fax: (316) 759-4507
Librarian **Darla Cooper** (316) 759-4207
Building 412, 22 SVS/SVRL, Fax: (316) 759-4254
53476 Wichita Street,
McConnell AFB, KS 67221-3610
E-mail: darla.cooper@us.af.mil

60th Air Mobility Wing (60 AMW)
Travis AFB, CA 94535-5000
Tel: (707) 424-2011 (Public Affairs) Fax: (707) 424-5936
Internet: www.travis.af.mil

Commander **Col Jeffrey Nelson USAF** (707) 424-2452

60th Air Mobility Wing *(continued)*

Executive Assistant **Capt Andrew Baer USAF** (707) 424-2454
Vice Commander
Col Matthew A. "Matt" Leard USAF (707) 424-2453
Operations Group Commander
Col Teresa Wayne USAF (707) 424-1110
Maintenance Group Commander
Col David Hammerschmidt USAF (707) 424-2656
Chief Master Sergeant
CMSgt Steve A. Nichols USAF (707) 424-5005
Freedom of Information Act Officer **Maria Morris** (707) 424-5668
Librarian **Marie Ludwig** (707) 424-4940
60 SVS/SVMG, Bldg. 436, Fax: (707) 424-3809
510 Travis Ave., Travis AFB, CA 94535-2168
Public Affairs Chief **Capt Lyndsey Horn USAF** (707) 424-2011
Public Affairs Secretary **Robert "Bobby" Textor** (707) 424-2011

62nd Airlift Wing (62 AW)
100 Colonel Joe Jackson Boulevard,
Joint Base Lewis-McChord, WA 98438
Tel: (253) 982-1110 Fax: (253) 982-5025 Internet: www.62aw.af.mil

Commander **Col Scovill W. Currin, Jr. USAF** (253) 982-2621
Education: Citadel; George Washington MA
Vice Commander **(Vacant)** (253) 982-2621
Chief Master Sergeant
CMSgt Jeffrey C. Sandusky USAF (253) 982-2621
Public Affairs Chief **Jason Waggoner** (253) 982-5638 ext. 8
Librarian **Cindy Spano** (253) 982-3454
851 Lincoln Boulevard, Ground Floor,
Joint Base Lewis-McChord, WA 98438-1317
Operations Group Commander
Col Mark S. Fuhrmann USAF (253) 982-2621
Maintenance Group Commander
Col Anthony Babcock USAF (253) 982-2621
Education: Air Force Acad BS;
Eisenhower National Security and Resource Strategy MS;
National Defense U MS; George Washington MA

89th Airlift Wing (89 AW)
1535 Command Drive, Suite AB-210,
Joint Base Andrews-Naval Air Facility Washington, MD 20762
Tel: (301) 981-3899 (Public Affairs) Fax: (301) 981-5921

Commander **Col Rebecca J. Sonkiss USAF** (301) 981-6011
Vice Commander **Col Samuel J. Chesnut USAF** (301) 981-6011
Chief Master Sergeant **(Vacant)** (301) 981-6011

92nd Air Refueling Wing (92 ARW)
Fairchild AFB, WA 99011
Tel: (509) 247-1212 (General Information)
Tel: (509) 247-5705 (Public Affairs) Fax: (509) 247-2120
Internet: www.fairchild.af.mil

Commander **Col Derek Salmi USAF** (509) 247-2124
Vice Commander **Col J. Scot Heathman USAF** (509) 247-2124
Chief Master Sergeant **CMSgt Lee P. Mills USAF** (509) 247-2124
Maintenance Group Commander
Col Alan T. Hart USAF (509) 247-2124
Education: Syracuse 1992 BS
Mission Support Group Commander
Col Yvonne S. Spencer USAF (509) 247-2124
E-mail: yvonne.s.spencer.mil@mail.mil
Operations Group Commander
Col Barry Cargle USAF (509) 247-2124
Director of Staff **Allard R. "Al" Carney** (509) 247-2124
Education: Air Force Acad 1977 BS; Illinois 1986 MS;
National Defense U 1997 MS
Public Affairs **A1C Sean Campbell USAF** (509) 247-5705

305th Air Mobility Wing (305 AMW)
Joint Base McGuire-Dix-Lakehurst, NJ 08641-5002
Tel: (609) 754-1100 (Base Operator)

Commander **Col Jacqueline D. Breeden USAF** (609) 754-3051
Vice Commander **Col David D. LeRoy USAF** (609) 754-3052
Command Chief Master Sergeant
CMSgt Brian D. Eastman USAF (609) 754-2174

★ Presidential Appointment Requiring Senate Confirmation ☆ Presidential Appointment □ Schedule C Appointment ◇ Career Senior Foreign Service Appointment
● Career Senior Executive Service (SES) Appointment ○ Non-Career Senior Executive Service (SES) Appointment ■ Postal Career Executive Service

314th Airlift Wing (314 AW)
1250 Thomas Avenue, Little Rock AFB, AR 72099-4940
Tel: (501) 987-3141 Tel: (501) 987-3601 (Public Affairs)
Fax: (501) 987-3753 Internet: www.littlerock.af.mil
E-mail: 19aw.paall@littlerock.af.mil (Public Affairs)

Commander **Col Stephen L. Hodge USAF** . . . . (501) 987-3141
Vice Commander **Col John M. Schutte USAF** . . . . (501) 987-3141
Chief Master Sergeant
CMSgt Justin W. Strain USAF . . . . (501) 987-3141

375th Airlift Mobility Wing (375 AMW)
Building 700 West, 901 South Drive, Scott AFB, IL 62225
Tel: (618) 256-4241 Fax: (618) 256-8837 Internet: www.scott.af.mil

Commander **Col Leslie A. Maher USAF** . . . . (618) 256-3751
Vice Commander **Col Joseph R. Meyer USAF** . . . . (618) 256-3751
Command Chief Master Sergeant **(Vacant)** . . . . (618) 256-5286

436th Airlift Wing
Dover AFB, DE 19902-7219
Tel: (302) 677-3000 Tel: (302) 677-3372 (Public Affairs)
Fax: (302) 677-2901 Internet: www.dover.af.mil

Commander **Col Joel W. Safranek USAF** . . . . (302) 677-4360
Vice Commander **Col Matthew E. Jones USAF** . . . . (302) 677-4360
Chief Master Sergeant
CMSgt Anthony W. Green USAF . . . . (302) 677-4360
Operations Group Commander
Col Larry Nance USAF . . . . (302) 677-3401
Freedom of Information Act Officer **Craig Gilbert** . . . . (302) 677-3642
Small Business Officer **Susan Bailey** . . . . (302) 677-2184

437th Airlift Wing (437 AW)
Joint Base Charleston, SC 29404-5154
Tel: (843) 963-3201 Fax: (843) 963-5604
E-mail: public.affairs@charleston.af.mil Internet: www.charleston.af.mil

Commander **Col Clinton Zumbrunnen USAF** . . . . (843) 963-3201
Vice Commander **Col Patrick Winstead USAF** . . . . (843) 963-3201
Chief Master Sergeant
CMSgt Jennifer L. Kersey USAF . . . . (843) 963-3201
Maintenance Group Commander
Maj Robert Johnson USAF . . . . (843) 963-3201
Operations Group Commander **(Vacant)** . . . . (843) 963-3201
Public Affairs Division Chief
Capt Christopher Love USAF . . . . (843) 963-5608
Library Director **Angela Aschenbrenner** . . . . (843) 963-5672
FL 4418, 106 W. McCaw St., Fax: (843) 963-3840
Joint Base Charleston, SC 29404-4700

U.S. Air Force Expeditionary Center (USAF EC)
5656 Texas Avenue, Joint Base McGuire-Dix-Lakehurst, NJ 08640-5403
Tel: (609) 754-7010 Internet: www.expeditionarycenter.af.mil

Commander **BrigGen John R. Gordy II USAF** . . . . (609) 754-7010
Education: North Carolina Charlotte 1988 BA; Webster 1996 MA; Air Command Col 2003 MA; National War Col 2008 MS
Executive Assistant **Felicia Pretty** . . . . (609) 754-7010
Mobilization Assistant **(Vacant)** . . . . (609) 754-7010
Vice Commander
BrigGen William M. "Bill" Knight USAF . . . . (609) 754-7010
Education: Auburn 1989 BS, 1990 MBA
Chief Master Sergeant **(Vacant)** . . . . (609) 754-7021

621st Contingency Response Wing
Joint Base McGuire-Dix-Lakehurst, NJ 08641-5002
Internet: www.expeditionarycenter.af.mil/units/621crw

Commander **Col Ryan T. Marshall USAF** . . . . (609) 754-6694
Vice Commander **(Vacant)** . . . . (609) 754-6694
Command Chief Master Sergeant **David M. Abell** . . . . (609) 754-6694
Education: Ashford 2013 BS

721st Air Mobility Operations Group (721 AMOG - Ramstein Air Base)
APO, AE 09094

Commander **Col Douglas Jackson USAF** 49 (6371) 46-4204
Deputy Commander **Col Robert Blake USAF** 49 (6371) 46-4204

43d Air Mobility Operations Group (43 AMOG)
259 Maynard Street, Pope AFB, NC 28308-2391
Tel: (910) 394-3223 (Freedom of Information Act Requests)
Fax: (910) 394-4266 Internet: www.pope.af.mil

Commander **Col Kelly Holbert USAF** . . . . (910) 394-3223

87th Air Base Wing (87 ABW)
Joint Base McGuire-Dix-Lakehurst, NJ 08641-5002
Tel: (609) 754-0870 (Public Affairs)

Commander **Col Neil R. Richardson USAF** . . . . (609) 754-0870
Deputy Commander **COL Charles W. Durr, Jr. USAR** . . . . (609) 754-0870
Education: Maryland
Chief Master Sergeant
CMSgt James E. Fitch II USAF . . . . (609) 754-0870
Executive Officer **Dr. Roderick Davis** . . . . (609) 754-0870
Contracting Officer **Maj Aarti U. Puri USAF** . . . . (609) 754-5926
Director of Operations **(Vacant)** . . . . (609) 754-0870
Freedom of Information Act Officer **Karen Leden** . . . . (609) 754-3445
E-mail: karen.leden@mcguire.af.mil
Public Affairs Chief **Maj Brian Wagner USAF** . . . . (609) 754-2104
E-mail: 87.abw.pa@us.af.mil

628th Air Base Wing (628 ABW)
Joint Base Charleston, SC 29404-5154
Tel: (843) 963-3419 Tel: (843) 963-5608 (Public Affairs)
Internet: http://www.jbcharleston.jb.mil/

Commander **Col Terrence A. Adams USAF** . . . . (843) 963-3419
Command Master Chief **CMDCM Jon Lonsdale USN** . . . (843) 963-3419

618th Air and Space Operations Center (Tanker Airlift Control Center)
2300 East Drive, Scott AFB, IL 62225-5406
Internet: www.618tacc.amc.af.mil

Commander **BrigGen John D. Lamontagne USAF** . . . . . (618) 229-2209
Mobilization Assistant
Col Kenneth R. Council, Jr. USAFR . . . . (618) 229-2209
Education: Embry-Riddle 1989 BS, 2008 MS
Vice Commander **Col Jimmy R. Canlas USAF** . . . . (618) 229-2209
Superintendent **CMSgt Ernest D. Crider USAF** . . . . (618) 229-2984

Air National Guard Units

101st Air Refueling Wing (101 ARW)
101 MAINEiac Avenue, Suite 505, Bangor, ME 04401-8009
Tel: (207) 626-4325 Internet: www.101arw.ang.af.mil

Commander **Col Frank W. Roy ANG** . . . . (207) 626-4325
Vice Commander **Col Matthew Brass ANG** . . . . (207) 626-4325
Freedom of Information Act Officer
TSgt Joseph Stalter ANG . . . . (207) 626-4325
Contracting/Small Business Officer
MSgt Daniel A. Boone, Jr. ANG . . . . (207) 626-4325
E-mail: daniel.a.boone3.mil@mail.mil

105th Airlift Wing (105 AW - Stewart Air National Guard Base)
Stewart Air National Guard Base, Newburgh, NY 12550-5076
Tel: (845) 563-2031 Fax: (845) 563-2013 Internet: www.105aw.ang.af.mil

Commander **Col Denise M. Donnell ANG** . . . . (845) 563-2001
Education: Georgetown 1993 BS; Air Command Col 2005; Air War Col 2008
Chief of Staff **LtCol Kristopher R. Geis USAF** . . . . (845) 563-2162
Vice Commander **Col Wilbur Biggin USAF** . . . . (845) 563-2001
Chief Master Sergeant
CMSgt Mark A. Cozzupoli ANG . . . . (845) 563-2001
Education: Manhattan Col 2002 BS; Mount St Mary 2007 MBA
Public Affairs Chief **MSgt Sara Pastorello USAF** . . . . . . (845) 563-2031
Operations Group Commander
LtCol Matthew Brenner USAF . . . . (845) 563-2000

107th Attack Wing
9910 Blewett Avenue, Niagara Falls, NY 14304
Tel: (716) 236-2000 Internet: www.107aw.ang.af.mil

Commander **Col Robert Kilgore ANG** . . . . (716) 236-2468
Education: Air Force Acad 1988 BS; Oklahoma 1999 MA
Vice Commander **Col Gary R. Charlton II ANG** . . . . (716) 236-2468

107th Attack Wing *(continued)*

Command Chief Master Sergeant
CMSgt Edward . Stefik USAF .... (716) 236-2468

109th Airlift Wing
One Air National Guard Road, Scotia, NY 12302-9752
Tel: (518) 344-2300 Fax: (518) 344-2530 Internet: www.109aw.ang.af.mil

Commander **Col Michele L. Kilgore ANG** .... (518) 344-2430
Vice Commander **Col Alan Ross ANG** .... (518) 344-2300
Command Chief Master Sergeant
CMSgt Denny L. Richardson ANG .... (518) 344-2300
Public Affairs Officer **TSgt Catharine Schmidt ANG** ... (518) 344-2352
E-mail: usaf.ny.109-aw.list.pa-public-affairs@mail.mil
Freedom of Information Act Monitor
MSgt Sarah Helligrass ANG .... (518) 344-2319
E-mail: sarah.m.helligrass.mil@mail.mil
Freedom of Information Act Officer (Alternate)
(Vacant) .... (518) 344-2429
Contracting/Small Business Officer
MSgt Wanda D. Yarbor ANG .... (518) 344-2300
E-mail: wanda.d.yarbor.mil@mail.mil

117th Air Refueling Wing (117 ARW)
5401 East Lake Boulevard, Birmingham, AL 35217-3545
Tel: (205) 714-2000 Fax: (205) 714-2224
Internet: www.117arw.ang.af.mil

Commander **Col Scott Grant ANG** .... (205) 714-2201
Vice Commander **Col Allen King ANG** .... (205) 714-2200
Command Chief Master Sergeant
CMSgt David Bullard ANG .... (205) 714-2000
Executive Officer **CAPT John Russell USN** .... (205) 714-2527

118th Wing (118 WG)
240 Knapp Boulevard, Nashville, TN 37217-2538
Tel: (615) 660-8062 Internet: http://www.118wg.ang.af.mil/

Commander **Col Keith A. Allbritten ANG** .... (615) 660-8000
Executive Officer **LtCol Marlin Malone, Jr. ANG** ..... (615) 660-8004
Public Affairs Officer **MSgt Jeremy Cornelius ANG** .... (615) 660-8062
Contracting Officer **SMSgt Fred Cawthon ANG**
Building 801, Room 123 .... (615) 660-8889

123rd Airlift Wing (123 AW)
1101 Grade Lane, Louisville, KY 40213-2678
Tel: (502) 413-4400 Fax: (502) 413-4676 Internet: www.123aw.ang.af.mil

Commander **Col David J. Mounkes USAF** .... (502) 413-4404
Education: Cal Poly San Luis Obispo 1989 BS;
Southern Baptist 2005 MDiv
Command Chief Master Sergeant
CMSgt Shane A. LaGrone ANG .... (502) 413-4404
Public Affairs **Maj Jackson Gabriel USAF** .... (502) 413-4589

128th Air Refueling Wing
1919 East Grange Avenue, Milwaukee, WI 53207-6142
Tel: (414) 944-8475 Fax: (414) 944-8259
E-mail: 128hq.publicaffairs@ang.af.mil Internet: www.128arw.ang.af.mil

Commander **Col James V. Locke USAF** .... (414) 944-8405
Vice Commander **Col Shawn Gaffney ANG** .... (414) 944-8475
Command Chief **CMSgt Thomas Fredrickson USAF** .... (414) 944-8475
Public Affairs Officer **Capt Beth Sawant ANG** .... (414) 944-8715

130th Airlift Wing (130 AW)
1679 Coonskin Drive, Charleston, WV 25311-5000
Tel: (304) 341-6000 Fax: (304) 341-6004 Internet: www.130aw.ang.af.mil

Commander **Col Johnny Ryan ANG** .... (304) 341-6130
Vice Commander **Col Michael O. Cadle ANG** .... (304) 341-6130
Command Chief Master Sergeant
CMSgt Kevin Cecil ANG .... (304) 341-6130
Public Affairs Officer **Capt Rachel Hughey ANG** .... (304) 341-6129
Freedom of Information Act Officer
TSgt Joshua Powell USAF .... (304) 341-6104
Contracting/Small Business Officer
MSgt Robert "Bob" Barker USAF .... (304) 341-6292
E-mail: robert.a.barker10.mil@mail.mil

134th Air Refueling Wing (134 ARW)
134 Briscoe Drive, McGhee Tyson ANG Base, TN 37777-6200
Tel: (865) 336-3203 Fax: (865) 336-3284
Internet: www.134arw.ang.af.mil

Commander **Col Martin L. "Lee" Hartley, Jr. ANG** ..... (865) 336-3203
Education: Air Force Acad BS; Liberty MBA
Executive Officer **Capt Stephanie McKeen ANG** ..... (865) 336-3205
Vice Commander **Col Bobby Underwood ANG** .... (865) 336-3203
Education: Tennessee BSA
Command Chief
CMSAF Stanley E. Drozdowski USAF .... (865) 336-3203
Public Affairs Officer **Capt Stephanie McKeen ANG** ... (865) 336-3205

137th Air Refueling Wing (137 ARW)
5624 Air Guard Drive, Oklahoma City, OK 73179-1067
Tel: (405) 686-5221 Fax: (405) 686-5812

Commander **Col Devin Wooden ANG** .... (405) 686-5220
Public Affairs Officer
1LT Michael "Mike" Campbell USAF .... (405) 686-5227
Freedom of Information Act Officer **(Vacant)** .... (405) 686-5848
Contracting/Small Business Officer **(Vacant)** .... (405) 686-5274

139th Airlift Wing (139 AW)
705 Memorial Drive, St. Joseph, MO 64503-9307
Tel: (816) 236-3201 Fax: (816) 236-3699 Internet: www.139aw.ang.af.mil

Commander **Col Edward E. Black ANG** .... (816) 236-3201
Vice Commander **Col John A. Cluck ANG** .... (816) 236-3201
Command Chief Master Sergeant
CMSgt Kris J. Neros ANG .... (816) 236-3201
Public Affairs Officer **Capt Rhonda Brown USAF** ...... (816) 236-3582

141st Air Refueling Wing (141 ARW - Fairchild AFB)
1403 West Wainwright Boulevard, Fairchild AFB, WA 99011-9417
Tel: (509) 247-7042 Fax: (509) 247-7002
Internet: www.141arw.ang.af.mil

Commander **Col Johan A. Deutscher USAF** .... (509) 247-7001
Executive Assistant **MSgt Katie Anderson ANG** ...... (509) 247-7001
Vice Commander **Col Kurt A. Tuininga ANG** .... (509) 247-7001
Chief Master Sergeant **CMSgt David E. Bishop ANG** ... (509) 247-7010
Wing Executive Officer and Community Manager
Maj Rona Ritchie ANG .... (509) 247-7003
Contracting and Small Business Officer
SMSgt Anthony Kuntz ANG .... (509) 247-7221

143rd Airlift Wing (143 AW)
One Minuteman Way, North Kingstown, RI 02852-7502
Tel: (401) 267-3200 Fax: (401) 886-1494 Internet: www.143aw.ang.af.mil

Commander **Col Michael A. Comstock ANG** .... (401) 267-3200
Education: Air Force Acad 1986 Fax: (401) 886-1494
Vice Commander **Col John Trevino USAF** .... (401) 267-3200
Chief Master Sergeant **CMSgt Jose Baltazar ANG** ...... (401) 267-3200
Public Affairs Officer **MSgt Janeen Miller ANG** .... (401) 267-3229
E-mail: usaf.ri.143-aw.list.pa@mail.mil
Freedom of Information Act Officer
Capt Brendan Duffy USAF .... (401) 267-3200
Contracting Officer **1st Lt Timothy Carron ANG** .... (401) 267-3200

145th Airlift Wing (145 AW)
4930 Minuteman Way, Charlotte, NC 28208-3866
Tel: (704) 391-4100 Fax: (704) 391-4196 Internet: www.145aw.ang.af.mil

Commander **Col Bryony Terrell ANG** .... (704) 391-4145
Education: Ohio 1997 BS
Vice Commander **Col Allan R. Cecil ANG** .... (704) 391-4345
Education: Belmont Abbey 1996 BABA
Executive Officer **Maj Lisa Dodge ANG** .... (704) 391-4245
Command Chief Master Sergeant
CMSgt Susan A. Dietz ANG .... (704) 391-4446
Maintenance Group Commander
LtCol Gary L. Dodge ANG .... (704) 391-4100
Education: LaVerne 1991 BS
Medical Group Commander
Col John W. Rogers ANG .... (704) 391-4124
Mission Support Group Commander
Col Russell L. Ponder ANG .... (704) 391-4124

(continued on next page)

★ Presidential Appointment Requiring Senate Confirmation ☆ Presidential Appointment □ Schedule C Appointment ◇ Career Senior Foreign Service Appointment
● Career Senior Executive Service (SES) Appointment ○ Non-Career Senior Executive Service (SES) Appointment ■ Postal Career Executive Service

DEPARTMENTS

DEPARTMENTS

145th Airlift Wing *(continued)*

Operations Group Commander
Col Miles K. Harkey ANG . . . . . (704) 391-4956
Public Affairs Officer **1st Lt Monica Ebert USAF** . . . . . (704) 391-4239
Fax: (704) 391-4320
Communications **(Vacant)** . . . . . (704) 391-4173

146th Airlift Wing (146 AW)
Channel Islands Air National Guard Station,
100 Mulcahey Drive, Port Hueneme, CA 93041-4001
Tel: (805) 986-7500 Fax: (805) 986-7437 Internet: www.146aw.ang.af.mil

Commander **Col Keith Y. Ward ANG** . . . . . (805) 986-7500
Vice Commander **Col Brian Kelly ANG** . . . . . (805) 986-7500
Chief Master Sergeant
CMSgt Cynthia Gregory USAF . . . . . (805) 986-7509
Chief Public Affairs Officer
Maj Kimberly Holman USAF . . . . . (805) 340-7301
Contracting Officer **SMSgt Jennifer Jackson ANG** . . . . . (805) 986-7970
Fax: (805) 986-7946

151st Air Refueling Wing (151 ARW)
765 North 2200 West, Salt Lake City, UT 84116-2999
Tel: (801) 245-2417 Fax: (801) 245-2447

Commander **Col Ryan Ogan ANG** . . . . . (801) 245-2307
Administrative Assistant
MSgt Jacqueline Clausen ANG . . . . . (801) 245-2308
E-mail: jacqueline.clausen@ang.af.mil
Chief of Information Systems
CMSgt Don Johnson USAF . . . . . (801) 245-2241
E-mail: webmaster@ang.af.mil

152nd Airlift Wing (152 AW)
1776 National Guard Way, Reno, NV 89502-4494
Tel: (775) 788-4500 Tel: (775) 788-4515 (Public Affairs)
Fax: (775) 788-4783 Internet: www.152aw.ang.af.mil

Commander **Col Eric Wade ANG** . . . . . (775) 788-4701
Vice Commander **Col Shanna Woyak ANG** . . . . . (775) 788-4701
Command Chief Master Sergeant
CMSgt Mark Prizina USAF . . . . . (775) 788-4701
Maintenance Group Commander
Capt Masten Bethel USAF . . . . . (775) 788-4500
Medical Group Commander **Col Martin A. Bain ANG** . . . (775) 788-4500
Mission Support Group Commander
Col Todd Starbuck ANG . . . . . (775) 788-4500
Operations Group Commander
Col Anthony Machabee ANG . . . . . (775) 788-4500
Commander, 152nd Intelligence Squadron
Col Brian J. Gunderson ANG . . . . . (775) 788-9380
Public Affairs Officer
Maj Jason Yuhasz ANG 152AW/PAO . . . . . (775) 788-4515
E-mail: usaf.nv.152-aw.list.pa-public-affairs@mail.mil
Contracting/Small Business Officer
MSgt Jason C. Huth ANG (Ret) . . . . . (775) 788-4662
E-mail: jason.c.huth.mil@mail.mil

153rd Airlift Wing (153 AW)
217 Dell Range Boulevard, Cheyenne, WY 82009
Tel: (307) 772-6750 (General Information) Fax: (307) 772-5010
Internet: www.153aw.ang.af.mil

Commander **Col Justin Walrath ANG** . . . . . (307) 772-6153
Vice Commander
Col David W. "Sheep" Herder ANG . . . . . (307) 772-6212
Command Chief Master Sergeant **(Vacant)** . . . . . (307) 772-5144
Public Affairs Executive Director **Deidre Forster** . . . . . (307) 431-4153
E-mail: deidre.m.forster.nfg@mail.mil Fax: (307) 772-5132

155th Air Refueling Wing (155 ARW)
1300 Military Road, Lincoln, NE 68508
Tel: (402) 309-1110 Fax: (402) 309-7310
Internet: http://www.155arw.ang.af.mil/

Commander **Col Robert Hargens ANG** . . . . . (402) 309-1111
Vice Commander **LtCol James Dalton ANG** . . . . . (402) 309-1111
Wing Command Chief **CMSgt Jeff Horne ANG** . . . . . (402) 309-1111

155th Air Refueling Wing *(continued)*

Public Affairs Officer **LtCol Kevin J. Hynes ANG** . . . . . (402) 309-7300
E-mail: kevin.j.hynes.mil@mail.mil
Base Contracting Officer **MSgt Tonja Buchholz ANG** . . . (402) 309-8254
E-mail: tonja.a.buchholz.mil@mail.mil Fax: (402) 309-7524

156th Airlift Wing (156 AW)
200 Jose A. Santana Tony Avenue, Carolina, PR 00979-1502
Fax: (787) 253-5280 Internet: http://www.156aw.ang.af.mil/

Commander **Col Raymond Figueroa ANG** . . . . . (787) 253-5101

157th Air Refueling Wing (157 ARW)
302 New Market Street, Portsmouth, NH 03803-0157
Tel: (603) 430-3577 Fax: (603) 430-3139
Internet: www.157arw.ang.af.mil

Commander **Col John W. "Pogo" Pogorek USAF** . . . . . (603) 430-2453
Vice Commander **LtCol William Davis ANG** . . . . . (603) 430-2453
Command Chief **CMSgt Matthew S. Heiman USAF** . . . . (603) 430-2453
Public Affairs Officer **Capt Emily O'Neil USAF** . . . . . (603) 340-3577
E-mail: 157arw.pa@ang.af.mil Fax: (603) 430-3413
Chief of Contracting **Scott L. Ballweg** . . . . . (603) 715-3670
E-mail: scott.l.ballweg.civ@mail.mil
Education: Granite State 2009 BA

161st Air Refueling Wing (161 ARW)
161st Air Refueling Wing, Arizona Air National Guard,
3200 East Old Tower Road, Phoenix, AZ 85034-7263
Tel: (602) 302-9000 Fax: (602) 302-9199
Internet: www.161arw.ang.af.mil

Commander **Col Patrick W. Donaldson ANG** . . . . . (602) 302-9200
Education: U St Thomas (MN) 1993 BA; Whitworth 1999 MBA
Secretary, Office Administrator
TSgt Maria Baceda USAF . . . . . (602) 302-9201
Vice Commander **Col E Hoyt Slocum ANG** . . . . . (602) 302-9200
Education: Embry-Riddle BS
Chief of Staff **LtCol Gabe D. Johnson ANG** . . . . . (602) 302-9200
Chief Master Sergeant **CMSgt Bert A. Reid USAF** . . . . . (602) 302-9200
Public Affairs Officer **Maj Candace N. Park ANG** . . . . . (602) 302-9449
Education: Arizona 2005 BA, 2014 MA

164th Airlift Wing (164 AW)
2815 Democrat Road, Memphis, TN 38118-1510
Tel: (901) 291-7111 Fax: (901) 291-7463 E-mail: 164aw.pa@ang.af.mil
Internet: www.164aw.ang.af.mil/

Commander **Col Raymond S. Robinson IV ANG** . . . . . (901) 291-7164
Vice Commander **(Vacant)** . . . . . (901) 291-7120
Command Chief **CMSgt Jimmie Jones ANG** . . . . . (901) 291-7463
Operations Group Commander
Col Joseph "Jody" Dickens ANG . . . . . (901) 291-7111

165th Airlift Wing (165 AW)
1401 Robert B. Miller, Jr. Drive, Garden City, GA 31408-9001
Internet: www.165aw.ang.af.mil

Commander **Col Rainer G. "Speedy" Gomez ANG** . . . . (912) 966-8290
Vice Commander **Col James P. "Jim" Marren ANG** . . . . (912) 966-8290
Education: Spring Hill 1988 BS
Command Chief **CMSgt Rodney L. Jenkins USAF** . . . . . (912) 966-8290
Education: St Leo U 1998 BA
Public Affairs Officer **Maj David C. Simons ANG** . . . . . (912) 966-8290
E-mail: 165aw.public_affairs@ang.af.mil

166th Airlift Wing (166 AW)
2600 Spruance Drive, New Castle, DE 19720
Tel: (302) 323-3535 (Command Post)
Tel: (302) 323-3369 (Public Affairs) E-mail: 166aw.pa@ang.af.mil
Internet: http://www.166aw.ang.af.mil/

Commander **Col Robert E. Culcasi ANG** . . . . . (302) 323-3535
Vice Commander **(Vacant)** . . . . . (302) 323-3535
Command Chief Master Sergeant
CMSgt Shaune Peters ANG . . . . . (302) 323-3535

★ Presidential Appointment Requiring Senate Confirmation ☆ Presidential Appointment □ Schedule C Appointment ◇ Career Senior Foreign Service Appointment
● Career Senior Executive Service (SES) Appointment ○ Non-Career Senior Executive Service (SES) Appointment ■ Postal Career Executive Service

167th Airlift Wing (167 AW)
Building 110, 222 Sabre Jet Boulevard, Martinsburg, WV 25405-7704
Tel: (304) 616-5272 Fax: (304) 616-5111
Internet: www.167aw.ang.af.mil/

Commander **Col David V. "DC" Cochran ANG** . . . . (304) 616-5167
Vice Commander **Col Rodney Neely ANG** . . . . (304) 616-5272
Chief Master Sergeant
CMSAF David W. Stevens ANG . . . . (304) 616-5272
Chief of Staff **Maj Lindsey Fletcher ANG** . . . . (304) 616-5272
Maintenance Group Commander
Col Christian Cunningham ANG . . . . (304) 616-5272
Mission Support Group Commander **(Vacant)** . . . . (304) 616-5272
Operations Group Commander
LtCol Martin E. Timkl USAF . . . . (304) 616-5100
Public Affairs Officer **1st Lt Stacy Gault ANG** . . . . (304) 616-5272
E-mail: 167aw.pa@ang.af.mil
Freedom of Information Act Officer
SSgt Katrina Santa Maria ANG . . . . (304) 616-5272

171st Air Refueling Wing (171 ARW)
300 Tanker Road, Room 4200, Coraopolis, PA 15108
Tel: (412) 776-8010 Internet: www.171arw.ang.af.mil

Commander **LtCol Mark Goodwill ANG** . . . . (412) 776-7321
Education: Penn State 1987 BS
Vice Commander **Col Joseph R. Olszewski USAF** . . . . . (412) 776-7321
Education: Embry-Riddle 1990 BS; California U (PA) 1998 MA; Air Command Col 2006; Air War Col 2009
Chief Master Sergeant **CMSgt Randy E. Miller ANG** . . . . (412) 776-7321
Maintenance Group Commander
LtCol Raymond Hyland ANG . . . . (412) 776-8010
Education: Kent State 1989 BS; Mountain State 2007 MS
Mission Support Group Commander **(Vacant)** . . . . (412) 776-7321
Operations Group Commander
Col Gilbert L. Patton ANG . . . . (412) 776-7321
E-mail: gilbert.l.patton.mil@mail.mil
Contracting Officer
MSgt Francis X. "Frank" McNulty ANG . . . . (412) 776-7685
E-mail: francis.x.mcnulty2.mil@mail.mil
Public Affairs Officer **Maj Karen Bogdan ANG** . . . . (412) 776-7321
E-mail: 171.arw.pa@ang.af.mil

172nd Airlift Wing (172 AW)
141 Military Drive, Jackson, MS 39232-8881
Tel: (601) 405-8300 Fax: (601) 405-8565 Internet: www.172aw.ang.af.mil

Commander **Col Tommy F. Tillman ANG** . . . . (601) 405-8300
Vice Commander **Col Trent J. Van Hulzen USAF** . . . . (601) 405-8300
Chief of Staff **LtCol Laura Odom USAF** . . . . (601) 405-8506
Contracting/Small Business Chief (Acting)
MSgt Amber Young ANG . . . . (601) 405-8494
Fax: (601) 405-8214
Webmaster **MSgt Edwin Levy ANG** . . . . (601) 405-8690

179th Airlift Wing (179 AW)
1947 Harrington Memorial Road, Mansfield, OH 44903-0179
Tel: (419) 520-6100 Fax: (419) 520-6479 Internet: www.179aw.ang.af.mil

Commander **Col Allison Miller ANG** . . . . (419) 520-6179
Education: Auburn (Montgomery) 1993 BS, 2013 MS
Vice Commander **Col Todd K. Thomas MCSE** . . . . (419) 520-6153
Education: Iowa 1988 BS; Air War Col 2008
Chief Master Sergeant **CMSgt Mark A. Dyer ANG** . . . . . . (419) 520-6578
Public Affairs Officer **1st Lt Paul Stennett ANG** . . . . (419) 520-6377
Education: Akron 2011

185th Air Refueling Wing (185 ARW)
2920 Headquarters Avenue, Sioux City, IA 51111-1300
Tel: (712) 233-0502 Internet: www.185arw.ang.af.mil

Commander **Col Lawrence L. Christensen ANG** . . . . (712) 233-0501
Vice Commander **Col James Walker USAF** . . . . (712) 233-0501
Command Chief **(Vacant)** . . . . (712) 233-0502
Mission Support Group Commander
Col Stephanie S. Samenus ANG . . . . (712) 233-0587
E-mail: stephanie.samenus@iasiou.ang.af.mil
Education: Missouri Western State Col 1987 BSBA

185th Air Refueling Wing *(continued)*

Base Contracting Officer **Allison Harbit** . . . . (712) 233-0512
Fax: (712) 233-0576
Public Affairs Officer **Maj Jennifer Carlson USAF** . . . . . . (712) 233-0809

186th Air Refueling Wing (186 ARW)
Key Field, 6225 M Street, Meridian, MS 39307-7112
Tel: (601) 484-9000 Fax: (601) 484-9699
Internet: http://www.186arw.ang.af.mil/

Commander **Col Edward H. Evans, Jr. USAF** . . . . (601) 484-9000
Public Affairs Officer **LtCol Brad Crawford USAF** . . . . . . (601) 484-9000
E-mail: usaf.ms.186-arw.mbx.public-affairs@mail.mil

190th Air Refueling Wing (190 ARW)
5920 Southeast Coyote Drive, Topeka, KS 66619-5370
Tel: (785) 861-4791 Fax: (785) 861-4266
Internet: www.190arw.ang.af.mil

Commander **Col G. Jarrod Frantz ANG** . . . . (785) 861-4791
Vice Commander **LtCol Dan Skoda USAF** . . . . (785) 861-4791
Command Chief Master Sergeant
CMSgt Von R. Burns ANG . . . . (785) 861-4791

North American Aerospace Defense Command (NORAD)
250 Vandenberg Street, Peterson AFB, CO 80914-5002
Tel: (719) 554-6889 (Public Affairs) Fax: (719) 554-3165 (Public Affairs)
E-mail: norpa@peterson.af.mil Internet: www.norad.mil

Commander **Gen Terrence J. O'Shaughnessy USAF** . . . (719) 554-6889
Education: Air Force Acad 1986 BS; Embry-Riddle 1996 MS; Air Command Col 1998; Indust'l Col Armed Forces 2003
Executive Officer **CAPT Steven A. Mucklow USN** . . . . (719) 554-6889
◇ Foreign Policy Advisor
Christopher J. "Chris" Sandrolini . . . . (719) 554-6889
Education: Chicago 1982 BA; Johns Hopkins 1984 MA
Special Assistant for Reserve Matters
BG John E. Cardwell USAR . . . . (719) 554-6889
Education: Tennessee; Army War Col MSS
Deputy Commander **LGen Christopher Coates CF** . . . . . . (719) 554-3005
250 Vandenberg Street, Peterson AFB, CO 80914-3801
Vice Commander, U.S. Element **(Vacant)** . . . . (719) 554-3892
250 Vandenberg Street, Peterson AFB, CO 80914-3801
Senior Enlisted Advisor
SgtMaj Paul G. McKenna USMC . . . . (719) 554-7688
Chief of Staff **MG Richard J. Gallant ARNG** . . . . (719) 554-6889
Deputy Chief of Staff for Communications and
Public Affairs Officer **(Vacant)** . . . . (719) 554-5889
Director, Command and Control Systems **(Vacant)** . . . . (719) 554-3475
Director, Cyberspace Operations
BrigGen Angela M. "Angie" Cadwell USAF . . . . (719) 554-5916
Vice Director, Operations
BrigGen Peter M. Fesler USAF . . . . (719) 554-6889

Integrated Command Center
250 Vandenberg Street, Peterson AFB, CO 80914-5002
Tel: (719) 554-7214

Director **(Vacant)** . . . . (719) 554-7214

Pacific Air Forces (PACAF)
Joint Base Pearl Harbor-Hickam, HI 96853
Fax: (808) 449-4521 Internet: www.pacaf.af.mil

Commander **Gen Charles Q. Brown, Jr. USAF** . . . . (808) 449-4501
Education: Texas Tech 1984 BSCE; Embry-Riddle 1994 MAS
Executive Officer **(Vacant)** . . . . (703) 697-7376
Mobilization Assistant to the Commander
MajGen Walter J. Sams USAFR . . . . (808) 449-4501
Education: Georgia 1984 BS; Embry-Riddle 1999 MAS
Deputy Commander **MajGen Russell L. Mack USAF** . . . . (808) 449-4501
Education: New Hampshire 1984 BSEE; Troy St (Montgomery) 1996 MPA
Chief Master Sergeant
CMSgt Anthony W. Johnson USAF . . . . (808) 449-2490
Education: Comm Col Air Force 2001 AAS; U Phoenix 2006 BS
Chief of Staff **MajGen Brian M. Killough USAF** . . . . (808) 449-2490

(continued on next page)

★ Presidential Appointment Requiring Senate Confirmation ☆ Presidential Appointment ☐ Schedule C Appointment ◇ Career Senior Foreign Service Appointment
● Career Senior Executive Service (SES) Appointment ○ Non-Career Senior Executive Service (SES) Appointment ■ Postal Career Executive Service

DEPARTMENTS

Pacific Air Forces *(continued)*

Air and Cyberspace Operations Director
BrigGen Stephen C. Williams USAF . . . . (808) 449-4501
Education: Air Force Acad 1989 BS; Embry-Riddle 2003 MS
Mobilization Assistant to the Air and Cyberspace Operations Director
BrigGen James N. Coombes ANG . . . . (808) 449-4501
Education: Auburn 1987 BS, 1994 MBA
Logistics, Engineering and Force Protection Director
(Vacant) . . . . (808) 449-2490
Logistics, Engineering and Force Protection Director
BrigGen Jeffrey R. King USAF . . . . (808) 449-2490
Programs and Analyses Director **(Vacant)** . . . . (808) 449-2490
Strategic Plans, Requirements and Programs Director
BrigGen Michael P. Winkler USAF . . . . (808) 449-2490
Command Surgeon **(Vacant)** . . . . (808) 449-4501

15th Wing
800 Scott Circle, Joint Base Pearl Harbor-Hickam, HI 96853-5328
Tel: (808) 449-1500 Fax: (808) 449-3017 E-mail: 15wg.pa@us.af.mil
Internet: www.15wing.af.mil

Commander **W. Halsey Burks USAF** . . . . (808) 449-1500
Education: Air Force Acad 1995 BS
Vice Commander **(Vacant)** . . . . (808) 449-1501
Chief Master Sergeant **CMSgt Michael Cole USAF** . . . . . (808) 449-1510
Command Post Chief **Maj Warren Reece USAF** . . . . (808) 448-6916
15 AW/CTC, 800 Hangar Avenue,
Joint Base Pearl Harbor-Hickam, HI 96853-5244
Staff Judge Advocate
LtCol Matthew McCall USAF . . . . (808) 449-1737 ext. 240
15 ABW/JA, 120 Sixth Street,
Joint Base Pearl Harbor-Hickam, HI 96853-5336

15th Maintenance Group (Joint Base Pearl Harbor-Hickam)
Commander **Col Dominic "Nic" Clementz USAF** . . . . . . (808) 449-1500

15th Medical Group (Joint Base Pearl Harbor-Hickam)
755 Scott Circle, Joint Base Pearl Harbor-Hickam, HI 96853-5399
Tel: (808) 448-6000

Commander **Col Kara Gormont USAF** . . . . (808) 448-6222
Executive Officer **Capt Rhoda Santos USAF** . . . . (808) 448-6222
Chief Master Sergeant **CMSgt Rickey L. Mann USAF** . . . (808) 448-6374

15th Operations Group (Joint Base Pearl Harbor-Hickam)
Commander **Col Jason King USAF** . . . . (808) 449-1543
E-mail: 15og.css.1@us.af.mil

647th Air Base Group (Joint Base Pearl Harbor-Hickam)
Commander **Col Douglas E. Pierce USAF** . . . . (808) 449-1579
Education: Citadel 1995 BS; South Carolina 2002 MA

36th Wing (36 WG)
Unit 14003, Box 25, APO, AP 96543-4003
Tel: (671) 366-4202 Fax: (671) 366-4242 Internet: www.andersen.af.mil

Commander **BrigGen Gentry Boswell USAF** . . . . (671) 366-4202
Education: Delta State 1991 BS; Embry-Riddle 2001 MA; Air U (USAF) 2005; Air War Col 2011 MSS
Vice Commander **Col Matthew J. Nicholson USAF** . . . . (671) 366-3600
Chief Master Sergeant **CMSgt Gary Szekely USAF** . . . . . (671) 366-3604

36th Maintenance Group (Andersen AFB)
Commander **(Vacant)** . . . . (671) 366-6150

36th Medical Group (Andersen AFB)
Unit 14010, APO, AP 96543-4003
Commander **Col Joel O. Almosara USAF** . . . . (671) 366-4270

36th Mission Support Group (Andersen AFB)
Unit 14003, Box 25, APO, AP 96543-4003
Commander **(Vacant)** . . . . (671) 366-4551

36th Operations Group (Andersen AFB)
Commander **Col Samuel White USAF** . . . . (671) 366-3664

5th Air Force (5AF)
Yokota Air Base, Japan
Mail: Unit 5068, APO, AP 96328-5068
Tel: 81 3117-55-2769 Tel: 81 3117-55-1110 (Base Operator)
Fax: 81 3117-55-2312 E-mail: 5AF.P@us.af.mil
Internet: www.5af.pacaf.af.mil

Commander, 5th Air Force/Commander, U.S. Forces Japan **LtGen Jerry P. Martinez USAF** 81 (3117) 55-4295
Education: Air Force Acad 1986 BSGS; Webster 1994 MBA
Mobilization Assistant to the Commander
Col Paul R. Fast USAF 81 3117-55-2769
Education: Miami U (OH) 1991 BSBA; U Phoenix 2004 MBA; Air Command Col 2006; Air War Col 2011
Deputy Commander, U.S. Forces Japan
BGen Christopher J. "C.J." Mahoney USMC 81 (3117) 55-4148
Vice Commander **BrigGen Todd A. Dozier USAF** 81 (3117) 55-4148
Command Master Sergeant
CMSgt Terrence A. Greene USAF 81 (3117) 55-4148
Education: U Phoenix 2010 BS

374th Airlift Wing (374 AW)
Yokota Air Base, Japan

Commander **Col Otis Jones USAF** 81 (3117) 55-8833
After Hours: 81 (3117) 55-2536
Vice Commander **Col Neil R. Richardson USAF** 81 (3117) 55-8833
Chief Master Sergeant **(Vacant)** 81 (3117) 55-8833
Maintenance Group Commander
Col Sean W. Robertson USAF 81 (3117) 55-8833
Mission Support Group Commander
Col Tanya J. Anderson USAF 81 (3117) 55-8833
Operations Group Commander
Col Mark J. Mullarkey USAF 81 (3117) 55-8833
Public Affairs **Sgt David Owsianka USAF** 81 (3117) 55-8833
E-mail: 374thaw.pa@yokota.af.mil
After Hours: 81 (3117) 55-2536

35th Fighter Wing (Misawa Air Base)
PSC 76, Unit 5003, APO, AP 96319
Tel: 81 3117-66-1110 E-mail: 35fwpa.media@misawa.af.mil
Internet: www.misawa.af.mil

Commander **Col Kristopher W. Struve USAF** 81 3117-66-1110
Vice Commander **Col Paul D. Kirmis USAF** 81 3117-66-1110
Chief Master Sergeant
CMSgt John C. Alsvig USAF 81 3117-66-1110

18th Wing (18 WG)
18 WG/PA, Unit 5141, Box 30, APO, AP 96368-5141
Tel: 81 (6117) 34-1509 Fax: 81 (6117) 34-2344
E-mail: 18wg.pa@kadena.af.mil Internet: www.kadena.af.mil

Commander **BrigGen Case Cunningham USAF** 81 (6117) 34-1110
Vice Commander **Col Richard C. Tanner USAF** 81 (6117) 34-1110
Chief Master Sergeant
CMSgt Michael R. Ditore USAF 81 (6117) 34-1110
Civil Engineer Group Commander
Col R. Scott Grainger USAF 81 (6117) 34-1110
Maintenance Group Commander
Col Tony S. Lombardo USAF 81 (6117) 34-1110
Mission Support Group Commander
Col Thang Tom Doan USAF . . . . 81 (6117] 34-1110
Operations Group Commander
Col Scott Rowe USAF 81 (6117) 34-1110

7th Air Force (7AF)
Unit 2047, APO, AP 96278-2047
Tel: 82 (31) 661-7001 Fax: 82 (31) 661-2767
Internet: www.7af.pacaf.af.mil

Commander **LtGen Kenneth S. Wilsbach USAF** 82 (31) 661-7001
Education: Florida 1985 BS; Embry-Riddle 1997 MAE; Indust'l Col Armed Forces 2003
Mobilization Assistant
Col Scheid P. Hodges USAFR . . . . (703) 692-6800
Education: Louisiana Tech U 1987 BS, 1988 MBA
Vice Commander
BrigGen Lansing R. "Lance" Pilch USAF 82 (31) 661-7001

★ Presidential Appointment Requiring Senate Confirmation ☆ Presidential Appointment ☐ Schedule C Appointment ◇ Career Senior Foreign Service Appointment
● Career Senior Executive Service (SES) Appointment ○ Non-Career Senior Executive Service (SES) Appointment ■ Postal Career Executive Service

7th Air Force *(continued)*

Chief Master Sergeant
CMSgt Scott W. Lumpkin USAF 82 (31) 661-6304
Education: American Military U 2011 BA

51st Fighter Wing (51 FW - Osan Air Base)
51 FW/PA, Unit 2067, APO, AP 96278-2067
Tel: 82 505-784-4044 Internet: www.osan.af.mil

Commander **Maj Gregory T. White ANG** 82 505-784-4044
Vice Commander **Jesse Friedel USAF** 82 505-784-4044
Chief Master Sergeant
CMSgt Philip B. Hudson USAF 82 505-784-4044
Maintenance Group Commander
Col M. Todd Hammond USAF 82 505-784-4044
Education: VMI 1993 BA; George Washington 2001 MA; Air Command Col 2006 MMAS
Mission Support Group Commander
Col Kevin R. Mantovani USAF 82 505-784-4044
Operations Group Commander
Col Larry Card II USAF 82 505-784-4044

11th Air Force (11AF - Joint Base Elmendorf-Richardson)
9480 Pease Avenue, Suite 111,
Joint Base Elmendorf-Richardson, AK 99506
Tel: (907) 552-2100 Fax: (907) 552-5411

Commander **LtGen Thomas A. Bussiere USAF** . . . . (907) 552-2100
Education: Norwich 1985 BSBusMgt; Air Command Col 2000; Air U (USAF) 2000 MA, 2001 MA; Air War Col 2004; Army War Col 2007 MSS
Executive Officer **Maj Gina M. Schneider USAF** . . . . . . (907) 552-2100
Vice Commander **Col Lars R. Hubert USAF** . . . . (907) 552-4100
Chief Master Sergeant **CMSgt Gay Veale USAF** . . . . (907) 552-2295
Public Affairs Director
Capt Anastasia Schmidt USAF . . . . (907) 552-2341
E-mail: anastasia.wasem@us.af.mil

3rd Wing (3 WG)
11550 Heritage Avenue, Joint Base Elmendorf-Richardson, AK 99506
Tel: (907) 552-0300 Fax: (907) 552-1085

Commander **(Vacant)** . . . . (907) 552-0300
Vice Commander **Col Harmon S. Lewis, Jr. USAF** . . . . . (907) 552-0300
Education: Air Force Acad 1995 BS; Joint Forces Staff Col 2008 MS; Naval War 2014 MA
Chief Master Sergeant **CMSgt Brian Stafford USAF** . . . . (907) 552-0304
Maintenance Group Commander **(Vacant)** . . . . (907) 552-3005
Operations Group Commander **(Vacant)** . . . . (907) 552-3003
Public Affairs Chief **Maj Angela Webb USAF** . . . . (907) 552-8153
E-mail: angela.webb@elmendorf.af.mil

354th Fighter Wing (354 FW)
Eielson AFB, AK 99702-5000
Tel: (907) 377-1110 Tel: (907) 377-3148 (Community Relations)
Tel: (907) 377-2441 (Contracting)
Tel: (907) 377-2107 (Freedom of Information Act Officer)
Tel: (907) 377-2116 (Public Affairs)
Tel: (907) 377-4183 (Small Business) E-mail: info@eielson.af.mil
Internet: www.eielson.af.mil

Commander **Col Benjamin Bishop USAF** . . . . (907) 377-6101
Vice Commander **Col Shawn E. Anger USAF** . . . . (907) 377-6101
Chief Master Sergeant **(Vacant)** . . . . (907) 377-6101
Maintenance Group Commander
Col Peter J. Gryzen USAF . . . . (907) 377-2207
Mission Support Group Commander
Col Chad Bondurant USAF . . . . (907) 377-3258
Operations Group Commander
Col Jacob Trigler USAF . . . . (907) 377-1110

673rd Air Base Wing (673ABW)
10471 20th Street, Suite 139,
Joint Base Elmendorf-Richardson, AK 99506
Tel: (907) 552-8151 Fax: (907) 552-5265 Internet: www.jber.af.mil

Commander **Col George "Dutch" Dietrich III USAF** . . . . (907) 552-8151
Executive Officer **Capt Joanna Everett USAF** . . . . (907) 552-6738

673rd Air Base Wing *(continued)*

Vice Commander **COL Adam W. Lange USA** . . . . (907) 552-8151
Executive Director
Col Donald C. Weckhorst USAF (Ret) . . . . (907) 552-8151
Chief Master Sergeant **CMSgt Charles C. Orf USN** . . . . . (907) 552-8151
Command Sergeant Major
CSM Jerry H. Byrd, Jr. USA . . . . (907) 552-8151
Civil Engineer Group Commander **(Vacant)** . . . . (907) 552-3007
Logistics Readiness Group Commander
Col Kirk Peterson USAF . . . . (907) 552-3264
Mission Support Group Commander
Col Dan Knight USAF . . . . (907) 552-3004
Contracting Squadron Commander
LtCol James Atchley USAF . . . . (907) 552-2810
E-mail: james.atchley@us.af.mil
Public Affairs Director **Maj Angela Webb USAF** . . . . (907) 552-8153
E-mail: angela.webb@elmendorf.af.mil

Air National Guard Units

168th Wing (168th Air Refueling Wing)
168 ARW, 2680 Flightline Avenue, Suite 117,
Eielson AFB, AK 99702-1740
Tel: (907) 377-8722 Fax: (907) 377-8712
Internet: www.168arw.ang.af.mil

Commander **Col Bryan S. White ANG** . . . . (907) 377-8722
Mission Support Group Commander
LtCol Jack R. Evans ANG . . . . (907) 377-8722
Chief Master Sergeant
CMSgt James Wolverton ANG . . . . (907) 377-8722
Public Affairs Officer
2nd Lt Francine St. Laurent USAF . . . . (907) 377-8734
Contracting Officer **MSgt Stacey L. Pfau ANG** . . . . (907) 377-8743
E-mail: stacey.l.pfau.mil@mail.mil

176th Wing (176 WG)
Joint Base Elmendorf-Richardson, AK 99506
Tel: (907) 552-3959 Internet: www.176wg.ang.af.mil

Commander **BrigGen Darrin Slaten ANG** . . . . (907) 551-1764
Executive Staff Officer **Maj Ashley Noruad ANG** . . . . (907) 551-1764
Vice Commander **Col Scott A. Coniglio ANG** . . . . (907) 552-1764
Command Chief Master Sergeant
CMSgt Delmar J. Schaefers ANG . . . . (907) 551-1764
Public Affairs Officer **Capt John Callahan ANG** . . . . (907) 552-3959
Information Manager **TSgt Ray Ileno ANG** . . . . (907) 551-1764
Contracting Officer **SMSgt Craig S. Wood ANG** . . . . (907) 551-0246
E-mail: craig.s.wood.mil@mail.mil

U.S. Air Forces in Europe and Air Forces Africa (USAFEAFARICA)

Ramstein Air Base, Kaiserslautern, Germany
Mail: HQ, U.S. Air Forces in Europe/Commander, Unit 3050, Box 1, APO, AE 09094-0501
Tel: 49 (6371) 47-6357 Fax: 49 (6371) 47-2705
Internet: www.usafe.af.mil

Commander **Gen Tod D. Wolters USAF** 49 (6371) 47-6357
E-mail: tod.d.wolters.mil@mail.mil
Education: Air Force Acad 1982 BS; Air Command Col 1995; Joint Forces Staff Col 1996; Embry-Riddle 1996 MS; Army War Col 2001 MSS
Deputy Commander
MajGen Timothy G. Fay USAF 49 (6371) 47-6357
Education: Air Force Acad 1987 BS; Cal State (Stanislaus) 1995 MBA
Air Force Reserve Mobilization Assistant
Col John Williams USAF 49 (6371) 47-6357
Command Chief Master Sergeant
CMSgt Phillip L. Easton USAF, USAF 49 (6371) 47-6357
Director, Logistics, Engineering and Force
Protection **BrigGen Roy-Alan C. Agustin USAF** 49 (6371) 47-6357
Director, Operations Strategic
Deterrence and Nuclear Integration
BrigGen Charles Corcoran USAF 49 (6371) 47-6357

(continued on next page)

★ Presidential Appointment Requiring Senate Confirmation ☆ Presidential Appointment □ Schedule C Appointment ◇ Career Senior Foreign Service Appointment
● Career Senior Executive Service (SES) Appointment ○ Non-Career Senior Executive Service (SES) Appointment ■ Postal Career Executive Service

U.S. Air Forces in Europe and Air Forces Africa *(continued)*

Director, Plans, Programs, and Analyses
BrigGen Michael G. Koscheski USAF 49 (6371) 47-6357
Education: Air Force Acad 1992 BS
Director, USAFE - United Kingdom
BrigGen Andrew P. Hansen USAF 49 (6371) 47-6357
Public Affairs Chief **Jerry Renne** 49 (6371) 47-6357

Kisling Non-Commissioned Officer (NCO) Academy – Kapaun Air Station
Kisling NCO Academy, USAFE/PME,
Unit 3345, Box 570, APO, AE 09094-5570
Tel: 49 (631) 536-6502 Fax: 49 (631) 536-7429

Commandant **(Vacant)** 49 (631) 536-6502

Warrior Preparation Center (WPC)
USAFE WPC, Kaiserstrasse 84, GEB 709, 67661 Kaiserslautern, Germany
Mail: WPC, Attn: CC, Unit 3050, Box 20, APO, AE 09094-5020
Tel: 49 (6371) 405-6001 Fax: 49 (6371) 536-6277

Commander **Col Michael Rider USAF** 49 (6371) 405-6001

3rd Air Force (3AF)
Ramstein Air Base, Kaiserslautern, Germany
Tel: 49 (6371) 405-1159 (Public Affairs)

Commander **MajGen John M. Wood USAF** 49 (6371) 47-6357
Education: UC Davis 1989 BS; Embry-Riddle 1996 MAS; Air Command Col 2001; Air War Col 2005
Mobilization Assistant
BrigGen Jeffrey K. Barnson USAFR 49 (6371) 405-1159
Education: Air Force Acad 1983 BS; Webster 1993 MA
Vice Commander
Col Joseph D. "Joe" McFall USAF 49 (6371) 47-6357
Education: Air Force Acad 1993 BS; Touro U International 2004 MBA; Naval Postgrad 2005 MA; National War Col 2012 MS
Chief Master Sergeant
CMSgt Anthony Cruz Munoz USAF 49 (6371) 47-6357

31st Fighter Wing
HQ 31st Fighter Wing, Public Affairs, Unit 6140, Box 100, Aviano AB, Italy, APO, AE 09601
Tel: 39 (0434) 30-7555 Internet: www.aviano.af.mil

Commander **Col Daniel T. "Dan" Lasica USAF** 39 (0434) 30-4700
Executive Officer **Col James L. Fisher USAF** 39 (0434) 30-4700
Vice Commander **Col David S. Chace USAF** 39 (0434) 30-4700
Education: Air Force Acad 1994 BS
Command Chief Master Sergeant
CMSgt Edwin V. Ludwigsen USAF 39 (0434) 30-4708
Public Affairs Officer **Capt Thomas Barger USAF** . . . 39 (0434) 30-7555
E-mail: 31FW.PA.webmaster@aviano.af.mil
Library Director **Tania Baker** 39 (0434) 30-7291
Base Library, FL 5682, 31 SVS/SVRL, Fax: 39 (0434) 30-5385
Unit 6122, Box 50, APO, AE 09601-2250
Internet: www.aviano.library.com
31st Operations Group Commander
Col Richard J. Nelson, Jr. USAF 39 (0434) 30-7555

39th Air Base Wing (Incirlik Air Base)
Unit 7090, Box 135, APO, AE 09824-0135
Internet: www.incirlik.af.mil

Commander **Col Britt K. Hurst USAF** 90 (322) 316-6060
Vice Commander **Col Brian A. Filler USAF** 90 (322) 316-6060
Chief Master Sergeant
CMSgt Jason T. Heilman USAF 90 (322) 316-6060

48th Fighter Wing (48 FW)
RAF Lakenheath, Brandon, Lakenheath, Suffolk IP 27 9PN, United Kingdom
Mail: Unit 5210, Box 215, APO, AE 09461-0125
Tel: 44 1638-54-110 Fax: 44 1638-525637
Internet: www.lakenheath.af.mil

Commander **COL William L. Marshall USA** 44 1638-524500

48th Fighter Wing *(continued)*

Royal Air Force Commander
SQNLDR Jerry Neild RAF 44 1638-521945
Vice Commander **Col John A. Kent USAF** 44 1638-524500
Command Chief
CMSgt Ernesto J. Rendon, Sr. USAF 44 1638-524500
Maintenance Group Commander
Col Steven P. Collen USAF 44 1638-524804
Education: Utah 1994 BS
Mission Support Group Commander
Col Christopher J. Leonard USAF 44 1638-524805
Education: Air Force Acad 1997 BSCE
Operations Group Commander
Col Jason A. Camilletti USAF 44 1638-524803
Public Affairs Chief **Maj Sybil Taunton USAF** 44 1638-522151
E-mail: 48fw.pa@lakenheath.af.mil

52nd Fighter Wing (52 FW)
Spangdahlem AB, 52 FW PA, Unit 3680, Box 220, APO, AE 09126
Tel: 49 656561-6012 Fax: 49 6656561-5254
Internet: www.spangdahlem.af.mil

Commander **Col Jason E. Bailey USAF** 49 656561-6012
Vice Commander **Col Tad D. Clark USAF** 49 656561-6012
Chief Master Sergeant **CMSgt Alvin R. Dyer USAF** 49 656561-6012
Maintenance Group Commander
Col Timothy "Tim" Trimmell USAF 49 656561-6012
Mission Support Group Commander
Col Marlyce K. Roth USAF 49 656561-6012
Munitions Maintenance Group Commander
LTC Mark L. Ashman USA 49 656561-6012
E-mail: mark.l.ashman.mil@mail.mil
Operations Group Commander
Col Anthony G. Retka USAF 49 656561-6012

86th Airlift Wing (86 AW)
Unit 3200 Box 330, APO, AE 09094-0330 (Ramstein Public Affairs)
Tel: 49 (6371) 47-9196 (Public Affairs) Internet: www.ramstein.af.mil

Commander
BrigGen Mark R. "Buzz" August USAF 49 (6371) 47-8686
Vice Commander **Col Joseph H. Wenckus USAF** 49 (6371) 47-8686
Vice Director **Scott C. Lockard** 49 (6371) 47-8686
Chief Master Sergeant
CMSgt Ernesto J. Rendon, Sr. USAF 49 (6371) 47-8686
Chief Public Affairs Officer
LtCol Joel Harper USAF 49 (6371) 47-9196
Public Affairs Officer
1st Lt Michelle Fletcher USAF 49 (6371) 47-9196
Secretary **Jutta Lausberg** 49 (6371) 47-8686

100th Air Refueling Wing (100 ARW - RAF Mildenhall)
RAF Mildenhall, Bury St. Edmunds, Suffolk, England IP28 8NF, United Kingdom
Mail: Unit 4840, Box 30, APO, AE 09459-8501
Tel: 44 1638-542252 Fax: 44 1638-543525
Internet: www.mildenhall.af.mil

Commander **Col Christopher R. Amrhein USAF** 44 1638-543262
Vice Commander **Col David M. Lenderman USAF** 44 1638-542252
Command Chief **MSgt Curtis A. Stanley USAF** 44 1638-542252
Education: Embry-Riddle 2011 BS

435th Air Ground Operations Wing (435 AGOW - Ramstein Air Base)
435th ABW/PA, Unit 3200, Box 330, APO, AE 09094
Tel: 49 (6371) 47-0435

Commander **Col Michael T. Rawls USAF** 49 (6371) 47-0435
Education: Kentucky 1992 BSEE
Chief Master Sergeant
CMSgt Heath T. Tempel USAF 49 (6371) 47-0435

★ Presidential Appointment Requiring Senate Confirmation ☆ Presidential Appointment □ Schedule C Appointment ◇ Career Senior Foreign Service Appointment
● Career Senior Executive Service (SES) Appointment ○ Non-Career Senior Executive Service (SES) Appointment ■ Postal Career Executive Service

United States Department of the Army

DEPARTMENTS

Contents

United States Department of the Army (USA)

The Pentagon, Washington, DC 20310
Tel: (703) 545-6700 (Department of Defense General Information)
Tel: (703) 695-2488 (Procurement Information)
Tel: (703) 697-8113 (Small and Minority Business Information)
Tel: (703) 695-0363 (Public Information) Tel: (703) 487-4600 (Publications Information - National Technical Information Service)
Tel: (703) 607-3377 (Freedom of Information/Privacy Act)
Tel: (703) 695-1578 (Army Inspector General's Hotline - DC Metropolitan Area) Tel: (800) 572-9000 (Army Inspector General's Hotline - Virginia)
Tel: (800) 752-9747 (Army Inspector General's Hotline - Continental US, Alaska and Hawaii) Internet: www.army.mil
Internet: www.usa.gov (Official US Government Website)

OFFICE OF THE SECRETARY OF THE ARMY

101 Army Pentagon, Room 3E700, Washington, DC 20310-0101
Fax: (703) 697-8036

Office of the Administrative Assistant to the Secretary (OAA)

105 Army Pentagon, Washington, DC 20310-0105
Fax: (703) 697-6194 E-mail: usarmy.pentagon.hqda-oaa.mbx.oaa-communications-poc@mail.mil

Military Postal Service Agency (MPSA)

2900 Crystal Drive, Suite 400, Arlington, VA 22202
Tel: (703) 545-5480
E-mail: usarmy.pentagon.hqda-mpsa.list.webmaster@mail.mil

Joint Military Postal Activity - Chicago (JMPA-C)

JT Weeker International and Military Service Center,
11600 West Irving Park Road, Chicago, IL 60666-9998
Tel: (650) 280-3715 E-mail: JMPA-PAC@usace.army.mil
Commander **CDR Vincent Webster USN** .... (650) 280-3715

Under Secretary of the Army

102 Army Pentagon, Washington, DC 20310-0102

OFFICE OF THE UNDER SECRETARY OF THE ARMY

102 Army Pentagon, Room 3E700, Washington, DC 20310-0102

Assistant Secretary of the Army for Installations, Energy and Environment (ASAIE)

110 Army Pentagon, Washington, DC 20310-0110
Tel: (703) 692-9800 Fax: (703) 692-9808

Strategic Integration

110 Army Pentagon, Washington, DC 20310-0110

Regional Environmental and Energy Office - Central

628 McClellan Avenue, Fort Leavenworth, KS 66027
Tel: (913) 684-4003 Fax: (816) 389-2006

Note: EPA Regions 6 and 7

Areas Covered: AR, IA, KS, LA, MO, NE, NM, OK, TX

Director **Stanley Rasmussen** .... (913) 684-4003
E-mail: stanley.l.rasmussen.civ@mail.mil
Deputy Director **David B. Snodgrass** .... (913) 684-4003
E-mail: david.b.snodgrass2.civ@mail.mil

Regional Environmental and Energy Office - Northern

Building E-4480, 5179 Hoadley Road,
Aberdeen Proving Ground, MD 21010-5401
Tel: (410) 278-6991 Fax: (410) 278-6171

Note: EPA Regions 1, 2, 3 and 5

Areas Covered: CT, DE, IL, IN, MA, MD, ME, MI, MN, NH, NJ, NY, OH, PA, PR, RI, VA, VI, VT, WI, WV

Director **Dr. James R. "Jim" Hartman PhD** .... (410) 276-6991
E-mail: james.r.hartman32.civ@mail.mil

Regional Environmental and Energy Office - Southern

60 West Forsythe Street SW, Room 10M15, Peachtree City, GA 30303
Tel: (404) 562-5023

Note: EPA Region 4

Areas Covered: AL, FL, GA, KY, MS, NC, SC, TN

Director **Susan P. Gibson** .... (404) 460-3131
E-mail: susan.p.gibson.civ@mail.mil

Regional Environmental and Energy Office - Western

U.S. Custom House, 721 19th Street, 4th Floor, Room 427,
Denver, CO 80202-2500
Tel: (303) 844-0950 Fax: (303) 844-0951

Note: EPA Regions 8, 9, 10

Areas Covered: AK, AZ, CA, CO, ID, MT, ND, NV, OR, SD, UT, WA, WY

Director **Mark A. Mahoney** .... (303) 844-0956
E-mail: mark.a.mahoney.civ@mail.mil

Director of the Army Staff

201 Army Pentagon, Washington, DC 20310-0201
Fax: (703) 695-6117

Field Operating Agencies/Staff Support Agencies

U.S. Army Combat Readiness/Safety Center (USACRC - Fort Rucker)
Building # 4905, Fifth Avenue, Fort Rucker, AL 36362-5363
Internet: https://safety.army.mil/

Director of Army Safety and Commanding General
BG Timothy J. Daugherty USA .... (703) 545-6700
Deputy Commander **COL Christopher Waters USA** ..... (334) 255-3075
Chief of Staff **David B. Parker** .... (334) 255-3075
Command Sergeant Major
CSM Ernest D. Bowen, Jr. USA .... (334) 255-3075
Senior Safety Advisor and Functional Chief Representative, Career Program-12
Dr. Brenda G. Miller .... (334) 255-2959
E-mail: brenda.g.miller.civ@mail.mil

U.S. Army Test and Evaluation Command (ATEC)
2202 Aberdeen Boulevard, Aberdeen Proving Ground, MD 21005
Tel: (443) 861-9731 E-mail: usarmy.APG.atec.mbx.atec-hq-pao@mail.mil
Internet: https://www.army.mil/atec/

Dugway Proving Ground - West Desert Test Center
CSTE-DTC-DP-PA, Dugway Proving Ground, Dugway, UT 84022-5000
Tel: (435) 831-3409

Commander **COL Sean G. Kirschner USA** .... (435) 831-3314
E-mail: sean.g.kirschner.mil@mail.mil
Education: Tulane 1992 BS; Webster 2004 MM; National War Col 2014 MNSSS
Public Affairs Specialist **Robert D. Saxon** .... (435) 831-3409
Fax: (435) 831-3410

U.S. Army Aberdeen Test Center (Aberdeen Proving Ground)
Commander, U.S. Army Aberdeen Test Center,
ATTN: TEDT-AT-CO, Aberdeen Proving Ground, MD 21005-5059
Tel: (410) 278-4639 Fax: (410) 278-3909 Internet: www.atc.army.mil

Commander **COL Morris L. Bodrick USA** .... (410) 306-4003
Technical Director **John Wallace** .... (410) 306-4003
Business Development Team Leader **Heather Hilton** ..... (410) 278-4037
E-mail: usarmy.apg.atec.mbx.apgr-atc-business@mail.mil

White Sands Missile Range (WSMR)
White Sands Missile Range, NM 88002-5047
Tel: (575) 678-1134 Fax: (575) 678-8903 Internet: www.wsmr.army.mil

Commanding General **BG Gregory J. Brady USA** ...... (575) 678-1134
E-mail: usarmy.wsmr.atec.mbx.wsmr-cg@mail.mil
Air Force Deputy **Maj Paul Dolce USAF** .... (575) 678-1251
Navy Deputy **LCDR Anthony C. Holmes USN** .... (575) 678-3896
● Executive Director **(Vacant)** .... (575) 678-1980
Command Sergeant Major
CSM William A. Wofford USA .... (575) 678-1980
Chief of Staff **Glen T. Adams** .... (575) 678-1980
Test Center Commander **COL David R. Cheney USA** .... (575) 678-1959
Public Affairs Chief **Robert Carver** .... (575) 678-1134
Assistant Director, Office of Small Business Programs
Gregory F. DeVogel .... (575) 678-1401
Fax: (575) 678-3883
Contracting Division Chief **(Vacant)** .... (575) 678-7307
Fax: (575) 678-2706

Yuma Proving Ground
Yuma Proving Ground, Yuma, AZ 85365
Tel: (928) 328-6533 Fax: (928) 328-6039
E-mail: usarmy.ypg.atec.list.public-affairs-office@mail.mil

Commander **COL Ross C. Poppenberger USA** .... (928) 328-2163
E-mail: ross.c.poppenberger.mil@mail.mil
Command Sergeant Major
CSM Jamathon Nelson USA .... (928) 328-6625
Yuma Test Center Commander
LTC Timothy E. Matthews USA .... (928) 328-6225
E-mail: timothy.e.matthews.mil@mail.mil

Yuma Proving Ground *(continued)*

Plans and Operations Director **Jeffrey B. Tatar** .... (928) 328-6519
E-mail: jeffrey.b.tatar.civ@mail.mil
Technical Director **Larry Bracamonte** .... (928) 328-2813
Director of Information Management **Steve B. Swain** .... (928) 328-2112
E-mail: steve.b.swain.civ@mail.mil
Freedom of Information Act Officer **Hernel A. Aitken** ... (928) 328-6161
E-mail: hernel.a.aitken.civ@mail.mil
Public Affairs Chief **Charles C. Wullenjohn** .... (928) 328-6189
E-mail: charles.c.wullenjohn.civ@mail.mil
Education: Humboldt State BA
Editor, "The Outpost" **Mark A. Schauer** .... (928) 328-6149
301 C Street, Yuma, AZ 85365

Cold Regions Test Center (Fort Wainwright)
Fort Wainwright, AK 99703
Tel: (907) 873-1930 Internet: http://www.crtc.army.mil/

Commander **LCDR Loren D. Todd USN** .... (907) 353-4215
E-mail: loren.d.todd.mil@mail.mil

Tropic Regions Test Center (Yuma Proving Ground)
Yuma Proving Ground, Yuma, AZ 85365
Tel: (928) 328-6671 E-mail: trtc@yuma.army.mil

Director **CDR Ernest E. Hugh USN (Ret)** .... (928) 328-2124
E-mail: ernest.e.hugh.civ@mail.mil

U.S. Army Operational Test Command (USAOTC - Fort Hood)
91012 Station Avenue, WFH, Fort Hood, TX 76544-5068
Tel: (254) 288-9606 Tel: (254) 288-9110 (Public Affairs)
Fax: (254) 288-1359 E-mail: usarmy.hood.atec.mbx.otc-pao@mail.mil
Internet: www.otc.army.mil

Commander **BG William D. "Hank" Taylor USA** .... (254) 288-9700
Deputy Commander and Chief of Staff
COL Christopher E. "Chris" Albus USA .... (254) 288-9500
○ Executive Director **John W. Diem** .... (254) 288-1057
Command Sergeant Major
CSM Mario O. Terenas USA .... (254) 288-9700
Financial Management Director
COL Archie P. Davis III USA (Ret) .... (254) 288-9114
Methodology and Analysis Director
COL William "Bill" Adams USA (Ret) .... (254) 288-9965
Operations Director **Col Thomas Jauquet USAF** .... (254) 288-1469
Fax: (254) 288-1704
Public Affairs Officer **Michael M. Novogradac** .... (254) 288-9110
E-mail: michael.m.novogradac.civ@mail.mil

★ Presidential Appointment Requiring Senate Confirmation ☆ Presidential Appointment □ Schedule C Appointment ◇ Career Senior Foreign Service Appointment
● Career Senior Executive Service (SES) Appointment ○ Non-Career Senior Executive Service (SES) Appointment ■ Postal Career Executive Service

Chief of Staff of the Army (CSA)
The Pentagon, Washington, DC 20310
Mail: 200 Army Pentagon, Washington, DC 20310-0200

OFFICE OF THE CHIEF
The Pentagon, Washington, DC 20310
Mail: 200 Army Pentagon, Washington, DC 20310-0200
Fax: (703) 614-5268 Internet: https://www.army.mil/leaders/csa/

Vice Chief of Staff
201 Army Pentagon, Washington, DC 20310-0201
Fax: (703) 693-3955 Internet: https://www.army.mil/leaders/vcsa/

Assistant Chief of Staff for Installation Management (ACSIM)
600 Army Pentagon, Washington, DC 20310-0600
Fax: (703) 693-3507 Internet: www.acsim.army.mil

U.S. Army Installation Management Command (IMCOM)
11711 N. IH-35, San Antonio, TX 78233
2405 Gun Shed Road, Fort Sam Houston, TX 78234-1223

U.S. Army Installation Management Command Europe (IMCOM Europe - Sembach Kaserne)
Unit 29353, Box 200, APO, AE 09014
Sembach Kaserne, 69126 Heidelberg, Germany
Tel: 49 (6221) 57-113

● Director **Michael D. Formica** 49 (6221) 57-113
E-mail: michael.d.formica.civ@mail.mil
Deputy Director **COL Todd J. Fish USA** 49 (6221) 57-113
Command Sergeant Major
CSM Ulysses D. Rayford USA 49 (6221) 57-113
Education: Excelsior
Chief of Staff **Kari Otto** 49 (6221) 57-113

U.S. Army Garrison Benelux (USAG Benelux)
Grand Rue, 56, Room 7950, Chievres, Belgium
Mail: HQ US Army Garrison Benelux,
Unit 21419, APO, AE 09708-1419
Tel: 32 68-27-5419 Fax: 32 68-27-5106
Internet: http://www.usagbenelux.eur.army.mil

Commander **COL Sean Hunt Kuester USA** 32 68-27-5410
Fax: 32 68-27-5661
Command Sergeant Major **CSM Samara L. Pitre USA** . . . 32 68-27-1320
Deputy to the Garrison Commander
Col Thomas C. Joyce USAF (Ret) 32 68-27-5410
Education: Virginia 1986 BA; Purdue 1991 MS Fax: 32 68-27-5661
Deputy Garrison Manager, Brussels
Raymond S. Myers 32 68-27-5419
Public Affairs Officer **Marie-Lise Baneton** 32 68-27-5419
E-mail: marielise.baneton2@us.army.mil
Webmaster **Jessica Ryan** 32 68-27-5910

U.S. Army Garrison Benelux-Schinnen (USAG Benelux-Schinnen)
Schinnen, Netherlands
Mail: U.S. Army Garrison - Schinnen, Attn: IMEU-SCH-ZA, Unit 21602, APO, AE 09703-1602
Tel: 31 (46) 443-7160 (Public Affairs) Fax: 31 (46) 443-7290
E-mail: paousagshi@benelux.army.mil
Internet: http://www.usagbenelux.eur.army.mil/

Deputy Garrison Manager
Chet Witkowski USA (Ret) 31 (46) 443-7160

AFNORTH International Library
Library Director **Carla Kruizinga** 31 (45) 526-2469
E-mail: carla.kruizingak@benelux.army.mil

U.S. Army Garrison Bavaria (Germany) (USAG Bavaria)
United States Army Garrison Bavaria,
Unit 28130, ATTN: IMEU-GRF-PA, APO, AE 09114
Tel: 49 (9641) 83-7390 Fax: 49 (9641) 83-6548
E-mail: usarmy.bavaria.imcom-europe.mbx.pao@mail.mil
Internet: www.grafenwoehr.army.mil

Commander **COL Lance C. Varney USA** 49 (9472) 83-1300
Deputy Commander **M. Annette Evans** 49 (9641) 83-7390
Education: New Mexico BBA; Oklahoma; Army War Col MSS
Deputy Manager, Garmisch Military Community
Mike Arnold 49 8821-750-3825
Deputy Manager, Hohenfels Military Community
Michael R. Mathews 49 (9641) 83-1500
Special Projects Officer
CPT Michael Morookian USA 49 (9641) 83-1310
Command Sergeant Major
CSM Micheal D. Sutterfield USA 49 (9641) 83-1320
Public Affairs Officer **Ray Johnson** 49 (9641) 83-8103

U.S. Army Garrison Italy (USAG Italy)
U.S. Army Garrison Vicenza, Vialle della Pace 193, 36100 Vicenza, Italy
Mail: U.S. Army Garrison Vicenza, Unit 31401, Box 41, APO, AE 09630
Tel: 39 (0444) 71-7866 E-mail: usarmy.vmc.pao@mail.mil
Internet: www.usag.vicenza.army.mil

Commander **COL Erik M. Berdy USA** 39 (0444) 71-7866
Deputy Garrison Commander
Frank W. Lands USA (Ret) 39 (0444) 71-7866
Education: Ohio State BS; Texas MPA; Army War Col MA
Command Sergeant Major
CSM Mason L. Bryant USA 39 (0444) 71-7866
Public Affairs Officer **Karin Martinez** 39 (0444) 61-8031
E-mail: usarmy.vmc.pao@mail.mil Fax: 39 (0444) 717-543

Darby Military Community
Livorno, Italy
Mail: Unit 31301, Box 1, APO, AE 09613
Tel: 39 (050) 54-7111

Deputy Garrison Manager **Catherine Miller** 39 (050) 54-7505

U.S. Army Garrison Rheinland-Pfalz (USAG Rheinland-Pfalz)
Building 2933, Pulaski Barracks, 67661 Kaiserslautern, Germany
Mail: HQ, U.S. Army Garrison Kaiserslautern,
ATTN: PAO Unit 23152, APO, AE 09227-3152
Tel: 49 (631) 34064213 Fax: 49 (631) 536-6097
Internet: http://www.rp.army.mil/

Commander **COL Jason T. Edwards USA** 49 (631) 34064135
Education: Central Michigan 1996 BS, 2005 MPA
Deputy Commander **Dr. Kevin L. Griess** 49 (631) 34064135
Command Sergeant Major
CMSgt D. "Brett" Waterhouse USAF 49 (631) 34064135

U.S. Army Garrison Stuttgart (Germany) (USAG Stuttgart)
Unit 30401, APO, AE 09107
Tel: 49 (7031) 15-1300
E-mail: usarmy.stuttgart.imcom-europe.mbx.usag-stuttgart-media@mail.mil
Internet: www.stuttgart.army.mil

Commander **COL Neal A. Corson USA** 49 (7031) 15-1300
Deputy to the Commander **Kathryn E. McNeely** 49 (7031) 15-1310
Command Sergeant Major
CSM Toese J. Tia, Jr. USA 49 (7031) 15-1320

U.S. Army Garrison Wiesbaden (Germany) (USAG Wiesbaden)
Wiesbaden Army Airfield, Wiesbaden, Germany
Mail: Unit 29623, APO, AE 09096
Tel: 49 (611) 705-5142 Fax: 49 (611) 705-6604
E-mail: army.wiesbadenpao@mail.mil Internet: www.wiesbaden.army.mil

Commander **COL Noah C. Cloud USA** 49 (611) 705-1500
Deputy to the Commander
COL Edward Douglas "Doug" Earle USA (Ret) . . . 49 (611) 705-1500
Education: Virginia 1975
Command Sergeant Major
CSM Chad L. Pinkston USA 49 (611) 705-1520

DEPARTMENTS

★ Presidential Appointment Requiring Senate Confirmation ☆ Presidential Appointment □ Schedule C Appointment ◇ Career Senior Foreign Service Appointment
● Career Senior Executive Service (SES) Appointment ○ Non-Career Senior Executive Service (SES) Appointment ■ Postal Career Executive Service

DEPARTMENTS

U.S. Army Installation Management Command Pacific (IMCOM Pacific)
Building 104, 132 Yamanaga Street, Fort Shafter, HI 96858-5520
Tel: (808) 438-1025 Fax: (808) 438-8690
Areas Covered: AK, HI, Japan, Korea

● Director **Christine T. Altendorf PhD, PE** . . . . (808) 438-1025
E-mail: christine.t.altendorf.civ@mail.mil
Education: Oklahoma State 1985 BS, 1987 MS, 1993 PhD
Deputy Director **COL William B. Johnson USA** . . . . (808) 438-1025
Command Sergeant Major **CSM Jason Schmidt USA** . . . (808) 438-1025
Chief of Staff **David Shafii** . . . . (808) 438-1025

U.S. Army Garrison Camp Humphreys (USAG Camp Humphreys)
USASA Area III, Unit 15716, APO, AP 96271-0716
Tel: 82 (31) 690-6108 Internet: https://www.army.mil/humphreys

Commander **COL Scott W. Mueller USA** 82 (31) 690-6108
Deputy to the Commander **Robert Brown** 82 (31) 690-6108
Deputy Commander for Transformation
COL Jon Nufable USA 82 (31) 690-6108
Command Sergeant Major
CSM Antonio R. Lopez USA 82 (31) 690-6108

U.S. Army Garrison Fort Greely (USAG Fort Greely)
Fort Greely, Delta Junction, AK 99731
Tel: (907) 873-7387 Fax: (907) 873-4631
E-mail: fgapao@greely.army.mil

Garrison Commander **LTC Michael Foote USA** . . . . (907) 873-7380
Deputy Commander **Craig H. Cugini** . . . . (907) 873-7384
E-mail: craig.h.cugini@us.army.mil
Command Sergeant Major
CSM Christopher E. Magee USA . . . . (907) 873-7386

U.S. Army Garrison Fort Wainwright (USAG Fort Wainwright)
Fort Wainwright, AK 99703
Tel: (907) 353-1110 Fax: (907) 353-7668
E-mail: usarmy.wainwright.imcom-pacific.list.pao@mail.mil (Public Affairs) Internet: www.wainwright.army.mil

Commander **COL Sean Fisher USA** . . . . (907) 353-7660
Education: Auburn; American Military U; Army War Col MSS
Deputy to the Commander **Angela M. Major** . . . . (907) 353-1110
Education: Minnesota (Crookston) BS
Command Sergeant Major
CSM Juan S. Cornett USA . . . . (907) 353-7665

U.S. Army Garrison Hawaii (USAG Hawaii)
745 Wright Avenue, WAAF, Schofield Barracks, HI 96857-5000
Tel: (808) 656-1153 Fax: (808) 656-3740

Garrison Commander
COL Stephen "Steve" Dawson USA . . . . (808) 656-1153
Executive Officer **Clyde Sage** . . . . (808) 656-1153
Deputy Garrison Commander **Michael S. Amarosa** . . . . . . (808) 656-0610
Garrison Command Sergeant Major
CSM Lisa Piette-Edwards USA . . . . (808) 656-1153
Chief Regional Contracting Officer
Timothy W. Powers . . . . (808) 656-0610

U.S. Army Garrison Japan (USAG Japan)
Unit 45006, APO, AP 96343-5006
Fax: 81 3117-634069 Internet: https://www.army.mil/risingsun

Commander **COL Phillip K. Gage USA** 81 46-407-7060
Command Sergeant Major **CSM Will E. Holland USA** . . . 81 46-407-7060

U.S. Army Garrison Kwajalein Atoll (USAG Kwajalein Atoll)
PSC 701, APO, AP 96555
Internet: https://www.army.mil/kwajalein

Commander **COL James DeOre, Jr. USA** 82 (31) 690-6108
Command Sergeant Major
CSM Todd J. Shirley USA 82 (31) 690-6108

U.S. Army Garrison Yongsan (South Korea) (USAG-Y)
Seoul, South Korea
Mail: Unit 15333, APO, AP 96205-5333
Fax: 82 (2) 7918-3021 Internet: https://www.army.mil/yongsan

Commander **COL Maria P. Eoff USA** 82 (2) 7918-7453
Deputy to the Commander **Tommy R. Mize** 82 (2) 7918-7442
E-mail: tommy.r.mize2.civ@mail.mil
Command Sergeant Major
CSM Joseph M. James, Jr. USA 82 (2) 7918-7448

U.S. Army Installation Management Command Readiness
Fort Bragg, NC 28307-5243
Tel: (210) 466-1505 Fax: (210) 295-2242

● Director **Brenda Lee McCullough** . . . . (210) 466-1507
Chief of Staff **(Vacant)** . . . . (210) 466-1507
Command Sergeant Major **CSM Ray Rocco USA** . . . . (210) 466-1507

Joint Base Lewis-McChord (JBLM)
Joint Base Lewis-McChord, WA 98433
Tel: (253) 967-0148
E-mail: usarmy.jblm.imcom.mbx.pao-public@mail.mil
Internet: www.lewis-mcchord.army.mil

Commander **COL Nicole M. Lucas USA** . . . . (253) 967-0005
Command Sergeant Major
CSM Richard T. Mulryan USA . . . . (253) 967-0033
Deputy Commander **Col William Percival USAF** . . . . (253) 967-0005
Senior Enlisted Advisor
CMSgt Nicholas Hollinger USAF . . . . (253) 967-0033
Chief of Staff **Thomas G. "Tom" Knight** . . . . (253) 967-0158
E-mail: thomas.g.knight.civ@mail.mil

U.S. Army Garrison Devens (MA) Reserve Training Forces Area (USAG Devens Reserve Training Forces Area)
1 Quebec Street, Devens, MA 01434-4424
Internet: www.devens.army.mil

Commander **LTC Efrem Z. Slaughter USA** . . . . (978) 796-2126
Deputy to the Garrison Commander
Steven B. "Steve" Hood . . . . (978) 796-2126
Command Sergeant Major **CSM Kelli M. Harr USA** . . . . . (978) 796-2126

U.S. Army Garrison Fort Bliss (USAG Fort Bliss)
IMBL - ZA, 1 Pershing Road, Fort Bliss, TX 79916
Tel: (915) 568-2121 Fax: (915) 568-0313
Internet: https://www.bliss.army.mil/garrison

Commander **COL Steve O. Murphy USA** . . . . (915) 568-2833
Deputy Commander **Bob Burns USA (Ret)** . . . . (915) 568-2873
Education: Florida 1984 BA
Command Sergeant Major
CSM Brian Holschbach USA . . . . (915) 568-2001
Public Affairs Officer **Guy Volb** . . . . (915) 568-4505

U.S. Army Garrison Fort Bragg (USAG Fort Bragg)
Fort Bragg, NC 28310
Tel: (910) 396-5620 Fax: (910) 396-4568

Commander **COL Kyle Reed USA** . . . . (910) 396-4011
Deputy Commander **Justin O. Mitchell** . . . . (910) 396-4011
Command Sergeant Major
CSM William D. Lohmeyer USA . . . . (910) 396-4011
Public Affairs Officer **Thomas D. "Tom" McCollum** . . . . (910) 396-2122
E-mail: thomas.d.mccollum2.civ@mail.mil

U.S. Army Garrison Fort Buchanan (USAG Fort Buchanan)
218 Brooke Street, Fort Buchanan, PR 00934
Fax: (787) 707-3362 Internet: www.buchanan.army.mil/

Commander **COL Guy D. Bass USAR** . . . . (787) 707-3440
Education: Northeast Louisiana
Deputy Commander **LTC Patrick J. Dillon USA** . . . . (787) 707-3440
Deputy to the Commander **William S. Leyh** . . . . (787) 707-3440
Command Sergeant Major
CSM Heriberto Quintana USA . . . . (787) 707-3440
Public Affairs Officer **Grissel Rosa** . . . . (787) 707-4486
E-mail: grissel.rosa@us.army.mil
E-mail: usarmy.buchanan.imcom-atlantic.list.pao@mail.mil

★ Presidential Appointment Requiring Senate Confirmation ☆ Presidential Appointment □ Schedule C Appointment ◇ Career Senior Foreign Service Appointment
● Career Senior Executive Service (SES) Appointment ○ Non-Career Senior Executive Service (SES) Appointment ■ Postal Career Executive Service

U.S. Army Garrison Fort Campbell (USAG Fort Campbell)
39 Normandy Boulevard, Fort Campbell, KY 42223-5617
Tel: (270) 798-9921 Tel: (270) 798-3025 (Public Affairs)

Commander **COL Joseph Kuchan USA** . . . . (270) 798-9921
Deputy to the Commander
COL Jonathan B. Hunter USA (Ret) . . . . (270) 798-9921
E-mail: jonathan.b.hunter.civ@mail.mil
Command Sergeant Major
CSM Jason W. Osborne USA . . . . (270) 798-9921

U.S. Army Garrison Fort Carson (USAG Fort Carson)
Fort Carson, CO 80913
Tel: (719) 526-1269 (Public Affairs) Fax: (719) 526-1021
E-mail: usarmy.carson.hqda-ocpa.list.pao-officer@mail.mil
Internet: www.carson.army.mil

Commander **COL Ronald P. Fitch, Jr. USA** . . . . (719) 526-1269
Deputy Garrison Commander
Roderick A. "Rod" Chisholm . . . . (719) 526-1269
Education: Colorado State 1977 BS
Command Sergeant Major
CSM David K. Burton USA . . . . (719) 526-1269

U.S. Army Garrison Fort Drum (USAG Fort Drum)
Fort Drum, NY 13602
Tel: (315) 772-6011 Internet: https://www.army.mil/drum

Commander **COL Kenneth "Dean" Harrison USA** . . . . . . (315) 772-5501
Education: Maryland Baltimore County 1987
Deputy to the Commander **Eric Wagenaar** . . . . (315) 772-5501
Command Sergeant Major **CSM Ryan L. Alfaro USA** . . . . (315) 772-5501

U.S. Army Garrison Fort Hood (USAG Fort Hood)
Building 1001, Room W321, Fort Hood, TX 76544-5000
E-mail: usarmy.hood.iii-corps.mbx.pao@mail.mil
Internet: http://www.hood.army.mil/

Commander **COL Henry C. "Hank" Perry, Jr. USA** . . . . . (254) 288-3451
Executive Assistant **(Vacant)** . . . . (210) 466-1505
Deputy to the Commander **Keith Gogas** . . . . (254) 287-2205
Executive Administrative Secretary **Susan Davis** . . . . . . (254) 287-2205
E-mail: susan.davis@us.army.mil
Command Sergeant Major **CSM Byron Larsen USA** . . . . . (254) 287-2205
Public Affairs Director **Thomas E. Rheinlander** . . . . (254) 287-0103
E-mail: thomas.e.rheinlander.civ@mail.mil
Education: Texas A&M 1980 BA
Command Information Chief and Social Media
Manager **David J. "Dave" Larsen** . . . . (254) 286-5139
E-mail: david.j.larsen.civ@mail.mil

U.S. Army Garrison Fort Hunter Liggett (USAG Fort Hunter Liggett)
IMSW-CST-ZAH, Fort Hunter Liggett, CA 93928-7000
Tel: (831) 386-2505 Fax: (831) 386-2011 Internet: www.liggett.army.mil/

Commander **COL Kerry E. Norman USA** . . . . (831) 386-2506
Deputy Commander **LTC Jason R. McKenzie USA** . . . . . . (831) 386-2505
Deputy to the Commander **Bran K. Adkins** . . . . (831) 386-2505
E-mail: brian.k.adkins.civ@mail.mil
Command Sergeant Major
CSM DeeAnn K. Dunstan USA . . . . (831) 386-2505

U.S. Army Garrison Fort Irwin (USAG Fort Irwin)
Fort Irwin, CA 92310
Tel: (760) 380-6268

Commander **COL Seth D. Krummrich USA** . . . . (760) 380-6268
Deputy to the Commander **Craig Fabrizio** . . . . (760) 380-6267
Command Sergeant Major
CSM Robert Edwards, Jr. USA . . . . (760) 380-6267

U.S. Army Garrison Fort McCoy (USAG Fort McCoy)
Fort McCoy, WI 54656-5263
Tel: (608) 388-2222 Fax: (608) 388-4237
E-mail: usarmy.mccoy.imcom-central.list.pao-admin@mail.mil
Internet: www.mccoy.army.mil

Commander **COL Hui Chae Kim USA** . . . . (608) 388-3001
E-mail: usarmy.mccoy.imcom-central.list.cmdgroup-admin@mail.mil
Deputy Commander **LTC Jared T. Corsi USAR** . . . . (608) 388-3405

U.S. Army Garrison Fort McCoy *(continued)*

Deputy to the Commander **James A. Chen** . . . . (608) 388-3705
Command Sergeant Major
CSM Frank T. Mathias USA . . . . (608) 388-3605
Contracting Director **Mary E. Purpus** . . . . (608) 388-2818
E-mail: mary.e.purpus.civ@mail.mil
E-mail: usarmy.mccoy.acc-micc.list.micc-admin@mail.mil
Freedom of Information Act Officer **Trudy L. Ward** . . . . . . (608) 388-4222
E-mail: usarmy.mccoy.imcom-central.list.dhr-foia@mail.mil
Public Affairs Officer **Tonya K. Townsell** . . . . (608) 388-4209
E-mail: usarmy.mccoy.imcom-central.list.pao-admin@mail.mil
Emergency Services Director **Mark Fritsche** . . . . (608) 388-4225
1680 West Eaton Street, Fort McCoy, WI 54656 Fax: (608) 388-4111
E-mail:
usarmy.mccoy.imcom-central.list.des-admin@mail.mil
Plans, Training, Mobilization and Security Director
Dale B. Stewart . . . . (608) 388-2203
110 East Headquarters Road, Fax: (608) 388-8487
Fort McCoy, WI 54656-5226
E-mail: dale.b.stewart.civ@mail.mil
E-mail: usarmy.mccoy.imcom-central.list.dptms-admin@mail.mil
Webmaster **(Vacant)** . . . . (608) 388-4209
E-mail: usarmy.mccoy.imcom-central.list.pao-admin@mail.mil

U.S. Army Garrison Fort Polk and Joint Readiness Training Center (USAG Fort Polk)
Building 350, 6661 Warrior Trail, Fort Polk, LA 71459-5249
Fax: (337) 531-6014 (Public Affairs) Internet: www.jrtc-polk.army.mil/

Commander **COL Jarrett A. Thomas II USA** . . . . (337) 531-1606
Building 1714, 6661 Warrior Trail, Fort Polk, LA 71459
Deputy to the Commander **Johnny Bevers** . . . . (337) 531-1606
Command Sergeant Major
CSM Jerry L. Dodson USA . . . . (337) 531-1606

U.S. Army Garrison Fort Riley (USAG Fort Riley)
Fort Riley, KS 66442
Tel: (785) 239-3911 Internet: www.riley.army.mil

Garrison Commander **COL Stephen Shrader USA** . . . . . . (785) 239-2092
Deputy Garrison Commander **Timothy Livsey** . . . . (785) 239-2092
Command Sergeant Major
CSM Andrew T. Bristow II USA . . . . (785) 239-2092

U.S. Army Garrison Fort Stewart (USAG Fort Stewart)
Building 624, 954 William H. Wilson Avenue,
Suite 130, Fort Stewart, GA 31314
Fax: (912) 767-9996 Internet: www.stewart.army.mil

Commander **COL Jason A. Wolter USA** . . . . (912) 767-8606
Deputy Commander **Henry Paul Stuart** . . . . (912) 767-8606
Education: Mississippi State 1972 BA
Command Sergeant Major
CSM Martin M. Conroy USA . . . . (912) 767-8606
Executive Officer **Wes Stephens** . . . . (912) 767-8606

U.S. Army Garrison White Sands (NM) Missile Range (USAG White Sands Missile Range)
100 Headquarters Avenue, White Sands Missile Range, NM 88002

Commander **COL Christopher J. Ward USA** . . . . (575) 678-2220
Deputy Commander **Timothy Anderson** . . . . (575) 678-2220
Command Sergeant Major
CSM Robert L. Parker II USA . . . . (575) 678-2220

U.S. Army Installation Management Command Sustainment
Redstone Arsenal, AL 35898
Tel: (210) 466-1507

● Director **Davis D. "Dave" Tindoll, Jr.** . . . . (210) 295-2082
Education: Eastern Kentucky BS
Command Sergeant Major
CSM Richard Sullivan III USA . . . . (210) 295-2082
Chief of Staff **COL Luke S. Green USA (Ret)** . . . . (210) 295-2082
Public Affairs Officer **Vicki M. Stapes** . . . . (210) 295-2277
E-mail: vicki.m.stapes@us.army.mil

★ Presidential Appointment Requiring Senate Confirmation ☆ Presidential Appointment ☐ Schedule C Appointment ◇ Career Senior Foreign Service Appointment
● Career Senior Executive Service (SES) Appointment ○ Non-Career Senior Executive Service (SES) Appointment ■ Postal Career Executive Service

Joint Base Myer-Henderson Hall (JBMHH)
IMNE-MYR, 204 Lee Avenue,
Joint Base Myer-Henderson Hall, VA 22211-1119
Tel: (703) 696-3250 Fax: (703) 696-2678 Internet: www.army.mil/jbmhh

Commander **COL Kimberly A. Peeples USA** . . . . (703) 696-3250
E-mail: kimberly.a.peeples.mil@mail.mil
Education: West Point
Deputy Commander **LtCol Eric W. Kelly USMC** . . . . (703) 696-3250
E-mail: eric.w.kelly.mil@mail.mil
Command Sergeant Major
CSM Stephen M. Harris USA . . . . (703) 696-3250
Public Affairs Director **Michael Howard** . . . . (703) 696-0584
Chief of Staff **Glenn A. Wait** . . . . (703) 696-3250
E-mail: glenn.a.wait.civ@mail.mil

U.S. Army Garrison Aberdeen (MD) Proving Ground (USAG APG)
U.S. Army Garrison Aberdeen Proving Ground,
2201 Aberdeen Boulevard, Aberdeen Proving Ground, MD 21005-5001
Tel: (410) 278-1147 Internet: www.apg.army.mil

Commander **COL Robert Phillips III USA** . . . . (410) 278-1511
Deputy to the Commanding General **(Vacant)** . . . . (410) 278-1511
Command Sergeant Major
CSM Jeffrey O. Adams USA . . . . (410) 278-1511
Freedom of Information Act Officer **Sandra Schiller** . . . . . (410) 436-3580
E-mail: sandra.schiller@us.army.mil
Public Affairs Office Chief **Kelly C. Luster** . . . . (410) 278-1147
E-mail: kelly.c.luster.civ@mail.mil

U.S. Army Garrison Adelphi (MD) Laboratory Center (USAG Adelphi Laboratory Center)
2800 Powder Mill Road, Adelphi, MD 20783-1197
E-mail: alc.public.affairs@gmail.com

Garrison Manager **William Cole** . . . . (301) 394-1385

U.S. Army Garrison Hunter Army Airfield (USAG Hunter Army Airfield)
Building 1201, 685 Horace Emmet Wilson Boulevard,
Hunter Army Airfield, GA 31409-5023
Tel: (912) 315-5617 (Public Affairs) Fax: (912) 315-4501
E-mail: usarmy.stewart.3-id.mbx.mbx-public-affairs1@mail.mil

Commander **LTC Kenneth M. Dwyer USA** . . . . (912) 315-5801
Deputy Commander **Ernest Tafoya** . . . . (912) 315-5801
Education: Eastern New Mexico
Command Sergeant Major
CSM LaVander R. Wilkerson USA . . . . (912) 315-5801

U.S. Army Garrison Fort A.P. Hill (USAG Fort A.P. Hill)
Building P00112, 18436 Fourth Street, Bowling Green, VA 22427-3114
Fax: (804) 633-8105 Internet: https://www.army.mil/aphill/

Commander **LTC Michael E. Gates USA** . . . . (804) 633-8206
Deputy to the Commander **(Vacant)** . . . . (804) 633-8206
Command Sergeant Major **(Vacant)** . . . . (804) 633-8205

U.S. Army Garrison Fort Belvoir (USAG Fort Belvoir)
8831 John J. Kingman Road, Fort Belvoir, VA 22060
Tel: (703) 805-5001 Internet: www.belvoir.army.mil

Commander **COL Michael H. Greenberg USA** . . . . (703) 805-2052
U.S. Army Garrison, Fort Belvoir Command Group,
9820 Flagler Road, Fort Belvoir, VA 22060-5932
Deputy to the Commander
Stephen W. "Steve" Brooks . . . . (703) 805-2052
E-mail: steve.brooks@us.army.mil
Command Sergeant Major
CSM Billie Jo Boersma USA . . . . (703) 805-3506
Personnel and Community Activities Director
George Dickson . . . . (703) 805-2532
Plans, Training, Mobilization and Security Director
(Vacant) . . . . (703) 805-4002
Public Affairs Director **Joe Richard** . . . . (703) 805-5001
Public Works Director **William "Bill" Sanders** . . . . (703) 806-3017
Resource Management Director **Mike Bidelman** . . . . (703) 805-1189

U.S. Army Garrison Fort Detrick (USAG Fort Detrick)
Patchel Street, Fort Detrick, MD 21702
Tel: (301) 619-8000 Fax: (301) 619-2515 Internet: www.detrick.army.mil

Commander **COL Scott M. Halter USA** . . . . (301) 619-7314
Deputy Commander
Gunnar G.F. Pedersen USA (Ret) . . . . (301) 619-3357
E-mail: gunnar.g.pedersen2.civ@mail.mil
Command Sergeant Major
CSM Marcos E. Muñoz USA . . . . (301) 619-3436
Forest Glen Annex Manager **Mark C. Dahlquist** . . . . (301) 619-8000
Education: Northern Michigan 1982 BS
Freedom of Information Act Officer **Valerie Wright** . . . . . (301) 619-8095

U.S. Army Garrison Fort Meade (USAG Fort Meade)
4551 Llewellyn Avenue, Fort George G. Meade, MD 20755-5000
Tel: (301) 677-4844 Fax: (301) 677-7602
Internet: www.ftmeade.army.mil

Garrison Commander **COL Erich C. Spragg USA** . . . . (301) 677-4844
Garrison Deputy Commander **John M. Moeller** . . . . (301) 677-4844
Education: West Point 1980 BS; USC MS; National War Col MS
Garrison Command Sergeant Major
CSM Brian S. Cullen USA . . . . (301) 677-2300
Freedom of Information Act Officer **Rodney Ramsey** . . . . (301) 677-1301
Information Officer **Michael Steele** . . . . (301) 677-1573
Fax: (301) 677-1305
Public Affairs Director **Chad T. Jones** . . . . (301) 677-1301
E-mail: chad.t.jones.civ@mail.mil Fax: (301) 677-1305
Training Officer **Robert Howard** . . . . (301) 677-2622
Fax: (301) 677-3100
Security Division Chief **(Vacant)** . . . . (301) 677-3400
Fax: (301) 677-6211
Emerging Media Manager **Alexandra Snyder** . . . . (301) 677-1109
Fax: (301) 677-1305

U.S. Army Garrison Natick (USAG Natick)
U.S. Army Soldier Systems Center, Kansas Street,
Natick, MA 01760-5000
Internet: www.natick.army.mil/garrison

Commander **LTC Bryan Martin USA** . . . . (508) 233-4205
E-mail: usarmy.natick.imcom-atlantic.mbx.nati-imne-ssc-za@mail.mil
Deputy Commander **Sean C. LeHane** . . . . (508) 233-4205
Command Sergeant Major
CSM Michael R. "Mike" Pintagro USA . . . . (508) 233-4205
E-mail: michael.pintagro@us.army.mil

U.S. Army Garrison Picatinny (NJ) Army Depot (USAG Picatinny Army Depot)
One Ramsey Avenue, Picatinny Arsenal, NJ 07806-5000
Tel: (973) 724-7011 Internet: www.pica.army.mil/garrison

Commander **LTC Jeffrey E. "Jeff" Ivey USA** . . . . (973) 724-7010
Deputy to the Garrison Commander
Fred Hankerson III . . . . (973) 724-2100
Command Sergeant Major **CSM Sheila E. Royal USA** . . . (973) 724-7012

U.S. Army Garrison Redstone (AL) Arsenal (Redstone Arsenal)
Redstone Arsenal, AL 35898
Fax: (256) 842-2991 Internet: www.garrison.redstone.army.mil

Commander **COL Kelsey Smith USA** . . . . (256) 876-8861
Command Sergeant Major **SGM Kim Bradshaw USA** . . . (256) 876-5331

U.S. Army Garrison Rock Island Arsenal (USAG-RIA)
One Rock Island Arsenal, Rock Island, IL 61299-6200
Tel: (309) 782-6001 Internet: www.usagria.army.mil

Commander **COL Stephen C. Marr USA** . . . . (309) 782-7722
E-mail: kenneth.j.tauke.mil@mail.mil
Deputy Commander **Joel G. Himsl** . . . . (309) 782-5555
Education: St John's U (MN) BA
Command Sergeant Major **CSM Brian Heffernan USA** . . . (309) 782-1332
Director, Network Enterprise Center **Scott E. Hary** . . . . . . (309) 782-1212
E-mail: scott.e.hary.civ@mail.mil
Chief, Network Enterprise Center Information Technology Systems Support Division
Anthony R. "Tony" Crossen . . . . (309) 782-0544
E-mail: anthony.r.crossen.civ@mail.mil

★ Presidential Appointment Requiring Senate Confirmation ☆ Presidential Appointment ☐ Schedule C Appointment ◇ Career Senior Foreign Service Appointment
● Career Senior Executive Service (SES) Appointment ○ Non-Career Senior Executive Service (SES) Appointment ■ Postal Career Executive Service

U.S. Army Garrison Yuma (AZ) Proving Ground (USAG Yuma Proving Ground)
Yuma Proving Ground, Yuma, AZ 85365

Manager **Gordon K. Rogers** .... (928) 328-3474
E-mail: gordon.k.rogers.civ@mail.mil
Public Affairs Chief **Charles C. Wullenjohn** .... (928) 328-6189
E-mail: charles.c.wullenjohn.civ@mail.mil
Education: Humboldt State BA

U.S. Army Support Activity Fort Dix (ASA-DIX)
Joint Base McGuire-Dix-Lakehurst, NJ 08640
Tel: (609) 562-1011 Fax: (609) 562-3337

Note: Fort Dix is a component of Joint Base McGuire-Dix-Lakehurst, administered by the 87th Air Base Wing, USAF.

Commander **COL Charles W. Durr USA** .... (609) 562-2458
Education: West Point
Deputy Commander **(Vacant)** .... (609) 562-2458
Command Sergeant Major
CSM Randy Gillespie USA .... (609) 562-2557

U.S. Army Installation Management Command Training
Fort Eustis, VA 23604

• Director **(Vacant)** .... (210) 466-1507

U.S. Army Garrison Carlisle (PA) Barracks (USAG Carlisle Barracks)
22 Ashburn Drive, Carlisle, PA 17013-5006

Commander **LTC Sally C. Hannan USA** .... (717) 245-4708
E-mail: sally.c.hannan.mil@mail.mil
Education: West Point 1998 BS
Command Sergeant Major
CSM Jamie M. Lethiecq USA .... (717) 245-4708

U.S. Army Garrison Fort Benning (USAG Fort Benning)
Fort Benning, GA 31905-5000
Tel: (706) 545-1500 Fax: (706) 545-6302
E-mail: usarmy.benning.imcom.mbx.pao@mail.mil
Internet: www.benning.army.mil/garrison

Commander **COL Clinton W. Cox USA** .... (706) 545-1500
E-mail: andrew.c.hilmes.mil@mail.mil
Deputy Garrison Commander **George Steuber** .... (706) 545-6041
E-mail: george.steuber@us.army.mil
Command Sergeant Major
CSM Connie L. Rounds USA .... (706) 545-1500
Director, Contracting **Steven "Steve" Sullivan** .... (706) 545-5173
Fax: (706) 545-6529

U.S. Army Garrison Fort Gordon (USAG Fort Gordon)
Fort Gordon, GA 30905-5000
Fax: (706) 791-5844

Commander **COL Jim Clifford USA** .... (706) 791-6300
Education: Rutgers BS; Webster MA;
Eisenhower National Security and Resource Strategy MS
Deputy to the Commander **John J. Curry** .... (706) 791-6300
E-mail: john.curry@us.army.mil
Command Sergeant Major
CSM Marcus L. Campbell USA .... (706) 791-6300
Inspector General **(Vacant)** .... (706) 791-6300

U.S. Army Garrison Fort Hamilton (USAG Fort Hamilton)
United States Army Garrison, Fort Hamilton,
Public Affairs Office, ATTN: ANFH-PA, 114 White Avenue,
Suite 2, Brooklyn, NY 11252-5700
Tel: (718) 630-4780 Fax: (718) 630-4709
Internet: www.hamilton.army.mil

Commander **COL Andrew S. Zieseniss USA** .... (718) 630-4780
Deputy Commander **Don Bradshaw** .... (718) 630-4780
Education: VMI
Command Sergeant Major **CSM LaShan Hayes USA** .... (718) 630-4780

U.S. Army Garrison Fort Huachuca (USAG Fort Huachuca)
2837 Boyd Avenue, Fort Huachuca, AZ 85613-7001
Fax: (520) 533-2572

Commander **COL Chad Rambo USA** .... (520) 533-1562
Fax: (520) 533-9266
Command Sergeant Major **CSM Marcus Jones USA** .... (520) 533-1100
Public Affairs Officer **Angela L. Camara** .... (520) 533-1850
E-mail: angela.l.camara.civ@mail.mil

U.S. Army Garrison Fort Jackson (USAG Fort Jackson)
Fort Jackson, SC 29207-5015
Tel: (803) 751-7613 Fax: (803) 751-6160
E-mail: usarmy.jackson.93-sig-bde.mbx.atzj-pao@mail.mil

Commander **COL Stephen Elder USA** .... (803) 751-7613
Command Sergeant Major
CSM John P. Drawbond USA .... (803) 751-7246

U.S. Army Garrison Fort Knox (USAG Fort Knox)
995, Fort Knox, KY 40121-2726
Tel: (502) 624-4985 (Public Affairs)
E-mail: usarmy.knox.imcom-atlantic.mbx.hdd@mail.mil
Internet: www.knox.army.mil/garrison

Commander **(Vacant)** .... (502) 624-3351
Deputy Commander **Emmet E. Holley** .... (502) 624-3351
E-mail: emmet.holley@us.army.mil
Education: Tennessee (Martin) 1976 BS; Western Kentucky 1988 MPA
Command Sergeant Major
CSM Bobby R. Wooldridge USA .... (502) 624-3351
E-mail: bobby.r.wooldridge.mil@mail.mil

U.S. Army Garrison Fort Leavenworth (USAG Fort Leavenworth)
Unit 1, 290 Grant Avenue, Fort Leavenworth, KS 66027
Tel: (913) 684-4448 (Staff Duty Offices) Tel: (913) 684-4021 (Directory)
E-mail: usarmy.leavenworth.imcom-central.mbx.pao-inbox@mail.mil

Commander **MAJ Marne Sutten USA** .... (913) 684-4448
E-mail: usarmy.leavenworth.imcom-west.mbx.garcmd@mail.mil
Deputy to the Commander **Jack Walker** .... (913) 684-4448
Command Sergeant Major **CSM Jon Y. Williams USA** ... (913) 684-4448

U.S. Army Garrison Fort Lee (USAG Fort Lee)
Building 12010, 3312 Adams Avenue,
Suite 208, Fort Lee, VA 23801-1723
Internet: www.lee.army.mil

Commander **COL Hollie Martin USA** .... (804) 734-7188
Deputy to the Commander **Patrick "Mac" MacKenzie** ... (804) 734-7188
Command Sergeant Major
CSM Vittorio F. DeSouza USA .... (804) 734-7188

U.S. Army Garrison Fort Leonard Wood (USAG Fort Leonard Wood)
320 Manscen Loop, Suite 120, Fort Leonard Wood, MO 65473
Tel: (573) 596-0131 ext. 34004 Fax: (573) 596-4006

Commander **COL Tracy L. Lanier USA** ...... (573) 596-0131 ext. 34004
Deputy Commander **Kathy Aydt** .... (573) 596-0131 ext. 34004
Education: Bradford BFA; Nova MBA
Command Sergeant Major
CSM Faith A.R. Alexander USA .... (573) 596-0131 ext. 34004

U.S. Army Garrison Fort Rucker (USAG Fort Rucker)
453 Novosel Street, Fort Rucker, AL 36362-5105
Fax: (334) 255-3843 E-mail: usarmy.rucker.usag.mbx.atzq-pao@mail.mil
Internet: www.rucker.army.mil/imcom

Commander **COL Brian E. Walsh USA** .... (334) 255-2095
Deputy to the Garrison Commander (Interim)
Sean M. Sparks .... (334) 255-2095
Command Sergeant Major
CSM Jasper C. Johnson USA .... (334) 255-9451

U.S. Army Garrison Fort Sill (USAG Fort Sill)
462 Hamilton Road, Fort Sill, OK 73503-1899
Internet: http://sill-www.army.mil

Commander **COL Samuel W. Curtis USA** .... (580) 442-3106
Command Sergeant Major
SGM Jonathan Lutgens USA .... (580) 442-3332

DEPARTMENTS

★ Presidential Appointment Requiring Senate Confirmation ☆ Presidential Appointment ☐ Schedule C Appointment ◇ Career Senior Foreign Service Appointment
● Career Senior Executive Service (SES) Appointment ○ Non-Career Senior Executive Service (SES) Appointment ■ Postal Career Executive Service

DEPARTMENTS

U.S. Army Garrison Presidio of Monterey (CA) (USAG Presidio of Monterey)
1759 Lewis Road, Monterey, CA 93940
Fax: (831) 242-6608 Internet: www.monterey.army.mil

Commander **COL Lawrence Brown USA** .... (831) 242-6601
Deputy to the Garrison Commander **Hugh H. Hardin** .... (831) 242-6001
E-mail: hugh.hardin@us.army.mil
Education: West Point BS
Command Sergeant Major
CSM Roberto Marshall USA .... (831) 242-6600
Director of Emergency Services **Shawn Marshall** .... (831) 242-7007
Public Affairs Officer **Jim Laughlin** .... (831) 242-5555
E-mail: presidiopao@gmail.com

U.S. Army Garrison West Point (USAG West Point)
Building 681, U.S. Military Academy, West Point, NY 10996
Tel: (845) 938-2022

Commander **COL Harris "Harry" Marson USA** .... (845) 938-2022
E-mail: 8gc@usma.edu
Deputy to the Garrison Commander
COL Thomas H. Cowan, Jr. USA (Ret) .... (845) 938-2022
Command Sergeant Major
CSM Kanisha S. Lamothe USA .... (845) 938-2022
Director, Civilian Personnel Advisory Center
Carol L. McQuinn .... (845) 938-2703
E-mail: carol.l.mcquinn.civ@mail.mil
Education: Northeastern BA
Director, Emergency Services **LTC Bryan Everly USA** ... (845) 938-2403
Director, Logistics **Paul Brown** .... (845) 938-2161
Director, Medical Activity
COL Brett H. Venable USA .... (845) 938-3305
Director, Morale, Welfare and Recreation
Brooke Haley .... (845) 938-2103
Director, Plans, Training, Mobilization and Security
Charles Peddy .... (845) 938-8845
E-mail: 8g3@usma.edu
Director, Public Works **Matthew Talaber** .... (845) 938-4407
Education: New York Inst Tech BA; Harvard 1996 MPA
Director, West Point Museum **David Reel** .... (845) 938-3617
E-mail: david.reel@us.army.mil
Education: Dickinson Col BA; NYU MA

United States Army Corps of Engineers (USACE)

Government Accounting Office Building,
441 G Street, NW, Washington, DC 20314-1000

Headquarters United States Army Corps of Engineers
441 G Street, NW, Washington, DC 20314
Tel: (202) 761-0001 Fax: (202) 761-0416
E-mail: usarmy.pentagon.hqda-oce.mbx.daen-zc@mail.mil

Humphreys Engineer Center Support Activity (HECSA)
7701 Telegraph Road, Alexandria, VA 22315-3860
Tel: (703) 428-6214 Fax: (703) 428-6188

Director **Dale F. Stoutenburgh** Room 1A01 .... (703) 428-7107
E-mail: dale.f.stoutenburgh@usace.army.mil
Deputy Director **Victor H. Stephenson** Room 1A01 ..... (703) 428-7328
Human Resources Officer **La Var M. Williams** .... (202) 761-1885
Government Accountability Office Building, 441 G Street, NW,
Room 6T92, Washington, DC 20314-1000
Chief Security Officer **Jeffrey W. Hill** .... (703) 761-8243
E-mail: jeffrey.w.hill@usace.army.mil
Deputy for Small Business **Deborah L. Ahn** .... (703) 428-7385
Librarian (Acting) **Victor H. Stephenson** .... (703) 428-7430
7701 Telegraph Road, Fax: (703) 428-6310
Alexandria, VA 22315-3868
Equal Employment Office Chief **Richard Harris** .... (202) 761-8613
441 G. Street, NW, Fax: (202) 761-5718
Room 6Q85, Washington, DC 20314-1000
E-mail: richard.harris12@usace.army.mil

Contracting Office (CEHEC-CT)
7701 Telegraph Road, Alexandria, VA 22315-3863
Tel: (703) 428-7153 Fax: (703) 428-8181

Chief **Sally Williams** .... (703) 428-7303
Kingman Building, Fax: (703) 428-8181
7701 Telegraph Road,
Room 1B01, Alexandria, VA 22315-3860

Office of Counsel (CEHEC-OC)
7701 Telegraph Road, Alexandria, VA 22315-3863
Tel: (703) 428-8160 Fax: (703) 428-7633

Counsel **Damon A. Roberts** .... (703) 428-6161
Kingman Building, Fax: (703) 428-7633
7701 Telegraph Road,
Room 2A01, Alexandria, VA 22315-3860
E-mail: damon.a.roberts@usace.army.mil

Resource Management Office (CEHEC-RM)
7701 Telegraph Road, Alexandria, VA 22315-3863
Tel: (703) 428-6390 Fax: (703) 428-7287

Chief **Wilett W. Bunton** .... (703) 428-6389
Kingman Building, Fax: (703) 428-7287
7701 Telegraph Road,
Room 1A20, Alexandria, VA 22315-3860
E-mail: wilett.bunton@usace.army.mil

Safety and Occupational Health Office (CEHEC-SH)
7701 Telegraph Road, Alexandria, VA 22315-3863
Fax: (703) 428-6034

Chief **Lloyd C. Roberts** .... (703) 428-7004
Kingman Building, Fax: (703) 428-6034
7701 Telegraph Road,
Room 2B06, Alexandria, VA 22315-3860
E-mail: lloyd.c.roberts@usace.army.mil

Institute for Water Resources (IWR)
Casey Building No. 2594, 7701 Telegraph Road,
Alexandria, VA 22315-3868
Fax: (703) 428-8171 Internet: www.iwr.usace.army.mil

Director
Dr. Joe D. Manous, Jr. PE, PhD, D.WRE Room 206 ... (703) 428-8015
Deputy Director **Dr. Robert W. Brumbaugh** .... (703) 428-7069
Casey Building No. 2594, 7701 Telegraph Road,
Room 292, Alexandria, VA 22315-3863
E-mail: robert.w.brumbaugh@usace.army.mil
Director, International Center for Integrated
Water Resources Management (Acting)
Dr. Robert W. Brumbaugh Room 206 .... (703) 428-8015
E-mail: robert.w.brumbaugh@usace.army.mil
USACE-ICIWaRM Director **Robert A. Pietrowsky** ...... (703) 428-8077
Education: SUNY (Stony Brook) BS; Poly Inst New York MS
USACE-ICIWaRM Deputy Director
William S. Logan Room 220D .... (703) 428-6054
Director, Navigation and Civil Works Decision Support
Center **Dr. Mark F. Sudol** .... (703) 428-7570
Casey Building No. 2594, 7701 Telegraph Road,
Room 280, Alexandria, VA 22315-3860
E-mail: mark.f.sudol@usace.army.mil
Director, Risk Management Center
Nathan J. Snorteland .... (303) 963-4573
12596 West Bayaud Avenue, Suite 400, Lakewood, CO 80228
Director, Waterborne Commerce Statistics Center
Thomas Podany .... (202) 761-0001
US Section, International Navigation Association
Anne R. Cann Casey Building No.2594, Room 277 .... (703) 428-9090
E-mail: anne.r.cann@usace.army.mil

Hydrologic Engineering Center (HEC)
609 Second Street, Davis, CA 95616
Tel: (530) 756-1104 Fax: (530) 756-8250
E-mail: webmaster-hec@usace.army.mil

Director **Christopher N. Dunn** .... (530) 756-1104
E-mail: christopher.n.dunn@usace.army.mil

★ Presidential Appointment Requiring Senate Confirmation ☆ Presidential Appointment □ Schedule C Appointment ◇ Career Senior Foreign Service Appointment
● Career Senior Executive Service (SES) Appointment ○ Non-Career Senior Executive Service (SES) Appointment ■ Postal Career Executive Service

Centers

Engineer Research and Development Center (ERDC)
3909 Halls Ferry Road, Vicksburg, MS 39180-6199
Tel: (601) 634-3111 (General Calls) Tel: (601) 634-2562 (Public Affairs)
Fax: (601) 634-2361 E-mail: ceerd-pa-z@erdc.usace.army.mil
Internet: www.erdc.usace.army.mil

● Director **Dr. David W. Pittman** .... (601) 634-3304
E-mail: david.w.pittman@usace.army.mil
Education: Mississippi State 1983 BSCE, 1988 MSCE; Texas 1993 PhD
● Deputy Director **Dr. Beth C. Fleming** .... (601) 634-1111
Education: Mississippi State 1988 BS, 1994 MS; LSU 2000 PhD
Commander **COL Ivan P. Beckman USA** .... (601) 634-2513
Deputy to the Commander **Henry S. McDevitt, Jr.** .... (601) 634-3506
E-mail: henry.s.mcdevitt@usace.army.mil
Education: Mississippi State
Associate Director **Patricia M. Sullivan** .... (601) 634-3065
Education: Tulane 1984 BCE; Mississippi State 1991 MCE

Coastal and Hydraulics Laboratory (CHL)
3909 Halls Ferry Road, Vicksburg, MS 39180-6199
E-mail: erdcinfo@usace.army.mil

● Director **(Vacant)** .... (601) 634-2001
Deputy Director **COL Jeffrey R. Eckstein USA, PE** .... (601) 634-4263
Education: West Point 1985 BSCE; U Washington 1994 MSCE

Cold Regions Research and Engineering Laboratory (CRREL)
72 Lyme Road, Hanover, NH 03755
Tel: (603) 646-4100 Fax: (603) 646-4178
E-mail: crrel-info@usace.army.mil

● Director **Dr. Joseph L. Corriveau PhD** .... (603) 646-4200
E-mail: joseph.l.corriveau.civ@mail.mil
Education: St Anselm 1981; Delaware 1983; Brown U 1989 PhD
Deputy Director **David B. Ringelberg** .... (603) 646-4201
Technical Director **Dr. Mark Moran** .... (603) 646-4100
Chief, Biogeochemical Sciences Branch **Dr. Justin B. Berman** .... (603) 646-4563
E-mail: justin.b.berman@usace.army.mil
Education: Illinois BS, MS, PhD
Chief, Engineering Resources Branch **Jared I. Oren** .... (603) 646-4458
E-mail: jared.i.oren@usace.army.mil
Chief, Force Projection and Sustainment Branch **Dr. Edel R. Cortez** .... (603) 646-4301
Chief, Management Integration Office **Kent Apley** .... (603) 646-4203
Chief, Remote Sensing and Water Resources Branch **Timothy Pangburn** .... (603) 646-4296
Education: Dartmouth 1981 ME
Chief, Research and Engineering Division (Acting) **Dr. Warren Wehmeyer** .... (603) 646-4794
Chief, Signature Physics Branch **Dr. Joyce A. Mechling** .... (603) 646-4261
E-mail: joyce.a.mechling@usace.army.mil
Chief, Terrestrial and Cryospheric Sciences Branch **Janet P. Hardy** .... (603) 646-4306
E-mail: janet.p.hardy@usace.army.mil
Public Affairs Specialist **Bryan R. Armbrust** .... (603) 646-4852
E-mail: bryan.r.armbrust@usace.army.mil

Construction Engineering Research Laboratory (CERL)
Champaign, IL 61826
Mail: P.O. Box 9005, Champaign, IL 61826-9005
Tel: (217) 352-6511 Fax: (217) 373-7208

● Director **Dr. Lance D. Hansen** .... (217) 352-6511
E-mail: lance.d.hansen@usace.army.mil
Education: West Point 1988 BS; Purdue 1995 MS, 2002 PhD
Deputy Director **Kirankumar Topudurti** .... (217) 352-6511
Public Affairs Communications Specialist **Michael R. Jazdyk** .... (217) 373-6714
E-mail: michael.r.jazdyk@usace.army.mil
Library Technician **Patricia K. "Pat" Lacey** .... (217) 373-7217
E-mail: patricia.k.lacey@usace.army.mil

Environmental Laboratory
3909 Halls Ferry Road, Vicksburg, MS 39180-6199
Internet: www.erdc.usace.army.mil/el E-mail: erdcinfo@usace.army.mil

● Director **Ilker R. Adiguzel** .... (601) 634-3943
E-mail: ilker.r.adiguzel@usace.army.mil
Education: Illinois DCE
Deputy Director **Dr. Jack E. Davis** .... (601) 634-2502
E-mail: jack.e.davis@usace.army.mil

Geospatial Research Laboratory (GRL)
Cude Building Number 2592, 7701 Telegraph Road,
Alexandria, VA 22315-3864
Tel: (703) 428-3736 Fax: (703) 428-8154 Internet: www.agc.army.mil

● Director **Gary W. Blohm** Cude Building No. 2592, Room 100-D .... (703) 428-3736
E-mail: gary.w.blohm.civ@mail.mil
Deputy Director **Valerie Carney** Cude Building No. 2592, Room 100-C .... (703) 428-3736

Geotechnical and Structures Laboratory
3909 Halls Ferry Road, Vicksburg, MS 39180-6199
Tel: (601) 634-3188 E-mail: erdcinfo@usace.army.mil
Internet: www.erdc.usace.army.mil/gsl

● Director **Bartley P. Durst** .... (601) 634-2226
E-mail: bartley.p.durst@usace.army.mil
Education: Mississippi State
Deputy Director **William P. Grogan PE, MASCE** .... (601) 634-2183
Education: Georgia Tech BSCE; Mississippi State MSCE; Texas A&M PhD

Information Technology Laboratory
3909 Halls Ferry Road, Vicksburg, MS 39180-6199
E-mail: erdcinfo@usace.army.mil Internet: www.erdc.usace.army.mil/itl

● Director **Dr. David A. Horner** .... (601) 634-3956
Deputy Director **Patti S. Duett** .... (601) 634-3789
E-mail: patti.s.duett@usace.army.mil

Huntsville (AL) Engineering and Support Center
4820 University Square, Huntsville, AL 35816
Mail: P.O. Box 1600, Huntsville, AL 35807
Tel: (256) 895-1300 Internet: www.hnc.usace.army.mil

Commander **COL John S. Hurley USA** .... (256) 895-1300
E-mail: john.s.hurley@usace.army.mil
Education: West Point BS, MA
Deputy Commander **LTC Hugh Darville USA** .... (256) 895-1302
Education: Texas A&M 1993 BS; Virginia MArch
Programs Director **Albert "Chip" Marin** .... (256) 895-1301
Education: Maine 1980 BS; US Army Command 1982 MA; Army War Col 2003 MS
Executive Liaison Officer **Martha Cook** .... (256) 895-1306
Audit Director **Lori Cordell-Meikle** .... (256) 895-1363
Business Director **Christina Freese** .... (256) 895-1246
Education: Athens State BBA; Webster MA
Contracting Director **Colleen J. O'Keefe** .... (256) 895-1110
E-mail: colleen.j.okeefe@usace.army.mil
Energy Division Chief **Paul R. Robinson** .... (256) 895-1541
E-mail: paul.r.robinson@usace.army.mil
Engineering Director **Boyce Ross** .... (256) 895-1900
Information Management Director **Mark Music** .... (256) 895-1260
Logistics Director **Chris DeMarcus** .... (256) 895-1681
Resource Management Director **Darrell Audwin Davis** .... (256) 895-1410
USACE Learning Center Director **John E. Barnett** .... (256) 895-7400
EIM Program Manager **John A. Trudell III** .... (256) 895-1322
E-mail: john.a.trudelliii@usace.army.mil
Energy Engineering Analysis Program Manager **Raúl E. Alonso** .... (256) 895-1710
E-mail: raul.e.alonso@usace.army.mil
Central Metering Program Manager **Michael A. Ott** .... (256) 895-1376
E-mail: michael.a.ott@usace.army.mil

DEPARTMENTS

★ Presidential Appointment Requiring Senate Confirmation ☆ Presidential Appointment ☐ Schedule C Appointment ◇ Career Senior Foreign Service Appointment
● Career Senior Executive Service (SES) Appointment ○ Non-Career Senior Executive Service (SES) Appointment ■ Postal Career Executive Service

DEPARTMENTS

US Army Corps of Engineers Divisions

Great Lakes and Ohio River Division

550 Main Street, Room 10524, Cincinnati, OH 45202-3215
Mail: P.O. Box 1159, Cincinnati, OH 45201-1159
Tel: (513) 684-3002 Fax: (513) 684-2085
Internet: www.lrd.usace.army.mil

Commander and Division Engineer
MG Richard Mark Toy USA, PE .... (513) 684-3002
E-mail: richard.m.toy@usace.army.mil
Education: West Point 1987 BS; Boston U 1991 MBA; UCLA 1996 MS; Indust'l Col Armed Forces 2010 MS
Executive Assistant
COL Kimberly A. Longoria USA .... (513) 684-3004
Deputy Commander **COL Paul Kremer USA** .... (513) 684-3003
Public Affairs Specialist **Jacqueline Y. "Jackee" Tate** ... (513) 684-3097
E-mail: jacqueline.y.tate@usace.army.mil
Human Resources Director **Oneda Lambert** .... (513) 684-2822
Programs Director **Stephen G. Durrett PE** .... (513) 684-3061
Education: Kentucky BSCE; Cincinnati MS
Regional Business Directorate **(Vacant)** .... (513) 684-3005
Resource Management Director **(Vacant)** .... (513) 684-3052
Provost Marshal **Joanne Rutledge** .... (513) 684-2698
E-mail: joanne.rutledge@usace.army.mil Fax: (513) 684-6218

Buffalo (NY) District

1776 Niagara Street, Buffalo, NY 14207-3199
Tel: (716) 879-4410 Fax: (716) 879-4434
Internet: www.lrb.usace.army.mil
Areas Covered: Massena, NY to Toledo, OH

Commander and District Engineer
LTC Jason A. Toth USA .... (716) 879-4200
Deputy Commander **MAJ Patrick Billmann USA** .... (716) 879-4201
Public Affairs Officer **Andrew A. "Andy" Kornacki** ..... (716) 879-4410
E-mail: andrew.a.kornacki@usace.army.mil

Chicago (IL) District

231 South LaSalle Street, Suite 1500, Chicago, IL 60604
Tel: (312) 846-5333 Fax: (312) 353-2169
Internet: www.lrc.usace.army.mil
Areas Covered: Civil Works (McHenry, Lake, Kane, DuPage, Cook and Will counties in IL; Lake, Porter and northern LaPorte counties in IN); Emergency Management (same as Civil Works plus entire Kankakee River basin); Regulatory (McHenry, Lake, Kane, DuPage, Cook and Will counties, IL)

Commander and District Engineer
COL Aaron W. Reisinger USA .... (312) 846-5333
Education: West Point 1994 BSME; Georgetown MS
Deputy Commander **LTC Jason Borg USA** .... (312) 846-5333
Deputy District Engineer
Katarzyna Chelkowska-Risley .... (312) 846-5302
Office of Counsel Chief **Kim Sabo** .... (312) 846-5350
Technical Services Division Chief **Linda Sorn** .... (312) 846-5400
Information Management Office Chief **Gabrielle Reed** ... (312) 846-5382
Safety Office Chief **Peter Flanagan** .... (312) 846-5340

Detroit (MI) District

477 Michigan Avenue, Detroit, MI 48226
Mail: P.O. Box 1027, Detroit, MI 48231-1027
Tel: (888) 694-8313 Fax: (313) 226-5993
Internet: www.lre.usace.army.mil
Areas Covered: Lake Huron; Lake Michigan; Lake Superior; Upper Lake Erie

Commander and District Engineer
LTC Greg Turner USA .... (313) 226-5763
Fax: (313) 226-6009
Deputy Commander **MAJ Scott D. Snyder USA** .... (313) 226-6572
Deputy District Engineer for Project Management
Scott J. Thieme .... (313) 226-2240
E-mail: scott.j.thieme@usace.army.mil
Personnel Officer **Adrienne Barber** .... (313) 226-2713
Counsel **(Vacant)** .... (313) 226-6822
Equal Employment Office Chief
Valerie "Val" Stevenson .... (313) 226-4744

Detroit (MI) District *(continued)*

Information Management Office Chief
Yolanda Mclaurin .... (313) 226-6448
Internal Review Office Chief **William "Bill" Stafford** .... (313) 226-6834
Logistics Management Office Chief **Sandra Watson** ..... (313) 226-7609
Public Affairs Officer **Lynn M. Rose** .... (313) 226-4680
E-mail: Lynn.M.Rose@usace.army.mil
Resource Management Office Chief **Erwin Dungy** .... (313) 226-5044
Safety and Occupational Health Chief **Scott Resch** ...... (313) 226-6810
Security and Law Enforcement Office Chief **(Vacant)** .... (313) 226-3465
Engineering and Technical Services Chief
Marie T. Strum .... (313) 226-6444
Great Lakes Hydraulics and Hydrology Office Chief
John Allis .... (313) 226-2137
Management Support Office Chief **Scott Theut** .... (313) 226-6787
Operations Office Chief **(Vacant)** .... (313) 226-5013
Regulatory Office Chief **(Vacant)** .... (313) 226-7732
Contracting Division Chief **Robert Alton** .... (313) 226-2134
Engineering Construction Division Chief **Phillip Ross** .... (313) 226-4761
Planning Chief **(Vacant)** .... (313) 226-7762

Huntington (WV) District

502 Eighth Street, Room 6300, Huntington, WV 25701-2070
Tel: (304) 399-5395 Fax: (304) 399-5076 E-mail: pa2@usace.army.mil
Internet: www.lrh.usace.army.mil

Commander and District Engineer
LTC William J. Miller USA .... (304) 399-5395
Fax: (304) 399-5591
Deputy Commander **(Vacant)** .... (304) 399-5251
Deputy District Engineer for Project Management
Joseph M. Savage .... (304) 399-5395
Deputy for Small Business **Eileen S. Hodges** .... (304) 399-5632
E-mail: eileen.s.hodges@usace.army.mil
Human Resources Officer **(Vacant)** .... (304) 399-5667
Security Officer **Sandra L. Hardwick** .... (304) 399-5612
E-mail: sandra.l.hardwick@usace.army.mil Fax: (304) 399-5581
Counsel Office Chief **Henry J. Iarrusso** .... (304) 399-5261
E-mail: henry.j.iarrusso@usace.army.mil
Equal Employment Opportunity Office Chief
Tracy D. Baker .... (304) 399-5214
E-mail: tracy.d.baker@usace.army.mil
Internal Review Office Chief **(Vacant)** .... (304) 399-5649
Public Affairs Office Chief **Brian Maka** .... (304) 399-5353
E-mail: brian.maka@usace.army.mil
Resource Management Office Chief **Crystal Adkins** ..... (304) 399-5250
Safety and Occupational Health Office Chief
Shereda Gorum .... (304) 399-5094
Planning Branch Chief **Amy Frantz** .... (304) 399-5802
Contracting Division Chief **Cheryl B. Fitzwater** .... (304) 399-5619
E-mail: cheryl.b.fitzwater@usace.army.mil
Engineering and Construction Division Chief
August W. Martin .... (304) 399-5254
Operations and Readiness Division Chief
Wayne Budrus .... (304) 399-5910
Planning, Programs and Project Management Division
Chief **Michael Keathley** .... (304) 399-5699
E-mail: michael.keathley@usace.army.mil
Real Estate Division Chief **Kenneth Bumgardner** .... (304) 399-5272
Strategic Integration Office Chief **Todd Mitchell** .... (304) 339-5021
Navigation Planning Center Chief **Patrick J. Donovan** ... (304) 399-6955
ACE-IT Chief **Kerry Campbell** .... (304) 399-5655

Louisville (KY) District

600 Dr. M.L. King Jr. Place, Louisville, KY 40202
Mail: P.O. Box 59, Louisville, KY 40201-0059
Tel: (502) 315-6106 Fax: (502) 315-6109
Internet: www.lrl.usace.army.mil

Commander **COL Antoinette R. Gant USA** .... (502) 315-6102
E-mail: antoinette.r.gant@usace.army.mil
Deputy Commander **LTC Robert Newbauer USA** .... (502) 315-6103
Deputy District Engineer **Linda R. Murphy PE** .... (502) 315-6104
E-mail: linda.r.murphy@usace.army.mil
Executive Liaison Officer **Rhiannon Ryan** .... (502) 315-6105

★ Presidential Appointment Requiring Senate Confirmation ☆ Presidential Appointment □ Schedule C Appointment ◇ Career Senior Foreign Service Appointment
● Career Senior Executive Service (SES) Appointment ○ Non-Career Senior Executive Service (SES) Appointment ■ Postal Career Executive Service

Louisville (KY) District *(continued)*

District Counsel **Janice E. Lengel** .... (502) 315-6641
E-mail: janice.e.lengel@usace.army.mil
Civilian Advisory Center Supervisor **Linda A. Miller** ..... (502) 315-6579
E-mail: linda.a.miller@usace.army.mil
Equal Employment Opportunity Office Chief
Brenda Smith .... (502) 315-6518
Information Technology Operations Officer
Marcella M. Denton .... (502) 315-6554
E-mail: marcella.m.denton@usace.army.mil
Internal Review Office Chief **Cowan W. Whitnable** ..... (502) 315-6607
E-mail: cowan.w.whitnable@usace.army.mil
Logistics Management Office Chief **Jane Myers** .... (502) 315-6631
Public Affairs Officer **Todd J. Hornback** .... (502) 315-6768
E-mail: todd.j.hornback@usace.army.mil
Safety Officer **Matthew H. Burg** .... (502) 315-7061
E-mail: matthew.h.burg@usace.army.mil
Construction Division Chief **Kirk P. Dailey** .... (502) 315-6116
E-mail: kirk.p.dailey@usace.army.mil
Contracting Division Director **Denise A. Bush** .... (502) 315-6209
E-mail: denise.a.bush@usace.army.mil
Engineering Division Chief **John R. Bock** .... (502) 315-6300
E-mail: john.r.bock@usace.army.mil
Operations and Readiness Division Chief
Eugene A. Dowell .... (502) 315-6731
Planning Programs Project Management Division Chief
(Acting) **Joanne M. Milo** .... (502) 315-6857
Real Estate Division Chief **Veronica A. Hiriams** .... (502) 315-7002
E-mail: veronica.a.hiriams@usace.army.mil
Small Business Deputy **Crystal M. May** .... (502) 315-6111
E-mail: crystal.m.may@usace.army.mil
Outreach Coordinator **Brandon R. Brummett** .... (502) 315-6883
E-mail: brandon.r.brummett@usace.army.mil
Strategic Communications Officer **Dan London** .... (502) 315-6597

Nashville (TN) District
P.O. Box 1070, Nashville, TN 37202-1070
Tel: (615) 736-7161 Fax: (615) 736-7065
Internet: www.lrn.usace.army.mil

Commander and District Engineer
LTC Stephen F. Murphy USA .... (615) 736-5626
Deputy Commander **MAJ Justin R. Toole USA** .... (615) 736-5627
Fax: (615) 736-2052
Deputy District Engineer for Project Management
Patty Coffey .... (615) 736-7836
Fax: (615) 736-2052
Chief, Engineering and Construction Division
Jimmy Waddle .... (615) 736-5647
Fax: (615) 736-2843
Chief, Information Technology Division **Ron Douglas** ... (615) 736-7161
Executive Officer **Joanne Mann** .... (615) 736-5601
Public Affairs Officer **William L. Peoples** .... (615) 736-7834
E-mail: william.l.peoples@usace.army.mil

Pittsburgh (PA) District
2200 William S. Moorhead Federal Building,
1000 Liberty Avenue, Pittsburgh, PA 15222-4186
Tel: (412) 395-7500 Fax: (412) 644-2811
Internet: www.lrp.usace.army.mil

Commander and District Engineer
COL Andrew J. "Coby" Short USA .... (412) 395-7103
Fax: (412) 644-4093
Deputy Commander **LTC Jonathan E. Klink USA** .... (412) 395-7102
Fax: (412) 644-4093
Deputy District Engineer **Lenna C. Hawkins** .... (412) 395-7102
E-mail: lenna.c.hawkins@usace.army.mil Fax: (412) 644-4093
ACE-IT Chief **Andrew Kramer** .... (412) 395-7538
Public Affairs Officer **Jeffrey S. "Jeff" Hawk** .... (412) 395-7501
E-mail: jeffrey.s.hawk@usace.army.mil

Mississippi Valley Division
1400 Walnut Street, Vicksburg, MS 39180
Mail: P.O. Box 80, Vicksburg, MS 39181-0080
Tel: (601) 634-5750 Fax: (601) 634-5029
E-mail: cemvd-pa@usace.army.mil Internet: www.mvd.usace.army.mil

Commander **MG Richard G. Kaiser USA** .... (601) 634-5750
Executive Assistant **Charles A. Camillo** .... (601) 634-7023
E-mail: charles.a.camillo@usace.army.mil
Deputy Commander **COL Robert A. Hilliard USA** .... (601) 634-5752
Business Resource Director **Joe L. Lemons** .... (601) 634-5776
Business Technical Division Chief
Michael A. "Mike" Turner .... (601) 634-5922
E-mail: mike.a.turner@usace.army.mil
Civil Works Integration Chief and Deputy of Programs
Renee N. Turner .... (601) 634-5799
Contracting Director **Wendell N. Norman** .... (601) 634-7135
E-mail: wendell.n.norman@usace.army.mil
Division Counsel **G. Rogers Sloan** .... (601) 634-5771
Equal Employment Office Chief **Brenda Jackson** .... (601) 634-5140
Human Resources Management Director **Joel Torres** ..... (601) 634-5166
● Programs Director **James A. "Jim" Bodron** .... (601) 634-5800
E-mail: james.a.bodron@usace.army.mil
Regional Business Director
Thomas A. Holden, Jr. PE .... (601) 634-5901
E-mail: thomas.a.holden@usace.army.mil
Education: West Point 1975 BSE; MIT MSCE; Army War Col MNSSS
Public Affairs Office Chief **Reagan B. Lauritzen** .... (601) 634-5760
E-mail: reagan.b.lauritzen@usace.army.mil
Education: Tulane 2006 BA; San Diego State 2013 MA
Public Affairs Office Deputy Chief **Pam Vedros** .... (601) 634-7783
E-mail: pam.vedros@mvd02.usace.army.mil
Administrative Officer **Edie Whittington** .... (601) 634-5768

Memphis (TN) District
167 North Main Street, Room B202, Memphis, TN 38103-1894
Tel: (901) 544-3005 Fax: (901) 544-3786
Internet: www.mvm.usace.army.mil

Commander and District Engineer
COL Michael A. "Mike" Ellicott, Jr. USA .... (901) 544-3221
Deputy Commander **MAJ Thomas Darrow USA** .... (901) 544-3223
Deputy for Project Management **James Jim Lloyd** ...... (901) 544-3223
District Counsel **LTC Suzy Mitchem USA (Ret)** .... (901) 544-3609
Operations Division Chief **Russell Davis** .... (901) 544-3356
Fax: (901) 544-3838
Engineering and Construction Division Chief
Donny Davidson .... (901) 544-3226
E-mail: donny.d.davidson@usace.army.mil Fax: (901) 544-3787
Education: U Memphis 1997 BS
Equal Employment Opportunity Office Chief
Dion M. Banks .... (901) 544-3501
Human Resource Officer **Fred Grittman** .... (901) 544-3105
Information Management Office Chief
Michael D. Chopard .... (901) 544-3135
Internal Review Office Chief **Leonardo Ramos** .... (901) 544-3579
Logistics Management Officer **Jimmy Longino** .... (901) 544-0812
Programs and Project Management Office Chief
(Vacant) .... (901) 544-0721
Fax: (901) 544-4041
Resource Management Office Chief **Voncile Williams** .... (901) 544-0782
Safety and Occupational Health Office Chief
Robert E. Shover .... (901) 544-3601
E-mail: robert.e.shover@usace.army.mil
Security and Law Enforcement Office Chief
Harold Harden .... (901) 544-4007
Public Affairs Officer **James T. "Jim" Pogue** .... (901) 544-4109
E-mail: james.t.pogue@usace.army.mil

★ Presidential Appointment Requiring Senate Confirmation ☆ Presidential Appointment ☐ Schedule C Appointment ◇ Career Senior Foreign Service Appointment
● Career Senior Executive Service (SES) Appointment ○ Non-Career Senior Executive Service (SES) Appointment ■ Postal Career Executive Service

New Orleans (LA) District
7400 Leake Avenue, New Orleans, LA 70118
Mail: P.O. Box 60267, New Orleans, LA 70160-0267
Tel: (504) 862-2077 Fax: (504) 862-1259
Internet: www.mvn.usace.army.mil

Commander and District Engineer
COL Michael N. Clancy USA .... (504) 862-2077
E-mail: michael.n.clancy@usace.army.mil
Deputy Commander **MAJ Jordan S. Davis USA** .... (504) 862-2077
Deputy District Engineer for Project Management
Mark R. Wingate .... (504) 862-2204
E-mail: mark.r.wingate@usace.army.mil
Education: New Orleans 1989 BSCE
Public Affairs Officer **Rickey D. Boyett** .... (504) 862-1524
E-mail: rickey.d.boyett@usace.army.mil
Training Officer **Vera-Ellen Trice** .... (504) 862-1042
ACE-IT Chief **David L. Berna** .... (504) 862-2121
E-mail: david.l.berna@usace.army.mil
Safety and Security Chief **LTC Stephen L. Hric USA** .... (504) 862-2205
Librarian **Sandra Brown** .... (504) 862-2559

Rock Island (IL) District
205 Rodman Avenue, Rock Island, IL 61299
Mail: P.O. Box 2004, Clock Tower Building, Rock Island, IL 61204-2004
Tel: (309) 794-4200 Fax: (309) 794-5793
Internet: www.mvr.usace.army.mil

District Commander
COL Steven M. "Steve" Sattinger USA .... (309) 794-5249
Deputy Commander **LTC Rachel A. Honderd USA** .... (309) 794-5253
E-mail: rachel.honderd@usace.army.mil
Deputy for Programs and Project Management
Dennis W. Hamilton .... (309) 794-5260
E-mail: dennis.w.hamilton@usace.army.mil
Executive Secretary **Melody McHugh** .... (309) 794-5249
Executive Assistant **Mari K. Fournier** .... (309) 794-5298
E-mail: mari.k.fournier@usace.army.mil
District Counsel **Rian W. Hancks** .... (309) 794-5417
E-mail: cemvr-oc@usace.army.mil
Outreach Planning **Angela M. Freyermuth** .... (309) 794-5341
Disadvantaged Business Utility Office **(Vacant)** .... (309) 794-5661
Central Area Office Area Engineer **Barbara L. Lester** .... (309) 794-5480
Education: Iowa State BA; Iowa MCE
Eastern Area Office Area Engineer **Jack McDaniel** .... (309) 794-4200
E-mail: jack.mcdaniel@usace.army.mil
Civilian Personnel Advisory Center Team Leader
Leona F. Vilmont .... (309) 794-5345
Construction Division Chief **Roger A. Perk** .... (309) 794-5227
Contracting Division Chief **Scott Harris** .... (309) 794-5628
E-mail: cemvr-ct@usace.army.mil
Corporation Communications Chief **Allen Marshall** .... (309) 794-5274
Emergency Management/Security Division Chief
Michael Lorah .... (309) 794-5230
E-mail: cemvr-eoc@usace.army.mil Fax: (309) 794-5404
Engineering & Construction Division Chief (Acting)
John T. Behrens .... (309) 794-5226
Equal Employment Opportunity Office Chief
Rachal Deahl .... (309) 794-5422
Information Management Chief
Thomas G. "Tom" Lafrenz .... (309) 794-5771
E-mail: thomas.g.lafrenz@usace.army.mil
Internal Review Chief **Michael E. Roarty** .... (309) 794-5652
E-mail: michael.e.roarty@usace.army.mil
Logistics Management Chief **Daniel Simon** .... (309) 794-5835
Operations Division Chief **Tom Heimond** .... (309) 794-5501
Mississippi River Operations Manager
Robert T. Germann .... (309) 794-4512
Real Estate Division Chief **Jodie Rowe** .... (309) 794-5234
Resource Management Chief **James Toohey** .... (309) 794-5242
Safety and Occupational Health Chief **Troy A. Larson** .... (309) 794-5280
E-mail: troy.a.larson@usace.army.mil
Library Director **Robert L. "Bob" Romic** .... (309) 794-5576
E-mail: robert.l.romic@usace.army.mil

Saint Louis (MO) District
Robert A. Young Federal Building, 1222 Spruce Street,
St. Louis, MO 63103-2833
Tel: (314) 331-8002 Tel: (314) 331-8068 Tel: (314) 331-8095
Fax: (314) 331-8005 Internet: www.mvs.usace.army.mil

Commander and District Engineer
COL Bryan K. Sizemore USA .... (314) 331-8010
Education: West Point 1986 BSE; Missouri (Rolla) MS;
Marine Corps U MMAS
Deputy District Engineer **LTC David Gordon USA** .... (314) 331-8014
E-mail: David.Gordon@usace.army.mil
Deputy District Engineer for Program Management
John N. Peukert .... (314) 331-8012
Education: Southeast Missouri State 2000 BA; Mississippi 2002 MA
Public Affairs Officer **Amanda Kruse** .... (314) 331-8095
E-mail: amanda.l.kruse@usace.army.mil
Small Business Officer **Karla L. Babb** .... (314) 331-8511
E-mail: karla.l.babb@usace.army.mil
District Counsel **William P. Levins** .... (314) 331-8196
E-mail: william.p.levins@usace.army.mil
Engineering and Construction Division Chief
David R. Busse .... (314) 331-8202
E-mail: david.r.busse@usace.army.mil
Construction Branch Chief **(Vacant)** .... (314) 331-8130
Operations Readiness Division Chief
Louis A. "Lou" Dell'Orco .... (314) 331-8100
Real Estate Division Chief **Jaclyn Wittenborn** .... (314) 331-8151
Readiness Branch Chief **Matthew J. "Matt" Hunn** .... (314) 331-8569
E-mail: matthew.j.hunn@usace.army.mil
ACE-IT Chief **Jule D. Bartels** .... (314) 331-8650
E-mail: Jule.D.Bartels@usace.army.mi

Saint Paul (MN) District
Corps of Engineers, Sibly Square at Mears Park, 190 Fifth Street, East,
Suite 401, St. Paul, MN 55101-1638
Tel: (651) 290-5200 Fax: (651) 290-5752
E-mail: cemvp-pa@usace.army.mil Internet: www.mvp.usace.army.mil

District Commander **COL Samuel Calkins USA** .... (651) 290-5300
Deputy Commander **LTC Jason Poth USA** .... (651) 290-5299
Deputy for Programs and Project Management
Judith L. A. DesHarnais .... (651) 290-5298
ACE-IT Chief **David A. "Dave" Himmerich** .... (651) 290-5807
E-mail: david.a.himmerich@usace.army.mil
Contracting Officer **Kevin Hendricks** .... (651) 290-5419
Librarian **(Vacant)** .... (651) 290-5680
Public Affairs Officer **Shannon L. Bauer** .... (651) 290-5108

Vicksburg (MS) District
4155 Clay Street, Vicksburg, MS 39183-3435
Tel: (601) 631-5000 Fax: (601) 631-5225
Internet: www.mvk.usace.army.mil

Commander and District Engineer
COL Michael C. Derosier USA .... (601) 631-5014
E-mail: cemvk-pa@usace.army.mil
Education: West Point 1992 BSCE
Deputy Commander **LTC Aaron W. Wolf USA** .... (601) 631-5014
Education: Wisconsin (Stevens Point) 1994
District Counsel **David Dyer** .... (601) 631-5074
Fax: (601) 631-5073
Chief, Engineering Division **Henry Dulaney** .... (601) 631-7724
E-mail: henry.a.dulaney@usace.army.mil
Chief, Equal Employment Opportunity Office
Frederick Austin .... (601) 631-5063
Chief, Information Management Office **Bill Bunevich** .... (601) 631-7292
Chief, Internal Review and Audit Compliance Office
(Acting) **Harold Germantyy** .... (601) 631-5031
Chief, Office of Small Business Programs
Demetric T. Erwin .... (601) 631-5951
E-mail: demetric.erwin@usace.army.mil
Chief, Operations Division **James Ross** .... (601) 631-5315
Education: Mississippi State BS, MS
Chief, Planning, Programs and Project Management
Division **Patricia "Pat" Hemphill** .... (601) 631-7933
Education: Mississippi State BSCE

Vicksburg (MS) District *(continued)*

Chief, Real Estate Division **Robert S. Wood** .... (601) 631-5220
E-mail: robert.s.wood@usace.army.mil
Chief, Resource Management Office **Carol Watkins** ..... (601) 631-5180
Chief, Safety and Occupational Health Office
William "Bill" Richards .... (601) 631-5091
Public Affairs Officer **Gregory C. Raimondo** .... (601) 631-5053
E-mail: gregory.c.raimondo@usace.army.mil

North Atlantic Division

Buildings 301 and 302, Fort Hamilton Military Community,
General Lee Avenue, Brooklyn, NY 11252
Tel: (347) 370-4550 Fax: (718) 765-7168
Internet: www.nad.usace.army.mil

Commander
MG Jeffrey L. Milhorn USA Building 302 .... (347) 370-4500
E-mail: jeffrey.l.milhorn.mil@mail.mil
Executive Officer **(Vacant)** .... (347) 370-4506
Deputy Commander
COL Corey M. Spencer USA Building 302 .... (347) 370-4501
● Director, Regional Business Directorate
COL Reinhard W. Koenig PE, USA (Ret) .... (347) 370-4555
Education: West Point 1986 BSCE; Rose-Hulman MS; National Defense U MS
● Director, Regional Programs Directorate (Interim)
Wesley E. Coleman, Jr. .... (347) 370-4629
Division Counsel **Maureen McAndrew** .... (347) 370-4522
Emergency Management Team **Michael Ganley** .... (347) 370-4576
Business Management Division **(Vacant)** .... (347) 370-4627
Business Technical Division **Alan Huntley** .... (347) 370-4664
E-mail: alan.huntley@usace.army.mil
Civil Works Integration Division
Joseph "Joe" Forcina .... (347) 370-4567
Military Integration Division **Thomas Harnedy** .... (347) 370-4604
Program Support Division **George Nieves** .... (347) 370-4556
E-mail: george.nieves@usace.army.mil
Security and Law Enforcement Chief **Gary L. Kehoe** .... (347) 370-4520
E-mail: gary.l.kehoe@usace.army.mil
Public Affairs Chief **Edward L. "Ed" Loomis** .... (347) 370-4550
E-mail: edward.loomis@usace.army.mil

Baltimore (MD) District

10 South Howard Street, Baltimore, MD 21201
Mail: P.O. Box 1715, Baltimore, MD 21203-1715
Tel: (410) 962-2809 Fax: (410) 962-3660
Internet: www.nab.usace.army.mil

Commander and District Engineer
LTC John T. Litz USA .... (410) 962-2809
E-mail: john.t.litz@usace.army.mil
Deputy Commander **MAJ Brad Morgan USA** .... (410) 962-4546
Deputy District Engineer for Programs and Project
Management **David "Dave" Morrow** .... (410) 962-7960
Deputy for Small Business **Tamika Gray** .... (410) 962-2809
E-mail: tamika.gray@usace.army.mil
Chief of Staff **Sara Robert** .... (410) 962-4547
E-mail: sara.robert@usace.army.mil
Chief, ACE-IT **Gary Maul** .... (410) 962-2809
Chief, Corporation Communications
Christopher Augsburger .... (410) 962-2809
E-mail: christopher.augsburger@usace.army.mil Fax: (410) 962-3660
Chief, Engineering Division **Ron Maj** .... (410) 962-2809
Chief, Operations Division **Dianne Edwardson** .... (410) 962-4458
Chief, Planning Division **Amy M. Guise** .... (410) 962-4900
Fax: (410) 385-5559
Chief, Real Estate Division **Susan Lewis** .... (410) 962-3000

New England District

696 Virginia Road, Concord, MA 01742-2751
Tel: (978) 318-8238 Fax: (978) 318-8850
Internet: www.nae.usace.army.mil E-mail: cenae-pa@usace.army.mil

Commander and District Engineer
COL William Conde USA .... (978) 318-8220
Deputy Commander and Deputy District Engineer
LTC Sonny B. Avichal USA .... (978) 318-8222

New England District *(continued)*

Deputy District Engineer for Programs and Project
Management **Scott E. Acone** .... (978) 318-8230
E-mail: scott.e.acone@usace.army.mil
Public Affairs Chief **Larry B. Rosenberg** .... (978) 318-8657
E-mail: larry.b.rosenberg@usace.army.mil
ACE-IT Chief **Gregory C. "Greg" Lantz** .... (978) 318-8187
E-mail: gregory.c.lantz@usace.army.mil
Construction Division Chief **Sean C. Dolan** .... (978) 318-8079
E-mail: sean.c.dolan@usace.army.mil
Contracting Division Chief **Sheila M. Winston** .... (978) 318-8159
E-mail: sheila.m.winston@usace.army.mil
Engineering/Planning Division Chief **(Vacant)** .... (978) 318-8194
Operations Division Chief **Eric Pedersen** .... (978) 318-8194
Programs Management Division Chief
Janet G. Harrington .... (978) 318-8620
E-mail: janet.g.harrington@usace.army.mil
Real Estate Division Chief **(Vacant)** .... (978) 318-8585
Small Business Office Chief **Eva Marie D'Antuono** ..... (938) 318-8427
E-mail: evamarie.d'antuono@usace.army.mil
Librarian and District Historian **(Vacant)** .... (978) 318-8349
E-mail: library@usace.army.mil

New York District

Jacob K. Javits Federal Building, 26 Federal Plaza,
New York, NY 10278-0090
Tel: (917) 790-8001 Fax: (212) 264-5947
Internet: www.nan.usace.army.mil

Commander and District Engineer
COL Thomas D. Asbery USA .... (917) 790-8000
Education: West Virginia 1994 BS; Virginia Tech MS
Secretary **Jessica Novick** .... (917) 790-8026
Deputy District Engineer for Programs and Project
Management **Joseph J. Seebode** .... (917) 790-8209
E-mail: joseph.j.seebode@usace.army.mil
ACE-IT Chief **Bhavesh Shah** .... (917) 790-8691
Construction Division Chief **Matthew A. Ludwig** .... (917) 790-8471
Contracting Division Chief **Francis Cashman** .... (917) 790-8173
E-mail: francis.cashman@usace.army.mil
Engineering Division Chief **Michael Rovi** .... (917) 790-8300
Operations Division Chief **Thomas M. Creamer** .... (917) 790-8400
Planning Division Chief **Clifford S. Jones** .... (917) 790-8700
Real Estate Division Chief
Noreen D. "Dean" Dresser .... (917) 790-8430
E-mail: noreen.d.dresser@usace.army.mil
District Counsel **Lorraine C. Lee** .... (917) 790-8055
Education: St John's U (NY) JD
Public Affairs Chief **Kenneth Wells** .... (917) 790-8007
E-mail: kenneth.wells@usace.army.mil
Program Manager **(Vacant)** .... (917) 790-8001
Security Specialist **William C. Kozak** .... (917) 790-8010
E-mail: william.c.kozak@usace.army.mil Fax: (212) 264-0541

Norfolk (VA) District

803 Front Street, Norfolk, VA 23510-1096
Tel: (757) 201-7601 Fax: (757) 201-7115
Internet: www.nao.usace.army.mil

Commander and District Engineer
COL Jason E. Kelly USA .... (757) 201-7601
E-mail: jason.e.kelly@usace.army.mil
Deputy Commander **MAJ Alexander Samms USA** ..... (757) 201-7603
Deputy District Engineer for Programs and Project
Management **Michael R. "Mike" Darrow PE, PMP** .... (757) 201-7601
E-mail: michael.r.darrow@usace.army.mil
Education: Clark U 1988 BS; Cornell 1998 ME
Public Affairs Chief **Mark W. Haviland** .... (757) 201-7606
E-mail: mark.w.haviland@usace.army.mil

DEPARTMENTS

★ Presidential Appointment Requiring Senate Confirmation ☆ Presidential Appointment □ Schedule C Appointment ◇ Career Senior Foreign Service Appointment
● Career Senior Executive Service (SES) Appointment ○ Non-Career Senior Executive Service (SES) Appointment ■ Postal Career Executive Service

DEPARTMENTS

Philadelphia (PA) District
The Wanamaker Building, 100 Penn Square, East,
Philadelphia, PA 19107-3390
Tel: (215) 656-6500 Fax: (215) 656-6820
Internet: http://www.nap.usace.army.mil/

Commander and District Engineer
LTC Kristen N. Dahle USA .... (215) 656-6501
E-mail: kristen.n.dahle@usace.army.mil
Deputy District Commander **MAJ Brian Corbin USA** .... (215) 656-6501
Deputy District Engineer for Programs and Project Management **Nathan Barcomb** .... (215) 656-6501
Chief Information Officer **Robert E. Hunter** .... (215) 656-6858
E-mail: robert.e.hunter@usace.army.mil Fax: (215) 656-6828
Public Affairs Officer **Edward C. Voigt** .... (215) 656-6515
E-mail: edward.c.voigt@usace.army.mil
Librarian **Linda C. Skale** .... (215) 656-6821
E-mail: linda.c.skale@usace.army.mil Fax: (215) 656-6828
Security and Law Enforcement Chief **Jermaine March** ... (215) 656-8696
Fax: (215) 656-6522
Secretary **Rosemary I. McMullen** .... (215) 656-6502
E-mail: rosemary.i.mcmullen@usace.army.mil

Marine Design Center
100 Penn Square, East, Philadelphia, PA 19107-3390
Tel: (215) 656-6850

Hull Section Chief **Timothy J. "Tim" Keyser PE** .... (215) 656-6171
Education: New Orleans 2003 BS

Northwestern Division
P.O. Box 2870, Portland, OR 97208-2870
Tel: (503) 808-3722 Internet: www.nwd.usace.army.mil

Commander and Division Engineer
BG D. Peter Helmlinger USA, PE .... (503) 808-3700
E-mail: peter.helmlinger@usace.army.mil
Education: West Point 1988 BSME; Stanford MSCE; Indust'l Col Armed Forces MS
Deputy Commander **COL Torrey A. DiCiro USA, PE** ..... (503) 808-3701
E-mail: torrey.a.diciro@usace.army.mil
Education: West Point 1993 BCE; Georgia Tech 2001 MCE, 2001 MBA
Executive Officer **Judith Hutchins** .... (503) 808-3703
Executive Secretary **Cheryl Long** .... (503) 808-3702
Director, Contracting **LTC Thomas R. Lutz USA** .... (503) 808-3797
Director, Human Resources **Kate Furlong-Borth** .... (503) 808-3786
Fax: (503) 808-3766
Director, Information Management **Dean Rychlik** .... (503) 808-3937
Director, Logistics Management **James McKinney** ...... (503) 808-3805
Fax: (503) 808-3749
● Director, Regional Business **Eric V. Hansen** .... (503) 808-3820
Education: Whitman 1993 BA; Washington State 1997 BS Fax: (503) 808-3750
Assistant Director, Small Business Programs (Acting)
Carol A. McIntyre .... (503) 808-3852
E-mail: carol.a.mcintyre@usace.army.mil
Regional Director, Programs **David J. Ponganis** .... (503) 808-3730
Education: UC Santa Cruz 1977; Stanford 1979 MSCE
Resource Management **James P. "Jim" Erzen** .... (503) 808-3770
E-mail: james.p.erzen@usace.army.mil Fax: (503) 808-3799
Division Counsel **Patrick Flachs** .... (503) 808-3762
Fax: (503) 808-3766
Equal Employment Opportunity Officer **(Vacant)** .... (503) 808-3792
Native American Coordinator **J.R. Inglis** .... (503) 808-4508
Director of Public Affairs **Matt Rabe** .... (503) 808-3710
E-mail: j.matt.rabe@usace.army.mil
Education: Concordia Col (OR) 1997 BA
Safety and Occupational Health Officer
CPT Anne Krake USA .... (503) 808-7973
Security and Law Enforcement Officer
CPT Aaron Hoffman USA (Ret) .... (503) 808-3982

Kansas City (MO) District
Richard Bolling Federal Building, 601 East 12th Street, Room 635, Kansas City, MO 64106-2824
Tel: (816) 389-3205 Fax: (816) 389-2027
Internet: www.nwk.usace.army.mil

Commander and District Engineer
COL Douglas B. Guttormsen USA .... (816) 389-3202
E-mail: douglas.b.guttormsen@usace.army.mil
Deputy Commander
MAJ Christopher Ryan Pevey USA .... (816) 389-3205
Deputy District Engineer for Project Management (Acting) **Rex W. Ostrander** .... (816) 389-3205
E-mail: rex.w.ostrander@usace.army.mil
Executive Officer **Larry L. Myers** .... (816) 389-3202
E-mail: larry.l.myers@usace.army.mil
Executive Secretary **(Vacant)** .... (816) 389-3202
Chief, ACE-IT **Steve R. Burns** .... (816) 389-3414
E-mail: steven.r.burns@usace.army.mil
Chief, Construction Division
Robert J. "Bob" Kreienheder .... (816) 389-3270
E-mail: robert.j.kreienheder@usace.army.mil
Chief, Engineering Division **David L. Mathews** .... (816) 389-3696
E-mail: david.l.mathews@usace.army.mil
Public Affairs Officer **David S. Kolarik** .... (816) 389-3072
E-mail: david.s.kolarik@usace.army.mil
Security Officer **Mark E. Asbury** .... (816) 389-3403
E-mail: mark.e.ashbury@usace.army.mil
Training Officer **Beverly B. Hogle** .... (816) 389-3785
E-mail: beverly.b.hogle@usace.army.mil

Omaha (NE) District
1616 Capitol Avenue, Omaha, NE 68102
Tel: (402) 995-2229 Tel: (888) 835-5971 Fax: (402) 779-2421
Internet: www.nwo.usace.army.mil

Commander and District Engineer
COL John L. Hudson USA .... (402) 995-2001
E-mail: john.l.hudson@usace.army.mil
Deputy Commander and Chief of Staff
MAJ James T. Startzell USA .... (402) 995-2002
Deputy District Engineer **Ted H. Streckfuss** .... (402) 995-2003
Information Technology Chief **George P. Keele** .... (402) 995-2553
E-mail: george.p.keele@usace.army.mil
Public Affairs Director
COL Thomas A. "Tom" O'Hara USA .... (402) 995-2416
E-mail: thomas.a.ohara@usace.army.mil
Deputy Public Affairs Director **Cheryl Moore** .... (402) 996-3802
Librarian **Barbara L. Slater** .... (402) 995-2535
E-mail: barbara.l.slater@usace.army.mil

Portland (OR) District
333 SW First, Portland, OR 97204-3495
Mail: P.O. Box 2946, Portland, OR 97208-2946
Tel: (503) 808-4510 Fax: (503) 808-4515
Internet: www.nwp.usace.army.mil

Commander and District Engineer
COL Aaron Dorf USA .... (503) 808-4501
Deputy Commander **MAJ John D. Cunningham USA** ... (503) 808-4501
Deputy District Engineer for Project Management
Kevin Brice .... (503) 808-4700
Librarian **Jennifer Muller** .... (503) 808-5140
Fax: (503) 808-5142

Seattle (WA) District
4735 East Marginal Way South, Seattle, WA 98134-2329
Mail: P.O. Box 3755, Seattle, WA 98124-3755
Tel: (206) 764-3750 Fax: (206) 764-6544
E-mail: paoteam@nws02.usace.army.mil
Internet: www.nws.usace.army.mil

Commander and District Engineer
COL Mark A. Geraldi USA .... (206) 764-3690
Executive Assistant **Susan L. Murphy** .... (206) 764-3693
Deputy Commander **LTC Andrew Olson USA** .... (206) 764-3691
Deputy District Engineer **Damon Lilly** .... (206) 764-3692
Deputy for Small Business **John Solomon** .... (206) 316-3990
E-mail: cenws-sb@usace.army.mil

★ Presidential Appointment Requiring Senate Confirmation ☆ Presidential Appointment ☐ Schedule C Appointment ◇ Career Senior Foreign Service Appointment
● Career Senior Executive Service (SES) Appointment ○ Non-Career Senior Executive Service (SES) Appointment ■ Postal Career Executive Service

Seattle (WA) District *(continued)*

District Counsel **Craig Juckniess** .... (206) 764-6834
E-mail: siri.c.nelson@usace.army.mil
Contracting Division Chief
Roger David "Dave" Williams .... (206) 764-3772
E-mail: roger.d.williams@usace.army.mil Fax: (206) 764-6817
Engineering Division Chief **JoAnn T. Walls** .... (206) 764-3776
Fax: (206) 764-4470
Operations Division Chief **Amy Reese** .... (206) 764-3431
Fax: (206) 764-3308
Planning Branch Chief **Laura Boerner** .... (206) 764-3600
Real Estate Division Chief **Patricia Fatherree** .... (206) 764-6571
Fax: (206) 764-6579
ACE-IT Chief **Tina AlSadhan** .... (206) 316-3900
Internal Review Office Chief **Julie Scheid** .... (206) 764-6868
Fax: (206) 764-6872
Logistics Management Office Chief **William Ratcliff** ..... (206) 764-3523
Fax: (206) 764-6989
Public Affairs Officer **Patricia C. Graesser** .... (206) 764-3760
E-mail: patricia.c.graesser@usace.army.mil Fax: (206) 764-3769
Public Affairs Specialist **Scott Lawrence** .... (206) 764-6896
Fax: (206) 764-3769
Public Affairs Assistant **(Vacant)** .... (206) 764-3750
Resource Management Office Chief
Robert L. "Rob" Frazier .... (206) 766-6977
E-mail: albert.candelaria@usace.army.mil Fax: (206) 764-6977
Safety and Occupational Health Office Chief
Timothy E. Grube .... (206) 764-3503
E-mail: timothy.e.grube@usace.army.mil Fax: (206) 764-6685
District Librarian **Shelly R. Trulson** .... (206) 764-3728
E-mail: shelly.r.trulson@usace.army.mil Fax: (206) 764-6444

Walla Walla (WA) District
201 North Third Avenue, Walla Walla, WA 99362-1876
Tel: (509) 527-7020 Fax: (509) 527-7824
E-mail: cenww-pa@usace.army.mil Internet: www.nww.usace.army.mil

District Commander **LTC Christian N. Dietz USA** .... (509) 527-7700
Education: Missouri Science and Tech 2005 MEM;
UCLA 2011 MEnvE
Deputy District Commander **MAJ Gregory Polk USA** ... (509) 527-7700
Deputy District Engineer for Project Management
Alan W. Feistner .... (509) 527-7020
Public Affairs Officer **Joseph Saxon** .... (509) 527-7020
E-mail: cenww-pa@usace.army.mil
Information Technology Officer **Javier "Javi" Lopez** .... (509) 527-7020
Deputy for Small Business **James Glynn** .... (509) 527-7434
E-mail: james.glynn@usace.army.mil
Librarian **Angie Camarillo** .... (509) 527-7427
E-mail: cenww-im-sl@usace.army.mil

Pacific Ocean Division (POD)
Building 525, Fort Shafter, Honolulu, HI 96858-5440
Tel: (808) 835-4700 Fax: (808) 835-4710
E-mail: pod-pao@usace.army.mil Internet: www.pod.usace.army.mil

Commander/Division Engineer
BG Thomas J. Tickner USA .... (808) 835-4700
Education: Penn State 1990 BSCE; Colorado 1999 MCE;
National Defense U 2013 MNSSS
Deputy Commander
COL Christopher D. Lestochi USA .... (808) 835-4700
E-mail: christopher.d.lestochi@usace.army.mil
Education: Penn State 1989 BS, MSCE; Army War Col MSS
Chief of Staff **James H. Proctor** .... (808) 835-4700
E-mail: james.h.proctor@usace.army.mil
Education: West Point 1966 BS; Miami MA;
US Army Command MMAS; Army War Col
Command Sergeant Major
CSM Patrickson Toussaint USA .... (808) 835-4700
● Regional Business Director **Gary Kitkowski PE** .... (808) 835-4650
E-mail: gary.kitkowski@usace.army.mil
Education: Hawaii BSCE
Human Resources Director **(Vacant)** .... (808) 835-4770
Information Management Director **(Vacant)** .... (808) 835-4785
Logistics Management Director **Richard Kim** .... (808) 835-4790
E-mail: timothy.c.moore@usace.army.mil

Pacific Ocean Division *(continued)*

● Director of Programs **(Vacant)** .... (808) 835-4610
Division Counsel **Rymn Parsons** .... (808) 835-4750
Education: Eisenhower Col 1977 AB; Albany Law 1981 JD;
Army War Col 2009 MSS; George Washington 1996 LLM
Chief of Public Affairs and Communication **(Vacant)** .... (808) 835-4715
E-mail: pod-pao@usace.army.mil
Contracting Office Chief **John A. Jacobson** .... (808) 835-4760
E-mail: john.a.jacobson@usace.army.mil
Education: Loyola Marymount 1989 BBA;
Webster U (Netherlands) 1994 MBA; Air Force Inst Tech 2004 MSM
Emergency Management Office Chief
Andrew R. Benziger .... (808) 835-4720
E-mail: andrew.r.benziger@usace.army.mil
Safety and Occupational Health Office Chief (Acting)
Francis W. Trent .... (202) 761-8548
E-mail: francis.w.trent@usace.army.mil

Alaska District
2204 Third Street, Joint Base Elmendorf-Richardson, AK 99506-1518
Mail: P.O. Box 6898, Joint Base Elmendorf-Richardson, AK 99506-0898
Tel: (907) 753-2522 Fax: (907) 753-5610
E-mail: public.affairs3@usace.army.mil Internet: www.poa.usace.army.mil

Commander/District Engineer
COL Phillip J. Borders USA .... (907) 753-2504
Executive Assistant **Jackie R. Leseman** .... (907) 753-2501
E-mail: jackie.r.leseman@usace.army.mil
Deputy Commander **LTC Penny M;. Bloedel USA** ...... (907) 753-2505
Education: West Point BS; Missouri Science and Tech 2006 MS;
Kansas State 2016 MA
Director of Programs and Project Management
Randall L. Bowker .... (907) 753-5728
E-mail: randall.l.bowker@usace.army.mil
Education: Alaska 1992 BSCE; Wayland Baptist 2007 MM
Deputy for Small Business **Ivonne Drake** .... (907) 753-5576
E-mail: ivonne.drake@usace.army.mil
Emergency Management Office Chief (Acting)
Herschel Deaton .... (907) 753-2666
Public Affairs Chief **Tom Findtner** .... (907) 753-2522
E-mail: tom.findtner@usace.army.mil
Regulatory Division Chief **David S. Hobbie** .... (907) 753-2782
E-mail: david.s.hobbie@usace.army.mil
Safety and Occupational Health Office Chief
David Prado .... (907) 753-5712
E-mail: david.prado@usace.army.mil

Far East District
Seoul, South Korea
Mail: U.S. Army Engineer District, Far East, Far East Unit 15546,
APO, AP 96205-0610
Tel: 82 (2) 2270-7300 Fax: 82 (2) 2270-7528
E-mail: dll-cepof-pa@usace.army.mil Internet: www.pof.usace.army.mil

Commander/District Engineer
COL Teresa Schlosser USA 82 (2) 2270-7300
Education: Montana 1994; Central Michigan MPA;
Army War Col MNSSS
Deputy Commander **LTC Dennis J. McGee USA** 82 (2) 2270-7300
Deputy Engineer **Richard "Rich" Byrd** 82 (2) 2270-7300
E-mail: jon.s.iwata@usace.army.mil
Education: Indiana Tech 1994 BSBA; Oklahoma 2000
Public Affairs Officer **Stephen Satkowski** 82 (2) 279-7301
E-mail: stephen.satkowski@usace.army.mil
Command Sergeant Major
CSM Robert L. "Bob" Stanek USAR 82 (2) 2270-7300
E-mail: robert.l.stanek@usace.army.mil
Education: North Dakota State

★ Presidential Appointment Requiring Senate Confirmation ☆ Presidential Appointment ☐ Schedule C Appointment ◇ Career Senior Foreign Service Appointment
● Career Senior Executive Service (SES) Appointment ○ Non-Career Senior Executive Service (SES) Appointment ■ Postal Career Executive Service

DEPARTMENTS

Honolulu (HI) District (Fort Shafter)
Building 230, U.S. Army Engineer District, Honolulu,
Fort Shafter, HI 96858-5440
Tel: (808) 835-4000 Fax: (808) 835-4019
E-mail: cepoh-pa@usace.army.mil Internet: www.poh.usace.army.mil

Commander/District Engineer
COL James D. Hoyman USA .... (808) 835-4000
E-mail: james.d.hoyman@usace.army.mil
Education: West Point 1998 BSCE; Missouri Science and Tech MM
Executive Assistant **Laureen Y. Spencer** .... (808) 835-4000
E-mail: laureen.y.spencer@usace.army.mil
Deputy District Commander
MAJ Thomas Piazze USA .... (808) 835-4000
Education: West Point 2001 BSE; Missouri 2005 MS
Deputy District Engineer and Chief of Programs and
Project Management **Stephen Cayetano PE** .... (808) 835-4000
Education: Hawaii BSCE
Emergency Management Division Chief **(Vacant)** .... (808) 835-4014
Deputy for Small Business **Catherine L. Yoza** .... (808) 835-4020
E-mail: catherine.l.yoza@usace.army.mil
Public Affairs Officer **Joseph "Joe" Bonfiglio** .... (808) 835-4004
E-mail: cepoh-pa@usace.army.mil

Japan District (Camp Zama)
Camp Zama, Japan
Mail: U.S. Army Engineer District, Japan,
Attn: Public Affairs Office, APO, AP 96338-5010
Tel: 81 (0462) 53-1890 Fax: 81 (462) 53-9461
E-mail: cepoj-pa@usace.army.mil Internet: www.poj.usace.army.mil

Commander/District Engineer
COL Rafael F. Pazos USA 81 (462) 53-1890
E-mail: cepoj-pa@usace.army.mil
Deputy Commander **LTC Daniel A. Segura USA** 81 (462) 53-1890
Deputy District Engineer for Programs and Project
Management **Raymond J. "Ray" McNeil** 81 (0462) 53-1890
E-mail: raymond.j.mcneil@usace.army.mil

South Atlantic Division
60 Forsyth Street, SW, Room 10M15, Atlanta, GA 30303-8801
Tel: (404) 562-5004 Fax: (404) 562-5002
Internet: www.sad.usace.army.mil

Commanding General **BG Diana M. Holland USA** ...... (404) 562-5006
Education: West Point 1990
Deputy Commander
COL C. Patrick Hogeboom IV USA, PE .... (404) 562-5007
Education: Virginia Tech BSCE; Missouri Science and Tech MS
Chief of Staff **George R. "Bob" Prince, Jr.** .... (404) 562-5125
Executive Officer **Joanne Crawford** .... (404) 562-5157
Executive Assistant **Narissia Skinner** .... (404) 562-5005
Public Affairs Officer **Robert G. Holland** .... (404) 562-5011
E-mail: robert.g.holland@usace.army.mil
Counsel **Cornelius W. "Neil" Purcell** .... (404) 562-5015
E-mail: cornelius.w.purcell@usace.army.mil
Construction and Operations Director
John D. Ferguson .... (404) 562-5125
E-mail: john.d.ferguson@usace.army.mil
Contracting Director **Heven Ford** .... (404) 562-5210
Human Resources Director **Carmallitica "Lisa" Davis** ... (404) 562-5030
E-mail: carmallitica.davis@usace.army.mil
Information Management Director **Thomas J. Linek** ..... (404) 562-5051
E-mail: thomas.j.linek@usace.army.mil
Internal Review Director **Bridget Butler** .... (404) 562-5071
Military Integration Division Chief **Torkild P. Brunso** .... (404) 562-5216
Education: Colorado Mines BS
Planning Director **Eric Bush** .... (404) 562-5220
Education: Florida State BS
• Programs Director **COL Alvin C. "Al" Lee USA (Ret)** ... (404) 562-5200
E-mail: alvin.b.lee@usace.army.mil
Education: Georgia Southern 1985 BBA; Saint Martin's U 1995 MS
Real Estate Director **William LeShore** .... (404) 562-5142
• Regional Business Director
Theodore A. "Tab" Brown .... (404) 562-5100
Resource Management Director **Kelly A. Daugherty** ..... (404) 562-5250
E-mail: kelly.a.daugherty@usace.army.mil

South Atlantic Division *(continued)*

Equal Employment Opportunity Office Chief
Jean W. Ellis .... (404) 562-5045
E-mail: jean.w.ellis@usace.army.mil
Safety and Occupational Health Office Chief
Gary D. McAlister .... (404) 562-5236
E-mail: gary.d.mcalister@usace.army.mil
Security and Law Enforcement Office Chief
Thomas F. Loree .... (404) 562-5157
E-mail: thomas.f.loree@usace.army.mil

Charleston (SC) District
69A Hagood Avenue, Charleston, SC 29403-5107
Tel: (843) 329-8004 Fax: (843) 329-2327
Internet: www.sac.usace.army.mil

Commander **LTC Jeffrey Palazzini USA** .... (843) 329-8000
Education: West Point BS; Wharton MBA
Deputy District Engineer **Lisa Metheney** .... (843) 329-8004
Chief, Corporate Communications **Glenn A. Jeffries** ..... (843) 329-8123
E-mail: cesac-pao@sac.usace.army.mil

Jacksonville (FL) District
701 San Marco Boulevard, Jacksonville, FL 32207
Tel: (904) 232-2568 Fax: (904) 232-2237
E-mail: publicmail.cesaj-cc@usace.army.mil
Internet: www.saj.usace.army.mil

District Commander
COL Andrew D. "Drew" Kelly USA .... (904) 232-2241
E-mail: andrew.d.kelly@usace.army.mil
Education: West Point BS; Missouri (Rolla) MS
Deputy District Commander
MAJ Joseph M. Sahl USA .... (561) 472-8891
Deputy District Commander for South Florida
LTC Jennifer Reynolds USA .... (904) 232-2242
Deputy District Engineer for Programs and Project
Management **Tim Murphy** .... (904) 232-3137
ACE-IT Chief **Guy T. Tate** .... (904) 232-2568
E-mail: guy.t.tate@usace.army.mil
Corporate Communications Chief **Mark C. Ray** .... (904) 232-1628
E-mail: mark.c.ray@usace.army.mil
Librarian **Oriana B. Armstrong** .... (904) 232-3643
Fax: (904) 232-1838

Mobile (AL) District
P.O. Box 2288, Mobile, AL 36628-0001
Tel: (251) 690-2511 Fax: (251) 690-2525
Internet: www.sam.usace.army.mil

Commander and District Engineer
COL Sebastien P. Joly USA .... (251) 690-2512
Deputy District Engineer for Latin America
LTC Frankie L. Flowers USA .... (251) 690-3094
Deputy Commander **LTC Andrew P. Yoder USA** .... (251) 690-2511
Deputy District Engineer for Programs and Project
Management **Peter F. Taylor, Jr.** .... (251) 690-2511
Chief of Staff **Kristina K. Mullins** .... (251) 690-2511
E-mail: kristina.k.mullins@usace.army.mil
District Counsel **Stephen "Steve" Sowell** .... (251) 690-2491
Construction Division Chief **George Condoyiannis** ..... (251) 690-2471
Contracting Division Chief **Jeffrey D. Burgess** .... (251) 441-5585
E-mail: jeffrey.d.burgess@usace.army.mil
Engineering Division Chief **Douglas C. Otto, Jr.** .... (251) 690-2611
Education: Auburn BSCE; Georgia Tech MSCE
Equal Employment Opportunity Officer
Catherine Cummings .... (251) 690-2510
Information Management Office Chief **Tim Tarver** .... (251) 690-2411
Internal Review Office Chief **Melissa Adkinson** .... (251) 690-3355
Legislative Chief **E. Patrick Robbins** .... (251) 690-2512
E-mail: ervin.p.robbins@usace.army.mil
Operations Division Chief **William Wynne Fuller** .... (251) 690-2576
Education: South Alabama BSCE
Planning and Environmental Division Chief
Curtis M. Flakes .... (251) 690-2777
E-mail: curtis.m.flakes@usace.army.mil
Public Affairs Chief **Cesar Yabor** .... (251) 690-3320

★ Presidential Appointment Requiring Senate Confirmation ☆ Presidential Appointment ☐ Schedule C Appointment ◇ Career Senior Foreign Service Appointment
● Career Senior Executive Service (SES) Appointment ○ Non-Career Senior Executive Service (SES) Appointment ■ Postal Career Executive Service

Mobile (AL) District *(continued)*

Real Estate Division Chief **Willie L. Patterson III EdD** . . . (251) 690-2511
E-mail: willie.l.patterson@usace.army.mil
Regulatory Division Chief **Craig J. Litteken** . . . . (251) 690-2658
Education: Southern Illinois BS; Missouri MS
Regional Logistics Management Office Chief
Valerie Alleyee-Robinson . . . . (251) 441-5191
Resource Management Office Chief **Brian Ivey** . . . . (251) 441-6055
Safety and Occupational Health Office Chief **(Vacant)** . . . . (251) 690-3088
Security and Law Enforcement Office Chief
Kenneth Earls . . . . (251) 690-2469
Small and Disadvantaged Business Utilization Office
Chief **Linda L. Spadaro** . . . . (251) 690-3597
E-mail: linda.l.spadaro@usace.army.mil
Central America Office in Charge
LTC Roberto Solórzano USA . . . . (251) 690-2511

Savannah (GA) District
100 West Oglethorpe Avenue, Savannah, GA 31402
Tel: (912) 652-5226 Fax: (912) 652-5222
Internet: www.sas.usace.army.mil

District Engineer **COL Daniel H. Hibner USA** . . . . (912) 652-5227
Deputy District Engineer
LTC Stephen Peterson USA, PE . . . . (912) 652-5225
Education: West Point BSCE; Missouri Science and Tech MSCE
Deputy District Engineer for Programs and Project
Management **Erik T. Blechinger** . . . . (912) 652-5220
Education: Wisconsin 1987 BSCE; Kansas 1997 MSCE
Executive Assistant and Congressional Liaison
Jeremy C. Keels . . . . (912) 652-5122
E-mail: jeremy.c.keels@usace.army.mil
Chief of Corporate Communications **Russell A. Wicke** . . . (912) 652-5777
E-mail: russell.a.wicker@usace.army.mil
Senior Public Affairs Officer **Billy E. Birdwell** . . . . (912) 652-5777
E-mail: billy.e.birdwell@usace.army.mil
Tel: (912) 652-5014
Chief Librarian **(Vacant)** . . . . (904) 232-3643
ACE-IT Chief **Herman H. Kramer** . . . . (912) 652-5178
E-mail: herman.h.kramer@usace.army.mil

Wilmington (NC) District
69 Darlington Avenue, Wilmington, NC 28403
Mail: P.O. Box 1890, Wilmington, NC 28402-1890
Tel: (910) 251-4000 Fax: (910) 251-4185
Internet: www.saw.usace.army.mil

Commander **COL Robert J. Clark USA** . . . . (910) 251-4501
Education: Vanderbilt 1995 BSCE; Webster MM; Army War Col MSS
Deputy Commander **LTC Yanson T. Cox USA** . . . . (910) 251-4502
Chief of Staff **George T. Burch** . . . . (910) 251-4628
E-mail: george.t.burch@saw02.usace.army.mil
Personnel Officer **(Vacant)** . . . . (910) 251-4869
Contracting Division Chief **John P. Mayo** . . . . (910) 251-4884
E-mail: john.p.mayo@usace.army.mil
Equal Employment Opportunity Office Chief
Renita W. McNeill . . . . (910) 251-4887
E-mail: renita.w.mcneill@saw02.usace.army.mil
Information Management Office Chief **John Hess** . . . . (910) 251-4657
Logistics Management Office Chief **(Vacant)** . . . . (910) 251-4800
District Counsel **(Vacant)** . . . . (910) 251-4499
Public Affairs Chief **Ann Johnson** . . . . (910) 251-4626
Fax: (910) 251-4618
Resource Management Office Chief **Michael Shaw** . . . . . . (910) 251-4792
Security and Law Enforcement Office Chief **Greg Barr** . . . (910) 251-4809
E-mail: gregory.e.barr@saw02.usace.army.mil
Safety and Occupational Health Office Chief
William F. Harris . . . . (910) 251-4698
E-mail: william.f.harris@saw02.usace.army.mil
Small Business Office Chief **Donna H. Walton** . . . . (910) 251-4452
E-mail: donna.h.walton@usace.army.mil
Emergency Management Division Chief
Ronald P. Stirrat . . . . (910) 251-4944
E-mail: ronald.p.stirrat@saw02.usace.army.mil
Operations Division Chief **Robert E. Sattin** . . . . (910) 251-4819
E-mail: robert.e.sattin@saw02.usace.army.mil

Wilmington (NC) District *(continued)*

Programs and Project Management Division Chief
Christine M. Brayman . . . . (910) 251-4478
Regulatory Division Chief **Scott C. McLendon** . . . . (910) 251-4952
Technical Services Division Chief **(Vacant)** . . . . (910) 251-4039
Auditor **Patricia A. Glover** . . . . (910) 251-4909

South Pacific Division
1455 Market Street, 20th Floor, San Francisco, CA 94103
Tel: (415) 503-6514 Fax: (415) 503-6642
Internet: www.spd.usace.army.mil

Commander **COL Kimberly M. Colloton USA** . . . . (415) 503-6501
Deputy Commander **COL Eric McFadden USA** . . . . (415) 503-6502
Education: Arizona State 1993 BSE
Contracting Director **James Deane "Jim" Bartha** . . . . . . (415) 503-6548
E-mail: jim.burtha@usace.army.mil
• Regional Programs Director **Cheree D. Peterson** . . . . (415) 503-6550
E-mail: cheree.d.peterson@usace.army.mil
Education: U Washington 1994 MPA
• Division Director of Regional Business **(Vacant)** . . . . (415) 503-6510

Albuquerque (NM) District
4101 Jefferson Plaza, NE, Albuquerque, NM 87109
Tel: (505) 342-3100 Fax: (505) 342-3197
Internet: www.spa.usace.army.mil

District Commander
LTC Larry "Dale" Caswell, Jr. USA . . . . (505) 342-3432
Deputy District Commander **MAJ John Miller USA** . . . . . (505) 342-3433
Deputy District Engineer **John R. D'Antonio, Jr. PE** . . . . (505) 342-3261
E-mail: john.r.d'antonio@usace.army.mil
Education: New Mexico 1979 BSCE
Contracting Division Chief **Leslie M. Molina** . . . . (505) 342-3460
E-mail: Leslie.M.Molina@usace.army.mil
District Counsel **LeeAnn M. Summer** . . . . (505) 342-3304
E-mail: leeann.m.summer@usace.army.mil
Engineering and Construction Division Chief
Art Maestas . . . . (505) 342-3436
Equal Employment Manager **(Vacant)** . . . . (505) 342-3383
Information Management Office Chief **Jack Ramsey** . . . . . (505) 342-3107
E-mail: jack.ramsey@usace.army.mil
Logistics Management Office Chief **Shirley A. Dehon** . . . (505) 342-3133
E-mail: shirley.a.dehon@usace.army.mil
Operations Division Chief **Mark E. Yuska** . . . . (505) 342-3608
E-mail: mark.e.yuska@usace.army.mil
Public Affairs Specialist **Mark T. Slimp** . . . . (505) 342-3171
E-mail: mark.t.slimp@usace.army.mil
Real Estate Division Chief **(Vacant)** . . . . (505) 342-3225
Resource Management Office Chief
Elizabeth McCullough . . . . (505) 342-3243
Safety and Occupational Health Office Manager
(Vacant) . . . . (505) 342-3175
Security and Law Enforcement Manager
Richard Maillet . . . . (505) 342-3137
Education: Florida Metro U 2007 BS
Administrative Officer **(Vacant)** . . . . (505) 342-3430
Webmaster **Cindy A. Romero** . . . . (505) 342-3114
E-mail: cindy.a.romero@usace.army.mil

Los Angeles (CA) District
915 Wilshire Boulevard, Suite 980, Los Angeles, CA 90017-3401
Mail: P.O. Box 532711, Los Angeles, CA 90053-2325
Tel: (213) 452-3333 Fax: (213) 452-4191
E-mail: publicaffairs.spl@usace.army.mil
Internet: www.spl.usace.army.mil

District Commander **COL Aaron Barta USA** . . . . (213) 452-3961
Deputy District Commander **MAJ Scotty Autin USA** . . . . (213) 452-3333
Education: West Point 2002 BS; Columbia MA
Deputy District Engineer **David Van Dorpe** . . . . (213) 452-3871
Education: Cal Poly (Pomona) 1994 BSCE
Public Affairs Chief **Thomas J. "Jay" Field** . . . . (213) 452-3920
E-mail: thomas.j.field@usace.army.mil

DEPARTMENTS

★ Presidential Appointment Requiring Senate Confirmation ☆ Presidential Appointment □ Schedule C Appointment ◇ Career Senior Foreign Service Appointment
● Career Senior Executive Service (SES) Appointment ○ Non-Career Senior Executive Service (SES) Appointment ■ Postal Career Executive Service

DEPARTMENTS

Sacramento (CA) District
1325 J Street, Room 1430, Sacramento, CA 95814-2922
Tel: (916) 557-7461 Fax: (916) 557-7859
Internet: www.spk.usace.army.mil

District Commander **COL David G. Ray USA** .... (916) 557-7490
Education: Colorado Mines BSCE; Missouri (Rolla) MEM
Executive Assistant **Jennifer L. Mijares** .... (916) 557-7490
Deputy District Commander
MAJ Rory C. Foster USA .... (916) 557-7490
E-mail: rory.c.foster.mil@mail.mil
Information Management Office Chief
William E. "Bill" McDaniel .... (916) 557-7668
E-mail: william.e.mcdaniel@usace.army.mil
Internal Review Office Chief **Clem G. Cantil** .... (916) 557-6894
E-mail: clem.g.cantil@usace.army.mil
Logistics Management Office Chief **Susan L. Bayless** ... (916) 557-7168
E-mail: susan.l.bayless@usace.army.mil
Safety and Occupational Health Office Chief
Shawn Curtis .... (916) 557-6973
Construction Operations Division Chief
Norbert F. Suter .... (916) 557-6714
Contracting Division Chief **Susan L. Yarbrough** .... (916) 557-5266
Education: Cal State (Chico) 1982 BS
Engineering Division Chief **Rick L. Poeppelman** .... (916) 557-7301
E-mail: rick.l.poeppelman@usace.army.mil
Planning Division Chief **Alicia E. Kirchner** .... (916) 557-6767
E-mail: alicia.e.kirchner@usace.army.mil
Programs and Project Management Division Chief
(Vacant) .... (916) 557-7490
Real Estate Acquisition Division Chief **Lisa M. Ng** ...... (916) 557-5225
E-mail: lisa.m.ng@usace.army.mil
Small Business Office Deputy Chief
Michelle D. Stratton .... (916) 557-7641
E-mail: michelle.d.stratton@usace.army.mil
Public Affairs Chief **Nancy E. Allen** .... (601) 619-9844
E-mail: nancy.e.allen@usace.army.mil
Education: Virginia Wesleyan 1999 BA
Security Officer **Robert Bastian** .... (916) 557-6920
District Librarian **(Vacant)** 820 .... (916) 557-6660
Fax: (916) 557-7091

San Francisco (CA) District
1455 Market Street, San Francisco, CA 94103
Tel: (415) 503-6700 Fax: (415) 503-6691
Internet: www.spn.usace.army.mil

Commander **LTC Travis T. Rayfield USA** .... (415) 503-6700
Deputy Commander **MAJ Kevin M. McCormick USA** ... (415) 503-6701
Contracting Division Chief **(Vacant)** .... (415) 503-6990
Engineering and Technical Services Division Chief
Lyn Gillespie .... (415) 503-6820
E-mail: lyn.gillespie@usace.army.mil
Operations and Readiness Division Chief
Nicholas Malasavage .... (415) 503-6915
Equal Employment Manager **Tamara Moland** .... (415) 503-6706
District Counsel **Merry Goodenough** .... (415) 503-6760
Education: UC Berkeley BS; San Diego State MPA; Baltimore JD; George Washington LLM
Logistics Chief **Boonchan "Mike" Pornnang** .... (415) 503-6970
E-mail: boonchan.pornnang@usace.army.mil
Project Management **Arijs A. Rakstins** .... (415) 503-6720
Public Affairs Chief **John D. Hardesty** .... (415) 503-6801
E-mail: john.d.hardesty@usace.army.mil
Regulatory Division Chief **Richard "Rick" Bottoms** ..... (415) 503-6771
Small Business Deputy **Shirley A. Turnbo** .... (415) 503-6987
E-mail: shirley.a.turnbo@usace.army.mil

Southwestern Division
1100 Commerce Street, Suite 831, Dallas, TX 75242-1317
Tel: (469) 487-7005 Tel: (469) 487-7007 (Personnel Locator)
Fax: (469) 487-7197 Fax: (469) 487-7198 (Alternate)
Internet: www.swd.usace.army.mil

Commander and Division Engineer
BG Paul E. Owen USA .... (469) 487-7005
E-mail: paul.owen@usace.army.mil
Education: West Point 1990 BS

Southwestern Division *(continued)*

Executive Assistant **Laura Lopez** .... (469) 487-7002
Deputy Commander **COL Kevin S. Brown USA** .... (469) 487-7005
Division Counsel **Nancye L. Bethurem** .... (469) 487-7008
E-mail: nancye.l.bethurem@usace.army.mil
Human Resources Manager **Benjamin Bracken** .... (469) 487-7123
E-mail: benjamin.r.bracken@usace.army.mil
Education: Creighton
Public Affairs Chief **Martha J. "Martie" Cenkci** .... (469) 487-7107
E-mail: martha.j.cenkci@usace.army.mil
Safety and Occupational Health Manager **Bruce Elliott** ... (469) 487-7017
Security and Law Enforcement Chief
Douglas "Doug" Benge .... (469) 487-7089
E-mail: douglas.benge@usace.army.mil
Chief, Regional Contracting Office **David M. Curry** ...... (469) 487-7013
E-mail: david.m.curry@usace.army.mil
● Programs Directorate Director **Mark L. Mazzanti** .... (469) 487-7028
E-mail: mark.l.mazzanti@usace.army.mil
● Regional Business Director **Pete G. Perez** .... (469) 487-7084
E-mail: pete.g.perez@usace.army.mil
Education: Texas A&M 1985 BSCE; Texas (San Antonio) 1997 MS
Assistant Director for Small Business Programs
Melea Crouse .... (469) 487-7105
E-mail: melea.crouse@usace.army.mil
Regulatory Officer **Vicki G. Dixon** .... (469) 487-7037
Business Resources Chief and Chief Financial Officer
Cheryl Partee .... (469) 487-7116
E-mail: cheryl.partee@usace.army.mil

Fort Worth (TX) District
Fritz B. Lanham Federal Building, 819 Taylor Street, Fort Worth, TX 76102-0300
P.O. Box 17300, Fort Worth, TX 76102-0300
Tel: (817) 886-1000 Fax: (817) 886-6451
Internet: www.swf.usace.army.mil

Commander and District Engineer
COL Kenneth Reed USA .... (817) 886-1515
Education: Alabama 1995; US Army Command
Deputy Commander **LTC Clay A. Morgan USA** .... (817) 886-1515
Deputy District Engineer **Eric Verwers** .... (817) 886-1516
Public Affairs Office Chief **Rhonda K. Paige** .... (817) 886-1312
E-mail: rhonda.k.paige@usace.army.mil
Public Affairs Officer **Clayton A. "Clay" Church** .... (817) 886-1314
E-mail: clayton.a.church@usace.army.mil
Contracting Division Chief **Katherine Freeman** .... (817) 886-1043
E-mail: kathrine.freeman@usace.army.mil
Deputy for Small Business **Carolyn L. Staten** .... (817) 886-1382
E-mail: carolyn.l.staten@usace.army.mil
Engineering and Construction Division Chief
Brian Giacomozzi .... (817) 886-1947
Regional Planning and Environmental Center (RPEC)
Chief **(Vacant)** .... (817) 886-1854
Real Estate Division Chief **Rocky D. Lee** .... (817) 886-1096
E-mail: rocky.d.lee@usace.army.mil
Logistics Management Office Chief **Tamara Mahaffey** ... (817) 886-1010
Operations Office Chief **Tim L. MacAllister** .... (817) 886-1567
Resource Management Office Chief **Robert T. Geiger** .... (817) 886-1426
E-mail: robert.t.geiger@usace.army.mil
Safety and Occupational Health Office Chief
Madeline Morgan .... (817) 886-1316
Chief of Information Technology **Donald Walker** .... (817) 886-1332
Security Office Specialist **(Vacant)** .... (817) 886-1438
Fax: (817) 886-6447
District Counsel **Rex Crosswhite** .... (817) 886-1140
Equal Employment Opportunity Manager **Vidal Gray** .... (817) 886-1321

Eastern Area Office
280 Miller Road, Bossier City, LA 71112-2505
Tel: (318) 676-3365 Fax: (318) 676-3370

Area Engineer **Gary Westby** .... (337) 531-2933

★ Presidential Appointment Requiring Senate Confirmation ☆ Presidential Appointment □ Schedule C Appointment ◇ Career Senior Foreign Service Appointment
● Career Senior Executive Service (SES) Appointment ○ Non-Career Senior Executive Service (SES) Appointment ■ Postal Career Executive Service

North Texas Resident Office
819 Taylor Street, Fort Worth, TX 76102-0300
Mail: P.O. Box 17388, Fort Worth, TX 76102-0388
Tel: (817) 886-1310 Fax: (817) 886-6446

Chief of Quality Assurance **Trevor Stockton** . . . . (817) 886-1949

San Antonio (TX) Area Office
2202 15th Street, Suite 12, Joint Base San Antonio, TX 78234
Tel: (210) 221-5492 Fax: (210) 221-5689

Area Engineer **Tom Smiley** . . . . (210) 221-5492

Galveston (TX) District
2000 Ft. Point Road, Galveston, TX 77550
Mail: P.O. Box 1229, Galveston, TX 77553-1229
Tel: (409) 766-3005 Fax: (409) 766-3049

Commander and District Engineer
LTC Lars N. Zetterstrom USA . . . . (409) 766-3001
Deputy District Commander **LTC Jay T. Luckritz USA** . . . (409) 766-3003
Deputy District Engineer **Dr. Edmond J. Russo, Jr.** . . . . . (409) 766-3109
E-mail: edmond.j.russo@usace.army.mil
Public Affairs Chief **LTC Mark Williford USA** . . . . (409) 766-3994
ACE-IT Chief **Thanh Nguyen** . . . . (409) 766-3197

Little Rock (AR) District
P.O. Box 867, Little Rock, AR 72203-0867
Tel: (501) 324-5551 Fax: (501) 324-5699
E-mail: ceswl-pa@swl02.usace.army.mil
Internet: www.swl.usace.army.mil/

Commander and District Engineer
COL Robert J. Dixon, Jr. USA . . . . (501) 324-5531
Education: Indiana BA
Deputy District Commander **(Vacant)** . . . . (501) 324-5531
● Deputy District Engineer for Project Management
Craig Pierce . . . . (501) 324-5531
Public Affairs Chief **Miles Brown** . . . . (501) 324-5551
E-mail: miles.brown@usace.army.mil Fax: (501) 324-6699
ACE-IT Chief **Brooke Reese** . . . . (501) 324-5551
Librarian **Shawn Snow** . . . . (501) 324-6167
Webmaster **Jay Woods** . . . . (501) 324-5551
E-mail: ceswl-pa@usace.army.mil

Tulsa (OK) District
1645 South 101 East Avenue, Tulsa, OK 74128-4609
Tel: (918) 669-7366 Fax: (918) 669-7368
E-mail: ceswt-pa@usace.army.mil Internet: www.swt.usace.army.mil

Commander and District Engineer
COL Christopher A. Hussin USA . . . . (918) 669-7201
E-mail: ceswt-de@usace.army.mil
Education: Wisconsin BS; US Army Command 2005
Deputy Commander **MAJ Richard T. Childers USA** . . . . . (918) 669-7201
Deputy District Engineer for Project Management
Lee Conley . . . . (918) 669-7201
E-mail: lee.conley@usace.army.mil
Public Affairs Officer **Edward W. "Ed" Johnson** . . . . (918) 669-7342

United States Military Academy (West Point) (USMA)

Official Mail and Distribution Center, 646 Swift Road,
West Point, NY 10996-1905
Tel: (845) 938-4011 Fax: (845) 938-7140 E-mail: 8sgs@usma.edu
Internet: www.usma.edu

Office of the Superintendent

Superintendent **LTG Darryl A. Williams USA** . . . . (845) 938-2610
Education: West Point 1983, MA
Executive Officer **LTC Charles Kean USA** . . . . (845) 938-8420
Aide de Camp **MAJ Burton D. Eissler USA** . . . . (845) 938-3301
Command Sergeant Major **CSM Jack H. Love USA** . . . . . (845) 938-4011
Secretary of the General Staff **LTC Justin Miller USA** . . . (845) 938-4200

Directorate of Admissions
Building 606, West Point, NY 10996
Tel: (845) 938-4041 Internet: http://admissions.usma.edu

Director **COL Deborah J. McDonald USA** . . . . (845) 938-4041
E-mail: admissions-info@usma.edu
Education: West Point 1985

Directorate of Intercollegiate Athletics
Army West Point Athletics, 639 Howard Road, West Point, NY 10996
Internet: http://goarmysports.com

Director **Boo Corrigan** . . . . (845) 938-3701

United States Military Academy Library
Jefferson Hall, 758 Cullum Road, West Point, NY 10996
Tel: (845) 938-8301 (Administration) Tel: (845) 938-2230 (Circulation)
Tel: (845) 938-8325 (Research and Reference)
Internet: www.library.usma.edu

Librarian and Associate Dean **Christopher Barth** . . . . (845) 938-3833
E-mail: christopher.barth@usma.edu

Office of the Chief of Staff
Chief of Staff **COL Mark Bieger USA** . . . . (845) 938-3419

G1 Personnel, Office of the Adjutant General (MAAG)
Griffin Hall, Building 622, West Point, NY 10996
Tel: (845) 938-3402

Adjutant General **LTC David J. McConnell USA** . . . . (845) 938-3402

G6 Office of the Chief Information Officer
Building 600, West Point, NY 10996

Chief Information Officer
COL Edward "Ed" Teague USA . . . . (845) 938-5569
E-mail: edward.teague@usma.edu
E-mail: 8ocio@usma.mil

Office of the Chaplain
Senior Chaplain **COL Matthew Pawlikowski USA** . . . . . . (845) 938-3316
E-mail: matthew.pawlikowski@usma.edu
E-mail: 8chap@usma.edu

Office of the Inspector General
Inspector General **LTC James "Jim" Osuna USA** . . . . . . (845) 938-8209

Office of the Staff Judge Advocate
Staff Judge Advocate **COL Erik L. Christiansen USA** . . . . (845) 938-3205
E-mail: 8sja@usma.edu

Directorate of Academy Advancement
Director **LTC Ken Heckel USA** . . . . (845) 938-3700
E-mail: ken.heckel@usma.edu

Public Affairs Office
646 Swift Road, West Point, NY 10996
Tel: (845) 938-3808 E-mail: 8pao@usma.edu
Internet: www.pointerview.com

Director **LTC Webster Wright III USA** . . . . (845) 938-3808
Chief, Policy and Plans **Joseph V. "Joe" Tombrello** . . . . (845) 938-3808
E-mail: joseph.tombrello@usma.edu
Public Affairs Director **LTC Chevelle Thomas USA** . . . . . (845) 670-8586
E-mail: chevelle.thomas2.mil@mail.mil

G8 Comptroller
Comptroller **COL Leslie Brehm USA** . . . . (845) 938-6947

Office of the Dean of the Academic Board
646 Swift Road, West Point, NY 10996
Fax: (845) 938-2202 E-mail: 8dean@usma.edu

Dean of Academic Board **BG Cindy R. Jebb USA** . . . . . . (845) 938-2000
E-mail: cindy.jebb@usma.edu
Education: West Point 1982 BS; Duke 1992 MA, 1997 PhD; Naval War 2000 MNSSS
Vice Dean of Academic Affairs
Rachel Sondheimer PhD . . . . (845) 938-8306

(continued on next page)

DEPARTMENTS

★ Presidential Appointment Requiring Senate Confirmation ☆ Presidential Appointment □ Schedule C Appointment ◇ Career Senior Foreign Service Appointment
● Career Senior Executive Service (SES) Appointment ○ Non-Career Senior Executive Service (SES) Appointment ■ Postal Career Executive Service

DEPARTMENTS

Office of the Dean of the Academic Board *(continued)*

Vice Dean of Operations
COL Michael "Mike" Yankovich USA . . . . (845) 938-5007
Vice Dean of Resources **COL David Lyle USA, PhD** . . . . (845) 938-3615
Academic Affairs and Registrar Services
Dr. James "Jim" Dalton . . . . (845) 938-2050
Education: Providence BA; Gannon MA; Naval War MA; Minnesota PhD
Dean's Operations Office **Bernadette D. Ortland** . . . . (845) 938-3134
Education: SUNY (Oneonta) BS; John Jay Col MPA
Information Technology
COL Edward "Ed" Teague USA . . . . (845) 938-5569
E-mail: edward.teague@usma.edu
Institute for Innovation and Development
Dr. Elizabeth Velilla . . . . (845) 938-2764
Plans and Resources **(Vacant)** . . . . (845) 938-5811

United States Corps of Cadets

Washington Hall, Building 745, West Point, NY 10996
Internet: www.westpoint.edu/uscc

Commandant of Cadets **MG Steven W. Gilland USA** . . . . (845) 938-3103
E-mail: 8uscc@usma.edu
Command Sergeant Major
CSM Thomas C. Kenny USA . . . . (845) 938-4601

Major U.S. Army Commands

Army and Air Force Exchange Service (AAFES)

3911 South Walton Walker Boulevard, Dallas, TX 75236-1598
Mail: P.O. Box 660202, Dallas, TX 75266-0202
Tel: (214) 312-2011 Fax: (214) 312-3000
Internet: http://shop.aafes.com/shop/

Director/Chief Executive Officer
Thomas C. "Tom" Shull . . . . (214) 312-3551
E-mail: shull@aafes.com
Education: West Point 1973 BS; Harvard 1981 MBA
Senior Enlisted Advisor **CMSgt Luis Reyes USAF** . . . . . . (214) 312-2260
E-mail: reyeslu@aafes.com
Deputy Director **(Vacant)** . . . . (214) 312-3631
President and Chief Merchandising Officer
Ana Middleton . . . . (214) 312-3351
Executive Vice President and Chief Financial Officer
James "Jim" Jordan . . . . (214) 312-2551
E-mail: jordan@aafes.com
Executive Vice President and Chief Human Resources Officer **Leigh A. Roop** . . . . (214) 312-3350
E-mail: roopl@aafes.com
Executive Vice President and Chief Information Officer
Philip R. "Phil" Stevens . . . . (214) 312-3371
E-mail: stevenspr@aafes.com
Executive Vice President and Chief Logistics Officer
Karen Stack . . . . (214) 312-3005
Executive Vice President and Chief Operating Officer
David "Dave" Nelson . . . . (214) 312-3663
E-mail: nelsonda@aafes.com
Senior Vice President, Audit and Inspector General
Kevin Iverson . . . . (214) 312-2465
E-mail: iversonk@aafes.com
Education: North Dakota 2002 MBA
Senior Vice President, Customer Relationship Management **Jim Skibo** . . . . (214) 312-5000
Senior Vice President, E-Commerce **Karen Cardin** . . . . (214) 312-3231
Senior Vice President, Exchange Credit
Jami Richardson . . . . (214) 312-3680
Senior Vice President, Omni Channel
Mickey Bradford . . . . (214) 312-6684
Senior Vice President, Services and Food
Trinidad "Trini" Saucedo . . . . (214) 312-6871
Senior Vice President, Supply Chain **Thomas Lozier** . . . . (214) 312-3042
Vice President, e-Business **Debra Zarsk** . . . . (214) 312-2425
Vice President, E-Commerce Merchandising and Operations **David Lemons** . . . . (214) 312-6320
Vice President, Food, Fuel and Theater Operations
Michael Deerhake . . . . (214) 312-2345

Army and Air Force Exchange Service *(continued)*

Vice President, Information Technology Development Services **Donald "Don" Covert** . . . . (214) 312-2561
E-mail: covert@aafes.com
Vice President, Loss Prevention **Eric Stewart** . . . . (214) 312-4777
Vice President, Main Store Hardlines Division
Chris Burton . . . . (214) 312-2306
Vice President, Main Store Softlines Division
Tamson Shelmire . . . . (214) 312-3625
Vice President, Marketing **Mark Morrell** . . . . (214) 312-2106
Vice President, Merchandising **(Vacant)** . . . . (214) 312-2011
Vice President, Omnichannel Marketing **Brad Nash** . . . . . . (214) 312-2035
Vice President, Real Estate
Michael J. "Mike" Smietana . . . . (214) 312-6579
Vice President, Services and Commercial Leasing
Darryl Porter . . . . (214) 312-3840
Vice President, Specialty Store Consumables Division
Sean Shaw . . . . (214) 312-3212
Vice President, Store Operations **Anthony Ventura** . . . . . . (214) 312-4495
E-mail: ventura@aafes.com
General Counsel **Dale Harbour** . . . . (214) 312-3126
E-mail: harbourd@aafes.com
Director of Staff **Thomas P. Ockenfels** . . . . (214) 312-3939
E-mail: ockenfelstp@aafes.com
Director, Corporate Procurement **Rod Sibila** . . . . (214) 312-4615
E-mail: sibilar@aafes.com
Information Technology Security Manager
Sun Ursini . . . . (214) 312-2561
E-mail: ursini@aafes.com
Infrastructure Manager **Clyde Todd** . . . . (214) 312-2561
E-mail: toddc@aafes.com

U.S. Army Cadet Command (ROTC)

Fort Knox, KY 40121-2726
Tel: (502) 624-3450 Internet: http://www.cadetcommand.army.mil/

Commanding General **BG John R. Evans, Jr. USA** . . . . . . (502) 624-3450
Chief of Staff **COL Janet R. Holliday USA** . . . . (502) 624-3450
Deputy Commanding General **(Vacant)** . . . . (502) 624-3450
Command Sergeant Major
CSM Kenneth J. Kraus USA . . . . (502) 624-3450

U.S. Army Drill Sergeant School

9574 Marion Avenue, Fort Jackson, SC 29207
Fax: (803) 751-0744 Internet: https://www.army.mil/drillsergeant/

Commandant **CSM Michael Berry USA** . . . . (803) 751-6672
Deputy Commandant **SGM Deedra A. Perez USA** . . . . . . (803) 751-6672

U.S. Army Forces Command (FORSCOM)

4700 Knox Street, Fort Bragg, NC 28310-5000
Tel: (910) 570-7200 Fax: (910) 570-1546
Internet: www.forscom.army.mil

11th Armored Cavalry Regiment

Building 182, B Avenue, Fort Irwin, CA 92310
P.O. Box 105068, Fort Irwin, CA 92310
Tel: (760) 380-8358 Fax: (760) 380-3601

Regimental Commander
COL Scott C. Woodward USA . . . . (760) 380-5740
Command Sergeant Major
CSM Michael Stunkard USA . . . . (760) 380-3499

I Corps

Joint Base Lewis-McChord, WA 98433-5000
Tel: (253) 967-0001 Fax: (253) 967-0717
Internet: https://www.army.mil/icorps

Note: I Corps is also a unit of U.S. Army Pacific

Commanding General **LTG Gary J. Volesky USA** . . . . (253) 967-0001
E-mail: gary.j.volesky.mil@mail.mil
Education: Eastern Washington 1983 BA; Air War Col MA; Princeton MA
Deputy Commanding General
MG William H. Graham USA . . . . (253) 967-0003

★ Presidential Appointment Requiring Senate Confirmation ☆ Presidential Appointment ☐ Schedule C Appointment ◇ Career Senior Foreign Service Appointment
● Career Senior Executive Service (SES) Appointment ○ Non-Career Senior Executive Service (SES) Appointment ■ Postal Career Executive Service

I Corps *(continued)*

Deputy Commanding General for Operations
BGen Michele-Henry St-Louis . . . . . . (253) 967-0001
Command Sergeant Major **(Vacant)** . . . . . . (253) 967-0001
Contracting Officer **Dia Cooper** . . . . . . (253) 967-3508
Fax: (253) 967-8137

7th Infantry Division (7th ID)
Harrison Hall, Joint Base Lewis-McChord, WA 98433-5000
Tel: (253) 477-5602
E-mail: usarmy.jblm.7-id.list.media-relations@mail.mil
Internet: https://www.army.mil/7thid (Army.mil Website)

Commanding General
BG Willard M. "Bill" Burleson III USA . . . . . . (253) 477-5602
Education: West Point 1988; Army War Col 2008 MSS
Deputy Commanding General for Operations **(Vacant)** . . . (253) 477-5602
Chief of Staff **COL David S. Doyle USA** . . . . . . (253) 477-5602
Education: West Point 1993 BS
Command Sergeant Major
CSM Stephen Helton USA . . . . . . (253) 477-5602

593rd Expeditionary Sustainment Command (593rd ESC - Joint Base Lewis-McChord)
Joint Base Lewis-McChord, WA 98433
Tel: (253) 967-9510 (Public Affairs Office)
E-mail: usarmy.jblm.593-esc.mbx.593rd-esc-pao@mail.mil
Internet: http://www.lewis-mcchord.army.mil/593csg/

Commanding General **COL James Moore USA** . . . . . . (253) 967-9510
Education: West Virginia State U BS; Troy State MPA
Command Sergeant Major
CSM Pamela K. Williams USA . . . . . . (253) 967-9510

III Corps (3rd Armored Corps)
Murphy Road and 53rd Street, Fort Hood, TX 76544-5000
Tel: (254) 287-7509 Tel: (254) 288-2023 (Civilian Locator)
Tel: (254) 287-1110 (Operator) Tel: (254) 287-0103 (Public Affairs)
E-mail: usarmy.hood.iii-corps.mbx.pao@mail.mil

Commanding General **LTG Paul E. Funk II USA** . . . . . . (254) 287-2206
Education: Montana State BA; Central Michigan MS
Executive Assistant **Patricia Rivera** . . . . . . (254) 287-7509
Executive Officer **LTC Stacy Moore USA** . . . . . . (254) 287-7509
Deputy Commanding General
BG Kenneth L. Kamper USA . . . . . . (254) 287-5203
Education: West Point BS
Deputy Commanding General (UK) **(Vacant)** . . . . . . (254) 287-5203
Chief of Staff **COL Todd M. Fox USA** . . . . . . (254) 287-7205
Command Sergeant Major
CSM Michael A. Crosby USA . . . . . . (254) 287-7904
Public Affairs Officer **COL Thomas Veale USA** . . . . . . (254) 286-5139
E-mail: thomas.f.veale.mil@mail.mil
E-mail: usarmy.hood.iii-corps.mbx.pao@mail.mil

1st Cavalry Division
Fort Hood, TX 76544
Tel: (254) 288-0928

Commanding General **BG Paul T. Calvert USA** . . . . . . (254) 287-3832
Deputy Commander (Home Station) **(Vacant)** . . . . . . (254) 287-3832
Deputy Commander (Maneuver)
COL Christopher R. "Chris" Norrie USA . . . . . . (254) 287-3832
Deputy Commander (Support)
COL Miles Brown USA . . . . . . (254) 287-3832
Command Sergeant Major **CSM Shane Pospisil USA** . . . (254) 287-3832
Chief of Staff **COL Matthew "Matt" Cody USA** . . . . . . (254) 287-3832
Public Affairs Officer **LTC Gabriel J. Ramirez USA** . . . . . (254) 286-5139

4th Infantry Division (Fort Carson)
Fort Carson, CO 80913

Commanding General **MG Randy A. George USA** . . . . . . (719) 503-0025
Education: West Point BS; Colorado Mines MS; Naval War MA
Deputy Commanding General
BG David M. "Dave" Hodne USA . . . . . . (719) 503-0025
Deputy Commanding General
BG William L. Thigpen USA . . . . . . (719) 526-0025
Education: Virginia State 1992; National War Col; Embry-Riddle

4th Infantry Division *(continued)*

Command Sergeant Major
CSM Timothy L. Metheny USA . . . . . . (719) 503-0025
Chief of Staff **(Vacant)** . . . . . . (719) 503-0025

XVIII Airborne Corps
XVIII ABN Corps and Fort Bragg, Armistead and Macomb Streets, Fort Bragg, NC 28310-5000
Tel: (910) 396-3111 Fax: (910) 396-4568
Note: Members of XVIII Airborne Corps are currently on deployment as part of Combined Joint Task Force Operation Inherent Resolve.

Commander **LTG Paul J. LaCamera USA** . . . . . . (910) 396-3111
E-mail: paul.j.lacamera.mil@mail.mil
Education: West Point 1985 BS; Naval War MNSSS; US Army Command
Deputy Commanding General
MG Brian J. McKiernan USAR . . . . . . (910) 396-3111
Education: Vanderbilt BE; George Mason MS; Army War Col MA
Deputy Commanding General, Operations
BGen Marc Gagne CF . . . . . . (910) 396-3111
Command Sergeant Major
CSM Charles W. Albertson USA . . . . . . (910) 396-1515
Public Affairs Officer **Thomas D. "Tom" McCollum**
Building 1-1326, IMSE-BRG-PA . . . . . . (910) 396-2122
E-mail: thomas.d.mccollum2.civ@mail.mil
Freedom of Information Act Officer
Douglas E. "Doug" Moore . . . . . . (910) 907-3642
E-mail: douglas.e.moore.civ@mail.mil
Contracting Officer **(Vacant)** . . . . . . (910) 396-4362
Small Business Officer **(Vacant)** . . . . . . (910) 396-4362

3rd Sustainment Command (Expeditionary) (3rd ESC)
Building M1436, 2400 Quartermaster Street, Fort Bragg, NC 28307
Tel: (910) 432-5319

Commander **Col James M. "Jim" Smith USAF** . . . . . . (910) 432-5319
Education: Air Force Acad 1997 BS; Air U (USAF) 2010 MA
Deputy Commander **COL Gregory Boyd USA** . . . . . . (910) 432-5319
Command Sergeant Major
CSM Bernard P. Smalls, Sr. USA . . . . . . (910) 432-5319

3rd Infantry Division (Fort Stewart)
Building HQ 001, 942 Dr. Ben Hall Place, Fort Stewart, GA 31314
Tel: (912) 767-5606 Tel: (912) 435-9950 (Public Affairs)
Fax: (912) 767-6673 Internet: www.stewart.army.mil

Commanding General
BG Leopoldo A. "Lee" Quintas, Jr. USA . . . . . . (912) 767-5606
E-mail: leopoldo.a.quintas.mil@mail.mil
Deputy Commanding General, Maneuver
COL Andrew C. Hilmes USA . . . . . . (912) 767-8633
Deputy Commander, Support
COL Marcus S. Evans USA . . . . . . (912) 767-8633
Command Sergeant Major **CSM Daniel Hendrex USA** . . . (912) 767-8633
Chief of Staff **COL Christopher Boyle USA** . . . . . . (912) 435-9753

10th Mountain Division (Light Infantry) (10th MD - Fort Drum)
10th Mountain Division (Light Infantry), Fort Drum, NY 13602-5000
Tel: (315) 772-6011 E-mail: pao@drum.army.mil (Public Affairs Office)
Internet: www.drum.army.mil

Commander **MG Walter E. Piatt USA** . . . . . . (315) 772-5565
Education: Lock Haven 1987 BS
Aide **CPT Kenneth Elgort USA** . . . . . . (315) 772-5565
Deputy Commanding General
BG Patrick J. Donahoe USA . . . . . . (315) 772-5565
Deputy Commanding General for Operations
COL Brian S. Eifler USA . . . . . . (315) 772-5565
E-mail: brian.s.eifler.mil@mail.mil
Deputy Commanding General for Support **(Vacant)** . . . . . . (315) 772-5565
Command Sergeant Major **CSM Jason Roark USA** . . . . . (315) 772-5565
Chief of Staff **(Vacant)** . . . . . . (315) 772-5565
Public Affairs Officer **MAJ Isaac Taylor USA** . . . . . . (315) 772-7634
Fax: (315) 772-8295
Deputy Public Affairs Officer **Julie A. Halpin** . . . . . . (315) 772-8286
E-mail: julie.a.halpin.civ@mail.mil

(continued on next page)

★ Presidential Appointment Requiring Senate Confirmation ☆ Presidential Appointment ☐ Schedule C Appointment ◇ Career Senior Foreign Service Appointment
● Career Senior Executive Service (SES) Appointment ○ Non-Career Senior Executive Service (SES) Appointment ■ Postal Career Executive Service

DEPARTMENTS

10th Mountain Division (Light Infantry) *(continued)*

Public Information/Media Relations Officer
Kathleen L. "Kae" Young .... (315) 772-5463
E-mail: kathleen.l.young4.civ@mail.mil
Small Business Specialist **Anthony J. Sligar** .... (315) 772-9909
Building T-45, 45 West Street, Fort Drum, NY 13602-5220
E-mail: anthony..sligar2.civ@mail.mil
Administrative Librarian **Allen R. Goudie** .... (315) 772-4734
4300 Camp Hale Road, Fort Drum, NY 13602-5284
E-mail: allen.r.goudie.naf@mail.mil
Installation Security Officer **James P. "Jim" Shaw** ...... (315) 772-5715
E-mail: james.p.shaw.civ@mail.mil
Training Chief **(Vacant)** .... (315) 772-1467
Webmaster **(Vacant)** .... (315) 772-1203

82nd Airborne Division
82nd Airborne Division, Fort Bragg, NC 28310-5000
Commanding General **MG James J. Mingus USA** ...... (910) 432-0661
Deputy Commanding General
BG Frederick M. O'Donnell USA .... (910) 432-0661
Deputy Commanding General for Interoperability
Brig James Learmont .... (910) 432-0661
Deputy Commanding General for Operations **(Vacant)** ... (910) 432-0661
Deputy Commanding General for Support **(Vacant)** ...... (910) 432-0661
Command Sergeant Major
CSM Michael A. Ferrusi USA .... (910) 432-0661
Chief of Staff **COL Brett T. Funck USA** .... (910) 432-0661
Education: West Point 1994 BS

101st Airborne Division (Air Assault)
101st Airborne Division (Air Assault), Fort Campbell, KY 42223-5627
Tel: (270) 798-2151 Fax: (270) 798-9800
Internet: www.campbell.army.mil
Commanding General **MG Andrew P. Poppas USA** ..... (270) 798-2151
Education: West Point BS
Deputy Commander **BG Richard F. Johnson ARNG** ..... (270) 798-9933
Deputy Commander (Operations)
BG John W. Brennan, Jr. USA .... (270) 798-2151
Deputy Commander (Support)
BG Kenneth T. "Todd" Royar USA .... (270) 798-2151
E-mail: kenneth.t.royar.mil@mail.mil
Chief of Staff **COL Jeffrey Thompson USA** .... (270) 956-4870
Command Sergeant Major **CSM Todd W. Sims USA** .... (270) 798-9607
Public Affairs Officer **LTC Martin O'Donnell USA** ...... (270) 798-9961

Headquarters, 1st Armored Division and Fort Bliss (Fort Bliss)
11685 Sergeant Major Boulevard, Fort Bliss, TX 79916-6812
Tel: (915) 744-6988 Fax: (915) 568-2995
E-mail: ATZC-CGP@bliss.army.mil Internet: https://www.bliss.army.mil
Commanding General **BG Patrick E. Matlock USA** ...... (915) 744-6988
E-mail: usarmy.bliss.1-ad.mbx.cg-fort-bliss@mail.mil
Education: West Point 1988
Deputy Commanding General (Operations)
COL James Gallivan USA .... (915) 744-6990
Deputy Commanding General (Rear)
Brig F. M. "Frazer" Lawrence .... (915) 744-6990
Deputy Commanding General (Support)
COL Scott M. Naumann USA .... (915) 744-6990
Chief of Staff **COL Charles D. Constanza USA** .... (915) 744-0905
Command Sergeant Major
CSM Daniel L. "Danny" Day USA .... (915) 744-6957
Public Affairs Officer **LTC Craig Childs USA** .... (915) 744-8406
Public Affairs Officer **MAJ Crystal X. Boring USA** ..... (915) 744-8406

Joint Readiness Training Center (Fort Polk)
Building 350, 6661 Warrior Trail, Fort Polk, LA 71459
Tel: (337) 531-2911 Fax: (337) 531-2403
E-mail: usarmy.polk.imcom.mbx.pao-ci@mail.mil
Internet: www.jrtc-polk.army.mil
Commanding General **BG Patrick D. Frank USA** .... (337) 531-1706
Command Sergeant Major **CSM David W. Bass USA** .... (337) 531-6699
Freedom of Information Act Officer **Connie Earl** .... (337) 531-1612
E-mail: usarmy.polk.imcom.mbx.dhr-foia-freedom-of-info@mail.mil

Joint Readiness Training Center *(continued)*

Public Affairs Officer **Troy D. Darr** .... (337) 531-1344
G2 Security **CPT Terrence Sadler USA** .... (337) 531-0613
Fax: (337) 531-0125

National Training Center (Fort Irwin)
983 Innerloop Road, Fort Irwin, CA 92310-5067
Mail: Public Affairs Office, P.O. Box 105067, Fort Irwin, CA 92310-5067
Tel: (760) 380-3750 Tel: (760) 380-4773 (Library) Fax: (760) 380-3075
Internet: www.irwin.army.mil
Commanding General
BG Jeffery D. Broadwater USA .... (760) 380-3261
Education: Kentucky 1989 BS; National Defense U MS
Chief of Staff **COL Matthew Moore USA** .... (760) 380-3261
Command Sergeant Major
CSM Matthew R. Lowe USA .... (760) 380-3319

32nd Army Air and Missile Defense Command (Fort Bliss)
Fort Bliss, TX 79916
Tel: (915) 568-9402 Internet: www.bliss.army.mil
Commanding General
BG Clement S. Coward, Jr. USA .... (915) 568-2043
Command Sergeant Major
CSM Stephen A. Burnley USA .... (915) 568-7618

20th Support Command (Chemical, Biological, Radiological, Nuclear and High Yield Explosives)
Edgewood Area, 5183 Blackhawk Road,
Aberdeen Proving Ground, MD 21010-5424
Tel: (410) 436-0330 (Main Office) Tel: (410) 436-6200 (Operations)
E-mail: usarmy.APG.20-cbrne.mbx.apgr-cbrne-pao@mail.mil
Internet: https://www.cbrne.army.mil/
Commanding General
BG James E. "Jim" Bonner, Jr. USA .... (410) 436-0330
Deputy Commanding Officer
COL Colin "Patrick" Nikkila USA .... (410) 436-0330
Chief of Staff **(Vacant)** .... (410) 436-0330
Command Sergeant Major
CSM Kenneth B. Graham USA .... (410) 436-0330

U.S. Army Reserve Command (USARC)
4710 Knox Street, Fort Bragg, NC 28310-5010
Tel: (910) 570-8330 (Public Affairs) Internet: http://www.usar.army.mil/
Commanding General **LTG Charles D. Luckey USAR** .... (703) 697-1784
2400 Army Pentagon, Washington, DC 20310-2400
Education: Virginia 1978 BA; Army War Col 2001 MSS
Deputy Commanding General
MG Scottie Dean Carpenter USAR .... (910) 570-8330
Chief of Staff **BG Alberto C. Rosende USAR** .... (910) 570-8330
Deputy Chief of Staff **COL Mark Towne USAR** .... (910) 570-8330
Command Sergeant Major
CSM Ted L. Copeland USAR .... (703) 695-1913
2400 Army Pentagon, Room 2B548, DAAR-ZX,
Washington, DC 20310-2400
Command Chief Warrant Officer
CW5 Hal Griffin III USA .... (910) 570-8330

9th Mission Support Command (9th MSC)
1557 Suehiro Road, Fort Shafter Flats, Honolulu, HI 96819-2135
Tel: (808) 438-1600 ext. 3301 (Public Affairs Office)
Fax: (808) 438-7190
Commander
BG Douglas F. "Doug" Anderson USAR ... (808) 438-1600 ext. 3290

80th Training Command (TASS)
6700 Strathmore Road, Richmond, VA 23237
Tel: (804) 271-5800 Internet: https://www.army.mil/80thtngcmd
Commanding General **MG Bruce E. Hackett USA** ...... (804) 271-5800
Deputy Commander
BG Fletcher V. Washington USA .... (804) 271-5800
Command Sergeant Major
CSM Dennis Thomas USAR .... (804) 271-5800
Chief Executive Officer **Michael Bland** .... (804) 271-5800

★ Presidential Appointment Requiring Senate Confirmation ☆ Presidential Appointment □ Schedule C Appointment ◇ Career Senior Foreign Service Appointment
● Career Senior Executive Service (SES) Appointment ○ Non-Career Senior Executive Service (SES) Appointment ■ Postal Career Executive Service

80th Training Command *(continued)*

Public Affairs Officer
LTC Crystal Shamlee USAR (Ret) .... (804) 377-6329
Commander, 102nd Training Division
BG Michael T. Harvey USAR .... (573) 596-0131

81st Regional Support Command (Fort Jackson)
81 Wildcat Way, Fort Jackson, SC 29207
Tel: (803) 751-5386 (General Inquiries)
Tel: (803) 751-9694 (Media Inquiries)
Areas Covered: AL, FL, GA, KY, LA, MS, NC, PR, SC, TN

Commanding General **MG Kenneth D. Jones USAR** .... (803) 751-3161
Deputy Commander **(Vacant)** .... (803) 751-3161
Public Affairs Officer **Michael Mascari** .... (803) 751-9694

84th Training Command
Building 203, 230 Old Ironside Avenue, Fort Knox, KY 40121
Tel: (502) 624-1134 (General Inquiries)
Tel: (502) 624-4411 (Media Inquiries)

Commander **MG Arlen R. "Ray" Royalty USAR** .... (502) 624-4411
Deputy Commander **(Vacant)** .... (502) 624-4411
Command Chief Warrant Officer
CW5 Steven D. Conrad USA .... (502) 624-4411
Command Sergeant Major
CSM Lawrence C. Arnold USAR .... (502) 624-4411

88th Regional Support Command (88th RSC)
60 South O Street, Fort McCoy, WI 54656
Tel: (608) 556-0336
Areas Covered: IL, IN, MI, MN, OH, WI

Commanding General **MG Patrick J. Reinert USAR** ..... (608) 556-0336
Education: Iowa State 1983 BA; Central U Iowa 1986 JD; Army War Col 2005 MS
Deputy Commanding General
BG Tony L. Wright USAR .... (608) 556-0336
Education: Ohio 1985 BS
Command Sergeant Major **CSM Earl Rocca USA** .... (608) 556-0336
Public Affairs Director **Catherine Carroll** .... (608) 388-0336
E-mail: 88rsc.pao@us.army.mil

416th Theater Engineer Command (416 ENCOM)
10S, 100 South Frontage Road, Darien, IL 60561
Tel: (630) 427-9700 (General Inquiries)
Tel: (630) 739-7177 (Media Inquiries)
Tel: (800) 315-6327 ext. 217 (Retention and Recruiting)
E-mail: usarmy.usarc.416-eng-cmd.list.public-affairs-all-users@mail.mil

Commander **MG Miyako N. Schanely USAR** .... (630) 427-9700
Education: West Point 1986 BS; Rochester MBA; Army War Col MSS
Deputy Commanding General
BG John J. Elam USAR .... (630) 427-9700
Education: Michigan State BSCE; Army War Col MSS
Deputy Commanding General - Support
BG Matthew V. Baker USAR .... (630) 427-9700
Education: Illinois (Chicago) BS; Army War Col MSS
Chief of Staff **COL James J. Kokaska USAR** .... (630) 427-9700
Education: Bradley 1982 BS; Missouri MS; Army War Col MSS
Commander, Contingency Response Unit
COL Brian T. Dixon USA .... (630) 427-9700
Education: Clarkson U 1989; Army War Col MSS
Command Sergeant Major **CSM Ty V. Emmans USAR** ... (630) 427-9700
Command Chief Warrant Officer **(Vacant)** .... (630) 427-9700

1st U.S. Army
Building 68, One Rock Island Arsenal, Rock Island, IL 61299-6200
Tel: (309) 782-9200 E-mail: usarmy.ria.1-army.mbx.first-army-hq-pao@mail.mil (Public Affairs Officer)
E-mail: usarmy.ria.1-army.mbx.first-army-hq-g6-webmaster@mail.mil (Webmaster) Internet: www.first.army.mil
Areas Covered: Continental United States, PR and VI

Commanding General (Acting)
MG Erik C. Peterson USA .... (309) 782-9200
Education: Idaho 1986
Deputy Commanding General for Operations
MG Jeffrey H. Holmes USA .... (309) 782-9200

1st U.S. Army *(continued)*

Deputy Commanding General for Support **(Vacant)** ...... (309) 782-9200
Command Sergeant Major
CSM Richard K. Johnson MC, USA .... (309) 782-9200
Chief of Staff **COL Shawn E. Klawunder USA** .... (309) 782-9200

1st Infantry Division (1ID)
Fort Riley, KS 66442-5016
Tel: (785) 239-3911 (Administration) Tel: (785) 239-8850 (Publications)
Fax: (785) 239-2592 Internet: www.1id.army.mil

Commanding General **MG John S. Kolasheski USA** .... (785) 239-3516
E-mail: john.s.kolasheski.mil@mail.mil
Deputy Commanding General (Maneuver)
COL Patrick R. Michaelis USA .... (785) 239-3516
E-mail: patrick.r.michaelis2.mil@mail.mil
Deputy Commanding General (Rear) **(Vacant)** .... (785) 239-3516
Deputy Commanding General (Support)
COL Todd R. Wasmund USA .... (785) 239-3516
Command Sergeant Major
CSM Craig A. Bishop USA .... (785) 239-2722
Chief of Staff **COL Curtis D. Taylor USA** .... (785) 239-2110
Public Affairs Officer **LTC Joey J. Sullinger USA** ...... (785) 239-2253
Contracting Director **Anthony Tiroch** .... (785) 239-9887
E-mail: usarmy.riley.acc-micc.list.micc-customers@mail.mil

1st Army Division West (Fort Hood)
Building 410, 761st Tank Battalion Avenue, Fort Hood, TX 76544
Tel: (254) 553-5003 (Public Affairs)
Internet: http://www.first.army.mil/divwest/

Commanding General **MG Erik C. Peterson USA** .... (254) 553-4949
Education: Idaho 1986
Deputy Commanding General for Operations **(Vacant)** ... (254) 553-4960
Deputy Commanding General for Support
BG William J. Edwards USA .... (254) 553-4949
Chief of Staff **COL Michael D. Henderson USA** .... (254) 553-4949
Command Sergeant Major **CSM John McDwyer USA** ... (254) 553-4962

5th U.S. Army/U.S. Army North (ARNORTH)
1400 East Grayson, Suite 152, Joint Base San Antonio, TX 78234-5000
Tel: (210) 221-0015 Fax: (210) 221-9289
Internet: https://twitter.com/usarmynorth

Commanding General **LTG Jeffrey S. Buchanan USA** ... (210) 221-0015
Education: Arizona 1982 BS
● Deputy to the Commanding General
Robert R. Naething .... (210) 221-0015
Deputy Commanding General - Operations
BG Richard C. Kim USA .... (210) 221-0015
Deputy Commanding General - Support
BG John B. Hashem ARNG .... (210) 221-0015
Chief of Staff **COL Niave F. Knell USA** .... (210) 221-0015
Command Sergeant Major
CSM Alberto Delgado USA .... (210) 221-0015
E-mail: ronald.e.orosz.mil@mail.mil
◇ Foreign Policy Advisor **Donald M. "Don" Sheehan** ..... (210) 221-0015
Education: George Mason 1991 MBA

U.S. Army Futures Command
Austin, TX 78731

Commanding General
GEN John M. "Mike" Murray USA .... (910) 570-7200

U.S. Army Materiel Command (AMC)
4400 Martin Road, Redstone Arsenal, AL 35898
Tel: (256) 450-6012 Internet: http://www.amc.army.mil/

U.S. Army Aviation and Missile Life Cycle Management Command (AMCOM)
AMSAM-PA, Redstone Arsenal, AL 35898-5020
Tel: (256) 876-4161 Fax: (256) 955-0133

Commanding General **BG Douglas M. Gabram USA** .... (256) 876-2101
AMSAM-CG, Redstone Arsenal, AL 35898-5000
Education: Bowling Green State 1984

(continued on next page)

★ Presidential Appointment Requiring Senate Confirmation ☆ Presidential Appointment ☐ Schedule C Appointment ◇ Career Senior Foreign Service Appointment
● Career Senior Executive Service (SES) Appointment ○ Non-Career Senior Executive Service (SES) Appointment ■ Postal Career Executive Service

DEPARTMENTS

U.S. Army Aviation and Missile Life Cycle Management Command *(continued)*

• Deputy to the Commanding General **William P. Marriott** . . . . (256) 842-9888
AMSAM-DC, Redstone Arsenal, AL 35898-5000
E-mail: william.p.marriott.civ@mail.mil

Chief of Staff **COL Shawn T. Prickett USA** . . . . (256) 876-1120
AMSAM-CS, Redstone Arsenal, AL 35898-5000

Command Sergeant Major **(Vacant)** . . . . (256) 876-1874
AMSAM-CSM, Redstone Arsenal, AL 35898-5000

• Aviation and Missile Research, Development and Engineering Center Director **(Vacant)** . . . . (256) 876-3322
AMSRD-AMR, Redstone Arsenal, AL 35898-5000

Chief Information Officer **Shirley Perkey** . . . . (256) 876-3514
AMSAM-CIO, Redstone Arsenal, AL 35898-5000

Congressional Affairs Officer **Julie A. Frederick** . . . . (256) 876-4163
AMSAM-PC, Redstone Arsenal, AL 35898-5000
E-mail: julie.a.frederick@us.army.mil

Public and Congressional Affairs Chief **Ann Jensis-Dale** . . . . (256) 842-3546
E-mail: ann.jensisdale2.civ@mail.mil

Webmaster **(Vacant)** . . . . (256) 876-5649
Information Systems Engineering,
AMSAM-CIO-A-I-P, Corporate Information Center,
U.S. Army Aviation and Missile Command,
Redstone Arsenal, AL 35898-5000

Corpus Christi (TX) Army Depot
308 Crecy Street, Corpus Christi, TX 78419-5260
Tel: (361) 961-3627 Fax: (361) 961-3039
Internet: https://www.ccad.army.mil/

Commander **COL Gail Atkins USA** . . . . (361) 961-3771
Deputy Commander **Mark Wagner** . . . . (361) 961-3371
Chief Operations Officer **Robert B. Sharp** . . . . (361) 961-6622
Chief of Staff **Cynthia A. "Annette" Cross** . . . . (361) 961-2028
E-mail: annette.cross@us.army.mil
Depot Command Sergeant Major **CSM Patricia A. Wahl USA** . . . . (361) 961-3627
Resource Management Officer **Jeffrey A. "Jeff" Fluegge** . . . . (361) 961-2271
Accessories and Rotor Blades Director **Rick Rincon** . . . . (361) 961-3622
Aircraft Production Director **Roy Hollins** . . . . (361) 961-2016
E-mail: roy.hollins@us.army.mil
Engine Director **(Vacant)** . . . . (361) 961-3561
Information Technology Director **Connie Salas** . . . . (361) 961-6358
E-mail: connie.salas@us.army.mil
Infrastructure Operations Director **Marc Gonzalez** . . . . (361) 961-2455
E-mail: marc.gonzalez2@us.army.mil
Manufacturing/Process Production Director **Don Dawson** . . . . (361) 961-4645
Power Train Director **Marco Garcia** . . . . (361) 961-2958
Production Engineering Director **Thomas Sandoval** . . . . (361) 961-3001
Production Management Director **Timothy Hillenburg** . . . (361) 961-3508
Quality Assurance Director **Richard Stevenson** . . . . (361) 961-3070
Chief Counsel **Alex Lopez** . . . . (361) 961-3432
E-mail: alex.lopez2@us.army.mil
Protocol Officer **Enrique Gonzalez** . . . . (361) 961-3600
Public Affairs Officer **Carla Johnson** . . . . (361) 961-3627
E-mail: usarmy.ccad.usamc.mbx.pao@mail.mil
Contracting/Small Business Officer **Rod Wolthoff** . . . . (361) 961-3957
E-mail: rod.wolthoff@us.army.mil
Security Office Chief **William Neal** . . . . (361) 961-6899
Equal Opportunity Manager **Glennis Ribblett** . . . . (361) 961-4317
Webmaster **Edward "Ed" Slonaker** . . . . (361) 961-2209
E-mail: ed.slonaker@us.army.mil

Letterkenny (PA) Army Depot
One Overcash Avenue, Chambersburg, PA 17201-4150
Tel: (717) 267-8111 Fax: (717) 267-9724
E-mail: usarmy.lead.usamc.mbx.lead-pao@mail.mil
Internet: www.letterkenny.army.mil

Commander **COL Stephen W. Ledbetter USA** . . . . (717) 267-8300
Education: Tennessee (Martin) 1993 BS
Deputy Commander **Damien Bess** . . . . (717) 267-8300
Education: Missouri (Rolla) MEM

Letterkenny (PA) Army Depot *(continued)*

Sergeant Major **SGM Richard A. Huff USA** . . . . (717) 267-8301
Freedom of Information Act Officer **Timothy K. Brendza** . . . . (717) 267-9286
E-mail: timothy.k.brendza.civ@mail.mil

Redstone Arsenal (AL)
U.S. Army Aviation and Missile Command,
Redstone Arsenal, AL 35898-5000
Tel: (256) 876-2151 Internet: www.garrison.redstone.army.mil

Commanding General **LTG Larry D. Wyche USA** . . . . (256) 876-2101
E-mail: larry.d.wyche.mil@mail.mil
Freedom of Information Act and Privacy Program Coordinator **Charmaine Howell** IMSE-RED-HRR . . . . (256) 876-6360
E-mail: charmaine.howell@us.army.mil Fax: (256) 876-2057
Small Business Officer **Kelly J. Rhodes** . . . . (717) 267-5313
Building 25, One Overcash Avenue, Chambersburg, PA 17201-4150
E-mail: kelly.j.rhodes.civ@mail.mil
Program Executive Officer, Aviation **BG Thomas H. Todd III USA** . . . . (256) 876-2151
Deputy Program Executive Officer, Aviation (Acting) **Rich Kretzschmar** . . . . (256) 313-4004
Chief Information Officer, PEO Aviation **Terry Carlson** . . . . (256) 313-4004

U.S. Army Chemical Materials Activity
E4585 Hoadley Road, ATTN: AMSCM-D,
Aberdeen Proving Ground, MD 21010-5424
Tel: (410) 436-4364 Fax: (410) 436-4932
Internet: https://www.cma.army.mil/

Director **COL Kelso C. Horne III USA** . . . . (410) 436-4364
Deputy Director **Frank J. Belcastro** . . . . (410) 436-2345
E-mail: frank.j.belcastro.civ@mail.mil

Program Executive Office, Assembled Chemical Weapons Alternatives (PEO ACWA)
5183 Blackhawk Road, Aberdeen Proving Ground, MD 21010-5424
Tel: (410) 436-3398 (Public Affairs) Fax: (410) 436-1992
Internet: www.peoacwa.army.mil

• Program Executive Officer **Michael S. "Mike" Abaie** . . . . (410) 436-3498
E-mail: michael.s.abaie.civ@mail.mil
Deputy Program Executive Officer (Acting) **Nicholas Stamatakis III** . . . . (410) 436-5691
Chief of Staff **Tamika D. "Tami" Atkins** . . . . (410) 436-0165
Public Affairs Officer **Katherine B. DeWeese** . . . . (410) 436-3398
E-mail: katherine.b.deweese.civ@mail.mil

Pueblo (CO) Chemical Depot
45825 Highway 96 East, Pueblo, CO 81006-9330
Tel: (719) 549-4135 (Public Affairs)

Commander **COL Christopher A. Grice USA** . . . . (719) 549-4141
Fax: (719) 549-4617
Site Project Manager, Pueblo Chemical Agent-Destruction Pilot Plant **Gregory B. Mohrman** . . . (719) 549-4135
Public Affairs **Lorraine Waters** . . . . (719) 549-4135
Fax: (719) 549-4866
Project Manager **Bret Griebenow** . . . . (719) 549-4135
Freedom of Information Act Officer **Larry Hornes** . . . . (719) 549-4141

U.S. Army Communications-Electronics Command (CECOM)
6002 Combat Drive, Floorl, Room D1-310A,
Aberdeen Proving Ground, MD 21005
Tel: (443) 861-6757 E-mail: usarmy.apg.cecom.mbx.cecom-pao@mail.mil
Internet: www.cecom.army.mil

Commanding General **MG Randy S. Taylor USA** . . . . (443) 861-6714
Deputy to the Commanding General **Larry M. Muzzelo** . . . . (443) 861-6714
Education: Penn State 1981 BSAE, 1983 MSAE; NJIT MSEE; Webster MA
Chief of Staff **COL Seena C. Tucker USA** . . . . (443) 861-6714
Command Sergeant Major **CSM Matthew D. McCoy USA** . . . . (443) 861-6714
Public Affairs Chief **Greg Mayhall** . . . . (443) 861-6757

★ Presidential Appointment Requiring Senate Confirmation ☆ Presidential Appointment ☐ Schedule C Appointment ◇ Career Senior Foreign Service Appointment
● Career Senior Executive Service (SES) Appointment ○ Non-Career Senior Executive Service (SES) Appointment ■ Postal Career Executive Service

U.S. Army Communications-Electronics Command *(continued)*

Public Affairs Officer **Paul D. Mehney** . . . . (443) 861-7062
E-mail: Paul.d.mehney.civ@mail.mil
Education: Michigan State 1998 BA

Tobyhanna (PA) Army Depot
11 Hap Arnold Boulevard, Tobyhanna, PA 18466-5000
Tel: (570) 615-7201 Fax: (570) 615-6061
Internet: www.tobyhanna.army.mil

Commander **COL Nathan M. Swartz USA** . . . . (570) 615-7201
Deputy Commander **Frank W. Zardecki** . . . . (570) 615-7201
E-mail: frank.w.zardecki.civ@mail.mil
Contracting Officer **Anthony Delicati** . . . . (570) 615-7232
Fax: (570) 615-6782
Protocol Officer **Karen M. Brusca** . . . . (570) 615-6223
E-mail: karen.m.brusca.civ@mail.mil
Public Affairs Officer **Kristyn Smith** . . . . (570) 615-7308

U.S. Army Joint Munitions Command (JMC)
One Rock Island Arsenal, Rock Island, IL 61299-5000
Tel: (309) 782-7649 Fax: (309) 782-3935
Internet: http://www.jmc.army.mil/Default.aspx

Commander **BG Michelle M.T. Letcher USA** . . . . (309) 782-7649
● Deputy to the Commander **Rhonda Vandecasteele** . . . . (309) 782-7649
Education: Western Illinois
Chief of Staff **COL Ronald D. "Dave" Brown USA** . . . . (309) 782-7649
Command Sergeant Major **(Vacant)** . . . . (309) 782-7649
Executive Director for Ammunition (Acting)
JoEtta Fisher . . . . (309) 782-7649

Anniston (AL) Munitions Center
7 Frankford Avenue, Anniston, AL 36201-4199
Tel: (256) 235-6281

Commander **LTC Roshun A. Steele USA** . . . . (256) 235-6281
Deputy to the Commander **Anthony L. Burdell** . . . . (256) 235-6281

Blue Grass (KY) Army Depot (BGAD)
431 Battlefield Memorial Highway, Richmond, KY 40475-5100
Tel: (859) 779-6246
Tel: (859) 779-6941 (Blue Grass Army Depot Public Affairs)
Tel: (859) 779-6897 (Blue Grass Chemical Activity Public Affairs)
Fax: (859) 779-6548 Internet: www.bluegrass.army.mil

Commander **COL Joseph "Joe" Kurz USA** . . . . (859) 779-6246
Civilian Executive **Stephen L. Sharp** . . . . (859) 779-6246
Director of Information Management
Thomas "Tom" Lane . . . . (859) 779-6391
E-mail: thomas.l.lane14.civ@mail.mil

Crane (IN) Army Ammunition Activity (CAAA)
300 Highway 361, Crane, IN 47522
Tel: (812) 854-5682 Fax: (812) 854-3963
E-mail: cdrsite@crane.army.mil Internet: www.crane.army.mil

Commander **LTC Michael Garlington USA** . . . . (812) 854-1484
Civilian Executive Assistant **Norman Thomas** . . . . (812) 854-3660
Webmaster **Cheri Barlow** . . . . (812) 854-3422

Hawthorne (NV) Army Depot
One South Maine Avenue, Hawthorne, NV 89415-9404
Tel: (775) 945-7001 Fax: (775) 945-7948
E-mail: usarmy.hawthorne.jmc.list.command@mail.mil

Commander **LTC Scott M. Bishop USA** . . . . (775) 945-7001
Deputy to the Commander **Larry M. Cruz** . . . . (775) 945-7002
Contracting/Small Business **Ken Thomas** . . . . (775) 945-7341

Holston (TN) Army Ammunition Plant
4509 West Stone Drive, Kingsport, TN 37660-1048
Tel: (423) 578-6285 Fax: (423) 247-8579
E-mail: campholstonaap@us.army.mil

Commander's Representative **Joseph R. Kennedy** . . . . (423) 578-6242
Contracting/Small Business **Lisa Sneed** . . . . (423) 578-6248

Iowa Army Ammunition Plant
17571 Highway 79, Middletown, IA 52638-5000
Tel: (319) 753-7710 Fax: (319) 753-7735

Commander **LTC Stephen T. Koehler USA** . . . . (319) 753-7200
Education: East Carolina 1998
Deputy to the Commander **Gifford Haddock** . . . . (319) 753-7200

Lake City (MO) Army Ammunition Plant
Independence, MO 64051-1000
Tel: (816) 796-7157 Fax: (816) 796-7124
E-mail: rock-lakecity@us.army.mil

Commander **LTC Dana Crow USA** . . . . (816) 796-7120
Civilian Executive Assistant **Tracy A. Cleaver** . . . . (816) 796-7113
E-mail: tracy.cleaver@us.army.mil Fax: (816) 796-7124
Education: Central Missouri State
Public Affairs Officer **Crystal Rankin** . . . . (816) 796-7157
E-mail: crystal.rankin@us.army.mil
Protocol Officer **Crystal Rankin** . . . . (816) 796-7157
E-mail: crystal.rankin@us.army.mil

Letterkenny (PA) Munitions Center
One Overcash Avenue, Chambersburg, PA 17201-4150
Tel: (717) 267-9954

Commander **LTC Jeffrey J. Ignatowski USA** . . . . (717) 267-9954
Education: Marquette 2000 BS
Civilian Executive Assistant **Edward E. Averill** . . . . (717) 267-9954

McAlester (OK) Army Ammunition Plant (McAAP)
1C Tree Road, McAlester, OK 74501-9002
Tel: (918) 420-6591 Fax: (918) 956-7581
Internet: http://www.mcaap.army.mil/

Commander **COL Joseph Blanding USA** . . . . (918) 420-6591
Civilian Deputy **Gary D. Reasnor** . . . . (918) 420-6591
E-mail: gary.reasnor@us.army.mil
Chief of Staff **Brian D. Lott** . . . . (918) 420-6591
Education: Southeastern Oklahoma St 1996 BS; Cameron 2001 MBA

Milan (TN) Army Ammunition Plant
2280 Highway 104 West, Suite One, Milan, TN 38358-3176
Tel: (731) 686-6087 Fax: (731) 686-6077

Commander's Representative **Britton G. Locke** . . . . (731) 686-6087

Pine Bluff (AR) Arsenal
10020 Kabrich Circle, Pine Bluff, AR 71602-9500
Tel: (870) 540-3000 Internet: www.pba.army.mil

Commander **COL Luis A. "Fred" Ortiz USA** . . . . (870) 540-3000

Radford (VA) Army Ammunition Plant (RFAAP)
Radford, VA 24143-0002
Mail: P.O. Box Two, Radford, VA 24143-0002
Tel: (540) 731-5785 Fax: (540) 639-7789 Internet: www.rfaap.army.mil

Commander **LTC James H. Scott III USA** . . . . (540) 731-5762
Civilian Executive Assistant **Jeffrey Bonnett** . . . . (540) 731-5761
Public Affairs Officer **Charles E. Saks, Jr.** . . . . (540) 731-5785
E-mail: charles.e.saks3.civ@mail.mil

Scranton (PA) Army Ammunition Plant
156 Cedar Avenue, Scranton, PA 18505-1138
Tel: (570) 340-1135 Fax: (570) 340-1189
E-mail: scaap@aco.pica.army.mil

Commander's Representative **Richard P. Hansen** . . . . (570) 340-1152
E-mail: richard.p.hansen.civ@mail.mil

Tooele (UT) Army Depot
Tooele, UT 84074-5000
Tel: (435) 833-2211 Fax: (435) 833-2810 Internet: www.tooele.army.mil

Commander **LTC James D. Brown USA** . . . . (435) 833-2211
Deputy to the Commander **Keith Siniscalchi** . . . . (435) 833-2211
E-mail: keith.siniscalchi@us.army.mil
Contracting Officer **Brenda R. Alverson** . . . . (435) 822-2616
E-mail: brenda.r.alverson.civ@mail.mil
Freedom of Information Act Officer **Kathy Anderson** . . . . (435) 833-3293
E-mail: kathy.anderson1@us.army.mil

(continued on next page)

DEPARTMENTS

Tooele (UT) Army Depot *(continued)*

Public Affairs Officer **Kathy Anderson** . . . . (435) 833-2693
E-mail: kathy.anderson1@us.army.mil
Training and Equal Employment Officer **Arthur Reilly** . . . (435) 833-2694
E-mail: arthur.reilly.civ@mail.mil
Information Management Division Director
Tom Duryea . . . . (435) 833-3070
E-mail: tom.duryea@us.army.mil Fax: (435) 833-3938

U.S. Army Research, Development and Engineering Command (RDECOM)
ATTN: Public Affairs Office, 3071 Aberdeen Boulevard,
Aberdeen Proving Ground, MD 20115
Tel: (443) 395-3922 Internet: www.army.mil/RDECOM/

Commanding General **MG Cedric T. Wins USA** . . . . (410) 278-0833
E-mail: cedric.t.wins.mil@mail.mil
Deputy Commanding General
BG Vincent F. Malone II USA . . . . (410) 278-0833
E-mail: vincent.f.malone.mil@mail.mil
Education: West Point
• Deputy to the Commanding General **John S. Willison** . . . (410) 278-0833
Chief of Staff **COL Raymond K. Compton USA** . . . . (410) 278-1190
Command Sergeant Major **CSM Jon Stanley USA** . . . . . . (410) 278-0833

U.S. Army Armament Research, Development and Engineering Center – Picatinny (NJ) (ARDEC - Picatinny Arsenal)
Picatinny Arsenal, NJ 07806-5000
Tel: (973) 724-6364 (Public Affairs) Fax: (973) 724-6582
Internet: www.ardec.army.mil

• Director **John F. Hedderich III** . . . . (973) 724-6365
E-mail: john.f.hedderich.civ@mail.mil
Military Deputy **COL Richard Hornstein USA** . . . . (973) 724-6365
Associate Director **Peter O'Neill** . . . . (973) 724-6365
Chief of Staff **Marie Felix** . . . . (973) 724-6365
Sergeant Major **(Vacant)** . . . . (973) 724-6365
Technology Director **Joseph Pelino** . . . . (973) 724-3457
E-mail: joseph.pelino.civ@mail.mil
Legal Office Chief **Denise C. Scott** . . . . (973) 724-3410
E-mail: denise.c.scott.civ@mail.mil
Small Business Officer **Eric J. Bankit** . . . . (973) 724-3068
E-mail: eric.j.bankit.civ@mail.mil Fax: (973) 724-3002
Public Affairs Officer **Timothy L. Rider** . . . . (973) 724-6365
E-mail: timothy.l.rider@us.army.mil
E-mail: usarmy.pica.ardec.mbx.picatinny-public-affairs@mail.mil
Chief Librarian **Suseela Chandrasekar** Building 59 . . . . . (973) 724-5898
Fax: (973) 724-3044
Librarian **Elizabeth Reisman** . . . . (973) 724-5350
E-mail: elizabeth.reisman@us.army.mil

U.S. Army Communications-Electronics Research, Development and Engineering Center (CERDEC)
6002 Combat Drive, Aberdeen Proving Ground, MD 21005
Fax: (443) 861-7726 Internet: www.cerdec.army.mil

• Director **Patrick J. O'Neill** . . . . (443) 861-7692
E-mail: patrick.j.oneill.civ@mail.mil
Education: Loyola U (Maryland) 1979 BS; Johns Hopkins 1983 MS; Indust'l Col Armed Forces 2000 MS

U.S. Army Edgewood Chemical Biological Center (ECBC)
AMSRD-ECB-AP, 5183 Blackhawk Road,
Aberdeen Proving Ground, MD 21010-5424
Tel: (410) 436-2456 Fax: (410) 436-6529
E-mail: usarmy.APG.ecbc.mbx.communications-office@mail.mil

Director **Dr. Eric Moore PhD** . . . . (410) 436-5501
Public Affairs Officer **Don Kennedy** . . . . (410) 436-7118
E-mail: usarmy.APG.ecbc.mbx.communications-office@mail.mil

U.S. Army Materiel Systems Analysis Activity
AMSRD-AMD-D, 392 Hopkins Road,
Aberdeen Proving Ground, MD 21005-5071
Tel: (410) 278-6614 Fax: (410) 278-6584 Internet: www.amsaa.army.mil

• Director **James Amato** . . . . (410) 278-6614
Deputy Director **COL David Dinger USA** . . . . (410) 278-6598
Education: West Point BS; Old Dominion MSEM

U.S. Army Materiel Systems Analysis Activity *(continued)*

Technical Director **Christopher J. Barrett** . . . . (410) 278-6590

U.S. Army Natick Soldier Systems Center (NSSC)
Kansas Street, Natick, MA 01760-5000
Tel: (508) 233-4300

Senior Commander **BG Vincent F. Malone II USA** . . . . . . (508) 233-5519
E-mail: vincent.f.malone.mil@mail.mil
Education: West Point
Deputy to the Commanding General
Christine T. Marsh . . . . (508) 233-4300
Public Affairs Chief **John Harlow** . . . . (508) 233-5340
Fax: (508) 233-5390
Natick Contracting Division Director **(Vacant)** . . . . (508) 233-4514
Small Business Advocate **Philip R. Varney** . . . . (508) 233-4995
E-mail: philip.r.varney.civ@mail.mil Fax: (508) 233-8676
Library Team Leader **Patricia E. Bremner** . . . . (508) 233-4249
E-mail: patricia.e.bremner.civ@mail.mil Fax: (508) 233-4248

U.S. Army Tank Automotive Research, Development and Engineering Center (TARDEC)
6501 East 11 Mile Road, Warren, MI 48397
Tel: (586) 282-6144 Fax: (586) 282-6013 Internet: www.army.mil/tardec

• Director **Dr. Paul D. Rogers** . . . . (586) 282-6144
E-mail: paul.d.rogers14.civ@mail.mil
Education: Michigan Tech 1988 BSME; Michigan (Dearborn) MS; Army War Col MSS; Michigan Tech 2004 PhD
• Executive Director, Research Technology and Integration (Acting) **Charles G. Coutteau** . . . . (586) 282-6391
Executive Director, Systems Integration and Engineering **Jennifer A. Hitchcock** . . . . (586) 282-7595
E-mail: magid.athnasios.civ@mail.mil
Education: Lawrence Tech BS; Oakland U MS; Lawrence Tech MS, 2014 DBA
Chief of Staff **David B. "Dave" Taylor USA (Ret)** . . . . . . (586) 282-7855
E-mail: david.b.taylor10.civ@mail.mil
Education: Citadel BA; Harvard MPA
Military Deputy **COL Kevin A. Vanyo USA** . . . . (586) 282-8030
E-mail: kevin.a.vanyo.mil@mail.mil
Chief Scientist **David J. Gorsich PhD** . . . . (586) 282-7413
E-mail: david.j.gorsich.civ@mail.mil
Education: Lawrence Tech 1990 BS; George Washington 1994 MS; MIT 2000 MA
Chief Roboticist **Dr. Robert W. Sadowski** . . . . (586) 282-8618

U.S. Army Research Laboratory (ARL)
2800 Powder Mill Road, Adelphi, MD 20783-1197
Tel: (301) 394-2515 Internet: www.arl.army.mil

Director **Dr. Philip Perconti DSc** . . . . (301) 394-1600
E-mail: philip.perconti.civ@mail.mil
Education: George Mason BSEE; Johns Hopkins MSEE; George Washington DSc
Deputy Director for Basic Science **(Vacant)** . . . . (919) 549-4201
P.O. Box 12211, Research Triangle Park, NC 27709
Military Deputy **COL Kevin L. Ellison USA** . . . . (301) 394-2515
Sergeant Major **SGM Keith Noland Taylor USA** . . . . (301) 394-2515
Education: Franklin U BS; Webster MSc
Associate Director for Plans and Programs
Todd E. Rosenberger . . . . (301) 394-1600
E-mail: todd.rosenberger@us.army.mil
Associate Director for Science and Technology
(Vacant) . . . . (301) 394-1600
Associate for Corporate Programs
CPT Jennifer Thurston USA . . . . (301) 394-4154
Associate for Laboratory Operations **Teresa Kines** . . . . (301) 394-1300
Deputy Associate for Laboratory Operations, Intelligence, and Security **Paul Watson** . . . . (301) 394-4166
Chief Procurement Officer **(Vacant)** . . . . (301) 394-4593
Chief Scientist **Dr. Joseph N. Mait** . . . . (301) 394-2515
E-mail: joseph.n.mait2.civ@mail.mil
Freedom of Information Act Officer **Tim Connolly** . . . . . . (301) 394-1073
E-mail: tim.connolly@us.army.mil
Deputy Chief Scientist **Dr. Mary Harper** . . . . (301) 394-2515
Outreach Program Manager **Dr. Vallen L. Emery, Jr.** . . . . . (301) 394-3585
E-mail: vallen.l.emery.civ@mail.mil

★ Presidential Appointment Requiring Senate Confirmation ☆ Presidential Appointment □ Schedule C Appointment ◇ Career Senior Foreign Service Appointment
● Career Senior Executive Service (SES) Appointment ○ Non-Career Senior Executive Service (SES) Appointment ■ Postal Career Executive Service

U.S. Army Research Laboratory *(continued)*

Public Affairs Office **Thomas Moyer** .... (301) 394-3590
E-mail: thomas.moyer@us.army.mil
Regional Director, ARL Central **Mark Tschopp** .... (301) 394-2515
Regional Director, ARL South **Heidi Maupin** .... (301) 394-2515
Regional Director, ARL West **(Vacant)** .... (301) 394-2515
Small Business Officer **David O. Christ** .... (919) 549-4278
E-mail: david.o.christ.civ@mail.mil

U.S. Army Research Office (USARO)
4300 South Miami Boulevard, Durham, NC 27703-9142
Mail: P.O. Box 12211, Research Triangle Park, NC 27709-2211
Tel: (919) 549-4201 Internet: www.aro.army.mil

● Director (Acting) **Dr. David M. Stepp** .... (919) 549-4203
E-mail: david.m.stepp.civ@mail.mil
Administrative Specialist **Tisha L. "Tish" Torgerson** ... (919) 549-4201
E-mail: tisha.l.torgerson.civ@mail.mil
Special Assistant to Director **Dr. Brian Ashford** .... (919) 549-4228
E-mail: brian.m.ashford.civ@mail.mil
Senior Scientist **Dr. Stephen J. Lee** .... (919) 549-4365
E-mail: stephen.j.lee28.civ@mail.mil
Associate Director for Business and Research Administration **Richard A. Freed** .... (919) 549-4335
Engineering Sciences Directorate Director **Dr. David M. Stepp** .... (919) 549-4251
E-mail: david.m.stepp.civ@mail.mil
Information Sciences Directorate Director **Dr. Randy A. Zachery** .... (919) 549-4368
E-mail: randy.a.zachery.civ@mail.mil
Physical Sciences Directorate Director **Dr. Hugh C. De Long** .... (919) 549-4319
E-mail: hugh.delong@us.af.mil
Education: Lebanon Valley 1982 BS; Rochester 1984 MS; Wyoming 1990 PhD
Attorney Advisor **John Stone** .... (919) 549-4292
Chief of Information Management **Jack K. "Kevin" Rappold** .... (919) 549-4299
E-mail: jack.k.rappold.civ@mail.mil
Technology Integration and Outreach Chief **Michael J. Caccuitto** .... (919) 549-4369
E-mail: michael.j.caccuitto.civ@mail.mil

Computational and Information Sciences Directorate (CISD)
● Director **Cynthia "Cindy" Bedell** .... (301) 394-2100
Education: MIT BS, MS

Human Research and Engineering Directorate (HRED)
● Director **J. Corde Lane** .... (410) 278-5800

Sensors and Electron Devices Directorate (SEDD)
● Director **(Vacant)** .... (301) 394-2002

Survivability/Lethality Analysis Directorate (SLAD)
● Director **Dr. Patrick Baker** .... (410) 278-6321
E-mail: patrick.j.baker26.civ@mail.mil
Education: Drexel BSME, MSME; Vanderbilt PhD

Vehicle Technology Directorate (VTD)
Director **(Vacant)** .... (216) 433-5742

Weapons and Materials Research Directorate (WMRD)
Weapons and Materials Research Directorate Director **Dr. Robert H. Carter PhD** .... (410) 306-0646

U.S. Army Sustainment Command (ASC)
Building 390, One Rock Island Arsenal, Rock Island, IL 61299
Internet: http://www.aschq.army.mil/

Commanding General **MG Duane A. Gamble USA** ..... (309) 782-5111
Education: Western Maryland 1985 BSBA; Florida Tech; Indust'l Col Armed Forces
Deputy Commanding General **(Vacant)** .... (309) 782-5111
● Deputy to the Commanding General **Michael R. Hutchison** .... (309) 782-5111
E-mail: michael.r.hutchison8.civ@mail.mil
Education: Saint Louis U BBA

U.S. Army Sustainment Command *(continued)*

Deputy Commanding General for Mobilization and Reserve Affairs **(Vacant)** .... (309) 782-5111
Chief of Staff **COL Steven L. Allen USA** .... (309) 782-5111
Executive Officer **LTC Jeff Milne USA** .... (309) 782-3765
Administrative Assistant **Cynthia L. "Cindy" Beserra** .... (309) 782-6111
Deputy Chief of Staff for Information Management, G-6 **COL Jason Woodford USA** .... (309) 782-7808
Deputy Chief of Staff for Operations Support, G3/5/7 **COL Grant L. Morris USA** .... (309) 782-0149
Command Sergeant Major **CSM Joe M. Ulloth USA** .... (309) 782-4480
Executive Director for Acquisition, Integration and Management **Carl Cartwright USA (Ret)** .... (309) 782-5111
Senior Warrant Officer **CW5 Kevin D. Kuhn USA** .... (309) 782-4480
Public Affairs Officer (Interim) **Rhys Fullerlove** .... (309) 782-5421
E-mail: usarmy.ria.asc.list.pa@mail.mil

Army Strategic Logistic Activity Charleston (SC) (ASLAC)
103 Guidance Road, Goose Creek, SC 29445-6060
Tel: (843) 794-4428 Fax: (843) 764-4430

General Manager **Vivian Freeman** .... (843) 794-4428

U.S. 403rd Army Field Support Brigade (403rd AFSB)
Daegu, South Korea
Mail: Unit # 15016, APO, AP 96218-5016
Tel: 82 (53) 470-6515 Fax: 82 (53) 470-8034
E-mail: 403-afsb.list.s3-ops@mail.mil

Commander **COL Renee Mann USA** 82 503-363-4600
Deputy to the Commander **Steven Risley** 82 503-363-4601
Command Sergeant Major **CSM Petra M. Casarez USA** 82 503-363-4603
S1 - Personnel and Administration Chief **Nicola A. Stephens** 82 503-363-6051
E-mail: nicola.a.stephens.civ@mail.mil
S2 - Security Chief **Stanley W. Wojtonik** 82 503-363-2222
E-mail: stanley.w.wojtonik.civ@mail.mil
S3 - Plans and Operations Chief **Clayton C. Gillyard** ... 82 803-363-4274
E-mail: clayton.c.gillyard.civ@mail.mil
S4 - Logistics Chief **Louis A. Sabia** 82 503-398-6744
E-mail: louis.a.sabia.civ@mail.mil
S6 - Information Management Chief **Jesse Meza** 82 503-363-4607
E-mail: jesse.meza.civ@mail.mil
S8 - Resource Management Chief **Young Kim** 82 503-368-7941
E-mail: young.k.kim6@mail.mil

U.S. Army Tank-automotive and Armaments Command (TACOM)
6501 East 11 Mile Road, Warren, MI 48397-5000
Tel: (586) 282-5000 Fax: (586) 282-5097
E-mail: usarmy.detroit.tacom.mail.lcmc-pao@mail.mil
Internet: https://www.army.mil/tacom

Commanding General **BG Daniel G. Mitchell USA** ...... (586) 282-5000
Fax: (586) 574-5038
Deputy to the Commander **Brian D. Butler** .... (586) 282-5134
E-mail: brian.d.butler8.civ@mail.mil Fax: (586) 282-8561
Education: Northern Michigan 1987 BS; US Army Command
Command Sergeant Major **CSM Ian C. Griffin USA** ..... (586) 282-5000
E-mail: jesse.l.sharpe.mil@mail.mil
Chief of Staff **COL Jeffrey D. Witt USA** .... (586) 282-5000
Deputy Chief of Staff **Annette Riggs** .... (586) 282-5000
Deputy Chief of Staff for Human Capital **Timothy F. "Tim" Tarczynski** .... (586) 282-6655
E-mail: timothy.f.tarczynski.civ@mail.mil Fax: (586) 282-2304
Freedom of Information Act Officer **Michele M. "Shelly" Pantalone** .... (586) 282-8099
E-mail: michele.m.pantalone.civ@mail.mil
Public Affairs Officer **Eric P. Emerton** .... (586) 282-5663
E-mail: usarmy.detroit.tacom.mail.lcmc-pao@mail.mil
● Contracting Officer **Kristan A. Mendoza** .... (586) 282-7027
E-mail: kristin.a.mendoza.civ@mail.mil
Small Business Officer **Marie T. Gapinski** .... (586) 282-6005
E-mail: marie.t.gapinski.civ@mail.mil

(continued on next page)

★ Presidential Appointment Requiring Senate Confirmation ☆ Presidential Appointment ☐ Schedule C Appointment ◇ Career Senior Foreign Service Appointment
● Career Senior Executive Service (SES) Appointment ○ Non-Career Senior Executive Service (SES) Appointment ■ Postal Career Executive Service

DEPARTMENTS

U.S. Army Tank-automotive and Armaments Command *(continued)*

Competition Advocate and Ombudsperson
LaRuth Shepherd . . . . (586) 282-6597
E-mail: laruth.shepherd.civ@mail.mil
Section 508 Coordinator [Section 508 Coordinator]
Stephen W. Barnes . . . . (586) 282-5860
E-mail: stephen.w.barnes6.civ@mail.mil

Anniston (AL) Army Depot
7 Frankford Avenue, Anniston, AL 36201-4199
Tel: (256) 235-7501 Fax: (256) 235-4695
E-mail: anadpaousers@us.army.mil

Commander **COL Martine Kidd USA** . . . . (256) 235-7511
Education: Methodist Col 1994; Eisenhower National Security and Resource Strategy
Contracting Officer **David Jesse Bunt** . . . . (256) 235-6231
E-mail: david.j.bunt2.mil@mail.mil
Freedom of Information Act Officer **Bruce L. Ellis** . . . . (256) 235-4741
E-mail: usarmy.anad.tacom.list.foia@mail.mil Fax: (256) 235-7799
Public Affairs Officer **Clester M. Burdell** . . . . (256) 235-6281
E-mail: clester.burdell@us.army.mil
Education: Jacksonville State BA

Integrated Logistics Support Center (ILSC)
6501 East 11 Mile Road, Warren, MI 48397
Tel: (586) 282-6090 Internet: www.tacom.army.mil/ilsc

● Executive Director (Acting) **Marion G. Whicker** . . . . (586) 282-5000
E-mail: marion.g.whicker.civ@mail.mil
Director, Soldier Readiness and Sustainment
Michael J. "Mike" Ahearn . . . . (508) 233-5525

Red River Army Depot
100 Main Drive, Texarkana, TX 75507-5000
Tel: (903) 334-4446 Fax: (903) 334-4411
E-mail: usarmy.rrad.usamc.list.tarr-ba@mail.mil

Commander **COL Stephen M. York USA** . . . . (903) 334-3111
Education: VCU 1993 BS; Florida Tech MS
Deputy Commander **James P. "Patton" Tidwell** . . . . (903) 334-2102
Chief of Staff **Theresa Weaver** . . . . (903) 334-4779
Director of Contracting **Donald E. "Don" Kennedy** . . . . (903) 334-3987
E-mail: donald.e.kennedy16.civ@mail.mil
E-mail: usarmy.rrad.acc.mbx.ccta-hdr@mail.mil
Director of Emergency Services **Wallace Embrey, Jr.** . . . . (903) 334-3151
E-mail: wallace.embrey@us.army.mil Fax: (903) 334-3841
Director of Information Management **Karen Hendricks** . . . (903) 334-3107
Director of Maintenance Logistics
James E. "Jamie" Bass . . . . (903) 334-2104
E-mail: james.e.bass.civ@mail.mil
Director of Maintenance Production **Mike Lockard** . . . . (903) 334-2104
E-mail: mike.lockard@us.army.mil
Director of Personnel **Jackie Johnson** . . . . (903) 334-3617
Director of Public Works **Mark Crawford** . . . . (903) 334-3115
E-mail: usarmy.rrad.usamc.mbx.tarr-o@mail.mil
Director of Resource Management
Michael Addington . . . . (903) 334-3145
E-mail: usarmy.rrad.usamc.list.tarr-r@mail.mil
Equal Opportunity Officer **Gwen Houston** . . . . (903) 334-3444
Integrated Business Management Office
Marshall McKellar . . . . (903) 334-5045
Internal Review and Audit Compliance Office
Eva M. Knight . . . . (903) 334-3222
E-mail: usarmy.rrad.usamc.list.tarr-i@mail.mil
Quality Assurance Officer **Tad Cunningham** . . . . (903) 334-2151
Protocol Officer **Tara Inman** . . . . (903) 334-2316
Public Affairs Officer **Adrienne Marie Brown** . . . . (903) 334-4446
Fax: (903) 334-4149

Rock Island (IL) Arsenal Joint Manufacturing and Technology Center (RIA-JMTC)
One Rock Island Arsenal, Rock Island, IL 61299-6200
Tel: (309) 782-6854 E-mail: rock-amsta-ri-mktg@conus.army.mil
Internet: ria-jmtc.ria.army.mil

Commander **COL Kenneth W. "Ken" Letcher USA** . . . . . (309) 782-6854

Sierra Army Depot
AMSTA-SI-CO, Herlong, CA 96113-5000
Tel: (530) 827-2111 Tel: (530) 827-4666 Fax: (530) 827-4767
Internet: www.sierra.army.mil

Commander **LTC Benjamin G. Johnson USA** . . . . (530) 827-2111
Deputy Commander
COL Donald C. "Don" Olson USA (Ret) . . . (530) 827-2111 ext. 4666
Education: Trinity U 1979
Chief of Staff **Aric A. Manner** . . . . (530) 827-2111 ext. 4665
Public Affairs Officer **Lori K. McDonald** . . . . (530) 827-4343
E-mail: lori.k.mcdonald@us.army.mil

Watervliet (NY) Arsenal
One Buffington Street, Watervliet, NY 12189-4050
Tel: (518) 266-5111 Tel: (518) 266-4294 (Public Affairs)
Internet: http://www.wva.army.mil/ Fax: (518) 266-4358

Commander **COL Milton G. "Milt" Kelly USA** . . . . (518) 266-4294
Education: Central Arkansas 1995
Purchasing Division Chief **(Vacant)** . . . . (518) 266-5309
Safety, Health and Environmental Division Chief
Matthew K. "Matt" Church . . . . (518) 266-5633
Emergency Planning Officer **Robert Pfeil** . . . . (518) 266-4772
E-mail: robert.pfeil@us.army.mil
Freedom of Information Act Officer **John Snyder** . . . . (518) 266-5055
E-mail: john.snyder@us.army.mil
Operations Officer and Chief of Staff **Barbara Hill** . . . . (518) 266-5702
Protocol Officer **Debra "Deb" Monaco** . . . . (518) 266-4153
Public Affairs Officer **John Snyder** . . . . (518) 266-5055
E-mail: john.snyder@us.army.mil
Small and Disadvantaged Business Utilization
Specialist **(Vacant)** . . . . (518) 266-4150
Internal Audit and Review Chief **(Vacant)** . . . . (518) 266-4204
Equal Employment Program Manager **(Vacant)** . . . . (518) 266-5308

Military Surface Deployment and Distribution Command (SDDC)
One Soldier Way, Scott AFB, IL 62225
Tel: (618) 220-6284 Fax: (618) 220-5020

Commanding General **MG Stephen E. Farmen USA** . . . . (618) 220-6284
709 Ward Drive Building 1990, Scott AFB, Belleville, IL 62225
E-mail: stephen.e.farmen.mil@mail.mil
Education: Richmond 1986 BA
Deputy Commander **COL Lillard Evans USA** . . . . (618) 220-6284
Deputy Commander for Mobilization
COL Martin F. Klein USAR . . . . (618) 220-6284
● Deputy to the Commander **Bryan R. Samson** . . . . (618) 220-5001
709 Ward Drive Building 1990, Scott AFB, Room 11N41, Belleville, IL 62225
E-mail: bryan.r.samson.civ@mail.mil
Education: Alfred BS; Iowa MBA
Chief of Staff **COL Zorn T. Sliman USA** . . . . (618) 220-6284
Command Sergeant Major **CSM Dana S. Mason USA** . . . (618) 220-6284
709 Ward Drive Building 1990, Scott AFB, Belleville, IL 62225
E-mail: dana.s.mason.mil@mail.mil

Transportation Engineering Agency (TEA)
Building 1990, 709 Ward Drive, Scott AFB, Belleville, IL 62225

● Director and Special Assistant for Transportation Engineering **Bruce A. Busler** . . . . (618) 220-5118
E-mail: bruce.a.busler.civ@mail.mil
Education: Air Force Acad 1979 BS; Air Force Inst Tech 1987 MS; National Defense U 1996 MS

597th Transportation Brigade
1012 Monroe Avenue, Joint Base Langley-Eustis, VA 23604
Tel: (757) 878-8067 Fax: (757) 878-1567

Commander **COL Frederick Christ USA** . . . . (757) 878-8067

★ Presidential Appointment Requiring Senate Confirmation ☆ Presidential Appointment □ Schedule C Appointment ◇ Career Senior Foreign Service Appointment
● Career Senior Executive Service (SES) Appointment ○ Non-Career Senior Executive Service (SES) Appointment ■ Postal Career Executive Service

U.S. Army Medical Command (MEDCOM)
Army Medicine, Sam Houston Place, Fort Sam Houston, TX 78234
Internet: https://www.army.mil/armymedicine

Regional Health Command - Europe (ERMC)
ERMC, Karlsruherstrasse 144, Gebaude 3607,
Room 207, 69126 Heidelberg, Germany
Mail: Europe Regional Medical Command,
MCEU, APO, AE 09042-0130
Tel: 49 (6371) 9464-2113
E-mail: usarmy.sembach.medcom-ermc.list.pao@mail.mil
Internet: http://rhce.amedd.army.mil/

Commanding General and U.S.
Army Europe Command Surgeon
BG Ronald T. Stephens USA 49 (6371) 9464-2113
Deputy Commander and Chief of Medical
Operations **(Vacant)** 49 (6371) 9464-2113
Command Sergeant Major
CSM Todd M. Garner USA 49 (6371) 9464-2113

U.S. Army Public Health Command - Europe (PHC-Europe)
Building 3809, Commander, USACHPPMEUR,
MCHB-AE, Kirchberg Kaserne, 66849 Landstuhl, Germany
Mail: Commander, USACHPPMEUR,
MCHB-AE, CMR 402, APO, AE 09180
Tel: 49 (6371) 9464-9703
Fax: 49 (6371) 86-7198 (Administrative Services)
E-mail: usarmy.landstuhl.medcom-phe.mbx.s3@mail.mil

Commander **COL Rebecca Porter USA** 49 (6371) 86-8084

Regional Health Command - Atlantic (RHC-A)
Fort Belvoir, VA 22060
Tel: (571) 231-5345
Areas Covered: CT, DE, IL, IN, KY, MA, MD, ME, MI, MN, NC, NH, NJ, NY, OH, PA, RI, VA, VT, WI, WV

Commanding General **BG Telita Crosland USA** .... (571) 231-5345
E-mail: telita.crosland.mil@mail.mil
Education: West Point 1989 BS; Uniformed Services MPH
Deputy Commanding General **(Vacant)** .... (571) 231-5345
E-mail: erik.h.torring.mil@mail.mil
Command Sergeant Major
CSM Diamond D. Hough USA .... (571) 231-5342
Chief of Staff **COL David Carpenter USA** .... (571) 231-5345
Assistant Chief of Staff **(Vacant)** .... (571) 231-5345

U.S. Army Public Health Command - Atlantic (PHC-Atlantic)
Commander, ATTN: MCHB-RN, Fort George G. Meade, MD 20755-5225
Tel: (301) 677-6502 Fax: (301) 677-7132
E-mail: usarmy.meade.medcom-phcr-n.list.web-contact@mail.mil

Commander **COL James Grady USA** .... (301) 677-6200
Secretary **Diane L. Stroud** .... (301) 677-6502
E-mail: diane.l.stroud.civ@mail.mil
Sergeant Major **CSM Eugene Larkins USA** .... (301) 677-6205
Executive Officer **MAJ Lesly Calix USA** .... (301) 677-3713
Deputy Commander **LTC Winico M. Martinez USA** ..... (301) 677-3713
Deputy Commander for Technical Services
MAJ Chanda M. Maneval USA .... (301) 677-3466
Environmental Health Engineering Division Chief
MAJ Katherine Kinder USA .... (301) 677-3668
Health Risk Management Chief
CPT Anthony A. John USA .... (301) 677-5120
E-mail: usarmy.meade.medcom-phcr-n.list.web-hrmd@mail.mil
Laboratory Sciences Chief **Melissa K. Miller** .... (301) 677-3806
Occupational Health Sciences Chief
MAJ Raushan Salaam USA .... (301) 677-3426
Budget Officer **Teresita Balajadia Craig** .... (301) 677-4252

Regional Health Command - Pacific (RHC-P)
Building 160, 160 Krukowski Road, Honolulu, HI 96859-5001
Tel: (808) 433-6661 Fax: (808) 433-4899
E-mail: shafter.medcom-rhc-p.list.dcomm@mail.mil
Internet: https://www.army.mil/rhcpacific (Pacific Regional Medical Command) Internet: https://www.tamc.amedd.army.mil/ (Tripler Army Medical Center)
Areas Covered: HI, Japan

Commanding General **BG Dennis P. LeMaster USA** ..... (808) 433-5716
E-mail: dennis.p.lemaster.mil@mail.mil
Command Sergeant Major
CSM Clark J. Charpentier USA .... (808) 433-6661
Education: Excelsior BS
Aide-de-Camp **CPT Anna-Marie Travis USA** .... (808) 433-6344
Deputy Commanding General
COL Michael L. Place USA .... (253) 967-8392
Madigan Army Medical Center, Fitzsimmons Drive,
Tacoma, WA 98431
Education: Uniformed Services MD
Deputy Commander for Clinical Services **(Vacant)** ...... (808) 433-6661
Tripler Army Medical Center Commander
COL Mary V. Krueger USA .... (808) 433-5716
Command Sergeant Major (Acting)
CSM Larry Reyes USA .... (808) 433-6661

Regional Health Command - Central (RHC-C)
2410 Stanley Road, Suite 120, Joint Base San Antonio, TX 78234-6230
Tel: (210) 295-2355 Internet: https://www.army.mil/RHCCentral
Areas Covered: AR, AZ, CO, IA, KS, LA, MO, MT, ND, NE, NM, OK, SD, TX, UT, WY

Commanding General **BG Jeffrey J. Johnson USA** ..... (210) 295-2355
Deputy Commanding General
BG George N. Appenzeller USA .... (210) 916-1125
Education: Tulane
Chief of Staff **COL John P. Lamoureux USA** .... (210) 295-2355
Education: Embry-Riddle BSE; Webster MSA
Command Sergeant Major **CSM Joseph L. Cecil USA** ... (210) 295-2355

U.S. Army Medical Department Center and School
3630 Stanley Road, Suite 301, Joint Base San Antonio, TX 78234-6100
Tel: (210) 221-8317 Fax: (210) 221-1198
Internet: www.cs.amedd.army.mil

Commanding General **MG Patrick D. Sargent USA** ..... (210) 221-6325
Command Sergeant Major
CSM William H. "Buck" O'Neal II USA .... (210) 221-8050

U.S. Army Public Health Center (Provisional) (USAPHC - Aberdeen Proving Ground)
5158 Blackhawk Road, Aberdeen Proving Ground, MD 21010-5403
Tel: (800) 222-9698 E-mail: usarmy.apg.medcom-phc.mbx.pao@mail.mil

Commander
CPT Diana M. Rommelfanger-Konkol USA .... (410) 436-4311

U.S. Army Medical Research and Materiel Command (USAMRMC)
504 Scott Street, Fort Detrick, MD 21702-5012
Tel: (301) 619-7613 Fax: (301) 619-2982 Internet: mrmc.amedd.army.mil

Commanding General **MG Barbara R. Holcomb USA** ... (301) 619-7636
E-mail: barbara.r.holcomb.mil@mail.mil
Education: Seattle BS; Kansas
Command Sergeant Major
CSM Timothy J. Sprunger USA .... (301) 619-3357
Public Affairs Officer **Lori Salvatore** .... (301) 619-2736
Fax: (301) 619-3320
Freedom of Information Act Officer **Sandra Rogers** ..... (301) 619-7118

U.S. Army Military District of Washington/Joint Force Headquarters - National Capital Region (JFHQ-NCR/MDW)
Building 39, 103 Third Avenue, Fort Lesley J. McNair, DC 20319-5058
Tel: (202) 685-2808 Fax: (202) 685-3481
E-mail: usarmy.mcnair.mdw.mbx.mediadesk-omb@mail.mil

Commander **MG Michael L. Howard USA** .... (202) 685-2807
Secretary to the Commanding General **Kai Brown** ..... (202) 685-2808
Aide-de-Camp **CPT Carl Stickeler USA** .... (202) 685-2807

(continued on next page)

DEPARTMENTS

U.S. Army Military District of Washington/Joint Force Headquarters - National Capital Region *(continued)*

Executive Officer **MAJ Beau J. Ashley USA** .... (202) 685-2817
• Deputy Commander **COL Egon Hawrylak USA (Ret)** .... (202) 685-0641
E-mail: egon.hawrylak@us.army.mil
Education: Toledo 1974; National War Col MS; Naval Postgrad MA
Deputy Commander **(Vacant)** .... (202) 685-0641
Inspector General **COL Gary Cunningham USA** .... (202) 685-2808
Command Sergeant Major
CSM Richard Woodring USA .... (202) 685-2923
E-mail: richard.a.woodring4.mil@mail.mil
Army Air Operations Group Commander
Christopher Scott "Chris" Ferris .... (202) 685-2807
Headquarters Battalion Commander
LTC Derrick Davis USA .... (703) 696-3569
Deputy Public Affairs Director
COL Sunset R. Belinsky USA .... (202) 685-2900
E-mail: sunset.r.belinsky.mil@mail.mil
Education: St Bonaventure 1997 BAJ; Georgetown 2013 MA

Arlington National Cemetery
Administration Building, Arlington, VA 22211-5003
Tel: (877) 907-8585 Internet: www.arlingtoncemetery.mil

• Executive Director of Army National Military Cemeteries **Karen L. Durham-Aguilera PE** .... (877) 907-8585
Education: Louisville BCE, MCE
• Superintendent **Katharine "Kate." Kelley** .... (877) 907-8585
Education: Villanova 1999 BA; Oklahoma 2003 MA; Naval War 2012 MA
Deputy Superintendent for Field Operations
Brion Moore .... (877) 907-8585
Deputy Superintendent for Cemetery Administration
Renea C. Yates .... (877) 907-8585
E-mail: renea.c.yates.civ@mail.mil
Public Affairs **Stephanie Russ** .... (877) 907-8585

U.S. Army Pacific Command (USARPAC)
Building T100, U.S. Army Pacific, ATTN: APPA,
Fort Shafter, HI 96858-5100
Tel: (808) 787-5862 Fax: (808) 438-6354
E-mail: sgsadmin@shafter.army.mil (Command Group)
E-mail: appaadm@shafter.army.mil (Public Affairs)

Commanding General **GEN Robert B. Brown USA** ..... (808) 787-5862
E-mail: robert.b.brown90.mil@mail.mil
Deputy Commanding General
MG John P. "Pete" Johnson USA .... (808) 787-5862
Deputy Commanding General, Army National Guard
MG Timothy M. McKeithen ARNG .... (808) 787-5862
E-mail: timothy.m.mckeithen.mil@mail.mil
Deputy Commanding General, North
MAJGEN Roger Noble .... (808) 787-5862
Deputy Commanding General, South **(Vacant)** .... (808) 787-5862
Chief of Staff **BG Peter B. Andrysiak USA** .... (808) 787-5862
Deputy Chief of Staff, G3/G5/G7
BG Jonathan E. "Jon" Howerton USA .... (808) 787-5862
Education: Texas Christian
Command Sergeant Major
CSM Benjamin Jones USA .... (808) 787-5862

8th Theater Sustainment Command
Fort Shafter, Honolulu, HI 96858-5440
Internet: https://www.army.mil/8thtsc

Commanding General **BG Charles R. Hamilton USA** .... (808) 438-0894
Deputy Commanding General
COL Douglas M. Vallejo USA .... (808) 438-5581
Education: West Point 1991 BS
Chief of Staff **COL Dennis H. Levesque USA** .... (808) 438-5581
Command Sergeant Major
CSM Maurice V. Chaplin USA .... (808) 438-5581

130th Engineer Brigade (Fort Shafter)
260 Williston Avenue, Wahiawa, HI 96857
Tel: (808) 655-8843

Commander **COL Danielle Ngo USA** .... (808) 655-8843

130th Engineer Brigade *(continued)*

Command Sergeant Major
CSM Patrickson Toussaint USA .... (808) 655-8843

94th Army Air and Missile Defense Command
Joint Base Pearl Harbor-Hickam, HI 96818
Fax: (808) 438-2775 E-mail: usarmy.shafter.94-aamdc.list.pao@mail.mil
Internet: https://www.army.mil/94thaamdc/

Commanding General **BG Michael T. Morrissey USA** ... (808) 438-3855
Command Sergeant Major **CSM Eric R. McCray USA** ... (808) 438-3855
Command Chief Warrant Officer
CW5 James E. Heck USA .... (808) 438-3855

U.S. Army Alaska (USARAK)
724 Postal Service Loop, Suite 5000,
Joint Base Elmendorf-Richardson, AK 99505-5000
Tel: (907) 384-2163 Fax: (907) 384-2913

Commander **MG Mark J. O'Neill USA** .... (907) 384-2163
Education: Norwich 1986
Deputy Commander, Operations
COL Roch Pelletier USA .... (907) 384-2163
Deputy Commander, Sustainment
COL Mark A. Colbrook USA .... (907) 384-2163
Command Sergeant Major
CSM Jeffrey R. Dillingham USA .... (907) 384-2156

U.S. Army Japan and I Corps (Forward) (USARJ)
Camp Zama, Japan
Mail: Commander, USARJ, Unit 45005, APO, AP 96343-5005
Tel: 81 046-263-5336 Fax: 81 3117-63-7554
Internet: www.usarj.army.mil

Commanding General **BG Viet Xuan Luong USA** 81 046-263-7452
E-mail: viet.x.luong.mil@mail.mil
Command Sergeant Major **CSM Richard Clark USA** ... 81 046-263-7452

25th Infantry Division
U.S. Army Garrison - Hawaii, Schofield Barracks, HI 96857
Tel: (808) 655-4907 Fax: (808) 655-9290

Commanding General **MG Ronald P. Clark USA** .... (808) 655-4823
Deputy Commanding General for Operations
COL Joel B. Vowell USA .... (808) 655-4991
Deputy Commanding General for Support
COL Andrew D. "Andy" Preston USA .... (808) 655-4991
Chief of Staff **COL David B. Womack USA** .... (808) 655-4823
Command Sergeant Major **CSM Brian Hester USA** ..... (808) 655-7110

Pohakuloa Training Area (HI) (PTA)
25th Infantry Division (L) and USARHAW, Schofield Barracks, HI 96857
Tel: (808) 969-2402 Fax: (808) 438-1643
Internet: www.garrison.hawaii.army.mil/pta

Commander **LTC Loreto V. Borce, Jr. USA** .... (808) 969-2402
Deputy Commander **Gregory R. Fleming** .... (808) 969-2404
Senior Enlisted Leader
CSM Luis E. Ortiz-Santiago USA .... (808) 969-2402

U.S. Army Recruiting Command (USAREC - Fort Knox)
Fort Knox, KY 40121-2726
Tel: (502) 626-0511 (Staff Duty Officer) Internet: www.usarec.army.mil

Commander **MG Frank M. Muth USA** .... (502) 626-0511
Executive Assistant **Jessica Miller** .... (502) 626-0511
Deputy Commanding General for Operations
BG Kevin Vereen USA .... (502) 626-0508
Education: Campbell 1988
Deputy Commander for Support
BG Jason L. Walrath USAR .... (502) 626-0508
Command Sergeant Major
CSM Tabitha A. Gavia USA .... (502) 626-0508
Chief of Staff **COL Isaac O. Johnson USA** .... (502) 626-0522
Chief Information Officer (G6) **Ronnie Creech** .... (502) 626-3258
E-mail: usarmy.knox.usarec.list.hq-g6@mail.mil

★ Presidential Appointment Requiring Senate Confirmation ☆ Presidential Appointment ☐ Schedule C Appointment ◇ Career Senior Foreign Service Appointment
● Career Senior Executive Service (SES) Appointment ○ Non-Career Senior Executive Service (SES) Appointment ■ Postal Career Executive Service

U.S. Army Special Operations Command (USASOC)
2929 Desert Storm Drive, ATTN: AOPA, Fort Bragg, NC 28310
Tel: (910) 432-6005 (Public Affairs) Fax: (910) 432-1046
E-mail: pao@soc.mil Internet: www.soc.mil

U.S. Army Training and Doctrine Command (TRADOC)
950 Jefferson Avenue, Fort Eustis, VA 23604
Tel: (757) 501-5886
E-mail: usarmy.jble.tradoc.mbx.hq-tradoc-pao@mail.mil
Internet: www.tradoc.army.mil

Defense Language Institute Foreign Language Center (DLIFLC)
Presidio of Monterey, CA 93944-5000
Tel: (831) 242-5118 Fax: (831) 242-6519 Internet: www.dliflc.edu

Commandant **COL Phillip J. Deppert USA** .... (831) 242-5200
E-mail: phillip.j.deppert.mil@mail.mil
Assistant Commandant **Col Wiley L. Barnes USAF** ...... (831) 242-5312
Education: Tennessee 1996 BA
Command Sergeant Major
CSM Ryan J. Ramsey USA .... (831) 242-5842

TRADOC Analysis Center (TRAC)
225 Sedgwick Avenue, Fort Leavenworth, KS 66027-2345
E-mail: trac.army@us.army.mil Internet: www.trac.army.mil

Director **Pamela I. Blechinger** .... (913) 684-5132
Deputy Director **COL David Tarvin USA** .... (913) 684-5132

U.S. Army Sergeants Major Academy (USASMA)
11291 SGT East Churchill Street, Fort Bliss, TX 79918-8002
Tel: (915) 744-2952

Commandant **CSM Jimmy J. Sellers USA** .... (915) 744-8009
Deputy Commandant **CSM Michael C. Henry USA** ..... (915) 744-8307
Chief of Staff **Jesse W. McKinney USA (Ret)** .... (915) 744-2967

U.S. Army War College (USAWC)
122 Forbes Avenue, Carlisle Barracks, Carlisle, PA 17013-5050
Tel: (717) 245-4400 E-mail: usarmy.carlisle.awc.mbx.atwc-cpa@mail.mil
Internet: www.carlisle.army.mil

Commandant, U.S. Army War College/Commanding General, Carlisle Barracks **MG John S. Kem USA** .... (717) 245-4400
E-mail: john.s.kem.mil@mail.mil
Education: Indust'l Col Armed Forces; Kellogg 1995 MBA; Northwestern 1995 MEnvE; US Army Command 1998
◇ Diplomatic Advisor to the Commandant
Ambassador Donald W. Koran .... (717) 245-4400
Education: Texas BA; Johns Hopkins MA, PhD
Deputy Commandant **COL Kimo C. Gallahue USA** ..... (717) 245-4400
Deputy Commandant - Reserve Affairs
BG Kelly Fisher USA .... (717) 245-4400
Education: Cal Poly San Luis Obispo MS
Provost **James G. Breckenridge PhD** .... (717) 245-4771
Chief of Staff **COL Gregg Thompson USA** .... (717) 245-4025
Command Sergeant Major
CSM Alan K. Hummel USA .... (717) 245-4101
E-mail: alan.k.hummel.mil@mail.mil
Public Affairs Officer **Carol A. Kerr** .... (717) 245-4389
E-mail: carol.a.kerr.civ@mail.mil
Contracting **Karen A. Kurzendoerfer** .... (717) 245-4609
E-mail: karen.a.kurzendoerfer.civ@mail.mil
Chief Librarian **Greta Braungard** .... (717) 245-4300

U.S. Army Warrant Officer Career College
Building 5302 (Swartworth Hall), Outlaw Street, Fort Rucker, AL 16048
Fax: (334) 255-1173

Commandant **COL Gary L. Thompson USA** .... (334) 255-3869
Deputy Commandant **CW5 Richard B. Ayers USA** ...... (334) 255-9031
E-mail: richard.b.ayers2.mil@mail.mil

Army Capabilities Integration Center (ARCIC)
950 Jefferson Avenue, Fort Eustis, VA 23604
Tel: (757) 501-6328 Internet: www.arcic.army.mil

Director **MG Eric J. Wesley USA** .... (757) 501-6328

Army Capabilities Integration Center *(continued)*

Deputy Director and Chief of Staff
MG John A. George USA .... (757) 501-6328
Command Sergeant Major **CSM Paul E. Biggs USA** ..... (757) 501-6328

U.S. Army Joint Modernization Command (JMC)
Fort Bliss, TX 79916
Tel: (915) 568-4250 Fax: (915) 569-8906

Commanding General **BG Johnny K. Davis USA** .... (915) 568-4250
Education: Cardinal Stritch U 1992 BS
Command Sergeant Major
CSM Wilbert E. Engram USA .... (915) 568-4250

Army Combined Arms Center (CAC)
Building 52, 415 Sherman Avenue, Unit 1, Fort Leavenworth, KS 66027
Tel: (913) 684-0020 Fax: (913) 684-4677 Internet: http://usacac.army.mil/

Commanding General **LTG Michael D. Lundy USA** ..... (913) 684-5621
Education: McNeese State 1987
Deputy Commanding General for Army National Guard **BG Troy D. Galloway ARNG** .... (913) 684-0020
Deputy Commanding General for Training
MG Maria R. Gervais USA .... (913) 684-5501
● Deputy to the Commanding General **Kirby Brown** .... (913) 684-5322
Provost, Army University **BG Scott L. Efflandt USA** .... (913) 684-3443
E-mail: scott.l.efflandt.mil@mail.mil
Command Sergeant Major **CSM Eric C. Dostie USA** .... (913) 684-0023
Chief of Staff **COL Edward T. Bohnemann USA** .... (913) 684-2761
Director, Combined Training Center Directorate
COL Robert J. Molinari USA .... (913) 684-0020
Public Affairs Officer **LTC Kirk A. Luedeke USA** .... (913) 684-2019
E-mail: kirk.a.luedeke.mil@mail.mil Fax: (913) 684-8513

U.S. Army Aviation Center of Excellence (Fort Rucker)
Fort Rucker, AL 36362-5033
Tel: (334) 255-2252 E-mail: usarmy.rucker.usag.mbx.atzq-pao@mail.mil
Internet: www.rucker.army.mil

Commanding General **MG William K. Gayler USA** ..... (334) 255-2600
E-mail: william.k.gayler.mil@mail.mil
Education: North Georgia BBA; US Army Command; National War Col
Deputy to the Commanding General
William G. "Bill" Kidd .... (334) 255-2808
E-mail: william.g.kidd2.civ@mail.mil
Education: Troy State 1986 BA; Webster 1994 MPA; Army War Col 2002 MSS
Deputy Commander
COL Thomas W. O'Connor, Jr. USA .... (334) 255-2252
Education: West Point 1994 BS
Deputy Commanding General, U.S. Army National Guard **BG Timothy E. "Tim" Gowen ARNG** ....(334) 255-2600
Chief of Staff **(Vacant)** .... (334) 255-2600
Command Sergeant Major
CSM Brian N. Hauke USA Building 114 .... (334) 255-2600
Chief Warrant Officer **CW5 Joseph B. Roland USA**.....(334) 255-2600
Contracting Director **Thomas Michael "Mike" Coburn** Building 5700, Directorate of Contracting ..... (334) 255-3404
E-mail: thomas.m.coburn.civ@mail.mil Fax: (334) 255-1231
Education: Austin Peay State BA; Florida Tech MA
Small Business Adviser **Michael J. Faire** ....(334) 255-3141
E-mail: michael.j.faire2.civ@mail.mil
TRADOC Capability Manager for Unmanned Aircraft Systems **(Vacant)** .... (334) 255-1801
Deputy TRADOC Capability Manager for Unmanned Aircraft Systems **Glenn A. Rizzi** .... (334) 255-0736
E-mail: glenn.a.rizzi.civ@mail.mil
Public Affairs Officer **Lisa E. Eichhorn** ....(334) 255-3404
Building 5700, 453 Novosel Avenue, Room 385, Fort Rucker, AL 36362-5033 Fax: (334) 255-1004
E-mail: usarmy.rucker.usag.mbx.atzq-pao@mail.mil
Freedom of Information Act Officer **Phaedra Lecuyer** ... (334) 255-2066
E-mail: phaedra.lecuyer@us.army.mil

(continued on next page)

★ Presidential Appointment Requiring Senate Confirmation ☆ Presidential Appointment □ Schedule C Appointment ◇ Career Senior Foreign Service Appointment
● Career Senior Executive Service (SES) Appointment ○ Non-Career Senior Executive Service (SES) Appointment ■ Postal Career Executive Service

DEPARTMENTS

U.S. Army Aviation Center of Excellence *(continued)*

Aviation Technical Librarian **Jill Redington** . . . . (334) 255-3912
Building 9204, Fax: (334) 255-2838
5th Avenue, Fort Rucker, AL 36362
E-mail: jill.redington@us.army.mil
Center Library Head Librarian **Alfred R. Edwards** . . . . . . (334) 255-3885

U.S. Army Aviation Museum (Fort Rucker)
Building 6000, Fort Rucker, AL 36362
Mail: P.O. Box 620610, Fort Rucker, AL 36362
Tel: (334) 598-2508 Fax: (334) 255-3054
Internet: http://www.armyaviationmuseum.org/

Director (Interim) **Robert D. Mitchell** . . . . (334) 255-1078
E-mail: robert.d.mitchell3.civ@mail.mil
E-mail: director@armyaviationmuseum.org
Curator **Robert D. Mitchell** . . . . (334) 255-1060
E-mail: robert.d.mitchell3.civ@mail.mil
E-mail: curator@armyaviationmuseum.org

U.S. Army Training Center (Fort Jackson)
U.S. Army Training Center, Fort Jackson, SC 29207-5015
Tel: (803) 751-1742 Fax: (803) 751-2722
Internet: http://jackson.armylive.dodlive.mil/

Commanding General
BG Milford H. "Beags" Beagle USA . . . . (803) 751-1742
Deputy Commander **COL Joseph McLamb USA** . . . . (803) 751-7622
Chief of Staff **COL Douglas "Doug" Walter USA** . . . . . . (803) 751-7414
Command Sergeant Major
CSM Jerimiah E. Gan USA . . . . (803) 751-7246

U.S. Army Combined Arms Support Command and Sustainment Center of Excellence (CASCOM)
Building 5020, 2221 Adams Avenue, Fort Lee, VA 23801-2102
Tel: (804) 734-6855 (Post Locator)
Tel: (804) 765-3000 (Post Information) Internet: www.cascom.army.mil

Commanding General **MG Rodney D. Fogg USA** . . . . (804) 734-1542
Executive Assistant to the Commanding General
Sheila Boone . . . . (804) 734-1542
Aide **CPT Lydia Koh USA** . . . . (804) 734-1585
● Deputy to the Commanding General **John E. Hall** . . . . (804) 734-1540
E-mail: john.e.hall58.civ@mail.mil
Education: Arkansas State BA; Stanford MA; Army War Col 1999
Executive Officer to the Deputy **Kayla Fabre** . . . . (804) 734-1540
Deputy Commanding General, Army Reserve
BG Stephen Iacovelli USA . . . . (804) 734-6855
Deputy Commanding General, National Guard
BG James E. "Eddie" Porter USA . . . . (804) 734-6855
Resource Management Director **Donald "Don" Hall** . . . . . (804) 765-0576
E-mail: donald.hall@us.army.mil
Command Sergeant Major
CSM Michael J. Perry III USA . . . . (804) 734-1358
Chief Warrant Officer
CW5 Richard C. Myers, Jr. USA . . . . (804) 734-2733
Public Affairs Specialist
Maj Daneta "Dani" Johnson USAF . . . . (804) 765-7197

Chief of Staff
Chief of Staff **COL Tamatha A. Patterson USA** . . . . (804) 734-1683
Deputy Chief of Staff **Lionel Compos** . . . . (804) 734-1683

Schools

U.S. Army Logistics University
Building 12420, 2401 Quarters Road, Fort Lee, VA 23801
Tel: (804) 765-8006 Tel: (804) 765-8440 (Duty Officer)
Fax: (804) 765-4655 E-mail: usarmy.lee.tradoc.mbx.leee-nlc@mail.mil
Internet: www.alu.army.mil

● President **Michael K. Williams** . . . . (804) 765-8006
Secretary **Mykeshia Tucker** . . . . (804) 765-8006
Commandant and Military Deputy to the President
COL James L. Godfrey USA . . . . (804) 765-8005
Civilian Deputy to the President
David J. "Dave" Rohrer . . . . (804) 765-8005
Executive Officer **Jeryle Jones** . . . . (804) 765-8004
E-mail: jeryle.jones@us.army.mil

U.S. Army Logistics University *(continued)*

Library Director **Tim Renick** . . . . (804) 765-8171
Fax: (804) 765-4660
Command Sergeant Major **CSM Jerome Smalls USA** . . . (804) 765-8040

U.S. Army Ordnance School
Building 5020, Fort Lee, VA 23801
Tel: (804) 765-7365 Fax: (804) 765-7367
Internet: www.goordnance.lee.army.mil

Commandant and Chief of Ordnance
BG Heidi J. Hoyle USA . . . . (804) 765-7365
Education: West Point
Executive Officer **MAJ Ebony Thomas USA** . . . . (804) 765-7396
Deputy to the Commandant for Training
Dr. Richard Armstrong . . . . (804) 765-1435
Education: Indiana 1979 BA, 1981 MS
Command Sergeant Major **CSM Terry D. Burton USA** . . . (804) 765-7363
Chief Warrant Officer **CW5 Norman G. May USA** . . . . . . (804) 765-7392

U.S. Army Quartermaster School
Building 5020, 2221 A Avenue, Fort Lee, VA 23801
Internet: www.quartermaster.army.mil

Quartermaster General Commandant
BG Douglas M. McBride USA . . . . (804) 734-3458
Administrative Assistant **Pamela Gray** . . . . (804) 734-3458
Chief of Staff **COL Marc Thoreson USA** . . . . (804) 734-3759
Deputy to the Commandant **Marshall J. Jones** . . . . (804) 734-3480
Education: Virginia State 1979 BS; Ohio State 1981 MS
Regimental Command Sergeant Major
CSM Sean J. Rice USA . . . . (804) 734-3248
Regimental Chief Warrant Officer
CW5 Jonathan O. Yerby USA . . . . (804) 734-3702

U.S. Army Soldier Support Institute
10000 Hampton Parkway, Fort Jackson, SC 29207-7025

Commander **COL Stephen K. "Steve" Aiton USA** . . . . . (803) 751-8000
E-mail: stephen.k.aiton.mil@mail.mil
Deputy Commander **COL James Bibb ARNG** . . . . (803) 751-8001
Command Sergeant Major
CSM Jorge Escobedo USA . . . . (803) 751-8005
Chief of Staff **COL Troy Anthony Clay USA** . . . . (803) 751-8006
Education: Monmouth U 1984 BSBA; US Army Command; Army War Col MSS; South Carolina MAcc

U.S. Army Transportation School
Building 5020, Fort Lee, VA 23801
Tel: (757) 878-5215

Chief of Transportation and Commandant
COL Jered Helwig USA . . . . (804) 765-7444
Assistant Commandant **COL Stephen J. Riley USA** . . . . . (804) 765-1958
Education: Siena Col 1991 BS
Command Sergeant Major
MSG Sheri J. English-Moss USA . . . . (804) 765-7226

U.S. Army Fires Center of Excellence
Fort Sill, OK 73503
Tel: (580) 442-3006 Internet: http://sill-www.army.mil/

Commanding General **MG Wilson A. Shoffner USA** . . . . (580) 442-3006
Education: West Point 1988
Deputy to the Commanding General
Joseph E. "Joe" Gallagher . . . . (580) 442-3205
Chief of Staff **COL Paul S. Hossenlopp USA** . . . . (580) 442-3205
E-mail: paul.s.hossenlopp.mil@mail.mil
Command Sergeant Major **CSM John W. Foley USA** . . . . (580) 442-3205

U.S. Army Air Defense Artillery School (ADA - Fort Sill)
Fort Sill, OK 73503
Tel: (580) 442-5377
E-mail: usarmy.sill.fcoe.mbx.ada-commandant-chief-km@mail.mil
Internet: http://sill-www.army.mil/adaschool

Commandant **COL Brian W. Gibson USA** . . . . (580) 442-5377
Chief Warrant Officer **CW5 Eric D. Maule USA** . . . . (580) 558-0777
Education: Western Illinois BA; U Phoenix MBA

★ Presidential Appointment Requiring Senate Confirmation ☆ Presidential Appointment ☐ Schedule C Appointment ◇ Career Senior Foreign Service Appointment
● Career Senior Executive Service (SES) Appointment ○ Non-Career Senior Executive Service (SES) Appointment ■ Postal Career Executive Service

U.S. Army Air Defense Artillery School *(continued)*

Command Sergeant Major
CSM Finis A. Dodson USA . . . . (580) 442-5377

U.S. Army Field Artillery School (USAFAS)
Fort Sill, OK 73503
Tel: (580) 442-3006 Fax: (580) 355-6756
Internet: sill-www.army.mil/USAFAS

Commandant **BG Stephen G. Smith USA** . . . . . . (580) 442-6604
Aide **1LT Joe Williams USA** . . . . . . (580) 442-6604
Deputy Commandant **COL Samuel Saine USA** . . . . . . (580) 442-6604
Chief Warrant Officer **CW5 John Robinson USA** . . . . (580) 442-3006
Command Sergeant Major **CSM Berk Parsons USA** . . . . (580) 442-6604
Chief Public Affairs Officer **Darrell D. Ames** . . . . . (580) 442-4500
Public Information Officer **Sharon McBride** . . . . . (580) 442-2384
Contracting Director **Sharon K. McKinzie** . . . . . . (580) 442-6561
E-mail: sharon.k.mckinzie.civ@mail.mil

U.S. Army Intelligence Center of Excellence (USAICoE - Fort Huachuca)
1903 Hatfield Street, Fort Huachuca, AZ 85616-6000

Commanding General/Commandant
BG Robert P. Walters, Jr. USA . . . . . . (520) 533-1140
Education: Maryland BA; Golden Gate MA; Webster MA; Army War Col MS
Chief of Staff **COL Douglas "Doug" Woodall USA** . . . . (520) 533-1142
Public Affairs Officer **Angela L. Camara** . . . . . . (520) 533-1850
E-mail: angela.l.camara.civ@mail.mil Fax: (520) 533-1280

344th Military Intelligence Battalion (Goodfellow AFB)
340 Fort Lancaster Avenue, Goodfellow AFB, TX 76908
Tel: (325) 654-5295

Commander **LTC Yukio Kuniyuki USA** . . . . . . (325) 654-3601

U.S. Army Maneuver Center of Excellence
Fort Benning, GA 31905-5000
Tel: (706) 545-5111
Tel: (706) 545-2218 (Public Affairs Staff Duty Office)
Fax: (706) 545-3287 Internet: www.benning.army.mil

Commanding General **BG Gary M. Brito USA** . . . . . . (706) 545-5111
Education: Penn State BS; Troy U MS
Deputy Commanding General
BG Rafael A. Ribas USA . . . . . . (706) 545-5111
Deputy to the Commanding General
Donald M. Sando . . . . . . (706) 545-5111
E-mail: donald.m.sando.civ@mail.mil
Chief of Staff **COL Andrew Cole, Jr. USA** . . . . . . (706) 545-5111
Command Sergeant Major **CSM Scott A. Brzak USA** . . . . (706) 545-5111
Public Affairs Chief
LTC Benjamin L. "Ben" Garrett USA (Ret) . . . . . (706) 545-9229
E-mail: benjamin.l.garrett4.civ@mail.mil

U.S. Army Armor School (Fort Benning)
Fort Benning, GA 31905-5000
Tel: (706) 545-3815 Internet: www.benning.army.mil/armor

Commandant **BG David A. Lesperance USA** . . . . . . (706) 545-3815
E-mail: david.a.lesperance.mil@mail.mil
Deputy Commandant **COL David S. Davidson USA** . . . . . (706) 545-3815
Command Sergeant Major
CSM Kevin J. Muhlenbeck USA . . . . . . (706) 545-3815
Executive Officer **MAJ David J. Bauer USA** . . . . . . (706) 545-3815
Freedom of Information Act Officer
Maureen Barefield . . . . . . (706) 545-5356
E-mail: maureen.a.barefield2.civ@mail.mil Fax: (706) 545-2719
Contracting/Small Business Officer **(Vacant)** . . . . . . (502) 624-8046
Donovan Research Library Chief
Ericka L. Loze-Hudson . . . . . . (706) 545-8591
Building 70, 7533 Holtz Street, Suite 1025, Fort Benning, GA 31905
E-mail: ericka.l.loze-hudson.civ@mail.mil
E-mail: usarmy.benning.mcoe.mbx.donovan-ref-desk@mail.mil
Education: Humboldt State BA; USC MLIS

U.S. Army Armor School *(continued)*

Barr Memorial Library Director **Michael Steinmacher** . . . (502) 624-5351
400 Quartermaster Street, Fax: (502) 624-7528
Fort Knox, KY 40121-5000
E-mail: usarmy.knox.imcom-atlantic.mbx.dfmwr-barr-library@mail.mil
Education: Bellarmine BA, MALS; Kentucky MLIS

U.S. Army Infantry School (Fort Benning)
Fort Benning, GA 31905-5000
Tel: (706) 545-2236 Fax: (706) 545-1516
Internet: www.benning.army.mil/infantry

Commandant **BG David M. "Dave" Hodne USA** . . . . . . (706) 545-2236
Command Sergeant Major
CSM Martin S. Celestine USA . . . . . . (706) 545-2236
Education: Troy State BS Fax: (706) 545-1215
Freedom of Information Act Coordinator
Maureen Barefield . . . . . . (706) 545-2236
E-mail: maureen.barefield@us.army.mil

U.S. Army Maneuver Support Center of Excellence
Fort Leonard Wood, MO 65473
Tel: (573) 596-0131 Tel: (573) 563-4145 (Public Affairs)
Fax: (573) 563-4012 Internet: www.wood.army.mil

Commanding General **MG Donna W. Martin USA** . . . . . . (573) 563-6116
E-mail: donna.w.martin.mil@mail.mil
● Deputy to the Commanding General
Michael McCarthy . . . . . . (573) 563-5521
Deputy to the Commanding General - Army National Guard **BG Thomas Fisher USA** . . . . . . (573) 596-0131
Chief of Staff **COL Heath C. Roscoe USA** . . . . . . (573) 563-6118
Command Sergeant Major **CSM Jon Stanley USA** . . . . . . (573) 563-6149
Public Affairs Director **Tiffany D. Wood** . . . . . . (573) 563-4013
E-mail: tiffany.d.wood@us.army.mil

U.S. Army Chemical, Biological, Radiological, and Nuclear School (CBRN School)
ATSN-CZ, 401 MANSCEN Loop, Suite 1041,
Fort Leonard Wood, MO 65473-8926
Tel: (573) 563-8053

Commandant **COL Antonio "Andy" Munera USA** . . . . . . (573) 563-8053
Assistant Commandant
COL Thomas A. "Tom" Duncan II USA . . . . . . (573) 563-8053
Chief of Staff **LTC Glen Wright USA** . . . . . . (573) 563-8052
Chief Warrant Officer **CW2 Jesse S. Deberry USA** . . . . . (573) 563-8053
Regimental Command Sergeant Major
CSM Henney M. Hodgkins USA . . . . . . (573) 563-8053

U.S. Army Engineer School
464 Manscen Loop, Suite 1661, Fort Leonard Wood, MO 65473
Tel: (573) 563-6192

Commandant **BG Robert F. Whittle, Jr. USA** . . . . . . (573) 563-6192
Chief Warrant Officer **CW5 Jerome Bussey USA** . . . . . . (573) 563-4088
Command Sergeant Major **CSM Trevor Walker USA** . . . . (573) 563-8060
Public Affairs Officer **Tiffany D. Wood** . . . . . . (573) 563-4013
E-mail: tiffany.d.wood.civ@mail.mil
Freedom of Information Act Officer
Joyce Stevens . . . . . . (573) 596-0131 ext. 65246
Contracting Director **James E. Tucker** . . . . . . (573) 596-0244
Supervisory Librarian **Rick Switzer** . . . . . . (573) 563-8154
Fax: (573) 563-4118

U.S. Army Military Police School
Fort Leonard Wood, MO 65473
Tel: (573) 563-3203
E-mail: usarmy.leonardwood.mp-schl.mbx.cybersquire@mail.mil
Internet: www.wood.army.mil/usamps

Commandant **BG Brian Bisacre USA** . . . . . . (573) 563-3203
E-mail: brian.r.bisacre.mil@mail.mil
Assistant Commandant
COL Eugenia K. Guilmartin USA . . . . . . (573) 563-8019
Regimental Command Sergeant Major
CSM James Breckinridge USA . . . . . . (573) 563-8018

DEPARTMENTS

★ Presidential Appointment Requiring Senate Confirmation ☆ Presidential Appointment □ Schedule C Appointment ◇ Career Senior Foreign Service Appointment
● Career Senior Executive Service (SES) Appointment ○ Non-Career Senior Executive Service (SES) Appointment ■ Postal Career Executive Service

DEPARTMENTS

U.S. Army Cyber Center of Excellence (Cyber CoE)
Fort Gordon, GA 30905-5000
Tel: (706) 791-2114 Fax: (706) 791-4438
E-mail: usarmy.gordon.usag.mbx.gordon-webmaster-mailbox@mail.mil
Internet: https://cybercoe.army.mil/

Commanding General
MG John B. Morrison, Jr. USA .... (706) 791-4588
E-mail: john.b.morrison.mil@mail.mil
Education: James Madison 1986 BBA; Webster MS; Indust'l Col Armed Forces MS
Aide **CPT Norton Langley USA** .... (706) 791-4588
● Deputy to the Commander **Robert V. Kazimer** .... (706) 791-3185
Chief of Staff
COL Samuel G. "Sam" Anderson USA .... (706) 791-4588
Command Sergeant Major
CSM Carlos M. Simmons USA .... (706) 791-2114
Chief Information Officer **Lisa McClease** .... (706) 791-5381
Fax: (706) 791-6188

Command Chief Warrant Officer
CW5 Abel Chavez USA .... (706) 791-2114
Freedom of Information Act Officer **(Vacant)** .... (706) 791-2004
Fax: (706) 791-6915
Protocol Officer **(Vacant)** .... (706) 791-0022
Fax: (706) 791-2478
Public Affairs Officer **Kimberly Wintrich** .... (706) 791-6011
Fax: (706) 791-2061
Small Business Officer **Rufus Gates** .... (706) 791-1817
E-mail: rufus.gates.civ@mail.mil Fax: (706) 791-8651
Contracting Director **Steven R. Boshears** .... (706) 791-1800
E-mail: steven.boshears@us.army.mil Fax: (706) 791-8651
Public Safety Director **John Houpt** .... (706) 791-3227
E-mail: john.houpt@us.army.mil Fax: (706) 791-0083
Training Director **COL William Churchwell USA** .... (706) 791-6206
Fax: (706) 791-7809

Librarian, Eisenhower Army Medical Center
Janet Millar .... (706) 787-6765
Eisenhower Army Medical Center, Room 4A-09, Fort Gordon, GA 30905 Fax: (706) 787-2327
E-mail: janet.millar@us.army.mil
Librarian, Woodworth Library (Acting) **Yadira Payne** .... (706) 791-2449
Building 33500, Woolworth Library, Fort Gordon, GA 30905-5282 Fax: (706) 791-3282

★ Presidential Appointment Requiring Senate Confirmation ☆ Presidential Appointment ☐ Schedule C Appointment ◇ Career Senior Foreign Service Appointment
● Career Senior Executive Service (SES) Appointment ○ Non-Career Senior Executive Service (SES) Appointment ■ Postal Career Executive Service

United States Department of the Navy

DEPARTMENTS

Contents

United States Department of the Navy (USN)

The Pentagon, Washington, DC 20350
Tel: (703) 545-6700 (Department of Defense General Information)
Tel: (901) 874-3388 (Navy Personnel Locator)
Tel: (703) 784-3942 (Marine Corps Personnel Locator)
Tel: (202) 685-6545 (Freedom of Information/Privacy Act)
Tel: (703) 614-2000 (News Media Office)
Tel: (703) 697-9020 (Public Information)
Internet: www.navy.mil (Navy's Official Website)
Internet: www.usno.navy.mil (Naval Observatory Homepage)
Internet: www.navyjobs.com (Navy Recruiting Homepage)
Internet: www.nrl.navy.mil (Naval Research Lab Homepage)
Internet: www.usa.gov (Official US Government Website)

OFFICE OF THE SECRETARY OF THE NAVY (SECNAV)

The Pentagon, Washington, DC 20350
Fax: (703) 693-9545

Office of Information (Public Affairs) (CHINFO)

The Pentagon, Room 4B463, Washington, DC 20350
Fax: (703) 697-8921

Navy Office of Information East (NAVINFOEAST)

805 Third Avenue, 9th Floor, New York, NY 10022-7513
Tel: (212) 784-0130 Fax: (212) 784-0139
Areas Covered: CT, DE, ME, MD, MA, NH, NJ, NY, PA, RI, VT, VA

Director **LCDR Corey Barker USN** .... (212) 784-0131
E-mail: corey.barker@navy.mil

Navy Office of Information West (NAVINFOWEST)

10880 Wilshire Boulevard, Suite 1220, Los Angeles, CA 90024-4113
Tel: (310) 235-7481 Fax: (310) 235-7856
Internet: www.navy.mil/local/navinfowest
Areas Covered: AK, AZ, CA, HI, ID, MT, NV, OR, UT, WA

Director (Acting) **CAPT Russell L. Coons USN** .... (310) 235-7481
E-mail: russell.l.coons1@navy.mil
Deputy Director **LCDR Renee F. Soltes USN** .... (310) 235-7481
E-mail: renee.soltes@navy.mil

United States Naval Academy (USNA)

121 Blake Road, Annapolis, MD 21402-5000
Tel: (410) 293-1000 Fax: (410) 293-3133
E-mail: mediarelations@usna.edu Internet: www.usna.edu

★ Superintendent
VADM Walter E. "Ted" Carter, Jr. USN .... (410) 293-1500
Education: Naval Acad 1981
Executive Assistant **(Vacant)** .... (410) 293-1500
Special Assistant and Speechwriter **(Vacant)** .... (410) 293-1500
Chief of Staff and Deputy to the Superintendent
CAPT George Lang USN .... (410) 293-1500
Fax: (410) 293-2303
Deputy for Information Technology
Louis J. "Lou" Giannotti .... (410) 293-1400
E-mail: giannott@usna.edu
Command Master Chief **(Vacant)** .... (410) 293-1000

United States Naval Academy *(continued)*

Ombudsman **Kristin Grow** .... (410) 980-2508
E-mail: ombudsmanusna@gmail.com

Office of the Commandant of Midshipmen

121 Blake Road, Annapolis, MD 21402-5000
Commandant **CAPT Robert B. Chadwick II USN** .... (410) 293-7005
Education: Naval Acad 1991
Deputy Commandant **CAPT Thomas J. Grady USN** ..... (410) 293-7002
E-mail: thomas@usna.edu

Academic Dean and Provost's Office

121 Blake Road, Annapolis, MD 21402-5000
Academic Dean and Provost **Dr. Andrew T. Phillips** ..... (410) 293-1583
E-mail: aphillip@usna.edu
Education: Penn State 1984 BS; Minnesota 1986 MS, 1988 PhD
Executive Assistant to the Dean
Capt Ross Pospisil USMC .... (410) 293-1583
Vice Academic Dean **Dr. Daniel O'Sullivan** .... (410) 293-1585
Associate Dean for Academic Affairs
Dr. Jennifer K. Waters .... (410) 293-1581
Education: Webb Inst 1991; Stevens 1993, 1995 PhD
Associate Dean for Finance and Military Affairs
Peter Nardi .... (410) 293-1582
E-mail: nardi@usna.edu
Associate Dean for Information and Library Director
Lawrence E. "Larry" Clemens .... (410) 293-6903
E-mail: clemens@usna.edu
Education: Maryland 1982 MLS
Associate Dean for Planning and Assessment
Dr. Katherine A. Cermak .... (410) 293-1579
Education: Loyola U (Chicago) PhD
Registrar **Christopher A. "Chris" Davis** .... (410) 293-6381
E-mail: cdavis@usna.edu
Education: Old Dominion PhD
Director, Academic Center **Bruce Bukowski** .... (410) 293-2934
E-mail: bukowski@usna.edu
Education: Wisconsin 1963 PhD
Director, Academic Counseling
Pamela "Pam" Schmitt .... (410) 293-6888
Director, Center for Regional Studies **(Vacant)** .... (410) 293-6307
Director, International Programs
Timothy A. "Tim" Disher .... (410) 293-2981
Director, Multimedia Support Center **(Vacant)** .... (410) 293-4028
Director, Research and Scholarship
Reza Malek-Madani .... (410) 293-2504
Education: Brown U 1979 PhD
Director, Teaching and Learning **Dr. Karyn Z. Sproles** ... (410) 293-2506

Division of Character Development and Training

121 Blake Road, Annapolis, MD 21402-5000
Internet: https://www.usna.edu/CDT/
Director **CAPT James Campbell USN (Ret)** .... (410) 293-1904
E-mail: campbelc@usna.edu

Division of Engineering and Weapons

590 Holloway Road, Annapolis, MD 21402
Tel: (410) 293-6310 Fax: (410) 293-2591
Director **CAPT Joseph "Joe" Reason USN** .... (410) 293-6311

★ Presidential Appointment Requiring Senate Confirmation ☆ Presidential Appointment ☐ Schedule C Appointment ◇ Career Senior Foreign Service Appointment
● Career Senior Executive Service (SES) Appointment ○ Non-Career Senior Executive Service (SES) Appointment ■ Postal Career Executive Service

DEPARTMENTS

Division of Humanities and Social Sciences
Director **Col Jon Aytes USMC** . . . . (410) 293-6301
E-mail: aytes@usna.edu

Division of Leadership Education and Development
Director **CAPT Michael D. Michel USN** . . . . (410) 293-6010
E-mail: michel@usna.edu
Education: Naval Acad 1989

Division of Mathematics and Science
572M Holloway Road, Stop 9A, Annapolis, MD 21402-5026
Tel: (410) 293-6330 Fax: (410) 293-2134
Director **CAPT David Roberts USN** . . . . (410) 293-6332
Deputy Director **CDR John Bleidorn USN** . . . . (410) 293-6601

Division of Professional Development
Director **CAPT Brian O'Donald USN** . . . . (410) 293-6002

Dean of Admissions
121 Blake Road, Annapolis, MD 21402-5000
Dean of Admissions **Stephen "Bruce" Latta** . . . . (410) 293-1857
E-mail: latta@usna.edu
Education: Naval Acad 1978 BAE

Athletics
121 Blake Road, Annapolis, MD 21402-5000
Director **Chet Gladchuk** . . . . (410) 293-8910
Deputy Director **Eric Ruden** . . . . (410) 293-8748
Education: Indiana 1986

Staff Judge Advocate's Office
121 Blake Road, Annapolis, MD 21402-5000
Fax: (410) 293-0005
Staff Judge Advocate **CAPT Larry Hill USN** . . . . (410) 293-1564

Under Secretary of the Navy
1000 Navy Pentagon, Room 4E720, Washington, DC 20350-1000
Fax: (703) 697-4982

Assistant Secretary of the Navy (Research, Development and Acquisition) (ASN RDA)
1000 Navy Pentagon, Washington, DC 20350-1000
Fax: (703) 614-3192

Office of Naval Research (ONR)
One Liberty Center, 875 North Randolph Street,
Suite 1425, Arlington, VA 22203
Tel: (703) 696-5031 Fax: (703) 696-5940
Internet: https://www.onr.navy.mil/

U.S. Naval Research Laboratory (NRL)
4555 Overlook Avenue, SW, Code 5660,
Code 1000, Washington, DC 20375-5320
Tel: (202) 767-3200 (Personnel Locator)
Tel: (202) 767-2541 (Public Affairs) Internet: www.nrl.navy.mil

U.S. Naval Research Laboratory Stennis Space Center
Stennis Space Center, MS 39529-5004
Fax: (228) 688-4920 Internet: www.nrlssc.navy.mil
Marine Geosciences Division Superintendent
Dr. Herbert C. Eppert, Jr. . . . . (228) 688-4650
Education: Florida 1961, 1963; Tulane 1967 PhD
Oceanography Division Superintendent
Dr. Ruth H. Preller . . . . (228) 688-4670 ext. 7300
E-mail: nrl7300@nrlssc.navy.mil
Public Affairs Officer **Shannon Mensi** . . . . (228) 688-4002
E-mail: shannon.mensi@nrlssc.navy.mil

Chief of Naval Operations (CNO)
2000 Navy Pentagon, Washington, DC 20350-2000

OFFICE OF THE CHIEF
2000 Navy Pentagon, Washington, DC 20350-2000
Tel: (703) 695-5664 Fax: (703) 693-9408

The Operating Forces

Military Sealift Command (MSC)
471 East C Street, Norfolk, VA 23511-2419
Tel: (757) 443-2839 (Public Affairs) Internet: www.msc.navy.mil
Note: Military Sealift Command is currently consolidating its offices at Naval Station Norfolk, Virginia, with an estimated completion date of September 30, 2019.

Area Commands

Military Sealift Command Atlantic (MSCLANT)
1283 Tow Way Drive, Norfolk, VA 23511-3496
Tel: (757) 443-5604 Tel: (757) 443-5776 (Public Affairs)
Commander **CAPT Hans E. Lynch USN** . . . . (757) 443-5604

Military Sealift Command Central/Commander, Task Force 53 (MSCCENT)
Manama, Bahrain
Tel: 973 1785-9479
Commander **CAPT Timothy Gibboney USN** 973 1785-9479

Military Sealift Command Europe and Africa (MSCEURAF)
MSCEURAF, Naples, Italy
Tel: 39 (081) 358-3803 Tel: 39 (081) 568-4096 (Public Affairs)
Commander **CAPT Eric L. Conzen USN** 39 (081) 568-3803

Military Sealift Command Far East (MSCFE)
Sembawang Wharves, Deptford Road, Singapore, 759657, Singapore
Tel: 65 6750-2743
Commander **CAPT Robert R. Williams USN** 65 6750-2743

Military Sealift Command Pacific (MSCPAC)
140 Sylvester Road, San Diego, CA 92106-5200
Tel: (619) 524-9600 Tel: (619) 524-9609 (Public Affairs)
Commander **CAPT Brett C. Hershman USN** . . . . (619) 524-9600
Public Affairs Officer **Sarah E. Burford** . . . . (619) 524-9609
E-mail: sarah.burford@navy.mil

Navy Installations Command (CNIC)
716 Sicard Street SE, Suite 1000, Washington Navy Yard, DC 20388-5380
Tel: (202) 433-3200 Fax: (202) 685-0270
E-mail: cnic_hq_public_affairs@navy.mil Internet: www.cnic.navy.mil
Commander **VADM Mary M. Jackson USN** . . . . (202) 433-3200
Education: Naval Acad 1988 BS
Executive Assistant **LCDR John Liddle USN** . . . . (202) 433-3200
● Deputy Commander **Joseph D. "Joe" Ludovici** . . . . (202) 433-3200
E-mail: joseph.ludovici@navy.mil
Education: Central Florida BSCE; U Washington MS
Executive Assistant to the Deputy Commander
Linda Melendy . . . . (202) 433-3200
Reserve Deputy Commander
RDML Matthew "Matt" O'Keefe USNR . . . . (202) 433-3200
Force Master Chief **CMDCM Steven Timmons USN** . . . . (202) 433-3200
Chief of Staff **CAPT Stephen Barnett USN** . . . . (202) 433-3200
Education: Troy State BSME, MBA
● Counsel **Josie C. Dristy** . . . . (202) 433-3200
Public Affairs Officer **CDR John Gay USN** . . . . (202) 685-0867

★ Presidential Appointment Requiring Senate Confirmation ☆ Presidential Appointment ☐ Schedule C Appointment ◇ Career Senior Foreign Service Appointment
● Career Senior Executive Service (SES) Appointment ○ Non-Career Senior Executive Service (SES) Appointment ■ Postal Career Executive Service

Joint Region Marianas
PSC 455, Box 152, FPO, AP 96540-1000
Tel: (671) 339-3200 Tel: (671) 339-2115 (Public Affairs)
Fax: (671) 339-2426 Internet: www.cnic.navy.mil/marianas

Deputy Commander **BrigGen Douglas A. Cox USAF** .... (671) 349-3200
Chief of Staff **CAPT Hans E. Sholley USN** .... (671) 349-3200
Executive Director **Col Michael J. Paulovich USMC** .... (671) 349-3200
Education: Naval War MA; Webster MBA, MA
Command Master Chief **CMDCM Brian Ortega USN** .... (671) 349-3200

Naval Base Guam
PSC 445, Box 152, FPO, AP 96540-1000
Tel: (671) 339-2663 (Public Affairs) Internet: www.cnic.navy.mil/guam

Commanding Officer **CAPT Jeffrey M. Grimes USN** .... (671) 339-4274
Executive Officer **CDR Jason Wilkerson USN** .... (671) 339-4226
Command Master Chief
CMDCM Kenyatter D. Ballard USN .... (671) 339-6163

Naval Computer and Telecommunications Station Guam
PSC 488, Box 101, FPO, AP 96537-1800
Tel: (671) 355-5311 Fax: (671) 355-5017

Commanding Officer **CDR Christina M. Hicks USN** ..... (671) 355-5311
Education: North Alabama 2000 BS; Old Dominion MEM; Naval Postgrad
Executive Officer **LCDR John L. Tomar USN** .... (671) 355-5312
E-mail: jimmie.nelson@fe.navy.mil
Senior Enlisted Leader **ITCS Patricia R. Crump USN** .... (671) 355-8843

Naval District Washington (DC) (NDW)
1141 Parsons Avenue, Washington, DC 20374
Internet: www.ndw.navy.mil
Areas Covered: Shore activities, commands, and personnel in DC, MD (except for Pentagon) and six VA counties (Arlington, Fairfax, Fauquier, Loudoun, Prince William, Stafford)

Commandant **CAPT Carl A. Lahti USN** .... (202) 433-2777
Chief of Staff **CAPT Roy Undersander USN** .... (202) 433-3737
Command Master Chief
CMDCM Scott A. Nagle USN .... (202) 433-2617
Regional Executive Director **Thomas F. McGuire** .... (202) 433-2777

Naval Air Facility Washington (DC) (NAF Washington - Joint Base Andrews)
Building 3198, 1 San Diego Loop,
Joint Base Andrews-Naval Air Facility Washington, MD 20762
Tel: (240) 857-4880 Fax: (240) 857-3425
Internet: https://www.navy.mil/local/nafdc/

Commander **CAPT Scott "Spark" Fuller USN** .... (240) 857-3755
Executive Officer **CDR Kyle M. Horlacher USN** .... (240) 857-4880
Command Master Chief **CMDCM Tracy L. Hunt USN** ... (240) 857-4880

Naval Air Station Patuxent River
Building 409, 22268 Cedar Point Road,
Suite 204, Patuxent River, MD 20670
Fax: (301) 342-5206 Internet: www.cnic.navy.mil/Patuxent

Commanding Officer **CAPT Jason Hammond USN** ..... (301) 342-3000
Executive Officer
CAPT Christopher A. "Chris" Cox USN .... (301) 342-3000
Command Master Chief **CMDCM Kevin V. Guy USN** .... (301) 342-3000
Public Affairs Officer **Patrick Gordon** .... (301) 757-3343
E-mail: shawn.d.graham1@navy.mil

Naval Support Activity Bethesda (NSAB)
Building Eleven, 8901 Wisconsin Avenue, Bethesda, MD 20889
Tel: (301) 538-2843 (Base Duty Officer)
Tel: (301) 295-4000 (Base Operator)

Commanding Officer
CAPT Marvin L. Jones MSC, USN .... (301) 538-2843
Education: Rollins 1987 BS
Executive Director **Willis E. "Bill" Meekins** .... (301) 538-2843
Senior Enlisted Leader **(Vacant)** .... (301) 538-2843

Naval Support Activity Washington
Building 101, 1411 Parsons Avenue SE,
Suite 339, Washington, DC 20374
Tel: (202) 433-3963 Fax: (202) 433-3379

Commanding Officer
CAPT Jeffrey J. "Jeff" Draeger USN .... (202) 433-3495
Deputy Commanding Officer **Gilbert Elliott, Jr.** .... (202) 433-3963
Executive Officer
CDR Anthony "Tony" Militello USN .... (202) 433-3689

Navy Region Europe, Africa, Southwest Asia
Naples, Italy
Mail: PSC 817, Box 108, FPO, AE 09622-0108
Tel: 39 (081) 568-5907

Commander
RADM Rick L. "Ricky" Williamson USN 39 (081) 568-5907
Education: Naval Acad 1985 BS
Executive Director **Linda Ward** 39 (081) 568-5907
Chief of Staff **CAPT Lawrence R. Vasquez USN** 39 (081) 568-5907
Education: Baruch Col BSBA; JFK School Govt MPA
Command Master Chief
CMDCM Matthew P. Logsdon USN 39 (081) 568-5907

Naval Air Station Sigonella (NASSIG)
PSC 812, Box 1000, FPO, AE 09627
Tel: 39 (095) 86-5440 Internet: www.cnic.navy.mil/Sigonella

Commander **CAPT Brent Trickel USN** 39 (095) 86-5440
Executive Officer **CDR Patrick J. Moran USN** 39 (095) 86-5440
Education: Jacksonville U 1992 BA; Naval Postgrad MA
Command Master Chief
CMDCM Michael Kaszubowski USN 39 (095) 86-5440
Public Affairs Officer **LT Paul Newell USN** 39 (095) 86-6986
E-mail: paul.newell@eu.navy.mil

Naval Station Rota
PSC 819, Box 1, FPO, AE 09645-1000
Tel: 34 95682-1680 Fax: 34 95682-1021
E-mail: coastline@navsta.rota.navy.mil

Commander, U.S. Naval Activities Spain
CAPT Michael MacNicholl USN 34 956-82-2440
Executive Officer **CDR Neil Hoffman USN** 34 956-82-2440
Command Master Chief
MCPO Gary Rosenbaum USN 34 956-82-2440
Education: Thomas Edison State BS
Administration **LT Toshi Williams USN** 34 956-82-2325
Protocol Officer **Roberto Fuertes** 34 956-82-2795
E-mail: n024@navsta.rota.navy.mil Fax: 34 956-82-2220
Public Affairs Officer **Brian Dietrick** 34 956-82-1680

Naval Support Activity, Naples, Italy (NSA Naples)
Naples, Italy
Mail: U.S. Naval Support Activity Naples Italy, PSC 817, Box 40, FPO, AE 09622
Tel: 39 (081) 568-5110 Fax: 39 (081) 568-5112

Commander **CAPT Todd Abrahamson USN** 39 (081) 568-6289
Senior Enlisted Officer
CMDCM Timothy A. Preabt USN 39 (081) 568-6289

Naval Support Activity Souda Bay
USNAVSUPPACT, PSC 814, Box 1, FPO, AE 09865-0061
Tel: 30 28210-21699 (Administration)
Tel: 30 28210-21244 (Public Affairs) Fax: 30 28210-21229
E-mail: soudabaypao@eu.navy.mil

Commander **CAPT Ryan T. Tewell USN** 30 28210-21231
Education: Naval Acad
Executive Officer **LCDR Joshua F. Jones USN** 30 28210-21231
Command Master Chief **CMDCM Neal T. Olds USN** 30 28210-21361
Public Affairs Officer **Jacquelynn E. "Jacky" Fisher** ... 30 28210-21244
E-mail: jacky.fisher@eu.navy.mil
Education: Troy State MPA

★ Presidential Appointment Requiring Senate Confirmation ☆ Presidential Appointment □ Schedule C Appointment ◇ Career Senior Foreign Service Appointment
● Career Senior Executive Service (SES) Appointment ○ Non-Career Senior Executive Service (SES) Appointment ■ Postal Career Executive Service

Navy Region Hawaii

850 Ticonderoga Street, Suite 110, Pearl Harbor, HI 96860-5101
Fax: (808) 473-2876 Internet: www.cnic.navy.mil/hawaii

Commander **RDML Brian P. Fort USN** . . . . (808) 473-2200
Chief of Staff **CAPT James W. Jenks USN** . . . . (808) 474-6219
Command Master Chief
CMDMC(SW) Gregory A. Vidaurri USN . . . . (808) 473-2200
Executive Director **Theresa A. Phillips** . . . . (808) 473-2200
Webmaster **Anna-Marie General** . . . . (808) 473-2924
Public Affairs Officer **Agnes Tauyan** . . . . (808) 554-4813

Joint Base Pearl Harbor-Hickam

850 Ticonderoga Street, Suite 100, Pearl Harbor, HI 96860-5102
Tel: (808) 473-2888 Fax: (808) 473-2876
Internet: www.cnic.navy.mil/pearlharbor-hickam

Commander **CAPT Jeff Bernard USN** . . . . (808) 473-2201
Education: New Mexico; U Memphis MBA
Deputy Commander **Col Douglas E. Pierce USAF** . . . . . . (808) 473-2201
Education: Citadel 1995 BS; South Carolina 2002 MA
Chief Staff Officer **CDR Corey D. Hurd USN** . . . . (808) 473-2132
Command Master Chief
CMDCM Allen V. Keller USN . . . . (808) 473-2201
Senior Enlisted Advisor - Air Force
CMSgt Michael Andrews USAF . . . . (808) 473-2888
Director, Public Affairs
LtCol Charles J. Anthony ANG . . . . (808) 473-2926

Navy Munitions Command East Asia Division

562 G Avenue, Ewa Beach, HI 96706-3381
Tel: (808) 471-1111 Fax: (808) 471-0985

Commanding Officer
CAPT Michael J. Singleton USN . . . . (808) 471-1111 ext. 100
E-mail: michael.j.singleton1@navy.mil
Executive Director **Kathleen Russell** . . . . (808) 471-1111 ext. 103
Executive Officer
CDR Kenneth Teasley USN . . . . (808) 471-1111 ext. 102
Privacy Officer **(Vacant)** . . . . (808) 471-1111 ext. 106
Contracting/Operations **Ryan Lotts** . . . . (808) 471-1111 ext. 103
Training Officer **(Vacant)** . . . . (808) 471-1111

Pacific Missile Range Facility Barking Sands (PMRF)

Kekaha, HI 96752
Mail: P.O. Box 128, Kekaha, HI 96752-0128
Tel: (808) 335-4255 Fax: (808) 335-4660

Commanding Officer
CAPT Vincent "Vinc" Johnson USN . . . . (808) 335-4251
Education: Naval Acad 1993 BS; Naval War 1996 MA
Executive Officer **CDR Daniel W. Kimberly USN** . . . . . . (808) 335-4252
Education: IU-Purdue U (Ft Wayne) 1997 BA
Command Master Chief **MCPO James C. Bibb USN** . . . . (808) 335-4234
Public Affairs Officer **(Vacant)** . . . . (808) 335-4740

Navy Region Mid-Atlantic (CNRMA)

1510 Gilbert Street, Norfolk, VA 23511-2737
Fax: (757) 444-2133 Internet: www.cnic.navy.mil/cnrma

Commander **RDML Charles W. "Chip" Rock USN** . . . . . (757) 322-2800
Education: Texas A&M BS; National War Col MNSSS
● Deputy Commander (Acting)
CAPT Gregory J. "Greg" Cornish USN (Ret) . . . . (757) 444-1380
Chief of Staff **CAPT Michael R. Moore USN** . . . . (757) 322-2800
Education: Naval Acad 1990
Command Master Chief **CMDCM Justin Gray USN** . . . . . (757) 322-2822

Navy Munitions Command - CONUS East Division

P.O. Drawer 410, Yorktown, VA 23691-0410
Tel: (757) 887-4888 Fax: (757) 887-4926 Fax: (757) 887-4550

Commanding Officer **James Jacobs** . . . . (757) 887-4888
Executive Director **Glenn E. Norton** . . . . (757) 887-4119
E-mail: glenn.norton@navy.mil
Executive Officer **CDR Kevin Downey USN** . . . . (757) 887-4889
Support Services Specialist **Elizabeth "Liz" Colson** . . . . . (757) 887-7632
E-mail: elizabeth.colson@navy.mil

Navy Munitions Command - CONUS East Division *(continued)*

Security Manager **(Vacant)** . . . . (757) 887-7349
Naval Weapons Station Yorktown, Fax: (757) 887-7715
P.O. Box 160 (Code 10),
Yorktown, VA 23691-0160

Naval Air Station Oceana

Naval Air Station Oceana, 1750 Tomcat Boulevard,
Virginia Beach, VA 23460-2191
Tel: (757) 433-2366

Commanding Officer **CAPT Chad P. Vincelette USN** . . . . (757) 433-2922
Executive Officer **CAPT John W. Hewitt USN** . . . . (757) 433-2923
Command Master Chief **CMDCM Lee Salas USN** . . . . (757) 433-2366
Public Affairs Officer **Jennifer Colazzi** . . . . (757) 433-3131
Fax: (757) 433-2629

Joint Expeditionary Base Little Creek-Fort Story (JEB Little Creek-Fort Story)

2600 Tarawa Court, Suite 100, Virginia Beach, VA 23459-3297
Tel: (757) 462-2640 (Public Affairs) Fax: (757) 462-8160 (Public Affairs)

Commander **CAPT Daniel J. Senesky USN** . . . . (757) 462-7231
Education: Penn State 1991 BA Fax: (757) 462-8422
Deputy Commander **LTC John W. Penree USA** . . . . (757) 462-7231
Executive Officer **CAPT Quinn Skinner USN** . . . . (757) 462-7211
Command Master Chief
CMDCM Brian T. Schlicht USN . . . . (757) 462-8426
Fax: (757) 462-8422
Freedom of Information Act Officer
CDR Andrew "Andy" House USN . . . . (757) 322-2934
E-mail: andrew.house@navy.mil
Education: North Carolina
Head Librarian **Brandy Jeschonek** . . . . (757) 422-7548 ext. 7525
Building Fax: (757) 422-7773
T-530,
Joint Expeditionary Base Little Creek-Fort Story, VA 23459-5067

Naval Station Great Lakes (NS Great Lakes)

Building 1, 2601E Paul Jones Street, Great Lakes, IL 60088
Tel: (847) 688-2961 Fax: (847) 688-4945
Internet: www.cnic.navy.mil/GreatLakes

Commander **CAPT Raymond C. Leung USN** . . . . (847) 688-2960
Executive Officer **CDR Omar G. Martinez USN** . . . . (847) 688-2960
Command Master Chief
CMDCM Ryan J. Lamkin USN . . . . (847) 688-2960

Naval Station Newport (RI)

Building 690, 690 Peary Street, Newport, RI 02841-1522
Tel: (401) 841-3456 Fax: (401) 841-2265

Commander **CAPT Ian Johnson USN** . . . . (401) 841-3715
Executive Officer **CDR Al L. Lima USN** . . . . (401) 841-3456
Command Master Chief **CMDCM Paul A. King USN** . . . . (401) 841-3456
Public Affairs Officer **Lisa Rama** . . . . (401) 841-3538
E-mail: lisa.rama@navy.mil

Naval Station Norfolk (VA)

1530 Gilbert Street, Suite 2000, Norfolk, VA 23511-2722
Tel: (757) 322-2366 Tel: (757) 444-0000 (Base Information Operator)
Fax: (757) 445-0947 Internet: https://cnic.navy.mil/norfolksta

Commanding Officer
CAPT Bradley N. "Brad" Rosen USN . . . . (757) 322-2302
Education: Naval Acad 1995 BS; JFK School Govt 2005 MPA
Executive Officer **(Vacant)** . . . . (757) 322-2302
Command Master Chief **CMDCM Marc Puco USN** . . . . . . (757) 444-4377

Naval Support Activity Hampton Roads (VA)

Building 140, 7918 Blandy Road, Suite 100, Norfolk, VA 23551-2419
Tel: (757) 836-1484 Fax: (757) 836-1897
Internet: www.cnic.navy.mil/norfolk

Commanding Officer **CAPT Jack Freeman USN** . . . . (757) 836-1488
Education: Radford 1990
Executive Officer **CDR John Graf USN** . . . . (757) 836-1962
Public Affairs Officer **Katisha R. Draughn-Fraguada** . . . . (757) 836-1484
E-mail: katisha.draughn-frag@navy.mil Fax: (757) 836-1897

★ Presidential Appointment Requiring Senate Confirmation ☆ Presidential Appointment □ Schedule C Appointment ◇ Career Senior Foreign Service Appointment
● Career Senior Executive Service (SES) Appointment ○ Non-Career Senior Executive Service (SES) Appointment ■ Postal Career Executive Service

Naval Submarine Base New London (CT)
Groton, CT 06349-5000
Tel: (860) 694-3011 (Base Locator) Tel: (860) 694-5980 (Public Affairs)
Fax: (860) 694-4699 Internet: www.cnic.navy.mil/NewLondon

Commanding Officer **CAPT Paul Whitescarver USN** .... (860) 694-3400
Fax: (860) 694-2653
Executive Officer **CDR Cory Dyer USN** .... (860) 694-3401
Command Master Chief
CMDCM Ronald L. Clark USN .... (860) 694-3860

Naval Weapons Station Earle (NJ)
201 Highway 34, Colts Neck, NJ 07722
Tel: (732) 866-2000 Fax: (732) 866-2175
Internet: www.cnic.navy.mil/earle

Commanding Officer **CAPT Pierre Fuller USN** .... (732) 866-2880
Executive Officer **LCDR Eric P. Rion USN** .... (732) 866-2879
Command Senior Chief
CMDCM Ronald Herman USN .... (732) 866-2032
Public Affairs Officer **Bill Addison** .... (732) 866-2171

Naval Weapons Station Yorktown (VA)
160 Main Road, Yorktown, VA 23691-0160
Tel: (757) 887-4000 Fax: (757) 887-7505
Internet: www.cnic.navy.mil/yorktown/index.htm

Commanding Officer **CAPT Matthew Kosnar USN** ..... (757) 887-4981
Executive Officer **LCDR Christian B. Dillard USN** ...... (757) 887-4242
Executive Officer **CDR Cassius A. Farrell USN** .... (757) 887-4000
Command Master Chief
CMDCM Michael A. Jones USN .... (757) 887-7120
Freedom of Information Act Officer **Albert Kirby** .... (757) 887-4444

Personnel Support Activity Detachment Naval Station Norfolk (VA)
1755 Powhatan Street, Suite 113, Norfolk, VA 23511-2984
Tel: (757) 445-4981 Fax: (757) 445-4392
Areas Covered: CT, DC, DE, FL, GA, IL, LA, MD, ME, MS, NC, NH, NJ, NY, PA, RI, SC, TN, TX, VA, WV, Cuba

Director **J.T. Kelley** .... (757) 445-4981
Assistant Director **Rocky Beasley** .... (757) 445-4981

Navy Region Northwest
1100 Hunley Road, Silverdale, WA 98315-1103
Tel: (360) 315-5000 Fax: (360) 315-5017
Internet: https://www.cnic.navy.mil/regions/cnrnw.html
Areas Covered: AK, ID, MT, OR, WA, WY

Commander
RADM Christopher S. "Scott" Gray USN .... (360) 315-5000
Chief of Staff **CAPT Thomas Zwolfer USN** .... (360) 315-5000
Command Master Chief
CMDMC Ted Calcaterra USN .... (360) 315-5002

Naval Air Station Whidbey Island (WA)
3730 North Charles Porter Avenue, Oak Harbor, WA 98278-5000
Tel: (360) 257-2631 Tel: (360) 257-2286 (Public Affairs)
Tel: (360) 279-1080 (Base Information) Fax: (360) 257-3972
Internet: www.cnic.navy.mil/Whidbey

Commanding Officer
CAPT Matthew L. "Matt" Arny USN .... (360) 257-2037
Executive Officer **CDR James F. Rankin USN** .... (360) 257-2011
Education: Naval Acad 1997; American Military U 2012 MNSSS
Command Master Chief
CMDCM Shane Cardon USN .... (360) 257-2037
Public Affairs Officer **Michael T. Welding** .... (360) 257-2962
E-mail: michael.welding@navy.mil

Naval Base Kitsap
120 South Dewey Street, Bremerton, WA 98314-5020
Tel: (360) 627-4024

Commanding Officer **CAPT Edward Schrader USN** ..... (360) 627-4000
Education: Naval Acad 1992 BS
Executive Officer **CDR Brian Rednour USN** .... (360) 627-4000
Command Master Chief **CMDCM James Willis USN** .... (360) 627-4000
Public Affairs Officer **Silvia L. Klatman** .... (360) 627-4030
E-mail: silvia.klatman@navy.mil Fax: (360) 627-4045

Naval Magazine Indian Island
100 Indian Island Road, Port Hadlock, WA 98339-9723
Tel: (360) 396-5227

Commanding Officer **CDR Rocky B. Pulley USN** .... (360) 396-5227

Naval Station Everett (WA)
2000 West Marine View Drive, Everett, WA 98207-5001
Tel: (425) 304-3000 (Public Information)
Internet: www.cnic.navy.mil/everett

Commanding Officer **CAPT Mark A. Lakamp USN** ..... (425) 304-3325
Executive Officer **CDR Rodman Burley USN** .... (425) 304-3325
Command Master Chief
CMDCM Brian Wojcicki USN .... (425) 304-3124
Public Affairs Officer **Kristin M. Ching** .... (425) 304-3202
E-mail: kristin.ching@navy.mil Fax: (425) 304-3096

Navy Region Southeast
Building 919, Naval Air Station, Suite 102, Jacksonville, FL 32212-0102
Mail: P.O. Box 102, Public Affairs, Naval Air Station, Jacksonville, FL 32212-0102
Tel: (904) 542-4032 Fax: (904) 542-2413
Internet: https://www.cnic.navy.mil/cnrse
Areas Covered: AL, FL, GA, KY, MS, NC, SC, TN, TX

Commander **RDML Babette "Bette" Bolivar USN** ...... (904) 542-4032
Education: Naval Acad 1985 BS; Troy State MM
● Executive Director **Bruce B. Cwalina** .... (904) 542-2326
Education: Maryland 1974 BA; George Washington 1982 BSA; Naval War 1995; George Washington 2003 MA
Chief of Staff **CAPT Sean P. Haley USN** .... (904) 542-4032
Education: Naval Acad 1992 BS
Command Master Chief
CMDCM David C. Twiford USN .... (904) 542-2403
Public Affairs Officer **Bill Dougherty** .... (904) 542-4032
E-mail: bill.dougherty@navy.mil

Naval Support Activity Mid-South
5722 Integrity Drive, Millington, TN 38054-5045
Tel: (901) 874-5111 Fax: (901) 874-7366 Fax: (901) 874-5649

Commanding Officer **CAPT Michael Wathen USN** ...... (901) 874-5102
Education: Oklahoma 1992 BS
Executive Officer **CDR Michael Mosi USN** .... (901) 874-5111
Education: Florida; Webster 2010 MBA
Command Master Chief
CMDCM Marilyn Kennard USN .... (901) 874-5111
Education: Park U BS; Arkansas MS
Contracting/Small Business Officer **(Vacant)** .... (901) 874-5271
Freedom of Information Act Officer **(Vacant)** .... (901) 874-5887
Public Affairs Officer **Amanda Moreno** .... (901) 874-5446
E-mail: amanda.moreno@navy.mil
Information Technology Director **Noah "Jake" Doss** .... (901) 874-7015
E-mail: noah.doss@navy.mil

Naval Air Station, Corpus Christi (TX)
11001 D Street, Suite 101, Corpus Christi, TX 78419-5021
Tel: (361) 961-2332 Fax: (361) 961-3402
Internet: www.cnic.navy.mil/corpuschristi

Commanding Officer **CAPT Philip M. Brock USN** ...... (361) 961-2332
Executive Officer **CDR David A. Cisneros USN** .... (361) 961-2331
Command Master Chief
CMDCM Gregory Williams USN .... (361) 961-2332
Public Affairs Officer **Fifi Kieschnick** .... (361) 961-2674
E-mail: fifi.kieschnick@navy.mil

Naval Air Station Jacksonville (FL)
6801 Roosevelt Boulevard, Jacksonville, FL 32212
Tel: (904) 542-2345 Fax: (904) 542-2413
Internet: www.cnic.navy.mil/Jacksonville

Commanding Officer **CAPT Michael Conner USN** ...... (904) 542-2334
Executive Officer **CAPT Brian Weiss USN** .... (904) 542-2336
Command Master Chief
CMDCM Jeffery Waters USN .... (904) 542-2934
Security Officer **Glenn D. Williams** .... (904) 542-0969
E-mail: glenn.williams@navy.mil Fax: (904) 542-2371

(continued on next page)

★ Presidential Appointment Requiring Senate Confirmation ☆ Presidential Appointment □ Schedule C Appointment ◇ Career Senior Foreign Service Appointment
● Career Senior Executive Service (SES) Appointment ○ Non-Career Senior Executive Service (SES) Appointment ■ Postal Career Executive Service

Naval Air Station Jacksonville (FL) *(continued)*

Public Affairs Officer **Kaylee Larocque** . . . . (904) 542-5588
E-mail: kaylee.larocque@navy.mil
Freedom of Information Act Officer
Mary Frances Chergi . . . . (904) 542-2941
E-mail: mary.chergi@navy.mil

Naval Air Station Joint Reserve Base Fort Worth (TX) (NAS JRB Fort Worth)
NAS JRB Fort Worth, Fort Worth, TX 76127
Tel: (817) 782-5000 Fax: (817) 782-7601
Internet: https://www.cnic.navy.mil/fortworth/index.htm

Commanding Officer
CAPT Jonathan R. Townsend USN . . . . (817) 782-7600
Communications Manager **Ronald Marchand** . . . . (817) 782-7400
E-mail: ronald.marchand1@navy.mil Fax: (817) 782-5776

Naval Air Station Joint Reserve Base New Orleans (LA) (NAS JRB New Orleans)
400 Russell Avenue, New Orleans, LA 70143-5012
Tel: (504) 678-3201 Fax: (504) 678-3244

Commanding Officer **CAPT Mark Sucato USNR** . . . . (504) 678-3201
Executive Officer **CDR Carina Maloney USN** . . . . (504) 678-3201
Command Master Chief **CMDCM Chad Helms USN** . . . . (504) 678-3201
Public Affairs Officer **Andrew F. Thomas** . . . . (504) 678-3201
E-mail: andrew.thomas2@navy.mil

Naval Air Station Key West (FL)
P.O. Box 9001, Key West, FL 33040-9001
Tel: (305) 293-2425 Fax: (305) 293-2627
Internet: www.cnic.navy.mil/keywest

Commanding Officer **CAPT Bobby Baker USN** . . . . (305) 293-2866
Executive Officer **CDR Gregory Brotherton USN** . . . . (305) 293-2866
Command Master Chief
CMDCM Craig Forehand USN . . . . (305) 293-2744
Public Affairs Officer **Andrea P. "Trice" Denny** . . . . (305) 293-2027
E-mail: andrea.denny@navy.mil

Naval Air Station, Kingsville (TX) (NAS Kingsville)
554 McCain Street, Kingsville, TX 78363-5054
Tel: (361) 516-6375 Tel: (361) 516-6481 Fax: (361) 516-6875
Internet: www.cnic.navy.mil/Kingsville

Commanding Officer **CAPT Erik A. Spitzer USN** . . . . (361) 516-6481
Executive Officer **CDR Kelly J. Richards USN** . . . . (361) 516-6482
Command Master Chief **CMDCM Tomas Garcia USN** . . . (361) 516-6495
Training Air Wing Two Commander
CAPT Richard A. Rivera USN . . . . (361) 516-1090

Naval Air Station Meridian (MS)
255 Rosenbaum Avenue, Suite 163, Meridian, MS 39309-5003
Tel: (601) 679-2602 Fax: (601) 679-3670
Internet: www.cnic.navy.mil/Meridian

Commanding Officer **CAPT Brian Horstman USN** . . . . . . (601) 679-2181
Executive Officer **CDR Matthew McGuire USN** . . . . (601) 679-2181
Public Affairs Officer **Penny Randall** . . . . (601) 679-2602

Naval Air Station Pensacola (FL) (NAS Pensacola)
Building 191, 190 Radford Boulevard, Pensacola, FL 32508-5217
Tel: (850) 452-4785 Fax: (850) 452-5977
Internet: www.cnic.navy.mil/Pensacola

Commanding Officer
CAPT Christopher T. Martin USN . . . . (850) 452-2713
Executive Officer **CDR Shawn Dominguez USN** . . . . (850) 452-2713
Public Affairs Officer **Patrick J. Nichols** . . . . (850) 452-4436
E-mail: patrick.j.nichols@navy.mil
E-mail: nasp_pao_webpage@navy.mil

Naval Air Station Whiting Field (FL)
7550 USS Essex Street, Room 206, Milton, FL 32570-6155
Tel: (850) 623-7341

Commanding Officer **CAPT Paul D. Bowdich USN** . . . . . (850) 623-7121
Education: US Merchant Marine Acad 1994

Naval Air Station Whiting Field (FL) *(continued)*

Executive Officer **CDR Donald L. Gaines USN** . . . . (850) 623-7121
E-mail: donald.l.gaines@navy.mil
Command Master Chief **Herbert "Lee" Stephens** . . . . . . (850) 623-7144
E-mail: herbert.stephens@navy.mil
Training Air Wing 5 Commodore
CAPT David Morris USN . . . . (850) 623-7555
Public Affairs Officer **Julie Ziegenhorn** . . . . (850) 623-7341
Information Systems Officer **JJ Adkison** . . . . (850) 623-7726

Naval Construction Battalion Center Gulfport (MS) (NCBC Gulfport)
4902 Marvin Shields Boulevard, Gulfport, MS 39501
Tel: (228) 871-2555 Fax: (228) 871-2389
Internet: www.cnic.navy.mil/gulfport E-mail: ncbc_gpt_pao@navy.mil

Commanding Officer
CAPT William L. Whitmire USN . . . . (228) 871-2699
Executive Officer **CDR Ronald Jenkins USN** . . . . (228) 871-3320
Command Master Chief
CMDCM David J. Garcia USN . . . . (228) 871-3320

Naval Station Guantanamo Bay
CO, PSC 1005, Box 25, FPO, AE 09593-0025
Tel: 53 99-4520 Fax: 53 99-4500

Commander **CAPT John "Fish" Fischer USN** 53 99-4400
Executive Officer **CDR David Walker USN** 53 99-4520
Command Master Chief **CMDCM Thomas Mace USN** 53 99-4520
Public Affairs Officer **Kelly Wirfel** 53 99-4520
E-mail: pao@gtmo.navy.mil

Naval Station Mayport (FL)
Mayport, FL 32228
Tel: (904) 270-5226 Fax: (904) 270-5683

Commanding Officer **CAPT David J. Yoder USN** . . . . (904) 270-5201
Executive Officer **CDR Patricia A. Tyler USN** . . . . (904) 270-5201
Command Master Chief **CMDCM Bill Houlihan USN** . . . . (904) 270-5201

Naval Submarine Base Kings Bay (GA)
Kings Bay, GA 31547-5000
Tel: (912) 573-4714 Fax: (912) 573-4717
Internet: www.cnic.navy.mil/kingsbay

Base Commander **CAPT Brian Lepine USN** . . . . (912) 573-4700
Executive Officer **CDR Eric J. Stein USN** . . . . (912) 573-4700
Command Master Chief
CMDCM Mitchell Burgin USN . . . . (912) 573-4700
Public Affairs Officer **Scott A. Bassett** . . . . (912) 573-4714
1063 USS Tennessee Avenue, Kings Bay, GA 31547
E-mail: scott.bassett@navy.mil

Naval Support Activity Panama City
101 Vernon Avenue, Panama City, FL 32407
Tel: (850) 230-7320

Commanding Officer **Jay Sego USN** . . . . (850) 230-7320
Executive Officer **LCDR Adam Walski USN** . . . . (850) 230-7320
Command Master Chief **MCPO Taryn Wilson USN** . . . . . (850) 230-7320

Navy Region Southwest
937 North Harbor Drive, San Diego, CA 92132-0058
Tel: (619) 532-1011
Areas Covered: AZ, CA, NV

Commander **RDML Yancy B. Lindsey USN** . . . . (619) 532-1011
Education: UC Berkeley 1986 BSME
Chief of Staff **CAPT Curtis Jones USN** . . . . (619) 532-1011
Command Master Chief
CMDCM Chad Lunsford USN . . . . (619) 532-1011
Executive Director **CAPT Joe Stuyvesant USN (Ret)** . . . (619) 532-1011

Naval Air Facility El Centro (CA) (NAF El Centro)
1605 Third Street, El Centro, CA 92243-5001
Tel: (760) 339-2401 Fax: (760) 339-2403
Internet: https://www.cnic.navy.mil/elcentro

Commanding Officer **CAPT Brent Alfonzo USN** . . . . (760) 339-2401
Secretary **Adela Coronado** . . . . (760) 339-2401

★ Presidential Appointment Requiring Senate Confirmation ☆ Presidential Appointment ☐ Schedule C Appointment ◇ Career Senior Foreign Service Appointment
● Career Senior Executive Service (SES) Appointment ○ Non-Career Senior Executive Service (SES) Appointment ■ Postal Career Executive Service

Naval Air Facility El Centro (CA) *(continued)*

Executive Officer **CDR Adam Schlismann USN** .... (760) 339-2402
Command Master Chief
CMDCM Jeremy Embree USN .... (760) 339-2437
Public Works Officer **LCDR Nathanael Overtree USN** ... (760) 339-2201
Security Officer **LT John Page USN** .... (760) 339-2663
Fax: (760) 339-2587
Public Affairs Officer **Kristopher Haugh** .... (760) 339-2519
E-mail: kristopher.haugh@navy.mil Fax: (760) 339-2699

Naval Air Station Fallon (NV)
4755 Pasture Road, Fallon, NV 89496
Tel: (775) 426-3000 Fax: (775) 426-2930
Internet: www.cnic.navy.mil/fallon

Commanding Officer **CAPT David Halloran USN** .... (775) 426-3000
Education: Arizona 1992
Executive Officer **CDR James P. Shell USN** .... (775) 426-3000
Command Master Chief **CMDCM Robert Boyd USN** .... (775) 426-3000
Public Affairs Officer **J. N. "Zip" Upham** .... (775) 426-2280
E-mail: zip.upham@navy.mil
Freedom of Information Act Officer
LT Victor Marquez USN .... (775) 426-3000

Naval Air Station Lemoore (CA) (NAS Lemoore)
730 Enterprise, Room 015, Lemoore, CA 93246-5001
Tel: (559) 998-3393

Commanding Officer **CAPT David James USN** .... (559) 998-3344
Executive Officer **CAPT John Brattain USN** .... (559) 998-3344
Command Master Chief **CMDCM James Cahill USN** .... (559) 998-3344

Naval Air Weapons Station, China Lake (CA) (NAWS China Lake)
China Lake, CA 93555-6100
Tel: (760) 939-1683 Fax: (760) 939-2796

Commanding Officer **CAPT Paul M. Dale USN** .... (760) 939-1683
Executive Officer **CDR Matthew Conliffe USN** .... (760) 939-1683
Command Master Chief
CMDCS Jose M. Ramos USN .... (760) 939-1683

Naval Base Coronado - Naval Air Station North Island (CA)
P.O. Box 357-033, Building 678, San Diego, CA 92135
Tel: (619) 545-8123 Fax: (619) 545-0182
Internet: www.cnic.navy.mil/coronado

Commanding Officer
CAPT Timothy J. "Tim" Slentz USN .... (619) 545-8163
Education: Notre Dame 1993; Troy U 1994 MSM; Naval War 2007 MA
Executive Officer **(Vacant)** .... (619) 545-8126
Command Master Chief
CMDCM Harlan B. Patawaran USN .... (619) 545-8126
Education: Southern Illinois BS
Public Affairs Officer **Sandy Duchac** .... (619) 545-8136
E-mail: nbcpao@navy.mil
Education: Arizona 1999 BFA

Naval Base San Diego (CA)
Building 72, 3455 Senn Road, San Diego, CA 92136-5084
Tel: (619) 556-2400 Fax: (619) 556-3338
Internet: https://www.cnic.navy.mil/SanDiego

Commanding Officer **CAPT Roy Love USN** .... (619) 556-2400
Executive Officer **CDR Jesse Lankford USN** .... (619) 556-2400
Command Master Chief **CMDCM Matt Ruane USN** ..... (619) 556-2415
Public Affairs Officer
PO1 Krishna M. "Krash" Jackson USN (Ret) .... (619) 556-7359
E-mail: tina.stallions@navy.mil Fax: (619) 556-1837

Naval Base Ventura County (NBVC)
NBVC, 311 Main Road, Suite 1, Port Hueneme, CA 93042
Tel: (805) 989-7209 (Quarterdeck)
Tel: (805) 989-1110 (Naval Base Ventura County - Point Mugu Base)
Tel: (805) 982-4711 (Naval Base Ventura County - Port Hueneme Base)
Fax: (805) 989-1728

Commanding Officer **CAPT Chris D. Janke USN** .... (805) 989-7904

Naval Base Ventura County *(continued)*

Chief Staff Officer
CAPT Douglas W. "Doug" King USN .... (805) 989-7905
Command Master Chief
CMDCM Martin T. Laurie USN .... (805) 989-8484
E-mail: nbvc_cmc@navy.mil
Public Affairs Officer **Theresa Miller** .... (805) 989-9234
Chief Information Technology Officer **Nancy Perez** ...... (805) 989-0823
E-mail: nancy.perez1@navy.mil
Webmaster **Theresa Miller** .... (805) 989-9234

Naval Weapons Station Seal Beach (CA)
800 Seal Beach Boulevard, Seal Beach, CA 90740-5000
Tel: (562) 626-7011 Fax: (562) 626-7900
Internet: www.cnic.navy.mil/sealbeach

Commanding Officer **CAPT Noel J. Dahlke USN** .... (562) 626-7901
Executive Officer **CDR John M. Quillinan USN** .... (562) 626-7901
Command Senior Chief **SCPO Kirby C. Lee USN** .... (562) 626-7011
Public Affairs Officer **Gregg T. Smith** .... (562) 626-7215
E-mail: gregg.smith@navy.mil
Freedom of Information Act Officer **Drew Martinez** ..... (562) 626-7392

Navy Reserve Forces Command (CNRFC)
1915 Forrestal Drive, Norfolk, VA 23551-4615
Tel: (757) 445-8500 Fax: (757) 444-7545

Commander **RADM Thomas W. Luscher USN** .... (757) 322-5600
E-mail: thomas.luscher@navy.mil
Education: Naval Acad 1986 BS; Army War Col MSS
Aide **LT Jon Bradner USN** .... (757) 322-5606
Education: Hobart & William Smith BA; Rhode Island MBA
Executive Director **Randy B. Johnson** .... (757) 322-5610
E-mail: randy.b.johnson@navy.mil
Command Master Chief
CMDCM Carrie J. Wentzel USN .... (757) 322-5657
Force Master Chief **CMDCM Christopher Kotz USN** .... (703) 695-3975
Commander, Naval Air Force Reserve
RADM William Michael "Sky" Crane USN .... (619) 767-7379
Education: Virginia Tech 1984 BSCE; Naval War MNSSS
Command Services (Administrative Department)
Director **LCDR Glenn Buni USN** .... (757) 322-5651
E-mail: glenn.buni@navy.mil
Family Support Programs Director **James D. Warren** .... (757) 322-6568
E-mail: james.d.warren@navy.mil
Force Chaplain **CAPT Timothy Lantz USN** .... (757) 322-5671
E-mail: timothy.lantz@navy.mil
Force Equal Opportunity Officer
CSCS Veronica Lawrence USN .... (757) 322-6656
E-mail: veronica.lawrence@navy.mil
Force Judge Advocate General
CAPT Matthew Foley USN .... (757) 322-5649
Force Medical Director
CAPT Nancy R. Delaney USN .... (757) 322-5645
E-mail: nancy.r.delaney@navy.mil
Human Resources Director **John Rowe** .... (757) 322-5661
E-mail: john.rowe1@navy.mil
Information Security Manager **Wanda Swindle** .... (757) 322-5752
E-mail: wanda.swindle@navy.mil
Inspector General **CAPT George Whitbred USN** .... (757) 322-5655
E-mail: george.whitbred@navy.mil
Protocol Officer **(Vacant)** .... (757) 322-5600
Safety Director **Cecilia Daley** .... (757) 322-5676
E-mail: cecilia.daley@navy.mil

Operational Test and Evaluation Force (OPTEVFOR)
7970 Diven Street, Norfolk, VA 23505
Tel: (757) 457-6018 Tel: (757) 282-5574 Fax: (757) 282-5532
Internet: www.public.navy.mil/cotf

Commander **RDML Paul A. "L.J." Sohl USN** .... (757) 282-5546
Education: MIT 1985 BS; Stanford MS
Deputy Commander **Carlton Hill** .... (757) 282-5546 ext. 3900
Chief of Staff
CAPT Michael D. Patterson USN .... (757) 282-5546 ext. 3283
Education: North Carolina State 1989 BSCE

(continued on next page)

★ Presidential Appointment Requiring Senate Confirmation ☆ Presidential Appointment □ Schedule C Appointment ◇ Career Senior Foreign Service Appointment
● Career Senior Executive Service (SES) Appointment ○ Non-Career Senior Executive Service (SES) Appointment ■ Postal Career Executive Service

Operational Test and Evaluation Force *(continued)*

Command Master Chief/Force Master Chief
CMDCM Donnie Novak USN . . . . (757) 282-5546 ext. 3107
E-mail: cmc@cotf.navy.mil
Chief Information Officer **Jessie McArthur** . . . . (757) 282-5546 ext. 3055
Comptroller and Resources Manager
Anthony "Tony" Starks . . . . (757) 282-5546 ext. 3312
E-mail: anthony.starks@cotf.navy.mil
Security Manager **Kevin Smith** . . . . (757) 282-5546 ext. 3002
Technical Director **Mark Lucas** . . . . (757) 282-5546 ext. 3115
Education: Penn State 1990 BS; Johns Hopkins 2002 MS
Training Director **Guy Cofield** . . . . (757) 282-5546 ext. 3069
E-mail: cofieldg@cotf.navy.mil

U.S. Fleet Forces Command (USFF)

COMUSFLTFORCOM (N02P), 1562 Mitscher Avenue,
Suite 250, Norfolk, VA 23551-2487
Tel: (757) 836-3630 Fax: (757) 836-3603

Commander
ADM Christopher W. "Chris" Grady USN . . . . (757) 836-3630
Education: Notre Dame Fax: (757) 836-5887
Special Assistant
RDML Edward B. "Ed" Cashman USN . . . . (757) 836-3630
Education: MIT 1987 BS; Maryland MS; Naval War MA
Deputy Commander **VADM Bruce H. Lindsey USN** . . . . . (757) 836-3636
Reserve Deputy Commander for Maritime Operations
RDML Brian S. Hurley USN . . . . (757) 836-3630
● Director, Fleet Personnel Development and Allocation
(N1) **Alfred H. Gonzalez** . . . . (757) 836-3630
Education: Naval Acad 1978 BS
Director, Fleet Safety & Occupational Health
(N01FS) **CAPT Brendan J. Murphy USN** . . . . (757) 836-3630
General Counsel (N01GC) **Michael E. McGregor** . . . . (757) 836-3630
E-mail: michael.mcgregor@navy.mil
Director, Public Affairs and Outreach (N01P)
CDR Mike Kaska USN . . . . (757) 836-3630
● Executive Director and Chief of Staff (N02)
Mark Honecker . . . . (757) 836-8630
Education: Pfeiffer U BS; American U MPA
Director, Joint/Fleet Maritime Operations (N3)
RDML Douglas Perry USN . . . . (757) 836-3630
Fleet Surgeon and Director, Health Services (N03H)
CAPT Paul Kane MC, USN . . . . (757) 836-3630
Reserve Fleet Surgeon
RADM Brian S. Pecha MC, USNR . . . . (757) 836-3630
Education: U San Francisco 1983 BS; Stanford MD
Fleet Marine Officer (N03M) **(Vacant)** . . . . (757) 836-3630
Director, Maritime Operations (N04)
RDML (Sel) Bret C. Batchelder USN . . . . (757) 836-3630
Director, Global Force Management (N04)
Edward J. Baron . . . . (757) 836-3630
Deputy Director, Maritime Operations (N04B)
Michael Durkin . . . . (757) 836-3630
Deputy Director, Maritime Operations Reserve
(N04R) **(Vacant)** . . . . (757) 836-3630
Director, Fleet Ordnance and Supply (N41)
RDML Thomas J. "Jack" Moreau SC, USN . . . . (757) 836-3630
Education: Rensselaer Poly 1990 BS
Director, Fleet Maintenance (N43)
RADM Mark R. Whitney USN . . . . (757) 836-3630
E-mail: mark.r.whitney@navy.mil
Education: Maine Maritime 1984 BS
● Director, Fleet Installations and Environment (N46)
Elizabeth Nashold . . . . (757) 836-3630
Director, Fleet Policy and International Engagement
(N5) **Christopher "C." Melhuish** . . . . (757) 836-3630
Director, Communications and Information Systems
(N6) **Francis A. "Skip" Hiser** . . . . (757) 492-8738
Education: South Carolina BS; Hawaii Pacific MS
Director, Joint Fleet Training (N7)
RDML (Sel) Timothy C. Kuehhas USN . . . . (757) 836-3630
● Director, Fleet Capabilities and Force Development
(N08/N09) **Mark E. Kosnik** . . . . (757) 836-3630
E-mail: mark.kosnik@navy.mil
Education: Notre Dame 1978; Naval Postgrad 1985 MS

U.S. Fleet Forces Command *(continued)*

Fleet Civil Engineer **RDML Darius Banaji USN** . . . . (757) 836-3630
E-mail: darius.banaji@navy.mil
Fleet Master Chief **CMDCM Richard P. O'Rawe USN** . . . (757) 836-6739

Naval Medical Center Camp Lejeune
Naval Hospital, 100 Brewster Boulevard, Camp Lejeune, NC 28547-2538
Tel: (910) 450-4300 Fax: (910) 450-4012
Internet: www.med.navy.mil/sites/nhcl

Commanding Officer
CAPT Jeffrey W. "Jeff" Timby MC, USN . . . . (910) 450-4007
E-mail: jeffrey.timby@usmc.mil
Education: Duke 1980; Temple 1984
Executive Officer **CAPT Shelley K. Perkins MC, USN** . . . (910) 450-4009
Education: Whittier BA
Command Master Chief
CMDCM Michelle L. Brooks USN . . . . (910) 450-4005
E-mail: michelle.brooks@navy.mil
Education: Park U BS
Director of Administration
CDR Danielle Wooten USN . . . . (910) 450-4300
Director of Public Affairs **CDR Kimberly Taylor USN** . . . (910) 450-3836
E-mail: kimberly.taylor@med.navy.mil
Medical Librarian **Joann T. Hall** . . . . (910) 450-4076

Naval Air Force, U.S. Atlantic Fleet

COMNAVAIRLANT, 1279 Franklin Street, Norfolk, VA 23511-2494
Tel: (757) 615-6026 Tel: (757) 836-4880 (Quarterdeck)
Fax: (757) 444-8700

Commander **RADM Roy J. Kelley USN** . . . . (757) 615-6026
E-mail: roy.kelley@navy.mil
Education: Southeastern Oklahoma St 1984 BS
Deputy Commander **RDML Scott D. Jones USN** . . . . (757) 615-6026
Chief of Staff **CAPT William Ewald USN** . . . . (757) 444-7451
Force Master Chief **FORCM Huben L. Phillips USN** . . . . (757) 444-8666
Public Affairs Officer
LCDR William M. "Mike" Kafka USN . . . . (757) 444-3373
E-mail: william.kafka@navy.mil Fax: (757) 444-3374

Naval Aviation Warfighting Development Center (NAWDC)

Building 465, 4755 Pasture Road, Fallon, NV 89496-5000
Tel: (775) 426-3773 (Administration Office) Fax: (775) 426-3958

Commander **RDML Daniel L. Cheever USN** . . . . (775) 426-3772
Director of Headquarters
CAPT Russell W. Jones USN . . . . (775) 426-3900

Naval Surface Force Atlantic (COMNAVSURFLANT)

Building NH-13, 1430 Mitscher Avenue, Norfolk, VA 23551-2494
Tel: (757) 836-3057 Fax: (757) 836-3281 Internet: www.surflant.navy.mil

Commander **RDML Jesse A. Wilson, Jr. USN** . . . . (757) 836-3000
Education: Naval Acad 1986 BS; Naval War 2001 MNSSS
Deputy Commander **(Vacant)** . . . . (757) 836-3284
Executive Director **David Volonino** . . . . (757) 836-3012
Chief of Staff **CAPT Clinton A. "Clint" Carroll USN** . . . . (757) 836-3002
Education: Naval Acad 1989 BS; San Diego State 2002 MBA
Assistant Chief of Staff
CAPT Hung Ba "H.B." Le USN . . . . (757) 836-3061
Force Master Chief **FORCM Kevin Goodrich USN** . . . . . . (757) 836-3046
Command Master Chief
CMDCM Steven W. Rioux USN . . . . (757) 836-3057

U.S. 2nd Fleet

Note: After being deactivated in 2011, the U.S. 2nd Fleet resumed operations on July 1, 2018.

Commander
VADM Andrew L. "Woody" Lewis USN . . . . (757) 615-6026
Education: Naval Acad 1985

★ Presidential Appointment Requiring Senate Confirmation ☆ Presidential Appointment ☐ Schedule C Appointment ◇ Career Senior Foreign Service Appointment
● Career Senior Executive Service (SES) Appointment ○ Non-Career Senior Executive Service (SES) Appointment ■ Postal Career Executive Service

U.S. Naval Forces Europe-Africa

U.S. Naval Forces Europe (COMUSNAVEUR), PSC 802, Box 13, FPO, AE 09499
Tel: 39 081-721-3004 Fax: 39 081-639-3038

Commander **ADM James G. Foggo III USN** 39 (081) 626-2319
Education: Naval Acad 1981
Deputy Commander
VADM Lisa M. Franchetti USN 39 (081) 568-4301
Education: Northwestern 1985 BS
Fleet Master Chief
FLTCM Raymond D. Kemp, Sr. USN 39 (081) 568-2958
Foreign Policy Advisor **Elizabeth A. Hopkins** 39 081-721-3004
Education: Middlebury; Fletcher Law & Diplomacy
Chief of Staff **RDML Matthew A. Zirkle USN** 39 (081) 568-4301
Command Master Chief
CMDCM James C. Wallace USN 39 (081) 568-4301
Director of Maritime Headquarters
RDML John Gumbleton USN 39 (081) 568-4301
Maritime Partnership Program Director
RDML (Sel) Shawn E. Duane USN 39 (081) 568-4301
Operations Director **RADM Thomas E. Ishee USN** . . . 39 (081) 568-4301
Education: Georgia 1987 BS; Texas 1995 MSEE
Force Surgeon **(Vacant)** 39 (081) 568-4301
Public Affairs Director **(Vacant)** 39 (081) 568-3070
U.S. Naval Forces Europe (COMUSNAVEUR), PSC 817, Box 70, FPO, AE 09622

U.S. Pacific Fleet (PACFLT)

250 Makalapa Drive, Pearl Harbor, HI 96860-3131
Tel: (808) 471-9727 Fax: (808) 474-5161
Internet: https://www.cpf.navy.mil/

Commander **ADM John C. Aquilino USN** . . . . (808) 471-9727
Education: Naval Acad 1984 BS
Deputy Commander **RDML Matthew J. Carter USN** . . . . (808) 471-9800
Education: VMI 1985
Reserve Director, Maritime Operations
RDML Kevin C. Hayes USNR . . . . (808) 471-9800
● Executive Director and Chief of Staff **Todd L. Schafer** . . . (808) 471-9727
Education: Wright State 1989 BSB; Webster 1992 MA; Troy State 1997 MBA; Air Command Col 1997
Fleet Master Chief **CMDCM James Honea USN** . . . . (808) 471-9727
● Director, Command, Control, Communications, Computers and Intelligence **(Vacant)** . . . . (808) 471-5209
Director, Communications and Information Systems
Robert A. Stephenson . . . . (808) 471-9727
Education: Naval Acad 1973
Director, Fleet Maintenance
RDML William C. Greene USN . . . . (808) 471-0401
Education: Florida BS, MBA
Director, Fleet Training **Mark T. Lagier** . . . . (808) 471-9727
Director, Intelligence and Information Operations
CAPT Dale C. Rielage USN . . . . (808) 471-0778
Director, Logistics, Fleet Supply and Ordnance
RDML Kristen B. Fabry USN . . . . (808) 471-9727
E-mail: kristen.fabry@navy.mil
Reserve Director, Logistics, Fleet Supply and Ordnance
RDML Jacquelyn McClelland USNR . . . . (808) 471-9727
Director, Maritime Headquarters
RDML James P. "Jim" Waters III USN . . . . (808) 471-9727
Director, Maritime Operations
RADM Marc H. Dalton USN . . . . (808) 471-9727
Education: Naval Acad 1987 BS
Director, Operations **(Vacant)** . . . . (808) 471-9727
Director, Plans and Policy **William J. Wesley** . . . . (808) 471-5790
Education: Pepperdine BA; Oklahoma MPA
Director, Total Fleet Force Manpower and Personnel
Lynn C. Simpson . . . . (808) 471-9393
Director, Warfare Requirements, Resources and Force Structure **Kenneth S. "Ken" Jordan USN (Ret)** . . . . . . (808) 471-9727
Director, Warfighting Assessment and Readiness
Patrick Molenda . . . . (808) 471-9727
Fleet Chaplain **CAPT David O. Bynum USN** . . . . (808) 471-9727
Fleet Civil Engineer **RDML John Adametz USN** . . . . (808) 472-1000
Education: VMI 1989 BSME; Penn State 1997 MSCE
Fleet Judge Advocate **CAPT Gregory Smith USN** . . . . . . (808) 471-0624

U.S. Pacific Fleet *(continued)*

Fleet Surgeon **CAPT Kris M. Belland MC, USN** . . . . (808) 471-9727
Inspector General **Judy Yamashita** . . . . (808) 471-9064
Public Affairs Officer and Communications Director
CAPT Charlie Brown USN . . . . (808) 471-3769

U.S. Naval Forces Japan

PSC 473, Box 12, FPO, AP 96349-0051
Tel: 81 (468) 16-1110 Internet: https://www.cnic.navy.mil/Japan

Commander
RDML Gregory J. "Greg" Fenton USN 81 (468) 16-7615
Executive Director **Robert Posthumus** 81 (468) 16-1110
Deputy Commander and Chief of Staff
CAPT Keith M. Henry USN 81 (468) 16-7615
Command Master Chief
CMDCM Steven J. Snyder USN 81 (468) 16-7615

Fleet Activities Yokosuka

COMFLEACT Yokosuka, PSC 473, Box 1, FPO, AP 96349-0001
Tel: 81 46-816-7300 Fax: 81 46-816-5353
Internet: www.cnic.navy.mil/yokosuka

Commander **CAPT Jeffrey J. Kim USN** 81 46-816-7300
Chief Staff Officer **CDR Terry P. McNamara USN** 81 46-816-7301
Command Master Chief
CMDCM Warren L. Britten USN 81 46-816-7058

U.S. Naval Forces Korea (CNFK - Yongsan Army Garrison)

Yongsan Army Garrison, Seoul, South Korea
Mail: COMNAVFORKOREA, Unit 15250, APO, AP 96205-0023
Tel: 82 (2) 7913-7251 Fax: 82 (2) 7913-9336
E-mail: 01p1@cnfk.navy.mil Internet: www.cnic.navy.mil/korea

Commander **RDML Michael E. Boyle USN** 82 (2) 7913-5127
Deputy Commander **CAPT Joseph Carrigan USN** 82 (2) 7913-5127
Command Master Chief
CMDCM Christopher Stone USN 82 (2) 7913-5127

Naval Air Force, U.S. Pacific Fleet

Building Eight, COMNAVAIRFOR, San Diego, CA 92135
Tel: (619) 545-1133 Fax: (619) 545-1140

Commander and Commander, Naval Air Forces
VADM DeWolfe H. "Chip" Miller III USN . . . . (619) 545-4390
Education: Naval Acad 1981; National Defense U MS
Executive Assistant **CDR Teddy Kribs USN** . . . . (619) 545-4390
Deputy Commander
RADM William Michael "Sky" Crane USN . . . . (619) 545-4390
Education: Virginia Tech 1984 BSCE; Naval War MNSSS
Director, Joint Strike Fighter Fleet Integration
RDML Dale E. Horan USN . . . . (619) 545-1133
Education: Naval Acad 1985 BSME; Naval Postgrad 1994 MSE; National War Col 2001 MNSSS
Chief of Staff **CAPT Jeffrey J. Czerewko USN** . . . . (619) 545-4390
Education: Naval Acad 1990
Force Master Chief **FORCM James Tocorzic USN** . . . . . . (619) 545-1133
● Executive Director **Bryan M. Scurry** . . . . (619) 545-1133
E-mail: bryan.scurry@navy.mil
Education: Colorado BS; Cal State (Northridge) MSME
Public Affairs Officer
CDR Ronald S. "Ron" Flanders USN . . . . (619) 767-1625
Education: Maryland University Col 1999 BA; San Diego State 2011 MA Fax: (619) 545-1140

Naval Surface Force, U.S. Pacific Fleet (COMNAVSURFPAC)

2841 Rendova Road, San Diego, CA 92155-5490
Tel: (619) 437-2942 Fax: (619) 437-2720
Internet: www.public.navy.mil/surfor

Commander **VADM Richard A. "Rich" Brown USN** . . . . (619) 437-2942
Education: Naval Acad 1985 BS; Naval Postgrad MS; Naval War MA
Deputy Commander **RDML John B. Mustin USN** . . . . (619) 437-2942
Education: Naval Acad 1990 BSE; Naval Postgrad MS; Babson MBA
● Executive Director **Jeffrey A. Klein** . . . . (619) 437-2942
Chief of Staff
CAPT Christopher "Chris" Engdahl USN . . . . (619) 437-2942
Force Master Chief **FORCM James W. Osborne USN** . . . (619) 437-2942

(continued on next page)

★ Presidential Appointment Requiring Senate Confirmation ☆ Presidential Appointment ☐ Schedule C Appointment ◇ Career Senior Foreign Service Appointment
● Career Senior Executive Service (SES) Appointment ○ Non-Career Senior Executive Service (SES) Appointment ■ Postal Career Executive Service

DEPARTMENTS

Naval Surface Force, U.S. Pacific Fleet *(continued)*

Public Affairs Officer **CDR John Perkins USN** .... (619) 437-2146

Submarine Force, U.S. Pacific Fleet (COMSUBPAC)
Building 619, COMSUBPAC, 1430 Morton Street,
Pearl Harbor, HI 96860-4664
Tel: (808) 473-0911 Fax: (808) 423-2732 E-mail: n00p3@csp.navy.mil
Internet: www.csp.navy.mil

Commander **RADM Daryl L. Caudle USN** .... (808) 473-0700
Aide **LT Jessica Wilcox USN** .... (808) 473-0153
● Executive Director **Donald L. Hoffer** .... (757) 836-4700
Norfolk, VA 23521
Director, Manpower and Personnel **Chris Kaiser** .... (808) 473-0911
Force Master Chief **FORCM Paul Davenport USN** ...... (808) 473-0700
Chief of Staff **CAPT Anthony C. Carullo USN** .... (808) 473-0700

U.S. 3rd Fleet (C3F)
53690 Tomahawk Drive, Suite 338, San Diego, CA 92147-5004
Tel: (619) 221-5287 (Quarterdeck)
Tel: (619) 767-4523 (Administrative Office) Fax: (619) 524-9562
Internet: https://www.navy.mil/local/c3f/

Commander **VADM John D. Alexander USN** .... (619) 524-9500
Education: Texas Tech BS; U London MA
Deputy Commander **RDML Darren J. Hanson USNR**.... (619) 524-9500
Chief of Staff **CAPT Sterling W. Dawley USN** .... (619) 524-9500
Assistant Chief of Staff for Requirements, Experimentation, and Innovation
CAPT Christopher E. Sund USN .... (619) 524-9500
Command Master Chief **CMDCM Jack Rallison USN** ... (619) 524-9500
Public Affairs Officer **CDR John Sage USN** .... (619) 524-9868

U.S. 7th Fleet (C7F)
Yokosuka, Japan
Mail: U.S. SEVENTH Fleet, Unit 25104, FPO, AP 96601-6003
Tel: 81 (468) 21-1910 (In-port, Yokosuka, Japan) Tel: (808) 653-1460
Tel: (808) 653-9730 (At Sea and In-port Public Affairs)
Fax: (808) 654-2134 E-mail: 0121@c7f.navy.mil (Public Affairs)
E-mail: 0122@c7f.navy.mil Internet: www.c7f.navy.mil

Commander **VADM Phillip G. "Phil" Sawyer USN** ... 81 (468) 16-7444
Education: Naval Acad 1983 BSE
Deputy Commander **RDML Joey B. Dodgen USNR** ... 81 (468) 16-7444
Chief of Staff **CAPT Jeffrey T. Griffin USN** 81 (468) 16-7445
Command Master Chief
CMDCM Benjamin T. Howat USN 81 (468) 16-7460
Public Affairs Officer **(Vacant)** .... (808) 653-2152
E-mail: webmaster@c7f.navy.mil

Logistics Group Western Pacific (COMLOG WESTPAC)
Sembawang Wharf, Deptford Road, Singapore, 759657, Singapore
Mail: COMLOG WESTPAC, PSC 470, Box 2400, FPO, AP 96534-2400
Tel: 65 6750-2466 Fax: 65 6750-2469 Internet: www.clwp.navy.mil

Commander **CAPT Murray J. "JT" Tynch III USN** 65 6750-2421
Chief of Staff **CAPT Randall H. Martin USN**............ 65 6750-2421
Command Master Chief **CMDCM Daniel Irwin USN**...... 65 6750-2421

Vice Chief of Naval Operations (VCNO)
2000 Navy Pentagon, Washington, DC 20350-2000
Tel: (703) 697-0436 Fax: (703) 614-0401

Navy Staff (N09B)
2000 Navy Pentagon, Washington, DC 20350-2000
Tel: (703) 692-9043 Fax: (703) 692-8809

Bureau of Medicine and Surgery (N093) (BUMED)
7700 Arlington Boulevard, Suite 5113, Falls Church, VA 22042
Tel: (703) 681-5200 Fax: (703) 681-9527 Internet: www.med.navy.mil

Navy Medicine Operational Training Center (NMOTC)
220 Hovey Road, Pensacola, FL 32508-1047
Tel: (850) 452-8144 Fax: (850) 452-3338

Commanding Officer
CAPT Theron C. Toole MC, USN .... (850) 452-4554
Executive Officer **CAPT Michael Kohler NC, USN** ...... (850) 452-4555
Command Senior Enlisted Leader
CMDCM Andrew Ali USN......................... (850) 452-4154
E-mail: nomi-cmc@med.navy.mil

Naval Survival Training Institute (NSTI)
220 Hovey Road, Pensacola, FL 32508-1047
Tel: (850) 452-2411 Fax: (850) 452-5968

Officer-in-Charge **CAPT Dan Patterson MSC, USN** ..... (850) 452-2411
E-mail: nomi-nstioic@med.navy.mil

Navy Medicine East (NME)
620 John Paul Jones Circle, Portsmouth, VA 23708-2197
Tel: (757) 953-5000

Commander **RDML Anne M. Swap USN**.............. (757) 953-7424
E-mail: anne.swap@navy.mil
Deputy Commander **(Vacant)**......................... (757) 953-7424
Executive Officer **CAPT Susan Herron USN** .... (757) 953-5000
Chief of Staff **CAPT Cynthia Gantt USN** .... (757) 953-5000
Command Master Chief **(Vacant)**..................... (757) 953-5000
Public Affairs Officer **Christina Johnson** .... (757) 953-1941
E-mail: christina.johnson@med.navy.mil
Freedom of Information Act Officer
CDR Robert Anselm USN .... (757) 953-5452
Webmaster **Bill Smith** .... (757) 953-4651
E-mail: NAVMEDEast-Webmaster@med.navy.mil

Navy Medicine West (NMW)
34800 Bob Wilson Drive, San Diego, CA 92134
Tel: (619) 767-6573

Commander **RDML Paul D. Pearigen USN** .... (619) 532-6400
E-mail: paul.pearigen@navy.mil
Education: Sewanee 1983 BA; Vanderbilt 1987 MD
Deputy Commander **RDML Mark E. Bipes USN**........ (619) 532-6400
Executive Officer **CAPT Shannon J. Johnson USN** ... (619) 532-6400
Command Master Chief (Surface Warfare)
CMDCM Loren D. Rucker USN.................... (619) 532-6400
Chief of Staff
CAPT Timothy H. "Tim" Weber MSC, USN .... (619) 532-6400
Public Affairs Officer **Regena Kowitz**................. (619) 532-9380
E-mail: usn.nmcsd-pao@mail.mil
Chief Librarian **Kathy Parker**........................ (619) 532-7950
E-mail: kathy.parker@navy.mil
Research Director, Mental Health Directorate
CDR Henry Kane USN .... (619) 532-5666

★ Presidential Appointment Requiring Senate Confirmation ☆ Presidential Appointment □ Schedule C Appointment ◇ Career Senior Foreign Service Appointment
● Career Senior Executive Service (SES) Appointment ○ Non-Career Senior Executive Service (SES) Appointment ■ Postal Career Executive Service

N1 Manpower, Personnel, Training, and Education/Chief of Naval Personnel (MPT&E/CNP)
Columbia Pike & Southgate Road, Arlington, VA 20370
Fax: (703) 604-5942 Internet: www.navy.mil/cnp

Navy Personnel Command
5720 Integrity Drive, Millington, TN 38055
Tel: (901) 874-3000 Fax: (901) 874-2600 E-mail: uasknpc@navy.mil

Deputy Chief of Naval Personnel and Commander
RDML Jeffrey W. "Jeff" Hughes USN .... (901) 874-3000
Education: Duke 1988 BSME
Assistant Deputy Chief of Naval Personnel/Deputy Commander **Diane L.H. Lofink** .... (901) 874-3000
Education: Rosary 1978 BA
Assistant Commander for Career Management
RDML Richard J. "Rick" Cheeseman USN .... (901) 874-3000
E-mail: rick.cheeseman@navy.mil
Executive Officer **CAPT Paul L. Dinius USN** .... (901) 874-3000
Force Master Chief **FORCM Scott A. Rossiter USN** .... (901) 874-3000
Section 508 Coordinator [Section 508 Coordinator]
Mitchell E. "Mitch" Kilgore .... (901) 874-4748
E-mail: mitch.kilgore@navy.mil

Navy Recruiting Command (CNRC)
Building 784, 5722 Integrity Drive, Millington, TN 38054-5054
Tel: (901) 874-9048 Fax: (901) 874-9074

Commander **RDML Brendan R. McLane USN** .... (901) 874-9048
Education: Naval Acad 1990
Deputy Commander
RDML Andrew J. Mueller USNR .... (901) 874-9048
Executive Director **Gary C. "Norm" Peterson** .... (901) 874-9048
Education: Oregon
Command Master Chief
CMDCM Donald A. Charbonneau USN .... (901) 874-9048
National Chief Recruiter
NCCM Franklin Tiongco USN .... (901) 874-9048
Public Affairs Officer
CDR Kristine "Kris" Garland USN .... (901) 874-9048
E-mail: kristine.garland@navy.mil

Navy Recruiting Orientation Unit (NORU)
385 Millington Avenue, Pensacola, FL 32508
Tel: (850) 452-5401 Fax: (850) 452-5383

Officer-in-Charge **CDR Mark E. Yates USN** .... (850) 452-5401
Assistant Officer-in-Charge
LCDR Matthew O'Brian USN .... (850) 452-5303
Command Master Chief **NCCM Gerald Allchin USN** .... (850) 452-5397

Major U.S. Naval Commands

Naval Air Systems Command (NAVAIR)
Building 2272, 47123 Buse Road, Suite 540,
Patuxent River, MD 20670-1547
Tel: (301) 757-7825 Fax: (301) 757-7756 E-mail: navairpao@navy.mil
Internet: www.navair.navy.mil

Fleet Readiness Center East (FRCE)
PSC Box 8021, Cherry Point, NC 28533-0021
Tel: (252) 464-7999

Commander **Col Clarence Harper III USMC** .... (252) 464-7999
Executive Officer **CAPT Mark E. Nieto USN** .... (252) 464-7999

Fleet Readiness Center Southeast (FRCSE)
Naval Air Station Jacksonville, 6801 Roosevelt Boulevard, Jacksonville, FL 32212
Tel: (904) 542-3526

Commander **CAPT Trent DeMoss USN** .... (904) 542-3526

Fleet Readiness Center Southwest (FRCSW)
Code 75000, P.O. Box 357058, San Diego, CA 92135-7058
Tel: (619) 545-3415 Fax: (619) 545-5127

Commanding Officer
CAPT Anthony "Tony" Jaramillo USN .... (619) 545-2200
Executive Officer **(Vacant)** .... (619) 545-2200
Command Master Chief
CMDCM Joel Rodriguez USN .... (619) 545-3415
Public Affairs Specialist **Michael A. "Mike" Furlano** .... (619) 545-0735
E-mail: michael.furlano@navy.mil

Fleet Readiness Center West (FRCW)
160 L Street, Lemoore, CA 93246

Commander **CAPT Bret Washburn USN** .... (301) 757-7825

Fleet Readiness Center Western Pacific (FRCWP)
PSC 477, Box 35, FPO, AP 96306
Internet: www.navair.navy.mil/napra

Commanding Officer
CDR James "Steve" Carmichael USN 81 46-776-3771
Executive Officer **CDR Holly M. Falconieri USN** 81 46-776-3771

Naval Air Warfare Center Aircraft Division (NAWCAD)
22473 Millstone Road, Patuxent River, MD 20670-5304
Tel: (301) 342-1133 Tel: (866) 242-2143 (Toll-free)
Fax: (301) 342-2143 Internet: http://www.navair.navy.mil/nawcad/
E-mail: nawcad.nbo@navy.mil

Commander **RDML John S. Lemmon USN** .... (301) 342-1100
E-mail: john.s.lemmon@navy.mil
Vice Commander **CAPT Craig E. Lee USN** .... (301) 342-1111
● Executive Director **Leslie D. Taylor** .... (301) 342-1133
Education: West Virginia Tech 1984 BSCE; Florida Tech 1990 MS
Command Master Chief
CMDCM Christopher W. Chelberg USN .... (301) 342-1100
Contracting Officer **John Bogoven** .... (301) 757-9748
Public Affairs Director **Timothy "Tim" Boulay** .... (301) 757-2211
Small Business Specialist **Melanie Roach** .... (301) 995-4260

Naval Air Warfare Center Training Systems Division (NAWCTSD)
12350 Research Parkway, Orlando, FL 32826
Tel: (407) 380-4000 Internet: http://www.navair.navy.mil/nawctsd/

Commanding Officer **CAPT Erik Etz USN** .... (407) 380-8128
E-mail: erik.etz@navy.mil
Technical Director **John Meyers** .... (407) 380-4000
Deputy Technical Director **Michael "Mike" Merritt** ..... (407) 380-8129
Education: Central Florida 1982 BA; Air Force Inst Tech 1984 MA
Director of Contracts **(Vacant)** .... (407) 380-8061

Naval Air Warfare Center Weapons Division (NAWCWD)
One Administration Circle, Stop 1002, China Lake, CA 93555
Tel: (760) 939-3511 (Public Affairs)
Internet: www.navair.navy.mil/nawcwd

Commander **RDML William Scott Dillon USN** .... (760) 939-3511
Fax: (760) 939-2056
Vice Commander **CDR Matthew Sniffin USN** .... (760) 939-2201
Executive Director and Director for Research and Engineering **Joan Johnson** .... (760) 939-3511
● Director, Range and Air Vehicle Modification and Instrumentation (5.2) **Thomas C. "Tom" Dowd** .... (760) 939-3511
Education: Boston U 1988 BS; Pepperdine 2005 MBA
Director, Software and Mission Systems Integration (4.5) **Harlan Kooima** .... (760) 939-7333
E-mail: harlan.kooima@navy.mil Fax: (760) 428-3043
Education: Iowa State 1988 BS
● Director, Weapons and Energetics (4.7) **Daniel "Dan" Carreño** .... (760) 939-3511
● National Director, Avionics, Sensors and Electronic Warfare (4.5) **Dr. Ronald E. Smiley PhD** .... (760) 939-3511
Education: Howard U 1970 BS; Pepperdine 1976 MBA; Claremont Grad 1985 MA, 1992 PhD

(continued on next page)

★ Presidential Appointment Requiring Senate Confirmation ☆ Presidential Appointment ☐ Schedule C Appointment ◇ Career Senior Foreign Service Appointment
● Career Senior Executive Service (SES) Appointment ○ Non-Career Senior Executive Service (SES) Appointment ■ Postal Career Executive Service

Naval Air Warfare Center Weapons Division *(continued)*

Public Affairs Officer **Renee Hatcher** . . . . (760) 939-3511
Fax: (760) 939-2056

Naval Education and Training Command (NETC)

250 Dallas Street, Pensacola, FL 32508-5220
Tel: (850) 452-4858 Fax: (850) 452-4900 Internet: www.netc.navy.mil

Center for Explosive Ordnance Disposal (EOD) and Diving (CNEODDIVE)

350 South Crag Road, Panama City, FL 32407-7016
Tel: (850) 235-5241 E-mail: ceodd.pao@navy.mil
Internet: www.netc.navy.mil/centers/ceneoddive

Commanding Officer **CAPT Robert R. Porter III USN** . . . (850) 235-5274
Command Master Chief
CMDCM Stephen J. Mulholland USN . . . . (850) 235-5793
Executive Director **George Delano** . . . . (850) 235-5254
Education: Murray State U 1971 BA, 1974 MACT

Center for Information Warfare Training (CIWT)

640 Roberts Avenue, Pensacola, FL 32511-5138
Tel: (850) 452-6512 Fax: (850) 452-6633 E-mail: ciwt_pao@navy.mil

Commanding Officer
CAPT Nicholas "Nick" Andrews II USN . . . . (850) 452-6516
Education: Boston U 1992; Naval War; Naval Postgrad; Joint Forces Staff Col
Executive Director **James E. "Jim" Hagy** . . . . (850) 452-6512
Executive Officer **CDR Jeffrey Buschmann USN** . . . . (850) 452-6512
Public Affairs Officer **Glenn Sircy** . . . . (850) 452-6672
Command Master Chief
MCPO Michael P. Bates USN . . . . (850) 452-6512

Center for Information Dominance Detachment (Goodfellow AFB)

170 Vance Street, Goodfellow AFB, TX 76908
Tel: (325) 654-5500

Officer-in-Charge **LCDR Austin Maxwell USN** . . . . (325) 654-5500

Information Warfare Training Command Corry Station

640 Roberts Avenue, Pensacola, FL 32511-5138
Tel: (850) 452-6618 (Quarterdeck)

Commanding Officer **CDR Chad M. Smith USN** . . . . (850) 452-6934
E-mail: chad.m.smith@navy.mil
Education: Miami U (OH) 1999 BS
Executive Officer **LCDR Phillip Hickman USN** . . . . (850) 452-6934
Senior Enlisted Leader **CMDCM Joanne Gibson USN** . . . (850) 452-6502

Center for Information Dominance Unit Hampton Roads (CID Unit Hampton Roads)

Layton Hall, 2088 Regulus Avenue, Virginia Beach, VA 23461-2099
Tel: (757) 492-0001

Commanding Officer **CDR Andrew W. Boyden USN** . . . . (757) 492-0001
Executive Officer
LCDR Anthony "Eric" Dobson USN . . . . (757) 492-0001
Senior Enlisted Advisor
CMDCM Daniel K. "Danny" Leek USN . . . . (757) 492-0001

Information Warfare Training Command Monterey (IWTC Monterey)

412 Rifle Range Road #228, Monterey, CA 93943
Tel: (831) 242-5142 (Quarterdeck)
Tel: (831) 760-0336 (Command Duty Officer)
Tel: (831) 242-5570 (Administration)
E-mail: info.ciddmonterey@navy.mil

Commanding Officer **CDR Mike Salehi USN** . . . . (831) 242-5142
Executive Officer
LCDR Andrew T. Michalowicz USN . . . . (831) 242-5142
Command Master Chief
MCPO Christopher Stevens USN . . . . (831) 242-5142

Center for Naval Aviation Technical Training (CNATT)

230 Chevalier Field Avenue, Suite C, Pensacola, FL 32508
Tel: (850) 452-8297

Commanding Officer **CAPT Eric J. Simon USN** . . . . (850) 452-7163

Center for Naval Aviation Technical Training *(continued)*

Executive Officer **CAPT Nate Schneider USN** . . . . (850) 452-7163
Command Master Chief
CTRCM Todd E. Strebin USN . . . . (850) 452-8028

Center for Surface Combat Systems (CSCS)

5395 First Street, Dahlgren, VA 22448
Tel: (540) 653-1031 Fax: (540) 653-2011
Internet: https://www.netc.navy.mil/centers/cscs/

Commanding Officer **CAPT Frank Castellano USN** . . . . . (540) 653-1023
Command Master Chief
CMDCM Thormod J. Forseth USN . . . . (540) 653-1031
Executive Officer
CDR Christopher S. Simmons USN . . . . (540) 653-1031

Fleet Anti-Submarine Warfare Training Center

33150 Destroyer Lane, Suite 401, San Diego, CA 92147
Tel: (619) 524-1689 Fax: (619) 524-1537

Commanding Officer
CAPT Ronald W. Toland, Jr. USN . . . . (619) 524-1665
Executive Officer
CDR Espiridion N. "Speedy" Limón USN . . . . (619) 524-1665
Command Master Chief
CMDCM Raul DeLaCruz USN . . . . (619) 524-5709
Public Affairs Officer **LT Joshua Pierce USN** . . . . (619) 553-0852

Naval Diving and Salvage Training Center (NDSTC)

350 South Crag Road, Panama City, FL 32407
Tel: (850) 234-4651

Commanding Officer **LCDR Sam Brasfield USN** . . . . (850) 234-4651
Executive Officer **LCDR Joseph Sandoval USN** . . . . (850) 234-4651
Education: New Mexico State BS
Command Master Chief
CMDCM Stephen D. Zentz USN . . . . (850) 234-4651

Naval Education and Training Professional Development Center (NETPDC)

6490 Saufley Field Road, Pensacola, FL 32509-5204
Tel: (850) 452-1001 Fax: (850) 452-1690

Commanding Officer
CAPT Kertreck V. Brooks DC, USN . . . . (850) 473-6004
Public Affairs Officer **Thomas D. "Tom" Updike** . . . . (850) 473-6132
E-mail: tom.updike@navy.mil

Submarine Learning Center (Naval Submarine Base New London, CT)

Box 29 - Building 166, Naval Submarine Base, Groton, CT 06349-1716
Tel: (860) 694-1716 Internet: https://www.netc.navy.mil/centers/slc/

Commanding Officer **CAPT Aaron M. Thieme USN** . . . . (860) 694-1716
Education: Vanderbilt 1992 BEE; Mississippi; Naval War
Executive Director **Jonathan P. "John" Houser** . . . . (860) 694-1716
Command Master Chief
CMDCM David Meadvin USN . . . . (860) 694-1716

Naval Submarine School (Naval Submarine Base New London, CT)

Box 700, Groton, CT 06349-5700
Tel: (860) 694-3914 Fax: (860) 694-3753

Commanding Officer **CAPT Jack Houdeshell USN** . . . . . (860) 694-3751
Education: Idaho BS
Executive Officer **LCDR Jon Cantor USN** . . . . (860) 694-3752
Command Master Chief
CMDCM(SS) Eric J. Murphy USN . . . . (860) 694-4955

Submarine Learning Center Detachment San Diego (CA)

544 White Road, San Diego, CA 92106-3550
Tel: (619) 553-7260 Tel: (619) 553-7219 (Public Affairs)
Fax: (619) 553-7236

Officer-in-Charge
CDR Matthew "Maka" Mazat USN . . . . (619) 553-7284

★ Presidential Appointment Requiring Senate Confirmation ☆ Presidential Appointment ☐ Schedule C Appointment ◇ Career Senior Foreign Service Appointment
● Career Senior Executive Service (SES) Appointment ○ Non-Career Senior Executive Service (SES) Appointment ■ Postal Career Executive Service

Submarine Learning Facility Norfolk (VA)
Building CEP-166, 1915 C Avenue, Norfolk, VA 23511-3791
Tel: (757) 444-7578 Fax: (757) 444-5793
Internet: www.netc.navy.mil/centers/slc/sublrnfacnfk

Commanding Officer
CDR Leighton J. "Pete" Pitre USN . . . . (757) 444-7578
Executive Officer **LCDR Greg Edwards USN** . . . . (757) 444-7578
Command Master Chief
MMCM Cynthia Huratiak USN . . . . (757) 444-7578

Naval Submarine Training Center Pacific
NSTCP, 1130 Bole Loop, Pearl Harbor, HI 96860-4437
Tel: (808) 473-3375 Fax: (808) 473-2559
Internet: https://www.netc.navy.mil/centers/slc/nstcp/

Commanding Officer **CAPT Andrew C. Hertel USN** . . . . . (808) 473-3375
Executive Officer **CDR Brett J. Sterneckert USN** . . . . (808) 473-3375
Command Master Chief **CMDCM Eric M. Baker USN** . . . (808) 473-5166

Trident Training Facility Bangor (WA) (TTF Bangor)
2000 Thresher Avenue, Silverdale, WA 98315
Tel: (360) 315-2000 Fax: (360) 315-2613
Internet: www.netc.navy.mil/centers/slc/ttfbangor

Commanding Officer **CAPT John W. Fancher USN** . . . . . (360) 315-2612
Executive Officer **CDR Darrell S. Lewis USN** . . . . (360) 315-2615
Command Master Chief
CMDCM Steven A. "Steve" Bradsher USN . . . . (360) 315-2620
Information Technology Director **Richard L. Creger** . . . . . (360) 315-2651
E-mail: richard.creger@navy.mil Fax: (360) 315-2651

Trident Training Facility Kings Bay (GA)
1040 USS Georgia Avenue, Kings Bay, GA 31547
Tel: (912) 573-3453 Internet: www.netc.navy.mil/centers/slc/ttfkb

Commanding Officer **CAPT Wayne Wall USN** . . . . (912) 573-3430
Executive Officer **CDR Scott Cullen USN** . . . . (912) 573-3430
Command Master Chief
CMDCM Matthew Suzor USN . . . . (912) 573-3335

Tactical Training Group, Pacific
53720 Horizon Drive, San Diego, CA 92147-5080
Tel: (619) 553-8341 Fax: (619) 553-4731 Internet: www.ttgp.navy.mil

Commander **CAPT Michael G. Dowling USN** . . . . (619) 553-8333
Executive Officer **CAPT Eric Stephen Pfister USN** . . . . . (619) 553-8334
Education: Virginia Tech 1989 BSCE
Senior Enlisted Leader **ETCM Latoya R. Corker USN** . . . (619) 553-8341

Training Support Center Great Lakes (TSCGL)
320A Dewey Avenue, Great Lakes, IL 60088-5100
Tel: (847) 688-3536 Internet: www.netc.navy.mil/centers/tscgl

Commanding Officer (Acting)
CAPT Edward L. Heflin USN . . . . (847) 688-3536
Executive Officer **CDR Jason Juergens USN** . . . . (847) 688-3536
Executive Director **Michael C. Bilak** . . . . (847) 688-3536
Education: Southern Illinois BS; San Diego State MA
Command Master Chief **CMDCM Randy Reid USN** . . . . . (847) 688-3536

Training Support Center Hampton Roads (TSCHR)
1912 Regulus Avenue, Virginia Beach, VA 23461-2098
Tel: (757) 492-6542 Fax: (757) 492-6775
Internet: https://www.netc.navy.mil/centers/tsc_hr/

Commander **CAPT Matthew Rick USN** . . . . (757) 492-6542
Education: Naval Acad 1994; Naval War 2006; National Defense U 2013
Executive Director **Robert Wydler** . . . . (757) 492-6413
Executive Officer **LCDR Mike Bubulka USN** . . . . (757) 492-6211
Command Master Chief
CMDCM Keith A. Webb USN . . . . (757) 492-6950

Training Support Center San Diego
3975 Norman Scott Road, San Diego, CA 92136
Internet: www.netc.navy.mil/centers/tscsd

Commanding Officer
CAPT Michael S. "Mike" Feyedelem USN . . . . (619) 556-8328

Training Support Center San Diego *(continued)*

Executive Officer **LCDR Justin Santos USN** . . . . (619) 556-9640
Executive Director **Scott Trulove** . . . . (619) 556-8327
Command Master Chief
CMDCM Christopher D. Cline USN . . . . (619) 556-8330

Chief of Naval Air Training (CNATRA)
NAS Corpus Christi, Ocean Drive, Corpus Christi, TX 78409
Tel: (361) 961-2284 Fax: (391) 961-3160 Internet: www.cnatra.navy.mil

Chief of Naval Air Training
RDML Gregory N. Harris USN . . . . (361) 961-2671
Chief of Staff **CAPT Scott Starkey USN** . . . . (361) 961-2284
Command Chief **(Vacant)** . . . . (361) 961-2284
Public Affairs Officer **Elizabeth "Liz" Feaster USN** . . . . . (361) 961-3666

Naval Nuclear Power Training Command (NNPTC)
Charleston Naval Weapons Station, 101 NNPTC Circle, Goose Creek, SC 29445-6324
Tel: (843) 794-8000 E-mail: pao4@navy.mil
Internet: www.netc.navy.mil/nnptc

Commanding Officer
CAPT Andrew G. Peterson III USN . . . . (843) 794-8000
Executive Officer **LCDR Sean Flanagan USN** . . . . (843) 794-8000
Command Master Chief
CMDCM Derek G. Gruell USN . . . . (843) 794-8000
E-mail: nnptc-cmc@navy.mil

Naval Postgraduate School
One University Circle, Naval Postgraduate School, Monterey, CA 93943-5001
Tel: (831) 656-2442 Fax: (831) 656-2337 Internet: www.nps.edu

President **VADM Ronald Arthur Route USN (Ret)** . . . . . (831) 656-2511
Education: Naval Acad 1971 BS; Naval Postgrad MS
President **VADM Ann Elisabeth Rondeau USN (Ret)** . . . (831) 656-2511
Note: On October 11, 2018, Secretary of the Navy Richard Spencer announced the assignment of Ann Rondeau as President, with an effective date to be announced.
Education: Eisenhower Col 1973 BA; Georgetown 1982 MA
Provost and Academic Dean **Steven R. Lerman** . . . . (831) 656-2371
Education: MIT 1972 BS, 1973 MS, 1975 PhD
Chief of Staff **CAPT Mike Ward USN** . . . . (831) 656-2973
Comptroller **Kevin Little** . . . . (831) 656-2508
Counsel **Katherine Ashton** . . . . (831) 656-3356
Dean of Research **Dr. Jeffrey D. Paduan** . . . . (831) 656-3671
Education: Michigan 1982 BSE; Oregon State 1987 PhD
Dean of Students
CAPT Markus J. Gudmundsson USN . . . . (831) 656-2291
Dean, Graduate School of Business and Public Policy
Dr. William Gates . . . . (831) 656-2471
Dean, Graduate School of Engineering and Applied Sciences **Dr. Clyde L. Scandrett** . . . . (831) 656-2660
Dean, Graduate School of International Studies
Dr. James Wirtz . . . . (831) 656-3781
Dean, Graduate School of Operational and Information Sciences **Dr. Gordon McCormick** . . . . (831) 656-7693
Director, Contracting and Logistics Management
Patricia Hirsch . . . . (831) 656-2470
Director, Human Resources
Ermelinda Rodriguez-Heffner . . . . (831) 656-3054
Director, Information Technology
Joseph "Joe" LoPiccolo . . . . (831) 656-2994
E-mail: jlopiccolo@nps.edu
E-mail: execdir@nps.edu
Facilities Manager (Acting) **Jeremy Laney** . . . . (831) 656-3058
Inspector General **Victor Jarrett** . . . . (831) 656-2190
Librarian **Eleanor Uhlinger** . . . . (831) 656-2343
E-mail: euhlinger@nps.edu
Public Affairs Office (Acting) **Dale M. Kuska** . . . . (831) 656-3567
E-mail: pao@nps.edu
Staff Judge Advocate **CDR Valerie Small USN** . . . . (831) 656-3610
Vice Provost for Academic Affairs
Dr. O. Douglas "Doug" Moses . . . . (831) 656-3218
Education: Cornell 1969 BA; San Diego State 1976 MBA; UCLA 1983 PhD

★ Presidential Appointment Requiring Senate Confirmation ☆ Presidential Appointment □ Schedule C Appointment ◇ Career Senior Foreign Service Appointment
● Career Senior Executive Service (SES) Appointment ○ Non-Career Senior Executive Service (SES) Appointment ■ Postal Career Executive Service

Naval Service Training Command (NSTC)
2601A Paul Jones Street, Great Lakes, IL 60088-2845
Tel: (847) 688-3400

Commander
RDML Michael D. "Mike" Bernacchi, Jr. USN . . . . (847) 688-3400
Education: Detroit
Chief of Staff **CAPT W. Douglas Pfeifle USN** . . . . (847) 688-3400
Command Master Chief
CMDCM Jimmy W. Hailey III USN . . . . (847) 688-3400
Executive Director **Dr. Guerry "Rusty" Hagins** . . . . (847) 688-3400
Public Affairs Officer **(Vacant)** . . . . (847) 688-4271 ext. 349

Navy Supply Corps School (NSCS)
1378 Porter Avenue, Newport, RI 02841
Tel: (401) 841-4800 Internet: www.netc.navy.mil/centers/css/nscs

Commanding Officer **CAPT Nickolas L. Rapley USN** . . . . (401) 841-4800
Executive Officer **William Barich** . . . . (401) 841-4800

Center for Service Support
1183 Cushing Road, Newport, RI 02841
Tel: (401) 841-1268 Internet: www.netc.navy.mil/centers/css

Commanding Officer **CAPT Jonathan Haynes USN** . . . . (401) 841-1268
Executive Director **Frederic M. Schomburg** . . . . (401) 841-1268
Command Master Chief **Craig Cole** . . . . (401) 841-1268

Naval War College (NWC)
686 Cushing Road, Newport, RI 02841-1207
Tel: (401) 841-2220 Fax: (401) 841-6309 Internet: www.usnwc.edu

President **RADM Jeffrey A. Harley USN** . . . . (401) 841-2266
E-mail: presidents_office@usnwc.edu
Education: Minnesota BA; Naval War MA
Provost **Dr. Lewis M. Duncan** . . . . (401) 841-7004
E-mail: lewis.duncan@usnwc.edu
Education: Rice 1973 BA, 1976 MS, 1977 PhD
Associate Provost **James E. "Jay" Hickey PhD** . . . . (401) 841-3499
E-mail: hickeyj@usnwc.edu
Education: Naval Acad 1980 BS; Troy U; King's Col (UK); Salve Regina U PhD
Deputy/Chief of Staff **Tamara K. Graham USN** . . . . (401) 841-2245
E-mail: tamara.graham@usnwc.edu
Dean of Academic Affairs **Phil M. Haun** . . . . (401) 841-6431
E-mail: phil.haun@usnwc.edu
Dean of International Programs **Thomas E. Mangold** . . . . (401) 841-2074
E-mail: thomas.mangold@usnwc.edu
Education: Harvard BA, MPA
Dean of Leadership and Ethics
RDML Margaret DeLuca Klein USN (Ret) . . . . (401) 841-3665
E-mail: margaret.klein@usnwc.edu
Dean of the College of Distance Education
Leonard Wildemann . . . . (401) 841-3780
E-mail: wildemal@usnwc.edu
Dean of the College of Maritime Operational Warfare
RADM Michael S. "Mike" White USN (Ret) . . . . (401) 841-7560
E-mail: michael.white@usnwc.edu
Education: Colorado 1983; Webster 2005 MA
Dean of Students **CAPT Patrick E. "Pat" Keyes USN** . . . (401) 841-6594
E-mail: patrick.keyes@usnwc.edu
E-mail: studentpoc@usnwc.edu
Library Director **Allen C. Benson PhD** . . . . (401) 841-2641
E-mail: allen.benson@usnwc.edu Fax: (401) 841-6491
Education: Minnesota 1974 BFA; Alabama 1993 MLS; Pittsburgh 2011 PhD
Chief Information Officer and Director of Information Resources **(Vacant)** . . . . (401) 841-6958

Naval Facilities Engineering Command (NAVFAC)
1322 Patterson Avenue, SE, Washington Navy Yard, DC 20374-5065
Tel: (202) 685-1423 (Public Affairs Office) Internet: www.navfac.navy.mil

Component Commands

Naval Facilities Engineering Command (NAVFAC) Atlantic (NAVFACLANT)
6506 Hampton Boulevard, Norfolk, VA 23508-1278
Tel: (757) 322-8000
Areas Covered: NC, PR, Caribbean, Central America, Cuba, South America
Public Affairs Officer **Michael "Mike" Andrews** . . . . (757) 322-8005
Fax: (757) 322-8219

Naval Facilities Engineering Command (NAVFAC) Europe, Africa and Southwest Asia (NAVFAC EURAFSWA)
Viale Porto Box 51, Naples, Italy
Mail: PSC 817, Box 51, FPO, AE 09622-0051
Tel: 39 (081) 568-7700
Commanding Officer **CAPT Maria Aguayo USN** 39 (081) 568-7700

Naval Facilities Engineering Command (NAVFAC) Mid-Atlantic (NAVFACMIDLANT)
9742 Maryland Avenue, Norfolk, VA 23511-3095
Tel: (757) 341-1410
Areas Covered: PA, VA, WV
Commander **CAPT Richard D. "Rick" Hayes III USN** . . . (757) 341-1431
E-mail: richard.d.hayes1@navy.mil
Executive Officer **CAPT Jeff Lengkeek USN** . . . . (757) 341-1431
Public Affairs Officer **JC Kreidel** . . . . (757) 341-1410

Naval Facilities Engineering Command (NAVFAC) Northwest (NAVFACNW)
1101 Tautog Circle, Silverdale, WA 98315-1101
Tel: (360) 396-0043 Fax: (360) 396-0855
Commanding Officer
CAPT Christopher M. "Chris" Kurgan USN . . . . (360) 396-0043
Education: Vanderbilt 1990 BE
Public Affairs Officer **Leslie Ann Yuenger** . . . . (360) 396-6387
E-mail: leslie.yuenger@navy.mil Fax: (360) 396-0852

Naval Facilities Engineering Command (NAVFAC) Southeast (NAVFAC SOUTHEAST)
Naval Air Station Jacksonville, Box 30, Jacksonville, FL 32212-0030
Tel: (904) 542-6633 Fax: (904) 542-6634
Executive Officer **CAPT Gil Manalo CEC, USN** . . . . (904) 542-6633
Public Affairs Officer **Susan Brink** . . . . (904) 542-6622
P.O. Box 30, Jacksonville, FL 32212-0030
E-mail: susan.brink@navy.mil
FOIA Coordinator **Pat Spann** . . . . (904) 542-5836
E-mail: pat.spann@navy.mil Fax: (904) 542-2220

Public Works Department, Pensacola (FL) (PWD-Pensacola)
Building 3560, 310 John Towers Road, Pensacola, FL 32508-5303
Tel: (850) 452-3131 Fax: (850) 452-2893
Public Works Officer **CDR Brent Paul USN** . . . . (850) 452-3131 ext. 3000
Operations Officer **(Vacant)** . . . . (850) 452-3131
Contracting Officer
LCDR Alfred Nuzzolo USN . . . . (850) 452-3131 ext. 3004
E-mail: alfred.nuzzolo@navy.mil

Naval Facilities Engineering Command (NAVFAC) Southwest (NAVFAC SWDIV)
1220 Pacific Highway, San Diego, CA 92132-5190
Tel: (619) 532-2317 Fax: (619) 532-3830
Commanding Officer **CAPT Mark K. Edelson USN** . . . . . (619) 532-2317
E-mail: mark.edelson@navy.mil
Education: VMI 1989 BS; Penn State 1997 MS
Executive Officer **CAPT Jeff Powell USN** . . . . (619) 532-2317
Public Affairs Officer **Lee Saunders** . . . . (619) 532-3100
E-mail: lee.saunders@navy.mil

★ Presidential Appointment Requiring Senate Confirmation ☆ Presidential Appointment ☐ Schedule C Appointment ◇ Career Senior Foreign Service Appointment
● Career Senior Executive Service (SES) Appointment ○ Non-Career Senior Executive Service (SES) Appointment ■ Postal Career Executive Service

Naval Facilities Engineering Command (NAVFAC) Washington (NAVFACWASH)
WNY Building 212, 1314 Harwood Street, SE,
Suite 426, Washington Navy Yard, DC 20374-5018
Tel: (202) 685-3300 Fax: (202) 433-5759
Areas Covered: MD, Naval District Washington, Northern VA

Commanding Officer
CAPT Andrew "Drew" Hascall USN .... (202) 685-3300
Public Affairs Officer **Regina F. "Gina" Adams** .... (202) 685-0384
E-mail: regina.adams@navy.mil
Lead Deputy for Small Business **(Vacant)** .... (202) 685-0088

Naval Facilities Engineering Command (NAVFAC) Pacific (NAVFACP)
258 Makalapa Drive, Suite 100, Pearl Harbor, HI 96860-3134
Tel: (808) 472-1000

Commander **RDML John Adametz USN** .... (808) 472-1000
Education: VMI 1989 BSME; Penn State 1997 MSCE
Vice Commander **CAPT Brian Weinstein USN** .... (808) 472-1000

Naval Facilities Engineering Command (NAVFAC) Far East (NAVFACFE)
Yokosuka, Japan
Mail: PSC 473, Box 13, FPO, AP 96349-0013
Tel: 81 46-816-7711 Fax: 81 616-043-7098
E-mail: navfacfe-pao@fe.navy.mil

Commanding Officer
CAPT Michael D. Kennedy, Jr. USN 81 46-816-7711

Naval Facilities Engineering Command (NAVFAC) Hawaii (NAVFAC Hawaii - Joint Base Pearl Harbor-Hickam)
400 Marshall Road, Joint Base Pearl Harbor-Hickam, HI 96860-3139
Tel: (808) 471-3926 Fax: (808) 471-5024

Commanding Officer **CAPT Marc R. Delao USN** .... (808) 471-3926
Command Information Officer **Brian Nobunaga** .... (808) 474-3954
E-mail: brian.nobunaga@navy.mil Fax: (808) 471-8659
Public Affairs Officer **Denise Emsley** .... (808) 471-7300
E-mail: denise.emsley@navy.mil Fax: (808) 474-5479

Naval Facilities Engineering Command (NAVFAC) Marianas
PSC 455, Box 195, FPO, AP 96540-2937
Tel: (671) 349-5100 Fax: (671) 349-7148

Commanding Officer **CAPT Daniel P. Turner USN** ...... (671) 349-5100
Executive Officer **CDR Paul Chan USN** .... (671) 349-5101
Operations Officer **CDR Warren LeBeau USN** .... (671) 349-5100
Director, Management Services **Arlene B. Sablan** .... (671) 349-5100
E-mail: arlene.sablan@fe.navy.mil

Specialty Centers

Naval Facilities Engineering and Expeditionary Warfare Center (NAVFAC EXWC)
1000 23rd Avenue, Port Hueneme, CA 93043-4301
Fax: (805) 982-5819

Commanding Officer **CAPT Mike Saum USN** .... (805) 982-1254
Education: Union Col (NY) 1992 BCE; UC Berkeley MCE
Executive Officer **CAPT Jeffrey Kilian USN** .... (805) 982-2111
Command Master Chief
CMDCM Shawn Hollister USN .... (805) 982-2111
Public Affairs Officer **MC Palmer Pinckney II USN** ..... (805) 982-2056
Education: UC Berkeley 1984 BA; Chapman 2012 BASc
Technical Director and SBIR Program Manager
Kail Macias .... (805) 982-2111
E-mail: Kail.macias@navy.mil
Education: Cal State (Northridge) 1990 BSME, 2001 MSE

Navy Crane Center
Norfolk Naval Shipyard, Building 491, Portsmouth, VA 23709
Tel: (757) 967-3803 Fax: (757) 967-3808

• Director **(Vacant)** .... (757) 967-3800

Naval Sea Systems Command (NAVSEA)
1333 Isaac Hull Avenue, SE, Washington Navy Yard, DC 20376-0001
Tel: (202) 781-1010 Tel: (202) 781-4123 (Media Inquiries)
Fax: (202) 781-0111 Internet: www.navsea.navy.mil

Naval Shipyards

Norfolk Naval Shipyard
Portsmouth, VA 23709-5000
Tel: (757) 396-8615

Commander **CAPT Kai O. Torkelson USN** .... (757) 396-9333
Executive Officer **CAPT Daniel M. Rossler USN** .... (757) 396-8615
Command Master Chief
CMDCM Michael L. Reese USN .... (757) 396-8615
Public Affairs Officer **Jeffrey R. "Jeff" Cunningham** ... (757) 396-9559
E-mail: jeffrey.r.cunningham@navy.mil Fax: (757) 396-8005

Pearl Harbor Naval Shipyard and Intermediate Maintenance Facility (PHNSY)
667 Safeguard, Suite 100, Pearl Harbor, HI 96860-5033
Tel: (808) 474-9119 Fax: (808) 474-9033

Commander **CAPT Gregory D. Burton USN** .... (808) 474-9119
Education: New Mexico 1991 BSME
Deputy Commander **CDR Scott E. Shea USN** .... (808) 474-9119
E-mail: scott.shea@navy.mil
Education: Thomas Edison State
Executive Director
CAPT Alexander S. Desroches USN (Ret) .... (808) 474-9119
Education: Missouri (Rolla) BSE; MIT MME
Command Master Chief
CMDCM James Schneider USN .... (808) 474-9119
• Nuclear Engineering and Planning Manager
Gregory Kaipo Crowell .... (808) 474-9119
Chief of Congressional and Public Affairs
Christian P. Hodge .... (808) 474-0272
Education: U Incarnate Word 2016 MA;
Texas State (San Marcos) 2002 BAS

Portsmouth Naval Shipyard
Portsmouth, NH 03804-5000
Tel: (207) 438-1000 Fax: (207) 438-1266

Commanding Officer **CAPT David S. Hunt USN** .... (207) 438-2700
Deputy Commander **CDR Ritchie Taylor USN** .... (207) 438-2700
Command Master Chief
CMDCM Ashley Roy Drake USN .... (207) 438-2700
Public Affairs Officer **Danna Eddy** .... (207) 438-3975
E-mail: danna.eddy@navy.mil

Puget Sound Naval Shipyard and Intermediate Maintenance Facility
1400 Farragut Avenue, Bremerton, WA 98314-5001
Tel: (360) 476-7111 Fax: (360) 476-0937

Shipyard Commander **CAPT Howard B. Markle USN** ... (360) 476-3161
E-mail: cindi.schaum@navy.mil Fax: (360) 476-8740
Commanding Officer **CAPT Eric Woelper USN** .... (360) 476-3161
Fax: (360) 476-8740
Executive Officer **CDR Jeffrey R. Shipman USN** .... (360) 476-3161
Command Master Chief
CMDCM Paul W. Coffin USN .... (360) 315-1103
Fax: (360) 476-8740

SUPSHIPs

Supervisor of Shipbuilding, Conversion and Repair, Bath (ME) (SUPSHIP Bath)
574 Washington Street, Bath, ME 04530-1905
Tel: (207) 442-2773 Fax: (207) 442-1420

Supervisor of Shipbuilding
CAPT Joseph M. "Joe" Tuite USN .... (207) 442-2253
Education: Naval Acad 1992 BSE; Naval Postgrad MSME
Deputy Supervisor of Shipbuilding **Robert J. Footer** .... (207) 442-2253
E-mail: footerrj@supship.navy.mil
Public Affairs **Kristen Mason** .... (207) 442-2731
Freedom of Information Act Officer
Donnie Spiegelman-Boyd .... (207) 442-3496
Fax: (207) 442-5400

(continued on next page)

★ Presidential Appointment Requiring Senate Confirmation ☆ Presidential Appointment □ Schedule C Appointment ◇ Career Senior Foreign Service Appointment
● Career Senior Executive Service (SES) Appointment ○ Non-Career Senior Executive Service (SES) Appointment ■ Postal Career Executive Service

Supervisor of Shipbuilding, Conversion and Repair, Bath (ME)
(continued)

Contracting Officer
CDR Jeffery J. "Jeff" Mason USN (207) 442-2471
E-mail: jeffery.mason@supshipba.navy.mil
Small Business Officer **Carol Britt** (207) 442-2738
E-mail: brittcl@supship.navy.mil
Training Officer **Tim Crossley** (207) 442-2156
Fax: (207) 442-3511
Security Manager **Russell "Russ" Wrede** (207) 442-3186
E-mail: robert.russell@navy.mil Fax: (207) 442-2718

Supervisor of Shipbuilding, Conversion and Repair, Gulf Coast (SUPSHIP Gulf Coast)
P.O. Box 7003, Pascagoula, MS 39568-7003
Tel: (228) 769-4247

Supervisor of Shipbuilding
CAPT Brian Lawrence USN (228) 769-4247

Supervisor of Shipbuilding, Conversion and Repair, Groton (CT) (SUPSHIP Groton)
73 Eastern Point Road, Groton, CT 06340
Tel: (860) 433-2459

Commanding Officer **CAPT Jeffrey Heydon USN** (860) 433-2459
Deputy Supervisor **Gary W. Kirkpatrick** (860) 433-2459

Supervisor of Shipbuilding, Conversion and Repair, Newport News (VA) (SUPSHIP Newport News)
Building Two, 4101 Washington Avenue, Newport News, VA 23607
Tel: (757) 380-4221

Commanding Officer **CAPT Jason Lloyd USN** (757) 380-4221
Deputy Supervisor **Todd Bockwoldt** (757) 380-4221
Education: Georgia Tech BE, ME

Navy Regional Maintenance Center (CNRMC)
9170 Second Avenue, Norfolk, VA 23511
Tel: (757) 444-3001

Commander **RDML James Downey USN** (757) 444-3001

Mid Atlantic Regional Maintenance Center (MARMC)
9170 Second Street, Suite 120, Norfolk, VA 23511-2393
9727 Avionics Loop, Norfolk, VA 23511-2124
Tel: (757) 443-3872 Tel: (757) 443-3872 ext. 1668 (Public Affairs)
E-mail: marmc_nrfk_1100p_public_affairs@navy.mil

Commanding Officer
CAPT Daniel L. Lannamann USN (757) 443-3872 ext. 4210
Executive Director **Dennis G. Bevington** (757) 443-3872 ext. 4116
Executive Officer
CAPT Steve W. Connell USN (757) 443-3872 ext. 4409
Command Master Chief
CMDCM Timothy D. Bailey USN (757) 443-3872

Southwest Regional Maintenance Center
3755 Brinzer Street, Suite One, San Diego, CA 92136-5299
Tel: (619) 556-1500 Fax: (619) 556-1715
Internet: http://www.swrmc.navy.mil/

Commander **CAPT David Hart USN** (619) 556-2071
Education: North Carolina State BS; Naval Postgrad MSME
Executive Officer **CDR Steven R. Reynolds USN** (619) 556-2071
Executive Director **John Robinson** (619) 556-2071
Education: Air Force Acad 1981 BSEE; Naval Postgrad 1987 MSME
Command Master Chief
CMDCM Asa Worcester USN (619) 556-2477

Naval Surface Warfare Center (NSWC)
1333 Isaac Hull Avenue, SE, Washington Navy Yard, DC 20376-0001

Commander
RDML Thomas J. "Tom" Anderson USN (202) 781-1010
E-mail: thomas.j.anderson3@navy.mil
Education: Boston U 1991 BS; Naval Postgrad MS
Executive Director **Donald F. McCormack** (202) 781-1715
E-mail: donald.mccormack@navy.mil
Education: UMass (Dartmouth) 1985 BSEE

Naval Surface Warfare Center, Carderock (MD) Division (NSWCCD)
9500 MacArthur Boulevard, West Bethesda, MD 20817-5700
Tel: (301) 227-1330

Commander **CAPT Mark R. Vandroff USN** (301) 227-1515
E-mail: mark.vandroff@navy.mil
● Technical Director (Acting) **Dr. Paul Shang** (301) 227-1628
E-mail: paul.shang@navy.mil
Corporate Information Services Director
Michael "Mike" Kirby (301) 227-1067
Small Business Specialist **Irene Katacinski** (215) 897-7596
5001 South Broad Street, Philadelphia, PA 19112-1403
Chief of Technology **Jack Templeton** (301) 227-5572
E-mail: jack.templeton@navy.mil
Environmental, Safety and Health Department Head
Joe Barger (301) 227-0144
Naval Architecture and Engineering Department
Michael S. Brown (301) 227-3412
Operations Department **Tamar Gallagher** (301) 227-2478
Ship Signatures Department **Dr. Paul Shang** (301) 227-1895
E-mail: paul.shang@navy.mil
Survivability, Structures and Materials Department
Gerard P. Mercier (301) 227-5068
Technical Information Center **Kenneth L. Myers** (301) 227-1319
E-mail: kenneth.l.myers@navy.mil Fax: (301) 227-4428

Naval Surface Warfare Center, Corona (CA) Division
2300 Fifth Street, Norco, CA 92860
Mail: P.O. Box 5000, Corona, CA 92878-5000
Tel: (951) 273-5000 Fax: (951) 273-4205

Commanding Officer
CAPT Richard A. Braunbeck III USN (951) 273-5123
● Technical Director **Dianne M. Costlow** (951) 273-5000
Education: Kansas State 1985 BSIE; Cal State (Dominguez) 1995
Public Affairs Officer **Troy Clarke** (951) 273-5137
E-mail: troy.clarke@navy.mil Fax: (951) 273-4655

Naval Surface Warfare Center, Crane (IN) Division (NSWC Crane)
300 Highway 361, Crane, IN 47522-5001
Tel: (812) 854-1762 Fax: (812) 854-4165 E-mail: info@crane.navy.mil

Commanding Officer **CAPT Mark Oesterreich USN** (812) 854-1210
Chief Engineer, Small Arms Weapons Systems Division **David Long** (812) 854-1762
Chief of Staff **Angie Lewis** (812) 854-1762
Education: Ball State
Chief Technology Officer **Rob Walker** (812) 854-1762
Education: Evansville BS; Rose-Hulman MS; Indiana MPA
Contracting Officer **Kelly Siffin** (812) 854-3705
E-mail: kelly.siffin@navy.mil
Corporate Communications **Sandy Zehr** (812) 854-1865
Corporate Operations Director **(Vacant)** (812) 854-1762
Deputy for Small Business **Matt Burkett** (812) 854-1542
E-mail: matt.burkett@navy.mil
Director Human Resources **Jim Harden** (812) 854-3838
Building 2, NAVSURFWARCENDIV, Code 0581, Crane, IN 47522-5001 Fax: (812) 854-1066
Director, Special Warfare and Expeditionary Systems Department **Patricia Herndon** (812) 854-1762
Manager, Maneuver and Engagement Division
Adam Parslay (812) 854-1762
Manager, Surveillance and Reconnaissance Systems Division **(Vacant)** (812) 854-1762
Project Manager, Applied Science and Demand Management Department **Eric Moody** (812) 854-1762
Public Affairs Officer **Pamela Ingram** (812) 854-3239
E-mail: pamela.ingram@navy.mil
Staffing and Classification Branch Manager, Human Resources Division **Lucinda "Cindy" Shirley** (812) 854-1762
● Technical Director **Dr. Brett Seidle** (812) 854-3666

★ Presidential Appointment Requiring Senate Confirmation ☆ Presidential Appointment ☐ Schedule C Appointment ◇ Career Senior Foreign Service Appointment
● Career Senior Executive Service (SES) Appointment ○ Non-Career Senior Executive Service (SES) Appointment ■ Postal Career Executive Service

Naval Surface Warfare Center, Dahlgren (VA) Division
Building 180, 6149 Welsh Road, Dahlgren, VA 22448-5100
Tel: (540) 653-8152 (Public Affairs)
Tel: (540) 653-8101 (Commanding Officer)
Tel: (540) 653-8291 (Base Operator) Fax: (540) 653-4679

Commander **CAPT Godfrey "Gus" Weekes USN** ...... (540) 653-8101
Education: Savannah State BS
• Technical Director **John G. Fiore** .... (540) 653-8103
Education: Drexel BSEE, MSEE
Corporate Communications **Alan Black** .... (540) 653-6011
E-mail: alan.black@navy.mil
Freedom of Information Act Officer **Laurie Muir** .... (540) 653-7578
E-mail: laurie.muir@navy.mil
Small Business Deputy **Kristofer "Kris" Parker** .... (540) 653-4806
E-mail: kristofer.parker@navy.mil
College Recruitment Program Manager
Margaret "Ally" Regan .... (540) 653-8941
17632 Dahlgren Road, Dahlgren, VA 22448-5154
E-mail: margaret.regan@navy.mil
Weapons, Control, Integration Department
John Lysher .... (540) 653-8535
E-mail: john.lysher@navy.mil
Electromagnetic and Sensors System Department
Darren Barnes .... (540) 653-1218
E-mail: darren.barnes@navy.mil
Corporate Operations Department
Michael "Mike" Purello .... (540) 653-2769
E-mail: michael.purello@navy.mil
Strategic and Computing Systems Department
Stephen K. "Kyle" Jones .... (540) 653-8111
E-mail: stephen.k.jones@navy.mil
Warfare Systems Engineering and Integration
Department **Stephanie Hornbaker** .... (540) 653-1446
E-mail: stephanie.hornbaker@navy.mil
Gun and Electric Weapon Systems Department
Michael "Mike" Till .... (540) 653-8831
E-mail: michael.till@navy.mil
Education: Notre Dame 1984 BSChE
Readiness and Training Systems Department
Bobby Stark .... (540) 653-2828
Librarian **Jon Dodd** .... (540) 653-2630
E-mail: jon.dodd@navy.mil

Naval Surface Warfare Center, Dahlgren Division Dam Neck Activity
1922 Regulus Avenue, Virginia Beach, VA 23461-2097
Tel: (757) 492-6155 Fax: (757) 492-8370

Commanding Officer
CDR Andrew "A.J." Hoffman USN .... (757) 492-6311
Education: North Carolina 1999 BA; Naval Postgrad 2006 MS
Director of Corporate Communications **(Vacant)** .... (757) 492-6155
Fax: (757) 492-8370
Chief of Staff **Nancy J. Maloy** .... (757) 492-6155
Technical Operations Manager
Dr. Martin "Marty" Irvine .... (757) 492-6155
E-mail: martin.irvine@navy.mil

Naval Surface Warfare Center, Indian Head (MD) Explosive Ordnance Disposal Technology Division (NSWC IHEODTD)
3767 Strauss Avenue, Suite 201, Indian Head, MD 20640
Tel: (301) 744-4304

Commander **CAPT Scott H. Kraft USN** .... (301) 744-4401
Executive Officer **(Vacant)** .... (301) 744-4401
Fax: (301) 744-4935
Technical Director **Ashley G. Johnson** .... (301) 744-6519
Education: Rochester 1987 BSME
Public Affairs Officer **Holly Dodds** .... (301) 744-6505
Contracts and Acquisition **Penny Kennedy** .... (301) 744-6626
Fax: (301) 744-6620
Librarian-in-Charge **Eugene Bruce** .... (301) 744-4742
Naval Surface Warfare Center, Building 299, Fax: (301) 744-4192
Indian Head, MD 20640

Naval Surface Warfare Center, Panama City (FL) Division
1700 Thomas Drive, Panama City, FL 32407
Tel: (850) 230-7400 (Main Line) Tel: (850) 234-4011 (Base Operator)

Commander **CAPT Aaron Peters USN** .... (850) 234-4201
• Technical Director **Edwin A. Stewart** .... (850) 234-4202
Education: Old Dominion 1985 BSEE, 1994 MBA
Freedom of Information Act Officer **Jim Sheperd** .... (850) 234-4915
Public Affairs Officer **Jacqui L. Barker** .... (850) 636-6168
Research and Technology Applications Office Director
Edward C. Linsenmeyer .... (850) 234-4161
110 Vernon Avenue, Panama City, FL 32407 Fax: (850) 235-5374
Small Business Specialist **Gerald Sorrell** .... (850) 235-5328
E-mail: gerald.sorrell@navy.mil

Naval Surface Warfare Center, Philadelphia (PA) Division
5001 South Broad Street, Philadelphia, PA 19112-1403
Tel: (215) 897-7700

Commanding Officer
CAPT Francis E. Spencer III USN .... (215) 897-7005

Naval Surface Warfare Center, Port Hueneme (CA) Division
4363 Missile Way, Port Hueneme, CA 93043-4307
Tel: (805) 228-8700 Fax: (805) 228-8244
E-mail: nswcphd_cco@navy.mil

Commanding Officer
CAPT Rafael "Ray" Acevedo USN .... (805) 228-8238
• Technical Director **Paul D. Mann** .... (805) 228-8238
Command Communications Manager **Michelle Heaton** ... (805) 228-5125
E-mail: michelle.harris@navy.mil

Naval Undersea Warfare Center (NUWC)
1176 Howell Street, Newport, RI 02841
Tel: (401) 832-6892

Commander **RDML Moises DelToro III USN** .... (202) 781-4005
E-mail: moises.deltoro@navy.mil
Executive Director **Donald F. McCormack** .... (202) 781-1715
E-mail: donald.mccormack@navy.mil
Education: UMass (Dartmouth) 1985 BSEE

Naval Undersea Warfare Center, Division Keyport (WA)
610 Dowell Street, Keyport, WA 98345-7610
Tel: (360) 396-2699 E-mail: kypt_pao@navy.mil

Commander **CAPT Jon H. Moretty USN** .... (360) 396-2340
Executive Officer **CDR Carlos J. Cintron USN** .... (360) 396-2340
E-mail: carlos.cintron@navy.mil
• Division Technical Director **Alan D. Kent** .... (360) 396-2987
Division Deputy Technical Director **Eric R. Gillespie** ..... (360) 396-2987
Public Affairs Officer **Wendy Miles** .... (360) 396-2699
E-mail: wendy.miles@navy.mil Fax: (360) 396-2387

Naval Undersea Warfare Center, Division Newport (RI)
1176 Howell Street, Newport, RI 02841
Tel: (401) 832-6892 Fax: (401) 832-4661

Commander **CAPT Michael R. Coughlin USN** .... (401) 832-3344
Education: Northwestern 1990 BS
• Technical Director **Ronald A. "Ron" Vien** .... (401) 832-3344
Deputy for Small Business **Stephen Stewart** .... (401) 832-1766
Commercial Acquisition Department, Building 11, Simonpetri Drive,
Code 00SB, Newport, RI 02841
Public Affairs Officer **David Sanders** .... (401) 832-3611
E-mail: david.sanders2@navy.mil

★ Presidential Appointment Requiring Senate Confirmation ☆ Presidential Appointment ☐ Schedule C Appointment ◇ Career Senior Foreign Service Appointment
● Career Senior Executive Service (SES) Appointment ○ Non-Career Senior Executive Service (SES) Appointment ■ Postal Career Executive Service

Naval Supply Systems Command (NAVSUP)

P.O. Box 2050, Mechanicsburg, PA 17055-0791
Building 309, 5450 Carlisle Pike, Mechanicsburg, PA 17055-0791
Tel: (717) 605-5954 (Media Inquiries and Corporate Communications)
Fax: (717) 605-5938
Internet: https://www.navsup.navy.mil/public/navsup/home/

NAVSUP Global Logistics Support

937 North Harbor Drive, Suite 1, San Diego, CA 92132-0001
Tel: (619) 532-2203 Fax: (619) 532-2304

Commander
RDML Grafton D. "Chip" Chase, Jr. USNR .... (619) 532-2203
Chief of Staff **CAPT Derric T. Turner USN** .... (619) 532-2200
Education: Naval Acad BS
Deputy Chief of Staff
LT Bobby Schmermund SC, USN .... (619) 532-2773
Flag Lieutenant **(Vacant)** .... (619) 532-4803
• Vice Commander **William E. Bickert, Jr.** .... (619) 532-2203
E-mail: william.bickert@navy.mil
Education: Villanova BS; Florida MBA
Command Master Chief
CMDCM Chris Fitzgerald USN .... (619) 532-4607

Fleet Logistics Center Jacksonville

110 Yorktown Avenue, Jacksonville, FL 32212
Tel: (904) 542-1000 Fax: (904) 542-5477

Commanding Officer
CAPT Matthew "Matt" Ott USN .... (904) 542-1263
Education: VMI; North Carolina MBA
Executive Officer **CDR Stuart M. Day USN** .... (904) 542-1003
Executive Director **Kevin F. Mooney** .... (904) 542-1000 ext. 219
Education: St Edward's BA; Naval Postgrad MS
Command Master Chief
MCPO Christopher E. Smith USN .... (904) 542-1000 ext. 141
Corporate Communications Director **Barbara Burch** .... (904) 542-4269

Fleet Logistics Center Norfolk

1968 Gilbert Street, Norfolk, VA 23511-3392
Tel: (757) 443-1013 Fax: (757) 443-1015

Commanding Officer **CAPT James M. Lowther USN** .... (757) 443-1001
Executive Officer **CAPT Craig L. Abraham USN** .... (757) 443-1001
Executive Director **Dale C. Rieck** .... (757) 443-1001
E-mail: dale.rieck@navy.mil
Education: South Carolina BS
Command Master Chief
CMDCM Claude M. Henderson, Jr. USN .... (757) 443-1153
Director of Corporate Communications
Thomas A. "Tom" Kreidel .... (757) 443-1013
E-mail: thomas.kreidel@navy.mil
Information Systems Coordinator **Chris Harris** .... (757) 443-1523
Deputy for Small Business **(Vacant)** .... (757) 443-1435

DLA Cheatham Annex

One C Street, DLA Cheatham Annex, Williamsburg, VA 23185-5830
Tel: (757) 887-7111 Tel: (757) 887-4154 Fax: (757) 887-7223

Director **Jeffry May** .... (757) 887-7111
E-mail: jeffry.may@dla.mil

Fleet Logistics Center Pearl Harbor (FLCPH)

1942 Gaffney Street, Suite 100, Pearl Harbor, HI 96860-4549
Fax: (808) 473-2578

Commanding Officer **CAPT Eric A. Morgan USN** .... (808) 473-0961
Education: Carnegie Mellon 1993 BS; Naval Postgrad
Executive Officer **CDR Michael S. Carl USN** .... (808) 473-0962
Executive Director **Mona A. Yamada** .... (808) 473-7672
E-mail: mona.yamada@navy.mil
Senior Enlisted Advisor **MCPO Gary Daniels USN** .... (808) 473-0961

Fleet Logistics Center Puget Sound (FLCPS)

467 W Street, Bremerton, WA 98314-5100
Tel: (360) 476-2914 Fax: (360) 476-0303

Commanding Officer **CAPT Bernard D. Knox USN** .... (360) 476-7525

Fleet Logistics Center Puget Sound *(continued)*

Executive Officer **CDR Derwin B. Proby SC, USN** .... (360) 476-7524
Education: Chapman
Executive Director **John H. Hornbrook III** .... (360) 476-7523

Fleet Logistics Center San Diego (FLCSD)

3985 Cummings Road, San Diego, CA 92213
Tel: (619) 556-2220 Fax: (619) 556-3049

Commanding Officer **CAPT Brian J. Anderson USN** .... (619) 556-2220
Education: St Michael's BS; Michigan State MBA
Executive Director **Chachi Gorman** .... (619) 556-2219
E-mail: chachi.gorman@navy.mil
Secretary **Sirell Lane** .... (619) 556-2220
E-mail: sirell.lane@navy.mil
Executive Officer **CDR Sean A. Neer USN** .... (619) 556-2217
Senior Enlisted Advisor **CMDCS Nicole Ellis USN** .... (619) 556-0412
Corporate Communications Director
Candice B. Villarreal .... (619) 556-2221
E-mail: candice.villarreal@navy.mil Fax: (619) 556-2239
Comptroller **David Donnell** .... (619) 532-3030
Office of Counsel **Robert McCall** .... (619) 556-5313
Business Director **William H. "Bill" Weinfurtner** .... (619) 556-2277
E-mail: william.weinfurtner@navy.mil
Contracts Director **CDR Joel P. Pitel USN** .... (619) 556-5312
Fuel Management Director **Daniel Maldonado** .... (619) 553-1312
Industrial Support Department Director **Craig Horton** .... (619) 556-8217
Personal Property Director
LCDR Troy Weidenmiller USN .... (619) 556-6683
E-mail: personal.property@navy.mil
Security Director **Alicia Braceland** .... (619) 556-3758
Supply Management Department Director
LCDR Brian P. Madden USN .... (619) 556-8388

Fleet Logistics Center Sigonella

PSC 812, Box 3560, FPO, AE 09627
Fax: 39 (095) 86-5064

Commanding Officer **CAPT Dion English USN** 39 (095) 86-2944
Executive Officer **CDR Terry C. Grigsby USN** 39 (095) 86-2944
Executive Director **Bong A. Cabling** 39 (095) 86-2944
Command Master Chief
CMDCM Mark Schlosser USN 39 (095) 86-2944

Fleet Logistics Center Yokosuka

PSC 473, Box 11, FPO, AP 96349-0011
Fax: 81 (468) 16-9104

Commanding Officer **CAPT Frank Nevarez USN** 81 (468) 16-7077
Executive Director
CAPT Andrew L. "Andy" Benson SC, USN (Ret) 81 (468) 16-7078
E-mail: andrew.l.benson@navy.mil
Executive Officer **CDR Jayson Cramer SC, USN** 81 (468) 16-7078
E-mail: jayson.cramer@navy.mil
Command Master Chief
CMDCM Steve E. Horton USN 81 (468) 16-7310

Space and Naval Warfare Systems Command (SPAWAR)

Building Old Town, 4301 Pacific Highway,
Building OT1, San Diego, CA 92110-3127
Fax: (619) 524-7010 Fax: (619) 524-3469 (Public Affairs)

Space and Naval Warfare (SPAWAR) Systems Center Atlantic (SSC Atlantic)

Building 3147, One Innovation Drive,
Floor 2, North Charleston, SC 29406
Tel: (843) 218-4000 Tel: (843) 218-3390

Commanding Officer **CAPT Wesley S. Sanders USN** .... (843) 218-5000
Education: Jacksonville U
Executive Officer **CDR Lane C. Askew USN** .... (843) 218-3390
• Executive Director **Christopher A. Miller** .... (843) 218-5009
Education: Vanderbilt BA
Command Master Chief
ITC Mildred Rivera-Fisher USN .... (843) 218-3390
Public Affairs Officer **Lonnie Cowart** .... (843) 218-5801

★ Presidential Appointment Requiring Senate Confirmation ☆ Presidential Appointment ☐ Schedule C Appointment ◇ Career Senior Foreign Service Appointment
● Career Senior Executive Service (SES) Appointment ○ Non Career Senior Executive Service (SES) Appointment ■ Postal Career Executive Service

Space and Naval Warfare (SPAWAR) Systems Center Pacific (SSC Pacific)

CO - Space and Naval Warfare Systems Center,
53560 Hull Street, San Diego, CA 92152-5001
Tel: (619) 553-3000 Tel: (619) 553-2717 (Public Affairs Office)
Fax: (619) 524-3469 Internet: www.public.navy.mil/spawar/pacific

Commanding Officer
CAPT Melvin K. "Mel" Yokoyama USN . . . . (619) 553-3000
Executive Director **Bill Bonwit** . . . . (619) 553-3010
Command Master Chief **LSC Rafael Rios, Jr. USN** . . . . . . (619) 553-3000
Contracts Director **Sharon Pritchard** . . . . (619) 553-4492
E-mail: sharon.pritchard@navy.mil
• Command and Control Department Head **(Vacant)** . . . . (619) 553-3400
Fax: (619) 553-4153
• Communications, Networks, and Cyber Security Department Head **Susie Hartzog** . . . . (619) 553-3800
E-mail: susie.hartzog@navy.mil
Education: San Diego 1989 BSEE
Deputy for Small Business Programs (Acting)
Jose Neto . . . . (619) 553-1128
E-mail: jose.neto@navy.mil
• Intelligence, Surveillance and Reconnaissance and Information Operations Department Head
Lynn Collins . . . . (619) 553-3700
Fax: (619) 553-5682
Logistics and Fleet Support Department Head
Mavis J. Machniak . . . . (619) 524-2481
Education: Cal State (Fresno) 1985 BSEE
Program and Project Management Department Head
Joseph "Joe" Adan . . . . (619) 553-3000
E-mail: joseph.adan@navy.mil
Science, Technology, and Netcentric Engineering Department Head **Dr. Stephen D. Russell** . . . . (619) 553-3500
Education: SUNY (Stony Brook) 1979 BS; Michigan 1981 MS, 1986 PhD
Fax: (619) 553-2951
Supply and Contracts Department Head
Tammy Sanchez . . . . (619) 553-3200
E-mail: tammy.sanchez@navy.mil Fax: (619) 553-4948
Pacific C4ISR Officer in Charge
CDR Remil Capili USN . . . . (808) 474-6043
Joint Base Pearl Harbor-Hickam, HI 96818
Legal Counsel **Scott E. Miller** . . . . (619) 553-4703
E-mail: scott.miller@navy.mil
Public Affairs Officer **James Fallin** . . . . (619) 553-2724

United States Marine Corps (USMC)

Arlington Annex, Columbia Pike and Southgate Road,
Arlington, VA 22204
Mail: Headquarters, U.S. Marine Corps,
3000 Marine Corps Pentagon, Washington, DC 20350-3000
Internet: www.marines.mil

OFFICE OF THE COMMANDANT

The Pentagon, 3000 Marine Pentagon, Washington, DC 20350-3000
Fax: (703) 697-7246 Internet: www.hqmc.marines.mil/cmc

Office of the Assistant Commandant

The Pentagon, Washington, DC 20350-3000
Fax: (703) 697-5399 Internet: www.hqmc.marines.mil/acmc

Installations and Logistics

3000 Marine Pentagon, Washington, DC 20350-3000
Tel: (703) 695-8644 Fax: (703) 614-4210
Internet: www.iandl.marines.mil/

Marine Corps Installations Command/Installations and Logistics Facilities (MCICOM/I&L LF)

3000 Marine Pentagon, Washington, DC 20350-3000
Tel: (703) 695-6824 Internet: www.mcicom.marines.mil

Marine Corps Installations East - Marine Corps Base, Camp Lejeune

PSC Box 20005, Camp Lejeune, NC 28542-0005
Tel: (910) 451-1113 (Information) Fax: (910) 451-5882
Internet: http://www.lejeune.marines.mil/

Commanding General **Col Michael L. Scalise USMC** . . . . (910) 451-2526
Chief of Staff **Col Thomas R. McCarthy USMC** . . . . (910) 451-2526
Sergeant Major **SgtMaj Charles A. Metger USMC** . . . . . (910) 451-2526
Aide **1stLt David Coffman USMC** . . . . (910) 451-2526
Base Librarian **Judy Bradford** . . . . (910) 451-2665
Fax: (910) 451-1871
Contracting Director and Small Business Officer
Sherry F. Gaylor . . . . (910) 451-7843
E-mail: sherry.gaylor@usmc.mil
Deputy Contracting Director **(Vacant)** . . . . (910) 451-7842
Freedom of Information Act Officer
John R. "J.R." Armour . . . . (910) 451-5415
E-mail: john.armour@usmc.mil
Base Operations Assistant Chief of Staff
Col Nick Davis USMC . . . . (910) 451-7391
Installation Security and Safety Assistant Chief of Staff
Col Eric Eldred USMC . . . . (910) 451-9349
Network Operations and Systems Officer
Donald H. Ruth . . . . (910) 450-5423
E-mail: donald.ruth@usmc.mil
Protocol Coordinator **Michael Dietz** . . . . (910) 451-2526
Public Affairs Officer **Nathaniel Fahy** . . . . (910) 451-7413
E-mail: nat.fahy@usmc.mil

Marine Corps Air Station Beaufort (SC)

P.O. Box 55001, Beaufort, SC 29904-5001
Tel: (843) 228-7121 Fax: (843) 228-7032
Internet: www.beaufort.marines.mil

Commanding Officer **Col Timothy P. Miller USMC** . . . . . (843) 228-7158
Executive Officer **LtCol Matthew Stover USMC** . . . . . . (843) 228-7121
Sergeant Major **SgtMaj Matthew A. Conrad USMC** . . . . (843) 228-7405
Historian and Freedom of Information Act Officer
Dorothy Mack . . . . (843) 228-7201
Public Affairs Officer **Capt Clayton Groover USMC** . . . . (843) 228-7121

Marine Corps Air Station New River (NC) (MCAS New River)

MCAS New River, PSC Box 21002, Jacksonville, NC 28545-1002
Tel: (910) 449-5432 Fax: (910) 449-5119
Internet: www.newriver.marines.mil

Commanding Officer **Col Russell Burton USMC** . . . . (910) 449-5431

(continued on next page)

★ Presidential Appointment Requiring Senate Confirmation ☆ Presidential Appointment □ Schedule C Appointment ◇ Career Senior Foreign Service Appointment
● Career Senior Executive Service (SES) Appointment ○ Non-Career Senior Executive Service (SES) Appointment ■ Postal Career Executive Service

Marine Corps Air Station New River (NC) *(continued)*

Executive Officer **LtCol Scott T. Trent USMC** .... (910) 449-5432
Sergeant Major **SgtMaj Robert F. Griffith USMC** .... (910) 449-6399
Public Affairs Chief **(Vacant)** .... (910) 449-5435

II Marine Expeditionary Force (II MEF - Marine Corps Base Camp Lejeune)

PSC Box 20080, Camp Lejeune, NC 28542-0080
Tel: (910) 451-8793 Internet: www.iimefpublic.usmc.mil

Commanding General
LtGen Robert F. Hedelund USMC .... (910) 451-8138
Deputy Commanding General **(Vacant)** .... (910) 451-8138
Sergeant Major
SgtMaj Richard D. "R.D." Thresher USMC .... (910) 451-8793
Command Master Chief
CMDCM Russell W. Folley USN .... (910) 451-8793

2nd Marine Division (Marine Corps Base Camp Lejeune)
PSC Box 20003, Camp Lejeune, NC 28542-0003
Tel: (910) 451-8319 Internet: www.2ndmardiv.marines.mil

Commanding General
MajGen David J. Furness USMC .... (910) 451-8319
E-mail: david.furness@usmc.mil
Education: VMI 1987
Assistant Division Commander
Col David L. Odom USMC .... (910) 451-8470
Sergeant Major **SgtMaj Alex M. Dobson USMC** .... (910) 451-8319
Command Master Chief
HMCM Jody Gene Fletcher MC, USN .... (910) 451-8319

2nd Marine Logistics Group (Marine Corps Base Camp Lejeune)
PSC Box 20002, Camp Lejeune, NC 28542-0002
Tel: (910) 451-5504 Internet: www.2ndmlg.marines.mil

Commanding General **BGen Kevin J. Stewart USMC** ... (910) 451-2702

Marine Corps Installations Pacific (MCIPAC)

Building One, Camp Butler, Okinawa, Japan
Tel: 81 (98) 970-3803 (Public Affairs) Internet: www.mcipac.marines.mil

Commanding General
BGen Paul J. Rock, Jr. USMC 81 (98) 970-3803
Education: Naval Acad 1988
Deputy Commander **Col David E. Jones USMC** 81 (98) 970-3803
Sergeant Major **SgtMaj Vincent F. Young USMC** 81 (98) 970-3803

Marine Corps Air Station Futenma
MCAS Futenma, Okinawa, Japan
Tel: 81 611-736-3100 Internet: http://www.mcasfutenma.marines.mil/

Commanding General **Col David Steele USMC** 81 611-736-3100
Education: George Mason 1995
Executive Officer **LtCol Nathan Hill USMC** 81 611-736-3100
Sergeant Major **SgtMaj William Harrington USMC** ... 81 611-736-3100

Marine Corps Air Station, Iwakuni, Japan (MCAS Iwakuni)
PSC 561 Box 1868, Iwakuni, Japan
Tel: 81 (827) 79-1110 Tel: 81 (827) 79-5551 (Public Affairs)
Internet: www.marines.mil/unit/mcasiwakuni

Commander **Col Richard F. Fuerst USMC** 81 (827) 79-1110
Sergeant Major
SgtMaj Joseph S. Gregory USMC .... 81 (827) 79-1110 ext. 2521

Marine Corps Base Hawaii - Kaneohe Bay (HI)
PAO, Box 63002, M.C.B.H. Kaneohe Bay, HI 96863-3002
Tel: (808) 257-8840 Tel: (808) 257-8852 (Base Hotline)
Fax: (808) 257-2511 Internet: www.mcbhawaii.marines.mil

Commanding Officer **Col Raul Lianez USMC** .... (808) 257-8877
Education: Naval Acad 1993 BS
Sergeant Major **SgtMaj Charles E. Wells USMC** .... (808) 257-3443

Marine Corps Installations West - Marine Corps Base Camp Pendleton (MCIWEST)

Camp Pendleton, CA 92055
Tel: (760) 725-5799 (Public Affairs) Internet: www.mciwest.marines.mil

Commander **BGen Kevin J. Killea USMC** .... (760) 725-5799
Deputy Commander **(Vacant)** .... (760) 725-5799
Sergeant Major **SgtMaj Julio E. Meza USMC** .... (760) 725-5799

Marine Corps Air Station, Miramar (CA) (MCAS Miramar)
P.O. Box 452017, San Diego, CA 92145-2017
Tel: (858) 577-6000 Fax: (858) 577-6001
Internet: http://www.miramar.marines.mil/

Commanding Officer **Col Charles B. Dockery USMC** .... (858) 577-4833
Executive Officer **LtCol Paul B. Kopacz USMC** .... (858) 577-1222
Command Sergeant Major
SgtMaj Mike Walten USMC .... (858) 577-6000

3rd Marine Aircraft Wing (3 MAW)
3d MAW, P.O. Box 452038, San Diego, CA 92145-2038
Tel: (858) 577-7300 Fax: (858) 577-6892

Commanding General
MajGen Kevin M. Iiams USMC .... (858) 577-7300
Assistant Wing Commander
Col Michael J. Borgschulte USMC .... (858) 577-6903
Command Master Chief
CMDCM Donald L. Davis, Jr. USN .... (858) 577-7300
Sergeant Major **SgtMaj Peter A. Siaw USMC** .... (858) 577-4613
E-mail: peter.siaw@usmc.mil
Commanding Officer, Marine Aircraft Group 39
Col Matthew Mowery USMC .... (858) 577-7300

Marine Corps Air Station, Yuma (AZ)
Yuma, AZ 85369
Tel: (928) 269-2275 Tel: (928) 269-2275 (Public Affairs)
Tel: (928) 269-2790 (Contracting/Purchasing)
Tel: (928) 269-2790 (Small Business Office) Fax: (928) 269-3282
Internet: www.mcasyuma.marines.mil

Commander **Col David A. Suggs USMC** .... (928) 269-3608
Sergeant Major **SgtMaj David M. Leikwold USMC** ..... (928) 269-2777

Office of Marine Corps Communications

The Pentagon, Washington, DC 20350
Tel: (703) 614-8010 Fax: (703) 697-5362
Internet: https://www.hqmc.marines.mil/ousmcc/

Los Angeles Public Affairs Office - Motion Picture and T.V. Liaison

10880 Wilshire Boulevard, Suite 1230, Los Angeles, CA 90024

Director **CAPT Russell L. Coons USN** .... (310) 235-7481
E-mail: russell.l.coons1@navy.mil

New York Public Affairs Office

805 Third Avenue, 9th Floor, New York, NY 10022-7513
Tel: (347) 292-8762 Fax: (212) 784-0169 E-mail: nycmarines@usmc.mil

Public Affairs Director **Maj Neil A. Ruggiero USMC** .... (212) 784-0160
E-mail: neil.ruggiero@usmc.mil

Marine Corps Base Quantico (VA) (MCB Quantico)

3250 Catlin Avenue, Quantico, VA 22134-5000
Tel: (703) 784-2741 Fax: (703) 784-0065
Internet: www.quantico.usmc.mil

Commander **Col Joseph M. Murray USMC** .... (703) 432-0322
Chief of Staff **Col Robert Boucher USMC** .... (703) 784-2741
E-mail: robert.boucher@usmc.mil
Sergeant Major **SgtMaj Michael W. Hensley USMC** .... (703) 784-2741
Public Affairs Officer
Maj Andrew J. Bormann USMC .... (703) 784-2741
E-mail: andrew.bormann@usmc.mil

★ Presidential Appointment Requiring Senate Confirmation ☆ Presidential Appointment □ Schedule C Appointment ◇ Career Senior Foreign Service Appointment
● Career Senior Executive Service (SES) Appointment ○ Non-Career Senior Executive Service (SES) Appointment ■ Postal Career Executive Service

Marine Barracks - Washington (DC)
Eighth & I Streets, SE, Washington, DC 20390
Tel: (202) 433-4891 Fax: (202) 433-9852
Internet: www.barracks.marines.mil

Commander **Col Donald J. Tomich USMC** .... (202) 433-4891
Executive Officer **LtCol Scott Clippinger USMC** .... (202) 433-4891
Sergeant Major **SgtMaj Matthew Hackett USMC** ...... (202) 433-4891
Public Affairs Officer
Capt Colleen McFadden USMC .... (202) 433-6660

U.S. Marine Forces Reserve (MARFORRES)

Joseph J. McCarthy Building, 2000 Opelousas Avenue,
New Orleans, LA 70146
Tel: (504) 256-8172 E-mail: mfrpao@usmc.mil

Commander, Marine Forces Reserve and Marine Forces North **MajGen Frederick M. Padilla USMC** .... (504) 256-8172
• Executive Director **Col Gregg T. Habel USMCR (Ret)** ... (504) 256-8172
Education: Naval Acad 1985
Chief of Staff **Col Gerry W. Leonard, Jr. USMC** .... (504) 256-8172
E-mail: gerry.leonard@usmc.mil
Vice Chief of Staff **Col Michael J. Flynn USMC** ...... (504) 256-8172
Education: UC Berkeley 1988
Sergeant Major **SgtMaj Scott D. Grade USMC** .... (504) 256-8172
Command Master Chief
CMDCM Ryan N. Strack USN .... (504) 256-8172
Public Affairs Officer
LtCol Tanya M. Murnock USMCR .... (504) 256-8172

4th Marine Logistics Group (4th MLG)
Joseph J. McCarthy Building, 2000 Opelousas Avenue,
New Orleans, LA 70146

Commanding General **BGen Karl Pierson USMC** .... (504) 913-6298
Education: William & Mary MBA; Army War Col MSS
Deputy Commander **(Vacant)** .... (504) 913-6298
Sergeant Major **SgtMaj Lanette N. Wright USMC** ...... (504) 697-7154
Chief of Staff **(Vacant)** .... (504) 697-7125

4th Marine Aircraft Wing (4th MAW)
Joseph J. McCarthy Building, 2000 Opelousas Avenue,
New Orleans, LA 70146
Tel: (504) 697-7763

Commanding General
BGen Bradley S. James USMC .... (504) 697-7763
Sergeant Major **SgtMaj Rodney L. Lane USMC** .... (504) 697-7763
Chief of Staff **Col William B. Johnson USMC** .... (504) 697-7763
Education: Texas 1986 BS
Assistant Wing Commander
Col Timothy L. Adams USMCR .... (504) 697-7763

4th Marine Division (4th MAR DIV)
Joseph J. McCarthy Building, 2000 Opelousas Avenue,
New Orleans, LA 70146
Tel: (504) 697-7911

Commanding General
BGen Michael S. Martin USMC .... (504) 697-7127
Sergeant Major **SgtMaj M. A. Miller USMC** .... (504) 678-0047
Chief of Staff **(Vacant)** .... (504) 678-6406

Marine Individual Reserve Support Organization (MIRSO)
Joseph J. McCarthy Building, 2000 Opelousas Avenue,
New Orleans, LA 70146
Tel: (800) 255-5082 E-mail: mcirsa_ima@usmc.mil

Commanding Officer **Col Torrin Miller USMCR** .... (504) 697-8499

Major U.S. Marine Corps Commands

U.S. Marine Corps Combat Development Command (MCCDC)

3300 Russell Road, Suite 202, Quantico, VA 22134-5111
Fax: (703) 784-3450 Internet: www.mccdc.marines.mil/

Commanding General and Deputy Commandant for Combat Development and Integration
LtGen David H. Berger USMC .... (703) 784-2416
Education: Tulane 1981 BS; Johns Hopkins MIPP
Deputy Commanding General and Assistant Deputy Commandant **MajGen Mark R. Wise USMC** .... (703) 784-2416
Education: U Washington
Sergeant Major
SgtMaj Thomas G. Eggerling USMC .... (703) 784-3999
Chief of Staff **Col Scott D. Leonard USMC** .... (703) 784-2665
E-mail: scott.d.leonard@usmc.mil
Education: VMI 1991 BSME
Administrative Chief **Eric Rodriguez** .... (703) 432-8562
Capabilities Development Director
BGen James H. Adams III USMC .... (703) 614-8610

Training and Education Command (TECOM)
1019 Elliot Road, Quantico, VA 22134-5111
Fax: (703) 784-0012 Internet: www.tecom.marines.mil

Commanding General **(Vacant)** .... (703) 784-3730
• Executive Deputy **Dennis C. Thompson** .... (703) 784-3730
E-mail: dennis.thompson@usmc.mil
Education: Penn State 1976 BS; Naval War 1998 MA; Golden Gate MPA
Sergeant Major **SgtMaj William J. Grigsby USMC** ..... (703) 784-3730
Weapons Training Battalion Commanding Officer
Col Timothy M. Parker USMC .... (703) 784-5084
27211 Garand Road, Quantico, VA 22134-5001

Marine Corps Air Ground Combat Center (MCAGCC)
Commanding General, Public Affairs Office, MAGTFTC/MCAGCC, Twentynine Palms, CA 92278-8200
Mail: P.O. Box 788200, Twentynine Palms, CA 92278-8200
Tel: (760) 830-6106 Fax: (760) 830-5474
Internet: www.29palms.marines.mil

Battalion Commanding Officer
LtCol Shane A. Edwards USMC .... (760) 830-7493
Battalion Executive Officer **Maj Davis USMC** .... (760) 830-7083
Battalion Sergeant Major
SgtMaj Michael B. Dutchin USMC .... (760) 830-6330
Commanding General, Marine Corps Air Ground Combat Center Training Command
BGen Roger Turner USMC .... (760) 830-6106
E-mail: roger.turner@usmc.mil Fax: (760) 830-6060
Sergeant Major, Marine Corps Air Ground Combat Center Training Command
SgtMaj Michael J. Hendges USMC .... (760) 830-6106

Marine Corps Mountain Warfare Training Center
Building 4048, MCMWTC, Highway 108, Bridgeport, CA 93517
Mail: Box 5002, Bridgeport, CA 93517-5002
Tel: (760) 932-1511 Fax: (760) 932-7706

Commander **LtCol Kevin H. Hutchison USMC** .... (760) 932-1411
E-mail: kevin.hutchison@usmc.mil
Sergeant Major **Matthew J. Fouss** .... (760) 932-1413

U.S. Marine Corps Detachment, Goodfellow Air Force Base
328 Fort Lancaster Avenue, Goodfellow AFB, TX 76908
Tel: (325) 654-5100

Commanding Officer
Maj Andrew H. Armstrong USMC .... (325) 654-5100

DEPARTMENTS

★ Presidential Appointment Requiring Senate Confirmation ☆ Presidential Appointment □ Schedule C Appointment ◇ Career Senior Foreign Service Appointment
● Career Senior Executive Service (SES) Appointment ○ Non-Career Senior Executive Service (SES) Appointment ■ Postal Career Executive Service

DEPARTMENTS

U.S. Marine Corps Forces Command (MARFORCOM)

1775 Forrestal Drive, Norfolk, VA 23551-2596
Tel: (757) 836-1500 Fax: (757) 836-1535
Internet: www.marforcom.marines.mil/

Commander **LtGen Mark A. Brilakis USMC** .... (757) 836-1517
Executive Assistant **Gwen Lipford** .... (757) 836-1517
Aide-de-Camp **Maj Rohit Masih USMC** .... (757) 836-1505
Deputy Commander **BGen Eric E. Austin USMC** .... (757) 836-1505
● Executive Director **Joseph W. Murphy** .... (757) 836-1533
Education: Naval Acad 1981; Naval Postgrad MS
Chief of Staff **Col James T. Iulo USMC** .... (757) 836-1500
Deputy Chief of Staff **Howard T. Parker, Jr.** .... (757) 836-1500
Command Master Chief
CMDCM Frank E. Johnson USN .... (757) 836-1500
Sergeant Major **SgtMaj Clifford W. Wiggins USMC** .... (757) 836-1514
Headquarters and Service Battalion Commanding Officer **Col Thomas H. Capell III USMC** .... (757) 836-1500
Deputy Public Affairs Officer
Maj Matthew Bellader USMC .... (757) 836-1581

Marine Corps Air Station Cherry Point (NC) (MCAS Cherry Point)

PCS Box 8006, Cherry Point, NC 28533-0003
Tel: (252) 466-3051 Tel: (252) 466-2811 (Information)
Fax: (252) 466-5201 Internet: www.cherrypoint.marines.mil

Commanding Officer **Col Todd Ferry USMC** .... (252) 466-2848
Education: Naval Acad 1992 BS
Executive Officer **LtCol Brian Moll USMC** .... (252) 466-2848
Sergeant Major **SgtMaj Paul McElearney USMC** .... (252) 466-2848
Protocol Officer/Secretary **Lori Crawford** .... (252) 466-2848

2nd Marine Aircraft Wing

PCS Box 8006, Cherry Point, NC 28533-0003
Tel: (252) 466-4313 Fax: (252) 466-2231
Internet: www.2ndmaw.marines.mil

Commanding General **BGen Karsten S. Heckl USMC** .... (252) 466-5488
E-mail: karsten.heckl@usmc.mil
Protocol Officer **Kelly Dippold** .... (252) 466-2434
E-mail: kelly.dippold@usmc.mil
Joint Public Affairs Office Director (Acting)
Mike Barton .... (252) 466-4241
E-mail: chpt.jpao.omb@usmc.mil
Librarian **Suzanne Shell** .... (252) 466-3532
Building 298, Fax: (252) 466-2476
Commanding General/ATTN: Station Library,
NCCS/MCPV, PSC Box 8009, Cherry Point, NC 28533-0009
E-mail: suzanne.shell@usmc.mil

U.S. Marine Corps Forces Pacific Command (MARFORPAC)

Camp H. M. Smith, HI 96861
Tel: (808) 477-8311 Fax: (808) 477-8721
Internet: www.marforpac.marines.mil

Commanding General
LtGen Lewis A. Craparotta USMC .... (808) 477-8600
Education: Vermont 1982 BA
Aide de Camp **Maj Ralph Tompkins USMC** .... (808) 477-8601
Foreign Policy Advisor **Mary-Gardner Coppola** .... (808) 477-8841
Deputy Commander **BGen Robert B. Sofge USMC** .... (808) 477-8600
Chief of Staff **Col Brian M. Howlett USMC** .... (808) 477-8606
Education: Marine Corps Command Col; Air War Col
● Executive Director **Craig B. Welden** .... (808) 477-8311
Command Master Chief
CMDCM Frank Dominguez USN .... (808) 477-8661
Force Sergeant Major
SgtMaj Robert K. Williamson USMC .... (808) 477-8604
E-mail: robert.k.williamson@usmc.mil
Protocol Officer **Sarah Radigan** .... (808) 477-8959
E-mail: sarah.radigan@usmc.mil
Deputy Public Affairs Director **Chuck Little** .... (808) 477-8308
E-mail: chuck.little@usmc.mil Fax: (808) 477-8715

U.S. Marine Corps Forces Pacific Command *(continued)*

Staff Secretary **Sarah Murphy** .... (808) 477-8606
E-mail: sarah.murphy@usmc.mil

U.S. Marine Corps Forces Special Operations Command (MARSOC)

PSC Box 20071, Camp Lejeune, NC 28542-0071
Tel: (910) 451-9070 Internet: www.marsoc.marines.mil

Commanding Officer **MajGen Daniel D. Yoo USMC** .... (910) 451-9064
Education: Arizona State 1984 BS; Naval War MA

U.S. Marine Corps Logistics Command (MARCORLOGCOM)

814 Radford Boulevard, Suite 20201, Albany, GA 31704
Tel: (229) 639-5201 Tel: (229) 639-6676 (G-1) Fax: (229) 639-5290
Fax: (229) 639-5480 (Communication Strategy and Operations Office)
Internet: www.logcom.marines.mil

Commanding General
BGen Joseph F. Shrader USMC .... (229) 639-5201
Executive Assistant **Deidre Groves** .... (229) 639-5201
● Executive Deputy **David R. Clifton** .... (229) 639-5201
E-mail: david.clifton@usmc.mil
Education: Citadel 1973 BS; Pepperdine 1976 MS; New Orleans 1981 MBA; Indust'l Col Armed Forces 1994 MS
Sergeant Major **SgtMaj Michael J. Rowan USMC** .... (229) 639-5510
E-mail: michael.rowan@usmc.mil

Marine Corps Logistics Base, Albany (GA)

814 Radford Boulevard, Suite 20302, Albany, GA 31704
Tel: (229) 639-5202 Tel: (229) 639-5212 (Freedom of Information Act)
Fax: (229) 639-5774 Internet: www.albany.marines.mil

Commanding Officer **Col Alphonso Trimble USMC** .... (229) 639-5202
E-mail: alphonso.trimble@usmc.mil
Executive Assistant **Laura Thorne** .... (229) 639-5202
Sergeant Major **SgtMaj Johnny L. Higdon USMC** .... (229) 639-5799
Executive Director **Leonard A. "Len" Housley** .... (229) 639-5202
E-mail: leonard.housley@usmc.mil
Education: Maryland BS; Alabama Huntsville MS; Army War Col 2013 MSS

Marine Corps Logistics Base, Barstow (CA) (MCLB Barstow)

Box 110100, Barstow, CA 92311-5050
Tel: (760) 577-6555 Tel: (760) 577-6211 (Directory Assistance)
Fax: (760) 577-6058 Internet: www.mclbbarstow.marines.mil

Commanding Officer **Col Craig C. Clemans USMC** .... (760) 577-6555
Executive Assistant **Katherine Fortune** .... (760) 577-6555
Executive Officer **LtCol Tim Silkowski USMC** .... (760) 577-6556
Sergeant Major **SgtMaj Sergio MartinezRuiz USMC** .... (760) 577-6238
Public Affairs Officer **Robert L. Jackson** .... (760) 577-6430
E-mail: robert.l.jackson@usmc.mil Fax: (760) 577-6350

Blount Island Command

5880 Channel View Boulevard, Jacksonville, FL 32226-3404
Tel: (904) 696-5100 Fax: (904) 696-5186 Internet: www.bic.usmc.mil
Internet: www.matcombic.usmc.mil

Commanding Officer **Col Andrew J. Bergen USMC** .... (904) 696-5100
Deputy Director **Col James D. Hooks USMC (Ret)** .... (904) 696-5100
E-mail: hooksjd@bic.usmc.mil
Education: Naval Acad
Senior Enlisted Advisor **1SG Fidel Chavez USMC** .... (904) 696-5100

U.S. Marine Corps Recruiting Command (MCRC)

3280 Russell Road, Quantico, VA 22134
Tel: (703) 784-9400 Fax: (703) 784-9863
Internet: www.mcrc.marines.mil/

Commanding General
MajGen James W. Bierman, Jr. USMC .... (703) 784-9400
E-mail: james.bierman@usmc.mil
General's Aide **Capt Charles Dowling USMC** .... (703) 784-9401

★ Presidential Appointment Requiring Senate Confirmation ☆ Presidential Appointment □ Schedule C Appointment ◇ Career Senior Foreign Service Appointment
● Career Senior Executive Service (SES) Appointment ○ Non-Career Senior Executive Service (SES) Appointment ■ Postal Career Executive Service

U.S. Marine Corps Recruiting Command *(continued)*

Sergeant Major
SgtMaj Michael "Mike" Lanpolsaen USMC .... (703) 784-9400
Comptroller **Mark Smith** .... (703) 784-9458
National Director of Advertising
LtCol Christian Devine USMC Room 9434 .... (703) 784-9434
E-mail: christian.devine@usmc.mil
Command, Control, Communications, and Computers
Systems **LtCol David G. "Dave" DiEugenio USMC** ... (703) 784-9465
Enlisted Recruitment Operations Section Head
LtCol Patrick Spencer USMC .... (703) 784-9403
Plans and Analysis Section Head
LtCol Jeffrey "Jeff" Scofield USMC .... (703) 784-9408
E-mail: jeffrey.scofield@usmc.mil
Officer Programs Assistant Chief of Staff
LtCol Isaiah Martinez USMC .... (703) 784-9449
Assistant Chief of Staff, G3
Col Jeffrey J. Kenney USMC .... (703) 784-9429
Assistant Chief of Staff, G4 **Steve Plato** .... (703) 784-9400

Eastern Recruiting Region (Marine Corps Recruit Depot Parris Island)

Marine Corps Recruit Depot, P.O. Box 19201,
Parris Island, SC 29905-9001
Tel: (843) 228-2111 (Base Operator)
Tel: (843) 228-3923 (Public Affairs Office)
Internet: www.mcrdpi.marines.mil

Commanding General
BGen James F. "Jim" Glynn USMC .... (843) 228-2111
Chief of Staff **Col Michael R. Bowersox USMC** .... (843) 228-2111
Education: Bowling Green State 1985 BS
Sergeant Major **SgtMaj Rafael Rodriguez USMC** .... (843) 228-2111

1st Marine Corps District

605 Stewart Avenue, Garden City, NY 11530-4761
Tel: (516) 228-5640
Internet: http://www.mcrc.marines.mil/1stmcd/UnitHome.aspx
Areas Covered: CT, ME, MA, NH, NJ, NY, PA, RI, VT

Commanding Officer **Col Ivan I. Monclova USMC** ...... (516) 228-5653

Public Affairs Branch

Public Affairs Chief **SSgt Jon Holmes USMC** .... (516) 228-5642
Public Affairs Officer **Capt Gerard Farao USMC** .... (516) 228-5640

4th Marine Corps District

Building 54, Suite 3, Box 806, New Cumberland, PA 17070-0806
Tel: (717) 770-4525 Fax: (717) 770-4533
Areas Covered: DE, portions of IN, KY, MD, Southeastern MI, NC, OH, VA, WV, DC

Commanding Officer **Col Robert M. Clark USMC** ...... (717) 770-4524
Sergeant Major **SgtMaj Mark Gonzalez USMC** .... (717) 770-4525
Webmaster **SSgt Steven "Steve" Cushman USMC** .... (717) 770-8126
E-mail: steven.cushman@marines.usmc.mil

Public Affairs Branch

Building 54, Suite 3, Box 806, New Cumberland, PA 17070
Tel: (717) 770-8123

Branch Chief
SSgt Steven "Steve" Cushman USMC
E-mail: steven.cushman@marines.usmc.mil

6th Marine Corps District (Marine Corps Recruit Depot Parris Island)

P.O. Box 19201, Parris Island, SC 29905-9001
Tel: (843) 228-3662 Fax: (843) 228-3034 Internet: www.6mcd.usmc.mil
Areas Covered: AL, FL, GA, LA, portions of NC, SC, TN and MS

Commanding Officer **Col William C. Gray USMC** ...... (843) 228-2726
Education: South Carolina 1993; U Phoenix 2003 MS; Naval War 2015
Executive Officer **LtCol Stephen Bates USMC** .... (843) 228-2587
Sergeant Major **SgtMaj Cortez L. Brown USMC** .... (843) 228-3662

Public Affairs Office

P.O. Box 19201, Parris Island, SC 29905
Tel: (843) 228-2773 Fax: (843) 228-3383

Public Affairs Officer **1stLt Savannah Frank USMC** .... (843) 228-2085
Public Affairs Chief **SSgt Jose Nava USMC** .... (843) 228-2782

Western Recruiting Region (Marine Corps Recruit Depot San Diego)

1600 Henderson Avenue, Suite 238, San Diego, CA 92140-5001
Tel: (619) 524-8704 Tel: (619) 524-8727 (Public Affairs)
Internet: http://www.mcrdsd.marines.mil/

Commanding General **BGen Ryan P. Heritage USMC** ... (619) 524-8704
Sergeant Major **SgtMaj Devon A. Lee USMC** .... (619) 524-8704
Chief of Staff **Col Jim G. Gruny USMC** .... (619) 524-8704

8th Marine Corps District

1513 Desert Storm Road, Fort Worth, TX 76127
Tel: (817) 782-6715

Commanding Officer
Col Keven W. Matthews USMC .... (817) 868-8026
Sergeant Major **SgtMaj Troy A. Nicks USMC** .... (817) 782-6715
Executive Officer
LtCol Christopher Halloway USMC .... (817) 782-6715

Public Affairs Branch

Public Affairs Officer **LCpl Luis Ramirez USMC** .... (817) 782-6777
E-mail: luis.ramirez@marines.usmc.mil
Public Affairs Chief **Sgt Melissa A. Latty USMC** ...... (817) 782-6777
E-mail: melissa.latty@marines.usmc.mil

9th Marine Corps District

Building 710, 3805 East 155th Street, Kansas City, MO 64147-1309
Tel: (847) 887-8323 (Public Affairs)
Internet: http://www.9thmcd.marines.mil/
Areas Covered: AR, IL, IN, IA, KS, MI, MN, MO, NE, ND, SD, WI

Commanding Officer **Col David M. Fallon USMC** .... (816) 843-3876
Education: Boston Col 1994; Naval Postgrad MS; Naval War MA
Executive Officer **LtCol Charles Winchester USMC** .... (847) 887-8323
Sergeant Major **(Vacant)** .... (847) 887-8323
Information Systems Management Officer **David Mann** ... (847) 887-8323
Fax: (816) 843-3982

Public Affairs Branch

Public Affairs Officer **Capt Jean Durham USMC** .... (224) 374-8895
Education: Savannah State 2011 BA Fax: (816) 843-3984

12th Marine Corps District (Recruiting Station Los Angeles)

Building Eight, 3704 Hochmuth Avenue, San Diego, CA 92140
Areas Covered: AK, AZ, CA, GU, HI, ID, NV, OR, UT, WA, WY, Japan, Okinawa

Commanding Officer **Col Terry M. Johnson USMC** ..... (619) 542-5554
E-mail: terry.m.johnson@usmc.mil
Sergeant Major
SgtMaj Bernard T. Jackson III USMC .... (619) 542-5554

DEPARTMENTS

★ Presidential Appointment Requiring Senate Confirmation ☆ Presidential Appointment ☐ Schedule C Appointment ◇ Career Senior Foreign Service Appointment
● Career Senior Executive Service (SES) Appointment ○ Non-Career Senior Executive Service (SES) Appointment ■ Postal Career Executive Service

United States Department of Education

Contents

United States Department of Education (ED)

Description: The Department of Education is responsible for ensuring equal access to education and promoting educational excellence.

400 Maryland Avenue, SW, Washington, DC 20202
Tel: (800) 421-3481 (Civil Rights Hotline)
Tel: (202) 245-6800 (Civil Rights Hotline - Washington, DC)
Tel: (800) 621-3115 (Defaulted Loans)
Tel: (877) 433-7827 (ED Pubs - Education Publications Center)
Tel: (800) 433-3243 (Federal Student Aid Information Center)
Tel: (202) 401-8365 (Freedom of Information and Privacy Act)
Tel: (202) 401-2000 (Information Resource Center - IRC)
Tel: (800) 872-5327 (Information Resource Center - IRC)
Tel: (800) 647-8733 (Inspector General's Fraud and Abuse Hot Line)
Tel: (800) 557-7392 (Loan Consolidation)
Tel: (800) 424-1616 (National Library of Education)
Tel: (202) 205-5015 (National Library of Education - Washington, DC)
Tel: (888) 625-2787 (NCLB - No Child Left Behind - Superintendent's Hotline) Tel: (202) 401-1576 (Press Office)
Tel: (800) 872-5327 (Public Information)
Tel: (202) 401-2000 (Public Information)
Tel: (800) 624-0100 (Safe and Drug-Free Schools)
Tel: (202) 260-3954 (Safe and Drug-Free Schools - Washington, DC)
Tel: (800) 251-7236 (School-to-Work Initiative)
E-mail: edpubs@inet.ed.gov (ED Pubs - Education Publications Center)
E-mail: library@ed.gov (National Library of Education)
E-mail: NCLBSUP@ed.gov (NCLB - No Child Left Behind - Superintendent's Hotline)
E-mail: press@ed.gov (Press Office) Internet: www.ed.gov
Internet: www2.ed.gov/about/open.html (Open Government Directive)
Internet: www.ed.gov/nclb (No Child Left Behind Website)
Internet: https://www.ed.gov/edpubs/ (Ed Pubs - Education Publications Center)
Internet: http://dashboard.ed.gov/ (United States Education Dashboard)

OFFICE OF THE SECRETARY

400 Maryland Avenue, SW, Washington, DC 20202-1510
Tel: (202) 401-3000 Fax: (202) 401-0596

Regional Offices

Region I

5 Post Office Square, 9th Floor, Boston, MA 02109
Tel: (617) 289-0100 Fax: (617) 289-0151
Areas Covered: CT, ME, MA, NH, RI, VT

Administrative Officer **Kin Cayon** .... (617) 289-0027
E-mail: kin.cayon@ed.gov

Office for Civil Rights - Boston Enforcement Office
5 Post Office Square, 8th Floor, Boston, MA 02109
Tel: (617) 289-0111 Fax: (617) 289-0150 E-mail: ocr.boston@ed.gov

Boston Office Director - Eastern Division Regional Director **Diane Henson** .... (617) 289-0037
E-mail: diane.henson@ed.gov
Chief Attorney **Adrienne Mundy-Shephard** .... (617) 289-0040
Education: Georgetown 1999 JD
Program Manager **(Vacant)** .... (617) 289-0111

Office of Inspector General
33 Arch Street, Suite 1101, Boston, MA 02110
Tel: (617) 289-0176 Fax: (617) 289-0156
Special Agent-in-Charge **(Vacant)** .... (617) 289-0174

Federal Student Aid
33 Arch Street, Boston, MA 02110
Fax: (617) 289-4724
Compliance Manager **Tracy M. Nave** Suite 1007A....... (617) 289-0145
E-mail: tracy.nave@ed.gov
Boston Training Delivery **(Vacant)** .... (617) 289-0144
Program Analyst **Holly Langer-Evans** .... (617) 289-0136
E-mail: holly.langer-evans@ed.gov
Education: Boston U 1977 BEd
Program Support Assistant **(Vacant)** .... (617) 289-0133

Region II

Financial Square, 32 Old Slip, 25th and 26th Floors, New York, NY 10005
Tel: (646) 428-3906 Fax: (646) 428-3904
Areas Covered: NJ, NY, PR, VI
Public Affairs Specialist **Jacquelyn Pitta** .... (646) 428-3906
E-mail: jacquelyn.pitta@ed.gov
Education Program Specialist **Taylor Owen Ramsey** ..... (646) 428-3899

Office for Civil Rights - New York Enforcement Office
32 Old Slip, New York, NY 10005
Fax: (646) 428-3843
Director **Timothy C.J. Blanchard** .... (646) 428-3805
E-mail: timothy.blanchard@ed.gov
Chief Program Manager **Naja Allen-Gill** .... (646) 428-3906
Chief Civil Rights Attorney **Rachel Pomerantz** Financial Square, 26th Floor....... (646) 428-3835
E-mail: rachel.pomerantz@ed.gov
Senior Attorney **Joy Purcell** .... (646) 428-3906
E-mail: joy.purcell@ed.gov
Investigator **Sammie O'Dolla** .... (646) 428-3781
Investigator **(Vacant)** .... (646) 428-3789
Administrative Officer **Diane S. Diggs** .... (646) 428-3811
E-mail: diane.diggs@ed.gov

Office of Inspector General
32 Old Slip, New York, NY 10005
Fax: (646) 428-3868
Regional Inspector General for Audit **Daniel P. Schultz** .... (646) 428-3888
E-mail: daniel.schultz@ed.gov

Office of Management
32 Old Slip, New York, NY 10005
Fax: (212) 264-4427
Personnel Management Specialist **(Vacant)** .... (646) 428-3794
Fax: (646) 428-3858

Federal Student Aid
32 Old Slip, New York, NY 10005
Director **Robin R. Shinn** .... (646) 428-3908
E-mail: robin.shinn@ed.gov

(continued on next page)

★ Presidential Appointment Requiring Senate Confirmation ☆ Presidential Appointment □ Schedule C Appointment ◇ Career Senior Foreign Service Appointment
● Career Senior Executive Service (SES) Appointment ○ Non-Career Senior Executive Service (SES) Appointment ■ Postal Career Executive Service

DEPARTMENTS

Federal Student Aid *(continued)*

Director, Clery Unit – Student Aid Enforcement Unit
Candace R. McLaren .... (646) 428-3906
Federal Student Aid Team Leader **Susan C. Ferraiole** .... (646) 428-3771
New York/Boston School Participation Division
Director **Betty Coughlin** Financial Square .... (646) 428-3737
Fax: (646) 428-3742
New York/Boston Compliance Manager
Christopher Curry .... (646) 428-3738
Institutional Improvement Specialist **Barbara Wingel** .... (646) 428-3760

Region III

Wanamaker Building, 100 Penn Square East,
Suite 505, Philadelphia, PA 19107
Tel: (215) 656-6010 Fax: (215) 656-6020
Areas Covered: DC, DE, MD, PA, VA, WV

Education Specialist **Elizabeth Williamson** .... (215) 656-6015
E-mail: elizabeth.williamson@ed.gov

Office for Civil Rights - District of Columbia Office
400 Maryland Avenue, SW, Washington, DC 20202
Tel: (202) 453-6020 TTY: (877) 521-2172 Fax: (202) 453-6021

Office for Civil Rights District of Columbia Office
Director **Alice Wender** .... (202) 453-5932
E-mail: alice.wender@ed.gov
Program Manager **(Vacant)** .... (202) 453-6020
Chief Civil Rights Attorney **(Vacant)** .... (202) 453-5918

Office for Civil Rights - Philadelphia Enforcement Office
100 Penn Square East, Philadelphia, PA 19107
Tel: (215) 656-8542 Fax: (215) 656-8605

Regional Director **Wendella P. Fox** Room 515 .... (215) 656-8542
E-mail: wendella.fox@ed.gov
Supervisory Management and Program Analyst
(Vacant) .... (215) 656-8542
Program Manager **Joseph P. Mahoney** .... (215) 656-8564
E-mail: joseph.mahoney@ed.gov
Chief Civil Rights Attorney **Judith O'Boyle** .... (215) 656-8572
E-mail: judith.oboyle@ed.gov

Office of Inspector General
100 Penn Square East, Philadelphia, PA 19107
Tel: (215) 656-6900 Fax: (215) 656-6397

Regional Inspector General for Audit
Bernard Tadley Room 502 .... (215) 656-6279
E-mail: bernard.tadley@ed.gov
Assistant Regional Inspector General for Audit
(Vacant) Room 502 .... (215) 656-6900
Assistant Special Agent-in-Charge **(Vacant)** .... (215) 656-6900

Office of Management
100 Penn Square East, Philadelphia, PA 19107

Human Resources Specialist **(Vacant)** .... (215) 656-6023

Federal Student Aid
100 Penn Square East, Philadelphia, PA 19107

Philadelphia Direct Loan School Relations Director
Nancy Gifford 513 .... (215) 656-6436
E-mail: nancy.gifford@ed.gov
Co-Team Lead **John Loreng** .... (215) 656-6437
Senior Training Specialist **Gregory Martin** .... (202) 219-7104
E-mail: gregory.martin@ed.gov
Senior Training Specialist **(Vacant)** .... (215) 656-6484
Information Technology Program Manager
Michael Burke .... (215) 656-6010
E-mail: michael.burke@ed.gov
Information Technology Program Manager
John Flannery .... (215) 656-6010
E-mail: john.flannery@ed.gov
Management and Program Analyst **Brian L. Ford** .... (215) 656-6010
Management and Program Analyst **Brandon Hellman** .... (215) 656-6010
Management and Program Analyst **Joel Sutherland** ..... (215) 656-6010

Federal Student Aid *(continued)*

Public Affairs Specialist **Jared Anderson** .... (215) 656-6010
E-mail: jared.anderson@ed.gov

Region IV

SNAFC, 61 Forsyth Street Southwest, Suite 18T15, Atlanta, GA 30303
Areas Covered: AL, FL, GA, KY, MS, NC, SC, TN

Office for Civil Rights – Atlanta Enforcement Office
61 Forsyth Street, SW, Suite 19T10, Atlanta, GA 30303
Tel: (404) 974-9406 TTY: (877) 521-2172

Director **Melanie Velez-Ruffin** .... (404) 974-9331
E-mail: melanie.velez@ed.gov
Chief Civil Rights Attorney **Deborah Floyd** .... (404) 974-9334
E-mail: deborah.floyd@ed.gov
Program Manager **(Vacant)** .... (404) 974-9406

Office of Communications and Outreach
61 Forsyth Street, SW, Suite 18T15, Atlanta, GA 30303
Tel: (404) 974-9450

Director **Dennis Bega** .... (404) 974-9452
E-mail: dennis.bega@ed.gov

Office of Inspector General
61 Forsyth Street, SW, Suite 19T30, Atlanta, GA 30303
Tel: (404) 974-9430

Regional Inspector General for Audit
Mildred "Milly" Blanes .... (404) 974-9416
E-mail: milly.blanes@ed.gov
Assistant Regional Inspector General for Audit
Christopher Gamble .... (404) 974-9417
E-mail: christopher.gamble@ed.gov
Special Agent-in-Charge **Yessyka Santana** .... (404) 974-9431

Office of Management
61 Forsyth Street, SW, Atlanta, GA 30303

Chief, Eastern Client Services Branch **Clayton Adams** ... (404) 974-9464

Federal Student Aid
SNAFC, 61 Forsyth Street, SW, Suite 18T30, Atlanta, GA 30303
Tel: (404) 974-9490

Business Operations Director **Douglas Lane** .... (404) 974-9244
E-mail: douglas.lane@ed.gov
Program Compliance Director **Robin S. Minor** .... (202) 377-3717
E-mail: robin.minor@ed.gov

Region V

500 West Madison Street, Chicago, IL 60661
Tel: (312) 730-1700 Fax: (312) 730-1704
Areas Covered: IL, IN, MI, MN, OH, WI

Public Affairs Officer **Julie Ewart** .... (312) 730-1583
E-mail: julie.ewart@ed.gov
Program Specialist **Shirley Jones** .... (312) 730-1706
E-mail: shirley.jones@ed.gov

Office for Civil Rights – Chicago Enforcement Office
500 West Madison Street, Chicago, IL 60661
Tel: (312) 730-1560 TTY: (312) 730-1609 Fax: (312) 730-1576

Director **Adele Rapport** .... (312) 730-1495
E-mail: adele.rapport@ed.gov
Chief Civil Rights Attorney **Karen Mines** .... (312) 730-1560
Program Manager **Algis Tamosiunas** .... (312) 730-1608
E-mail: algis.tamosiunas@ed.gov

Cleveland Enforcement Office
600 Superior Avenue, East, Room 750, Cleveland, OH 44114
Tel: (216) 522-4970 TTY: (216) 522-4944 Fax: (216) 522-2573

Director **Meenakshi Morey "Meena" Chandra** .... (216) 522-2677
E-mail: meena.morey.chandra@ed.gov
Chief Attorney **Traci Lynn Ext** .... (216) 522-2671
E-mail: traci.ext@ed.gov
Education: Rice 1995 BA; Harvard 1998 JD

★ Presidential Appointment Requiring Senate Confirmation ☆ Presidential Appointment ☐ Schedule C Appointment ◇ Career Senior Foreign Service Appointment
● Career Senior Executive Service (SES) Appointment ○ Non-Career Senior Executive Service (SES) Appointment ■ Postal Career Executive Service

Office of Inspector General
500 West Madison Street, Chicago, IL 60661
Fax: (312) 730-1626

Regional Inspector General for Audit
Gary D. Whitman . . . . . (312) 730-1658
E-mail: gary.whitman@ed.gov
Special Agent In Charge **Thomas D. "Tom" Utz, Jr.** . . . . (312) 730-1652
Assistant Special Agent in Charge **John Woolley** . . . . . . (312) 730-1700

Office of Management
500 West Madison Street, Chicago, IL 60661

Regional Personnel Officer **Theresa "Terry" Ralidak** . . . . (312) 730-1546
E-mail: terry.ralidak@ed.gov
Regional Training and Development Center Career Counselor **(Vacant)** . . . . . (312) 730-1700

Federal Student Aid
500 West Madison Street, Suite 1520, Chicago, IL 60661
Tel: (800) 621-3115 Tel: (312) 730-1477 Fax: (312) 730-1455

Chicago Service Center Director **(Vacant)** . . . . . (312) 730-1477
Northern Region Partner Services Director **(Vacant)** Suite 1551 . . . . . (312) 730-1477
Fax: (312) 730-1503
Chicago Team Lead **Douglas Parrott** Suite 1576 . . . . . (312) 730-1477
E-mail: douglas.parrott@ed.gov
Co-Team Lead **Earl Flurkey** Suite 1576 . . . . . (312) 730-1477
E-mail: earl.flurkey@ed.gov
Chicago Training Officer **(Vacant)** Suite 1576 . . . . . (312) 730-1477

Region VI

199 Bryan Street, Suite 1510, Dallas, TX 75201-6817
Tel: (214) 661-9500 Fax: (214) 661-9594
Areas Covered: AR, LA, NM, OK, TX

Public Affairs Specialist **(Vacant)** . . . . . (214) 661-9500
Special Assistant **(Vacant)** . . . . . (214) 661-9500

Office for Civil Rights – Dallas Enforcement Office
1999 Bryan Street, Dallas, TX 75201-6817
Tel: (214) 661-9600 Fax: (214) 661-9583

Director **Taylor D. August** . . . . . (214) 661-9603
199 Bryan Street, Suite 1620, Dallas, TX 75201-6817
E-mail: taylor.august@ed.gov
Chief Civil Rights Attorney **Angela Hights** . . . . . (214) 661-9621
199 Bryan Street, Suite 1620, Dallas, TX 75201-6817
E-mail: angela.hights@ed.gov
Program Manager **Gregory McGee** . . . . . (214) 661-9674
199 Bryan Street, Dallas, TX 75201-6817
E-mail: gregory.mcgee@ed.gov

Office of Inspector General
1999 Bryan Street, Dallas, TX 75201-6817
Tel: (214) 661-9530 Fax: (214) 661-9531

Assistant Regional Inspector General for Audit
Myra Hamilton . . . . . (214) 661-9530
199 Bryan Street, Suite 1440, Dallas, TX 75201-6817
E-mail: myra.hamilton@ed.gov
Special Agent-in-Charge **Neil E. Sanchez** Suite 1440 . . . . (214) 661-9530

Federal Student Aid
1999 Bryan Street, Dallas, TX 75201-6817
Tel: (214) 661-9490 Fax: (214) 661-9662

Partner Services - Southern Region Director
Jerry Wallace . . . . . (214) 661-9515
199 Bryan Street, Fax: (214) 661-9581
Room 1540, Dallas, TX 75201-6817
E-mail: jerry.wallace@ed.gov
Division Director **Cynthia "Jessie" Thornton** . . . . . (214) 661-9457
199 Bryan Street, Suite 1410, Dallas, TX 75201-6817
E-mail: cynthia.thornton@ed.gov
Case Manager **Jesus Moya** . . . . . (214) 661-9472
E-mail: jesus.moya@ed.gov
Case Manager **Kimberly Peeler** . . . . . (214) 661-9471
E-mail: kimberly.peeler@ed.gov

Federal Student Aid *(continued)*

Forensic Accountant **Ernest Kinneer** . . . . . (214) 661-9490
E-mail: ernest.kinneer@ed.gov

Region VII

One Petticoat Lane, 1010 WalnutStreet,
Suite 452, Kansas City, MO 64106
Tel: (816) 268-0400 Fax: (816) 268-0407
Areas Covered: IA, KS, MO, NE

Regional Director **(Vacant)** . . . . . (404) 974-9452
Atlanta Federal Center, 61 Forsyth Street, SW,
Suite 19T40, Atlanta, GA 30303

Office for Civil Rights – Kansas City Enforcement Office
1010 Walnut Street, Kansas City, MO 64106
Tel: (877) 521-2172 Tel: (816) 268-0550 Fax: (816) 268-0599
E-mail: ocr.kansascity@ed.gov
Areas Covered: KS, MO, NE, OK, SD

Director **Joshua Douglass** . . . . . (816) 268-0550
E-mail: joshua.douglass@ed.gov
Chief Attorney **(Vacant)** . . . . . (816) 268-0579

Office of Inspector General
1010 Walnut Street, Kansas City, MO 64106
Tel: (816) 268-0500 Fax: (816) 823-1398

Regional Inspector General for Audit
Gary D. Whitman . . . . . (816) 268-0500
E-mail: gary.whitman@ed.gov
Assistant Regional Inspector General for Audit
Lisa Robinson . . . . . (816) 268-0519
E-mail: lisa.robinson@ed.gov
Special Agent-in-Charge (Chicago, IL)
Neil E. Sanchez . . . . . (214) 661-9546
Harwood Building, 199 Bryan Street,
Room 1440, Dallas, TX 75201-6817

Office of Management
One Petticoat Lane, 1010 WalnutStreet, Kansas City, MO 64106
Fax: (206) 607-1662

Human Resources Specialist **Susan Pearce** . . . . . (312) 730-1544
E-mail: susan.pearce@ed.gov

Federal Student Aid
1010 Walnut Street, Suite 336, Kansas City, MO 64106
Tel: (816) 268-0410
Tel: (800) 433-3243 (Federal Student Aid Information Center)
Fax: (816) 823-1402
Areas Covered: IA, KS, KY, MO, NE, TN

Kansas City Area Case Director **Ralph A. LoBosco** . . . . . (816) 268-0410
Kansas City Training Delivery **David Bartlett** . . . . . (816) 268-0410
E-mail: david.bartlett@ed.gov
Team Leader **Dvak Corwin** . . . . . (816) 268-0410
E-mail: dvak.corwin@ed.gov
Institutional Review Specialist **Donica Barnett** . . . . . (816) 268-0410
Institutional Review Specialist **Isabel Williams** . . . . . (816) 268-0410

Region VIII

Cesar Chavez Memorial Building, 1244 Speer Boulevard,
Suite 310, Denver, CO 80204-3582
Tel: (303) 844-3544 Fax: (303) 844-2524
Areas Covered: CO, MT, ND, SD, UT, WY

Public Affairs Specialist **Helen Littlejohn** . . . . . (303) 844-3546
E-mail: helen.littlejohn@ed.gov

Office for Civil Rights – Denver Enforcement Office
Cesar Chavez Memorial Building, 1244 Speer Boulevard,
Suite 300, Denver, CO 80204-3582
Tel: (303) 844-5695 TTY: (303) 844-3417 Fax: (303) 844-4303
Areas Covered: AZ, CO, MT, NM, UT, WY

Director **Aaron Romine** Room 300 . . . . . (303) 844-5695
E-mail: aaron.romine@ed.gov

(continued on next page)

★ Presidential Appointment Requiring Senate Confirmation ☆ Presidential Appointment ☐ Schedule C Appointment ◇ Career Senior Foreign Service Appointment
● Career Senior Executive Service (SES) Appointment ○ Non-Career Senior Executive Service (SES) Appointment ■ Postal Career Executive Service

Office for Civil Rights – Denver Enforcement Office *(continued)*

Chief Civil Rights Attorney **Erica Austin** .... (303) 844-5695
E-mail: erica.austin@ed.gov
Program Manager **Stephen Chen** .... (303) 844-5695

Office of Management
1244 Speer Boulevard, Denver, CO 80204-3582
Tel: (202) 260-4412 Fax: (303) 844-3708

Human Resources Specialist **Anthony Bell** Cesar Chavez Memorial Building, Suite 353 .... (202) 260-4412
E-mail: anthony.bell@ed.gov Fax: (303) 844-2524

Federal Student Aid
1244 Speer Boulevard, Suite 201, Denver, CO 80204-3582
Fax: (303) 844-5756

Area Case Director **(Vacant)** .... (303) 844-4178
Denver Training Officer **Margaret Day** .... (303) 844-3146
E-mail: margaret.day@ed.gov
Denver Training Officer **Deborah Tarpley** .... (303) 844-3683
E-mail: deborah.tarpley@ed.gov
Associate Director for Compliance **(Vacant)** .... (303) 844-3544
Institutional Review Specialist **Derita S. Hall** .... (303) 844-0518
Education: Albany State U 2008 MPA; Walden 2014 PhD
Tribal College and University Training (TCU) Team Leader **John Gritts** .... (303) 844-3148

Region IX

50 Beale Street, Suite 9700, San Francisco, CA 94105
Tel: (415) 486-5700 Fax: (415) 486-5719
Areas Covered: AZ, CA, HI, GU, NV, American Samoa, Guam, Confederation of the Northern Mariana Islands, Federated States of Micronesia, Republic of the Marshall Islands, Republic of Palau

Office for Civil Rights – San Francisco Enforcement Office
50 United Nations Plaza, San Francisco, CA 94102
Tel: (415) 486-5555 Fax: (415) 486-5570

Regional Director **Laura Faer** .... (415) 486-5567
E-mail: laura.faer@ed.gov
Education: Columbia 2003 JD

Office of Communications and Outreach
50 Beale Street, San Francisco, CA 94105

Director **Joe Barison** .... (415) 486-5707

Office of Inspector General
501 I Street, Sacramento, CA 95814

Regional Inspector General for Audit **Raymond "Ray" Hendren** Suite 9-200 .... (916) 930-2399
E-mail: ray.hendren@ed.gov Fax: (916) 930-2390
Special Agent-in-Charge **(Vacant)** .... (562) 980-4132
One World Trade Center, Suite 1200, Long Beach, CA 90831 Fax: (562) 980-4143

Office of Management
50 Beale Street, San Francisco, CA 94105
Tel: (415) 486-5710 Fax: (415) 486-5706

Human Resource Officer **Christine Reese** Suite 9300 .... (415) 486-5541
E-mail: christine.reese@ed.gov

Federal Student Aid
50 Beale Street, San Francisco, CA 94105

School Participation Team Director **Martina Fernandez-Rosario** .... (415) 486-5605
E-mail: martina.fernandez-rosario@ed.gov

Region X

Jackson Federal Building, 915 Second Avenue, Room 3362, Seattle, WA 98174-1099
Tel: (206) 607-1655 Fax: (206) 607-1661
Areas Covered: AK, ID, OR, WA

Public Affairs Specialist **Linda Pauley** .... (206) 607-1655
E-mail: linda.pauley@ed.gov

Office for Civil Rights – Seattle Enforcement Office
Jackson Federal Building, 915 Second Avenue, Room 3310, Seattle, WA 98174-1099
Tel: (206) 607-1600 TTY: (206) 607-1647 Fax: (206) 607-1601

Seattle Enforcement Office Director **Linda Mangel** ...... (206) 607-1600
Chief Attorney **Sarah Dunne** .... (206) 607-1640
E-mail: sarah.dunne@ed.gov

Office of Human Resources
915 Second Avenue, Seattle, WA 98174-1099
Tel: (206) 607-1667 Fax: (206) 607-1662

Human Resource Specialist **Isaac "Ike" Gilbert** Jackson Federal Building, Room 3388 .... (206) 607-1667
E-mail: ike.gilbert@ed.gov

Federal Student Aid
915 Second Avenue, Room 390, Seattle, WA 98174-1099
Tel: (206) 615-2594 Fax: (206) 615-2508

Senior Institutional Review Specialist **Gayle Palumbo** ... (415) 486-5614
50 Beale Street, Room 9808, San Francisco, CA 94105
E-mail: gayle.palumbo@ed.gov
Seattle Performance Improvement Duty Station Director **Michael Cagle** .... (206) 615-2594
E-mail: michael.cagle@ed.gov
Training Delivery Manager **Suzanne Scheldt** .... (206) 615-2583
E-mail: suzanne.scheldt@ed.gov
Training Delivery Manager **Kimberly "Kim" Wells** ...... (206) 615-2594
E-mail: kimberly.wells@ed.gov

★ Presidential Appointment Requiring Senate Confirmation ☆ Presidential Appointment □ Schedule C Appointment ◇ Career Senior Foreign Service Appointment
● Career Senior Executive Service (SES) Appointment ○ Non-Career Senior Executive Service (SES) Appointment ■ Postal Career Executive Service

United States Department of Energy

Contents

United States Department of Energy (DOE)

Description: The Department of Energy is responsible for pursuing long-term, high-risk research; developing energy technology; marketing federal power; promoting energy conservation; providing data collection and analysis programs; and overseeing the nation's nuclear weapons and energy regulatory programs.

Forrestal Building, 1000 Independence Avenue, SW,
Washington, DC 20585 (Mailing Address for All Locations)
Tel: (202) 586-5000 (Personnel Locator)
Tel: (202) 586-5575 (Public Inquiry)
Tel: (202) 586-5955 (Freedom of Information/Privacy Act)
Tel: (877) 337-3463 (Clean Cities Hotline) Tel: (877) 337-3463 (EERE - Energy Efficiency and Renewable Energy Information Center)
Tel: (202) 586-4073 (Inspector General's Hotline - DC Metropolitan Area)
Tel: (800) 541-1625 (Inspector General's Hotline - Continental US)
TTY: (800) 877-8339 (Federal Information Relay Service)
Internet: www.energy.gov Internet: www.usa.gov

OFFICE OF THE SECRETARY

Forrestal Building, 1000 Independence Avenue, SW,
Washington, DC 20585-1000
Tel: (202) 586-6210 Fax: (202) 586-4403

Office of the Deputy Secretary (DS)

Forrestal Building, 1000 Independence Avenue, SW,
Washington, DC 20585
Fax: (202) 586-7210

Office of Inspector General (IG)

Forrestal Building, 1000 Independence Avenue, SW,
Washington, DC 20585-0102
Tel: (202) 586-1818

Office of Audits and Inspections (OAS)

Forrestal Building, 1000 Independence Avenue, SW,
Washington, DC 20585
Fax: (202) 586-0099

Central Region

• Deputy Assistant Inspector General for Audits **Jack D. Rouch** .... (240) 562-1702
E-mail: jack.rouch@ee.doe.gov

Albuquerque (NM) Office of Audit Services

P.O. Box 5400, Albuquerque, NM 87185
Tel: (505) 845-5554

Assistant Director **Aldric G. Hill** .... (505) 845-6229
E-mail: aldric.hill@nnsa.doe.gov

Los Alamos (NM) Office of Audit Services

Office of Inspector General, 528 - 35th Street,
Mail Stop B211, Los Alamos, NM 87545-5001
Tel: (505) 665-6513 Fax: (505) 667-7631

Team Leader **(Vacant)** .... (505) 665-6513

Eastern Region

P.O. Box 2001, Oak Ridge, TN 37831
Tel: (865) 576-7839 Fax: (865) 241-3897

• Deputy Assistant Inspector General for Audits and Inspections **Debra K. Solmonson** .... (865) 576-5772
E-mail: solmonsondk@oigor.doe.gov

Eastern Region *(continued)*

Executive Secretary **Patricia H. Bowerman** .... (865) 576-5774
E-mail: bowermanph@oigor.doe.gov
Assistant Division Director **Philip D. Beckett** .... (865) 576-7400
E-mail: beckettp@oigor.doe.gov
Assistant Division Director **Dawnya D. Hathaway** .... (865) 241-5390
E-mail: hathawayd@oigor.doe.gov
Assistant Division Director **Marilyn E. Richardson** .... (202) 586-4624
E-mail: marilyn.richardson@hq.doe.gov
Team Leader **Phillip L. Holbrook, Jr.** .... (865) 576-7844
E-mail: holbrookpl@oigor.doe.gov

Chicago (IL) Office of Audit Services

Building 310, 9800 South Cass Avenue, Lemont, IL 60439
Fax: (630) 252-3650

Team Leader **William R. "Bill" Lubecke** .... (630) 252-2345
E-mail: william.lubecke@science.doe.gov

Oak Ridge (TN) Office of Inspections

P.O. Box 2001, Mail Stop B8-27, Oak Ridge, TN 37831
Tel: (865) 576-7839

Team Leader **Phillip L. Holbrook, Jr.** .... (865) 576-7844
E-mail: holbrookpl@oigor.doe.gov

Oak Ridge (TN) Office of Audit Services

P.O. Box 2001, Mail Stop B8-27, Oak Ridge, TN 37831
Tel: (865) 576-5774 Fax: (865) 576-3213

Assistant Division Director **Karen Morrow** .... (865) 241-1842
E-mail: morrowkd@oigor.doe.gov

Pittsburgh (PA) Office of Audit Services

P.O. Box 10940, Pittsburgh, PA 15236-0940
626 Cochrans Mill Road, P.O. Box 10690, Pittsburgh, PA 15236-0940
Tel: (412) 386-4782 Fax: (412) 386-5048

Team Leader **Veronica L. Rutt** .... (412) 386-5042
E-mail: veronica.rutt@netl.doe.gov
Director, Office of Environment, Science, and Corporate Audits **(Vacant)** .... (412) 386-6526
Secretary **Michele L. Crivello** .... (412) 386-5866
E-mail: michele.crivello@netl.doe.gov

Savannah River (SC) Office of Audit Services

Building 703-41A, Savannah River Site, Aiken, SC 29802
Tel: (803) 725-2241 Fax: (803) 725-7592

Group Leader **Troy McGahee** .... (803) 725-1275
E-mail: troy.mcgahee@srs.gov

Western Region

P.O. Box 5400, Albuquerque, NM 87185-5400
Fax: (505) 845-4644

• Deputy Assistant Inspector General for Audits and Inspections **(Vacant)** .... (505) 845-4739
Director **Judy Jew** .... (505) 845-4739

Albuquerque (NM) Office of Inspections

P.O. Box 5400, Albuquerque, NM 87185
Tel: (505) 845-5153 Fax: (505) 845-4644

Team Leader **(Vacant)** .... (505) 845-5153

★ Presidential Appointment Requiring Senate Confirmation ☆ Presidential Appointment □ Schedule C Appointment ◇ Career Senior Foreign Service Appointment
● Career Senior Executive Service (SES) Appointment ○ Non-Career Senior Executive Service (SES) Appointment ■ Postal Career Executive Service

DEPARTMENTS

Las Vegas (NV) Office of Audit Services
P.O. Box 98518, Mail Stop 574, Las Vegas, NV 89193-8518
Tel: (702) 295-0779 Fax: (702) 295-0255
Team Leader **Crystal A. Miller** .... (702) 295-0779
E-mail: crystal.miller@doe.gov

Livermore (CA) Office of Audit Services
P.O. Box 808, Mail Stop L-369, Livermore, CA 94550
Tel: (925) 423-7278
Team Leader **Dulce Pamela "Pamela" Baizas** .... (925) 424-3234
E-mail: pamela.baizas@nnsa.doe.gov

Livermore (CA) Office of Inspections
P.O. Box 2254, Livermore, CA 94551
Tel: (925) 422-2889
Team Leader **(Vacant)** .... (925) 422-1989

Office of Investigations
Forrestal Building, 1000 Independence Avenue, SW,
Washington, DC 20585
Fax: (202) 586-0754

Central Investigations Operations
P.O. Box J657, Albuquerque, NM 87185
Special Agent-in-Charge **James F. Breckenridge** .... (505) 845-5572

Eastern Investigation Operations
1000 Independence Avenue, SW, Suite 8F-037, Washington, DC 20585
Tel: (202) 586-3084 Fax: (202) 586-3697
Special Agent-in-Charge
Richard A. "Rick" Sample, Jr. .... (865) 576-9200

Oak Ridge (TN) Field Office
P.O. Box 6318, Oak Ridge, TN 37831
115 Union Valley Road, Oak Ridge, TN 37830 (Mail. Night Mail)
Tel: (865) 576-9588 Fax: (865) 576-8111
Supervisory Criminal Investigator
Richard A. "Rick" Sample, Jr. .... (865) 576-9202
Special Agent **Ryan M. Baker** .... (865) 576-3655
Special Agent **Jeffrey W. "Jeff" Inman** .... (865) 576-4071
Special Agent **Jonathan M. Lamb** .... (865) 576-9588
Special Agent **Laura M. Slatton** .... (865) 574-9827

Pittsburgh (PA) Field Office
Building 141, 626 Cochrans Mill Road, Pittsburgh, PA 15236-0940
P.O. Box 10940, Pittsburgh, PA 15236-0940
Fax: (412) 386-4971
Special Agent **Loran A. DeHonney** .... (412) 386-6185
E-mail: loran.dehonney@netl.doe.gov

Savannah River (SC) Field Office
Road 1, Building 703-41A, Aiken, SC 29802
P.O. Box 447, New Ellenton, SC 29809
Tel: (803) 725-7319 Fax: (803) 725-5384
Assistant Special Agent in Charge **Kevin P. Childress** .... (803) 725-7319
Special Agent **Christopher M. Campbell** .... (803) 725-8419
Special Agent **Steven R. Driver** .... (803) 725-7323
Special Agent **Anthony C. Ginn** .... (803) 725-5346
Special Agent **Kevin D. Gordon** .... (803) 725-5936
Special Agent **(Vacant)** .... (803) 725-2635

Western Investigation Operations
1838 Terminal Drive, Suite A, Richland, WA 99354
Tel: (509) 376-6361 Fax: (509) 376-7458
Special Agent-in-Charge **Scott A. Berenberg** .... (925) 423-8678

Albuquerque (NM) Field Office
Pennsylvania and H Streets, Kirtland Air Force Base,
Albuquerque, NM 87116
P.O. Box 5657, Albuquerque, NM 87185
Tel: (505) 845-4009 Fax: (505) 845-4663
Assistant Special Agent-in-Charge **(Vacant)** .... (505) 845-4009

Albuquerque (NM) Field Office *(continued)*
Special Agent **Joseph R. Davila III** .... (505) 845-5091
E-mail: joseph.davila@nnsa.doe.gov
Special Agent **Anthony J. Montoya** .... (505) 845-6313
E-mail: anthony.montoya@doe.gov

Denver (CO) Field Office
12155 West Alameda Parkway, Lakewood, CO 80228-2802
P.O. Box 281213, Lakewood, CO 80228-8213
Tel: (720) 962-7539 Fax: (720) 962-7554
Special Agent **(Vacant)** .... (720) 962-7539
Special Agent **(Vacant)** .... (720) 962-7539

Idaho Falls (ID) Field Office
1580 Sawtelle Street, Idaho Falls, ID 83415-2508
P.O. Box 51566, Idaho Falls, ID 83405-1566
Tel: (208) 526-4225 Fax: (208) 526-4175
Special Agent **Charles T. McDevitt** .... (208) 526-4225
Special Agent **Raymond E. Soske** .... (208) 526-4227

Las Vegas (NV) Field Office
P.O. Box 98518, Las Vegas, NV 89193-8518
Tel: (702) 295-0877
Special Agent **(Vacant)** .... (702) 295-0877

Livermore (CA) Field Office
Lawrence Livermore National Laboratory, L-368,
7000 East Avenue, T3527, Livermore, CA 94550
P.O. Box 2270, Livermore, CA 94551
Tel: (925) 422-3245 Fax: (925) 422-3230
Assistant Special Agent in Charge
Christopher D. "Chris" Burris .... (925) 422-2885
Special Agent **Scott A. Berenberg** .... (925) 423-8678

Richland (WA) Field Office
1838 Terminal Drive, Suite A, Richland, WA 99354
Tel: (509) 376-8828 Fax: (509) 376-7458
Assistant Special Agent-in-Charge **Shawn Dionida** .... (509) 376-8783
Special Agent **Patrick D. McGlinn** .... (509) 376-8533
Special Agent **Karrisa E. D. Otero** .... (509) 372-0349
Special Agent **Trevor Pearson** .... (509) 376-3830

Office of the Under Secretary of Energy (S3)
Forrestal Building, 1000 Independence Avenue, SW,
Washington, DC 20585
Tel: (202) 586-7700 Fax: (202) 586-0148

ASSISTANT SECRETARY FOR ELECTRICITY (OE)
Forrestal Building, 1000 Independence Avenue, SW,
Suite 8H033, Washington, DC 20585
Tel: (202) 586-1411 Fax: (202) 586-1472

Bonneville Power Administration (BPA)
905 NE 11th Avenue, Portland, OR 97232
P.O. Box 3621, Portland, OR 97208-3621
Tel: (503) 230-3000 Fax: (503) 230-5026 Internet: www.bpa.gov

Office of the Administrator (A)
905 NE 11th Avenue, Portland, OR 97232
Tel: (503) 230-5102 Fax: (503) 230-4018
● Administrator and Chief Executive Officer
[Senior Agency Official for Records Management]
Elliot E. Mainzer .... (503) 230-5102
E-mail: eemainzer@bpa.gov
Education: UC Berkeley 1989 BA; Yale 1998 MBA
Executive Officer **Sandra A. "Sandy" Boardman** .... (503) 230-5102
E-mail: sxboardman@bpa.gov

★ Presidential Appointment Requiring Senate Confirmation ☆ Presidential Appointment □ Schedule C Appointment ◇ Career Senior Foreign Service Appointment
● Career Senior Executive Service (SES) Appointment ○ Non-Career Senior Executive Service (SES) Appointment ■ Postal Career Executive Service

Office of the Deputy Administrator
● Deputy Administrator **Daniel M. "Dan" James** .... (503) 230-4452
E-mail: mjames@bpa.gov
Education: Pacific U 1987 BA

Communications (DK)
Tel: (503) 230-5131
Director **Scott R. Simms** .... (503) 230-3567
E-mail: srsimms@bpa.gov

Compliance, Audit, Risk and Equal Employment Opportunity
● Executive Vice President (Acting)
Thomas A. McDonald .... (503) 230-3251
E-mail: tamcdonald@bpa.gov

Corporate Strategy (S)
● Director **(Vacant)** .... (503) 230-3408

Intergovernmental Affairs
Director **Peter T. Cogswell** .... (503) 230-5227
E-mail: ptcogswell@bpa.gov

Office of the Chief Administrative Officer (N)
905 NE 11th Avenue, Portland, OR 97232
Fax: (503) 230-4508 Fax: (503) 230-5374
● Chief Administrative Officer **John L. Hairston** .... (503) 230-5262
E-mail: jlhairston@bpa.gov

Office of the Chief Financial Officer
905 NE 11th Avenue, Portland, OR 97232
Fax: (503) 230-5316
● Executive Vice President and Chief Financial Officer
Michelle L. Manary .... (503) 230-3421
E-mail: mlmanary@bpa.gov
Education: Linfield; Willamette MBA, MPA

Office of the Chief Operating Officer
905 NE 11th Avenue, Portland, OR 97232
● Chief Operating Officer **Janet C. Herrin** .... (503) 230-3311
E-mail: jcherrin@bpa.gov
Education: Willamette BA; Colorado State MS; Tennessee MBA

Business Transformation Office (B)
Deputy Executive Vice President **Nita M. Zimmerman** ... (503) 230-3935

Contracting Activity
Director **Nicholas Jenkins** .... (503) 230-5498
E-mail: nmjenkins@bpa.gov

Environment, Fish and Wildlife (E)
905 NE 11th Avenue, Portland, OR 97232
Fax: (503) 230-4563
● Vice President **Scott Armentrout** .... (503) 230-3076
Education: Oregon State 1989 BS
Deputy Vice President **Gregory J. Dondlinger** .... (503) 230-5065

Power Services (P)
905 NE 11th Avenue, Portland, OR 97232
Fax: (503) 230-7333
● Senior Vice President **Joel D. Cook** .... (360) 418-2245

Energy Efficiency
905 NE 11th Avenue, Portland, OR 97232
Fax: (503) 230-5147
Vice President **Kim T. Thompson** .... (503) 230-3408
E-mail: ktthompson@bpa.gov

Generation Asset Management
● Vice President **Kieran P. Connolly** .... (503) 230-4680
E-mail: kpconnolly@bpa.gov
Education: Willamette BS; Portland MBA

Northwest Requirements Marketing (PS)
● Vice President **Garry R. Thompson** .... (503) 230-4452
E-mail: grthompson@bpa.gov

Bulk Marketing (PT)
● Vice President **Suzanne Bennett Cooper** .... (503) 230-5077
E-mail: sbcooper@bpa.gov

Transmission Services (T)
5411 NE Highway 99, Vancouver, WA 98666-0491
P.O. Box 491 – T/Ditt2, Vancouver, WA 98666-0491
Fax: (360) 418-2516
● Senior Vice President **Richard Labib Shaheen** .... (360) 418-2122
E-mail: rlshaheen@bpa.gov

Planning and Asset Management
● Vice President **Jeffrey W. "Jeff" Cook** .... (360) 418-2306
E-mail: jwcook@bpa.gov

Transmission Field Services (TF)
● Vice President **Robin R. Furrer** .... (360) 418-2245
E-mail: rrfurrer@bpa.gov

Transmission Marketing and Sales (TS)
● Vice President **(Vacant)** .... (503) 230-5858

Office of the General Counsel
905 NE 11th Avenue, Portland, OR 97232
Fax: (503) 230-7405
● Executive Vice President and General Counsel
Mary K. Jensen .... (503) 230-5758
E-mail: mkjensen@bpa.gov

Southeastern Power Administration (SEPA)

1166 Athens Tech Road, Elberton, GA 30635
Tel: (706) 213-3800 Fax: (706) 213-3884 E-mail: info2@sepa.doe.gov
Internet: energy.gov/sepa
Areas Covered: AL, FL, GA, IL, KY, MS, NC, SC, TN, VA, WV

● Administrator **Kenneth E. Legg** .... (706) 213-3800
E-mail: ken.legg@sepa.doe.gov
Assistant Administrator, Finance and Marketing
Virgil Hobbs .... (706) 213-3838
E-mail: virgil.hobbs@sepa.doe.gov
Assistant Administrator, Human Resources and Administration [Senior Agency Official for Records Management, Federal Vendor Engagement Official]
Joel W. Seymour .... (706) 213-3810
E-mail: joels@sepa.doe.gov
Assistant Administrator, Power Resources
Herbert R. "Herb" Nadler .... (706) 213-3853
E-mail: herbn@sepa.doe.gov
Attorney-Adviser **Leon Jourolmon** .... (706) 213-3807
E-mail: leon.jourolmon@sepa.doe.gov
Information Management **Dale Jett** .... (706) 213-3830
E-mail: dalej@sepa.doe.gov
Librarian **Denise Moon** .... (706) 213-3815
Public Affairs Specialist **(Vacant)** .... (706) 213-3812

Southwestern Power Administration (SWPA)

One West Third Street, Tulsa, OK 74103-3502
Tel: (918) 595-6600 Fax: (918) 595-6755 E-mail: info@swpa.gov
Internet: www.swpa.gov
Areas Covered: AR, KS, LA, MO, OK, TX

● Administrator and Chief Executive Officer [Senior Agency Official for Records Management, Federal Vendor Engagement Official]
Michael S. "Mike" Wech .... (417) 891-2626
E-mail: mike.wech@swpa.gov
Education: Nebraska 1982
Executive Assistant **(Vacant)** .... (918) 595-6606
Fax: (918) 595-6656

Office of Diversity
Diversity Program Manager **Bradley S. "Brad" Shaff** .... (918) 595-6696
E-mail: brad.shaff@swpa.gov

★ Presidential Appointment Requiring Senate Confirmation ☆ Presidential Appointment ☐ Schedule C Appointment ◇ Career Senior Foreign Service Appointment
● Career Senior Executive Service (SES) Appointment ○ Non-Career Senior Executive Service (SES) Appointment ■ Postal Career Executive Service

Office of Power Delivery
2858 South Golden Avenue, Springfield, MO 65807-3213
Deputy Administrator **(Vacant)** .... (417) 891-2626

Office of Corporate Compliance
Senior Vice President
Elmer Keith "Keith" Blackstone .... (918) 595-6618
E-mail: keith.blackstone@swpa.gov

Division of Environmental, Security, Safety and Health
Director/Program Manager **Danny Johnson** .... (918) 595-6781
Security Officer **James "Jay" Parvin** .... (918) 595-6741
E-mail: james.parvin@swpa.gov

Office of General Counsel
One West Third Street, Tulsa, OK 74103-3502
Fax: (918) 595-6755
General Counsel **Laurence J. "Larry" Yadon II** .... (918) 595-6607
E-mail: laurence.yadon@swpa.gov

Division of Human Resources Management
Senior Human Resources Business Partner (Acting)
Elmer Keith "Keith" Blackstone .... (918) 595-6618
E-mail: keith.blackstone@swpa.gov

Division of Information Technology
Director/Chief Information Officer **(Vacant)** .... (918) 595-6600

Division of Reliability Compliance
Compliance Supervisor **Tracey L. Stewart** .... (918) 595-6677

Office of Corporate Operations
One West Third Street, Tulsa, OK 74103-3502
Fax: (918) 595-6656
Senior Vice President and Chief Operating Officer
Marshall S. Boyken .... (918) 595-6646

Division of Acquisitions and Facilities Services
Director/Contracting Officer **Sean L. Long** .... (918) 595-6740
E-mail: sean.long@swpa.gov

Division of Financial Management
Director/Chief Financial Officer
Douglas J. "Doug" Hart .... (918) 595-6631

Division of Power Marketing and Transmission Strategy
Vice President **Aiden Smith** .... (918) 595-6764

Division of Resources and Rates
Director/Civil Engineer (Hydrologic) **Fritha Ohlson** .... (918) 595-6684

Division of Maintenance
Director/Program Manager **Kenny V. Broadaway** .... (870) 268-2509
305 North Floyd Street, Fax: (870) 932-6153
Jonesboro, AR 72401-1908

Division of Scheduling and Operations
Vice President of Operations **(Vacant)** .... (417) 891-2626

Division of System Protection and Communications
Director **Douglas E. "Doug" Johnson** .... (417) 891-2669
Fax: (417) 891-2693

Division of Transmission Engineering and Planning
Director/Electrical Engineer **Carlos E. Valencia** .... (918) 595-6707

Western Area Power Administration (WAPA)
12155 West Alameda Parkway, Lakewood, CO 80228-2802
P.O. Box 281213, Lakewood, CO 80228-8213
Tel: (720) 962-7000 (Information) Tel: (720) 962-7050 (Public Affairs)
Fax: (720) 962-7059 E-mail: publicaffairs@wapa.gov
Internet: www.wapa.gov
Areas Covered: AZ, CA, CO, western IA, KS, western MN, MT, NE, NV, NM, ND, SD, western TX, UT, WY

● Administrator and Chief Executive Officer
[Senior Agency Official for Records Management]
Mark A. Gabriel .... (720) 962-7077
E-mail: gabriel@wapa.gov
Education: Fordham 1976 BA
Administrative Assistant **Miriam Pena** .... (720) 962-7077
E-mail: pena@wapa.gov
Chief of Staff **Erin A. Green** .... (720) 962-7016
E-mail: egreen@wapa.gov
Senior Vice President and Assistant Administrator for
Corporate Liaison **Dionne E. Thompson** .... (720) 962-7000
Forrestal Building, Fax: (202) 586-6261
1000 Independence Avenue, SW,
Room 8G-027, Washington, DC 20585-1290
Education: Harvard 1989 BA; Virginia JD
● Senior Vice President and General Counsel
John Bremer .... (720) 962-7019
E-mail: bremer@wapa.gov
Chief Strategy Officer **Jennifer R. Rodgers** .... (720) 962-7099
Education: Colorado State BA; Colorado (Colo Springs) MBA
Chief Public Affairs Officer **Teresa Waugh** .... (720) 962-7051
E-mail: waugh@wapa.gov
Economic Impact and Diversity Office Manager
Charles Marquez .... (720) 962-7044
E-mail: marquez@wapa.gov
Power Marketing Advisor **Rodney G. Bailey** .... (801) 524-4007
E-mail: rbailey@wapa.gov

Office of the Chief Administrative Officer
● Senior Vice President and Chief Administrative Officer
(Acting) **Tracey A. LeBeau** .... (720) 962-7710
E-mail: lebeau@wapa.gov
Education: Stanford 1991 AB; Iowa 1994 JD

Office of the Chief Financial Officer (OCFO)
● Senior Vice President and Chief Financial Officer
Dennis Sullivan .... (720) 962-7501
E-mail: dsullivan@wapa.gov
Education: UMass (Amherst) 1990 BSAcc;
Colorado (Denver) 2002 MBA
Budget and Analysis Officer **(Vacant)** .... (720) 962-7450
Compliance and Audit Liaison Officer **Lisa Hansen** .... (720) 962-7513
E-mail: hansen@wapa.gov
Financial Operations Officer **Lynn Hahn** .... (720) 962-7456

Office of the Chief Information Officer
Senior Vice President and Chief Information Officer
(Acting) **Michael M. "Mike" Montoya** .... (720) 962-7130
E-mail: mmontoya@wapa.gov
Vice President of Information Technology Enterprise
Management **Michael M. "Mike" Montoya** .... (720) 962-7130
E-mail: mmontoya@wapa.gov
Vice President, Cyber Security **James Ball** .... (720) 962-7572
E-mail: ball@wapa.gov

Office of the Chief Operating Officer
● Executive Vice President and Chief Operating Officer
Kevin Howard .... (720) 962-7241
E-mail: howard@wapa.gov
Education: Colorado State 1988 BSE
● Senior Vice President and Transmission Infrastructure
Program Manager **Tracey A. LeBeau** .... (720) 962-7710
E-mail: lebeau@wapa.gov
Education: Stanford 1991 AB; Iowa 1994 JD
Vice President of Engineering **Ross Clark** .... (720) 962-7338
Vice President of Natural Resources (Acting)
Matt Blevins .... (720) 962-7261

Office of the Chief Operating Officer *(continued)*

Vice President of Procurement **John Athanasiou** . . . . (720) 962-7155
E-mail: athanasi@wapa.gov
Vice President of Technical Services
Steven M. "Steve" Yexley . . . . (720) 962-7245
E-mail: yexley@wapa.gov
Aviation Manager **Rich Westra** . . . . (720) 962-7431
Electric Power Training Center Manager **Kyle Conroy** . . . . (720) 962-7351
E-mail: conroy@wapa.gov
Director of Security **Pernell "Bruce" Watson** . . . . (720) 962-7290
Education: Air Force Acad 1989 BS; Cardinal Stritch U 2004 MS
Director of Safety **Kevin Ripplinger** . . . . (720) 962-7292
E-mail: ripplinger@wapa.gov

Colorado River Storage Project Management Center (CRSP)
299 South Main Street, Suite 200?, Salt Lake City, UT 84111
Tel: (801) 524-5493 Fax: (801) 524-5017

Manager **Steven R. "Steve" Johnson** . . . . (801) 524-6372
E-mail: johnsons@wapa.gov
Executive Assistant **Roberta Sweeney** . . . . (801) 524-5494
E-mail: sweeney@wapa.gov
Manager, Energy Management and Marketing **(Vacant)** . . . (970) 240-3028
Manager, Management and Technical Services
Brian J. Sadler . . . . (801) 524-5506
E-mail: sadler@wapa.gov
Manager, Power Marketing **Brent Osiek** . . . . (801) 524-5399
E-mail: osiek@wapa.gov

Desert Southwest Regional Office (DSW)
615 South 43rd Avenue, Phoenix, AZ 85009-5313
P.O. Box 6457, Phoenix, AZ 85005-6457
Tel: (602) 605-2525 Fax: (602) 605-2630
Internet: www.wapa.gov/regions/DSW

● Senior Vice President and Regional Manager
Ronald E. "Ron" Moulton . . . . (602) 605-2668
E-mail: moulton@wapa.gov
Education: USC 1988 MSEE; Utah 1998 MBA
Executive Administrative Assistant
Sylvia A. Gallardo . . . . (602) 605-2639
E-mail: sgallardo@wapa.gov
Assistant Regional Manager for Federal Power Systems
Jack D. Murray . . . . (602) 605-2442
E-mail: jmurray@wapa.gov
Assistant Regional Manager for Financial Management
Ethel Redhair . . . . (602) 605-2566
Assistant Regional Manager for Management Services
Leonard Mathieu . . . . (602) 605-2404
E-mail: mathieu@wapa.gov Fax: (602) 605-2483
Assistant Regional Manager for Power System
Maintenance **Jimmy Kendrick** . . . . (602) 605-2440
Assistant Regional Manager for Power System
Operations **Teresita Amaro** . . . . (602) 605-2605
E-mail: amaro@wapa.gov
Accounting Manager **Anna E. "Beth" Kozik** . . . . (602) 605-2835
Budget and Alternative Finance Manager **(Vacant)** . . . . . . (602) 605-2832
Energy Management and Marketing Manager
John Paulsen . . . . (602) 605-2557
E-mail: paulsen@wapa.gov
Environmental Manager **Linda Marianito** . . . . (602) 605-2524
Maintenance, Engineering and Construction Manager
(Vacant) . . . . (602) 605-2694
Transmission Planning Manager
Michael D. "Mike" Olson . . . . (602) 605-2617
Operations Reliability and Balancing Manager
(Vacant) . . . . (602) 605-2876
Personnel Manager **Barbara B. South** . . . . (602) 605-2770
E-mail: south@wapa.gov
Power Contracts and Energy Services Manager
Patricia Weeks . . . . (602) 605-2594
Procurement Manager **Byron McCollum** . . . . (720) 962-7154
E-mail: mccollum@wapa.gov
Protection and Communication Manager **(Vacant)** . . . . (602) 605-2605
Resource and Planning Manager
Christina M. "Tina" Ramsey . . . . (602) 605-2565
E-mail: ramsey@wapa.gov Fax: (602) 605-2569

Desert Southwest Regional Office *(continued)*

Safety and Security Manager **Troy E. Henry** . . . . (602) 605-2695
E-mail: thenry@wapa.gov
Transmission Lines and Substations Manager **(Vacant)** . . . (602) 605-2756
Engineering Office Team Leader **Roger Moody** . . . . (602) 605-2697
Field Team Leader **Gary P. Lachvayder** . . . . (602) 605-2694
Project Engineer Team Leader
Donald L. "Don" Byron . . . . (602) 605-2685
Rates Team Leader **Scott Lund** . . . . (602) 605-2442
System Support Team Leader **(Vacant)** . . . . (602) 605-2730
Contracting Officer's Representative for
Computer-Aided Design (CAD) **(Vacant)** . . . . (602) 605-2532
Supervisory Control and Data Acquisition (SCADA)
Supervisor **Matthew Powel "Matt" Schmehl** . . . . (602) 605-2784
E-mail: schmehl@wapa.gov
Information Technology Contract Support Services
Albert T. Slucher . . . . (602) 605-2608
E-mail: slucher@wapa.gov
Reliability Compliance Advisor **(Vacant)** . . . . (602) 605-2638
Remarketing Specialist **Michael J. "Mike" Simonton** . . . (602) 605-2675
E-mail: simonton@wapa.gov
System Integration Specialist **(Vacant)** . . . . (602) 605-2651
Realty Officer **(Vacant)** . . . . (602) 605-2554
Realty Specialist **(Vacant)** . . . . (602) 605-2580

Rocky Mountain Regional Office (RM)
5555 East Crossroads Boulevard, Loveland, CO 80538-8986
P.O. Box 3700, Loveland, CO 80539-3003
Tel: (970) 461-7200 Fax: (970) 461-7213

● Senior Vice President and Regional Manager
Michael D. "Mike" McElhany . . . . (970) 461-7200
E-mail: mcelhany@wapa.gov
Education: North Dakota State BSEE
Executive Assistant **Heather Bredesen** . . . . (970) 461-7382
Environmental Manager **Brian J. Little** . . . . (970) 461-7287
E-mail: blittle@wapa.gov
Financial Manager **Larry Maass** . . . . (970) 461-7245
E-mail: maass@wapa.gov
Human Resources Advisor **Ruby Dunbar** . . . . (970) 461-7202
E-mail: dunbar@wapa.gov
Information Technology Manager **Brett M. Fisher** . . . . (970) 461-7275
E-mail: bfisher@wapa.gov
Maintenance Manager **Nicholas S. "Nic" Klemm** . . . . . . (970) 461-7205
E-mail: klemm@wapa.gov Fax: (970) 461-7452
Operations Manager **Darren A. Buck** . . . . (916) 353-4016
E-mail: dbuck@wapa.gov
Power Marketing Manager **David J. Neumayer** . . . . (307) 232-5200
E-mail: neumayer@wapa.gov
Procurement Manager **Corinna Gonzalez** . . . . (970) 545-1292
E-mail: cgonzalez@wapa.gov
Property Management Specialist **Patrick J. Kearney** . . . . . (970) 461-7697
E-mail: kearney@wapa.gov
Rates Manager **Sheila Cook** . . . . (970) 461-7211
E-mail: scook@wapa.gov
Reliability and Transmission Switching Manager
(Vacant) . . . . (970) 461-7200
Safety and Security Manager **William Neil Schnyer** . . . . . (970) 461-7449
E-mail: schnyer@wapa.gov
Supervisory Electrical Engineer
Robert H. "Bob" Easton . . . . (970) 461-7272
E-mail: aeaston@wapa.gov
Transmission Scheduling and Security Manager
Peter D. Heiman . . . . (602) 605-4475
E-mail: heiman@wapa.gov
Administrative Officer **Kellie Petty** . . . . (970) 461-7202
E-mail: petty@wapa.gov

Sierra Nevada Regional Office (SN)
114 Parkshore Drive, Folsom, CA 95630-4710
Tel: (916) 353-4400 Fax: (916) 985-1930
Areas Covered: Northern and central CA; northern NV

● Senior Vice President and Regional Manager **(Vacant)** . . . (916) 353-4418
Restructuring Advisor **Howard Hirahara** . . . . (916) 353-4019
Administrative Officer **(Vacant)** . . . . (916) 353-4400

(continued on next page)

★ Presidential Appointment Requiring Senate Confirmation ☆ Presidential Appointment □ Schedule C Appointment ◇ Career Senior Foreign Service Appointment
● Career Senior Executive Service (SES) Appointment ○ Non-Career Senior Executive Service (SES) Appointment ■ Postal Career Executive Service

DEPARTMENTS

Sierra Nevada Regional Office *(continued)*

Administrative Assistant **Alexia Mendoza** . . . . (916) 353-4418
E-mail: mendoza@wapa.gov
Environmental Manager
Gerald D. "Jerry" Robbins, Jr. . . . . (916) 353-4032
E-mail: grobbins@wapa.gov
Financial Manager **Janice Nations** . . . . (916) 353-4057
E-mail: nations@wapa.gov
Maintenance Manager **Arun Sethi** . . . . (602) 605-4090
Fax: (602) 352-2484
Line Maintenance **Brian Adams** . . . . (530) 247-6710
E-mail: badams@wapa.gov
Maintenance Engineering **Wilson A. Head** . . . . (916) 353-4779
E-mail: head@wapa.gov
Protection and Communications **Daryl Rictor** . . . . (916) 353-4574
E-mail: rictor@wapa.gov
Substation Maintenance **Jim Higgins** . . . . (916) 353-4030
E-mail: higgins@wapa.gov
Operations Manager **(Vacant)** . . . . (916) 353-4008
Chief Dispatcher **Carl E. Dobbs** . . . . (916) 353-4612
E-mail: dobbs@wapa.gov Fax: (916) 353-2232
Transmission Scheduling and Security Manager
Ira A. Witherspoon . . . . (916) 353-4659
E-mail: withersp@wapa.gov Fax: (916) 353-2232
Power Operations Advisor **Russell Knight** . . . . (916) 353-4523
E-mail: rknight@wapa.gov
Power Marketing Manager **Sonja A. Anderson** . . . . (916) 353-4421
Contracts and Energy Services **Jeanne Haas** . . . . (916) 353-4438
E-mail: haas@wapa.gov Fax: (916) 985-1931
Rates **Regina A. Rieger** . . . . (916) 353-4629
E-mail: rieger@wapa.gov
Resources and Scheduling **Tong Wu** . . . . (916) 353-4016
E-mail: wu@wapa.gov
Settlements and Power Billings Manager **(Vacant)** . . . . . . (916) 353-4400
Safety Manager **Matt Monroe** . . . . (916) 353-4461
E-mail: monroe@wapa.gov Fax: (916) 985-1935
Human Resources Specialist **Perry A. Deiwert** . . . . (916) 353-4458
E-mail: deiwert@wapa.gov
Supervisory Contract Specialist **Jennifer R. Borghese** . . . (916) 353-4469
E-mail: borghese@wapa.gov

Upper Great Plains Regional Office (UGP)
2900 4th Avenue North, Billings, MT 59101-1266
P.O. Box 35800, Billings, MT 59107-5800
Tel: (406) 255-2800 Fax: (406) 255-2900

● Senior Vice President and Regional Manager
Jody S. Sundsted . . . . (406) 255-2910
E-mail: sundsted@wapa.gov
Education: Montana State BS
Administrative Assistant **Anthony Chavez** . . . . (406) 255-2802
E-mail: chavez@wapa.gov
Vice President of Information Technology
James C. Phillips . . . . (406) 255-2850
E-mail: jphillips@wapa.gov Fax: (406) 255-2900
Environmental Manager **Matthew L. Marsh** . . . . (406) 255-2811
Financial Manager **Traci J. Albright** . . . . (406) 247-7448
Maintenance Manager **Bruce A. Harrington** . . . . (605) 353-2500
200 Fourth Street, SW, Huron, SD 57350-2474
E-mail: bharring@wapa.gov
Power Marketing Manager **(Vacant)** . . . . (406) 244-2911
Safety and Security Manager **James Withers** . . . . (406) 255-2815
E-mail: jwithers@wapa.gov
Transmission System Planning Manager
Gayle R. Nansel . . . . (406) 247-7437
E-mail: nansel@wapa.gov
Administrative Officer **Robin R. Johnson** . . . . (406) 247-7426
E-mail: rrjohnsn@wapa.gov
Tel: (803) 952-8870

Construction
200 Fourth Street, SW, Huron, SD 57350-2474
Tel: (605) 353-2670 Fax: (605) 353-2673

Manager **Trevor J. Howard** . . . . (605) 353-2690

Montana Maintenance
P.O. Box 145, Fort Peck, MT 59223-0145
Tel: (406) 526-3421 Fax: (406) 526-8501

Manager **Timothy J. "Tim" Padden** . . . . (406) 526-8504
E-mail: padden@wapa.gov

North Dakota Maintenance
707 North Bismarck Expressway, Bismarck, ND 58501-3308
P.O. Box 1173, Bismarck, ND 58502-1173
Tel: (701) 221-4500 Fax: (701) 221-4526

Manager **Marc J. Kress** . . . . (701) 221-4544
E-mail: kress@wapa.gov

South Dakota Maintenance
200 Fourth Street, SW, Huron, SD 57350-2474
Tel: (605) 352-8112 Fax: (605) 353-2512

Manager (Acting) **David R. Hinders** . . . . (605) 353-2555
E-mail: hinders@wapa.gov

Upper Great Plains Operations (UGPO)
1330 41st Street, SE, Watertown, SD 57201
P.O. Box 790, Watertown, SD 57201-0790
Tel: (605) 882-7300 Fax: (605) 882-7409

Operations Manager **Lloyd A. Linke** . . . . (605) 882-7500
Transmission Scheduling and Generation Control
Manager **Craig T. Speidel** . . . . (605) 882-7576
Transmission Dispatch Manager **Michael M. Kirwan** . . . . . (605) 882-7539

ASSISTANT SECRETARY FOR ENERGY EFFICIENCY AND RENEWABLE ENERGY (EERE)

Forrestal Building, 1000 Independence Avenue, SW,
Mail Stop EE-1, Washington, DC 20585
Tel: (202) 586-9220 Fax: (202) 586-9260 Internet: www.eere.energy.gov

Golden (CO) Field Office (GFO)

15013 Denver West Parkway, Golden, CO 80401
Tel: (240) 562-1800 Fax: (240) 562-1750

● Director **Derek Passarelli** . . . . (240) 562-1742
E-mail: derek.passarelli@ee.doe.gov
Education: Stanford 1985 BA, 1985 MA; Georgetown 1988 JD
Chief of Staff **Tertia Speiser** . . . . (240) 562-1637
E-mail: tertia.speiser@ee.doe.gov

Equal Employment Office
Director **Brian D. Sutherland** . . . . (240) 562-1320

Office of Chief Counsel
Chief Counsel (Acting) **Reesha K. Trznadel** . . . . (240) 562-1801
E-mail: reesha.trznadel@hq.doe.gov
Freedom of Information Act (FOIA) Specialist
Michele H. Altieri . . . . (720) 356-1427
E-mail: michele.altieri@ee.doe.gov

Field Operations Division (GFO-2)
15013 Denver West Parkway, Golden, CO 80401
Fax: (240) 356-1780

● Director **(Vacant)** . . . . (240) 562-1403
Administrative Assistant **Kamala B. Quintana** . . . . (240) 562-1515

Office of National Laboratory Oversight (GFO-2N)
Director **(Vacant)** . . . . (720) 356-1800

National Renewable Energy Laboratory (NREL)
15013 Denver West Parkway, Golden, CO 80401
Tel: (303) 275-3000 Tel: (303) 275-4090 (Public Affairs)
Fax: (303) 275-3097 Fax: (303) 630-2119 (Public Affairs)
Internet: www.nrel.gov

Director **Dr. Martin Keller** . . . . (303) 275-3011

★ Presidential Appointment Requiring Senate Confirmation ☆ Presidential Appointment ☐ Schedule C Appointment ◇ Career Senior Foreign Service Appointment
● Career Senior Executive Service (SES) Appointment ○ Non-Career Senior Executive Service (SES) Appointment ■ Postal Career Executive Service

Operations
Deputy Laboratory Director and Chief Operating Officer **Bobi Garrett** .... (303) 275-3070
Education: Montana State BS; U Washington MBA
Executive Director, Strategic Initiatives
Robin L. Newmark .... (303) 275-4602

Energy Systems Integration
15013 Denver West Parkway, Golden, CO 80401
Internet: www.nrel.gov/esif
Associate Laboratory Director **Juan Torres** .... (303) 275-3094
Education: Southern Colorado BSEE; New Mexico MSEE
Center Director for ESIF (Energy Systems Integration Facility) **Chad Blake** .... (303) 619-5888
Director, Power Systems Engineering Center
Benjamin "Ben" Kroposki .... (303) 275-2979

Facilities and Operations
Associate Laboratory Director **Julie Baker** .... (303) 275-3004
Education: Idaho BS Fax: (303) 275-3097
Contracts and Business Services Director **Paul Pierson** ... (303) 275-3132
E-mail: Paul.Pierson@nrel.gov
Quality Management Office Director **Henry Higaki** ...... (303) 275-4212
E-mail: henry.higaki@nrel.gov
Chief Financial Officer **Owen F. Barwell** .... (303) 275-4555
Education: Lancaster (UK) BS Fax: (303) 275-4520
Chief Human Resources Officer **Deb Doel-Hammond** ... (303) 275-3000
Education: Pepperdine EdD
Chief Information Officer **Dr. James M. Lyall** .... (303) 275-4599
E-mail: James.Lyall@nrel.gov
Security and Emergency Preparedness Director
Joseph Thill .... (303) 275-4645
E-mail: joseph.thill@nrel.gov Fax: (303) 275-4668
Technical Librarian Lead **Tami Sandberg** .... (303) 275-4024
E-mail: tami.sandberg@nrel.gov Fax: (303) 630-2045

Innovation Partnering and Outreach
Associate Laboratory Director for Innovation Partnering and Outreach **William T. "Bill" Farris** ...... (303) 275-3069
Education: U Washington 1984 BS, 1987 MS; National Tech 2000 MS
Technology Transfer Director **Kristin Gray** .... (303) 275-3050

Institutional Planning, Integration and Development
Executive Director **David "Dave" Mooney** .... (303) 384-6782
E-mail: david.mooney@nrel.gov
Public Affairs/Communications Director **Sarah Sloan** .... (303) 275-4090
E-mail: sarah.sloan@nrel.gov Fax: (303) 630-2119

Scientific Computing and Energy Analysis (SCEA)
Associate Laboratory Director **Robert W. Leland** .... (303) 275-3009
Education: Michigan State 1985 BS; Oxford (UK) 1989 DPhil
Deputy Associate Laboratory Director
Douglas J. "Doug" Arent .... (303) 384-7502

Science and Technology
15013 Denver West Parkway, Golden, CO 80401
Fax: (303) 275-3097
Deputy Laboratory Director **Peter F. Green** .... (303) 275-3008
Education: Hunter 1981 BA; Cornell 1983 MS, 1985 PhD

BioEnergy Science and Technology
15013 Denver West Parkway, Golden, CO 80401
Internet: www.nrel.gov/bioenergy
Associate Laboratory Director **Adam Bratis** .... (303) 384-7852
E-mail: adam.bratis@nrel.gov

Materials and Chemical Science and Technology (MCST)
15013 Denver West Parkway, Golden, CO 80401
Associate Laboratory Director **William "Bill" Tumas** .... (303) 384-7955
E-mail: bill.tumas@nrel.gov
Education: Ithaca 1980 BA; Stanford 1985 PhD

Mechanical and Thermal Systems Engineering (MTES)
15013 Denver West Parkway, Golden, CO 80401
Associate Lab Director **Johney Boyd Green, Jr.** .... (303) 275-3043
E-mail: johney.green@nrel.gov
Education: U Memphis BME; Georgia Tech MME, PhD

Procurement Operations Division (GFO-3)
Director [Federal Vendor Engagement Official]
(Vacant) .... (720) 356-1800

ASSISTANT SECRETARY FOR FOSSIL ENERGY (FE)
Forrestal Building, 1000 Independence Avenue, SW,
Room 4G-084, Mail Stop FE-1, Washington, DC 20585
Tel: (202) 586-6660 Fax: (202) 586-7847

National Energy Technology Laboratory (NETL)
626 Cochrans Mill Road, P.O. Box 10690, Pittsburgh, PA 15236-0940
Tel: (541) 967-5892 (Albany) Tel: (304) 285-4764 (Morgantown)
Tel: (412) 386-4984 (Pittsburgh) Fax: (541) 967-5936 (Albany)
Fax: (304) 285-4919 (Morgantown)
Fax: (304) 285-4292 (Morgantown, Alternate)
Fax: (412) 386-5746 (Pittsburgh)
Fax: (412) 386-4604 (Pittsburgh, Alternate) Internet: www.netl.doe.gov
● Director **Dr. Brian J. Anderson PhD** .... (412) 386-4867
Education: West Virginia 2000 BS; MIT 2004 MS, 2005 PhD
● Deputy Director and Chief Operating Officer
Linda S. Kimberling .... (304) 285-6581
E-mail: linda.kimberling@netl.doe.gov
Education: Southern IL Edwardsville 1984 BS, 1986 MS; Capella U 2008 PhD
Associate Director, Strategic Partnerships
Michael K. "Mike" Knaggs .... (304) 285-4926
Equal Employment Opportunity Manager **(Vacant)** .... (412) 386-4654
Fax: (412) 386-6514
Supervisory Administrative Specialist
Kristine L. "Kristie" Brokaw .... (412) 386-5024
626 Cochrans Mill Road, P.O. Box 10940, Pittsburgh, PA 15236-0940
E-mail: kristine.brokaw@netl.doe.gov

Science and Technology Strategic Plans and Programs
Deputy Director **Randall W. Gentry** .... (412) 386-7302

Research and Innovation Center (R&IC)
3610 Collins Ferry Road, P.O. Box 880, Morgantown, WV 26507-0880
● Executive Director **Bryan D. Morreale** .... (412) 386-5929
626 Cochrans Mill Road, P.O. Box 10690, Pittsburgh, PA 15236-0940
E-mail: bryan.morreale@netl.doe.gov
Education: Pittsburgh PhD
Deputy Executive Director **(Vacant)** .... (541) 967-5892
Associate Deputy Director of Outreach and Administration **Jimmy D. Thornton** .... (304) 285-4427
E-mail: jimmy.thornton@netl.doe.gov
Education: West Virginia 1994 BS, 1999 MS
Associate Deputy Director of Research and Development **Randall "Randy" Gemmen** .... (304) 285-4536
Education: Michigan 1991 PhD
Supervisory Administrative Specialist
Stacy B. Jamison .... (304) 285-0232
E-mail: stacy.jamison@netl.doe.gov Fax: (304) 285-4848

Technology Development and Integration Center
● Executive Director (Acting) **Charles M. "Chuck" Zeh** ... (304) 285-4265
3610 Collins Ferry Road, P.O. Box 880, Morgantown, WV 26507-0880
E-mail: czeh@netl.doe.gov
Education: SUNY (Buffalo) BSChE
Supervisory Administrative Specialist **Jill R. Roberts** .... (304) 285-4148
3610 Collins Ferry Road, P.O. Box 880, Morgantown, WV 26507-0880
E-mail: jill.roberts@netl.doe.gov

★ Presidential Appointment Requiring Senate Confirmation ☆ Presidential Appointment ☐ Schedule C Appointment ◇ Career Senior Foreign Service Appointment
● Career Senior Executive Service (SES) Appointment ○ Non-Career Senior Executive Service (SES) Appointment ■ Postal Career Executive Service

Strategic Center for Coal (SCC)
626 Cochrans Mill Road, P.O. Box 10690, Pittsburgh, PA 15236-0940
● Director **(Vacant)** .... (541) 967-5892

Strategic Center for Natural Gas and Oil
Director **Jared Ciferno** .... (412) 386-5862
Education: Pittsburgh 1999 BSChE, 2005 MSChE
Deputy Director **Maria Vargas** .... (412) 386-5470
626 Cochrans Mill Road, P.O. Box 10940, Pittsburgh, PA 15236-0940
Administrative Specialist **Debra M. Turner** .... (304) 285-0238
3610 Collins Ferry Road, P.O. Box 880, Morgantown, WV 26507-0880
E-mail: debra.turner@netl.doe.gov

Laboratory Operations Center
3610 Collins Ferry Road, P.O. Box 880, Morgantown, WV 26507-0880
● Director **(Vacant)** .... (304) 285-4265
Supervisory Administrative Specialist
Regina "Dena" Pride .... (304) 285-2099
E-mail: regina.pride@netl.doe.gov

Office of Chief Counsel (OCC)
● Chief Counsel **Susan E. Malie** .... (412) 386-5501
E-mail: susan.malie@netl.doe.gov
Education: Duquesne BA, JD

ASSISTANT SECRETARY FOR NUCLEAR ENERGY (NE)
Forrestal Building, 1000 Independence Avenue, SW,
Washington, DC 20585
Tel: (202) 586-2240 Fax: (202) 586-8353
Fax: (202) 586-0698 (Alternate)

Deputy Assistant Secretary for Idaho Site Operations and Contractor Assurance
1955 Fremont Avenue, Idaho Falls, ID 83415
Tel: (208) 526-8070 Internet: www.id.doe.gov
● Deputy Assistant Secretary [Federal Vendor Engagement Official] **Richard B. "Rick" Provencher** .... (208) 526-7300
E-mail: provenrb@id.doe.gov
Executive Secretary **Judith N. "Judi" Stevenson** .... (208) 526-8070
● Principal Deputy Manager for Nuclear Energy
Alan Lee Gunn .... (208) 526-5759
E-mail: gunnal@id.doe.gov
Public Affairs Officer **Timothy B. "Tim" Jackson** .... (208) 526-8484
E-mail: jacksotb@id.doe.gov Fax: (208) 526-8789

Office of Administrative Support
1955 Fremont Avenue, Idaho Falls, ID 83415
Fax: (208) 526-7407
● Deputy Manager **Amy E. Grose** .... (208) 526-5711
E-mail: groseae@id.doe.gov
Budget and Cost Management Division Director
Mark L. Searle .... (208) 526-5454
E-mail: searleml@id.doe.gov
Contract Management Division Director
Michael L. Adams .... (208) 526-5277
E-mail: adamsml@id.doe.gov
Supervisory Contract Specialist **Elliot Dye** .... (208) 526-9593
E-mail: dyeej@id.doe.gov
Financial Services and Resources Division Director
Kelly D. Lemons .... (208) 526-5453
E-mail: lemonskd@id.doe.gov

Office of the Chief Counsel (OCC)
1955 Fremont Avenue, Idaho Falls, ID 83415
Tel: (208) 526-0276 Fax: (208) 526-7632
Chief Counsel (Acting)
Margaret B. "Peggy" Hinman .... (208) 526-7109
E-mail: hinmanmb@id.doe.gov

Office of Operations Support
1955 Fremont Avenue, Idaho Falls, ID 83415
Tel: (208) 526-0960 Fax: (208) 526-5678
● Deputy Manager **Robert D. "Bob" Boston** .... (208) 526-8932
E-mail: bostonrd@id.doe.gov
Environment and Sustainability Division Director
Teresa L. Perkins .... (208) 526-1483
E-mail: perkintl@id.doe.gov
Operational and Program Assurance Director
Robert Dary "Dary" Newbry .... (208) 526-5859
E-mail: newbryrd@id.doe.gov
Quality and Safety Division Director **Mark D. Gardner** .... (208) 526-5655
E-mail: gardnemd@id.doe.gov
Security Division Director **SoLita M. Greene** .... (208) 526-2216
E-mail: greenesm@id.doe.gov
Supervisory Physical Scientist **(Vacant)** .... (208) 526-3508
Fax: (208) 526-1926

Idaho Cleanup Project
1955 Fremont Avenue, Idaho Falls, ID 83415
Tel: (208) 526-6736 Fax: (208) 526-5678
● Deputy Manager **John P. "Jack" Zimmerman** .... (208) 526-3811
E-mail: zimmerjp@id.doe.gov Fax: (208) 526-7245
● Associate Deputy Manager **Connie M. Flohr** .... (208) 526-8838
E-mail: flohrcm@id.doe.gov
Configuration Management and Project Controls Assistant Manager **Mark L. Searle** .... (208) 526-5454
E-mail: searleml@id.doe.gov Fax: (208) 526-7407
Facility and Material Disposition Assistant Manager
Kenneth R. "Ken" Whitham .... (208) 526-5698
E-mail: whithakr@id.doe.gov

Idaho National Laboratory (INL)
995 University Blvd, Idaho Falls, ID 83401
P.O. Box 1625, Idaho Falls, ID 83415
Tel: (800) 708-2680 (General Information) Tel: (866) 495-7440
Fax: (208) 526-4563 Internet: www.inl.gov
Note: Idaho National Laboratory is operated for the Department of Energy by Battelle Energy Alliance (BEA).
Laboratory Director **Mark T. Peters** .... (208) 526-2057
E-mail: mark.peters@inl.gov
Education: Auburn BS; Chicago 1992 PhD
Administrative Assistant **Laurie Christensen** .... (208) 526-6528
E-mail: laurie.christensen@inl.gov
Associate Laboratory Director, Energy and Environmental Science and Technology
Todd E. Combs .... (208) 526-5315
Associate Laboratory Director, Nuclear Science and Technology **John C. Wagner** .... (800) 708-2680
E-mail: john.wagner@inl.gov
Associate Laboratory Director, National and Homeland Security **Zachary Tudor** .... (208) 526-5051
E-mail: Zachary.Tudor@inl.gov
Deputy Laboratory Director for Management and Operations and Chief Operating Officer
Juan Alvarez .... (208) 526-9128
E-mail: juan.alvarez@inl.gov
Deputy Laboratory Director for Science and Technology and Chief Research Officer **(Vacant)** .... (208) 526-0707
Associate Laboratory Director, Materials and Fuels Complex **Ronald Allen "Ron" Crone** .... (208) 533-7125
Associate Laboratory Director, Advanced Test Reactor
Sean O'Kelly .... (208) 533-4710
Director for Audits **Fredrick G. Pieper** .... (208) 526-4513
E-mail: frederick.pieper@inl.gov
Business Management Director, Chief Financial Officer
Dennis Newby .... (208) 526-0980
Environment, Safety, and Health Director
Carol Mascareñas .... (208) 526-0633
E-mail: carolyn.mascarenas@inl.gov
Facilities and Site Services Director **Carlo Melbihess** .... (208) 526-8688
General Counsel **Mark Olsen** .... (208) 526-1994
E-mail: mark.olsen@inl.gov

★ Presidential Appointment Requiring Senate Confirmation ☆ Presidential Appointment ☐ Schedule C Appointment ◇ Career Senior Foreign Service Appointment
● Career Senior Executive Service (SES) Appointment ○ Non-Career Senior Executive Service (SES) Appointment ■ Postal Career Executive Service

Idaho National Laboratory *(continued)*

Human Resources and Diversity Programs Director
Mark Holubar . . . . (208) 526-9028
E-mail: mark.holubar@inl.gov

Partnerships, Engagement and Technology Deployment Director **Amy Lientz** . . . . (208) 526-0137

ATR Life Extension Manager, Battelle Energy Alliance
Paul Henslee . . . . (208) 526-3722
E-mail: paul.henslee@inl.gov

Nuclear Energy Oak Ridge Site Office (NE-ORSO)
200 Administration Road, Oak Ridge, TN 37830
Tel: (865) 576-2535 Fax: (865) 241-4439

● Manager (Acting) **Mary McCune** . . . . (301) 903-8152
E-mail: mary.mccune@nuclear.energy.gov Fax: (301) 903-5005

Regulatory Management Team Leader
Randall M. "Randy" DeVault . . . . (865) 241-8277
E-mail: devaultrm@neor.doe.gov

Office of the Under Secretary for Science (S4)

Forrestal Building, 1000 Independence Avenue, SW,
Room 7A-075, Mail Stop S-4, Washington, DC 20585
Tel: (202) 586-0505 Fax: (202) 586-8693

ASSISTANT SECRETARY FOR ENVIRONMENTAL MANAGEMENT (EM)

Forrestal Building, 1000 Independence Avenue, SW,
Washington, DC 20585-0113
Tel: (202) 586-7709 Fax: (202) 586-9100 Internet: www.em.doe.gov

Office of Field Operations (EM-3)

Field Sites

Carlsbad (NM) Field Office (CBFO)
4021 National Parks Highway, Carlsbad, NM 88220
Tel: (800) 336-9477 E-mail: infocntr@wipp.ws
Internet: www.wipp.energy.gov

● Manager **Todd A. Shrader** . . . . (575) 234-7300
E-mail: todd.shrader@cbfo.doe.gov Fax: (575) 234-7694

Environmental Management Consolidated Business Center (EMCBC)
250 East 5th Street, Suite 500, Cincinnati, OH 45202
Tel: (513) 246-0500 Fax: (513) 246-0526 Internet: www.emcbc.doe.gov

● Director **Jeffrey Kash "Kash" Grimes** . . . . (513) 246-1050
E-mail: kash.grimes@emcbc.doe.gov
Education: Kentucky 1983 BBA, 1986 JD; Naval Postgrad 1998 MS

● Deputy Director **(Vacant)** . . . . (513) 246-0500

Associate Deputy Director
Kenneth P. "Ken" Armstrong . . . . (513) 246-1375
E-mail: ken.armstrong@emcbc.doe.gov

Office of Chief Counsel
250 East 5th Street, Cincinnati, OH 45202
Internet: www.emcbc.doe.gov/Office/LegalService

● Chief Counsel **Mell J. Roy** . . . . (513) 246-0585
E-mail: mell.roy@emcbc.doe.gov Fax: (513) 246-0524
Education: Denver BS, BA, JD

Attorney **George W. Hellstrom** . . . . (859) 219-4005
E-mail: george.hellstrom@lex.doe.gov

Attorney **Simon Paul Lipstein** . . . . (303) 994-4315
E-mail: simon.lipstein@emcbc.doe.gov

Acquisition and Litigation Division
Supervisory General Attorney **Brady L. Jones III** . . . . (513) 246-0543
E-mail: brady.jones@emcbc.doe.gov

Attorney **Sky Smith** . . . . (513) 246-0510
E-mail: sky.smith@emcbc.doe.gov

Acquisition and Litigation Division *(continued)*

Attorney **Paul S. Sian** . . . . (202) 586-7532
E-mail: paul.sian@emcbc.doe.gov

Attorney **Rachna Talwar** . . . . (513) 744-2196
E-mail: rachna.talwar@emcbc.doe.gov

Attorney **Paul L. Whalen** . . . . (513) 246-0577
E-mail: paul.whalen@emcbc.doe.gov

General and Environmental Law Division
Supervisory General Attorney **Thomas "Tom" Aug** . . . . . (513) 246-0543
E-mail: thomas.aug@emcbc.doe.gov

Attorney **Angela R. Elder** . . . . (513) 246-0589
E-mail: angela.elder@emcbc.doe.gov

Attorney **Jay A. Jalovec** . . . . (513) 246-0608
E-mail: jay.jalovec@emcbc.doe.gov

Attorney **Elizabeth C. Rose** . . . . (513) 246-0571
E-mail: elizabeth.rose@emcbc.doe.gov

Attorney **Randolph T. "Randy" Tormey** . . . . (513) 246-0583
E-mail: randy.tormey@emcbc.doe.gov

Support and Information Access Division
Lead Paralegal Specialist **Scott D. Lucarelli** . . . . (513) 246-0497
E-mail: scott.lucarelli@emcbc.doe.gov

Paralegal **Michelle Farris** . . . . (513) 246-0522
E-mail: michelle.farris@emcbc.doe.gov

Legal Assistant **Kyle Smith** . . . . (513) 246-0561
E-mail: kyle.smith@emcbc.doe.gov

Government Information Specialist **David J. Ford** . . . . (513) 246-0585
E-mail: david.ford@emcbc.doe.gov

Office of Civil Rights and Diversity
250 East 5th Street, Cincinnati, OH 45202
Internet: www.emcbc.doe.gov/Office/CivilRights

Assistant Director **Sheila L. Gilliam** . . . . (513) 744-0968
E-mail: sheila.gilliam@emcbc.doe.gov

Office of Contracting
Assistant Director **Tamara L. Miles** . . . . (513) 246-1367
E-mail: tamara.miles@emcbc.doe.gov Fax: (513) 246-0529

Office of Cost Estimating
Assistant Director **Marwood A. "Allen" Moe** . . . . (513) 246-0230
E-mail: allen.moe@emcbc.doe.gov

Office of Financial Management
Assistant Director **David A. Arvin** . . . . (513) 744-0960
Education: Anderson U BAcc; Syracuse MBA Fax: (513) 246-0527

Human Resources Advisory Office
250 East 5th Street, Cincinnati, OH 45202
Internet: www.emcbc.doe.gov/Office/HumanResources

Senior Human Resources Business Partner
Kimberly S. Dellinger . . . . (513) 246-0520
E-mail: kimberly.dellinger@emcbc.doe.gov

Office of Information Resource Management
Assistant Director **Ward E. Best** . . . . (513) 246-0530
E-mail: ward.best@emcbc.doe.gov
Education: Michigan State 1980 BSE

Office of Technical Support and Asset Management
Assistant Director **John J. Rampe** . . . . (303) 994-3916
E-mail: john.rampe@emcbc.doe.gov Fax: (518) 395-7403

Field Operations

Energy Technology Engineering Center (ETEC)
4100 Guardian, Suite 160, Simi Valley, CA 93063
Tel: (805) 416-0990 Fax: (855) 658-8695 Internet: www.etec.energy.gov

Federal Project Director **John Jones** . . . . (805) 416-0990
E-mail: john.jones@emcbc.doe.gov

Deputy Federal Project Director
Stephanie "Stephie" Jennings . . . . (805) 416-0990
E-mail: stephanie.jennings@emcbc.doe.gov

DEPARTMENTS

★ Presidential Appointment Requiring Senate Confirmation ☆ Presidential Appointment □ Schedule C Appointment ◇ Career Senior Foreign Service Appointment
● Career Senior Executive Service (SES) Appointment ○ Non-Career Senior Executive Service (SES) Appointment ■ Postal Career Executive Service

Environmental Management Nevada Program (EM-NV)
Tel: (702) 295-3521 E-mail: envmgt@nnsa.doe.gov

Program Manager **Robert F. "Rob" Boehlecke** . . . . (702) 295-2099
E-mail: robert.boehlecke@nnsa.doe.gov

Deputy Program Manager for Operations
Wilhelm R. "Bill" Wilborn . . . . (702) 295-3188
E-mail: bill.wilborn@nnsa.doe.gov Fax: (702) 295-5300
Education: UNLV 1996 BS

Deputy Program Manager for Operations Support
Catherine E. Hampton . . . . (702) 295-4542
E-mail: catherine.hampton@em.doe.gov

West Valley (NY) Demonstration Project (WVDP)
10282 Rock Springs Road, West Valley, NY 14171-9799
Fax: (716) 942-4703 Internet: https://www.wv.doe.gov/

Director **Bryan C. Bower** . . . . (716) 942-4368
E-mail: bryan.bower@hq.doe.gov

Deputy Director **Craig R. Rieman** . . . . (716) 942-4312
E-mail: craig.rieman@emcbc.doe.gov

Program Manager **Carol L. Streczywilk** . . . . (716) 942-4011

Lead Physical Scientist **Moira N. Maloney** . . . . (716) 942-4255

Lead Physical Scientist **(Vacant)** . . . . (716) 942-4783

Lead General Engineer **Daniel W. Sullivan** . . . . (716) 942-4016

Hanford (WA) Site
2420 Stevens Center Place, Richland, WA 99352
Internet: www.hanford.gov

Richland (WA) Operations Office (RL)
2420 Stevens Center Place, MSIN: H5-20, Richland, WA 99352
P.O. Box 550, Richland, WA 99352
Tel: (509) 376-7395 Fax: (509) 376-4789
Internet: www.hanford.gov/page.cfm/RL

● Manager **Doug S. Shoop** . . . . (509) 376-7395
E-mail: doug.shoop@rl.doe.gov Fax: (509) 376-4789

● Deputy Manager **Jose M. "Joe" Franco** . . . . (509) 376-7395
E-mail: joe.franco@rl.doe.gov
Education: New Orleans 2000 BE

● Chief Counsel **Ralph Paul "Paul" Detwiler** . . . . (509) 376-4603
E-mail: paul.detwiler@rl.doe.gov Fax: (509) 376-4590
Education: Dartmouth AB; Cornell PhD; George Washington JD

Chief Information Officer **Benjamin A. "Ben" Ellison** . . . (509) 376-5318
E-mail: ben.ellison@rl.doe.gov

Employee Concerns Program Manager
Michael L. Collins . . . . (509) 376-2891
E-mail: michael.collins1@rl.doe.gov

Defense Nuclear Facilities Safety Board (DNFSB) Site
Representative **Padraic "Pat" Fox** . . . . (509) 373-3838
E-mail: padraic_k_fox@rl.gov

Defense Nuclear Facilities Safety Board (DNFSB) Site
Representative **David Gutowski** . . . . (509) 373-0101
E-mail: daveg@dnfsb.gov

Business and Financial Operations
2420 Stevens Center Place, MSIN: A7-27, Richland, WA 99352

● Assistant Manager **Greg A. Jones** . . . . (509) 372-8977
E-mail: gregory.jones@rl.doe.gov

Deputy Assistant Manager
Douglas T. "Doug" Aoyama . . . . (509) 376-4959
E-mail: douglas.aoyama@rl.doe.gov

Budget Division Director **Mark A. Coronado** . . . . (509) 376-5363
E-mail: mark.coronado@rl.doe.gov Fax: (509) 372-2114

Finance Division Director **Thomas L. "Tom" Toon** . . . . . . (509) 376-8515
Education: Cal State (Fresno) 1985 BS

Human Resources Activity Office Senior Business
Partner **Connie G. Nottingham** . . . . (509) 373-6288
E-mail: connie.nottingham@rl.doe.gov Fax: (509) 376-5335

Procurement Services Division Director
Sally A. Sieracki . . . . (509) 376-8948
E-mail: sally.sieracki@rl.doe.gov Fax: (509) 376-5378

Communications and External Affairs
2420 Stevens Center Place, MSIN: A7-75, Richland, WA 99352

Communications Manager **Theodore Erik "Erik" Olds** . . . (509) 372-8656
E-mail: theodore_e_erik_olds@rl.doe.gov
Education: UNLV, MAC

Mission Support (AMMS)
2420 Stevens Center Place, MSIN: A4-19, Richland, WA 99352

● Assistant Manager **Jeffrey A. Frey** . . . . (509) 376-7727
E-mail: jeffrey.frey@rl.doe.gov

Deputy Assistant Manager **Jeffery L. Bird** . . . . (509) 376-0440
E-mail: jeffery.bird@rl.doe.gov

Security, Emergency Services and Information
Management Division Director **Corey A. Low** . . . . (509) 376-4820
E-mail: corey.low@rl.doe.gov Fax: (509) 376-1002

Infrastructure and Services Division Director
Sharee Dickinson . . . . (509) 376-1793
E-mail: sharee.dickinson@rl.doe.gov

Site Stewardship Division Director **H. Boyd Hathaway** . . . (509) 376-7340
E-mail: boyd.hathaway@rl.doe.gov Fax: (509) 376-1466

River and Plateau
● Assistant Manager **Jose M. "Joe" Franco** . . . . (509) 376-8806
E-mail: joe.franco@rl.doe.gov Fax: (509) 373-0726
Education: New Orleans 2000 BE

Deputy Assistant Manager **(Vacant)** . . . . (509) 376-6363

Plutonium Finishing Plant Closure Division Director
Thomas K. "Tom" Teynor . . . . (509) 376-6363
Education: Naval Acad 1979 BS

River Corridor Division Director **Mark S. French** . . . . (509) 373-9863

Soil and Groundwater Division Director
Michael W. Cline . . . . (509) 376-6070

Waste Management and D&D Division Director
Oliver A. "Al" Farabee . . . . (509) 376-8089

Safety and Environment (AMSE)
2420 Stevens Center Place, MSIN: A5-14, Richland, WA 99352

● Assistant Manager **William F. Hamel, Jr.** . . . . (509) 371-6727
E-mail: william_f_hamel@orp.doe.gov

Deputy Assistant Manager **Brian J. Stickney** . . . . (509) 376-9079
E-mail: brian_j_stickney@orp.doe.gov

Environmental, Safety, and Quality Division Director
Joseph M. Sondag . . . . (509) 373-9179

Operations Oversight Division Director (Acting)
James E. Spets . . . . (509) 373-0140

Nuclear Safety Division Director
Joseph J. "Joe" Waring . . . . (509) 373-7687
E-mail: joseph.waring@rl.doe.gov

Office of River Protection (ORP)
DOE ORP, 2440 Stevens Center Place,
H660, Richland, WA 99354
P.O. Box 450, Richland, WA 99353
Tel: (509) 372-2315 Fax: (509) 372-0712
E-mail: orp_web_information@rl.gov
Internet: https://www.hanford.gov/page.cfm/ORP

● Manager **Brian Vance** . . . . (509) 372-2315
E-mail: brian.t.vance@orp.doe.gov
Education: Penn State BS; North Carolina MBA

● Deputy Manager **Benton J. "Ben" Harp** . . . . (509) 376-1462
E-mail: benton_j_ben_harp@orp.doe.gov

Chief of Staff **Mark G. Edgren** . . . . (509) 376-6700
E-mail: mark_g_edgren@orp.doe.gov Fax: (509) 372-0712

● Technical and Regulatory Support Assistant Manager
Robert G. "Rob" Hastings . . . . (509) 376-9824
E-mail: robert_hastings@orp.doe.gov

● Tank Farms Assistant Manager **Glyn D. Trenchard** . . . . . . (509) 373-4016
E-mail: Glyn_D_Trenchard@orp.doe.gov

Contracts and Property Manager **Marc T. McCusker** . . . . . (509) 376-2760
E-mail: marc_t_mccusker@orp.doe.gov
Education: McMurry

● Waste Treatment Plant Start-Up, Commissioning, and
Integration Director **Delmar L. Noyes** . . . . (509) 376-5166
E-mail: Delmar_L_Noyes@orp.doe.gov

★ Presidential Appointment Requiring Senate Confirmation ☆ Presidential Appointment ☐ Schedule C Appointment ◇ Career Senior Foreign Service Appointment
● Career Senior Executive Service (SES) Appointment ○ Non-Career Senior Executive Service (SES) Appointment ■ Postal Career Executive Service

Office of River Protection *(continued)*

- ● Waste Treatment and Immobilization Plant Project Director **Thomas W. Fletcher** . . . . (509) 376-4941
  E-mail: Thomas_W_Fletcher@orp.doe.gov
- Communications Director **Carrie C. Meyer** . . . . (509) 372-0810
  E-mail: carrie_c_meyer@orp.doe.gov
- Legal Counsel **Mark D. Silberstein** . . . . (509) 376-2380
  E-mail: Mark.Silberstein@rl.doe.gov
- Public Affairs **Paula Call** . . . . (509) 376-2048
  E-mail: paula.call@orp.doe.gov
- Public Affairs **Capt Yvonne Levardi USAF** . . . . (509) 376-8625
  E-mail: yvonne_levardi@orp.doe.gov
  Education: Eastern Washington 1996 BA

Los Alamos (NM) Field Office (EM-LA)

1900 Diamond Drive, MS-M984, Los Alamos, NM 87544
Tel: (505) 665-5658 E-mail: publicaffairs.emla@em.doe.gov

- ● Manager **Douglas E. "Doug" Hintze** . . . . (505) 665-5820
  E-mail: douglas.hintze@em.doe.gov
- Deputy Manager **Stephen G. Hoffman** . . . . (505) 606-0960
  E-mail: stephen.hoffman@em.doe.gov

Oak Ridge Office of Environmental Management (OREM)

200 Administration Road, Oak Ridge, TN 37830
Tel: (865) 576-0742 Fax: (865) 576-3799
E-mail: OakRidgeEM@orem.doe.gov

- ● Manager **John A. "Jay" Mullis** . . . . (865) 241-3706
  E-mail: jay.mullis@orem.doe.gov
  Education: Citadel BSEE
- ● Deputy Manager **(Vacant)** . . . . (865) 576-0742
- Senior Technical Advisor **Brenda L. Hawks** . . . . (865) 576-2503
  E-mail: brenda.hawks@orem.doe.gov
- Chief of Staff **(Vacant)** . . . . (865) 574-1626
- ETTP Portfolio Federal Project Director **Wendy A. Cain** . . . . (865) 574-9130
  E-mail: wendy.cain@orem.doe.gov
  Education: West Virginia BS; Tennessee MS
- ORNL Portfolio Federal Project Director **William G. "Bill" McMillan, Jr.** . . . . (865) 241-6426
  E-mail: bill.mcmillan@orem.doe.gov
- Y-12 Portfolio Federal Project Director **Brian Thomas Henry** . . . . (865) 241-8340
  E-mail: brian.henry@orem.doe.gov Fax: (865) 241-3314
  Education: Tennessee Tech BSE
- Engineering, Safety, and Quality Division Director **(Vacant)** . . . . (865) 241-3706
  Fax: (865) 241-0317
- Quality and Mission Support Division Director **David G. Adler** . . . . (865) 576-4094
  E-mail: david.adler@orem.doe.gov
  Education: Rutgers BSc; Michigan MS
  - Associate Director, Planning and Execution Division **Alan Stokes** . . . . (865) 576-8096
    E-mail: alan.stokes@orem.doe.gov
- Operations Management Division Director **Larry D. Perkins** . . . . (865) 574-8268
  E-mail: perkinsl@neor.doe.gov

Portsmouth/Paducah Project Office (PPPO)

1017 Majestic Drive, Suite 200, Lexington, KY 40513
Tel: (859) 219-4010 Fax: (859) 219-4098 E-mail: pppoinfo@lex.doe.gov

- ● Manager **Robert E. Edwards III** . . . . (859) 219-4002
  E-mail: robert.edwards@lex.doe.gov
- Deputy Manager **Joel B. Bradburne** . . . . (740) 897-3822
  E-mail: joel.bradburne@lex.doe.gov
  Education: Bridgewater Col BS

Savannah River (SC) Operations Office (SR)

P.O. Box A, Aiken, SC 29802-0900
Tel: (800) 278-5009 Fax: (803) 952-8144 Internet: sro.srs.gov

- ● Manager **Michael D. "Mike" Budney** . . . . (800) 278-5009
  E-mail: michael.budney@srs.gov
  Education: Naval Acad 1980 BS; Naval Postgrad 1987 MSEE; Maryland University Col 2007 MBA

Savannah River (SC) Operations Office *(continued)*

- ● Deputy Manager **Terrel J. "Terry" Spears** . . . . (803) 208-6072
  E-mail: terrel.spears@srs.gov
  Education: Florida 1982 BS; South Carolina 1992 ME
- ● Associate Deputy Manager **Thomas Johnson, Jr.** . . . . (803) 952-8135
  E-mail: thomas.johnson@srs.gov
- ● Chief Counsel **Lucy M. Knowles** . . . . (803) 952-7618
  E-mail: lucy.knowles@srs.gov
- Office of Civil Rights **Dorothy A. Famber** . . . . (803) 952-7646
  E-mail: dorothy.famber@srs.gov
- Office of Acquisitions Management Director **Jeffrey C. "Craig" Armstrong** . . . . (803) 952-9345
  E-mail: craig.armstrong@srs.gov
- Office of External Affairs Lead **(Vacant)** . . . . (803) 952-7684

Office of Human Capital Management

P.O. Box A, Aiken, SC 29802
Tel: (803) 952-5978 Fax: (803) 952-7711

- Director (Acting) **Lee H. Moody** . . . . (803) 952-5978
  E-mail: lee.moody@srs.gov

Office of Safeguards, Security and Emergency Services

P.O. Box A, Aiken, SC 29802
Tel: (803) 952-5544 Fax: (803) 952-7852

- Director **Ronald T. Bartholomew** . . . . (803) 952-5544
  E-mail: ronald.bartholomew@srs.gov
- Safeguards Division Director **(Vacant)** . . . . (803) 952-6830
- Security Programs and Emergency Services Division Director **William C. Dennis, Jr.** . . . . (803) 952-6655
  E-mail: william.dennis@srs.gov
- Cyber and Information Technology Division Director **Lewann M. Belton** . . . . (803) 952-7705
  E-mail: lewann.belton@srs.gov

Office of the Assistant Manager for Organizational Culture, Safety, and Quality Assurance

P.O. Box A, Aiken, SC 29802
Tel: (803) 952-8581 Fax: (803) 952-7065

- Assistant Manager (Acting) **Dannie S. "Scott" Nicholson** . . . . (803) 952-9299
  E-mail: scott.nicholson@srs.gov
- Performance Assurance Division Director **Charles C. Harris** . . . . (803) 952-8379
  E-mail: charles.harris@srs.gov
- Technical Support Division Director **Phillip "Phil" Giles, Jr.** . . . . (803) 208-6084
  E-mail: phillip-doe.giles@srs.gov

Office of the Assistant Manager for Infrastructure and Environmental Stewardship

P.O. Box A, Aiken, SC 29802
Tel: (803) 952-8187 Fax: (803) 952-7710

- ● Assistant Manager (Acting) **Angelia Holmes** . . . . (803) 952-8593
  E-mail: angelia.holmes@srs.gov
- Environmental Quality and Management Division Director **(Vacant)** . . . . (803) 952-8272
- Infrastructure and Area Completion Division Director **David J. Bender** . . . . (803) 952-8696
  E-mail: david.bender@srs.gov

Office of the Assistant Manager for Integration and Planning

P.O. Box A, Aiken, SC 29802
Tel: (803) 952-8422 Fax: (803) 952-9591

- ● Assistant Manager **John A. Lopez** . . . . (803) 952-6376
  E-mail: john.lopez@srs.gov
- Management Systems Division Director **Sharon J. Robinson** . . . . (803) 952-7947
  E-mail: sharon.robinson@srs.gov
- Mission Planning Division Director **William Dale "Bill" Clark, Jr.** . . . . (803) 952-6014

DEPARTMENTS

★ Presidential Appointment Requiring Senate Confirmation ☆ Presidential Appointment ☐ Schedule C Appointment ◇ Career Senior Foreign Service Appointment
● Career Senior Executive Service (SES) Appointment ○ Non-Career Senior Executive Service (SES) Appointment ■ Postal Career Executive Service

Office of the Assistant Manager for Mission Support
P.O. Box A, Aiken, SC 29802
Tel: (803) 952-8422 Fax: (803) 952-9591

● Assistant Manager (Acting) **Jennifer J. Nelson** .... (803) 952-7219
E-mail: jennifer.nelson@srs.gov

Office of the Assistant Manager for Nuclear Material Stabilization
P.O. Box A, Aiken, SC 29802
Tel: (803) 208-3927 Fax: (803) 208-3983

● Assistant Manager **Michael A. Mikolanis** .... (803) 952-8187
E-mail: michael.mikolanis@srs.gov
Nuclear Material Engineering Division Director
James D. Kekacs .... (803) 208-1526
E-mail: james.kekacs@srs.gov
Nuclear Material Operations Division Director
Linda M. Quarles .... (803) 208-0445
E-mail: linda-m.quarles@srs.gov
Nuclear Material Programs Division Director
Philip A. "Tony" Polk .... (803) 208-2854
E-mail: tony.polk@srs.gov

Office of the Assistant Manager for Waste Disposition
P.O. Box A, Aiken, SC 29802
Tel: (803) 208-6710 Fax: (803) 208-6441

● Assistant Manager **James L. Folk, Jr.** .... (803) 208-6710
E-mail: james.folk@srs.gov
Waste Disposition Engineering Division Director
Mark A. Smith .... (803) 208-8898
Waste Disposition Operations Division Director
(Vacant) .... (803) 208-6084
Waste Disposition Program Division Director
Jean M. Ridley .... (803) 208-6075
E-mail: jean.ridley@srs.gov Fax: (803) 208-6441
Salt Waste Processing Facility Project Office Director
Pamela A. Marks .... (803) 208-7220
E-mail: pamela.horning@srs.gov

Office of the Chief Financial Officer (OCFO)
P.O. Box A, Aiken, SC 29802
Tel: (803) 952-9175 Fax: (803) 952-6027

Chief Financial Officer **Bruce Martin** .... (803) 557-9550
Budget Division Director **Mitzi Lynn Francis** .... (803) 952-7450
E-mail: mitzi.francis@srs.gov

OFFICE OF SCIENCE (OS)

Forrestal Building, 1000 Independence Avenue, SW,
Room 7B-058, Mail Stop SC-1, Washington, DC 20585
Tel: (202) 586-5430 Fax: (202) 586-4120 Internet: science.energy.gov

Office of the Deputy Director for Field Operations (SC-3)

1000 Independence Avenue, SW, Washington, DC 20585
Tel: (202) 586-5434 Fax: (202) 586-4120

Site Offices

Ames (IA) Site Office (AMSO)
9800 South Cass Avenue, Argonne, IL 60439
Tel: (630) 252-6167 Fax: (630) 252-2855
Internet: https://science.energy.gov/amso/

Site Manager **Cynthia K. Baebler** .... (630) 252-1563
E-mail: cynthia.baebler@science.doe.gov
Education: Wisconsin BSIE; George Washington MS
Contracting Officer **Jennifer A. Stricker** .... (630) 252-2408
E-mail: jennifer.stricker@science.doe.gov
Education: Northern Illinois BS; Lewis U MBA
Field Representative **Bruce A. Goplin** .... (515) 294-8037
E-mail: bruce.goplin@science.doe.gov
Management and Program Analyst **Kelly A. Lieser** ...... (630) 252-6167
E-mail: kelly.lieser@science.doe.gov

Ames (IA) Laboratory
Technical and Administrative Services Facility (TASF),
2408 Pammel Drive, Ames, IA 50011-1015
Tel: (515) 294-2770 E-mail: info@ameslab.gov
Internet: www.ameslab.gov

Director **Dr. Adam J. Schwartz** .... (515) 294-2770
E-mail: ajschwartz@ameslab.gov Fax: (515) 294-4456
Education: Pittsburgh 1985 BS, 1989 MS, 1991 PhD
Deputy Director **Thomas A. "Tom" Lograsso** .... (515) 294-5722
E-mail: lograsso@ameslab.gov Fax: (515) 294-4456
Education: Michigan Tech 1980 BS, 1983 MS, 1986 PhD
Internal Auditor **Fran M. Dunshee** .... (515) 294-8098
E-mail: dunshee@ameslab.gov Fax: (515) 294-3958

Communications
2408 Pammel Drive, Ames, IA 50011-1015
Tel: (515) 294-9557 Fax: (515) 294-3226

Manager **Alissa Brammer** .... (515) 294-1048
E-mail: abrammer@ameslab.gov

Environment, Safety, and Health (ESH)
2408 Pammel Drive, Ames, IA 50011-1015
Tel: (515) 294-2153

Manager **Sean Whalen** .... (515) 294-4965
E-mail: sbwhale@ameslab.gov

Information Systems (IS)
2408 Pammel Drive, Ames, IA 50011-1015
E-mail: is@ameslab.gov E-mail: networks@ameslab.gov
E-mail: webmaster@ameslab.gov

Manager **Diane R. Den Adel** .... (515) 294-1061
E-mail: ddenadel@ameslab.gov Fax: (515) 294-5638
Director and Chief Information Officer
Jennifer Lohrbach .... (515) 294-5070
E-mail: lohrbach@ameslab.gov
Education: Iowa State 1999 BS

Operations
Chief Operations Officer **Mark L. Murphy** .... (515) 294-2618
E-mail: murphy@ameslab.gov Fax: (515) 294-4456
General Counsel **Barbara A. Biederman** .... (515) 294-0147

Accounting
Director **John Clough** .... (515) 294-5623
Fax: (515) 294-3958

Budget
Manager **Stephanie Boersma** .... (515) 294-8785
E-mail: boersma@ameslab.gov Fax: (515) 294-1389

Facilities and Engineering Services (FES)
Facilities Services Manager **Douglas Hoenig** .... (515) 294-0930
Engineering Services Manager
Terrance R. "Terry" Herrman .... (515) 294-7896
Fax: (515) 294-0568

Human Resources Office
Director **Lynnette Witt** .... (515) 294-5740
E-mail: witt@ameslab.gov

Purchasing and Property Services
2408 Pammel Drive, Ames, IA 50011-1015
E-mail: purchasing@ameslab.gov

Manager (Interim) **Andrew Saxton** .... (515) 294-4191
E-mail: saxton@ameslab.gov

Safeguards and Security
2408 Pammel Drive, Ames, IA 50011-1015
Tel: (515) 294-3483

Facility Security Officer and Program Director
Jeffrey "Jeff" Bartine .... (515) 294-4743
E-mail: bartine@ameslab.gov Fax: (515) 294-2155

★ Presidential Appointment Requiring Senate Confirmation ☆ Presidential Appointment ☐ Schedule C Appointment ◇ Career Senior Foreign Service Appointment
● Career Senior Executive Service (SES) Appointment ○ Non-Career Senior Executive Service (SES) Appointment ■ Postal Career Executive Service

Science and Programs

Chief Research Officer **(Vacant)** .... (515) 294-9649
Applied Mathematics and Computational Sciences
Program Director **Mark S. Gordon** .... (515) 294-0452
E-mail: mark@si.fi.ameslab.gov Fax: (515) 294-5204
Chemical and Biological Sciences Division Director
(Interim) **Marek Pruski** .... (515) 294-2017
Division of Materials Sciences and Engineering
Director **Matthew J. "Matt" Kramer** .... (515) 294-0276
Fax: (515) 294-8727
Simulation, Modeling, and Decision Science Director
Kenneth Mark "Mark" Bryden .... (515) 294-3891
Fax: (515) 294-3261

Critical Materials Institute

2332 Pammel Drive, 134 Wilhelm Hall, Iowa State University, Ames, IA 50011-1025
Tel: (515) 296-4500 Internet: https://cmi.ameslab.gov/

Director **Dr. Chris Haase** .... (515) 296-4500
Education: Ohio State 1990 BS; Erasmus U Rotterdam (Netherlands) 2000 MBA; Chicago MS, 1996 PhD

Argonne (IL) Site Office (SC-ASO)

9800 South Cass Avenue, Argonne, IL 60439
Tel: (630) 252-8637 Fax: (630) 252-2361
Internet: https://science.energy.gov/aso/

● Manager **Dr. Joanna M. Livengood** .... (630) 252-2366
E-mail: joanna.livengood@science.doe.gov
Deputy Manager (Acting) **Rock Aker** .... (630) 252-5663
E-mail: rock.aker@science.doe.gov
Education: Purdue 1979 BS
Business Management Division Director (Acting)
Margaret L. Marks .... (630) 252-2692
Education: Illinois State 1979 BS
Environment, Safety, and Health Division Director
(Acting) **Donald E. "Eric" Dallmann** .... (630) 252-3340
E-mail: eric.dallmann@science.doe.gov
Infrastructure, Programs, and Projects Division Director
Margaret L. Marks .... (630) 252-2692
E-mail: margaret.marks@science.doe.gov
Education: Illinois State 1979 BS

Argonne (IL) National Laboratory (ANL)

9700 South Cass Avenue, Argonne, IL 60439-4801
Tel: (630) 252-2000 Fax: (630) 252-7923 Internet: www.anl.gov

Director **Paul K. Kearns** .... (630) 252-3051
E-mail: pkearns@anl.gov
Education: Purdue BS, MS, PhD
Chief of Staff **Megan Claire Clifford** .... (630) 252-4470
E-mail: mclifford@anl.gov
Education: George Washington 1998 BBA
Senior Science Advisor **Dr. Supratik Guha** .... (630) 252-7740
Deputy Director for Science/Chief Research Officer
(Vacant) .... (773) 834-2001
Chief Communications Officer **Leslie H. Krohn** .... (630) 252-5953
E-mail: lkrohn@anl.gov
Education: Notre Dame BA; Northwestern MS
Director, Government Affairs
Norman D. "Norm" Peterson .... (630) 252-7229
Director, Audit, Quality, and Oversight **Denise J. Price** ... (630) 252-3034
Fax: (630) 252-3679
Director, Office of Strategy, Performance, and Risk
Greg Morin .... (630) 252-4871
E-mail: gmorin@anl.gov
General Counsel (Interim) **Glenn E. McKeown** .... (630) 252-6186
Fax: (630) 252-5966

Computing, Environment and Life Sciences (CELS)

9700 South Cass Avenue, Argonne, IL 60439-4801
Fax: (630) 252-6333 Internet: www.anl.gov/cels

Associate Laboratory Director **Rick L. Stevens** .... (630) 252-3378
Deputy Associate Laboratory Director
Robin L. Graham .... (630) 252-5677

Computing, Environment and Life Sciences *(continued)*

Deputy Associate Laboratory Director
Michael E. Papka .... (630) 252-1556
Education: Northern Illinois 1990 BS; Illinois (Chicago) 1994 MSEE; Chicago 2002 MS
Chief Operations Officer **Devin S. Hodge** .... (630) 252-7834
Fax: (630) 252-3115
Senior Computational Scientist
Raymond A. "Ray" Bair Building 240, Room 4122 ... (630) 252-5751
E-mail: rbair@anl.gov
Director, Biosciences Division
Philippe Henri Noirot Building 446, Room A192 ..... (630) 252-3731
Director, Computational Science Division
Paul Messina Building 240, Room 5156 .... (630) 252-3045
E-mail: messina@anl.gov
Director, Environmental Science Division
M. Cristina Negri .... (630) 252-9662
E-mail: cnegri@anl.gov Fax: (630) 252-5880
Co-Director, Northwestern Argonne Institute of Science
and Engineering **Peter H. "Pete" Beckman** .... (630) 252-9020
E-mail: beckman@mcs.anl.gov
Education: Indiana 1993 PhD
Director, Leadership Computing Facility
Michael E. Papka Building 240 .... (630) 252-1556
E-mail: papka@anl.gov Fax: (630) 252-6333
Education: Northern Illinois 1990 BS; Illinois (Chicago) 1994 MSEE; Chicago 2002 MS
Director, Mathematics and Computer Science Division
Valerie E. Taylor .... (630) 252-8808
E-mail: vtaylor@anl.gov

Energy and Global Security (EGS)

9700 South Cass Avenue, Argonne, IL 60439-4801
Fax: (630) 252-5318 Internet: www.anl.gov/egs/energy-and-global-security

Associate Laboratory Director
Jeffrey L. "Jeff" Binder .... (630) 252-6511
E-mail: jlbinder@anl.gov
Education: Illinois 1985 BS, 1987 MS, 1990 PhD; Chicago 2003 MBA
Chief Operating Officer **Balendra Sutharshan** .... (630) 252-6601
Director, National Security Programs **Keith Bradley** ..... (630) 252-6194
E-mail: ksbradley@anl.gov Fax: (630) 252-9868
Director, Manufacturing Science and Engineering
Dr. Santanu Chaudhuri PhD .... (630) 252-1404
E-mail: schaudhuri@anl.gov
Education: SUNY (Stony Brook) 2003 PhD
Director, Energy Systems Division
Dr. Donald G. Hillebrand .... (630) 252-6502
E-mail: hillebrand@anl.gov Fax: (630) 252-5132
Education: Oakland U 1984 BS, 1986 MS, 1995 PhD
Director, Center for Transportation Research
Ann Schlenker .... (630) 252-5542
E-mail: aschlenker@anl.gov Fax: (630) 252-3443
Director, Global Security Sciences (Interim)
George Vukovich .... (630) 252-6247
E-mail: gvukovich@anl.gov Fax: (630) 252-9868
Director, Risk and Infrastructure Science Center
David K. "Dave" Brannegan .... (630) 252-0932
E-mail: dbrannegan@anl.gov
Director, Nuclear Engineering Division
Jordi Roglans-Ribas .... (630) 252-6283
E-mail: roglans@anl.gov Fax: (630) 252-5161
Director, Chain Reaction Innovations **John A. Carlisle** ... (815) 272-3969
E-mail: carlisle@anl.gov
Director, Transportation Research and Computing
Center **Hubert Ley** .... (630) 252-8224
Fax: (630) 252-5203

Photon Sciences (PS)

9700 South Cass Avenue, Argonne, IL 60439-4801
Tel: (630) 252-7950 Fax: (630) 252-4599
Internet: https://www.aps.anl.gov/

Associate Laboratory Director **Stephen K. Streiffer** ..... (630) 252-7990
Education: Rice 1987; Stanford 1993 PhD

(continued on next page)

★ Presidential Appointment Requiring Senate Confirmation ☆ Presidential Appointment □ Schedule C Appointment ◇ Career Senior Foreign Service Appointment
● Career Senior Executive Service (SES) Appointment ○ Non-Career Senior Executive Service (SES) Appointment ■ Postal Career Executive Service

DEPARTMENTS

Photon Sciences *(continued)*

Deputy Associate Laboratory Director, Accelerators
Robert O. "Bob" Hettel .... (630) 252-6128
Education: Harvey Mudd BS
Deputy Associate Laboratory Director, X-Ray Science
Dennis M. Mills .... (630) 252-5680
Deputy Associate Laboratory Director, Operations
George Srajer .... (630) 252-3267
Education: U Belgrade 1980 BS; Brandeis 1988 PhD
Director, Accelerator Systems Division **John M. Byrd** .... (630) 252-5392
E-mail: jbyrd@anl.gov
Director, Advanced Photon Source
Stephen K. Streiffer .... (630) 252-7990
E-mail: streiffer@anl.gov
Education: Rice 1987; Stanford 1993 PhD
Director, APS Engineering Support Division
John P. Connolly IV .... (630) 252-5259
Fax: (630) 252-9250
Director, X-Ray Science Division **Jonathan C. Lang** .... (630) 252-0122
Fax: (630) 252-3222
Director, Advanced Photon Source Upgrade Project
Robert O. "Bob" Hettel .... (630) 252-6128
Education: Harvey Mudd BS

Physical Sciences and Engineering (PSE)
9700 South Cass Avenue, Argonne, IL 60439-4801
Fax: (630) 252-5318 Internet: http://www.anl.gov/pse/

Associate Laboratory Director (Interim)
Michael R. Norman .... (630) 252-3518
Chief Operations Officer **Maria Curry-Nkansah** .... (630) 252-6737
Director, Nanoscience and Technology Division
Dr. Supratik Guha Building 440, Room A-202 .... (630) 252-7740
E-mail: sguha@anl.gov Fax: (630) 252-6866
Director, Chemical Sciences and Engineering Division
Cynthia Jenks .... (630) 252-4640
Education: UCLA 1986 BSChE; Columbia 1988 MSChE, 1991 MPhil, 1992 PhD
Director, High Energy Physics Division
Marcellinus W. Demarteau .... (630) 252-5130
E-mail: mdemarteau@anl.gov
Director, Materials Science Division (Interim)
John Mitchell .... (630) 252-5852
E-mail: mitchell@anl.gov
Director, Physics Division **Kawtar Hafidi** .... (630) 252-4012
E-mail: kawtar@anl.gov

Science and Technology Partnerships and Outreach (STPO)
Associate Laboratory Director and Chief Technology Officer **Suresh Sunderrajan** .... (630) 252-8111
Education: MIT ScM; North Carolina State PhD

Deputy Director for Operations
9700 South Cass Avenue, Argonne, IL 60439-4801
Fax: (630) 252-7923

Deputy Director for Operations and Chief Operations Officer (Interim) **Kim C. Sawyer** .... (703) 229-9856
Education: Robert Morris U (PA) BS; UMass (Lowell) 1989 MS
Chief Financial Officer **Jeffrey C. Purnell** .... (630) 252-6840
Fax: (630) 252-6397
Chief Human Resources Officer **Julie Nuter** .... (630) 252-3445
E-mail: jnuter@anl.gov Fax: (630) 252-9396
Education: Benedictine U PhD
Chief Information Officer **Stuart "Stu" Hannay** .... (630) 252-7815
E-mail: stu@anl.gov Fax: (630) 252-9689
Deputy Chief Information Officer and Chief Information Security Officer **Michael A. Skwarek** ..... (630) 252-0572
E-mail: mskwarek@anl.gov
Director, Health, Safety, and Environment
Elizabeth Dunn .... (630) 252-8274
E-mail: edunn@anl.gov Fax: (630) 252-5778
Director, Infrastructure Services **Gail Y. Stine** .... (630) 252-8930
Fax: (630) 252-8400

Berkeley (CA) Site Office
One Cyclotron Road, Berkeley, CA 94720
Tel: (510) 486-5784

● Manager **Paul M. Golan** .... (510) 495-2395
E-mail: pgolan@lbl.gov
Education: Loyola U (Chicago) 1985 BS

Lawrence Berkeley (CA) National Laboratory (LBL)
One Cyclotron Road, Mail Stop 65, Berkeley, CA 94720
Tel: (510) 486-5771 Fax: (510) 486-6641 Internet: www.lbl.gov

Director **Michael S. "Mike" Witherell** .... (510) 486-5111
Chief of Staff **Margaret Dick** .... (510) 486-4317
E-mail: mkdick@lbl.gov
Administrative Assistant **Andrea Schreffler** .... (510) 486-7272
Deputy Director for Research **Horst D. Simon** .... (510) 486-7377
E-mail: hdsimon@lbl.gov Fax: (510) 642-6340
Education: Technical U (Berlin); UC Berkeley 1982 PhD
Director for Institutional Assurance and Integrity
(Interim) **Theresa A. Triplett** .... (510) 486-7401
Director, Office of Internal Audit Services **Adel Flores** ... (510) 486-4472
E-mail: anflores@lbl.gov
Director, Office of Planning and Strategic Development
Kristin Balder-Froid .... (510) 486-6060
E-mail: khbalder-froid@lbl.gov
Chief Sustainability Officer **John D. Elliott** .... (510) 486-7188
Education: Stanford BS; UC Berkeley MS
Chief Science and Technology Officer for Biosciences
Jay D. Keasling .... (510) 495-2620
Education: Nebraska 1986 BS; Fax: (510) 495-2630
Michigan 1988 MS, 1991 PhD

Brookhaven (NY) Site Office (BHSO)
Building 464, 53 Bell Avenue, Upton, NY 11973
Tel: (631) 344-3425 Fax: (631) 344-3444 E-mail: telldoe@bnl.gov
Internet: science.energy.gov/bhso

● Site Manager (Acting) **Robert P. Gordon** .... (631) 344-3346
E-mail: robert.gordon@science.doe.gov
Deputy Site Manager **Robert P. Gordon** .... (631) 344-3346
E-mail: robert.gordon@science.doe.gov
Assistant Chief Counsel **Louis F. "Lou" Sadler** .... (631) 344-3435
E-mail: lou.sadler@science.doe.gov Fax: (631) 344-7347
Attorney Advisor **Michael M. McCann** .... (631) 344-3440
E-mail: michael.mccann@science.doe.gov
Business Management Division Director (Acting)
Louis F. "Lou" Sadler .... (631) 344-3435
Operations Management Division Director
Maria V. Dikeakos .... (631) 344-5434
Education: Cooper Union 1993 BS; Stanford 1995 MS; Harvard 2003 MPH
Project Management Division Director **Joseph Eng** ...... (631) 344-7982
E-mail: joseph.eng@science.doe.gov
Federal Project Director **Robert M. Caradonna** .... (631) 344-2945

Brookhaven (NY) National Laboratory (BNL)
P.O. Box 5000, Upton, NY 11973-5000
Tel: (631) 344-8000 Fax: (631) 344-3000 Internet: www.bnl.gov

Director **Dr. Doon Gibbs** .... (631) 344-4608
E-mail: gibbs@bnl.gov
Education: Utah 1977 BS; Illinois 1979 MS, 1982 PhD
Deputy Director for Operations **Jack W. Anderson** ...... (631) 344-7474
E-mail: janderson@bnl.gov
Deputy Director for Science and Technology
Robert E. Tribble .... (631) 344-3177
E-mail: rtribble@bnl.gov
Education: Missouri 1969 BS; Princeton 1973 PhD
Chief Intellectual Property Counsel **(Vacant)** .... (631) 344-3035
Planning, Performance and Quality Management Director (Interim) **Jack W. Anderson** .... (631) 344-7474
E-mail: janderson@bnl.gov
Internal Audit Director **Roy Garbarino** .... (631) 344-4179
E-mail: rgarbarino@bnl.gov Fax: (631) 344-4852
Education: Colorado BAcc

★ Presidential Appointment Requiring Senate Confirmation ☆ Presidential Appointment □ Schedule C Appointment ◇ Career Senior Foreign Service Appointment
● Career Senior Executive Service (SES) Appointment ○ Non-Career Senior Executive Service (SES) Appointment ■ Postal Career Executive Service

Brookhaven (NY) National Laboratory *(continued)*

General Counsel **Anne Troutman** .... (631) 344-8629
E-mail: troutman@bnl.gov
Education: Albany Law 1982 JD
RIKEN BNL Research Center Director **Hideto En'yo** .... (631) 355-2555
E-mail: henyo@bnl.gov
Education: U Tokyo PhD
Counterintelligence Officer **Randy Biegelman** .... (631) 344-2234
E-mail: biegelman@bnl.gov

Stakeholder and Community Relations
P.O. Box 5000, Upton, NY 11973-5000
Internet: https://www.bnl.gov/externalaffairs/

Director **David J. Manning** .... (631) 344-4747
E-mail: dmanning@bnl.gov
Education: Alberta BA, BLL
Stakeholder Relations Manager **Nora Sundin** .... (631) 344-4458
E-mail: nsundin@bnl.gov Fax: (631) 344-3654
Educational Programs Manager **Ken White** .... (631) 344-7171
E-mail: kwwhite@bnl.gov Fax: (631) 344-5832
Media and Communications Manager
Peter "Pete" Genzer .... (631) 344-3174
E-mail: genzer@bnl.gov Fax: (631) 334-3368
Education: SUNY (New Paltz) 1993 BA;
SUNY (Stony Brook) 2006 MA

Business Services
P.O. Box 5000, Upton, NY 11973-5000
Internet: www.bnl.gov/busops

Associate Laboratory Director and Chief Financial
Officer **George Clark** .... (631) 344-7755
E-mail: gclark@bnl.gov
Education: U Washington MBA
Budget Office Manager **Barbara Carreras** .... (631) 344-3313
E-mail: carreras@bnl.gov
Fiscal Services Division Manager **Peter Ferrara** .... (631) 344-2460
Education: SUNY (Binghamton) 1983 BSAcc Fax: (631) 344-6243
Prime Contract Manager **Brian Boyle** .... (631) 344-2750
E-mail: brianb@bnl.gov

Information Technology Division
P.O. Box 5000, Upton, NY 11973-5000
Internet: www.bnl.gov/itd

Chief Information Officer **Thomas Schlagel** .... (631) 344-8765
E-mail: schlagel@bnl.gov
Education: Carleton 1984 BA; Illinois 1985 MS, 1990 PhD

Property and Procurement Management Division
P.O. Box 5000, Upton, NY 11973-5000
Fax: (631) 344-5499 E-mail: ppmhelp@bnl.gov
Internet: www.bnl.gov/ppm

Manager (Interim) **Kevin J. Fox** .... (631) 344-6185
E-mail: kjfox@bnl.gov

Computational Science Initiative (CSI)
P.O. Box 5000, Upton, NY 11973-5000
Fax: (631) 344-5751

Associate Laboratory Director
Kerstin Kleese van Dam .... (631) 344-6019
E-mail: kleese@bnl.gov
Deputy Director **Francis J. "Frank" Alexander** .... (631) 344-4899
E-mail: falexander@bnl.gov
Chief Scientist **Robert Harrison** .... (631) 344-8676
E-mail: rharrison@bnl.gov
Chair, Computer Science and Mathematics
Barbara M.P. Chapman .... (631) 344-8445
Chair, Center for Data-Driven Discovery
Shantenu Jha .... (631) 344-4780
Chair, Computational Science Laboratory
Nicholas "Nick" D'Imperio .... (631) 344-8607
Chair, Computing for National Security **Adolfy Hoisie** ... (631) 344-4874
E-mail: ahoisie@bnl.gov
Chair, BNL Scientific Data and Computing Center
Eric Lancon .... (631) 344-3829

Technology Commercialization and Partnerships (TCP)
P.O. Box 5000, Upton, NY 11973-5000
Tel: (631) 344-4919 Fax: (631) 344-3729

Director **(Vacant)** .... (631) 344-3177
Manager, Research Partnerships **Erick Hunt** .... (631) 344-2103
E-mail: ehunt@bnl.gov
Education: Boston Col BA; Stetson JD

Energy and Photon Sciences
P.O. Box 5000, Upton, NY 11973-5000
Fax: (631) 344-3075 Internet: www.bnl.gov/energysci

Associate Laboratory Director **Jim Misewich** .... (631) 344-3501
E-mail: misewich@bnl.gov
Education: Cornell 1984 PhD
Deputy Associate Laboratory Director **Dr. John P. Hill** ... (631) 344-3736
E-mail: hill@bnl.gov
Education: Imperial Col (UK) 1986 BSc; MIT 1992 PhD

Chemistry Department
P.O. Box 5000, Upton, NY 11973-5000
Tel: (631) 344-4301 Fax: (631) 344-7993

Chair **Alex Harris** .... (631) 344-4301
E-mail: harris@bnl.gov

Condensed Matter Physics and Materials Science Department
P.O. Box 5000, Upton, NY 11973-5000
Internet: www.bnl.gov/cmpmsd

Chair **Robert Konik** .... (631) 344-3225
E-mail: rmk@bnl.gov
Electron Spectroscopy Group Leader
Peter D. Johnson .... (631) 344-3705
E-mail: pdj@bnl.gov
Education: Warwick (UK) 1978 PhD
Senior Physicist **John M. Tranquada** .... (631) 344-7547
Education: Pomona 1977 BA; U Washington 1983 PhD

Sustainable Energy Technologies Department
P.O. Box 5000, Upton, NY 11973-5000
Internet: www.bnl.gov/set

Chair **J. Patrick "Pat" Looney** .... (631) 344-3798
E-mail: jlooney@bnl.gov
Education: Delaware 1984 BS; Penn State 1986 MS, 1987 PhD
Energy Conversion Group Leader
Dr. Thomas "Tom" Butcher .... (631) 344-7196
E-mail: butcher@bnl.gov
Energy Policy and Technology Analysis Group Leader
Paul "Chip" Friley .... (631) 344-3160
E-mail: pfriley@bnl.gov
Renewable Energy Group Leader **Robert Lofaro** .... (631) 344-7191
E-mail: lofaro@bnl.gov

National Synchrotron Light Source II
P.O. Box 5000, Upton, NY 11973-5000
Internet: www.bnl.gov/ps

Director **Dr. John P. Hill** .... (631) 344-3736
Education: Imperial Col (UK) 1986 BSc; MIT 1992 PhD
Accelerator Division Director (Interim) **Timur Shaftan** ... (631) 344-5144
Photon Division Director **Paul Zschack** .... (631) 344-8703

Environment, Safety, and Health (ES&H)
P.O. Box 5000, Upton, NY 11973-5000
Internet: www.bnl.gov/esh

Associate Laboratory Director **Gail G. Mattson** .... (631) 344-2842
E-mail: gmattson@bnl.gov Fax: (631) 344-5584
Education: Baker U 1973 BS;
U Washington 1982 MSE
Deputy Associate Laboratory Director
Steven A. Coleman .... (631) 344-8705
E-mail: coleman@bnl.gov Fax: (631) 344-7091
Environmental Protection Division Manager
Jason Remien .... (631) 344-3477
E-mail: remien@bnl.gov Fax: (631) 344-7334

(continued on next page)

DEPARTMENTS

★ Presidential Appointment Requiring Senate Confirmation ☆ Presidential Appointment □ Schedule C Appointment ◇ Career Senior Foreign Service Appointment
● Career Senior Executive Service (SES) Appointment ○ Non-Career Senior Executive Service (SES) Appointment ■ Postal Career Executive Service

DEPARTMENTS

Environment, Safety, and Health *(continued)*

Radiological Control Division Program Manager
Dennis Ryan . . . . . . (631) 344-5528
E-mail: dryan@bnl.gov
Education: SUNY (Stony Brook) 2007 MS

Safety and Health Services Division Program Manager
Michael "Mike" Clancy, Jr. . . . . . . (631) 344-7651
E-mail: clancy@bnl.gov Fax: (631) 344-3223

Environmental, Biology, Nuclear Science and Nonproliferation
P.O. Box 5000, Upton, NY 11973-5000
Internet: www.bnl.gov/ebnn

Associate Laboratory Director **Martin Schoonen** . . . . . . (631) 344-4014
E-mail: mschoonen@bnl.gov
Education: Penn State 1989 PhD

Biology Department
P.O. Box 5000, Upton, NY 11973-5000
Tel: (631) 344-3415 Fax: (631) 344-3407

Chair **John Shanklin** . . . . . . (631) 344-3414

Environmental and Climate Sciences Department
P.O. Box 5000, Upton, NY 11973-5000
Internet: www.bnl.gov/envsci

Chair (Interim) **Alice Cialella** . . . . . . (631) 344-3286

Nuclear Science and Technology Department
P.O. Box 5000, Upton, NY 11973-5000
Tel: (631) 344-2716 Fax: (631) 344-7650 Internet: www.bnl.gov/NST

Chairman **Dr. William C. Horak** . . . . . . (631) 344-2627
Education: Illinois BS, MS, PhD

Advanced Materials for Energy Systems Group Leader
Lynne Ecker . . . . . . (631) 344-2538
E-mail: lecker@bnl.gov

National Nuclear Data Center Leader
Michal W. Herman . . . . . . (631) 344-2802
E-mail: mwherman@bnl.gov

Nuclear Analysis Group Leader (Acting)
Dr. David Diamond . . . . . . (631) 344-2604

Systems Engineering Group Leader
James "Jim" Higgins III . . . . . . (631) 344-2432
E-mail: higgins@bnl.gov

Nonproliferation and National Security Department
P.O. Box 5000, Upton, NY 11973-5000
Tel: (631) 344-7517 Fax: (631) 344-5266 Internet: www.bnl.gov/nns

Chair **Susan Pepper** . . . . . . (631) 344-5979
E-mail: pepper@bnl.gov Fax: (631) 344-5266

International Safeguards Project Office Head
Raymond "Ray" Diaz . . . . . . (631) 344-5902
E-mail: diazr@bnl.gov

Nonproliferation and Homeland Security Field Support Group Leader **Biays Bowerman** . . . . . . (631) 344-2946
E-mail: bowerman@bnl.gov

Nonproliferation Policy and Implementation Group Leader **Lisa Toler** . . . . . . (631) 344-2276
E-mail: lttoler@bnl.gov

Radiation Detector and Nonproliferation Research and Development Group Leader **Peter Vanier** . . . . . . (631) 344-3535
E-mail: vanier@bnl.gov

Nuclear and Particle Physics (NPP)
P.O. Box 5000, Upton, NY 11973-5000
Fax: (631) 344-5830 Internet: www.bnl.gov/npp

Associate Laboratory Director **Berndt Mueller** . . . . . . (631) 344-5397
E-mail: bmueller@bnl.gov
Education: Johann Goethe Universitat PhD

Deputy Associate Laboratory Director for Strategic Program Development **David Asner** . . . . . . (631) 344-2829
E-mail: dasner@bnl.gov
Education: Waterloo 1991 BSc; UC San Diego 1994 MS; UC Santa Barbara 2000 Ph.D.

Nuclear and Particle Physics *(continued)*

Instrumentation Division Manager **David Asner** . . . . . . (631) 344-2829
E-mail: dasner@bnl.gov
Education: Waterloo 1991 BSc; UC San Diego 1994 MS; UC Santa Barbara 2000 Ph.D.

Superconducting Magnet Division Manager
Peter J. Wanderer, Jr. . . . . . . (631) 344-7687
E-mail: wanderer@bnl.gov Fax: (631) 344-2190
Education: Yale 1970 PhD

Collider-Accelerator Department
P.O. Box 5000, Upton, NY 11973-5000
Tel: (631) 344-4619 Fax: (631) 344-5954 Internet: www.bnl.gov/CAD

Chairman **Thomas Roser** . . . . . . (631) 344-7084

Department Administrator and Business Finance
Stephanie Lamontagne . . . . . . (631) 344-7141
E-mail: stephl@bnl.gov

Accelerator Division Head **Wolfram Fischer** . . . . . . (631) 344-5452
E-mail: wfischer@bnl.gov

Experimental Support and Facilities Division Head
William Christie . . . . . . (631) 344-7137
E-mail: christie@bnl.gov

Relativistic Heavy Ion Collider Project
P.O. Box 5000, Upton, NY 11973-5000
Tel: (631) 344-5590 Fax: (631) 344-2588 Internet: www.bnl.gov/rhic

Director **Vladimir Litvinenko** . . . . . . (631) 344-2570
E-mail: vl@bnl.gov

Physics Department
P.O. Box 5000, Upton, NY 11973-5000
Fax: (631) 344-5568 Internet: www.bnl.gov/physics

Chair **Hong Ma** . . . . . . (631) 344-2919

Assistant to the Chair for Nuclear Physics
Dr. Edward O'Brien . . . . . . (631) 344-4318
E-mail: eobrien@bnl.gov

Deputy Chair, Atlas **(Vacant)** . . . . . . (631) 344-3740

Administrative Officer **Robert Ernst** . . . . . . (631) 344-2153
E-mail: ernst@bnl.gov

Librarian **(Vacant)** . . . . . . (631) 344-2396

Accelerator Test Facility Group Leader **Ilan Ben-Zvi** . . . . . . (631) 344-5143

Advanced Accelerator Group Leader
Dr. Robert B. Palmer . . . . . . (631) 344-2842
E-mail: palmer@bnl.gov
Education: Imperial Col (UK) PhD

Electronic Detector Group Leader **Steven H. Kettell** . . . . . . (631) 344-5323

High Energy Theory Group Leader
Hooman Davoudiasl . . . . . . (631) 344-3856
E-mail: hooman@bnl.gov

Lattice Gauge Theory Group Leader
Dr. Frithjof Karsch . . . . . . (631) 344-8015

Nuclear Theory Group Leader **Raju Venugopalan** . . . . . . (631) 344-2341
E-mail: rajuv@bnl.gov

Omega Group Leader **Michael Begel** . . . . . . (631) 344-3403
E-mail: begel@bnl.gov

PHENIX Group Leader **David Morrison** . . . . . . (631) 344-5840

Physics Applications Software Group Leader
Alexei A. Klimentov . . . . . . (631) 344-7855
E-mail: aak@bnl.gov

RHIC/Atlas Computing Facility Group Leader
Eric Lancon . . . . . . (631) 344-3829

RHIC Spin Physics Group Leader **Elke Aschenauer** . . . . . . (631) 344-4769

STAR Group Leader **Zhangbu Xu** . . . . . . (631) 344-3955

Facilities and Operations
P.O. Box 5000, Upton, NY 11973-5000

Associate Laboratory Director
Thomas "Tom" Daniels . . . . . . (631) 344-4752
E-mail: tdaniels@bnl.gov
Education: Villanova BSME; Manhattan Col MSME

Emergency Services, Laboratory Protection Division Director **Mike Venegoni** . . . . . . (631) 344-3108

Energy and Utilities Division Manager
Christopher "Chris" Bruno . . . . . . (631) 344-8262
E-mail: cbruno@bnl.gov Fax: (631) 344-7656

★ Presidential Appointment Requiring Senate Confirmation ☆ Presidential Appointment ☐ Schedule C Appointment ◇ Career Senior Foreign Service Appointment
● Career Senior Executive Service (SES) Appointment ○ Non-Career Senior Executive Service (SES) Appointment ■ Postal Career Executive Service

Facilities and Operations *(continued)*

Guest Services Division Manager **Jeffrey J. Swenson** . . . (631) 344-2525
E-mail: swenson@bnl.gov Fax: (631) 344-2940
Integrated Facility Management Division Manager
Mark Davis . . . . (631) 344-2165
Modernization Project Office Director
Peggy Caradonna . . . . (631) 344-4752
Operational Support and Planning Division Manager
Raymond Costa . . . . (631) 344-8227
Fax: (631) 344-5999
Production Division Manager **Thomas "Tom" Roza** . . . . . (631) 344-3085
Safeguard and Security, Laboratory Protection Division
Director **Leonard Butera** . . . . (631) 344-8000
Site Planning and Infrastructure Management Division
Manager **Martin Fallier** . . . . (631) 344-3475

Human Resources
Associate Laboratory Director and Chief Human
Resources Officer **Robert "Bob" Lincoln** . . . . (631) 344-7435
E-mail: rlincoln@bnl.gov
Education: Ohio State BS
Guest User Visitor (GUV) Center Manager
Kathleen "Kathy" Nasta . . . . (631) 344-7114
E-mail: nasta@bnl.gov
Diversity Office Director **Shirley Kendall** . . . . (631) 344-3318
E-mail: kendall@bnl.gov Fax: (631) 344-5305

Fermi (IL) Site Office (SC-FSO)
P.O. Box 2000, Mail Stop 118, Batavia, IL 60510
Tel: (630) 840-3281 Fax: (630) 840-3285 Internet: science.energy.gov/fso

● Site Manager **Michael J. "Mike" Weis** . . . . (630) 840-2304
E-mail: michael.weis@science.doe.gov
Deputy Site Manager **Mark E. Bollinger** . . . . (630) 840-8130
E-mail: mark.bollinger@science.doe.gov
Education: Indiana 1992 MS

Fermi (IL) National Accelerator Laboratory (Fermilab)
Kirk Road and Pine Street, Batavia, IL 60510
P.O. Box 500, Batavia, IL 60510
Tel: (630) 840-3000 Fax: (630) 840-4343 E-mail: fermilab@fnal.gov
Internet: www.fnal.gov

Director **Nigel Lockyer** . . . . (630) 840-3211
E-mail: lockyer@fnal.gov Fax: (630) 840-2900
Education: York (Canada) 1975;
Ohio State 1980 PhD
Chief of Staff **Hema Ramamoorthi** . . . . (630) 840-6723
E-mail: hema@fnal.gov
Deputy Director for Research
Dr. Joseph "Joe" Lykken . . . . (630) 840-4689
E-mail: lykken@fnal.gov Fax: (630) 840-2900
Education: MIT 1982 PhD

Accelerator Division (AD)
Kirk Road and Pine Street, Batavia, IL 60510
Internet: ad.fnal.gov

Head **Michael A. "Mike" Lindgren** . . . . (630) 840-8409

Accelerator Physics Center
Kirk Road and Pine Street, Batavia, IL 60510
Tel: (630) 840-2880 Fax: (630) 840-6039 E-mail: apc@fnal.gov
Internet: apc.fnal.gov

Director **Vladimir Shiltsev** . . . . (630) 840-5241

Office of the Chief Financial Officer (CFO)
Kirk Road and Pine Street, Batavia, IL 60510

Chief Financial Officer and Finance Section Head
Vanessa Peoples . . . . (630) 840-2573
Deputy Section Head **Jeffrey W. Irvin** . . . . (630) 840-2404
Accounting Department Head
Michael F. "Mike" Rhoades . . . . (630) 840-5807
Budget Office Head **Denise C. Keiner** . . . . (630) 840-6462
E-mail: dkeiner@fnal.gov
Procurement Department Head **Joseph P. Collins** . . . . (630) 840-4169
E-mail: jcollins@fnal.gov

Office of the Chief Information Officer (CIO)
Kirk Road and Pine Street, Batavia, IL 60510
Internet: computing.fnal.gov

Associate Lab Director for
Computing/Chief Information Officer
Elizabeth S. "Liz" Sexton-Kennedy . . . . (630) 840-4974

Core Computing Division
Division Head **Jon A. Bakken** . . . . (630) 840-4790
E-mail: bakken@fnal.gov

Scientific Computing Division
Division Head **Panagiotis Spentzouris** . . . . (630) 840-4342
E-mail: spentz@fnal.gov

Office of the Chief Operating Officer
Chief Operating Officer **Timothy I. "Tim" Meyer** . . . . (630) 840-6650
E-mail: meyertim@fnal.gov

Office of Communication
Communication Director
Kathleen L. "Katie" Yurkewicz . . . . (630) 840-4112
E-mail: katie@fnal.gov

Office of General Counsel
Kirk Road and Pine Street, Batavia, IL 60510
Internet: http://www.fnal.gov/directorate/Legal/

General Counsel **John Myer** . . . . (630) 840-3252
Deputy General Counsel **Beth Fancsali** . . . . (630) 840-2027
E-mail: fancsali@fnal.gov
Legal Office Administrator **Karen M. Bormann** . . . . (630) 840-3572
E-mail: kbormann@fnal.gov

Facilities Engineering Services Section (FESS)
Kirk Road and Pine Street, Batavia, IL 60510
Internet: fess.fnal.gov

Section Head **Karen Kosky** . . . . (630) 840-2565
E-mail: kkosky@fnal.gov
Education: Wisconsin 1995 BSCE; Purdue 1997 MSE
Deputy Section Head **(Vacant)** . . . . (630) 840-2565

Workforce Development and Resources Section
Kirk Road and Pine Street, Batavia, IL 60510

Head **Kay A. Van Vreede** . . . . (630) 840-3396
E-mail: vanvreed@fnal.gov
Deputy Head **Barbara P. Brooks** . . . . (630) 840-5021
E-mail: bbrooks@fnal.gov

Office of Partnerships and Technology Transfer
Manager **Cherri Schmidt** . . . . (630) 840-5178

Illinois Accelerator Research Center (IARC)
Kirk Road and Pine Street, Batavia, IL 60510
Internet: iarc.fnal.gov

Director (Interim) **Cherri Schmidt** . . . . (630) 840-5178

Office of the Chief Project Officer
Chief Project Officer **Robert S. "Bob" Tschirhart** . . . . . . (630) 840-4100

Office of the Chief Research Officer (CRO)
Chief Research Officer **Dr. Joseph "Joe" Lykken** . . . . (630) 840-4689
Education: MIT 1982 PhD

Center for Particle Astrophysics
Kirk Road and Pine Street, Batavia, IL 60510
Internet: http://astro.fnal.gov/

Director **Dr. Craig J. Hogan** . . . . (630) 840-5523
Education: Harvard 1976 AB; Cambridge (UK) 1980 PhD
Deputy Head **Dan A. Bauer** . . . . (630) 840-4771

Compact Muon Solenoid (CMS) Center
Kirk Road and Pine Street, Batavia, IL 60510
Internet: http://cms.fnal.gov/

Center Director **Anadi Canepa** . . . . (630) 840-5402

Neutrino Division
Kirk Road and Pine Street, Batavia, IL 60510
Internet: http://neutrinophysics.fnal.gov/

Head **Stephen J. "Steve" Brice** .... (630) 840-8748

Particle Physics Division
Kirk Road and Pine Street, Batavia, IL 60510
Internet: http://ppd.fnal.gov/

Head **Joshua A. "Josh" Frieman** .... (630) 840-2226
Deputy Head **Kevin A. Burkett** .... (630) 840-2391
Deputy Head **Jonathan Lewis** .... (630) 840-3779

Office of the Chief Safety Officer
Chief Safety Officer **Martha E. Michels** .... (630) 840-3511
E-mail: martha@fnal.gov

Office of the Chief Technology Officer (CTO)
Kirk Road and Pine Street, Batavia, IL 60510
Internet: td.fnal.gov

Chief Technology Officer and Technical Division Head
Sergey Belomestnykh .... (630) 840-5015
Deputy Head **Anna Grassellino** .... (630) 840-2458
Associate Head **Alexandr Romanenko** .... (630) 840-2770
Associate Head **Romesh C. Sood** .... (630) 840-4071
Associate Head **(Vacant)** .... (630) 840-2137

Long-Baseline Neutrino Facility Project (LBNF)
Kirk Road and Pine Street, Batavia, IL 60510
Internet: lbnf.fnal.gov

Project Director **Christopher J. "Chris" Mossey PE** .... (630) 840-6444
Education: Cornell 1981 BSEE; Stanford 1991 MS

Proton Improvement Plan-II Project (PIP-II)
Internet: https://pip2.fnal.gov/

Project Director **Dr. Lia Merminga** .... (630) 840-6922

Oak Ridge National Laboratory (ORNL) Site Office (SC-OSO)
P.O. Box 2008, Oak Ridge, TN 37831
Tel: (865) 576-0710 Fax: (865) 576-4511

• Manager **Johnny O. Moore** .... (865) 576-3536
E-mail: johnny.moore@science.doe.gov
Deputy Manager **Michele G. Branton** .... (865) 576-4530
E-mail: michele.branton@science.doe.gov
Operations and Oversight Division Director
Martha J. Kass .... (865) 576-0717
Fax: (865) 574-9275
Mission Integration and Projects Division Director
H. Randall Fair .... (865) 574-8643
E-mail: randall.fair@science.doe.gov Fax: (865) 482-5022

Oak Ridge (TN) National Laboratory (ORNL)
One Bethel Valley Road, Oak Ridge, TN 37831-6037
P.O. Box 2008, Oak Ridge, TN 37831-6037
Tel: (865) 574-1000 Fax: (865) 241-2967 Internet: www.ornl.gov

Director **Dr. Thomas Zacharia** .... (865) 574-4897
E-mail: zachariat@ornl.gov
Education: National Tech Karnataka 1980 BSEE; Mississippi 1984 MS; Clarkson U 1987 PhD
Deputy Director for Operations
Jeffrey W. "Jeff" Smith .... (865) 574-4322
Education: Ohio State 1981 BS
Deputy Director for Science and Technology
Dr. Michelle V. Buchanan .... (865) 574-1144
Education: Kansas BA; Wisconsin PhD

Information Technology Services Division (ITS)
One Bethel Valley Road, Oak Ridge, TN 37831-6037
Tel: (865) 241-3657 Fax: (865) 241-1055

Chief Information Officer **Michael E. "Mike" Bartell** .... (865) 241-3657
E-mail: bartellm@ornl.gov
Education: Mount St Mary's 1974 BS; American U (Attended); George Washington (Attended)

Information Technology Services Division *(continued)*

Deputy Chief Information Officer
Kristofer L. "Kris" Torgerson .... (865) 241-3624
E-mail: torgersonkl@ornl.gov
Chief Information Security Officer **Kevin A. Kerr** .... (865) 576-1995
E-mail: kerrka@ornl.gov

Internal Audit Directorate (IA)
Director **C. Gail Lewis** .... (865) 241-3737
Fax: (865) 576-1092
Executive Secretary **Sandy Glazier** .... (865) 241-6974
Fax: (865) 241-7595
Staff Concerns Coordinator **Robert L. "Bob" Stewart** ... (865) 576-1762
E-mail: stewartrn@ornl.gov Fax: (865) 241-6261

Legal Directorate
One Bethel Valley Road, Oak Ridge, TN 37831-6037
Fax: (865) 241-4456

General Counsel **Rachel H. Blumenfeld** .... (865) 574-1389
E-mail: blumenfeldrh@ornl.gov

Institutional Planning and Integrated Performance Management (IPIPM)
One Bethel Valley Road, Oak Ridge, TN 37831-6037
Fax: (865) 576-6183

Institutional Planning Director **Celia Merzbacher** .... (865) 576-2723
Integrated Performance Management Director
Brian Weston .... (865) 241-3985

Oak Ridge (TN) Institute for Science and Education (ORISE)
Oak Ridge Associated Universities, 130 Badger Avenue, Oak Ridge, TN 37830
P.O. Box 117, MS 22, Oak Ridge, TN 37831-0117
Tel: (865) 574-7607 E-mail: oriseinfo@orise.orau.gov
Internet: http://orise.orau.gov

Director **William J. "Jim" Vosburg** .... (865) 576-0631
E-mail: jim.vosburg@orau.org
Director, Business Operations **Phil Andrews** .... (865) 576-3057
Director, Information Technology Services
Chester Keith Maze .... (865) 576-0781

Research Library (RL)
One Bethel Valley Road, Oak Ridge, TN 37831-6037
Tel: (865) 574-6744 (Service Desk) Fax: (865) 574-6745
Internet: www.ornl.gov/content/research-library

Director **Bob Conrad** .... (865) 574-4872
E-mail: conradre@ornl.gov Fax: (865) 574-6915
Administrative Assistant **Karen Kolopus** .... (865) 574-6735
E-mail: kolopuskm@ornl.gov
Coordinator, Electronic Resources Management and Acquisitions **Anna Galyon** .... (865) 576-8027
E-mail: galyonar@ornl.gov
Education: Tennessee 2002 BA; Mid Tennessee State 2007 MA; Tennessee 2009 MS
Metadata and Cataloging Librarian **Kathryn E. Knight** ... (865) 241-0367
E-mail: knightke@ornl.gov

Business Services Directorate
One Bethel Valley Road, Oak Ridge, TN 37831-6037
Fax: (865) 241-7595

Chief Financial Officer **J. Scott Branham** .... (865) 241-7614
E-mail: branhams@ornl.gov Fax: (865) 241-7595
Education: Concord Col 1989 BS; Auburn 1998 MBA
Executive Secretary **Renee Evans** .... (865) 241-5851
Fax: (865) 574-4159
Prime Contract Administration and Services Manager
Nicole Elizabeth Porter .... (865) 574-2227
E-mail: porterne1@ornl.gov Fax: (865) 241-9914
Accounting Services Director **Libby D. Brown** .... (865) 574-5062
Business Management Services Director
Deborah U. "Debbie" Mann .... (865) 241-8657
Fax: (865) 576-8346

★ Presidential Appointment Requiring Senate Confirmation ☆ Presidential Appointment ☐ Schedule C Appointment ◇ Career Senior Foreign Service Appointment
● Career Senior Executive Service (SES) Appointment ○ Non-Career Senior Executive Service (SES) Appointment ■ Postal Career Executive Service

Business Services Directorate *(continued)*

Business Operations and Strategy Services Director
Sylvia S. Davis . . . . (865) 574-0228
Fax: (865) 576-8346

Retirement Services Director **Mark Benjamin Keck** . . . . (865) 241-6215

Acquisition Management Services
One Bethel Valley Road, Oak Ridge, TN 37831-6037
Internet: web.ornl.gov/adm/contracts

Director **Brooks C. Baldwin** . . . . (865) 576-7151
E-mail: baldwinbc@ornl.gov Fax: (865) 241-9903

Computing and Computational Sciences Directorate (CCS)
One Bethel Valley Road, Oak Ridge, TN 37831-6037
Fax: (865) 574-4839 Internet: www.ornl.gov/directorate/ccsd

Associate Laboratory Director
Dr. Jeffrey A. "Jeff" Nichols . . . . (865) 574-6224
E-mail: nicholsja@ornl.gov

Deputy Associate Laboratory Director **(Vacant)** . . . . (865) 241-9392

Director, Computational Sciences and Engineering Division **Shaun S. Gleason** . . . . (865) 574-8521
E-mail: gleasonss@ornl.gov Fax: (865) 576-6183
Education: Tennessee 2001 PhD

Director, Computer Science and Mathematics Division
Arthur Bernard "Barney" Maccabe . . . . (865) 241-6504
E-mail: maccabeab@ornl.gov Fax: (865) 574-6076

Director, Directorate Operations **Becky J. Verastegui** . . . . (865) 576-1955
Fax: (865) 241-1055

Director, Artificial Intelligence Program
David E. Womble . . . . (865) 576-9087
E-mail: womblede@ornl.gov

Director, Industrial Partnerships Program
Suzy P. Tichenor . . . . (703) 413-7846
E-mail: tichenorsp@ornl.gov

Director, Joint Institute for Computational Sciences
Anthony "Tony" Mezzacappa . . . . (865) 574-6113
E-mail: mezzacappaa@ornl.gov Fax: (865) 576-4368

Director, Leadership Computing Facility
Arthur S. "Buddy" Bland . . . . (865) 576-6727
E-mail: blandas@ornl.gov
Tel: (865) 241-9578

Director, Oak Ridge Climate Change Science Institute
Stan D. Wullschleger . . . . (865) 574-7839

National Center for Computational Sciences (NCCS)
One Bethel Valley Road, Oak Ridge, TN 37831-6037
Tel: (865) 241-7202 E-mail: info@olcf.ornl.gov
Internet: https://www.olcf.ornl.gov/

Director **James J. Hack** . . . . (865) 574-6334
E-mail: jhack@ornl.gov Fax: (865) 576-4368
Education: Lyndon State 1974 BS; Colorado State 1977 MS, 1980 PhD

Director of Science **Jack C. Wells** . . . . (865) 241-2853
E-mail: wellsjc@ornl.gov

Environment, Safety, and Health Directorate (ESH)
One Bethel Valley Road, Oak Ridge, TN 37831-6037
Fax: (865) 576-4891

Director **John E. Powell** . . . . (865) 241-1550
E-mail: powellje@ornl.gov
Executive Assistant **Gina O'Brien** . . . . (865) 241-1550

Director, Environmental Protection Division
David Dillon Skipper . . . . (865) 576-5748
Fax: (865) 576-3515

Director, Health Services Division **Carol H. Scott** . . . . (865) 574-7431
E-mail: scottch@ornl.gov Fax: (865) 576-5381

Director, Transportation and Waste Management Division **Jeff H. Shelton** . . . . (865) 576-6401
Fax: (865) 576-3515

Director, Nuclear and Radiological Protection Division
Michael W. "Mike" Stafford . . . . (865) 241-5144
E-mail: staffordmw@ornl.gov Fax: (865) 241-7660

Director, Safety Services Division **Sharon C. Kohler** . . . . (865) 574-4337
E-mail: kohlersc@ornl.gov Fax: (865) 574-6617

Operations Manager **Sharon C. Kohler** . . . . (865) 574-4337

Facilities and Operations Directorate
One Bethel Valley Road, Oak Ridge, TN 37831-6037
Fax: (865) 241-7610

Director **Jimmy E. Stone** . . . . (865) 241-6911
E-mail: stoneje@ornl.gov

Executive Secretary **Angela "Angie" Raby** . . . . (865) 576-1996

Director, Facilities Management Division
Ann Bryant Weaver . . . . (865) 576-8689
E-mail: bryantar@ornl.gov Fax: (865) 241-5673

Director, Integrated Operations Support Division
Kimberly B. "Kim" Jeskie . . . . (865) 574-4945

Director, Laboratory Protection Division
William J. "Bill" Manuel . . . . (865) 576-1165
E-mail: manuelwj@ornl.gov Fax: (865) 241-8305

Director, Logistical Services Division **(Vacant)** . . . . (865) 576-5640
Fax: (865) 574-6028

Director, Modernization Project Office
Randall Curtis "Randy" Pickens . . . . (865) 576-3975
Fax: (865) 576-2893

Director, Reservation Natural Resources Management
Neil R. Giffen . . . . (865) 241-9421
Fax: (865) 576-9938

Director, Utilities **Robert N. "Bob" Baugh** . . . . (865) 574-4295

Human Resources Directorate
One Bethel Valley Road, Oak Ridge, TN 37831-6037
Fax: (865) 241-2977

Director **Deborah R. "Debbie" Stairs** . . . . (865) 574-4189
E-mail: stairsdr@ornl.gov
Education: Tennessee PhD
Executive Assistant **Susan P. Noe** . . . . (865) 574-5006
E-mail: noesp@ornl.gov

Office of Communications and External Relations (CER)
One Bethel Valley Road, Oak Ridge, TN 37831-6037
Fax: (865) 574-0595 Internet: www.ornl.gov/content/communications

Director **David Keim** . . . . (865) 576-9122
E-mail: keimdm@ornl.gov
Education: Ohio 1990 BS

Energy and Environmental Sciences Directorate (EES)
One Bethel Valley Road, Oak Ridge, TN 37831-6037
Tel: (865) 574-4333 Fax: (865) 574-9869 E-mail: estessa@ornl.gov
Internet: web.ornl.gov/sci/ees

Associate Laboratory Director
Mohammad "Moe" Khaleel . . . . (865) 574-4333
Education: Washington State 1988 MS, 1991 PhD

Director, Biosciences Division
Anthony Vito "Tony" Palumbo . . . . (865) 574-5845
Fax: (865) 574-9223

Director, Climate and Environmental Sciences Division
Stan D. Wullschleger . . . . (865) 574-7839

Director, Electricity and Energy Reliability Program
Thomas J. "Tom" King, Jr. . . . . (865) 241-5756
E-mail: kingtjjr@ornl.gov Fax: (865) 576-7572

Director, Energy and Transportation Science Division
Xin Sun . . . . (865) 576-3711
E-mail: sunx1@ornl.gov

Director, Advanced Manufacturing Program
Craig A. Blue . . . . (865) 574-4351
E-mail: blueca@ornl.gov

Director, Building Technologies Program
Ronald D. "Ron" Ott, Sr. . . . . (865) 574-5172

Director, Sustainable Transportation Program
Claus Daniel . . . . (865) 946-1544
E-mail: danielc@ornl.gov

Director, Electrical and Electronics Systems Research Division **Richard A. "Rick" Raines** . . . . (865) 241-7390
E-mail: rainesra@ornl.gov

Research Operations Manager **Dwight Clayton** . . . . (865) 576-8134

DEPARTMENTS

★ Presidential Appointment Requiring Senate Confirmation ☆ Presidential Appointment ☐ Schedule C Appointment ◇ Career Senior Foreign Service Appointment
● Career Senior Executive Service (SES) Appointment ○ Non-Career Senior Executive Service (SES) Appointment ■ Postal Career Executive Service

DEPARTMENTS

Global Security Directorate (GS)
One Bethel Valley Road, Oak Ridge, TN 37831-6037
Tel: (865) 576-3846 Fax: (865) 574-1260

Associate Laboratory Director **Dr. James S. Peery** . . . . . . (865) 576-0154
E-mail: peeryjs@ornl.gov
Education: Texas A&M PhD
Executive Assistant **Jennifer M. Baker** . . . . (865) 574-5006
E-mail: bakerjm@ornl.gov
Chief Scientist **(Vacant)** . . . . (865) 576-3846
Director, Oak Ridge Counterintelligence **Selin Warnell** . . . (865) 574-6770
Fax: (865) 241-0240
Director, DOE-IN Programs **Kendall L. Card** . . . . (865) 241-6635
E-mail: cardk@ornl.gov Fax: (865) 574-8814
Education: Vanderbilt 1977 BSME;
Naval War MA
Director, Defense and Homeland Security
Dr. Nicholas J. "Nick" Prins . . . . (865) 241-0137
E-mail: prinsnj@ornl.gov
Education: Hope BS; Naval Postgrad MS; Air Force Inst Tech PhD
Director, Intelligence Programs
John D. "J.D." Stauffer . . . . (865) 241-6580
E-mail: staufferjd@ornl.gov Fax: (865) 574-8814
Education: Colorado 1983 BA;
Defense Intelligence 1989 MSS; Naval War 1995 MS;
Indust'l Col Armed Forces 2001 MS

Neutron Sciences Directorate (NScD)
One Bethel Valley Road, Oak Ridge, TN 37831-6037
Fax: (865) 576-3041 Internet: neutrons.ornl.gov

Associate Laboratory Director **Paul A. Langan** . . . . (865) 241-1499
E-mail: langanpa@ornl.gov

Biology and Soft Matter Division
One Bethel Valley Road, Oak Ridge, TN 37831-6037
Fax: (865) 574-2053 Internet: neutrons.ornl.gov/bsmd

Director **Wim Bras** . . . . (865) 576-0666
E-mail: brasw@ornl.gov

Chemical and Engineering Materials Division (CEMD)
One Bethel Valley Road, Oak Ridge, TN 37831-6037
Fax: (865) 574-6080

Director **Richard Ibberson** . . . . (865) 574-4962
E-mail: ibbersonrm@ornl.gov
Education: Durham (UK) 1986 BSc; U Reading (UK) 1993 PhD

Instrument and Source Division (ISD)
One Bethel Valley Road, Oak Ridge, TN 37831-6037
Fax: (865) 241-6909

Director **Donald H. "Don" Abercrombie** . . . . (865) 241-5736
E-mail: abercrombidh@ornl.gov

Neutron Data Analysis and Visualization Division
One Bethel Valley Road, Oak Ridge, TN 37831-6037
Fax: (865) 576-3041

Director **Thomas E. Proffen** . . . . (865) 576-8633
E-mail: tproffen@ornl.gov
Education: Ludwig Maximillian U 1995 PhD

Quantum Condensed Matter Division (QCMD)
One Bethel Valley Road, Oak Ridge, TN 37831-6037
Fax: (865) 574-2033

Director **Stephen E. Nagler** . . . . (865) 574-5240
E-mail: naglerse@ornl.gov

Research Accelerator Division (RAD)
One Bethel Valley Road, Oak Ridge, TN 37831-6037
Fax: (865) 574-6617

Director **Dr. Fulvia C. Pilat** . . . . (865) 576-9315
E-mail: pilatfc@ornl.gov

Research Reactors Division (RRD)
One Bethel Valley Road, Oak Ridge, TN 37831-6037
Fax: (865) 574-0967

Director **Tim P. Powers** . . . . (865) 576-5563
E-mail: powerstp@ornl.gov

Scientific and Program Services Office
One Bethel Valley Road, Oak Ridge, TN 37831-6037

Manager **Crystal A. Schrof** . . . . (865) 574-9228

Nuclear Science and Engineering Directorate (NSED)
One Bethel Valley Road, Oak Ridge, TN 37831-6037
Fax: (865) 241-7603

Associate Laboratory Director **Alan S. Icenhour** . . . . (865) 576-5315
E-mail: icenhouras@ornl.gov

Physical Sciences Directorate (PSD)
One Bethel Valley Road, Oak Ridge, TN 37831-6037
Internet: www.ornl.gov/directorate/psd

Associate Laboratory Director **Dr. David Jarvis Dean** . . . . (865) 576-1219
E-mail: deandj@ornl.gov
Education: Tennessee (Chattanooga) 1985 BSc; Vanderbilt 1991 Ph.D.
Executive Secretary **Cathy L. Cheverton** . . . . (865) 574-4329

Center for Nanophase Materials Sciences (CNMS)
One Bethel Valley Road, Oak Ridge, TN 37831-6037
Fax: (865) 574-1753 Internet: www.ornl.gov/facility/cnms

Director **Hans M. Christen** . . . . (865) 574-5081
Deputy Director **Bobby G. Sumpter** . . . . (865) 574-4973

Chemical Sciences Division (CSD)
One Bethel Valley Road, Oak Ridge, TN 37831-6037
Fax: (865) 574-4902 Internet: www.ornl.gov/division/csd

Division Director **Dr. Phillip F. Britt** . . . . (865) 574-4986

Materials Science and Technology Division
One Bethel Valley Road, Oak Ridge, TN 37831-6037
Internet: www.ornl.gov/division/mstd

Director **Jeremy T. Busby** . . . . (865) 241-4622
E-mail: busbyjt@ornl.gov

Physics Division
One Bethel Valley Road, Oak Ridge, TN 37831-6037
Internet: www.phy.ornl.gov

Director **(Vacant)** . . . . (865) 574-5229
Fax: (865) 576-8746

Partnerships Directorate
One Bethel Valley Road, Oak Ridge, TN 37831-6037
Fax: (865) 574-4180 Internet: www.ornl.gov/partnerships/partnerships

Director (Acting) **Dr. Thomas Zacharia** . . . . (865) 574-4897
E-mail: zachariat@ornl.gov
Education: National Tech Karnataka 1980 BSEE; Mississippi 1984 MS;
Clarkson U 1987 PhD

Finance and Administration
Business Manager **Leroy Sims** . . . . (865) 574-2615
E-mail: simsl@ornl.gov

Industrial and Economic Development Partnerships
Director **Thomas C. "Tom" Rogers** . . . . (865) 241-2149
E-mail: rogerstc@ornl.gov
Education: Michigan State BA; North Carolina MRP

Intellectual Property
Managing Attorney **Marc T. Filigenzi** . . . . (865) 576-6883
E-mail: filigenzimt@ornl.gov

Licensing
Group Leader **Jennifer T. Caldwell** . . . . (865) 574-4180
E-mail: caldwelljt@ornl.gov

★ Presidential Appointment Requiring Senate Confirmation ☆ Presidential Appointment ☐ Schedule C Appointment ◇ Career Senior Foreign Service Appointment
● Career Senior Executive Service (SES) Appointment ○ Non-Career Senior Executive Service (SES) Appointment ■ Postal Career Executive Service

Sponsored Research
Sponsored Research Group Leader **Mark E. Reeves** ..... (865) 576-2577
Education: North Alabama 1977 BS; Tennessee 1982 PhD; Colorado State 2001 MBA

Technology Transfer
Technology Transfer Director
Michael Joseph "Mike" Paulus .... (865) 574-1051
Education: Tennessee BSEE; Dayton MSEE; Tennessee PhD

U.S. ITER Project
One Bethel Valley Road, Oak Ridge, TN 37831-6037
Fax: (865) 574-6108 Internet: www.usiter.org
Project Manager **Dr. Ned R. Sauthoff** .... (865) 574-5947
E-mail: sauthoffnr@ornl.gov

Pacific Northwest Site Office (PNSO)
P.O. Box 350, Mail Stop K9-42, Richland, WA 99352
Tel: (509) 372-4005 Fax: (509) 372-4532
● Site Manager **Roger E Snyder** .... (509) 372-4005
E-mail: roger.snyder@pnso.science.doe.gov Fax: (509) 372-4532
Deputy Site Manager **Julie K. Erickson** .... (509) 942-4695
E-mail: julie.erickson@pnso.science.doe.gov Fax: (509) 372-4532

Pacific Northwest National Laboratory (PNNL)
902 Battelle Boulevard, Richland, WA 99352
P.O. Box 999, Richland, WA 99352
Tel: (888) 375-7665 (Toll Free) Tel: (509) 375-2121 (Switchboard)
Fax: (509) 375-6844 Internet: www.pnnl.gov
Note: Managed and Operated by Battelle for the U.S. Department of Energy.
Director **Steven F. Ashby** .... (509) 375-4550
E-mail: sfashby@pnnl.gov
Education: Santa Clara U 1982 BS; Illinois 1987 PhD
Deputy Director for Operations and Chief Operating Officer **Michael H. Schlender** .... (509) 375-5911
Deputy Director for Science and Technology
Malin Young .... (509) 375-6616
Chief Information Officer and Associate Laboratory Director for Communications and Information Technology **Brian Abrahamson** .... (509) 372-6927

Office of General Counsel (OGC)
902 Battelle Boulevard, Richland, WA 99352
Tel: (509) 375-3784 Fax: (509) 375-2592
General Counsel **Vincent A. Branton** .... (509) 375-2633
E-mail: vincent.branton@pnnl.gov
Education: Tennessee 1989 BS; Stetson 1999 JD
Assistant General Counsel **Brian Cable** .... (509) 375-6814
Assistant General Counsel **Steven D. Cooke** .... (509) 375-2891
Assistant General Counsel **David A. Maestas** .... (509) 375-4360
Assistant General Counsel **Alan C. Rither** .... (509) 375-2218
E-mail: alan.rither@pnnl.gov

Audit Services
902 Battelle Boulevard, Richland, WA 99352
Fax: (509) 375-2092
Director and Chief Audit Executive **Kevin R. Ensign** .... (509) 375-2486
E-mail: kevin.ensign@pnnl.gov

Business Services
Associate Laboratory Director and Chief Financial Officer **Tracie Cowen** .... (509) 372-6305
Education: Arizona State 1990 BSAcc; U Washington 1993 MBA
Business Development and Analysis Department Manager **Iris Anderson** .... (509) 375-2823

Earth and Biological Sciences Directorate (EBSD)
902 Battelle Boulevard, Richland, WA 99352
Internet: www.pnnl.gov/science
Associate Laboratory Director **Allison A. Campbell** ..... (509) 371-6000
E-mail: allison.campbell@pnnl.gov
Education: Gettysburg 1985 BA; SUNY Col (Buffalo) 1991 PhD

Atmospheric Sciences and Global Change Division
902 Battelle Boulevard, Richland, WA 99352
Internet: www.pnnl.gov/atmospheric
Director **Ian Kraucunas** .... (509) 372-6713
Chief Scientist for Climate Change
Philip "Phil" Rasch .... (509) 372-4464
Education: U Washington 1976 BA, 1976 BS; Florida State MA, PhD

Biological Sciences Division
902 Battelle Boulevard, Richland, WA 99352
Internet: www.pnnl.gov/biology
Director **Katrina Waters** .... (509) 375-3982

William R. Wiley Environmental Molecular Sciences Laboratory (EMSL)
902 Battelle Boulevard, Richland, WA 99352
Tel: (509) 371-6003 E-mail: emsl@pnnl.gov Internet: www.emsl.pnnl.gov
Director (Acting) **Dr. Harvey Bolton, Jr.** .... (509) 371-6958
E-mail: harvey.bolton@pnnl.gov
Education: Rhode Island 1979 BS; Washington State 1983 MS, 1985 PhD

Energy and Environment Directorate
902 Battelle Boulevard, Richland, WA 99352
Internet: energyenvironment.pnnl.gov
Associate Laboratory Director **Jud W. Virden** .... (509) 375-6512
Education: U Washington BS, PhD
Chief Operations Officer
Lawrence O. "Larry" Casazza .... (509) 375-4333
Chief Science and Technology Officer
Dr. Sue B. Clark .... (509) 372-6180
E-mail: sue.clark@pnnl.gov
Education: Lander 1984 BS; Florida State 1987 MS, 1989 PhD
Chief Architect for Electric Grid Transformation
Jeffrey D. Taft .... (509) 372-4171

Earth Systems Science Division (ESSD)
902 Battelle Boulevard, Richland, WA 99352
Internet: http://essd.pnnl.gov/
Director **Wayne L. Johnson** .... (509) 372-4791
E-mail: wayne.johnson@pnnl.gov

Energy Processes and Materials Division
902 Battelle Boulevard, Richland, WA 99352
Internet: energy-proc-mat.pnnl.gov
Director **Cynthia A. "Cindy" Powell** .... (509) 375-3645
E-mail: cynthia.powell@pnnl.gov
Education: Clemson BS; Case Western MS, PhD

Coastal Sciences Division
902 Battelle Boulevard, Richland, WA 99352
Internet: https://marine.pnnl.gov/
Director **Charles A. "Charlie" Brandt** .... (360) 681-4594
E-mail: charles.brandt@pnnl.gov
Education: Oregon State BS; Duke PhD

Marine Sciences Laboratory (MSL)
1529 West Sequim Bay Road, Sequim, WA 98382
Fax: (360) 681-3699
Director **Charles A. "Charlie" Brandt** .... (360) 681-4594
Education: Oregon State BS; Duke PhD

Nuclear Sciences Division
902 Battelle Boulevard, Richland, WA 99352
Director **Paul R. Bredt** .... (509) 375-6812

Electricity Infrastructure and Buildings Division
Manager **Steve A. Shankle** .... (509) 372-4322
Chief Cyber Security Program Manager **Paul Skare** ...... (888) 375-7665
Education: Minnesota 1984

DEPARTMENTS

★ Presidential Appointment Requiring Senate Confirmation ☆ Presidential Appointment ☐ Schedule C Appointment ◇ Career Senior Foreign Service Appointment
● Career Senior Executive Service (SES) Appointment ○ Non-Career Senior Executive Service (SES) Appointment ■ Postal Career Executive Service

Human Resources (HR)
902 Battelle Boulevard, Richland, WA 99352
Tel: (509) 375-2450 Fax: (509) 375-2899

Director **Cheri C. Wideman** .... (509) 375-3990
Education: Michigan State BA; Cornell MA
Equal Employment Opportunity Manager
James R. "Jim" Blount .... (509) 375-2114
Human Resources Information Systems Manager
Duane E. Klotz .... (509) 375-2581

National Security Directorate
902 Battelle Boulevard, Richland, WA 99352
Fax: (509) 372-2255 Internet: www.pnnl.gov/nationalsecurity

Associate Laboratory Director, National Security
Anthony J. "Tony" Peurrung .... (509) 372-6375
Fax: (509) 372-6506
Executive Assistant **Julie A. Nelson** .... (509) 375-6604
Chief Operating Officer **Tammy P. Taylor** .... (509) 375-6714
Education: New Mexico State 1994 BS; Georgia Tech 1999 PhD
Chief Science and Technology Officer
Robert "Bob" Runkle .... (509) 375-1966
Security Operations Director **Cindy L. Parnell** .... (509) 372-4953

Project Management Offices
Chemical, Biological, Nuclear Surety and Signatures
Manager **William G. "Bill" Richmond** .... (509) 372-6315
Global Security Implementation Manager
Mario Pereira .... (509) 372-4131
Special Programs Manager **Tricia A. Lewallen** .... (509) 375-5925
Integrated Systems Solutions Manager
Robert C. "Bob" Thompson .... (509) 371-6761

Program Development Office
Director **Deborah K. Gracio** .... (509) 375-6362
National Nuclear Security Administration Programs
Manager **Daniel L. Stephens** .... (509) 372-6109
Department of Defense Programs Manager
Dr. L. Wayne Brasure .... (202) 646-5025
Education: Michigan 1980 BS; USC 1983 MS;
Air Force Inst Tech 1985 MS; New Mexico 1991 PhD
Homeland Security Programs Manager
Christopher L. "Chris" Aardahl .... (509) 375-7210
Special Programs Manager **Dennis B. Nelson** .... (509) 372-4688

Computational and Analytics Division
Director **William A. "Bill" Pike** .... (509) 375-2689

Operational Systems and Technology Division
Director **Keith D. Freier** .... (509) 375-6744

Signatures Science and Technology Division
Director (Acting) **Kristin Omberg** .... (509) 375-2934

Operational Systems
902 Battelle Boulevard, Richland, WA 99352
P.O. Box 999, Richland, WA 99352
Tel: (509) 375-3747 Fax: (509) 375-2290

Associate Laboratory Director for Operations
Dr. Larry E. Maples .... (509) 375-3747
E-mail: larry.maples@pnnl.gov
Executive Director of External Affairs
Paula X. Linnen .... (509) 375-2450
E-mail: paula.linnen@pnnl.gov
Director of Laboratory Planning and Performance
Management **John P. LaFemina** .... (509) 375-6806
Education: Rensselaer Poly 1981 BS; Penn State 1983 MS, 1985 PhD
Director, Research Partnerships **Suresh Baskaran** .... (509) 375-6483

Physical and Computational Sciences Directorate (PCSD)
902 Battelle Boulevard, Richland, WA 99352
Tel: (509) 375-2121 Internet: www.pnnl.gov/science

Associate Laboratory Director
Louis "Lou" Terminello .... (509) 371-6790
E-mail: louis.terminello@pnnl.gov

Physical and Computational Sciences Directorate *(continued)*

Chief Scientist for Computing **James A. "Jim" Ang** .... (509) 372-4540
Education: Grinnell BS; UC Berkeley MSME, Ph.D.

Advanced Computing, Mathematics, and Data
902 Battelle Boulevard, Richland, WA 99352
Internet: www.pnnl.gov/computing

Director **Nathan Baker** .... (509) 375-3997

Physical Sciences Division (PSD)
902 Battelle Boulevard, Richland, WA 99352
Internet: www.pnnl.gov/psd

Director **Wendy J. Shaw** .... (509) 375-5922

Small Business Program
P.O. Box 999, Richland, WA 99352
Tel: (509) 372-4060 Fax: (509) 371-7530
E-mail: small.business@pnnl.gov

Small Business Program Manager **Brianna Durkin** .... (509) 371-7742
Contracts Manager **Dana Storms** .... (509) 375-4343
Contracts Specialist **Andrea Fernandez** .... (509) 375-6534
E-mail: Andrea.Fernandez@pnnl.gov
Contracts Specialist **William K. "Kevin" Grubbs** .... (509) 372-4050
E-mail: kevin.grubbs@pnnl.gov
Contracts Specialist **Kevin Heaton** .... (509) 375-6715
E-mail: kevin.heaton@pnnl.gov
Contracts Specialist **Rolando Lara** .... (509) 372-6733
E-mail: rolando@pnnl.gov
Contracts Specialist **David Slater** .... (509) 371-7187
E-mail: david.slater@pnnl.gov

Technology Deployment and Outreach
902 Battelle Boulevard, Richland, WA 99352
Tel: (509) 375-3700 Fax: (509) 375-2221

Director **(Vacant)** .... (509) 375-2614
Economic Development Office Manager
Gary E. Spanner .... (509) 372-4296
Media and External Communications Director
Greg L. Koller .... (509) 372-4864
Technology Commercialization Director **(Vacant)** .... (509) 372-3700

Princeton (NJ) Site Office (PSO)
P.O. Box 102, Princeton, NJ 08542
Tel: (609) 243-3700 Fax: (609) 243-2032
Internet: https://science.energy.gov/pso/

● Site Manager **Peter O. Johnson** .... (609) 243-3706
E-mail: peter.johnson@science.doe.gov
Contracting Officer **Kim E. Tafe** .... (609) 243-3708
E-mail: kim.tafe@science.doe.gov
General Engineer **Jeffrey "Jeff" Makiel** .... (609) 243-3721
E-mail: jeffrey.makiel@science.doe.gov

Stanford (CA) Site Office
2575 Sand Hill Road, Menlo Park, CA 94025
Tel: (650) 926-2505 Fax: (650) 926-3210

Site Manager **Paul M. Golan** .... (650) 926-3208
Education: Loyola U (Chicago) 1985 BS

SLAC National Accelerator Laboratory (SLAC)
2575 Sand Hill Road, Menlo Park, CA 94025
Tel: (650) 926-3300 Internet: www.slac.stanford.edu

Vice President **Dr. William J. Madia** .... (650) 926-8757
E-mail: madia@stanford.edu
Education: Indiana 1969 BS, 1971 MS; Virginia Tech 1975 PhD
Director **Dr. Chi-Chang Kao** .... (650) 926-3699
E-mail: ckao@slac.stanford.edu
Education: National Taiwan U 1980 BChE; Cornell 1988 PhD
Executive Assistant **Andrea Reed** .... (650) 926-8746
E-mail: andrear@slac.stanford.edu
Deputy Director **Norbert Holtkamp** .... (650) 926-7449
E-mail: norbert.holtkamp@slac.stanford.edu
Executive Assistant **Yvonne Concepcion** .... (650) 926-8747
E-mail: cyvonne@slac.stanford.edu

★ Presidential Appointment Requiring Senate Confirmation ☆ Presidential Appointment ☐ Schedule C Appointment ◇ Career Senior Foreign Service Appointment
● Career Senior Executive Service (SES) Appointment ○ Non-Career Senior Executive Service (SES) Appointment ■ Postal Career Executive Service

SLAC National Accelerator Laboratory *(continued)*

Deputy Director of Operations and Chief Operating Officer **Brian Sherin** .... (650) 926-5082
Education: UC Davis 1982 BS; San José State 1988 MA — Fax: (650) 926-8705
Chief Administrative Officer **Angel M. Smith** .... (650) 926-8751
Federal Project Director **Kevin D. Bazzell** .... (650) 926-2513
Laboratory Counsel **Saurabh Anand** .... (650) 926-8708
Fax: (650) 926-8705

Accelerator Directorate
2575 Sand Hill Road, Menlo Park, CA 94025
Internet: www-public.slac.stanford.edu/accelerator

Associate Laboratory Director (Acting) **Bruce M. Dunham** .... (650) 926-4340

Business and Technology Services (BTS)
2575 Sand Hill Road, Menlo Park, CA 94025
Internet: www-group.slac.stanford.edu/ocfo

Director and Chief Financial Officer **Suzanne M.P. Hansen** .... (650) 926-2625
Education: Washington State 1985 BA, 1989 MBA
Chief Information Officer **Theresa Bamrick** .... (650) 926-4245
E-mail: tbamrick@slac.stanford.edu
Education: Charter Oak State BA

Energy Sciences Directorate
2575 Sand Hill Road, Menlo Park, CA 94025

Associate Laboratory Director **Tony F. Heinz** .... (650) 926-2414
Education: Stanford 1978 BS; UC Berkeley 1982 PhD
Deputy Associate Laboratory Director and Chief Technology Officer **Dr. Mark A. Hartney** .... (650) 926-4805
Education: MIT BS, MS; UC Berkeley PhD

Environment, Safety and Health Division (ESH)
2575 Sand Hill Road, Menlo Park, CA 94025
Fax: (650) 926-3030 Internet: www-group.slac.stanford.edu/esh

Director and Chief Safety Officer **Carole Fried** .... (650) 926-2339
E-mail: carolef@slac.stanford.edu

Fundamental Physics Directorate
Director and Chief Research Officer **JoAnne L. Hewett** .... (650) 926-4424

Office of Strategic Planning
2575 Sand Hill Road, Menlo Park, CA 94025

Director (Acting) **Norbert Holtkamp** .... (650) 926-7449

Linac Coherent Light Source Directorate (LCLS)
2575 Sand Hill Road, Menlo Park, CA 94025
Fax: (690) 926-4695

Associate Laboratory Director **Anthony Michael "Mike" Dunne** .... (650) 926-2936
Education: Imperial Col (UK) PhD

Stanford Synchrotron Radiation Lightsource Directorate (SSRL)
2575 Sand Hill Road, Menlo Park, CA 94025
Internet: www-ssrl.slac.stanford.edu

Associate Laboratory Director **Kelly J. Gaffney** .... (650) 926-2382

Technology and Innovation Directorate (TID)
Associate Laboratory Director **Michael V. Fazio** .... (650) 926-5765

Thomas Jefferson Site Office (SC-TJSO)
12000 Jefferson Avenue, Newport News, VA 23606
Tel: (757) 269-7140 Fax: (757) 269-7146

● Site Manager **Joseph Mann "Joe" Arango III** .... (757) 269-5094
E-mail: arango@jlab.org
Education: Naval Acad BS; Virginia Tech MS
Deputy Site Manager **Scott Mallette** .... (757) 269-7142
E-mail: mallette@jlab.org
Education: Purdue BS, BSE; Dayton MS

Thomas Jefferson National Accelerator Facility (JLAB)
Jefferson Lab, 12000 Jefferson Avenue, Newport News, VA 23606
Tel: (757) 269-7100 Fax: (757) 269-7398 E-mail: jlabinfo@jlab.org
Internet: https://www.jlab.org/

Director **Stuart D. Henderson** .... (757) 269-7552
E-mail: stuart@jlab.org
Education: Vanderbilt BSChem; Yale 1991 PhD
Deputy Director for Science **Robert McKeown** .... (757) 269-6481

Accelerator Division
12000 Jefferson Avenue, Newport News, VA 23606
Fax: (757) 269-6099 Internet: www.jlab.org/accel

Associate Director **Dr. Andrei Seryi** .... (757) 269-7100

Experimental Nuclear Physics Division
Associate Director **Dr. Rolf Ent PhD** .... (757) 269-7373
Education: Vrije U (Amsterdam) 1985 BS, 1989 PhD

Theoretical and Computational Physics Division
12000 Jefferson Avenue, Newport News, VA 23606
Fax: (757) 269-7002

Associate Director **Jianwei Qiu** .... (757) 269-6026

Office of the Chief Operating Officer
12000 Jefferson Avenue, Newport News, VA 23606
Fax: (757) 269-7398

Chief Operations Officer **Michael W. "Mike" Maier** .... (757) 269-7538
E-mail: mmaier@jlab.org
Communications Manager **Lauren Hansen** .... (757) 269-7689
E-mail: lhansen@jlab.org
Human Resources Manager **Rhonda M. Barbosa** .... (757) 269-5991
E-mail: rbarbosa@jlab.org
Education: Christopher Newport BASW; George Washington MS

Finance and Business Operations
Chief Financial Officer and Business Services Manager **Joseph "Joe" Scarcello** .... (757) 269-7027
Education: New Orleans 1979 BSBA

Engineering Division
12000 Jefferson Avenue, Newport News, VA 23606
Internet: www.jlab.org/eng

Division Manager **Will Oren** .... (757) 269-7344

Environmental Safety, Healthy, and Quality Division
12000 Jefferson Avenue, Newport News, VA 23606
Fax: (757) 269-6050

Associate Director **Mary K. Logue** .... (757) 269-7447
E-mail: logue@jlab.org
Education: Notre Dame BS; Northwestern MS

Information Technology Division
12000 Jefferson Avenue, Newport News, VA 23606
Fax: (757) 269-5427

Chief Information Officer **Amber S. Boehnlein** .... (757) 269-7536
E-mail: amber@jlab.org
Education: Miami U (OH) 1984 BS; Florida State 1990 PhD
Chief Technology Officer **Drew Weisenberger** .... (757) 269-7090
E-mail: drew@jlab.org

Integrated Support Center (ISC)
1000 Independence Avenue, SW, Washington, DC 20585
Internet: science.energy.gov/isc

Note: The ISC is a virtual organization comprised of the combined support capabilities of offices in Chicago, Illinois, and Oak Ridge, Tennessee.

Chicago (IL) Office (SC-CH)
9800 South Cass Avenue, Argonne, IL 60439
Fax: (630) 252-9473

● Manager (Acting) **John D. Greenwood** .... (630) 252-2018
E-mail: John.Greenwood@science.doe.gov
Secretary **Kimberly S. Simpson** .... (630) 252-2700
E-mail: kimberly.simpson@science.doe.gov

(continued on next page)

★ Presidential Appointment Requiring Senate Confirmation ☆ Presidential Appointment ☐ Schedule C Appointment ◇ Career Senior Foreign Service Appointment
● Career Senior Executive Service (SES) Appointment ○ Non-Career Senior Executive Service (SES) Appointment ■ Postal Career Executive Service

DEPARTMENTS

Chicago (IL) Office *(continued)*

• Deputy Manager **John D. Greenwood** .... (630) 252-2018
E-mail: john.greenwood@science.doe.gov
Communications Office Director (Acting)
Peter R. "Pete" Siebach .... (630) 252-2007
E-mail: peter.siebach@science.doe.gov
Diversity Manager **Jaime Claudio, Jr.** .... (630) 252-2321
E-mail: jaime.claudio@science.doe.gov

Office of Acquisition and Assistance
9800 South Cass Avenue, Lemont, IL 60439
Tel: (630) 252-2339 Fax: (630) 252-5045

• Assistant Manager **Patricia J. Schuneman** .... (630) 252-2339
E-mail: patricia.schuneman@science.doe.gov
Lead Contract Specialist, Acquisitions Group
John P. Motz .... (630) 252-2152
Supervisory Contract Specialist, Non-M&O Policy
Group **Dennis L. Wilson** .... (630) 252-2069
E-mail: dennis.wilson@science.doe.gov

Office of Chief Counsel (OCC)
9800 South Cass Avenue, Building 350, Argonne, IL 60439-4899
Tel: (630) 252-2031 Fax: (630) 252-2183

• Chief Counsel **James Melbourn Durant III** .... (630) 252-2034
E-mail: james.durant@science.doe.gov
Director, General Law Division
Kimberly McMahon "Kim" Donham .... (630) 252-2038
E-mail: kim.donham@science.doe.gov
Director, Intellectual Property Law Division
Michael J. "Mike" Dobbs .... (630) 252-2164
E-mail: mike.dobbs@science.doe.gov

Office of Chief Financial Officer (CFO)
9800 South Cass Avenue, Lemont, IL 60439
Tel: (630) 252-2414 Fax: (630) 252-2015

• Chief Financial Officer **John D. Greenwood** .... (630) 252-2018
E-mail: john.greenwood@science.doe.gov
Supervisory Accountant **(Vacant)** .... (630) 252-2414
Supervisory Budget Analyst **Ramona F. Nykodem** ...... (630) 252-6047
E-mail: ramona.nykodem@science.doe.gov

Office of Safety, Technical and Infrastructure Services
9800 South Cass Avenue, Lemont, IL 60439
Tel: (630) 252-2476 Fax: (630) 252-2654

• Assistant Manager **Karl G. Moro** .... (630) 252-2065
E-mail: karl.moro@science.doe.gov
Safeguards and Security Services Director **(Vacant)** ...... (630) 252-2476

Oak Ridge (TN) Office (SC-OR)

200 Administration Road, Oak Ridge, TN 37830
Mail: P.O. Box 2001, Oak Ridge, TN 37831
Fax: (865) 576-0006

• Manager **Dr. Kenneth R. Tarcza** .... (865) 576-4446
E-mail: kenneth.tarcza@science.doe.gov
Deputy Manager **Geoffrey G. "Geoff" deBeauclair** ..... (865) 576-4442
E-mail: geoffrey.debeauclair@science.doe.gov
Diversity Programs Manager **Moses Madera** .... (865) 576-4988
E-mail: moses.madera@science.doe.gov
Human Resources Advisory Office Director
Adolphus Brown .... (865) 576-4757
E-mail: adolphus.brown@science.doe.gov Fax: (865) 241-9499

Office of the Chief Counsel (CC-10)
9800 South Cass Avenue, Lemont, IL 60439
Tel: (865) 576-1200 Fax: (865) 576-1556

• Chief Counsel **Donald F. "Don" Thress, Jr.** .... (865) 576-1200
E-mail: don.thress@science.doe.gov
Assistant Chief Counsel for Contracts and General Law
Wendy E. Bryant .... (865) 576-1210
E-mail: wendy.bryant@science.doe.gov
Assistant Chief Counsel for Intellectual Property and
Technology Transfer **Emily G. Schneider** .... (865) 576-1077
E-mail: emily.schneider@science.doe.gov

Office of the Chief Counsel *(continued)*

Assistant Chief Counsel for Regulatory and General
Law **Kimberly S. Walling** .... (865) 576-1213
E-mail: kimberly.walling@science.doe.gov

Administration (AD-40)
200 Administration Road, Oak Ridge, TN 37830
Tel: (865) 576-9603 Fax: (865) 576-0006

Assistant Manager for Administration
John C. Shewairy .... (865) 576-9603
E-mail: john.shewairy@science.doe.gov
Facilities, Information, and Reservation Management
Division Director **Johnathan J. Sitzlar** .... (865) 241-5869
Administrative Specialist (Acting) **Robin E. Duncan** ..... (865) 576-9603
E-mail: robin.duncan@science.doe.gov

Safety and Technical Services (SE-30)
Oak Ridge, TN 37831
P.O. Box 2001, Oak Ridge, TN 37831-8501
Tel: (865) 576-0830 Fax: (865) 576-5038

• Assistant Manager (Acting) **Pauline L. Douglas** .... (865) 576-9171
E-mail: pauline.douglas@science.doe.gov
Deputy Assistant Manager **(Vacant)** .... (865) 576-8018
Fax: (865) 576-7298
Health and Safety Services Division Director **(Vacant)** ... (865) 576-0830
Environmental and Quality Services Division Director
(Vacant) .... (865) 574-0960
Engineering and ISC Services Division Director
(Vacant) .... (865) 574-0960

Financial Management (FM-70)
200 Administration Road, Oak Ridge, TN 37830
Tel: (865) 576-0770 Fax: (865) 576-9686

• Assistant Manager/Chief Financial Officer
Marcia J. Bischak .... (865) 576-4446
E-mail: marcie.bischak@science.doe.gov
Financial Evaluation and Accountability Division
Director **Vicki Keith** .... (865) 576-0697
Oak Ridge Financial Service Center Director
Roger Scott "Scott" Frank .... (865) 576-4677
Fax: (865) 574-5374
Financial Systems and Reporting Branch Chief
(Acting) **Rosemary Farsoun Smith** .... (865) 241-6766
E-mail: rosemary.smith@science.doe.gov Fax: (865) 574-5374

New Brunswick Laboratory Program Office (SC-NBL)

9800 South Cass Avenue, Building 350, Argonne, IL 60439-4899
Fax: (630) 252-6256 E-mail: usdoe.nbl@science.doe.gov
Internet: science.energy.gov/nbl

• Program Director **Yacouba Diawara** .... (865) 252-2446
E-mail: yacouba.diawara@science.doe.gov
Secretary **(Vacant)** .... (630) 252-2451
Deputy Director **Peter Mason** .... (630) 252-2458
E-mail: peter.mason@science.doe.gov
Physical Scientist **Paul Croatto** .... (630) 252-6662
E-mail: paul.croatto@science.doe.gov

★ Presidential Appointment Requiring Senate Confirmation ☆ Presidential Appointment □ Schedule C Appointment ◇ Career Senior Foreign Service Appointment
● Career Senior Executive Service (SES) Appointment ○ Non-Career Senior Executive Service (SES) Appointment ■ Postal Career Executive Service

DEPARTMENTS

Federal Energy Regulatory Commission (FERC)

888 First Street, NE, Washington, DC 20426
Tel: (202) 502-8200 (General Information, Personnel Locator)
Internet: www.ferc.gov
Internet: www.ferc.gov/open.asp (Open Government Initiative)

OFFICES OF THE COMMISSIONERS

Note: A commissioner may continue to serve after the expiration of his/her term until a successor is nominated and confirmed, or until the sitting commissioner is reappointed and confirmed, but shall not serve beyond the end of the session of Congress in which such term expires.

Regional Offices

Atlanta (GA) Regional Office

Gwinnett Commerce Center, 3700 Crestwood Parkway, NW, Suite 950, Duluth, GA 30096
Fax: (678) 245-3010
Areas Covered: AL, AR, FL, GA, LA, MS, NC, OK, PR, SC, TN, TX, VA

Regional Engineer **Wayne B. King** .... (678) 245-3075
E-mail: wayne.king@ferc.gov
Dam Safety Branch Chief 1 **Randal Pool** .... (678) 245-3079
E-mail: randal.pool@ferc.gov
Dam Safety Branch Chief 2 **William J. Brown** .... (678) 245-3070
E-mail: william.brown2@ferc.gov

Chicago (IL) Regional Office (CRO)

Kluczynski Federal Building, 230 South Dearborn Street, Suite 3130, Chicago, IL 60604
Tel: (312) 596-4430 Fax: (312) 596-4460
Areas Covered: IL, IN, IA, KS, KY, MI, MN, MO, NE, ND, OH, SD, WI

Regional Engineer **John A. Zygaj** .... (312) 596-4437
E-mail: john.zygaj@ferc.gov
Dam Safety Branch Chief 1 **Olaf Weeks** .... (312) 596-4451
E-mail: olaf.weeks@ferc.gov
Dam Safety Branch Chief 2 **Kevin C. Griebenow** .... (312) 596-4436
E-mail: Kevin.Griebenow@ferc.gov

New York (NY) Regional Office

19 West 34th Street, Suite 400, New York, NY 10001
Tel: (212) 273-5900 Fax: (212) 631-8124
Areas Covered: NY, NJ, PA, WV, MD, DE

Regional Engineer **John Spain** .... (212) 273-5954
Hydropower Resource Assistant **Donna Samuel** .... (212) 273-5903
E-mail: donna.samuel@ferc.gov
Dam Safety Branch Chief 1
Malayandy "Mike" Thiagaram .... (212) 273-5920
Dam Safety Branch Chief 2 **Nicholas Agnoli** .... (212) 273-5906
Dam Safety Branch Chief 3 **Prapa Haran** .... (212) 273-5935

Portland (OR) Regional Office (PRO)

805 Southwest Broadway, Suite 550, Portland, OR 97205
Tel: (503) 552-2700 Fax: (503) 552-2799
Areas Covered: AK, ID, MT, OR, WA, WY

Regional Engineer **Douglas "Doug" Johnson** .... (503) 552-2715
Dam Safety Branch Chief 1 **Karl F. Swanson** .... (503) 552-2734
Dam Safety Branch Chief 2
Kathleen "Katie" Clarkson .... (503) 552-2723

San Francisco (CA) Regional Office (SFRO)

100 First Street, Suite 2300, San Francisco, CA 94105
Tel: (415) 369-3300 Fax: (415) 369-3322
Areas Covered: AZ, CA, CO, HI, NM, NV, UT

Regional Engineer **Frank L. Blackett** .... (415) 369-3318
Dam Safety Branch Chief 1 **Vinh Duc Tran** .... (415) 369-3396
Dam Safety Branch Chief 2 **John Onderdonk** .... (415) 369-3300

★ Presidential Appointment Requiring Senate Confirmation ☆ Presidential Appointment ☐ Schedule C Appointment ◇ Career Senior Foreign Service Appointment
● Career Senior Executive Service (SES) Appointment ○ Non-Career Senior Executive Service (SES) Appointment ■ Postal Career Executive Service

United States Department of Health and Human Services

DEPARTMENTS

Contents

United States Department of Health and Human Services (HHS)

Description: The Department of Health and Human Services provides health, income, and security programs for all U.S. citizens. The department administers programs for the nation's children and families, coordinates health care financing, oversees the research and regulatory functions of the Office of the Assistant Secretary for Health, conducts medical research through the National Institutes of Health, and regulates the purity of food, drugs, and cosmetics through the Food and Drug Administration.

Hubert H. Humphrey Building, 200 Independence Avenue, SW, Washington, DC 20201
Tel: (877) 696-6775 (Toll Free)
Tel: (301) 443-2475 (Procurement Information)
Tel: (202) 690-6617 (Grants Information)
Tel: (202) 690-6343 (Press Office)
Tel: (202) 690-7453 (Freedom of Information/Privacy Act)
Tel: (800) 447-8477 (Inspector General's Hotline) Tel: (301) 443-1240 (Food and Drug Administration Consumer Complaint Line)
Tel: (800) 311-3435 (Hospital Infections Program) Internet: www.hhs.gov
Internet: www.healthcare.gov Internet: www.cuidadodesalud.gov
Internet: https://www.hhs.gov/open/index.html (Open Government Directive Website)

OFFICE OF THE SECRETARY (OS)

Hubert H. Humphrey Building, 200 Independence Avenue, SW, Washington, DC 20201
Tel: (202) 690-7000 Fax: (202) 690-7755

Office of the Deputy Secretary

Hurbert H. Humphrey Building, 200 Independence Avenue, SW, Washington, DC 20201
Fax: (202) 690-7755

Office of Intergovernmental and External Affairs (IEA)

Hubert H. Humphrey Building, 200 Independence Avenue, SW, Washington, DC 20201
Tel: (202) 690-6060 Fax: (202) 205-2727 E-mail: hhsiea@hhs.gov

Regional Directors

Region 1 - Boston (MA)

John F. Kennedy Federal Building, Government Center, Room 2100, Boston, MA 02203
Tel: (617) 565-1500 Fax: (617) 565-1491
Areas Covered: CT, ME, MA, NH, RI, VT

□ Regional Director **John McGough** .... (617) 565-1501
E-mail: John.Mcgough@hhs.gov Fax: (617) 565-1491
Executive Officer **Paul Jacobsen** .... (617) 565-1502
E-mail: paul.jacobsen@hhs.gov
Education: Northeastern

Office of General Counsel

J. F. Kennedy Federal Building, Suite 2100, Boston, MA 02203
Fax: (617) 565-4809

● Chief Counsel **(Vacant)** .... (617) 565-2382

Office of Inspector General

John F. Kennedy Federal Building, Government Center, Boston, MA 02203
Tel: (617) 565-1050 Fax: (617) 565-3750

Regional Inspector General for Audit Services **David Lamir** Room 2425 .... (617) 565-2704
E-mail: david.lamir@oig.hhs.gov

Office of Inspector General *(continued)*

Regional Inspector General for Evaluation and Inspections **Joyce Greenleaf** Room 2225 .... (617) 565-1057
Fax: (617) 565-3751
Regional Special Agent in Charge **Phillip M. Coyne** ..... (617) 565-2672
Fax: (617) 565-4186

Region 2 - New York (NY)

Jacob K. Javits Federal Building, 26 Federal Plaza, Room 3835, New York, NY 10278
Tel: (212) 264-4600 Fax: (212) 264-3620
Areas Covered: NJ, NY, PR, VI

□ Regional Director **Anthony C. Ferreri** .... (202) 260-6348
E-mail: Anthony.Ferreri@hhs.gov
Executive Officer **Dennis E. Gonzalez** .... (212) 264-4600
E-mail: dennis.gonzalez@hhs.gov
Intergovernmental Affairs Specialist **Sean Hightower** .... (212) 264-0131
Fax: (212) 264-3620

Office of General Counsel (GC)

Jacob K. Javits Federal Building, 26 Federal Plaza, Room 3908, New York, NY 10278
Tel: (212) 264-4610 Fax: (212) 264-6364

● Chief Counsel **(Vacant)** .... (212) 264-4610

Office of Inspector General (IG)

26 Federal Plaza, New York, NY 10278
Tel: (212) 264-4620 Fax: (212) 264-6307

Regional Inspector General for Audit Services **James P. Edert** Jacob K. Javits Federal Building, Room 3900A .... (212) 264-4620
E-mail: james.edert@oig.hhs.gov
Regional Inspector General, Regional Coordinator, Office of Investigations **(Vacant)** Jacob K. Javits Federal Building, Room 13-124 .... (212) 264-4620
Regional Inspector General, Office of Evaluations and Inspections **Jodi D. Nudelman** Jacob K. Javits Federal Building, Room 41-106 .... (212) 264-2779

Region 3 - Philadelphia (PA)

150 South Independence Mall West, Suite 436, Philadelphia, PA 19106-3499
Tel: (215) 861-4633 Fax: (215) 861-4625
Areas Covered: DE, DC, MD, PA, VA, WV

□ Regional Director **Matthew E. Baker** .... (215) 861-4648
E-mail: Matthew.Baker@hhs.gov
Education: Elmira 1988 BS
Executive Officer **Melissa A. Herd** .... (215) 861-4362
E-mail: melissa.herd@hhs.gov
Intergovernmental Affairs Specialist **Thomas Harris** ..... (215) 861-4633

Program Support Center

150 South Independence Mall West, Philadelphia, PA 19106-3499
Tel: (215) 861-4667 Fax: (215) 861-4665

Administrative Manager (STG Contractor) **Emily Yaskowski** .... (215) 861-4422
E-mail: emily.yaskowski@psc.hhs.gov

★ Presidential Appointment Requiring Senate Confirmation ☆ Presidential Appointment □ Schedule C Appointment ◇ Career Senior Foreign Service Appointment
● Career Senior Executive Service (SES) Appointment ○ Non-Career Senior Executive Service (SES) Appointment ■ Postal Career Executive Service

DEPARTMENTS

Office of General Counsel

• Chief Counsel **James C. Newman** .... (215) 861-4456
E-mail: james.newman@hhs.gov

Office of Inspector General

Regional Inspector General for Audit **Jason Jelen** ...... (215) 861-4470
E-mail: jason.jelen@oig.hhs.gov
Regional Inspector General for Evaluations and Inspections **Linda Ragone** .... (215) 861-4561
Regional Inspector General for Investigations **Nicolas "Nick" DiGiulio** .... (215) 861-4584
Fax: (215) 861-4596

Region 4 - Atlanta (GA)

Atlanta Federal Center, 61 Forsyth Street, SW,
Suite 5B95, Atlanta, GA 30303-8901
Tel: (404) 562-7888 Fax: (404) 562-7899
Areas Covered: AL, FL, GA, KY, MS, NC, SC, TN

□ Regional Director **Renee Louise-Jacisin Ellmers RN** .... (404) 562-7888
E-mail: renee.ellmers@hhs.gov Fax: (404) 562-7899
Education: Oakland U 1990 BSN
Executive Officer **Natalia Cales** .... (404) 562-7893
E-mail: natalia.cales@hhs.gov

Office of General Counsel

61 Forsyth Street, SW, Room 5M60, Atlanta, GA 30303-8909
Fax: (404) 562-7855

• Chief Counsel **Dana Petti** .... (404) 562-7840
E-mail: dana.petti@hhs.gov

Office of Inspector General

61 Forsyth Street, SW, Atlanta, GA 30303-8909
Fax: (404) 562-7794

Regional Inspector General for Audits **Lori S. Pilcher** .... (404) 562-7750
E-mail: lori.pilcher@oig.hhs.gov
Regional Inspector General for Evaluation and Inspections **Dwayne F. Grant** .... (404) 562-7734
Special Agent-in-Charge **Derrick Jackson** .... (404) 562-7625

Region 5 - Chicago (IL)

233 North Michigan Avenue, Suite 1300, Chicago, IL 60601
Tel: (312) 353-5160 Fax: (312) 353-4144
Areas Covered: IL, IN, MI, MN, OH, WI

□ Regional Director **Douglas S. O'Brien** .... (312) 353-5160
E-mail: Douglas.Obrien@hhs.gov Fax: (312) 353-4144
Education: Notre Dame 1985 BA
Executive Officer **Sam Gabuzzi** .... (312) 353-5132
E-mail: sam.gabuzzi@hhs.gov
Public Affairs Specialist **Lauren Eiten** .... (312) 886-2896
E-mail: lauren.eiten@hhs.gov
Public Affairs Specialist **Gregg Ross** .... (312) 886-1788
E-mail: gregg.ross@hhs.gov

Program Support Center - Regional Administrative Operations Service

233 North Michigan Avenue, Suite 755, Chicago, IL 60601
Fax: (312) 353-1194 Internet: www.psc.gov

Senior Administrative Manager **Michael Downing** ...... (312) 353-0682
E-mail: michael.downing@hhs.gov

Office of General Counsel

233 North Michigan Avenue, Suite 700, Chicago, IL 60601
Tel: (312) 886-1716

• Chief Counsel **Alan S. Dorn** .... (312) 886-1707
E-mail: alan.dorn@hhs.gov

Office of Inspector General

233 North Michigan Avenue, Room 1360, Chicago, IL 60601
Fax: (312) 353-3814

Regional Inspector General for Audit Services **Sheri L. Fulcher** .... (312) 353-2621
E-mail: sheri.fulcher@oig.hhs.gov

Office of Inspector General *(continued)*

Regional Inspector General for Evaluation and Inspections **Thomas F. "Tom" Komaniecki** .... (312) 353-8823
E-mail: thomas.komaniecki@oig.hhs.gov

Office of Investigations

233 North Michigan Avenue, Suite 1330, Chicago, IL 60601
Fax: (312) 353-0147

Special Agent in Charge, Investigations Office **Lamont Pugh** .... (312) 353-5700
E-mail: lamont.pugh@oig.hhs.gov

Region 6 - Dallas (TX)

1301 Young Street, Suite 1124, Dallas, TX 75202
Tel: (214) 767-3301 Fax: (214) 767-3617
Areas Covered: AR, LA, NM, OK, TX

□ Regional Director (Acting) **Mervin D. Turner** .... (214) 767-0778
E-mail: Mervin.Turner@HHS.GOV
Executive Officer **Julia L. Lothrop** .... (214) 767-3301
E-mail: julia.lothrop@hhs.gov

Office of General Counsel

1301 Young Street, Room 1138, Dallas, TX 75202
Tel: (214) 767-2995 Fax: (214) 767-3473

• Chief Counsel (Acting) **Mervin D. Turner** .... (214) 767-0778
E-mail: Mervin.Turner@HHS.GOV

Office of Inspector General

Audit **Patricia M. "Trish" Wheeler** .... (214) 767-8414
E-mail: trish.wheeler@oig.hhs.gov
Evaluation and Inspections **Ruth Ann Dorrill** .... (469) 263-6154
Investigations **C.J. Porter** .... (214) 767-8406
Fax: (214) 767-4291

Region 7 - Kansas City (MO)

Federal Building, 601 East 12th Street,
Suite S1801, Kansas City, MO 64106
Tel: (816) 426-2821 Fax: (816) 426-2834
Areas Covered: IA, KS, MO, NE

□ Regional Director **Jeff Kahrs** .... (816) 426-2925
E-mail: Jeff.Kahrs@hhs.gov Fax: (816) 426-2834
Education: Wichita State BA; Washburn 1993 JD

Office of General Counsel

601 East 12th Street, Suite N1800, Kansas City, MO 64106
Fax: (816) 426-3550

• Chief Counsel **Randall Butler** .... (816) 426-5533
E-mail: randy.butler@hhs.gov

Office of Inspector General

Office of Audit Services Regional Inspector General **Patrick "Pat" Cogley** Suite 284A .... (816) 426-3200
E-mail: patrick.cogley@oig.hhs.gov Fax: (816) 426-3655
Office of Evaluation and Inspections Regional Inspector General **Brian T. Whitley** .... (816) 426-4966
Fax: (816) 426-2146
National External Audit Review Center Manager **Gregory B. "Greg" Dowell** .... (816) 426-7734
323 West Eighth Street, Room 514, Kansas City, MO 64105
E-mail: greg.dowell@oig.hhs.gov

Office of Investigations (OI)

1201 Walnut, Suite 920, Kansas City, MO 64106
Fax: (816) 426-4979

Special Agent-in-Charge **(Vacant)** .... (816) 426-2821

Program Support Center (PSC)

601 East 12th Street, Suite S1801, Kansas City, MO 64106

Administrative Operations Services Manager **Andrew S. "Andy" Groebe** .... (816) 426-3491
E-mail: andrew.groebe@psc.hhs.gov

★ Presidential Appointment Requiring Senate Confirmation ☆ Presidential Appointment □ Schedule C Appointment ◇ Career Senior Foreign Service Appointment
• Career Senior Executive Service (SES) Appointment ○ Non-Career Senior Executive Service (SES) Appointment ■ Postal Career Executive Service

Region 8 - Denver (CO)
1961 Stout Street, Room 08.148, Denver, CO 80294
Tel: (303) 844-3372 Fax: (303) 844-4545
Areas Covered: CO, MT, ND, SD, UT, WY

□ Regional Director **Brian E. Shiozawa** .... (303) 844-7299
E-mail: Brian.Shiozawa@hhs.gov
Education: Stanford BS; U Washington 1981 MD

Office of General Counsel
1961 Stout Street, Room 08.148, Denver, CO 80294
Tel: (303) 844-5101 Fax: (303) 844-6665

● Chief Counsel **Scott Driggs** .... (303) 844-7801
E-mail: scott.driggs@hhs.gov

Office of Inspector General
Assistant Special Agent-in-Charge **(Vacant)** .... (303) 844-7813

Program Support Center- Building Operation Services
1961 Stout Street, Floor 8 - 148, Denver, CO 80294
Fax: (303) 844-2394

Regional Account Manager **Carolyn Sailer** .... (303) 844-7882
E-mail: carolyn.sailer@hhs.gov

Region 9 - San Francisco (CA)
90 Seventh Street, Suite 5-100, San Francisco, CA 94103
Tel: (415) 437-8500
Areas Covered: AZ, CA, GU, HI, NV, American Samoa, Pacific Islands

□ Regional Director **(Vacant)** .... (415) 437-8500
Executive Officer **Kevin Milne** .... (415) 437-8177
E-mail: Kevin.Milne@hhs.gov

Office of General Counsel
90 Seventh Street, Room 4-500, San Francisco, CA 94103
Tel: (415) 437-8181

Chief Counsel **Kevin Milne** Suite 4-500 .... (415) 437-8177
E-mail: kevin.milne@hhs.gov

Office of Inspector General
Regional Inspector General **Blaine B. Collins** .... (415) 437-8500
E-mail: blaine.collins@oig.hhs.gov
Regional Inspector General for Audit
Lori Ahlstrand Suite 3-650 .... (415) 437-8360
E-mail: lori.ahlstrand@oig.hhs.gov
Education: U Washington 1986 BABA
Deputy Regional Inspector General for Evaluations and Inspections **Michael Henry** Suite 3-600 .... (415) 437-7919
Special Agent-in-Charge (Investigations)
(Vacant) Suite 3-510 .... (925) 356-7809
Special Agent-in-Charge, Los Angeles Region
Christian J. Schrank .... (714) 712-7710
Fax: (714) 712-7702

Region 10 - Seattle (WA)
Columbia Center, 701 Fifth Avenue, Suite 1660, Seattle, WA 98104
Tel: (206) 615-2010 Fax: (206) 615-2087
Areas Covered: AK, ID, OR, WA

□ Regional Director **John R. Graham** .... (206) 615-2010
E-mail: John.Graham@hhs.gov
Education: Royal Military Canada BA; London Business (UK) MBA
Executive Officer **Barbara Greene** .... (206) 615-2011
E-mail: barbara.greene@hhs.gov
Regional Outreach Specialist **(Vacant)** .... (206) 615-2010

Office of General Counsel
Columbia Tower, 701 Fifth Avenue, Suite 1620, Seattle, WA 98104
Tel: (206) 615-2268 Fax: (206) 615-2286

● Chief Counsel **Pamela K. Parker** .... (206) 615-2278
E-mail: pamela.parker@hhs.gov

Office of Inspector General
2201 Sixth Avenue, Room 237, Mail Stop 80, Seattle, WA 98121
Fax: (206) 615-2258

Audit Manager **Gerald J. Illies** .... (206) 615-2342
E-mail: Gerald.Illies@oig.hhs.gov
Regional Coordinator **(Vacant)** .... (206) 615-2010

Office of the Assistant Secretary for Health (OASH)
Hubert H. Humphrey Building, 200 Independence Avenue, SW, Washington, DC 20201
Tel: (202) 690-7850 (Public Information)
Tel: (800) 342-2437 (AIDS Hot Line) Fax: (202) 690-6960
Internet: www.hhs.gov/ash/

Regional Offices

Region 1 - Boston (MA)
John F. Kennedy Federal Building, 15 New Sudbury Street, Room 2100, Boston, MA 02203
Fax: (617) 565-1491
Areas Covered: CT, ME, MA, NH, RI, VT

● Regional Health Administrator **Betsy F. Rosenfeld** ...... (617) 565-1505
E-mail: betsy.rosenfeld@hhs.gov
Education: Harvard 1988 BS, JD
Deputy Regional Health Administrator **(Vacant)** .... (617) 565-1505
Administrative Assistant **Tina B. DeLima** .... (617) 565-1507
E-mail: tina.delima@hhs.gov

Office of Family Planning
15 New Sudbury Street, Room 2126, Boston, MA 02203
Fax: (617) 565-4265

Public Health Advisor **Natalia T. Guevara** .... (617) 565-1070

Office of Minority Health (OMH)
Regional Minority Health Consultant
Georgia M. Simpson .... (617) 565-1062

Office on Women's Health (OWH)
Regional Women's Health Coordinator
Laurie Robinson .... (617) 565-1071

Region 2 - New York (NY)
26 Federal Plaza, Room 3835, New York, NY 10278
Tel: (212) 264-2560 Fax: (212) 264-1324
Areas Covered: NJ, NY, PR, VI

● Regional Health Administrator (Acting)
April Smith-Hirak .... (212) 264-2560
E-mail: michelle.davis@hhs.gov
Deputy Regional Health Administrator
April Smith-Hirak .... (212) 264-2560
Regional Minority Health Consultant **Marline Vignier** .... (212) 264-2560
Regional Women's Health Coordinator
Sandra Bennett-Pagan .... (212) 264-4628
Public Health Advisor **Delores Stewart** Room 38-100 ... (212) 264-3935

Region 3 - Philadelphia (PA)
The Public Ledger Building, 150 South Independence Mall West, Suite 436, Philadelphia, PA 19106-3499
Tel: (215) 861-4639 Fax: (215) 861-4617
Areas Covered: DE, DC, MD, PA, VA, WV

● Regional Health Administrator **Dalton Paxman** .... (215) 861-4639
E-mail: dalton.paxman@hhs.gov
Deputy Regional Health Administrator **Mahal Lalvani** .... (215) 861-4641
Fax: (215) 861-4617
Administrative Assistant **Brenda Solomon** .... (215) 861-4640
Regional Women's Health Coordinator
Sarah L. Shrimplin .... (215) 861-4620
Minority Health Consultant **(Vacant)** .... (215) 861-4639
Regional Program Consultant, Family Planning
Dickie Lynn Gronseth .... (215) 861-4656
Regional Program Consultant, Family Planning
Christine Woolslayer .... (215) 861-4766
Fax: (215) 861-4617

(continued on next page)

★ Presidential Appointment Requiring Senate Confirmation ☆ Presidential Appointment □ Schedule C Appointment ◇ Career Senior Foreign Service Appointment
● Career Senior Executive Service (SES) Appointment ○ Non-Career Senior Executive Service (SES) Appointment ■ Postal Career Executive Service

Region 3 - Philadelphia (PA) *(continued)*

Regional Resource Consultant (HIV/AIDS Minority Initiative) **(Vacant)** .... (215) 861-4639

Region 4 - Atlanta (GA)

Atlanta Federal Center, 61 Forsyth Street SW,
Suite 5B95, Atlanta, GA 30303
Tel: (404) 562-7890 Fax: (404) 562-7899
E-mail: hhsoashregion4@hhs.gov
Areas Covered: AL, FL, GA, KY, MS, NC, SC, TN

● Regional Health Administrator **(Vacant)** .... (404) 562-7890
Deputy Regional Health Administrator **(Vacant)** .... (404) 562-7906
Regional Women's Health Coordinator **Lenee Simon** .... (404) 562-7907
Regional Minority Health Consultant
Arlene M. Lester Presser DDS .... (404) 562-7905
Regional Program Consultant for the Office of Family Planning **Edecia Richards** .... (404) 562-7900

Region 5 - Chicago (IL)

233 North Michigan Avenue, Suite 1300, Chicago, IL 60601
Tel: (312) 353-1385 Fax: (312) 353-0718
Areas Covered: IL, IN, MI, MN, OH, WI

● Regional Health Administrator (Acting)
Anna T. Gonzales .... (312) 886-3880
E-mail: anna.gonzales@hhs.gov Fax: (312) 353-0718
Deputy Regional Health Administrator **(Vacant)** .... (312) 353-1385
Regional Minority Health Consultant
Mildred C. Hunter .... (312) 353-1386
Regional Nurse Consultant **Antonio Vargas** .... (312) 886-3864
Regional Program Consultant **Anthony Harden** .... (312) 886-0391
Regional Women's Health Coordinator
Michelle Hoersch .... (312) 353-8122
Education: DePaul
Executive Assistant **Erica Moorer** .... (312) 353-1385
Fax: (312) 353-0718

Region 6 - Dallas (TX)

1301 Young Street, Suite 1124, Dallas, TX 75202
Tel: (214) 767-3879 Fax: (214) 767-3209
Internet: http://www.hhs.gov/ophs/rha/region6/index.html
Areas Covered: AR, LA, NM, OK, TX

● Regional Health Administrator
CAPT Mehran S. Massoudi USPHS .... (214) 767-8433
E-mail: mehran.massoudi@hhs.gov Fax: (214) 767-3209
Education: Pittsburgh MPH, PhD
Deputy Regional Health Administrator **(Vacant)** .... (214) 767-3660
Executive Assistant **(Vacant)** .... (214) 767-8387
Public Health Advisor
CDR Stacy Harper USPHS, RDH, MPH .... (214) 767-3490
E-mail: stacy.harper@hhs.gov

Family Planning Program Section

1301 Young Street, Room 1124, Dallas, TX 75202
Fax: (214) 767-3209

Regional Program Consultant for Family Planning Services **Liese A. Sherwood-Fabre PhD** .... (214) 767-3060
Education: Texas Christian 1978 BA; Indiana 1984 PhD Fax: (214) 767-3209
Public Health Advisor **CAPT Alisha R. Acker USPHS** .... (214) 767-3088

HIV - AIDS Regional Resource Network

1301 Young Street, Dallas, TX 75202
Fax: (214) 767-3209

Regional Resource Consultant **Regina Waits** .... (214) 767-6084
Education: Wiley 1989 BS

Minority Health Section

1301 Young Street, Room 1124, Dallas, TX 75202
Fax: (214) 767-3209

Minority Health Consultant **CAPT James LaVelle Dickens USPHS, DNP, NP, FAANP** .... (214) 767-3882

Women's Health Section

1301 Young Street, Room 1124, Dallas, TX 75202
Fax: (214) 767-3209

Women's Health Coordinator
CDR Angela Girgenti USPHS, RDH, MPH .... (214) 767-3523

Region 7 - Kansas City (MO)

Federal Building, 601 East 12th Street,
Room S1801, Kansas City, MO 64106
Tel: (816) 426-3291 Fax: (816) 426-2178
Areas Covered: IA, KS, MS, NE

● Regional Health Administrator **(Vacant)** .... (816) 426-3291
Deputy Regional Health Administrator
CDR Shary Jones USPHS .... (816) 426-3330
Minority Health Coordinator **Corstella Henley** Richard Bolling Federal Building, Suite 1801 .... (816) 426-3291
Regional Medical Reserve Corps Coordinator **(Vacant)** .... (816) 426-3291
3030 W 9th Street, Lawrence, KS 66049
Regional Resource Coordinator for HIV/AIDs
Angela Williams .... (816) 426-3296
Family Planning Regional Program Consultant
(Vacant) .... (816) 426-3291
Family Planning Regional Program Consultant
Dustin Rider .... (816) 426-2924
Regional Women's Health Coordinator
Joyce Townser RN, BSN .... (816) 426-2926
Education: Missouri (Kansas City) BSN; Central Michigan MSA

Region 8 - Denver (CO)

1961 Stout Street, Denver, CO 80294
Tel: (303) 844-6163 Fax: (303) 844-2019
Areas Covered: CO, MT, ND, SD, UT, WY

● Regional Health Administrator (Acting)
Laurie Konsella .... (303) 844-7854
E-mail: laurie.konsella@hhs.gov
Administrative Assistant **(Vacant)** .... (303) 844-6163
Deputy Regional Health Administrator
Laurie Konsella .... (303) 844-7854
Family Planning Project Officer **Traci Pole** .... (303) 844-7856
Family Planning Consultant **(Vacant)** .... (303) 844-7856
Minority Health Consultant **(Vacant)** .... (303) 844-7858
Women's Health Coordinator **Susana Calderon** .... (303) 844-7859
Program Assistant **Linda Stopp** .... (303) 844-7891
E-mail: linda.stopp@hhs.gov

Region 9 - San Francisco (CA)

90 Seventh Street, Suite 5-100, San Francisco, CA 94103
Tel: (415) 437-8096 Fax: (415) 437-8004
Areas Covered: AZ, CA, HI, NV, Guam, American Samoa, Commonwealth of the Northern Marianas Islands, Federated States of Micronesia, Republic of the Marshall Islands, Palau

● Regional Health Administrator (Acting)
CAPT Brad Austin USPHS, MPH, FACHE .... (415) 437-8386
E-mail: Brad.Austin@hhs.gov Fax: (415) 437-8388
Administrative Assistant **Denise Farr** .... (415) 437-8096
● Deputy Regional Health Administrator (Acting)
Kay A. Strawder JD, MSW .... (415) 437-8119
E-mail: kay.strawder@hhs.gov Fax: (415) 437-8004
Pacific Health Unit **Subroto Banerji** .... (415) 437-8114
Regional Minority Health Coordinator **(Vacant)** .... (415) 437-8124
Regional Women's Health Coordinator
Kay A. Strawder JD, MSW .... (415) 437-8119
Public Health Advisor **Sheila L. James** .... (415) 437-8075
Fax: (415) 437-8004
Regional Family Planning Consultant **Rebecca McTall** .... (415) 437-8403
Regional Program Consultant **(Vacant)** .... (415) 437-7984

★ Presidential Appointment Requiring Senate Confirmation ☆ Presidential Appointment ☐ Schedule C Appointment ◇ Career Senior Foreign Service Appointment
● Career Senior Executive Service (SES) Appointment ○ Non-Career Senior Executive Service (SES) Appointment ■ Postal Career Executive Service

Region 10 - Seattle (WA)
Columbia Center, 701 Fifth Avenue, Suite 1600, Mail Stop 20, Seattle, WA 98104
Tel: (206) 615-2469 Fax: (206) 615-2481
Areas Covered: AK, ID, OR, WA

Regional Health Administrator (Acting)
Renee Bouvion MPH .... (206) 615-3667
Education: U Washington MPH
Deputy Regional Health Administrator
Karen J. Matsuda MN, RN .... (206) 615-2469
Regional Family Planning Consultant
Louis "Lou" Glass USPHS .... (206) 615-2776
Regional Minority Health Consultant **Jesus Reyna** .... (206) 615-3678
Regional Women's Health Coordinator
Renee Bouvion MPH .... (206) 615-3667
Education: U Washington MPH

Office of the Assistant Secretary for Preparedness and Response (ASPR)

Hubert H. Humphrey Building, 200 Independence Avenue, SW, Room 639D, Washington, DC 20201
Tel: (202) 205-2882 Fax: (202) 690-6512 Internet: www.phe.gov

Office of Emergency Management (OEM)

Hubert H. Humphrey Building, 200 Independence Avenue, SW, Room 638G, Washington, DC 20201
Tel: (202) 205-8387 Fax: (202) 260-6056 E-mail: ASPROEM@hhs.gov

Regional Offices

Region 1 - Boston (MA)
John F. Kennedy Federal Building, 15 New Sudbury Street, Room 2100, Boston, MA 02203
Fax: (615) 622-0252

Regional Administrator **Gary J. Kleinman** .... (617) 565-1159
E-mail: gary.kleinman@hhs.gov
Regional Emergency Coordinator
Gregory T. Banner CEM .... (617) 565-1485
E-mail: gregory.banner@hhs.gov
Regional Emergency Coordinator
Mark C. N. Libby RN, EMT-P .... (617) 565-1481
E-mail: mark.libby@hhs.gov Fax: (763) 431-8986

Region 2 - New York (NY)
Jacob K. Javitz Federal Building, 26 Federal Plaza, Room 38-100, New York, NY 10278
Tel: (212) 680-3611

Supervisory Regional Emergency Coordinator
Murad Raheem .... (212) 264-4494
E-mail: murad.raheem@hhs.gov Fax: (212) 264-3424
Regional Emergency Coordinator
CAPT Andrew Chen USPHS .... (212) 264-2745
E-mail: andrew.chen@hhs.gov Fax: (212) 264-3424

Region 3 - Philadelphia (PA)
150 South Independence Mall West, Suite 436, Philadelphia, PA 19106-3499
Fax: (215) 861-4363

Supervisory Regional Emergency Administrator
Harry Mayer .... (215) 861-4413
E-mail: harry.mayer@hhs.gov
Regional Emergency Coordinator **Emily Falone** .... (215) 861-4390
E-mail: emily.falone@hhs.gov
Regional Emergency Coordinator
CAPT Stephen Formanski USPHS .... (215) 861-4398
E-mail: stephen.formanski@hhs.gov

Region 4 - Atlanta (GA)
Atlanta Federal Center, 61 Forsyth Street, SW, Suite 5B-95, Atlanta, GA 30303-8909
Tel: (404) 562-7936 Fax: (404) 562-7913

Supervisory Regional Emergency Coordinator
CAPT Thomas "Tom" Bowman USPHS .... (404) 562-7912
E-mail: thomas.bowman@hhs.gov
Education: Delaware Valley 1979 ScB; Jacksonville State 2009 ScM

Region 4 - Atlanta (GA) *(continued)*

Regional Emergency Coordinator **Jeanette Dickinson** .... (404) 562-7679
E-mail: jeanette.dickinson@hhs.gov
Regional Emergency Coordinator
CAPT Charles Weir USPHS .... (404) 562-7936
E-mail: charles.weir@hhs.gov

Region 5 - Chicago (IL)
233 North Michigan Avenue, Suite 1300, Chicago, IL 60601-5519
Tel: (312) 353-9763 Fax: (312) 353-7800

Regional Administrator **CAPT Janet Odom USPHS** .... (312) 886-0696
E-mail: janet.odom@hhs.gov
Regional Emergency Coordinator **Todd Stankewicz** .... (312) 353-4515
E-mail: todd.stankewicz@hhs.gov
Regional Emergency Coordinator
Anthony J. Voirin Room 354 .... (415) 385-6451
E-mail: anthony.voirin@hhs.gov

Region 6 - Dallas (TX)
854 Avenue R, Grand Prairie, TX 75050
Fax: (972) 606-8940

Supervisory Regional Emergency Coordinator
CAPT Mick Cote USPHS .... (214) 601-1101
E-mail: mick.cote@hhs.gov
Regional Emergency Coordinator
CDR Mark Byrd USPHS .... (817) 403-8742
E-mail: mark.byrd@hhs.gov
Regional Emergency Coordinator
CAPT Louis A. "Skip" Lightner, Jr. USPHS .... (972) 606-6472
E-mail: louis.lightner@hhs.gov
Regional Emergency Coordinator
CDR Amy O. Taylor USPHS .... (972) 606-6190
E-mail: amyo.taylor@hhs.gov

Region 7 - Kansas City (MO)
Bolling Federal Building, 601 East 12th Street, Room S1801, Kansas City, MO 64106
Fax: (816) 426-2834

Supervisory Regional Emergency Coordinator
CAPT Dana L. Hall USPHS .... (816) 426-2828
E-mail: dana.hall@hhs.gov
Regional Emergency Coordinator
CAPT Scott Lee USPHS .... (816) 426-3490
E-mail: scott.lee@hhs.gov
HPP Field Project Officer **Angela Krutsinger** .... (816) 426-3290
E-mail: angela.krutsinger@hhs.gov

Region 8 - Denver (CO)
Byron G. Rogers Federal Building, 999 18th Street South Terrace, Room 1456, Denver, CO 80202
Fax: (303) 844-7274

Regional Administrator
CDR Ronald R. Pinheiro USPHS .... (303) 844-7273
E-mail: ronald.pinheiro@hhs.gov

Region 9 - San Francisco (CA)
Federal Building, 90 Seventh Street, San Francisco, CA 94103
Fax: (415) 437-8388

Regional Administrator **Mark D. Young** .... (415) 633-5500
E-mail: mark.young@hhs.gov
Regional Emergency Coordinator
CAPT Brad Austin USPHS, MPH, FACHE .... (415) 437-8386
E-mail: brad.austin@hhs.gov

Region 10 - Seattle (WA)
2201 Sixth Avenue, Suite 900 Blanchard Plaza, MS-20, Seattle, WA 98121
Fax: (206) 615-2481

Regional Administrator **Rick Buell** .... (206) 615-3600
E-mail: rick.buell@hhs.gov
Regional Emergency Coordinator
CAPT John Smart USPHS .... (206) 615-2506
E-mail: john.smart@hhs.gov

(continued on next page)

★ Presidential Appointment Requiring Senate Confirmation ☆ Presidential Appointment ☐ Schedule C Appointment ◇ Career Senior Foreign Service Appointment
● Career Senior Executive Service (SES) Appointment ○ Non-Career Senior Executive Service (SES) Appointment ■ Postal Career Executive Service

DEPARTMENTS

Region 10 - Seattle (WA) *(continued)*

Regional Emergency Coordinator
Andrew C. Stevermer ARNP . . . . (206) 615-2266
E-mail: andrew.stevermer@hhs.gov

Office for Civil Rights (OCR)

Hubert H. Humphrey Building, 200 Independence Avenue, SW, Room 515F, Washington, DC 20201
Tel: (202) 619-0403 Fax: (202) 619-3437 E-mail: ocrmail@hhs.gov
Internet: www.hhs.gov/ocr

Operations and Resources Division
Hubert H. Humphrey Building, 200 Independence Avenue, SW, Room 509-F4, Washington, DC 20201
Fax: (202) 619-3437

● Deputy Director **Steven D. "Steve" Novy** . . . . (202) 619-0553
E-mail: steve.novy@hhs.gov

Eastern and Caribbean Region
26 Federal Plaza, Room 3312, New York, NY 10278
Tel: (800) 368-1019 Fax: (212) 264-3039

Regional Manager
Linda C. Colon Jacob K. Javits Federal Building . . . . . . (212) 264-4136
E-mail: linda.colon@hhs.gov
Deputy Regional Manager
(Vacant) Jacob K. Javits Federal Building . . . . (212) 264-3313

Kansas City Region
601 East 12th Street, Room 353, Kansas City, MO 64106
Tel: (800) 368-1019

Regional Manager **Steven M. Mitchell** . . . . (816) 426-2157
E-mail: steven.mitchell@hhs.gov

Mid-Atlantic Region
150 South Independence Mall West, Suite 372, Philadelphia, PA 19106-3499
Tel: (215) 861-4441 Fax: (215) 861-4431

Regional Manager **Barbara J. Holland** . . . . (215) 861-4447
E-mail: barbara.holland@hhs.gov

Midwest Region
233 North Michigan Avenue, Suite 240, Chicago, IL 60601
Tel: (800) 368-1019 Fax: (312) 886-1807

Regional Manager **(Vacant)** . . . . (800) 368-1019
Deputy Regional Manager **(Vacant)** . . . . (312) 886-5887

New England Region
15 New Sudbury Street, Room 1875, Boston, MA 02203
Tel: (800) 368-1019 Fax: (617) 565-3809

Regional Manager **Susan Rhodes** . . . . (617) 565-1347
John F. Kennedy Federal Building, Government Center, Room 1875, Boston, MA 02203
E-mail: susan.rhodes@hhs.gov

Pacific Region
90 7th Street, Room 4-105, San Francisco, CA 94103
Tel: (800) 368-1019

Regional Manager **Michael S. Leoz** . . . . (415) 437-8330
90 Seventh Street, Suite 4-100, San Francisco, CA 94103
E-mail: michael.leoz@hhs.gov

Rocky Mountain Region
1961 Stout Street, Room 08-148, Denver, CO 80294
Tel: (800) 368-1019

Regional Manager **Andrea Oliver** . . . . (303) 844-7839
E-mail: andrea.oliver@hhs.gov

Southeast Region
61 Forsyth Street SW, Suite 16T70, Atlanta, GA 30303
Tel: (800) 368-1019 Fax: (404) 562-7881

Regional Manager **Timothy Noonan** . . . . (404) 562-7453
E-mail: timothy.noonan@hhs.gov

Southwest Region
1301 Young Street, Suite 1169, Dallas, TX 75202
Tel: (800) 368-1019 Fax: (206) 615-2297

Regional Manager
Marisa Smith 11th Floor, Room 1169 . . . . (214) 767-4058
E-mail: marisa.smith@hhs.gov

Administration for Children and Families (ACF)

330 C Street, SW, Washington, DC 20201
Tel: (202) 401-9373 (Child Support Information)
Tel: (888) 747-1861 (Freedom of Information/Privacy Act Information)
Internet: www.acf.hhs.gov

OFFICE OF THE ASSISTANT SECRETARY

Mary E. Switzer Building, 330 C Street, SW, Washington, DC 20201
Fax: (202) 401-4678

Office of Regional Operations (ORO)

370 L'Enfant Promenade, SW, Washington, DC 20447
Tel: (202) 401-4802 Fax: (202) 401-5706
Internet: www.acf.hhs.gov/programs/oro

Regional Offices

Region 1 - Boston (MA)
John F. Kennedy Federal Building, Government Center, Room 2000, Boston, MA 02203
Tel: (617) 565-1020 Fax: (617) 565-2493
Internet: www.acf.hhs.gov/programs/region1
Areas Covered: CT, ME, MA, NH, RI, VT

Regional Administrator **Elaine Zimmerman** . . . . (617) 565-1020
E-mail: elaine.zimmerman@acf.hhs.gov
Regional Program Manager, Child Care **Shireen Riley** . . . (617) 565-1152
Regional Program Manager, Child Support Enforcement **Michael R. Ginns** . . . . (617) 565-2456
E-mail: michael.ginns@acf.hhs.gov
Regional Program Manager, Children's Bureau
Bob Cavanaugh . . . . (617) 565-2449
Regional Program Manager, Temporary Assistance to Needy Families (TANF) **Carol Monteiro** . . . . (617) 565-2462
Grants Officer **George Barnwell** . . . . (617) 565-1403
E-mail: george.barnwell@acf.hhs.gov
Administrative Assistant **Maureen F. Walsh** . . . . (617) 565-1115

Region 2 - New York (NY)
26 Federal Plaza, Room 4114, New York, NY 10278
Tel: (212) 264-2890 Fax: (212) 264-4881
Internet: https://www.acf.hhs.gov/programs/region2
Areas Covered: NJ, NY, PR, VI

● Regional Administrator **Joyce A. Thomas** . . . . . (212) 264-2890 ext. 103
E-mail: joyce.thomas@acf.hhs.gov
Education: Northern Iowa BA, MA
Regional Program Manager, Child Care
Magdamari Marcano . . . . (212) 264-2890
Regional Program Manager, Child Support Enforcement **Jens Feck** . . . . (787) 766-5196 ext. 2
350 Carlos Chardon Avenue, San Juan, PR 00918
E-mail: jens.feck@acf.hhs.gov
Regional Program Manager, Children's Bureau
Alfonso F. Nicholas . . . . (212) 264-2890

★ Presidential Appointment Requiring Senate Confirmation ☆ Presidential Appointment ☐ Schedule C Appointment ◇ Career Senior Foreign Service Appointment
● Career Senior Executive Service (SES) Appointment ○ Non-Career Senior Executive Service (SES) Appointment ■ Postal Career Executive Service

Region 2 - New York (NY) *(continued)*

Regional Program Manager, Temporary Assistance to Needy Families (TANF) **Shantel Mickens** . . . . (212) 264-2890
Fax: (212) 264-0013

Grants Officer **Clinton McGrane** . . . . (212) 264-2890 ext. 176
E-mail: clinton.mcgrane@acf.hhs.gov

Region 3 - Philadelphia (PA)

150 South Independence Mall West, Suite 864,
Philadelphia, PA 19106-3499
Tel: (215) 861-4000 Fax: (215) 861-4070
Internet: www.acf.hhs.gov/programs/region3
Areas Covered: DE, DC, MD, PA, VA, WV

● Regional Administrator (Acting) **Joyce A. Thomas** . . . . (212) 264-2890 ext. 103
E-mail: joyce.thomas@acf.hhs.gov
Education: Northern Iowa BA, MA

Regional Program Manager, Child Care **Beverly Wellons** . . . . (215) 861-4020

Regional Program Manager, Child Support Enforcement **Juanita DeVine** . . . . (215) 861-4054
E-mail: juanita.devine@acf.hhs.gov

Regional Program Manager, Children's Bureau **Lisa Pearson** . . . . (215) 861-4030

Regional Program Manager, Temporary Assistance to Needy Families (TANF) **Eileen Friedman** . . . . (215) 861-4058

Grants Officer **Calvin Mitchell** . . . . (215) 861-4027
E-mail: calvin.mitchell@acf.hhs.gov

Region 4 - Atlanta (GA)

61 Forsyth Street, SW, Suite 4M60, Atlanta, GA 30303-8909
Tel: (404) 562-2800 Fax: (404) 562-2981
Internet: www.acf.hhs.gov/programs/region4
Areas Covered: AL, FL, GA, KY, MS, NC, SC, TN

● Regional Administrator **Carlis V. Williams** . . . . (404) 562-2929
E-mail: carlis.williams@acf.hhs.gov Fax: (404) 562-2980
Education: Ball State BS, MA

Regional Program Manager, Child Care **Eric Blanchette** . . . . (404) 562-2782

Regional Program Manager, Child Support Enforcement **Jacqueline Mull** . . . . (404) 562-2958
E-mail: jacqueline.mull@acf.hhs.gov

Regional Program Manager, Children's Bureau **Shalonda Cawthon** . . . . (404) 562-2242

Regional Program Manager, Temporary Assistance to Needy Families (TANF) **LaMonica Shelton** . . . . (404) 562-2938

Grants Officer **Cheryl A. Pressley** . . . . (404) 562-7662
E-mail: cheryl.pressley@acf.hhs.gov

Region 5 - Chicago (IL)

233 North Michigan Avenue, Suite 400, Chicago, IL 60601-5519
Tel: (312) 353-4237 Fax: (312) 353-2204 E-mail: chicago@acf.hhs.gov
Internet: www.acf.hhs.gov/programs/region5
Areas Covered: IL, IN, MI, MN, OH, WI

● Regional Administrator **Angela Green** . . . . (312) 886-6375
E-mail: angela.green@acf.hhs.gov Fax: (312) 353-7828

Regional Program Manager, Child Care **(Vacant)** . . . . (312) 353-4237

Regional Program Manager, Child Support Enforcement **Michael "Mike" Vicars** . . . . (312) 886-5339
E-mail: mike.vicars@acf.hhs.gov

Regional Program Manager, Temporary Assistance to Needy Families (TANF) **Thomas Schindler** . . . . (312) 886-9540

Regional Program Manager, Youth Services **William "Bill" Clair** . . . . (312) 353-0166

Grants Officer **Eric Staples** . . . . (312) 353-6350
E-mail: eric.staples@acf.hhs.gov

Region 6 - Dallas (TX)

1301 Young Street, Room 914, Dallas, TX 75202
Tel: (214) 767-9648 Fax: (214) 767-3743 E-mail: dallas@acf.hhs.gov
Areas Covered: AR, LA, NM, OK, TX

● Regional Administrator **LaKesha Pope Jackson** . . . . (214) 767-2821
E-mail: lakesha.popejackson@acf.hhs.gov Fax: (214) 767-3743

Region 6 - Dallas (TX) *(continued)*

Regional Program Manager, Child Care **Gwendolyn G. Jones** . . . . (214) 767-3849
Fax: (214) 767-8124

Regional Program Manager, Child Support Enforcement **James V. Travis** . . . . (214) 767-6239
E-mail: james.travis@acf.hhs.gov Fax: (214) 767-8890

Regional Program Manager, Children's Bureau **Janis Brown** . . . . (214) 767-8466
Education: Texas 2001 MSSW Fax: (214) 767-8890

Regional Program Manager, Temporary Assistance to Needy Families (TANF) **Larry D. McDowell** . . . . (214) 767-7327

Grants Officer **Ray M. Bishop** . . . . (214) 767-8849
E-mail: ray.bishop@acf.hhs.gov Fax: (214) 767-8890

Region 7 - Kansas City (MO)

Federal Building, 601 East 12th Street,
Room 349, Kansas City, MO 64106-2808
Tel: (816) 426-3981 Fax: (816) 426-2888
Internet: https://www.acf.hhs.gov/programs/region7
Areas Covered: IA, KS, MO, NE

Regional Administrator (Acting) **Angela Green** . . . . (312) 886-6375
E-mail: angela.green@acf.hhs.gov Fax: (312) 353-7828

Region 8 - Denver (CO)

1961 Stout Street, Room 08-148, Denver, CO 80294
Tel: (303) 844-3100 Fax: (303) 844-1188 E-mail: region8@acf.hhs.gov
Internet: www.acf.hhs.gov/programs/region8
Areas Covered: CO, MT, ND, SD, UT, WY

● Regional Administrator **Nikki Hatch** . . . . (303) 844-1211
E-mail: nikki.hatch@acf.hhs.gov

Management Analyst **Carol D. Delgado** . . . . (303) 844-1169

Region 9 - San Francisco (CA)

90 Seventh Street, 9th Floor, San Francisco, CA 94103
Tel: (415) 437-8400 Fax: (415) 437-8436
Internet: www.acf.hhs.gov/programs/region9
Areas Covered: AZ, CA, HI, NV, American Samoa, Commonwealth of the Northern Mariana Islands, Federated State of Micronesia, Guam, Republic of the Marshall Islands, Republic of Palau

Regional Administrator (Acting) **Elaine Zimmerman** . . . . (617) 565-1020

Region 10 - Seattle (WA)

701 Fifth Avenue, Suite 1510, Seattle, WA 98104
Tel: (206) 615-2547 Fax: (206) 615-2574
Internet: www.acf.hhs.gov/programs/region10
Areas Covered: AK, ID, OR, WA

Regional Administrator (Acting) **Nikki Hatch** . . . . (303) 844-1211
E-mail: nikki.hatch@acf.hhs.gov Fax: (303) 844-2624

Regional Program Manager, Child Care **Paul Noski** . . . . . . (206) 615-2609

Regional Program Manager, Child Support Enforcement **Donna C. Hengeveld** . . . . (206) 615-3769
E-mail: donna.hengeveld@acf.hhs.gov

Regional Program Manager, Children's Bureau **Tina Naugler** . . . . (206) 615-3657

Regional Program Manager, Temporary Assistance to Needy Families (TANF) **Frank Shields** . . . . (206) 615-2569

Grants Officer **Patricia L. Fisher** . . . . (206) 615-2614
E-mail: patricia.fisher@acf.hhs.gov

DEPARTMENTS

★ Presidential Appointment Requiring Senate Confirmation ☆ Presidential Appointment ☐ Schedule C Appointment ◇ Career Senior Foreign Service Appointment
● Career Senior Executive Service (SES) Appointment ○ Non-Career Senior Executive Service (SES) Appointment ■ Postal Career Executive Service

DEPARTMENTS

Administration for Community Living (ACL)

Hubert H. Humphrey Building, 200 Independence Avenue, SW, Washington, DC 20201
Internet: www.acl.gov

OFFICE OF THE ADMINISTRATOR

Office of Regional Operations

One Massachusetts Avenue, NW, Washington, DC 20201-1401
Director **Robert D. "Bob" Logan** .... (202) 795-7388

Region 1 - Boston (MA)
John F. Kennedy Federal Building, Room 2075, Boston, MA 02203
Tel: (617) 565-1158 Fax: (617) 565-4511
Areas Covered: CT, ME, MA, NH, RI, VT

Regional Administrator **Kathleen F. Otte** .... (212) 264-5767
26 Federal Plaza, Fax: (212) 264-0114
Room 38-102, New York, NY 10278
E-mail: kathleen.otte@acl.hhs.gov

Region 2 - New York (NY)
26 Federal Plaza, Room 38-102, New York, NY 10278
Tel: (212) 264-2976 Fax: (212) 264-0114
Areas Covered: DE, DC, MD, NJ, NY, PA, PR, VA, VI, WV

Regional Administrator **Kathleen F. Otte** .... (212) 264-5767
E-mail: kathleen.otte@acl.hhs.gov

Region 3 - Philadelphia (PA)
Public Ledger Building, 150 South Independence Mall West, Philadelphia, PA 19106-3499
Tel: (215) 861-4719 Fax: (215) 861-4625

Regional Administrator
Constantinos I. "Costas" Miskis .... (202) 868-9384
61 Forsyth Street SW, Fax: (404) 562-7598
Room 5-M69, Atlanta, GA 30303
E-mail: constantinos.miskis@acl.hhs.gov
Education: Florida International BA; Florida 1995 JD

Region 4 - Atlanta (GA)
Atlanta Federal Center, 61 Forsyth Street, SW, Suite 5M69, Atlanta, GA 30303-8909
Tel: (404) 562-7600 Fax: (404) 562-7598
Areas Covered: AL, FL, GA, KY, MS, NC, SC, TN

Regional Administrator
Constantinos I. "Costas" Miskis .... (404) 562-7600
E-mail: constantinos.miskis@aoa.hhs.gov
Education: Florida International BA; Florida 1995 JD

Region 5 - Chicago (IL)
233 North Michigan Avenue, Suite 790, Chicago, IL 60601-5519
Tel: (312) 353-3141 Fax: (312) 886-8533
Areas Covered: AK, IL, IN, KS, MI, MO, MN, NE, OH, WI

Regional Administrator **James "Jim" Varpness** .... (312) 938-9857
E-mail: jim.varpness@acl.hhs.gov Fax: (312) 886-8536

Region 6 - Dallas (TX)
1301 Young Street, Suite 736, Dallas, TX 75202-4325
Tel: (214) 767-2971 Fax: (214) 767-2951
Areas Covered: AR, LA, NM, OK, TX

Regional Administrator **Percy Devine III** .... (303) 844-7815
Areas Covered: Region VI (AR, LA, OK, NM. TX) and Region VIII (CO, MT, ND, SD, UT, WY) Fax: (303) 844-2943
999 18th Street, South Terrace, Suite 496, Denver, CO 80202-2466
E-mail: percy.devine@aoa.hhs.gov

Region 7 - Kansas City (MO)
601 East 12th Street, Kansas City, MO 64106

Regional Administrator **James "Jim" Varpness** .... (312) 938-9857
233 North Michigan Avenue, Fax: (312) 886-8536
Room 790, Chicago, IL 60601-5519
E-mail: jim.varpness@acl.hhs.gov

Region 8 - Denver (CO)
1961 Stout Street, Mail Room 08-148, Denver, CO 80294
Tel: (303) 844-2951 Fax: (303) 844-2943
Areas Covered: CO, MT, ND, SD, UT, WY

Regional Administrator **Percy Devine III** .... (303) 844-7815
Areas Covered: Region VI (AR, LA, OK, NM. TX) and Region VIII (CO, MT, ND, SD, UT, WY)
E-mail: percy.devine@aoa.hhs.gov

Region 9 - San Francisco (CA)
90 Seventh Street, Suite T-8100, San Francisco, CA 94103
Tel: (415) 437-8780 Fax: (415) 437-8782
Areas Covered: AS, AZ, CA, Commonwealth of the Northern Mariana Islands, GU, HI, NV

Regional Administrator **David A. Ishida** .... (415) 437-8780
E-mail: david.ishida@aoa.hhs.gov

Region 10 - Seattle (WA)
Blanchard Plaza, RX-33, 2201 Sixth Avenue, Suite 859, Seattle, WA 98121-1826
Tel: (206) 615-2298 Fax: (206) 615-2305
Areas Covered: AK, ID, OR, WA

Regional Administrator **David A. Ishida** .... (415) 437-8780
90 Seventh Street, Fax: (415) 437-8782
Suite T-8100, San Francisco, CA 94103
E-mail: david.ishida@aoa.hhs.gov

Centers for Disease Control and Prevention (CDC)

1600 Clifton Road, NE, Atlanta, GA 30333
Tel: (800) 232-4636 (General Information)
TTY: (888) 232-6348 (CDC Information - TTY)
Tel: (404) 639-3311 (Personnel Locator)
Tel: (888) 232-3299 (Auto Facsimile Service)
Fax: (404) 332-4565 (International Travelers Health Information)
Internet: www.cdc.gov Internet: www.flu.gov (Flu Information)

OFFICE OF THE DIRECTOR

1600 Clifton Road, NE, Atlanta, GA 30333
Fax: (404) 639-7111

National Institute for Occupational Safety and Health (NIOSH)

Patriots Plaza 1, 395 E Street, SW, Suite 9200, Washington, DC 20201
Fax: (202) 245-0664 Internet: www.cdc.gov/niosh

Appalachian Laboratories for Occupational Safety and Health

Health Effects Laboratory Division (HELD)
1095 Willowdale Road, Morgantown, WV 26505
Fax: (304) 285-6126

Director **Donald "Don" Beezhold PhD** .... (304) 285-5963
E-mail: don.beezhold@cdc.hhs.gov
Deputy Director **Robert Lanciotti** .... (304) 285-6279
E-mail: robert.lanciotti@cdc.hhs.gov
Chief, Allergy and Clinical Immunology Branch
John D. Noti .... (304) 285-6322
E-mail: ivr2@cdc.gov
Chief, Biostatistics and Epidemiology Branch
(Vacant) Room 4201 .... (800) 232-4636

★ Presidential Appointment Requiring Senate Confirmation ☆ Presidential Appointment ☐ Schedule C Appointment ◇ Career Senior Foreign Service Appointment
● Career Senior Executive Service (SES) Appointment ○ Non-Career Senior Executive Service (SES) Appointment ■ Postal Career Executive Service

Health Effects Laboratory Division *(continued)*

Chief, Engineering and Control Technology Branch
(Acting) **Robert Lanciotti** Room 2203 .... (304) 285-6279
E-mail: rkl6@cdc.gov
Chief, Exposure Assessment Branch
(Vacant) Room 3207 .... (800) 232-4636
Chief, Pathology and Physiological Research Branch
Jeffrey S. "Jeff" Fedan .... (304) 285-5766
E-mail: jsf2@cdc.gov
Chief, Toxicology and Molecular Biology Branch
Stephen H. "Steve" Reynolds Room 3012 .... (304) 285-5806

Respiratory Health Division (RHD)
1095 Willowdale Road, Morgantown, WV 26505
Fax: (304) 285-5861

Director **David N. Weissman MD** Room 2920 .... (304) 285-5749
E-mail: david.weissman@cdc.hhs.gov
Deputy Director
Douglas O. Johns MS, PhD Room 2919 .... (304) 285-6384
E-mail: wix7@cdc.gov
Chief, Field Studies Branch
Paul K. Henneberger Room 2817 .... (304) 285-6161
E-mail: paul.henneberger@cdc.hhs.gov
Chief, Surveillance Branch **Eileen Storey** .... (304) 285-6382
E-mail: eileen.storey@cdc.hhs.gov

Safety Research Division (SRD)
1095 Willowdale Road, Morgantown, WV 26505
Fax: (304) 285-6046

Director **Dawn N. Castillo MPH** Room 1920 .... (304) 285-5894
E-mail: dawn.castillo@cdc.hhs.gov
Deputy Director
Timothy J. "Tim" Pizatella Room 1919 .... (304) 285-6003
E-mail: timothy.pizatella@cdc.hhs.gov
Chief, Analysis and Field Evaluations Branch
CAPT James W. Collins USPHS, PhD Room 1815 .... (304) 285-5998
E-mail: james.collins@cdc.hhs.gov
Education: Georgia Tech BME; West Virginia MSME; Johns Hopkins PhD
Chief, Protective Technology Branch
Hongwei Hsiao PhD Room G815 .... (304) 285-5910
E-mail: hongwei.hsiao@cdc.hhs.gov
Chief, Surveillance and Field Investigations Branch
John R. Myers Room 1817 .... (304) 285-6005
E-mail: john.myers@cdc.hhs.gov Fax: (304) 285-5774

National Personal Protective Technology Laboratory (NPPTL)

626 Cochrans Mill Road, Pittsburgh, PA 15236
Fax: (412) 386-6111 Internet: www.cdc.gov/niosh/npptl

Director
Maryann M. D'Alessandro Building 20, Room 301 ... (412) 386-4033
E-mail: maryann.dalessandro@cdc.hhs.gov
Deputy Director **Jonathan V. "Jon" Szalajda** .... (412) 386-6627
E-mail: zfx1@cdc.gov
Chief, Confirming, Verification and Standards Development Branch **David C. Chirdon** .... (412) 386-6111
E-mail: yev8@cdc.gov
Chief, Evaluation and Test Branch **(Vacant)** .... (412) 386-6627
Chief, Technology Research Branch
Ronald E. "Ron" Shaffer Building 29, Room 100 ..... (412) 386-4001
E-mail: ronald.shaffer@cdc.hhs.gov Fax: (412) 386-6864
Associate Director for Science **Christopher C. Coffey** .... (304) 285-5958
1095 Willowdale Road, Morgantown, WV 26505 Fax: (304) 285-6321
E-mail: christopher.coffey@cdc.hhs.gov

Office of Mine Safety and Health Research (OMSHR)

626 Cochrans Mill Road, Pittsburgh, PA 15236
Tel: (412) 386-5302

Associate Director for Mining **Jessica Elzea Kogel** ...... (404) 498-2580
1600 Clifton Road, NE, Atlanta, GA 30333
E-mail: kqy7@cdc.gov
Education: UC Berkeley BS; Indiana MS, PhD

Office of Mine Safety and Health Research *(continued)*

Management and Program Analyst **Marie I. Chovanec** ... (412) 386-5302
E-mail: mchovanec@cdc.gov

Division of Mining Research Operations (DMRO)
626 Cochrans Mill Road, Pittsburgh, PA 15236
Fax: (412) 386-6614

Director
Rudy J. "R.J." Matetic Building 1, Room 200 .... (412) 386-6601
E-mail: rmatetic@cdc.gov
Secretary **Berni Metzger** .... (412) 386-4541
E-mail: metzger@cdc.gov
Deputy Director **Adam K. Smith** .... (412) 386-6028
E-mail: eyv7@cdc.gov
Chief of Staff **Jeffrey H. "Jeff" Welsh** .... (412) 386-4040
E-mail: jeffrey.welsh@cdc.hhs.gov
Chief, Disaster Fires and Explosions Branch
Gerrit R. Goodman Building 1, Room 215 .... (412) 386-4455
E-mail: gerrit.goodman@cdc.hhs.gov Fax: (412) 386-6595
Chief, Hearing Loss Prevention Branch
Patrick G. Dempsey Building 1, Room 21 .... (412) 386-6480
E-mail: pbd8@cdc.gov
Chief, Human Factors Branch
Dana Willmer Building 1, Room 201 .... (412) 386-6648
Chief, Dust Ventilation and Toxic Substance Branch
John Drew Potts Building 3, Room 317 .... (412) 386-4487
E-mail: jdu1@cdc.gov
Chief, Ground Control Branch (Acting)
Jack D. Trackemas .... (412) 386-6781
E-mail: xek6@cdc.gov
Chief, Health, Communication, Surveillance and Research Support Branch
Robert F. "Bob" Randolph .... (412) 386-4660
E-mail: rgr4@cdc.gov Fax: (412) 386-4865

Spokane Mining Research Division
Spokane Research Laboratory, 315 East Montgomery Avenue, Spokane, WA 99207
Tel: (509) 354-8005

Director **Todd M. Ruff MS, PE** .... (509) 354-8003
E-mail: truff2@cdc.gov
Secretary **Linda R. Burrow** .... (509) 354-8005
E-mail: lburrow@cdc.gov

Robert A. Taft Laboratories

1090 Tusculum Avenue, Cincinnati, OH 45226

Associate Director for Cincinnati Operations
Larry J. Elliott .... (513) 533-6891
E-mail: larry.elliott@cdc.hhs.gov
Associate Director for Financial Services
Martha A. DiMuzio .... (513) 533-6805
E-mail: mad2@cdc.gov

Applied Research and Technology Division (DART)
1090 Tusculum Avenue, Cincinnati, OH 45226
Fax: (513) 533-8510

Director (Interim) **Samuel E. Glover** .... (513) 533-6829
E-mail: seg3@cdc.gov Fax: (513) 533-6817
Deputy Director (Acting) **Ken Mead** .... (513) 841-4385
E-mail: kcm3@cdc.gov Fax: (513) 841-4506
Chief, Biomonitoring and Health Assessment Branch
(Vacant) .... (800) 232-4636
Chief, Chemical Exposure and Monitoring Branch
Robert P. "Bob" Streicher .... (513) 841-4296
E-mail: robert.streicher@cdc.hhs.gov Fax: (513) 458-7189
Chief, Engineering and Physical Hazards Branch
(Vacant) .... (513) 841-4378
Chief, Organizational Science and Human Factors Branch **Naomi Swanson** .... (513) 533-8165
E-mail: naomi.swanson@cdc.hhs.gov Fax: (513) 533-8596

DEPARTMENTS

★ Presidential Appointment Requiring Senate Confirmation ☆ Presidential Appointment □ Schedule C Appointment ◇ Career Senior Foreign Service Appointment
● Career Senior Executive Service (SES) Appointment ○ Non-Career Senior Executive Service (SES) Appointment ■ Postal Career Executive Service

DEPARTMENTS

Compensation Analysis and Support Division
1090 Tusculum Avenue, Cincinnati, OH 45226
Tel: (513) 533-6800 E-mail: dcas@cdc.gov

Director **Stuart L. Hinnefeld** .... (513) 533-6825
E-mail: stuart.hinnefeld@cdc.hhs.gov
Deputy Director **David S. "Dave" Sundin** .... (513) 533-6802
E-mail: david.sundin@cdc.hhs.gov

Education and Information Division (EID)
1090 Tusculum Avenue, Cincinnati, OH 45226
Fax: (513) 533-8588

Director **Paul A. Schulte** .... (513) 533-8302
E-mail: paul.schulte@cdc.hhs.gov
Deputy Director (Acting) **Sarah Unthanks** .... (513) 533-8147
E-mail: soh0@cdc.gov
Associate Director for Nanotechnology
Charles L. Geraci .... (513) 533-8339
E-mail: ciu9@cdc.gov
Chief, Document Development Branch
Thomas J. "T.J." Lentz .... (513) 533-8260
E-mail: thomas.lentz@cdc.hhs.gov
Chief, Information Resources Branch
Donna Van Bogaert .... (513) 533-6873
E-mail: ili4@cdc.gov
Chief, Risk Evaluation Branch
Christine W. Whittaker .... (513) 533-8439
E-mail: cts6@cdc.gov
Chief, Training Research and Evaluation Branch
(Vacant) .... (513) 533-8581

Surveillance, Hazard Evaluations and Field Studies Division (DSHEFS)
1150 Tusculum Avenue, Cincinnati, OH 45226
Fax: (513) 841-4483

Director **Teresa M. Schnorr** .... (513) 841-4428
E-mail: teresa.schnorr@cdc.hhs.gov
Deputy Director **(Vacant)** .... (800) 232-4636
5555 Ridge Avenue, Room 40A, Cincinnati, OH 45213
Chief, Hazard Evaluations and Technical Assistance Branch **Allison L. Tepper** .... (513) 841-4425
5555 Ridge Avenue, Room 220, Cincinnati, OH 45213
E-mail: allison.tepper@cdc.hhs.gov
Chief, Industry-Wide Studies Branch
Elizabeth Whelan .... (513) 841-4437
5555 Ridge Avenue, Room B10A, Cincinnati, OH 45213
E-mail: elizabeth.whelan@cdc.hhs.gov
Chief, Surveillance Branch **Marie Sweeney** .... (513) 841-4102
5555 Ridge Avenue, Room B416, Cincinnati, OH 45213
E-mail: marieharing.sweeney@cdc.hhs.gov

Western States Division
P.O. Box 25226, Denver, CO 80225
Tel: (509) 354-8066

Director **Ryan Hill** .... (509) 354-8064
E-mail: gii9@cdc.gov Fax: (303) 236-6072
Deputy Director **Kara R. Perritt MS** .... (509) 354-8066
E-mail: kip4@cdc.gov Fax: (304) 285-5774

Alaska Pacific Office
Grace Hall, 4230 University Drive, Suite 310, Anchorage, AK 99508
Tel: (907) 271-2382

Associate Director **Jennifer M. Lincoln** .... (509) 354-8065
E-mail: jxw7@cdc.gov

Deputy Director for Non-Infectious Diseases (DDNID)
1600 Clifton Road, NE, Atlanta, GA 30333

National Center for Environmental Health/Agency for Toxic Substances and Disease Registry (NCEH/ATSDR)
Centers for Disease Control, 1600 Clifton Road, NE,
Mail Stop F-61, Atlanta, GA 30333
Tel: (770) 488-0604 Fax: (770) 488-3385 Internet: www.cdc.gov/nceh
Note: The Agency for Toxic Substances and Disease Registry, while an operational division of the Department of Health and Human Services, is managed through a common Office of the Director with the National Center for Environmental Health of the Centers for Disease Control and Prevention.

Agency for Toxic Substances and Disease Registry Divisions (ATSDR)
Director **Eric J. Wortman** .... (202) 245-0616

Division of Community Health Investigations (DCHI)
4770 Buford Highway, NE, Mail Stop F59, Atlanta, GA 30341
Tel: (770) 488-0706 Fax: (770) 488-1544

Director (Acting) **Susan M. Moore** .... (770) 488-0706
E-mail: sym8@cdc.gov

Eastern Branch
Branch Chief **Sharon O. Williams-Fleetwood** .... (770) 488-0743

Region 1 - Boston (MA)
One Congress Street, Suite 1100, Boston, MA 02114-2023
Tel: (617) 918-1495 Fax: (617) 918-1494
Areas Covered: Connecticut, Maine, Massachusetts, New Hampshire, Rhode Island, and Vermont

Regional Director
CDR Tarah Somers USPHS, MPH, RN .... (617) 918-1493
Regional Representative **CAPT Gary D. Perlman MPH, CPO, RS, EMT, DAAS** .... (617) 918-1492
Education: Yale 1990 MPH
Health Physicist **Michael D. Brooks** .... (617) 918-1490
E-mail: mdb7@cdc.gov
Administrative Support/SEEP **(Vacant)** .... (617) 918-1495

Region 2 - New York, NY
290 Broadway, North, New York, NY 10007
Building 209, 2890 Woodbridge Avenue, Edison, NJ 08837 (Edison, NJ Office)
Tel: (212) 637-4305 Tel: (732) 906-6931 (Edison, NJ Office)
Fax: (212) 673-3253 Fax: (732) 321-4365 (Edison, NJ Office)
Areas Covered: New Jersey, New York, The Commonwealth of Puerto Rico, and the United States Virgin Islands

Regional Director **(Vacant)** 20th Floor .... (212) 637-4306
Regional Representative and Environmental Health Scientist **LCDR Elena Vaouli USPHS** 20th Floor ...... (732) 321-4465
Environmental Health Scientist (Toxicologist)
Luis Rivera-Gonzalez PhD .... (732) 906-6933
Administrative Assistant
Antoinette "Micki" Jones 20th Floor .... (212) 637-4305
E-mail: amj3@cdc.gov

Region 3 - Philadelphia (PA)
1650 Arch Street, Philadelphia, PA 19103-2029
Tel: (215) 814-3140 Fax: (215) 814-3033
Areas Covered: Delaware, District of Columbia, Maryland, Pennsylvania, Virginia, and West Virginia

Regional Director **Lora Werner** .... (215) 814-3141
Regional Representative and Environmental Health Scientist **(Vacant)** .... (215) 814-3139
Regional Representative and Senior Toxicologist
Karl Markiewicz PhD .... (215) 814-3149
Regional Representative and Toxicologist
Christine E. Lloyd MPH .... (215) 814-3142
Environmental Health Scientist **Ana E. Pomales** .... (215) 814-5716

★ Presidential Appointment Requiring Senate Confirmation ☆ Presidential Appointment □ Schedule C Appointment ◇ Career Senior Foreign Service Appointment
● Career Senior Executive Service (SES) Appointment ○ Non-Career Senior Executive Service (SES) Appointment ■ Postal Career Executive Service

Region 3 - Philadelphia (PA) *(continued)*

Administrative Support/SEEP **Patricia "Pat" Giles** . . . . . . (215) 814-3141
E-mail: kvt9@cdc.gov

Central Branch
Branch Chief **Richard "Rick" Gillig** Mail Stop F-58 . . . . . (770) 488-3723
Education: Georgia Tech 1987 MCR

Region 4 - Atlanta (GA)
Atlanta Federal Center, 61 Forsyth Street SW,
Room 7T90, Atlanta, GA 30303
Tel: (404) 562-1788 Fax: (404) 562-1790
Areas Covered: Alabama, Florida, Georgia, Kentucky, Mississippi, North Carolina, South Carolina, and Tennessee

Regional Director **John Wheeler** . . . . (404) 562-1782
Regional Representative and Health Scientist
Leann Bing . . . . (404) 562-1784
Regional Representative and Public Health Advisor
Carl B. Blair . . . . (404) 562-1786
Health Educator **Sue Casteel** . . . . (404) 562-0637
E-mail: aov2@cdc.gov

Region 5 - Chicago (IL)
77 West Jackson Boulevard, Room 413, Mail Stop: ATSD-4J,
Chicago, IL 60604
Tel: (312) 886-0840 Fax: (312) 886-6066
Areas Covered: Illinois, Indiana, Michigan, Minnesota, Ohio and Wisconsin

Regional Director **Mark D. Johnson PhD** . . . . (312) 353-3436
Regional Representative and Research Officer
CAPT Michelle Colledge USPHS . . . . (312) 886-1462
Brownfields Coordinator **Laurel A. Berman** . . . . (312) 886-7476
Chief Medical Officer
Michelle T. Watters MD, MPH, PhD . . . . (312) 353-2979
Secretary **Peggy S. Graham** . . . . (312) 886-0480
E-mail: psg1@cdc.gov

Region 6 - Dallas (TX)
1445 Ross Avenue, Dallas, TX 75202
Tel: (214) 665-8361 Fax: (214) 665-2237
Areas Covered: Arkansas, Louisiana, New Mexico, Oklahoma, and Texas

Regional Director **George L. Pettigrew** . . . . (214) 665-8361
Regional Representative **Jennifer L. Lyke** . . . . (214) 665-8362
Regional Representative
James "Patrick" Young USPHS . . . . (214) 665-8562

Western Branch
Branch Chief (Acting) **Alan W. Yarbrough** . . . . (770) 488-3655

Region 7 - Kansas City (MO)
Robert J. Dole Federal Courthouse, 500 State Avenue,
Suite 182, Kansas City, KS 66101
Fax: (913) 551-1315
Areas Covered: Iowa, Kansas, Missouri, and Nebraska

Regional Director **E. Spencer Williams** . . . . (913) 551-1310
Regional Representative **Erin J. Evans** . . . . (913) 551-1311
Regional Representative and Environmental Health
Scientist **Cory Kokko** . . . . (913) 551-1312

Region 8 - Denver (CO)
999 18th Street, Suite 300, Denver, CO 80202-2466
Tel: (303) 312-7010 Fax: (303) 312-7018
Areas Covered: Colorado, Montana, North Dakota, South Dakota, Utah, and Wyoming

Regional Director **Dan C. Strausbaugh** . . . . (303) 312-7010
Environmental Health Scientist **David Dorian** . . . . (303) 312-7011
Environmental Health Scientist **Chris Maniglier-Poulet** . . . (303) 312-7013
Toxicologist and Health Assessor **Scott Sudweeks** . . . . . . (303) 312-6580
E-mail: zdg1@cdc.gov
Administrative Support/SEEP **Shirley McDaniel** . . . . (303) 312-7012
E-mail: whv4@cdc.gov

Montana Office
10 West 15th Street, Suite 3200, Helena, MT 59626
Tel: (406) 457-5007 Fax: (406) 457-5055
Regional Representative **Dan C. Strausbaugh** . . . . (406) 457-5007

Region 9 - San Francisco (CA)
75 Hawthorne Street, Suite 100, Mail Stop: HHS-1,
San Francisco, CA 94105-3901
Tel: (415) 947-4318 Tel: (415) 947-4323
Areas Covered: Arizona, California, Hawaii, Nevada, the Pacific Islands and Tribal Nations

Regional Director (Acting) **Libby Vianu** . . . . (415) 947-4319
Health Educator **Jamie Rayman** . . . . (415) 947-4318
Regional Representative and Environmental Health
Scientist **Libby Vianu** . . . . (415) 947-4319
Regional Representative **Benjamin Gerhardstein** . . . . (415) 947-4316

Region 10 - Seattle (WA)
1200 Sixth Avenue, Suite 1910, Seattle, WA 98101
Tel: (206) 553-1049 Fax: (206) 553-2142
Areas Covered: Alaska, Idaho, Oregon, and Washington

Regional Director **Rhonda S. Kaetzel PhD** . . . . (206) 553-0530
Environmental Health Scientist and Health Assessor
Debra Gable . . . . (206) 553-1796
Environmental Health Scientist and Medical Officer
Dr. Arthur Wendel MD, MPH . . . . (206) 553-0454
Environmental Health Scientist and Regional
Representative **Joseph M. "Joe" Sarcone** . . . . (907) 271-4073
Alaska Office, 222 West Eighth Avenue,
Room 261, Anchorage, AK 99513

Washington DC Office
William Jefferson Clinton Federal Building,
1200 Pennsylvania Avenue, NW, Mail Code 5203-P,
Washington, DC 20460
Mail: 2777 South Crystal Drive, 5th Floor, Arlington, VA 22202
Tel: (703) 603-8765 Fax: (703) 603-8987 (Crystal Gateway)
Fax: (202) 260-6606 (Waterside Mall)

Regional Director and EPA Liaison
Steven Jones . . . . (703) 603-8729 (Crystal Gateway)
Regional Representative and Environmental Health
Scientist **Deborah Burgin** . . . . (703) 603-8813
Regional Representative and Environmental Health
Scientist **Dana Williams** . . . . (703) 603-0723
Administrative Support/SEEP **Cory Bautista** . . . . (703) 603-8765
E-mail: zzr4@cdc.gov

Centers for Medicare and Medicaid Services (CMS)

7500 Security Boulevard, Baltimore, MD 21244-1850
Tel: (410) 786-3000 Tel: (800) 638-6833 (Medicare Hotline)
Internet: www.cms.gov

OFFICE OF THE ADMINISTRATOR

200 Independence Avenue, SW, Washington, DC 20201
Tel: (202) 690-6726 Fax: (202) 690-6262

Operations

7500 Security Boulevard, Baltimore, MD 21244-1850
Tel: (410) 786-3151

● Chief Operating Officer **(Vacant)** . . . . (202) 260-6131
Deputy Chief Operating Officer **Karen E. Jackson** . . . . . . (410) 786-0079
Education: Michigan MPP

★ Presidential Appointment Requiring Senate Confirmation ☆ Presidential Appointment ☐ Schedule C Appointment ◇ Career Senior Foreign Service Appointment
● Career Senior Executive Service (SES) Appointment ○ Non-Career Senior Executive Service (SES) Appointment ■ Postal Career Executive Service

Regional Offices

Region 1 - Boston (MA)

John F. Kennedy Federal Building, Government Center,
Room 2325, Boston, MA 02203
Fax: (617) 565-1339
Areas Covered: CT, ME, MA, NH, RI, VT

● Regional Administrator **Raymond Hurd** . . . . . (617) 565-1188
E-mail: raymond.hurd@cms.hhs.gov
Executive Secretary **Nycole Tramble** . . . . . (617) 565-1188
E-mail: nycole.tramble@cms.hhs.gov
Deputy Regional Administrator **Barbara Manning** . . . . . (617) 565-1182
E-mail: barbara.manning@cms.hhs.gov
Chief Medical Officer **(Vacant)** . . . . . (617) 565-1319

Division of Survey and Certification

J.F. Kennedy Federal Building, Boston, MA 02203
Fax: (617) 565-4835

Associate Regional Administrator (Acting)
Lauren Reinertsen . . . . . (202) 616-2443
E-mail: lauren.reinertsen@cms.hhs.gov Fax: (443) 380-5176
Branch Manager **Hyosim Seon-Spada** John F. Kennedy Federal Building, Government Center, Room 2275 . . . . . (617) 565-9160
E-mail: hyosim.seon-spada@cms.hhs.gov
Branch Manager **Daniel M. Kristola** John F. Kennedy Federal Building, Government Center, Room 2275 . . . . . (617) 565-4487

Division of Financial Management and Fee for Service Operations

John F. Kennedy Federal Building, Government Center,
Room 2375, Boston, MA 02203
Tel: (617) 565-1233 Fax: (617) 565-3856

Associate Regional Administrator
Barbara "Barb" Veno . . . . . (617) 565-1331
E-mail: barbara.veno@cms.hhs.gov
Financial Management Chief **Wendell C. Cosgrove** . . . . . (617) 565-1292
Medicare Operations Branch Chief **Susan P. Kossler** . . . . . (617) 565-1275

Division of Medicaid and Children's Health Operations

John F. Kennedy Federal Building, Government Center,
Room 2275, Boston, MA 02203
Tel: (617) 565-1230 Fax: (617) 565-1083

Associate Regional Administrator **Richard R. McGreal** . . . (617) 565-1226
E-mail: richard.mcgreal@cms.hhs.gov
Medicaid Financial Management Branch Chief
Robert J. Parris . . . . . (617) 565-1242
E-mail: robert.parris@cms.hhs.gov
Medicaid Program Branch Chief **Stephen C. Mills** . . . . . (617) 565-1281
E-mail: stephen.mills@cms.hhs.gov

Division of Medicare Health Plans Operations

John F. Kennedy Federal Building, Government Center,
Room 2375, Boston, MA 02203
Tel: (617) 565-1232 Fax: (617) 565-3856

Associate Regional Administrator
Douglas J. Edwards . . . . . (617) 565-1321
E-mail: douglas.edwards1@cms.hhs.gov
Customer Relations Branch Chief **Ashley Hashem** . . . . . (617) 565-1234
Medicare Advantage Health Plans Branch Chief
Adele H. Pietrantoni . . . . . (617) 565-1266
E-mail: adele.pietrantoni@cms.hhs.gov

Division of Quality Improvement

John F. Kennedy Federal Building, Government Center,
Room 2350, Boston, MA 02203
Tel: (617) 565-1323 Fax: (617) 565-4835

Associate Regional Administrator
Annette E. Kussmaul . . . . . (617) 565-1323
E-mail: annette.kussmaul@cms.hhs.gov

Region 2 - New York (NY)

26 Federal Plaza, Room 3811, New York, NY 10278
Tel: (212) 616-2222
Areas Covered: NJ, NY, PR, VI

● Regional Administrator **Raymond Hurd** . . . . . (617) 565-1182
John F. Kennedy Government Building,
Government Center, Boston, MA 02203
E-mail: raymond.hurd@cms.hhs.gov
● Consortium Administrator **James T. Kerr** . . . . . (212) 616-2205
E-mail: james.kerr@cms.hhs.gov
Education: Rensselaer Poly BSME, MS; Mount Sinai Medicine MBA
Special Assistant **Tammee Young** . . . . . (212) 616-2423
E-mail: tammee.young@cms.hhs.gov
Deputy Regional Administrator **Gilbert Kunken** . . . . . (212) 616-2205
E-mail: gilbert.kunken@cms.hhs.gov
Executive Officer **Tanya L. Carolina** . . . . . (212) 616-2318
E-mail: tanya.carolina@cms.hhs.gov
Chief Medical Officer **Nilsa Gutierrez** . . . . . (212) 616-2212
Puerto Rico Field Office Director **Marina Diaz** . . . . . (787) 294-1681
E-mail: marina.diaz@cms.gov

Division of Medicaid and Children's Health Operations

26 Federal Plaza, New York, NY 10278
Tel: (212) 616-2400 Fax: (443) 380-8892

Associate Regional Administrator **Michael Melendez** . . . . (212) 616-2430
E-mail: michael.melendez@cms.hhs.gov
Medicaid Management Branch Manager
Ricardo Holligan . . . . . (212) 616-2424
E-mail: ricardo.holligan@cms.hhs.gov
Medicaid Program Services Branch Manager
Nicole M. McKnight . . . . . (212) 616-2429
E-mail: Nicole.McKnight@cms.hhs.gov Fax: (443) 380-5155

Division of Financial Management and Fee for Service Operations

26 Federal Plaza, New York, NY 10278
Tel: (212) 616-2500 Fax: (443) 380-8922

Associate Regional Administrator **Victoria Abril** . . . . . (212) 616-2505
Financial Control Branch Manager
George Fantaousakis . . . . . (212) 616-2546
E-mail: george.fantaousakis@cms.hhs.gov
Program Integrity Branch Manager **Denise Molloy** . . . . . (212) 616-2524
E-mail: denise.molloy@cms.hhs.gov

Division of Medicare Health Plans Operations

26 Federal Plaza, New York, NY 10278
Tel: (212) 616-2300 Fax: (443) 380-8882

Associate Regional Administrator **Heather Lang** . . . . . (212) 616-2358
Customer Relations Branch Manager **Nancy Ng** . . . . . (212) 616-2323
Health Plans Branch Manager **Michael Regusters** . . . . . (212) 616-2332
E-mail: michael.regusters@cms.hhs.gov
Medicare Advantage Branch Manager
Rachel D. Walker . . . . . (212) 616-2353

Division of Survey and Certification

Associate Regional Administrator
J. William Roberson . . . . . (617) 565-1327
John F. Kennedy Government Building,
Government Center, Boston, MA 02203
Certification and Enforcement Branch Manager
Lauren Reinertsen . . . . . (212) 616-2443
E-mail: lauren.reinertsen@cms.hhs.gov
Survey Branch Manager **Nancy L. Miller** . . . . . (212) 616-2442
E-mail: nancy.miller@cms.hhs.gov Fax: (443) 380-5116

Region 3 - Philadelphia (PA)

The Public Ledger Building, 150 South Independence Mall West,
Suite 216, Philadelphia, PA 19106-3499
Tel: (215) 861-4140 Fax: (215) 861-4240
Areas Covered: DE, DC, MD, PA, VA, WV

● Regional Administrator **Nancy Bolton O'Connor** . . . . . (215) 861-4140
E-mail: nancy.oconnor@cms.hhs.gov
Deputy Regional Administrator **Roseanne Buccine** . . . . . (215) 861-4140

★ Presidential Appointment Requiring Senate Confirmation ☆ Presidential Appointment ☐ Schedule C Appointment ◇ Career Senior Foreign Service Appointment
● Career Senior Executive Service (SES) Appointment ○ Non-Career Senior Executive Service (SES) Appointment ■ Postal Career Executive Service

Region 3 - Philadelphia (PA) *(continued)*

Special Assistant **Sharon Graham** . . . . (215) 861-4304
Executive Officer **Anne Nelson** . . . . (215) 861-4748

Division of Medicaid and Children's Health Operations
150 South Independence Mall West, Philadelphia, PA 19106-3499
Tel: (215) 861-4155 Fax: (215) 861-4280

Associate Regional Administrator **Francis McCullough** . . . . (215) 861-4157
Financial Review Branch Manager **(Vacant)** . . . . (215) 861-4155
Program Oversight Branch Manager **Sabrina Tillman-Boyd** . . . . (215) 861-4721

Division of Management and Financial Operations
150 South Independence Mall West, Philadelphia, PA 19106-3499
Tel: (215) 861-4262 Fax: (215) 861-4254

Associate Regional Administrator **Charlotte Foster** . . . . . . (215) 861-4219

Division of Medicare Health Plans Operations
150 South Independence Mall West, Philadelphia, PA 19106-3499
Fax: (215) 861-4176

Associate Regional Administrator **(Vacant)** . . . . (215) 861-4140
Health Plans Branch North West Manager **Tamara M. "Tammy" McCloy** . . . . (215) 861-4220
Beneficiary Services Southeast Manager **(Vacant)** . . . . (215) 861-4152
Medicare Branch Chief **(Vacant)** . . . . (215) 861-4762

Northeast Consortium Division of Survey and Certification
150 South Independence Mall West, Philadelphia, PA 19106-3499
Fax: (215) 861-4146

Associate Administrator **(Vacant)** . . . . (215) 861-4140
John F. Kennedy Government Building, Government Center, Boston, MA 02203
Consortium Survey and Certification Operations Manager **(Vacant)** . . . . (215) 861-4313
Certification and Enforcement Branch 3 Manager **(Vacant)** . . . . (215) 861-4311
Survey Branch 3 Manager **Michele D. Clinton** . . . . (215) 861-4320

Region 4 - Atlanta (GA)
Atlanta Federal Center, 61 Forsyth Street, Suite 4T20, Atlanta, GA 30303-8909
Tel: (404) 562-7150 Fax: (404) 562-7162
Areas Covered: AL, NC, SC, FL, GA, KY, MS, TN

● Regional Administrator for Dallas/Atlanta **Angela M. Brice Smith** . . . . (214) 767-6425
1301 Young Street, Dallas, TX 75202
E-mail: angela.brice-smith@cms.hhs.gov
Deputy Regional Administrator **Gilbert "Gil" Silva** . . . . . . (404) 562-7154
E-mail: gil.silva@cms.hhs.gov
Executive Assistant **Joyce A. Jones** . . . . (404) 562-7168
E-mail: joyce.jones@cms.hhs.gov
Media Affairs Officer **April M. Washington** . . . . (404) 562-7903
1301 Young Street, Dallas, TX 75202
E-mail: april.washington@hhs.gov
Special Assistant **(Vacant)** . . . . (404) 562-7150

Division of Financial Management and Fee for Service Operations
61 Forsyth Street, SW, Atlanta, GA 30303-8909
Tel: (404) 562-7300 (Beneficiaries A and B) Fax: (404) 562-7350

Associate Regional Administrator **Kristen Dixon** . . . . (404) 562-7368
1301 Young Street, Dallas, TX 75202 Fax: (443) 380-5941
Medicare Financial Management Branch Chief **Cherie F. Weatherington** . . . . (404) 562-7319
Program Integrity Branch Chief (Acting) **Cherie F. Weatherington** . . . . (404) 562-7319
Health Services Specialist **(Vacant)** . . . . (404) 562-7300

Division of Medicaid Health Plans Operations
61 Forsyth Street, SW, Atlanta, GA 30303-8909
Tel: (404) 562-7500 (Beneficiaries C and D) Fax: (404) 562-7386

Associate Regional Administrator **Jackie L. Glaze** . . . . (404) 562-7417
Medicare Health Plans Operations Branch Chief **Melanie Johnson** . . . . (404) 562-0151
Senior Policy Specialist **Colleen Carpenter** . . . . (404) 562-7242
Special Assistant **Alexander Bates** . . . . (404) 562-7250

Division of Medicaid and Children's Health Operations
61 Forsyth Street, SW, Atlanta, GA 30303-8909
Tel: (404) 562-7400 Fax: (404) 562-7482

Associate Regional Administrator **Jackie L. Glaze** . . . . (404) 562-7417
E-mail: jackie.glaze@cms.hhs.gov
Professional Health Advocacy and Analysis Branch Manager **Joyce Wilkerson** . . . . (404) 562-7426

Division of Survey and Certification Operations
Associate Regional Administrator for Survey and Certification (Acting) **Linda Smith** . . . . (404) 562-7150
Long-Term Care Certification and Enforcement Branch Manager **Stephanie M. Davis** . . . . (404) 562-7471
Non-Long-Term Care Certification and Enforcement Branch Manager **Hulio Griffin** . . . . (404) 562-7320
Survey and Certification Review Branch Manager **(Vacant)** . . . . (404) 562-7467
Survey and Certification Technical Advisor **Larry Clemonts** . . . . (404) 562-7433
Secretary **(Vacant)** . . . . (404) 562-7150

Region 5 - Chicago (IL)
233 North Michigan Avenue, Suite 600, Chicago, IL 60601-5519
Tel: (312) 886-6432 Fax: (312) 353-0252
Areas Covered: IL, IN, MI, MN, OH, WI

● Consortium Administrator (Acting) **Verlon Johnson** . . . . . (312) 886-5343
E-mail: verlon.johnson@cms.hhs.gov
Executive Secretary **Charlamia "Charla" Jordan** . . . . . . (312) 353-1753
E-mail: charlamia.jordan@cms.hhs.gov
Deputy Regional Administrator **(Vacant)** . . . . (312) 886-6432
Medical Officer **Robert Furno** . . . . (312) 353-1350
Information Technology Specialist **Karlos S. Dodson** . . . . (312) 353-2889
E-mail: karlos.dodson@cms.hhs.gov

Division of Medicaid and Children's Health Operations
233 North Michigan Avenue, Chicago, IL 60601-5519
Tel: (312) 353-8050 Fax: (312) 353-3866

Associate Regional Administrator **Verlon Johnson** . . . . . . (312) 886-5343
E-mail: verlon.johnson@cms.hhs.gov
Illinois/Indiana/Ohio Financial Management Manager **Todd McMillion** . . . . (312) 353-9860
E-mail: todd.mcmillion@cms.hhs.gov
Illinois/Indiana/Ohio Operations Branch Manager **Tannisse L. Joyce** . . . . (312) 886-5121
E-mail: Tannisse.Joyce@cms.hhs.gov Fax: (443) 380-6695
Michigan/Minnesota/Wisconsin Financial Management Manager **Celestine J. Curry** . . . . (312) 353-2869
E-mail: celestine.curry@cms.hhs.gov
Michigan/Minnesota/Wisconsin Operations Branch Manager **Mara Siler-Price** . . . . (312) 886-5353
E-mail: mara.siler-price@cms.hhs.gov
Management Analyst **Shantell L. Franklin** . . . . (312) 353-8050
E-mail: shantell.franklin@cms.hhs.gov

Division of Medicare Financial Management and Fee for Service Operations
233 North Michigan Avenue, Chicago, IL 60601-5519
Tel: (312) 353-9841 Fax: (312) 353-9474

Associate Regional Administrator **Jorge Nevarez** . . . . (312) 886-2749
Fax: (443) 380-5038
Medicare Financial Management Branch Manager **Gloria Walker** . . . . (312) 353-9857
E-mail: gloria.walker@cms.hhs.gov

(continued on next page)

★ Presidential Appointment Requiring Senate Confirmation ☆ Presidential Appointment ☐ Schedule C Appointment ◇ Career Senior Foreign Service Appointment
● Career Senior Executive Service (SES) Appointment ○ Non-Career Senior Executive Service (SES) Appointment ■ Postal Career Executive Service

Division of Medicare Financial Management and Fee for Service Operations *(continued)*

Medicare Operations Branch Manager
Kristine Scherbring ..... (312) 353-3756
E-mail: Kristine.Scherbring@cms.hhs.gov Fax: (443) 380-7146
Management Analyst **Bertha A. Lopez-Rivera** ..... (312) 353-9841
E-mail: bertha.lopez@cms.hhs.gov

Division of Medicare Health Plans Operations

233 North Michigan Avenue, Chicago, IL 60601-5519
Tel: (312) 353-8056 Fax: (312) 353-5927

Associate Regional Administrator
Raymond "Ray" Swisher ..... (312) 353-3620
E-mail: Raymond.Swisher@cms.hhs.gov Fax: (443) 380-6740
Customer Relations Branch Manager **Lisa Riley** ..... (312) 353-1708
Health Plans Branch Manager **Dolores Perteet** ..... (312) 353-9864
Education: Yale 1978 MSN, 1979 MPH
Medicare Advantage Branch Manager **(Vacant)** ..... (312) 353-8056
Management Analyst **Brenita Betts** ..... (312) 353-8056

Midwestern Consortium Division of Survey and Certification

233 North Michigan Avenue, Chicago, IL 60601-5519
Tel: (312) 886-9599 Fax: (312) 886-2303

Consortium Survey and Certification Officer
Nadine F. Renbarger ..... (312) 886-0783
Consortium Survey and Certification Operations Manager **(Vacant)** ..... (312) 886-5344
Survey Branch 1 Manager **Stephen Pelinski** ..... (312) 886-5215
E-mail: stephen.pelinski@cms.hhs.gov
Survey Branch 2 Manager **Christine Vause** ..... (312) 353-9613
E-mail: christine.vause@cms.hhs.gov
Non Long-Term Care Branch Manager
Pam L. Thomas ..... (312) 886-5561
E-mail: pam.thomas@cms.hhs.gov
Long-Term Care Branch Manager **Gregg Brandush** ..... (312) 353-1567
E-mail: gregg.brandush@cms.hhs.gov
Survey and Certification Coordination Manager
Marilyn Hirsch ..... (312) 353-1798
Technical Advisor **Elizabeth Honiotes** ..... (312) 353-1588

Region 6 - Dallas (TX)

1301 Young Street, Suite 714, Dallas, TX 75202
Tel: (214) 767-6423 ext. 6 E-mail: rodalora@cms.hhs.gov
Areas Covered: AR, LA, NM, OK, TX

Regional Administrator for Dallas/Atlanta
(Vacant) ..... (214) 767-6423 ext. 6
Deputy Regional Administrator **Lisa M. McAdams** ..... (214) 767-6427
E-mail: lisa.mcadams@cms.hhs.gov Fax: (443) 380-6497
● Consortium Administrator **Renard L. Murray** ..... (404) 562-7150
61 Forsyth Street, SW, Suite 4T20, Atlanta, GA 30303-8909
E-mail: renard.murray@cms.hhs.gov
Education: Xavier (LA) 1984 BS

Division of Medicaid and Children's Health Operations

1301 Young Street, Dallas, TX 75202
Fax: (443) 380-8896 E-mail: rodalmso@cms.hhs.gov

Associate Regional Administrator **Bill Brooks** ..... (214) 767-6495
E-mail: bill.brooks@cms.hhs.gov
Financial and Program Operations Branch Chief
Dorothy Ferguson ..... (214) 767-6495
Medicaid/SCHIP Policy Branch Chief **Billy Bob Farrell** ... (214) 767-6495

Division of Medicare Financial Management and Fee for Service Operations

1301 Young Street, Dallas, TX 75202
Fax: (443) 380-8926 E-mail: rodalfm@cms.hhs.gov

Associate Regional Administrator **Charna R. Pettaway** ... (214) 767-0250
E-mail: charna.pettaway@cms.hhs.gov
Medicare Fee for Service Branch Chief
Bobbie Sullivan ..... (214) 767-6422
Medicare Financial Management Branch Chief
Lindsey R. Kittrell ..... (214) 767-6416
Fax: (443) 380-6518

Division of Medicare Health Plan Operations

1301 Young Street, Suite 827, Dallas, TX 75202
E-mail: rodalbs@cms.hhs.gov

Associate Regional Administrator **Arthur W. Pagan** ..... (214) 767-4471
Customer Relations Branch Chief **Michael K. Moore** ..... (214) 767-6390
E-mail: michael.moore@cms.hhs.gov Fax: (443) 380-7118
Medicare Advantage and Health Plans Branch Chief
April Forsythe ..... (214) 767-6487
E-mail: april.forsythe@cms.hhs.gov Fax: (443) 380-7129

Division of Quality Improvement

1301 Young Street, Dallas, TX 75202
Fax: (443) 380-8867

Associate Regional Administrator **Shalon C. Quinn** ..... (214) 767-4441
E-mail: Shalon.Quinn@cms.hhs.gov Fax: (443) 380-6391

Division of Survey and Certification

1301 Young Street, Dallas, TX 75202
Fax: (443) 380-8869 E-mail: rodalmso@cms.hhs.gov

Associate Regional Administrator **Gerardo Ortiz** ..... (214) 767-6341
E-mail: gerardo.ortiz@cms.hhs.gov Fax: (443) 380-6409
Long Term Care Certification and Enforcement Branch Chief **Karen J. Hillman** ..... (214) 767-2091
Fax: (443) 380-5482
Non-Long Term Care Certification and Enforcement Branch Chief **Shannon Hills-Cline** ..... (214) 767-4400
Survey Branch Chief **(Vacant)** ..... (214) 767-6423 ext. 6

Region 7 - Kansas City (MO)

Richard Bolling Federal Building, 601 East 12th Street, Room 355, Kansas City, MO 64106
Tel: (816) 426-5233 Fax: (816) 426-3548
Areas Covered: IA, KS, MO, NE

● Consortium Administrator (Acting)
Gregory R. "Greg" Dill ..... (415) 744-3505
E-mail: gregory.dill@cms.hhs.gov
Special Assistant **Nancy L. Schmidt** ..... (816) 426-6519
E-mail: nancy.schmidt@cms.hhs.gov
Deputy Regional Administrator **Neil Thowe** ..... (816) 426-5233
Executive Officer **Kevin Nathan** ..... (816) 426-6335
E-mail: kevin.nathan@cms.hhs.gov

Division of Medicaid and Children's Health Operations

Richard Bolling Federal Building, 601 East 12th Street, Room 322, Kansas City, MO 64106
Tel: (816) 426-5925 Fax: (816) 426-3727

Associate Regional Administrator **James G. Scott** ..... (816) 426-5925
E-mail: james.scott1@cms.hhs.gov
Financial Management and Systems Branch Chief
Leticia Barraza ..... (816) 426-6424
E-mail: leticia.barraza@cms.hhs.gov
Program Services Branch Chief **Megan Buck** ..... (816) 426-6314
E-mail: megan.buck@cms.hhs.gov

Division of Financial Management and Fee For Service Operations

Richard Bolling Federal Building, 601 East 12th Street, Room 312, Kansas City, MO 64106
Tel: (816) 426-5033 Fax: (816) 426-3760

Associate Regional Administrator **John Hannigan** ..... (303) 844-5738
1961 Stout Street, Denver, CO 80294
E-mail: john.hannigan@cms.hhs.gov

Division of Medicare Health Plans Operations

Richard Bolling Federal Building, 601 East 12th Street, Room 235, Kansas City, MO 64106
Tel: (816) 426-6534 Fax: (816) 426-7604

Associate Regional Administrator **Judith A. Flynn** ..... (816) 426-6534
E-mail: judith.flynn@cms.hhs.gov
Customer Relations Branch Manager **Amy Flynn** ..... (816) 426-6475

★ Presidential Appointment Requiring Senate Confirmation ☆ Presidential Appointment □ Schedule C Appointment ◇ Career Senior Foreign Service Appointment
● Career Senior Executive Service (SES) Appointment ○ Non-Career Senior Executive Service (SES) Appointment ■ Postal Career Executive Service

Division of Medicare Health Plans Operations *(continued)*

Medicare Advantage and Health Plans Branch Manager
Dale A. Ferguson .... (816) 426-6530
E-mail: dale.ferguson@cms.hhs.gov

Division of Quality Improvement
Richard Bolling Federal Building, 601 East 12th Street, Room 301, Kansas City, MO 64106
Tel: (816) 426-5746 Fax: (816) 426-5525

Associate Regional Administrator **Trevor Stone** .... (816) 426-6377
E-mail: trevor.stone@cms.hhs.gov

Division of Survey and Certification
Richard Bolling Federal Building, 601 East 12th Street, Room 301, Kansas City, MO 64106
Tel: (816) 426-2011 Fax: (816) 426-6769

Survey and Certification Branch LTC Chief
Darla McCloskey .... (816) 426-6557
E-mail: darla.mccloskey@cms.hhs.gov
Survey and Certification Branch NLTC Chief
Victoria F. Vachon .... (816) 426-6354
E-mail: victoria.vachon@cms.hhs.gov

Region 8 - Denver (CO)
1600 Broadway, Suite 700, Denver, CO 80202
Tel: (303) 844-2111 Fax: (303) 844-6374
Areas Covered: CO, MT, ND, SD, UT, WY

● Regional Administrator **Jeffrey Y. "Jeff" Hinson** .... (303) 844-7055
E-mail: jeffrey.hinson@cms.hhs.gov
Deputy Regional Administrator **Diane L. Moll** .... (303) 844-7057
E-mail: diane.moll@cms.hhs.gov Fax: (443) 380-5490
Special Assistant **(Vacant)** .... (303) 844-2111
Executive Officer **Susan Augustin** .... (303) 844-7118
E-mail: susan.augustin@cms.hhs.gov Fax: (443) 380-5222

Division of Medicaid and Children's Health Operations
1600 Broadway, Denver, CO 80202
Tel: (303) 844-2111 Fax: (303) 844-3753

Associate Regional Administrator **Richard C. Allen** ...... (303) 844-1370
E-mail: richard.allen@cms.hhs.gov
Financial Management Branch Chief **Trinia J. Hunt** ...... (303) 844-7066
E-mail: trinia.hunt@cms.hhs.gov
State Programs Branch Chief **(Vacant)** .... (303) 844-2111
Survey Branch Chief **(Vacant)** .... (303) 844-4723
Certification Branch Manager **(Vacant)** .... (303) 844-2111

Division of Medicare Operations
1600 Broadway, Denver, CO 80202
Tel: (303) 844-2111 Fax: (303) 844-3753

Associate Regional Administrator **(Vacant)** .... (303) 844-2111
Customer Relations Branch Chief **Karen J. Hill** .... (303) 844-7906
Medicare Administration Branch Chief **Anne M. Kane** ... (303) 844-7122
E-mail: anne.kane@cms.hhs.gov
Medicare Financial Management Branch Chief
(Vacant) .... (303) 844-2111

Region 9 - San Francisco (CA)
90 Seventh Street, Suite 5-300, SW, San Francisco, CA 94103-6706
Tel: (415) 744-3501 Fax: (415) 744-3517 E-mail: rosfoora@cms.hhs.gov
Areas Covered: AS, AZ, CA, GU, HI, NV, Commonwealth of Northern Marianas Islands

● Regional Administrator **(Vacant)** .... (415) 744-3501
Deputy Regional Administrator **Catherine Kortzeborn** ... (415) 744-3507
E-mail: catherine.kortzeborn@cms.hhs.gov
Pacific Area Representative **Thomas C. "Tom" Duran** ... (808) 541-2732
300 Ala Moana Boulevard, Room 6-225, Honolulu, HI 96850
Mail: P.O. Box 50081, Honolulu, HI 96850

Division of Medicaid and Children's Health Operations
90 Seventh Street, San Francisco, CA 94103
Tel: (415) 744-3568 Fax: (415) 744-2933
E-mail: rosfomcd@cms.hhs.gov

Associate Regional Administrator
Henrietta C. Sam-Louie .... (415) 744-3742
E-mail: henrietta.sam-louie@cms.hhs.gov
Financial Management Branch Manager (Acting)
Jeanie Chan .... (415) 744-3596
State Programs Branch Manager (Acting)
Kristin C. Dillon .... (443) 380-6255
Note: Acting State Program Branch Manager until Cynthia Nanes returns.
State Programs Branch Manager **Cynthia Nanes** .... (415) 744-2977
Note: On extended leave starting July 3, 2018.

Division of Medicare Financial Management
90 Seventh Street, San Francisco, CA 94103
Tel: (415) 744-3658 Fax: (415) 744-2706 E-mail: rosfofm@cms.hhs.gov

Associate Regional Administrator **Lorelei Piantedosi** .... (415) 744-3642
Medicare Program Protection Branch Manager
Kirk M. Sadur .... (415) 744-3655
E-mail: kirk.sadur@cms.hhs.gov
Financial Oversight and Reimbursement Branch
Manager **Gregory Snyder** .... (415) 744-3734

Division of Medicare Health Plans Operations
90 Seventh Street, San Francisco, CA 94103
Tel: (415) 744-3617 Fax: (415) 744-3761
E-mail: rosfodhpp@cms.hhs.gov

Associate Regional Administrator **Ann Duarte** .... (415) 744-3770
E-mail: ann.duarte@cms.hhs.gov
Branch A Manager **Deanna Gee** .... (415) 744-3675
Branch B Manager **Ayanna Busby-Jackson** .... (415) 744-3615
Customer Relations Branch Manager **Max T. Wong** ...... (415) 744-3609

Division of Survey and Certification
90 Seventh Street, San Francisco, CA 94103
Tel: (415) 744-3696 Fax: (415) 744-2692 E-mail: rosfoso@cms.hhs.gov

Associate Regional Administrator **Steven Chickering** .... (415) 744-3682
E-mail: steven.chickering@cms.hhs.gov
Survey and Certification Branch 4 Manager
Paula Perse .... (415) 744-3746
E-mail: paula.perse@cms.hhs.gov
Survey and Certification Branch 5 Manager
Rufus Arther .... (415) 744-3803
E-mail: rufus.arther@cms.hhs.gov
Survey and Certification Branch 6 Manager
Karen Fuller .... (415) 744-3741

Region 10 - Seattle (WA)
2201 Sixth Avenue, Room 801, MS/RX-40, Seattle, WA 98121-2500
Tel: (206) 615-2306 Fax: (206) 615-2027
Areas Covered: AK, ID, OR, WA

● Regional Administrator **John T. Hammarlund** .... (206) 615-2306
E-mail: john.hammarlund@cms.hhs.gov
Special Assistant **Teresa Cumpton** .... (206) 615-2391
E-mail: teresa.cumpton@cms.hhs.gov
Deputy Regional Administrator **Darryl N. Means** .... (206) 615-2306
E-mail: darryl.means@cms.hhs.gov
Public Affairs Director **(Vacant)** .... (206) 615-2306
Executive Officer **Debra "Debbie" Snyder** .... (206) 615-2308
E-mail: debra.snyder@cms.hhs.gov
Chief Medical Officer **Dr. Nancy L. Fisher MD** .... (206) 615-2390

Division of Medicare Financial Management and Fee for Service Operations
2201 Sixth Avenue, Seattle, WA 98121-1826
Tel: (206) 615-2331 Fax: (206) 615-2472

Associate Regional Administrator **Brian Flett** .... (206) 615-2094

★ Presidential Appointment Requiring Senate Confirmation ☆ Presidential Appointment □ Schedule C Appointment ◇ Career Senior Foreign Service Appointment
● Career Senior Executive Service (SES) Appointment ○ Non-Career Senior Executive Service (SES) Appointment ■ Postal Career Executive Service

DEPARTMENTS

Division of Medicaid and Children's Health Operations
Associate Regional Administrator **David Meacham** . . . . . . (206) 615-2356
E-mail: david.meacham@cms.hhs.gov

Division of Medicare Health Plans Operations (DMHPO)
2201 Sixth Avenue, Seattle, WA 98121-1826
Fax: (206) 615-2363 Fax: (206) 615-2093

Associate Regional Administrator
Brenda Suiter Mail Stop 44 . . . . (206) 615-2371
E-mail: brenda.suiter@cms.hhs.gov Fax: (206) 615-2363

Division of Quality Improvement
2201 Sixth Avenue, Seattle, WA 98121-1826
Fax: (206) 615-2434

Associate Regional Administrator **Shane Illies** . . . . (206) 615-2366

Division of Survey and Certification
2201 Sixth Avenue, Seattle, WA 98121-1826
Fax: (415) 744-2692

Western Consortium Surveyor and Certification Officer
Steven Chickering . . . . (415) 744-3682
90 Seventh Street, Fax: (415) 744-2692
Room 443F, San Francisco, CA 94103-6706

Food and Drug Administration (FDA)
10903 New Hampshire Avenue, Silver Spring, MD 20993
Tel: (301) 827-4573 (General Information)
Tel: (301) 827-3742 (Employee Research and Information Center)
Tel: (888) 463-6332 (FDA Consumer Complaint Coordinator)
Internet: www.fda.gov

OFFICE OF THE COMMISSIONER (OC)
White Oak Building One, 10903 New Hampshire Avenue,
Room 2217, Silver Spring, MD 20993
Tel: (301) 796-5000 Fax: (301) 847-3531

Office of Regulatory Affairs (ORA)
White Oak Building 31, 10903 New Hampshire Avenue,
Silver Spring, MD 20993
Tel: (301) 796-8800 Fax: (301) 595-7943 Internet: www.fda.gov/ora

District Offices

Atlanta (GA) District Office
60 Eighth Street, NE, Atlanta, GA 30309
Tel: (404) 253-1161 Fax: (404) 253-1202

District Director **Ingrid A. Zambrana** . . . . (404) 253-1284
E-mail: ingrid.zambrana@fda.hhs.gov Fax: (404) 253-2257
Secretary **Terry E. Jackson** . . . . (404) 253-2282
E-mail: terry.jackson@fda.hhs.gov Fax: (404) 253-1202
Compliance Branch Director **Derek C. Price** . . . . (404) 253-2277
E-mail: derek.price@fda.hhs.gov Fax: (404) 253-1205
Investigations Branch Director **(Vacant)** . . . . (404) 253-1161
Management and Program Support Branch Director
Arnisa M. Raiford . . . . (404) 253-1257
E-mail: arnisa.raiford@fda.hhs.gov Fax: (404) 253-1206
Public Affairs Specialist **Joann M. Pittman** . . . . (404) 253-1272
E-mail: joann.pittman@fda.hhs.gov

Baltimore (MD) District Office
6000 Metro Drive, Suite 101, Baltimore, MD 21215
Tel: (410) 779-5455 Fax: (410) 779-5707
Areas Covered: DC, MD, VA, WV

District Director **Evelyn Bonnin** . . . . (410) 779-5424
E-mail: evelyn.bonnin@fda.hhs.gov
Administrative Management Director
Joanne V. Macon . . . . (410) 779-5406
E-mail: joanne.macon@fda.hhs.gov
Compliance Branch Director **Randy F. Pack** . . . . (410) 779-5417

Baltimore (MD) District Office *(continued)*

Investigations Branch Director **Martin J. Guardia** . . . . (410) 779-5430
Fax: (410) 779-5707
Consumer Complaints Coordinator **Jennie Hallinan** . . . . . (410) 779-5713
Recalls Coordinator **Ruark Lanham** . . . . (410) 779-5414
Public Affairs Specialist **(Vacant)** . . . .(410) 779-5426

Chicago (IL) District Office
550 West Jackson Boulevard, 15th Floor, Chicago, IL 60661-5716
Tel: (312) 353-5863 Fax: (312) 596-4187

District Director **William R. Weissinger** . . . . (312) 596-4210
E-mail: william.weissinger@fda.hhs.gov
Compliance Branch Director **Nicholas F. Lyons** . . . . (312) 596-4220
Consumer Complaint Coordinator
Christinae R. Hudson . . . . (312) 353-7840
Emergency Response Coordinator **Joseph D. Cooper** . . . . (312) 596-4252
Investigations Branch Director **Tamara M. Qtami** . . . . (312) 596-4240
Recall Coordinator **Mennie C. Eldridge** . . . . (312) 596-4239
Administrative Officer **Oenia Watkins** . . . . (312) 596-4230
E-mail: oenia.watkins@fda.hhs.gov
Public Affairs Specialist **(Vacant)** . . . . (312) 353-5863
Program Support Specialist **Cheryl Alvarez** . . . . (312) 596-4228
E-mail: cheryl.alvarez@fda.hhs.gov
State Liaison **Maria Diaz** . . . . (312) 596-4265

Cincinnati (OH) District Office
6751 Steger Drive, Cincinnati, OH 45237-3097
Tel: (513) 679-2700 Fax: (513) 679-2771

District Director **Steven B. Barber** . . . . (513) 679-2700 ext. 2116
Compliance Branch Director **Toniette Williams** . . . . (513) 679-2700
Investigations Branch Director
Heather A. McCauley . . . . (513) 679-2700 ext. 2241
Supervisory Administrative Management
Officer **Felisha Howell** . . . . (513) 679-2700 ext. 2110
E-mail: felisha.howell@fda.hhs.gov Fax: (513) 679-2771

Dallas (TX) District Office
4040 North Central Expressway, Suite 300, Dallas, TX 75204
Tel: (214) 253-5200

District Director **Edmundo Garcia, Jr.** . . . . (214) 253-5201

Denver (CO) District Office
Building 20, Denver Federal Center, Sixth Avenue and Kipling Street,
Denver, CO 80225-0087
Mail: P.O. Box 25087, Denver, CO 80225-0087
Tel: (303) 236-3017 Fax: (303) 236-3100
Areas Covered: CO, NM, UT, WY

District Director **LaTonya M. Mitchell** . . . . (303) 236-3016
Administrative Officer **Kathleen Davis** . . . . (303) 236-3017
Note: On detail.
Compliance Branch Director **Kimetha King** . . . . (303) 236-3041
Investigations Branch Director **Mark Harris** . . . . (303) 236-3017
Investigations Branch Deputy Director **(Vacant)** . . . . (303) 236-3017
Laboratory Branch Director **Mark Madson** . . . .(303) 236-3060

Detroit (MI) District Office
300 River Place, Suite 5900, Detroit, MI 48207
Tel: (313) 393-8100 Fax: (313) 393-8139 Fax: (313) 393-8140
Areas Covered: IN, MI

District Director **Art O. Czabaniuk** . . . . (313) 393-8154
Fax: (313) 393-8105
Public Affairs Specialist **Dawn Cargle Pyant** . . . .(313) 393-8196
E-mail: dawn.pyant@fda.gov
Supervisory Administrative Specialist **(Vacant)** . . . .(313) 393-8100
Compliance Branch Director **(Vacant)** . . . .(313) 393-8110
Investigations Branch Director **Keith J. Jasukaitis** . . . . . . (313) 393-8141
Laboratory Director **(Vacant)** . . . . (313) 393-8100

Florida (FL) District Office
15100 Northwest 67th Avenue, Suite 400, Miami Lakes, FL 33014
Tel: (407) 475-4700 Fax: (407) 475-4768

District Director **Susan M. Turcovski** . . . . (407) 475-4702
Deputy District Director **Elizabeth W. Ormond** . . . . (407) 475-4703
E-mail: elizabeth.ormond@fda.hhs.gov Fax: (407) 475-4774
Program Support Specialist **(Vacant)** . . . . (407) 475-4700
Compliance Branch Director **Blake Bevill** . . . . (407) 475-4734
Investigations Branch Director **Kathleen Sinninger** . . . . (407) 475-4715
Public Affairs Specialist **Charles S. Watson** . . . . (407) 475-4756
E-mail: charles.watson@fda.hhs.gov
Supervisory Administrative Specialist
Wilberto Otero-Cruz . . . . (407) 475-4752
E-mail: wilberto.otero-cruz@fda.hhs.gov Fax: (407) 475-4770

Kansas City (KS) District Office
8050 Marshal Drive, Suite 205, Lenexa, KS 66214
Tel: (913) 495-5100

District Director **Cheryl A. Bigham** . . . . (913) 495-5108
Deputy District Director **Ann M. Adams** . . . . (913) 495-5111
Supervisory Administrative Management Specialist
Amy R. Meeks . . . . (913) 495-5138
Fax: (913) 495-5144
Investigations Branch Director **(Vacant)** . . . . (913) 495-5100
Compliance Branch Director **Miguel A. Hernandez** . . . . (913) 495-5101
Public Affairs Officer **(Vacant)** . . . . (913) 752-2141

Saint Louis (MO) Branch Office
15 Sunnen Drive, Suite 113, St. Louis, MO 63143-3800
Tel: (314) 645-1167 Fax: (314) 645-2969

Supervisor **Mary K. Concannon** . . . . (314) 645-1167 ext. 124
Fax: (314) 645-2969

Los Angeles (CA) District Office
19701 Fairchild, Irvine, CA 92612
Tel: (949) 608-2900 Fax: (949) 608-4415

● District Director **Steven E. Porter** Room 2172 . . . . (949) 608-4448
E-mail: steven.porter@fda.hhs.gov
Public Affairs Officer **Rosario Quintanilla-Vior** . . . . (949) 608-4407
E-mail: rosario.vior@fda.hhs.gov
Compliance Branch Director **Kelly D. Sheppard** . . . . (949) 608-4426
E-mail: kelly.sheppard@fda.hhs.gov
Domestic Investigations Section Director
Monica Maxwell . . . . (949) 608-4454
E-mail: monica.maxwell@fda.hhs.gov
Imports Branch Director **Daniel R. "Dan" Solis** . . . . (562) 256-9202
E-mail: dan.solis@fda.hhs.gov
Supervisory Administrative Officer
Alessande R. Velez . . . . (949) 608-4411
E-mail: alessande.velez@fda.hhs.gov

Minneapolis (MN) District Office
250 Marquette Avenue, Suite #600, Minneapolis, MN 55401
Tel: (612) 334-4100 Fax: (612) 334-4134

District Director **Dr. Michael Dutcher DVM** . . . . (612) 758-7124
E-mail: michael.dutcher@fda.hhs.gov
Secretary **Olga Jonas** . . . . (612) 758-7123
E-mail: olga.jonas@fda.hhs.gov
Compliance Branch Director
Christopher K. "Chris" VanTwuyver . . . . (612) 758-7112
E-mail: chris.vantwuyver@fda.hhs.gov
Investigations Branch Director
Gregory W. "Greg" Smith . . . . (612) 758-7155
Public Affairs Specialist **Susan A. Seefeld** . . . . (612) 758-7130
E-mail: susan.seefeld@fda.hhs.gov
Administrative Officer **Cynthia Grindahl** . . . . (612) 758-7144
E-mail: cynthia.grindahl@fda.hhs.gov

New England District Office
One Montvale Avenue, Stoneham, MA 02180-3400
Tel: (781) 587-7500 Fax: (781) 587-7556

Director **Joseph Mastrisciano** . . . . (781) 587-7490
E-mail: joseph.matrisciano@fda.hhs.gov

New England District Office *(continued)*

Secretary **(Vacant)** . . . . (781) 587-7500
Compliance Branch Director **(Vacant)** . . . . (781) 587-7484
Investigations Branch Director **Lori A. Holmquist** . . . . (781) 587-7437
312 Fore Street, Fax: (207) 221-2381
Room 103, Portland, ME 04101
E-mail: lori.holmquist@fda.hhs.gov
Public Affairs Specialist **Mary B. Yebba** . . . . (781) 587-7466
E-mail: mary.yebba@fda.hhs.gov

New Jersey (NJ) District Office
Waterview Corporate Center, 10 Waterview Boulevard,
3rd Floor, Parsippany, NJ 07054
Tel: (973) 331-4900 Fax: (973) 331-4969

District Director **Diana Amador-Toro** . . . . (973) 331-4901
E-mail: diana.amador@fda.hhs.gov
Public Affairs Specialist **Joan G. Lytle** . . . . (732) 390-3823
629 Cranbury Road, East Brunswick, NJ 08816
E-mail: joan.lytle@fda.hhs.gov
Compliance Branch Director **Stephanie Durso** . . . . (973) 331-4911
E-mail: Stephanie.Durso@fda.hhs.gov Fax: (973) 331-4969
Investigations Branch Director **Nerizza B. Guerin** . . . . (856) 290-4040
E-mail: Nerizza.Guerin@fda.hhs.gov Fax: (856) 783-1513

New Orleans (LA) District Office
Building 200, 404 BNA Drive, Suite 500, Nashville, TN 37217
Tel: (615) 366-7801 Fax: (615) 366-7802

Director **Ruth P. Dixon** . . . . (615) 366-7803
Deputy Director **Kimberley L. McMillan** . . . . (615) 366-7811
E-mail: kimberly.mcmillan@fda.hhs.gov Fax: (615) 366-7812
Investigations Branch Director **Thomas D. Clarida** . . . . (615) 366-7827
Investigations Branch Deputy Director
Krista W. Whitten . . . . (615) 366-7842
E-mail: krista.whitten@fda.hhs.gov
Management and Program Support Branch Director
Tammara P. Threats . . . . (615) 366-7830
E-mail: tammara.threats@fda.hhs.gov
Administrative Management Specialist
Mary D. Torasso . . . . (615) 366-7825
E-mail: mary.torasso@fda.hhs.gov
Supervisor **Richard L. Garcia** . . . . (615) 366-7820
E-mail: richard.garcia@fda.hhs.gov
Supervisor **Danielle M. Maddox** . . . . (615) 366-7981
E-mail: danielle.maddox@fda.hhs.gov
Supervisor **(Vacant)** . . . . (615) 366-7816
Supervisor **(Vacant)** . . . . (615) 366-7813
Public Affairs Specialist **(Vacant)** . . . . (615) 366-7801
Fax: (615) 366-7805

New York (NY) District Office
158 - 15 Liberty Avenue, Jamaica, NY 11433-1034
Tel: (718) 340-7000 Fax: (718) 662-5665 Internet: www.fda.gov/ora
Areas Covered: New York State (Downstate and Upstate)

● District Director **Ronald Pace** . . . . (718) 662-5447
E-mail: ronald.pace@fda.hhs.gov
Secretary to the District Director **Elsie Tamay** . . . . (718) 662-5456
E-mail: elsie.tamay@fda.hhs.gov
Deputy Director **Matthew Palo USPHS** . . . . (718) 662-5552
Domestic Compliance Branch Director
Anna Alexander . . . . (718) 662-5683
E-mail: anna.alexander@fda.hhs.gov
Downstate Import Operations Branch Director
Dawne M. Hines . . . . (718) 662-5461
Fax: (718) 662-5662
Upstate Import Operations Branch Director
Sandra K. Sylvester . . . . (716) 846-6221
E-mail: sandra.sylvester@fda.hhs.gov
Public Affairs Specialist **Dilcia Granville** . . . . (718) 662-5445
E-mail: dilcia.granville@fda.hhs.gov Fax: (718) 662-5665

DEPARTMENTS

★ Presidential Appointment Requiring Senate Confirmation ☆ Presidential Appointment □ Schedule C Appointment ◇ Career Senior Foreign Service Appointment
● Career Senior Executive Service (SES) Appointment ○ Non-Career Senior Executive Service (SES) Appointment ■ Postal Career Executive Service

DEPARTMENTS

Buffalo (NY) Branch Office
Theater Place, 622 Main Street, Suite 100, Buffalo, NY 14202
Tel: (716) 846-6200 Fax: (716) 846-6303
Areas Covered: NY (except NYC metropolitan area)

Domestic Compliance Branch Director **(Vacant)** ....(716) 846-6200
Fax: (716) 551-4499
Management and Program Support Branch Director
(Vacant) ....(716) 846-6214
Upstate Import Operations Branch Director
Sandra K. Sylvester ....(716) 846-6221
Health Communications Specialist
Diana D. Monaco RDN, CDN, FAND ....(716) 846-6204
E-mail: diana.monaco@fda.hhs.gov

Philadelphia (PA) District Office
U.S. Customs House, 200 Chestnut Street,
Room 900, Philadelphia, PA 19106
Tel: (215) 597-4390 Fax: (215) 597-4660
Areas Covered: DE, PA

District Director **Anne Johnson** ....(215) 717-3003
E-mail: anne.johnson@fda.hhs.gov
Public Affairs Specialist **Anitra Brown-Reed** ....(215) 717-3004
E-mail: anitra.brownreed@fda.hhs.gov
Pre-Approval Inspection Manager **Gayle S. Lawson** ....(215) 717-3737
Fax: (215) 597-0875
Compliance Branch Chief **(Vacant)** ....(215) 597-4390
Investigations Branch Chief **Karyn M. Campbell** ....(215) 717-3731
E-mail: karyn.campbell@fda.hhs.gov
Supervisory Management **Zavia V. Forney** ....(215) 717-3011
E-mail: zavia.forney@fda.hhs.gov

San Francisco (CA) District Office
1431 Harbor Bay Parkway, Alameda, CA 94502-7096
Tel: (510) 337-6700 Fax: (510) 337-6859

District Director **Darla R. Bracy** ....(510) 337-6733
E-mail: darla.bracy@fda.hhs.gov
Deputy Director **(Vacant)** ....(510) 337-6700
Administrative Officer **Katrina E. Damiani** ....(510) 337-6872
E-mail: katrina.damiani@fda.hhs.gov
Public Affairs Specialist **Mary Ellen Taylor** ....(510) 337-6888
E-mail: maryellen.taylor@fda.hhs.gov Fax: (510) 337-6708
Compliance for Division of West Coast Imports
Director **Lawton W. Lum** ....(510) 337-6792
Laboratory Operations
Thomas H. "Tom" Sidebottom ....(510) 337-6825
District Specialist **(Vacant)** ....(510) 337-6771
Investigations Operations **Luis A. Solorzano** ....(510) 287-2712
Fax: (510) 337-6702

San Juan (PR) District Office
466 Fernandez Juncos Avenue, San Juan, PR 00901-3223
Tel: (787) 729-8500 Fax: (787) 729-6851

District Director **Ramón A. Hernández** ....(787) 729-8588
Fax: (787) 729-6747
Compliance Officer **Nancy Rosado** ....(787) 729-8683
E-mail: nancy.rosado@fda.hhs.gov Fax: (787) 729-8829
Compliance Branch Director **Edwin Ramos** ....(787) 729-8662
Investigations Branch Director **(Vacant)** ....(787) 729-8500
Supervisory Investigator **Frances L. DeJesus** ....(787) 729-8543
E-mail: frances.dejesus@fda.hhs.gov Fax: (787) 729-8768
Public Affairs Officer **Nilda Villegas** ....(787) 729-8517
E-mail: nilda.villegas@fda.hhs.gov

Seattle (WA) District Office
22215 26th Ave., Suite 210, Bothell, WA 98021
Tel: (425) 302-0340 Fax: (425) 302-0402
Areas Covered: AK, ID, MT, OR, WA

District Director and Program Division Director
Miriam R. Burbach ....(425) 302-0420
Compliance Director **Lisa M. Althar** ....(425) 302-0412
Fax: (425) 302-0402
Investigations Director **(Vacant)** ....(425) 302-0435

Seattle (WA) District Office *(continued)*

Administrative Officer **Ngoc-Lan Nguyen** ....(425) 302-0370
E-mail: ngoc-lan.nguyen@fda.hhs.gov
Public Affairs Specialist **(Vacant)** ....(425) 302-0340

Health Resources and Services Administration (HRSA)

Parklawn Building, 5600 Fishers Lane, Rockville, MD 20857
Tel: (301) 443-2216 Internet: www.hrsa.gov

OFFICE OF THE ADMINISTRATOR

Parklawn Building, 5600 Fishers Lane, Rockville, MD 20857
Fax: (301) 443-1246

Office of Regional Operations

Parklawn Building, 5600 Fishers Lane, Rockville, MD 20857
Fax: (301) 443-2173

Regional Divisions

Region 1 - Boston (MA)
John F. Kennedy Federal Building, Room 1826, Boston, MA 02203
Tel: (617) 565-1420 Fax: (617) 565-3044
Areas Covered: CT, MA, ME, NH, RI, VT

Regional Administrator **Jeffrey Beard** ....(617) 565-1460
E-mail: jeffrey.beard@hrsa.hhs.gov
Deputy Regional Administrator **Christopher Bersani** ....(617) 565-1470
E-mail: christopher.bersani@hrsa.hhs.gov Fax: (301) 451-5552

Region 2 - New York (NY)
26 Federal Plaza, Room 3337, New York, NY 10278
Tel: (212) 264-4498 Fax: (212) 264-2673

Regional Administrator **Ronald Moss** ....(212) 264-2664
E-mail: rmoss@hrsa.gov
Deputy Regional Administrator **Cheryl Donald** ....(212) 264-2768
E-mail: cheryl.donald@hrsa.hhs.gov Fax: (212) 264-4497

Region 3 - Philadelphia (PA)
Public Ledger Building, 150 South Independence Mall West,
Suite 1172, Philadelphia, PA 19106-3499
Tel: (215) 861-4411 Fax: (215) 861-4385

Regional Administrator **Pamela Kania** ....(215) 861-4628
E-mail: pamela.kania@hrsa.hhs.gov
Deputy Regional Administrator **Leah Suter** ....(215) 861-4078
E-mail: leah.suter@hrsa.hhs.gov

Region 4 - Atlanta (GA)
SAMNUN Atlanta Federal Center, 61 Forsyth Street, SW,
Suite 3M60, Atlanta, GA 30303-8909
Tel: (404) 562-4140 Fax: (404) 562-7974
Areas Covered: AL, GA, FL, KY, MS, NC, SC, TN

Regional Administrator **Lisa Mariani** ....(404) 562-4144
E-mail: lisa.mariani@hrsa.hhs.gov
Deputy Regional Administrator **Natalie Perry** ....(404) 562-4103
E-mail: natalie.perry@hrsa.hhs.gov

Region 5 - Chicago (IL)
233 North Michigan Avenue, Suite 200, Chicago, IL 60601
Tel: (312) 353-6835 Fax: (312) 353-2832

Regional Administrator **Tamara Cox** ....(312) 353-8121
E-mail: tamara.cox@hrsa.hhs.gov
Deputy Regional Administrator **(Vacant)** ....(312) 353-6835

Region 6 - Dallas (TX)
1301 Young Street, Suite 1040, Dallas, TX 75202
Tel: (214) 767-3872 Fax: (214) 767-3923

Regional Administrator **(Vacant)** ....(214) 767-3872
Deputy Regional Administrator (Acting)
Martha Culver ....(214) 767-3342
E-mail: Martha.Culver@hrsa.hhs.gov

Region 6 - Dallas (TX) *(continued)*

Administrative Officer **Carla Williams** . . . . (214) 767-3072
E-mail: carla.williams@hrsa.hhs.gov

Region 7 - Kansas City (MO)
601 East 12th Street, Suite 250, Kansas City, MO 64106
Tel: (816) 426-5226 Fax: (816) 426-6323

Regional Administrator **Lisa J. Goschen** . . . . (816) 426-5203
E-mail: lisa.goschen@hrsa.hhs.gov
Deputy Regional Administrator **Nancy Rios-Brooks** . . . . . (816) 426-5206
E-mail: nancy.rios@hrsa.hhs.gov Fax: (816) 426-6323

Region 8 - Denver (CO)
Federal Office Building, 999 18th Street South Terrace,
Room 409, Denver, CO 80202
Fax: (303) 844-0002

Regional Administrator **Nicholas C. Zucconi** . . . . (303) 844-7879
Fax: (303) 844-0002
Deputy Regional Administrator **(Vacant)** . . . . (301) 443-2216
Administrative Officer **Ellen Ingram** . . . . (303) 844-3375
E-mail: ellen.ingram@hrsa.hhs.gov

Region 9 - San Francisco (CA)
90 Seventh Street, San Francisco, CA 94103
Tel: (415) 437-8090 Fax: (415) 437-7664

Regional Administrator **Dr. John Moroney** . . . . (415) 437-8159
E-mail: jmoroney@hrsa.gov
Deputy Regional Administrator **Lorenzo Taylor** . . . . (415) 437-8125
E-mail: lorenzo.taylor@hrsa.hhs.gov Fax: (415) 437-7664

Region 10 - Seattle (WA)
701 Fifth Avenue, 15th Floor, Suite 1520, Mail Stop 23,
Seattle, WA 98104
Tel: (206) 615-2490 Fax: (206) 615-2500

Regional Administrator **Sharon Turner** . . . . (206) 615-2059
E-mail: sharon.turner@hrsa.hhs.gov
Deputy Regional Administrator **Eric Bradford** . . . . (206) 615-2518
E-mail: eric.bradford@hrsa.hhs.gov
Administrative Officer **Frederick Bueno** . . . . (206) 615-2490
E-mail: frederick.bueno@hrsa.hhs.gov
Program Integrity Analyst **Randall "Randy" Alley** . . . . . (206) 615-2620
E-mail: randall.alley@hrsa.hhs.gov
Program Integrity Analyst **Nikita Baker** . . . . (206) 615-2639
E-mail: nikita.baker@hrsa.hhs.gov
Program Integrity Analyst **Elizabeth Naftchi** . . . . (206) 615-2046
E-mail: elizabeth.naftchi@hrsa.hhs.gov
Senior Public Health Analyst **Carolyn Gleason** . . . . . . (206) 615-2486
E-mail: carolyn.gleason@hrsa.hhs.gov
Public Health Analyst **Aphrodyi Antoine** . . . . (206) 615-2058
Public Health Analyst **Matthew Feist** . . . . (206) 615-2488
E-mail: matthew.feist@hrsa.hhs.gov
Public Health Analyst **Gary Gant** . . . . (206) 615-2318
Public Health Analyst **Maria Garcia** . . . . (206) 615-2636
E-mail: maria.garcia@hrsa.hhs.gov
Public Health Analyst **Lorrie Grevstad** . . . . (206) 615-3891
Public Health Analyst **Gabriele Colangelo** . . . . (206) 615-2490

Indian Health Service (IHS)

5600 Fishers Lane, Rockville, MD 20857
TTY: (301) 443-6394 Internet: www.ihs.gov

OFFICE OF THE DIRECTOR (OD)

5600 Fishers Lane, Rockville, MD 20857
Fax: (301) 443-4794

Field Operations

Deputy Director for Field Operations (Acting)
RADM Kevin D. Meeks USPHS . . . . (405) 951-3774
Education: East Central U

Great Plains Area Indian Health Service

Federal Building, 115 Fourth Avenue, SE, Aberdeen, SD 57401
Tel: (605) 226-7581 Fax: (605) 226-7541
Areas Covered: IA, NE, ND, SD

• Area Director **(Vacant)** . . . . (605) 226-7581
Deputy Area Director, Behavioral Health
Emily Williams . . . . (605) 226-7791
Fax: (605) 226-7543
Deputy Area Director, Indian Health Policy **(Vacant)** . . . . (605) 226-7581
Deputy Area Director, Management Operations
Daniel Davis . . . . (605) 226-7776
Environmental Health and Engineering Associate
Director (Acting) **Daniel Davis** . . . . (605) 226-7776
Chief Medical Officer **Lee Lawrence** . . . . (605) 226-7581
Deputy Chief Medical Officer **Patrick J. Fullerton** . . . . . (605) 226-7265
Medical Care Evaluation Program Manager **(Vacant)** . . . . (605) 226-7581

Belcourt (ND) Service Unit (Quentin N. Burdick Memorial Healthcare Facility)
Quentin N. Burdick Memorial Health Care Facility, Belcourt, ND 58316
Mail: P.O. Box 160, Belcourt, ND 58316
Tel: (701) 477-6111 Fax: (701) 477-8410

Chief Executive Officer **Shelly R. Harris** . . . . (701) 477-6111
E-mail: shelly.harris@ihs.gov
Deputy Chief Executive Officer **Duane Marcellais** . . . . . (701) 477-6111
E-mail: duane.marcellais@ihs.gov
Administrative Officer **(Vacant)** . . . . (701) 477-6111
Clinical Director (Acting) **Paula Bercier** . . . . . . (701) 477-6111 ext. 8444
E-mail: paula.bercier@ihs.gov

Cheyenne River (SD) Service Unit (Eagle Butte Indian Health Service)
Eagle Butte IHS Indian Hospital, Eagle Butte, SD 57625
P.O. Box 1012, Eagle Butte, SD 57625
Tel: (605) 964-7724

Chief Executive Officer **Charles Fischer** . . . . (605) 964-7724
Clinical Director **Rodney Vizcarra** . . . . (605) 964-7724

Crow Creek (SD) Service Unit (Fort Thompson Indian Health Center)
Fort Thompson PHS Indian Health Center, Fort Thompson, SD 57339
P.O. Box 200, Fort Thompson, SD 57339
Tel: (605) 245-2285 Fax: (605) 245-2384

Chief Executive Officer (Acting) **Dale Buckles** . . . . (605) 245-1549
Administrative Officer **Dale Buckles** . . . . (605) 245-1549
E-mail: dale.buckles@ihs.gov
Clinical Director **Dr. H. John McFee** . . . . (605) 245-2285
Computer Specialist (Acting) **Helen Thiry-Chmela** . . . . . (605) 245-1564
E-mail: helen.thiry-chmela@ihs.gov

Elbow Woods (ND) Service Unit
1058 College Drive, New Town, ND 58763-4400
Tel: (701) 627-4750 Fax: (701) 627-2809

Chief Executive Officer **Kathy Eagle** . . . . (701) 627-4750 ext. 7791
Administrative Officer **Melissa Brady** . . . . (701) 627-7614
E-mail: melissa.brady@ihs.gov

Fort Totten (ND) Service Unit (Spirit Lake Health Center)
Spirit Lake Indian Health Center, Fort Totten, ND 58335
P.O. Box 200, Fort Totten, ND 58335
Tel: (701) 766-1600 Fax: (701) 766-4295

Chief Executive Officer **(Vacant)** . . . . (701) 766-1600
Administrative Officer **Dixie Omen** . . . . (701) 766-1600
E-mail: Dixie.Omen@ihs.gov
Clinical Director **(Vacant)** . . . . (701) 766-1600

DEPARTMENTS

★ Presidential Appointment Requiring Senate Confirmation ☆ Presidential Appointment ☐ Schedule C Appointment ◇ Career Senior Foreign Service Appointment
● Career Senior Executive Service (SES) Appointment ○ Non-Career Senior Executive Service (SES) Appointment ■ Postal Career Executive Service

DEPARTMENTS

Lower Brule (SD) Service Unit (Lower Brule Indian Health Clinic)
Lower Brule IHS Indian Health Center, P.O. Box 248,
Lower Brule, SD 57548
Tel: (605) 473-5544 Fax: (605) 473-5677

Chief Executive Officer **(Vacant)** .... (605) 473-5544
Administrative Officer **Kimberly Craig** .... (605) 473-5544
E-mail: kimberly.craig@ihs.gov
Clinical Director (Acting) **Kyrstin Reimann** .... (605) 473-5526
Nursing Director **Kimm Schweitzer** .... (605) 473-5526
Fax: (605) 473-5677
Chief Pharmacist **Deb Odens** .... (605) 473-8225

Omaha-Winnebago (NE) Service Unit (Winnebago PHS Indian Hospital)
Winnebago Indian Hospital, P.O. Box HH, Winnebago, NE 68071
Tel: (402) 878-2231

Chief Executive Officer **Danelle Smith** .... (402) 878-2231
Clinical Director **Lynelle Noisy Hawk** .... (402) 878-2231
Office Automation Clerk **Michelle Thomas** .... (402) 878-2231 ext. 2150
E-mail: Michelle.Thomas@ihs.gov
Pharmacy Director **Susan Porter** .... (402) 878-2231 ext. 2040
Purchasing Officer **Ursula R. Maslonka** .... (402) 878-2231
E-mail: ursula.maslonka@ihs.hhs.gov

Pine Ridge (SD) Service Unit (Pine Ridge Indian Hospital)
Pine Ridge IHS Indian Hospital, East Highway 18, P.O. Box 1201,
Pine Ridge, SD 57770
Tel: (605) 867-5131 Fax: (605) 867-3271

Chief Executive Officer **Mark Meersman** .... (605) 867-3389
E-mail: mark.meersman@ihs.gov
Deputy Chief Executive Officer **(Vacant)** .... (605) 867-3021
Administrative Officer **Duane Ross** .... (605) 867-3040
E-mail: duane.ross@ihs.gov
Clinical Director **Alma Tatum** .... (605) 867-5131 ext. 3104
E-mail: alma.tatum@ihs.gov
Information Technology Specialist **(Vacant)** .... (605) 867-5131

Kyle (SD) PHS Health Center
1000 Health Center Road, Kyle, SD 57752
Mail: P.O. Box 540, Kyle, SD 57752
Tel: (605) 455-2451 Fax: (605) 455-2808
Fax: (605) 455-1589 (Administration)

Health Center Director **Sophia Conroy** .... (605) 867-3021
Clinical Supervisor **Dr. Kimberly Montileaux DPM** .... (605) 455-8250
Administrative Support Assistant **(Vacant)** .... (605) 455-2451
Information Technology Specialist
Edwin Harris .... (605) 455-2451 ext. 8273
E-mail: edwin.harris@ihs.gov

Wanblee (SD) PHS Health Center
210 1st Street, Wanblee, SD 57577

Health Center Director **Francine Red Willow** .... (605) 462-5622

Rapid City (SD) Service Unit (Sioux San Indian Health Hospital)
Rapid City IHS Hospital, 3200 Canyon Lake Drive, Rapid City, SD 57702
Tel: (605) 355-2500 Fax: (605) 355-2504

Chief Executive Officer **Joseph "Joe" Amiotte** .... (605) 355-2494
Deputy Chief Executive Officer **(Vacant)** .... (605) 355-2322
Chief Medical Director **(Vacant)** .... (605) 355-2500

Rosebud (SD) Service Unit (Rosebud Comprehensive Healthcare Facility)
Rosebud Comprehensive Health Care Facility,
Soldier Creek Road, Rosebud, SD 57570
Rosebud Comprehensive Health Care Facility, P.O. Box 400,
Rosebud, SD 57570
Fax: (605) 747-2216

Chief Executive Officer **Arlene Lester** .... (605) 747-2231
Deputy Chief Executive Officer **Shannon J. Hopkins** .... (605) 747-2231
E-mail: shannon.hopkins@ihs.gov
Clinical Director **(Vacant)** .... (605) 747-2231 ext. 3

Sisseton-Wahpeton (SD) Service Unit (Woodrow Wilson Keeble Memorial Health Care Center)
100 Lake Traverse Drive, P.O. Box 189, Sisseton, SD 57262
Tel: (605) 698-7606 Fax: (605) 698-4270

Chief Executive Officer **Randy Jordan** .... (605) 742-3614
Administrative Officer **Gail Williams** .... (605) 742-3617
E-mail: gail.williams@ihs.gov Fax: (605) 698-3774
Clinical Director (Acting)
Dr. Thanigasalam "Mason" Arumuganathan .... (605) 742-3825
Nursing Director **Jacqueline "Jackie" Birney** .... (605) 742-3686

Standing Rock (ND) Service Unit (Standing Rock IHS Health Center)
Fort Yates IHS Indian Hospital, Fort Yates, ND 58538
P.O. Box J, Fort Yates, ND 58538
Tel: (701) 854-3831 Fax: (701) 854-7399

Chief Executive Officer **Jana Gipp** .... (701) 854-8211
Administrative Officer **Percetta Red Willow** .... (701) 854-8279
E-mail: percetta.redwillow@ihs.gov
Clinical Director **Sara Jumping Eagle** .... (701) 854-8210

McLaughlin (SD) PHS Indian Health Center
P.O. Box 879, McLaughlin, SD 57642
701 East Sixth Street, McLaughlin, SD 57642
Tel: (605) 823-4459 Fax: (605) 823-4818

Administrative Officer **Arlene M. Krulish** .... (605) 823-4458
E-mail: arlene.krulish@ihs.gov Fax: (701) 766-1627

Wagner (SD) Service Unit (Wagner Indian Health Services)
Wagner PHS Health Care Center, 111 Washington Street,
Wagner, SD 57380
P.O. Box 490, Wagner, SD 57380
Tel: (605) 384-3621 Fax: (605) 384-5229

Chief Executive Officer
Michael "Mike" Horned Eagle .... (605) 384-3621
Administrative Officer **Rebecca Jandreau Picotte** .... (605) 384-3621
E-mail: rebecca.jandreaupicotte@ihs.gov
Medical Officer **Grisel Rodriguez** .... (605) 384-3621

Alaska Area Indian Health Service
Alaska Native Health Service, 4141 Ambassador Drive,
Suite 300, Anchorage, AK 99508-5928
Tel: (907) 729-3686
Areas Covered: AK

● Director **Christopher "Chris" Mandregan, Jr. MPH** .... (907) 729-3686
E-mail: chris.mandregan@ihs.gov
Education: Washington State BABA; Hawaii MPH
Secretary **Marlene McGlashan** .... (907) 729-3683
E-mail: marlene.mcglashan@ihs.gov
Deputy Director and Chief Medical Officer **(Vacant)** .... (907) 729-3686
Assistant Regional Counsel **(Vacant)** .... (907) 729-3686
701 Fifth Avenue, Seattle, WA 98104
Planning, Evaluation and Health Statistics Division
Director **Diana Roberts** .... (907) 729-3665
E-mail: diana.roberts@ihs.gov
Western Region Liaison **Martha Wanca** .... (907) 729-3686
E-mail: martha.wanca@ihs.gov Fax: (907) 729-1312

Office of Acquisition Management (OAM)
Acquisition and Property Management Officer
Burton "Burt" Humphrey .... (907) 729-2965
E-mail: burton.humphrey@ihs.hhs.gov

Office of Environmental Health and Engineering
4141 Ambassador Drive, Anchorage, AK 99508-5928
Tel: (907) 729-3508 Fax: (907) 729-5690

Director **Denman Ondelacy** .... (907) 729-3501
E-mail: denman.ondelacy@ihs.gov

★ Presidential Appointment Requiring Senate Confirmation ☆ Presidential Appointment ☐ Schedule C Appointment ◇ Career Senior Foreign Service Appointment
● Career Senior Executive Service (SES) Appointment ○ Non-Career Senior Executive Service (SES) Appointment ■ Postal Career Executive Service

Office of Financial Management
4141 Ambassador Drive, Anchorage, AK 99508-5928
Tel: (907) 729-2870 Fax: (907) 729-2889

Director **Lyle Claw** .... (907) 729-2870

Office of Human Resources
4141 Ambassador Drive, Anchorage, AK 99508-5928
Tel: (907) 729-1323 Fax: (907) 729-1312

Director (Acting) **Jeanne Smith** .... (916) 930-3981 ext. 335
E-mail: jeanne.taylor@ihs.gov

Office of Tribal Programs
4141 Ambassador Drive, Anchorage, AK 99508-5928
Tel: (907) 729-3677 Fax: (907) 729-3678

Director **Lanie Fox** .... (907) 729-3677

Albuquerque (NM) Area Indian Health Service

5300 Homestead Road, NE, Albuquerque, NM 87110
Tel: (505) 248-4500 Fax: (505) 248-4115
Areas Covered: CO, NM, TX

• Director **Dr. Leonard D. Thomas MD** .... (505) 256-6735
E-mail: leonard.thomas@ihs.gov Fax: (505) 248-4624
Education: Fort Lewis BS;
New Mexico 1996 MD
Chief Medical Officer **(Vacant)** .... (505) 248-4500
Tribal Support Office Director **R.C. Begay** .... (505) 248-4549
E-mail: r.c.begay@ihs.hhs.gov Fax: (505) 248-4624
Executive Officer **Sandra Winfrey** .... (505) 256-6736
E-mail: sandra.winfrey@ihs.gov Fax: (505) 248-4624

Division of Accounting/Budget
Director **Rhonda Robinson-Boal** .... (505) 248-4582
E-mail: rhonda.robinson-boal@ihs.gov Fax: (505) 248-4631

Division of Clinical Quality
5300 Homestead Road, NE, Albuquerque, NM 87110
Fax: (505) 248-4257

Director **(Vacant)** .... (505) 248-4500
Behavioral Health Consultant
Christopher L. "Chris" Fore .... (505) 274-4095
Diabetes Consultant **Harriet Hosetosavit** .... (505) 248-4219
Health Promotion Disease Prevention Coordinator
Theresa Clay .... (505) 248-4772
E-mail: theresa.clay@ihs.gov

Division of Contracts, Grants and Procurement
Director **Veronica Zuni** .... (505) 248-4565
E-mail: veronica.zuni@ihs.gov Fax: (505) 248-4641

Division of Environmental Health and Engineering
5300 Homestead Road, NE, Albuquerque, NM 87110
Tel: (505) 248-4600 Fax: (505) 248-4678

Director **Russel Pederson** .... (505) 248-4275
E-mail: russel.pederson@ihs.hhs.gov
Environmental Health Services Director
Richard Turner .... (505) 248-4262
Environmental Health Support Center Director (Acting)
Richard Turner .... (505) 248-4258
Health Facilities Management Director
Thomas "Tom" Plummer .... (505) 248-4262
Property Management and Supply Director **(Vacant)** ..... (505) 248-4593
Sanitation Facilities Construction Director
Chris Bradley .... (505) 248-4595

Division of Human Resources
Director **Raelyn Pecos** .... (505) 248-4512
E-mail: raelyn.pecos@ihs.hhs.gov

Division of Information Management Services
Director **Joseph F. Lucero** .... (505) 248-4566
E-mail: joseph.lucero@ihs.gov Fax: (505) 248-4172

New Sunrise Regional Treatment Center
P.O. Box 210, San Fidel, NM 87049
Tel: (505) 552-5500 Fax: (505) 552-5530

Program Director **Clarissa "Janay" Cedar Face** .... (505) 248-4082
E-mail: Clarissa.CedarFace@ihs.gov

Acoma-Canoncito Laguna Indian Health Service Hospital
P.O. Box 130, San Fidel, NM 87049
Tel: (505) 552-5300 Fax: (505) 552-5490

Chief Executive Officer **Melody Price-Yonts** .... (505) 552-5305
Administrative Officer **Barbara Felipe** .... (505) 552-5303
E-mail: bfelipe@abq.ihs.gov
Clinical Director **James Urbina** .... (505) 552-5300
Director of Nursing **Melissa Wyaco** .... (505) 552-5324

Albuquerque (NM) Service Unit
Albuquerque (NM) Indian Health Center,
801 Vassar Drive, NE, Albuquerque, NM 87106
Tel: (505) 248-4000 Fax: (505) 248-7814

Chief Executive Officer **John Rael** .... (505) 248-4064
Clinical Director (Acting) **Miranda Durham** .... (505) 248-4000

Jicarilla (NM) Service Unit (Dulce Health Center)
P.O. Box 187, Dulce, NM 87528
Tel: (575) 759-3291 Fax: (575) 759-3651

Chief Executive Officer **Sandra Lahi** .... (575) 759-7200
E-mail: sandra.lahi@ihs.gov

Mescalero (NM) Service Unit (Mescalero Indian Hospital)
Mescalero PHS Indian Hospital, Mescalero, NM 88340
P.O. Box 210, Mescalero, NM 88340

Chief Executive Officer **Dorlynn Simmons** .... (575) 464-3801
E-mail: dorlynn.simmons@ihs.hhs.gov
Budget Analyst/Human Resources **Rainey Enjady** .... (575) 464-3804
E-mail: rainey.enjady@ihs.hhs.gov
Managed Care Director **(Vacant)** .... (505) 248-4500
Nursing Director **Yolanda Adams** .... (575) 464-3873
E-mail: yolanda.adams@ihs.hhs.gov

Santa Fe (NM) Indian Hospital (SFIH)
Santa Fe PHS Indian Hospital, 1700 Cerrillos Road, Santa Fe, NM 87501
Tel: (505) 988-9821

Chief Executive Officer **Leslie D. Dye** .... (505) 946-9204
Administrative Officer **(Vacant)** .... (505) 946-9202
Clinical Director **Bret Smoker** .... (505) 946-9272
Human Resources Director **(Vacant)** .... (505) 946-9238
Support Services Supervisor **(Vacant)** .... (505) 946-9237
Fax: (505) 986-0751

Santa Clara PHS Indian Health Center
RR5, Box 446, Espanola, NM 87532
Tel: (505) 988-9821 Fax: (505) 753-5039

Health Center Director **(Vacant)** .... (505) 753-9421 ext. 215
Administrative Assistant **Arlene Cata** .... (505) 753-9421 ext. 210
E-mail: arlene.cata@ihs.hhs.gov

Taos-Picuris PHS Indian Health Center
P.O. Box 1956, Taos, NM 87571
Tel: (505) 758-4224

Chief Executive Officer (Acting) **Theresa Dyess** .... (575) 758-6974
Fax: (575) 751-5210
Clinical Director **Paige Gerling** .... (575) 758-6916
Administrative Officer **Gail W. Osborne** .... (575) 758-4224
E-mail: gail.osborne@ihs.hhs.gov

Southern Colorado Ute Service Unit (Ignacio Health Clinic) (SCUSU)
P.O. Box 778, Ignacio, CO 81137
Tel: (970) 563-4581 Fax: (970) 563-0206

Chief Executive Officer **(Vacant)** .... (970) 563-4581

DEPARTMENTS

★ Presidential Appointment Requiring Senate Confirmation ☆ Presidential Appointment □ Schedule C Appointment ◇ Career Senior Foreign Service Appointment
● Career Senior Executive Service (SES) Appointment ○ Non-Career Senior Executive Service (SES) Appointment ■ Postal Career Executive Service

DEPARTMENTS

Southern Ute Health Center
P.O. Box 899, Ignacio, CO 81137
Tel: (970) 563-4581 Fax: (970) 563-0206 (Administration)

Health Center Director **(Vacant)** ....(970) 563-4581

Ute Mountain Ute Health Center
Complex D, Resting Willow Road, Towaoc, CO 81334
Mail: P.O. Box 49, Towaoc, CO 81334
Tel: (970) 565-4441 Fax: (970) 565-4784

Health Center Director **Kyle "Clinton" Gropp** ....(970) 565-4441
Tel: (970) 565-4441 219
Senior Medical Officer/Clinical Director
Matthew Clark ....(970) 565-4441 ext. 240
E-mail: matthew.clark@ihs.hhs.gov

Ysleta del Sur (TX) Service Unit
9314 Juanchido Lane, El Paso, TX 79907
Tel: (915) 858-1076 Fax: (915) 858-2367

Director **Martin Lopez, Jr.** ....(915) 858-1076
Medical Director **Lorena Silvestre-Tobias** ....(915) 858-1076
Medical Assistant **(Vacant)** ....(915) 858-1076

Zuni (NM) Service Unit
Zuni Indian Hospital, P.O. Box 467, Zuni, NM 87327
Tel: (505) 782-4431 Fax: (505) 782-7405

Chief Executive Officer **Jean Otholé** ....(505) 782-7304
E-mail: jean.othole@ihs.hhs.gov
Administrative Officer **(Vacant)** ....(505) 782-4431
Clinical Director **Thomas Faber** ....(505) 782-7301
Nursing Director **Theresa M. "Terry" Kanesta-Brislin** ...(505) 782-7302
E-mail: terry.kanesta-brislin@ihs.hhs.gov
Quality Improvement/Risk Management
Rebecca Grizzle ....(505) 782-7533

Bemidji (MN) Area Indian Health Service

522 Minnesota Avenue NW, Bemidji, MN 56601-3062
Tel: (218) 444-0452 Fax: (218) 444-0461
Areas Covered: MI, MN, WI

● Area Director **Keith Longie** ....(218) 444-0452
E-mail: keith.longie@ihs.gov
Education: Southern Oregon State 1974 BS; UC Berkeley 1977 MPH
Chief Financial Officer **Jeff Bingham** ....(218) 444-0466
E-mail: jeff.bingham@ihs.gov
Chief Information Officer **Verna Kuka** ....(218) 368-0093
E-mail: verna.kuka@ihs.gov
Chief Medical Officer **Dr. Antonio Guimaraes** ....(218) 335-0552
E-mail: antonio.guimaraes@ihs.gov
Director, Office of Environmental Health and
Engineering **(Vacant)** ....(218) 444-0452
Chief, Sanitation Facilities Construction Branch
Craig Morin ....(218) 444-0504
Health Professions Recruiter
Anthony "Tony" Buckanaga ....(218) 444-0486
E-mail: tony.buckanaga@ihs.gov Fax: (218) 444-0498
Agency Lead Negotiator **Chris Poole** ....(218) 444-0475
E-mail: Chris.Poole@ihs.gov
Senior Contract Officer **William Fisher** ....(218) 444-0478
E-mail: william.fisher@ihs.gov Fax: (218) 444-0484
Contract Health Service Officer **(Vacant)** ....(218) 444-0452

Greater Leech Lake (MN) Service Unit
PHS Indian Hospital, 425 Seventh Street, NW, Cass Lake, MN 56633
Tel: (218) 335-3200 Fax: (218) 335-3300

Chief Executive Officer **Louis Erdrich** ....(218) 444-0507
Fax: (218) 444-0510
Administrative Secretary **(Vacant)** ....(218) 335-3200
Clinical Director **(Vacant)** ....(218) 335-3270
Administrative Officer **Terrance Lascano** ....(218) 335-3206
E-mail: terrance.lascano@ihs.gov

Red Lake (MN) Service Unit
PHS Indian Hospital, Highway 1, Redlake, MN 56671
Tel: (218) 679-3912 Fax: (218) 679-0181

Service Unit Director **Norine Smith** ....(218) 679-3912
Administrative Officer **Linda Bedeau** ....(218) 679-3912 ext. 4208
E-mail: linda.bedeau2@ihs.gov
Administrative Clerk **Rhonda G. Wipf** ....(218) 679-3912
E-mail: rhonda.wipf@ihs.gov
Clinical Director **Dr. Paul Ditmanson** ....(218) 444-0545
Information Technology Manager **Andric Fisher** ....(218) 214-0068
E-mail: Andric.Fisher@ihs.gov

White Earth (MN) Service Unit
40520 County Highway 34, Ogema, MN 56569
358, White Earth, MN 56591
Tel: (218) 983-4300 Fax: (218) 983-6217

Service Unit Director and Chief Executive Officer
Alan Fogarty ....(218) 983-6214
Administrative Officer **(Vacant)** ....(218) 983-4300 ext. 6333
Clinical Director **(Vacant)** ....(218) 983-4300 ext. 6243
Optometry Director **David J. Bellware** ....(218) 983-6295
Education: Bowling Green State 1990 BS;
Southern Col Optometry 1996 DO
Dental Services Chief **Toby Imler** ....(218) 983-6285
E-mail: toby.imler@ihs.gov
Mental Health Services Chief **Dr. Darryl R. Zitzow** ......(218) 983-6325
Computer Specialist **Joel Privette** ....(218) 983-6321
E-mail: joel.privette@ihs.gov
Pharmacy Services **Judy L. Rose** ....(218) 983-6372

St. Croix Tribal Health Clinic
4404 State Road 70, Webster, WI 54893
Tel: (715) 349-8554 Fax: (715) 349-2559

Health Center Director **Sarah Cormell** ....(715) 349-8554 ext. 5257

Bad River Health Services
53585 Nokomis Road, Ashland, WI 54806
Tel: (715) 682-7133 Fax: (715) 685-7857

Clinic Administrator **Debra Tutor** ....(715) 682-7133
Facilities Manager **Michael Wiggins, Jr.** ....(715) 682-7111

Fond du Lac Clinic
Min-no-aya-win Human Services, 927 Trettel Lane, Cloquet, MN 55720
Tel: (218) 879-1227 Fax: (218) 879-3750

Human Services Director **Samuel "Sam" Moose** ....(218) 879-1227
Associate Director **Jennifer DuPuis** ....(218) 879-1227
Associate Director **Marilyn Grover** ....(218) 879-1227
Associate Director **Nate Sandman** ....(218) 879-1227
Clinical Director **(Vacant)** ....(218) 879-1227

Billings (MT) Area Indian Health Service

Judge Jameson Federal Building, 2900 Fourth Avenue North,
Billings, MT 59101
Mail: P.O. Box 36600, Billings, MT 59107
Tel: (406) 247-7248 Fax: (406) 247-7230
Areas Covered: MT, WY

● Director **Dorothy A. Dupree MBA** ....(406) 247-7248
E-mail: dorothy.dupree@ihs.gov
Education: North Dakota BA; Arizona MBA
Executive Director **Bryce Redgrave** ....(406) 247-7248
E-mail: bryce.redgrave@ihs.gov
Director of Field Operations **Andrew Delgado** ....(406) 247-7077
E-mail: Andrew.Delgado@ihs.gov
Chief Medical Officer **Dr. Jonathan Gilbert MD** ....(406) 247-7110
Administrative Support Associate Director and
Executive Officer **(Vacant)** ....(406) 247-7248
Environmental Health and Engineering Office
Associate Director **(Vacant)** ....(406) 247-7248
Health Care Programs Office Associate Director
Dr. Jonathan Gilbert MD ....(406) 247-7110
Information Management Office Associate Director
Arlene "Dina" Hansen ....(406) 247-7158
E-mail: dina.hansen@ihs.gov

★ Presidential Appointment Requiring Senate Confirmation ☆ Presidential Appointment □ Schedule C Appointment ◇ Career Senior Foreign Service Appointment
● Career Senior Executive Service (SES) Appointment ○ Non-Career Senior Executive Service (SES) Appointment ■ Postal Career Executive Service

Billings (MT) Area Indian Health Service *(continued)*

Tribal Programs Office Associate Director **(Vacant)** . . . . . . (406) 247-7248

Blackfeet (MT) Service Unit
Browning PHS Hospital, Hospital Circle, Browning, MT 59417
P.O. Box 760, Browning, MT 59417
Tel: (406) 338-6100 Fax: (406) 338-2959

Chief Executive Officer **Garland Stiffarm** . . . . (406) 247-8917
Clinical Director/Medical Officer **Ernest J. Gray** . . . . (406) 338-6100
Administrative Officer **Tina Russell** . . . . (406) 338-6151
E-mail: Tina.Russell@ihs.gov

Crow (MT) Service Unit
One Hospital Road, Crow Agency, MT 59022

Chief Executive Officer **Darren Crowe** . . . . (406) 638-3468
Administrative Officer **Roberta Spotted Horse** . . . . (406) 638-3373
E-mail: roberta.spottedhorse@ihs.gov

Crow/Northern Cheyenne (MT) Hospital
Crow/Northern Cheyenne Hospital, Crow Agency, MT 59022
P.O. Box 9, Crow Agency, MT 59022
Tel: (406) 638-3500 Fax: (406) 638-3569

Chief Medical Officer **(Vacant)** . . . . (406) 638-3339
Clinical Director **(Vacant)** . . . . (406) 638-3500
Administrative Officer **Roberta Spotted Horse** . . . . (406) 638-3373
E-mail: roberta.spottedhorse@ihs.gov

Lodge Grass (MT) Indian Health Clinic
Harding Avenue, Lodge Grass, MT 59050
P.O. Box 780, Lodge Grass, MT 59050
Tel: (406) 639-2317 Fax: (406) 639-2976

Medical Officer **Melanie Walker FNP** . . . . (406) 639-2317
Administrative Officer **Henrietta Whiteman** . . . . (406) 638-2626
E-mail: Henrietta.Whiteman@ihs.gov

Fort Belknap (MT) Service Unit
669 Agency Main Street, Harlem, MT 59526
Tel: (406) 353-3100 Fax: (406) 353-3227

Chief Executive Officer **Jacquelyn James** . . . . (406) 353-3191
E-mail: jacquelyn.james@ihs.gov
Clinical Director **Dr. Gregory M. Smith** . . . . (406) 353-3119
E-mail: gregory.smith@ihs.gov
Executive Secretary **Wanda Allen** . . . . (406) 353-3192
E-mail: wanda.allen@ihs.gov
Administrative Officer **Charlotte Lamebull** . . . . (406) 353-3193
E-mail: charlotte.lamebull@ihs.gov
Administrative Assistant **Wanda Brown** . . . . (406) 353-3247
E-mail: wanda.brown@ihs.gov
Information Technology Specialist **Mikealinda Grant** . . . . (406) 353-3186
E-mail: mikealinda.grant@ihs.gov

Fort Peck (MT) Service Unit
P.O. Box 67, Poplar, MT 59255
Tel: (406) 768-3491 Fax: (406) 768-3603

Service Unit Director **Julie Bemer** . . . . (406) 768-2101
Administrative Officer **Mary Ellen Frislie** . . . . (406) 768-3491
E-mail: maryellen.frislie@ihs.hhs.gov
Chief Medical Officer (Acting) **Peter Arosemena** . . . . (406) 768-2166
Clinical Manager **Kelly Loringer** . . . . (406) 768-3491
Medical Officer **Peter Arosemena** . . . . (406) 768-2166
Family Nurse Practitioner **(Vacant)** . . . . (406) 768-3491
Information Technology Specialist **Mike Lafloe** . . . . (406) 768-3491
E-mail: mike.lafloe@ihs.gov

Wolf Point Indian Health Center
P.O. Box 729, Wolf Point, MT 59201
Tel: (406) 653-1641 Fax: (406) 653-3728

Medical Officer **Dr. Robert Apgar MD** . . . . (406) 768-3491
Clinical Manager **Loren Bisbee** . . . . (406) 653-1641
E-mail: loren.bisbee@ihs.hhs.gov
Clinic Psychologist **Michael Tilus** . . . . (503) 414-5598

Northern Cheyenne (MT) Service Unit
Lame Deer Indian Health Center, Lame Deer, MT 59043
Mail: P.O. Box 70, Lame Deer, MT 59043
Tel: (406) 477-4400 Fax: (406) 477-4427

Chief Executive Officer **Debby Bends** . . . . (406) 477-4410
E-mail: debby.bends@ihs.hhs.gov
Administrative Officer **Crystal Colliflower** . . . . (406) 477-4402
E-mail: crystal.colliflower@ihs.gov
Clinical Director **(Vacant)** . . . . (406) 477-4400
Chief Medical Officer **(Vacant)** . . . . (406) 477-4400
Site Manager **Leah Walkingbear** . . . . (406) 477-4406
E-mail: leah.walkingbear@ihs.gov
Quality Assurance Coordinator **Cheyenne Tallbull** . . . . (406) 477-4454
E-mail: cheyenne.tallbull@ihs.hhs.gov

Wind River (WY) Service Unit
Fort Washakie PHS Indian Health Center,
29 Washakie Park Road, Fort Washakie, WY 82514
P.O. Box 128, Fort Washakie, WY 82514
Tel: (307) 332-7300 Fax: (307) 332-3949

Chief Executive Officer (Acting) **Greg Ault** . . . . (406) 247-7140
E-mail: Greg.Ault@ihs.gov Fax: (406) 247-7229
Chief Medical Officer **Dr. Garth Reber** . . . . (307) 335-5968
Administrative Officer (Acting)
JoLynn Davis . . . . (307) 332-7300 ext. 5963
E-mail: JoLynn.Davis@ihs.gov

Arapahoe (WY) PHS Indian Health Center
Araphoe PHS Indian Health Center, 14 Great Plains Road,
Arapahoe, WY 82510
Mail: P.O. Box 1310, Riverton, WY 82501
Tel: (307) 856-9281 Fax: (307) 856-1630

Clinical Services Administrator **Larron Dolence** . . . . (307) 335-5963
Administrative Officer **(Vacant)** . . . . (307) 856-9281

California Area Indian Health Service
John E. Moss Federal Building, 650 Capitol Mall,
Suite 7-100, Sacramento, CA 95814
Tel: (916) 930-3981 Fax: (916) 930-3951 Fax: (916) 930-3952
Areas Covered: CA, HI

● Area Director **Beverly Miller CPA** . . . . (916) 930-3981 ext. 312
E-mail: beverly.miller@ihs.gov
Chief Medical Officer **Charles Magruder** . . . . (916) 930-3981 ext. 367
Indian Self-Determination Program Manager **(Vacant)** . . . . (916) 930-3981
Office of Public Health Associate Director
Steve J. Riggio DDS . . . . (916) 930-3981 ext. 322
Fax: (916) 930-3952
Information Systems Coordinator
Robert G. Gemmell . . . . (916) 930-3981 ext. 326
E-mail: robert.gemmell@ihs.hhs.gov

Office of Environmental Health and Engineering (OEHE)
650 Capitol Mall, Sacramento, CA 95814
Tel: (916) 930-3945 Fax: (916) 930-3954

Associate Director
Donald "Don" Brafford PE . . . . (916) 930-3981 ext. 339
E-mail: Donald.Brafford@ihs.gov Fax: (916) 930-3954
Director, Environmental Health Services Division
(Vacant) . . . . (916) 930-3945
Deputy Director, Environmental Health
Services Division **(Vacant)** . . . . (916) 930-3981 ext. 356
Director, Health Facilities Engineering
Division **CDR Paul Frazier USPHS** . . . . (916) 930-3981 ext. 365
Director, Sanitation Facilities Construction Division
(Vacant) . . . . (916) 930-3945
Deputy Director, Sanitation
Facilities Construction Division
Christopher Brady PE . . . . (916) 930-3981 ext. 340
E-mail: chris.brady@ihs.gov

DEPARTMENTS

★ Presidential Appointment Requiring Senate Confirmation ☆ Presidential Appointment ☐ Schedule C Appointment ◇ Career Senior Foreign Service Appointment
● Career Senior Executive Service (SES) Appointment ○ Non-Career Senior Executive Service (SES) Appointment ■ Postal Career Executive Service

DEPARTMENTS

Office of Management Support (OMS)
650 Capitol Mall, Sacramento, CA 95814
Tel: (916) 930-3927 Fax: (916) 930-3952

Area Executive and Finance Officer **(Vacant)** .... (916) 930-3981 ext. 335
Financial Management Officer
Jeffrey "JT" Turner .... (916) 930-3981 ext. 309
E-mail: feffrey.turner@ihs.gov
Regional Human Resources Specialist
Jeanne Smith .... (916) 930-3981 ext. 335
E-mail: jeanne.taylor@ihs.gov
Chief Contracting Officer **(Vacant)** .... (916) 930-3927

Consolidated Tribal Health Project
6991 North State Street, Redwood Valley, CA 95470
Mail: P.O. Box 387, Calpella, CA 95418
Tel: (707) 485-5115 Fax: (707) 485-1585 Internet: http://www.cthp.org/

Executive Director **Richard W. Matens** .... (707) 485-5115
E-mail: rmatens@cthp.org
Behavioral Health Director **Melonie Ulzila** ..... (707) 485-5115 ext. 5607
E-mail: mulzila@cthp.org
Dental Director **Mary Ann Gonzalez** .... (707) 485-5115 ext. 5634
E-mail: mgonzalez@cthp.org Fax: (707) 485-5127
Fiscal Officer **Richard Nakamura** .... (707) 485-5115

Pit River Health Service, Inc.
36977 Park Avenue, Burney, CA 96013
Tel: (530) 335-5090 Fax: (530) 335-5241

Executive Director **Glenna Moore** .... (530) 335-5090
Chief Financial Officer **Jeremy Wheeler** .... (530) 335-5090
Computer Systems Manager
Richard Johnston .... (530) 335-3651 ext. 121
E-mail: richardj@pitriverhealthservice.org Fax: (530) 335-3221

Nashville (TN) Area Indian Health Service
711 Stewart's Ferry Pike, Nashville, TN 37214-2634
Tel: (615) 467-1500 Fax: (615) 467-1580
Internet: http://www.ihs.gov/nashville/
Areas Covered: Eastern United States

● Area Director **(Vacant)** .... (615) 467-1500
Emergency Operations and Security Manager
Harold Jones .... (615) 467-1509
E-mail: harold.jones@ihs.gov Fax: (615) 467-2963
Chief Medical Officer **Gloria Grim** .... (615) 467-1500
Dental Officer **(Vacant)** .... (615) 467-1500
Fax: (615) 467-1585
Personnel Management Division Director
Raelyn Pecos .... (505) 248-4510
5300 Homestead Rd., NE, Albuquerque, NM 87110
E-mail: raelyn.pecos@ihs.gov
Tel: (505) 248-4744
Executive Officer **Mark Skinner** .... (615) 467-1537
E-mail: mark.skinner@ihs.hhs.gov

Office of Environmental Health and Engineering
711 Stewart's Ferry Pike, Nashville, TN 37214-2634
Tel: (615) 467-1535 Fax: (615) 467-1586

Director (Acting) **Darrall Tillock** .... (615) 467-1616
5300 Homestead Rd., NE, Albuquerque, NM 87110
Environmental Health Service Division Director
(Acting) **Kit Grosch** .... (615) 467-1622
Facilities Engineering Division Director
Allen Bollinger .... (615) 467-1514
Sanitation Facilities Construction Division Chief
(Vacant) .... (615) 467-1535

Office of Tribal Activities (OTA)
711 Stewart's Ferry Pike, Nashville, TN 37214-2634
Fax: (615) 467-1587

Director **Ashley Metcalf** .... (615) 495-1297

Cherokee Indian Hospital (CIH)
Cherokee Indian Hospital, 188 Hospital Road,
Box C-268, Cherokee, NC 28719
Tel: (828) 497-9163 Fax: (828) 497-5343

Chief Executive Officer **Casey Cooper** .... (828) 497-9163 ext. 201
Chief Operating Officer **Sonya Wachacha** .... (828) 497-9163
Chief Information Officer **Hugh Lambert** .... (828) 497-9163
E-mail: hugh.lambert@cherokeehospital.org
Clinical Director **Dr. Michael Toedt USPHS, MD** .... (301) 443-1619
Pharmacy Director **(Vacant)** .... (828) 497-9163 ext. 6366

Unity Healing Center (UHC)
448 Sequoyah Trail Drive, Cherokee, NC 28719
P.O. Box 201, Cherokee, NC 28719
Tel: (828) 497-3958 Fax: (828) 497-6826

Director **Tiara Ruff** .... (828) 497-3958 ext. 203

Navajo Area Indian Health Service
Highway 264 West to (St. Michaels), Window Rock, AZ 86515
P.O. Box 9020, Window Rock, AZ 86515-9020
Tel: (928) 871-4811 Fax: (928) 871-5896
Internet: https://www.ihs.gov/Navajo/
Areas Covered: Navajo Nation: Northeastern AZ, Northwestern NM, Southern UT

● Director **(Vacant)** .... (928) 871-4811
Chief Information Officer **Robina P. Henry** .... (928) 871-1426
E-mail: robina.henry@ihs.gov
Chief Executive Officer **Priscilla "Patti" Whitethorne** ... (928) 697-4233
E-mail: Priscilla.Whitethorne@ihs.gov
Executive Officer **Dee Hutchison** .... (928) 871-5812
E-mail: Dee.Hutchison@ihs.gov
Equal Employment Opportunity/Civil Rights Officer
Tilda Smith .... (928) 871-1304
E-mail: tilda.smith@ihs.gov
Administrative Services Director **(Vacant)** .... (928) 871-5812
Contracts and Grants Director **(Vacant)** .... (928) 871-5890
Financial Management Director
Margaret Morgan-Benally .... (928) 871-5860
Health Promotion and Disease Prevention Coordinator
Marie Nelson .... (928) 871-1338
Office of Indian Self-Determination Director
Alva R. Tom .... (928) 871-1444
E-mail: alva.tom@ihs.gov Fax: (928) 871-5819
Personnel Management Director **(Vacant)** .... (928) 871-4811
Program Planning and Evaluation Director
Genevieve L. Notah .... (928) 871-5836
Fax: (928) 871-1322

Office of Environmental Health and Engineering
Highway 264 West to (St. Michaels), Window Rock, AZ 86515
Tel: (928) 871-5852 Fax: (928) 871-1462

Director **Roger Slape** .... (928) 871-5857
E-mail: roger.slape@ihs.gov
Biomedical Engineering Director **Harlen Yazzie** .... (928) 871-5889
Fax: (928) 871-1478
Environmental Health Service Director
Gordon D. Tsatoke .... (928) 871-5855
Facilities Management Director (Acting)
Candace Tsingine .... (928) 871-1331
Fax: (928) 871-1478
Occupational Health and Safety Management Director
(Vacant) .... (928) 871-5852
Sanitation Facilities Construction Director **(Vacant)** ...... (928) 871-5852

Office of Professional Standards and Recruitment
Highway 264 West to (St. Michaels), Window Rock, AZ 86515
Tel: (928) 871-5880 Fax: (928) 871-5868

Physician Recruiter **Brenda Martin** .... (928) 871-5884
Nursing Retention and Recruitment Director
Jeannette Yazzie .... (928) 871-5842
E-mail: jeannette.yazzie@ihs.gov Fax: (928) 871-1365

★ Presidential Appointment Requiring Senate Confirmation ☆ Presidential Appointment ☐ Schedule C Appointment ◇ Career Senior Foreign Service Appointment
● Career Senior Executive Service (SES) Appointment ○ Non-Career Senior Executive Service (SES) Appointment ■ Postal Career Executive Service

Chinle (AZ) Service Unit (Chinle Comprehensive Health Care Facility)
Chinle PHS Indian Hospital, Chinle, AZ 86503
P.O. Drawer PH, Chinle, AZ 86503
Tel: (928) 674-7001 Fax: (928) 674-7008

Chief Executive Officer **(Vacant)** .... (928) 674-7001
Administrative Officer **(Vacant)** .... (928) 674-7001
Clinical Director **Eric Ritchie** .... (928) 674-7019

Tsaile (AZ) PHS Indian Health Center
P.O. Box 467, Tsaile, AZ 86556
Tel: (928) 724-3600 Fax: (928) 724-3605

Facility Director **(Vacant)** .... (928) 724-3600
Clinical Director **Dr. Carolyn Johnson** .... (928) 724-3603
E-mail: carolyn.johnson2@ihs.gov
Information Technology Specialist **Merle Chato** .... (928) 724-3719
E-mail: merle.chato@ihs.gov

Crownpoint (NM) Service Unit (Crownpoint Health Care Facility)
Crownpoint PHS Indian Hospital, Crownpoint, NM 87313
P.O. Box 358, Crownpoint, NM 87313-0358
Tel: (505) 786-5291 Fax: (505) 786-6440

Chief Executive Officer **Anslem Roanhorse** .... (505) 786-6313
Clinical Director **Charlene Avery** .... (505) 786-6354

Gallup (NM) Service Unit (Gallup Indian Medical Center)
Gallup Indian Medical Center, 516 East Nizhoni Boulevard, Gallup, NM 87301
Mail: P.O. Box 1337, Gallup, NM 87305
Tel: (505) 722-1000 Fax: (505) 722-1397 (Administration)

Chief Executive Officer **(Vacant)** .... (505) 722-1000
Clinical Director **Dr. Loretta J. Christensen MD** .... (505) 722-1482
Quality Management Director (Acting) **Jennifer Moore** .... (505) 722-1621
Information Technology Supervisor **Adrian C. Haven** .... (505) 722-1300
E-mail: adrian.haven@ihs.gov
Health System Administrator **Virgil L. Davis** .... (505) 722-1400
E-mail: virgil.davis@ihs.gov

Tohatchi (NM) PHS Indian Health Center (Tohatchi Health Care Center)
07 Choosgai Drive, Tohatchi, NM 87325
P.O. Box 142, Tohatchi, NM 87325
Tel: (505) 733-8100 Fax: (505) 733-8239

Health Systems Administrator **Fawn Damon** .... (505) 733-8415
E-mail: fawn.damon@ihs.gov
Supervisory Clinical Nurse **(Vacant)** .... (505) 733-8230
Chief Pharmacist **Kofi Sallar** .... (505) 733-8218
General Supply Technician **Phillip Smith** .... (505) 733-8271
E-mail: phillip.smith2@ihs.gov

Kayenta (AZ) Service Unit (Kayenta Health Center)
Kayenta PHS Indian Health Center, Kayenta, AZ 86033
P.O. Box 368, Kayenta, AZ 86033
Tel: (928) 697-4000

Chief Nurse Executive **Wanda Begay** .... (928) 697-4236
Administrative Officer **Vanessa C. Williams** .... (928) 697-4226
Clinical Director **Barbara Vize** .... (928) 697-4237
E-mail: barbara.vize@ihs.gov
Education: Minnesota 1990 MD

Inscription House PHS Indian Health Center (Inscription House Health Center)
PHS Indian Health Center, Highway 98, Navajo Route 16, Tonalea, AZ 86044
P.O. Box 7397, Shonto, AZ 86054
Tel: (928) 672-3000 Fax: (928) 672-3005

Health Systems Administrator **Delaine M. Alley** .... (928) 672-3046
E-mail: delaine.alley@ihs.gov

Shiprock (NM) Service Unit (Shiprock - Northern Navajo Medical Center)
P.O. Box 160, Shiprock, NM 87420
Tel: (505) 368-6001 Fax: (505) 368-6260

Service Unit Director **Fannessa Comer** .... (505) 368-6006
Chief Information Officer **Roland Chapman** .... (505) 368-6107
E-mail: roland.chapman@ihs.gov
Administrative Officer **Carenda Robinson** .... (505) 368-6007
E-mail: carenda.robinson@ihs.gov
Clinical Director (Acting) **Ouida Vincent** .... (505) 368-6008
Medical Librarian **(Vacant)** .... (505) 368-7062
Supervisory Information Technology Specialist **Tina Nelson** .... (505) 368-6195
Information Technology Specialist **Samuel Namoki** .... (505) 368-6193
E-mail: samuel.namoki@ihs.gov

Dzilth-Na-O-Dith-Hle Health Center - Bloomfield (NM)
Dzilth-Na-O-Dith-Hle Health Center, 6 Road 7586, Bloomfield, NM 87413
Tel: (505) 960-1801 Fax: (505) 368-8009

Facility Director **Laverne J. Miles** .... (505) 368-8002
Executive Assistant **LouElla Bitanny** .... (505) 368-8001
E-mail: louella.bitanny@ihs.gov
Clinical Director (Acting) **Dr. Bryan Harber** .... (505) 368-8083
Fax: (505) 368-6459
Business Office Supervisor **Arlene Sandoval** .... (505) 368-8015
Dental Facility Supervisor **Dr. Bryan Harber** .... (505) 368-8083
General Service **(Vacant)** .... (505) 960-1801
Human Resource Specialist **Gloria Redhorse-Charley** .... (505) 368-6095
E-mail: gloria.redhorse-charley@ihs.gov
Laboratory Services Supervisor **Deborah Denetclaw** .... (505) 368-8056
Education: New Mexico State SB
Maintenance Department Supervisor **Ernest L. Sandoval** .... (505) 368-6755
Medical Records Supervisor **Theresa Victor** .... (505) 368-8021
Mental Health Specialist **Pat Moran** .... (505) 368-8152
Optometrist **Thomas Hurst** .... (505) 368-8091
Pharmacist **(Vacant)** .... (505) 368-8140
Public Health Nursing Supervisor **Joann King** .... (505) 368-7400
Radiologic Diagnostic Technologist **Nicole M. Tsosie** .... (505) 368-7150
Supervisory Clinical Nurse **David Hodgins** .... (505) 368-8122

Tuba City (AZ) Regional Health Care Corporation (TCRHCC)
P.O. Box 600, Tuba City, AZ 86045
Tel: (928) 283-2501 Fax: (928) 283-2828 Internet: www.tchealth.org

Chief Executive Officer **Lynette Bonar** .... (928) 283-2501
E-mail: lynette.bonar@tchealth.org
Chief Medical Officer **James Kyle PhD** .... (928) 283-2587

Winslow (AZ) Service Unit
Winslow Indian Health Care Center, 500 North Indiana Avenue, Winslow, AZ 86047
Tel: (928) 289-4646 Fax: (928) 289-6229

Chief Executive Officer **Sally N. Pete** .... (928) 289-6100
Chief Financial Officer **Karen Leuppe** .... (928) 289-4646
Chief Medical Officer **Frank Armao** .... (928) 289-6233
Director for Community Health **Rod Antone** .... (928) 289-8033
Clinical Nursing Executive **Valarie Kelley** .... (928) 289-6110

Oklahoma City (OK) Area Indian Health Service
701 Market Drive, Oklahoma City, OK 73114
Tel: (405) 951-3820 Fax: (405) 951-3780
Areas Covered: KS, OK, TX

● Director **CAPT Travis E. Watts USPHS** .... (405) 951-3829
E-mail: Travis.Watts@ihs.gov
Chief Medical Officer **Greggory "Greg" Woitte** .... (405) 951-3776
Equal Employment Opportunity Manager **(Vacant)** .... (405) 951-3948
Public Affairs Liaison **Dora Birdhead** .... (405) 951-3724
E-mail: dora.birdhead@ihs.gov

★ Presidential Appointment Requiring Senate Confirmation ☆ Presidential Appointment □ Schedule C Appointment ◇ Career Senior Foreign Service Appointment
● Career Senior Executive Service (SES) Appointment ○ Non-Career Senior Executive Service (SES) Appointment ■ Postal Career Executive Service

Office of Area Office Operations
Assistant Area Director for Area Office Operations
Ronald Grinnell .... (405) 951-3995
E-mail: ronald.grinnell@ihs.gov
Assistant Area Director for Environmental Health and Engineering **Harold Cully** .... (405) 951-3853
E-mail: harold.cully@ihs.gov
Acquisition Management Division Director
Ronda M. Longbrake Trowman .... (405) 951-3999
E-mail: ronda.longbrake@ihs.gov
Financial Management Division Director
Carla Despain .... (405) 951-3911
Human Resources Officer **Shirl Eastep** .... (405) 951-3951
E-mail: shirl.eastep@ihs.gov
Tribal Self-Determination Officer **Lindsay King** .... (405) 951-3733
E-mail: lindsay.king@ihs.gov

Office of Field Operations
Purchase Referred Care Director **Taveah A. George** ..... (405) 951-3723
E-mail: taveah.george@ihs.gov
Health Information Management Director
Jennifer Farris .... (405) 951-3708
E-mail: jennifer.farris@ihs.gov
Business Office Coordinator **Sandra L. Sealey** .... (580) 354-5000
E-mail: Sandra.Sealey@ihs.gov
Performance Improvement Consultant **(Vacant)** .... (405) 257-7315

Division of Information Technology and Telecommunications
Director **Robert "Bobby" Villines** .... (405) 951-3803
E-mail: Bobby.Villines@ihs.gov Fax: (405) 951-6065

Claremore (OK) Service Unit
101 South Moore Avenue, Claremore, OK 74017
Tel: (918) 342-6200 Fax: (918) 342-6436
Director **George L. Valliere** .... (918) 342-6427
Administrative Officer **Carl Murray** .... (918) 342-6200
E-mail: carl.murray@ihs.gov
Clinical Director **Gary Lang** .... (918) 342-6394

Clinton (OK) Service Unit
PHS Indian Hospital, Clinton, OK 73601
Mail: RR 1 Box 3060, Clinton, OK 73601
Tel: (580) 331-3300 Fax: (580) 323-2884 ext. 211
Chief Executive Officer (Acting) **Joseph Bryant** .... (580) 331-3300
Administrative Officer (Acting) **Andrea Klimo** .... (580) 331-3300
E-mail: andrea.klimo@ihs.gov
Clinical Director **Sarah Hartnett** .... (580) 331-3306

El Reno (OK) Indian Health Center
1631-A East Highway 66, El Reno, OK 73036
Tel: (405) 234-8400 Fax: (405) 262-8099
Facility Unit Director **Kelly Factor** .... (405) 422-8440
E-mail: kelly.factor@ihs.gov

Watonga (OK) Indian Health Center
1305 S. Clarence Nash Boulevard, Watonga, OK 73772
Tel: (580) 623-4991 Fax: (580) 623-5490
Facility Unit Director **Andrea Jackson** .... (580) 331-3300
Clinical Director **Sarah Hartnett** .... (580) 331-3306

Haskell Indian Health Center (HHC)
2415 Massachusetts Street, Lawrence, KS 66046-4808
Tel: (785) 843-3750 Fax: (785) 843-8815
Chief Executive Officer **Kelly Battese** .... (785) 843-8815
E-mail: sharon.dawes@ihs.gov
Clinical Director **Dr. Mark James** .... (785) 843-3750
E-mail: mark.james@ihs.gov

Holton (OK) Service Unit (Whitecloud Health Station)
3313-B Thrasher Road, White Cloud, KS 66094
Tel: (785) 595-3450
Facility Director **Kelly Battese** .... (785) 832-4824
E-mail: kelly.battese@ihs.gov

Kickapoo Health Center
1117 Goldfinch Road, Horton, KS 66439
Tel: (785) 486-2154
Facility Director **Paul Austin** .... (785) 486-2154
E-mail: Paul.Austin@ihs.gov

Prairie Band Potawatomi Family Health Center
11400 158 Road, Mayetta, KS 66509
Tel: (785) 966-8200
Facility Director **Jay Mooney** .... (785) 966-8200

Lawton (OK) Service Unit (Lawton Indian Hospital)
PHS Indian Hospital, 1515 Lawrie Tatum Road, Lawton, OK 73501
Tel: (580) 353-0350 Fax: (580) 353-0350 ext. 206
Chief Executive Officer **Dr. Greg A. Ketcher** .... (580) 354-5102
Fax: (580) 354-5105
Administrative Officer **John Bear** .... (580) 354-5103
E-mail: john.bear@ihs.hhs.gov
Clinical Director **Dr. Richard Chadek** .... (580) 354-5270

Anadarko (OK) Indian Health Center (Anadarko Health Center)
P.O. Box 828, Anadarko, OK 73005
201 E. Parker McKenzie Drive, Anadarko, OK 73005
Tel: (405) 247-7900 Tel: (405) 247-7931 (Appointments)
Tel: (405) 247-7928 (Medical Records) Fax: (405) 247-4945
Fax: (405) 247-2342 (Medical Records)
Facility Unit Director **Terry Hunter** .... (405) 247-7901

Carnegie (OK) Indian Health Center (Carnegie Indian Health Station)
1/2 Mile West on Highway 9, Carnegie, OK 73015
Mail: P.O. Box 1120, Carnegie, OK 73015
Tel: (580) 654-1100 Fax: (580) 654-2533
Facility Director **Terry Hunter** .... (405) 247-7901
E-mail: terry.hunter@ihs.gov

Pawnee (OK) Indian Health Center
Public Health Service, 1201 Heritage Circle, Pawnee, OK 74058
Tel: (918) 762-2517 Fax: (918) 762-2729
Chief Executive Officer **Seneca Smith** .... (918) 762-6625
Administrative Officer **Jeri Coats** .... (918) 762-6682
E-mail: Jeri.Coats@ihs.gov
Clinical Director **michelle kimmel** .... (918) 762-2517

Wewoka (OK) Service Unit
PHS Indian Health Center, Wewoka, OK 74884
P.O. Box 1475, Wewoka, OK 74884-1475
Tel: (800) 390-5181 Fax: (405) 257-2051
Chief Executive Officer **Sarrel Smith** .... (405) 257-7326
Administrative Officer **Andy Wilson** .... (405) 257-7343
Clinical Director **Dr. Ronald Fried** .... (405) 257-7334
Information Technology Specialist **Stace Harjo** .... (405) 257-7338
E-mail: stace.harjo@ihs.gov

Phoenix (AZ) Area Indian Health Service
40 North Central Avenue, Suite 600, Phoenix, AZ 85004-4450
Tel: (602) 364-5039 Fax: (602) 364-5042
Areas Covered: AZ, NV, UT

● Director
RADM Charles Ty Reidhead USPHS, MD Suite 601 .. (602) 364-5039
E-mail: ty.reidhead@ihs.gov
Administrative Assistant **Carrie Lewis** .... (602) 364-5347
E-mail: carrie.lewis@ihs.gov
Director of Business Development (Acting)
Arikah McClary .... (602) 364-5117
Director of Field Operations **Holly Elliott** .... (602) 364-5039
Executive Officer (Acting) **Douglas W. Ward** .... (602) 364-5163
E-mail: doug.ward@ihs.gov
Administrative Assistant to the Executive Officer
Michelle Sager Suite 601 .... (602) 364-5347
E-mail: michelle.sager@ihs.gov
Chief Information Officer **Constance James** ... (602) 263-1200 ext. 1928
E-mail: constance.james@ihs.gov

★ Presidential Appointment Requiring Senate Confirmation ☆ Presidential Appointment ☐ Schedule C Appointment ◇ Career Senior Foreign Service Appointment
● Career Senior Executive Service (SES) Appointment ○ Non-Career Senior Executive Service (SES) Appointment ■ Postal Career Executive Service

Phoenix (AZ) Area Indian Health Service *(continued)*

Chief Medical Officer **CAPT Marie Russell USPHS** ..... (602) 364-5039
Clinical Support Center Director **Wesley Picciotti** .... (602) 364-7777
Contract Health Service Office Director
Julia Ysaguirre .... (602) 364-5140
E-mail: julia.ysaguirre@ihs.gov
Environmental Health Office Director
CAPT Michael Welch USPHS .... (602) 364-5068
Health Programs Office Director **Cynthia Claus PhD** .... (602) 364-5169
E-mail: cynthia.claus@ihs.gov
Information Resources Management Director
Lee Stern .... (602) 364-5287
E-mail: lee.stern@ihs.gov Fax: (602) 364-5311
Self-Determination Director **Randall Morgan** .... (602) 364-5351
Physician Recruiter **Kevin Long** .... (602) 364-5039
Privacy Coordinator **Maria Strom** .... (602) 364-5149
E-mail: Maria.Strom@ihs.gov

Office of Administration (OA)
40 North Central Avenue, Phoenix, AZ 85004-4450
Fax: (602) 364-5042

Director **Douglas W. Ward** .... (602) 364-5163
E-mail: Doug.Ward@ihs.gov
Employee/Labor Relations Officer **Naomi White** .... (602) 364-5247
Equal Employment Opportunity Officer
Michelle Homer .... (602) 364-5265
E-mail: michelle.homer@ihs.gov
Property Management Officer **Jeremy Woodruff** .... (602) 364-5367
Southwest Regional Personnel Officer **Cathy Ayatta** ..... (602) 364-5248
E-mail: cathy.ayatta@ihs.gov
Indian Health Service Commissioned Corps Liaison
Stephen Navarro .... (602) 364-5039
E-mail: stephen.navarro@ihs.gov
Acquisition Management Division Chief
Verna Kuwanhoyioma .... (602) 364-5012
E-mail: verna.kuwanhoyioma@ihs.gov
Facilities Management Branch Chief (Acting)
Steve McGovern .... (602) 364-5086
Financial Management Branch Chief **Carey Tso** .... (602) 364-5039

Colorado River (AZ) Service Unit (Parker Indian Health Center)
Parker PHS Indian Hospital, 12033 Agency Road, Parker, AZ 85344
Tel: (928) 669-2137 Fax: (928) 669-5860

Chief Executive Officer **Elizabeth Helsel** .... (928) 669-3114
Clinical Director **(Vacant)** .... (928) 669-2137
Chief Information Officer **Jaylynn Saavedra** .... (928) 669-3112
E-mail: jaylynn.saavedra@ihs.gov
Information Technology Specialist **(Vacant)** .... (928) 669-2137

Peach Springs (AZ) PHS Indian Health Center
P.O. Box 190, Peach Springs, AZ 86434-0190
Tel: (928) 769-2204 Fax: (928) 769-2701

Facility Director **Daniel Cox** .... (928) 769-2910
E-mail: daniel.cox@ihs.gov

Supai Health Station
P.O. Box 129, Supai, AZ 86435
Tel: (928) 448-2641 Fax: (928) 448-2312

Facility Director **(Vacant)** .... (928) 769-2900

Elko (NV) Service Unit
515 Shoshone Circle, Elko, NV 89801
Tel: (775) 738-2252 Fax: (775) 748-1455
Areas Covered: Northeastern NV

Chief Executive Officer (Acting)
Loren Ellery .... (775) 738-2252 ext. 1401
E-mail: loren.ellery@ihs.gov
Clinical Director **Kirin Madden** .... (775) 748-1416

Fort Yuma (AZ) Service Unit
P.O. Box 1368, Yuma, AZ 85366-1368
Tel: (760) 572-4105 Fax: (760) 572-4183

Chief Executive Officer **(Vacant)** .... (760) 572-4100

Fort Yuma (AZ) Service Unit *(continued)*

Administrative Officer (Acting) **Yvonne Galvan** .... (760) 572-4137
E-mail: yvonne.yazzie@ihs.hhs.gov
Clinical Director (Acting) **Cynthia A. Long** .... (760) 572-4100

Hopi Service Unit (Hopi Health Care Center)
P.O. Box 4000, Polacca, AZ 86042
Tel: (928) 737-6002 Tel: (928) 737-6000 (Automated)
Fax: (928) 737-6001

Chief Executive Officer **Mose Herne** .... (928) 737-6000
Chief Operations Officer **David Tonemah** .... (928) 737-6013
Clinical Director **Darren Vicenti MD** .... (928) 737-6140
Chief Nursing Executive **Maria Grace Gomes** .... (928) 737-6370
Quality Management Director **Kendra Bonin** .... (928) 737-6024
Secretary **Carla Harvey** .... (928) 737-6000

Phoenix (AZ) Service Unit (Phoenix Indian Medical Center)
Phoenix Indian Medical Center, 4212 North 16th Street,
Phoenix, AZ 85016
Tel: (602) 263-1200 Fax: (602) 263-1618

Chief Executive Officer **(Vacant)** .... (602) 263-1200
Chief Financial Officer **Paulla Henderson** .... (602) 263-1599
Chief Information Officer **Darrin I'atala** .... (602) 263-1658
E-mail: darrin.i'atala@ihs.gov
Chief Operating Officer **Deanna J. Dick** .... (602) 263-1582
Health System Specialist **Rinda L. Bradley** ..... (602) 263-1200 ext. 122
E-mail: rinda.bradley@ihs.gov
Director, Inpatient and Specialty Services
Laura Tillman .... (602) 263-1674
Librarian **Rebecca Swift** .... (602) 263-1200 ext. 1777
E-mail: rebecca.swift@ihs.gov Fax: (602) 263-1577

Salt River Clinic (SRC)
10005 East Osborn Road, Scottsdale, AZ 85256
Tel: (480) 946-9066 Fax: (480) 946-9415

Clinical Administrator (Acting) **Karen Camilli** .... (480) 946-9066
E-mail: karen.camilli@ihs.gov
Supervisory Nurse **Barbara Asher** .... (480) 946-9066 ext. 4508
E-mail: barbara.asher@ihs.hhs.gov
Pharmacist (Acting) **Robert Boyle** .... (480) 946-9066 ext. 4508
E-mail: robert.boyle@ihs.gov

San Carlos (AZ) Service Unit
San Carlos PHS Indian Hospital, 223 Seneca Lane, San Carlos, AZ 85550
Mail: P.O. Box 208, San Carlos, AZ 85550-0208
Tel: (928) 475-7350

Chief Executive Officer (Acting)
Dr. Robert H. Harry MD .... (928) 475-7350
Chief Financial Officer **Vivie Hosteenez** .... (928) 475-7319
Administrative Officer **Shirley Boni** .... (928) 475-7348
Clinical Director **Dr. Carol Frost Lee** .... (928) 475-7219

Bylas Health Center (Clarence Wesley Health Center)
101 Medical Drive, Bylas, AZ 85530
P.O. Box 208, San Carlos, AZ 85550
Tel: (928) 475-2686 Fax: (928) 475-7377

Facility Director (Acting) **Dr. Carol Frost Lee** .... (928) 475-7349

San Carlos Apache Tribe Health Center
Facility Director **Deven Parlikar** .... (928) 475-2686

Schurz (NV) Service Unit (Schurz Health Center)
1150 Financial Boulevard, Suite 500, Reno, NV 89502
Drawer A, Schurz, NV 89427
Tel: (775) 331-7901 Fax: (775) 359-1464

Chief Executive Officer **Loren Ellery** .... (775) 331-7901 ext. 234

Washoe Tribal Health Center (WTHC)
1559 Watasheamu Drive, Gardnerville, NV 89460
Tel: (775) 265-4215 Fax: (775) 265-3429

Executive Director **(Vacant)** .... (775) 265-4215

★ Presidential Appointment Requiring Senate Confirmation ☆ Presidential Appointment ☐ Schedule C Appointment ◇ Career Senior Foreign Service Appointment
● Career Senior Executive Service (SES) Appointment ○ Non-Career Senior Executive Service (SES) Appointment ■ Postal Career Executive Service

DEPARTMENTS

Uintah and Ouray (UT) Service Unit (Fort Duchesne PHS Indian Health Center)
Fort Duchesne PHS Indian Health Center, Fort Duchesne, UT 84026
P.O. Box 160, Fort Duchesne, UT 84026
Tel: (435) 722-5122 Fax: (435) 722-9137

Chief Executive Officer (Acting) **Dr. Lawrence Zubel** .... (435) 725-6803
Administrative Officer **(Vacant)** .... (435) 722-5122
Nursing Director **Jonathan Flitton** .... (435) 725-6861
E-mail: jonathan.flitton@ihs.gov

Whiteriver (AZ) Service Unit (Whiteriver PHS Indian Hospital)
Whiteriver Indian Hospital, 200 West Hospital Highway, MP-342, Whiteriver, AZ 85941
P.O. Box 860, Whiteriver, AZ 85941-0860
Tel: (928) 338-4911 Fax: (928) 338-3522

Chief Executive Officer **Michelle Martinez** .... (928) 338-3549
Clinical Director **James McAuley** .... (928) 338-4911
Administrative Officer **(Vacant)** .... (928) 338-4911

Cibecue (AZ) PHS Indian Health Center (Cibecue Satellite Office)
Two West Third Street, Cibecue, AZ 85911
Mail: P.O. Box 80039, Cibecue, AZ 85911
Tel: (928) 332-2560 Fax: (928) 332-2418

Director **Michelle Martinez** .... (928) 332-2560

Portland (OR) Area Office Indian Health Service (PAO)
1414 Northwest Northrup Street, Suite 800, Portland, OR 97209
Tel: (503) 414-5555 Fax: (503) 414-5554
Areas Covered: ID, OR, WA

• Director **Dean M. Seyler** .... (503) 414-7746
E-mail: dean.seyler@ihs.hhs.gov
Secretary **Asha Petoskey** .... (503) 414-7746 ext. 5558
E-mail: asha.petoskey@ihs.gov
• Deputy Director
Dr. Stephen Miles Rudd MD .... (503) 414-5555 ext. 3552
E-mail: stephen.rudd@ihs.gov
Tribal/Service Unit Operations Director **(Vacant)** .... (503) 414-7746
Chief Medical Officer
Dr. Stephen Miles Rudd MD .... (503) 414-5555 ext. 3552
Diabetes Consultant **(Vacant)** .... (503) 414-5550
Division of Information Resources Management
Jonathan Hubbard .... (503) 414-7752
E-mail: jonathan.hubbard@ihs.gov

Clinical Support
Director
Jonathan Merrell RN, BSN, MBA, USPHS (Ret) .... (503) 414-5555
E-mail: jonathan.merrell@ihs.gov Fax: (503) 414-7795
Dental Consultant **(Vacant)** .... (503) 414-5594

Office of Administration and Management (OAM)
Executive Officer **Ann Arnett** .... (503) 414-7746
E-mail: ann.arnett@ihs.gov
Acquisition Division Director **(Vacant)** .... (503) 414-5528
Financial Management Division Director **(Vacant)** .... (503) 414-5555
Client Services Division Director **Margaret Witt** .... (503) 414-7732
E-mail: margaret.witt@ihs.gov Fax: (503) 414-7723

Office of Environmental Health and Engineering
Director **Richard R. Truitt** .... (503) 414-7783
E-mail: richard.truitt@ihs.hhs.gov
Environmental Health Services Director **(Vacant)** .... (503) 414-5555
Sanitation Facilities Construction Division Director
Mathew Martinson .... (503) 414-7780

Colville (WA) Service Unit
Colville IHS Indian Health Center, Highway 155, Nespelem, WA 99155
Mail: P.O. Box 71, Highway 155, Nespelem, WA 99155
Tel: (509) 634-2900 Fax: (509) 634-2946

Chief Executive Officer **Colleen Cawston** .... (509) 634-2933
Clinical Director **Dr. Loren Lewis MD** .... (509) 634-2913
Education: Utah MPH; Nevada (Reno) MD

Colville (WA) Service Unit *(continued)*

Information Technology Specialist **Jody George** .... (509) 634-2923
E-mail: jody.george@ihs.gov
Administrative Officer (Acting) **Brian Nanamkin** .... (509) 634-2924
E-mail: brian.nanamkin@ihs.gov

Fort Hall (ID) Service Unit (Not-Tsoo Gah-Nee Indian Health Center)
Fort Hall Indian Health Service, Mission Road, Fort Hall, ID 83203
P.O. Box 717, Fort Hall, ID 83203
Tel: (208) 238-2400 Fax: (208) 238-5463

Chief Executive Officer **Shirley D. Alvarez** .... (208) 238-5493
Clinical Director **Christopher Nield** .... (208) 238-5455
Administrative Officer **(Vacant)** .... (208) 238-2400

Warm Springs (OR) Health and Wellness Center
P.O. Box 1209, Warm Springs, OR 97761
Tel: (541) 553-1196 Fax: (541) 553-2126

Service Unit Director **Carol A. Prevost** .... (541) 553-1196
Clinical Director **Rachel Locker** .... (541) 553-1196
Quality Assurance Coordinator **Diane Fuller** .... (541) 553-1196

Wellpinit (WA) Service Unit (David C. Wynecoop Memorial Clinic)
David C. Wynecoop Memorial Clinic, Wellpinit, WA 99040
P.O. Box 357, Wellpinit, WA 99040
Tel: (509) 258-4517 Fax: (509) 258-7152

Service Unit Director **Marcus C. Martinez** .... (509) 258-4517 ext. 100
Administrative Officer **(Vacant)** .... (509) 258-4517 ext. 103
Clinical Director **Margaret Koepping** .... (509) 258-4517
Facilities **Steven "Steve" Abrahamson** .... (509) 258-4517
Medical Equipment Specialist **(Vacant)** .... (509) 258-4517

Western Oregon Service Unit (Chemawa Health Center)
Chemawa Indian Health Center, 3750 Chemawa Road, NE, Salem, OR 97305
Tel: (503) 304-7600 Fax: (503) 304-7678

Service Unit Director **Laura Herbison** .... (503) 304-7240
Clinical Director **(Vacant)** .... (503) 304-7625
Administrative Officer **Teresa Barbo** .... (503) 304-7667
E-mail: teresa.barbo@ihs.gov

Yakama (WA) Service Unit
Yakama PHS Indian Health Center, 401 Buster Road, Toppenish, WA 98948-9792
Tel: (509) 865-2102 Fax: (509) 865-6237

Service Unit Director **Jay Sampson** .... (509) 865-2102 ext. 273
Clinical Director **Michelle Womack** .... (509) 865-2102 ext. 285
Human Resource Specialist **(Vacant)** .... (509) 865-2102
Administrative Assistant **Stacy Palmer-Hill** .... (509) 865-2102 ext. 396
E-mail: Stacy.Hill@ihs.gov

Tucson (AZ) Area Indian Health Service
7900 South "J" Stock Road, Tucson, AZ 85746-7012
Tel: (520) 295-2550 Fax: (520) 295-2602
Areas Covered: South Central AZ

• Director **Dixie Gaikowski** .... (520) 295-2405
E-mail: dixie.gaikowski@ihs.gov
Education: South Dakota State BS
Executive Officer **Mark Bigbey** .... (520) 295-2405
E-mail: mark.bigbey@ihs.gov
Financial Management Officer **Vivian A. Draper** .... (520) 295-2452
E-mail: vivian.draper@ihs.gov
Chief Information Officer **(Vacant)** .... (520) 295-2523
Chief Medical Officer **Daniel Marino** .... (520) 295-2401
Area Contracting Officer **(Vacant)** .... (520) 295-2550
Equal Opportunity Employment Counselor **(Vacant)** .... (520) 295-2485

Sells (AZ) Service Unit
Sells PHS Indian Hospital, Highway 86 and Topawa Road, Sells, AZ 85634
P.O. Box 548, Sells, AZ 85634
Tel: (520) 383-7251 Fax: (520) 383-7216

Chief Executive Officer **Troy Klarkowski** .... (520) 383-7251
Clinical Services Division Director **Andrew Terranella** . . . (520) 383-7453
E-mail: andrew.terranella@ihs.gov
Hospital Nursing Division Director **Donna Hobbs** .... (520) 383-7256
E-mail: donna.hobbs@ihs.hhs.gov
Executive Assistant **(Vacant)** .... (520) 383-7251

San Xavier PHS Indian Health Center
7900 South "J" Stock Road, Tucson, AZ 85746-7012
Tel: (520) 295-2550 Fax: (520) 295-2609

Health Center Director **Ellamae Dayzie** .... (520) 295-2480
E-mail: ellamae.dayzie@ihs.gov
Administrative Officer **Rozina Taylor** .... (520) 295-2680
E-mail: rozina.taylor@ihs.hhs.gov

Santa Rosa PHS Indian Health Center
HC 01, Box 8700, Sells, AZ 85634
Tel: (520) 383-5570 Fax: (520) 383-5572

Facility Director (Acting) **Cynthia Manuel** .... (520) 383-6011

DEPARTMENTS

★ Presidential Appointment Requiring Senate Confirmation ☆ Presidential Appointment ☐ Schedule C Appointment ◇ Career Senior Foreign Service Appointment
● Career Senior Executive Service (SES) Appointment ○ Non-Career Senior Executive Service (SES) Appointment ■ Postal Career Executive Service

United States Department of Homeland Security

DEPARTMENTS

Contents

DEPARTMENTS

United States Department of Homeland Security (DHS)

Description: The Department of Homeland Security is charged with protecting the nation against domestic threats. Through its component agencies, it analyzes threats and intelligence, guards borders and airports, protects and enhances critical infrastructure, and coordinates the nation's response to emergencies and disasters.

Department of Homeland Security, Washington, DC 20528
Tel: (202) 282-8000 Internet: www.dhs.gov
Internet: www.dhs.gov/open-government (Open Government Initiative)

OFFICE OF THE SECRETARY

Department of Homeland Security, Washington, DC 20528
Fax: (202) 282-9188

Office of the Deputy Secretary

Federal Law Enforcement Training Centers (FLETC)

Glynco Facility, 1131 Chapel Crossing Road, Glynco, GA 31524
Tel: (912) 267-2070 Fax: (912) 267-2071 Internet: www.fletc.gov

Office of the Deputy Director
1131 Chapel Crossing Road, Glynco, GA 31524
Tel: (912) 267-2070 Fax: (912) 267-2071

Regional and International Training Directorate
Glynco Facility, 1131 Chapel Crossing Road, Glynco, GA 31524
Fax: (912) 280-5159

Artesia Center
1300 West Richey Avenue, Artesia, NM 88210
Tel: (575) 748-8000 Fax: (575) 748-8100 E-mail: fletc-artesia@dhs.gov

● Site Director **Terry Todd** .... (575) 746-5717
E-mail: terry.todd@dhs.gov

Charleston Center
2000 Bainbridge Avenue, Charleston, SC 29405
Tel: (843) 566-8551 Fax: (843) 743-2104
E-mail: fletc-charleston@dhs.gov

Site Director **Wayne Anderson** .... (843) 566-7710

Cheltenham Center
9000 Commo Road, Cheltenham, MD 20623-5000
Tel: (301) 868-5830 Fax: (301) 868-6549
E-mail: fletc-webmasterche@dhs.gov

Site Director **Daniel W. "Danny" Auer** .... (301) 868-5461

Office of Inspector General (IG)

245 Murray Lane, SW, Mail Stop 0305, Washington, DC 20528
1120 Vermont Avenue, NW, Washington, DC 20005
Tel: (202) 254-4100 Fax: (202) 254-4285
E-mail: dhs-oig.officepublicaffairs@oig.dhs.gov Internet: www.oig.dhs.gov

Office of Audits

Department of Homeland Security, Washington, DC 20528
Fax: (202) 254-4285

Chicago (IL) Field Office
55 West Monroe Street, Suite 1010, Chicago, IL 60603
Tel: (312) 886-6300 Fax: (312) 886-6308
Areas Covered: IA, IL, IN, KS, MI, MO, MN, NE, ND, OH, SD, TN, WV, WI

Field Audit Director **(Vacant)** .... (312) 886-0118
Audit Manager **Cheryl Jones** .... (312) 886-0121
E-mail: cheryl.jones@dhs.gov
Education: DePaul 1983 BS
Audit Manager **Bradley Mosher** .... (312) 886-0142
E-mail: bradley.mosher@dhs.gov
Education: Southern Illinois 1983 BS; Benedictine 1989 MBA
Audit Manager **(Vacant)** .... (312) 886-0127

Houston (TX) Field Office
1800 West Loop South, Suite 300, Houston, TX 77027
Tel: (713) 212-4350 Fax: (713) 212-4361

Audit Manager **J. Eric Barnett** .... (713) 212-4350
E-mail: eric.barnett@dhs.gov
Audit Manager **Johnson Joseph** .... (713) 212-4350
Audit Manager **LaParacina Williams** .... (713) 212-4350
E-mail: laparacina.williams@dhs.gov

Philadelphia (PA) Field Office
Cherry Hill, NJ 08002
Fax: (856) 661-3347

Director **Patrick O'Malley** .... (856) 596-3822
E-mail: patrick.omalley@dhs.gov
Audit Manager **Robert Ferrara** .... (856) 596-3810
E-mail: robert.ferrara@dhs.gov
Audit Manager **Christine Haynes** .... (856) 596-3827
E-mail: christine.haynes@dhs.gov
Audit Manager **(Vacant)** .... (856) 596-3825

Miami (FL) Field Office
3401 SW 160th Avenue, Suite 320, Miramar, FL 33027
Tel: (954) 538-7842 Fax: (954) 602-1034

Director **Maryann Pereira** .... (954) 538-7848

Office of Investigations (INV)

Department of Homeland Security, Washington, DC 20528
Fax: (202) 254-4285

Atlanta (GA) Field Office
10 Tenth Street, Suite 750, Atlanta, GA 30309
Tel: (404) 832-6730 Fax: (404) 832-6646

Special Agent-in-Charge **James E. Ward** .... (404) 832-6730

(continued on next page)

Atlanta (GA) Field Office *(continued)*

Administrative Officer **Cherrie Jordan** . . . . (404) 832-6733
E-mail: cherrie.jordan@dhs.gov

Dallas (TX) Field Office
7460 Warren Parkway, Suite 275A, Frisco, TX 75034
Tel: (214) 436-5250 Fax: (214) 436-5251

Special Agent-in-Charge **David Green** . . . . (713) 212-4301
E-mail: david.green@oig.dhs.gov
Assistant Special Agent-in-Charge **(Vacant)** . . . . (214) 436-5250

Chicago (IL) Field Office
55 West Monroe Street, Suite 1050, Chicago, IL 60603
Tel: (312) 886-2800 Fax: (312) 886-2804
Areas Covered: IL, IN, IA, KY, KS MI, MN, NE, ND, OH, SD, WI

Special Agent-in-Charge **Armando Lopez** . . . . (312) 886-2800
Administrative Officer **Dollena McIntyre** . . . . (312) 886-2800
E-mail: dollena.mcintyre@dhs.gov

Houston (TX) Field Office
1800 West Loop South, Suite 300, Houston, TX 77027
Tel: (713) 212-4300 Fax: (713) 212-4363
Areas Covered: LA, TX

Special Agent-in-Charge **David Green** . . . . (713) 212-4300

Los Angeles (CA) Field Office
222 North Sepulveda Boulevard, Suite 1640, El Segundo, CA 90245-4320
Tel: (310) 665-7320 Fax: (310) 665-7309

Special Agent-in-Charge **Tom Merchant** . . . . (310) 665-7320
Administrative Officer **Gail D. Lindsey** . . . . (310) 665-7320
E-mail: gail.lindsey@dhs.gov

McAllen (TX) Field Office
Bentsen Tower, 1701 West Business Highway 83,
Suite 250, McAllen, TX 78501-5160
Tel: (956) 664-8010 Fax: (956) 618-8151

Resident Agent-in-Charge **(Vacant)** . . . . (956) 664-8010

Miami (FL) Field Office
3401 SW 160th Avenue, Suite 401, Miramar, FL 33027
Tel: (954) 538-7555 Fax: (954) 602-1033
Areas Covered: FL, PR, VI

Special Agent-in-Charge **Jay Donly** . . . . (954) 538-7555

Philadelphia (PA) Field Office
5002 Lincoln Drive West, Suite B, Marlton, NJ 08053
Tel: (856) 596-3800 Fax: (856) 810-3410
Areas Covered: CT, DE, MA, MD, ME, NH, NJ, NY, PA, RI, VT

Special Agent-in-Charge **Gregory K. Null** . . . . (856) 596-3800
Assistant Special Agent-in-Charge **Julio Santana** . . . . (856) 596-3800
Administrative Officer **Brianna Brown** . . . . (856) 596-3800
E-mail: brianna.brown@oig.dhs.gov

San Diego (CA) Field Office
701 B Street, Suite 560, San Diego, CA 92101
Tel: (619) 235-2501

Special Agent-in-Charge **Amanda Thandi** . . . . (619) 235-2501
Assistant Special Agent-in-Charge **David Canez** . . . . (619) 235-2501
Administrative Officer **Elizabeth Maldonado** . . . . (619) 235-2501
E-mail: elizabeth.maldonado@dhs.gov

El Centro (CA) Area Office
516 Industry Way, Suite B, Imperial, CA 92251
Tel: (760) 335-3900 Fax: (760) 335-3726

Resident Agent-in-Charge **Angie Cuevas** . . . . (760) 335-3900
E-mail: angie.cuevas@dhs.gov
Administrative Officer **Rosario Carrion** . . . . (760) 335-3900
E-mail: rosario.carrion@dhs.gov

San Francisco Field Office
300 Frank H. Owaga Plaza, Suite 275, Oakland, CA 94612
Tel: (510) 637-4311 Fax: (510) 637-4327
Areas Covered: CA, CO, NV, UT

Special Agent-in-Charge **Thomas E. Meyer** . . . . (510) 637-4338

Office of Emergency Management Oversight (EMO)

Department of Homeland Security, Washington, DC 20528
Fax: (202) 254-4285

Central Regional Office
7460 Warren Parkway, Suite 275, Frisco, TX 75034
Tel: (214) 436-5200 Tel: (214) 395-2132 Fax: (214) 436-5201

● Director, North **Paige Hamrick** . . . . (214) 436-5231
E-mail: paige.hamrick@oig.dhs.gov
● Director, South **(Vacant)** . . . . (214) 436-5220
Administrative Officer **Sonja Popovich** . . . . (214) 436-5200
E-mail: sonja.popovich@oig.dhs.gov

Eastern Regional Office
10 Tenth Street, Suite 750, Atlanta, GA 30309
Tel: (404) 832-6700

Director **David Kimble** . . . . (404) 832-6700
E-mail: david.kimble@dhs.gov
Education: Southeastern Louisiana

Western Regional Office
300 Frank Ogawa Plaza, Suite 275, Oakland, CA 94612
Tel: (510) 637-1463 Fax: (510) 637-1484

Director **Humberto Melara** . . . . (510) 637-1463

CYBERSECURITY AND INFRASTRUCTURE SECURITY AGENCY (CISA)

Department of Homeland Security, Washington, DC 20528

Note: On November 16, 2018, President Trump signed into law the Cybersecurity and Infrastructure Security Agency Act of 2018, which elevates the mission of the former National Protection and Programs Directorate within DHS and establishes the Cybersecurity and Infrastructure Security Agency (CISA).

Office of the Under Secretary

Department of Homeland Security, Washington, DC 20528
Tel: (703) 235-1482 Fax: (703) 235-1488

Office of the Federal Protective Service (FPS)
800 North Capitol Street, NW, Suite 500, Washington, DC 20002
Tel: (202) 732-8000 Fax: (202) 732-8109

Federal Protective Service - National Capital Region
1900 Half Street, SW, Suite 5000, Washington, DC 20528
Tel: (202) 245-2300 Fax: (202) 245-2306
Areas Covered: DC, MD, VA

Regional Director (Acting) **Maybelle Hallman** . . . . (202) 245-2300
Deputy Director **Maybelle Hallman** . . . . (202) 245-2300

Federal Protective Service - Region 1
10 Causeway Street, Room 935, Boston, MA 02222-1054
Tel: (617) 565-6360
Tel: (617) 565-1212 (24-Hour Emergency Control Number)
Fax: (617) 565-6364
Areas Covered: CT, MA, ME, NH, RI, VT

Regional Director **Timothy G. Bane** . . . . (617) 565-6360
E-mail: timothy.bane@dhs.gov
Deputy Regional Director **Suzanne MacMullin** . . . . (617) 565-6360
E-mail: suzanne.macmullin@dhs.gov
Mission Support Branch Chief (Acting)
Thomas McGoff . . . . (617) 565-6360
Threat Management Branch Chief **Jeff Steely** . . . . (617) 565-6360
Administrative Assistant **Lisena Paul** . . . . (617) 565-6360
E-mail: lisena.paul@dhs.gov

★ Presidential Appointment Requiring Senate Confirmation ☆ Presidential Appointment □ Schedule C Appointment ◇ Career Senior Foreign Service Appointment
● Career Senior Executive Service (SES) Appointment ○ Non-Career Senior Executive Service (SES) Appointment ■ Postal Career Executive Service

Federal Protective Service - Region 2
Jacob K. Javitz Federal Building, 26 Federal Plaza,
Room 17-130, New York, NY 10278
Tel: (646) 589-6000
Areas Covered: NJ, NY, PR, VI

Regional Director **Anthony Levey** .... (646) 589-6000 ext. 5
Deputy Director **Chris Pappas** .... (646) 589-6000
E-mail: chris.pappas@dhs.gov
Caribbean Branch Chief **Clyde Beatty** .... (787) 766-5395
Federico Degetau Federal Building, Carlos Chardon Avenue,
Hato Rey, PR 00918
Criminal Investigations **(Vacant)** .... (646) 589-6000
Metropolitan Branch Chief **Chris Barnes** .... (646) 589-6000
Mission Support Branch Chief
Martin McRimmon .... (646) 589-6000 ext. 6
E-mail: martin.mcrimmon@dhs.gov
New Jersey Branch Chief **Neil Ford** .... (973) 645-4790
970 Broad Street, Newark, NJ 07102
Upstate Branch Chief **Neil Ford** .... (518) 431-4302
Regional Control Center **Kenneth Johnson** .... (646) 589-6000
E-mail: kenneth.johnson@dhs.gov
Training Officer **Tony Wong** .... (646) 589-6000

Federal Protective Service - Region 3
Mellon Independence Center, 701 Market Street,
Suite 4200, Philadelphia, PA 19106
Tel: (215) 521-2150 Fax: (215) 521-2169
Areas Covered: DE, MD, PA, VA, WV

Regional Director **Cathy C. Long** .... (215) 521-7823

Federal Protective Service - Region 4
Martin Luther King, Jr. Federal Building,
180 Spring Street, SW, Atlanta, GA 30303
Areas Covered: AL, FL, GA, KY. MS, NC, SC, TN

Regional Director (Acting) **Shirley Reed** .... (404) 893-1500
Deputy Regional Director **(Vacant)** .... (404) 893-1500
Regional Threat Manager **Curtis Houston** .... (404) 893-1500
Operations Branch Chief **King Cooper** .... (404) 893-1500
E-mail: king.cooper@dhs.gov
Support Services Branch Chief
Annette L. Taylor USMC (Ret) .... (404) 893-1500

Federal Protective Service - Region 5
Kluczynski Federal Building, 230 South Dearborn Street,
Room 3540, Chicago, IL 60604
Tel: (312) 353-0933 Fax: (312) 353-0143
Areas Covered: IL, IN, MI, MN, OH, WI

Regional Director **Clifford T. Hughes** .... (312) 353-0933
Education: Johns Hopkins 2010 MA

Federal Protective Service - Region 6
601 East 12th Street, Suite W0261, Kansas City, MO 64106
Tel: (816) 426-2155
Areas Covered: IA, KS, MO, NE

Regional Director **David S. Thomas** .... (816) 426-2155
E-mail: david.thomas@dhs.gov
Deputy Director **Derrick Reuschlein** .... (816) 426-2155

Federal Protective Service - Region 7
1901 North State Highway 360, Suite 500, Grand Prairie, TX 75050
Tel: (817) 649-6200 Fax: (817) 649-7221
Areas Covered: AR, LA, NM, OK, TX

Regional Director **Matthew Brand** .... (817) 649-6200
E-mail: matthew.brand@dhs.gov

Federal Protective Service - Region 8
Building 44, Denver Federal Center, Denver, CO 80225-0266
Tel: (303) 236-7931 Fax: (303) 236-7965
Areas Covered: CO, MT, ND, SD, UT, WY

Regional Director **Donald Cooper** .... (303) 236-7931

Federal Protective Service - Region 9
450 Golden Gate Avenue, 5th Floor West, San Francisco, CA 94102-3434
Tel: (415) 522-3440 Fax: (415) 522-3218
Areas Covered: AZ, CA, HI, NV

Regional Director **Mario Canton** .... (415) 522-3449
Administrative Officer **Alex Borkowski** .... (415) 522-3440

Federal Protective Service - Region 10
32125 32nd Avenue South, Federal Way, WA 98001
Tel: (877) 437-7411 Fax: (253) 815-4739
Areas Covered: AK, ID, OR, WA

Regional Director **Gabriel Russell** .... (877) 437-7411

DEPARTMENTS

Federal Emergency Management Agency (FEMA)

Federal Center Plaza, 500 C Street, SW, Washington, DC 20472
Tel: (202) 646-2500 (Public Information)
Tel: (202) 646-4006 (Procurement Information)
Tel: (800) 323-8603 (Fraud Hotline) Fax: (202) 646-3930
Internet: www.fema.gov Internet: m.fema.gov (Mobile Website)
Internet: www.fema.gov/esp (Spanish-Language FEMA Website)
Internet: www.ready.gov (Emergency Preparation Website)

OFFICE OF THE ADMINISTRATOR

Federal Center Plaza, 500 C Street, SW, Washington, DC 20472

Office of Regional Operations

Director **Elizabeth Edge** .... (202) 646-3900
E-mail: elizabeth.edge@dhs.gov
Education: Connecticut Col BA

National Incident Management Assistance Team - East (IMAT - East)
● Federal Coordinating Officer **(Vacant)** .... (202) 646-2500

National Incident Management Assistance Team - West (IMAT - West)
● Federal Coordinating Officer **Kevin Hannes** .... (940) 230-6639
Note: Kevin Hannes is serving as Federal Coordinating Officer in charge of Hurricane Harvey relief efforts.
E-mail: kevin.hannes@fema.dhs.gov
Education: Naval Postgrad
Federal Disaster Recovery Coordinator
Michael S. "Mike" Byrne .... (940) 230-6639
Education: Queens Col (NY) 1995 BA

Office of Response and Recovery (ORR)

Federal Center Plaza, 500 C Street, SW, Washington, DC 20472
Tel: (202) 646-3888 Fax: (202) 212-1002

Response Directorate
Federal Center Plaza, 500 C Street, SW, Washington, DC 20472
Tel: (202) 646-3692 Fax: (202) 646-4060

Disaster Emergency Communications Division
Federal Center Plaza, 500 C Street, SW, Washington, DC 20472

MERS Detachments

MERS (Mobile Emergency Response Support) Detachment - Bothell (WA)
Federal Regional Center, 200 228th Street SW, Bothell, WA 98021-8665
Fax: (425) 487-4435 Fax: (425) 487-4404 (24 Hour Fax)

Chief **Lee W. Champagne** .... (425) 487-4401
E-mail: lee.champagne@fema.dhs.gov
Education: Oregon State 1971 BA; Naval Postgrad 1976 MA

★ Presidential Appointment Requiring Senate Confirmation ☆ Presidential Appointment ☐ Schedule C Appointment ◇ Career Senior Foreign Service Appointment
● Career Senior Executive Service (SES) Appointment ○ Non-Career Senior Executive Service (SES) Appointment ■ Postal Career Executive Service

MERS (Mobile Emergency Response Support) Detachment - Denton (TX)
Federal Regional Center, 800 North Loop 288, Denton, TX 76209-3698
Tel: (940) 898-5280 Fax: (940) 898-5512
E-mail: fema-moc-denton@fema.dhs.gov
Chief **Michael "Mike" Eaton** .... (940) 898-5101

MERS (Mobile Emergency Response Support) Detachment - Denver (CO)
P.O. Box 261424, Lakewood, CO 80226-9424
Tel: (303) 235-4878 Fax: (303) 235-4684
Chief **Stephen M. "Steve" Sterling** .... (303) 235-4878

MERS (Mobile Emergency Response Support) Detachment - Frederick (MD)
4420 Buckeystown Pike, Frederick, MD 21704
Chief **Patrick J. Casey** .... (301) 874-4220

MERS (Mobile Emergency Response Support) Detachment - Maynard (MA)
65 Old Marlboro Road, Maynard, MA 01754
Tel: (978) 461-5510 Tel: (978) 461-5501 (After 3 p.m. EST)
Fax: (978) 461-5574
Chief **Peter Koutrouba** .... (978) 461-5510

MERS (Mobile Emergency Response Support) Detachment - Thomasville (GA)
404 South Pinetree Boulevard, Thomasville, GA 31792
Tel: (229) 225-4738 Fax: (229) 225-4737
Chief **Kevin Bell** .... (229) 225-4735

Regional Administrators

Region 1
99 High Street, Sixth Floor, Boston, MA 02110-2320
Tel: (617) 956-7506 Fax: (617) 956-7519
Internet: www.fema.gov/region-i-ct-me-ma-nh-ri-vt
Areas Covered: CT, ME, MA, NH, RI, VT

○ Regional Administrator (Acting) **Paul F. Ford** .... (617) 956-7566
Deputy Regional Administrator (Acting)
Doug Wolcott .... (617) 956-7506
E-mail: doug.wolcott@fema.dhs.gov
Executive Secretary **Deborah Miller** .... (617) 956-7522
Public Affairs Officer **Dennis W. Pinkham** .... (617) 956-7547
E-mail: dennis.pinkham@fema.dhs.gov

Grants Division
99 High Street, Sixth Floor, Boston, MA 02110-2320
Director **Vida Morkunas** .... (617) 956-7567
E-mail: vida.morkunas@fema.dhs.gov

Mission Support Division
99 High Street, Sixth Floor, Boston, MA 02110-2320
Fax: (617) 956-7526
Director **Doug Wolcott** .... (617) 956-7511
E-mail: doug.wolcott@fema.dhs.gov
Information Technology Branch Chief **Mike Kershaw** .... (617) 832-4770
Fax: (617) 832-4773

Mitigation Division
99 High Street, Sixth Floor, Boston, MA 02110-2320
Fax: (617) 956-7574
Director **Dean Savramis** .... (617) 956-7564
E-mail: dean.savramis@fema.dhs.gov
Floodplain Management and Insurance Branch Chief
Rick Nicholas .... (617) 956-7571
Hazard Mitigation Assistance Branch Chief
Richard Verville .... (617) 956-7564
E-mail: richard.verville@fema.dhs.gov
Risk Analysis Branch Chief **Marilyn Hilliard** .... (617) 956-7536
Fax: (617) 956-7574

National Preparedness Division
99 High Street, Sixth Floor, Boston, MA 02110-2320
Fax: (617) 956-7538
National Preparedness Director and Federal Preparedness Coordinator **Daniel McElhinney** .... (617) 956-7506
E-mail: dan.mcelhinney@fema.dhs.gov
Individual Community Outreach Branch Chief
(Vacant) .... (617) 956-7594
Integrations Branch Chief **(Vacant)** .... (617) 832-4799
Program Coordination and Grants Branch Chief
(Vacant) .... (617) 956-7567
Regional Exercise Officer **Christopher Lynch** .... (617) 832-4795
E-mail: Christopher.lynch4@fema.dhs.gov
Technology Hazard Branch Chief **Steve Coleman** .... (617) 956-7567

Recovery Division
99 High Street, Sixth Floor, Boston, MA 02110-2320
Fax: (617) 956-7507
Director **Robert Grimley** .... (617) 956-7594
E-mail: robert.grimley@fema.dhs.gov
Education: Bridgewater Col BA; St Mary's U (TX) 1999 MA
Individual Assistance Branch Chief **Becky Szymcik** .... (617) 956-7565
E-mail: becky.szymcik@fema.dhs.gov Fax: (617) 832-4794
Public Assistance Branch Chief **Thomas Perry** .... (617) 832-4765
Fax: (617) 956-7507

Response Division
99 High Street, Sixth Floor, Boston, MA 02110-2320
Director **Mark Gallagher** .... (617) 956-7504
E-mail: mark.gallagher1@fema.dhs.gov Fax: (617) 956-7507

Region 2
Jacob K. Javits Federal Building, 26 Federal Plaza, Room 1311, New York, NY 10278-0002
Tel: (212) 680-3600 Fax: (212) 680-3681
Internet: www.fema.gov/region-ii
Areas Covered: NJ, NY, PR, VI

○ Regional Administrator **Thomas Von Essen** .... (212) 680-3612
Deputy Regional Administrator
Dr. Ahsha N. Tribble PhD .... (212) 680-3600
E-mail: ahsha.tribble@fema.dhs.gov
Education: Florida A&M 1992 BS; Florida State 1999 MS; Oklahoma 2003 PhD
Defense Coordinating Officer
COL Scott W. Heintzelman USA .... (212) 295-5210
Note: Until January 2019.
E-mail: Scott.W.Heintzelman.mil@mail.mil
Education: Army War Col 2012 MSS
External Affairs Director
Capt Donald A. "Don" Caetano USMC (Ret) .... (212) 680-3616
Federal Coordinating Officer **Sadie Bynum** .... (212) 680-3600
Education: Jacksonville State MPA
Federal Coordinating Officer **Seamus Leary** .... (732) 866-2931
Education: Marist 2003 MPA
Federal Coordinating Officer **William L. "Bill" Vogel** .... (212) 680-3600
Federal Coordinating Officer **Lai Sun Yee** .... (202) 368-0384
Education: Cornell BA, JD; Naval Postgrad MA
Federal Preparedness Coordinator **(Vacant)** .... (212) 680-8507

Caribbean Area Division
New San Juan Office Building, 159 Calle Chardon, Sixth Floor, Hato Rey, PR 00918
Mail: P.O. Box 70105, San Juan, PR 00936
Tel: (787) 296-3500 Fax: (787) 296-3542
Director **Alejandro de la Campa** .... (787) 296-3501
E-mail: alejandro.delacampa@fema.dhs.gov

Mission Support Division
Division Director (Acting) **John Covell** .... (212) 680-3617
E-mail: john.covell@fema.dhs.gov
Administrative and Finance Branch Chief
Michael Wagner .... (212) 680-3646
E-mail: michael.wagner@fema.dhs.gov
Information Technology Branch Chief **(Vacant)** .... (212) 680-8697

★ Presidential Appointment Requiring Senate Confirmation ☆ Presidential Appointment □ Schedule C Appointment ◇ Career Senior Foreign Service Appointment
● Career Senior Executive Service (SES) Appointment ○ Non-Career Senior Executive Service (SES) Appointment ■ Postal Career Executive Service

Mitigation Division

Director **Michael F. "Mike" Moriarty** . . . . . . (347) 838-0427
E-mail: michael.moriarty@fema.dhs.gov
Education: Dayton BA; NYU MPA; Seton Hall JD

Deputy Director **William "Bill" McDonnell** . . . . . . (212) 680-3622
E-mail: William.McDonnell@fema.dhs.gov

Risk Analysis Branch Chief (Acting)
J. Andrew Martin . . . . . . (202) 716-2721
E-mail: Andrew.Martin@fema.dhs.gov
Education: Wright State 2002 BS

Environmental Planning and Historic Preservation Branch Chief **John McKee** . . . . . . (212) 680-8810
E-mail: John.McKee@fema.dhs.gov

Hazard Mitigation Branch Chief **Robert Tranter** . . . . . . (212) 680-3628
E-mail: Robert.tranter@fema.dhs.gov

Flood Management and Insurance Branch Chief
Scott Duell . . . . . . (347) 633-4308
E-mail: scott.duell@fema.dhs.gov

Program Management Branch Chief
Glenny Rodriguez . . . . . . (212) 720-9676
E-mail: Glenny.Rodriguez@fema.dhs.gov

Sandy Branch Chief **Luis Avila** . . . . . . (212) 680-3628
E-mail: Luis.Avila@fema.dhs.gov

Protection and National Preparedness Division

Division Director **Lawrence O'Reilly** . . . . . . (212) 680-8828
E-mail: Lawrence.OReilly@fema.dhs.gov

Regional Exercise Officer
Christopher "Chris" Cammarata . . . . . . (212) 680-3684
E-mail: christopher.cammarata@fema.dhs.gov
Education: Marist 2015 MPA

Recovery Division

Division Director **Heather Smith** . . . . . . (212) 680-8552
E-mail: heather.smith@fema.dhs.gov

Deputy Division Director **Ana Morales** . . . . . . (212) 680-3676

Response Division

Director (Acting) **Alan Neidermeyer** . . . . . . (212) 680-8614
E-mail: alan.neidermeyer@fema.dhs.gov

Operations Branch Chief **Alexander Greenberg** . . . . . . (212) 680-3607

Technological Hazards Branch Chief
Susan D.C. O'Neill . . . . . . (212) 680-8507
E-mail: susan.oneill@fema.dhs.gov

Region 3

One Independence Mall, 615 Chestnut Street,
6th Floor, Philadelphia, PA 19106
Tel: (215) 931-5757 Tel: (215) 931-5608 Fax: (215) 931-5621
Internet: www.fema.gov/region-iii
Areas Covered: DE, DC, MD, PA, VA, WV

● Regional Administrator **MaryAnn E. Tierney** . . . . . . (215) 931-5600
E-mail: maryann.tierney@fema.dhs.gov
Education: American U BA

Administrative Assistant **Diane Faso** . . . . . . (215) 931-5608

● Deputy Regional Administrator **Janice Barlow** . . . . . . (215) 931-5757
E-mail: janice.barlow@fema.dhs.gov
Education: Connecticut Col 1982 MA; Penn State (Great Valley) 2003 MEd

Chief of Staff **Mary McKenna** . . . . . . (215) 931-5509
E-mail: mary.mckenna@fema.dhs.gov

External Affairs Division Director
Daniel "Dan" Stoneking . . . . . . (215) 931-5614
E-mail: daniel.stoneking@fema.dhs.gov

External Affairs Specialist **David Thomason** . . . . . . (215) 931-5706
E-mail: david.thomason@fema.dhs.gov

External Affairs Specialist **Amanda Hancher** . . . . . . (215) 931-5716
E-mail: amanda.hancher@fema.dhs.gov

External Affairs Specialist **William Powell** . . . . . . (215) 931-5949
E-mail: william.powell@fema.dhs.gov

Recovery Division

Director **Steve Simpson** . . . . . . (215) 931-5717
E-mail: steve.simpson@fema.dhs.gov

Deputy Director **Michael Senycz** . . . . . . (215) 931-5632
E-mail: michael.senycz@fema.dhs.gov

Recovery Division *(continued)*

Individual Assistance Branch Chief **Robert Hoban** . . . . . . (215) 931-5548
E-mail: robert.hoban@fema.dhs.gov

Public Assistance Branch Chief **Emily Breslin** . . . . . . (215) 931-5661

Response Division

Director **Kelly Wolslayer** . . . . . . (215) 931-2897
E-mail: kelly.wolslayer@fema.dhs.gov

Mitigation Division

Internet: https://www.fema.gov/region-iii-mitigation

Director **(Vacant)** . . . . . . (215) 931-5669

Deputy Director **April Cummings** . . . . . . (215) 931-5635
Education: Marquette 2003 BA; Vermont 2006 MS

Hazard Mitigation Branch Chief **Nancy Carpenter** . . . . . . (215) 931-5508
E-mail: nancy.carpenter@fema.dhs.gov

Floodplain Management and Insurance Branch Chief
Nicole Lick . . . . . . (215) 931-5625
E-mail: nicole.lick@fema.dhs.gov

Risk Analysis Branch Chief **Kathryn Lipiecki** . . . . . . (215) 931-5655
E-mail: kathryn.lipiecki@fema.dhs.gov

Grants Division

E-mail: FEMA-R3-Grants-Division@fema.dhs.gov
Internet: https://www.fema.gov/region-iii-grants

Director **Regeane Frederique** . . . . . . (215) 931-5569
E-mail: Regeane.Frederique@fema.dhs.gov Fax: (215) 931-5621

Mission Support Division

Director **Lilian Hutchinson** . . . . . . (215) 931-5510
E-mail: lilian.hutchinson@fema.dhs.gov

Administration Services Branch Chief **(Vacant)** . . . . . . (215) 931-5552

Information Technology Branch Supervisory Computer Specialist **Chuck Goehringer** . . . . . . (215) 931-5696

National Preparedness Division

Director **(Vacant)** . . . . . . (215) 931-5641

Federal Preparedness Branch Chief **Steven Whitesell** . . . . (215) 931-5735
E-mail: steven.whitesell@fema.dhs.gov Fax: (215) 931-5539

Regional Integration Branch Chief **John Brasko** . . . . . . (215) 931-5630
E-mail: John.Brasko@fema.dhs.gov

Technological Hazard Branch Chief **Thomas Scardino** . . . (215) 931-5546
E-mail: thomas.scardino@fema.dhs.gov

Region 4

3003 Chamblee Tucker Road, Atlanta, GA 30341
Tel: (770) 220-5200 Tel: (770) 220-5226 (Media Inquiries)
Fax: (770) 220-5230
Areas Covered: AL, FL, GA, KY, MS, NC, SC, TN

● Regional Administrator **Gracia B. Szczech** . . . . . . (770) 220-5220
E-mail: gracia.szczech@fema.dhs.gov

Special Assistant to the Administrator
George Yearwood . . . . . . (770) 220-5225
E-mail: george.yearwood@fema.dhs.gov

Executive Assistant **Denise Harris** . . . . . . (770) 220-5224

● Deputy Regional Administrator **Robert Samaan** . . . . . . (770) 220-5224
E-mail: robert.samaan@fema.dhs.gov
Education: Lee U BA; George Washington MA

Regional Counsel **Stuart Baker** . . . . . . (770) 220-5200

Assistant Regional Counsel **(Vacant)** . . . . . . (770) 220-5200

External Affairs Officer **Mary Hudak** . . . . . . (770) 220-5226
E-mail: mary.hudak@fema.dhs.gov

● Federal Coordinating Officer
Elizabeth "Libby" Turner . . . . . . (678) 491-0412
E-mail: Libby.Turner@fema.dhs.gov
Education: Bob Jones U 1980 BS; Furman 1989 MA

Grants Management

3003 Chamblee Tucker Road, Atlanta, GA 30341

Director **Sharrie Abrams** . . . . . . (770) 220-5231
E-mail: sharrie.abrams@fema.dhs.gov

Deputy Director (Acting) **Maxine Frederick** . . . . . . (770) 220-5460

(continued on next page)

DEPARTMENTS

★ Presidential Appointment Requiring Senate Confirmation ☆ Presidential Appointment □ Schedule C Appointment ◇ Career Senior Foreign Service Appointment
● Career Senior Executive Service (SES) Appointment ○ Non-Career Senior Executive Service (SES) Appointment ■ Postal Career Executive Service

DEPARTMENTS

Grants Management *(continued)*

Grants Business Branch Chief
Steven "Steve" Denham .... (770) 220-5200
E-mail: steven.denham@fema.dhs.gov

Mission Support Division
3003 Chamblee Tucker Road, Atlanta, GA 30341

Director **Elton Andrew Newton** .... (770) 220-5558
E-mail: eltonandrew.newton@fema.dhs.gov
Administrative Services Branch Chief
Jefferson Oakes .... (770) 220-8772
E-mail: jefferson.oakes@fema.dhs.gov
Information Technology Branch Chief **Jeffrey S. Hill** ... (770) 220-5257
E-mail: jeffrey.hill@fema.dhs.gov
Freedom of Information Act Officer **Mary Barnes** ..... (770) 220-5482
E-mail: mary.barnes@fema.dhs.gov

Mitigation Division
3003 Chamblee Tucker Road, Atlanta, GA 30341

Director **Jesse Munoz** .... (770) 220-5212
E-mail: jesse.munoz@fema.dhs.gov
Floodplain Management and Insurance Branch Chief
Susan Wilson .... (770) 220-5414
E-mail: susan.wilson@fema.dhs.gov
Hazard Mitigation Assistance Branch Chief
Jacky Bell .... (770) 220-5439
E-mail: jacky.bell@fema.dhs.gov
Risk Analysis Branch Chief **Robert "Rob" Lowe** ...... (770) 220-5438
E-mail: robert.lowe@fema.dhs.gov
Regional Environmental Officer
Dr. Stephanie Madson .... (770) 220-5387
E-mail: stephanie.madson@fema.dhs.gov

National Preparedness Division
3003 Chamblee Tucker Road, Atlanta, GA 30341
Tel: (770) 220-3155 Fax: (770) 220-3113

Director **MG W. Montague Winfield USA (Ret)** .... (770) 220-3147
Education: Virginia State BS

Recovery Division
3003 Chamblee Tucker Road, Atlanta, GA 30341

Director **Terry L. Quarles** .... (770) 220-5301
E-mail: terry.quarles@fema.dhs.gov
Deputy Director **Gary Bruey** .... (770) 220-5331
E-mail: gary.bruey@fema.dhs.gov
Individual Assistance Branch Chief **Jackie Reginello** .... (770) 220-5255
E-mail: jackie.reginello@fema.dhs.gov
Public Assistance Branch Chief **Valerie Rhoads** .... (770) 220-5618
E-mail: valerie.rhoads@fema.dhs.gov

Response Division
3003 Chamblee Tucker Road, Atlanta, GA 30341

Director **Gwen Keenan** .... (770) 220-5319
E-mail: Gwen.Keenan@fema.dhs.gov
Education: US Coast Guard Acad 1987 BS; Maryland 1998 MA
Operations Planning Branch Chief **Lora W. Goza** .... (770) 220-5589
E-mail: Lora.Goza@fema.dhs.gov
Operations Integration Branch Chief **Terry Brown** .... (770) 220-3173
E-mail: terry.brown@fema.dhs.gov
Regional Response Coordination Center Branch Chief
Stacy Gunnin .... (770) 220-5280
E-mail: stacy.gunnin@fema.dhs.gov
Disaster Emergency Communications **Donnie Monette** ... (770) 220-5361
E-mail: Donnie.Monette@fema.dhs.gov
Hurricane Program Manager **Brandon Bolinski** .... (770) 220-5430
E-mail: brandon.bolinski@fema.dhs.gov
Incident Management Assistance Team
Glen R. Sachtleben .... (770) 220-8825
E-mail: glen.sachtleben@fema.dhs.gov
Education: Michigan Tech 1974 BSF
Logistics Branch Chief **Kertz Hare** .... (770) 220-5333
E-mail: kertz.hare@fema.dhs.gov

Region 5
536 South Clark Street, Sixth Floor, Chicago, IL 60605-1521
Tel: (312) 408-5500 Fax: (312) 408-5234
Internet: www.fema.gov/region-v
Areas Covered: IL, IN, MI, MN, OH, WI

○ Regional Administrator **James K. Joseph** .... (312) 408-5503
E-mail: james.joseph@fema.dhs.gov
Deputy Regional Administrator **Janet M. Odeshoo** ..... (312) 408-5500
E-mail: janet.odeshoo@fema.dhs.gov
Administrative Specialist **Cheryl Pestka** .... (312) 408-5505
E-mail: cheryl.pestka@fema.dhs.gov
Emergency Analyst **Thomas "Tom" Mefferd** .... (312) 408-5378
E-mail: thomas.mefferd@fema.dhs.gov
Senior Advisor **Morgan B. Geiger** .... (312) 408-5360
Congressional Liaison **Dan Shulman** .... (312) 408-4427
Education: American U BA; Washington U (MO) JD
External Affairs Officer **Mark Peterson** .... (312) 408-4469
E-mail: mark.peterson2@fema.dhs.gov
Education: Dayton 2005 JD
Law Enforcement Liaison **(Vacant)** .... (312) 408-4490
Regional Counsel **Maureen P. Cunningham** .... (312) 408-5500
Education: Notre Dame 1989 JD
Tribal Liaison **William "Bill" Sulinckas** .... (312) 408-5210
E-mail: william.sulinckas@fema.dhs.gov

Grants Management Division
536 South Clark Street, Sixth Floor, Chicago, IL 60605-1521

Director **Iris Andrade** .... (312) 408-5405
E-mail: iris.andrade@fema.dhs.gov

Logistics Division
536 South Clark Street, Sixth Floor, Chicago, IL 60605-1521

Branch Chief **Morgan B. Geiger** .... (312) 408-5581
E-mail: morgan.geiger@hq.dhs.gov

Mission Support Division
536 South Clark Street, Sixth Floor, Chicago, IL 60605-1521
Fax: (312) 408-5521

Mission Support Director **Donald Mobley** .... (312) 408-5592
E-mail: donald.mobley@fema.dhs.gov
Administrative Services Branch Chief
Nicholas Mueller .... (312) 408-5438
E-mail: nicholas.mueller@fema.dhs.gov
Grants Business Branch Chief **William Ryan** .... (312) 408-5584
E-mail: william.ryan@fema.dhs.gov
Grants Programs Management Branch Chief **(Vacant)** .... (312) 408-5584
Information Technology Branch Chief
Kenneth "Ken" Howdeshell .... (312) 408-4463
E-mail: kenneth.howdeshell@dhs.gov

Mitigation Division
536 South Clark Street, Sixth Floor, Chicago, IL 60605-1521

Director **Mary Beth Caruso** .... (312) 408-5570
Floodplain Management and Insurance Branch Chief
Eric Kuklewski .... (312) 408-5589
E-mail: eric.kuklewski@fema.dhs.gov
Hazard Mitigation Assistance Branch Chief
Anna Pudlo .... (312) 408-5320
Risk Analysis Branch Chief **Melissa Janssen** .... (312) 408-5500
E-mail: melissa.janssen@fema.dhs.gov

National Preparedness Division
536 South Clark Street, Sixth Floor, Chicago, IL 60605-1521

National Preparedness Director **Michael S. Chesney** ..... (312) 408-5592
Education: Northern Illinois 1983 BA; US Army Command 1994 MS; Army War Col 2006 MS
Regional Integration Branch Chief **William Wooten** ..... (312) 408-5359
Technical Hazards Branch Chief **Sean O'Leary** .... (312) 408-5366
E-mail: sean.oleary@fema.dhs.gov
Regional Exercise Officer **Marc Chmielewski** .... (312) 408-4448
E-mail: Marc.chmielewski@fema.dhs.gov

★ Presidential Appointment Requiring Senate Confirmation ☆ Presidential Appointment □ Schedule C Appointment ◇ Career Senior Foreign Service Appointment
● Career Senior Executive Service (SES) Appointment ○ Non-Career Senior Executive Service (SES) Appointment ■ Postal Career Executive Service

Recovery Division
536 South Clark Street, Sixth Floor, Chicago, IL 60605-1521
Fax: (312) 408-5599

Director **Fredric "Fred" Kaehler** .... (312) 408-5589
E-mail: fredric.kaehler@fema.dhs.gov
Individual Assistance Branch Chief **Jean McGhee** .... (312) 408-5554
E-mail: jean.mcghee@fema.dhs.gov
Public Assistance Branch Chief **Amanda Ratliff** .... (312) 408-5440

Response Division
536 South Clark Street, Sixth Floor, Chicago, IL 60605-1521
Fax: (312) 408-5599

Director **Paul A. Preusse** .... (312) 408-5500
E-mail: paul.preusse@fema.dhs.gov
Education: US Coast Guard Acad 1978 BS; Tennessee 1985 MS
Voluntary Agency Liaison **Sara Echols** .... (312) 408-5358
Operational Planning Branch Chief **Gus Wufkuhle** .... (312) 408-5366
Operations Integration Branch Chief **William King** .... (312) 408-5528
E-mail: william.king3@fema.dhs.gov
Regional Response Coordination Center (RRCC) Branch Chief **Lemorris Graham** .... (312) 408-5365
E-mail: lemorris.graham@fema.dhs.gov

Region 6
FRC 800 North Loop 288, Denton, TX 76209-3698
Tel: (940) 898-5399 Fax: (940) 898-5325
Areas Covered: AR, LA, NM, OK, TX

● Regional Administrator **George A. "Tony" Robinson** .... (940) 898-5399
E-mail: tony.robinson@fema.dhs.gov
Deputy Administrator **Moises Dugan** .... (940) 898-5399
E-mail: moises.dugan@fema.dhs.gov
Education: Texas BA
Executive Specialist **Kate McWilliams** .... (940) 898-5399
Federal Coordinating Officer **Gerard Stolar** .... (940) 898-5399
E-mail: gerard.stolar@fema.dhs.gov
Mobile Emergency Response Support Detachment Chief **Richard "Dick" Harmon** .... (940) 898-5101
E-mail: richard.harmon@fema.dhs.gov

Louisiana Recovery Office (LRO)
1500 Main Street, Baton Rouge, LA 70802
Tel: (225) 339-6610

Director **Thomas "Mike" Womack** .... (225) 339-6610
Education: Mississippi BA

Grants Management Division (GMD)
FRC 800 North Loop 288, Denton, TX 76209-3698

Grants Director **Mark D. Price** .... (940) 898-5399

Mission Support Division
FRC 800 North Loop 288, Denton, TX 76209-3698

Director **Kelli LaPoint** .... (940) 898-5146
Information Technology Branch Chief **Joshua Herrell** .... (940) 898-5399

Mitigation Division
FRC 800 North Loop 288, Denton, TX 76209-3698
Tel: (940) 898-5127

Director **Sandra A. "Sandy" Keefe** .... (940) 898-5146
E-mail: sandra.keefe@fema.dhs.gov
Deputy Director and Risk Analysis Branch Chief **Gary Zimmerer** .... (940) 898-5161
E-mail: gary.zimmerer@fema.dhs.gov
Hazard Mitigation Assistance Branch Chief **Camille Crain** .... (940) 898-5207
E-mail: h-camille.crain@fema.dhs.gov
Environmental Planning and Historic Preservation Branch Chief **Kevin Jaynes** .... (940) 383-7224
E-mail: kevin.jaynes@fema.dhs.gov

National Preparedness Division
FRC 800 North Loop 288, Denton, TX 76209-3698

Director and Federal Preparedness Coordinator **Randy Meshell** .... (940) 898-5118
E-mail: randy.meshell@fema.dhs.gov

National Preparedness Division *(continued)*

Deputy Division Director/Program Coordination Branch Chief **Lisa Hammond** .... (940) 898-5416
E-mail: lisa.hammond@fema.dhs.gov
Regional Integration Branch Chief **Shyrlee Fox** .... (940) 898-5327
E-mail: shyrlee.fox@fema.dhs.gov
Technological Hazards Branch Chief **Denise Bordelom** .... (940) 898-5399
E-mail: denise.bordelom@fema.dhs.gov
Regional Exercise Officer **Justin F. Breeding** .... (940) 898-5185
E-mail: Justinf.breeding@fema.dhs.gov

Recovery Division
FRC 800 North Loop 288, Denton, TX 76209-3698
Tel: (940) 898-5144 Internet: https://www.fema.gov/r6-recovery

Director **Traci Lea Brasher** .... (940) 898-5436
Education: Northcentral U 2012 EdD
Deputy Division Director **Dave Lebsack** .... (940) 898-5339
E-mail: david.lebsack@fema.dhs.gov
Individual Assistance Branch Chief **Lori LaFon** .... (940) 898-5281
E-mail: lori.lafon@fema.dhs.gov
Public Assistance Branch Chief **Bill Boone** .... (940) 898-5520
Community Planning and Capacity Building Coordinator **(Vacant)** .... (940) 898-5400

Response Division
FRC 800 North Loop 288, Denton, TX 76209-3698

Director **Kenneth G. Clark** .... (940) 255-0577
Deputy Division Director **Andrew T. Sabata** .... (940) 898-5399
Operations Branch Chief **(Vacant)** .... (940) 383-7205

Region 7
9221 Ward Parkway, Suite 300, Kansas City, MO 64114-3372
Tel: (816) 283-7061 Fax: (816) 283-7582
Internet: www.fema.gov/region-vii
Areas Covered: IA, KS, MO, NE

○ Regional Administrator **Paul J. Taylor** .... (816) 283-7061
Education: West Point BS; Louisville MPA
Deputy Regional Administrator **Kathy D. Fields** .... (816) 283-7062
Education: Central Missouri BS
Executive Assistant **Carol Gomez** .... (816) 283-7060
Emergency Analyst **(Vacant)** .... (816) 283-7008
Public Affairs Officer **Michael "Mike" Cappannari** .... (816) 283-7080
E-mail: michael.cappannari@fema.dhs.gov
Education: Connecticut 2001 BA, 2004 MPA

Mission Support Division
Director **Jeffrey Smith** .... (816) 283-7087
E-mail: jeffrey.smithl@fema.dhs.gov
Administrative Services Branch Chief **(Vacant)** .... (816) 283-7043
Grant Program Branch Chief **(Vacant)** .... (816) 283-7040
Information Technology Branch Chief **Kevin Fitts** .... (816) 283-7508
E-mail: kevin.fitts@fema.dhs.gov

Mitigation Division
Director **Michael Scott** .... (816) 283-7004
Hazard Mitigation Assistance Branch Chief **(Vacant)** .... (816) 283-7012
Flood Plain Management and Insurance Branch Chief **Dean Ownby** .... (816) 283-7045
E-mail: dean.ownby@fema.dhs.gov
Risk Analysis Branch Chief **Richard Leonard** .... (816) 283-7009
E-mail: richard.leonard@fema.dhs.gov

National Preparedness Division
Director **Dennis J. Prevett** .... (816) 283-7076
Regional Integration Branch Chief **Richard "Rick" Jordan** .... (816) 283-7926
E-mail: rick.jordan@dhs.gov
Technological Hazards Branch Chief **Charles "Chuck" Gregg** .... (816) 283-7007
E-mail: charles.gregg@fema.dhs.gov
Regional Exercise Officer **Alan Garrison** .... (816) 283-7021
E-mail: Alan.garrison@fema.dhs.gov

★ Presidential Appointment Requiring Senate Confirmation ☆ Presidential Appointment □ Schedule C Appointment ◇ Career Senior Foreign Service Appointment
● Career Senior Executive Service (SES) Appointment ○ Non-Career Senior Executive Service (SES) Appointment ■ Postal Career Executive Service

Recovery Division
9221 Ward Parkway, Kansas City, MO 64114-3372
Fax: (816) 283-7042

Director **Keith Dupont** .... (816) 283-7032
Individual Assistance Branch Chief **Candy Newman** ... (816) 283-7038
E-mail: candy.newman@fema.dhs.gov
Public Assistance Branch Chief
James "Jim" Nelson .... (816) 283-7903
E-mail: james2.nelson@fema.dhs.gov

Response Division
Director **Dan Best** .... (816) 283-7027
E-mail: dan.best@fema.dhs.gov
Disaster Planning Operations Branch Chief
Rodney Butts .... (816) 283-0726
Logistics Plans Branch Chief **Bryan Grable** .... (816) 283-7506
Operations Branch Chief **James Donley** .... (816) 283-7010
Regional Response Coordinating Center Branch Chief
(Vacant) .... (816) 283-7066

Region 8
Building 710, Denver Federal Center, Sixth Avenue and Kipling Street, Denver, CO 80225-0267
Mail: P.O. Box 25267, Denver, CO 80225-0267
Tel: (303) 235-4800 Fax: (303) 235-4976
Internet: www.fema.gov/region-viii-co-mt-nd-sd-ut-wy
Areas Covered: CO, MT, ND, SD, UT, WY

● Regional Administrator **Lee dePalo** .... (303) 235-4812
E-mail: lee.depalo@fema.dhs.gov
Education: Air Force Acad 1986 BS; Webster 1991 MS; US Army Command 1998; Air War Col 2001, 2005; Air U (USAF) 2005 MSS
Policy Advisor **(Vacant)** .... (303) 235-4775
External Affairs Director **Stacie Greff** .... (303) 235-4774
E-mail: stacie.greff@fema.dhs.gov
Public Affairs Officer **(Vacant)** .... (303) 235-4909
Deputy Regional Administrator **Nancy Dragani** .... (303) 235-4840
E-mail: nancy.dragani@fema.dhs.gov
Education: Old Dominion 1994 BA
Environmental Officer **Steven Hardegen** .... (303) 235-4714
E-mail: steven.hardegen@fema.dhs.gov
Federal Coordinating Officer **Nancy Casper** .... (303) 235-4928
E-mail: nancy.casper@fema.dhs.gov
Federal Coordinating Officer **Tom McCool** .... (303) 231-1953
Federal Coordinating Officer
James "Ricky" Stephenson .... (303) 235-4304
E-mail: james.stephenson@fema.dhs.gov
Federal Disaster Recovery Coordinator
Ryan Rockabrand .... (303) 235-4973
E-mail: ryan.rockabrand@fema.dhs.gov
Regional Counsel **Jennifer Dick** .... (303) 235-4903
Tribal Liaison **Megan Floyd** .... (303) 235-4638
E-mail: megan.floyd@fema.dhs.gov
Tribal Relations Specialist **John VanPool** .... (303) 235-4971
E-mail: john.vanpool@fema.dhs.gov
Chemical Stockpile Emergency Preparedness Program Manager **Cheryl Layman** .... (303) 235-4800
E-mail: cheryl.layman@fema.dhs.gov

Grants Division
Building 710, Denver Federal Center, Sixth Avenue and Kipling Street, Denver, CO 80225-0267
Fax: (303) 235-4857

Director **Bradford "Brad" Hufford** .... (303) 235-4871
E-mail: bradford.hufford@fema.dhs.gov

Mission Support Division
Building 710, Denver Federal Center, Sixth Avenue and Kipling Street, Denver, CO 80225-0267
Fax: (303) 235-4924

Director **Charles "Bunk" Lawley** .... (303) 235-4709
E-mail: charles.lawley@fema.dhs.gov

Mission Support Division *(continued)*

Administrative Services Branch Chief
Michael "Mike" Ordonez .... (303) 235-4768
E-mail: michael.ordonez@fema.dhs.gov
Information Technology Branch Chief **Eddie Martin** .... (303) 235-4918
E-mail: edwin.martin@fema.dhs.gov
Support Services Branch Chief **(Vacant)** .... (303) 235-4916

Mitigation Division
Building 710, Denver Federal Center, Sixth Avenue and Kipling Street, Denver, CO 80225-0267
Fax: (303) 235-4849

Director **Jeanine D. Petterson** .... (303) 235-4830
E-mail: jeanine.petterson@fema.dhs.gov
Floodplain Management and Insurance Branch Chief
Jeffrey Herd .... (303) 235-4906
E-mail: jeffrey.herd@fema.dhs.gov
Hazard Mitigation Assistance Branch Chief
Mike Hillenburg .... (303) 235-4875
E-mail: mike.hillenburg@fema.dhs.gov
Risk Analysis Branch Chief **Ryan Pietramali** .... (303) 235-4836
E-mail: ryan.pietramali@fema.dhs.gov

National Preparedness Division
Building 710, Denver Federal Center, Sixth Avenue and Kipling Street, Denver, CO 80225-0267
Fax: (303) 235-4857

Federal Preparedness Coordinator **Lanney Holmes** .... (303) 235-4629
E-mail: lanney.holmes@fema.dhs.gov
Grants Program Management Branch Chief
Dan Carlson .... (303) 235-4825
E-mail: dan.carlson@fema.dhs.gov
Regional Integration Branch Chief **Jeffrey Gafkjen** .... (303) 235-4725
E-mail: jeffrey.gafkjen@fema.dhs.gov
Technical Hazards Branch Chief **(Vacant)** .... (303) 235-4737
Regional Exercise Officer **Andrew Batten** .... (303) 235-4356
E-mail: Andrew.batten@fema.dhs.gov

Recovery Division
Building 710, Denver Federal Center, Sixth Avenue and Kipling Street, Denver, CO 80225-0267
Fax: (303) 235-4939

Director **Thomas "Tom" Carroll** .... (303) 235-4910
E-mail: thomas.carroll@fema.dhs.gov
Deputy Director **Donovan Puffer** .... (303) 235-4632
E-mail: donovan.puffer@fema.dhs.gov
Individual Assistance Branch Chief **Brannen Ulrick** .... (303) 235-4897
E-mail: brannen.ulrick@fema.dhs.gov
Public Assistance Branch Chief **Tom Bush** .... (303) 235-4860
E-mail: tom.bush@fema.dhs.gov

Response Division
Building 710, Denver Federal Center, Sixth Avenue and Kipling Street, Denver, CO 80225-0267
Fax: (303) 235-4777

Director **Nathan Knapp** .... (303) 235-4344
E-mail: nathan.knapp@fema.dhs.gov
Operations Integration Branch Chief **J. Kevin Moore** .... (303) 235-4917
Planning Branch Chief **Patricia Gray** .... (303) 235-4901
IMAT Team Lead **(Vacant)** .... (303) 235-4736

Region 9
1111 Broadway, Suite 1200, Oakland, CA 94607-4052
Tel: (510) 627-7100 Fax: (510) 627-7112
Areas Covered: AZ, CA, HI, NV, Pacific Island Trust Territories

● Regional Administrator **Robert J. "Bob" Fenton, Jr.** .... (510) 627-7104
E-mail: robert.fenton@fema.dhs.gov
Deputy Regional Administrator **William "Bill" Roche** .... (510) 627-7100
E-mail: william.roche@fema.dhs.gov
Education: Washington & Jefferson 1981 BS
Regional Counsel **John P. "J.P." Henderson** .... (510) 627-7055
External Affairs Director **David G. Passey** .... (510) 627-7054
E-mail: david.passey@fema.dhs.gov
Education: BYU

★ Presidential Appointment Requiring Senate Confirmation ☆ Presidential Appointment ☐ Schedule C Appointment ◇ Career Senior Foreign Service Appointment
● Career Senior Executive Service (SES) Appointment ○ Non-Career Senior Executive Service (SES) Appointment ■ Postal Career Executive Service

Region 9 *(continued)*

Congressional and Intergovernmental Affairs
Casey DeShong .... (510) 627-7785
E-mail: casey.deshong@fema.dhs.gov
External Affairs Officer **Brandi Richard** .... (510) 627-7006
E-mail: brandi.richard@fema.dhs.gov
External Affairs Specialist **Veronica Verde** .... (626) 431-3843
E-mail: veronica.verde@fema.dhs.gov
Private Sector Liaison **Michael Cummings** .... (510) 627-7220
E-mail: michael.cummings@fema.dhs.gov
Speakers' Bureau Coordinator **(Vacant)** .... (510) 627-7079
Senior Policy Advisor **Jeffery Reilly** .... (510) 627-7102

Grants Division
1111 Broadway, Suite 1200, Oakland, CA 94607-4052
Tel: (510) 627-7121
Director **Karen E. Armes** .... (510) 627-7132
E-mail: karen.armes@fema.dhs.gov

Grants Branch
1111 Broadway, Suite 1200, Oakland, CA 94607-4052
Fax: (510) 627-7126
Chief **Paulene Graham-Melton** .... (510) 627-7269
Services Chief **Michelle Weaver** .... (510) 627-7021
E-mail: michelle.weaver@fema.dhs.gov

Mission Support Division
1111 Broadway, Suite 1200, Oakland, CA 94607-4052
Fax: (510) 627-7213
Director **Tammy L. Littrell** .... (510) 627-7110

Administrative Services Branch
1111 Broadway, Suite 1200, Oakland, CA 94607-4052
Fax: (510) 627-7031
Chief **Michael Lull** .... (510) 627-7128
E-mail: michael.lull@fema.dhs.gov

Employee Services Branch
Chief **Debbie Lewis** .... (510) 627-7001
E-mail: debbie.lewis@fema.dhs.gov

Information Technology Branch
1111 Broadway, Suite 1200, Oakland, CA 94607-4052
Fax: (510) 627-7141
Chief **Stephen Bryson** .... (510) 627-7141
E-mail: stephen.bryson@fema.dhs.gov

Mitigation Division
1111 Broadway, Suite 1200, Oakland, CA 94607-4052
Fax: (510) 627-7141
Director **Jeffrey "Jeff" Lusk** .... (510) 627-7116
E-mail: jeffrey.lusk@fema.dhs.gov
Executive Assistant **Tracy Walton** .... (510) 627-7162
Mitigation Outreach Specialist **Frank Mansell** .... (510) 368-0877
E-mail: frank.mansell@fema.dhs.gov

Flood Plain Management and Insurance Branch
1111 Broadway, Suite 1200, Oakland, CA 94607-4052
Fax: (510) 627-7147
Chief **Gregor Blackburn** .... (510) 627-7186
E-mail: gregor.blackburn@fema.dhs.gov

Hazard Mitigation Assistance Branch
1111 Broadway, Suite 1200, Oakland, CA 94607-4052
Tel: (510) 627-7147
Chief **Robert McCord** .... (510) 627-7059
E-mail: robert.mccord@fema.dhs.gov

Risk Analysis Branch
1111 Broadway, Suite 1200, Oakland, CA 94607-4052
Tel: (510) 627-7147
Chief **Juliette Hayes** .... (510) 627-7211
E-mail: juliette.hayes@fema.dhs.gov

National Preparedness Division (R9-NP)
1111 Broadway, Suite 1200, Oakland, CA 94607-4052
Fax: (510) 627-7214
Federal Preparedness Coordinator **Robert Pesapane** ..... (510) 627-7037
Deputy Federal Preparedness Coordinator
Sally M. Ziolkowski .... (510) 627-7116
E-mail: sally.ziolkowski@fema.dhs.gov

Preparedness and Analysis Branch
Branch Chief **Joel Palmer** .... (510) 627-7053
E-mail: joel.palmer@fema.dhs.gov

Regional Integration Branch (R9-NP-PC)
1111 Broadway, Suite 1200, Oakland, CA 94607-4052
Fax: (510) 627-7214
Chief **Fred Wehrenberg** .... (510) 627-7020
E-mail: fred.wehrenberg@fema.dhs.gov

Technological Hazard Branch
1111 Broadway, Suite 1200, Oakland, CA 94607-4052
Fax: (510) 627-7214
Chief **Johanna Johnson** .... (510) 627-7240
E-mail: johanna.johnson@fema.dhs.gov

Pacific Area Division
Building 520, 546 Bonney Loop, Fort Shafter, Honolulu, HI 96858-5000
Fax: (808) 851-7927
Areas Covered: Territory of American Samoa, Territory of Guam, Commonwealth of the Northern Mariana Islands, Republic of the Marshall Islands, Federated States of Micronesia, Republic of Palau
Director, Readiness **Colby Stanton** .... (808) 851-7918
E-mail: colby.stanton@fema.dhs.gov
Director, Field Operations **Tracy Haynes** .... (808) 851-7909

Recovery Division
1111 Broadway, Suite 1200, Oakland, CA 94607-4052
Fax: (510) 627-7270
Director **(Vacant)** .... (510) 627-7262
Deputy Director **Mark Wingate** .... (510) 627-7188

Individual Assistance Branch
1111 Broadway, Suite 1200, Oakland, CA 94607-4052
Fax: (510) 627-7049
Chief **Maggie de la Matta** .... (510) 627-7253
E-mail: magda.de-la-matta@fema.dhs.gov

Infrastructure Branch
1111 Broadway, Suite 1200, Oakland, CA 94607-4052
Fax: (510) 627-7270
Chief **Michael Gayrard** .... (510) 627-7077

Response Division
Director **James "Jim" Cho** .... (510) 627-7136

Logistics Branch
Chief **Shawn Matz** .... (510) 627-7035

Operations Branch
1111 Broadway, Suite 1200, Oakland, CA 94607-4052
Fax: (510) 627-7270
Operations Manager **Mark Armstrong** .... (510) 627-7038
E-mail: mark.armstrong@fema.dhs.gov

Planning Branch
Chief **Dennis McKeown** .... (510) 627-7040
E-mail: dennis.mckeown@fema.dhs.gov

Regional Response Coordination Center/Watch Branch
Response Coordination and Watch Branch Chief
(Vacant) .... (510) 627-7018

Southern California Area Field Office
Director **Josie Arcurio** .... (626) 731-3706
E-mail: josie.arcurio@fema.dhs.gov

★ Presidential Appointment Requiring Senate Confirmation ☆ Presidential Appointment ☐ Schedule C Appointment ◇ Career Senior Foreign Service Appointment
● Career Senior Executive Service (SES) Appointment ○ Non-Career Senior Executive Service (SES) Appointment ■ Postal Career Executive Service

DEPARTMENTS

Region 10
Federal Regional Center, 130 228th Street SW, Bothell, WA 98021-9796
Tel: (425) 487-4600 Fax: (425) 487-4622
Areas Covered: AK, ID, OR, WA

○ Regional Administrator **Michael "Mike" O'Hare** .... (425) 487-4604
Education: Southampton Col 1984 BA
Secretary **Sheri Arcon** .... (425) 487-4604
Deputy Regional Administrator **Sharon Loper** .... (425) 487-4608
E-mail: sharon.loper@fema.dhs.gov
Chief of Staff **Patrick G. Marcham** .... (425) 487-4725
E-mail: patrick.marcham@fema.dhs.gov
External Affairs Officer **Ryan Ike** .... (425) 487-4600
E-mail: ryan.ike@fema.dhs.gov Fax: (425) 487-4690

Grants Programs Division
Director **Christine "Chris" Jonientz-Trisler** .... (425) 487-4689
E-mail: chris.jonientz-trisler@fema.dhs.gov

Mission Support Division
Director **Robert Miyamura** .... (425) 487-4600
E-mail: robert.miyamura@fema.dhs.gov
Administrative Services Branch Chief **Ted Bullock** .... (425) 487-4600

Mitigation Division
Director **Mark Carey** .... (425) 487-4682
E-mail: mark.carey@fema.gov

National Preparedness Division
Director **Scott D. Zaffram** .... (425) 487-4704
E-mail: Scott.Zaffram@fema.dhs.gov
Planning and Readiness Branch Chief **Phil Bakke** .... (425) 487-4646
Regional Exercise Officer **Stephen "Steve" Simerly** .... (425) 487-4605
E-mail: Stephen.simerly@fema.dhs.gov

Recovery Division
Director **Vincent J. "Vince" Maykovich** .... (425) 487-4685
E-mail: vincent.maykovich@fema.dhs.gov
Education: Webster 2009 MA
Individual Assistance Branch Chief (Acting)
Lisa Davidson .... (425) 487-4630
Public Assistance Branch Chief (Acting)
Anna Daggett .... (425) 487-4630

Response Division
Director **Lon Biasco** .... (425) 487-4600

United States Citizenship and Immigration Services (USCIS)
U.S. Citizenship and Immigration Services,
20 Massachusetts Avenue, NW, Washington, DC 20529
Tel: (800) 375-5283 (National Customer Service Center)
Tel: (800) 870-3676 (Forms Request Line)
TTY: (800) 767-1833 (National Customer Service Center)
Internet: www.uscis.gov

OFFICE OF THE DIRECTOR
20 Massachusetts Avenue, NW, Washington, DC 20529
Fax: (202) 272-8010

Field Operations Directorate
20 Massachusetts Avenue, NW, Washington, DC 20529
Fax: (202) 272-1008

Central Region
4500 Fuller Drive, Irving, TX 75038
Tel: (972) 893-5495 Fax: (972) 893-5403
Areas Covered: CO, ID, IL, IN, KS, KY, MN, MO, MT, NE, NM, OH, OK, TX, UT, WI

Regional Director (Acting) **Tony Bryson** .... (972) 893-5495
E-mail: tony.r.bryson@uscis.dhs.gov

Central Region *(continued)*
Operations Support Specialist **Lalinda Hudson** .... (972) 893-5495
Associate Regional Director **Kevin Gallagher** .... (972) 893-5495
Chief of Staff **Lynn Langton** .... (972) 893-5495
E-mail: lynn.langton@dhs.gov
Human Resources Assistant Director **Nancy Varga** .... (972) 893-5495
Mission Support Assistant Director **Roy Castillo** .... (972) 893-5495
Congressional Affairs Officer **William Housden** .... (972) 893-5495
Regional Counsel **William Finley** .... (972) 893-5495
E-mail: william.finley@dhs.gov

District 12 - Detroit (MI) Office
11411 East Jefferson Avenue, Detroit, MI 48214
District Director **Mirash "Mick" Dedvukaj** .... (313) 926-4206
Field Office Director **Michael Klinger** .... (313) 926-4348
E-mail: michael.klinger@dhs.gov

District 13 - Cleveland (OH) Office
A.J. Celebrezze Federal Building, 1240 East Ninth Street, Room 501, Cleveland, OH 44199
Tel: (216) 622-4647 Fax: (216) 522-7039
District Director **Mark B. Hansen** .... (216) 622-4680
Field Office Director **Karyn Zarlenga** .... (216) 622-4631

Cincinnati (OH) Sub-Office
J.W.P. Federal Building, 550 Main Street, Room 4001, Cincinnati, OH 45202-5298
Fax: (513) 744-0091
Field Office Director (Acting) **Julie Decker** .... (513) 744-0050

Columbus (OH) Sub-Office
395 East Broad Street, Suite 100, Columbus, OH 43215
Tel: (614) 225-3502 Fax: (614) 564-2881
Field Office Director **Stephanie Reither** .... (614) 225-3502

Indianapolis (IN) Sub-Office
Gateway Plaza, 950 North Meridian Street, Room 400, Indianapolis, IN 46204-3915
Tel: (317) 554-8485 Fax: (317) 554-8454
Field Office Director **Kamsing Lee** .... (317) 554-8485

Louisville (KY) Sub-Office
Gene Snyder U.S. Customhouse and Courthouse, 601 West Broadway, Suite 606, Louisville, KY 40202-2250
Tel: (502) 855-3500 Fax: (502) 855-3536
Field Office Director **Larry Kammerer** .... (502) 855-3539

District 14 - Chicago (IL) Office
101 West Congress Parkway, Room 500, Chicago, IL 60605
Tel: (312) 239-5900 Fax: (312) 705-6810
District Director **Thomas M. Cioppa** .... (312) 239-5905
E-mail: thomas.m.cioppa@uscis.dhs.gov
Chief of Staff **Aphrodite Loutas** .... (312) 239-5905
Field Office Director **Martha Medina-Maltes** .... (312) 239-5900

Milwaukee (WI) Field Office
310 East Knapp Street, Milwaukee, WI 53202
Tel: (414) 326-3026 Fax: (414) 238-6898
Field Office Director **Kay F. Leopold** .... (414) 326-3026
E-mail: kay.f.leopold@uscis.dhs.gov

District 15 - Kansas City (MO) Office
10320 NW Prairie View Road, Kansas City, MO 64153
Tel: (816) 621-2882 Fax: (816) 581-6352
District Director **David Douglas** .... (816) 621-2882
Field Office Director **Michelle Perry** .... (816) 621-2882
Fax: (816) 891-7006

Des Moines (IA) Field Office
210 Walnut Street, Room 215, Des Moines, IA 50302
Tel: (515) 564-4761 Fax: (515) 243-7322
Field Office Director **Marta Nickols** .... (515) 564-4761

★ Presidential Appointment Requiring Senate Confirmation ☆ Presidential Appointment □ Schedule C Appointment ◇ Career Senior Foreign Service Appointment
● Career Senior Executive Service (SES) Appointment ○ Non-Career Senior Executive Service (SES) Appointment ■ Postal Career Executive Service

Omaha (NE) Field Office
1717 Avenue H, Omaha, NE 68100
Tel: (402) 633-4000 Fax: (402) 341-9050
Field Office Director **William "Bill" Connor** . . . . (402) 633-4000

Saint Louis (MO) Sub-Office
Robert A. Young Federal Building, 1222 Spruce Street, Room 2.205, St. Louis, MO 63103-2815
Tel: (314) 539-5601 Fax: (314) 539-5655
Field Office Director (Acting) **Eunita "Nina" Miller** . . . . (314) 539-5601

Saint Paul (MN) Field Office
250 Marquette Avenue, Suite 710, Bloomington, MN 55401
Tel: (612) 876-3398 Fax: (612) 313-9035
Field Office Director **Leslie Tritten** . . . . (612) 876-3398

Wichita Field (KS) Field Office
271 West 3rd Street, N., Suite 1050, Wichita, KS 67202-1212
Tel: (316) 293-2440 Fax: (316) 265-5666
Field Office Director **Dawn C. Henderson** . . . . (316) 293-2440

District 33 - Dallas (TX) Office
6500 Campus Circle Drive East, Irving, TX 75063
Tel: (972) 582-5777 Fax: (972) 582-5871
District Director (Acting) **Tracy Tarango** . . . . (972) 582-5777
Deputy District Director **Tracy Tarango** . . . . (972) 582-5777
Field Office Director **Wilhelm Bierman** . . . . (972) 582-5777

Oklahoma City (OK) Field Office
4400 Southwest 44th Street, Suite A, Oklahoma City, OK 73119
Fax: (405) 219-3141
Field Office Director (Acting) **Wallace Carroll** . . . . (405) 219-3190

District 17 - Houston (TX) Office
810 Gears Road, Suite 100, Houston, TX 77067
Fax: (281) 260-4104
District Director **Tony Bryson** . . . . (281) 539-7041
E-mail: tony.r.bryson@uscis.dhs.gov
Field Office Director **Mark Siegl** . . . . (281) 539-7011

District 18 - San Antonio (TX) Office
20760 U.S. Highway 281, Suite A, San Antonio, TX 78258
Tel: (210) 564-2700 Fax: (210) 564-3615
District Director **Mario Ortiz** . . . . (210) 564-2700
Chief of Staff **Susie Quintana** . . . . (210) 564-2700
Field Office Director **Gary Garman** . . . . (210) 564-3602
Fax: (210) 564-2788

Albuquerque (NM) Field Office
1551 Mercantile Avenue, NE, Suite A, Albuquerque, NM 87107
Tel: (505) 924-6600 Fax: (505) 924-6630
Field Office Director **Jesse Mendez** . . . . (505) 924-6600

El Paso (TX) Field Office
1545 Hawkins Boulevard, Suite 167, El Paso, TX 79925
Tel: (915) 774-5722 Fax: (915) 225-1743
● Field Office Director **Raymond Adams** . . . . (915) 774-5722

Harlingen (TX) Field Office
1717 Zoy Street, Harlingen, TX 78552
Tel: (956) 430-5967 Fax: (956) 389-7553
Field Office Director **Norma A. Limon** . . . . (956) 430-5967
E-mail: norma.a.limon@uscis.dhs.gov

District 19 - Denver (CO) Office
12484 East Weaver Place, Centennial, CO 80111
Tel: (720) 852-6900 Fax: (720) 852-6908
District Director **Angela K. "Kristi" Barrows** . . . . (720) 852-6900
E-mail: angela.k.barrows@uscis.dhs.gov
Field Office Director **Andrew Lambrecht** . . . . (720) 852-6900

Boise (ID) Field Office
1185 South Vinnell Way, Boise, ID 83709
Tel: (208) 377-6560 Fax: (208) 377-6581
Field Office Director **John McCarthy** . . . . (208) 377-6560

Helena (MT) Field Office
754 River Rock Drive, Helena, MT 59602
Tel: (406) 441-3334 Fax: (406) 441-3309
Field Office Director **Jodi Bard** . . . . (406) 441-3334

Salt Lake City (UT) Field Office
660 South 200 East, Suite 400, Salt Lake City, UT 84111
Tel: (801) 320-6900 Fax: (801) 320-6902
Field Office Director **Laura K. McNeer** . . . . (801) 320-6900
Education: Xavier (OH) BA; Ohio State MA

Northeast Region
70 Kimball Avenue, South Burlington, VT 05403-6813
Tel: (802) 660-5000 Fax: (802) 660-5114
Areas Covered: CT, DC, MA, MD, ME, NH, NJ, NY, PA, RI, VA, VT
Regional Director **Lori A. Pietropaoli** . . . . (802) 660-5000
Chief of Staff **Andrew V. Fontanez** . . . . (802) 660-5006
E-mail: andrew.v.fontanez@uscis.dhs.gov
Regional Counsel **Suzanne McGregor** . . . . (802) 660-5043
E-mail: suzanne.m.mcgregor@dhs.gov
Public Affairs Officer **Anita Rios Moore** . . . . (802) 660-5029
Operations Support Specialist **Vicki L. Wells** . . . . (802) 660-5000
E-mail: vicki.l.wells@uscis.dhs.gov

Field Support Center
Director **(Vacant)** . . . . (802) 872-4102
Human Resources and Career Development Director **Steven Dykeman** . . . . (802) 660-5075
E-mail: steven.dykeman@dhs.gov
Information Resources Management Director **(Vacant)** . . . (802) 872-9410
Security Director **Danielle Esposito** . . . . (802) 859-1919
E-mail: danielle.esposito@dhs.gov Fax: (802) 859-1939
Training Director **(Vacant)** . . . . (802) 288-7910
Fax: (802) 660-5130

District 1 - Boston (MA) Office
John F. Kennedy Federal Building, 15 New Sudbury Street, Room E-160, Boston, MA 02203
Fax: (617) 565-4534
District Director **Denis C. Riordan** . . . . (617) 565-9555
Field Office Director **Michael "Mike" McCleary** . . . . (617) 565-9555

Portland (ME) Field Office
176 Gannett Drive, South Portland, ME 04106-6909
Fax: (207) 253-3001
Field Office Director **Cindy C. Lembarra** . . . . (207) 253-3008
E-mail: Cindy.C.Lembarra@uscis.dhs.gov
Education: Vermont

Providence (RI) Field Office
200 Dyer Street, Providence, RI 02903-3993
Fax: (401) 277-1209
Field Office Director **Adam Bergeron** . . . . (401) 277-1200

District 2 - Buffalo (NY) Office
306 Delaware Avenue, Buffalo, NY 14202-2404
Fax: (716) 551-3131
District Director **Edward A. Newman** . . . . (716) 843-7900

Albany (NY) Field Office
1086 Troy-Schenectady Road, Latham, NY 12110
Fax: (518) 786-3220
Field Office Director **Gwynne Dinolfo** . . . . (518) 786-3210

Hartford (CT) Field Office
Ribicoff Federal Building, 450 Main Street, Hartford, CT 06103-3060
Fax: (860) 728-2355
Field Office Director **Nieves Cardinale** . . . . (860) 728-2300

★ Presidential Appointment Requiring Senate Confirmation ☆ Presidential Appointment ☐ Schedule C Appointment ◇ Career Senior Foreign Service Appointment
● Career Senior Executive Service (SES) Appointment ○ Non-Career Senior Executive Service (SES) Appointment ■ Postal Career Executive Service

Saint Albans (VT) Field Office
64 Gricebrook Road, St. Albans, VT 05478
Fax: (802) 527-3262
Field Office Director **Michael Paul** .... (802) 528-2000

District 3 - New York City (NY) Office
Jacob K. Javits Federal Building, 26 Federal Plaza,
Room 14-102, New York, NY 10278
Fax: (212) 264-4146
● District Director **Thomas M. Cioppa** .... (212) 264-3972

Long Island (NY) Field Office
30 Barretts Avenue, Holtsville, NY 11742
Tel: (631) 687-8800
Field Office Director **Elizabeth Miller** .... (631) 687-8800

Queens (NY) Field Office
26 Federal Plaza, New York, NY 10278
Tel: (212) 264-5705
Field Office Director **Brian Meier** .... (212) 264-5705
E-mail: brian.meier@uscis.dhs.gov

District 4 - Newark (NJ) Office
Peter Rodino Federal Building, 970 Broad Street, Newark, NJ 07102
Fax: (973) 645-2304
District Director **John E. Thompson** .... (973) 639-6899
E-mail: john.e.thompson@uscis.dhs.gov

District 5 - Philadelphia (PA) Office
30 North 41st Street, Philadelphia, PA 19104
Fax: (215) 255-4999
District Director **Anna Chau** .... (267) 292-6700

Pittsburgh (PA) Field Office
777 Penn Center Boulevard, Suite 600, Pittsburgh, PA 15235
Fax: (412) 390-3950
Field Office Director **Michael Horvath** .... (412) 390-3900

District 6 - Baltimore (MD) Office
3701 Koppers Street, Baltimore, MD 21227
Tel: (410) 962-2008 Fax: (410) 962-7555
District Director **Gregory L. "Greg" Collett** .... (410) 962-2008
Education: Towson State U 1989 BA

District 7 - Fairfax (VA) Office
2675 Prosperity Avenue, Fairfax, VA 22031
Fax: (703) 285-6024
District Director **Sarah Taylor** .... (703) 285-6027

Norfolk (VA) Field Office
Norfolk Commerce Park, 5280 Henneman Drive, Norfolk, VA 23513
Fax: (757) 858-6273
Field Office Director **Frank Reffel** .... (757) 466-3100

Southeast Region
390 North Orange Avenue, Suite 1943, Orlando, FL 32801
Tel: (407) 237-8800 Fax: (407) 237-8995
Areas Covered: AR, FL, GA, LA, NC, PR, SC, TN, VI
Regional Director **CAPT Mark E. Dolan USCG (Ret)** .... (407) 237-8811
Education: US Coast Guard Acad 1986 BS; Naval War 2000 MA; Naval Postgrad MA

District 8 - Atlanta (GA) Office
2150 Parklake Drive NE, Atlanta, GA 30345
Tel: (770) 508-1866 Fax: (770) 508-1899
District Director **Denise Frazier** .... (770) 508-1829
Chief of Staff **Paul Onyango** .... (770) 508-1706
Field Office Director **Kevin Riddle** .... (770) 508-1650
Education: Illinois 2000; Hawaii 2006

Charleston (SC) Field Office
1821 Sam Rittenberg Boulevard, Charleston, SC 29407
Tel: (843) 556-6039 Fax: (843) 556-9026
Field Office Director **Warren Janssen** .... (843) 852-5444

Charlotte (NC) Field Office
6130 Tyvola Centre Drive, Charlotte, NC 28217
Tel: (704) 936-5105 Fax: (704) 936-5245
Field Office Director **Amra Beslagic** .... (704) 936-5101

Greer (SC) Field Office
501 Pennsylvania Avenue, Greer, SC 29652
Tel: (864) 968-3950 Fax: (864) 879-3829
Field Office Director **Jaclyn Williams** .... (864) 968-3951

Montgomery (AL) Field Office
3381 Atlanta Highway, Montgomery, AL 36109
Field Office Director **Nicolas Bartell** .... (334) 244-4501
E-mail: nicolas.bartell@uscis.dhs.gov

Raleigh-Durham (NC) Field Office
301 Roycroft Drive, Durham, NC 27703
Tel: (919) 998-5851 Fax: (919) 541-4810
Field Office Director **Jay Weselmann** .... (919) 998-5851
E-mail: jay.weselmann@uscis.dhs.gov

District 9 - Miami (FL) Office
8801 Northwest Seventh Avenue, Miami, FL 33150
Tel: (305) 762-8205 Fax: (305) 762-8225
District Director **Linda Swacina** .... (305) 762-8205

Charlotte-Amalie (VI) Field Office
8000 Nisky Center, First Floor South, Suite 1A, St. Thomas, VI 00802
Tel: (340) 774-1390 Fax: (340) 776-4981
Field Office Director **Lorelie Conner** .... (340) 774-1390 ext. 249

Hialeah (FL) Field Office
5880 NW 183rd Street, Hialeah, FL 33015
Tel: (305) 818-5205 Fax: (305) 818-5392
Field Office Director **Enid Stulz** .... (305) 818-5205

Kendall (FL) Field Office
14675 SW 120th Street, Miami, FL 32216
Tel: (305) 383-4705 Fax: (305) 383-4880
Field Office Director **Kristian Parker** .... (305) 383-4705

Oakland Park (FL) Field Office
4451 NW 31st Avenue, Oakland Park, FL 33309
Tel: (954) 677-7105 Fax: (954) 677-7108
Field Office Director **Emigdio Martinez** .... (954) 677-7105

San Juan (PR) Field Office
Plaza 273, 273 Ponce de Leon Avenue,
Suite 1100, San Juan, PR 00917
Fax: (787) 773-8556
Field Office Director **Deliana Gonzalez-Ferrer** .... (787) 773-8532
E-mail: Deliana.Gonzalez-Ferrer@uscis.dhs.gov

District 10 - Tampa (FL) Office
5629 Hoover Boulevard, Tampa, FL 33634
Fax: (813) 288-1229
District Director **Michael R. Borgen** .... (813) 712-8933
E-mail: michael.r.borgen@uscis.dhs.gov

Fort Myers (FL) Field Office
4220 Executive Circle, Suite 1, Fort Myers, FL 33916
Tel: (239) 274-5241
Field Office Director **Shelly Randall** .... (239) 274-5241
E-mail: shelly.d.randall@uscis.dhs.gov

★ Presidential Appointment Requiring Senate Confirmation ☆ Presidential Appointment □ Schedule C Appointment ◇ Career Senior Foreign Service Appointment
● Career Senior Executive Service (SES) Appointment ○ Non-Career Senior Executive Service (SES) Appointment ■ Postal Career Executive Service

Jacksonville (FL) Field Office
4121 Southpoint Boulevard, Jacksonville, FL 32216-0930
Fax: (904) 232-2388
Field Office Director **Lisa Bradley** .... (904) 245-7848

Orlando (FL) Field Office
6680 Corporate Centre, Orlando, FL 32827
Fax: (407) 855-3616
Field Office Director **Kimberly D. Dean** .... (407) 858-3625
E-mail: kimberly.d.dean@uscis.dhs.gov

West Palm Beach (FL) Field Office
9300 Belvedere Road, Royal Palm Beach, FL 33411
Tel: (561) 904-4100 Fax: (561) 904-4250
Field Office Director **Wendy Wilcox** .... (561) 904-4110

District 11 - New Orleans (LA) Office
1250 Poydras Street, Suite 1800, New Orleans, LA 70113
Tel: (504) 571-2500 Fax: (504) 836-3452
District Director **Cindy Gomez** .... (504) 571-2520

Fort Smith (AR) Field Office
4624 Kelley Highway, Fort Smith, AR 72904
Tel: (479) 573-2027 Fax: (479) 573-2067
Field Office Director **Christina Olguin** .... (479) 573-2027

Memphis (TN) Field Office
80 Monroe Avenue, 7th Floor, Memphis, TN 38105
Fax: (901) 544-3507
Field Office Director **Lynuel W. Dennis** .... (901) 820-2601

Western Region
24000 Avila Road, Laguna Niguel, CA 92677
Mail: P.O. Box 30080, Laguna Niguel, CA 92607-0080
Tel: (949) 360-2995 Fax: (949) 360-3081
Areas Covered: AK, AZ, CA, GU, HI, NV, OR, WA
● Regional Director **Carolyn L. Muzyka** .... (949) 360-2995
E-mail: carolyn.muzyka@dhs.gov

District 20 - Seattle (WA) Office
12500 Tukwila International Boulevard, Seattle, WA 98168-2506
Tel: (206) 277-9010 Fax: (206) 277-9083
District Director **Anne Arries Corsano** .... (206) 277-9010

Anchorage (AK) Field Office
620 East 10th Avenue, Suite 102, Anchorage, AK 99501
Tel: (907) 271-4064 Fax: (907) 271-6444
Field Office Director **Terry J. Charbonneau** .... (907) 271-4064

Portland (OR) Field Office
1455 NW Overton Street, Suite 1, Portland, OR 97209
Tel: (503) 326-6898 Fax: (503) 326-3566
Field Office Director **Richard L. Miller** .... (503) 326-6898
Community Relations Officer **Ed Sale** .... (503) 326-6898
E-mail: ed.sale@dhs.gov

Spokane (WA) Sub-Office
U.S. Courthouse Building, West 920 Riverside,
Room 691, Spokane, WA 99201
Field Office Director **Chrysta Stock** .... (509) 353-4699

Yakima (WA) Sub-Office
415 North Third Street, Yakima, WA 98901
P.O. Box 49, Yakima, WA 98902
Tel: (509) 454-5407 Fax: (509) 575-5910
Officer-in-Charge **Siw Bay-Hansen** .... (509) 454-5407

District 21 - San Francisco (CA) Office
444 Washington Street, San Francisco, CA 94111
Tel: (415) 248-8863 Fax: (415) 844-5260
District Director **John M. Kramar** .... (415) 248-8863

District 22 - Sacramento (CA) Office
650 Capital Mall, Sacramento, CA 95814
Tel: (916) 498-6469 Fax: (916) 498-5878
District Director **Monica Toro** .... (916) 498-6469
Field Office Director **Elisabeth E. Clerie** .... (916) 498-6469

Fresno (CA) Field Office
744 P Street, Suite 120, Fresno, CA 93721
Fax: (559) 444-2820
Field Office Director **Lynn Q. Feldman** .... (559) 444-2811
Education: Chicago-Kent 2000 JD

District 23 - Los Angeles (CA) Office
Federal Building, 300 North Los Angeles Street,
Room 7671, Los Angeles, CA 90012
Tel: (213) 830-8041 Fax: (213) 830-5077
Note: In June 2018, USCIS announced that it will be creating a new office in Los Angeles "to review and initiate the civil denaturalization process against individuals who had been ordered removed and intentionally used multiple identities in order to defraud the government and the American people to obtain citizenship."
● District Director **Donna P. Campagnolo** .... (213) 830-8041
E-mail: donna.p.campagnolo@uscis.dhs.gov

Santa Ana (CA) Field Office
34 Civic Center Plaza, Santa Ana, CA 92701
Tel: (714) 972-6612 Fax: (714) 972-6613
Field Office Director **David Lester** .... (714) 972-6612

District 24 - San Diego (CA) Office
880 Front Street, Suite 1234, San Diego, CA 92101
Fax: (619) 450-4809 E-mail: ask.cis.snd@dhs.gov
District Director **Alanna Y. Ow** .... (619) 450-4889
E-mail: alanna.y.ow@uscis.dhs.gov

District 25 - Phoenix (AZ) Office
1330 South 16th Street, Phoenix, AZ 85034
Tel: (602) 462-2500 Fax: (602) 462-2504
Director **Al Gallmann** .... (602) 462-2501
Fax: (602) 379-4409

Las Vegas (NV) Field Office
3373 Pepper Lane, Las Vegas, NV 89120
Tel: (702) 388-5875 Fax: (702) 388-5823
Field Office Director **Jeanne M. Kent** .... (702) 388-5875
E-mail: jeanne.m.kent@uscis.dhs.gov

Reno (NV) Field Office
1351 Corporate Boulevard, Reno, NV 89502
Tel: (775) 784-5175 Fax: (775) 784-5899
Field Office Director **Walter L. Haith** .... (775) 784-5175
E-mail: walter.l.haith@uscis.dhs.gov

Tucson (AZ) Field Office
4475 South Coach Drive, Tucson, AZ 85714
Tel: (520) 620-7550 Fax: (520) 620-4581
Field Office Director **Julie M. Hashimoto** .... (520) 620-7580

District 26 - Honolulu (HI) Office
595 Ala Moana Boulevard, Honolulu, HI 96813-4999
Tel: (808) 532-2700 Fax: (808) 532-7489
District Director **David G. Gulick** .... (808) 532-2700

Guam Field Office
770 East Sunset Boulevard, Suite 185, Barrigada, GU 96913
Tel: (671) 472-7206 Fax: (671) 472-7275
Field Office Director **Rebecca F. Maliuwelur** .... (671) 472-7206
E-mail: Rebecca.F.Maliuwelur@uscis.dhs.gov

Administrative Center
24000 Avila Road, Laguna Niguel, CA 92677
Tel: (949) 360-3124 Fax: (949) 360-3138
Director **(Vacant)** .... (949) 360-3124

(continued on next page)

★ Presidential Appointment Requiring Senate Confirmation ☆ Presidential Appointment ☐ Schedule C Appointment ◇ Career Senior Foreign Service Appointment
● Career Senior Executive Service (SES) Appointment ○ Non-Career Senior Executive Service (SES) Appointment ■ Postal Career Executive Service

DEPARTMENTS

DEPARTMENTS

Administrative Center *(continued)*

Equal Employment Opportunity Assistant Center Director **(Vacant)** .... (949) 360-3192
Facilities and Engineering Division Assistant Center Director **Hector Montalvo** .... (949) 360-3048
Finance Support Service Assistant Center Director **Mary Anne Thomson** .... (949) 360-3153
Human Resources Director **Peggy Gaethke** .... (949) 360-2054
E-mail: peggy.gaethke@dhs.gov
Property Management and Procurement Assistant Center Director **Tracy Swilley** .... (949) 425-7035
E-mail: tracy.swilley@dhs.gov
Security Assistant Center Director (Interim) **Evelyn Flores** .... (866) 960-8312
E-mail: evelyn.flores@dhs.gov

Operations
24000 Avila Road, Laguna Niguel, CA 92677

Regional Director **Ellen Woo** .... (949) 360-2995
Staff Operations Associate Regional Director **Gloria Kee** .... (949) 360-3029
Adjudications Assistant Regional Director **James Booe** .... (949) 360-3314
Border Patrol Assistant Regional Director **Robert W. "Bob" Gilbert** .... (949) 360-2995
E-mail: robert.gilbert@dhs.gov
Inspections Assistant Regional Director **Peter Gordon** .... (949) 360-3045
Intelligence Assistant Regional Director **Stephen A. Shanks** .... (949) 360-3128
Investigations Assistant Regional Director **Anthony Esposito** .... (949) 360-3007
Asset Forfeiture Area Director **Kenneth Takeda** .... (949) 360-3085
Resource Management Director **Marta Kavanaugh** .... (949) 360-3351

Refugee, Asylum, and International Operations Directorate (RAIO)

20 Massachusetts Avenue, NW, Washington, DC 20529
Fax: (202) 272-1676

Asylum Division

20 Massachusetts Avenue, NW, Washington, DC 20529
Fax: (202) 272-1681

Arlington (VA) Office
1525 Wilson Boulevard, Suite 300, Arlington, VA 22209
Tel: (703) 235-4100 Fax: (703) 812-8455
Areas Covered: DC, GA, MD, NC, VA

Director **Jedidah "Jeddy" Hussey** .... (703) 235-4100
Deputy Director **Antonio Donis** .... (703) 235-4100

Chicago (IL) Office
181 West Madison Street, Suite 3000, Chicago, IL 60602
Tel: (312) 849-5200 Fax: (312) 849-5206
Areas Covered: ID, IL, IN, IA, KS, KY, MI, MN, MO, MT, NE, ND, OH, SD, WI

Director **Kenneth S. Madsen** .... (312) 849-5200

Houston (TX) Office
16630 Imperial Valley Drive, Suite 200, Houston, TX 77060
Tel: (281) 931-2100
Areas Covered: AR, CO, LA, MS, NM, OK, TN, TX, UT, WY

Director **Robert Daum** .... (281) 931-2100

Los Angeles (CA) Office
1585 South Manchester Avenue, Anaheim, CA 92802
Mail: P.O. Box 65015, Anaheim, CA 92815
Tel: (714) 808-8207 Fax: (714) 635-9136
Areas Covered: Arizona, California (counties of Los Angeles, Orange, Riverside, San Bernardino, San Luis Obispo, Santa Barbara, Ventura, Imperial, and San Diego), Hawaii, Nevada (southern portion), Guam

• Director **David M. Radel** .... (714) 808-8205
E-mail: David.M.Radel@uscis.dhs.gov

Los Angeles (CA) Office *(continued)*

Deputy Director **Marianne X. Hong** .... (714) 808-8206
E-mail: Marianne.x.hong@uscis.dhs.gov

Miami (FL) Office
1501 Biscayne Boulevard, Suite 300, Miami, FL 33132
Tel: (786) 456-2900 Fax: (786) 456-2910
Areas Covered: Florida, Puerto Rico, U.S. Virgin Islands

Director **Varsenik L. Papazian** .... (786) 456-2900
E-mail: varsenik.l.papazian@uscis.dhs.gov
Supervisory Mission Support Specialist **Hilda Gutierrez** .... (786) 456-2900
Mission Support Specialist **Sharon Turner** .... (786) 456-2900
Deputy Director **Kimberly M. Aguilar** .... (786) 456-2900
E-mail: kimberly.m.aguilar@uscis.dhs.gov

Newark (NJ) Office
1200 Wall St. West, 4th Floor, Lyndhurst, NJ 07071
Tel: (201) 508-6100 Fax: (201) 531-1877
Areas Covered: CT, DE, ME, MA, NH, NJ, portions of NY (New York City [Manhattan and the Bronx], Albany region, Buffalo region), portions of Pennsylvania, RI, VT

Director **Susan "Sue" Raufer** .... (201) 508-6100
E-mail: susan.raufer@uscis.dhs.gov
Deputy Director **(Vacant)** .... (201) 508-6100
Chief of Staff **Lorie Heinrich** .... (201) 508-6100
E-mail: lorie.heinrich@uscis.dhs.gov

New York (NY) Office
1065 Stewart Avenue, Suite 200, Bethpage, NY 11714
Tel: (516) 261-0000 E-mail: newyork.asylum@uscis.dhs.gov
Areas Covered: New York (excluding Albany region, Buffalo region, and the boroughs of Manhattan and the Bronx)

Director **Patricia A. Menges** .... (516) 261-0000
E-mail: patricia.menges@uscis.dhs.gov
Deputy Director **Mathew C. Varghese** .... (516) 261-0000
E-mail: mathew.c.varghese@uscis.dhs.gov

San Francisco (CA) Office
75 Hawthorne Street, 7th Floor, San Francisco, CA 94105
P.O. Box 77530, San Francisco, CA 94105
Tel: (415) 575-1300 Fax: (415) 293-1270
Areas Covered: AK, CA (Counties of Alameda, Alpine, Amador, Butte, Calaveras, Colusa, Contra Costa, Del Norte, El Dorado, Fresno, Glenn, Humboldt, Inyo, Kern, Kings, Lake, Lassen, Madera, Marin, Mariposa, Mendocino, Merced, Modoc, Mono, Monterey, Napa, Nevada, Placer, Plumas, Sacramento, San Benito, San Francisco, San Joaquin, San Mateo, Santa Clara, Santa Cruz, Shasta, Sierra, Siskiyou, Solano, Sonoma, Stanislaus, Sutter, Tehama, Trinity, Tulare, Tuolumne, Yolo, and Yuba), Northern NV, OR, WA

Director **Emilia M. Bardini** .... (415) 575-1300
E-mail: emilia.m.bardini@uscis.dhs.gov
Deputy Director **Carlton Yue** .... (415) 575-1300
E-mail: carlton.yue@uscis.dhs.gov

Service Center Operations Directorate (SCOPS)

20 Massachusetts Avenue, NW, Washington, DC 20529
Tel: (202) 272-1505 Fax: (202) 272-1543

California Service Center
24000 Avila Road, 2nd Floor, Laguna Niguel, CA 92677
Mail: P.O. Box 30040, Laguna Niguel, CA 92607-0040
Tel: (949) 389-3003 Fax: (949) 389-3251

Director **Kathy A. Baran** .... (949) 389-3003
Education: SUNY (Albany) 1978 BA; San Diego State 1988 MA; Indust'l Col Armed Forces 2007 MS
Deputy Director **Donna Campolagnolo** .... (949) 389-3220
Fax: (949) 389-3497
Chief of Staff **John P. Abram** .... (949) 389-3051

★ Presidential Appointment Requiring Senate Confirmation ☆ Presidential Appointment □ Schedule C Appointment ◇ Career Senior Foreign Service Appointment
● Career Senior Executive Service (SES) Appointment ○ Non-Career Senior Executive Service (SES) Appointment ■ Postal Career Executive Service

Nebraska Service Center
P.O. Box 82521, Lincoln, NE 68501-2521
Tel: (402) 474-5012 Fax: (402) 219-6050

Director **F. Gerard "Jerry" Heinauer** .... (402) 474-5012
Deputy Director **Marilyn P. Wiles** .... (402) 474-5012
Chief of Staff **Neil Jacobson** .... (402) 474-5012
E-mail: neil.jacobson@dhs.gov

Texas Service Center
8001 North Stemmons Freeway, Dallas, TX 75247
Tel: (214) 962-2626 Fax: (214) 962-1451

Director **Gregorgy A. "Greg" Richardson** .... (214) 962-2626
E-mail: gregory.a.richardson@uscis.dhs.gov
Deputy Director **Kirt Thompson** .... (214) 962-2626
Chief of Staff **Marnie K. Grimes** .... (214) 962-2626
E-mail: marnie.k.grimes@uscis.dhs.gov

Vermont Service Center
75 Lower Welden Street, St. Albans, VT 05479-0001
Tel: (802) 527-4700 Fax: (802) 527-4862

Director **Laura B. Zuchowski** .... (802) 527-4700
E-mail: laura.zuchowski@dhs.gov
Deputy Director **Cara Selby** .... (802) 527-4700
Chief of Staff **Sandra Bushey** .... (802) 527-4700

United States Coast Guard (USCG)
2703 Martin Luther King Jr. Avenue, SE, Washington, DC 20593-7714
Tel: (202) 475-3519 (Freedom of Information/Privacy Act)
Internet: www.uscg.mil

COMMANDANT OF THE COAST GUARD (CG-00)
COMMANDANT (CG-00), 2703 Martin Luther King Jr. Avenue, SE, STOP 7000, Washington, DC 20593-7213
Fax: (202) 372-8302

Office of Governmental and Public Affairs (CG-092)
2703 Martin Luther King Jr. Avenue, SE, Stop 7103, Washington, DC 20593-7714
Tel: (202) 372-4600 Fax: (202) 372-8312

Historian's Office (CG-09224)
2703 Martin Luther King Jr. Avenue, SE, Stop 7103, Washington, DC 20593-7714
Fax: (202) 372-4984

U.S. Coast Guard Exhibit Center
7945 Fernham Lane, Forestville, MD 20747
Tel: (301) 763-4008 Fax: (301) 763-4009

Curator **Arlyn S. Danielson** .... (301) 763-4008

United States Coast Guard Centers, Commands, Installations and Institutions

Aviation Training Center (ATC)
8501 Tanner Williams Road, Mobile, AL 36608-8322
Tel: (251) 441-6401 Tel: (251) 441-6861 (After 4 p.m.)
Tel: (251) 441-6122 (Administration Office) Fax: (251) 441-6815

Commanding Officer
CAPT William E. Sasser, Jr. USCG .... (251) 441-6401
Information Resource Management Officer **Ray Evans** ... (251) 441-6098
Fax: (251) 441-6558
Public Affairs Officer **LT John Barrett USCG** .... (251) 441-6432

Facilities Design and Construction Center (FDCC)
5505 Robin Hood Road, Suite K, Norfolk, VA 23513-2431
Tel: (757) 852-3400 Fax: (757) 852-3495

Commanding Officer **CDR Patrick Dugan USCG** .... (757) 852-3400
Chief of Contracting **Pamela J. "Pam" Argilan** .... (757) 852-3449

Facilities Design and Construction Center *(continued)*

Executive Director **CDR Cesar Acosta USCG** .... (757) 852-3400
E-mail: cesar.c.acosta@uscg.mil

U.S. Coast Guard Aviation Logistics Center (ALC)
Elizabeth City, NC 27909-5001
Fax: (252) 335-6735 Internet: www.uscg.mil/alc

Commanding Officer
CAPT Randal A. "Randy" Hartnett USCG .... (252) 335-6191
E-mail: randal.a.hartnett@uscg.mil
Education: US Coast Guard Acad 1990 BS; Purdue MS
Secretary to Commanding Officer **Jeff Gardiner** .... (252) 335-6191
Executive Officer
CDR Matthew R. "Matt" Farnen USCG .... (252) 335-6192
E-mail: matthew.r.farnen@uscg.mil
Command Master Chief **CMC Ann Logan USCG** .... (252) 202-6127
Aviation Logistics Division
CDR David W. Hatchett USCG .... (252) 335-6842
E-mail: david.w.hatchett@uscg.mil
Business Operations Division Chief **(Vacant)** .... (252) 334-5103
Chief of Contracting Office **David S. Burgess** .... (252) 335-6436
E-mail: david.s.burgess@uscg.mil
Engineering Services Division Chief
CDR Jeffrey R. Graham USCG .... (252) 335-6943
E-mail: jeffrey.r.graham@uscg.mil
Engineering Services Division Program Manager
Carol M. Frey .... (252) 335-6064
E-mail: carol.m.frey@uscg.mil
LRS Division Chief
CDR Christopher M. Huberty USCG .... (252) 335-6837
E-mail: christopher.m.huberty@uscg.mil
MRR Division Chief **Mark Lay** .... (252) 335-6067
MRS Division Chief **CDR Steve Walsh USCG** .... (252) 335-6597
SRR Division Chief **CDR Todd C. Troup USCG** .... (252) 335-6039
E-mail: todd.c.troup@uscg.mil
Industrial Operations Division Chief
CDR Craig Murray USCG .... (252) 384-7329
Information Systems Division Chief
CDR Michael Woodrum USCG .... (252) 335-6165
E-mail: adam.g.bentley@uscg.mil
Operations Division Chief
CDR Susan M. Maitre USCG .... (252) 335-6594
E-mail: susan.m.maitre@uscg.mil
Work Force Management Staff **Cindy Soules** .... (252) 335-6120
Small Business Specialist **Patrick Morris** .... (252) 335-6669
E-mail: william.p.morris@uscg.mil
Small Business Specialist **Sherri L. Peele** .... (252) 335-6768
E-mail: sherri.l.peele@uscg.mil

U.S. Coast Guard Aviation Technical Training Center (ATTC)
Building 4, 1664 Weeksville Road, Elizabeth City, NC 27909
Tel: (252) 722-2606

Commander **CAPT Lance C. Belben USCG** .... (252) 335-6208
Education: US Coast Guard Acad 1994 BS
Executive Officer **CDR Timothy Schmitz USCG** .... (252) 335-6160
Training Officer **LCDR Andrew R. Campbell USCG** .... (252) 335-6271
Command Master Chief **CMC Ann Logan USCG** .... (252) 202-6127

U.S. Coast Guard Research and Development Center (RDC)
One Chelsea Street, New London, CT 06320
Tel: (860) 271-2600 Fax: (860) 441-2792

Commanding Officer
CAPT Gregory C. Rothrock USCG .... (860) 271-2600
Education: US Coast Guard Acad BSME; Northeastern MS
Executive Director **Bert N. Macesker** .... (860) 271-2610
E-mail: bert.n.macesker@uscg.mil
Resource Director **(Vacant)** .... (860) 271-2600
Technical Director **Timothy R. Girton** .... (860) 271-2600
Public Affairs Officer **CDR Michael L. Turner USCG** .... (860) 271-2882
E-mail: michael.l.turner@uscg.mil

★ Presidential Appointment Requiring Senate Confirmation ☆ Presidential Appointment ☐ Schedule C Appointment ◇ Career Senior Foreign Service Appointment
● Career Senior Executive Service (SES) Appointment ○ Non-Career Senior Executive Service (SES) Appointment ■ Postal Career Executive Service

DEPARTMENTS

U.S. Coast Guard Training Center - Cape May (NJ) (TRACEN Cape May)

One Munro Avenue, Cape May, NJ 08204
Tel: (609) 898-6900

Commanding Officer **CAPT Owen L. Gibbons USCG** . . . (609) 898-6901
E-mail: owen.l.gibbons@uscg.mil
Secretary **Tina Walker** . . . (609) 898-6901
Command Master Chief **MCPO David Pace USCG** . . . (609) 898-6923
Executive Officer **CDR Brian C. Krautler USCG** . . . (609) 898-6901
E-mail: brian.c.krautler@uscg.mil
Public Affairs Officer **CWO John D. Edwards USCG** . . . (609) 898-6362
E-mail: john.d.edwards@uscg.mil

U.S. Coast Guard Training Center - Petaluma (CA) (TRACEN Petaluma)

599 Tomales Road, Petaluma, CA 94952-5000
Tel: (707) 765-7320 Fax: (707) 765-7329

Commanding Officer **CAPT Paul A. Flynn USCG** . . . (707) 765-7320
E-mail: paul.a.flynn@uscg.mil
Executive Officer **CDR Brian Neier USCG** . . . (707) 765-7320
Command Master Chief
CMC Thomas D. Daniels USCG . . . (707) 765-7320
Administrative Assistant **Joy M. Connors** . . . (707) 765-7320
E-mail: joy.m.connors@uscg.mil
Librarian **Jason Van Zant** . . . (707) 765-7580
Webmaster **Cameron Huff** . . . (707) 765-7784

U.S. Coast Guard Training Center - Yorktown (VA) (TRACEN Yorktown)

End of State Route 238, Yorktown, VA 23690-5000
Tel: (757) 856-2212 Fax: (757) 856-2329
Internet: www.uscg.mil/tcyorktown

Commanding Officer
CAPT John C. "Jay" Vann USCG . . . (757) 856-2212
Education: US Coast Guard Acad 1992 BSCE; Florida State MS
Administrative Assistant **Denise Serio** . . . (757) 856-2212
Executive Officer **CAPT Bowen Spievack USCG** . . . (757) 856-2212
Education: Georgetown 1997 BS; Northeastern 2001 JD
Command Master Chief
CMC Stephen Dykema USCG . . . (757) 856-2144
Chief of Training **CDR Scott S. Casad USCG, CPT** . . . (757) 856-2000
E-mail: scott.s.casad@uscg.mil
Public Affairs Officer **LT Kelli M. Dougherty USCG** . . . (757) 856-2989
E-mail: kelli.m.dougherty@uscg.mil

U.S. Coast Guard Sector New York

212 Coast Guard Drive, Staten Island, NY 10305
Tel: (718) 354-4004 Fax: (718) 354-4009

Commanding Officer **CAPT Michael H. Day USCG** . . . (718) 354-4003
Education: Naval War MNSSS; Bridgewater State U MPA
Public Affairs Officer **Ann Marie Gordon** . . . (718) 354-4069
Fax: (718) 354-4027

U.S. Coast Guard Surface Forces Logistics Center (SFLC)

2401 Hawkins Point Road, Baltimore, MD 21226-5000
Tel: (410) 762-6010 Tel: (800) 336-7430 Fax: (410) 762-6070
Internet: www.uscg.mil/sflc

Commanding Officer **CAPT Chad L. Jacoby USCG** . . . (410) 762-6012
Education: US Coast Guard Acad 1992; MIT MEM
Executive Director **Kenneth R. Burgess, Jr.** . . . (410) 762-6010
Command Master Chief **Robert Jeffries** . . . (410) 762-6425
Small Boat Production Line Product Manager
CDR Seth J. Denning USCG . . . (410) 762-6164
Small Boat Production Line Deputy Product Manager
Randy L. Gardner . . . (410) 762-6736

U.S. Coast Guard Yard

2401 Hawkins Point Road, Baltimore, MD 21226
Tel: (410) 789-1600 Fax: (410) 636-7990

Commanding Officer **CAPT Matthew W. Lake USCG** . . . (410) 636-3271
E-mail: matthew.w.lake@uscg.mil
Executive Officer **CDR Christopher Wolfe USCG** . . . (410) 636-3271
Command Senior Chief **SSCS Robert Proctor USCG** . . . (410) 636-7713

U.S. Coast Guard Yard *(continued)*

Facilities Engineer **LCDR John Adams USCG** . . . (410) 636-4097
Education: US Coast Guard Acad 2005 BSCE; Illinois 2010 MSCE
Financial Manager **Timothy "Tim" Howard** . . . (410) 636-3639
Education: Bob Jones U 1999 BS; American Military U 2011 MBA
Industrial Manager **CAPT Vincent J. Skwarek USCG** . . . (410) 636-3208
E-mail: vincent.j.skwarek@uscg.mil
Military Support Division Chief
LT David "Dave" Rott USCG . . . (410) 636-4149
E-mail: isaac.l.saenz@uscg.mil
Communications Manager
Dorothy E. "Dottie" Mitchell . . . (410) 636-7238
E-mail: dottie.e.mitchell@uscg.mil
Education: Maryland BA; Col Notre Dame (CA) MA
Quality and Safety Manager **Roger Taylor** . . . (410) 636-3597

Deputy Commandant for Mission Support (CG-DCMS)

2703 Martin Luther King Jr. Avenue, SE, Washington, DC 20593-7714
Tel: (202) 372-4546 Fax: (202) 372-4973
Internet: https://www.dcms.uscg.mil/

United States Coast Guard Academy (USCGA)

31 Mohegan Avenue, New London, CT 06320
Tel: (860) 444-8444 Fax: (860) 444-8639
Internet: https://www.uscga.edu/

Administration

Superintendent **RDML James E. Rendon USCG** . . . (860) 444-8285
E-mail: james.e.rendon@uscg.mil
Education: US Coast Guard Acad 1983 BSCE;
National War Col 2005 MS
Executive Assistant **Bonnie L. Fogell** . . . (860) 444-8285
E-mail: bonnie.l.fogell@uscg.mil
Assistant Superintendent
CAPT Ronald A. LaBrec USCG . . . (860) 444-8286
E-mail: ronald.a.labrec@uscg.mil
Command Master Chief
CMC Brett L. VerHulst USCG . . . (860) 444-8444
E-mail: brett.l.verhulst@uscg.mil
Dean, Academics **CAPT Kurt J. Colella USCG, PhD** . . . (860) 444-8275
E-mail: kurt.j.colella@uscga.edu
Education: US Coast Guard Acad 1981 BS; MIT; Connecticut PhD
Associate Dean **CAPT Gregory J. Hall USCG, USCG** . . . (860) 444-8393
E-mail: gregory.hall@uscga.edu
Education: Tufts 2006 PhD
Assistant Dean, Academics
LCDR Meghan K. Steinhaus USCG . . . (860) 444-8532
Commandant of Cadets
CAPT Melissa L. Rivera USCG . . . (860) 444-8280
E-mail: melissa.l.rivera@uscg.mil
Commanding Officer, Barque Eagle
CAPT Matthew T. "Matt" Meilstrup USCG . . . (860) 439-1562
Director, Admissions
CAPT Robert E. McKenna USCG . . . (860) 444-8503
E-mail: robert.e.mckenna@uscga.edu
Director, Athletics **Timothy M. Fitzpatrick** . . . (860) 444-8600
E-mail: Timothy.M.Fitzpatrick@uscga.edu
Chief Information Officer
CDR Christopher M. Armstrong USCG . . . (860) 701-6194
E-mail: christopher.m.armstrong@uscga.edu

★ Presidential Appointment Requiring Senate Confirmation ☆ Presidential Appointment ☐ Schedule C Appointment ◇ Career Senior Foreign Service Appointment
● Career Senior Executive Service (SES) Appointment ○ Non-Career Senior Executive Service (SES) Appointment ■ Postal Career Executive Service

Deputy Commandant for Operations (CG-DCO)

2703 Martin Luther King Jr. Avenue, SE, Washington, DC 20593-7714
Fax: (202) 372-8342

Coast Guard Investigative Service (CGIS)

2703 Martin Luther King Jr. Avenue, SE,
Suite 3i14-00, Mail Stop 3703, Washington, DC 20593-7301
Tel: (202) 372-3000 Fax: (202) 372-3062

Coast Guard Investigative Service Central Region Office

1240 East 9th Street, Cleveland, OH 44199-2060
Tel: (216) 902-6136 Fax: (216) 902-6143
Areas Covered: IA, IL, (north of I-70), IN (North of I-74), MI, MN (East of the Mississippi River; North of I-494), ND (North of I-94), WI

Special Agent-in-Charge **Neal R. Marzloff** . . . . (216) 902-6137
E-mail: neal.r.marzloff@uscg.mil
Assistant Special Agent-in-Charge **Michael LeClair** . . . . . . (216) 902-6139

Coast Guard Investigative Service Chesapeake Region Office

Federal Building, 431 Crawford Street, Portsmouth, VA 23704-5004
Tel: (757) 398-6268 Fax: (757) 398-6506
Areas Covered: MD, NC, SC, VA, WV

Special Agent-in-Charge **Marty J. Martinez** . . . . (757) 398-6845
E-mail: marty.j.martinez@uscg.mil
Assistant Special Agent-in-Charge **Kelly Hoyle** . . . . (757) 398-6292

Coast Guard Investigative Service Gulf Region Office

F. Edward Hebert Federal Building, 600 South Maestrie Place,
Suite 635, New Orleans, LA 70130
Tel: (504) 589-4929 Fax: (504) 589-6262
Areas Covered: AL, AR, FL (panhandle), IL (South of I-70), IN (South of I-74), KS, KY, LA, MN (West of Mississippi River; South of I-494), MS, MO, NE, ND (South of I-94), OK, PA (West of I-81), SD, TN, TX (East of 103 W longitude)

Special Agent-in-Charge **Brian J. Jeanfreau** . . . . (504) 589-4929
E-mail: brian.j.jeanfreau@uscg.mil
Assistant Special Agent-in-Charge **Paul Shultz** . . . . (504) 589-4929

Coast Guard Investigative Service New England Region Office

Building 8, Coast Guard Base, 427 Commercial Street,
Boston, MA 02110
Tel: (617) 557-9091 Fax: (617) 557-9097
Areas Covered: CT, ME, MA, NH, NY (east of I-81), PA (east of I-81), RI, VT

Special Agent-in-Charge **Richard D. Cox** . . . . (617) 557-9091
E-mail: richard.d.cox@uscg.mil
Assistant Special Agent-in-Charge **(Vacant)** . . . . (617) 557-9077

Coast Guard Investigative Service New York Field Office

Battery Park Building, One South Street,
Third Floor, New York, NY 10004
Tel: (212) 668-7048 Fax: (212) 668-7050
Areas Covered: NJ, NY, PA

Special Agent In Charge **Otis Harris** . . . . (212) 668-5982
Assistant Special Agent in Charge **Eric J. O'Hearn** . . . . . . (212) 668-5984

Coast Guard Investigative Service Northwest Region Office

Jackson Federal Building, 915 Second Avenue,
Suite 3406, Seattle, WA 98174-1067
Tel: (206) 220-7308 Fax: (206) 220-7173
Areas Covered: AK, ID, MT, OR, WA, WY

Special Agent-in-Charge **Jonathan N. Sall** . . . . (206) 220-7300
E-mail: jonathan.n.sall@uscg.mil
Assistant Special Agent-in-Charge **Helena T. Chavez** . . . . (206) 220-7299
E-mail: helena.t.chavez@uscg.mil

Coast Guard Investigative Service Pacific Region Office

Building 18, Coast Guard Island, Alameda, CA 94501-5100
Tel: (510) 437-3406 Fax: (510) 437-3411
Areas Covered: AZ, CA, CO, HI, GU, NV, NM, TX (west of 103 W longitude), UT

Special Agent-in-Charge **Jon C. Finnegan** . . . . (510) 437-3409

Coast Guard Investigative Service Pacific Region Office *(continued)*

Assistant Special Agent-in-Charge **Eric G. Holm** . . . . (510) 437-3410
E-mail: eric.g.holm@uscg.mil

Coast Guard Investigative Service Southeast Region Office

909 S.E. First Avenue, Room 490, Miami, FL 33130
Tel: (305) 278-6850 Fax: (305) 415-7018
Areas Covered: FL (except panhandle), GA, PR, VI

Special Agent-in-Charge **Thomas E. "Tom" Robarge** . . . (305) 415-7013
Assistant Special Agent-in-Charge **Zinnia James** . . . . (305) 415-7014
E-mail: zinnia.james@uscg.mil

DEPARTMENTS

Atlantic Area (LANTAREA)

431 Crawford Street, Portsmouth, VA 23704
Tel: (757) 398-6287 Fax: (757) 391-8123
Areas Covered: AL, AR, CO, CT, DE, DC, FL, GA, IL, IN, IA, KS, KY, LA, ME, MD, MA, MI, MN, MS, MO, NE, NH, NJ, NM, NY, NC, ND, OH, OK, Panama Canal Zone, PA, PR, RI, SC, SD, TN, TX, VT, VI

Commander Atlantic Area/Commander U.S. Defense Force East **VADM Scott A. Buschman USCG** . . . . (757) 398-6287
E-mail: scott.a.buschman@uscg.mil
Education: US Coast Guard Acad BSCE; George Washington MPA; Sloan MBA
Administrative Specialist **Paula Marcangelo** . . . . (757) 398-6521
E-mail: paula.marcangelo@uscg.mil
Deputy Commander **RADM Todd A. Sokalzuk USCG** . . . (757) 398-6521
E-mail: todd.a.sokalzuk@uscg.mil
Reserve Chief of Staff **CAPT Julia A. Hein USCG** . . . . . . (757) 398-6288
E-mail: julia.a.hein@uscg.mil
Command Master Chief **CMC James H. Bach USCG** . . . . (757) 398-6345
E-mail: james.h.bach@uscg.mil
Reserve Command Master Chief **CMC Robert J. "Joe" Pasqua USCGR** . . . . (757) 398-6368
Education: Excelsior 2011 BS
Chief of Staff **CAPT Edward M. "Ted" St. Pierre USCG** . . . . (757) 398-6288
Executive Assistant **CDR Gretchen Bailey USCG** . . . . . . (757) 398-6379
Command, Control and Communications Division Chief **(Vacant)** . . . . (757) 398-6437
Operations Division Chief **CAPT Sean Regan USCG** . . . . (757) 398-6412
Atlantic Command Center Chief **CDR Linda M. Hoerster USCG** . . . . (757) 398-6700
Plans and Exercises Division Chief **(Vacant)** . . . . (757) 398-6365

1st Coast Guard District

408 Atlantic Avenue, Boston, MA 02110-3350
Tel: (800) 848-3942 Tel: (800) 223-8310 (CCGDONE Boating Hotline-Recorded Messages Only) Tel: (617) 223-8171
Fax: (617) 223-8078
Areas Covered: CT, ME, MA, NH, Northern NJ, NY (metro NYC and Long Island), RI, VT

Commander **RDML Andrew J. "Andy" Tiongson USCG** . . . . (617) 223-8480
E-mail: andrew.j.tiongson@uscg.mil
Executive Assistant **CDR Carolyn Leonard-Cho USCG** . . . . (617) 223-8514
Fax: (617) 223-8115
Chief of Staff **CAPT Gregory D. Case USCG** . . . . (617) 223-8473
E-mail: gregory.d.case@uscg.mil Fax: (617) 223-8115
Education: Southern Illinois BA; U Washington MS
Command Master Chief **MCPO William D. Hollandsworth USCG** . . . . (617) 223-8450
Reserve Command Master Chief **MCPO Rashaun R. Morris USCG** . . . . (617) 223-8450
Chaplain **CDR David A. Shirk USN** . . . . (617) 223-8314
Civilian Personnel Liaison Officer **Todd A. Merrick** . . . . . . (617) 223-3494
E-mail: todd.a.merrick@uscg.mil Fax: (617) 223-3495
District Legal Officer **(Vacant)** . . . . (617) 223-8500
Administration Branch Chief **CWO Steve Merchant USCG** . . . . (617) 223-8167
Fax: (617) 223-8078

(continued on next page)

★ Presidential Appointment Requiring Senate Confirmation ☆ Presidential Appointment □ Schedule C Appointment ◇ Career Senior Foreign Service Appointment
● Career Senior Executive Service (SES) Appointment ◎ Non-Career Senior Executive Service (SES) Appointment ■ Postal Career Executive Service

DEPARTMENTS

1st Coast Guard District *(continued)*

External Affairs Division Chief
CAPT Edward J. Marohn USCG .... (617) 223-8203
E-mail: edward.j.marohn@uscg.mil Fax: (617) 223-8523
Public Affairs Officer
LT Karen L. Kutkiewicz USCG .... (617) 223-8519
E-mail: karen.l.kutkiewicz@uscg.mil Fax: (617) 223-8523
Planning and Force Readiness Division
CAPT Jerry W. Davenport USCG .... (617) 223-8340
E-mail: jerry.w.davenport@uscg.mil
Response Division Chief **(Vacant)** .... (617) 223-8457
Incident Management Branch Chief **(Vacant)** .... (617) 223-8461
Fax: (617) 223-8471
Law Enforcement Branch Chief
CAPT Brian Fiedler USCG .... (617) 223-8426
Fax: (617) 223-8074
Waterways Management Branch Chief
CAPT Matthew B. Stuck USCG .... (617) 223-8355
E-mail: matthew.b.stuck@uscg.mil
Prevention Officer **CAPT Byron L. Black USCG** .... (617) 223-8214
E-mail: byron.l.black@uscg.mil Fax: (617) 223-8291
Information and Communications Resources
Management Staff Chief/Webmaster **Matthew Carty** ... (617) 223-8492

5th Coast Guard District
431 Crawford Street, Portsmouth, VA 23704-5004
Tel: (757) 398-6640 Fax: (757) 398-1707
Areas Covered: DE, DC, MD, Southern NJ, NC, Eastern PA, VA

Commander **RDML Keith M. Smith USCG** .... (757) 398-6640
E-mail: keith.m.smith@uscg.mil
Education: Cal State (Long Beach)
Chief of Staff **(Vacant)** .... (757) 398-1704
Command Master Chief
CMC Leonard Barbazon USCG .... (757) 398-6640
Chief of Planning and Force Readiness
CAPT Anthony S. Lloyd USCG .... (757) 398-6640
E-mail: anthony.s.lloyd@uscg.mil
Education: Naval War 2001 MNSSS
Chief of Prevention **CAPT Jerry Barnes USCG** .... (757) 398-6691
Education: US Coast Guard Acad BSE; Michigan MSE
Chief of Response **CAPT William J. Lane USCG** .... (757) 398-6676

7th Coast Guard District
Brickell Plaza Federal Building, 909 SE First Avenue,
Room 944, Miami, FL 33131
Tel: (305) 415-6670 Fax: (305) 415-6674
Areas Covered: FL, GA, PR, SC, VI

Commander **RDML Peter J. Brown USCG** .... (305) 415-6670
E-mail: peter.j.brown@uscg.mil
Education: US Coast Guard Acad 1985; Miami 1991
Executive Administrator **Robert W. Sova** .... (305) 415-6670
E-mail: robert.w.sova@uscg.mil
Chief of Staff **CAPT Austin Gould USCG** .... (305) 415-6670
Command Master Chief
CMC Devin R. Spencer USCG .... (305) 415-6677
E-mail: devin.r.spencer@uscg.mil
Reserve Command Master Chief
CMC Janine M. Tschantz-Hahn USCGR .... (305) 415-6677
E-mail: janine.m.tschantz-hahn@uscg.mil
Command Chaplain **CDR Santiago Rodriguez USN** .... (305) 415-6675
E-mail: Santiago.Rodriguez@uscg.mil

8th Coast Guard District
500 Poydras Street, Suite 1324, New Orleans, LA 70130-3396
Fax: (504) 589-2077
Areas Covered: AL, AR, CO, FL (panhandle), Southwestern GA, IL (except north of 41 N longitude and east of 90 W longitude), IN (south of 41 N latitude), IA, KS, KY, LA, MO, MS, NE, NM, ND, OH (south of 41 N latitude), OK, PA (south of 41 N latitude and west of 70 W longitude), SD, TN, TX, WV, WY

Commander **RADM Paul F. Thomas USCG** .... (504) 589-6298
E-mail: paul.f.thomas@uscg.mil
Education: US Coast Guard Acad 1985 BS; MIT 1990 MS; Dalhousie 1992 MBA

8th Coast Guard District *(continued)*

Chief of Staff **CAPT Andrew M. Sugimoto USCG** ..... (504) 589-6298
E-mail: andrew.m.sugimoto@uscg.mil
Civil Rights Officer **Dean Vesone** .... (504) 671-2043
Contingency Preparedness Officer
CAPT Orin E. Rush USCG .... (504) 671-2059
E-mail: orin.e.rush@uscg.mil
External Affairs Officer **LCDR B.J. Coffman USCG** .... (504) 671-2018
Legal Officer **CAPT Philip C. Schifflin USCG** .... (504) 671-2036
Telecommunications Officer
CWO2 John Marshall USCG .... (504) 671-2215
Command Master Chief **CMC Heath B. Jones USCG** ... (504) 671-2006
E-mail: heath.b.jones@uscg.mil
Reserve Command Master Chief
CMC James R. Wood USCGR .... (985) 380-5313
Administration Division Chief
CAPT Teri Jordan USCG .... (504) 671-2173
Outer Continental Shelf Division Chief
CAPT Joshua D. Reynolds USCG .... (504) 671-2150
E-mail: joshua.d.reynolds@uscg.mil
Prevention Division Chief
CDR Emily C. Saddler USCG .... (504) 671-2087
E-mail: emily.c.saddler@uscg.mil
Response Division Chief **(Vacant)** .... (504) 671-2230
Western Rivers Coordinator
CAPT Christopher K. "Chris" Palmer USCG .... (504) 671-2263
E-mail: christopher.k.palmer@uscg.mil
Chaplain **CDR Lynn W. Christensen USCG** .... (757) 398-6287
E-mail: lynn.w.christensen@uscg.mil

9th Coast Guard District
A.J. Celebrezze Federal Building, 1240 East Ninth Street,
Cleveland, OH 44199-2060
Tel: (216) 902-6001 Fax: (216) 902-6018
Areas Covered: Great Lakes Area

District Commander **RDML Joanna M. Nunan USCG** ... (216) 902-6001
Education: Rensselaer Poly 1991 MBA
Administrative Assistant **Crystal M. Kinnaird** .... (216) 902-6001
E-mail: crystal.m.kinnaird@uscg.mil
Chief of Staff
CAPT Nicholas A. "Nick" Bartolotta USCG .... (216) 902-6001
E-mail: nicholas.a.bartolotta@uscg.mil
Senior Reserve Officer
CAPT Martha J. LaGuardia USCGR .... (216) 902-6001
E-mail: martha.j.laguardia@uscg.mil
Command Master Chief **CMC Jahmal Perreira USCG** ... (216) 902-6001
Response Division Chief **CAPT Tim Wendt USCG** ...... (216) 902-6063
External Affairs Officer **LT Marvin Kimmel USCG** ...... (216) 902-6020
Chaplain **LCDR Ronald S. O'Dell, Jr. USCG** .... (216) 902-6006

Pacific Area (PACAREA)
Building 51-6, Coast Guard Island, Alameda, CA 94501-5100
Tel: (510) 437-3522 Fax: (510) 437-3774
Areas Covered: AZ, CA, GU, HI, ID, MT, NV, OR, UT, WA

Commander **VADM Linda L. Fagan USCG** .... (510) 437-3522
E-mail: linda.l.fagan@uscg.mil
Education: US Coast Guard Acad 1985 BS; U Washington 2000 MMA; Indust'l Col Armed Forces 2008 MA
Executive Assistant **(Vacant)** .... (510) 437-3522
Deputy Commander
RDML Nathan A. "Nate" Moore USCG .... (510) 437-3522
Senior Reserve Officer **CAPT Mark Murakami USCG** ... (510) 437-3522
Chief of Staff **(Vacant)** .... (510) 437-3522
Command Master Chief
CMC Adwoa S. Hendricks USCG .... (510) 437-3070
Reserve Command Master Chief
CMC Timothy A. Beard USCGR .... (510) 437-3522
Chaplain **CAPT John A. Swanson USN** .... (510) 437-3067
E-mail: john.a.swanson@uscg.mil
Director, Naval Defense Forces West
CAPT Timothy Callahan USCG .... (510) 437-3404
External Affairs Staff Chief **Charlie Richards** .... (510) 437-3099
Command, Control and Communications Division
Chief **(Vacant)** .... (510) 437-3608

★ Presidential Appointment Requiring Senate Confirmation ☆ Presidential Appointment ☐ Schedule C Appointment ◇ Career Senior Foreign Service Appointment
● Career Senior Executive Service (SES) Appointment ○ Non-Career Senior Executive Service (SES) Appointment ■ Postal Career Executive Service

Pacific Area *(continued)*

Intelligence Division Chief **(Vacant)** .... (510) 437-2911
Operations Division Chief **(Vacant)** .... (510) 437-3908
Operations Analysis Division Chief
Jean A. Dominguez .... (510) 437-3634
Preparedness Division Chief **(Vacant)** .... (510) 437-3248
Resource Management and Administration Division
Chief **(Vacant)** .... (510) 437-3011

11th Coast Guard District
Building 52, Coast Guard Island, Alameda, CA 94501-5100
Tel: (510) 437-3968 Fax: (510) 437-5793
Areas Covered: AZ, CA, NV, UT

Commander **RDML Peter W. Gautier USCG** .... (510) 437-3968
E-mail: peter.w.gautier@uscg.mil
Education: US Coast Guard Acad 1987 BS; Michigan MSChE; National War Col MA
Secretary to the Commander **(Vacant)** .... (510) 437-3968
Chief of Staff **CAPT James B. "Jim" Pruett USCG** .... (510) 437-5623
E-mail: james.b.pruett@uscg.mil
Education: Cal State (Chico) 1990 BA; Golden Gate 2003 JD
Command Master Chief
CMC Ryan J. Fahlenkamp USCG .... (510) 437-5367
Bridge Section Chief **Carl T. Hausner** .... (510) 437-3516
Prevention Chief **CAPT William M. Drelling USCG** ..... (510) 437-5754
Response Chief **Gregory Burg** .... (510) 437-5397

13th Coast Guard District
3590 Federal Building, 915 Second Avenue, Seattle, WA 98174-1067
Tel: (206) 220-7090 Fax: (206) 220-7092 E-mail: d13ipa@uscg.mil
Areas Covered: ID, MT, OR, WA

Commander **RDML David G. Throop USCG** .... (206) 220-7090
E-mail: david.g.throop@uscg.mil
Administrative Assistant **Jamie H. Belouskas** .... (206) 220-7090
E-mail: jamie.h.belouskas@uscg.mil
Command Master Chief
MCPO Jason K. Wong USCG .... (206) 220-7090
E-mail: Jason.K.Wong@uscg.mil
Chief of Staff **CAPT Brendan C. McPherson USCG** .... (206) 220-7091
E-mail: brendan.c.mcpherson@uscg.mil

14th Coast Guard District
300 Ala Moana Boulevard, 9th Floor, Honolulu, HI 96850-4982
Tel: (808) 535-3230 Fax: (808) 535-3209
Areas Covered: Hawaiian Islands to Indian Ocean

Commander **RDML Kevin E. Lunday USCG** .... (808) 535-3201
E-mail: kevin.e.lunday@uscg.mil
Education: National War Col 2008 MS
Chief of Staff **(Vacant)** .... (808) 535-3202
Command Master Chief **CMC Lori Fields USCG** .... (808) 535-3230
Maritime Safety and Security Team Commanding
Officer **(Vacant)** .... (808) 842-2768
Prevention Division Chief
CAPT Malcolm McLellan USCG .... (808) 535-3401
External Affairs Officer **LCDR Warren Wright USCG** .... (808) 535-3441
Public Affairs Officer **LT Scott S. Carr USCG** .... (808) 535-3230
E-mail: scott.s.carr@uscg.mil
Purchasing/Contracting Officer
LCDR Felicia Butalia USCG .... (808) 535-3281
Webmaster **Ervin B. Lawson** .... (808) 535-3444
E-mail: ervin.b.lawson@uscg.mil

17th Coast Guard District
Federal Office Building, 709 West Ninth Street,
Room 651, Juneau, AK 99801
Mail: P.O. Box 25517, Juneau, AK 99802-5517
Tel: (907) 463-2065 Fax: (907) 463-2037
E-mail: d17-dg-publicaffairs@uscg.mil
Areas Covered: AK

Commander **RDML Matthew T. Bell, Jr. USCG** .... (907) 463-2028
Education: Northern Arizona 1984 BS, 1993 MS
Chief of Staff **CAPT Laura M. Dickey USCG** .... (907) 463-2029
E-mail: laura.m.dickey@uscg.mil

17th Coast Guard District *(continued)*

Command Master Chief **CMC Clinton R. Self USCG** .... (907) 463-2036

United States Customs and Border Protection (CBP)

1300 Pennsylvania Avenue, NW, Washington, DC 20229
Tel: (202) 344-2001 (Personnel Locator)
Tel: (202) 344-1350 (Library and Information Center)
Tel: (202) 325-8000 (CBP Info Center) Fax: (202) 344-1380
Internet: www.cbp.gov

OFFICE OF THE COMMISSIONER

1300 Pennsylvania Avenue, NW, Room 4.4A, Washington, DC 20229
Tel: (202) 344-2001 Fax: (202) 344-1380

Enterprise Services (ES)

Office of Finance (OF)

1300 Pennsylvania Avenue, NW, Washington, DC 20229
Tel: (202) 344-2300 Fax: (202) 344-2360

Financial Systems Division
6650 Telecom Drive, Indianapolis, IN 46278
Fax: (317) 298-1013
Director **Sherri D. Jordan** .... (317) 614-4624

Organizational Resources and Support
6650 Telecom Drive, Indianapolis, IN 46278
Fax: (317) 298-1593
Director **John Dickerson** .... (317) 298-1142

National Finance Center
6650 Telecom Drive, Indianapolis, IN 46278
Fax: (317) 298-1012
Director **Pamela A. Miller** .... (317) 298-1567
Management and Program Analyst **Natasha Wolske** ... (317) 298-1222

Office of Training and Development

1300 Pennsylvania Avenue, NW, Washington, DC 20229
Tel: (202) 325-7100 Fax: (202) 344-2520

Advanced Training Center
400 Koonce Road, Harpers Ferry, WV 25425
Tel: (304) 724-5800
Director **Clark J. Messer** .... (304) 724-5827

CBP Field Operations Academy
1131 Chapel Crossing Road, Glynco, GA 31524
Tel: (912) 261-4526 Fax: (912) 261-4031
Director **Michael "Mike" Brown** .... (912) 554-4995
Legal Counsel **Russell Jokinen** .... (912) 267-2552
Education: Northern Michigan 1980 BS

U.S. Border Patrol Academy
1300 West Richey, Artesia, NM 88210
Tel: (575) 748-8032 Fax: (505) 746-8319
Chief **Dan M. Harris, Jr.** .... (575) 746-8360
Education: Angelo State BA

★ Presidential Appointment Requiring Senate Confirmation ☆ Presidential Appointment □ Schedule C Appointment ◇ Career Senior Foreign Service Appointment
● Career Senior Executive Service (SES) Appointment ○ Non-Career Senior Executive Service (SES) Appointment ■ Postal Career Executive Service

Office of Field Operations (OFO)

1300 Pennsylvania Avenue, NW, Washington, DC 20229
Tel: (202) 344-1620 Fax: (202) 344-2777

Atlanta Field Operations

1699 Phoenix Parkway, Suite 400, College Park, GA 30349-5565
Tel: (678) 284-5900 Fax: (678) 284-5932

Director **Reginald I. Manning** .... (678) 284-5900
Assistant Director, Border Security
Michael S. Denning .... (678) 284-5900
Assistant Director, Mission Support **Patti S. Crow** .... (770) 994-4106
Deputy Assistant Director, Mission Support
(Logistics) **Cherisse Rountree** .... (678) 284-5900
Assistant Director, Trade Operations **Petrina O. Evans** ... (678) 284-5900
E-mail: petrina.o.evans@cbp.dhs.gov
Press Officer **Sean Crep** .... (678) 284-5915

Atlanta (GA) Port
157 Tradeport Drive, Suite C, Atlanta, GA 30354
Tel: (404) 675-1300 Tel: (404) 675-1302 (Cargo Office)
Fax: (404) 675-1231
Port Director **Carey T. Davis** .... (404) 675-1300
E-mail: carey.t.davis@cbp.dhs.gov

Brunswick (GA) Port
1609 Gloucester Street, Brunswick, GA 31520-7146
Fax: (912) 262-0235
Port Director **Tracy Harris** .... (912) 262-6692

Charleston (SC) Area Port
200 East Bay Street, Charleston, SC 29403
Fax: (843) 579-6610
Port Director **Robert A. Fencel** .... (843) 579-6500
E-mail: robert.a.fencel@cbp.dhs.gov

Charleston (WV) Port
176 Airport Road, Charleston, WV 25311-1081
Fax: (304) 347-5520
Port Director **(Vacant)** .... (304) 347-5204

Charlotte (NC) Area Port
1901 Cross Beam Road, Charlotte, NC 28217-2823
Tel: (704) 329-6120 Fax: (704) 329-6103
Port Director **Patricia Fitzpatrick** .... (704) 329-6151

Columbia (SC) Port
2355-A Airport Boulevard, Columbia, SC 29170
Fax: (803) 822-5055
Port Director **Jerry Wilson** .... (803) 822-5251

Georgetown (SC) Port
1100 Jetport Road, Myrtle Beach, SC 29577-4201
Fax: (843) 916-0442
Officer in Charge **Charles E. Sasser** .... (843) 916-0438

Greensboro/Winston-Salem (NC) Port
532 North Regional Road, Suite C, Greensboro, NC 27409-9057
Fax: (336) 668-7364
Port Director **Charles S. "Steve" Bowie** .... (336) 668-7272
E-mail: steve.bowie@dhs.gov

Greenville-Spartanburg (SC) Port
150-A West Phillips Road, Greer, SC 29650-4721
Fax: (864) 848-3454
Port Director **Wayne Henson** .... (864) 877-8006

Morehead City (NC) Port
534 North 35th Street, Suite H, Morehead City, NC 28557-4257
Tel: (252) 726-5845 Fax: (252) 726-6159
Port Director **Kevin O'Brien** .... (252) 726-5845
E-mail: kevin.m.obrien@cbp.dhs.gov

Myrtle Beach (SC) Port
1100 Jetport Road, Myrtle Beach, SC 29577-4201
Fax: (843) 916-0442
Officer in Charge **Charles E. Sasser** .... (843) 916-0438

Norfolk (VA) Area Port
101 East Main Street, Norfolk, VA 23510-1605
Fax: (757) 533-4273
Port Director **Mark J. Laria** .... (757) 533-4200
E-mail: mark.j.laria@cbp.dhs.gov

Raleigh-Durham (NC) Port
2400 John Brantley Boulevard, Morrisville, NC 27560
Fax: (919) 840-0627
Port Director **Ronald L. Jackson** .... (919) 674-3400

Richmond (VA) Port
Ivor-Massey Building, 5707 Huntsman Road,
Suite I-104, Richmond, VA 23250-2415
Fax: (804) 226-1197
Port Director **Brett Marshall** .... (804) 226-9675

Savannah (GA) Area Port
One East Bay Street, Savannah, GA 31401-1224
Fax: (912) 447-9407
Port Director **Lisa Beth Brown** .... (912) 447-9400

Wilmington (NC) Port
721 Medical Center Drive, Suite 200, Wilmington, NC 28401-7054
Fax: (910) 772-5907
Port Director **Scott Opalka** .... (910) 772-5900

Baltimore Field Operations

217 East Redwood Street, 12th Floor, Baltimore, MD 21202
Tel: (410) 962-6200 Fax: (410) 962-2423

● Director **Casey Owen Durst** .... (410) 962-6200

Baltimore (MD) Service Port
40 South Gay Street, Suite 110, Baltimore, MD 21202
Tel: (410) 962-2666 Fax: (410) 962-9335
Port Director **Dianna Bowman** .... (410) 962-2666

Harrisburg (PA) Area Port
Port of Harrisburg, 1215 Manor Drive,
Suite 301, Harrisburg, PA 17055
Tel: (717) 691-7136 Fax: (717) 691-7107
Port Director **Michelle Stover** .... (717) 691-7136 ext. 1

Philadelphia (PA) Service Port
Second and Chestnut Streets, Room 102, Philadelphia, PA 19106
Tel: (215) 717-5800 Fax: (215) 597-8370
Port Director **(Vacant)** .... (215) 717-5800

Pittsburgh (PA) Port
P.O. Box 12445, Pittsburgh, PA 15231
Tel: (412) 472-0804 Fax: (412) 472-0809
Port Director **Susan P. Anderson** .... (412) 472-0806
E-mail: susan.p.anderson@cbp.dhs.gov

Wilmington (DE) - Chester (PA) Port
908 New Churchman's Road, Suite C, New Castle, DE 19720
Tel: (302) 326-0600 Fax: (302) 326-0828
Port Director **Donald Josey** .... (302) 326-0600 ext. 101

Washington-Dulles (VA) Port
22685 Holiday Park Drive, Suite 15, Sterling, VA 20598
Tel: (703) 318-5900 Fax: (703) 318-6706
Port Director **Wayne R. Biondi** .... (703) 318-5900
E-mail: wayne.r.biondi@cbp.dhs.gov

★ Presidential Appointment Requiring Senate Confirmation ☆ Presidential Appointment ☐ Schedule C Appointment ◇ Career Senior Foreign Service Appointment
● Career Senior Executive Service (SES) Appointment ○ Non-Career Senior Executive Service (SES) Appointment ■ Postal Career Executive Service

Boston Field Operations
10 Causeway Street, Room 801, Boston, MA 02222-1056
Tel: (617) 565-6208 Fax: (617) 565-6277
Areas Covered: CT, ME, MA, NH, RI, VT

Director **William A. Ferrara** . . . . . (617) 565-6208
E-mail: william.a.ferrara@cbp.dhs.gov
Staff Assistant **(Vacant)** . . . . . (617) 565-6208
Public Affairs Liaison **Sean D. Smith** . . . . . (617) 565-6332
Public Affairs Specialist **(Vacant)** . . . . . (207) 532-5644
155 Gannett Drive, South Portland, ME 04106

Boston (MA) Area Port
10 Causeway Street, Room 603, Boston, MA 02222-1007
Tel: (617) 565-6149 Fax: (617) 565-6137
Port Director **Clint Lamm** . . . . . (617) 565-6149

Calais (ME) Port of Entry
180 International Avenue, Calais, ME 04619
Tel: (207) 904-3001 Fax: (207) 904-3009
Port Director (Acting) **Dan Ramboer** . . . . . (207) 904-3001

Derby Line (VT) Area Port
Interstate 91 South, Derby Line, VT 05830-9003
Tel: (802) 873-3219 Fax: (802) 873-3628
Port Director **David Mantione** . . . . . (802) 873-3219

Hartford (CT) Area Port
International Arrivals Building, Bradley International Airport, Windsor Locks, CT 06096
Tel: (860) 292-1314 Fax: (860) 627-6761
Port Director **Nancy Graham** . . . . . (860) 292-1314

Highgate Springs (VT) Area Port
480 Welcome Center Road, Swanton, VT 05488-8887
Tel: (802) 868-2778 Fax: (802) 868-2373
Port Director **Ronald L. Stanley** . . . . . (802) 868-2778
E-mail: ronald.l.stanley@cbp.dhs.gov

Houlton (ME) Area Port
27 Customs Loop, Houlton, ME 04730-3307
Tel: (207) 532-2131 ext. 0 Fax: (207) 532-4153
Port Director **Chris Doughty** . . . . . (207) 532-2131 ext. 0

Portland (ME) Area Port
155 Gannett Drive, South Portland, ME 04106
Tel: (207) 771-3600 Fax: (207) 771-3608
Area Port Director **Keith Fleming** . . . . . (207) 771-3605

Saint Albans (VT) Port
50 South Main Street, Room 100R, St. Albans, VT 05478-2215
Tel: (802) 524-6527 Fax: (802) 527-6258
Area Port Director **(Vacant)** . . . . . (802) 524-6527 ext. 3301

Buffalo Field Operations
300 Airborne Parkway, Suite 300, Buffalo, NY 14225
Tel: (716) 626-0400 Fax: (716) 626-1164
Director **Rose Hilmey** . . . . . (716) 626-0400 ext. 201
Assistant Director, Trade Operations **Richard Roberts** . . . . (716) 626-0400
Press Officer **Aaron Bowker** . . . . . (716) 626-0400 ext. 261
E-mail: aaron.e.bowker@cbp.dhs.gov

Albany (NY) Port
445 Broadway, Albany, NY 12207
Tel: (518) 431-0200 Fax: (518) 431-0203
Director **Drew Wescott** . . . . . (518) 431-0200

Alexandria Bay (NY) Port
46735 I-81, Alexandria Bay, NY 13607
Tel: (315) 482-2065 Fax: (315) 482-5304
Director **Tim Walker** . . . . . (315) 482-2065

Buffalo (NY) Area Port
726 Exchange Street, Room 400, Buffalo, NY 14210
Tel: (716) 843-8300 Fax: (716) 843-8522
Director **Cary Frieling** . . . . . (716) 843-8300

Champlain (NY) Area Port
237 West Service Road, Champlain, NY 12919
Tel: (518) 298-8311 Fax: (518) 298-8395
Director **Paul Stephan Mongillo** . . . . . (518) 298-8311

Rochester (NY) Port
Greater Rochester International Airport, 1200 Brooks Avenue, Rochester, NY 14624
Tel: (585) 263-6293 Fax: (585) 263-5828
Director **Ronald Menz** . . . . . (585) 263-6293

Syracuse (NY) Port
152 Air Cargo Road, Suite 201, North Syracuse, NY 13212
Tel: (315) 455-8446 Fax: (315) 454-8224
Director **David Harris** . . . . . (315) 455-8446

Caribbean Area - San Juan Field Operations
City View Plaza Tower II, #48 Road. 165 km 1.2, Guaynabo, PR 00968
Tel: (787) 729-6950 Fax: (787) 729-6978
Director **(Vacant)** . . . . . (787) 729-6950
Press Officer **Brenda Padial** . . . . . (787) 729-6999

Charlotte-Amalie (VI) Area Port
5500 Veterans Drive, St. Thomas, VI 00801
Tel: (340) 774-2510 Fax: (340) 776-3489
Area Port Director **Louis Harrigan** . . . . . (340) 774-2510 ext. 222

Saint Croix (VI) Service Port
Henry E. Rohlsen Airport, Kingshill, St. Croix, VI 00850
Tel: (340) 773-1490 Fax: (340) 778-7419
Port Director **Vinroy Douglas** . . . . . (340) 773-1490 ext. 222

San Juan (PR) Service - Area Port
Tel: (787) 729-6850 Fax: (787) 729-6678
Area Port Director **Edwin Cruz** . . . . . (787) 729-6850

Chicago Field Operations
610 Canal Street, 3rd Floor, Chicago, IL 60607-4523
Tel: (312) 542-5700 Fax: (312) 542-5790
Director, Field Operations **Robert E. White** . . . . . (312) 542-5700
E-mail: robert.e.white@cbp.dhs.gov
Education: Chicago 2010
Assistant Director, Border Security
Steven T. "Steve" Artino . . . . . (312) 542-5700
E-mail: steven.t.artino@cbp.dhs.gov
Assistant Director, Mission Support **Charles E. Young** . . . (312) 542-5700
E-mail: charles.e.young@cbp.dhs.gov
Assistant Director, Trade Operations **Jack Bebinger** . . . . . (312) 542-5700
E-mail: jack.bebinger@cbp.dhs.gov
Press Officer **Steven P. Bansbach** . . . . . (773) 462-9477
E-mail: steven.p.bansbach@cbp.dhs.gov

Ashtabula-Conneaut (OH) Port
1170 Lake Avenue, Ashtabula, OH 44004
Tel: (440) 964-2510 Fax: (440) 964-2478
Port Director **Cynthia Verbiak** . . . . . (440) 964-2510
E-mail: cynthia.verbiak@cbp.dhs.gov

Chicago (IL) Service - Area Port
5600 Pearl Street, Rosemont, IL 60018
Tel: (847) 928-3000 Fax: (847) 928-5115
Port Director **Matthew S. Davies** . . . . . (847) 928-5110
E-mail: matthew.s.davies@cbp.dhs.gov

DEPARTMENTS

Cincinnati (OH) - Erlanger (KY) Ports
4243 Olympic Boulevard, Suite 210, Erlanger, KY 41018
Tel: (859) 282-7203 Fax: (859) 282-8914

Port Director **Richard L. Gillespie** .... (859) 282-6308 ext. 102
E-mail: richard.l.gillespie@cbp.dhs.gov

Cleveland (OH) Service - Area Port
6747 Engle Road, Middleburg Heights, OH 44130-7939
Tel: (440) 891-3800 Fax: (440) 891-3836

Port Director **Marc A. Hurteau** .... (440) 891-3804
E-mail: marc.a.hurteau@cbp.dhs.gov

Columbus (OH) Port
6431 Alum Creek Drive, Suite A, Groveport, OH 43125
Tel: (614) 497-1865 Fax: (614) 497-3559

Port Director **Theodore "Ted" Thomas** .... (614) 497-1865 ext. 115
E-mail: theodore.thomas@cbp.dhs.gov

Davenport (IA) - Rock Island, Moline (IL) Ports
2480 69th Avenue, Moline, IL 61265
Tel: (309) 799-8129 Fax: (309) 799-8124

Port Director **Maurice A. Howe** .... (309) 799-8129

Dayton (OH) Port
3800 Wright Drive, Vandalia, OH 45377
Tel: (937) 890-7633 Fax: (937) 890-7485

Port Director **Gary G. Speckhard** .... (937) 890-7633 ext. 125
E-mail: gary.g.speckhard@cbp.dhs.gov

Des Moines (IA) Port
Des Moines International Airport, 6000 Fleur Drive,
Des Moines, IA 50321
Tel: (515) 284-4403 Fax: (515) 256-5514

Port Director **Jerry N. Soard** .... (515) 284-4403
E-mail: jerry.n.soard@cbp.dhs.gov

Erie (PA) Port
4459 West 12th Street, Erie, PA 16505-3003
Tel: (814) 833-1355 Fax: (814) 835-2152

Port Director **Steven McGreevey** .... (814) 833-1355

Evansville (IN) Port
New Federal Building, 101 NW Martin Luther King Boulevard,
Room 116, Evansville, IN 47708
Tel: (812) 465-6413

Port Director **Steven Harriss** .... (812) 465-6413

Green Bay (WI) Port
Austin Straubel Field, 2077 Airport Drive,
2nd Floor, Green Bay, WI 54313
Tel: (920) 496-0606 Fax: (920) 496-1455

Port Director **Chad Shulfer** .... (920) 496-0606

Indianapolis (IN) Port
6801 Pierson Drive, Indianapolis, IN 46241
Tel: (317) 248-4060 Fax: (317) 248-4174

Port Director **James E. Moore** .... (317) 248-4068
E-mail: james.e.moore2@cbp.dhs.gov

Kansas City (MO) Service Port
4100 North Mulberry Drive, Suite 110, Kansas City, MO 64116
Tel: (816) 584-1994 Fax: (816) 584-8431

Port Director **Peggy J. Kraft** .... (816) 584-1994 ext. 8600
E-mail: peggy.j.kraft@cbp.dhs.gov

Louisville (KY) Service Port
650 Administrative Drive, Louisville International Airport,
Louisville, KY 40209
Tel: (502) 368-5604 Fax: (502) 368-5319

Port Director **Thomas Mahn** .... (502) 368-5604 ext. 107
E-mail: thomas.jr.mahn@cbp.dhs.gov

Milwaukee (WI) Service - Area Port
4915 South Howell Avenue, Suite 200, Milwaukee, WI 53223
Mail: P.O. Box 370920, Milwaukee, WI 53237-0920
Tel: (414) 486-7790 Fax: (414) 486-7819

Port Director **William Braun** .... (414) 486-7790 ext. 123
E-mail: william.braun@dhs.gov

Minneapolis (MN) Service Port
5600 West American Boulevard, Bloomington, MN 55437
Tel: (952) 857-3100 Fax: (952) 857-3230

Port Director **Kathleen M. Koetz** .... (952) 857-3236 ext. 145
E-mail: kathleen.m.koetz@cbp.dhs.gov

Omaha (NE) Port
3737 Orvilla Plaza, Omaha, NE 68110
Tel: (402) 341-0240 Fax: (402) 341-2117

Port Director **Leo E. Hachey** .... (402) 341-0240
E-mail: leo.e.hachey@cbp.dhs.gov

Peoria (IL) International Airport
6100 West Dirksen Parkway, Peoria, IL 61607
Tel: (309) 697-4329 Fax: (309) 697-2699

Port Director **Daniel R. Hartzler** .... (309) 697-4329
E-mail: daniel.r.hartzler@cbp.dhs.gov

Racine (WI) Port
3239 North Green Bay Road, Room 207, Racine, WI 53404
Tel: (262) 633-0286 Fax: (262) 633-4054

Port Director **Paul A. Bisswurm** .... (262) 633-0286 ext. 142
E-mail: paul.a.bisswurm@cbp.dhs.gov

Rockford (IL) Port
Greater Rockford Airport, 50 Airport Drive, Rockford, IL 61109
Tel: (815) 968-0661 Fax: (815) 965-6611

Port Director **Theodore S. "Ted" Williams** .... (815) 968-0661
E-mail: theodore.s.williams@cbp.dhs.gov

Sioux Falls (SD) Port
One Weather Lane, Room 100, Sioux Falls, SD 57104
Tel: (605) 338-4384 Fax: (605) 336-7046

Port Director **Michael P. Horan** .... (605) 338-4384
E-mail: michael.p.horan@cbp.dhs.gov

Saint Louis (MO) Service - Area Port
4477 Woodson Road, Suite 200, St. Louis, MO 63134
Tel: (314) 429-8100 Fax: (314) 429-8193

Port Director **Joseph Lanzante** .... (314) 429-8100

Springfield (MO) Port
5141 West Cargo, Springfield, MO 65803
Tel: (417) 831-4035 Fax: (417) 868-0546

Port Director **Hezekiah "Ky" Neuleib** .... (417) 831-4035
E-mail: hezekiah.neuleib@cbp.dhs.gov

Toledo - Sandusky - Port Clinton (OH) Ports
709 SE Catawba Road, Port Clinton, OH 43452
Tel: (419) 732-4446 Fax: (419) 259-3703

Port Director **Sheryl D. Monette** .... (419) 732-4446
E-mail: sheryl.d.monette@cbp.dhs.gov

Wichita (KS) Port
1700 Airport Road, Wichita, KS 67209
Tel: (316) 613-4194 Fax: (316) 613-4195

Port Director **Douglas C. Grove** .... (316) 613-4194
E-mail: douglas.c.grove@cbp.dhs.gov

Detroit Field Operations

211 West Fort Street, Suite1200, Detroit, MI 48226
Tel: (313) 496-2155 Tel: (313) 442-0370 (Customer Information)
Fax: (313) 226-6066

Director **Christopher M. "Chris" Perry** .... (313) 496-2155
Education: SUNY (Buffalo); Towson State U MA;
Loyola Col (MD) 1998 MBA

★ Presidential Appointment Requiring Senate Confirmation ☆ Presidential Appointment □ Schedule C Appointment ◇ Career Senior Foreign Service Appointment
● Career Senior Executive Service (SES) Appointment ○ Non-Career Senior Executive Service (SES) Appointment ■ Postal Career Executive Service

Detroit Field Operations *(continued)*

Assistant Director For Trade Operations
Tinesha L. Cherry . . . . (313) 496-2155

Battle Creek (MI) Port of Entry
4950 Dickman Road, Battle Creek, MI 49015
Tel: (269) 965-3349 Fax: (269) 965-0661

Port Director **Ken Bagwell** . . . . (269) 965-3349

Detroit (MI) Area Port
2810B West Fort Street, Suite 123, Detroit, MI 48216
Tel: (313) 964-7830 Fax: (313) 964-2109

Port Director **Marty Raybon** . . . . (313) 964-7830

Detroit (MI) Metropolitan Airport - Area Port
Edward H. McNamara Terminal, 2596 Wordgateway Place, Detroit, MI 48242
Tel: (734) 941-6180 Fax: (734) 941-6690

Port Director **Devin Chamberlain** . . . . (734) 941-6180 ext. 100

Grand Rapids (MI) Port of Entry
6450 Air Cargo Drive, Grand Rapids, MI 49512
Tel: (616) 942-5245 Fax: (616) 285-0188

Port Director **Robert "Bob" Pykosz** . . . . (616) 942-5245

Port Huron (MI) Area Port
526 Water Street, Room 301, Port Huron, MI 48060
Tel: (810) 985-7125 Fax: (810) 985-3516

Port Director **Andrew Douglas** . . . . (810) 985-7125

Saginaw/Bay City/Flint Port of Entry
8500 Garfield Road, Suite 103, Freeland, MI 48623
Tel: (989) 695-2871 Fax: (989) 695-2809

Port Director **Robert Nasser** . . . . (989) 695-2871

Sault Sainte Marie (MI) Area Port
900 International Bridge Plaza, Room 113, Sault Sainte Marie, MI 49783
Tel: (906) 632-7221 Fax: (906) 632-0978

Port Director **Patrick Wilson** . . . . (906) 632-7221

El Paso Field Operations
9400 Viscount Boulevard, El Paso, TX 79925-7040
Tel: (915) 633-7300 Fax: (915) 633-7290

• Director **Hector A. Mancha, Jr.** . . . . (915) 730-7201
E-mail: hector.a.mancha@cbp.dhs.gov Fax: (915) 633-7345
Education: Texas
Special Assistant **Marianne Martinez** . . . . (915) 730-7201
Assistant Director for Field Operations **(Vacant)** . . . . (915) 633-7300
Assistant Director for Mission Support
Christopher A. "Chris" Saindon . . . . (915) 730-7204
Education: New Mexico State 1980 AA; Cameron 2001 BSGS
Assistant Director for Trade **(Vacant)** . . . . (915) 633-7300

Albuquerque (NM) Port of Entry
2200 Sunport Boulevard SE, Albuquerque, NM 87106
Tel: (505) 346-6992 Fax: (505) 346-6995

Port Director **Tracy S. Thorpe** . . . . (505) 346-6992
E-mail: tracy.s.thorpe@cbp.dhs.gov

El Paso (TX) Service Port
3600 East Paisano Drive, El Paso, TX 79905
Tel: (915) 730-7004 Fax: (915) 730-7091

Service Port Director **Beverly Good** . . . . (915) 730-7004

Rio Grande City (TX) Port of Entry
317 South Pete Diaz Avenue, Rio Grande City, TX 78582
Tel: (956) 487-1650 Fax: (956) 487-1649

Port Director **David John Gonzalez** . . . . (956) 487-1650

Santa Teresa (NM) Port of Entry
170 Pete Domenici Highway, Santa Teresa, NM 88008
P.O. Box 1439, Santa Teresa, NM 88008
Tel: (915) 730-7436 Fax: (915) 730-7405

Port Director **Charles G. Perez** . . . . (915) 730-7436
Education: New Mexico State 1986

Houston Field Operations
2323 South Shepherd Drive, Suite 1200, Houston, TX 77019
Tel: (713) 387-7200 Fax: (713) 387-7212

Director of Field Operations **Judson W. Murdock II** . . . . . (713) 387-7210
Assistant Director For Trade Operations **Lynn Fallik** . . . . . (713) 387-7291
E-mail: lynn.fallik@cbp.dhs.gov

Dallas-Fort Worth (TX) Service - Area Port
7501 Esters Boulevard, Suite 160, Irving, TX 75063
Mail: P.O. Box 619050, Dallas, TX 75261
Tel: (972) 870-7460 Fax: (972) 870-7553

Port Director **Cleatus Hunt** . . . . (972) 870-7552
Assistant Port Director **O'Ruill D. McCanlas** . . . . (972) 870-7549

Houston (TX) Airport Service Port
2350 North Sam Houston Parkway East, Suite 1000, Houston, TX 77032
Tel: (281) 985-6700 Fax: (281) 985-6706

Port Director **(Vacant)** . . . . (281) 985-6712

Houston/Galveston (TX) Seaport
7141 Office City Drive, Houston, TX 77087
Fax: (713) 454-8065 Fax: (713) 454-8062

Area Director **Roderick "Rod" Hudson** . . . . (713) 454-8029

Laredo Field Operations
109 Shiloh Drive, Suite 300, Laredo, TX 78045
Tel: (956) 753-1768 Fax: (956) 753-1754

• Director **David P. Higgerson** . . . . (956) 753-1768
E-mail: david.p.higgerson@cbp.dhs.gov
Assistant Director For Trade Operations
Bradd M. Skinner . . . . (956) 753-1768
E-mail: bradd.m.skinner@cbp.dhs.gov
Education: Ohio Wesleyan
Press Officer **Mucia C. Dovalina** . . . . (956) 753-1703

Laredo (TX) Service Port
Building 2, Lincoln-Juarez Bridge, Laredo, TX 78040
Mail: P.O. Box 3130, Laredo, TX 78044-3130
Tel: (956) 523-7300 Fax: (956) 523-7313

Port Director **Gregory "Greg" Alvarez** . . . . (956) 523-7414
Assistant Port Director for Passenger Processing
Adriana Arce . . . . (956) 523-7387
Assistant Port Director for Trade Operations
Alberto Flores . . . . (956) 523-7414

Los Angeles Field Operations
One World Trade Center, Room 705, Long Beach, CA 90831
Mail: P.O. Box 32689, Long Beach, CA 90832-2639
Tel: (562) 980-3100 Fax: (562) 980-3107

Director **Carlos C. Martel** . . . . (562) 980-3100
E-mail: carlos.c.martel@cbp.dhs.gov
Education: UCLA
Assistant Director, Border Security and Facilitation
(Acting) **Thomas Reis** . . . . (562) 980-3100
E-mail: thomas.reis@cbp.dhs.gov
Assistant Director, Mission Support **Jeanette Lewis** . . . . . (562) 980-3100
E-mail: jeannette.lewis@cbp.dhs.gov
Assistant Director, Trade Operations
Elva M. Muneton . . . . (562) 980-3100
Chief Public Affairs Liaison
Darryl Tamayo Room 741 . . . . (562) 366-5772
Fax: (562) 980-3359

★ Presidential Appointment Requiring Senate Confirmation ☆ Presidential Appointment □ Schedule C Appointment ◇ Career Senior Foreign Service Appointment
● Career Senior Executive Service (SES) Appointment ○ Non-Career Senior Executive Service (SES) Appointment ■ Postal Career Executive Service

Los Angeles Airport
11099 La Cienega Boulevard, Room 201-H, Los Angeles, CA 90045
Tel: (310) 215-2618 Fax: (310) 215-2013

● Area Port Director (Acting) **Loretta Sanchez** . . . . (310) 665-4638
E-mail: loretta.sanchez@cbp.dhs.gov

Los Angeles-Long Beach Seaport
301 East Ocean Boulevard, Long Beach, CA 90802
Tel: (562) 366-5700 Fax: (562) 628-7900

Port Director **LaFonda D. Sutton-Burke** . . . . (562) 366-5700
E-mail: lafonda.d.sutton-burke@cbp.dhs.gov
Education: Central Oklahoma BA

Miami Field Operations
909 SE First Avenue, Suite 980, Miami, FL 33131
Tel: (305) 810-5120 Fax: (305) 810-5143

Director **Diane J. Sabatino** . . . . (305) 810-5120
E-mail: diane.j.sabatino@cbp.dhs.gov
Education: Fordham BA
Executive Assistant **Judy C. Cottle** . . . . (305) 810-5120
Deputy Director **Daniel "Danny" Alonso** . . . . (305) 810-5181
E-mail: daniel.alonso@cbp.dhs.gov
Assistant Director, Border Security **(Vacant)** . . . . (305) 810-5120
Assistant Director, Mission Support **Leona Haynes** . . . . . . (305) 810-5104
Assistant Director, Trade Operations **Gregory McCann** . . . (305) 810-5125
Public Affairs Officer **Michael Silva** Suite 734 . . . . (786) 354-5055
E-mail: michael.silva@cbp.dhs.gov

Miami (FL) Service Port
Concourse D- North Terminal, 4200 NW 21st Street,
Second Floor, Miami, FL 33122
Mail: 6601 NW 25th Street, Miami, FL 33122
Tel: (786) 476-3100 Fax: (786) 476-3149

Port Director **Christopher D. Maston** . . . . (786) 476-3100
E-mail: christopher.d.maston@cbp.dhs.gov

Miami (FL) Seaport
903 South America Way, Miami, FL 33132
Tel: (305) 536-4758 Fax: (305) 536-4716

Port Director **Jorge L. Roig** . . . . (305) 536-4758
E-mail: jorge.l.roig@cbp.dhs.gov

Port of Key West (FL)
301 Simonton Street, Key West, FL 33040
Tel: (305) 296-5411 Fax: (305) 293-7224

Port Director **Stephen Bausmith** . . . . (305) 296-5411

Port of Port Everglades (Fort Lauderdale, FL)
1800 Eller Drive, Suite 104, Fort Lauderdale, FL 33316
Tel: (954) 761-2001 Fax: (954) 761-2088

Port Director **Jorge L. Roig** . . . . (954) 761-2001
E-mail: jorge.l.roig@cbp.dhs.gov

Port of West Palm Beach (FL)
One East 11th Street, Room 323, Box #4, Riviera Beach, FL 33404
Tel: (561) 844-1703 Fax: (561) 844-2254

Port Director **Jennifer Connors** . . . . (561) 844-1703

New Orleans Field Operations
423 Canal Street, New Orleans, LA 70130
Tel: (504) 670-2404 Fax: (504) 670-2286

Director **Vanessa Vargas** . . . . (504) 670-2404
Public Affairs Officer **Nancy Bonnaffons** . . . . (504) 670-2124
Fax: (504) 670-2286

Memphis (TN) Service Port
2813 Business Park Drive, Memphis, TN 38118
Tel: (901) 480-4000

Port Director **Patrick T. "Pat" McCumber** . . . . (901) 480-4000
E-mail: patrick.t.mccumber@cbp.dhs.gov
Area Port Director **Lori Breakstone** . . . . (901) 480-4000

Mobile (AL) Service Port
150 North Royal Street, Room 3004, Mobile, AL 36602
Tel: (251) 378-7600 Fax: (251) 378-7680

Port Director **Anthony A. Acrey** . . . . (251) 378-7600
E-mail: anthony.a.acrey@cbp.dhs.gov
Assistant Port Director **Christina Allen** . . . . (251) 441-5107
Assistant Port Director **Scott Walters** . . . . (251) 441-5106

New Orleans (LA) Service Port
423 Canal Street, Room 260, New Orleans, LA 70130
Tel: (504) 670-2391 Fax: (504) 670-2123

Port Director **Vernon T. Foret** . . . . (504) 670-2391
E-mail: vernon.t.fornet@cbp.dhs.gov
Education: Southeastern Louisiana
Assistant Director for Tactical Affairs **Mark Choina** . . . . . (504) 670-2391
Assistant Director for Trade **Troy A. Simon** . . . . (504) 670-2391
E-mail: troy.a.simon@cbp.dhs.gov

New York Field Operations
One World Trade Center, Suite 50.200, New York, NY 10007
Tel: (646) 733-3100 Fax: (646) 733-3245

● Field Operations Director (Acting)
Francis J. "Frank" Russo . . . . (646) 733-3100
E-mail: francis.j.russo@cbp.dhs.gov
Assistant Director for Border Security
Francis J. "Frank" Russo . . . . (646) 733-3113
E-mail: francis.j.russo@cbp.dhs.gov
Assistant Director for Mission Support
Karen Dugan-Rivera . . . . (646) 733-3267
Assistant Director for Trade and Cargo Security
Leon Hayward . . . . (646) 733-3230
E-mail: leon.hayward@cbp.dhs.gov
Press Officer **Anthony Bucci** . . . . (646) 733-3275
E-mail: anthony.bucci@cbp.dhs.gov
Public Affairs Liaison **Andrija Dandridge** . . . . (646) 733-3215

John F. Kennedy International Airport Area
Building 77, John F. Kennedy International Airport, Jamaica, NY 11430
Tel: (718) 487-5164 Fax: (718) 487-5191

Port Director **Francis J. "Frank" Russo** . . . . (718) 487-5164
E-mail: francis.j.russo@cbp.dhs.gov

New York-Newark Area
1100 Raymond Boulevard, Newark, NJ 07102
Tel: (973) 368-6000 Fax: (201) 443-0550

Port Director **Richard F. DiNucci** . . . . (973) 368-6000
E-mail: richard.f.dinucci@cbp.dhs.gov
Education: Colorado 1987 BA

Portland Field Operations
33 New Montgomery Street, Suite 1600, San Francisco, CA 94105
Tel: (415) 744-1530 Fax: (415) 744-1530

Director **Brian J. Humphrey** Room 1620 . . . . (415) 744-1530
Assistant Director, Field Operations - Border Security
Leticia Romero . . . . (415) 744-1530
E-mail: leticia.romero@dhs.gov
Assistant Director, Field Operations - Mission Support
Lamar Witmer . . . . (503) 744-1530
P.O. Box 55580, Portland, OR 97238-5580
Assistant Director, Field Operations - Trade
Dora Murphy . . . . (415) 744-1530 ext. 233
E-mail: dora.murphy@cbp.dhs.gov

Anchorage (AK) Service - Area Port
605 West Fourth Avenue, Room 203, Anchorage, AK 99501-2252
Tel: (907) 271-2675 Fax: (907) 271-2684

Area Port Director **Lance Robinson** . . . . (907) 271-2675

Denver (CO) Service - Area Port
183000 East 71st Avenue, Suite 200, Denver, CO 80249
Tel: (303) 375-4500 Fax: (303) 307-9660

Area Port Director **LaShanda Jones** . . . . (303) 375-4500

★ Presidential Appointment Requiring Senate Confirmation ☆ Presidential Appointment ☐ Schedule C Appointment ◇ Career Senior Foreign Service Appointment
● Career Senior Executive Service (SES) Appointment ○ Non-Career Senior Executive Service (SES) Appointment ■ Postal Career Executive Service

Portland (OR) Service - Area Port
8337 Northeast Alderwood Road, Portland, OR 97220
Mail: P.O. Box 55580, Portland, OR 97238-5580
Tel: (503) 326-2865 Fax: (503) 326-3511
Area Port Director **John Barnes** .... (503) 326-2865

San Diego Field Operations
610 West Ash Street, Suite 1200, San Diego, CA 92101
Tel: (619) 652-9966 Fax: (619) 645-6644
Director **Peter "Pete" Flores** .... (619) 652-9966
E-mail: peteromero.flores@cbp.dhs.gov
Education: San Diego State BS
Field Training Coordinator **Dennis Nelson** ..... (619) 652-9966 ext. 113
Press Officer **Angela De Cima** .... (619) 744-5292

Andrade Port of Entry
235 Andrade Road, Winterhaven, CA 92283
Tel: (760) 572-0089 Fax: (760) 572-2704
Port Director **David Sarrasin** .... (760) 572-0089

Calexico (CA) Port of Entry
P.O. Box 632, Calexico, CA 92232
Tel: (760) 768-7000 Fax: (760) 357-3748
Port Director **David Salazar** .... (760) 768-7000

Otay Mesa (CA) Cargo Facility
9777 Via De La Amistad, San Diego, CA 92173
Tel: (619) 671-8064 Fax: (619) 661-3049
Port Director **Rosa E. Hernandez** .... (619) 690-7675
E-mail: rosa.e.hernandez@cbp.dhs.gov

San Diego (CA) Port of Entry
610 West Ash Street, Suite 1005, San Diego, CA 92101
Tel: (619) 685-4300 Fax: (619) 685-4397
Port Director **William P. Snyder** .... (619) 685-4300
E-mail: william.p.snyder@cbp.dhs.gov

San Ysidro-Otay Mesa Ports of Entry
720 East San Ysidro Boulevard, San Ysidro, CA 92173
Tel: (619) 690-8800 Fax: (619) 662-7162
Port Director **Sidney K. Aki** .... (619) 690-8830
E-mail: sidney.k.aki@cbp.dhs.gov

Tecate (CA) Port of Entry
405 Tecate Road, Tecate, CA 91980
Tel: (619) 938-8330 Fax: (619) 938-8304
Port Director **Carlos Silva** .... (619) 938-8330

San Francisco Field Operations
33 New Montgomery Street, Room 1620, San Francisco, CA 94105
Tel: (415) 744-1530 Fax: (415) 744-7005
Director **Brian J. Humphrey** .... (415) 744-1530
Staff Assistant **Thomas B. Walsh** .... (415) 744-1530 ext. 234
E-mail: thomas.b.walsh@cbp.dhs.gov
Assistant Director, Field Operations - Border Security
Leticia Romero .... (415) 744-1530
E-mail: leticia.romero@dhs.gov
Assistant Director, Field Operations - Mission Support
Lamar Witmer .... (503) 744-1530
P.O. Box 55580, Portland, OR 97238-5580
Assistant Director, Field Operations - Trade
Dora Murphy .... (415) 744-1530 ext. 233
E-mail: dora.murphy@cbp.dhs.gov
Public Affairs Liaison
Francis "Frank" Falcon .... (415) 744-1530 ext. 237
E-mail: francis.falcon@cbp.dhs.gov

Honolulu (HI) Service - Area Port
300 Ala Moana Boulevard, Suite 2500, Honolulu, HI 96850
Tel: (808) 237-4601 Fax: (808) 237-4617
Port Director **Bruce Murley** .... (808) 237-4601

San Francisco (CA) Service - Area Port
555 Battery Street, San Francisco, CA 94111
Tel: (415) 744-1530 Fax: (415) 744-7005
Port Director **(Vacant)** .... (415) 744-1530

Seattle Field Operations
9901 Pacific Highway, Blaine, WA 98230
Tel: (206) 370-3800 Fax: (206) 553-1401
Areas Covered: MT; ND; ID: along Canadian border; MN: along Canadian border as far east as Grand Portage; WA: except south of Olympia in western WA
Director of Field Operations (Interim)
Michael S. Denning .... (206) 370-3800
Public Affairs Chief **Jayson Givens** .... (360) 961-1403

Blaine (WA) Service Port
9901 Pacific Highway, Blaine, WA 98230
Tel: (360) 332-5771
Area Port Director **Ken Williams** .... (360) 332-6500
Assistant Port Director **John Dahm** .... (360) 332-6500
Assistant Port Director **Terry Schulze** .... (360) 332-6500

Great Falls (MT) Service Port
1620 Airport Drive, Great Falls, MT 59404-5508
Tel: (406) 453-0861 Fax: (406) 453-5688
Area Port Director **Daniel Escobedo** .... (406) 453-0861

Pembina (ND) Service Port
112 West Stutsman, Pembina, ND 58271-4102
Tel: (701) 825-5800 Fax: (701) 825-5980
Area Port Director **Jason Schmelz** .... (701) 825-5800
E-mail: jason.schmelz@dhs.gov

Seattle (WA) Service Port
17801 Pacific Highway S, Seattle, WA 98158-2940
Tel: (206) 901-3200 Fax: (206) 553-2940
Area Port Director **Mark W. Wilkerson** .... (206) 901-3200

Tampa Field Operations
1624 East Seventh Avenue, Suite 301, Tampa, FL 33605
Tel: (813) 712-6100 Fax: (813) 225-7110
Director **Diane J. Sabatino** .... (305) 810-5120
E-mail: diane.j.sabatino@cbp.dhs.gov
Education: Fordham BA
Assistant Director for Border Security **(Vacant)** .... (305) 810-5181
Assistant Director for Mission Support **Leona Haynes** ... (305) 810-5107
Assistant Director for Trade **Gregory McCann** .... (305) 810-5104
Supervisory Mission Support Specialist **Ron Johnson** ... (813) 712-6100

Jacksonville (FL) Area Port
10426 Alter Drive, Jacksonville, FL 32226
Tel: (904) 714-3100 Fax: (904) 360-5026
Director **Jennifer Bradshaw** .... (904) 714-3100
E-mail: jennifer.bradshaw@cbp.dhs.gov

Orlando (FL) Orlando International Airport
9043 Tradeport Drive, Orlando, FL 32827
Tel: (407) 240-4462 Fax: (407) 240-7689
Director **Gaetano Cordone** .... (407) 240-4462

Tampa (FL) Area Port
1624 East Seventh Avenue, Suite 101, Tampa, FL 33605
Tel: (813) 712-6000 Fax: (813) 225-7309
Director **Radames Torres** .... (813) 712-6000

Tucson Field Operations
4740 North Oracle Road, Suite 310, Tucson, AZ 85705
Tel: (520) 407-2300 Fax: (520) 407-2350
Director, Field Operations **(Vacant)** .... (520) 407-2325
Assistant Director Field Operations, Border Security
(Vacant) .... (520) 407-2325

(continued on next page)

DEPARTMENTS

★ Presidential Appointment Requiring Senate Confirmation ☆ Presidential Appointment ☐ Schedule C Appointment ◇ Career Senior Foreign Service Appointment
● Career Senior Executive Service (SES) Appointment ○ Non-Career Senior Executive Service (SES) Appointment ■ Postal Career Executive Service

Tucson Field Operations *(continued)*

Assistant Director Field Operations, Capital Improvements **Mark Jankowski** . . . . . . (520) 407-2317
Assistant Director Field Operations, Mission Support **Mark Jankowski** . . . . . . (520) 407-2342
Assistant Director Field Operations, Trade **Guadalupe Ramirez, Jr.** . . . . . . (520) 407-2325
E-mail: guadalupe.ramirezjr@cbp.dhs.gov
Public Affairs Officer **Teresa G. Small** . . . . . . (520) 407-2319
E-mail: teresa.g.small@cbp.dhs.gov
Office of Information Technology Specialist **Josh Lippman** . . . . . . (520) 407-2331
Staff Assistant **Veronica Lopez** . . . . . . (520) 407-2325

Douglas (AZ) Port
First Street and Pan American Avenue, Douglas, AZ 85607
Tel: (520) 364-8486 Fax: (520) 364-2313
Port Director **Margaret Baldenegro** . . . . . . (520) 364-8486

Lukeville (AZ) Port
P.O. Box C, Lukeville, AZ 85341
Tel: (520) 387-5671 Fax: (520) 387-5309
Port Director **Peter Bachelier** . . . . . . (520) 387-5671

Naco (AZ) Port
3867 South Towner Avenue, Naco, AZ 85620
Tel: (520) 432-5349 Fax: (520) 432-7798
Port Director **Margaret Baldenegro** . . . . . . (520) 432-5349

Nogales (AZ) Port
Nine North Grand Avenue, Nogales, AZ 85621
Tel: (520) 375-5785 Fax: (520) 287-1420
Port Director **Michael Humphries** . . . . . . (520) 375-5785

Phoenix (AZ) Port
3002 East Old Tower Road, Room 400, Phoenix, AZ 85034
Tel: (602) 914-1400 Fax: (602) 914-1409
Port Director **Luz Galarza** . . . . . . (602) 914-1427

San Luis (AZ) Port
P.O. Box 7050, San Luis, AZ 85349
Tel: (928) 627-8854 Fax: (928) 627-9850
Port Director **John A. Schwamm** . . . . . . (928) 627-8854

Sasabe (AZ) Port
P.O. Box 306, Sasabe, AZ 85633
Tel: (520) 823-4230 Fax: (520) 823-4270
Port Director **Kenneth Baxter** . . . . . . (520) 823-4231

Tucson (AZ) Port
7150 South Tucson Boulevard, Tucson, AZ 85706
Tel: (520) 799-8348 Fax: (520) 799-8388
Port Director **Roger F. Wheaton** . . . . . . (520) 799-8348 ext. 223
E-mail: roger.f.wheaton@cbp.dhs.gov

Phoenix-Mesa Gateway User Fee Airport
5803 South Sossaman Road, Suite 109, Mesa, AZ 85212
Tel: (480) 279-2928 Fax: (480) 279-2833
SCI **Luz Galarza** . . . . . . (480) 279-2928

Scottsdale (AZ) User Fee Airport
15041 North Airport Drive, Room 105, Scottsdale, AZ 86260
Tel: (480) 312-8483
SCI **Luz Galarza** . . . . . . (480) 312-8483

Air and Marine Operations (AMO)

1300 Pennsylvania Avenue, NW, Room 6.4A, Washington, DC 20229
Fax: (202) 344-3960

National Air and Training Center
5020 South Meridian Ave, Oklahoma City, OK 73119
Tel: (405) 319-6400 Fax: (405) 319-6489
Director **Trevor Buhler** . . . . . . (405) 319-6409
Bellingham Air Operations Director **David Dunn** . . . . . . (360) 734-7557
3871 Airport Way, Bellingham, WA 98225

Air and Marine Operations Center (AMOC)
Building 605, 1355 Customs Way, March Air Reserve Base, CA 92518
Tel: (951) 656-8000 Fax: (951) 656-8070
● Executive Director **(Vacant)** . . . . . . (951) 656-8001
Deputy Director **Kimberly "Kim" Garcia** . . . . . . (951) 656-8002
E-mail: kim.garcia@dhs.gov
Director, Intelligence **Dan Brick** . . . . . . (951) 656-0901
Public Information Officer **(Vacant)** . . . . . . (951) 656-8037
Human Resources Specialist **Lasherry Granger** . . . . . . (951) 656-8004
Director, Operations **Keith Jones** . . . . . . (951) 656-0921
Director, Systems Management **Sherry A. Ziegler** . . . . . . (951) 656-8083
Facilities Manager **Michael Callis** . . . . . . (951) 656-8007

National Air Security Operations Center - Albuquerque
P.O. Box 9209, Albuquerque, NM 87119
Tel: (505) 366-2800 Fax: (505) 346-6431
Areas Covered: New Mexico, West Texas
Director **Andy Campbell** . . . . . . (505) 366-2871

National Air Security Operations Center - Jacksonville (P-3 Operations Center - Jacksonville)
6222 New World Avenue, Jacksonville, FL 32212
Tel: (904) 594-5000 Fax: (904) 778-1853
Director **Robert Blanchard** . . . . . . (904) 594-5000

National Air Security Operations Center - Corpus Christi (P-3 Operations Center - Corpus Christi)
845 First Street, SE, NAS, Corpus Christi, TX 78419
Mail: P.O. Box 18900, Corpus Christi, TX 78480-8900
Tel: (361) 698-6700 Fax: (361) 698-6890
Director of Air Operations **William Allen Durham** . . . . . . (361) 698-6701
Education: Texas A&M
Deputy Director of Air Operations **Troy Meridith** . . . . . . (361) 698-6700

Caribbean Air and Marine Branch
P.O. Box 250429, Aguadilla, PR 00604-0429
Tel: (787) 819-5083 Fax: (787) 819-3800
Fax: (787) 819-3814 (Operations)
Director of Air and Marine Operations **Johnny Morales** . . . . . . (787) 819-5083
Fax: (787) 819-3813

Jacksonville Air and Marine Branch
Box 115 - NAS, Jacksonville, FL 32212
Tel: (904) 680-6794 Fax: (904) 680-6725
Areas Covered: Northern FL, GA, NC, PA, SC, VA
Director of Aviation Operations (Acting) **Iain Henry** . . . . . . (904) 680-6794
Director of Marine Operations **Allen Gustafson** . . . . . . (904) 680-6794

Miami Air and Marine Branch
P.O. Box 901349, Homestead, FL 33090-1349
Tel: (305) 258-5550 Fax: (305) 257-3697
Areas Covered: Southern FL
Director for Air Operations **Jeff Maher** . . . . . . (305) 258-5550 ext. 101

New Orleans Air and Marine Branch
P.O. Box 1439, Hammond, LA 70404
Tel: (985) 902-2200 Fax: (985) 902-2286
Areas Covered: AL, FL (panhandle region), IL, IN, KY, LA, MI, MS, OH, TN
Director, Air Operations **Francisco Rodriguez** . . . . . . (985) 902-2200

★ Presidential Appointment Requiring Senate Confirmation ☆ Presidential Appointment ☐ Schedule C Appointment ◇ Career Senior Foreign Service Appointment
● Career Senior Executive Service (SES) Appointment ○ Non-Career Senior Executive Service (SES) Appointment ■ Postal Career Executive Service

New Orleans Air and Marine Branch *(continued)*

Director, Marine Operations **Jaime Garcia** ....(985) 902-2200

San Angelo Air and Marine Branch
P.O. Box 62390, San Angelo, TX 76906
Tel: (325) 224-1400 Fax: (325) 224-1475
Areas Covered: KS, ND, NE, OK, SD, portions of TX

Air Operations Director **Jeremy Battenfield** ....(325) 224-1400
Deputy Air Operations Director **Brian Thomas** ....(325) 224-1470

San Diego Air and Marine Branch
P.O. Box 357013, Building 1480, NASNI, San Diego, CA 92135-7013
Tel: (619) 522-6100 Fax: (619) 522-6118
Areas Covered: CA, OR, WA

Director of Aviation Operations **Hunter Davis** ...(619) 522-6100 ext. 101
Director of Marine Operations **Jeremy Thompson** ......(619) 522-6100

Tucson Air Branch
P.O. Box 15009, DMAFB, Tucson, AZ 85708-5001
Tel: (520) 584-2400 Fax: (520) 584-2414
Areas Covered: AZ, ID, NV, UT

Director of Air Operations **(Vacant)** ....(520) 584-2400

U.S. Border Patrol (USBP)

Ronald Reagan International Trade Center,
1300 Pennsylvania Avenue, NW, Room 6.5E, Washington, DC 20229
Fax: (202) 344-3160

U.S. Border Patrol Sectors

Big Bend Border Patrol Sector
P.O. Box I, Marfa, TX 79843
Tel: (432) 729-5200 Tel: (888) 536-6204 Fax: (432) 729-5498
Areas Covered: The Big Bend Sector covers over 135,000 square miles encompassing over 118 counties in Texas and Oklahoma. Big Bend Sector is responsible for the largest geographical area of any sector along the Southwest border. Border Patrol agents in the Big Bend Sector are responsible for over 420 miles of river border.

● Chief Patrol Agent **Robert L. Boatright** ....(432) 729-5200
Deputy Chief Patrol Agent **Victor M. Velazquez** ....(432) 729-5200
Public Affairs Officer **(Vacant)** ....(432) 729-5217

Blaine Border Patrol Sector
2410 Nature's Pathway, Blaine, WA 98230-9114
Tel: (360) 332-9200 Tel: (360) 332-8781 (Public Affairs)
Fax: (360) 332-9263
Areas Covered: The Sector services Alaska, Oregon and the western half of the State of Washington.

Chief Patrol Agent **Brian J. Martin** ....(360) 332-9200
E-mail: brian.j.martin@cbp.dhs.gov
Deputy Chief Patrol Agent **Chris Bippley** ....(360) 332-9200

Buffalo Border Patrol Sector
201 Lang Boulevard, Grand Island, NY 14072
Tel: (716) 774-7200 Fax: (716) 773-2387
Areas Covered: The Sector is responsible for 450 miles of border with Canada from the Ohio/Pennsylvania state line to Jefferson County, NY. The sector also encompasses most of NY, and all of PA, MD, VA, and WV

Chief Patrol Agent (Acting) **Eduardo Payan** ....(716) 774-7200
Deputy Chief Patrol Agent (Acting) **Paul Thaver** ....(716) 774-7200
Mission Support Specialist **Stephanie D. Greco** ....(716) 774-7236
E-mail: stephanie.d.greco@cbp.dhs.gov
Lead Mission Support Specialist, Workforce
Management **Michael Miller** ....(716) 774-7200
Fax: (716) 773-2347
Mission Support Specialist, Training/Workforce
Management **Kelly Gallagher** ....(716) 774-7200
E-mail: kelly.gallagher@dhs.gov

Del Rio Border Patrol Sector
2401 Dodson Avenue, Del Rio, TX 78840
Tel: (830) 778-7000 Tel: (830) 778-7050 (Public Affairs)
Fax: (830) 778-7807
Areas Covered: The Sector area of responsibility covers 59,541 square miles of Texas, and reaches more than 300 miles into Texas from the U.S.-Mexico border.

● Chief Patrol Agent **Felix Chavez** ....(830) 778-7000
Education: Ashford BA
Deputy Chief Patrol Agent **Matthew J. Hudak** ....(830) 778-7000
E-mail: matthew.hudak@cbp.dhs.gov
Supervisory Border Patrol Agent **David R. Vera** ....(830) 778-7000
E-mail: david.r.vera@cbp.dhs.gov
Public Affairs Officer **Dennis P. Smith** ....(830) 778-7051
E-mail: dennis.p.smith@cbp.dhs.gov

Detroit Border Patrol Sector
Building 1516, 26000 South Street, Selfridge ANGB, MI 48045
Mail: P.O. Box 450040, Selfridge ANGB, MI 48045-0040
Tel: (586) 239-2160 Fax: (586) 307-2171
Areas Covered: The Sector area of responsibility includes Illinois, Indiana, Michigan, and Ohio.

Chief Patrol Agent **Douglas Harrison** ....(586) 239-2160
Deputy Chief Patrol Agent **Tony Barker** ....(586) 239-2160
Border Community Liaison **Geoffrey M. Ramer** ....(586) 239-5059
E-mail: geoffrey.m.ramer@cbp.dhs.gov

El Centro Border Patrol Sector
211 West Aten Road, Imperial, CA 92251
Tel: (760) 335-5700 Fax: (760) 335-5819
Areas Covered: The Sector covers the counties of Imperial and Riverside, California.

Chief Patrol Agent **Gloria I. Chavez** ....(760) 355-5700
Deputy Chief Patrol Agent **Ryan J. Scudder** ....(760) 335-5809
E-mail: ryan.j.scudder@cbp.dhs.gov

El Paso Border Patrol Sector
8901 Montana Avenue, El Paso, TX 79925-1212
Tel: (915) 834-8350 Tel: (915) 834-8312 (Public Affairs)
Fax: (915) 782-4333
Areas Covered: The Sector covers 125,500 square miles including the entire state of New Mexico and the two western most counties in Texas, Hudspeth and El Paso.

Chief Patrol Agent **Aaron A. Hull** ....(915) 834-8307
Deputy Chief Patrol Agent **Chris T. Clem** ....(915) 834-8302
Director of Air Operations **(Vacant)** ....(915) 782-2300

Grand Forks Border Patrol Sector
2320 South Washington Street, Grand Forks, ND 58201
Tel: (701) 772-3056 Fax: (701) 772-5031
Areas Covered: The Sector covers North Dakota, Minnesota, Wisconsin, South Dakota, Iowa, Nebraska, Kansas, and Missouri.

Chief Patrol Agent **Aaron M. Heitke** ....(701) 772-3056
E-mail: aaron.heitke@dhs.gov
Deputy Chief Patrol Agent **Andrew J. Althoff** ....(701) 772-3056
E-mail: andrew.j.althoff@cbp.dhs.gov
Public Affairs Officer, Special Operations Supervisor
Jesse Lindemer ....(701) 772-3056
E-mail: jesse.g.lindemer@cbp.dhs.gov
Border Community Liaison **Ryan C. Gilberg** ....(701) 772-3056

Havre Border Patrol Sector
2605 Fifth Avenue, SE, Havre, MT 59501
P.O. Box 810, Havre, MT 59501
Tel: (406) 262-5600 Fax: (406) 262-5681
Areas Covered: CO, portions of ID, UT, WY, and 454 miles of border area between MT and Canada.

Chief Patrol Agent **Sean L. McGoffin** ....(406) 262-5600
Deputy Chief Patrol Agent **(Vacant)** ....(406) 262-5600
Public Affairs Officer/Assistant Chief Patrol Agent
Michael Rappold ....(406) 262-5645
E-mail: michael.rappold@cbp.dhs.gov

DEPARTMENTS

★ Presidential Appointment Requiring Senate Confirmation ☆ Presidential Appointment ☐ Schedule C Appointment ◇ Career Senior Foreign Service Appointment
● Career Senior Executive Service (SES) Appointment ○ Non-Career Senior Executive Service (SES) Appointment ■ Postal Career Executive Service

Houlton Border Patrol Sector
96 Calais Road, Hodgdon, ME 04730
Tel: (207) 532-6521 Tel: (800) 851-8727 Fax: (207) 532-3123
Fax: (207) 532-5645
Areas Covered: ME

Chief Patrol Agent **Daniel Hiebert** .... (207) 532-6521
Deputy Chief Patrol Agent **Jason Schneider** .... (207) 532-6521

Laredo Border Patrol Sector
207 West Del Mar Boulevard, Laredo, TX 78041
Tel: (956) 764-3200 Tel: (956) 764-3349 (Public Affairs)
Fax: (956) 764-3236
Areas Covered: The Sector encompasses 101 counties and covers 94,499 square miles of southwest and northeast Texas. The Rio Grande River is both the southwest and international boundary. The Laredo Sector is situated between the Del Rio and Marfa Sectors on the west and the Rio Grande Valley Sector on the southeast. The northern boundary extends to the Oklahoma border.

● Chief Patrol Agent (Interim) **Felix Chavez** .... (956) 764-3200
Education: Ashford BA
Deputy Chief Patrol Agent **Jason D. Owens** .... (956) 764-3200
Education: National War Col

Miami Border Patrol Sector
15720 Pines Boulevard, Pembroke Pines, FL 33027
Tel: (954) 965-6300 Fax: (954) 965-6321
Areas Covered: The Sector covers the states of Florida, Georgia, North Carolina and South Carolina.

Chief Patrol Agent **John R. Modlin** .... (954) 965-6300 ext. 104
E-mail: john.r.modlin@dhs.gov
Deputy Chief Patrol Agent **(Vacant)** .... (954) 965-6300
Public Affairs Officer/Assistant Chief Patrol Agent **Frank Miller** .... (954) 965-6300 ext. 106

New Orleans Border Patrol Sector
423 Canal Street, Suite 409-L, New Orleans, LA 70130
Tel: (504) 376-2800 Fax: (504) 376-2806
Areas Covered: The New Orleans Sector has jurisdiction over a seven-state area, encompassing 592 counties and parishes and approximately 362,310 square miles, including Louisiana, Mississippi, Alabama, Arkansas, Kentucky, Tennessee, and a portion of the Florida panhandle.

Chief Patrol Agent (Acting) **Joseph A. Banco** .... (504) 376-2800
E-mail: joseph.a.banco@cbp.dhs.gov
Deputy Chief Patrol Agent (Acting) **Teresa Pedregon** .... (504) 376-2800
E-mail: teresa.pedregon@cbp.dhs.gov
Operations Division Chief **Teresa Pedregon** .... (504) 376-2800
E-mail: teresa.pedregon@cbp.dhs.gov

Ramey Border Patrol Sector
P.O. Box 250467, Aguadilla, PR 00604
Tel: (787) 890-4747 Fax: (787) 882-3541
Areas Covered: The Sector covers Puerto Rico and U.S. Virgin Islands.

Chief Patrol Agent **Ramiro S. Cerrillo** .... (787) 890-4901
E-mail: ramiro.s.cerrillo@cbp.dhs.gov
Deputy Chief Patrol Agent **Xavier A. Morales** .... (787) 890-4902
E-mail: xavier.a.morales@cbp.dhs.gov
Border Community Liaison **Edgardo M. Milan** .... (787) 890-4747 ext. 4975

Rio Grande Valley Border Patrol Sector
4400 South Expressway 281, Edinburg, TX 78539
Tel: (956) 289-4800 Tel: (956) 289-4845 (Public Affairs)
Fax: (956) 289-4807
Areas Covered: The Sector covers 17,000 square miles of Southeast Texas, including the following counties: Cameron, Willacy, Hidalgo, Starr, Brooks, Kenedy, Kleberg, Nueces, San Patricio, Jim Wells, Bee, Refugio, Calhoun, Goliad, Victoria, Dewitt, Jackson, and Lavaca.

Chief Patrol Agent **Manuel J. "Manny" Padilla, Jr.** ..... (956) 289-4800
Staff Assistant to the Chief Patrol Agent **Rebecca Balli** .... (956) 289-4824
Deputy Chief Patrol Agent **Raul L. Ortiz** .... (956) 289-4800

San Diego Border Patrol Sector
2411 Boswell Road, Chula Vista, CA 91914-3519
Tel: (619) 216-4000 Tel: (619) 216-4182 (Public Affairs)
Fax: (619) 216-4034
Areas Covered: The Sector covers the entire San Diego County.

Chief Patrol Agent **Rodney S. Scott** .... (619) 216-4006
E-mail: rodney.s.scott@cbp.dhs.gov
Deputy Chief Patrol Agent (Acting) **Roy D. Villareal** .... (619) 216-4006
E-mail: roy.d.villareal@cbp.dhs.gov

Spokane Border Patrol Sector
10710 North Newport Highway, Spokane, WA 99218
Tel: (509) 353-2747 Fax: (509) 353-2736
Areas Covered: The Sector covers eastern Washington and Idaho, and western Montana up to the Continental Divide.

Chief Patrol Agent **Henry Rolon** .... (509) 353-2747
E-mail: henry.rolon@dhs.gov
Deputy Chief Patrol Agent **David BeMiller** .... (509) 353-2747
Public Affairs Officer/Supervisory Border Patrol Agent **(Vacant)** .... (509) 353-2747

Swanton Border Patrol Sector
155 Grand Avenue, Swanton, VT 05488
Tel: (802) 868-3361 Fax: (802) 868-3337 Fax: (802) 868-5804
Areas Covered: The Swanton Sector area of responsibility encompasses some 24,000 square miles and includes the State of Vermont; Clinton, Essex, Franklin, St. Lawrence and Herkimer counties of New York; and Coos, Grafton and Carroll counties of New Hampshire. This area includes 261 miles of International Boundary, from the Maine-New Hampshire state line on the east. Of the 261 miles of border, 173 miles are land border and 88 miles are water boundary, chiefly the St. Lawrence River.

Chief Patrol Agent **John C. Pfeifer** .... (802) 868-3361
E-mail: john.pfeifer@dhs.gov
Deputy Chief Patrol Agent **Robert Garcia** .... (802) 868-3361
Assistant Chief Patrol Agent **Todd A. Jewell** .... (802) 868-3361
E-mail: todd.jewell@dhs.gov
Assistant Chief Patrol Agent **Bradley Curtis** .... (802) 868-3361
Assistant Chief Patrol Agent **(Vacant)** .... (802) 868-3361
Assistant Chief Patrol Agent **(Vacant)** .... (802) 868-3361
Supervisory Border Patrol Agent **(Vacant)** .... (802) 868-3361
Public Affairs Officer **Brad Brandt** .... (802) 868-3361
Director of Mission Support **Nicole Johnson** .... (802) 868-3361
E-mail: nicole.johnson@dhs.gov

Tucson Border Patrol Sector
2430 South Swan Road, Tucson, AZ 85711
Tel: (520) 748-3000 Fax: (520) 748-3236
Areas Covered: The sector area of responsibility encompasses Arizona, except for Yuma, La Paz and Mojave Counties.

Chief Patrol Agent **Rodolfo Karisch** .... (520) 748-3000
E-mail: rodolfo.karisch@dhs.gov
Deputy Chief Patrol Agent **Jeffrey D. "Jeff" Self** .... (520) 748-3000
Field Technology Supervisor **Gary Weaver** .... (520) 748-3048
Lead Field Technology Officer **(Vacant)** .... (520) 748-3074
Security Manager **Patrick Moore** .... (520) 748-3257
E-mail: patrick.moore@dhs.gov

Yuma Border Patrol Sector
4035 South Avenue A, Yuma, AZ 85365-5002
Tel: (928) 341-6500
Areas Covered: The Sector patrols 118 miles of border with Mexico, between the Yuma-Pima County line in Arizona and the Imperial Sand Dunes in California. The sector has responsibility for Yuma, La Paz and Mojave Counties in Arizona, the Eastern-most areas of Imperial, Riverside, and Los Angeles Counties in California, and the four Southern-most counties in Nevada.

Chief Patrol Agent **Anthony J. Porvaznik** .... (928) 341-6500
E-mail: anthony.j.porvaznik@cbp.dhs.gov
Education: Ashford
Deputy Chief Patrol Agent **Carl E. Landrum** .... (928) 341-6500
E-mail: carl.e.landrum@cbp.dhs.gov
Education: U Phoenix BS; Army War Col MSS

★ Presidential Appointment Requiring Senate Confirmation ☆ Presidential Appointment □ Schedule C Appointment ◇ Career Senior Foreign Service Appointment
● Career Senior Executive Service (SES) Appointment ○ Non-Career Senior Executive Service (SES) Appointment ■ Postal Career Executive Service

Yuma Border Patrol Sector *(continued)*

Assistant Chief Patrol Agent **Frank Amarillas** .... (928) 341-6500
Assistant Chief Patrol Agent **Desi Deleon** .... (928) 341-6500
E-mail: desi.deleon@dhs.gov
Assistant Chief Patrol Agent **Carlos Dominguez** .... (928) 341-6500
Assistant Chief Patrol Agent **Daniel Hann** .... (928) 341-6500
Assistant Chief Patrol Agent **Wayne Preston** .... (928) 341-6500
Assistant Chief Patrol Agent **Kevin Villegas** .... (928) 341-6500

United States Immigration and Customs Enforcement (ICE)

500 12th Street, SW, Washington, DC 20536
Tel: (202) 732-3000 Fax: (202) 732-3060 Internet: www.ice.gov

OFFICE OF THE DIRECTOR

500 12th Street, SW, Washington, DC 20536
Tel: (202) 732-3000 Fax: (202) 732-3050

Office of the Deputy Director

500 12th Street, SW, Washington, DC 20536
Tel: (202) 732-3000

Office of Enforcement and Removal Operations (ERO)

500 12th Street, SW, Washington, DC 20536
Tel: (202) 732-3100 Fax: (202) 732-3115

Boston Field Office
1000 District Avenue, Burlington, MA 10803
Tel: (781) 359-7500 E-mail: Boston.Outreach@ice.dhs.gov

Field Office Director **Chris Cronen** .... (781) 359-7500
E-mail: Chris.M.Cronen@ice.dhs.gov

Chicago Field Office
101 West Congress Parkway, 4th Floor, Chicago, IL 60605
Tel: (312) 347-2400 E-mail: chicago.outreach@ice.dhs.gov

Field Office Director **Ricardo A. Wong** .... (312) 347-2400
E-mail: ricardo.a.wong@ice.dhs.gov

Eloy (AZ) Detention Center
1705 East Hanna Road, Eloy, AZ 85231
Tel: (520) 466-4141 Fax: (520) 466-7750

Note: The Eloy Detention Center is operated privately for ICE by the company CoreCivic.

Warden **Michael J. Donahue** .... (520) 466-4141
E-mail: michael.donahue@corecivic.com
Education: New Haven BA
Assistant Warden **Todd Wasmer** .... (520) 466-4141
Education: Grand Canyon 2012 BAS, 2014 MA

Los Angeles Field Office
300 North Los Angeles Street, Room 7631, Los Angeles, CA 90012
Tel: (213) 830-7911 E-mail: LosAngeles.Outreach@ice.dhs.gov

● Director **(Vacant)** .... (213) 830-7911

Newark Field Office
970 Broad Street, 11th Floor, Newark, NJ 07102
Tel: (973) 645-3666 E-mail: Newark.Outreach@ice.dhs.gov

Director **John Tsoukaris** .... (973) 645-3666
Public Affairs Officer **Emilio Karim Dabul** .... (973) 645-3666
Education: SUNY (Albany) BA

Philadelphia Field Office
1600 Callowhill Street, 6th Floor, Philadelphia, PA 19130
Tel: (215) 656-7164 E-mail: philadelphia.outreach@ice.dhs.gov

Director **Thomas R. Decker** .... (215) 656-7164
E-mail: thomas.r.decker@ice.dhs.gov

San Diego Field Office
880 Front Street, Suite 2232, San Diego, CA 92101
Tel: (619) 436-0410 E-mail: SanDiego.Outreach@ice.dhs.gov

● Director of Field Operations Detention and Removal
Gregory J. "Greg" Archambeault .... (619) 436-0410
E-mail: gregory.j.archambeault@ice.dhs.gov
Education: San Diego State BS
Deputy Office Director **Jack Bennett** .... (619) 436-0410
Deputy Office Director **John A. Garzon** .... (619) 436-0410
E-mail: john.a.garzon@ice.dhs.gov

Office of Homeland Security Investigations (HSI)

500 12th Street, SW, Washington, DC 20536
Tel: (202) 732-5100 Fax: (202) 732-5126

Special Agent-in-Charge (SAC) Offices

SAC Atlanta
1100 Centre Parkway, Atlanta, GA 30344
Tel: (404) 346-2300 Fax: (404) 346-2374 Fax: (404) 763-5919

Special Agent-in-Charge **Nick S. Annan** .... (404) 346-2300

SAC Baltimore
40 South Gay Street, 3rd Floor, Baltimore, MD 21202
Tel: (410) 962-2620 Fax: (410) 962-3469

Special Agent-in-Charge (Acting) **Cardell Morant** .... (410) 962-2620

SAC Boston
10 Causeway Street, Room 722, Boston, MA 02222-1054
Tel: (617) 565-7402 Fax: (617) 565-7422

Special Agent-in-Charge **Peter Fitzhugh** .... (617) 565-7402
Deputy Special Agent-in-Charge **Michael S. Shea** .... (617) 565-7402
E-mail: michael.s.shea@ice.dhs.gov

SAC Buffalo
1780 Wehrle Drive, Suite D, Williamsville, NY 14221
Tel: (716) 565-2039 Fax: (716) 565-9509

● Special Agent In Charge **Kevin Kelly** .... (716) 565-2039

SAC Chicago
One Tower Lane, Suite 1600, Oakbrook Terrace, IL 60181
Tel: (630) 574-4600 Fax: (630) 574-2889

● Special Agent-in-Charge **James "Jim" Gibbons** .... (630) 574-4172

SAC Dallas
125 East John Carpenter Freeway, Suite 800, Irving, TX 75062
Tel: (972) 444-7300 Fax: (972) 444-7461

Special Agent-in-Charge **Katrina W. Berger** .... (972) 444-7306
E-mail: katrina.berger@ice.dhs.gov
Education: Virginia Tech 1989 BA; Nova Southeastern 1993 JD; Loyola U (New Orleans)

SAC Denver
5445 DTC Parkway, Suite 600, Greenwood Village, CO 80111
Tel: (303) 721-3000 Fax: (303) 721-3003

Special Agent-in-Charge **Steven "Steve" Cagen** .... (303) 721-3001
Deputy Special Agent-in-Charge **John Eisert** .... (303) 721-3000
Assistant Special Agent-in-Charge **Walter Moran** .... (303) 721-3011
E-mail: walter.moran@dhs.gov
Assistant Special Agent-in-Charge **Elizabeth Perino** ..... (303) 721-3000

Salt Lake City (UT) Sub-Office
46 West 300 South, Suite 206, Salt Lake City, UT 84101
Tel: (801) 886-7500

Assistant Special Agent-in-Charge **Jonathan Lines** ...... (801) 886-7500
E-mail: jonathan.lines@dhs.gov

SAC Detroit
477 Michigan Avenue, Suite 1850, Detroit, MI 48226-2521
Tel: (313) 226-0500 Fax: (313) 226-6282

● Special Agent-in-Charge **Steve Francis** .... (313) 226-0700

DEPARTMENTS

★ Presidential Appointment Requiring Senate Confirmation ☆ Presidential Appointment ☐ Schedule C Appointment ◇ Career Senior Foreign Service Appointment
● Career Senior Executive Service (SES) Appointment ○ Non-Career Senior Executive Service (SES) Appointment ■ Postal Career Executive Service

SAC El Paso
11541 Montana Avenue, El Paso, TX 79936
Tel: (915) 856-2315 Fax: (915) 857-6083
Special Agent-in-Charge **Jack P. Staton** .... (915) 856-2315

SAC Honolulu
595 Ala Moana Boulevard, Honolulu, HI 96850
Tel: (808) 532-3785 Fax: (808) 532-4689
Special Agent-in-Charge **Joanna Ip** .... (808) 532-3746

SAC Houston
4141 North Sam Houston Parkway, East #300, Houston, TX 77032
Tel: (281) 985-0500 Fax: (281) 985-0505
Special Agent-in-Charge **Mark B. Dawson** .... (281) 985-0500
E-mail: mark.b.dawson@ice.dhs.gov

SAC Los Angeles
501 West Ocean Boulevard, Suite 7200, Long Beach, CA 90802-4213
Tel: (562) 624-3800 Fax: (562) 590-9604
Special Agent-in-Charge
Joseph "Joe" Macias .... (562) 624-3800 ext. 3998
E-mail: Joseph.Macias@ice.dhs.gov
Education: St John's U (NY) 1984 BA
Deputy Special Agent-in-Charge **Dawn Barriteau** .... (562) 624-3904
Deputy Special Agent-in-Charge **Garrick Carlton** .... (562) 624-3904

SAC Miami
11226 Northwest 20th Street, Miami, FL 33172
Tel: (305) 597-6000 Fax: (305) 597-6227
Special Agent-in-Charge **Mark Selby** .... (305) 597-6000

SAC Minneapolis/St. Paul
One Federal Drive, Suite 1340, Minneapolis, MN 55111
Tel: (612) 843-8800 Tel: (612) 843-8985 (Public Affairs)
Fax: (612) 843-8921
Special Agent-in-Charge **(Vacant)** .... (612) 843-8800

SAC Newark
620 Frelinghuysen Avenue, 2nd Floor, Newark, NJ 07114
Tel: (973) 776-5500 Fax: (973) 776-5650
Special Agent-in-Charge **Andrew McLees** .... (973) 776-5509
E-mail: andrew.mclees@dhs.gov

SAC New Orleans
1250 Poydras Street, Suite 2200, New Orleans, LA 70113
Tel: (504) 310-8800 Fax: (504) 310-8900
● Special Agent-in-Charge **Jere Miles** .... (504) 310-8800
Public Affairs Officer **Thomas Byrd** .... (504) 310-8887

SAC New York
601 West 26th Street, 7th Floor, New York, NY 10001
Tel: (646) 230-3200 Fax: (646) 230-3255
● Special Agent-in-Charge **Angel M. Melendez** .... (646) 230-3478
E-mail: angel.m.melendez@ice.dhs.gov
Education: Puerto Rico 1992 BBA

SAC Philadelphia
220 Chestnut Street, Room 200, Philadelphia, PA 19106
Tel: (215) 717-4800 Fax: (215) 717-4805
Special Agent-in-Charge **Marlon V. Miller** .... (215) 717-4844
Staff Assistant **Dianna Fulton** .... (215) 717-4836
E-mail: dianna.fulton@ice.dhs.gov

SAC Phoenix
4041 North Central Avenue, Suite 1650, Phoenix, AZ 85012
Tel: (602) 200-2200 Fax: (602) 514-7790
Special Agent-in-Charge **A. Scott Brown** .... (602) 200-2200
Deputy Special Agent-in-Charge **Lon D. Weigand II** ..... (602) 200-2200

SAC San Antonio
1015 Jackson-Keller Road, Suite 200, San Antonio, TX 78213
Tel: (210) 979-4500 Fax: (210) 979-4643
Special Agent-in-Charge **Shane M. Folden** .... (210) 979-4500
E-mail: shane.m.folden@ice.dhs.gov

SAC San Diego
880 Front Street, Suite 3200, San Diego, CA 92101
Tel: (619) 744-4600 Fax: (619) 557-7275
● Special Agent-in-Charge **David Shaw** .... (619) 744-4600

SAC San Juan
Capitol Office Building, 800 Ponce de Leon Avenue,
12th Floor, Santurce, PR 00908
Tel: (787) 729-5151 Fax: (787) 729-6646
Special Agent-in-Charge **Ricardo Mayoral** .... (787) 729-5151

SAC San Francisco
630 Sansome Street, Room 890, San Francisco, CA 94111
Tel: (415) 844-5455 Fax: (510) 267-3870
● Special Agent-in-Charge **Ryan L. Spradlin** .... (415) 844-5455
E-mail: ryan.l.spradlin@ice.dhs.gov
Education: San José State

SAC Seattle
1000 Second Avenue, Suite 2300, Seattle, WA 98104
Tel: (206) 442-2200 Fax: (206) 442-2201
● Special Agent-in-Charge **Brad Bench** .... (206) 442-2200

SAC Tampa
2203 North Lois Avenue, Suite 600, Tampa, FL 33607
Tel: (813) 357-7000 Fax: (813) 348-1877
Special Agent-in-Charge **James C. Spero** .... (813) 357-7000
E-mail: james.c.spero@ice.dhs.gov
Education: St John's U (NY) 1992 BA

DSAC Tucson
7400 North Oracle Road, Suite 242, Tucson, AZ 85704
Tel: (520) 229-5100 Fax: (520) 229-5160
Deputy Special Agent-in-Charge **Francisco Burrola** ...... (520) 229-5100

SAC Washington, DC
2675 Prosperity Avenue, Fairfax, VA 20598-5114
Tel: (703) 285-6700 Fax: (703) 285-6709
Special Agent-in-Charge **Patrick "PJ" Lechleitner** ...... (703) 285-6700
Deputy Special Agent-in-Charge **Tracy J. Cormier** .... (703) 285-6817
Education: Maine

United States Secret Service (USSS)
Building 410, 245 Murray Drive, SW, Washington, DC 20223
Internet: www.secretservice.gov

OFFICE OF THE DIRECTOR
245 Murray Drive, SW, Washington, DC 20223
Tel: (202) 406-5700 Fax: (202) 406-5246

Field Offices

Albuquerque (NM) Field Office
Compass Bank Building, 505 Marquette Street, NW,
Suite 1700, Albuquerque, NM 87102
Tel: (505) 248-5290 Fax: (505) 248-5296
Resident Agent-in-Charge **Britton Yee** .... (505) 248-5290

★ Presidential Appointment Requiring Senate Confirmation ☆ Presidential Appointment ☐ Schedule C Appointment ◇ Career Senior Foreign Service Appointment
● Career Senior Executive Service (SES) Appointment ○ Non-Career Senior Executive Service (SES) Appointment ■ Postal Career Executive Service

Atlanta (GA) Field Office
Peachtree Summit Federal Building, 401 West Peachtree Street, NW, Suite 2900, Atlanta, GA 30308
Tel: (404) 331-6111 Fax: (404) 331-5058
Areas Covered: Northern Judicial District of Georgia
Special Agent-in-Charge **Kenneth J. "Ken" Cronin** . . . . . (404) 331-6111
Administrative Officer **Christine Heeger** . . . . (404) 331-6111

Albany (GA) Resident Office
410 West Broad Avenue, Suite 410, Albany, GA 31701
Mail: P.O. Box 1093, Albany, GA 31702
Tel: (229) 430-8442 Fax: (229) 430-8441
Resident Agent in Charge **Clint Bush** . . . . (229) 430-8442

Savannah (GA) Resident Office
33 Bull Street, Room 570, Savannah, GA 31401
Tel: (912) 652-4401 Fax: (912) 652-4062
Resident Agent in Charge **Glen M. Kessler** . . . . (912) 652-4401

Baltimore (MD) Field Office
Tower One, 100 South Charles Street, 11th Floor, Baltimore, MD 21201
Tel: (443) 263-1000 Fax: (443) 263-1100
Internet: www.secretservice.gov
Areas Covered: MD, except Montgomery and Prince George's Counties
Special Agent-in-Charge **Christopher "Chris" Caruso** . . . (443) 263-1000

Birmingham (AL) Field Office
Daniel Building, 15 South 20th Street, Suite 1125, Birmingham, AL 35233
Tel: (205) 731-1144 Fax: (205) 731-0007
Special Agent-in-Charge **Michael A. Williams** . . . . (205) 731-1144
E-mail: michael.a.williams@usss.dhs.gov
Assistant Special Agent-in-Charge **Robert Holloway** . . . . . (205) 731-1144
Administrative Officer **Heather Pinkham** . . . . (205) 731-1144

Jackson (MS) Resident Office
Dr. A. H. McCoy Federal Building, 100 West Capitol Street, Suite 840, Jackson, MS 39269
Tel: (601) 965-4436 Fax: (601) 965-4012
Resident Agent-in-Charge **Shawn Wolfe** . . . . (601) 965-4436

Mobile (AL) Resident Office
Parkview Office Building, 182 St. Francis Street, Suite 200, Mobile, AL 36602-3501
Tel: (251) 441-5851 Fax: (251) 441-5250
Resident Agent-in-Charge **Brian O'Neil** . . . . (251) 441-5851

Montgomery (AL) Resident Office
One Commerce Street, Suite 605, Montgomery, AL 36104
Tel: (334) 223-7601 Fax: (334) 223-7523
Resident Agent-in-Charge **Clayton D. Slay** . . . . (334) 223-7601
E-mail: clayton.slay@usss.dhs.gov

Boston (MA) Field Office
Thomas P. O'Neill, Jr., Federal Building, 10 Causeway Street, Room 447, Boston, MA 02222-1054
Tel: (617) 565-5640 Fax: (617) 565-5659
Areas Covered: MA, ME, NH, RI, VT
Special Agent-in-Charge **Stephen A. Marks** . . . . (617) 565-5640
E-mail: stephen.a.marks@usss.dhs.gov
Administrative Officer **Sophia Lithotomos** . . . . (617) 565-5640

Burlington (VT) Resident Agency
P.O. Box 906, Burlington, VT 05402
Tel: (802) 651-4091 Fax: (802) 651-6820
Resident Agent-in-Charge **(Vacant)** . . . . (802) 651-4091

Manchester (NH) Resident Office
1750 Elm Street, Suite 802, Manchester, NH 03104
Tel: (603) 626-7026 Fax: (603) 626-5653
Resident Agent-in-Charge **Timothy Benitez** . . . . (603) 626-5631

Portland (ME) Resident Office
Tower B, 100 Middle Street, 2nd Floor, Portland, ME 04101
Tel: (207) 780-3493 Fax: (207) 780-3301
Resident Agent-in-Charge **David Watson** . . . . (207) 780-3493

Providence (RI) Resident Office
The Federal Center, 380 Westminster Street, Room 343, Providence, RI 02903
Tel: (401) 331-6456 Fax: (401) 528-4394
Resident Agent-in-Charge **Brian Deck** . . . . (401) 331-6456

Buffalo (NY) Field Office
City Center, 598 Main Street, Suite 300, Buffalo, NY 14202
Tel: (716) 551-4401 Fax: (716) 551-5075
Special Agent-in-Charge **Lewis Robinson** . . . . (716) 551-4401
E-mail: lewis.robinson@usss.dhs.gov
Administrative Officer **Karen Hajiaskari** . . . . (716) 551-4401
E-mail: karen.hajiaskari@usss.dhs.gov

Albany (NY) Resident Office
39 N. Pearl Street, 2nd Floor, Albany, NY 12207
Tel: (518) 427-0400 Fax: (518) 436-9635
Resident Agent-in-Charge **Jon Murphy** . . . . (518) 427-0400
E-mail: jon.murphy@usss.dhs.gov

Rochester (NY) Resident Agency
1820 HSBC Plaza, 100 Chestnut Street, Rochester, NY 14604
Tel: (585) 232-4160 Fax: (585) 232-4662
Senior Resident Agent **Bradley Jacobs** . . . . (585) 232-4160
E-mail: brad.jacobs@usss.dhs.gov

Syracuse (NY) Resident Office
James M. Hanley Federal Building, 100 South Clinton Street, Syracuse, NY 13260
P.O. Box 7006, Federal Station, Syracuse, NY 13261
Tel: (315) 448-0304 Fax: (315) 448-0302
Resident Agent-in-Charge **Tim Kirk** . . . . (315) 448-0304
E-mail: tkirk@usss.dhs.gov

Charlotte (NC) Field Office
One Fairview Center, 6302 Fairview Road, Suite 400, Charlotte, NC 28210
Tel: (704) 442-8370 Fax: (704) 442-8369
Special Agent-in-Charge
Reginald "Reggie" Dematteis . . . . (704) 442-8370
Administrative Officer **Carnita B. Maxwell** . . . . (704) 442-8370

Greensboro (NC) Resident Office
4905 Koger Boulevard, Suite 220, Greensboro, NC 27407
Tel: (336) 547-4180 Fax: (336) 547-4185
Resident Agent-in-Charge **Curtis High** . . . . (336) 547-4180
E-mail: curtis.high@usss.dhs.gov

Raleigh (NC) Resident Office
4700 Falls of Neuese Road, Suite 295, Raleigh, NC 27609
Tel: (919) 790-2834 Fax: (919) 790-2832
Resident Agent-in-Charge **Robert Trumbo** . . . . (919) 790-2834
E-mail: robert.trumbo@usss.dhs.gov

Wilmington (NC) Resident Office
Summit Center, 1717 Shipyard Boulevard, Suite 340, Wilmington, NC 28403
Tel: (910) 313-3043 Fax: (910) 313-3169
Resident Agent-in-Charge **John Kendall** . . . . (910) 313-3043
E-mail: john.kendall@usss.dhs.gov

Chicago (IL) Field Office
525 West Van Buren, Suite 900, Chicago, IL 60607
Tel: (312) 353-5431 Fax: (312) 353-1225
Special Agent-in-Charge **John A. Koleno** . . . . (312) 353-5431
Supervisory Administrative Specialist **Tina Muscarello** . . . (312) 353-5431

★ Presidential Appointment Requiring Senate Confirmation ☆ Presidential Appointment □ Schedule C Appointment ◇ Career Senior Foreign Service Appointment
● Career Senior Executive Service (SES) Appointment ○ Non-Career Senior Executive Service (SES) Appointment ■ Postal Career Executive Service

DEPARTMENTS

Madison (WI) Resident Agency
660 West Washington Avenue, Suite 305, Madison, WI 53703
Tel: (608) 264-5191 Fax: (608) 264-5592
Resident Agent **Jack F. Leskovar** .... (608) 264-5191

Milwaukee (WI) Resident Office
U.S. Federal Courthouse, 517 East Wisconsin Avenue,
Room 572, Milwaukee, WI 53202
Tel: (414) 297-3587 Fax: (414) 297-3595
Resident Agent-in-Charge **Cary Dyer** .... (414) 297-3587
E-mail: cary.dyer@usss.dhs.gov

Springfield (IL) Resident Office
3161 West White Oaks Drive, Suite 201, Springfield, IL 62704
Tel: (217) 726-8453 Fax: (217) 726-8430
Resident Agent-in-Charge **William Shink** .... (217) 726-8453

Cincinnati (OH) Field Office
550 Main Street, Cincinnati, OH 45202-5298
Tel: (513) 684-3585 Fax: (513) 684-3436
Special Agent-in-Charge **Yvonne A. DiCristoforo** .... (513) 684-3585

Columbus (OH) Resident Office
500 South Front Street, Columbus, OH 43215
Tel: (614) 469-7370 Fax: (614) 469-2049
Resident Agent-in-Charge **Allen Biladeau** .... (614) 469-7370

Dayton (OH) Resident Office
200 West 2nd Street, Dayton, OH 45402
Tel: (937) 222-2013 Fax: (937) 225-2724
Resident Agent in Charge **Kevin Dye** .... (937) 222-2013

Cleveland Field Office
6450 Rockside Woods Boulevard, South,
Suite 200, Independence, OH 44131-2230
Tel: (216) 750-2058 Fax: (216) 750-2067
Special Agent-in-Charge **Jonathan Schuck** .... (216) 750-2058
Assistant Special Agent-in-Charge **Richard Hurst** .... (216) 750-2058
E-mail: richard.hurst@usss.dhs.gov

Toledo (OH) Resident Office
Four Seagate, Suite 702, Toledo, OH 43604
Tel: (419) 259-6434 Fax: (419) 259-6437
Resident Agent-in-Charge **Scott Anderson** .... (419) 259-6434

Columbia (SC) Field Office
United States Secret Service, 107 Westpark Boulevard,
Suite 301, Columbia, SC 29210
Tel: (803) 772-4015 Fax: (803) 772-1920
Special Agent-in-Charge **John Hirt** .... (803) 772-4015
Assistant Special Agent-in-Charge **Patrick Keegan** ...... (803) 772-4015

Charleston (SC) Resident Office
1671 Belle Isle Avenue, Suite 225, Mt. Pleasant, SC 29464
Tel: (843) 388-0305 Fax: (843) 388-0946
Resident Agent-in-Charge **John C. Kenney** .... (843) 388-0305
E-mail: john.kenney@usss.dhs.gov

Greenville (SC) Resident Office
301 North Main Street, Suite 1803, Greenville, SC 29601
Tel: (864) 233-1490 Fax: (864) 235-6237
Resident Agent-in-Charge **(Vacant)** .... (864) 233-1490

Dallas (TX) Field Office
125 East John Carpenter Freeway, Suite 300, Irving, TX 75062-2752
Tel: (972) 868-3200 Fax: (972) 868-3222
Special Agent-in-Charge **William Noonan** .... (972) 868-3202
Assistant Special Agent-in-Charge **Adrian Andrews** ..... (972) 868-3103
Assistant Special Agent-in-Charge **Jimmy Boen** .... (972) 868-3104

Lubbock (TX) Resident Agency
1205 Texas Avenue, Room 815, Lubbock, TX 79401
Mail: P.O. Box 2975, Lubbock, TX 79408
Tel: (806) 472-7347 Fax: (806) 472-7542
Senior Resident Agent **Oscar Rosales** .... (806) 472-7347
E-mail: oscar.rosales@usss.dhs.gov

Tyler (TX) Resident Agency
6101 South Broadway, Suite 420, Tyler, TX 75703
Tel: (903) 534-2933 Fax: (903) 581-9569
Resident Agent **Todd Hiles** .... (903) 534-2933

Waco (TX) Resident Office
P.O. Box 20905, Waco, TX 76702-0905
Tel: (254) 741-0576 Fax: (254) 776-0413
Resident Agent-in-Charge **Scott Deford** .... (254) 741-0576

Denver (CO) Field Office
5619 DTC Parkway, Suite 400, Greenwood Village, CO 80111
Tel: (303) 850-2700 Fax: (303) 850-2750
Special Agent-in-Charge **(Vacant)** .... (303) 850-2700
Cheyenne (WY) Domicile Special Agent **Rick L. Near** ... (307) 772-2380
P.O. Box 145, Cheyenne, WY 82003 Fax: (307) 772-2387

Boise (ID) Resident Agency
Federal Building and U.S. Courthouse, 550 West Fort Street,
Room 732, Boise, ID 83724
Tel: (208) 334-1403 Fax: (208) 334-1289
Resident Agent **Robert N. Harrell** .... (208) 334-1403
E-mail: robert.harrell@usss.dhs.gov

Salt Lake City (UT) Resident Office
57 West 200 South, Salt Lake City, UT 84101
Tel: (801) 524-5910 Fax: (801) 524-6216
Resident Agent-in-Charge **William "Bill" Bishop** .... (801) 524-5910

Detroit (MI) Field Office
Patrick V. McNamara Federal Building, 477 Michigan Avenue,
Suite 1000, Detroit, MI 48226
Tel: (313) 226-6400 Fax: (313) 226-3952
Special Agent-in-Charge **Douglas J. Zloto** .... (313) 226-6400
Assistant Special Agent-in-Charge **(Vacant)** .... (313) 226-6400
Administrative Officer **Cathy A. Evoy** .... (313) 226-6400
E-mail: cathy.evoy@usss.dhs.gov

Grand Rapids (MI) Resident Agency
330 Ionia Avenue NW, Suite 302, Grand Rapids, MI 49503
Tel: (616) 454-4671 Fax: (616) 454-5816
Resident Agent-in-Charge **Steven C. McMahon** .... (616) 456-4671

Saginaw (MI) Resident Agency
4805 Towne Centre Road, Suite 105, Saginaw, MI 48604
Tel: (989) 497-0580 Fax: (989) 497-0610
Resident Agent-in-Charge **Peter J. Schloop** .... (989) 497-0580
E-mail: peter.schloop@usss.dhs.gov

Honolulu (HI) Field Office
Prince Jonah Kuhio Kalanianaole Federal Building,
300 Ala Moana Boulevard, Room 6-210, Honolulu, HI 96850
P.O. Box 50046, Honolulu, HI 96850
Tel: (808) 541-1912 Fax: (808) 545-4490
Special Agent-in-Charge **Steven M. Stanford** .... (808) 541-1912
Administrative Officer **Janette Lentz-Hill** .... (808) 541-1912

Houston (TX) Field Office
1801 Allen Parkway, Suite 200, Houston, TX 77019
Tel: (713) 868-2299 Fax: (713) 374-3705
Special Agent-in-Charge **Douglas W. Thigpen** .... (713) 868-2299
E-mail: douglas.thigpen@usss.dhs.gov
Deputy Special Agent-in-Charge **William H. Smarr** ...... (713) 868-2299
E-mail: william.smarr@usss.dhs.gov

Houston (TX) Field Office *(continued)*

Assistant Special Agent-in-Charge **John W. Durkan** . . . . . (713) 868-2299
E-mail: john.durkan@usss.dhs.gov
Supervisory Administrative Specialist
Lydia Hernandez . . . . (713) 868-2299
E-mail: lydia.hernandez@usss.dhs.gov
Administrative Officer **Veronica "Ronnie" Almanza** . . . . (713) 868-2299
E-mail: veronica.almanza@usss.dhs.gov

Austin (TX) Resident Office
Federal Building, 300 East Eighth Street,
Room 972, Austin, TX 78701
Tel: (512) 916-5103 Fax: (512) 916-5365
Resident Agent-in-Charge **Steven Hampton** . . . . (512) 916-5103

Mexico City Resident Office
Mexico City Resident Office, Embajada De Los Estados Unidos,
Paseo De La Reforma 305, 06500 Mexico City, Mexico
P.O. Box 9000, Brownsville, TX 78520-0900
Tel: 52 (55) 5080-2212 Fax: 52 (55) 5080-2048
Resident Agent-in-Charge
Christopher G. Campbell 52 (55) 5080-2212

Indianapolis (IN) Field Office
151 North Delaware Street, Suite 825, Indianapolis, IN 46204
Tel: (317) 635-6420 Fax: (317) 635-6290
Special Agent-in-Charge **Paul R. Dvorak** . . . . (317) 635-6420
E-mail: paul.r.dvorak@usss.dhs.gov
Education: Alabama Birmingham BS
Administrative Officer **Carolyn L. Feltner** . . . .(317) 635-6420
E-mail: cfeltner@usss.dhs.gov

Jacksonville (FL) Field Office
5200 Belfort Road, 2nd Floor, Suite 200, Jacksonville, FL 32256
Tel: (904) 296-0133 Fax: (904) 296-0188
Special Agent-in-Charge **Neil Melofchik** . . . .(904) 296-0133
Education: Stockton State BS
Assistant Special Agent-in-Charge **Thomas G. Lascell** . . . (904) 296-0133
Administrative Officer **Karen Bethurem** . . . .(904) 296-0133

Tallahassee (FL) Resident Office
3520 Thomasville Road, Suite 301, Tallahassee, FL 32309
Tel: (850) 942-9523 Fax: (850) 942-9526
Resident Agent-in-Charge **Peter Stacey** . . . . (850) 942-9523
E-mail: peter.stacey@usss.dhs.gov

Kansas City (MO) Field Office
1150 Grand Avenue, Suite 510, Kansas City, MO 64106
Tel: (816) 460-0600 Fax: (816) 283-0321
Assistant Special Agent-in-Charge **David Stutheit** . . . .(816) 460-0600
E-mail: david.stutheit@usss.dhs.gov
Education: Washburn 1988 BA
Administrative Officer **Tobi Garcia** . . . . (816) 460-0600
E-mail: tobi.garcia@usss.dhs.gov

Des Moines (IA) Resident Agency
210 Walnut Street, Des Moines, IA 50309
Tel: (515) 284-4565 Fax: (515) 284-4566
Senior Resident Agent **(Vacant)** . . . .(515) 284-4565
Administrative Officer **Tammie Mahnken** . . . .(515) 284-4565
E-mail: tmahnken@usss.dhs.gov

Omaha (NE) Resident Office
2707 North 108th Street, Suite 301, Omaha, NE 68164
Tel: (402) 965-9670 Fax: (402) 445-9638
Resident Agent-in-Charge **Paul Brandenburg** . . . . (402) 965-9670
Education: Northwestern Col (MN) BA
Administrative Officer **Bethany Soukup** . . . .(402) 965-9670
E-mail: bethany.cooney@usss.dhs.gov

Springfield (MO) Resident Agency
901 East Saint Louis Street, Suite 306, Springfield, MO 65806
Tel: (417) 864-8340 Fax: (417) 864-8676
Resident Agent **Greg Enyart** . . . . (417) 864-8340

Wichita (KS) Resident Agency
Epic Center, 301 North Main, Suite 275, Wichita, KS 67202
Tel: (316) 267-1452 Fax: (316) 269-6154
Senior Resident Agent **Gregory "Greg" Tiano** . . . . (316) 267-1452
E-mail: gregory.tiano@usss.dhs.gov

Las Vegas (NV) Field Office
600 Las Vegas Boulevard, South, Suite 700, Las Vegas, NV 89101
Tel: (702) 868-3000 Fax: (702) 868-0000
Special Agent-in-Charge **Brian G. Spellacy** . . . . (702) 868-3000

Little Rock (AR) Field Office
111 Center Street, Suite 1700, Little Rock, AR 72201
Tel: (501) 324-6241 Fax: (501) 324-6097
Special Agent-in-Charge **(Vacant)** . . . . (501) 324-6241
Administrative Officer **Terry Gamble** . . . . (501) 324-6241

Los Angeles (CA) Field Office
U.S. Secret Service Los Angeles Field Office, 725 South Figueroa Street,
Suite 1300, Los Angeles, CA 90017-5418
Tel: (213) 894-4830 Fax: (213) 533-4725
Special Agent-in-Charge **L. Robert Savage III** . . . . (213) 894-4830
Ventura (CA) Resident Agent in Charge **Doug Cohen** . . . . (805) 383-5745
5051 Verdugo Way, Fax: (805) 389-0381
Suite 31C, Camarillo, CA 93012

Riverside (CA) Resident Agency
4371 Latham Street, Suite 203, Riverside, CA 92501
Tel: (951) 276-6781 Fax: (951) 276-6637
Resident Agent-in-Charge **John K. Clifton** . . . . (951) 276-6781

Santa Ana (CA) Resident Agency
200 West Santa Ana Boulevard, Suite 500, Santa Ana, CA 92701-4164
Tel: (714) 246-8257 Fax: (714) 246-8261
Resident Agent-in-Charge **Tin T. Nguyen** . . . . (714) 246-8257

Louisville (KY) Field Office
2002 Papa John's Boulevard, Suite 200, Louisville, KY 40299
Tel: (502) 582-5171 Fax: (502) 582-6329
Special Agent-in-Charge **Richard "Rich" Ferretti** . . . . (502) 582-5171
E-mail: richard.ferretti@usss.dhs.gov
Administrative Officer **Elizabeth Roy** . . . . (502) 582-5171
E-mail: elizabeth.roy@usss.dhs.gov

Lexington (KY) Resident Agency
3141 Beaumont Center, Suite 201, Lexington, KY 40513
Tel: (859) 223-2358 Fax: (859) 223-1819
Resident Agent **Jon Oldham** . . . . (859) 223-2358

Memphis (TN) Field Office
5350 Poplar Avenue, Suite 204, Memphis, TN 38119
Tel: (901) 544-0333 Fax: (901) 544-0342
Special Agent-in-Charge **James "Jim" Hawkins** . . . . (901) 544-0333
E-mail: james.hawkins@usss.dhs.gov

Miami (FL) Field Office
10350 NW, 112 Avenue, Miami, FL 33178
Tel: (305) 863-5000 Fax: (305) 863-5025
● Special Agent-in-Charge **Brian Swain** . . . . (305) 863-5000
Administrative Officer **Bianca Clark** . . . . (305) 863-5127
Fax: (305) 863-5130

★ Presidential Appointment Requiring Senate Confirmation ☆ Presidential Appointment □ Schedule C Appointment ◇ Career Senior Foreign Service Appointment
● Career Senior Executive Service (SES) Appointment ○ Non-Career Senior Executive Service (SES) Appointment ■ Postal Career Executive Service

San Juan (PR) Resident Agency
1510 Franklin Delano Roosevelt Avenue,
Suite 3B, Guaynabo, PR 00968
Tel: (787) 277-1515 Fax: (787) 277-1537
Resident Agent-in-Charge **Carlos Colon** . . . . (787) 277-1515

West Palm Beach (FL) Resident Agency
505 South Flagler Drive, Suite 800, West Palm Beach, FL 33401
Tel: (561) 659-0184 Fax: (561) 655-8484
Resident Agent-in-Charge **Robert Pearce** . . . . (561) 659-0184

Minneapolis (MN) Field Office
U.S. Courthouse, 300 South Fourth Street,
Suite 750, Minneapolis, MN 55415
Tel: (612) 348-1800 Fax: (612) 348-1807
Special Agent-in-Charge **Edward "Joe" Scargall** . . . . (612) 348-1800
Administrative Officer **Jodi Vandewalker** . . . . (612) 348-1800
Fargo (ND) Special Agent **John A. Kelly** . . . . (701) 239-5070
P.O. Box 590, Fargo, ND 58102 Fax: (701) 239-5071

Sioux Falls (SD) Resident Agency
P.O. Box 2240, Sioux Falls, SD 57101
Tel: (605) 330-4565 Fax: (605) 330-4523
Resident Agent **Randy Walker** . . . . (605) 330-4565
E-mail: randy.walker@usss.dhs.gov

Nashville (TN) Field Office
223 Rosa L. Parks Avenue, Suite 400, Nashville, TN 37203
Tel: (615) 736-5841 Fax: (615) 736-5848
Special Agent-in-Charge **William Todd Hudson** . . . . (615) 736-5841
Assistant Special Agent-in-Charge **Gregory A. Mays** . . . . (615) 736-5841
Administrative Officer **Kari Sanders** . . . . (615) 736-5841

Chattanooga (TN) Resident Agency
Post Office Building, Martin Luther King Boulevard & Georgia Avenue,
Room 204, Chattanooga, TN 37401
P.O. Box 6279, Chattanooga, TN 37401-6279
Tel: (423) 752-5125 Fax: (423) 752-5130
Resident Agent-in-Charge **Juan Alicea** . . . . (423) 752-5125

New Orleans (LA) Field Office
3900 North Causeway Boulevard, Suite 1400, Metairie, LA 70002
Tel: (504) 841-3260 Fax: (504) 841-3270
Special Agent-in-Charge **Anthony Bynum** . . . . (504) 841-3260
E-mail: anthony.bynum@usss.dhs.gov
Assistant Special Agent-in-Charge **Darin Lake** . . . . (504) 841-3260

Baton Rouge (LA) Resident Agency
Center 425, 2600 City Place, Baton Rouge, LA 70808
Tel: (225) 389-0763 Fax: (225) 389-0325
Resident Agent in Charge **Luis Velez** . . . . (225) 925-5436
Fax: (225) 925-5440

Shreveport (LA) Resident Agency
401 Edwards Street, Suite 525, Shreveport, LA 71101
Tel: (318) 676-3500 Fax: (318) 676-3502
Resident Agent **Darin Craft** . . . . (318) 676-3500

New York (NY) Field Office
335 Adams Street, Brooklyn, NY 11201
Tel: (718) 840-1000 Fax: (718) 625-3719
Special Agent-in-Charge **David E. Beach** . . . . (718) 722-0713
E-mail: david.e.beach@usss.dhs.gov

John F. Kennedy Airport Resident Office
Building 59, 230-59 Rockaway Boulevard,
Suite 265, Springfield Gardens, NY 11413
Tel: (718) 553-0911 Fax: (718) 553-7626
Resident Agent-in-Charge **Joseph Ciglirano** . . . . (718) 553-0911

Melville (NY) Resident Agency
35 Pinelawn Road, Suite 216E, Melville, NY 11747-3154
Tel: (631) 293-4028
Resident Agent-in-Charge **Steven Choma** . . . . (631) 293-4028

New Haven (CT) Resident Agency
265 Church Street, Suite 1201, New Haven, CT 06510
Mail: P.O. Box 45, New Haven, CT 06501
Tel: (203) 865-2449 Fax: (203) 865-2525
Resident Agent-in-Charge **Peter Quinn** . . . . (203) 865-2449

White Plains (NY) Resident Agency
140 Grand Street, Suite 300, White Plains, NY 10601-1877
Tel: (914) 682-6300 Fax: (914) 682-6182
Resident Agent-in-Charge **(Vacant)** . . . . (914) 682-6300

Newark (NJ) Field Office
290 Headquarters Plaza, Morristown, NJ 07960-3990
Tel: (973) 971-3100 Fax: (973) 984-5822
Special Agent-in-Charge **Mark F. McKevitt** . . . . (973) 971-3100
E-mail: mark.f.mckevitt@usss.dhs.gov

Trenton (NJ) Resident Office
Clarkson S. Fisher Federal Building and Courthouse,
402 East State Street, Suite 3000, Trenton, NJ 08608
Tel: (609) 989-2008 Fax: (609) 989-2174
Resident Agent-in-Charge **Preston B. Fairlamb** . . . . (609) 989-2008
E-mail: preston.fairlamb@usss.dhs.gov

Oklahoma City (OK) Field Office
210 Park Avenue, Suite 1100, Oklahoma City, OK 73102
Tel: (405) 272-0630 Fax: (405) 270-0767
Special Agent-in-Charge **Kenneth Valentine** . . . . (405) 272-0630

Tulsa (OK) Resident Office
Pratt Tower, 125 West 15th Street, Suite 400, Tulsa, OK 74119-3824
Tel: (918) 581-7272 Fax: (918) 581-7626
Resident Agent-in-Charge **Douglas Farrell** . . . . (918) 581-7272

Orlando (FL) Field Office
390 North Orange Avenue, Suite 1300, Orlando, FL 32801
Tel: (407) 648-6333 Fax: (407) 648-6606
Special Agent-in-Charge **(Vacant)** . . . . (407) 648-6333

Philadelphia (PA) Field Office
7236 Federal Building, 600 Arch Street, Philadelphia, PA 19106-1676
Tel: (215) 861-3300 Fax: (215) 861-3311
Special Agent-in-Charge **James Henry** . . . . (215) 861-3300
Administrative Officer **Karyn Casares** . . . . (215) 446-6492
E-mail: karyn.casares@usss.dhs.gov

Atlantic City (NJ) Resident Office
English Creek Corporate Center, 500 Scarborough Drive,
Suite 301, Egg Harbor Township, NJ 08234
Tel: (609) 383-8687 Fax: (609) 383-8310
Resident Agent-in-Charge **Timothy Jordan** . . . . (609) 383-8687

Harrisburg (PA) Resident Agency
P.O. Box 1244, Harrisburg, PA 17108
Fax: (717) 236-2461
Resident Agent **Kenneth Werley** . . . . (717) 234-0214
P.O. Box 1244, Harrisburg, PA 17108

Scranton (PA) Resident Office
P.O. Box 247, Scranton, PA 18501
Tel: (570) 346-5781 Fax: (570) 346-3003
Resident Agent-in-Charge **Richard Reese** . . . . (570) 346-5781
E-mail: richard.reese@usss.dhs.gov

★ Presidential Appointment Requiring Senate Confirmation ☆ Presidential Appointment ☐ Schedule C Appointment ◇ Career Senior Foreign Service Appointment
● Career Senior Executive Service (SES) Appointment ○ Non-Career Senior Executive Service (SES) Appointment ■ Postal Career Executive Service

Wilmington (DE) Resident Office
500 Delaware Avenue, Suite 910, Wilmington, DE 19801
Tel: (302) 573-6188 Fax: (302) 573-6190
Resident Agent-in-Charge **Robert Walker** .... (302) 573-6188

Phoenix (AZ) Field Office
3200 North Central Avenue, Suite 1450, Phoenix, AZ 85012
Tel: (602) 640-5580 Fax: (602) 640-5505
Special Agent-in-Charge **Cristina Beloud** .... (602) 640-5580
E-mail: cristina.beloud@usss.dhs.gov
Administrative Officer **Cortrenia McGorry** .... (602) 640-5580
E-mail: cortrenia.mcgorry@usss.dhs.gov

Tucson (AZ) Resident Agency
One South Church Avenue, Room 1950, Tucson, AZ 85701
Tel: (520) 622-6822 Fax: (520) 622-6830
Resident Agent **Glenn Dennis** .... (520) 622-6822

Pittsburgh (PA) Field Office
2 Chatham Center, 112 Washington Place,
Suite 1610, Pittsburgh, PA 15219
Tel: (412) 281-7825 Fax: (412) 281-7914
Special Agent-in-Charge **Tim Burke** .... (412) 281-7825
Administrative Officer **Christi Shreckengost** .... (412) 281-7825
Erie (PA) Domicile Special Agent
David "Dave" Halushka .... (814) 833-5352

Charleston (WV) Resident Agency
BB & T Square, 300 Summers Street,
Suite 910, Charleston, WV 25301-1692
Tel: (304) 347-5188 Fax: (304) 347-5187
Resident Agent-in-Charge **Thomas Fleming** .... (304) 347-5188

Richmond (VA) Field Office
600 East Main Street, Suite 1910, Richmond, VA 23219-2441
Tel: (804) 592-3086
Special Agent-in-Charge **Douglas Mease** .... (804) 592-3086
E-mail: douglas.mease@usss.dhs.gov
Assistant Special Agent-in-Charge
Joseph "Joe" Morrison .... (804) 592-3086

Norfolk (VA) Resident Office
Federal Office Building, 200 Granby Street,
Suite 640, Norfolk, VA 23510
Tel: (757) 441-3200 Fax: (757) 441-3811
Resident Agent-in-Charge (Acting) **Douglas Mease** .... (757) 441-3200
E-mail: douglas.mease@usss.dhs.gov

Roanoke (VA) Resident Agency
105 Franklin Road, SW, Suite 2, Roanoke, VA 24011
Tel: (540) 857-2208 Fax: (540) 857-2151
Resident Agent in Charge **George Purefoy** .... (540) 857-2208

Sacramento (CA) Resident Office
501 I Street, Suite 9-500, Sacramento, CA 95814-2322
Tel: (916) 325-5481 Fax: (916) 930-2140
Areas Covered: CA: Alpine, Amador, Butte, Calaveras, Colusa, El Dorado, Glenn, Lassen, Modoc, Mono, Nevada, Placer, Plumas, Sacramento, San Joaquin, Shasta, Sierra, Siskiyou, Solano, Stanislaus, Sutter, Tehama, Trinity, Tuolumne, Yolo, and Yuba Counties
Resident Agent-in-Charge **Scott Gillingham** .... (916) 325-5481

Fresno (CA) Resident Office
5200 North Palm Avenue, Suite 207, Fresno, CA 93704
Tel: (559) 487-5204 Fax: (559) 487-5013
Internet: www.secretservice.gov
Areas Covered: CA: Fresno, Inyo, Kern, Kings, Madera, Mariposa, Merced, and Tulare Counties
Resident Agent-in-Charge **(Vacant)** .... (559) 487-5204

Reno (NV) Resident Office
100 West Liberty Street, Suite 850, Reno, NV 89501
Tel: (775) 784-5354
Areas Covered: NV: Churchill, Douglas, Elko, Eureka, Humboldt, Lander, Lyon, Mineral, Pershing, Storey, and Washoe Counties
Resident Agent-in-Charge **George Cheretis** .... (775) 784-5354

Saint Louis (MO) Field Office
111 South 10th Street, Suite 11-346, St. Louis, MO 63102
Tel: (314) 539-2238 Fax: (314) 539-2567
Special Agent-in-Charge **(Vacant)** .... (314) 539-2238
Assistant Special Agent-in-Charge **Trevor R. Fenwick** .... (314) 539-2238

San Antonio (TX) Field Office
One International Centre, 100 NE Loop 410,
Suite 1200, San Antonio, TX 78216
Tel: (210) 308-6220 Fax: (210) 308-6230
Areas Covered: San Antonio and Rio Grande Valley; Southwest TX
Special Agent-in-Charge **Lee Dotson** .... (210) 308-6220
Office Manager **Charlotte Bennett** .... (210) 308-6220

El Paso (TX) Resident Office
211 North Florence Street, Suite 300, El Paso, TX 79901
Tel: (915) 532-2144 Fax: (915) 532-2154
Areas Covered: El Paso and Midland, TX
Resident Agent-in-Charge **Edwardo Garcia** .... (915) 532-2144

San Diego (CA) Field Office
550 West C Street, Suite 660, San Diego, CA 92101-3531
Tel: (619) 557-5640 Fax: (619) 557-6658
Special Agent-in-Charge **Scott Christensen** .... (619) 557-5640
Administrative Officer **Mildred Shane** .... (619) 557-5640

San Francisco (CA) Field Office
1700 Montgomery Street, Suite 300, San Francisco, CA 94111
Tel: (415) 576-1210 Fax: (415) 576-1154
Areas Covered: CA (Counties of Alameda, Contra Costa, Del Norte, Humboldt, Lake, Marin, Mendocino, Napa, San Francisco, San Mateo, Sonoma)
Special Agent-in-Charge **Thomas C. "Tom" Edwards** ... (415) 576-1210
Education: UC San Diego BA
Administrative Officer **Helen P. Erhard** .... (415) 576-1210
E-mail: herhard@usss.dhs.gov
Information Technology Specialist **Kevin Chan** .... (415) 576-1210
E-mail: kevin.chan@usss.dhs.gov

San Jose (CA) Resident Office
280 South First Street, Suite 1111, San Jose, CA 95113
Tel: (408) 535-5288 Fax: (408) 535-5292
Areas Covered: CA (Counties of Monterey, San Benito, Santa Clara, Santa Cruz)
Resident Agent-in-Charge **Shawn M. Bradstreet** .... (408) 535-5288
Education: Cedarville U BA

Seattle (WA) Field Office
Jackson Federal Building, 915 Second Avenue,
Room 806, Seattle, WA 98174
Tel: (206) 553-1922 Fax: (206) 220-6479
Special Agent-in-Charge **Robert Kierstead** .... (206) 553-1922
E-mail: robert.kierstead@usss.dhs.gov

Anchorage (AK) Resident Agency
Federal Building & U.S. Courthouse, 222 West Seventh Avenue,
Room 559, Anchorage, AK 99513-7592
Tel: (907) 271-5148 Fax: (907) 271-3727
Resident Agent **(Vacant)** .... (907) 271-5148

Billings (MT) Resident Agency
401 North 31st Street, Suite 600, Billings, MT 59101
Tel: (406) 245-8585 Fax: (406) 245-2123
Resident Agent **Ian Blair** .... (406) 245-8585

Portland (OR) Resident Office
805 SW Broadway, Suite 520, Portland, OR 97205
Tel: (503) 326-2162 Fax: (503) 326-3258
Resident Agent-in-Charge **Justin Borne** . . . . (503) 326-2162

Spokane (WA) Resident Office
528 East Spokane Falls Boulevard, Suite 600, Spokane, WA 99202
Tel: (509) 353-2532 Fax: (509) 353-2871
Resident Agent-in-Charge **Gregory Ligouri** . . . . (509) 353-2532

Tampa (FL) Field Office
Robert Timberlake Federal Building Annex, 501 East Polk Street, Suite 1101, Tampa, FL 33602
Tel: (813) 228-2636 Fax: (813) 228-2618
Special Agent-in-Charge **Billy Joe Powers** . . . . (813) 228-2636
Assistant Special Agent-in-Charge **Patrick Henry** . . . . (813) 228-2636

Fort Myers (FL) Resident Agency
Huntington Bank Center, 2000 Main Street, Room 804, Fort Myers, FL 33901
Tel: (239) 334-0660 Fax: (239) 334-4833
Resident Agent in Charge **Jeff Kelly** . . . . (239) 334-0660

Washington (DC) Field Office
1100 L Street, NW, Suite 6000, Washington, DC 20005-4035
Mail: 245 Murray Drive, SW, T-5, Washington, DC 20223
Tel: (202) 406-8000 Fax: (202) 406-8008
Special Agent-in-Charge **Brian J. Ebert** . . . . (202) 406-8000
E-mail: brian.ebert@usss.dhs.gov

Transportation Security Administration (TSA)

East Building, 601 South 12th Street, Arlington, VA 20598
Fax: (571) 227-4400 Internet: www.tsa.gov

OFFICE OF THE ADMINISTRATOR

East Building, 601 South 12th Street, Arlington, VA 20598
Tel: (571) 227-2801 Fax: (571) 227-1398

Office of the Deputy Administrator

East Building, 601 South 12th Street, Arlington, VA 20598
Fax: (571) 227-1398

Office of Law Enforcement - Federal Air Marshal Service (FAMS)

601 South 12th Street, Mail Stop 6105, Arlington, VA 20598
Tel: (703) 487-3400 Fax: (703) 487-3405

Federal Air Marshal Service - Atlantic City (NJ)
Building 202, FAMS, Atlantic City, NJ 08405
Tel: (609) 813-3300 Fax: (609) 813-3309
Special Agent-in-Charge for Training **(Vacant)** . . . . (609) 813-3453

Office of Security Operations (OSO)

East Building, 601 South 12th Street, Arlington, VA 20598
Fax: (571) 227-1399

Area Directors

Abilene Regional Airport - Transportation Security Administration
1215 East South 11th Street, Suite B, Abilene, TX 79602
P.O. Box 60, Abilene, TX 79604
Tel: (806) 740-8011
Areas Covered: The FSD for this airport is also responsible for the San Angelo Regional Airport
Federal Security Director **Amy Williams** . . . . (806) 740-8011

Albany International Airport - Transportation Security Administration
Albany International Airport, 737 Albany Shaker Road, Albany, NY 12211
Tel: (518) 452-4247 E-mail: albcoordinationcenter@tsa.dhs.gov
Internet: www.albanyairport.com
Federal Security Director **Bart R. Johnson** . . . . (518) 452-4247
Education: Empire Col 2004 BS

Albuquerque International Sunport - Transportation Security Administration
2920A Yale Boulevard, SE, Albuquerque, NM 87106
Tel: (505) 246-4100 Fax: (505) 247-4593 Internet: www.cabq.gov/airport
Federal Security Director **Jesse C. Sanchez** . . . . (505) 246-4100
E-mail: jesse.c.sanchez@tsa.dhs.gov

Antonio B. Won Pat Guam International Airport - Transportation Security Administration
770 East Sunset Boulevard, Suite 163, Tiyan, GU 96913
Tel: (671) 642-7600 Fax: (671) 642-7645
Federal Security Director **Jenel L. Cline** . . . . (808) 838-2501
E-mail: jenel.cline@tsa.dhs.gov

Atlantic City International Airport - Transportation Security Administration
Civil Terminal, 3 Canale Drive, Suite 106, Egg Harbor Township, NJ 08234
Tel: (609) 645-3833 Fax: (609) 407-7132
Federal Security Director **Thomas Carter** . . . . (609) 645-3833
E-mail: Thomas.Carter@tsa.dhs.gov

Austin Straubel International Airport - Transportation Security Administration
2077 Airport Drive, Suite 3, Green Bay, WI 54313
Tel: (920) 593-3167 Fax: (920) 327-7612
Areas Covered: The Federal Security Director for this airport is also responsible for airports in Rhinelander-Onieta, Ironwood, Escanaba, Kingsford, Calumet, and Gwinn, MI
Federal Security Director **Mark Lendvay** . . . . (920) 593-3167

Austin-Bergstrom International Airport - Transportation Security Administration
Building 310, 6800 Burleson Road, Suite 160, Austin, TX 78744
Tel: (512) 530-2001
Federal Security Director **Michael D. Scott** . . . . (512) 691-7847
E-mail: michael.scott@dhs.gov

Baltimore-Washington International Airport - Transportation Security Administration (BWI)
801 International Drive, Linthicum Heights, MD 21090
Tel: (410) 859-7027 (Public Affairs Office) Internet: www.bwiairport.com
Federal Security Director **Andrea R. Mishoe** . . . . (410) 689-3676

Bangor International Airport - Transportation Security Administration
287 Godfrey Boulevard, Bangor, ME 04401
Tel: (207) 974-4212 Fax: (207) 945-3607 E-mail: admin@flybangor.com
Internet: www.flybangor.com
Areas Covered: The Federal Security Director for this airport is also responsible for airports in Bar Harbor, Rockland, and Presque Isle, ME
Federal Security Director **(Vacant)** . . . . (207) 974-4212
Airport Director **Anthony P. Caruso, Jr.** . . . . (207) 992-4605
E-mail: tcaruso@flybangor.com
Assistant Airport Director **James Canders** . . . . (207) 992-4601

★ Presidential Appointment Requiring Senate Confirmation ☆ Presidential Appointment ☐ Schedule C Appointment ◇ Career Senior Foreign Service Appointment
● Career Senior Executive Service (SES) Appointment ○ Non-Career Senior Executive Service (SES) Appointment ■ Postal Career Executive Service

Baton Rouge Metropolitan Airport - Transportation Security Administration
9191 Plank Road, Baton Rouge, LA 70811
Tel: (504) 472-9365 Fax: (225) 355-6617 Internet: www.flybtr.com
Areas Covered: The Federal Security Director for this airport is also responsible for Lafayette Regional Airport and Lake Charles Regional Airport, LA
Federal Security Director **Johnny Eason** .... (504) 472-9369

Bill and Hillary Clinton National Airport - Transportation Security Administration
One Airport Road, Little Rock, AR 72202-4402
Tel: (501) 212-2001 Fax: (501) 396-7020
Areas Covered: The Federal Security Director for this airport is also responsible for El Dorado Airport, El Dorado, AR; Fort Smith Municipal Airport, Fort Smith, AR; Harrison Airport, Harrison, AR; Hot Springs Airport, Hot Springs, AR; and Northwest Arkansas Regional Airport, Jonesboro Regional Airport, AR.
Federal Security Director **Louis Traverzo** .... (501) 212-2004
E-mail: louis.traverzo@dhs.gov
Education: St Norbert BA; Shippensburg MPA

Billings Logan International Airport - Transportation Security Administration
1737 U.S. Highway 3, Billings, MT 59105
Tel: (406) 255-2004 Fax: (406) 657-6583
Areas Covered: The Federal Security Director for this airport is also responsible for all airports in MT.
Federal Security Director **Daniel P. Fevold** .... (406) 255-2004
Administrative Officer **John Merritt** .... (406) 255-2005
E-mail: john.merritt@dhs.gov

Missoula International Airport - Transportation Security Administration
100 West Railroad Street, Suite 101, Missoula, MT 59802
Tel: (406) 329-4305 Fax: (406) 543-0539
Areas Covered: The Assistant Federal Security Director for this airport is also responsible for Glacier Park International Airport, Kalispell, MT; Great Falls International Airport, Great Falls, MT; and Helena Regional Airport, Helena, MT.
Assistant Federal Security Director **Kurt Carlson** .... (406) 329-4407

Birmingham International Airport - Transportation Security Administration
6500 43rd Avenue North, Suite 100, Birmingham, AL 35206
Tel: (205) 510-1701 Fax: (205) 599-6232
Note: The Federal Security Director for this airport is also responsible for Huntsville International Airport, Huntsville, AL, and Northwest Alabama Regional Airport, Muscle Shoals, AL.
Federal Security Director **Gail R. Linkins** .... (205) 665-9738
E-mail: gail.r.linkins@tsa.dhs.gov

Bismarck Municipal Airport - Transportation Security Administration
Building 17, 2301 University Drive, Bismarck, ND 58504
Note: The Federal Security Director for this airport is also responsible for airports in Fargo, Grand Forks, Minot, Dickinson, Williston, Jamestown, and Devil's Lake.
Federal Security Director for North Dakota
David Durgan .... (701) 255-5301
919 South Seventh Street, Suite 303, Bismarck, ND 58504

Hector International Airport - Transportation Security Administration
2801 32nd Avenue NW, Fargo, ND 58102
Tel: (701) 239-5693 Fax: (701) 239-5680
Federal Security Director **David Durgan** .... (701) 255-5301

Bloomington-Normal Airport - Central Illinois Regional Airport - Transportation Security Administration
2901 East Empire, Suite 200, Bloomington, IL 61704
Tel: (309) 662-2583 Internet: www.cira.com
Assistant Federal Security Director **(Vacant)** .... (309) 662-2583

Blue Grass Airport - Transportation Security Administration
4000 Terminal Drive, Suite 217, Lexington, KY 40510
Tel: (859) 252-0120 Internet: www.bluegrassairport.com
Assistant Federal Security Director **(Vacant)** .... (859) 252-0120

Boise Air Terminal - Gowen Field - Transportation Security Administration
3201 Airport Way, Suite 1200, Boise, ID 83705
Tel: (208) 338-8200 TTY: (208) 383-3137 Fax: (208) 334-1206
Areas Covered: The FSD for this airport is also responsible for all federal airports in the State of Idaho.
Federal Security Director **Andrew L. "Andy" Coose** .... (208) 338-8200
E-mail: andrew.coose@tsa.dhs.gov
Education: Northwest Nazarene Col BIA; Colorado State MBA

Idaho Falls Regional Airport - Transportation Security Administration
1585 North Skyline Drive, Idaho Falls, ID 83402
Tel: (208) 338-8200 Tel: (208) 334-1196 (Regional Operations Center)
Fax: (208) 334-1206 Fax: (208) 334-1198 (Regional Operations Center)
Areas Covered: The Federal Security Director for this airport is also responsible for Jackson Hole Airport, Jackson, WY.
Federal Security Director **Andrew L. "Andy" Coose** .... (208) 338-8200
E-mail: andrew.coose@tsa.dhs.gov
Education: Northwest Nazarene Col BIA; Colorado State MBA

Bradley International Airport - Transportation Security Administration
334 Ella Grasso Turnpike, Suite 200, Windsor Locks, CT 06096
Tel: (860) 804-4117 Fax: (860) 292-9656
Internet: www.bradleyairport.com
Federal Security Director **William Csontos** .... (860) 804-4105

Buffalo-Niagara International Airport - Transportation Security Administration
4200 Genesee Street, Cheektowaga, NY 14225
Tel: (716) 635-1200 Fax: (716) 633-7596
Areas Covered: The FSD for this airport is also responsible for Niagara Falls International Airport, Niagara Falls, NY.
Federal Security Director **Bart R. Johnson** .... (716) 635-1200
Education: Empire Col 2004 BS

Burbank-Glendale-Pasadena Airport - Transportation Security Administration
2919 West Empire Avenue, Burbank, CA 91504-3108
Tel: (818) 840-6300 Internet: www.burbankairport.com
Areas Covered: The FSD for this airport is also responsible for the Bob Hope Airport, Burbank, CA
Federal Security Director **Anita Minaei** .... (818) 840-6300

Burlington International Airport - Transportation Security Administration
110 Kimball Avenue, Suite 100, South Burlington, VT 05403
Tel: (802) 951-3512 Fax: (802) 863-9062 Internet: www.btv.aero
Areas Covered: The Federal Security Director for this airport is also responsible for the Lebanon, NH, Municipal Airport; the Clinton County Airport in Plattsburgh, NY; and the Rutland State Airport, VT; Adirondack Regional Airport, NY.
Federal Security Director **Bruce McDonald** .... (802) 951-3512
E-mail: bruce.mcdonald@dhs.gov

★ Presidential Appointment Requiring Senate Confirmation ☆ Presidential Appointment □ Schedule C Appointment ◇ Career Senior Foreign Service Appointment
● Career Senior Executive Service (SES) Appointment ○ Non-Career Senior Executive Service (SES) Appointment ■ Postal Career Executive Service

Capital City Airport - Transportation Security Administration
Capital Region Airport Authority, 4100 Capital City Boulevard, Lansing, MI 48906
Tel: (517) 321-6121 (General) Tel: (517) 886-7001 (TSA)
Fax: (517) 321-6197
Areas Covered: The Federal Security Director for this airport is also responsible for Bishop International Airport, Flint, MI; and MBS International Airport, Freeland, MI.
Federal Security Director **Denise T. Amicucci** .... (517) 886-7001
E-mail: denise.amicucci@dhs.gov
Education: Walsh Col 1999 MA

Charleston International Airport - Transportation Security Administration
5300 International Boulevard, Suite C-104, Charleston, SC 29418
Tel: (843) 302-8000 Internet: www.chs-airport.com
Note: The Federal Security Director for this airport is also responsible for Asheville Regional Airport, Fletcher, NC, and Greenville-Spartanburg Airport, Greer, SC.
Federal Security Director **Steven Corey** .... (843) 302-8000

Charlotte-Douglas International Airport - Transportation Security Administration
3800 Arco Corp Drive, Suite 400, Charlotte, NC 28273
Areas Covered: The Federal Security Director for this airport is also responsible for Asheville Regional Airport.
Federal Security Director **Kevin Frederick** .... (704) 916-3310
E-mail: kevin.frederick@dhs.gov

Charlottesville - Albemarle Airport - Transportation Security Administration
1540 Airport Road, Charlottesville, VA 22911
Tel: (804) 226-8547 Internet: www.gocho.com
Areas Covered: The Federal Security Director for this airport is also responsible for Lynchburg Regional Airport, Lynchburg, VA; and Shenandoah Valley Airport, Weyers Cave, VA.
Federal Security Director **Chuck Burke** .... (804) 226-8547
E-mail: chuck.burke@dhs.gov

Cherry Capital Airport - Transportation Security Administration
727 Sly Dont Drive, Traverse City, MI 49686
Tel: (231) 946-6009
Areas Covered: The Federal Security Director for this airport is also responsible for Alpena County Regional Airport, Alpena, MI; Chippewa County International Airport, Kincheloe, MI; Delta County Airport, Escanaba, MI; Ford Airport, Iron Mountain, MI; Gogebic-Iron County Airport, Ironwood, MI; Houghton County Memorial Airport, Calumet, MI; Pellston Regional Airport of Emmet County, Pellston, MI Sawyer International Airport, Gwihn, MI.
Federal Security Director **Roger Dubuc** .... (231) 929-5339

Chicago Midway Airport - Transportation Security Administration
5333 South Laramie Avenue, Suite 220, Chicago, IL 60638
Tel: (773) 838-0600 Fax: (773) 948-6153
Federal Security Director
CDR Kevin G. McCarthy USN (Ret) .... (773) 498-1322
Education: Naval Acad 1981 BS
Assistant Federal Security Director **(Vacant)** .... (773) 498-1322

Chicago O'Hare International Airport - Transportation Security Administration
P.O. Box 661010, Chicago, IL 60666-1010
Fax: (773) 894-0251 Internet: www.ohare.com
Federal Security Director **Darryl Sterr** .... (847) 720-0101

Cincinnati-Northern Kentucky International Airport - Transportation Security Administration
3900 Olympic Boulevard, Suite 200, Erlanger, KY 41018
Tel: (859) 488-0274 Fax: (859) 372-9739
Federal Security Director **Ray Williams** .... (859) 488-0282
E-mail: ray.williams@tsa.dhs.gov

Cleveland Hopkins International Airport - Transportation Security Administration
20445 Emerald Parkway Drive, Suite 300, Cleveland, OH 44135
Tel: (216) 362-4220 Fax: (216) 265-1663
Federal Security Director **Donald "Don" Barker III** ...... (216) 362-4913
E-mail: donald.barker@dhs.gov
Education: Penn State BS; U Phoenix MBA

Colorado Springs Municipal Airport - Transportation Security Administration
985 Space Center Drive, Suite 210, Colorado Springs, CO 80915
Tel: (719) 622-5980 Fax: (719) 591-8872
Assistant Federal Security Director **(Vacant)** .... (719) 622-5982

Columbia Metropolitan Airport - Transportation Security Administration
3000 Aviation Way, West Columbia, SC 29170
Tel: (803) 822-1904 Tel: (803) 822-5020 (Public Relations)
Fax: (803) 822-5141 Internet: www.columbiaairport.com
Areas Covered: The Federal Security Director for this airport is also responsible for Florence Regional Airport, SC, and Bush Field Airport, Augusta, GA.
Federal Security Manager **Roger Edwards** .... (803) 451-5151

Commonwealth Ports Authority - Transportation Security Administration
Saipan International Airport, P.O. Box 501055, Saipan, MP 96950
Tel: (670) 322-6004 Fax: (670) 234-5962
E-mail: cpa.admin@pticom.com Internet: http://cpa.gov.mp
Deputy Federal Security Director **(Vacant)** .... (670) 322-6007

Corpus Christi International Airport - Transportation Security Administration
1000 International Drive, Suite TSA, Corpus Christi, TX 78406-1811
Tel: (361) 693-3811 Fax: (361) 299-8743
Assistant Federal Security Director/Generalist
John Seelmann .... (361) 693-3813

Cyril E. King International Airport - Transportation Security Administration
Cyril E. King Airport, Terminal, 2nd Floor, St. Thomas, VI 00802
Tel: (340) 715-2277 Fax: (340) 779-6028
Federal Security Director **Jose Baquero** .... (340) 779-6045
E-mail: jose.baquero@dhs.gov

Dallas Fort Worth International Airport - Transportation Security Administration
3200 East Airfield Drive, Dallas Fort Worth Airport, TX 75261
Tel: (469) 948-1810 Tel: (469) 948-1828 (Customer Service Line)
Federal Security Director **Michael Donnelly** .... (469) 948-1823
E-mail: michael.donnelly@tsa.dhs.gov

Dallas Love Field - Transportation Security Administration
3890 West Northwest Highway, Suite 102, Dallas, TX 75220
Tel: (469) 221-2080 Fax: (469) 335-5090
Federal Security Director **Amy Williams** .... (469) 221-2084

★ Presidential Appointment Requiring Senate Confirmation ☆ Presidential Appointment ☐ Schedule C Appointment ◇ Career Senior Foreign Service Appointment
● Career Senior Executive Service (SES) Appointment ○ Non-Career Senior Executive Service (SES) Appointment ■ Postal Career Executive Service

Dane County Regional Airport - Transportation Security Administration
2701 International Lane, Suite 106, Madison, WI 53704
Tel: (608) 395-6015
Areas Covered: The Federal Security Director for this airport is also responsible for airports in La Crosse and Eau Claire, WI
Federal Security Director **Mark Lendvay** .... (608) 395-6001

Daytona Beach International Airport - Transportation Security Administration
700 Catalina Drive, Suite 103, Daytona Beach, FL 32114
Fax: (386) 239-3524
Assistant Federal Security Director **Eric Fisher** .... (386) 947-7502

Denver International Airport - Transportation Security Administration
8400 Peña Boulevard, Mail Box 492125, Denver, CO 80249
Tel: (303) 348-7679 Fax: (303) 342-6518
Federal Security Director **Lawrence "Larry" Nau** .... (303) 348-7648
E-mail: lawrence.nau@tsa.dhs.gov
Deputy Federal Security Director **Anne Catron** .... (303) 348-7648
E-mail: anne.catron@tsa.dhs.gov
Assistant Federal Security Director - Mission Support
KC Wurtsbaugh .... (303) 348-7589
E-mail: kc.wurtsbaugh@tsa.dhs.gov
Assistant Federal Security Director - Screening
Roberto Brito .... (720) 479-3121
E-mail: roberto.brito@tsa.dhs.gov

Des Moines International Airport - Transportation Security Administration
5921 Southeast 14th Street, Suite 1200, Des Moines, IA 50320
Tel: (515) 473-9408 Fax: (515) 953-1490
Areas Covered: The Federal Security Director for this airport is also responsible for Dubuque Regional Airport, Eastern Iowa Airport, Fort Dodge Regional Airport, Mason City Municipal Airport, Sioux Gateway Airport, Southeast Iowa Regional Airport, and Waterloo Municipal Airport.
Federal Security Director **David W. Dailey** .... (515) 473-9408
E-mail: david.dailey@tsa.dhs.gov
Education: U Phoenix 2010 AA

Detroit Metro Wayne County Airport - Transportation Security Administration
11100 Metro Airport Center Drive, Suite 160, Romulus, MI 48174
Tel: (734) 995-2999 Fax: (734) 955-8603
Federal Security Director **Juan Sanchez** .... (734) 942-2999
Deputy Federal Security Director **Sophia Tallant** .... (734) 942-2999

Duluth International Airport - Transportation Security Administration
4701 Grinden Drive, Duluth, MN 55811
Fax: (218) 727-2960
Assistant Federal Security Director **Dan Monette** .... (218) 727-7430

Eagle County Regional Airport - Transportation Security Administration
2828 Walker Field Drive, Grand Junction, CO 81506
Tel: (970) 242-0505
Regional Federal Security Director **(Vacant)** .... (970) 242-0505

El Paso International Airport - Transportation Security Administration
1200 Golden Key Circle, Suite 260, El Paso, TX 79925
Tel: (915) 774-4600 Fax: (915) 599-3729
Internet: www.elpasointernationalairport.com
Federal Security Director **Tim Berroyer** .... (915) 774-4600

Eppley Airfield - Transportation Security Administration
1102 East Hartman Avenue, Omaha, NE 68110-2808
Tel: (402) 457-1528 Fax: (402) 345-3015
Federal Security Director **Michael Fowler** .... (402) 457-1528

Fairbanks International Airport - Transportation Security Administration
5904 Old Airport Way, Suite 2B, Fairbanks, AK 99709
Tel: (907) 452-9413 (Administration) Fax: (907) 458-2070
Internet: www.dot.state.ak.us/faiiap
Federal Security Director **Brian Cahill** .... (907) 771-2901
E-mail: brian.cahill@tsa.dhs.gov
Education: Chapman BA

Fort Lauderdale - Hollywood International Airport - Transportation Security Administration
1050 Lee Wagener Boulevard, Suite 303, Fort Lauderdale, FL 33315
Tel: (954) 308-5530 Fax: (954) 359-0854
Federal Security Director **Jason Martin** .... (954) 308-5530

Fresno Yosemite International Airport - Transportation Security Administration
City of Fresno - Department of Airports,
4995 East Clinton Way, Fresno, CA 93727
Tel: (559) 456-6828 Fax: (559) 456-6835 Internet: www.flyfresno.com
Federal Security Director **(Vacant)** .... (559) 456-6828

General Mitchell International Airport - Transportation Security Administration
5007 South Howell Avenue, Suite 200, Milwaukee, WI 53207
Federal Security Director **Mark Lendvay** .... (414) 238-6015

George Bush Intercontinental Airport - Transportation Security Administration
3838 North Sam Houston Parkway East,
Suite 510, Houston, TX 77032
Tel: (281) 848-2940 Fax: (281) 986-4121
Federal Security Director **Gerry Phelan** .... (281) 848-2940
E-mail: gerry.phelan@tsa.dhs.gov
Education: Warner Southern BA

Gerald R. Ford International Airport - Transportation Security Administration
4665 Broadmoor Avenue, SE, Suite 250, Grand Rapids, MI 49512
Tel: (616) 554-1079 Fax: (616) 554-9444
Federal Security Director **Roger Dubuc** .... (616) 554-1079

Grand Junction - Transportation Security Administration
2828 Walker Field Drive, Suite 209, Grand Junction, CO 81506
Tel: (970) 242-0505 Fax: (970) 242-4699
Federal Security Director **(Vacant)** .... (970) 242-0505

Greater Peoria Regional Airport - Transportation Security Administration
6100 West Dirksen Parkway, Peoria, IL 61607
Tel: (309) 634-6657 Fax: (309) 634-6659
Internet: www.flypia.com/index.php
Security Manager **(Vacant)** .... (309) 757-6617

Greater Rochester International Airport - Transportation Security Administration
One Airport Way, Suite 200, Rochester, NY 14624
Tel: (585) 279-6028 Fax: (585) 328-1124
Areas Covered: The Federal Security Director for this airport is also responsible for Elmira-Corning Regional Airport, Horseheads, NY
Federal Security Director **John McCaffrey** .... (585) 279-6001
E-mail: john.mccaffrey@dhs.gov
Assistant Federal Security Director for Operations
(Vacant) .... (585) 279-6022

(continued on next page)

★ Presidential Appointment Requiring Senate Confirmation ☆ Presidential Appointment ☐ Schedule C Appointment ◇ Career Senior Foreign Service Appointment
● Career Senior Executive Service (SES) Appointment ○ Non-Career Senior Executive Service (SES) Appointment ■ Postal Career Executive Service

Greater Rochester International Airport - Transportation Security Administration *(continued)*

Assistant Federal Security Director for Law Enforcement **Clancy McMahon** .... (585) 279-6003
E-mail: clancy.mcmahon@ole.tsa.dhs.gov

Gulfport-Biloxi International Airport - Transportation Security Administration
14035 Airport Road, Suite N, Gulfport, MS 39503
Tel: (228) 822-8305 Fax: (228) 563-7331 Internet: www.gulfcoast.org/gpt

Assistant Federal Security Director-Generalist **Gregory Dion** .... (228) 822-8303
E-mail: gregory.dion@dhs.gov

Human Resources Assistant **Lucretia Lott** .... (228) 822-8307
E-mail: lucretia.lott@dhs.gov Fax: (228) 563-1558

Harrisburg International Airport - Transportation Security Administration
517 Airport Drive, Middletown, PA 17057

Federal Security Director **David Marshall** .... (717) 948-4808

Hartsfield-Jackson Atlanta International Airport - Transportation Security Administration
3848 Northwest Drive, College Park, GA 30337
Tel: (404) 460-2280 Internet: www.atlanta-airport.com

Federal Security Director **Mary Leftridge Byrd** .... (404) 460-2280
Education: Penn State BS

Deputy Federal Security Director **Ronnie Edge** .... (404) 460-2280

Huntsville International Airport - Transportation Security Administration
Port of Huntsville, Box 20008, 1000 Glenn Hearn Boulevard, Huntsville, AL 35824
Tel: (256) 772-1368 Fax: (256) 772-9158

Deputy Federal Security Director **Samuel W. Bucy** ...... (256) 772-4802
E-mail: samuel.bucy@dhs.gov
Education: Auburn

Honolulu International Airport - Transportation Security Administration
300 Rodgers Boulevard, #45, Honolulu, HI 96819
Tel: (808) 838-2501 Fax: (808) 831-4619

Federal Security Director **Jenel L. Cline** .... (808) 831-4604
E-mail: jenel.cline@dhs.gov

Indiana Airports - Transportation Security Administration
1843 Commerce Drive, Suite 200, South Bend, IN 46628-5594
Tel: (574) 520-2000
Areas Covered: The Federal Security Director is responsible for all commercial airports in Indiana.

Federal Security Director **Aaron Batt** .... (317) 612-9000
Education: Purdue ABS

Evansville Regional Airport - Transportation Security Administration
7801 Bussing Drive, Evansville, IN 47725-6799
Tel: (812) 435-1513 Fax: (812) 434-4673

Transportation Security Manager **Mark A. Appler** .... (812) 435-1513

Jackson-Evers International Airport - Transportation Security Administration
10 Canebrake Boulevard, Suite 310, Flowood, MS 39232
Tel: (601) 936-1702 Fax: (601) 939-4711
Areas Covered: The Federal Security Director for this airport is also responsible for Golden Triangle Regional Airport, Columbus, MS; Gulfport/Biloxi International Airport, Gulfport, MS; Hattiesburg-Laurel Regional Airport, Moselle, MS; Meridian Regional Airport, Meridian, MS; Mid Delta Regional Airport, Greenville, MS; and Tupelo Regional Airport, Tupelo, MS.

Federal Security Director **David C. Wynn** .... (601) 936-1701
E-mail: david.wynn@dhs.gov

Jacksonville International Airport - Transportation Security Administration
14201 Pecan Park Road, Jacksonville, FL 32218
Tel: (904) 380-2016 Fax: (904) 741-9520 Internet: www.jaa.aero

Federal Security Director **(Vacant)** .... (904) 380-2016

James M. Cox Dayton International Airport
303 Corporate Center Drive, Suite 200, Vandalia, OH 45377
Fax: (937) 890-6265

Federal Security Director **John Barker** .... (937) 454-2413

John F. Kennedy International Airport - Transportation Security Administration
TSA, 230 - 59 Rockaway Boulevard, Suite 210, Jamaica, NY 11413
Tel: (718) 244-4444 Fax: (718) 553-2154
Internet: www.kennedyairport.com/aviation/jfkhomemain.html

Federal Security Director **(Vacant)** .... (718) 244-4444

John Wayne Airport - Transportation Security Administration
881 Airport Way, Santa Ana, CA 92707
Tel: (949) 862-5533

Federal Security Director (Acting) **Boyd Keith Jeffries** ... (949) 862-5533

Juneau International Airport - Transportation Security Administration
8800 Glacier Highway, Suite 217, Juneau, AK 99801
Tel: (907) 713-3301 Fax: (907) 586-7687
Areas Covered: The Federal Security Director for this airport is also responsible for Gustavas Airport, Gustavas, AK; Ketchikan International Airport, Ketchikan, AK; Petersburg Airport, Petersburg, AK; Sitka Rocky Guitierrez Airport, Sitka, AK; Wrangell Airport, Wrangell, AK; and Yakutat Airport, Yakutat, AK.

Federal Security Director **Brian Cahill** .... (907) 713-3301
E-mail: brian.cahill@tsa.dhs.gov
Education: Chapman BA

Kahului Airport - Transportation Security Administration
425 Koloa Street, Suite 106, Koloa, HI 96732
Tel: (808) 872-0221 Fax: (808) 873-3618

Kansas City International Airport - Transportation Security Administration
12200 North Ambassador Drive, Suite 212, Kansas City, MO 64163
Tel: (816) 243-6261 Fax: (816) 243-7540

Deputy Federal Security Director **Angela Brooks** .... (816) 243-6261

Kona International Airport - Transportation Security Administration
Kona International Airport at Ke-ahole, 73-5618 Maiau Street, Suite A101, Kailua Kona, HI 96740
Tel: (808) 331-6901 Fax: (808) 327-5916
Areas Covered: The Federal Security Director for this airport is also responsible for Hilo International Airport, Hilo, HI.

Federal Security Director **Jenel L. Cline** .... (808) 831-4604
E-mail: jenel.cline@dhs.gov

LaGuardia Airport - Transportation Security Administration
P.O. Box 441, Flushing, NY 11371

Federal Security Director **Robert A. Duffy** .... (718) 662-5000

Lambert - St. Louis International Airport - Transportation Security Administration
10701 Lambert International Boulevard, St. Louis, MO 63145-0212
Tel: (314) 656-1153

Federal Security Director **James "Jim" Spriggs** .... (314) 656-1160

Lehigh Valley International Airport - Transportation Security Administration
961 Marcon Boulevard, Suite 105, Allentown, PA 18109
Tel: (484) 834-8201 Fax: (610) 231-1789 Internet: www.lvia.org
Areas Covered: The Assistant Federal Security Director for this airport is also responsible for Reading Regional Airport, Reading, PA; Wilkes Barre/Scranton International Airport, Avoca, PA; and Williamsport Regional Airport, Montoursville, PA.
Assistant Federal Security Director (Generalist)
Michael Kichline . . . . . (484) 834-8201

Lihue Airport - Transportation Security Administration
4820A Rice Street, Lihue, HI 96766
Tel: (808) 241-4501 Fax: (808) 241-7765
Federal Security Director **Jenel L. Cline** . . . . . (808) 241-4501
E-mail: jenel.cline@dhs.gov

Logan International Airport - Transportation Security Administration
Two Service Road East, Boston, MA 02128
Tel: (617) 561-2000 Fax: (617) 568-0554
Federal Security Director **Robert Allison** . . . . . (617) 568-8901
E-mail: robert.allison@dhs.gov Fax: (617) 568-8902

Long Island MacArthur Airport - Transportation Security Administration
100 Arrival Avenue, Suite 100, Ronkonkoma, NY 11779
Tel: (631) 580-6748
Assistant Federal Security Director **Joseph Modica** . . . . . (631) 807-7788
E-mail: joseph.modica@tsa.dhs.gov

Los Angeles International Airport - Transportation Security Administration
P.O. Box 92214, 6th Floor, Los Angeles, CA 90045
Tel: (310) 242-2901 Fax: (310) 641-2817
Federal Security Director
Boyd Keith Jeffries . . . . . (310) 242-2901 ext. 9044
Deputy Federal Security Director **Martin Elam** . . . . . (310) 242-2902
Assistant Federal Security Director for Mission Support
George Andler . . . . . (310) 242-2902
Assistant Federal Security Director for Mission Support
(Vacant) . . . . . (310) 242-2901

Louis Armstrong New Orleans International Airport - Transportation Security Administration
120 Mallard Street, Suite 200, St. Rose, LA 70087
Tel: (504) 472-9365 Fax: (504) 465-5033 Internet: www.flymsy.com
Federal Security Director **Johnny Eason** . . . . . (504) 472-9365
E-mail: johnny.eason@dhs.gov
Administrative Officer **Beverly Thompson** . . . . . (504) 472-9365
E-mail: beverly.thompson@dhs.gov

Louisville International Airport - Transportation Security Administration
600 Terminal Drive, Louisville, KY 40209
Tel: (502) 413-0900 Fax: (502) 363-2517
Federal Security Director **Ray Williams** . . . . . (502) 413-0905
E-mail: ray.williams@tsa.dhs.gov

Lubbock International Airport - Transportation Security Administration
4630 50th Street, Suite 107, Lubbock, TX 79414
Tel: (806) 740-8011 Fax: (806) 740-8161
Areas Covered: The Federal Security Director for this airport is also responsible for Abilene Regional Airport, Abilene, TX; Amarillo International Airport, Amarillo, TX; Midland International Airport, Midland, TX; and San Angelo Regional Airport, San Angelo, TX.
Federal Security Director **Michael A. "Mike" Scott** . . . . . (806) 740-8011
E-mail: michael.a.scott@tsa.dhs.gov
Education: Stevens BSE, MS

Luis Munoz Marin International Airport - Transportation Security Administration
Terminal D, Suite 4010, Carolina, PR 00979
Tel: (787) 253-4591 Fax: (787) 253-4688
Federal Security Director **Jose Baquero** . . . . . (787) 253-5496
E-mail: jose.baquero@dhs.gov
Assistant Federal Security Director, Screening
Jose Rivera . . . . . (787) 253-4591
E-mail: jose.a.rivera1@dhs.gov
Education: Inter American 1996 BMS

Manchester Airport - Transportation Security Administration
Four Technology Drive, Londonderry, NH 03053
Tel: (603) 666-7420 Fax: (603) 666-7546
Areas Covered: The Federal Security Director for this airport is also responsible for Lebanon Municipal Airport, Lebanon, NH.
Federal Security Director **Robert C. Krekorian** . . . . . (603) 666-7420
E-mail: robert.krekorian@dhs.gov

McCarran International Airport - Transportation Security Administration
6750 Via Austi Parkway, Suite 200, Las Vegas, NV 89119
Tel: (702) 577-9018 Fax: (702) 261-6682 Internet: http://mccarran.com
Federal Security Director **Karen Burke** . . . . . (702) 577-9401
E-mail: karen.burke@tsa.dhs.gov
Education: Northwestern 1969 BA; Naval Postgrad 2008 MNSSS

Miami International Airport - Transportation Security Administration
8400 NW 36th Street, Suite 300, Miami, FL 33166
Internet: www.miami-airport.com
Federal Security Director
CAPT Daniel A. Ronan USCG (Ret) . . . . . (305) 421-2445
E-mail: daniel.a.ronan@tsa.dhs.gov Fax: (305) 526-2600

Minneapolis-St. Paul International Airport - Transportation Security Administration
2001 Killebrew Drive, Suite 400, Bloomington, MN 55425
Tel: (952) 229-3850 Fax: (952) 851-5643
Internet: www.mspairport.com (Minneapolis-St. Paul Airport)
Federal Security Director **Clifford Van Leuven** . . . . . (952) 229-3850
Education: South Florida BA
Deputy Federal Security Director
David "Dave" McMahon . . . . . (952) 229-3850

Mobile Regional Airport - Transportation Security Administration
P.O. Box 88048, Mobile, AL 36608
Federal Security Director **Gail R. Linkins** . . . . . (251) 665-9738
E-mail: gail.r.linkins@tsa.dhs.gov

Montgomery Regional - Dannelly Field Airport - Transportation Security Administration
4525 Executive Park Drive, Suite 202, Montgomery, AL 36116
Transportation Security Manager **Michael McNeal** . . . . . (334) 286-7502

Myrtle Beach International Airport - Transportation Security Administration
1100 Jetport Road, Myrtle Beach, SC 29577
Tel: (843) 443-9500 Fax: (843) 626-9096
Federal Security Director **Blake Strickland** . . . . . (843) 443-9500
Fax: (843) 626-4392

DEPARTMENTS

★ Presidential Appointment Requiring Senate Confirmation ☆ Presidential Appointment ☐ Schedule C Appointment ◇ Career Senior Foreign Service Appointment
● Career Senior Executive Service (SES) Appointment ○ Non-Career Senior Executive Service (SES) Appointment ■ Postal Career Executive Service

Nashville International Airport - Transportation Security Administration
TSA, One Terminal Drive, Suite 321, Nashville, TN 37214
Fax: (615) 695-4385
Areas Covered: The Federal Security Director for this airport is also responsible for Chattanooga Metropolitan Airport, Chattanooga, TN; McGhee Tyson Airport, Alcoa, TN; Memphis International Airport, Memphis, TN; and Tri-Cities Regional Airport, Blountville, TN.

Federal Security Director **Stephen N. "Steve" Wood** . . . (615) 354-6701
E-mail: stephen.wood@dhs.gov
Education: Georgia Southern BS; Indust'l Col Armed Forces MS; US Army Command

Coordination Center Manager **Bill Riker** . . . . (865) 474-6741

Natrona County International Airport - Transportation Security Administration
8500 Airport Parkway, Suite 217, Casper, WY 82604
Tel: (307) 995-3615
Areas Covered: The Federal Security Director for this airport is also responsible for Cheyenne Airport, Cheyenne, WY; Gillette-Campbell County Airport, Gillette, WY; Laramie Regional Airport, Laramie, WY; Riverton Regional Airport, Riverton, WY; Rock Springs-Sweetwater County Airport, Rocksprings, WY; Sheridan County Airport, Sheridan, WY; Worland Municipal Airport, Worland, WY; and Yellowstone Regional Airport, Cody, WY; and all other airports in WY.

Federal Security Director **Rick Gordon** . . . . (307) 995-3601
E-mail: rick.gordon@tsa.dhs.gov

Newark Liberty International Airport - Transportation Security Administration
614 Frelinghuysen Avenue, 3rd Floor, Newark, NJ 07114
Tel: (908) 787-0555 Fax: (973) 286-4934
Internet: www.panynj.gov/airports/newark-liberty.html

Federal Security Director **Thomas Carter** . . . . (908) 787-0555
E-mail: Thomas.Carter@tsa.dhs.gov

Norfolk International Airport - Transportation Security Administration
5800 Lake Wright Drive, Suite 200, Norfolk, VA 23502
Tel: (757) 892-8021 Fax: (757) 459-4931

Assistant Federal Security Director
Jeffrey "Jeff" Horowitz . . . . (757) 892-8021
E-mail: jeffrey.horowitz@dhs.gov
Education: SUNY (Empire State) BA

Norman Y. Mineta San Jose International Airport - Transportation Security Administration
1735 Technology Drive, Suite 240, San Jose, CA 95110
Tel: (408) 961-0370 Fax: (408) 451-1285 Internet: www.sjc.org
Areas Covered: The Federal Security Director for this airport is also responsible for Modesto Municipal Airport, Modesto, CA; and Monterey Peninsula Airport, Monterey, CA.

Federal Security Director **Robert B. Nowland** . . . . (408) 961-0352
E-mail: robert.nowland@dhs.gov

Ontario International Airport - Transportation Security Administration
5676 West Century Boulevard, Suite 3000, Los Angeles, CA 90045
Tel: (310) 242-2956

Assistant Federal Security Director **Jason Pantages** . . . . . (310) 242-2956
E-mail: jason.pantages@tsa.dhs.gov

Orlando International Airport - Transportation Security Administration
5850 T. G. Lee Boulevard, Suite 610, Orlando, FL 32822
Tel: (407) 563-4067 Fax: (407) 852-9286

Federal Security Director **Jerry Henderson** . . . . (407) 563-4067
E-mail: jerry.henderson@tsa.dhs.gov
Education: Colorado State BSBA; Embry-Riddle MBA

Deputy Federal Security Director **Steven M. Hanson** . . . . (407) 563-4067
E-mail: steven.m.hanson@tsa.dhs.gov

Palm Beach International Airport - Transportation Security Administration
3200 Belvedere Road, Suite A-124, West Palm Beach, FL 33406
Tel: (561) 616-9650 Fax: (561) 615-7085 Internet: www.pbia.org

Federal Security Director **Pete R. Garcia** . . . . (561) 227-5022

Palm Springs International Airport - Transportation Security Administration
3400 East Tahquitz Canyon Way, Suite 10, Palm Springs, CA 92262
Tel: (760) 833-9303 Fax: (760) 318-8845
Areas Covered: Palm Springs International Airport

Federal Security Director **(Vacant)** . . . . (760) 833-9301

Pensacola International Airport - Transportation Security Administration
700 South Palafox Street, Suite 205, Pensacola, FL 32501
Fax: (850) 433-2534

Federal Security Director **(Vacant)** . . . . (850) 436-7101

Philadelphia International Airport - Transportation Security Administration
Two International Plaza, Suite 640, Philadelphia, PA 19113
Tel: (610) 537-1000

Federal Security Director **(Vacant)** . . . . (610) 537-1010
Executive Assistant **Lorianne Malagesi** . . . . (610) 537-1011

Phoenix Sky Harbor International Airport - Transportation Security Administration
410 North 44th Street, Suite 300, Phoenix, AZ 85008
Tel: (480) 375-2600 Fax: (602) 231-0160

Regional Security Director **Jerry Agnew** . . . . (480) 375-2525

Piedmont Triad International Airport - Transportation Security Administration
7029 Albert Pick Road, Suite 203, Greensboro, NC 27409
Tel: (919) 337-9751 Fax: (336) 665-7091

Federal Security Director **Elizabeth "Beth" Walker** . . . . . (336) 358-4401

Pittsburgh International Airport - Transportation Security Administration
P.O. Box 12315, Pittsburgh, PA 15231
Tel: (412) 472-3525 Internet: www.pitairport.com

Federal Security Director **Karen Keys-Turner** . . . . (412) 714-0700
Assistant Federal Security Director for Inspections
Robert Shaffer . . . . (412) 714-0450
Assistant Federal Security Director for Screening
Thomas A. Zoppetti . . . . (412) 714-0551
Deputy Assistant Federal Security Director for Screening **David Myers** . . . . (412) 714-0650
E-mail: nicholas.bruich@dhs.gov

Port Columbus International Airport - Transportation Security Administration
2780 Airport Drive, Room 200, Columbus, OH 43219
Fax: (614) 337-4407

Federal Security Director **Donald "Don" Barker III** . . . . . . (614) 479-2901
E-mail: donald.barker@dhs.gov
Education: Penn State BS; U Phoenix MBA

Portland International Airport - Transportation Security Administration
P.O. Box 55910, Portland, OR 97238
Tel: (503) 889-3071 Fax: (503) 493-1834
Areas Covered: All commercial airports in Oregon

Federal Security Director **Michael T. "Mike" Irwin** . . . . . . (503) 889-3050
E-mail: michael.irwin@dhs.gov
Assistant Federal Security Director - Mission Support
Tina A. Burke . . . . (503) 889-3055
E-mail: tina.burke@dhs.gov

★ Presidential Appointment Requiring Senate Confirmation ☆ Presidential Appointment ☐ Schedule C Appointment ◇ Career Senior Foreign Service Appointment
● Career Senior Executive Service (SES) Appointment ○ Non-Career Senior Executive Service (SES) Appointment ■ Postal Career Executive Service

Eugene Airport - Mahlon Sweet Field - Transportation Security Administration
TSA, Mahlon Sweet Eugene Airport, 28845 Lockheed Drive, Eugene, OR 97402
Tel: (541) 688-8434 Fax: (541) 688-3170
Areas Covered: The Assistant Federal Security Director for this airport is also responsible for Redmond Airport-Roberts Field.
Assistant Federal Security Director **Donald Wilson** ...... (541) 852-5490
E-mail: donald.wilson@dhs.gov
Supervisory Transportation Security Officer
Dean Inouye .... (541) 688-8434

Rogue Valley International - Medford Airport - Transportation Security Administration
1030 Terminal Loop Parkway, Medford, OR 97504
Tel: (541) 776-3731 Fax: (541) 776-3741
Assistant Federal Security Director **Terry Coleman** ...... (541) 776-3721

Portland International Jetport - Transportation Security Administration
1001 Westbrook Street, Portland, ME 04102
Tel: (207) 541-2602 Fax: (207) 541-0005
Assistant Federal Security Director **Rick Kelly** .... (207) 541-2602

Quad City International Airport - Transportation Security Administration
2200 69th Avenue, Moline, IL 61265
Mail: P.O. Box 9029, Moline, IL 61265
Tel: (309) 757-6601 Fax: (309) 797-3074 Internet: www.qcairport.com
Federal Security Director
LtCol John W. Hursey USAF (Ret) .... (309) 757-6620
E-mail: john.hursey@dhs.gov
Education: McKendree 1985 BS; Golden Gate 1989 MPA

Raleigh-Durham International Airport - Transportation Security Administration
One Copley Parkway, Suite 600, Morrisville, NC 27560
Fax: (919) 388-5826
Federal Security Director **Beth G. Walker**..............(919) 337-9751

Reno-Tahoe International Airport - Transportation Security Administration
1755 East Plumb Lane, Suite 241, Reno, NV 89502
Tel: (775) 334-7700
Federal Security Director **(Vacant)**.....................(775) 334-7715

Richmond International Airport - Transportation Security Administration
Capital Region Airport Commission, One Richard E. Byrd Terminal Drive, Richmond, VA 23250-2400
Tel: (804) 226-3000 Internet: www.flyrichmond.com
• Federal Security Director **Chuck Burke** .... (804) 612-5871
E-mail: chuck.burke@dhs.gov

Roanoke Regional Airport - Transportation Security Administration
5251 Concourse Drive, Suite 2B, Roanoke, VA 24019
Tel: (540) 362-1999 (Airport Commission) Tel: (540) 265-6072
Fax: (540) 265-6074 Internet: www.roanokeairport.com
Areas Covered: The Federal Security Director for this airport is also responsible for Greenbriar Valley Airport, Lewisburg, WV; Mercer County Airport, Bluefield, WV; and Raleigh County Memorial Airport, Beaver, WV.
Transportation Security Manager **Robin Trimble** .... (540) 265-6072

Rochester International Airport - Transportation Security Administration
7600 Helgerson Drive, SW, Rochester, MN 55902
Tel: (507) 289-8123 Fax: (507) 289-8134
Transportation Security Manager
Kenneth "Ken" Rowe.............................(507) 289-8123
E-mail: kenneth.rowe1@dhs.gov

Ronald Reagan Washington National Airport - Transportation Security Administration
c/o Metropolitan Washington Airports Authority, One Aviation Circle, Washington, DC 20001-6000
Tel: (703) 603-1550
Internet: www.metwashairports.com/reagan/reagan.htm
Federal Security Director **Kerwin Wilson** ....(703) 603-1502

Sacramento International Airport - Transportation Security Administration (SMF)
The Sacramento County Airport System, 6900 Airport Boulevard, Sacramento, CA 95837
Tel: (916) 929-5411 Tel: (916) 874-0719 (Public Relations)
Fax: (916) 874-0636 E-mail: market@saccounty.net
Internet: www.sacramento.aero
Areas Covered: The Federal Security Director for this airport is also responsible for Arcata-Eureka Airport, Eureka, CA; Chico Municipal Airport, Chico, CA; Crescent City Airport, Crescent City, CA; and Redding Municipal Airport, Redding, CA.
Federal Security Director **Sid Hanna**..................(916) 830-0220

Salt Lake City International Airport - Transportation Security Administration
776 North Terminal Drive, Salt Lake City, UT 84122
Internet: www.slcairport.com
Federal Security Director **Ronald J. "Ron" Malin**.......(801) 606-6015
E-mail: ronald.malin@dhs.gov

San Antonio International Airport - Transportation Security Administration
70 NE Loop 410, Suite 1000, San Antonio, TX 78216
Tel: (210) 507-3151 Fax: (210) 308-3292
Federal Security Director **Jesus S. Presas** .... (210) 507-3150
Assistant Federal Security Director, Law Enforcement
Nathan A. Gulick .... (210) 507-3174
E-mail: nathan.gulick@ole.tsa.dhs.gov
Assistant Federal Security Director, Mission Support
Tommy Johnson ....(210) 507-3157

San Diego International Airport - Transportation Security Administration
2305 Historic Decatur Road, Suite 201, San Diego, CA 92106
Tel: (619) 321-1330 Fax: (619) 523-2656
Federal Security Director **(Vacant)**....................(619) 321-1330

San Francisco International Airport - Transportation Security Administration
P.O. Box 251926, San Francisco, CA 94125
Tel: (650) 266-1900
Federal Security Director **Fred Lau** .... (650) 266-1900
E-mail: fred.lau@dhs.gov
Education: San Francisco State U BA
Deputy Federal Security Director **Anthony Mira** .... (650) 207-5860
E-mail: anthony.mira@dhs.gov

Santa Barbara Municipal Airport - Transportation Security Administration
6144 Calle Real, Suite 201, Goleta, CA 93117
Federal Security Director **Anita Minaei**................(805) 681-0801

DEPARTMENTS

★ Presidential Appointment Requiring Senate Confirmation ☆ Presidential Appointment □ Schedule C Appointment ◇ Career Senior Foreign Service Appointment
● Career Senior Executive Service (SES) Appointment ○ Non-Career Senior Executive Service (SES) Appointment ■ Postal Career Executive Service

Sarasota Bradenton International Airport - Transportation Security Administration
6004 Airport Circle, Sarasota, FL 34243
Tel: (941) 360-8359 Fax: (941) 358-7679 Internet: www.srq-airport.com
Assistant Federal Security Director **Jean Barnes** . . . . (941) 360-8359
E-mail: jean.barnes@dhs.gov

Savannah/Hilton Head International Airport - Transportation Security Administration
Savannah Airport Commission, 468 Airways Avenue, Savannah, GA 31408
Tel: (912) 963-4904 Fax: (912) 965-0632
E-mail: info@savannahairport.com
Areas Covered: The Federal Security Director for this airport is also responsible for commercial airports in Albany, Athens, August, Brunswick, Columbus, and Valdosta in Georgia as well as Hilton Head Island in South Carolina.
Federal Security Director **James Scott** . . . . (912) 963-4904

Seattle-Tacoma International Airport - Transportation Security Administration
18000 International Boulevard, #200, Seattle, WA 98188
Tel: (206) 214-1106 Fax: (206) 248-7588
Federal Security Director **Jeff Holmgren** . . . . (206) 214-1153
E-mail: jeff.holmgren@tsa.dhs.gov

Shreveport Regional Airport - Transportation Security Administration
5103 Hollywood Avenue, Shreveport, LA 71109
Tel: (318) 635-7663 Fax: (318) 635-5633
Internet: www.ci.shreveport.la.us/dept/airport
Assistant Federal Security Director/Generalist
Martin Wright Suite 200 . . . . (318) 635-7663

Sioux Falls Regional Airport - Transportation Security Administration
1610 North Minnesota Avenue, Suite 210, Sioux Falls, SD 57104
Tel: (605) 330-2500 Fax: (605) 330-2552
Areas Covered: The Federal Security Director for this airport is also responsible for Aberdeen Regional Airport, Aberdeen, SD; Brookings Municipal Airport, Brookings, SD; Huron Regional Airport, Huron SD; Pierre Regional Airport, Pierre, SD; Rapid City Regional Airport, Rapid City, SD; and Watertown Regional Airport, Watertown, SD.
Federal Security Director **J. Mark Heisey** . . . . (605) 330-2500
E-mail: mark.heisey@tsa.dhs.gov
Education: Old Dominion BSBA; Naval Postgrad MS

Southwest Florida International Airport - Transportation Security Administration
11000 Terminal Access Drive, Suite 8635, Fort Myers, FL 33913
Tel: (239) 210-6405 Fax: (239) 561-0926 Internet: www.flylcpa.com
Areas Covered: The Federal Security Director for this airport is also responsible for Naples Municipal Airport, Naples, FL.
Federal Security Director **(Vacant)** . . . . (239) 210-6405

Spokane International Airport - Transportation Security Administration
7904 West Pilot Drive, Spokane, WA 99224
Tel: (509) 626-5400 Internet: www.spokaneairports.net
Areas Covered: The Federal Security Director for this airport is also responsible for Pangborn Municipal Airport, East Wenatchee, WA; Pullman/Moscow Regional Airport, Pullman, WA; Tri-cities Airport, Pasco, WA; Walla Walla Airport, Walla Walla, WA; Yakima Airport, Yakima, WA
Federal Security Director **David Redencher** . . . . (509) 626-5410

Tri-Cities Airport/Port of Pasco - Transportation Security Administration
3601 North 20th Avenue, Pasco, WA 99301
Internet: www.portofpasco.org
Areas Covered: The Federal Security Director for this airport is also responsible for Eastern Oregon Regional Airport, Pendelton, OR; Walla Walla Regional Airport, Walla Walla, WA; and Yakima Air Terminal - McAllister Airport, Yakima, WA.
Assistant Federal Security Director **Don Burton** . . . . (509) 543-1501

Springfield - Branson Regional Airport - Transportation Security Administration
2530 North Airport Plaza Avenue, Springfield, MO 65803
Tel: (417) 829-8300 Fax: (417) 829-3842
Assistant Federal Security Director **Chuck Kirkland** . . . . . . (417) 829-8300

Syracuse - Hancock International Airport - Transportation Security Administration
152 Aircargo Road, Syracuse, NY 13212
Tel: (315) 455-3300 E-mail: information@syrairport.org
Internet: www.syrairport.org
Areas Covered: The Federal Security Director for this airport is also responsible for Binghampton Regional Airport, Johnson City, NY; Massena International Airport, Massena, NY; Ogdensburg International Airport, Ogdensburg, NY; Oneida County, Rome, NY; Tompkins County Airport, Ithaca, NY; and Watertown International Airport, Dexter, NY.
Federal Security Director **Bart R. Johnson** . . . . (315) 455-3300
Education: Empire Col 2004 BS

Tallahassee Regional Airport - Transportation Security Administration
3300 Capital Circle, SW, Suite 33, Tallahassee, FL 32310
Tel: (850) 504-6214 Fax: (850) 574-4299
Areas Covered: The Federal Security Director for this airport is also responsible for Dothan-Houston County Airport, Dothan, AL; Southwest Georgia Regional Airport, Albany, GA; and Valdosta Municipal Airport, Valdosta, GA.
Federal Security Director **(Vacant)** . . . . (904) 380-2016
14201 Pecan Park Road, Jacksonville, FL 32218

Tampa International Airport - Transportation Security Administration
5521 West Spruce Street, Suite B-33, Tampa, FL 33607
Tel: (813) 227-4037 Fax: (813) 348-1557
Areas Covered: The Federal Security Director for this airport is also responsible for Sarasota-Bradenton and St. Petersburg-Clearwater International Airports.
Federal Security Director **Kirk Skinner** . . . . (813) 227-4037

Ted Stevens Anchorage International Airport - Transportation Security Administration
4000 West 50th Avenue, Suite 300, Anchorage, AK 99502
Tel: (907) 771-2905 Fax: (907) 271-2266
Federal Security Director (Acting) **Peter Duffy** . . . . (907) 771-2945
E-mail: peter.duffy@tsa.dhs.gov

T.F. Green Airport - Transportation Security Administration
475 Kilvert Street, Suite 220, Warwick, RI 02886
Tel: (401) 734-1900 Fax: (401) 736-9406
Areas Covered: The Federal Security Director for this airport is also responsible for Barnstable Municipal Airport, Hyannis, MA; Martha's Vineyard Airport, Vineyard Haven, MA; Nantucket Memorial Airport, Nantucket, MA; and Provincetown Airport, Provincetown, MA.
Federal Security Director **Daniel Burche** . . . . (401) 736-9102
E-mail: daniel.burche@tsa.dhs.gov

★ Presidential Appointment Requiring Senate Confirmation ☆ Presidential Appointment □ Schedule C Appointment ◇ Career Senior Foreign Service Appointment
● Career Senior Executive Service (SES) Appointment ○ Non-Career Senior Executive Service (SES) Appointment ■ Postal Career Executive Service

Tucson International Airport - Transportation Security Administration
6550 South Bay Colony Drive, Suite 120, Tucson, AZ 85706
Tel: (520) 806-8880 Fax: (520) 746-8440

Assistant Federal Security Director
Charles E. "Charlie" Sparks . . . . (520) 806-8880
Assistant Federal Security Director - Law Enforcement
(Vacant) . . . . (520) 806-8880

Valley International Airport - Transportation Security Administration
3002 Heritage Way, Harlingen, TX 78550
Tel: (956) 430-5468 Internet: www.flythevalley.com
Areas Covered: The Federal Security Director for this airport is also responsible for Brownsville/South Padre International Airport, Brownsville, TX; and McAllen-Miller International Airport, McAllen, TX.

Federal Security Director **Ed Loya** . . . . (956) 430-5468

Washington-Dulles International Airport - Transportation Security Administration
45045 Aviation Drive, Sterling, VA 20598
Tel: (703) 662-2222 Fax: (703) 661-6777
Internet: www.mwaa.com/dulles

Federal Security Director **Scott Johnson** . . . . (703) 662-2222

Wichita Mid-Continent Airport - Transportation Security Administration
2299 Airport Road, Wichita, KS 67209
Tel: (316) 946-4700 Fax: (316) 945-1791
Areas Covered: The Federal Security Director for this airport is also responsible for Dodge City Regional Airport, Dodge City, KS; Garden City Municipal Airport, Garden City, KS; Great Bend Municipal Airport, Great Bend, KS; Hays Regional Airport, Hays, KS; Liberal Municipal Airport, Liberal, KS; and Salina Municipal Airport, Salina, KS.

Federal Security Director **Jason "Jay" Brainard** . . . . (316) 946-4700
E-mail: jay.brainard@tsa.dhs.gov

Will Rogers World Airport - Transportation Security Administration
5700 SW 36th Street, Suite A, Oklahoma City, OK 73179
Tel: (405) 702-7500 Fax: (405) 684-2419 Internet: www.flyokc.com
Areas Covered: The Federal Security Director for this airport is also responsible for Enid Woodring Municipal Airport, Enid, OK.

Federal Security Director **Steven "Steve" Crawford** . . . . (405) 702-7507
Assistant Federal Security Director **Doug Townson** . . . . . . (405) 702-7507

William P. Hobby Airport - Transportation Security Administration
8876 Gulf Freeway, Suite 125, Houston, TX 77017
Fax: (713) 641-8721

Federal Security Director **Hector Vela** . . . . (713) 454-8804

Wilmington International Airport - Transportation Security Administration
1740 Airport Boulevard, Wilmington, NC 28405
Tel: (910) 815-4583 Fax: (910) 815-4564

Assistant Federal Security Director **Cathy English** . . . . (910) 815-4583
E-mail: cathy.english@dhs.gov

Yeager Airport - Transportation Security Administration
John D. Rockefeller IV Terminal Building,
Central West Virginia Regional Airport Authority, 100 Airport Road, Suite 167, Charleston, WV 25311
Tel: (304) 340-9202 Fax: (304) 347-5178 E-mail: fly@yeagerairport.com
Internet: www.yeagerairport.com
Areas Covered: The Federal Security Director for this airport is also responsible for Benedum Airport, Bridgeport, WV; Morgantown Municipal Airport, Morgantown, WV; Tri-State Airport, Huntington, WV; and Wood County Airport, Parkersburg, WV.

Federal Security Director **John Allen** . . . . (304) 340-9187

★ Presidential Appointment Requiring Senate Confirmation ☆ Presidential Appointment □ Schedule C Appointment ◇ Career Senior Foreign Service Appointment
● Career Senior Executive Service (SES) Appointment ○ Non-Career Senior Executive Service (SES) Appointment ■ Postal Career Executive Service

United States Department of Housing and Urban Development

DEPARTMENTS

Contents

United States Department of Housing and Urban Development (HUD)

Description: The Department of Housing and Urban Development insures home mortgages and loans for home improvement, channels funds from investors into the mortgage industry, makes direct loans for construction or rehabilitation of housing projects for the elderly and disabled, subsidizes low- and moderate-income housing, provides grants to encourage community development, and promotes and enforces fair and equal housing opportunity laws.

Robert C. Weaver Federal Building, 451 Seventh Street, SW,
Mail Stop UE, Washington, DC 20410
Tel: (202) 708-1112 (Headquarters - Washington DC)
Tel: (202) 708-1422 (Personnel Locator)
Tel: (202) 708-0685 (Public Affairs)
Tel: (202) 708-0408 (Employment Information)
Tel: (202) 708-3866 (Freedom of Information)
Tel: (202) 708-1290 (Procurement/Contracts Information)
Tel: (202) 708-1420 (Program Information Center)
Tel: (202) 708-0390 (Office of Inspector General Hotline - DC Metropolitan Area) Tel: (800) 347-3735 (Office of Inspector General Hotline - Continental US, Alaska and Hawaii)
Tel: (800) 669-9777 (HUD Housing Discrimination Hotline)
Tel: (202) 708-3151 (HUD User Line - Publications Information/Reference Service - DC Metropolitan Area)
Tel: (800) 245-2691 (HUD User Line - Publications Information/Reference Service - Continental US, Alaska and Hawaii) Tel: (800) 333-4636 (Telephone Directory)
TTY: (202) 708-1455 (Personnel Locator) Internet: www.hud.gov
Internet: http://espanol.hud.gov Internet: www.huduser.org (HUD User Line - Publications Information/Reference Service Homepage)
Internet: www.usa.gov (Official US Government Website)

OFFICE OF THE SECRETARY

Robert C. Weaver Federal Building, 451 Seventh Street, SW,
Mail Stop S, Washington, DC 20410
Tel: (202) 708-3750 Fax: (202) 619-8153

Office of the Deputy Secretary

Robert C. Weaver Federal Building, 451 Seventh Street, SW,
Room 10100, Mail Code SD, Washington, DC 20410
Fax: (202) 708-2706

Assistant Deputy Secretary for Field Policy and Management (FPM)

451 Seventh Street, SW, Room 7108, Mail Stop SDF,
Washington, DC 20410
Tel: (202) 708-2426 Fax: (202) 708-1558

○ Assistant Deputy Secretary for Field Policy and Management **Matthew F. Hunter** .... (202) 708-2426
E-mail: matthew.f.hunter@hud.gov
● Associate Assistant Deputy Secretary (Acting) **Timothy M. "Tim" Smyth** .... (202) 402-2439
E-mail: timothy.m.smyth@hud.gov
Program Analyst **Crystal Kelley** .... (202) 708-2426
● Senior Advisor **(Vacant)** .... (202) 708-2426
Special Assistant **Alexander Stowe** .... (202) 402-5309
Special Assistant **Angela L. Beckles** .... (202) 402-5967
● Director of Field Operations **Jaime E. Forero** .... (202) 402-6036
E-mail: jaime.e.forero@hud.gov
Administrative Management Specialist **Angel Fountain-Cooper** .... (202) 708-2426
Web Manager **Diane J. Fournier** .... (860) 240-9729
E-mail: diane.j.fournier@hud.gov
Web Manager **David W. Lockwood** .... (714) 955-0902
E-mail: david.w.lockwood@hud.gov

Assistant Deputy Secretary for Field Policy and Management *(continued)*

Director, Budget and Financial Management **Paul A. Scott** .... (202) 708-2426
E-mail: paul.a.scott@hud.gov
Disaster Recovery Coordinator (Regions I-V) **Tony X. Hebert** .... (678) 732-2075
Disaster Recovery Coordinator (Regions VI-X) **Edward Ellis** .... (202) 708-2426

Region I - New England

Boston Regional Office

Thomas P. O'Neill Jr. Federal Building, 10 Causeway Street,
Third Floor, Boston, MA 02222-1092
Tel: (617) 994-8200 TTY: (617) 565-6557
Tel: (617) 994-8218 (FOIA Requester Service Center.)
Fax: (617) 565-6558
Areas Covered: CT, ME, MA, NH, RI, VT

□ Regional Administrator **David E. Tille** .... (617) 994-8223
E-mail: david.e.tille@hud.gov Fax: (617) 565-7313
Deputy Regional Administrator **Nicholas R. White** .... (617) 994-8218
E-mail: nicholas.r.white@hud.gov
Management Analyst **Taylor M. Bryan** .... (617) 994-8230
E-mail: taylor.m.bryan@hud.gov
Management Analyst **Erika Koizumi** .... (617) 994-8200
E-mail: erika.koizumi@hud.gov
Management Analyst **Kara E. Norman** .... (617) 994-8200
E-mail: kara.e.norman@hud.gov
Management Analyst **Tanetta Williams** .... (617) 994-8223
E-mail: tanetta.williams@hud.gov
Public Affairs Specialist **Rhonda M. Siciliano** .... (617) 994-8355
E-mail: rhonda.m.siciliano@hud.gov
Regional Web Manager **Diane J. Fournier** .... (860) 240-9729
E-mail: ma_webmanager@hud.gov
Labor Relations Director **William A. Pickett** .... (617) 994-8232
E-mail: william.a.pickett@hud.gov Fax: (617) 565-5257
Regional IT Field Services Director **Charles A. Bragg** .... (617) 994-8296
E-mail: charles.a.bragg@hud.gov

Office of General Counsel

10 Causeway Street, Room 310, Boston, MA 02222-1092
Tel: (617) 994-8250 Fax: (617) 565-7337

Regional Counsel **Miniard Culpepper** .... (617) 994-8250
E-mail: miniard_culpepper@hud.gov
Education: Brandeis 1976 BA; Suffolk 1981 JD; Howard U 1989 MDiv
Deputy Regional Counsel **Derya Samadi** .... (617) 994-8250
E-mail: derya.samadi@hud.gov
Litigation Associate Field Counsel **(Vacant)** .... (617) 994-8250
Program Operations Associate Field Counsel **(Vacant)** .... (617) 994-8250

Office of Inspector General

490 L'Enfant Plaza East, SW, #2206, Washington, DC 20024
Tel: (617) 994-8380 Fax: (617) 565-6878

New England (Region 1) Regional Inspector General for Audit **Ann Marie Henry** .... (617) 994-8380
10 Causeway Street, Room 370, Boston, MA 02222-1092
New England (Region 1) Special Agent in Charge **Christina D. Scaringi** .... (617) 994-8450
10 Causeway Street, Room 360, Boston, MA 02222-1092

★ Presidential Appointment Requiring Senate Confirmation ☆ Presidential Appointment □ Schedule C Appointment ◇ Career Senior Foreign Service Appointment
● Career Senior Executive Service (SES) Appointment ○ Non-Career Senior Executive Service (SES) Appointment ■ Postal Career Executive Service

Office of Community Planning and Development
10 Causeway Street, Room 535, Boston, MA 02222-1092
Tel: (617) 994-8350 Fax: (617) 565-5442

Director **Robert D. Shumeyko** .... (617) 994-8376
E-mail: robert.shumeyko@hud.gov
Program Manager **Paul M. Connolly** .... (617) 994-8592
E-mail: paul.m.connolly@hud.gov
Program Support Specialist **David M. Manganis** .... (617) 994-8367
E-mail: david.m.manganis@hud.gov
Relocation Specialist **Nancy A. Scoppa** .... (617) 994-8357
Environmental Officer **Martha Curran** .... (617) 994-8363
Grant Manager [Disaster Recovery] **Michael Casper** ..... (617) 994-8411
Fax: (617) 565-5442
Grant Manager [Disaster Recovery] **Lois A. Gaetz** ...... (617) 994-8360
Fax: (617) 656-5442
Grant Manager [Disaster Recovery] **Samantha Graves** ... (617) 994-8353
Grant Manager **Stephanie J. Harrington** .... (617) 994-8373
Grant Manager **William M. Hodgdon** .... (617) 994-8354
Grant Manager [Disaster Recovery] **Cynthia E. Lopez** ... (617) 994-8364
Grant Manager **Cleonie H. Mainvielle** .... (617) 994-8520
Grant Manager **Lynn M. Morrow** .... (603) 666-7510 ext. 3027
Grant Manager **Adam C. Ploetz** .... (617) 994-8351
Grant Manager **Laura B. Schiffer** .... (617) 994-8359
Grant Manager **Amy E. Yuhasz** .... (617) 994-8504

Office of Fair Housing
10 Causeway Street, Room 321, Boston, MA 02222-1092
Tel: (617) 994-8300 Tel: (617) 994-8335 (Hot Line, Complaints)
Tel: (800) 827-5005 (Hot Line, Complaints) Fax: (617) 565-7313

Boston Program Center Director **Robert D. Forti** .... (617) 994-8316
E-mail: robert.d.forti@hud.gov
Fair Housing Enforcement Branch Chief
Daniel Weaver .... (617) 994-8307
E-mail: daniel.j.weaver@hud.gov
Intake/Assessment Branch Chief **(Vacant)** .... (617) 994-8308
Program Compliance Branch Chief **(Vacant)** .... (617) 994-8305

Office of Public Housing
10 Causeway Street, Room 553, Boston, MA 02222-1092
Tel: (617) 994-8400 Fax: (617) 565-7305

Director **Marilyn B. O'Sullivan** .... (617) 994-8420
E-mail: marilyn.b.o'sullivan@hud.gov
Deputy Director **Robert P. Cwieka** .... (617) 994-8418
E-mail: robert_p._cwieka@hud.gov
Program Assistant **Hersh Goldman** .... (617) 994-8435
Program Assistant **Regina M. Johnston** .... (617) 994-8430
Program Analyst **Jennifer E. Hatch** .... (617) 994-8407
E-mail: jennifer.h.hatch@hud.gov

Production Division
10 Causeway Street, Room 301, Boston, MA 02222-1092
Tel: (617) 994-8500 Fax: (617) 565-6557

Director **Stacey Ashmore** .... (212) 542-7840
E-mail: stacey.l.ashmore@hud.gov

Asset Management Division
Director **Joseph A. "Joe" Crisafulli** .... (617) 994-8582
Account Executive Branch 1 Chief **Daniel J. Rogers** ..... (617) 994-8524
E-mail: daniel.j.rogers@hud.gov
Senior Project Manager **Paul Armstrong** .... (617) 994-8569
E-mail: paul.armstrong@hud.gov
Senior Project Manager **Loren Bernardi** .... (617) 994-8537
E-mail: loren.bernardi@hud.gov
Senior Project Manager **Teresa Cline** .... (617) 994-8534
Senior Project Manager **Kim Cuscuna** .... (617) 994-8527
Senior Project Manager **Nancy Gentile** .... (617) 994-8532
Senior Project Manager **Jerry Melillo** .... (617) 994-8550
Senior Project Manager **Warren Mroz** .... (617) 994-8543
Senior Project Manager **Elaine Ormond** .... (617) 994-8544
Senior Project Manager **Jim Polito** .... (617) 994-8515
Project Manager **Christopher J. Curran** .... (617) 994-8533
Project Manager **Winifred V. Day** .... (617) 994-8547
Project Manager **Kevin N. Elliott** .... (617) 994-8552

Asset Management Division *(continued)*

Project Manager **Lauren Hennessy** .... (617) 994-8548
Project Manager **Paul Krzewick** .... (617) 994-8551
Project Manager **Pamela Perry** .... (617) 994-8531
Construction Analyst **James Drazen** .... (617) 994-8565
Senior Architect **Guillermo Bahamon** .... (617) 994-8526

Administrative Service Center 1
Administrative Officer **Karen Zitnay** Room 365 .... (617) 994-8288
Labor Relations Specialist **Cedric Wright** Room 373 ..... (617) 994-8217

Bangor (ME) Field Office
202 Harlow Street, Room D20200, Bangor, ME 04401-4901
Tel: (207) 945-0467 TTY: (800) 877-8339 Fax: (207) 945-0533

Field Office Director **William D. Burney, Jr.** .... (207) 945-0467
E-mail: william.d.burney@hud.gov
Customer Service Representative **Ann C. Martin** .... (207) 945-0467
E-mail: ann.c.martin@hud.gov Fax: (207) 945-0533
Senior Management Analyst **(Vacant)** .... (207) 945-0469

Burlington (VT) Field Office
95 Saint Paul Street, Suite 440, Burlington, VT 05401-4486
Tel: (802) 951-6290 Fax: (802) 951-6298 TTY: (800) 877-8339

Field Office Director **Michael F. McNamara** ... (802) 951-6290 ext. 3004
E-mail: michael.f.mcnamara@hud.gov
Housing Program Specialist **(Vacant)** .... (802) 951-6290

Hartford (CT) Field Office
20 Church Street, Floor 10, Hartford, CT 06103-3220
Tel: (860) 240-4800 TTY: (800) 877-8339 Fax: (860) 240-4850

Field Office Director **Suzanne C. Piacentini** .... (860) 240-9702
E-mail: suzanne.piacentini@hud.gov
Administrative Officer **Thomas P. Bussiere** .... (860) 240-9765
E-mail: thomas.p.bussiere@hud.gov Fax: (860) 240-4853
Chief Counsel **(Vacant)** .... (860) 240-9731
Fax: (860) 240-4858
Senior Management Analyst **Stella Spyropoulos** .... (860) 240-9725
Senior Management Analyst **Marc J. Boucher** .... (860) 240-4818
Management Analyst **Carmen L. Rodriguez** .... (860) 240-9700
OIG/Connecticut State Senior Auditor
Kristen J. Ekmalian .... (860) 240-9744
E-mail: kekmalian@hudoig.gov Fax: (617) 565-6878
Office of Community Planning and Development
Director **Alanna Cavanagh Kabel** .... (860) 240-9770
Multifamily Program Center Director
Richard P. "Rick" Daugherty .... (860) 240-9720
E-mail: richard.p.daugherty@hud.gov Fax: (860) 240-4851
Public Housing Director **Jennifer R. Gottlieb-Elazhari** ... (860) 240-9757
E-mail: jennifer.r.gottlieb@hud.gov Fax: (860) 240-4854

Manchester (NH) Field Office
Norris Cotton Federal Building, 275 Chestnut Street,
4th Floor, Manchester, NH 03101
Tel: (603) 666-7510 TTY: (603) 666-7518 Fax: (603) 666-7667

Field Office Director **Gregory G. Carson** ...... (603) 666-7510 ext. 3016
E-mail: gregory.carson@hud.gov
Chief Counsel **(Vacant)** .... (603) 666-7510
Management Analyst **Jessica O'Meara** .... (603) 666-7510 ext. 3048
Multifamily Program Center Director **(Vacant)** .... (603) 666-7510
Faith-Based Liaison **(Vacant)** .... (617) 994-8216
10 Causeway Street, Boston, MA 02222-1092

Providence (RI) Field Office
Providence Field Office, One Weybosset Hill, 33 Broad Street,
Floor 4, Providence, RI 02903
Tel: (401) 277-8300 TTY: (401) 277-8391 Fax: (401) 277-8398

Field Office Director **Nancy D. Smith Greer** .... (401) 277-8301
E-mail: nancy.smithgreer@hud.gov
Chief Counsel **(Vacant)** .... (401) 277-8307
Management Analyst/Web Coordinator
Deborah B. Hall .... (401) 277-8303
E-mail: deborah.b.hall@hud.gov

★ Presidential Appointment Requiring Senate Confirmation ☆ Presidential Appointment ☐ Schedule C Appointment ◇ Career Senior Foreign Service Appointment
● Career Senior Executive Service (SES) Appointment ○ Non-Career Senior Executive Service (SES) Appointment ■ Postal Career Executive Service

Providence (RI) Field Office *(continued)*

Multifamily Program Center Director
Christine M. Keshura .... (401) 277-8322
E-mail: christine.m.keshura@hud.gov
Senior Project Manager **William F. Morales** .... (401) 277-8324
Project Manager **Colleen M. Judge** .... (401) 277-8321

Region II - New York - New Jersey

New York Regional Office

26 Federal Plaza, New York, NY 10278-0068
Tel: (212) 264-8000 TTY: (212) 264-0927 Fax: (212) 264-0246
Areas Covered: NJ, NY

□ Regional Administrator **Lynne M. Patton** .... (212) 542-7109
E-mail: lynne.m.patton@hud.gov
Education: Miami 1996 BA
Secretary **Angelique M. Urbina** .... (212) 542-7109
E-mail: angelique.m.urbina@hud.gov
Senior Advisor **Stephen E. Murphy** .... (212) 542-7111
E-mail: stephen.e.murphy@hud.gov
Senior Management Analyst **Angela Aloia** .... (212) 542-7162
Deputy Regional Administrator (Acting)
Stephen E. Murphy .... (212) 542-7111
E-mail: stephen.e.murphy@hud.gov
Public Affairs Officer **Charles E. McNally** .... (212) 542-7647
E-mail: charles.e.mcnally@hud.gov
Public Affairs Officer **Olga R. Alvarez** .... (212) 542-7142
E-mail: olga.r.alvarez@hud.gov
Regional Faith-Based Coordinator **Earleene A. Sealy** .... (212) 542-7152
E-mail: earleene.a.sealy@hud.gov
Supervisory Management Analyst [FOIA Public Liaison] **Marvin Adam Glantz** .... (212) 542-7158
Operations Specialist and Co-op Coordinator
Henry Comas .... (212) 542-7116
Operations Specialist and Homeless Coordinator
Samuel E. Miller .... (212) 542-7144
Operations Specialist and FOIA Liaison
Maria Cestaro .... (212) 542-7537
E-mail: maria.cestaro@hud.gov
Operations Analyst **Eileen Rivera** .... (212) 542-7101
Customer Service Representative **Curtis Houston** .... (212) 542-7170
Senior Management Analyst **Justin Scheid** .... (212) 542-7146
□ Advisor **Barbara Gruson** .... (212) 542-7342
E-mail: barbara.gruson@hud.gov
Contractor Industrial Relations Specialist
Loretta Franco .... (212) 542-7160
E-mail: loretta.franco@hud.gov
Contractor Industrial Relations Specialist **Cory Chu** .... (212) 542-7148
E-mail: cory.chu@hud.gov

Office of Counsel

26 Federal Plaza, New York, NY 10278-0068
Fax: (212) 246-8000
Regional Counsel **Ventura Simmons** .... (212) 542-7204
E-mail: ventura.a.simmons@hud.gov

Office of Inspector General

26 Federal Plaza, New York, NY 10278-0068
New York/New Jersey District Inspector General for Audit **(Vacant)** .... (212) 542-9784
Fax: (212) 264-1400
New York/New Jersey Special Agent-in-Charge
(Vacant) .... (212) 542-7955
Fax: (212) 264-4933

Office of the Chief Procurement Officer

26 Federal Plaza, New York, NY 10278-0068
Director **(Vacant)** .... (212) 542-7310
Fax: (212) 264-8521

Office of Community Planning and Development

26 Federal Plaza, New York, NY 10278-0068
Fax: (212) 264-0993
Director **Vincent Hom** .... (212) 542-7401
E-mail: vincent.hom@hud.gov
Deputy Director **Nicholas J. Andreo** .... (212) 542-7421
E-mail: Nicholas.J.Andreo@hud.gov

Office of Fair Housing and Equal Opportunity

26 Federal Plaza, Room 3532, New York, NY 10278-0068
Tel: (212) 542-7519 TTY: (212) 264-0927 Fax: (212) 264-9829
New York Fair Housing and Equal Opportunity Region II Director **Jay Golden** .... (212) 542-7507
E-mail: jay.golden@hud.gov
New York Fair Housing and Equal Opportunity Center Director **Jo Antoinette Frey** .... (212) 542-7527
E-mail: jo-ann.frey@hud.gov
Intake Branch Chief **(Vacant)** .... (212) 542-7536
Program Compliance Branch Chief
Natasha M. Saxton .... (212) 542-7512
E-mail: natasha.saxton@hud.gov
Equal Opportunity Specialist **Jennifer Liebman** .... (212) 542-7518
E-mail: jennifer.m.liebman@hud.gov
Education: Sarah Lawrence 2001 BA; Chicago 2002 MA; Illinois 2007 JD

Office of Field Administrative Resources

26 Federal Plaza, New York, NY 10278-0068
Fax: (312) 353-0121
Director **Lisa T. Surplus** .... (212) 542-7331
77 West Jackson Boulevard, Chicago, IL 60604-3507 Fax: (212) 542-7330
E-mail: lisa_t._surplus@hud.gov
Deputy Director **(Vacant)** .... (212) 264-8000
Human Resources Division Director **(Vacant)** .... (312) 913-8533
77 West Jackson Boulevard, Chicago, IL 60604-3507
Information Technology Division Director
Raymond Y. Chan .... (212) 542-7373
E-mail: raymond.y.chan@hud.gov Fax: (212) 264-2398

Office of Housing

26 Federal Plaza, New York, NY 10278-0068
Tel: (212) 542-7701 Fax: (212) 264-2281
Director, New York Multifamily HUB
Arden A. Sokolow .... (212) 542-7701
E-mail: arden.a.sokolow@hud.gov
Operations Division Director **Brett Wise** .... (212) 542-7888
E-mail: brett.wise@hud.gov
Asset Management Director **Dean J. Santa** .... (212) 542-7821
E-mail: dean.j.santa@hud.gov
Production Division Director **Stacey L. Ashmore** .... (212) 542-7840
Information Specialist **James Shelton** .... (212) 542-7716
Education: North Carolina Asheville 2011 BA

Office of Public Housing

26 Federal Plaza, New York, NY 10278-0068
Fax: (212) 542-7680
Director **Luigi D'Ancona** .... (212) 542-7649
Fax: (212) 542-7680
Quality Assurance Team Director
Cynthia M. McKnight .... (212) 542-7615
E-mail: cynthia.m.mcknight@hud.gov
Housing Management Division Director
Christopher J. Ingram .... (212) 542-7642
Planning and Analysis Division Director
Carmen M. Rivera .... (212) 542-7638
E-mail: carmen.m.rivera@hud.gov
Technical Services Division Director **Suen Ping Yip** .... (212) 542-7610

Albany (NY) Field Office

52 Corporate Circle, Albany, NY 12203-5121
Tel: (518) 862-2804 Fax: (518) 464-4300
Field Office Director (Acting)
James C. Brylinski .... (716) 551-5755 ext. 5200
E-mail: james.c.brylinski@hud.gov

(continued on next page)

★ Presidential Appointment Requiring Senate Confirmation ☆ Presidential Appointment □ Schedule C Appointment ◇ Career Senior Foreign Service Appointment
● Career Senior Executive Service (SES) Appointment ○ Non-Career Senior Executive Service (SES) Appointment ■ Postal Career Executive Service

Albany (NY) Field Office *(continued)*

Administrative Officer **Patricia E. Warn** . . . . (518) 862-2808
E-mail: patricia.e.warn@hud.gov
New York/New Jersey District Inspector
General for Audit **(Vacant)** . . . . (518) 464-4200 ext. 2892
Fax: (518) 464-4397

Albany Financial Operations Center Director
Michael C. DeMarco . . . . (518) 862-2859
E-mail: michael.demarco@hud.gov Fax: (518) 485-9035
Asset Recovery Division Director **Brian M. Dillon** . . . . . (518) 862-2819
Fax: (518) 485-9035

Insurance Operations Director **Patrick W. Porter** . . . . (518) 862-2881
E-mail: patrick.w.porter@hud.gov Fax: (518) 485-9035

Buffalo (NY) Area Office
Lafayette Court, 465 Main Street, 2nd Floor, Buffalo, NY 14203-1780
Tel: (716) 551-5755 TTY: (716) 551-5787 Fax: (716) 551-5752
Internet: www.hud.gov

Field Office Director (Acting)
James C. Brylinski . . . . (716) 551-5755 ext. 5200
E-mail: james.c.brylinski@hud.gov
Chief Counsel **James C. Brylinski** . . . . (716) 551-5755 ext. 5200
E-mail: james.c.brylinksi@hud.gov
Chief Economist **(Vacant)** . . . . (716) 551-5755 ext. 5004
Labor Relations Specialist **Gary J. Kinsel** . . . . . (716) 551-5755 ext. 5003
E-mail: gary.j.kinsel@hud.gov

Office of Inspector General
465 Main Street, Buffalo, NY 14203-1780
Fax: (716) 551-3179

Buffalo Area District Inspector General for
Audit **Paul Zausen** . . . . (716) 551-5755 ext. 5900
E-mail: paul.zausen@hud.gov
Buffalo Area Special Agent-in-Charge **(Vacant)** . . . . (716) 551-5755

Community Planning and Development Division
465 Main Street, Buffalo, NY 14203-1780
Fax: (716) 551-5634

Director **William T. O'Connell** . . . . (716) 551-5755 ext. 5800
E-mail: william.t.oconnell@hud.gov
Program Manager **Kenneth R. Naples** . . . . (716) 551-5755 ext. 5815

Fair Housing and Equal Opportunity
465 Main Street, Buffalo, NY 14203-1780
Fax: (716) 551-5171

Director **Andrij O. Pryshlak** . . . . (716) 551-5755 ext. 5600
E-mail: andrij.pryshlak@hud.gov

Multifamily Housing
465 Main Street, Buffalo, NY 14203-1780
Fax: (716) 551-3252

Chief, Account Executive Branch
Laurie Beardi . . . . (716) 551-5755 ext. 5522
E-mail: laurie.a.beardi@hud.gov
Education: Medaille 2000 BS

Office of Public Housing
465 Main Street, Buffalo, NY 14203-1780
Fax: (716) 551-4789

Director **Lisa Pugliese** . . . . (716) 551-5755 ext. 5400
E-mail: lisa.m.pugliese@hud.gov

Newark (NJ) Field Office
One Newark Center, 1085 Raymond Boulevard,
13th Floor, Newark, NJ 07102-5260
Tel: (973) 776-7310 TTY: (973) 645-3298 Fax: (973) 645-6423
Internet: www.hud.gov/local/njn/

Field Office Director **Maria Maio-Messano** . . . . (973) 776-7310
E-mail: maria.m.messano@hud.gov
Chief Counsel **Shie-Fong Sun** . . . . (973) 776-7325
E-mail: shie-fong.sun@hud.gov
Environmental Specialist **Michael R. Furda** . . . . (973) 776-7310
E-mail: michael.r.furda@hud.gov
Labor Relations Specialist **David J. Bosakowski** . . . . (973) 776-7310

Newark (NJ) Field Office *(continued)*

Operations Specialist **Alan Gelfand** . . . . (973) 776-7310
E-mail: alan.gelfand@hud.gov

Community Planning and Development
1085 Raymond Boulevard, Newark, NJ 07102-5260

Director **Annemarie C. Uebbing** . . . . (973) 776-7288
E-mail: annemarie.c.uebbing@hud.gov

Housing
1085 Raymond Boulevard, Newark, NJ 07102-5260

Director **Mary Ann Diak-Stern** . . . . (973) 622-7900 ext. 7257
Single Family Marketing Representative
Stuart S. Mindes . . . . (973) 622-7900 ext. 7361
E-mail: stuart.s.mindes@hud.gov

Office of Public Housing
1085 Raymond Boulevard, Newark, NJ 07102-5260

Director **Theresa L. Arce** . . . . (973) 776-7250
E-mail: theresa.l.arce@hud.gov

Region III - Mid-Atlantic

Philadelphia Regional Office

The Wanamaker Building, 100 Penn Square East,
Philadelphia, PA 19107-3380
Tel: (215) 656-0500 TTY: (800) 877-8339 Fax: (215) 656-3433
Areas Covered: DE, DC, MD, PA, VA, WV

□ Regional Administrator **Joseph J. "Joe" DeFelice** . . . . . . (215) 430-6635
E-mail: joseph.j.defelice@hud.gov Fax: (215) 656-3445
Executive Secretary **Shana Robinson** . . . . (215) 430-6632
E-mail: shana.robinson@hud.gov
□ Senior Advisor **Elvis Solivan** . . . . (215) 861-7565
Deputy Regional Administrator **Richard M. Ott** . . . . (215) 430-6621
E-mail: richard.m.ott@hud.gov
Regional Labor Relations Officer **Debra Bensala** . . . . (215) 430-6648
E-mail: debra.bensala@hud.gov Fax: (215) 430-6764
Regional Public Affairs Specialist **Nika V. Edwards** . . . . . (215) 430-6622
E-mail: nika.v.edwards@hud.gov
Regional Public Affairs Specialist
Sheppard V. Williams . . . . (215) 861-6628
E-mail: sheppard.williams@hud.gov
Regional Public Affairs Specialist **Lisa A. Wolfe** . . . . (215) 430-6640
E-mail: lisa.a.wolfe@hud.gov

Office of the Chief Procurement Officer
100 Penn Square East, Philadelphia, PA 19107-3380

Northern Field Contracting Operations Director
Shelli J. Waltz . . . . (215) 430-6721
E-mail: shelli.j.waltz@hud.gov Fax: (215) 656-3453
Small Business Specialist **Patrick "Pat" McQuoid** . . . . . . (215) 656-0674

Office of Counsel
100 Penn Square East, Philadelphia, PA 19107-3380

Regional Counsel **Sheryl L. Johnson** . . . . (215) 430-6655
E-mail: sheryl.johnson@hud.gov Fax: (215) 401-2115
Deputy Regional Counsel **Sonya M. Kaloyanides** . . . . (215) 430-6671
E-mail: sonya.m.kaloyanides@hud.gov Fax: (215) 656-3446

Office of Inspector General
100 Penn Square East, Philadelphia, PA 19107-3380
Tel: (215) 656-0500 Fax: (215) 656-3409

Regional Inspector General for Audit
Dave Kasperowicz . . . . (215) 430-6730
E-mail: dkasperowicz@hudoig.gov
Special Agent-in-Charge **Bertrand N. Nelson** . . . . (215) 430-6756

Office of Community Planning and Development
100 Penn Square East, Philadelphia, PA 19107-3380
Tel: (215) 656-0500 Fax: (215) 656-3442

Director **Nadab O. Bynum** . . . . (215) 861-7652
Economic Development Specialist **Andrea Edwards** . . . . . (215) 861-7658
E-mail: andrea.edwards@hud.gov

★ Presidential Appointment Requiring Senate Confirmation ☆ Presidential Appointment □ Schedule C Appointment ◇ Career Senior Foreign Service Appointment
● Career Senior Executive Service (SES) Appointment ○ Non-Career Senior Executive Service (SES) Appointment ■ Postal Career Executive Service

Office of Community Planning and Development *(continued)*

Environmental Officer **Paul J. Lehmann** . . . . (215) 430-6636
E-mail: paul.j.lehmann@hud.gov
Financial Analyst **Stephanie W Satiah** . . . . (215) 861-7653
E-mail: stephanie.w.satiah@hud.gov
Healthy Homes Representative **Edward Thomas** . . . . (215) 861-7670
Program Manager **David M. Collins** . . . . (215) 861-7659
E-mail: david.m.collins@hud.gov
Program Manager **Mandy Wampler** . . . . (215) 861-7664
E-mail: mandy.wampler@hud.gov
Relocation Specialist **Michael Szupper** . . . . (215) 861-7669
E-mail: michael.szupper@hud.gov
CPD Representative **Crystal I. Edwards** . . . . (215) 861-7657

Office of Fair Housing and Equal Opportunity - Philadelphia Hub
100 Penn Square East, Philadelphia, PA 19107-3380
Tel: (215) 861-7646 TTY: (215) 656-3450
Tel: (888) 799-2085 (Fair Housing Hotline) Fax: (215) 656-3449

Director **Melody C. Taylor** . . . . (215) 861-7643
E-mail: melody.c.taylor@hud.gov
Intake/Assessment Branch Chief **(Vacant)** . . . . (215) 861-7622
Enforcement Branch Chief **Roberto H. Chavez** . . . . (215) 861-7625
E-mail: roberto.h.chavez@hud.gov
Philadelphia Center Director **Barbara R. Delaney** . . . . (215) 861-7637
E-mail: barbara.r.delaney@hud.gov

Office of Public Housing
100 Penn Square East, Philadelphia, PA 19107-3380
Tel: (215) 656-0500 Fax: (215) 656-3442

Director **Monica A. Hawkins** . . . . (215) 861-7593
E-mail: monica.a.hawkins@hud.gov
Division A Director **(Vacant)** . . . . (215) 656-0500
Division B Director **Judith "Judy" Axler** . . . . (215) 861-7604
E-mail: judith.r.axler@hud.gov

Administrative Service Center 1 - New York and Chicago
100 Penn Square East, Philadelphia, PA 19107-3380

Regional Support Manager **Antoinette Perry Banks** . . . . . (215) 430-6705
E-mail: antoinette.p.banks@hud.gov Fax: (215) 656-3433
Human Resources Staff Coordinator **(Vacant)** . . . . (215) 430-6640
Fax: (215) 656-3437
IT Field Service Delivery Manager **Debbie Jankowski** . . . (215) 430-6689
E-mail: debbie.jankowski@hud.gov Fax: (215) 656-3499
Education: Rutgers 1985 BEc;
St Joseph's U 1990 MBA

Philadelphia Single Family Homeownership Center
100 Penn Square East, Philadelphia, PA 19107-3380
Tel: (800) 225-5342 Fax: (215) 656-3456

Director **Julie Shaffer** . . . . (800) 225-5342
E-mail: julie.shaffer@hud.gov
Deputy Director **Anthony Triolo** . . . . (215) 861-7252
E-mail: anthony.triolo@hud.gov
Director, Operations and Customer Service Division
Chris Boguslaw . . . . (215) 861-7241
Processing and Underwriting Division Director
Andrew D. "Andy" Cianci . . . . (215) 861-7687
E-mail: andrew.cianci@hud.gov Fax: (215) 656-3436
Insuring and Underwriting Branch 1 Chief
Debbie Maldonado . . . . (215) 861-7276
E-mail: deborah.maldonad@hud.gov
Insuring and Underwriting Branch 2 Chief
Joyce R. Jones . . . . (215) 861-7519
E-mail: joyce.r.jones@hud.gov
Insuring and Underwriting Branch 3 Chief
John J. Phillips . . . . (215) 430-7298
E-mail: john.j.phillips@hud.gov
Insuring and Underwriting Branch 4 Chief
Charles J. Anderson . . . . (215) 861-7281
E-mail: charles.j.anderson@hud.gov
Processing and Underwriting Division Technical
Branch 1 Chief **Michael H. McArdle** . . . . (215) 861-7689
E-mail: michael.h.mcardle@hud.gov

Philadelphia Single Family Homeownership Center *(continued)*

Processing and Underwriting Division Technical
Branch 2 Chief **Krish Raja** . . . . (215) 861-7539
E-mail: krish.raja@hud.gov
Program Support Division Director
Elizabeth M. Cahall . . . . (215) 861-7236
E-mail: elizabeth.cahall@hud.gov Fax: (215) 656-3443
Quality Assurance Division Director (Acting)
Andy V. DiPietro . . . . (215) 861-7220
E-mail: andy.v.dipietro@hud.gov Fax: (215) 656-3457
Field Review Branch 1 Chief (Acting)
Joyce Tate Cech . . . . (215) 861-7225
Field Review Branch 2 Chief **Patricia Peiffer** . . . . (215) 861-7209
E-mail: patricia.peiffer@hud.gov
Field Review Branch 3 Chief **John F. Van de Zilver** . . . (215) 861-7226
E-mail: john.f.vandezilver@hud.gov
Real Estate Owned Division Director **Michael Curry** . . . . . (215) 861-7181
E-mail: michael.j.curry@hud.gov Fax: (215) 656-3491
Real Estate Owned Compliance Branch Chief
Valerie I. McCoy . . . . (215) 861-7230
E-mail: valerie.l.mccoy@hud.gov
Real Estate Owned Marketing Branch Chief
David B. Marshall . . . . (215) 861-7193
E-mail: david.b.marshall@hud.gov
Real Estate Owned Property Maintenance Branch
Chief **John Thress** . . . . (215) 861-7193
E-mail: john.thress@hud.gov
Management Analyst **Richard J. Young** . . . . (215) 861-7693

Philadelphia Multifamily Hub
100 Penn Square East, Philadelphia, PA 19107-3380
Tel: (215) 656-0500 Fax: (215) 656-3427

Director **(Vacant)** . . . . (212) 542-7701
26 Federal Plaza, New York, NY 10278-0068
Branch Chief **Randall J. Scheetz** . . . . (215) 861-7576
Operations Division Director **(Vacant)** . . . . (215) 861-7565
Project Management Director **(Vacant)** . . . . (215) 861-7556
Senior Project Manager **(Vacant)** . . . . (215) 430-6717
Contract Administration Oversight Monitor
Carolyn M. Anastasi . . . . (215) 861-7551
E-mail: carolyn.m.anastasi@hud.gov
Information Specialist **(Vacant)** . . . . (215) 861-7555
Development and Production, Appraiser **(Vacant)** . . . . (215) 861-7578
Performance-Based Contract Monitoring, Senior Project
Manager **Nunzia A. "Nancy" Luberto** . . . . (215) 861-7577
E-mail: nunzia.a.luberto@hud.gov

Baltimore (MD) Field Office
City Crescent Building, 10 South Howard Street,
5th Floor, Baltimore, MD 21201-2505
Tel: (410) 962-2520 TTY: (410) 209-6681 Fax: (410) 209-6671
Internet: www.hud.gov/local/bal

Field Office Director **Carol Bryant Payne** . . . . (410) 209-6557
Fax: (410) 209-6670
Regional Support Manager **Antoinette Perry Banks** . . . (410) 209-6527
E-mail: antoinette.p.banks@hud.gov
Chief Counsel **Sorella Jacobs** . . . . (410) 209-6598
E-mail: sorella.jacobs@hud.gov
Environmental Officer **Susanne A. Sotirchos** . . . . (410) 209-6546
E-mail: suzanne.a.sotirchos@hud.gov
Management Analyst **Patrick R. Wallis** . . . . (410) 209-6587

Community Planning and Development Division
10 South Howard Street, Baltimore, MD 21201-2505
Fax: (410) 209-6672

Director **Charles E. Halm** . . . . (410) 209-6541
E-mail: charles.e.halm@hud.gov
Program Assistant **(Vacant)** . . . . (410) 962-2520

Fair Housing and Equal Opportunity Program Center
10 South Howard Street, Baltimore, MD 21201-2505
Tel: (410) 209-6640 Fax: (410) 209-6673

Director **Debra E. McGhee** . . . . (410) 209-6562
E-mail: debra.e.mcghee@hud.gov

(continued on next page)

DEPARTMENTS

Fair Housing and Equal Opportunity Program Center *(continued)*

Program Compliance Branch Chief **Rachel L. Leach** ..... (410) 209-6548
Fax: (410) 209-6673

Multifamily Northeast Region Baltimore Satellite Office
10 South Howard Street, Baltimore, MD 21201-2505
Fax: (410) 209-6675

Asset Management Division Director - Satellite Coordinator **Brenda J. Brown** ..... (410) 209-6510
E-mail: brenda.j.brown@hud.gov Fax: (410) 209-6675
Account Executive Branch Chief **Judith Parker** ..... (410) 209-6569
Resolution Specialist Branch Chief **Lisa C. Ellis** ..... (410) 209-6505
Technical Specialist Branch Chief **Richard M. Harding** ... (410) 209-6524
Underwriting Branch Chief **Yvette B. Jackson** ..... (410) 209-6550

Public Housing Program Hub
10 South Howard Street, Baltimore, MD 21201-2505

Director **William D. Tamburrino** ..... (410) 209-6595
E-mail: william.d.tamburrino@hud.gov
Division Director **Russell L. Desouza** ..... (410) 209-6522
E-mail: russell.l.desouza@hud.gov Fax: (410) 209-6678

Charleston (WV) Field Office
414 Summers Street, Suite 110, Charleston, WV 25301
Tel: (304) 347-7000 TTY: (304) 347-5332 Fax: (304) 347-7050

Field Office Director **Julie A. Alston** ..... (304) 347-7402
E-mail: julie.a.alston@hud.gov
Chief Information Officer (Acting) **Julie A. Alston** ..... (304) 347-7402
E-mail: julie.a.alston@hud.gov
Support Services Specialist **Charlotte Rose Puryear** ... (304) 347-7044
E-mail: charlotte.rose.puryear@hud.gov
Fair Housing Division Equal Opportunity Specialist **(Vacant)** ..... (304) 347-7020

District of Columbia Field Office
820 First Street, NE, Suite 300, Washington, DC 20002-4205
Tel: (202) 275-9200 TTY: (202) 275-0772 Fax: (202) 275-6381
E-mail: dc_webmanager@hud.gov

Field Office Director **Marvin W. Turner** ..... (202) 275-9200
E-mail: marvin.w.turner@hud.gov
Chief Counsel **Russell S. Conlan** ..... (202) 275-9200 ext. 6270
E-mail: russell.s.conlan@hud.gov
Administrative Officer **(Vacant)** ..... (202) 275-9200 ext. 6297
Fax: (202) 275-0779
Management Analyst **Belinda Fadlelmola** ..... (202) 275-6280
Management Analyst **Lorraine Richardson** ..... (202) 275-6274
Customer Service Representative **Janice Everett** ..... (202) 275-6360

Community Planning and Development Division
820 First Street, NE, Washington, DC 20002-4205
Tel: (202) 275-9200 ext. 6266 Fax: (202) 275-4190

Director **Michael D. Rose** ..... (202) 275-6266
E-mail: michael.rose@hud.gov

Fair Housing and Equal Opportunity - Program Operations and Compliance Office
820 First Street, NE, Washington, DC 20002-4205
Tel: (202) 275-2987 Fax: (202) 275-6387

Director **Steven M. Paikin** ..... (202) 275-6305
E-mail: steven.m.paikin@hud.gov

Housing
820 First Street, NE, Washington, DC 20002-4205

Multifamily Program Center **Robert J. Ford** ..... (202) 275-6273
E-mail: Robert.J.Ford@hud.gov Fax: (202) 275-6382
Single Family Marketing and Outreach Supervisor **Colleen A. Weiser** ..... (202) 275-6288
Education: Cal State (Northridge) 1980 MA

Office of Public Housing
820 First Street, NE, Washington, DC 20002-4205
Tel: (202) 275-9200 Fax: (202) 275-6690

Director **Christine Jenkins** ..... (202) 275-6306
E-mail: christine.jenkins@hud.gov
Regional Public Housing Director **Debra Torres** ..... (216) 357-7785

Pittsburgh (PA) Field Office
1000 Liberty Avenue, Pittsburgh, PA 15222
Tel: (412) 644-5846 TTY: (866) 592-3875 Fax: (412) 644-6499

Field Office Director **Jane E. Miller** ..... (412) 644-6436
E-mail: jane.e.miller@hud.gov Fax: (412) 644-4240
Education: Duquesne 1979 BS
Regional Support Manager **Antoinette Perry Banks** ..... (410) 209-6529
E-mail: antoinette.p.banks@hud.gov
Chief Counsel **Sarah Pietragallo JD** ..... (412) 644-6414
E-mail: sarah.g.pietragallo@hud.gov Fax: (412) 644-6893
Education: Kenyon 1997 BA; Columbus Law 2002 JD
Pittsburgh Area District Inspector General for Audit **Chandra Dey** ..... (412) 644-6372
E-mail: cdey@hudoig.gov Fax: (412) 644-4589
Education: Siena Col 1979 BA
Pittsburgh Area Special Agent-in-Charge **William J. Foley** ..... (412) 644-6598 ext. 1
E-mail: wfoley@hud.gov Fax: (412) 644-4589
Education: Pittsburgh 1988 BA
Community Planning and Development Office Director **John E. Tolbert III** ..... (412) 644-5846
E-mail: john.e.tolbert@hud.gov
Education: Pittsburgh 1981 MA
Fair Housing and Equal Opportunity Program Director **(Vacant)** ..... (412) 644-5846
Senior Account Executive **Gary Possage** ..... (412) 644-6399
E-mail: gary.o.passage@hud.gov Fax: (412) 644-5872
Senior Account Executive **(Vacant)** ..... (412) 644-5846
Public Housing Director **Jacqueline A. Molinaro-Thompson** ..... (412) 644-6529
E-mail: j.molinarothompson@hud.gov Fax: (412) 644-5486
Education: Duquesne 1981 BS

Richmond (VA) Field Office
600 East Broad Street, 3rd Floor, Richmond, VA 23219-1800
Tel: (800) 842-2610 TTY: (800) 877-8339 Fax: (804) 822-4807
Internet: www.hud.gov/virginia

Field Office Director **Carrie S. Schmidt** ..... (800) 842-2610
Chief Counsel **Brad E. Rader** ..... (804) 822-4814
E-mail: brad.e.rader@hud.gov
Community Planning and Development Division Director **Ronnie J. Legette** ..... (804) 822-4831
Virginia Multifamily Program Center Director **(Vacant)** ... (800) 842-2610
Multifamily Production Chief **(Vacant)** ..... (800) 842-2610
Single Family Division Supervisory Housing Program Officer **(Vacant)** ..... (800) 842-2610
Public Housing Office Director (Acting) **Catherine D. Lamberg** ..... (804) 822-4898
E-mail: catherine.d.lamberg@hud.gov Fax: (804) 771-2264
Senior Single Family Housing Specialist **Virginia F. Holman** ..... (804) 771-2100 ext. 4911
E-mail: virginia.f.holman@hud.gov Fax: (804) 771-2296
Environmental Protection Specialist **Kerry Johnson** ..... (804) 771-2100 ext. 4803
E-mail: kerry.johnson@hud.gov
Senior Management Analyst **Anne Davis** ..... (804) 822-4802
E-mail: anne.davis@hud.gov
Senior Management Analyst **Toni D. Schmiegelow** ..... (804) 822-4925
Labor Relations Specialist **(Vacant)** ..... (804) 771-2100 ext. 4606
Multifamily Quality Assurance Officer **(Vacant)** ..... (804) 771-2100 ext. 4845
Fax: (804) 771-2296

Fair Housing and Equal Opportunity Director/Government Technical Representative (Acting) **Steven M. Paikin** ..... (804) 822-4837
E-mail: steven.m.paikin@hud.gov

★ Presidential Appointment Requiring Senate Confirmation ☆ Presidential Appointment ☐ Schedule C Appointment ◇ Career Senior Foreign Service Appointment
● Career Senior Executive Service (SES) Appointment ○ Non-Career Senior Executive Service (SES) Appointment ■ Postal Career Executive Service

Richmond (VA) Field Office *(continued)*

Inspector General/Virginia State Special
Agent-in-Charge **(Vacant)** . . . . (804) 771-2100 ext. 4891
Fax: (804) 771-2065

Wilmington (DE) Field Office
One Rodney Square, 920 King Street, Suite 404, Wilmington, DE 19801
Tel: (302) 573-6300 Fax: (302) 573-6259

Field Office Director **Maria L. Bynum** . . . . (302) 573-6300
E-mail: maria.l.bynum@hud.gov
Education: Hampton 1982 BA
Senior Management Analyst **(Vacant)** . . . . (302) 573-6300
Customer Service Representative **David A. Sillery** . . . . (302) 573-6300

Region IV - Southeast

Atlanta Regional Office
Five Points Plaza Building, 40 Marietta Street, NW, Atlanta, GA 30303
Tel: (404) 331-5136 TTY: (404) 730-2654 Fax: (404) 730-2392
Areas Covered: AL, FL, GA, KY, MS, NC, PR, SC, TN

○ Regional Administrator **Denise C. Cleveland-Leggett** . . . (404) 331-5001
E-mail: denise.c.cleveland-leggett@hud.gov
Deputy Regional Administrator **Christopher D. Taylor** . . . (678) 732-2009
400 West Bay Street, Jacksonville, FL 32202
E-mail: christopher.d.taylor@hud.gov
Administrative Assistant **Donald E. Wooten** . . . . . . (678) 732-2009
E-mail: donald.e.wooten@hud.gov
Atlanta Field Office Director **Luis Rolle** . . . . (305) 536-4456
Fax: (305) 536-5765
Economic and Market Analysis Director
Charles P. Hugghins . . . . (678) 732-2033
E-mail: charles.p.hugghins@hud.gov
Labor Relations Director **(Vacant)** . . . . (678) 732-2041
Senior Public Affairs Specialist
[Webmaster] **Joseph J. "Joe" Phillips** . . . . . . (678) 732-2943 ext. 2017
E-mail: joseph.j.phillips@hud.gov Fax: (404) 730-2365
□ Supervisor Management Analyst **(Vacant)** . . . . (404) 331-5136
Supervisory Environmental Officer **Sandra L. Frye** . . . . . . (678) 732-2727
E-mail: Sandra.L.Frye@hud.gov
Training Officer **(Vacant)** . . . . (404) 331-5001 ext. 2192
Fax: (404) 730-9415
Training Officer **(Vacant)** . . . . (404) 331-4111

Office of Counsel
40 Marietta Street, NW, Atlanta, GA 30303
Fax: (404) 730-3315

Regional Counsel **Sharon M. Swain** . . . . (678) 732-2646
E-mail: sharon.m.swain@hud.gov
Deputy Regional General Counsel **(Vacant)** . . . . (404) 331-5001 ext. 2023
Civil Rights Associate Field Counsel
(Vacant) . . . . (404) 331-5001 ext. 2078
Litigation and Administrative Law Associate
Field Counsel **(Vacant)** . . . . (404) 331-5001 ext. 2171
Program Enforcement Associate Field
Counsel **(Vacant)** . . . . (404) 331-5001 ext. 2025
Program Services Associate Field Counsel
Dhoya Z. Bentley . . . . (404) 331-5001 ext. 2020
E-mail: dhoya.z.bentley@hud.gov

Office of Community Planning and Development
40 Marietta Street, NW, Atlanta, GA 30303
Tel: (404) 331-5001 Fax: (404) 331-6997

Director **Rufus Washington** . . . . (678) 732-2545
E-mail: rufus.washington@hud.gov
Program Manager **Stephen F. Hand** . . . . (678) 732-2950
E-mail: stephen.f.hand@hud.gov

Office of Fair Housing and Equal Opportunity
40 Marietta Street, NW, Atlanta, GA 30303
Tel: (404) 331-5140 TTY: (404) 730-2654 Tel: (800) 440-8091

Atlanta Hub Director **Natasha J. Watson** . . . . (678) 732-2163
E-mail: natasha.j.watson@hud.gov Fax: (404) 331-4069
Atlanta FHEO Center Director **(Vacant)** . . . . (678) 732-2163
Fax: (404) 331-4069

Office of Fair Housing and Equal Opportunity *(continued)*

Enforcement Branch Chief **(Vacant)** . . . . (404) 331-5001
Intake/Assess Branch Chief **(Vacant)** . . . . (404) 331-5001 ext. 2475
Program Operations Branch Chief **(Vacant)** . . . . (404) 331-5001 ext. 2496

Office of Inspector General
Richard B. Russell Federal Building, 75 Spring Street, SW,
Atlanta, GA 30303
Tel: (404) 331-5001

Southeast/Caribbean Inspector General for
Audit **Gregory Johnson** . . . . (404) 331-5001 ext. 2392
E-mail: Gregory.Johnson@hud.gov Fax: (404) 730-2382
Southeast/Caribbean Special Agent-in-Charge **(Vacant)** . . . (678) 732-2514
Fax: (404) 331-1243

Office of Public Housing
40 Marietta Street, NW, Atlanta, GA 30303
Tel: (678) 732-2258 Tel: (404) 331-4138 (Planning and Analysis Staff)
Fax: (404) 331-1022

Director **Ada H. Holloway** . . . . (404) 331-5001 ext. 2516
E-mail: ada.h.holloway@hud.gov
Regional Public Housing Director **Ellis Henry** . . . . (904) 208-6093
Operations Director **Clamentine V. Melvin** . . . . (404) 331-4766 ext. 2511
E-mail: clamentine.v.melvin@hud.gov
Technical Director **(Vacant)** . . . . (404) 331-5001
Financial Analyst **Jorge L. Torres** . . . . (404) 331-4888 ext. 3442
E-mail: jorge.l.torres@hud.gov

Atlanta Homeownership Center
40 Marietta Street, NW, Atlanta, GA 30303
Tel: (404) 331-1263 Fax: (404) 730-2364

Director **N. Daniel Rogers III** . . . . (404) 331-1263 ext. 2359
E-mail: dan.rogersiii@hud.gov
Deputy Director **Glenn Dumont** . . . . (404) 331-1263 ext. 2674
E-mail: glenn.l.dumont@hud.gov
Operations and Customer Service Division
Director **Yvielle Edwards-Lee** . . . . (404) 331-1263 ext. 2380
Columbia (SC) Customer Service Branch #1 Chief
Cynthia G. Lowery . . . . (803) 765-5847
E-mail: cynthia.g.lowery@hud.gov
Process and Underwriting Division Director
Valerie D. Williams . . . . (404) 331-1263 ext. 2784
E-mail: valerie.d.williams@hud.gov
Insurance and Underwriting Branch #1 Chief
Linn Lawrence . . . . (678) 732-2657
E-mail: linn.lawrence@hud.gov
Insurance and Underwriting Branch #2 Chief
Agustin Mujica . . . . (678) 732-2707
E-mail: agustin.mujica@hud.gov
Technical Support Branch #1 Chief
Malcolm Jefferson . . . . (404) 331-1263 ext. 2340
E-mail: malcolm.jefferson@hud.gov
Technical Support Branch #2 Chief
Carl E. Heckman . . . . (404) 331-1263 ext. 2687
E-mail: carl.e.heckman@hud.gov
Program Support Division Director
Gayle F. Knowlson . . . . (404) 331-1263 ext. 2345
E-mail: gayle.f.knowlson@hud.gov
Program Support Branch Director –
Marketing, Education and Outreach
Daniel Patrick Ellis . . . . (404) 331-1263 ext. 2696
E-mail: daniel.patrick.ellis@hud.gov
Program Support Branch Director – FHA's
Single Family Nonprofits Program
Rachel L. Allen . . . . (404) 331-1263 ext. 2141
E-mail: rachel.l.allen@hud.gov
Quality Assurance Division Director
Kevin A. Shearer . . . . (404) 331-1263 ext. 2678
E-mail: kevin.a.shearer@hud.gov
Field Review Branch #1 Chief **Valerie J. Williams** . . . . . (404) 331-1263
E-mail: valerie.j.williams@hud.gov
Field Review Branch #2 Chief
Dorian M. Humphrey . . . . (678) 732-2520
E-mail: dorian.m.humphrey@hud.gov

(continued on next page)

DEPARTMENTS

★ Presidential Appointment Requiring Senate Confirmation ☆ Presidential Appointment □ Schedule C Appointment ◇ Career Senior Foreign Service Appointment
● Career Senior Executive Service (SES) Appointment ○ Non-Career Senior Executive Service (SES) Appointment ■ Postal Career Executive Service

DEPARTMENTS

Atlanta Homeownership Center *(continued)*

Field Review Branch #3 Chief
Nora G. Kittrell .... (404) 331-1263 ext. 2704
E-mail: nora_g._kittrell@hud.gov
Real Estate Owned Division Director
Ralph Jackson .... (404) 331-1263 ext. 2153
E-mail: ralph.jackson@hud.gov
Real Estate Owned Branch #1 Chief
Debra "Debbie" Bonelli .... (404) 331-1263 ext. 2073
E-mail: debbie.bonelli@hud.gov
Real Estate Owned Branch #2 Chief
Joyce M. Ledlow-Dorsey .... (404) 331-1263 ext. 2492
E-mail: joyce.m.ledlowdorsey@hud.gov
Real Estate Owned Branch #3 Chief **Felicia D. Parks** ... (404) 331-1263
E-mail: felicia.d.parks@hud.gov

Atlanta Multifamily Hub
40 Marietta Street, NW, Atlanta, GA 30303
Tel: (404) 331-5001 Fax: (404) 331-4089

Director **Ruben J. Brooks** .... (678) 732-2743
Multifamily Property Disposition Center
Director **(Vacant)** .... (404) 331-5001 ext. 2187
Multifamily Property Disposition Sales
Team Chief **(Vacant)** .... (404) 331-5001 ext. 2760
Senior Project Manager **Cynthia Gordon-Benson** ..... (678) 732-2737
Operations Director **Marcia D. Ringo** .... (678) 732-2350
E-mail: marcia.d.ringo@hud.gov

Birmingham (AL) Field Office
Medical Forum Building, 950 22nd Street North,
Suite 900, Birmingham, AL 35203-5301
Tel: (205) 731-2617 TTY: (800) 548-2546 Fax: (205) 731-2593

Field Office Director **Patricia A. "Pat" Hoban-Moore** ... (205) 745-4301
E-mail: Patricia.Hoban-Moore@hud.gov
Education: Wayne State U; Georgia MPA
Chief Counsel **Elizabeth B. Joiner** .... (205) 731-2616
E-mail: elizabeth.b.joiner@hud.gov Fax: (205) 731-2639
Community Planning and Development Director
(Acting) **Renee Ryles** .... (202) 402-4609
E-mail: renee.ryles@hud.gov
Education: Morgan State 1981
Fair Housing and Equal Opportunity Division Director
(Vacant) .... (205) 745-4313
Fax: (205) 731-2395
Public Housing Director **Velma Byron** .... (787) 766-5400 ext. 2078
E-mail: velma.m.byron@hud.gov Fax: (205) 731-2502
Regional Public Housing Director **Ellis Henry** .... (904) 208-6093
Administrative Officer **Gale L. Harris** .... (205) 745-4305
E-mail: gale.l.harris@hud.gov Fax: (205) 731-2639

Columbia (SC) Field Office
Strom Thurmond Federal Building, 1835 Assembly Street,
13th Floor, Columbia, SC 29201-2480
Tel: (803) 765-5592 TTY: (803) 253-3071 Fax: (803) 765-5515

● Field Office Director (Acting) **Michael German** .... (803) 765-5592
E-mail: michael.german@hud.gov Fax: (803) 253-3043
Management Information Specialist
Douglas L. Bouknight .... (803) 765-5532
E-mail: douglas.l.bouknight@hud.gov
Community Planning and Development Office Director
Bradley S. "Brad" Evatt .... (803) 765-5344
Fair Housing and Equal Opportunity Office/Program
Operations and Compliance Center Director
Patricia W. Green .... (803) 765-5938
E-mail: pat.w.green@hud.gov Fax: (803) 253-3427
Public Housing Office Director **Eric Bickley** .... (803) 253-3238
E-mail: eric.bickley@hud.gov Fax: (803) 253-3428
Regional Public Housing Director **Ellis Henry** .... (904) 208-6093

Greensboro (NC) Field Office
Asheville Building, 1500 Pinecroft Road,
Suite 401, Greensboro, NC 27407-3838
Tel: (336) 547-4000 TTY: (336) 547-4054 Fax: (336) 547-4138

Field Office Director **Curtis L. Davis** .... (336) 547-4001 ext. 2064
E-mail: curtis.l.davis@hud.gov

Greensboro (NC) Field Office *(continued)*

Administrative Officer **Patricia T. Royal** ...... (336) 547-4000 ext. 2425
E-mail: patricia.t.royal@hud.gov Fax: (336) 547-4015
Chief Counsel **Jonathan S. Anderson** .... (336) 851-8169
E-mail: jonathan.s.anderson@hud.gov Fax: (336) 547-4113
North Carolina District Inspector General for
Audit **(Vacant)** .... (336) 547-4056 ext. 2409
North Carolina Area Special Agent-in-Charge **(Vacant)** ... (336) 547-4000
Community Planning and Development Office Director
Matthew T. King .... (336) 547-4000
E-mail: matthew.t.king@hud.gov
Public Housing Office Director (Acting) **Shirley Wong** ... (336) 851-8086
E-mail: shirley.wong@hud.gov Fax: (336) 547-4129
Regional Public Housing Director **Ellis Henry** .... (904) 208-6093
Fair Housing and Equal Opportunity Director
(Vacant) .... (336) 547-4000 ext. 2039
Fax: (336) 547-4146
Public Housing Division Director **Courtney Kyles** .... (336) 851-8072
E-mail: courtney.n.kyles@hud.gov Fax: (336) 547-4120
Asset Management Branch Chief **(Vacant)** ... (336) 547-4034 ext. 2001
Out Stational/Atlanta Marketing and
Outreach **(Vacant)** .... (336) 547-4053 ext. 2113
Fax: (336) 547-4121

Jackson (MS) Field Office
Dr. A. H. McCoy Federal Building, 100 West Capitol Street,
Room 910, Jackson, MS 39269-1096
Tel: (601) 965-4700 TTY: (601) 965-4171 Fax: (601) 965-4773

Field Office Director **Jerrie G. Magruder** ..... (601) 965-4700 ext. 2105
E-mail: jerrie.g.magruder@hud.gov
Chief Counsel **(Vacant)** .... (601) 965-4700
Community Planning and Development Program
Manager **Donnetta McAdoo** .... (601) 608-1796
E-mail: donnetta.mcadoo@hud.gov
Fair Housing and Equal Opportunity Director
Marilyn Moore-Lemons .... (601) 608-1804
E-mail: marilyn.moore-lemons@hud.gov Fax: (601) 965-4764
Public Housing Office Director **Sheila W. Jackson** ...... (601) 608-1729
Regional Public Housing Director **Ellis Henry** .... (904) 208-6093
Program Assistant **Linda Magee** .... (601) 608-1766 ext. 2910
E-mail: linda.s.magee@hud.gov

Jacksonville (FL) Field Office
Charles E. Bennett Federal Building, 400 West Bay Street,
Suite 1015, Jacksonville, FL 32202
Tel: (904) 232-1241 Tel: (904) 232-1777 ext. 2510 (Fair Housing, Program Operations and Compliance Center) TTY: (904) 232-2631
Fax: (904) 232-3759

Director **Alesia Scott-Ford** .... (904) 208-6139
E-mail: alesia.scott-ford@hud.gov
Administrative Officer **(Vacant)** .... (904) 232-1241
Chief Counsel **Ingrid Suarez-Osborn** .... (904) 208-6120
Inspector General/Jacksonville Area District Inspector
General for Audit **Antonio A. Bailey** .... (904) 208-6109
E-mail: abailey@hudoig.gov
Community Planning and Development Director
(Acting) **Thomas "Tom" Bilodeau** .... (904) 208-6001
Fair Housing Compliance Director **(Vacant)** .... (904) 208-6186
Multifamily Housing Division Director
Daniel M. Ortiz .... (904) 208-6137
E-mail: daniel.ortiz@hud.gov
Public Housing Office Director (Acting) **Uche Oluku** .... (305) 520-5091
E-mail: uche.a.oluku@hud.gov Fax: (904) 232-1721
Regional Public Housing Director **Ellis Henry** .... (904) 208-6093

Knoxville (TN) Field Office
John J. Duncan Federal Building, 710 Locust Street,
3rd Floor, Knoxville, TN 37902-2526
Tel: (865) 545-4370

Field Office Director **Bob W. Cook** .... (865) 474-8205
Chief Counsel **Mary Brewer** .... (865) 545-4400 ext. 110
E-mail: mary.b.brewer@hud.gov Fax: (865) 545-4579

★ Presidential Appointment Requiring Senate Confirmation ☆ Presidential Appointment ☐ Schedule C Appointment ◇ Career Senior Foreign Service Appointment
● Career Senior Executive Service (SES) Appointment ○ Non-Career Senior Executive Service (SES) Appointment ■ Postal Career Executive Service

Knoxville (TN) Field Office *(continued)*

Inspector General/Knoxville Inspector General for Audit **David Butcher** .... (865) 545-4400 ext. 118
E-mail: david.butcher@hud.gov Fax: (865) 545-4572
Community Planning and Development Office Director **Mary C. Wilson** .... (865) 474-8225 ext. 125
Fair Housing and Equal Opportunity/Program Compliance Center Director (Acting) **Zachary D. Blair** .... (615) 515-8597
E-mail: zachary.d.blair@hud.gov
Housing/Multifamily Housing Program Center Director **Jeffrey A. Fleming** .... (678) 732-2316
E-mail: Jeffrey.A.Fleming@hud.gov
Housing/Single Family Housing Division Housing Program Specialist **Robert A. Bright** .... (865) 474-8212
Public Housing Office Director **Tosha LeSure** .... (615) 515-8520
E-mail: Tosha.LeSure@hud.gov Fax: (615) 736-2385
Regional Public Housing Director **Ellis Henry** .... (904) 208-6093
Management Analyst **Suzanne E. Wright** .... (865) 474-8206
E-mail: suzanne.e.wright@hud.gov
Equal Opportunity Specialist **Kim R. Harris** .... (502) 618-8125
Equal Opportunity Specialist **Michele Roundtree** .... (502) 618-8148

Louisville (KY) Field Office
601 West Broadway, Louisville, KY 40202
Tel: (502) 582-5251 TTY: (800) 648-6056 Fax: (502) 582-6074
Internet: www.hud.gov/kentucky

Field Office Director **Michael L. Browder, Sr.** .... (502) 618-8114
E-mail: michael.l.browder@hud.gov
Regional Support Manager **Jenna L. Sappenfield** .... (502) 618-8149
E-mail: jenna.sappenfield@hud.gov Fax: (502) 582-6683
Administrative Project Manager **Jinger Coffelt** .... (502) 618-8115
E-mail: jinger.coffelt@hud.gov
Administrative Regional Support Manager **Patricia C. "Patty" Whitehouse** .... (502) 618-8157
E-mail: patty.c.whitehouse@hud.gov
Chief Counsel **(Vacant)** .... (502) 582-5251
Community Planning and Development Division Director (Acting) **Renee Ryles** .... (402) 292-4609
E-mail: renee.ryles@hud.gov Fax: (502) 582-5300
Education: Morgan State 1981
Fair Housing Compliance Director **(Vacant)** .... (502) 582-5251
Housing Counseling Program Specialist **Jane D. Charida** .... (502) 618-8111
Housing Counseling Program Specialist **Robin Penick** .... (502) 618-8144
Multifamily Housing Director **(Vacant)** .... (502) 582-5251
Public Housing Office Director **Carol C. Spencer** .... (502) 618-8152
E-mail: carol.c.spencer@hud.gov Fax: (502) 582-6558
Regional Public Housing Director **(Vacant)** .... (502) 582-5251
Senior Analyst [Public Affairs] **Deborah L. Knight** ...... (502) 618-8129
E-mail: deborah.l.knight@hud.gov

Memphis (TN) Field Office
One Memphis Place, 200 Jefferson Avenue, Suite 300, Memphis, TN 38103-2389
Tel: (901) 544-3367 Fax: (901) 544-3697

Field Office Director **Sernorma L. Mitchell** .... (901) 544-3367
Web Manager **George H. Denton** .... (901) 544-3262
E-mail: george.h.denton@hud.gov

Public Housing Hub
One Memphis Place, 200 Jefferson Avenue, Suite 300, Memphis, TN 38103-2389
Tel: (901) 544-3373 Fax: (901) 544-3181

Director **Reginald Marable** .... (901) 544-3544
E-mail: reginald.marable@hud.gov Fax: (615) 736-2385

Miami (FL) Field Office
Brickell Plaza Federal Building, 909 First Avenue, SE, Suite 500, Miami, FL 33131
Tel: (888) 696-4687 (Homeownership Center)
Tel: (888) 297-8685 (Loss Mitigation) Tel: (305) 536-4456
Fax: (305) 536-4698

Field Office Director **Jose Cintron** .... (305) 520-5026
E-mail: jose.cintron@hud.gov
Administrative Officer **Michelle S. Cazanas** .... (305) 520-5100
E-mail: michelle.s.cazanas@hud.gov Fax: (305) 536-4765
Chief Counsel **Gail Ash Dotson** .... (305) 536-4563 ext. 2285
E-mail: gail.a.dotson@hud.gov
Consumer/Public Affairs Officer **Gloria Shanahan** ...... (305) 520-5030
E-mail: gloria.shanahan@hud.gov
Community Planning and Development Division Director **Ann D. Chavis** .... (305) 520-5010 ext. 2223
E-mail: ann.d.chavis@hud.gov
Fair Housing and Equal Opportunity/Program Operations and Compliance Center Director **Vicki D. Johnson** .... (305) 520-5044
E-mail: vicki.d.johnson@hud.gov Fax: (305) 536-4863
Homeownership Center/Program Support Supervisory Program Support **(Vacant)** .... (305) 536-4579
Fax: (305) 536-5678
Multifamily Housing Division Director **Daniel M. Ortiz** .... (904) 208-6137
E-mail: daniel.ortiz@hud.gov Fax: (305) 536-4789
Public Housing Office Director **Uche Oluku** .... (305) 520-5091
Fax: (305) 536-5662
Regional Public Housing Director **Ellis Henry** .... (904) 208-6093
Office of Inspector General/Resident Agent-in-Charge **Scott J. Tanchak** .... (305) 536-3087

Nashville (TN) Field Office
235 Cumberland Bend Drive, Suite 200, Nashville, TN 37228-1803
Tel: (615) 736-5600 TTY: (866) 503-0264 Fax: (615) 736-7848

Field Office Director **Sernorma L. Mitchell** .... (615) 515-8510
Associate Regional Counsel for Housing Finance and Procurement **(Vacant)** .... (615) 736-5740 ext. 7322

Office of Legal Counsel
235 Cumberland Bend Drive, Nashville, TN 37228-1803

Chief Counsel **Mary Brewer** .... (615) 515-8590
E-mail: mary.b.brewer@hud.gov Fax: (615) 736-2110

Office of Housing - Multifamily Program Center
235 Cumberland Bend Drive, Nashville, TN 37228-1803

Multifamily Program Center Field Director **(Vacant)** ..... (615) 736-5600
Fax: (615) 736-5998

Office of Public Housing - Program Center
235 Cumberland Bend Drive, Nashville, TN 37228-1803

Program Center Coordinator **Tosha LeSure** .... (615) 515-8520
E-mail: Tosha.LeSure@hud.gov Fax: (615) 736-2385
Regional Public Housing Director **Ellis Henry** .... (904) 208-6093

San Juan (PR) Field Office
Parque Las Americas I, 235 Federico Costa Street, Suite 200, San Juan, PR 00918
Tel: (787) 766-5400 TTY: (787) 766-5909
TTY: (787) 766-5909 (Fair Housing and Equal Opportunity)
Fax: (787) 766-5995

Field Office Director **Efrain Maldonado** .... (787) 766-5400
E-mail: efrain.maldonado@hud.gov Fax: (787) 766-5995
Administrative Officer **Gabriel Ferrer** .... (787) 766-5400 ext. 2089
E-mail: gabriel.ferrer@hud.gov Fax: (787) 766-5227
Chief Regional Counsel **Maria Teresa Pombo** .... (787) 766-5400 ext. 2048
E-mail: teresa.pombo@hud.gov Fax: (787) 766-6107
Assistant Inspector General/Caribbean District Inspector General for Audit Region 4 **Michael A. Rivera** .... (787) 766-5202 ext. 221
E-mail: michael.a.rivera@hud.gov Fax: (787) 766-6386
Community Planning and Development Office Director **Olga L. De La Rosa** .... (787) 274-5802

(continued on next page)

★ Presidential Appointment Requiring Senate Confirmation ☆ Presidential Appointment □ Schedule C Appointment ◇ Career Senior Foreign Service Appointment
● Career Senior Executive Service (SES) Appointment ○ Non-Career Senior Executive Service (SES) Appointment ■ Postal Career Executive Service

DEPARTMENTS

San Juan (PR) Field Office *(continued)*

Public Housing Office Director
Antonio Cordova . . . . (787) 766-5400 ext. 2032
E-mail: antonio.cordova@hud.gov Fax: (787) 766-6504
Regional Public Housing Director **Ellis Henry** . . . . (904) 208-6093
Public Affairs Specialist **Gloria Shanahan** . . . . . (305) 536-5678 ext. 2254
909 First Avenue, SE, Miami, FL 33131
E-mail: gloria.shanahan@hud.gov
Multifamily Housing Division Director
Daniel M. Ortiz . . . . (904) 208-6137
909 First Avenue, SE, Miami, FL 33131

Region V - Midwest

Chicago Regional Office

Ralph H. Metcalfe Federal Building, 77 West Jackson Boulevard, Chicago, IL 60604-3507
Tel: (312) 353-5680 Fax: (312) 913-8293
Areas Covered: IL, IN, MI, MN, OH, WI

○ Regional Administrator **Joseph P. "Joe" Galvan** . . . . (312) 353-5680
E-mail: Joe.P.Galvan@hud.gov
Education: Illinois (Chicago) BS
● Deputy Regional Administrator
James A. "Jim" Cunningham . . . . (312) 353-6236
E-mail: james.a.cunningham@hud.gov
Supervisory Management Analyst
Catherine S. Peterson . . . . (312) 913-8662
E-mail: catherine.s.peterson@hud.gov
Senior Management Analyst **Larry Anderson** . . . . (312) 913-8696
E-mail: larry.anderson@hud.gov
Senior Management Analyst **Brian Gillen** . . . . (312) 913-8090
E-mail: brian.gillen@hud.gov
Senior Management Analyst **(Vacant)** . . . . (312) 353-5680
Public Affairs Officer **Gina Rodriguez-Berinde** . . . . (312) 913-8332
E-mail: Gina.Rodriguez@hud.gov
Regional Labor Relations Officer **Yvonne Matthews** . . . . (312) 913-8092
Economic and Market Analysis Division Regional Director **Donald L. "Don" Darling** . . . . (312) 913-8663
E-mail: Donald.l.darling@hud.gov

Office of General Counsel

77 West Jackson Boulevard, Chicago, IL 60604-3507
Fax: (312) 886-4944

Regional Counsel **Courtney Minor** . . . . (312) 913-8615
E-mail: courtney.b.minor@hud.gov Fax: (312) 353-4944
Education: Northwestern BA; UCLA MBA, JD
Deputy Assistant General Counsel **Janet Elson** . . . . (312) 913-8604
E-mail: janet.elson@hud.gov

Office of Inspector General

77 West Jackson Boulevard, Chicago, IL 60604-3507
Tel: (312) 353-7832 Fax: (312) 353-8866

Midwest District Inspector General for Audit
Kelly Anderson . . . . (312) 913-8684
E-mail: kelly.anderson@hud.gov
Midwest Special Agent-in-Charge
Bradley L. "Brad" Geary . . . . (312) 913-8476
Fax: (312) 353-3188

Office of Community Planning and Development

77 West Jackson Boulevard, Chicago, IL 60604-3507
Tel: (312) 353-1696 Fax: (312) 353-5417

Director **Donald "Don" Kathan** . . . . (312) 913-8713
E-mail: donald.g.kathan@hud.gov
Deputy Director **Raymond Canchola** . . . . (312) 913-8714
E-mail: raymond.canchola@hud.gov
Entitlement Programs and HOME Program Manager
Kimberly Danna-Mulick . . . . (312) 913-8737
E-mail: kimberly.danna@hud.gov
Homeless Programs Manager **Darrel Bugajsky** . . . . (312) 913-8716
E-mail: darrel.bugajsky@hud.gov
Homeless Programs Manager **Nora Lally** . . . . (312) 913-8738
E-mail: nora.m.lally@hud.gov
Education: John Carroll 1994 BA; Pennsylvania 1999 MSW

Office of Eastern - Woodlands Native American Programs

77 West Jackson Boulevard, Chicago, IL 60604-3507
Tel: (800) 735-3239 Fax: (312) 353-8936

Area Administrator **Mark Butterfield** . . . . (312) 913-8750
E-mail: mark.butterfield@hud.gov
Administrator Advisor **Kimberly McMorris** . . . . (312) 913-8027
E-mail: kimberly.n.mcmorris@hud.gov
Grants Evaluation Specialist Lead **David C. Thomas** . . . . . (312) 913-8774
E-mail: david.c.thomas@hud.gov
Grants Management Director **Elton Jones** . . . . (312) 913-8765
E-mail: elton.jones@hud.gov

Office of Fair Housing and Equal Opportunity

77 West Jackson Boulevard, Chicago, IL 60604-3507
Tel: (312) 353-7776 ext. 2453 TTY: (312) 353-7143 Fax: (312) 886-2837

Regional Director
Maurice J. "Maury" McGough . . . . (312) 353-7776 ext. 8400
E-mail: maurice.j.mcgough@hud.gov
Chicago Program Center Director **Kimberly Nevels** . . . . . . (312) 913-8429
E-mail: kimberly.nevels@hud.gov Fax: (312) 886-2837
Enforcement Branch I Chief **(Vacant)** . . . . (312) 913-8403
Enforcement Branch II Chief **(Vacant)** . . . . (312) 913-8423
Intake/Assessment Branch Chief [Legal Advisor]
Merilyn D. Brown . . . . (312) 913-8457
E-mail: merilyn.d.brown@hud.gov
Programs and Compliance Branch Chief **(Vacant)** . . . . . . (312) 913-8452

Office of Field and Administrative Resources

77 West Jackson Boulevard, Chicago, IL 60604-3507
Tel: (312) 353-6236 Tel: (312) 353-8515 (Human Resources)
Fax: (312) 353-0121

Administrative Resources Division Director
Wayne E. Popelka . . . . (312) 913-8524
E-mail: wayne.e.popelka@hud.gov
Support Services Supervisor **(Vacant)** . . . . (312) 913-8524
Information Technology Division Director
Linda Jasper . . . . (312) 913-8544
E-mail: linda.jasper@hud.gov Fax: (312) 353-1954
Information Technology Branch Chief **(Vacant)** . . . . (312) 913-8544

Office of Human Resources

77 West Jackson Boulevard, Chicago, IL 60604-3507
Tel: (312) 353-5950

Director of Human Resources **James E. Fruge** . . . . (312) 913-8533
E-mail: james.e.fruge@hud.gov

Office of Public Housing

77 West Jackson Boulevard, Chicago, IL 60604-3507
Tel: (312) 353-1915 Fax: (312) 886-4060

Director **Daniel W. Sherrod** . . . . (312) 913-8300
E-mail: daniel.w.sherrod@hud.gov Fax: (312) 913-8889
Operations Division Director **Towanda S. Macon** . . . . (312) 913-8318
E-mail: towanda.s.macon@hud.gov
Technical Services Division Director **Eleny Ladias** . . . . . . (312) 913-8313
E-mail: eleny.ladias@hud.gov
Regional Public Housing Director **Kelley D. Lyons** . . . . . . (313) 234-7376

Multifamily Housing Division

77 West Jackson Boulevard, Chicago, IL 60604-3507
Fax: (312) 353-1690

Director **Daniel J. Burke** . . . . (312) 913-8152
E-mail: daniel.j.burke@hud.gov
Project Management Director **Debbie L. Gray** . . . . (312) 913-8142
E-mail: debbie.gray@hud.gov
Director of Operations **Mary Anderson** . . . . (312) 913-8102
Supervisory Project Manager **Darletta Baugh** . . . . (312) 913-8160
Supervisory Project Manager **Gail Burks** . . . . (312) 913-8121
Supervisory Project Manager **Sharon King** . . . . (312) 913-8126
Supervisory Project Manager **Ryan Lafollette** . . . . (312) 913-8181
Senior Project Coordinator **Mary E. Watkins** . . . . (312) 913-8552

Housing Financial Management Center

77 West Jackson Boulevard, Chicago, IL 60604-3507

Financial Management Director **(Vacant)** . . . . (312) 913-8589

★ Presidential Appointment Requiring Senate Confirmation ☆ Presidential Appointment □ Schedule C Appointment ◇ Career Senior Foreign Service Appointment
● Career Senior Executive Service (SES) Appointment ○ Non-Career Senior Executive Service (SES) Appointment ■ Postal Career Executive Service

Cleveland (OH) Field Office
U.S. Bank Centre Building, 1350 Euclid Avenue,
Suite 500, Cleveland, OH 44115-1815
Tel: (216) 357-7900 Fax: (216) 357-7920 Internet: www.hud.gov/local/cle

Field Office Director **Pamela Ashby** .... (216) 357-7651
E-mail: pamela.ashby@hud.gov
Administrative Officer **Reshemah Haggins** .... (216) 357-7661
E-mail: reshemah.haggins@hud.gov
Inspector General Special Agent-in-Charge **Eric Bizjak** ... (216) 357-7801
E-mail: eric.bizjak@hud.gov
Chief Counsel **Raymond C. Keyser** .... (216) 357-7681
Senior Management Analyst [Webmaster] **Lucy Miller** .... (216) 357-7654
E-mail: lucy.miller@hud.gov
Management Analyst **Barbara Dunlap** .... (216) 357-7652
Regional Public Housing Director **(Vacant)** .... (216) 357-7900
Public Housing Division Director **Brian D. Murray** ..... (216) 357-7780
E-mail: brian.d.murray@hud.gov
Cleveland Multifamily Branch Chief **(Vacant)** .... (216) 357-7900
Multifamily Program Center Chief Underwriter
(Vacant) .... (216) 357-7691
Single Family Housing Team Leader **John Schuster** ... (216) 357-7724
E-mail: john.schuster@hud.gov
Recovery and Prevention (Corps) **(Vacant)** .... (216) 357-7900
Labor Relations Specialist **(Vacant)** .... (312) 913-8127
Web Manager **Gwen Hampton** .... (216) 357-7655
E-mail: gwen.hampton@hud.gov
Computer Specialist **Joan Chernin** .... (216) 357-7663
E-mail: joan.chernin@hud.gov Fax: (216) 357-7915

Columbus (OH) Field Office
Bricker Federal Building, 200 North High Street,
7th Floor, Columbus, OH 43215-2499
Tel: (614) 469-5737 Fax: (614) 428-0615

Field Office Director **Thomas H. Leach** .... (614) 280-6111
E-mail: thomas.h.leach@hud.gov
Administrative Officer **Kenneth "Ken" Hamilton** ..... (614) 280-6102
E-mail: ken.hamilton@hud.gov Fax: (614) 280-6174
Chief Counsel **(Vacant)** .... (614) 469-5737
Assistant Regional Inspector General for Audit
Kimberly Toler .... (614) 280-6144
E-mail: ktoler@hudoig.gov Fax: (614) 469-6711
Community Planning and Development
Division Director **Jorgelle Lawson** .... (614) 469-5737 ext. 8254
Environmental Staff **Ross S. Carlson, Jr.** .... (614) 280-6090
E-mail: ross.carlson@hud.gov Fax: (614) 280-6175
Fair Housing and Equal Opportunity Director **(Vacant)** ... (614) 469-5737
Enforcement Chief **Francis Smith** .... (614) 280-6128
Program Operations Chief **Elva Lewis** .... (614) 280-6112
E-mail: elva.lewis@hud.gov
Senior Management Analyst **Barry A. Roberts** .... (614) 280-6126

Housing
200 North High Street, Columbus, OH 43215-2499
Tel: (614) 280-6159 Fax: (614) 280-6180

Ohio Multifamily Branch Chief **Janice M. Shriver** ...... (614) 280-6120
E-mail: janice.m.shriver@hud.gov Fax: (614) 280-6180
Operations Officer **(Vacant)** .... (614) 280-6159

Detroit (MI) Field Office
Patrick V. McNamara Federal Building, 477 Michigan Avenue,
Suite 1710, Detroit, MI 48226-2592
Tel: (313) 226-7900 Fax: (313) 226-5611

Field Office Director **Michael L. Polsinelli** ..... (313) 226-7900 ext. 7502
E-mail: michael.l.polsinelli@hud.gov
Chief Counsel **Amanda J. Shaughnessy** .... (313) 234-7432
Community Planning and Development
Director **Keith E. Hernandez** .... (313) 234-7326 ext. 6059
E-mail: keith.e.hernandez@hud.gov
Senior Management Analyst **Daniel J. Huyck** .... (313) 234-7327
Operations Analyst and FOIA Liaison
Carol T. Harper-Berry .... (313) 226-7900 ext. 7368
E-mail: carol.t.harper-berry@hud.gov Fax: (313) 226-5611
Management Analyst **Anthony P. Martin** .... (313) 234-7339
E-mail: anthony.p.martin@hud.gov

Detroit (MI) Field Office *(continued)*

Customer Service Representative
Anne "Annie" Olgetree .... (313) 234-7369
E-mail: annie.olgetree@hud.gov
Administrative Officer **Gloria D. Smart** .... (313) 226-7900 ext. 7305
E-mail: gloria.d.smart@hud.gov

Office of Housing
477 Michigan Avenue, Detroit, MI 48226-2592
Fax: (313) 226-2002

Multifamily Hub Director
Barbara Chiapella .... (313) 226-7900 ext. 7490
E-mail: barbara.chiapella@hud.gov
Multifamily Director of Operations **(Vacant)** .... (313) 226-7900

Office of Public Housing
477 Michigan Avenue, Detroit, MI 48226-2592
Fax: (313) 226-6160

Director **Douglas C. Gordon** .... (313) 234-7463
E-mail: douglas.c.gordon@hud.gov
Regional Public Housing Director **Kelley D. Lyons** ...... (313) 234-7376

Office of Operations
477 Michigan Avenue, Detroit, MI 48226-2592

Operations Director **Ratico J. Lake** .... (313) 226-7900 ext. 7461
E-mail: ratico.j.lake@hud.gov
Asset Management Director **Susie Sapilewski** .... (313) 234-7521

Indianapolis (IN) Field Office
Minton Capehart Federal Building, 575 N. Pennsylvania Street,
Suite 655, Indianapolis, IN 46204-1555
Tel: (317) 226-6303 TTY: (800) 743-3333 Fax: (317) 226-6317

Field Office Director **John R. Hall** .... (317) 957-7273
E-mail: John.R.Hall@hud.gov
Support Services Specialist **(Vacant)** .... (317) 226-6303 ext. 6309
Chief Counsel **Keith W. Lerch** .... (317) 957-7279
E-mail: keith.w.lerch@hud.gov
Education: Yale 1970 JD
Special Agent for the Inspector General
Cari D. Hess .... (317) 226-6303 ext. 5427
Community Planning and Development
Director (Acting) **John Dorgan** .... (317) 226-6303 ext. 6790
E-mail: john.dorgan@hud.gov
Fair Housing and Equal Opportunity Director
Phillip C. Shelton .... (317) 226-6263
E-mail: phillip.c.shelton@hud.gov
Program Center Coordinator (Acting)
Lucia M. Clausen .... (317) 957-7341
E-mail: lucia.m.clausen@hud.gov
Multifamily Housing Division Director
Eileen R. Mitcheltree .... (317) 226-6303 ext. 7302
E-mail: eileen.r.mitcheltree@hud.gov
Public Housing Office Coordinator (Acting)
Kimberly A. Wize .... (317) 957-7345
E-mail: Kimberly.Wize@hud.gov
Regional Public Housing Director **(Vacant)** .... (317) 226-6303

Milwaukee (WI) Field Office
310 West Wisconsin Avenue, Suite 950, Milwaukee, WI 53203-2289
Tel: (414) 297-3214 Fax: (414) 935-6775
Internet: www.hud.gov/local/mil

Field Office Director **Dale A. Darrow** .... (414) 935-6640
E-mail: dale.a.darrow@hud.gov
Chief Counsel **(Vacant)** .... (414) 729-7312
Community Planning and Development Director
(Acting) **Renee Ryles** .... (202) 402-4609
E-mail: renee.ryles@hud.gov
Education: Morgan State 1981
Senior Management Analyst **(Vacant)** .... (414) 935-6603
Management Analyst **(Vacant)** .... (414) 935-6605
Multifamily Program Center Director
Joseph Thibedeau .... (414) 297-3214 ext. 6696
E-mail: joseph.thibedeau@hud.gov

(continued on next page)

DEPARTMENTS

★ Presidential Appointment Requiring Senate Confirmation ☆ Presidential Appointment ☐ Schedule C Appointment ◇ Career Senior Foreign Service Appointment
● Career Senior Executive Service (SES) Appointment ○ Non-Career Senior Executive Service (SES) Appointment ■ Postal Career Executive Service

Milwaukee (WI) Field Office *(continued)*

Project Management (Asset Management) Chief **Michael D. Furnner** . . . . (414) 297-3214 ext. 6682
Project Management (Production) Chief **(Vacant)** . . . . (414) 297-3214 ext. 6692
Fair Housing and Equal Opportunity Director **(Vacant)** . . . (414) 935-6661
Public Housing/Program Center Coordinator **John Finger** . . . . (414) 297-3214 ext. 6729
E-mail: john.finger@hud.gov
Customer Service Representative **Sonya L. Medina** . . . . (414) 935-6604
Regional Public Housing Director **(Vacant)** . . . . (414) 297-3214

Minneapolis (MN) Field Office
212 Third Avenue South, Ste 150, Minneapolis, MN 55401
Tel: (612) 370-3000 TTY: (612) 370-3186 Fax: (612) 370-3218

Field Office Director **Michele K. Smith** . . . . (612) 370-3288
E-mail: michele.k.smith@hud.gov
Chief Counsel **Judith "Judy" Tucker** . . . . (612) 370-3198
E-mail: judy.tucker@hud.gov Fax: (612) 370-3187
Inspector General/Special Agent-in-Charge for Investigation **Brian Besch** . . . . (612) 370-3130
Fax: (612) 370-3039
Community Planning and Development Office Director **Marcia A. Kolb** . . . . (612) 370-3055
E-mail: marcia.a.kolb@hud.gov
Program Manager **(Vacant)** . . . . (612) 370-3019 ext. 2105
Housing/Single Family Division Director **Anita Olson** . . . . (612) 370-3000 ext. 2289
E-mail: anita.olson@hud.gov Fax: (612) 370-3218
Operations Branch Chief **Ray Stiles** . . . . (612) 370-3000 ext. 2267
E-mail: ray.stiles@hud.gov
Project Team Chief **Laura Simpson** . . . . (612) 370-3000 ext. 2250
Public Housing Office Director **Lucia M. Clausen** . . . . (612) 957-7341
E-mail: lucia.m.clausen@hud.gov Fax: (612) 370-3003
Labor Relations Staff **Loretta A. Szweduik** . . . . (612) 370-3000 ext. 2284
E-mail: loretta.a.szweduik@hud.gov
Senior Management Analyst **James A. Baltazar** . . . . (612) 370-2078
Customer Service Representative **Susan Seifert** . . . . (612) 370-2100
Management Analyst (Community Initiatives) **Jacob S. Akervik** . . . . (612) 370-3282

Region VI - Southwest

Fort Worth Regional Office
801 Cherry Street, Suite 2500, Unit #45, Fort Worth, TX 76102
Tel: (817) 978-5600 Fax: (817) 978-5567
Areas Covered: AR, LA, NM, OK, TX

○ Regional Administrator **Elizabeth A. "Beth" Van Duyne** Unit 45 . . . . (817) 978-5568
● Deputy Regional Administrator **(Vacant)** . . . . (817) 978-5600
Contracting Operations Branch Chief **Cathy J. Baker** . . . . (817) 978-5404
E-mail: cathy.j.baker@hud.gov Fax: (817) 978-5431
Information Technology Division Director **Michael J. Martinez** . . . . (817) 978-5422
E-mail: michael.j.martinez@hud.gov Fax: (817) 978-5432
Supervisory Regional Economist **Leon Vertz** . . . . (817) 978-9414
E-mail: leon.d.vertz@hud.gov
Tel: (817) 978-9405
Regional Labor Relations Officer **Jerlinda D. Banks** . . . . (817) 978-5619
E-mail: jerlinda.d.banks@hud.gov Fax: (817) 978-5565
Public Affairs Officer **Patricia A. Campbell** Unit 45, Room 2500 . . . . (817) 978-5600
E-mail: patricia.a.campbell@hud.gov
Education: St John's U (NY) 1973 BA; American U 1983 MS

Office of Administration and Field Support
801 Cherry Street, Fort Worth, TX 76102

Regional Support Manager **Deborah J. Dunn** . . . . (817) 978-5521
E-mail: deborah.j.dunn@hud.gov

Office of Community Planning and Development
801 Cherry Street, Fort Worth, TX 76102
Tel: (817) 978-5933 Fax: (817) 978-5559

Director **Shirley J. Henley** . . . . (817) 978-5951

Office of Community Planning and Development *(continued)*

Deputy Director **(Vacant)** . . . . (817) 978-5824
Program Management Team 1 Manager **Stephen L. Eberlein** . . . . (817) 978-5956
Program Management Team 2 Manager **(Vacant)** . . . . (817) 978-5936

Office of Counsel
801 Cherry Street, Fort Worth, TX 76102
Tel: (817) 978-5987 Fax: (817) 978-5563

Regional Counsel **William J. Daley** . . . . (817) 978-5990
E-mail: william.j.daley@hud.gov

Office of Fair Housing and Equal Opportunity
801 Cherry Street, Fort Worth, TX 76102
Tel: (817) 978-5900 TTY: (817) 978-5595 Fax: (817) 978-5876

Fair Housing and Equal Opportunity Southwest Hub Director **Garry L. Sweeney** . . . . (817) 978-5868
E-mail: garry.l.sweeney@hud.gov
Program Center Director **Thurman G. Miles** . . . . (817) 978-5870
E-mail: thurman.g.miles@hud.gov
Enforcement Branch Chief **Robert A. Avila** . . . . (817) 978-5898
E-mail: robert.a.avila@hud.gov Fax: (817) 978-5876
Intake/Assessment Branch Chief **Patrick L. Banis** . . . . (817) 978-5922
E-mail: patrick.l.banis@hud.gov Fax: (817) 978-5876
Programs and Compliance Branch Chief **Bonita Howard** . . . . (817) 978-5595

Office of the Chief Human Capital Officer
801 Cherry Street, Fort Worth, TX 76102
Tel: (817) 978-5500 Fax: (817) 978-6008

Human Resources Coordinator **(Vacant)** . . . . (817) 978-5513
Fax: (817) 978-5554
Training Consultant **(Vacant)** . . . . (817) 978-5516
Human Resources Employee Labor Relations Branch Chief **D'Andra A. Hankinson** . . . . (817) 978-5608
E-mail: d'andra.a.hankinson@hud.gov Fax: (817) 978-5564
Human Resources Staffing and Classification Branch Chief **(Vacant)** . . . . (817) 978-5515
Fax: (817) 978-5554

Office of Housing
801 Cherry Street, Fort Worth, TX 76102
Tel: (817) 978-5763 Fax: (817) 978-6018

Multifamily Regional Director **Mary V. Walsh** . . . . (817) 978-5807
E-mail: Mary.V.Walsh@hud.gov Fax: (817) 978-5748
Director of Operations **Desiree Miles** . . . . (817) 978-5842
Fax: (817) 978-6018
Single Family Housing Division Director **(Vacant)** . . . . (817) 978-5763

Office of Inspector General
801 Cherry Street, Fort Worth, TX 76102
Tel: (817) 978-5440 Fax: (817) 978-2052

Southwest District Inspector General for Audit **(Vacant)** . . . . (817) 978-5440
819 Taylor Street, Room 13A09, Fort Worth, TX 76102 Fax: (817) 978-9316
Southwest Special Agent-in-Charge **Phyllis Grissom-Robinson** Unit #45 . . . . (817) 978-5446
Fax: (817) 978-2052

Office of Public Housing
801 Cherry Street, Fort Worth, TX 76102
Tel: (817) 978-5700 Fax: (817) 978-5756

Regional Public Housing Director **Donna L. Wickes** . . . . (713) 718-3273
E-mail: donna.l.wickes@hud.gov
PIH Division Director **Regina Hawkins** . . . . (817) 978-5716
Technical Division Director **Carrie E. Dobbins** . . . . (817) 978-5727
E-mail: carrie.e.dobbins@hud.gov

CFO Accounting Center
801 Cherry Street, Fort Worth, TX 76102
Internet: www.hud.gov/offices/cfo/center.cfm

Director **Otis Jones** . . . . (817) 978-5911
E-mail: otis.jones@hud.gov

★ Presidential Appointment Requiring Senate Confirmation ☆ Presidential Appointment □ Schedule C Appointment ◇ Career Senior Foreign Service Appointment
● Career Senior Executive Service (SES) Appointment ○ Non-Career Senior Executive Service (SES) Appointment ■ Postal Career Executive Service

CFO Accounting Center *(continued)*

Funds Control Division Director **Peter M. Engelbert** . . . . (817) 978-5694
Funds Control Branch I Chief **Kimberly K. Erdmann** . . . . (817) 978-5576
Funds Control Branch II Chief (Acting) **Peter M. Engelbert** . . . . (817) 978-5694
Payments and Collection Division Director **Mary Lou Dominguez** . . . . (817) 978-5669
Commercial Payment Branch Chief **Sabrina Ascencio** . . . . (817) 978-5660
Program Payments Branch Chief **Steve R. Caero** . . . . (817) 978-5677
Reports and Control Division Director (Acting) **Otis Jones** . . . . (817) 978-5911
Resolution Specialist Branch Chief **Michael A. Gamez** . . . (817) 978-9419
Education: Texas 2004 BS

Albuquerque (NM) Field Office
500 Gold Avenue SW, Ste. 7301, Albuquerque, NM 87103-0906
Tel: (505) 346-6463 TTY: (800) 877-8339 (Relay Operator)
Fax: (505) 346-6927

Deputy Administrator for Southwest Office of Native American Programs **David W. Southerland** . . . . (505) 346-6925
E-mail: david.w.southerland@hud.gov
Community Planning and Development Director **Leticia Ibarra** . . . . (505) 346-7361
E-mail: leticia.ibarra@hud.gov
Field Office Director (Acting) **Leslie Ann Bradley** . . . . (817) 978-9406
E-mail: leslieann.bradley@hud.gov
Public Housing Director **Floyd R. Duran** . . . . (505) 346-7392
E-mail: floyd.duran@hud.gov
Housing/Multifamily Housing Branch Senior Project Manager **Gloria Garcia** . . . . (505) 346-7380
E-mail: gloria.garcia@hud.gov
Administrative Officer **Elizabeth R. Ramirez** . . . . (505) 346-7349
E-mail: elizabeth.r.ramirez@hud.gov

Houston (TX) Field Office
1301 Fannin, Suite 2200, Houston, TX 77002
Tel: (713) 718-3199 TTY: (800) 877-8339 Fax: (713) 718-3255

Field Office Director **Dr. Edward L. Pringle** . . . . (713) 718-3199
E-mail: edward.l.pringle@hud.gov

Administrative Service Center 2
1301 Fannin, Houston, TX 77002
Tel: (713) 718-3111

Administrative Officer **Roger Harvey** . . . . (713) 718-3111
E-mail: roger.harvey@hud.gov

Housing
1301 Fannin, Houston, TX 77002
Tel: (713) 718-3137

Multi-Family Housing Division **(Vacant)** . . . . (817) 978-5781
Single Family Housing Division **(Vacant)** . . . . (713) 718-3137

Office of Community Planning and Development
1301 Fannin, Houston, TX 77002

Director **Stacia L. Johnson** . . . . (713) 718-3279
E-mail: stacia..johnson@hud.gov

Office of Counsel
1301 Fannin, Houston, TX 77002
Tel: (713) 718-3126

Chief Counsel **(Vacant)** . . . . (713) 718-3126

Office of Fair Housing and Equal Opportunity
1301 Fannin, Houston, TX 77002
Fax: (713) 718-5447

Director **Christina Lewis** . . . . (713) 718-3189
E-mail: christina.lewis@hud.gov

Office of Inspector General
1301 Fannin, Houston, TX 77002

Senior Auditor **Jacob Williams** . . . . (713) 718-3199
E-mail: jacob.williams@hud.gov

Office of Public Housing
1301 Fannin, Houston, TX 77002
Tel: (713) 718-3214

Director **Lorraine Walls** . . . . (713) 718-3214
E-mail: lorraine.d.walls@hud.gov
Regional Public Housing Director **Donna L. Wickes** . . . . (713) 718-3273

Little Rock (AR) Field Office
Metropolitan National Bank Building, 425 West Capitol Avenue, Suite 1000, Little Rock, AR 72201-3488
Tel: (501) 918-5700 TTY: (501) 324-5931 Fax: (501) 324-7168

Field Office Director **Wanda C. Merritt** . . . . (501) 918-5701
E-mail: wanda.c.merritt@hud.gov Fax: (501) 324-6142
Administrative Officer **(Vacant)** . . . . (713) 718-3111
1301 Fannin, Houston, TX 77002
Community Planning and Development Division Director **Clinton E. Johnson** . . . . (501) 918-5739
E-mail: clinton.e.johnson@hud.gov
Fair Housing and Equal Opportunity **(Vacant)** . . . . (501) 918-5708
Fax: (501) 324-6296
Housing/Multifamily Housing Division Director **(Vacant)** . . . . (501) 918-5712
Fax: (501) 324-5203
Asset Management Supervisory Project Manager **(Vacant)** . . . . (501) 918-5715
Production Branch Supervisory Project Manager **(Vacant)** . . . . (501) 918-5723
Housing/Single Family Housing Program Support Specialist **Don Mayor** . . . . (501) 918-5756
E-mail: don.m.mayor@hud.gov Fax: (501) 324-5952
Public Housing Division Director **Johnny Wooley** . . . . (501) 918-5750
E-mail: johnny.wooley@hud.gov Fax: (501) 324-5448
Chief Counsel **Jessica Lee** . . . . (501) 918-5702
E-mail: jessica.l.lee@hud.gov Fax: (501) 324-5413

New Orleans (LA) Field Office
Hale Boggs Federal Building, 500 Poydras Street, 9th Floor, New Orleans, LA 70130-3099
Tel: (504) 671-3001 Tel: (888) 297-8685 (Housing Hotline)
TTY: (800) 877-8339 TTY: (504) 671-3049 Fax: (504) 671-3751

Field Office Director **Earl Randall III** . . . . (504) 671-3797
Chief Counsel **Bam V. Gressett** . . . . (504) 671-3796
E-mail: bam.v.gressett@hud.gov
Community Planning and Development Division Director **Cheryl S. Breaux** . . . . (504) 671-3007
E-mail: cheryl.s.breaux@hud.gov
Community Planning and Development Specialist **Sonya M. Brister** . . . . (504) 671-3017
E-mail: sonya.m.brister@hud.gov
Community Planning and Development Specialist **Adriane Burgess** . . . . (504) 671-3786
E-mail: adriane.t.burgess@hud.gov
Fair Housing and Equal Opportunity Director **(Vacant)** . . . (504) 671-3739
Supervisory Program Operations Compliance Branch **Jan Kearney-King** . . . . (504) 671-3731
E-mail: jan.kearney-king@hud.gov
Public Housing Deputy Director **Cheryl J. Williams** . . . . (504) 671-3793
E-mail: cheryl.j.williams@hud.gov
Administrative Officer **Romona P. Augillard** . . . . (504) 671-3723
E-mail: romona.p.augillard@hud.gov Fax: (504) 671-3727
Webmaster **(Vacant)** . . . . (504) 671-3755

Oklahoma City (OK) Field Office
301 NW 6th Street, Suite 200, Oklahoma City, OK 73102
Tel: (405) 609-8400 Fax: (405) 609-8982

Field Office Director **Sharon Gordon-Ribeiro** . . . . (405) 609-8522
E-mail: sharon.gordon-ribeiro@hud.gov
Administrative Officer **Mark Gregory Young** . . . . (405) 609-8479
E-mail: mark.gregory.young@hud.gov Fax: (405) 609-8981
Chief Counsel **Mikel K. Anderson** . . . . (405) 609-8430
E-mail: mikel.k.anderson@hud.gov Fax: (405) 609-8404
Inspector General/Audit **Tamara Wallinger** . . . . (405) 609-8608
E-mail: twallinger@hudoig.gov
Inspector General/Investigation **Brock Minnick** . . . . (405) 609-8601

(continued on next page)

DEPARTMENTS

★ Presidential Appointment Requiring Senate Confirmation ☆ Presidential Appointment □ Schedule C Appointment ◇ Career Senior Foreign Service Appointment
● Career Senior Executive Service (SES) Appointment ○ Non-Career Senior Executive Service (SES) Appointment ■ Postal Career Executive Service

Oklahoma City (OK) Field Office *(continued)*

Community Planning and Development Director
Earl M. Cook .... (202) 402-4609
E-mail: earl.m.cook@hud.gov
Education: Maryland 1977 BA

Fair Housing and Equal Opportunity Division
Thurman G. Miles .... (817) 978-5870
E-mail: thurman.g.miles@hud.gov

National Servicing and Loss Mitigation Center Director
Matt B. Martin .... (405) 609-8533
E-mail: matt.b.martin@hud.gov Fax: (405) 609-8405

National Servicing and Loss Mitigation Center Deputy Director **Felicia B. Jones** .... (405) 609-8444
E-mail: felicia.b.jones@hud.gov Fax: (405) 609-8405

Public Housing Division Director **Greg J. Jungman** ..... (405) 609-8562
E-mail: greg.j.jungman@hud.gov Fax: (405) 609-8530

Office of Southern Plains Native American Housing Programs
301 NW 6th Street, Oklahoma City, OK 73102
Tel: (405) 609-8520

Administrator **Wayne Sims** .... (405) 609-8520
E-mail: wayne.sims@hud.gov Fax: (405) 609-8403

San Antonio (TX) Field Office
Hipolito Garcia Federal Building, 615 East Houston Street, Suite 347, San Antonio, TX 78205-2001
Tel: (210) 475-6806 TTY: (210) 475-6885 Fax: (210) 472-6804

Field Office Director **Zuleika K. Morales-Romero** ...... (210) 475-6806
E-mail: zuleika.morales-romero@hud.gov

Regional Support Manager
Tammye Hildamar Treviño EDFP .... (817) 978-5965
E-mail: tammye.h.trevino@hud.gov
Education: Texas (San Antonio) BA; Sul Ross State MBA

Chief Counsel **(Vacant)** .... (210) 475-6806

Inspector General/San Antonio Area District Inspector General for Audit **(Vacant)** .... (210) 475-6895
Fax: (210) 472-6901

Community Planning and Development Division Director **Elva F. Garcia** .... (210) 475-6866
E-mail: elva.f.garcia@hud.gov

Fair Housing and Equal Opportunity Division/Program Operations and Compliance Center Team Leader
Thurman G. Miles .... (817) 978-5870
E-mail: thurman.g.miles@hud.gov

Multifamily Housing Division Director **(Vacant)** .... (210) 475-6832

Public Housing Office Director **David Pohler** .... (210) 475-6860
E-mail: david.pohler@hud.gov Fax: (210) 472-6816

Single Family Housing Division Supervisor **(Vacant)** ..... (210) 475-6817
Fax: (210) 472-6753

Tulsa (OK) Field Office
110 West 7th Street, Suite 1110, Tulsa, OK 74119
Tel: (918) 292-8900 Fax: (918) 292-8983 Internet: www.hud.gov

Field Office Director **Sharon Gordon-Ribeiro** .... (918) 292-8910

Administrator Officer **Mark Gregory Young** .... (405) 609-8479
E-mail: mark.gregory.young@hud.gov Fax: (918) 292-8995

Housing/Single Family National Servicing Center, Branch 3 Director **Kasey Watson** .... (918) 292-8957

Region VII - Great Plains

Kansas City Regional Office

400 State Avenue, Room 200, Kansas City, KS 66101-2406
Tel: (913) 551-5462 Tel: (913) 551-5644 (General Information)
TTY: (913) 551-6972 Fax: (913) 551-5469
Areas Covered: IA, KS, MO, NE

□ Regional Administrator **Jason M. Mohr** .... (913) 551-5462
E-mail: jason.m.mohr@hud.gov

Deputy Regional Administrator **Bruce L. Ladd** .... (913) 551-5537
E-mail: bruce.l.ladd@hud.gov

Labor Relations Officer **Fannie J. Woods** .... (913) 551-5577
E-mail: fannie.j.woods@hud.gov

Senior Environmental Officer **Paul F. Mohr** .... (913) 551-5704
E-mail: paul.f.mohr@hud.gov

Kansas City Regional Office *(continued)*

Public Affairs **Agatha R. Gutierrez** .... (913) 551-6803
E-mail: agatha.r.gutierrez@hud.gov

Information Technology Field Service Manager
Bruce R. Watkins .... (913) 551-6968
E-mail: bruce.r.watkins@hud.gov

Office of Counsel
400 State Avenue, Kansas City, KS 66101-2406
Tel: (913) 551-5891 Fax: (913) 551-5857

Regional Counsel **Gayle E. Bohling** .... (913) 551-6736
E-mail: gayle.e.bohling@hud.gov

Attorney-Advisor **Guillermo "Billy" Mejia** .... (913) 551-5532
E-mail: guillermo.mejia@hud.gov
Education: Missouri (Kansas City) 2015 JD, 2016 MPA

Office of Inspector General
400 State Avenue, Kansas City, KS 66101-2406
Tel: (913) 551-5870 (Audits) Tel: (913) 551-5866 (Investigations)
Fax: (913) 551-5877 (Audits) Fax: (913) 551-5496 (Investigations)

Regional Inspector General **Ronald J. Hosking** .... (913) 551-5872
E-mail: rhosking@hudoig.gov

Special Agent-in-Charge **Michael V. "Mike" Powell** ..... (913) 551-5407

Office of Community Planning and Development
400 State Avenue, Kansas City, KS 66101-2406
Tel: (913) 551-5484 Fax: (913) 551-5859

Director **Dana T. Buckner** .... (913) 551-5546
E-mail: dana.t.buckner@hud.gov

Office of Public Housing
400 State Avenue, Kansas City, KS 66101-2406
Tel: (913) 551-6916 Fax: (913) 551-6981

Director **Frances M. Cleary** .... (913) 551-5702
E-mail: frances.m.cleary@hud.gov

Public Housing Division Director **Julie A. Miles** .... (913) 551-5529
E-mail: julie.a.miles@hud.gov

Low-Income Housing Tax Credit Team Lead
Mark A. Heap .... (913) 955-2810
E-mail: mark.a.heap@hud.gov

Office of Fair Housing and Equal Opportunity
400 State Avenue, Kansas City, KS 66101-2406
Tel: (913) 551-6958 TTY: (913) 551-6972 Fax: (913) 551-6856

Kansas City Fair Housing HUB Director
Gregory B. King .... (913) 551-5447
E-mail: gregory.b.king@hud.gov

Compliance Branch, Supervisory Equal Opportunity Chief **(Vacant)** .... (913) 551-5890

Enforcement Branch, Supervisory Equal Opportunity Chief **Tiana N. Alexander** .... (913) 551-5584

Intake/Assessment Branch Chief **Anthony L. May** .... (913) 551-6898
E-mail: anthony.l.may@hud.gov

Office of Multifamily Housing
400 State Avenue, Kansas City, KS 66101-2406
Tel: (913) 551-6812 Fax: (913) 551-6818

Director **Edward P. Manning** .... (913) 551-5537
E-mail: edward.p.manning@hud.gov

Office of Administration
400 State Avenue, Kansas City, KS 66101-2406
Tel: (913) 551-5411 Fax: (913) 551-5416

Regional Support Manager **(Vacant)** .... (913) 551-5412

Information Technology Chief Information Officer
Brent G. Ericson .... (402) 492-3105
1616 Capitol Avenue, Omaha, NE 68102
E-mail: Brent.G.Ericson@hud.gov

★ Presidential Appointment Requiring Senate Confirmation ☆ Presidential Appointment □ Schedule C Appointment ◇ Career Senior Foreign Service Appointment
● Career Senior Executive Service (SES) Appointment ○ Non-Career Senior Executive Service (SES) Appointment ■ Postal Career Executive Service

Des Moines (IA) Field Office
Neal Smith Federal Building, 210 Walnut Street,
Room 937, Des Moines, IA 50309-2155
Tel: (515) 284-4512 TTY: (800) 877-8339 Fax: (515) 284-4743

Field Office Director **Steven "Steve" Eggleston** .... (515) 284-4512
E-mail: steven.eggleston@hud.gov
Chief Counsel **James V. "Jim" Provenzale** .... (515) 284-4496
Fair Housing Specialist **(Vacant)** .... (515) 284-4706
Supervisory Project Manager **(Vacant)** .... (515) 284-4736
Webmaster **(Vacant)** .... (515) 284-4512

Omaha (NE) Field Office
Edward Zorinsky Federal Building, 1616 Capitol Avenue,
Suite 329, Omaha, NE 68102
Tel: (402) 492-3100 TTY: (402) 492-3183 Fax: (402) 492-3150

Field Office Director **Earl E. Redrick** .... (402) 492-3134
E-mail: earl.e.redrick@hud.gov Fax: (402) 492-3150
Chief Counsel **(Vacant)** .... (402) 492-3100
Administrative Officer **Denise M. Cernik** .... (402) 492-3177
E-mail: denise.m.cernik@hud.gov
Community Planning and Development Director
F. Tim Severin .... (402) 492-3145
E-mail: tim.severin@hud.gov
Fair Housing and Equal Opportunity Specialist
(Vacant) .... (402) 492-3100
Public Housing Director **Denise Gipson** .... (402) 492-3137
E-mail: denise.e.gipson@hud.gov

St. Louis (MO) Field Office
Robert A. Young Federal Building, 1222 Spruce Street,
Ste. 3203, St. Louis, MO 63103-2836
Tel: (314) 418-5400 TTY: (314) 418-5219 Fax: (314) 418-5247
Internet: www.hud.gov/local/stl

Field Office Director **James M. Heard** .... (314) 418-5245
E-mail: james.m.heard@hud.gov
Chief Counsel (Acting) **Gayle E. Bohling** .... (913) 551-6736
E-mail: gayle.e.bohling@hud.gov Fax: (913) 551-5857
Inspector General for Audit **Carrie Gray** .... (314) 539-6342
E-mail: carrie.gray@hud.gov Fax: (314) 539-6306
Special Agent-in-Charge **(Vacant)** .... (314) 539-6193
Community Planning and Development Office Director
Dee Ann Ducote .... (314) 418-5405
E-mail: deeann.ducote@hud.gov
Fair Housing and Equal Opportunity Supervisory Equal
Opportunity Specialist **Natasha J. Watson** .... (913) 551-5447
E-mail: natasha.j.watson@hud.gov Fax: (913) 551-6856
Public Housing Program Center Director
Craig Dobson .... (314) 418-5230
E-mail: craig.dobson@hud.gov Fax: (314) 539-6508

Region VIII - Rocky Mountain

Denver Regional Office
1670 Broadway, 25th Floor, Denver, CO 80202-4801
Tel: (303) 672-5440 TTY: (303) 672-5022 Fax: (303) 672-5004
Internet: www.hud.gov/local/index.cfm?state=co&topic=offices
Areas Covered: CO, MT, ND, SD, UT, WY

□ Regional Administrator **(Vacant)** .... (303) 672-5440
Deputy Regional Administrator **Eric R. Cobb** ... (800) 543-9378 ext. 1526
E-mail: eric.r.cobb@hud.gov
Public Affairs Officer **Christine Baumann** .... (202) 708-0980
E-mail: christine.a.baumann@hud.gov Fax: (303) 672-5308
Management Analyst **Winifred Jean Cole** .... (303) 672-5000
Sustainability Officer **Guadalupe M. Herrera** .... (303) 839-2651
Healthy Homes Representative **Abigail "Abby" Hugill** ... (303) 672-5165
E-mail: abigail.h.hugill@hud.gov
Supervisory Analyst **Effie L. Russell** .... (303) 672-5289
Regional Web Manager **(Vacant)** .... (303) 672-5440
Regional Support Manager
Michael P. "Mike" Westra .... (913) 551-5411
E-mail: Michael.P.Westra@hud.gov
Program Analyst **Sebastian Dawiskiba** .... (303) 672-5012

Office of Counsel
1670 Broadway, Denver, CO 80202-4801
Tel: (303) 672-5409 Fax: (303) 672-5027

Regional Counsel **Matthew Mussetter** .... (303) 672-4509
E-mail: matthew.mussetter@hud.gov
Deputy Regional Counsel **Lisa K. Coronado** .... (303) 672-5381
E-mail: lisa.k.coronado@hud.gov
Associate Regional Counsel for Litigation
Nicole A. Allard .... (303) 672-5306
E-mail: nicole.a.allard@hud.gov
Trial Attorney **Jesse Loper** .... (303) 672-5019 ext. 1342
E-mail: jesse.loper@hud.gov

Office of Inspector General
1670 Broadway, Denver, CO 80202-4801
Tel: (303) 672-5452

Rocky Mountain Assistant Special
Agent-in-Charge **David R. Barnes** .... (303) 672-5350 ext. 1732
Fax: (303) 672-5087

Office of Community Planning and Development
1670 Broadway, Denver, CO 80202-4801
Tel: (303) 672-5414 Fax: (303) 672-5028

Director **Aaron B. Gagne** .... (303) 672-5076
E-mail: aaron.b.gagne@hud.gov
Deputy Director **(Vacant)** .... (303) 672-5414 ext. 1324
Program Manager **Kathleen Burke** .... (303) 839-2634
Program Manager **(Vacant)** .... (303) 672-5071

Office of Fair Housing and Equal Opportunity
1670 Broadway, Denver, CO 80202-4801
Tel: (303) 672-5437 TTY: (303) 672-5248 Fax: (303) 672-5026

Director **Col Amy M. Frisk USAF (Ret)** .... (303) 672-5151
E-mail: amy.m.frisk@hud.gov
Denver Program Center Director **(Vacant)** .... (303) 672-5155
Compliance Branch Chief/Supervisory EEO
Specialist **James Whiteside** .... (303) 672-5026
E-mail: james.c.whiteside@hud.gov
Enforcement Branch Chief
Christopher Vogel .... (303) 672-5437 ext. 1389
E-mail: christopher.vogel@hud.gov
Intake Branch Chief
Lynn Neely-Edmonds .... (303) 672-5437 ext. 1364
E-mail: lynn.neely-edmonds@hud.gov

Office of Human Resources
1670 Broadway, Denver, CO 80202-4801
Tel: (303) 672-5259 TTY: (303) 672-5042 Fax: (303) 672-5010

Supervisory Human Resources Specialist
Paula Z. Lopez .... (303) 672-5218 ext. 5218
E-mail: paula.z.lopez@hud.gov Fax: (303) 672-5010
Employee and Labor Relations Chief **Cheryl Eddings** .... (303) 672-5259

Office of Public Housing
1670 Broadway, Denver, CO 80202-4801
Tel: (303) 672-5372 Fax: (303) 672-5065

Director **Janice L. Rodriquez** .... (303) 672-5402
E-mail: janice.rodriquez@hud.gov
Division A Director **(Vacant)** .... (303) 672-5402
Regional Public Housing Director **Velma C. Navarro** .... (303) 672-5234
Education: Colorado State BS; U Phoenix MBA

Western (Denver) Field Contracting Operations
1670 Broadway, Denver, CO 80202-4801
Tel: (303) 672-5281 Fax: (303) 672-5062

Director **(Vacant)** .... (303) 672-5281
Program and REO Support Branch Chief
Edgar A. Cross .... (303) 672-5367
E-mail: edgar.a.cross@hud.gov
Small Business Specialist **Darrell D. Rishel** .... (303) 839-2622
Fax: (303) 672-5062

DEPARTMENTS

★ Presidential Appointment Requiring Senate Confirmation ☆ Presidential Appointment □ Schedule C Appointment ◇ Career Senior Foreign Service Appointment
● Career Senior Executive Service (SES) Appointment ○ Non-Career Senior Executive Service (SES) Appointment ■ Postal Career Executive Service

Office of Field Administrative Resources
1670 Broadway, Denver, CO 80202-4801

Supervisory Management and Budget Director
Robert D. Johnson .... (303) 672-5475
E-mail: Robert.D.Johnson@hud.gov
Regional Support Manager
Michael P. "Mike" Westra .... (303) 672-5251 ext. 1755
E-mail: michael_p._westra@hud.gov
Information Technology Division Director
Ronald L. "Ron" Wall .... (303) 672-5267 ext. 1860
E-mail: ronald.l.wall@hud.gov
Program Management Division Director **(Vacant)**........ (303) 672-5256

Denver Multifamily Hub
1670 Broadway, Denver, CO 80202-4801
Tel: (303) 672-5343 TTY: (303) 672-5113 Fax: (303) 672-5388

Multifamily Hub Housing Division Director (Acting)
Adela M. Escalante.............................. (303) 672-5417
E-mail: adela.escalante@hud.gov
Funding Specialist **Rayeann Abraham** .... (303) 672-5440
Program Analyst **Lisa A. Roner** .... (303) 672-5395
E-mail: lisa.a.roner@hud.gov
Grant Specialist **Rhonda L. Horn**..................... (303) 672-1608
E-mail: rhonda.l.horn@hud.gov
Grant Specialist **Darlene S. Matushefske** .... (303) 672-5474
E-mail: darlene.s.matushefske@hud.gov

Northern Plains Office of Native American Programs
1670 Broadway, Denver, CO 80202-4801
Tel: (303) 672-5465 TTY: (303) 672-5116 Fax: (303) 672-5003

Director **Randall R. "Randy" Akers**.................. (303) 672-5160
E-mail: randall.r.akers@hud.gov
Grants Evaluation Division Director **Melissa West** ...... (303) 672-5352
E-mail: melissa.west@hud.gov
Grants Management Division Director **Lori Roget** .... (303) 672-5175

Office of Housing – Denver Homeownership Center
1670 Broadway, Denver, CO 80202-4801
Tel: (303) 672-5244 Tel: (800) 543-9378 TTY: (303) 672-5325
Fax: (303) 672-5040

Director **Scott E. Bice**.............................. (303) 675-1639
E-mail: scott.e.bice@hud.gov
Deputy Director **Elaine A. Roberts** .... (303) 675-1698
E-mail: elaine.a.roberts@hud.gov
Processing and Underwriting Division
Director **Amy K. Trujillo** .... (303) 672-5342 ext. 5058
E-mail: amy.k.trujillo@hud.gov
Insurance and Underwriting Branch 1 Chief
Chris Malone .... (303) 672-5342 ext. 5299
E-mail: chris.malone@hud.gov
Insurance and Underwriting Branch 2 Chief
Melanie Brazil-Aksland................. (800) 225-5342 ext. 3817
Technical Support Branch Team 1 Chief
Simon L. Willis, Jr. .... (800) 225-5342 ext. 2664
E-mail: simon.l..jr.willis@hud.gov
Technical Support Branch Team 2 Chief
Juan C. Sola.......................... (800) 225-5342 ext. 3801
E-mail: juan.sola@hud.gov
Program Operations and Customer Service
Deputy Director **Daniel Richardson**......... (800) 225-5342 ext. 5266
E-mail: daniel.richardson@hud.gov
Program Support Division Director **Jeffrey M. Burton** ... (303) 861-3814
E-mail: jeffrey.m.burton@hud.gov
Quality Assurance Division Director **Kay Baker** .... (303) 675-1680
E-mail: Karen.Baker@hud.gov
Field Review Branch 1 Chief **Paul Will** ...... (800) 225-5342 ext. 1630
E-mail: paul.will@hud.gov
Field Review Branch 2 Chief
Robert C. Mitchell .... (800) 225-5342 ext. 2655
E-mail: Robert.C.Mitchell@hud.gov
Field Review Branch 3 Chief
Laura L. Bullock .... (303) 672-5215 ext. 1940
E-mail: Laura.L.Bullock@hud.gov

Office of Housing – Denver Homeownership Center *(continued)*

Real Estate Owned Division Director
Andrew R. Eckel .... (800) 225-5342 ext. 1635
E-mail: andrew.r.eckel@hud.gov
Real Estate Owned Branch 1 Division
Chief **Emilie Helms** .... (800) 225-5342 ext. 2659
E-mail: emilie.helms@hud.gov

Casper (WY) Field Office
Federal Office Building, 150 East B Street,
Room 1010, Casper, WY 82601
Tel: (888) 245-2994 Tel: (307) 261-6250 TTY: (307) 261-5252
Fax: (307) 261-6245
Field Office Director **Lyle J. Konkol** .... (307) 261-6251

Fargo (ND) Field Office
Federal Building North, 657 Second Avenue,
Room 366, Fargo, ND 58102-2483
P.O. Box 2483, Fargo, ND 58102-2483
Tel: (701) 239-5136 Fax: (701) 239-5249

Field Office Director **Joel D. Manske** .... (701) 293-2828
Operations Specialist **Oswald S. Scantlebury** .... (701) 293-2831
E-mail: oswald.s.scantlebury@hud.gov
Quality Assurance Specialist **Dean J. Fischer** .... (701) 293-2834
E-mail: dean.j.fischer@hud.gov
Program Assistant **Patricia M. Petry** .... (701) 293-2830
E-mail: patricia.m.petry@hud.gov

Helena (MT) Field Office
Paul G. Hatfield U.S. Courthouse, 901 Front Street,
Suite 1300, Helena, MT 59626
Tel: (406) 449-5050 Fax: (406) 449-5052

Field Office Director **Erik Amundson** .... (406) 447-1488
Customer Service Representative **(Vacant)** .... (406) 449-5050
Housing Specialist **Patricia "Pat" Heiser** .... (406) 447-1484
E-mail: patricia.e.heiser@hud.gov

Salt Lake City (UT) Field Office
125 South State Street, Suite 3001, Salt Lake City, UT 84138-1105
Tel: (801) 524-6070 Tel: (800) 225-5342 (Toll Free) Fax: (801) 524-6816
Internet: www.hud.gov/local/index.cfm?state=ut

Field Office Director (Acting) **Kelly L. Jorgensen** .... (801) 524-6070
Secretary **(Vacant)** .... (801) 524-6070
Senior Management Analyst **Pauline K. Zvonkovic** ...... (801) 524-6076
E-mail: pauline.zvonkovic@hud.gov
Management Analyst **Jeff L. Stowell** .... (801) 524-6071
E-mail: jeff.l.stowell@hud.gov

Sioux Falls (SD) Field Office
4301 West 57th Street, Suite 101, Sioux Falls, SD 57108
Tel: (605) 330-4223 Fax: (605) 330-4465

Field Office Director **Roger D. Jacobs** .... (605) 731-7693
Customer Service Representative **Lisa M. Wright** ...... (605) 330-4223
E-mail: lisa.m.wright@hud.gov
Housing Program Specialist **Jacqueline L. Westover** .... (605) 370-5146
E-mail: jacqueline.l.westover@hud.gov
SD Webmaster **(Vacant)** .... (605) 330-4223

Region IX - Pacific - Hawaii

San Francisco Regional Office
1 Sansome Street, Suite 1200, San Francisco, CA 94104
Tel: (415) 489-6410 Tel: (415) 489-6700 Tel: (800) 347-3739
TTY: (415) 489-6564 Fax: (415) 489-6419
Areas Covered: AZ, CA, HI, NV

○ Regional Administrator **James "Jimmy" Stracner** ...... (415) 489-6412
Deputy Regional Administrator **Wayne Sauseda** .... (415) 489-6400
E-mail: wayne.sauseda@hud.gov
Education: U San Francisco; U Pacific
Supervisory Management Analyst **Barbara A. Arch** ...... (415) 489-6600
E-mail: barbara.a.arch@hud.gov

★ Presidential Appointment Requiring Senate Confirmation ☆ Presidential Appointment ☐ Schedule C Appointment ◇ Career Senior Foreign Service Appointment
● Career Senior Executive Service (SES) Appointment ○ Non-Career Senior Executive Service (SES) Appointment ■ Postal Career Executive Service

San Francisco Regional Office *(continued)*

Information Technology Service Delivery Manager
Daigo Maydwell .... (415) 489-6477
E-mail: Daigo.C.Maydwell@hud.gov
Public Affairs Officer and Homeless Liaison
Eduardo "Ed" Cabrera .... (415) 489-6407
E-mail: eduardo.cabrera@hud.gov
Senior Management Analyst
David W. Lockwood .... (714) 796-5577 ext. 3004
Supervisory Management Analyst **Cynthia L. Abbott** .... (415) 489-6400
E-mail: cynthia.l.abbott@hud.gov
Senior Management Analyst, Freedom of Information Act (FOIA) Liaison **Myrna Pascual** .... (415) 489-6400
E-mail: myrna.b.pascual@hud.gov
FOIA Liaison **Toulu Thao** .... (415) 489-6404
E-mail: toulu.thao@hud.gov
Clerk **Mark S. Higuera** .... (415) 489-6408

Office of Counsel
1 Sansome Street, San Francisco, CA 94104
Tel: (415) 489-6500 Fax: (415) 489-6601

Regional Counsel (Acting) **Michael Propst** .... (415) 489-6510
Deputy Regional General Counsel **Mary C. Merchant** .... (415) 489-6515
E-mail: mary.c.merchant@hud.gov

Office of Inspector General
1 Sansome Street, San Francisco, CA 94104
Tel: (415) 489-6683 Fax: (415) 489-6689

Assistant Regional Inspector General for Audit
James Brady .... (415) 489-6697
E-mail: james.brady@hud.gov
Pacific/Hawaii Special Agent-in-Charge **James Luu** ...... (415) 489-6685
Fax: (415) 489-6689

Office of Community Planning and Development
1 Sansome Street, Ste. 1200, San Francisco, CA 94104
Tel: (415) 489-6597 Fax: (415) 489-6602

Director **Kimberly Nash** .... (415) 489-6572
E-mail: kimberly.y.nash@hud.gov
Team 1 Program Manager **Winston D. Moy** .... (415) 489-6586
E-mail: winston.d.moy@hud.gov
Team 4 Program Manager **Angelo C. Tom** .... (415) 489-6596
E-mail: angelo.tom@hud.gov

Office of Fair Housing and Equal Opportunity
1 Sansome Street, San Francisco, CA 94104
Tel: (415) 489-6524 TTY: (415) 436-6594 Fax: (415) 489-6559

Regional Director **Anne T. Quesada** .... (415) 489-6526
E-mail: Anne.Quesada@hud.gov Fax: (415) 489-6560
Deputy Director **Kenneth J. Carroll** .... (415) 489-6524

San Francisco Center
1 Sansome Street, San Francisco, CA 94104

Director **Kenneth J. Carroll** .... (415) 489-6536
E-mail: kenneth.j.carroll@hud.gov
Complaint Intake/Assessment Branch Chief
Paul E. Smith .... (415) 489-6524
E-mail: paul.e.smith@hud.gov

Office of Housing
1 Sansome Street, San Francisco, CA 94104
Tel: (415) 489-6603 Fax: (415) 489-6608

Pacific/Hawaii Multifamily Housing HUB Director
Thomas W. "Tom" Azumbrado .... (415) 489-6603
E-mail: thomas.azumbrado@hud.gov
Operations Director
Christopher J. "Chris" Thornton .... (415) 489-6493
E-mail: christopher.j.thornton@hud.gov
Director of Project Management **John Matters** .... (415) 489-6613
Fax: (415) 489-6620
Santa Ana Homeownership Center Real Estate Owned Division Director (Acting) **Shelby Rigg** ...... (800) 796-5577
Desk Officer **Suzette Agans** .... (202) 402-5089

Office of Human Resources
1 Sansome Street, San Francisco, CA 94104
Tel: (415) 489-6715 TTY: (415) 489-6564 Fax: (415) 489-6725

Director **Ginger Richardson** .... (415) 489-6400
Computer Services Director and CIO **Joanne Lee** .... (415) 489-6476
E-mail: joanne.lee@hud.gov Fax: (415) 489-6711
Supervisory Personnel Management Specialist
Sharon M. Lacy .... (415) 489-6703
E-mail: sharon.m.lacy@hud.gov Fax: (415) 489-6710

Office of Public Housing
1 Sansome Street, San Francisco, CA 94104
Tel: (415) 489-6426 Fax: (415) 489-6459

Director **Gerard Windt** .... (415) 489-6444
E-mail: Gerard.Windt@hud.gov
Division A Director (Operations)
Melina M. Whitehead .... (415) 489-6426
E-mail: melina.m.whitehead@hud.gov
Division B Director (Management) **(Vacant)** .... (415) 489-6426
Regional Public Housing Director **Edward Moses** .... (213) 534-2481

Honolulu (HI) Field Office
1132 Bishop Street, Suite 1400, Honolulu, HI 96813
Tel: (808) 457-4662 TTY: (808) 522-8193 Fax: (808) 457-4694
Internet: www.hud.gov/local/hi/community/contacts.cfm

Administrative Officer (Acting) **Kristie Reese** .... (602) 379-7119
E-mail: kristie.v.reese@hud.gov
Chief Counsel **(Vacant)** .... (808) 457-4662
Community Planning and Development Office Director
Mark A. Chandler .... (808) 457-4678
E-mail: mark.a.chandler@hud.gov
Customer Service Representative **Peter D. Howell** ...... (808) 457-4662
Fair Housing and Equal Opportunity Lead
Jelani M. Madaraka .... (808) 457-4693
E-mail: jelani.m.madaraka@hud.gov
Field Office Director **BrigGen Ryan T. Okahara ANG** ... (808) 457-4665
E-mail: ryan.t.okhara@hud.gov
Education: Hawaii BS; Webster MA
Multifamily Honolulu Program Lead **Raymond Gota** ... (808) 457-4691
Public and Indian Housing Director **Jesse Wu** .... (808) 457-4668
Education: Illinois; MIT 1997

Las Vegas (NV) Field Office
302 East Carson Avenue, Suite 400, Las Vegas, NV 89101-5911
Tel: (702) 366-2100 Fax: (702) 388-6244

Field Office Director **Tamara S. Thomas** .... (702) 366-2100
E-mail: tamara.s.thomas@hud.gov Fax: (702) 388-6244
Administrative Officer **Robbie L. Bradford** .... (702) 366-2112
E-mail: robbie.l.bradford@hud.gov
Multifamily Housing Management Branch Supervisory Project Manager **Frank J. Castro** .... (702) 366-2120
E-mail: frank.j.castro@hud.gov
Senior Management Analyst-Office of Field Policy and Management **Phyllis A. Hargrove** .... (702) 366-2142
E-mail: phyllis.a.hargrove@hud.gov
Management Analyst - Office of Field Policy and Management **Mimi M. Woodruff** .... (702) 366-2116
E-mail: mimi.m.woodruff@hud.gov
Senior Community Planning and Development Representative **(Vacant)** .... (702) 366-2113
Single Family Management Branch Team Leader
Kristine S. Douglas .... (702) 366-2131
E-mail: kristine.s.douglas@hud.gov
Multifamily Housing Project Manager
Cheryl Borgstrom .... (702) 366-2124
E-mail: cheryl.borgstrom@hud.gov
Multifamily Housing Project Manager **Mary E. Cain** ..... (702) 366-2122
E-mail: mary.e.cain@hud.gov

Reno (NV) Area Office
745 West Moana Lane, Suite 360, Reno, NV 89509
Tel: (775) 824-3700 TTY: (775) 784-5971 Fax: (775) 824-4978

Director **(Vacant)** .... (775) 784-4978
Management Analyst **Janet LeVesque** .... (775) 824-3706

(continued on next page)

DEPARTMENTS

Reno (NV) Area Office *(continued)*

Customer Service Representative **Luthene Andrews** ..... (775) 824-3701

Los Angeles (CA) Field Office
300 North Los Angeles Street, Suite 4054, Los Angeles, CA 90012
Tel: (213) 894-8000 TTY: (213) 894-7038 Fax: (213) 894-8107

Field Office Director **Ray Brewer** ..... (213) 894-8007
E-mail: ray.w.brewer@hud.gov
Chief Counsel **Lora Han** ..... (808) 780-0674
Special Agent-in-Charge **James Todak** ..... (213) 534-2510
Community Planning and Development Office Director (Acting) **Chin Woo Choi** ..... (213) 534-2571
Fair Housing and Equal Opportunity Office/Program Operations and Compliance Center Director **David T. Quezada** ..... (213) 534-2600
E-mail: david.quezada@hud.gov Fax: (213) 894-8123
Multifamily Housing Office Director **Thomas W. "Tom" Azumbrado** ..... (213) 534-2704
Fax: (213) 894-8132
Public Housing Office Director **Marcie Chavez** ..... (213) 534-2602
E-mail: marcie.p.chavez@hud.gov Fax: (213) 894-8125
Economic and Market Analysis Staff **Jerry Nakano** ..... (213) 534-2464
E-mail: ikuo.j.nakano@hud.gov
Environmental Staff **(Vacant)** ..... (213) 534-2578
Administrative Service Center Officer **Twila L. Bonds** ..... (213) 534-2700
E-mail: twila.l.bonds@hud.gov Fax: (213) 894-8096

Phoenix (AZ) Field Office
One North Central Avenue, Suite 600, Phoenix, AZ 85004-2361
Tel: (602) 379-7100 TTY: (602) 379-7181 Fax: (602) 379-3985
Internet: http://espanol.hud.gov

Field Office Director **Stephanie L. Smelnick** ..... (602) 379-7120
E-mail: stephanie.l.smelnick@hud.gov
Administrative Officer **Kristie Reese** ..... (602) 379-7119
E-mail: kristie.v.reese@hud.gov
Chief Counsel **Monica Garcia** ..... (602) 379-7104
E-mail: monica.n.garcia@hud.gov
Multifamily Program Branch Chief **Mary Ellen McFarlane** ..... (303) 672-5411
E-mail: mary.e.mcfarlane@hud.gov
Senior Management Analyst **Kenneth A. "Ken" Einbinder** ..... (602) 379-7103
E-mail: kenneth.a.einbinder@hud.gov
Management Analyst, Single-Family Asset Management **Stacey A. Brown** ..... (602) 379-7133
E-mail: stacey.a.brown@hud.gov
CPD Program Manager (Acting) **Kimberly Nash** ..... (415) 489-6572
Public Housing Director **Charron T Alfonso** ..... (602) 379-7118
Assistant Regional Inspector General for Audit **Martin Herrera** ..... (602) 379-7243
E-mail: mherrera@hudoig.gov

Southwest Office of Native American Programs
One North Central Avenue, Suite 600, Phoenix, AZ 85004-2361
Tel: (602) 379-7200 TTY: (602) 379-7181 Fax: (602) 379-3101

Administrator (Acting) **David W. Southerland** ..... (505) 346-6925
E-mail: david.w.southerland@hud.gov
Administrative Advisor **(Vacant)** ..... (602) 379-7200
Grants Evaluation Director **Rebecca L. Halloran** ..... (602) 379-7210
E-mail: rebecca.l.halloran@hud.gov
Grants Management Director **Robert J. "Bob" Holden** ..... (602) 379-7192
E-mail: robert.j.holden@hud.gov

Santa Ana (CA) Field Office
Santa Ana Federal Building, 34 Civic Center Plaza, Room 7015, Santa Ana, CA 92701
Tel: (714) 796-5577 Fax: (714) 796-1285

Field Office Director **Ray Brewer** ..... (213) 534-2503
E-mail: ray.brewer@hud.gov

Santa Ana (CA) Homeownership Center
Santa Ana Federal Building, 34 Civic Center Plaza, Room 7015, Santa Ana, CA 92701-4003
Tel: (714) 796-1200 Fax: (714) 796-1281

Director **Thomas A. Rose** ..... (714) 955-0920
E-mail: thomas.a.rose@hud.gov Fax: (714) 796-5528
TTY: (800) 225-5342
Deputy Director **Stephen F. "Steve" Gargano** ..... (714) 796-3615
E-mail: stephen.f.gargano@hud.gov

Region X - Northwest - Alaska

Seattle Regional Office
Seattle Federal Office Building, 909 First Avenue, Suite 200, Seattle, WA 98104-1000
Tel: (206) 220-5101 Fax: (206) 220-5108
Internet: www.hud.gov/washington
Areas Covered: AK, ID, OR, WA

□ Regional Administrator **Jeffrey "Jeff" McMorris** ..... (206) 220-5374
Deputy Regional Administrator **Michael S. Look** ..... (206) 220-5101 ext. 5374
E-mail: michael.s.look@hud.gov
Supervisory Operations Officer **Diana deForest** ..... (206) 220-6222
Economic and Market Analysis **Tom E. Aston** ..... (206) 220-5382
E-mail: tom.aston@hud.gov Fax: (206) 220-5194
Labor Relations (Acting) **Sandra Antrillo** ..... (303) 672-5012
Note: Based in Denver (Region VII) Office. 1670 Broadway, Denver, CO 80202-4801
E-mail: sandra.antrillo@hud.gov
Public Affairs Officer **Leland Jones** ..... (206) 220-5356
E-mail: leland.jones@hud.gov
Regional Web Manager **Helen A. Savoye Minor** ..... (509) 368-3205
E-mail: helen.a.savoye@hud.gov
Senior Executive Human Resources **Daniel Raymond** ..... (206) 220-5340
E-mail: daniel.raymond@hud.gov

Administrative Service Center 3
909 First Avenue, Seattle, WA 98104-1000
Tel: (206) 220-5100 Fax: (206) 220-5133

Support Services Branch 2 Chief **(Vacant)** ..... (206) 220-5100
Information Technology Service Delivery Manager **(Vacant)** ..... (206) 220-6249

Office of Counsel
909 First Avenue, Seattle, WA 98104-1000
Tel: (206) 220-5191 Fax: (206) 220-5194

Regional Counsel **Mona Fandel** ..... (206) 220-5445
E-mail: mona.fandel@hud.gov

Office of Inspector General
909 First Avenue, Seattle, WA 98104-1000
Tel: (206) 220-6444 Fax: (206) 220-5159

Assistant Regional Inspector General for Audit **(Vacant)** ..... (206) 220-6444
Northwest/Alaska Inspector General for Investigation **(Vacant)** ..... (206) 220-5120
Fax: (206) 220-5160

Office of Community Planning and Development
909 First Avenue, Seattle, WA 98104-1000
Tel: (206) 220-5150 Fax: (206) 220-5403

Director **John W. "Jack" Peters** ..... (206) 220-5268
E-mail: jack.peters@hud.gov
Deputy Director **(Vacant)** ..... (206) 220-5375

Office of Fair Housing and Equal Opportunity
909 First Avenue, Seattle, WA 98104-1000
Tel: (206) 220-5170 TTY: (206) 220-5185 Tel: (800) 877-0246
Fax: (206) 220-5447

Regional Director **(Vacant)** ..... (206) 220-5170

★ Presidential Appointment Requiring Senate Confirmation ☆ Presidential Appointment □ Schedule C Appointment ◇ Career Senior Foreign Service Appointment
● Career Senior Executive Service (SES) Appointment ○ Non-Career Senior Executive Service (SES) Appointment ■ Postal Career Executive Service

Office of Public Housing
909 First Avenue, Seattle, WA 98104-1000
Tel: (206) 220-5290 Fax: (206) 220-5255

Director **Harlan L. Stewart** .... (206) 220-6220
E-mail: harlan_stewart@hud.gov
Deputy Director **(Vacant)** .... (206) 220-6211

Housing and Equal Opportunity Enforcement Center
909 First Avenue, Seattle, WA 98104-1000

Program Center Director and Compliance Branch Chief
(Vacant) .... (206) 220-5304
Enforcement/Intake Branch Chief **Yvonne Marte** .... (206) 220-5297
E-mail: yvonne.marte@hud.gov

Office of Native American Programs
909 First Avenue, Seattle, WA 98104-1000
Tel: (206) 220-5270 Fax: (206) 220-5234

Administrator **Ken A. Bowring** .... (206) 220-5391
E-mail: ken_a._bowring@hud.gov
Grants Evaluation Division Director **Julie Kander** .... (206) 220-5397
E-mail: julie.kander@hud.gov
Grants Management Division Director
Thomas Carney .... (206) 220-6204
E-mail: tom_carney@hud.gov

Anchorage (AK) Field Office
3000 C Street, Suite 401, Anchorage, AK 99503
Tel: (907) 677-9800 TTY: (800) 770-8973 Fax: (907) 677-9803
Internet: www.hud.gov/local/anc

Office of Field Policy and Management - Field Office
Director **Colleen K. Bickford** .... (907) 677-9830
E-mail: colleen.bickford@hud.gov Fax: (907) 677-9805
Community Planning and Development Director
Carma E. Reed .... (907) 677-9890
E-mail: carma.reed@hud.gov
Regional Public Affairs Officer **Leland Jones** .... (206) 220-5356
E-mail: leland.jones@hud.gov Fax: (206) 220-5108
Senior Management Analyst **Ann Gravier** .... (907) 677-9833
Customer Service Representative **Jennifer Dickson** ...... (907) 677-9836

Office of Alaska Native American Programs
3000 C Street, Anchorage, AK 99503
Tel: (907) 677-9890 Fax: (607) 677-9802

Administrator **Bill Zachares** .... (907) 677-9860
E-mail: bill.zachares@hud.gov
Grants Evaluation Division Director **Dianna Alcantra** .... (907) 677-9870
E-mail: dianna.alcantra@hud.gov
Grants Management Division Director
Andy Concepcion .... (907) 677-9880
E-mail: andy.concepcion@hud.gov

Boise (ID) Field Office
1249 S Vinnell Way, Suite 108, Boise, ID 83709
Tel: (208) 334-1990 Fax: (208) 334-9648

Field Office Director **(Vacant)** .... (208) 334-1990
Senior Management Analyst **Brian Dale** .... (208) 334-1338
Management Analyst **(Vacant)** .... (208) 334-1990
Public Affairs Officer **Leland Jones** .... (206) 220-5356
E-mail: leland.jones@hud.gov

Portland (OR) Field Office
Edith Green-Wendell Wyatt Federal Office Building,
1220 SW 3rd Avenue, Suite 400, Portland, OR 97204-2825
Tel: (971) 222-2600 Fax: (971) 222-0357

Field Office Director **Tony Ramirez** .... (971) 222-2601
E-mail: tony.ramirez@hud.gov
Management Analyst **Lea Anderson** .... (971) 222-1877
Chief Counsel **(Vacant)** .... (971) 222-2600
Regional Public Affairs Officer **Leland Jones** .... (206) 220-5356
E-mail: leland.jones@hud.gov
Community Planning and Development Division
Director **(Vacant)** .... (971) 222-2612

Portland (OR) Field Office *(continued)*

Fair Housing and Equal Opportunity Director
Ife Asantewa .... (971) 222-2633
E-mail: ife.asantewa@hud.gov Fax: (971) 222-2671
Public Housing Office/Program Center Coordinator
Laure Rawson .... (971) 222-2666
E-mail: laure.rawson@hud.gov Fax: (971) 222-2673
Customer Service Representative **Julian Rose** .... (971) 222-2600

DEPARTMENTS

★ Presidential Appointment Requiring Senate Confirmation ☆ Presidential Appointment □ Schedule C Appointment ◇ Career Senior Foreign Service Appointment
● Career Senior Executive Service (SES) Appointment ○ Non-Career Senior Executive Service (SES) Appointment ■ Postal Career Executive Service

United States Department of the Interior

DEPARTMENTS

Contents

United States Department of the Interior (DOI)

Description: The Department of the Interior manages nationally owned public lands and natural resources, American Indian reservation communities, and island territories under United States administration. Other functions include assessing American mineral resources, as well as preserving both the environmental and cultural heritage of American national parks and historic sites.

1849 C Street, NW, Washington, DC 20240
Tel: (202) 208-7220 (Personnel Locator)
Tel: (202) 208-6416 (Public Information/Communications)
Tel: (202) 208-3424 (Fraud, Abuse and Mismanagement Hotline - DC Metropolitan Area) Tel: (800) 424-5081 (Fraud, Abuse and Mismanagement Hotline - Continental US, Alaska and Hawaii)
E-mail: open@ios.doi.gov (Open Government Directive Email)
Internet: www.doi.gov
Internet: https://www.doi.gov/open (Open Government Directive Website)

OFFICE OF THE SECRETARY

1849 C Street, NW, Mail Stop 7328, Washington, DC 20240
Tel: (202) 208-7351 Fax: (202) 208-6956

Office of the Deputy Secretary (DS)

1849 C Street, NW, Washington, DC 20240
Fax: (202) 219-1873

Office of Inspector General (IG)

1849 C Street, NW, Mail Stop 4428, Washington, DC 20240
Tel: (202) 208-5745 Tel: (202) 208-5300 (Hot Line)
Tel: (800) 424-5081 (Hotline) Fax: (703) 487-5402 Fax: (202) 208-6062
Internet: www.doioig.gov

Audits, Inspections and Evaluations

1849 C Street, NW, Washington, DC 20240
Tel: (202) 208-5745 Fax: (202) 208-6062

Central Regional Office

12345 West Alameda Parkway, Suite 300, Lakewood, CO 80228
Tel: (303) 236-8296

Regional Manager **Amy R. Billings** .... (303) 236-8282
E-mail: amy_billings@doioig.gov Fax: (303) 236-8211

Western Regional Office

Federal Building, 2800 Cottage Way,,
Suite E-2712, Sacramento, CA 95825
Tel: (916) 978-5650 Fax: (916) 978-5656

Regional Manager **Michael P. Colombo** .... (916) 978-5650
E-mail: michael_p_colombo@doioig.gov

Investigations

1849 C Street, NW, Washington, DC 20240
Tel: (202) 208-6752 TTY: (202) 208-2420 Fax: (202) 208-6062

Central Region Investigations

12345 West Alameda Parkway, Suite 300, Lakewood, CO 80228
Tel: (303) 236-8296 Fax: (303) 236-8279
E-mail: jack_rohmer@doioig.gov

Special Agent-in-Charge **David House** .... (303) 236-9892

Albuquerque (NM) Field Office

AFC Building 1, 2424 Louisiana Boulevard, NE,
Room 250, Albuquerque, NM 87110
Tel: (505) 346-2720 Fax: (505) 346-2744

Resident Agent-in-Charge **Art Willhite** .... (505) 346-2720

Billings (MT) Field Office

2602 First Avenue North, Room 136, Billings, MT 59101
Tel: (406) 657-6298 Fax: (406) 657-6319

Resident Agent-in-Charge **Joseph Waller** .... (406) 657-6323

Eastern Region Investigations

381 Elden Street, Suite 3000, Herndon, VA 20170-4817
Tel: (703) 487-8057 Fax: (703) 487-8053

Atlanta (GA) Field Office

2300 Lake Park Drive, Suite 215, Smyrna, GA 30081
Tel: (770) 801-7920 Fax: (770) 801-7924

Resident Agent-in-Charge **Gaddis "Mike" Ishee** .... (770) 801-7920

Western Region Investigations

Federal Building, 2800 Cottage Way, Suite E-2708,
Sacramento, CA 95825
Tel: (916) 978-5630 Fax: (916) 978-5635

Assistant Special Agent-in-Charge **Eric May** .... (916) 978-5630

Hawaii Field Office

1132 Bishop Street, Suite 2300, Honolulu, HI 96813
Tel: (808) 525-5310 Fax: (808) 525-5349

Resident Agent-in-Charge **Dean Tsukada** .... (808) 525-5320

Office of the Solicitor

1849 C Street, NW, Room 6352, Washington, DC 20240
Tel: (202) 208-4423 Fax: (202) 208-5584

Regional Offices

Alaska Region

4230 University Drive, Suite 300, Anchorage, AK 99508-4664
Tel: (907) 271-4131 Fax: (907) 271-4143
Areas Covered: AK

● Regional Solicitor **Joshua Kindred** .... (907) 271-4131
E-mail: joshua.kindred@sol.doi.gov
Executive Assistant **(Vacant)** .... (907) 271-4131

Intermountain Region

6201 Federal Building, 125 South State Street, Salt Lake City, UT 84138
Tel: (801) 524-5677 Fax: (801) 524-4506
Areas Covered: UT, AZ, parts of NV

● Regional Solicitor (Acting) **John W. Steiger** .... (801) 524-5677 ext. 233
E-mail: john.steiger@sol.doi.gov
Deputy Regional Solicitor **(Vacant)** .... (801) 524-5677 ext. 233
Staff Assistant **Kelly Flynn** .... (801) 524-5677 ext. 222
E-mail: kelly.flynn@sol.doi.gov

★ Presidential Appointment Requiring Senate Confirmation ☆ Presidential Appointment □ Schedule C Appointment ◇ Career Senior Foreign Service Appointment
● Career Senior Executive Service (SES) Appointment ○ Non-Career Senior Executive Service (SES) Appointment ■ Postal Career Executive Service

DEPARTMENTS

Phoenix (AZ) Field Office
401 West Washington Street, Space 44, Phoenix, AZ 85003
Tel: (602) 364-7880 Fax: (602) 364-7885

Field Solicitor **Wonsook Sprague** .... (602) 364-7880 ext. 7
E-mail: wonsook.sprague@sol.doi.gov

Northeast Region
One Gateway Center, Suite 612, Newton, MA 02458-2881
Tel: (617) 527-3400 Fax: (617) 527-6848
Areas Covered: CT, DE, IL, IN, ME, MD, MA, MI, MN, NH, NJ, NY, ND, OH, PA, RI, SD, VT, VA, WV, WI

Regional Solicitor **Peg Romanik** .... (202) 208-5578
E-mail: peg.romanik@sol.doi.gov
Field Solicitor **Andrew Tittler** .... (617) 527-3400
E-mail: andrew.tittler@sol.doi.gov
Attorney Advisor **Martha F. Ansty** .... (802) 662-5305
E-mail: martha.ansty@sol.doi.gov
Education: Duquesne JD
Attorney Advisor **Susan Amanda Bossie** .... (617) 527-3400
E-mail: susan.bossie@sol.doi.gov
Attorney Advisor **Mark D. Barash** .... (617) 527-3400
E-mail: mark.barash@sol.doi.gov
Attorney Advisor **David J. Gately, Jr.** .... (617) 527-3400
E-mail: david.gately@sol.doi.gov
Attorney Advisor **Brianna C. Kenny** .... (617) 527-3400
E-mail: brianna.kenny@sol.doi.gov
Attorney Advisor **David S. Rothstein** .... (413) 253-8600
E-mail: dave_s_rothstein@fws.gov
Attorney Advisor **Lea J. Tyhach** .... (617) 527-3400
E-mail: lea.tyhach@sol.doi.gov
Education: Cornell BS; Boston Col JD

Pittsburgh (PA) Field Office
Three Parkway Center, Suite 385, Pittsburgh, PA 15220
Tel: (412) 937-4000 Fax: (412) 937-4003

Field Solicitor **Wayne Babcock** .... (412) 937-4020
E-mail: wayne.babcock@sol.doi.gov
Attorney Advisor **Kelly Bakayza** .... (412) 937-4006
E-mail: kelly.bakayza@sol.doi.gov
Attorney Advisor **Steve Barcley** .... (412) 937-4007
E-mail: steve.barcley@sol.doi.gov
Attorney Advisor **Kimberly Gilmore** .... (412) 937-4017
E-mail: kimberly.gilmore@sol.doi.gov
Attorney Advisor **Stephen Mahoney** .... (412) 937-4009
E-mail: stephen.mahoney@sol.doi.gov
Attorney Advisor **(Vacant)** .... (412) 937-4000

Twin Cities (MN) Field Office
5600 West American Boulevard, Suite 270, Bloomington, MN 55437-1458
Tel: (612) 713-7100 Fax: (612) 713-7121

Field Solicitor **Tony A. Sullins** .... (612) 713-7100
E-mail: tony.sullins@sol.doi.gov
Attorney Advisor **Courtney L. Allensworth** .... (612) 713-7100
E-mail: courtney.allensworth@sol.doi.gov
Attorney Advisor **Hannah B. Bolt** .... (612) 713-7100
E-mail: hannah.bolt@sol.doi.gov
Attorney Advisor **Caitlin Coomes** .... (612) 713-7100
E-mail: caitlin.coomes@sol.doi.gov
Attorney Advisor **Alex Dyste** .... (612) 713-7100
E-mail: alex.dyste@sol.doi.gov
Attorney Advisor **Teresa M. Garrity** .... (612) 713-7100
E-mail: teresa.garrity@sol.doi.gov
Attorney Advisor **Alice Peterson** .... (612) 713-7100
E-mail: alice.peterson@sol.doi.gov
Attorney Advisor **Kara G. Pfister** .... (612) 713-7100
E-mail: kara.pfister@sol.doi.gov
Attorney Advisor **Carrie A. Prokop** .... (612) 713-7100
E-mail: carrie.prokop@sol.doi.gov
Attorney Advisor **Sharon E. Pudwill** .... (612) 713-7100
E-mail: sharon.pudwill@sol.doi.gov
Attorney Advisor **Stuart Radde** .... (612) 713-7100
E-mail: stuart.radde@sol.doi.gov

Pacific Northwest Region
805 SW Broadway, Suite 600, Portland, OR 97205
Tel: (503) 231-2126 Fax: (503) 231-2166
Areas Covered: ID, OR, WA

● Regional Solicitor **Lynn Peterson** .... (503) 231-2125
E-mail: lynn.peterson@sol.doi.gov
Assistant Regional Solicitor **Brad Grenham** .... (503) 231-2143
Assistant Regional Solicitor **Nolan Shishido** .... (503) 231-2126
Assistant Regional Solicitor **Frank S. Wilson** .... (503) 231-2132
E-mail: frank.wilson@sol.doi.gov

Boise (ID) Field Office
U.S. Department of the Interior, University Plaza, 960 Broadway Avenue, Suite 400, Boise, ID 83706
Tel: (208) 334-1911 Fax: (208) 334-1919

Field Solicitor **Kathleen M. Carr** .... (208) 334-1911 ext. 1
E-mail: kathleen.carr@sol.doi.gov

Pacific Southwest Region
Federal Building, 2800 Cottage Way, Room E-1712,
Sacramento, CA 95825
Tel: (916) 978-6131 Fax: (916) 978-5694
Areas Covered: CA, HI, NV, Pacific Islands

● Regional Solicitor **(Vacant)** .... (916) 978-6131
Staff Attorney **Amy Aufdemberge** .... (916) 978-6131
E-mail: amy.aufdemberge@sol.doi.gov
Staff Attorney **Janell Bogue** .... (916) 978-6131
E-mail: janell.bogue@sol.doi.gov
Staff Attorney **Cheryll Dobson** .... (916) 978-6131
E-mail: cheryll.dobson@sol.doi.gov
Staff Attorney **Janet Fealk** .... (916) 978-6131
E-mail: janet.fealk@sol.doi.gov
Staff Attorney **Karen Koch** .... (916) 978-6131
E-mail: karen.koch@sol.doi.gov
Staff Attorney **Kevin Mack** .... (916) 978-6131
E-mail: kevin.mack@sol.doi.gov
Staff Attorney **Luke Miller** .... (916) 978-6131
E-mail: luke.miller@sol.doi.gov
Staff Attorney **Erica L. B. Niebauer** .... (916) 978-6131
E-mail: erica.niebauer@sol.doi.gov
Staff Attorney **Kerry O'Hara** .... (916) 978-6131
E-mail: kerry.o'hara@sol.doi.gov
Staff Attorney **Stephen R. "Steve" Palmer** .... (916) 978-6131
E-mail: steve.palmer@sol.doi.gov
Staff Attorney **Veronica Rowan** .... (916) 978-6131
E-mail: veronica.rowan@sol.doi.gov
Staff Attorney **John "Kevin" Tanaka** .... (916) 978-6131
E-mail: kevin.tanaka@sol.doi.gov
Staff Attorney **Nancy Zahedi** .... (916) 978-6131
E-mail: nancy.zahedi@sol.doi.gov

San Francisco (CA) Field Office
333 Bush Street, Suite 775, San Francisco, CA 94104
Tel: (510) 817-1460 Fax: (510) 419-0143

Field Solicitor (Acting) **Karen Glasgow** .... (415) 296-3381
E-mail: karen.glasgow@sol.doi.gov

Rocky Mountain Region
755 Parfet Street, Suite 151, Lakewood, CO 80215
Tel: (303) 445-0600 Fax: (303) 231-5363
Areas Covered: CO, IA, KS, MO, NE, WY

● Regional Solicitor **Matthew J. McKeown** .... (303) 445-0625
E-mail: matthew.mckeown@sol.doi.gov
Education: McGill (Canada) 1989 BA; Oregon 1994 JD
Staff Assistant **(Vacant)** .... (303) 445-0600 ext. 558
Assistant Regional Solicitor **Terri Debin** .... (303) 445-0600 ext. 335
E-mail: terri.debin@sol.doi.gov
Assistant Regional Solicitor **Ratna C. Gupta** .... (303) 445-0600
Assistant Regional Solicitor **Dana Jacobsen** .... (303) 445-0600 ext. 336
E-mail: dana.jacobsen@sol.doi.gov
Assistant Regional Solicitor **(Vacant)** .... (303) 231-5353 ext. 447

★ Presidential Appointment Requiring Senate Confirmation ☆ Presidential Appointment ☐ Schedule C Appointment ◇ Career Senior Foreign Service Appointment
● Career Senior Executive Service (SES) Appointment ○ Non-Career Senior Executive Service (SES) Appointment ■ Postal Career Executive Service

Billings (MT) Field Office
U.S. Department of the Interior, 2021 4th Avenue North,
Suite 112, Billings, MT 59101
Tel: (406) 247-7583 Fax: (406) 247-7587

Legal Technician/Administrative Officer **Rita Graeber** .... (406) 247-7583
E-mail: rita.graeber@sol.doi.gov
Field Solicitor **Karan L. Dunnigan** .... (406) 247-7583
E-mail: karan.dunnigan@sol.doi.gov
Attorney-Advisor **John C. Chaffin** .... (406) 247-7583
E-mail: john.chaffin@sol.doi.gov
Attorney-Advisor **Roselyn Rennie** .... (406) 247-7583
E-mail: roselyn.rennie@sol.doi.gov
Attorney-Advisor **Curt Sholar** .... (406) 247-7583
E-mail: curt.sholar@sol.doi.gov
Attorney-Advisor **Bryan Wilson** .... (406) 247-7583
E-mail: bryan.wilson@sol.doi.gov
Attorney-Advisor **(Vacant)** .... (406) 247-7583
Paralegal **Robin Deguara** .... (406) 247-7583
E-mail: robin.deguara@sol.doi.gov
File Clerk **(Vacant)** .... (406) 247-7583

Southeast Region
Richard B. Russell Federal Building, 75 Spring Street, SW,
Suite 304, Atlanta, GA 30303
Tel: (404) 331-4447 Fax: (404) 730-2682
Areas Covered: AL, AR, FL, GA, KY, LA, MS, NC, SC, TN, PR, VI

• Regional Solicitor **Shannon Goessling** .... (404) 331-4447
E-mail: shannon.goessling@sol.doi.gov
Deputy Regional Solicitor **(Vacant)** .... (404) 331-4447 ext. 227
Assistant Regional Solicitor **(Vacant)** .... (404) 331-4447 ext. 228
Staff Assistant **Cheryl Brown** .... (404) 331-4447 ext. 223
E-mail: cheryl.brown@sol.doi.gov

Knoxville (TN) Field Office
800 South Gay Street, Suite 800, Knoxville, TN 37902
Tel: (865) 545-4294 Fax: (865) 545-4314

Field Solicitor **John W. Austin** .... (865) 545-4315
E-mail: john.austin@sol.doi.gov
Assistant Field Solicitor **(Vacant)** .... (865) 545-4294

Southwest Region
505 Marquette Avenue, NW, Suite 1800, Albuquerque, NM 87102
Tel: (505) 248-5600 Fax: (505) 248-5623
Areas Covered: AZ, CO, NM, OK, TX

• Regional Solicitor **Lance Wenger** .... (505) 248-5600
E-mail: lance.wenger@sol.doi.gov
Assistant Regional Solicitor **Frank R. Lupo** .... (505) 248-5611
E-mail: frank.lupo@sol.doi.gov
Attorney **Evan Blackstone** .... (505) 248-5606
Attorney **Theresa D. Copeland** .... (505) 248-5605
E-mail: theresa.copeland@sol.doi.gov
Education: New Mexico 2005 JD
Attorney **Stephanie Kiger** .... (505) 248-5600
E-mail: stephanie.kiger@sol.doi.gov
Education: American U BA; Arizona MA; U Washington 1999 JD
Attorney **Joan D. Marsan** .... (505) 248-5618
E-mail: joah.marsan@sol.doi.gov
Attorney **Jared M. Slade** .... (505) 248-5615
E-mail: jared.slade@sol.doi.gov
Attorney **Justin S. Tade** .... (505) 988-6721
E-mail: justin.tade@sol.doi.gov
Paralegal **Donna Sanchez** .... (505) 248-5610
E-mail: donna.sanchez@sol.doi.gov
Staff Assistant **Sarah St. John** .... (505) 248-5619
E-mail: sarah.stjohn@sol.doi.gov

Tulsa (OK) Field Office
7906 East 33rd Street, Suite 100, Tulsa, OK 74145
Tel: (918) 669-7730 Fax: (918) 669-7736

Field Solicitor **Alan Woodcock** .... (918) 669-7730 ext. 225
E-mail: alan.woodcock@sol.doi.gov
Attorney **Charles R. Babst, Jr.** .... (918) 669-7730 ext. 224
E-mail: charles.babst@sol.doi.gov

Tulsa (OK) Field Office *(continued)*

Attorney **Conor Cleary** .... (918) 669-7730 ext. 226
E-mail: conor.cleary@sol.doi.gov
Attorney **Martin Steinmetz** .... (918) 669-7730 ext. 231
E-mail: martin.steinmetz@sol.doi.gov
Paralegal **Karen Armendariz** .... (918) 669-7730 ext. 234
Paralegal **Kristina Tryon** .... (918) 669-7730 ext. 230
Legal Assistant **Jamie Belton** .... (918) 669-7730 ext. 229
Legal Assistant **Cathey King** .... (918) 669-7730 ext. 221

Office of the Special Trustee for American Indians (OST)

1849 C Street, NW, Washington, DC 20240
Tel: (202) 208-4866 Fax: (202) 208-7545 Internet: www.doi.gov/ost

Office of Trust Records
4400 Masthead Street, NE, Room 130, Albuquerque, NM 87109
Tel: (505) 816-1600 Fax: (505) 816-1612

• Director **Karen B. Foster** .... (505) 816-1600
E-mail: karen_foster@ost.doi.gov

Office of Trust Review and Audit (OTRA)
4400 Masthead Street, NE, Mail Stop 225, Albuquerque, NM 87109
Tel: (505) 816-1253 Fax: (505) 816-1366
Director **Elizabeth Wells Shollenberger** .... (505) 816-1253

Trust Beneficiary Call Center
4400 Masthead Street, NE, Albuquerque, NM 87109
Director **Bryan Marozas** .... (505) 816-1330

Trust Funds Investments Office
4400 Masthead Street, NE, Albuquerque, NM 87109
Director **(Vacant)** .... (505) 816-1100
1849 C Street, NW, Washington, DC 20240

Trust Funds Management Office
4400 Masthead Street, NE, Albuquerque, NM 87109
Financial Systems Administrator **Dianne Moran** .... (505) 816-1060
1849 C Street, NW, Washington, DC 20240

Trust Funds Accounting Division
1849 C Street, NW, Washington, DC 20240
Director **Sim-Wing Gohard** .... (505) 816-1336

Reporting and Reconciliation Office
4400 Masthead Street, NE, Albuquerque, NM 87109
Director **Robert Winter** .... (505) 816-1142
1849 C Street, NW, Washington, DC 20240

Regional Trust Administrators
4400 Masthead Street, NE, Albuquerque, NM 87109

• Great Plains and Alaska Regional Trust Administrator **Timothy Lake** .... (605) 698-4906
E-mail: timothy_lake@ost.doi.gov
• Navajo and Southwest Regional Trust Administrator **Margaret Williams** .... (505) 816-1052
E-mail: margaret_williams@ost.doi.gov
• Northwest and Western Regional Trust Administrator **Melvin Burch** .... (505) 816-1465
E-mail: melvin_burch@ost.doi.gov
• Midwest, Rocky Mountain and Pacific Regional Trust Administrator **Tom Reynolds** .... (505) 816-1108
• Southern Plains, Eastern Oklahoma, and Eastern Regional Trust Administrator **Robert Craff** .... (505) 816-1462
E-mail: robert_craff@ost.doi.gov

★ Presidential Appointment Requiring Senate Confirmation ☆ Presidential Appointment □ Schedule C Appointment ◇ Career Senior Foreign Service Appointment
● Career Senior Executive Service (SES) Appointment ○ Non-Career Senior Executive Service (SES) Appointment ■ Postal Career Executive Service

DEPARTMENTS

Fish and Wildlife and Parks (FWP)
1849 C Street, NW, Washington, DC 20240

OFFICE OF THE ASSISTANT SECRETARY (AS)
1849 C Street, NW, Washington, DC 20240
Tel: (202) 208-4416 Fax: (202) 208-4684

United States Fish and Wildlife Service (FWS)
1849 C Street, NW, Washington, DC 20240
Tel: (202) 208-4717 Fax: (202) 208-6817 Internet: www.fws.gov

★ Director-Designate **Aurelia Skipwith** .... (202) 208-4545

External Affairs (EA)
1849 C Street, NW, Washington, DC 20240
Fax: (202) 501-6589

National Conservation Training Center (NCTC)
Shepherd Grade Road, Route One, Box 166, Shepherdstown, WV 25443
Tel: (304) 876-7263 Internet: http://training.fws.gov

● Director **Jay Slack** .... (304) 876-7263
Deputy Director **James B. "Jim" Willis** .... (304) 876-7263
Librarian **(Vacant)** .... (304) 876-7399
Webmaster **Kathleen Loerich** .... (304) 876-7434
E-mail: kathleen_loerich@fws.gov

Law Enforcement
5275 Leesburg Pike, Falls Church, VA 22041-3803
Tel: (703) 358-1949 Fax: (703) 358-2271 Internet: www.fws.gov/le

National Fish and Wildlife Forensics Laboratory (FWRL)
1490 East Main Street, Ashland, OR 97520
Tel: (541) 482-4191 Fax: (541) 482-4989 Internet: www.lab.fws.gov

Laboratory Director
Kenneth W. "Ken" Goddard .... (541) 482-4191 ext. 507
Deputy Lab Director
Edgard O. "Ed" Espinoza .... (541) 482-4191 ext. 513
Administration and Technical Support Branch
Chief **Darrell D. Hegdahl** .... (541) 482-4191 ext. 501
Forensic Branch Chief **(Vacant)** .... (541) 482-4191
Chemistry Team Leader **Dr. Mark A. Kirms** .... (541) 482-4191
Criminalistics Team Leader **(Vacant)** .... (541) 482-4191 ext. 530
Genetics Team Leader **Mary Burnham Curtis** ... (541) 482-4191 ext. 522
Morphology Team Leader **Barry Baker** .... (541) 482-4191
Pathology Team Leader **Tabitha Viner** .... (541) 482-4191
Education: Maryland Baltimore County 1994

Regional Offices

Region 1 - Pacific Region
Eastside Federal Complex, 911 NE 11th Avenue,
Portland, OR 97232-4181
Tel: (503) 231-6119 Fax: (503) 872-2716 Internet: www.fws.gov/pacific
Areas Covered: GU, HI, ID, OR, WA, Pacific Islands

● Regional Director **Robyn Thorson** .... (503) 231-6119
E-mail: robyn_thorson@fws.gov
Education: Oregon 1982 JD
Deputy Regional Director **Theresa "Terry" Rabot** ...... (503) 231-6119

Budget and Administration
911 NE 11th Avenue, Portland, OR 97232-4181
Tel: (503) 231-6115 Fax: (503) 872-2811

Assistant Regional Director **Kevin Bumatay** .... (503) 231-6115
E-mail: kevin_bumatay@fws.gov
Education: Florida BS; Maryland MBA
Budget and Finance Division Chief **Cheri Frazell** .... (503) 736-4755
Diversity and Civil Rights Chief **Dana Perez** .... (503) 231-2260
E-mail: dana_perez@fws.gov

Budget and Administration *(continued)*

Lesbian, Gay, Bisexual, and Transgender Special
Emphasis Program Manager **Anthony Wynn** .... (503) 231-3231
E-mail: anthony_wynn@fws.gov
Regional Equal Employment Opportunity Counselor
Cris Stemler-Ross .... (503) 231-2081
E-mail: cris_stemler-ross@fws.gov
Contracting and General Services Division Chief
Frank Lee .... (503) 872-2827
Engineering Division Chief **Gary Blefgen** .... (503) 231-2016
Safety Branch Manager **Gary Wilson** .... (503) 231-2330
E-mail: gary_wilson@fws.gov
Safety Specialist **Alan Williams** .... (503) 231-2327
E-mail: alan_williams@fws.gov
Information Technology Management Division Chief
Michael "Mike" Fields .... (503) 231-2165
E-mail: mike_fields@fws.gov
Human Resources Division Chief **David Clark** .... (503) 231-6141
E-mail: david_c_clark@fws.gov
Employee Relations Specialist **Jeff Hardgrove** .... (503) 231-6141
E-mail: jeff_hardgrove@fws.gov
Administrative Assistant **(Vacant)** .... (503) 231-6115

Ecological Services
911 NE 11th Avenue, Portland, OR 97232-4181
Tel: (503) 231-6151 Fax: (503) 231-2240

Assistant Regional Director **Rolland White** .... (503) 231-6151
Deputy Assistant Regional Director (Acting)
Rachel Merkel .... (503) 231-6151
Division of Natural Resource Conservation, Chief
(Vacant) .... (503) 231-2013
Endangered Species Program Supervisor
Marilet Zablan .... (503) 231-2345

External Affairs
911 NE 11th Avenue, Portland, OR 97232-4181
Tel: (503) 231-6120

Assistant Regional Director **Jason Holm** .... (503) 231-2264
Public Affairs Chief **Miel Corbett** .... (503) 231-6211
E-mail: miel.corbett@fws.gov

Fisheries
911 NE 11th Avenue, Portland, OR 97232-4181
Tel: (503) 872-2763 Fax: (503) 231-2062

Assistant Regional Director **Roy Elicker** .... (503) 872-2763
Education: Lewis & Clark 1982 JD

Law Enforcement
911 NE 11th Avenue, Portland, OR 97232-4181
Tel: (503) 231-6170 Fax: (503) 231-6197

Special Agent-in-Charge **James Ashburner** .... (503) 231-6945
Assistant Special Agent-in-Charge **(Vacant)** .... (503) 231-6925

Migratory Birds and State Programs
Eastside Federal Complex, 911 NE 11th Avenue,
Portland, OR 97232-4181
Tel: (503) 231-6159 Fax: (503) 231-2019

Assistant Regional Director **Nanette Seto** .... (503) 736-4749
Education: Hawaii

National Wildlife Refuge System
911 NE 11th Avenue, Portland, OR 97232-4181
Tel: (503) 231-6214

Regional Chief **Kevin Foerster** .... (503) 231-6214
Fax: (503) 231-6837
Deputy Chief **Kim Trust** .... (503) 231-6214
Fax: (503) 231-6837
Realty and Refuge Lands Division Chief
Charles J. Houghten .... (503) 231-6214
Education: Western Michigan 1976 BPA; Utah State 1984 MLA
Natural and Cultural Resources Division Chief
Kim Trust .... (503) 231-6214
Fax: (503) 231-6837

★ Presidential Appointment Requiring Senate Confirmation ☆ Presidential Appointment □ Schedule C Appointment ◇ Career Senior Foreign Service Appointment
● Career Senior Executive Service (SES) Appointment ○ Non-Career Senior Executive Service (SES) Appointment ■ Postal Career Executive Service

National Wildlife Refuge System *(continued)*

Office of Refuge Law Enforcement Division Chief
Jeremy Bucher .... (503) 231-6214
E-mail: jeremy_bucher@fws.gov Fax: (503) 872-2709
Planning Services Division Chief **Charles J. Houghten** East Side Federal Complex, Floor 3, West ... (503) 231-6214
Education: Western Michigan 1976 BPA; Utah State 1984 MLA
Visitor Services and Communication Branch Chief
Michael Marxen .... (503) 872-2700
Fax: (503) 231-6187
Refuge Supervisor, Region 1 **Sylvia Pelizza** .... (503) 872-2723
Administrative Assistant **(Vacant)** .... (503) 231-6214

Science Applications

911 NE 11th Avenue, Portland, OR 97232-4181
Internet: https://www.fws.gov/pacific/Climatechange/

Assistant Regional Director **Stephen Zylstra** .... (503) 231-6237
Education: Colorado State 1993 BS; George Mason PhD

Field Offices

Idaho Fish and Wildlife Office
1387 South Vinnell Way, Suite 368, Boise, ID 83709
Tel: (208) 378-5243 Fax: (208) 378-5262 Internet: http://idahoes.fws.gov

State Supervisor **Greg Hughes** .... (208) 378-5243
State Deputy Supervisor **(Vacant)** .... (208) 378-5243
External Affairs Officer **(Vacant)** .... (208) 378-5243
Administrative Officer **Cathy L. Rogers** .... (208) 378-5387
E-mail: cathy_rogers@fws.gov

Pacific Islands Office
Prince Jonah Kuhio Kalanianaole Federal Building,
300 Ala Moana Boulevard, Room 3-122, Honolulu, HI 96850
Box 50187, Honolulu, HI 96850-0052
Tel: (808) 792-9400 Fax: (808) 792-9581
Internet: www.fws.gov/pacificislands
Areas Covered: HI, American Samoa, Commonwealth of the Northern Mariana Islands, Federated States of Micronesia, Guam, Republic of Palau, Republic of the Marshall Islands, U.S. territories in the Pacific (Midway, Wake, Johnston and Palmyra Atolls; Howland, Baker and Jarvis Islands; Kingman Reef)

Ecological Services Field Supervisor **Mary Abrams** ...... (808) 792-9400
Refuges and Wildlife Project Leader
Barry W. Stieglitz .... (808) 792-9540
Fax: (808) 792-9585
Law Enforcement Senior Resident Agent
Keith Swindle .... (808) 861-8525
Public Affairs Officer **Megan Nagel** .... (808) 792-9594
E-mail: megan_nagel@fws.gov

Washington Fish and Wildlife Office
510 Desmond Drive, SE, Suite 102, Lacey, WA 98503
Tel: (360) 753-9440 Fax: (360) 753-9008
Internet: https://www.fws.gov/wafwo/
Areas Covered: Western WA

State Supervisor **Eric Rickerson** .... (360) 753-6039
Education: Oregon State BS
Deputy State Supervisor **Bradley "Brad" Thompson** .... (360) 753-4652
Administrative Officer **Natalie Lasher** .... (360) 753-4328
Consultation and Technical Assistance Division Manager **Curtis Tanner** .... (360) 753-4326
Environmental Assistance and Restoration Division Manager **Mary Root** .... (360) 753-9547
E-mail: mary_root@fws.gov
Listing and Recovery Division Manager
Thomas "Tom" McDowell .... (360) 753-6046
Information, Education and Outreach Supervisor
Ann Froschauer .... (360) 753-4370
E-mail: ann_froschauer@fws.gov
Information Technology Management Supervisor
Zuma Martin .... (360) 753-6049
E-mail: zuma_martin@fws.gov

Region 2 – Southwest Region

500 Gold Avenue, SW, Albuquerque, NM 87102
P.O. Box 1306, Albuquerque, NM 87103-1306
Tel: (505) 248-6282 Fax: (505) 248-6910
Internet: www.fws.gov/southwest
Areas Covered: AZ, NM, OK, TX

● Regional Director (Acting) **Joy E. Nicholopoulos** .... (505) 248-6283
E-mail: joy_nicholopoulos@fws.gov Fax: (505) 248-6287
Education: New Mexico State 1996 PhD
● Deputy Regional Director (Acting) **James Broska** .... (505) 248-6928
E-mail: james_broska@fws.gov
Assistant Regional Director for Science Applications
James Broska .... (505) 248-6928

Budget and Administration

500 Gold Avenue, SW, Albuquerque, NM 87102
Tel: (505) 248-6808 Fax: (505) 248-6459

Assistant Regional Director **Ann Hammond** .... (505) 248-6808
E-mail: ann_hammond@fws.gov
Budget and Finance Division Chief **Terri Braden** .... (505) 248-6824
Fax: (505) 248-6798
Contracting and General Services Division Chief
Rey Aragon .... (505) 248-6794
Fax: (505) 248-6791
Engineering Division Chief **(Vacant)** .... (505) 248-7956
Fax: (505) 248-7950
Information Resources and Technology Management Division Chief **Gerry Gajeton** .... (505) 248-6851
Personnel Management Officer **(Vacant)** .... (505) 248-6808

Diversity and Civil Rights Program

500 Gold Avenue, SW, Albuquerque, NM 87102
Tel: (505) 248-7838 Fax: (505) 248-7837

Division Chief **Kary Allen** .... (505) 248-6818

Ecological Services

500 Gold Avenue, SW, Albuquerque, NM 87102
Tel: (505) 248-6920 Fax: (505) 248-6922 E-mail: r2esweb@fws.gov

Assistant Regional Director **Edward D. "Ted" Koch** ..... (505) 248-6920
Education: Southern Connecticut State U BS; Idaho State MS
Threatened and Endangered Species Division Chief
Susan Jacobsen .... (505) 248-6641

External Affairs

500 Gold Avenue, SW, Albuquerque, NM 87102
Tel: (505) 248-6911 Fax: (505) 248-6915

Assistant Regional Director **(Vacant)** .... (505) 248-6911
Executive Assistant **Phoebe Comeau** .... (505) 248-6912

Fisheries

500 Gold Avenue, SW, Albuquerque, NM 87102
Tel: (505) 248-6865 Fax: (505) 248-6845

Assistant Regional Director **Stuart Jacks** .... (505) 248-6865

Law Enforcement

500 Gold Avenue, SW, Albuquerque, NM 87102
Tel: (505) 248-7889 Fax: (505) 248-7899

Special Agent-in-Charge **Phillip Land** .... (505) 248-7889

Migratory Birds

500 Gold Avenue, SW, Albuquerque, NM 87102

Migratory Birds Division Chief **Scott Carleton** .... (575) 646-7196
Education: Southern Nazarene 1995 BS; Fax: (505) 248-6674
Arkansas 2002 MS; Wyoming 2009 PhD

National Wildlife Refuge System

500 Gold Avenue, SW, Albuquerque, NM 87102
Tel: (505) 248-6804 Fax: (505) 248-6497

Regional Coordinator **Aaron Archibeque** .... (505) 248-6908

★ Presidential Appointment Requiring Senate Confirmation ☆ Presidential Appointment ☐ Schedule C Appointment ◇ Career Senior Foreign Service Appointment
● Career Senior Executive Service (SES) Appointment ○ Non-Career Senior Executive Service (SES) Appointment ■ Postal Career Executive Service

DEPARTMENTS

State Programs
500 Gold Avenue, SW, Albuquerque, NM 87102
Federal Assistance Division Chief **Cliff Schleusner** ...... (505) 248-7450

Region 3 – Midwest Region
5600 West American Boulevard, Suite 990, Bloomington, MN 55437-1458
Tel: (612) 713-5360 Fax: (612) 713-5280 Internet: http://midwest.fws.gov
Areas Covered: IL, IN, IA, MI, MN, MO, OH, WI

● Regional Director (Acting) **Charles M. Wooley** .... (612) 713-5301
E-mail: charles_wooley@fws.gov
Education: Wisconsin (Stevens Point)
Executive Assistant **Conni Conner** .... (612) 713-5301
E-mail: conni.conner@fws.gov
Deputy Regional Director **Charles M. Wooley** .... (612) 713-5301
Education: Wisconsin (Stevens Point)
External Affairs Assistant Regional Director
Charles Traxler .... (612) 713-5310
E-mail: charles_traxler@fws.gov
Intergovernmental Affairs Liaison **Garrett Peterson** .... (612) 713-5311
Migratory Birds and State Programs Assistant Regional Director **Tom Cooper** .... (612) 713-5338
Science Applications Assistant Regional Director
Craig Czarnecki .... (612) 713-5180

Budget and Administration
5600 West American Boulevard, Bloomington, MN 55437-1458
Tel: (612) 713-5306 Fax: (612) 713-5308
Assistant Regional Director **Chris Jensen** .... (612) 713-5306

Ecological Services
5600 West American Boulevard, Bloomington, MN 55437-1458
Tel: (612) 713-5350 Fax: (612) 713-5292
Assistant Regional Director **Lori H. Nordstrom** .... (612) 713-5345

Indiana Field Office
620 South Walker Street, Bloomington, IN 47403-2121
Tel: (812) 334-4261 Fax: (812) 334-4273
Field Supervisor **Scott E. Pruitt** .... (812) 334-4261 ext. 200
Northern Indiana Ecological Services Sub-Office
Biologist **Elizabeth McCloskey** .... (219) 983-9753
P.O. Box 2616, Chesterton, IN 46304-2616 Fax: (219) 983-9816

Chicago Illinois Field Office
230 South Dearborn Street, Suite 3300, Chicago, IL 60604
Tel: (312) 216-4720 Fax: (312) 837-1788
Internet: www.fws.gov/midwest/chicago
Field Supervisor **Louise Clemency** .... (312) 216-4733
Administrative Officer **Luis Zaragoza** .... (312) 405-1278
E-mail: Luis_Zaragoza@fws.gov
Endangered Species Program Supervisor
Kristopher Lah .... (312) 216-4735
Environmental Contaminants Specialist
Edward "Ed" Karecki .... (312) 216-4734
Fish and Wildlife Biologist **Shawn Cirton** .... (312) 216-4728
Fish and Wildlife Biologist
Catherine "Cathy" Pollack .... (312) 216-4731
Fish and Wildlife Biologist **Kristen Voorhies** .... (312) 216-4720
Habitat Restoration Coordinator
Michael "Mike" Redmer .... (312) 216-4732
Administrative Assistant **(Vacant)** .... (312) 216-4720

Missouri Field Office
101 Park de Ville Drive, Suite A, Columbia, MO 65203-2132
Tel: (573) 234-2132 Fax: (573) 234-2181
Field Supervisor **Amy Salveter** .... (573) 234-2132 ext. 104
Administrative Officer **(Vacant)** .... (573) 234-2132 ext. 165

Ohio Field Office
4625 Morse Road, Suite 104, Columbus, OH 43230
Tel: (614) 416-8993 E-mail: ohio@fws.gov
Field Supervisor **(Vacant)** .... (614) 416-8993

Michigan Field Office
2651 Coolidge Road, Suite 101, East Lansing, MI 48823
Tel: (517) 351-2555 Fax: (517) 351-1443 E-mail: eastlansing@fws.gov
Internet: www.fws.gov/midwest/eastlansing
Field Supervisor **Scott Hicks** .... (517) 351-6274

Wisconsin Field Office
2661 Scott Tower Drive, New Franken, WI 54229-9565
Tel: (920) 866-1717 Fax: (920) 866-1710 E-mail: greenbay@fws.gov
Areas Covered: WI (except for the main stem of the Mississippi River and Duluth/Superior Harbor)
Field Supervisor **Peter "Pete" Fasbender** ...... (952) 252-0092 ext. 210
4101 American Boulevard, Bloomington, MN 55425-1665
E-mail: peter_fasbender@fws.gov

Illinois and Iowa Field Office
1511 47th Avenue, Moline, IL 61265
Tel: (309) 757-5800 Fax: (309) 757-5807 E-mail: RockIsland@fws.gov
Field Supervisor **Kraig A. McPeek** .... (309) 757-5800 ext. 202
Education: Augustana (IL) 2001
Assistant Field Supervisor **(Vacant)** .... (309) 757-5800

Minnesota Field Office
4101 American Boulevard, Bloomington, MN 55425-1665
Tel: (952) 252-0092 Fax: (952) 646-2873 E-mail: twincities@fws.gov
Internet: https://www.fws.gov/midwest/twincities
Field Office Supervisor
Peter "Pete" Fasbender .... (952) 252-0092 ext. 210

Fisheries
5600 West American Boulevard, Bloomington, MN 55437-1458
Tel: (612) 713-5111 Fax: (612) 713-5289
Assistant Regional Director **Todd Turner** .... (612) 713-5102
Executive Assistant **Kevin Alban** .... (612) 713-5133
Deputy Assistant Regional Director **Aaron Woldt** .... (612) 713-5110

Green Bay Fish and Wildlife Conservation Office
2661 Scott Tower Drive, New Franken, WI 54229-9565
Tel: (920) 866-1717 Fax: (920) 866-1710
E-mail: greenbayfisheries@fws.gov
Internet: www.fws.gov/midwest/GreenBayFisheries
Project Leader **(Vacant)** .... (920) 866-1717
Administrative Officer **Bernadette Madison** .... (920) 866-1745
E-mail: bernadette_madison@fws.gov

Law Enforcement
5600 West American Boulevard, Bloomington, MN 55437-1458
Tel: (612) 713-5320 Fax: (612) 713-5283
Special Agent-in-Charge **Gregory M. Jackson** .... (612) 713-5320
Assistant Special Agent-in-Charge
Warren "Andy" Buhl .... (612) 713-5320
E-mail: warren_buhl@fws.gov

National Wildlife Refuge System
5600 West American Boulevard, Bloomington, MN 55437-1458
Tel: (612) 713-5400 Fax: (612) 713-5288
Chief **Charles Blair** .... (612) 713-5401

Fergus Falls Wetland Management District
18965 County Highway 82, Fergus Falls, MN 56537-7726
Tel: (218) 739-2291 Fax: (218) 739-9534
Areas Covered: MN
Wetland Manager **(Vacant)** .... (218) 739-2291

Region 4 – Southeast Region
1875 Century Boulevard, Suite 400, Atlanta, GA 30345-3319
Tel: (404) 679-4000 Fax: (404) 679-4006
Internet: http://southeast.fws.gov
Areas Covered: AL, AR, FL, GA, KY, LA, MS, NC, SC, TN, PR, VI

● Regional Director (Acting) **Michael "Mike" Oetker** ..... (404) 679-4000
E-mail: michael_oetker@fws.gov
Education: Iowa State; Michigan State

★ Presidential Appointment Requiring Senate Confirmation ☆ Presidential Appointment ☐ Schedule C Appointment ◇ Career Senior Foreign Service Appointment
● Career Senior Executive Service (SES) Appointment ○ Non-Career Senior Executive Service (SES) Appointment ■ Postal Career Executive Service

Region 4 – Southeast Region *(continued)*

Assistant to the Regional Director
Acquanetta Reese .... (404) 679-4000 ext. 44002
E-mail: acquanette_reese@fws.gov

Deputy Regional Director
Michael "Mike" Oetker .... (404) 679-4000 ext. 44005
E-mail: michael_oetker@fws.gov
Education: Iowa State; Michigan State

Assistant to the Deputy Regional Director
Laura Maloof .... (404) 679-4000 ext. 44003

Budget and Administration

1875 Century Boulevard, Atlanta, GA 30345
Tel: (404) 679-4086 Fax: (404) 679-4102

Assistant Regional Director **Jacquelyn Hall** .... (404) 679-4087
Budget and Finance Division Chief (Acting)
Gerald Elrod .... (404) 679-4094
Contracting and General Services Division Chief
Steven "Steve" Sponaugle .... (404) 679-4026
E-mail: steve_sponaugle@fws.gov
Diversity and Civil Rights Division Chief **Kary Allen** .... (404) 679-4197
Engineering Division Chief **Brian Ellington** .... (404) 679-4103
Human Resources Division Chief **Keith Williams** .... (404) 679-4023
Information Technology Division Chief **John Taitano** .... (404) 679-4129
Safety and Occupational Health Division Chief
Brian Hardison .... (404) 679-4185

Ecological Services

1875 Century Boulevard, Atlanta, GA 30345
Tel: (404) 679-7140 Fax: (404) 679-7081

Assistant Regional Director (Acting) **Todd Hopkins** ..... (404) 679-7140
E-mail: todd_hopkins@fws.gov
Deputy Assistant Regional Director
Franklin J. "Jack" Arnold III .... (404) 679-7311
Ecological Services Program Supervisor
Michelle Eversen .... (404) 679-4108
Conservation Partnerships Division Chief
Aaron Valenta .... (404) 679-4144
Environmental Quality Division Chief **Robert Tawes** .... (404) 679-7142
Endangered Species Division Chief **Timothy Merritt** ..... (404) 679-7082

External Affairs

1875 Century Boulevard, Atlanta, GA 30345
Tel: (404) 679-7289 Fax: (404) 679-7286

Assistant Regional Director
Jeffrey M. "Jeff" Fleming .... (404) 679-7287
Government Affairs Specialist **Kristen Peters** .... (404) 679-7172
Media Relations Specialist and Native American
Liaison **Mel Davis** .... (404) 679-7289
Media Relations Specialist and Native American
Liaison **Dan Chapman** .... (404) 679-7289
Media Relations Specialist and Native American
Liaison **Elsie Davis** .... (404) 679-7289
Public Affairs Specialist **Nanciann Regalado** .... (404) 679-4161
E-mail: nanciann_regalado@fws.gov
Web Manager **Roy Hewitt** .... (404) 679-7306
E-mail: roy_hewitt@fws.gov

Fisheries

1875 Century Boulevard, Atlanta, GA 30345
Tel: (404) 679-4157 Fax: (404) 679-4141

Assistant Regional Director **Allan Brown** .... (404) 679-7082
Deputy Assistant Regional Director **(Vacant)** .... (404) 679-7324
Program Supervisor **Cynthia Williams** .... (404) 679-4148
Program Supervisor **(Vacant)** .... (386) 467-2374
Program Supervisor **(Vacant)** .... (706) 838-4723

Law Enforcement

1875 Century Boulevard, Atlanta, GA 30345
Tel: (404) 679-7057 Fax: (404) 679-7065
Internet: http://southeast.fws.gov/law

Special Agent-in-Charge **Luis Santiago** .... (404) 679-7057

Law Enforcement *(continued)*

Assistant Special Agent-in-Charge **Darwin Huggins** ..... (404) 679-7043

Migratory Birds and State Programs

1875 Century Boulevard, Atlanta, GA 30345
Tel: (404) 679-4159 Fax: (404) 679-4180 (Migratory Birds)
Internet: www.fws.gov/southeast/birds

Assistant Regional Director, Migratory Birds Division
Laurel Barnhill .... (404) 679-4159
Federal Aid Division Chief **Mike Piccirilli** .... (404) 679-4154

Refuges

1875 Century Boulevard, Atlanta, GA 30345
Tel: (404) 679-7154 Fax: (404) 679-7259

Chief **David Viker** .... (404) 679-7152
Education: Florida
Deputy Chief **Brett Hunter** .... (404) 679-7155
Assistant Deputy Regional Chief **Brett Hunter** .... (404) 679-7155
Realty Division Chief **Steven "Steve" Seibert** .... (404) 679-7164
Refuge Supervisor Area I **Mindy Gautreaux** .... (404) 679-7167
Refuge Supervisor Area II **(Vacant)** .... (404) 679-7157
Refuge Supervisor Area III **Daffny Pitchford** .... (404) 679-7163

Region 5 – Northeast Region

300 Westgate Center Drive, Hadley, MA 01035-9589
Tel: (413) 253-8200 Fax: (413) 253-8308 E-mail: northeast@fws.gov
Internet: www.fws.gov/northeast
Areas Covered: CT, DE, ME, MD, MA, NH, NJ, NY, PA, RI, VT, VA, WV, D.C.

● Regional Director **Wendi Weber** .... (413) 253-8300
E-mail: wendi_weber@fws.gov
Deputy Regional Director **Deborah Rocque** .... (413) 253-8301

Budget and Administration

300 Westgate Center Drive, Hadley, MA 01035-9589
Tel: (413) 253-8598 Fax: (413) 253-8293

Assistant Regional Director **Henry Chang** .... (413) 253-8613
E-mail: henry_chang@fws.gov
Deputy Assistant Regional Director **Glenn Davis** .... (413) 253-8256
Chief, Budget and Finance **Chris Nolan** .... (413) 253-8227
E-mail: chris_nolan@fws.gov
Chief, CGS-Hurricane Sandy Procurement
Lisa Virgilio .... (413) 253-8243
Chief, Contracting and General Services
Shannon Blackburn .... (413) 253-8748
E-mail: shannon_blackburn@fws.gov
Informal EEO Complaints Manager **(Vacant)** .... (413) 253-8598
Chief, Engineering (Acting) **Teri Neyhart** .... (413) 253-8598
Chief, Human Resources **Tiffany McFadden** .... (413) 253-8598
E-mail: tiffany_mcfadden@fws.gov
Chief, Information Technology Management
Eric McVey .... (413) 253-8330
Fax: (413) 253-8353
Chief, Safety and Occupational Health **David Dorough** ... (413) 253-8311

Ecological Services

300 Westgate Center Drive, Hadley, MA 01035-9589
Tel: (413) 253-8304 Fax: (413) 253-8482

Assistant Regional Director - Ecological Services
Paul Phifer PhD .... (413) 253-8304
Education: Boston Col; Minnesota PhD
Deputy Assistant Regional Director **Spencer Simon** ..... (413) 253-8578
Endangered Species Division Chief
Martin "Marty" Miller .... (413) 253-8615
Environmental Restoration and Review Division Chief
(Vacant) .... (413) 253-8646

Chesapeake Bay Field Office
177 Admiral Cochrane Drive, Annapolis, MD 21401
Tel: (410) 573-4599 Fax: (410) 266-9127
Internet: https://www.fws.gov/chesapeakebay/

Supervisor **Genevieve LaRouche** .... (410) 573-4573
E-mail: genevieve_larouche@fws.gov
Coastal Program Supervisor **Dan Murphy** .... (410) 573-4521
Contaminants Program Supervisor **Sherry Krest** .... (410) 573-4525
Invasive Species Program Supervisor **Julie Slacum** ...... (410) 573-4595
E-mail: julie_thompson@fws.gov
Federal Projects Program Supervisor **Chris Guy** .... (410) 573-4529
E-mail: chris_guy@fws.gov
Habitat Restoration and Partners Program Supervisor **Richard "Rich" Starr** .... (410) 573-4583
E-mail: rich_starr@fws.gov
Permits Program Supervisor **Chris Guy** .... (410) 573-4529
E-mail: chris_guy@fws.gov
Streams and Watershed Restoration Program Supervisor **Richard "Rich" Starr** .... (410) 573-4583
E-mail: rich_starr@fws.gov
Liaison to Chesapeake Bay Program **Mike Slattery** ...... (410) 260-2487
E-mail: michael_slattery@fws.gov
Computer Specialist **(Vacant)** .... (410) 573-4563
Administrative Officer **(Vacant)** .... (410) 573-4568

Delaware Bay Estuary Project
2610 Whitehall Neck Road, Smyrna, DE 19977
TTY: (800) 232-5460 Tel: (302) 653-9152 Fax: (302) 653-9421

Field Supervisor **Gregory Breese** .... (302) 653-9152 ext. 115

Maine Fish and Wildlife Service Complex
306 Hatchery Road, East Orland, ME 04431
Tel: (207) 469-7300 Fax: (207) 902-1588
Internet: www.fws.gov/mainefieldoffice

Field Supervisor **Anna Harris** .... (207) 902-1567

New England Field Office
70 Commercial Street., Suite 300, Concord, NH 03301
Tel: (603) 223-2541 Fax: (603) 223-0104
Internet: www.fws.gov/newengland

Supervisor **Thomas R. "Tom" Chapman** .... (603) 227-6410

New Jersey Field Office
Atlantic Professional Park, 4 East Jimmie Leeds Road, Galloway, NJ 08205
Tel: (609) 646-9310 Tel: (609) 383-3938 Fax: (609) 646-0352
E-mail: newjerseyfieldoffice@fws.gov Internet: http://njfieldoffice.fws.gov

Administrator **Eric Schrading** .... (609) 383-3938 ext. 5272
E-mail: eric_schrading@fws.gov
Partners Private Lands Coordinator **Elizabeth Ciuzio "Beth" Freiday** .... (609) 383-3938 ext. 5263
Environmental Contaminants Supervisory Fish and Wildlife Biologist **(Vacant)** .... (609) 383-3938 ext. 26
Senior Fish and Wildlife Biologist (Environmental Contaminants) **Melissa Foster** .... (609) 383-3938 ext. 5262
E-mail: melissa_foster@fws.gov
Senior Fish and Wildlife Biologist (Environmental Contaminants) **Clay Stern** .... (609) 383-3938 ext. 5280
E-mail: clay_stern@fws.gov
Federal Activities and Endangered Species Supervisory Fish and Wildlife Biologist **Ron Popowski** .... (609) 241-7065
Senior Fish and Wildlife Biologist (Endangered Species) **Wendy Walsh** ...... (609) 383-3938 ext. 5274
Senior Fish and Wildlife Biologist (Federal Activities) **Steve Mars** .... (609) 383-3938 ext. 5267
Division of Law Enforcement - Special Agent **Ryan Bessey** .... (856) 327-0821 ext. 5277
Administrative Officer **Laura Perlick** .... (609) 383-3938 ext. 5270
Information Technology Specialist **(Vacant)** .... (609) 646-9310

New York Field Office
3817 Luker Road, Cortland, NY 13045
Tel: (607) 753-9334 Fax: (607) 753-9699
Internet: www.fws.gov/northeast/nyfo/
Areas Covered: NY

Supervisor **David Stilwell** .... (607) 753-9334

Pennsylvania Field Office
110 Radnor Road, Suite 101, State College, PA 16801
Tel: (814) 234-4090 Fax: (814) 234-0748
Areas Covered: PA

Supervisor and Project Leader **Sonja Jahrsdoerfer** .... (814) 234-4090 ext. 7474

Rhode Island Field Office
Rhode Island Field Office, 50 Bend Road, Charlestown, RI 02813
Tel: (401) 364-9124 Fax: (401) 364-0170 E-mail: fw5es_rifo@fws.gov

Northeast Region Refuges Manager **Charles E. VanDemoer** Rhode Island National Wildlife Refuge Complex .... (401) 364-9124
E-mail: charlie_vandemoer@fws.gov
Southern New England-New York Bight Coastal Ecosystems Program Project Leader **Thomas R. "Tom" Chapman** .... (603) 223-2541
70 Commercial Street, Suite 300, Concord, NH 03301 Fax: (603) 223-0104
E-mail: tom_chapman@fws.gov

Virginia Field Office
6669 Short Lane, Gloucester, VA 23061-4410
Tel: (804) 693-6694 Fax: (804) 693-9032
Internet: www.fws.gov/northeast/virginiafield

Field Supervisor **Cindy A. Schulz** .... (804) 824-2426
Assistant Supervisor for Endangered Species and Conservation Planning Assistance **Troy Andersen** ...... (804) 824-2428
Assistant Supervisor for Environmental Contaminants **Susan Lingenfelser** .... (804) 824-2415
E-mail: susan_lingenfelser@fws.gov

West Virginia Field Office
694 Beverly Pike, Elkins, WV 26241
Tel: (304) 636-6586 Fax: (304) 636-7824

Supervisor **John Schmidt** .... (304) 636-6586 ext. 16

External Affairs (EA)
300 Westgate Center Drive, Hadley, MA 01035-9589

Assistant Regional Director for External Affairs **Kyla Hastie** .... (413) 253-8325
Deputy Assistant Regional Director and Congressional Liaison **Christine Eustis** .... (413) 253-8321
Chief, Public Affairs **Terri Edwards** .... (413) 253-8324

Fisheries
300 Westgate Center Drive, Hadley, MA 01035-9589
Tel: (413) 253-8402 Fax: (413) 253-8488

Assistant Regional Director **Sherry White** .... (413) 253-8296
Fax: (413) 253-8293
Deputy Assistant Regional Director **Lowell Whitney** ..... (413) 253-8405

Lake Champlain Fish and Wildlife Resources Office
Winston Prouty Federal Building, 11 Lincoln Street, Essex Junction, VT 05452
Tel: (802) 872-0629 Fax: (802) 872-9704 E-mail: fw5fr_lcfwro@fws.gov

Project Leader **Helen Person** .... (802) 872-0629 ext. 12

Migratory Birds
300 Westgate Center Drive, Hadley, MA 01035-9589
Tel: (413) 253-8273 Fax: (413) 253-8293

Chief **Pamela Toschik** .... (413) 253-8610
Bird Habitat Programs Chief **(Vacant)** .... (413) 253-8273
Bird Population Programs Chief **Scott Johnston** .... (413) 253-8557
Permits Branch Chief **(Vacant)** .... (413) 253-8273

★ Presidential Appointment Requiring Senate Confirmation ☆ Presidential Appointment ☐ Schedule C Appointment ◇ Career Senior Foreign Service Appointment
● Career Senior Executive Service (SES) Appointment ○ Non-Career Senior Executive Service (SES) Appointment ■ Postal Career Executive Service

Migratory Birds *(continued)*

Leadership and Employee Development Chief
Jennifer Jones .... (304) 870-4614

National Wildlife Refuge System
300 Westgate Center Drive, Hadley, MA 01035-9589
Tel: (413) 253-8306 Fax: (413) 253-8468

Regional Chief **Scott Kahan** .... (413) 253-8550
Deputy Regional Chief **Sharon Marino** .... (413) 253-8579
Realty Division Chief **Mark Maghini** .... (413) 253-8590
Refuge Field Support Division Chief **Deborah Long** ..... (413) 253-8527

Science Applications
300 Westgate Center Drive, Hadley, MA 01035-9589

Assistant Regional Director **Kenneth D. Elowe PhD** ..... (413) 253-8273
Education: Bowdoin BS; UMass (Amherst) MS, PhD
Regional Scientist **Richard O. "Rick" Bennett PhD** ..... (413) 253-8273
Education: Fairleigh Dickinson BS; Adelphi MS; Rhode Island PhD

Wildlife and Sport Fish Restoration
300 Westgate Center Drive, Hadley, MA 01035-9589

Assistant Regional Director **Colleen Sculley** .... (413) 253-8501

Office of Law Enforcement
300 Westgate Center Drive, Hadley, MA 01035-9589
Tel: (413) 253-8274 Fax: (413) 253-8459

Special Agent-in-Charge
Honora G. "Honnie" Gordon .... (413) 253-8274
Assistant Special Agent-in-Charge **Jeffrey Odom** .... (413) 253-8341
E-mail: jeff_odom@fws.gov

Region 6 – Mountain-Prairie Region
134 Union Boulevard, Lakewood, CO 80228-1807
P.O. Box 25486, DFC, Denver, CO 80225-0486
Tel: (303) 236-7920 Fax: (303) 236-8295 Internet: www.r6.fws.gov
Areas Covered: CO, KS, MT, NE, ND, SD, UT, WY

● Regional Director **Noreen E. Walsh** .... (303) 236-7920
Education: Michigan State BS; Colorado State MS
Deputy Regional Director **Matthew J. "Matt" Hogan** ... (303) 236-7920
Education: LeMoyne-Owen 1990 BA
Webmaster **(Vacant)** .... (303) 236-4487

Budget and Administration
134 Union Boulevard, Lakewood, CO 80228
Tel: (303) 236-7917 Fax: (303) 236-6958

Assistant Regional Director (Acting)
Clinton "Clint" Riley .... (303) 236-5231
E-mail: clinton_riley@fws.gov
Budget and Finance Officer **(Vacant)** .... (303) 236-4456
Contracting Officer **(Vacant)** .... (303) 236-3636
Human Resources Officer **Michelle Rockwell** .... (303) 236-4738
Regional Engineer **Lorri Harper** .... (303) 236-4478
Regional Safety Manager **Jim Chandler** .... (303) 236-8193
Information Technology and Resources Management
Stephen A. Smith .... (303) 236-4583
E-mail: stephen_a_smith@fws.gov

External Affairs
134 Union Boulevard, Lakewood, CO 80228
Tel: (303) 236-7905 Fax: (303) 236-3815 E-mail: r6ea_web@fws.gov

Assistant Regional Director **Anna Muñoz** .... (303) 236-4510
Deputy Assistant Regional Director and Legislative Affairs Specialist **Roya Mogadam** .... (303) 236-4572
E-mail: roya_mogadam@fws.gov
Public Affairs Specialist **Michael D'Agostino MPA** ...... (303) 236-4588
E-mail: michael_dagostino@fws.gov
Public Affairs Specialist **Robert "Steve" Segin** .... (303) 236-4578
Public Affairs Specialist **Jennifer Strickland** .... (303) 236-7905
E-mail: jennifer_strickland@fws.gov
Public Affairs Assistant **Denise Sanchez** .... (303) 236-2985
E-mail: denise_sanchez@fws.gov

External Affairs *(continued)*

Digital Communications Specialist **(Vacant)** .... (303) 236-7905

Ecological Services
134 Union Boulevard, Lakewood, CO 80228
Tel: (303) 236-4211 Fax: (303) 236-0027

Assistant Regional Director **Michael "Mike" Thabault** ... (303) 236-4210
Deputy Assistant Regional Director **Nicole Alt** .... (303) 236-4213
Division Chief **Marjorie "Marj" Nelson** .... (303) 236-4258
Classification and Recovery Branch Chief **(Vacant)** ...... (303) 236-4211
Decision Support Branch Chief **Kate Norman** .... (303) 236-4214
Landscape Conservation and Restoration Branch Chief
Maria Boroja .... (303) 236-4518

Fisheries
134 Union Boulevard, Lakewood, CO 80228
Tel: (303) 236-4517 Fax: (303) 236-8163

Assistant Regional Director **Gregory Gerlich** .... (303) 236-4580

Law Enforcement
134 Union Boulevard, Lakewood, CO 80228
Tel: (303) 236-7540 Fax: (303) 236-7901

Special Agent In Charge **Steve Oberholtzer** .... (303) 236-7893
Assistant Special Agent in Charge **(Vacant)** .... (303) 236-7791

Migratory Birds and State Programs
134 Union Boulevard, Lakewood, CO 80228
Tel: (303) 236-8155 Fax: (303) 236-8192

Assistant Regional Director **Clinton "Clint" Riley** .... (303) 236-5231
Federal Aid Division Chief **Steve Jose** .... (303) 236-4411
Migratory Birds Chief **Casey Stemler** .... (303) 236-4403

National Wildlife Refuge System (NWRS)
134 Union Boulevard, Lakewood, CO 80228
Tel: (303) 236-8145 Fax: (303) 236-4792

Assistant Regional Director **Will Meeks** .... (303) 236-4303

Water Resources
134 Union Boulevard, Lakewood, CO 80228
Tel: (303) 236-5322 Fax: (303) 236-4224
Internet: https://www.fws.gov/mountain-prairie/wtr/

Chief **Megan "Meg" Estep** .... (303) 236-4491

Region 7 – Alaska Region
1011 East Tudor Road, Anchorage, AK 99503
Tel: (907) 786-3309 Fax: (907) 786-3306
E-mail: ak_externalaffairs@fws.gov Internet: http://alaska.fws.gov
Areas Covered: AK

● Regional Director (Acting) **Karen P. Clark** .... (907) 786-3542
E-mail: karen_clark@fws.gov
Deputy Regional Director **Karen P. Clark** .... (907) 786-3542

Budget and Administration
1011 East Tudor Road, Mail Stop 385, Anchorage, AK 99503
Fax: (907) 786-3848

Assistant Regional Director **Douglas Mills** .... (907) 786-3619
E-mail: douglas_mills@fws.gov
Deputy Assistant Regional Director **(Vacant)** .... (907) 786-3481
Budget and Finance Chief **Sheri Frazell** .... (907) 786-3619
Contracting and General Services Chief
Alissa Varrati Mail Stop 171 .... (907) 786-3439
FOIA Officer **Lynne N. Santos** .... (907) 786-3544
E-mail: lynne_santos@fws.gov
Human Resources Officer
Helen Stewart Mail Stop 111 .... (907) 786-3307
E-mail: helen_stewart@fws.gov
Information Technology Management Chief (Acting)
Mike Lewis .... (907) 786-3347
1011East Tudor Road, Mail Stop 271, Anchorage, AK 99503 Fax: (907) 786-3652

(continued on next page)

DEPARTMENTS

Budget and Administration *(continued)*

Regional Engineer/Engineering Division Chief
Gary Blefgen .... (907) 786-3862
1011 East Tudor Road, Mail Stop 131, Anchorage, AK 99503

Regional Safety Manager **Mark Ilg** .... (907) 786-3309
E-mail: mark_ilg@fws.gov

Diversity and Civil Rights Programs
1011 East Tudor Road, Mail Stop 301, Anchorage, AK 99503
Tel: (907) 786-3328 Fax: (907) 786-3552

Chief **Mike Lewis** .... (907) 786-3518

Alaska Resources Library
Library Building, 3211 Providence Drive,
Room 111, Anchorage, AK 99503
Tel: (907) 272-7547 Fax: (907) 786-7652

Librarian **Steven "Steve" Johnson** .... (907) 786-7661
E-mail: steven_johnson@fws.gov

Reference Services Coordinator **(Vacant)** .... (907) 786-7660

External Affairs
1011 East Tudor Road, Mail Stop 101, Anchorage, AK 99503
Tel: (907) 786-3695 Fax: (907) 786-3495

Assistant Regional Director **Sara Boario** .... (907) 786-3431
Alaska Native Affairs Specialist **Crystal Leonetti** .... (907) 786-3868
Chief of Media **Andrea Medeiros** .... (907) 786-3695

Fisheries - Ecological Services
1011 East Tudor Road, Mail Stop 385, Anchorage, AK 99503
Tel: (907) 786-3544 Fax: (907) 786-3848

Assistant Regional Director **Mary A. Colligan** .... (907) 786-3668
E-mail: mary_colligan@fws.gov

Secretary **Lucille Frerich** .... (907) 786-3856
E-mail: lucille_frerich@fws.gov

Endangered Species Coordinator **Drew Crane** .... (907) 786-3323

Conservation Genetics Laboratory
1011 East Tudor Road, Mail Stop 255, Anchorage, AK 99503
Tel: (907) 786-3858 Fax: (907) 786-3978

Supervisory Geneticist **John Wenburg** .... (907) 786-3858

Fisheries and Habitat Conservation
1011 East Tudor Road, Anchorage, AK 99503
Fax: (907) 786-3350 Fax: (907) 786-3978

Deputy Assistant Regional Director **Steve Klosiewski** ... (907) 786-3523

Fish and Wildlife Biologist (Coastal/Partners)
John DeLapp .... (907) 786-3925

Regional Environmental Contaminants Coordinator
Lori Verbrugge .... (907) 786-3329
Fax: (907) 786-3350

Fishery Subsistence Coordinator **Jerry Berg** .... (907) 786-3830

Habitat Restoration and Partnership Coordinator
David Wigglesworth .... (907) 786-3925

Marine Mammals Management Office
1011 East Tudor Road, Anchorage, AK 99503
Tel: (800) 362-5148 Tel: (907) 786-3800 Fax: (907) 786-3816

Division Chief **Patrick Lemons** .... (907) 786-3668
Supervisory Wildlife Biologist **James MacCracken** ..... (907) 786-3803

Anchorage Fish and Wildlife Conservation Office
4700 BLM Road, Anchorage, AK 99507
Tel: (907) 271-2888 Fax: (907) 271-2786
Internet: alaska.fws.gov/fisheries/fieldoffice/anchorage

Conservation Supervisor **Stewart Cogswell** .... (907) 271-2787
E-mail: stewart_cogswell@fws.gov

Administration Officer **Gary Goldberg** .... (907) 786-3813
E-mail: gary_goldberg@fws.gov

Administration Assistant **Catherine "Cathy" Shaw** ..... (907) 271-2888
E-mail: catherine_shaw@fws.gov

Ecological Services Branch Chief **Douglass Cooper** ..... (907) 271-1467
E-mail: douglass_cooper@fws.gov

Anchorage Fish and Wildlife Conservation Office *(continued)*

Fish and Wildlife Biologist **Elizabeth B. Benolkin** ..... (907) 271-2718
Education: Pittsburgh 1994 BA; Alaska (Fairbanks) 2009 MS

Fish and Wildlife Biologist **Kevin Foley** .... (907) 271-2788
E-mail: kevin_foley@fws.gov

Fish and Wildlife Biologist **Leah Kenney** .... (907) 271-2440
E-mail: leah_kenney@fws.gov

Fish and Wildlife Biologist **Betsy McCracken** .... (907) 271-2783

Fish and Wildlife Biologist **Daniel Rinella** .... (907) 271-2871
E-mail: daniel_rinella@fws.gov

Fish and Wildlife Biologist
Jennifer "Jennie" Spegon .... (907) 271-2768
E-mail: jennifer_j_spegon@fws.gov

Fish and Wildlife Biologist **Catherine Yeargan** .... (907) 271-2066
E-mail: catherine_yeargan@fws.gov

Fisheries Branch Chief **Jonathon "Jon" Gerken** .... (907) 271-2776

Habitat Restoration Branch Chief **Trent Liebich** .... (907) 271-1798
E-mail: trent_liebich@fws.gov

Civil Engineer (Hydraulics) **Heather Hanson** .... (907) 271-2786
E-mail: heather_hanson@fws.gov Fax: (907) 271-2736

Fish and Wildlife Hydrologist **Franklin Dekker** .... (907) 271-2888

Juneau Satellite Office
3000 Vintage Boulevard, Suite 201, Juneau, AK 99801-7100
Tel: (907) 780-1160 Fax: (907) 586-7099 E-mail: juneau@fws.gov
Internet: alaska.fws.gov/fisheries/fieldoffice/juneau

Southeast Alaska Coordinator
Stephen "Steve" Brockmann .... (907) 780-1181

Habitat Restoration Coordinator **Neil Stichert** .... (907) 780-1180
Raptor Specialist **Steven A. "Steve" Lewis** .... (907) 780-1163
Fish and Wildlife Biologist **(Vacant)** .... (907) 780-1160
Wildlife Biologist **Deborah "Debbie" Groves** .... (907) 780-1174
Wildlife Biologist **Michelle Kissling** .... (907) 780-1168

Kenai Fish and Wildlife Field Office
43655 Kalifornsky Beach Road, Kenai, AK 99669
P.O. Box 1670, Kenai, AK 99611
Tel: (907) 262-9863 Fax: (907) 262-7145 E-mail: r7kfa@mail.fws.gov
Areas Covered: Region VII fisheries program in South Central Alaska, parts of Western Alaska and the Aleutian Islands

Field Supervisor **Jeff Anderson** .... (907) 262-9803
E-mail: jeffry_anderson@fws.gov

Biological Science Technician **James "Jim" Boersma** ... (907) 262-9863

Fish and Wildlife Biologist **Cheryl N. Anderson** .... (907) 262-9863
E-mail: cheryl_anderson@fws.gov

Fish and Wildlife Biologist **Heather Fuller** .... (907) 260-0130
E-mail: heather_fuller@fws.gov

Fish and Wildlife Biologist **Emily Munter** .... (907) 260-0124
E-mail: emily_munter@fws.gov

Fishery Biologist **Ken Gates** .... (907) 262-9863
Fishery Biologist **Ken Harper** .... (907) 262-9863 ext. 222
Fishery Biologist **Steve Miller** .... (907) 543-1009
Fishery Biologist **(Vacant)** .... (907) 262-9863

International Affairs
1011 East Tudor Road, Anchorage, AK 99503
Tel: (907) 786-3850 Fax: (907) 786-3898

International Affairs Specialist
Gilbert Castellanos Mail Stop 101 .... (907) 786-3850
E-mail: gilbert_castellanos@fws.gov

Law Enforcement
1011 East Tudor Road, Anchorage, AK 99503
Tel: (907) 786-3311 Fax: (907) 786-3313

Special Agent-in-Charge **Ryan Noel** Mail Stop 151 ...... (907) 786-3331
E-mail: ryan_noel@fws.gov

Assistant Special Agent-in-Charge
Rory Stark Mail Stop 151 .... (907) 786-3330

Migratory Birds and State Programs
1011 East Tudor Road, Mail Stop 371, Anchorage, AK 99503
Tel: (907) 786-3545 Fax: (907) 786-3575

Assistant Regional Director **(Vacant)** .... (907) 786-3545

★ Presidential Appointment Requiring Senate Confirmation ☆ Presidential Appointment ☐ Schedule C Appointment ◇ Career Senior Foreign Service Appointment
● Career Senior Executive Service (SES) Appointment ○ Non-Career Senior Executive Service (SES) Appointment ■ Postal Career Executive Service

Migratory Birds and State Programs *(continued)*

Administrative Assistant **(Vacant)** .... (907) 786-3545
Budget Analyst **Williard "Will" Lacy** .... (907) 786-3392
E-mail: willard_lacy@fws.gov
Grants Fiscal Specialist **(Vacant)** .... (907) 786-3878

Division of Federal Assistance
1011 East Tudor Road, Mail Stop 261, Anchorage, AK 99503
Tel: (907) 786-3545 Fax: (907) 786-3575

Chief **Steve Kline** .... (907) 786-3322
Fish and Wildlife Biologist/Grant Specialist **(Vacant)** ..... (907) 786-3631
Program Administrative Assistant **Rocel Hogue** .... (907) 786-3363

Migratory Birds Co-Management Council
1011 East Tudor Road, Mail Stop 201, Anchorage, AK 99503
Tel: (907) 786-3887 Fax: (907) 786-3938

Executive Director **Patty Schwalenberg** .... (907) 562-6647
Wildlife Biologist **Donna Dewhurst** .... (907) 786-3499
Wildlife Biologist **Kay Larson-Blair** .... (907) 786-3663

Division of Migratory Bird Management
1011 East Tudor Road, Mail Stop 201, Anchorage, AK 99503
Tel: (907) 786-3443 Fax: (907) 786-3641

Chief/Migratory Bird Coordinator (Acting) **Eric Taylor** ... (907) 786-3446
E-mail: eric_taylor@fws.gov
Secretary/Administrative Assistant **Paul Matusewic** ..... (907) 786-3443
Fish and Wildlife Biologist **(Vacant)** .... (907) 786-3945
Outreach Biologist **Tamara Zeller** .... (907) 786-3517
Permits Clerk **Beth Pattinson** .... (907) 786-3693
E-mail: beth_pattinson@fws.gov
Wildlife Biologist **Jordan Muir** .... (907) 786-3503

Nongame Bird Management
1011 East Tudor Road, Mail Stop 201, Anchorage, AK 99503
Tel: (907) 786-3444 Fax: (907) 786-3641

Branch Chief (Acting) **Dave Irons** .... (907) 786-3376
Administrative Assistant **(Vacant)** .... (907) 786-3444
Biological Science Technician **Robert Kaler** .... (907) 786-3984
Biological Science Technician
Elizabeth "Liz" Labunski .... (907) 786-3865
Biological Science Technician **Michelle St. Peters** ...... (907) 786-3691
Biological Science Technician **(Vacant)** .... (907) 786-3979
Raptor Management Supervisor and Wildlife Biologist
Steve B. Lewis .... (907) 780-1163
Wildlife Biologist **Dave Irons** .... (907) 786-3376
Wildlife Biologist **Jim Johnson** .... (907) 786-3423
Wildlife Biologist **Katherine J. Kuletz** .... (907) 786-3453
Wildlife Biologist **Richard Lanctot** .... (907) 786-3609
Wildlife Biologist **(Vacant)** .... (907) 786-3672

Waterfowl Management
1101 East Tudor Road, Mail Stop 201, Anchorage, AK 99503
Tel: (907) 786-3443 Fax: (907) 786-3641

Branch Chief **Eric Taylor** .... (907) 786-3446
E-mail: eric_taylor@fws.gov
Wildlife Biologist/Pilot **Heather Wilson** .... (907) 786-3460
Wildlife Biologist/Pilot **(Vacant)** .... (907) 271-5235
Wildlife Biologist **Tim Bowman** .... (907) 786-3569
Wildlife Biologist **Julian Fischer** .... (907) 786-3644
Wildlife Biologist **Dennis Marks** .... (907) 786-3987
Wildlife Biologist **Bob Platte** .... (907) 786-3565
Wildlife Biologist **David Safine** .... (907) 786-3908
Wildlife Biologist (Biometrical Emphasis) **(Vacant)** ...... (907) 786-3504

Waterfowl Management - Fairbanks
1412 Airport Way, Fairbanks, AK 99701-5824
Tel: (907) 456-0256 Fax: (907) 456-0346

Project Leader/Wildlife Biologist/Pilot **(Vacant)** .... (907) 456-0341
Wildlife Biologist/Pilot **(Vacant)** .... (907) 456-0256

Waterfowl Management - Juneau
3000 Vintage Boulevard, Juneau, AK 99801
Tel: (907) 780-1160 Fax: (907) 586-7244

Wildlife Biologist **Deborah "Debbie" Groves** .... (907) 780-1173
Wildlife Biologist **(Vacant)** .... (907) 786-3849

Waterfowl Management - Soldotna
P.O. Box 1670, Kenai, AK 99611
Tel: (907) 260-0124 Fax: (907) 262-7145

Wildlife Biologist **(Vacant)** .... (907) 260-0124

National Wildlife Refuge System
1011 East Tudor Road, Mail Stop 225, Anchorage, AK 99503
Tel: (907) 786-3665 Fax: (907) 786-3998
Areas Covered: Bristol Bay/Kodiak, Yukon-Kuskokwin Delta, and Bering Sea/Aleutian Ecosystems

Regional Chief **Mitchell R. Ellis** .... (907) 786-3354
E-mail: mitch_ellis@fws.gov
Deputy Chief **Socheata "Soch" Lor** .... (907) 271-2787
E-mail: socheata_lor@fws.gov
Education: Ripon BS; Cornell MS; Missouri PhD
Aircraft Manager **Nathan Olson** .... (907) 786-3368
Budget and Information Management Chief
Christopher Schiltz .... (907) 786-3665
E-mail: christopher_schiltz@fws.gov
Senior Budget Analyst **Ruth Johnson** .... (907) 786-3540
Planning Chief **Ryan Mollnow** .... (907) 786-3326
E-mail: ryan_mollnow@fws.gov
Law Enforcement Chief **Jim Hjelmgren** .... (907) 786-3354
Realty and Natural Resource Chief
Douglas "Doug" Campbell .... (907) 786-3907
Archaeologist **Edward J. Decleva** .... (907) 786-3399
Natural Resource Chief **Ryan Mollnow** .... (907) 786-3326
Operations Branch Chief **(Vacant)** .... (907) 786-3907
Refuge Supervisor **Douglas "Doug" Damberg** .... (907) 786-3329
Refuge Supervisor **Ronnie Sanchez** .... (907) 786-3555
Visitor Services Chief **Debbie Steen** .... (907) 786-3665
E-mail: debbie_steen@fws.gov

Division of Refuges - Fire Management Coordinator
1011 East Tudor Road, Anchorage, AK 99503
Tel: (907) 786-3354 Fax: (907) 786-3932 E-mail: r7fire@fws.gov

Fire Management Coordinator **Doug Alexander** .... (907) 786-3497

Subsistence Management
1011 East Tudor Road, Anchorage, AK 99503
Tel: (907) 786-3888 Fax: (907) 786-3898

Assistant Regional Director
Eugene R. "Gene" Peltola, Jr. .... (907) 786-3484
Secretary **Pamela Raygor** .... (907) 786-3484
E-mail: pamela_raygor@fws.gov
Deputy Assistant Regional Director **Thomas Doolittle** ... (907) 786-3871
Native Liaison **Orville Lind** .... (907) 786-3953
E-mail: orville_lind@fws.gov
State Subsistence Liaison **George Pappas** .... (907) 786-3822

Ecological Services - Northern Ecoregion

Region 8 – Pacific Southwest Region
2800 Cottage Way, Suite W-2606, Sacramento, CA 95825
Tel: (916) 414-6464 Fax: (916) 414-6486 Internet: www.fws.gov/cno
Areas Covered: CA, NV

● Regional Director (Acting) **Angela Picco** .... (916) 414-6498
E-mail: angela_picco@fws.gov
Deputy Regional Director **Jody Holzworth** .... (916) 414-6467
Executive Secretary **Wanda Cantrell** .... (916) 414-6467
E-mail: wanda_cantrell@fws.gov
Assistant Regional Director, Budget and Administration
Kevin Bumatay .... (916) 414-6498
E-mail: kevin_bumatay@fws.gov
Education: Florida BS; Maryland MBA
Assistant Regional Director, Science Applications
Larry Rabin .... (916) 414-6450

(continued on next page)

★ Presidential Appointment Requiring Senate Confirmation ☆ Presidential Appointment □ Schedule C Appointment ◇ Career Senior Foreign Service Appointment
● Career Senior Executive Service (SES) Appointment ○ Non-Career Senior Executive Service (SES) Appointment ■ Postal Career Executive Service

DEPARTMENTS

Region 8 – Pacific Southwest Region *(continued)*

Executive Assistant **Angelia Davenport** .... (916) 414-6498
E-mail: angelica_davenport@fws.gov
Assistant Regional Director, Migratory Birds
Amedee Brickey .... (916) 414-6464
Executive Assistant **(Vacant)** .... (916) 414-6694
Assistant Regional Director, Ecological Services
Michael "Mike" Fris .... (916) 414-6464
E-mail: michael_fris@fws.gov
Executive Assistant **April Evans** .... (916) 414-6516
E-mail: april_evans@fws.gov
Assistant Regional Director, External Affairs (Acting)
John Heil .... (916) 414-6636
Executive Assistant **Angelia Davenport** .... (916) 414-6498
E-mail: angelia_davenport@fws.gov
Assistant Regional Director, Fish and Aquatic
Conservation **Dan Castleberry** .... (916) 414-6464
Executive Assistant **Matthew Sullivan** .... (916) 414-6464
E-mail: matthew_sullivan@fws.gov
Regional Chief, National Wildlife Refuge System
Polly Wheeler .... (916) 414-6468
E-mail: polly_wheeler@fws.gov
Executive Assistant **Nicole Sedlacek** .... (916) 414-6468
E-mail: nicole_sedlacek@fws.gov

Carlsbad (CA) Fish and Wildlife Office (CFWO)
2177 Salk Avenue, Suite 250, Carlsbad, CA 92008
Tel: (760) 431-9440 Fax: (760) 431-9624 Internet: www.fws.gov/carlsbad
Areas Covered: Southern CA

Field Supervisor **G. Mendel Stewart** .... (760) 431-9440 ext. 211
Education: Western Kentucky BS; U Memphis MPA
Deputy Field Supervisor **Scott A. Sobiech** ..... (760) 431-9440 ext. 248
Geographic Information and IT Division
Chief **Tony McKinney** .... (760) 431-9440 ext. 259
Fax: (760) 930-0846
Conservation Partnerships Program Division
Chief **Clark Winchell** .... (760) 431-9440 ext. 259
Fax: (760) 431-9624
Environmental Contaminants Division Chief
Carol Roberts .... (760) 431-9440 ext. 271
Fax: (760) 431-9170
Public Affairs Division Chief
Jane Hendron .... (760) 431-9440 ext. 205
E-mail: jane_hendron@fws.gov Fax: (760) 431-5901
Recovery Division Chief **Bradd Bridges** ...... (760) 431-9440 ext. 221
Fax: (760) 431-5901
Assistant Field Supervisor (Coastal)
Karen Goebel .... (760) 431-9440 ext. 296
Division Chief (Coastal Office)
Jonathan Snyder .... (760) 431-9440 ext. 307
Division Chief (Coastal Office)
Doreen Stadtlander .... (760) 431-9440 ext. 223
Division Chief (Coastal Office) **David Zoutenkyk** ..... (760) 431-9440
Assistant Field Supervisor (Palm Springs)
Ken Corey .... (760) 322-2070 ext. 401
Fax: (760) 322-4648
Division Chief (Palm Springs Office)
Karin Cleary-Rose .... (760) 322-2070 ext. 406
Division Chief (Palm Springs Office)
Brian Croft .... (760) 322-2070 ext. 410
Division Chief (Palm Springs Office)
Jenness McBride .... (760) 322-2070 ext. 403
Division Chief (Palm Springs Office)
Peter Sorensen .... (760) 322-2070 ext. 402
Fax: (760) 322-4648

Reno Fish and Wildlife Office (RFWO)
Nevada Fish and Wildlife Office, 1340 Financial Boulevard,
Suite 234, Reno, NV 89502-7147
Tel: (775) 861-6300 Fax: (775) 861-6301 Internet: www.fws.gov/nevada

Field Supervisor **Carolyn Swed** .... (775) 861-6337
Assistant Deputy Field Supervisor **Shawna Theisen** ..... (775) 861-6300
4701 North Torrey Pines Drive, Reno, NV 89130-2301
Assistant Field Supervisor **Justin Barrett** .... (775) 861-6300
4701 North Torrey Pines Drive, Reno, NV 89130-2301

Reno Fish and Wildlife Office *(continued)*

Assistant Field Supervisor, Las Vegas **(Vacant)** .... (775) 861-6300
4701 North Torrey Pines Drive, Reno, NV 89130-2301
Deputy Field Supervisor, Reno **LeeAnn Carranza** .... (775) 861-6300
Contaminants **(Vacant)** .... (775) 861-6300
Administrative Officer **Mark Fabes** .... (775) 861-6389
E-mail: mark_fabes@fws.gov
Fishery Program Manager **Lisa Heki** .... (775) 861-6300
Computer Specialist **Victor Cobos** .... (775) 861-6300
E-mail: victor_cobos@fws.gov
Public Affairs Officer **Daniel "Dan" Hottle** .... (775) 861-6300
E-mail: daniel_hottle@fws.gov
Public Affairs Specialist **Joseph "Joe" Barker** .... (775) 861-6300
Conservation Partnerships Coordinator **Susan Abele** ..... (775) 861-6300
Desert Tortoise Coordinator **Roy Averill-Murray** .... (775) 861-6300
Schoolyard Habitat Coordinator **Michelle Hunt** .... (775) 861-6300

Sacramento (CA) Fish and Wildlife Office
2800 Cottage Way, Room W-2605, Sacramento, CA 95825
Tel: (916) 414-6600 Fax: (916) 414-6710

Field Supervisor **Jennifer Norris** .... (916) 414-6700
E-mail: jennifer_norris@fws.gov
Deputy Field Supervisor **Jan Knight** .... (916) 414-6700
E-mail: jan_knight@fws.gov

Ventura (CA) Fish and Wildlife Office (VFWO)
2493 Portola Road, Suite B, Ventura, CA 93003
Tel: (805) 644-1766 Fax: (805) 644-3958 E-mail: ventura@fws.gov
Internet: www.fws.gov/ventura
Areas Covered: Los Angeles (North and Western), Mono, Monterey, San Benito, San Bernardino, Santa Barbara, Santa Cruz, San Luis Obispo, Ventura counties

Field Supervisor
Stephen P. "Steve" Henry .... (805) 644-1766 ext. 53333

National Park Service (NPS)

1849 C Street, NW, Washington, DC 20240
Tel: (202) 208-4747 (General Information)
Tel: (202) 208-6843 (Office of the Director) Fax: (202) 219-0910
E-mail: asknps@nps.gov Internet: www.nps.gov
Internet: www.recreation.gov

★ Director (Acting)
Paul Daniel "Dan" Smith Room 3113 .... (202) 208-3818
E-mail: paul_smith@nps.gov
★ Director-Designate **Raymond David Vela** .... (202) 208-4747
E-mail: raymond_vela@nps.gov
Education: Texas A&M International BS
Deputy Director **Paul Daniel "Dan" Smith** .... (202) 208-3818
E-mail: paul_smith@nps.gov

Deputy Director for Operations (DDO)

1849 C Street, NW, Washington, DC 20240
Fax: (202) 273-0896

U.S. Park Police (USPP)
1100 Ohio Drive, SW, Washington, DC 20224
Tel: (202) 619-7350 Fax: (202) 205-7981 Internet: www.nps.gov/uspp

New York Field Office (NYFO)
Building 275, Floyd Bennett Field, Brooklyn, NY 11234
Tel: (718) 354-4586

Commander **John Lauro** .... (718) 354-4586
E-mail: john_lauro@nps.gov

San Francisco Field Office (SFFO)
1217 Ralston Avenue, San Francisco, CA 94129
Tel: (415) 561-5505

Commander **Noreen Schirmer** .... (415) 561-5149

★ Presidential Appointment Requiring Senate Confirmation ☆ Presidential Appointment ☐ Schedule C Appointment ◇ Career Senior Foreign Service Appointment
● Career Senior Executive Service (SES) Appointment ○ Non-Career Senior Executive Service (SES) Appointment ■ Postal Career Executive Service

Natural Resource Stewardship and Science

1201 Oakridge Drive, Suite 200, Fort Collins, CO 80525
Tel: (970) 267-2151 Fax: (202) 273-4431

Air Resources Division
12795 West Alameda Parkway, Lakewood, CO 80228
Chief **Carol McCoy** Room 215 .... (303) 969-2096
Education: Brown U; Michigan MPP; Georgetown JD

Biological Resources Management Division
1201 Oakridge Drive, Fort Collins, CO 80525
Chief **Elaine F. Leslie** Room 200 .... (970) 267-2135
Restoration and Adaptation Branch Chief **(Vacant)** .... (970) 267-2151

Geologic Resources Division
12795 West Alameda Parkway, Lakewood, CO 80228
Fax: (303) 987-6792 Internet: http://www.nature.nps.gov/geology/
Chief **David Steensen** Room 221 .... (303) 969-2014

Social Science Division
1201 Oakridge Drive, Fort Collins, CO 80525
Fax: (970) 225-3579 Internet: http://www.nature.nps.gov/socialscience/
Management Analyst **Pamela Ziesler PhD** .... (970) 225-3564
Education: Embry-Riddle BAE; Central Florida MS; Colorado State PhD

Water Resources Division
1201 Oakridge Drive, Fort Collins, CO 80525
Tel: (970) 225-3500 Fax: (970) 225-9965
Chief and Supervisory Hydrologist **Dr. Forrest "Ed" Harvey** Room 250 .... (970) 225-3511
Education: Olivet Nazarene BS; Purdue MS; Waterloo PhD

Park Planning, Facilities, and Lands

1849 C Street, NW, 10th Floor, Washington, DC 20240
Fax: (202) 273-3242

Denver Service Center (DSC)
12795 West Alameda Parkway, Room 303, Lakewood, CO 80228
P. O. Box 25287, Denver, CO 80225-0287
Tel: (303) 969-2100 Fax: (303) 969-2195 E-mail: dsc_director@nps.gov
Internet: www.nps.gov/dsc

- ● Director **Ray Todd** .... (303) 969-2801
E-mail: ray_todd@nps.gov
Education: Michigan BS; Oregon MARC

Chief of Staff **Samantha Richardson** .... (303) 969-2825
E-mail: samantha_richardson@nps.gov
Budget Officer **Joel Siderius** .... (303) 969-2520
E-mail: joel_siderius@nps.gov
Contracting Services **Lori Irish** .... (303) 987-6776
E-mail: lori_irish@nps.gov
Design and Construction Division Chief **(Vacant)** .... (303) 969-2459
Information Management **Carol Simpson** .... (303) 969-2534
E-mail: carol_simpson@nps.gov
Education: Utah BA; Oregon MLIS
Partnerships **Linda Moery** .... (303) 969-2411
Planning **(Vacant)** .... (303) 969-2208
Public Affairs **Sally Mayberry** .... (303) 969-2588
E-mail: sally_mayberry@nps.gov
Technical Branch Chief **Mike Eissenberg** .... (303) 969-2488
Transportation **George Tait** .... (303) 969-2688

Harpers Ferry Center
Harpers Ferry Center for Media Services,
67 Mather Place, Harpers Ferry, WV 25425
Mail: P.O. Box 50, Harpers Ferry, WV 25425
Tel: (304) 535-5050 Internet: www.nps.gov/hfc
Director (Acting) **Robert Clark** .... (304) 535-5050
E-mail: robert_clark@nps.gov
Administrative Assistant **(Vacant)** .... (304) 535-6104

Construction Program Management Division
12795 West Alameda Parkway, Lakewood, CO 80225
Mail: P.O. Box 25287, Denver, CO 80225
Fax: (303) 969-2423
Program Manager **(Vacant)** .... (303) 969-2178

Park Facility Management Division
1201 Eye Street, NW, 10th Floor, Washington, DC 20005
Fax: (202) 371-6675
Chief **Robert "Bob" Wilbur** .... (202) 513-7034

Regional Offices

Alaska Region

240 West 5th Avenue, Room 114, Anchorage, AK 99501
Tel: (907) 644-3510 Fax: (907) 644-3816 Internet: www.nps.gov/akso
Areas Covered: AK

- ● Regional Director **Dr. Herbert C. "Bert" Frost** .... (907) 644-3510
E-mail: Bert_Frost@nps.gov
E-mail: akro_regional_director@nps.gov
Education: BYU BS, MS; Maine 1994 PhD
Executive Assistant **Yolanda Tankersley** .... (907) 644-3501
E-mail: yolanda_tankersley@nps.gov

Deputy Regional Director **Joel Hard** .... (907) 644-3506
Associate Regional Director, Administration **Christina Caswell** .... (907) 644-3504
E-mail: christina_caswell@nps.gov
Assistant Regional Director, Communications, Science and Partnerhsip **Leigh A. Welling** .... (907) 644-3510
E-mail: leigh_welling@nps.gov
Education: Colorado BA; Oregon State MS, 1996 PhD
Associate Regional Director, Resources **Debora Cooper** .... (907) 644-3505
Acquisition/Property Management **Yvonne Finley** .... (907) 644-3303
E-mail: yvonne_finley@nps.gov
Chief Ranger – Ranger Services **Lindy Mihata** .... (907) 644-3406
E-mail: lindy_mihata@nps.gov
Concessions **Kelly Chang** .... (907) 644-3361
Cultural Resources **Jennifer Pederson** .... (907) 644-3456
Fax: (907) 644-3811
Education and Interpretation **Rebecca Talbott** .... (907) 644-3371
Education: Oregon State; JFK School Govt MPA Fax: (907) 644-3801
Equal Opportunity Officer **Barbara Green** .... (907) 644-3348
E-mail: barbara_green@nps.gov
GIS and Information Resources **(Vacant)** .... (907) 644-3510
Information Technology **Keith Burgess** .... (907) 644-3703
E-mail: keith_burgess@nps.gov Fax: (907) 644-3812
Inventory and Monitoring **Jim Lawler** .... (907) 644-3699
Lands **Robert Childers** .... (907) 644-3426
Fax: (907) 644-3807
Native Liaison **Adrienne Sleek** .... (907) 644-3510
Natural Resources **Jason P. Taylor** .... (907) 644-3571
Planning, Design and Maintenance **John Chekan** .... (907) 644-3381
Fax: (907) 644-3804
Planning and Compliance **Brooke Merrell** .... (907) 644-3526
Rivers and Trails Conservation Assistance **Paul Clark** .... (907) 644-3586
Education: Pacific Lutheran 1999 BA Fax: (907) 644-3807
Workforce Management **(Vacant)** .... (907) 644-3510
Webmaster **Judy Kesler** .... (907) 644-3513
E-mail: judy_kesler@nps.gov
Administrative Support Assistant **Oliver Dillard** .... (907) 644-3514
E-mail: oliver_dillard@nps.gov

Parks

Alagnak Wild River
P.O. Box 7, King Salmon, AK 99613
Tel: (907) 246-3305 Fax: (907) 246-2116 Internet: www.nps.gov/alag
Superintendent **Mark Sturm** .... (907) 246-2154

Aleutian World War II National Historic Area
240 West 5th Avenue, Room 114, Anchorage, AK 99501
Tel: (907) 644-3472 Fax: (907) 644-3816 Internet: www.nps.gov/aleu
Program Manager **Rachel Mason PhD** .... (907) 644-3472

DEPARTMENTS

Aniakchak National Monument and Preserve
P.O. Box 7, King Salmon, AK 99613
Tel: (907) 246-3305 Fax: (907) 246-4286 Internet: www.nps.gov/ania
Superintendent **Mark Sturm** .... (907) 246-2154

Bering Land Bridge National Preserve
P.O. Box 220, Nome, AK 99762
Tel: (907) 443-2522 Fax: (907) 443-6139 Internet: www.nps.gov/bela
Superintendent **Jeanette Koelsch** .... (907) 443-2522

Cape Krusenstern National Monument
P.O. Box 1029, Kotzebue, AK 99752
Tel: (907) 442-3890 Fax: (907) 442-8316 Internet: www.nps.gov/cakr
Superintendent **Maija Lukin** .... (907) 442-3890

Denali National Park and Preserve
P.O. Box 9, Denali National Park, AK 99755
Tel: (907) 683-2294 Fax: (907) 683-9617 Internet: www.nps.gov/dena
Superintendent **Don Striker** .... (907) 683-2294

Gates of the Arctic National Park and Preserve
4175 Geist Road, Fairbanks, AK 99709-3420
Tel: (907) 457-5752 Fax: (907) 455-0601 Internet: www.nps.gov/gaar
Superintendent **Greg Dudgeon** .... (907) 455-0614

Glacier Bay National Park and Preserve
P.O. Box 140, Gustavus, AK 99826
Tel: (907) 697-2232 Fax: (907) 697-2654
E-mail: glba_administration@nps.gov Internet: www.nps.gov/glba
Superintendent **Philip Hooge** .... (907) 697-2230

Katmai National Park and Preserve
P.O. Box 7, King Salmon, AK 99613
Tel: (907) 246-3305 Fax: (907) 246-2116 Internet: www.nps.gov/katm
Superintendent **Mark Sturm** .... (907) 246-2154

Kenai Fjords National Park
P.O. Box 1727, Seward, AK 99664
Tel: (907) 422-0500 Fax: (907) 422-0571 Internet: www.nps.gov/kefj
Superintendent **Eric Beach** .... (907) 422-0500

Klondike Gold Rush National Historical Park
P.O. Box 517, Skagway, AK 99840
Tel: (907) 983-2921 Fax: (907) 983-9249 Internet: www.nps.gov/klgo
Superintendent **Michael "Mike" Tranel** .... (907) 983-2921
Education: Notre Dame; Iowa

Kobuk Valley National Park
P.O. Box 1029, Kotzebue, AK 99752
Tel: (907) 442-3890 Fax: (907) 442-8316 Internet: www.nps.gov/kova
Superintendent **Maija Lukin** .... (907) 442-3890

Lake Clark National Park and Preserve
240 West 5th Avenue, Suite 236, Anchorage, AK 99508
Tel: (907) 644-3626 Fax: (907) 644-3810 Internet: www.nps.gov/lacl
Superintendent **Susan Green** .... (907) 644-3627

Noatak National Preserve
P.O. Box 1029, Kotzebue, AK 99752
Tel: (907) 442-3890 Fax: (907) 442-8316 Internet: www.nps.gov/noat
Superintendent **Maija Lukin** .... (907) 442-3890

Sitka National Historical Park
106 Metlakatla Street, Sitka, AK 99835
P.O. Box 738, Sitka, AK 99835
Tel: (907) 747-6281 Fax: (907) 747-5938 Internet: www.nps.gov/sitk
Superintendent **David Elkowitz** .... (907) 747-6281

Wrangell-St. Elias National Park and Preserve
P.O. Box 439, Copper Center, AK 99573
Tel: (907) 822-5234 Fax: (907) 822-7216 Internet: www.nps.gov/wrst
Superintendent **Ben Bobowski** .... (907) 822-5234

Yukon-Charley Rivers National Preserve
4175 Geist Road, Fairbanks, AK 99709-3420
Tel: (907) 457-5752 Fax: (907) 457-2247 Internet: www.nps.gov/yuch
Superintendent **Greg Dudgeon** .... (907) 457-5752

Intermountain Region
12795 West Alameda Parkway, Lakewood, CO 80228
P.O. Box 25287, Denver, CO 80225-0287
Tel: (303) 969-2500 Fax: (303) 969-2785
Areas Covered: AZ, CO, MT, NM, OK, TX, UT, WY

● Regional Director **Sue E. Masica** .... (303) 969-2503
E-mail: Sue_Masica@nps.gov
Education: Austin Col BA; Texas MPA

Deputy Regional Director and Chief of Staff **(Vacant)** .... (303) 969-2856

Deputy Regional Director for Operations **Colin Campbell** .... (303) 969-2503
Education: Cal Poly San Luis Obispo 1980 BS

Associate Regional Director for Business and Technology **(Vacant)** .... (303) 969-2544

Comptroller **Melinda Dominguez** .... (303) 969-2589
E-mail: melinda_dominguez@nps.gov

Associate Regional Director for Communications and External Relations **Rick Frost** .... (303) 987-6732
E-mail: rick_frost@nps.gov

Associate Regional Director for Facilities and Lands **(Vacant)** .... (303) 969-2801

Associate Regional Director for Human Resources **Annette Martinez** .... (303) 969-2506

Associate Regional Director for Resources and Science **(Vacant)** .... (303) 969-2073

Associate Regional Director for Workforce Management **Annette Martinez** .... (303) 969-2506
E-mail: annette_martinez@nps.gov

National Natural Landmarks Regional Coordinator **Heather "Heath" Eggleston** .... (303) 969-2945

Southern Arizona Office (SOAR)
2120 North Central, Suite 120, Phoenix, AZ 85004-1455
Tel: (602) 794-3804 Fax: (602) 794-3835
Director **Sherry Plowman** .... (602) 794-3809

Western Archeological and Conservation Center
255 North Commerce Park Loop, Tucson, AZ 85745
Tel: (520) 791-6400 Fax: (520) 791-6479
Center Chief **Stephanie "Tef" Rodeffer** .... (520) 791-6401
E-mail: tef_rodeffer@nps.gov

Colorado Plateau Cluster of National Parks

Arches National Park
2282 South West Resource Boulevard, Moab, UT 84532
Tel: (435) 719-2100 Fax: (435) 719-2305 Internet: www.nps.gov/arch
Superintendent **Kate Cannon** .... (435) 719-2100

Aztec Ruins National Monument
84 County Road 2900, Aztec, NM 87410-9715
Tel: (505) 334-6174 Fax: (505) 334-6372 Internet: www.nps.gov/azru
Superintendent **Richard "Michael" Quijano-West** .... (505) 334-6174 ext. 222

Bryce Canyon National Park
P.O. Box 64021, Bryce Canyon, UT 84764-0201
Tel: (435) 834-5322 Fax: (435) 834-4102 Internet: www.nps.gov/brca
Superintendent **Sue Fritzke** .... (435) 834-5322

Canyon de Chelly National Monument
P.O. Box 588, Chinle, AZ 86503
Tel: (928) 674-5500 Fax: (928) 674-5507 Internet: www.nps.gov/cach
Superintendent **Lyn Carranza** .... (928) 674-5500 ext. 224
Education: New Mexico State 1994 BA

★ Presidential Appointment Requiring Senate Confirmation ☆ Presidential Appointment ☐ Schedule C Appointment ◇ Career Senior Foreign Service Appointment
● Career Senior Executive Service (SES) Appointment ○ Non-Career Senior Executive Service (SES) Appointment ■ Postal Career Executive Service

Canyonlands National Park
2282 S. West Resource Boulevard, Moab, UT 84532
Tel: (435) 719-2313 Fax: (435) 719-2300 Internet: www.nps.gov/cany
Superintendent **Kate Cannon** .... (435) 719-2101

Capitol Reef National Park
HC 70, Box 15, Torrey, UT 84775-9602
Tel: (435) 425-3791 Fax: (435) 425-3026 Internet: www.nps.gov/care
Superintendent (Acting) **Pam Rice** .... (435) 425-3791 ext. 4100

Cedar Breaks National Monument
2390 West Highway 56, Suite 11, Cedar City, UT 84720-2606
Tel: (435) 586-9451 Fax: (435) 586-3813 Internet: www.nps.gov/cebr
Superintendent **Paul Roelandt** .... (435) 586-9451 ext. 4421

Chaco Culture National Historical Park
P.O. Box 220, Nageezi, NM 87037
Tel: (505) 786-7014 Fax: (505) 786-7061 Internet: www.nps.gov/chcu
Superintendent (Acting) **Aaron Adams** .... (505) 334-6174 ext. 226

Colorado National Monument
Fruita, CO 81521-0001
Tel: (970) 858-3617 Fax: (970) 858-0372 Internet: www.nps.gov/colm
Superintendent **Ken Mabery** .... (970) 858-3617 ext. 301

Dinosaur National Monument
4545 East Highway 40, Dinosaur, CO 81610-9724
Tel: (970) 374-3000 Fax: (970) 374-3003 Internet: www.nps.gov/dino
Superintendent **Mark Foust** .... (970) 374-3000
Education: UC Davis 1989 BS

El Malpais National Monument
123 East Roosevelt, Grants, NM 87020
Tel: (505) 285-4641 Fax: (505) 285-5661 Internet: www.nps.gov/elma
Superintendent **Mitzi Frank** .... (505) 285-4641 ext. 12
Education: South Dakota State 1981 BA

El Morro National Monument
RT 2, P.O. Box 43, Ramah, NM 87321-9603
Tel: (505) 783-4226 Fax: (505) 783-4689 Internet: www.nps.gov/elmo
Superintendent **Mitzi Frank** .... (505) 783-4226
Education: South Dakota State 1981 BA

Fossil Butte National Monument
P.O. Box 592, Kemmerer, WY 83101-0592
Tel: (307) 877-4455 Fax: (307) 877-4457 Internet: www.nps.gov/fobu
Superintendent **Angela Wetz** .... (307) 877-4455

Glen Canyon National Recreation Area
P.O. Box 1507, Page, AZ 86040-1507
Tel: (928) 608-6200 Fax: (928) 608-6283 Internet: www.nps.gov/glca
Superintendent **Nyra Akins** .... (928) 608-6205

Golden Spike National Historic Site
P.O. Box 897, Brigham City, UT 84302
Tel: (435) 471-2209 Fax: (435) 471-2341 Internet: www.nps.gov/gosp
Superintendent **Leslie Crossland** .... (435) 471-2209 ext. 23
Education: Utah State BS

Grand Canyon National Park
P.O. Box 129, Grand Canyon, AZ 86023
Tel: (928) 638-7888 Fax: (928) 638-7815 Internet: www.nps.gov/grca
Superintendent **Christine S. "Chris" Lehnertz** .... (928) 638-7945
Education: Colorado
Deputy Superintendent **Diane Chalfant** .... (928) 638-7888

Hovenweep National Monument
McElmo Route, Cortez, CO 81321
Tel: (970) 562-4282 Fax: (970) 562-4283 Internet: www.nps.gov/hove
Superintendent **Jeannine McElveen** .... (970) 562-4282

Hubbell Trading Post National Historic Site
P.O. Box 150, Ganado, AZ 86505-0150
Tel: (928) 755-3475 Fax: (928) 755-3405 Internet: www.nps.gov/hutr
Superintendent **Lloyd Masayumptewa** .... (928) 755-3475 ext. 224

Mesa Verde National Park
P.O. Box 8, Mesa Verde, CO 81330-0008
Tel: (970) 529-4600 Fax: (970) 529-4637 Internet: www.nps.gov/meve
Superintendent **Cliff Spencer** .... (970) 529-4465
Education: Pierce Col AA; Cal State (Northridge) BS

Natural Bridges National Monument
HC 60, Box 1, Lake Powell, UT 84533-0101
Tel: (435) 692-1234 Fax: (435) 692-1111 Internet: www.nps.gov/nabr
Superintendent and Chief Law Enforcement
Ranger **Jim Dougan** .... (435) 692-1234 ext. 15
Education: Utah State BS; Arizona State MA

Navajo National Monument
HC 71, Box 3, Tonalea, AZ 86044-9704
Tel: (928) 672-2700 Fax: (928) 672-2703 Internet: www.nps.gov/nava
Superintendent **Alden Miller** .... (928) 672-2710
Education: UMass (Amherst) BS

Petrified Forest National Park
P.O. Box 2217, Petrified Forest National Park, AZ 86028
Tel: (928) 524-6228 Fax: (928) 524-3567 Internet: www.nps.gov/pefo
Superintendent **Bradley Traver** .... (928) 524-6228 ext. 265
Education: Worcester Polytech BS

Pipe Spring National Monument
HC 65, Box 5, Fredonia, AZ 86022
Tel: (928) 643-7105 Fax: (928) 643-7583 Internet: www.nps.gov/pisp
Superintendent **(Vacant)** .... (928) 643-7105 ext. 212

Rainbow Bridge National Monument
c/o Glen Canyon National Recreation Area, P.O. Box 1507, Page, AZ 86040-1507
Tel: (928) 608-6200 Fax: (928) 608-6283 Internet: www.nps.gov/rabr
Superintendent **Todd Brindle** .... (928) 608-6200
Education: Penn State (Attended); Florida 1975

Sand Creek Massacre National Historic Site
249, Eads, CO 81036
Tel: (719) 729-3003 Fax: (719) 438-5410
Superintendent **Alexa Roberts** .... (719) 729-3003

Sunset Crater Volcano National Monument
6400 North Highway 89, Flagstaff, AZ 86004
Tel: (928) 526-0502 Fax: (928) 714-0565 Internet: www.nps.gov/sucr
Superintendent **Kayci Cook-Collins** .... (928) 526-1157 ext. 227
Education: Northern Arizona 1983 BS

Timpanogos Cave National Monument
RR 3, Box 200, American Fork, UT 84003-9803
Tel: (801) 756-5239 Fax: (801) 756-5661 Internet: www.nps.gov/tica
Superintendent **Jim Ireland** .... (801) 756-5239 ext. 101
Education: Arizona BA

Walnut Canyon National Monument
6400 North Highway 89, Flagstaff, AZ 86004
Tel: (928) 526-3367 Fax: (928) 527-0246 Internet: www.nps.gov/waca
Superintendent **Kayci Cook-Collins** .... (928) 526-1157 ext. 227
Education: Northern Arizona 1983 BS

Wupatki National Monument
6400 North Highway 89, Flagstaff, AZ 86004
Tel: (928) 679-2365 Fax: (928) 679-2349 Internet: www.nps.gov/wupa
Superintendent **Kayci Cook-Collins** .... (928) 526-1157 ext. 227
Education: Northern Arizona 1983 BS

★ Presidential Appointment Requiring Senate Confirmation ☆ Presidential Appointment □ Schedule C Appointment ◇ Career Senior Foreign Service Appointment
● Career Senior Executive Service (SES) Appointment ○ Non-Career Senior Executive Service (SES) Appointment ■ Postal Career Executive Service

Yucca House National Monument
c/o Mesa Verde National Park, P.O. Box 8, Mesa Verde, CO 81330-0008
Tel: (970) 529-4465 Fax: (970) 529-4637 Internet: www.nps.gov/yuho

Superintendent **Cliff Spencer** .... (970) 529-4465
Education: Pierce Col AA; Cal State (Northridge) BS

Zion National Park
Springdale, UT 84767-1099
Tel: (435) 772-3256 Fax: (435) 772-3426 Internet: www.nps.gov/zion

Superintendent **Jeff Bradybaugh** .... (435) 772-0140
Education: South Dakota State BS; New Mexico State MS

Long Distance Trails Office (California, Mormon Pioneer, Oregon, Pony Express National Historic Trails)
324 South State Street, Suite 250, P.O. Box 45155,
Salt Lake City, UT 84145-0155
Tel: (801) 741-1012 Fax: (801) 741-1102

Superintendent **Aaron Mahr** .... (505) 988-6736
P.O. Box 728, Santa Fe, NM 87504-0728

Rocky Mountain Cluster of National Parks

Bent's Old Fort National Historic Site
35110 Highway 194 East, La Junta, CO 81050-2300
Tel: (719) 383-5010 Fax: (719) 383-2129
E-mail: BEOL_administration@nps.gov Internet: www.nps.gov/beol

Superintendent **Alexa Roberts** .... (719) 383-5010 ext. 112

Bighorn Canyon National Recreation Area
P.O. Box 7458, Fort Smith, MT 59035
Tel: (406) 666-2412 Fax: (406) 666-2415 Internet: www.nps.gov/bica

Superintendent (Acting) **Regina Klondit** .... (406) 666-2412

Black Canyon of the Gunnison National Park
102 Elk Creek, Gunnison, CO 81230
Tel: (970) 641-2337 Fax: (970) 641-3127
E-mail: cure_vis_mail@nps.gov Internet: www.nps.gov/blca

Superintendent **Bruce Noble** .... (970) 641-2337
Education: Wyoming BA, MA

Curecanti National Recreation Area
102 Elk Creek, Gunnison, CO 81230
Tel: (970) 641-2337 Fax: (970) 641-3127
E-mail: cure_vis_mail@nps.gov Internet: www.nps.gov/cure

Superintendent **Bruce Noble** .... (970) 641-2337
Education: Wyoming BA, MA

Devils Tower National Monument
P.O. Box 10, Devils Tower, WY 82714-0010
Tel: (307) 467-5283 Fax: (307) 467-5350 Internet: www.nps.gov/deto

Superintendent **Tim Reid** .... (307) 467-5283 ext. 213

Florissant Fossil Beds National Monument
P.O. Box 185, Florissant, CO 80816-0185
Tel: (719) 748-3253 Fax: (719) 748-3164 Internet: www.nps.gov/flfo

Superintendent **(Vacant)** .... (719) 748-3253

Fort Laramie National Historic Site
HC 72, P.O. Box 389, Fort Laramie, WY 82212-0086
Tel: (307) 837-2221 Fax: (307) 837-2120 Internet: www.nps.gov/fola

Superintendent **Thomas M. "Tom" Baker** ..... (307) 837-2221 ext. 3004

Glacier National Park
P.O. Box 128, West Glacier, MT 59936-0128
Tel: (406) 888-7800 Fax: (406) 888-7808 Internet: www.nps.gov/glac

Superintendent **Jeff Mow** .... (406) 888-7901

Grand Teton National Park
P.O. Drawer 170, Moose, WY 83012-0170
Tel: (307) 739-3300 Fax: (307) 739-3440 Internet: www.nps.gov/grte

● Superintendent **Raymond David Vela** .... (307) 739-3300 ext. 3413
E-mail: david_vela@nps.gov
Education: Texas A&M International BS

Grand Teton National Park *(continued)*

Deputy Superintendent **Gopaul Noojibail** .... (307) 739-3300
Education: Earlham; Indiana

Grant-Kohrs Ranch National Historic Site
266 Warren Lane, Deer Lodge, MT 59722-0790
Tel: (406) 846-2070 Fax: (406) 846-3962 Internet: www.nps.gov/grko

Superintendent **Jacqueline "Jacque" Lavelle** ... (406) 846-2070 ext. 221

Great Sand Dunes National Park and Preserve
11500 Highway 150, Mosca, CO 81146-9798
Tel: (719) 378-6300 Fax: (719) 378-6310 Internet: www.nps.gov/grsa

Superintendent (Acting) **Scott Stonem** .... (719) 378-6311

John D. Rockefeller, Jr. Memorial Parkway
c/o Grand Teton National Park, P.O. Drawer 170, Moose, WY 83012-0170
Tel: (307) 739-3300 Fax: (307) 739-3438 Internet: www.nps.gov/jodr
Note: Grand Teton National Park administers John D. Rockefeller Memorial Parkway.

Superintendent **Raymond David Vela** .... (307) 739-3300 ext. 3413
Education: Texas A&M International BS

Little Bighorn Battlefield National Monument
P.O. Box 39, Crow Agency, MT 59022-0039
Tel: (406) 638-3201 Fax: (406) 638-2623
E-mail: libi_administration@nps.gov Internet: www.nps.gov/libi

Superintendent **(Vacant)** .... (406) 638-3204

Rocky Mountain National Park
1000 Highway 36, Estes Park, CO 80517-8397
Tel: (970) 586-1206 Fax: (970) 586-1310
E-mail: ROMO_information@nps.gov Internet: www.nps.gov/romo

Superintendent **Darla Sidles** .... (970) 586-1475

Yellowstone National Park
P.O. Box 168, Yellowstone National Park, WY 82190-0168
Tel: (307) 344-7381 Fax: (307) 344-2005 Internet: www.nps.gov/yell

Superintendent **Cameron "Cam" Sholly** .... (402) 661-1520
Education: St Mary's Col (CA); Duke

Deputy Superintendent **Patrick "Pat" Kenney** .... (307) 344-7381
Education: Wisconsin

Southwest Cluster of National Parks

Alibates Flint Quarries National Monument
c/o Lake Meredith National Recreation Area, P.O. Box 1460,
Fritch, TX 79036-1460
Tel: (806) 857-3151 Fax: (806) 857-2319 Internet: www.nps.gov/alfl

Superintendent **Robert "Bob" Maguire** .... (806) 857-3151 ext. 300

Amistad National Recreation Area
HCR 3, Box 5J, Del Rio, TX 78840-9350
Tel: (830) 775-7491 Fax: (830) 778-0760 Internet: www.nps.gov/amis

Superintendent **Christopher Ryan** .... (830) 775-7492 ext. 2201

Bandelier National Monument
15 Entrance Road, Los Alamos, NM 87544
Tel: (505) 672-3861 ext. 720 Fax: (505) 672-9714
Internet: www.nps.gov/band

Superintendent **Jason Lott** .... (505) 672-3861 ext. 501

Big Bend National Park
P.O. Box 129, Big Bend National Park, TX 79834-0129
Tel: (432) 477-2251 Fax: (432) 477-1175 Internet: www.nps.gov/bibe

Superintendent **Cindy Ott-Jones** .... (432) 477-1102

Big Thicket National Preserve
3785 Milam Street, Beaumont, TX 77701
Tel: (409) 951-6700 Fax: (409) 951-6868 Internet: www.nps.gov/bith

Superintendent **Wayne Prokopetz** .... (409) 951-6801
Education: Utah (ABD)

★ Presidential Appointment Requiring Senate Confirmation ☆ Presidential Appointment □ Schedule C Appointment ◇ Career Senior Foreign Service Appointment
● Career Senior Executive Service (SES) Appointment ○ Non-Career Senior Executive Service (SES) Appointment ■ Postal Career Executive Service

Capulin Volcano National Monument
P.O. Box 40, Capulin, NM 88414
Tel: (505) 278-2201 Fax: (505) 278-2211 Internet: www.nps.gov/cavo
Superintendent **Peter Armato** . . . . (505) 278-2201 ext. 210
Education: Marin; Nevada (Reno); Western Washington MS

Carlsbad Caverns National Park
3225 National Parks Highway, Carlsbad, NM 88220
Tel: (505) 785-2232 Fax: (505) 785-2133 Internet: www.nps.gov/cave
Superintendent **Douglas S. Neighbor** . . . . (505) 785-3020
Education: Texas A&M 1989 BS

Casa Grande Ruins National Monument
1100 Ruins Drive, Coolidge, AZ 85228
Tel: (520) 723-3172 Fax: (520) 723-7209 Internet: www.nps.gov/cagr
Superintendent **Karl Pierce** . . . . (520) 723-3172
Education: UC Davis 1987

Chamizal National Memorial
800 South San Marcial Street, El Paso, TX 79905-4123
Tel: (915) 532-7273 Fax: (915) 532-7240 Internet: www.nps.gov/cham
Superintendent
Fernando Gus "Gus" Sanchez . . . . (915) 532-7273 ext. 108

Chickasaw National Recreation Area
1008 West Second, Sulphur, OK 73086-4814
Tel: (580) 622-7234 Fax: (580) 622-2296 Internet: www.nps.gov/chic
Superintendent **William Wright** . . . . (580) 622-7234

Chiricahua National Monument
12856 East Rhyolite Creek Road, Willcox, AZ 85643
Tel: (520) 824-3560 Fax: (520) 824-3421 Internet: www.nps.gov/chir
Superintendent **Allen S. Etheridge** . . . . (520) 366-5515 ext. 2101
Education: Mid Tennessee State

Coronado National Memorial
4101 East Montezuma Canyon Road, Hereford, AZ 85615
Tel: (520) 366-5515 Fax: (520) 366-0302 Internet: www.nps.gov/coro
Superintendent **Allen S. Etheridge** . . . . (520) 366-5515 ext. 2101
Education: Mid Tennessee State

Fort Bowie National Historic Site
c/o Chiricahua National Monument, 12856 East Rhyolite Creek Rd., Willcox, AZ 85643
Tel: (520) 847-2500 Fax: (520) 824-3421 Internet: www.nps.gov/fobo
Superintendent **Allen S. Etheridge** . . . . (520) 366-5515 ext. 2101
Education: Mid Tennessee State

Fort Davis National Historic Site
P.O. Box 1456, Lt. Flipper Drive, Fort Davis, TX 79734
Tel: (432) 426-3225 Fax: (432) 426-3122 Internet: www.nps.gov/foda
Superintendent **Barney Riley** . . . . (432) 426-3225 ext. 221

Fort Union National Monument
P.O. Box 127, Watrous, NM 87753
Tel: (505) 425-8025 Fax: (505) 454-1155 Internet: www.nps.gov/foun
Superintendent **Charles Strickfaden** . . . . (505) 425-8025 ext. 222
Education: Cal Poly San Luis Obispo BS

Gila Cliff Dwellings National Monument
HC 68, Box 100, Silver City, NM 88061
Tel: (575) 536-9461 Fax: (575) 536-9344 Internet: www.nps.gov/gicl
Superintendent (Acting) **Kevin Tillman** . . . . (575) 536-9461

Guadalupe Mountains National Park
HC 60, Box 400, Salt Flat, TX 79847-9400
Tel: (915) 828-3251 Fax: (915) 828-3269 Internet: www.nps.gov/gumo
Superintendent **Eric J. Brunnemann** . . . . (915) 828-3251 ext. 104
Education: Texas 1984 BA, 1988 MA; New Mexico 1995 MA

Hohokam Pima National Monument
c/o Casa Grande Ruins National Monument, 1100 Ruins Dr., Coolidge, AZ 85228
Tel: (520) 723-3172 Fax: (520) 723-7209 Internet: www.nps.gov/pima
Superintendent **Karl Pierce** . . . . (520) 723-3172 ext. 121
Education: UC Davis 1987

Lake Meredith National Recreation Area
P.O. Box 1460, Fritch, TX 79036
Tel: (806) 857-3151 Fax: (806) 857-2319 Internet: www.nps.gov/lamr
Superintendent **Robert "Bob" Maguire** . . . . (806) 857-3151

Lyndon B. Johnson National Historical Park
P.O. Box 329, Johnson City, TX 78636
Tel: (830) 868-7128 Fax: (830) 868-7863 Internet: www.nps.gov/lyjo
Superintendent **Susan McDonald** . . . . (830) 868-7128

Manhattan Project National Historical Park
12795 West Alameda Parkway, Lakewood, CO 80225
25287, Lakewood, CO 80225
Tel: (303) 969-2700
Note: The Manhattan Project National Historic Park is jointly administered by the National Park Service and the Department of Energy.
Superintendent **Kris Kirby** . . . . (303) 969-2700

Montezuma Castle National Monument
P.O. Box 219, Camp Verde, AZ 86322
Tel: (928) 567-5276 Fax: (928) 567-3597 Internet: www.nps.gov/moca
Superintendent **Dorothy FireCloud** . . . . (928) 567-5276 ext. 223

Organ Pipe Cactus National Monument
10 Organ Pipe Drive, Ajo, AZ 85321-9626
Tel: (520) 387-6849 Fax: (520) 387-7144 Internet: www.nps.gov/orpi
Superintendent **(Vacant)** . . . . (520) 387-6849

Padre Island National Seashore
P.O. Box 181300, Corpus Christi, TX 78480-1300
Tel: (361) 949-8173 Fax: (361) 949-8023 Internet: www.nps.gov/pais
Superintendent **Mark Spier** . . . . (361) 949-8173 ext. 222
Education: Colorado State 1978 BA

Palo Alto Battlefield National Historic Site
1623 Central Boulevard, Suite 213, Brownsville, TX 78520-8326
Tel: (956) 541-2785 Fax: (956) 541-6356 Internet: www.nps.gov/paal
Superintendent **Mark Spier** . . . . (956) 541-2785 ext. 222
Education: Colorado State 1978 BA

Pecos National Historical Park
P.O. Box 418, Pecos, NM 87552-0418
Tel: (505) 757-7241 Fax: (505) 757-8460 Internet: www.nps.gov/peco
Superintendent **Karl Cordova** . . . . (505) 757-7241 ext. 2

Petroglyph National Monument
6001 Unser Boulevard, NW, Albuquerque, NM 87120
Tel: (505) 899-0205 Fax: (505) 899-0207 Internet: www.nps.gov/petr
Superintendent **Dennis A. Vásquez** . . . . (505) 899-0205 ext. 222
Education: Texas (El Paso) 1983 BS

Rio Grande del Norte National Monument
226 Cruz Alta Road, Taos, NM 87571
Superintendent **John R. Bailey** . . . . (575) 751-4703

Rio Grande Wild and Scenic River
c/o Big Bend National Park, P.O. Box 129,
Big Bend National Park, TX 79834-0129
Tel: (432) 477-2251 Fax: (432) 477-1175 Internet: www.nps.gov/rigr
Superintendent **Cindy Ott-Jones** . . . . (915) 477-1102

Saguaro National Park
3693 South Old Spanish Trail, Tucson, AZ 85730-5601
Tel: (520) 733-5100 Fax: (520) 733-5183 Internet: www.nps.gov/sagu
Superintendent **(Vacant)** . . . . (520) 733-5101

★ Presidential Appointment Requiring Senate Confirmation ☆ Presidential Appointment □ Schedule C Appointment ◇ Career Senior Foreign Service Appointment
● Career Senior Executive Service (SES) Appointment ○ Non-Career Senior Executive Service (SES) Appointment ■ Postal Career Executive Service

DEPARTMENTS

Salinas Pueblo Missions National Monument
P.O. Box 517, Mountainair, NM 87036
Tel: (505) 847-2585 Fax: (505) 847-2441 Internet: www.nps.gov/sapu

Superintendent **Glenn Fulfer** .... (505) 847-2585 ext. 26

San Antonio Missions National Historical Park
2202 Roosevelt Avenue, San Antonio, TX 78210-4919
Tel: (210) 534-8833 Fax: (210) 534-1106 Internet: www.nps.gov/saan

Superintendent **Mardi Arce** .... (210) 534-8875
Education: Buena Vista Col 1985 BA

Tonto National Monument
HC 02, Box 4602, Roosevelt, AZ 85545
Tel: (928) 467-2241 Fax: (928) 467-2225 Internet: www.nps.gov/tont

Superintendent **Duane Hubbard** .... (928) 467-2241 ext. 8101

Tule Springs Fossil Beds National Monument
601 Nevada Highway, Boulder City, NV 89005-2426

Superintendent **Jonathon "Jon" Burpee** .... (702) 902-0431
Education: U Washington BA

Tumacacori National Historical Park
P.O. Box 8067, Tumacacori, AZ 85640
Tel: (520) 398-2341 Fax: (520) 398-9271 Internet: www.nps.gov/tuma

Superintendent **Bob Love** .... (520) 398-2341
Education: Cal State (Chico) BA

Tuzigoot National Monument
c/o Montezuma Castle National Monument, P.O. Box 219,
Camp Verde, AZ 86322
Tel: (928) 567-5276 Fax: (928) 567-3597 Internet: www.nps.gov/tuzi

Superintendent **Dorothy FireCloud** .... (928) 567-5276 ext. 223

Valles Caldera National Preserve
39201 Highway 4, Jemez Springs, NM 87025
Mail: P.O. Box 359, Jemez Springs, NM 87025
Tel: (575) 829-4100 Fax: (575) 829-4141
Internet: http://www.nps.gov/vall E-mail: info@vallescaldera.gov

Superintendent **Jorge Silva-Banuelos** .... (575) 829-4100
Education: San Diego
Administrative Officer **Marin Karraker** .... (575) 829-4100
Administrative Clerk **Lenda Folks** .... (505) 465-8056
E-mail: lenda_folks@nps.gov
Budget Technician **Joyce McHugh** .... (575) 829-4100
E-mail: joyce_mchugh@nps.gov

Washita Battlefield National Historic Site
P.O. Box 890, Cheyenne, OK 73628-0890
Tel: (580) 497-2742 Fax: (580) 497-2712 Internet: www.nps.gov/waba

Superintendent
Matthew Tucker "Tucker" Blythe .... (580) 497-2742 ext. 3001

White Sands National Monument
P.O. Box 1086, Holloman AFB, NM 88330-1086
Tel: (575) 479-6124 Fax: (575) 479-4333 Internet: www.nps.gov/whsa

Superintendent **Marie Frias-Sauter** .... (575) 479-6124
Education: Georgia BA

Long Distance Group Office (Santa Fe Trail - Trail of Tears) and El Camino Real de Tierra Adentro
P.O. Box 728, Santa Fe, NM 87504-0728
Tel: (505) 988-6888 Fax: (505) 986-5214

Superintendent **Aaron Mahr** .... (505) 988-6888

Midwest Region
601 Riverfront Drive, Omaha, NE 68102
Tel: (402) 661-1736
Areas Covered: AR, IL, IN, IA, KS, MI, MN, MO, NE, ND, OH, SD, WI

● Regional Director (Acting) **Craig A. Kenkel** .... (402) 661-1736
E-mail: craig_kenkel@nps.gov
Deputy Regional Director **Patricia Trap** .... (402) 661-1522
E-mail: patricia_trap@nps.gov

Midwest Region *(continued)*

Associate Regional Director, Administration and Information Technology **Clara Wooden** .... (402) 661-1974
E-mail: clara_wooden@nps.gov
Contracting Chief **George Sievers** .... (402) 661-1606
E-mail: george_sievers@nps.gov
Associate Regional Director, Cultural Resource **Robert "Bob" Bryson** .... (402) 437-5392 ext. 107
Education: Oregon 1989 PhD
Associate Regional Director, Equal Employment Opportunity **Clara Wooden** .... (402) 661-1974
E-mail: clara_wooden@nps.gov
Associate Regional Director, Natural Resource Stewardship and Science **Nancy Finley** .... (402) 661-1536
Associate Regional Director, Operations Interpretation and Education **James A. Loach** .... (402) 661-1702
Chief, Education and Interpretation **Tom Richter** .... (402) 661-1892
E-mail: tom_richter@nps.gov
Chief, Facility Maintenance and Design **Duane Bubac** .... (402) 661-1720
Associate Regional Director for Legislation, Communications, Planning and Partnerships **Nancy Finley** .... (402) 661-1536
E-mail: nancy_finley@nps.gov
Planning and Compliance Chief **Tokey Boswell** .... (402) 661-1840
Assistant Regional Director, Comptroller **Connie Dworak** .... (402) 661-1628
E-mail: connie_dworak@nps.gov
Chief, Information Technology **Jenifer Noss** .... (402) 661-1624
E-mail: jenifer_noss@nps.gov
Chief Ranger **Tim "TC" Colyer** .... (402) 661-1736
Education: Penn Col Tech 1990 AS

Agate Fossil Beds National Monument
301 River Road, Harrison, NE 69346
Tel: (308) 668-2211 Fax: (308) 668-2318 Internet: www.nps.gov/agfo

Superintendent **James Hill** .... (308) 668-2211 ext. 770

Apostle Islands National Lakeshore
415 Washington Avenue, Bayfield, WI 54814
Tel: (715) 779-3397 Fax: (715) 779-3049 Internet: www.nps.gov/apis

Superintendent **Robert J. "Bob" Krumenaker** .... (715) 779-3397
Education: Brown U 1979 BS; Yale 1982 MFS
Resource Education Chief **Myra Foster** .... (715) 779-3397
E-mail: myra_foster@nps.gov

Arkansas Post National Memorial
1741 Old Post Road, Gillett, AR 72055
Tel: (870) 548-2207 Fax: (870) 548-2431
E-mail: arpo_historian@nps.gov Internet: www.nps.gov/arpo

Superintendent **Karen Bradford** .... (870) 548-2207

Badlands National Park
25216 Ben Reifel Road, Interior, SD 57750
P.O. Box 6, Interior, SD 57750
Tel: (605) 433-5361 Fax: (605) 433-5404 Internet: www.nps.gov/badl

Superintendent **Michael D. "Mike" Pflaum** .... (605) 433-5361
Education: Mankato State 1978 BS

Brown vs. Board of Education National Historic Site
1515 SE Monroe Street, Topeka, KS 66612
Tel: (785) 354-4273 Fax: (785) 354-7213 Internet: www.nps.gov/brvb

Superintendent **Sherda Williams** .... (785) 354-4273

Buffalo National River
402 North Walnut Street, Suite 136, Harrison, AR 72601
Tel: (870) 741-5443 Tel: (870) 439-2502 (Visitor Information)
Fax: (870) 741-7286 Internet: www.nps.gov/buff

Superintendent **Laura Miller** .... (870) 741-5443

★ Presidential Appointment Requiring Senate Confirmation ☆ Presidential Appointment ☐ Schedule C Appointment ◇ Career Senior Foreign Service Appointment
● Career Senior Executive Service (SES) Appointment ○ Non-Career Senior Executive Service (SES) Appointment ■ Postal Career Executive Service

Central High School National Historic Site
2125 Daisy L. Gaston Bates Drive, Little Rock, AR 72202
Tel: (501) 374-1957 Fax: (501) 301-7762
E-mail: chsc_visitor_center@nps.gov
Superintendent **Robin White** .... (501) 396-3002
Chief of Education and Interpretation **David Kilton** ...... (501) 396-3006
Administrative Officer **Marchelle Williams** .... (501) 396-3002
Facility Manager **Evan Webber** .... (501) 396-3080

Charles Young Buffalo Soldiers National Monument
1120 US Route 42 East, Wilberforce, OH 45385
Tel: (937) 352-6757 Internet: www.nps.gov/chyo
Superintendent **Joy Kinard** .... (937) 352-6757
Education: Howard U MA, PhD

Cuyahoga Valley National Park
15610 Vaughn Road, Brecksville, OH 44141
Tel: (216) 524-1497 (Visitor Information)
Tel: (440) 546-5991 (Visitor Information) Fax: (440) 546-5989
E-mail: cuva_info@nps.gov Internet: www.nps.gov/cuva
Superintendent **Craig A. Kenkel** .... (440) 546-5903

Dayton Aviation Heritage National Historical Park
16 South Williams Street, Dayton, OH 45402
P.O. Box 9280, Wright Brothers Station, Dayton, OH 45409
Tel: (937) 225-7705 (Wright-Dunbar Interpretive Center)
Tel: (937) 425-0008 (Huffman Prairie Interpretive Center)
Fax: (937) 222-4512 Internet: www.nps.gov/daav
Superintendent **(Vacant)** .... (937) 225-7705

Effigy Mounds National Monument
151 Highway 76, Harpers Ferry, IA 52146
Tel: (563) 873-3491 Fax: (563) 873-3743 Internet: www.nps.gov/efmo
Superintendent **James A. "Jim" Nepstad** .... (563) 873-3491
Education: Wisconsin BS

First Ladies National Historic Site
205 Market Avenue South, Canton, OH 44702
Tel: (330) 452-0876 Fax: (330) 456-3414 Internet: www.nps.gov/fila
Site Manager **Craig A. Kenkel** .... (330) 452-0876

Fort Larned National Historic Site
1767 Kansas Highway 156, Larned, KS 67550-9733
P.O. Box 69, Larned, KS 67550-9733
Tel: (620) 285-6911 Fax: (620) 285-3571 Internet: www.nps.gov/fols
Superintendent **Betty Boyko** .... (620) 285-6911

Fort Scott National Historic Site
Old Fort Boulevard, Fort Scott, KS 66701
P.O. Box 918, Fort Scott, KS 66701
Tel: (620) 223-0310 Fax: (620) 223-0188 Internet: www.nps.gov/fosc
Superintendent **Betty Boyko** .... (620) 223-0310

Fort Smith National Historic Site
301 Parker Avenue, Fort Smith, AR 72902
P.O. Box 1406, Fort Smith, AR 72902
Tel: (479) 783-3961 Fax: (479) 783-5307 Internet: www.nps.gov/fosm
Superintendent **Lisa Conard-Frost** .... (479) 783-3961

Fort Union Trading Post National Historic Site
601 Riverfront Drive, Omaha, NE 68102
Tel: (701) 572-9083 Fax: (701) 572-7321 Internet: www.nps.gov/fous
Superintendent **Andrew E. Banta** .... (701) 572-9083

Gateway Arch National Park
11 North Fourth Street, St. Louis, MO 63102
Tel: (314) 655-1600 Fax: (314) 655-1641 Internet: www.nps.gov/jeff
Superintendent **Michael M. "Mike" Ward** .... (314) 655-1600

George Rogers Clark National Historical Park
401 South Second Street, Vincennes, IN 47591
Tel: (812) 882-1812 (Park Headquarters)
Tel: (812) 882-1776 (Visitor Information) Fax: (812) 882-7270
Internet: www.nps.gov/gero
Superintendent **Frank W. Doughman** .... (812) 882-1776 ext. 202
Education: Maine

George Washington Carver National Monument
5646 Carver Road, Diamond, MO 64840
Tel: (417) 325-4151 Fax: (417) 325-4231 Internet: www.nps.gov/gwca
Superintendent **James Heaney** .... (417) 325-4151

Grand Portage National Monument
315 South Broadway, Grand Marais, MN 55604
P.O. Box 668, Grand Marais, MN 55604
Tel: (218) 387-2788 (Park Headquarters)
Tel: (218) 475-2202 (Stockade Ranger Station) Fax: (218) 387-2790
Internet: www.nps.gov/grpo
Superintendent (Acting) **Craig Hansen** .... (701) 745-3741 ext. 202

Harry S. Truman National Historic Site
223 North Main Street, Independence, MO 64050
Tel: (816) 254-2720 (Park Headquarters)
Tel: (816) 254-9929 (Visitor Information) Fax: (816) 254-4491
Internet: www.nps.gov/hstr
Superintendent **Carol Dage** .... (816) 254-2720

Herbert Hoover National Historic Site
110 Parkside Drive, West Branch, IA 52358
P.O. Box 607, West Branch, IA 52358-0607
Tel: (319) 643-2541 TTY: (319) 643-2594 Fax: (319) 643-5367
Internet: www.nps.gov/heho
Superintendent **Pete Swisher** .... (319) 643-7870
Education: Western Illinois BS

Homestead National Monument of America
8523 West State Highway 4, Beatrice, NE 68310
Tel: (402) 223-3514 Fax: (402) 228-4231 Internet: www.nps.gov/home
Superintendent **Mark Engler** .... (402) 223-3514

Hopewell Culture National Historical Park
16062 State Route 104, Chillicothe, OH 45601
Tel: (740) 774-1126 Fax: (740) 774-1140 Internet: www.nps.gov/hocu
Superintendent **Karen Dorn** .... (740) 774-1126

Hot Springs National Park
101 Reserve Street, Hot Springs, AR 71901
Tel: (501) 623-2824 (Park Headquarters)
Tel: (501) 624-2701 (Visitor Information) Fax: (501) 624-3458
Internet: www.nps.gov/hosp
Superintendent **(Vacant)** .... (501) 623-2824
Management Analyst **Tricia Horn** .... (501) 620-6730
Chief of Resources Management and Visitor Services
(Acting) **Mark Scott** .... (501) 620-6861
Facilities Manager (Acting) **Mark Scott** .... (501) 620-6861
Natural Resources Physical Scientist **Shelley Todd** ...... (501) 620-6751
Administrative Officer **(Vacant)** .... (501) 623-2824

Ice Age National Scenic Trail
700 Rayovac Drive, Suite 100, Madison, WI 53711
Tel: (608) 441-5610 Fax: (608) 441-5606
Internet: http://www.nps.gov/iatr/index.htm
Superintendent **(Vacant)** .... (608) 441-5610

Indiana Dunes National Lakeshore
1100 North Mineral Springs Road, Porter, IN 46304
Tel: (219) 926-7561 Fax: (219) 926-6153 Internet: www.nps.gov/indu
Superintendent **Paul R. Labovitz** .... (219) 395-1699
Education: Penn State BS; Frostburg State U 1987 MBA

DEPARTMENTS

★ Presidential Appointment Requiring Senate Confirmation ☆ Presidential Appointment □ Schedule C Appointment ◇ Career Senior Foreign Service Appointment
● Career Senior Executive Service (SES) Appointment ○ Non-Career Senior Executive Service (SES) Appointment ■ Postal Career Executive Service

DEPARTMENTS

Isle Royale National Park
800 East Lakeshore Drive, Houghton, MI 49931-1869
Tel: (906) 482-0984 Fax: (906) 482-8753 Internet: www.nps.gov/isro
Superintendent **Phyllis Green** .... (906) 482-0984

James A. Garfield National Historic Site
8095 Mentor Avenue, Mentor, OH 44606
Tel: (440) 255-8722 Fax: (440) 974-2045 Internet: www.nps.gov/jaga
Site Manager **Craig A. Kenkel** .... (440) 255-8722 ext. 238

Jewel Cave National Monument
Building B12, 11149 US Highway 16, Custer, SD 57730
P.O. Box 60AA , RR1, Custer, SD 57730
Tel: (605) 673-2288 Fax: (605) 673-3294
E-mail: jeca_interpretation@nps.gov Internet: www.nps.gov/jeca
Superintendent **Nancy Martinz** .... (605) 673-8300

Keweenaw National Historical Park
25970 Red Jacket Road, Calumet, MI 49913
P.O. Box 471, Calumet, MI 49913-0471
Tel: (906) 337-3168 Fax: (906) 337-3169 Internet: www.nps.gov/kewe
Superintendent **Wyndeth Davis** .... (906) 337-3168
Education: Oregon BS, MS

Knife River Indian Villages National Historic Site
564 County Road 37, Stanton, ND 58571
P.O. Box 9, Stanton, ND 58571
Tel: (701) 745-3300 Fax: (701) 745-3708 Internet: www.nps.gov/knri
Superintendent (Acting) **Brenda Todd** .... (701) 745-3300

Lewis and Clark National Historic Trail
601 Riverfront Drive, Omaha, NE 68102
Tel: (402) 661-1804 Fax: (402) 661-1807 Internet: www.nps.gov/lewi
Superintendent **Mark Weekley** .... (402) 661-1806
Education: Minnesota BS; Iowa State BLA, MLA

Lincoln Boyhood National Memorial
3027 East South Street, Lincoln City, IN 47552-1816
P.O. Box 1816, Lincoln City, IN 47552-1816
Tel: (812) 937-4541 Fax: (812) 937-9929 Internet: www.nps.gov/libo
Superintendent **Kendell Thompson** .... (812) 937-4541

Lincoln Home National Historic Site
413 South 8th Street, Springfield, IL 62701-1905
Tel: (217) 492-4241 Fax: (217) 492-4673 Internet: www.nps.gov/liho
Superintendent **Timothy S. Good** .... (217) 391-3222

Midwest Archeological Center
Federal Building, 100 Centennial Mall North,
Room 474, Lincoln, NE 68508-3873
Tel: (402) 437-5392 Fax: (402) 437-5098
Center Manager **Robert "Bob" Bryson** .... (402) 437-5392 ext. 107
Education: Oregon 1989 PhD
Archeologist and Park Archeology Program
Manager **(Vacant)** .... (402) 437-5392 ext. 140

Minuteman Missile National Historic Site
21280 SD Highway 240, Philip, SD 57750
Tel: (605) 433-5552 Fax: (605) 433-5558 Internet: www.nps.gov/mimi
Superintendent **Eric Leonard** .... (605) 433-5552

Mississippi National River and Recreation Area
111 East Kellogg Boulevard, Suite 105, St. Paul, MN 55101
Tel: (651) 290-4160 (Park Headquarters)
Tel: (651) 293-0200 (Visitor Information) Fax: (651) 290-3214
Internet: www.nps.gov/miss
Superintendent **John Anfinson** .... (651) 293-8432

Mount Rushmore National Memorial
Building 31, 1300 Highway 244, Suite 1, Keystone, SD 57751
Tel: (605) 574-2523 Fax: (605) 574-2307 Internet: www.nps.gov/moru
Superintendent **Cheryl A. Schreier** .... (605) 574-3131
E-mail: cheryl_schreier@nps.gov
Education: Wisconsin (Stevens Point) BS

Nicodemus National Historic Site
304 Washington Avenue, Bogue, KS 67625-3015
Tel: (785) 839-4233 Fax: (785) 839-4325 Internet: www.nps.gov/nico
Superintendent (Acting) **Sherda Williams** .... (785) 354-4273

Niobrara - Missouri National Scenic Riverways
P.O. Box 319, Valentine, NE 69201
Tel: (402) 376-1901 Fax: (402) 376-1949 Internet: www.nps.gov/niob
Superintendent **Stephen G. Thede** .... (402) 376-1901 ext. 114
E-mail: steve_thede@nps.gov

Ozark National Scenic Riverways
404 Watercress Drive, Van Buren, MO 63965
P.O. Box 490, Van Buren, MO 63965
Tel: (573) 323-4236 Fax: (573) 323-4140 Internet: www.nps.gov/ozar
Superintendent **Lawrence E. "Larry" Johnson** .... (573) 323-4236
E-mail: larry_johnson@nps.gov
Education: Iowa State BS

North Country National Scenic Trails
P.O. Box 288, Lowell, MI 49331
Tel: (616) 319-7906 Fax: (608) 441-5606
Internet: http://www.nps.gov/noco/index.htm
Superintendent **Mark Weaver** .... (608) 441-5610
Fax: (608) 441-5606

Pea Ridge National Military Park
15930 Highway 62, Garfield, AR 72732
P.O. Box 700, Pea Ridge, AR 72751
Tel: (479) 451-8122 Fax: (479) 451-0219 Internet: www.nps.gov/peri
Superintendent **Kevin Eads** .... (479) 451-8122
E-mail: kevin_eads@nps.gov
Education: Northeastern State BS; Arkansas (Monticello) MS

Perry's Victory and International Peace Memorial
93 Delaware Avenue, Put-in-Bay, OH 43456
P.O. Box 549, Put-in-Bay, OH 43456
Tel: (419) 285-2184 Fax: (419) 285-2516 Internet: www.nps.gov/pevi
Superintendent **Barbara Fearon** .... (419) 285-2184

Pictured Rocks National Lakeshore
N8391 Sand Point Road, Munising, MI 49862-0040
P.O. Box 40, Munising, MI 49862-0040
Tel: (906) 387-2607 (Park Headquarters)
Tel: (906) 387-3700 (Visitor Information) Fax: (906) 387-4025
Internet: www.nps.gov/piro
Superintendent **David Horne** .... (906) 387-2607 ext. 1202
Education: Humboldt State BS

Pipestone National Monument
36 Reservation Avenue, Pipestone, MN 56164
Tel: (507) 825-5464 Fax: (507) 825-5466 Internet: www.nps.gov/pipe
Superintendent **Lauren Blacik** .... (402) 661-1584

President William Jefferson Clinton Birthplace Home National Historic Site
117 South Hervey Street, Hope, AR 71801-4208
Tel: (870) 777-4455 Internet: http://www.nps.gov/wicl/index.htm
Superintendent **Tarona Armstrong** .... (870) 777-4455

River Raisin National Battlefield Park
1403 Elm Avenue, Monroe, MI 48161
Mail: P.O. Box 2229, Monroe, MI 48161
Tel: (734) 243-7136
Superintendent **Scott J. Bentley** .... (734) 243-7136

★ Presidential Appointment Requiring Senate Confirmation ☆ Presidential Appointment ☐ Schedule C Appointment ◇ Career Senior Foreign Service Appointment
● Career Senior Executive Service (SES) Appointment ○ Non-Career Senior Executive Service (SES) Appointment ■ Postal Career Executive Service

Saint Croix - Lower Saint Croix National Scenic Riverways
401 Hamilton Street, North, Saint Croix Falls, WI 54024
P.O. Box 708, Saint Croix Falls, WI 54024-0708
Tel: (715) 483-3284 Fax: (715) 483-3288 Internet: www.nps.gov/sacn

Superintendent **Christopher "Chris" Stein** ....(715) 483-2290
E-mail: chris_stein@nps.gov
Education: Utah State BS

Scotts Bluff National Monument
190276 Old Oregon Trail, Gering, NE 69341
P.O. Box 27, Gering, NE 69341
Tel: (308) 436-4340 Fax: (308) 436-7611 Internet: www.nps.gov/scbl

Superintendent **Dan Morford** .... (308) 436-4340
E-mail: dan_morford@nps.gov

Sleeping Bear Dunes National Lakeshore
9922 Front Street, Highway M-72, Empire, MI 49630
Tel: (231) 326-5134 Fax: (231) 326-5382
E-mail: slbe_interpretation@nps.gov Internet: www.nps.gov/slbe

Superintendent **Scott Tucker** .... (231) 326-5134
E-mail: scott_tucker@nps.gov

Tallgrass Prairie National Preserve
226 Broadway, Cottonwood Falls, KS 66845-0585
Tel: (620) 273-6034 (Administrative Headquarters)
Tel: (620) 273-8494 (Park Headquarters) Fax: (620) 273-8950
Internet: www.nps.gov/tapr

Superintendent **(Vacant)** .... (620) 273-6034 ext. 280

Theodore Roosevelt National Park
P.O. Box 7, Medora, ND 58645-0007
Tel: (701) 623-4466 (Park Headquarters)
Tel: (701) 842-2333 (Visitor Information) Fax: (701) 623-4840
Internet: www.nps.gov/thro

Superintendent **Wendy Ross** .... (701) 623-4466
E-mail: wendy_ross@nps.gov
Education: Middlebury BA

Ulysses S. Grant National Historic Site
7400 Grant Road, St. Louis, MO 63123
Tel: (314) 842-3298 Fax: (314) 842-1659 Internet: www.nps.gov/ulsg

Superintendent **Nichole McHenry** ....(402) 661-1978
E-mail: nichole_mchenry@nps.gov

Voyageurs National Park
3131 Highway 53 South, International Falls, MN 56649
Tel: (218) 283-6600 (Park Headquarters)
Tel: (218) 286-5258 (Visitor Information) Fax: (218) 285-7407
Internet: www.nps.gov/voya

Superintendent **Bob DeGross** ....(218) 283-6606
E-mail: bob_degross@nps.gov

William Howard Taft National Historic Site
2038 Auburn Avenue, Cincinnati, OH 45219
Tel: (513) 684-3262 ext. 301 Fax: (513) 684-3627
Internet: www.nps.gov/wiho

Superintendent **Hugh Hawthorne** .... (575) 536-9461
Education: Idaho 1982 BA

Wilson's Creek National Battlefield
6424 West Farm Road 182, Republic, MO 65738
Tel: (417) 732-2662 Fax: (417) 732-1167 Internet: www.nps.gov/wicr

Superintendent **T. John Hillmer** ....(417) 732-2662
E-mail: t_john_hillmer@nps.gov

Wind Cave National Park
26611 US Highway 385, Hot Springs, SD 57747
Mail: RR 1, Box 190 - WCNP, Hot Springs, SD 57747-9430
Tel: (605) 745-4600 Fax: (605) 745-4207 Internet: www.nps.gov/wica

Superintendent **Vidal Davila** ....(605) 745-4600
E-mail: vidal_davila@nps.gov

Pullman National Monument
11141 South Cottage Grove Avenue, Chicago, IL 60628
Tel: (773) 264-7431

Superintendent **Kathleen "Kathy" Schneider** ....(773) 468-3284

National Capital Region (NCR)
1100 Ohio Drive, SW, 3rd Floor, Washington, DC 20242
Tel: (202) 619-7023 Fax: (202) 619-7220
Areas Covered: Washington, DC metropolitan area including some parks in MD, VA, WV

● Regional Director (Acting) **Rick Obernesser** .... (907) 822-7202
E-mail: rick_obernesser@nps.gov
Education: Cal State (Sacramento) 1973 BS
Deputy Regional Director
Lisa Mendelson-Ielmini Third Floor .... (202) 619-7194
Education: Washington Col 1985 BA; Virginia 1990 MPL
Associate Regional Director for Communications
Jennifer Mummart .... (202) 619-7023
Education: Richmond; American U
Associate Regional Director for Youth and Community Engagement **Wendy O'Sullivan** .... (202) 619-7492
E-mail: wendy_o'sullivan@nps.gov
Comptroller **Shelly Murray** First Floor .... (202) 619-7309
Safety and Occupational Health Manager
Tony Moreland .... (202) 619-7261
E-mail: tony_moreland@nps.gov

Administration
1100 Ohio Drive, SW, Washington, DC 20242
Tel: (202) 619-7200 Fax: (202) 619-7199

Associate Regional Director, Administration
Nancie Ames Second Floor .... (202) 619-7286
E-mail: nancie_ames@nps.gov
Contracting **(Vacant)** Annex .... (202) 619-7200
Facilities Chief **(Vacant)** .... (202) 619-7200
Finance Office **(Vacant)** .... (202) 619-7200
Human Resources Officer
Charles Richardson Second Floor .... (202) 619-7217
E-mail: charles_richardson@nps.gov
Information Management **Jeff Burrows** .... (202) 692-6006
E-mail: jeff_burrows@nps.gov
Property Director **Laren Beasley** First Floor .... (202) 619-7181
Records/FOIA Coordinator **Taylor Beckett** .... (202) 619-7200
E-mail: taylor_beckett@nps.gov

Lands, Planning and Design
1100 Ohio Drive, SW, Washington, DC 20242
Tel: (202) 619-7023 Fax: (202) 401-0017

Associate Regional Director, Lands, Planning and Design **Peter G. May** .... (202) 619-7025
Education: Georgetown BA; Maryland MAR
Deputy Associate, Lands, Planning and Design
Doug Jacobs .... (202) 619-7038
Land Resources Program Center **Melissa Mooza** .... (202) 619-7464
E-mail: melissa_mooza@nps.gov
Museum Resource Center Director **(Vacant)** .... (202) 619-7023
Regional Land Use Liaison **Glenn DeMarr** .... (202) 619-7027
Regional Legislative Coordinator
(Vacant) Second Floor .... (202) 619-7097
Associate Director for Resource, Stewardship and Science **Perry Wheelock** .... (202) 619-7088
Education: Pennsylvania; George Washington

Operations and Education
1100 Ohio Drive, SW, Washington, DC 20242
Tel: (202) 619-7142 Fax: (202) 619-7225

Associate Regional Director, Operations and Education
(Vacant) Third Floor .... (202) 619-7245
Business Services **Dave M. Moore** Third Floor .... (202) 619-7404
Chief of Interpretation and Education
Linda Lutz-Ryan .... (202) 619-7245
Facilities Services Administrator **(Vacant)** Third Floor .... (202) 619-7200
Public Health **Jeremy Mason** .... (202) 619-7070
E-mail: jeremy_mason@nps.gov

(continued on next page)

DEPARTMENTS

Operations and Education *(continued)*

Ranger Services Division **Will Reynolds** . . . . (202) 619-7057

National Mall and Memorial Parks
1100 Ohio Drive, SW, Washington, DC 20242
Tel: (202) 485-9880 Fax: (202) 426-9309

● Superintendent **(Vacant)** . . . . (202) 485-9880
Deputy Superintendent for Operations
Karen Cucurullo . . . . (202) 245-4661
Deputy Superintendent for Planning **(Vacant)** . . . . (202) 485-9880

American Veterans Disabled for Life Memorial
150 Washington Avenue SW, Washington, DC 20024
Tel: (800) 331-7590
Superintendent **(Vacant)** . . . . (800) 331-7590

Antietam National Battlefield
P.O. Box 158, Sharpsburg, MD 21782-0158
Tel: (301) 432-5124 Fax: (301) 432-4590 Internet: www.nps.gov/anti
Superintendent **Susan Trail** . . . . (301) 432-7648
Education: Maryland PhD

Arlington House, The Robert E. Lee Memorial
George Washington Memorial Parkway, McLean, VA 22101
Tel: (703) 557-0613 Fax: (703) 289-2598
E-mail: gwmp_superintendent@nps.gov Internet: www.nps.gov/arho
Superintendent **Brandon Bies** . . . . (703) 235-1530

Belmont-Paul Women's Equality National Monument
144 Constitution Avenue, NE, Washington, DC 20002-5608
Tel: (202) 546-1210 Internet: https://www.nps.gov/bepa
Superintendent **(Vacant)** . . . . (202) 546-1210

Catoctin Mountain Park
6602 Foxville Road, Thurmont, MD 21788-1598
Tel: (301) 663-9330 Fax: (301) 271-2764 Internet: www.nps.gov/cato
Superintendent **Rick Slade** . . . . (301) 663-9388
Education: Kansas; Virginia

Chesapeake and Ohio Canal National Historical Park
1850 Dual Highway, Suite 100, Hagerstown, MD 21740
Tel: (301) 739-4200 Fax: (301) 739-5275 Fax: (301) 739-6179
Internet: www.nps.gov/choh
Superintendent **Kevin Brandt** . . . . (301) 714-2201

Clara Barton National Historic Site
700 George Washington Memorial Parkway Headquarters,
McLean, VA 22101
Tel: (301) 492-6245 Fax: (301) 289-2598
E-mail: gwmp_superintendent@nps.gov Internet: www.nps.gov/clba
Site Manager **(Vacant)** . . . . (301) 492-6245

Constitution Gardens
900 Ohio Drive, SW, Washington, DC 20024
Tel: (202) 426-6841 Fax: (202) 426-1844 Internet: www.nps.gov/coga
Superintendent **(Vacant)** . . . . (202) 245-4660

Ford's Theatre National Historic Site
900 Ohio Drive, SW, Washington, DC 20024
Tel: (202) 426-6924 Fax: (202) 426-1845 Internet: www.nps.gov/foth
Site Manager **William Cheek** . . . . (202) 426-6924

Fort Washington Park
13551 Fort Washington Road, Fort Washington, MD 20744
Tel: (301) 763-4600 Fax: (301) 763-1389 Internet: www.nps.gov/fowa
Superintendent **Christine Smith** . . . . (301) 763-4600

Franklin Delano Roosevelt Memorial
900 Ohio Drive, SW, Washington, DC 20024
Tel: (202) 426-6841 Fax: (202) 426-1844 Internet: www.nps.gov/fdrm
Superintendent (Acting) **Cassius M. Cash** . . . . (202) 485-9880
Education: Arkansas (Pine Bluff) BS

Frederick Douglass National Historic Site
1411 W Street, SE, Washington, DC 20020-4813
Tel: (202) 426-5961 Fax: (202) 426-0880 Internet: www.nps.gov/frdo
Site Manager **Julie Kutruff** . . . . (202) 426-5961
Curator **Ka'mal McClarin** . . . . (202) 690-5161
Education: Howard U 2012 PhD

George Washington Memorial Parkway
Turkey Run Park, McLean, VA 22101
Tel: (703) 289-2500 Fax: (703) 289-2598
E-mail: gwmp_superintendent@nps.gov Internet: www.nps.gov/gwmp
Superintendent **Alex Romero** . . . . (703) 289-2503

Greenbelt Park
6565 Greenbelt Road, Greenbelt, MD 20770
Tel: (301) 344-3948 Fax: (301) 344-3736 Internet: www.nps.gov/gree
Superintendent (Acting) **Makayah Royal** . . . . (202) 619-7092
1100 Ohio Drive, SW, Washington, DC 20224

Harpers Ferry National Historical Park
P.O. Box 65, Harpers Ferry, WV 25425
Tel: (304) 535-6224 Fax: (304) 535-6244 Internet: www.nps.gov/hafe
Superintendent **(Vacant)** . . . . (304) 535-6224

Korean War Veterans Memorial
900 Ohio Drive, SW, Washington, DC 20024
Tel: (202) 426-6841 Fax: (202) 426-1844 Internet: www.nps.gov/kwvm
Superintendent (Acting) **Cassius M. Cash** . . . . (202) 485-9880
Education: Arkansas (Pine Bluff) BS

Lincoln Memorial
900 Ohio Drive, SW, Washington, DC 20024
Tel: (202) 426-6841 Fax: (202) 426-1844 Internet: www.nps.gov/linc
Superintendent (Acting) **Cassius M. Cash** . . . . (202) 485-9880
Education: Arkansas (Pine Bluff) BS

Lyndon Baines Johnson Memorial Grove on the Potomac
Turkey Run Park, McLean, VA 22101
Tel: (703) 289-2500 Fax: (703) 289-2598
E-mail: gwmp_superintendent@nps.gov Internet: www.nps.gov/lyba
Superintendent (Acting) **Cassius M. Cash** . . . . (202) 485-9880
Education: Arkansas (Pine Bluff) BS

Manassas National Battlefield Park
12521 Lee Highway, Manassas, VA 20109
Tel: (703) 754-1861 Fax: (703) 754-1107 Internet: www.nps.gov/mana
Superintendent **Jon G. "J. J." James** . . . . (703) 754-1861
Education: William & Mary BA

Martin Luther King, Jr. Memorial
900 Ohio Drive, SW, Washington, DC 20024
Superintendent (Acting) **Cassius M. Cash** . . . . (202) 485-9880
Education: Arkansas (Pine Bluff) BS

Mary McLeod Bethune Council House National Historic Site
1318 Vermont Avenue, NW, Washington, DC 20005
Tel: (202) 673-2402 Fax: (202) 673-2414 Internet: www.nps.gov/mamc
Superintendent **(Vacant)** . . . . (202) 673-2402

Monocacy National Battlefield
4801 Urbana Pike, Frederick, MD 21704
Tel: (301) 698-6247 (Law Enforcement and Facilities Management Offices) Tel: (301) 696-8650 (Administrative Headquarters)
Tel: (301) 662-3515 (Visitor Center) Fax: (301) 662-3420
Internet: www.nps.gov/mono
Superintendent **Christopher J. Stubbs** . . . . (301) 694-3147

National Park Service Liaison to the White House
1849 C Street, NW, Room 1426, Washington, DC 20240
Tel: (202) 208-1631 Fax: (202) 619-6353

National Park Service Liaison to the White House
John Stanwich . . . . . (202) 619-6344
1100 Ohio Drive, SW, Room 344, Washington, DC 20242
Education: London School Econ (UK) MS
Deputy Liaison **(Vacant)** . . . . . (202) 619-6344
1100 Ohio Drive, SW, 344, Washington, DC 20242
President's Park Division **Peter Lonsway** . . . . . (202) 208-1638

National Mall
900 Ohio Drive, SW, Washington, DC 20024
Tel: (202) 426-6841 Fax: (202) 426-1844 E-mail: national_mall@nps.gov
Internet: www.nps.gov/nama

Superintendent (Acting) **Cassius M. Cash** . . . . . (202) 485-9880
Education: Arkansas (Pine Bluff) BS

Piscataway Park
1900 Anacostia Drive, SE, Washington, DC 20020
13351 Fort Washington Road, Fort Washington, MD 20744
Tel: (301) 763-4600 Fax: (301) 763-1389 Internet: www.nps.gov/pisc

Superintendent **Christine Smith** . . . . . (301) 839-1176

Potomac Heritage National Scenic Trail
P.O. Box B, Harpers Ferry, WV 25425
Tel: (304) 535-4014 Fax: (304) 535-4020
Internet: www.nps.gov/gwmp/vapa/pht.htm

Superintendent **Donald "Don" Briggs** . . . . . (304) 535-4016

Prince William Forest Park
18100 Park Headquarters Road, Triangle, VA 22172
Tel: (703) 221-4706 Fax: (703) 221-4322 Internet: www.nps.gov/prwi

Superintendent **Vidal Martinez** . . . . . (703) 221-2925

Rock Creek Park
3545 Williamsburg Lane, NW, Washington, DC 20008-1207
Tel: (202) 895-6070 Fax: (202) 282-7612 Internet: www.nps.gov/rocr

Superintendent **Julia Washburn** . . . . . (202) 895-6001
Education: Mount Holyoke BS; Bank Street

Theodore Roosevelt Island
George Washington Memorial Parkway, McLean, VA 22101
Tel: (703) 289-2500 Fax: (703) 289-2598
E-mail: gwmp_superintendent@nps.gov Internet: www.nps.gov/this

Superintendent **Alex Romero** . . . . . (703) 289-2500

Thomas Jefferson Memorial
900 Ohio Drive, SW, Washington, DC 20024
Tel: (202) 426-6841 Fax: (202) 426-1844 Internet: www.nps.gov/thje

Superintendent (Acting) **Cassius M. Cash** . . . . . (202) 485-9880
Education: Arkansas (Pine Bluff) BS

Vietnam Veterans Memorial
900 Ohio Drive, SW, Washington, DC 20024
Tel: (202) 426-6841 Fax: (202) 426-1844 Internet: www.nps.gov/vive

Superintendent (Acting) **Cassius M. Cash** . . . . . (202) 485-9880
Education: Arkansas (Pine Bluff) BS

Washington Monument
900 Ohio Drive, SW, Washington, DC 20024
Tel: (202) 426-6841 Fax: (202) 426-1844 Internet: www.nps.gov/wamo

Superintendent (Acting) **Cassius M. Cash** . . . . . (202) 485-9880
Education: Arkansas (Pine Bluff) BS

Wolf Trap National Park for the Performing Arts
1551 Trap Road, Vienna, VA 22182
Tel: (703) 255-1800 Fax: (703) 255-1971 Internet: www.nps.gov/wotr

Director **George Liffert** . . . . . (703) 255-1808

World War I Memorial
Superintendent (Acting) **Cassius M. Cash** . . . . . (202) 485-9880
Education: Arkansas (Pine Bluff) BS

World War II Memorial
900 Ohio Drive, SW, Washington, DC 20024
Fax: (202) 426-9309

Superintendent (Acting) **Cassius M. Cash** . . . . . (202) 485-9880
Education: Arkansas (Pine Bluff) BS

Northeast Regional Office
U.S. Customs House, 200 Chestnut Street,
5th Floor, Philadelphia, PA 19106-2818
Tel: (215) 597-7013 Fax: (215) 597-0815 Internet: www.nps.gov/nero
Areas Covered: CT, DE, ME, MD, MA, NH, NJ, NY, PA, RI, VT, VA, WV

● Regional Director (Acting)
Deborah L. "Debbie" Conway . . . . . (215) 597-7013
E-mail: deborah_conway@nps.gov
Education: Hiram 1988 BA
Confidentiality Assistant to the Regional Director
Rochelle Williams . . . . . (215) 597-7018
E-mail: rochelle_williams@nps.gov
Deputy Regional Director for Park Operations
Jonathan "Jon" Meade . . . . . (215) 597-9014
Associate Regional Director for Administration
(Acting) **Alexa Molnar** . . . . . (215) 597-7065
E-mail: alexa_molnar@nps.gov
Associate Regional Director for Construction and
Management **(Vacant)** . . . . . (215) 597-6474
Associate Regional Director, Natural Resource
Stewardship and Science **Frank R. Hays** . . . . . (215) 597-7013
Education: Arizona BS; Northern Arizona MPA
Associate Regional Director for Planning, Facilities,
and Conservation Assistance **Brian R. Strack** . . . . . (215) 597-1788
Fax: (215) 597-2337
Chief of Communications and Legislative Affairs
Jane Ahern . . . . . (215) 597-0865
E-mail: jane_ahern@nps.gov
Chief of Business Services **(Vacant)** . . . . . (215) 597-9014
Chief Historian **Christine Arato** . . . . . (504) 589-3882
Education: Harvard 2008 BA
Chief, Interpretation, Education and Partnership
Development **(Vacant)** . . . . . (215) 597-7056
Chief, Inventory and Monitoring **Jim Comiskey** . . . . . (215) 597-7056
Chief, Law Enforcement and Emergency Operations
Lorena Harris . . . . . (215) 597-3679
Fax: (215) 597-8641
Chief, Natural Resources **Carmen Chapin** . . . . . (215) 597-7700
Regional Comptroller **Alexa Molnar** . . . . . (215) 597-7065
E-mail: alexa_molnar@nps.gov Fax: (215) 597-9656
Freedom of Information Act Coordinator
Annette Sasso . . . . . (215) 597-7384
E-mail: annette_sasso@nps.gov
Employee Development Specialist **Mariah Cisse** . . . . . (215) 597-7071
Information Technology Specialist **Heidi Graham** . . . . . (215) 597-6850
E-mail: heidi_graham@nps.gov Fax: (215) 597-6900
Human Resource Manager **Melissa Sims** . . . . . (215) 597-7013
E-mail: melissa_sims@nps.gov
Education: West Point 1997 BS
Equal Employment Opportunity Manager
Eileen White . . . . . (215) 597-7123
E-mail: eileen_white@nps.gov
Education: Penn State BS; London School Econ (UK) MSc

Acadia National Park
P.O. Box 177, Bar Harbor, ME 04609-0177
Tel: (207) 288-3338 TTY: (207) 288-8800 Fax: (207) 288-8813
Internet: www.nps.gov/acad

Superintendent (Acting) **Michael Madell** . . . . . (207) 288-8701

Adams National Historical Park
135 Adams Street, Quincy, MA 02169
Tel: (617) 770-1175 Fax: (617) 472-7562 Internet: www.nps.gov/adam

Superintendent **Marianne Peak** . . . . . (617) 773-1177

★ Presidential Appointment Requiring Senate Confirmation ☆ Presidential Appointment □ Schedule C Appointment ◇ Career Senior Foreign Service Appointment
● Career Senior Executive Service (SES) Appointment ○ Non-Career Senior Executive Service (SES) Appointment ■ Postal Career Executive Service

African Burial Ground National Monument
290 Broadway, New York, NY 10007
Tel: (212) 637-2019 Fax: (212) 227-2026 Internet: www.nps.gov/afbg

Superintendent **Shirley McKinney** .... (212) 825-6991
Education: Kentucky State BS

Allegheny Portage Railroad National Historic Site
110 Federal Park Road, Gallitzin, PA 16641
Tel: (814) 886-6150 Fax: (814) 886-6117 Internet: www.nps.gov/alpo

Superintendent **Stephen M. Clark** .... (814) 886-6150

Appalachian National Scenic Trail
252 McDowell Street, Harpers Ferry, WV 25425 (Fed Ex Delivery)
Mail: P.O. Box 50, Harpers Ferry, WV 25425
Tel: (304) 535-6278 Fax: (304) 535-6270 Internet: www.nps.gov/appa

Superintendent **Wendy Janssen** .... (304) 535-6279
Education: Rutgers BA
Assistant Park Manager **(Vacant)** .... (304) 535-6170
Chief Ranger **Todd Remaley** .... (304) 535-6171
E-mail: todd_remaley@nps.gov

Appomattox Court House National Historical Park
P.O. Box 218, Route 24, Appomattox, VA 24522
Tel: (434) 352-8987 Fax: (434) 352-8330 Internet: www.nps.gov/apco

Superintendent **Robin Snyder** .... (434) 352-8987 ext. 221

Assateague Island National Seashore
7206 National Seashore Lane, Berlin, MD 21811
Tel: (410) 641-1441 Fax: (410) 641-1099 Internet: www.nps.gov/asis

Superintendent **Deborah Darden** .... (410) 641-1441
Secretary **Karen Rodney** .... (410) 641-1441
E-mail: karen_rodney@nps.gov

Blackstone River Valley National Heritage Corridor
One Depot Square, Woonsocket, RI 02895
Tel: (508) 234-4242 Fax: (401) 762-0530 Internet: www.nps.gov/blac

Superintendent **Meghan Kish** .... (508) 996-4095 ext. 6100
Education: Stanford BS

Blackstone River Valley National Historical Park
670 Linwood Avenue, Suite #10, Whitinsville, MA 05188
Tel: (508) 234-4242

Superintendent **Meghan Kish** .... (508) 996-4095 ext. 6100
Education: Stanford BS

Bluestone National Scenic River
P.O. Box 246, Glen Jean, WV 25846
Tel: (304) 465-0508 Fax: (304) 465-0591 Internet: www.nps.gov/blue

Superintendent **Lizzie Watts** .... (304) 465-0508

Booker T. Washington National Monument
12130 Booker T. Washington Highway, Hardy, VA 24101
Tel: (540) 721-2094 Fax: (540) 721-8311 Internet: www.nps.gov/bowa

Superintendent (Acting) **Timothy G. "Timbo" Sims** .... (540) 721-2094

Boston African American National Historic Site
14 Beacon Street, Suite 503, Boston, MA 02108
Tel: (617) 742-5415 Fax: (617) 720-0848 Internet: www.nps.gov/boaf

Superintendent **Michael Creasey** .... (617) 742-5415

Boston Harbor Islands National Recreation Area
408 Atlantic Avenue, Suite 225, Boston, MA 02210-3350
Tel: (617) 223-8666 Fax: (617) 223-8671 Internet: www.nps.gov/boha

Superintendent **Giles Parker** .... (617) 223-8669

Boston National Historical Park
Charlestown Navy Yard, Boston, MA 02129-4543
Tel: (617) 242-5642
Tel: (617) 242-5601 (Charlestown Navy Yard Visitor Information Center)
Fax: (617) 242-6006 Internet: www.nps.gov/bost

Superintendent **Michael Creasey** .... (617) 242-5642

Cape Cod National Seashore
99 Marconi Site Road, Wellfleet, MA 02667
Tel: (508) 255-3421 Fax: (508) 349-9052 Internet: www.nps.gov/caco

Superintendent **Brian Carlstrom** .... (970) 267-2151 ext. 212
Education: George Mason 1989 BS, MA
Deputy Superintendent **Kathy Tevyaw** .... (508) 771-2144

Captain John Smith Chesapeake National Historic Trail
410 Severn Avenue, Annapolis, MD 21403
Tel: (410) 260-2470 Fax: (410) 263-2135 Internet: www.nps.gov/cajo

Superintendent **Charles "Chuck" Hunt** .... (410) 260-2471

Castle Clinton National Monument
Battery Park, New York, NY 10004
Tel: (212) 344-7220 Fax: (212) 825-9363 Internet: www.nps.gov/cacl

Superintendent **Shirley McKinney** .... (212) 825-6990
Education: Kentucky State BS

Cedar Creek and Belle Grove National Historical Park
P.O. Box 700, Middletown, VA 22645
Tel: (540) 868-9176 Fax: (540) 869-4527 Internet: www.nps.gov/cebe

Superintendent **Jennifer Flynn** .... (540) 999-3500 ext. 3200

Chesapeake Bay Gateways Network
410 Severn Avenue, Suite 109, Annapolis, MD 21403
Tel: (410) 260-2470 Fax: (410) 263-2135 Internet: www.nps.gov/cbpo

Superintendent **Charles "Chuck" Hunt** .... (410) 260-2471

Colonial National Historical Park
P.O. Box 210, Yorktown, VA 23690
Tel: (757) 898-3400 Fax: (757) 898-6346 Internet: www.nps.gov/colo

Superintendent **Kym Hall** .... (757) 898-3400

Coltsville National Historical Park
Superintendent **James Woolsey** .... (215) 597-7013

Delaware and Lehigh National Heritage Corridor
2750 Hugh Moore Park Road, Easton, PA 18042
Tel: (610) 923-3548 Fax: (610) 961-9357 E-mail: dele3@fast.net
Internet: www.nps.gov/dele

Executive Director **Elissa Garofalo** .... (610) 923-3548 ext. 234

Delaware National Scenic River
c/o Delaware Water Gap National Recreation Area,
HQ River Road off Route 209, Bushkill, PA 18324
Tel: (570) 426-2452 Fax: (570) 426-2402 Internet: www.nps.gov/dele

Superintendent **(Vacant)** .... (570) 426-2452

Delaware Water Gap National Recreation Area
River Road, Bushkill, PA 18324
Tel: (570) 426-2435 Fax: (570) 426-2407 Internet: www.nps.gov/dewa

Superintendent **(Vacant)** .... (570) 426-2418

Edgar Allan Poe National Historic Site
532 North Seventh Street, Philadelphia, PA 19123
Tel: (215) 597-8780 Fax: (215) 597-1901
E-mail: inde_poe_house@nps.gov Internet: www.nps.gov/edal

Superintendent **(Vacant)** .... (215) 597-8780

Eisenhower National Historic Site
97 Taneytown Road, Gettysburg, PA 17325
Tel: (717) 338-9114 Fax: (717) 338-0821
E-mail: eise_site_manager@nps.gov Internet: www.nps.gov/eise

Superintendent **Ed W. Clark** .... (717) 338-9114

Eleanor Roosevelt National Historic Site
4097 Albany Post Road, Hyde Park, NY 12538
Tel: (845) 229-9115 Fax: (845) 229-0739 Internet: www.nps.gov/elro

Superintendent **Lawrence "Larry" Turk** .... (845) 229-9115 ext. 2033

Erie Canalway National Heritage Corridor
P.O. Box 219, Waterford, NY 12188
Tel: (518) 237-7000 Fax: (518) 237-7640 Internet: www.nps.gov/erie
Executive Director **Bob Radliff** . . . . (518) 237-7000 ext. 204

Essex National Heritage Area
Essex National Heritage Commission, Inc.,
140 Washington Street, Salem, MA 01970
Tel: (978) 740-0444 Fax: (978) 744-6473 Internet: www.nps.gov/esse
Chief Executive Officer **Annie C. Harris** . . . . (978) 740-0444

Federal Hall National Memorial
26 Wall Street, New York, NY 10005
Tel: (212) 825-6990 Fax: (212) 825-6874 Internet: www.nps.gov/feha
Superintendent **Shirley McKinney** . . . . (212) 825-6990
Education: Kentucky State BS

Fire Island National Seashore
120 Laurel Street, Patchogue, NY 11772-3596
Tel: (631) 687-4750 Fax: (631) 289-4898
E-mail: fiis_interpretation@nps.gov Internet: www.nps.gov/fiis
Superintendent **Chris Soller** . . . . (631) 687-4752

First State National Historic Park
211 Delaware Street, New Castle, DE 19720
Tel: (302) 824-3530
Superintendent **Ethan McKinley** . . . . (302) 544-6363
Education: Denver

Flight 93 National Memorial
109 West Main Street, Suite 104, Somerset, PA 15501-2035
Tel: (814) 893-5503 Fax: (814) 443-2180 Internet: www.nps.gov/flni
Superintendent **Stephen M. Clark** . . . . (814) 893-6531

Fort McHenry National Monument and Historic Shrine
2400 East Fort Avenue, Baltimore, MD 21230
Tel: (410) 962-4290 Fax: (410) 962-2500 Internet: www.nps.gov/fomc
Superintendent **Tina Cappetta** . . . . (410) 962-4290 ext. 101
Education: Maryland

Fort Monroe National Monument
41 Bernard Road, Fort Monroe, VA 23651
Tel: (757) 722-3678 Internet: www.nps.gov/fomr
Superintendent **(Vacant)** . . . . (757) 722-3678

Fort Necessity National Battlefield
One Washington Parkway, Farmington, PA 15437
Tel: (724) 329-5512 Fax: (724) 329-8682 Internet: www.nps.gov/fone
Superintendent **Stephen M. Clark** . . . . (814) 893-6531

Fort Stanwix National Monument
112 East Park Street, Rome, NY 13440
Tel: (315) 336-3113 Fax: (315) 334-5051 Internet: www.nps.gov/fost
Superintendent **Frank Barrows** . . . . (315) 336-3113

Frederick Law Olmsted National Historic Site
99 Warren Street, Brookline, MA 02445
Tel: (617) 566-1689 Fax: (617) 232-4073 Internet: www.nps.gov/frla
Superintendent **Myra Harrison** . . . . (617) 566-1689 ext. 201
Head Ranger **Alan Banks** . . . . (617) 566-1689 ext. 221
Fax: (617) 232-3964

Fredericksburg and Spotsylvania National Military Park
120 Chatham Lane, Fredericksburg, VA 22405
Tel: (540) 693-3200 Fax: (540) 371-1907 Internet: www.nps.gov/frsp
Superintendent **Kirsten Talken-Spaulding** . . . . . (540) 693-3200 ext. 1010

Friendship Hill National Historic Site
c/o Fort Necessity National Battlefield,
One Washington Parkway, Farmington, PA 15437
Tel: (724) 725-9190 Fax: (724) 329-8682 Internet: www.nps.gov/frhi
Superintendent **Stephen M. Clark** . . . . (814) 893-6531

Gateway National Recreation Area
210 New York Avenue, Staten Island, NY 10305
Tel: (718) 338-3338 Tel: (718) 354-4665 (Public Affairs Office)
Fax: (718) 338-3876 Fax: (718) 354-4605 (Public Affairs Fax)
Internet: www.nps.gov/gate
Superintendent **Jennifer T. Nersesian** . . . . (718) 354-4661
Education: Rutgers MPP

Gauley River National Recreation Area
P.O. Box 246, Glen Jean, WV 25846
Tel: (304) 465-0508 Fax: (304) 465-0591 Internet: www.nps.gov/gari
Superintendent **Lizzie Watts** . . . . (304) 465-0508

General Grant National Memorial
Riverside Drive and 122nd Street, New York, NY 10027
Tel: (212) 825-6990 Fax: (212) 932-9631 Internet: www.nps.gov/gegr
Superintendent **Shirley McKinney** . . . . (212) 825-6990
Education: Kentucky State BS

George Washington Birthplace National Monument
1732 Popes Creek Road, Washington's Birthplace, VA 22443
Tel: (804) 224-1732 Fax: (804) 224-2142 Internet: www.nps.gov/gewa
Superintendent **Melissa K. Cobern** . . . . (804) 224-1732 ext. 224
Education: Montevallo AB; Memphis State MA

Germantown White House
5442 Germantown Avenue, Philadelphia, PA 19144
Tel: (215) 597-7120 Fax: (215) 597-0321
Superintendent **Cynthia "Cindy" MacLeod** . . . . (215) 597-7120
Education: Virginia MA

Gettysburg National Military Park
1195 Baltimore Pike, Suite 100, Gettysburg, PA 17325
Tel: (717) 334-1124 Fax: (717) 334-1891 Internet: www.nps.gov/gett
Superintendent **Ed W. Clark** . . . . (717) 334-1124

Gloria Dei Church National Historic Site
Columbus Boulevard and Christian Street, Philadelphia, PA 19147
Tel: (215) 389-1513 Fax: (215) 597-1416 Internet: www.nps.gov/glde
Superintendent **Cynthia "Cindy" MacLeod** . . . . (215) 597-7120
Education: Virginia MA

Governors Island National Monument
Battery Maritime Building Slip 7, 10 South Street,
New York, NY 10004-1900
Tel: (212) 825-3045 Fax: (212) 825-3055 Internet: www.nps.gov/gois
Superintendent **Shirley McKinney** . . . . (212) 825-6991
Education: Kentucky State BS

Great Egg Harbor National Scenic and Recreational River
U.S. Custom House, 200 Chestnut Street,
3rd Floor, Philadelphia, PA 19106
Tel: (215) 597-5823 Fax: (215) 597-5747 Internet: www.nps.gov/greg
National Wild and Scenic Rivers Coordinator **(Vacant)** . . . (215) 597-1581

Hamilton Grange National Memorial
287 Convent Avenue, New York, NY 10005
Tel: (212) 825-6690 Fax: (212) 825-6874 Internet: www.nps.gov/hagr
Superintendent **Shirley McKinney** . . . . (212) 825-6990
Education: Kentucky State BS

Hampton National Historic Site
535 Hampton Lane, Towson, MD 21286
Tel: (410) 823-1309 Fax: (410) 823-8394 Internet: www.nps.gov/hamp
Superintendent **Tina Cappetta** . . . . (410) 823-1309 ext. 101
Education: Maryland

Harriet Tubman National Historical Park
Superintendent **Robert Parker** . . . . (267) 838-2376
Education: North Carolina A&T BA; North Carolina State 2001 MA

DEPARTMENTS

★ Presidential Appointment Requiring Senate Confirmation ☆ Presidential Appointment ☐ Schedule C Appointment ◇ Career Senior Foreign Service Appointment
● Career Senior Executive Service (SES) Appointment ○ Non-Career Senior Executive Service (SES) Appointment ■ Postal Career Executive Service

Harriet Tubman Underground Railroad National Monument
Superintendent **Robert Parker** . . . . (267) 838-2376
Education: North Carolina A&T BA; North Carolina State 2001 MA

Home of Franklin D. Roosevelt National Historic Site
4097 Albany Post Road, Hyde Park, NY 12538
Tel: (845) 229-9115 Fax: (845) 229-0739 Internet: www.nps.gov/hofr
Superintendent **Lawrence "Larry" Turk** . . . . (845) 229-9115 ext. 2033

Hopewell Furnace National Historic Site
Two Mark Bird Lane, Elverson, PA 19520
Tel: (610) 582-8773 TTY: (610) 582-2093 Fax: (610) 582-2768
E-mail: hofu_superintendent@nps.gov Internet: www.nps.gov/hofu
Superintendent **Kate Hammond** . . . . (610) 582-8773 ext. 230
Librarian **Rebecca "Becky" Ross** . . . . (610) 582-8773 ext. 240

Independence National Historical Park
143 South Third Street, Philadelphia, PA 19106
Tel: (215) 965-2305 TTY: (215) 597-1785 Fax: (215) 597-1003
Internet: www.nps.gov/inde
Superintendent [Section 508 Coordinator]
Cynthia "Cindy" MacLeod . . . . (215) 965-2305
Education: Virginia MA

Jamestown National Historic Site
P.O. Box 210, Yorktown, VA 23690
Tel: (757) 898-2401 Fax: (757) 229-4273 Internet: www.nps.gov/jame
Superintendent **Kym Hall** . . . . (757) 898-2401

Johnstown Flood National Memorial
733 Lake Road, South Fork, PA 15956
Tel: (814) 495-4643 Fax: (814) 495-7463 Internet: www.nps.gov/jofl
Superintendent **Stephen M. Clark** . . . . (814) 893-6531

John F. Kennedy National Historic Site
83 Beals Street, Brookline, MA 02446
Tel: (617) 566-1689 Fax: (617) 730-9884 E-mail: mava_info@nps.gov
Internet: www.nps.gov/jofi
Superintendent **Myra Harrison** . . . . (617) 566-1689 ext. 201

Katahdin Woods and Waters National Monument
200 Chestnut Street, Philadelphia, PA 19106
Tel: (207) 456-6001
Superintendent **Tim Hudson** . . . . (215) 597-7013
Community Planner **Christina Marts** . . . . (215) 597-7013

Longfellow National Historic Site
105 Brattle Street, Cambridge, MA 02138
Tel: (617) 566-1689 Fax: (617) 497-8718 Internet: www.nps.gov/long
Superintendent **Myra Harrison** . . . . (617) 587-6449 ext. 201
Curator **David Daly** . . . . (617) 876-4491 ext. 12

Lowell National Historical Park
67 Kirk Street, Lowell, MA 01852-1029
Tel: (978) 275-1700 TTY: (978) 970-5002 Fax: (978) 275-1762
Internet: www.nps.gov/lowe
Superintendent **Celeste Bernardo** . . . . (978) 275-1703
Education: Northeastern BA, MA

Lower East Side Tenement Museum
103 Orchard Street, New York, NY 10002
Tel: (212) 431-0233 Fax: (212) 431-0402 Internet: www.tenement.org
Internet: www.nps.gov/loea
President and Superintendent **Morris Vogel** . . . . (212) 431-0233
E-mail: mvogel@tenement.org
Education: Brandeis; Chicago PhD

Maggie L. Walker National Historic Site
3215 East Broad Street, Richmond, VA 23223
Tel: (804) 771-2017 Fax: (804) 771-8522 Internet: www.nps.gov/mawa
Superintendent **Dave Ruth** . . . . (804) 226-1981 ext. 5031

Marsh-Billings-Rockefeller National Historical Park
54 Elm Street, Woodstock, VT 05091
P.O. Box 178, Woodstock, VT 05091
Tel: (802) 457-3368 Fax: (802) 457-3405 Internet: www.nps.gov/mabi
Superintendent **Rick Kendall** . . . . (802) 457-3368 ext. 215

Martin Van Buren National Historic Site
1013 Old Post Road, Kinderhook, NY 12106
Tel: (518) 758-9689 Fax: (518) 758-6986 Internet: www.nps.gov/mava
Superintendent **Lawrence "Larry" Turk** . . . . (845) 229-9115 ext. 2033

Minute Man National Historical Park
174 Liberty Street, Concord, MA 01742
Tel: (978) 318-7811 Fax: (978) 318-7801 E-mail: mima_infor@nps.gov
Internet: www.nps.gov/mima
Superintendent **B. J. Dunn** . . . . (978) 369-6993

Morristown National Historical Park
30 Washington Place, Morristown, NJ 07960-4299
Tel: (973) 766-8224 Tel: (973) 543-4030 (Jockey Hollow Visitor Center)
Fax: (973) 539-8361 E-mail: morr_administration@nps.gov
Internet: www.nps.gov/morr
Superintendent **Thomas E. Ross** . . . . (973) 984-2182 ext. 200
Chief of Cultural Resources **Jude Pfister** . . . . (973) 984-2313 ext. 204
E-mail: jude_pfister@nps.gov

New Bedford Whaling National Historical Park
33 William Street, New Bedford, MA 02740
Tel: (508) 996-4095 Fax: (508) 984-1250
E-mail: nebe_superintendent@nps.gov Internet: www.nps.gov/nebe
Superintendent **Meghan Kish** . . . . (508) 996-4095 ext. 6100
Education: Stanford BS

New Jersey Coastal Heritage Trail Route
P.O. Box 568, Newport, NJ 08345
Tel: (215) 597-1581 Fax: (609) 894-7330
E-mail: neje_interpretation@nps.gov Internet: www.nps.gov/neje
Project Director **Philip G. "Phil" Correll** . . . . (215) 597-1581

New River Gorge National River
P.O. Box 246, Glen Jean, WV 25846
Tel: (304) 465-0508 Fax: (304) 465-0591 Internet: www.nps.gov/neri
Superintendent **Lizzie Watts** . . . . (304) 465-0508

Paterson Great Falls National Historic Park
72 McBride Avenue, Paterson, NJ 07501
Tel: (201) 314-3977 Internet: www.nps.gov/pagr
Superintendent **Darren Boch** . . . . (201) 314-3977

Petersburg National Battlefield
1539 Hickory Hill Road, Petersburg, VA 23803
Tel: (804) 732-4210 Fax: (804) 732-3615 Internet: www.nps.gov/pete
Superintendent **Lewis Rogers** . . . . (804) 732-3531
Education: Slippery Rock U

Quinebaug and Shetucket Rivers Valley National Heritage Corridor
The Last Green Valley, 111 Main Street, Danielson, CT 06239-0029
Tel: (860) 774-3300 Fax: (860) 928-2189
Internet: http://thelastgreenvalley.org/
Executive Director **Lois Bruinooge** . . . . (860) 774-3300

Richmond National Battlefield Park
3215 East Broad Street, Richmond, VA 23223
Tel: (804) 771-2808 Fax: (804) 771-8522 Internet: www.nps.gov/rich
Superintendent **Dave Ruth** . . . . (804) 226-1981 ext. 5031

Roger Williams National Memorial
282 North Main Street, Providence, RI 02903
Tel: (401) 521-7266 Fax: (401) 521-7239 Internet: www.nps.gov/rowi
Superintendent **Meghan Kish** . . . . (401) 521-7266
Education: Stanford BS

★ Presidential Appointment Requiring Senate Confirmation ☆ Presidential Appointment ☐ Schedule C Appointment ◇ Career Senior Foreign Service Appointment
● Career Senior Executive Service (SES) Appointment ○ Non-Career Senior Executive Service (SES) Appointment ■ Postal Career Executive Service

Roosevelt Campobello International Park
Executive Secretary, P.O. Box 97, Lubec, ME 04652
459 Route 774, New Brunswick, Canada
Tel: (506) 752-2922 Fax: (506) 752-6000 Internet: www.nps.gov/roca
Superintendent **James Carr** .... (506) 752-2922

Saint Croix Island International Historic Site
c/o Acadia National Park, P.O. Box 177, Bar Harbor, ME 04609-0177
Tel: (207) 288-3338 Fax: (207) 288-8813 Internet: www.nps.gov/sacr
Superintendent **Kevin Schneider** .... (207) 288-3338 ext. 8702
Education: Colorado State 1998 BS

Saint-Gaudens National Historic Site
139 Saint-Gaudens Road, Cornish, NH 03745
Tel: (603) 675-2175 Fax: (603) 675-2701 Internet: www.nps.gov/saga
Superintendent **Rick Kendall** .... (603) 675-2175 ext. 143

Saint Paul's Church National Historic Site
897 South Columbus Avenue, Mount Vernon, NY 10550
Tel: (914) 667-4116 Fax: (914) 667-3024 Internet: www.nps.gov/sapa
Site Manager **David Osborn** .... (914) 667-4116

Salem Maritime National Historic Site
160 Derby Street, Salem, MA 01970
Tel: (978) 740-1680 Fax: (978) 740-1685 Internet: www.nps.gov/sama
Superintendent **Paul DePrey** .... (978) 740-1684

Sagamore Hill National Historic Site
20 Sagamore Hill Road, Oyster Bay, NY 11771-1807
Tel: (516) 922-4271 Fax: (516) 922-4792 Internet: www.nps.gov/sahi
Superintendent **Kelly Fuhrmann** .... (516) 922-4788
Cultural Resources Chief **Susan Sarna** .... (516) 922-4271

Saratoga National Historical Park
648 Route 32, Stillwater, NY 12170-1604
Tel: (518) 670-2985 Fax: (518) 664-9830 E-mail: sara_info@nps.gov
Internet: www.nps.gov/sara
Superintendent **Amy Bracewell** .... (518) 670-2940

Saugus Iron Works National Historic Site
244 Central Street, Saugus, MA 01906
Tel: (781) 233-0050 Fax: (781) 231-7345 Internet: www.nps.gov/sair
Superintendent **Paul DePrey** .... (781) 233-0050

Shenandoah National Park
3655 U.S. Highway 211 East, Luray, VA 22835
Tel: (540) 999-3500 Fax: (540) 999-3601 Internet: www.nps.gov/shen
Superintendent **Jennifer Flynn** .... (540) 999-3500 ext. 3200
E-mail: jennifer_flynn@nps.gov

Springfield Armory National Historic Site
One Armory Square, Suite 2, Springfield, MA 01105-1299
Tel: (413) 734-6478 Fax: (413) 747-8062 Internet: www.nps.gov/spar
Superintendent **James Woolsey** .... (413) 271-3980
Museum Curator **Alex MacKenzie** .... (413) 271-3971
E-mail: alex_mackenzie@nps.gov

Statue of Liberty - Ellis Island National Monuments
Liberty Island, New York, NY 10004
Tel: (212) 363-3206 Tel: (212) 363-3200 (Information)
Fax: (212) 363-6304 Internet: www.nps.gov/elis
Internet: www.nps.gov/stli
Superintendent **John Piltzecker** .... (646) 356-2101
Education: Fairleigh Dickinson
Deputy Superintendent **Cherie Butler** .... (212) 363-3206

Steamtown National Historic Site
150 South Washington Avenue, Scranton, PA 18503
Tel: (570) 340-5206 TTY: (570) 340-5207 Tel: (888) 693-9391
Fax: (570) 340-5235 Internet: www.nps.gov/stea
Superintendent **Debbie Conway** .... (570) 340-5206
Education: Hiram 1988 BA

Stonewall National Monument
26 Wall Street, New York, NY 10005
Tel: (212) 668-2577
Superintendent **Shirley McKinney** .... (212) 825-6991
Education: Kentucky State BS

Thaddeus Kosciuszko National Memorial
301 Pine Street, Philadelphia, PA 19106
Tel: (215) 597-9618 Internet: www.nps.gov/thko
Superintendent **Cynthia "Cindy" MacLeod** .... (215) 597-9618
Education: Virginia MA

Theodore Roosevelt Birthplace National Historic Site
28 East 20th Street, New York, NY 10003
P.O. Box 26 Wall Street, New York, NY 10005
Tel: (212) 825-6990 Fax: (212) 677-3587 E-mail: masi_thrb@nps.gov
Internet: www.nps.gov/thrb
Superintendent **Shirley McKinney** .... (212) 825-6990
Education: Kentucky State BS

Theodore Roosevelt Inaugural National Historic Site
641 Delaware Avenue, Buffalo, NY 14202
Tel: (716) 884-0095 Fax: (716) 884-0330 Internet: www.nps.gov/thri
Superintendent **Stanton H. Hudson, Jr.** .... (716) 884-0095

Thomas Edison National Historic Site
211 Main Street, West Orange, NJ 07052-5612
Tel: (973) 736-0550 TTY: (973) 243-9122 Fax: (973) 736-6567
E-mail: edis_archives@nps.gov Internet: www.nps.gov/edis
Superintendent **Thomas E. Ross** .... (973) 539-2016 ext. 27
Archivist **Leonard De Graaf** .... (973) 736-0550 ext. 22
E-mail: leonard_degraaf@nps.gov

Thomas Stone National Historic Site
6655 Rosehill Road, Port Tobacco, MD 20677
Tel: (301) 392-1776 Fax: (301) 934-8793 Internet: www.nps.gov/thst
Superintendent **Melissa K. Cobern** .... (804) 224-1732 ext. 224
1732 Popes Creek Road, Washington's Birthplace, VA 22443
Education: Montevallo AB; Memphis State MA

Touro Synagogue National Historic Site
72 Touro Street, Newport, RI 02840
Tel: (401) 847-4794 Fax: (401) 847-8121
E-mail: info@tourosynagogue.org Internet: www.nps.gov/tosy
Executive Director **Rabbi Mendel** .... (401) 847-4794 ext. 7

Upper Delaware Scenic and Recreational River
274 River Road, Beach Lake, PA 18405
Tel: (717) 685-4871 Fax: (570) 729-8565
E-mail: upde_interpretation@nps.gov Internet: www.nps.gov/upde
Superintendent **Kristina "Kris" Heister** .... (717) 685-4871
Education: Salisbury State U 1989 BS; Penn State 1995 MS

Valley Forge National Historical Park
1400 North Outer Line Drive, King of Prussia, PA 19406
Tel: (610) 783-1037 Fax: (610) 783-1038 Internet: www.nps.gov/vafo
Superintendent **Steven Sims** .... (610) 783-1037

Roosevelt - Vanderbilt Mansion National Historic Site
4097 Albany Post Road, Hyde Park, NY 12538
Tel: (845) 229-9115 Fax: (845) 229-0739 Internet: www.nps.gov/vama
Superintendent **Lawrence "Larry" Turk** .... (845) 229-9115 ext. 2033

Weir Farm National Historic Site
735 Nod Hill Road, Wilton, CT 06897
Tel: (203) 834-1896 Fax: (203) 834-2421 Internet: www.nps.gov/wefa
Superintendent **Linda Cook** .... (203) 834-1896 ext. 23

Women's Rights National Historical Park
136 Fall Street, Seneca Falls, NY 13148
Tel: (315) 568-2991 Tel: (315) 568-0024 (Information Desk)
Fax: (315) 568-2141 Internet: www.nps.gov/wori
Superintendent **Noemi "Ami" Ghazala** .... (315) 568-2772

★ Presidential Appointment Requiring Senate Confirmation ☆ Presidential Appointment ☐ Schedule C Appointment ◇ Career Senior Foreign Service Appointment
● Career Senior Executive Service (SES) Appointment ○ Non-Career Senior Executive Service (SES) Appointment ■ Postal Career Executive Service

DEPARTMENTS

Pacific West Region
333 Bush Street, Suite 500, San Francisco, CA 94104
Tel: (415) 623-2100
Areas Covered: AS, CA, CNMI, GU, HI, ID, NV, OR, WA

● Regional Director **Stanley "Stan" Austin** .... (415) 623-2100
E-mail: stan_austin@nps.gov
Education: Rutgers BS
Secretary **Karen Washington** .... (415) 623-2102
E-mail: karen_washington@nps.gov
Deputy Regional Director **Katarina Tuovinen** .... (415) 623-2100
Acquisition Division **Jamie Sherrill** .... (415) 623-2250
E-mail: jamie_sherrill@nps.gov
Facility Management Division
David F. "Dave" Kruse .... (415) 623-2270
Education: Oregon
Budget **Aaron Dowe** .... (415) 623-2141
E-mail: aaron_dowe@nps.gov
Finance **(Vacant)** .... (415) 623-2100
Human Resources **Susan Michl** .... (415) 623-2160
Assistant Regional Director **(Vacant)** .... (415) 623-2100
Assistant Regional Director, Communications
Stephanie Burkhart .... (415) 623-2103
E-mail: stephanie_burkhart@nps.gov Fax: (510) 817-1325
Concessions Division **Trystan Stern** .... (415) 623-2220
Information Technology Division **David Quitevis** .... (415) 623-2241
E-mail: david_quitevis@nps.gov
Deputy Regional Director for Public Use Management
Martha J. Lee .... (415) 623-2106
Education: Stanford
Fire Management Division **(Vacant)** .... (415) 623-2100
Interpretation Division **Sheri Forbes** .... (415) 623-2301
Partnerships Division **Ray Murray** .... (510) 817-1439
E-mail: ray_murray@nps.gov
Chief Ranger – Visitor Protection Division (Acting)
Rene Buehl .... (415) 623-2181
Fax: (510) 817-1488
Deputy Regional Director for Resource Management
and Planning **Chip Jenkins** .... (206) 220-4020
909 First Avenue, Seattle, WA 98104 Fax: (206) 220-4160
Cultural Resources Division **Dr. David Louter** .... (206) 220-4137
909 First Avenue, Seattle, WA 98104
E-mail: david_louter@nps.gov
Education: Montana BA; U Washington MA, PhD
Natural Resources Division Director **Jay Goldsmith** .... (415) 623-2206
Planning Division Administrator **Martha Crusius** .... (415) 623-2310
Safety Division **Stacy C. Wertman** .... (415) 623-2350

Pacific West Regional Office- Seattle
909 First Avenue, Seattle, WA 98104
Tel: (206) 220-4000 Fax: (206) 220-4160
Deputy Regional Director (Acting) **Tracy Swartout** .... (206) 220-4000

Big Hole National Battlefield
P.O. Box 237, Wisdom, MT 59761
Tel: (406) 689-3155 Fax: (406) 689-3151 Internet: www.nps.gov/biho
Superintendent **Mandy Wick** .... (406) 689-3155

City of Rocks National Reserve
3035 Elba Almo Road, Almo, ID 83312
P.O. Box 169, Almo, ID 83312
Tel: (208) 824-5519 Fax: (208) 824-5563 Internet: www.nps.gov/ciro
Superintendent **Wallace Keck** .... (208) 824-5911

Crater Lake National Park
P.O. Box 7, Crater Lake, OR 97604-0007
Tel: (541) 594-3000 Fax: (541) 594-3010 Internet: www.nps.gov/crla
Superintendent **Craig Ackerman** .... (541) 594-3000

Craters of the Moon National Monument
P.O. Box 29, Arco, ID 83213-0029
Tel: (208) 527-3257 Fax: (208) 527-3073 Internet: www.nps.gov/crmo
Superintendent **(Vacant)** .... (208) 527-3257

Ebey's Landing National Historical Reserve
P.O. Box 774, Coupeville, WA 98239-0774
Tel: (360) 678-6084 Fax: (360) 678-2246 Internet: www.nps.gov/ebla
Superintendent (Acting) **Roy Zipp** .... (360) 678-6084

Fort Vancouver National Historic Site
612 East Reserve Street, Vancouver, WA 98661-3811
Tel: (360) 696-7655 Fax: (360) 696-7657 Internet: www.nps.gov/fova
Superintendent **Tracy Fortmann** .... (360) 816-6205

Hagerman Fossil Beds National Monument
221 North State Street, Hagerman, ID 83332-0570
P.O. Box 570, Hagerman, ID 83332-0570
Tel: (208) 933-4100 Fax: (208) 837-4857 Internet: www.nps.gov/hafo
Superintendent **Wade Vagias** .... (208) 933-4100

John Day Fossil Beds National Monument
HC 82, Box 126, Kimberly, OR 97848-9701
Tel: (541) 987-2333 Fax: (541) 987-2336 Internet: www.nps.gov/joda
Superintendent (Acting) **Christopher Collins** .... (541) 987-2333

Klondike Gold Rush National Historical Park - Seattle Unit
319 Second Avenue, Seattle, WA 98104
Tel: (206) 220-4240 Fax: (206) 381-0664 Internet: www.nps.gov/klse
Superintendent **Charles Beall** .... (206) 220-4240
Education: Cal State (Sacramento); Maryland University Col MA
Chief of Interpretation **Julie Fonseca de Borges** .... (206) 220-4231
Education: North Texas MA

Lake Chelan National Recreation Area (LCNRA)
810 State Route 20, Sedro Woolley, WA 98284
Tel: (360) 856-5700 Fax: (360) 856-1934 Internet: www.nps.gov/lach
Superintendent **Karen Taylor-Goodrich** .... (360) 854-7200

Lake Roosevelt National Recreation Area
1008 Crest Drive, Coulee Dam, WA 99116-1259
P.O. Box 37, Coulee Dam, WA 99116-1259
Tel: (509) 633-9441 Fax: (509) 633-9184 Internet: www.nps.gov/laro
Superintendent **Dan Foster** .... (509) 633-9441
Education: BYU BS

Lewis and Clark National Historical Park
Route 3, Box 604-FC, Astoria, OR 97103-9803
Tel: (503) 861-2471 TTY: (503) 861-1620 Fax: (503) 861-2585
Internet: www.nps.gov/lewi
Superintendent **John Buppee** .... (503) 861-2471

Mount Rainier National Park (MRNP)
Tahoma Woods, Star Route, Ashford, WA 98304-9751
Tel: (360) 569-2211 Fax: (360) 569-2170 Internet: www.nps.gov/mora
Superintendent **Randy King** .... (360) 569-2211 ext. 2302
Education: Michigan State BS

Nez Perce National Historical Park
Route 1, Spalding, ID 83540
Mail: P.O. Box 100, Spalding, ID 83540
Tel: (208) 843-7009 Fax: (208) 843-2124 Internet: www.nps.gov/nepe
Superintendent **Mike Gauthier** .... (208) 843-7009
Librarian/Archivist **Robert Applegate** .... (208) 843-7009
E-mail: robert_applegate@nps.gov

North Cascades National Park (NCNP)
810 State Route 20, Sedro Woolley, WA 98284
Tel: (360) 856-5700 Fax: (360) 856-1934 Internet: www.nps.gov/noca
Superintendent **Karen Taylor-Goodrich** .... (360) 854-7200

Olympic National Park (ONP)
600 East Park Avenue, Port Angeles, WA 98362-6757
Tel: (360) 565-3130 Fax: (360) 565-3015 Internet: www.nps.gov/olym
Superintendent **Sarah Creachbaum** .... (360) 565-3002
Deputy Superintendent **Lee Taylor** .... (360) 565-3003

★ Presidential Appointment Requiring Senate Confirmation ☆ Presidential Appointment ☐ Schedule C Appointment ◇ Career Senior Foreign Service Appointment
● Career Senior Executive Service (SES) Appointment ○ Non-Career Senior Executive Service (SES) Appointment ■ Postal Career Executive Service

Olympic National Park *(continued)*

Librarian **Greg Marsh** ....(360) 565-3138
Olympic National Park Visitor Center, Fax: (360) 565-3147
3002 Mount Angeles Road,
Port Angeles, WA 98362-6798
E-mail: greg_marsh@nps.gov

Oregon Caves National Monument and Preserve
19000 Caves Highway, Cave Junction, OR 97523-9716
Tel: (541) 592-2100 Fax: (541) 592-3981 Internet: www.nps.gov/orca

Superintendent **Vicki Snitzler**.........................(541) 592-2100
Education: Wisconsin

Ross Lake National Recreation Area
810 State Route 20, Sedro Woolley, WA 98284
Tel: (360) 856-5700 Fax: (360) 856-1934 Internet: www.nps.gov/rola

Superintendent **Karen Taylor-Goodrich** ....(360) 854-7200

San Juan Island National Historical Park
125 Spring Street, Friday Harbor, WA 98250-0429
P.O. Box 429, Friday Harbor, WA 98250-0429
Tel: (360) 378-2240 Fax: (360) 378-2615 Internet: www.nps.gov/sajh

Superintendent **Elexis Fredy**..........................(360) 378-2240

Whitman Mission National Historic Site
Route 2, Box 247, Walla Walla, WA 99362-9699
Tel: (509) 522-6360 Fax: (509) 522-6355 Internet: www.nps.gov/whmi

Superintendent **Tim Nitz**.................................(509) 522-6360

Pacific Great Basin Support Office
Jackson Center One, 1111 Jackson Street,
Suite 700, Oakland, CA 94607
Tel: (510) 817-1300 Fax: (510) 419-0197

Cabrillo National Monument
1800 Cabrillo Memorial Drive, San Diego, CA 92106-3601
Tel: (619) 557-5450 Fax: (619) 557-5469 Internet: www.nps.gov/cabr

Superintendent **Andrea Compton** ....(619) 557-5450

Castle Mountains National Monument
2701 Barstow Road, Barstow, CA 92311
Tel: (760) 252-6100 Fax: (760) 252-6174

Note: On February 12, 2016, President Obama signed a proclamation declaring the Castle Mountains National Monument.

Superintendent **Todd Suess** ....(760) 252-6100
Education: Minnesota 1988 BS

Cesar E. Chavez National Monument
29700 Woodford Tehachapi Road, Keene, CA 93531

Superintendent **Ruben Andrade**......................(661) 823-6134

Channel Islands National Park
1901 Spinnaker Drive, Ventura, CA 93001
Tel: (805) 658-5700 Fax: (805) 658-5799 Internet: www.nps.gov/chis

Superintendent **Russell Galipeau**.....................(805) 658-5702

Death Valley National Park
P.O. Box 579, Death Valley, CA 92328
Tel: (760) 786-3243 Fax: (760) 786-3283 Internet: www.nps.gov/deva

Superintendent **Mike Reynolds** ....(760) 786-3240
Education: Indiana BS; Arizona State MS

Devils Postpile National Monument
Three Rivers, CA 93271
Tel: (559) 565-3101 Fax: (559) 565-3730 Internet: www.nps.gov/depo

Superintendent **Deanna M. Dulen**.....................(559) 565-3101

Eugene O'Neill National Historic Site
P.O. Box 280, Danville, CA 94526
Tel: (925) 838-0249 Fax: (925) 838-9471 Internet: www.nps.gov/euon

Superintendent **Tom Leatherman** ....(925) 838-0249 ext. 6301
Education: UC Santa Cruz BA

Fort Point National Historic Site
P.O. Box 29333, Presidio of San Francisco, CA 94129
Tel: (415) 556-1693 Fax: (415) 556-4390 Internet: www.nps.gov/fopo

Superintendent (Acting) **Aaron Roth**..................(415) 556-1693

Golden Gate National Recreation Area
Fort Mason, Building 201, Savannah River Site, San Francisco, CA 94123
Tel: (415) 561-4720 Fax: (415) 561-4710 Internet: www.nps.gov/goga

Superintendent (Acting) **Craig A. Kenkel** ....(415) 561-4720

Great Basin National Park
Baker, NV 89311
Tel: (775) 234-7331 Fax: (775) 234-7269 Internet: www.nps.gov/grba

Superintendent **Steven Mietz**.........................(775) 234-7331

John Muir National Historic Site
4202 Alhambra Avenue, Martinez, CA 94553
Tel: (925) 228-8860 Fax: (925) 228-8192 Internet: www.nps.gov/jomu

Superintendent **Tom Leatherman** ....(925) 228-8860 ext. 6301
Education: UC Santa Cruz BA

Joshua Tree National Park
74485 National Park Drive, Twentynine Palms, CA 92277
Tel: (760) 367-5500 Fax: (760) 367-6392 Internet: www.nps.gov/jotr

Superintendent **David A. Smith**.......................(760) 367-5500
Education: UC Berkeley 1990 BA; Austin State MS

Juan Bautista de Anza National Historic Trail
1111 Jackson Street, Suite 700, Oakland, CA 94607
Tel: (510) 817-1438 Fax: (510) 419-0197 Internet: www.nps.gov/juba

Superintendent **Naomi Torres**.........................(415) 623-2340

Kings Canyon National Park
Three Rivers, CA 93271
Tel: (559) 565-3341 Fax: (559) 565-3730 Internet: www.nps.gov/seki

Superintendent **Woody Smeck**.......................(559) 565-3341

Lake Mead National Recreation Area
601 Nevada Highway, Boulder City, NV 89005-2426
Tel: (702) 293-8920 Fax: (702) 293-8936 Internet: www.nps.gov/lame

● Superintendent **Lizette Richardson** ....(702) 293-8922
E-mail: Lizette_Richardson@nps.gov
Education: Manhattan Col BS

Lassen Volcanic National Park
P.O. Box 100, Mineral, CA 96063-0100
Tel: (530) 595-4444 Fax: (530) 595-3262 Internet: www.nps.gov/lavo

Superintendent **Steve Gibbons** ....(530) 595-4444
Education: Miami BA

Lava Beds National Monument
P.O. Box 867, Tulelake, CA 96134
Tel: (530) 667-2282 Fax: (530) 667-2737 Internet: www.nps.gov/labe

Superintendent **Larry Whalon**.........................(530) 667-2282

Manzanar National Historic Site
P.O. Box 426, Independence, CA 93526
Tel: (760) 878-2194 Fax: (760) 878-2949 Internet: www.nps.gov/manz

Superintendent **Bernadette N. Johnson** ....(760) 878-2194

Mojave National Preserve
2701 Barstow Road, Barstow, CA 92311
Tel: (760) 252-6100 Fax: (760) 252-6174 Internet: www.nps.gov/moja

Superintendent **Todd Suess** ....(760) 252-6100
Education: Minnesota 1988 BS

Muir Woods National Monument
Mill Valley, CA 94941
Tel: (415) 388-2596 Fax: (415) 389-6957 Internet: www.nps.gov/muwo

Superintendent **Emily Levine** ....(415) 388-2596

★ Presidential Appointment Requiring Senate Confirmation ☆ Presidential Appointment □ Schedule C Appointment ◇ Career Senior Foreign Service Appointment
● Career Senior Executive Service (SES) Appointment ○ Non-Career Senior Executive Service (SES) Appointment ■ Postal Career Executive Service

DEPARTMENTS

Pinnacles National Park
5000 Highway 4146, Paicines, CA 95043
Tel: (831) 389-4485 Fax: (831) 389-4489 Internet: www.nps.gov/pinn
Superintendent **Karen Beppler-Dorn** .... (831) 389-4485

Point Reyes National Seashore
Point Reyes Station, CA 94956
Tel: (415) 464-5100 Fax: (415) 663-8132 Internet: www.nps.gov/pore
Superintendent **Cicely Muldoon** .... (415) 464-5101

Redwood National State Park
1111 Second Street, Crescent City, CA 95531
Tel: (707) 464-6101 Fax: (707) 464-1812 Internet: www.nps.gov/redw
Superintendent **Stephen "Steve" Prokop** .... (707) 465-7300
Education: San Francisco State U 1993 MPA
North District Supervisory Park Ranger
Gregory Morse .... (707) 465-7787
E-mail: gregory_morse@nps.gov
South District Supervisory Park Ranger **Laura Denny** .... (707) 465-7750

Rosie the Riveter/WWII Homefront National Historical Park
1401 Marina Way South, Suite B, Richmond, CA 94804
Tel: (510) 232-5050 Fax: (510) 232-5504 Internet: www.nps.gov/rori
Superintendent **Tom Leatherman** .... (925) 838-0249 ext. 6301
Education: UC Santa Cruz BA

San Francisco Maritime National Historical Park
Fort Mason, Building E, Room 265, San Francisco, CA 94123
Tel: (415) 561-7000 Fax: (415) 561-1624 Internet: www.nps.gov/safr
Superintendent **Kevin Hendricks** .... (415) 561-7000
Education: UC Berkeley 1984 BS

Santa Monica Mountains National Recreation Area
401 West Hillcrest Drive, Thousand Oaks, CA 91360-4223
Tel: (805) 370-2300 Fax: (805) 370-1850 Internet: www.nps.gov/samo
Superintendent **David Szymanski** .... (805) 370-2300

Sequoia National Park
Three Rivers, CA 93271
Tel: (559) 565-3341 Fax: (559) 565-3730 Internet: www.nps.gov/seki
Superintendent **Woody Smeck** .... (559) 565-3341

Whiskeytown-Shasta-Trinity National Recreation Area
P.O. Box 188, Whiskeytown, CA 96095
Tel: (530) 242-3400 Fax: (530) 246-5154 Internet: www.nps.gov/whis
Superintendent **Jim Milestone** .... (530) 242-3400

Yosemite National Park
P.O. Box 577, Yosemite National Park, CA 95389
Tel: (209) 372-0200 Fax: (209) 372-0220 Internet: www.nps.gov/yose
● Superintendent **Michael T. "Mike" Reynolds** .... (202) 208-4621
E-mail: michael_reynolds@nps.gov
Education: UC Santa Barbara; Regis U MBA

Pacific West Region - Honolulu
300 Ala Moana Boulevard, Honolulu, HI 96850
P.O. Box 50165, Honolulu, HI 96850
Tel: (808) 541-2693 Fax: (808) 541-3696
Area Manager **Melia Lane-Kamahele** .... (808) 541-2693 ext. 729

Ala Kahakai National Historical Trail
Ala Kahakai National Historic Trail, 73-4768 Kanalani Street #14,
Kailua Kona, HI 96740
Tel: (808) 329-2288 Fax: (808) 329-2597 Internet: www.nps.gov/alka
Superintendent **Aric Arakaki** .... (808) 326-6012 ext. 101

Haleakala National Park
P.O. Box 369, Makawao, HI 96768
Tel: (808) 572-4400 Fax: (808) 572-4407 Internet: www.nps.gov/hale
Superintendent **Natalie Gates** .... (808) 572-4401
Education: Cornell VMD; UC Berkeley MS

Hawaii Volcanoes National Park
P.O. Box 52, Hawaii National Park, HI 96718
Tel: (808) 985-6000 Fax: (808) 967-8186 Internet: www.nps.gov/havo
Superintendent **Cindy Orlando** .... (808) 985-6025

Honouliuli National Monument
300 Ala Moana Boulevard, Room 6226, Honolulu, HI 96850
Tel: (808) 725-6149
Superintendent **Jacqueline Ashwell** .... (808) 725-6149

Kalaupapa National Historical Park
P.O. Box 2222, Kalaupapa, HI 96742
Tel: (808) 567-6802 Fax: (808) 567-6729 Internet: www.nps.gov/kala
Superintendent **Erika Stein** .... (808) 567-6802 ext. 7

Kaloko-Honokohau National Historical Park
73-4768 Kanalani Street #14, Kailua Kona, HI 96740
Tel: (808) 329-2288 Fax: (808) 329-2597 Internet: www.nps.gov/kaho
Superintendent **(Vacant)** .... (808) 329-2288

National Park of American Samoa
Pago Pago, AS 96799
Tel: (684) 633-7082 Fax: (684) 633-7085 Internet: www.nps.gov/npsa
Superintendent **Scott Burch** .... (684) 633-7082

Pu'uhonua o Honaunau National Historical Park
P.O. Box 129, Honaunau, HI 96726
Tel: (808) 328-2288 Fax: (808) 328-9485 Internet: www.nps.gov/puho
Superintendent **Tammy Duchesne** .... (808) 328-2326 ext. 1201
Education: Tulane 1996 BA; U Guam 2004 MA
Park Ranger **Charles T. "Kale" Hua** .... (808) 328-2326 ext. 1241
Fax: (808) 328-8251

Pu'ukohola Heiau National Historic Site
62-3601 Kawaihae Road, Kamuela, HI 96743
Tel: (808) 882-7218 Fax: (808) 882-1215 Internet: www.nps.gov/puhe
Superintendent **Daniel Kawaiaea** .... (808) 882-7218 ext. 7

World War II Valor in the Pacific National Monument
One Arizona Memorial Place, Honolulu, HI 96818
Tel: (808) 422-3300 Fax: (808) 483-8606 Internet: www.nps.gov/usar
Superintendent **Jacqueline Ashwell** .... (808) 266-0826
Chief of Cultural and Natural Resources
Scott Pawlowski .... (808) 422-3333

War in the Pacific National Historical Park
460 North Marine Drive, Piti, GU 96915
Tel: (671) 477-7278 ext. 1001 Fax: (671) 477-7281
Internet: www.nps.gov/wapa
Superintendent **Jim Richardson** .... (671) 447-7278 ext. 1003
Education: Nebraska BB

Southeast Region
Atlanta Federal Center, 100 Alabama Street, SW, Atlanta, GA 30303
Tel: (404) 507-5604 Fax: (404) 562-3263
Areas Covered: AL, FL, GA, KY, LA, MS, NC, PR, SC, TN, VI
● Regional Director **Robert A. "Bob" Vogel** .... (404) 507-5604
E-mail: Bob_Vogel@nps.gov
Education: Tennessee BS
Executive Assistant **Whitny Howeth** .... (404) 507-5604
E-mail: whitny_howeth@nps.gov
Special Assistant **(Vacant)** .... (404) 507-5604
Deputy Regional Director (Acting) **Sarah Craighead** .... (270) 758-2184
Education: Transylvania 1978 BA
Deputy Regional Director **(Vacant)** .... (404) 507-5604
1 Mammoth Cave Parkway, Mammoth Cave, KY 42259-0007
Deputy Regional Director **(Vacant)** .... (404) 507-5604
Communications Assistant Regional Director **(Vacant)** ... (404) 507-5604
Equal Employment Opportunity Assistant Regional
Director **Lynda D. Glover** .... (404) 507-5738
E-mail: lynda_glover@nps.gov

★ Presidential Appointment Requiring Senate Confirmation ☆ Presidential Appointment ☐ Schedule C Appointment ◇ Career Senior Foreign Service Appointment
● Career Senior Executive Service (SES) Appointment ○ Non-Career Senior Executive Service (SES) Appointment ■ Postal Career Executive Service

Southeast Region *(continued)*

Regional Comptroller **Michael Andrew Byrd** . . . . (404) 507-5610
E-mail: michael_byrd@nps.gov Fax: (404) 562-3264
Education: Hampton; Syracuse MBA
Chief, Information Technology **Joycine Lowe** . . . . (404) 507-5675
E-mail: joycine_lowe@nps.gov
Chief Ranger **Scott Larson** . . . . (404) 507-5604
E-mail: scott_larson@nps.gov

Administration
100 Alabama Street, SW, Atlanta, GA 30303
Tel: (404) 507-5610 Fax: (404) 562-3263

Associate Regional Director **Ed Buskirk** . . . . (404) 507-5610
E-mail: ed_buskirk@nps.gov

Cultural Resources Stewardship
100 Alabama Street, SW, Atlanta, GA 30303
Tel: (404) 507-5841 Fax: (404) 562-3263

Chief of Cultural Resources **Dan Scheidt** . . . . (404) 507-5787

Natural Resources Stewardship and Service
100 Alabama Street, SW, Atlanta, GA 30303
Tel: (404) 562-3279 Fax: (404) 562-3263

Chief of Natural Resources **Darrell L. Echols** . . . . (404) 507-5813

Interpretation and Education
100 Alabama Street, SW, Atlanta, GA 30303
Tel: (404) 562-3100 Fax: (404) 562-3263

Chief of Interpretation and Education **(Vacant)** . . . . (404) 562-3100
Special Assistant to the Regional Director **(Vacant)** . . . . . . (404) 562-3100
Chief, Land Resources Program **Nancy Carter** . . . . (404) 562-3100
E-mail: nancy_carter@nps.gov

Southeast Region National Park Service Sites
100 Alabama Street, SW, Atlanta, GA 30303
Tel: (404) 507-5600

Architectural Cyclic Chief **(Vacant)** . . . . (404) 507-5713
Fax: (404) 562-3257
Contracting and Property Management Chief
Jeffrey Shaffer . . . . (404) 507-5749
E-mail: jeffrey_shaffer@nps.gov
Human Resources Chief **Barbara Stegall** . . . . (404) 507-5761
E-mail: barbara_stegall@nps.gov
Law Enforcement Chief **David Horne** . . . . (906) 387-2607 ext. 1202
E-mail: david_horne@nps.gov
Education: Humboldt State BS
Facility Management Division Chief **Brad Shattuck** . . . . . (404) 507-5600
Fax: (404) 562-3257
Facility Support Division Chief **(Vacant)** . . . . (404) 507-5697 ext. 707
Natural Resources Technical Assistance Chief **(Vacant)** . . . (404) 507-5600
Planning and Compliance Division Chief **Ben West** . . . . . (404) 507-5700
Fax: (404) 562-3257
Recreation Grants Chief **(Vacant)** . . . . (404) 507-5686
Fax: (404) 562-3246
Rivers, Trails and Conservation Assistance Chief
Deirdre "Dee" Hewitt . . . . (404) 507-5691
Fax: (404) 562-3246

Abraham Lincoln Birthplace National Historic Site
2995 Lincoln Farm Road, Hodgenville, KY 42748
Tel: (270) 358-3137 Fax: (270) 358-3874 Internet: www.nps.gov/abli

Superintendent **Jay Grass** . . . . (270) 358-3137

Andersonville National Historic Site
496 Cemetery Road, Andersonville, GA 31711
Tel: (229) 924-0343 Fax: (229) 928-9640 Internet: www.nps.gov/ande

Superintendent **Charles Sellars** . . . . (229) 924-0343 ext. 105

Andrew Johnson National Historic Site
121 Monument Avenue, Greeneville, TN 37743-5552
Tel: (423) 639-3711 Fax: (423) 798-0754 Internet: www.nps.gov/anjo

Superintendent **(Vacant)** . . . . (423) 639-3711

Big Cypress National Preserve
33100 Tamiami Trail East, Ochopee, FL 34141-9710
Tel: (239) 695-2000 Fax: (239) 695-0416 Internet: www.nps.gov/bicy

Superintendent **Tamara "Tammy" Whittington** . . . . (239) 695-1101
Education: Colorado Mines 1989 BS
Deputy Superintendent **(Vacant)** . . . . (239) 695-2000

Big South Fork National River and Recreation Area
4564 Leatherwood Road, Oneida, TN 37841
Tel: (423) 569-9778 Fax: (423) 569-5505 Internet: www.nps.gov/biso

Superintendent **Niki S. Nicholas** . . . . (423) 569-9778
Education: Northwestern; Tennessee MS; Virginia Tech PhD

Birmingham Civil Rights National Monument
1510 5th Ave North, Birmingham, Birmingham, AL 35203

Superintendent **Reggie Tiller** . . . . (404) 507-5605

Biscayne National Park
9700 Southwest 328th Street, Homestead, FL 33033-5634
Tel: (305) 230-1144 Fax: (305) 230-1190 Internet: www.nps.gov/bisc

Superintendent **Margaret Goodro** . . . . (786) 335-3646

Blue Ridge Parkway
199 Hemphill Knob Road, Asheville, NC 28803
Tel: (828) 271-4779 Fax: (828) 271-4117 Internet: www.nps.gov/blri

Superintendent **J. D. "J.D." Lee** . . . . (828) 271-4779

Brices Cross Roads National Battlefield Site
2680 Natchez Trace Parkway, Tupelo, MS 38804
Tel: (662) 680-4025 Fax: (662) 680-4035 Internet: www.nps.gov/brcr

Superintendent **Mary Risser** . . . . (662) 680-4025

Buck Island Reef National Monument
2100 Church Street, Route 100, St. Croix, VI 00820-5402
Tel: (340) 773-1460 Fax: (340) 778-8460 Internet: www.nps.gov/buis

Superintendent **Joel Tutein** . . . . (340) 773-1460 ext. 1

Canaveral National Seashore
212 Washington Avenue, Titusville, FL 32796
Tel: (321) 267-1110 Fax: (321) 264-2906 Internet: www.nps.gov/cana

Superintendent (Acting) **Kristen Kneifl** . . . . (321) 267-1110 ext. 14
Education: Nebraska BS

Cane River Creole National Historical Park and Heritage Area
400 Rapides Drive, Natchitoches, LA 71457
Tel: (318) 352-0383 Fax: (318) 352-4549 Internet: www.nps.gov/cari

Superintendent **(Vacant)** . . . . (318) 352-0383 ext. 22

Cape Hatteras National Seashore
1401 National Park Road, Manteo, NC 27954
Tel: (252) 473-2111 Fax: (252) 473-2595 Internet: www.nps.gov/caha

Superintendent **David "Dave" Hallac** . . . . (252) 473-2111
Education: Vermont 1999 MS

Cape Lookout National Seashore
131 Charles Street, Harkers Island, NC 28531
Tel: (252) 728-2250 Fax: (252) 728-2160 Internet: www.nps.gov/calo

Superintendent (Acting) **Michael Gutia** . . . . (252) 728-2250

Carl Sandburg Home National Historic Site
81 Carl Sandburg Lane, Flat Rock, NC 28731-9766
Tel: (828) 693-4178 Fax: (828) 693-4179 Internet: www.nps.gov/carl

Superintendent (Acting) **R. Steven Kidd** . . . . (828) 693-4178

Castillo de San Marcos National Monument
One South Castillo Drive, St. Augustine, FL 32084
Tel: (904) 829-6506 Fax: (904) 823-9388 Internet: www.nps.gov/casa

Superintendent **Gordon J. Wilson** . . . . (904) 829-6506 ext. 221

DEPARTMENTS

★ Presidential Appointment Requiring Senate Confirmation ☆ Presidential Appointment ☐ Schedule C Appointment ◇ Career Senior Foreign Service Appointment
● Career Senior Executive Service (SES) Appointment ○ Non-Career Senior Executive Service (SES) Appointment ■ Postal Career Executive Service

Charles Pinckney National Historic Site
1214 Middle Street, Sullivan's Island, SC 29482
Tel: (843) 883-3123 Fax: (843) 881-7070 Internet: www.nps.gov/chpi

Superintendent **Timothy G. "Tim" Stone** .... (843) 883-3123
Education: Washington U (MO) BS

Chattahoochee River National Recreation Area
1978 Island Ford Parkway, Atlanta, GA 30350-3400
Tel: (678) 538-1200 Fax: (770) 392-7045 Internet: www.nps.gov/chat

Superintendent **William "Bill" Cox** .... (678) 538-1221
Education: Georgia BS; Arizona 1980 MS

Chickamauga and Chattanooga National Military Park
P.O. Box 2128, Fort Oglethorpe, GA 30742
Tel: (423) 752-5213 Fax: (423) 752-5215 Internet: www.nps.gov/chch

Superintendent **Brad Bennett** .... (423) 752-5213 ext. 115
Education: USC BA

Christiansted National Historic Site
2100 Church Street, Route 100, Danish Custom's House, King Wharfs, St. Croix, VI 00820-5402
Tel: (340) 773-1460 Fax: (340) 778-8460 Internet: www.nps.gov/chri

Superintendent **Joel Tutein** .... (340) 773-1460

Congaree National Park
100 National Park Road, Hopkins, SC 29061
Tel: (803) 776-4396 Fax: (803) 783-4241 Internet: www.nps.gov/cosw

Superintendent **(Vacant)** .... (803) 776-4396

Cowpens National Battlefield
P.O. Box 308, Chesnee, SC 29323
Tel: (864) 461-2828 Fax: (864) 461-7077 Internet: www.nps.gov/cowp

Superintendent **John Slaughter** .... (864) 461-2828

Cumberland Gap National Historical Park
P.O. Box 1848, Middlesboro, KY 40965
Tel: (606) 248-2817 Fax: (606) 248-7276 Internet: www.nps.gov/cuga

Superintendent **Sula Jacobs** .... (606) 248-2817 ext. 1052
Education: Washington and Lee BA; UC Berkeley MPP

Cumberland Island National Seashore
P.O. Box 806, 129 Osborne Street, Saint Mary's, GA 31558
Tel: (912) 882-4336 Fax: (912) 882-5688 Internet: www.nps.gov/cuis

Superintendent **Gary Ingram** .... (912) 882-4336 ext. 227

De Soto National Memorial
P.O. Box 15390, 75th Street, NW, Bradenton, FL 34280-5390
Tel: (941) 792-0458 Fax: (941) 792-1403 Internet: www.nps.gov/deso

Superintendent **Jorge Acevedo** .... (941) 792-0458
Education: Puerto Rico BA

Dry Tortugas National Park
40001 State Road 9336, Homestead, FL 33034-6733
Tel: (305) 242-7710 Fax: (305) 242-7711 Internet: www.nps.gov/drto

Superintendent **Pedro Ramos** .... (305) 242-7712
Education: UMass (Amherst) 1990 BS
Deputy Superintendent **Justin Unger** .... (305) 242-7713
Education: Kansas BS, 2005 MPA

Everglades National Park
40001 State Road 9336, Homestead, FL 33034-6733
Tel: (305) 242-7710 Fax: (305) 242-7711 Internet: www.nps.gov/ever

Superintendent **Pedro Ramos** .... (305) 242-7712
Education: UMass (Amherst) 1990 BS
Deputy Superintendent **Justin Unger** .... (305) 242-7713
Education: Kansas BS, 2005 MPA

Fort Caroline National Memorial
13165 Mount Pleasant Road, Jacksonville, FL 32225
Tel: (904) 221-5568 Fax: (904) 641-3798 Internet: www.nps.gov/foca

Superintendent **Chris Hughes** .... (904) 221-5568
Education: Auburn; Georgia State

Fort Donelson National Battlefield
174 National Cemetery Drive, P.O. Box 434, Dover, TN 37058-0434
Tel: (931) 232-5348 Fax: (931) 232-6331 Internet: www.nps.gov/fodo

Superintendent **Brian K. McCutchen** .... (931) 232-5348 ext. 105
Education: Southeast Missouri State 1992 BS, 1995 MA

Fort Frederica National Monument
6515 Frederica Road, Saint Simons Island, GA 31522
Tel: (912) 638-3639 Fax: (912) 638-5357 Internet: www.nps.gov/fofr

Superintendent **Gary Ingram** .... (912) 882-4336 ext. 227

Fort Matanzas National Monument
5635 A1A South, Saint Augustine, FL 32080
Tel: (904) 471-0116 Fax: (904) 471-7605 Internet: www.nps.gov/foma

Superintendent **Gordon J. Wilson** .... (904) 829-6506

Fort Moultrie Site
1214 Middle Street, Sullivan's Island, SC 29482
Tel: (843) 883-3124 Fax: (843) 883-3910
Internet: www.nps.gov/fosu/historyculture/fort_moultrie.htm

Superintendent **Timothy G. "Tim" Stone** .... (843) 883-3123 ext. 14
Education: Washington U (MO) BS

Fort Pulaski National Monument
U.S. Highway 80 East, P.O. Box 30757, Savannah, GA 31410-0757
Tel: (912) 786-8182 Fax: (912) 786-6023 Internet: www.nps.gov/fopu

Superintendent **Melissa Memory** .... (912) 786-8182

Fort Raleigh National Historic Site
1401 National Park Drive, Manteo, NC 27954
Tel: (252) 473-2111 Fax: (252) 473-2595 Internet: www.nps.gov/fora

Superintendent **David "Dave" Hallac** .... (252) 473-2111
Education: Vermont 1999 MS

Fort Sumter National Monument
1214 Middle Street, Sullivan's Island, SC 29482
Tel: (843) 883-3123 Fax: (843) 883-3910 Internet: www.nps.gov/fosu

Superintendent **Timothy G. "Tim" Stone** .... (843) 883-3114
Education: Washington U (MO) BS

Freedom Riders National Monument
1029 Gurnee Ave, Anniston, AL 36201

Superintendent **Reggie Tiller** .... (404) 507-5605

Great Smoky Mountains National Park
107 Park Headquarters Road, Gatlinburg, TN 37738
Tel: (865) 436-1201 Fax: (865) 436-1204 Internet: www.nps.gov/grsm

Superintendent (Acting) **Cassius M. Cash** .... (202) 485-9880
Education: Arkansas (Pine Bluff) BS
Deputy Superintendent **Clayton Jordan** .... (865) 436-1201

Guilford Courthouse National Military Park
2332 New Garden Road, Greensboro, NC 27410-2355
Tel: (336) 288-1776 Fax: (336) 282-2296 Internet: www.nps.gov/guco

Superintendent **Doyle Sapp** .... (336) 288-1776

Gulf Islands National Seashore
1801 Gulf Breeze Parkway, Gulf Breeze, FL 32563
Tel: (850) 934-2600 Fax: (850) 930-9654 Internet: www.nps.gov/guis

Superintendent **Daniel R. Brown** .... (850) 934-2600
Education: Adams State

Horseshoe Bend National Military Park
11288 Horseshoe Bend Road, Daviston, AL 36256-9751
Tel: (256) 234-7111 Fax: (256) 329-9905 Internet: www.nps.gov/hobe

Superintendent **Barbara Tagger** .... (256) 234-7111

Jean Lafitte National Historical Park and Preserve
419 Decatur Street, New Orleans, LA 70130-1035
Tel: (504) 589-3882 Fax: (504) 589-3851 Internet: www.nps.gov/jela

Superintendent **Lance Hatten** .... (504) 589-3882 ext. 108

Jimmy Carter National Historic Site
300 North Bond Street, Plains, GA 31780
Tel: (229) 824-4104 Fax: (229) 824-3441 Internet: www.nps.gov/jica

Superintendent **Barbara Judy** . . . . (229) 824-4104
Education: Virginia BS; UC Berkeley MArch

Kennesaw Mountain National Battlefield Park
905 Kennesaw Mountain Drive, Kennesaw, GA 30152
Tel: (770) 427-4686 Fax: (770) 528-8399 Internet: www.nps.gov/kemo

Superintendent **Nancy Walther** . . . . (770) 427-4686 ext. 223

Kings Mountain National Military Park
2625 Park Road, Blacksburg, SC 29702
Tel: (864) 936-7921 Fax: (864) 936-9897 Internet: www.nps.gov/kimo

Superintendent **John Slaughter** . . . . (864) 936-7921

Little River Canyon National Preserve
2141 Gault Avenue North, Fort Payne, AL 35967
Tel: (256) 845-9605 Fax: (256) 997-9129 Internet: www.nps.gov/liri

Superintendent **Stephen "Steve" Black** . . . . (256) 845-9605 ext. 217
Education: Kansas State 1987 BS

Mammoth Cave National Park
P.O. Box 7, Mammoth Cave, KY 42259
Tel: (270) 758-2180 Fax: (270) 758-2349 Internet: www.nps.gov/maca

Superintendent **Barclay Trimble** . . . . (270) 758-2184
Education: Texas (San Antonio) 1989 BBA
Deputy Superintendent **Bruce M. Powell** . . . . (270) 758-2186

Martin Luther King, Jr. National Historic Park
450 Auburn Avenue, NE, Atlanta, GA 30312
Tel: (404) 331-5190 Fax: (404) 730-3112 Internet: www.nps.gov/malu

Note: On January 8, 2018, the President signed into law: H.R. 267, the "Martin Luther King, Jr. National Historical Park Act," which redesignates the Martin Luther King, Junior, National Historic Site in the State of Georgia as the Martin Luther King, Jr. National Historical Park.

Superintendent **Judy Forte** . . . . (404) 331-5190
Deputy Superintendent **(Vacant)** . . . . (404) 331-5190

Moores Creek National Battlefield
40 Patriots Hall Drive, Currie, NC 28435
Tel: (910) 283-5591 Fax: (910) 283-5769 Internet: www.nps.gov/mocr

Superintendent **Ricardo P. Perez** . . . . (910) 283-5591

Natchez National Historical Park
640 South Canal Street, Box E, Natchez, MS 39120
Tel: (601) 442-7047 Fax: (601) 442-8845 Internet: www.nps.gov/natc

Superintendent **Kathleen Bond** . . . . (601) 442-7047 ext. 13

Natchez Trace Parkway
2680 Natchez Trace Parkway, Tupelo, MS 38804
Tel: (662) 680-4025 Fax: (662) 680-4035 Internet: www.nps.gov/natr

Superintendent **Mary Risser** . . . . (662) 680-4005

New Orleans Jazz National Historical Park
419 Decatur Street, Fourth Floor, Suite 2400, New Orleans, LA 70130
Tel: (504) 589-4841 Fax: (504) 589-4845 Internet: www.nps.gov/neor

Superintendent **Lance Hatten** . . . . (504) 589-4806 ext. 22

Ninety Six National Historic Site
P.O. Box 418, Ninety Six, SC 29666
Tel: (864) 543-4068 Fax: (864) 543-2058 Internet: www.nps.gov/nisi

Superintendent **John Slaughter** . . . . (864) 543-4068

Obed Wild and Scenic River
P.O. Box 429, 208 North Maiden Street, Wartburg, TN 37841
Tel: (423) 346-6294 Fax: (423) 346-3362 Internet: www.nps.gov/obed

Superintendent **Niki S. Nicholas** . . . . (423) 569-9778
Education: Northwestern; Tennessee MS; Virginia Tech PhD

Ocmulgee National Monument
1207 Emery Highway, Macon, GA 31217-4399
Tel: (478) 752-8257 Fax: (478) 752-8259 Internet: www.nps.gov/ocmu

Superintendent **James "Jim" David** . . . . (478) 752-8257 ext. 211

Reconstruction Era National Monument
P.O. Box 1719, Beaufort, SC 29901

Superintendent **Tracy Stakely** . . . . (404) 507-5605
Education: LSU MLA

Russell Cave National Monument
3729 County Road 98, Bridgeport, AL 35740
Tel: (256) 495-2672 Fax: (256) 495-9220 Internet: www.nps.gov/ruca

Superintendent **Stephen "Steve" Black** . . . . (256) 495-2672
Education: Kansas State 1987 BS

San Juan National Historic Site
Fort San Cristobal, 501 Norzagaray Street, Old San Juan, PR 00901
Tel: (787) 729-6777 Fax: (787) 405-8712 Internet: www.nps.gov/saju

Superintendent **Walter Chavez** . . . . (787) 729-6777 ext. 3

Selma to Montgomery National Historic Trail
7002 U.S. Highway 80, Hayneville, AL 36040-4612
Tel: (334) 877-1983 Fax: (334) 877-1985 Internet: www.nps.gov/semo

Superintendent **Sandy Taylor** . . . . (334) 877-1984

Shiloh National Military Park
1055 Pittsburg Landing Road, Shiloh, TN 38376
Tel: (731) 689-5275 Fax: (731) 689-5450 Internet: www.nps.gov/shil

Superintendent **Dale Wilkerson** . . . . (731) 689-5275
Education: Mount Olive BS; Campbell MBA

Southeast Archeological Center
Johnson Building, 2035 East Paul Dirac Drive,
Suite 120, Tallahassee, FL 32310
Tel: (850) 580-3011 Fax: (850) 580-2884 Internet: www.nps.gov/seac

Director **David Morgan** . . . . (850) 580-3011 ext. 123

Stones River National Battlefield
3501 Old Nashville Highway, Murfreesboro, TN 37129
Tel: (615) 893-9501 Fax: (615) 893-9508 Internet: www.nps.gov/stri

Superintendent **Brenda Waters** . . . . (615) 893-9501
Education: Boise State BS; Idaho MS

Timucuan Ecological and Historic Preserve
83165 Mount Pleasant Road, Jacksonville, FL 32225
Tel: (904) 221-5568 Fax: (904) 221-5248 Internet: www.nps.gov/timu

Superintendent **Chris Hughes** . . . . (904) 221-5568
Education: Auburn; Georgia State

Tupelo National Battlefield
2680 Natchez Trace Parkway, Tupelo, MS 38804
Tel: (662) 680-4014 Fax: (601) 680-4015 Internet: www.nps.gov/tupe

Superintendent **Mary Risser** . . . . (601) 680-4025

Tuskegee Airmen National Historic Site
1616 Chappie James Avenue, Tuskegee, AL 36083
Tel: (334) 724-0922 Fax: (334) 724-0952 Internet: www.nps.gov/tuai

Superintendent **Sandy Taylor** . . . . (334) 724-0922

Tuskegee Institute National Historic Site
1212 West Montgomery Road, Tuskegee Institute, AL 36088-0010
Tel: (334) 727-6390 Fax: (334) 727-4597 Internet: www.nps.gov/tuin

Superintendent **Sandy Taylor** . . . . (334) 727-6390

Vicksburg National Military Park
3201 Clay Street, Vicksburg, MS 39183
Tel: (601) 636-0583 Fax: (601) 636-9497 Internet: www.nps.gov/vick

Superintendent **Bill Justice** . . . . (601) 636-0583
Education: American U BA

DEPARTMENTS

DEPARTMENTS

Virgin Islands National Park
1300 Cruz Bay Creek, Saint John, VI 00831
Tel: (340) 776-6201 Fax: (340) 693-9301 Internet: www.nps.gov/viis

Superintendent **Brion FitzGerald** .... (340) 776-6201 ext. 242
Education: East Carolina BS

Wright Brothers National Memorial
1401 National Park Road, Manteo, NC 27954
Tel: (252) 473-2111 Fax: (252) 473-2595 Internet: www.nps.gov/wrbr

Superintendent **David "Dave" Hallac** .... (252) 473-2111
Education: Vermont 1999 MS

Indian Affairs (IA)
1849 C Street, NW, Washington, DC 20240

OFFICE OF THE ASSISTANT SECRETARY
1849 C Street, NW, Mail Stop 4660, Washington, DC 20240
Tel: (202) 208-7163 Fax: (202) 208-5320

Bureau of Indian Affairs (BIA)
1849 C Street, NW, Washington, DC 20240
E-mail: feedback@bia.gov Internet: www.indianaffairs.gov

Office of the Director
1849 C Street, NW, Mail Stop 4606, Washington, DC 20240
Tel: (202) 208-5116 Fax: (202) 208-6334

Office of Field Operations
1849 C Street, NW, Washington, DC 20240
Tel: (202) 208-5116 Fax: (202) 208-6334

● Director **Jim James** Room 4606 .... (202) 208-5116
E-mail: jim.james@bia.gov
● Deputy Director (Acting) **Jim James** .... (202) 208-5116
E-mail: jim.james@bia.gov
Special Assistant **Donna Bia** Room 4606 .... (202) 513-0778

Alaska Regional Office
3601 C Street, Suite 1100, Anchorage, AK 99503
Tel: (907) 586-7204
Areas Covered: AK

● Regional Director (Acting)
Eugene R. "Gene" Peltola, Jr. .... (907) 271-1828
E-mail: eugene.peltola@bia.gov
Deputy Regional Director - Trust Services
Lynn Polacca .... (907) 271-4088 ext. 1572
Deputy Regional Director - Native Services
Cathy Cline .... (907) 586-7204
E-mail: cathy.cline@bia.gov
Housing Specialist **Dewayne Cooper** .... (907) 586-7204
E-mail: dewayne.cooper@bia.gov
Human Services **Gloria Gorman** .... (907) 586-7611 ext. 4111
E-mail: gloria.gorman@bia.gov
Natural Resources Manager **Keith Kahklen** .... (907) 586-7618 ext. 4004
Regional Budget/Accounting Officer **Chih S. Chen** ...... (907) 271-1708
E-mail: chih.chen@bia.gov
Regional Realty Officer **Cyril Andrews** .... (907) 271-1553
Subsistence Program Manager **Dr. Glenn Chen** .... (907) 271-4173
Rights Protection Specialist **Gary Hanson** .... (907) 271-4097
E-mail: gary.hanson@bia.gov
Supervisory Information Technology Specialist
Marilyn Lucero .... (907) 586-7204
Fax: (907) 586-7170
Self Determination Specialist **Dolores Ayotte** .... (907) 271-4086
E-mail: dolores.ayotte@bia.gov
Environmental and Cultural Resources Director
(Vacant) .... (907) 271-4030
Transportation Director **Stuart Hartford** .... (907) 271-6984
Fax: (907) 271-2133

Fairbanks (AK) Agency
101 - 12th Avenue, Room 166, Fairbanks, AK 99701-6270
Tel: (907) 456-0222 Tel: (800) 822-3596 Fax: (907) 456-0225

Superintendent **Lesley DeWilde** .... (907) 456-0229

West-Central Alaska Agency
3601 C Street, Suite 1100, Anchorage, AK 99503
Tel: (907) 271-4088 Tel: (800) 645-8465 ext. 3
Tel: (800) 645-8465 ext. 5 Fax: (907) 271-4836

Zone Manager **Jennifer Cesar** .... (907) 271-4021
E-mail: jennifer.cesar@bia.gov Fax: (907) 271-4015
Deputy Regional Director - Trust Services
Lynn Polacca .... (907) 271-4088 ext. 1572

Eastern Regional Office
545 Marriott Drive, Suite 700, Nashville, TN 37214
Tel: (615) 564-6500 Fax: (615) 564-6701
Areas Covered: AL, CT, FL, LA, ME, MA, MS, NY, NC, RI, SC, TN

● Regional Director **Bruce Maytubby** .... (615) 564-6500
E-mail: bruce.maytubby@bia.gov

Eastern Oklahoma Regional Office
3100 West Peak Boulevard, Muskogee, OK 74401
Tel: (918) 781-4608 Fax: (918) 781-4604
Areas Covered: Eastern OK

● Regional Director (Acting) **Eddie Streater** .... (918) 781-4608
E-mail: eddie.streater@bia.gov
Staff Assistant **Letha Wilson** .... (918) 781-4608
E-mail: letha.wilson@bia.gov
Environmental, Safety, and Cultural Resources
Mosby Halterman .... (918) 781-4608
E-mail: mosby.halterman@bia.gov
Field Support Manager **(Vacant)** .... (918) 781-4699

Administrative Services
3100 West Peak Boulevard, Muskogee, OK 74401
Fax: (918) 781-4621

Budget Officer **Kelly Harjo** .... (918) 781-4620
E-mail: kelly.harjo@bia.gov
Contracts Specialist **Katheryn "Katie" Impson** .... (918) 781-4612
E-mail: katheryn.impson@bia.gov
Property Management **Janine Bond** .... (918) 781-4659
Fax: (918) 781-4627

Indian Services
3100 West Peak Boulevard, Muskogee, OK 74401
Tel: (918) 781-4608

Social Worker **Clarissa Cole** .... (918) 781-4613
E-mail: clarissa.cole@bia.gov
Tribal Government Officer **Diane Buck** .... (918) 781-4685
E-mail: diane.buck@bia.gov Fax: (918) 781-4649
Self Determination Officer **Sherri Smith** .... (918) 781-4646
Fax: (918) 781-4663

Supervisory Highway Transportation
3100 West Peak Boulevard, Muskogee, OK 74401
Tel: (918) 781-4636 Fax: (918) 781-4640

Supervisory Highway Engineer **Barry Hughes** .... (918) 781-4680

Trust Services
3100 West Peak Boulevard, Muskogee, OK 74401
Tel: (918) 781-4608 Fax: (918) 781-4604

Deputy Regional Director **Jessie Huff Durham** .... (918) 781-4608
Legal Administrative Specialist **Leslie Chambers** .... (918) 781-4608
E-mail: leslie.chambers@bia.gov
Natural Resources Officer **Brent Gohring** .... (918) 781-4642
Fax: (918) 781-4644
Regional Lands Records Officer **Cristy McSpadden** ..... (918) 781-4608
Regional Realty Officer **Annette Jenkins** .... (918) 781-4658
Fax: (918) 781-4637

★ Presidential Appointment Requiring Senate Confirmation ☆ Presidential Appointment ☐ Schedule C Appointment ◇ Career Senior Foreign Service Appointment
● Career Senior Executive Service (SES) Appointment ○ Non-Career Senior Executive Service (SES) Appointment ■ Postal Career Executive Service

Great Plains Regional Office
115 Fourth Avenue, SE, Suite 400, Aberdeen, SD 57401-4384
Tel: (605) 226-7343 Fax: (605) 226-7446
Areas Covered: NE, ND, SD

● Regional Director (Acting) **Richard "Glen" Melville** .... (605) 226-7343
E-mail: glen.melville@bia.gov
Staff Assistant to the Regional Director
Anne-Marie Tso .... (605) 226-7343
Deputy Regional Director - Indian Services
Danelle Daugherty .... (605) 226-7343
Deputy Regional Director - Trust Services
Gregg Bourland .... (605) 226-7343

Administration
Accounting Officer **(Vacant)** .... (605) 226-7422
Budget Officer **Ernest J. Pourier** .... (605) 226-7742
E-mail: ernestj.pourier@bia.gov
Contracting Officer **Raelynn Her Many Horses** .... (605) 226-7745
E-mail: raelynn.hermanyhorses@bia.gov
Facilities Management Officer **John Langley** .... (605) 226-0877
Information Operations Officer **Damar Dore** .... (605) 226-7485
Property Management Officer **Scott Whit-Horn** .... (605) 226-7343
Records Management Officer **Kevin McNulty** .... (605) 226-7421
Safety Management Officer **Wayne LaBelle** .... (605) 226-7467
E-mail: wayne.labelle@bia.gov Fax: (605) 226-7658
Self-Determination Officer **Krisanne Stevens** .... (605) 226-7343
Supervisory Environmental Protection Specialist
Marilyn Bercier .... (605) 226-7656
Fax: (605) 226-7757
Supervisory Legal Administrative Specialist
Faith Justice .... (605) 226-7666
E-mail: faith.justice@bia.gov Fax: (605) 266-7371
Supervisory Social Worker **(Vacant)** .... (605) 226-7343

Programs
Department of Transportation - Roads
Thomas Croymans .... (605) 226-7645
E-mail: thomas.croymans@bia.gov
Housing Officer **Art Hacker** .... (605) 226-7441
E-mail: art.hacker@bia.gov
Natural Resources Officer **Diane Mann-Klager** .... (605) 226-7621
Real Estate Services Officer **Rick Clifford** .... (605) 226-7618
Human Services Specialist **Dawn Muth** .... (605) 226-7351
Land Titles and Records Officer **Rick Zephier** .... (605) 226-7393
E-mail: rick.zephier@bia.gov
Tribal Operations Specialist **Todd Gravelle** .... (605) 226-7376

Midwest Regional Office
5600 West American Boulevard, Suite 500, Bloomington, MN 55437-1458
Tel: (612) 725-4500 Fax: (612) 713-4401
Areas Covered: IA, IN, MI, MN, WI

● Regional Director (Acting) **Scott Sufficool** .... (612) 725-4500
Deputy Director for Tribal Services **(Vacant)** .... (612) 725-4500
Deputy Director for Trust **Tammie Poitra** .... (612) 725-4503
Archaeologist **Timothy Guyah** .... (612) 725-4511
Environmental, Cultural and Safety Division
Scott Doig .... (612) 725-4510
E-mail: scott.doig@bia.gov
Facilities Manager **Loren Welch** .... (612) 725-4519
Financial Manager **Priscilla Westlund** .... (612) 725-4531
Fishery Biologist **Merben Cebrian** .... (612) 713-4400
Hydrologist **Mary Manydeeds** .... (612) 725-4539
Information Operation Director **Allen Canfield** .... (612) 725-4515
E-mail: allen.canfield@bia.gov
Realty Officer **Diane Baker** .... (612) 725-4586
Regional Forester **(Vacant)** .... (612) 725-4500
Road Engineer **Todd Kennedy** .... (612) 725-4551
Self Determination Officer **Michelle Corbine** .... (612) 725-4507
Social Worker **Valerie Vasquez** .... (612) 725-4572
E-mail: valerie.vasquez@bia.gov
Tribal Operations Officer **Sherrel LaPointe** .... (612) 725-4554

Navajo Regional Office
P.O. Box 1060, Gallup, NM 87305-1060
Tel: (505) 863-8314 Fax: (505) 863-8324
Areas Covered: Navajo Reservation only in AZ, NM, UT

● Regional Director **(Vacant)** .... (505) 863-8314
Deputy Regional Director - Indian Services
Harold "Jess" Brien .... (505) 863-8264
E-mail: harold.brien@bia.gov
Deputy Regional Director - Trust Services
John Halliday .... (505) 863-8221
Superintendent - Eastern Navajo Agency
Lester Tsosie .... (505) 786-6032
Fax: (505) 786-6111

Administration
Budget Officer **Duwayne Begay** .... (505) 863-8233
Fax: (505) 863-8269
Computer Services **David Cheatham** .... (505) 863-8433
E-mail: david.cheatham@bia.gov
Contracting Officer **Lynelle Benallie** .... (505) 863-8404
E-mail: lynelle.benallie@bia.gov
Environmental Services **George Padilla** .... (505) 863-8434
E-mail: george.padilla@bia.gov
Facility Management Officer **Joseph Bitsie** .... (505) 863-8278
Fax: (505) 863-8421
Finance Officer **(Vacant)** .... (505) 863-8236
Housing Program Officer **Karlene E. Zajicek** .... (505) 863-8486
E-mail: karlene.zajicek@bia.gov
Natural Resources Division Director **Calvert Curley** .... (505) 863-8463
Fax: (505) 863-8480
Personnel Officer **Marsha Tashe-Wyaco** .... (505) 563-3170
E-mail: marsha.tashewyaco@bia.gov
Property Management Officer **Fern Becenti** .... (505) 863-8224
Safety Officer **Todd Reber** .... (505) 786-6191
Self-Determination **Orlinda Platero** .... (505) 863-8311
Social Worker **Jane Jackson Bear** .... (505) 863-9213
Fax: (505) 863-8292
Tribal Operations Specialist **Cheryl Curley** .... (505) 863-8220

Programs
Division of Engineering and Technical Support
Pearl Chamberlin .... (505) 863-8217
E-mail: pearl.chamberlin@bia.gov Fax: (505) 863-8214
Division of Environmental Quality Act Compliance
Review **Harrilene Yazzie** .... (505) 863-8287
Division of Probate and Estate Services
Christina Ashley .... (928) 871-5935
E-mail: christina.ashley@bia.gov Fax: (928) 871-5943
Fire Management Officer **Dale Glenmore** .... (928) 729-7390
Fax: (928) 729-5029
Federal Indian Minerals Office **(Vacant)** .... (505) 863-8314
Forestry **(Vacant)** .... (505) 863-8483
Law Enforcement **Roanna Bennett** .... (505) 863-8317
E-mail: roanna.bennett@bia.gov
Natural Resources **(Vacant)** .... (505) 863-8314
Navajo Partitioned Lands Office **Amos Johnson** .... (928) 674-5109
Real Estate Services Officer **Simone Jones** .... (505) 863-8314
Road Engineer **Herby Larsen** .... (505) 863-8281
Fax: (505) 863-8355

Northwest Regional Office
911 Federal Building, NE 11th Avenue, Portland, OR 97232-4169
Tel: (503) 231-6702 Fax: (503) 231-6791
Areas Covered: ID, OR, WA and portions of AK and MT.

● Regional Director (Acting) **Tammie Poitra** .... (612) 725-4503
E-mail: tammie.poitra@bia.gov
Deputy Regional Director, Indian Services
Twyla Stange .... (503) 231-6727
Deputy Regional Director, Trust Services **Bodie Shaw** .... (503) 231-6705
Natural Resource Officer **David Redhorse** .... (503) 231-6927
Realty Officer **Sherry Johns** .... (503) 872-2879
E-mail: sherry.johns@bia.gov
Supervisory Forester **Dale Sebastian** .... (503) 231-6802
Supervisory Highway Engineer **Kurt Fredenberg** .... (503) 872-2870

(continued on next page)

★ Presidential Appointment Requiring Senate Confirmation ☆ Presidential Appointment ☐ Schedule C Appointment ◇ Career Senior Foreign Service Appointment
● Career Senior Executive Service (SES) Appointment ○ Non-Career Senior Executive Service (SES) Appointment ■ Postal Career Executive Service

DEPARTMENTS

DEPARTMENTS

Northwest Regional Office *(continued)*

Special Agent In Charge **Richard "Glen" Melville** ...... (503) 231-2283
E-mail: richard.melville@bia.gov
Superintendent (Acting) **Joseph Holford** .... (509) 634-2333

Pacific Regional Office
Federal Building, 2800 Cottage Way, Sacramento, CA 95825
Tel: (916) 978-6000 Fax: (916) 978-6099
Areas Covered: CA

● Regional Director **Amy L. Dutschke** .... (916) 978-6007
E-mail: amy.dutschke@bia.gov

Division of Environmental, Cultural Resources Management and Safety
Chief **John Rydzik** .... (916) 978-6051

Indian Services
2800 Cottage Way, Sacramento, CA 95825
Deputy Director **Dale Risling, Sr.** .... (916) 978-6147

Trust Services
Deputy Regional Director, Trust Services
Kevin Bearquiver .... (916) 978-6006
E-mail: kevin.bearquiver@bia.gov

Central California Agency
650 Capitol Mall, Suite 8-500, Sacramento, CA 95814
Tel: (916) 930-3680 Fax: (916) 930-3780
Superintendent **Troy Burdick** .... (916) 930-3776

Northern California Agency
1900 Churn Creek Road, Suite 300, Redding, CA 96002-0292
P.O. Box 494879, Redding, CA 96049
Tel: (530) 223-7960 Fax: (530) 224-7749
Superintendent **Dr. Virgil Akins** .... (530) 223-7961

Palm Springs Field Office
P.O. Box 2245, Palm Springs, CA 92263
3700A Tachevah Drive, Suite 201, Palm Springs, CA 92262
Tel: (760) 416-2133 Fax: (760) 416-2687
Superintendent **Ollie Beyal** .... (760) 416-2133

Southern California Agency
1451 Research Park Drive, Suite 100, Riverside, CA 92507
Tel: (951) 276-6624 Fax: (951) 276-6641
Superintendent **Javin Moore** .... (951) 276-6624 ext. 222
Secretary to the Superintendent
Sandra Hansen .... (951) 276-6624 ext. 223
E-mail: sandra.hansen@bia.gov
Deputy Superintendent for Trust Services
Joann Koda .... (951) 276-6624 ext. 228
Information Technology Specialist
Oliver Reeves .... (951) 276-6624 ext. 300
E-mail: oliver.reeves@bia.gov
Natural Resources Officer **(Vacant)** .... (951) 276-6624
Real Estate Officer **(Vacant)** .... (951) 276-6624

Rocky Mountain Regional Office
2021 4th Avenue North, Billings, MT 59101
Tel: (406) 247-7943 Fax: (406) 247-7976
Areas Covered: MT, WY

● Regional Director **Darryl LaCounte** .... (406) 247-7943 ext. 223
E-mail: darryl.lacounte@bia.gov
Staff Assistant **Jamie Ereaux** .... (406) 247-7943
E-mail: jamie.ereaux@bia.gov
Deputy Regional Director - Indian Services (Acting)
Susan Messerly .... (406) 247-7943
Deputy Regional Director - Trust Services **(Vacant)** ...... (406) 247-7943
Computer Specialist **John McNeal** .... (406) 247-7928
E-mail: john.mcneal@bia.gov Fax: (406) 247-7979

Administration
Budget Officer **Randi Hodge** .... (406) 247-7985
E-mail: randi.hodge-adams@bia.gov
Contracting Officer **Alvin Windy Boy** .... (406) 247-7941
E-mail: alvin.windyboy@bia.gov
Equal Employment Opportunity Manager **(Vacant)** .... (406) 247-7913
Acquisition and Property Management **Buddy Ereaux** .... (406) 247-7939
E-mail: buddy.ereaux@bia.gov
General Engineer-Facilities Management **Bruce Ward** .... (406) 657-6682
Ethics Officer **Michael Adams** .... (406) 247-7943
E-mail: michael.adams@bia.gov

Programs
Criminal Investigator **(Vacant)** .... (406) 657-5936
Education Line Officer **(Vacant)** .... (406) 247-7953
Forester **Caleb Cain** .... (406) 247-7949
Water Resources Officer (Acting) **John Anevski** .... (406) 247-7998
Housing Officer **JoEllen Cree** .... (406) 247-7978
E-mail: joellen.cree@bia.gov
Indian Services Officer **Louise Zokan-Delos Reyes** ..... (406) 247-7988
E-mail: louise.reyes@bia.gov
Indian Services Specialist **JoEllen Cree** .... (406) 247-7978
Loan Specialist **(Vacant)** .... (406) 247-7963
Network Administrator **(Vacant)** .... (406) 247-7928
Fax: (406) 247-7979
Realty Officer **(Vacant)** .... (406) 247-7935
Supervisor/General Engineer **Richard Tapto** .... (406) 657-6675

Southern Plains Regional Office
Southern Plains Regional Office, BIA, P.O 368, Anadarko, OK 73005
Tel: (405) 247-6673 Fax: (405) 247-5611
Areas Covered: KS, SE Nebraska, Western OK, TX

● Regional Director **Jessie Huff Durham** .... (405) 247-6673
E-mail: jessie.durham@bia.gov
Deputy Regional Director - Indian Services
Terry Bruner .... (405) 247-6673 ext. 209
Deputy Regional Director - Trust Services
R. Gabe Morgan .... (405) 247-6673
Budget Specialist **Gerald Haunpo** .... (405) 247-1604
E-mail: gerald.haunpo@bia.gov
Contracting Officer **Jocelyn Little Chief** .... (405) 247-1527
E-mail: jocelyn.littlechief@bia.gov
Facilities Manager **Frank Tartsah** .... (405) 247-5059 ext. 220
Finance Officer **Barbara Nixon** .... (405) 247-1551
Highway Engineer **Tom Simpson** .... (405) 247-6386 ext. 203
Housing Officer **Roman Johnson** .... (405) 247-6120
E-mail: roman.johnson@bia.gov
Human Resources Management Officer
Jeannie Cooper .... (405) 247-1535
E-mail: jeannie.cooper@bia.gov
Information Technology Specialist Supervisor
Rhonda Roundtree .... (405) 247-6673
Land Titles and Records Manager **Jamie Allen** .... (405) 247-6673
Loan Specialist **Freida Satepeahtaw** .... (405) 247-6140
Fax: (405) 247-2581
Management Analyst **Rolanda Talley** .... (405) 247-6673
Natural Resources Officer **John Warthington** .... (405) 247-6673
Property Management Officer **Wynette Satoe** .... (405) 247-1649
Realty Officer **Sandy Ray** .... (405) 247-6673
Safety Officer **(Vacant)** .... (405) 247-5059 ext. 221
Self-Determination Officer (Acting) **Kelly Moore** .... (405) 247-1574
E-mail: kelly.moore@bia.gov
Supervisory Social Worker **Ofelia de la Rosa** .... (405) 247-1585
E-mail: ofelia.delarosa@bia.gov Fax: (405) 247-2895
Tribal Government Officer **Sherry Lovin** .... (405) 247-1534

Southwest Regional Office
1001 Indian School Road, NW, Albuquerque, NM 87104
Tel: (505) 563-3103 Fax: (505) 563-3101
Areas Covered: CO, NM

● Regional Director **(Vacant)** .... (505) 563-3103
Administrative Assistant **Amoretta Aragon** .... (505) 563-3103

★ Presidential Appointment Requiring Senate Confirmation ☆ Presidential Appointment □ Schedule C Appointment ◇ Career Senior Foreign Service Appointment
● Career Senior Executive Service (SES) Appointment ○ Non-Career Senior Executive Service (SES) Appointment ■ Postal Career Executive Service

Administration
Deputy Regional Director **Gregory C. Mehojah** . . . . (505) 563-3106
Accounting **Cecilia Clark** . . . . (505) 563-3151
E-mail: ceciliaclark@bia.gov
Contracts and Grants **Jeff Sena** . . . . (505) 563-3007
E-mail: jeff.sena@bia.gov
Credit and Financing **Mary Alsace Laframboise** . . . . (505) 563-5470
Facility Management (Acting) **Becenti Wilson** . . . . (505) 563-3313
Forestry **Andrew Quam** . . . . (505) 563-3385
Justice Services Officer **William McClure** . . . . (505) 563-3840
Natural Resources **Christopher Banet** . . . . (505) 563-3403
Human Capital Officer **Glenda Yellowhorse** . . . . (505) 563-3103
Property and Supply **Marty Yazzie** . . . . (505) 563-3120
Real Estate **Douglas Hickman** . . . . (505) 563-3330
Roads **Angela Arviso** . . . . (505) 563-3446
Social Services **Sandra McCook** . . . . (505) 563-3520
E-mail: sandramccook@bia.gov
Tribal Government **Patricia Mattingly** . . . . (505) 563-3103
Water Rights Protection **Christopher Banet** . . . . (505) 563-3403

Western Regional Office
2600 North Central Avenue, 13th Floor, Phoenix, AZ 85004
Tel: (602) 379-6600 Fax: (602) 379-4413
Areas Covered: AZ, NV, UT

• Regional Director **Bryan L. Bowker** . . . . (602) 379-6600
E-mail: bryan.bowker@bia.gov
Deputy Regional Director **Carolyn "Carol" Richards** . . . . (602) 379-4002
Security Specialist **Colleen Florence** . . . . (602) 379-4010
E-mail: colleen.florence@bia.gov
Trust Records Officer **Thomas Hemstreet** . . . . (602) 379-6600
E-mail: thomas_hemstreet@ost.doi.gov

Administration
Budget Officer **(Vacant)** . . . . (602) 379-6600
Contracting Officer **Renee Holly** . . . . (602) 379-6760
E-mail: renee.holly@bia.gov
Safety Officer **Vanessa Duncan** . . . . (602) 379-6755
Supply Management Officer **Janie Petersen** . . . . (602) 379-6761
Supervisory Accountant **Eunice Clah-Netson** . . . . (602) 379-3677
Facilities Manager **Erwin Kaisem** . . . . (602) 379-6755

Indian Services
Deputy Regional Director, Indian Services
Carolyn "Carol" Richards . . . . (602) 379-4189
Housing Program Officer **Nancy Jones** . . . . (602) 379-3083
E-mail: nancy.jones@bia.gov
Tribal Operations Officer **Sharlot Johnson** . . . . (602) 379-6786
Regional Road Engineer **David Smith** . . . . (602) 379-6782
Regional Social Worker **Marjorie Eagleman** . . . . (602) 379-6785
E-mail: marjorie.eagleman@bia.gov
Self-Determination Specialist **Glennn Schaeffer** . . . . (602) 379-4189

Trust Services
Deputy Regional Director, Trust Services (Acting)
Rodney McVey . . . . (602) 379-6600
Environmental Scientist **John Krause** . . . . (602) 379-3723
E-mail: john.krause@bia.gov
Environmental Protection Officer (Acting)
Charles "Chip" Lewis . . . . (602) 379-6750
E-mail: charles.lewis@bia.gov
Realty Officer **Stan Webb** . . . . (602) 379-6781
Natural Resources Division Chief **Cathy Wilson** . . . . (602) 379-4511
Regional Forester **Leon Ben, Jr.** . . . . (602) 379-6798
Probates Legal Administrative Specialist (Acting)
Pamela Kessay . . . . (602) 379-4299

Information Technology
2600 North Central Avenue, Phoenix, AZ 85004
Fax: (602) 379-4075
Lead Supervisory Information Technology Specialist
Jeffry White . . . . (602) 379-3099
Zone Manager **John Ashley** . . . . (602) 379-3099
E-mail: john.ashley@bia.gov

Land and Minerals Management (LMM)
1849 C Street, NW, Washington, DC 20240

OFFICE OF THE ASSISTANT SECRETARY
1849 C Street, NW, Washington, DC 20240
Fax: (202) 208-3619

Bureau of Land Management (BLM)
1849 C Street, NW, Washington, DC 20240
Fax: (202) 208-5242 Internet: www.blm.gov

National Operations Center (NOC)
Denver Federal Center, Building 50, Denver, CO 80225
P.O. Box 25047, Denver, CO 80225-0047
Tel: (303) 236-8857 Fax: (303) 236-6450
• Director **Howard M. Cantor** . . . . (303) 236-8857
Associate Chief Information Officer
Robert A. "Bob" Casias . . . . (303) 236-8857

Division of Business Services (DBS)
Denver Federal Center, Building 50, Denver, CO 80225
Fax: (303) 236-6459
Chief (Acting) **Alan R. McConnell** . . . . (303) 236-6369
E-mail: amcconnell@blm.gov

Accounting Operations Branch
Denver Federal Center, Building 50, Denver, CO 80225
Fax: (303) 236-6412
Division Chief **Alan R. McConnell** . . . . (303) 236-6369

Architecture and Engineering Branch
Denver Federal Center, Building 50, Denver, CO 80225
Fax: (303) 236-1176
Branch Chief **(Vacant)** . . . . (303) 236-1160

Financial Services Branch
Denver Federal Center, Building 50, Denver, CO 80225
Fax: (303) 236-7124
Branch Chief **Michael J. "Mike" Conkey** . . . . (303) 236-5401

National Acquisitions Branch
Denver Federal Center, Building 50, Denver, CO 80225
Branch Chief **Lorna M. Gunning** . . . . (303) 236-6309
E-mail: lgunning@blm.gov
Education: Stonehill 1983 BA

National Property and Support Branch
Denver Federal Center, Building 50, Denver, CO 80225
Fax: (303) 236-0561
Branch Chief (Acting) **Carol Hooper** . . . . (303) 236-6335

Division of Human Resources Services (DHRS)
Denver Federal Center, Building 50, Denver, CO 80225
Fax: (303) 236-6685
Division Chief (Acting) **Federica H. Lee** . . . . (303) 236-6505
E-mail: flee@blm.gov

Employee Benefits Services Branch
Denver Federal Center, Building 50, Denver, CO 80225
Branch Chief **Marie S. Piltz-Elliott** . . . . (303) 236-0159
E-mail: mpiltz@blm.gov

Internal Human Resources Services Branch
Denver Federal Center, Building 50, Denver, CO 80225
Branch Chief **(Vacant)** . . . . (303) 236-0486

★ Presidential Appointment Requiring Senate Confirmation ☆ Presidential Appointment □ Schedule C Appointment ◇ Career Senior Foreign Service Appointment
● Career Senior Executive Service (SES) Appointment ○ Non-Career Senior Executive Service (SES) Appointment ■ Postal Career Executive Service

DEPARTMENTS

Position Classification Services Branch
Denver Federal Center, Building 50, Denver, CO 80225
Fax: (303) 236-8632
Branch Chief **Todd W. Ryan** .... (303) 236-6669
E-mail: tryan@blm.gov

Security Operations Branch
Denver Federal Center, Building 50, Denver, CO 80225
Branch Chief (Acting) **Kimberly K. Rose** .... (303) 236-6690
E-mail: krose@blm.gov

Division of Information Resource Management (IRM) Support Services (DIRM)
Denver Federal Center, Building 50, Denver, CO 80225
Fax: (303) 236-3327
Division Chief (Acting) **Janet L. McCormick** .... (303) 236-8857
E-mail: j1mccorm@blm.gov

Mission Applications Branch
Denver Federal Center, Building 50, Denver, CO 80225
Fax: (303) 236-0558
Branch Chief **(Vacant)** .... (303) 236-7058

Projects, Engineering and Development Branch
Denver Federal Center, Building 50, Denver, CO 80225
Fax: (303) 236-1974
Branch Chief **Daniel C. "Dan" Ialenti** .... (303) 236-1049
E-mail: dialenti@blm.gov

Division of Resources Services (DRS)
Denver Federal Center, Building 50, Denver, CO 80225
Fax: (303) 236-6450
Division Chief **Roxanne D. Falise** .... (303) 236-2700

Assessment and Monitoring Branch
Denver Federal Center, Building 50, Denver, CO 80225
Branch Chief **Robert A. Boyd** .... (303) 236-5428

Program Operations Branch
Denver Federal Center, Building 50, Denver, CO 80225
Branch Chief **Jamie L. Sellar-Baker** .... (303) 236-0402

Resource Data Branch
Denver Federal Center, Building 50, Denver, CO 80225
Branch Chief **(Vacant)** .... (303) 236-9940

Technical Operations Branch
Denver Federal Center, Building 50, Denver, CO 80225
Fax: (303) 236-3508
Branch Chief **(Vacant)** .... (303) 236-7198

Resources and Planning Directorate
1849 C Street, NW, Mail Stop 5644-M1B, Washington, DC 20240
Tel: (202) 208-4364 Fax: (202) 208-5010

National Wild Horses and Burros Division
20 M Street, SE, Washington, DC 20003
Tel: (202) 912-7648 Fax: (202) 912-7182

Billings (MT) Field Office
5001 Southgate Drive, Billings, MT 59101
Tel: (406) 896-5013 Fax: (406) 896-5281
E-mail: mt_billings_fo@blm.gov
Wild Horse and Burro Specialist **(Vacant)** .... (406) 896-5013

Burns District Office
28910 Highway 20 West, Hines, OR 97738
Tel: (541) 573-4400 Fax: (541) 573-4411
Supervisory Wild Horse Specialist **Robert N. Sharp** .... (541) 573-4429

California State Office
2800 Cottage Way, Suite W-1834, Sacramento, CA 95825
Tel: (916) 978-4400 Fax: (916) 978-4416
Wild Horse and Burro Specialist **Amy Dumas** .... (916) 978-4678

Eagle Lake (CA) Field Office
2550 Riverside Drive, Susanville, CA 96130
Tel: (530) 257-0456 Fax: (530) 257-4831
Wild Horse and Burro Program Assistant
Videll Retterath .... (530) 254-6575
Litchfield WH&B Corrals, Fax: (530) 254-6762
474-000 Highway 395 East, Litchfield, CA 96117

Eastern States Office
20 M Street, SE, Washington, DC 20003
Tel: (202) 912-7701 Fax: (202) 912-7710
State Director (Acting) **Mitchell "Mitch" Leverette** .... (202) 912-7113
Education: Col Charleston BS; Sul Ross State MS

Elm Creek (NE) Wild Horse and Burro Center
P.O. Box 160, Elm Creek, NE 68836
Tel: (308) 856-4498 Fax: (308) 856-4523
Facility Manager **Joseph A. "Joe" Stratton** .... (308) 856-4498
Education: Iowa State 1987 BS; New Mexico State MS

Idaho State Office
1387 South Vinnell Way, Boise, ID 83709
Tel: (208) 373-4000 Fax: (208) 373-3899
Program Manager **Christopher L. "Chris" Robbins** .... (208) 373-3804

Jackson (MS) Field Office
273 Market Street, Flowood, MS 39232
Tel: (601) 919-4650 Tel: (888) 274-2133 Fax: (601) 919-4700
Lead Wild Horse and Burro Specialist **Carey Frost** .... (601) 715-9711

Milwaukee (WI) Field Office
626 East Wisconsin Avenue, Suite 200, Milwaukee, WI 53202
Tel: (414) 297-4407 Tel: (800) 293-1781 Fax: (414) 297-4442
Wild Horse and Burro Specialist
Steven S. "Steve" Meyer .... (414) 297-4407

Moore (OK) Field Station
221 North Service Road, Moore, OK 73160-4946
Fax: (405) 790-1050
Wild Horse and Burro Facility Manager
Patrick Hofmann .... (405) 238-7138
Wild Horse and Burro Facility Manager
Patricia B. "Pat" Williams .... (405) 222-8676
Wild Horse and Burro Assistant Facility Manager
Gary D. Hughes .... (405) 238-7138

Palomino Valley Center
15780 State Route 445, Reno, NV 89510
P.O. Box 3270, Sparks, NV 89432
Tel: (775) 475-2222 Fax: (775) 475-2053
Operations Manager **John J. Neill** .... (775) 475-2222

Phoenix (AZ) District Office
21605 North Seventh Avenue, Phoenix, AZ 85027
Tel: (623) 580-5500 Fax: (623) 580-5580
Wild Horse and Burro Specialist **Mary Pyles** .... (623) 580-5662

Rock Springs (WY) District Office
280 Highway 191 North, Rock Springs, WY 82901
Tel: (307) 352-0256 Fax: (307) 352-0329
Wild Horse and Burro Specialist **(Vacant)** .... (307) 352-0331

Utah State Office
440 West 200 Street, Suite 50, Salt Lake City, UT 84101
P.O. Box 45155, Salt Lake City, UT 84145-0155
Fax: (801) 539-4074
Wild Horse and Burro Specialist **Gus Warr** .... (801) 539-4057

State Offices

Alaska State Office
Federal Building and U.S. Courthouse, 222 West Seventh Avenue, Room 13, Anchorage, AK 99513-7599
Tel: (907) 271-5066 (Equal Employment Opportunity Office)
Tel: (907) 271-5076 Fax: (907) 271-4596 Internet: www.ak.blm.gov

● State Director **Karen Mouritsen** .... (907) 271-5066
E-mail: kmourits@blm.gov
Education: Texas 1983 BS, 1992 JD

Alaska Lands and Cadastral Survey
222 West Seventh Avenue, Anchorage, AK 99513-7599
Tel: (907) 271-4591 Fax: (907) 271-3144
Deputy State Director (Acting) **Erika L. Reed** .... (907) 271-6613

Resources
222 West Seventh Avenue, Anchorage, AK 99513-7599
Tel: (907) 271-5477 Fax: (907) 271-5479
Deputy State Director **Steven M. "Steve" Cohn** .... (907) 271-4413

Support Services
222 West Seventh Avenue, Anchorage, AK 99513-7599
Deputy State Director **Leslie B. Holland** .... (907) 271-4598

Anchorage (AK) District Office
4700 BLM Road, Anchorage, AK 99507
Tel: (907) 267-1246 Fax: (907) 267-1267
District Manager **Mark Spencer** .... (907) 267-1264

Anchorage Field Office
6881 Elmore Road, Anchorage, AK 99507-2599
Tel: (907) 267-1246 Tel: (800) 478-1263 Fax: (907) 267-1267
E-mail: blm_ak_afo_general_delivery@blm.gov
Field Manager **Bonnie M. Million** .... (907) 267-1246

Nome (AK) Field Station
P.O. Box 925, Nome, AK 99762
Tel: (907) 443-2177 Fax: (907) 443-3611
Natural Resources Program Coordinator **Tom Sparks** .... (907) 443-2177

Glennallen Field Office
Mile 186.5 Glen Highway, Glennallen, AK 99588
P.O. Box 147, Glennallen, AK 99588
Tel: (907) 822-3217 Fax: (907) 822-7335
E-mail: blm_ak_gfo_general_delivery_@blm.gov
Field Manager **(Vacant)** .... (907) 822-3217

Fairbanks (AK) District Office
222 University Avenue, Fairbanks, AK 99709
Tel: (907) 474-2200 Tel: (800) 437-7021 Fax: (907) 474-2280
E-mail: FairbanksDistrict@blm.gov
District Manager **Geoff Beyersdorf** .... (907) 474-2216

Arctic Division Office
222 University Avenue, Fairbanks, AK 99709
Tel: (907) 474-2200 Tel: (800) 437-7021 Fax: (907) 474-2280
E-mail: arctic@blm.gov
Field Manager **Stacie J. McIntosh** .... (907) 474-2310

Central Yukon Field Office
222 University Avenue, Fairbanks, AK 99709
Tel: (907) 474-2200 Tel: (800) 437-7021 Fax: (907) 474-2280
E-mail: CentralYukon@blm.gov
Field Manager **Timothy J. "Tim" LaMarr** .... (907) 474-2356

Barrow (AK) Field Station
P.O. Box 250, Barrow, AK 99723
Tel: (907) 852-2757 Fax: (907) 852-2785
Bureau of Land Management Liaison **Roy M. Nageak** ... (907) 474-2200

Eastern Interior Field Office
222 University Avenue, Fairbanks, AK 99709
Tel: (907) 474-2320 Tel: (800) 437-7021 Fax: (907) 474-2280
E-mail: EasternInterior@blm.gov
Field Manager **Adam D. Carr** .... (907) 474-2320

Kotzebue (AK) Field Station
P.O. Box 1049, Kotzebue, AK 99775
Tel: (907) 442-3430 Fax: (907) 442-2720
Field Manager **(Vacant)** .... (907) 442-3430

Alaska Fire Service (AFS)
Building 1541 Gaffney Road, Fort Wainwright, AK 99703
P.O. Box 35005, Fort Wainwright, AK 99703-0005
Tel: (907) 356-5511 Fax: (907) 356-5518
Manager **Kent W. Slaughter** .... (907) 356-5505

Office of Pipeline Monitoring
222 West Seventh Avenue, Anchorage, AK 99513-7599
Tel: (907) 271-1309 Fax: (907) 262-0690
Authorized Officer **Erika L. Reed** .... (907) 271-1371
Deputy Authorized Officer **Nolan Heath** .... (907) 271-1371

Arizona State Office
One North Central Avenue, Phoenix, AZ 85004
Tel: (602) 417-9200 Fax: (602) 417-9556 E-mail: asoweb_az@blm.gov

● State Director **Raymond "Ray" Suazo** .... (602) 417-9500
E-mail: rmsuazo@blm.gov
Education: New Mexico Highlands BA

Associate State Director
Deborah K. "Deb" Rawhouser .... (602) 417-9500

Deputy State Director, Business and Support Services
Gera A. Ashton .... (602) 417-9202
E-mail: gashton@blm.gov

Communications Deputy State Director
Maj Amber L. Cargile USAF .... (602) 417-9504
Education: Indiana (Kokomo) 1990 BSBehavSci

Equal Employment Opportunity Program Manager
Lillian R. Robinson .... (602) 417-9218
E-mail: lrobinso@blm.gov

Organizational Development Specialist **(Vacant)** .... (602) 417-9274
Fax: (602) 417-9470

Records Management Specialist **Theresa Davis** .... (602) 417-9354
E-mail: t8davis@blm.gov

Public Affairs Specialist **Adam T. Eggers** .... (602) 417-9499
E-mail: aeggers@blm.gov

Arizona Strip District Office
345 East Riverside Drive, St. George, UT 84790-9000
Tel: (435) 688-3200 Fax: (435) 688-3258 E-mail: asdo_az@blm.gov
District Manager **Michael Herder** .... (435) 688-3200

Colorado River District Office
2610 Sweetwater Avenue, Lake Havasu City, AZ 86406-9071
Tel: (928) 505-1200 Fax: (928) 505-1208
District Manager **William Mack, Jr.** .... (928) 505-1200
Fax: (928) 505-1208

Kingman (AZ) Field Office
2755 Mission Boulevard, Kingman, AZ 86401
Tel: (928) 718-3700 Fax: (928) 718-3761
Field Manager **Amanda M. Dodson** .... (928) 718-3701

Lake Havasu (AZ) Field Office
2610 Sweetwater Avenue, Lake Havasu City, AZ 86406-9071
Tel: (928) 505-1200 Tel: (888) 213-2582
Field Manager **Jason R. West** .... (928) 505-1205

Yuma (AZ) Field Office
7341 East 30th Street, Suite A, Yuma, AZ 85365
Tel: (928) 317-3200 Fax: (928) 317-3250 E-mail: yfoweb_az@blm.gov
Manager **John MacDonald** .... (928) 317-3201

★ Presidential Appointment Requiring Senate Confirmation ☆ Presidential Appointment □ Schedule C Appointment ◇ Career Senior Foreign Service Appointment
● Career Senior Executive Service (SES) Appointment ○ Non-Career Senior Executive Service (SES) Appointment ■ Postal Career Executive Service

DEPARTMENTS

Gila (AZ) District Office
3201 E. Universal Way, Tucson, AZ 85756
Tel: (520) 258-7200 Fax: (520) 258-7238
District Manager **Timothy R. "Tim" Shannon** .... (520) 258-7279

Safford (AZ) Field Office
711 - 14th Avenue, Safford, AZ 85546
Tel: (928) 348-4400 Fax: (928) 348-4450
Field Manager **Scott Cooke** .... (928) 348-4400
E-mail: scooke@blm.gov
Assistant Field Manager **Thomas "Tom" Schnell** .... (928) 348-4420
E-mail: tschnell@blm.gov

Tucson (AZ) Field Office
3201 E. Universal Way, Tucson, AZ 85756
Tel: (520) 258-7200 Fax: (520) 258-7238
Manager **(Vacant)** .... (520) 258-7200

Phoenix (AZ) District Office
21605 North Seventh Avenue, Phoenix, AZ 85027
Tel: (623) 580-5500 Fax: (623) 580-5580 E-mail: pfoweb_az@blm.gov
District Manager **Leon Thomas, Jr.** .... (623) 580-5600
Public Affairs Specialist **(Vacant)** .... (623) 580-5500

Hassayampa (AZ) Field Office
21605 North Seventh Avenue, Phoenix, AZ 85027
Tel: (623) 580-5500 Fax: (623) 580-5580
Field Manager **David Rem "Rem" Hawes** .... (623) 580-5530

Lower Sonoran (AZ) Field Office
21605 North Seventh Avenue, Phoenix, AZ 85027
Tel: (623) 580-5500 Fax: (623) 580-5580
Field Manager **Edward J. "Ed" Kender** .... (623) 580-5616

California State Office
2800 Cottage Way, Room. W-1623, Sacramento, CA 95825
Tel: (916) 978-4400 Fax: (916) 978-4416
Internet: https://www.blm.gov/california
● State Director **Jerome E. "Jerry" Perez** .... (916) 978-4600
E-mail: jperez@blm.gov
Education: West Virginia BS; Columbus Law 2005 JD
Associate State Director **Joseph R. "Joe" Stout** .... (916) 978-4600
Deputy State Director, Communications (Acting)
Erica E. St. Michel .... (916) 978-4611
E-mail: estmichel@blm.gov
Deputy State Director, Energy and Minerals
James V. "Jim" Scrivner .... (916) 978-4361
E-mail: jscrivne@blm.gov
Deputy State Director, External Affairs
Martha L. Maciel .... (916) 978-4616
E-mail: mmaciel@blm.gov
Deputy State Director, Natural Resources
Danielle K. Chi .... (916) 978-4637
Fax: (916) 978-4657

California Desert District Office
22835 Calle San Juan de Los Lagos, Moreno Valley, CA 92553
Tel: (951) 697-5200 Fax: (951) 697-5299
District Manager **Beth E. Ransel** .... (951) 697-5200
Associate Director Manager (Acting)
Dana M. Dennison .... (951) 697-5200

Barstow (CA) Field Office
2601 Barstow Road, Barstow, CA 92311
Tel: (760) 252-6000 Fax: (760) 252-6099
Manager **Katrina Symons** .... (760) 252-6004

El Centro (CA) Field Office
1661 South Fourth Street, El Centro, CA 92243
Tel: (760) 337-4400 Fax: (760) 337-4490
Manager **Thomas "Tom" Zale** .... (760) 337-4400
Chief of Law Enforcement **(Vacant)** .... (760) 337-4400

Needles (CA) Field Office
1303 South US Highway 95, Needles, CA 92363
Tel: (760) 326-7000 Fax: (760) 326-7099
Field Manager (Acting) **Michael W. Ahrens** .... (760) 326-7031

Palm Springs / South Coast (CA) Field Office
1201 Bird Center Drive, Palm Springs, CA 92262
Tel: (760) 833-7100 Fax: (760) 833-7199
Field Manager **(Vacant)** .... (760) 833-7100

Ridgecrest (CA) Field Office
300 South Richmond Road, Ridgecrest, CA 93555
Tel: (760) 384-5400 Fax: (760) 384-5499
Field Office Manager **Carl B. Symons** .... (760) 384-5405

Central California District Office
5152 Hillsdale Circle, El Dorado Hills, CA 95762
Tel: (916) 941-3101 Fax: (916) 941-3199
District Manager **Este A. Stifel** .... (916) 941-3101
Associate District Manager **Ruben Leal** .... (916) 941-3101
Public Affairs Officer **Serena Baker** .... (916) 941-3146
E-mail: sbaker@blm.gov

Bakersfield (CA) Field Office
3801 Pegasus Drive, Bakersfield, CA 93308-6837
Tel: (661) 391-6000 Fax: (661) 391-6041
Field Manager **Gabriel R. "Gabe" Garcia** .... (661) 391-6139
Education: Cal State (Chico) 2002; National U MA

Bishop (CA) Field Office
940 2nd Avenue, Marina, CA 93933-6009
Tel: (831) 582-2200 Fax: (831) 582-2266
Field Manager **Steven L. "Steve" Nelson** .... (760) 872-5011

Central Coast (CA) Field Office
940 2nd Avenue, Marina, CA 93933-6009
Tel: (831) 582-2200 Fax: (831) 630-5055
Field Office Manager **Benjamin Z. Blom** .... (831) 582-2200

Mother Lode (CA) Field Office
5152 Hillsdale Circle, El Dorado Hills, CA 95762
Tel: (916) 941-3101 Fax: (916) 941-3199
Field Manager **William S. "Bill" Haigh** .... (916) 941-3102

Ukiah (CA) Field Office
2550 North State Street, Ukiah, CA 95482
Tel: (707) 468-4000 Fax: (707) 468-4027
Field Manager **Amanda James** .... (707) 468-4070
Education: Montana BS

Northern California District Office
355 Hemsted Drive, Redding, CA 96002
Tel: (530) 224-2100 Fax: (530) 224-2172
District Manager **Alan R. Bittner** .... (530) 224-2100
Education: Cornerstone U BS
Associate District Manager **Dereck C. Wilson** .... (530) 224-2100

Applegate Field Office
708 West 12th Street, Alturas, CA 96101
Tel: (530) 233-4666 Fax: (530) 233-5696
Field Manager **Craig R. Drake** .... (530) 233-4666

Arcata (CA) Field Office
1695 Heindon Road, Arcata, CA 95521-4573
Tel: (707) 825-2300 Fax: (707) 825-2301 E-mail: caweb330@ca.blm.gov
Manager **Molly Brown** .... (707) 825-2309

★ Presidential Appointment Requiring Senate Confirmation ☆ Presidential Appointment ☐ Schedule C Appointment ◇ Career Senior Foreign Service Appointment
● Career Senior Executive Service (SES) Appointment ○ Non-Career Senior Executive Service (SES) Appointment ■ Postal Career Executive Service

Eagle Lake (CA) Field Office
2950 Riverside Drive, Susanville, CA 96130
Tel: (530) 257-0456 Fax: (530) 257-4831
E-mail: blm_ca_eagle_lake_fo_email@blm.gov

● Field Manager (Acting) **Emily S. Ryan** .... (530) 252-5309
E-mail: esryan@blm.gov

Redding (CA) Field Office
6640 Lockheed Drive, Redding, CA 96002
Tel: (530) 224-2100 Fax: (530) 224-2172

Field Manager **Jennifer L. Mata** .... (530) 224-2102

Surprise (CA) Field Station
P.O. Box 460, Cedarville, CA 96104
Tel: (530) 279-6101 Fax: (530) 279-2171

Manager **Craig R. Drake** .... (530) 233-7904
708 West 12th Street, Alturas, CA 96101

Colorado State Office
2850 Youngfield Street, Lakewood, CO 80215-7076
Tel: (303) 239-3600 Fax: (303) 239-3933 Internet: www.co.blm.gov

● State Director **Jamie E. Connell** .... (303) 239-3600
Education: Kalamazoo 1989; Michigan 1993 MS
Associate State Director **Gregory "Greg" Shoop** .... (303) 239-3700
Deputy State Director, Energy, Lands and Minerals
Lonny R. Bagley .... (303) 239-3923
E-mail: lbagley@blm.gov
Deputy State Director, Support Services
David McCormack .... (303) 239-3957
Communications Director **Steven Hall** .... (303) 239-3672
E-mail: sbhall@blm.gov
Manager, Office of Civil Rights (Acting) **Rosene Vigil** ... (303) 239-3661
E-mail: rvigil@blm.gov
Deputy State Director, Resources and Fire
Brian St. George .... (303) 239-3768

Rocky Mountain District Office
3028 East Main Street, Canon City, CO 81212
Tel: (719) 269-8500 Fax: (719) 269-8599

District Manager **Tom Heinlein** .... (719) 269-8554

Del Norte Ranger District
13308 West Highway 160, Del Norte, CO 81132

Field Manager **Martha Williamson** .... (719) 657-3321

Royal Gorge (CO) Field Office
3028 East Main Street, Canon City, CO 81212
Tel: (719) 269-8500 Fax: (719) 269-8599

Field Manager **Keith Berger** .... (719) 269-8500
BLM River Manager **John Nahomenuk** .... (719) 539-7289
307 West Sackett, Salida, CO 81201 Fax: (719) 539-3771
E-mail: jnahomen@blm.gov

San Luis Valley (CO) Field Office
1313 East Highway 160, Monte Vista, CO 81144
Tel: (719) 852-7074 Fax: (719) 655-2502

Field Manager **Melissa K. Garcia** .... (719) 852-7074
E-mail: mgarcia@blm.gov
Education: Colorado BS; Wyoming MS

Browns Canyon National Monument
Note: The Browns Canyon National Monument. The monument is jointly administered by the Bureau of Land Management and the United States Forest Service.

Monument Manager **Melissa K. Garcia** .... (719) 269-8724
Education: Colorado BS; Wyoming MS

Northwest District Office
2815 H Road, Grand Junction, CO 81506
Tel: (970) 244-3000 Fax: (970) 244-3083

District Manager **Andrew Archuleta** .... (970) 244-3000
Education: Colorado State BS,

Colorado River Valley Field Office
2300 River Frontage Road, Silt, CO 81652
Tel: (970) 876-9000

Field Manager **Karl Mendonca** .... (970) 876-9004
Education: Colorado State BF

Grand Junction (CO) Field Office
2815 H Road, Grand Junction, CO 81506
Tel: (970) 244-3000 Fax: (970) 244-3083
E-mail: gjfo_webmail@co.blm.gov

Field Manager **Katie Stevens** .... (970) 244-3000
Dominguez-Escalante National Conservation Area
Manager **Collin Ewing** .... (970) 244-3049
McInnis Canyons National Conservation Area Manager
Collin Ewing .... (970) 244-3049

Kremmling (CO) Field Office
2103 East Park Avenue, P.O. Box 68, Kremmling, CO 80459
Tel: (970) 724-3000 Fax: (970) 724-3066

Field Manager **(Vacant)** .... (970) 724-3000

Little Snake (CO) Field Office
455 Emerson Street, Craig, CO 81625
Tel: (970) 826-5000 Fax: (970) 826-5002

Field Office Manager **Bruce L. Sillitoe** .... (970) 826-5089
Education: Utah State BS; UNLV MBA

White River (CO) Field Office
220 East Market, Meeker, CO 81641
Tel: (970) 878-3800 Fax: (970) 878-3805

Field Manager **Kent Walter** .... (970) 878-3800

Southwest District Office
2465 South Townsend Avenue, Montrose, CO 81401
Tel: (970) 240-5300 Fax: (970) 240-5367

District Manager **Joseph F. "Joe" Meyer** .... (970) 244-3066

Gunnison (CO) Field Office
210 West Spencer Avenue, Gunnison, CO 81230
Tel: (970) 642-4940 Fax: (970) 642-4990

Field Manager **Elijah Waters** .... (970) 642-4941

San Juan Public Lands Center
15 Burnett Court, Durango, CO 81301
Tel: (970) 247-4874 TTY: (970) 385-1257 Fax: (970) 385-1243

Forest Supervisor **Kara Chadwick** .... (970) 247-4874
Note: On detail.
Forest Supervisor **(Vacant)** .... (970) 247-4874

Tres Rios (CO) Field Office
29211 Highway 184, Dolores, CO 81323
Fax: (970) 882-6841

Field Manager **Connie J. Clementson** .... (970) 882-6808

Uncompahgre (CO) Field Office
2465 South Townsend Avenue, Montrose, CO 81401
Tel: (970) 240-5300 TTY: (970) 240-5366 Fax: (970) 240-5367

Field Manager **Greg Larson** .... (970) 240-5315
Associate Field Manager **Stacy D. Whitt** .... (970) 240-5309

Eastern States Office
20 M Street, SE, Suite 950, Washington, DC 20003
Tel: (202) 912-7700 Fax: (202) 912-7186 Internet: www.blm.gov/es
Areas Covered: AR, IA, LA, MN, MO, all states east of and bordering the Mississippi River

● State Director (Acting) **Mitchell "Mitch" Leverette** ..... (202) 912-7113
E-mail: mleveret@blm.gov
Education: Col Charleston BS; Sul Ross State MS
Associate State Director **Barbara Eggers** .... (202) 912-7703
Deputy State Director, Business Resources
Monique McDonald-Harris .... (202) 912-7750
E-mail: m1mcdona@blm.gov

(continued on next page)

★ Presidential Appointment Requiring Senate Confirmation ☆ Presidential Appointment □ Schedule C Appointment ◇ Career Senior Foreign Service Appointment
● Career Senior Executive Service (SES) Appointment ○ Non-Career Senior Executive Service (SES) Appointment ■ Postal Career Executive Service

DEPARTMENTS

Eastern States Office *(continued)*

Deputy State Director, Natural Resources **Alana Fink** .... (202) 912-7700
Chief Cadastral Surveyor **Dominica Van Koten** .... (202) 912-7353

Lower Potomac Field Office
10406 Gunston Road, Lorton, VA 22079
Tel: (703) 339-8009 Fax: (703) 339-3479
E-mail: esmeadowood@es.blm.gov

Field Manager (Acting) **Zachary T. "Zach" Reichold** .... (703) 339-3467

Northeastern States Field Office
626 East Wisconsin Avenue, Suite 200, Milwaukee, WI 53202-4617
Tel: (414) 297-4400 Fax: (414) 297-4409

Field Manager **Dean S. Gettinger** .... (414) 297-4402
Associate Field Manager **Randall "Randy" Anderson** ... (414) 297-4402
Assistant District Manager, Support Services
Gabriele B. Thompson .... (414) 297-4419
Assistant Field Manager for Minerals **Theresa Bodus** .... (414) 297-4420
Supervisory Wild Horse and Burro Specialist
Steven S. "Steve" Meyer .... (414) 297-4407
Fax: (414) 297-4442
Public Affairs Officer **Martha "Marie" Malik** .... (414) 297-1236
E-mail: mmalik@blm.gov

Southeastern States District
273 Market Street, Flowood, MS 39232
Tel: (601) 919-4650 Fax: (601) 919-4703

District Manager **Robert "Bob" Swithers** .... (601) 919-4650
Associate District Manager **(Vacant)** .... (601) 977-5415
Assistant Field Manager for Minerals **Elizabeth Ivy** ...... (601) 977-5427
Assistant Field Manager for Minerals and Lands
(Vacant) .... (601) 977-5400
Administrative Officer **Jeanette McGrew** .... (601) 977-5401
Public Affairs Specialist **Shayne Banks** .... (601) 919-4650
E-mail: shayne_banks@blm.gov
Supervisory Range Technician **Lamar Liddell** .... (601) 977-5433
Wildlife Biologist **Jody B. Peters** .... (406) 262-2832

Idaho State Office
1387 South Vinnell Way, Boise, ID 83709
Tel: (208) 373-4000 Fax: (208) 373-4005 Internet: www.id.blm.gov

● State Director (Acting) **Peter J. Ditton** .... (208) 373-4001
E-mail: pditton@blm.gov
Education: Montana Mineral
Associate State Director (Acting) **Meagan M. Conry** .... (208) 373-4001
Fax: (208) 373-4005

Deputy State Director for Resource Services
June Shoemaker .... (208) 373-3801
Fax: (208) 373-3805

Deputy State Director for Support Services
Michelle G. Ryerson .... (208) 373-3901
E-mail: mryerson@blm.gov Fax: (208) 373-3949
Engineering and Geographic Sciences Manager
(Vacant) .... (208) 373-3951
Equal Employment Manager **Maria L Simmons** .... (208) 373-4011
E-mail: msimmons@blm.gov Fax: (208) 373-4009
Resources and Science Supervisory Resource Manager
(Vacant) .... (208) 373-3813
Safety and Occupational Health Manager (Acting)
Timothy J. "Tim" Burke .... (208) 373-4030
E-mail: tburke@blm.gov Fax: (208) 373-3805
Human Resources Officer **Charles B. Pendleton** .... (208) 373-3920
E-mail: cbpendleton@blm.gov
Cadastral Survey Chief **Timothy A. Quincy** .... (208) 373-3981
Fax: (208) 373-3988
Lands, Minerals, Water Rights Branch Chief
James "Jim" Fincher .... (208) 373-3827
Senior Advisor for Energy and Transmission
David H. Murphy .... (208) 373-3874
E-mail: dmurphy@blm.gov
Education: Michigan MS
Budget Officer **Barbara N. Loving** .... (208) 373-3822
E-mail: bloving@blm.gov

Idaho State Office *(continued)*

Equal Employment Manager **Maria L. Simmons** .... (208) 373-4011
Fax: (208) 373-4050

Office of Communications
1387 South Vinnell Way, Boise, ID 83709
Tel: (208) 373-4001

Deputy State Director (Acting) **Venitia Gempler** .... (208) 373-4016
E-mail: vgempler@blm.gov Fax: (208) 373-4019

Fire and Aviation
1387 South Vinnell Way, Boise, ID 83709
Fax: (208) 373-3850

State Fire Management Officer
Michael L. "Mike" Morcom .... (208) 373-3851

Boise District Office
3948 Development Avenue, Boise, ID 83705
Tel: (208) 384-3300 TTY: (208) 384-3496 Fax: (208) 384-3326

District Manager **Lara E. Douglas** .... (208) 384-3391
Fire Management Officer **Andy Delmas** .... (208) 384-3401
Operations Manager **William Kelley** .... (208) 384-3417
Public Affairs Officer **Mary J. "M.J." Byrne** .... (208) 384-3393
E-mail: mbyrne@blm.gov
Education: Albertson BA; Boise State MS; George Washington MPA
Administrative Officer **Marscha Buchanan** .... (208) 384-3364
E-mail: mbuchanan@blm.gov

Bruneau Field Office
3948 Development Avenue, Boise, ID 83705
Tel: (208) 384-3300 Fax: (208) 384-3326
E-mail: blm_id_bruneauoffice@blm.gov

Field Manager (Acting) **TJ Clifford** .... (208) 384-3341

Four Rivers Field Office
3948 Development Avenue, Boise, ID 83705
Tel: (208) 384-3300 Fax: (208) 384-3493
E-mail: blm_id_fourriversoffice@blm.gov

Field Manager **Tate Fischer** .... (208) 384-3430

Owyhee Field Office
20 First Avenue West, Marsing, ID 83639
Tel: (208) 896-5912 Fax: (208) 896-5940
E-mail: blm_id_owyheeoffice@blm.gov

Field Manager (Acting) **Lance K. Okeson** .... (208) 896-5912

Coeur d'Alene District Office
3815 Schreiber Way, Coeur d'Alene, ID 83815
Tel: (208) 769-5000 Fax: (208) 769-5050
E-mail: blm_id_coeurd'aleneoffice@blm.gov

District Manager **Linda A. Clark** .... (208) 769-5000
Assistant Fire Management Officer **Lonnie Newton** ..... (208) 769-5017
Public Affairs Specialist **Suzanne Endsley** .... (208) 769-5004
E-mail: sendsley@blm.gov

Coeur d'Alene Field Office
3815 Schreiber Way, Coeur d'Alene, ID 83815
Tel: (208) 769-5000 Fax: (208) 769-5050 E-mail: idcda_fo@blm.gov

Field Manager **Kurt Pavlat** .... (208) 769-5038

Cottonwood Field Office
1 Butte Drive, Cottonwood, ID 83522
Tel: (208) 962-3245 Fax: (208) 962-3275
E-mail: blm_id_cottonwoodoffice@blm.gov

Field Manager **Richard White** .... (208) 962-3256

Idaho Falls District Office
1405 Hollipark Drive, Idaho Falls, ID 83401
Tel: (208) 524-7500 Fax: (208) 524-7505

District Manager **Mary D'Aversa** .... (208) 524-7555
Education: Montana State (Billings)
Associate District Manager **Lance R. Brady** .... (208) 524-7500

★ Presidential Appointment Requiring Senate Confirmation ☆ Presidential Appointment □ Schedule C Appointment ◇ Career Senior Foreign Service Appointment
● Career Senior Executive Service (SES) Appointment ○ Non-Career Senior Executive Service (SES) Appointment ■ Postal Career Executive Service

Idaho Falls District Office *(continued)*

Fire Management Officer **Joel Gosswiller** ....(208) 524-7601
Operations Manager **Michaela Moen** ....(208) 524-7516
Resource Coordinator **Jason S. Wright**................(208) 524-7542

Challis Field Office
1151 Blue Mountain Road, Challis, ID 83226
Tel: (208) 879-6200 Fax: (208) 879-6219
E-mail: BLM_ID_ChallisOffice@blm.gov

Field Manager (Acting) **Erin Darboven** ....(208) 879-6200

Pocatello Field Office
4350 South Cliffs Drive, Pocatello, ID 83204
Tel: (208) 478-6340 Fax: (208) 478-6376
E-mail: blm_id_pocatellooffice@blm.gov

Field Manager **Melissa D. Warren** ....(208) 478-6340

Salmon Field Office
1207 South Challis Street, Salmon, ID 83467
Tel: (208) 756-5400 Fax: (208) 756-5436

Field Manager **Linda Price** ....(208) 756-5410
Education: Arizona State

Upper Snake Field Office
1405 Hollipark Drive, Idaho Falls, ID 83401-2100
Tel: (208) 524-7500 Fax: (208) 524-7505

Field Manager **Jeremy Casterson** ....(208) 524-7500

Twin Falls District Office
2878 Addison Avenue East, Twin Falls, ID 88301
Tel: (208) 735-2060 Fax: (208) 735-2076

District Manager (Acting) **Elizabeth A. Maclean**........(208) 736-2382
Public Affairs Specialist **Heather Tiel-Nelson** ....(208) 736-2352
E-mail: hnelson@blm.gov
Planning and Environmental Coordinator **Lisa Criswell** ...(208) 736-7270
Resource Coordinator **Elena Shaw** ....(208) 735-2065
Fire Management Officer **Thomas Hayes** ....(208) 735-4602
Support Services Manager **Brenda Gifford** ....(208) 735-2064
E-mail: bgifford@blm.gov

Burley Field Office
15 East 200 South, Burley, ID 83318
Tel: (208) 677-6600 Fax: (208) 677-6699

Field Manager **Kenneth J. "Ken" Crane** ....(208) 736-2369

Jarbidge Field Office
2536 Kimberly Road, Twin Falls, ID 83301
Tel: (208) 736-2350 Fax: (208) 736-2375
E-mail: blm_id_jarbidgeoffice@blm.gov

Field Manager **Elliot J. Traher** ....(208) 732-2380

Shoshone Field Office
400 West F Street, Shoshone, ID 83352
Tel: (208) 732-7200 Fax: (208) 732-7317
E-mail: blm_id_shoshoneoffice@blm.gov

Field Manager **Codie J. Martin** ....(208) 732-7200

Craters of the Moon National Monument
400 West F Street, Shoshone, ID 83352

Craters of the Moon National Monument Manager
Holly Crawford ....(208) 732-7288

Montana/Dakotas State Office
5001 Southgate Drive, Billings, MT 59101
Tel: (406) 896-5000 Fax: (406) 896-5298 E-mail: mtinfo@mt.blm.gov
Areas Covered: MT, ND, SD

● State Director (Acting) **Kim A. "Al" Nash** ....(406) 896-5000
E-mail: kanash@blm.gov
Education: Iowa State
Associate State Director **Diane M. Friez** ....(406) 233-2827
Deputy State Director, Division of Energy, Minerals, and Realty **Donato J. "Don" Judice** ....(406) 896-5003

Montana/Dakotas State Office *(continued)*

Deputy State Director, Division of Resources, Planning and Fire (Acting) **Mike Philbin** ....(406) 896-5003
Deputy State Director, Division of Support Services
Stephen R. "Steve" Thompson ....(406) 896-5001
E-mail: sthompso@blm.gov
Communications Chief **Kim A. "Al" Nash** ....(406) 896-5000
E-mail: kanash@blm.gov
Education: Iowa State
Equal Employment Opportunity Manager
Sara L. Romero-Minkoff ....(406) 896-5180
E-mail: sminkoff@blm.gov Fax: (406) 896-5282

Billings (MT) Field Office
5001 Southgate Drive, Billings, MT 59101
Tel: (406) 896-5013 Fax: (406) 896-5281
E-mail: mt_billings_fo@blm.gov

Field Manager **James M. "Jim" Sparks** ....(406) 896-5013

Eastern Montana/Dakotas District Office
111 Garryowen Road, Miles City, MT 59301-0940
Tel: (406) 233-2800 Fax: (406) 233-2921

District Manager (Acting) **Todd D. Yeager** ....(406) 233-2800

Miles City (MT) Field Office
111 Garryowen Road, Miles City, MT 59301-0940
Tel: (406) 233-2800 Fax: (406) 233-2921 E-mail: mcfoinfo@mt.blm.gov

Field Manager **Eric D. Lepisto** ....(406) 233-2800

North Dakota Field Office
99 23rd Avenue West, Suite A, Dickinson, ND 58601
Tel: (701) 227-7700 Fax: (701) 227-7701
E-mail: mt_north_dakota_fo@blm.gov

Field Manager **Loren C. Wickstrom** ....(701) 227-7713

South Dakota Field Office
309 Bonanza Street, Belle Fourche, SD 57717
Tel: (605) 892-7000 Fax: (605) 892-7015
E-mail: mt_south_dakota_fo@blm.gov

Field Manager **Lori "Chip" Kimball** ....(605) 892-7001

North Central Montana District Office
920 Northeast Main, Lewistown, MT 59457
Tel: (406) 538-1900 Fax: (406) 538-1904

District Manager **Mark Albers** ....(406) 538-1900
Fax: (406) 538-1904

Glasgow (MT) Field Office
5 Lasar Drive, Glasgow, MT 59230
Tel: (406) 228-3750 Fax: (406) 228-3751
E-mail: BLM_MT_Glasgow_FO@blm.gov

Field Manager **Patrick T. "Pat" Gunderson**............(406) 228-3758
Civil Engineering Technician **Dean D. Jensen** ....(406) 228-3757
Hydrologist **Thomas G. Probert** ....(406) 228-3750
Park Ranger **Alexandra Burke**.......................(406) 228-3750
Rangeland Management Specialist
Raymond N. Neumiller ....(406) 228-3750
Rangeland Management Specialist **Lindsay Roberts** .....(406) 228-3750
Wildlife Biologist **Mike Borgreen** ....(406) 228-3750
Administrative Support Assistant **Stacie L. Canen** ....(406) 228-3750
E-mail: scanen@blm.gov

Great Falls (MT) Oil and Gas Field Office
1101 15th Street North, Great Falls, MT 59403
Tel: (406) 791-7700 Fax: (406) 731-5303
E-mail: BLM_MT_Oil_and_Gas_Field_Office@blm.gov

Field Manager **Dale H. Manchester** ....(406) 791-7789
Budget Analyst **(Vacant)**............................(406) 791-7700
Geologist **Tessa L. Wallace** ....(406) 791-7768
Legal Instruments Examiner **Toni R. Dittmann** ....(406) 791-7792
E-mail: tdittman@blm.gov

(continued on next page)

★ Presidential Appointment Requiring Senate Confirmation ☆ Presidential Appointment ☐ Schedule C Appointment ◇ Career Senior Foreign Service Appointment
● Career Senior Executive Service (SES) Appointment ○ Non-Career Senior Executive Service (SES) Appointment ■ Postal Career Executive Service

DEPARTMENTS

Great Falls (MT) Oil and Gas Field Office *(continued)*

Petroleum Engineer **Dale H. Manchester** . . . . (406) 791-7767
E-mail: dmanches@blm.gov
Petroleum Engineer **(Vacant)** . . . . (406) 791-7700
Petroleum Engineering Technician **Chad A. Hoskins** . . . . . (406) 791-7785
E-mail: choskins@blm.gov
Petroleum Engineering Technician
Steven R. McCracken . . . . (406) 791-7784
E-mail: smccrack@blm.gov
Physical Science Technician **Lottie L. Hufford** . . . . (406) 791-7783
Administrative Support Assistant **(Vacant)** . . . . (406) 791-7792

Havre (MT) Field Office
3990 Highway Two West, Havre, MT 59501
Tel: (406) 262-2820 Fax: (406) 262-2856
E-mail: BLM_MT_Havre_FO@blm.gov

Field Manager **(Vacant)** . . . . (406) 262-2820
Archaeologist **Joshua J. Chase** . . . . (406) 262-2840
Civil Engineering Technician **(Vacant)** . . . . (406) 262-2820
Natural Resource Specialist **Kirsten M. Boyle** . . . . (406) 262-2829
Natural Resource Specialist **Kenneth C. Keever** . . . . (406) 262-2828
Planning and Environmental Specialist **Cassie Powell** . . . . (406) 262-2837
Rangeland Management Specialist **Abby L. Hall** . . . . (406) 262-2833
Rangeland Management Specialist (Acting)
Benjamin J. Hileman . . . . (406) 262-2826
Rangeland Management Specialist
Jeremy C. McKellar . . . . (406) 262-2845
Realty Specialist **Micah R. Lee** . . . . (406) 262-2851
Wildlife Biologist **Craig B. Miller** . . . . (406) 262-2849
Administrative Support Assistant **(Vacant)** . . . . (406) 262-2820

Lewistown (MT) Field Office
920 Northeast Main, Lewistown, MT 59457
Tel: (406) 538-1900 Fax: (406) 538-1904
E-mail: mt_lewistown_fo@blm.gov

Field Manager (Acting) **Brett A. Blumhardt** . . . . (406) 538-1900
Fax: (406) 538-1904

Malta (MT) Field Office
501 South Second Street East, Malta, MT 59538
Tel: (406) 654-5100 Fax: (406) 654-5150
E-mail: blm_mt_malta_fo@blm.gov

Field Manager **Tom Darrington** . . . . (406) 654-5131
Civil Engineering Technician **Craig Mayfield** . . . . (406) 654-5114
Outdoor Recreation Planner **Jason J. Snellman** . . . . (406) 654-5124
Rangeland Management Specialist **Adrienne M. Lipka** . . . (406) 654-5116
Soil Scientist **Joshua D. Sorlie** . . . . (406) 654-5100
Engineering Equipment Operator **Hal Moore** . . . . (406) 654-5100

Western Montana District Office
106 North Parkmont, Butte, MT 59701
Tel: (406) 533-7600 Fax: (406) 533-7660

District Manager **Richard M. Hotaling** . . . . (406) 533-7600

Butte (MT) Field Office
106 North Parkmont, Butte, MT 59701
Tel: (406) 533-7600 Fax: (406) 533-7660
E-mail: blm_mt_butte_fo@blm.gov Internet: www.mt.blm.gov/bdo

Field Manager **Scott Haight** . . . . (406) 533-7629
Education: Rocky Mt Col (MT) BS

Dillon (MT) Field Office
1005 Selway Drive, Dillon, MT 59725-9431
Tel: (406) 683-8000 Fax: (406) 683-8066 E-mail: mt_dillon_fo@blm.gov

Field Manager **Cornelia H. Hudson** . . . . (406) 683-8023

Missoula (MT) Field Office
3255 Ft. Missoula Road, Missoula, MT 59804-7293
Tel: (406) 329-3914 Fax: (406) 329-3721
E-mail: mt_missoula_fo@blm.gov

Field Manager **Joe L. Ashor** . . . . (406) 329-3717

Nevada State Office
1340 Financial Boulevard, Reno, NV 89502
Tel: (775) 861-6400 Fax: (775) 861-6601 Internet: www.blm.gov/nv
Areas Covered: NV

● State Director **(Vacant)** . . . . (775) 861-6400
Associate State Director **Marci Todd** . . . . (775) 861-6591
Budget Officer **Mary Laub** . . . . (775) 861-6400
E-mail: mlaub@blm.gov
Deputy State Director for Minerals Management
Brian C. Amme . . . . (775) 861-6585
Deputy State Director for Natural Resources, Lands and Planning **Raul Morales** . . . . (775) 861-6464
Deputy State Director for Support Services (Acting)
Nancy Taylor . . . . (775) 861-6410
Equal Employment Opportunity Manager (Acting)
Sandra H. "Sandi" Martinez . . . . (505) 438-7687
Human Resources Chief **Debi L. Petosky** . . . . (775) 861-6433
E-mail: dpetosky@blm.gov
Office of Communications Chief
Stephen D. Clutter USAF (Ret) . . . . (775) 861-6629
E-mail: sclutter@blm.gov
Education: Troy U MA; Naval War MA; U Washington
Office of Law Enforcement, Special Agent-in-Charge
Zachary Oper . . . . (775) 861-6667

Gold Butte National Monument
Monument Manager **(Vacant)** . . . . (801) 539-4001

Battle Mountain (NV) District Office
50 Bastian Road, Battle Mountain, NV 89820
Tel: (775) 635-4000 Fax: (775) 635-4034

District Manager **Doug Furtado** . . . . (775) 635-4010

Mount Lewis (NV) Field Office
50 Bastian Road, Battle Mountain, NV 89820
Tel: (775) 635-4000 Fax: (775) 635-4034

Field Manager (Acting) **John Gant Massey** . . . . (775) 635-4000

Tonopah (NV) Field Office
1553 South Main Street, Tonopah, NV 89049-0911
Mail: P.O. Box 911, Tonopah, NV 89049
Tel: (775) 482-7800 Fax: (775) 482-7810

Field Manager **Timothy J. Coward** . . . . (775) 482-7830

Carson City (NV) District Office
5665 Morgan Mill Road, Carson City, NV 89701-1448
Tel: (775) 885-6000 Fax: (775) 885-6147

District Manager **Colleen M. Dulin** . . . . (775) 885-6000
Education: Oregon
Associate Manager (Acting) **Paul J. Fuselier** . . . . (775) 885-6000
Public Information Officer **Lisa Ross** . . . . (775) 885-6107
E-mail: lross@blm.gov
IT Specialist **Mike Grimes** . . . . (775) 885-6147
E-mail: mgrimes@blm.gov

Elko (NV) District Office
3900 East Idaho Street, Elko, NV 89801
Tel: (775) 753-0200 Fax: (775) 753-0255

District Manager **Jill Silvey** . . . . (775) 753-0200
Associate District Manager **(Vacant)** . . . . (775) 753-0200
Geologist **Tom Schmidt** . . . . (775) 753-0343
Wildlife Biologist **Ken Wilkinson** . . . . (775) 753-0351

Ely (NV) District Office
702 North Industrial Way, HC33 Box 33500, Ely, NV 89301-9408
Tel: (775) 289-1800 Fax: (775) 289-1910 E-mail: eyfoweb@blm.gov

District Manager **(Vacant)** . . . . (775) 289-1800
Egan Field Office Manager **Jill Moore** . . . . (775) 289-1847
Schell Field Office Manager **(Vacant)** . . . . (775) 289-1827

★ Presidential Appointment Requiring Senate Confirmation ☆ Presidential Appointment ☐ Schedule C Appointment ◇ Career Senior Foreign Service Appointment
● Career Senior Executive Service (SES) Appointment ○ Non-Career Senior Executive Service (SES) Appointment ■ Postal Career Executive Service

Caliente (NV) Field Office
Building 1, US Highway 93, Caliente, NV 89008
Tel: (775) 726-8100 Fax: (775) 726-8111
Field Manager **Christopher J. Carlton** .... (775) 726-8109

Southern Nevada District Office
4701 North Torrey Pines Drive, Reno, NV 89130-2301
Tel: (702) 515-5000 Fax: (702) 515-5111
District Manager **Timothy Z. "Tim" Smith** .... (702) 515-5093
Assistant Field Manager for Support Services
Ian Glander .... (702) 515-5103
Secretary (Office Automation) **Terri Halbardier** .... (702) 515-5187
E-mail: mhalbardier@blm.gov

Winnemucca (NV) District Office
5100 East Winnemucca Boulevard, Winnemucca, NV 89445
Tel: (775) 623-1500
District Manager **Michael Toombs** .... (775) 623-1501
Public Affairs Officer **Joseph E. Wilcox** .... (775) 623-1500
E-mail: jwilcox@blm.gov

New Mexico State Office
301 Dinosaur Trail, Santa Fe, NM 87508
P.O. Box 27115, Santa Fe, NM 87502-0115
Tel: (505) 954-2000 Fax: (505) 954-2115 Internet: www.blm.gov/nm
Areas Covered: KS, NM, OK, TX
● State Director (Acting) **Aden L. Seidlitz** .... (505) 954-2222
E-mail: aseidlitz@blm.gov
Associate State Director **(Vacant)** .... (505) 954-2222
Deputy State Director for Land and Resources
Melanie G. Barnes .... (505) 954-2180
Fax: (505) 954-2010
Deputy State Director for Minerals **Sheila K. Mallory** .... (505) 954-2134
Deputy State Director for Support Services **(Vacant)** ..... (505) 954-2000
Communications Chief **Donna Hummel** .... (505) 954-2018
E-mail: dhummel@blm.gov
Equal Employment Opportunity Manager **(Vacant)** .... (505) 954-2000

Amarillo (TX) Field Office
801 South Fillmore Street, Amarillo, TX 79101-3545
Tel: (806) 356-1000 Fax: (806) 356-1041
Field Manager **Samuel R.M. Burton** .... (806) 356-1025

Oklahoma Field Office
Five Partners Place, 201 Stephenson Parkway, Norman, OK 73019
Tel: (405) 234-5900
Field Manager **Robert W. Pawelek** .... (405) 234-5900

Moore (OK) Field Station
200 NW 4th Street, Room 2401, Oklahoma City, OK 73102
Tel: (405) 234-5900
Field Station Manager **(Vacant)** .... (405) 234-5902

Remote Horse and Burro Staff
Remote Staff **Cody Bedford** .... (817) 307-3827
P.O. Box 235 PR 2751, Decatur, TX 76234 Fax: (940) 466-9114
Remote Staff **Jimmy Galloway** .... (817) 821-0141
417 Ridgeview Circle, Keller, TX 76248 Fax: (817) 431-7094
Remote Staff **Patrick Hofmann** .... (405) 238-7138
Pauls Valley Facility Manager, P.O. Box 847, Pauls Valley, OK 73075
Remote Staff **Gary D. Hughes** .... (405) 238-7138
Remote Staff **Patricia B. "Pat" Williams** .... (405) 579-7180
Fax: (405) 579-7101

Albuquerque (NM) District Office
100 Sun Avenue NE, Suite 330, Albuquerque, NM 87109-4676
Tel: (505) 761-8700 Fax: (505) 761-8911
District Manager **Danita T. Burns** .... (505) 761-8951

Rio Puerco (NM) Field Office
100 Sun Avenue NE, Suite 330, Albuquerque, NM 87109-4676
Tel: (505) 761-8700 Fax: (505) 761-8911
Field Manager **Angel Martinez** .... (575) 761-8918
435 Montano Road, NE, Albuquerque, NM 87107-4935

Socorro (NM) Field Office
901 South Highway 85, Socorro, NM 87801-4648
Tel: (575) 835-0412 Fax: (575) 835-0223
Field Manager **Mark W. Matthews** .... (575) 838-1250

Farmington (NM) District Office
6251 College Boulevard, Suite A, Farmington, NM 87402
Tel: (505) 564-7600 Tel: (800) 842-3127 Fax: (505) 564-7608
District Manager **Victoria R. Barr** .... (505) 564-7618

Farmington (NM) Field Office
6251 College Boulevard, Farmington, NM 87402
Tel: (505) 564-7600 Tel: (800) 842-3127 Fax: (505) 564-7608
Field Manager **(Vacant)** .... (505) 564-7612

Taos (NM) Field Office
226 Cruz Alta Road, Taos, NM 87571
Tel: (575) 758-8851 Fax: (575) 758-1620
Field Manager **Jeffrey J. Tafoya** .... (575) 751-4700

Las Cruces (NM) District Office
1800 Marquess Street, Las Cruces, NM 88005
Tel: (575) 525-4300 Fax: (575) 525-4412
District Manager **William T. "Bill" Childress** .... (575) 525-4499

Organ Mountains-Desert Peaks National Monument (OMDP)
1800 Marquess Street, Las Cruces, NM 88005
Tel: (575) 522-1219
Monument Manager **Diane E. Prather** .... (575) 525-4309

Pecos (NM) District Office
2909 West Second Street, Roswell, NM 88201-2019
Tel: (575) 627-0272 Fax: (575) 627-0276
District Manager **James K. "Jim" Stovall** .... (575) 627-0290

Carlsbad (NM) Field Office
620 East Greene, Carlsbad, NM 88220-6292
Tel: (575) 234-5972 Fax: (575) 885-9264
Associate Field Manager **George H. MacDonnell** .... (575) 234-5901

Roswell (NM) Field Office
2909 West Second Street, Roswell, NM 88201-2019
Tel: (575) 627-0272 Fax: (575) 627-0276
Field Manager **Charles Schmidt** .... (575) 627-0224

Oregon / Washington State Office
1220 SW 3rd Avenue, Portland, OR 97204
P.O. Box 2965, Portland, OR 97208-2965
TTY: (503) 808-6372 Tel: (503) 808-6001 Fax: (503) 808-6308
E-mail: blm_or_so_land_office@blm.gov Internet: www.blm.gov/or
Areas Covered: OR, WA
● State Director **(Vacant)** .... (503) 808-6372
Executive Staff Assistant **Annette Fournier** .... (503) 808-6026
E-mail: afournie@blm.gov
Associate State Director **Theresa Hanley** .... (503) 808-6026
Executive Staff Assistant **Juliane Tilton** .... (503) 808-6026
E-mail: jtilton@blm.gov
Deputy State Director **Jody Weil** .... (503) 808-6287
E-mail: jweil@blm.gov
Deputy State Director for Communications
Gina Owens .... (503) 808-6287
E-mail: gowens@blm.gov
Deputy State Director for Management Services
Andrew M. "Andy" Smith .... (503) 808-6091
E-mail: asmith@blm.gov

(continued on next page)

★ Presidential Appointment Requiring Senate Confirmation ☆ Presidential Appointment ☐ Schedule C Appointment ◇ Career Senior Foreign Service Appointment
● Career Senior Executive Service (SES) Appointment ○ Non-Career Senior Executive Service (SES) Appointment ■ Postal Career Executive Service

DEPARTMENTS

Oregon / Washington State Office *(continued)*

Deputy State Director for Resource Planning, Use and Protection (Acting) **Lee Folliard** . . . . . (503) 808-6372
Equal Employment Opportunity Manager **Toya L. Bligen** . . . . . (503) 808-6341
E-mail: tlbaker@blm.gov
Forestry Section Chief **Richard A. Schultz** . . . . . (503) 808-6234
System Administration Section Chief **Stephanie Solorzano** . . . . . (503) 808-6274
E-mail: sscolorza@blm.gov
Human Resources Officer **Julie M. Dean** . . . . . (503) 808-6025
E-mail: jmdean@blm.gov

Burns District Office
28910 Highway 20 West, Hines, OR 97738
Tel: (541) 573-4400 Fax: (541) 573-4411
E-mail: blm_or_bu_mail@blm.gov
District Manager (Acting) **Holly M. Orr** . . . . . (541) 573-4501
Associate District Manager **Holly M. Orr** . . . . . (541) 573-4501
Andrews Resource Area Field Manager **Rhonda B Karges** . . . . . (541) 573-4433
Three Rivers Resource Area Field Manager **Richard Roy** . . . . . (541) 573-4425
Administrative Officer **Susan K. Hueckman** . . . . . (541) 573-4403
E-mail: shueckma@blm.gov
Public Affairs Specialist/Webmaster **Tara Martinak** . . . . . (541) 573-4519
E-mail: tmartina@blm.gov

Coos Bay District Office
1300 Airport Lane, North Bend, OR 97459
Tel: (541) 756-0100 Fax: (541) 751-4303
E-mail: blm_or_cb_mail@blm.gov
District Manager **Kathy Westenskow** . . . . . (541) 756-0100
Associate District Manager **(Vacant)** . . . . . (541) 751-4239
Field Manager **Todd D. Buchholz** . . . . . (541) 751-4350
Myrtlewood Resource Area Field Manager **(Vacant)** . . . . . (541) 756-0100
Public Affairs Officer **Megan Harper** . . . . . (541) 751-4353
E-mail: m1harper@blm.gov

Eugene (OR) District Office
3106 Pierce Parkway, Suite E, Springfield, OR 97477
Tel: (541) 683-6600 Fax: (541) 683-6981
E-mail: blm_or_eu_mail@blm.gov
Note: In September 2014, the Bureau of Land Management announced the consolidation of the Eugene and Salem District Offices. The consolidation is expected to be completed by 2017.
District Manager **Kathryn "Kathy" Stangl** . . . . . (541) 683-6988
Associate District Manager **Patricia Mallette** . . . . . (541) 683-6992
Siuslaw Resource Area Field Manager **Mike Korn** . . . . . (541) 683-6792
Upper Willamette Resource Area Field Manager **William O. Sullivan** . . . . . (541) 683-6287
Public Affairs Officer **Jennifer Velez** . . . . . (541) 683-6415
E-mail: jvelez@blm.gov

Lakeview (OR) District Office
1301 South "G" Street, Lakeview, OR 97630
Tel: (541) 947-2177 Fax: (541) 947-6399
E-mail: blm_or_lv_mail@blm.gov
District Manager **(Vacant)** . . . . . (541) 947-2177
Associate District Manager **Loretta V. Chandler** . . . . . (541) 947-6101
Lakeview Resource Area Field Manager **James "Todd" Forbes** . . . . . (541) 947-6102
Education: Oregon State 1993 BS
Administrative Officer **(Vacant)** . . . . . (541) 947-6202
Public Affairs Officer **Larissa Bogardus** . . . . . (541) 947-6237
E-mail: lbogardus@blm.gov

Klamath Falls Field Office
Building 25, 2795 Anderson Avenue, Klamath Falls, OR 97603
Tel: (541) 883-6916 Fax: (541) 884-2097
E-mail: blm_or_kf_mail@blm.gov
Field Manager **Donald Holmstrom** . . . . . (541) 885-4101
Education: Montana BS

Medford (OR) District Office
3040 Biddle Road, Mail Code 110, Medford, OR 97504
Tel: (541) 618-2200 Fax: (541) 618-2400 TTY: (866) 296-3823
E-mail: blm_or_md_mail@blm.gov
District Manager **Elizabeth R. Burghard** . . . . . (541) 618-2200
Associate District Manager **Mary Smelcer** . . . . . (541) 618-2440
Ashland Resource Area Field Manager **John Gerritsma** . . . . . (541) 618-2438
Field Manager **Genivieve D. Rasmussen** . . . . . (541) 618-2348

Grants Pass Interagency Office
2164 N.E. Spalding Avenue, Grants Pass, OR 97526
Tel: (541) 471-6500 Fax: (541) 471-6514
Field Manager **Allen Bollschweiler** . . . . . (541) 471-6653
2164 Northeast Spalding Avenue, Grants Pass, OR 97526

Prineville (OR) District Office
3050 NE Third, Prineville, OR 97754
Tel: (541) 416-6700 Fax: (541) 416-6798
E-mail: blm_or_pr_mail@blm.gov
District Manager **Carol Benkosky** . . . . . (541) 416-6730
Associate District Manager **William I. Dean** . . . . . (541) 416-6732
Central Oregon Resource Area Field Manager **Homer F. "Chip" Faver** . . . . . (541) 416-6731
Deschutes Resource Area Field Manager **Jeffrey H. Kitchens** . . . . . (541) 416-6766

Roseburg (OR) District Office
777 NW Garden Valley Boulevard, Roseburg, OR 97471
Tel: (541) 440-4930 Fax: (541) 440-4948
E-mail: blm_or_rb_mail@blm.gov
District Manager **Heather L. Whitman** . . . . . (541) 440-4930
Associate District Manager **Barbara L. Machado** . . . . . (541) 464-3202
South River Field Manager **Steven D. "Steve" Lydick** . . . (541) 464-3211
Swiftwater Field Manager **Max Yager** . . . . . (541) 464-3388
Support Services Division Chief **John Royce** . . . . . (541) 464-3281

Salem (OR) District Office
1717 Fabry Road, SE, Salem, OR 97306
Tel: (503) 375-5646 Fax: (503) 375-5622
E-mail: blm_or_sa_mail@blm.gov
District Manager **Kim Titus** . . . . . (503) 375-5646
Associate District Manager **David O. Howell** . . . . . (503) 375-5642
Cascades Resource Area Field Manager **John Huston** . . . . (503) 315-5969
Marys Peak Resource Area Field Manager **Paul Gigan** . . . (503) 315-5968

Spokane (WA) District Office
1103 North Fancher, Mail Code 130, Spokane Valley, WA 99212-1275
Tel: (509) 536-1200 Fax: (509) 536-1275
E-mail: blm_or_sp_mail@blm.gov
District Manager **Linda A. Clark** . . . . . (509) 536-1262
Associate District Manager **Michelle L. Brown** . . . . . (509) 536-1200
Border Field Office Manager **Lindsey G. Babcock** . . . . . (509) 536-1200

San Juan Islands National Monument
1103 North Fancher, Spokane Valley, WA 99212-1275
Tel: (360) 468-3051
Monument Manager **Marcia deChadenedes** . . . . . (360) 468-3051

Wenatchee Field Office
915 North Walla Walla, Wenatchee, WA 98801
Tel: (509) 665-2100 Fax: (509) 665-2121
E-mail: blm_or_wn_mail@blm.gov
Field Manager **Aron King** . . . . . (509) 665-2100

Vale (OR) District Office
100 Oregon Street, Code 030, Vale, OR 97918
Tel: (541) 473-3144 Fax: (541) 473-6213
E-mail: blm_or_vl_mail@blm.gov
District Manager **Don Gonzalez** . . . . . (541) 473-3144

★ Presidential Appointment Requiring Senate Confirmation ☆ Presidential Appointment ☐ Schedule C Appointment ◇ Career Senior Foreign Service Appointment
● Career Senior Executive Service (SES) Appointment ○ Non-Career Senior Executive Service (SES) Appointment ■ Postal Career Executive Service

Vale (OR) District Office *(continued)*

Baker Resource Area Field Manager **(Vacant)** .... (541) 523-1431
3285 11th Street, Baker City, OR 97814
Jordan Resource Area Field Manager
Thomas Pat Ryan .... (541) 473-6277
Malheur Resource Area Field Manager
Thomas Pat Ryan .... (541) 473-6277
National Historic Oregon Trail Interpretive Center
Manager **Sarah LeCompte** .... (541) 523-1825
P.O. Box 987, Baker City, OR 97814-0987 Fax: (541) 523-1834
Lead Civil Engineer **Vernon R. "Vern" Pritchard** .... (541) 473-6267
Supervisory Multi-Resource Specialist
Jonathan E. Westfall .... (541) 473-6335

Utah State Office

440 West 200 South, Suite 500, Salt Lake City, UT 84101
Tel: (801) 539-4001 Fax: (801) 539-4237
E-mail: blm_ut_so_mail@blm.gov Internet: https://www.blm.gov/utah
Areas Covered: UT

● State Director **Edwin L. "Ed" Roberson** .... (801) 539-4010
E-mail: eroberso@blm.gov
Education: Auburn BS, MURP

Bears Ears National Monument
Monument Manager **(Vacant)** .... (801) 539-4001

Canyon Country District
82 East Dogwood, Moab, UT 84532
Tel: (435) 259-2100 Fax: (435) 259-2106 E-mail: utmbmail@blm.gov
District Manager **Lance C. Porter** .... (435) 259-2100

Moab (UT) Field Office
82 East Dogwood, Moab, UT 84532
Tel: (435) 259-2100 Fax: (435) 259-2106
E-mail: blm_ut_mb_mail@blm.gov
Field Manager **Christina Price** .... (435) 259-2100

Monticello (UT) Field Office
365 North Main Street, Monticello, UT 84535
Tel: (435) 587-1500 Fax: (435) 587-1518
Field Manager **Donald K. Hoffheins** .... (435) 587-1506

Color Country District
176 East D.L. Sargent Drive, Cedar City, UT 84720
Tel: (435) 865-3000 Fax: (435) 865-3058 E-mail: utccmail@blm.gov
District Manager **Ahmed F. Mohsen** .... (435) 865-3000
Education: Nevada (Reno) BS

Cedar City (UT) Field Office
176 East D.L. Sargent Drive, Cedar City, UT 84720
Tel: (435) 865-3000 Fax: (435) 865-3058
Field Manager **(Vacant)** .... (435) 865-3006

Henry Mountains (UT) Field Station
380 South 100 West, Hanksville, UT 84734
Tel: (435) 542-3461 Fax: (435) 542-3016
Field Station Manager **Sue L. Fivecoat** .... (435) 542-3461

Kanab (UT) Field Office
669 South Highway 89A, Kanab, UT 84741
Tel: (435) 644-1200 Fax: (435) 644-1299 E-mail: utknmail@blm.gov
Field Manager **Harry A. Barber** .... (435) 644-1271

Richfield (UT) Field Office
150 East 900 North, Richfield, UT 84701
Tel: (435) 896-1500 Fax: (435) 896-1550 E-mail: utrfmail@blm.gov
Field Manager **Wayne A. Wetzel** .... (435) 896-1501

Saint George (UT) Field Office
345 East Riverside Drive, St. George, UT 84790
Tel: (435) 688-3200 Fax: (435) 688-3252 E-mail: utsgmail@blm.gov
Field Manager (Acting) **Dawna E. Ferris** .... (435) 688-3200

Grand Staircase - Escalante National Monument (GSENM)
669 South Highway 89A, Kanab, UT 84741
Tel: (435) 644-1200 Fax: (435) 644-1250
E-mail: escalante_interagency@blm.gov
Note: On December 4, 2017, Donald Trump issued a proclamation modifying the boundaries of Grand Staircase Escalante National Monument to three units named Grand Staircase, Kaiparowits, and Escalante Canyons.
Monument Manager **Cynthia "Cindy" Staszak** .... (435) 644-1240

Escalante Field Station
755 West Main Street, Escalante, UT 84726
Tel: (435) 826-5600 Fax: (435) 826-5650
E-mail: Mail_UT-Escalante@ut.blm.gov
Field Station Manager **Drew Parkin** .... (435) 826-5629

Green River District
170 South 500 East, Vernal, UT 84078
Tel: (435) 781-4400 Fax: (435) 781-4410 E-mail: utvnmail@blm.gov
District Manager **Gary Torres** .... (435) 781-4401

Price (UT) Field Office
125 South 600 West, Price, UT 84501
Tel: (435) 636-3600 Fax: (435) 636-3657 E-mail: utprmail@blm.gov
Field Manager (Acting) **Deej Brown** .... (435) 636-3637

Vernal (UT) Field Office
170 South 500 East, Vernal, UT 84078
Tel: (435) 781-4400 Fax: (435) 781-4410 E-mail: utvnmail@blm.gov
Field Manager **Ester McCullough** .... (435) 781-3416

West Desert District
2370 South Decker Lake Boulevard, West Valley City, UT 84119
Tel: (801) 977-4300 Fax: (801) 977-4397 E-mail: utslmail@blm.gov
District Manager **Kevin E. Oliver** .... (801) 977-4310

Fillmore (UT) Field Office
35 East 500 North, Fillmore, UT 84631
Tel: (435) 743-3100 Fax: (435) 743-3135 E-mail: utfmmail@blm.gov
Field Manager **Michael D. Gates** .... (435) 743-3163

Salt Lake (UT) Field Office
2370 South Decker Lake Boulevard, West Valley City, UT 84119
Tel: (801) 977-4300 Fax: (801) 977-4397
Field Manager **Matthew A. Preston** .... (801) 977-4350

Wyoming State Office

5353 Yellowstone Road, Cheyenne, WY 82009-4137
P.O. Box 1828, Cheyenne, WY 82003-1828
Tel: (307) 775-6256 Fax: (307) 775-6082
E-mail: state_office_wymail@blm.gov
Areas Covered: NE, WY

● State Director **Mary Jo Rugwell** .... (307) 775-6001
E-mail: mrugwell@blm.gov
Education: Chapman BS; Wyoming MPA
Executive Assistant **Jessica M. Camargo** .... (307) 775-6001
E-mail: jessica_camargo@blm.gov
Associate State Director **Larry K. Claypool** .... (307) 775-6001
Deputy State Director, Communications
Kristen J. Lenhardt .... (307) 775-6015
E-mail: klenhard@blm.gov Fax: (307) 775-6003
Deputy State Director for Resources Policy and
Management **Buddy W. Green** .... (307) 775-6113
Deputy State Director for Minerals and Lands
Duane W. Spencer .... (307) 775-6146
Education: Wyoming BS Fax: (307) 775-6203
Deputy State Director for Support Services
Brian W. Davis .... (307) 775-6044

★ Presidential Appointment Requiring Senate Confirmation ☆ Presidential Appointment □ Schedule C Appointment ◇ Career Senior Foreign Service Appointment
● Career Senior Executive Service (SES) Appointment ○ Non-Career Senior Executive Service (SES) Appointment ■ Postal Career Executive Service

DEPARTMENTS

DEPARTMENTS

High Desert District Office
280 Highway 191 North, Rock Springs, WY 82901
Tel: (307) 352-0256 Fax: (307) 352-0329
E-mail: rock_springs_wymail@blm.gov

District Manager **Timothy J. "Tim" Wakefield** .... (307) 352-0256
Education: Colorado State BS, MSc
Wyoming Landscape Conservation Initiative Coordinator **Stephanie G. Anderson** .... (307) 352-0227

Kemmerer (WY) Field Office
430 N. Highway 189, Kemmerer, WY 83101
Tel: (307) 828-4500 Fax: (307) 828-4539
E-mail: kemmerer_wymail@blm.gov

Field Manager **William "Aaron" Mier** .... (307) 828-4502

Pinedale (WY) Field Office
1625 West Pine, Pinedale, WY 82941-0768
P.O. Box 768, Pinedale, WY 82941-0768
Tel: (307) 367-5300 Fax: (307) 367-5329
E-mail: pinedale_wymail@blm.gov

Field Manager **Caleb M. Hiner** .... (307) 367-5302
Education: Idaho State BS

Rawlins (WY) Field Office
1300 North Third, Rawlins, WY 82301-2407
P.O. Box 2407, Rawlins, WY 82301-2407
Tel: (307) 328-4200 Fax: (307) 328-4224
E-mail: rawlins_wymail@blm.gov

Field Manager **Dennis J. Carpenter** .... (307) 328-4209

Rock Springs (WY) Field Office
280 Highway 191 North, Rock Springs, WY 82901-3448
Tel: (307) 352-0256 Fax: (307) 352-0329
E-mail: rock_springs_wymail@blm.gov

Field Manager **Kimberlee Foster** .... (307) 352-0201

High Plains District Office
2987 Prospector Drive, Casper, WY 82604-2968
Tel: (307) 261-7600 Fax: (307) 261-7587
E-mail: casper_wymail@blm.gov

District Manager **Stephanie A. Connolly** .... (307) 261-7777

Buffalo (WY) Field Office
1425 Fort Street, Buffalo, WY 82834-2436
Tel: (307) 684-1100 Fax: (307) 684-1122
E-mail: buffalo_wymail@blm.gov

Manager **(Vacant)** .... (307) 684-1100

Casper (WY) Field Office
2987 Prospector Drive, Casper, WY 82604-2968
Tel: (307) 261-7600 Fax: (307) 261-7587
E-mail: casper_wymail@blm.gov

Field Manager **(Vacant)** .... (307) 261-7600

Newcastle (WY) Field Office
1101 Washington Boulevard, Newcastle, WY 82701-2972
Tel: (307) 746-6600 Fax: (307) 746-6639

Field Manager **Richard C. "Rick" Miller** .... (307) 746-6602
Assistant Field Manager **Jim D. Hutchinson** .... (307) 746-6612

Wind River/Bighorn Basin District Office
101 South 23rd Street, Worland, WY 82401
Tel: (307) 347-5100 Fax: (307) 347-5228
E-mail: worland_wymail@blm.gov

District Manager **Kimber "Kim" Liebhauser** .... (307) 347-5243

Cody (WY) Field Office
1002 Blackburn, Cody, WY 82414-8464
P.O. Box 518, Cody, WY 82414-8464
Tel: (307) 578-5900 Fax: (307) 578-5939 E-mail: cody_wymail@blm.gov

Field Manager **Cade R. Powell** .... (307) 578-5915

Lander (WY) Field Office
1335 Main, Lander, WY 82520-0589
Tel: (307) 332-8400 Fax: (307) 332-2318
E-mail: lander_wymail@blm.gov

Field Manager **(Vacant)** .... (307) 332-8400

Worland (WY) Field Office
101 South 23rd Street, Worland, WY 82401
Tel: (307) 347-5100 Fax: (307) 347-5228
E-mail: worland_wymail@blm.gov

Field Manager **Michael J. "Mike" Phillips** .... (307) 347-5297

Bureau of Ocean Energy Management (BOEM)
1849 C Street, NW, Washington, DC 20240
Tel: (202) 208-6300 Fax: (202) 208-6048 Internet: www.boem.gov

Alaska Region
3801 Centerpoint Drive, Suite 500, Anchorage, AK 99503
Tel: (907) 334-5200 Fax: (907) 334-5202

● Regional Director **Dr. James J. "Jim" Kendall, Jr.** ..... (907) 334-5200
E-mail: james.kendall@boem.gov
Education: Old Dominion 1978 BS; Texas A&M 1983 PhD
Deputy Regional Director **(Vacant)** .... (907) 334-5200
Public Affairs Specialist **John T. Callahan** .... (907) 334-5208
E-mail: john.callahan@boem.gov

Gulf of Mexico Region
1201 Elmwood Park Boulevard, Mail Stop GM333C,
New Orleans, LA 70123-2394
Tel: (504) 736-2592 Fax: (504) 731-7802

● Regional Director **Michael "Mike" Celata** .... (504) 736-2592
E-mail: michael.celata@boem.gov
Education: Bowdoin 1980 BA
Deputy Regional Director **Barry Obiol** .... (504) 736-2592
E-mail: barry.obiol@boem.gov
Director, Office of the Environment **Terri Thomas** .... (504) 736-2759
Leasing and Plans Supervisor **Jaron E. Ming JD** .... (504) 736-7531
E-mail: jaron.ming@boem.gov
Education: Georgetown BA; Miami MA, JD
Organizational Development and Support Manager **W. Scott Bodet** .... (504) 736-6713
E-mail: scott.bodet@boem.gov
Public Affairs Specialist **Caryl Fagót** .... (504) 736-2592
E-mail: caryl.fagot@boem.gov
Resource Evaluation Regional Supervisor **Matthew "Matt" Wilson** .... (504) 736-2592
E-mail: matthew.wilson@boem.gov
Senior Advisor **Michele M. Daigle PMP** .... (504) 736-2681
E-mail: michele.daigle@boem.gov
Education: LSU 1984 BSEE

Pacific Region
760 Paseo Camarillo, Suite 102, Camarillo, CA 93010-6064
Tel: (805) 384-6305 Fax: (805) 388-1049

Regional Director **Joan R. Barminski** .... (805) 384-6318
Education: Smith BA
Supervisor, Office of Strategic Resources **Douglas P. "Doug" Boren** .... (805) 384-6384
E-mail: douglas.boren@boem.gov
Supervisor, Office of Environment **Richard R. Yarde** ..... (805) 384-6383
E-mail: richard.yarde@boem.gov
Public Affairs Specialist **John D. Romero** .... (805) 384-6324
E-mail: john.romero@boem.gov
Deputy Regional Director **Thomas J. Liu** .... (805) 384-6317
E-mail: thomas.liu@boem.gov

★ Presidential Appointment Requiring Senate Confirmation ☆ Presidential Appointment ☐ Schedule C Appointment ◇ Career Senior Foreign Service Appointment
● Career Senior Executive Service (SES) Appointment ○ Non-Career Senior Executive Service (SES) Appointment ■ Postal Career Executive Service

Bureau of Safety and Environmental Enforcement (BSEE)

1849 C Street NW, Washington, DC 20240
45600 Woodland Road, Sterling, VA 20166
Tel: (202) 208-6184 Fax: (202) 208-7242 Internet: www.bsee.gov

Alaska Region

3801 Centerpoint Drive, Suite 500, Anchorage, AK 99503
Tel: (907) 334-5300 Fax: (907) 334-5202

Regional Director **Mark Fesmire JD** .... (907) 334-5300
Education: New Mexico; Texas Tech JD

Gulf of Mexico Region

1201 Elmwood Park Boulevard, New Orleans, LA 70123-2394

● Regional Director **Lars Herbst** .... (504) 736-2589
E-mail: lars.herbst@bsee.gov
Education: LSU BSPE

Pacific Region

760 Paseo Camarillo, First Floor, Suite 102, Camarillo, CA 93010-6064
Tel: (805) 384-6300 Tel: (800) 672-2627

Regional Director **(Vacant)** .... (805) 384-6300

Office of Surface Mining Reclamation and Enforcement (OSMRE)

1849 C Street, NW, Room 4513, Washington, DC 20240
Fax: (202) 219-3106 Internet: www.osmre.gov

Appalachian Regional Office

Three Parkway Center, Pittsburgh, PA 15220
Tel: (412) 937-2828 Fax: (412) 937-2903 Internet: www.arcc.osmre.gov/
Areas Covered: GA, KY, MD, MA, MI, NY, NC, OH, PA, RI, TN, VA, WV

Regional Director **Thomas D. Shope** .... (412) 937-2828
Education: West Virginia BSE; Duquesne JD
Technical Support Division Chief **Lois Uranowski** ...... (412) 937-2909
Freedom of Information Act Coordinator **Julia Moore** ... (412) 937-2146

Big Stone Gap (VA) Area Office

1941 Neeley Road, Compartment 116,
Suite 201, Big Stone Gap, VA 24219
Tel: (276) 523-4303 Fax: (276) 523-5053

Area Office Manager **Ian B. Dye, Jr.** .... (276) 523-0022 ext. 16

Charleston (WV) Field Office

1027 Virginia Street, East, Charleston, WV 25301
Tel: (304) 347-7158 Fax: (304) 347-7170 E-mail: chfo@osmre.gov

Director **Roger W. Calhoun** .... (304) 347-7158
Education: West Virginia

Knoxville (TN) Field Office

710 Locust Street, 2nd Floor, Knoxville, TN 37902
Tel: (865) 545-4103 Fax: (865) 545-4111

Director **(Vacant)** .... (865) 545-4103
Information Technology Specialist
Daniel J. Lewis .... (865) 545-4103 ext. 163
E-mail: dlewis@osmre.gov

Lexington (KY) Field Office

2675 Regency Road, Lexington, KY 40503
Tel: (859) 260-3900 Fax: (859) 260-8410

Director (Acting) **Lois Uranowski** .... (412) 937-2805
Program Manager (Program Support) **Corey Miller** ...... (859) 260-3916
Administrative Officer **Elizabeth A. Cox** .... (859) 260-3927
E-mail: lcox@osmre.gov
Information Technology Specialist
William "Bill" Arthur .... (859) 260-3905
E-mail: barthur@osmre.gov

Pittsburgh Field Division - Columbus (OH) Area Office

4605 Morse Road, Columbus, OH 43230
Tel: (614) 416-2238

Division Chief **Benjamin "Ben" Owens** .... (412) 937-2827
Three Parkway Center, Pittsburgh, PA 15220
Secretary **Lisa Henderson** .... (412) 937-2855
E-mail: lhenderson@osmre.gov

Pittsburgh Field Division - Harrisburg (PA) Area Office

215 Limekiln Road, New Cumberland, PA 17070
Tel: (717) 730-6985

Division Chief **Benjamin "Ben" Owens** .... (412) 937-2827

Pittsburgh Field Division - Pittsburgh (PA) Area Office

Three Parkway Center, Pittsburgh, PA 15220

Division Chief **Benjamin "Ben" Owens** .... (412) 937-2827

Mid-Continent Regional Office

501 Belle Street, Room 216, Alton, IL 62002
Tel: (618) 463-6460 Fax: (618) 463-6470 Internet: www.mcrcc.osmre.gov
Areas Covered: AL, AR, IL, IN, IA, KS, LA, MS, MO, OK, TX

● Regional Director **Leonard "Len" Meier** .... (618) 463-6460
South Interior Building, 1951 Constitution Avenue, NW,
Room 252, Washington, DC 20240
E-mail: lmeier@osmre.gov

Alton (IL) Field Office

501 Belle Street, Room 216, Alton, IL 62002
Tel: (618) 463-6460 Fax: (618) 463-6470

Chief **Leonard "Len" Meier** .... (618) 463-6463 ext. 5109

Birmingham (AL) Field Office

135 Gemini Circle, Suite 215, Homewood, AL 35209
Tel: (205) 290-7282 Fax: (205) 290-7280

Director (Acting) **William L. "Bill" Joseph** .... (205) 290-7282

Tulsa (OK) Field Office

1645 South 101st East Avenue, Suite 145, Tulsa, OK 74128-4629
Tel: (918) 581-6430 Fax: (918) 581-6419

Director (Acting) **William L. "Bill" Joseph** .... (205) 290-7282

Program Support Division

Chief **Paul Ehret** .... (618) 463-6463 ext. 5129
Education: Southern Illinois 1975 BS, 1979 MS

Program and Technology Support Branch

Chief **Paul Fritsch** .... (618) 463-6463 ext. 5113

Technical Services Branch

Chief **Kim Quinn** .... (618) 463-6460

Western Regional Office

1999 Broadway, Suite 3320, Denver, CO 80202-5733
Mail: P.O. Box 46667, Denver, CO 80201-6667
Tel: (303) 293-5000 Fax: (303) 293-5006
Areas Covered: AK, CO, MT, NM, ND, UT, WA, WY, the Hopi, Crow, and Northern Cheyenne Tribes, and the Navajo Nation

Regional Director **David Berry** .... (303) 293-5001

Denver (CO) Field Division

1999 Broadway, Suite 3320, Denver, CO 80202-5733
Mail: P.O. Box 46667, Denver, CO 80201-6667
Tel: (303) 293-5000

Division Chief **Jeffrey Fleischman** .... (303) 293-6550
E-mail: jfleischman@osmre.gov

Casper (WY) Field Office

Federal Building, 150 E. B Street, Room 1018, Casper, WY 82601-1018
Tel: (307) 261-6550 Fax: (307) 261-6552
Areas Covered: MT, ND, SD, WY

Director **Jeffrey Fleischman** .... (307) 261-6550

★ Presidential Appointment Requiring Senate Confirmation ☆ Presidential Appointment ☐ Schedule C Appointment ◇ Career Senior Foreign Service Appointment
● Career Senior Executive Service (SES) Appointment ○ Non-Career Senior Executive Service (SES) Appointment ■ Postal Career Executive Service

DEPARTMENTS

Program Support Division
1999 Broadway, Suite 3320, Denver, CO 80202-5733
Fax: (303) 293-5032

Division Manager **Marcelo Calle** .... (303) 293-5035
E-mail: mcalle@osmre.gov

Albuquerque (NM) Area Office
435 Montano Road, NE, Albuquerque, NM 87107-4935

Manager **Marcelo Calle** .... (303) 293-5035

Technology Management Division
1999 Broadway, Suite 3320, Denver, CO 80202-5733
Fax: (303) 293-5058

Division Manager **Robert Welsh** .... (303) 293-5080

Policy, Management and Budget (PMB)

1849 C Street, NW, Mail Stop 5110 MIB, Washington, DC 20240
Tel: (202) 208-1927 Fax: (202) 513-0734 Internet: www.doi.gov/pmb

OFFICE OF THE ASSISTANT SECRETARY

1849 C Street, NW, Washington, DC 20240
Fax: (202) 513-0734

Office of Natural Resources Revenue (ONRR)

1849 C Street, NW, Mail Stop 4211, Washington, DC 20240
Tel: (202) 513-0604 Fax: (202) 628-3430 Internet: www.onrr.gov

● Director **Gregory J. "Greg" Gould** .... (202) 513-0603
E-mail: greg.gould@onrr.gov
Education: SUNY (Cortland) 1983 BS; George Mason 1993 MA

● Deputy Director **James D. "Jim" Steward** .... (303) 231-3715
Building 85, Sixth Avenue and Kipling Street, Denver, CO 80225
E-mail: jim.steward@onrr.gov
Education: Nebraska BSChE, MBA

Chief of Staff **Jennifer Goldblatt** .... (202) 513-0604
E-mail: jennifer.goldblatt@onrr.gov

Appeals and Regulations Program Manager
Bonnie Robson .... (303) 231-3729
Sixth Avenue and Kipling Street, Denver, CO 80225

Program Director, Coordination, Enforcement, Valuation, and Appeals **John Mehlhoff** .... (303) 231-3080
Building 85, Sixth Avenue and Kipling Street, Denver, CO 80225

Public Affairs Officer **(Vacant)** .... (202) 513-0604

Workforce Development **Joseph Coleman** .... (303) 231-3392
Building 85, Sixth Avenue and Kipling Street, Denver, CO 80225

Asset Valuation
Denver Federal Center, Building 85, West Sixth Avenue and Kipling Street, Lakewood, CO 80225
P.O. Box 25165, Mail Stop 350B1, Denver, CO 80225
Fax: (303) 231-3473

Program Director **Michael DeBerard** .... (303) 231-3884

Audit and Compliance Management
Denver Federal Center, Building 85, Sixth and Kipling Streets, Denver, CO 80225
P.O. Box 25165, Mail Stop 350B1, Denver, CO 80225
Tel: (303) 231-3400 Fax: (303) 231-3194
Internet: http://www.onrr.gov/ACM/

● Program Director **Paul G. Tyler** .... (303) 231-3413
E-mail: paul.tyler@onrr.gov

Central Audit and Compliance
P.O. Box 25165, Denver, CO 80225
Tel: (303) 231-3301

Manager **John Barder** .... (303) 231-3702
Fax: (303) 231-3722

Southern Audit and Compliance Manager
Barbara Lambert .... (303) 231-3124
E-mail: barbara.lambert@onrr.gov

Central Audit and Compliance *(continued)*

State and Indian Coordination Program Manager
Patrick Milano .... (303) 231-3124

Western Audit and Compliance Manager
Judith "Judi" Clark .... (303) 231-3537
E-mail: judith.clark@onrr.gov

Dallas, TX Team Leader **Allen McDaniel** .... (214) 640-9030
4050 Alpha Road, Suite 420, Farmers Branch, TX 75244-4201
E-mail: allen.mcdaniel@onrr.gov

Oklahoma City Team Leader **Shawna Schimke** .... (405) 879-6006
4013 Northwest Expressway, Suite 230, Oklahoma City, OK 73116-1697
E-mail: shawna.schimke@onrr.gov

Financial and Production Management (FPM)
Denver Federal Center, Building 85, Sixth Avenue and Kipling Street, Denver, CO 80225-0046
P.O. Box 25165, Mail Stop 350B1, Denver, CO 80225
Tel: (303) 231-3116 Fax: (303) 231-3508

● Program Director **Kimbra Davis** .... (303) 231-3514

Secretary **Ellie Arden** .... (303) 231-3523
E-mail: ellie.arden@onrr.gov

Financial Management Manager **(Vacant)** .... (303) 231-3116

Reporting and Solid Mineral Services Manager
Lee Ann Martin .... (303) 231-3313

Budget Officer **Renee Magalong** .... (303) 231-3986
E-mail: renee.magalong@onrr.gov

Information Technology Center (ITC)
Denver Federal Center, Building 85, Sixth and Kipling Streets, Denver, CO 80225
P.O. Box 25165, Denver, CO 80225
Tel: (303) 231-3749 Fax: (303) 231-3362

Infrastructure and Digital Services Manager
Patricia L. Damon .... (303) 231-3956
E-mail: patricia.damon@onrr.gov

Information Access Manager **Ralph Johnson** .... (303) 231-3666
E-mail: ralph.johnson@onrr.gov

Policy and International Affairs (P&IA)

1849 C Street, NW, Mail Stop 5120, Washington, DC 20240
Tel: (202) 208-4852 Fax: (202) 208-1067

Office of Environmental Policy and Compliance (OEPC)

1849 C Street, NW, Mail Stop 2462, Washington, DC 20240
Tel: (202) 208-3891 Fax: (202) 208-6970 Internet: www.doi.gov/oepc

Regional Offices

Alaska Region
1689 C Street, Room 119, Anchorage, AK 99501-5126
Tel: (907) 271-5011 Fax: (907) 271-4102
Areas Covered: AK

Regional Environmental Officer **Philip Johnson** .... (907) 271-5011
E-mail: philip_johnson@ios.doi.gov

Regional Environmental Protection Specialist
Grace Cochon .... (907) 271-5011
E-mail: grace_cochon@ios.doi.gov

Albuquerque (NM) Region
1001 Indian School Road, NW, Suite 348, Albuquerque, NM 87104
Tel: (505) 563-3572 Fax: (505) 563-3066
Internet: www.doi.gov/oepc/albuquerque.html
Areas Covered: AR, LA, NM, OK, TX

Regional Environmental Officer **Stephen R. Spencer** .... (505) 563-3572
E-mail: stephen_spencer@ios.doi.gov
Education: Ohio State 1975 BS; Miami U (OH) 1977 MS; Houston 1982 PhD

★ Presidential Appointment Requiring Senate Confirmation ☆ Presidential Appointment ☐ Schedule C Appointment ◇ Career Senior Foreign Service Appointment
● Career Senior Executive Service (SES) Appointment ○ Non-Career Senior Executive Service (SES) Appointment ■ Postal Career Executive Service

Atlanta (GA) Region
75 Ted Turner Drive, Suite 1144, Atlanta, GA 30303
Tel: (404) 331-4524 Fax: (404) 331-1736
Areas Covered: AL, FL, GA, KY, MS, NC, PR, SC, TN, VI

Regional Environmental Protection Specialist
Joyce A. Stanley . . . . (404) 331-4524
E-mail: joyce_stanley@ios.doi.gov

Boston (MA) Region
15 State Street, Floor 8, Boston, MA 02109-3572
Tel: (617) 223-8565 Fax: (617) 223-8569
Areas Covered: CT, ME, MA, NH, NJ, NY, RI, VT

Regional Environmental Officer **Andrew L. Raddant** . . . . (617) 223-8565
E-mail: andrew_raddant@ios.doi.gov
Regional Environmental Protection Specialist
Diane Lazinsky . . . . (617) 223-8565
E-mail: diane_lazinsky@ios.doi.gov

Denver (CO) Region
Denver Federal Center, Building 67, Sixth Avenue and Kipling Streets, Room 118, Denver, CO 80225
P.O. Box 25007 (D-108), Denver, CO 80225-0007
Tel: (303) 445-2500 Fax: (303) 445-6320
Internet: www.doi.gov/oepc/denver.html
Areas Covered: CO, IA, KS, MO, MT, NE, ND, SD, UT, WY

Regional Environmental Officer **Courtney Hoover** . . . . (303) 445-2500
E-mail: courtney_hoover@ios.doi.gov
Regional Environmental Protection Specialist
Ryan Sloan . . . . (303) 445-2500
E-mail: ryan_sloan@ios.doi.gov

Philadelphia (PA) Region
U.S. Customs House, 200 Chestnut Street, Room 244, Philadelphia, PA 19106-2904
Tel: (215) 597-5378 Fax: (215) 597-9845
Areas Covered: DE, DC, IL, IN, MD, MI, MN, OH, PA, VA, WV, WI

Regional Environmental Officer **Lindy Nelson** . . . . (215) 597-5378
E-mail: lindy_nelson@ios.doi.gov
Regional Environmental Protection Assistant
Valincia Darby . . . . (215) 597-5378
E-mail: valincia_darby@ios.doi.gov

Portland (OR) Region
620 Southwest Main Street, Room 201, Portland, OR 97205
Tel: (503) 326-2489 Fax: (503) 326-2494
Internet: www.doi.gov/oepc/portland.html
Areas Covered: ID, OR, WA

Regional Environmental Officer **Allison O'Brien** . . . . (503) 807-3829
E-mail: allison_o'brien@ios.doi.gov
Regional Environmental Protection Specialist
Brian Milchak . . . . (503) 326-2489
E-mail: brian_milchak@ios.doi.gov

San Francisco (CA) Region
333 Bush Street, Suite 515, San Francisco, CA 94104
Tel: (415) 296-3350 Fax: (415) 773-8334
Areas Covered: AZ, CA, GU, HI, NV, Pacific Islands Territories

Regional Environmental Officer **Janet Whitlock** . . . . (415) 296-3350
E-mail: janet_whitlock@ios.doi.gov

Technology, Information, and Business Services

● Deputy Assistant Secretary
Elena Gonzalez Room 5120 . . . . (202) 208-1927
E-mail: elena_gonzalez@ios.doi.gov

Office of Aviation Services

300 East Mallard Drive, Suite 200, Boise, ID 83706-3991
Tel: (208) 433-5000 Fax: (208) 433-5007 Internet: http://oas.doi.gov/

Alaska Region
4405 Lear Court, Anchorage, AK 99502-1032
Tel: (907) 271-3700 Fax: (907) 271-4788
Areas Covered: AK, HI
Regional Director **Kevin Fox** . . . . (907) 271-3700

Eastern Region
3190 Northeast Expressway, Suite 250, Atlanta, GA 30341-5323
Tel: (770) 458-7474
Areas Covered: AL, AR, CT, DE, FL, GA, IL, IN, IA, KS, KY, LA, ME, MD, MA, MI, MN, MS, MO, NE, NH, NJ, NY, NC, ND, OH, OK, PA, PR, RI, SC, SD, TN, TX, VT, VA, VI, WV, WI
Eastern Regional Director **Frank Crump III** . . . . (770) 280-7245

Western Region
Areas Covered: AZ, CA, CO, ID, MT, NV, NM, OR, UT, WA, WY

Western Region - Boise Office
960 Broadway Avenue, Suite 300, Boise, ID 83706
Tel: (208) 334-9310 Fax: (208) 334-9303
Western Region Director **Gary Kunz** . . . . (208) 334-9310

Water and Science (WS)

1849 C Street, NW, Washington, DC 20240
Tel: (202) 208-3186

OFFICE OF THE ASSISTANT SECRETARY

1849 C Street, NW, Mail Stop 6640, Washington, DC 20240
Tel: (202) 208-3186 Fax: (202) 208-6948

Central Utah Project Completion Act Office
302 East 1860 South, Provo, UT 84606
Fax: (801) 379-1209 Internet: http://www.cupcao.gov
Program Director **Reed R. Murray** . . . . (801) 379-1237
Education: BYU 1986 BCE
Program Coordinator **Lee Baxter** . . . . (801) 379-1174
Program Coordinator **Russ Findlay** . . . . (801) 379-1084

United States Geological Survey (USGS)

U.S. Geological Survey National Center,
12201 Sunrise Valley Drive, Reston, VA 20192
Tel: (703) 648-4000 (Public Information)
Tel: (703) 648-4455 (Legislative Information)
Tel: (888) 275-8747 (Earth Science Information Center)
Tel: (800) 435-7627 (Information Services)
Tel: (888) 275-8747 (United States Geological Survey)
Fax: (703) 648-4454 Internet: www.usgs.gov

Core Science Systems

12201 Sunrise Valley Drive, Reston, VA 20192

National Geospatial Programs Office

National Geospatial Technical Operations Center - Denver (CO)
Sixth Avenue and Kipling Street, Mail Stop 510, Denver, CO 80225-0046
Tel: (303) 202-4115
Denver Center Chief **Ronald "Ron" Lofton** . . . . (303) 202-4115

National Geospatial Technical Operations Center - Rolla (MO) (NGTOC)
1400 Independence Road, Rolla, MO 65401-2602
Tel: (573) 308-3500 (Earth Science Information) Tel: (573) 308-3800
Fax: (573) 308-3652 Internet: http://mcmcweb.er.usgs.gov
Rolla Center Chief **Eric W. Constance** . . . . (573) 308-3685

DEPARTMENTS

★ Presidential Appointment Requiring Senate Confirmation ☆ Presidential Appointment ☐ Schedule C Appointment ◇ Career Senior Foreign Service Appointment
● Career Senior Executive Service (SES) Appointment ○ Non-Career Senior Executive Service (SES) Appointment ■ Postal Career Executive Service

Ecosystems
12201 Sunrise Valley Drive, Reston, VA 20192
Tel: (703) 648-4050 Fax: (703) 648-7031
Internet: http://ecosystems.usgs.gov

Cooperative Research Units (CRU)
12201 Sunrise Valley Drive, MS303, Reston, VA 20192
Tel: (703) 648-4260 Fax: (703) 648-4269 Internet: www.coopunits.org

Unit Supervisor - Round Hill
185, Round Hill, VA 20142
Unit Supervisor **Dr. Kevin Whalen** .... (703) 269-7711

Unit Supervisor - Leetown
USGS-BRD, Leetown Science Center, 11700 Leetown Road,
Kearneysville, WV 25430
Tel: (304) 724-4411 Fax: (304) 724-4415
Unit Supervisor **Dr. Michael W. Tome** .... (304) 724-4411
Education: Penn State 1978 BS; Maine 1981 MS; Michigan 1986 PhD

Unit Supervisor - Pagosa Springs
1135 Park Avenue, Unit 904, Pagosa Springs, CO 81147
Tel: (303) 656-0906 Fax: (303) 236-1451
Unit Supervisor **(Vacant)** .... (303) 236-1454

Cooperative Units

Alabama Cooperative Fish and Wildlife Research Unit
School of Forestry and Wildlife Services, 602 Duncan Drive,
Auburn University, Auburn, AL 36849-5418
Tel: (334) 844-4796 Fax: (334) 887-1084 E-mail: coop-unit@auburn.edu
Unit Leader **Dr. J. Barry Grand** .... (334) 844-4796
Assistant Leader - Fish **Dr. Elise Irwin** .... (334) 844-4796
Assistant Leader - Wildlife **Conor McGowan** .... (334) 844-4796
Education: Wake Forest 2000 BS; North Carolina State 2004 MS; Missouri 2008 PhD

Alaska Cooperative Fish and Wildlife Research Unit
209 Irving I Building, University of Alaska, Fairbanks, AK 99775-7020
P.O. Box 757020, Fairbanks, AK 99775-7020
Tel: (907) 474-7661 Fax: (907) 474-7872 E-mail: fyunit@uaf.edu
Unit Leader **Dr. Brad Griffith** .... (907) 474-5067
Education: Missouri 1969 BA; Oregon State 1977 MS; Idaho 1988 PhD
Assistant Unit Leader **Jeffrey Falke** .... (907) 474-6044
Assistant Unit Leader **Mark Wipfli** .... (907) 474-6654
Education: Michigan State 1992 PhD
Fiscal Officer **Monica Armbruster** .... (907) 474-5924
E-mail: mlarmbruster@alaska.edu
Senior Scientist **Dr. A. David McGuire** .... (907) 474-6242
Administrative Assistant **Kathleen R. "Kathy" Pearse** ... (907) 474-7661
E-mail: krpearse@alaska.edu

Arizona Cooperative Fish and Wildlife Research Unit
104 Biological Sciences East Building,
University of Arizona, Tucson, AZ 85721
Tel: (520) 621-1959 Fax: (520) 621-8801
E-mail: azcoopunit@ag.arizona.edu
Unit Leader **Dr. Scott Bonar** .... (520) 349-1894
Education: Evansville 1983 BS; U Washington 1990 PhD
Assistant Unit Leader **Melanie Culver** .... (520) 626-3775

Arkansas Cooperative Fish and Wildlife Research Unit
Biological Sciences, SCEN-632, University of Arkansas,
Fayetteville, AR 72701
Tel: (479) 575-6709 Fax: (479) 575-3330 E-mail: coopunit@uark.edu
Unit Leader **Dr. David G. Krementz** .... (479) 575-7560
Assistant Unit Leader **Dr. Daniel "Dan" Magoulick** ..... (479) 575-5449

California Cooperative Fish and Wildlife Research Unit
Humboldt State University, One Harpst Street, Arcata, CA 95521-8299
Tel: (707) 826-3268 Fax: (707) 826-3269 E-mail: cuca@humboldt.edu
Unit Leader **Dr. Margaret A. "Peggy" Wilzbach** .... (707) 826-5645
Education: Illinois 1976 BS, 1978 MS; Oregon State 1985 PhD

Colorado Cooperative Fish and Wildlife Research Unit
201 J.V.K. Wagar Building, Colorado State University,
Fort Collins, CO 80523-1484
Tel: (970) 491-5396 Fax: (970) 491-1413
E-mail: coopunit@warnercnr.colostate.edu
Internet: www.colostate.edu/depts/coopunit
Unit Leader **Dr. Dana Winkelman** .... (970) 491-1414
Education: Nevada (Reno) 1984 BS, 1987 MS; Georgia 1994 PhD
Assistant Unit Leader **Mevin Hooten** .... (970) 491-1415
E-mail: mevin.hooten@colostate.edu
Assistant Unit Leader **Bill Kendall** .... (970) 491-7066
Accounting Technician **Gabriele Engler** .... (970) 491-6942

Florida Cooperative Fish and Wildlife Research Unit
University of Florida, Building 810, Gainesville, FL 32611-0485
Box 110485, University of Florida, Gainesville, FL 32611-0485
Tel: (352) 846-0534 Fax: (352) 846-0841 E-mail: coop@wec.ufl.edu
Internet: http://www.coopunits.org/Florida/
Unit Leader **Abby Powell** .... (352) 846-0543
Education: Cornell 1980 BS; San Diego State 1986 MS; Minnesota 1992 PhD
Assistant Unit Leader **Dr. Raymond Carthy** .... (352) 846-0545
Education: Manhattan Col 1980 BS; Slippery Rock U 1983 MS; Florida 1996 PhD

Georgia Cooperative Fish and Wildlife Research Unit
D. B. Warnell School of Forest Resources, University of Georgia,
D. W. Brooks Drive, Room 3-428, Athens, GA 30602-2152
Tel: (706) 542-5260 Fax: (706) 542-8356
E-mail: coopunit@forestry.uga.edu
Unit Leader **Dr. Cecil A. Jennings** .... (706) 542-4837
Assistant Leader **Brian Irwin** .... (706) 542-0790
Assistant Leader **Clinton Moore** .... (706) 542-1166

Hawaii Cooperative Fishery Research Unit
University of Hawaii, Dean Hall, 2540 Campus Road,
Room 2, Honolulu, HI 96822
Tel: (808) 956-8350 Fax: (808) 956-9812
Unit Leader **(Vacant)** .... (808) 587-7454
Assistant Leader **(Vacant)** .... (808) 956-8350

Idaho Cooperative Fish and Wildlife Research Unit
College of Natural Resources, Sixth and Line Streets,
Room 103, Moscow, ID 83844-1141
College of Natural Resources, Room 103, P.O. Box 441141,
Moscow, ID 83844-1141
Tel: (208) 885-6336 Fax: (208) 885-9080 E-mail: idcfwru@uidaho.edu
Unit Leader **Courtney Conway** .... (208) 885-6176
Assistant Unit Leader **Christine Moffitt** .... (208) 885-7047
Assistant Unit Leader **Michael C. Quist** .... (208) 885-4064

Iowa Cooperative Fish and Wildlife Research Unit
Department of Natural Resource, Ecology and Management,
Iowa State University, Ames, IA 50011-3221
Tel: (515) 294-3056 Fax: (515) 294-5468 E-mail: coopunit@iastate.edu
Unit Leader **Robert "Bob" Klaver** .... (515) 294-7639
Education: Iowa State 1971 BS; Montana 1974 BS, 1977 MS; South Dakota State 2001 PhD
Assistant Unit Leader **Dr. Clay Pierce** .... (515) 294-3159
Education: Mankato State 1980 BS; Kentucky 1982 MS; Maryland 1987 PhD

Kansas Cooperative Fish and Wildlife Research Unit
205 Leasure Hall, Kansas State University, Manhattan, KS 66506-3501
Tel: (785) 532-6070 Fax: (785) 532-7159 E-mail: kscfwru@ksu.edu
Internet: http://www.coopunits.org/Kansas/

Unit Leader **David A. "Dave" Haukos** . . . . (785) 532-5761
Education: South Dakota State 1986 BS; Texas Tech 1988 MS, 1991 PhD

Assistant Unit Leader **Dr. Martha E. Mather** . . . . (785) 532-6522
Education: Denison 1978 BS; Ohio State 1985 MS, 1990 PhD

Louisiana Cooperative Fish and Wildlife Research Unit
124 Forestry-Wildlife-Fisheries Building,
School of Renewable Natural Resources,
Louisiana State University, Baton Rouge, LA 70803-6202
Tel: (225) 578-4179 Fax: (225) 578-4144 E-mail: lacoop@lsu.edu
Internet: http://www.coopunits.org/Louisiana/

Unit Leader **Sammy King** . . . . (225) 578-7564

Assistant Unit Leader **Megan K. G. La Peyre** . . . . (225) 578-4180
E-mail: mlapey@lsu.edu

Maine Cooperative Fish and Wildlife Research Unit
5755 Nutting Hall, University of Maine,
Room 258, Orono, ME 04469-5755
Tel: (207) 581-2870 Fax: (207) 581-2858
E-mail: usgs@umenfa.maine.edu

Unit Leader **Dr. Cyndy Loftin** . . . . (207) 581-2843
Education: Virginia 1984 BA; Auburn 1987 MS; Florida 1998 PhD

Assistant Unit Leader **Joseph Zydlewski** . . . .(207) 581-2853
E-mail: jzydlewski@usgs.gov
Education: Bates 1990 BS; UMass (Amherst) 1997 PhD

Maryland Cooperative Fish and Wildlife Research Unit
Trigg Hall, University of Maryland (Eastern Shore),
Room 1120, Princess Anne, MD 21853-1299
Tel: (410) 651-7663 Fax: (410) 651-7662
E-mail: mdcoopunit@mail.umes.edu

Unit Leader **(Vacant)** . . . .(410) 651-7654

Assistant Leader **(Vacant)** . . . .(410) 651-7664

Massachusetts Cooperative Fish and Wildlife Research Unit
Holdsworth Natural Resources Center, University of Massachusetts,
Amherst, MA 01003-4220
Tel: (413) 545-0398 Fax: (413) 545-4358
E-mail: macoopunit@forwild.umass.edu

Unit Leader **Dr. Stephen DeStefano** . . . . (413) 545-4889

Assistant Leader **Allison Roy** . . . .(413) 545-4895
E-mail: aroy@eco.umass.edu

Minnesota Cooperative Fish and Wildlife Research Unit
Department of Fisheries, Wildlife, and Conservation Biology,
University of Minnesota, St. Paul, MN 55108-6124
Tel: (612) 624-3421 Fax: (612) 625-5299

Unit Leader **Dr. David E. Andersen** . . . . (612) 626-1222

Assistant Unit Leader **Dr. David C. Fulton** . . . . (612) 625-5256

Mississippi Cooperative Fish and Wildlife Research Unit
100 Thompson Hall, Stone Boulevard, Mississippi State, MS 39762
MS 9691, Mississippi State, MS 39762
Tel: (662) 325-2643 Fax: (662) 325-4763
E-mail: mscoopunit@cfr.msstate.edu

Unit Leader **Dr. Harold "Hal" Schramm** . . . . (662) 325-7495
Education: Southern Illinois 1977 PhD

Assistant Unit Leader
Dr. Leandro Esteban "Steve" Miranda . . . .(662) 325-3217
E-mail: smiranda@cfr.msstate.edu
Education: Morehead State 1977 BS; Auburn 1981 MS; Mississippi State 1986 PhD

Assistant Unit Leader **Dr. Francisco Vilella** . . . . (662) 325-0784
E-mail: fvilella@cfr.msstate.edu
Education: Hofstra 1983 MS; LSU 1989 PhD

Missouri Cooperative Fish and Wildlife Research Unit
302 Anheuser-Busch Natural Resources Building,
University of Missouri, Columbia, MO 65211-7240
Tel: (573) 882-3634 Fax: (573) 884-5070 E-mail: coopunit@missouri.edu

Unit Leader **Craig P. Paukert** . . . .(573) 882-3524

Assistant Unit Leader **Elisabeth "Lisa" Webb** . . . .(573) 882-3634

Montana Cooperative Fishery Research Unit
Montana State University, Lewis Hall,
Room 301, Bozeman, MT 59717-3460
P.O. Box 173460, Bozeman, MT 59717-3460
Tel: (406) 994-4549 Fax: (406) 994-7479
E-mail: mtfcoopunit@montana.edu

Unit Leader - Fish **Dr. Alexander "Al" Zale** . . . .(406) 994-2380

Assistant Unit Leader - Fish **Dr. Christopher S. Guy** . . . . (406) 994-3491
E-mail: cguy@montana.edu

Montana Cooperative Wildlife Research Unit
Natural Science Building 205, University of Montana,
Missoula, MT 59812-1120
Tel: (406) 243-5372 Fax: (406) 243-6064
E-mail: coopunit@umontana.edu

Unit Leader **Dr. Michael "Mike" Mitchell** . . . .(406) 243-4390

Assistant Unit Leader **Dr. Thomas E. Martin** . . . .(406) 243-5372
E-mail: Tom.Martin@umontana.edu

Nebraska Cooperative Fish and Wildlife Research Unit
University of Nebraska-Lincoln, 422 Hardin Hall,
Lincoln, NE 68583-0711
Tel: (402) 472-0449 Fax: (402) 472-2722

Unit Leader **Craig Allen** . . . .(402) 472-0229
Education: Florida 1997 PhD

Assistant Leader **Kevin Pope** . . . .(402) 472-7028

Assistant Leader - Ecology **Joseph "TJ" Fontaine** . . . . . . (402) 472-0339

New Mexico Cooperative Fish and Wildlife Research Unit
New Mexico State University, 2980 South Espina, Knox Hall,
Room 132, Las Cruces, NM 88003-0003
P.O. Box 30003, MSC 4901, Las Cruces, NM 88003-0003
Tel: (575) 646-6053 Fax: (575) 646-1281 E-mail: coopunit@nmsu.edu

Unit Leader **Dr. Colleen A. Caldwell** . . . . (575) 646-8126
Education: Texas A&M 1982 BS; Texas State (San Marcos) 1985 MS; Tennessee 1988 PhD

Assistant Leader - Fish **Scott Carleton** . . . .(575) 646-7196
E-mail: scarleton@usgs.gov
Education: Southern Nazarene 1995 BS; Arkansas 2002 MS; Wyoming 2009 PhD

Assistant Leader - Wildlife **James W. Cain** . . . . (575) 646-3382
E-mail: jwcain@nmsu.edu
Education: Colorado State 1997 BS; Cal State (Sacramento) 2001 MS; Arizona 2006 PhD

New York Cooperative Fish and Wildlife Research Unit
Cornell University, Fernow Hall, Room 206F, Ithaca, NY 14853-3001
Tel: (607) 255-2839 Fax: (607) 255-1895
E-mail: dnrcru-mailbox@cornell.edu

Unit Leader **Angela Fuller** . . . .(607) 255-2841
Education: Maine (Machias) 1996 BS; Maine 1999 MS, 2006 PhD

Assistant Unit Leader **(Vacant)** . . . .(607) 255-4665

North Carolina Cooperative Fish and Wildlife Research Unit
North Carolina State University, Department of Zoology,
Raleigh, NC 27695-7617
Mail: Campus Box 7617, North Carolina State University,
Raleigh, NC 27695-7617
Tel: (919) 515-2631 Fax: (919) 515-4454 E-mail: nc_cfwru@ncsu.edu

Unit Leader **Dr. Thomas J. Kwak** . . . .(919) 513-2696
Education: Illinois 1981 BS, 1983 MS; Minnesota 1993 PhD

Assistant Leader - Ecology
Dr. Theodore R. "Ted" Simons . . . .(919) 515-2689
Education: Wisconsin 1975 BS; U Washington 1979 MS, 1983 PhD

(continued on next page)

DEPARTMENTS

North Carolina Cooperative Fish and Wildlife Research Unit *(continued)*

Assistant Leader - Fish **Dr. Joseph E. Hightower** . . . . (919) 515-8836
E-mail: jhightower@ncsu.edu
Education: North Carolina State 1978 BS; Georgia 1981 MS, 1984 PhD

Assistant Leader - Wildlife **Dr. Jaime A. Collazo** . . . . (919) 515-8837
E-mail: jaime_collazo@ncsu.edu
Education: Puerto Rico BS; Idaho MS; Iowa State PhD

Oklahoma Cooperative Fish and Wildlife Research Unit
Oklahoma State University, 007 Agriculture Hall,
Stillwater, OK 74078-3051
Tel: (405) 744-6342 Fax: (405) 744-5006 E-mail: coopunit@okstate.edu
Internet: http://www.coopunits.org/Oklahoma/

Unit Leader (Acting) **Shannon K. Brewer** . . . . (405) 744-9841
Education: Missouri Western State U 2001 BS; Missouri 2004 MS, 2008 PhD

Assistant Leader - Ecology **Shannon K. Brewer** . . . . (405) 744-9841
E-mail: skbrewer@usgs.gov
Education: Missouri Western State U 2001 BS; Missouri 2004 MS, 2008 PhD

Assistant Leader - Fish **Dr. Jim Long** . . . . (405) 744-6342

Oregon Cooperative Fish and Wildlife Research Unit
104 Nash Hall, Oregon State University, Corvallis, OR 97331-3803
Tel: (541) 737-1938 Fax: (541) 737-3590
E-mail: or_cfwru@oregonstate.edu

Unit Leader - Fish **Dr. Carl B. Schreck** . . . . (541) 737-1961
Assistant Leader - Fish **Dr. James T. Peterson** . . . . (541) 737-1963
Unit Leader - Wildlife **Dr. Daniel D. Roby** . . . . (541) 737-1955
Unit Scientist **Katie Dugger** . . . . (541) 737-2473

Pennsylvania Cooperative Fish and Wildlife Research Unit
419 Forest Resources Building, Pennsylvania State University,
University Park, PA 16802-1100
Tel: (814) 865-4511 Fax: (814) 863-4710
E-mail: l-coopunits@lists.psu.edu

Unit Leader **Dr. Duane R. Diefenbach** . . . . (814) 865-3992
Assistant Unit Leader - Fish **Dr. Tyler Wagner** . . . .(814) 865-4511
Assistant Leader - Wildlife **W. David Walter** . . . . (814) 867-4763
E-mail: wdwalter@psu.edu

South Dakota Cooperative Fish and Wildlife Research Unit
Department of Wildlife and Fisheries Sciences,
South Dakota State University, Box 2140B, Biostress Lab,
Room 138, Brookings, SD 57007-1696
Northern Plains Biostress Lab, Rm. 138, South Dakota State U,
Brookings, SD 57007-1696
Tel: (605) 688-6121 Fax: (605) 688-4515

Unit Leader **Dr. Steven R. Chipps** . . . . (605) 688-5467
Education: Davis & Elkins 1989 BS; West Virginia 1992 MS; Idaho 1997 PhD

Assistant Leader - Ecology **Larry Gigliotti** . . . . (605) 688-6717
E-mail: larry.gigliotti@sdstate.edu
Education: Penn State 1975 BS; Michigan State 1983 MS, 1989 PhD

Assistant Leader - Wildlife **Joshua Stafford** . . . . (605) 688-5759
E-mail: joshua.stafford@sdstate.edu
Education: Oregon State 1997 BS; South Dakota State 2000 MS; Mississippi State 2004 PhD

Tennessee Cooperative Fishery Research Unit
Tennessee Tech University, 205 Pennebaker Hall, 1100 North Dixie Avenue, Cookeville, TN 38505-0001
Mail: Tennessee Tech University, Box 5114, Cookeville, TN 38505-0001
Tel: (931) 372-3094 Fax: (931) 372-6257 E-mail: coopunit@tntech.edu

Unit Leader **Mark W. Rogers** . . . .(931) 372-3032
Assistant Leader **(Vacant)** . . . .(931) 372-3086

Texas Cooperative Fish and Wildlife Research Unit
Texas Tech University, 15th Street and Boston,
Room 218, Lubbock, TX 79409-2120
Tel: (806) 742-2851 Fax: (806) 742-2946 E-mail: txcoop@ttu.edu
Internet: http://www.coopunits.org/Texas/

Unit Leader **Dr. Reynaldo Patino** . . . . (806) 742-2851
Assistant Leader - Fish **(Vacant)** . . . . (806) 742-2851
Assistant Leader - Wildlife **Clint Boal** . . . .(806) 742-2851
E-mail: clint.boal@ttu.edu
Education: Arizona 1991 BS, 1993 MS, 1997 PhD

Utah Cooperative Fish and Wildlife Research Unit
Utah State University, 5290 University Boulevard, NR 108,
Logan, UT 84322-5290
Tel: (435) 797-7565 Fax: (435) 797-4025 E-mail: utcoop@cnr.usu.edu

Unit Leader **Phaedra Budy** . . . . (435) 797-7564
Assistant Unit Leader **Dr. Thomas C. Edwards** . . . .(435) 797-2529

Vermont Cooperative Fish and Wildlife Research Unit
310 Aiken Center, School of Natural Resources, University of Vermont,
Burlington, VT 05405
Tel: (802) 656-3011 Fax: (802) 656-8683 E-mail: vtcfwru@uvm.edu

Unit Leader **Dr. Donna L. Parrish** . . . . (802) 656-2693
Education: Southeast Missouri State BS; Murray State U MS; Ohio State PhD

Assistant Unit Leader **Dr. Therese "Terri" Donovan** . . . . . (802) 656-2516
E-mail: tdonovan@uvm.edu
Education: Eastern Illinois 1984 BS, 1986 BS, 1986 MS; Missouri 1994 PhD

Virginia Cooperative Fish and Wildlife Research Unit
106 Cheatham Hall, Virginia Polytechnic Institute & State University,
Blacksburg, VA 24061
Tel: (540) 231-4934 Fax: (540) 231-7580
E-mail: vacfwru@listserve.vt.edu

Unit Leader **William Mark Ford** . . . . (540) 231-5927
Assistant Unit Leader **Dr. Paul L. Angermeier** . . . .(540) 231-4501

Washington Cooperative Fish and Wildlife Research Unit
Fishery Sciences Building, University Of Washington
School of Aquatic and Fishery Scien, 1122 NE Boat Street,
Box 355020, Seattle, WA 98195-5020
Tel: (206) 543-6475 Fax: (206) 616-9012
E-mail: washcoop@u.washington.edu

Unit Leader **(Vacant)** . . . .(206) 543-6475
Assistant Unit Leader **Dr. Glenn R. VanBlaricom** . . . . (206) 543-6475
Education: U Washington 1972 BS; UC San Diego 1978 PhD

West Virginia Cooperative Fish and Wildlife Research Unit
Division of Forestry, College of Agriculture and Forestry,
P.O. Box 6125, 322 Percival Hall, West Virginia University,
Morgantown, WV 26506-6125
WV University/Div. of Forestry, P.O. Box 6125, 322 Percival,
Morgantown, WV 26506-6125
Tel: (304) 293-3794 Fax: (304) 293-4826 E-mail: wvcoop@wvu.edu

Unit Leader **Dr. Patricia "Pat" Mazik** . . . .(304) 293-4943
Assistant Leader - Fish **Dr. Stuart Welsh** . . . . (304) 293-5006
E-mail: swelsh@wvu.edu

Assistant Leader - Wildlife **Dr. Petra B. Wood** . . . .(304) 293-5090

Wisconsin Cooperative Fishery Research Unit
College of Natural Resources, University of Wisconsin,
1900 Franklin Street, Room 0163, Stevens Point, WI 54481-3897
Tel: (715) 346-2178 Fax: (715) 346-3624 E-mail: coopfish@uwsp.edu

Unit Leader **Dan Isermann** . . . . (715) 346-3221
Education: Southern Illinois 1997 BS; Tennessee Tech 2000 MS; South Dakota State 2003 PhD

Assistant Unit Leader **Wes Larson** . . . . (715) 346-2178
E-mail: wes.larson@uwsp.edu

Wisconsin Cooperative Wildlife Research Unit
Dept. of Wildlife Ecology, University of Wisconsin,
Room 204, Russell Laboratories, 1630 Linden Drive,
Madison, WI 53706-1598
Tel: (608) 263-4519 Fax: (608) 262-9922
E-mail: coopunit@marlplus.wisc.edu

Unit Leader **Dr. Christine Ribic** . . . . (608) 263-6556
E-mail: caribic@wisc.edu

Wyoming Cooperative Fish and Wildlife Research Unit
Biological Science Building, Room 419,
University of Wyoming, 16th and Gibbon Streets,
Laramie, WY 82071-3166
Biological Science Building, Box 3166, University of Wyoming,
Laramie, WY 82071-3166
Tel: (307) 766-5415 Fax: (307) 766-5400 E-mail: wyo-coop@uwyo.edu

Unit Leader **Dr. Matthew Kauffman PhD** . . . . . . (307) 766-6404
Education: Oregon BS; UC Santa Cruz PhD
Assistant Leader - Fish **Annika Walters** . . . . (307) 766-5473
Assistant Leader - Wildlife **Anna Chalfoun PhD** . . . . (307) 766-6966
Education: Smith BA; Missouri MS; Montana PhD

Natural Hazards

12201 Sunrise Valley Drive, Reston, VA 20192
Fax: (703) 648-7031

Earthquake Hazards Program
12201 Sunrise Valley Drive, Mail Stop 905, Reston, VA 20192
Fax: (703) 648-6717 Internet: http://earthquake.usgs.gov/

Menlo Park Science Center
345 Middlefield Road, Mail Stop 977, Menlo Park, CA 94025-3561
Tel: (650) 329-4668 Fax: (650) 329-5163

Director **Stephen H. Hickman** . . . . (650) 329-4807
345 Middlefield Road, Room 3A-129, Menlo Park, CA 94025-3561
Education: MIT PhD
Deputy Director **Keith L. Knudsen** . . . . (650) 329-5154
Education: Carleton BS; Humboldt State MS
Administrative Officer **Jane Meyer** . . . . (650) 329-4741
E-mail: jmeyer@usgs.gov
Education: San José State 1984 BS, 1995 MBA
Public Information Officer **Susan Garcia** . . . . . . (650) 329-4668
E-mail: garcia@usgs.gov
Research Geophysicist **Thomas Brocher** . . . . (650) 329-4737
345 Middlefield Road, Room 3-202B, Menlo Park, CA 94025
Education: Michigan 1975 BS; Princeton 1980 PhD

Volcano Hazards Program
12201 Sunrise Valley Drive, Reston, VA 20192
E-mail: vhpweb@usgs.gov Internet: http://volcanoes.usgs.gov

Alaska Volcano Observatory
Gould Hall, Room 109, 4200 University Drive, Anchorage, AK 99508
Tel: (907) 786-7479 Fax: (907) 786-7401

Note: Though physically located in the Alaska Science Center in Anchorage, the Alaska Volcano Observatory Scientist-in-Charge reports to the Volcano Hazards Team Chief Scientist in the United States Geological Survey's Southwest Area Regional Executive Office.

Scientist-in-Charge **Michelle Coombs PhD** . . . . . . (907) 786-7403
Education: Williams BS
Geophysicist **John A. Power** . . . . (907) 786-7426

California Volcano Observatory
345 Middlefield Road, Menlo Park, CA 94025-3561
Fax: (650) 329-5203

Scientist-in-Charge **Margaret T. Mangan** . . . . . . (650) 329-5738

Cascades Volcano Observatory
CVO 1300 SE Cardinal Court, Vancouver, WA 98683
Tel: (360) 993-8973 Fax: (360) 993-8980
Internet: http://volcanoes.usgs.gov/observatories/calvo/

Scientist-in-Charge **Seth Moran PhD** . . . . (360) 993-8934
Education: U Washington 1992, 1997 PhD Fax: (360) 993-8980

Hawaii Volcano Observatory
Hawaii Volcano Observatory, P.O. Box 51,
Room 1137, Hawaii National Park, HI 96708-0051
Tel: (808) 967-8819 Fax: (808) 967-8890

Scientist-in-Charge **Christina "Tina" Neal** . . . . . . (808) 967-8853

Yellowstone Volcano Observatory
345 Middlefield Road, Menlo Park, CA 94025-3561
Fax: (650) 329-5203 Internet: http://volcanoes.usgs.gov/yvo

Scientist-in-Charge **Jacob B. Lowenstern PhD** . . . . (650) 329-5238

Water

U.S. Geological Survey National Center,
12201 Sunrise Valley Drive, Reston, VA 20192
Tel: (703) 648-5041 Fax: (703) 648-5002 Internet: https://water.usgs.gov

Office of the Chief Scientist

Office of Groundwater
12201 Sunrise Valley Drive, Reston, VA 20192
Tel: (703) 648-5001 Internet: https://water.usgs.gov/ogw

Geophysics Branch
11 Sherman Place, Unit 5015, Storrs, CT 06269
Tel: (860) 487-7402 Fax: (860) 487-8802
Internet: https://water.usgs.gov/ogw/bgas/

Chief **John W. Lane, Jr. PhD** . . . . (860) 487-7402 ext. 813
Research Hydrologist **Martin Briggs PhD** . . . (860) 487-7402 ext. 819
Research Hydrologist
Frederick D. "Fred" Day-Lewis PhD . . . . (860) 487-7402 ext. 821
Research Hydrologist **Neil Terry** . . . . (860) 487-7402 ext. 18
Hydrologist **Cian B. Dawson** . . . . (860) 377-7081
Hydrologist **Carole D. Johnson** . . . . . . (860) 487-7402 ext. 817
Hydrologist **Eric A. White** . . . . (860) 487-7402 ext. 823
Hydrologist **John H. Williams** . . . . (518) 285-5670
Physical Scientist **Alison C. Waxman** . . . . (860) 487-7402 ext. 810
Emeritus **Frederick L. Paillet** . . . . (860) 487-7402

Office of Science and Research
12201 Sunrise Valley Drive, Reston, VA 20192
Tel: (703) 648-5041 Fax: (703) 648-5002

Central Regional Research Branch
Denver Federal Center, Building 53, Room H-2822, Denver, CO 80225
Denver Federal Center, P.O. Box 25046, MS 418, Denver, CO 80225
Tel: (303) 236-5021 Fax: (303) 236-5034

Branch Chief **(Vacant)** . . . . (303) 236-5022

Eastern Regional Research Branch
12201 Sunrise Valley Drive, MS 432, Reston, VA 20192
Tel: (703) 648-5823 Fax: (703) 648-5832

Branch Chief **Pierre D. Glynn** . . . . (703) 648-5823

Western Regional Research Branch
345 Middlefield Road, Mail Stop 466, Menlo Park, CA 94025
Fax: (650) 329-4463

Branch Chief **Dr. Joseph R. "Joe" Holomuzki** . . . . (650) 329-4419
McKelvey Building, 345 Middlefield Road,
Mail Stop 466, Menlo Park, CA 94025-3561

Office of Surface Water
12201 Sunrise Valley Drive, Mail Stop 415, Reston, VA 20192
Tel: (703) 648-5301 Fax: (703) 648-6693

Hydrologic Instrumentation Facility (HIF)
USGS Building 2101, Stennis Space Center, MS 39529-6000
Tel: (800) 382-0634 Fax: (228) 688-1577 Internet: water.usgs.gov/hif

Chief **(Vacant)** . . . . (800) 382-0634

DEPARTMENTS

★ Presidential Appointment Requiring Senate Confirmation ☆ Presidential Appointment ☐ Schedule C Appointment ◇ Career Senior Foreign Service Appointment
● Career Senior Executive Service (SES) Appointment ○ Non-Career Senior Executive Service (SES) Appointment ■ Postal Career Executive Service

Office of Water Quality
12201 Sunrise Valley Drive, MS 412, Reston, VA 20192
Tel: (703) 648-6862 Fax: (703) 648-6693
Internet: https://water.usgs.gov/owq

National Water Quality Laboratory
Denver Federal Center, Building 95, Entrance E3, Denver, CO 80225
P.O. Box 25585, Denver, CO 80225-0585
Tel: (303) 236-2000 Fax: (303) 236-3499 Internet: http://nwql.usgs.gov

Chief (Acting) **Jeff McCoy** .... (303) 236-3940
E-mail: jefmccoy@usgs.gov
Assistant Chief **David Reppert** .... (303) 236-3548
Administrative Services Chief **Patricia Bergstrom** .... (303) 236-3570
Analytical Services Chief **Duane Wydoski** .... (303) 236-3240
Information Technology Chief
Thomas J. "Tom" Bushly .... (303) 236-3722
E-mail: tjbushly@usgs.gov
Methods Research and Development Chief **(Vacant)** .... (303) 236-2000
Safety, Health and Environment Sciences Chief
Carlos Arozarena .... (303) 236-3302
Support Services Chief **Milton Marshall** .... (303) 236-3715
Quality Assurance Chief **Tim Oden** .... (303) 236-2000

Quality Systems Branch (QSB)
Denver Federal Center, Building 95, Denver, CO 80225
P.O. Box 25046, Denver, CO 80225
Tel: (303) 236-1835 Fax: (303) 236-1880

Chief **George F. Ritz** .... (303) 236-1835

National Water Quality Assessment Program (NAWQA)
National Center, 12201 Sunrise Valley Drive,
Mail Stop 413, Reston, VA 20192
Tel: (703) 648-5012 Tel: (703) 648-5716 Fax: (703) 648-6693
Internet: https://water.usgs.gov/nawqa

Pesticide National Synthesis
Placer Hall, 6000 J Street, Sacramento, CA 95819-6129
Tel: (916) 278-3094 Fax: (916) 278-3071

Project Chief **Robert J. Gilliom** .... (916) 278-3094

Central Region
Denver Federal Center, Mail Stop 406, Denver, CO 80225
Mail: P.O. Box 25046, Denver, CO 80225
Tel: (303) 236-1461 Fax: (303) 236-1451

Central Area Coordinator **Gary L. Rowe, Jr.** .... (303) 236-1461

Acadian-Pontchartrain Field Office
3535 South Sherwood Forest Boulevard,
Suite 120, Baton Rouge, LA 70816
Fax: (225) 298-5490

Project Chief **Dennis K. Demcheck** .... (225) 298-5481 ext. 3214

Central Nebraska Basins Field Office
5231 South 19th Street, Lincoln, NE 68512
Tel: (402) 328-4100 Fax: (402) 328-4101

Superintendent **(Vacant)** .... (402) 328-4100

Eastern Iowa Basins Field Office
Federal Building, 400 South Clinton Street,
Room 269, Iowa City, IA 52244
Tel: (319) 358-3611 Fax: (319) 358-3606

Supervisory Hydrologist **Stephen Kalkhoff** .... (319) 358-3611
Education: Bemidji State 1978 BS

High Plains Ground Water Study Unit
Denver Federal Center, Mail Stop 415, Denver, CO 80225

Project Chief **(Vacant)** .... (303) 236-1461

Northern Rockies Intermontane Basins Field Office
230 Collins Road, Boise, ID 83702-4520
Tel: (208) 387-1300 Fax: (208) 387-1372

Supervisory Hydrologist **(Vacant)** .... (208) 387-1324

Ozark Plateau Field Office
401 Hardin Road, Little Rock, AR 72211
Tel: (501) 228-3600 Fax: (501) 228-3601

Project Chief/Hydrologist **James C. "Jim" Petersen** .... (501) 228-3620

Rio Grande Valley Field Office
5338 Montgomery Boulevard NE, Suite 400, Albuquerque, NM 87109
Tel: (505) 830-7900 Fax: (505) 830-7998

Project Chief **Dianna Crilley** .... (505) 830-7951
Education: Maine (Farmington) BS; Temple 2004 MS

South Central Texas Field Office
1505 Ferguson Lane, Austin, TX 78754
Tel: (512) 927-3500 Fax: (512) 927-3590

Project Chief **Joseph P. Capesius** .... (512) 927-3570
Education: Northern Iowa 1992 BA; Denver 1996 MA

South Platte River Basin Field Office
Denver Federal Center, Mail Stop 415, Denver, CO 80225

Project Chief **(Vacant)** .... (303) 236-6873

Upper Colorado River Basin Field Office
DFC Building 53, West Sixth Avenue and Kipling Street,
Denver, CO 80225
Fax: (303) 236-4912

Supervisory Hydrologist (Acting) **Peter McMahon** .... (303) 236-6899

Upper Mississippi River Basin Field Office
Federal Building, 2280 Woodale Drive, Mounds View, MN 55112-4900
Tel: (763) 783-3100 Fax: (763) 783-3103

Project Chief **James R. "Jim" Stark** .... (763) 783-3230

Yellowstone River Basin Field Office
2617 East Lincolnway, Suite B, Cheyenne, WY 82001-5662
Tel: (307) 778-2931 Fax: (307) 778-2764

Project Chief **Peter R. Wright** .... (406) 656-1444

Northeast and Midwest Areas
12201 Sunrise Valley Drive, Mail Stop 413, Reston, VA 20192-0523
Tel: (703) 648-5811 Fax: (614) 430-7777

Regional NAWQA Program Officer **(Vacant)** .... (703) 648-5811
6480 Doubletree Avenue, Columbus, OH 43229-1111

Southeast Area
3850 Holcomb Bridge Road, Norcross, GA 30092
Tel: (615) 837-4706 Internet: https://water.usgs.gov/nawqa

Assistant Regional Hydrologist for NAWQA **(Vacant)** .... (615) 837-4706
640 Grassmere Park Drive, Nashville, TN 37211

Mississippi Embayment Branch
308 South Airport Road, Pearl, MS 39208-6649
Tel: (601) 933-2982 Fax: (601) 933-2901
Internet: http://ms.water.usgs.gov/ms_proj/nawqa

Project Chief **Richard A. Rebich** .... (601) 933-2928

Mobile River and Tributaries Branch
75 Technacenter Drive, Montgomery, AL 36117
Fax: (334) 395-4168
Internet: http://al.water.usgs.gov/pubs/mobl/basin-description.html

Project Chief **Maurice W. "Rick" Treece** .... (334) 395-4126

Santee Basin and Coastal Drainages Branch
Stephenson Center, Suite 129, 720 Gracern Road, Columbia, SC 29210
Tel: (803) 750-6141 Fax: (803) 750-6181
Internet: http://sc.water.usgs.gov/nawqa

Project Chief (Acting) **Celeste A. Journey** .... (803) 750-6141

★ Presidential Appointment Requiring Senate Confirmation ☆ Presidential Appointment ☐ Schedule C Appointment ◇ Career Senior Foreign Service Appointment
● Career Senior Executive Service (SES) Appointment ○ Non-Career Senior Executive Service (SES) Appointment ■ Postal Career Executive Service

Western Region
345 Middlefield Road, Menlo Park, CA 94025
Fax: (650) 329-4463
Areas Covered: AK, AZ, CA, HI, ID, NV, OR, UT, WA

Associate Regional Hydrologist **Dennis D. Lynch** . . . . (503) 251-3265
2130 SW 5th Avenue, Portland, OR 97201
Education: Oregon BS; U Washington MS

Central Arizona Basins Field Office
520 North Park Avenue, Suite 221, Tucson, AZ 85719
Tel: (520) 670-6671 ext. 223 Fax: (520) 670-5592

Project Chief **David W. Anning** . . . . (928) 556-7139

Central Columbia Plateau Field Office
934 Broadway, Suite 300, Tacoma, WA 98402
Tel: (253) 552-1600 Fax: (253) 552-1581

Project Chief **Robert W. Black** . . . . (253) 552-1687
Project Chief, Puget Sound Basin Study Unit **(Vacant)** . . . (253) 552-1644

Great Salt Lake Basins Field Office
2329 Orton Circle, West Valley City, UT 84119-2047
Tel: (801) 908-5063 Fax: (801) 908-5001
Internet: http://ut.water.usgs.gov/nawqa

Project Chief **Susan A. Thiros** . . . . (801) 908-5063

Nevada Basin and Range Field Office
2730 Deer Run Road, Carson City, NV 89704
Tel: (775) 887-7692 Fax: (775) 887-7629

Project Chief **Jena Huntington** . . . . (775) 887-7692

Sacramento Basin Field Office
Placer Hall, 6000 J Street, Room 3000I, Sacramento, CA 95819-6129
Tel: (916) 278-3077 Fax: (916) 278-3071

Project Chief **Joseph Domagalski** . . . . (916) 278-3077

San Joaquin-Tulare Field Office
Placer Hall, 6000 J Street, Room 3000H, Sacramento, CA 95819-6129
Tel: (916) 278-3076 Fax: (916) 278-3071

Project Chief (Acting) **Joseph Domagalski** . . . . (916) 278-3077

Southern California Coastal Drainages
4165 Spruance Road, Suite 200, San Diego, CA 92101
Tel: (619) 225-6151 Fax: (619) 225-6101

Project Chief (Acting) **Joseph Domagalski** . . . . (916) 278-3077

Upper Snake River Field Office
230 Collins Road, Boise, ID 83702-4520
Fax: (208) 387-1372

Project Chief **(Vacant)** . . . . (208) 387-1335

Willamette Basin Field Office
2130 SW 5th Avenue, Portland, OR 97201
Tel: (503) 251-3200 Fax: (503) 251-3470

Project Chief **Hank Johnson** . . . . (503) 251-3472
Education: Virginia Tech 1992 BS; Oregon Graduate 1996 MS
Assistant Regional Hydrologist
Matthew W. Johnston . . . . (503) 251-3200

Office of the Deputy Associate Director

Deputy Associate Director (Acting)
Johnathan R. "John" Bumgarner MS150 . . . . (505) 830-7901

Alaska Area Regional Director Office

4210 University Drive, Anchorage, AK 99508-4650
Tel: (907) 786-7000 Fax: (907) 786-7020
Areas Covered: AK

● Regional Director **Aimee M. Devaris** . . . . (907) 786-7091
E-mail: adevaris@usgs.gov
Deputy Regional Executive **Dee Williams** . . . . (907) 786-7000

Alaska Science Center (ASC)
4210 University Drive, Anchorage, AK 99508-4650
Tel: (907) 786-7000 Fax: (907) 786-7150 E-mail: dc_ak@usgs.gov
Internet: http://alaska.usgs.gov

Director **Christian E. Zimmerman** . . . . (907) 786-7071
Education: Humboldt State BS; Oregon State MS

Midwest Region Regional Director Office

1451 Green Road, Ann Arbor, MI 48105-2807
Tel: (734) 214-7206 Fax: (734) 214-7231
Areas Covered: ND, SD, NE, MN, IA, IL, IN, KY, MI, MN, OH, ND, NE, SD, WI

Regional Director **Leon M. Carl** . . . . (734) 214-7207
Education: Michigan 1974 BS, 1976 MS, 1980 PhD
Deputy Regional Director for Operations
Linda E. Leake . . . . (608) 781-6263
2630 Fanta Reed Road, La Crosse, WI 54603
Education: Sierra 1991 AS
Deputy Regional Director for Science **Danielle Hawks** . . . (734) 214-7258
Regional Management Officer **Debra Malone** . . . . (734) 214-7225
E-mail: dmalone@usgs.gov
Regional Program Analyst **Kaleb Blodgett** . . . . (734) 214-7202
E-mail: kkblodgett@usgs.gov
Midwest Area Science Coordinator **(Vacant)** . . . . (734) 214-7206
Great Lakes Area Coordinator **(Vacant)** . . . . (734) 214-7206
6520 Mercantile Way, Lansing, MI 48911-5991
Staff Scientist **Sandra Morrison** . . . . (734) 214-9393

Columbia Environmental Research Center (CERC)
4200 New Haven Road, Columbia, MO 65201-9634
Tel: (573) 875-5399 Fax: (573) 876-1896 Internet: www.cerc.usgs.gov
Areas Covered:

Director **Rip S. Shively** . . . . (573) 876-1900
E-mail: rsshively@usgs.gov
Deputy Center Director **(Vacant)** . . . . (573) 875-5399

Jackson (WY) Field Research Station
1475 Fish Hatchery Road, Jackson, WY 83001-1089
Tel: (307) 733-2314 Fax: (307) 739-9268

Station Leader **Aida Farag** . . . . (307) 733-2314 ext. 11

Yankton (SD) Field Research Station
31247 - 436th Avenue, Yankton, SD 57078-6364
Tel: (605) 665-9217 Fax: (605) 665-9335

Station Leader **Kevin Buhl** . . . . (605) 665-9217

Great Lakes Science Center (GLSC)
1451 Green Road, Ann Arbor, MI 48105-2807
Tel: (734) 994-3331 Fax: (734) 994-8780 Internet: www.glsc.usgs.gov

Director **Russell M. "Russ" Strach** . . . . (734) 214-7200
Education: Cornell 1987 BS; Idaho 1990 MS

National Wildlife Health Center (NWHC)
6006 Schroeder Road, Madison, WI 53711-6223
Tel: (608) 270-2400 Fax: (608) 270-2415 Internet: www.nwhc.usgs.gov
Areas Covered: Nationwide and selected international

Center Director **Dr. Jonathan M. Sleeman PhD** . . . . (608) 270-2401
E-mail: jsleeman@usgs.gov
Education: Cambridge (UK) 1989 BA, 2004 MA

Northern Prairie Wildlife Research Center (NPWRC)
8711 37th Street, SE, Jamestown, ND 58401-7317
Tel: (701) 253-5500 Fax: (701) 253-5553 Internet: www.npwrc.usgs.gov

Director **Robert A. Gleason** . . . . (701) 253-5546
Education: Humboldt State 1991 BS, 1996 MS; South Dakota State 2001 PhD
Deputy Director **Mark H. Sherfy PhD** . . . . (701) 253-5504
Education: William & Mary 1988 BS; New Hampshire 1992 MS; Virginia Tech 1999 PhD

DEPARTMENTS

★ Presidential Appointment Requiring Senate Confirmation ☆ Presidential Appointment ☐ Schedule C Appointment ◇ Career Senior Foreign Service Appointment
● Career Senior Executive Service (SES) Appointment ○ Non-Career Senior Executive Service (SES) Appointment ■ Postal Career Executive Service

Black Hills (SD) Field Station
Wind Cave National Park, 26611 U.S. Highway 385,
Hot Springs, SD 57747
Tel: (605) 745-1191 Fax: (605) 745-1162

Principal Investigator **Dr. Amy J. Symstad** .... (605) 745-1191
Education: MIT 1992 BS; Minnesota 1998 PhD Fax: (605) 745-1162

Minnesota Field Station
University of Minnesota, Gabbert Raptor Center,
1920 Fitch Avenue, St. Paul, MN 55108
Tel: (651) 649-5231 Fax: (651) 649-5233

● Principal Investigator **(Vacant)** .... (612) 624-4716
Department of Fisheries, Wildlife, Fax: (612) 625-5299
and Conservation Biology,
204 Hodson Hall, 1980 Folwell Avenue,
University of Minnesota, St. Paul, MN 55108

● Senior Research Scientist **Dr. L. David "Dave" Mech** .... (651) 649-5231
E-mail: david_mech@usgs.gov
Education: Cornell 1958 BS; Purdue 1962 PhD

Research Wildlife Biologist **Dr. Diane L. Larson** .... (651) 649-5041
USDA Forest Service Building, Fax: (651) 649-5040
1561 Lindig Street,
University of Minnesota, St. Paul, MN 55108
Education: Colorado 1978 BA, 1984 MA; Illinois 1991 PhD

Upper Midwest Environmental Sciences Center (UMESC)
2630 Fanta Reed Road, La Crosse, WI 54603
Tel: (608) 783-6451 Fax: (608) 783-6066
Internet: https://www.usgs.gov/centers/umesc/connect
Areas Covered: Nationwide

Center Director **Mark Gaikowski** .... (608) 781-6284
E-mail: mgaikowski@usgs.gov
Education: South Dakota 1991 BS, 1994 MA

Deputy Director **(Vacant)** .... (608) 783-6451

Administrative Officer **Nick Andrews** .... (608) 783-6451

Chief, Aquatic Ecosystem Health Branch
Mark Gaikowski .... (608) 781-6284
Education: South Dakota 1991 BS, 1994 MA

Chief, Long Term Resource Monitoring Branch
Jennifer Sauer .... (608) 781-6376

Librarian **Lisa Hein** .... (608) 781-6215 ext. 215
E-mail: lhein@usgs.gov

Illinois Water Science Center
405 North Goodwin Avenue, Urbana, IL 61801
Tel: (217) 328-8747 Fax: (217) 328-9770 E-mail: dc_il@usgs.gov
Internet: http://il.water.usgs.gov

Director **Amy M. Beussink** .... (319) 471-3449
400 South Clinton Street, Room 269, Iowa City, IA 52244

Indiana Water Science Center
5957 Lakeside Boulevard, Indianapolis, IN 46278
Tel: (317) 290-3333 Fax: (317) 290-3313
Internet: http://in.water.usgs.gov

Director **Michael S. "Mike" Griffin** .... (317) 600-2721

Iowa Water Science Center
Federal Building, 400 South Clinton Street, Room 269,
Iowa City, IA 52240
P.O. Box 1230, Iowa City, IA 52244
Tel: (319) 337-4191 Fax: (319) 358-3606
Internet: http://ia.water.usgs.gov

Director **Amy M. Beussink** .... (573) 308-3667

Kentucky Water Science Center
9818 Bluegrass Parkway, Louisville, KY 40299
Tel: (502) 493-1900 Fax: (502) 493-1909
Internet: http://ky.water.usgs.gov

Director **Michael S. "Mike" Griffin** .... (502) 493-1913

Deputy Director **Peter "Pete" Cinotto** .... (502) 493-1930

Michigan Water Science Center
6520 Mercantile Way, Suite Five, Lansing, MI 48911
Tel: (517) 887-8903 Fax: (517) 887-8937
Internet: http://mi.water.usgs.gov

Director **John F. Walker** .... (517) 887-8906

Minnesota Water Science Center
2280 Woodale Drive, Mounds View, MN 55112
Tel: (763) 783-3100 Fax: (763) 783-3103 E-mail: dc_mn@usgs.gov
Internet: http://mn.usgs.gov

Director **John F. Walker** .... (608) 821-3810
Fax: (763) 783-3103

Missouri Water Science Center
1400 Independence Road, Mail Stop 100, Rolla, MO 65401
Tel: (573) 308-3667 Fax: (573) 308-3645
Internet: http://mo.water.usgs.gov

Director **Amy M. Beussink** .... (573) 308-3667

Nebraska Water Science Center
5231 South 19th Street, Lincoln, NE 68512
Tel: (402) 328-4100 Fax: (402) 328-4101 E-mail: gs-w-ne_fb@usgs.gov
Internet: http://ne.water.usgs.gov

Director (Acting) **Jason Lambrecht** .... (402) 328-4100

Information Technology Specialist **Kurt D. Schultz** ...... (402) 328-4171

Information Technology Specialist **Kelly M. Snow** .... (402) 328-4172

Administrative Officer **Lisa B. Dietsch** .... (402) 328-4116

North Dakota Water Science Center (NDWSC)
821 East Interstate Avenue, Bismarck, ND 58503
Tel: (701) 250-7400 Fax: (701) 250-7492
Internet: http://nd.water.usgs.gov

Director **Joyce E. "Judy" Williamson** .... (605) 394-3219

Ohio Water Science Center
6480 Doubletree Avenue, Columbus, OH 43229-1111
Tel: (614) 430-7700 Fax: (614) 430-7777
Internet: http://oh.water.usgs.gov

Director **James R. Morris** .... (614) 430-7702

South Dakota Water Science Center
1608 Mountain View Road, Rapid City, SD 57702
Tel: (605) 394-3200 Fax: (605) 355-4523
Internet: http://sd.water.usgs.gov

Director **Joyce E. "Judy" Williamson** .... (605) 394-3219

Wisconsin Water Science Center
8505 Research Way, Middleton, WI 53562-3581
Tel: (608) 828-9901 Fax: (608) 821-3817 E-mail: dc_wi@usgs.gov
Internet: http://wi.water.usgs.gov

Director **John F. Walker** .... (608) 821-3810

Northeast Area Regional Director Office
953 National Center, 12201 Sunrise Valley Drive, Reston, VA 20192
Tel: (703) 648-6660 Fax: (703) 648-6684
Areas Covered: CT, DE, DC, ME, MD, MA, MI, NH, NJ, NY, PA, RI, VT, VA, WV

Regional Director **Michael H. "Mike" Tupper** .... (703) 648-6660
12201 Sunrise Valley Drive, Mail Stop 953, Reston, VA 20192

Deputy Regional Executive **Daniel J. Hippy** .... (703) 648-5293
12201 Sunrise Valley Drive, Mail Stop 953, Reston, VA 20192-0002

Regional Management Officer **Dirk C. Van Dyk** .... (703) 648-6150
12201 Sunrise Valley Drive, MS 953, Reston, VA 20192
E-mail: dvandyk@usgs.gov

Regional Program Officer **(Vacant)** .... (703) 648-5114
12201 Sunrise Valley Drive, MS 953, Reston, VA 20192

Regional Coordinator **Glenn Holcomb** .... (304) 724-4526
11649 Leetown Road, Fax: (304) 724-4505
Mail Stop 156, Kearneysville, WV 25430
E-mail: gholcomb@usgs.gov

★ Presidential Appointment Requiring Senate Confirmation ☆ Presidential Appointment □ Schedule C Appointment ◇ Career Senior Foreign Service Appointment
● Career Senior Executive Service (SES) Appointment ○ Non-Career Senior Executive Service (SES) Appointment ■ Postal Career Executive Service

Northeast Area Regional Director Office *(continued)*

Chesapeake Bay Coordinator **Scott W. Phillips** . . . . (443) 498-5552
5522 Research Park Drive, Baltimore, MD 21228 Fax: (443) 498-5510
Education: James Madison 1981 BS;
George Washington 1983 MS

Eastern Energy Resources Science Center
12201 Sunrise Valley Drive, Room 4C300, Mail Stop 956,
Reston, VA 20192-0523
Fax: (703) 648-6419 Internet: energy.er.usgs.gov

Center Director **Daniel O. "Dan" Hayba** . . . . (703) 648-6327
Education: Wooster 1976 BA; Penn State 1979 MS; Illinois PhD
Associate Center Director **Tina Roberts-Ashby** . . . . (703) 648-6543
Team Secretary **Kathleen M. Spiegelberg** . . . . (703) 648-6407
Administrative Officer **Shirlie A. McManus** . . . . (703) 648-5825
E-mail: smcmanus@usgs.gov

Eastern Geology and Paleoclimate Science Center
12201 Sunrise Valley Drive, Room 3C200, Mail Stop 926A,
Reston, VA 20192-0523
Tel: (703) 648-4000 Fax: (703) 648-6953

Director **Chris Bernhardt** . . . . (703) 648-6071

Eastern Minerals and Environmental Resources Science Center (EMERSC)
12201 Sunrise Valley Drive, Mail Stop 954, Reston, VA 20192-0523
Fax: (703) 648-6383 Internet: http://minerals.usgs.gov/east/index.html

Chief Scientist and Director **Daniel O. "Dan" Hayba** . . . . (703) 648-6327
Education: Wooster 1976 BA; Penn State 1979 MS; Illinois PhD

Patuxent Wildlife Research Center
12100 Beech Forest Road, Laurel, MD 20708
Tel: (301) 497-5500 Fax: (301) 497-5505 Internet: www.pwrc.usgs.gov

Center Director **John B. French** . . . . (301) 497-5502

Leetown Science Center (LSC)
11649 Leetown Road, Kearneysville, WV 25430
Tel: (304) 724-4400 Fax: (304) 724-4410 Internet: www.lsc.usgs.gov

Director **A. William "Bill" Palmisano** . . . . (304) 724-4400

Maryland, Delaware, and the District of Columbia Water Science Center
5522 Research Park Drive, Baltimore, MD 21228
Tel: (443) 498-5500 (Baltimore (MD) Office)
Tel: (302) 734-2506 (Dover (DE) Office)
Tel: (301) 687-0919 (Frostburg (MD) Office) Tel: (888) 826-3130
Fax: (443) 498-5510 (Baltimore (MD) Office)
Fax: (302) 734-2964 (Dover (DE) Office) E-mail: dc_md@usgs.gov
Internet: http://de.water.usgs.gov
Areas Covered: DE, DC, MD

Director **Mary Kay Foley** . . . . (443) 498-5501

National Minerals Information Center
12201 Sunrise Valley Drive, Room 3B310, Mail Stop 988,
Reston, VA 20192
Fax: (703) 648-4995

Director **Steven M. Fortier** . . . . (703) 648-4920
Secretary **(Vacant)** . . . . (703) 648-6660
Associate Director **Michael J. Magyar** . . . . (703) 648-4910
Data Collection and Coordination Branch Chief
Shonta E. Osborne . . . . (703) 648-7971
Global Minerals Analysis Branch Chief
Steven D. "Steve" Textoris . . . . (703) 648-4976
Fax: (703) 648-7737
Materials Flow Analysis Section Chief
Nedal T. Nassar . . . . (703) 648-7725
Statistics and Information Systems Branch Chief
(Acting) **Michael J. Magyar** . . . . (703) 648-4910
Administrative Officer **Kathi L. Stone** . . . . (703) 648-6137
E-mail: kstone@usgs.gov

Mineral Commodities Branch
308 South Airport Road, Pearl, MS 39208-6649
Fax: (703) 648-7757

Chief **Elizabeth Scott Sangine** . . . . (703) 648-7720
Fax: (703) 648-7757

New England Water Science Center (NEng WSC)
331 Commerce Way, Suite Two, Pembroke, NH 03275
Internet: http://newengland.water.usgs.gov/

Director **Keith W. Robinson** . . . . (603) 226-7807

Associate Director for Hydrologic Surveillance Programs
Associate Director **Robert M. Lent** . . . . (207) 626-6602
196 Whitten Road, Augusta, ME 04330

Connecticut Hydrologic Surveillance Operations
101 Pitkin Street, East Hartford, CT 06108
Tel: (860) 291-6740

Chief **Timothy Sargent** . . . . (860) 291-6754

Maine Hydrologic Surveillance Operations
196 Whitten Road, Augusta, ME 04330
Tel: (207) 622-8201 Fax: (207) 622-8204 E-mail: dc_me@usgs.gov
Internet: http://me.water.usgs.gov

Chief **Nicholas W. Stasulis** . . . . (207) 626-6612

Massachusetts-Rhode Island Hydrologic Surveillance Operations
10 Bearfoot Road, Northborough, MA 01532
Tel: (508) 490-5000 Fax: (508) 490-5068
Internet: http://ma.water.usgs.gov
Areas Covered: MA, RI

Chief **Richard Verdi** . . . . (508) 490-5064

New Hampshire-Vermont Hydrologic Surveillance Operations
331 Commerce Way, Suite Two, Pembroke, NH 03275
Tel: (603) 226-7800 Fax: (603) 226-7894 E-mail: dc_nh@usgs.gov
Internet: http://nh.water.usgs.gov

Chief **Richard Kiah** . . . . (603) 226-7819

New Jersey Water Science Center
3450 Princeton Pike, Suite 110, Lawrenceville, NJ 08428
Tel: (609) 771-3900 Fax: (609) 771-3915
Internet: http://nj.water.usgs.gov

Director **Richard H. Kropp** . . . . (609) 771-3901

New York Water Science Center
425 Jordan Road, Troy, NY 12180-8349
Tel: (518) 285-5600 Fax: (518) 285-5601 E-mail: dc_ny@usgs.gov
Internet: http://ny.usgs.gov

Director **Robert F. Breault** . . . . (518) 285-5661
Education: UMass (Lowell) 1993 BS, 1999 MS
Associate Director (Acting) **Gary Wall** . . . . (518) 285-5621
Administrative Officer **Tracy Bristol-Strock** . . . . (518) 285-5626
E-mail: tbristol@usgs.gov

Pennsylvania Water Science Center
215 Limekiln Road, New Cumberland, PA 17070
Tel: (717) 730-6900 Fax: (717) 730-6997
Internet: http://pa.water.usgs.gov

Director **James B. Campbell** . . . . (717) 730-6912
Secretary **Julie Bricker** . . . . (717) 730-6946
E-mail: jbricker@usgs.gov
Administrative Officer **Georganne M. Gillespie** . . . . (717) 730-6921
E-mail: gmgilles@usgs.gov
Administrative Operations Assistant **Generosa Burkett** . . . (717) 730-6906
E-mail: gburkett@usgs.gov
Administrative Specialist **Colleen Ceric** . . . . (717) 730-6922
E-mail: cceric@usgs.gov

Office of the Associate Director for Research and Scientific Services
Associate Director for Scientific Investigations and
Research **Curtis Schreffler** . . . . (717) 730-6913

DEPARTMENTS

★ Presidential Appointment Requiring Senate Confirmation ☆ Presidential Appointment ☐ Schedule C Appointment ◇ Career Senior Foreign Service Appointment
● Career Senior Executive Service (SES) Appointment ○ Non-Career Senior Executive Service (SES) Appointment ■ Postal Career Executive Service

DEPARTMENTS

Office of the Assistant Director for Hydrologic Surveillance and Data Management
Assistant Director for Hydrologic Surveillance and Data Management **Marla Stuckey** . . . . (717) 730-6950
Assistant Director and Surface Water Specialist **Robert A. Hainly** . . . . (717) 730-6971

Virginia Water Science Center
1730 East Parham Road, Richmond, VA 23228-2202
Tel: (804) 261-2600 Fax: (804) 261-2657
Internet: http://va.water.usgs.gov
Director **Mark R. Bennett** . . . . (804) 261-2643

West Virginia Water Science Center
11 Dunbar Street, Charleston, WV 25301
Tel: (304) 347-5130 Fax: (304) 347-5133 E-mail: dc_wv@usgs.gov
Internet: http://wv.water.usgs.gov
Director **Mark R. Bennett** . . . . (804) 344-2590
1730 East Parham Road, Richmond, VA 23228-2202
Assistant Director **George E. Harlow** . . . . (804) 261-2631
1730 East Parham Road, Richmond, VA 23228-2202

Woods Hole Science Center
384 Woods Hole Road, Quissett Campus, Woods Hole, MA 02543-1598
Tel: (508) 548-8700 Fax: (508) 457-2310
Internet: http://woodshole.er.usgs.gov
Director **E. Robert "Rob" Thieler** . . . . (508) 457-2211

Northwest Area Regional Director Office
909 First Avenue, 8th Floor, Seattle, WA 98104
Tel: (206) 220-4600 Fax: (206) 220-4624
Areas Covered: ID, OR, WA, WY, MT
Regional Director **Richard Ferrero** . . . . (206) 220-4600
Executive Secretary **Angela E. Freeman** . . . . (206) 220-4600
E-mail: aefreeman@usgs.gov
Deputy Regional Director **Marijke Van Heeswijk** . . . . (206) 220-4606
Associate Regional Director **(Vacant)** . . . . (206) 220-4600
Regional Management Officer **Curtis W. Hoesing** . . . . (206) 220-4620
E-mail: choesing@usgs.gov
Science Program Officer **Lief R. Horwitz** . . . . (206) 220-4616
Regional Science Coordinator **William "Bill" Labiosa** . . . (206) 220-4563
Education: Davidson 1990 BS; Duke 1993 MS; Stanford 1996 MS, 2006 PhD
Executive Assistant **(Vacant)** . . . . (206) 220-4600

Forest and Rangeland Ecosystem Science Center (FRESC)
777 NW 9th Street, Suite 400, Corvallis, OR 97330
Tel: (541) 750-1030 Fax: (541) 750-1069 Internet: http://fresc.usgs.gov
Center Director **Ken Berg** . . . . (541) 750-1031

Geologic Hazards Science Center
P.O. Box 25046, Denver, CO 80225
Tel: (303) 273-8582 Fax: (303) 273-8583
Director **Jill McCarthy** . . . . (303) 273-8579
Denver Federal Center, Box 25046, MS 966, Denver, CO 80225
Mail: 1711 Illinois Street, Golden, CO 80401
Associate Director **Linda K. Pratt** . . . . (303) 273-8507
Denver Federal Center, Box 25046, MS-966, Denver, CO 80225

Idaho Water Science Center
230 Collins Road, Boise, ID 83702-4520
Tel: (208) 387-1300 Fax: (208) 387-1372
Internet: http://id.water.usgs.gov
Director (Acting) **Kyle W. Blasch** . . . . (208) 387-1321
Education: MIT 1994 BS, 1994 MS; Arizona PhD
Budget Analyst **Diana J. Knapek** . . . . (208) 387-1397
E-mail: dianaj@usgs.gov
Associate Director, Scientific Investigations **Gregory M. Clark** . . . . (208) 387-1300
Education: Southern Illinois 1985 BS; Colorado State 1988 MS
Procurement **Crystal Sverdsten** . . . . (208) 387-1388
E-mail: crystals@usgs.gov

Idaho Water Science Center *(continued)*
Information Technology Program Management **Chad Hicks** . . . . (208) 387-1370
E-mail: chicks@usgs.gov
Information Technology Specialist **Robert Hollis** . . . . (208) 387-1360
E-mail: rhollis@usgs.gov
Supervisory Technical Information and Reports Specialist **Tim Merrick** . . . . (208) 387-1305
E-mail: trmerrick@usgs.gov

Northern Rocky Mountain Science Center (NOROCK)
2327 University Way, Suite Two, Bozeman, MT 59715
Tel: (406) 994-5304 Fax: (406) 994-6556 Internet: www.nrmsc.usgs.gov
Director **Jeffrey L. "Jeff" Kershner** . . . . (406) 994-5304

Oregon Water Science Center
2130 SW 5th Avenue, Portland, OR 97201
Tel: (503) 251-3200 Fax: (503) 251-3470 E-mail: info-or@usgs.gov
Internet: http://or.water.usgs.gov
Director **James D. Crammond** . . . . (503) 251-3204
Associate Director **(Vacant)** . . . . (503) 251-3200
Hydrologist **Kathryn Kuivila** . . . . (503) 251-3257
Hydrologist **Anthony J. Tesoriero** . . . . (503) 251-3202
Education: SUNY (Buffalo) BA; Arizona State MS; Oregon Graduate PhD

Administrative Services Section
Administrative Officer **Gary M. Yerks** . . . . (503) 251-3210
E-mail: gyerks@usgs.gov
Budget Analyst **Joseph P. Jenkins** . . . . (503) 251-3256
E-mail: jjenkins@usgs.gov
Financial Specialist **Andrew L. Kerslake** . . . . (503) 251-3253
Management Analyst **Matthew D. Dale** . . . . (503) 251-3292

Hydrologic Data Section
Supervisory Hydrologist and Data Chief **Keith Overton** . . . . (503) 251-3246

Information Section
Supervisory Hydrologist **John S. Williams** . . . . (503) 251-3220
Hydrologist, National Water Quality Program **Leonard L. Orzol** . . . . (503) 251-3270
Education: Portland State BS, MS
Hydrologist, Outreach **Steven Sobieszczyk** . . . . (503) 251-3208
Education: Wisconsin (Oshkosh) BS; Portland State MS
Information Technology Specialist, National Water Quality Program **Kenneth A. Skach** . . . . (503) 251-3285
E-mail: kaskach@usgs.gov

Studies Section
Supervisory Hydrologist **Terrence Conlon** . . . . (503) 251-3232

Medford Field Office
4890 North Runway Drive, Medford, OR 97502
Tel: (541) 776-4256 Fax: (541) 776-4257
Supervisory Hydrologic Technician and Field Office Chief **Frank S. Johnson** . . . . (541) 776-4283
4890 North Runway Drive, Central Point, Central Point, OR 97502 Fax: (541) 776-4257
Hydrologic Technician **Bryan Coorlim** . . . . (541) 776-4282
Hydrologic Technician **Thomas P. Craig** . . . . (541) 776-4281
Hydrologic Technician **Timothy L. Dalrymple** . . . . (541) 776-4281
Hydrologic Technician **Kent Doughty** . . . . (541) 776-4280
Hydrologic Technician **Tyler C. Kappen** . . . . (541) 776-4259
Hydrologic Technician **Christopher McWhorter** . . . . (541) 776-4280
Hydrologic Technician **Mark D. Schuster** . . . . (541) 776-4279
Hydrologic Technician **Randy M. Spitzer** . . . . (541) 776-4282
Hydrologic Technician **John T. Swiecichowski** . . . . (541) 776-4256

Portland Field Office
Supervisory Hydrologic Technician **Roy Wellman** . . . . (503) 251-3295
Cartographer, Scientific Publishing Network **Jacqueline C. Olson** . . . . (503) 251-3268

★ Presidential Appointment Requiring Senate Confirmation ☆ Presidential Appointment □ Schedule C Appointment ◇ Career Senior Foreign Service Appointment
● Career Senior Executive Service (SES) Appointment ○ Non-Career Senior Executive Service (SES) Appointment ■ Postal Career Executive Service

Portland Field Office *(continued)*

Hydrologist and Regional Safety Officer
Fred W. Simonds .... (503) 251-3262
E-mail: wsimonds@usgs.gov
Hydrologist, Geology, Minerals, Energy and Geophysics Science Center **Charles Cannon** .... (503) 251-3273
Education: Portland State 2008 BS
Hydrologic Technician **Amarys Acosta** .... (503) 251-3265
Hydrologic Technician **Sylas Daughtrey** .... (503) 251-3235
Hydrologic Technician **Lori L. Fischer** .... (503) 251-3275
Hydrologic Technician **Peter Koestner** .... (503) 251-3261
Hydrologic Technician **Dale A. Melton** .... (503) 251-3214
Hydrologic Technician **Gregory W. Olsen** .... (503) 251-3267
Hydrologic Technician **Matthew J. Smith** .... (503) 251-3211

Washington Water Science Center
934 Broadway, Suite 300, Tacoma, WA 98402
Tel: (253) 552-1600 Fax: (253) 552-1581 E-mail: dc_wa@usgs.gov
Internet: http://wa.water.usgs.gov
Center Director **Cynthia "Cindi" Barton** .... (253) 552-1602

Western Fisheries Research Center (WFRC)
6505 NE 65th Street, Seattle, WA 98115-5016
Tel: (206) 526-6282 Fax: (206) 526-6654 Internet: http://wfrc.usgs.gov
Center Director **Jill Rolland** .... (206) 526-6291
E-mail: jrolland@usgs.gov

Columbia River Research Laboratory (CRRL)
5501- A Cook - Underwood Road, Cook, WA 98605-9717
Tel: (509) 538-2299 Fax: (509) 538-2843
Laboratory Director **Stephen M. "Steve" Waste** .... (509) 538-2936
E-mail: swaste@usgs.gov

Klamath Falls Field Station (OR) (KFFS)
2795 Anderson Avenue, Suite 106, Klamath Falls, OR 97603
Tel: (541) 273-8689 Fax: (541) 273-8692
Field Station Leader **Eric Janney** .... (541) 273-8689 ext. 202

Marrowstone Marine Field Station (MMFS)
616 Marrowstone Point Road, Nordland, WA 98358
Tel: (360) 385-1007 Fax: (360) 385-7207
Field Station Leader **Paul Hershberger** .... (360) 385-1007 ext. 225

Wyoming-Montana Water Science Center
3162 Bozeman Avenue, Helena, MT 59601 (Helena Office)
521 Progress Circle, Suite Six, Cheyenne, WY 82007 (Cheyenne Office)
Tel: (406) 457-5900 (Helena Office)
Tel: (307) 778-2931 (Cheyenne Office)
Fax: (406) 457-5990 (Helena Office)
Fax: (307) 778-2764 (Cheyenne Office) E-mail: dc_wy@usgs.gov
Internet: http://wy.water.usgs.gov
Director **John M. Kilpatrick** .... (406) 457-5902

Pacific Regional Area Director Office

Placer Hall, 6000 J Street, Suite 5000, Sacramento, CA 95819-6129
Tel: (916) 278-9551 Fax: (916) 278-9546
Areas Covered: CA, GU, HI, NV
Regional Director **Mark K. Sogge** .... (916) 278-9551
Education: San José State; UC Davis
Executive Assistant **Rachel A. Sackett** .... (916) 278-9551
Deputy Regional Director **Jane A. Reid** .... (831) 460-7402
E-mail: jareid@usgs.gov
Associate Regional Director **Darrin M. Thome** .... (916) 278-9561
Regional Hazards Coordinator **Dale A. Cox** .... (916) 997-4209
E-mail: dacox@usgs.gov
Regional Management Officer **Rona Y. Peters** .... (916) 278-9558
E-mail: rypeters@usgs.gov
Program Officer **(Vacant)** .... (916) 278-9559
Administrative Officer **(Vacant)** .... (916) 278-9368

California Water Science Center
Placer Hall, 6000 J Street, Sacramento, CA 95819-6129
Tel: (916) 278-3000 Fax: (916) 278-3070 E-mail: dc_ca@usgs.gov
Internet: http://ca.water.usgs.gov
Director **Eric G. Reichard** .... (619) 225-6134
4165 Spruance Road, Suite 200, San Diego, CA 92101
Deputy Director **Mary H. Johannis** .... (916) 278-3097
Associate Director of Data **Dianna Crilley** .... (619) 225-6150
Education: Maine (Farmington) BS; Temple 2004 MS
Associate Director of Projects **Anke Mueller-Solger** ..... (916) 278-3198
Administrative Officer **Glenn A. Henz** .... (916) 278-3101
E-mail: ghenz@usgs.gov
Safety Officer **Stephen T. Schmitt** .... (916) 278-3253
Science Communications **Laurel Rogers** .... (619) 225-6104

Geology, Minerals, Energy, and Geophysics Science Center (GMEG)
345 Middlefield Road, Menlo Park, CA 94025-3561
Fax: (650) 329-4936 Internet: http://geomaps.wr.usgs.gov/gmeg/
Director **Colin Williams** .... (650) 329-4881
E-mail: colin@usgs.gov

Nevada Water Science Center (NWSC)
2730 North Deer Run Road, Room 203, Carson City, NV 89701
Tel: (775) 887-7600 Fax: (775) 887-7629 E-mail: dc_nv@usgs.gov
Internet: http://nevada.usgs.gov
Director **David L. Berger** .... (775) 887-7658
Administrative Officer **Stacy Masters** .... (775) 887-7657
E-mail: smasters@usgs.gov
Center Data Chief **Steven Berris** .... (775) 887-7693
E-mail: snberris@usgs.gov
Hydrologic Technician **Todd Geiger** .... (702) 564-4510
Hydrologic Technician **Bryce Redinger** .... (775) 887-7751
Hydrologic Technician **Breann Roerick** .... (808) 690-9569
Hydrologist **Nora C. Nelson** .... (702) 564-4611
Information Technology Specialist **Jerome Hunter** ...... (702) 564-4522
E-mail: jhunter@usgs.gov
Information Technology Specialist **Stuart Wilson** .... (775) 887-7608
E-mail: swwilson@usgs.gov
National Watershed Boundary Dataset Team Lead
Susan Buto .... (775) 887-7663
Program Analyst **Lacey Triplett** .... (702) 564-4546

Pacific Coastal and Marine Science Center (PCMSC)
2885 Mission Street, Santa Cruz, CA 95060
Tel: (831) 427-4450 Fax: (831) 427-4709
Internet: http://walrus.wr.usgs.gov/
Center Director and Chief Scientist **Guy Gelfenbaum** .... (831) 460-7417
E-mail: ggelfenbaum@usgs.gov
Education: Wisconsin BS; U Washington PhD
Deputy Director (Acting) **Nadine Golden** .... (831) 460-7530
E-mail: ngolden@usgs.gov
Assistant Deputy Director **Susan "Susie" Cochran** ..... (831) 460-7545
E-mail: scochran@usgs.gov
Administrative Officer **Paulette Zamora** .... (831) 460-7431
E-mail: pzamora@usgs.gov
Marine Facility Superintendent (Acting) **Tim Elfers** ...... (831) 460-7479

Pacific Island Ecosystems Research Center (PIERC)
Building 176, 1845 Wasp Boulevard, Honolulu, HI 96818
Tel: (808) 690-9604 Fax: (808) 690-9599
Internet: www.usgs.gov/centers/pierc
Center Director **Gordon W. Tribble PhD** .... (808) 985-6457
Building 344, Chain of Craters Road, Hawaii National Park, HI 96718
E-mail: gtribble@usgs.gov
Education: UC Santa Barbara 1979 BS; Hawaii 1990 PhD
Budget Analyst **Debbie Cobb** .... (808) 587-7453
E-mail: dcobb@usgs.gov
Education: Hawaii 1996 BS

DEPARTMENTS

★ Presidential Appointment Requiring Senate Confirmation ☆ Presidential Appointment □ Schedule C Appointment ◇ Career Senior Foreign Service Appointment
● Career Senior Executive Service (SES) Appointment ○ Non-Career Senior Executive Service (SES) Appointment ■ Postal Career Executive Service

Haleakala Field Station
P.O. Box 246, Makawao, HI 96768
Tel: (808) 572-4470 Fax: (808) 572-1304

Program Field Leader **Dr. Steve Hess** . . . . (808) 985-6410
E-mail: shess@usgs.gov
Education: Florida State 1987 BS; Montana 1995 MS; Montana State 2002 PhD

Kilauea Field Station
Building 344, Chain of Craters Road, Hawaii National Park, HI 96718
Tel: (808) 985-6410 Fax: (808) 967-8568

Station Leader and Wildlife Biologist **Dr. Steve Hess** . . . . (808) 985-6410
E-mail: shess@usgs.gov
Education: Florida State 1987 BS; Montana 1995 MS; Montana State 2002 PhD

Biologist **Dr. Jim Jacobi** . . . . (808) 985-6411
E-mail: jjacobi@usgs.gov
Education: UC Riverside 1970 BS; Hawaii 1990 PhD

Botanist **Stephanie Yelenik** . . . . (808) 967-7396 ext. 6440
E-mail: syelenik@usgs.gov
Education: UC Berkeley 1997 BA; U Cape Town (S Africa) 2000 MSc; UC Santa Barbara 2009 PhD

Ecologist **Dr. Dennis LaPointe** . . . . (808) 985-6413
E-mail: dlapointe@usgs.gov
Education: UMass (Amherst) 1978 BS, 1982 MS, 2000 PhD

Ecologist **(Vacant)** . . . . (808) 985-6410

Microbiologist **Dr. Carter Atkinson** . . . . (808) 985-6401
E-mail: catkinson@usgs.gov
Education: Dickinson Col 1976 BS; LSU Health Sciences Ctr 1981 MS; Florida 1985 PhD

Wildlife Biologist **Dr. Paul Banko** . . . . (808) 967-7396 ext. 235
E-mail: pbanko@usgs.gov
Education: U Washington 1972 BS, 1988 PhD

Wildlife Biologist **Dr. Michelle Reynolds** . . . . (808) 985-6416
E-mail: mreynolds@usgs.gov
Education: Virginia Tech BS; Old Dominion MSc; Virginia Tech 2003 PhD

Pacific Islands Water Science Center
Inouye Regional Center Building 176,
1845 Wasp Boulevard, Honolulu, HI 96818
Tel: (808) 690-9600 Fax: (808) 690-9599
Internet: http://hi.water.usgs.gov
Areas Covered: HI and Western Pacific

Center Director **Stephen S. "Steve" Anthony** . . . . (808) 690-9600

Western Ecological Research Center (WERC)
Modoc Hall, 3020 State University Drive East,
Room 3006, Sacramento, CA 95819
Tel: (916) 278-9485 Fax: (916) 278-9475 Internet: www.werc.usgs.gov

Director **A. Keith Miles** . . . . (916) 278-9572
Education: Howard U 1972 BS; Oregon State 1976 MS, 1987 PhD

Western Geographic Science Center (WGSC)
345 Middlefield Road, MS 531, Menlo Park, CA 94025
Fax: (650) 329-4249

Director **Susan Benjamin** . . . . (650) 329-5049
E-mail: sbenjamin@usgs.gov
Education: San José State 1983 BA, 1988 MA

Southwest Area Regional Director Office
Denver Federal Center, Denver, CO 80225
Mail: P.O. Box 25046, Mail Stop 911, Denver, CO 80225
Tel: (303) 236-5438 Fax: (303) 236-5448
Areas Covered: AZ, CO, KS, OK, NM, TX, UT

● Regional Director (Acting) **William R. Guertal** . . . . (703) 648-5060
E-mail: wguertal@usgs.gov
Education: Ohio State 1983 BS, 1987 MS; North Carolina State 1992 PhD

Deputy Regional Director for Operations **Peter Griffiths** . . . . (303) 236-5023

Deputy Regional Director for Science **(Vacant)** . . . . (303) 236-6484

Regional Management Officer **Eric F. Hensel** . . . . (303) 236-5435
E-mail: efhensel@usgs.gov

Arizona Water Science Center
520 North Park Avenue, Suite 221, Tucson, AZ 85719
Tel: (520) 670-6671 Fax: (520) 670-5592 E-mail: dc_az@usgs.gov
Internet: http://az.water.usgs.gov

Director **James M. Leenhouts** . . . . (520) 670-6671 ext. 278
Education: Oberlin 1990 BA; Arizona 1994 MS, 2000 PhD

Astrogeology Science Center
2255 North Gemini Drive, Flagstaff, AZ 86001
Tel: (928) 556-7011 Fax: (928) 556-7014
Internet: http://astrogeology.usgs.gov/

Chief Scientist **Laszlo P. Kestay** . . . . (928) 556-7002
E-mail: laz@usgs.gov
Education: Texas 1988 BS; Caltech 1993 MS, 1994 PhD

Central Energy Resources Science Center (CERSC)
25046 Mail Stop 939, Denver, CO 80225
Tel: (303) 236-1647 Fax: (303) 236-5888

Director **(Vacant)** . . . . (303) 236-1647
Denver Federal Center, Box 25046, MS 939, Denver, CO 80225

Associate Director **David A. Ferderer** . . . . (303) 236-3611
Denver Federal Center, Box 25046, MS 939, Denver, CO 80225
E-mail: dferdere@usgs.gov

Lead Scientist **Susan M. Hall** . . . . (303) 236-1656
E-mail: susanhall@usgs.gov

Administrative Assistant **Mirian J. Cuara** . . . . (303) 236-1647
E-mail: mcuara@usgs.gov

Central Mineral Environmental Resources Science Center
25046 Mail Stop 973, Denver, CO 80225
Tel: (303) 236-1800 Fax: (303) 236-1811

Director (Acting) **Warren C. Day** . . . . (303) 236-1800
Denver Federal Center, Box 25046, MS 973, Denver, CO 80225

Administrative Officer **Jennifer George** . . . . (303) 236-1823
Denver Federal Center, Box 25046, MS 973, Denver, CO 80225

Colorado Water Science Center (CWSC)
Building 53, Denver Federal Center, Sixth Avenue and Kipling Street, Denver, CO 80225-0046
Box 25046, MS 415, Lakewood, CO 80225-0046
Tel: (303) 236-6900 Fax: (303) 236-4912 Internet: co.water.usgs.gov

Director **David P. Mau** . . . . (303) 236-6900

Crustal Geophysics and Geochemistry Science Center
25046 Mail Stop 964, Denver, CO 80225-0046
Fax: (303) 236-1229

Director (Acting) **Allison Shipp** . . . . (573) 876-1888
Denver Federal Center, Box 25046, MS 964, Denver, CO 80225

Characterization Branch Chief **Ruth E. Wolf** . . . . (303) 236-2470
Denver Federal Center, Box 25046, MS 973, Denver, CO 80225

Administrative Officer (Acting) **Jennifer George** . . . . (303) 236-5451
Box 25046, Denver, CO 80225

Imaging Branch Chief **Michael H. Powers** . . . . (303) 236-1349
Box 25046, Denver, CO 80225

Fort Collins Science Center (FCSC)
2150 Centre Avenue, Building C, Fort Collins, CO 80526-8118
Tel: (970) 226-9100 Fax: (970) 226-9230
Internet: https://www.usgs.gov/centers/fort

Center Director **Sharon K. Taylor PhD** . . . . (970) 226-9238

Aquatic Systems Branch (AS)
2150 Centre Avenue, Building C, Fort Collins, CO 80526-8118

Branch Chief **Quan Dong** . . . . (970) 226-9175

Ecosystem Dynamics Branch
2150 Centre Avenue, Building C, Fort Collins, CO 80526-8118
Tel: (970) 226-9218 Fax: (970) 226-9230

Branch Chief **Zachary "Zack" Bowen** . . . . (970) 226-9218
Education: North Alabama PhD

★ Presidential Appointment Requiring Senate Confirmation ☆ Presidential Appointment ☐ Schedule C Appointment ◇ Career Senior Foreign Service Appointment
● Career Senior Executive Service (SES) Appointment ○ Non-Career Senior Executive Service (SES) Appointment ■ Postal Career Executive Service

Information Science Branch (IS)
2150 Centre Avenue, Building C, Fort Collins, CO 80526-8118
Tel: (970) 226-9366 Fax: (970) 226-9230

Branch Chief **Tim Kern** .... (970) 226-9366
E-mail: kernt@usgs.gov

Invasive Species Science Branch (ISS)
2150 Centre Avenue, Building C, Fort Collins, CO 80526-8118
Tel: (970) 226-9144 Fax: (970) 226-9230

Branch Chief **Robert "Bob" Reed** .... (970) 226-9464

Social and Economic Analysis Branch
2150 Centre Avenue, Building C, Fort Collins, CO 80526-8118
Tel: (970) 226-9314 Fax: (970) 226-9230

Branch Chief **Rudolph "Rudy" Schuster** .... (970) 226-9165

Trust Species and Habitats Branch (TSH)
2150 Centre Avenue, Building C, Fort Collins, CO 80526-8118
Tel: (970) 226-9499 Fax: (970) 226-9230

Branch Chief **Patricia "Patty" Stevens** .... (970) 226-9499
E-mail: stevensp@usgs.gov
Education: Colorado State MS

Geosciences and Environmental Change Science Center (GECSC)
P.O. Box 25046, Mail Stop 201, Denver, CO 80225
Tel: (303) 236-5345 Fax: (303) 236-5690 Internet: http://esp.cr.usgs.gov

Director **Eugene "Buddy" Schweig III** .... (303) 236-5344
Denver Federal Center, Box 25046, MS 980, Denver, CO 80225
E-mail: schweig@usgs.gov
Education: Missouri 1976 BS; Stanford 1983 MS, 1985 PhD

Kansas Water Science Center
1217 Biltmore Drive, Lawrence, KS 66049
Tel: (785) 760-0187 Fax: (785) 832-3500
Internet: http://ks.water.usgs.gov

Director **Andrew Ziegler** .... (785) 832-3539
Administrative Officer **Victoria P. Lewis** .... (785) 832-3510
E-mail: vmerrill@usgs.gov
Information Technology Specialist **Jeff Miller** .... (785) 832-3552
E-mail: jlmiller@usgs.gov
Public Affairs Coordinator **(Vacant)** .... (785) 832-3570
Supervisory Hydrologist **(Vacant)** .... (785) 832-3516

New Mexico Water Science Center (NMWSC)
6700 Edith Boulevard, NE, Albuquerque, NM 87113
Tel: (505) 830-7900 Fax: (505) 830-7998 Internet: nm.water.usgs.gov

Director **Johnathan R. "John" Bumgarner** .... (505) 830-7901

Oklahoma Water Science Center
202 NW 66th Street, Building 7, Oklahoma City, OK 73116
Tel: (405) 810-4400 Fax: (405) 843-7712 E-mail: dc_ok@usgs.gov
Internet: http://ok.water.usgs.gov

Director (Acting) **Jason M. Lewis** .... (405) 810-4404

Southwest Biological Science Center
2255 North Gemini Drive, MS-9394, Flagstaff, AZ 86001
Tel: (928) 556-7094 Fax: (928) 556-7092 Internet: sbsc.wr.usgs.gov
Areas Covered: Colorado River from Lake Powell to Upper Lake Mead, AZ; Colorado Plateau in CO/UT/AZ/NM; Sonoran Desert in AZ/Northern Mexico/UT

Center Director **David E. Lytle PhD** .... (928) 556-7094
Education: Macalester BA; Maine MS; Minnesota PhD
Deputy Center Director **Theodore S. Melis PhD** .... (928) 556-7282
Secretary **Serena Mankiller** .... (928) 556-7094
E-mail: smankiller@usgs.gov
Administrative Officer **Chris Schill** .... (928) 556-7093
E-mail: cschill@usgs.gov
Chief Information Officer **Devon Ambler** .... (928) 556-7383
E-mail: dambler@usgs.gov
Dryland Ecosystem Branch Chief **Jayne Belnap PhD** .... (435) 719-2331
2290 Southwest Resource Boulevard, Moab, UT 84532
Education: UC Santa Cruz 1980 BS; Stanford 1983 MS; BYU 1991 PhD

Southwest Biological Science Center *(continued)*

River Research and Restoration Branch Chief
Scott P. VanderKooi .... (928) 556-7094
Education: Oregon State 1991 BS, 1999 MS
Information Technology Program Manager **Rian Bogle** . . . (928) 556-7212
E-mail: rbogle@usgs.gov
Public Outreach Coordinator **Todd Wojtowicz** .... (928) 556-7390
E-mail: twojtowicz@usgs.gov
Webmaster **Todd Wojtowicz** .... (928) 556-7390
E-mail: twojtowicz@usgs.gov

Texas Water Science Center
501 West Felix Street, Fort Worth, TX 76115
Tel: (512) 927-3500 Fax: (512) 927-3590 Internet: http://tx.usgs.gov

Director **Timothy H. "Tim" Raines** .... (817) 263-9545 ext. 201

Utah Water Science Center
2329 West Orton Circle, Salt Lake City, UT 84119
Tel: (801) 908-5000 Fax: (801) 908-5001 E-mail: dc_ut@usgs.gov
Internet: http://ut.water.usgs.gov

Director **Cory Angeroth** .... (801) 908-5048

Southeast Regional Director Office

1770 Corporate Drive, Suite 500, Norcross, GA 30093
Tel: (678) 924-6700
Areas Covered: AL, AR, FL, GA, LA, MS, NC, PR, SC, TN, VI,

Regional Director **Holly S. Weyers** .... (678) 924-6609
Deputy Regional Director for Operations
Marjorie S. "Marge" Davenport .... (678) 924-6608
Deputy Regional Director for Science
James E. "Jim" Stefanov .... (573) 514-4281
4200 New Haven Road, Columbia, MO 65201-9634
Education: Illinois State 1982 BS; Fort Hays State 1985 MSc
Everglades Study Unit Coordinator
Nicholas G. Aumen .... (954) 377-5917
3205 College Avenue, Fort Lauderdale, FL 33314
E-mail: naumen@usgs.gov
Regional Management Officer **Kim Crutchfield** .... (803) 750-6123
720 Gracern Road, Columbia, SC 29210
E-mail: kcrutch@usgs.gov
Science Advisor for Programs **Holly S. Weyers** .... (703) 715-7020
Science Advisor for the Gulf Coast
Gregory "Greg" Steyer .... (225) 578-7201
Education: Maryland 1985 BS; Louisiana (Lafayette) 1988 MS; LSU 2008 PhD

Alabama Water Science Center
75 TechnaCenter Drive, Montgomery, AL 36117
Tel: (334) 395-4120 Fax: (534) 395-4168
Internet: http://al.water.usgs.gov

Director **Athena P. Clark** .... (334) 395-4141
Education: Alabama 1986 BS; Auburn 1990 MS, 1992 BS

Arkansas Water Science Center
401 Hardin Road, Little Rock, AR 72211
Tel: (501) 228-3600 Fax: (501) 228-3601
Internet: http://ar.water.usgs.gov

Director **W. Scott Gain** .... (601) 933-2900

Caribbean Water Science Center
GSA Center, 651 Federal Drive, Suite 400-15, Guaynabo, PR 00965-5703
Tel: (787) 749-7400 Fax: (787) 749-7401
Internet: http://pr.water.usgs.gov

Director **David M. Sumner** .... (813) 498-5025
E-mail: dmsumner@usgs.gov

Caribbean Florida Water Science Center
12703 Research Parkway, Orlando, FL 32826
Tel: (407) 803-5500 Fax: (407) 803-5501
Internet: http://fl.water.usgs.gov/

Director **David M. Sumner** .... (813) 498-5025

★ Presidential Appointment Requiring Senate Confirmation ☆ Presidential Appointment ☐ Schedule C Appointment ◇ Career Senior Foreign Service Appointment
● Career Senior Executive Service (SES) Appointment ○ Non-Career Senior Executive Service (SES) Appointment ■ Postal Career Executive Service

DEPARTMENTS

Florida Water Science Center
4446 Pet Lane, Suite 108, Lutz, FL 33559
Tel: (813) 498-5000 Fax: (813) 498-5002
Internet: http://fl.water.usgs.gov/
Director **David M. Sumner** .... (813) 498-5025

St. Petersburg (FL) Coastal and Marine Science Center (SPCMSC)
600 Fourth Street South, St. Petersburg, FL 33701
Tel: (727) 502-8000 Fax: (727) 502-8001
Internet: http://coastal.er.usgs.gov/
Center Director (Acting) **Dianna Hogan** .... (703) 648-7240
Deputy for Operations **Christopher "Chris" Reich** ...... (727) 502-8032
Deputy for Science (Acting) **Nathaniel Plant** .... (727) 502-8072

South Atlantic Water Science Center - Georgia
1770 Corporate Drive, Norcross, GA 30093
Tel: (678) 924-6700 Fax: (678) 924-6710
Internet: http://ga.water.usgs.gov
Associate Director **John M. Shelton** .... (803) 750-6112
Fax: (803) 750-6181

Louisiana Water Science Center
3535 South Sherwood Forest Boulevard, Suite 120,
Baton Rouge, LA 70816
Tel: (225) 298-5481 Fax: (225) 298-5490
Internet: http://la.water.usgs.gov
Director **W. Scott Gain** .... (225) 298-5481
Assistant Director for Investigations
John Lovelace .... (225) 298-5481 ext. 3210
Baton Rouge Field Headquarters Supervisor
Hydrologic Technician **Garron Ross** .... (225) 298-5481 ext. 3225
E-mail: gbross@usgs.gov
Computer Services Section Supervisor
Scott H. Beddingfield .... (225) 298-5481 ext. 3224
E-mail: sbedding@usgs.gov
Database Management/Quality Assurance
Unit Supervisor Hydrologic Technician
David Walters .... (225) 298-5481 ext. 3120
E-mail: djwalter@usgs.gov
Supervisory Hydrologist
Dennis K. Demcheck .... (225) 298-5481 ext. 3214
Supervisor Hydrologist - Ruston Field Office
Benton McGee .... (318) 251-9630 ext. 19
3095 West California Avenue, Ruston, LA 71270
E-mail: bdmcgee@usgs.gov
Surface Water Specialist **Michael S. Runner** .... (601) 933-2941
Water Quality Services Unit Supervisor
Hydrologist **Cheryl R. Joseph** .... (225) 298-5481 ext. 3133

Mississippi Water Science Center
308 South Airport Road, Pearl, MS 39208-6649
Tel: (601) 933-2900 Fax: (601) 933-2901
Internet: http://ms.water.usgs.gov
Director **W. Scott Gain** .... (601) 933-2900
Hydrologic Data Section Chief **Michael S. Runner** ...... (601) 933-2941
Administrative Operations Assistant **Amanda Jackson** ... (601) 933-2914
E-mail: adavis@usgs.gov

Wetland and Aquatic Research Center (WARC)
7920 Northwest 71st Street, Gainesville, FL 32653
Tel: (352) 378-8181 Fax: (352) 378-4956
Director **Kenneth G. "Ken" Rice** .... (352) 264-3544
Education: North Carolina State 1986 BS; Florida 1992 MS, 1996 PhD
Deputy Director **(Vacant)** .... (352) 378-8181
Center Management Officer **Melissa Chavis** .... (337) 266-8804
3535 South Sherwood Forest Boulevard, Baton Rouge, LA 70816
E-mail: machavis@usgs.gov
Coastal Restoration Assessment Branch Chief
Tomma Barnes .... (337) 266-8520
Baton Rouge, LA 70803
Forest Ecology Branch Chief **Scott A. Wilson** .... (337) 266-8644
700 Cajundome Boulevard, Lafayette, LA 70506
E-mail: wilsons@usgs.gov
Education: New Orleans 1990 BS; Louisiana (Lafayette) 2001 MS, 2006 PhD

Wetland and Aquatic Research Center *(continued)*
Imperiled and Invasive Aquatic Species Branch Chief
Deborah Epperson PhD .... (352) 264-3515
700 Cajundome Boulevard, Lafayette, LA 70506
E-mail: depperson@usgs.gov
Spatial Analysis Branch Chief **Scott A. Wilson** .... (337) 266-8644
700 Cajundome Boulevard, Lafayette, LA 70506
Education: New Orleans 1990 BS; Louisiana (Lafayette) 2001 MS, 2006 PhD
Wetlands Ecology Branch Chief **Scott A. Wilson** .... (337) 266-8644
700 Cajundome Boulevard, Lafayette, LA 70506
E-mail: wilsons@usgs.gov
Education: New Orleans 1990 BS; Louisiana (Lafayette) 2001 MS, 2006 PhD
Contracting Officer **Sheryl Carriere** .... (337) 266-8521
700 Cajundome Boulevard, Lafayette, LA 70506
E-mail: carrieres@usgs.gov
Information Technology Specialist **George Ravain** .... (337) 266-8688
700 Cajundome Boulevard, Lafayette, LA 70506
E-mail: ravain@usgs.gov

South Atlantic Water Science Center - North Carolina
3916 Sunset Ridge Road, Raleigh, NC 27607
Tel: (919) 571-4000 Fax: (919) 571-4041
Internet: http://nc.water.usgs.gov
Director **Eric W. Strom** .... (803) 750-6109
720 Gracern Road, Columbia, SC 29210

South Atlantic Water Science Center - South Carolina
720 Gracern Road, Suite 129, Columbia, SC 29210-7651
Tel: (803) 750-6100 Fax: (803) 750-6181
Internet: http://sc.water.usgs.gov
Director **Eric W. Strom** .... (803) 750-6109

Tennessee Water Science Center
640 Grassmere Park, Suite 100, Nashville, TN 37211
Tel: (615) 837-4700 Fax: (615) 837-4799
Internet: http://tn.water.usgs.gov
Director **W. Scott Gain** .... (615) 837-4701
Assistant Director **Michael W. Bradley** .... (615) 837-4703
Assistant Director **Shannon D. Williams** .... (615) 837-4755
Assistant Director **William J. Wolfe** .... (615) 837-4756
Administrative Officer **Sheila C. Bernard** .... (615) 837-4710
E-mail: sbernard@usgs.gov

Bureau of Reclamation (USBR)
1849 C Street, NW, Washington, DC 20240
Tel: (202) 513-0501 Fax: (202) 513-0309 Internet: www.usbr.gov

Operations
1849 C Street, NW, Washington, DC 20240
Fax: (202) 513-0319

Regional Offices

Great Plains Regional Office
Federal Office Building, 2021 4th Avenue North, Billings, MT 59101
P.O. Box 36900, Billings, MT 59107-6900
Tel: (406) 247-7600 Fax: (406) 247-7604 Internet: www.usbr.gov/gp
Areas Covered: Eastern CO, KS, MT, NE, ND, OK, SD, TX, WY
● Regional Director **Michael S. "Mike" Black** .... (406) 247-7600
E-mail: mblack@usbr.gov
Education: South Dakota Mines 1986 BSME
Executive Assistant **Terri Currid** .... (406) 247-7111
E-mail: tcurrid@usbr.gov
Deputy Regional Director **Christopher Beardsley** .... (406) 247-7600
Education: James Madison BBA
Secretary **Julie Bohm** .... (406) 247-7601
Deputy Regional Director **John F. Soucy** .... (406) 247-7600
Human Resources Manager **Joan Berlinger** .... (406) 247-7600
E-mail: jberlinger@usbr.gov

★ Presidential Appointment Requiring Senate Confirmation ☆ Presidential Appointment □ Schedule C Appointment ◇ Career Senior Foreign Service Appointment
● Career Senior Executive Service (SES) Appointment ○ Non-Career Senior Executive Service (SES) Appointment ■ Postal Career Executive Service

Great Plains Regional Office *(continued)*

Regional Chief Information Officer
Maureen D. Wambeke .... (406) 247-7600
E-mail: mwambeke@usbr.gov
Education: Montana State (Billings) 1991 BSBA
Supervisory Public Affairs Specialist
Tyler A. Johnson .... (406) 247-7609
E-mail: tjohnson@usbr.gov
Education: Montana State BS
Special Agent **Ian Canaan** .... (406) 247-7600
E-mail: icanaan@usbr.gov

Dakotas Area Office
304 East Broadway, Bismarck, ND 58501
P.O. Box 1017, Bismarck, ND 58502
Tel: (701) 250-4242 Fax: (701) 250-4326

Area Manager **Arden Freitag** .... (701) 250-4242
Computer Specialist **Rod Wanner** .... (701) 221-1241
E-mail: rwanner@usbr.gov

Pierre (SD) Field Office
810 West Fifth Street, Pierre, SD 57501
Tel: (605) 945-2980 Fax: (605) 945-2969

Engineer **(Vacant)** .... (605) 945-2980 ext. 3003
Civil Engineer **Stacy Froelich** .... (605) 945-2980 ext. 3004
Civil Engineer/Technician **(Vacant)** .... (605) 945-2980
Civil Engineer/Technician **(Vacant)** .... (605) 945-2980
Industrial Water Specialist **Nolan Orr** .... (605) 945-2980 ext. 3007
Secretary **Lori R. Olson** .... (605) 945-2980 ext. 3001
E-mail: lolson@usbr.gov

Eastern Colorado Area Office
11056 West County Road 18E, Loveland, CO 80537-9711
Tel: (970) 962-4410 Fax: (970) 663-3212

Area Manager **Signe Snortland** .... (970) 962-4410
Deputy Area Manager **Monica Griffett** .... (970) 962-4410

Montana Area Office
Jameson Building, 2900 Fourth Avenue, North, Suite 501, Billings, MT 59101
P.O. Box 30137, Billings, MT 59107-0137
Tel: (406) 247-7298 Fax: (406) 247-7338

Area Manager **Steve Davies** .... (406) 247-7298
Computer Specialist **Catherine "Cathy" Ames** .... (406) 247-7328
E-mail: cames@usbr.gov

Nebraska - Kansas Area Office
1706 West Third Street, R.R. 1, McCook, NE 69001
P.O. Box 1607, Grand Island, NE 68802-1607
Tel: (308) 345-4400 Fax: (308) 346-6470
Internet: https://www.usbr.gov/gp/nkao

Area Manager **Aaron Thompson** .... (308) 345-1027
Administrative Officer **(Vacant)** .... (308) 389-4400
Purchasing Agent **Todd Wagner** .... (308) 345-4400
E-mail: twagner@usbr.gov
Information Technology Specialist **Jeffrey Almosara** .... (308) 389-4622
E-mail: jalmosara@usbr.gov

Oklahoma - Texas Area Office
5316 Highway 290 West, Suite 110, Austin, TX 78735-8931
Tel: (512) 899-4150 Fax: (512) 899-4179

Area Manager **Mark A. Trevino** .... (512) 899-4150
E-mail: mtrevino@usbr.gov
Administrative Officer **Kimberley Parish** .... (512) 899-4165
E-mail: kparish@usbr.gov

Austin (TX) Reclamation Office
5316 Highway 290 West, Suite 110, Austin, TX 78735-8931
Tel: (512) 899-4150 Fax: (512) 899-4179

Supervisory Program Coordinator **Collins Balcombe** .... (512) 899-4162
E-mail: cbalcombe@usbr.gov
Budget Analyst **Janna Fisher** .... (512) 899-4168
Environmental Projection Specialist **Trent Parish** .... (512) 899-4157

Austin (TX) Reclamation Office *(continued)*

Computer Specialist **Norma Kelvin** .... (512) 899-4177
E-mail: nkelvin@usbr.gov
Special Projects Coordinator **Thomas Michalewicz** .... (512) 899-4166
E-mail: tmichalewicz@usbr.gov
Civil Engineer **(Vacant)** .... (512) 899-4167

Oklahoma City (OK) Reclamation Office
5924 Northwest 2nd Street, Suite 200, Oklahoma City, OK 73127-6514
Tel: (405) 470-4800 Fax: (405) 470-4807

Deputy Area Manager **James Allard** .... (405) 470-4800
E-mail: jallard@usbr.gov
Geologist **(Vacant)** .... (405) 470-4800
Natural Resources Specialist **Precious Braggs** .... (405) 470-4800
Natural Resources Specialist **Meyer Jay** .... (405) 470-4800
Natural Resources Specialist **Cody McCrackin** .... (405) 470-4800
Realty Specialist **Ashley Dixson** .... (405) 470-4800
Supervisory NRS Specialist **Jeff Tompkins** .... (405) 470-4800
Repayment Specialist **Linda Temple** .... (405) 470-4800
Archaeologist **Kate Ellison** .... (405) 470-4800
Supervisory Civil Engineer
Matthew R. "Matt" Warren .... (405) 470-4800
Civil Engineer **Anna Hoag** .... (405) 470-4800
Civil Engineer **Oliver Lorenzo** .... (405) 470-4800
Civil Engineer **Goran Radinovic** .... (405) 470-4800
Civil Engineering Technician **Adam Milligan** .... (405) 470-4800
E-mail: amilligan@usbr.gov

Wyoming Area Office
705 Pendell Boulevard, Mills, WY 82644
P.O. Box 1630, Mills, WY 82644
Tel: (307) 261-5671 Fax: (307) 261-5683

Area Manager **Carlie A. Ronca** .... (307) 261-5671

Lower Colorado Regional Office
Bureau of Reclamation, Boulder City, NV 89006
P.O. Box 61470, Boulder City, NV 89006-1470
Tel: (702) 293-8000 Fax: (702) 293-8333 Internet: www.usbr.gov/lc
Areas Covered: Most of AZ, Southern CA, Southern NV, portions of NM, portions of UT

● Regional Director **Terrance J. "Terry" Fulp PhD** .... (702) 293-8401
E-mail: tfulp@usbr.gov
Education: Tulsa BS; Stanford MS; Colorado MS; Colorado Mines PhD
Deputy Regional Director **Jacklynn L. "Jaci" Gould** .... (702) 293-8411
Education: Colorado BS, MPA
Deputy Regional Director **Jennifer McCloskey** .... (702) 293-8411
Education: Arizona BA; Thunderbird International MBA
External Affairs Officer
Jeannette "Rose" Davis MPA .... (702) 293-8421
E-mail: jdavis@usbr.gov
Education: Northern Arizona 1982; Boise State 2005 MPA
Financial Management Office Director **Stacy Wade** .... (702) 293-8457
Human Resources Manager **John Cardiff** .... (702) 293-8155
Information Technology Security Manager
Tracy Callen-Young .... (702) 293-8214
E-mail: tcallen-young@usbr.gov
Public Affairs Officer **Patti Aaron** .... (702) 293-8000
E-mail: paaron@usbr.gov

Boulder Canyon Operations Office
P.O. Box 61470, Boulder City, NV 89006-1470
Tel: (702) 293-8373 Fax: (702) 293-8454

Office Chief **Steven C. Hvinden** .... (702) 293-8414
Education: North Dakota State BS, MS
Deputy Office Chief **(Vacant)** .... (702) 293-8495

Lower Colorado Dams Office
P.O. Box 60400, Boulder City, NV 89006-0400
Tel: (702) 494-2302 Fax: (702) 494-2297

Area Manager (Acting) **Terri Saumier** .... (702) 494-2822
Facility Manager (Davis) **Vincent Lammers** .... (928) 754-3626
Davis Dam, Bullhead City, AZ 86429
Facility Manager (Hoover) **Mark Cook** .... (702) 494-2301

(continued on next page)

★ Presidential Appointment Requiring Senate Confirmation ☆ Presidential Appointment □ Schedule C Appointment ◇ Career Senior Foreign Service Appointment
● Career Senior Executive Service (SES) Appointment ○ Non-Career Senior Executive Service (SES) Appointment ■ Postal Career Executive Service

DEPARTMENTS

Lower Colorado Dams Office *(continued)*

Facility Manager (Parker) **John Steffen** . . . . (760) 663-3712 ext. 329
Business Services Chief **Cristina Hayden** . . . . (702) 494-2781
Engineering Chief **(Vacant)** . . . . (702) 494-2823
Information Technology Manager **David Scott** . . . . (702) 494-2820
E-mail: dscott@usbr.gov
Maintenance Chief **Steve Valderrama** . . . . (702) 494-2282
Management Services Chief **Beth Young** . . . . (702) 494-2352
Operations Chief **Bob Vallely** . . . . (702) 293-8532
Program Assistant **Connie Hack** . . . . (702) 494-2840
E-mail: chack@usbr.gov
Property/Warehouse Services Chief **Randy Unverrich** . . . . (702) 494-2513
Safety and Occupational Health Manager
Kevin McDowell . . . . (702) 494-2359
Support Services Chief **(Vacant)** . . . . (702) 494-2302
Tour Operations Manager **(Vacant)** . . . . (702) 494-2859

Phoenix (AZ) Area Office
6150 West Thunderbird Road, Glendale, AZ 85306
Tel: (623) 773-6200 Fax: (623) 773-6485
Internet: www.usbr.gov/lc/phoenix

Area Manager **Leslie Meyers** . . . . (623) 773-6200
Fax: (623) 773-6480
Deputy Area Manager **Alexander Smith** . . . . (623) 773-6250
Financial Management Manager **Deanna Diehn** . . . . (623) 773-6220
E-mail: ddiehn@usbr.gov
Administrative Services Division Chief
Maria Quijada-Lopez . . . . (623) 773-6420
E-mail: mquijadalopez@usbr.gov
Engineering Division Chief **Jeffrey Riley** . . . . (623) 773-6430
Environmental Resource Management Division Chief
Sean Heath . . . . (623) 773-6200
Program Development Division Chief **Mary Reece** . . . . . . (623) 773-6279
Water and Lands Division Chief **Peter O. Castaneda** . . . . (623) 773-6240
Native American Affairs Office Manager
Lawrence Marquez . . . . (623) 773-6213

Yuma (AZ) Area Office (YAO)
7301 Calle Agua Salada, Yuma, AZ 85364
Tel: (928) 343-8100 Fax: (928) 343-8320 Internet: www.usbr.gov/lc/yuma

Area Manager **Maria Ramirez** . . . . (928) 343-8155
Education: U Phoenix; Norwich
Deputy Area Manager **Michael D. "Mike" Norris** . . . . (928) 343-8155
Management Support Office Director **Owen Fulsome** . . . . (928) 343-8138
E-mail: ofulsome@usbr.gov
Operations and Maintenance Office Director
Edward G. Virden . . . . (928) 343-8109
Resource Management Office Director
Christopher Wallis . . . . (928) 343-8215
Technical Support Office Director **Carrie Scott** . . . . (928) 343-8342

Southern California Area Office
27226 Via Industria, Suite A, Temecula, CA 92590
Tel: (951) 695-5310 Fax: (951) 695-5319
Internet: https://www.usbr.gov/lc/socal/

Area Manager **John "Jack" Simes** . . . . (951) 695-5310
Area Engineer **Dennis Wolfe** . . . . (951) 695-5310 ext. 101
Area Planning Officer **John "Jack" Simes** . . . . . (951) 695-5310 ext. 102
Environmental Specialist
Douglas "Doug" McPherson . . . . (951) 695-5310 ext. 104
Water Conservation Specialist
Debra "Deb" Whitney . . . . (951) 695-5310 ext. 105
Water Resources Manager **Leslie Cleveland** . . . . . (951) 695-5310 ext. 103
Administrative Support Assistant
Arthur "Art" Buchanon . . . . (951) 695-5310 ext. 100
E-mail: abuchanon@usbr.gov

Mid-Pacific Regional Office
Federal Building, 2800 Cottage Way, Sacramento, CA 95825
Tel: (916) 978-5100 Fax: (916) 978-5114 Internet: www.usbr.gov/mp
Areas Covered: Central and Northern CA, Northern NV, Portions of OR

● Regional Director (Acting) **Michael J. Ryan** . . . . (916) 978-5100
E-mail: mryan@usbr.gov Fax: (916) 978-5005
Education: Montana State 1984 BS

Mid-Pacific Regional Office *(continued)*

Executive Assistant **Alene Thomas** . . . . (916) 978-5100
Deputy Regional Director **Ali Forsythe** . . . . (916) 978-5100
Education: UC Santa Barbara BS
Assistant Regional Director, Business Services
Travis Bryant Aberle . . . . (916) 978-5100
E-mail: taberle@usbr.gov
Education: Cal State (Sacramento) BA
Financial Management Division Chief
Rodney Whitfield . . . . (916) 978-5364
Acquisition Services Manager **Brenda Davis** . . . . (916) 978-5130
E-mail: bdavis@usbr.gov
Administrative Services Manager **Melinda A. Jones** . . . . . (916) 978-5151
E-mail: majones@usbr.gov
Regional Engineer **Steven Melavic** . . . . (916) 978-5302
Environmental Affairs Manager **Anastasia Leigh** . . . . (916) 978-5568
Human Resources Manager **Kathleen Schulz** . . . . (916) 978-5477
E-mail: kschulz@usbr.gov
Regional Planning Officer **David van Rijn** . . . . (916) 978-5100
Education: George Mason BA
Program Coordination Office Manager
Ann Lubas-Williams . . . . (916) 978-5024
E-mail: alubaswilliams@usbr.gov
Resource Management Manager **Richard J. Woodley** . . . . (916) 978-5201
Safety, Health and Security Manager **Jaymes Hovinga** . . . (916) 978-5576
Public Affairs Officer **Erin C. Curtis** . . . . (916) 978-5100
E-mail: ecurtis@blm.gov
Education: Cal State (Long Beach) MPA; Cal State (Sacramento) BA
Deputy Public Affairs Officer **Wilbert Louis Moore** . . . . (916) 978-5102
E-mail: wmoore@usbr.gov
Education: National U
Equal Employment Manager **Tom Nichols** . . . . (916) 978-5571
Information Management Services Manager
Michael Rosenberger . . . . (916) 978-5449
E-mail: mrosenberger@usbr.gov

Bay-Delta Office
2800 Cottage Way, Sacramento, CA 95825
Tel: (916) 414-2400 Fax: (916) 414-2439

Office Manager **(Vacant)** . . . . (916) 414-2400
Deputy Manager **Mario Manzo** . . . . (916) 414-2400
Education: Arizona BEc
Area Manager **David Mooney** . . . . (916) 414-2400

Central California Area Office
7794 Folsom Dam Road, Folsom, CA 95630
Tel: (916) 988-1707 Fax: (916) 989-7208

Area Manager **Drew Lessard** . . . . (916) 989-7267

Central Valley Operations Office
3310 El Camino Avenue, Room 300, Sacramento, CA 95821
Tel: (916) 979-2180 Fax: (916) 979-2494

Operations Manager **Jeffrey "Jeff" Rieker** . . . . (916) 979-2180
Education: Missouri (Rolla) 1999 BS; Colorado State 2003 MS, 2011 PhD
Deputy Operations Manager **Kristin White** . . . . (916) 979-2180
Education: Florida Tech BSCE; Houston MCE
Operations Support Supervisor **David Ramirez** . . . . (916) 979-0259
E-mail: daramirez@usbr.gov

Klamath Basin Area Office
6600 Washburn Way, Klamath Falls, OR 97603
Tel: (541) 883-6935 Fax: (541) 884-9053
Internet: www.usbr.gov/mp/kbao

Administrative Officer **Deborah Leighton** . . . . (541) 880-2553

Lahontan Basin Area Office
705 North Plaza, Suite 320, Carson City, NV 89701
Tel: (775) 882-3436 Fax: (775) 882-7592 Fax: (775) 884-8376

Area Manager **Terri Edwards** . . . . (775) 884-8356
Education: Arizona BBA; Webster MBA
Deputy Area Manager **Roger Worsley** . . . . (775) 884-8356
Administrative Officer **Linda Mulkey** . . . . (775) 884-8343
E-mail: lmulkey@usbr.gov

★ Presidential Appointment Requiring Senate Confirmation ☆ Presidential Appointment □ Schedule C Appointment ◇ Career Senior Foreign Service Appointment
● Career Senior Executive Service (SES) Appointment ○ Non-Career Senior Executive Service (SES) Appointment ■ Postal Career Executive Service

Mid-Pacific Construction Office
1140 West Wood Street, Willows, CA 95988
P.O. Box 988, Willows, CA 95988
Tel: (530) 934-7066 Fax: (530) 934-7679
Construction Engineer **Richard A. Welsh** .... (530) 892-6262
Administrative Officer **Melanie L. Ross-Nichols** .... (530) 934-1362

Northern California Area Office
16349 Shasta Dam Boulevard, Shasta Lake, CA 96019-8400
Tel: (530) 275-1554 Fax: (530) 275-2441
Area Manager **Donald "Don" Bader** .... (530) 275-1554
Education: Wyoming
Administrative Officer **Janell A. Desmond** .... (530) 276-2006

South-Central California Area Office
1243 N Street, Fresno, CA 93721-1813
Tel: (559) 487-5116 Fax: (559) 487-5397
Area Manager **Michael P. Jackson PE** .... (559) 487-5116
Education: U Pacific BSCE
Deputy Area Manager **Duane Stroup** .... (559) 487-5118
Administrative Officer **DeAnn Brown** .... (559) 487-5119

Pacific Northwest Regional Office
1150 North Curtis Road, Suite 100, Boise, ID 83706-1234
Tel: (208) 378-5012 Fax: (208) 378-5019 Internet: www.usbr.gov/pn
Areas Covered: ID, Western MT, OR, WA
● Regional Director **Lorri J. Gray** .... (208) 378-5012
E-mail: lgray@usbr.gov
Education: U Phoenix BSBA
Deputy Regional Director for Natural Resources and External Affairs **David Mabe** .... (208) 378-5012
Education: Idaho BS
Deputy Regional Director for Power and Infrastructure
Robert Skordas .... (208) 378-5300
Deputy Regional Director **Jennifer Carrington** .... (208) 378-5300
Regional Public Affairs Officer **Michael Coffey** .... (208) 378-6203
Human Resources Manager
Nathan "Nate" Shimatsu .... (208) 378-5052
E-mail: nshimatsu@usbr.gov
EEO Manager **Bert Salisbury** .... (208) 378-5032
E-mail: bsalisbury@usbr.gov
EEO Specialist **Augustin Andrade** .... (208) 378-5050
E-mail: aandrade@usbr.gov
EEO Specialist **Luz Moreno** .... (208) 378-5160
E-mail: Lmoreno@usbr.gov

Bend (OR) Field Office
1375 Southeast Wilson Avenue, Suite 100, Bend, OR 97702-1435
Field Office Manager **Gregg Garnett** .... (208) 378-5012

Ephrata (WA) Field Office
P.O. Box 815, Ephrata, WA 98823
Field Office Manager **Marc Maynard** .... (509) 754-0200

Grand Coulee (WA) Power Office
P.O. Box 620, Grand Coulee, WA 99133-0620
Tel: (509) 633-1360 Fax: (509) 633-9138
Power Manager **Coleman Smith, Jr.** .... (509) 633-9507
Deputy Power Manager **Tim Koczur** .... (509) 633-1360
Education: Missouri (Rolla) BEE; Embry-Riddle
Deputy Power Manager for Engineering
Doug Anderson .... (509) 633-1360
Education: Montana State BS; Montana MBA
Physical Security Supervisor **Dale Carriere** .... (509) 633-9598
E-mail: dcarriere@usbr.gov
Administrative Officer **Matthew Tillman** .... (509) 633-9104
E-mail: mtillman@usbr.gov
Public Affairs Officer **Lynne Brougher** .... (509) 633-9503
Power Plant Operator **Randy Rothwell** .... (509) 633-1360

Hungry Horse (MT) Field Office
P.O. Box 190130, Hungry Horse, MT 59919-0130
Tel: (406) 387-5241 Fax: (406) 387-4012
Project Superintendent **Dennis Philmon** .... (406) 387-5241 ext. 313
E-mail: dphilmon@usbr.gov
Support Services Supervisor
Prudence M. Crampton .... (406) 387-5241 ext. 347
E-mail: pcrampton@usbr.gov

Pacific Northwest Construction Office
3701 River Road, Yakima, WA 98902-7306
Project Construction Engineer **Brandt Demars** .... (509) 454-5618

Umatilla (OR) Field Office
32871 Diagonal Road, Hermiston, OR 97838
Field Office Manager **Sean Kimbrel PE** .... (541) 571-2345

Yakima (WA) Field Office
1917 Marsh Road, Yakima, WA 98901
Tel: (509) 575-5848 Fax: (509) 454-5611
Field Office Manager **Chad Stuart** .... (509) 575-5848
Education: Oregon BS
Production Controller **Dorthey Pettit** .... (509) 575-5848 ext. 237
E-mail: dpettit@pn.usbr.gov

Columbia-Cascades Area Office
1917 Marsh Road, Yakima, WA 98901-2058
Tel: (509) 575-5848 Fax: (509) 454-5611
Area Manager **Dawn Wiedmeier** .... (509) 575-5848 ext. 200
Education: Slippery Rock State BS
Deputy Area Manager **Carolyn Chad** .... (509) 575-5848 ext. 255
Education: Humboldt State BS
Administrative Officer **Katrina Gorman** .... (509) 575-5848 ext. 271
E-mail: kgorman@usbr.gov
Information Technology Supervisor
Keith Griffith .... (509) 575-5848 ext. 268
Secretary **Paul Hernandez** .... (509) 575-5848 ext. 200
E-mail: ngalvez@usbr.gov

Snake River Area Office
230 Collins Road, Boise, ID 83702
Tel: (208) 383-2200 Fax: (208) 383-2237
Area Manager **Roland Springer** .... (208) 678-0461
E-mail: rspringer@usbr.gov
Education: MIT BCE, MCE; Cornell MBA

Upper Snake Field Office
470 22nd Street, Heyburn, ID 83336
Tel: (208) 678-0461 Fax: (208) 678-4321
Assistant Area Manager **Ryan Newman** .... (208) 678-0461 ext. 10
Education: South Dakota State BS, MSc
Natural Resource Manager
Robert L. "Hap" Boyer .... (208) 678-0461 ext. 15
Supervisory Civil Engineer **Jerry Cheek** .... (208) 678-0461 ext. 20
Education: Montana State 1991 BSCE
Water Operations Manager **(Vacant)** .... (208) 678-0461

Upper Colorado Regional Office
125 South State Street, Room 8100, Salt Lake City, UT 84138-1147
Tel: (801) 524-3603 Fax: (801) 524-5499 Internet: www.usbr.gov/uc
Areas Covered: North Western AZ, Western CO, NM, Western TX, UT
● Regional Director **Brent Rhees** .... (801) 524-3600
E-mail: brhees@usbr.gov
Education: Utah State
Executive Assistant **Stacie Wylie** .... (801) 524-3605
Special Assistant **Deborah Lawler** .... (801) 524-3606
Deputy Regional Director **Brent N. Esplin** .... (801) 524-3603
Education: Utah State BS, MS
Deputy Regional Director **Daniel C. Picard** .... (801) 524-3602
Education: Idaho BS, JD
Public Affairs Officer **Marlon Duke** .... (801) 524-3774
Webmaster **(Vacant)** .... (801) 524-3603

DEPARTMENTS

★ Presidential Appointment Requiring Senate Confirmation ☆ Presidential Appointment ☐ Schedule C Appointment ◇ Career Senior Foreign Service Appointment
● Career Senior Executive Service (SES) Appointment ○ Non-Career Senior Executive Service (SES) Appointment ■ Postal Career Executive Service

Acquisition Management Division
125 South State Street, Salt Lake City, UT 84138-1147
Tel: (801) 524-3762 Fax: (801) 524-3857

Manager **James Durrant** ... (801) 524-3854

Environmental Resources Division
125 South State Street, Salt Lake City, UT 84138-1147
Tel: (801) 524-3880 Fax: (801) 524-5499

Manager **Kathleen E. Callister** ... (801) 524-3712
E-mail: kcallister@usbr.gov
Adaptive Management Group Chief **Katrina Grantz** ... (801) 524-3880
Environmental Compliance Group Chief
Nancy Coulam ... (801) 524-3684
E-mail: ncoulam@usbr.gov

Financial Management Division
125 South State Street, Salt Lake City, UT 84138-1147
Tel: (801) 524-3804 Fax: (801) 524-5499

Manager **Mary Halverson** ... (801) 524-3613
E-mail: mhalverson@usbr.gov
Budget Group Chief **LuAnna Lambert** ... (801) 524-3683
E-mail: llambert@usbr.gov

Human Resources Division
125 South State Street, Salt Lake City, UT 84138-1147
Tel: (801) 524-3686 Fax: (801) 524-3187

Manager **Sue Frigm** ... (801) 524-3865
Employee and Labor Relations Group Chief
Sterling Egan ... (801) 524-3650
E-mail: segan@usbr.gov
Staffing and Classification Group Chief
Carol Avei-Ross ... (801) 524-3686

Information Resources Division
125 South State Street, Salt Lake City, UT 84138-1147
Tel: (801) 524-3746 Fax: (801) 524-5499

Manager **(Vacant)** ... (801) 524-3746
Equal Employment Opportunity Officer **Tim Coplin** ... (801) 524-3746
Librarian **Chantel Bouchard** ... (801) 524-3767
E-mail: cbouchard@usbr.gov

Power Office
125 South State Street, Salt Lake City, UT 84138-1147
Tel: (801) 524-3620 Fax: (801) 524-3828
Internet: https://www.usbr.gov/uc/power/

Power Manager **Talmadge Oxford** ... (801) 524-3628
E-mail: toxford@usbr.gov

Resource Management Division
125 South State Street, Salt Lake City, UT 84138-1147
Tel: (801) 524-3769 Fax: (801) 524-3858

Director **(Vacant)** ... (801) 524-3769
Land Resources Group Chief **David Krueger** ... (801) 524-3638
Water Resources Group Chief **Malcolm M. Wilson** ... (801) 524-3709

Technical Services Division
125 South State Street, Salt Lake City, UT 84138-1147
Tel: (801) 524-3769 Fax: (801) 524-3858

Manager **Wayne Xia** ... (801) 524-3702
E-mail: wxia@usbr.gov
Safety, Security and Dam Safety Division Chief
(Acting) **Kenneth "Ken" Rice** ... (505) 462-3558
Engineering Services Group Chief **Jay Bytheway** ... (801) 524-3690
Safety Group Chief **Dan Mitchell** ... (801) 524-3636
E-mail: dmitchell@usbr.gov Fax: (801) 524-5499
Security and Dam Safety Group Chief (Acting)
Kenneth "Ken" Rice ... (505) 462-3558
E-mail: krice@usbr.gov
Water Quality Group Chief **Kib Jacobson** ... (801) 524-3753

Albuquerque (NM) Area Office
555 Broadway, NE, Suite 100, Albuquerque, NM 87102-2162
Tel: (505) 462-3540 Fax: (505) 462-3794
Areas Covered: Alamosa, CO; NM; Southwestern TX

Area Manager **Jennifer Faler** ... (505) 462-3540
E-mail: jfaler@usbr.gov
Education: UC Davis MS
Deputy Area Manager **Jim Wilber** ... (505) 462-3594
E-mail: jwilber@usbr.gov
Secretary **(Vacant)** ... (505) 462-3542
Assistant Area Manager **Kenneth "Ken" Rice** ... (505) 462-3558
E-mail: krice@usbr.gov
Assistant Area Manager **Sean Torpey** ... (505) 462-3542
E-mail: storpey@usbr.gov
Assistant Area Manager **Art Valverde** ... (505) 462-3542
E-mail: avalverde@usbr.gov
Business Operation Division Manager
Catherine "Cat" Wheeler ... (505) 462-3561
Environment Division Manager **David Scruggs** ... (505) 462-3594
Facilities and Lands Division Manager
LeAnn Woodruff ... (505) 462-3553
Information Technology Specialist/Supervisor
James Lane ... (505) 462-3566
Information Technology Specialist/Systems
Administrator **Esteban Herrerra** ... (505) 462-3562
E-mail: eherrerra@usbr.gov
Technical Services Division Manager **(Vacant)** ... (505) 462-3540
Water Management Division Manager
Yvette McKenna ... (505) 462-3579
Safety and Occupational Health Specialist
Robert Morton ... (505) 462-3605
E-mail: rmorton@usbr.gov

Alamosa (CO) Field Division
10900 Highway 160 East, Alamosa, CO 81101-9518
Tel: (719) 589-5855 Fax: (719) 589-5379

Manager **Russell Plummer** ... (719) 589-5855

Chama (NM) Field Division
193 North Pinon Drive, Chama, NM 87520
P.O. Box 426, Chama, NM 87520-0426
Tel: (505) 756-2175 Fax: (505) 756-2453

Manager **Victor Salazar** ... (505) 756-2175
E-mail: vsalazar@usbr.gov

El Paso (TX) Field Office
10737 Gateway West, Suite 350, El Paso, TX 79935
Tel: (915) 534-6300 Fax: (915) 534-6299

Manager **Gerardo Melendez** ... (915) 534-6300
E-mail: gmelendez@usbr.gov

Elephant Butte Field Division
HC-32, Box 312, Truth or Consequences, NM 87901-9802
Tel: (575) 894-6661 Fax: (575) 894-3651

Facility Manager **Billy Elbrock** ... (575) 894-6661

Socorro (NM) Field Division
2401 State Road 1, Socorro, NM 87801
P.O. Box VV, Socorro, NM 87801
Tel: (575) 835-1202 Fax: (575) 835-3023

Manager **James "Jim" Jones** ... (575) 835-1202
E-mail: jjones@usbr.gov

Colorado River Storage Project

Curecanti Field Division
1820 South Rio Grande Avenue, Montrose, CO 81401
Fax: (970) 240-6304

Manager **Larry Lingerfelt** ... (970) 240-6306
Administrative Services Group Manager **Kay Schritter** ... (970) 240-6301
E-mail: kschritter@usbr.gov

★ Presidential Appointment Requiring Senate Confirmation ☆ Presidential Appointment □ Schedule C Appointment ◇ Career Senior Foreign Service Appointment
● Career Senior Executive Service (SES) Appointment ○ Non-Career Senior Executive Service (SES) Appointment ■ Postal Career Executive Service

Flaming Gorge Field Division
5995 Flaming Gorge Visitor Center, Dutch John, UT 84023
Tel: (435) 885-3106 Fax: (435) 885-3224

Manager **C. Steve Hulet** .... (435) 885-3231
Administrative Officer **Roxann Reid** .... (435) 885-3220
E-mail: rreid@usbr.gov
Engineer **Kasey Frandsen** .... (435) 885-3225
Operations and Maintenance Group Supervisor **John Morton** .... (435) 885-3234
Contract Specialist **Jennifer Handy** .... (435) 885-3228
E-mail: jhandy@usbr.gov

Four Corners Construction Office
1235 La Plata Highway, Farmington, NM 87401
Tel: (505) 324-5000 Fax: (505) 326-4388

Construction Engineer **Barry Longwell** .... (505) 324-5001

Provo (UT) Area Office
302 East 1860 South, Provo, UT 84606-7317
Tel: (801) 379-1000 Fax: (801) 379-1159
Internet: www.usbr.gov/uc/provo
Areas Covered: Southern ID, UT, Southwestern WY

Area Manager **Wayne Pullan** .... (801) 379-1100
Secretary **Donna Strait** .... (801) 379-1101
E-mail: dstrait@usbr.gov
Deputy Area Manager **Kent Kofford** .... (801) 379-1151

Western Colorado Area Office
445 West Gunnison Avenue, Suite 221, Grand Junction, CO 81501
Tel: (970) 248-0600 Fax: (970) 248-0601

Manager **Edward Warner** .... (970) 248-0600
Public Affairs Specialist **Justyn Liff** .... (970) 248-0625
E-mail: jliff@usbr.gov
Education: Mesa State 2002 BA

Policy, Administration, and Budget (PAB)

1849 C Street, NW, Washington, DC 20240

● Deputy Commissioner **Grayford F. "Gray" Payne** .... (202) 513-0517
Education: George Mason 1980 BS Fax: (202) 513-0323
Executive Assistant **(Vacant)** .... (202) 513-0509

Information Resources Office
Denver Federal Center, Building 67, Sixth and Kipling Streets, Denver, CO 80225
Mail: P.O. Box 25007, Denver, CO 80225-0007
Tel: (303) 445-3000

Associate Chief Information Officer **Karla Smiley** .... (303) 445-3000
E-mail: ksmiley@do.usbr.gov
Education: Florida Tech MBA; Davenport BA
Information Technology Program Manager (Security) **(Vacant)** Room 380 .... (303) 445-3000
Fax: (303) 445-6364
Information Technology Services Division Manager **Jeff Hoffman** Room 1200 .... (303) 445-3000
E-mail: jhoffman@usbr.gov

Mission Support Organization
Denver Federal Center, Building 67, Sixth and Kipling Streets, Room 394, Denver, CO 80225
Mail: P.O. Box 25007, Denver, CO 80225-0007
Fax: (720) 544-4771 Internet: www.usbr.gov/mso/

Director **Elizabeth Cordova-Harrison** .... (303) 445-2783
E-mail: eharrison@usbr.gov
Acquisition and Assistance Management Division Chief **Diana M. Terrell** .... (303) 445-2349
Business Analysis Division Chief **Heidi Morrow** .... (303) 445-3436
Finance and Accounting Division Chief **Deborah Nicholson** .... (303) 445-3514
Financial and Business Management System Division Chief **(Vacant)** .... (303) 445-2701

Policy and Administration (PPS)
Denver Federal Center, Building 67, Sixth and Kipling Streets, Room 1418, Denver, CO 80225
Mail: P.O. Box 25007, Denver, CO 80225-0007
E-mail: ethics@usbr.gov

● Director **Ruth Welch** .... (202) 513-0501
Education: Western State Col 1986 BA; Colorado (Denver) 2000 MPA
Executive Assistant **(Vacant)** .... (303) 445-2830
Deputy Ethics Counselor **James Gibson** .... (303) 445-2727
Land Resources Division Manager **(Vacant)** .... (303) 445-2900
Fax: (303) 445-6690
Maintenance Services Division Manager **(Vacant)** .... (202) 513-0501
Reclamation Law and Administration Division Manager **Karl Stock** .... (303) 445-2642
E-mail: kstock@usbr.gov Fax: (303) 445-6683
Senior Advisor for Design, Estimating and Construction Oversight and Dam Safety Officer **Brian Becker** .... (303) 445-2776
Education: North Dakota BSCE

Civil Rights Division
Denver Federal Center, Building 67, Sixth and Kipling Streets, Room 360, Denver, CO 80225
Mail: P.O. Box 25007, Denver, CO 80225-0007
Tel: (303) 445-3680 Tel: (303) 445-6385

Civil Rights Manager **Lara Grillos** .... (303) 445-3680
E-mail: lgrillos@usbr.gov
Secretary **Leticia "Letty" Gonzales** .... (303) 445-3680
E-mail: LGonzales@usbr.gov

Human Resources Division
Denver Federal Center, Building 67, Sixth and Kipling Streets, Room 348, Denver, CO 80225
Mail: P.O. Box 25007, Denver, CO 80225-0007

Division Manager **Carl A. Durrett** .... (303) 445-2642
E-mail: cdurrett@usbr.gov

Security, Safety and Law Enforcement (SSLE)
Denver Federal Center, Building 67, Sixth and Kipling Streets, Denver, CO 80225
Mail: P.O. Box 25007, Denver, CO 80225

● Director **Karen A. Knight PE** .... (303) 445-3044
E-mail: kknight@usbr.gov
Education: Missouri (Rolla) BS; Virginia Tech MSCE
Deputy Director **Phoebe Percell** .... (303) 445-3736
E-mail: ppercell@usbr.gov
Special Agent-in-Charge **(Vacant)** .... (202) 208-3186
Information Sharing and Law Enforcement Support **Justin M. Kearns** .... (303) 445-3959
Fax: (303) 445-6573
Safety and Health Office Manager **Monte Bowman** .... (303) 445-2695
E-mail: mbowman@usbr.gov Fax: (303) 445-6376
Chief Security Officer **Ronald J. "Rusty" Schuster** .... (303) 445-3377
E-mail: rschuster@usbr.gov Fax: (303) 445-6573
Chief, Program and Emergency Management Office **William Shipp** .... (303) 445-2799
Education: Yale 2001 MS, 2002 MPhil Fax: (303) 445-6464

DEPARTMENTS

★ Presidential Appointment Requiring Senate Confirmation ☆ Presidential Appointment ☐ Schedule C Appointment ◇ Career Senior Foreign Service Appointment
● Career Senior Executive Service (SES) Appointment ○ Non-Career Senior Executive Service (SES) Appointment ■ Postal Career Executive Service

United States Department of Justice

DEPARTMENTS

Contents

United States Department of Justice (DOJ)

Description: The Department of Justice serves as counsel to the U.S. Government, enforces the law, protects the public from criminals and subversion, ensures healthy business competition, and safeguards consumers. In its capacity as counsel, the department manages all cases involving the United States Federal Government.

Robert F. Kennedy Building, 950 Pennsylvania Avenue, NW, Washington, DC 20530-2001
Tel: (202) 514-2000 (Personnel Locator)
Tel: (202) 307-2000 (Procurement Information)
Tel: (202) 514-2007 (Public Information)
Tel: (202) 514-3642 (Freedom of Information/Privacy Act)
Tel: (202) 514-2001 (Office of the Attorney General)
Tel: (800) 869-4499 (Inspector General's Hot Line)
Tel: (800) 514-0301 (Americans with Disabilities Act Information)
Fax: (202) 514-4371 Internet: www.justice.gov
Internet: www.justice.gov/open (Open Government Directive)
Internet: www.usa.gov (Official US Government Website)

OFFICE OF THE ATTORNEY GENERAL

Robert F. Kennedy Building, 950 Pennsylvania Avenue, NW, Washington, DC 20530-2001
Tel: (202) 514-2001 Fax: (202) 307-6777
Internet: https://www.justice.gov/ag

Office of the Deputy Attorney General (ODAG)

Robert F. Kennedy Building, 950 Pennsylvania Avenue, NW, Washington, DC 20530
Tel: (202) 514-2101 Fax: (202) 514-0467 Internet: www.justice.gov/dag

Office of the Associate Attorney General (OASG)

Robert F. Kennedy Building, 950 Pennsylvania Avenue, NW, Room 5706, Washington, DC 20530
Tel: (202) 514-9500 Fax: (202) 514-0238 Internet: www.justice.gov/asg

Antitrust Division (ATR)

950 Pennsylvania Avenue, NW, Room 3109, Washington, DC 20530
Tel: (202) 514-2401 Fax: (202) 616-2645 E-mail: antitrust@usdoj.gov
Internet: www.justice.gov/atr

Field Offices

Chicago (IL) Field Office
Rookery Building, 209 South LaSalle Street, Suite 600, Chicago, IL 60604
Tel: (312) 984-7200 Fax: (312) 984-7299 E-mail: chicago.atr@usdoj.gov
Areas Covered: CO, IL, IN, IA, KS, Western MI, MN, MO, NE, ND, SD, WI

● Chief **Frank J. Vondrak** .... (312) 984-7219
Note: In November 2018 it was announced that Mr. Vondrak was planning on retiring from his position.
E-mail: frank.vondrak@usdoj.gov
Head Secretary **Oscar L. Dixon, Jr.** .... (312) 984-7200
E-mail: oscar.dixon@usdoj.gov
Assistant Chief **Michael Loterstein** .... (312) 984-7217
E-mail: michael.loterstein@usdoj.gov
Assistant Chief **Kalina M. Tulley** .... (312) 984-7299
E-mail: kalina.tulley@usdoj.gov
Administrative Assistant **Linda F. Irvin** .... (312) 984-7200
E-mail: linda.irvin@usdoj.gov

New York (NY) Field Office
26 Federal Plaza, Suite 3630, New York, NY 10278-0004
Tel: (212) 335-8000 Fax: (212) 335-8021 E-mail: newyork.atr@usdoj.gov
Areas Covered: CT, ME, MA, NH, Northern NJ, NY, RI, VT

● Chief **Jeffrey Martino** .... (212) 335-8019
E-mail: jeffrey.martino@usdoj.gov
Head Secretary **Eleanor Wu Clifford** .... (212) 335-8018
E-mail: eleanor.clifford@usdoj.gov
Assistant Chief **Sean M. Farrell** .... (212) 335-8025
E-mail: sean.farrell@usdoj.gov
Assistant Chief **Joseph Muoio, Jr.** .... (212) 335-8007
E-mail: joseph.muoio@usdoj.gov
Office Services Specialist **Mary Alice Baker** .... (212) 335-8132
E-mail: mary.baker@usdoj.gov
IT Specialist **Adam High** .... (212) 335-8027
E-mail: adam.high@usdoj.gov

San Francisco (CA) Field Office
U.S. Courthouse, 450 Golden Gate Avenue, Room 10-0101, San Francisco, CA 94102-3478
Tel: (415) 934-5426 Fax: (415) 934-5399 E-mail: sanfran.atr@usdoj.gov
Areas Covered: AK, AZ, CA, HI, ID, MT, NV, OR, UT, WA, WY

● Chief (Acting) **Manish Kumar** .... (415) 934-5333
Education: Minnesota 2008 JD
Legal Secretary **(Vacant)** .... (415) 934-5300
Assistant Chief **Manish Kumar** .... (415) 934-5300
E-mail: manish.kumar@usdoj.gov
Education: Minnesota 2008 JD
Assistant Chief **Katrina Rouse** .... (202) 934-5346
E-mail: katrina.rouse@usdoj.gov
Education: Columbia 2004 BA; Stanford 2009 JD

Civil Division (CIV)

Robert F. Kennedy Building, 950 Pennsylvania Avenue, NW, Washington, DC 20530
Tel: (202) 514-3301 Fax: (202) 514-8071 Internet: www.justice.gov/civil

Commercial Litigation Branch

1100 L Street, NW, Washington, DC 20530
Tel: (202) 514-3301 Fax: (202) 514-7968

International Trade Field Office
26 Federal Plaza, Suite 346, New York, NY 10278
Tel: (212) 264-9230 Fax: (212) 264-1916

Attorney-in-Charge **(Vacant)** .... (212) 264-9240
Assistant Director **Amy M. Rubin** .... (212) 264-9237
E-mail: amy.rubin@usdoj.gov
Senior Trial Counsel **Justin R. Miller** .... (212) 264-9241
E-mail: justin.r.miller@usdoj.gov
Senior Trial Counsel **Aimee Lee** .... (212) 264-9253
E-mail: aimee.lee@usdoj.gov
Attorney **Beverly A. Farrell** .... (212) 264-0483
E-mail: beverly.farrell@usdoj.gov
Attorney **Jason Kenner** .... (212) 264-9236
E-mail: jason.kenner@usdoj.gov
Attorney **Edward Kenny** .... (212) 264-0480
E-mail: edward.kenny@usdoj.gov
Attorney **Peter Mancuso** .... (212) 264-0484
E-mail: peter.mancuso@usdoj.gov

(continued on next page)

International Trade Field Office *(continued)*

Attorney **Marcella Powell** .... (212) 264-1873
E-mail: marcella.powell@usdoj.gov
Attorney **Jamie L. Shookman** .... (212) 264-2107
E-mail: jamie.shookman@usdoj.gov
Attorney **Alexander Vanderweide** .... (212) 264-0482
E-mail: alexander.vanderweide@usdoj.gov
Supervisory Office Manager **Katrina Nieves** .... (212) 264-9231
Senior Paralegal **Cylena Abrahams** .... (212) 264-9233
Paralegal **Avril Montanti** .... (212) 264-4907
Legal Assistant **Rodrigo Patino** .... (212) 264-3584
Legal Assistant **Alvar Lam** .... (212) 264-9234

Torts Branch
Robert F. Kennedy Building, 950 Pennsylvania Avenue, NW,
Room 3131, Washington, DC 20530
Fax: (202) 616-5200

West Coast Office (Admiralty)
U.S. Courthouse, 450 Golden Gate Avenue,
Room 7-5395, San Francisco, CA 94102
P.O. Box 36028, San Francisco, CA 94102
Tel: (415) 436-6630 Fax: (415) 436-6632

• Attorney-in-Charge **R. Michael "Mike" Underhill** .... (415) 436-6648
E-mail: mike.underhill@usdoj.gov
Secretary **(Vacant)** .... (415) 436-6639
Assistant Attorney-in-Charge **Eric Kaufman-Cohen** .... (415) 436-6630
Senior Admiralty Counsel **(Vacant)** .... (415) 436-6635
Trial Attorney **Vickey L. Quinn** .... (415) 436-6644
E-mail: vickey.l.quinn@usdoj.gov
Trial Attorney **(Vacant)** .... (415) 436-6647
Legal Assistant **Bonnie Li** .... (415) 436-6631
E-mail: bonnie.li@usdoj.gov

Community Relations Service (CRS)
Bicentennial Building, 600 E Street, NW,
Suite 6000, Washington, DC 20530
Tel: (202) 305-2935 Fax: (202) 305-3003 Internet: www.justice.gov/crs

Region 1 (New England)
408 Atlantic Avenue, Suite 222, Boston, MA 02110
Tel: (617) 424-5715 Fax: (617) 424-5727
Areas Covered: CT, MA, ME, NH, RI, VT

Regional Director **(Vacant)** .... (617) 424-5715
Senior Conciliation Specialist **(Vacant)** .... (617) 424-5715
Conciliation Specialist **Muhammad Ali Salaam** .... (617) 424-5715

Region 2 (Northeast)
Jacob K. Javits Federal Building, 26 Federal Plaza,
Room 36-118, New York, NY 10278
Tel: (212) 264-0700 Fax: (212) 264-2143
Areas Covered: NJ, NY, PR, VI

Regional Director (Acting) **O. Ben Lieu** .... (212) 264-0700
Conciliation Specialist **Matthew T. Lattimer** .... (212) 264-0700
Conciliation Specialist **Linda Ortiz** .... (212) 264-0700

Region 3 (Mid-Atlantic)
Second and Chestnut Streets, Room 208, Philadelphia, PA 19106
Tel: (215) 597-2344 Fax: (215) 597-9148
Areas Covered: DC, DE, MD, PA, VA, WV

Regional Director **Harpreet Singh Mokha** .... (215) 597-9946 ext. 14
E-mail: harpreet.mokha@usdoj.gov
Conciliation Specialist **Charles Phillips** .... (215) 597-2508
E-mail: charles.phillips@usdoj.gov
Conciliation Specialist **Suzanne Buchanan** .... (215) 597-4470
E-mail: suzanne.buchanan@usdoj.gov

Region 4 (Southeast)
Sam Nunn Atlanta Federal Center, 61 Forsyth Street, SW,
Suite 7B65, Atlanta, GA 30303-2525
Tel: (404) 331-6883 Fax: (404) 331-4471
Internet: https://www.justice.gov/crs
Areas Covered: AL, FL, GA, KY, MS, NC, SC, TN

Regional Director **Thomas Battles** .... (404) 331-6883
Conciliation Specialist **Walter Atkinson** .... (404) 331-6883
Conciliation Specialist **(Vacant)** .... (404) 331-6883
Conciliation Specialist **(Vacant)** .... (404) 331-6883

Miami (FL) Field Office
Claude Pepper Federal Plaza, 51 SW First Avenue,
Suite 624, Miami, FL 33130
Tel: (305) 536-5206 Fax: (305) 536-6778
Conciliation Specialist **Mildred Duprey-Derobles** .... (305) 536-5206

Region 5 (Midwest)
230 South Dearborn, Suite 2130, Chicago, IL 60604
Tel: (312) 353-4391 Fax: (312) 353-4390
Internet: https://www.justice.gov/crs
Areas Covered: IL, IN, MI, MN, OH, WI

Regional Director **Mary "Meg" Gorecki** .... (312) 353-4391
Administrative Assistant **(Vacant)** .... (312) 353-4391
Senior Conciliation Specialist **Kenith Bergeron** .... (312) 353-4728
Conciliation Specialist **(Vacant)** .... (312) 353-4391
Conciliation Specialist **(Vacant)** .... (312) 353-4356

Detroit (MI) Field Office
Federal Building, 211 West Fort Street,
Suite 1404, Detroit, MI 48226
Tel: (313) 226-4010 Fax: (313) 226-2568
Manager **Daedra A. Von Mike McGhee** .... (313) 226-4010

Region 6 (Southwest)
1999 Bryan Street, Suite 2050, Dallas, TX 75201
Tel: (214) 655-8175 Fax: (214) 655-8184
Areas Covered: AR, LA, NM, OK, TX

Regional Director **Synthia Taylor** .... (214) 655-8189
E-mail: synthia.taylor@usdoj.gov
Senior Conciliation Specialist **(Vacant)** .... (214) 655-8185
Conciliation Specialist **(Vacant)** .... (713) 718-4861
Administrative Assistant **(Vacant)** .... (214) 655-8175

Houston (TX) Field Office
515 Rusk Avenue, Room 12605, Houston, TX 77002
Tel: (713) 718-4861 Fax: (713) 718-4862
Conciliation Specialist **Kim Milstead** .... (713) 718-4861
E-mail: kim.milstead@usdoj.gov

Region 7 (Central)
601 East 12th Street, Kansas City, MO 64106-2808
Tel: (816) 426-7434 Fax: (816) 426-7441
Areas Covered: IA, KS, MO, NE

Regional Director **(Vacant)** .... (816) 426-7433
Senior Conciliation Specialist **(Vacant)** .... (816) 426-7436
Conciliation Specialist **Darryck Dean** .... (816) 426-7437
E-mail: darryck.dean@usdoj.gov
Conciliation Specialist **Rita Valenciano** .... (816) 426-7436
E-mail: rita.valenciano@usdoj.gov

Region 8 (Rocky Mountain)
Caesar Chavez Federal Building, 1244 Speer Boulevard,
Suite 650, Denver, CO 80204-3584
Tel: (303) 844-2973 Fax: (303) 844-2907
Areas Covered: CO, MT, ND, SD, UT, WY

Regional Director (Acting) **Rosa Salamanca** .... (303) 844-2906
Senior Conciliation Specialist **Rosa Salamanca** .... (303) 844-2974
Conciliation Specialist **Christopher Chalberg** .... (303) 844-2973
Conciliation Specialist **Jason Cvancara** .... (303) 844-2973

Region 9 (Western)
888 South Figueroa Street, Suite 2010, Los Angeles, CA 90017
Tel: (213) 894-2941 Fax: (213) 894-2880
Areas Covered: AZ, CA, GU, HI, NV

Regional Director **Ronald Wakabayashi** . . . . (213) 894-2941
E-mail: ronald.wakabayashi@usdoj.gov
Conciliation Specialist **Marquez Equalibria** . . . . (213) 894-2941
Conciliation Specialist **Sarah Majdiak** . . . . (213) 894-2941
E-mail: sarah.majdiak@usdoj.gov
Education: New Mexico 2002 MPA
Conciliation Specialist **James A. Williams III** . . . . (213) 894-2941
Administrative Assistant **(Vacant)** . . . . (213) 894-2941

San Francisco (CA) Field Office
90 Seventh Street, room 30300, San Francisco, CA 94103
Tel: (415) 744-6565 Fax: (415) 744-6590

Senior Conciliation Specialist **Justin Lock** . . . . (415) 744-6565
E-mail: justin.lock@usdoj.gov
Conciliation Specialist **Sarah Majdiak** . . . . (415) 744-6565
E-mail: sarah.majdiak@usdoj.gov
Education: New Mexico 2002 MPA

Region 10 (Northwest)
Jackson Federal Building, 915 Second Avenue,
Room 1808, Seattle, WA 98174
Tel: (206) 220-6700 Fax: (206) 220-6706
Areas Covered: AK, ID, OR, WA

Regional Director **Carol A. Russo** . . . . (206) 220-6700
Conciliation Specialist **(Vacant)** . . . . (206) 220-6700
Conciliation Specialist **John Yasutake** . . . . (206) 220-6700
Executive Administrative Assistant **(Vacant)** . . . . (206) 220-6700

Environment and Natural Resources Division (ENRD)
Robert F. Kennedy Building, 950 Pennsylvania Avenue, NW,
Washington, DC 20530
Tel: (202) 514-2701 Fax: (202) 514-0557
E-mail: webcontentmgr.enrd@usdoj.gov Internet: www.justice.gov/enrd

Field Offices

Anchorage (AK) Office
801 B Street, Suite 504, Anchorage, AK 99501-3657
Tel: (907) 271-4273 Fax: (907) 271-5827

Field Attorney **Dean Dunsmore** . . . . (907) 271-4273
E-mail: dean.dunsmore@usdoj.gov

Denver (CO) Office
1961 Stout Street, 8th Floor, Denver, CO 80294-1823
Tel: (303) 844-1899 Fax: (303) 844-1350
Areas Covered: AZ, CA, CO, ID, MT, NM, ND, OR, SD, UT, WA, WY

Environmental Defense Section Senior Counsel
David A. Carson . . . . (303) 844-1349
E-mail: david.a.carson@usdoj.gov
Environmental Defense Section Senior Counsel
Alan D. Greenberg . . . . (303) 844-1366
E-mail: alan.greenberg@usdoj.gov
Environmental Defense Section Senior Trial Counsel
Mark Nitczynski . . . . (303) 844-1498
E-mail: mark.nitczynski@usdoj.gov
Environmental Enforcement Section Trial Attorney
Jerel L. Ellington . . . . (303) 844-1363
E-mail: jerry.l.ellington@usdoj.gov
Environmental Enforcement Section Trial Attorney
James "Jim" Freeman . . . . (303) 844-1489
E-mail: james.freeman@usdoj.gov
Environmental Enforcement Section Trial Attorney
John Moscato . . . . (303) 844-1380
E-mail: john.moscato@usdoj.gov
Environmental Defense Section Trial Attorney
(Vacant) . . . . (303) 844-1362
Indian Resources Section Trial Attorney
Bradley S. Bridgewater . . . . (303) 844-1359
E-mail: bradley.s.bridgewater@usdoj.gov

Denver (CO) Office *(continued)*
Indian Resources Section Trial Attorney
David "Dave" Harder . . . . (303) 844-1372
E-mail: david.harder@usdoj.gov
Natural Resources Section Trial Attorney
James DuBois . . . . (303) 844-1375
E-mail: james.dubois@usdoj.gov
Administrative Officer **David "Dave" Jones** . . . . (303) 844-1807

San Francisco (CA) Office
301 Howard Street, Suite 1050, San Francisco, CA 94105
Tel: (415) 744-6491 Fax: (415) 744-6476

Environmental Enforcement Section Trial Attorney
Elise Feldman . . . . (415) 744-6491
E-mail: elise.feldman@usdoj.gov
Environmental Enforcement Section Trial Attorney
Rachel Hankey . . . . (415) 744-6491
E-mail: rachel.hankey@usdoj.gov
Education: NYU 2002 JD
Environmental Enforcement Section Trial Attorney
Brad O'Brien . . . . (415) 744-6491
E-mail: brad.o'brien@usdoj.gov
Natural Resources Section Trial Attorney
David B. Glazer . . . . (415) 744-6491
E-mail: david.glazer@usdoj.gov
Education: Yale 1982 BA
Paralegal Specialist **Bernice Yee** . . . . (415) 744-6491
E-mail: bernice.yee@usdoj.gov

Seattle (WA) Office
7600 Sand Point Way, NE, Seattle, WA 98115-0070
Environmental Enforcement Section Trial Attorney
Kent Hanson . . . . (206) 526-6617
E-mail: kent.hanson@usdoj.gov
Environmental Enforcement Section Trial Attorney
Jim Nicoll . . . . (206) 526-6616
Environmental Enforcement Section Trial Attorney
Rachel Roberts . . . . (206) 526-6617
E-mail: rachel.roberts@usdoj.gov
Environmental Enforcement Section Trial Attorney
Michael Zevenbergen . . . . (206) 526-6607
E-mail: michael.zevenbergen@usdoj.gov
Environmental Enforcement Section Trial Attorney
Erika Zimmerman . . . . (206) 526-6608
E-mail: erika.zimmerman@usdoj.gov

Executive Office for United States Trustees (EOUST)
441 G Street, NW, Suite 6150, Washington, DC 20530
Tel: (202) 307-1391 Fax: (202) 307-0672 Internet: www.justice.gov/ust

National Bankruptcy Training Institute
National Advocacy Center, 1620 Pendleton Street, Columbia, SC 29201
Tel: (803) 705-5131 Fax: (803) 705-5305

Chief **Scott A. Farrow** . . . . (803) 705-5131
E-mail: scott.a.farrow@usdoj.gov

Region 1
John W. McCormack Post Office and Courthouse, 5 Post Office Square,
10th Floor, Suite 1000, Boston, MA 02109
Tel: (617) 788-0400 Fax: (617) 565-6368
Internet: https://www.justice.gov/ust-regions-r01
Areas Covered: ME, MA, NH, RI

U.S. Trustee **William K. Harrington** . . . . (617) 788-0440
Administrative Officer **Dianne P. Dugan** . . . . (215) 597-9593
E-mail: dianne.p.dugan@usdoj.gov
Information Technology Specialist **Louie Salcedo** . . . . (617) 788-0403
E-mail: louie.salcedo@usdoj.gov Fax: (617) 565-5601

Boston (MA) Field Office
John W. McCormack Post Office and Courthouse, 5 Post Office Square,
10th Floor, Suite 1000, Boston, MA 02109
Tel: (617) 788-0400 Fax: (617) 565-6368

Assistant U.S. Trustee **John P. Fitzgerald III** . . . . (617) 788-0401

Manchester (NH) Field Office
1000 Elm Street, Suite 605, Manchester, NH 03101
Tel: (603) 666-7908 Fax: (603) 666-7913
Assistant U.S. Trustee **Geraldine L. Karonis** . . . . (603) 666-7908

Portland (ME) Field Office
537 Congress Street, Room 303, Portland, ME 04101
Tel: (207) 780-3564 Fax: (207) 780-3568
Assistant U.S. Trustee **Stephen G. Morrell** . . . . . (207) 780-3564 ext. 205

Providence (RI) Field Office
One Exchange Terrace, Suite 431, Providence, RI 02903
Tel: (401) 528-5551 Fax: (401) 528-5163
Assistant U.S. Trustee **Gary L. Donahue** . . . . (401) 528-5552

Worcester (MA) Field Office
446 Main Street, 14th Floor, Worcester, MA 01608
Tel: (508) 793-0555 Fax: (508) 793-0558
Assistant U.S. Trustee **Richard T. King** . . . . (508) 793-0555

Region 2
201 Varick St, Suite 1006, New York, NY 10014
Tel: (212) 510-0500 Fax: (212) 668-2256 Fax: (212) 668-2361
Internet: https://www.justice.gov/ust-regions-r02
Areas Covered: CT, NY, VT
U.S. Trustee **William K. Harrington** . . . . (212) 510-0500 ext. 207
Senior Bankruptcy Analyst **(Vacant)** . . . . (212) 510-0500 ext. 220
Information Technology Specialist
Carol A. Porter . . . . (212) 510-0500 ext. 230
E-mail: carol.a.porter@usdoj.gov
Administrative Officer
Jennifer L. Weston-Spotts . . . . (212) 510-0500 ext. 225
E-mail: jennifer.weston@usdoj.gov

Albany (NY) District Office
74 Chapel Street, Suite 200, Albany, NY 12207
Tel: (518) 434-4553 Fax: (518) 434-4459
Assistant U.S. Trustee **Lisa M. Penpraze** . . . . (518) 434-4969

Brooklyn (NY) District Office
201 Varick St, Room 1006, New York, NY 10014
Tel: (212) 510-0500 Fax: (212) 668-2255
Assistant U.S. Trustee (Acting)
Christine H. Black . . . . (631) 715-7800 ext. 228

Buffalo (NY) District Office
300 Pearl Street, Suite 401, Buffalo, NY 14202
Tel: (716) 551-5541 Fax: (716) 551-5560
Assistant U.S. Trustee **Joseph W. Allen** . . . . (716) 551-5541 ext. 231

Central Islip (NY) District Office
560 Federal Plaza, Suite 560, Central Islip, NY 11722-4456
Tel: (631) 715-7800 Fax: (631) 715-7777
Assistant U.S. Trustee **Christine H. Black** . . . . . (631) 715-7800 ext. 5792

New Haven (CT) District Office
150 Court Street, Room 302, New Haven, CT 06510-2055
Tel: (203) 773-2210 Fax: (203) 773-2217
Assistant U.S. Trustee **Kim McCabe** . . . . (203) 773-2210 ext. 233
Office Automation Clerk **Nicole Neely** . . . . (203) 773-2210 ext. 221
E-mail: nicole.neely@usdoj.gov

Manhattan (NY) District Office
201 Varick St, Suite 1006, New York, NY 10014
Tel: (212) 510-0500 Fax: (212) 668-2255
Assistant U.S. Trustee **Linda A. Riffkin** . . . . (212) 510-0500 ext. 233

Rochester (NY) District Office
100 State Street, Room 609, Rochester, NY 14614
Tel: (585) 263-5812 Fax: (585) 263-5862
Assistant U.S. Trustee **Kathleen Dunivin Schmitt** . . . . (585) 263-5706

Utica (NY) District Office
10 Broad Street, Room 105, Utica, NY 13501
Tel: (315) 793-8191 Fax: (315) 793-8133
Assistant U.S. Trustee **Guy A. Van Baalen** . . . . (315) 793-8191

Region 3
833 Chestnut Street, Suite 500, Philadelphia, PA 19107
Tel: (215) 597-4411 Fax: (215) 597-5795
Internet: https://www.justice.gov/ust-regions-r03
Areas Covered: DE, NJ, PA
U.S. Trustee (Acting) **Andrew R. "Andy" Vara** . . . . (215) 597-4411

Harrisburg (PA) Field Office
228 Walnut Street, Suite 1190, Harrisburg, PA 17101
Mail: P.O. Box 969, Harrisburg, PA 17108-0969
Tel: (717) 221-4515 Fax: (717) 221-4554
Assistant U.S. Trustee **Anne K. Fiorenza** . . . . (717) 221-4515

Newark (NJ) Field Office
One Newark Center, Suite 2100, Newark, NJ 07102
Tel: (973) 645-3014 Fax: (973) 645-5993
Assistant U.S. Trustee **Martha Hildebrandt** . . . . (973) 645-5912
Secretary **Ivette Gerhard** . . . . (973) 645-3014
E-mail: ivette.gerhard@usdoj.gov

Philadelphia (PA) Field Office
833 Chestnut Street, Suite 500, Philadelphia, PA 19107
Tel: (215) 597-4411 Fax: (215) 597-5795
Assistant U.S. Trustee **Frederic J. Baker** . . . . (215) 597-5816

Pittsburgh (PA) Field Office
1001 Liberty Avenue, Suite 970, Pittsburgh, PA 15222
Tel: (412) 644-4756 Fax: (412) 644-4785
Assistant U.S. Trustee **Joseph S. Sisca** . . . . (412) 644-4756

Wilmington (DE) Field Office
844 King Street, Lockbox #35, Suite 2207, Wilmington, DE 19801
Tel: (302) 573-6491 Fax: (302) 573-6497
Assistant U.S. Trustee **Thomas Patrick Tinker** . . . . (302) 573-6493

Region 4
Strom Thurmond Federal Building, 1835 Assembly Street,
Suite 953, Columbia, SC 29201
Tel: (803) 765-5250 Fax: (803) 765-5260
Internet: https://www.justice.gov/ust-regions-r04
Areas Covered: DC, MD, SC, VA, WV
U.S. Trustee (Acting) **John P. Fitzgerald III** . . . . (803) 765-5250
Administrative Officer **Shelly R. Thompson** . . . . (803) 765-5238
E-mail: shelly.r.thompson@usdoj.gov
Bankruptcy Analyst **B. Anne Hiers** . . . . (803) 765-5237
Legal Assistant **(Vacant)** . . . . (803) 765-5234

Alexandria (VA) Field Office
115 South Union Street, Suite 210, Alexandria, VA 22314
Tel: (703) 557-7176 Fax: (703) 557-7279
Assistant U.S. Trustee **Joseph A. Guzinski** . . . . (703) 557-7274
Education: Virginia 1983 JD

Baltimore (MD) Field Office
101 West Lombard Street, Suite 2625, Baltimore, MD 21201
Tel: (410) 962-4300 Fax: (410) 962-3537
Assistant U.S. Trustee **Gerard R. Vetter** . . . . (410) 962-4422

Charleston (WV) Field Office
300 Virginia Street East, Room 2025, Charleston, WV 25301
Tel: (304) 347-3400 Fax: (304) 347-3402
Assistant U.S. Trustee **Debra A. Wertman** . . . . (304) 347-3405

Columbia (SC) Field Office
Strom Thurmond Federal Building, 1835 Assembly Street, Suite 953, Columbia, SC 29201
Tel: (803) 765-5250 Fax: (803) 765-5260
Assistant U.S. Trustee **John Timothy Stack** .... (803) 765-5218

Greenbelt (MD) Field Office
6305 Ivy Lane, Suite 600, Greenbelt, MD 20770
Tel: (301) 344-6216 Fax: (301) 344-8431
Assistant U.S. Trustee **Gerard R. Vetter** .... (301) 344-6216

Norfolk (VA) Field Office
200 Granby Street, Room 625, Norfolk, VA 23510
Tel: (757) 441-6012 Fax: (757) 441-3266
Assistant U.S. Trustee **Kenneth N. Whitehurst III** .... (757) 441-6919

Richmond (VA) Field Office
701 East Broad Street, Suite 4304, Richmond, VA 23219
Tel: (804) 771-2310 Fax: (804) 771-2330
Assistant U.S. Trustee **Robert B. Van Arsdale** .... (804) 771-2327

Roanoke (VA) Field Office
First Campbell Square Building, 210 First Street, SW, Suite 505, Roanoke, VA 24011
Tel: (540) 857-2806 Fax: (540) 857-2844
Assistant U.S. Trustee **Margaret K. Garber** .... (804) 771-2327

Region 5
400 Poydras Street, Suite 2110, New Orleans, LA 70130
Tel: (504) 589-4018 Fax: (504) 589-4096
Internet: https://www.justice.gov/ust-regions-r05
Areas Covered: LA, MS
U.S. Trustee (Acting) **David Walter "Dave" Asbach** .... (504) 589-4018
Secretary **(Vacant)** .... (504) 589-2662
Standing Trustee Coordinator **(Vacant)** .... (504) 589-2591
Administrative Officer **Shelly R. Thompson** .... (504) 589-2666
E-mail: shelly.r.thompson@usdoj.gov
Information Technology Specialist **John E. Bagby** .... (504) 589-2667
E-mail: john.e.bagby@usdoj.gov

Jackson (MS) Field Office
501 East Court Street, Suite 6-430, Jackson, MS 39201
Tel: (601) 965-5241 Fax: (601) 965-5226
Assistant U.S. Trustee **Ronald H. McAlpin** .... (601) 965-5247

New Orleans (LA) Field Office
400 Poydras Street, Suite 2110, New Orleans, LA 70130
Tel: (504) 589-4018 Fax: (504) 589-4096
Assistant U.S. Trustee **Mary Langston** .... (504) 589-4093

Shreveport (LA) Field Office
300 Fannin Street, Suite 3196, Shreveport, LA 71101-3079
Tel: (318) 676-3456 Fax: (318) 676-3212
Assistant U.S. Trustee **Ronald H. McAlpin** .... (318) 676-3556

Region 6
Earle Cabell Federal Building, 1100 Commerce Street, Room 976, Dallas, TX 75242
Tel: (214) 767-8967 Fax: (214) 767-8971
E-mail: ustp.region06@usdoj.gov
Internet: https://www.justice.gov/ust-regions-r06
Areas Covered: TX (Northern & Eastern Judicial districts)
U.S. Trustee **William T. Neary** .... (214) 767-1070
Education: Vanderbilt 1979; Southern Methodist 1982 JD
Secretary **Julie S. Vega** .... (214) 767-1245
E-mail: julie.vega@usdoj.gov
Assistant U.S. Trustee **Lisa L. Lambert** .... (214) 767-1080
Administrative Officer **Elaine A. Thompson** .... (404) 331-4437 ext. 110

Tyler (TX) Field Office
110 North College Avenue, Suite 300, Tyler, TX 75702
Tel: (903) 590-1450 Fax: (903) 590-1461
Assistant U.S. Trustee **Timothy W. O'Neal** ..... (903) 590-1450 ext. 215
Education: Boston U 1981; Houston 1986 JD

Region 7
515 Rusk Avenue, Suite 3516, Houston, TX 77002-2604
Tel: (713) 718-4650 Fax: (713) 718-4670
Internet: www.justice.gov/ust/r07
Areas Covered: TX (Southern & Western Judicial districts)
U.S. Trustee (Acting) **Henry G. Hobbs, Jr.** .... (713) 718-4650
Administrative Officer
Nathalie V. Brumfield-Brown .... (713) 718-4650 ext. 244
E-mail: nathalie.brumfield-brown2@usdoj.gov
Information Technology Specialist
Thomas Crouse .... (713) 718-4650 ext. 245
E-mail: thomas.crouse@usdoj.gov

Austin (TX) Field Office
903 San Jacinto Boulevard, Suite 230, Austin, TX 78701-2450
Tel: (512) 916-5328 Fax: (512) 916-5331
Assistant U.S. Trustee **Henry G. Hobbs, Jr.** .... (512) 916-5329

Corpus Christi (TX) Field Office
606 North Carancahua, Room 1107, Corpus Christi, TX 78476-1736
Tel: (361) 888-3261 Fax: (361) 888-3263
Assistant U.S. Trustee
Diane Grittman Livingstone .... (713) 718-4650 ext. 23

Houston (TX) Field Office
515 Rusk Avenue, Suite 3516, Houston, TX 77002-2604
Tel: (713) 718-4650 Fax: (713) 718-4680
Assistant U.S. Trustee
Diane Grittman Livingstone .... (713) 718-4650 ext. 242

San Antonio (TX) Field Office
615 East Houston Street, Suite 533, San Antonio, TX 78205-2055
P.O. Box 1539, San Antonio, TX 78295-1539
Tel: (210) 472-4640 Fax: (210) 472-4649
Assistant U.S. Trustee **Nancy Ratchford** .... (210) 472-4647 ext. 223

Region 8
One Memphis Place, 200 Jefferson Avenue, Suite 400, Memphis, TN 38103
Tel: (901) 544-3251 Fax: (901) 544-4138
Internet: https://www.justice.gov/ust-regions-r08
Areas Covered: KY, TN
U.S. Trustee (Acting) **Paul A. Randolph** .... (901) 544-3251
Secretary **(Vacant)** .... (901) 544-3251
Administrative Officer **Jennifer L. Weston-Spotts** ...... (901) 544-3251
E-mail: jennifer.weston-spotts@usdoj.gov
Information Technology Specialist
Steven R. "Randy" Underwood .... (901) 544-3666
E-mail: steven.r.underwood@usdoj.gov

Chattanooga (TN) Field Office
Historic U.S. Courthouse, 31 East 11th Street, 4th Floor, Chattanooga, TN 37402
Tel: (423) 752-5153 Fax: (423) 752-5161
Assistant U.S. Trustee **Kimberly C. Swafford** .... (423) 752-5153

Knoxville (TN) Office
800 Market Street, Suite 114, Knoxville, TN 37902
Tel: (865) 545-4324 Fax: (865) 545-4325
Assistant U.S. Trustee (Acting) **Kimberly C. Swafford** ... (865) 545-4324
E-mail: kim.c.swafford@usdoj.gov

Lexington (KY) Field Office
100 East Vine Street, Suite 500, Lexington, KY 40507
Tel: (859) 233-2822 Fax: (859) 233-2834
Assistant U.S. Trustee **John L. Daugherty** ...... (859) 233-2822 ext. 113
Fax: (859) 233-2834

Louisville (KY) Field Office
Gene Snyder Courthouse, 601 West Broadway,
Room 512, Louisville, KY 40202
Tel: (502) 582-6000 Fax: (502) 582-6147

Assistant U.S. Trustee **Charles Merrill** . . . . (502) 582-6000 ext. 234

Memphis (TN) Regional Office
One Memphis Place, 200 Jefferson Avenue,
Suite 400, Memphis, TN 38103
Tel: (901) 544-3251 Fax: (901) 544-4138

Assistant U.S. Trustee **Sean M. Haynes** . . . . (901) 544-3251

Nashville (TN) Field Office
701 Broadway, Suite 318, Nashville, TN 37203
Tel: (615) 736-2254 Fax: (615) 736-2260

Assistant U.S. Trustee (Acting)
Kimberly C. Swafford . . . . (615) 736-2254 ext. 232

Region 9
Howard M. Mentzenbaum U.S. Courthouse, 201 Superior Avenue East,
Suite 441, Cleveland, OH 44114-1240
Tel: (216) 522-7800 Fax: (216) 522-7193
Internet: https://www.justice.gov/ust-regions-r09
Areas Covered: MI, OH

U.S. Trustee **Daniel M. McDermott** . . . . (216) 522-7800 ext. 230
Administrative Officer **Mary Ellen Gonzalez** . . . . (216) 522-7800 ext. 225
E-mail: mary.e.gonzalez@usdoj.gov
Information Technology Specialist **(Vacant)** . . . . . (216) 522-7800 ext. 228
Regional Bankruptcy Analyst
Christopher "Chris" Sonson . . . . (216) 522-7800 ext. 238

Cincinnati (OH) Field Office
36 East Seventh Street, Suite 2030, Cincinnati, OH 45202
Tel: (513) 684-6988 Fax: (513) 684-6994
Areas Covered: Cincinnati

Assistant U.S. Trustee **Monica Kindt** . . . . (513) 684-6988 ext. 226

Cleveland (OH) Field Office
Howard M. Metzebbaum U.S. Courthouse, 201 Superior Avenue East,
Suite 441, Cleveland, OH 44114-1240
Tel: (216) 522-7800 Fax: (216) 522-7193
Areas Covered: Northern OH

Assistant U.S. Trustee
Andrew R. "Andy" Vara . . . . (216) 522-7800 ext. 229

Columbus (OH) Field Office
170 North High Street, Suite 200, Columbus, OH 43215-2403
Tel: (614) 469-7411 Fax: (614) 469-7448
Areas Covered: Southern OH (except Cincinnati)

Assistant U.S. Trustee **MaryAnne Wilsbacher** . . . (614) 469-7411 ext. 212
Education: West Virginia 1987 BSJ; Toledo 1990 JD

Detroit (MI) Field Office
211 West Fort Street, Suite 700, Detroit, MI 48226
Tel: (313) 226-7999 Fax: (313) 226-7952
Areas Covered: Eastern MI

Assistant U.S. Trustee **Paul J. Randel** . . . . (313) 226-4541

Grand Rapids (MI) Field Office
125 Ottawa Street, Suite 200R, Grand Rapids, MI 49503
Tel: (616) 456-2002 Fax: (616) 456-2550
Areas Covered: Western MI

Assistant U.S. Trustee **Matthew Cheney** . . . . (616) 456-2002 ext. 116

Region 10
101 West Ohio Street, Suite 1000, Indianapolis, IN 46204
Tel: (317) 226-6101 Fax: (317) 226-6356
Internet: https://www.justice.gov/ust-regions-r10
Areas Covered: IL (Northern, Southern, and Central Districts), IN

U.S. Trustee **Nancy J. Gargula** . . . . (317) 226-6101
Education: Ball State 1977 BA; Notre Dame 1981 JD

Region 10 *(continued)*

Administrative Officer **Pamela S. Hillman** . . . . (317) 226-6101
E-mail: pam.s.hillman@usdoj.gov
Secretary **(Vacant)** . . . . (317) 226-6101
Senior Bankruptcy Analyst **(Vacant)** . . . . (317) 226-6101
Information Technology Specialist **Terri A. Bevan** . . . . (317) 226-6101
E-mail: terri.bevan@usdoj.gov

Indianapolis (IN) Field Office
101 West Ohio Street, Suite 1000, Indianapolis, IN 46204
Tel: (317) 226-6101 Fax: (317) 226-6356
Areas Covered: IN (Southern Judicial District)

Assistant U.S. Trustee **Ronald J. Moore** . . . . (317) 226-6101

Peoria (IL) Field Office
401 Main Street, Suite 1100, Peoria, IL 61602
Tel: (309) 671-7854 Fax: (309) 671-7857
Areas Covered: IL (Central and Southern Judicial Districts)

Assistant U.S. Trustee (Acting) **Susan Jaffe Roberts** . . . . (574) 236-8140
Education: Baltimore 2001 JD

South Bend (IN) Field Office
100 East Wayne Street, Room 555, South Bend, IN 46601-2349
Tel: (574) 236-8105 Fax: (574) 236-8163
Areas Covered: IN (Northern Judicial District)

Assistant U.S. Trustee **Susan Jaffe Roberts** . . . . (574) 236-8105
Education: Baltimore 2001 JD
Secretary **(Vacant)** . . . . (574) 236-8105

Region 11
219 South Dearborn Street, Room 873, Chicago, IL 60604
Tel: (312) 886-5785 Fax: (312) 886-5794
Internet: https://www.justice.gov/ust-regions-r11
Areas Covered: IL (Northern Judicial District), WI (Eastern and Western Judicial Districts)

U.S. Trustee **Patrick S. Layng** . . . . (312) 886-5785
Education: Illinois, JD
Administrative Officer **Pamela S. Hillman** . . . . (312) 886-5785
E-mail: pam.s.hillman@usdoj.gov
Information Technology Specialist
Keith E. Manikowski . . . . (312) 886-5785
E-mail: keith.manikowski@usdoj.gov

Chicago (IL) Field Office
219 South Dearborn Street, Room 873, Chicago, IL 60604
Tel: (312) 886-5785 Fax: (312) 886-5794

Assistant U.S. Trustee **Adam Brief** . . . . (312) 886-5785

Madison (WI) Field Office
780 Regent Street, Suite 304, Madison, WI 53715
Tel: (608) 264-5522 Fax: (608) 264-5182

Assistant U.S. Trustee **Mary Jensen** . . . . (608) 264-5522

Milwaukee (WI) Field Office
Federal Courthouse, 517 East Wisconsin Avenue,
Room 430, Milwaukee, WI 53202
Tel: (414) 297-4499 Fax: (414) 297-4478

Assistant U.S. Trustee **David Walter "Dave" Asbach** . . . . (414) 297-4499

Region 12
111 7th Avenue SE, Room 280, Cedar Rapids, IA 52401
Tel: (319) 364-2211 Fax: (319) 364-7370
Internet: https://www.justice.gov/ust-regions-r12
Areas Covered: IA, MN, ND, SD

U.S. Trustee (Acting) **James L. Snyder** . . . . (319) 364-2211
Assistant U.S. Trustee **Janet G. Reasoner** . . . . . . (319) 364-2211 ext. 230
Education: Iowa 1981 JD

Des Moines (IA) Field Office
Federal Building, 210 Walnut Street, Room 793, Des Moines, IA 50309
Tel: (515) 284-4982 Fax: (515) 284-4986

Assistant U.S. Trustee **James L. Snyder** . . . . (515) 284-4985

★ Presidential Appointment Requiring Senate Confirmation ☆ Presidential Appointment ☐ Schedule C Appointment ◇ Career Senior Foreign Service Appointment
● Career Senior Executive Service (SES) Appointment ○ Non-Career Senior Executive Service (SES) Appointment ■ Postal Career Executive Service

Minneapolis (MN) Field Office
1015 U.S. Courthouse, 300 South Fourth Street, Minneapolis, MN 55415
Tel: (612) 334-1350 Fax: (612) 335-4032
Assistant U.S. Trustee **Robert B. Raschke** . . . . (612) 664-5509

Sioux Falls (SD) Field Office
314 South Main Street, Suite 303, Sioux Falls, SD 57104
Tel: (605) 330-4450 Fax: (605) 330-4456
Assistant U.S. Trustee (Acting) **James L. Snyder** . . . . (515) 284-4982

Region 13
Charles Evans Whittaker U.S. Courthouse, 400 East Ninth Street, Suite 3440, Kansas City, MO 64106
Tel: (816) 512-1940 Fax: (816) 512-1967
Internet: https://www.justice.gov/ust-regions-r13
Areas Covered: AR, MO, NE
U.S. Trustee (Acting) **Daniel J. Casamatta** . . . . (816) 512-1940
E-mail: daniel.j.casamatta@usdoj.gov Fax: (816) 512-1964
Assistant U.S. Trustee **Daniel J. Casamatta** . . . . (816) 512-1943

Little Rock (AR) Field Office
200 West Capitol, Suite 1200, Little Rock, AR 72201
Tel: (501) 324-7357 Fax: (501) 324-7388
Assistant U.S. Trustee **Charles W. Tucker** . . . . (501) 324-7357

Omaha (NE) Field Office
111 South 18th Plaza, Room 1148, Omaha, NE 68102
Tel: (402) 221-4300 Fax: (402) 221-4383
Assistant U.S. Trustee (Acting) **Jerry L. Jensen** . . . . (402) 221-4300

Saint Louis (MO) Field Office
111 South 10th Street, Room 6353, St. Louis, MO 63102
Tel: (314) 539-2976 Fax: (314) 539-2990
Assistant U.S. Trustee **Paul A. Randolph** . . . . (314) 539-2976

Region 14
230 North First Avenue, Suite 204, Phoenix, AZ 85003-1706
Tel: (602) 682-2600 Fax: (602) 514-7270
Internet: https://www.justice.gov/ust-regions-r14
Areas Covered: AZ
U.S. Trustee **Ilene J. Lashinsky** . . . . (602) 682-2623
Education: Arizona State 1969, 1972 JD
Assistant U.S. Trustee **Elizabeth C. Amorosi** . . . . (602) 682-2619
Information Technology Specialist **Bryan People** . . . . (602) 682-2600
E-mail: bryan.people@usdoj.gov
Information Technology Specialist **(Vacant)** . . . . (602) 682-2600
Administrative Officer **Ronaele Creel** . . . . (602) 682-2611
E-mail: ronaele.creel2@usdoj.gov

Region 15
402 West Broadway, Suite 600, San Diego, CA 92101-8511
Tel: (619) 557-5013 Fax: (619) 557-5339
E-mail: ustp.region15@usdoj.gov
Internet: https://www.justice.gov/ust-regions-r15
Areas Covered: CA (Southern Judicial District), GU, HI, Commonwealth of the Northern Mariana Islands (CNMI)
U.S. Trustee (Acting) **Tiffany L. Carroll** . . . . (619) 557-5013
Education: Pitzer; Seattle JD
Administrative Officer **Ronaele Creel** . . . . (619) 557-5013 ext. 6226
E-mail: ronaele.creel2@usdoj.gov
Information Technology Specialist **Bryan People** . . . . (619) 557-5013
E-mail: bryan.people@usdoj.gov

Hagatna (GU) Field Office
Sirena Plaza Building, 108 Hernan Cortes, Suite 131, Hagatna, GU 96932
Tel: (671) 472-7336 Fax: (671) 472-7344
Assistant U.S. Trustee **Curtis B. Ching** . . . . (808) 552-8154
E-mail: curtis.b.ching@usdoj.gov

Honolulu (HI) Field Office
1132 Bishop Street, Suite 602, Honolulu, HI 96813-2830
Tel: (808) 522-8150 Fax: (808) 522-8156
Assistant U.S. Trustee **Curtis B. Ching** . . . . (808) 522-8154
Bankruptcy Analyst **Anson T. Okimoto** . . . . (808) 522-8153

San Diego (CA) Field Office
880 Front Street, Third Floor, Suite 3230, San Diego, CA 92101-8511
Tel: (619) 557-5013 Fax: (619) 557-5339
Assistant U.S. Trustee (Acting) **Elizabeth C. Amorosi** . . . (619) 557-5013

Region 16
915 Wilshire Boulevard, Suite 1850, Los Angeles, CA 90017
Tel: (213) 894-6811 Fax: (213) 894-2603
Internet: www.justice.gov/ust/r16
Areas Covered: CA (Central Judicial District)
U.S. Trustee **Peter C. Anderson** . . . . (213) 894-0405
Education: USC 1979; Loyola Law 1982 JD
Assistant U.S. Trustee **Jill Sturtevant** . . . . (213) 894-3701
Administrative Officer **Liz G. Espinoza** . . . . (213) 894-0411
E-mail: liz.espinoza@usdoj.gov

Riverside (CA) Field Office
3801 University Avenue, Suite 720, Riverside, CA 92501
Tel: (951) 276-6990 Fax: (951) 276-6973
Assistant U.S. Trustee **Abram S. Feuerstein** . . . . (951) 276-6975

Santa Ana (CA) Field Office
411 West Fourth Street, Suite 7160, Santa Ana, CA 92701-8000
Tel: (714) 338-3400 Fax: (714) 338-3421
Assistant U.S. Trustee **Frank M. Cadigan** . . . . (714) 338-3405

Woodland Hills (CA) Field Office
21051 Warner Center Lane, Suite 115, Woodland Hills, CA 91367
Tel: (818) 716-8800 Fax: (818) 716-1576
Note: The Woodland Hills office staff work out of the Los Angeles office.
Assistant U.S. Trustee **Jennifer L. Braun** . . . . (213) 894-3240

Region 17
450 Golden Gate Avenue, Floor 5, Suite 05-0153, San Francisco, CA 94102
Tel: (415) 705-3300 Fax: (415) 705-3367
Internet: https://www.justice.gov/ust-regions-r17
Areas Covered: CA (Eastern & Northern Judicial Districts), NV
U.S. Trustee **Tracy Hope Davis** . . . . (415) 705-3300
Senior Bankruptcy Analyst **Michael O. Sorgaard** . . . . (415) 705-3307
Administrative Officer **Nathalie V. Brumfield-Brown** . . . . (713) 718-4650
E-mail: nathalie.brumfield-brown@usdoj.gov
IT Manager **(Vacant)** . . . . (415) 705-3308
IT Specialist **John R. Hayden** . . . . (415) 705-3350
E-mail: john.hayden@usdoj.gov
Assistant U.S. Trustee **Donna S. Tamanaha** . . . . (415) 705-3300

Fresno (CA) Field Office
Office of U.S. Trustee, United States Courthouse, 2500 Tulare Street, Fresno, CA 93721
Tel: (559) 487-5002 Fax: (559) 487-5030
Assistant U.S. Trustee **Gregory Powell** . . . . (559) 487-5002 ext. 225
Trial Attorney **Terri Didion** . . . . (559) 487-5002 ext. 235
E-mail: terri.didion@usdoj.gov
Trial Attorney **Robin Tubesing** . . . . (559) 487-5002 ext. 224
E-mail: robin.tubesing@usdoj.gov
Secretary **(Vacant)** . . . . (559) 487-5002 ext. 232

Las Vegas (NV) Field Office
300 Las Vegas Boulevard South, Suite 4300, Las Vegas, NV 89101
Tel: (702) 388-6600 Fax: (702) 388-6658
Assistant U.S. Trustee **Nicholas Strozza** . . . . (702) 388-6600 ext. 235
Trial Attorney **Edward M. McDonald** . . . . (702) 388-6600 ext. 234
E-mail: edward.m.mcdonald@usdoj.gov
Trial Attorney **(Vacant)** . . . . (702) 388-6600 ext. 229
Trial Attorney **(Vacant)** . . . . (702) 388-6600

★ Presidential Appointment Requiring Senate Confirmation ☆ Presidential Appointment □ Schedule C Appointment ◇ Career Senior Foreign Service Appointment
● Career Senior Executive Service (SES) Appointment ○ Non-Career Senior Executive Service (SES) Appointment ■ Postal Career Executive Service

DEPARTMENTS

Oakland (CA) Field Office
Federal Building, 1301 Clay Street, Suite 690N, Oakland, CA 94612-5202
Tel: (510) 637-3200 Fax: (510) 637-3220

Assistant U.S. Trustee **Timothy S. Laffredi** .... (415) 252-2080
Trial Attorney **Lynette C. Kelly** .... (415) 252-2065
E-mail: lynette.c.kelly@usdoj.gov
Trial Attorney **(Vacant)** .... (415) 252-2062
Trial Attorney **Margaret H. McGee** .... (415) 252-2065

Reno (NV) Field Office
300 Booth Street, Suite 3009, Reno, NV 89509
Tel: (775) 784-5335 Fax: (775) 784-5531

Assistant U.S. Trustee **Nicholas Strozza** .... (775) 784-5335
Trial Attorney **(Vacant)** .... (775) 784-5052

Sacramento (CA) Field Office
501 I Street, Suite 7-500, Sacramento, CA 95814-2322
Tel: (916) 930-2100 Fax: (916) 930-2099

Assistant U.S. Trustee **Antonia G. Darling** .... (916) 930-2090
Trial Attorney **Jason Blumberg** .... (916) 930-2076
E-mail: jason.blumberg@usdoj.gov
Trial Attorney **Allen C. Massey** .... (916) 930-0281

San Jose (CA) Field Office
280 South First Street, Suite 268, San Jose, CA 95113
Tel: (408) 535-5525 Fax: (408) 535-5532

Assistant U.S. Trustee **Timothy S. Laffredi** .... (408) 535-5525

San Francisco (CA) Field Office
235 Pine Street, Suite 700, San Francisco, CA 94104
Tel: (415) 705-3333 Fax: (415) 705-3379

Assistant U.S. Trustee **Timothy S. Laffredi** .... (415) 705-3341
Trial Attorney **Marta Villacorta** .... (415) 705-3339
E-mail: marta.villacorta@usdoj.gov

Region 18
700 Stewart Street, Suite 5103, Seattle, WA 98101-1271
Tel: (206) 553-2000 Fax: (206) 553-2566
Internet: https://www.justice.gov/ust-regions-r18
Areas Covered: AK, ID, MT, OR, WA

U.S. Trustee (Acting) **Gregory Garvin** .... (206) 553-2000
Fax: (206) 553-2566

Anchorage (AK) Field Office
605 West Fourth Avenue, Suite 258, Anchorage, AK 99501
Tel: (907) 271-2600 Fax: (907) 271-2610

Assistant U.S. Trustee **Gary W. Dyer** .... (206) 533-2000 ext. 229
Fax: (907) 271-2610
Trial Attorney **Kathryn Perkins** .... (206) 553-2000 ext. 265
Bankruptcy Analyst **Martha A. Van Draanen** ... (206) 553-2000 ext. 263
Paralegal Specialist **Cori Gustafson** .... (206) 553-2000 ext. 242

Boise (ID) Field Office
720 Park Boulevard, Suite 220, Boise, ID 83712
Tel: (208) 334-1300 Fax: (208) 334-9756

Assistant U.S. Trustee **David W. Newman** ..... (208) 334-1300 ext. 2222
Trial Attorney **(Vacant)** .... (208) 334-1300 ext. 2228

Eugene (OR) Field Office
405 East Eighth Avenue, Room 1100, Eugene, OR 97401
Tel: (541) 465-6330 Fax: (541) 465-6335

Assistant U.S. Trustee (Acting) **Jonas V. Anderson** ..... (541) 465-6561
Education: Duke 2008 JD

Great Falls (MT) Field Office
301 Central Avenue, Suite 204, Great Falls, MT 59401
Tel: (406) 761-8777 Fax: (406) 761-8895

Assistant U.S. Trustee **David W. Newman** ...... (406) 761-8777 ext. 104

Portland (OR) Field Office
620 SW Main Avenue, Suite 213, Portland, OR 97205
Tel: (503) 326-4000 Fax: (503) 326-7658

Assistant U.S. Trustee (Acting) **Jonas V. Anderson** ..... (503) 326-4004
Education: Duke 2008 JD

Seattle (WA) Field Office
700 Stewart Street, Suite 5103, Seattle, WA 98101-1271
Tel: (206) 553-2000 Fax: (206) 553-2566

Assistant U.S. Trustee **Gary W. Dyer** .... (206) 553-2000 ext. 229

Spokane (WA) Field Office
Federal Courthouse, 920 West Riverside Avenue,
Room 593, Spokane, WA 99201
Tel: (509) 353-2999 Fax: (509) 353-3124

Assistant U.S. Trustee **Gary W. Dyer** .... (509) 353-2999 ext. 110

Region 19
Bryon G. Rogers Federal Building, 1961 Stout Street,
Suite 12-200, Denver, CO 80294
Tel: (303) 312-7230 Fax: (303) 312-7259
Internet: https://www.justice.gov/ust-regions-r19
Areas Covered: CO, UT, WY

U.S. Trustee (Interim) **Patrick S. Layng** .... (303) 312-7233
Education: Illinois, JD
Administrative Officer **Eric M. Campany** .... (303) 312-7235
E-mail: eric.campany@usdoj.gov
Regional Supervisory Auditor **Krista Hale** .... (303) 312-7998
E-mail: krista.hale@usdoj.gov

Cheyenne (WY) Field Office
308 West 21st Street, Room 203, Cheyenne, WY 82001
Tel: (307) 772-2790 Fax: (307) 772-2795

Assistant U.S. Trustee **Daniel J. Morse** .... (307) 772-2793

Denver (CO) Field Office
999 - 18th Street, Suite 1551, Denver, CO 80202
Tel: (303) 312-7230 Fax: (303) 312-7259

Assistant U.S. Trustee **Gregory Garvin** .... (303) 312-7230

Salt Lake City (UT) Field Office
Ken Garff Building, 405 South Main Street,
Suite 300, Salt Lake City, UT 84111
Tel: (801) 524-5734 Fax: (801) 524-5628

Assistant U.S. Trustee **James "Vince" Cameron** .... (801) 524-5149

Region 20
301 North Main, Suite 1150, Wichita, KS 67202
Tel: (316) 269-6637 Fax: (316) 269-6182
Areas Covered: KS, NM, OK

U.S. Trustee (Interim) **Ilene J. Lashinsky** .... (316) 269-6637
Education: Arizona State 1969, 1972 JD
Administrative Officer **S. Michele Cox** .... (316) 269-6607
E-mail: s.michele.cox@usdoj.gov
Information Technology Specialist (Acting)
Thomas Crouse .... (713) 718-4650 ext. 232
E-mail: thomas.crouse@usdoj.gov
Information Technology Specialist (Acting)
Theresa C. Garcia .... (303) 312-7240
E-mail: theresa.garcia@usdoj.gov
Senior Bankruptcy Analyst **Edward B. Walsh** .... (316) 269-6217

Albuquerque (NM) Field Office
421 Gold Avenue, SW, Room 112, Albuquerque, NM 87102
P.O. Box 608, Albuquerque, NM 87102
Tel: (505) 248-6544 Fax: (505) 248-6558

Assistant U.S. Trustee (Acting) **Charles S. Glidewell** .... (505) 248-6549

★ Presidential Appointment Requiring Senate Confirmation ☆ Presidential Appointment □ Schedule C Appointment ◇ Career Senior Foreign Service Appointment
● Career Senior Executive Service (SES) Appointment ○ Non-Career Senior Executive Service (SES) Appointment ■ Postal Career Executive Service

Oklahoma City (OK) Field Office
Old Postal Building, 215 Dean A. McGee Avenue, 4th Floor, Oklahoma City, OK 73102
Tel: (405) 231-5950 Fax: (405) 231-5958

Assistant U.S. Trustee **Charles S. Glidewell** . . . . (405) 231-5950

Tulsa (OK) Field Office
224 South Boulder Avenue, Suite 225, Tulsa, OK 74103
Tel: (918) 581-6670 Fax: (918) 581-6674

Assistant U.S. Trustee **Katherine Vance** . . . . (918) 581-6686

Wichita (KS) Field Office
301 North Main, Suite 1150, Wichita, KS 67202
Tel: (316) 269-6637 Fax: (316) 269-6182

Assistant U.S. Trustee **Jordan Sickman** . . . . (316) 269-6176

Region 21
Richard B. Russell Federal Building, 75 Ted Turner Drive, SW, Suite 362, Atlanta, GA 30303
Tel: (404) 331-4437 Fax: (404) 331-4464
Internet: https://www.justice.gov/ust-regions-r21
Areas Covered: FL, GA, PR, VI

U.S. Trustee (Interim) **Daniel M. McDermott** . . . (216) 522-7800 ext. 230

Atlanta (GA) Field Office
Richard B. Russell Federal Building, 75 Spring Street, SW, Suite 362, Atlanta, GA 30303
Tel: (404) 331-4437 Fax: (404) 331-4464

Assistant U.S. Trustee **Guy G. Gebhardt** . . . . (404) 331-4437 ext. 120

Macon (GA) Field Office
440 Martin L. King, Jr. Boulevard, Suite 302, Macon, GA 31201-7910
Tel: (478) 752-3544 Fax: (478) 752-3549

Assistant U.S. Trustee **Elizabeth A. Hardy** . . . . (478) 752-3401

Miami (FL) Field Office
Claude Pepper Federal Building, 51 SW First Avenue, Suite 1204, Miami, FL 33130
Tel: (305) 536-7285 Fax: (305) 536-7360

Assistant U.S. Trustee **Steven R. Turner** . . . . (305) 536-7354

Orlando (FL) Field Office
400 West Washington Street, Suite 1101, Orlando, FL 32801-2440
Tel: (407) 648-6301 Fax: (407) 648-6323

Assistant U.S. Trustee **Charles R. Sterbach** . . . . . (407) 648-6301 ext. 121

San Juan (PR) Field Office
Edificio Ochoa, 500 Tanca Street, Suite 301, San Juan, PR 00901-1922
Tel: (787) 729-7444 Fax: (787) 729-7449

Assistant U.S. Trustee **Monsita Lecaroz Arribas** . . . . (787) 729-7453

Savannah (GA) Field Office
Two East Bryan Street, Suite 725, Savannah, GA 31401
P.O. Box 10487, Savannah, GA 31412
Tel: (912) 652-4112 Fax: (912) 652-4123

Assistant U.S. Trustee **Matthew Mills** . . . . (912) 652-4117

Tallahassee (FL) Field Office
110 East Park Avenue, Suite 128, Tallahassee, FL 32301
Tel: (850) 942-1660 Fax: (850) 942-1669

Assistant U.S. Trustee **Charles F. Edwards** . . . . (850) 942-1661

Tampa (FL) Field Office
501 East Polk Street, Suite 1200, Tampa, FL 33602
Tel: (813) 228-2000 Fax: (813) 228-2303

Assistant U.S. Trustee
Cynthia P. "Cindy" Burnette . . . . (813) 228-2000 ext. 229
Assistant U.S. Trustee **Thomas Patrick Tinker** . . . . (302) 573-6538

Office of the Inspector General (OIG)
950 Pennsylvania Avenue, NW, Suite 4706, Washington, DC 20530
Tel: (202) 514-3435 Fax: (202) 514-4001 Internet: www.justice.gov/oig

Audit Division
1425 New York Avenue, NW, Suite 5000, Washington, DC 20530

Atlanta (GA) Regional Audit Office
75 Ted Turner Drive S.W., Suite 1130, Atlanta, GA 30303
Tel: (404) 331-5928 Fax: (404) 331-5046
Areas Covered: AL, FL, GA, MS, NC, PR, SC, TN, VI

Regional Audit Manager **Ferris B. Polk** . . . . (404) 331-5928
E-mail: ferris.b.polk@usdoj.gov
Program Specialist **Tonithia Reid** . . . . (404) 331-5928
Assistant Regional Audit Manager **Joel Smith** . . . . (404) 331-5928
Assistant Regional Audit Manager **Nathaniel Strohl** . . . . . (404) 331-5928
E-mail: nathaniel.strohl@usdoj.gov
Assistant Regional Audit Manager **Barbara Williams** . . . . (404) 331-5928
E-mail: barb.williams@usdoj.gov
Assistant Regional Audit Manager **Allen Wood** . . . . (404) 331-5928

Chicago (IL) Regional Audit Office
500 West Madison Street, Suite 1121, Chicago, IL 60661
Tel: (312) 353-1203 Fax: (312) 886-0513
Areas Covered: IL, IN, IA, KY, MI, MN, MO, OH, WI

Regional Audit Manager **Carol S. Taraszka** . . . . (312) 353-1203
E-mail: carol.s.taraszka@usdoj.gov
Assistant Regional Audit Manager **Todd A. Anderson** . . . (312) 353-1203
E-mail: todd.a.anderson@usdoj.gov
Assistant Regional Audit Manager
Dominic S. Gagliardi . . . . (312) 353-1203
E-mail: dominic.s.gagliardi@usdoj.gov
Assistant Regional Audit Manager **Michelle Proesel** . . . . . (312) 353-1203
E-mail: michelle.m.proesel@usdoj.gov

Denver (CO) Regional Audit Office
1120 Lincoln Street, Suite 1500, Denver, CO 80203
Tel: (303) 864-2000 Fax: (303) 864-2004
Areas Covered: AZ, CO, ID, KS, MT, ND, NE, NM, SD, UT, WY

Regional Audit Manager **David M. Sheeren** . . . . (303) 864-2000
Assistant Regional Audit Manager **Sean B. Haynes** . . . . . (303) 864-2000
E-mail: sean.b.haynes@usdoj.gov
Assistant Regional Audit Manager
Rebecca M. Quinson . . . . (303) 864-2000
E-mail: rebecca.m.quinson@usdoj.gov

Philadelphia (PA) Regional Audit Office
701 Market Street, Suite 201, Philadelphia, PA 19106
Tel: (215) 580-2111 Fax: (215) 597-1348

Regional Audit Manager **Thomas O. Puerzer** . . . . (215) 580-2111
E-mail: thomas.o.puerzer@usdoj.gov
Assistant Regional Audit Manager
Dirk W. Schumacher . . . . (215) 580-2111
E-mail: dirk.w.schumacher@usdoj.gov
Assistant Regional Audit Manager
Martin L. Ward CPA . . . . (215) 580-2111
E-mail: martin.l.ward@usdoj.gov
Assistant Regional Audit Manager **(Vacant)** . . . . (215) 580-2111

San Francisco (CA) Regional Audit Office
90 7th Street, Suite 3-100, San Francisco, CA 94103
Tel: (415) 436-9627 Fax: (415) 503-1417
Areas Covered: AK, AS, CA, Commonwealth of the Northern Mariana Islands, GU, HI, NV, OR, Trust Territory of the Pacific Islands, WA

Regional Audit Manager **David J. Gaschke** . . . . (415) 554-8109
E-mail: david.j.gaschke@usdoj.gov
Assistant Regional Audit Manager **John I. Provan** . . . . (415) 554-8109
E-mail: john.i.provan@usdoj.gov
Assistant Regional Audit Manager **Stacey L. Scull** . . . . . . (415) 554-8109
E-mail: stacey.l.scull@usdoj.gov

★ Presidential Appointment Requiring Senate Confirmation ☆ Presidential Appointment ☐ Schedule C Appointment ◇ Career Senior Foreign Service Appointment
● Career Senior Executive Service (SES) Appointment ○ Non-Career Senior Executive Service (SES) Appointment ■ Postal Career Executive Service

Washington (DC) Regional Audit Office
1401 S. Clark Street, Suite 9000, Arlington, VA 22202
Tel: (703) 413-1801 Fax: (703) 413-1833
Areas Covered: DC, MD, VA, WV

Regional Audit Manager **John J. Manning** . . . . (202) 616-4688
E-mail: john.manning@usdoj.gov
Assistant Regional Audit Manager **Shenika Cox** . . . . (202) 616-4688
E-mail: shenika.cox@usdoj.gov
Assistant Regional Audit Manager **David M. Hudson** . . . . (202) 616-4688
E-mail: david.m.hudson@usdoj.gov
Assistant Regional Audit Manager **Melissa Mulhollen** . . . (202) 616-4688
E-mail: melissa.mulhollen@usdoj.gov
Assistant Regional Audit Manager **Allison Russo** . . . . (202) 616-4688
E-mail: allison.russo@usdoj.gov

Investigations Division
1425 New York Avenue, NW, Suite 7100, Washington, DC 20530

Chicago (IL) Field Office
500 West Madison Street, 11th Floor, Chicago, IL 60661
P.O. Box 1802, Chicago, IL 60601
Tel: (312) 886-7050 Fax: (312) 886-7065

Special Agent-in-Charge **John F. Oleskowicz** . . . . (312) 886-7050
E-mail: john.f.oleskowicz@usdoj.gov
Assistant Special Agent-in-Charge **Kevin Shirley** . . . . (312) 886-7050

Detroit (MI) Area Office
211 West Fort Street, Suite 1402, Detroit, MI 48226
Tel: (313) 226-4005 Fax: (313) 226-4006

Assistant Special Agent in Charge **Kevin Shirley** . . . . (313) 226-4005

Dallas (TX) Field Office
Brookhollow Riverside, 2505 State Highway 360,
Suite 410, Grand Prairie, TX 75050
Tel: (817) 385-5200 Fax: (817) 385-5206

Special Agent In Charge **Monte A. Cason** . . . . (817) 385-5200
Assistant Special Agent in Charge **Sean P. Carson** . . . . . . (817) 385-5200

Houston (TX) Area Office
701 San Jacinto, Suite 146, Houston, TX 77002
Tel: (713) 718-4888 Fax: (713) 718-4706

Assistant Special Agent-in-Charge **Douglas B. Bruce** . . . . (713) 718-4888

El Paso (TX) Area Office
4050 Rio Bravo, Suite 135, El Paso, TX 79902
Tel: (915) 577-0102 Fax: (915) 577-9012

Contact Senior Special Agent **Eric S. Benn** . . . . (915) 577-0102

Denver (CO) Field Office
1120 Lincoln Street, Suite 1501, Denver, CO 80203
Tel: (303) 335-4201 Fax: (303) 335-4002

Special Agent-in-Charge **Sandra D. Barnes** . . . . (303) 335-4201
Assistant Special Agent-in-Charge **(Vacant)** . . . . (303) 335-4201
Special Agent **Jeffrey W. Campbell** . . . . (303) 335-4201
Criminal Investigator **Paul E. Sullivan** . . . . (303) 335-4201
Criminal Investigator **Craig M. Trautner** . . . . (303) 335-4201
Administrative Assistant **Cynthia K. Jensen** . . . . (303) 335-4201
E-mail: cynthia.k.jensen@usdoj.gov

Tucson (AZ) Area Office
300 West Congress Street, Suite 5000 FB34, Tucson, AZ 85701
Tel: (520) 620-7390 Fax: (520) 670-7301

Special Agent-in-Charge **James Greer** . . . . (520) 620-7390

Los Angeles (CA) Field Office
330 North Brand Boulevard, Suite 1000, Glendale, CA 91203
Tel: (818) 543-1172 Fax: (818) 637-5082

Special Agent-in-Charge **James K. Cheng** . . . . (818) 543-1172
Assistant Special Agent-in-Charge **Shroyer Zackary** . . . . . (818) 543-1172

San Francisco (CA) Area Office
90 7th Street, Suite 3-100, San Francisco, CA 94103
Tel: (415) 554-1402 Fax: (415) 503-1417

Assistant Special Agent-in-Charge **Michael Barranti** . . . . . (415) 554-1402

Miami (FL) Field Office
510 Shotgun Road, Suite 200, Sunrise, FL 33326
Tel: (954) 496-8178 Fax: (954) 496-8436
Areas Covered: AL, FL, GA, MS, SC, TN and the Caribbean

Special Agent-in-Charge **Robert A. Bourbon** . . . . (954) 496-8178
Assistant Special Agent-in-Charge **James Boyersmith** . . . (954) 496-8178

Atlanta (GA) Area Office
60 Forsyth Street, SW, Suite 8M45, Atlanta, GA 30303
Tel: (404) 588-3870 Fax: (404) 588-3871

Assistant Special Agent in Charge **Eddie D. Davis** . . . . (404) 562-1980

New York (NY) Field Office
One Battery Park Plaza, 29th Floor, New York, NY 10004
Tel: (212) 824-3650 Fax: (212) 771-1000
Areas Covered: CT, DE, ME, MA, NH, NJ, NY, PA, RI, VT, Western Europe, Former Soviet Union countries.

Special Agent-in-Charge **Ronald G. Gardella** . . . . (212) 824-3650
Assistant Special Agent-in-Charge **Guido Modano** . . . . . . (212) 824-3650
Assistant Special Agent-in-Charge **Kurt R. Jebitsch** . . . . . (212) 824-3650
Investigative Specialist **Luz H. Duque** . . . . (212) 824-3650
E-mail: luz.h.duque@usdoj.gov
Investigative Specialist **(Vacant)** . . . . (212) 824-3650

Boston (MA) Area Office
U.S. Court House, One Court House Way,
Room 9200, Boston, MA 02210
Tel: (617) 748-3218 Fax: (617) 748-3995

Senior Special Agent **(Vacant)** . . . . (617) 748-3219
Special Agent **Daniel Benedict** . . . . (617) 748-3218
Special Agent **Dennis Matulewicz** . . . . (617) 748-3218
Special Agent **(Vacant)** . . . . (617) 748-3330

New Jersey Area Office
50 West State Street, 1006, Trenton, NJ 08608
Tel: (609) 989-2698 Fax: (609) 989-2213

Senior Special Agent **Frank Adamo** . . . . (609) 883-5439
Special Agent **(Vacant)** . . . . (609) 989-2698
Special Agent **(Vacant)** . . . . (609) 989-2698

Washington (DC) Field Office
1401 S. Clark Street, Suite 9000, Arlington, VA 22202
Tel: (703) 413-1865 Fax: (703) 413-1833

Special Agent-in-Charge **Michael P. Tompkins** . . . . (202) 616-4766
Assistant Special Agent-in-Charge **(Vacant)** . . . . (202) 616-4766
Assistant Special Agent-in-Charge **(Vacant)** . . . . (202) 616-4766

Executive Office for Immigration Review (EOIR)
Skyline Towers, 5107 Leesburg Pike, Falls Church, VA 22041
Tel: (703) 305-0289 Fax: (703) 605-0365 E-mail: pao.eoir@usdoj.gov
Internet: www.justice.gov/eoir

Office of the Chief Immigration Judge (OCIJ)
Skyline Towers, 5107 Leesburg Pike,
Room 2500, Falls Church, VA 20530
Tel: (703) 305-1247
Internet: https://www.justice.gov/eoir/board-of-immigration-appeals

United States Immigration Courts

U.S. Immigration Court - Adelanto (CA) Detention Facility
10250 Rancho Road, Suite 201A, Adelanto, CA 92301
Tel: (760) 561-6500

Immigration Judge **Maria Bjornerud** . . . . (760) 246-5404
E-mail: maria.bjornerud@usdoj.gov

U.S. Immigration Court - Adelanto (CA) Detention Facility *(continued)*

Immigration Judge **Amy Lee** .... (760) 246-5404
E-mail: amy.lee@usdoj.gov
Immigration Judge **James M. Left** .... (760) 246-5404
E-mail: james.m.left@usdoj.gov
Immigration Judge **Jose Luis "Joe" Penalosa, Jr.** .... (760) 246-5404
Education: UCLA 1986 BA; Arizona State 1989 JD
Immigration Judge **Sandra J. Santos-Garcia** .... (760) 246-5404
E-mail: sandra.j.santos-garcia@usdoj.gov
Immigration Judge **(Vacant)** .... (760) 246-5404
Court Administrator **Hilma Torres** .... (760) 246-5404

U.S. Immigration Court - Arlington (VA)

1901 South Bell Street, Suite 200, Arlington, VA 22202
Tel: (703) 603-1300
Internet: https://www.justice.gov/eoir/arlington-immigration-court

Immigration Judge **Quynh Vu Bain** .... (703) 603-1300
E-mail: quynh.bain2@usdoj.gov
Immigration Judge **John M. Bryant** .... (703) 603-1300
E-mail: john.m.bryant@usdoj.gov
Immigration Judge **Lawrence O. Burman** .... (703) 603-1300
E-mail: lawrence.burman@usdoj.gov
Immigration Judge **Raphael Choi** .... (703) 603-1300
E-mail: raphael.choi@usdoj.gov
Education: Iowa State 1996 BA; Wisconsin 2002 JD
Immigration Judge **Karen M. Donoso-Stevens** .... (229) 838-1320
Education: Detroit Law JD
Immigration Judge **Roxanne Hladylowycz** .... (703) 603-1300
E-mail: roxanne.hladylowycz@usdoj.gov
Immigration Judge **Jungyoun Traci Hong** .... (703) 603-1300
E-mail: j.traci.hong@usdoj.gov
Immigration Judge **Paul McCloskey** .... (703) 603-1300
E-mail: paul.a.mccloskey@usdoj.gov
Education: Towson State U 1996 BS; Maryland 1999 JD
Immigration Judge **Francisco Mendez** .... (703) 603-1300
E-mail: francisco.mendez@usdoj.gov
Education: Fordham 1992 BA, 1995 JD
Immigration Judge **Helaine R. Perlman** .... (703) 603-1300
E-mail: helaine.perlman@usdoj.gov
Education: Columbia 1997 BA; NYU 2002 JD
Immigration Judge **Thomas G. Snow** .... (703) 603-1300
E-mail: thomas.snow@usdoj.gov
Education: William & Mary 1977 BA; Virginia 1980 MA, 1982 JD
Immigration Judge **Vance H. Spath** .... (703) 603-1300
E-mail: vance.h.spath@usdoj.gov
Education: Virginia Wesleyan U 1987 BA; Quinnipiac U 1991 JD; Judge Advocate Gen 2001 ML
Immigration Judge **Emmett D. Soper** .... (703) 603-1300
E-mail: emmett.soper@usdoj.gov
Immigration Judge **Cynthia Shepherd Torg** .... (318) 335-0365
E-mail: cynthia.torg@usdoj.gov
Education: Virginia 1989 BA, 1992 JD
Court Administrator **Deborah Castro** .... (703) 603-1300
E-mail: deborah.castro@usdoj.gov

Falls Church Immigration Adjudication Center

Immigration Judge **Audra R. Behne** .... (703) 603-1300
Education: Cal State (Northridge) 1992 BA; Southwestern 1995 JD
Immigration Judge **Lisa Ann J. De Cardona** .... (703) 603-1300
Immigration Judge **Emily N. Farrar-Crockett** .... (703) 603-1300
Education: Murray State Col 1997 BS; Tulane 2001 JD
Immigration Judge **George J. Ward, Jr.** .... (703) 603-1300
Education: Bucknell 1988 BA; St John's U (NY) 1993 JD
Court Administrator (Acting) **Nicole Wiggs** .... (703) 603-1300
E-mail: nicole.wiggs@usdoj.gov

U.S. Immigration Court - Atlanta (GA)

180 Ted Turner Drive, SW, Suite 241, Atlanta, GA 30303
Tel: (404) 331-0907
Internet: https://www.justice.gov/eoir/atlanta-immigration-court

Immigration Judge **Michael P. Baird** .... (404) 331-0907
E-mail: michael.p.baird@usdoj.gov
Education: Clayton State 1989 BBA; Georgia State 1992 JD

U.S. Immigration Court - Atlanta (GA) *(continued)*

Immigration Judge **William A. Cassidy** .... (404) 331-0907
E-mail: william.cassidy@usdoj.gov
Immigration Judge **Scott D. Criss** .... (404) 331-0907
E-mail: scott.d.criss@usdoj.gov
Immigration Judge **Wayne K. Houser, Jr.** .... (404) 331-0907
E-mail: wayne.houser@usdoj.gov
Education: Tennessee 1976 BA; Memphis State 1978 PhD
Immigration Judge **Sirce E. Owen** .... (404) 331-0907
E-mail: sirce.e.owen@usdoj.gov
Education: Johns Hopkins 1996 BS; Georgia State 2002 MBA, 2005 JD
Immigration Judge **Jonathan Dan Pelletier** .... (404) 331-0907
E-mail: dan.pelletier@usdoj.gov
Immigration Judge **Earle B. Wilson** .... (404) 331-0907
E-mail: earle.wilson2@usdoj.gov
Education: Atlantic Union 1979 BS; Howard U 1989 JD
Court Administrator **Cynthia Long** .... (404) 331-0907
E-mail: cynthia.long@usdoj.gov
Immigration Judge **Njeri B. Maldonado** .... (404) 331-0907
E-mail: njeri.b.maldonado@usdoj.gov

U.S. Immigration Court - Aurora (CO)

3130 N. Oakland Street, Aurora, CO 80010
Tel: (303) 361-0488

Immigration Judge **Steven Caley** .... (415) 705-4415
E-mail: steven.caley@usdoj.gov
Immigration Judge **Nina M. Carbone** .... (303) 361-0488
E-mail: nina.m.carbone@usdoj.gov
Immigration Judge **Elizabeth McGrail** .... (303) 361-0488
E-mail: elizabeth.mcgrail@usdoj.gov
Court Administrator **Fayne Overton** .... (303) 361-0488
E-mail: fayne.overton@usdoj.gov

U.S. Immigration Court - Baltimore (MD)

George M. Fallon Federal Building, 31 Hopkins Plaza, Room 440, Baltimore, MD 21201
Tel: (410) 962-3092
Internet: https://www.justice.gov/eoir/baltimore-immigration-court

Immigration Judge **David W. Crosland** .... (410) 962-3092
E-mail: david.crosland@usdoj.gov
Education: Auburn 1959 BS; Alabama 1966 JD
Immigration Judge **Lisa Dornell** .... (410) 962-3092
E-mail: lisa.dornell@usdoj.gov
Immigration Judge **Elizabeth A. Kessler** .... (410) 962-3092
E-mail: elizabeth.kessler@usdoj.gov
Education: Columbia 1987 BA; Yale 1992 MA, 1992 JD
Immigration Judge **David C. Koelsch** .... (410) 962-3092
E-mail: david.koelsch@usdoj.gov
Education: Michigan State 1988 BA; Catholic U 1994 JD
Immigration Judge **Zakia Mahasa** .... (410) 962-3092
E-mail: zakia.mahasa@usdoj.gov
Education: Maryland 1981 BBA, 1986 JD
Immigration Judge **Denise N. Slavin** .... (410) 962-3092
E-mail: denise.slavin@usdoj.gov
Immigration Judge **Phillip T. Williams** .... (410) 962-3092
E-mail: phillip.williams@usdoj.gov
Education: Temple 1978 BA; Howard U 1981 MA, 1986 JD
Court Administrator **Brenda L. Cook** .... (410) 962-3092
E-mail: brenda.l.cook@usdoj.gov

U.S. Immigration Court - Batavia (NY)

Batavia Federal Detention Facility, 4250 Federal Drive, Room F108, Batavia, NY 14020
Tel: (585) 345-4300
Internet: https://www.justice.gov/eoir/batavia-immigration-court

Immigration Judge **Steven J. Connelly** .... (585) 345-4300
E-mail: steven.j.connelly@usdoj.gov
Education: SUNY (Buffalo) 1983 BA, 1986 JD
Immigration Judge **Philip J. Montante, Jr.** .... (585) 345-4300
E-mail: philip.montante@usdoj.gov
Education: Cumberland 1972 JD
Court Administrator **Christopher E. Hess** .... (585) 345-4300
E-mail: christopher.hess@usdoj.gov

★ Presidential Appointment Requiring Senate Confirmation ☆ Presidential Appointment □ Schedule C Appointment ◇ Career Senior Foreign Service Appointment
● Career Senior Executive Service (SES) Appointment ○ Non-Career Senior Executive Service (SES) Appointment ■ Postal Career Executive Service

DEPARTMENTS

U.S. Immigration Court - Boston (MA)

John F. Kennedy Federal Building, 15 New Sudbury Street, Room 320, Boston, MA 02203
Tel: (617) 565-3080
Internet: https://www.justice.gov/eoir/boston-immigration-court

Immigration Judge **Steven F Day** .... (617) 565-3080
E-mail: steven.f.day@usdoj.gov
Immigration Judge **Robin E. Feder** .... (617) 565-3080
E-mail: robin.feder@usdoj.gov
Education: Illinois 1980 BA; George Washington 1983 JD
Immigration Judge **Paul M. Gagnon** .... (617) 565-3080
E-mail: paul.gagnon@usdoj.gov
Education: New Hampshire 1971 BA; Suffolk 1977 JD
Immigration Judge **Todd A. Masters** .... (213) 894-2811
E-mail: todd.a.masters@usdoj.gov
Education: Naval Acad 1992 BS; Maryland 1993 MA; Boston Col 2005 JD
Immigration Judge **Brenda M. O'Malley** .... (617) 565-3080
Education: Boston U 1992 BA; Suffolk 1995 JD
Immigration Judge **Maureen S. O'Sullivan** .... (617) 565-3080
E-mail: maureen.o'sullivan@usdoj.gov
Education: UCLA 1978 BA; Antioch Col 1981 JD; Harvard 1986 ML
Immigration Judge **Jose A. Sanchez** .... (617) 565-3080
E-mail: jose.a.sanchez@usdoj.gov
Immigration Judge **Mario J. Sturla** .... (617) 565-3080
Immigration Judge **Gwendylan Tregerman** .... (617) 565-3080
Court Administrator (Acting) **Pietro Cicolini** .... (617) 565-3080
E-mail: pietro.cicolini@usdoj.gov
Administrative Assistance **Tracy Polite-Jackson** .... (617) 565-3080
E-mail: tracy.polite-jackson@usdoj.gov

U.S. Immigration Court - Buffalo (NY)

130 Delaware Avenue, Suite 410, Buffalo, NY 14202
Tel: (716) 551-3442
Internet: https://www.justice.gov/eoir/buffalo-immigration-court

Immigration Judge **Denise Hochul** .... (716) 551-3442
E-mail: denise.hochul@usdoj.gov
Immigration Judge **Walter Hammele Ruehle** .... (716) 551-3442
E-mail: walter.ruehle@usdoj.gov
Immigration Judge **(Vacant)** .... (716) 551-3442
Court Administrator **Stephanie L. Kerr** .... (716) 551-3442
E-mail: stephanie.kerr@usdoj.gov

U.S. Immigration Court - Charlotte (NC)

5701 Executive Center Drive, Suite 400, Charlotte, NC 28212
Tel: (704) 817-6140

Immigration Judge **V. Stuart Couch** .... (704) 817-6140
E-mail: stuart.couch@usdoj.gov
Education: Duke 1987 BA; Campbell 1996 JD; George Washington 2008 ML
Immigration Judge **Theresa Holmes-Simmons** .... (704) 817-6140
E-mail: theresa.simmons@usdoj.gov
Immigration Judge **Barry Pettinato** .... (704) 817-6140
E-mail: barry.pettinato2@usdoj.gov
Court Administrator **R. Elliott Edwards** .... (704) 817-6140
E-mail: r.elliott.edwards@usdoj.gov

U.S. Immigration Court - Chicago (IL)

525 West Van Buren, Suite 500, Chicago, IL 60607
Tel: (312) 697-5800
Internet: https://www.justice.gov/eoir/chicago-immigration-court

Immigration Judge **Samuel B. Cole** .... (312) 855-2324
E-mail: samuel.b.cole@usdoj.gov
Immigration Judge **Kathryn L. DeAngelis** .... (312) 855-2324
E-mail: kathryn.deangelis@usdoj.gov
Immigration Judge **James R. Fujimoto** .... (312) 855-2324
E-mail: james.fujimoto@usdoj.gov
Immigration Judge **Jennie L. Giambastiani** .... (312) 855-2324
E-mail: jennie.giambastiani@usdoj.gov
Immigration Judge **Elizabeth G. Lang** .... (312) 855-2324
E-mail: elizabeth.g.lang@usdoj.gov
Immigration Judge **Patrick M. McKenna** .... (312) 855-2324
E-mail: patrick.m.mckenna@usdoj.gov
Education: DePauw 1998 BA; Notre Dame 2001 JD

U.S. Immigration Court - Chicago (IL) *(continued)*

Immigration Judge **Jennifer I. Peyton** .... (312) 697-5800
Immigration Judge **Robin J. Rosche** .... (312) 855-2324
E-mail: robin.j.rosche@usdoj.gov
Immigration Judge **Kaarina Salovaara** .... (312) 855-2324
Education: Smith 1976 BA; Virginia 1990 JD
Immigration Judge **Eva S. Saltzman** .... (312) 855-2324
Court Administrator (Acting) **R. Elliott Edwards** .... (312) 855-2324
E-mail: r.elliott.edwards@usdoj.gov

U.S. Immigration Court - Cleveland (OH)

801 West Superior Avenue, Suite 13-100, Cleveland, OH 44113
Tel: (216) 802-1100

Immigration Judge **Alison Brown** .... (216) 802-1100
Immigration Judge **Keith Hunsucker** .... (216) 802-1100
Immigration Judge **Jonathan W. Owens** .... (216) 802-1100
Education: Michigan 1997 BA; Detroit Law 2005 JD
Immigration Judge **Christopher R Seppanen** .... (216) 802-1100
Immigration Judge **David C. Whipple** .... (216) 802-1100
Court Administrator **James W. Roder** .... (216) 802-1100
E-mail: james.roder@usdoj.gov

U.S. Immigration Court - Dallas (TX)

1100 Commerce Street, Room 1060, Dallas, TX 75242
Tel: (214) 767-1814
Internet: https://www.justice.gov/eoir/dallas-immigration-court

Immigration Judge **Xiomara D. Davis-Gumbs** .... (214) 767-1814
E-mail: xiomara.d.davis-gumbs@usdoj.gov
Immigration Judge **Robert Wayne Kimball** .... (214) 767-1814
E-mail: r.wayne.kimball@usdoj.gov
Immigration Judge **James A. Nugent** .... (214) 767-1814
E-mail: james.a.nugent@usdoj.gov
Immigration Judge **Richard R. Ozmun** .... (214) 767-1814
E-mail: richard.ozmun@usdoj.gov
Immigration Judge **Deitrich H. Sims** .... (214) 767-1814
E-mail: deitrich.sims@usdoj.gov
Court Administrator **Barbara T. Baker** .... (214) 767-1814
E-mail: barbara.t.baker@usdoj.gov

U.S. Immigration Court - Denver (CO)

1961 Stout Street, Suite 3103, Denver, CO 80294
Tel: (303) 844-5815

Immigration Judge **Melanie K. Corrin** .... (303) 844-5815
E-mail: melanie.k.corrin@usdoj.gov
Immigration Judge **Ivan Gardzelewski** .... (303) 844-5815
E-mail: ivan.e.gardzelewski@usdoj.gov
Immigration Judge **Alison R. Kane** .... (303) 844-5815
E-mail: alison.kane@usdoj.gov
Immigration Judge **Matthew W. Kaufman** .... (303) 844-5815
E-mail: matthew.w.kaufman@usdoj.gov
Immigration Judge **Donald C. O'Hare** .... (303) 844-5815
E-mail: donald.o'hare@usdoj.gov
Immigration Judge **Eileen R. Trujillo** .... (303) 844-5815
E-mail: eileen.r.trujillo@usdoj.gov
Education: Harvard 1986 BA; Boalt Hall 1990 JD
Court Administrator **Jason E. Burke** .... (303) 844-5815
E-mail: jason.burke@usdoj.gov

U.S. Immigration Court - Detroit (MI)

477 Michigan Avenue, Suite 440, Detroit, MI 48226
Tel: (313) 226-2603
Internet: https://www.justice.gov/eoir/detroit-immigration-court

Immigration Judge **Jennifer M. Gorland** .... (313) 226-2603
E-mail: jennifer.m.gorland@usdoj.gov
Immigration Judge **Mark Jebson** .... (313) 226-2603
E-mail: mark.jebson@usdoj.gov
Immigration Judge **David H. Paruch** .... (313) 226-2603
E-mail: david.h.paruch@usdoj.gov
Immigration Judge **(Vacant)** .... (313) 226-2603
Court Administrator **Shandra Shelley** .... (313) 226-2603 ext. 204

★ Presidential Appointment Requiring Senate Confirmation ☆ Presidential Appointment □ Schedule C Appointment ◇ Career Senior Foreign Service Appointment
● Career Senior Executive Service (SES) Appointment ○ Non-Career Senior Executive Service (SES) Appointment ■ Postal Career Executive Service

U.S. Immigration Court - Otay Mesa (CA)

7488 Calzada de la Fuente, San Diego, CA 92154
Tel: (619) 661-5600
Internet: https://www.justice.gov/eoir/otay-mesa-immigration-court

Immigration Judge **Olga Attia** .... (619) 661-5600
Immigration Judge **Zsa Zsa De Paolo** .... (619) 661-5600
E-mail: zsazsa.depaolo@usdoj.gov
Immigration Judge **Catherine E. Halliday-Roberts** ...... (619) 661-5600
E-mail: catherine.halliday-roberts@usdoj.gov
Immigration Judge **Robert B.C. McSeveney** .... (619) 661-5600
E-mail: robert.mcseveney@usdoj.gov
Immigration Judge **Jonathan S. "Scott" Simpson** ..... (619) 661-5600
E-mail: scott.simpson@usdoj.gov
Education: Wabash Col 1995 BA; Seton Hall 1998 JD
Court Administrator **Glenda Viray** .... (619) 661-5600
E-mail: glenda.viray@usdoj.gov

U.S. Immigration Court - Otero (NM)

26 McGregor Range Rd, Door #1, Chaparral, NM 88081
Tel: (915) 313-8755

Immigration Judge **Lorely Ramirez Fernandez** .... (915) 313-8755
Immigration Judge **Kathleen "Kathy" French** .... (915) 313-8755
Education: US Coast Guard Acad 1982 BS; George Mason 1997 JD
Immigration Judge **Jacinto Palomino** .... (915) 313-8755
Immigration Judge **Brock Taylor** .... (415) 705-4415
E-mail: brock.taylor2@usdoj.gov
Education: BYU 2001 BA; Duke 2005 MPP; Harvard 2005 JD
Court Administrator (Acting) **Barbara T. Baker** .... (915) 313-8755
E-mail: barbara.baker@usdoj.gov

U.S. Immigration Court - Elizabeth (NJ)

625 Evans Street, Room 148A, Elizabeth, NJ 07201
Tel: (908) 787-1355
Internet: https://www.justice.gov/eoir/elizabeth-immigration-court

Immigration Judge **Dorothy Harbeck** .... (908) 787-1390
E-mail: dorothy.harbeck@usdoj.gov
Immigration Judge **Mirlande Tadal** .... (908) 787-1390
E-mail: mirlande.tadal@usdoj.gov
Court Administrator **Paul Friedman** .... (908) 787-1355
Education: Staten Island 2011 BA

U.S. Immigration Court - Eloy (AZ) Detention Center

1705 East Hanna Road, Suite 366, Eloy, AZ 85131
Tel: (520) 466-3671
Internet: https://www.justice.gov/eoir/eloy-immigration-court

Immigration Judge **Julian Castaneda** .... (520) 466-3671
E-mail: julian.castaneda@usdoj.gov
Education: Texas (San Antonio) 1997 BA; South Dakota 2005 JD
Immigration Judge **Richard Phelps** .... (520) 466-3671
E-mail: richard.phelps@usdoj.gov
Immigration Judge **Jennifer I. Gaz** .... (520) 466-3671
E-mail: jennifer.gaz@usdoj.gov
Court Administrator **Victoria Padilla** .... (520) 466-3671
E-mail: victoria.padilla@usdoj.gov

U.S. Immigration Court - El Paso (TX)

700 East San Antonio Avenue, Suite 750, El Paso, TX 79901
Tel: (915) 534-6020
Internet: https://www.justice.gov/eoir/el-paso-immigration-courts

Immigration Judge **Robert S. Hough** .... (915) 534-6020
E-mail: robert.hough@usdoj.gov
Education: Tulane 1979, 1982 JD
Immigration Judge **Dean Tuckman** .... (229) 838-1320
E-mail: dean.s.tuckman@usdoj.gov
Education: Pittsburgh JD
Immigration Judge **Nathan L. Herbert** .... (915) 225-0750
E-mail: nathan.herbert@usdoj.gov
Education: Western Michigan 2003 BA; Michigan State 2008 JD
Court Administrator **Rodney D. Buckmire** .... (915) 534-6020
E-mail: rodney.buckmire@usdoj.gov

Fort Worth Immigration Adjudications Center

Immigration Judge **Eric C. Bales** .... (915) 534-6020
Education: Texas A&M 1998 BA; Ave Maria Law 2008 JD
Immigration Judge **Monica Thompson Guidry** .... (915) 534-6020
Education: Sam Houston State 1984 BS, 1987 MA; South Texas 1997 JD
Immigration Judge **Brandon L. Hart** .... (915) 534-6020
Education: BYU 1993 BS; Utah 1996 JD; McGill (Canada) 2007 ML
Immigration Judge **Richard C. Jacobs** .... (717) 755-7555
Education: San Francisco State U 1994 BA; Miami 2000 JD
Immigration Judge **Joseph T. Leonard** .... (717) 755-7555
E-mail: joseph.t.leonard@usdoj.gov
Education: Texas A&M 1999 BA; Texas 2002 JD
Immigration Judge **Hugo R. Martinez** .... (717) 755-7555
E-mail: hugo.r.martinez@usdoj.gov
Education: Texas Wesleyan U 2001 BA; Texas 2004 JD
Immigration Judge **Jennifer A. May** .... (213) 894-2811
E-mail: jennifer.a.may@usdoj.gov
Education: William Jewell 1992 BA; Missouri (Kansas City) 1996 JD

U.S. Immigration Court - El Paso (TX) Service Processing Center

8915 Montana Avenue, Suite 100, El Paso, TX 79925
Tel: (915) 771-1600

Immigration Judge **William L. Abbott** .... (915) 771-1600
E-mail: william.abbott@usdoj.gov
Immigration Judge **Guadalupe R. Gonzalez** .... (915) 771-1600
E-mail: guadalupe.r.gonzalez@usdoj.gov
Immigration Judge **Sunita Mahtabfar** .... (915) 771-1600
E-mail: sunita.mahtabfar@usdoj.gov
Immigration Judge **Michael S. Pleters** .... (915) 771-1600
E-mail: michael.pleters@usdoj.gov
Immigration Judge **Stephen Ruhle** .... (915) 771-1600
E-mail: stephen.ruhle@usdoj.gov
Court Administrator **Jose A. Quinonez** .... (915) 771-1600
E-mail: jose.quinonez@usdoj.gov

U.S. Immigration Court - Fishkill (NY) Downstate Correctional Facility

Downstate Correctional Facility, 121 Red Schoolhouse Road, Fishkill, NY 12524
Tel: (845) 838-5700
Internet: https://www.justice.gov/eoir/fishkill-immigration-court

Immigration Judge **Roger Frederick Sagerman** .... (845) 838-5700
E-mail: roger.sagerman@usdoj.gov
Education: Tufts 1988 BA; Buffalo 1993 JD
Court Administrator (Acting) **Regina M. Rau** .... (845) 838-5700
E-mail: regina.rau@usdoj.gov

U.S. Immigration Court - Florence (AZ)

3260 North Pinal Parkway Avenue, Florence, AZ 85132
Tel: (520) 868-3341
Internet: https://www.justice.gov/eoir/fishkill-immigration-court

Immigration Judge **Robert Coughlon** .... (520) 868-3341
Immigration Judge **Molly S. Frazer** .... (520) 868-3341
Immigration Judge **Bruce A. Taylor** .... (520) 868-3341
E-mail: bruce.taylor@usdoj.gov
Education: Vermont 1972 BA; Cleveland-Marshall 1974 JD
Immigration Judge **Cara Knapp** .... (520) 868-3341
Court Administrator **Cheryl King** .... (520) 868-3341
E-mail: cheryl.king@usdoj.gov

U.S. Immigration Court - Fort Snelling

Bishop Henry Whipple Federal Building, 1 Federal Drive, Suite 1850, Fort Snelling, MN 55111
Tel: (612) 725-3765
Internet: https://www.justice.gov/eoir/bloomington-immigration-court

Immigration Judge **M. Audrey Carr** .... (612) 725-3765
E-mail: audrey.carr@usdoj.gov
Education: Earlham 1996 BA; Rensselaer Poly 1994 BBA; St Mary's U (MN) 1997 JD
Immigration Judge **Katherine L. Hansen** .... (612) 725-3765
E-mail: katherine.l.hansen@usdoj.gov
Immigration Judge **Kristin W. Olmanson** .... (612) 725-3765
E-mail: kristin.olmanson@usdoj.gov

(continued on next page)

DEPARTMENTS

★ Presidential Appointment Requiring Senate Confirmation ☆ Presidential Appointment ☐ Schedule C Appointment ◇ Career Senior Foreign Service Appointment
● Career Senior Executive Service (SES) Appointment ○ Non-Career Senior Executive Service (SES) Appointment ■ Postal Career Executive Service

DEPARTMENTS

U.S. Immigration Court - Fort Snelling *(continued)*

Immigration Judge **Sarah Mazzie** .... (612) 725-3765
E-mail: sarah.mazzie@usdoj.gov
Immigration Judge **Ryan R. Wood** .... (612) 725-3765
E-mail: ryan.wood@usdoj.gov
Court Administrator (Acting) **Betty Jones** ...... (612) 725-3765 ext. 235

U.S. Immigration Court - Guaynabo (PR)
San Patricio Office Center, 7 Tabonuco Street,
Room 401, Guaynabo, PR 00968-4605
Tel: (787) 749-4386
Internet: https://www.justice.gov/eoir/guaynabo-puerto-rico-immigration-court
Immigration Judge **Irma Lopez-Defillo** .... (787) 749-4386
Court Administrator **Luis Quiles** .... (787) 749-4386
E-mail: luis.quiles@usdoj.gov

U.S. Immigration Court - Harlingen (TX)
2009 West Jefferson Ave, Suite 300, Harlingen, TX 78550
Tel: (956) 427-8580
Internet: https://www.justice.gov/eoir/harlingen-immigration-court
Immigration Judge **Howard E. Achtsam** .... (956) 427-8582
E-mail: howard.e.achtsam@usdoj.gov
Immigration Judge **Charlotte D. Brown** .... (956) 427-8580
E-mail: charlotte.d.brown@usdoj.gov
Immigration Judge **Sean D. Clancy** .... (956) 427-8582
E-mail: sean.d.clancy@usdoj.gov
Education: Mississippi 1993 BA; Washington and Lee 1996 JD
Immigration Judge **Daniel B. Gilbert** .... (956) 427-8582
Education: Cardozo 2008 JD
Immigration Judge **Delia I. Gonzalez** .... (956) 427-8582
E-mail: delia.i.gonzalez@usdoj.gov
Court Administrator **Jennifer Cunningham** .... (956) 427-8582
E-mail: jennifer.cunningham@usdoj.gov

U.S. Immigration Court - Hartford (CT)
AA Ribicoff Federal Building and Courthouse, 450 Main Street,
Room 628, Hartford, CT 06103-3015
Tel: (860) 240-3881
Immigration Judge **Daniel A. Morris** .... (860) 240-3881
E-mail: daniel.morris@usdoj.gov
Education: Nebraska (Omaha) 1976 BS; Creighton 1981 MBA, 1981 JD
Immigration Judge **Michael W. Straus** .... (860) 240-3881
E-mail: michael.straus@usdoj.gov
Immigration Judge **Philip Verrillo** .... (860) 240-3881
E-mail: philip.verrillo@usdoj.gov
Education: Central Conn State U 1991 BA; New England 1995 JD
Court Administrator **Pietro Cicolini** .... (860) 240-3881
E-mail: pietro.cicolini@usdoj.gov

U.S. Immigration Court - Honolulu (HI)
Prince Kuhio U.S. Courthouse and Federal Building,
300 Ala Moana Boulevard, Room 8-112, Honolulu, HI 96850
Tel: (808) 541-1870
Internet: https://www.justice.gov/eoir/honolulu-immigration-court
Immigration Judge **Dayna M. Beamer** .... (808) 541-1870
E-mail: dayna.beamer@usdoj.gov
Immigration Judge **Clarence M. Wagner** .... (808) 541-1870
E-mail: clarence.m.wagner@usdoj.gov
Education: Hampton 1993 BS; Southern U Law 1997 JD; Georgetown 1999 ML
Court Administrator **Glenda Viray** .... (808) 541-1870
E-mail: glenda.viray@usdoj.gov

U.S. Immigration Court - Houston (TX)
Continental Center II, 600 Jefferson Street,
Ninth Floor, Suite 900, Houston, TX 77002
Tel: (713) 718-3870 Fax: (713) 718-3014
Internet: https://www.justice.gov/eoir/houston-immigration-court
Immigration Judge **Nimmo Bhagat** .... (713) 718-3870
E-mail: nimmo.bhagat@usdoj.gov

U.S. Immigration Court - Houston (TX) *(continued)*

Immigration Judge **Chris A. Brisack** .... (713) 718-3870
E-mail: chris.brisack@usdoj.gov
Education: Nebraska 1981; Houston 1985 JD
Immigration Judge **John R. Doolittle II** .... (415) 705-4415
E-mail: john.r.doolittle@usdoj.gov
Education: Tampa 1989 BS; Washburn 1994 JD; Army War Col 2014 MS
Immigration Judge **Gary E. Endelman** .... (713) 718-3870
E-mail: gary.e.endelman@usdoj.gov
Education: Virginia BA; Delaware PhD; Houston JD
Immigration Judge **Marcos Gemoets** .... (415) 705-4415
E-mail: marcos.gemoets@usdoj.gov
Immigration Judge **Stephanie E. Gorman** .... (415) 705-4415
E-mail: stephanie.gorman@usdoj.gov
Immigration Judge **Monique Harris** .... (713) 718-3870
E-mail: monique.harris@usdoj.gov
Immigration Judge **Richard A. Jamadar** .... (415) 705-4415
E-mail: richard.jamadar@usdoj.gov
Immigration Judge **Georgina M. Picos** .... (713) 718-3870
E-mail: georgina.m.picos@usdoj.gov
Immigration Judge **Clarease Rankin Yates** .... (713) 718-3870
E-mail: clarease.yates@usdoj.gov
Court Administrator **Melba J. Bennett** .... (713) 650-7838
E-mail: melba.bennett@usdoj.gov

U.S. Immigration Court - Houston (TX) Service Processing Center
5520 Greens Road, Houston, TX 77032
Tel: (281) 594-5600
Internet: https://www.justice.gov/eoir/houston-immigration-court
Immigration Judge **Saul E. Greenstein** .... (281) 594-5600
E-mail: saul.e.greenstein@usdoj.gov
Education: Brooklyn 1994 BA; Cardozo 1997 JD
Immigration Judge **Lisa Luis** .... (281) 594-5600
E-mail: lisa.luis2@usdoj.gov
Education: Houston 1990 BS, 1994 JD
Immigration Judge **Richard D. Walton** .... (281) 594-5600
E-mail: richard.d.walton@usdoj.gov
Court Administrator **Mark Russelburg** .... (281) 594-5601
E-mail: mark.russelburg@usdoj.gov

U.S. Immigration Court - Imperial (CA)
2409 La Brucherie Road, Imperial, CA 92251
Tel: (760) 370-5200
Internet: https://www.justice.gov/eoir/imperial-immigration-court
Immigration Judge **E. Mark Barcus** .... (760) 370-5200
E-mail: e.mark.barcus@usdoj.gov
Immigration Judge **Paul Habich** .... (760) 370-5200
Immigration Judge **Jaime Jasso** .... (717) 755-7555
E-mail: jaime.jasso@usdoj.gov
Education: Stanford 1995 BA; Whittier 1998 JD
Court Administrator **Gracie D. Gray** .... (760) 370-5200
E-mail: gracie.gray@usdoj.gov

U.S. Immigration Court - Kansas City (MO)
2345 Grand Boulevard, Suite 525, Kansas City, MO 64108
Tel: (816) 581-5000
Immigration Judge **Glen R. Baker** .... (816) 581-5000
E-mail: glen.baker@usdoj.gov
Immigration Judge **Justin W. Howard** .... (816) 581-5000
E-mail: justin.w.howard@usdoj.gov
Immigration Judge **Jayme Salinardi** .... (816) 581-5000
E-mail: jayme.salinardi@usdoj.gov
Court Administrator **Betty Jones** .... (816) 581-5000
E-mail: betty.jones@usdoj.gov

U.S. Immigration Court - Las Vegas (NV)
110 North City Parkway, Suite 400, Las Vegas, NV 89106
Tel: (702) 458-0227
Internet: https://www.justice.gov/eoir/las-vegas-immigration-court
Immigration Judge **Munish Sharda** .... (702) 458-0227

★ Presidential Appointment Requiring Senate Confirmation ☆ Presidential Appointment ☐ Schedule C Appointment ◇ Career Senior Foreign Service Appointment
● Career Senior Executive Service (SES) Appointment ○ Non-Career Senior Executive Service (SES) Appointment ■ Postal Career Executive Service

U.S. Immigration Court - Las Vegas (NV) *(continued)*

Immigration Judge **An Mai Nguyen** . . . . (702) 458-0227
E-mail: an.nguyen@usdoj.gov
Court Administrator **Rachel Newsome** . . . . (702) 458-0227
E-mail: rachel.newsome@usdoj.gov

U.S. Immigration Court - Los Angeles (CA)

606 South Olive Street, 15th Floor, Los Angeles, CA 90014
Tel: (213) 894-2811
Internet: https://www.justice.gov/eoir/los-angeles-immigration-court

Immigration Judge **Janette L. Allen** . . . . (213) 894-2811
E-mail: janette.l.allen@usdoj.gov
Education: Trinity U 2004 BA; American U 2008 JD
Immigration Judge **Lori R. Bass** . . . . (213) 894-2811
E-mail: lori.r.bass@usdoj.gov
Education: South Florida 1978 BA; St Thomas U 1988 JD
Immigration Judge **David Burke** . . . . (213) 894-2811
E-mail: david.burke@usdoj.gov
Immigration Judge **Kerri A. Calcador** . . . . (213) 894-2811
E-mail: kerri.calcador@usdoj.gov
Immigration Judge **Hye Y. Chon** . . . . (213) 894-2811
E-mail: hye.y.chon@usdoj.gov
Education: UCLA 1995 BA; Hastings 1999 JD
Immigration Judge **Philip J. Costa** . . . . (213) 894-2811
Education: NYU 1989 BA, 1992 JD
Immigration Judge **Jankhana Desai** . . . . (213) 894-2811
E-mail: jankhana.desai@usdoj.gov
Immigration Judge **Arlene Dorfman** . . . . (213) 894-2811
Immigration Judge **Timothy Everett** . . . . (213) 894-2811
E-mail: timothy.everett@usdoj.gov
Immigration Judge **LtCol Leon Francis USMC** . . . . (213) 894-2811
E-mail: leon.j.francis@usdoj.gov
Education: Boise State 1993 BA; Gonzaga 1996 JD; Judge Advocate Gen 2009 ML
Immigration Judge **Robert Fellrath** . . . . (213) 894-2811
Education: Notre Dame 1996 BA, 1999 JD
Immigration Judge **Marni Guerrero** . . . . (213) 894-2811
E-mail: marni.guerrero@usdoj.gov
Education: Arizona State 1999 BS, 2003 JD
Immigration Judge **Anna Ho** . . . . (213) 894-2811
E-mail: anna.ho@usdoj.gov
Immigration Judge **Natalie B. Huddleston** . . . . (213) 894-2811
Education: Notre Dame 2001 BA, 2004 JD
Immigration Judge **Carlos R. Juelle** . . . . (213) 894-2811
E-mail: carlos.r.juelle@usdoj.gov
Education: UCLA 1989 BA; Pepperdine 1996 JD
Immigration Judge **Jan D. Latimore** . . . . (213) 894-2811
E-mail: jan.latimore@usdoj.gov
Immigration Judge **Amy Lee** . . . . (213) 894-2811
E-mail: amy.lee@usdoj.gov
Immigration Judge **Monica M. Little** . . . . (213) 894-2811
E-mail: monica.m.little@usdoj.gov
Immigration Judge **Nicholas A. Martz** . . . . (213) 894-2811
E-mail: nicholas.a.martz@usdoj.gov
Education: Boston Col 1998 BA; Florida State 2007 JD
Immigration Judge **Nancy E. Miller** . . . . (213) 894-2811
Education: UCLA 1974 BA; Southwestern 1984 JD
Immigration Judge **Jeffrey S. Miller** . . . . (213) 894-2811
E-mail: jeffrey.s.miller@usdoj.gov
Education: Berry 1996 BS; Florida Coastal 2006 JD
Immigration Judge **William Neumeister** . . . . (213) 894-2811
E-mail: william.david.neumeister@usdoj.gov
Immigration Judge **Lee O'Connor** . . . . (213) 894-2811
E-mail: lee.oconnor@usdoj.gov
Immigration Judge **Jeannette L. Park** . . . . (213) 894-2811
E-mail: jeannette.park@usdoj.gov
Education: UC Berkeley 1996 BA; Boston Col 2000 JD
Immigration Judge **Sebastian Thomas Patti** . . . . (213) 894-2811
Education: Duke 1975 BA; Kansas 1978 JD
Immigration Judge **Rose C. Peters** . . . . (213) 894-2811
E-mail: rose.peters@usdoj.gov
Immigration Judge **Anne K. Perry** . . . . (213) 894-2811
E-mail: anne.perry@usdoj.gov
Education: UCLA 1978 BA; Loyola Law 1981 JD
Immigration Judge **Rachel A. Ruane** . . . . (213) 894-2811

U.S. Immigration Court - Los Angeles (CA) *(continued)*

Immigration Judge **Anita L. Simons** . . . . (213) 894-2811
E-mail: anita.l.simons@usdoj.gov
Education: Arizona 1999 BA; James Rogers Law 2005 JD
Immigration Judge **D. D. Sitgraves** . . . . (213) 894-2811
E-mail: d.sitgraves@usdoj.gov
Immigration Judge **Christine E. Stancill** . . . . (213) 894-2811
E-mail: christine.stancill@usdoj.gov
Immigration Judge **A. Ashley Tabaddor** . . . . (213) 894-2811
E-mail: ashley.tabaddor@usdoj.gov
Education: UCLA 1994 BA; Hastings 1997 JD
Immigration Judge **Gita Vahid-Tehrani** . . . . (213) 894-2811
E-mail: gita.vahid@usdoj.gov
Education: UCLA 1984 BA; Whittier 1991 JD
Immigration Judge **Joyce Bakke Varzandeh** . . . . (213) 894-2811
E-mail: joyce.bakke.varzandeh@usdoj.gov
Immigration Judge **Veronica S. Villegas** . . . . (213) 894-2811
E-mail: veronica.s.villegas@usdoj.gov
Immigration Judge **Bridget Virchis** . . . . (213) 894-2811
E-mail: bridget.virchis@usdoj.gov
Immigration Judge **Jason R. Waterloo** . . . . (213) 894-2811
E-mail: jason.waterloo@usdoj.gov
Education: Penn State 2004 BS; West Virginia 2007 JD
Court Administrator (Acting) **Jason E. Burke** . . . . (213) 894-2811
E-mail: jason.burke@usdoj.gov
Deputy Court Administrator **(Vacant)** . . . . (213) 894-2811
Administrative Support Assistant **(Vacant)** . . . . (213) 894-2811

U.S. Immigration Court- Los Angeles Detained (CA)

300 North Los Angeles Street, Room 4330, Los Angeles, CA 90012
Tel: (213) 576-4701

Immigration Judge **Nathan N. Aina** . . . . (213) 576-4701
Immigration Judge **Carlos E. Maury** . . . . (213) 576-4701
Immigration Judge **Tara Naselow-Nahas** . . . . (213) 576-4701
Immigration Judge **Kevin W. Riley** . . . . (213) 576-4701
Immigration Judge **Frank M. Travieso** . . . . (213) 576-4701
Education: Cal State (Fullerton) 1982 BA; Loyola Law 1995 JD
Deputy Court Administrator **Jeanette P. Patron** . . . . (213) 576-4701
E-mail: jeanette.patron@usdoj.gov

U.S. Immigration Court - Memphis (TN)

80 Monroe Avenue, Suite 501, Memphis, TN 38103
Tel: (901) 528-5883
Internet: https://www.justice.gov/eoir/memphis-immigration-court

Immigration Judge **Richard J. Averwater** . . . . (901) 528-5883
E-mail: richard.averwater@usdoj.gov
Immigration Judge **Rebecca L. Holt** . . . . (901) 528-5883
E-mail: rebecca.l.holt@usdoj.gov
Immigration Judge **Vernon Benet Miles** . . . . (901) 528-5883
E-mail: vernon.b.miles@usdoj.gov
Court Administrator **J. Thomas Davis** . . . . (901) 528-5883
E-mail: thomas.davis@usdoj.gov

U.S. Immigration Court - Miami (FL)

One Riverview Square, 333 South Miami Avenue,
Suite 700, Miami, FL 33130
Tel: (305) 789-4221 Fax: (305) 530-7001
Internet: https://www.justice.gov/eoir/miami-immigration-court

Immigration Judge **Scott G. Alexander** . . . . (305) 789-4221
E-mail: scott.alexander@usdoj.gov
Immigration Judge **Javier E. Balasquide** . . . . (305) 789-4221
E-mail: javier.e.balasquide@usdoj.gov
Immigration Judge **Teofilo Chapa** . . . . (305) 789-4221
E-mail: teofilo.chapa@usdoj.gov
Immigration Judge **Timothy M. Cole** . . . . (305) 789-4221
E-mail: timothy.m.cole@usdoj.gov
Immigration Judge **Jonathan Daniel Dowell** . . . . (305) 789-4221
E-mail: daniel.dowell@usdoj.gov
Immigration Judge **Madeline Garcia** . . . . (415) 705-4415
E-mail: madeline.garcia2@usdoj.gov
Immigration Judge **Deborah K. Goodwin** . . . . (415) 705-4415
E-mail: deborah.k.goodwin@usdoj.gov
Immigration Judge **Dalin R. Holyoak** . . . . (305) 789-4221
E-mail: dalin.r.holyoak@usdoj.gov

(continued on next page)

★ Presidential Appointment Requiring Senate Confirmation ☆ Presidential Appointment ☐ Schedule C Appointment ◇ Career Senior Foreign Service Appointment
● Career Senior Executive Service (SES) Appointment ○ Non-Career Senior Executive Service (SES) Appointment ■ Postal Career Executive Service

DEPARTMENTS

U.S. Immigration Court - Miami (FL) *(continued)*

Immigration Judge **Michael C. Horn** . . . . . (305) 789-4221
E-mail: michael.horn@usdoj.gov
Immigration Judge **Stephen E. Mander** . . . . . (305) 789-4221
E-mail: stephen.mander@usdoj.gov
Immigration Judge **Anthony E. Maingot** . . . . . (305) 789-4221
E-mail: anthony.e.maingot@usdoj.gov
Immigration Judge **Denise A. Marks Lane** . . . . . (305) 789-4221
E-mail: denise.lane@usdoj.gov
Immigration Judge **Lourdes B. Martinez-Esquivel** . . . . . (305) 789-4221
E-mail: lourdes.martinez-esquivel@usdoj.gov
Education: Georgetown 1983 BSBA; Florida International 1987 MBA; Boston Col 1990 JD
Immigration Judge **Rene D. Mateo** . . . . . (305) 789-4221
E-mail: rene.d.mateo@usdoj.gov
Immigration Judge **Marsha K. Nettles** . . . . . (305) 789-4221
E-mail: marsha.k.nettles@usdoj.gov
Immigration Judge **Jennifer L. Page-Lozano** . . . . . (305) 789-4221
E-mail: jennifer.l.page-lozano@usdoj.gov
Immigration Judge **G. William Riggs** . . . . . (305) 789-4221
E-mail: george.w.riggs@usdoj.gov
Immigration Judge **Lourdes Rodriguez de Jongh** . . . . . (305) 789-4221
E-mail: lourdes.rodriguez.de.jongh@usdoj.gov
Immigration Judge **Charles J. Sanders** . . . . . (305) 789-4221
E-mail: charles.sanders@usdoj.gov
Immigration Judge **Rico M. Sogocio** . . . . . (229) 838-1320
E-mail: rico.sogocio@usdoj.gov
Education: Columbus Law JD
Immigration Judge **Lilliana Torreh-Bayouth** . . . . . (305) 789-4221
E-mail: lilliana.torreh-bayouth@usdoj.gov
Immigration Judge **Gabriel C. Videla** . . . . . (305) 789-4221
E-mail: gabriel.videla@usdoj.gov
Immigration Judge **Michael Walleisa** . . . . . (305) 789-4221
E-mail: michael.walleisa@usdoj.gov
Education: Philadelphia Col Textiles 1981 BS; Temple 1985 JD
Court Administrator **Jorge Rodriguez** . . . . . (305) 789-4221
Deputy Court Administrator **Dania Perdomo-Borras** . . . . . (305) 789-4221
E-mail: dania.perdomo-borras@usdoj.gov
Administrative Assistant **Eliana M. Urquiza** . . . . . (305) 808-9464
E-mail: eliana.urquiza@usdoj.gov

U.S. Immigration Court - Miami (FL) Krome Service Processing Center

Building 1, 18201 SW 12th Street, Suite C, Miami, FL 33194
Mail: P.O. Box 940998, Miami, FL 33194
Tel: (786) 422-8700
Internet: https://www.justice.gov/eoir/miami-krome-immigration-court

Immigration Judge **Barry S. Chait** . . . . . (786) 422-8700
E-mail: barry.s.chait@usdoj.gov
Immigration Judge **Rex J. Ford** . . . . . (786) 422-8700
E-mail: rex.ford@usdoj.gov
Immigration Judge **Adam Opaciuch** . . . . . (786) 422-8700
E-mail: adam.opaciuch@usdoj.gov
Immigration Judge **Maria M. Lopez-Enriquez** . . . . . (786) 422-8700
E-mail: maria.m.lopez-enriquez@usdoj.gov
Education: Florida 1988 BS, 1991 JD; Florida International 1993 MIB
Immigration Judge **John Opaciuch** . . . . . (786) 422-8700
E-mail: john.opaciuch@usdoj.gov
Court Administrator **Jorge Rodriguez** . . . . . (786) 422-8700
E-mail: jorge.rodriguez@usdoj.gov

U.S. Immigration Court - Napanoch (NY) Ulster Correctional Facility

Berme Road, P.O. Box 800, Napanoch, NY 12458
Tel: (845) 647-5506
Internet: https://www.justice.gov/eoir/ulster-immigration-court

Immigration Judge **Roger Frederick Sagerman** . . . . . (845) 647-5506
E-mail: roger.sagerman@usdoj.gov
Education: Tufts 1988 BA; Buffalo 1993 JD
Immigration Judge **Nelson Vargas-Padilla** . . . . . (845) 647-5506
E-mail: nelson.vargas-padilla@usdoj.gov
Education: SUNY (Albany) 1990 BA; Buffalo 1994 JD
Court Administrator (Acting) **Regina M. Rau** . . . . . (845) 647-5506
E-mail: regina.rau@usdoj.gov

U.S. Immigration Court - Newark (NJ)

970 Broad Street, Suite 1200, Newark, NJ 07102
Tel: (973) 645-3524
Internet: https://www.justice.gov/eoir/newark-immigration-court

Immigration Judge **David Cheng** . . . . . (973) 645-3524
E-mail: david.cheng@usdoj.gov
Immigration Judge **Amit Chugh** . . . . . (973) 645-3524
E-mail: amit.chugh@usdoj.gov
Immigration Judge **Leo A. Finston** . . . . . (973) 645-3524
E-mail: leo.finston@usdoj.gov
Education: CUNY 1988 BA; Cardozo 1991 JD
Immigration Judge **Annie S. Garcy** . . . . . (973) 645-3524
E-mail: annie.s.garcy@usdoj.gov
Immigration Judge **Elise Manuel** . . . . . (973) 645-3524
E-mail: elise.manuel@usdoj.gov
Immigration Judge **Arya S. Ranasinghe** . . . . . (973) 645-3524
E-mail: arya.s.ranasinghe@usdoj.gov
Education: SUNY (Stony Brook) 2002 BA; Touro 2006 JD
Immigration Judge **Ramin Rastegar** . . . . . (973) 645-3524
E-mail: ramin.rastegar@usdoj.gov
Immigration Judge **Alberto J. Riefkohl** . . . . . (973) 645-3524
E-mail: alberto.riefkohl@usdoj.gov
Immigration Judge **Shifra Rubin** . . . . . (973) 645-3524
E-mail: shifra.rubin@usdoj.gov
Court Administrator **Yolanda English** . . . . . (973) 645-3524
E-mail: yolanda.english@usdoj.gov

U.S. Immigration Court - New Orleans (LA)

One Canal Place, 365 Canal Street, Suite 2450, New Orleans, LA 70130
Tel: (504) 589-3992
Internet: https://www.justice.gov/eoir/new-orleans-immigration-court

Immigration Judge **Joseph B. La Rocca** . . . . . (504) 589-3992
E-mail: joseph.larocca@usdoj.gov
Immigration Judge **Eric W. Marsteller** . . . . . (504) 589-3992
Immigration Judge **Charlotte S. Marquez** . . . . . (504) 589-3992
E-mail: charlotte.marquez@usdoj.gov
Court Administrator **Hunter Johnson** . . . . . (504) 589-3992
E-mail: hunter.johnson@usdoj.gov

U.S. Immigration Court - Federal Plaza, New York (NY)

Jacob K. Javits Federal Building, 26 Federal Plaza,
12th Floor, Room 1237, New York, NY 10278
Tel: (917) 454-1040 Fax: (212) 264-1070
Internet: https://www.justice.gov/eoir/new-orleans-immigration-court

Immigration Judge **Terry A. Bain** . . . . . (917) 454-1040
E-mail: terry.bain@usdoj.gov
Immigration Judge **Noel A. Brennan** . . . . . (917) 454-1040
E-mail: noel.brennan@usdoj.gov
Education: Marywood Col 1969 BA; George Washington 1972 MA; Georgetown 1985 JD
Immigration Judge **Patricia L. Buchanan** . . . . . (917) 454-1040
E-mail: patricia.l.buchanan@usdoj.gov
Immigration Judge **Olivia L. Cassin** . . . . . (917) 454-1040
E-mail: olivia.l.cassin@usdoj.gov
Immigration Judge **Jesse B. Christensen** . . . . . (917) 454-1040
E-mail: jesse.b.christensen@usdoj.gov
Education: Colorado 1997 BA; Iowa 2000 JD
Immigration Judge **Raisa Cohen** . . . . . (917) 454-1040
E-mail: raisa.cohen@usdoj.gov
Immigration Judge **Charles R. Conroy** . . . . . (917) 454-1040
E-mail: charles.conroy@usdoj.gov
Immigration Judge **Paula Donnolo** . . . . . (917) 454-1040
E-mail: paula.donnolo@usdoj.gov
Immigration Judge **Evalyn P. Douchy** . . . . . (917) 454-1040
E-mail: evalyn.p.douchy@usdoj.gov
Immigration Judge **Samuel M. Factor** . . . . . (917) 454-1040
E-mail: sam.factor@usdoj.gov
Education: CUNY 1995 BA, 2002 BS; Cardozo 1998 JD
Immigration Judge **Vivienne E. Gordon-Uruakpa** . . . . . (917) 454-1040
Immigration Judge **Howard C. Hom** . . . . . (917) 454-1040
Immigration Judge **Amiena A. Khan** . . . . . (917) 454-1040
E-mail: amiena.a.khan@usdoj.gov
Immigration Judge **Margaret M. Kolbe** . . . . . (917) 454-1040
E-mail: margaret.m.kolbe@usdoj.gov

★ Presidential Appointment Requiring Senate Confirmation ☆ Presidential Appointment ☐ Schedule C Appointment ◇ Career Senior Foreign Service Appointment
● Career Senior Executive Service (SES) Appointment ○ Non-Career Senior Executive Service (SES) Appointment ■ Postal Career Executive Service

U.S. Immigration Court - Federal Plaza, New York (NY) *(continued)*

Immigration Judge **Brigitte LaForest** .... (917) 454-1040
E-mail: brigitte.laforest@usdoj.gov
Immigration Judge **Elizabeth A. Lamb** .... (917) 454-1040
E-mail: elizabeth.lamb@usdoj.gov
Immigration Judge **Frederic G. Leeds** .... (917) 454-1040
E-mail: frederic.g.leeds@usdoj.gov
Immigration Judge **Frank James Loprest, Jr.** .... (917) 454-1040
E-mail: f.james.loprest.jr@usdoj.gov
Education: Cornell 1982 BA; Notre Dame 1989 JD
Immigration Judge **Lena Golovnin** .... (917) 454-1040
E-mail: lena.golovnin@usdoj.gov
Education: Hunter 2002 BA; Thomas M Cooley 2008 JD
Immigration Judge **Cynthia Gordon** .... (917) 454-1040
Education: Hamilton 1990 BA; Cornell 1993 JD
Immigration Judge **Maria Lurye** .... (917) 454-1040
E-mail: maria.lurye@usdoj.gov
Immigration Judge **James M. McCarthy** .... (917) 454-1040
Immigration Judge **Michael G. McFarland** .... (410) 962-3092
E-mail: michael.g.mcfarland@usdoj.gov
Education: NYU 2004 BA, 2007 JD
Immigration Judge **Maria E. Navarro** .... (617) 565-3080
E-mail: maria.e.navarro@usdoj.gov
Immigration Judge **Barbara A. Nelson** .... (917) 454-1040
E-mail: barbara.nelson2@usdoj.gov
Immigration Judge **Col Brian T. Palmer USMC** .... (917) 454-1040
E-mail: brian.t.palmer@usdoj.gov
Education: SUNY (Brockport) 1982 BA;
Western New England 1986 JD; Judge Advocate Gen 1992 ML
Immigration Judge **Aviva L. Poczter** .... (917) 454-1040
E-mail: aviva.l.poczter@usdoj.gov
Immigration Judge **Douglas B. Schoppert** .... (917) 454-1040
E-mail: douglas.schoppert@usdoj.gov
Immigration Judge **Alice Segal** .... (917) 454-1040
E-mail: alice.segal@usdoj.gov
Education: Pennsylvania 1992 BA; George Washington 1995 JD
Immigration Judge **Helen Sichel** .... (917) 454-1040
E-mail: helen.sichel@usdoj.gov
Immigration Judge **Oshea Denise Spencer** .... (703) 603-1300
E-mail: oshea.d.spencer@usdoj.gov
Education: Texas 1994 BA, 1997 JD
Immigration Judge **Jem C. Sponzo** .... (917) 454-1040
E-mail: jem.c.sponzo@usdoj.gov
Immigration Judge **Donald W. Thompson** .... (917) 454-1040
Immigration Judge **Virna A. Wright** .... (917) 454-1040
E-mail: virna.a.wright@usdoj.gov
Education: Rutgers 1990 BA; Cornell 1993 JD
Immigration Judge **Randa Zagzoug** .... (917) 454-1040
E-mail: randa.zagzoug@usdoj.gov
Court Administrator (Acting) **Regina M. Rau** .... (917) 454-1040
E-mail: regina.rau@usdoj.gov
Deputy Court Administrator **Regina M. Rau** .... (917) 454-1040
E-mail: regina.rau@usdoj.gov

U.S. Immigration Court - Varick Street, New York (NY)
201 Varick Street, Room 1140, New York, NY 10014
Tel: (212) 620-6279
Internet: https://www.justice.gov/eoir/varick-street-immigration-court

Immigration Judge **Thomas J. Mulligan** .... (212) 620-6279
E-mail: thomas.mulligan@usdoj.gov
Education: St John's U (NY) 1974 BS; Long Island 1977 MPS;
St John's U (NY) 1982 JD
Immigration Judge **Mimi Tsankov** .... (212) 620-6279
E-mail: mimi.tsankov@usdoj.gov
Education: James Madison 1986 BA; Virginia 1990 MA, 1990 JD
Immigration Judge **Lauren Weintraub** .... (212) 620-6279
Court Administrator (Acting) **Regina M. Rau** .... (212) 620-6279
E-mail: regina.rau@usdoj.gov

U.S. Immigration Court - Oakdale (LA) Federal Detention Center
1900 East Whatley Road, Oakdale, LA 71463
P.O. Box 750, Oakdale, LA 71463
Tel: (318) 335-0365
Internet: https://www.justice.gov/eoir/oakdale-immigration-court

Immigration Judge **Grady Crooks** .... (318) 335-0365
E-mail: grady.crooks@usdoj.gov
Education: North Dakota State 1996 BS;
George Washington 1999 MA; Rutgers 2004 JD
Immigration Judge **John A. Duck, Jr.** .... (318) 335-0365
E-mail: john.duck@usdoj.gov
Immigration Judge **Steven B. Fuller** .... (318) 335-0365
E-mail: steven.fuller@usdoj.gov
Education: Auburn 1997 BA; Regent U 2000 JD
Immigration Judge **Brent H. Landis** .... (318) 335-0365
E-mail: brent.landis@usdoj.gov
Education: Metropolitan State U 1982 BA; DePaul 1985 JD
Immigration Judge **LCDR Scott W. Laragy USN** .... (318) 335-0365
E-mail: scott.laragy@usdoj.gov
Education: Loyola U (New Orleans) 1991 BA, 1994 JD
Immigration Judge **Angela M. Munson** .... (318) 335-0365
Education: Georgia State 1990 BA; Tulane 1994 JD
Immigration Judge **Agnelis L. Reese** .... (318) 335-0365
E-mail: agnelis.reese@usdoj.gov
Immigration Judge **Cassie A. Thogersen** .... (318) 335-0365
E-mail: cassie.thogersen@usdoj.gov
Education: Southeastern Louisiana 1993 BA;
Washington U (MO) 1996 MSW; Wisconsin 1999 JD
Court Administrator **Hunter Johnson** .... (318) 335-0365
E-mail: hunter.johnson@usdoj.gov

U.S. Immigration Court - Omaha (NE)
1717 Avenue H, Suite 100, Omaha, NE 68110
Tel: (402) 348-0310

Immigration Judge **Jack L. Anderson** .... (402) 348-0310
E-mail: jack.anderson@usdoj.gov
Immigration Judge **Matthew E. Morrissey** .... (402) 348-0310
E-mail: matthew.e.morrissey@usdoj.gov
Immigration Judge **Abby L. Meyer** .... (402) 348-0310
E-mail: abby.l.meyer@usdoj.gov
Education: Simpson (CA) 2004 BA; Nebraska (Omaha) 2007 JD
Court Administrator **Henry Atkinson** .... (402) 348-0314
E-mail: henry.atkinson@usdoj.gov

U.S. Immigration Court - Orlando (FL)
3535 Lawton Road, Suite 200, Orlando, FL 32803
Tel: (407) 722-8900
Internet: https://www.justice.gov/eoir/orlando-immigration-court

Immigration Judge **Yon K. Alberdi** .... (407) 722-8900
E-mail: yon.k.alberdi@usdoj.gov
Immigration Judge **Kevin Chapman** .... (407) 722-8900
E-mail: kevin.chapman@usdoj.gov
Immigration Judge **Victoria L. Ghartey** .... (407) 722-8900
E-mail: victoria.ghartey@usdoj.gov
Immigration Judge **Stuart F. Karden** .... (407) 722-8900
E-mail: stuart.karden@usdoj.gov
Education: Michigan 1973 BA; Miami 1976 JD
Immigration Judge **Daniel Lippman** .... (407) 722-8900
E-mail: dan.lippman@usdoj.gov
Immigration Judge **Rafael B. Ortiz-Segura** .... (407) 722-8900
E-mail: rafael.ortiz@usdoj.gov
Court Administrator **Christina Parsons** .... (407) 722-8900
E-mail: christina.parsons@usdoj.gov

U.S. Immigration Court - Pearsall (TX)
566 Veterans Drive, Pearsall, TX 78601
Tel: (210) 368-5700

Immigration Judge **Stuart D. Alcorn** .... (210) 368-5700
E-mail: stuart.d.alcorn@usdoj.gov
Education: Southern Mississippi 1994 BA; Texas Southern 2004 JD
Immigration Judge **D'Anna H. Freeman** .... (210) 368-5700
E-mail: danna.h.freeman@usdoj.gov
Immigration Judge **Robert Reid McKee** .... (210) 368-5700
E-mail: robert.r.mckee@usdoj.gov

(continued on next page)

DEPARTMENTS

U.S. Immigration Court - Pearsall (TX) *(continued)*

Immigration Judge **(Vacant)** .... (210) 368-5700
Court Administrator (Acting) **Daniel Ponce de Leon** .... (210) 368-5700
E-mail: daniel.ponce.de.leon@usdoj.gov

U.S. Immigration Court - Philadelphia (PA)

Robert Nix Federal Building and Courthouse, 900 Market Street, Suite 504, Philadelphia, PA 19107
Tel: (215) 656-7000 Fax: (267) 387-4190
Internet: https://www.justice.gov/eoir/philadelphia-pa

Immigration Judge **John B. Carle** .... (215) 656-7000
E-mail: john.b.carle@usdoj.gov
Immigration Judge **Lisa Ann J. De Cardona** .... (215) 656-7000
Immigration Judge **Charles M. Honeyman** .... (215) 656-7000
E-mail: charles.honeyman@usdoj.gov
Immigration Judge **Rosalind K. Malloy** .... (215) 656-7000
E-mail: rosalind.malloy@usdoj.gov
Immigration Judge **Steven Morley** .... (215) 656-7000
E-mail: steven.morley@usdoj.gov
Immigration Judge **Dinesh C. Verma** .... (215) 656-7000
E-mail: dinesh.c.verma@usdoj.gov
Court Administrator **Alterra Alicea** .... (215) 656-7000 ext. 33
E-mail: alterra.alicea@usdoj.gov

U.S. Immigration Court - Phoenix (AZ)

200 East Mitchell Drive, Suite 200, Phoenix, AZ 85012
Tel: (602) 640-2747
Internet: https://www.justice.gov/eoir/phoenix-immigration-court

Immigration Judge **Silvia R. Arellano** .... (602) 640-2747
E-mail: silvia.r.arellano@usdoj.gov
Education: Arizona State 1974 BA, 1978 JD
Immigration Judge **LaMonte S. Freerks** .... (602) 640-2747
E-mail: lamonte.freerks@usdoj.gov
Immigration Judge **Linda Spencer-Walters** .... (602) 640-2747
E-mail: linda.spencer-walters@usdoj.gov
Court Administrator (Acting) **Corey Graff** .... (602) 640-2747
E-mail: corey.graff@usdoj.gov

U.S. Immigration Court - Portland (OR)

1220 SW Third Avenue, Suite 500, Portland, OR 97204
Tel: (503) 326-6341
Internet: https://www.justice.gov/eoir/portland-immigration-court

Immigration Judge **Christopher Joren Lyons** .... (503) 326-6341
E-mail: joren.lyons@usdoj.gov
Education: UC Berkeley 1994 BA; Boalt Hall 1999 JD
Immigration Judge **Richard Zanfardino** .... (503) 326-6341
E-mail: richard.zanfardino@usdoj.gov
Immigration Judge **(Vacant)** .... (503) 326-6341
Court Administrator (Acting) **Joseph A. Neifert** .... (503) 326-6341
E-mail: joseph.neifert@usdoj.gov

U.S. Immigration Court - Port Isabel (TX)

Port Isabel Processing Center, 27991 Buena Vista Boulevard, Los Fresnos, TX 78566
Tel: (956) 254-5700

Immigration Judge **Barbara Cigarroa** .... (956) 547-1789
E-mail: barbara.cigarroa@usdoj.gov
Immigration Judge **John Grasty Crews II** .... (956) 547-1789
E-mail: john.g.crews@usdoj.gov
Education: Boston U 1981 BA; Southern Methodist 1985 JD
Immigration Judge **Morris I. Onyewuchi** .... (956) 547-1789
E-mail: morris.i.onyewuchi@usdoj.gov
Immigration Judge **Frank T. Pimentel** .... (956) 547-1789
Immigration Judge **(Vacant)** .... (956) 547-1789
Immigration Judge **(Vacant)** .... (956) 547-1789
Court Administrator (Acting) **Jennifer Cunningham** .... (956) 547-1789
E-mail: jennifer.cunningham@usdoj.gov

U.S. Immigration Court - Salt Lake City (UT)

2975 South Decker Lake Drive, Suite 200, West Valley City, UT 84119-6094
Tel: (801) 524-3000

Immigration Judge **David C. Anderson** .... (801) 524-3000
E-mail: david.anderson@usdoj.gov
Immigration Judge **Cristopher M. Greer** .... (801) 524-3000
E-mail: christopher.m.greer@usdoj.gov
Immigration Judge **P. Michael Truman** .... (801) 524-3000
Court Administrator (Acting) **Rachel Newsome** .... (801) 524-3000
E-mail: rachel.newsome@usdoj.gov

U.S. Immigration Court - San Antonio (TX)

800 Dolorosa Street, Suite 300, San Antonio, TX 78207
106 S. St. Mary's St., Suite 600, San Antonio, TX 78205 (Annex)
Tel: (210) 472-6637
Internet: https://www.justice.gov/eoir/san-antonio-immigration-court

Immigration Judge **Justin F. Adams** .... (210) 472-6637
E-mail: justin.adams@usdoj.gov
Immigration Judge **Margaret D. Burkhart** .... (210) 472-6637
E-mail: margaret.burkhart@usdoj.gov
Immigration Judge **Thomas G. Crossan, Jr.** .... (210) 472-6637
E-mail: thomas.g.crossan@usdoj.gov
Education: Idaho 1979 BA, 1983 JD
Immigration Judge **Yvonne S. Gonzalez** .... (210) 472-6637
Immigration Judge **Craig A. Harlow** .... (210) 472-6637
E-mail: craig.harlow@usdoj.gov
Immigration Judge **Anibal Martinez** .... (210) 472-6637
E-mail: anibal.martinez@usdoj.gov
Immigration Judge **Cythia Lafuente-Gaona** .... (215) 656-7000
E-mail: cynthia.lafuente-gaona@usdoj.gov
Immigration Judge **Charles M. McCullough** .... (617) 565-3080
E-mail: charles.m.mccullough@usdoj.gov
Immigration Judge **Daniel J. "Dan" Santander** .... (210) 472-6637
E-mail: daniel.j.santander@usdoj.gov
Education: Arizona 1990 BS, 1994 JD
Immigration Judge **Eric J. Tijerina** .... (210) 472-6637
E-mail: eric.j.tijerina@usdoj.gov
Education: Texas 1991 BA; Texas Christian 1996 MBA; St Mary's U (TX) 2006 JD
Immigration Judge **Meredith Tyrakoski** .... (210) 472-6637
Court Administrator **Daniel Ponce de Leon** .... (210) 472-6637
E-mail: daniel.ponce.de.leon@usdoj.gov

U.S. Immigration Court - San Diego (CA)

401 West A Street, Suite 800, San Diego, CA 92101
Tel: (619) 557-6052
Internet: https://www.justice.gov/eoir/san-diego-immigration-court

Immigration Judge **Christine A. Bither** .... (619) 557-6052
E-mail: christine.bither@usdoj.gov
Immigration Judge **Jesus Clemente** .... (619) 557-6052
E-mail: jesus.clemente@usdoj.gov
Immigration Judge **James A. DeVitto** .... (619) 557-6052
E-mail: james.devitto2@usdoj.gov
Immigration Judge **Henry P. "Hank" Ipema, Jr.** .... (619) 557-6052
E-mail: hank.p.ipema@usdoj.gov
Immigration Judge **Philip S. Law** .... (619) 557-6052
E-mail: philip.law@usdoj.gov
Immigration Judge **Renee L. Renner** .... (619) 557-6052
E-mail: renee.renner@usdoj.gov
Education: Florida 1976 BA, 1979 JD; San Diego 1992 LLM; Naval War 1999; Army War Col 2002 MS
Immigration Judge **Jeffrey L. Romig** .... (619) 557-6052
E-mail: jeff.romig@usdoj.gov
Education: Duquesne 1981 BA; Pittsburgh 1985 MA, 1985 JD
Court Administrator **Rene Cervantes** .... (619) 557-6052
E-mail: rene.cervantes@usdoj.gov

U.S. Immigration Court - San Francisco (CA)

120 Montgomery Street, Suite 800, San Francisco, CA 94104
Tel: (800) 898-7180 (24 Hours) Tel: (415) 705-4415
Internet: https://www.justice.gov/eoir/san-francisco-immigration-court

Assistant Chief Immigration Judge **(Vacant)** .... (415) 705-4415

U.S. Immigration Court - San Francisco (CA) *(continued)*

Immigration Judge **Victoria L. Argumedo** . . . . (415) 705-4415
E-mail: victoria.l.argumedo@usdoj.gov
Immigration Judge **Valerie A. Burch** . . . . (415) 705-4415
Immigration Judge **Ila C. Deiss** . . . . (415) 705-4415
E-mail: ila.c.deiss@usdoj.gov
Immigration Judge **Laura C. Figueroa** . . . . (415) 705-4415
E-mail: laura.c.figueroa@usdoj.gov
Education: Texas (San Antonio) 2003 BA; Southern Methodist 2007 JD
Immigration Judge **Loreto Geisse** . . . . (415) 705-4415
E-mail: loreto.geisse@usdoj.gov
Immigration Judge **Charles S. Greene III** . . . . (415) 705-4415
Immigration Judge **Miriam R. Hayward** . . . . (415) 705-4415
E-mail: miriam.hayward@usdoj.gov
Immigration Judge **Jacqueline J. Jackson** . . . . (415) 705-4415
E-mail: jacqueline.j.jackson@usdoj.gov
Education: Stanford 1986 BA; UCLA 1989 JD; Army War Col 2013 MSS
Immigration Judge **Jeremiah Johnson** . . . . (415) 705-4415
E-mail: jeremiah.johnson@usdoj.gov
Immigration Judge **Dana Leigh Marks** . . . . (415) 705-4415
E-mail: dana.marks@usdoj.gov
Immigration Judge **Dion A. Morwood** . . . . (415) 705-4415
E-mail: dion.a.morwood@usdoj.gov
Education: Utah State 2000 BA; BYU 2008 JD
Immigration Judge **Julie L. Nelson** . . . . (415) 705-4415
E-mail: julie.l.nelson@usdoj.gov
Immigration Judge **Patrick S. O'Brien** . . . . (415) 705-4415
E-mail: patrick.s.o'brien@usdoj.gov
Immigration Judge **Joseph Y. Park** . . . . (415) 705-4415
E-mail: joseph.y.park@usdoj.gov
Immigration Judge **Robin Kandell Paulino** . . . . (415) 705-4415
Immigration Judge **Laura L. Ramirez** . . . . (415) 705-4415
E-mail: laura.ramirez@usdoj.gov
Immigration Judge **Patrick S. Savage** . . . . (415) 705-4415
E-mail: patrick.s.savage@usdoj.gov
Immigration Judge **Ilyce S. Shugall** . . . . (415) 705-4415
E-mail: ilyce.shugall@usdoj.gov
Immigration Judge **Shadee M. Star** . . . . (415) 705-4415
E-mail: shadee.m.star@usdoj.gov
Education: Cal State (Fullerton) 1996 BA; Stetson 1999 JD
Immigration Judge **Arwen Swink** . . . . (415) 705-4415
E-mail: arwen.a.swink@usdoj.gov
Immigration Judge **Elizabeth L. Young** . . . . (415) 705-4415
E-mail: elizabeth.l.young@usdoj.gov
Court Administrator **Maria Jauregui** . . . . (415) 705-4415
E-mail: maria.jauregui@usdoj.gov

U.S. Immigration Court - Seattle (WA)

1000 Second Avenue, Suite 2500, Seattle, WA 98104
Tel: (206) 553-5953
Internet: https://www.justice.gov/eoir/san-francisco-immigration-court

Immigration Judge **Paul A. DeFonzo** . . . . (206) 553-5953
E-mail: paul.defonzo@usdoj.gov
Immigration Judge **Brett M. Parchert** . . . . (206) 553-5953
E-mail: brett.parchert@usdoj.gov
Immigration Judge **(Vacant)** . . . . (206) 553-5953
Court Administrator **Randall M. "Randy" Bruns** . . . . (206) 553-5953
E-mail: randall.m.bruns@usdoj.gov

U.S. Immigration Court - Stewart (GA)

146 CCA Road, Lumpkin, GA 31815
PO Box 248, Lumpkin, GA 31815
Tel: (229) 838-1320

Immigration Judge **Randall Wilson Duncan** . . . . (229) 838-1320
E-mail: randall.duncan@usdoj.gov
Education: John Marshall JD
Immigration Judge **Jeffery R. Nance** . . . . (229) 838-1320
E-mail: jeffery.r.nance@usdoj.gov
Education: BYU 1985 BA; J Reuben Clark Law 1988 JD; Judge Advocate Gen 1997 ML
Immigration Judge **Dan Trimble** . . . . (229) 838-1320
E-mail: dan.trimble@usdoj.gov
Education: West Point 1975 BS; Case Western 1981 JD

U.S. Immigration Court - Stewart (GA) *(continued)*

Immigration Judge **(Vacant)** . . . . (229) 838-1320
Court Administrator **Ray Bethune** . . . . (229) 838-1320
E-mail: ray.bethune@usdoj.gov

U.S. Immigration Court - Tacoma (WA)

1623 East J. Street, Suite Three, Tacoma, WA 98421
Tel: (253) 779-6020 Fax: (253) 779-6001

Immigration Judge **Tammy Fitting** . . . . (253) 779-6020
E-mail: tammy.fitting@usdoj.gov
Immigration Judge **Charles Neil Floyd** . . . . (253) 779-6020
E-mail: charles.n.floyd@usdoj.gov
Education: Harding 1991 BS; Arkansas 1997 JD
Immigration Judge **John C. Odell** . . . . (253) 779-6020
E-mail: john.odell@usdoj.gov
Court Administrator (Acting) **Joseph A. Neifert** . . . . (253) 779-6020
E-mail: joseph.neifert@usdoj.gov

U.S. Immigration Court - Tucson (AZ)

300 West Congress Street, Suite 300, Tucson, AZ 85701
Tel: (520) 670-5212

Immigration Judge **John W. Davis** . . . . (520) 670-5212
E-mail: john.davis@usdoj.gov
Education: Nebraska (Omaha) 1981 BA; Creighton 1987 JD; Judge Advocate Gen 1997 LLM
Immigration Judge **Sean H. Keenan** . . . . (520) 670-5212
E-mail: sean.keenan@usdoj.gov
Immigration Judge **Thomas M. O'Leary** . . . . (520) 670-5212
E-mail: thomas.o'leary@usdoj.gov
Court Administrator **Corey Graff** . . . . (520) 670-5212
E-mail: corey.graff@usdoj.gov

U.S. Immigration Court - York (PA)

3400 Concord Road, Suite 2, York, PA 17402
P.O. Box 20370, York, PA 17402
Tel: (717) 755-7555
Internet: https://www.justice.gov/eoir/york-immigration-court

Immigration Judge **John P. Ellington** . . . . (717) 755-7555
E-mail: john.p.ellington@usdoj.gov
Immigration Judge **Kuyomars "Q." Golparvar** . . . . (717) 755-7555
E-mail: kuyomars.q.golparvar@usdoj.gov
Immigration Judge **Alice Song Hartye** . . . . (717) 755-7555
E-mail: alice.s.hartye@usdoj.gov
Education: Dickinson Col 2000 BA; Penn State 2005 JD
Court Administrator **Tina Barrow** . . . . (717) 755-7555
E-mail: tina.barrow@usdoj.gov

U.S. Immigration Court - Louisville (KY)

332 West Broadway, 11th Floor, Louisville, KY 40202
Tel: (502) 340-2000

Court Administrator **Hunter Johnson** . . . . (502) 340-2000
E-mail: hunter.johnson@usdoj.gov

DEPARTMENTS

★ Presidential Appointment Requiring Senate Confirmation ☆ Presidential Appointment □ Schedule C Appointment ◇ Career Senior Foreign Service Appointment
● Career Senior Executive Service (SES) Appointment ○ Non-Career Senior Executive Service (SES) Appointment ■ Postal Career Executive Service

DEPARTMENTS

Executive Office for United States Attorneys (EOUSA)

Robert F. Kennedy Building, 950 Pennsylvania Avenue, NW, Washington, DC 20530
Tel: (202) 252-1000 Fax: (202) 252-1001
Internet: www.justice.gov/usao/eousa

Office of the Director

Robert F. Kennedy Building, 950 Pennsylvania Avenue, NW, Room 2242, Washington, DC 20530
Tel: (202) 252-1000 Fax: (202) 252-1001

Office of the Deputy Director for Legal Management

Office of Legal Education (National Advocacy Center)
1620 Pendelton Street, Columbia, SC 29201
Tel: (803) 705-5100 Fax: (803) 705-5110
Internet: https://www.justice.gov/usao/training

● Associate Director **Cammy Chandler** .... (803) 705-5102
E-mail: cammy.chandler@usdoj.gov
Deputy Director **Col Calvin L. Lewis USAF** .... (803) 705-5102
E-mail: calvin.lewis@usdoj.gov

District Offices

Alabama - Middle District

131 Clayton Street, Montgomery, AL 36104
P.O. Box 197, Montgomery, AL 36101-0197
Tel: (334) 223-7280 Fax: (334) 223-7560
Internet: https://www.justice.gov/usao-mdal

★ U.S. Attorney **Louis V. Franklin, Sr.** .... (334) 223-7280
E-mail: louis.franklin@usdoj.gov
Secretary to the U.S. Attorney **Debbie Shaw** .... (334) 223-7280
E-mail: debbie.shaw@usdoj.gov
First Assistant U.S. Attorney **A. Clark Morris** .... (334) 223-7280
E-mail: clark.morris@usdoj.gov
Senior Litigation Counsel and Assistant U.S. Attorney
Jerusha T. Adams .... (334) 223-7280
E-mail: jerusha.adams@usdoj.gov
Asset Forfeiture Assistant U.S. Attorney
Kevin Davidson .... (334) 223-7280
E-mail: kevin.davidson@usdoj.gov
Drug Task Force Lead Assistant U.S. Attorney
Verne H. Speirs .... (334) 223-7280
E-mail: verne.speirs@usdoj.gov
Law Enforcement Coordination Manager
Douglas Howard .... (334) 223-7280
E-mail: douglas.howard@usdoj.gov
Victim/Witness Coordinator
Jacqueline "Jackie" Vickers .... (334) 223-7280
E-mail: jackie.vickers@usdoj.gov
Administrative Officer **Retta C. Goss** .... (334) 223-7280
E-mail: retta.goss@usdoj.gov
Budget Officer **Sherri C. Hamilton** .... (334) 223-7280
E-mail: sherri.c.hamilton@usdoj.gov
Information Technology Specialist **Jordan Oakley** .... (334) 223-7280
E-mail: jordan.oakley@usdoj.gov
Information Technology Systems Manager
Randy Durden .... (334) 223-7280
E-mail: randy.durden@usdoj.gov
Public Affairs Officer **A. Clark Morris** .... (334) 223-7280
E-mail: clark.morris@usdoj.gov

Civil Division
131 Clayton Street, Montgomery, AL 36104
Tel: (334) 223-7280 Fax: (334) 223-7560

Chief **Stephen M. "Steve" Doyle** .... (334) 223-7280
E-mail: stephen.doyle@usdoj.gov
Assistant U.S. Attorney [District Election Officer]
A. Clark Morris .... (334) 223-7280
E-mail: clark.morris@usdoj.gov
Assistant U.S. Attorney **James "Jim" DuBois** .... (334) 223-7280
E-mail: james.dubois2@usdoj.gov

Civil Division *(continued)*

Assistant U.S. Attorney **Jeshua Adams** .... (334) 223-7280
E-mail: jeshua.adams@usdoj.gov

Criminal Division
131 Clayton Street, Montgomery, AL 36104
Tel: (334) 223-7280 Fax: (334) 223-7135

Chief **(Vacant)** .... (334) 223-7280
Deputy Chief **Verne H. Speirs** .... (334) 223-7280
E-mail: verne.speirs@usdoj.gov
Assistant U.S. Attorney **Brandon Bates** .... (334) 223-7280
E-mail: brandon.bates@usdoj.gov
Assistant U.S. Attorney **Ben M. Baxley** .... (334) 223-7280
E-mail: ben.baxley@usdoj.gov
Assistant U.S. Attorney **Bradley Bodiford** .... (334) 223-7280
E-mail: bradley.bodiford@usdoj.gov
Assistant U.S. Attorney **Todd Brown** .... (334) 223-7280
E-mail: todd.brown@usdoj.gov
Assistant U.S. Attorney **John Geer** .... (334) 223-7280
E-mail: john.geer@usdoj.gov
Assistant U.S. Attorney **Curtis Ivy, Jr.** .... (334) 223-7280
E-mail: curtis.ivy@usdoj.gov
Assistant U.S. Attorney **Steven Lee** .... (334) 223-7280
E-mail: steven.lee@usdoj.gov
Assistant U.S. Attorney **Randolph R. Neeley** .... (334) 223-7280
E-mail: rand.neeley@usdoj.gov
Assistant U.S. Attorney **Susan Redmond** .... (334) 223-7280
E-mail: susan.redmond@usdoj.gov
Assistant U.S. Attorney **Hollie Reed** .... (334) 223-7280
E-mail: Hollie.reed@usdoj.gov
Assistant U.S. Attorney **Jonathan Ross** .... (334) 223-7280
E-mail: jonathan.ross@usdoj.gov
Assistant U.S. Attorney **Sandra J. Stewart** .... (334) 223-7280
E-mail: sandra.stewart@usdoj.gov
Assistant U.S. Attorney **Joshua Wendall** .... (334) 223-7280
E-mail: joshua.wendall@usdoj.gov
Assistant U.S. Attorney/Health Care Fraud Coordinator
Denise Simpson .... (334) 223-7280
E-mail: denise.simpson@usdoj.gov

Financial Litigation Unit
131 Clayton Street, Montgomery, AL 36104
Tel: (334) 223-7280 Fax: (334) 223-7418

Lead Attorney (Acting) **Stephen M. "Steve" Doyle** ..... (334) 223-7280
E-mail: stephen.doyle@usdoj.gov

Alabama - Northern District

1801 Fourth Avenue North, Birmingham, AL 35203-2101
Tel: (205) 244-2001 Fax: (205) 244-2183
Internet: https://www.justice.gov/usao-ndal

★ U.S. Attorney **Jay E. Town** .... (205) 244-2216
E-mail: jay.e.town@usdoj.gov
Education: Notre Dame 1995 BA; Seton Hall 1998 JD
Executive Assistant to the U.S. Attorney
Stacy M. Crane .... (205) 244-2015
First Assistant U.S. Attorney **Lloyd C. Peeples** .... (205) 244-2216
E-mail: lloyd.peeples@usdoj.gov
Education: Washington and Lee BA; Cumberland JD
Crisis Management Coordinator **Henry B. Cornelius** ..... (205) 244-2213
Law Enforcement Coordinator Manager
Lyndon J. Laster .... (205) 244-2092
E-mail: lyndon.laster@usdoj.gov
Victim-Witness Coordinator
Tonja Benninger Holtkamp .... (205) 244-2093
E-mail: tonja.benninger@usdoj.gov
Administrative Officer **China M. Davidson** .... (205) 244-2030
E-mail: china.davidson@usdoj.gov
Deputy Administrative Officer **(Vacant)** .... (205) 244-2001
Administrative Services Specialist
Christopher J. Givens .... (205) 244-2050
E-mail: christopher.givens@usdoj.gov
Human Resources Officer **Donzella L. Walton** .... (205) 244-2070
E-mail: donzella.walton@usdoj.gov

★ Presidential Appointment Requiring Senate Confirmation ☆ Presidential Appointment □ Schedule C Appointment ◇ Career Senior Foreign Service Appointment
● Career Senior Executive Service (SES) Appointment ○ Non-Career Senior Executive Service (SES) Appointment ■ Postal Career Executive Service

Alabama - Northern District *(continued)*

Human Resources Specialist **Jane M. McGuire** . . . . (205) 244-2071
E-mail: jane.mcguire@usdoj.gov
Intelligence Specialist **Tammy R. Davis** . . . . (205) 244-2188
Litigation Support Specialist **Valeria "Val" Swann** . . . . . . (205) 244-2081
E-mail: valeria.swann@usdoj.gov
Systems Manager **P. Tracy Stewart** . . . . (205) 244-2080
E-mail: tracy.stewart@usdoj.gov
Executive Assistant U.S. Attorney **Robert O. Posey** . . . . . (205) 244-2001
E-mail: robert.posey@usdoj.gov

Appellate Division

Chief **Michael B. Billingsley** . . . . (205) 244-2157
E-mail: michael.billingsley@usdoj.gov
Assistant U.S. Attorney **(Vacant)** . . . . (205) 244-2234
Assistant U.S. Attorney **Praveen S. Krishna** . . . . (205) 244-2168
E-mail: praveen.krishna@usdoj.gov
Assistant U.S. Attorney **Jenny L. Smith** . . . . (205) 244-2105
E-mail: jenny.smith@usdoj.gov

Civil Division

Chief **Lane H. Woodke** . . . . (205) 244-2107
E-mail: lane.woodke@usdoj.gov
Deputy Chief **Jason R. Cheek** . . . . (205) 244-2104
E-mail: jason.cheek@usdoj.gov
Assistant U.S. Attorney **Sarah Canzoniero Blutter** . . . . . . (205) 244-2119
E-mail: sarah.blutter@usdoj.gov
Education: Columbia 2000 BA; Virginia 2003 JD
Assistant U.S. Attorney **Margaret Lester Marshall** . . . . . . (205) 244-2104
E-mail: margaret.marshall@usdoj.gov
Assistant U.S. Attorney **Jack B. Hood** . . . . (205) 244-2103
E-mail: jack.hood@usdoj.gov
Assistant U.S. Attorney **Don B. Long** . . . . (205) 244-2106
E-mail: don.long2@usdoj.gov
Education: Texas 2008 JD
Assistant U.S. Attorney **Richard E. O'Neal** . . . . (205) 244-2120
E-mail: richard.o'neal@usdoj.gov
Assistant U.S. Attorney **John "Jay" Saxon** . . . . (205) 244-2217
E-mail: jay.saxon@usdoj.gov
Education: Ohio State 2011 JD
Assistant U.S. Attorney **Edward Q. Ragland** . . . . (205) 244-2109
E-mail: ed.ragland@usdoj.gov
Assistant U.S. Attorney **Carla Ward** . . . . (205) 244-2185
E-mail: carla.ward@usdoj.gov

Civil Rights Unit

131 Clayton Street, Montgomery, AL 36104
Tel: (205) 244-2001

Chief **Tamarra Matthews-Johnson** . . . . (205) 244-2203
E-mail: tamarra.matthews-johnson@usdoj.gov
Assistant U.S. Attorney **Carla Ward** . . . . (205) 244-2185
E-mail: carla.ward@usdoj.gov

Criminal Division

Chief **Michael W. Whisonant** . . . . (205) 244-2241
E-mail: mike.whisonant@usdoj.gov
Deputy Chief (Drugs, Guns, Violent Crimes)
William G. Simpson . . . . (205) 244-2207
E-mail: bill.simpson@usdoj.gov
Deputy Chief (Public Corruption, Fraud, Civil Rights, Environmental) **Tamarra Matthews-Johnson** . . . . (205) 244-2203
E-mail: tamarra.matthews-johnson@usdoj.gov
Deputy Chief (Terrorism, Cybercrime, Child Exploitation, Asset Forfeiture) **Daniel J. Fortune** . . . . . . (205) 244-2156
E-mail: daniel.fortune@usdoj.gov
Asset Forfeiture Unit Assistant U.S. Attorney
Thomas E. Borton IV . . . . (205) 244-2131
E-mail: thomas.borton@usdoj.gov
Education: Alabama 2001 JD
Assistant U.S. Attorney **Melissa K. Atwood** . . . . (205) 244-2159
E-mail: melissa.atwood@usdoj.gov
Assistant U.S. Attorney **Manu K. Balachandran** . . . . (205) 244-2108
E-mail: manu.balachandran@usdoj.gov
Assistant U.S. Attorney **Erica W Barnes** . . . . (205) 244-2228
E-mail: erica.barnes@usdoj.gov

Criminal Division *(continued)*

Assistant U.S. Attorney **Xavier O. Carter, Sr.** . . . . (205) 244-2229
E-mail: xavier.carter@usdoj.gov
Assistant U.S. Attorney **Henry B. Cornelius** . . . . (205) 244-2213
E-mail: henry.cornelius@usdoj.gov
Assistant U.S. Attorney **Chinelo Dike-Minor** . . . . (205) 244-2139
E-mail: chinelo.dike-minor@usdoj.gov
Assistant U.S. Attorney **John B. "Brad" Felton** . . . . (205) 244-2256
E-mail: brad.felton@usdoj.gov
Assistant U.S. Attorney **Nicole Grosnoff** . . . . (205) 244-2132
E-mail: nicole.s.grosnoff@usdoj.gov
Assistant U.S. Attorney **Elizabeth A. Holt** . . . . (205) 244-2022
E-mail: elizabeth.holt@usdoj.gov
Assistant U.S. Attorney **Robin B. Mark** . . . . (205) 244-2154
E-mail: robin.mark@usdoj.gov
Assistant U.S. Attorney **George A. Martin** . . . . (205) 244-2254
E-mail: george.martin@usdoj.gov
Assistant U.S. Attorney **Tamarra Matthews-Johnson** . . . (205) 244-2203
E-mail: tamarra.matthews-johnson@usdoj.gov
Assistant U.S. Attorney **Kathryn McHugh** . . . . (205) 244-2155
E-mail: kathryn.mchugh@usdoj.gov
Assistant U.S. Attorney **John P. "Pat" Meadows** . . . . (205) 244-2214
E-mail: pat.meadows@usdoj.gov
Assistant U.S. Attorney **Michael A. Royster** . . . . (205) 244-2242
E-mail: michael.royster@usdoj.gov
Assistant U.S. Attorney **Austin D. Shutt** . . . . (205) 244-2212
E-mail: austin.shutt@usdoj.gov
Assistant U.S. Attorney **L. James "Jim" Weil, Jr.** . . . . (205) 244-2242
E-mail: jim.weil@usdoj.gov

Drug Task Force

Lead Assistant U.S. Attorney **Gregory R. Dimler** . . . . (205) 244-2223
E-mail: greg.dimler@usdoj.gov
Assistant U.S. Attorney **Mohmmad Khatib** . . . . (205) 244-2160
E-mail: mohammad.khatib@usdoj.gov
Assistant U.S. Attorney **Kathryn McHugh** . . . . (205) 244-2242
E-mail: kathryn.mchugh@usdoj.gov
Assistant U.S. Attorney **Austin D. Shutt** . . . . (205) 244-2212
E-mail: austin.shutt@usdoj.gov

Huntsville (AL) Office

400 Meridian Street, Suite 304, Huntsville, AL 35801
Tel: (256) 534-8285 Fax: (256) 539-3270

Branch Chief and Assistant U.S. Attorney
Laura D. Hodge . . . . (256) 551-7363
E-mail: laura.hodge@usdoj.gov
Assistant U.S. Attorney **Davis A. Barlow** . . . . (256) 551-7353
E-mail: davis.barlow@usdoj.gov
Assistant U.S. Attorney **Mary Stuart Burrell** . . . . (256) 551-7365
E-mail: mary.stuart.burrell@usdoj.gov
Assistant U.S. Attorney **(Vacant)** . . . . (256) 551-7362
E-mail: david.estes@usdoj.gov
Assistant U.S. Attorney **Jonathan S. Keim** . . . . (256) 551-7354
E-mail: jonathan.keim@usdoj.gov
Assistant U.S. Attorney **Russell E. Penfield** . . . . (256) 551-7361
E-mail: russell.penfield@usdoj.gov

Alabama - Southern District

Renaissance Riverview Plaza Office Building, 63 South Royal Street, Suite 600, Mobile, AL 36602
Tel: (251) 441-5845 Fax: (251) 441-5277
Internet: www.justice.gov/usao/als

★ U.S. Attorney **Richard W. Moore** . . . . (251) 441-5845
E-mail: richard.moore@usdoj.gov
Education: Spring Hill BS; Cumberland JD
□ Secretary to the U.S. Attorney **Nancy Dixon** . . . . (251) 441-5845
E-mail: nancy.dixon@usdoj.gov
First Assistant U.S. Attorney **Donna Dobbins** . . . . (251) 441-5845
E-mail: donna.dobbins@usdoj.gov
Appellate Chief **(Vacant)** . . . . (251) 411-5845
Law Enforcement Coordination Specialist
Thomas Loftis . . . . (251) 441-5845
E-mail: thomas.loftis@usdoj.gov
Intelligence Specialist **(Vacant)** . . . . (251) 441-5845

(continued on next page)

★ Presidential Appointment Requiring Senate Confirmation ☆ Presidential Appointment □ Schedule C Appointment ◇ Career Senior Foreign Service Appointment
● Career Senior Executive Service (SES) Appointment ○ Non-Career Senior Executive Service (SES) Appointment ■ Postal Career Executive Service

DEPARTMENTS

Alabama - Southern District *(continued)*

Crisis Management Coordinator **(Vacant)** .... (251) 441-5845
Technology Specialist **Joshua Smith** .... (251) 415-7108
E-mail: joshua.smith@usdoj.gov Fax: (251) 441-6526
Victim-Witness Specialist **Eric T. Day** .... (251) 441-5845
E-mail: eric.day@usdoj.gov
Administrative Officer (Acting) **Dana Butler** .... (251) 441-5845

Civil Division

Chief **Steven E. Butler** .... (251) 441-5845
E-mail: steven.butler@usdoj.gov
Assistant U.S. Attorney **Daryl Atchison** .... (251) 441-5845
E-mail: daryl.atchison@usdoj.gov
Assistant U.S. Attorney **(Vacant)** .... (251) 441-5845
Assistant U.S. Attorney
BrigGen Patricia N. "Patty" Beyer USAFR .... (251) 441-5845
E-mail: patricia.beyer@usdoj.gov
Assistant U.S. Attorney **Deidre Colson** .... (251) 441-5845
E-mail: deidre.colson@usdoj.gov
Assistant U.S. Attorney **Erica Hilliard** .... (251) 441-5845
E-mail: erica.hilliard@usdoj.gov
Assistant U.S. Attorney **Alex F. Lankford IV** .... (251) 441-5845
E-mail: alex.lankford@usdoj.gov
Assistant U.S. Attorney **Suntrease Williams-Maynard** ... (251) 441-5845
E-mail: suntrease.williams-maynard@usdoj.gov
Assistant U.S. Attorney **Holly Wiseman** .... (251) 441-5845
E-mail: holly.wiseman@usdoj.gov

Criminal Division

Chief **Vicki Davis** .... (251) 441-5845
E-mail: vicki.davis@usdoj.gov
Deputy Criminal Chief **Sean Costello** .... (251) 441-5845
E-mail: sean.costello@usdoj.gov
Assistant U.S. Attorney **Michael D. "Mike" Anderson** ... (251) 441-5845
E-mail: mike.d.anderson@usdoj.gov
Assistant U.S. Attorney **Gloria A. Bedwell** .... (251) 441-5845
E-mail: gloria.bedwell@usdoj.gov
Assistant U.S. Attorney **Christopher Bodnar** .... (251) 441-5845
E-mail: christopher.bodnar@usdoj.gov
Education: Texas 2008 JD
Assistant U.S. Attorney **Greg A. Bordenkircher** .... (251) 441-5845
E-mail: greg.bordenkircher@usdoj.gov
Assistant U.S. Attorney **Deborah A. Griffin** .... (251) 441-5845
E-mail: deborah.griffin@usdoj.gov
Assistant U.S. Attorney **Sinan Kalayoglu** .... (251) 441-5845
E-mail: sinan.kalayoglu@usdoj.gov
Assistant U.S. Attorney **George F. May** .... (251) 441-5845
E-mail: george.may@usdoj.gov
Assistant U.S. Attorney **Maria E. Murphy** .... (251) 441-5845
E-mail: maria.murphy@usdoj.gov
Assistant U.S. Attorney **Michele O'Brien** .... (251) 441-5845
E-mail: michele.obrien@usdoj.gov
Assistant U.S. Attorney **Gina Vann** .... (251) 441-5845
E-mail: gina.vann@usdoj.gov
Assistant U.S. Attorney **(Vacant)** .... (251) 441-5845
Assistant U.S. Attorney **(Vacant)** .... (251) 441-5845
Assistant U.S. Attorney **(Vacant)** .... (251) 441-5845
Assistant U.S. Attorney **(Vacant)** .... (251) 441-5845

Alaska District

Federal Building and U.S. Courthouse, 222 West Seventh Avenue, #9, Room 253, Anchorage, AK 99513-7567
Tel: (907) 271-5071 Fax: (907) 271-3224
Internet: www.justice.gov/usao/ak

★ U.S. Attorney **Bryan Schroder** .... (907) 271-5071
E-mail: bryan.schroder@usdoj.gov
Secretary to the U.S. Attorney **Chloe Martin** .... (907) 271-4244
E-mail: chloe.martin@usdoj.gov
First Assistant U.S. Attorney **Bryan Wilson** .... (907) 271-3207
E-mail: Bryan.Wilson@usdoj.gov
Criminal Division Chief and Assistant U.S. Attorney
Frank V. Russo .... (907) 271-3207
E-mail: Frank.Russo@usdoj.gov

Alaska District *(continued)*

Deputy Criminal Division Chief and Assistant U.S. Attorney **Steven E. "Steve" Skrocki** .... (907) 271-5071
E-mail: Steven.Skrocki@usdoj.gov
Civil Division Chief and Assistant U.S. Attorney
Richard Pomeroy .... (907) 271-5071
E-mail: richard.pomeroy@usdoj.gov
Asset Forfeiture Unit Assistant U.S. Attorney **(Vacant)** ... (907) 271-5071
Drug Task Force Assistant U.S. Attorney
Stephan Collins .... (907) 271-5071
E-mail: stephan.collins@usdoj.gov
Assistant U.S. Attorney **Adam Alexander** .... (907) 271-2309
E-mail: adam.alexander@usdoj.gov
Assistant U.S. Attorney **Joseph W. "Joe" Bottini** ...... (907) 271-5071
E-mail: joe.bottini@usdoj.gov
Assistant U.S. Attorney **Thomas "Tom" Bradley** .... (907) 271-5071
E-mail: thomas.bradley@usdoj.gov
Assistant U.S. Attorney **Kelly Cavanaugh** .... (907) 271-5071
E-mail: kelly.cavanaugh@usdoj.gov
Assistant U.S. Attorney **JoAnn Farrington** .... (907) 271-5071
E-mail: JoAnn.Farrington@usdoj.gov
Assistant U.S. Attorney **John Fonstad** .... (907) 271-4274
E-mail: john.fonstad@usdoj.gov
Education: Michigan 2007 JD
Assistant U.S. Attorney **Andrea W. Hattan** .... (907) 271-5071
E-mail: andrea.hattan@usdoj.gov
Education: Seton Hall 2005 JD
Assistant U.S. Attorney **Sara Gray** .... (907) 271-4264
E-mail: sara.gray@usdoj.gov
Assistant U.S. Attorney **Susan Lindquist** .... (907) 271-5071
E-mail: Susan.Lindquist@usdoj.gov
Assistant U.S. Attorney **Retta-Rae Randall** .... (907) 271-5071
E-mail: Retta.Randall@usdoj.gov
Assistant U.S. Attorney **Kyle Reardon** .... (907) 271-5071
Assistant U.S. Attorney **Kimberly "Kim" Sayers-Fay** .... (907) 271-5071
E-mail: kim.sayers-fay@usdoj.gov
Assistant U.S. Attorney **Andrea "Aunnie" Steward** ..... (907) 271-5071
E-mail: aunnie.steward@usdoj.gov
Assistant U.S. Attorney **William Taylor** .... (907) 271-2305
E-mail: william.taylor@usdoj.gov
Assistant U.S. Attorney **Anne Veldhuis** .... (907) 271-2174
E-mail: anne.veldhuis@usdoj.gov
Assistant U.S. Attorney **Jonas Walker** .... (907) 271-3983
E-mail: jonas.walker@usdoj.gov
Administrative Officer **Brenda Spicer** .... (907) 271-5071
E-mail: brenda.spicer@usdoj.gov
Administrative Support Specialist **Lisa Brune** .... (907) 271-5071
E-mail: lisa.brune@usdoj.gov
Automated Litigation Support Specialist
Jodi Bradison .... (907) 271-5071
E-mail: jodi.bradison@usdoj.gov
Budget Officer **Traci D. Ross** .... (907) 271-5071
E-mail: traci.ross@usdoj.gov
Intelligence Officer **John Wallace** .... (907) 271-5071
E-mail: john.wallace@usdoj.gov
Law Enforcement Committee Coordinator
John Wallace .... (907) 271-5071
Office Automation Assistant, Administrative Division
Alesia Gordon .... (907) 271-3977
Office Automation Assistant, Criminal Division
(Vacant) .... (907) 271-5071
Legal Assistant - Administration **James Yeckley** .... (907) 271-5071
E-mail: james.yeckley@usdoj.gov
Legal Assistant Civil Division **Davina Stallworth** .... (907) 271-5071
E-mail: davina.stallworth@usdoj.gov
Legal Assistant Criminal Division **Blair Bowman** .... (907) 271-4802
E-mail: blair.bowman@usdoj.gov
Legal Assistant Criminal Division **Cassandra Mello** ..... (907) 271-3296
E-mail: cassandra.mello@usdoj.gov
Legal Assistant Criminal Division **(Vacant)** .... (907) 271-2302
Supervisory Paralegal Specialist, Criminal Division
Sean Robinson .... (907) 271-5071
Paralegal Specialist, Criminal Division
Monica Johnson .... (907) 271-5071
E-mail: monica.johnson2@usdoj.gov

★ Presidential Appointment Requiring Senate Confirmation ☆ Presidential Appointment ☐ Schedule C Appointment ◇ Career Senior Foreign Service Appointment
● Career Senior Executive Service (SES) Appointment ○ Non-Career Senior Executive Service (SES) Appointment ■ Postal Career Executive Service

Alaska District *(continued)*

Paralegal Specialist, Criminal Division **Jamie Keen** ...... (907) 271-4262
E-mail: jamie.keen@usdoj.gov
Paralegal Specialist, Criminal Division **Jennifer Lotz** .... (907) 271-5071
E-mail: jennifer.lotz@usdoj.gov
Legal Assistant Financial Litigation Unit **(Vacant)** .... (907) 271-5071
Paralegal Finance Litigation Unit **David Urrea** .... (907) 271-5071
Paralegal Financial Litigation Unit **Kathey Virgin** .... (907) 271-5071
E-mail: kathey.virgin@usdoj.gov
Paralegal Specialist Civil Division
Christine "Christy" Dollerhide .... (907) 271-5071
Paralegal Specialist Civil Division
Deborah "Debbie" Simpson .... (907) 271-5071
E-mail: deborah.simpson@usdoj.gov
Systems Manager **Renee Robinson** .... (907) 271-5071
E-mail: renee.robinson@usdoj.gov
Victim/Witness Specialist **(Vacant)** .... (907) 271-5071
Assistant Information Technology Specialist
Kimberly Hooper .... (907) 271-4054
E-mail: Kimberly.Hooper@usdoj.gov
Reentry and Community Outreach Coordinator
Yulonda Candelario .... (907) 271-5071

Fairbanks (AK) Office

Federal Building and U.S. Courthouse, 101 12th Avenue,
Room 310, Box 2, Fairbanks, AK 99701
Tel: (907) 456-0245 Fax: (907) 456-0309

Assistant U.S. Attorney **Stephen "Steve" Cooper** ...... (907) 456-0245
E-mail: stephen.cooper@usdoj.gov
Paralegal Specialist **Robert Knight** .... (907) 456-0245
E-mail: robert.knight@usdoj.gov

Juneau (AK) Office

Federal Building & U.S. Courthouse, 709 West Ninth Street,
Room 937, Juneau, AK 99802
P.O. Box 21627, Juneau, AK 99802
Tel: (907) 796-0400 Fax: (907) 796-0409

Assistant U.S. Attorney **Jack S. Schmidt** .... (907) 796-0400
E-mail: jack.schmidt@usdoj.gov
Paralegal **Ryhana Akhund** .... (907) 796-0400

Arizona District

Two Renaissance Square, 40 North Central Avenue,
Suite 1200, Phoenix, AZ 85004-4408
Tel: (602) 514-7500 Fax: (602) 514-7693
Internet: https://www.justice.gov/usao-az

★ U.S. Attorney (Acting) **Elizabeth A. "Betsy" Strange** ... (602) 514-7500
E-mail: elizabeth.strange@usdoj.gov
Secretary to the U.S. Attorney **Victoria Vasquez** ...... (520) 620-7348
E-mail: victoria.vasquez@usdoj.gov
First Assistant U.S. Attorney
Elizabeth A. "Betsy" Strange .... (602) 514-7518
E-mail: elizabeth.strange@usdoj.gov
Executive Assistant U.S. Attorney **Glenn McCormick** .... (602) 514-7699
Chief Assistant U.S. Attorney **(Vacant)** .... (602) 514-7500
Deputy Administrative Officer **Brandon Brokaw** .... (602) 514-7600
E-mail: brandon.brokaw@usdoj.gov
Community Outreach Director **Cosme Lopez** .... (602) 514-7456
E-mail: cosme.lopez@usdoj.gov
Law Enforcement Coordinator **(Vacant)** .... (602) 514-7573
Public Affairs Officer **Cosme Lopez** .... (602) 514-7500
E-mail: cosme.lopez@usdoj.gov
Systems Manager **James "Jim" Walsh** .... (602) 514-7642
E-mail: james.walsh@usdoj.gov
Victim Witness Coordinator **(Vacant)** .... (602) 514-7595

Appellate Division

Chief **Robert L. Miskell** .... (602) 514-7500
E-mail: robert.miskell@usdoj.gov
Deputy Chief **Krissa M. Lanham** .... (602) 514-7689
E-mail: krissa.lanham@usdoj.gov
Education: Yale JD
Assistant U.S. Attorney **(Vacant)** .... (602) 514-7505

Civil Division

Chief **Diana Varela** .... (602) 514-7743
E-mail: diana.varela@usdoj.gov
Deputy Chief **Peter M. Lantka** .... (602) 514-7739
E-mail: peter.lantka@usdoj.gov
Education: Illinois 1999 BA; Valparaiso 2002 JD
Assistant U.S. Attorney **Paul A. Bullis** .... (602) 514-7659
E-mail: paul.bullis@usdoj.gov
Education: Arizona 1979 BA; Georgetown 1982 JD
Assistant U.S. Attorney **Ann E. Harwood** .... (602) 514-7740
E-mail: ann.harwood@usdoj.gov
Assistant U.S. Attorney **Emory T. Hurley** .... (602) 514-7749
E-mail: emory.hurley@usdoj.gov
Assistant U.S. Attorney **Peter Kozinets** .... (602) 514-7525
E-mail: peter.kozinets@usdoj.gov
Assistant U.S. Attorney **Lon Leavitt** .... (602) 514-7500
E-mail: lon.r.leavitt@usdoj.gov
Assistant U.S. Attorney **Anne E. Nelson** .... (602) 514-7500
E-mail: anne.nelson@usdoj.gov
Education: Arizona 2005 BA; James Rogers Law 2010 JD
Assistant U.S. Attorney **(Vacant)** .... (602) 514-7566
Assistant U.S. Attorney **(Vacant)** .... (602) 514-7500

Criminal Division

Chief **Raymond Woo** .... (602) 514-7520
E-mail: raymond.woo@usdoj.gov
Deputy Chief **Glenn McCormick** .... (602) 514-7669
E-mail: glenn.mccormick@usdoj.gov
Deputy Chief **Dimitra Sampson** .... (602) 514-7584
E-mail: dimitra.sampson@usdoj.gov
Deputy Chief **Keith Vercauteren** .... (602) 514-7621
E-mail: keith.vercauteren@usdoj.gov
Deputy Chief **(Vacant)** .... (602) 514-7517
Assistant U.S. Attorney **Kristen Brook** .... (602) 514-7503
Assistant U.S. Attorney **Roger W. Dokken** .... (602) 514-7523
E-mail: roger.dokken@usdoj.gov
Assistant U.S. Attorney **Frank Galati** .... (602) 514-7582
E-mail: frank.galati@usdoj.gov
Assistant U.S. Attorney **Maria Gutierrez** .... (602) 514-7520
E-mail: maria.gutierrez@usdoj.gov
Assistant U.S. Attorney **Charles F. "Chuck" Hyder** ...... (602) 514-7565
E-mail: chuck.hyder@usdoj.gov
Assistant U.S. Attorney **Melissa Karlen** .... (602) 514-7688
E-mail: melissa.karlen@usdoj.gov
Assistant U.S. Attorney **Christine D. Keller** .... (602) 514-7500
E-mail: christine.keller@usdoj.gov
Assistant U.S. Attorney **James R. "Jim" Knapp** .... (602) 514-7675
E-mail: james.knapp3@usdoj.gov
Education: Arizona State BA, JD
Assistant U.S. Attorney **Brian G. Larson** .... (602) 514-7532
E-mail: brian.larson@usdoj.gov
Assistant U.S. Attorney **Kathy Lemke** .... (602) 514-7544
E-mail: kathy.lemke@usdoj.gov
Assistant U.S. Attorney **Jennifer Levinson** .... (602) 514-7501
E-mail: jennifer.levinson@usdoj.gov
Assistant U.S. Attorney **James "Jim" Morse, Jr.** .... (602) 514-7619
E-mail: james.morse@usdoj.gov
Assistant U.S. Attorney **Walter Perkel** .... (602) 514-7572
E-mail: walter.perkel@usdoj.gov
Assistant U.S. Attorney **Margaret Perlmeter** .... (602) 514-7500
E-mail: margaret.perlmeter@usdoj.gov
Assistant U.S. Attorney **Kevin Rapp** .... (602) 514-7609
E-mail: kevin.rapp@usdoj.gov
Assistant U.S. Attorney **Gary Restaino** .... (602) 514-7736
E-mail: gary.restaino@usdoj.gov
Assistant U.S. Attorney **Peter S. Sexton** .... (602) 514-7508
E-mail: peter.sexton@usdoj.gov
Assistant U.S. Attorney **Tracy Van Buskirk** .... (602) 514-7610
E-mail: tracy.van.buskirk@usdoj.gov
Assistant U.S. Attorney **Mark J. Wenker** .... (602) 514-7748
E-mail: mark.wenker@usdoj.gov
Assistant U.S. Attorney **Cassie Woo** .... (602) 514-7691
E-mail: cassie.woo@usdoj.gov

★ Presidential Appointment Requiring Senate Confirmation ☆ Presidential Appointment ☐ Schedule C Appointment ◇ Career Senior Foreign Service Appointment
● Career Senior Executive Service (SES) Appointment ○ Non-Career Senior Executive Service (SES) Appointment ■ Postal Career Executive Service

DEPARTMENTS

National Security Section
Chief **David Pimsner** .... (602) 514-7512
E-mail: david.pimsner@usdoj.gov
Legal Assistant **Charles "Chuck" Bailey** .... (602) 514-7577
E-mail: charles.bailey@usdoj.gov

Flagstaff (AZ) Office
123 North San Francisco Street, Suite 410, Flagstaff, AZ 86001
Tel: (928) 556-0833 Fax: (928) 556-0759
Supervisory Assistant U.S. Attorney
Patrick J. Schneider .... (928) 556-0833
E-mail: patrick.schneider@usdoj.gov
Assistant U.S. Attorney **Camille Bibles** .... (928) 556-0833
E-mail: camille.bibles@usdoj.gov
Assistant U.S. Attorney **Paul Stearns** .... (928) 556-0833
E-mail: paul.stearns@usdoj.gov
Assistant U.S. Attorney **(Vacant)** .... (928) 556-0833

Tucson (AZ) Office
405 West Congress Street, Suite 4800, Tucson, AZ 85701-5040
Tel: (520) 620-7300 Fax: (520) 620-7320
Chief Assistant U.S. Attorney (Acting)
Elizabeth A. "Betsy" Strange .... (520) 620-7300
E-mail: elizabeth.strange@usdoj.gov

Civil Division
Chief **Janet K. Martin** .... (520) 620-7493
E-mail: janet.martin@usdoj.gov
Assistant U.S. Attorney **Denise Faulk** .... (520) 620-7442
E-mail: denise.faulk@usdoj.gov
Assistant U.S. Attorney **Jane Westby** .... (520) 620-7333
E-mail: jane.westby@usdoj.gov
Assistant U.S. Attorney **Angela W. Woolridge** .... (520) 620-7339
E-mail: angela.woolridge@usdoj.gov
Assistant U.S. Attorney **(Vacant)** .... (520) 620-7408

Appellate Division
Chief **Robert L. Miskell** .... (520) 620-7300
E-mail: robert.miskell@usdoj.gov
Assistant U.S. Attorney **Christina M. Cabanillas** .... (520) 620-7377
E-mail: christina.cabanillas@usdoj.gov
Assistant U.S. Attorney **Erica A. McCallum** .... (520) 620-7371
Assistant U.S. Attorney **(Vacant)** .... (520) 620-7313

Criminal Division
Chief **Nicole P. Savel** .... (520) 620-7391
E-mail: nicole.savel@usdoj.gov
Deputy Chief **David P. Flannigan** .... (520) 620-7364
E-mail: david.flannigan@usdoj.gov
Deputy Chief **Liza M. Granoff** .... (520) 620-7474
E-mail: liza.granoff@usdoj.gov
Deputy Chief **(Vacant)** .... (520) 620-7351
Senior Litigation Counsel, Asset Forfeiture
Reese V. Bostwick .... (520) 620-7383
E-mail: reese.bostwick@usdoj.gov
Senior Litigation Counsel, OCDETF **(Vacant)** .... (520) 620-7473
Assistant U.S. Attorney **Joshua Ackerman** .... (520) 620-7355
E-mail: josh.ackerman@usdoj.gov
Assistant U.S. Attorney **Beverly K. Anderson** .... (520) 620-7330
E-mail: bev.anderson@usdoj.gov
Assistant U.S. Attorney **Raquel N. Arellano** .... (520) 620-7382
Assistant U.S. Attorney **Patrick T. Barry** .... (520) 620-7352
Assistant U.S. Attorney **Monte C. Clausen** .... (520) 620-7412
E-mail: monte.clausen@usdoj.gov
Assistant U.S. Attorney **Carmen F. Corbin** .... (520) 620-7263
E-mail: carmen.corbin@usdoj.gov
Assistant U.S. Attorney **Ann Demarais** .... (520) 620-7159
E-mail: ann.demarais@usdoj.gov
Assistant U.S. Attorney **Carin C. Duryee** .... (520) 620-7427
E-mail: carin.duryee@usdoj.gov
Assistant U.S. Attorney **Jesse J. Figueroa** .... (520) 620-7372
E-mail: jesse.figueroa@usdoj.gov
Assistant U.S. Attorney
Wallace H. "Wally" Kleindienst .... (520) 620-7578
Assistant U.S. Attorney **Lawrence Lee** .... (520) 620-7308

Criminal Division *(continued)*
Assistant U.S. Attorney **Cory M. Picton** .... (520) 620-7426
Assistant U.S. Attorney **Karen E. Rolley** .... (520) 620-7357
Assistant U.S. Attorney **Serra M. Tsethlikai** .... (520) 620-7358
Assistant U.S. Attorney **Rui Wang** .... (520) 620-7422
Assistant U.S. Attorney **Jane Westby** .... (520) 620-7333
E-mail: jane.westby@usdoj.gov
Assistant U.S. Attorney **David R. Zipps** .... (520) 620-7471
Assistant U.S. Attorney **(Vacant)** .... (520) 620-7370
Assistant U.S. Attorney **(Vacant)** .... (520) 620-7437
Assistant U.S. Attorney **(Vacant)** .... (520) 620-7355
Victim Witness Specialist **Mary-Anne Estrada** .... (520) 620-7431
E-mail: mary-anne.estrada@usdoj.gov
Victim Witness Specialist **(Vacant)** .... (520) 620-7367

Yuma (AZ) Office
4035 South Avenue A, Yuma, AZ 85365
Tel: (928) 314-6410 Tel: (928) 314-6411
Supervisory Assistant U.S. Attorney **Fred Cocio** .... (928) 314-6410
E-mail: fred.cocio@usdoj.gov
Assistant U.S. Attorney **John Ballos** .... (928) 314-6402
E-mail: john.ballos@usdoj.gov
Assistant U.S. Attorney **Louis Uhl** .... (928) 314-6410
E-mail: louis.uhl@usdoj.gov

Arkansas - Eastern District
Metropolitan National Bank Building, 425 West Capitol Avenue,
Suite 500, Little Rock, AR 72201
P.O. Box 1229, Little Rock, AR 72203-1229
Tel: (501) 340-2600 Fax: (501) 340-2728
Internet: www.justice.gov/usao/are
★ U.S. Attorney **J. Cody Hiland** .... (501) 340-2600
E-mail: cody.hiland@usdoj.gov
Education: Central Arkansas; Arkansas (Little Rock) JD
Secretary to the U.S. Attorney **(Vacant)** .... (501) 340-2600
Fax: (501) 340-2727
First Assistant U.S. Attorney **Patrick C. Harris** .... (501) 340-2600
E-mail: pat.harris@usdoj.gov
Intelligence Research Specialist **Scott Hendriks** .... (501) 340-2673
E-mail: scott.hendriks@usdoj.gov
Law Enforcement Committee Coordinator
Paulette Chappelle .... (501) 340-2667
Systems Manager **Andrew Oyemola** .... (501) 340-2665
E-mail: andrew.oyemola@usdoj.gov
Victim-Witness Coordinator **Amanda Warford** .... (501) 340-2648
E-mail: amanda.warford@usdoj.gov

Civil Division
Metropolitan National Bank Building, 425 West Capitol,
Suite 100, Little Rock, AR 72201
Tel: (501) 340-2600 Fax: (501) 340-2730
Chief **Richard M. Pence** .... (501) 340-2600
E-mail: richard.pence@usdoj.gov
Assistant U.S. Attorney **Jamie Dempsey** .... (501) 340-2600
E-mail: jamie.dempsey@usdoj.gov
Assistant U.S. Attorney **Lindsey Lorence** .... (501) 340-2600
E-mail: lindsey.lorence@usdoj.gov
Assistant U.S. Attorney **Stacey McCord** .... (501) 340-2600
E-mail: stacey.mccord@usdoj.gov
Assistant U.S. Attorney **Shannon S. Smith** .... (501) 340-2600
E-mail: shannon.smith@usdoj.gov

Criminal Division
Metropolitan National Bank Building, 425 West Capitol,
Suite 100, Little Rock, AR 72201
Fax: (501) 340-2725
Chief **John Ray White** .... (501) 340-2600
E-mail: john.white@usdoj.gov
Deputy Chief **Anne Gardner** .... (501) 340-2600
E-mail: anne.gardner2@usdoj.gov
Chief, Organized Crime **Anne Gardner** .... (501) 340-2600
E-mail: anne.gardner2@usdoj.gov

★ Presidential Appointment Requiring Senate Confirmation ☆ Presidential Appointment □ Schedule C Appointment ◇ Career Senior Foreign Service Appointment
● Career Senior Executive Service (SES) Appointment ○ Non-Career Senior Executive Service (SES) Appointment ■ Postal Career Executive Service

Criminal Division *(continued)*

Assistant U.S. Attorney **Ali Ahmad** . . . . (501) 340-2600
E-mail: ali.ahmad@usdoj.gov
Education: Michigan 2004 JD
Assistant U.S. Attorney **Allison Bragg** . . . . (501) 340-2600
E-mail: allison.bragg@usdoj.gov
Assistant U.S. Attorney **Hunter Bridges** . . . . (501) 340-2600
E-mail: hunter.bridges@usdoj.gov
Assistant U.S. Attorney **Liza Brown** . . . . (501) 340-2600
E-mail: liza.brown@usdoj.gov
Assistant U.S. Attorney **Kristin Bryant** . . . . (501) 340-2600
E-mail: kristin.bryant@usdoj.gov
Assistant U.S. Attorney **Chris Givens** . . . . (501) 340-2600
E-mail: chris.givens@usdoj.gov
Assistant U.S. Attorney **Michael Gordon** . . . . (501) 340-2600
E-mail: michael.gordon@usdoj.gov
Assistant U.S. Attorney **Jana Harris** . . . . (501) 340-2600
E-mail: jana.harris@usdoj.gov
Assistant U.S. Attorney **Angela Jegley** . . . . (501) 340-2600
E-mail: angela.jegley@usdoj.gov
Assistant U.S. Attorney **Stephanie Mazzanti** . . . . (501) 340-2600
E-mail: stephanie.mazzanti@usdoj.gov
Education: Arkansas 2006 JD
Assistant U.S. Attorney **Cameron McCree** . . . . (501) 340-2600
E-mail: cameron.mccree@usdoj.gov
Education: Arkansas JD
Assistant U.S. Attorney **Benecia Moore** . . . . (501) 340-2600
E-mail: benecia.moore@usdoj.gov
Assistant U.S. Attorney **Alex Morgan** . . . . (501) 340-2600
E-mail: alex.morgan@usdoj.gov
Assistant U.S. Attorney **Erin O'Leary-Chalk** . . . . (501) 340-2600
E-mail: erin.o'leary@usdoj.gov
Assistant U.S. Attorney **Julie Peters** . . . . (501) 340-2600
E-mail: julie.peters@usdoj.gov
Assistant U.S. Attorney **Edward O. Walker** . . . . (501) 340-2600
E-mail: edward.o.walker@usdoj.gov
Assistant U.S. Attorney **(Vacant)** . . . . (501) 340-2600

Arkansas - Western District

414 Parker Street, Fort Smith, AR 72901
Tel: (479) 783-5125 Fax: (479) 783-0578 Fax: (479) 785-2442
Internet: https://www.justice.gov/usao-wdar

★ U.S. Attorney **Duane A. Kees** . . . . (479) 783-5125
Education: Arkansas BA, JD
Secretary to the U.S. Attorney **Joyce Snow** . . . . (479) 783-5125
First Assistant U.S. Attorney
Kenneth P. "Kenny" Elser . . . . (479) 783-5125
E-mail: kenny.elser@usdoj.gov
Administrative Officer **Denise Daniels** . . . . (479) 783-5125
E-mail: denise.daniels@usdoj.gov
Intelligence Specialist **Daren Fowler** . . . . (479) 783-5125
E-mail: daren.fowler@usdoj.gov
LECC Coordinator **Charlie Robbins** . . . . (479) 783-5125
Systems Manager **Justin Trice** . . . . (479) 783-5125
E-mail: justin.trice@usdoj.gov
Victim-Witness Coordinator **Laura Johnson** . . . . (479) 783-5125
E-mail: laura.johnson@usdoj.gov

Civil Division

Chief **Deborah J. "Debbie" Groom** . . . . (479) 783-5125
E-mail: debbie.groom@usdoj.gov

Criminal Division

Chief **Clay Fowlkes** . . . . (479) 783-5125
E-mail: clay.fowlkes@usdoj.gov
Deputy Chief **(Vacant)** . . . . (479) 783-5125
Asset Forfeiture Chief **Aaron Jennen** . . . . (479) 783-5125
E-mail: aaron.jennen@usdoj.gov
Organized Crime Drug Enforcement Task Force Chief
Clay Fowlkes . . . . (479) 783-5125
E-mail: clay.fowlkes@usdoj.gov
Assistant United States Attorney **Brandon Carter** . . . . (479) 783-5125

California - Central District

312 North Spring Street, Suite 1200, Los Angeles, CA 90012
Tel: (213) 894-2400 (Main Line) Tel: (213) 894-2434
Fax: (213) 894-0141 Internet: www.justice.gov/usao/cac

★ U.S. Attorney **Nicola T. "Nick" Hanna** . . . . (213) 894-2434
E-mail: nicola.hanna@usdoj.gov
Education: UC San Diego BA; Georgetown JD
Secretary to the U.S. Attorney **Melena Malunao** . . . . (213) 894-2434
E-mail: melena.malunao@usdoj.gov
First Assistant U.S. Attorney **Sandra R. Brown** . . . . (213) 894-2434
U.S. Courthouse, 312 North Spring Street, Los Angeles, CA 90012
E-mail: sandra.brown@usdoj.gov
Executive Assistant U.S. Attorney **Wesley L. Hsu** . . . . (213) 894-2434
E-mail: wesley.hsu@usdoj.gov
Education: Yale 1993 BA, 1996 JD
Counsel to the United States Attorney
Bruce K. Riordan . . . . (213) 894-2434
Chief Assistant for Trials, Integrity, and
Professionalism **Robert E. Dugdale** . . . . (213) 894-2400
E-mail: robert.dugdale@usdoj.gov
Director of Administration **Kenneth A. "Ken" Martin** . . . (213) 894-8792
E-mail: ken.martin@usdoj.gov
Assistant Director, Litigation Support
Richard Bernales . . . . (213) 894-2434
Administrative Services Chief **(Vacant)** . . . . (213) 894-0608
Criminal Dockets Chief **(Vacant)** . . . . (213) 894-2434
Financial Services Chief **(Vacant)** . . . . (213) 894-2434
Human Resources Chief **Ann Quinn** . . . . (213) 894-2434
E-mail: ann.quinn@usdoj.gov
Information Technology Chief **Martin Jones** . . . . (213) 894-2434
E-mail: martin.jones@usdoj.gov
Crisis Management Coordinator **(Vacant)** . . . . (213) 894-2434
Law Enforcement Committee Coordinator **(Vacant)** . . . . . . (213) 894-2434
Librarian **Cornell H. Winston** . . . . (213) 894-2419
U.S. Courthouse, 312 North Spring Street,
Room 1214, Los Angeles, CA 90012
E-mail: cornell.h.winston@usdoj.gov
Public Information Officer **Thom Mrozek** . . . . (213) 894-6947
E-mail: thom.mrozek@usdoj.gov
Intelligence Specialist **Andrea Caston** . . . . (213) 894-2434
E-mail: andrea.caston@usdoj.gov
Victim-Witness Coordinator **Jeff Alabaso** . . . . (213) 894-7627
U.S. Courthouse, 312 North Spring Street,
Room 1311, Los Angeles, CA 90012
E-mail: jeff.alabaso@usdoj.gov

Civil Division

Federal Building, 300 North Los Angeles Street,
Suite 7516, Los Angeles, CA 90012
Tel: (213) 894-2404

Chief **Dorothy A. Schouten** . . . . (213) 894-2404
E-mail: dorothy.schouten@usdoj.gov
Civil Appeals Section Chief **Jessica Cheh** . . . . (213) 894-2404
E-mail: jessica.cheh@usdoj.gov
Civil Fraud Section Chief **David K. Barrett** . . . . (213) 894-0522
E-mail: david.barrett@usdoj.gov
Financial Litigation Section Chief
Indira J. Cameron-Banks . . . . (213) 894-2404
E-mail: indira.j.cameron-banks@usdoj.gov

Criminal Division

312 North Spring Street, Los Angeles, CA 90012
Fax: (213) 894-0141

Chief **Lawrence S. Middleton** . . . . (213) 894-4685
E-mail: lawrence.middleton@usdoj.gov
Deputy Chief **Scott Matthew Garringer** . . . . (213) 894-6772
E-mail: scott.garringer@usdoj.gov
Education: Iowa; UCLA JD
Appeals Section Chief **Ashley Aull** . . . . (213) 894-3391
E-mail: ashley.aull@usdoj.gov
Asset Forfeiture Section Chief **Steven R. Welk** . . . . (213) 894-6166
E-mail: steven.welk@usdoj.gov
Cyber and Intellectual Property Crime Section Chief
Tracy Wilkison . . . . (213) 894-3045
E-mail: tracy.wilkison@usdoj.gov

(continued on next page)

★ Presidential Appointment Requiring Senate Confirmation ☆ Presidential Appointment ☐ Schedule C Appointment ◇ Career Senior Foreign Service Appointment
● Career Senior Executive Service (SES) Appointment ○ Non-Career Senior Executive Service (SES) Appointment ■ Postal Career Executive Service

DEPARTMENTS

Criminal Division *(continued)*

Environmental Crimes Section Chief **Joseph O. Johns** . . . (213) 894-4536
E-mail: joseph.johns@usdoj.gov
General Crimes Chief **Lizabeth A. Rhodes** . . . . (213) 894-3424
E-mail: lizabeth.rhodes@usdoj.gov
Major Frauds Section Chief **George S. Cardona** . . . . (213) 894-3868
E-mail: george.s.cardona@usdoj.gov
National Security Section Chief **Patricia A. Donahue** . . . . (213) 894-0721
E-mail: patricia.donahue@usdoj.gov
Organized Crime and Drug Enforcement Task Force Section Chief **Kevin M. Lally** . . . . (213) 894-2170
E-mail: kevin.lally@usdoj.gov
Public Corruption and Civil Rights Chief **Mack E. Jenkins** . . . . (213) 894-2434
E-mail: mack.jenkins@usdoj.gov
Violent and Organized Crime Section Chief **Justin Rhoades** Room 1547 . . . . (213) 894-1785
E-mail: justin.rhoades@usdoj.gov
Assistant U.S. Attorney **(Vacant)** . . . . (213) 894-3899

Tax Division
Federal Building, 300 North Los Angeles Street, Suite 7211, Los Angeles, CA 90012

Chief **Sandra R. Brown** . . . . (213) 894-5810
E-mail: sandra.brown@usdoj.gov

Riverside (CA) Office
3880 Lemon Street, Suite 210, Riverside, CA 92501
Tel: (951) 276-6210 Fax: (951) 276-6202

Chief **Joseph Widman** . . . . (951) 276-6945
E-mail: joseph.widman@usdoj.gov

Santa Ana (CA) Office
411 West Fourth Street, Suite 8000, Santa Ana, CA 92701-4599
Tel: (714) 338-3540 Fax: (714) 338-3708

Assistant U.S. Attorney-in-Charge **Dennise D. Willett** . . . . (714) 338-3500
E-mail: dennise.willett@usdoj.gov

California - Eastern District
501 I Street, Suite 10-100, Sacramento, CA 95814
Tel: (916) 554-2700 TTY: (916) 554-2124 Fax: (916) 554-2900
Internet: https://www.justice.gov/usao-edca

★ U.S. Attorney **McGregor W. "Greg" Scott** . . . . (916) 554-2730
E-mail: mcgregor.scott@usdoj.gov
Education: Santa Clara U 1985 BA; Hastings 1989 JD
Secretary to the U.S. Attorney **Deb Buckett** . . . . (916) 554-2730
Senior Counsel to the U.S. Attorney **Duce Rice** . . . . (559) 497-4000
E-mail: duce.rice@usdoj.gov
First Assistant U.S. Attorney (Acting) **Phillip Talbert** . . . . . (916) 554-2798
E-mail: phillip.talbert@usdoj.gov
Press Officer **Lauren Horwood** . . . . (916) 554-2706
Executive Assistant U.S. Attorney **Michele Beckwich** . . . . (916) 554-2740
Administrative Officer **Jacquelyn C. "Jackie" Strong** . . . (916) 554-2714
E-mail: jackie.strong@usdoj.gov
Anti-Terrorism Advisory Council Coordinator **Jean Hobler** . . . . (916) 554-2700
E-mail: jean.hobler@usdoj.gov
District Office Security Manager **James Ham** . . . . (916) 554-2700
E-mail: james.ham@usdoj.gov
Information Technology Specialist **Tammy Metz** . . . . (916) 554-2742
E-mail: tammy.metz@usdoj.gov
Information Technology Specialist **Sharon Sumrak** . . . . . . (916) 554-2753
E-mail: sharon.sumrak@usdoj.gov
Law Enforcement Committee Coordinator **Timothy Johnstone** . . . . (916) 554-2712
E-mail: timothy.johnstone@usdoj.gov
Records Coordinator **Tracy Remitz** . . . . (916) 554-2700
E-mail: tracy.remitz@usdoj.gov
Supervisor, Computer Technology **Gina Alires** . . . . (916) 554-2746
E-mail: gina.alires@usdoj.gov
Victim-Witness Coordinator **Helene J. Tenette** . . . . (916) 554-2776
E-mail: helene.tenette@usdoj.gov

California - Eastern District *(continued)*

Special Prosecutions Unit Chief **Matthew D. Segal** . . . . . (916) 554-2700
E-mail: matthew.segal@usdoj.gov
Education: Yale 2002 JD

Civil Division
Civil Chief **David T. Shelledy** . . . . (916) 554-2700
E-mail: david.shelledy@usdoj.gov
Education: Yale 1990 LLM
Affirmative Civil Litigation Chief **Kelli L. Taylor** . . . . (916) 554-2700
E-mail: kelli.l.taylor@usdoj.gov
Civil Defense Chief **Edward Olsen** . . . . (916) 554-2700
E-mail: edward.olsen@usdoj.gov
Assistant U.S. Attorney **(Vacant)** . . . . (916) 554-2700
Assistant U.S. Attorney **Victoria L. Boesch** . . . . (916) 554-2700
E-mail: victoria.boesch@usdoj.gov
Assistant U.S. Attorney **Gregory Broderick** . . . . (916) 554-2700
E-mail: gregory.broderick@usdoj.gov
Assistant U.S. Attorney **Kurt Didier** . . . . (916) 554-2700
E-mail: kurt.didier@usdoj.gov
Assistant U.S. Attorney **Lynn Trinka Ernce** . . . . (916) 554-2700
E-mail: lynn.trinka.ernce@usdoj.gov
Assistant U.S. Attorney **Colleen M. Kennedy** . . . . (916) 554-2700
E-mail: colleen.m.kennedy@usdoj.gov
Education: Duke AB; Yale JD
Assistant U.S. Attorney **Kevin Khasigian** . . . . (916) 554-2700
E-mail: kevin.khasigian@usdoj.gov
Education: McGeorge 2007 JD
Assistant U.S. Attorney **Chi Soo Kim** . . . . (916) 554-2700
E-mail: chi.soo.kim@usdoj.gov
Education: Vanderbilt 2004 JD
Assistant U.S. Attorney **Bobbie J. Montoya** . . . . (916) 554-2700
E-mail: bobbie.montoya@usdoj.gov
Assistant U.S. Attorney **Catherine J. Swann** . . . . (916) 554-2700
E-mail: catherine.swann@usdoj.gov
Assistant U.S. Attorney **(Vacant)** . . . . (916) 554-2700
Assistant U.S. Attorney **(Vacant)** . . . . (916) 554-2700
Assistant U.S. Attorney **(Vacant)** . . . . (916) 554-2700
Assistant U.S. Attorney **(Vacant)** . . . . (916) 554-2700

Criminal Division
Chief - Criminal Division **John K. Vincent** . . . . (916) 554-2795
E-mail: john.vincent@usdoj.gov
Education: Notre Dame BA, JD
Appeals and Training Chief **Camil A. Skipper** . . . . (916) 554-2700
E-mail: camil.skipper@usdoj.gov
Crisis Management Coordinator **Michael Beckwith** . . . . . . (916) 554-2700
E-mail: michael.beckwith@usdoj.gov
Computer Crimes Chief **Sharon Goin** . . . . (916) 554-2700
E-mail: sharon.goin@usdoj.gov
Narcotics and Violent Crimes Chief **Richard J. Bender** . . . . (916) 554-2700
E-mail: richard.bender@usdoj.gov
Special Prosecutions Unit Chief **Matthew D. Segal** . . . . . (916) 554-2700
E-mail: matthew.segal@usdoj.gov
Education: Yale 2002 JD
White Collar Crime Chief **Michael Anderson** . . . . (916) 554-2700
E-mail: michael.anderson@usdoj.gov
Assistant U.S. Attorney **Amanda Beck** . . . . (916) 554-2700
E-mail: amanda.beck@usdoj.gov
Assistant U.S. Attorney **Lee Bickley** . . . . (916) 554-2700
E-mail: lee.bickley@usdoj.gov
Assistant U.S. Attorney **Heiko P. Coppola** . . . . (916) 554-2700
E-mail: heiko.coppola@usdoj.gov
Assistant U.S. Attorney **Nirav K. Desai** . . . . (916) 554-2700
E-mail: nirav.desai@usdoj.gov
Assistant U.S. Attorney **Jared Dolan** . . . . (916) 554-2700
E-mail: jared.dolan@usdoj.gov
Education: Stetson 2007 JD
Assistant U.S. Attorney **Andre Espinosa** . . . . (916) 554-2700
E-mail: andre.espinosa@usdoj.gov
Assistant U.S. Attorney **Brian Fogerty** . . . . (916) 554-2700
E-mail: brian.fogerty@usdoj.gov
Assistant U.S. Attorney **Christopher Hales** . . . . (916) 554-2700
E-mail: christopher.hales@usdoj.gov

★ Presidential Appointment Requiring Senate Confirmation ☆ Presidential Appointment ☐ Schedule C Appointment ◇ Career Senior Foreign Service Appointment
● Career Senior Executive Service (SES) Appointment ○ Non-Career Senior Executive Service (SES) Appointment ■ Postal Career Executive Service

Criminal Division *(continued)*

Assistant U.S. Attorney **Paul Hemesath** . . . . (916) 554-2700
E-mail: paul.hemesath@usdoj.gov
Assistant U.S. Attorney **Jason Hitt** . . . . (916) 554-2700
E-mail: jason.hitt@usdoj.gov
Assistant U.S. Attorney **Jean Hobler** . . . . (916) 554-2700
E-mail: jean.hobler@usdoj.gov
Assistant U.S. Attorney **John Kucera** . . . . (916) 554-2700
Education: John Marshall 2003 JD
Assistant U.S. Attorney **Justin Lee** . . . . (916) 554-2700
E-mail: justin.lee@usdoj.gov
Assistant U.S. Attorney **Katherine Lydon** . . . . (916) 554-2700
E-mail: katherine.lydon@usdoj.gov
Assistant U.S. Attorney **Matthew T. Morris** . . . . (916) 554-2700
E-mail: matthew.morris@usdoj.gov
Assistant U.S. Attorney **Todd A. Pickles** . . . . (916) 554-2700
E-mail: todd.pickles@usdoj.gov
Education: Georgetown 1997 BA; San Francisco Law 2001 JD
Assistant U.S. Attorney **Michelle Rodriguez** . . . . (916) 554-2700
E-mail: michelle.rodriguez@usdoj.gov
Assistant U.S. Attorney **Rosanne Rust** . . . . (916) 554-2700
E-mail: rosanne.rust@usdoj.gov
Assistant U.S. Attorney **Matthew D. Segal** . . . . (916) 554-2700
E-mail: matthew.segal@usdoj.gov
Education: Yale 2002 JD
Assistant U.S. Attorney **Jill Thomas** . . . . (916) 554-2700
E-mail: jill.thomas@usdoj.gov
Assistant U.S. Attorney **Shelley Weger** . . . . (916) 554-2700
E-mail: shelley.weger@usdoj.gov
Assistant U.S. Attorney **Samuel Wong** . . . . (916) 554-2700
E-mail: samuel.wong@usdoj.gov
Assistant U.S. Attorney **Roger Yang** . . . . (916) 554-2706
E-mail: roger.yang@usdoj.gov
Assistant U.S. Attorney **Matthew Yelovich** . . . . (916) 554-2706
E-mail: matthew.yelovich@usdoj.gov
Executive U.S. Attorney **Michele Beckwith** . . . . (916) 554-2700
E-mail: michele.beckwith@usdoj.gov
Special Assistant U.S. Attorney **(Vacant)** . . . . (916) 554-2700

Fresno (CA) Office

2500 Tulare Street, Suite 4401, Fresno, CA 93721
Tel: (559) 497-4000 TTY: (559) 498-7499 Fax: (559) 497-4099

Chief **Kirk E. Sherriff** . . . . (559) 497-4000
E-mail: kirk.e.sherriff@usdoj.gov
Chief, Narcotics and Violent Crimes **Kevin P. Rooney** . . . . (559) 497-4000
Chief, White Collar Crime Section **Henry Carbajal** . . . . . . (559) 497-4000
E-mail: henry.carbajal@usdoj.gov
Information Technology Specialist **Donna Dotson** . . . . (559) 497-4000
E-mail: donna.dotson@usdoj.gov

Civil Division

Assistant U.S. Attorney **Alyson Berg** . . . . (559) 497-4000
E-mail: alyson.berg@usdoj.gov
Assistant U.S. Attorney **Benjamin Hall** . . . . (559) 497-4000
E-mail: benjamin.hall@usdoj.gov
Assistant U.S. Attorney **Jeffrey L. Lodge** . . . . (559) 497-4000
E-mail: jeffrey.lodge@usdoj.gov
Assistant U.S. Attorney **Jeffery A. Spivak** . . . . (559) 497-4000
E-mail: jeffrey.spivak@usdoj.gov
Assistant U.S. Attorney **Patrick Suter** . . . . (559) 497-4000
E-mail: patrick.suter@usdoj.gov
Assistant U.S. Attorney **Vincente Tennerelli** . . . . (559) 497-4000
E-mail: vincente.tennerelli@usdoj.gov
Assistant U.S. Attorney **(Vacant)** . . . . (559) 497-4000

Criminal Division

Assistant U.S. Attorney **Melanie Alsworth** . . . . (559) 497-4000
E-mail: melanie.alsworth@usdoj.gov
Assistant U.S. Attorney **Christopher D. Baker** . . . . (559) 497-4000
E-mail: christopher.d.baker@usdoj.gov
Assistant U.S. Attorney **Brian K. Delaney** . . . . (661) 852-2470
E-mail: brian.delaney@usdoj.gov
Education: Illinois (Chicago) BSCrimJ; DePaul JD
Assistant U.S. Attorney **Patrick Delahunty** . . . . (559) 497-4000
E-mail: patrick.delahunty@usdoj.gov

Criminal Division *(continued)*

Assistant U.S. Attorney **Brian W. Enos** . . . . (559) 497-4000
E-mail: brian.enos@usdoj.gov
Assistant U.S. Attorney **Karen A. Escobar** . . . . (559) 497-4000
E-mail: karen.escobar@usdoj.gov
Assistant U.S. Attorney **David L. Gappa** . . . . (559) 497-4000
E-mail: david.gappa@usdoj.gov
Assistant U.S. Attorney **Daniel Griffin** . . . . (559) 497-4000
E-mail: daniel.griffin@usdoj.gov
Assistant U.S. Attorney **Mark J. McKeon** . . . . (559) 497-4000
E-mail: mark.mckeon@usdoj.gov
Assistant U.S. Attorney **Laurel J. Montoya** . . . . (559) 497-4000
E-mail: laurel.j.montoya@usdoj.gov
Assistant U.S. Attorney **Grant B. Rabenn** . . . . (559) 497-4000
E-mail: grant.rabenn@usdoj.gov
Assistant U.S. Attorney **Vincenza Rabenn** . . . . (559) 497-4000
E-mail: vincenza.rabenn@usdoj.gov
Assistant U.S. Attorney **Dawrence W. Rice** . . . . (559) 497-4000
Assistant U.S. Attorney **Megan A.S. Richards** . . . . (559) 497-4000
E-mail: megan.richards@usdoj.gov
Assistant U.S. Attorney **Kimberly Sanchez** . . . . (559) 497-4000
E-mail: kimberly.sanchez@usdoj.gov
Assistant U.S. Attorney **Angela Scott** . . . . (559) 497-4000
E-mail: angela.scott3@usdoj.gov
Assistant U.S. Attorney **Kathleen A. Servatius** . . . . (559) 497-4000
E-mail: kathleen.servatius@usdoj.gov
Assistant U.S. Attorney **Michael G. Tierney** . . . . (559) 497-4000
E-mail: michael.tierney@usdoj.gov
Assistant U.S. Attorney **(Vacant)** . . . . (559) 497-4000
Assistant U.S. Attorney **(Vacant)** . . . . (559) 497-4000
Assistant U.S. Attorney **(Vacant)** . . . . (559) 497-4000

California - Northern District

U.S. Courthouse, 450 Golden Gate Avenue,
11th Floor, San Francisco, CA 94102
Tel: (415) 436-7200 TTY: (415) 436-7221 Fax: (415) 436-7234
Internet: https://www.justice.gov/usao-edca

★ U.S. Attorney (Acting) **Alex Tse** . . . . (415) 436-6938
E-mail: alex.tse@usdoj.gov
★ U.S. Attorney-Designate **David L. Anderson** . . . . (415) 436-6938
Education: San José State 1985 BSAcc; Stanford 1990 JD
Secretary to the U.S. Attorney **Orisme Carminati** . . . . . . (415) 436-7143
E-mail: orisme.carminati@usdoj.gov
First Assistant U.S. Attorney **Alex Tse** . . . . (415) 436-6783
E-mail: alex.tse@usdoj.gov
Executive Assistant U.S. Attorney **Joshua Eaton** . . . . (415) 436-6958
Counsel to the U.S. Attorney **J. Douglas Wilson** . . . . (415) 436-7200
E-mail: douglas.wilson@usdoj.gov
Administrative Officer **Jennifer Crnkovich** . . . . (415) 436-6992
E-mail: jennifer.crnkovich@usdoj.gov
Administrative Service Supervisor **(Vacant)** . . . . (510) 637-3721
Senior Budget Analyst **Michael Alice** . . . . (415) 436-7313
Fax: (415) 436-7333
Information Technology Manager **Brian Wickett** . . . . (415) 436-7183
E-mail: brian.wickett@usdoj.gov
Public Affairs Officer **Abraham Simmons** . . . . (415) 436-6599
E-mail: abraham.simmons@usdoj.gov
Law Enforcement Coordinator **Annemarie Conroy** . . . . . . (415) 436-7067
E-mail: annemarie.conroy@usdoj.gov
Victim-Witness Program Manager **Maureen French** . . . . . (415) 436-6993
E-mail: maureen.french@usdoj.gov
Intelligence Research Specialist **(Vacant)** . . . . (415) 436-7200
Librarian **Janice Litten** . . . . (415) 436-7037
E-mail: janice.litten@usdoj.gov

Civil Division

450 Golden Gate, San Francisco, CA 94102
Tel: (415) 436-7137 Fax: (415) 436-6748

Chief **Sara Winslow** . . . . (415) 436-6855
E-mail: sara.winslow@usdoj.gov
Deputy Chief **Jonathan "John" Lee** . . . . (415) 436-7137
E-mail: jonathan.lee@usdoj.gov
Deputy Chief **(Vacant)** . . . . (415) 436-6925

(continued on next page)

DEPARTMENTS

★ Presidential Appointment Requiring Senate Confirmation ☆ Presidential Appointment □ Schedule C Appointment ◇ Career Senior Foreign Service Appointment
● Career Senior Executive Service (SES) Appointment ○ Non-Career Senior Executive Service (SES) Appointment ■ Postal Career Executive Service

DEPARTMENTS

Civil Division *(continued)*

Deputy Chief of Financial Litigation Unit
Steven Saltiel .... (415) 436-6996
E-mail: steven.saltiel@usdoj.gov
Assistant U.S. Attorney **Abraham Simmons** .... (415) 436-7264
E-mail: abraham.simmons@usdoj.gov
Assistant U.S. Attorney **(Vacant)** .... (415) 436-6962
Assistant U.S. Attorney **(Vacant)** .... (415) 436-7025
Environment and Natural Resources Unit Chief
Sara Winslow .... (415) 436-7180
E-mail: sara.winslow@usdoj.gov
Tax Division Chief **Thomas G. Moore** .... (415) 436-7137
E-mail: thomas.moore@usdoj.gov

Criminal Division
450 Golden Gate, San Francisco, CA 94102
Tel: (415) 436-7200 Fax: (415) 436-7009

Chief **Barbara J. Valliere** .... (415) 436-7200
E-mail: barbara.valliere@usdoj.gov
Appellate Chief **J. Douglas Wilson** .... (415) 436-7039
Anti-Terrorism Task Force Coordinator **Elise Becker** .... (415) 436-7200
Asset Forfeiture Unit Assistant U.S. Attorney
David Countryman .... (415) 436-6816
E-mail: david.countryman@usdoj.gov
Asset Forfeiture Unit Assistant U.S. Attorney
(Vacant) .... (415) 436-6857
Cybercrimes Chief **Matthew Parrella** .... (415) 436-7200
E-mail: matthew.parrella@usdoj.gov
Economic Crimes and Security Fraud Chief
Kyle Waldinger .... (415) 436-7200
E-mail: kyle.waldinger@usdoj.gov
Assistant U.S. Attorney **Kirstin Ault** .... (415) 436-6940
E-mail: kirstin.ault@usdoj.gov
Assistant U.S. Attorney **Peter Axelrod** .... (415) 436-6774
E-mail: peter.axelrod@usdoj.gov
Assistant U.S. Attorney **Chinhayi Cadet** .... (415) 436-7073
E-mail: chinhayi.cadet@usdoj.gov
Assistant U.S. Attorney **Julie Garcia** .... (415) 436-6758
E-mail: julie.garcia@usdoj.gov
Assistant U.S. Attorney **Robin Harris** .... (415) 436-7016
Assistant U.S. Attorney **Tom Colton** .... (415) 436-6833
Assistant U.S. Attorney **Erin Cornell** .... (415) 436-7200
E-mail: erin.cornell@usdoj.gov
Education: UC San Diego 2000 BA; U San Francisco 2003 JD
Assistant U.S. Attorney **Gregg Lowder** .... (415) 436-7044
E-mail: gregg.lowder@usdoj.gov
Assistant U.S. Attorney **Robert Rees** .... (415) 436-7210
E-mail: robert.rees@usdoj.gov
Education: NYU 2003 JD
Assistant U.S. Attorney **Colin C. Sampson** .... (415) 436-6747
E-mail: colin.sampson@usdoj.gov
Education: UCLA BA; Stanford JD
Assistant U.S. Attorney **Kyle Waldinger** .... (415) 436-6830
E-mail: kyle.waldinger@usdoj.gov
Assistant U.S. Attorney **(Vacant)** .... (510) 637-3709
Assistant U.S. Attorney **(Vacant)** .... (415) 436-7223
Narcotics Section Chief **(Vacant)** .... (415) 436-7249
E-mail: tom.colthurst@usdoj.gov
National Security Section Chief **Elise Becker** .... (415) 436-6878
E-mail: elise.becker@usdoj.gov
National Security Section Deputy Chief **(Vacant)** .... (408) 535-5061
150 Almaden Blvd., Suite 900, San Jose, CA 95113
Organized Crime Strike Force Chief
Stephen James Meyer .... (415) 436-6959
E-mail: stephen.meyer@usdoj.gov Fax: (415) 436-6401
Education: Brooklyn Law 2002 JD

Oakland (CA) Office
1301 Clay Street, Suite 340S, Oakland, CA 94612
Tel: (510) 637-3680 TTY: (510) 637-3678 Fax: (510) 637-3724

Chief **Garth E. Hire** .... (510) 637-3680
E-mail: garth.hire@usdoj.gov
Supervisory Legal Assistant
Kathleen "Katie" Turner .... (510) 637-3680
E-mail: kathleen.turner@usdoj.gov

Criminal Division
Chief **Barbara J. Valliere** .... (510) 637-3680
E-mail: barbara.valliere@usdoj.gov
Deputy Chief **(Vacant)** .... (510) 637-3680
Assistant U.S. Attorney **(Vacant)** .... (510) 637-3771
Assistant U.S. Attorney **Andrew Huang** .... (510) 637-3703
E-mail: andrew.huang@usdoj.gov

Drug Task Force
Assistant U.S. Attorney **(Vacant)** .... (510) 637-3709

San Jose (CA) Office
150 Almaden Boulevard, Suite 900, San Jose, CA 95113
Tel: (408) 535-5061 TTY: (408) 535-3960 Fax: (408) 535-5066
Fax: (408) 535-5081
Chief **Jeff Nedrow** .... (408) 535-5061
E-mail: jeff.nedrow@usdoj.gov

Civil Division
150 Almaden Blvd., San Jose, CA 95113
Fax: (408) 535-5081
Assistant U.S. Attorney **Claire Cormier** .... (408) 535-5082
E-mail: claire.cormier@usdoj.gov

Criminal Division
150 Almaden Blvd., San Jose, CA 95113
Fax: (408) 535-5066
Assistant U.S. Attorney **Gary Fry** .... (408) 535-5051
E-mail: gary.fry@usdoj.gov
Assistant U.S. Attorney **Tim Lucy** .... (408) 535-5054
Assistant U.S. Attorney **Stephen James Meyer** .... (408) 535-5061
E-mail: stephen.meyer@usdoj.gov
Education: Brooklyn Law 2002 JD
Assistant U.S. Attorney **Michael Pitman** .... (408) 535-5061
E-mail: michael.pitman@usdoj.gov
Education: UC Santa Cruz 1997 BA; Georgetown 2002 JD
Assistant U.S. Attorney **Amber Rosen** .... (408) 535-5046
E-mail: amber.rosen@usdoj.gov

Computer Hacking and Intellectual Property
Assistant U.S. Attorney **Matthew Parrella** .... (408) 535-5596
E-mail: matthew.parrella@usdoj.gov

Drug Task Force
Assistant U.S. Attorney **John Glang** .... (408) 535-5084
E-mail: john.glang@usdoj.gov

Strike Force
Assistant U.S. Attorney **Tim Lucy** .... (408) 535-5054

California - Southern District
Federal Office Building, 880 Front Street,
Room 6293, San Diego, CA 92101-8893
Tel: (619) 557-5610 Fax: (619) 546-0620
Internet: https://www.justice.gov/usao-sdca

★ U.S. Attorney (Interim) **Adam L. Braverman** .... (619) 546-5690
E-mail: adam.braverman@usdoj.gov
Education: George Washington 2000 JD
★ U.S. Attorney-Designate **Robert S. Brewer, Jr.** .... (619) 546-5690
Education: Lawrence U 1968 BA; San Diego 1975 JD
First Assistant U.S. Attorney **Alana W. Robinson** .... (619) 546-9608
E-mail: alana.robinson@usdoj.gov
Executive Assistant U.S. Attorney **Blair C. Perez** .... (619) 546-7963
E-mail: blair.perez@usdoj.gov
Administrative Assistant to the First Assistant and Executive Assistant U.S. Attorneys
Hortencia Barajas .... (619) 546-8639
Administrative Officer **Mary Tracy** .... (619) 546-9966
E-mail: mary.tracy@usdoj.gov
Human Resources Officer **Sylvia Rojas** .... (619) 546-8973
E-mail: sylvia.rojas@usdoj.gov
Law Enforcement Committee Coordinator
Kristen Dennis .... (619) 546-8817
E-mail: kristen.dennis@usdoj.gov

★ Presidential Appointment Requiring Senate Confirmation ☆ Presidential Appointment □ Schedule C Appointment ◇ Career Senior Foreign Service Appointment
● Career Senior Executive Service (SES) Appointment ○ Non-Career Senior Executive Service (SES) Appointment ■ Postal Career Executive Service

California - Southern District *(continued)*

Victim-Witness Coordinator **Polly M. Montano** . . . . (619) 546-8921
E-mail: polly.montano@usdoj.gov

Civil Division

Assistant U.S. Attorney, Chief **Thomas C. Stahl** . . . . (619) 546-7767
E-mail: thomas.stahl@usdoj.gov
Education: San Diego State BA; San Diego JD

Assistant U.S. Attorney, Deputy Chief **Katherine L. Parker** . . . . (619) 546-7634
E-mail: katherine.parker@usdoj.gov

Assistant U.S. Attorney, Deputy Chief **Joseph P. Price, Jr.** . . . . (619) 546-7642
E-mail: joseph.price@usdoj.gov

Special Assistant U.S. Attorney **Samuel W. Bettwy** . . . . . (619) 546-7125

Assistant U.S. Attorney **Dylan Aste** . . . . (619) 546-7621
E-mail: dylan.aste@usdoj.gov

Assistant U.S. Attorney **Daniel E. Butcher** . . . . (619) 546-7696

Assistant U.S. Attorney **Steve B. Chu** . . . . (619) 546-7167
E-mail: steve.chu@usdoj.gov

Assistant U.S. Attorney **Rebecca Church** . . . . (619) 546-7721
E-mail: rebecca.church@usdoj.gov

Assistant U.S. Attorney **Beth Clukey** . . . . (619) 546-7344
E-mail: beth.clukey@usdoj.gov

Assistant U.S. Attorney **Glen F. Dorgan** . . . . (619) 546-7665
E-mail: glen.dorgan@usdoj.gov

Assistant U.S. Attorney **Michael Garabed** . . . . (619) 546-7703
E-mail: michael.garabed@usdoj.gov

Assistant U.S. Attorney **Kyle W. Hoffman** . . . . (619) 546-6987
E-mail: kyle.hoffman@usdoj.gov

Assistant U.S. Attorney **Douglas Keehn** . . . . (619) 546-7573
E-mail: douglas.keehn@usdoj.gov

Assistant U.S. Attorney **George V. Manahan** . . . . (619) 546-7607
E-mail: george.manahan@usdoj.gov
Education: Harvard

Assistant U.S. Attorney **Brett Norris** . . . . (619) 546-7620
E-mail: brett.norris@usdoj.gov

Assistant U.S. Attorney **Steven J. Poliakoff** . . . . (619) 546-7058
E-mail: steve.poliakoff@usdoj.gov

Assistant U.S. Attorney **Joseph J. Purcell** . . . . (619) 546-7643
E-mail: joseph.purcell@usdoj.gov

Assistant U.S. Attorney **Dianne M. Schweiner** . . . . (619) 546-7654
E-mail: dianne.schweiner@usdoj.gov

Assistant U.S. Attorney **Paul L. Starita** . . . . (619) 546-8402
E-mail: paul.starita@usdoj.gov

Assistant U.S. Attorney **Valerie Torres** . . . . (619) 546-7644
E-mail: valerie.torres@usdoj.gov

Assistant U.S. Attorney **David B. Wallace** . . . . (619) 546-7669
E-mail: dave.wallace@usdoj.gov

Assistant U.S. Attorney **(Vacant)** . . . . (619) 557-5610

Criminal Division

Chief **Peter G. Ko** . . . . (619) 546-6762
E-mail: peter.ko2@usdoj.gov

Deputy Chief **(Vacant)** . . . . (619) 546-6768

Criminal Division Senior Litigation Counsel **Todd W. Robinson** . . . . (619) 546-7699
E-mail: todd.robinson@usdoj.gov

Criminal Division Senior Litigation Counsel **Michael G. Wheat** . . . . (619) 546-8437
E-mail: michael.wheat@usdoj.gov

Foreign Affairs Coordinator **Robert Ciaffa** . . . . (619) 546-6752
E-mail: robert.ciaffa@usdoj.gov

Appellate Section

Assistant U.S. Attorney, Chief **Helen Hong** . . . . (619) 546-7359
E-mail: helen.hong@usdoj.gov

Assistant U.S. Attorney **D. Benjamin Holley** . . . . (619) 546-7952
E-mail: benjamin.holley@usdoj.gov

Assistant U.S. Attorney **Emily J. Keifer** . . . . (619) 546-7319
E-mail: emily.keifer@usdoj.gov

Assistant U.S. Attorney **Colin McDonald** . . . . (619) 546-9144
E-mail: colin.mcdonald@usdoj.gov

Assistant U.S. Attorney **Mark R. Rehe** . . . . (619) 546-7986
E-mail: mark.rehe@usdoj.gov

Appellate Section *(continued)*

Assistant U.S. Attorney **Daniel E. Zipp** . . . . (619) 546-8463
E-mail: daniel.zipp@usdoj.gov

Criminal Enterprises Section

Assistant U.S. Attorney, Chief **Linda A. Frakes** . . . . (619) 546-6793
E-mail: linda.frakes@usdoj.gov

Assistant U.S. Attorney, Deputy Chief **(Vacant)** . . . . (619) 546-6717

Assistant U.S. Attorney, Deputy Chief **Joseph S. Green** . . . . (619) 546-6955
E-mail: joseph.green@usdoj.gov

Assistant U.S. Attorney, Deputy Chief **David Leshner** . . . . (619) 546-7921
E-mail: david.leshner@usdoj.gov

Assistant U.S. Attorney, Deputy Chief **Timothy F. Salel** . . . . (619) 546-8055
E-mail: timothy.salel@usdoj.gov

Assistant U.S. Attorney **Patrick Bumatay** . . . . (619) 546-8450
E-mail: patrick.bumatay@usdoj.gov

Assistant U.S. Attorney **Luella M. Caldito** . . . . (619) 546-6732
E-mail: luella.caldito@usdoj.gov

Assistant U.S. Attorney **Jose Castillo** . . . . (619) 564-6745
E-mail: jose.castillo3@usdoj.gov

Assistant U.S. Attorney **David P. Finn** . . . . (619) 546-1342
E-mail: david.finn@usdoj.gov

Assistant U.S. Attorney **Orlando B. Gutierrez** . . . . (619) 546-6758
E-mail: orlando.gutierrez@usdoj.gov

Assistant U.S. Attorney **Sherri Walker Hobson** . . . . (619) 546-6986
E-mail: sherri.hobson@usdoj.gov

Assistant U.S. Attorney **Joshua Jones** . . . . (619) 546-9744
E-mail: joshua.jones@usdoj.gov

Assistant U.S. Attorney **Jonathan I. Shapiro** . . . . (619) 546-8225
E-mail: jonathan.shapiro@usdoj.gov

Assistant U.S. Attorney **Lara W. Worm** . . . . (619) 546-9697
E-mail: lara.worm@usdoj.gov

Assistant U.S. Attorney **(Vacant)** . . . . (619) 546-6758

Assistant U.S. Attorney **(Vacant)** . . . . (619) 546-6717

Assistant U.S. Attorney **(Vacant)** . . . . (619) 557-5610

Assistant U.S. Attorney **(Vacant)** . . . . (619) 557-5610

Fast-Track Sentencing Unit

Assistant U.S. Attorney, Deputy Chief **(Vacant)** . . . . (619) 546-6952

Assistant U.S. Attorney **Charlotte E. Kaiser** . . . . (619) 546-7282
E-mail: charlotte.kaiser@usdoj.gov
Education: Chicago 1995 BA; Northwestern 2001 JD

Assistant U.S. Attorney **Ryan Sausedo** . . . . (619) 546-9689
E-mail: ryan.sausedo@usdoj.gov

Assistant U.S. Attorney **(Vacant)** . . . . (619) 546-6760

Financial Litigation Unit

Assistant U.S. Attorney, FLU Coordinator **Leah R. Bussell** . . . . (619) 546-6727
E-mail: leah.bussell@usdoj.gov

Assistant U.S. Attorney **Laura Grimes** . . . . (619) 546-7748
E-mail: laura.grimes@usdoj.gov

Assistant U.S. Attorney **Carol M. Lee** . . . . (619) 546-7584
E-mail: carol.lee@usdoj.gov

Assistant U.S. Attorney **Daniel C. Silva** . . . . (619) 546-9713
E-mail: daniel.c.silva@usdoj.gov

Assistant U.S. Attorney **Thomas Watkinson III** . . . . (619) 546-8861
E-mail: thomas.watkinson@usdoj.gov

Grand Jury Section

Assistant U.S. Attorney **Janaki S. Gandhi** . . . . (619) 546-8817
E-mail: janaki.gandhi@usdoj.gov

Assistant U.S. Attorney **Connie Wu** . . . . (619) 546-8592
E-mail: connie.wu@usdoj.gov

Intake Unit

Assistant U.S. Attorney, Intake Unit Deputy Chief **Arnold Dale Blankenship** . . . . (619) 546-6705
E-mail: dale.blankenship@usdoj.gov

Assistant U.S. Attorney, Intake Unit Deputy Chief **Caroline Han** . . . . (619) 546-6968
E-mail: caroline.han@usdoj.gov

Assistant U.S. Attorney **Adriana Ahumada** . . . . (619) 546-8971
E-mail: adriana.ahumada@usdoj.gov

(continued on next page)

★ Presidential Appointment Requiring Senate Confirmation ☆ Presidential Appointment ☐ Schedule C Appointment ◇ Career Senior Foreign Service Appointment
● Career Senior Executive Service (SES) Appointment ○ Non-Career Senior Executive Service (SES) Appointment ■ Postal Career Executive Service

DEPARTMENTS

Intake Unit *(continued)*

Assistant U.S. Attorney **Francis DiGiacco** . . . . (619) 546-6771
E-mail: francis.digiacco@usdoj.gov
Assistant U.S. Attorney **Kevin Mokhtari** . . . . (619) 546-8402
E-mail: kevin.mokhtari@usdoj.gov

General Crimes Section

Assistant U.S. Attorney, Chief **(Vacant)** . . . . (619) 546-6692
Assistant U.S. Attorney, Deputy Chief
Joseph M. Orabona . . . . (619) 546-7951
E-mail: joseph.orabona@usdoj.gov
Assistant U.S. Attorney, Deputy Chief **Fred Sheppard** . . . (619) 546-8237
E-mail: fred.sheppard@usdoj.gov
Senior Assistant U.S. Attorney **Michael E. Lasater** . . . . . . (619) 546-7462
E-mail: michael.lasater@usdoj.gov
Education: San Diego JD
Assistant U.S. Attorney **Christopher M. Alexander** . . . . . (619) 546-6665
E-mail: christopher.m.alexander@usdoj.gov
Assistant U.S. Attorney **Lawrence A. Casper** . . . . (619) 546-6734
E-mail: lawrence.casper@usdoj.gov
Assistant U.S. Attorney **Alexandra Foster** . . . . (619) 546-6735
E-mail: alexandra.foster@usdoj.gov
Assistant U.S. Attorney **Andrew R. Haden** . . . . (619) 546-6961
E-mail: andrew.haden@usdoj.gov
Assistant U.S. Attorney **Michael J. Heyman** . . . . (619) 546-9615
E-mail: michael.j.heyman@usdoj.gov
Assistant U.S. Attorney **Alessandra P. Serano** . . . . (619) 546-8014
E-mail: alessandra.p.serano@usdoj.gov
Assistant U.S. Attorney **Lara A. Stingley** . . . . (619) 546-8403
E-mail: lara.stingley@usdoj.gov
Assistant U.S. Attorney **(Vacant)** . . . . (619) 557-5610
Assistant U.S. Attorney **(Vacant)** . . . . (619) 546-9613
International Coordinator **Mark W. Conover** . . . . (619) 546-6763
E-mail: mark.conover@usdoj.gov
Assistant U.S. Attorney **(Vacant)** . . . . (619) 557-5610

Major Frauds

Assistant U.S. Attorney, Chief **Phillip L. B. Halpern** . . . . . (619) 546-6964
E-mail: phillip.halpern@usdoj.gov
Assistant U.S. Attorney, Principal Deputy Chief
Eric J. Beste . . . . (619) 546-6695
E-mail: eric.beste@usdoj.gov
Education: Oxford (UK) 1990 URGD; Pennsylvania 1991 AB; Northwestern 1994 JD
Assistant U.S. Attorney, Deputy Chief **(Vacant)** . . . . (619) 546-8068
Assistant U.S. Attorney **Emily Allen** . . . . (619) 546-9738
E-mail: emily.allen@usdoj.gov
Education: Harvard 2004 JD
Assistant U.S. Attorney **Valerie H. Chu** . . . . (619) 546-6750
E-mail: valerie.chu@usdoj.gov
Assistant U.S. Attorney **Andrew Galvin** . . . . (619) 546-9721
E-mail: andrew.galvin@usdoj.gov
Assistant U.S. Attorney **Rebecca Kanter** . . . . (619) 546-7304
E-mail: rebecca.kanter@usdoj.gov
Education: UC Irvine BA; UCLA 2003 JD
Assistant U.S. Attorney **Melanie K. Pierson** . . . . (619) 546-7976
E-mail: melanie.pierson@usdoj.gov
Assistant U.S. Attorney **Nicholas W. Pilchak** . . . . (619) 546-9709
E-mail: nicholas.pilchak@usdoj.gov
Assistant U.S. Attorney **Mark W. Pletcher** . . . . (619) 546-9714
E-mail: mark.pletcher@usdoj.gov
Assistant U.S. Attorney **Christopher P. Tenorio** . . . . (619) 546-8413
E-mail: christopher.tenorio@usdoj.gov
Assistant U.S. Attorney **Michelle L. Wasserman** . . . . (619) 546-8431
E-mail: michelle.wasserman@usdoj.gov
Education: Harvard 2007 JD
Assistant U.S. Attorney **(Vacant)** . . . . (619) 546-7053
Assistant U.S. Attorney **(Vacant)** . . . . (619) 546-7928

National Security and Cybercrimes Section

Chief of National Security and Cybercrimes
John N. Parmley . . . . (619) 546-7957
E-mail: john.parmley@usdoj.gov
Assistant U.S. Attorney **Sabrina L. Fève** . . . . (619) 546-6786
E-mail: sabrina.feve@usdoj.gov
Education: Williams 1997 BA; Harvard 2002 JD

National Security and Cybercrimes Section *(continued)*

Assistant U.S. Attorney **Shane P. Harrigan** . . . . (619) 546-6981
E-mail: shane.harrigan@usdoj.gov
Assistant U.S. Attorney **Michael J. Kaplan** . . . . (619) 546-7927
E-mail: michael.kaplan@usdoj.gov
Assistant U.S. Attorney **Michelle Pettit** . . . . (619) 546-7972
E-mail: michelle.pettit@usdoj.gov
Assistant U.S. Attorney **(Vacant)** . . . . (619) 546-7957

Reactive Crimes Section

Assistant U.S. Attorney, Principal Deputy Chief
(Vacant) . . . . (619) 557-5610
Assistant U.S. Attorney, Deputy Chief **Tara McGrath** . . . . (619) 546-7930
E-mail: tara.mcgrath@usdoj.gov
Senior Assistant U.S. Attorney **(Vacant)** . . . . (619) 546-7964
Senior Assistant U.S. Attorney **(Vacant)** . . . . (619) 546-6784
Diversion Coordinator **(Vacant)** . . . . (619) 564-6720
Assistant U.S. Attorney **Carlos Arguello** . . . . (619) 546-6684
E-mail: carlos.arguello2@usdoj.gov
Assistant U.S. Attorney **Matthew Brehm** . . . . (760) 370-3028
E-mail: matthew.brehm@usdoj.gov
Assistant U.S. Attorney **Janet Cabral** . . . . (619) 546-8715
E-mail: janet.cabral@usdoj.gov
Education: Notre Dame 1993 JD
Assistant U.S. Attorney **Jarad Hodes** . . . . (619) 546-7432
E-mail: jarad.hodes@usdoj.gov
Assistant U.S. Attorney **Benjamin Katz** . . . . (619) 546-8971
E-mail: benjamin.katz@usdoj.gov
Assistant U.S. Attorney **Brandon Kimura** . . . . (619) 546-9614
E-mail: brandon.kimura@usdoj.gov
Education: Santa Clara U 2005 JD
Assistant U.S. Attorney **Joseph S. Smith, Jr.** . . . . (619) 546-8299
E-mail: joseph.smith@usdoj.gov
Assistant U.S. Attorney **Lawrence E. Spong** . . . . (619) 546-8401
E-mail: larry.spong@usdoj.gov
Assistant U.S. Attorney **(Vacant)** . . . . (619) 546-7235
Assistant U.S. Attorney **(Vacant)** . . . . (619) 557-5610
Assistant U.S. Attorney **(Vacant)** . . . . (619) 557-5610
Assistant U.S. Attorney **(Vacant)** . . . . (619) 557-5610

Imperial County Office - El Centro

516 Industry Way, #C, Imperial, CA 92251
Tel: (760) 370-0893 Fax: (760) 335-3975

Assistant U.S. Attorney **(Vacant)** . . . . (760) 370-3037
Assistant U.S. Attorney **Rosario Gonzalez** . . . . (619) 546-8384
E-mail: rosario.gonzalez@usdoj.gov
Assistant U.S. Attorney **Christine M. Ro** . . . . (760) 355-2230
E-mail: christine.ro@usdoj.gov

Colorado District

1225 - 17th Street, Suite 700, Denver, CO 80202
Tel: (303) 454-0100 Fax: (303) 454-0400
Internet: https://www.justice.gov/usao-co

★ U.S. Attorney **Jason R. Dunn** . . . . (303) 454-0100
E-mail: jason.r.dunn@usdoj.gov
Education: Colorado 1993 BS, 1998 MPA, 2001 JD
First Assistant U.S. Attorney **Matthew Kirsch** . . . . (303) 454-0100
E-mail: matthew.kirsch@usdoj.gov
Executive United States Attorney **J. Chris Larson** . . . . . . (303) 454-0100
E-mail: j.chris.larson@usdoj.gov
Project Safe Neighborhood Assistant U.S. Attorney
Kurt Bohn . . . . (303) 454-0100
E-mail: kurt.bohn@usdoj.gov
Law Enforcement Coordinator **David M. Gaouette** . . . . . . (303) 454-0100
E-mail: david.gaouette@usdoj.gov
Education: Florida State 1976; Denver 1982 JD
Victim-Witness Specialist **Donna Summers** . . . . (303) 454-0100
E-mail: donna.summers@usdoj.gov
Information Technology Specialist and Litigation Support **Daniel Keener** . . . . (303) 454-0100
E-mail: daniel.keener@usdoj.gov
Legal Administration Specialist/FOIA **(Vacant)** . . . . (303) 454-0100
Public Affairs Specialist **Jeffrey Dorschner** . . . . (303) 454-0100
E-mail: jeffrey.dorschner@usdoj.gov

★ Presidential Appointment Requiring Senate Confirmation ☆ Presidential Appointment ☐ Schedule C Appointment ◇ Career Senior Foreign Service Appointment
● Career Senior Executive Service (SES) Appointment ○ Non-Career Senior Executive Service (SES) Appointment ■ Postal Career Executive Service

Colorado District *(continued)*

Regional Security Specialist **(Vacant)** .... (303) 454-0100
Executive Assistant/Office Manager **Cathy Olguin** .... (303) 454-0100

Administrative Division
1801 California Street, Suite 1600, Denver, CO 80202
Fax: (303) 454-0405

Chief **Marilyn Ferguson** .... (303) 454-0100
E-mail: marilyn.ferguson@usdoj.gov
Human Resources Specialist **Gloria Engle** .... (303) 454-0100
E-mail: gloria.engle@usdoj.gov
Human Resources Assistant **Alexandria Suazo** .... (303) 454-0100
E-mail: alexandria.suazo@usdoj.gov
Human Resources Assistant **(Vacant)** .... (303) 454-0100
Supervisor Administrative Services Specialist **Bonnie Vigil** .... (303) 454-0100
E-mail: bonnie.vigil@usdoj.gov
Administrative Services Specialist **Jeffrey Hernandez** .... (303) 454-0100
E-mail: jeffrey.hernandez@usdoj.gov
Administrative Specialist **Victoria "Tori" Soltis** .... (303) 454-0100
E-mail: victoria.soltis@usdoj.gov
Administrative Assistant and Receptionist **(Vacant)** ...... (303) 454-0100
Budget Officer **Mary Nevares** .... (303) 454-0100
E-mail: mary.nevares@usdoj.gov
Budget Analyst **Joanne Gienger** .... (303) 454-0100
E-mail: joanne.gienger@usdoj.gov
Financial Technician **Alexandra Ornelas** .... (303) 454-0100
E-mail: alexandra.ornelas@usdoj.gov
Information Technology Director **Mark Pittington** .... (303) 454-0100
E-mail: mark.pittington@usdoj.gov
Information Technology Director **Steve Brooks** .... (303) 454-0100
E-mail: steven.brooks@usdoj.gov
Information Technology Specialist and Litigation Support **Ed Medina** .... (303) 454-0100
Information Technology Specialist and Litigation Support **(Vacant)** .... (303) 454-0100

Appellate Division
1801 California Street, Suite 1600, Denver, CO 80202
Tel: (303) 454-0461

Appellate Chief **Bishop Grewell** .... (303) 454-0100
E-mail: bishop.grewell@usdoj.gov
Assistant U.S. Attorney **Paul Farley** .... (303) 454-0100
E-mail: paul.farley@usdoj.gov
Education: Colorado BA; Denver JD
Assistant U.S. Attorney **Michael Johnson** .... (303) 454-0100
E-mail: michael.johnson5@usdoj.gov
Assistant U.S. Attorney **James C. Murphy** .... (303) 454-0100
E-mail: james.murphy@usdoj.gov
Assistant U.S. Attorney **Karl Schock** .... (303) 454-0100
E-mail: karl.schock@usdoj.gov
Assistant U.S. Attorney **(Vacant)** .... (303) 454-0100
Paralegal **Carmen Gibson** .... (303) 454-0248
E-mail: carmen.gibson@usdoj.gov Fax: (303) 454-0403
Paralegal **Ma-Linda LaFollette** .... (303) 454-0100

Asset Recovery Division
1801 California Street, Suite 1600, Denver, CO 80202
Fax: (303) 454-0402

Chief **Tonya Andrews** .... (303) 454-0100
E-mail: tonya.andrews@usdoj.gov
Assistant U.S. Attorney **Laura Hurd** .... (303) 454-0100
E-mail: laura.hurd@usdoj.gov
Assistant U.S. Attorney **H. Wayne Campbell** .... (303) 454-0100
E-mail: wayne.campbell@usdoj.gov
Paralegal **Charisha Cruz** .... (303) 454-0100
E-mail: charisha.cruz@usdoj.gov Fax: (303) 454-0402

Civil Division
1801 California Street, Suite 1600, Denver, CO 80202
Fax: (303) 454-0404

Chief **Kevin Traskos** .... (303) 454-0100
E-mail: kevin.traskos@usdoj.gov

Civil Division *(continued)*

Deputy Chief **Amanda Rocque** .... (303) 454-0100
E-mail: amanda.rocque@usdoj.gov
Deputy Chief **Marcy Cook** .... (303) 454-0100
E-mail: marcy.cook@usdoj.gov
Paralegal **Cheriene Nowick** .... (303) 454-0100
Fax: (303) 454-0402
Paralegal **Megan Ingebrigtsen** .... (303) 454-0100
Fax: (303) 454-0402
Paralegal **Teresa Robinson** .... (303) 454-0100
Fax: (303) 454-0402
Affirmative Civil Enforcement Assistant U.S. Attorney/Senior Litigation Chief **Marcy Cook** .... (303) 454-0100
E-mail: marcy.cook@usdoj.gov
Affirmative Civil Enforcement Assistant U.S. Attorney **Hetal Doshi** .... (303) 454-0100
E-mail: hetal.doshi@usdoj.gov
Affirmative Civil Enforcement, Mortgage Fraud Assistant U.S. Attorney **Shiwon Choe** .... (303) 454-0100
E-mail: shiwon.choe@usdoj.gov
Affirmative Civil Enforcement Auditor **(Vacant)** .... (303) 454-0100
Financial Fraud Assistant U.S. Attorney **Lila Batemen** ... (303) 454-0100
E-mail: lila.bateman@usdoj.gov
Financial Analyst, Affirmative Civil Enforcement **Laura Keane** .... (303) 454-0100
E-mail: laura.keane@usdoj.gov
Defensive Litigation Assistant U.S. Attorney **Jacon Licht-Steenfat** .... (303) 454-0100
E-mail: jacob.licht-steenfat@usdoj.gov
Defensive Litigation Assistant U.S. Attorney **J. B. Garcia** .... (303) 454-0100
E-mail: j.b.garcia@usdoj.gov
Defensive Litigation Assistant U.S. Attorney **Timothy Jafek** .... (303) 454-0100
E-mail: timothy.jafek@usdoj.gov
Defensive Litigation Assistant U.S. Attorney **Mark S. Pestal** .... (303) 454-0100
E-mail: mark.pestal@usdoj.gov
Defensive Litigation Assistant U.S. Attorney **Susan Prose** .... (303) 454-0100
E-mail: susan.prose@usdoj.gov
Defensive Litigation Assistant U.S. Attorney **Katherine Ross** .... (303) 454-0100
E-mail: katherine.ross@usdoj.gov
Defensive Litigation Assistant U.S. Attorney **Juan G. Villaseñor** .... (303) 454-0100
E-mail: juan.villasenor@usdoj.gov
Financial Litigation Unit Supervisor **Patricia McGee-Wake** .... (303) 454-0100
E-mail: patricia.mcgee-wake@usdoj.gov
Financial Litigation Unit Paralegal **Carolyn Dean** .... (303) 454-0100
E-mail: carolyn.dean@usdoj.gov Fax: (303) 454-0407
Affirmative Civil Enforcement, Health Care Fraud Assistant U.S. Attorney **Edwin Winstead** .... (303) 454-0100
E-mail: edwin.winstead@usdoj.gov
Defensive Litigation, Health Care Fraud Assistant U.S. Attorney **Mark S. Pestal** .... (303) 454-0100
E-mail: mark.pestal@usdoj.gov
Health Care Fraud Paralegal **Lisa Lara** .... (303) 454-0100

Criminal Division
1801 Califonia Street, Suite 600, Denver, CO 80202
Fax: (303) 454-0402

Chief **Suneeta Hazra** .... (303) 454-0100
E-mail: suneeta.hazra@usdoj.gov
Economic Crimes Chief **Martha A. Paluch** .... (303) 454-0100
E-mail: martha.paluch@usdoj.gov
Economic Crimes Assistant U.S. Attorney **Patricia Davies** .... (303) 454-0100
E-mail: patricia.davies@usdoj.gov
Economic Crimes Assistant U.S. Attorney **John Haried** .... (303) 454-0100
E-mail: john.haried@usdoj.gov
Economic Crimes Assistant U.S. Attorney **(Vacant)** .... (303) 454-0100

(continued on next page)

Criminal Division *(continued)*

Economic Crimes Assistant U.S. Attorney
Chris Larson . . . . (303) 454-0100
E-mail: chris.larson@usdoj.gov
Economic Crimes Assistant U.S. Attorney **Tim Neff** . . . . (303) 454-0100
E-mail: tim.neff@usdoj.gov
Economic Crimes Assistant U.S. Attorney
Pegeen D. Rhyne . . . . (303) 454-0100
E-mail: pegeen.rhyne@usdoj.gov
Economic Crimes Assistant U.S. Attorney
Kenneth Harmon . . . . (303) 454-0100
E-mail: kenneth.harmon@usdoj.gov
Economic Crimes Assistant U.S. Attorney **(Vacant)** . . . . (303) 454-0100
Auditor of Economic Crimes **Richard "Rich" Zoeter** . . . (303) 454-0100
E-mail: richard.zoeter@usdoj.gov
Auditor **Dana Chamberlin** . . . . (303) 454-0100
E-mail: dana.chamberlin@usdoj.gov
Health Care Fraud Assistant U.S. Attorney/ Senior Litigation Chief **Anna Edgar** . . . . (303) 454-0100
Education: Georgetown 2006 JD
Major Crimes Section Chief **Bradley W. "Brad" Giles** . . . (303) 454-0100
Major Crimes Assistant U.S. Attorney
Rebecca Weber . . . . (303) 454-0100
E-mail: rebecca.weber@usdoj.gov
Major Crimes Assistant U.S. Attorney **Kurt Bohn** . . . . (303) 454-0100
Major Crimes Assistant U.S. Attorney **(Vacant)** . . . . (303) 454-0100
Major Crimes Assistant U.S. Attorney
Jeremy Sibert . . . . (303) 454-0100
E-mail: jeremy.sibert@usdoj.gov
Major Crimes Assistant U.S. Attorney
Jason St. Julien . . . . (303) 454-0100
Drug Enforcement Task Force Section Co-Chief
(Vacant) . . . . (303) 454-0100
Fax: (303) 454-0401
Drug Enforcement Task Force Section Co-Chief
(Vacant) . . . . (303) 454-0100
Chief Counsel, Special Projects **Stephanie Podolak** . . . . (303) 454-0100
E-mail: stephanie.podolak@usdoj.gov
Organized Crime Drug Enforcement Task Force Assistant U.S. Attorney **Bryan D. Fields** . . . . (303) 454-0100
E-mail: bryan.fields3@usdoj.gov Fax: (303) 454-0401
Education: Pennsylvania 2009 JD
Organized Crime Drug Enforcement Task Force Assistant U.S. Attorney **Edwin Garreth Winstead** . . . (303) 454-0100
Education: Colorado 2011 JD
Organized Crime Drug Enforcement Task Force Assistant U.S. Attorney **Barbara Skalla** . . . . (303) 454-0100
E-mail: barbara.skalla@usdoj.gov
Organized Crime Drug Enforcement Task Force Assistant U.S. Attorney **Guy Till** . . . . (303) 454-0100
E-mail: guy.till@usdoj.gov
Organized Crime Drug Enforcement Task Force Assistant U.S. Attorney **James Boma** . . . . (303) 454-0100
E-mail: james.boma@usdoj.gov
Organized Crime Drug Enforcement Task Force Assistant U.S. Attorney **(Vacant)** . . . . (303) 454-0100
Organized Crime Drug Enforcement Task Force Assistant U.S. Attorney **(Vacant)** . . . . (303) 454-0100
Organized Crime Drug Enforcement Task Force Special Assistant U.S. Attorney **Peter McNeilly** . . . . (303) 454-0100
E-mail: peter.mcneilly@usdoj.gov
Organized Crime Drug Enforcement Task Force Auditor **Scott Gammel** . . . . (303) 454-0100
E-mail: scott.gammel@usdoj.gov
Organized Crime Drug Enforcement Task Force Paralegal **Charlotte Musser** . . . . (303) 454-0100
E-mail: charlotte.musser@usdoj.gov

Special Prosecutions Division

Special Prosecutions Section Chief/CHIP
Judith Smith . . . . (303) 454-0100
Note: CHIP stands for Computer Hacking and Intellectual Property Fax: (303) 454-0403
Special Prosecutions Assistant U.S. Attorney
Colleen Covell . . . . (303) 454-0100

Special Prosecutions Division *(continued)*

Special Prosecutions Assistant U.S. Attorney
Gregory Holloway . . . . (303) 454-0100
E-mail: gregory.holloway@usdoj.gov
Special Prosecutions Assistant U.S. Attorney
Alecia Riewerts . . . . (303) 454-0100
Special Prosecutions Assistant U.S. Attorney
Valeria Spencer . . . . (303) 454-0100
E-mail: valeria.spencer@usdoj.gov
Special Prosecutions Assistant U.S. Attorney
David Tonini . . . . (303) 454-0100
E-mail: david.tonini@usdoj.gov
Special Prosecutions Assistant U.S. Attorney
(Vacant) . . . . (303) 454-0100

Durango Office

103 Sheppard Drive, Suite 215, Durango, CO 81303
Tel: (970) 247-1514 Fax: (970) 247-8619

Branch Chief and Senior Litigation Chief
James Candelaria . . . . (970) 247-1514
E-mail: james.candelaria@usdoj.gov
Assistant U.S. Attorney **(Vacant)** . . . . (970) 247-3102
Assistant U.S. Attorney **Dondi Osborne** . . . . (970) 247-3103
E-mail: dondi.osborne@usdoj.gov
Paralegal **(Vacant)** . . . . (970) 247-3104

Grand Junction Office

205 North Fourth Street, Suite 400, Grand Junction, CO 81501
Tel: (970) 257-7113 Fax: (970) 248-3630

Assistant U.S. Attorney **Peter Hautzinger** . . . . (970) 257-7113
E-mail: peter.hautzinger@usdoj.gov
Legal Assistant **Cosandra Foster** . . . . (970) 241-3843

Connecticut District

Connecticut Financial Center, 157 Church Street,
23rd Floor, New Haven, CT 06510
Tel: (203) 821-3700 Fax: (203) 773-5376
Internet: https://www.justice.gov/usao-ct

★ U.S. Attorney **John H. Durham** . . . . (203) 821-3700
Education: Colgate 1972; Connecticut 1975 JD
Secretary to the U.S. Attorney **Judith "Judi" Dauria** . . . (203) 821-3700
E-mail: judi.dauria@usdoj.gov
First Assistant U.S. Attorney **(Vacant)** . . . . (203) 821-3700
Counsel to the U.S. Attorney **(Vacant)** . . . . (203) 821-3700
Executive Assistant U.S. Attorney **Peter S. Jongbloed** . . . (203) 821-3700
E-mail: peter.jongbloed@usdoj.gov
Administrative Officer **Michele Genden** . . . . (203) 821-3700
E-mail: michele.genden@usdoj.gov
Budget Officer **Ruth Matthews** . . . . (203) 821-3700
E-mail: ruth.matthews@usdoj.gov
Human Resources Officer **(Vacant)** . . . . (203) 821-3700
Systems Manager and Coordinator **(Vacant)** . . . . (203) 821-3700
Law Enforcement Coordination Specialist **(Vacant)** . . . . (860) 947-1101
Public Affairs Specialist **Thomas Carson** . . . . (203) 821-3722
Victim-Witness Specialist **(Vacant)** . . . . (203) 821-3700
Senior Litigation Counsel **(Vacant)** . . . . (203) 696-3000

Civil Division

Chief **John B. Hughes** . . . . (203) 821-3700
E-mail: john.hughes@usdoj.gov
Affirmative Civil Enforcement Unit Chief
Richard M. Molot . . . . (203) 821-3700
E-mail: richard.molot2@usdoj.gov
Defensive Unit Chief **Michelle L. McConaghy** . . . . (203) 821-3700
E-mail: michelle.mcconaghy@usdoj.gov
Education: Roger Williams 2005 JD
Financial Litigation Unit Supervisor
Christine Sciarrino . . . . (203) 821-3700
E-mail: christine.sciarrino@usdoj.gov
Assistant U.S. Attorney **Douglas Morabito** . . . . (203) 821-3700
E-mail: douglas.morabito@usdoj.gov
Assistant U.S. Attorney **Lauren M. Nash** . . . . (203) 821-3700
E-mail: lauren.nash@usdoj.gov

★ Presidential Appointment Requiring Senate Confirmation ☆ Presidential Appointment □ Schedule C Appointment ◇ Career Senior Foreign Service Appointment
● Career Senior Executive Service (SES) Appointment ○ Non-Career Senior Executive Service (SES) Appointment ■ Postal Career Executive Service

Civil Division *(continued)*

Assistant U.S. Attorney **Alan M. Soloway** . . . . (203) 821-3700
E-mail: alan.soloway@usdoj.gov
Assistant U.S. Attorney **David X. Sullivan** . . . . (203) 821-3700
E-mail: david.sullivan@usdoj.gov
Assistant U.S. Attorney **Anne F. Thidemann** . . . . (203) 821-3700
E-mail: anne.thidemann@usdoj.gov
Education: Ohio JD
Assistant U.S. Attorney **Julie G. Turbert** . . . . (203) 821-3700
E-mail: julie.turbert@usdoj.gov

Criminal Division

Chief **William J. Nardini** . . . . (203) 821-3700
E-mail: william.nardini@usdoj.gov
Financial Fraud and Public Corruption Unit Chief
David E. Novick . . . . (203) 821-3700
E-mail: david.novick@usdoj.gov
Financial Fraud and Public Corruption Unit Deputy
Chief **Michael S. McGarry** . . . . (203) 821-3700
E-mail: michael.mcgarry@usdoj.gov
Major Crimes Unit Chief **Sarah P. Karwan** . . . . (203) 821-3700
E-mail: sarah.p.karwan@usdoj.gov
Education: Connecticut JD
Major Crimes Unit Chief **Sarala V. Nagala** . . . . (203) 821-3700
E-mail: sarala.nagala@usdoj.gov
National Security and Cybercrimes Unit Chief
Peter S. Jongbloed . . . . (203) 821-3700
E-mail: peter.jongbloed@usdoj.gov
National Security and Cybercrimes Unit Deputy
Chief **Vanessa Richards** . . . . (203) 821-3700
E-mail: vanessa.richards@usdoj.gov
National Security and Cybercrimes Unit Deputy
Chief **(Vacant)** . . . . (203) 821-3700
Anti-Terrorism Advisory Council Coordinator
Stephen B. Reynolds . . . . (203) 821-3700
Education: Hamilton 1993 BA; Cornell 1997 JD
Strike Force Unit Chief **Raymond F. Miller** . . . . (203) 821-3700
E-mail: ray.miller2@usdoj.gov
Violent Crimes and Narcotics Unit Chief **S. Dave Vatti** . . . (203) 821-3700
E-mail: dave.vatti@usdoj.gov
Violent Crimes and Narcotics Unit Deputy Chief
Michael J. "Mike" Gustafson . . . . (203) 821-3700
E-mail: mike.gustafson@usdoj.gov
Violent Crimes and Narcotics Unit Deputy Chief
Anthony E. Kaplan . . . . (203) 821-3700
E-mail: anthony.kaplan@usdoj.gov
Drug Enforcement Task Force Chief **Peter D. Markle** . . . (203) 821-3700
E-mail: peter.markle@usdoj.gov
Drug Enforcement Task Force Deputy Chief
H. Gordon Hall . . . . (203) 821-3700
E-mail: gordon.hall@usdoj.gov
Project Safe Neighborhoods Coordinator
S. Dave Vatti . . . . (203) 821-3700
Appellate Unit Chief **Sandra S. Glover** . . . . (203) 821-3700
E-mail: sandra.glover@usdoj.gov
Appellate Unit Deputy Chief **Marc Harris Silverman** . . . (203) 821-3700
E-mail: marc.silverman@usdoj.gov
Education: Yale 2003 BA, 2006 JD
Senior Litigation Counsel **Anthony E. Kaplan** . . . . (203) 821-3700
E-mail: anthony.kaplan@usdoj.gov
Assistant U.S. Attorney **Patrick F. Caruso** . . . . (203) 821-3700
E-mail: patrick.caruso@usdoj.gov
Assistant U.S. Attorney **David T. Huang** . . . . (203) 821-3700
E-mail: david.huang@usdoj.gov
Assistant U.S. Attorney **Anastasia M. King** . . . . (203) 821-3700
E-mail: anastasia.king@usdoj.gov
Assistant U.S. Attorney **Henry K. Kopel** . . . . (203) 821-3700
E-mail: henry.kopel@usdoj.gov
Assistant U.S. Attorney **Michael E. Runowicz** . . . . (203) 821-3700
E-mail: mike.runowicz@usdoj.gov
Assistant U.S. Attorney **Christopher W. Schmeisser** . . . . (203) 821-3700
E-mail: christopher.schmeisser@usdoj.gov
Assistant U.S. Attorney **David J. Sheldon** . . . . (203) 821-3700
E-mail: david.sheldon@usdoj.gov
Assistant U.S. Attorney **Susan Wines** . . . . (203) 821-3700
E-mail: susan.wines@usdoj.gov

Bridgeport (CT) Office

RBS Financial Center, 1000 Lafayette Boulevard,
10th Floor, Bridgeport, CT 06604
Tel: (203) 696-3000 Fax: (203) 579-5550

Supervisory Assistant U.S. Attorney **(Vacant)** . . . . (203) 696-3000
Civil Division Assistant U.S. Attorney
Brenda Moss Green . . . . (203) 696-3000
E-mail: brenda.green@usdoj.gov
Civil Division Assistant U.S. Attorney **(Vacant)** . . . . (203) 696-3000
Criminal Division Assistant U.S. Attorney
Harold H. Chen . . . . (203) 696-3000
E-mail: harold.chen@usdoj.gov
Education: Yale 1991 BA; Duke 1996 JD
Criminal Division Assistant U.S. Attorney **(Vacant)** . . . . . . (203) 696-3000
Criminal Division Assistant U.S. Attorney **(Vacant)** . . . . . . (203) 696-3000
Drug Enforcement Task Force Assistant U.S. Attorney
Alina P. Reynolds . . . . (203) 696-3000
E-mail: alina.reynolds@usdoj.gov

Hartford (CT) Office

Federal Building and U.S. Court House, 450 Main Street,
Room 328, Hartford, CT 06103
Tel: (860) 947-1101

Supervisory Assistant U.S. Attorney **Brian P. Leaming** . . . (860) 947-1101
E-mail: brian.leaming@usdoj.gov
Intelligence Research Specialist **(Vacant)** . . . . (860) 947-1101
Senior Litigation Counsel **(Vacant)** . . . . (860) 941-1101

Civil Division

Assistant U.S. Attorney **Carolyn Ikari** . . . . (860) 947-1101
E-mail: carolyn.ikari@usdoj.gov
Assistant U.S. Attorney **Gabriel J. Vidoni** . . . . (860) 947-1101
E-mail: gabriel.vidoni@usdoj.gov
Assistant U.S. Attorney **(Vacant)** . . . . (860) 941-1101

Criminal Division

Assistant U.S. Attorney **Deborah R. Slater** . . . . (860) 947-1101
E-mail: deborah.slater@usdoj.gov
Assistant U.S. Attorney **Geoffrey M. Stone** . . . . (860) 947-1101
E-mail: geoffrey.stone@usdoj.gov
Assistant U.S. Attorney **S. Dave Vatti** . . . . (860) 947-1101
E-mail: dave.vatti@usdoj.gov
Assistant U.S. Attorney **(Vacant)** . . . . (860) 947-1101

Delaware District

1007 Orange Street, Suite 700, Wilmington, DE 19801
P.O. Box 2046, Wilmington, DE 19899-2046
Tel: (302) 573-6277 Fax: (302) 573-6220
Internet: https://www.justice.gov/usao-de

★ U.S. Attorney **David C. Weiss** . . . . (302) 573-6277
E-mail: david.weiss@usdoj.gov
Education: Washington U (MO) BS; Widener JD
Secretary to the U.S. Attorney **Miranda Keith** . . . . (302) 573-6277
E-mail: miranda.keith@usdoj.gov
First Assistant U.S. Attorney **Shannon T. Hanson** . . . . (302) 573-6277
E-mail: shannon.hanson@usdoj.gov
Administrative Officer **Randall Lohan** . . . . (302) 573-6277
E-mail: randall.lohan@usdoj.gov
Deputy Administrative Officer **(Vacant)** . . . . (302) 573-6277
Law Enforcement Coordinator/Press Officer
Kimberlynn Reeves . . . . (302) 573-6277
E-mail: kimberlynn.reeves@usdoj.gov
Victim-Witness Coordinator **Susan Alfree** . . . . (302) 573-6277
E-mail: susan.alfree@usdoj.gov
Systems Manager **David Flint** . . . . (302) 573-6277
E-mail: david.flint@usdoj.gov

Civil Division

Chief **Jennifer L. Hall** . . . . (302) 573-6277
E-mail: jennifer.hall@usdoj.gov
Assistant U.S. Attorney **Laura Hatcher** . . . . (302) 573-6277
Assistant U.S. Attorney **Ellen W. Slights** . . . . (302) 573-6277
E-mail: ellen.slights@usdoj.gov

(continued on next page)

★ Presidential Appointment Requiring Senate Confirmation ☆ Presidential Appointment ☐ Schedule C Appointment ◇ Career Senior Foreign Service Appointment
● Career Senior Executive Service (SES) Appointment ○ Non-Career Senior Executive Service (SES) Appointment ■ Postal Career Executive Service

DEPARTMENTS

Civil Division *(continued)*

Assistant U.S. Attorney **Jennifer Welsh** .... (302) 573-6277
E-mail: jennifer.welsh@usdoj.gov
Assistant U.S. Attorney **Lesley Wolf** .... (302) 573-6277
E-mail: lesley.wolf@usdoj.gov
Assistant U.S. Attorney **(Vacant)** .... (302) 573-6277
Assistant U.S. Attorney **(Vacant)** .... (302) 573-6277

Criminal Division
Chief **Shawn Weede** .... (302) 573-6277
E-mail: shawn.weede@usdoj.gov
Education: Pennsylvania 2002 JD
Assistant U.S. Attorney **Whitney Cloud** .... (302) 573-6277
E-mail: whitney.cloud@usdoj.gov
Assistant U.S. Attorney **Edmond Falgowski** .... (302) 573-6277
E-mail: edmond.falgowski@usdoj.gov
Assistant U.S. Attorney **Alexander P. Ibrahim** .... (302) 573-6277
E-mail: alexander.ibrahim@usdoj.gov
Education: Penn State 2007 BA; Virginia 2010 JD
Assistant U.S. Attorney **Robert Kravetz** .... (302) 573-6277
E-mail: robert.kravetz@usdoj.gov
Assistant U.S. Attorney **Daniel Logan** .... (302) 573-6277
E-mail: daniel.logan@usdoj.gov
Assistant U.S. Attorney **Alexander Mackler** .... (302) 573-6277
E-mail: alexander.mackler@usdoj.gov
Education: Pennsylvania 2005 BS; William & Mary 2014 JD
Assistant U.S. Attorney **Jamie McCall** .... (302) 573-6277
E-mail: jamie.mccall@usdoj.gov
Assistant U.S. Attorney **Robert J. Prettyman** .... (302) 573-6277
E-mail: robert.prettyman@usdoj.gov
Assistant U.S. Attorney **Graham L. Robinson** .... (302) 573-6277
E-mail: graham.robinson@usdoj.gov
Education: BYU 2007 BSE; Delaware 2009 MA; J Reuben Clark Law 2012 JD

District of Columbia District
555 Fourth Street, NW, Washington, DC 20530
Tel: (202) 252-7566 Fax: (202) 305-0266
Internet: https://www.justice.gov/usao-dc

★ U.S. Attorney **Jessie K. Liu** .... (202) 252-6600
E-mail: jessie.liu@usdoj.gov
Education: Harvard 1995 BA; Yale 1998 JD
Executive Assistant **Elizabeth Fisher** .... (202) 252-1816
Principal Assistant U.S. Attorney **Alessio Evangelsta** .... (202) 252-6602
E-mail: alessio.evangelista@usdoj.gov
Education: SUNY (Geneseo) 1991 BA; Syracuse 1995 JD
Executive Assistant **(Vacant)** .... (202) 252-6615
Executive Assistant U.S. Attorney for External Affairs
Wendy Pohlhaus .... (202) 252-6612
E-mail: wendy.pohlhaus@usdoj.gov
Education: Miami 1990 JD
Supervisory Community Outreach Specialist
Brenda J. Horner .... (202) 698-0825
Executive Assistant U.S. Attorney for Management
Denise Simmonds .... (202) 252-6621
E-mail: denise.simmonds@usdoj.gov
Executive Assistant U.S. Attorney for Operations
(Vacant) .... (202) 252-6603
Administrative Officer **Ralph B. Cox** .... (202) 252-7627
E-mail: ralph.cox@usdoj.gov
Victim/Witness Assistance Unit Chief **(Vacant)** .... (202) 252-7187
Special Counsel to the U.S. Attorney
Renata Cooper Esq. .... (202) 252-6606
E-mail: renata.cooper@usdoj.gov
Special Counsel to the U.S. Attorney **(Vacant)** .... (202) 252-6606
Chief Information Officer **(Vacant)** .... (202) 252-0882
Budget Officer **(Vacant)** Room 5207 .... (202) 252-1723
Librarian **Lisa Kosow** Room 8222-A .... (202) 252-6659
E-mail: lisa.kosow2@usdoj.gov
Office Services Manager **Lee Pensmith** .... (202) 252-7634
E-mail: lee.pensmith@usdoj.gov
Human Resources Officer **(Vacant)** Room 5300 I ...... (202) 252-7629
Intelligence Specialist **John Marsh** .... (202) 252-6862
E-mail: john.marsh@usdoj.gov

District of Columbia District *(continued)*
Systems Manager **Karen T. Kress** .... (202) 252-0822
E-mail: karen.kress@usdoj.gov
Special Counsel for Professional Development
Denise Simmonds .... (301) 492-5513
Antiterrorism Officer/LECC Manager
Christopher Brophy .... (202) 252-6857
E-mail: christopher.brophy@usdoj.gov

Appellate Division
555 Fourth Street, NW, Washington, DC 20530
Fax: (202) 514-8779

Chief **Elizabeth Trosman** .... (202) 252-6784
E-mail: elizabeth.trosman@usdoj.gov
Assistant to the Chief **Lori Buckler** .... (202) 252-6775
E-mail: lori.buckler@usdoj.gov
Deputy Chief **Elizabeth Danello** .... (202) 252-6768
E-mail: elizabeth.danello@usdoj.gov
Deputy Chief **Chrisellen R. Kolb** .... (202) 252-6833
E-mail: chrisellen.r.kolb@usdoj.gov
Deputy Chief **John Mannarino** .... (202) 514-7118
E-mail: john.mannarino@usdoj.gov
Deputy Chief **(Vacant)** .... (202) 252-6784
Supervisory Paralegal Specialist **(Vacant)** .... (202) 252-7566

Civil Division
555 Fourth Street, NW, Washington, DC 20530
Tel: (202) 252-2563 Fax: (202) 514-8781 Fax: (202) 514-8780

Chief **Daniel Van Horn** .... (202) 514-7151
E-mail: daniel.vanhorn@usdoj.gov
Assistant to the Chief **Cynthia Parker** .... (202) 514-7166
E-mail: cindy.parker@usdoj.gov
Deputy Chief **Doris D. Coles-Huff** .... (202) 514-7170
E-mail: doris.coles@usdoj.gov
Deputy Chief **Robin N. Meriweather** .... (202) 514-7135
E-mail: robin.meriweather@usdoj.gov
Education: Michigan BA; Yale JD
Deputy Chief **(Vacant)** .... (202) 252-2563
Deputy Chief **(Vacant)** .... (202) 514-7168
Appellate Counsel **R. Craig Lawrence** .... (202) 278-3307
E-mail: craig.lawrence@usdoj.gov
Support Staff Manager **Pamela Lawson** .... (202) 514-6200
E-mail: pamela.lawson@usdoj.gov

Criminal Division
555 Fourth Street, NW, Washington, DC 20530
Tel: (202) 252-6766 Fax: (202) 514-8782

Chief **Jonathan M. Malis** .... (202) 252-6782
E-mail: jonathan.m.malis@usdoj.gov
Deputy Chief **(Vacant)** .... (202) 252-7842
Asset Forfeiture Unit Chief **(Vacant)** .... (202) 252-6766
Federal Major Crimes Section Chief **(Vacant)** .... (202) 252-7900
Fraud and Public Corruption Section Chief
[District Election Officer] **T. Patrick Martin** .... (202) 252-6766
E-mail: patrick.martin@usdoj.gov
Education: Northwestern 1997 JD
National Security Section Chief
Gregg Maisel Room 11-453 .... (202) 252-7812
E-mail: gregg.maisel@usdoj.gov
Special Counsel for National Security **(Vacant)** .... (202) 353-8831
Organized Crime and Narcotics Trafficking Section
Chief **(Vacant)** Room 4804 .... (202) 252-7683
Assistant U.S. Attorney **John Crabb, Jr.** .... (202) 252-6766
Assistant U.S. Attorney **Michael C. DiLorenzo** .... (202) 252-6766
Assistant U.S. Attorney **Zia Faruqui** .... (202) 252-6766
Assistant U.S. Attorney **Emily A. Miller** .... (202) 252-6766
Education: Michigan 1993 BA; George Washington 1996 JD
Assistant U.S. Attorney **Erik Kenerson** .... (202) 252-6766
Education: Case Western 2004 BA; Georgetown 2007 JD
Assistant U.S. Attorney **Sonali D. Patel** .... (202) 252-6766
Education: UC Irvine 1997 BS; UCLA 2000 MSW
Assistant U.S. Attorney **Scott L. Sroka** .... (202) 252-6766
Assistant U.S. Attorney **Derrick Williams** .... (202) 252-6766
Education: Boston Col 2004 BA; Vanderbilt 2009 JD

★ Presidential Appointment Requiring Senate Confirmation ☆ Presidential Appointment ☐ Schedule C Appointment ◇ Career Senior Foreign Service Appointment
● Career Senior Executive Service (SES) Appointment ○ Non-Career Senior Executive Service (SES) Appointment ■ Postal Career Executive Service

Special Proceedings Division
Chief **(Vacant)** Room 10-836 .... (202) 252-7566

Superior Court Division
555 Fourth Street, NW, Washington, DC 20530
Tel: (202) 514-7379 Fax: (202) 307-3221

Chief **Richard S. Tischner** Room 3205 .... (202) 252-7274
E-mail: richard.s.tischner@usdoj.gov
Deputy Chief **Michelle Jackson** .... (202) 252-7275
E-mail: michelle.jackson@usdoj.gov
Homicide Section Chief **Jeffrey Ragsdale** .... (202) 252-7268
Felony Major Crimes Section Chief **Jeffrey Ragsdale** .... (202) 252-7268
General Crimes Section Chief
Lisa Baskerville-Greene .... (202) 252-7279
Sex Offense and Domestic Violence Section Chief
(Vacant) .... (202) 252-7282
Sex Offense and Domestic Violence Prosecutor
(Vacant) .... (202) 514-7379

Florida - Middle District
Park Tower, 400 North Tampa Street, Suite 3200, Tampa, FL 33602
Tel: (813) 274-6000 Fax: (813) 274-6358
Internet: https://www.justice.gov/usao-mdfl

★ U.S. Attorney **Maria Chapa Lopez** .... (813) 274-6000
E-mail: maria.chapa@usdoj.gov
Education: Texas BA; South Texas JD; Judge Advocate Gen LLM
First Assistant U.S. Attorney **W. Stephen Muldrow** ..... (813) 274-6467
E-mail: w.stephen.muldrow@usdoj.gov
Executive Assistant U.S. Attorney **Todd Grandy** .... (813) 274-6343
E-mail: todd.grandy@usdoj.gov
Public Affairs Specialist **William Daniels** .... (813) 274-6388
E-mail: william.daniels@usdoj.gov
Law Enforcement Coordination Specialist
Eric Johnson .... (813) 274-6092
E-mail: eric.johnson@usdoj.gov

Administration Division
400 North Tampa Street, Suite 3200, Tampa, FL 33602
Fax: (813) 274-6358

Director **Jeffrey Hahn** .... (813) 274-6302
E-mail: jeffrey.hahn@usdoj.gov Fax: (813) 274-6074
Budget Officer **Evelyn Restaino** .... (813) 274-6007
E-mail: evelyn.restaino@usdoj.gov
Human Resources Officer **Dawn McCourt** .... (813) 274-6006
E-mail: dawn.mccourt@usdoj.gov
Litigation Support Manager **(Vacant)** .... (813) 274-6000
Support Services Manager **Tracy Ray** .... (813) 274-6013
E-mail: tracy.ray@usdoj.gov
Systems Manager **(Vacant)** .... (813) 274-6010

Appellate Division
400 North Tampa Street, Suite 3200, Tampa, FL 33602
Fax: (813) 274-6102

Chief **David P. Rhodes** .... (813) 274-6305
E-mail: david.rhodes@usdoj.gov
Deputy Chief, Appellate Division **Linda McNamara** ..... (813) 274-6306
E-mail: linda.mcnamara@usdoj.gov
Assistant U.S. Attorney **Todd Grandy** .... (813) 274-6307
E-mail: todd.grandy@usdoj.gov
Assistant U.S. Attorney **Yvette Rhodes** .... (813) 274-6330
E-mail: yvette.rhodes@usdoj.gov
Assistant U.S. Attorney **Peter J. Sholl** .... (813) 274-6327
E-mail: peter.sholl@usdoj.gov
Assistant U.S. Attorney **(Vacant)** .... (813) 274-6329

Civil Division
400 North Tampa Street, Suite 3200, Tampa, FL 33602
Fax: (813) 274-6198

Chief **Randy Harwell, Jr.** .... (813) 274-6332
E-mail: randy.harwell@usdoj.gov
Deputy Chief **Sean J. Flynn** .... (813) 274-6333
E-mail: sean.flynn2@usdoj.gov
Education: Colorado 1996 BA; Notre Dame 2002 JD

Civil Division *(continued)*

Assistant U.S. Attorney **Jennifer Corinis** .... (813) 274-6310
E-mail: jennifer.corinis@usdoj.gov
Assistant U.S. Attorney **Charles Harden** .... (813) 274-6316
E-mail: charles.harden@usdoj.gov
Assistant U.S. Attorney **John Rudy** .... (813) 274-6319
E-mail: john.rudy@usdoj.gov
Assistant U.S. Attorney **Kenneth Stegeby** .... (813) 274-6303
E-mail: kenneth.stegeby@usdoj.gov
Assistant U.S. Attorney **(Vacant)** .... (813) 274-6321
Assistant U.S. Attorney/ACE Coordinator **(Vacant)** ...... (813) 274-6335
Assistant U.S. Attorney/Social Security **(Vacant)** .... (813) 274-6334

Criminal Division
400 North Tampa Street, Suite 3200, Tampa, FL 33602
Fax: (813) 274-6108

Chief (North) **Roger B. Handberg** .... (813) 274-6000
E-mail: roger.handberg@usdoj.gov
Chief (South) **Rachelle DesVaux Bedke** .... (813) 274-6000
E-mail: rachelle.bedke@usdoj.gov
Asset Forfeiture Chief **Anita M. Cream** .... (813) 274-6301
E-mail: anita.cream@usdoj.gov Fax: (813) 274-6220
Opioid Fraud Prosecutor **Kelley Howard-Allen** .... (813) 274-6313
E-mail: kelley.howard@usdoj.gov
Asset Forfeiture Assistant U.S. Attorney
Josephine W. "Josie" Thomas .... (813) 274-6086
E-mail: josie.thomas@usdoj.gov
Economic Crimes Section Deputy Chief **(Vacant)** .... (813) 274-6317
Fax: (813) 274-6103
Economic Crimes Assistant U.S. Attorney
Cherie Krigsman .... (813) 274-6344
E-mail: cherie.krigsman@usdoj.gov
Economic Crimes Assistant U.S. Attorney
Thomas Palermo .... (813) 274-6355
E-mail: thomas.palermo@usdoj.gov
Education: Florida State 2001 JD; U London 2002 LLM
Economic Crimes Assistant U.S. Attorney
Jay Trezevant .... (813) 274-6312
E-mail: jay.trezevant@usdoj.gov
Economic Crimes Assistant U.S. Attorney **(Vacant)** .... (813) 274-6354
Economic Crimes Assistant U.S. Attorney **(Vacant)** .... (813) 274-6339
Economic Crimes Assistant U.S. Attorney **(Vacant)** .... (813) 274-6323
Economic Crimes Assistant U.S. Attorney **(Vacant)** .... (813) 274-6336
Narcotics Section Senior Deputy Chief **Joseph Ruddy** ... (813) 274-6338
E-mail: joseph.ruddy@usdoj.gov Fax: (813) 274-6125
Narcotics Section Deputy Chief
James Conway "Jim" Preston .... (813) 274-6326
E-mail: james.preston@usdoj.gov
Narcotics Assistant U.S. Attorney **Jeffrey Miller** .... (813) 274-6348
E-mail: jeffrey.miller2@usdoj.gov
Narcotics Assistant U.S. Attorney **James Muench** ..... (813) 274-6345
E-mail: james.muench2@usdoj.gov
Narcotics Assistant U.S. Attorney
Christopher Murray .... (813) 274-6356
E-mail: christopher.murray@usdoj.gov
Narcotics Assistant U.S. Attorney **Matthew H. Perry** ... (813) 274-6466
E-mail: matthew.perry@usdoj.gov
Narcotics Assistant U.S. Attorney **Greg Pizzo** .... (813) 301-3003
Narcotics Assistant U.S. Attorney **(Vacant)** .... (813) 274-6341
Organized Crime Section Deputy Chief **(Vacant)** .... (813) 274-6000
Organized Crime Section Assistant U.S. Attorney
(Vacant) .... (813) 274-6309
Organized Crime Special Assistant U.S. Attorney
Shauna Hale .... (813) 274-6347
E-mail: shauna.hale@usdoj.gov

General Crimes Section
Deputy Chief **Simon Gaugush** .... (813) 274-6318
E-mail: simon.gaugush@usdoj.gov Fax: (813) 274-6178
Assistant U.S. Attorney **Stacie Harris** .... (813) 274-6346
E-mail: stacie.harris@usdoj.gov
Assistant U.S. Attorney **Jay Hoffer** .... (813) 274-6000
E-mail: jay.hoffer@usdoj.gov
Education: Yale 1977 BA, 1980 JD

(continued on next page)

★ Presidential Appointment Requiring Senate Confirmation ☆ Presidential Appointment □ Schedule C Appointment ◇ Career Senior Foreign Service Appointment
● Career Senior Executive Service (SES) Appointment ○ Non-Career Senior Executive Service (SES) Appointment ■ Postal Career Executive Service

DEPARTMENTS

General Crimes Section *(continued)*

Assistant U.S. Attorney **Amanda Kaiser** . . . . (813) 274-6315
E-mail: amanda.kaiser@usdoj.gov
Assistant U.S. Attorney **Colleen Murphy-Davis** . . . . (813) 274-6331
E-mail: colleen.murphy@usdoj.gov
Assistant U.S. Attorney **Amanda Riedel** . . . . (813) 274-6340
E-mail: amanda.riedel@usdoj.gov
Assistant U.S. Attorney **(Vacant)** . . . . (813) 274-6351

Fort Myers (FL) Office

2110 First Street, Suite 3-137, Fort Myers, FL 33901
Tel: (239) 461-2200 Fax: (239) 461-2219

Chief **Jesus M. Casas** . . . . (239) 461-2200
E-mail: jesus.m.casas@usdoj.gov

Civil Division

Assistant U.S. Attorney **Kyle Cohen** . . . . (239) 461-2245
E-mail: kyle.cohen@usdoj.gov

Criminal Division

Assistant U.S. Attorney **(Vacant)** . . . . (239) 461-2200
Assistant U.S. Attorney **David G. Lazarus** . . . . (239) 461-2200
E-mail: david.lazarus@justice.usdoj.gov
Assistant U.S. Attorney **Jeffrey Michelland** . . . . (239) 461-2200
E-mail: jeffrey.michelland@usdoj.gov
Assistant U.S. Attorney **(Vacant)** . . . . (239) 461-2200

Asset Forfeiture

Assistant U.S. Attorney **(Vacant)** . . . . (239) 461-2200

Jacksonville (FL) Office

300 North Hogan Street, Suite 700, Jacksonville, FL 32202
Tel: (904) 301-6300 Fax: (904) 301-6310

Chief **Julie Hackenberry** . . . . (904) 301-6300
E-mail: julie.hackenberry@usdoj.gov
Office Manager **Michael J. Brown** . . . . (904) 301-6300

Civil Division

Assistant U.S. Attorney **(Vacant)** . . . . (904) 301-6300
Assistant U.S. Attorney **Collette Cunningham** . . . . (904) 301-6300
E-mail: collette.cunningham@usdoj.gov
Assistant U.S. Attorney **Laura Lothman** . . . . (904) 301-6300
E-mail: laura.lothman@usdoj.gov
Assistant U.S. Attorney **(Vacant)** . . . . (904) 301-6300

Criminal Division

Deputy Chief **Mac Heavener** . . . . (904) 301-6300
E-mail: mac.heavener@usdoj.gov
Special Assistant U.S. Attorney **(Vacant)** . . . . (904) 301-6300
Assistant U.S. Attorney **D. Rodney Brown** . . . . (904) 301-6300
E-mail: rodney.brown@usdoj.gov
Assistant U.S. Attorney **Dale Campion** . . . . (904) 301-6300
E-mail: dale.campion@usdoj.gov
Assistant U.S. Attorney
Arnold Bernard "Chip" Corsmeier . . . . (904) 301-6300
E-mail: chip.corsmeier@usdoj.gov
Assistant U.S. Attorney **Mark Devereaux** . . . . (904) 301-6300
E-mail: mark.devereaux@usdoj.gov
Assistant U.S. Attorney **A. Tysen Duva** . . . . (904) 301-6300
E-mail: tysen.duva@usdoj.gov
Education: Florida 2002 JD
Assistant U.S. Attorney **Kevin Frein** . . . . (904) 301-6300
E-mail: kevin.frein@usdoj.gov
Assistant U.S. Attorney **Bonnie Glober** . . . . (904) 301-6300
E-mail: bonnie.glober@usdoj.gov
Assistant U.S. Attorney **Kelly Karase** . . . . (904) 301-6300
E-mail: kelly.karase@usdoj.gov
Assistant U.S. Attorney **Diidri Robinson** . . . . (904) 301-6300
E-mail: diidri.robinson@usdoj.gov
Assistant U.S. Attorney **Jay Taylor** . . . . (904) 301-6300
E-mail: jay.taylor@usdoj.gov
Assistant U.S. Attorney **(Vacant)** . . . . (904) 301-6300
Assistant U.S. Attorney **(Vacant)** . . . . (904) 301-6300
Senior Litigation Counsel **(Vacant)** . . . . (904) 301-6300

Asset Forfeiture

Assistant U.S. Attorney **Bonnie Glober** . . . . (904) 301-6300
E-mail: bonnie.glober@usdoj.gov

Ocala (FL) Office

35 SE First Avenue, Suite 300, Ocala, FL 34471
Tel: (352) 547-3600 Fax: (352) 547-3623

Chief **Carlos A. Perez** . . . . (352) 547-3600
E-mail: carlos.a.perez@usdoj.gov
Assistant U.S. Attorney **Robert E. Bodnar, Jr.** . . . . (352) 547-3605
E-mail: robert.bodnar@usdoj.gov
Assistant U.S. Attorney **(Vacant)** . . . . (352) 547-3600
Officer Manager **(Vacant)** . . . . (352) 547-3600

Orlando (FL) Office

501 West Church Street, Suite 300, Orlando, FL 32805
Tel: (407) 648-7500 Fax: (407) 648-7643

Chief **Katherine Ho** . . . . (407) 648-7500
E-mail: katherine.ho@usdoj.gov
Deputy Chief **(Vacant)** . . . . (407) 648-7500
Officer Manager **Joey Chigro** . . . . (407) 648-7500

Appellate Division

Assistant U.S. Attorney **Roberta Bodnar** . . . . (407) 648-7500
E-mail: roberta.bodnar@usdoj.gov
Assistant U.S. Attorney **(Vacant)** . . . . (407) 648-7501

Civil Division

Assistant U.S. Attorney **Ralph E. Hopkins** . . . . (407) 648-7500
E-mail: ralph.hopkins@usdoj.gov
Assistant U.S. Attorney **Scott H. Park** . . . . (407) 648-7500
E-mail: scott.park@usdoj.gov
Assistant U.S. Attorney **Julie Posteraro** . . . . (407) 648-7500
E-mail: julie.posteraro@usdoj.gov
Assistant U.S. Attorney **(Vacant)** . . . . (407) 648-7500
Assistant U.S. Attorney **(Vacant)** . . . . (407) 648-7514

Criminal Division

Assistant U.S. Attorney **Vincent Chiu** . . . . (407) 648-7500
E-mail: vincent.chiu@usdoj.gov
Assistant U.S. Attorney **Karen L. Gable** . . . . (407) 648-7500
E-mail: karen.gable@usdoj.gov
Assistant U.S. Attorney **Shawn Napier** . . . . (407) 648-7500
E-mail: shawn.napier@usdoj.gov
Education: Capital U 2001 JD
Assistant U.S. Attorney **J. Bishop Ravenel** . . . . (407) 648-7500
E-mail: bishop.ravenel@usdoj.gov
Assistant U.S. Attorney **Joseph Schuster** . . . . (407) 648-7500
E-mail: joseph.schuster@usdoj.gov

Asset Forfeiture

Assistant U.S. Attorney **Nicole Andrejko** . . . . (407) 648-7500
E-mail: nicole.andrejko@usdoj.gov

Florida - Northern District

111 North Adams Street, 4th Floor, Tallahassee, FL 32301
Tel: (850) 942-8430 Fax: (850) 942-8429
Internet: www.justice.gov/usao/fln

★ U.S. Attorney **Christopher Canova** . . . . (850) 942-8430
Note: Serving an appointed term.
E-mail: chris.canova@usdoj.gov
★ U.S. Attorney-Designate **Lawrence "Larry" Keefe** . . . . . . (850) 942-8430
Education: Florida BA, JD
Secretary to the U.S. Attorney **Libby Stinger** . . . . (850) 942-8430
Counsel to the U.S. Attorney **(Vacant)** . . . . (850) 942-8430
First Assistant U.S. Attorney **Karen E. Rhew-Miller** . . . . . (850) 942-8430
E-mail: karen.rhew-miller@usdoj.gov
Law Enforcement Coordination Director **(Vacant)** . . . . (850) 942-8430
OCDETF Chief Assistant U.S. Attorney
Eric K. Mountin . . . . (850) 942-8430
E-mail: eric.mountin@usdoj.gov
Senior Litigation Counsel **Leah A. Butler** . . . . (850) 444-4000
Systems Manager **Skylar Smith** . . . . (850) 942-8530

Appellate Division
Chief Assistant U.S. Attorney (Acting)
Karen E. Rhew-Miller .... (850) 942-8430
E-mail: karen.rhew-miller@usdoj.gov
Senior Appellate Counsel **Robert G. Davies** .... (850) 942-8430

Civil Division
Chief **Michael J. Harwin** .... (850) 942-8430
Education: Northwestern 1998 BA; Emory 2001 JD
Chief Assistant U.S. Attorney **(Vacant)** .... (850) 942-8430
Assistant U.S. Attorney **Jonathan D. Letzring** .... (850) 942-8430
E-mail: jonathan.letzring@usdoj.gov

Criminal Division
Chief **Karen E. Rhew-Miller** .... (850) 942-8430
Supervisory Assistant U.S. Attorney **(Vacant)** .... (850) 942-8430
Assistant U.S. Attorney **Jason Coody** .... (850) 942-8430
Assistant U.S. Attorney **Herbert Lindsey** .... (850) 942-8430
Assistant U.S. Attorney **Winifred L.A. Nesmith** .... (850) 942-8430
E-mail: winifred.nesmith@usdoj.gov
Assistant U.S. Attorney **Corey J. Smith** .... (850) 942-8430
Assistant U.S. Attorney **James Ustynoski** .... (850) 942-8430
Assistant U.S. Attorney **(Vacant)** .... (850) 942-8430
Assistant U.S. Attorney **(Vacant)** .... (850) 942-8430

Gainesville (FL) Office
300 East University Avenue, Suite 310, Gainesville, FL 32601
Tel: (352) 378-0996 Fax: (352) 338-7981

Supervisory Assistant U.S. Attorney **Jonell L. Lucca** ..... (352) 378-0996
E-mail: jonell.lucca@usdoj.gov
Education: Notre Dame 2001 JD
Assistant U.S. Attorney **Gregory McMahon** .... (352) 378-0996
E-mail: gregory.mcmahon@usdoj.gov
Assistant U.S. Attorney **Frank T. Williams** .... (352) 378-0996
E-mail: frank.williams@usdoj.gov

Pensacola (FL) Office
21 East Garden Street, Suite 300, Pensacola, FL 32502
Tel: (850) 444-4000

Supervisory Assistant U.S. Attorney **Nancy J. Hess** ..... (850) 444-4000
Administrative Officer **Floyd Boyer** .... (850) 942-8430
E-mail: floyd.boyer@usdoj.gov

Civil/Appellate Division
Appellate Chief **Robert G. Davies** .... (850) 444-4000
Civil Chief **(Vacant)** .... (850) 444-4000
Assistant U.S. Attorney **Leah A. Butler** .... (850) 444-4000
E-mail: leah.butler@usdoj.gov
Assistant U.S. Attorney **Len Register** .... (850) 444-4000
E-mail: len.register@usdoj.gov
Assistant U.S. Attorney **(Vacant)** .... (850) 444-4000
Assistant U.S. Attorney **(Vacant)** .... (850) 444-4000

Criminal Division
Managing Assistant U.S. Attorney **Jeffrey M. Tharp** ..... (850) 444-4000
E-mail: jeffrey.tharp@usdoj.gov
Assistant U.S. Attorney **Tiffany H. Eggers** .... (850) 444-4000
E-mail: tiffany.eggers@usdoj.gov
Assistant U.S. Attorney **David L. Goldberg** .... (850) 444-4000
E-mail: david.goldberg@usdoj.gov
Assistant U.S. Attorney **Alicia H. Forbes** .... (850) 444-4000
E-mail: alicia.kim@usdoj.gov
Assistant U.S. Attorney **Edwin F. Knight** .... (850) 444-4000
E-mail: edwin.knight@usdoj.gov
Assistant U.S. Attorney **J. Ryan Love** .... (850) 444-4000
E-mail: ryan.love@usdoj.gov
Assistant U.S. Attorney **James Ustynowski** .... (850) 444-4000

Florida - Southern District
99 NE Fourth Street, Suite 800, Miami, FL 33132
Tel: (305) 961-9001 Fax: (305) 530-7679
Internet: www.justice.gov/usao/fls

★ U.S. Attorney **Ariana Fajardo Orshan** .... (305) 961-9001
E-mail: ariana.fajardo.orshan@usdoj.gov
Education: Florida International BS; Nova Southeastern JD
Executive Assistant U.S. Attorney **(Vacant)** .... (305) 961-9289
Special Counsel for Public Affairs **(Vacant)** .... (305) 961-9174
Senior Litigation Counsel **Thomas J. Mulvihill** .... (305) 961-9424
E-mail: thomas.mulvihill@usdoj.gov

Administration Division
400 North Tampa Street, Suite 3200, Tampa, FL 33602
Fax: (305) 530-7679

Administrative Officer **Helen Grill** .... (305) 961-9259
E-mail: helen.grill@usdoj.gov
Deputy Administrative Officer **(Vacant)** .... (305) 961-9113
Administrative Services Manager **Sandra Ortiz** .... (305) 961-9250
E-mail: sandra.ortiz@usdoj.gov
Human Resources Officer **Cynthia Hampton** .... (305) 961-9241
E-mail: cynthia.hampton@usdoj.gov
District Security Manager **Juan C. Fernandez** .... (305) 961-9037
E-mail: juan.c.fernandez@usdoj.gov
IT Manager **Jacqueline "Jacquie" Varela-Grajurdo** .... (305) 961-9218
E-mail: jacquie.varela@usdoj.gov

Appellate Division
400 North Tampa Street, Suite 3200, Tampa, FL 33602
Tel: (305) 961-9005 Fax: (305) 530-7214

Chief **Anne R. Schultz** .... (305) 961-9117
E-mail: anne.schultz@usdoj.gov
Deputy Chief **Kathleen M. Salyer** .... (305) 961-9130
E-mail: kathleen.salyer@usdoj.gov
Assistant U.S. Attorney **Jonathan Colan** .... (305) 961-9383
E-mail: jonathan.colan@usdoj.gov
Supervisory Assistant U.S. Attorney **(Vacant)** .... (305) 961-9325
Assistant U.S. Attorney **Carol Herman** .... (305) 961-9115
E-mail: carol.herman@usdoj.gov
Assistant U.S. Attorney **Lisa Hirsch** .... (305) 961-9214
E-mail: lisa.hirsch@usdoj.gov
Assistant U.S. Attorney **Lisette Reid** .... (305) 961-9129
E-mail: lisette.reid@usdoj.gov
Assistant U.S. Attorney **Laura Rivero** .... (305) 961-9433
E-mail: laura.rivero@usdoj.gov
Assistant U.S. Attorney **Lisa Rubio** .... (305) 961-9114
E-mail: lisa.rubio@usdoj.gov
Assistant U.S. Attorney **Stephen Schlessinger** .... (305) 961-9199
E-mail: stephen.schlessinger@usdoj.gov
Education: Yale 1970 BA
Assistant U.S. Attorney **Shannon Shaw** .... (305) 961-9336
E-mail: shannon.shaw@usdoj.gov
Education: Vanderbilt 2011 JD
Assistant U.S. Attorney **Madeleine R. Shirley** .... (305) 961-9127
E-mail: madeleine.shirley@usdoj.gov
Assistant U.S. Attorney **Emily Smachetti** .... (305) 961-9295
E-mail: emily.smachetti@usdoj.gov

Asset Forfeiture Division
400 North Tampa Street, Suite 3200, Tampa, FL 33602
Tel: (305) 961-9007 Fax: (305) 536-7599

Chief **Gerardo Simms** .... (305) 961-9035
E-mail: gerardo.simms@usdoj.gov
Deputy Chief **Michelle Alvarez** .... (305) 961-9088
E-mail: michelle.alvarez@usdoj.gov
Assistant U.S. Attorney **Alison Lehr** .... (305) 961-9176
E-mail: alison.lehr@usdoj.gov
Assistant U.S. Attorney **Karen E. Moore** .... (305) 961-9030
E-mail: karen.moore@usdoj.gov
Assistant U.S. Attorney **Arimentha Walkins** .... (305) 961-9091
E-mail: arimentha.walkins@usdoj.gov

★ Presidential Appointment Requiring Senate Confirmation ☆ Presidential Appointment □ Schedule C Appointment ◇ Career Senior Foreign Service Appointment
● Career Senior Executive Service (SES) Appointment ○ Non-Career Senior Executive Service (SES) Appointment ■ Postal Career Executive Service

DEPARTMENTS

Civil Division
400 North Tampa Street, Suite 3200, Tampa, FL 33602
Tel: (305) 961-9003 Fax: (305) 530-7139

Chief **Wendy Jacobus** (305) 961-9301
E-mail: wendy.jacobus@usdoj.gov
Deputy Chief **Maureen Donlan** (305) 961-9334
E-mail: maureen.donlan@usdoj.gov
Deputy Chief **Veronica Harrell-James** (305) 961-9327
E-mail: veronica.harrell-james@usdoj.gov
Senior Litigation Counsel **Dexter Lee** (305) 961-9320
Assistant U.S. Attorney **Stephanie Fidler** (305) 961-9073
E-mail: stephanie.fidler@usdoj.gov
Assistant U.S. Attorney **Mark A. Lavine** (305) 961-9303
E-mail: mark.lavine@usdoj.gov
Assistant U.S. Attorney **Larry Rosen** (305) 961-9321
E-mail: larry.rosen@usdoj.gov
Assistant U.S. Attorney **(Vacant)** (305) 961-9331
Assistant U.S. Attorney **Karin Wherry** (305) 961-9016
E-mail: karin.wherry@usdoj.gov
Assistant U.S. Attorney **Charles White** (305) 961-9286
E-mail: charles.white@usdoj.gov
Supervisory Assistant U.S. Attorney **(Vacant)** (305) 961-9335

Financial Litigation Unit
Assistant U.S. Attorney **(Vacant)** (305) 961-9310
Assistant U.S. Attorney **(Vacant)** (305) 961-9204

Criminal Division
99 NE Fourth Street, Miami, FL 33132
Fax: (305) 530-7950

Chief **Edward N. Stamm** (305) 961-9164
E-mail: edward.stamm@usdoj.gov
Deputy Chief **Kenneth Noto** (305) 961-9416
E-mail: kenneth.noto@usdoj.gov

Economic and Environmental Crimes Section
99 NE Fourth Street, Miami, FL 33132
Tel: (305) 961-9004 Fax: (305) 530-6168

Chief (Acting) **Joan Silverstein** (305) 961-9121
E-mail: joan.silverstein@usdoj.gov
Deputy Chief **Luis Perez** (305) 961-9428
E-mail: luis.perez@usdoj.gov
Deputy Chief **Thomas Watts-Fitzgerald** (305) 961-9413
E-mail: thomas.watts-fitzgerald@usdoj.gov
Senior Litigation Counsel **Caroline Heck Miller** (305) 961-9432
E-mail: caroline.miller@usdoj.gov
Assistant U.S. Attorney **Jose Bonau** (305) 961-9426
E-mail: jose.bonau@usdoj.gov
Assistant U.S. Attorney **Christopher Clark** (305) 961-9167
E-mail: christopher.clark@usdoj.gov
Assistant U.S. Attorney **Michael Davis** (305) 961-9027
E-mail: michael.davis2@usdoj.gov
Assistant U.S. Attorney **(Vacant)** (305) 961-9184
Assistant U.S. Attorney **Lois Foster-Steers** (305) 961-9203
E-mail: lois.foster-steers@usdoj.gov
Assistant U.S. Attorney **Randy Katz** (954) 356-7255 ext. 3620
E-mail: randy.katz@usdoj.gov
Education: Duke 2001 JD
Assistant U.S. Attorney **Ana Maria Martinez** (305) 961-9431
E-mail: ana.maria.martinez@usdoj.gov
Assistant U.S. Attorney **Marc Osborne** (305) 961-9198
E-mail: marc.osborne@usdoj.gov
Assistant U.S. Attorney **Peter Outerbridge** (305) 961-9326
E-mail: peter.outerbridge@usdoj.gov
Assistant U.S. Attorney **Karen Rochlin** (305) 961-9234
E-mail: karen.rochlin@usdoj.gov
Assistant U.S. Attorney **Kimberly A. Selmore** (305) 961-9189
E-mail: kim.selmore@usdoj.gov
Assistant U.S. Attorney **Alicia Shick** (954) 356-7355
500 East Broward Boulevard, Fort Lauderdale, FL 33394
E-mail: alicia.shick@usdoj.gov
Assistant U.S. Attorney **(Vacant)** (305) 961-9277
Deputy Chief **(Vacant)** (305) 961-9322

Major Crimes Section
99 NE Fourth Street, Miami, FL 33132
Tel: (305) 961-9006 Fax: (305) 530-7976

Chief **Randy Hummel** (305) 961-9043
E-mail: randy.hummel@usdoj.gov
Deputy Chief **Peter R. Forand** (305) 961-9060
E-mail: peter.forand@usdoj.gov
Deputy Chief **Rosa Rodriguez-Mera** (954) 356-7255
E-mail: rosa.rodriguez-mera@usdoj.gov
Deputy Chief **(Vacant)** (305) 961-9034
Deputy Chief **(Vacant)** (305) 961-9033
Assistant U.S. Attorney **(Vacant)** (305) 961-9414
Assistant U.S. Attorney **(Vacant)** (305) 961-9001

Narcotics Section
99 NE Fourth Street, Miami, FL 33132
Tel: (305) 961-9007 Fax: (305) 536-7213

Chief **Lynn Kirkpatrick** (305) 961-9289
E-mail: lynn.kirkpatrick@usdoj.gov
Deputy Chief **Richard Getchell** (305) 961-9281
E-mail: richard.getchell@usdoj.gov
Deputy Chief **Robin W. Waugh** (305) 961-9239
E-mail: robin.waugh@usdoj.gov
Deputy Chief **(Vacant)** (305) 961-9009
Senior Litigation Counsel **Richard "Dick" Gregorie** (305) 961-9148
E-mail: dick.gregorie@usdoj.gov
OCDETF Coordinator **Mary Virginia King** (305) 961-9418
E-mail: mary.v.king@usdoj.gov
Assistant U.S. Attorney **Michael Gilfarb** (305) 961-9029
E-mail: michael.gilfarb@usdoj.gov
Assistant U.S. Attorney **Yvonne Rodriguez-Schack** (305) 961-9014
E-mail: yvonne.rodriguez-schack@usdoj.gov
Assistant U.S. Attorney **Frank Tamen** (305) 961-9022
E-mail: frank.tamen@usdoj.gov
Assistant U.S. Attorney **(Vacant)** (305) 715-7646
Assistant U.S. Attorney **(Vacant)** (305) 961-9012

High Intensity Drug Trafficking Areas (HIDTA)
99 NE Fourth Street, Miami, FL 33132
Fax: (305) 715-7639

Assistant U.S. Attorney
Juan Antonio "Tony" Gonzalez (305) 597-1973
E-mail: juan.antonio.gonzalez@usdoj.gov
Assistant U.S. Attorney **Francisco "Frank" Maderal** (305) 715-7643
E-mail: francisco.maderal@usdoj.gov

Organized Crime Section
Assistant U.S. Attorney **Robert Lehner** (305) 961-9020
E-mail: robert.lehner@usdoj.gov
Education: Columbia 1961 DJur

Public Integrity and National Security Section
99 NE Fourth Street, Miami, FL 33132
Tel: (305) 961-9001 Fax: (305) 536-4675

Chief **Robert Senior** (305) 961-9291
E-mail: robert.senior@usdoj.gov
Deputy Chief **(Vacant)** (305) 961-9292
Senior Litigation Counsel **(Vacant)** (305) 961-9274
Assistant U.S. Attorney **Eloisa D. Fernandez** (305) 961-9025
E-mail: eloisa.d.fernandez@usdoj.gov
Assistant U.S. Attorney **Ricardo Del Toro** (305) 961-9025
Assistant U.S. Attorney **Rick Del Toro** (305) 961-9104
Assistant U.S. Attorney **Allyson Fritz** (305) 961-9287
E-mail: allyson.fritz@usdoj.gov
Assistant U.S. Attorney **Susan Osborne** (305) 961-9104
E-mail: susan.osborne@usdoj.gov
Assistant U.S. Attorney **Michael Thakur** (305) 961-9104
E-mail: michael.thakur@usdoj.gov

Special Prosecutions Section
Chief **Barbara Martinez** (305) 961-9146
E-mail: barbara.martinez@usdoj.gov
Deputy Chief **Anthony Lacosta** (305) 961-9280
E-mail: anthony.lacosta@usdoj.gov

★ Presidential Appointment Requiring Senate Confirmation ☆ Presidential Appointment ☐ Schedule C Appointment ◇ Career Senior Foreign Service Appointment
● Career Senior Executive Service (SES) Appointment ○ Non-Career Senior Executive Service (SES) Appointment ■ Postal Career Executive Service

Special Prosecutions Section *(continued)*

Deputy Chief **(Vacant)** .... (305) 961-9013
Assistant U.S. Attorney **Gera R. Peoples** .... (305) 961-9314
E-mail: gera.peoples@usdoj.gov
Assistant U.S. Attorney **Marlene Rodriguez** .... (305) 961-9206
E-mail: marlene.rodriguez@usdoj.gov

Fort Lauderdale Office
500 East Broward Boulevard, 7th Floor, Fort Lauderdale, FL 33394
Tel: (954) 356-7255 Fax: (954) 356-7336
Administrative Officer **Susan "Sue" Fernandez** .... (954) 660-5926
E-mail: sue.fernandez@usdoj.gov

Appellate Division
Assistant U.S. Attorney **Robert B. Cornell** .... (954) 660-5697
E-mail: robert.b.cornell@usdoj.gov
Assistant U.S. Attorney **Phillip DiRosa** .... (954) 660-5959
E-mail: phillip.dirosa@usdoj.gov

Asset Forfeiture Unit
500 East Broward Boulevard, Fort Lauderdale, FL 33394
Fax: (954) 356-7336
Assistant U.S. Attorney **(Vacant)** .... (954) 660-5774 ext. 3614

Civil Unit
500 East Broward Boulevard, Fort Lauderdale, FL 33394
Fax: (954) 356-7180
Deputy Chief **Marilynn K. Lindsey** .... (954) 356-7255 ext. 3610
E-mail: marilynn.lindsey@usdoj.gov
Assistant U.S. Attorney **David Mellinger** ...... (954) 356-7255 ext. 3612
E-mail: david.mellinger@usdoj.gov
Assistant U.S. Attorney **(Vacant)** .... (954) 356-7255 ext. 3599

Criminal Division
Deputy Chief and Assistant U.S. Attorney-in-Charge **(Vacant)** .... (954) 356-7255 ext. 3558

Economic Crimes Section
500 East Broward Boulevard, Fort Lauderdale, FL 33394
Fax: (954) 356-7336
Chief (Acting) **Neil Karadbil** .... (954) 356-7255
E-mail: neil.karadbil@usdoj.gov
Senior Litigation Counsel **Neil Karadbil** .... (954) 356-7255
Assistant U.S. Attorney **Laurence M. "Larry" Bardfeld** .... (954) 356-7255 ext. 3611
E-mail: laurence.bardfeld@usdoj.gov
Assistant U.S. Attorney **Jennifer Keene** .... (954) 356-7255 ext. 3596
E-mail: jennifer.keene@usdoj.gov
Assistant U.S. Attorney **Bertha Mitrani** .... (954) 356-7255 ext. 3511
E-mail: bertha.mitrani@usdoj.gov
Assistant U.S. Attorney **(Vacant)** .... (954) 356-7255 ext. 3613
Assistant U.S. Attorney **(Vacant)** .... (954) 356-7255 ext. 3593
Special Assistant U.S. Attorney **Marc Anton** ... (954) 356-7255 ext. 3608
E-mail: marc.anton@usdoj.gov

Narcotics and Violent Crimes Section
500 East Broward Boulevard, Fort Lauderdale, FL 33394
Fax: (954) 356-7228
Chief **Bruce Brown** .... (954) 356-7255 ext. 3514
E-mail: bruce.brown2@usdoj.gov
Assistant U.S. Attorney **Scott Behnke** .... (954) 660-5698
E-mail: scott.behnke@usdoj.gov
Assistant U.S. Attorney **Donald Chase** .... (954) 660-5693
E-mail: donald.chase@usdoj.gov
Assistant U.S. Attorney **Terry Lindsey** .... (954) 660-5957
E-mail: terry.lindsey@usdoj.gov
Assistant U.S. Attorney **Paul Schwartz** .... (954) 356-7255 ext. 3577
E-mail: paul.schwartz@usdoj.gov
Assistant U.S. Attorney **Julia Vaglienti** .... (954) 356-7255 ext. 3509
E-mail: julia.vaglienti@usdoj.gov
Assistant U.S. Attorney **(Vacant)** .... (954) 356-7255 ext. 3512

Organized Crime Section
500 East Broward Boulevard, Fort Lauderdale, FL 33394
Tel: (954) 356-7392 Fax: (954) 356-7230
Chief **Jeffrey Kaplan** .... (954) 356-7255 ext. 3515
E-mail: jeffrey.kaplan@usdoj.gov
Assistant U.S. Attorney **Lawrence Lavecchio** .... (954) 356-7255 ext. 3588
E-mail: lawrence.lavecchio@usdoj.gov
Assistant U.S. Attorney **(Vacant)** .... (954) 356-7255 ext. 3515
Assistant U.S. Attorney **(Vacant)** .... (954) 356-7255 ext. 3587

Fort Pierce Office
1111 SE Federal Highway, Suite 314, Stuart, FL 34994
Tel: (772) 466-0899
Assistant U.S. Attorney **Diana Acosta** .... (772) 466-0899
E-mail: diana.acosta@usdoj.gov
Assistant U.S. Attorney **(Vacant)** .... (772) 466-0899

West Palm Beach Office
500 South Australian Avenue, Suite 400, West Palm Beach, FL 33401
Tel: (561) 820-8711
Deputy Chief **Rolando Garcia** .... (561) 820-8711 ext. 3010
E-mail: rolando.garcia@usdoj.gov
Assistant U.S. Attorney **(Vacant)** .... (561) 209-1036

Asset Forfeiture Unit
500 South Australian Avenue, Suite 400, West Palm Beach, FL 33401
Fax: (561) 655-9785
Assistant U.S. Attorney **Antonia Barnes** .... (561) 209-1035
E-mail: antonia.barnes@usdoj.gov
Assistant U.S. Attorney **Mark Lester** .... (561) 820-8711 ext. 3056
E-mail: mark.lester@usdoj.gov

Criminal I
500 South Australian Avenue, Suite 400, West Palm Beach, FL 33401
Fax: (561) 659-4526
Chief **Rolando Garcia** .... (561) 820-8711 ext. 3010
E-mail: rolando.garcia@usdoj.gov
Assistant U.S. Attorney **Stephen Carlton** ...... (561) 820-8711 ext. 3053
E-mail: stephen.carlton@usdoj.gov
Assistant U.S. Attorney **John McMillan** .... (561) 820-8711 ext. 3008
E-mail: john.mcmillan@usdoj.gov
Assistant U.S. Attorney **Alan Lothrop Morris** .... (561) 820-8711 ext. 3013
E-mail: lothrop.morris@usdoj.gov
Assistant U.S. Attorney **Ann Marie C. Villafana** .... (561) 820-8711 ext. 3047
E-mail: ann.marie.c.villafana@usdoj.gov
Assistant U.S. Attorney **William Zloch** .... (561) 820-8711 ext. 3022
E-mail: william.zloch@usdoj.gov
Assistant U.S. Attorney **Roger Harris Stefin** ... (561) 820-8711 ext. 3034
E-mail: roger.stefin@usdoj.gov

Criminal II
500 South Australian Avenue, Suite 400, West Palm Beach, FL 33401
Fax: (561) 820-8777
Chief **Adrienne Rabinowitz** .... (561) 209-1039
E-mail: adrienne.rabinowitz@usdoj.gov
Assistant U.S. Attorney **Carolyn Bell** .... (561) 209-1042
E-mail: carolyn.bell@usdoj.gov
Assistant U.S. Attorney **Ellen Cohen** .... (561) 209-1046
E-mail: ellen.cohen@usdoj.gov
Assistant U.S. Attorney **Lauren Jorgensen** .... (561) 209-1027
E-mail: lauren.jorgensen@usdoj.gov
Assistant U.S. Attorney **(Vacant)** .... (561) 209-1043
Assistant U.S. Attorney **(Vacant)** .... (561) 209-1011

DEPARTMENTS

★ Presidential Appointment Requiring Senate Confirmation ☆ Presidential Appointment □ Schedule C Appointment ◇ Career Senior Foreign Service Appointment
● Career Senior Executive Service (SES) Appointment ○ Non-Career Senior Executive Service (SES) Appointment ■ Postal Career Executive Service

DEPARTMENTS

Georgia - Middle District

300 Mulberry Street, Suite 400, Macon, GA 31201
P.O. Box 1702, Macon, GA 31202-1702
Tel: (478) 752-3511 Fax: (478) 621-2655
Fax: (478) 621-2667 (Administration) Fax: (478) 621-2679 (Personnel)
E-mail: mdga@hom.net Internet: https://www.justice.gov/usao-mdga

★ U.S. Attorney **Charles E. Peeler** .... (478) 621-2600
Education: Georgia BS, JD
Secretary to the U.S. Attorney **Karen F. Moore** .... (478) 621-2606
E-mail: karen.f.moore@usdoj.gov Fax: (478) 621-2604
First Assistant U.S. Attorney
G. F. "Pete" Peterman III .... (478) 621-2601
E-mail: pete.peterman@usdoj.gov
Chief Administrative Officer **Dale Vaughn** .... (478) 621-2612
E-mail: dale.vaughn@usdoj.gov
Press Information Officer **Pamela "Pam" Lightsey** ...... (478) 621-2602
E-mail: pam.lightsey@usdoj.gov
Information Technology Specialist **Joey Hitchock** .... (478) 621-2734
E-mail: joey.hitchcock@usdoj.gov
Information Technology Specialist **Keli Maire** .... (478) 621-2609
E-mail: keli.maire@usdoj.gov
Law Enforcement Coordinator
Pamela "Pam" Lightsey .... (478) 621-2603
E-mail: pam.lightsey@usdoj.gov
Victim-Witness Coordinator **Cathy Barnes** .... (478) 621-2634
E-mail: cathy.barnes@usdoj.gov

Civil Division

300 Mulberry Street, Suite 400, Macon, GA 31201
Tel: (478) 752-3511 Fax: (478) 621-2737

Chief **Bernard Snell** .... (478) 621-2732
E-mail: bernard.snell@usdoj.gov
Assistant U.S. Attorney - Senior Litigation Counsel
(Vacant) .... (478) 621-2729
Assistant U.S. Attorney **Stewart Brown** .... (478) 621-2690
E-mail: stewart.brown@usdoj.gov
Assistant U.S. Attorney **Aimee Hall** .... (478) 621-2663
E-mail: aimee.hall@usdoj.gov
Assistant U.S. Attorney **Barbara Parker** .... (478) 621-2733
E-mail: barbara.parker@usdoj.gov
Assistant U.S. Attorney **Todd Swanson** .... (478) 621-2728
E-mail: todd.swanson@usdoj.gov
Assistant U.S. Attorney **Taylor McNeill** .... (478) 621-2729
E-mail: taylor.mcneill@usdoj.gov

Criminal Division

300 Mulberry Street, Suite 400, Macon, GA 31201
Tel: (478) 752-3511 Fax: (478) 621-2655

Chief **Michael T. "Mike" Solis** .... (478) 621-2640
E-mail: mike.solis@usdoj.gov
Deputy Criminal Division Chief and Assistant U.S.
Attorney **Danial A. Bennett** .... (478) 621-2731
E-mail: danial.bennett@usdoj.gov
Assistant U.S. Attorney **Tamara Jarrett** .... (478) 621-2638
E-mail: tamara.jarrett@usdoj.gov
Assistant U.S. Attorney **Charles Calhoun** .... (478) 621-2649
E-mail: charles.calhoun@usdoj.gov
Assistant U.S. Attorney **Kimberly Easterling** .... (478) 621-2627
E-mail: kimberly.easterling@usdoj.gov
Assistant U.S. Attorney **Lindsay Feinberg** .... (478) 621-2685
E-mail: lindsay.feinberg@usdoj.gov
Assistant U.S. Attorney **Elizabeth S. Howard** .... (478) 621-2645
E-mail: elizabeth.s.howard@usdoj.gov
Assistant U.S. Attorney **Peter Leary** .... (478) 621-2642
E-mail: peter.leary@usdoj.gov
Assistant U.S. Attorney **Paul McCommon** .... (478) 621-2632
E-mail: paul.mccommon@usdoj.gov
Assistant U.S. Attorney **Robert McCullers** .... (478) 621-2730
E-mail: robert.mccullers@usdoj.gov
Assistant U.S. Attorney **Sonja B. Profit** .... (478) 621-2648
E-mail: sonja.b.profit@usdoj.gov
Assistant U.S. Attorney **Michelle L. "Mikki" Schieber** ... (478) 621-2623
E-mail: mikki.schieber@usdoj.gov
Education: Illinois State 1985 BS; Mercer 1992 JD

Criminal Division *(continued)*

Community Relations Specialist
Pamela "Pam" Lightsey .... (478) 621-2603
E-mail: pam.lightsey@usdoj.gov Fax: (478) 621-2605
Intelligence Research Specialist **Gregory D. Armes** ..... (478) 621-2643
E-mail: gregory.d.armes@usdoj.gov Fax: (478) 621-2682
Victim-Witness Specialist **Cathy Barnes** .... (478) 621-2634
E-mail: cathy.barnes@usdoj.gov
Law Enforcement Committee Coordinator
Pamela "Pam" Lightsey .... (478) 621-2603
E-mail: pam.lightsey@usdoj.gov

Albany (GA) Branch Office

C.B. King U.S. Courthouse, 201 West Broad Avenue,
2nd Floor, Albany, GA 31701
P.O. Box 366, Albany, GA 31702-9917
Tel: (229) 430-7754 Fax: (229) 430-7766

Assistant U.S. Attorney **Alan Dasher** .... (229) 430-7718
E-mail: alan.dasher@usdoj.gov
Criminal Division Assistant U.S. Attorney **(Vacant)** ...... (229) 430-7758
Assistant U.S. Attorney **Leah E. McEwen** .... (229) 430-7757
E-mail: leah.e.mcewen@usdoj.gov

Columbus (GA) Branch Office

Sun Trust Building, 1246 First Avenue,
3rd Floor, Columbus, GA 31901
P.O. Box 2568, Columbus, GA 31902-2568
Tel: (706) 649-7700 Fax: (706) 649-7667

Assistant U.S. Attorney **Melvin E. Hyde** .... (706) 649-7728
E-mail: melvin.e.hyde@usdoj.gov
Assistant U.S. Attorney **Crawford L. Seals** .... (706) 649-7733
E-mail: crawford.l.seals@usdoj.gov
Assistant U.S. Attorney **(Vacant)** .... (706) 649-7731
Assistant U.S. Attorney **(Vacant)** .... (706) 649-7734

Georgia - Northern District

75 Ted Turner Drive, SW, Suite 600, Atlanta, GA 30303
Tel: (404) 581-6000 Fax: (404) 581-6181
Internet: https://www.justice.gov/usao-ndga

★ U.S. Attorney **Byung Jin "B.J." Pak** .... (404) 581-6000
E-mail: byung.pak@usdoj.gov
First Assistant U.S. Attorney **Kurt R. Erskine** .... (404) 581-6000
E-mail: kurt.erskine@usdoj.gov
Executive Assistant U.S. Attorney
Charysse L. Alexander .... (404) 581-6000
E-mail: charysse.alexander@usdoj.gov
Administrative Officer **Gregory R. Marshall** .... (404) 581-6000
E-mail: greg.marshall@usdoj.gov
Information Technology (Systems) Manager
David W. Houston .... (404) 581-6000
E-mail: david.houston@usdoj.gov
Intelligence Research Specialist **Eric De La Barre** ...... (404) 581-6000
E-mail: eric.delabarre@usdoj.gov
Law Enforcement Coordination Manager and
Community Programs **Diane "Didi" Nelson** .... (404) 581-6000
E-mail: didi.nelson@justice.usdoj.gov
Public Affairs Officer **Robert Page** .... (404) 581-6000
E-mail: robert.page@usdoj.gov
Victim/Witness Specialist **Christie Smith Jones** .... (404) 581-6000
E-mail: christie.jones@usdoj.gov

Civil Division

Chief, Assistant U.S. Attorney **Lori M. Beranek** .... (404) 581-6000
Deputy Chief, Assistant U.S. Attorney
Neeli Ben-David .... (404) 581-6000
E-mail: Neeli.ben-David@usdoj.gov
Deputy Chief, Assistant U.S. Attorney **Darcy F. Coty** .... (404) 581-6000
E-mail: Darcy.Coty@usdoj.gov

Affirmative Litigation and Civil Defensive Section

Assistant U.S. Attorney **Armen Adzhemyan** .... (404) 581-6000
E-mail: armen.adzhemyan@usdoj.gov

★ Presidential Appointment Requiring Senate Confirmation ☆ Presidential Appointment ☐ Schedule C Appointment ◇ Career Senior Foreign Service Appointment
● Career Senior Executive Service (SES) Appointment ○ Non-Career Senior Executive Service (SES) Appointment ■ Postal Career Executive Service

Affirmative Litigation and Civil Defensive Section *(continued)*

Assistant U.S. Attorney **Lena M. Amanti** .... (404) 581-6000
E-mail: lena.amanti@usdoj.gov
Education: Pomona 1998 BA; Pennsylvania 2003 JD

Assistant U.S. Attorney **Lisa D. Cooper** .... (404) 581-6000
E-mail: lisa.cooper@usdoj.gov

Assistant U.S. Attorney **Aileen M. Bell Hughes** .... (404) 581-6000
E-mail: aileen.bell.hughes@usdoj.gov

Assistant U.S. Attorney **Tiffany Johnson** .... (404) 581-6000
E-mail: Tiffany.Johnson2@usdoj.gov

Assistant U.S. Attorney **Gabriel Mendel** .... (404) 581-6000
E-mail: gabriel.mendel@usdoj.gov

Assistant U.S. Attorney **David O'Neal** .... (404) 581-6000
E-mail: david.oneal@usdoj.gov

Assistant U.S. Attorney **R. David Powell** .... (404) 581-6000
E-mail: r.david.powell@usdoj.gov

Assistant U.S. Attorney **Melaine A. Williams** .... (404) 581-6000
E-mail: melaine.williams@usdoj.gov

Assistant U.S. Attorney **Paris Wynn** .... (404) 581-6000
E-mail: paris.wynn@usdoj.gov

Assistant U.S. Attorney **(Vacant)** .... (404) 581-6000

Assistant U.S. Attorney **(Vacant)** .... (404) 581-6000

Financial Litigation Unit

Chief, Assistant U.S. Attorney **Cynthia B. Smith** .... (404) 581-6000
E-mail: Cynthia.Smith@usdoj.gov

Assistant U.S. Attorney **(Vacant)** .... (404) 581-6000

Assistant U.S. Attorney **(Vacant)** .... (404) 581-6000

Criminal Division

Chief, Assistant U.S. Attorney **Yonette M. Buchanan** .... (404) 581-6000
E-mail: Yonette.Buchanan@usdoj.gov

Deputy Chief, Assistant U.S. Attorney **Glenn D. Baker** ... (404) 581-6000
E-mail: Glenn.Baker@usdoj.gov

Deputy Chief, Assistant U.S. Attorney
Jill E. Steinberg .... (404) 581-6000
E-mail: Jill.Steinberg@usdoj.gov
Education: Georgia 1995 BA; Duke 1998 JD

Senior Litigation Counsel **William L. McKinnon** .... (404) 581-6000
E-mail: william.mckinnon@usdoj.gov

Senior Litigation Counsel **William R. Toliver** .... (404) 581-6000
E-mail: william.toliver@usdoj.gov

Senior Litigation Counsel **(Vacant)** .... (404) 581-6000

Senior Trial Counsel **Thomas A. Devlin, Jr.** .... (404) 581-6000

Outreach Coordinator, Assistant U.S. Attorney
(Vacant) .... (404) 581-6000

Public Corruption Chief **Kurt R. Erskine** .... (404) 581-6000
E-mail: kurt.erskine@usdoj.gov

Public Corruption Deputy Chief **Jeffrey W. Davis** .... (404) 581-6000
E-mail: jeffrey.davis@usdoj.gov

Appellate and Legal Advice Section

Chief, Assistant U.S. Attorney
Lawrence S. Sommerfeld .... (404) 581-6000
E-mail: lawrence.sommerfeld@usdoj.gov

Assistant U.S. Attorney **Christopher C. Bly** .... (404) 581-6000
E-mail: chris.bly@usdoj.gov
Education: Emory 2002 JD

Assistant U.S. Attorney **J. Elizabeth McBath** .... (404) 581-6000
E-mail: elizabeth.mcbath@usdoj.gov

Special Assistant U.S. Attorney **Erin Sanders** .... (404) 581-6000
E-mail: erin.sanders@usdoj.gov

Asset Forfeiture Section

Chief **Dahil D. Goss** .... (404) 581-6000
E-mail: dahil.goss@usdoj.gov

Assistant U.S. Attorney **Michael John Brown** .... (404) 581-6000

Assistant U.S. Attorney **Kelly Connors** .... (404) 581-6000
E-mail: kelly.connors@usdoj.gov

Assistant U.S. Attorney **Thomas Krepp** .... (404) 581-6000
E-mail: thomas.krepp@usdoj.gov

Assistant U.S. Attorney **Jenny R. Turner** .... (404) 581-6000
E-mail: jenny.turner@usdoj.gov

Assistant U.S. Attorney **(Vacant)** .... (404) 581-6000

Complex Frauds Section

Chief, Assistant U.S. Attorney **Stephen H. McClain** ..... (404) 581-6000
E-mail: Stephen.McClain@usdoj.gov

Deputy Chief, Assistant U.S. Attorney
Jeffery A. Brown .... (404) 581-6000
E-mail: Jeff.A.Brown@usdoj.gov

Deputy Chief, Assistant U.S. Attorney
Christopher J. Huber .... (404) 581-6000
E-mail: Chris.Huber@usdoj.gov

Deputy Chief, Assistant U.S. Attorney **(Vacant)** .... (404) 581-6000

Deputy Chief, Assistant U.S. Attorney **(Vacant)** .... (404) 581-6000

Assistant U.S. Attorney **Lynsey Barron** .... (404) 581-6000
E-mail: lynsey.barron@usdoj.gov

Assistant U.S. Attorney **Alana R. Black** .... (404) 581-6000
E-mail: alana.black@usdoj.gov

Assistant U.S. Attorney **Tracia King** .... (404) 581-6000

Assistant U.S. Attorney **Thomas Krepp** .... (404) 581-6000
E-mail: Thomas.Krepp@usdoj.gov

Assistant U.S. Attorney **Bernita B. Malloy** .... (404) 581-6000
E-mail: bernita.malloy@usdoj.gov

Assistant U.S. Attorney **John Russell Phillips** .... (404) 581-6000
E-mail: russell.phillips@usdoj.gov

Assistant U.S. Attorney **Jolee Porter** .... (404) 581-6000
E-mail: Jolee.Porter@usdoj.gov

Assistant U.S. Attorney **Cassandra J. Schansman** .... (404) 581-6000
E-mail: Cassandra.Schansman@usdoj.gov

Assistant U.S. Attorney **Alex R. Sistla** .... (404) 581-6000
E-mail: Alex.Sistla@usdoj.gov
Education: Pennsylvania 2005 JD

Special Assistant U.S. Attorney **Diane Schulman** .... (404) 581-6000
E-mail: diane.schulman@usdoj.gov

Intake Section

Chief, Assistant U.S. Attorney **Mary Jane Stewart** ...... (404) 581-6000
E-mail: mary.jane.stewart@usdoj.gov

Assistant U.S. Attorney **Mary C. Roemer** .... (404) 581-6000
E-mail: mary.roemer@usdoj.gov

Special Assistant U.S. Attorney **(Vacant)** .... (404) 581-6000

Narcotics and Organized Crime Drug Enforcement Task Force (OCDETF) Section

Chief, Assistant U.S. Attorney
Elizabeth M. Hathaway .... (404) 581-6000
E-mail: elizabeth.hathaway@usdoj.gov

Deputy Chief, Assistant U.S. Attorney
Michael V. Herskowitz .... (404) 581-6000
E-mail: michael.herskowitz@usdoj.gov

Deputy Chief, Assistant U.S. Attorney **Lisa W. Tarvin** .... (404) 581-6000
E-mail: lisa.tarvin@usdoj.gov

Deputy Chief, Assistant U.S. Attorney **(Vacant)** .... (404) 581-6000

Assistant U.S. Attorney **Laurel R. Boatright** .... (404) 581-6000
E-mail: laurel.boatright@usdoj.gov

Assistant U.S. Attorney **Garrett Bradford** .... (404) 581-6000
E-mail: garrett.bradford@usdoj.gov

Assistant U.S. Attorney **Brock Brockington** .... (404) 581-6000

Assistant U.S. Attorney **Ryan Christian** .... (404) 581-6000

Assistant U.S. Attorney **Dashene Cooper** .... (404) 581-6000

Assistant U.S. Attorney **Nicholas Hartigan** .... (404) 581-6000
E-mail: nicholas.hartigan@usdoj.gov

Assistant U.S. Attorney **Vivek Kothari** .... (404) 581-6000
E-mail: vivek.kothari@usdoj.gov

Assistant U.S. Attorney **Sandy Strippoli** .... (404) 581-6000
E-mail: sandy.strippoli@usdoj.gov

Assistant U.S. Attorney **Trevor Wilmot** .... (404) 581-6000
E-mail: trevor.wilmot@usdoj.gov

Assistant U.S. Attorney **Jennifer Whitfield** .... (404) 581-6000
E-mail: jennifer.whitfield2@usdoj.gov

OCDETF Coordinator/ Assistant U.S. Attorney
Michael F. Smith .... (404) 581-6000
E-mail: michael.f.smith@usdoj.gov

Assistant U.S. Attorney **(Vacant)** .... (404) 581-6000

Special Assistant U.S. Attorney **DeLana Jones** .... (404) 581-6000
E-mail: delana.jones@usdoj.gov

Special Assistant U.S. Attorney **Katie Terry** .... (404) 581-6000
E-mail: katie.terry@usdoj.gov

Special Assistant U.S. Attorney **(Vacant)** .... (404) 581-6000

★ Presidential Appointment Requiring Senate Confirmation ☆ Presidential Appointment ☐ Schedule C Appointment ◇ Career Senior Foreign Service Appointment
● Career Senior Executive Service (SES) Appointment ○ Non-Career Senior Executive Service (SES) Appointment ■ Postal Career Executive Service

DEPARTMENTS

Major Crime Section

Chief, Assistant U.S. Attorney **Yonette M. Buchanan** . . . . (404) 581-6000
E-mail: yonette.buchanan@usdoj.gov
Deputy Chief, Assistant U.S. Attorney **Kim S. Dammers** . . . . (404) 581-6000
E-mail: kim.dammers@usdoj.gov
Deputy Chief, Assistant U.S. Attorney **Katherine M. Hoffer** . . . . (404) 581-6000
E-mail: katherine.hoffer@usdoj.gov
Deputy Chief, Assistant U.S. Attorney **Richard S. Moultrie, Jr.** . . . . (404) 581-6000
E-mail: richard.moultrie@usdoj.gov
Assistant U.S. Attorney **Ryan K. Buchanan** . . . . (404) 581-6000
E-mail: ryan.buchanan@usdoj.gov
Education: Samford 2001 BS; Vanderbilt 2005 JD
Assistant U.S. Attorney **Matthew Carrico** . . . . (404) 581-6000
E-mail: matthew.carrico@usdoj.gov
Assistant U.S. Attorney **Phyllis Clerk** . . . . (404) 581-6000
E-mail: phyllis.clerk@usdoj.gov
Assistant U.S. Attorney **L. Skye Davis** . . . . (404) 581-6000
E-mail: skye.davis@usdoj.gov
Assistant U.S. Attorney **Stephanie Gabay-Smith** . . . . (404) 581-6000
E-mail: stephanie.smith@usdoj.gov
Assistant U.S. Attorney **Brent A. Gray** . . . . (404) 581-6000
E-mail: brent.gray@usdoj.gov
Assistant U.S. Attorney **Bret Hobson** . . . . (404) 581-6000
E-mail: bret.hobson@usdoj.gov
Assistant U.S. Attorney **Paul R. Jones** . . . . (404) 581-6000
E-mail: paul.jones@usdoj.gov
Assistant U.S. Attorney **Jennifer Keene** . . . . (404) 581-6000
E-mail: jennifer.keen@usdoj.gov
Assistant U.S. Attorney **Tracia King** . . . . (404) 581-6000
E-mail: tracia.king@usdoj.gov
Assistant U.S. Attorney **Jessica Morris** . . . . (404) 581-6000
E-mail: jessica.morris3@usdoj.gov
Education: Dartmouth 2001 BA; Georgia 2007 JD
Assistant U.S. Attorney **(Vacant)** . . . . (404) 581-6000
Assistant U.S. Attorney **Joseph A. Plummer** . . . . (404) 581-6000
E-mail: joe.plummer@usdoj.gov
Assistant U.S. Attorney **Jolee Porter** . . . . (404) 581-6000
E-mail: jolee.porter@usdoj.gov
Assistant U.S. Attorney **Suzette A. Smikle** . . . . (404) 581-6000
E-mail: suzette.smikle@usdoj.gov
Assistant U.S. Attorney **William G. Traynor** . . . . (404) 581-6000
E-mail: will.traynor@usdoj.gov
Assistant U.S. Attorney **Mary Webb** . . . . (404) 581-6000
E-mail: mary.webb@usdoj.gov
Assistant U.S. Attorney **(Vacant)** . . . . (404) 581-6000
Special Assistant U.S. Attorney **Wylly Jordan** . . . . (404) 581-6000
E-mail: wylly.jordan@usdoj.gov

Georgia - Southern District

22 Barnard Street, Suite 300, Savannah, GA 31401
P.O. Box 8970, Savannah, GA 31412
Tel: (912) 652-4422 Fax: (912) 652-4388
Internet: https://www.justice.gov/usao-sdga

★ U.S. Attorney **Bobby L. Christine ARNG** . . . . (912) 652-4422
E-mail: bobby.christine@usdoj.gov
Education: Georgia BA; Cumberland JD
Secretary to the U.S. Attorney **Alice Ball** . . . . (912) 652-4422
E-mail: alice.ball@usdoj.gov
First Assistant U.S. Attorney **David H. Estes** . . . . (912) 652-4422
E-mail: david.estes@usdoj.gov
Administrative Officer **Charlie Bourne** . . . . (912) 652-4422
E-mail: charlie.bourne@usdoj.gov
Victim-Witness Specialist **Iverna Campbell** . . . . (912) 652-4422
E-mail: iverna.campbell@usdoj.gov
Victim-Witness Specialist **Debra Jones** . . . . (912) 652-4422
E-mail: debra.jones@usdoj.gov
Law Enforcement Committee Coordinator **Dan Drake** . . . . (912) 652-4422
E-mail: dan.drake@justice.usdoj.gov
Supervisory Computer Specialist **(Vacant)** . . . . (912) 652-4422

Appellate Division

Chief **R. Brian Tanner** . . . . (912) 652-4422
E-mail: brian.tanner@justice.usdoj.gov
Education: Georgia Tech 1998 BS; Emory 2001 JD
Assistant U.S. Attorney **James C. Stuchell** . . . . (912) 652-4422
E-mail: james.stuchell@justice.usdoj.gov

Civil Division

Chief **Shannon Statkus** . . . . (706) 826-4522
E-mail: shannon.statkus@usdoj.gov
Deputy Chief **Thomas "Tommy" Clarkson** . . . . (912) 652-4520
Assistant U.S. Attorney **(Vacant)** . . . . (912) 652-4422
E-mail: thomas.clarkson@usdoj.gov
Assistant U.S. Attorney **(Vacant)** . . . . (912) 652-4422
Assistant U.S. Attorney **(Vacant)** . . . . (912) 652-4422

Criminal Division

Chief **Brian T. Rafferty** . . . . (912) 652-4422
E-mail: brian.rafferty@usdoj.gov
Deputy Chief **Karl I. Knoche** . . . . (912) 652-4422
E-mail: karl.knoche@usdoj.gov
Counter Terrorism Assistant U.S. Attorney **Charlie Bourne** . . . . (912) 201-2526
E-mail: charlie.bourne@justice.usdoj.gov
Assistant U.S. Attorney **Xavier C. Cunningham** . . . . (912) 652-4422
E-mail: xavier.cunningham@usdoj.gov
Assistant U.S. Attorney **Greg Gilluly** . . . . (912) 652-4422
E-mail: greg.gilluly@usdoj.gov
Assistant U.S. Attorney **Tania Groover** . . . . (912) 653-4422
E-mail: tania.groover@usdoj.gov
Assistant U.S. Attorney **Theodore Hertzberg** . . . . (912) 652-4422
E-mail: theodore.hertzberg@usdoj.gov
Assistant U.S. Attorney **Matthew Josephson** . . . . (912) 652-4422
E-mail: matthew.josephson@usdoj.gov
Assistant U.S. Attorney **Tara Lyons** . . . . (912) 652-4422
E-mail: tara.lyons@usdoj.gov
Assistant U.S. Attorney **Scarlett Nokes** . . . . (912) 652-4422
E-mail: scarlett.nokes@usdoj.gov
Senior Litigation Counsel **(Vacant)** . . . . (912) 652-4422
Senior Litigation Counsel **(Vacant)** . . . . (912) 652-4422

Augusta (GA) Office

600 James Brown Boulevard, Suite 200, Augusta, GA 30901
Tel: (706) 724-0517 Fax: (706) 724-7728

Branch Chief **Patricia Rose** . . . . (706) 826-4520
E-mail: patricia.rose@usdoj.gov
Criminal Division Deputy Chief and Assistant U.S. Attorney **Nancy C. Greenwood** . . . . (706) 724-0517
E-mail: nancy.greenwood@usdoj.gov
Civil Division Assistant U.S. Attorney **(Vacant)** . . . . (706) 826-4520
Criminal Division Assistant U.S. Attorney **(Vacant)** . . . . (706) 724-0517
E-mail: lamont.belk@usdoj.gov
Criminal Division Assistant U.S. Attorney **(Vacant)** . . . . (706) 724-0517
E-mail: troy.clark@justice.usdoj.gov
Appellate Criminal Division Assistant U.S. Attorney **Patricia Green Rhodes** . . . . (706) 724-0517
E-mail: patricia.rhodes@usdoj.gov

Guam District - Northern Marianas District

108 Hernan Cortez, Suite 500, Agana, GU 96910
Tel: (671) 472-7332 Fax: (671) 472-7334

★ U.S. Attorney (Interim) **Shawn N. Anderson** . . . . (671) 472-7332
E-mail: shawn.anderson@usdoj.gov
Education: Oregon State BS; Willamette JD
Secretary **(Vacant)** . . . . (671) 472-7332 ext. 142
Law Enforcement Committee/Victim-Witness Coordinator **Salome Blas** . . . . (671) 472-7332 ext. 144
E-mail: salome.blas@usdoj.gov
Administrative Officer **Ed Talato** . . . . (671) 472-7332 ext. 106
E-mail: ed.talato@usdoj.gov

★ Presidential Appointment Requiring Senate Confirmation ☆ Presidential Appointment ☐ Schedule C Appointment ◇ Career Senior Foreign Service Appointment
● Career Senior Executive Service (SES) Appointment ○ Non-Career Senior Executive Service (SES) Appointment ■ Postal Career Executive Service

Civil Division
108 Hernan Cortez Avenue, Hagatna, GU 96910
Tel: (671) 472-7332 ext. 121 Fax: (671) 472-7215

Chief **Mikel Schwab** . . . . (671) 472-7332 ext. 107
E-mail: mikel.schwab@usdoj.gov
Assistant U.S. Attorney **Jessica F. Cruz** . . . . (671) 472-7332 ext. 139
E-mail: jessica.f.cruz@usdoj.gov

Criminal Division
108 Hernan Cortez Avenue, Hagatna, GU 96910
Fax: (671) 472-7334 Fax: (671) 472-7229

First Assistant U.S. Attorney
Shawn N. Anderson . . . . (671) 472-7332 ext. 116
E-mail: shawn.anderson@usdoj.gov
Education: Oregon State BS; Willamette JD
Assistant U.S. Attorney **Belinda C. Alcantara** . . . (671) 472-7332 ext. 143
E-mail: belinda.alcantara@usdoj.gov
Assistant U.S. Attorney **Garth R. Backe** . . . . (671) 472-7332
E-mail: garth.backe@usdoj.gov
Education: LSU 1998 BA, 2002 JD, 2002 BCL
Assistant U.S. Attorney **Frederick A. Black** . . . . . (671) 472-7332 ext. 141
E-mail: frederick.black@usdoj.gov
Assistant U.S. Attorney **Rosetta San Nicolas** . . . (671) 472-7332 ext. 115
E-mail: rosetta.sannicolas@usdoj.gov
Assistant U.S. Attorney **(Vacant)** . . . . (671) 479-4122 ext. 120
Asset Forfeiture Unit Assistant U.S. Attorney
Shawn N. Anderson . . . . (671) 472-7332 ext. 146
Education: Oregon State BS; Willamette JD
Senior Litigation Counsel **Marivic P. David** . . . . (671) 472-7332

Commonwealth of the Northern Mariana Islands Office
Horiguchi Building, 3rd Floor, Saipan, MP 96950
P.O. Box 500377, Saipan, MP 96950-0377
Tel: (670) 236-2980 Fax: (670) 236-2945

Assistant U.S. Attorney **(Vacant)** . . . . (670) 236-2987
Legal Assistant **Marylynn Yamada-Sablan** . . . . (670) 236-2978
E-mail: marylynn.yamada-sablan@usdoj.gov

Hawaii District
300 Ala Moana Boulevard, Room 6-100, Honolulu, HI 96850
Tel: (808) 541-2850 Fax: (808) 541-2958
Internet: https://www.justice.gov/usao-sdga

★ U.S. Attorney **Kenji M. Price** . . . . (808) 541-2850
E-mail: kenji.price@usdoj.gov
Education: Gonzaga 2002 BA; Pennsylvania 2010 JD
Secretary to the U.S. Attorney **Cheri Abing** . . . . (808) 541-2850
E-mail: cheri.abing@justice.usdoj.gov
First Assistant U.S. Attorney **Elliot Enoki** . . . . (808) 541-2850
E-mail: elliot.enoki@usdoj.gov
Administrative Officer **Thomas Huyer** . . . . (808) 541-2850
E-mail: thomas.huyer@usdoj.gov
Law Enforcement Coordinator **Wesley J. Wong** . . . . (808) 541-2850
E-mail: wesley.wong@usdoj.gov
Education: UC Berkeley BA; UC Davis JD; NYU LLM
Systems Manager **Randal Wong** . . . . (808) 541-2850
E-mail: randal.wong@usdoj.gov

Civil Division
Chief **Tom Helper** . . . . (808) 541-2850
E-mail: tom.helper@usdoj.gov
Assistant U.S. Attorney **Michael Albanese** . . . . (808) 541-2850
E-mail: michael.albanese@usdoj.gov
Assistant U.S. Attorney **Morgan Early** . . . . (808) 541-2850
E-mail: morgan.early@usdoj.gov
Assistant U.S. Attorney **Edric Ching** . . . . (808) 541-2850
E-mail: edric.ching@usdoj.gov
Assistant U.S. Attorney **Rachel Moriyama** . . . . (808) 541-2850
E-mail: rachel.moriyama@usdoj.gov
Assistant U.S. Attorney **Harry Yee** . . . . (808) 541-2850
E-mail: harry.yee@usdoj.gov

Criminal Division
Chief **Thomas J. "Tom" Brady** . . . . (808) 541-2850
E-mail: tom.brady@usdoj.gov

Criminal Division *(continued)*

Assistant U.S. Attorney **Larry Butrick** . . . . (808) 541-2850
E-mail: larry.butrick@usdoj.gov
Assistant U.S. Attorney **Darren Ching** . . . . (808) 541-2850
E-mail: darren.ching@usdoj.gov
Assistant U.S. Attorney **Mark A. Inciong** . . . . (808) 541-2850
E-mail: mark.inciong@usdoj.gov
Assistant U.S. Attorney **Ronald G. Johnson** . . . . (808) 541-2850
E-mail: ron.johnson@usdoj.gov
Assistant U.S. Attorney **Thomas "Tom" Muehleck** . . . . . (808) 541-2850
E-mail: tom.muehleck@usdoj.gov
Assistant U.S. Attorney **Margaret Nammar** . . . . (808) 541-2850
E-mail: margaret.nammar@usdoj.gov
Assistant U.S. Attorney **Michael D. "Mike" Nammar** . . . . (808) 541-2850
E-mail: mike.nammar@usdoj.gov
Assistant U.S. Attorney **Marion Percell** . . . . (808) 541-2850
E-mail: marion.percell@usdoj.gov
Assistant U.S. Attorney **Rebecca Perlmutter** . . . . (808) 541-2850
E-mail: rebecca.perlmutter@usdoj.gov
Education: Wisconsin 2004 JD
Assistant U.S. Attorney **Tony R. Roberts** . . . . (808) 541-2850
E-mail: troberts@usa.doj.gov
Assistant U.S. Attorney **Marshall Silverberg** . . . . (808) 541-2850
E-mail: marshall.silverberg@usdoj.gov
Assistant U.S. Attorney **Ken Sorenson** . . . . (808) 541-2850
E-mail: ken.sorenson@usdoj.gov
Assistant U.S. Attorney **Chris Thomas** . . . . (808) 541-2850
E-mail: chris.thomas@usdoj.gov
Assistant U.S. Attorney **Lawrence "Larry" Tong** . . . . (808) 541-2850
E-mail: larry.tong@usdoj.gov
Assistant U.S. Attorney **Marc A. Wallenstein** . . . . (808) 541-2850
E-mail: marc.wallenstein@usdoj.gov
Education: Harvard 2002 AB; Yale 2006 JD
Assistant U.S. Attorney **Gregg Yates** . . . . (808) 541-2850
E-mail: gregg.yates@usdoj.gov
Drug and Organized Crime Section Chief
Thomas "Tom" Muehleck . . . . (808) 541-2850
E-mail: tom.muehleck@usdoj.gov
Fraud and Financial Crime Section Chief
Lawrence "Larry" Tong . . . . (808) 541-2850
Special Crime Section Chief **Thomas J. "Tom" Brady** . . . (808) 541-2850
E-mail: tom.brady@usdoj.gov

Idaho District
Washington Group Plaza IV, 800 E. Park Boulevard,
Suite 600, Boise, ID 83712-7788
Tel: (208) 334-1211 Fax: (208) 334-9375
Internet: https://www.justice.gov/usao-id

★ U.S. Attorney **Bart M. Davis** . . . . (208) 334-1211 (Boise)
E-mail: bart.davis@usdoj.gov
Education: BYU 1977 BA; Idaho 1980 JD
First Assistant U.S. Attorney **Rafael M. Gonzalez, Jr.** . . . . (208) 334-1211
E-mail: rafael.gonzalez@usdoj.gov Fax: (208) 334-1038
Secretary to the U.S. Attorney **(Vacant)** . . . . (208) 334-1211
Administrative Officer **Tonya M. Montesano** . . . . (208) 334-1211
E-mail: tonya.montesano@usdoj.gov Fax: (208) 334-9375
Law Enforcement Committee Coordinator
Tim Hawkins . . . . (208) 334-1211
E-mail: tim.hawkins@usdoj.gov Fax: (208) 334-1413
Victim-Witness Coordinator **Kristi Johnson** . . . . (208) 334-1211
E-mail: kristi.johnson@usdoj.gov Fax: (208) 334-1038
Asset Forfeiture Unit Assistant U.S. Attorney **(Vacant)** . . . (208) 334-1211
ALS/Assistant Systems Manager
Pamela J. "Pam" Rocca . . . . (208) 334-1211
E-mail: pam.rocca2@usdoj.gov
Public Information Officer **Barbara Layman** . . . . (208) 334-1211
E-mail: barbara.layman@usdoj.gov
Systems Manager **Joel Hawker** . . . . (208) 334-1211
E-mail: joel.hawker@usdoj.gov
IT Specialist **(Vacant)** . . . . (208) 334-1211
Fax: (208) 334-9375

DEPARTMENTS

Civil Division
Washington Group Buuilding Four, 800 E. Park Boulevard,
Suite 600, Boise, ID 83712-7788
Fax: (208) 334-1414

Chief **Syrena Case Hargrove** . . . . (208) 334-1211
E-mail: syrena.hargrove@usdoj.gov
Education: Harvard 1997 JD
Assistant U.S. Attorney **Christine England** . . . . (208) 334-1211
E-mail: christine.england@usdoj.gov
Assistant U.S. Attorney **Jessica Gunder** . . . . (208) 334-1211
E-mail: jessica.gunder@usdoj.gov
Education: Missouri 2007 JD
Assistant U.S. Attorney **Joanne P. Rodriguez** . . . . (208) 334-1211
E-mail: joanne.rodriguez@usdoj.gov
Assistant U.S. Attorney **Nicholas J. "Nick" Woychick** . . . (208) 334-1211
E-mail: nick.woychick@usdoj.gov
Assistant U.S. Attorney **(Vacant)** . . . . (208) 334-1211

Criminal Division
Washington Group Building Four, 800 E. Park Boulevard,
Suite 600, Boise, ID 83712-7788
Fax: (208) 334-1413

Chief **Aaron N. Lucoff** . . . . (208) 334-1211
E-mail: aaron.lucoff@usdoj.gov
Assistant U.S. Attorney **Christopher S. Atwood** . . . . (208) 334-1211
E-mail: christopher.atwood@usdoj.gov
Assistant U.S. Attorney **Darci Ward** . . . . (208) 334-1211
E-mail: darci.ward@usdoj.gov
Assistant U.S. Attorney **Joshua D. Hurwit** . . . . (208) 334-1211
E-mail: joshua.hurwit@usdoj.gov
Education: Stanford 2002 BA; Harvard 2006 JD
Assistant U.S. Attorney **Melissa Lou** . . . . (208) 334-1211
E-mail: melissa.lou@usdoj.gov
Assistant U.S. Attorney **Kevin T. Maloney** . . . . (208) 334-1211
E-mail: kevin.maloney@usdoj.gov
Assistant U.S. Attorney **Christian S. Nafzger** . . . . (208) 334-1211
E-mail: christian.nafzger@usdoj.gov
Assistant U.S. Attorney **Heather S. Patricco** . . . . (208) 334-1211
E-mail: heather.patricco@usdoj.gov
Assistant U.S. Attorney **Justin D. Whatcott** . . . . (208) 334-1211
E-mail: justin.whatcott@usdoj.gov
Assistant U.S. Attorney **(Vacant)** . . . . (208) 334-1211
Senior Litigation Counsel **Raymond E. Patricco, Jr.** . . . . . (208) 334-1211
E-mail: raymond.patricco@usdoj.gov

Coeur d'Alene (ID) Office
6450 North Mineral Drive, Suite 210, Coeur d'Alene, ID 83815
Tel: (208) 667-6568 Fax: (208) 667-0814

Branch Manager **Traci J. Whelan** . . . . (208) 667-6568
E-mail: traci.whelan@usdoj.gov
Assistant U.S. Attorney **Michael W. "Mike" Mitchell** . . . . (208) 667-6568
E-mail: mike.mitchell@usdoj.gov
Assistant U.S. Attorney **(Vacant)** . . . . (208) 667-6568
Assistant U.S. Attorney **(Vacant)** . . . . (208) 667-6568

Pocatello (ID) Office
801 East Sherman, Room 192, Pocatello, ID 83201
Tel: (208) 478-4166 Fax: (208) 478-4175

Branch Manager **Jack B. Haycock** . . . . (208) 478-4166
E-mail: jack.haycock@usdoj.gov
Assistant U.S. Attorney **Ann T. Wick** . . . . (208) 478-4166
E-mail: ann.wick@usdoj.gov
Assistant U.S. Attorney **Michael J. Fica** . . . . (208) 478-4166
E-mail: michael.fica@usdoj.gov

Illinois - Northern District
Dirksen Federal Building, 219 South Dearborn Street,
5th Floor, Chicago, IL 60604
Tel: (312) 353-5300 Fax: (312) 353-2067
Internet: https://www.justice.gov/usao-ndil

★ U.S. Attorney **John R. Lausch** . . . . (859) 233-2661
E-mail: john.lausch@usdoj.gov
Education: Harvard 1992 AB; Northwestern 1996 JD

Illinois - Northern District *(continued)*

Counsel to the U.S. Attorney **Morris O. Pasqual** . . . . (312) 886-7637
E-mail: morris.pasqual@usdoj.gov
Secretary to the U.S. Attorney **(Vacant)** . . . . (312) 886-1321
Public Affairs Specialist **Joseph Fitzpatrick** . . . . (312) 353-5318
E-mail: joseph.fitzpatrick2@usdoj.gov
First Assistant U.S. Attorney **(Vacant)** . . . . (312) 353-5306
Senior Litigation Counsel **(Vacant)** . . . . (312) 886-1328
Litigation Counsel **Diane MacArthur** . . . . (312) 353-5352
E-mail: diane.macarthur@usdoj.gov
Litigation Counsel **(Vacant)** . . . . (312) 353-5300
Executive Assistant U.S. Attorney **Meghan C. Stack** . . . . . (312) 353-4045
E-mail: meghan.stack@usdoj.gov
Executive Assistant U.S. Attorney **(Vacant)** . . . . (312) 353-1983
Appellate Division Chief **Debra R. Bonamici** . . . . (312) 353-3741
E-mail: debra.bonamici@usdoj.gov
Civil Division Chief **Thomas P. Walsh** . . . . (312) 353-5312
E-mail: thomas.walsh2@usdoj.gov
Criminal Division Chief **Brian Hayes** . . . . (312) 353-4307
E-mail: brian.hayes@usdoj.gov
Criminal Division Associate Chief **(Vacant)** . . . . (312) 353-1980
Financial Litigation Section Chief **(Vacant)** . . . . (312) 353-1980
General Crimes Section Chief **Lindsay Jenkins** . . . . (312) 353-0962
E-mail: lindsay.jenkins@usdoj.gov
Financial Crimes Section Chief **Rick Young** . . . . (312) 886-7660
E-mail: rick.young@usdoj.gov
National Security and Cybercrimes Section Chief
(Vacant) . . . . (312) 886-3389
Narcotics Section Chief **Christopher P. Hotaling** . . . . (312) 353-5324
E-mail: christopher.hotaling@usdoj.gov
Education: Duke BA; Virginia 2000 JD
Securities and Commodities Fraud Section Chief
Jason Yonan . . . . (312) 353-0708
E-mail: jason.yonan@usdoj.gov
Education: Illinois State 1997 BS; Illinois 2002 JD
Public Corruption and Organized Crime Section Chief
Laurie J. Barsella . . . . (312) 353-5300
E-mail: laurie.barsella@usdoj.gov
Violent Crimes Section Chief **Ronald L. DeWald, Jr.** . . . . (312) 886-4187
E-mail: ronald.dewald@usdoj.gov
Special Assistant U.S. Attorney **Jonathan Baum** . . . . (312) 353-5349
E-mail: jonathan.baum@usdoj.gov
Special Assistant U.S. Attorney **Catherine Dick** . . . . (312) 886-3482
E-mail: catherine.dick@usdoj.gov
Education: Harvard 2005 JD
Special Assistant U.S. Attorney **Jared Jodrey** . . . . (312) 353-5358
E-mail: jared.jodrey@usdoj.gov
Special Assistant U.S. Attorney **Kristin Linsley** . . . . (312) 353-5361
E-mail: kristin.linsley@usdoj.gov
Special Assistant U.S. Attorney **Jill Kolinski** . . . . (312) 353-4129
E-mail: jill.kolinski@usdoj.gov
Special Assistant U.S. Attorney **William P. Novak** . . . . . . (312) 697-4073
E-mail: william.novak@usdoj.gov
Special Assistant U.S. Attorney **(Vacant)** . . . . (312) 353-5300
Assistant U.S. Attorney **Georgia Alexakis** . . . . (312) 353-8897
E-mail: georgia.alexakis@usdoj.gov
Education: Harvard 2000 AB; Northwestern 2006 JD
Assistant U.S. Attorney **Susan Willoughby Anderson** . . . (312) 886-9082
E-mail: willoughby.anderson@usdoj.gov
Assistant U.S. Attorney **Jeannice Appenteng** . . . . (312) 353-5357
E-mail: jeannice.appenteng@usdoj.gov
Assistant U.S. Attorney **Tiffany Ardam** . . . . (312) 353-0951
E-mail: tiffany.ardam@usdoj.gov
Assistant U.S. Attorney **Kavitha Babu** . . . . (312) 353-1980
E-mail: kavitha.babu@usdoj.gov
Assistant U.S. Attorney **Carol A. Bell** . . . . (312) 353-8898
E-mail: carol.bell@usdoj.gov
Assistant U.S. Attorney **Albert Berry** . . . . (312) 886-7855
E-mail: albert.berry@usdoj.gov
Assistant U.S. Attorney **Yasmin N. Best** . . . . (312) 469-6024
E-mail: yasmin.best@usdoj.gov
Assistant U.S. Attorney **Amarjeet Bhachu** . . . . (312) 469-6212
E-mail: amarjeet.bhachu@usdoj.gov
Assistant U.S. Attorney **Bethany K. Biesenthal** . . . . (312) 886-7629
E-mail: bethany.biesenthal@usdoj.gov

★ Presidential Appointment Requiring Senate Confirmation ☆ Presidential Appointment □ Schedule C Appointment ◇ Career Senior Foreign Service Appointment
● Career Senior Executive Service (SES) Appointment ○ Non-Career Senior Executive Service (SES) Appointment ■ Postal Career Executive Service

Illinois - Northern District *(continued)*

Assistant U.S. Attorney **David E. Bindi** . . . . (312) 886-7643
E-mail: david.bindi@usdoj.gov

Assistant U.S. Attorney **Debra R. Bonamici** . . . . (312) 353-3741
E-mail: debra.bonamici@usdoj.gov

Assistant U.S. Attorney **Aaron Bond** . . . . (312) 469-6047
E-mail: aaron.bond@usdoj.gov

Assistant U.S. Attorney **Gina E. Brock** . . . . (312) 353-7919
E-mail: gina.brock@usdoj.gov

Assistant U.S. Attorney **Timothy J. Chapman** . . . . (312) 353-1925
E-mail: timothy.chapman@usdoj.gov

Assistant U.S. Attorney **Kalia Coleman** . . . . (312) 353-3540
E-mail: kalia.coleman@usdoj.gov

Assistant U.S. Attorney **John D. Cooke** . . . . (312) 353-8788
E-mail: john.cooke@usdoj.gov

Assistant U.S. Attorney **Yusef Dale** . . . . (312) 886-7645
E-mail: yusef.dale@usdoj.gov

Assistant U.S. Attorney **Jeremy Daniel** . . . . (312) 469-6314
E-mail: jeremy.daniel@usdoj.gov

Assistant U.S. Attorney **Vikas Didwania** . . . . (312) 353-0517
E-mail: vikas.didwania@usdoj.gov
Education: Chicago 2009 JD

Assistant U.S. Attorney **Steven Dollear** . . . . (312) 353-5359
E-mail: steven.dollear@usdoj.gov
Education: Loyola U (Chicago) 2002 JD

Assistant U.S. Attorney **Sean Driscoll** . . . . (312) 469-6151
E-mail: sean.driscoll@usdoj.gov

Assistant U.S. Attorney **William Dunne** . . . . (312) 353-2815
E-mail: william.dunne@usdoj.gov

Assistant U.S. Attorney **Katie Durick** . . . . (312) 886-2035
E-mail: katie.durick@usdoj.gov

Assistant U.S. Attorney **James Durkin** . . . . (312) 353-6630
E-mail: james.durkin@usdoj.gov

Assistant U.S. Attorney **Matthew S. Ebert** . . . . (312) 353-5354
E-mail: matthew.ebert@usdoj.gov

Assistant U.S. Attorney **Scott M. Edenfield** . . . . (312) 353-5277
E-mail: scott.edenfield@usdoj.gov

Assistant U.S. Attorney **Nicholas Eichenseer** . . . . (312) 353-1412
E-mail: nicholas.eichenseer@usdoj.gov
Education: Northwestern 2000 BS; Wisconsin 2006 JD

Assistant U.S. Attorney **Andrew H. Erskine** . . . . (312) 353-1875
E-mail: andrew.erskine@usdoj.gov
Education: Illinois 2004 BS, 2004 MS

Assistant U.S. Attorney **Michael Ferrara** . . . . (312) 886-7649
E-mail: michael.ferrara@usdoj.gov
Education: Boston Col 1998 BA; Stanford 2003 JD

Assistant U.S. Attorney **Peter M. Flanagan** . . . . (312) 469-6235
E-mail: peter.flanagan@usdoj.gov

Assistant U.S. Attorney **Sean J.B. Franzblau** . . . . (312) 371-4171
E-mail: sean.franzblau@usdoj.gov

Assistant U.S. Attorney **Stuart D. Fullerton** . . . . (312) 353-5266
E-mail: stuart.fullerton@usdoj.gov

Assistant U.S. Attorney **Matthew M. Getter** . . . . (312) 886-7651
E-mail: matthew.getter@usdoj.gov

Assistant U.S. Attorney **Nani Gilkerson** . . . . (312) 469-6049
E-mail: nani.gilkerson@usdoj.gov

Assistant U.S. Attorney **Kelly M. Greening** . . . . (312) 371-3191
E-mail: kelly.greening@usdoj.gov

Assistant U.S. Attorney **Helene B. Greenwald** . . . . (312) 469-6296
E-mail: helene.greenwald@usdoj.gov

Assistant U.S. Attorney **Kelly Guzman** . . . . (815) 353-1598
E-mail: kelly.guzman@usdoj.gov

Assistant U.S. Attorney **Jonathan C. Haile** . . . . (312) 886-2055
E-mail: jonathan.haile@usdoj.gov

Assistant U.S. Attorney **Virginia Hancock** . . . . (312) 353-1998
E-mail: virginia.hancock@usdoj.gov

Assistant U.S. Attorney **Sunil R. Harjani** . . . . (312) 353-9353
E-mail: sunil.harjani@usdoj.gov
Education: Northwestern 2000 JD

Assistant U.S. Attorney **Brian R. Havey** . . . . (312) 353-1857
E-mail: brian.havey@usdoj.gov

Assistant U.S. Attorney **Bolling Haxall** . . . . (312) 353-8728
E-mail: bolling.haxall@usdoj.gov

Assistant U.S. Attorney **Scott Heffron** . . . . (312) 886-4190
E-mail: scott.heffron@usdoj.gov

Illinois - Northern District *(continued)*

Assistant U.S. Attorney **Stephen L. Heinze** . . . . (312) 886-1265
E-mail: stephen.heinze@usdoj.gov

Assistant U.S. Attorney **Matthew Hernandez** . . . . (312) 353-4317
E-mail: matthew.hernandez@usdoj.gov

Assistant U.S. Attorney **William R. Hogan, Jr.** . . . . (312) 886-4185
E-mail: william.hogan@usdoj.gov

Assistant U.S. Attorney **Erik A. Hogstrom** . . . . (312) 353-8709
E-mail: erik.hogstrom@usdoj.gov
Education: Michigan 2004 JD

Assistant U.S. Attorney **Rebekah Holman** . . . . (312) 469-6233
E-mail: rebekah.holman@usdoj.gov

Assistant U.S. Attorney **Christopher P. Hotaling** . . . . (312) 353-5324
E-mail: christopher.hotaling@usdoj.gov
Education: Duke BA; Virginia 2000 JD

Assistant U.S. Attorney **Nathalina A. Hudson** . . . . (312) 353-1123
E-mail: nathalina.hudson@usdoj.gov
Education: Duke 2001 JD

Assistant U.S. Attorney **Lindsay Jenkins** . . . . (312) 353-0962
E-mail: lindsay.jenkins@usdoj.gov

Assistant U.S. Attorney **Lela D. Johnson** . . . . (312) 353-4320
E-mail: lela.johnson@usdoj.gov

Assistant U.S. Attorney **Patrick W. Johnson** . . . . (312) 353-5327
E-mail: patrick.johnson@usdoj.gov

Assistant U.S. Attorney **Barry Jonas** . . . . (312) 886-8027
E-mail: barry.jonas@usdoj.gov

Assistant U.S. Attorney **Andrianna D. Kastanek** . . . . (312) 886-0974
E-mail: andrianna.kastanek@usdoj.gov

Assistant U.S. Attorney **Erin Kelly** . . . . (312) 886-9083
E-mail: erin.kelly@usdoj.gov

Assistant U.S. Attorney **Kathryn A. Kelly** . . . . (312) 353-1936
E-mail: kathryn.kelly@usdoj.gov

Assistant U.S. Attorney **Michael Kelly** . . . . (312) 353-4220
E-mail: michael.kelly@usdoj.gov
Education: Illinois 2003 BSEE; Chicago 2006 JD

Assistant U.S. Attorney **Nicole Kim** . . . . (312) 886-7635
E-mail: nicole.kim@usdoj.gov
Education: Wesleyan U 1996 BA; U Washington 2000 JD

Assistant U.S. Attorney **Patrick J. King** . . . . (312) 353-5341
E-mail: patrick.king@usdoj.gov

Assistant U.S. Attorney **Edward G. Kohler** . . . . (312) 353-4086
E-mail: edward.kohler@usdoj.gov

Assistant U.S. Attorney **Prashant Kolluri** . . . . (312) 886-9085
E-mail: prashant.kolluri@usdoj.gov

Assistant U.S. Attorney **Angel Krull** . . . . (312) 886-2954
E-mail: angel.krull@usdoj.gov

Assistant U.S. Attorney **Matthew Kutcher** . . . . (312) 469-6132
E-mail: matthew.kutcher@usdoj.gov

Assistant U.S. Attorney **Stephen C. Lee** . . . . (312) 353-4127
E-mail: stephen.lee@usdoj.gov

Assistant U.S. Attorney **Jennie H. Levin** . . . . (312) 353-5372
E-mail: jennie.levin@usdoj.gov

Assistant U.S. Attorney **Kurt N. Lindland** . . . . (312) 353-4163
E-mail: kurt.lindland@usdoj.gov

Assistant U.S. Attorney **Ernest Y. Ling** . . . . (312) 353-5870
E-mail: ernest.ling@usdoj.gov

Assistant U.S. Attorney **Donald Lorenzen** . . . . (312) 353-5330
E-mail: donald.lorenzen@usdoj.gov

Assistant U.S. Attorney **Matthew F. Madden** . . . . (312) 886-2050
E-mail: matthew.madden@usdoj.gov
Education: Illinois 2002 JD

Assistant U.S. Attorney **Kathryn Malizia** . . . . (312) 353-5319
E-mail: kathryn.malizia@usdoj.gov

Assistant U.S. Attorney **Daniel E. May** . . . . (312) 353-8694
E-mail: daniel.may@usdoj.gov

Assistant U.S. Attorney **Heather K. McShain** . . . . (312) 353-1414
E-mail: heather.mcshain@usdoj.gov
Education: Notre Dame 1999 JD

Assistant U.S. Attorney **Sheri H. Mecklenburg** . . . . (312) 469-6030
E-mail: sheri.mecklenburg@usdoj.gov

Assistant U.S. Attorney **Maureen E. Merin** . . . . (312) 353-1457
E-mail: maureen.merin@usdoj.gov
Education: Chicago 2004 JD

Assistant U.S. Attorney **John D. Mitchell** . . . . (312) 353-5159
E-mail: john.mitchell@usdoj.gov
Education: Loyola U (Chicago) 2004 JD

(continued on next page)

DEPARTMENTS

Illinois - Northern District *(continued)*

Assistant U.S. Attorney **Charles Mulaney** . . . . . (312) 469-6042
E-mail: charles.mulaney@usdoj.gov
Assistant U.S. Attorney **Madeleine S. Murphy** . . . . . (312) 886-2070
E-mail: madeleine.murphy@usdoj.gov
Assistant U.S. Attorney **Brian P. Netols** . . . . . (312) 353-4128
E-mail: brian.netols@usdoj.gov
Assistant U.S. Attorney **Sarah North** . . . . . (312) 353-1413
E-mail: sarah.north@usdoj.gov
Assistant U.S. Attorney **Craig A. Oswald** . . . . . (312) 886-9080
E-mail: craig.oswald@usdoj.gov
Assistant U.S. Attorney **Derek R. Owens** . . . . . (312) 697-4071
E-mail: derek.owens@usdoj.gov
Assistant U.S. Attorney **Jordan M. Matthews** . . . . . (312) 697-4090
E-mail: jordan.matthews@usdoj.gov
Education: Pennsylvania 2009 JD
Assistant U.S. Attorney **Abigail Peluso** . . . . . (312) 353-5342
E-mail: abigail.peluso@usdoj.gov
Assistant U.S. Attorney **Michelle M. Petersen** . . . . . (312) 886-7655
E-mail: michelle.petersen@usdoj.gov
Assistant U.S. Attorney **Shoba Pillay** . . . . . (312) 886-7631
E-mail: shoba.pillay@usdoj.gov
Assistant U.S. Attorney **Elizabeth Pozolo** . . . . . (312) 469-6131
E-mail: elizabeth.pozolo@usdoj.gov
Education: DePaul 2008 JD
Assistant U.S. Attorney **Eric S. Pruitt** . . . . . (312) 353-5496
E-mail: eric.pruitt@usdoj.gov
Education: John Marshall 2001 JD
Assistant U.S. Attorney **Allison Ray** . . . . . (312) 353-6117
E-mail: allison.ray@usdoj.gov
Education: Harvard AB, 2012 JD
Assistant U.S. Attorney **Renai S. Rodney** . . . . . (312) 353-4064
E-mail: renai.rodney@usdoj.gov
Assistant U.S. Attorney **Tobara Richardson** . . . . . (312) 469-6305
E-mail: tobara.richardson@usdoj.gov
Assistant U.S. Attorney **Jessica Romero** . . . . . (312) 353-4137
E-mail: jessica.romero@justice.usdoj.gov
Assistant U.S. Attorney **Richard Rothblatt** . . . . . (312) 353-4558
E-mail: richard.rothblatt@usdoj.gov
Assistant U.S. Attorney **Peter S. Salib** . . . . . (312) 697-4092
E-mail: peter.salib@usdoj.gov
Assistant U.S. Attorney **Katherine A. Sawyer** . . . . . (312) 697-4089
E-mail: katherine.sawyer@usdoj.gov
Education: Washington College of Law 2004 JD
Assistant U.S. Attorney **Matthew M. Schneider** . . . . . (312) 886-0973
E-mail: matthew.schneider@usdoj.gov
Assistant U.S. Attorney **Douglas Snodgrass** . . . . . (312) 886-2065
E-mail: douglas.snodgrass@usdoj.gov
Assistant U.S. Attorney **Ankur Srivastava** . . . . . (312) 353-3148
E-mail: ankur.srivastava@usdoj.gov
Assistant U.S. Attorney **Meghan C. Stack** . . . . . (312) 353-4045
E-mail: meghan.stack@usdoj.gov
Assistant U.S. Attorney **Jacqueline O. Stern** . . . . . (312) 353-5329
E-mail: jacqueline.stern@usdoj.gov
Assistant U.S. Attorney **Christopher Stetler** . . . . . (312) 353-7602
E-mail: christopher.stetler@usdoj.gov
Assistant U.S. Attorney **Joseph A. Stewart** . . . . . (312) 469-6008
E-mail: joseph.stewart@usdoj.gov
Assistant U.S. Attorney **Timothy J. "Tim" Storino** . . . . . (312) 353-5347
E-mail: tim.storino@usdoj.gov
Education: Notre Dame 2002 BA, 2005 JD
Assistant U.S. Attorney **Sarah E. Streicker** . . . . . (312) 353-1415
E-mail: sarah.streicker@usdoj.gov
Assistant U.S. Attorney **Devlin Su** . . . . . (312) 886-0667
E-mail: devlin.su@usdoj.gov
Assistant U.S. Attorney **Kruti Trivedi** . . . . . (312) 353-5323
E-mail: kruti.trivedi@usdoj.gov
Assistant U.S. Attorney **Paul H. Tzur** . . . . . (312) 697-4032
E-mail: paul.tzur@usdoj.gov
Assistant U.S. Attorney **Cornelius Vandenberg** . . . . . (312) 353-5310
E-mail: cornelius.vandenberg@usdoj.gov
Assistant U.S. Attorney **Kristen Viglione** . . . . . (312) 353-5340
E-mail: kristen.viglione@usdoj.gov
Assistant U.S. Attorney **Grayson Walker** . . . . . (312) 697-4091
E-mail: grayson.walker@usdoj.gov

Illinois - Northern District *(continued)*

Assistant U.S. Attorney **Brian S. Wallach** . . . . . (312) 886-7625
E-mail: brian.wallach@usdoj.gov
Education: Yale 2003 BA; Georgetown 2007 JD
Assistant U.S. Attorney **Linda A. Wawzenski** . . . . . (312) 353-1994
E-mail: linda.wawzenski@usdoj.gov
Assistant U.S. Attorney **Katherine Welsh** . . . . . (312) 469-6309
E-mail: katherine.welsh@usdoj.gov
Assistant U.S. Attorney **Elizabeth A. Wilson** . . . . . (312) 353-5331
E-mail: elizabeth.wilson@usdoj.gov
Assistant U.S. Attorney **Sheri Wong** . . . . . (312) 697-4069
E-mail: sheri.wong@usdoj.gov
Assistant U.S. Attorney **Misty Wright** . . . . . (312) 886-2061
E-mail: misty.wright@usdoj.gov
Education: Harvard 2013 JD

Administration

Administrative Officer **Paul J. Borowitz** . . . . . (312) 353-5302
E-mail: paul.borowitz@usdoj.gov
Information Technology Officer **(Vacant)** . . . . . (312) 353-5300
Human Resources Officer **Vicky Gehrt** . . . . . (312) 353-8405
E-mail: vicky.gehrt@usdoj.gov
Budget Officer **Amanda Cross** . . . . . (312) 353-1124
E-mail: amanda.cross@usdoj.gov
Law Enforcement Committee Coordinator
Kim Nerheim . . . . . (312) 353-5489
E-mail: kimberly.nerheim@usdoj.gov
Systems Manager **Denise M. Pec** . . . . . (312) 886-7658
E-mail: denise.pec@usdoj.gov

Rockford (IL) Office

327 South Church Street, Rockford, IL 61101
Tel: (815) 987-4444 Fax: (815) 987-4236

Assistant U.S. Attorney-in-Charge **John G. McKenzie** . . . (815) 987-4444
E-mail: john.mckenzie@usdoj.gov
Assistant U.S. Attorney **Talia Bucci** . . . . . (815) 987-4451
E-mail: talia.bucci@usdoj.gov
Assistant U.S. Attorney **Michael D. Love** . . . . . (815) 987-4444
E-mail: michael.love@usdoj.gov
Assistant U.S. Attorney **Monica V. Mallory** . . . . . (815) 987-4444
E-mail: monica.mallory@usdoj.gov
Assistant U.S. Attorney **Joseph Pedersen** . . . . . (815) 987-4453
E-mail: joseph.pedersen@usdoj.gov
Assistant U.S. Attorney
Margaret Schneider-Remillard . . . . . (815) 987-4458
E-mail: margaret.schneider@usdoj.gov

Illinois - Central District

318 South Sixth Street, Springfield, IL 62701-1806
Tel: (217) 492-4450 Fax: (217) 492-4512
Internet: https://www.justice.gov/usao-cdil

★ U.S. Attorney (Interim) **John E. Childress** . . . . . (217) 492-4450
E-mail: john.childress@usdoj.gov
Education: Indiana; Duke
★ U.S. Attorney-Designate **John C. Milhiser** . . . . . (217) 492-4450
Secretary to U.S. Attorney **(Vacant)** . . . . . (217) 492-4469
First Assistant U.S. Attorney **Patrick D. Hansen** . . . . . (217) 492-4450
E-mail: patrick.hansen@usdoj.gov
Administrative Officer **Jack E. Pascoe** . . . . . (217) 492-4450
E-mail: jack.pascoe@usdoj.gov
Appellate Chief **Gregory Walters** . . . . . (217) 492-4450
Immigration Coordinator **(Vacant)** . . . . . (217) 492-4450
Law Enforcement Coordinator **Michael Emery** . . . . . (217) 492-4450
Victim-Witness Coordinator **Sharon J. Paul** . . . . . (217) 492-4450
E-mail: sharon.paul@usdoj.gov
Librarian **(Vacant)** . . . . . (217) 492-4450
Systems Manager **Michael Morgan** . . . . . (217) 492-4450
E-mail: michael.morgan@usdoj.gov
IT Specialist **James M. "Jimmy" Henton** . . . . . (217) 492-4450
E-mail: jimmy.henton@usdoj.gov

Civil Division

Chief **Carl L. Noel** . . . . . (217) 492-4450

★ Presidential Appointment Requiring Senate Confirmation ☆ Presidential Appointment □ Schedule C Appointment ◇ Career Senior Foreign Service Appointment
● Career Senior Executive Service (SES) Appointment ○ Non-Career Senior Executive Service (SES) Appointment ■ Postal Career Executive Service

Civil Division *(continued)*

Assistant U.S. Attorney **Hilary W. Frooman** . . . . (217) 492-4450
E-mail: hilary.frooman@usdoj.gov
Assistant U.S. Attorney **(Vacant)** . . . . (217) 492-4450

Criminal Division

Chief **(Vacant)** . . . . (217) 492-4450
Supervisor **(Vacant)** . . . . (217) 492-4450
Asset Forfeiture Unit Chief **Gregory M. Gilmore** . . . . (217) 492-4450
E-mail: greg.gilmore@usdoj.gov
Senior Litigation Counsel **Donald Alegro** . . . . (217) 492-4450
Assistant U.S. Attorney **Timothy A. Bass** . . . . (217) 492-4450
E-mail: tim.bass@usdoj.gov
Assistant U.S. Attorney **Crystal Correa** . . . . (217) 492-4450
E-mail: crystal.correa@usdoj.gov
Assistant U.S. Attorney **Gregory K. Harris** . . . . (217) 492-4450
E-mail: gregory.harris@usdoj.gov
Assistant U.S. Attorney **Matt Weir** . . . . (217) 492-4450
Assistant U.S. Attorney **Victory Yanz** . . . . (217) 492-4450
Assistant U.S. Attorney **(Vacant)** . . . . (217) 492-4450

Peoria (IL) Office

One Technology Plaza, 211 Fulton Street,
Suite 400, Peoria, IL 61602-1348
Tel: (309) 671-7050 Fax: (309) 671-7259

Branch Chief **Darilynn J. Knauss** . . . . (309) 671-7050
E-mail: darilynn.knauss@usdoj.gov
Assistant U.S. Attorney **Ronald Hanna** . . . . (309) 671-7050
E-mail: ronald.hanna@usdoj.gov
Assistant U.S. Attorney **Greggory Walters** . . . . (309) 671-7050
E-mail: greggory.walters@usdoj.gov
Civil Division Assistant U.S. Attorney **Kimberly Klient** . . . (309) 671-7050
Criminal Division Assistant U.S. Attorney **(Vacant)** . . . . . . (309) 671-7050
Criminal Division Assistant U.S. Attorney **(Vacant)** . . . . . . (309) 671-7050
Drug Task Force Lead Assistant U.S. Attorney
K. Tate Chambers . . . . (309) 671-7050
E-mail: tate.chambers@usdoj.gov

Rock Island (IL) Office

1830 Second Avenue, 2nd Floor, Rock Island, IL 61201
Tel: (309) 793-5884 Fax: (309) 793-5663

Branch Chief **John Mehochko** . . . . (309) 793-5884
E-mail: john.mehochko@usdoj.gov
Assistant U.S. Attorney **Donald B. Allegro** . . . . (309) 793-5884
E-mail: don.allegro@usdoj.gov
Assistant U.S. Attorney **Linda J. Mott** . . . . (309) 793-5884
E-mail: linda.j.mott@usdoj.gov
Assistant U.S. Attorney **Kevin Knight** . . . . (309) 793-5884
E-mail: kevin.knight@usdoj.gov
Education: Marquette 2009 BA; Notre Dame 2012 JD

Urbana (IL) Office

201 South Vine Street, Suite 226, Urbana, IL 61801
Tel: (217) 373-5875 Fax: (217) 373-5891

Branch Supervisor (Acting) **Eugene L. Miller** . . . . (217) 373-5875
E-mail: eugene.miller@usdoj.gov
Assistant U.S. Attorney **Katherine Boyle** . . . . (217) 373-5875
E-mail: katherine.boyle@usdoj.gov
Assistant U.S. Attorney **Elham Peirson** . . . . (217) 373-5875
E-mail: elly.peirson@usdoj.gov
Civil Division Assistant U.S. Attorney **David H. Hoff** . . . . (217) 373-5875
E-mail: david.hoff@usdoj.gov
Criminal Division Assistant U.S. Attorney
Eugene L. Miller . . . . (217) 373-5875
E-mail: eugene.miller@usdoj.gov
Anti-Terrorism Advisory Council Coordinator **(Vacant)** . . . (217) 373-5875
Assistant U.S. Attorney **Ryan Finlen** . . . . (217) 373-5875
E-mail: ryan.finlen@usdoj.gov

Illinois - Southern District

Nine Executive Drive, Fairview Heights, IL 62208
Tel: (618) 628-3700 Fax: (618) 628-3730
Internet: https://www.justice.gov/usao-sdil

★ U.S. Attorney (Acting) **Steven Weinhoeft** . . . . (618) 628-3700
E-mail: steven.weinhoeft@usdoj.gov
Secretary to U.S. Attorney **Karen Harriman** . . . . (618) 628-3700
E-mail: karen.harriman@usdoj.gov
First Assistant U.S. Attorney **Steven Weinhoeft** . . . . (618) 628-3700
Administrative Officer **Julie Crowe** . . . . (618) 628-3700
Law Enforcement Committee Coordinator **Greg Cueto** . . . (618) 628-3700
Victim-Witness Coordinator **Julie Swanston** . . . . (618) 628-3700
E-mail: julie.swanston@usdoj.gov
Intelligence Specialist **Mario Jimenez** . . . . (618) 628-3700
E-mail: mario.jimenez@usdoj.gov
IT Specialist **Michael McAfee** . . . . (618) 628-3700
E-mail: michael.mcafee@usdoj.gov
IT Specialist **Joyce Voss** . . . . (618) 628-3700
E-mail: joyce.voss@usdoj.gov

Civil Division

Chief **Nathan E. Wyatt** . . . . (618) 628-3700
E-mail: nathan.wyatt@usdoj.gov
Education: Illinois 2001 JD
Assistant U.S. Attorney **Nicholas Biersbach** . . . . (618) 628-3770
E-mail: nicholas.biersbach@usdoj.gov
Assistant U.S. Attorney **Adam Hanna** . . . . (618) 628-3700
E-mail: adam.hanna@usdoj.gov
Assistant U.S. Attorney **Jennifer Hudson** . . . . (618) 628-3700
E-mail: jennifer.hudson2@usdoj.gov
Assistant U.S. Attorney **Laura J. Jones** . . . . (618) 628-3700
E-mail: laura.jones@usdoj.gov
Assistant U.S. Attorney **David J. Pfeffer** . . . . (618) 628-3700
E-mail: david.j.pfeffer@usdoj.gov
Assistant U.S. Attorney **Nathan Stump** . . . . (618) 628-3700
E-mail: nathan.stump@usdoj.gov

Criminal Division

Chief **(Vacant)** . . . . (618) 628-3700
Organized Crime Drug Enforcement Task Force
Division Chief **(Vacant)** . . . . (618) 628-3700
Fraud and Corruption Chief **(Vacant)** . . . . (618) 628-3700
Assistant U.S. Attorney **Stephen B. Clark** . . . . (618) 628-3700
E-mail: stephen.clark@usdoj.gov
Assistant U.S. Attorney **Robert L. Garrison** . . . . (618) 628-3700
E-mail: robert.l.garrison@usdoj.gov
Assistant U.S. Attorney **Daniel T. Kapsak** . . . . (618) 628-3828
E-mail: dan.kapsak@usdoj.gov
Assistant U.S. Attorney **Ranley R. Killian** . . . . (618) 628-3700
E-mail: ranley.killian@usdoj.gov
Assistant U.S. Attorney **Kit R. Morrissey** . . . . (618) 628-3700
E-mail: kit.morrissey@usdoj.gov
Assistant U.S. Attorney **Michael J. Quinley** . . . . (618) 628-3700
E-mail: michael.j.quinley@usdoj.gov
Assistant U.S. Attorney **Laura Reppert** . . . . (618) 628-3700
E-mail: laura.reppert@usdoj.gov
Assistant U.S. Attorney **Angela Scott** . . . . (618) 628-3700
E-mail: angela.scott@usdoj.gov
Education: Southern Illinois 1997 BS, 2000 JD
Assistant U.S. Attorney **Norman R. Smith** . . . . (618) 628-3700
E-mail: norman.smith@usdoj.gov
Assistant U.S. Attorney **Monica A. Stump** . . . . (618) 628-3700
E-mail: monica.stump@usdoj.gov
Assistant U.S. Attorney **Ali Summers** . . . . (618) 628-3700
E-mail: ali.summers@usdoj.gov
Assistant U.S. Attorney **Scott A. Verseman** . . . . (618) 628-3700
E-mail: scott.verseman@usdoj.gov

Benton (IL) Office

402 West Main Street, Benton, IL 62812
Tel: (618) 439-3808 Fax: (618) 439-2401

Branch Manager **George A. Norwood** . . . . (618) 439-3808
E-mail: george.norwood@usdoj.gov

(continued on next page)

★ Presidential Appointment Requiring Senate Confirmation ☆ Presidential Appointment □ Schedule C Appointment ◇ Career Senior Foreign Service Appointment
● Career Senior Executive Service (SES) Appointment ○ Non-Career Senior Executive Service (SES) Appointment ■ Postal Career Executive Service

DEPARTMENTS

Benton (IL) Office *(continued)*

Criminal Division Assistant U.S. Attorney
Thomas E. Leggans .... (618) 439-3808
E-mail: thomas.leggans@usdoj.gov
Criminal Division Assistant U.S. Attorney
Amanda A. Robertson .... (618) 439-3808
E-mail: amanda.robertson@usdoj.gov
Criminal Division Assistant U.S. Attorney **(Vacant)** ...... (618) 439-3808

Indiana - Northern District

5400 Federal Plaza, Suite 1500, Hammond, IN 46320
Tel: (219) 937-5500 Fax: (219) 852-2770
Internet: https://www.justice.gov/usao-ndin

★ U.S. Attorney **Thomas L. Kirsch II** .... (219) 937-5500 ext. 15601
E-mail: thomas.kirsch@usdoj.gov
Secretary to the U.S. Attorney **(Vacant)** ..... (219) 937-5500 ext. 15682
First Assistant U.S. Attorney **Clifford D. Johnson** .... (574) 236-8287
E-mail: clifford.johnson@usdoj.gov
Public Affairs Specialist/Information Officer
Ryan Holmes .... (219) 937-5500 ext. 15666
E-mail: ryan.holmes@usdoj.gov
Senior Litigation Counsel **Robin Morlock** ..... (219) 937-5500 ext. 5611
E-mail: robin.morlock@usdoj.gov
Victim-Witness Specialist **Sally Haviar** .... (219) 937-5500 ext. 15665
E-mail: sally.haviar@usdoj.gov
Administrative Officer **Kenneth Potchen** ..... (219) 937-5500 ext. 15613
E-mail: kenneth.potchen@usdoj.gov
Budget Officer **Jun Zhang** .... (219) 937-5500 ext. 15622
E-mail: jun.zhang3@usdoj.gov
Systems Manager **Chad Hunter** .... (219) 937-5500 ext. 15620
E-mail: chad.hunter@usdoj.gov
Webmaster **Chad Hunter** .... (219) 937-5500 ext. 15620
E-mail: chad.hunter@usdoj.gov

Civil Division

Chief **Orest Szewciw** .... (219) 937-5500 ext. 5612
E-mail: orest.szewciw@usdoj.gov
Assistant U.S. Attorney **Wayne Ault** .... (219) 937-5500 ext. 5650
E-mail: wayne.ault@usdoj.gov
Assistant U.S. Attorney **Sharon Jefferson** ..... (219) 937-5500 ext. 5681
E-mail: sharon.jefferson@usdoj.gov
Assistant U.S. Attorney **Robin Morlock** .... (219) 937-5500 ext. 5611
E-mail: robin.morlock@usdoj.gov
Assistant U.S. Attorney **Abizer Zanzi** .... (219) 937-5500 ext. 5651
E-mail: abizer.zanzi@usdoj.gov
Education: Pennsylvania 2000 BA; Duke 2005 JD

Criminal Division

Chief **Daniel L. Bella** .... (219) 937-5500 ext. 15609
E-mail: daniel.bella@usdoj.gov
Supervisory Assistant U.S. Attorney
Gary Bell .... (219) 937-5500 ext. 15656
E-mail: gary.bell@usdoj.gov
Supervisory Assistant U.S. Attorney
(Vacant) .... (219) 937-5500 ext. 15634
Assistant U.S. Attorney **Philip Benson** .... (219) 937-5500 ext. 15608
E-mail: philip.benson@usdoj.gov
Assistant U.S. Attorney
Diane L. Berkowitz .... (219) 937-5500 ext. 15657
E-mail: diane.berkowitz@usdoj.gov
Assistant U.S. Attorney
Jennifer S. Chang-Adiga .... (219) 937-5500 ext. 5658
E-mail: jennifer.chang@usdoj.gov
Education: Stanford 2003 JD
Assistant U.S. Attorney **Toi D. Houston** ...... (219) 937-5500 ext. 15653
E-mail: toi.houston@usdoj.gov
Assistant U.S. Attorney **Joshua Kolar** .... (219) 937-5500 ext. 15659
E-mail: joshua.kolar@usdoj.gov
Assistant U.S. Attorney **Jill Koster** .... (219) 937-5500
E-mail: jill.koster@usdoj.gov
Assistant U.S. Attorney **Dean Lanter** .... (219) 937-5500 ext. 15677
E-mail: dean.lanter@usdoj.gov
Assistant U.S. Attorney **David Nozick** .... (219) 937-5500 ext. 15655
E-mail: david.nozick@usdoj.gov

Criminal Division *(continued)*

Assistant U.S. Attorney **Nicholas J. Padilla** ... (219) 937-5500 ext. 15652
E-mail: nick.padilla@usdoj.gov
Assistant U.S. Attorney
Thomas S. Ratcliffe .... (219) 937-5500 ext. 15654
E-mail: thomas.ratcliffe@usdoj.gov
Education: Vanderbilt 1993 BA; Northwestern 1997 JD
Assistant U.S. Attorney **(Vacant)** .... (219) 937-5500 ext. 15678

Fort Wayne (IN) Office

1300 South Harrison Street, Room 3128, Fort Wayne, IN 46802
Tel: (260) 422-2595 Fax: (260) 426-1616

Supervisory Assistant U.S. Attorney **Tina L. Nommay** ... (260) 422-2595
E-mail: tina.nommay@usdoj.gov
Civil Division Assistant U.S. Attorney
Deborah Leonard .... (260) 422-2595
E-mail: deborah.leonard@usdoj.gov
Criminal Division Assistant U.S. Attorney
Anthony Geller .... (260) 422-2595
E-mail: anthony.geller@usdoj.gov
Criminal Division Assistant U.S. Attorney
Nathaniel Henson .... (260) 422-2595
E-mail: nathaniel.henson@usdoj.gov
Education: Valparaiso 2004 JD
Criminal Division Assistant U.S. Attorney
Lovita Morris King .... (260) 422-2595
E-mail: lovita.morris.king@usdoj.gov
Criminal Division Assistant U.S. Attorney
Lesley Miller Lowery .... (260) 422-2595
E-mail: lesley.millerlowery@usdoj.gov

South Bend (IN) Office

204 South Main Street, Room MO-1, South Bend, IN 46601
Tel: (574) 236-8287 Fax: (574) 236-8155

First Assistant U.S. Attorney **Clifford D. Johnson** .... (574) 236-8287
E-mail: clifford.johnson@usdoj.gov
Supervisory Assistant U.S. Attorney **Kenneth Hays** ...... (574) 236-8287
E-mail: kenneth.hays@usdoj.gov
Criminal Division Assistant U.S. Attorney
Jesse Barrett .... (574) 236-8287
E-mail: jesse.barrett@usdoj.gov
Criminal Division Assistant U.S. Attorney **(Vacant)** ...... (574) 236-8287
Criminal Division Assistant U.S. Attorney
John Maciejczyk .... (574) 236-8287
E-mail: john.maciejczyk@usdoj.gov
Criminal Division Assistant U.S. Attorney
Frank Schaffer .... (574) 236-8286
E-mail: frank.schaffer@usdoj.gov
Criminal Division Assistant U.S. Attorney **(Vacant)** ...... (574) 236-8287
Criminal Division Assistant U.S. Attorney **(Vacant)** ...... (574) 236-8287
Senior Litigation Counsel **(Vacant)** .... (574) 236-8287

Indiana - Southern District

10 West Market Street, Suite 2100, Indianapolis, IN 46204
Tel: (317) 226-6333 Fax: (317) 226-6125 (Criminal)
Fax: (317) 226-5027 (Civil) Internet: https://www.justice.gov/usao-sdin

★ U.S. Attorney **Joshua J. Minkler** .... (317) 226-6333
E-mail: josh.minkler@usdoj.gov
Staff Assistant to the U.S. Attorney **Carrie Griffin** ...... (317) 226-6333
First Assistant U.S. Attorney (Acting) **Joe H. Vaughn** .... (317) 226-6333
E-mail: joe.vaughn@usdoj.gov
Senior Litigation Counsel **Bradley L. Blackington** .... (317) 226-6333
E-mail: bradley.blackington@usdoj.gov
Senior Litigation Counsel **Steven D. DeBrota** .... (317) 226-6333
E-mail: steve.debrota@usdoj.gov
Administrative Officer **(Vacant)** .... (317) 226-6333
Fax: (317) 226-5176

Appellate Division

Chief **Bob Wood** .... (317) 226-6333
E-mail: bob.wood@usdoj.gov

★ Presidential Appointment Requiring Senate Confirmation ☆ Presidential Appointment ☐ Schedule C Appointment ◇ Career Senior Foreign Service Appointment
● Career Senior Executive Service (SES) Appointment ○ Non-Career Senior Executive Service (SES) Appointment ■ Postal Career Executive Service

Civil Division
10 West Market Street, Indianapolis, IN 46204
Fax: (317) 226-5027

Chief **Jill E. Julian** .... (317) 226-6333
E-mail: jill.julian@usdoj.gov
Assistant U.S. Attorney **Debra Richards** .... (317) 226-6333
E-mail: debra.richards@usdoj.gov
Assistant U.S. Attorney **Shelese Woods** .... (317) 226-6333
E-mail: shelese.woods@usdoj.gov

Criminal Division
10 West Market Street, Suite 2100, Indianapolis, IN 46204
Fax: (317) 226-6125

Chief (Acting) **Winfield D. Ong** .... (317) 226-6333
E-mail: winfield.ong@usdoj.gov
Education: DePauw 1980 BA; Northwestern 1985 JD
Assistant U.S. Attorney **Matthew Lasher** .... (317) 226-6333
E-mail: matthew.lasher@usdoj.gov
Education: Indiana JD
Assistant U.S. Attorney **Nicholas "Nick" Linder** .... (317) 226-6333
E-mail: nick.linder@usdoj.gov
Assistant U.S. Attorney **Jeffrey D. Preston** .... (317) 226-6333
E-mail: jeffrey.preston@usdoj.gov
Assistant U.S. Attorney **Cynthia Ridgeway** .... (317) 226-6333
E-mail: cynthia.ridgeway@usdoj.gov
Assistant U.S. Attorney **Matthew Rinka** .... (317) 226-6333
E-mail: matthew.rinka@usdoj.gov
Assistant U.S. Attorney **Brad Shepard** .... (317) 226-6333
E-mail: brad.shepard@usdoj.gov
Asset Forfeiture Assistant U.S. Attorney
Winfield D. Ong .... (317) 226-6333
E-mail: winfield.ong@usdoj.gov
Education: DePauw 1980 BA; Northwestern 1985 JD

Drug Unit
10 West Market Street, Suite 2100, Indianapolis, IN 46204
Fax: (317) 226-5953

Chief **Barry D. Glickman** .... (317) 226-6333
E-mail: barry.glickman@usdoj.gov
Assistant U.S. Attorney **Bradley L. Blackington** .... (317) 226-6333
E-mail: bradley.blackington@usdoj.gov
Assistant U.S. Attorney **Michelle P. Brady** .... (317) 226-6333
E-mail: michelle.brady@usdoj.gov
Assistant U.S. Attorney **MaryAnn Mindrum** .... (317) 226-6333
E-mail: maryann.mindrum@usdoj.gov
Assistant U.S. Attorney **(Vacant)** .... (317) 226-6333
Assistant U.S. Attorney **(Vacant)** .... (317) 226-6333

National Terrorism Unit
Chief **(Vacant)** .... (317) 226-6333

Evansville (IN) Office
101 NW Martin Luther King, Jr. Boulevard,
Suite 250, Evansville, IN 47708
Fax: (812) 465-6444

Assistant U.S. Attorney **Kyle M. Sawa** .... (812) 465-6475
E-mail: kyle.sawa@usdoj.gov
Education: Indiana 2005 BA; George Washington 2009 JD
Assistant U.S. Attorney **Lauren Wheatley** .... (812) 465-6475
E-mail: lauren.wheatley@usdoj.gov
Assistant U.S. Attorney **(Vacant)** .... (812) 465-6475

Iowa - Northern District
111 7th Avenue SE, Box 1, Cedar Rapids, IA 52401
Tel: (319) 363-6333 TTY: (319) 286-9258 Fax: (319) 363-1990
Internet: https://www.justice.gov/usao-ndia

★ U.S. Attorney **Peter E. Deegan, Jr.** .... (319) 363-6333
E-mail: peter.deegan@usdoj.gov
Senior Litigation Counsel **Richard L. Murphy** .... (319) 363-6333
First Assistant U.S. Attorney **Sean R. Berry** .... (319) 363-6333
E-mail: sean.berry@usdoj.gov
Education: Notre Dame 1982 BBA; Northwestern 1987 JD
Administrative Officer **Misti Kloubec** .... (319) 363-6333
E-mail: misti.kloubec@usdoj.gov

Iowa - Northern District *(continued)*

Law Enforcement Committee Coordinator **(Vacant)** .... (319) 363-6333
Victim Assistance Specialist **Holly Elliott** .... (319) 363-6333
E-mail: holly.elliott@usdoj.gov
Civil Division Chief **Jacob A. Schunk** .... (319) 363-6333
E-mail: jacob.schunk@usdoj.gov
Education: Concordia U (WI) 2001 BA; St Thomas U 2004 JD
Criminal Division Chief **(Vacant)** .... (319) 363-6333
Deputy Criminal Chief **Matthew J. Cole** .... (319) 363-6333
E-mail: matthew.cole@usdoj.gov
Deputy Criminal Chief **MG Patrick J. Reinert USAR** .... (319) 363-6333
E-mail: pat.reinert@usdoj.gov
Education: Iowa State 1983 BA; Central U Iowa 1986 JD; Army War Col 2005 MS
Appellate Chief **Mark Tremmel** .... (319) 363-6333
E-mail: mark.tremmel@usdoj.gov
Assistant U.S. Attorney **Dan Chatham** .... (319) 363-6333
E-mail: dan.chatham@usdoj.gov
Education: Iowa 2007 JD
Assistant U.S. Attorney **Lyndie Freeman** .... (319) 363-6333
E-mail: lyndie.freeman@usdoj.gov
Assistant U.S. Attorney **Justin Lightfoot** .... (319) 363-6333
E-mail: justin.lightfoot@usdoj.gov
Assistant U.S. Attorney **Martin J. McLaughlin** .... (319) 363-6333
Assistant U.S. Attorney **Tony Morfit** .... (319) 363-6333
Assistant U.S. Attorney **Emily Nydle** .... (319) 363-6333
E-mail: emily.nydle@usdoj.gov
Assistant U.S. Attorney **Daniel C. Tvedt** .... (319) 363-6333
E-mail: daniel.tvedt@usdoj.gov
Assistant U.S. Attorney **Timothy L. Vavricek** .... (319) 363-6333
E-mail: tim.vavricek@usdoj.gov
Education: Iowa 2000 JD
Assistant U.S. Attorney **Lisa C. Williams** .... (319) 363-6333
E-mail: lisa.williams@usdoj.gov
Assistant U.S. Attorney **Stephanie J. Wright** .... (319) 363-6333
E-mail: stephanie.wright@usdoj.gov
Special Assistant U.S. Attorney **Drew Inman** .... (319) 363-6333
E-mail: drew.inman@usdoj.gov
Intelligence Specialist **Todd A. Voter** .... (319) 363-6333
E-mail: todd.voter@usdoj.gov
Systems Manager **Ashlee Plotz** .... (319) 363-6333
E-mail: ashlee.plotz@usdoj.gov

Sioux City (IA) Office
600 Fourth Street, Suite 670, Sioux City, IA 51101
Tel: (712) 255-6011 TTY: (712) 258-4761 Fax: (712) 252-2034

Branch Chief **Timothy Duax** .... (712) 255-6011
E-mail: timothy.duax@usdoj.gov
Criminal Division Deputy Chief **Jack H. Lammers** .... (712) 255-6011
E-mail: jack.lammers@usdoj.gov
Assistant U.S. Attorney
James D. "Jamie" Bowers, Jr. .... (712) 255-6011
E-mail: jamie.bowers@usdoj.gov
Assistant U.S. Attorney **Forde Owens Fairchild** .... (712) 255-6011
E-mail: forde.fairchild@usdoj.gov
Assistant U.S. Attorney **Kevin Fletcher** .... (712) 255-6011
E-mail: kevin.fletcher@usdoj.gov
Assistant U.S. Attorney **Kathryn "Katie" Hayden** .... (712) 255-6011
E-mail: kathryn.hayden@usdoj.gov
Assistant United States Attorney **Shawn S. Wehde** .... (712) 255-6011
E-mail: shawn.wehde@usdoj.gov
Special Assistant U.S. Attorney **Ajay Alexander** .... (712) 255-6011
E-mail: ajay.alexander@usdoj.gov
Special Assistant U.S. Attorney **Mikala Steenholdt** .... (712) 255-6011
E-mail: mikala.steenholdt@usdoj.gov

Iowa - Southern District
U.S. Courthouse Annex, 110 East Court Avenue,
Suite 286, Des Moines, IA 50309-2053
Tel: (515) 473-9300 Fax: (515) 473-9298
Internet: https://www.justice.gov/usao-sdia

★ U.S. Attorney **Marc L. Krickbaum** .... (515) 473-9300
E-mail: marc.krickbaum@usdoj.gov
Secretary to the U.S. Attorney **(Vacant)** .... (515) 473-9347

(continued on next page)

DEPARTMENTS

Iowa - Southern District *(continued)*

First Assistant U.S. Attorney **(Vacant)** .... (515) 473-9300
Administrative Officer **Deb Harvey** .... (515) 473-9333
E-mail: deborah.harvey@usdoj.gov
Community Outreach Coordinator **(Vacant)** .... (515) 473-9267
Victim-Witness Program Manager **Terrell Patrick** .... (515) 473-9318
E-mail: terrell.patrick@usdoj.gov
Systems Manager **(Vacant)** .... (515) 473-9331

Civil Division
110 East Court Avenue, Suite 286, Des Moines, IA 50309-2053
Fax: (515) 284-6492 Fax: (515) 473-9282

Chief **William C. Purdy** .... (515) 473-9315
Appellate Chief **Mary C. Luxa** .... (515) 473-9303
E-mail: mary.luxa@usdoj.gov
Assistant U.S. Attorney **Rachel Scherle** .... (515) 473-9357
E-mail: rachel.scherle@usdoj.gov
Assistant U.S. Attorney **Adam Kerndt** .... (515) 473-9309
E-mail: adam.kerndt@usdoj.gov

Criminal Division
110 East Court Avenue, Suite 286, Des Moines, IA 50309-2053
Fax: (515) 284-6281

Chief **Andrew H. Kahl** .... (515) 473-9311
E-mail: andrew.kahl@usdoj.gov
Deputy Chief **Debra L. Scorpiniti** .... (515) 473-9316
E-mail: debra.scorpiniti@usdoj.gov
Special Assistant U.S. Attorney **(Vacant)** .... (515) 473-9305
Assistant U.S. Attorney **Virginia Bruner** .... (515) 473-9324
E-mail: virginia.bruner@usdoj.gov
Assistant U.S. Attorney **Craig Gaumer** .... (515) 473-9317
Assistant U.S. Attorney **Bradley Price** .... (515) 473-9256
E-mail: bradley.price@usdoj.gov
Assistant U.S. Attorney **Mikaela Shotwell** .... (515) 473-9284
E-mail: mikaela.shotwell@usdoj.gov
Assistant U.S. Attorney **(Vacant)** .... (515) 473-9320
Assistant U.S. Attorney **(Vacant)** .... (515) 473-9329
Fax: (515) 473-9292
Senior Litigation Counsel **Jason Griess** .... (515) 473-9302
E-mail: jason.griess2@usdoj.gov

Council Bluffs Branch Office
8 South Sixth Street, Room 348, Council Bluffs, IA 51501
Tel: (712) 328-1612 Fax: (712) 328-4048

Assistant U.S. Attorney **Richard Rothrock** .... (712) 328-1612
E-mail: richard.rothrock@usdoj.gov

Quad-Cities Branch Office
131 East Fourth Street, Davenport, IA 52801
Tel: (563) 449-5432 Fax: (563) 449-5433

Branch Chief **Richard Westphal** .... (563) 449-5421
Assistant U.S. Attorney **Ashley Corkery** .... (563) 449-5405
E-mail: ashley.corkery@usdoj.gov
Assistant U.S. Attorney **Clifford R. Cronk III** .... (563) 449-5415
E-mail: cliff.cronk@usdoj.gov
Special Assistant U.S. Attorney **Will Ripley** .... (563) 449-5432
E-mail: william.ripley@usdoj.gov

Kansas District
1200 Epic Center, 301 North Main Street, Wichita, KS 67202
Tel: (316) 269-6481 Fax: (316) 269-6481
Internet: https://www.justice.gov/usao-ks

★ U.S. Attorney **Stephen R. McAllister** .... (913) 551-6730
E-mail: stephen.mcallister@usdoj.gov
Education: Kansas 1985 BA, 1988 JD
Secretary to the U.S. Attorney **Linda Smith** .... (913) 551-6730
E-mail: linda.smith2@usdoj.gov
First Assistant U.S. Attorney **Emily B. Metzger** .... (785) 295-2850
E-mail: emily.metzger@usdoj.gov
Administrative Officer **(Vacant)** .... (316) 269-6481
Law Enforcement Coordinator **(Vacant)** .... (316) 269-6481
Victim-Witness Coordinator **Kim Reese** .... (316) 269-6481
E-mail: kim.reese@usdoj.gov

Kansas District *(continued)*

Victim-Witness Coordinator **(Vacant)** .... (316) 269-6481
Budget Officer **Frank Prevost** .... (316) 269-6481
E-mail: frank.prevost@usdoj.gov
Personnel Officer **Amy Ayala** .... (316) 269-6481
E-mail: amy.ayala@usdoj.gov
Librarian **Phyllis A. Creed** .... (316) 269-6481
E-mail: phyllis.creed@usdoj.gov
Systems Manager **David Steeby** .... (316) 269-6481
E-mail: david.steeby@usdoj.gov

Civil Division
Chief **Emily B. Metzger** .... (316) 269-6481
E-mail: emily.metzger@usdoj.gov
Special Assistant U.S. Attorney **(Vacant)** .... (316) 269-6481
Assistant U.S. Attorney **Jason Oller** .... (316) 269-6481
E-mail: jason.oller@usdoj.gov
Assistant U.S. Attorney **Brian Sheern** .... (316) 269-6481
E-mail: brian.sheern@usdoj.gov

Criminal Division
Chief **Jared Maag** .... (785) 295-2850
E-mail: jared.maag@usdoj.gov
Special Assistant U.S. Attorney **(Vacant)** .... (316) 269-6481
Criminal Division Coordinator/ Assistant U.S. Attorney
Debra L. Barnett .... (316) 269-6481
E-mail: debra.barnett@usdoj.gov
Assistant U.S. Attorney **Brent I. Anderson** .... (316) 269-6481
E-mail: brent.anderson@usdoj.gov
Assistant U.S. Attorney **Mona L. Furst** .... (316) 269-6481
E-mail: mona.furst@usdoj.gov
Assistant U.S. Attorney **Annette B. Gurney** .... (316) 269-6481
E-mail: annette.gurney@usdoj.gov
Assistant U.S. Attorney **Jason Hart** .... (316) 269-6481
Assistant U.S. Attorney **David M. Lind** .... (316) 269-6481
E-mail: david.lind@usdoj.gov
Assistant U.S. Attorney **Alan G. Metzger** .... (316) 269-6481
E-mail: alan.metzger@usdoj.gov
Assistant U.S. Attorney **Aaron Smith** .... (316) 269-6481
Assistant U.S. Attorney **Matt Treaster** .... (316) 269-6481
E-mail: matt.treaster@usdoj.gov

Kansas City (KS) Office
Federal Building, 500 State Avenue, Suite 360, Kansas City, KS 66101
Tel: (913) 551-6730 Fax: (913) 551-6541

Assistant U.S. Attorney/Branch Manager
Christopher Allman .... (913) 551-6730
E-mail: chris.allman@usdoj.gov

Civil Division
Assistant U.S. Attorney/Branch Manager
Christopher Allman .... (913) 551-6730
E-mail: chris.allman@usdoj.gov
Assistant U.S. Attorney **Robin Anderson** .... (913) 551-6730
E-mail: robin.anderson@usdoj.gov
Assistant U.S. Attorney **Jon Fleenor** .... (913) 551-6730
E-mail: jon.fleenor@usdoj.gov
Assistant U.S. Attorney **Leon J. Patton** .... (913) 551-6730
E-mail: leon.patton@usdoj.gov
Assistant U.S. Attorney **Andrea Taylor** .... (913) 551-6730
E-mail: andrea.taylor@usdoj.gov
Assistant U.S. Attorney **(Vacant)** .... (913) 551-6730

Criminal Division
Criminal Division Coordinator **(Vacant)** .... (913) 551-6730
Special Assistant U.S. Attorney **Trent Krug** .... (913) 551-6730
E-mail: trent.krug@usdoj.gov
Assistant U.S. Attorney **Tris Hunt** .... (913) 551-6730
E-mail: tris.hunt@usdoj.gov
Assistant U.S. Attorney **Scott Rask** .... (913) 551-6730
E-mail: scott.rask@usdoj.gov
Assistant U.S. Attorney **Terra Morehead** .... (913) 551-6730
E-mail: terra.morehead@usdoj.gov
Assistant U.S. Attorney **Christopher "Chris" Oakley** .... (913) 551-6730
E-mail: chris.oakley@usdoj.gov

★ Presidential Appointment Requiring Senate Confirmation ☆ Presidential Appointment ☐ Schedule C Appointment ◇ Career Senior Foreign Service Appointment
● Career Senior Executive Service (SES) Appointment ○ Non-Career Senior Executive Service (SES) Appointment ■ Postal Career Executive Service

Criminal Division *(continued)*

Assistant U.S. Attorney **Kurt Shernuk** . . . . . (913) 551-6730
E-mail: kurt.shernuk@usdoj.gov
Assistant U.S. Attorney **David Smith** . . . . . (913) 551-6730
E-mail: david.smith@usdoj.gov
Assistant U.S. Attorney **Jabari Wamble** . . . . . (913) 551-6730
E-mail: jabari.wamble@usdoj.gov
Assistant U.S. Attorney **David Zabel** . . . . . (913) 551-6730
E-mail: david.zabel@usdoj.gov
Assistant U.S. Attorney **(Vacant)** . . . . . (913) 551-6730

Topeka (KS) Office
Federal Building, 444 SE Quincy Street,
Suite 290, Topeka, KS 66683
Tel: (785) 295-2850 Fax: (785) 295-2853

Assistant U.S. Attorney/Branch Manager
Jackie A. Rapstine . . . . . (785) 295-2850
E-mail: jackie.rapstine@usdoj.gov

Civil Division
Assistant U.S. Attorney **D. Brad Bailey** . . . . . (785) 295-2850
E-mail: brad.bailey@usdoj.gov
Assistant U.S. Attorney **Thomas G. "Tom" Luedke** . . . . . (785) 295-2850
E-mail: tom.luedke@usdoj.gov
Assistant U.S. Attorney **Tanya S. Wilson** . . . . . (785) 295-2850
E-mail: tanya.wilson@usdoj.gov
Assistant U.S. Attorney **(Vacant)** . . . . . (785) 295-2850

Criminal Division
Criminal Division Coordinator **Jared Maag** . . . . . (785) 295-2850
E-mail: jared.maag@usdoj.gov
Appellate Chief **James Brown** . . . . . (785) 295-2850
E-mail: james.brown@usdoj.gov
Senior Litigation Counsel **(Vacant)** . . . . . (785) 295-2850
Assistant U.S. Attorney **Richard L. Hathaway** . . . . . (785) 295-2850
E-mail: rich.hathaway@usdoj.gov
Assistant U.S. Attorney **Gregory A. Hough** . . . . . (785) 295-2850
E-mail: greg.hough@usdoj.gov
Assistant U.S. Attorney **Christine Kenney** . . . . . (785) 295-2850
E-mail: christine.kenney@usdoj.gov
Assistant U.S. Attorney **Anthony W. Mattivi** . . . . . (785) 295-2850
E-mail: anthony.mattivi@usdoj.gov
Assistant U.S. Attorney **(Vacant)** . . . . . (785) 295-2850
Assistant U.S. Attorney **(Vacant)** . . . . . (785) 295-2850

Kentucky - Eastern District
260 West Vine Street, Suite 300, Lexington, KY 40507
Tel: (859) 233-2661 Fax: (859) 233-2666

★ U.S. Attorney-Designate **Robert M. Duncan, Jr.** . . . . . (859) 233-2661
Education: Centre BA; Kentucky JD
Secretary to the U.S. Attorney **Melanie LeTourneau** . . . (859) 685-4802
E-mail: melanie.letourneau@usdoj.gov
First Assistant U.S. Attorney **Carlton S. Shier IV** . . . . . (859) 233-2661
E-mail: carlton.shier@usdoj.gov
Managing Assistant U.S. Attorney **Jason Parman** . . . . . (606) 864-5523
E-mail: jason.parman@usdoj.gov
Administrative Officer (Acting) **Carlton S. Shier IV** . . . . . (859) 685-4804
E-mail: carlton.shier@usdoj.gov
Law Enforcement Committee Coordinator **Allen Love** . . . . (859) 233-2661
Victim-Witness Coordinator **Jenny Parker** . . . . . (859) 685-4899
E-mail: jenny.parker@usdoj.gov
HR Specialist **Lois Elam** . . . . . (859) 685-4929
E-mail: lois.elam@usdoj.gov
Systems Manager **Traci Davis-Smith** . . . . . (859) 685-4917
E-mail: traci.davis-smith@usdoj.gov
Systems Manager **Robin Gosper** . . . . . (859) 685-4918
E-mail: robin.gosper@usdoj.gov

Civil Division
260 West Vine Street, Suite 300, Lexington, KY 40507
Fax: (859) 233-2533

Chief **Lee Gentry** . . . . . (859) 233-2661
E-mail: lee.gentry@usdoj.gov
Asset Forfeiture Unit Assistant U.S. Attorney **(Vacant)** . . . (859) 233-2661

Civil Division *(continued)*

Fraud Unit Chief **Paul McCaffrey** . . . . . (859) 685-4820
E-mail: paul.mccaffrey@usdoj.gov
Assistant U.S. Attorney **Christine Corndorf** . . . . . (859) 685-4848
E-mail: christine.corndorf@usdoj.gov
Assistant U.S. Attorney **Katie Crytzer** . . . . . (859) 685-4815
E-mail: katherine.crytzer@usdoj.gov
Assistant U.S. Attorney **Rajbir Datta** . . . . . (859) 685-4923
E-mail: rajbir.datta@usdoj.gov
Assistant U.S. Attorney **Tiffany Fleming** . . . . . (859) 685-4835
E-mail: tiffany.fleming@usdoj.gov
Assistant U.S. Attorney **Daniel Hancock** . . . . . (859) 685-4829
E-mail: daniel.hancock@usdoj.gov
Education: Kentucky 2011 JD
Assistant U.S. Attorney **Cheryl Morgan** . . . . . (859) 233-2661
E-mail: cheryl.morgan@usdoj.gov
Assistant U.S. Attorney **Wade Napier** . . . . . (859) 233-2661
E-mail: wade.napier@usdoj.gov
Assistant U.S. Attorney **Callie R. Owen** . . . . . (859) 685-4901
E-mail: callie.r.owen@usdoj.gov
Education: Kentucky 2000 JD
Assistant U.S. Attorney **Carrie Pond** . . . . . (859) 685-4869
E-mail: carrie.pond@usdoj.gov
Assistant U.S. Attorney **Jennifer Williams** . . . . . (859) 685-4862
E-mail: jennifer.williams@usdoj.gov
Assistant U.S. Attorney **(Vacant)** . . . . . (859) 685-4830
Assistant U.S. Attorney **(Vacant)** . . . . . (859) 233-2661
Assistant U.S. Attorney **(Vacant)** . . . . . (859) 233-2661
Senior Litigation Counsel **Hydee Hawkins** . . . . . (859) 233-2661
E-mail: hydee.hawkins@usdoj.gov

Criminal Division
260 West Vine Street, Suite 300, Lexington, KY 40507
Fax: (859) 233-2747

Chief **Ronald L. Walker** . . . . . (859) 233-2661
E-mail: ron.walker@usdoj.gov
Senior Litigation Counsel **(Vacant)** . . . . . (859) 233-2661
Appellate Division Chief **Charles Wisdom** . . . . . (859) 233-2661
E-mail: charles.wisdom@usdoj.gov
Assistant U.S. Attorney **Kathryn Anderson** . . . . . (859) 685-4885
E-mail: kathryn.anderson@usdoj.gov
Assistant U.S. Attorney **Andrew T. Boone** . . . . . (859) 685-4841
E-mail: andrew.boone2@usdoj.gov
Education: George Washington 2001 BA, 2004 JD
Assistant U.S. Attorney **Gary Todd Bradbury** . . . . . (859) 685-4898
E-mail: gary.t.bradbury@usdoj.gov
Assistant U.S. Attorney **Lauren Bradley** . . . . . (859) 685-4876
E-mail: lauren.bradley@usdoj.gov
Assistant U.S. Attorney **Rob Duncan** . . . . . (859) 233-2661
E-mail: rob.duncan@usdoj.gov
Assistant U.S. Attorney **John Grant** . . . . . (859) 233-2661
Assistant U.S. Attorney **Neeraj Gupta** . . . . . (859) 685-4843
E-mail: neeraj.gupta@usdoj.gov
Assistant U.S. Attorney **David A. Marye** . . . . . (859) 685-4873
E-mail: david.mayre@usdoj.gov
Assistant U.S. Attorney **Erin May-Roth** . . . . . (859) 233-2661
Education: Kentucky 2004 JD
Assistant U.S. Attorney **Cynthia Rieker** . . . . . (859) 685-4853
E-mail: cynthia.rieker@usdoj.gov
Assistant U.S. Attorney **Dimitry Slavin** . . . . . (859) 685-4899
E-mail: dimitry.slavin@usdoj.gov
Assistant U.S. Attorney **Andrew E. Smith** . . . . . (859) 685-4849
E-mail: andrew.e.smith@usdoj.gov
Assistant U.S. Attorney **Kate Smith** . . . . . (859) 685-4855
E-mail: kate.smith@usdoj.gov
Assistant U.S. Attorney **Kenneth R. Taylor** . . . . . (859) 233-2661
E-mail: ken.taylor@usdoj.gov
Assistant U.S. Attorney **Roger West** . . . . . (859) 685-4895
E-mail: roger.west@usdoj.gov

DEPARTMENTS

★ Presidential Appointment Requiring Senate Confirmation ☆ Presidential Appointment ☐ Schedule C Appointment ◇ Career Senior Foreign Service Appointment
● Career Senior Executive Service (SES) Appointment ○ Non-Career Senior Executive Service (SES) Appointment ■ Postal Career Executive Service

DEPARTMENTS

Fort Mitchell (KY) Office
207 Grandview Drive, Suite 400, Fort Mitchell, KY 41017
Tel: (859) 655-3200 Fax: (859) 655-3211

Managing Assistant U.S. Attorney **Robert McBride** ...... (859) 655-3200
E-mail: robert.mcbride@usdoj.gov
Education: Dayton 1992 JD
Assistant U.S. Attorney **Tony Bracke** .... (859) 655-3200
E-mail: tony.bracke@usdoj.gov
Assistant U.S. Attorney **Elaine M. Leonhard** .... (859) 655-3200
Education: Cincinnati 2001 BA; Salmon P Chase 2004 JD
Assistant U.S. Attorney **Wade Napier** .... (859) 655-3200
E-mail: wade.napier@usdoj.gov
Assistant U.S. Attorney **Laura K. Voorhees** .... (859) 655-3200
E-mail: laura.voorhees@usdoj.gov
Legal Assistant **(Vacant)** .... (859) 652-7040

London (KY) Office
601 Meyers Baker Road, Suite 200, London, KY 40741
Tel: (606) 864-5523 Fax: (606) 864-3590

Managing Assistant U.S. Attorney **Jason Parman** .... (606) 864-5523
E-mail: jason.parman@usdoj.gov
Assistant U.S. Attorney **Taylor Broadhead** .... (606) 864-5523
E-mail: taylor.broadhead@usdoj.gov
Assistant U.S. Attorney **Sam Dotson** .... (606) 864-5523
Assistant U.S. Attorney **Andrew Trimble** .... (606) 864-4838
E-mail: andrew.trimble@usdoj.gov
Assistant U.S. Attorney **Gregory Rosenberg** .... (606) 864-5834
E-mail: gregory.rosenberg2@usdoj.gov

Kentucky - Western District
717 West Broadway, Louisville, KY 40202
Tel: (502) 582-5911 Fax: (502) 582-5097
Internet: https://www.justice.gov/usao-wdky

★ U.S. Attorney **Russell M. Coleman** .... (502) 582-5911
E-mail: russell.coleman@usdoj.gov
Education: Kentucky 1998 BA, 2004 JD
Assistant to the U.S. Attorney **Wendy McCormick** ..... (502) 625-7053
E-mail: wendy.mccormick@usdoj.gov
First Assistant U.S. Attorney **John E. Kuhn, Jr.** .... (502) 625-5902
E-mail: john.kuhn2@usdoj.gov
Administrative Officer **Charlene Hood** .... (502) 582-6989
E-mail: charlene.hood@usdoj.gov
Budget Analyst **Kimberly Sunderhaus** .... (502) 582-5939
E-mail: kim.sunderhaus@usdoj.gov
Human Resources Officer **Sandra "Sandy" Focken** ..... (502) 582-5998
Grand Jury Coordinator **Lauren Stinson** .... (502) 582-6326
Law Enforcement Coordinator **(Vacant)** .... (502) 582-6892
Public Information Officer **Stephanie Collins** .... (502) 708-3200
E-mail: stephanie.collins@usdoj.gov Fax: (502) 582-5097
Victim-Witness Specialist **Helena Auberry** .... (502) 625-7040
E-mail: helena.auberry@usdoj.gov
Systems Manager **Robert Metzger** .... (502) 582-6420
E-mail: robert.metzger@usdoj.gov

Civil Division
717 West Broadway, Louisville, KY 40202
Fax: (502) 625-7110

Chief **(Vacant)** .... (502) 625-7044
Assistant U.S. Attorney **William F. "Bill" Campbell** ..... (502) 582-6773
E-mail: bill.campbell@usdoj.gov
Assistant U.S. Attorney **Michael D. Ekman** .... (502) 625-7102
E-mail: michael.ekman@usdoj.gov
Assistant U.S. Attorney **Jay Gilbert** .... (502) 625-7103
E-mail: jay.gilbert@usdoj.gov
Assistant U.S. Attorney **Benjamin S. Schecter** .... (502) 582-6061
E-mail: Ben.Schecter@usdoj.gov
Assistant U.S. Attorney **(Vacant)** .... (502) 582-5911
Assistant U.S. Attorney **(Vacant)** .... (502) 582-5911
Assistant U.S. Attorney **(Vacant)** .... (502) 582-5911

Criminal Division
717 West Broadway, Louisville, KY 40202
Fax: (502) 582-5067

Chief **Michael A. Bennett** .... (502) 582-6023
E-mail: michael.bennett3@usdoj.gov
Deputy Chief **Bryan R. Calhoun** .... (502) 625-7064
E-mail: bryan.calhoun@usdoj.gov
Deputy Chief **Thomas W. Dyke** .... (502) 625-7042
E-mail: tom.dyke@usdoj.gov
Assistant U.S. Attorney **Robert Bonar** .... (502) 582-7062
E-mail: robert.bonar@usdoj.gov
Assistant U.S. Attorney **Terry M. Cushing** .... (502) 582-6936
E-mail: terry.cushing@usdoj.gov
Assistant U.S. Attorney **J. Scott Davis** .... (502) 582-6988
E-mail: scott.davis@usdoj.gov
Assistant U.S. Attorney **Larry Fentress** .... (502) 582-6772
E-mail: larry.fentress@usdoj.gov
Assistant U.S. Attorney **Marisa J. Ford** .... (502) 582-5930
E-mail: marisa.ford@usdoj.gov
Assistant U.S. Attorney **Amanda Gregory** .... (502) 582-5016
E-mail: amanda.gregory@usdoj.gov
Assistant U.S. Attorney **Laura L. Hall** .... (502) 582-5901
E-mail: laura.hall@usdoj.gov
Assistant U.S. Attorney **Lettricea Jefferson-Webb** ...... (502) 582-6480
E-mail: lettricea.jefferson-webb@usdoj.gov
Assistant U.S. Attorney **Joshua Judd** .... (502) 625-7049
E-mail: joshua.judd@usdoj.gov
Education: Washington College of Law 2003 JD
Assistant U.S. Attorney **Daniel Kinnicutt** .... (502) 625-7408
E-mail: daniel.kinnicutt@usdoj.gov
Assistant U.S. Attorney **Jo Ellen Lawless** .... (502) 625-7065
E-mail: Jo.Lawless@usdoj.gov
Assistant U.S. Attorney **A. Spencer McKiness** .... (502) 582-6987
E-mail: spencer.mckiness@usdoj.gov
Assistant U.S. Attorney **Randy Ream** .... (502) 582-6981
E-mail: randy.ream@usdoj.gov
Assistant U.S. Attorney **Mac Shannon** .... (502) 582-6294
E-mail: mac.shannon@usdoj.gov
Assistant U.S. Attorney **Jason Snyder** .... (502) 582-6993
Education: Centre AB; Louisville JD
Assistant U.S. Attorney **Amy M. Sullivan** .... (502) 582-5449
E-mail: amy.sullivan@usdoj.gov
Assistant U.S. Attorney **Monica Wheatley** .... (502) 582-5938
E-mail: monica.wheatley@usdoj.gov
Assistant U.S. Attorney **Stephanie Dotson Zimdahl** .... (502) 582-6217
E-mail: stephanie.zimdahl@usdoj.gov
Education: Northwestern 2005 JD
Assistant U.S. Attorney **(Vacant)** .... (502) 625-7079
Assistant U.S. Attorney **(Vacant)** .... (502) 625-7075

Paducah (KY) Office
501 Broadway, Room 29, Paducah, KY 42001
Tel: (270) 442-7104 Fax: (270) 444-6794

Assistant U.S. Attorney **Nute Bonner** .... (270) 443-7104
E-mail: nute.bonner@usdoj.gov
Assistant U.S. Attorney **Seth Hancock** .... (270) 443-2899
E-mail: seth.hancock@usdoj.gov
Assistant U.S. Attorney **(Vacant)** .... (270) 443-6188

Louisiana - Eastern District
650 Poydras Street, Suite 1600, New Orleans, LA 70130
Tel: (504) 680-3000 Fax: (504) 589-4510
Internet: https://www.justice.gov/usao-edla

★ U.S. Attorney **Peter G. Strasser** .... (504) 680-3078
E-mail: peter.strasser@usdoj.gov
Education: Virginia BA; Washington and Lee JD
Secretary to the U.S. Attorney **Anna Christman** .... (504) 680-3171
E-mail: anna.christman@usdoj.gov
First Assistant U.S. Attorney/Criminal Division Chief
(Vacant) .... (504) 680-3000
Criminal Division Chief **Duane Evans** .... (504) 680-3000
E-mail: duane.evans@usdoj.gov

★ Presidential Appointment Requiring Senate Confirmation ☆ Presidential Appointment □ Schedule C Appointment ◇ Career Senior Foreign Service Appointment
● Career Senior Executive Service (SES) Appointment ○ Non-Career Senior Executive Service (SES) Appointment ■ Postal Career Executive Service

Louisiana - Eastern District *(continued)*

Criminal Division Deputy Chief (Acting)
Gregory M. "Gregg" Kennedy (504) 680-3000
E-mail: gregg.kennedy@usdoj.gov
Criminal Division Deputy Chief **(Vacant)** (504) 680-3000
Executive Assistant U.S. Attorney **Sharon Smith** (504) 680-3000
E-mail: sharon.d.smith@usdoj.gov
Appellate Division Chief and Assistant U.S. Attorney
Kevin G. Boitmann (504) 680-3000
E-mail: kevin.boitmann@usdoj.gov
Anti-Terrorism Unit Chief
Gregory M. "Gregg" Kennedy (504) 680-3103
E-mail: gregg.kennedy@usdoj.gov
Asset Forfeiture Unit Assistant U.S. Attorney
Jeffrey Sandman (504) 680-3000
E-mail: jeff.sandman@usdoj.gov
Civil Division Chief **Peter Mansfield** (504) 680-3000
E-mail: peter.mansfield@usdoj.gov
Civil Division Deputy Chief **(Vacant)** (504) 680-3000
Cybercrimes Unit Chief **Brian Klebba** (504) 680-3034
E-mail: brian.klebba@usdoj.gov
Fraud Unit Chief **Brian Klebba** (504) 680-3000
E-mail: brian.klebba@usdoj.gov
Organized Crime Drug Enforcement Task Force Unit
Supervisor **(Vacant)** (504) 680-3000
Public Integrity Unit Chief **Tracey Knight** (504) 680-3000
E-mail: tracey.knight@usdoj.gov
Violent Crimes Unit Supervisor **(Vacant)** (504) 680-3000
Assistant U.S. Attorney **Hayden Brockett** (504) 680-3012
E-mail: hayden.brockett@usdoj.gov
Education: St John's Col (MD) 2004 BA; George Washington 2009 JD
Assistant U.S. Attorney **Jeffrey Sandman** (504) 680-3012
E-mail: jeff.sandman@usdoj.gov
Assistant U.S. Attorney **Paige O'Hale** (504) 680-3012
E-mail: paige.ohale@usdoj.gov
Education: North Carolina 2011 JD
Special Assistant U.S. Attorney **John F. Butler** (504) 680-3012
E-mail: john.f.butler@usdoj.gov
Senior Litigation Counsel **Fred P. Harper, Jr.** (504) 680-3000
E-mail: fred.harper@usdoj.gov
Education: LSU 1976 JD
Senior Litigation Counsel **(Vacant)** (504) 680-3000
Victim-Witness Coordinator **Donna Duplantier** (504) 680-3000
E-mail: donna.duplantier@usdoj.gov
Systems Manager **(Vacant)** (504) 680-3090

Louisiana - Western District

300 Fannin Street, Suite 3201, Shreveport, LA 71101-3068
Tel: (318) 676-3600 TTY: (318) 676-3680 Fax: (318) 676-3641
Fax: (318) 676-3654 Internet: https://www.justice.gov/usao-wdla

★ U.S. Attorney **David C. Joseph** (703) 299-3700
Education: Oklahoma 1999 BBA; LSU 2003 JD
Counsel to the U.S. Attorney **(Vacant)** (318) 676-3600
Legal Assistant to the U.S. Attorney
Katina Freeman (337) 262-3600
E-mail: katina.freeman@usdoj.gov
First Assistant U.S. Attorney **Alexander C. Van Hook** (318) 676-3600
E-mail: alexander.van.hook@usdoj.gov
Legal Assistant **Lisa Langley** (318) 676-3600
E-mail: lisa.langley@usdoj.gov

Administrative Division

Administrative Officer **Vicki Willmon** (318) 676-3600
E-mail: vicki.willmon@usdoj.gov
Budget Officer **Samuel Glass** (318) 676-3600
E-mail: samuel.glass@usdoj.gov
Systems Manager **Sean Myrick** (318) 676-3600
E-mail: sean.myrick@usdoj.gov
Administrative Specialist **Dee A. Breedlove** (318) 676-3600
E-mail: dee.breedlove@usdoj.gov
Human Resources Specialist **Kelly D. Holland** (318) 676-3600
E-mail: kelly.d.holland@usdoj.gov
Litigation Support Specialist **Karen B. Levo** (318) 676-3600
E-mail: karen.levo@usdoj.gov

Civil Division

Chief **Katherine W. Vincent** (337) 262-6618
E-mail: katherine.vincent@usdoj.gov
Assistant U.S. Attorney **Shannon Brown** (318) 676-3600
E-mail: shannon.brown@usdoj.gov
Assistant U.S. Attorney **Cristina Walker** (318) 676-3600
E-mail: cristina.walker@usdoj.gov
Assistant U.S. Attorney **(Vacant)** (318) 676-3600

Criminal Division

Chief **Cytheria Jernigan** (318) 676-3600
E-mail: cytheria.jernigan@usdoj.gov
Deputy Chief **(Vacant)** (318) 676-3600
Lead OCDETF Attorney **Robert Abendroth** (318) 676-3600
E-mail: robert.abendroth@usdoj.gov
Assistant U.S. Attorney OCDETF **(Vacant)** (318) 676-3600
Assistant U.S. Attorney **Earl M. Campbell** (318) 676-3600
E-mail: earl.campbell@usdoj.gov
Assistant U.S. Attorney **John A. Crawford** (318) 676-3600
E-mail: john.crawford2@usdoj.gov
Assistant U.S. Attorney **Tiffany Fields** (318) 676-3600
E-mail: tiffany.fields2@usdoj.gov
Assistant U.S. Attorney **Brian C. Flanagan** (318) 676-3600
E-mail: brian.flanagan@usdoj.gov
Assistant U.S. Attorney **Tennille Gilreath** (318) 676-3600
E-mail: tennille.gilreath@usdoj.gov
Assistant U.S. Attorney **C. Mignonne Griffing** (318) 676-3600
E-mail: mingonne.griffing@usdoj.gov
Assistant U.S. Attorney **MIchael O'Mara** (318) 676-3600
E-mail: michael.omara@usdoj.gov
Assistant U.S. Attorney **Seth Reeg** (318) 676-3600
E-mail: seth.reeg@usdoj.gov
Senior Litigation Counsel **Allison Bushnell** (318) 676-3600
Victim-Witness Coordinator **Vicki T. Chance** (318) 676-3600
E-mail: vicki.chance@usdoj.gov

Lafayette (LA) Office

800 Lafayette Street, Suite 2200, Lafayette, LA 70501
Tel: (337) 262-6618 TTY: (337) 262-6650
Fax: (337) 262-6682 Fax: (337) 262-6680 (Criminal)
Internet: https://www.justice.gov/usao-wdla

Administrative Services Specialist
Melanie Hutchinson (337) 262-6618
E-mail: melanie.hutchinson@usdoj.gov

Civil Division

Civil Chief **Katherine W. Vincent** (337) 262-6618
E-mail: katherine.vincent@usdoj.gov
Assistant U.S. Attorney **Jennifer B. Frederick** (337) 262-6618
E-mail: jennifer.frederick@usdoj.gov
Assistant U.S. Attorney **Karen J. King** (337) 262-6618
E-mail: karen.king@usdoj.gov
Assistant U.S. Attorney **Desiree Williams** (337) 262-6618
E-mail: desiree.williams@usdoj.gov

Criminal Division

Chief **Richard A. Willis** (337) 262-6618
E-mail: richard.willis@usdoj.gov
Apellate Chief **Camille A. Domingue** (337) 262-6618
E-mail: camille.domingue@usdoj.gov
Assistant U.S. Attorney **Robert Abendroth** (337) 262-6618
E-mail: robert.abendroth@usdoj.gov
Assistant U.S. Attorney **David J. Ayo** (337) 262-6618
E-mail: david.ayo@usdoj.gov
Education: Southwestern Louisiana 1998; Mississippi 2002 JD
Assistant U.S. Attorney **Jamilla Bynog** (337) 262-6618
E-mail: jamilla.bynog@usdoj.gov
Assistant U.S. Attorney **Daniel J. McCoy** (337) 262-6618
E-mail: daniel.j.mccoy@usdoj.gov
Assistant U.S. Attorney **Joseph T. Mickel** (337) 262-6618
E-mail: joseph.mickel@usdoj.gov
Assistant U.S. Attorney **Thomas F. Phillips** (337) 262-6618
E-mail: thomas.phillips3@usdoj.gov
Assistant U.S. Attorney **Dominic Rossetti** (337) 262-6618
E-mail: dominic.rossetti@usdoj.gov

(continued on next page)

Criminal Division *(continued)*

Assistant U.S. Attorney **Kelly P. Uebinger** . . . . (337) 262-6618
E-mail: kelly.uebinger@usdoj.gov
Assistant U.S. Attorney [Lead Litigation Counsel]
John Luke Walker . . . . (337) 262-6618
E-mail: john.walker2@usdoj.gov
Assistant U.S. Attorney **(Vacant)** . . . . (337) 262-6618

Louisiana - Middle District

Russell B. Long Federal Building, 777 Florida Street,
Suite 208, Baton Rouge, LA 70801-1717
Tel: (225) 389-0443 Fax: (225) 389-0561
Internet: https://www.justice.gov/usao-mdla

★ U.S. Attorney **Brandon J. Fremin** . . . . (225) 389-0443
Education: Southeastern Louisiana BA; LSU Hebert Law JD
Secretary to the U.S. Attorney **Danette Willis** . . . . (225) 389-0443
E-mail: danette.willis@usdoj.gov
First Assistant U.S. Attorney **Ellison Travis** . . . . (225) 389-0443
E-mail: ellison.travis@usdoj.gov
Education: LSU BA; LSU Hebert Law 1988 JD
Administrative Officer **Miriam Fontaine** . . . . (225) 389-0443
E-mail: miriam.fontaine@usdoj.gov
Law Enforcement Committee Coordinator
Collins Harper . . . . (225) 389-0443
Victim-Witness Coordinator **Holly Sheets** . . . . (225) 389-0443
E-mail: holly.sheets@usdoj.gov
Systems Manager **Daryl Blink** . . . . (225) 389-0443
E-mail: daryl.blink@usdoj.gov

Civil Division

777 Florida Street, Baton Rouge, LA 70801
Tel: (225) 389-0443 Fax: (225) 389-0685

Chief **John J. Gaupp** . . . . (225) 389-0443
E-mail: john.gaupp@usdoj.gov
Assistant U.S. Attorney **Susan C. Amundson** . . . . (225) 389-0443
E-mail: susan.amundson@usdoj.gov
Assistant U.S. Attorney **James P. Thompson** . . . . (225) 389-0443
Assistant U.S. Attorney **(Vacant)** . . . . (225) 389-0443
Assistant U.S. Attorney **(Vacant)** . . . . (225) 389-0443

Criminal Division

777 Florida Street, Baton Rouge, LA 70801
Tel: (225) 389-0443 Fax: (225) 389-0561

Chief **René I. Salomon** . . . . (225) 389-0443
E-mail: rené.salomon@usdoj.gov
Deputy Chief **Jennifer M. Kleinpeter** . . . . (225) 389-0443
E-mail: jennifer.kleinpeter@usdoj.gov
Senior Litigation Counsel **M. Patricia Jones** . . . . (225) 389-0443
E-mail: patricia.jones@usdoj.gov
Assistant U.S. Attorney **Ryan Crosswell** . . . . (225) 389-0443
E-mail: ryan.crosswell@usdoj.gov
Assistant U.S. Attorney **Helina S. Dayries** . . . . (225) 389-0443
E-mail: helina.dayries@usdoj.gov
Assistant U.S. Attorney **Michael J. Jefferson** . . . . (225) 389-0443
E-mail: michael.jefferson@usdoj.gov
Assistant U.S. Attorney **Cam T. Le** . . . . (225) 389-0443
Assistant U.S. Attorney **Frederick A. Menner, Jr.** . . . . (225) 389-0443
E-mail: fred.menner@usdoj.gov
Assistant U.S. Attorney **Robert Piedrahita** . . . . (225) 389-0443
E-mail: robert.piedrahita@usdoj.gov
Assistant U.S. Attorney **Paul Pugliese** . . . . (225) 389-0443
Assistant U.S. Attorney **Ryan Rezaei** . . . . (225) 389-0443
Assistant U.S. Attorney **Kevin Sanchez** . . . . (225) 389-0443
E-mail: kevin.sanchez2@usdoj.gov
Assistant U.S. Attorney **Peter J. Smyczek** . . . . (225) 389-0443
Assistant U.S. Attorney **Alan Stevens** . . . . (225) 389-0443
E-mail: alan.stevens@usdoj.gov
Assistant U.S. Attorney **Lyman E. Thornton III** . . . . (225) 389-0443
E-mail: lyman.thornton@usdoj.gov
Education: LSU, JD
Assistant U.S. Attorney **Elizabeth White** . . . . (225) 389-0443
Assistant U.S. Attorney **(Vacant)** . . . . (225) 389-0443
Assistant U.S. Attorney **(Vacant)** . . . . (225) 389-0443

Maine District

East Tower, 100 Middle Street, 6th Floor, Portland, ME 04101
Tel: (207) 780-3257 TTY: (207) 780-3060 Fax: (207) 780-3304

★ U.S. Attorney **Halsey B. Frank** . . . . (207) 780-3257
E-mail: halsey.frank@usdoj.gov
Education: Wesleyan U; Boston U JD
Secretary to the U.S. Attorney **Laurie Janson** . . . . (207) 780-3257
E-mail: laurie.janson@usdoj.gov
Law Enforcement Coordinator **Heather Putnam** . . . . (207) 780-3257
E-mail: heather.putnam@usdoj.gov
Victim Witness Coordinator **Heather Putnam** . . . . (207) 780-3257
E-mail: heather.putnam@usdoj.gov
Administrative Officer **Sandra Dow** . . . . (207) 780-3257
E-mail: sandra.dow@usdoj.gov
IT Systems Manager **Karen Dube** . . . . (207) 780-3257
E-mail: karen.dube@usdoj.gov
Intelligence Research Specialist
Mark Winter . . . . (207) 780-3257 ext. 3242
E-mail: mark.winter@usdoj.gov

Appellate Section

Chief **(Vacant)** . . . . (207) 780-3257
Assistant U.S. Attorney **Renee M. Bunker** . . . . (207) 780-3257
E-mail: renee.bunker@usdoj.gov

Civil Division

Chief **John G. Osborn** . . . . (207) 780-3257
Assistant U.S. Attorney **Benjamin C. Block** . . . . (207) 780-3214
E-mail: benjamin.block@usdoj.gov
Education: Virginia 2004 JD
Assistant U.S. Attorney **James Concannon** . . . . (207) 780-3257
E-mail: james.concannon@usdoj.gov
Education: Columbia 2011 JD
Assistant U.S. Attorney **Julia Lipez** . . . . (207) 780-3257
E-mail: julia.lipez@usdoj.gov

Criminal Division

Chief **Jonathan R. Chapman** . . . . (207) 780-3257
E-mail: jon.chapman@usdoj.gov
Anti-Terrorism Coordinator **Mark Winter** . . . . (207) 780-3257
E-mail: mark.winter@usdoj.gov
Asset Forfeiture Unit Assistant U.S. Attorney
Donald E. Clark . . . . (207) 780-3257
E-mail: donald.clark@usdoj.gov
Narcotics Section/Organized Crime Drug Enforcement
Task Force Assistant U.S. Attorney **(Vacant)** . . . . (207) 780-3257
First Assistant U.S. Attorney
Richard W. Murphy . . . . (207) 780-3257 ext. 3250
Assistant U.S. Attorney **David B. Joyce** . . . . (207) 780-3257
E-mail: david.joyce@usdoj.gov
Education: Miami 2004 JD
Assistant U.S. Attorney **James W. Chapman** . . . . (207) 780-3257
E-mail: james.w.chapman@usdoj.gov
Assistant U.S. Attorney **Michael J. Conley** . . . . (207) 780-3257
E-mail: michael.conley@usdoj.gov
Assistant U.S. Attorney **Andrew Lizotte** . . . . (207) 780-3257
E-mail: andrew.lizotte@usdoj.gov
Assistant U.S. Attorney **Darcie McElwee** . . . . (207) 780-3257
E-mail: darcie.mcelwee@usdoj.gov
Assistant U.S. Attorney **Sheila W. Sawyer** . . . . (207) 780-3257
E-mail: sheila.sawyer@usdoj.gov
Education: Cornell 1985 BA; Fordham 1988 JD
Assistant U.S. Attorney **Jeanne Semivan** . . . . (207) 780-3257
E-mail: Jeanne.semivan@usdoj.gov
Education: Case Western 2006 BA; Boston Col 2009 BA
Assistant U.S. Attorney **Craig M. Wolff** . . . . (207) 780-3257
E-mail: craig.wolff@usdoj.gov

Bangor (ME) Office

202 Harlow Street, Room 111, Bangor, ME 04401
Tel: (207) 945-0373 TTY: (207) 945-0307 Fax: (207) 945-0319

Branch Chief **Todd Lowell** . . . . (207) 945-0373
E-mail: todd.lowell@usdoj.gov
Assistant U.S. Attorney **Joel Casey** . . . . (207) 945-0373
E-mail: joel.casey@usdoj.gov

★ Presidential Appointment Requiring Senate Confirmation ☆ Presidential Appointment ☐ Schedule C Appointment ◇ Career Senior Foreign Service Appointment
● Career Senior Executive Service (SES) Appointment ○ Non-Career Senior Executive Service (SES) Appointment ■ Postal Career Executive Service

Bangor (ME) Office *(continued)*

Assistant U.S. Attorney **Gail Fisk Malone** . . . . (207) 945-0373
E-mail: gail.f.malone@usdoj.gov
Assistant U.S. Attorney **James M. Moore** . . . . (207) 945-0373
E-mail: james.moore@usdoj.gov
Assistant U.S. Attorney **Andrew McCormick** . . . . (207) 945-0373
Assistant U.S. Attorney **Jody Mullis** . . . . (207) 945-0373
E-mail: jody.mullis@usdoj.gov
Assistant U.S. Attorney **Chris Ruge** . . . . (207) 945-0373
E-mail: chris.ruge@usdoj.gov
Deputy Administrative Officer **Katrina Martin** . . . . (207) 945-0373
E-mail: katrina.martin@usdoj.gov

Maryland District

36 South Charles Street, 4th Floor, Baltimore, MD 21201
Tel: (410) 209-4800 Fax: (410) 962-3124 Fax: (410) 962-0122
Internet: www.justice.gov/usao/md

★ U.S. Attorney **Robert K. "Rob" Hur** . . . . (410) 209-4800
E-mail: robert.hur@usdoj.gov
Education: Harvard 1995 AB; Stanford 2001 JD
Secretary to the U.S. Attorney **Marcia Murphy** . . . . (410) 209-4800
E-mail: marcia.murphy@usdoj.gov
First Assistant U.S. Attorney **Stephen M. Schenning** . . . . (410) 209-4800
E-mail: stephen.schenning@usdoj.gov
Administrative Officer **Patrick Dunn** . . . . (410) 209-4800
E-mail: patrick.dunn@usdoj.gov
Law Enforcement Coordinator **Steven Hess** . . . . (410) 209-4800
E-mail: steven.hess@usdoj.gov
Assistant U.S. Attorney and Appellate Chief **(Vacant)** . . . . (301) 344-4433
Assistant U.S. Attorney (OCDETF/HIDTA Coordinator) **Michael Hanlon** . . . . (410) 209-4800
E-mail: michael.hanlon@usdoj.gov

Civil Division

Chief, Civil Division **Allen F. Loucks** . . . . (410) 209-4800
E-mail: allen.loucks@usdoj.gov
Assistant Chief, Assistant U.S. Attorney (Health Care Fraud Coordinator) **Thomas Corcoran** . . . . (410) 209-4800
E-mail: thomas.corcoran@usdoj.gov
Assistant U.S. Attorney **Jane Andersen** . . . . (410) 209-4800
E-mail: jane.andersen@usdoj.gov
Assistant U.S. Attorney **Tarra DeShields** . . . . (410) 209-4800
E-mail: tarra.deshields@usdoj.gov
Assistant U.S. Attorney **Molissa Farber** . . . . (410) 209-4800
E-mail: molissa.farber@usdoj.gov
Assistant U.S. Attorney **Rebecca Koch** . . . . (410) 209-4800
E-mail: rebecca.koch@usdoj.gov
Assistant U.S. Attorney **Vickie E. LeDuc** . . . . (410) 209-4800
E-mail: vickie.leduc@usdoj.gov
Assistant U.S. Attorney **Sarah Marquardt** . . . . (410) 209-4800
E-mail: sarah.marquardt@usdoj.gov
Assistant U.S. Attorney **Roann Nichols** . . . . (410) 209-4800
E-mail: roann.nichols@usdoj.gov
Assistant U.S. Attorney **Matthew P. Phelps** . . . . (410) 209-4800
E-mail: matthew.phelps@usdoj.gov
Assistant U.S. Attorney **Neil White** . . . . (301) 344-4433
E-mail: neil.white@usdoj.gov
Assistant U.S. Attorney **(Vacant)** . . . . (301) 344-4433
Assistant U.S. Attorney (Affirmative Civil Enforcement) **(Vacant)** . . . . (410) 209-4800
Assistant U.S. Attorney **(Vacant)** . . . . (410) 209-4800

Criminal Division

Chief **(Vacant)** . . . . (410) 209-4800
Asset Forfeiture and Money Laundering Section Chief **(Vacant)** . . . . (410) 209-4800
Fraud and Corruption Section Chief **Kathleen O. Gavin** . . . . (410) 209-4800
E-mail: kathleen.gavin@usdoj.gov
Fraud and Corruption Section Deputy Chief **Martin J. "Marty" Clarke** . . . . (410) 209-4800
E-mail: marty.clarke@usdoj.gov
Major Crimes Section Chief **Sandra Wilkinson** . . . . (410) 209-4800
E-mail: sandra.wilkinson@usdoj.gov

Criminal Division *(continued)*

Major Crimes Section Deputy Chief **Michael Cunningham** . . . . (410) 209-4800
E-mail: michael.cunningham@usdoj.gov
National Security Section Chief **Harvey E. Eisenberg** . . . . (410) 209-4800
E-mail: harvey.eisenberg@usdoj.gov
Narcotics Section Chief **Robert Harding** . . . . (410) 209-4800
E-mail: robert.harding@usdoj.gov
Narcotics Section Deputy Chief **Christopher Romano** . . . (410) 209-4800
E-mail: christopher.romano@usdoj.gov
Violent Crimes Section Chief **Clinton J. Fuchs** . . . . (410) 209-4800
E-mail: clinton.fuchs@usdoj.gov
Violent Crimes Section Deputy Chief **James Wallner** . . . . (410) 209-4800
E-mail: james.wallner@usdoj.gov
Assistant U.S. Attorney **Dana Brusca** . . . . (410) 209-4800
E-mail: dana.brusca@usdoj.gov
Education: Northwestern 2010 JD
Assistant U.S. Attorney **Paul Budlow** . . . . (410) 209-4800
E-mail: paul.budlow@usdoj.gov
Assistant U.S. Attorney **Kenneth Clark** . . . . (410) 209-4800
E-mail: kenneth.clark@usdoj.gov
Assistant U.S. Attorney **Sean R. Delaney** . . . . (410) 209-4800
E-mail: sean.delaney@usdoj.gov
Assistant U.S. Attorney **Ayn Ducao** . . . . (410) 209-4800
E-mail: ayn.ducao@usdoj.gov
Education: Harvard 2001 JD
Assistant U.S. Attorney **Daniel C. Gardner** . . . . (410) 209-4800
E-mail: daniel.gardner@usdoj.gov
Assistant U.S. Attorney **Joshua Ferrentino** . . . . (410) 209-4800
E-mail: joshua.ferrentino@usdoj.gov
Assistant U.S. Attorney **Tamera Fine** . . . . (410) 209-4800
E-mail: tamera.fine@usdoj.gov
Assistant U.S. Attorney **Clinton J. Fuchs** . . . . (410) 209-4800
E-mail: clinton.fuchs@usdoj.gov
Assistant U.S. Attorney **Jefferson M. Gray** . . . . (410) 209-4800
E-mail: jefferson.m.gray@usdoj.gov
Assistant U.S. Attorney **Bonnie S. Greenberg** . . . . (410) 209-4800
E-mail: bonnie.greenberg@usdoj.gov
Assistant U.S. Attorney **Harry Gruber** . . . . (410) 209-4800
E-mail: harry.gruber@usdoj.gov
Assistant U.S. Attorney **Derek Hines** . . . . (410) 209-4800
E-mail: derek.hines@usdoj.gov
Assistant U.S. Attorney **Christina Hoffman** . . . . (410) 209-4800
E-mail: christina.hoffman@usdoj.gov
Assistant U.S. Attorney **Matthew Maddox** . . . . (410) 209-4800
E-mail: matthew.maddox2@usdoj.gov
Assistant U.S. Attorney **Christine Manuelian** . . . . (410) 209-4800
E-mail: christine.manuelian@usdoj.gov
Assistant U.S. Attorney **Peter J. Martinez** . . . . (410) 209-4800
E-mail: peter.martinez@usdoj.gov
Assistant U.S. Attorney **Joyce K. McDonald** . . . . (410) 209-4800
E-mail: joyce.mcdonald@usdoj.gov
Assistant U.S. Attorney **Patricia McLane** . . . . (410) 209-4800
E-mail: patricia.mclane@usdoj.gov
Assistant U.S. Attorney **Jason Medinger** . . . . (410) 209-4800
E-mail: jason.medinger@usdoj.gov
Assistant U.S. Attorney **David Metcalf** . . . . (410) 209-4800
E-mail: david.metcalf@usdoj.gov
Assistant U.S. Attorney **Judson T. Mihok** . . . . (410) 209-4800
E-mail: judson.mihok@usdoj.gov
Assistant U.S. Attorney **Seema Mittal** . . . . (410) 209-4800
E-mail: seema.mittal@usdoj.gov
Education: George Washington 2008 JD
Assistant U.S. Attorney **Zachary A. Myers** . . . . (410) 209-4800
E-mail: zachary.myers@usdoj.gov
Assistant U.S. Attorney **Paul Riley** . . . . (410) 209-4800
E-mail: paul.riley@usdoj.gov
Assistant U.S. Attorney **Philip Selden** . . . . (410) 209-4800
E-mail: philip.selden@usdoj.gov
Education: Columbia 2007 JD
Assistant U.S. Attorney **John Sippel** . . . . (410) 209-4800
E-mail: john.sippel@usdoj.gov
Assistant U.S. Attorney **Zachary Stendig** . . . . (410) 209-4800
E-mail: zachary.stendig@usdoj.org

(continued on next page)

DEPARTMENTS

★ Presidential Appointment Requiring Senate Confirmation ☆ Presidential Appointment ☐ Schedule C Appointment ◇ Career Senior Foreign Service Appointment
● Career Senior Executive Service (SES) Appointment ○ Non-Career Senior Executive Service (SES) Appointment ■ Postal Career Executive Service

DEPARTMENTS

Criminal Division *(continued)*

Assistant U.S. Attorney **James G. Warwick** .... (410) 209-4800
E-mail: james.warwick@usdoj.gov
Assistant U.S. Attorney **Leo J. Wise** .... (410) 209-4800
E-mail: leo.wise@usdoj.gov
Education: Johns Hopkins; Harvard 2003 JD
Assistant U.S. Attorney **Rachel M. Yasser** .... (410) 209-4800
E-mail: rachel.yasser@usdoj.gov
Assistant U.S. Attorney **Aaron Zelinsky** .... (410) 209-4800
Note: On detail.
E-mail: aaron.zelinsky@usdoj.gov
Education: Yale 2010 JD
Assistant U.S. Attorney **(Vacant)** .... (410) 209-4800
Assistant U.S. Attorney **(Vacant)** .... (410) 209-4800

Greenbelt (MD) Office

6500 Cherrywood Lane, Room 400, Greenbelt, MD 20770
Tel: (301) 344-4433 Fax: (301) 344-4516

Southern Division Chief **(Vacant)** .... (301) 344-4433
Southern Division Principal Deputy Chief **Kristi O'Malley** .... (301) 344-4433
E-mail: kristi.o'malley@usdoj.gov
Deputy Chief for Litigation **Bryan Foreman** .... (301) 344-4433
Senior Litigation Counsel **(Vacant)** .... (301) 344-4433
Assistant U.S. Attorney **Adam Ake** .... (301) 344-4433
E-mail: adam.ake@usdoj.gov
Assistant U.S. Attorney **Joseph Baldwin** .... (301) 344-4433
Assistant U.S. Attorney **Kelly O. Hayes** .... (301) 344-4433
E-mail: kelly.hayes@usdoj.gov
Assistant U.S. Attorney **Menaka Kalaskar** .... (301) 344-4433
E-mail: menaka.kalaskar@usdoj.gov
Assistant U.S. Attorney **Lindsay E. Kaplan** .... (301) 344-4433
E-mail: lindsay.kaplan@usdoj.gov
Assistant U.S. Attorney **Ray McKenzie** .... (301) 344-4433
E-mail: ray.mckenzie@usdoj.gov
Assistant U.S. Attorney **Nicolas Mitchell** .... (301) 344-4433
E-mail: nicolas.mitchell@usdoj.gov
Assistant U.S. Attorney **William Moomau** .... (301) 344-4433
E-mail: william.moomau@usdoj.gov
Assistant U.S. Attorney **Jane F. Nathan** .... (301) 344-4433
E-mail: jane.nathan@usdoj.gov
Assistant U.S. Attorney **Michael Packard** .... (301) 344-4433
Assistant U.S. Attorney **Erin Pulice** .... (301) 344-4433
E-mail: erin.pulice@usdoj.gov
Assistant U.S. Attorney **David I. Salem** .... (301) 344-4433
E-mail: david.salem@usdoj.gov
Assistant U.S. Attorney **Thomas Sullivan** .... (301) 344-4433
E-mail: thomas.sullivan@usdoj.gov
Assistant U.S. Attorney **Jennifer Sykes** .... (301) 344-4433
E-mail: jennifer.sykes2@usdoj.gov
Assistant U.S. Attorney **Hollis R. Weisman** .... (301) 344-4433
E-mail: hollis.weisman@usdoj.gov
Assistant U.S. Attorney **Thomas P. Windom** .... (301) 344-4433
E-mail: thomas.windom@usdoj.gov
Education: Harvard 2000 AB; Virginia 2005 JD

Massachusetts District

John Joseph Moakley U.S. Courthouse, One Courthouse Way,
Suite 9200, Boston, MA 02210
Tel: (617) 748-3100 Fax: (617) 748-3953
Internet: https://www.justice.gov/usao-ma

★ U.S. Attorney **Andrew E. Lelling** .... (617) 748-3100
E-mail: andrew.lelling@usdoj.gov
Education: SUNY (Binghamton) BA; Pennsylvania JD
Secretary to U.S. Attorney **Nancy Rojas** .... (617) 748-3100
E-mail: nancy.rojas@usdoj.gov
Public Affairs Specialist **Christina Dilorio-Sterling** ...... (617) 748-3100
First Assistant U.S. Attorney **(Vacant)** .... (617) 748-3100
Counsel to the U.S. Attorney **(Vacant)** .... (617) 748-3100
Victim - Witness Coordinator **Kathleen M. Griffin** ...... (617) 748-3100
E-mail: kathleen.griffin@usdoj.gov
Administrative Officer **Paul W. Havey** .... (617) 748-3100
E-mail: paul.havey@usdoj.gov

Appeals Division

Chief **Dina M. Chaitowitz** .... (617) 748-3100
E-mail: dina.chaitowitz@usdoj.gov

Asset Forfeiture Unit

John Joseph Moakley US Courthouse, One Court House Way,
Suite 9200, Boston, MA 02210
Fax: (617) 748-3967 Fax: (617) 748-3111

Chief **Doreen Rachal** .... (617) 748-3100
E-mail: doreen.rachal@usdoj.gov

Civil Division

John Joseph Moakley US Courthouse, One Court House Way,
Suite 9200, Boston, MA 02210
Fax: (617) 748-3969 Fax: (617) 748-3217

Chief **Mary Murrane** .... (617) 748-3100
E-mail: mary.murrane@usdoj.gov

Criminal Division

Chief **Cynthia Young** .... (617) 748-3100
Deputy Chief **James D. Herbert** .... (617) 748-3100
E-mail: james.herbert@usdoj.gov
Cybercrime Unit Chief **Amy Burkart** .... (617) 748-3100
E-mail: amy.burkart@usdoj.gov
Education: Dartmouth 1997 BA; NYU 2001 JD
Assistant U.S. Attorney **Stephen E. Frank** .... (617) 748-3100
Education: Harvard 2004 JD

Economic Crimes Unit

John Joseph Moakley Building, One Court House Way,
Suite 9200, Boston, MA 02210
Fax: (617) 740-3156

Chief **Stephen E. Frank** .... (617) 748-3100
E-mail: stephen.frank@usdoj.gov
Education: Harvard 2004 JD

Financial Litigation Unit

John Joseph Moakley US Courthouse, One Court House Way,
Suite 9200, Boston, MA 02210
Fax: (617) 748-3248

Chief **(Vacant)** .... (617) 748-3100

Health Care Fraud Unit

John Joseph Moakley US Courthouse, One Court House Way,
Suite 9200, Boston, MA 02210
Fax: (617) 748-3610

Chief **Nathaniel Yeager** .... (617) 748-3100
E-mail: nathaniel.yeager@usdoj.gov

Major Crimes Unit

John Joseph Moakley US Courthouse, One Court House Way,
Suite 9200, Boston, MA 02210
Fax: (617) 748-3104 Fax: (617) 748-3234

Chief **Lori J. Holik** .... (617) 748-3100
E-mail: lori.holik@usdoj.gov
Assistant U.S. Attorney **B. Stephanie Siegmann** .... (617) 748-3100

Narcotics and Money Laundering Unit

Chief **Linda Marie Ricci** .... (617) 748-3100
Education: Yale 1994 JD

Organized Crime Drug Enforcement Task Force Unit

John Joseph Moakley US Courthouse, One Court House Way,
Suite 9200, Boston, MA 02210
Fax: (617) 748-3156 Fax: (617) 748-3164

Chief **Nathaniel Mendell** .... (617) 748-3100
E-mail: nathaniel.mendell@usdoj.gov

★ Presidential Appointment Requiring Senate Confirmation ☆ Presidential Appointment ☐ Schedule C Appointment ◇ Career Senior Foreign Service Appointment
● Career Senior Executive Service (SES) Appointment ○ Non-Career Senior Executive Service (SES) Appointment ■ Postal Career Executive Service

Public Corruption and Special Prosecutions Unit
John Joseph Moakley US Courthouse, One Court House Way,
Suite 9200, Boston, MA 02210
Fax: (617) 748-3357 Fax: (617) 748-3357

Chief **Fred M. Wyshak, Jr.** .... (617) 748-3100
E-mail: fred.wyshak@usdoj.gov

Strike Force Unit
John Joseph Moakley US Courthouse, One Court House Way,
Suite 9200, Boston, MA 02210
Fax: (617) 748-3214

Chief **Glenn Mackinlay** .... (617) 748-3100
E-mail: glenn.mackinlay@usdoj.gov

Springfield (MA) Office
United States Courthouse, 300 State Street,
Suite 230, Springfield, MA 01105-2926
Tel: (413) 785-0235 Fax: (413) 785-0394

Chief **Kevin O'Regan** .... (413) 785-0235
E-mail: kevin.o'regan@usdoj.gov

Worcester (MA) Office
Donohue Federal Building, 595 Main Street,
Suite 206, Worcester, MA 01608
Tel: (508) 368-0100 Fax: (508) 756-7120

Chief **Karin Bell** .... (508) 368-0100
E-mail: karin.bell@usdoj.gov
Education: Harvard 2002 JD

Michigan - Eastern District
211 West Fort Street, Suite 2001, Detroit, MI 48226-3211
Tel: (313) 226-9100 TTY: (313) 226-9560 Fax: (313) 226-4609
Internet: https://www.justice.gov/usao-edmi

★ U.S. Attorney (Interim) **Matthew Schneider** .... (313) 226-9100
Note: On June 25, 2018, the nomination for Matthew J. Schneider to be the United States Attorney for the Eastern District of Michigan was sent to the United States Senate. Mr. Schneider is currently serving as Interim United States Attorney for the District.
Education: Michigan State 1996 BA; Michigan 2000 JD
Secretary to the U.S. Attorney **Stacey Harris** .... (313) 226-9100
E-mail: stacey.harris@usdoj.gov

First Assistant U.S. Attorney **Saima Mohsin** .... (313) 226-9100
E-mail: saima.mohsin@usdoj.gov
Executive Assistant U.S. Attorney **Kevin M. Mulcahy** .... (313) 226-9100
E-mail: kevin.mulcahy@usdoj.gov
Senior Counsel **(Vacant)** .... (313) 226-9100
Administrative Officer **Keri Miller** .... (313) 226-9100
E-mail: keri.miller@usdoj.gov
District Office Security Manager **Todd Paxton** .... (313) 226-9100
E-mail: todd.paxton@usdoj.gov
Immigration Coordinator **(Vacant)** .... (313) 226-9100
Law Enforcement Manager **Robert Poikey** .... (313) 226-9100
E-mail: robert.poikey@usdoj.gov
Librarian **Shannon Bass** .... (313) 226-9100
E-mail: shannon.bass@usdoj.gov
Public Affairs Officer **Gina Balaya** .... (313) 226-9758
E-mail: gina.balaya@usdoj.gov
Records Coordinator **(Vacant)** .... (313) 226-9100
Systems Manager **Danette Scagnetti** .... (313) 226-9100
E-mail: danette.scagnetti@usdoj.gov
Victim-Witness Coordinator **Sandy Palazzolo** .... (313) 226-9100
E-mail: sandy.palazzolo@usdoj.gov

Appellate Division
Chief **Andrew Goetz** .... (313) 226-9100
E-mail: andrew.goetz@usdoj.gov
Education: Michigan 2007 JD
Assistant U.S. Attorney **(Vacant)** .... (313) 226-9518

Civil Division
Chief **Peter A. Caplan** .... (313) 226-9100
E-mail: peter.caplan@usdoj.gov
Supervisory Assistant U.S. Attorney **(Vacant)** .... (313) 226-9786

Civil Division *(continued)*
Affirmative Litigation Chief **Caroline Burgunder** .... (313) 226-9100
E-mail: caroline.burgunder@usdoj.gov
Asset Forfeiture and Financial Litigation Chief
Linda Auoate .... (313) 226-9100
E-mail: linda.aouate@usdoj.gov
Civil Rights Chief **Susan DeClercq** .... (313) 226-9100
E-mail: susan.declercq@usdoj.gov
Defensive Litigation Chief **Vanessa Mays** .... (313) 226-9100
E-mail: vanessa.mays@usdoj.gov
Assistant U.S. Attorney **Jacqueline M. "Jackie" Hotz** ... (313) 226-9108
E-mail: jackie.hotz@usdoj.gov
Assistant U.S. Attorney **Derri T. Thomas** .... (313) 226-9153
E-mail: derri.thomas@usdoj.gov
Assistant U.S. Attorney **Leslie Matuja Wizner** .... (313) 226-9766
E-mail: leslie.wizner@usdoj.gov
Assistant U.S. Attorney **(Vacant)** .... (313) 226-9573
Assistant U.S. Attorney **(Vacant)** .... (313) 226-9520
Assistant U.S. Attorney **(Vacant)** .... (313) 226-9100

Criminal Division
Chief **Mark D. Chutkow** .... (313) 226-9100
E-mail: mark.chutkow@usdoj.gov
Education: Yale 1987 BA
Senior Litigation Counsel **(Vacant)** .... (313) 226-9100
Supervisory Assistant U.S. Attorney **Robert P. Cares** .... (313) 226-9736
E-mail: robert.cares@usdoj.gov
Supervisory Assistant U.S. Attorney **Lynn A. Helland** .... (313) 226-9730
E-mail: lynn.helland@usdoj.gov
Supervisory Assistant U.S. Attorney **Sheldon N. Light** ... (313) 226-9732
E-mail: sheldon.light@usdoj.gov
Complex Crimes Chief **(Vacant)** .... (313) 226-0816
Drug Task Force Chief **Julie Beck** .... (313) 226-9100
E-mail: julie.beck@usdoj.gov
General Crimes Chief **Matthew Roth** .... (313) 226-9100
E-mail: matthew.roth@usdoj.gov
General Crimes Deputy Chief **Sara Woodward** .... (313) 226-9100
E-mail: sara.woodward@usdoj.gov
Health Care Fraud Chief **Wayne F. Pratt** .... (313) 226-9100
E-mail: wayne.pratt@usdoj.gov
Health Care Fraud Deputy Chief **(Vacant)** .... (313) 226-9100
National Security Chief **Cathleen Corken** .... (313) 226-9100
E-mail: cathleen.corken@usdoj.gov
Public Corruption Chief **David Gardey** .... (313) 226-9100
E-mail: david.gardey@usdoj.gov
Violent and Organized Crime Chief **Eric M. Straus** .... (313) 226-9100
E-mail: eric.straus@usdoj.gov
White Collar Crime Chief **John Neal** .... (313) 226-9100
E-mail: john.neal@usdoj.gov
Assistant U.S. Attorney **R. Michael Bullotta** .... (313) 226-9100
Assistant U.S. Attorney **Frances Carlson** .... (313) 226-9100
E-mail: frances.carlson@usdoj.gov
Assistant U.S. Attorney **Kenneth R. Chadwell** .... (313) 226-9689
E-mail: ken.chadwell@usdoj.gov
Assistant U.S. Attorney **John C. Engstrom** .... (313) 226-9571
E-mail: john.engstrom@usdoj.gov
Assistant U.S. Attorney **Gary M. Felder** .... (313) 226-9742
E-mail: gary.felder@usdoj.gov
Assistant U.S. Attorney **(Vacant)** .... (313) 226-9577
Assistant U.S. Attorney **Carl Gilmer-Hill** .... (313) 226-9100
E-mail: carl.gilmer-hill@usdoj.gov
Assistant U.S. Attorney **Jerome F. Gorgon, Jr.** .... (313) 226-9676
E-mail: jerome.gorgon@usdoj.gov
Education: Michigan 2002 JD
Assistant U.S. Attorney **Terrence R. Haugabook** .... (313) 226-9157
E-mail: terrence.haugabook@usdoj.gov
Assistant U.S. Attorney **Daniel R. Hurley** .... (313) 226-9100
E-mail: daniel.hurley@usdoj.gov
Assistant U.S. Attorney **Stanley J. "Lee" Janice** .... (313) 226-9740
E-mail: lee.janice@usdoj.gov
Assistant U.S. Attorney **Bruce C. Judge** .... (313) 226-9100
E-mail: bruce.judge@usdoj.gov
Assistant U.S. Attorney **David E. Morris** .... (313) 226-9646
E-mail: david.morris@usdoj.gov

(continued on next page)

DEPARTMENTS

★ Presidential Appointment Requiring Senate Confirmation ☆ Presidential Appointment ☐ Schedule C Appointment ◇ Career Senior Foreign Service Appointment
● Career Senior Executive Service (SES) Appointment ○ Non-Career Senior Executive Service (SES) Appointment ■ Postal Career Executive Service

DEPARTMENTS

Criminal Division *(continued)*

Assistant U.S. Attorney **Sarah Resnick Cohen** . . . . (313) 226-9637
E-mail: sarah.cohen@usdoj.gov
Assistant U.S. Attorney **Karen L. Reynolds** . . . . (313) 226-9672
E-mail: karen.reynolds@usdoj.gov
Assistant U.S. Attorney **April N. Russo** . . . . (313) 226-9770
E-mail: april.russo@usdoj.gov
Education: Colorado Col 2006 BA; American U 2008 MA; Virginia 2011 JD
Assistant U.S. Attorney **William J. Sauget** . . . . (313) 226-9575
E-mail: william.sauget@usdoj.gov
Assistant U.S. Attorney **Christopher Varner** . . . . (313) 226-9100
E-mail: christopher.varner@usdoj.gov
Assistant U.S. Attorney **Ronald W. Waterstreet** . . . . (313) 226-9593
E-mail: ronald.waterstreet@usdoj.gov
Assistant U.S. Attorney **Craig A. Weier** . . . . (313) 226-9678
E-mail: craig.weier@usdoj.gov

Bay City (MI) Office
101 First Street, Suite 200, Bay City, MI 48708
Tel: (989) 895-5712 TTY: (989) 895-2501 Fax: (989) 895-5790

Supervisory Assistant U.S. Attorney **Anthony Vance** . . . . (989) 891-5712
E-mail: anthony.vance@usdoj.gov
Assistant U.S. Attorney **Roy Kranz** . . . . (989) 895-5712
E-mail: roy.kranz@usdoj.gov
Assistant U.S. Attorney **Janet L. Parker** . . . . (989) 895-5712
E-mail: janet.parker2@usdoj.gov
Assistant U.S. Attorney **Anca I. Pop** . . . . (989) 895-5790
Note: On detail.
E-mail: anca.pop@usdoj.gov
Education: Michigan State 2006 JD
Assistant U.S. Attorney **(Vacant)** . . . . (989) 895-5712

Flint (MI) Office
210 Federal Building, 600 Church Street, Suite 200, Flint, MI 48502
Tel: (810) 766-5177 TTY: (810) 766-5100 Fax: (810) 766-5427

Supervisory Assistant U.S. Attorney **Anthony Vance** . . . . (810) 766-5177
E-mail: anthony.vance@usdoj.gov
Assistant U.S. Attorney **Nancy A. Abraham** . . . . (810) 766-5020
E-mail: nancy.abraham@usdoj.gov
Assistant U.S. Attorney **Jules Deporre** . . . . (810) 766-5177
E-mail: jules.deporre@usdoj.gov
Assistant U.S. Attorney **Christopher Rawsthorne** . . . . (810) 766-5020
E-mail: christopher.rawsthorne@usdoj.gov
Assistant U.S. Attorney **(Vacant)** . . . . (810) 766-5177

Michigan - Western District
330 Ionia NW, Suite 501, Grand Rapids, MI 49503
P.O. Box 208, Grand Rapids, MI 49501-0208
Tel: (616) 456-2404 Fax: (616) 456-2408
Internet: https://www.justice.gov/usao-wdmi

★ U.S. Attorney (Acting) **Andrew Byerly Birge** . . . . (616) 456-2404
E-mail: andrew.birge@usdoj.gov
Administrative Assistant to the U.S. Attorney **Breanne Warner** . . . . (616) 456-2404
First Assistant U.S. Attorney **Andrew Byerly Birge** . . . . . . (616) 456-2404
E-mail: andrew.birge@usdoj.gov
Administrative Officer **Sheryl A. Brugh** . . . . (616) 456-2404
E-mail: sheryl.brugh@usdoj.gov
Administrative Service Specialist **Kelly Johnson** . . . . (616) 456-2404
E-mail: kelly.johnson@usdoj.gov
Supervisory Administrative Services Specialist **Warren Olsen** . . . . (616) 456-2404
E-mail: warren.olson@usdoj.gov
Law Enforcement Committee Coordinator **Kaye D. Hooker** . . . . (616) 456-2404
Librarian **(Vacant)** . . . . (616) 456-2404
Public Information Officer **Kaye D. Hooker** . . . . (616) 456-2404
E-mail: kaye.hooker@usdoj.gov
Systems Manager **Roger Hensley** . . . . (616) 456-2404
E-mail: roger.hensley@usdoj.gov
Assistant Systems Manager **Tom Keating** . . . . (616) 456-2404
E-mail: tom.keating@usdoj.gov

Michigan - Western District *(continued)*

Victim-Witness Coordinator **Kathy Schuette** . . . . (616) 456-2404
E-mail: kathy.schuette@usdoj.gov
Victim-Witness Coordinator **Janet Strahan** . . . . (616) 456-2404
E-mail: janet.strahan@usdoj.gov

Civil Division
Chief **Ryan Cobb** . . . . (616) 456-2404
E-mail: ryan.cobb@usdoj.gov
Assistant U.S. Attorney **Carrie Almassian** . . . . (616) 456-2404
Assistant U.S. Attorney **Jeanne F. Long** . . . . (616) 456-2404
E-mail: jeanne.long@usdoj.gov
Education: Michigan 2007 JD
Assistant U.S. Attorney **Michael L. Shiparski** . . . . (616) 456-2404
E-mail: mike.shiparski@usdoj.gov
Assistant U.S. Attorney **Adam Townshend** . . . . (616) 456-2404
E-mail: adam.townshend@usdoj.gov
Assistant U.S. Attorney **(Vacant)** . . . . (616) 456-2404

Criminal Division
Chief/Assistant U.S. Attorney **Nils Kessler** . . . . (616) 456-2404
E-mail: nils.kessler@usdoj.gov
Deputy Chief **Daniel Y. Mekaru** . . . . (616) 456-2404
E-mail: daniel.mekaru@usdoj.gov
Senior Litigative Counsel **(Vacant)** . . . . (616) 456-2404
Executive Counsel **Donald Daniels** . . . . (616) 456-2404
E-mail: donald.daniels@usdoj.gov
Anti-Terrorism Advisory Council Coordinator **Clay Matthew West** . . . . (616) 456-2404
E-mail: clay.west@usdoj.gov
Education: Harvard 1997 AB; Cambridge (UK) 1998 MPhil; Yale 2001 JD
Appellate Coordinator **Jennifer L. McManus** . . . . (616) 456-2404
E-mail: jennifer.mcmanus@usdoj.gov
Asset Forfeiture Coordinator **Joel Fauson** . . . . (616) 456-2404
E-mail: joel.fauson@usdoj.gov
Drug Unit Chief **(Vacant)** . . . . (616) 456-2404
Tribal Liaison **Jeffrey J. Davis** . . . . (616) 456-2404
Assistant U.S. Attorney **Raymond E. Beckering III** . . . . . . (616) 456-2404
E-mail: ray.beckering@usdoj.gov
Assistant U.S. Attorney **Sally Berens** . . . . (616) 456-2404
E-mail: sally.berens@usdoj.gov
Education: Chicago 2001 JD
Assistant U.S. Attorney **Andrew Byerly Birge** . . . . (616) 456-2404
E-mail: andrew.birge@usdoj.gov
Assistant U.S. Attorney **Mark V. Courtade** . . . . (616) 456-2404
E-mail: mark.courtade@usdoj.gov
Assistant U.S. Attorney **Joel Fauson** . . . . (616) 456-2404
E-mail: joel.fauson@usdoj.gov
Assistant U.S. Attorney **Hagen W. Frank** . . . . (616) 456-2404
E-mail: hagen.frank@usdoj.gov
Assistant U.S. Attorney **Tessa Hessmiller** . . . . (616) 456-2404
E-mail: tessa.hessmiller@usdoj.gov
Assistant U.S. Attorney **Sean Lewis** . . . . (616) 456-2404
E-mail: sean.lewis@usdoj.gov
Assistant U.S. Attorney **Michael A. MacDonald** . . . . (616) 456-2404
E-mail: michael.macdonald@usdoj.gov
Assistant U.S. Attorney **Christopher O'Connor** . . . . (616) 456-2404
E-mail: christopher.oconnor@usdoj.gov
Assistant U.S. Attorney **B. Rene Shekmer** . . . . (616) 456-2404
E-mail: rene.shekmer@usdoj.gov
Assistant U.S. Attorney **Ronald M. Stella** . . . . (616) 456-2404
Assistant U.S. Attorney **Clay Stiffler** . . . . (616) 456-2404
E-mail: clay.stiffler@usdoj.gov
Assistant U.S. Attorney **Timothy P. VerHey** . . . . (616) 456-2404
E-mail: timothy.verhey@usdoj.gov
Assistant U.S. Attorney **Clay Matthew West** . . . . (616) 456-2404
E-mail: clay.west@usdoj.gov
Education: Harvard 1997 AB; Cambridge (UK) 1998 MPhil; Yale 2001 JD
Assistant U.S. Attorney **(Vacant)** . . . . (616) 456-2404
Assistant U.S. Attorney **(Vacant)** . . . . (616) 456-2404
Assistant U.S. Attorney **(Vacant)** . . . . (616) 456-2404
Assistant U.S. Attorney **(Vacant)** . . . . (616) 456-2404

Lansing (MI) Office
315 West Allegan, Room 252, Lansing, MI 48933
Tel: (517) 377-1577 Fax: (517) 377-1698
Assistant U.S. Attorney **(Vacant)** .... (517) 377-1577

Marquette (MI) Office
First Merit Bank, 1930 U.S. 41 West, 2nd Floor, Marquette, MI 49855
Tel: (906) 226-2500 Fax: (906) 226-3700
Assistant U.S. Attorney **Paul D. Lochner** .... (906) 226-2500
E-mail: paul.lochner@usdoj.gov
Assistant U.S. Attorney **Hannah Bobee** .... (906) 226-2500
E-mail: hannah.bobee@usdoj.gov
Assistant U.S. Attorney **Maarten Vermaat** .... (906) 226-2500
E-mail: maarten.vermaat@usdoj.gov
Education: Yale 1999 JD

Minnesota District
600 U.S. Courthouse, 300 South Fourth Street, Minneapolis, MN 55415
Tel: (612) 664-5600 Tel: (651) 848-1950 (St. Paul, MN Office)
Fax: (612) 664-5787 Internet: https://www.justice.gov/usao-mn
★ U.S. Attorney **Erica H. MacDonald** .... (612) 664-5600
E-mail: erica.macdonald@usdoj.gov
Education: Notre Dame BA; DePaul JD
Secretary to the U.S. Attorney **Tammie Cuddihy** ...... (612) 664-5665
E-mail: tammie.cuddihy@usdoj.gov
First Assistant U.S. Attorney **W. Anders Folk** .... (612) 664-5600
E-mail: anders.folk@usdoj.gov
Education: Minnesota 1998 BA, 1998 JD
Senior Litigation Counsel **Andrew S. Dunne** .... (612) 664-5600
Senior Litigation Counsel **David MacLaughlin** .... (612) 664-5600
Administrative Officer **Keith Collier** .... (612) 664-5600
Human Resources Officer **Joan Potter** .... (612) 664-5585
E-mail: joan.potter@usdoj.gov
Systems Manager **Daniel "Dan" McConville** .... (612) 664-5600
E-mail: daniel.mcconville@usdoj.gov
Secretary to the U.S. Attorney **Deb Kapinrs** .... (612) 664-5657

Civil Division
Chief **Ana Voss** .... (612) 664-5600
E-mail: ana.voss@usdoj.gov
Deputy Chief **Anne M. Bildtsen** .... (612) 664-5600
E-mail: ann.bildtsen@usdoj.gov

Criminal Division
Chief **Tracy L. Perzel** .... (612) 664-5600
E-mail: tracy.perzel@usdoj.gov
Appellate Chief **Lisa Kirkpatrick** .... (612) 848-1927
E-mail: lisa.kirkpatrick@usdoj.gov
Deputy Criminal Chief for Fraud and Public Corruption **Timothy G. Rank** .... (612) 664-5600
E-mail: timothy.rank@usdoj.gov
Deputy Criminal Chief for Major Crimes and Priority Prosecutions **Karen B. Schommer** .... (612) 664-5600
E-mail: karen.schommer@usdoj.gov
Deputy Criminal Chief for Organized Crime Drug Enforcement Task Force and Violent Crimes **Andrew S. Dunne** .... (612) 664-5600
E-mail: andrew.dunne@usdoj.gov

Saint Paul (MN) Office
404 United States Courthouse, 316 North Robert Street, St. Paul, MN 55101
Tel: (651) 848-1950 Fax: (651) 848-1943
Branch Chief **Lisa Kirkpatrick** .... (612) 848-1927

Mississippi - Northern District
900 Jefferson Avenue, Oxford, MS 38655-3608
Tel: (662) 234-3351 Fax: (662) 234-4818
E-mail: usa-msn-oxford@usdoj.gov
★ U.S. Attorney **William Chad Lamar** .... (662) 234-3351
Education: Millsaps; Mississippi JD
Secretary to the U.S. Attorney **(Vacant)** .... (662) 234-3351
First Assistant U.S. Attorney **(Vacant)** .... (662) 234-3351

Mississippi - Northern District *(continued)*
Administrative Officer **Gerald Coleman** .... (662) 234-3351
E-mail: gerald.coleman@usdoj.gov
Law Enforcement Coordinator **Randall M. "Randy" Corban** .... (662) 234-3351
E-mail: randy.corban@usdoj.gov
Victim-Witness Coordinator **Jorge Torres** .... (662) 234-3351
Intelligence Specialist **James Paul Rowlett** .... (662) 234-3351
Public Affairs Officer **(Vacant)** .... (662) 234-3351

Civil Division
900 Jefferson Avenue, Oxford, MS 38655-3608
Fax: (662) 234-3318
Chief **William C. Martin** .... (662) 234-3351
Assistant U.S. Attorney **John E. Gough, Jr.** .... (662) 234-3351
E-mail: john.gough@usdoj.gov
Assistant U.S. Attorney **Ava N. Jackson** .... (662) 234-3351
E-mail: ava.jackson@usdoj.gov
Assistant U.S. Attorney **Feleica T. Wilson** .... (662) 234-3351
E-mail: feleica.wilson@usdoj.gov
Assistant U.S. Attorney **Samuel D. Wright** .... (662) 234-3351
E-mail: samuel.wright@usdoj.gov
Assistant U.S. Attorney **(Vacant)** .... (662) 234-3351
Paralegal Specialist **(Vacant)** .... (662) 234-3351

Criminal Division
900 Jefferson Avenue, Oxford, MS 38655-3608
Fax: (662) 234-0657
Chief **(Vacant)** .... (662) 234-3351
Drug Task Force Lead Assistant U.S. Attorney **Scott F. Leary** .... (662) 234-3351
E-mail: scott.leary@usdoj.gov
Assistant U.S. Attorney **Susan S. Bradley** .... (662) 234-3351
E-mail: susan.bradley@usdoj.gov
Assistant U.S. Attorney **Robert W. Coleman** .... (662) 234-3351
E-mail: robert.coleman@usdoj.gov
Assistant U.S. Attorney **Clayton A. Dabbs** .... (662) 234-3351
E-mail: clay.dabbs@usdoj.gov
Assistant U.S. Attorney **Chad M. Doleac** .... (662) 234-3351
E-mail: chad.doleac@usdoj.gov
Assistant U.S. Attorney **Michael Hallock** .... (662) 234-3351
E-mail: michael.hallock@usdoj.gov
Education: Arizona 2005 BA; Chicago-Kent 2008 JD
Assistant U.S. Attorney **Clyde McGee IV** .... (662) 234-3351
E-mail: clyde.mcgee@usdoj.gov
Assistant U.S. Attorney **Robert H. Mims** .... (662) 234-3351
E-mail: robert.mims@usdoj.gov
Assistant U.S. Attorney **Paul D. Roberts** .... (662) 234-3351
E-mail: paul.roberts@usdoj.gov
Assistant U.S. Attorney **Jamiel M. Wiggins** .... (662) 234-3351
E-mail: jamiel.wiggins@usdoj.gov
Assistant U.S. Attorney **(Vacant)** .... (662) 234-3351

Mississippi - Southern District
501 East Court Street, Suite 4-430, Jackson, MS 39201
Tel: (601) 965-4480 Fax: (601) 965-4409
Internet: https://www.justice.gov/usao-sdms
★ U.S. Attorney **D. Michael Hurst, Jr.** .... (601) 965-4480
E-mail: mike.hurst@usdoj.gov
Education: Millsaps 1997 BA; George Washington 2000 JD
Secretary to the U.S. Attorney **Sheila Wilbanks** .... (601) 973-2852
E-mail: sheila.wilbanks@usdoj.gov
First Assistant U.S. Attorney **Harold Brittain** .... (228) 563-1560
E-mail: harold.brittain@usdoj.gov
Administrative Officer **(Vacant)** .... (601) 965-4480
Law Enforcement Committee Coordinator **Jesse Bingham** .... (601) 965-4480
E-mail: jesse.bingham@usdoj.gov
Personnel Manager **Cindy Pittman** .... (601) 973-2861
Systems Manager **(Vacant)** .... (601) 973-2809
Webmaster **Gordon Huey** .... (601) 965-2807
E-mail: gordon.huey@usdoj.gov

★ Presidential Appointment Requiring Senate Confirmation ☆ Presidential Appointment ☐ Schedule C Appointment ◇ Career Senior Foreign Service Appointment
● Career Senior Executive Service (SES) Appointment ○ Non-Career Senior Executive Service (SES) Appointment ■ Postal Career Executive Service

DEPARTMENTS

Civil Division
Chief **Mitzi Dease Paige** .... (601) 965-4480
E-mail: mitzi.paige@usdoj.gov
Assistant U.S. Attorney **Pshon Barrett** .... (601) 965-4480
E-mail: pshon.barrett@usdoj.gov
Assistant U.S. Attorney **Keith French** .... (601) 965-4480
E-mail: keith.french@usdoj.gov
Assistant U.S. Attorney **Kristi Johnson** .... (601) 965-4480
E-mail: kristi.johnson2@usdoj.gov
Assistant U.S. Attorney **Candace Mayberry** .... (601) 965-4480
E-mail: candace.mayberry@usdoj.gov
Assistant U.S. Attorney **Lynn Murray** .... (601) 965-4480
E-mail: lynn.murray@usdoj.gov
Assistant U.S. Attorney **Marc Perez** .... (601) 965-4480
E-mail: marc.perez@usdoj.gov
Assistant U.S. Attorney **David Usry** .... (601) 965-4480
E-mail: david.usry@usdoj.gov

Criminal Division
Chief **Darren LaMarca** .... (601) 965-4480
E-mail: darren.lamarca@usdoj.gov
Drug Task Force Lead Assistant U.S. Attorney
Jerry Rushing .... (601) 965-4480
E-mail: jerry.rushing@usdoj.gov
Assistant U.S. Attorney **Jennifer Case** .... (601) 965-4480
E-mail: jennifer.case@usdoj.gov
Assistant U.S. Attorney **Erin Chalk** .... (601) 965-4480
E-mail: erin.chalk@usdoj.gov
Assistant U.S. Attorney **Carla Clark** .... (601) 965-4480
E-mail: carla.clark@usdoj.gov
Assistant U.S. Attorney **Dave Fulcher** .... (601) 965-4480
E-mail: dave.fulcher@usdoj.gov
Assistant U.S. Attorney **Glenda Haynes** .... (601) 965-4480
E-mail: glenda.haynes@usdoj.gov
Assistant U.S. Attorney **Greg Kennedy** .... (601) 965-4480
E-mail: greg.kennedy@usdoj.gov
Assistant U.S. Attorney **Pat Lemon** .... (601) 965-4480
E-mail: pat.lemon@usdoj.gov
Assistant U.S. Attorney **John Meynardie** .... (601) 965-4480
E-mail: john.meynardie@usdoj.gov
Assistant U.S. Attorney **Abe Mcglothin** .... (601) 965-4480
E-mail: abe.mcglothin@usdoj.gov
Assistant U.S. Attorney **Keesha Middleton** .... (601) 965-4480
E-mail: keesha.middleton@usdoj.gov
Assistant U.S. Attorney **Mary Helen Wall** .... (601) 965-4480
Assistant U.S. Attorney **Christopher Wansley** .... (601) 965-4480
E-mail: christopher.wansley@usdoj.gov

Gulfport (MS) Office
1575 20th Avenue, Gulfport, MS 39501
Tel: (228) 563-1560 Fax: (228) 435-3303
Assistant U.S. Attorney **Stanley B. Harris** .... (228) 563-1560
Civil Division Assistant U.S. Attorney
Cynthia Eldridge .... (228) 563-1560
Civil Division Assistant U.S. Attorney
Stephen R. Graben .... (228) 563-1560
E-mail: stephen.graben@usdoj.gov
Criminal Division Supervisory Assistant U.S. Attorney
Jay Golden .... (228) 563-1560
E-mail: jay.golden@usdoj.gov
Criminal Division Assistant U.S. Attorney
Gaines Cleveland .... (228) 563-1560
E-mail: gaines.cleveland@usdoj.gov
Criminal Division Assistant U.S. Attorney
Shundral Cole .... (228) 563-1560
E-mail: shundral.cole@usdoj.gov
Criminal Division Assistant U.S. Attorney
Andrea Cabell Jones .... (228) 563-1560
E-mail: andrea.jones@usdoj.gov
Education: Sophie Newcomb 1983 BA; Mississippi 1986 JD
Criminal Division Assistant U.S. Attorney
Kathlyn Van Buskirk .... (228) 563-1560
E-mail: kathlyn.vanbuskirk@usdoj.gov
Criminal Division Assistant U.S. Attorney
Annette Williams .... (228) 563-1560

Missouri - Eastern District
Thomas F. Eagleton U.S. Courthouse, 111 South 10th Street,
Room 20.333, St. Louis, MO 63102
Tel: (314) 539-2200 Fax: (314) 539-2309
Internet: https://www.justice.gov/usao-edmo
★ U.S. Attorney **Jeffrey B. Jensen** .... (314) 539-2200
E-mail: jeff.jensen@usdoj.gov
Secretary to the U.S. Attorney **Terri L. Dougherty** .... (314) 539-2200
E-mail: terri.dougherty@usdoj.gov
First Assistant U.S. Attorney **Carrie Costantin** .... (314) 539-2200
E-mail: carrie.costantin@usdoj.gov
Executive Assistant U.S. Attorney **Reginald Harris** .... (314) 539-2200
E-mail: reginald.harris@usdoj.gov
Administrative Officer **Gary Livingston** .... (314) 539-2200
E-mail: gary.livingston@usdoj.gov
Public Affairs Officer **(Vacant)** .... (314) 539-2200
Law Enforcement Committee Coordinator
Ronald J. Scaggs .... (314) 539-2200
E-mail: ron.scaggs@usdoj.gov
Victim Advocate **Kimberly Sanders** .... (314) 539-2200
E-mail: kimberly.sanders@usdoj.gov
Systems Manager **Dianne Michels** .... (314) 539-2200
E-mail: dianne.michels@usdoj.gov

Civil Division
Chief **Nicholas P. Llewellyn** .... (314) 539-3280
E-mail: nicholas.llewellyn@usdoj.gov
Financial Litigation Unit Supervisor **Karen Wilke** .... (314) 539-2200
E-mail: karen.wilke@usdoj.gov
Assistant U.S. Attorney **Josh Jones** .... (314) 539-3280
E-mail: josh.jones@usdoj.gov
Education: Georgia 2000 JD
Assistant U.S. Attorney **Roger Keller** .... (314) 539-3280
E-mail: roger.keller@usdoj.gov
Assistant U.S. Attorney **Andy Lay** .... (314) 539-3280
Assistant U.S. Attorney **Steven Luther** .... (314) 539-3280
E-mail: steven.luther@usdoj.gov
Assistant U.S. Attorney **Suzanne Moore** .... (314) 539-3280
E-mail: suzanne.moore@usdoj.gov
Assistant U.S. Attorney **A. Jane Rund** .... (314) 539-3280
Assistant U.S. Attorney **Karin Schute** .... (314) 539-3280
E-mail: karin.schute@usdoj.gov
Assistant U.S. Attorney **Jane Berman Shaw** .... (314) 539-3280
E-mail: jane.shaw@usdoj.gov
Assistant U.S. Attorney **(Vacant)** .... (314) 539-3280

Criminal Division
Chief **James E. Crowe, Jr.** .... (314) 539-2200
E-mail: james.crowe@usdoj.gov
Deputy Chief **Patrick Judge** .... (314) 539-2200
E-mail: patrick.judge@usdoj.gov
Regional Drug Task Force Coordinator
James C. Delworth .... (314) 539-2200
E-mail: james.delworth@usdoj.gov
Senior Litigation Counsel **Thomas Albus** .... (314) 539-2200
White Collar and General Crime Unit Supervisor
Jeanette Graviss .... (314) 539-2200
White Collar and General Crime Unit Supervisor
Howard J. Marcus .... (314) 539-2200
E-mail: howard.marcus@usdoj.gov
White Collar and General Crime Unit Supervisor
(Vacant) .... (314) 539-2200
Appellate Chief **Tiffany Becker** .... (314) 539-2200
E-mail: tiffany.becker@usdoj.gov
Assistant U.S. Attorney **Kyle Bateman** .... (314) 539-2200
Assistant U.S. Attorney **Tracy Berry** .... (314) 539-2220
E-mail: tracy.berry@usdoj.gov
Assistant U.S. Attorney **John Bird** .... (314) 539-2200
E-mail: john.bird@usdoj.gov
Assistant U.S. Attorney **Charles Birmingham** .... (314) 539-2200
E-mail: charles.birmingham@usdoj.gov
Assistant U.S. Attorney **Gwendolyn E. Carroll** .... (314) 539-2200
E-mail: gwendolyn.e.carroll@usdoj.gov
Assistant U.S. Attorney **Stephen Casey** .... (314) 539-2200
Education: Regent U JD

★ Presidential Appointment Requiring Senate Confirmation ☆ Presidential Appointment ☐ Schedule C Appointment ◇ Career Senior Foreign Service Appointment
● Career Senior Executive Service (SES) Appointment ○ Non-Career Senior Executive Service (SES) Appointment ■ Postal Career Executive Service

Criminal Division *(continued)*

Assistant U.S. Attorney **Dianna Collins** .... (314) 539-2200
Assistant U.S. Attorney **John T. Davis** .... (314) 539-2200
Assistant U.S. Attorney **Angie Danis** .... (314) 539-2200
E-mail: angie.danis@usdoj.gov
Assistant U.S. Attorney **Edward Dowd III** .... (314) 539-2200
E-mail: edward.dowd@usdoj.gov
Assistant U.S. Attorney **Matthew Drake** .... (314) 539-2200
E-mail: matthew.drake@usdoj.gov
Assistant U.S. Attorney **Sayler Anne Ault Fleming** ..... (314) 539-2200
Education: Mississippi State 2001 BACCY; Vanderbilt 2006 JD
Assistant U.S. Attorney **Anthony Franks** .... (314) 539-2200
Assistant U.S. Attorney **Dean R. Hoag** .... (314) 539-2200
E-mail: dean.hoag@usdoj.gov
Assistant U.S. Attorney **Rodney Holmes** .... (314) 539-2200
E-mail: rodney.holmes@usdoj.gov
Assistant U.S. Attorney **Sara Koppenaal** .... (314) 539-2200
E-mail: sara.koppenaal@usdoj.gov
Assistant U.S. Attorney **Linda Lane** .... (314) 539-2200
E-mail: linda.lane@usdoj.gov
Assistant U.S. Attorney **Colleen Lang** .... (314) 539-2200
E-mail: colleen.lang@usdoj.gov
Assistant U.S. Attorney **Rob Livergood** .... (314) 539-2200
E-mail: rob.livergood@usdoj.gov
Assistant U.S. Attorney **John Mantovani** .... (314) 539-2200
E-mail: john.mantovani@usdoj.gov
Assistant U.S. Attorney **Dorothy L. McMurtry** .... (314) 539-2200
E-mail: dorothy.mcmurtry@usdoj.gov
Assistant U.S. Attorney **Thomas S. Rea** .... (314) 539-2200
E-mail: thomas.rea@usdoj.gov
Assistant U.S. Attorney **Beth Orwick** .... (314) 539-2200
E-mail: beth.orwick@usdoj.gov
Assistant U.S. Attorney **Thomas J. Mehan** .... (314) 539-2200
E-mail: thomas.mehan@usdoj.gov
Assistant U.S. Attorney **Michael Reilly** .... (314) 539-2200
E-mail: michael.reilly@usdoj.gov
Assistant U.S. Attorney **Gil Sison** .... (314) 539-2200
Assistant U.S. Attorney **Kenneth R. Tihen** .... (314) 539-2200
E-mail: kenneth.tihen@usdoj.gov
Assistant U.S. Attorney **John J. Ware** .... (314) 539-2200
E-mail: john.ware@usdoj.gov
Assistant U.S. Attorney **Jennifer Winfield** .... (314) 539-2200
Assistant U.S. Attorney **Sirena Wissler** .... (314) 539-2200
E-mail: sirena.wissler@usdoj.gov
Assistant U.S. Attorney **Lisa Yemm** .... (314) 539-2200
E-mail: lisa.yemm@usdoj.gov
Assistant U.S. Attorney **(Vacant)** .... (314) 539-2200
Assistant U.S. Attorney **(Vacant)** .... (314) 539-2200
Assistant U.S. Attorney **(Vacant)** .... (314) 539-2200
Assistant U.S. Attorney **(Vacant)** .... (314) 539-2200

Cape Girardeau (MO) Office

Rush H. Limbaugh, Sr. U.S. Courthouse,
555 Independence Street, Cape Girardeau, MO 63701
Tel: (573) 334-3736 Fax: (573) 335-2393

Chief **Larry H. Ferrell** .... (573) 334-3736
E-mail: larry.ferrell@usdoj.gov
Special Assistant U.S. Attorney **Timothy Willis** .... (573) 334-3736
E-mail: timothy.willis@usdoj.gov
Assistant U.S. Attorney **Paul W. Hahn** .... (573) 334-3736
E-mail: paul.hahn@usdoj.gov
Assistant U.S. Attorney **Keith D. Sorrell** .... (573) 334-3736
Assistant U.S. Attorney **John "Jack" Koester** .... (573) 334-3736
E-mail: john.koester@usdoj.gov

Missouri - Western District

Charles Evans Whittaker Courthouse, 400 East Ninth Street,
Room 5510, Kansas City, MO 64106
Tel: (816) 426-3122 Fax: (816) 426-4210
Internet: https://www.justice.gov/usao-wdmo

★ U.S. Attorney **Timothy "Tim" Garrison** .... (816) 426-3122
E-mail: timothy.garrison@usdoj.gov
Education: Drury U BS; Missouri MPA, JD
Executive Secretary **Jeanne Morgan** .... (816) 426-4319

Missouri - Western District *(continued)*

First Assistant U.S. Attorney **David Ketchmark** .... (816) 426-3122
E-mail: david.ketchmark@usdoj.gov
Senior Litigation Counsel **David Raskin** .... (816) 426-3122
E-mail: david.raskin@usdoj.gov
Administrative Officer **Christy Rodriguez** .... (816) 426-3122
E-mail: christy.rodriguez@usdoj.gov
Public Affairs Officer **Don Ledford** .... (816) 426-3122
E-mail: don.ledford@usdoj.gov
Law Enforcement Coordinator **Les Kerr** .... (816) 426-3122
Victim Assistance Specialist **Tina Sutter** .... (816) 426-3122
E-mail: tina.sutter@usdoj.gov
Victim Assistance Specialist **Rebekah Jackson** .... (816) 426-3122
E-mail: rebekah.jackson@usdoj.gov
Systems Manager **Bill Waldram** .... (816) 426-3122
E-mail: william.waldram@usdoj.gov

Appellate Division

Chief **Curt Bohling** .... (816) 426-3122
E-mail: curt.bohling@usdoj.gov
Assistant U.S. Attorney **Phil Koppe** .... (816) 426-3122
E-mail: phil.koppe@usdoj.gov

Civil Division

Charles Evans Whitaker US Courthouse,
400 East Ninth Street, Kansas City, MO 64106
Fax: (816) 426-3165

Deputy U.S. Attorney **Jeff Ray** .... (816) 426-3122
E-mail: jeffrey.ray@usdoj.gov
Monetary Penalties Unit Chief **Stacey Perkins-Rock** ..... (816) 426-3122
E-mail: stacey.perkins-rock@usdoj.gov
Assistant U.S. Attorney **Amy Blackburn** .... (816) 426-4269
E-mail: amy.blackburn@usdoj.gov
Assistant U.S. Attorney **Thomas M. Larson** .... (816) 426-3130
E-mail: thomas.larson@usdoj.gov
Assistant U.S. Attorney **Jerry Short** .... (816) 426-3122
E-mail: jerry.short@usdoj.gov
Assistant U.S. Attorney **Matt Sparks** .... (816) 426-3122
E-mail: matt.sparks@usdoj.gov
Assistant U.S. Attorney **Charles Thomas** .... (816) 426-3122
E-mail: charles.thomas@usdoj.gov
Assistant U.S. Attorney **Cari Walsh** .... (816) 426-3130
E-mail: cari.walsh@usdoj.gov
Assistant U.S. Attorney **Cindi Woolery** .... (816) 426-3130
E-mail: cindi.woolery@usdoj.gov

Criminal Division

Chief **Gene Porter** .... (816) 426-3122
E-mail: gene.porter@usdoj.gov
Computer Crimes and Child Exploitation Unit Chief
Teresa Moore .... (816) 426-3122
E-mail: teresa.moore2@usdoj.gov
Fraud and Corruption Unit Chief
Kathleen "Kate" Mahoney .... (816) 426-3122
E-mail: kate.mahoney@usdoj.gov
Narcotics and Violent Crimes Unit Chief **Jeff Valenti** .... (816) 426-3122
E-mail: jeff.valenti@usdoj.gov
Narcotics and Violent Crimes Deputy Chief
Patrick Edwards .... (816) 426-3122
E-mail: patrick.edwards@usdoj.gov
Narcotics and Violent Crimes Deputy Chief
Jess Michaelsen .... (816) 426-2605
E-mail: jess.michaelsen@usdoj.gov
Assistant U.S. Attorney **Trey Alford** .... (816) 426-3122
E-mail: trey.alford@usdoj.gov
Assistant U.S. Attorney **David Barnes** .... (816) 426-3122
E-mail: david.barnes@usdoj.gov
Assistant U.S. Attorney **Paul S. Becker** .... (816) 426-3122
E-mail: paul.becker@usdoj.gov
Assistant U.S. Attorney **Jane Brown** .... (816) 426-2605
E-mail: jane.brown@usdoj.gov
Assistant U.S. Attorney **Adam Caine** .... (816) 426-3122
E-mail: adam.caine@usdoj.gov
Assistant U.S. Attorney **Brian Casey** .... (816) 426-3122
E-mail: brian.casey@usdoj.gov

(continued on next page)

DEPARTMENTS

★ Presidential Appointment Requiring Senate Confirmation ☆ Presidential Appointment ☐ Schedule C Appointment ◇ Career Senior Foreign Service Appointment
● Career Senior Executive Service (SES) Appointment ○ Non-Career Senior Executive Service (SES) Appointment ■ Postal Career Executive Service

DEPARTMENTS

Criminal Division *(continued)*

Assistant U.S. Attorney **Bruce Clark** .... (816) 426-3122
E-mail: bruce.clark2@usdoj.gov
Assistant U.S. Attorney **Catherine Connelly** .... (816) 426-3122
E-mail: catherine.connelly@usdoj.gov
Assistant U.S. Attorney **Patrick Daly** .... (816) 426-3122
E-mail: patrick.daly@usdoj.gov
Assistant U.S. Attorney **Justin G. Davids** .... (816) 426-3122
E-mail: justin.davids@usdoj.gov
Education: Yale 2001 BA; Columbia 2005 JD
Assistant U.S. Attorney **Alison Dunning** .... (816) 426-3122
E-mail: alison.dunning@usdoj.gov
Assistant U.S. Attorney **Mike Green** .... (816) 426-3122
E-mail: mike.green@usdoj.gov
Assistant U.S. Attorney **Stefan Hughes** .... (816) 426-3122
E-mail: stefan.hughes@usdoj.gov
Assistant U.S. Attorney **Bradley "Brad" Kavanaugh** .... (816) 426-3122
E-mail: bradley.kavanaugh@usdoj.gov
Assistant U.S. Attorney **David Luna** .... (816) 426-3122
E-mail: david.luna@usdoj.gov
Assistant U.S. Attorney **Joseph "Joe" Marquez** .... (816) 426-3122
E-mail: joseph.marquez@usdoj.gov
Assistant U.S. Attorney **Jeffrey McCarther** .... (816) 426-3122
E-mail: jeffrey.mccarther@usdoj.gov
Assistant U.S. Attorney **William Meiners** .... (816) 426-3122
E-mail: william.meiners@usdoj.gov
Assistant U.S. Attorney **Emily Morgan** .... (816) 426-4290
E-mail: emily.morgan2@usdoj.gov
Assistant U.S. Attorney **Bruce Rhoades** .... (816) 426-4278
E-mail: bruce.rhoades@usdoj.gov
Assistant U.S. Attorney **Rudolph R. Rhodes IV** .... (816) 426-3122
E-mail: rudolph.rhodes@usdoj.gov
Assistant U.S. Attorney **Brent Venneman** .... (816) 426-3122
E-mail: brent.venneman@usdoj.gov
Assistant U.S. Attorney **Matthew "Matt" Wolesky** ..... (816) 426-2771
E-mail: matthew.wolesky@usdoj.gov

Jefferson City (MO) Office
80 Lafayette St, Ste. 2100, Jefferson City, MO 65101
Tel: (573) 634-8214 Fax: (573) 634-8723

Supervisory Assistant U.S. Attorney **Mike Oliver** .... (573) 634-8214
E-mail: mike.oliver@usdoj.gov
Assistant U.S. Attorney **Lauren Kummerer** .... (573) 634-8214
E-mail: lauren.kummerer@usdoj.gov
Assistant U.S. Attorney **Jim Lynn** .... (573) 634-8214
E-mail: jim.lynn@usdoj.gov
Assistant U.S. Attorney **Larry Miller** .... (573) 634-8214
E-mail: larry.miller@usdoj.gov
Assistant U.S. Attorney **Ashley Turner** .... (573) 634-8214
E-mail: ashley.turner@usdoj.gov
Special Assistant United States Attorney **Aaron Jolly** .... (573) 634-8214
E-mail: aaron.jolly@usdoj.gov

Springfield (MO) Office
901 St. Louis Street, Suite 500, Springfield, MO 65806-2512
Tel: (417) 831-4406 Fax: (417) 831-0078

Supervisory Assistant U.S. Attorney **Randy Eggert** ...... (417) 831-4406
E-mail: randy.eggert@usdoj.gov
Assistant U.S. Attorney **Patrick A. N. Carney** .... (417) 831-4406
E-mail: patrick.carney@usdoj.gov
Assistant U.S. Attorney **Casey Clark** .... (417) 831-4406
E-mail: casey.clark@usdoj.gov
Assistant U.S. Attorney **(Vacant)** .... (417) 831-4406
Assistant U.S. Attorney **Cynthia Hyde** .... (417) 831-4406
E-mail: cynthia.hyde@usdoj.gov
Assistant U.S. Attorney **James "Jim" Kelleher** .... (417) 831-4406
E-mail: james.kelleher@usdoj.gov
Assistant U.S. Attorney **Abram "Abe" McGull** .... (417) 831-4406
E-mail: abram.mcgull@usdoj.gov
Assistant U.S. Attorney **Ami Miller** .... (417) 831-4406
E-mail: ami.miller@usdoj.gov
Assistant U.S. Attorney **Steven Mohlhenrich** .... (417) 831-4406
E-mail: steven.mohlhenrich@usdoj.gov

Springfield (MO) Office *(continued)*

Assistant U.S. Attorney **Nhan Nguyen** .... (417) 831-4406
E-mail: nhan.nguyen@usdoj.gov
Assistant U.S. Attorney **(Vacant)** .... (417) 831-4406

Montana District
2601 Second Ave North, Suite 3200, Billings, MT 59101
Tel: (406) 657-6101 Fax: (406) 657-6989
Internet: https://www.justice.gov/usao-mt

★ U.S. Attorney **Kurt G. Alme** .... (406) 457-5120
E-mail: kurt.alme@usdoj.gov
Education: Colorado 1989 BS; Harvard 1992 JD
Secretary to the U.S. Attorney
Cassandra "Cassie" Potter .... (406) 457-5120
E-mail: cassie.potter@usdoj.gov
Appellate Division Chief **Leif M. Johnson** .... (406) 657-6101
E-mail: leif.johnson@usdoj.gov
Civil Division Chief **Victoria L. Francis** .... (406) 657-6101
E-mail: victoria.francis@usdoj.gov
Assistant U.S. Attorney **Zeno Benjamin Baucus** .... (406) 657-6101
E-mail: zeno.baucus@usdoj.gov
Education: Stanford 1999 BA; Georgetown 2004 JD
Assistant U.S. Attorney **(Vacant)** .... (406) 657-6101
Assistant U.S. Attorney **Brendan McCarthy** .... (406) 657-6101
E-mail: brendan.mccarthy@usdoj.gov
Assistant U.S. Attorney **Colin Rubich** .... (406) 657-6101
E-mail: colin.rubich@usdoj.gov
Assistant U.S. Attorney **Mark S. Smith** .... (406) 657-6101
Victim-Witness Specialist **(Vacant)** .... (406) 657-6101
Systems Manager **Jason Ferree** .... (406) 657-6101
E-mail: jason.ferree@usdoj.gov
Administrative Officer **Kora L. Connolly** .... (406) 657-6101
E-mail: kora.connolly@usdoj.gov

Indian Country Crime Unit
Deputy Chief and Assistant U.S. Attorney
Lori Harper Suek .... (406) 657-6101
E-mail: lori.suek@usdoj.gov
Assistant U.S. Attorney **Jessica A. Betley** .... (406) 761-7715
E-mail: jessica.betley@usdoj.gov
Assistant U.S. Attorney **Ryan G. Weldon** .... (406) 761-7715
E-mail: ryan.weldon@usdoj.gov
Education: Montana 2009 JD
Assistant U.S. Attorney **(Vacant)** .... (406) 761-7715
Assistant U.S. Attorney **(Vacant)** .... (406) 657-6101
Assistant U.S. Attorney **(Vacant)** .... (406) 457-5120

Butte (MT) Office
Federal Building, 400 North Main, Suite 181, Butte, MT 59701
Tel: (406) 723-6611 Fax: (406) 723-5002

Assistant U.S. Attorney **(Vacant)** .... (406) 723-6611

Great Falls (MT) Office
119 First Avenue North, Number 300, Great Falls, MT 59401
P.O. Box 3447, Great Falls, MT 59403-3447
Tel: (406) 761-7715 Fax: (406) 453-9973

Assistant U.S. Attorney **Jeffrey K. Starnes** .... (406) 761-7715
E-mail: jeff.starnes@usdoj.gov
Assistant U.S. Attorney **(Vacant)** .... (406) 761-7715
Executive Assistant U.S. Attorney **(Vacant)** .... (406) 761-7715
Victim-Witness Specialist **Keri Brehm-Leggett** .... (406) 761-7715
E-mail: kerri.leggett@usdoj.gov

Helena (MT) Office
100 North Park Avenue, Suite 100, Helena, MT 59601
Tel: (406) 457-5120 Fax: (406) 457-5130

Criminal Division Chief **Joseph E. Thaggard** .... (406) 457-5120
E-mail: joseph.thaggard@usdoj.gov
Assistant U.S. Attorney **Melissa Hornbein** .... (406) 457-5120
E-mail: melissa.hornbein@usdoj.gov
Assistant U.S. Attorney **Chad Spraker** .... (406) 657-6101
E-mail: chad.spraker@usdoj.gov

★ Presidential Appointment Requiring Senate Confirmation ☆ Presidential Appointment □ Schedule C Appointment ◇ Career Senior Foreign Service Appointment
● Career Senior Executive Service (SES) Appointment ○ Non-Career Senior Executive Service (SES) Appointment ■ Postal Career Executive Service

Helena (MT) Office *(continued)*

Assistant U.S. Attorney **Paulette Stewart** . . . . . (406) 457-5120
E-mail: paulette.stewart@usdoj.gov
Intelligence Specialist **Michael Rankin** . . . . . (406) 457-5120
E-mail: michael.rankin@usdoj.gov
Assistant U.S. Attorney **(Vacant)** . . . . . (406) 457-5120
Assistant U.S. Attorney **(Vacant)** . . . . . (406) 457-5120

Missoula (MT) Office

105 East Pine, 2nd Floor, Missoula, MT 59802
P.O. Box 8329, Missoula, MT 59807-8329
Tel: (406) 542-8851 Fax: (406) 542-1476

First Assistant U.S. Attorney **Joe Phaggard** . . . . . (406) 542-8851
Deputy Criminal Division Chief and Assistant U.S. Attorney **(Vacant)** . . . . . (406) 542-8851
Organized Crime Drug Enforcement Task Force Assistant U.S. Attorney **(Vacant)** . . . . . (406) 542-8851
Assistant U.S. Attorney **Megan Dishong** . . . . . (406) 542-8851
E-mail: megan.dishong@usdoj.gov
Education: Wooster 2000 BA; Montana 2007 JD
Assistant U.S. Attorney **Cyndee Peterson** . . . . . (406) 542-8851
E-mail: cyndee.peterson@usdoj.gov

Nebraska District

1620 Dodge Street, Suite 1400, Omaha, NE 68102-1506
Tel: (800) 899-9124 Tel: (402) 661-3700 Fax: (402) 345-6958
Internet: https://www.justice.gov/usao-ne

★ U.S. Attorney **Joseph P. Kelly** . . . . . (402) 661-3700
E-mail: joe.kelly@usdoj.gov
Education: Nebraska BA, JD
Secretary to the U.S. Attorney **Colleen MacDonald** . . . . (402) 661-3700
E-mail: colleen.macdonald@usdoj.gov
First Assistant U.S. Attorney **Jan W. Sharp** . . . . . (402) 661-3700
E-mail: jan.sharp@usdoj.gov
Administrative Officer **Denise M. Smith** . . . . . (402) 661-3700
E-mail: denise.smith@usdoj.gov
HIDTA Coordinator **(Vacant)** . . . . . (402) 661-3700
Law Enforcement Coordinator **(Vacant)** . . . . . (402) 661-3700
Victim-Witness Coordinator **(Vacant)** . . . . . (402) 661-3700
Computer Programmer Analyst **Jason D. Bray** . . . . . (402) 661-3700
E-mail: jason.bray@usdoj.gov

Civil Division

Chief **Robert L. Homan** . . . . . (402) 661-3700
E-mail: robert.homan@usdoj.gov
Assistant U.S. Attorney **Timothy Hook** . . . . . (402) 437-5241
E-mail: tim.hook@usdoj.gov
Assistant U.S. Attorney **Laurie Kelly** . . . . . (402) 661-3700
E-mail: laurie.kelly@usdoj.gov
Assistant U.S. Attorney **(Vacant)** . . . . . (402) 661-3700
Assistant U.S. Attorney **(Vacant)** . . . . . (402) 661-3700

Criminal Division

Chief **Jan W. Sharp** . . . . . (402) 661-3700
E-mail: jan.sharp@usdoj.gov
Supervisory Assistant U.S. Attorney **John E. Higgins** . . . . (402) 661-3700
E-mail: john.higgins@usdoj.gov
Assistant U.S. Attorney **Donald Kleine** . . . . . (402) 437-5241
E-mail: donald.kleine@usdoj.gov
Assistant U.S. Attorney **Susan Lehr** . . . . . (402) 661-3700
Assistant U.S. Attorney **Matthew Molsen** . . . . . (402) 661-3700
E-mail: matthew.molsen@usdoj.gov
Assistant U.S. Attorney **Michael P. Norris** . . . . . (402) 661-3700
E-mail: michael.norris@usdoj.gov
Assistant U.S. Attorney **Douglas R. "Doug" Semisch** . . . (402) 661-3700
E-mail: doug.semisch@usdoj.gov
Assistant U.S. Attorney **Lecia Wright** . . . . . (402) 661-3700
E-mail: lecia.wright@usdoj.gov
Assistant U.S. Attorney **(Vacant)** . . . . . (402) 661-3700
Assistant U.S. Attorney **(Vacant)** . . . . . (402) 661-3700
Assistant U.S. Attorney **(Vacant)** . . . . . (402) 661-3700

Lincoln (NE) Office

Federal Building, 100 Centennial Mall North, Suite 487, Lincoln, NE 68508-3865
Tel: (800) 889-9123 Tel: (402) 437-5241 Fax: (402) 437-5390

Supervisory Assistant U.S. Attorney **Steven A. Russell** . . . . . (402) 437-5241
E-mail: steve.russell@usdoj.gov
Assistant U.S. Attorney **Sara E. Fullerton** . . . . . (402) 437-5241
E-mail: sara.fullerton@usdoj.gov

Nevada District

333 Las Vegas Boulevard South, Suite 5000, Las Vegas, NV 89101
Tel: (702) 388-6336 Fax: (702) 388-6296
Internet: https://www.justice.gov/usao-nv

★ U.S. Attorney (Interim) **Dayle Elieson** . . . . . (702) 388-6336
E-mail: dayle.elieson@usdoj.gov
★ U.S. Attorney-Designate **Nicholas A. Trutanich** . . . . . (702) 388-6336
Secretary to the U.S. Attorney **Ashlin Brown** . . . . . (702) 388-6336
E-mail: ashlin.brown@usdoj.gov
First Assistant U.S. Attorney **Steven W. Myhre** . . . . . (702) 388-6336
E-mail: steven.myhre@usdoj.gov
Administrative Officer **Burton J. Carle** . . . . . (702) 388-6336
E-mail: burton.carle@usdoj.gov
Human Resources Specialist **(Vacant)** . . . . . (702) 388-6336
Fax: (702) 388-6735
Supervisory Information Technology Specialist **Angel Beltran** . . . . . (702) 388-6336
E-mail: angel.beltran@usdoj.gov Fax: (702) 388-6735
Public Affairs Officer **(Vacant)** . . . . . (702) 388-6336

Appellate Division

333 Las Vegas Boulevard, South, Las Vegas, NV 89101
Tel: (702) 388-6336

Chief **Elizabeth White** . . . . . (702) 388-6336
E-mail: elizabeth.white@usdoj.gov Fax: (702) 388-6418

Civil Division

333 Las Vegas Boulevard, South, Las Vegas, NV 89101
Tel: (702) 388-6336 Fax: (702) 388-6787

Chief **Blaine T. Welsh** . . . . . (702) 388-6336
E-mail: blaine.welsh@usdoj.gov
Health Care Fraud Assistant U.S. Attorney **Roger W. Wenthe** . . . . . (702) 388-6336
E-mail: roger.wenthe@usdoj.gov

Criminal Division

333 Las Vegas Boulevard, South, Las Vegas, NV 89101
Tel: (702) 388-6336

Chief **Daniel R. Schiess** . . . . . (702) 388-6336
E-mail: dan.schiess@usdoj.gov
Team 1 Deputy Chief **Cristina Silva** . . . . . (702) 388-6336
E-mail: cristina.silva@usdoj.gov
Team 2 Deputy Chief **(Vacant)** . . . . . (702) 388-6336
Team 3 Deputy Chief **Pam Martin** . . . . . (702) 388-6336
E-mail: pam.martin@usdoj.gov

Reno (NV) Office

100 West Liberty Street, Suite 600, Reno, NV 89501
Tel: (775) 334-3342 Fax: (775) 784-5181

Assistant U.S. Attorney-in-Charge **Sue Fahami** . . . . . (775) 334-3342

Civil Division

333 Las Vegas Boulevard, South, Las Vegas, NV 89101
Tel: (775) 784-5438 Fax: (775) 784-5181

Assistant U.S. Attorney **Gregory W. Addington** . . . . . (775) 784-5438
E-mail: greg.addington@usdoj.gov

Criminal Division

333 Las Vegas Boulevard, South, Las Vegas, NV 89101
Tel: (775) 784-5438 Fax: (775) 784-5181

Narcotics and Violent Crimes Assistant U.S. Attorney **James E. Keller** . . . . . (775) 784-5438

(continued on next page)

★ Presidential Appointment Requiring Senate Confirmation ☆ Presidential Appointment □ Schedule C Appointment ◇ Career Senior Foreign Service Appointment
● Career Senior Executive Service (SES) Appointment ○ Non-Career Senior Executive Service (SES) Appointment ■ Postal Career Executive Service

Criminal Division *(continued)*

White Collar and Economic Crimes Assistant U.S. Attorney **Brian L. Sullivan** .... (775) 784-5438
E-mail: brian.sullivan@usdoj.gov

New Hampshire District

James C. Cleveland Federal Building, 53 Pleasant Street, Concord, NH 03301-3904
Tel: (603) 225-1552 Fax: (603) 225-1470
Internet: https://www.justice.gov/usao-nh

★ U.S. Attorney **Scott W. Murray** .... (603) 225-1552
Education: New Hampshire BA, MPA; Pierce Law JD
Secretary to U.S. Attorney **Mary Ellen McMahon** ..... (603) 225-1552
E-mail: maryellen.mcmahon@usdoj.gov
First Assistant U.S. Attorney **John J. Farley III** .... (603) 225-1552
E-mail: john.farley@usdoj.gov
Administrative Officer **Philip DeVincent** .... (603) 225-1552
E-mail: philip.devincent@usdoj.gov
Administrative Services Specialist **Denise Philbrick** .... (603) 225-1552
E-mail: denise.philbrick@usdoj.gov
Budget Analyst **Thomas Kasyan** .... (603) 225-1552
E-mail: thomas.kasyan@usdoj.gov
Financial Technician **Janna Foote** .... (603) 225-1552
Human Resources Specialist **Holly R. Boyson** .... (603) 230-2544
E-mail: holly.boyson@usdoj.gov
Systems Manager **Jessica Magdziasz** .... (603) 225-1552
E-mail: jessica.magdziasz@usdoj.gov
Law Enforcement Coordination Specialist **Joseph Cafarelli** .... (603) 225-1552
Victim Witness Specialist **Jennifer Hunt** .... (603) 225-1552

Civil Division

James C. Cleveland Federal Building, 53 Pleasant Street, Concord, NH 03301
Fax: (603) 225-1470

Chief **T. David Plourde** .... (603) 225-1552
E-mail: david.plourde@usdoj.gov
Assistant U.S. Attorney **Michael T. McCormack** .... (603) 225-1552
E-mail: michael.mccormack@usdoj.gov
Assistant U.S. Attorney **Robert Rabuck** .... (603) 225-1552
Assistant U.S. Attorney **Terry Ollila** .... (603) 225-1552

Criminal Division

James C. Cleveland Federal Building, 53 Pleasant Street, Concord, NH 03301
Fax: (603) 225-1470

Chief **Mark Zuckerman** .... (603) 225-1552
E-mail: mark.zuckerman@usdoj.gov
Deputy Chief **(Vacant)** .... (603) 225-1552
Senior Litigation Counsel **Robert Kinsella** .... (603) 225-1552
E-mail: robert.kinsella@usdoj.gov
Assistant U.S. Attorney **Seth Aframe** .... (603) 225-1552
E-mail: seth.aframe@usdoj.gov
Assistant U.S. Attorney **Jennifer C. Davis** .... (603) 225-1552
E-mail: jennifer.c.davis@usdoj.gov
Assistant U.S. Attorney **Helen White Fitzgibbon** .... (603) 225-1552
E-mail: helen.fitzgibbon@usdoj.gov
Assistant U.S. Attorney **Michael J. Gunnison** .... (603) 225-1552
E-mail: michael.gunnison@usdoj.gov
Assistant U.S. Attorney **Arnold H. Huftalen** .... (603) 225-1552
E-mail: arnold.huftalen@usdoj.gov
Assistant U.S. Attorney **Shane Kelbley** .... (603) 225-1552
E-mail: shane.kelbley@usdoj.gov
Assistant U.S. Attorney **William Morse** .... (603) 225-1552
E-mail: william.morse@usdoj.gov
Assistant U.S. Attorney **Alfred Rubega** .... (603) 225-1552
E-mail: alfred.rubega@usdoj.gov
Assistant U.S. Attorney **Debra M. Walsh** .... (603) 225-1552
E-mail: deb.walsh@usdoj.gov
Assistant U.S. Attorney **(Vacant)** .... (603) 225-1552
Assistant U.S. Attorney **(Vacant)** .... (603) 225-1552
Assistant U.S. Attorney **(Vacant)** .... (603) 225-1552

New Jersey District

970 Broad Street, Suite 700, Newark, NJ 07102
Tel: (973) 645-2700 Fax: (973) 645-2702
Internet: https://www.justice.gov/usao-nj

★ U.S. Attorney (Interim) **Craig Carpenito** .... (973) 645-2700
E-mail: craig.carpenito@usdoj.gov
Executive Assistant to the U.S. Attorney **Nancy Manteiga** .... (973) 645-2700
E-mail: nancy.manteiga@usdoj.gov
First Assistant U.S. Attorney **Rachael A. Honig** .... (973) 645-2700
E-mail: rachael.honig@usdoj.gov
Education: Chicago 1995 BA, 1999 JD
Executive Assistant U.S. Attorney **Sabrina G. Comizzoli** .... (973) 645-2700
E-mail: sabrina.comizzoli@usdoj.gov
Deputy U.S. Attorney for the Southern Vicinages **(Vacant)** .... (973) 645-2700
Counsel to the United States Attorney **John M. Fietkiewicz** .... (973) 645-2700
Counsel to the United States Attorney **(Vacant)** .... (973) 645-2700
Administrative Officer **Donna A. Fisher** .... (973) 645-2700
E-mail: donna.fisher@usdoj.gov
Public Affairs Officer **Matthew Reilly** .... (973) 645-2888
E-mail: matthew.reilly@usdoj.gov
Victim-Witness Coordinator **Shirley Estreicher** .... (973) 645-2700
E-mail: shirley.estreicher@usdoj.gov

Appellate Division

970 Broad Street, Suite 700, Newark, NJ 07102
Tel: (973) 645-2755

Chief **Mark E. Coyne** .... (973) 245-2700
E-mail: mark.coyne@usdoj.gov
Deputy Chief **(Vacant)** .... (973) 245-2700
Assistant U.S. Attorney **Bruce P. Keller** .... (973) 245-2700
E-mail: bruce.keller@usdoj.gov
Education: Cornell 1976 BS; Boston U 1979 JD
Assistant U.S. Attorney **John F. Romano** .... (973) 245-2700
E-mail: john.romano@usdoj.gov
Education: St John's U (NY) 2004 JD
Assistant U.S. Attorney **(Vacant)** .... (973) 245-2700

Civil Division

Chief **Caroline A. Sadlowski** .... (973) 645-2700
E-mail: caroline.sadlowski@usdoj.gov
Education: Harvard 1993 AB, 1996 MA; Michigan 2000 JD
Deputy Chief **Leticia B. Vandehaar** .... (973) 645-2700
E-mail: leticia.vandehaar@usdoj.gov
Deputy Chief **Kristin L. Vassallo** .... (973) 645-2700
E-mail: kristin.vassallo@usdoj.gov
Deputy Chief **(Vacant)** .... (973) 645-2700
Senior Litigation Counsel **Daniel J. Gibbons** .... (973) 645-2700
E-mail: daniel.gibbons@usdoj.gov
Senior Litigation Counsel **Anthony J. LaBruna, Jr.** ...... (973) 645-2700
E-mail: anthony.labruna@usdoj.gov
Senior Litigation Counsel **(Vacant)** .... (973) 645-2700
Civil Rights Unit Chief **Michael Campion** .... (973) 645-2700
E-mail: michael.campion@usdoj.gov
Assistant U.S. Attorney **Christopher D. Amore** .... (973) 645-2700
E-mail: christopher.amore@usdoj.gov
Assistant U.S. Attorney **Jordan Anger** .... (973) 645-2700
E-mail: jordan.anger@usdoj.gov
Assistant U.S. Attorney **Frances C. Bajada** .... (973) 645-2700
E-mail: frances.bajada@usdoj.gov
Education: Baruch Col BA; New York Law JD
Assistant U.S. Attorney **Catherine R. Murphy** .... (973) 645-2700
E-mail: catherine.murphy@usdoj.gov
Assistant U.S. Attorney **Susan R. Millenky** .... (973) 645-2700
E-mail: susan.millenky@usdoj.gov
Assistant U.S. Attorney **Eamonn O'Hagan** .... (973) 645-2700
E-mail: eamonn.ohagan@usdoj.gov
Education: Boston Col 2004 JD
Assistant U.S. Attorney **Mark C. Orlowski** .... (973) 645-2700
E-mail: mark.orlowski@usdoj.gov
Assistant U.S. Attorney **Valorie D. Smith** .... (973) 645-2700
E-mail: valorie.d.smith@usdoj.gov

Civil Division *(continued)*

Assistant U.S. Attorney **Allan B. K. Urgent** . . . . (973) 645-2700
E-mail: allan.urgent@usdoj.gov
Education: Fordham 1997 JD
Assistant U.S. Attorney **(Vacant)** . . . . (973) 645-2700

Criminal Division

Chief **Thomas J. Eicher** . . . . (973) 645-2700
E-mail: thomas.eicher@usdoj.gov
Deputy Chief **(Vacant)** . . . . (973) 645-2700
Deputy Chief **John Gay** . . . . (973) 645-2700
E-mail: john.gay@usdoj.gov
Asset Forfeiture and Money Laundering Unit Chief (Acting) **Barbara A. Ward** . . . . (973) 645-2700
E-mail: barbara.ward@usdoj.gov
Economic Crimes Unit Chief **Paul A. Murphy** . . . . (973) 645-2700
E-mail: paul.murphy@usdoj.gov
Education: Georgetown 1985 AB; St John's U (NY) 1990 JD
General Crimes Unit Chief **Zach Intrater** . . . . (973) 645-2700
E-mail: zach.intrater@usdoj.gov
Healthcare and Government Fraud Unit Chief **Jacob T. Elberg** . . . . (973) 645-2700
E-mail: jacob.elberg@usdoj.gov
Education: Harvard 2003 JD
Narcotics/OCDETF Unit Chief **Ronnell L. Wilson** . . . . (973) 645-2700
E-mail: ronnell.wilson@usdoj.gov
National Security Unit Chief **Anthony C. Moscato** . . . . . . (973) 645-2700
E-mail: anthony.moscato@usdoj.gov
Education: Columbia 1967 BA; George Washington 1970 JD
Organized Crime/Gangs Unit Chief **David E. Malagold** . . . . (973) 645-2700
E-mail: david.malagold@usdoj.gov
Education: NYU 2001 JD
Economic Crimes/Computer Hacking and IP Section Unit Deputy Chief **(Vacant)** . . . . (973) 645-2700
General Crimes Unit Deputy Chief **Mary Toscano** . . . . (973) 645-2700
E-mail: mary.toscano2@usdoj.gov
Healthcare and Government Fraud Unit Deputy Chief **Joseph G. Mack** . . . . (973) 645-2700
E-mail: joseph.mack@usdoj.gov
Senior Litigation Counsel **Andrew Leven** . . . . (973) 645-2700
Education: Ithaca 1982 BS; Syracuse 1986 JD
Senior Litigation Counsel **Margaret Ann Mahoney** . . . . . (973) 645-2700
Senior Litigation Counsel **(Vacant)** . . . . (973) 645-2700
Senior Litigation Counsel **(Vacant)** . . . . (973) 645-2700
Senior Litigation Counsel **(Vacant)** . . . . (973) 645-2700
Assistant U.S. Attorney **Sharon E. Ashe** . . . . (973) 645-2700
E-mail: sharon.ashe@usdoj.gov
Assistant U.S. Attorney **Osmar J. Benvenuto** . . . . (973) 645-2700
E-mail: osmar.benvenuto@usdoj.gov
Assistant U.S. Attorney **Jamari Buxton** . . . . (973) 645-2700
E-mail: jamari.buxton@usdoj.gov
Assistant U.S. Attorney **Dennis C. Carletta** . . . . (973) 645-2700
E-mail: dennis.carletta@usdoj.gov
Assistant U.S. Attorney **Shana W. Chen** . . . . (973) 645-2700
E-mail: shana.chen@usdoj.gov
Education: Georgetown 2001 JD
Assistant U.S. Attorney **Bernard J. Cooney** . . . . (973) 645-2700
E-mail: bernard.cooney@usdoj.gov
Assistant U.S. Attorney **Sarah Devlin** . . . . (973) 645-2700
E-mail: sarah.devlin2@usdoj.gov
Assistant U.S. Attorney **James M. Donnelly** . . . . (973) 645-2700
E-mail: james.donnelly@usdoj.gov
Assistant U.S. Attorney **David M. Eskew** . . . . (973) 645-2700
E-mail: david.eskew@usdoj.gov
Education: St John's U (NY) 2004 JD
Assistant U.S. Attorney **Robert L. Frazer** . . . . (973) 645-2700
E-mail: robert.frazer@usdoj.gov
Assistant U.S. Attorney **Peter W. Gaeta** . . . . (973) 645-2700
E-mail: peter.gaeta@usdoj.gov
Assistant U.S. Attorney **Deborah J. Gannett** . . . . (973) 645-2700
E-mail: deborah.gannett@usdoj.gov
Assistant U.S. Attorney **Lorraine S. Gerson** . . . . (973) 645-2700
E-mail: lorraine.gerson@usdoj.gov

Criminal Division *(continued)*

Assistant U.S. Attorney **Dara A. Govan** . . . . (973) 645-2700
E-mail: dara.govan@usdoj.gov
Education: Morgan State 1998 BS; Rutgers 2001 JD
Assistant U.S. Attorney **Charles Graybow** . . . . (973) 645-2700
E-mail: charles.graybow@usdoj.gov
Assistant U.S. Attorney **Nicholas P. Grippo** . . . . (973) 645-2700
E-mail: nicholas.grippo@usdoj.gov
Assistant U.S. Attorney **Joshua Hafetz** . . . . (973) 645-2700
E-mail: joshua.hafetz@usdoj.gov
Assistant U.S. Attorney **Lakshmi Herman** . . . . (973) 645-2700
E-mail: lakshmi.herman@usdoj.gov
Assistant U.S. Attorney **Justin S. Herring** . . . . (973) 645-2700
E-mail: justin.herring@usdoj.gov
Assistant U.S. Attorney **Courtney Howard** . . . . (973) 645-2700
E-mail: courtney.howard@usdoj.gov
Assistant U.S. Attorney **Andrew D. Kogan** . . . . (973) 645-2700
E-mail: andrew.kogan@usdoj.gov
Assistant U.S. Attorney **Joyce M. Malliet** . . . . (973) 645-2700
E-mail: joyce.malliet@usdoj.gov
Assistant U.S. Attorney **Sara Merin** . . . . (973) 645-2700
E-mail: sara.merin@usdoj.gov
Assistant U.S. Attorney **Joseph N. Minish** . . . . (973) 645-2700
E-mail: joseph.minish@usdoj.gov
Assistant U.S. Attorney **Francisco J. Navarro** . . . . (973) 645-2700
E-mail: francisco.navarro@usdoj.gov
Assistant U.S. Attorney **Kathleen P. O'Leary** . . . . (973) 645-2700
E-mail: kathleen.o'leary@usdoj.gov
Assistant U.S. Attorney **Andrew S. Pak** . . . . (973) 645-2700
E-mail: andrew.pak@usdoj.gov
Assistant U.S. Attorney **Jonathan Peck** . . . . (973) 645-2700
E-mail: jonathan.peck@usdoj.gov
Assistant U.S. Attorney **Jonathan W. Romankow** . . . . . . (973) 645-2700
E-mail: jonathan.romankow@usdoj.gov
Assistant U.S. Attorney **Daniel Shapiro** . . . . (973) 645-2700
E-mail: daniel.shapiro@usdoj.gov
Assistant U.S. Attorney **Karen D. Stringer** . . . . (973) 645-2700
E-mail: karen.stringer@usdoj.gov
Assistant U.S. Attorney **Adam N. Subervi** . . . . (973) 645-2700
E-mail: adam.subervi@usdoj.gov
Education: Seton Hall 1997 BA; Rutgers (Newark) 2000 JD
Assistant U.S. Attorney **Brian L. Urbano** . . . . (973) 645-2700
E-mail: brian.urbano@usdoj.gov
Assistant U.S. Attorney **Danielle A. Walsman** . . . . (973) 645-2700
E-mail: danielle.walsman@usdoj.gov
Assistant U.S. Attorney **Melissa M. Wangenheim** . . . . . . (973) 645-2700
E-mail: melissa.wangenheim@usdoj.gov
Assistant U.S. Attorney **Meredith J. Williams** . . . . (973) 645-2700
E-mail: meredith.williams@usdoj.gov

Special Prosecutions Division

Chief **James B. Nobile** . . . . (973) 645-2700
E-mail: james.nobile@usdoj.gov
Senior Litigation Counsel **J Fortier Imbert** . . . . (973) 645-2700
Senior Litigation Counsel **Mark J. McCarren** . . . . (973) 645-2700
Senior Litigation Counsel **Leslie F. Schwartz** . . . . (973) 645-2700
Assistant U.S. Attorney **Rahul Agarwal** . . . . (973) 645-2700
E-mail: rahul.agarwal@usdoj.gov
Education: Columbia 2006 JD
Assistant U.S. Attorney **Lee S. Cortes, Jr.** . . . . (973) 645-2700
E-mail: lee.cortes@usdoj.gov
Education: King's Col (UK) 2000 BA; Fordham 2003 JD
Assistant U.S. Attorney **Shirley U. Emehelu** . . . . (973) 645-2700
E-mail: shirley.emehelu@usdoj.gov
Assistant U.S. Attorney **Cari Fais** . . . . (973) 645-2700
E-mail: cari.fais@usdoj.gov
Assistant U.S. Attorney **David W. Feder** . . . . (973) 645-2700
E-mail: david.feder@usdoj.gov
Education: Fordham 2007 JD
Assistant U.S. Attorney **Vikas Khanna** . . . . (973) 645-2700
E-mail: vikas.khanna@usdoj.gov
Education: Harvard JD
Assistant U.S. Attorney **Barbara Llanes** . . . . (973) 645-2700
E-mail: barbara.llanes@usdoj.gov

(continued on next page)

★ Presidential Appointment Requiring Senate Confirmation ☆ Presidential Appointment □ Schedule C Appointment ◇ Career Senior Foreign Service Appointment
● Career Senior Executive Service (SES) Appointment ○ Non-Career Senior Executive Service (SES) Appointment ■ Postal Career Executive Service

DEPARTMENTS

Special Prosecutions Division *(continued)*

Assistant U.S. Attorney **Jacques S. Pierre** . . . . (973) 645-2700
E-mail: jacques.pierre@usdoj.gov
Assistant U.S. Attorney **(Vacant)** . . . . (973) 645-2700
Assistant U.S. Attorney **(Vacant)** . . . . (973) 645-2700
Assistant U.S. Attorney **(Vacant)** . . . . (973) 645-2700

Camden (NJ) Office

Camden Federal Building and U.S. Courthouse, 401 Market Street, 4th Floor, Camden, NJ 08101
Tel: (856) 757-5026 Tel: (856) 757-5412 (Civil Division)
Fax: (856) 968-4917 Fax: (856) 757-5416 (Civil Division)

Assistant U.S. Attorney-in-Charge **R. Stephen Stigall** . . . . (856) 757-5026
E-mail: stephen.stigall@usdoj.gov
Deputy Assistant U.S. Attorney-in-Charge **Matthew Skahill** . . . . (856) 757-5026
E-mail: matthew.skahill@usdoj.gov
Appellate Division Assistant U.S. Attorney **Norman J. Gross** . . . . (856) 757-5026
E-mail: norman.gross@usdoj.gov
Appellate Division Assistant U.S. Attorney **Glenn J. Moramarco** . . . . (856) 757-5026
E-mail: glenn.moramarco@usdoj.gov
Appellate Division Assistant U.S. Attorney **Deborah A. Prisinzano Mikkelsen** . . . . (856) 757-5026
E-mail: deborah.mikkelsen@usdoj.gov
Education: Virginia 2001 JD
Senior Litigation Counsel **(Vacant)** . . . . (856) 757-5412
Senior Litigation Counsel **Jason M. Richardson** . . . . . . (856) 757-5026
Civil Division Assistant U.S. Attorney **Elizabeth A. Pascal** . . . . (856) 757-5412
E-mail: elizabeth.pascal@usdoj.gov
Civil Division Assistant U.S. Attorney **Anne B. Taylor** . . . . (856) 757-5412
E-mail: anne.taylor@usdoj.gov
Education: Georgetown 2007 JD
Criminal Division Assistant U.S. Attorney **Sara A. Aliabadi** . . . . (856) 757-5026
Criminal Division Assistant U.S. Attorney **Patrick C. Askin** . . . . (856) 757-5026
Criminal Division Assistant U.S. Attorney **Jacqueline M. Carle** . . . . (856) 757-5026
Criminal Division Assistant U.S. Attorney **Diana V. Carrig** . . . . (856) 757-5026
Criminal Division Assistant U.S. Attorney **Matthew T. Smith** . . . . (856) 757-5026
Education: Holy Cross Col 1995 BA; Emory 1998 MS; Rutgers (Camden) 2001 JD
Criminal Division Assistant U.S. Attorney **R. David Walk** . . . . (856) 757-5026

Trenton (NJ) Office

402 East State Street, Suite 400, Trenton, NJ 08608
Tel: (609) 989-2190 Fax: (609) 989-2275
Fax: (609) 989-2360 (Civil Division)
Fax: (609) 989-0583 (Criminal Division)

Assistant U.S. Attorney-in-Charge **Eric W. Moran** . . . . (609) 989-2190
E-mail: eric.moran@usdoj.gov
Deputy Chief **(Vacant)** . . . . (609) 989-2190
Civil Division Assistant U.S. Attorney **David Bober** . . . . . (609) 989-2190
E-mail: david.bober@usdoj.gov
Education: Seton Hall 2002 JD
Criminal Division Assistant U.S. Attorney **Brendan Day** . . . . (609) 989-2190
E-mail: brendan.day@usdoj.gov
Criminal Division Assistant U.S. Attorney **R. Joseph Gribko** . . . . (609) 989-2190
E-mail: joseph.gribko@usdoj.gov
Criminal Division Assistant U.S. Attorney **Molly S. Lorber** . . . . (609) 989-2190
E-mail: molly.lorber@usdoj.gov
Criminal Division Assistant U.S. Attorney **Fabiana Pierre-Louis** . . . . (609) 989-2190
E-mail: fabiana.pierre-louis@usdoj.gov
Education: Rutgers 2002 BA; Rutgers (Camden) 2006 JD

Trenton (NJ) Office *(continued)*

Criminal Division Assistant U.S. Attorney **Elisa T. Wiygul** . . . . (609) 989-2190
E-mail: elisa.wiygul@usdoj.gov
Education: Yale JD
Criminal Division Assistant U.S. Attorney **Sarah M. Wolfe** . . . . (609) 989-2190
E-mail: sarah.wolfe@usdoj.gov
Criminal Division Assistant U.S. Attorney **(Vacant)** . . . . . . (609) 989-2190

New Mexico District

201 Third Street, NW, Suite 900, Albuquerque, NM 87102
P.O. Box 607, Albuquerque, NM 87103-0607
Tel: (505) 346-7274 Fax: (505) 346-7296
E-mail: usanm.webmaster@usdoj.gov
Internet: https://www.justice.gov/usao-nm

★ U.S. Attorney **John C. Anderson** . . . . (505) 346-7274
Education: Bowdoin 1997 AB; Fordham 2003 JD
Executive Assistant U.S. Attorney and Public Affairs Officer **Elizabeth Martinez** . . . . (505) 346-7274
E-mail: elizabeth.martinez@usdoj.gov
Secretary to the U.S. Attorney **Annamarie Maresca** . . . . (505) 346-7274
E-mail: annamarie.maresca@usdoj.gov
First Assistant U.S. Attorney **James "Jim" Tierney** . . . . . (505) 346-7274
E-mail: jim.tierney@usdoj.gov
Director of Administration **Ruth Cox** . . . . (505) 346-7274
E-mail: ruth.cox@usdoj.gov Fax: (505) 346-6890
Victim-Witness Coordinator **Anita Perry** . . . . (505) 346-7274
E-mail: anita.perry@usdoj.gov Fax: (505) 346-7208
District Office Security Manager **(Vacant)** . . . . (505) 346-7274
Supervisory IT Manager **Edmund Lee** . . . . (505) 346-7274
E-mail: edmund.lee@usdoj.gov
Human Resources Officer **Audrey Sullivan** . . . . (505) 346-7274
E-mail: audrey.sullivan@usdoj.gov
Budget Officer **(Vacant)** . . . . (505) 346-7274

Appeals Division

201 Third Street, NW, Albuquerque, NM 87102
Tel: (505) 346-7274

Appeals Chief **James Braun** . . . . (505) 346-7274
E-mail: james.braun@usdoj.gov
Assistant U.S. Attorney **David N. Williams** . . . . (505) 346-7274
E-mail: david.williams@usdoj.gov
Assistant U.S. Attorney/Organized Crime Drug Enforcement Task Forces **James Braun** . . . . (505) 346-7274
E-mail: james.braun@usdoj.gov

Civil Division

201 Third Street, NW, Albuquerque, NM 87102
Tel: (505) 346-7274 Fax: (505) 346-7205

Civil Division Chief **Michael Hoses** . . . . (505) 346-7274
E-mail: michael.hoses@usdoj.gov Fax: (505) 346-7205
Assistant U.S. Attorney **Ruth F. Keegan** . . . . (505) 346-7274
E-mail: ruth.f.keegan@usdoj.gov
Assistant U.S. Attorney **Erin Langenwalter** . . . . (505) 346-7274
E-mail: erin.langenwalter@usdoj.gov
Assistant U.S. Attorney **Manuel Lucero** . . . . (505) 346-7274
E-mail: manny.lucero@usdoj.gov
Assistant U.S. Attorney **Roberto Ortega** . . . . (505) 346-7274
E-mail: roberto.ortega@usdoj.gov
Assistant U.S. Attorney **Howard Thomas** . . . . (505) 346-7274
E-mail: howard.thomas@usdoj.gov
Assistant U.S. Attorney **(Vacant)** . . . . (505) 346-7274

Criminal Division

201 Third Street, NW, Albuquerque, NM 87102
Tel: (505) 346-7274 Fax: (505) 346-6887

Criminal Division Chief **Jack E. Burkhead** . . . . (505) 346-7274
Supervisory Assistant U.S. Attorney/Fraud and Public Corruption Section **Jonathon Gerson** . . . . (505) 346-7274
E-mail: jonathon.gerson@usdoj.gov
Supervisory Assistant U.S. Attorney/General Crimes Section **Kimberly Brawley** . . . . (505) 346-7274
E-mail: kimberly.brawley@usdoj.gov

★ Presidential Appointment Requiring Senate Confirmation ☆ Presidential Appointment ☐ Schedule C Appointment ◇ Career Senior Foreign Service Appointment
● Career Senior Executive Service (SES) Appointment ○ Non-Career Senior Executive Service (SES) Appointment ■ Postal Career Executive Service

Criminal Division *(continued)*

Supervisory Assistant U.S. Attorney/Indian Country Section **(Vacant)** . . . . . (505) 346-7274
Supervisory Assistant U.S. Attorney/National Security Section **Fred J. Federici** . . . . . (505) 346-7274
E-mail: fred.federici@usdoj.gov
Supervisory Assistant U.S. Attorney/Organized Crime Section **Joel R. Meyers** . . . . . (505) 346-7274
E-mail: joel.meyers@usdoj.gov
Assistant U.S. Attorney **Rumaldo Armijo** . . . . . (505) 346-7274
E-mail: rumaldo.armijo@usdoj.gov
Assistant U.S. Attorney **Norman Cairns** . . . . . (505) 346-7274
E-mail: norman.cairns@usdoj.gov
Assistant U.S. Attorney **Nicholas J. Ganjei** . . . . . (505) 346-7274
E-mail: nicholas.j.ganjei@usdoj.gov
Education: Boalt Hall 2005 JD
Assistant U.S. Attorney **Kristopher N. Houghton** . . . . . (505) 346-7274
E-mail: kristopher.houghton@usdoj.gov
Education: New Mexico 2008 JD
Assistant U.S. Attorney **Samuel A. Hurtado** . . . . . (505) 346-7274
E-mail: samuel.a.hurtado@usdoj.gov
Assistant U.S. Attorney **Holland S. Kastrin** . . . . . (505) 346-7274
E-mail: holland.s.kastrin@usdoj.gov
Assistant U.S. Attorney **Stephen R. Kotz** . . . . . (505) 346-7224
E-mail: steve.kotz@usdoj.gov
Assistant U.S. Attorney **Shana B. Long** . . . . . (505) 346-7274
E-mail: shana.b.long@usdoj.gov
Assistant U.S. Attorney **Sarah Mease** . . . . . (505) 346-7274
E-mail: sarah.mease@usdoj.gov
Assistant U.S. Attorney **Paige Messec** . . . . . (505) 346-7274
E-mail: paige.messec@usdoj.gov
Assistant U.S. Attorney **Paul Mysliwiec** . . . . . (505) 346-7274
E-mail: paul.mysliwiec@usdoj.gov
Assistant U.S. Attorney **Kyle Nayback** . . . . . (505) 346-7274
E-mail: kyle.nayback2@usdoj.gov
Assistant U.S. Attorney **Jeremy A. Pena** . . . . . (505) 346-7274
E-mail: jeremy.pena@usdoj.gov
Assistant U.S. Attorney **Elaine Ramirez** . . . . . (505) 346-7274
E-mail: elaine.ramirez@usdoj.gov
Assistant U.S. Attorney **Jennifer M. Rozzoni** . . . . . (505) 346-7274
E-mail: jennifer.m.rozzoni@usdoj.gov
Assistant U.S. Attorney **Raquel Ruiz-Velez** . . . . . (505) 346-7274
E-mail: raquel.ruiz.velez@usdoj.gov
Assistant U.S. Attorney **Sasha Siemel** . . . . . (505) 346-7274
E-mail: sasha.siemel@usdoj.gov
Assistant U.S. Attorney **Paul Spiers** . . . . . (505) 346-7274
E-mail: paul.spiers@usdoj.gov
Assistant U.S. Attorney **Jon Stanford** . . . . . (505) 346-7274
E-mail: jon.stanford@usdoj.gov
Assistant U.S. Attorney **Sean J. Sullivan** . . . . . (505) 346-7274
E-mail: sean.j.sullivan@usdoj.gov
Assistant U.S. Attorney **Reeve Swainston** . . . . . (505) 346-7274
E-mail: reeve.swainston@usdoj.gov
Assistant U.S. Attorney **Niki Tapia-Brito** . . . . . (505) 346-7274
E-mail: niki.tapia-brito@usdoj.gov
Assistant U.S. Attorney **Shaheen Torgoley** . . . . . (505) 346-7274
E-mail: shaheen.torgoley@usdoj.gov
Assistant U.S. Attorney **Presiliano Torrez** . . . . . (505) 346-7274
E-mail: presiliano.torrez@usdoj.gov
Education: Harvard 1999 AB; London School Econ (UK) 2001 MS; Stanford 2005 JD
Assistant U.S. Attorney **Timothy Vasquez** . . . . . (505) 346-7274
E-mail: timothy.vasquez@usdoj.gov
Assistant U.S. Attorney **David M. Walsh** . . . . . (505) 346-7274
E-mail: david.m.walsh@usdoj.gov
Assistant U.S. Attorney **Lynn Wang** . . . . . (505) 346-7274
E-mail: lynn.wang@usdoj.gov
Assistant U.S. Attorney **Novaline Wilson** . . . . . (505) 346-7274
E-mail: novaline.wilson@usdoj.gov

Las Cruces (NM) Office
555 South Telshor, Suite 300, Las Cruces, NM 88011
Tel: (575) 522-2304 Fax: (575) 522-2391

Deputy Chief, Criminal Division **Renee Camacho** . . . . . (575) 522-2304
E-mail: renee.camacho@usdoj.gov

Las Cruces (NM) Office *(continued)*

Assistant U.S. Attorney/Trial Group Supervisor **Alfred Perez** . . . . . (575) 522-2304
E-mail: alfred.perez@usdoj.gov
Assistant U.S. Attorney/Trial Group Supervisor **Richard C. Williams** . . . . . (575) 522-2304
E-mail: richard.c.williams@usdoj.gov
Senior Litigation Counsel/OCDETF and Strike Force Coordinator **Terri Abernathy** . . . . . (575) 522-2304
E-mail: terri.abernathy@usdoj.gov
Assistant U.S. Attorney **Maria Armijo** . . . . . (505) 522-2304
E-mail: maria.armijo@usdoj.gov
Assistant U.S. Attorney **Randy Castellano** . . . . . (575) 522-2304
E-mail: randy.castellano@usdoj.gov
Assistant U.S. Attorney **Sarah M. Davenport** . . . . . (575) 522-2304
E-mail: sarah.m.davenport@usdoj.gov
Assistant U.S. Attorney **Amanda Gould** . . . . . (575) 522-2304
E-mail: amanda.gould@usdoj.gov
Assistant U.S. Attorney **Aaron O. Jordan** . . . . . (575) 522-2304
E-mail: aaron.o.jordan@usdoj.gov
Assistant U.S. Attorney **Luis A. Martinez** . . . . . (575) 522-2304
E-mail: luis.a.martinez@usdoj.gov
Assistant U.S. Attorney **Mark Saltman** . . . . . (575) 522-2304
E-mail: mark.saltman@usdoj.gov
Assistant U.S. Attorney **Alexander Shapiro** . . . . . (575) 522-2304
E-mail: alexander.shapiro@usdoj.gov
Assistant U.S. Attorney **(Vacant)** . . . . . (575) 522-2304
Assistant U.S. Attorney **(Vacant)** . . . . . (575) 522-2304
Special Assistant U.S. Attorney **Selesia Winston** . . . . . (575) 522-2304
E-mail: selesia.winston@usdoj.gov
Special Assistant U.S. Attorney **(Vacant)** . . . . . (575) 522-2304

New York - Eastern District
271 Cadman Plaza East, Brooklyn, NY 11201
Tel: (718) 254-7000 Fax: (718) 254-6479
Internet: https://www.justice.gov/usao-edny

★ U.S. Attorney (Interim) **Richard P. Donoghue** . . . . . (718) 254-7000
E-mail: richard.donoghue@usdoj.gov
Secretary to the U.S. Attorney **Lisa Alper** . . . . . (718) 254-7000
E-mail: lisa.alper@usdoj.gov
Chief Assistant U.S. Attorney **(Vacant)** . . . . . (718) 254-7000
Fax: (718) 254-6300
Secretary to the Chief Assistant U.S. Attorney **Lisa Alper** . . . . . (718) 254-7000
E-mail: lisa.alper@usdoj.gov
Executive Assistant U.S. Attorney **William J. Muller** . . . . . (718) 254-7000
E-mail: william.muller@usdoj.gov Fax: (718) 254-6329
Secretary to the Executive Assistant U.S. Attorney **(Vacant)** . . . . . (718) 254-7000
Fax: (718) 254-6329
Law Enforcement Coordinator **Richard Capobianco** . . . . . (718) 254-7000
E-mail: richard.capobianco@usdoj.gov
Public Information Officer **(Vacant)** . . . . . (718) 254-7000
Victim - Witness Coordinator **Lisa Foster** . . . . . (718) 254-7000
E-mail: lisa.foster@usdoj.gov
Webmaster **Richard Woo** . . . . . (718) 254-7000
E-mail: richard.woo@usdoj.gov

Administrative Division
271 Cadman Plaza East, Brooklyn, NY 11201
Administrative Officer **(Vacant)** . . . . . (718) 254-7000
Fax: (718) 254-6587
Deputy Administrative Officer **Mary Breen** . . . . . (718) 254-7000
E-mail: mary.breen@usdoj.gov
Systems Manager **Shafiul Khan** . . . . . (718) 254-7000
E-mail: shafiul.khan@usdoj.gov
Support Services Supervisor **Marc Caffray** . . . . . (718) 254-7000
E-mail: marc.caffray@usdoj.gov
Budget Officer **(Vacant)** . . . . . (718) 254-7000
Fax: (718) 254-6550
Budget Analyst **(Vacant)** . . . . . (718) 254-7000
Security Officer **Richard Capobianco** . . . . . (631) 715-7000
610 Federal Plaza, Central Islip, NY 11722
E-mail: richard.capobianco@usdoj.gov
Management Analyst **(Vacant)** . . . . . (718) 254-7000

(continued on next page)

DEPARTMENTS

★ Presidential Appointment Requiring Senate Confirmation ☆ Presidential Appointment □ Schedule C Appointment ◇ Career Senior Foreign Service Appointment
● Career Senior Executive Service (SES) Appointment ○ Non-Career Senior Executive Service (SES) Appointment ■ Postal Career Executive Service

Administrative Division *(continued)*

Librarian **John Malone** . . . . . (718) 254-6306
E-mail: john.malone@usdoj.gov

Appeals Division
271 Cadman Plaza East, Brooklyn, NY 11201
Fax: (718) 254-6325

Appeals Division Chief/Ethics Advisor/Professional Responsibility Officer **(Vacant)** . . . . . (718) 254-7000
Deputy Chief **Emily Berger** . . . . . (718) 254-7000
E-mail: emily.berger@usdoj.gov
Deputy Chief **David C. James** . . . . . (718) 254-7000
E-mail: david.james@usdoj.gov
Assistant U.S. Attorney **Susan Corkery** . . . . . (718) 254-7000
E-mail: susan.corkery@usdoj.gov
Assistant U.S. Attorney **(Vacant)** . . . . . (718) 254-7000

Civil Division
One Pierrepont Plaza, Brooklyn, NY 11201
Tel: (718) 254-7000 Fax: (718) 254-8701

Chief **Susan L. Riley** . . . . . (718) 254-7000
E-mail: susan.riley@usdoj.gov Fax: (718) 254-7483
Principal Deputy Chief **Gail Matthews** . . . . . (718) 254-7000
E-mail: gail.matthews@usdoj.gov
Deputy Chief **Artemis Lekakis** . . . . . (718) 254-7000
E-mail: artemis.lekakis@usdoj.gov
Affirmative Enforcement Chief **Richard K. Hayes** . . . . . (718) 254-7000
E-mail: richard.hayes@usdoj.gov
Civil Appeals Chief **Varuni Nelson** . . . . . (718) 254-7000
E-mail: varuni.nelson@usdoj.gov
Civil Rights Chief **Michael Goldberger** . . . . . (718) 254-7000
E-mail: michael.goldberger@usdoj.gov
Chief of Environmental Litigation **Sandra Levy** . . . . . (718) 254-7000
E-mail: sandra.levy@usdoj.gov
Chief of Trial Training **(Vacant)** . . . . . (718) 254-7000
Employment Discrimination Chief **Catherine M. Mirabile** . . . . . (718) 254-7000
E-mail: catherine.m.mirabile@usdoj.gov
Financial Litigation Unit Chief **Beth P. Schwartz** . . . . . (718) 254-7000
E-mail: beth.schwartz@usdoj.gov
Health Care Fraud Chief **(Vacant)** . . . . . (718) 254-7000
Senior Trial Counsel **F. Franklin Amanat** . . . . . (718) 254-7000
E-mail: franklin.amanat@usdoj.gov
Senior Trial Counsel **Kevan Cleary** . . . . . (718) 254-7000
E-mail: kevan.cleary@usdoj.gov
Assistant U.S. Attorney **Kenneth Abell** . . . . . (718) 254-7000
E-mail: kenneth.abell@usdoj.gov
Assistant U.S. Attorney **Matthew R. Belz** . . . . . (718) 254-7000
E-mail: matthew.belz@usdoj.gov
Assistant U.S. Attorney **Mary M. Dickman** . . . . . (718) 254-7000
E-mail: mary.dickman@usdoj.gov
Assistant U.S. Attorney **Kelly Horan** . . . . . (718) 254-7000
E-mail: kelly.horan@usdoj.gov
Assistant U.S. Attorney **Claire S. Kedeshian** . . . . . (718) 254-7000
E-mail: claire.kedeshian@usdoj.gov
Assistant U.S. Attorney **Evan P. Lestelle** . . . . . (718) 254-7000
E-mail: evan.lestelle@usdoj.gov
Assistant U.S. Attorney **Orelia Merchant** . . . . . (718) 254-7000
E-mail: orelia.merchant@usdoj.gov
Assistant U.S. Attorney **Matthew J. Modafferi** . . . . . (718) 254-7000
E-mail: matthew.modafferi@usdoj.gov
Assistant U.S. Attorney **Elliot Schachner** . . . . . (718) 254-7000
E-mail: elliot.schachner@usdoj.gov
Assistant U.S. Attorney **Clayton Solomon** . . . . . (718) 254-7000
E-mail: clayton.solomon@usdoj.gov
Assistant U.S. Attorney **Josephine M. Vella** . . . . . (718) 254-7000
E-mail: josephine.vella@usdoj.gov
Assistant U.S. Attorney **Alex Weinberg** . . . . . (718) 254-7000
E-mail: alex.weinberg@usdoj.gov
Education: Brooklyn Law 2010 JD
Special Assistant U.S. Attorney **(Vacant)** . . . . . (718) 254-7000
Special Assistant U.S. Attorney **(Vacant)** . . . . . (718) 254-7000
Social Security Litigation Chief **Kathleen Mahoney** . . . . . (718) 254-7000
E-mail: kathleen.mahoney@usdoj.gov

Criminal Division
271 Cadman Plaza East, Brooklyn, NY 11201
Tel: (718) 254-7614 (Business and Securities Fraud Hotline)
Tel: (718) 254-6582 (General Crimes Hotline)
Tel: (718) 254-6581 (Narcotics Hotline)
Tel: (718) 254-6584 (Public Integrity Hotline)
Tel: (718) 254-6583 (Organized Crime and Racketeering Hotline)
Tel: (718) 254-6580 (Violent Criminal Enterprises Hotline)
Fax: (718) 254-6324

Chief **James D. Gatta** . . . . . (718) 254-7000
E-mail: james.gatta@usdoj.gov
Education: Fordham 1998 BA, 2002 JD
Deputy Chief **(Vacant)** . . . . . (718) 254-7000
Chief of Appeals/Professional Responsibility Officer **(Vacant)** . . . . . (718) 254-7000
Senior Litigation Counsel **(Vacant)** . . . . . (718) 254-7000
Business/Securities Fraud Section Chief **James F. "Jay" McMahon** . . . . . (718) 254-7000
E-mail: james.mcmahon@usdoj.gov Fax: (718) 254-7499
Education: Fordham JD
Business/Security Fraud Deputy Chief **(Vacant)** . . . . . (718) 254-7000
Business/Security Fraud Senior Trial Counsel **Walter Norkin** . . . . . (718) 254-7000
E-mail: walter.norkin@usdoj.gov
Education: NYU 2000 JD
Assistant U.S. Attorney **(Vacant)** . . . . . (718) 254-7000
Assistant U.S. Attorney **Tanya Y. Hill** . . . . . (718) 254-7000
E-mail: tanya.hill@usdoj.gov
Assistant U.S. Attorney **Shannon Jones** . . . . . (718) 254-7000
E-mail: shannon.jones@usdoj.gov
Assistant U.S. Attorney **(Vacant)** . . . . . (718) 254-7000
Assistant U.S. Attorney **(Vacant)** . . . . . (718) 254-7000
Civil Rights Litigation Section Chief **Taryn A. Merkl** . . . . . (718) 254-7000
E-mail: taryn.merkl@usdoj.gov
Education: Columbia 2000 JD
Senior Litigation Counsel **(Vacant)** . . . . . (718) 254-7000
Fax: (718) 254-6076
Assistant U.S. Attorney **Amy Busa** . . . . . (718) 254-7000
One Pierrepont Plaza, Brooklyn, NY 11201
E-mail: amy.busa@usdoj.gov
Assistant U.S. Attorney **Carrie N. Capwell** . . . . . (718) 254-7000
E-mail: carrie.capwell@usdoj.gov
Education: Georgetown 1998 JD
Assistant U.S. Attorney **Charles S. Kleinberg** . . . . . (718) 254-7000
E-mail: charles.kleinberg@usdoj.gov
Intake and Arraignments Section Chief **Judith A. "Judy" Philips** . . . . . (718) 254-7000
E-mail: judy.philips@usdoj.gov Fax: (718) 254-6482
Narcotics Chief **(Vacant)** . . . . . (718) 254-7000
Narcotics Deputy Chief **(Vacant)** . . . . . (718) 254-7000
Assistant U.S. Attorney **(Vacant)** . . . . . (718) 254-7000
Organized Crime and Racketeering Section Chief **Elizabeth Geddes** . . . . . (718) 254-7000
E-mail: elizabeth.geddes@usdoj.gov Fax: (718) 254-6480
Deputy Chief, Organized Crime **James D. Gatta** . . . . . (718) 254-6339
E-mail: james.gatta@usdoj.gov
Education: Fordham 1998 BA, 2002 JD
General Crimes Chief **(Vacant)** . . . . . (718) 254-7000
Assistant U.S. Attorney **Lauren Elbert** . . . . . (718) 254-7000
E-mail: lauren.elbert@usdoj.gov
Deputy Chief, General Crimes **(Vacant)** . . . . . (718) 254-7000
Assistant U.S. Attorney **James Loonam** . . . . . (718) 254-7000
E-mail: james.loonam@usdoj.gov
Assistant U.S. Attorney **Jonathan P. Lax** . . . . . (718) 254-7000
E-mail: jonathan.lax@usdoj.gov
Assistant U.S. Attorney **Patricia Notopoulos** . . . . . (718) 254-7000
E-mail: patricia.notopoulos@usdoj.gov
Assistant U.S. Attorney **David Pitluck** . . . . . (718) 254-7000
E-mail: david.pitluck@usdoj.gov
Assistant U.S. Attorney **Michael H. Warren** . . . . . (718) 254-7000
E-mail: michael.warren@usdoj.gov
Public Integrity Chief **(Vacant)** . . . . . (718) 254-7000
Fax: (718) 254-6180

★ Presidential Appointment Requiring Senate Confirmation ☆ Presidential Appointment ☐ Schedule C Appointment ◇ Career Senior Foreign Service Appointment
● Career Senior Executive Service (SES) Appointment ○ Non-Career Senior Executive Service (SES) Appointment ■ Postal Career Executive Service

Criminal Division *(continued)*

Assistant U.S. Attorney **Douglas M. Pravda** . . . . (718) 254-7000
E-mail: douglas.pravda@usdoj.gov
Education: Harvard 2001 JD

Deputy Chief, Public Integrity Section
Paul Tuchmann . . . . (718) 254-7000
E-mail: paul.tuchmann@usdoj.gov
Education: Harvard 2002 JD

Violent Crimes and Terrorism Section Chief
Zainab Ahmad . . . . (718) 254-7000
Note: On detail to the Office of the Special Counsel. Fax: (718) 254-6480
E-mail: zainab.ahmad@usdoj.gov

Assistant U.S. Attorney **Saritha Komatireddy** . . . . (718) 254-7000
E-mail: saritha.komatireddy@usdoj.gov
Education: Harvard, JD

Deputy Chief, Violent Crimes **(Vacant)** . . . . (718) 254-7000

Assistant U.S. Attorney **Ian Richardson** . . . . (718) 254-7000
E-mail: ian.richardson@usdoj.gov
Education: UC Berkeley 2005 BA; Columbia 2010 JD

Assistant U.S. Attorney **James P. McDonald** . . . . (718) 254-7000
Education: Bowdoin 2005 AB; Duke 2009 JD

Assistant U.S. Attorney **Alexander F. Mindlin** . . . . (718) 254-7000
E-mail: alexander.mindlin@usdoj.gov
Education: Harvard 2002 BA; NYU 2011 JD

Assistant U.S. Attorney **Sylvia Shweder** . . . . (718) 254-7000
E-mail: sylvia.shweder@usdoj.gov

Long Island Office

610 Federal Plaza, Central Islip, NY 11722-4454
Tel: (631) 715-7900 Fax: (631) 715-7922

Assistant U.S. Attorney-in-Charge **Nicole Boeckmann** . . . (631) 715-7900
E-mail: nicole.boeckmann@usdoj.gov

Office Manager **(Vacant)** . . . . (631) 715-7900

Civil Division

610 Federal Plaza, Central Islip, NY 11722-4454
Fax: (631) 715-7920

Chief **(Vacant)** . . . . (631) 715-7900

Deputy Chief **Charles Kelly** . . . . (631) 715-7900
E-mail: charles.kelly@usdoj.gov

Assistant U.S. Attorney **James Knapp** . . . . (631) 715-7900
E-mail: james.knapp@usdoj.gov

Assistant U.S. Attorney **Vincent Lipari** . . . . (631) 715-7900
E-mail: vincent.lipari@usdoj.gov

Criminal Division

610 Federal Plaza, Central Islip, NY 11722-4454
Fax: (631) 715-7922

Chief **Nicole Boeckmann** . . . . (631) 715-7874
E-mail: nicole.boeckmann@usdoj.gov

Deputy Chief **(Vacant)** . . . . (718) 254-7000

Deputy Chief **(Vacant)** . . . . (631) 715-7900

Criminal Investigator **(Vacant)** . . . . (631) 715-7900

Narcotics Deputy Chief **(Vacant)** . . . . (718) 254-7000

Assistant U.S. Attorney **Carrie N. Capwell** . . . . (631) 715-7900
E-mail: carrie.capwell@usdoj.gov
Education: Georgetown 1998 JD

Assistant U.S. Attorney **John J. Durham** . . . . (718) 254-7000
E-mail: john.durham2@usdoj.gov
Education: Col Holy Cross 1998 BA; Connecticut 2001 JD

Assistant U.S. Attorney **Lara Treinis Gatz** . . . . (631) 715-7900
E-mail: lara.gatz@usdoj.gov

Assistant U.S. Attorney **(Vacant)** . . . . (631) 715-7900

Assistant U.S. Attorney **Burton T. Ryan** . . . . (631) 715-7900
E-mail: burton.ryan@usdoj.gov

Assistant U.S. Attorney **(Vacant)** . . . . (631) 715-7900

Assistant U.S. Attorney/Project Safe Childhood Task Force **Allen L. Bode** . . . . (631) 715-7900
E-mail: allen.bode@usdoj.gov

New York - Northern District

James M. Hanley Federal Building, 100 South Clinton Street, Room 900, Syracuse, NY 13261-7198
P.O. Box 7198, Syracuse, NY 13261-7198
Tel: (315) 448-0672 Fax: (315) 448-0689
Internet: https://www.justice.gov/usao-ndny

★ U.S. Attorney (Interim) **Grant C. Jaquith** . . . . (518) 431-0247
E-mail: grant.jaquith@usdoj.gov
Education: Presbyterian Col 1979; Florida 1982 JD

Paralegal to the U.S. Attorney **(Vacant)** . . . . (518) 431-0247

First Assistant U.S. Attorney **Grant C. Jaquith** . . . . (518) 431-0247
E-mail: grant.jaquith@usdoj.gov
Education: Presbyterian Col 1979; Florida 1982 JD

Executive Assistant U.S. Attorney for Community and Public Affairs **Linda Powers** . . . . (315) 448-0672
E-mail: linda.powers@usdoj.gov

Administrative Officer **Martha J. Stratton** . . . . (315) 448-0672
E-mail: martha.stratton@usdoj.gov

Law Enforcement Committee Coordinator
Armond Scipione . . . . (315) 448-0672

Systems Manager **William Eckert** . . . . (315) 448-0672
E-mail: william.eckert@usdoj.gov

Syracuse Office Manager **Lisa M. Fletcher** . . . . (315) 448-0672

Appellate Division

James M. Hanely Federal Building, 100 South Clinton Street, Syracuse, NY 13261
Fax: (315) 448-0689

Appellate Chief **Steven D. Clymer** . . . . (315) 448-0672
E-mail: steven.d.clymer@usdoj.gov
Education: Cornell 1983, 1986 JD

Civil Division

James M. Hanely Federal Building, 100 South Clinton Street, Syracuse, NY 13261
Fax: (315) 448-0646

Chief **Thomas Spina, Jr.** . . . . (518) 431-0247
E-mail: thomas.spina@usdoj.gov
Education: Siena Col 1982; Albany Law 1995 JD

Assistant U.S. Attorney **Mary Langan** . . . . (315) 448-0672
E-mail: mary.langan@usdoj.gov

Assistant U.S. Attorney **William F. Larkin** . . . . (315) 448-0672
E-mail: william.larkin@usdoj.gov

Assistant U.S. Attorney **Ransom P. Reynolds** . . . . (315) 448-0672
E-mail: ransom.p.reynolds@usdoj.gov

Assistant U.S. Attorney **Charles E. Roberts** . . . . (315) 448-0672
E-mail: charles.roberts@usdoj.gov

Assistant U.S. Attorney **(Vacant)** . . . . (315) 448-0672

Criminal Division

James M. Hanely Federal Building, 100 South Clinton Street, Syracuse, NY 13261
Fax: (315) 448-0689

Chief **Elizabeth C. Coombe** . . . . (315) 448-0672
E-mail: elizabeth.c.coombe@usdoj.gov

Deputy Chief **(Vacant)** . . . . (518) 431-0247

Assistant U.S. Attorney and National Security Coordinator **Stephen C. Green** . . . . (315) 448-0672
E-mail: stephen.green@usdoj.gov

Assistant U.S. Attorney and Senior Litigation Counsel
Edward R. Broton . . . . (315) 448-0672
E-mail: ed.broton@usdoj.gov
Education: Canisius 1975 BS; Albany Law 1979 JD

Assistant U.S. Attorney **Rick Bellis** . . . . (315) 448-0672

Assistant U.S. Attorney **Nicolas Commandeur** . . . . (315) 448-0672
E-mail: nicolas.commandeur@usdoj.gov

Assistant U.S. Attorney **Rajit S. Dosanjh** . . . . (315) 448-0672
E-mail: rajit.s.dosanjh@usdoj.gov

Assistant U.S. Attorney **Carl G. Eurenius** . . . . (315) 448-0672
E-mail: carl.eurenius@usdoj.gov

Assistant U.S. Attorney **Lisa M. Fletcher** . . . . (315) 448-0672
E-mail: lisa.fletcher@usdoj.gov

Assistant U.S. Attorney **Carla B. Freedman** . . . . (315) 448-0672
E-mail: carla.freedman@usdoj.gov

(continued on next page)

DEPARTMENTS

Criminal Division *(continued)*

Assistant U.S. Attorney **Emmett O'Hanlon** .... (315) 448-0672
Assistant U.S. Attorney **Michael Perry** .... (315) 448-0672
E-mail: michael.perry@usdoj.gov
Education: Harvard 2009 JD
Assistant U.S. Attorney **Carina Schoenberger** .... (315) 448-0672
E-mail: carina.schoenberger@usdoj.gov
Assistant U.S. Attorney **Richard R. Southwick** .... (315) 448-0672
E-mail: richard.southwick@usdoj.gov
Assistant U.S. Attorney **Tamara Thompson** .... (315) 448-0672
E-mail: tamara.thompson@usdoj.gov

Organized Crime Drug Enforcement Task Force
James M. Hanely Federal Building, 100 South Clinton Street, Syracuse, NY 13261
Fax: (315) 448-0689

Chief **Daniel Hanlon** .... (518) 431-0247
E-mail: daniel.hanlon@usdoj.gov

Albany (NY) Office
James T. Foley Courthouse, 445 Broadway, Room 218, Albany, NY 12207
Tel: (518) 431-0247 Fax: (518) 431-0249

Office Chief **Thomas Spina, Jr.** .... (518) 431-0247
E-mail: thomas.spina@usdoj.gov
Education: Siena Col 1982; Albany Law 1995 JD

Asset Forfeiture Unit
James M. Hanely Federal Building, 100 South Clinton Street, Syracuse, NY 13261
Fax: (518) 431-0249

Assistant U.S. Attorney **Tamara Thompson** .... (315) 448-0672
E-mail: tamara.thompson@usdoj.gov

Civil Division
James M, Hanely Federal Building, 100 South Clinton Street, Syracuse, NY 13261
Fax: (518) 431-0249

Assistant U.S. Attorney **Cathleen Clark** .... (518) 431-0247
Assistant U.S. Attorney **John D. Hoggan, Jr.** .... (518) 431-0247
E-mail: john.hoggan@usdoj.gov
Education: Cornell 1999 JD
Assistant U.S. Attorney **Adam Katz** .... (518) 431-0247
E-mail: adam.katz@usdoj.gov
Assistant U.S. Attorney **Karen Lesperance** .... (518) 431-0247
E-mail: karen.lesperance@usdoj.gov

Criminal Division
James M. Hanely Federal Building, 100 South Clinton Street, Syracuse, NY 13261
Fax: (518) 431-0249

Assistant U.S. Attorney **Michael Barnett** .... (518) 431-0247
E-mail: michael.barnett@usdoj.gov
Assistant U.S. Attorney **Richard Belliss** .... (518) 431-0247
E-mail: richard.belliss@usdoj.gov
Assistant U.S. Attorney **Jeffrey Coffman** .... (518) 431-0247
E-mail: jeffrey.coffman@usdoj.gov
Assistant U.S. Attorney **Emily Farber** .... (518) 431-0247
E-mail: emily.farber@usdoj.gov
Assistant U.S. Attorney **Edward P. Grogan** .... (518) 431-0247
E-mail: edward.grogan@usdoj.gov
Assistant U.S. Attorney **Wayne Meyers** .... (518) 431-0247
Assistant U.S. Attorney **Sean O'Dowd** .... (518) 431-0247
E-mail: sean.odowd@usdoj.gov
Assistant U.S. Attorney **Elizabeth Rabe** .... (518) 431-0247
E-mail: elizabeth.rabe@usdoj.gov
Assistant U.S. Attorney **Kofi Sansculotte** .... (518) 431-0247
E-mail: kofi.sansculotte@usdoj.gov
Assistant U.S. Attorney **Robert A. Sharpe** .... (518) 431-0247
E-mail: robert.sharpe@usdoj.gov
Assistant U.S. Attorney **Solomon Shinerock** .... (518) 431-0247
E-mail: solomon.shinerock@usdoj.gov
Education: Washington College of Law 2009 JD

Criminal Division *(continued)*

Assistant U.S. Attorney **Paul D. Silver** .... (518) 431-0247
E-mail: paul.silver@usdoj.gov
Special Assistant U.S. Attorney **Jason White** .... (518) 431-0247
E-mail: jason.white@usdoj.gov

Binghamton (NY) Office
Federal Building, 15 Henry Street, Room 304, Binghamton, NY 13901
Tel: (607) 773-2887 Fax: (607) 773-2901

Assistant U.S. Attorney **Miroslav "Miro" Lovric** .... (607) 773-2887
E-mail: miro.lovric@usdoj.gov

Plattsburgh (NY) Office
14 Durkee Street, Suite 340, Plattsburgh, NY 12910
Tel: (518) 314-7800 Fax: (518) 314-7811

Assistant U.S. Attorney **Douglas Collyer** .... (518) 314-7800
Assistant U.S. Attorney **Elizabeth Horsman** .... (518) 314-7800
Assistant U.S. Attorney **Katherine Kopita** .... (518) 314-7800
Assistant U.S. Attorney **Cyrus P.W. Rieck** .... (518) 314-7800
Education: Miami 2008 JD

New York - Southern District
One St. Andrew's Plaza, New York, NY 10007
Tel: (212) 637-2200 Internet: https://www.justice.gov/usao-sdny

★ U.S. Attorney **Geoffrey S. Berman** .... (212) 637-1025
E-mail: geoffrey.berman@usdoj.gov
Education: Pennsylvania 1981 BA; Stanford 1984 JD
Chief Counsel to the United States Attorney **(Vacant)** .... (212) 637-2200
Senior Counsel to the United States Attorney **Audrey Strauss** .... (212) 637-2200
Education: Barnard 1968 BA; Columbia 1971 JD
Administrative Assistant to the U.S. Attorney **Hilary Nabhan** .... (212) 637-2582
Deputy U.S. Attorney **Robert S. Khuzami** .... (212) 637-2200
E-mail: robert.khuzami@usdoj.gov
Education: Rochester 1979; Boston U 1983 JD
Associate U.S. Attorney **John M. McEnany** .... (212) 637-2571
E-mail: john.mcenany@usdoj.gov
Executive Assistant U.S. Attorney **Neil M. Corwin** ...... (212) 637-2707
E-mail: neil.corwin@usdoj.gov
Education: Amherst 1981 BS; NYU 1985 JD
Administrative Officer **Edward Tyrrell** .... (212) 637-2269
E-mail: edward.tyrrell@usdoj.gov
Deputy Administrative Officer **James Bullock** .... (212) 637-2584
Chief Public Information Officer **James M. "Jim" Margolin** .... (212) 637-2600
E-mail: james.margolin@usdoj.gov
Senior Public Affairs Officer and Director of New Media **(Vacant)** .... (212) 637-2600

Civil Division
86 Chambers Street, New York, NY 10007

Chief **Jeffrey S. Oesstericher** .... (212) 637-2698
E-mail: jeffrey.oesstericher@usdoj.gov
Education: Yale 1990 JD
Deputy Chief **David S. Jones** .... (212) 637-2739
E-mail: david.jones@usdoj.gov
Deputy Chief **Sarah S. Normand** .... (212) 637-2709
E-mail: sarah.normand@usdoj.gov
Education: Georgetown 1991 JD
Chief Appellate Attorney **Benjamin Torrance** .... (212) 637-2706
E-mail: benjamin.torrance@usdoj.gov
Education: Columbia 2000 JD
Civil Frauds Co-Chief **Pierre Armand** .... (212) 637-2724
E-mail: pierre.armand@usdoj.gov
Civil Frauds Co-Chief **(Vacant)** .... (212) 637-2714
Civil Rights Unit Chief **David Kennedy** .... (212) 637-2733
E-mail: david.kennedy2@usdoj.gov
Civil Rights Unit Deputy Chief **Laura Eshkenazi** ...... (212) 637-2758
Environmental Protection Unit Chief **Robert Yalen** ...... (212) 637-2734
E-mail: robert.yalen@usdoj.gov

★ Presidential Appointment Requiring Senate Confirmation ☆ Presidential Appointment ☐ Schedule C Appointment ◇ Career Senior Foreign Service Appointment
● Career Senior Executive Service (SES) Appointment ○ Non-Career Senior Executive Service (SES) Appointment ■ Postal Career Executive Service

Civil Division *(continued)*

Financial Litigation Unit Chief
Kathleen A. Zebrowski . . . . . (212) 637-2710
E-mail: kathleen.zebrowski@usdoj.gov
Tax and Bankruptcy Unit Chief **Jeannette A. Vargas** . . . . (212) 637-2739
E-mail: jeannette.vargas@usdoj.gov
Education: Harvard 1995 BA; Yale 2000 JD
Tax and Bankruptcy Unit Deputy Chief
Lawrence "Larry" Fogelman . . . . . (212) 637-2739
E-mail: lawrence.fogelman@usdoj.gov
Budget and Fiscal Officer **Wanda Yu** . . . . . (212) 637-2666
E-mail: wanda.yu@usdoj.gov
Personnel Officer **Ruby Hopkins** . . . . . (212) 637-2659
E-mail: ruby.hopkins@usdoj.gov
Office Manager **Carmen Sepulveda** . . . . . (212) 637-2767
E-mail: carmen.sepulveda@usdoj.gov
Civil Clerk Office Chief **(Vacant)** . . . . . (212) 637-1563
Paralegal Manager **Lisa Jones** . . . . . (212) 637-2694

Criminal Division
One St. Andrew's Plaza, New York, NY 10007
Tel: (212) 637-2200

Chief **Lisa Zornberg** . . . . . (212) 637-2200
E-mail: lisa.zornberg@usdoj.gov
Deputy Chief **Andrew Dunber** . . . . . (212) 637-2563
Deputy Chief **Diane Gujarati** . . . . . (212) 637-2200
E-mail: diane.gujarati@usdoj.gov
Education: Barnard 1990 BA; Yale 1995 JD
Deputy Chief **Bonnie B. Jonas** . . . . . (212) 637-2472
E-mail: bonnie.jonas@usdoj.gov
Education: Wharton 1991 BS; Columbia 1995 JD
Deputy Chief **Janis M. Echenberg** . . . . . (212) 637-2265
E-mail: janis.echenberg@usdoj.gov
Chief Appellate Attorney **Michael A. "Mike" Levy** . . . . . (212) 637-1044
Complex Frauds Chief **Stephen Smith** . . . . . (212) 637-2330
Complex Frauds Deputy Chief **Nicole Fridander** . . . . . (212) 637-2211
General Crimes Co-Chief **(Vacant)** . . . . . (212) 637-2262
General Crimes Co-Chief **(Vacant)** . . . . . (212) 637-1110
Terrorism and International Narcotics Co-Chief
(Vacant) . . . . . (212) 637-2200
Terrorism and International Narcotics Co-Chief
(Vacant) . . . . . (212) 637-2407
Narcotics Co-Chief **Paul Krieger** . . . . . (212) 637-1084
E-mail: paul.krieger@usdoj.gov
Education: Harvard JD
Narcotics Co-Chief **Jessica Ortiz** . . . . . (212) 637-2212
E-mail: jessica.ortiz@usdoj.gov
Violent and Organized Crime Co-Chief
Laurie A. Korenbaum . . . . . (212) 637-2266
E-mail: laurie.korenbaum@usdoj.gov
Education: NYU 1985; Brooklyn Law 1996 JD
Violent and Organized Crime Co-Chief
Michael McGinnis . . . . . (212) 637-2305
E-mail: michael.mcginnis@usdoj.gov
Senior Trial Counsel **Stanley Okula** . . . . . (212) 637-1585
E-mail: stan.okula@usdoj.gov
Assistant U.S. Attorney **Andrew Beaty** . . . . . (212) 637-2200
Assistant U.S. Attorney **Emil Bove III** . . . . . (212) 637-2200
Assistant U.S. Attorney **Nicholas Chiuchiolo** . . . . . (212) 637-2200
Education: SUNY (Albany) 2007 BA; Columbia 2010 JD
Assistant U.S. Attorney **Andrew J. DeFilippis** . . . . . (212) 637-2200
Assistant U.S. Attorney **David W. Denton, Jr.** . . . . . (212) 637-2200
Education: Yale 2007 BA; Harvard 2011 JD
Assistant U.S. Attorney **Ilan Graff** . . . . . (212) 637-2200
Education: Harvard 2009 JD
Assistant U.S. Attorney **Amanda Houle** . . . . . (212) 637-2200
Education: Fordham 2009 JD
Assistant U.S. Attorney **Sidhardha Karamaju** . . . . . (212) 637-2200
Education: Washington U (MO) JD
Assistant U.S. Attorney **Jane Kim** . . . . . (212) 637-2200
Assistant U.S. Attorney **Matthew Laroche** . . . . . (212) 637-2200
Education: Albany Law 2010 JD
Assistant U.S. Attorney **Michael D. Lockard** . . . . . (212) 637-2200
Assistant U.S. Attorney **Daniel Noble** . . . . . (212) 637-2200
Education: Yale 2008 JD

Criminal Division *(continued)*

Assistant U.S. Attorney **George D. Turner** . . . . . (212) 637-2200
Assistant U.S. Attorney **Daniel C. Richenthal** . . . . . (212) 637-2200
Assistant U.S. Attorney **Niketh Velamoor** . . . . . (212) 637-2200
Education: Columbia 2001; Harvard 2004 JD
Assistant U.S. Attorney **Brendan Quigley** . . . . . (212) 637-2200
Education: Georgetown JD
Special Assistant U.S. Attorney, Criminal Division
Dean Sovolos . . . . . (212) 637-2200
Assistant U.S. Attorney **Douglas Zolkind** . . . . . (212) 637-2200

White Plains (NY) Office
300 Quarropas Street, Third Floor, White Plains, NY 10601
Tel: (914) 993-1900 Fax: (914) 682-3392

Co-Chief **Perry A. Carbone** . . . . . (914) 993-1908
E-mail: perry.carbone@usdoj.gov
Co-Chief **(Vacant)** . . . . . (914) 993-1908
Deputy Chief **(Vacant)** . . . . . (914) 993-1908
Senior Litigation Counsel **Elliott Jacobson** . . . . . (914) 993-1940
E-mail: elliott.jacobson@usdoj.gov

New York - Western District
138 Delaware Avenue, Buffalo, NY 14202
Tel: (716) 843-5700 Fax: (716) 551-3052
Internet: https://www.justice.gov/usao-wdny

★ U.S. Attorney (Acting) **James P. Kennedy, Jr.** . . . . . (716) 843-5700
E-mail: jp.kennedy@usdoj.gov
Secretary to U.S. Attorney **Karen A. Brown** . . . . . (716) 843-5836
E-mail: karen.brown@usdoj.gov
First Assistant U.S. Attorney
James P. Kennedy, Jr. . . . . . (716) 843-5700 ext. 892
E-mail: jp.kennedy@usdoj.gov
Senior Litigation Counsel **(Vacant)** . . . . . (716) 843-5805
Administrative Officer **Amy Shantler** . . . . . (716) 843-5826
E-mail: amy.shantler@usdoj.gov
Health Care Investigator **(Vacant)** . . . . . (716) 843-5700
Human Resources Officer **(Vacant)** . . . . . (716) 843-5878
Computer Technology Division Chief
Nicholas G. Baldauf . . . . . (716) 843-5815
E-mail: nicholas.baldauf@usdoj.gov
Law Enforcement Coordinating Committee
Coordinator **Samuel M. Palmiere** . . . . . (716) 843-5700 ext. 842
E-mail: samuel.palmiere@usdoj.gov
Public Affairs Officer **Barbara J. Burns** . . . . . (716) 843-5700 ext. 817
E-mail: barbara.burns@usdoj.gov
Supervisory Legal Assistant **Karen Barone** . . . . . (716) 843-5700 ext. 865
Supervisory Legal Assistant **Karen A. Brown** . . . . . (716) 716-5836
Supervisory Legal Assistant **(Vacant)** . . . . . (716) 716-5700 ext. 857
Victim Witness Coordinator **(Vacant)** . . . . . (716) 843-5700 ext. 828
Litigation Support Manager **Craig R. Bowman** . . . . . (716) 843-5832

Appeals Unit
Chief, Assistant U.S. Attorney
Joseph J. Karaszewski . . . . . (716) 843-5700 ext. 837
E-mail: joseph.j.karaszewski@usdoj.gov
Assistant U.S. Attorney **(Vacant)** . . . . . (716) 843-5700
Assistant U.S. Attorney **(Vacant)** . . . . . (716) 843-8688
Assistant U.S. Attorney **Monica J. Richards** . . . . . (716) 843-5700 ext. 852
E-mail: monica.richards@usdoj.gov

Asset Forfeiture Financial Litigation Unit
Chief **Richard D. Kaufman** . . . . . (716) 843-5700 ext. 871
E-mail: richard.kaufman@usdoj.gov
Deputy Chief **Kevin D. Robinson** . . . . . (716) 843-5700 ext. 804
E-mail: kevin.d.robinson@usdoj.gov
Assistant U.S. Attorney **Grace M. Carducci** . . . . . (585) 263-6760 ext. 2254
Assistant U.S. Attorney **Mary C. Kane** . . . . . (716) 843-5700 ext. 809
E-mail: mary.kane@usdoj.gov
Assistant U.S. Attorney **Kathryn L. Smith** . . . . . (585) 263-6760 ext. 2261
E-mail: kathryn.l.smith@usdoj.gov

Civil Division
Chief **Mary Pat Fleming** . . . . . (716) 843-5700 ext. 867
E-mail: mary.pat.fleming@usdoj.gov

(continued on next page)

★ Presidential Appointment Requiring Senate Confirmation ☆ Presidential Appointment □ Schedule C Appointment ◇ Career Senior Foreign Service Appointment
● Career Senior Executive Service (SES) Appointment ○ Non-Career Senior Executive Service (SES) Appointment ■ Postal Career Executive Service

Civil Division *(continued)*

Senior Litigation Counsel
Mary K. "Molly" Roach (716) 843-5700 ext. 866
E-mail: mary.k.roach@usdoj.gov
Assistant U.S. Attorney **Michael Cerrone** (716) 843-5700 ext. 851
E-mail: michael.cerrone@usdoj.gov
Assistant U.S. Attorney **Kathleen A. Lynch** (716) 843-5700 ext. 830
E-mail: kathleen.lynch@usdoj.gov
Assistant U.S. Attorney **(Vacant)** (716) 843-5700
Assistant U.S. Attorney **(Vacant)** (716) 843-5700

Criminal Division
138 Delaware Avenue, Buffalo, NY 14202
Tel: (716) 843-5700

Criminal Chief **Joseph M. Guerra III** (716) 843-5700 ext. 824
E-mail: joseph.m.guerra@usdoj.gov

Fraud and Corruption Section
Chief, Fraud and Corruption
Russell T. Ippolito, Jr. (716) 843-5700 ext. 805
E-mail: russell.ippolito@usdoj.gov
Assistant U.S. Attorney **Marie P. Grisanti** (716) 843-5700 ext. 818
E-mail: marie.grisanti@usdoj.gov
Assistant U.S. Attorney **Mary Ellen Kresse** (716) 843-5700 ext. 888
E-mail: maryellen.kresse@usdoj.gov
Assistant U.S. Attorney **Maura O'Donnell** (716) 843-5700 ext. 816
E-mail: maura.odonnell@usdoj.gov
Assistant U.S. Attorney
Elizabeth Russo-Moellering (716) 843-5700 ext. 872
E-mail: elizabeth.moellering@usdoj.gov
Assistant U.S. Attorney **(Vacant)** (716) 843-5700

General Crimes Section
Chief **Michael "Mike" DiGiacomo** (716) 843-5700 ext. 885
E-mail: michael.digiacomo@usdoj.gov
Special Assistant U.S. Attorney **(Vacant)** (716) 843-5831
Assistant U.S. Attorney **John D. Fabian** (716) 843-5700 ext. 819
E-mail: john.fabian@usdoj.gov
Assistant U.S. Attorney **Aaron Mango** (716) 843-5882
E-mail: aaron.mango@usdoj.gov
Assistant U.S. Attorney **(Vacant)** (716) 843-5822
Assistant U.S. Attorney **(Vacant)** (716) 843-5700 ext. 868
Assistant U.S. Attorney **(Vacant)** (716) 843-5700

Narcotics and Organized Crime Section
Chief **Timothy C. Lynch** (716) 843-5846
E-mail: timothy.lynch@usdoj.gov
Deputy Chief **Joseph M. Tripi** (716) 843-5700 ext. 839
E-mail: joseph.tripi@usdoj.gov
Assistant U.S. Attorney **Michael J. Adler** (716) 843-5857
E-mail: michael.adler@usdoj.gov
Assistant U.S. Attorney **Brendan Cullinane** (716) 843-5875
Assistant U.S. Attorney **Michael Felicetta** (716) 843-5893
E-mail: michael.felicetta@usdoj.gov
Assistant U.S. Attorney **Joel L. Violanti** (716) 843-5700 ext. 854
E-mail: joel.l.violanti@usdoj.gov
Assistant U.S. Attorney
Edward "Ned" White (716) 843-5700 ext. 862
E-mail: edward.white@usdoj.gov
Assistant U.S. Attorney **Wei Xiang** (716) 843-5700 ext. 806
E-mail: wei.xiang@usdoj.gov
Assistant U.S. Attorney **(Vacant)** (716) 843-5811
Assistant U.S. Attorney **(Vacant)** (716) 843-5863
District Office Security Manager **Meghan A. Tokash** (716) 843-5860
E-mail: meghan.tokash@usdoj.gov
Assistant U.S. Attorney **(Vacant)** (716) 843-5700

Rochester (NY) Office
620 Federal Building, 100 State Street, Rochester, NY 14614
Tel: (585) 263-6760 Fax: (585) 263-6226

Assistant U.S. Attorney-in-Charge
Richard A. Resnick (585) 263-6760 ext. 23949
E-mail: richard.resnick@usdoj.gov

Rochester (NY) Office *(continued)*

Chief of General Crimes Section
Tiffany Lee (585) 263-6760 ext. 23951
E-mail: tiffany.lee@usdoj.gov
Chief of Narcotics and Organized Crime
Section **Brett A. Harvey** (585) 263-6760 ext. 23949
E-mail: brett.harvey@usdoj.gov
Assistant U.S. Attorney **Melissa M. Marangola** (585) 263-6760
E-mail: melissa.marangola@usdoj.gov
Civil Division Assistant U.S. Attorney
Katherine Smith (585) 263-6760 ext. 23961
E-mail: katherine.smith@usdoj.gov
Criminal Division Assistant U.S. Attorney
Grace M. Carducci (585) 263-6760 ext. 23954
E-mail: grace.carducci@usdoj.gov
Criminal Division Assistant U.S. Attorney
John Field (585) 263-6760 ext. 23933
E-mail: john.field@usdoj.gov
Criminal Division Assistant U.S. Attorney
Craig Gestring (585) 263-6760 ext. 23979
E-mail: craig.gestring@usdoj.gov
Criminal Division Assistant U.S. Attorney
Douglas Gregory (585) 263-6760 ext. 23938
E-mail: douglas.gregory@usdoj.gov
Criminal Division Assistant U.S. Attorney
Robert A. Marangola (585) 263-6760 ext. 23980
E-mail: robert.marangola@usdoj.gov
Criminal Division Assistant U.S. Attorney
Marisa J. Miller (585) 263-6760 ext. 23965
Criminal Division Assistant U.S. Attorney
Charles E. Moynihan (585) 263-6760 ext. 23971
E-mail: charles.moynihan@usdoj.gov
Criminal Division Assistant U.S. Attorney
Everardo "Andy" Rodriguez (585) 263-6760 ext. 23950
E-mail: everardo.rodriguez@usdoj.gov
Criminal Division Assistant U.S. Attorney
Bradley E. Tyler (585) 263-6760 ext. 23931
E-mail: bradley.e.tyler@usdoj.gov
Criminal Division Assistant U.S. Attorney
(Vacant) (585) 263-6760 ext. 23951
Criminal Division Assistant U.S. Attorney **(Vacant)** (585) 263-6760
Supervisory Paralegal Specialist
Lori Pietrzykowski (585) 263-6760 ext. 23928
Victim Witness Coordinator **Kim Pettit** (585) 263-6760 ext. 972
E-mail: kim.pettit@usdoj.gov

North Carolina - Eastern District
Terry Sanford Federal Building and U.S. Courthouse,
310 New Bern Avenue, Suite 800, Raleigh, NC 27601-1461
Tel: (919) 856-4530 Fax: (919) 856-4487
Internet: https://www.justice.gov/usao-wdny

★ U.S. Attorney **Robert J. "Bobby" Higdon, Jr.** (919) 856-4530
E-mail: bobby.higdon@usdoj.gov
Secretary to the U.S. Attorney **Sara Harrington** (919) 856-4530
First Assistant U.S. Attorney **John Stuart Bruce** (919) 856-4850
E-mail: john.bruce@usdoj.gov
Education: North Carolina 1975, 1978 JD
Administrative Officer **Bret E. Lopes** (919) 856-4530
E-mail: bret.lopes@usdoj.gov
Personnel Officer **Sherry E. Bowden** (919) 856-4530
E-mail: sherry.bowden@usdoj.gov
Law Enforcement Committee Coordinator
Donald P. Connelly (919) 856-4530
E-mail: don.connelly@usdoj.gov
Victim-Witness Coordinator **Michelle D. Scott** (919) 856-4530
E-mail: michelle.scott@usdoj.gov
Librarian **Dakeisa Parker** (919) 856-4872
E-mail: dakeisa.parker@usdoj.gov
Systems Manager **Patrick Reynolds** (919) 856-4530
E-mail: patrick.reynolds@usdoj.gov
Administrative Services Specialist/Purchasing Officer
Janae McKay (919) 856-4530
Information Technology Specialist **(Vacant)** (919) 856-4530

★ Presidential Appointment Requiring Senate Confirmation ☆ Presidential Appointment ☐ Schedule C Appointment ◇ Career Senior Foreign Service Appointment
● Career Senior Executive Service (SES) Appointment ○ Non-Career Senior Executive Service (SES) Appointment ■ Postal Career Executive Service

Appellate Division
Appellate Division Chief and Assistant U.S. Attorney
Jennifer May-Parker .... (919) 856-4530
E-mail: jennifer.may-parker@usdoj.gov
Education: SUNY (Geneseo) 1988 BA; SUNY Col (Buffalo) 1991 JD
Assistant U.S. Attorney **Kristine L. Fritz** .... (919) 856-4530
E-mail: kristine.fritz@usdoj.gov
Education: Washington & Jefferson 2002 BA; Duquesne 2006 JD
Assistant U.S. Attorney **Phillip Rubin** .... (919) 856-4530
E-mail: phillip.rubin@usdoj.gov
Assistant U.S. Attorney **Seth Morgan Wood** .... (919) 856-4530
E-mail: seth.wood@usdoj.gov
Education: Virginia 2003 JD
Assistant U.S. Attorney **(Vacant)** .... (919) 856-4530
Assistant U.S. Attorney **(Vacant)** .... (919) 856-4530

Civil Division
Assistant U.S. Attorney **(Vacant)** .... (919) 856-4530
Civil Division Chief and Assistant U.S. Attorney
G. Norman Acker III .... (919) 856-4530
E-mail: norman.acker@usdoj.gov
Deputy Chief and Assistant U.S. Attorney
Joshua B. Royster .... (919) 856-4530
E-mail: joshua.royster@usdoj.gov
Assistant U.S. Attorney **Matthew L. Fesak** .... (919) 856-4530
E-mail: matthew.fesak@usdoj.gov
Assistant U.S. Attorney **Neal I. Fowler** .... (919) 856-4530
E-mail: neal.fowler@usdoj.gov
Assistant U.S. Attorney **Michael G. James** .... (919) 856-4530
Assistant U.S. Attorney **Stephen A. West** .... (919) 856-4530
E-mail: steve.west@usdoj.gov
Assistant U.S. Attorney **Sharon C. Wilson** .... (919) 856-4530
E-mail: sharon.wilson2@usdoj.gov
Assistant U.S. Attorney **(Vacant)** .... (919) 856-4530
Assistant U.S. Attorney **(Vacant)** .... (919) 856-4319
Assistant U.S. Attorney **(Vacant)** .... (919) 856-4530

Criminal Division
Criminal Division Chief and Assistant U.S. Attorney
Leslie Cooley .... (919) 856-4530
E-mail: leslie.cooley@usdoj.gov
Organized Crime Drug Enforcement Task Force Chief
and Assistant U.S. Attorney **Toby Lathan** .... (919) 856-4530
E-mail: tody.lathan@usdoj.gov
Deputy Chief **Felice M. Corpening** .... (919) 856-4530
Assistant U.S. Attorney **J. Frank Bradsher** .... (919) 856-4530
E-mail: frank.bradsher@usdoj.gov
Assistant U.S. Attorney **David A. Bragdon** .... (919) 856-4808
Education: Virginia JD
Assistant U.S. Attorney **Katherine Burnette** .... (919) 856-4530
Assistant U.S. Attorney **William Gilmore** .... (919) 856-4530
E-mail: william.gilmore@usdoj.gov
Assistant U.S. Attorney **Eric D. Goulian** .... (919) 856-4530
Assistant U.S. Attorney **Edward D. Gray** .... (919) 856-4530
Assistant U.S. Attorney **John Holbrook** .... (919) 856-4530
Assistant U.S. Attorney **Adam Hulbig** .... (919) 856-4530
Assistant U.S. Attorney **Jane J. Jackson** .... (919) 856-4530
Assistant U.S. Attorney **Jason Kellhofer** .... (919) 856-4530
E-mail: jason.kellhofer@usdoj.gov
Assistant U.S. Attorney **Sebastian Kielmanovich** .... (919) 856-4530
E-mail: sebastian.kielmanovich@usdoj.gov
Assistant U.S. Attorney **Brad Knott** .... (919) 856-4530
Assistant U.S. Attorney **Barbara D. Kocher** .... (919) 856-4530
Assistant U.S. Attorney **James J. Kurosad** .... (919) 856-4530
Assistant U.S. Attorney **Scott Lemmon** .... (252) 830-0335
Assistant U.S. Attorney **Susan Menzer** .... (919) 856-4530
E-mail: susan.menzer@usdoj.gov
Assistant U.S. Attorney **Brian Meyers** .... (919) 856-4530
Assistant U.S. Attorney **Eleanor Morales** .... (919) 856-4530
Assistant U.S. Attorney **Ethan A. Ontjes** .... (919) 856-4530
Assistant U.S. Attorney **Banumathi Rangarajan** .... (919) 856-4359
Assistant U.S. Attorney **Rudy E. Renfer** .... (919) 856-4530
Assistant U.S. Attorney **Evan Rikhye** .... (919) 856-4530
Education: Washington College of Law 2001 JD
Assistant U.S. Attorney **Jennifer Wells** .... (919) 856-4530

Criminal Division *(continued)*
Assistant U.S. Attorney **(Vacant)** .... (919) 856-4530
OCEDTF Special Assistant U.S. Attorney **(Vacant)** ...... (919) 856-4530
Special Assistant U.S. Attorney **Glenn Perry** .... (919) 856-4530
Special Assistant U.S. Attorney **(Vacant)** .... (919) 856-4530
Special Assistant U.S. Attorney **(Vacant)** .... (919) 856-4530
Special Assistant U.S. Attorney **(Vacant)** .... (919) 856-4530

North Carolina - Middle District
101 South Edgeworth Street, 4th Floor, Greensboro, NC 27401
Tel: (336) 333-5351 Fax: (336) 333-5438
Internet: https://www.justice.gov/usao-mdnc

★ U.S. Attorney **Matthew G.T. "Matt" Martin** .... (336) 333-5351
E-mail: matthew.martin@usdoj.gov
Education: North Carolina BA; North Carolina Asheville JD
First Assistant U.S. Attorney **Sandra Hairston** .... (336) 333-5351
E-mail: sandra.hairston@usdoj.gov
Civil Division Chief and Assistant U.S. Attorney
Lynne Klauer .... (336) 333-5351
E-mail: lynne.klauer@usdoj.gov Fax: (336) 333-5257
Criminal Division Chief and Assistant U.S. Attorney
Clifton T. Barrett .... (336) 333-5351
Fax: (336) 333-5381
Deputy Criminal Chief and Assistant U.S. Attorney
Stephen T. Inman .... (336) 333-5351
E-mail: stephen.inman@usdoj.gov
Assistant U.S. Attorney **Lisa Boggs** .... (336) 333-5351
E-mail: lisa.boggs@usdoj.gov
Assistant U.S. Attorney **Frank J. Chut** .... (336) 333-5351
E-mail: frank.chut@usdoj.gov
Education: Duke, JD
Assistant U.S. Attorney **Michael A. DeFranco** .... (336) 333-5351
E-mail: michael.defranco@usdoj.gov
Assistant U.S. Attorney **Robert Hamilton** .... (336) 333-5351
E-mail: robert.hamilton@usdoj.gov
Assistant U.S. Attorney **Eric Iverson** .... (336) 333-5351
E-mail: eric.iverson@usdoj.gov
Assistant U.S. Attorney **Michael F. Joseph** .... (336) 333-5351
Assistant U.S. Attorney **Joanna McFadden** .... (336) 333-5351
E-mail: joanna.mcfadden@usdoj.gov
Assistant U.S. Attorney **Angela H. Miller** .... (336) 333-5351
E-mail: angela.miller@usdoj.gov
Assistant U.S. Attorney **Kyle Pousson** .... (336) 333-5351
E-mail: kyle.pousson@usdoj.gov
Assistant U.S. Attorney **Anand P. Ramaswamy** .... (336) 333-5351
E-mail: anand.ramaswamy@usdoj.gov
Education: North Carolina Greensboro BA; North Carolina 1997 JD
Assistant U.S. Attorney **Cheryl Sloan** .... (336) 333-5351
E-mail: cheryl.sloan@usdoj.gov
Assistant U.S. Attorney **(Vacant)** .... (336) 333-5351
Administrative Officer **Raquel Niles** .... (336) 333-5351
E-mail: raquel.niles@usdoj.gov
Victim-Witness Specialist **Marsha Thompson** .... (336) 333-5351
Systems Manager **Timothy Brooks** .... (336) 333-5351
E-mail: tim.brooks@usdoj.gov
Systems Manager **(Vacant)** .... (336) 333-5351
LEC Coordinator **Randy Tysinger** .... (336) 333-5351
E-mail: randy.tysinger@usdoj.gov

Winston-Salem (NC) Office
Federal Building, 251 North Main Street,
Room 505, Winston-Salem, NC 27101
Tel: (336) 631-5268 Fax: (336) 631-5308

Assistant U.S. Attorney **Joan Binkley** .... (336) 333-5268
E-mail: joan.binkley@usdoj.gov
Assistant U.S. Attorney **Randall Galyon** .... (336) 631-5268
E-mail: randall.galyon@usdoj.gov
Assistant U.S. Attorney **Graham T. Green** .... (336) 333-5268
E-mail: graham.green@usdoj.gov
Education: Appalachian State; Campbell JD
Assistant U.S. Attorney **Robert A. Lang** .... (336) 631-5268
E-mail: rob.lang@usdoj.gov

(continued on next page)

DEPARTMENTS

★ Presidential Appointment Requiring Senate Confirmation ☆ Presidential Appointment ☐ Schedule C Appointment ◇ Career Senior Foreign Service Appointment
● Career Senior Executive Service (SES) Appointment ○ Non-Career Senior Executive Service (SES) Appointment ■ Postal Career Executive Service

Winston-Salem (NC) Office *(continued)*

Assistant U.S. Attorney **Terry M. Meinecke** .... (336) 333-5268
E-mail: terry.meinecke@usdoj.gov
Education: North Carolina Greensboro BA; Nebraska JD

North Carolina - Western District

Carillon Building, 227 West Trade Street,
Suite 1650, Charlotte, NC 28202
Tel: (704) 344-6222 Fax: (704) 277-0259
Internet: www.justice.gov/usao-wdnc

★ U.S. Attorney **R. Andrew Murray** .... (704) 344-6222
Education: North Carolina Charlotte 1989 BA; North Carolina 1992 JD
Special Assistant to the U.S. Attorney **Lia Bantavani** ... (704) 344-6222
E-mail: lia.bantavani@usdoj.gov
Administrative Officer **Rhonda Ramsey** .... (704) 344-6222
E-mail: rhonda.ramsey@usdoj.gov
First Assistant U.S. Attorney **Corey Ellis** .... (704) 344-6222
E-mail: corey.ellis@usdoj.gov
Law Enforcement Committee Coordinator
Fred Hudson .... (704) 344-6222
Victim-Witness Coordinator **Shirley Rutledge** .... (704) 344-6222
E-mail: shirley.rutledge@usdoj.gov
Automated Litigation Support Specialist
Timothy Dunbar .... (704) 344-6222
E-mail: tim.dunbar@usdoj.gov
Systems Manager **Ricky Vidarte** .... (704) 344-6222
E-mail: ricky.vidarte@usdoj.gov

Asset Forfeiture

Assistant U.S. Attorney **Benjamin Bain-Creed** .... (704) 344-6222
E-mail: benjamin.bain-creed@usdoj.gov
Assistant U.S. Attorney **(Vacant)** .... (704) 344-6222

Civil Division

Chief Assistant U.S. Attorney **Gill P. Beck** .... (828) 271-4661
Assistant U.S. Attorney **(Vacant)** .... (704) 344-6222
Assistant U.S. Attorney **(Vacant)** .... (704) 344-6222
Affirmative Civil Enforcement Assistant U.S. Attorney
(Vacant) .... (704) 344-6222

Criminal Division

Chief **Dana O. Washington** .... (704) 344-6222
E-mail: dana.washington@usdoj.gov
Deputy Chief **Kelli Ferry** .... (704) 344-6222
E-mail: kelli.ferry@usdoj.gov
Deputy Chief **(Vacant)** .... (704) 344-6222
Assistant U.S. Attorney **Tom O'Malley** .... (704) 344-6222
E-mail: tom.omalley@usdoj.gov
Assistant U.S. Attorney **Kenneth Smith** .... (704) 344-6222
E-mail: kenneth.smith@usdoj.gov

Drug Task Force

Assistant U.S. Attorney **Jennifer Dillon** .... (704) 344-6222
E-mail: jennifer.dillon@usdoj.gov
Assistant U.S. Attorney **Robert "Bob" Gleason** .... (704) 344-6222
E-mail: robert.gleason@usdoj.gov
Assistant U.S. Attorney **Elizabeth Greene** .... (704) 344-6222
E-mail: elizabeth.greene@usdoj.gov
Assistant U.S. Attorney **Steve Kaufman** .... (704) 344-6222
E-mail: steve.kaufman@usdoj.gov
Assistant U.S. Attorney **Cortney Randall** .... (704) 344-6222
E-mail: cortney.randall@usdoj.gov
Assistant U.S. Attorney **Craig Randall** .... (704) 344-6222
E-mail: craig.randall@usdoj.gov

Asheville (NC) Office

U.S. Courthouse, 100 Otis Street, Room 207, Asheville, NC 28801-2611
Tel: (828) 271-4661 Fax: (828) 271-4670

Civil Division Chief **(Vacant)** .... (828) 271-4661
Appellate Division Assistant U.S. Attorney
Amy E. Ray .... (828) 271-4661
E-mail: amy.ray@usdoj.gov
Education: Florida State 1995 JD
Asset Forfeiture Unit Assistant U.S. Attorney **(Vacant)** ... (828) 271-4661

Asheville (NC) Office *(continued)*

Criminal Division Assistant U.S. Attorney
Richard Edwards .... (828) 271-4661
E-mail: richard.edward2@usdoj.gov
Criminal Division Assistant U.S. Attorney
Donald Gast .... (828) 271-4661
E-mail: don.gast@usdoj.gov
Criminal Division Assistant U.S. Attorney
John Pritchard .... (828) 271-4661
E-mail: john.pritchard@usdoj.gov
Drug Task Force Assistant U.S. Attorney
Thomas Kent .... (828) 271-4661
E-mail: thomas.kent@usdoj.gov
Assistant U.S. Attorney **David Thorneloe** .... (828) 271-4661
E-mail: david.thorneloe@usdoj.gov
Victim-Witness Coordinator **Lynne W. Crout** .... (828) 271-4661
E-mail: lynne.crout@usdoj.gov

North Dakota District

Quentin N. Burdick U.S. Courthouse, 655 First Avenue, North,
Suite 250, Fargo, ND 58102-4932
Tel: (701) 297-7400 Fax: (701) 297-7405
Internet: https://www.justice.gov/usao-nd

★ U.S. Attorney **Christopher C. Myers** .... (701) 297-7400
E-mail: christopher.c.myers@usdoj.gov
Education: Drake JD
★ U.S. Attorney-Designate **Drew Howard Wrigley** .... (701) 297-7400
Education: North Dakota BA; Washington College of Law 1991 JD
First Assistant U.S. Attorney **Keith W. Reisenauer** ...... (701) 297-7400
E-mail: keith.reisenauer@usdoj.gov
Education: North Dakota JD
Administrative Officer **Stuard Eidenschink** .... (701) 297-7400
E-mail: stu.eidenschink@usdoj.gov
Civil Chief **Kent S. Rockstad** .... (701) 297-7400
P.O. Box 699, Bismarck, ND 58502
E-mail: kent.rockstad@usdoj.gov
Education: North Dakota JD
Assistant U.S. Attorney **Melissa Burkland** .... (701) 297-7400
E-mail: melissa.burkland@usdoj.gov
Education: North Dakota JD
Assistant U.S. Attorney **Nicholas Whitney Chase** .... (701) 297-7400
E-mail: nick.chase@usdoj.gov
Education: North Dakota JD
Assistant U.S. Attorney **Matt Greenley** .... (701) 297-7400
E-mail: matthew.greenley@usdoj.gov
Assistant U.S. Attorney **Megan A. Healy** .... (701) 297-7400
E-mail: megan.healy@usdoj.gov
Education: Concordia Col Moorhead MN 2002 BA;
Minnesota 2007 JD
Assistant U.S. Attorney **Tara Iversen** .... (701) 297-7400
E-mail: tara.iversen@usdoj.gov
Assistant U.S. Attorney **Janice M. Morley** .... (701) 297-7400
E-mail: jan.morley@usdoj.gov
Education: North Dakota JD
Assistant U.S. Attorney **Jennifer Klemetsrud Puhl** ...... (701) 297-7400
E-mail: jennifer.puhl@usdoj.gov
Education: North Dakota 1997 BA, 2000 JD
Assistant U.S. Attorney **Jake Rodenbiker** .... (701) 297-7400
E-mail: jake.rodenbiker@usdoj.gov
Assistant U.S. Attorney **Brett M. Shasky** .... (701) 297-7400
E-mail: brett.shasky@usdoj.gov
Education: North Dakota JD
Financial Litigation Unit **Nicole Olson** .... (701) 297-7400
E-mail: nicole.olson@usdoj.gov
Librarian **Denise Fuchs** .... (701) 297-7400
E-mail: denise.fuchs@usdoj.gov
Systems Manager **Ray Bakke** .... (701) 297-7400
E-mail: raymond.bakke@usdoj.gov
Intelligence Specialist/Law Enforcement Coordinator
Terry Van Horn .... (701) 297-7400
E-mail: terry.vanhorn@usdoj.gov
Victim - Witness Coordinator **Dimple Smith** .... (701) 297-7400
E-mail: dimple.smith@usdoj.gov

★ Presidential Appointment Requiring Senate Confirmation ☆ Presidential Appointment ☐ Schedule C Appointment ◇ Career Senior Foreign Service Appointment
● Career Senior Executive Service (SES) Appointment ○ Non-Career Senior Executive Service (SES) Appointment ■ Postal Career Executive Service

Bismarck (ND) Office
U.S. Post Office and Courthouse, 220 East Rosser Avenue, Room 372, Bismarck, ND 58501
Mail: P.O. Box 699, Bismarck, ND 58502-0699
Tel: (701) 530-2420 Fax: (701) 530-2421

Assistant U.S. Attorney/Criminal Chief **(Vacant)** .... (701) 530-2420
Assistant U.S. Attorney **Gary L. Delorme** .... (701) 530-2420
E-mail: gary.delorme@usdoj.gov
Assistant U.S. Attorney **Dawn Deitz** .... (701) 530-2420
E-mail: dawn.deitz@usdoj.gov
Assistant U.S. Attorney **Jonathan O'Konek** .... (701) 530-2420
E-mail: jonathan.okonek@usdoj.gov
Assistant U.S. Attorney **Brandi Sasse Russell** .... (701) 530-2420
E-mail: brandi.russell@usdoj.gov
Assistant U.S. Attorney **James P. Thomas** .... (701) 530-2420
E-mail: james.p.thomas@usdoj.gov
Assistant U.S. Attorney **Rick Lee Volk** .... (701) 530-2420
E-mail: rick.volk@usdoj.gov
Education: North Dakota JD
Assistant U.S. Attorney **David D. Hagler** .... (701) 530-2420
E-mail: david.hagler@usdoj.gov
Education: North Dakota JD
Victim - Witness Coordinator **Beth Lang** .... (701) 530-2420
E-mail: beth.lang@usdoj.gov

Ohio - Northern District
801 West Superior Avenue, Suite 400, Cleveland, OH 44113
Tel: (216) 622-3600 TTY: (216) 522-3086
Fax: (216) 522-3370 (Administrative Division)
Fax: (216) 522-7545 (Executive Division)
Fax: (216) 522-2806 (Law Enforcement Committee Coordinator)
Fax: (216) 522-7358 (Major Fraud and Corruption)
Fax: (216) 522-7499 (Organized Crime Drug Enforcement Task Force)
Internet: https://www.justice.gov/usao-ndoh

★ U.S. Attorney **Justin E. Herdman** .... (216) 622-3600
E-mail: justin.herdman@usdoj.gov
Education: Ohio 1996 BA; Glasgow (Scotland) 1998 MPhil; Harvard 2001 JD
Secretary to the U.S. Attorney **(Vacant)** .... (216) 622-3652
First Assistant U.S. Attorney **Bridget M. Brennan** .... (216) 622-3656
E-mail: bridget.brennan@usdoj.gov
Administration Director **Renee G. Sykora** .... (216) 622-3613
E-mail: renee.sykora@usdoj.gov
Deputy Director **Donald Loechler** .... (216) 622-3611
E-mail: donald.loechler@usdoj.gov
Budget Officer **Heidi Lyons** .... (216) 622-3626
E-mail: heidi.lyons@usdoj.gov
Personnel Officer **Renee Mackey** .... (216) 622-3615
E-mail: renee.mackey@usdoj.gov
Public Information Officer **Michael "Mike" Tobin** .... (216) 622-3651
E-mail: michael.tobin@usdoj.gov
Law Enforcement Manager **Craig A. Tame** .... (216) 622-3644
Systems Manager **Michael Godshalk** .... (216) 622-3621
E-mail: michael.godshalk@usdoj.gov
Victim-Witness Specialist **Darla R. Pendergrass** .... (216) 622-3725
E-mail: darla.pendergrass@usdoj.gov
Litigation Support Specialist **(Vacant)** .... (216) 622-3767
Litigation Support Specialist **Judith "Judy" Spar** .... (216) 622-3981

Asset Forfeiture Unit
801 West Superior Avenue, Cleveland, OH 44113
Tel: (216) 622-3743 Fax: (216) 522-7499

Assistant U.S. Attorney **James L. Morford** .... (216) 622-3743
E-mail: james.morford@usdoj.gov
Assistant U.S. Attorney **Phillip J. Tripi** .... (216) 622-3769
E-mail: phillip.tripi@usdoj.gov

Civil Division
801 West Superior Avenue, Cleveland, OH 44113
Tel: (216) 622-3670 Fax: (216) 522-4982

Chief **Lynne H. Buck** .... (216) 622-3712
E-mail: lynne.buck@usdoj.gov
Deputy Chief **Kent W. Penhallurick** .... (216) 622-3682
E-mail: kent.penhallurick@usdoj.gov

Civil Division *(continued)*

Deputy Chief **Alex A. Rokakis** .... (216) 622-3673
E-mail: alex.rokakis@usdoj.gov
Assistant U.S. Attorney **Renee Bacchus** .... (216) 622-3707
E-mail: renee.bacchus@usdoj.gov
Assistant U.S. Attorney **James R. Bennett** .... (216) 622-3988
E-mail: james.bennett@usdoj.gov
Assistant U.S. Attorney **Lisa Hammond Johnson** .... (216) 622-3679
E-mail: lisa.hammond.johnson@usdoj.gov
Assistant U.S. Attorney **Michelle Heyer** .... (216) 622-3686
E-mail: michelle.heyer@usdoj.gov
Assistant U.S. Attorney **Steven J. Paffilas** .... (216) 622-3698
E-mail: steven.paffilas@usdoj.gov
Assistant U.S. Attorney **Marlon A. Primes** .... (216) 622-3684
E-mail: marlon.primes@usdoj.gov
Assistant U.S. Attorney **Heather Tonsing Volosin** .... (216) 622-3797
E-mail: heather.tonsing.volosin@usdoj.gov
Assistant U.S. Attorney **(Vacant)** .... (216) 622-3718
Assistant U.S. Attorney **(Vacant)** .... (216) 622-3911
Assistant U.S. Attorney **(Vacant)** .... (216) 622-3670
Auditor **(Vacant)** .... (216) 622-3779

Criminal Division
801 West Superior Avenue, Cleveland, OH 44113
Tel: (216) 622-3874 Fax: (216) 522-8354

Chief **Robert E. "Bob" Bulford** .... (216) 622-3754
Chief, Major and Cyber Crimes Unit **Edward F. Feran** ... (216) 622-3709
E-mail: edward.feran@usdoj.gov
Deputy Chief, Major and Cyber Crimes Unit **Carol M. Skutnik** .... (216) 622-3785
E-mail: carol.skutnik@usdoj.gov
Chief, Major Fraud and Corruption Unit **(Vacant)** .... (216) 622-3847
Deputy Chief, Major Fraud and Corruption Unit **Michael Collyer** .... (216) 622-3888
E-mail: michael.collyer@usdoj.gov
Chief, National Security, Human Rights and OC Unit **(Vacant)** .... (216) 622-3840
Deputy Chief, National Security, Human Rights and OC Unit **Matthew W. Shepherd** .... (216) 622-3859
E-mail: matthew.shepherd@usdoj.gov
Chief, Organized Crime Drug Enforcement Task Force Unit **Joseph M. Pinjuh** .... (216) 622-3771
E-mail: joseph.pinjuh@usdoj.gov
Deputy Chief, Organized Crime Drug Enforcement Task Force **Michelle Baeppler** .... (216) 622-3995
E-mail: michelle.baeppler@usdoj.gov
Assistant U.S. Attorney **Duncan T. Brown** .... (216) 622-3933
E-mail: duncan.brown@usdoj.gov
Assistant U.S. Attorney **Robert F. Corts** .... (216) 622-3957
E-mail: robert.corts@usdoj.gov
Assistant U.S. Attorney **Matthew J. Cronin** .... (216) 622-3995
E-mail: matthew.cronin@usdoj.gov
Assistant U.S. Attorney **Henry DeBaggis** .... (216) 622-3929
E-mail: henry.debaggis@usdoj.gov
Assistant U.S. Attorney **Miranda E. Dugi** .... (216) 622-3844
E-mail: miranda.dugi@usdoj.gov
Assistant U.S. Attorney **Laura M. Ford** .... (216) 622-3817
E-mail: laura.ford@usdoj.gov
Assistant U.S. Attorney **Kelly L. Galvin** .... (216) 622-3731
E-mail: kelly.l.galvin@usdoj.gov
Assistant U.S. Attorney **Justin Gould** .... (216) 622-3869
E-mail: justin.gould@usdoj.gov
Assistant U.S. Attorney **Om M. Kakani** .... (216) 622-3756
E-mail: om.kakani@usdoj.gov
Assistant U.S. Attorney **Robert W. Kern** .... (216) 622-3836
E-mail: robert.kern@usdoj.gov
Assistant U.S. Attorney **Kendra Klump** .... (216) 622-3689
E-mail: kendra.klump@usdoj.gov
Assistant U.S. Attorney **Dan R. Ranke** .... (216) 622-3753
E-mail: daniel.ranke@usdoj.gov
Assistant U.S. Attorney **Chelsea Rice** .... (216) 622-3752
E-mail: chelsea.rice@usdoj.gov
Assistant U.S. Attorney **Daniel J. Riedl** .... (216) 622-3669
E-mail: daniel.riedl@usdoj.gov

(continued on next page)

★ Presidential Appointment Requiring Senate Confirmation ☆ Presidential Appointment ☐ Schedule C Appointment ◇ Career Senior Foreign Service Appointment
● Career Senior Executive Service (SES) Appointment ○ Non-Career Senior Executive Service (SES) Appointment ■ Postal Career Executive Service

DEPARTMENTS

Criminal Division *(continued)*

Assistant U.S. Attorney **Michael A. Sullivan** . . . . (216) 622-3977
E-mail: michael.a.sullivan@usdoj.gov
Assistant U.S. Attorney **Margaret Sweeney** . . . . (216) 622-3990
E-mail: margaret.sweeney@usdoj.gov
Auditor **(Vacant)** . . . . (216) 622-3830
Intelligence Research Specialist **Janeth Herman** . . . . (216) 622-3730

Akron (OH) Office

Two South Main Street, Room 208, Akron, OH 44308
Tel: (330) 375-5716 Fax: (330) 375-5492

Branch Chief **Robert E. "Bob" Bulford** . . . . (330) 761-0517
Civil Division Assistant U.S. Attorney **(Vacant)** . . . . (330) 761-0523
Chief, Appellate Unit **(Vacant)** . . . . (330) 761-0524
Assistant U.S. Attorney **(Vacant)** . . . . (330) 761-0519
Assistant U.S. Attorney **Rebecca C. Lutzko** . . . . (330) 761-0530
E-mail: rebecca.lutzko@usdoj.gov
Criminal Division Assistant U.S. Attorney **(Vacant)** . . . . . . (330) 761-0521
Criminal Division Assistant U.S. Attorney **(Vacant)** . . . . . . (330) 761-0518

Toledo (OH) Office

Four Seagate, 3rd Floor, Toledo, OH 43604
Tel: (419) 259-6376 Fax: (419) 259-6360

Branch Chief **Ava Rotell-Dustin** . . . . (419) 241-0767
E-mail: ava.rotell.dustin@usdoj.gov
Civil Division Assistant U.S. Attorney
Angelita Cruz Bridges . . . . (419) 241-0715
E-mail: angelita.bridges@usdoj.gov
Civil Division Assistant U.S. Attorney
Guillermo Rojas . . . . (419) 241-0716
E-mail: guillermo.rojas@usdoj.gov
Civil Division Assistant U.S. Attorney **(Vacant)** . . . . (419) 241-0718
Criminal Division Assistant U.S. Attorney
Gene Crawford . . . . (419) 241-0726
E-mail: gene.crawford@usdoj.gov
Criminal Division Assistant U.S. Attorney
Michael J. Freeman . . . . (419) 241-0724
E-mail: michael.freeman2@usdoj.gov
Criminal Division Assistant U.S. Attorney
Noah P. Hood . . . . (419) 241-0725
E-mail: noah.hood@usdoj.gov
Criminal Division Assistant U.S. Attorney
Alissa Sterling . . . . (419) 241-0727
E-mail: alissa.sterling@usdoj.gov
Criminal Division Assistant U.S. Attorney
Thomas P. Weldon . . . . (419) 241-0721
E-mail: thomas.weldon@usdoj.gov
Paralegal Specialist **Gretchen Croniser** . . . . (419) 241-0714
E-mail: gretchen.croniser@usdoj.gov
Paralegal Specialist **Jennifer Ramon** . . . . (419) 241-0738
E-mail: jennifer.ramon@usdoj.gov

Youngstown (OH) Office

City Center One, 100 East Federal Plaza,
Suite 325, Youngstown, OH 44503
Tel: (330) 746-7974 Fax: (330) 746-0239

Criminal Division Assistant U.S. Attorney
Jason M. Katz . . . . (330) 746-7974
E-mail: jason.katz@usdoj.gov
Criminal Division Assistant U.S. Attorney
David M. "Dave" Toepfer . . . . (330) 746-6986
E-mail: david.toepfer@usdoj.gov

Ohio - Southern District

200 West Second Street, Suite 200, Dayton, OH 43215
Tel: (614) 469-5715 Fax: (614) 469-7769
Internet: https://www.justice.gov/usao-sdoh

★ U.S. Attorney **Benjamin Charles Glassman** . . . . (614) 469-5715
E-mail: benjamin.glassman@usdoj.gov
Education: Harvard 2000 JD
Executive Assistant **(Vacant)** . . . . (614) 469-5715
First Assistant U.S. Attorney **Vipal J. Patel** . . . . (614) 469-5715
E-mail: vipal.patel@usdoj.gov

Ohio - Southern District *(continued)*

Executive Assistant U.S. Attorney
Mark T. D'Alessandro . . . . (614) 469-5715
E-mail: mark.dalessandro@usdoj.gov

Criminal Division

200 West Second Street, Dayton, OH 43215
Fax: (937) 225-2564

Deputy Criminal Chief **Laura I. Clemmens** . . . . (614) 469-5715
Assistant U.S. Attorney **Dominick S. Gerace II** . . . . (937) 225-2910
E-mail: doninick.gerace@usdoj.gov
Education: Georgetown 2007 JD
Assistant U.S. Attorney **Andrew J. Hunt** . . . . (614) 469-5715
Assistant U.S. Attorney **Dwight K. Keller** . . . . (614) 469-5715
E-mail: dwight.keller@usdoj.gov
Assistant U.S. Attorney **Sheila G. Lafferty** . . . . (614) 469-5715
E-mail: sheila.lafferty@usdoj.gov
Assistant U.S. Attorney **SaMee Harden** . . . . (937) 225-2910
E-mail: samee.harden@usdoj.gov
Assistant U.S. Attorney **Amy Smith** . . . . (937) 225-2910
E-mail: Amy.smith2@usdoj.gov
Assistant U.S. Attorney **Pamela M. Stanek** . . . . (937) 225-2910
E-mail: pamela.stanek@usdoj.gov
Assistant U.S. Attorney **Brent G. Tabacchi** . . . . (614) 469-5715
E-mail: brent.tabacchi@usdoj.gov
Education: Illinois 2001 JD

Cincinnati (OH) Office

221 East Fourth Street, Suite 400, Cincinnati, OH 45202
Tel: (513) 684-3711 Fax: (513) 684-6710

Criminal Chief **Kenneth L. Parker** . . . . (614) 684-3711
E-mail: kenneth.parker@usdoj.gov
Deputy Criminal Chief **Emily Glatfelter** . . . . (513) 684-3711
E-mail: emily.glatfelter@usdoj.gov
Victim-Witness Specialist **Krista Zeller** . . . . (513) 684-3711
E-mail: krista.zeller@usdoj.gov Fax: (513) 684-6385

Civil Division

200 West Second Street, Dayton, OH 43215
Tel: (513) 684-3711 Fax: (513) 684-6972

Deputy Chief **Matthew Horwitz** . . . . (513) 684-3711
E-mail: matthew.horwitz@usdoj.gov
Senior Litigation Counsel **(Vacant)** . . . . (513) 684-3711
Assistant U.S. Attorney **Margaret Castro** . . . . (513) 684-3711
E-mail: margaret.castro@usdoj.gov
Assistant U.S. Attorney **William B. "Bill" King II** . . . . (513) 684-3711
E-mail: bill.king@usdoj.gov

Criminal Division

200 West Second Street, Dayton, OH 43215
Tel: (513) 684-3711 Fax: (513) 684-6385

Assistant U.S. Attorney/Appellate Chief **(Vacant)** . . . . (513) 684-3711
Assistant U.S. Attorney/Organized Crime Drug
Enforcement Task Force Chief **Michael Hunter** . . . . (513) 684-3711
Assistant U.S. Attorney **Megan Gaffney** . . . . (513) 684-3711
E-mail: megan.gaffney@usdoj.gov
Education: Harvard 2009 JD
Assistant U.S. Attorney **Kyle J. Healey** . . . . (513) 684-3711
E-mail: kyle.healey@usdoj.gov
Assistant U.S. Attorney **Karl Kadon** . . . . (513) 684-3711
Assistant U.S. Attorney **Timothy D. Oakley** . . . . (513) 684-3711
E-mail: tim.oakley@usdoj.gov
Assistant U.S. Attorney **Matthew C. Singer** . . . . (513) 684-3711
E-mail: matthew.singer@usdoj.gov
Education: Cincinnati 2001 BA, 2008 JD
Assistant U.S. Attorney **Anthony Springer** . . . . (513) 684-3711
E-mail: anthony.springer@usdoj.gov
Assistant U.S. Attorney **Ebunoluwa Taiwo** . . . . (513) 684-3711
E-mail: ebunoluwa.taiwo@usdoj.gov
Assistant U.S. Attorney **Alexis Zouhary** . . . . (513) 684-3711
E-mail: alexis.zouhary@usdoj.gov
Law Enforcement Coordination Specialist **Brian Capps** . . . (513) 684-3711
E-mail: brian.capps@usdoj.gov

★ Presidential Appointment Requiring Senate Confirmation ☆ Presidential Appointment ☐ Schedule C Appointment ◇ Career Senior Foreign Service Appointment
● Career Senior Executive Service (SES) Appointment ○ Non-Career Senior Executive Service (SES) Appointment ■ Postal Career Executive Service

Columbus (OH) Office

200 West Second Street, Suite 200, Dayton, OH 43215
Tel: (614) 469-5715 Fax: (614) 469-2200

Assistant U.S. Attorney/Branch Chief **Gary L. Spartis** .... (513) 684-3711
E-mail: gary.spartis@usdoj.gov
Administrative Officer **Jessica Gourley** .... (614) 469-5715
E-mail: jessica.gourley@usdoj.gov Fax: (614) 469-7769
Victim-Witness Coordinator **Barbara E. Vanarsdall** ...... (614) 469-5715
E-mail: barbara.vanarsdall@usdoj.gov
Systems Manager **Christopher Smith** .... (614) 469-5715
E-mail: christopher.smith5@usdoj.gov
IT Specialist **Kevin Baker** .... (614) 469-5715
E-mail: kevin.baker@usdoj.gov

Civil Division

200 West Second Street, Dayton, OH 43215
Tel: (614) 469-5715 Fax: (614) 469-5240

Deputy Chief **(Vacant)** .... (614) 469-5715
Assistant U.S. Attorney **Bethany Hamilton** .... (614) 469-5715
E-mail: bethany.hamilton@usdoj.gov
Assistant U.S. Attorney **Andrew M. Malek** .... (614) 469-5715
E-mail: andrew.malek@usdoj.gov
Assistant U.S. Attorney **John J. Stark** .... (614) 469-5715
E-mail: john.stark@usdoj.gov
Assistant U.S. Attorney **Christopher R. Yates** .... (614) 469-5715
E-mail: christopher.yates@usdoj.gov
Assistant U.S. Attorney **Leah Wolfe** .... (614) 469-5715
E-mail: leah.wolfe@usdoj.gov

Criminal Division

200 West Second Street, Dayton, OH 43215
Tel: (614) 469-5715 Fax: (614) 469-5653

Deputy Chief **Brenda Shoemaker** .... (614) 469-5715
E-mail: brenda.shoemaker@usdoj.gov
Deputy Criminal Chief OCDETF **Michael Hunter** .... (614) 469-5715
E-mail: michael.hunter@usdoj.gov
Appellate Chief **Mary Beth Young** .... (614) 469-5715
E-mail: mary.beth.young@usdoj.gov
Assistant U.S. Attorney **David J. Bosley** .... (614) 469-5715
E-mail: dave.bosley@usdoj.gov
Assistant U.S. Attorney **Daniel A. Brown** .... (614) 469-5715
E-mail: dan.brown@usdoj.gov
Assistant U.S. Attorney **David M. DeVillers** .... (614) 469-5715
E-mail: dave.devillers@usdoj.gov
Assistant U.S. Attorney **Salvador A. Dominguez** .... (614) 469-5715
E-mail: sal.dominguez@usdoj.gov
Assistant U.S. Attorney **Peter Glenn-Applegate** .... (614) 469-5715
E-mail: peter.glenn-applegate@usdoj.gov
Assistant U.S. Attorney **Jonathan Grey** .... (614) 469-5715
E-mail: jonathan.grey@usdoj.gov
Assistant U.S. Attorney **Heather Hill** .... (614) 469-5715
E-mail: heather.hill@usdoj.gov
Assistant U.S. Attorney **Kevin W. Kelley** .... (614) 469-5715
E-mail: kevin.kelley@usdoj.gov
Assistant U.S. Attorney **Jessica Knight** .... (614) 469-5715
E-mail: jessica.knight@usdoj.gov
Assistant U.S. Attorney **Noah Litton** .... (614) 469-5715
E-mail: noah.litton@usdoj.gov
Assistant U.S. Attorney **J. Michael Marous** .... (614) 469-5715
E-mail: mike.marous@usdoj.gov
Assistant U.S. Attorney **Brian Martinez** .... (614) 469-5715
E-mail: brian.martinez2@usdojo.gov
Assistant U.S. Attorney **Timothy "Tim" Prichard** .... (614) 469-5715
E-mail: tim.prichard@usdoj.gov
Assistant U.S. Attorney **Douglas W. Squires** .... (614) 469-5715
E-mail: douglas.squires@usdoj.gov

Dayton Office

200 West Second Street, Suite 200, Dayton, OH 45402
Tel: (937) 225-2910

Civil Chief **(Vacant)** .... (614) 469-5715
Assistant U.S. Attorney **Kevin Koller** .... (937) 225-2910
E-mail: kevin.koller@usdoj.gov

Dayton Office *(continued)*

Assistant U.S. Attorney **Brandi M. Stewart** .... (937) 225-2910
E-mail: brandi.stewart@usdoj.gov
Assistant U.S. Attorney **(Vacant)** .... (614) 469-5715
Victim-Witness Specialist **Acquanette Lindsay** .... (937) 225-2910
E-mail: acquanette.lindsay@usdoj.gov

Oklahoma - Eastern District

1200 West Okmulgee Street, Muskogee, OK 74401
Tel: (918) 684-5100 Fax: (918) 684-5130
Internet: https://www.justice.gov/usao-edok

★ U.S. Attorney **Brian J. Kuester** .... (918) 684-5100
E-mail: brian.kuester@usdoj.gov
Education: Central Missouri State 1990 BS; Tulsa 2000 JD
Administrative Officer **Daniel Edwards** .... (918) 684-5131
E-mail: dan.edwards@usdoj.gov
First Assistant U.S. Attorney **Douglas A. Horn** .... (918) 684-5100
E-mail: doug.horn@usdoj.gov
Law Enforcement Committee Coordinator **(Vacant)** ...... (918) 684-5100
Victim-Witness Specialist **Mary Jo Speaker** .... (918) 684-5100
E-mail: maryjo.speaker@usdoj.gov
Systems Manager/Webmaster **Dan Cott** .... (918) 684-5100
E-mail: dan.cott@usdoj.gov

Civil Division

Civil Division Chief and Assistant U.S. Attorney
Susan Brandon .... (918) 684-5100
E-mail: susan.brandon@usdoj.gov
Assistant U.S. Attorney **Michael Cooper** .... (918) 684-5100
E-mail: michael.cooper@usdoj.gov
Assistant U.S. Attorney **Cheryl R. Triplett** .... (918) 684-5100
E-mail: cheryl.triplett@usdoj.gov
Assistant U.S. Attorney **(Vacant)** .... (918) 684-5100

Criminal Division

Assistant U.S. Attorney **Dean Burris** .... (918) 684-5100
E-mail: dean.burris@usdoj.gov
Assistant U.S. Attorney **Linda Epperley** .... (918) 684-5100
E-mail: linda.epperley@usdoj.gov
Assistant U.S. Attorney **Timothy Hammer** .... (918) 684-5100
E-mail: timothy.hammer@usdoj.gov
Assistant U.S. Attorney **Kristin Harrington** .... (918) 684-5100
E-mail: kristin.harrington@usdoj.gov
Assistant U.S. Attorney **Shannon L. Henson** .... (918) 684-5100
E-mail: shannon.henson@usdoj.gov
Assistant U.S. Attorney **Melody Noble Nelson** .... (918) 684-5100
E-mail: melody.nelson@usdoj.gov
Assistant U.S. Attorney **Edward "Ed" Snow** .... (918) 684-5100
E-mail: ed.snow@usdoj.gov
Assistant U.S. Attorney **Rob Wallace** .... (918) 684-5100
E-mail: rob.wallace@usdoj.gov
Education: Oklahoma 1985, 1988 JD
Chief Assistant U.S. Attorney **Chris Wilson** .... (918) 684-5100
E-mail: chris.wilson@usdoj.gov

Oklahoma - Northern District

110 West Seventh Street, Suite 300, Tulsa, OK 74119
Tel: (918) 382-2700 Fax: (918) 560-7938
Internet: https://www.justice.gov/usao-ndok

★ U.S. Attorney **R. Trent Shores** .... (918) 382-2700
E-mail: r.trent.shores@usdoj.gov
Education: Vanderbilt; Oklahoma JD
Secretary to the U.S. Attorney **Anna Montgomery** .... (918) 382-2700
E-mail: anna.montgomery@usdoj.gov
First Assistant U.S. Attorney **Loretta F. Radford** .... (918) 382-2700
E-mail: loretta.radford@usdoj.gov
Senior Litigation Counsel **(Vacant)** .... (918) 382-2700
Administrative Officer **(Vacant)** .... (918) 382-2700
Law Enforcement Coordinator **(Vacant)** .... (918) 382-2700
Victim-Witness Specialist **Gayla C. Stewart** .... (918) 382-2700
E-mail: gayla.stewart@usdoj.gov
Systems Manager **Hank Hampton** .... (918) 382-2700
E-mail: hank.hampton@usdoj.gov

★ Presidential Appointment Requiring Senate Confirmation ☆ Presidential Appointment □ Schedule C Appointment ◇ Career Senior Foreign Service Appointment
● Career Senior Executive Service (SES) Appointment ○ Non-Career Senior Executive Service (SES) Appointment ■ Postal Career Executive Service

DEPARTMENTS

Appellate Division

Assistant U.S. Attorney **Leena M. Alam** . . . . . . (918) 382-2700
E-mail: leena.alam@usdoj.gov

Civil Division

Chief **Cathryn "Cathy" McClanahan** . . . . . . (918) 382-2700
E-mail: cathy.mcclanahan@usdoj.gov
Assistant U.S. Attorney **(Vacant)** . . . . . . (918) 382-2700
Assistant U.S. Attorney **Jeffrey A. Gallant** . . . . . . (918) 382-2700
E-mail: jeff.gallant@usdoj.gov
Assistant U.S. Attorney **Marianne Hardcastle** . . . . . . (918) 382-2700
E-mail: marianne.hardcastle@usdoj.gov
Assistant U.S. Attorney **Thomas Scott Woodward** . . . . . . (918) 382-2700
E-mail: scott.woodward@usdoj.gov
Education: Texas 1972; Oklahoma City 1981 JD

Criminal Division

Chief **Joseph F. "Joe" Wilson** . . . . . . (918) 382-2700
E-mail: joe.wilson@usdoj.gov
Deputy Chief **Timothy L. "Tim" Faerber** . . . . . . (918) 382-2700
E-mail: tim.faerber@usdoj.gov
Assistant U.S. Attorney **Shannon Cozzoni** . . . . . . (918) 382-2700
E-mail: shannon.cozzoni@usdoj.gov
Assistant U.S. Attorney **Catherine J. Depew** . . . . . . (918) 382-2700
E-mail: catherine.depew@usdoj.gov
Assistant U.S. Attorney **Andrew "A.J." Hofland** . . . . . . (918) 382-2700
E-mail: andrew.hofland@usdoj.gov
Assistant U.S. Attorney **Neal C. Hong** . . . . . . (918) 382-2700
E-mail: neal.hong@usdoj.gov
Assistant U.S. Attorney **Clinton J. "Clint" Johnson** . . . . . . (918) 382-2700
E-mail: clinton.j.johnson@usdoj.gov
Assistant U.S. Attorney **Eric Johnston** . . . . . . (918) 382-2700
E-mail: eric.johnston@usdoj.gov
Assistant U.S. Attorney **Kevin C. Leitch** . . . . . . (918) 382-2700
E-mail: kevin.leitch@usdoj.gov
Assistant U.S. Attorney **Allen J. Litchfield** . . . . . . (918) 382-2700
E-mail: allen.j.litchfield@usdoj.gov
Assistant U.S. Attorney **Charles M. McLoughlin** . . . . . . (918) 382-2700
E-mail: charles.mcloughlin@usdoj.gov
Organized Crime Drug Enforcement Task Force
Assistant U.S. Attorney **Joel-lyn A. McCormick** . . . . . . (918) 382-2700
E-mail: joel-lyn.a.mccormick@usdoj.gov
Organized Crime Drug Enforcement Task Force
Assistant U.S. Attorney **Robert T. "Rob" Raley** . . . . . . (918) 382-2700
E-mail: rob.raley@usdoj.gov

Oklahoma - Western District

Oklahoma Tower, 210 Park Avenue, Suite 400,
Oklahoma City, OK 73102-5602
Tel: (405) 553-8700 Fax: (405) 553-8888
Internet: https://www.justice.gov/usao-wdok

★ U.S. Attorney (Acting) **Robert J. Troester** . . . . . . (405) 553-8720
E-mail: robert.troester@usdoj.gov
Secretary to the U.S. Attorney **Nikki Winters** . . . . . . (405) 553-8731
E-mail: nikki.winters@usdoj.gov
First Assistant U.S. Attorney **Robert J. Troester** . . . . . . (405) 553-8842
E-mail: robert.troester@usdoj.gov
Assistant U.S. Attorney **Nicholas J. Patterson** . . . . . . (405) 553-8842
E-mail: nicholas.patterson@usdoj.gov
Executive Assistant U.S. Attorney **Robert J. Troester** . . . . (405) 553-8809
E-mail: robert.troester@usdoj.gov
Administrative Officer **Lisa Engelke** . . . . . . (405) 553-8777
E-mail: lisa.engelke@usdoj.gov
Immigration Coordinator **(Vacant)** . . . . . . (405) 553-8700
Law Enforcement Committee Coordinator
James Mogren . . . . . . (405) 553-8926
Victim-Witness Specialist **Beverly LaRue** . . . . . . (405) 553-8872
E-mail: beverly.larue@usdoj.gov
Personnel Management Specialist **Denea Wylie** . . . . . . (405) 553-8776
Systems Manager **Gary Murray** . . . . . . (405) 553-8780
E-mail: gary.murray@usdoj.gov

Appellate Division

Chief **(Vacant)** . . . . . . (405) 553-8741

Appellate Division *(continued)*

Assistant U.S. Attorney **Steven W. Creager** . . . . . . (405) 553-8726
E-mail: steven.w.creager@usdoj.gov

Civil Division

Chief **Kay Sewell** . . . . . . (405) 553-8805
E-mail: kay.sewell@usdoj.gov
Education: Oklahoma 1984 JD
Assistant U.S. Attorney **Rebecca Frazier** . . . . . . (405) 553-8831
E-mail: rebecca.frazier@usdoj.gov
Assistant U.S. Attorney **Ronald R. Gallegos** . . . . . . (405) 553-8844
E-mail: ron.gallegos@usdoj.gov
Assistant U.S. Attorney **Tom Majors** . . . . . . (405) 553-8814
E-mail: tom.majors@usdoj.gov
Assistant U.S. Attorney **Scott Maule** . . . . . . (405) 553-8832
E-mail: scott.maule@usdoj.gov

Criminal Division

Chief **Scott E. Williams** . . . . . . (405) 553-8752
E-mail: scott.e.williams@usdoj.gov
Deputy Chief **(Vacant)** . . . . . . (405) 553-8846
Deputy Chief **(Vacant)** . . . . . . (405) 553-8752
Asset Recovery Unit Leader **Don Evans** . . . . . . (405) 553-8831
E-mail: don.evans@usdoj.gov
Drug Task Force Unit Leader **(Vacant)** . . . . . . (405) 553-8846
Fraud/Corruption Unit Leader **(Vacant)** . . . . . . (405) 553-8740
Assistant U.S. Attorney **Julia Barry** . . . . . . (405) 553-8755
E-mail: julia.barry@usdoj.gov
Education: NYU JD
Assistant U.S. Attorney **Kerry Blackburn** . . . . . . (405) 553-8700
Assistant U.S. Attorney **Charles Brown** . . . . . . (405) 553-8871
E-mail: charles.brown4@usdoj.gov
Assistant U.S. Attorney **Brandon Hale** . . . . . . (405) 553-8813
E-mail: brandon.hale@usdoj.gov
Assistant U.S. Attorney **Lori Hines** . . . . . . (405) 553-8853
E-mail: lori.hines@usdoj.gov
Assistant U.S. Attorney **Jessica Cárdenas Jarvis** . . . . . . (405) 553-8868
E-mail: jessica.jarvis@usdoj.gov
Assistant U.S. Attorney **Kerry A. Kelly** . . . . . . (405) 553-8700
Education: Oklahoma 1977 JD
Assistant U.S. Attorney **Ed Kumiega** . . . . . . (405) 553-8849
E-mail: ed.kumiega@usdoj.gov
Assistant U.S. Attorney **Amanda Maxfield-Green** . . . . . . (405) 553-8770
Assistant U.S. Attorney **David McCrary** . . . . . . (405) 553-8739
Assistant U.S. Attorney **Rozia McKinney-Foster** . . . . . . (405) 553-8806
E-mail: rozia.mckinney-foster@usdoj.gov
Education: Oklahoma City 1980 JD
Assistant U.S. Attorney **Arvo Mikkanen** . . . . . . (405) 553-8737
E-mail: arvo.mikkanen@usdoj.gov
Education: Dartmouth 1983 BA; Yale 1986 JD
Assistant U.S. Attorney **Tim Ogilvie** . . . . . . (405) 553-8851
E-mail: tim.ogilvie@usdoj.gov
Education: Oklahoma City 1987 JD
Assistant U.S. Attorney **Jessica Perry** . . . . . . (405) 553-8754
E-mail: jessica.perry@usdoj.gov
Assistant U.S. Attorney **Dave Petermann** . . . . . . (405) 553-8855
E-mail: david.petermann@usdoj.gov
Assistant U.S. Attorney **Travis Smith** . . . . . . (405) 553-8772
Assistant U.S. Attorney **Chris Stephens** . . . . . . (405) 553-8783
E-mail: chris.stephens@usdoj.gov
Assistant U.S. Attorney **Scott E. Williams** . . . . . . (405) 553-8808
Assistant U.S. Attorney **(Vacant)** . . . . . . (405) 553-8736
Assistant U.S. Attorney **Ashley Oltshuler** . . . . . . (405) 553-8700

Oregon District

Mark O. Hatfield U.S. Courthouse, 1000 SW Third Avenue,
Suite 600, Portland, OR 97204-2902
Tel: (503) 727-1000 Fax: (503) 727-1117
Internet: https://www.justice.gov/usao-or

★ U.S. Attorney **Billy J. Williams** . . . . . . (503) 727-1000
E-mail: bill.williams@usdoj.gov
Education: Washington State 1981 BA; Willamette 1989 JD
Secretary to U.S. Attorney **Andrea Rocksund** . . . . . . (503) 727-1000
E-mail: andrea.rocksund@usdoj.gov

Oregon District *(continued)*

First Assistant U.S. Attorney (Acting) **Scott Asphaug** . . . (503) 727-1000
E-mail: scott.asphaug@usdoj.gov
Assistant U.S. Attorney-in-Charge **Helen Cooper** . . . . (503) 727-1000
E-mail: helen.cooper@usdoj.gov
Assistant U.S. Attorney **Scott Bradford** . . . . (503) 727-1000
Education: BYU BA; Gonzaga JD
Assistant U.S. Attorney **Hannah Horsley** . . . . (503) 727-1000
E-mail: hannah.horsley@usdoj.gov
Immigration Coordinator **Greg R. Nyhus** . . . . (503) 727-1000
E-mail: greg.r.nyhus@usdoj.gov
Appellate Chief **Kelly Zusman** . . . . (503) 727-1000
E-mail: kelly.zusman@usdoj.gov
Education: Oregon 1989 JD
Asset Forfeiture Chief **Katie DeVillers** . . . . (503) 727-1000
E-mail: katie.de.villers@usdoj.gov
Civil Chief **Renata Gowie** . . . . (503) 727-1000
E-mail: renata.gowie@usdoj.gov
Criminal Chief **Pamela Holsinger** . . . . (503) 727-1000
E-mail: pamela.holsinger@usdoj.gov
Organized Crime Drug Enforcement Task Force Chief
Thomas "Tom" Edmonds . . . . (503) 727-1000
Administrative Officer **Angela Zerbe-Darnell** . . . . (503) 727-1000
E-mail: renata.gowie@usdoj.gov
Records Coordinator **Michelle Volker** . . . . (503) 727-1000
E-mail: michelle.volker@usdoj.gov

Eugene (OR) Office

405 East 8th Ave, Suite 2400, Eugene, OR 97401
Tel: (541) 465-6771 Fax: (541) 465-6582

Assistant U.S. Attorney-in-Charge **Helen Cooper** . . . . (541) 465-6771
E-mail: helen.cooper@usdoj.gov Fax: (541) 465-6840

Medford (OR) Office

310 West Sixth Street, Medford, OR 97501
Mail: 24 Mistletoe, Medford, OR 97501
Tel: (541) 776-3564 Fax: (541) 776-3583

Assistant U.S. Attorney-in-Charge **Helen Cooper** . . . . (541) 776-3564
E-mail: helen.cooper@usdoj.gov

Pennsylvania - Eastern District

615 Chestnut Street, Suite 1250, Philadelphia, PA 19106
Tel: (215) 861-8200 Fax: (215) 861-8618
Internet: https://www.justice.gov/usao-edpa

★ U.S. Attorney **William M. McSwain Esq.** . . . . (215) 861-8200
E-mail: william.mcswain@usdoj.gov
Education: Yale 1991 BA; Harvard 2000 JD
Secretary to the U.S. Attorney **Nancy McElroy Dick** . . . (215) 861-8553
E-mail: nancy.dick@usdoj.gov
First Assistant U.S. Attorney
Jennifer Arbittier Wlliams . . . . (215) 861-8200
Secretary to the First Assistant U.S. Attorney
Pamela Maffei . . . . (215) 861-8657
E-mail: pamela.maffei@usdoj.gov
Deputy U.S. Attorney **Louis D. Lappen** . . . . (215) 861-8200
Executive Assistant U.S. Attorney for Community
Outreach and Special Programs **Robert K. Reed** . . . . (215) 861-8422
E-mail: robert.reed@usdoj.gov
Administrative Officer **(Vacant)** . . . . (215) 861-8403
Media Contact **Michele Mucellin** . . . . (215) 861-8218
E-mail: michele.mucellin@usdoj.gov
Systems Manager **Dawn Ferrell** . . . . (215) 861-8650
E-mail: dawn.ferrell@usdoj.gov
Victim-Witness Coordinator **(Vacant)** . . . . (215) 861-8905

Civil Division

Chief **Gregory B. David** . . . . (215) 861-8282
E-mail: gregory.david@usdoj.gov
Education: Virginia 2000 BA; Pennsylvania 2004 MA, 2004 JD
Legal Assistant **Desiree Wilkins** . . . . (215) 861-8375
E-mail: desiree.wilkins@usdoj.gov
Chief, Affirmative Litigation **Charlene K. Fullmer** . . . . (215) 861-8301
E-mail: charlene.fullmer@usdoj.gov
Deputy Chief, Defensive Litigation **(Vacant)** . . . . (215) 861-8306

Civil Division *(continued)*

Senior Litigation Counsel **Susan Dein Bricklin** . . . . (215) 861-8318
E-mail: susan.bricklin@usdoj.gov
Assistant U.S. Attorney **Judith A. Amorosa** . . . . (215) 861-8869
E-mail: judith.amorosa@usdoj.gov
Assistant U.S. Attorney **Susan R. Becker** . . . . (215) 861-8310
E-mail: susan.becker@usdoj.gov
Assistant U.S. Attorney **Richard M. Bernstein** . . . . (215) 861-8334
E-mail: richard.bernstein@usdoj.gov
Assistant U.S. Attorney **Colin M. Cherico** . . . . (215) 861-8788
E-mail: colin.cherico@usdoj.gov
Assistant U.S. Attorney **John T. Crutchlow** . . . . (215) 861-8622
E-mail: john.crutchlow@usdoj.gov
Assistant U.S. Attorney **David A. Degnan** . . . . (215) 861-8522
E-mail: david.degnan@usdoj.gov
Assistant U.S. Attorney **Veronica J. Finkelstein** . . . . (215) 861-8598
E-mail: veronica.finkelstein@usdoj.gov Fax: (215) 861-8618
Assistant U.S. Attorney **Eric D. Gill** . . . . (215) 861-8250
E-mail: eric.gill@usdoj.gov
Assistant U.S. Attorney **Landon Y. Jones** . . . . (215) 861-8323
E-mail: landon.jones@usdoj.gov
Education: Michigan 2004 JD
Assistant U.S. Attorney **Paul W. Kaufman** . . . . (215) 861-8579
E-mail: paul.kaufman2@usdoj.gov
Assistant U.S. Attorney **Michael S. Macko** . . . . (215) 861-8415
E-mail: michael.macko@usdoj.gov
Education: Pennsylvania 2006 JD
Assistant U.S. Attorney **Richard J. Mentzinger, Jr.** . . . . . . (215) 861-8316
E-mail: rick.mentzinger@usdoj.gov
Assistant U.S. Attorney **Viveca D. Parker** . . . . (215) 861-8443
E-mail: viveca.parker@usdoj.gov
Assistant U.S. Attorney **Scott W. Reid** . . . . (215) 861-8358
E-mail: scott.reid@usdoj.gov
Education: West Chester 1996 BS; Widener 2002 JD
Assistant U.S. Attorney **Jacqueline C. Romero** . . . . (215) 861-8470
E-mail: jacqueline.romero@usdoj.gov
Assistant U.S. Attorney **Mark J. Sherer** . . . . (215) 861-8445
E-mail: mark.sherer@usdoj.gov
Assistant U.S. Attorney **Stacey L. B. Smith** . . . . (215) 861-8348
E-mail: stacey.smith@usdoj.gov
Assistant U.S. Attorney **Anthony St. Joseph** . . . . (215) 861-8492
E-mail: anthony.stjoseph@usdoj.gov
Assistant U.S. Attorney **Gerald B. Sullivan** . . . . (215) 861-8786
E-mail: gerald.sullivan@usdoj.gov
Assistant U.S. Attorney **Joel M. Sweet** . . . . (215) 861-8581
E-mail: joel.sweet@usdoj.gov
Assistant U.S. Attorney **(Vacant)** . . . . (215) 861-8380
Assistant U.S. Attorney **(Vacant)** . . . . (215) 861-8263

Criminal Division

Chief **Denise S. Wolf** . . . . (215) 861-8570
E-mail: denise.wolf@usdoj.gov
Supervisory Legal Assistant **Kathie Smith** . . . . (215) 861-8421
E-mail: kathie.smith@usdoj.gov
Deputy Chief for White Collar Crime and Terrorism
M. Taylor Aspinwall . . . . (215) 861-8264
E-mail: taylor.aspinwall@usdoj.gov
Deputy Chief for Narcotics and Violent Crime
Christine E. Sykes . . . . (215) 861-8441
E-mail: christine.sykes@usdoj.gov
Deputy Chief, Asset Recovery & Victim Witness
Joseph F. Minni . . . . (215) 861-8574
E-mail: joseph.minni@usdoj.gov
Crisis Management Coordinator (CMC) and District
Office Security Manager (DOSM) **Jose R. Arteaga** . . . . (215) 861-8711
E-mail: jose.arteaga@usdoj.gov
Appeals Chief **Robert A. "Bob" Zauzmer** . . . . (215) 861-8568
E-mail: bob.zauzmer@usdoj.gov
Asset Forfeiture, Victim Witness Program, and Trial
Advocacy Program Chief **Sarah L. Grieb** . . . . (215) 861-8461
E-mail: sarah.grieb@usdoj.gov
Computer Crime, Child Exploitation and Intellectual
Property Crimes Chief **(Vacant)** . . . . (215) 861-8599
Economic Crimes Chief and Crisis Management
Coordinator **Richard W. Goldberg** . . . . (215) 861-8439
E-mail: richard.goldberg2@usdoj.gov

(continued on next page)

DEPARTMENTS

★ Presidential Appointment Requiring Senate Confirmation ☆ Presidential Appointment ☐ Schedule C Appointment ◇ Career Senior Foreign Service Appointment
● Career Senior Executive Service (SES) Appointment ○ Non-Career Senior Executive Service (SES) Appointment ■ Postal Career Executive Service

Criminal Division *(continued)*

Economic Crimes Deputy Chief **Daniel A. Velez** . . . . (215) 861-8454
E-mail: daniel.velez@usdoj.gov
Health Care and Government Fraud and Environmental Crime Chief **Mary E. Crawley** . . . . (215) 861-8519
E-mail: mary.crawley2@usdoj.gov
Narcotics and Organized Crime Chief
Thomas R. Perricone . . . . (215) 861-8419
E-mail: thomas.perricone@usdoj.gov
Narcotics and Organized Crime Deputy Chief
Faithe Moore Taylor . . . . (215) 861-8515
E-mail: faithe.taylor@usdoj.gov
Official Corruption, Tax Fraud and Civil Rights Chief
Richard P. Barrett . . . . (215) 861-8420
E-mail: richard.barrett3@usdoj.gov
Violent Crimes and Firearms Chief **(Vacant)** . . . . (215) 861-8438
Violent Crimes and Firearms Deputy Chief
Eric B. Henson . . . . (215) 861-8312
E-mail: eric.henson@usdoj.gov
Senior Litigation Counsel **Anthony J. Wzorek** . . . . (215) 861-8469
E-mail: anthony.wzorek@usdoj.gov
Assistant U.S. Attorney **Elizabeth F. Abrams** . . . . (215) 861-8670
E-mail: elizabeth.abrams@usdoj.gov
Assistant U.S. Attorney **Salvatore L. Astolfi** . . . . (215) 861-8431
E-mail: salvatore.astolfi@usdoj.gov
Assistant U.S. Attorney **Lauren R. Baer** . . . . (215) 861-8338
E-mail: lauren.baer@usdoj.gov
Assistant U.S. Attorney **Roberta Benjamin** . . . . (215) 861-8407
E-mail: roberta.benjamin@usdoj.gov
Assistant U.S. Attorney **Eric A. Boden** . . . . (215) 861-8327
E-mail: eric.boden@usdoj.gov
Assistant U.S. Attorney **Jason P. Bologna** . . . . (215) 861-8499
E-mail: jason.bologna@usdoj.gov
Assistant U.S. Attorney **Frank R. Costello, Jr.** . . . . (215) 861-8442
E-mail: frank.costello@usdoj.gov
Assistant U.S. Attorney **Mary Kay Costello** . . . . (215) 861-8923
E-mail: marykay.costello@usdoj.gov
Assistant U.S. Attorney **Priya T. DeSouza** . . . . (215) 861-8344
E-mail: priya.desouza@usdoj.gov
Assistant U.S. Attorney **Christopher Diviny** . . . . (215) 861-8205
E-mail: christopher.diviny@usdoj.gov
Assistant U.S. Attorney **Michael T. Donovan** . . . . (215) 861-8631
E-mail: michael.donovan@usdoj.gov
Assistant U.S. Attorney **Katherine Driscoll** . . . . (215) 861-8253
E-mail: katherine.driscoll@usdoj.gov
Assistant U.S. Attorney **Mark B. Dubnoff** . . . . (215) 861-8397
E-mail: mark.dubnoff@usdoj.gov
Assistant U.S. Attorney **Robert E. Eckert** . . . . (215) 861-8630
E-mail: robert.eckert@usdoj.gov
Assistant U.S. Attorney **Anita Eve** . . . . (215) 861-8577
E-mail: anita.eve@usdoj.gov
Assistant U.S. Attorney **Andrea G. Foulkes** . . . . (215) 861-8685
E-mail: andrea.foulkes@usdoj.gov
Assistant U.S. Attorney **Alicia M. Freind** . . . . (215) 861-8677
E-mail: alicia.freind@usdoj.gov
Assistant U.S. Attorney **John M. Gallagher** . . . . (215) 861-8636
E-mail: john.gallagher3@usdoj.gov
Assistant U.S. Attorney **Vineet Gauri** . . . . (215) 861-8644
E-mail: vineet.gauri@usdoj.gov
Assistant U.S. Attorney **Eric Gibson** . . . . (215) 861-8261
Assistant U.S. Attorney **Albert S. Glenn** . . . . (215) 861-8900
E-mail: albert.glenn@usdoj.gov
Assistant U.S. Attorney **Joel D. Goldstein** . . . . (215) 861-8429
E-mail: joel.goldstein@usdoj.gov
Assistant U.S. Attorney **Paul Gray** . . . . (215) 861-8257
E-mail: paul.gray@usdoj.gov
Assistant U.S. Attorney **Karen L. Grigsby** . . . . (215) 861-8572
E-mail: karen.grigsby@usdoj.gov
Assistant U.S. Attorney **Randall P. Hsia** . . . . (215) 861-8204
E-mail: randall.hsia@usdoj.gov
Assistant U.S. Attorney **David J. Ignall** . . . . (215) 861-8687
E-mail: david.j.ignall@usdoj.gov
Assistant U.S. Attorney **Jennifer B. Jordan** . . . . (215) 861-8462
E-mail: jennifer.jordan@usdoj.gov
Assistant U.S. Attorney **Joseph A. LaBar** . . . . (215) 861-8516
E-mail: joseph.labar@usdoj.gov

Criminal Division *(continued)*

Assistant U.S. Attorney **Frank A. Labor III** . . . . (215) 861-8675
E-mail: frank.labor@usdoj.gov
Assistant U.S. Attorney **Joseph T. Labrum III** . . . . (215) 861-8412
E-mail: joseph.labrum@usdoj.gov
Assistant U.S. Attorney **M. Beth Leahy** . . . . (215) 861-8343
E-mail: mary.beth.leahy@usdoj.gov
Assistant U.S. Attorney **Jeanine M. Linehan** . . . . (215) 861-8303
E-mail: jeanine.linehan@usdoj.gov
Assistant U.S. Attorney **Robert J. Livermore** . . . . (215) 861-8464
E-mail: robert.j.livermore@usdoj.gov
Assistant U.S. Attorney **Michael S. "Mike" Lowe** . . . . (215) 861-8534
E-mail: mike.lowe@usdoj.gov
Assistant U.S. Attorney **Laurie Magid** . . . . (215) 861-8513
E-mail: laurie.magid@usdoj.gov
Education: Pennsylvania 1982 BS; Columbia 1985 JD
Assistant U.S. Attorney **Christopher J. Mannion** . . . . (215) 861-8673
E-mail: christopher.mannion@usdoj.gov
Education: Villanova 2009 JD
Assistant U.S. Attorney **Jerome Maiatico** . . . . (215) 861-8258
E-mail: jerome.maiatico@usdoj.gov
Assistant U.S. Attorney **Terri A. Marinari** . . . . (215) 861-8466
E-mail: terri.marinari@usdoj.gov
Assistant U.S. Attorney **Karen S. Marston** . . . . (215) 861-8291
E-mail: karen.s.marston@usdoj.gov
Assistant U.S. Attorney **Maureen McCartney** . . . . (215) 861-8564
E-mail: maureen.mccartney@usdoj.gov
Assistant U.S. Attorney **Bernadette McKeon** . . . . (215) 861-8326
E-mail: bernadette.mckeon2@usdoj.gov
Assistant U.S. Attorney **Emily McKillip** . . . . (215) 861-8416
E-mail: emily.mckillip@usdoj.gov
Education: Bryn Mawr 1981 AB; Yale 1984 JD
Assistant U.S. Attorney **Mark S. Miller** . . . . (215) 861-8357
E-mail: mark.miller6@usdoj.gov
Assistant U.S. Attorney **Michelle L. Morgan** . . . . (215) 861-8458
E-mail: michelle.morgan2@usdoj.gov
Assistant U.S. Attorney **Patrick J. Murray** . . . . (215) 861-8456
E-mail: patrick.j.murray@usdoj.gov
Assistant U.S. Attorney **Kishan Nair** . . . . (215) 861-8411
E-mail: kishan.nair@usdoj.gov
Assistant U.S. Attorney **Jessica Natali** . . . . (215) 861-8505
E-mail: jessica.natali@usdoj.gov
Assistant U.S. Attorney **K. T. Newton** . . . . (215) 861-8329
E-mail: kt.newton@usdoj.gov
Assistant U.S. Attorney **Jonathan B. Ortiz** . . . . (215) 861-8305
E-mail: jonathan.ortiz2@usdoj.gov
Assistant U.S. Attorney **Yvonne O. Osirim** . . . . (215) 861-8207
E-mail: yvonne.osirim@usdoj.gov
Assistant U.S. Attorney **Tomika S. Patterson** . . . . (215) 861-8328
E-mail: tomika.stevens.patterson@usdoj.gov
Assistant U.S. Attorney **James Pavlock** . . . . (215) 861-8339
E-mail: james.pavlock@usdoj.gov
Assistant U.S. Attorney **James Petkun** . . . . (215) 861-8658
E-mail: james.petkun@usdoj.gov
Education: Villanova 2007 JD
Assistant U.S. Attorney **Andrea Nicole Phillips** . . . . (215) 861-8447
E-mail: andrea.phillips@usdoj.gov
Assistant U.S. Attorney **Michelle T. Rotella** . . . . (215) 861-8471
E-mail: michelle.rotella@usdoj.gov
Assistant U.S. Attorney **Nancy Rue** . . . . (215) 861-8683
E-mail: nancy.rue@usdoj.gov
Assistant U.S. Attorney **Andrew J. Schell** . . . . (215) 861-8646
E-mail: andrew.schell@usdoj.gov
Assistant U.S. Attorney **Paul G. Shapiro** . . . . (215) 861-8325
E-mail: paul.shapiro@usdoj.gov
Assistant U.S. Attorney **Judy Goldstein Smith** . . . . (215) 861-8511
Assistant U.S. Attorney **MaryTeresa Soltis** . . . . (215) 861-8445
E-mail: mary.soltis@usdoj.gov
Assistant U.S. Attorney **Sherri A. Stephan** . . . . (215) 861-8585
E-mail: sherri.stephan2@usdoj.gov
Assistant U.S. Attorney **Nelson S.T. Thayer, Jr.** . . . . (215) 861-8855
E-mail: nelson.thayer@usdoj.gov
Assistant U.S. Attorney **David E. Troyer** . . . . (215) 861-8475
E-mail: david.troyer@usdoj.gov

Criminal Division *(continued)*

Assistant U.S. Attorney **Virgil B. Walker** . . . . (215) 861-8446
E-mail: virgil.walker@usdoj.gov
Assistant U.S. Attorney **Jennifer A. Williams** . . . . (215) 861-8474
E-mail: jennifer.a.williams@usdoj.gov
Education: Maine 2003 JD
Assistant U.S. Attorney **Melanie B. Wilmoth** . . . . (215) 861-8603
E-mail: melanie.babb.wilmoth@usdoj.gov
Assistant U.S. Attorney **Nancy B. Winter** . . . . (215) 861-8473
E-mail: nancy.winter@usdoj.gov
Assistant U.S. Attorney **Bea L. Witzleben** . . . . (215) 861-8680
E-mail: bea.witzleben@usdoj.gov
Assistant U.S. Attorney **Linwood C. Wright, Jr.** . . . . (215) 861-8512
E-mail: l.c.wright@usdoj.gov
Assistant U.S. Attorney **Thomas M. Zaleski** . . . . (215) 861-8460
E-mail: tom.zaleski@usdoj.gov
Assistant U.S. Attorney **Ewald Zittlau** . . . . (215) 861-8407
E-mail: ewald.zittlau@usdoj.gov

Pennsylvania - Middle District

Federal Building, 228 Walnut Street, Room 220,
Harrisburg, PA 17108-1754
Federal Building, P.O. Box 11754, Harrisburg, PA 17108-1754
Tel: (717) 221-4482 Fax: (717) 221-4582

★ U.S. Attorney **David J. Freed** . . . . (717) 221-4482
E-mail: david.j.freed@usdoj.gov
Education: Washington and Lee BA; Dickinson Law JD
First Assistant U.S. Attorney **Bruce D. Brandler** . . . . (717) 221-4482
E-mail: bruce.brandler@usdoj.gov
Law Enforcement Committee Coordinator **(Vacant)** . . . . . . (717) 221-4482
Victim-Witness Coordinator **Laurie Reiley** . . . . (717) 221-4482
E-mail: laurie.reiley@usdoj.gov
Smart on Crime Coordinator **William S. Houser** . . . . (717) 221-4482
E-mail: william.houser@usdoj.gov
Smart on Crime Coordinator **Daryl Bloom** . . . . (717) 221-4482
E-mail: daryl.bloom@usdoj.gov

Civil Division

228 Walnut Street, Harrisburg, PA 17101
Fax: (717) 221-2246

Chief **Kate L. Mershimer** . . . . (717) 221-4482
E-mail: kate.l.mershimer@usdoj.gov
Civil Appeals Chief **Carlo D. "Carl" Marchioli** . . . . (717) 221-4482
E-mail: carlo.d.marchioli@usdoj.gov
Education: Bucknell 2007 BA; Harvard 2010 JD
Assistant U.S. Attorney **Mark E. Morrison** . . . . (717) 221-4482
E-mail: mark.e.morrison@usdoj.gov
Assistant U.S. Attorney **D. Brian Simpson** . . . . (717) 221-4482
E-mail: d.brian.simpson@usdoj.gov
Assistant U.S. Attorney **Melissa A. Swauger** . . . . (717) 221-4482
E-mail: melissa.swauger@usdoj.gov
Education: Hood 1992; Widener 1998 JD
Assistant U.S. Attorney **(Vacant)** . . . . (717) 221-4482
Assistant U.S. Attorney **(Vacant)** . . . . (717) 221-4482

Criminal Division

Chief **John C. Gurganus, Jr.** . . . . (717) 221-4482
E-mail: john.gurganus@usdoj.gov
Deputy Chief **Eric Pfisterer** . . . . (717) 221-4482
E-mail: eric.pfisterer@usdoj.gov
Criminal Appeals, Chief **Stephen Cerutti** . . . . (717) 221-4482
E-mail: stephen.cerutti@usdoj.gov
Assistant U.S. Attorney **William A. Behe** . . . . (717) 221-4482
E-mail: william.behe@usdoj.gov
Assistant U.S. Attorney **Daryl Bloom** . . . . (717) 221-4482
E-mail: daryl.bloom@usdoj.gov
Assistant U.S. Attorney **Stephen Cerutti** . . . . (717) 221-4482
Assistant U.S. Attorney **James Clancy** . . . . (717) 221-4482
E-mail: james.clancy@usdoj.gov
Assistant U.S. Attorney **Michael Consiglio** . . . . (717) 221-4482
E-mail: michael.consiglio@usdoj.gov
Assistant U.S. Attorney **Kim D. Daniel** . . . . (717) 221-4482
E-mail: kim.daniel@usdoj.gov

Criminal Division *(continued)*

Assistant U.S. Attorney **Meredith Taylor** . . . . (717) 221-4482
E-mail: meredith.taylor@usdoj.gov
Assistant U.S. Attorney **Joseph J. Terz** . . . . (717) 221-4482
E-mail: joseph.terz@usdoj.gov
Assistant U.S. Attorney **(Vacant)** . . . . (717) 221-4482

Scranton (PA) Office

William J. Nealon Federal Building, 235 North Washington Avenue,
Suite 311, Scranton, PA 18501-0309
P.O. Box 309, Scranton, PA 18501-0309
Tel: (570) 348-2800 Fax: (570) 348-2037

Deputy Civil Division Chief and Assistant U.S.
Attorney **Michael "Mike" Thiel** . . . . (570) 348-2800
E-mail: mike.thiel@usdoj.gov
Civil Division Assistant U.S. Attorney
J. Justin Blewitt . . . . (570) 348-2800
E-mail: justin.blewitt@usdoj.gov
Civil Division Assistant U.S. Attorney **Timothy Judge** . . . (570) 348-2800
E-mail: timothy.judge@usdoj.gov
Criminal Division Chief **(Vacant)** . . . . (570) 348-2800
Criminal Division Deputy Chief
John C. Gurganus, Jr. . . . . (570) 348-2800
E-mail: john.gurganus@usdoj.gov
Criminal Division Assistant U.S. Attorney **(Vacant)** . . . . . . (570) 348-2800
Criminal Division Assistant U.S. Attorney
Evan J. Gotlob . . . . (570) 348-2800
E-mail: evan.j.gotlob@usdoj.gov
Criminal Division Assistant U.S. Attorney
Todd Hinkley . . . . (570) 348-2800
E-mail: todd.hinkley@usdoj.gov
Criminal Division Assistant U.S. Attorney
Robert O'Hara . . . . (570) 348-2800
E-mail: robert.o'hara@usdoj.gov
Criminal Division Assistant U.S. Attorney
Michelle Olshefski . . . . (570) 348-2800
E-mail: michelle.olshefski@usdoj.gov
Criminal Division Assistant U.S. Attorney
Fran Sempa . . . . (570) 348-2800
E-mail: fran.sempa@usdoj.gov
Senior Litigation Counsel **William S. Houser** . . . . (717) 221-4482
E-mail: william.houser@usdoj.gov
Administrative Officer **Linda L. Smith** . . . . (570) 348-2800
Budget Officer **(Vacant)** . . . . (570) 348-2800
Personnel Officer **Christine Osborne** . . . . (570) 348-2800
E-mail: christine.osborne@usdoj.gov
Purchasing Officer **Sharon Jones** . . . . (570) 348-2800
E-mail: sharon.jones2@usdoj.gov

Williamsport (PA) Office

Federal Building, 240 West Third Street,
Suite 316, Williamsport, PA 17701-6465
Tel: (570) 326-1935 Fax: (570) 326-7954

Branch Chief **George J. Rocktashel** . . . . (570) 326-1935
E-mail: george.rocktashel@usdoj.gov
Criminal Division Assistant U.S. Attorney
Geoffrey McArthur . . . . (570) 326-1935
E-mail: geoffrey.macarthur@usdoj.gov
Criminal Division Assistant U.S. Attorney **(Vacant)** . . . . . . (570) 326-1935

Pennsylvania - Western District

U.S. Post Office and Courthouse Building, 700 Grant Street,
Suite 4000, Pittsburgh, PA 15219
Tel: (412) 644-3500 Fax: (412) 644-4549
Internet: https://www.justice.gov/usao-wdpa

★ U.S. Attorney **Scott W. Brady** . . . . (412) 894-7325
Education: Harvard 1991 AB; Dickinson Law 2001 JD
Executive Assistant to the U.S. Attorney **(Vacant)** . . . . . . (412) 894-7333
Deputy U.S. Attorney **(Vacant)** . . . . (412) 894-7329
First Assistant U.S. Attorney **Soo C. Song** . . . . (412) 894-7329
E-mail: soo.song@usdoj.gov
Education: Yale; George Washington JD

(continued on next page)

DEPARTMENTS

★ Presidential Appointment Requiring Senate Confirmation ☆ Presidential Appointment ☐ Schedule C Appointment ◇ Career Senior Foreign Service Appointment
● Career Senior Executive Service (SES) Appointment ○ Non-Career Senior Executive Service (SES) Appointment ■ Postal Career Executive Service

DEPARTMENTS

Pennsylvania - Western District *(continued)*

Secretary to the First Assistant U.S. Attorney
Anne E. Foley . . . . . (412) 894-7360
E-mail: anne.foley@usdoj.gov
Counsel for Ethics **Lee J. Karl** . . . . . (412) 894-7488
E-mail: lee.karl@usdoj.gov
Education: Pittsburgh 2001 JD
Counsel for Professional Responsibility
Marshall J. Piccinini . . . . . (412) 644-3500
E-mail: marshall.piccinini@usdoj.gov
Counsel for Professional Responsibility
Christy Wiegand . . . . . (412) 894-7452
E-mail: christy.wiegand@usdoj.gov
Appeals Chief **Rebecca Ross Haywood** . . . . . (412) 894-7353
E-mail: rebecca.haywood@usdoj.gov
Education: Princeton; Michigan 1994 JD
Civil Division Chief **Michael A. Comber** . . . . . (412) 894-7416
E-mail: michael.comber@usdoj.gov
Education: Purdue; Duquesne JD
Criminal Division Chief
Stephen R. "Steve" Kaufman . . . . . (412) 894-7377
Education: Allegheny; Harvard JD
Civil Rights, Exploitation and Corruption Section
Chief **Shaun E. Sweeney** . . . . . (412) 644-3500
E-mail: shaun.sweeney@usdoj.gov
National Security, Cyber and Fraud Section Chief
Paul E. Hull . . . . . (412) 644-3500
E-mail: paul.hull@usdoj.gov
Violent Crimes Section Chief **Troy Rivetti** . . . . . (412) 644-3500
E-mail: troy.rivetti@usdoj.gov
Erie Division Chief/Assistant U.S. Attorney
Marshall J. Piccinini . . . . . (814) 452-2906
United States Attorney's Office, Fax: (814) 455-6951
17 South Park Row,
Room A-330, Erie, PA 16501
E-mail: marshall.piccinini@usdoj.gov
Johnstown Division Chief/Assistant U.S. Attorney
(Vacant) . . . . . (814) 533-4547
United States Attorney's Office, Fax: (814) 533-4545
Penn Traffic Building, 319 Washington Street,
Suite 200, Johnstown, PA 15901
E-mail: stephanie.haines@usdoj.gov
Administrative Officer **Barbara A. "Barb" Bacvinskas** . . . (412) 894-7322
E-mail: barbara.bacvinskas@usdoj.gov
Budget Officer **(Vacant)** . . . . . (412) 894-7394
Personnel Officer **Nicole L. Huff** . . . . . (412) 894-7384
E-mail: nicole.huff@usdoj.gov
Public Affairs Officer **Margaret Philbin** . . . . . (412) 894-7312
E-mail: margaret.philbin@usdoj.gov
Supervisory IT Specialist **Adam M. Stahl** . . . . . (412) 894-7396
E-mail: adam.stahl@usdoj.gov
Victim-Witness Specialist **Adrienne R. Howe** . . . . . (412) 894-7400
E-mail: adrienne.howe@usdoj.gov

Puerto Rico District

350 Carlos Chardon Street, Torre Chardon,
Suite 1201, San Juan, PR 00918
Tel: (787) 766-5656 Fax: (787) 766-5632
Internet: www.justice.gov/usao/districts/pr.html

★ U.S. Attorney **Rosa Emilia Rodriguez-Velez** . . . . . (787) 766-5656
E-mail: rosa.e.rodriguez@usdoj.gov
Education: Sacred Heart (PR) 1973; Inter American 1977 JD, ML
Secretary **Ivette Figueroa** . . . . . (787) 766-5656
E-mail: ivette.figueroa@usdoj.gov
First Assistant U.S. Attorney **Timothy Henwood** . . . . . (787) 766-5656
E-mail: timothy.henwood@usdoj.gov
Education: Indiana JD
Appellate Division Chief and Assistant U.S. Attorney
Mariana E. Bauza . . . . . (787) 766-5656
E-mail: mariana.e.bauza@usdoj.gov
Education: Harvard 2003 JD
Civil Division Chief and Assistant U.S. Attorney
Hector Ramirez . . . . . (787) 766-5656
E-mail: hector.ramirez@usdoj.gov

Puerto Rico District *(continued)*

Criminal Division Chief and Assistant U.S. Attorney
Jose Capo . . . . . (787) 766-5656
E-mail: jose.capo2@usdoj.gov
Criminal Division Deputy Chief and Assistant U.S.
Attorney **Myriam Y. Fernandez** . . . . . (787) 766-5656
E-mail: myriam.y.fernandez@usdoj.gov
Criminal Division Deputy Chief and Assistant U.S.
Attorney **Julia Diaz-Rex** . . . . . (787) 766-5656
E-mail: julia.diaz-rex@usdoj.gov
Criminal Division Deputy Chief and Assistant U.S.
Attorney **Nicholas Cannon** . . . . . (787) 766-5656
E-mail: nicholas.cannon@usdoj.gov
Education: Richmond 2006 JD
Violent Crime Deputy Chief and Assistant U.S.
Attorney **Jenifer Hernandez** . . . . . (787) 766-5656
E-mail: jenifer.hernandez@usdoj.gov
Senior Litigation Counsel **Jose Ruiz** . . . . . (787) 766-5656
E-mail: jose.ruiz3@usdoj.gov
Administrative Officer **Lisa F. Western** . . . . . (787) 766-5656
E-mail: lisa.f.western@usdoj.gov
Human Resources Officer **Carmen Pura Lopez** . . . . . (787) 282-1873
E-mail: c.pura.lopez@usdoj.gov
Supervisory Information Technology Specialist
(Vacant) . . . . . (787) 766-5656
Fax: (787) 766-5193

Rhode Island District

50 Kennedy Plaza, 8th Floor, Providence, RI 02903
Tel: (401) 709-5000 Fax: (401) 709-5001
Internet: https://www.justice.gov/usao-ri

★ U.S. Attorney **Stephen G. Dambruch** . . . . . (401) 709-5000
E-mail: stephen.dambruch@usdoj.gov
Education: Providence 1982 BA; Boston Col 1985 JD
★ U.S. Attorney-Designate **Aaron L. Weisman** . . . . . (401) 709-5000
Education: Brandeis BA; Cardozo JD
Secretary to the U.S. Attorney **Sheila Grant** . . . . . (401) 709-5051
E-mail: sheila.grant@usdoj.gov
First Assistant U.S. Attorney **Richard B. Myrus** . . . . . (401) 709-5000
E-mail: richard.myrus@usdoj.gov
Education: Columbia 1984 BA; UC San Diego 1992 MA; Fordham 1995 JD
Administrative Officer **Robin S. Downey** . . . . . (401) 709-5000
E-mail: robin.downey@usdoj.gov
Budget Officer **Vincent Onorato** . . . . . (401) 709-5000
E-mail: vincent.onorato@usdoj.gov
Public Information Officer **Jim Martin** . . . . . (401) 709-5357
E-mail: usari.media@usdoj.gov
Systems Manager **Troy Edwards** . . . . . (401) 709-5000
E-mail: troy.edwards@usdoj.gov

Civil Division

Chief/Assistant U.S. Attorney **Richard B. Myrus** . . . . . (401) 709-5000
E-mail: richard.myrus@usdoj.gov
Education: Columbia 1984 BA; UC San Diego 1992 MA; Fordham 1995 JD
Assistant U.S. Attorney **Zachary A. Cunha** . . . . . (401) 709-5000
E-mail: zachary.cunha@usdoj.gov
Assistant U.S. Attorney **Leslie Kane** . . . . . (401) 709-5000
E-mail: leslie.kane@usdoj.gov
Assistant U.S. Attorney **Mary E. Rogers** . . . . . (401) 709-5000
E-mail: mary.rogers@usdoj.gov
Education: Marquette 1980 BA; Suffolk JD
Assistant U.S. Attorney **Bethany N. Wong** . . . . . (401) 709-5000
E-mail: bethany.wong@usdoj.gov
Assistant U.S. Attorney **Amy R Romero** . . . . . (401) 709-5000
E-mail: amy.romero@usdoj.gov

Criminal Division

Chief/Assistant U.S. Attorney **William Ferland** . . . . . (401) 709-5000
E-mail: william.ferland@usdoj.gov
Appellate Section Chief **Donald C. Lockhart** . . . . . (401) 709-5000
Organized Crime Chief and Assistant U.S. Attorney
William Ferland . . . . . (401) 709-5000
E-mail: william.ferland@usdoj.gov

★ Presidential Appointment Requiring Senate Confirmation ☆ Presidential Appointment ☐ Schedule C Appointment ◇ Career Senior Foreign Service Appointment
● Career Senior Executive Service (SES) Appointment ○ Non-Career Senior Executive Service (SES) Appointment ■ Postal Career Executive Service

Criminal Division *(continued)*

Organized Crime Drug Enforcement Task Force Chief and Assistant U.S. Attorney **Paul Daly, Jr.** . . . . (401) 709-5000
E-mail: paul.daly@usdoj.gov
Assistant Deputy Chief **Sandra R. Hebert** . . . . (401) 709-5000
E-mail: sandra.hebert@usdoj.gov
Assistant U.S. Attorney **Zechariah Chafee** . . . . (401) 709-5000
E-mail: zechariah.chafee@usdoj.gov
Assistant U.S. Attorney **Ly T. Chin** . . . . (401) 709-5000
E-mail: ly.chin@usdoj.gov
Education: William & Mary 1999 BA; Washington and Lee 2003 JD
Assistant U.S. Attorney **Terrence P. Donnelly** . . . . (401) 709-5000
E-mail: terrence.donnelly@usdoj.gov
Assistant U.S. Attorney **Dulce Donovan Esq.** . . . . (401) 709-5000
E-mail: dulce.donovan@usdoj.gov
Education: Bates BA; Cornell 1993 JD
Assistant U.S. Attorney **Ronald R. Gendron** . . . . (401) 709-5000
E-mail: ronald.gendron@usdoj.gov
Assistant U.S. Attorney **Denise M. Barton** . . . . (401) 709-5000
E-mail: denise.barton@usdoj.gov
Assistant U.S. Attorney **John P. McAdams** . . . . (401) 709-5000
E-mail: john.mcadams@usdoj.gov
Assistant U.S. Attorney **Richard W. Rose** . . . . (401) 709-5000
E-mail: richard.rose@usdoj.gov
Education: Rhode Island Col; Northeastern JD
Assistant U.S. Attorney **Milind Shah** . . . . (401) 709-5000
E-mail: milind.shah@usdoj.gov
Assistant U.S. Attorney **Gerard B. Sullivan** . . . . (401) 709-5000
E-mail: gerard.sullivan@usdoj.gov
Assistant U.S. Attorney **Lee Vilker** . . . . (401) 709-5000
E-mail: lee.vilker@usdoj.gov
Education: Brandeis; NYU JD

South Carolina District

Wells Fargo Building, 1441 Main Street,
Suite 500, Columbia, SC 29201
Tel: (803) 929-3000 Fax: (803) 254-2912 Fax: (803) 254-2943
Fax: (803) 254-2889 Internet: https://www.justice.gov/usao-sc

★ U.S. Attorney-Designate **Cheryl A. "Sherri" Lydon** . . . . . (803) 929-3000
E-mail: sherri.lydon@usdoj.gov
Education: Clemson 1983 BA; South Carolina 1987 JD
Secretary to the U.S. Attorney **Ramona Geiger** . . . . (803) 929-3005
E-mail: ramona.geiger@usdoj.gov
First Assistant U.S. Attorney **Lance Crick** . . . . (803) 929-3000
E-mail: lance.crick@usdoj.gov
Secretary to the First Assistant U.S. Attorney **Kelly Reynolds** . . . . (803) 929-3006
E-mail: kelly.reynolds@usdoj.gov
Administrative Officer **John Fonville** . . . . (803) 929-3074
E-mail: john.fonville@usdoj.gov
Personnel Officer **(Vacant)** . . . . (803) 929-3096
Law Enforcement Coordinator **Rebecca C. Plyler** . . . . (803) 929-3009
Victim-Witness Coordinator **Candace Shepherd** . . . . (803) 929-3012
E-mail: candace.shepherd@usdoj.gov
Appellate Division Chief **Robert "Bob" Daley** . . . . (803) 929-3000
E-mail: bob.daley@usdoj.gov
Civil Division Chief and Assistant U.S. Attorney **Barbara Bowens** . . . . (803) 929-3054
E-mail: barbara.bowens@usdoj.gov
Deputy Civil Division Chief and Assistant U.S. Attorney **Jennifer Aldrich** . . . . (803) 929-3052
E-mail: jennifer.aldrich@usdoj.gov
Criminal Division Chief and Assistant U.S. Attorney **Nancy Wicker** . . . . (803) 929-3081
E-mail: nancy.wicker@usdoj.gov
Deputy Criminal Division Chief and Assistant U.S. Attorney **(Vacant)** . . . . (803) 929-3081
General Crimes Section Chief and Assistant U.S. Attorney **Jay Richardson** . . . . (803) 929-3063
Narcotics Section Chief and Assistant U.S. Attorney **Andy Moorman** . . . . (803) 929-3000
Violent Crimes Section Chief and Assistant U.S. Attorney **J.D. Rowell** . . . . (803) 929-3000
Asset Forfeiture Unit Assistant U.S. Attorney **Carrie Fisher-Sherrard** . . . . (864) 282-2111

South Carolina District *(continued)*

Financial Litigation Unit Assistant U.S. Attorney **Ann Young** . . . . (803) 929-3055
Organized Crime Drug Enforcement Task Force Assistant U.S. Attorney **Andy Moorman** . . . . (803) 929-3036
Systems Manager **Raul Cruz** . . . . (803) 929-3099

Charleston (SC) Office

151 Meeting Street, Suite 200, Charleston, SC 29402
P.O. Box 978, Charleston, SC 29402
Tel: (843) 727-4381 Fax: (843) 727-4443

Assistant U.S. Attorney-in-Charge **Nathan Williams** . . . . . (843) 727-4381
E-mail: nathan.williams@usdoj.gov

Florence (SC) Office

John L. McMillan Federal Building, 401 West Evans Street,
Room 222, Florence, SC 29501
P.O. Box 1567, Florence, SC 29503-1567
Tel: (843) 665-6688 Fax: (843) 678-8809

Assistant U.S. Attorney-in-Charge **A. Bradley Parham** . . . (843) 665-6688

Greenville (SC) Office

One Liberty Square Building, 55 Beattie Place,
Suite 700, Greenville, SC 29601
Tel: (864) 282-2100 Fax: (864) 233-3158

Assistant U.S. Attorney-in-Charge **Lance Crick** . . . . (864) 282-2100
E-mail: lance.crick@usdoj.gov

South Dakota District

325 South First Avenue, Suite 300, Sioux Falls, SD 57104
P.O. Box 2638, Sioux Falls, SD 57101-2638
Tel: (605) 330-4400 Fax: (605) 330-4410
Internet: https://www.justice.gov/usao-sd

★ U.S. Attorney **Ronald A. Parsons, Jr.** . . . . (605) 330-4400
E-mail: ronald.parsons@usdoj.gov
Education: Minnesota BA; South Dakota JD
Secretary to the U.S. Attorney **Rebecca Anderson** . . . . . (605) 357-2304
E-mail: rebecca.anderson@usdoj.gov
First Assistant U.S. Attorney **(Vacant)** . . . . (605) 224-5402
Administrative Officer **(Vacant)** . . . . (605) 357-2337
Law Enforcement Coordinator **(Vacant)** . . . . (605) 330-4400
Systems Manager **James Lichty** . . . . (605) 357-2370
E-mail: james.lichty@usdoj.gov
Victim-Witness Coordinator **Marlys Big Eagle** . . . . (605) 224-5402
E-mail: marlys.bigeagle@usdoj.gov
Special Assistant U.S. Attorney **Debra Flute** . . . . (605) 330-4400

Civil Division

Civil Division Chief **Diana J. Ryan** . . . . (605) 357-2340
E-mail: diana.ryan@usdoj.gov
Assistant U.S. Attorney **Meghan Roche** . . . . (605) 357-2341
E-mail: meghan.roche@usdoj.gov
Assistant U.S. Attorney **(Vacant)** . . . . (605) 357-2343
Assistant U.S. Attorney **Camela Theeler** . . . . (605) 357-2342
E-mail: camela.theeler@usdoj.gov

Criminal Division

Assistant U.S. Attorney and Criminal Chief **Dennis R. Holmes** . . . . (605) 357-2350
E-mail: dennis.holmes@usdoj.gov
Appeals Chief **Kevin Koliner** . . . . (605) 330-4400
E-mail: kevin.koliner@usdoj.gov
Assistant U.S. Attorney **Jeff Clapper** . . . . (605) 357-2351
E-mail: jeff.clapper@usdoj.gov
Assistant U.S. Attorney **John Haak** . . . . (605) 357-2352
E-mail: john.haak@usdoj.gov
Assistant U.S. Attorney **Ann Hoffman** . . . . (605) 357-2363
E-mail: ann.hoffman@usdoj.gov
Assistant U.S. Attorney **Connie Larson** . . . . (605) 357-2362
E-mail: connie.larson@usdoj.gov
Assistant U.S. Attorney **(Vacant)** . . . . (605) 357-2353

★ Presidential Appointment Requiring Senate Confirmation ☆ Presidential Appointment ☐ Schedule C Appointment ◇ Career Senior Foreign Service Appointment
● Career Senior Executive Service (SES) Appointment ○ Non-Career Senior Executive Service (SES) Appointment ■ Postal Career Executive Service

DEPARTMENTS

Pierre (SD) Office

337 Federal Building and U.S. Courthouse,
225 South Pierre Street, Pierre, SD 57501
P.O. Box 7249, Pierre, SD 57501-7240
Tel: (605) 224-5402 Fax: (605) 224-8305

Supervisory Assistant U.S. Attorney **Tim Maher** . . . . (605) 224-5402
E-mail: tim.maher@usdoj.gov
Civil Division Assistant U.S. Attorney **Cheryl DuPris** . . . . (605) 224-5402
E-mail: cheryl.dupris@usdoj.gov
Criminal Division Assistant U.S. Attorney
Meghan Dilges . . . . (605) 224-5402
E-mail: meghan.dilges@usdoj.gov
Criminal Division Assistant U.S. Attorney **Jay Miller** . . . . (605) 224-5402
E-mail: jay.miller@usdoj.gov
Criminal Division Assistant U.S. Attorney **Troy Morley** . . . (605) 224-5402
E-mail: troy.morley@usdoj.gov
Criminal Division Assistant U.S. Attorney **(Vacant)** . . . . . . (605) 224-5402
Criminal Division Assistant U.S. Attorney **(Vacant)** . . . . . . (605) 224-5402

Rapid City (SD) Office

515 Ninth Street, Room 201, Rapid City, SD 57701
Tel: (605) 342-7822 Fax: (605) 342-1108

Supervisory Assistant U.S. Attorney
Gregg S. Peterman . . . . (605) 342-7822
E-mail: gregg.peterman@usdoj.gov
Criminal Division Assistant U.S. Attorney
Sarah B. Collins . . . . (605) 342-7822
E-mail: sarah.b.collins@usdoj.gov
Criminal Division Assistant U.S. Attorney
Eric D. Kelderman . . . . (605) 342-7822
E-mail: eric.kelderman@usdoj.gov
Education: Creighton 2001 JD
Criminal Division Assistant U.S. Attorney
Benjamin Patterson . . . . (605) 342-7822
E-mail: ben.patterson@usdoj.gov
Criminal Division Assistant U.S. Attorney
Megan Poppen . . . . (605) 342-7822
E-mail: megan.poppen@usdoj.gov
Criminal Division Assistant U.S. Attorney
Kathryn Rich . . . . (605) 342-7822
E-mail: kathryn.rich@usdoj.gov
Education: South Dakota 2009 JD
Victim-Witness Specialist **Aileen Crawford** . . . . (605) 342-7822
E-mail: aileen.crawford@usdoj.gov

Tennessee - Eastern District

800 Market Street, Suite 211, Knoxville, TN 37902
Tel: (865) 545-4167 Fax: (865) 545-4176
Internet: www.justice.gov/usao/tne

★ U.S. Attorney **J. Douglas "Doug" Overbey** . . . . (865) 545-4167
E-mail: douglas.overbey@usdoj.gov
Education: Carson-Newman 1976 BA; Tennessee 1979 JD
First Assistant U.S. Attorney **Nancy S. Harr** . . . . (865) 545-4167
E-mail: nancy.harr@usdoj.gov
Administrative Officer **Connie Moody** . . . . (865) 545-4167
E-mail: connie.moody@usdoj.gov
Budget Officer **Sharon Sellers** . . . . (865) 545-4167
E-mail: sharon.sellers@usdoj.gov
Human Resource Officer **Cheryl Lykens** . . . . (865) 545-4167
E-mail: cheryl.lykens@usdoj.gov
Records Management Officer **Susan Leonard** . . . . (865) 545-4167
E-mail: susan.leonard@usdoj.gov
Systems Manager **(Vacant)** . . . . (865) 545-4167
Law Enforcement Committee Coordinator
Sharry Dedman-Beard . . . . (865) 545-4167
E-mail: sherry.dedman-beard@usdoj.gov
Victim-Witness Coordinator **(Vacant)** . . . . (865) 545-4167
Intelligence Specialist **Paul Trask** . . . . (865) 545-4167
E-mail: paul.trask@usdoj.gov

Civil Division

Chief **Loretta Harber** . . . . (865) 545-4167
E-mail: loretta.harber@usdoj.gov

Civil Division *(continued)*

Social Security Assistant U.S. Attorney (Acting)
Loretta Harber . . . . (865) 545-4167
E-mail: loretta.harber@usdoj.gov
Assistant U.S. Attorney **Robert McConkey** . . . . (865) 545-4167
E-mail: robert.mcconkey@usdoj.gov
Assistant U.S. Attorney **(Vacant)** . . . . (865) 545-4167
Assistant U.S. Attorney **(Vacant)** . . . . (865) 545-4167

Criminal Division

Chief **(Vacant)** . . . . (865) 545-4167
Supervisory Assistant U.S. Attorney **Charles Atchley** . . . . (865) 545-4167
E-mail: charles.atchley@usdoj.gov
Supervisory Assistant U.S. Attorney **Debra Breneman** . . . (865) 545-4167
E-mail: debra.breneman@usdoj.gov
Supervisory Assistant U.S. Attorney **David Jennings** . . . . (865) 545-4167
E-mail: david.jennings@usdoj.gov
Supervisory Assistant U.S. Attorney **(Vacant)** . . . . (865) 545-4167
Assistant U.S. Attorney **Cynthia Davidson** . . . . (865) 545-4167
E-mail: cynthia.davidson@usdoj.gov
Assistant U.S. Attorney **F. M. "Trey" Hamilton** . . . . (865) 545-4167
E-mail: trey.hamilton@usdoj.gov
Assistant U.S. Attorney **David Lewen** . . . . (865) 545-4167
E-mail: david.lewen@usdoj.gov
Assistant U.S. Attorney **Kelly Norris** . . . . (865) 545-4167
E-mail: kelly.norris@usdoj.gov
Assistant U.S. Attorney **Tracy Stone** . . . . (865) 545-4167
E-mail: tracy.stone@usdoj.gov
Assistant U.S. Attorney **Jeffrey E. Theodore** . . . . (865) 545-4167
E-mail: jeffrey.theodore@usdoj.gov
Assistant U.S. Attorney **(Vacant)** . . . . (865) 545-4167
Assistant U.S. Attorney **(Vacant)** . . . . (865) 545-4167
Appellate Assistant U.S. Attorney **(Vacant)** . . . . (865) 545-4167
Asset Forfeiture Assistant U.S. Attorney **Frank Dale** . . . . . (865) 545-4167
E-mail: frank.dale@usdoj.gov
Organized Crime Drug Enforcement Task Force
Assistant U.S. Attorney **Caryn Hebets** . . . . (423) 282-1889
E-mail: caryn.hebets@usdoj.gov

Chattanooga (TN) Office

1110 Market Street, Suite 301, Chattanooga, TN 37402
Tel: (423) 752-5140 Fax: (423) 752-5150

Supervisory Assistant U.S. Attorney/Lead OCDETF
Assistant U.S. Attorney **Scott Winne** . . . . (423) 752-5140
E-mail: scott.winne@usdoj.gov
Civil Division Assistant U.S. Attorney
M. Kent Anderson . . . . (423) 752-5140
E-mail: kent.anderson@usdoj.gov
Civil Division Assistant U.S. Attorney **Tammy Combs** . . . (423) 752-5140
E-mail: tammy.combs@usdoj.gov

Criminal Division

Supervisory Assistant U.S. Attorney **Scott Winne** . . . . (423) 752-5140
Assistant U.S. Attorney **Terra Bay** . . . . (423) 752-5140
Assistant U.S. Attorney **James Brooks** . . . . (423) 752-5140
E-mail: james.brooks@usdoj.gov
Assistant U.S. Attorney **(Vacant)** . . . . (423) 752-5140
Assistant U.S. Attorney **Chris Poole** . . . . (423) 752-5140
E-mail: chris.poole@usdoj.gov
Assistant U.S. Attorney **Michael Porter** . . . . (423) 752-5140
E-mail: michael.porter2@usdoj.gov
Education: Case Western 2002 JD
Assistant U.S. Attorney **Gregg L. Sullivan** . . . . (423) 752-5140
E-mail: gregg.sullivan@usdoj.gov
Assistant U.S. Attorney **Jay Woods** . . . . (423) 752-5140

Greeneville (TN) Office

220 West Depot Street, Suite 423, Greeneville, TN 37743
Tel: (423) 639-6759 Fax: (423) 639-6451

Supervisory Assistant U.S. Attorney
Robert M. Reeves . . . . (423) 639-6759
E-mail: robert.reeves@usdoj.gov

Greeneville (TN) Office *(continued)*

Criminal Division Assistant U.S. Attorney
Greg Bowman .... (423) 639-6759
E-mail: greg.bowman@usdoj.gov
Criminal Division Assistant U.S. Attorney
J. Christian Lampe .... (423) 639-6759
E-mail: christian.lampe@usdoj.gov
Criminal Division Assistant U.S. Attorney
Nicholas Regalia .... (423) 639-6759
E-mail: nicholas.regalia@usdoj.gov
Criminal Division Assistant U.S. Attorney
Helen Smith .... (423) 639-6759
E-mail: helen.smith@usdoj.gov
Criminal Division Assistant U.S. Attorney **(Vacant)** ...... (423) 282-1889
Criminal Division Assistant U.S. Attorney **(Vacant)** ...... (423) 639-6759
Criminal Division Assistant U.S. Attorney **(Vacant)** ...... (423) 639-6759
Criminal Division Assistant U.S. Attorney **(Vacant)** ...... (423) 639-6759

Tennessee - Middle District

110 Ninth Avenue South, Suite A-961, Nashville, TN 37203-3870
Tel: (615) 736-5151 Fax: (615) 736-5323
Internet: https://www.justice.gov/usao-mdtn

★ U.S. Attorney **Donald Q. Cochran, Jr.** .... (615) 736-5151
Education: Vanderbilt BA, JD
Secretary to the U.S. Attorney **Darlene Danielson** ..... (615) 736-5151
E-mail: darlene.danielson@usdoj.gov
Victim-Witness Coordinator **John Hernandez** .... (615) 736-5151
E-mail: john.hernandez@usdoj.gov
First Assistant U.S. Attorney **John L. "Jack" Smith** ..... (615) 736-5151
E-mail: jack.smith2@usdoj.gov
Education: Harvard 1994 JD
Senior Litigation Counsel **(Vacant)** .... (615) 736-5151
Law Enforcement Committee Coordinator
David Boling .... (615) 736-5151
Human Resources Specialist **Dawn Woodside** .... (615) 736-5151
E-mail: dawn.woodside@usdoj.gov
Administrative Officer **Keith Preston** .... (615) 736-5151
E-mail: keith.preston@usdoj.gov

Civil Division

Chief **Mark Wildasin** .... (615) 736-5151
E-mail: mark.wildasin@usdoj.gov
Assistant U.S. Attorney **Ellen M. Bowden** .... (615) 736-5151
Assistant U.S. Attorney **Jason S. Ehrlinspiel** .... (615) 736-5151
E-mail: jason.ehrlinspiel@usdoj.gov
Assistant U.S. Attorney **Steve Jordan** .... (615) 736-5151
E-mail: steve.jordan@usdoj.gov
Assistant U.S. Attorney **Delk Kennedy** .... (615) 736-5151
E-mail: delk.kennedy@usdoj.gov
Assistant U.S. Attorney **Amanda Klops** .... (615) 736-5151
Assistant U.S. Attorney **Mercedes C. Maynor-Faulcon** ... (615) 736-5151
E-mail: mercedes.maynor-faulcon@usdoj.gov
Assistant U.S. Attorney **Michael L. Roden** .... (615) 736-5151
E-mail: michael.roden@usdoj.gov
Assistant U.S. Attorney **Christopher Sabis** .... (615) 736-5151
E-mail: christopher.sabis@usdoj.gov
Assistant U.S. Attorney **(Vacant)** .... (615) 736-5151
Financial Litigation Unit Debt Collection Agent
Amanda Griggs .... (615) 736-5151
E-mail: amanda.griggs@usdoj.gov

Criminal Division

Chief **Jimmie Lynn Ramsaur** .... (615) 736-5151
E-mail: jimmie.lynn.ramsaur@usdoj.gov
Deputy Chief **Brent Hannafan** .... (615) 736-5151
E-mail: brent.hannafan@usdoj.gov
Deputy Chief **John K. Webb** .... (615) 736-5151
Deputy Chief **Phil Wehby** .... (615) 736-5151
Assistant U.S. Attorney **Siji Moore** .... (615) 736-5151
Assistant U.S. Attorney **Sara Beth Myer** .... (615) 736-5151
Assistant U.S. Attorney **Courtney Coker** .... (615) 736-5151
Assistant U.S. Attorney
S. Carran "Carrie" Daughtrey .... (615) 736-5151
E-mail: carrie.daughtrey@usdoj.gov
Education: Vanderbilt BS; Wisconsin; Vanderbilt 1994 JD

Criminal Division *(continued)*

Assistant U.S. Attorney **Lee Deneke** .... (615) 736-5151
E-mail: lee.deneke@usdoj.gov
Assistant U.S. Attorney **Lynne Ingram** .... (615) 736-5151
E-mail: lynne.ingram@usdoj.gov
Assistant U.S. Attorney **Thomas Jaworski** .... (615) 736-5151
Assistant U.S. Attorney **Byron M. Jones** .... (615) 736-5151
E-mail: byron.jones@usdoj.gov
Assistant U.S. Attorney **Sunny Koshy** .... (615) 736-5151
E-mail: sunny.koshy@usdoj.gov
Assistant U.S. Attorney **Clay Lee** .... (615) 736-5151
E-mail: clay.lee@usdoj.gov
Assistant U.S. Attorney **Joseph Montmimy** .... (615) 736-5151
Assistant U.S. Attorney **Henry Leventis** .... (615) 736-5151
Assistant U.S. Attorney **Sara Beth Myers** .... (615) 736-5151
Education: Duke BA; Yale MA; Vanderbilt JD
Assistant U.S. Attorney **Ryan Rayboulb** .... (615) 736-5151
Assistant U.S. Attorney **Katie Risinger** .... (615) 736-5151
Assistant U.S. Attorney **Ahmed Safeeullah** .... (615) 736-5151
E-mail: ahmed.safeeullah@usdoj.gov
Assistant U.S. Attorney **Ben Schraber** .... (615) 736-5151
Assistant U.S. Attorney **Stephanie Toussaint** .... (615) 736-5151
E-mail: stephanie.toussaint@usdoj.gov
Assistant U.S. Attorney **Cecil Van Devenber** .... (615) 736-5151
Assistant U.S. Attorney **Van Vincent** .... (615) 736-5151
E-mail: van.vincent@usdoj.gov
Administrative Officer **Keith Preston** .... (615) 736-4515
E-mail: keith.preston@usdoj.gov

Tennessee - Western District

Clifford Davis Federal Building, 167 North Main Street,
Suite 800, Memphis, TN 38103
Tel: (901) 544-4231 Fax: (901) 544-4230
Internet: https://www.justice.gov/usao-wdtn

★ U.S. Attorney **D. Michael Dunavant** .... (901) 544-4231
E-mail: michael.dunavant@usdoj.gov
Education: Tennessee 1992 BA; Mississippi 1995 JD
Special Counsel **(Vacant)** .... (901) 544-4231
Secretary to the U.S. Attorney (Acting)
LaRita Bearden .... (901) 544-4231
E-mail: larita.bearden@usdoj.gov
First Assistant U.S. Attorney
Joseph "Joe" Murphy, Jr. .... (901) 544-4231
E-mail: joe.murphy@usdoj.gov
Education: Lambuth BA; U Memphis JD
Executive Assistant United States Attorney
C. David Biggers .... (901) 544-4231
E-mail: david.biggers@usdoj.gov
Administrative Officer **Demetrice Rufus** .... (901) 544-4231
Budget Officer **Denise Johnson** .... (901) 544-4231
E-mail: denise.johnson@usdoj.gov
Personnel Officer **Donald Stinson** .... (901) 544-4231
E-mail: donald.stinson@usdoj.gov
Law Enforcement Committee Coordinator
Timothy M. Kring .... (901) 544-4231
E-mail: timothy.kring@usdoj.gov
Victim-Witness Specialist **LaRita Bearden** .... (901) 544-4231
E-mail: larita.bearden@usdoj.gov
Information Technology Manager **Chris Miller** .... (901) 544-4231
E-mail: chris.miller@usdoj.gov

Civil Division

Chief and Senior Litigation Counsel **Bill Siler** .... (901) 544-4231
E-mail: bill.siler@usdoj.gov
Bankruptcy/Collections Assistant U.S. Attorney
Barbara Zoccola .... (901) 544-4010
E-mail: barbara.zoccola@usdoj.gov
Assistant U.S. Attorney **David Brackstone** .... (901) 544-4231
E-mail: david.brackstone@usdoj.gov
Assistant U.S. Attorney **S. Keenan Carter** .... (901) 544-4231
E-mail: keenan.carter@usdoj.gov
Assistant U.S. Attorney **Monica Simmons** .... (901) 544-4231
E-mail: monica.simmons@usdoj.gov
Assistant U.S. Attorney **Matt Waldrop** .... (901) 544-4231

(continued on next page)

★ Presidential Appointment Requiring Senate Confirmation ☆ Presidential Appointment ☐ Schedule C Appointment ◇ Career Senior Foreign Service Appointment
● Career Senior Executive Service (SES) Appointment ○ Non-Career Senior Executive Service (SES) Appointment ■ Postal Career Executive Service

DEPARTMENTS

Civil Division *(continued)*

Health Care Fraud Assistant U.S. Attorney
Stuart Canale . . . . . (901) 544-4231
E-mail: stuart.canale@usdoj.gov

Criminal Division

Chief **Joseph "Joe" Murphy, Jr.** . . . . . (901) 544-4231
Education: Lambuth BA; U Memphis JD
Deputy Chief **Carroll Andre III** . . . . . (901) 544-4231
Senior Litigation Counsel **Tony Arvin** . . . . . (901) 544-4231
Assistant U.S. Attorney **J. William Crow** . . . . . (901) 544-4231
Assistant U.S. Attorney **Christopher Cotten** . . . . . (901) 544-4231
Assistant U.S. Attorney **Lorraine Craig** . . . . . (901) 544-4231
E-mail: lorraine.craig@usdoj.gov
Assistant U.S. Attorney **Dean DeCandia** . . . . . (901) 544-4231
E-mail: dean.decandia@usdoj.gov
Assistant U.S. Attorney **Damon Griffin** . . . . . (901) 544-4231
Assistant U.S. Attorney **Debra Ireland** . . . . . (901) 544-4231
E-mail: deb.ireland@usdoj.gov
Assistant U.S. Attorney **Murrell Martindale** . . . . . (901) 544-4231
Assistant U.S. Attorney **Bayonle Osundare** . . . . . (901) 544-4231
E-mail: bayonle.osundare@usdoj.gov
Assistant U.S. Attorney **David Pritchard** . . . . . (901) 544-4231
E-mail: david.pritchard@usdoj.gov
Assistant U.S. Attorney **Elizabeth Rogers** . . . . . (901) 544-4231
E-mail: elizabeth.rogers@usdoj.gov
Education: Harvard 2000 JD
Assistant U.S. Attorney **Reagan Taylor** . . . . . (901) 544-4231
E-mail: reagan.taylor2@usdoj.gov
Assistant U.S. Attorney **Kasey Weiland** . . . . . (901) 544-4231
E-mail: kasey.weiland2@usdoj.gov
Special Assistant U.S. Attorney **(Vacant)** . . . . . (901) 544-4231
Community Outreach Specialist **Cherri Green** . . . . . (901) 544-4231

Drug Task Force

Assistant U.S. Attorney **Mark Erskine** . . . . . (901) 544-4231
E-mail: mark.erskine@usdoj.gov

Jackson (TN) Office

109 South Highland, Suite 300, Jackson, TN 38301
Tel: (731) 422-6220 Fax: (731) 422-6668

Branch Chief **Victor "Vic" Ivy** . . . . . (731) 422-6220
E-mail: vic.ivy@usdoj.gov
Deputy Chief **James Powell** . . . . . (731) 422-6220
E-mail: james.powell@usdoj.gov
Organized Crime Drug Enforcement Task Force Chief
Beth Boswell . . . . . (731) 422-6220
E-mail: beth.boswell@usdoj.gov
Assistant U.S. Attorney **Taylor Eskridge** . . . . . (731) 422-6220
E-mail: taylor.eskridge@usdoj.gov
Assistant U.S. Attorney **Matthew Wilson** . . . . . (731) 422-6220
E-mail: matthew.wilson@usdoj.gov

Texas - Eastern District

Federal Building, 350 Magnolia Avenue,
Suite 150, Beaumont, TX 77701
Tel: (409) 839-2538 Fax: (409) 839-2550
Internet: https://www.justice.gov/usao-edtx

★ U.S. Attorney **Joseph D. Brown** . . . . . (409) 839-2538
Education: Texas 1992 BA; Southern Methodist 1995 JD
Secretary to the U.S. Attorney **Sharon Beckum** . . . . . (409) 839-2538
E-mail: sharon.beckum@usdoj.gov
First Assistant U.S. Attorney **Brit Featherston** . . . . . (409) 839-2538
E-mail: brit.featherston@usdoj.gov
Attorney in Charge **Matt Quinn** . . . . . (409) 839-2538
E-mail: matt.quinn@usdoj.gov
Administrative Officer **Gretchen Randall** . . . . . (409) 839-2538
E-mail: gretchen.randall@usdoj.gov
Personnel Officer **Princess Franklin** . . . . . (409) 839-2538
E-mail: princess.franklin@usdoj.gov
Public Affairs Specialist/Law Enforcement Coordinator
Davilyn Walston . . . . . (409) 839-2538
E-mail: davilyn.walston@usdoj.gov

Texas - Eastern District *(continued)*

Systems Manager **Fredrick Schultz** . . . . . (409) 839-2538
E-mail: fredrick.schultz@usdoj.gov
Systems Manager/Webmaster
Joseph "Butch" Henderson . . . . . (409) 839-2538
E-mail: joseph.henderson@usdoj.gov

Civil Division

Assistant U.S. Attorney **Michael Lockhart** . . . . . (409) 839-2538
E-mail: michael.lockhart@usdoj.gov
Assistant U.S. Attorney **Andrea Parker** . . . . . (409) 839-2538
E-mail: andrea.parker@usdoj.gov

Criminal Division

Chief **Alan R. Jackson** . . . . . (936) 590-1400
E-mail: alan.jackson@usdoj.gov
Assistant U.S. Attorney **Joseph R. "Joe" Batte** . . . . . (409) 839-2538
E-mail: joe.batte@usdoj.gov
Assistant U.S. Attorney **Michelle Englade** . . . . . (409) 839-2538
E-mail: michelle.englade@usdoj.gov
Assistant U.S. Attorney **Randall L. Fluke** . . . . . (409) 839-2538
E-mail: randall.fluke@usdoj.gov
Assistant U.S. Attorney **Russell James** . . . . . (409) 839-2538
E-mail: russell.james@usdoj.gov
Assistant U.S. Attorney **John Ross** . . . . . (409) 839-2538
E-mail: john.ross@usdoj.gov
Assistant U.S. Attorney **Kate Rumsey** . . . . . (409) 839-2538
E-mail: kate.rumsey@usdoj.gov
Assistant U.S. Attorney **(Vacant)** . . . . . (409) 839-2538
Assistant U.S. Attorney **(Vacant)** . . . . . (409) 839-2538

Lufkin (TX) Office

Bank of America Building, 415 South First Street,
Suite 201, Lufkin, TX 75901
Tel: (936) 639-4003 Fax: (936) 639-4033

Assistant U.S. Attorney **Lauren Gaston** . . . . . (936) 639-4003
Assistant U.S. Attorney **(Vacant)** . . . . . (936) 639-4003

Plano (TX) Office

101 East Park Boulevard, Suite 500, Plano, TX 75074-6749
Tel: (972) 509-1201 Fax: (972) 509-1209

Attorney-in-Charge **Kevin McClendon** . . . . . (972) 509-1201
E-mail: kevin.mcclendon@usdoj.gov
Assistant U.S. Attorney **Tracey Batson** . . . . . (972) 509-1201
E-mail: tracey.batson@usdoj.gov
Assistant U.S. Attorney **Chris Eason** . . . . . (972) 509-1201
E-mail: chris.eason@usdoj.gov
Assistant U.S. Attorney **Ernest Gonzalez** . . . . . (972) 509-1201
E-mail: ernest.gonzalez@usdoj.gov
Assistant U.S. Attorney **Terri L. Hagan** . . . . . (972) 509-1201
E-mail: terri.hagan@usdoj.gov
Assistant U.S. Attorney **Camelia Lopez** . . . . . (972) 509-1201
E-mail: camelia.lopez@usdoj.gov
Assistant U.S. Attorney **Marisa Miller** . . . . . (972) 509-1201
E-mail: marisa.miller@usdoj.gov
Assistant U.S. Attorney **Heather Rattan** . . . . . (972) 509-1201
E-mail: heather.rattan@usdoj.gov
Assistant U.S. Attorney **Milton Andrew Stover** . . . . . (972) 509-1201
E-mail: andrew.stover@usdoj.gov
Assistant U.S. Attorney **Bradley Visosky** . . . . . (972) 509-1201
E-mail: bradley.visosky@usdoj.gov
Education: Texas 2001 JD
Assistant U.S. Attorney **James Andrew Williams** . . . . . (972) 509-1201
E-mail: james.williams@usdoj.gov
Assistant U.S. Attorney **(Vacant)** . . . . . (972) 509-1201
Assistant U.S. Attorney **(Vacant)** . . . . . (972) 509-1201
Assistant U.S. Attorney **(Vacant)** . . . . . (972) 509-1201
Systems Manager **Frank Peters** . . . . . (972) 509-1201
E-mail: frank.peters@usdoj.gov

Sherman (TX) Office
1800 Teague Drive, Suite 500, Sherman, TX 75090
Tel: (903) 868-9454 Fax: (903) 892-2792

Attorney in Charge **Maureen Clancey Smith** .... (903) 868-9454
E-mail: maureen.smith@usdoj.gov
Assistant U.S. Attorney **William "Will" Tatum** .... (409) 839-2538
E-mail: william.tatum@usdoj.gov
Assistant U.S. Attorney **(Vacant)** .... (903) 868-9454
Assistant U.S. Attorney **(Vacant)** .... (903) 868-9454
Assistant U.S. Attorney **(Vacant)** .... (903) 868-9454

Texarkana (TX) Office
U.S. Courthouse, 500 State Line Avenue North,
Room 402, Texarkana, TX 75501
Tel: (903) 794-9481 Fax: (903) 792-5164

Assistant U.S. Attorney **Ryan Locker** .... (903) 794-9481
E-mail: ryan.locker@usdoj.gov

Tyler (TX) Office
110 North College, Suite 700, Tyler, TX 75702
Tel: (903) 590-1400 Fax: (903) 590-1436

Victim-Witness Specialist **(Vacant)** .... (903) 590-1400
Systems Manager **(Vacant)** .... (903) 590-1400

Civil Division
Civil Division Chief and Assistant U.S. Attorney
Randi D. Russell .... (903) 590-1400
E-mail: randi.russell@usdoj.gov
Assistant U.S. Attorney **James Gillingham** .... (903) 590-1400
E-mail: james.gillingham@usdoj.gov
Assistant U.S. Attorney **Robert Wells** .... (903) 590-1400
E-mail: robert.wells@usdoj.gov
Assistant U.S. Attorney **Ruth H. Yeager** .... (903) 590-1400
E-mail: ruth.yeager@usdoj.gov

Criminal Division
Criminal Division Chief **Alan R. Jackson** .... (903) 590-1400
E-mail: alan.jackson@usdoj.gov
Attorney in Charge **(Vacant)** .... (903) 590-1400
Assistant U.S. Attorney Appellate Chief
Traci L. Kenner .... (903) 590-1400
E-mail: traci.kenner@usdoj.gov
Assistant U.S. Attorney **Frank Coan** .... (903) 590-1400
E-mail: frank.coan@usdoj.gov
Assistant U.S. Attorney **Mary Ann Cozby** .... (903) 590-1400
E-mail: mary.ann.cozby@usdoj.gov
Assistant U.S. Attorney **Tom Gibson** .... (903) 590-1400
E-mail: tom.gibson@usdoj.gov
Assistant U.S. Attorney **Allen H. Hurst** .... (903) 590-1400
E-mail: allen.hurst@usdoj.gov
Assistant U.S. Attorney **Nathaniel Kummerfeld** .... (903) 590-1400
E-mail: nathaniel.kummerfeld@usdoj.gov
Assistant U.S. Attorney **Jim Noble** .... (903) 590-1400
E-mail: james.noble@usdoj.gov
Assistant U.S. Attorney **(Vacant)** .... (903) 590-1400
Special Assistant U.S. Attorney **Kenneth McGurk** .... (903) 590-1400
E-mail: kenneth.mcgurk@usdoj.gov

Texas - Northern District
Earle Cabell Federal Building, 1100 Commerce Street,
3rd Floor, Dallas, TX 75242-1699
Tel: (214) 659-8600 Fax: (214) 659-8806
Internet: https://www.justice.gov/usao-ndtx

★ U.S. Attorney **Erin Nealy Cox** .... (214) 659-8600
E-mail: erin.nealycox@usdoj.gov
Education: Texas BBA; Southern Methodist JD
Secretary to the U.S. Attorney **(Vacant)** .... (214) 659-8600
First Assistant U.S. Attorney **Tanya K. Pierce** .... (214) 659-8600
E-mail: tanya.k.pierce@usdoj.gov
Education: North Texas 1980 BA; Texas Tech 1984 JD
Executive Assistant U.S. Attorney **Jennifer Tourje** .... (214) 659-8600
E-mail: jennifer.tourje@usdoj.gov
Administrative Officer **Brian Barr** .... (214) 659-8600
E-mail: brian.barr@usdoj.gov

Texas - Northern District *(continued)*
Paralegal **Lisa Slimak** .... (214) 659-8600
Public Affairs Officer **(Vacant)** .... (214) 659-8600
Law Enforcement Coordinator **Dow Croyle** .... (214) 659-8600
E-mail: dow.croyle@usdoj.gov
Civil Division Chief (Acting) **Scott Hogan** .... (214) 659-8600
E-mail: scott.hogan@usdoj.gov
Civil Division Deputy Chief **Scott Hogan** .... (214) 659-8600
E-mail: scott.hogan@usdoj.gov
Criminal Chief **Steve P. Fahey** .... (214) 659-8600
E-mail: steve.p.fahey@usdoj.gov
Criminal Deputy Chief **Rick Calvert** .... (214) 659-8600
E-mail: rick.calvert@usdoj.gov
Criminal Deputy Chief **Melissa Childs** .... (214) 659-8600
E-mail: melissa.childs@usdoj.gov
Criminal Deputy Chief **Katherine Miller** .... (214) 659-8600
E-mail: katherine.miller@usdoj.gov
Criminal Deputy Chief **Lisa Miller** .... (214) 659-8600
E-mail: lisa.miller@usdoj.gov
Criminal Deputy Chief **(Vacant)** .... (214) 659-8600
Organized Crime Drug Enforcement Task Force Lead
Assistant U.S. Attorney **Suzanna Etessam** .... (214) 659-8600
E-mail: suzanna.etessam@usdoj.gov

Abilene (TX) Office
341 Pine Street, Suite 2101, Abilene, TX 79601
Tel: (325) 672-8160 Fax: (325) 673-3139

Criminal Deputy Chief **Jeff Haag** .... (325) 672-8160
E-mail: jeff.haag@usdoj.gov

Amarillo (TX) Office
Amarillo National Plaza Two, 500 South Taylor Street,
Suite 300, Amarillo, TX 79101-2442
Tel: (806) 324-2356 Fax: (806) 324-2399

Criminal Division Deputy Chief **Jeff Haag** .... (806) 472-7351
E-mail: jeff.haag@usdoj.gov

Fort Worth (TX) Office
Burnett Plaza, 801 Cherry Street, Unit #4,
Suite 1700, Fort Worth, TX 76102-6882
Tel: (817) 252-5200 Fax: (817) 252-5455

Civil Division Deputy Chief **Tami Parker** .... (817) 252-5200
E-mail: tami.parker@usdoj.gov
Criminal Deputy Chief **Alex Lewis** .... (817) 252-5232
E-mail: alex.lewis@usdoj.gov

Lubbock (TX) Office
U.S. Federal Building, 1205 Texas Avenue,
Suite 700, Lubbock, TX 79401-4002
Tel: (806) 472-7351 Fax: (806) 472-7394

Criminal Division Deputy Chief **Jeff Haag** .... (806) 472-7351
E-mail: jeff.haag@usdoj.gov

Texas - Southern District
1000 Louisiana Street, Suite 2300, Houston, TX 77002
P.O. Box 61129, Houston, TX 77208-1129
Tel: (713) 567-9000 Fax: (713) 718-3300 E-mail: usatty.txs@usdoj.gov
Internet: https://www.justice.gov/usao-sdtx

★ U.S. Attorney-Designate **Ryan K. Patrick** .... (713) 567-9300
E-mail: ryan.patrick@usdoj.gov
Education: Baylor 2001 BBA; South Texas 2006 JD
Secretary **Maria Lerma** .... (713) 567-9310
E-mail: maria.lerma@usdoj.gov
First Assistant U.S. Attorney **Abe Martinez** .... (713) 567-9000
E-mail: abe.martinez@usdoj.gov
Executive Assistant U.S. Attorney - Litigation Support
Vernon Lewis .... (713) 567-9000
E-mail: vernon.lewis@usdoj.gov
Administrative Officer **Rodney Mattix** .... (713) 567-9317
E-mail: rodney.mattix@usdoj.gov Fax: (713) 718-3306
Law Enforcement Committee Coordinator **(Vacant)** ...... (713) 567-9336
Victim-Witness Coordinator **Kesha Miller** .... (713) 567-9335
E-mail: kesha.miller@usdoj.gov

(continued on next page)

★ Presidential Appointment Requiring Senate Confirmation ☆ Presidential Appointment □ Schedule C Appointment ◇ Career Senior Foreign Service Appointment
● Career Senior Executive Service (SES) Appointment ○ Non-Career Senior Executive Service (SES) Appointment ■ Postal Career Executive Service

DEPARTMENTS

Texas - Southern District *(continued)*

Public Affairs Specialist **Angela C. Dodge** . . . . (713) 567-9388
E-mail: angela.dodge@usdoj.gov
Librarian **(Vacant)** . . . . (713) 567-9337

Appellate Division
1000 Louisiana Street, Houston, TX 77002
Fax: (713) 718-3302
Chief **(Vacant)** . . . . (713) 567-9000

Asset Forfeiture Division
1000 Louisiana Street, Houston, TX 77002
Fax: (713) 718-3304
Chief **Susan "Sue" Kempner** . . . . (713) 567-9565

Civil Division
1000 Louisiana Street, Houston, TX 77002
Fax: (713) 718-3309
Chief **Keith Wyatt** . . . . (713) 567-9713
E-mail: keith.wyatt@usdoj.gov

Criminal Division
1000 Louisiana Street, Houston, TX 77002
Fax: (713) 718-3361
Division Chief **Michael Wright** . . . . (713) 567-9584
E-mail: michael.wright@usdoj.gov

Brownsville (TX) Office
600 East Harrison, Suite 201, Brownsville, TX 78520-5106
Tel: (956) 548-2554 Fax: (956) 548-2549
Assistant U.S. Attorney-in-Charge
Richard "Rick" Lara . . . . (956) 983-6001
E-mail: rick.lara@usdoj.gov

Corpus Christi (TX) Office
Wilson Plaza, 800 North Shoreline Boulevard,
Suite 500, Corpus Christi, TX 78401
Tel: (361) 888-3111 Fax: (361) 888-3200
Assistant U.S. Attorney-in-Charge **Julie Hampton** . . . . (361) 903-7921
E-mail: julie.hampton@usdoj.gov
Education: North Carolina 1999 BA; Campbell 2002 JD

Laredo (TX) Office
1100 Matamoros Street, Suite 200, Laredo, TX 78040-4912
P.O. Box 1179, Laredo, TX 78042-1179
Tel: (956) 723-5523 Fax: (956) 726-2266
Assistant U.S. Attorney-in-Charge
Jose Angel Moreno . . . . (956) 721-4958
E-mail: jose.moreno@usdoj.gov

McAllen (TX) Office
Bentsen Tower, 1701 West Highway 83,
Suite 600, McAllen, TX 78501-5160
Tel: (956) 630-3173 Fax: (956) 618-8016
Assistant U.S. Attorney-in-Charge **James Sturgis** . . . . (956) 992-9359
E-mail: james.sturgis@usdoj.gov

Victoria (TX) Office
312 South Main, 3rd Floor, Victoria, TX 77901
P.O. Box 2685, Victoria, TX 77902-2685
Tel: (361) 576-9988 Fax: (361) 579-6820
Note: Currently being served by the Corpus Christi Office.
Assistant U.S. Attorney-in-Charge **Julie Hampton** . . . . (361) 576-9988
E-mail: julie.hampton@usdoj.gov
Education: North Carolina 1999 BA; Campbell 2002 JD

Texas - Western District
601 NW Loop 410, Suite 600, San Antonio, TX 78216
Tel: (210) 384-7100 Fax: (210) 384-7106
Internet: https://www.justice.gov/usao-wdtx

★ U.S. Attorney **John F. Bash** . . . . (210) 384-7400
E-mail: john.bash@usdoj.gov
Education: Harvard 2003 AB, 2006 JD
Secretary to the U.S. Attorney **Addie Cote** . . . . (512) 916-5858
E-mail: addie.cote@usdoj.gov Fax: (512) 916-5855
Counselor to the U.S. Attorney **Mickey Tapken** . . . . (210) 384-7100
First Assistant U.S. Attorney **Richard L. Durbin, Jr.** . . . . . (210) 384-7400
E-mail: richard.durbin@usdoj.gov
Secretary to the First Assistant U.S. Attorney
Addie Cote . . . . (210) 384-7400
E-mail: addie.cote@usdoj.gov Fax: (210) 384-7460
Executive Assistant U.S. Attorney **Sharon Pierce** . . . . (210) 384-7100
Law Enforcement Coordinating Committee **(Vacant)** . . . . . (210) 384-7100
Victim-Witness Coordinator (Austin) **Kathi West** . . . . (512) 916-5858
816 Congress Avenue, Austin, TX 78701
E-mail: kathi.west@usdoj.gov
Victim-Witness Coordinator (El Paso) **Thelma Luna** . . . . . (915) 534-6884
Federal Building, 700 East San Antonio,
Suite 200, El Paso, TX 79901
E-mail: thelma.luna@usdoj.gov
Victim-Witness Coordinator (San Antonio)
Danielle Deisch . . . . (210) 384-7100
E-mail: danielle.deisch@usdoj.gov
Administrative Officer **Dianne Dziuk** . . . . (210) 384-7200
E-mail: dianne.dziuk@usdoj.gov
Budget Officer **Ed Cimmino** . . . . (210) 384-7100
E-mail: ed.cimmino@usdoj.gov
Deputy Administrative Officer **Steven Garza** . . . . (210) 384-7200
E-mail: steven.garza@usdoj.gov
Human Resources Officer **Linda A. Dickson** . . . . (210) 384-7200
E-mail: linda.dickson@usdoj.gov
Public Affairs Officer **Daryl Fields** . . . . (210) 384-7100
E-mail: daryl.fields@usdoj.gov
LIONS Systems Manager **Robin Sandin** . . . . (210) 384-7200
E-mail: robin.sandin@usdoj.gov
Systems Manager **Robert Mercer** . . . . (210) 384-7200
E-mail: robert.mercer@usdoj.gov
Litigation Support Specialist **Lora Makowski** . . . . (210) 384-7100
E-mail: lora.makowski@usdoj.gov

Civil Division
Chief **John Paniszczyn** . . . . (210) 384-7300
E-mail: john.paniszczyn@usdoj.gov
Deputy Chief **Joe Rodriguez** . . . . (210) 384-7300
E-mail: joe.rodriguez@usdoj.gov
Affirmative Civil Enforcement Chief **John LoCurto** . . . . . (210) 384-7300
E-mail: john.locurto@usdoj.gov
Assets Forfeiture Fund and Field Offices Chief
(Vacant) . . . . (210) 384-7300
Financial Litigation Unit Chief **Kristy Callahan** . . . . (210) 384-7250
E-mail: kristy.callahan@usdoj.gov
Assistant U.S. Attorney **Gary Anderson** . . . . (210) 384-7300
E-mail: gary.anderson@usdoj.gov
Assistant U.S. Attorney **Clayton Diedrichs** . . . . (210) 384-7300
E-mail: clayton.diedrichs@usdoj.gov
Assistant U.S. Attorney **James Dingivan** . . . . (210) 384-7300
E-mail: james.dingivan@usdoj.gov
Education: Wake Forest 2005 BA; Emory 2008 JD
Assistant U.S. Attorney **James F. "Jim" Gilligan, Jr.** . . . . (210) 384-7300
E-mail: jim.gilligan@usdoj.gov
Assistant U.S. Attorney **Susan Strawn** . . . . (210) 384-7300
E-mail: susan.strawn@usdoj.gov

Criminal Division
Chief **Margaret F. Leachman** . . . . (210) 384-7100
E-mail: margaret.leachman@usdoj.gov
Chief (San Antonio) **Erica Giese** . . . . (210) 384-7131
E-mail: erica.giese@usdoj.gov
Appellate Section Chief **Joe Gay** . . . . (210) 384-7090
E-mail: joseph.gay@usdoj.gov

★ Presidential Appointment Requiring Senate Confirmation ☆ Presidential Appointment ☐ Schedule C Appointment ◇ Career Senior Foreign Service Appointment
● Career Senior Executive Service (SES) Appointment ○ Non-Career Senior Executive Service (SES) Appointment ■ Postal Career Executive Service

Criminal Division *(continued)*

Asset Forfeiture Section Chief **Diana Cruz-Zapata** ...... (210) 384-7040
E-mail: diana.cruz-zapata@usdoj.gov
Major Crimes Section Chief **Jose Contreras** .... (210) 384-7150
E-mail: jose.contreras@usdoj.gov
OCDETF Section Chief **Russell Leachman** .... (210) 384-7100
E-mail: russell.leachman@usdoj.gov
White Collar Crime Chief **Mark Roomberg** .... (210) 384-7179
E-mail: mark.roomberg@usdoj.gov
Senior Litigation Counsel **(Vacant)** .... (210) 384-7400
Special Assistant U.S. Attorney **(Vacant)** .... (210) 384-7150
Assistant U.S. Attorney **James K. "Jim" Blankinship** ... (210) 384-7100
E-mail: jim.blankinship@usdoj.gov
Assistant U.S. Attorney **Priscilla Garcia** .... (210) 384-7025
E-mail: priscilla.garcia@usdoj.gov
Assistant U.S. Attorney **Mike Hardy** .... (210) 384-7150
E-mail: mike.hardy@usdoj.gov
Assistant U.S. Attorney **Bill Harris** .... (210) 384-7150
E-mail: bill.harris@usdoj.gov
Assistant U.S. Attorney **Charles Jenkins** .... (210) 384-7100
E-mail: charles.jenkins@usdoj.gov
Assistant U.S. Attorney **Diane Kirstein** .... (210) 384-7150
E-mail: diane.kirstein@usdoj.gov
Assistant U.S. Attorney **Matthew Lathrop** .... (210) 384-7150
E-mail: matthew.lathrop@usdoj.gov
Assistant U.S. Attorney **Thomas P. "Tom" Moore** ...... (210) 384-7150
E-mail: tom.moore@usdoj.gov
Assistant U.S. Attorney **Karen Norris** .... (210) 384-7025
E-mail: karen.norris@usdoj.gov
Assistant U.S. Attorney **Walter L. "Bud" Paulissen** ..... (210) 384-7150
E-mail: bud.paulissen@usdoj.gov
Assistant U.S. Attorney **Christina Playton** .... (210) 384-7150
E-mail: christina.playton@usdoj.gov
Assistant U.S. Attorney **Sam Ponder** .... (210) 384-7025
E-mail: sam.ponder@usdoj.gov
Assistant U.S. Attorney **Angela S. "Angie" Raba** .... (210) 384-7090
E-mail: angie.raba@usdoj.gov
Assistant U.S. Attorney **Bettina Richardson** .... (210) 384-7150
E-mail: bettina.richardson@usdoj.gov
Assistant U.S. Attorney **David Shearer** .... (210) 384-7150
E-mail: david.shearer@usdoj.gov
Assistant U.S. Attorney **Charlie Strauss** .... (210) 384-7025
E-mail: charlie.strauss@usdoj.gov
Assistant U.S. Attorney **Gregory J. Surovic** .... (210) 384-7020
E-mail: greg.surovic@usdoj.gov
Assistant U.S. Attorney **Tracy Thompson** .... (210) 384-7150
E-mail: tracy.thompson@usdoj.gov
Assistant U.S. Attorney **Sarah Wannarka** .... (210) 384-7150
E-mail: sarah.wannarka@usdoj.gov
Special Assistant U.S. Attorney **(Vacant)** .... (210) 384-7150

Alpine - Pecos (TX) Office

2500 North Highway 118, Alpine, TX 79830
Tel: (432) 837-7332 Fax: (432) 837-7485

Chief **James J. "Jay" Miller, Jr.** .... (432) 837-7332
E-mail: jay.miller2@usdoj.gov
Criminal Division Assistant U.S. Attorney
Sandra L. "Sandy" Stewart .... (432) 837-7332
E-mail: sandy.stewart@usdoj.gov
Assistant U.S. Attorney **Layton Duer** .... (432) 837-7332
E-mail: layton.duer@usdoj.gov
Assistant U.S. Attorney **Monty Kimball** .... (432) 837-7332
E-mail: monty.kimball@usdoj.gov

Austin (TX) Office

816 Congress Avenue, Suite 1000, Austin, TX 78701
Tel: (512) 916-5858 Fax: (512) 916-5854

Chief **Ashley Hoff** .... (512) 916-5858
E-mail: ashley.hoff@usdoj.gov
Deputy Chief **Michelle Fernald** .... (512) 916-5858
E-mail: michelle.fernald@usdoj.gov
Victim-Witness Coordinator **Kathi West** .... (512) 916-5858
E-mail: kathi.west@usdoj.gov

Civil Division
Assistant U.S. Attorney **Steven Bass** .... (512) 916-5858
E-mail: steven.bass@usdoj.gov
Assistant U.S. Attorney **(Vacant)** .... (512) 916-5858
Assistant U.S. Attorney **(Vacant)** .... (512) 916-5858

Criminal Division
Assistant U.S. Attorney **Alan M. Buie** .... (512) 916-5858
E-mail: alan.buie@usdoj.gov
Assistant U.S. Attorney **Matthew Devlin** .... (512) 916-5858
E-mail: matt.devlin@usdoj.gov
Assistant U.S. Attorney **Matthew Harding** .... (512) 916-5858
E-mail: matt.harding@usdoj.gov
Education: Texas 2010 JD
Assistant U.S. Attorney **(Vacant)** .... (512) 916-5858
Assistant U.S. Attorney **(Vacant)** .... (512) 916-5858

Del Rio (TX) Office

U.S. Courthouse, 111 East Broadway, Room 300, Del Rio, TX 78840
Tel: (830) 703-2025 Fax: (830) 703-3741

Chief **Patrick Burke** .... (830) 703-2025
E-mail: patrick.burke@usdoj.gov
Deputy Chief **Meghan McCalla** .... (830) 703-2025
E-mail: meghan.mccalla@usdoj.gov
Assistant U.S. Attorney **Daniel Castillo** .... (830) 703-2025
E-mail: daniel.castillo@usdoj.gov
Assistant U.S. Attorney **Elizabeth Cunningham** .... (830) 703-2025
E-mail: elizabeth.cunningham@usdoj.gov
Assistant U.S. Attorney **Matthew Devlin** .... (830) 703-2025
E-mail: matt.devlin@usdoj.gov
Assistant U.S. Attorney **Michelle Fernald** .... (830) 703-2025
E-mail: michelle.fernald@usdoj.gov
Assistant U.S. Attorney **Douglas Gardner** .... (830) 703-2025
E-mail: douglas.gardner@usdoj.gov
Assistant U.S. Attorney **Dan Guess** .... (830) 703-2025
E-mail: dan.guess@usdoj.gov
Assistant U.S. Attorney **Mark Marshall** .... (830) 703-2025
E-mail: mark.marshall@usdoj.gov
Assistant U.S. Attorney **Sharon Pierce** .... (830) 703-2025
E-mail: sharon.pierce@usdoj.gov
Assistant U.S. Attorney **Gregg N. Sofer** .... (830) 703-2025
E-mail: gregg.sofer@usdoj.gov
Assistant U.S. Attorney **Grant Sparks** .... (830) 703-2025
E-mail: grant.sparks@usdoj.gov
Assistant U.S. Attorney **Mark Stelmach** .... (830) 703-2025
E-mail: mark.stelmach@usdoj.gov
Assistant U.S. Attorney **(Vacant)** .... (830) 703-2025
Assistant U.S. Attorney **(Vacant)** .... (830) 703-2025

El Paso (TX) Office

Federal Building, 700 East San Antonio,
Suite 200, El Paso, TX 79901
Tel: (915) 534-6884 Fax: (915) 534-6024

Chief **Jose Luis Gonzalez** .... (915) 534-6884
E-mail: jose.gonzalez@usdoj.gov
Senior Litigation Counsel **Debra Kanof** .... (915) 534-6884
E-mail: debra.kanof@usdoj.gov
Complex Fraud and Public Corruption Chief
Donna Miller .... (915) 534-6884
E-mail: donna.miller@usdoj.gov
General Crimes Chief **Laura Franco-Gregory** .... (915) 534-6884
E-mail: laura.gregory@usdoj.gov
General Crimes Deputy Chief **Steven R. Spitzer** .... (915) 534-6884
E-mail: steven.r.spitzer@usdoj.gov
OCDETF Chief Assistant U.S. Attorney **(Vacant)** .... (915) 534-6884
OCDETF Deputy Chief Assistant U.S. Attorney
(Vacant) .... (915) 534-6884

Asset Forfeiture Division
Assistant U.S. Attorney **Anna Arreola** .... (915) 534-6884
E-mail: anna.arreola@usdoj.gov
Education: Stanford 2002 JD

DEPARTMENTS

★ Presidential Appointment Requiring Senate Confirmation ☆ Presidential Appointment □ Schedule C Appointment ◇ Career Senior Foreign Service Appointment
● Career Senior Executive Service (SES) Appointment ○ Non-Career Senior Executive Service (SES) Appointment ■ Postal Career Executive Service

DEPARTMENTS

Civil Division

Assistant U.S. Attorney **Eduardo "Eddie" Castillo** (915) 534-6884
E-mail: eddie.castillo@usdoj.gov
Assistant U.S. Attorney **Magdalena G. "Maggie" Jara** (915) 534-6884
E-mail: magdalena.jara@usdoj.gov
Assistant U.S. Attorney **Angelica Saenz** (915) 534-6884
E-mail: angelica.saenz@usdoj.gov

Criminal Division

Assistant U.S. Attorney **Jose Luis Acosta** (915) 534-6884
E-mail: jose.l.acosta@usdoj.gov
Assistant U.S. Attorney **Patricia Acosta** (915) 534-6884
E-mail: patricia.acosta@usdoj.gov
Assistant U.S. Attorney **Patricia Aguayo** (915) 534-6884
E-mail: patricia.aguayo@usdoj.gov
Assistant U.S. Attorney **Joseph E. Blackwell** (915) 534-6884
E-mail: joseph.blackwell@usdoj.gov
Assistant U.S. Attorney **Mara Blatt** (915) 534-6884
E-mail: mara.blatt@usdoj.gov
Assistant U.S. Attorney **Juanita Fielden** (915) 534-6884
E-mail: juanita.fielden@usdoj.gov
Assistant U.S. Attorney **Stephen G. "Steve" Garcia** (915) 534-6884
E-mail: stephen.garcia@usdoj.gov
Assistant U.S. Attorney **Ian Hanna** (915) 534-6884
E-mail: ian.hanna@usdoj.gov
Assistant U.S. Attorney **Carlos Hermosillo** (915) 534-6884
E-mail: carlos.hermosillo@usdoj.gov
Assistant U.S. Attorney **John Johnston** (915) 534-6884
E-mail: john.johnston@usdoj.gov
Assistant U.S. Attorney **Gregory E. McDonald** (915) 534-6884
E-mail: gregory.mcdonald@usdoj.gov
Assistant U.S. Attorney **Daphne Newaz** (915) 534-6884
E-mail: daphne.newaz@usdoj.gov
Assistant U.S. Attorney **Rifian Newaz** (915) 534-6884
E-mail: rifian.newaz@usdoj.gov
Assistant U.S. Attorney **Andres Ortega** (915) 534-6884
E-mail: andres.ortega@usdoj.gov
Assistant U.S. Attorney **Stanley M. Serwatka, Jr.** (915) 534-6884
E-mail: stanley.serwatka@usdoj.gov
Assistant U.S. Attorney **James Christopher "Chris" Skillern** (915) 534-6884
E-mail: chris.skillern@usdoj.gov
Assistant U.S. Attorney **Kristal Wade** (915) 534-6884
E-mail: kristal.wade@usdoj.gov
Assistant U.S. Attorney **Michael Waits** (915) 534-6884
E-mail: michael.waits@usdoj.gov
Assistant U.S. Attorney **Richard Watts** (915) 534-6884
E-mail: richard.watts@usdoj.gov
Assistant U.S. Attorney **Michael Whyte** (915) 534-6884
E-mail: michael.whyte@usdoj.gov

Midland (TX) Office

400 West Illinois Street, Suite 1200, Midland, TX 79702
Tel: (432) 686-4110 Fax: (432) 686-4131

Chief **William F. "Bill" Lewis** (432) 686-4110
E-mail: william.lewis@usdoj.gov
Assistant U.S. Attorney **Glenn Harwood** (432) 686-4110
E-mail: glenn.harwood@usdoj.gov
Assistant U.S. Attorney **Latawn Warsaw** (432) 686-4110
E-mail: latawn.warsaw@usdoj.gov
Assistant U.S. Attorney **Brandi Young** (432) 686-4110
E-mail: brandi.young@usdoj.gov

Waco (TX) Office

800 Franklin Avenue, Suite 280, Waco, TX 76701
Tel: (254) 750-1580 Fax: (254) 750-1599

Chief **Mark Frazier** (254) 750-1580
E-mail: mark.frazier@usdoj.gov
Assistant U.S. Attorney **Gregory S. Gloff** (254) 750-1580
E-mail: greg.gloff@usdoj.gov
Assistant U.S. Attorney **Mary Kucera** (254) 750-1580
E-mail: mary.kucera@usdoj.gov
Assistant U.S. Attorney **Stephanie Smith-Burris** (254) 750-1580
E-mail: stephanie.smith-burris@usdoj.gov

Waco (TX) Office *(continued)*

Assistant U.S. Attorney **(Vacant)** (254) 750-1580

Utah District

111 South Main Street, Suite 1800, Salt Lake City, UT 84111-2176
Tel: (801) 524-5682 Fax: (801) 524-6924
Internet: https://www.justice.gov/usao-ut

★ U.S. Attorney **John W. Huber** (801) 325-3224
E-mail: john.huber@usdoj.gov
First Assistant U.S. Attorney **(Vacant)** (801) 325-3322
Executive Assistant U.S. Attorney **Andrew Choate** (801) 325-1423
E-mail: andrew.choate@usdoj.gov
Administrative Officer **Linda J. McFarlane** (801) 325-3208
E-mail: linda.mcfarlane@usdoj.gov
Budget Officer **Kelli L. Divino** (801) 325-3207
E-mail: kelli.divino@usdoj.gov
Personnel Officer **Danna M. Reichert** (801) 325-3242
E-mail: danna.reichert@usdoj.gov
Systems Administrator **Barbara Atencio** (801) 325-3330
E-mail: barbara.atencio@usdoj.gov
Law Enforcement Committee Coordinator/Press Officer **Melodie Rydalch** (801) 325-3206
Victim-Witness Coordinator **Candelaria "Candy" Bennett** (801) 325-3256
E-mail: candelaria.bennett@usdoj.gov
Librarian **Allison Turner** (801) 325-3304
E-mail: allison.turner@usdoj.gov
Contracting Officer **Kristy Begay** (801) 325-1416
E-mail: kristy.begay@usdoj.gov

Civil Division

Chief **Jared C. Bennett** (801) 325-3259
E-mail: jared.bennett@usdoj.gov
Education: Utah 2001 JD
Deputy Chief **Daniel D. Price** (801) 325-3234
E-mail: daniel.price@usdoj.gov
Assistant U.S. Attorney **Carra Cadman** (801) 325-3371
E-mail: carra.cadman@usdoj.gov
Assistant U.S. Attorney **John Mangum** (801) 325-3216
E-mail: john.mangum@usdoj.gov
Education: Chicago 1980 JD
Assistant U.S. Attorney **Allison J. Moon** (801) 325-3319
E-mail: allison.moon@usdoj.gov
Education: UC Santa Barbara 2005 BA; Boston U 2009 JD
Assistant U.S. Attorney **Sandra Steinvoort** (801) 325-3233
E-mail: sandra.steinvoort@usdoj.gov
Assistant U.S. Attorney **(Vacant)** (801) 325-3250
Assistant U.S. Attorney **(Vacant)** (801) 325-3236

Criminal Division

Chief **(Vacant)** (801) 325-3251
Deputy Chief **David F. Backman** (801) 325-3315
E-mail: david.backman@usdoj.gov
Civil Rights and Public Corruption Section Chief **Richard W. Daynes** (801) 325-3361
E-mail: richard.daynes@usdoj.gov
Narcotics Section Chief **Vernon Stejskal** (801) 325-1404
E-mail: vernon.stejskal@usdoj.gov
Violent Crime Section Chief **Karin Fojtik** (801) 325-3229
E-mail: karin.fojtik@usdoj.gov
Violent Crime Section Deputy Chief **Drew Yeates** (801) 325-3252
E-mail: drew.yeates@usdoj.gov
White Collar Chief **Robert A. "Rob" Lund** (801) 325-3314
E-mail: robert.lund@usdoj.gov
Senior Litigation Counsel **Trina A. Higgins** (801) 325-3356
E-mail: trina.higgins@usdoj.gov
Senior Litigation Counsel **(Vacant)** (801) 325-3267
Assistant U.S. Attorney **Amanda A. Berndt** (801) 325-3267
E-mail: amanda.berndt@usdoj.gov
Assistant U.S. Attorney **Cy Castle** (801) 325-3214
E-mail: cy.castle@usdoj.gov
Assistant U.S. Attorney **Aaron Clark** (801) 325-1405
E-mail: aaron.clark@usdoj.gov
Assistant U.S. Attorney **Carol Dain** (801) 325-3353
E-mail: carol.dain@usdoj.gov

★ Presidential Appointment Requiring Senate Confirmation ☆ Presidential Appointment ☐ Schedule C Appointment ◇ Career Senior Foreign Service Appointment
● Career Senior Executive Service (SES) Appointment ○ Non-Career Senior Executive Service (SES) Appointment ■ Postal Career Executive Service

DEPARTMENTS

Criminal Division *(continued)*

Assistant U.S. Attorney **Lake Dishman** . . . . (801) 325-1409
E-mail: lake.dishman@usdoj.gov
Assistant U.S. Attorney **Adam S. Elggren** . . . . (801) 325-3316
E-mail: adam.elggren@usdoj.gov
Assistant U.S. Attorney **Carlos A. Esqueda** . . . . (801) 325-3352
E-mail: carlos.esqueda@usdoj.gov
Assistant U.S. Attorney **Mark Y. Hirata** . . . . (801) 325-3239
E-mail: mark.hirata@usdoj.gov
Assistant U.S. Attorney **Michael P. Kennedy** . . . . (801) 325-3300
E-mail: michael.kennedy@usdoj.gov
Education: George Mason 1993 JD
Assistant U.S. Attorney **Paul Kohler** . . . . (435) 680-4421
Note: Operates out of a branch office.
E-mail: paul.kohler@usdoj.gov
Assistant U.S. Attorney **Lynda R. Krause** . . . . (801) 325-3354
E-mail: lynda.krause@usdoj.gov
Assistant U.S. Attorney **Andrea Martinez** . . . . (801) 325-1406
E-mail: andrea.martinez@usdoj.gov
Assistant U.S. Attorney **Victoria McFarland** . . . . (801) 325-3373
E-mail: victoria.mcfarland@usdoj.gov
Assistant U.S. Attorney **Stephen Nelson** . . . . (801) 325-3235
E-mail: stephen.nelson@usdoj.gov
Assistant U.S. Attorney **Bryan Reeves** . . . . (801) 325-3303
E-mail: bryan.reeves@usdoj.gov
Assistant U.S. Attorney **Elizabethanne C. Stevens** . . . . . . (801) 325-3257
E-mail: elizabethanne.stevens@usdoj.gov
Assistant U.S. Attorney **Jacob Strain** . . . . (801) 325-3285
E-mail: jacob.strain@usdoj.gov
Assistant U.S. Attorney **Jeannette F. Swent** . . . . (801) 325-3220
E-mail: jeannette.swent@usdoj.gov
Education: Yale 1982 MPhil, 1984 PhD; Stanford 1991 JD
Assistant U.S. Attorney **Michael Thorpe** . . . . (801) 325-1410
E-mail: michael.thorpe@usdoj.gov
Assistant U.S. Attorney **Veda M. Travis** . . . . (801) 325-3295
E-mail: veda.travis@usdoj.gov
Assistant U.S. Attorney **Mark K. Vincent** . . . . (801) 325-3249
E-mail: mark.vincent@usdoj.gov
Education: Pepperdine 1987 JD
Assistant U.S. Attorney **Felice J. Viti** . . . . (801) 325-3230
E-mail: felice.viti@usdoj.gov
Education: Fordham 1983 JD
Assistant U.S. Attorney **Stewart C. Walz** . . . . (801) 325-3238
E-mail: stewart.walz@usdoj.gov
Education: Vanderbilt 1976 JD
Assistant U.S. Attorney **Isaac Workman** . . . . (801) 325-3377
E-mail: isaac.workman@usdoj.gov
Assistant U.S. Attorney **Stewart Young** . . . . (801) 325-3213
E-mail: stewart.young@usdoj.gov
Assistant U.S. Attorney **(Vacant)** . . . . (801) 325-1439
Assistant U.S. Attorney **(Vacant)** . . . . (801) 325-3229
Assistant U.S. Attorney **(Vacant)** . . . . (801) 325-3256
Assistant U.S. Attorney **(Vacant)** . . . . (801) 325-1403

Vermont District

U.S. Federal Building, 11 Elmwood Avenue,
3rd Floor, Burlington, VT 05401
P.O. Box 570, Burlington, VT 05402
Tel: (802) 951-6725 Fax: (802) 951-6540
Internet: https://www.justice.gov/usao-vt

★ U.S. Attorney **Christina E. Nolan** . . . . (802) 951-6725
E-mail: christina.nolan@usdok.gov
Education: Vermont BA; Boston Col 2004 JD
Secretary to the U.S. Attorney **Laura Harvey** . . . . (802) 951-6725
E-mail: laura.harvey@usdoj.gov
First Assistant U.S. Attorney **Eugenia A.P. Cowles** . . . . . . (802) 951-6725
E-mail: eugenia.cowles@usdoj.gov
Administrative Officer **Lisa J. Graves** . . . . (802) 951-6725
E-mail: lisa.j.graves@usdoj.gov
Law Enforcement Coordinator **Kraig LaPorte** . . . . (802) 951-6725
E-mail: kraig.laporte@usdoj.gov
Victim/Witness Coordinator **Aimee Stearns** . . . . (802) 951-6725
E-mail: aimee.stearns@usdoj.gov

Vermont District *(continued)*

Systems Manager **Charlene Tallman** . . . . (802) 951-6725
E-mail: charlene.tallman@usdoj.gov
Records Coordinator **Charlene Tallman** . . . . (802) 951-6725
E-mail: charlene.tallman@usdoj.gov

Civil Division

11 Elmwood Avenue, Burlington, VT 05401
Tel: (802) 951-6725

Civil Chief **Nikolas Kerest** . . . . (802) 951-6725
E-mail: nikolas.kerest@usdoj.gov
Assistant U.S. Attorney **Owen Foster** . . . . (802) 951-6725
Assistant U.S. Attorney **Ben Weathers-Lowin** . . . . (802) 951-6725
E-mail: ben.weathers-lowin@usdoj.gov
Assistant U.S. Attorney **Melissa A. D. Ranaldo** . . . . (802) 951-6725
E-mail: melissa.ranaldo@usdoj.gov

Criminal Division

11 Elmwood Avenue, Burlington, VT 05401
Tel: (802) 951-6725

Chief **Paul Van de Graaf** . . . . (802) 951-6725
E-mail: paul.van.de.graaf@usdoj.gov
Assistant U.S. Attorney **Nate Burris** . . . . (802) 951-6725
E-mail: nate.burris@usdoj.gov
Assistant U.S. Attorney **John Boscia** . . . . (802) 951-6725
Assistant U.S. Attorney **William B. Darrow** . . . . (802) 951-6725
E-mail: bill.darrow@usdoj.gov
Assistant U.S. Attorney **Timothy C. Doherty** . . . . (802) 951-6725
E-mail: timothy.c.doherty@usdoj.gov
Education: Yale 2003 JD
Assistant U.S. Attorney **Kevin J. Doyle** . . . . (802) 951-6725
E-mail: kevin.doyle@usdoj.gov
Assistant U.S. Attorney **Michael P. Drescher** . . . . (802) 951-6725
E-mail: michael.drescher@usdoj.gov
Assistant U.S. Attorney **Wendy L. Fuller** . . . . (802) 951-6725
E-mail: wendy.fuller@usdoj.gov
Assistant U.S. Attorney **Barbara A. Masterson** . . . . (802) 951-6725
E-mail: barbara.masterson@usdoj.gov
Assistant U.S. Attorney **Jonathan Ophardt** . . . . (802) 951-6725
E-mail: jon.ophardt@usdoj.gov
Education: Duke 2010 JD
Assistant U.S. Attorney **Joseph R. Perella** . . . . (802) 951-6725
E-mail: joseph.perella@usdoj.gov
Assistant U.S. Attorney **Gregory Waples** . . . . (802) 951-6725
E-mail: gregory.waples@usdoj.gov
Education: Yale 1971 BA

Rutland (VT) Office

151 West Street, Room 304, Rutland, VT 05701
P.O. Box 10, Rutland, VT 05701
Tel: (802) 773-0231 Fax: (802) 773-0214

Assistant U.S. Attorney **(Vacant)** . . . . (802) 951-6725

Virgin Islands District

Ron DeLugo Federal Building and U.S. Courthouse, 5500 Veterans Drive,
Room 260, St. Thomas, VI 00802-6424
Tel: (340) 774-5757 Fax: (340) 776-3474
Internet: https://www.justice.gov/usao-vi

★ U.S. Attorney **Gretchen C. F. Shappert** . . . . (340) 773-3920
E-mail: gretchen.shappert@usdoj.gov
Education: Duke BA; Washington and Lee 1980 JD
Secretary to the U.S. Attorney **(Vacant)** . . . . (340) 773-3920
Administrative Officer **(Vacant)** . . . . (340) 774-5757
First Assistant U.S. Attorney **(Vacant)** . . . . (340) 774-5757
Special Litigation Counsel **Kim L. Chisholm** . . . . (340) 774-5757
E-mail: kim.chisholm@usdoj.gov
Budget Officer **(Vacant)** . . . . (340) 774-5757
Law Enforcement Coordinator Specialist
James Latham . . . . (340) 774-5757
E-mail: james.latham@usdoj.gov
Victim-Witness Specialist **Antoinette M. James** . . . . (340) 773-3920
E-mail: antoinette.james@usdoj.gov

(continued on next page)

★ Presidential Appointment Requiring Senate Confirmation ☆ Presidential Appointment ☐ Schedule C Appointment ◇ Career Senior Foreign Service Appointment
● Career Senior Executive Service (SES) Appointment ○ Non-Career Senior Executive Service (SES) Appointment ■ Postal Career Executive Service

DEPARTMENTS

Virgin Islands District *(continued)*

Assistant U.S. Attorney **Meredith Edwards** .... (340) 774-5757
E-mail: meredith.edwards@usdoj.gov
Assistant U.S. Attorney **Tasheika Hanson** .... (340) 774-5757
Assistant U.S. Attorney **Inez Zlasvoda** .... (340) 774-5757

Civil Division
Civil Chief (Acting) **Angela Tyson-Floyd** .... (340) 774-5757
E-mail: angela.floyd@usdoj.gov
Assistant U.S. Attorney **Angela Tyson-Floyd** .... (340) 774-5757
E-mail: angela.floyd@usdoj.gov
Assistant U.S. Attorney **Sansara Cannon** .... (340) 774-5757
E-mail: sansara.cannon@usdoj.gov
Assistant U.S. Attorney **(Vacant)** .... (340) 774-5757

Criminal Division
Chief **Christian Fisanick** .... (340) 774-5757
Organized Crime Drug Enforcement Task Force
Assistant U.S. Attorney **(Vacant)** .... (340) 774-5757
Assistant U.S. Attorney **Alphonso Andrews, Jr.** .... (340) 774-5757
E-mail: alphonso.andrews@usdoj.gov
Assistant U.S. Attorney **Kim L. Chisholm** .... (340) 774-5757
E-mail: kim.chisholm@usdoj.gov
Assistant U.S. Attorney **Everard Potter** .... (340) 774-5757
E-mail: everard.potter@usdoj.gov
Assistant U.S. Attorney **Delia Smith** .... (340) 774-5757
E-mail: delia.smith@usdoj.gov
Assistant U.S. Attorney **Emily Wasserman** .... (340) 774-5757
Assistant U.S. Attorney **David White** .... (340) 774-5757
E-mail: david.white@usdoj.gov
Assistant U.S. Attorney **Rhonda Williams-Henry** .... (340) 774-5757
E-mail: rhonda.williams-henry@usdoj.gov
Assistant U.S. Attorney **Sigrid Tejos-Protte** .... (340) 774-5757

Saint Croix (VI) Office
1108 King Street, Suite 201, Christiansted, VI 00820-4951
Tel: (340) 773-3920 Fax: (340) 773-1407

Senior Litigation Counsel **Kim L. Chisholm** .... (340) 773-3920
E-mail: kim.chisholm@usdoj.gov
Branch Administrative Officer **Ingrid Richardson** .... (340) 773-3920
E-mail: ingrid.richardson@usdoj.gov

Civil Division
Assistant U.S. Attorney **(Vacant)** .... (340) 773-3920
Assistant U.S. Attorney **(Vacant)** .... (340) 773-3920
Assistant U.S. Attorney **(Vacant)** .... (340) 773-3920

Criminal Division
Deputy Chief **Alphonso Andrews, Jr.** .... (340) 773-3920
E-mail: alphonso.andrews@usdoj.gov
Assistant U.S. Attorney **Rhonda Williams-Henry** .... (340) 773-3920
E-mail: rhonda.williams-henry@usdoj.gov

Virginia - Eastern District
2100 Jamieson Avenue, Alexandria, VA 22314-5794
Tel: (703) 299-3700 Fax: (703) 299-3983
Internet: https://www.justice.gov/usao-edva

★ U.S. Attorney **G. Zachary "Zach" Terwilliger** .... (703) 299-3700
E-mail: zachary.terwilliger@usdoj.gov
Secretary to the U.S. Attorney **Fay Brundage** .... (703) 299-3700
E-mail: fay.brundage@usdoj.gov
First Assistant U.S. Attorney **(Vacant)** .... (703) 299-3700
Administrative Officer **Arline Gause** .... (703) 299-3700
Public Information Officer **Joshua Stueve** .... (703) 842-4050
Note: On detail to the Office of Special Counsel.
E-mail: joshua.stueve@usdoj.gov
Systems Manager **Katy Law** .... (703) 299-3700
E-mail: katy.law@usdoj.gov
Victim-Witness Coordinator **(Vacant)** .... (703) 299-3700

Civil Division
Chief **Lauren A. Wetzler** .... (703) 299-3700
E-mail: lauren.wetzler@usdoj.gov
Education: Harvard 2000 BA; Yale 2004 JD

Civil Division *(continued)*
Deputy Chief **R. Joseph Sher** .... (703) 299-3700
Education: NYU BA, MA; Michigan State JD

Criminal Division
Chief **Robert W. "Bob" Wiechering** .... (804) 819-5400
Education: Ohio State JD
Deputy Chief and Assistant U.S. Attorney **(Vacant)** .... (804) 819-5400
Chief, Appellate Division **(Vacant)** .... (703) 299-3700
Chief, Financial Crime and Public Corruption **(Vacant)** ... (703) 299-3700
Chief, Major Crimes **Morris Parker** .... (703) 299-3700
E-mail: morris.parker@usdoj.gov
Chief, Major Frauds **(Vacant)** .... (703) 299-3700
Chief, Narcotics Unit **Morris Parker** .... (703) 299-3700
E-mail: morris.parker@usdoj.gov
Chief, National Security **Daniel "Danny" Grooms** .... (703) 299-3700
E-mail: daniel.grooms@usdoj.gov
Education: Harvard 2002 JD
Chief, Organized Crime and Drug Enforcement Task Force **(Vacant)** .... (757) 591-4000
Chief, Terrorism Unit **Daniel "Danny" Grooms** .... (703) 299-3700
E-mail: daniel.grooms@usdoj.gov
Education: Harvard 2002 JD

Newport News (VA) Office
Newport News (VA) Office, 721 Lakefront Commons, Suite 300, Newport News, VA 23606
Tel: (757) 591-4000 Fax: (757) 591-0866

Managing Assistant United States Attorney **Howard Zlotnick** .... (757) 591-4000
E-mail: howard.zlotnick@usdoj.gov

Norfolk (VA) Office
101 West Main Street, Suite 8000, Norfolk, VA 23510
Tel: (757) 441-6331 Fax: (757) 441-6689

Managing Assistant U.S. Attorney **(Vacant)** .... (757) 441-6331

Richmond (VA) Office
600 East Main Street, Suite 1800, Richmond, VA 23219
Tel: (804) 819-5400 Fax: (804) 771-2316

Managing Assistant U.S. Attorney **Stephen W. Miller** ... (804) 819-5400
E-mail: stephen.miller@usdoj.gov

Virginia - Western District
BB&T Building, 310 First Street, SW, Room 906, Roanoke, VA 24011
P.O. Box 1709, Roanoke, VA 24008-1709
Tel: (540) 857-2250 Fax: (540) 857-2614
Internet: https://www.justice.gov/usao-wdva

★ U.S. Attorney **Thomas T. Cullen** .... (540) 857-2250
E-mail: thomas.cullen2@usdoj.gov
Education: Furman 2000 BA; William & Mary 2004 JD
Secretary to the U.S. Attorney **Ashley Neese** .... (540) 857-2977
Fax: (540) 857-2179
First Assistant U.S. Attorney **Stephen "Steve" Pfleger** .... (540) 857-2250
E-mail: stephen.pfleger@usdoj.gov
Education: Princeton 1983; Cornell 1986 JD
Administrative Officer **Jason Austin** .... (540) 857-2929
E-mail: jason.austin@usdoj.gov
Community Outreach Coordinator **Erin Kulpa** .... (434) 293-4283
255 West Main Street, Charlottesville, VA 22901
E-mail: erin.kulpa@usdoj.gov
Law Enforcement Committee Coordinator **Isaac "Zac" Van Patten** .... (540) 857-2959
E-mail: isaac.vanpatten@usdoj.gov
Victim-Witness Coordinator **Al Smith** .... (540) 857-2957
E-mail: albert.smith@usdoj.gov
Webmaster **Deborah J. "Debbie" Wood** .... (540) 857-2760
E-mail: debbie.wood@usdoj.gov
Personnel Specialist **Jason Austin** .... (540) 857-2929
E-mail: jason.austin@usdoj.gov Fax: (540) 857-2179

★ Presidential Appointment Requiring Senate Confirmation ☆ Presidential Appointment ☐ Schedule C Appointment ◇ Career Senior Foreign Service Appointment
● Career Senior Executive Service (SES) Appointment ○ Non-Career Senior Executive Service (SES) Appointment ■ Postal Career Executive Service

Asset Forfeiture Unit
BB&T Building, 310 First Street, SW, Roanoke, VA 24011
Tel: (540) 857-2250

Assistant U.S. Attorney **(Vacant)** .... (540) 857-2250

Civil Division
BB&T Building, 310 First Street, SW, Roanoke, VA 24011
Tel: (540) 857-2250 Fax: (540) 857-2283

Chief **Anthony "Tony" Giorno** .... (540) 857-2254
E-mail: anthony.giorno@usdoj.gov

Assistant U.S. Attorney **Sara B. Winn** .... (540) 857-2984
E-mail: sara.winn@usdoj.gov
Education: Minnesota 1988 BS; Hamline 1993 JD

Assistant U.S. Attorney **(Vacant)** .... (540) 857-2761

Assistant U.S. Attorney **(Vacant)** .... (540) 857-2256

Criminal Division
BB&T Building, 310 First Street, SW, Roanoke, VA 24011
Tel: (540) 857-2250

Chief **Stephen "Steve" Pfleger** .... (540) 857-2250
E-mail: stephen.pfleger@usdoj.gov
Education: Princeton 1983; Cornell 1986 JD

Deputy Chief **Craig J. Jacobsen** .... (540) 857-2252
Education: UC Berkeley 1984 BA; Santa Clara U 1988 JD

Senior Litigation Counsel **Donald R. Wolthuis** .... (540) 857-2762
E-mail: donald.wolthuis@usdoj.gov
Education: Mary Washington Col 1977 BA; William & Mary 1980 JD

Assistant U.S. Attorney **R. Andrew Bassford** .... (540) 857-2799
E-mail: andrew.bassford@usdoj.gov
Education: Georgetown 1986 BSFS; Virginia 1998 JD

Assistant U.S. Attorney **Daniel "Dan" Bubar** .... (540) 857-2880
E-mail: daniel.bubar@usdoj.gov

Assistant U.S. Attorney **Charlene Day** .... (540) 278-1485
E-mail: charlene.day@usdoj.gov Fax: (540) 857-2179
Education: Virginia 1992 BA; Indiana 1997 JD

Assistant U.S. Attorney **C. Patrick Hogeboom III** .... (540) 857-2217
E-mail: pat.hogeboom@usdoj.gov Fax: (540) 857-2179
Education: New Mexico State 1971 BS; Gonzaga 1986 JD

Assistant U.S. Attorney **Ashley Neese** .... (540) 857-2938
Education: Emory & Henry 2004 BA; Ohio Northern 2007 JD

Assistant U.S. Attorney **Laura Rottenborn** .... (540) 857-2250
E-mail: laura.rottenborn@usdoj.gov

Assistant U.S. Attorney **Jennie L. M. Waering** .... (540) 857-2257
E-mail: jennie.waering@usdoj.gov
Education: Lynchburg 1976; Richmond 1981 JD

Abingdon (VA) Office
310 Cummings Street, Suite A, Abingdon, VA 24210
Tel: (276) 628-4161 Fax: (276) 628-7399

Managing Assistant U. S. Attorney
S. Randall "Randy" Ramseyer .... (276) 628-4161
E-mail: randy.ramseyer@usdoj.gov
Education: Wilmington Col (OH) 1986 BA; Vanderbilt 1990 JD

Assistant U.S. Attorney **Jennifer Bockhorst** .... (276) 628-4161
E-mail: jennifer.bockhorst@usdoj.gov
Education: Delaware 1993 BA; New Mexico 1996 MA; Stanford 2001 JD

Assistant U.S. Attorney **Zachary T. Lee** .... (276) 628-4161
E-mail: zachary.lee@usdoj.gov
Education: Washington and Lee 1998 BA; Wyoming 2001 JD

Charlottesville (VA) Office
255 West Main Street, Room 130, Charlottesville, VA 22902
Tel: (434) 293-4283 Fax: (434) 293-4910

Managing Assistant U.S. Attorney
Ronald "Ron" Huber .... (434) 293-4283
E-mail: ron.huber@usdoj.gov
Education: Michigan State 1984 BA; George Mason 1989 JD

Assistant U.S. Attorney **Stephen Curran** .... (434) 293-4283
E-mail: stephen.curran@usdoj.gov

Assistant U.S. Attorney **Nancy S. Healey** .... (434) 293-4283
E-mail: nancy.healey@usdoj.gov
Education: Northwestern BA; George Washington 1986 JD

Charlottesville (VA) Office *(continued)*

Assistant U.S. Attorney **Jean B. Hudson** .... (434) 293-4283
E-mail: jean.hudson@usdoj.gov
Education: North Carolina Greensboro 1978 BM; Washington and Lee 1985 JD

Assistant U.S. Attorney **Christopher Kavanaugh** .... (434) 293-4283
E-mail: christopher.kavanaugh@usdoj.gov

Assistant U.S. Attorney **Erin Kulpa** .... (434) 293-4283
E-mail: erin.kulpa@usdoj.gov

Harrisonburg (VA) Office
116 North Main Street, Room 130, Harrisonburg, VA 22802
Tel: (540) 432-6636 Fax: (540) 433-9296

Branch Manager **Jeb T. Terrien** .... (540) 432-6636
E-mail: jeb.terrien@usdoj.gov
Education: Virginia 1994 BA; Tulane 1997 JD

Assistant U.S. Attorney **Grayson Hoffman** .... (540) 432-6636
E-mail: grayson.hoffman@usdoj.gov

Assistant U.S. Attorney **Elizabeth Wright** .... (540) 432-6636
E-mail: elizabeth.wright@usdoj.gov

Washington - Eastern District
Federal Courthouse, 920 West Riverside Avenue, Room 340, Spokane, WA 99201
P.O. Box 1494, Spokane, WA 99210-1494
Tel: (509) 353-2767 Fax: (509) 353-2766

★ U.S. Attorney (Interim) **Joseph H. Harrington** .... (509) 353-2767
E-mail: joseph.harrington@usdoj.gov

First Assistant U.S. Attorney **(Vacant)** .... (509) 353-2767

Administrative Officer **Heidi J. Krummel** .... (509) 353-2767
E-mail: heidi.krummel@usdoj.gov

Intelligence Research Specialist **(Vacant)** .... (509) 353-2767

Law Enforcement Coordinator **(Vacant)** .... (509) 353-2767

Systems Manager **Doug Rowland** .... (509) 353-2767
E-mail: doug.rowland@usdoj.gov

Victim-Witness Coordinator **Amy L. Mayther** .... (509) 353-2767
E-mail: amy.mayther@usdoj.gov

Investigator **Kathy S. Fagyas** .... (509) 353-2767

Investigator **Jeanne Harkleroad** .... (509) 353-2767

Civil Division
920 West Riverside Avenue, Spokane, WA 99201
Fax: (509) 353-2766

Chief **Timothy M. Durkin** .... (509) 353-2767
E-mail: tim.durkin@usdoj.gov

Financial Litigation Unit Assistant U.S. Attorney
Esther Darnell .... (509) 353-2767
E-mail: esther.darnell@usdoj.gov

Assistant U.S. Attorney **Rudy J. Verschoor** .... (509) 353-2767
E-mail: rudy.j.verschoor@usdoj.gov

Assistant U.S. Attorney **Vanessa Waldres** .... (509) 353-2767

Assistant U.S. Attorney **Joseph "Joe" Derrig** .... (509) 353-2767
E-mail: joseph.derrig@usdoj.gov

Criminal Division

Chief **Russell E. Smoot** .... (509) 353-2767
E-mail: russell.e.smoot@usdoj.gov

Supervisory Assistant U.S. Attorney **(Vacant)** .... (509) 353-2767

Assistant U.S. Attorney **Caitlin Baunsgard** .... (509) 353-2767
E-mail: caitlin.baunsgard@usdoj.gov

Assistant U.S. Attorney **Matthew Duggan** .... (509) 353-2767

Assistant U.S. Attorney **James "Jim" Goeke** .... (509) 353-2767
E-mail: james.goeke@usdoj.gov

Assistant U.S. Attorney **Earl A. Hicks** .... (509) 353-2767
E-mail: earl.hicks@usdoj.gov

Assistant U.S. Attorney **George J.C. Jacobs** .... (509) 353-2767

Assistant U.S. Attorney **Jared C. Kimball** .... (509) 353-2767
E-mail: jared.c.kimball@usdoj.gov

Assistant U.S. Attorney **Stephanie J. Lister** .... (509) 353-2767
E-mail: stephanie.lister@usdoj.gov

Assistant U.S. Attorney **Timothy J. Ohms** .... (509) 353-2767
E-mail: timothy.ohms@usdoj.gov

Assistant U.S. Attorney **Tyler H.L. Tornabene** .... (509) 353-2767

(continued on next page)

★ Presidential Appointment Requiring Senate Confirmation ☆ Presidential Appointment ☐ Schedule C Appointment ◇ Career Senior Foreign Service Appointment
● Career Senior Executive Service (SES) Appointment ○ Non-Career Senior Executive Service (SES) Appointment ■ Postal Career Executive Service

Criminal Division *(continued)*

Assistant U.S. Attorney **Stephanie A. Van Marter** . . . . . . (509) 353-2767
E-mail: stephanie.vanmarter@usdoj.gov
Assistant U.S. Attorney **(Vacant)** . . . . . . (509) 353-2767
Assistant U.S. Attorney **(Vacant)** . . . . . . (509) 353-2767
Assistant U.S. Attorney **(Vacant)** . . . . . . (509) 353-2767

Yakima (WA) Office

402 East Yakima Avenue, Suite 210, Box 4065, Yakima, WA 98901-2760
Tel: (509) 454-4425 Fax: (509) 454-4435

Supervisory Assistant U.S. Attorney **(Vacant)** . . . . . . (509) 454-4425
Assistant U.S. Attorney **Ian Garriques** . . . . . . (509) 454-4425
E-mail: ian.garriques@usdoj.gov
Assistant U.S. Attorney **Thomas J. Hanlon** . . . . . . (509) 454-4425
Assistant U.S. Attorney **Ben Seal** . . . . . . (509) 454-4425
Assistant U.S. Attorney **(Vacant)** . . . . . . (509) 454-4425
Assistant U.S. Attorney **(Vacant)** . . . . . . (509) 454-4425
Assistant U.S. Attorney **(Vacant)** . . . . . . (509) 454-4425
Victim-Witness Specialist **Adela Garza** . . . . . . (509) 454-4425

Washington - Western District

700 Stewart Street, Suite 5220, Seattle, WA 98101
Tel: (206) 553-7970 Fax: (206) 553-0882
Internet: https://www.justice.gov/usao-wdwa

★ U.S. Attorney (Interim) **Annette L. Hayes** . . . . . . (206) 553-7970
E-mail: annette.hayes@usdoj.gov
★ U.S. Attorney-Designate **Brian T. Moran** . . . . . . (206) 553-7970
Education: Middlebury 1982 BA; U Puget Sound 1987 JD
Executive Specialist to the U.S. Attorney **(Vacant)** . . . . . (206) 553-7970
First Assistant U.S. Attorney
Helen J. "Micki" Brunner . . . . . . (206) 553-7970
E-mail: micki.brunner@usdoj.gov
Executive Assistant U.S. Attorney **(Vacant)** . . . . . . (206) 553-7970
Law Enforcement Coordinator **(Vacant)** . . . . . . (206) 553-7970
Victim-Witness Coordinator **Tracy Orcutt** . . . . . . (206) 553-7970
E-mail: tracy.orcutt@usdoj.gov
Administrative Officer **Michael Marzano** . . . . . . (206) 553-7970
Human Resources Officer **Gerri Cerna** . . . . . . (206) 553-7970
E-mail: gerri.cerna@usdoj.gov
Systems Manager **Robert Jones** . . . . . . (206) 553-7970

Civil Division

Chief **Kerry Keefe** . . . . . . (206) 553-7970
E-mail: kerry.keefe@usdoj.gov
Deputy Chief **Kristin Johnson** . . . . . . (206) 553-7970
E-mail: kristin.johnson@usdoj.gov
Assistant U.S. Attorney **Tricia Boerger** . . . . . . (206) 553-7970
E-mail: tricia.boerger@usdoj.gov
Assistant U.S. Attorney **Lisca Borichewski** . . . . . . (206) 553-7970
E-mail: lisca.borichewski@usdoj.gov
Assistant U.S. Attorney **Priscilla Chan** . . . . . . (206) 553-7970
E-mail: priscilla.chan@usdoj.gov
Assistant U.S. Attorney **David East** . . . . . . (206) 553-7970
E-mail: david.east@usdoj.gov
Assistant U.S. Attorney **Christina Fogg** . . . . . . (206) 553-7970
E-mail: christina.fogg@usdoj.gov
Assistant U.S. Attorney **Kyle A. Forsyth** . . . . . . (206) 553-7970
E-mail: kyle.forsyth@usdoj.gov
Education: Whitworth 1999 BA; Notre Dame 2003 JD
Assistant U.S. Attorney **Brian C. Kipnis** . . . . . . (206) 553-7970
E-mail: brian.kipnis@usdoj.gov
Assistant U.S. Attorney **Sarah Morehead** . . . . . . (206) 553-7970
E-mail: sarah.moreland@usdoj.gov
Education: Hamilton 1995 BA; Georgetown 1999 JD
Assistant U.S. Attorney **Whitney Passmore** . . . . . . (206) 553-7970
E-mail: whitney.passmore@usdoj.gov
Education: Wake Forest 2008 JD
Assistant U.S. Attorney **Kayla Stahman** . . . . . . (206) 553-7970
E-mail: kayla.stahman@usdoj.gov
Assistant U.S. Attorney **(Vacant)** . . . . . . (206) 553-7970
Assistant U.S. Attorney **(Vacant)** . . . . . . (206) 553-7970

Criminal Division

Chief **Tessa M. Gorman** . . . . . . (206) 553-7970
E-mail: tessa.gorman@usdoj.gov
Education: Yale 1993 BA; UC Berkeley JD

Appeals Section

Supervisor **Helen J. "Micki" Brunner** . . . . . . (206) 553-7970
Assistant U.S. Attorney **Teal Miller** . . . . . . (206) 553-7970
E-mail: teal.miller@usdoj.gov
Assistant U.S. Attorney **Michael Morgan** . . . . . . (206) 553-7970
E-mail: michael.morgan2@usdoj.gov

Asset Forfeiture Section

Assistant U.S. Attorney **Michelle Jensen** . . . . . . (206) 553-7970
E-mail: michelle.jensen@usdoj.gov
Assistant U.S. Attorney **Matthew H. Thomas** . . . . . . (206) 553-7970
E-mail: matthew.h.thomas@usdoj.gov
Assistant U.S. Attorney **(Vacant)** . . . . . . (206) 553-7970

Complex Crimes Section

Supervisor **Andrew C. Friedman** . . . . . . (206) 553-7970
E-mail: andrew.friedman@usdoj.gov
Education: Yale 1986 BA
Assistant U.S. Attorney **Justin W. Arnold** . . . . . . (206) 553-7970
E-mail: justin.arnold@usdoj.gov
Assistant U.S. Attorney **Matthew "Matt" Diggs** . . . . . . (206) 553-7970
E-mail: matthew.diggs@usdoj.gov
Assistant U.S. Attorney **Mike Dion** . . . . . . (206) 553-7970
E-mail: michael.dion@usdoj.gov
Assistant U.S. Attorney **Francis Franze-Nakamura** . . . . . . (206) 553-7970
E-mail: frances.franze-nakamura@usdoj.gov
Education: Yale 1998 BA; Michigan 2003 JD
Assistant U.S. Attorney **Mike Lang** . . . . . . (206) 553-7970
E-mail: mike.lang@usdoj.gov
Assistant U.S. Attorney **Steven "Steve" Masada** . . . . . . (206) 553-7970
E-mail: steven.masada@usdoj.gov
Assistant U.S. Attorney **Susan Roe** . . . . . . (206) 553-7970
E-mail: susan.roe@usdoj.gov
Assistant U.S. Attorney **Brian Werner** . . . . . . (206) 553-7970
E-mail: brian.werner@usdoj.gov
Assistant U.S. Attorney **Seth Wilkinson** . . . . . . (206) 553-7970
E-mail: seth.wilkinson@usdoj.gov
Education: Michigan 2001 JD

Criminal Enterprises Section

Supervisor **Sarah Vogel** . . . . . . (206) 553-7970
E-mail: sarah.vogel@usdoj.gov
Assistant U.S. Attorney **Andy Colasurdo** . . . . . . (206) 553-7970
Assistant U.S. Attorney **Vincent Lombardi** . . . . . . (206) 553-7970
E-mail: vince.lombardi@usdoj.gov
Assistant U.S. Attorney **Kate S. Vaughan** . . . . . . (206) 553-7970
E-mail: kate.vaughan@usdoj.gov
Education: U Washington 2004 JD
Assistant U.S. Attorney **(Vacant)** . . . . . . (206) 553-7970
Assistant U.S. Attorney **(Vacant)** . . . . . . (206) 553-7970
Assistant U.S. Attorney **(Vacant)** . . . . . . (206) 553-7970
Special Assistant U.S. Attorney **(Vacant)** . . . . . . (206) 553-7970

General Crimes I

Supervisor **Kathryn Frierson** . . . . . . (206) 553-7970
Assistant U.S. Attorney **Cecelia Gregson** . . . . . . (206) 553-7970
E-mail: cecelia.gregson@usdoj.gov
Assistant U.S. Attorney **Amy Jaquette** . . . . . . (206) 553-7970
Assistant U.S. Attorney **Matthew Hampton** . . . . . . (206) 553-7970
E-mail: matthew.hampton@usdoj.gov
Education: Washington U (MO) JD
Assistant U.S. Attorney **Donald M. "Don" Reno, Jr.** . . . . . (206) 553-7970
E-mail: don.reno@usdoj.gov
Assistant U.S. Attorney **Siddharth Velamoor** . . . . . . (206) 553-7970
E-mail: siddharth.velamoor@usdoj.gov
Assistant U.S. Attorney **(Vacant)** . . . . . . (206) 553-7970

General Crimes II

Supervisor **Jim Oesterle** . . . . . . (206) 553-7970
E-mail: jim.oesterle@usdoj.gov

★ Presidential Appointment Requiring Senate Confirmation ☆ Presidential Appointment □ Schedule C Appointment ◇ Career Senior Foreign Service Appointment
● Career Senior Executive Service (SES) Appointment ○ Non-Career Senior Executive Service (SES) Appointment ■ Postal Career Executive Service

General Crimes II *(continued)*

Assistant U.S. Attorney **Benjamin Diggs** . . . . (206) 553-7970
E-mail: benjamin.diggs@usdoj.gov
Assistant U.S. Attorney **Grady Leupold** . . . . (206) 553-7970
E-mail: grady.leupold@usdoj.gov
Assistant U.S. Attorney **Nicholas Manheim** . . . . (206) 553-7970
E-mail: nicholas.manheim@usdoj.gov
Assistant U.S. Attorney **Andre Penalver** . . . . (206) 553-7970
E-mail: andre.penalver@usdoj.gov
Assistant U.S. Attorney **Barbara J. "Barb" Sievers** . . . . . (206) 553-7970
E-mail: barbara.sievers@usdoj.gov

Terrorism and Violent Crimes Section
Supervisor **Todd Greenberg** . . . . (206) 553-7970
Deputy Supervisor **Bruce Miyake** . . . . (206) 553-7970
E-mail: bruce.miyake@usdoj.gov
Assistant U.S. Attorney **Erin Becker** . . . . (206) 553-7970
E-mail: erin.becker@usdoj.gov
Assistant U.S. Attorney **Rebecca "Becca" Cohen** . . . . (206) 553-7970
E-mail: rebecca.cohen@usdoj.gov
Assistant U.S. Attorney **J. Tate London** . . . . (206) 553-7970
E-mail: tate.london@usdoj.gov
Assistant U.S. Attorney **Ye Ting Woo** . . . . (206) 553-7970
E-mail: ye-ting.woo@usdoj.gov
Assistant U.S. Attorney **Tom Woods** . . . . (206) 553-7970

Tacoma (WA) Office
Tacoma Financial Center, 1201 Pacific Avenue,
Suite 700, Tacoma, WA 98402
Tel: (253) 428-3810

Supervisor **David Reese Jennings** . . . . (253) 428-3810
E-mail: david.r.jennings@usdoj.gov
Civil Division Assistant U.S. Attorney [District Election Official] **Arlen R. Storm** . . . . (253) 428-3800
E-mail: arlen.storm@usdoj.gov
Special Criminal Division Assistant U.S. Attorney **(Vacant)** . . . . (206) 553-7970
Criminal Division Assistant U.S. Attorney **Gregory A. Gruber** . . . . (253) 428-3800
E-mail: gregory.a.gruber@usdoj.gov
Criminal Division Assistant U.S. Attorney **Matthew H. Thomas** . . . . (253) 428-3800
E-mail: matthew.h.thomas@usdoj.gov
Criminal Division Assistant U.S. Attorney **(Vacant)** . . . . . . (253) 428-3800
Criminal Division Assistant U.S. Attorney **(Vacant)** . . . . . . (206) 553-7970
Criminal Division Assistant U.S. Attorney **(Vacant)** . . . . . . (206) 553-7970
Assistant U.S. Attorney **Marci Ellsworth** . . . . (206) 553-7970
E-mail: mari.ellsworth@usdoj.gov
Assistant U.S. Attorney **Grady Leupold** . . . . (206) 553-7970
E-mail: grady.leupold@usdoj.gov

West Virginia - Northern District
Federal Building, 1125 Chapline Street,
Suite 3000, Wheeling, WV 26003
Tel: (304) 234-0100 Fax: (304) 234-0110 (Main)
Fax: (304) 234-0112 (Civil) Fax: (304) 234-0111 (Criminal)

★ U.S. Attorney **William J. Powell** . . . . (304) 234-0100
E-mail: william.powell@usdoj.gov
Education: Salem Col 1982 BA; West Virginia 1985 JD
Executive Assistant to the U.S. Attorney **Ashley Meghan Lough** . . . . (304) 234-0100
E-mail: ashley.lough@usdoj.gov
Education: Indiana 2007
First Assistant U.S. Attorney **Randolph John "Randy" Bernard** . . . . (304) 234-0100
Administrative Officer **Fawn E. Thomas** . . . . (304) 234-7709
E-mail: fawn.thomas@usdoj.gov
Budget Officer **Sybil D. Ott** . . . . (304) 234-0100
E-mail: sybil.ott@usdoj.gov
Public Affairs Specialist **Stacy Bishop** . . . . (304) 234-0100
Systems Manager **Thomas Gibson** . . . . (304) 234-0100
E-mail: thomas.gibson@usdoj.gov
Support Services Specialist **Chad Lough** . . . . (304) 234-0100
E-mail: chad.lough@usdoj.gov

West Virginia - Northern District *(continued)*

Administrative Technician/Receptionist **Kyla Civitillo** . . . . . (304) 234-0100
Law Enforcement Coordinator **Gary M. Gaus** . . . . (304) 234-0100
E-mail: gary.gaus@usdoj.gov
FSA Records Manager **(Vacant)** . . . . (304) 234-0100
FSA Data Analyst **(Vacant)** . . . . (304) 234-0100

Civil Division
1125-1141 Chapline Street, Wheeling, WV 26003
Tel: (304) 234-0100 Fax: (304) 234-0112

Chief **Helen Campbell Altmeyer** . . . . (304) 234-0100
E-mail: helen.altmeyer@usdoj.gov
Assistant U.S. Attorney **Jarod J. Douglas** . . . . (304) 234-0100
E-mail: jarod.j.douglas@usdoj.gov
Paralegal Specialist **Susan M. Collins** . . . . (304) 234-0100
E-mail: susan.collins@usdoj.gov
Lead Legal Assistant **Janet K. Evick** . . . . (304) 234-0100
E-mail: janet.evick@usdoj.gov
Health Care Fraud Auditor **Donald W. Shelek** . . . . (304) 234-0100
E-mail: donald.shelek@usdoj.gov
FSA Legal Clerk **(Vacant)** . . . . (304) 234-0100
FSA Paralegal IV **(Vacant)** . . . . (304) 234-0100

Criminal Division
1125-1141 Chapline Street, Wheeling, WV 26003
Tel: (304) 234-0100 Fax: (304) 234-0111

Chief **Paul T. Camilletti** . . . . (304) 234-0100
E-mail: paul.camilletti@usdoj.gov
Deputy Chief **(Vacant)** . . . . (304) 234-0100
Financial Crimes Unit Coordinator **(Vacant)** . . . . (304) 234-0100
Assistant U.S. Attorney **Robert H. McWilliams, Jr.** . . . . . . (304) 234-0100
E-mail: rob.mcwilliams@usdoj.gov
Assistant U.S. Attorney **David J. Perri** . . . . (304) 234-0100
E-mail: david.perri@usdoj.gov
Assistant U.S. Attorney **Michael D. Stein** . . . . (304) 234-0100
E-mail: michael.stein@usdoj.gov
Assistant U.S. Attorney **Stephen L. Vogrin** . . . . (304) 234-0100
E-mail: stephen.vogrin@usdoj.gov
Victim Witness Coordinator **Christina J. Frizzell** . . . . (304) 234-0100
E-mail: chris.frizzell@usdoj.gov
Supervisory Paralegal Specialist **(Vacant)** . . . . (304) 234-0100
Legal Assistant **Rebecca R. Moore** . . . . (304) 234-0100
E-mail: becky.moore@usdoj.gov
Legal Assistant **(Vacant)** . . . . (304) 234-0100
FSA Senior Law Clerk **L. Danae DeMasi** . . . . (304) 234-0100
E-mail: danae.demasi@usdoj.gov
FSA Clerk **Lori A. Farmer** . . . . (304) 234-0100
E-mail: lori.farmer@usdoj.gov
FSA Data Analyst **(Vacant)** . . . . (304) 234-0100

Clarksburg (WV) Office
Federal Center, 320 West Pike Street,
Suite 300, Clarksburg, WV 26301-2710
Tel: (304) 623-7030 Fax: (304) 623-7031

Assistant U.S. Attorney-in-Charge **Tracy Cook** . . . . (304) 623-7030
Assistant U.S. Attorney **Andrew R. Cogar** . . . . (304) 623-7030
E-mail: andy.cogar@usdoj.gov
Assistant U.S. Attorney **Zelda E. Wesley** . . . . (304) 623-7030
E-mail: zelda.wesley@usdoj.gov
Assistant U.S. Attorney **Stephen D. Warner** . . . . (304) 623-7030
Intelligence Specialist **(Vacant)** . . . . (304) 623-7030
Legal Assistant **Laurel K. Jones** . . . . (304) 623-7030
E-mail: laurel.k.jones@usdoj.gov
Legal Assistant **Lisa Bishop** . . . . (304) 623-7030
Legal Assistant **Michelle E. Longerbeam** . . . . (304) 623-7030

Elkins (WV) Office
Federal Building, 300 Third Street, Suite 300, Elkins, WV 26241
P.O. Box 190, Elkins, WV 26241-0190
Tel: (304) 636-1739 Fax: (304) 636-1967

Assistant U.S. Attorney **Stephen D. Warner** . . . . (304) 636-1739

(continued on next page)

★ Presidential Appointment Requiring Senate Confirmation ☆ Presidential Appointment ☐ Schedule C Appointment ◇ Career Senior Foreign Service Appointment
● Career Senior Executive Service (SES) Appointment ○ Non-Career Senior Executive Service (SES) Appointment ■ Postal Career Executive Service

Elkins (WV) Office *(continued)*

Financial Litigation Paralegal Specialist **Cheryl J. Given** . . . . (304) 636-1739
E-mail: cheryl.given@usdoj.gov
Financial Litigation Paralegal Specialist **(Vacant)** . . . . (304) 636-1739

Martinsburg (WV) Office

217 West King Street, Suite 400, Martinsburg, WV 25401
Tel: (304) 262-0590 Fax: (304) 262-0591

Assistant U.S. Attorney-in-Charge (Acting) **Paul T. Camilletti** . . . . (304) 262-0590
E-mail: paul.camilletti@usdoj.gov
Assistant U.S. Attorney **Shawn Adkins** . . . . (304) 262-0590
E-mail: shawn.adkins@usdoj.gov
Assistant U.S. Attorney **Anna Krafskin** . . . . (304) 262-0590
Assistant U.S. Attorney **Lara K. Omps-Botteicher** . . . . (304) 262-0590
E-mail: lara.omps-botteicher@usdoj.gov
Assistant U.S. Attorney **Erin Reisenweber** . . . . (304) 262-0590
E-mail: erin.reisenweber@usdoj.gov
Education: Boston Col BA; Pittsburgh MLS; West Virginia 2003 JD
Legal Assistant **Leanna B. Murray** . . . . (304) 262-0590
E-mail: leanna.murray@usdoj.gov
Legal Assistant **Sheryl Weller** . . . . (304) 262-0590
Paralegal Specialist **Tracie L. Weaver** . . . . (304) 262-0590
E-mail: tracie.weaver@usdoj.gov

West Virginia - Southern District

300 Virginia Street East, Room 4000, Charleston, WV 25301
P.O. Box 1713, Charleston, WV 25326
Tel: (304) 345-2200 Fax: (304) 347-5104
Internet: https://www.justice.gov/usao-sdwv

★ U.S. Attorney **Michael B. "Mike" Stuart** . . . . (304) 345-2200
Education: West Virginia 1995 BA, 1995 BSBA; Boston U 2000 JD
Secretary to the U.S. Attorney **Vicky L. Dickerson** . . . . (304) 345-2200
E-mail: vicky.dickerson@usdoj.gov
Administrative Officer **Robin Y. Justice** . . . . (304) 345-2200
E-mail: robin.justice@usdoj.gov
Systems Manager **Kelvin Romero** . . . . (304) 345-2200
E-mail: kelvin.romero@usdoj.gov

Civil Division

Civil Division Chief and Assistant U.S. Attorney **Fred B. Westfall, Jr.** . . . . (304) 345-2200
E-mail: fred.westfall@usdoj.gov
Education: Ashland 1980 BSBA; Toledo 1983 JD
Assistant U.S. Attorney **Alan G. McGonigal** . . . . (304) 345-2200
E-mail: alan.mcgonigal@usdoj.gov
Assistant U.S. Attorney **Matthew C. Lindsay** . . . . (304) 345-2200
E-mail: matthew.lindsay@usdoj.gov
Assistant U.S. Attorney **Jennifer M. Mankins** . . . . (304) 345-2200
E-mail: jennifer.mankins@usdoj.gov

Criminal Division

First Assistant U.S. Attorney **Lisa G. Johnston** . . . . (304) 345-2200
E-mail: lisa.johnston@usdoj.gov
Criminal and Appellate Chief and Assistant U.S. Attorney **L. Anna Forbes** . . . . (304) 345-2200
E-mail: anna.forbes@usdoj.gov
Deputy Criminal Chief and Assistant U.S. Attorney **John J. Frail** . . . . (304) 345-2200
E-mail: john.frail@usdoj.gov
Education: Charleston 1980 BA; West Virginia 1983 JD
Deputy Criminal Chief, White Collar, Special Crimes and Public Integrity **Philip H. Wright** . . . . (304) 345-2200
E-mail: philip.wright@usdoj.gov
Assistant U.S. Attorney **C. Haley Bunn** . . . . (304) 345-2200
E-mail: haley.bunn@usdoj.gov
Assistant U.S. Attorney **Monica D. Coleman** . . . . (304) 345-2200
E-mail: monica.coleman@usdoj.gov
Assistant U.S. Attorney **J. Matthew Davis** . . . . (304) 345-2200
E-mail: matt.davis@usdoj.gov
Asset Forfeiture Assistant U.S. Attorney **Christopher R. Arthur** . . . . (304) 345-2200
E-mail: chris.arthur@usdoj..gov

Criminal Division *(continued)*

Assistant U.S. Attorney **Erik S. Goes** . . . . (304) 345-2200
E-mail: erik.goes@usdoj.gov
Assistant U.S. Attorney **Joshua C. "Josh" Hanks** . . . . (304) 345-2200
E-mail: josh.hanks@usdoj.gov
Assistant U.S. Attorney **Jennifer R. Herrald** . . . . (304) 345-2200
E-mail: jennifer.herrald@usdoj.gov
Assistant U.S. Attorney **Meredith G. Thomas** . . . . (304) 345-2200
E-mail: meredith.thomas@usdoj.gov
Assistant U.S. Attorney **Emily Wasserman** . . . . (304) 345-2200
E-mail: emily.wasserman@usdoj.gov
Education: Middlebury BA; Duke JD
Assistant U.S. Attorney **Gabriele Wohl** . . . . (304) 345-2200
E-mail: gabriele.wohl@usdoj.gov
Education: West Virginia 2009 JD
Assistant U.S. Attorney **Steven I. Loew** . . . . (304) 345-2200
E-mail: stevn.loew2@usdoj.gov
Counsel to United States Attorney and Assistant U.S. Attorney **(Vacant)** . . . . (304) 345-2200
Senior Litigation Counsel **R. Gregory McVey** . . . . (304) 345-2200
E-mail: greg.mcvey@usdoj.gov

Beckley (WV) Office

U.S. Courthouse and IRS Complex, 110 North Heber Street, Room 257, Beckley, WV 25801
Tel: (304) 253-6722 Fax: (304) 253-9206

Assistant U.S. Attorney **Timothy D. Boggess** . . . . (304) 253-6722
E-mail: timothy.boggess@usdoj.gov
Assistant U.S. Attorney **John L. File** . . . . (304) 253-6722
E-mail: john.file@usdoj.gov

Huntington (WV) Office

Sydney L. Christie Federal Building, 845 Fifth Avenue, Room 209, Huntington, WV 25701
Tel: (304) 529-5799 Fax: (304) 529-5545

Assistant U.S. Attorney **Joseph F. Adams** . . . . (304) 529-5799
E-mail: joe.adams@usdoj.gov
Assistant U.S. Attorney **W. Clinton Carte** . . . . (304) 529-5799
E-mail: clint.carte@usdoj.gov
Assistant U.S. Attorney **Stephanie S. Taylor** . . . . (304) 529-5799
E-mail: stephanie.taylor2@usdoj.gov

Wisconsin - Eastern District

Federal Courthouse, 517 East Wisconsin Avenue, Room 530, Milwaukee, WI 53202
Tel: (414) 297-1700 Fax: (414) 297-1738
Internet: https://www.justice.gov/usao-edwi

★ U.S. Attorney **Matthew D. Krueger** . . . . (414) 297-1700
E-mail: matthew.krueger@usdoj.gov
Secretary to the U.S. Attorney **Nancy Zepnick** . . . . (414) 297-1700
E-mail: nancy.zepnick@usdoj.gov
First Assistant U.S. Attorney **Richard Glen "Rick" Frohling** . . . . (414) 297-1700
Education: Yale 1993 BA
Secretary to the First Assistant U.S. Attorney **Nancy Zepnick** . . . . (414) 297-1700
E-mail: nancy.zepnick@usdoj.gov
Administrative Officer **Robert Sperry** . . . . (414) 297-1700
E-mail: robert.sperry@usdoj.gov
Budget Officer **LaQuisha Schroeder** . . . . (414) 297-1700
E-mail: laquisha.schroeder@usdoj.gov
Law Enforcement Committee Coordinator **Dean Puschnig** . . . . (414) 297-1700
E-mail: dean.puschnig@usdoj.gov
Victim-Witness Coordinator **Erin Morgan** . . . . (414) 297-1700
E-mail: erin.morgan@usdoj.gov
Personnel Officer **Kristie Schwark** . . . . (414) 297-1700
E-mail: kristie.schwark@usdoj.gov
Systems Manager **Christine Pinkowsky** . . . . (414) 297-1700
E-mail: christine.pinkowsky@usdoj.gov

Civil Division

Chief **Susan M. Knepel** . . . . (414) 297-1700
E-mail: susan.knepel@usdoj.gov

★ Presidential Appointment Requiring Senate Confirmation ☆ Presidential Appointment ☐ Schedule C Appointment ◇ Career Senior Foreign Service Appointment
● Career Senior Executive Service (SES) Appointment ○ Non-Career Senior Executive Service (SES) Appointment ■ Postal Career Executive Service

DEPARTMENTS

Civil Division *(continued)*

Deputy Chief **(Vacant)** . . . . (414) 297-1700
Assistant U.S. Attorney **Michael A. Carter** . . . . (414) 297-1700
E-mail: michael.a.carter@usdoj.gov
Assistant U.S. Attorney **Maura Flaherty** . . . . (414) 297-1700
E-mail: maura.flaherty@usdoj.gov
Assistant U.S. Attorney **Charles A. Guadagnino** . . . . (414) 297-1700
E-mail: charles.guadagnino@usdoj.gov
Assistant U.S. Attorney **Brian Pawlak** . . . . (414) 297-1700
E-mail: brian.pawlak@usdoj.gov
Assistant U.S. Attorney **Lisa T. Warwick** . . . . (414) 297-1700
E-mail: lisa.warwick@usdoj.gov
Assistant U.S. Attorney **Lisa Yun** . . . . (414) 297-1700
E-mail: lisa.yun@usdoj.gov
Assistant U.S. Attorney **Christian R. Larsen** . . . . (414) 297-1700

Criminal Division

Chief **Paul L. Kanter** . . . . (414) 297-1700
E-mail: paul.kanter@usdoj.gov
Deputy Chief/Financial Fraud **Kelly Watzka** . . . . (414) 297-1700
Deputy Chief **Keith S. Alexander** . . . . (414) 297-1700
E-mail: keith.alexander@usdoj.gov
Education: Notre Dame 2003 JD
Deputy Chief **(Vacant)** . . . . (414) 297-1700
Assistant U.S. Attorney **Benjamin Wesson** . . . . (414) 297-1700
Assistant U.S. Attorney **William J. Lipscomb** . . . . (414) 297-1700
E-mail: william.lipscomb@usdoj.gov
Assistant U.S. Attorney **Matthew L. Jacobs** . . . . (414) 297-1700
Assistant U.S. Attorney **Scott Campbell** . . . . (414) 297-1700
E-mail: scott.campbell@usdoj.gov
Assistant U.S. Attorney **Michael J. Chmelar** . . . . (414) 297-1700
E-mail: michael.chmelar@usdoj.gov
Assistant U.S. Attorney **Robert Brady** . . . . (414) 297-1700
Assistant U.S. Attorney **Zachary J. Corey** . . . . (414) 297-1700
E-mail: zachary.corey@usdoj.gov
Education: Cornell 2009 JD
Assistant U.S. Attorney **Megan Paulson** . . . . (414) 297-1700
E-mail: megan.paulson@usdoj.gov
Assistant U.S. Attorney **Andrew Maier** . . . . (414) 297-1700
E-mail: andrew.maier@usdoj.gov
Assistant U.S. Attorney **Gregory J. "Greg" Haanstad** . . . . (414) 297-1700
E-mail: greg.haanstad@usdoj.gov
Assistant U.S. Attorney **Gail J. Hoffman** . . . . (414) 297-1700
E-mail: gail.hoffman@usdoj.gov
Assistant U.S. Attorney **Margaret B. Honrath** . . . . (414) 297-1700
E-mail: margaret.honrath@usdoj.gov
Assistant U.S. Attorney **Daniel R. Humble** . . . . (414) 297-1700
E-mail: daniel.humble@usdoj.gov
Assistant U.S. Attorney **Stephen A. Ingraham** . . . . (414) 297-1700
E-mail: stephen.ingraham@usdoj.gov
Assistant U.S. Attorney **Jonathan H. Koenig** . . . . (414) 297-1700
E-mail: jonathan.h.koenig@usoj.gov
Education: Georgetown 1987 AB; William & Mary 1995 JD
Assistant U.S. Attorney **Carol Kraft** . . . . (414) 297-1700
E-mail: carol.kraft@usdoj.gov
Assistant U.S. Attorney **Laura Kwaterski** . . . . (414) 297-1700
E-mail: laura.kwaterski@usdoj.gov
Assistant U.S. Attorney **Elizabeth Monfils** . . . . (414) 297-1700
E-mail: elizabeth.monfils@usdoj.gov
Assistant U.S. Attorney **Karine Moreno-Taxman** . . . . (414) 297-1700
E-mail: karine.moreno-taxman@usdoj.gov
Assistant U.S. Attorney **Benjamin W. Proctor** . . . . (414) 297-1700
E-mail: benjamin.proctor@usdoj.gov
Assistant U.S. Attorney **William Roach** . . . . (414) 297-1700
E-mail: william.roach@usdoj.gov
Assistant U.S. Attorney **Benjamin Taibleson** . . . . (414) 297-1700
Assistant U.S. Attorney **Rebecca Taibleson** . . . . (414) 297-1700
E-mail: rebecca.taibleson@usdoj.gov
Education: Yale 2010 JD
Assistant U.S. Attorney **Melvin K. Washington** . . . . (414) 297-1700
E-mail: melvin.washington@usdoj.gov
Assistant U.S. Attorney **Lisa Wesley** . . . . (414) 297-1700
E-mail: lisa.wesley@usdoj.gov
Assistant U.S. Attorney **Adam Ptashkin** . . . . (414) 297-1700

Wisconsin - Western District

222 West Washington Avenue, Suite 700, Madison, WI 53703
Tel: (608) 264-5158 TTY: (608) 264-5006 Fax: (608) 264-5172

★ U.S. Attorney **Scott C. Blader** . . . . (608) 264-5158
E-mail: scott.c.blader@usdoj.gov
Education: Wisconsin (Oshkosh) 1996 BA; Marquette 1996 JD
Secretary to the U.S. Attorney **(Vacant)** . . . . (608) 264-5158
First Assistant U.S. Attorney
Stephen P. "Steve" Sinnott . . . . (608) 264-5158
E-mail: steve.sinnott@usdoj.gov
Administrative Officer **Brian M. McCarthy** . . . . (608) 264-5158
E-mail: brian.mccarthy@usdoj.gov
Law Enforcement Committee Coordinator
Myra J. Longfield . . . . (608) 264-5158
Victim-Witness Coordinator **(Vacant)** . . . . (608) 264-5158
Senior Systems Manager **(Vacant)** . . . . (608) 264-5158
ALS Manager **(Vacant)** . . . . (608) 264-5158

Civil Division

Civil Division Chief and Assistant U.S. Attorney
Leslie K. Herje . . . . (608) 264-5158
E-mail: leslie.herje@usdoj.gov
Assistant U.S. Attorney **David Conway** . . . . (608) 264-5158
E-mail: david.conway@usdoj.gov
Assistant U.S. Attorney **Daniel Fruchter** . . . . (608) 264-5158
E-mail: daniel.fruchter@usdoj.gov
Assistant U.S. Attorney **Richard Humphrey** . . . . (608) 264-5158
E-mail: richard.humphrey@usdoj.gov
Assistant U.S. Attorney **Heidi L. Luehring** . . . . (608) 264-5158
E-mail: heidi.luehring@usdoj.gov
Assistant U.S. Attorney **Barbara Oswald** . . . . (608) 264-5158
E-mail: barbara.oswald@usdoj.gov

Criminal Division

Criminal Division Chief and Assistant U.S. Attorney
Laura Przybylinksi Finn . . . . (608) 264-5158
Senior Litigation Counsel and Assistant U.S. Attorney
Timothy M. O'Shea . . . . (608) 264-5158
E-mail: tim.oshea@usdoj.gov
Organized Crime Drug Enforcement Task Force Unit Chief and Assistant U.S. Attorney
Jeffrey M. Anderson . . . . (608) 264-5158
E-mail: jeff.anderson@usdoj.gov
Asset Forfeiture Unit Assistant U.S. Attorney
Elizabeth Altman . . . . (608) 264-5158
E-mail: elizabeth.altman@usdoj.gov
Assistant U.S. Attorney **Meredith Duchemin** . . . . (608) 264-5158
E-mail: meredith.duchemin@usdoj.gov
Assistant U.S. Attorney **Daniel Graber** . . . . (608) 264-5158
E-mail: dan.graber@usdoj.gov
Assistant U.S. Attorney **Alice H. Green** . . . . (608) 264-5158
E-mail: alice.green@usdoj.gov
Assistant U.S. Attorney **Darren Halverson** . . . . (608) 264-5158
E-mail: darren.halverson@usdoj.gov
Education: Georgetown 2011 JD
Assistant U.S. Attorney **Peter M. Jarosz** . . . . (608) 264-5158
E-mail: peter.jarosz2@usdoj.gov
Assistant U.S. Attorney **David Reinhard** . . . . (608) 264-5158
E-mail: david.reinhard@usdoj.gov
Assistant U.S. Attorney **Rita M. Rumbelow** . . . . (608) 264-5158
E-mail: rita.rumbelow@usdoj.gov
Assistant U.S. Attorney **Antonio "Tony" Trillo** . . . . (608) 264-5158
E-mail: antonio.trillo@usdoj.gov
Assistant U.S. Attorney **(Vacant)** . . . . (608) 264-5158

Wyoming District

J.C. O'Mahoney Federal Building, 2120 Capitol Avenue, Room 4002, Cheyenne, WY 82001
P.O. Box 668, Cheyenne, WY 82003-0668
Tel: (307) 772-2124 Fax: (307) 772-2123
Internet: https://www.justice.gov/usao-wy

★ U.S. Attorney **Mark A. Klaassen** . . . . (307) 772-2124
E-mail: mark.klaassen@usdoj.gov
First Assistant U.S. Attorney **John R. Green** . . . . (307) 772-2124
E-mail: john.green@usdoj.gov

(continued on next page)

★ Presidential Appointment Requiring Senate Confirmation ☆ Presidential Appointment ☐ Schedule C Appointment ◇ Career Senior Foreign Service Appointment
● Career Senior Executive Service (SES) Appointment ○ Non-Career Senior Executive Service (SES) Appointment ■ Postal Career Executive Service

Wyoming District *(continued)*

Administrative Officer **John R. Powell** . . . . (307) 772-2124
E-mail: john.powell@usdoj.gov
Budget Officer **Patsy Wrede** . . . . (307) 772-2124
E-mail: patsy.wrede@usdoj.gov
Intelligence Officer **John R. Powell** . . . . (307) 772-2124
E-mail: john.powell@usdoj.gov
Law Enforcement Coordination Specialist and Press Officer **John R. Powell** . . . . (307) 772-2124
E-mail: john.powell@usdoj.gov
Victim-Witness Specialist **Vicki Powell** . . . . (307) 772-2124
E-mail: vpowell@usa.doj.gov
Systems Manager **Richard Peterson** . . . . (307) 772-2124
E-mail: richard.peterson@usdoj.gov

Civil Division

Supervisory Assistant U.S. Attorney/Civil Division Chief/Executive Assistant **Nick Vassallo** . . . . (307) 772-2124
E-mail: nick.vassallo@usdoj.gov
Assistant U.S. Attorney **C. Levi Martin** . . . . (307) 772-2124
Assistant U.S. Attorney **(Vacant)** . . . . (307) 772-2124
Assistant U.S. Attorney **(Vacant)** . . . . (307) 772-2124

Criminal Division

Chief **Robert Murray** . . . . (307) 772-2124
Executive U.S. Attorney **Lisa E. Leschuck** . . . . (307) 772-2124
E-mail: lisa.leschuck@usdoj.gov
Assistant U.S. Attorney **Timothy J. Forwood** . . . . (307) 772-2124
E-mail: timothy.forwood@usdoj.gov
Assistant U.S. Attorney **Thomas A. Szott** . . . . (307) 772-2124
E-mail: thomas.szott@usdoj.gov
Assistant U.S. Attorney **(Vacant)** . . . . (307) 772-2124

Casper (WY) Office

Dick Cheney Federal Building, 100 East B Street, Suite 2211, Casper, WY 82601
Tel: (307) 261-5434 Fax: (307) 261-5471

Supervisory Assistant U.S. Attorney/Branch Office Chief **Stephanie Sprecher** . . . . (307) 261-5434
E-mail: stephanie.sprecher@usdoj.gov
Senior Litigation Counsel **David Kubichek** . . . . (307) 261-5434
E-mail: david.kubichek@usdoj.gov
Criminal Division Assistant U.S. Attorney **Stephanie A. Hambrick** . . . . (307) 261-5434
E-mail: stephanie.hambrick@usdoj.gov
Criminal Division Assistant U.S. Attorney **(Vacant)** . . . . . . (307) 261-5434

Lander (WY) Branch Office

331 Main Street, Suite A, Lander, WY 82520
PO Box 449, Lander, WY 82520
Tel: (307) 332-8195 Fax: (307) 332-7104

Supervisory Assistant U.S. Attorney/Branch Office Chief **Kerry Jacobson** . . . . (307) 332-8195
E-mail: kerry.jacobson@usdoj.gov
Criminal Division Assistant U.S. Attorney **Jason M. Conder** . . . . (307) 332-8195
E-mail: jason.conder@usdoj.gov

Yellowstone (WY) Branch Office

P.O. Box 703, Yellowstone National Park, WY 82190-0703
Tel: (307) 690-7394

Assistant U.S. Attorney **Francis Leland Pico** . . . . (307) 690-7394

Bureau of Alcohol, Tobacco, Firearms and Explosives (ATF)

Ariel Rios Federal Building, 99 New York Avenue, NE, Washington, DC 20226
Tel: (202) 648-7777 (General Information)
Tel: (888) 283-3473 (Arson Hotline) Tel: (888) 283-2662 (Bomb Hotline)
Tel: (888) 283-4867 (Report Illegal Firearms Activity)
Tel: (888) 930-9275 (Firearms Theft Hotline)
Tel: (800) 788-7133 (Firearms Tracing Center)
Tel: (800) 578-7223 (Law Enforcement Use)
Tel: (800) 659-6242 (Report Stolen, Hijacked or Seized Cigarettes)
Tel: (800) 283-8477 (Other Criminal Activity) Internet: www.atf.gov

OFFICE OF THE DIRECTOR

Ariel Rios Federal Building, 99 New York Avenue, NE, Suite 5S.100, Washington, DC 20226
Tel: (202) 648-8700 Fax: (202) 648-9622

Office of Chief Counsel (OCC)

Ariel Rios Federal Building, 99 New York Avenue, NE, Washington, DC 20226
Tel: (202) 648-7000 Fax: (202) 648-9600

Associate Chief Counsel - Central

525 West Van Buren Street, Suite 600, Chicago, IL 60607
Tel: (312) 846-8890 Fax: (312) 846-8891

Associate Chief Counsel **Erika L. Ritt** . . . . (312) 846-8892
E-mail: erika.ritt@atf.gov

Division Counsel - Chicago (IL)

525 West Van Buren Street, Suite 600, Chicago, IL 60607
Tel: (312) 846-8893
Areas Covered: IL, Northern IN

Division Counsel **Jason Libby** . . . . (312) 846-8893

Division Counsel - Columbus (OH)

37 West Street, Suite 400, Columbus, OH 43215
Tel: (614) 827-8400 Fax: (614) 827-8401
Areas Covered: IN, OH

Division Counsel **Dianna Bessemer** . . . . (614) 827-8400
E-mail: dianne.bessemer@atf.gov

Division Counsel - Detroit (MI)

Division Counsel **(Vacant)** . . . . (313) 202-3421

Division Counsel - Louisville (KY)

600 Dr. Martin Luther King Jr. Place, Room 354, Louisville, KY 40202
Tel: (502) 753-3507 Fax: (502) 753-3501
Areas Covered: KY

Deputy Associate Chief Counsel - Central **Mark J. Lowney** . . . . (502) 753-3507

Division Counsel - New Orleans (LA)

One Galleria Boulevard, Suite 1700, Metairie, LA 70001

Division Counsel **Elizabeth D. Chatelain** . . . . (504) 841-7000
Attorney Advisor **Michele L. Thielhorn** . . . . (504) 841-7011

Division Counsel - Saint Paul (MN)

30 East Seventh Street, Suite 1900, St. Paul, MN 55101-4910

Division Counsel **Patricia R. Cangemi** . . . . (651) 726-0219

Associate Chief Counsel - East

The Curtis Center, 601 Walnut Street, Philadelphia, PA 19106
Tel: (215) 446-7830 Fax: (215) 446-7831

Associate Chief Counsel **Jeffrey A. Cohen** . . . . (215) 446-7832

★ Presidential Appointment Requiring Senate Confirmation ☆ Presidential Appointment ☐ Schedule C Appointment ◇ Career Senior Foreign Service Appointment
● Career Senior Executive Service (SES) Appointment ○ Non-Career Senior Executive Service (SES) Appointment ■ Postal Career Executive Service

Division Counsel - Baltimore (MD)
31 Hopkins Plaza, 5th Floor, Baltimore, MD 21201
Tel: (443) 965-2000

Division Counsel **David Rose** . . . . . (443) 965-2000
E-mail: david.rose@atf.gov

Division Counsel - Boston (MA)
10 Causeway Street, Boston, MA 02222-1047
Tel: (617) 557-1214
Areas Covered: MA

Division Counsel **S. Roy Chabra** . . . . . (617) 557-1214
E-mail: s.chabra@atf.gov

Division Counsel - Newark (NJ)
One Garret Mountain Plaza, Suite 500, Woodland Park, NJ 07424
Tel: (973) 413-1179

Division Counsel **Lisa A. Jakubczyk** . . . . . (973) 413-1179
E-mail: lisa.jakubczyk@atf.gov

Division Counsel- New York (NY)
241 37th Street, 3rd Floor, Brooklyn, NY 11232
Tel: (718) 541-0388 Fax: (718) 650-4091

Division Counsel **Matthew Myerson** . . . . . (718) 541-0388
E-mail: matthew.myerson@atf.gov

Division Counsel - Philadelphia (PA)
The Curtis Center, 601 Walnut Street,
Suite 1000E, Philadelphia, PA 19106
Tel: (215) 446-7836 Fax: (215) 446-7831
Areas Covered: DE, MD, NJ, PA

Division Counsel **J. Kevin White** . . . . . (215) 446-7833
E-mail: j.white@atf.gov

Division Counsel - Washington (DC)
90 K Street NE, 9th Floor, Washington, DC 20002
Tel: (202) 648-8010 Fax: (202) 648-8001
Areas Covered: DC

Division Counsel **James Vann** . . . . . (202) 648-8119
E-mail: james.vann@atf.gov

Associate Chief Counsel - Southeast
6701 Carmel Road, Charlotte, NC 28226
Tel: (704) 716-1800 Fax: (704) 716-1801

Associate Chief Counsel **David C. Lieberman** . . . . . (704) 716-1800
E-mail: david.lieberman@atf.gov

Division Counsel - Atlanta (GA)
2600 Century Parkway, NE, Suite 300, Atlanta, GA 30345
Tel: (404) 417-2600 Fax: (404) 417-2691

Division Counsel **Harry Foster** . . . . . (404) 417-2600
E-mail: harry.foster@atf.gov
Legal Technician **(Vacant)** . . . . . (404) 417-2697

Division Counsel - Charlotte (NC)
Division Counsel **Keith M. Cave** . . . . . (704) 716-1800

Division Counsel - Miami (FL)
Division Counsel **Robert J. Wilder** . . . . . (305) 597-4960

Division Counsel - Nashville (TN)
5300 Maryland Way, Brentwood, TN 37027
Tel: (615) 565-1400 Fax: (615) 565-1401

Division Counsel **B. Todd Martin** . . . . . (615) 565-1400

Division Counsel - Tampa (FL)
400 North Tampa Street, Tampa, FL 33602
Tel: (813) 202-7300 Fax: (813) 202-7301

Deputy Associate Chief Counsel
Eileen L. Husselbaugh . . . . . (813) 202-7300

Associate Chief Counsel - Southwest
1114 Commerce Street, Room 303, Dallas, TX 75242-1004
Tel: (469) 227-4440 Fax: (469) 227-4435

Associate Chief Counsel **Dean Andrews** . . . . . (469) 227-4440

Division Counsel - Dallas (TX)
Division Counsel **Kellie Hohenshelt** . . . . . (469) 227-4300

Division Counsel - Houston (TX)
Division Counsel **Don Calvert** . . . . . (281) 716-8200

Division Counsel - Kansas City (MO)
2600 Grand Avenue, Suite 200, Kansas City, MO 64108
Tel: (816) 559-0700 Fax: (816) 559-0701
Areas Covered: Iowa, Kansas, Missouri, Nebraska

Division Counsel **Mark Curzydlo** . . . . . (816) 559-0700

Associate Chief Counsel - West
6701 Carmel Rd, Suite 200, Charlotte, NC 28226
Tel: (704) 716-1807
Areas Covered: CA, GU, HI, ID, NV, OR, WA

Associate Chief Counsel **David C. Lieberman** . . . . . (704) 716-1807
E-mail: david.lieberman@atf.gov

Division Counsel - Denver (CO)
Division Counsel **Stuart Browne** . . . . . (303) 575-7600

Division Counsel - Los Angeles (CA)
Division Counsel **Paul J. Ware** . . . . . (818) 265-2500

Division Counsel - Phoenix (AZ)
Division Counsel **Thomas E. Karmgard** . . . . . (602) 776-5400

Division Counsel - San Francisco (CA)
Division Counsel **Melissa S. Delvecchio** . . . . . (925) 557-2800

Division Counsel - Seattle (WA)
Division Counsel **John Tibbetts** . . . . . (206) 204-3205

Office of Enforcement Programs and Services (OEPS)

Ariel Rios Federal Building, 99 New York Avenue, NE,
Washington, DC 20226
Fax: (202) 648-9757

Firearms and Explosives Services Division
244 Needy Road, Martinsburg, WV 25401
Tel: (304) 616-4590 Fax: (304) 616-4591

Chief **Gary R. Taylor** . . . . . (304) 616-4590
E-mail: gary.r.taylor@atf.gov
Firearms and Explosives Import Branch Chief
William Majors . . . . . (304) 616-4590
Deputy Chief **(Vacant)** . . . . . (304) 616-4590
Federal Explosives Licensing Center Chief
Christopher Reeves . . . . . (304) 616-4590
Federal Firearms Licensing Center Chief
Tracey Robertson . . . . . (304) 616-4608

National Tracing Center Division
244 Needy Road, Martinsburg, WV 25401
Tel: (800) 788-7133 Fax: (304) 260-5342

Chief **Charles J. Houser** . . . . . (304) 260-1500
E-mail: charles.houser@atf.gov
Education: Grand Valley State BS; US Army Command
Deputy Chief **Tyson Arnold** . . . . . (304) 260-1500
Firearms Tracing Branch Chief **David A. Scott** . . . . . (304) 260-1500
E-mail: david.scott@atf.gov
Law Enforcement Support Branch Chief
Larry R. Penninger . . . . . (304) 260-1500
E-mail: larry.r.penninger@usdoj.gov
Tracing Operations and Records Management Branch
Chief **Edward E. Stely** . . . . . (304) 260-1500
E-mail: edward.e.stely@atf.gov

(continued on next page)

★ Presidential Appointment Requiring Senate Confirmation ☆ Presidential Appointment □ Schedule C Appointment ◇ Career Senior Foreign Service Appointment
● Career Senior Executive Service (SES) Appointment ○ Non-Career Senior Executive Service (SES) Appointment ■ Postal Career Executive Service

National Tracing Center Division *(continued)*

Division Operations Officer **(Vacant)** .... (304) 260-1500
Internet Investigations Center Director **(Vacant)** .... (800) 788-7133

Office of Field Operations (OFO)

Ariel Rios Federal Building, 99 New York Avenue, NE,
Washington, DC 20226
Tel: (202) 648-8410 Fax: (202) 648-9608

Field Divisions

Atlanta (GA) Field Division

2600 Century Parkway, NE, Suite 300, Atlanta, GA 30345
Tel: (404) 417-2600 Fax: (404) 417-2601 E-mail: atlantadiv@atf.gov
Areas Covered: GA

• Special Agent-in-Charge **Wayne L. Dixie, Jr.** .... (404) 417-2600
E-mail: wayle.l.dixie@atf.gov
Assistant Special Agent-in-Charge **(Vacant)** .... (404) 417-2600
Assistant Special Agent-in-Charge **John Schmidt** .... (404) 417-2600
Director of Industry Operations **Diana Mitchell** .... (404) 417-2600
Division Operations Officer **Chad D. Munn** .... (404) 417-2600
Public Information Officer **Larry Priester** .... (404) 417-2600

Atlanta (GA) Field Offices

Atlanta (GA) Group II
2600 Century Parkway NE, Suite 300, Atlanta, GA 30345
Tel: (404) 315-4500 Fax: (404) 315-4502
Group Supervisor/Special Agent **Will Creech** .... (404) 315-4500

Atlanta (GA) Group III
2600 Century Parkway NE, Suite 300, Atlanta, GA 30345
Tel: (404) 315-4500 Fax: (404) 315-4503
Group Supervisor/Special Agent **Michael Desmond** ..... (404) 417-1300
E-mail: micheal.desmond@atf.gov

Atlanta (GA) Group IV
2635 Century Parkway, 10th Floor, Atlanta, GA 30345
Tel: (404) 315-4500 Fax: (404) 315-4501
Group Supervisor/Special Agent **Robert Davis** .... (404) 638-7642
E-mail: robert.davis@atf.gov Fax: (404) 815-5541

Atlanta (GA) Group V (Industry Operations)
2600 Century Parkway, NE, Suite 300, Atlanta, GA 30345
Tel: (404) 417-2670 Fax: (404) 417-2688
Area Supervisor (Industry Operations)
Paulean Wooley .... (404) 417-2670

Atlanta (GA) Group VI (Intelligence)
2600 Century Parkway, NE, Suite 300, Atlanta, GA 30345
Tel: (404) 417-2650 Fax: (404) 315-4599
Group Supervisor/Special Agent **Cheryl Harrell** .... (404) 417-2662
E-mail: cheryl.harrell@atf.gov

Atlanta (GA) Group VII
2600 Century Parkway NE, Suite 300, Atlanta, GA 30345
Tel: (404) 315-4570 Fax: (404) 315-4571
Group Supervisor **Brent Quinn** .... (404) 730-1370
E-mail: brent.quinn@atf.gov

Atlanta (GA) Group VIII (Industry Operations)
2600 Century Parkway, NE, Atlanta, GA 30345
Area Supervisor (Industry Operations) **Liza Ryan** .... (404) 417-2670

Macon (GA) Field Office

1645 Forest Hill Road, Room 200, Macon, GA 31210-1602
Tel: (478) 405-2440 Fax: (478) 405-2441
Resident Agent-in-Charge/Special Agent
William Panoke .... (478) 405-2510

Macon (GA) II Industry Operations

1645 Forest Hill Road, Suite 200, Macon, GA 31210-1602
Supervisor **David Cagle** .... (478) 405-2520
Fax: (478) 405-2451

Savannah (GA) Field Office

56 Park of Commerce Boulevard, Suite B, Savannah, GA 31405
Tel: (912) 650-6550 Fax: (912) 650-6551
Resident Agent-in-Charge/Special Agent
Timothy Graden .... (912) 650-6550

Baltimore (MD) Field Division

G. H. Fallon Building, 31 Hopkins Plaza,
5th Floor, Baltimore, MD 21201-2825
Tel: (443) 965-2000 Fax: (443) 965-2001
Areas Covered: DE, MD

• Special Agent-in-Charge **Robert Cekada** .... (443) 965-2000
E-mail: robert.cekada@usdoj.gov
Assistant Special Agent-in-Charge **Jordi Clop** .... (443) 965-2000
E-mail: jordi.clorp@atf.gov
Assistant Special Agent-in-Charge **Matthew Varisco** .... (443) 965-2000
E-mail: matthew.varisco@atf.gov
Director of Industry Operations **Michael Fronczak** ...... (443) 965-2000
Public Information Officer **Amanda Hils** .... (443) 965-2007
E-mail: amanda.hils@atf.gov Fax: (443) 965-2001

Baltimore (MD) Field Offices

Baltimore (MD) I Arson and Explosives
31 Hopkins Plaza, 5th Floor, Baltimore, MD 21201
Tel: (443) 965-2050 Fax: (443) 965-2051
Group Supervisor **Eric Pena** .... (443) 965-2052
E-mail: eric.pena@atf.gov

Baltimore (MD) II - HIDTA
31 Hopkins Plaza, 5th Floor, Baltimore, MD 21201
Tel: (410) 579-5011 Fax: (410) 579-5137
Group Supervisor **Shannon Day-Hill** .... (410) 579-5011
E-mail: shannon.day@atf.gov

Baltimore (MD) III - Violent Crime Impact Team
31 Hopkins Plaza, 5th Floor, Baltimore, MD 21201
Tel: (443) 965-2070 Fax: (443) 965-2071
Group Supervisor **Timothy Lee** .... (443) 965-2070
E-mail: timothy.lee@atf.gov

Baltimore (MD) IV - Intelligence
31 Hopkins Plaza, 5th Floor, Baltimore, MD 21201
Tel: (443) 965-2100 Fax: (443) 965-2101
Group Supervisor **Troy Dannenfelser** .... (443) 965-2100
E-mail: troy.dannenfelser@atf.gov

Baltimore (MD) V - Industry Operations
31 Hopkins Plaza, 5th Floor, Baltimore, MD 21201-2585
Tel: (443) 965-2120 Fax: (443) 965-2121
Areas Covered: DE, MD
Area Supervisor **Christopher S. Turett** .... (443) 965-2120

Baltimore (MD) VI - Firearms Trafficking Team
31 Hopkins Plaza, 5th Floor, Baltimore, MD 21201
Tel: (443) 965-2170 Fax: (443) 965-2051
Group Supervisor **Kimberly Drielak** .... (443) 965-2170
E-mail: kimberly.drielak@atf.gov

Delaware Field Office

1007 North Orange Street, Suite 201, Wilmington, DE 19801
Tel: (302) 252-0110 Fax: (302) 252-0129
Resident Agent-in-Charge **John Oakey** .... (302) 252-0110
E-mail: john.oakey@atf.gov

★ Presidential Appointment Requiring Senate Confirmation ☆ Presidential Appointment □ Schedule C Appointment ◇ Career Senior Foreign Service Appointment
● Career Senior Executive Service (SES) Appointment ○ Non-Career Senior Executive Service (SES) Appointment ■ Postal Career Executive Service

Wilmington (DE) II Industry Operations
1007 Orange Street, Suite 201, Wilmington, DE 19801
Tel: (443) 965-2120 Fax: (302) 252-0137

Area Supervisor **Christopher S. Turett** . . . . (443) 965-2120
E-mail: chris.turett@atf.gov

Hyattsville (MD) I Field Office
Aerospace Building, 10210 Greenbelt Road,
Suite 770, Lanham, MD 20706
Tel: (301) 397-2640 Fax: (301) 397-2679

Resident Agent-in-Charge **Frank Oliver** . . . . (240) 965-3061
E-mail: frank.oliver@atf.gov

Hyattsville (MD) II Field Office
7833 Walker Drive, Suite 580, Greenbelt, MD 20770
Tel: (301) 446-6520 Fax: (301) 446-6521

Resident Agent-in-Charge **Stacy Brown** . . . . (301) 446-6520
E-mail: stacy.brown@atf.gov

Boston (MA) Field Division
Thomas P. O'Neill Federal Building, 10 Causeway Street,
Room 791, Boston, MA 02222
Tel: (617) 557-1200 Fax: (617) 557-1201 E-mail: bostondiv@atf.gov
Areas Covered: CT, ME, MA, NH, RI, VT

• Special Agent-in-Charge **Mickey D. Leadingham** . . . . (617) 557-1200
E-mail: mickey.leadingham@atf.gov
Assistant Special Agent-in-Charge **Kenneth K. Kwak** . . . . (617) 557-1200
E-mail: kenneth.kwak@atf.gov
Assistant Special Agent-in-Charge **Larry Panetta** . . . . (617) 557-1200
E-mail: larry.panetta@atf.gov
Director of Industry Operations **(Vacant)** . . . . (617) 557-1200
Division Counsel **S. Roy Chabra** . . . . (617) 557-1200
E-mail: s.chabra@atf.gov
Public Information Officer
Matthew H. O'Shaughnessy . . . . (617) 557-1200

Boston (MA) Field Office
Thomas P. O'Neill Federal Building, 10 Causeway Street,
Room 791, Boston, MA 02222

Boston II Field Office Group Supervisor
James M. Ferguson . . . . (617) 557-1220
E-mail: james.ferguson@atf.gov
Boston III Field Office Group Supervisor
Rossin Marchetti . . . . (617) 557-1230
E-mail: rossin.marchetti@atf.gov
Boston IV Field Office Resident Agent-in-Charge
Kathleen M. Dowd . . . . (617) 557-1240
E-mail: kathleen.dowd@atf.gov
Boston V Industry Operations Area Supervisor
Wayne Bittencourt . . . . (617) 557-1250
Boston VI Office Group Supervisor **Mike Payne** . . . . (617) 557-1326
E-mail: mike.payne@atf.gov

Burlington (VT) Field Office
30 Main Street, Suite 430, Burlington, VT 05401
Tel: (802) 865-4020 Fax: (802) 865-4021

Resident Agent-in-Charge **Craig Roetner** . . . . (802) 865-4020
E-mail: craig.roetner@atf.gov

Hartford (CT) Field Office (Industry Operations)
450 Main Street, Room 610, Hartford, CT 06103-3002
Tel: (860) 240-3400 Fax: (860) 240-3404
Areas Covered: CT, Western MA, VT

Area Supervisor **Nealy Earl** . . . . (860) 240-3400
E-mail: nealy.earl@atf.gov

Hartford (CT) Field Office (Law Enforcement)
Capitol Place, 21 Oak Street, Suite 303, Hartford, CT 06106
Tel: (860) 293-2540 Fax: (860) 293-2579

Resident Agent in Charge **Mark Bakuchi** . . . . (860) 293-2540

Manchester (NH) Field Office
55 Constitution Drive, 2nd Floor, Bedford, NH 03110
Tel: (603) 471-1283 Fax: (603) 471-9024

Resident Agent-in-Charge **Amanda Cahill** . . . . (603) 471-1283

New Haven (CT) Field Office
150 Court Street, Room 211, New Haven, CT 06510-2055
Tel: (203) 773-2060 Fax: (203) 773-2330

Resident Agent-in-Charge **Michael Zeppieri** . . . . (203) 773-2060
E-mail: michael.zeppieri@atf.gov

Portland (ME) Field Office
68 Marginal Way, 3rd Floor, Portland, ME 04101
Tel: (207) 780-3324 Fax: (207) 780-3625

Resident Agent-in-Charge **Douglas Kirk** . . . . (207) 780-3324
E-mail: douglas.kirk@atf.gov

Providence (RI) Field Office
380 Westminster Mall, Room 569, Providence, RI 02903-3246
Tel: (401) 528-4366 Fax: (401) 528-4840

Resident Agent-in-Charge **John Hayes** . . . . (401) 528-4366

Worcester (MA) Satellite Office
120 Front Street, Room 610, Worcester, MA 01608-1401
Tel: (508) 793-0240 Fax: (508) 793-0271

Resident Agent-in-Charge **West Jackson** . . . . (508) 793-0240

Springfield (MA) Field Office
1550 Main Street, Room 317, Springfield, MA 01103-1422
Tel: (413) 731-6200 Fax: (413) 785-0362

Resident Agent-in-Charge **West Jackson** . . . . (413) 731-6200

Charlotte (NC) Field Division
6701 Carmel Road, Suite 200, Charlotte, NC 28226
Tel: (704) 716-1800 Fax: (704) 716-1801
Internet: www.atf.gov/field/charlotte/index.html
Areas Covered: NC, SC

• Special Agent-in-Charge
Christopher J. "C.J." Hyman . . . . (704) 716-1800
Secretary to the Special Agent-in-Charge
Christine Yost . . . . (704) 716-1800
Assistant Special Agent-in-Charge
David Riddleburger . . . . (704) 716-1800
Assistant Special Agent-in-Charge **Ernesto Diaz** . . . . (803) 251-4612
Strom Thurmond Federal Building, Fax: (803) 251-4613
1835 Assembly Street,
Room 375, Columbia, SC 29201
E-mail: ernesto.diaz@atf.gov
Director Industry Operations **Stephen B. Albro** . . . . (704) 716-1800
Division Operations Officer **Winfred Pressley** . . . . (704) 716-1800
Public Information Officer **Gerod King** . . . . (704) 716-1800

Charleston (SC) Field Office
One Poston Road, Suite 325, Charleston, SC 29407
Tel: (843) 763-3683 Fax: (843) 763-8848

Resident Agent-in-Charge **Scott Perala** . . . . (843) 763-3683

Charlotte (NC) Field Office
6701 Carmel Road, Suite 200, Charlotte, NC 28226
Tel: (704) 716-1800

Charlotte Group I Supervisor **Anthony Spotswood** . . . . . (704) 716-1810
Fax: (704) 716-1811
Charlotte Group II Supervisor **Joshua Bezy** . . . . (704) 716-1820
Fax: (704) 716-1821
Charlotte Group III (Industry Operations) Area
Supervisor **Cathy Morrison** . . . . (704) 716-1830
Fax: (704) 716-1831
Charlotte Group IV Group Supervisor **Shawn Arthur** . . . . (704) 716-1840
E-mail: shawn.arthur@atf.gov Fax: (704) 716-1841

★ Presidential Appointment Requiring Senate Confirmation ☆ Presidential Appointment □ Schedule C Appointment ◇ Career Senior Foreign Service Appointment
● Career Senior Executive Service (SES) Appointment ○ Non-Career Senior Executive Service (SES) Appointment ■ Postal Career Executive Service

Columbia (SC) Field Office
Strom Thurmond Federal Building, 1835 Assembly Street, Room 309, Columbia, SC 29201
Tel: (803) 251-4600 Fax: (803) 251-4601
Resident Agent-in-Charge **Eddie Eubanks** .... (803) 251-4600
Area Supervisor **(Vacant)** .... (803) 251-4640

Fayetteville (NC) Field Office
225 Green Street, Suite 300, Fayetteville, NC 28301
Tel: (910) 483-3030 Fax: (910) 323-2258
Resident Agent-in-Charge **Nathan Honaker** .... (910) 483-3030
E-mail: nathan.honaker@atf.gov

Greensboro (NC) Field Office
1801 Stanley Road, Suite 300, Greensboro, NC 27407
Tel: (336) 235-4900 Fax: (336) 235-4901
Greensboro Group I Resident Agent-in-Charge **Jason Walsh** .... (336) 235-4900
Greensboro Group II (Industry Operations) Area Supervisor **Sheila R. Hall** .... (336) 235-4950
Fax: (336) 235-4951

Greenville (SC) Field Office
301 North Main Street, Suite 1802, Greenville, SC 29601
Tel: (864) 282-2937 Fax: (864) 282-2958
Resident Agent-in-Charge **Michael Dixon** .... (864) 282-2937
E-mail: michael.dixon@atf.gov

Raleigh (NC) Field Office
The North Tower, 4700 Falls of the Neuse Road, Suite 395, Raleigh, NC 27609
Tel: (919) 719-2021 Fax: (919) 719-2022
Resident Agent-in-Charge **Timothy L. Sloan** .... (919) 719-2021

Wilmington (NC) Field Office
3205 Randall Parkway, Suite 202, Wilmington, NC 28403
Tel: (910) 343-6801 Fax: (910) 343-6827
Resident Agent-in-Charge **Shawn Stallo** .... (910) 343-6801

Chicago (IL) Field Division
525 West Van Buren, Suite 600, Chicago, IL 60607
Tel: (312) 846-7200 Fax: (312) 846-7201 E-mail: chicagodiv@atf.gov
Areas Covered: IL
● Special Agent-in-Charge **Celinez Nuñez** .... (312) 846-7200
E-mail: celinez.nunez@atf.gov
Assistant Special Agent-in-Charge **Raymond E. Fragoso** .... (312) 846-7200
E-mail: raymond.fragoso@atf.gov
Assistant Special Agent-in-Charge **(Vacant)** .... (312) 846-7200
Director of Industry Operations **Thomas Arnold** .... (312) 846-7200
Public Information Officer **Rhonda Daho** .... (312) 846-7200

Chicago (IL) Field Office
525 West Van Buren Street, Suite 600, Chicago, IL 60607
Tel: (312) 846-7200 Fax: (312) 846-7201
Chicago I Group Supervisor **Mark Anton** .... (312) 846-7230
Chicago II Group Supervisor (Acting) **Kevin Biesty** .... (312) 846-7250
Chicago III Group Supervisor (Acting) **Bill Bollenburg** .... (312) 846-7270
Chicago IV Group Supervisor **Bennie Mims** .... (312) 846-8850
E-mail: bennie.mims@atf.gov
Chicago V Group Supervisor (Acting) **C. Hoffman** .... (312) 846-8870

Downers Grove (IL) Field Office
3250 Lacey Road, Suite 400, Downers Grove, IL 60515
Tel: (630) 725-5220 Fax: (630) 725-5249
Downers Grove I Group Supervisor **Timothy Wilson** .... (630) 725-5220
Downers Grove II Group Supervisor (Acting) **Erin Silk** .... (630) 725-5230
Downers Grove III Industry Operations Area Supervisor **Stephen Pratt** .... (630) 725-5290
E-mail: stephen.pratt@atf.gov

Fairview Heights (IL) Field Office
333 Salem Place, Suite 205, Fairview Heights, IL 62208
Tel: (618) 632-9380 Fax: (618) 632-8479
Resident Agent-in-Charge **Paul Heiser** .... (618) 632-9380
Fairview Heights II Industry Operations Area Supervisor **Lisa Storey** .... (618) 632-0704
E-mail: lisa.storey@atf.gov

Springfield (IL) I Field Office
3161 West White Oaks Drive, Suite 200, Springfield, IL 62704
Tel: (217) 547-3650 Fax: (217) 547-3651
Resident Agent-in-Charge **Thomas Dart** .... (217) 547-3650
Springfield II Industry Operations Area Supervisor **Stephen Pratt** .... (217) 547-3675
E-mail: stephen.pratt@atf.gov

Columbus (OH) Field Division
230 West Street, Suite 400, Columbus, OH 43215
Tel: (614) 827-8400 Fax: (614) 827-8401 E-mail: columbusdiv@atf.gov
Areas Covered: IN, OH
● Special Agent-in-Charge **Trevor Velinor** .... (614) 827-8450
E-mail: trevor.velinor@atf.gov
Assistant Special Agent-in-Charge **Roland Herndon** .... (614) 827-8400
E-mail: roland.herndon@atf.gov
Assistant Special Agent-in-Charge **Kyle A. Walton** .... (614) 827-8400
Director, Industry Operations **Judyth LeDoux** .... (614) 827-8400
Division Counsel **Dianna Bessemer** .... (614) 827-8400
E-mail: dianna.bessemer@atf.gov
Public Information Officer **Suzanne Dabkowski** .... (614) 827-8400

Cincinnati (OH) Field Offices
2012 Ronald Reagan Drive, Suite 8503, Cincinnati, OH 45236
Areas Covered: Northern KY, Southern OH
Cincinnati I Field Office Resident Agent-in-Charge **Clayton Merrill** .... (513) 684-3354
Fax: (513) 684-6359
Cincinnati II (Industry Operations) Field Office Area Supervisor **Terry Legg** Suite 8507 .... (513) 684-3351
Fax: (513) 684-6455

Cleveland (OH) Field Offices
5005 Rockside Road, Suite 700, Independence, OH 44130-6828
Areas Covered: Northern OH
Cleveland I Field Office/Group Supervisor **William Hall** .... (216) 573-8100
E-mail: william.hall@atf.gov Fax: (216) 573-8101
Cleveland II Field Office/Group Supervisor **Eric Frey** .... (216) 573-8120
Fax: (216) 573-8121
Cleveland III (Industry Operations) Field Office Area Supervisor **Richard Ridenbaugh** .... (216) 573-8140
Fax: (216) 573-8141

Columbus (OH) Field Offices
230 West Street, Suite 400, Columbus, OH 43215
Columbus I Field Office Resident Agent-in-Charge **Robert Patrizi** .... (614) 827-8450
Fax: (614) 827-8462
Columbus (Industry Operations) Satellite Office Area Supervisor **Terry Legg** .... (614) 827-8470
Fax: (614) 827-8467
Columbus II Field Office Group Supervisor **Joe Delucio** .... (614) 827-8430
Fax: (614) 827-8431

Indianapolis (IN) Field Offices
151 North Delaware Street, Suite 1000, Indianapolis, IN 46204-2517
Indianapolis I Field Office Group Supervisor **Patrick W. Hand** .... (317) 287-3500
E-mail: patrick.hand@atf.gov Fax: (317) 287-3501
Indianapolis II (Industry Operations) Field Office Area Supervisor **Nena R. Fisher** .... (317) 287-3500
E-mail: nena.fisher@atf.gov Fax: (317) 287-3502

★ Presidential Appointment Requiring Senate Confirmation ☆ Presidential Appointment ☐ Schedule C Appointment ◇ Career Senior Foreign Service Appointment
● Career Senior Executive Service (SES) Appointment ○ Non-Career Senior Executive Service (SES) Appointment ■ Postal Career Executive Service

Indianapolis (IN) Field Offices *(continued)*

Indianapolis III Field Office Group Supervisor
Robert Bryson .... (317) 287-3500
E-mail: robert.bryson@atf.gov Fax: (317) 287-3503

Evansville Satellite Office
101 Northwest Martin Luther King, Room 101, Evansville, IN 47708
Tel: (812) 461-5000 Fax: (812) 465-5121

Resident Agent in Charge **Patrick W. Hand** .... (812) 461-5000
E-mail: patrick.hand@atf.gov

Toledo (OH) Field Office
Four Seagate, 433 North Summit Street,
Suite 701, Toledo, OH 46304-1551
Tel: (419) 245-5115 Fax: (419) 245-5120

Resident Agent-in-Charge/Special Agent
Michael Medlin .... (419) 245-5115

Youngstown (OH) Field Office
8544 Hickory Hill Drive, Suite 100, Poland, OH 44514
Tel: (330) 707-2300 Fax: (330) 707-2301

Resident Agent-in-Charge **Robert L. Miller** .... (330) 707-2300
E-mail: robert.miller@atf.gov

Dallas (TX) Field Division
1114 Commerce Street, Dallas, TX 75242
Tel: (469) 227-4300 Fax: (469) 227-4302 E-mail: dallasdiv@atf.gov

● Special Agent In Charge **William A. Temple** .... (469) 227-4300
Assistant Special Agent in Charge **Vincent Pallozzi** ..... (469) 227-4300
Assistant Special Agent in Charge **(Vacant)** .... (469) 227-4300
Director of Industry Operations **Kevin R. Murphy** .... (469) 227-4300
E-mail: kevin.r.murphy@atf.gov
Public Information Officer **Scott Ragsdale** .... (469) 227-4300
Division Counsel **Dean Andrews** .... (469) 227-4440
Fax: (469) 227-4435
Division Counsel **Kellie Hohenshelt** .... (469) 227-4440
Fax: (469) 227-4435
Audit Manager **Hope Alcorta** .... (469) 227-4300
E-mail: hope.alcorta@atf.gov

Dallas (TX) Field Office
1114 Commerce Street, Room 303, Dallas, TX 75242
Tel: (469) 227-4300

Dallas I (Intelligence) Group Supervisor **Steve Toth** ..... (469) 227-4350
Dallas II (Arson and Explosives) Group Supervisor
Marty Roy .... (469) 227-4370
Dallas III (Firearms Trafficking) Group Supervisor
(Vacant) .... (469) 227-4395
Fax: (469) 227-4396
Dallas IV (HIDTA) Group Supervisor **John Pias** .... (972) 915-9570
8404 Esters Boulevard, Fax: (972) 915-9518
Suite 100, Irving, TX 75063
Dallas V (Industry Operations) Group Supervisor
Scena Webb .... (469) 227-4415
Dallas VI (Industry Operations) Area Supervisor
(Vacant) .... (469) 227-4430
Dallas VII (Firearms Trafficking) Group Supervisor
Joseph "Joe" Patterson .... (469) 227-4395
E-mail: joseph.patterson@atf.gov Fax: (469) 227-4363
Tactical Operations Officer **(Vacant)** .... (469) 227-5500
Fax: (214) 221-3391

El Paso (TX) Field Office
303 North Oregon, Suite 500, El Paso, TX 79901-7020
Tel: (915) 534-6449 Fax: (915) 534-6453

Resident Agent in Charge **Corey Hill** .... (915) 832-6200
E-mail: corey.hill@atf.gov
El Paso Group Three Resident Agent in Charge
(Vacant) .... (915) 534-6449
Industry Operations Supervisor **Eric Caviness** .... (915) 534-6475

Fort Worth (TX) Field Office
6000 Western Place, Suite 400, Fort Worth, TX 76107
Tel: (817) 862-2800 Fax: (817) 862-2824

Resident Agent in Charge **Blake Gordon** .... (817) 862-2800
Explosives Enforcement Officer **Johnnie Green** .... (817) 862-2800
E-mail: johnnie.green@atf.gov
Industry Operations Area Supervisor **Sherry Perales** ..... (817) 862-2850

Lubbock (TX) Field Office
Sentry Plaza III, 5214 68th Street, Suite 300, Lubbock, TX 79424-1722
Tel: (806) 783-2700 Fax: (806) 783-2701

Resident Agent in Charge **(Vacant)** .... (806) 783-2700

Oklahoma City (OK) Field Office
901 NE 122nd Street, Suite 200, Oklahoma City, OK 73114
Tel: (405) 748-8291 Fax: (405) 748-8295

Resident Agent in Charge **(Vacant)** .... (405) 297-5060
Industry Operations Area Supervisor **Justin Demaree** ... (405) 297-5073
E-mail: justin.demaree@atf.gov

Tulsa (OK) Field Office
Pratt Towers, 125 West 15th Street, Suite 600, Tulsa, OK 74119-3822
Tel: (918) 594-1800 Fax: (918) 594-1801

Resident Agent in Charge **Justin Demaree** .... (918) 594-1800
E-mail: justin.demaree@atf.gov

Tyler (TX) Field Office
110 North College, Suite 1500, Tyler, TX 75702-7231
Tel: (903) 590-1475 Fax: (903) 590-1498

Resident Agent in Charge **Mike Graham** .... (903) 590-1475
E-mail: mike.graham@atf.gov

Denver (CO) Field Division
950 17th Street, Suite 1800, Denver, CO 80202
Tel: (303) 575-7600 Fax: (303) 575-7601

● Special Agent In Charge
Debora "Debbie" Livingston .... (303) 575-7600
Assistant Special Agent in Charge
W. Terry Henderson .... (303) 575-7600
Assistant Special Agent in Charge **Ronald Humphries** ... (303) 575-7600
E-mail: ronald.humphries@atf.gov
Director of Industry Operations **Paul Brown** .... (303) 575-7600
E-mail: paul.brown@atf.gov
Public Information Officer **Mary Markos** .... (303) 575-7611

Billings (MT) Field Office
2929 Third Avenue North, Billings, MT 59101
Tel: (406) 657-9700

Resident Agent in Charge **Scott Dvorak** .... (406) 657-9700
Fax: (406) 657-9701

Cheyenne (WY) Field Office
2120 Capitol Avenue, Cheyenne, WY 82001
Tel: (307) 633-9400

Resident Agent in Charge **Travis Riddle** .... (307) 633-9400
Fax: (307) 633-9401

Lander (WY) Satellite Office
980 12th Street, Lander, WY 82520
P.O. Box 1010, Lander, WY 82520
Tel: (307) 332-0920 Fax: (307) 332-0930

Special Agent **Jay Johnson** .... (307) 332-0920
Special Agent **(Vacant)** .... (307) 332-0920

Colorado Springs (CO) Field Office
5755 Mark Pabling Boulevard, Colorado Springs, CO 80919
Tel: (719) 445-5690 Fax: (719) 445-5691

Resident Agent in Charge **(Vacant)** .... (719) 445-5690

DEPARTMENTS

★ Presidential Appointment Requiring Senate Confirmation ☆ Presidential Appointment □ Schedule C Appointment ◇ Career Senior Foreign Service Appointment
● Career Senior Executive Service (SES) Appointment ○ Non-Career Senior Executive Service (SES) Appointment ■ Postal Career Executive Service

DEPARTMENTS

Denver (CO) Field Office
950 17th Street, Denver, CO 80202
Tel: (303) 844-7600 Fax: (303) 844-7601
Areas Covered: CO, UT, WY

Denver I Group Supervisor **Joshua Hernandez** . . . . (303) 575-7690
E-mail: joshua.hernandez@atf.gov Fax: (303) 575-7691
Denver II (Arson and Explosives) Group Supervisor
Tim Kelly . . . . (303) 575-7750
Fax: (303) 575-7751
Denver III (Industry Operations) Area Supervisor
Rebecca Solis . . . . (303) 575-7640
E-mail: rebecca.solis@atf.gov Fax: (303) 575-7641
Denver IV Group Supervisor **Jeffrey Russell** . . . . (303) 575-7720
Fax: (303) 575-7721
Denver VI Area Supervisor **Lacie Peterson** . . . . (303) 575-7640
Fax: (303) 575-7641

Helena (MT) Field Office
10 West 15th Street, Helena, MT 59626
Tel: (406) 441-3160

Area Supervisor **Kirk Nelson** . . . . (406) 441-3160
Resident Agent in Charge **Nat Olsen** . . . . (406) 441-3160

Missoula (MT) Satellite Office
200 East Broadway, Room 334, Missoula, MT 59802
Tel: (406) 721-2611

Special Agent **William "Bud" Ramsey** . . . . (406) 721-2611 ext. 1
Fax: (406) 721-7325

Salt Lake City (UT) Field Office
257 East 200 South, Salt Lake City, UT 84111-2048
Tel: (801) 524-7070 Fax: (801) 524-7050

Resident Agent in Charge **Brian Embley** . . . . (801) 524-7070
Area Supervisor **Tim Mawhinney** . . . . (801) 524-7000

Detroit (MI) Field Division
1155 Brewery Park Boulevard, Suite 300, Detroit, MI 48207-2602
Tel: (313) 202-3400 Fax: (313) 202-3445 E-mail: detroitdiv@atf.gov
Internet: www.atf.gov/field/detroit/index.html
Areas Covered: MI

● Special Agent-in-Charge **James M. Deir** . . . . (313) 202-3434
E-mail: james.deir@atf.gov
Assistant Special Agent-in-Charge **(Vacant)** . . . . (313) 202-3504
Assistant Special Agent-in-Charge **(Vacant)** . . . . (313) 259-3436
Director of Industry Operations **Scott Mendoza** . . . . (313) 202-3400
Public Information Officer **Ronnie Dahl** . . . . (313) 202-3578

Ann Arbor (MI) Field Office
200 East Liberty, Suite 308, Ann Arbor, MI 48104
Tel: (313) 202-3525 Fax: (313) 202-3445

Resident Agent-in-Charge **Scott Toth** . . . . (313) 202-3525

Flint (MI) Field Office
Northbank Center, 432 North Saginaw Street,
Suite 605, Flint, MI 48502
Tel: (810) 341-5710 Fax: (810) 341-5711

Resident Agent-in-Charge **Alan Jakubowski** . . . . (810) 341-5712

Grand Rapids (MI) I Field Office (Enforcement)
38 West Fulton, Suite 200, Grand Rapids, MI 49503
Tel: (616) 301-6100 Fax: (616) 732-2783

Resident Agent-in-Charge **Justin Herman** . . . . (616) 301-6108

Grand Rapids (MI) II Field Office (Industry Operations)
38 West Fulton, Suite 200, Grand Rapids, MI 49503
Tel: (616) 301-6100 Tel: (616) 456-2923

Area Supervisor **Lori Morell** . . . . (616) 301-6101

Houston (TX) Field Division
5825 North Sam Houston Parkway, Suite 300, Houston, TX 77086
Tel: (281) 716-8200 Fax: (281) 716-8219
Internet: www.atf.gov/field/houston/index.html
Areas Covered: South TX

● Special Agent-in-Charge **Frederick J. Milanowski** . . . . . . (281) 716-8200
Education: Central Michigan 1990 BBA; Detroit Law 1998 MA; Marine Corps U 2009 MS
Assistant Special Agent-in-Charge **Gary A. Orchowski** . . . (281) 372-2900
E-mail: gary.orchowski@atf.gov
Assistant Special Agent-in-Charge **Arthur Peralta** . . . . (281) 716-8202
E-mail: arthur.peralta@atf.gov
Assistant Special Agent-in-Charge **Crisanto Perez** . . . . (210) 805-2727
E-mail: crisanto.perez@usdoj.gov
Area Supervisor **(Vacant)** . . . . (281) 716-8200
Area Supervisor/Industry Operations **Derek Ball** . . . . (281) 716-8200
Director of Industry Operations **Tanarra James** . . . . (281) 716-8204
Public Information Officer **Nicole Strong** . . . . (281) 716-8207
E-mail: nicole.strong@atf.gov

Austin (TX) Field Office
9009 Mountain Ridge Drive, Suite 220, Austin, TX 78759
Tel: (512) 349-4545 Fax: (512) 349-4550

Resident Agent-in-Charge **Daniel Jones** . . . . (512) 349-4545
E-mail: daniel.jones@atf.gov

Beaumont (TX) Field Office
2615 Calder Avenue, Suite 330, Beaumont, TX 77702
Tel: (409) 981-6670 Fax: (409) 981-6671

Resident Agent-in-Charge **Larry Sanders** . . . . (409) 981-6670
E-mail: larry.sanders@atf.gov

Corpus Christi (TX) Field Office
802 North Carancahua, Suite 1670, Corpus Christi, TX 78470
Tel: (361) 888-3391 Fax: (361) 888-3395

Resident Agent-in-Charge **Richard "Rick" Miller** . . . . (361) 888-3391
E-mail: richard.miller@atf.gov

Houston (TX) Area Office
5825 N. Sam Houston Pkwy W, Suite 300, Houston, TX 77086
Tel: (281) 716-8200 Fax: (281) 716-8219

Houston I Supervisor **Tom Tallas** 300 . . . . (281) 716-9900
Houston II Supervisor **George Taylor** . . . . (281) 716-8780
Houston III Supervisor (Arson Explosives Task Force)
Gena Alvarez 300 . . . . (281) 716-8260
E-mail: gena.alvarez@atf.gov
Houston IV Supervisor **Kirk Tinker** . . . . (281) 716-9903
E-mail: kirk.tinker@atf.gov
Houston V Supervisor (High Intensity Drug Trafficking Area) **Rich Bohan** . . . . (281) 372-3010
Area Supervisor/Industry Operations Group VI
Valentina Close . . . . (281) 716-8338
E-mail: valentina.close@atf.gov
Area Supervisor/Industry Operations Group VII
Derek Ball . . . . (281) 716-8360
E-mail: derrek.ball@atf.gov
Group VIII Supervisor **Daniel Casey** . . . . (281) 716-9933
E-mail: daniel.casey@atf.gov
Group IX Supervisor **Delmaria Cole-Bigelow** . . . . (281) 716-8234
E-mail: delmaria.cole-bigelow@atf.gov

Laredo (TX) Field Office
5810 San Bernardo, Suite 350, Laredo, TX 78041
Tel: (956) 764-7940

Resident Agent-in-Charge **Arthur Gonzalez** . . . . (956) 764-7940

McAllen (TX) Field Office
1100 East Laurel Avenue, Suite 301, McAllen, TX 78504
Tel: (956) 661-7930

Resident Agent-in-Charge **R. Mark Wilson** . . . . (956) 661-7930
Resident Agent-in-Charge **(Vacant)** . . . . (956) 661-7930
Area Supervisor **Edward Saavedra** . . . . (956) 661-7950

★ Presidential Appointment Requiring Senate Confirmation ☆ Presidential Appointment ☐ Schedule C Appointment ◇ Career Senior Foreign Service Appointment
● Career Senior Executive Service (SES) Appointment ○ Non-Career Senior Executive Service (SES) Appointment ■ Postal Career Executive Service

San Antonio (TX) Field Office
6100 Bandera Road, Suite 701, San Antonio, TX 78238
Tel: (210) 805-2727 Fax: (210) 805-2791

Area Supervisor Industry Operations **Enrique Franco** .... (210) 805-2777
E-mail: enrique.franco@atf.gov
Resident Agent in Charge **Bartholomew Mora** .... (210) 805-2727
E-mail: bartholomew.mora@atf.gov
Resident Agent in Charge **David Robeson** .... (210) 805-2727

Kansas City (MO) Field Division
1251 NW Briarcliff Parkway, Suite 600, Kansas City, MO 64116
Tel: (816) 559-0700 Fax: (816) 559-0701
Areas Covered: IA, KS, MO, NE

● Special Agent-in-Charge **George Lauder** .... (816) 559-0700
E-mail: george.lauder@atf.gov
Assistant Special Agent-in-Charge **(Vacant)** .... (816) 559-0700
Assistant Special Agent-in-Charge
Frederic D. Winston .... (314) 269-2200
E-mail: frederic.d.winston@usdoj.gov
Director of Industry Operations **William J. Miller** .... (816) 559-0700
Division Operations Officer **(Vacant)** .... (816) 559-0700
Public Information Officer **John Ham** .... (816) 559-0700
E-mail: john.ham@atf.gov

Cape Girardeau (MO) Field Office
Auburn Park, 3065 William Street, Suite 301, Cape Girardeau, MO 63703
Tel: (573) 331-7300 Fax: (573) 334-0603

Resident Agent-in-Charge/Special Agent
Dimechi Herring .... (573) 331-7300
E-mail: dimechi.herring@atf.gov
Investigative Analyst **Anthony Thompson** .... (573) 331-7300

Des Moines (IA) Field Office
210 Walnut, Room 707, Des Moines, IA 50309
Tel: (515) 362-4000 Fax: (515) 362-4002

Resident Agent-in-Charge/Special Agent
Donald Dockendorff .... (515) 362-4000
Investigative Analyst **Sherry Wells** .... (515) 362-4000

Kansas City (MO) Field Offices
2600 Grand Avenue, Suite 200, Kansas City, MO 64108
Tel: (816) 559-0700 Fax: (816) 559-0701

Group I Supervisor **Scott O'Brien** .... (816) 559-0710
Fax: (816) 559-0711
Investigative Analyst **Crystal Cooper** .... (816) 559-0710
Group II Supervisor **David Lin** .... (816) 559-0720
E-mail: david.lin@atf.gov Fax: (816) 559-0721
Investigative Analyst **Lorraine Lordi** .... (816) 559-0720
Group III Area Supervisor (Industry Operations)
Andrew Jensen .... (816) 559-0730
E-mail: andrew.jensen@atf.gov Fax: (816) 559-0731
Industry Operations Analyst **(Vacant)** .... (816) 559-0730
Fax: (816) 559-0731
Group IV Supervisor (Intelligence) **Matthew Brown** .... (816) 746-4962
10220 Northwest Ambassador Drive, Fax: (816) 746-9711
Suite 620, Kansas City, MO 64153
Investigative Analyst **Patty Bergloff** .... (816) 746-4962
10220 Northwest Ambassador Drive,
Suite 620, Kansas City, MO 64153
Group V Supervisor **Eric Immesberger** .... (816) 559-0850
E-mail: eric.immesberger@atf.gov Fax: (816) 559-0831
Investigative Analyst **Allison Robb** .... (816) 559-0850
E-mail: allison.brown@atf.gov
Group VI Supervisor **Richard Lake** .... (816) 559-0730
E-mail: richard.lake@atf.gov Fax: (816) 559-0815
Investigative Analyst **Barbara Tomlin** .... (816) 559-0730

Omaha (NE) Field Office
17310 Wright Street, Suite 204, Omaha, NE 68130
Tel: (402) 952-2605 Fax: (402) 952-2606

Resident Agent-in-Charge **Michael Parker** .... (402) 952-2605
Investigative Analyst **John Aasdemore** .... (402) 952-2605

Omaha (NE) Field Office *(continued)*

Group II Area Supervisor (Industry Operations)
Cannon Kinchelow .... (402) 952-2635
E-mail: cannon.kinchelow@atf.gov
Investigative Analyst **(Vacant)** .... (402) 952-2635

Saint Louis (MO) Field Office
1222 Spruce Street, Room 6.205, St. Louis, MO 63103
Tel: (314) 269-2200
Areas Covered: Eastern MO
Group I Supervisor **Chris Rodgers** .... (314) 269-2200
Fax: (314) 269-2238
Investigative Analyst **Nancy Woods** .... (314) 269-2200
Group II Supervisor **Andre Miller** .... (314) 269-2200
Fax: (314) 269-2237
Investigative Analyst **(Vacant)** .... (314) 269-2200
Group III Area Supervisor (Industry Operations)
Ron Young .... (314) 269-2250
Fax: (314) 369-2265
Investigative Analyst **Darrin Hutson** .... (314) 269-2250

Saint Louis Assistant Special Agent-in-Charge Office
1222 Spruce Street, Room 6.205, St. Louis, MO 63103
Tel: (314) 269-2250 Fax: (314) 269-2245
Assistant Special Agent-in-Charge (Criminal
Enforcement) **(Vacant)** .... (314) 768-3157
Administrative Assistant **(Vacant)** .... (314) 269-2242

Springfield (MO) Field Office
901 St. Louis, Suite 201, Springfield, MO 65806
Tel: (417) 837-2100 Fax: (417) 837-2156
Resident Agent-in-Charge **Joe Shepherd** .... (417) 837-2100
Investigative Analyst **Morgan Baker** .... (417) 837-2100

Wichita (KS) Field Office
301 North Main Street, Suite 225, Wichita, KS 67202
Tel: (316) 269-6229 Fax: (316) 269-6220
Resident Agent-in-Charge **Creighton Bradt** .... (316) 269-6229
Investigative Analyst **Sattin Janserv** .... (316) 269-6229

Los Angeles (CA) Field Division
550 North Brand Boulevard, Suite 800, Glendale, CA 91203
Tel: (818) 265-2500 Fax: (818) 265-2501
Internet: www.atf.gov/field/losangeles/index.html
Areas Covered: South CA
● Special Agent-in-Charge **William P. "Bill" McMullan** .... (818) 265-2500
E-mail: william.mcmullan@atf.gov
Executive Assistant **Phyllis Castrejon** .... (818) 265-2500
E-mail: phyllis.castrejon@atf.gov
Assistant Special Agent-in-Charge **John D'Angelo** ...... (818) 265-2500
E-mail: john.d'angelo@atf.gov
Assistant Special Agent-in-Charge **Monique Villegas** .... (213) 534-2500
Director of Industry Operations **(Vacant)** .... (818) 265-2500
Division Operations Officer **Susan K. Raichel** .... (213) 534-2500
Public Information Officer **Giagi Colburn** .... (818) 265-2507
E-mail: giagi.colburn@atf.gov

El Centro (CA) Field Office
2437 Enterprise Trail, Imperial, CA 92251
Tel: (818) 265-3732 Fax: (818) 265-3731
Resident Agent in Charge **Chad Key** .... (818) 265-3732
E-mail: chad.key@atf.gov

Glendale (CA) Field Office I
550 North Brand Boulevard, Suite 800, Glendale, CA 91203
Tel: (818) 265-7032 Fax: (818) 265-2511
Group Supervisor **John R. Osborn III** .... (818) 265-2510
E-mail: john.osborn@atf.gov

DEPARTMENTS

★ Presidential Appointment Requiring Senate Confirmation ☆ Presidential Appointment □ Schedule C Appointment ◇ Career Senior Foreign Service Appointment
● Career Senior Executive Service (SES) Appointment ○ Non-Career Senior Executive Service (SES) Appointment ■ Postal Career Executive Service

Glendale (CA) Field Office II
550 North Brand Boulevard, 8th Floor, Glendale, CA 91203
Tel: (818) 265-2530 Fax: (818) 265-2531
Group Supervisor **Carmine Downey** . . . . (818) 265-2530
E-mail: carmine.downey@atf.gov

Glendale (CA) Field Office III
550 North Brand Boulevard, 8th Floor, Glendale, CA 91203
Tel: (818) 265-2540 Fax: (818) 265-2541
Area Supervisor **Antonia Reza** . . . . (818) 265-2540
E-mail: antonia.reza@atf.gov

Glendale (CA) Field Office IV
550 North Brand Avenue, 8th Floor, Glendale, CA 91203
Tel: (818) 265-2550 Fax: (818) 265-2551
Group Supervisor **Christopher Bombardiere** . . . . (818) 265-2550
E-mail: christopher.bombardiere@atf.gov

Glendale (CA) Field Office V
550 North Brand Boulevard, Suite 800, Glendale, CA 91203
Tel: (818) 265-2560 Fax: (818) 265-2561
Group Supervisor (Acting) **Joshua Jackson** . . . . (818) 756-4350
E-mail: joshua.jackson@atf.gov

Long Beach (CA) Field Office
301 East Ocean Boulevard, Suite 2050, Long Beach, CA 90802
Tel: (818) 265-3760 Fax: (818) 265-3761
Resident Agent in Charge **Daryl Thomas** . . . . (818) 265-3760
E-mail: darryl.thomas@atf.gov

Los Angeles (CA) Field Office I
888 South Figueroa Street, Suite 1170, Los Angeles, CA 90017
Tel: (818) 265-8020 Fax: (818) 265-8021
Resident Agent in Charge **Matthew Collins** . . . . (213) 265-8020
E-mail: matthew.collins@atf.gov

Los Angeles (CA) Field Office II
888 South Figueroa Street, Room 1050, Los Angeles, CA 90017
Tel: (818) 265-8050 Fax: (818) 265-8051
Resident Agent in Charge **Kenneth Tomlinson** . . . . (818) 265-8050
E-mail: kenneth.tomlinson@atf.gov

Riverside (CA) Field Office
3801 University Avenue, Suite 670, Riverside, CA 92501
Tel: (951) 320-7560 Fax: (951) 320-7562
Resident Agent-in-Charge **Adam Ekstrom** . . . . (951) 276-6031
E-mail: adam.ekstrom@atf.gov

Riverside (CA) Satellite Office (IO)
3801 University Avenue, Suite 670, Riverside, CA 92501
Tel: (858) 966-1030 Fax: (858) 966-1021
Investigator **Thomas Chimileski** . . . . (951) 320-7560
E-mail: thomas.chimileski@atf.gov

San Diego (CA) Field Office I
9449 Balboa Ave., Suite 200, San Diego, CA 92123
Tel: (858) 966-1010 Fax: (858) 966-1021
Resident Agent-in-Charge **Brad Galvan** . . . . (619) 966-1010
E-mail: brad.galvan@atf.gov

San Diego (CA) Field Office II
9449 Balboa Ave., Suite 200, San Diego, CA 92123
Tel: (858) 966-1030 Fax: (858) 966-1021
Resident Agent-in-Charge **Jin Chah** . . . . (858) 966-1030
E-mail: jin.chah@atf.gov

San Diego (CA) Field Office III (IO)
9449 Balboa Ave., Suite 200, San Diego, CA 92123
Tel: (858) 966-1030 Fax: (858) 966-1021
Area Supervisor **Juan Lopez** . . . . (858) 966-1030
E-mail: juan.lopez@atf.gov

San Diego (CA) Field Office IV
5901 Priestly Drive, Suite 304, Carlsbad, CA 92008
Tel: (818) 265-3700 Fax: (818) 265-3701
Resident Agent in Charge **Armando Hernandez** . . . . (818) 265-3700
E-mail: armando.hernandez@atf.gov

Santa Ana (CA) Field Office I
34 Civic Center Plaza, Room 6121, Santa Ana, CA 92701
Tel: (714) 347-9100 Fax: (714) 347-9101
Resident Agent-in-Charge **Bryan Berryman** . . . . (714) 347-9100
E-mail: bryan.berryman@atf.gov

Santa Ana (CA) Field Office II (IO)
34 Civic Center Plaza, Room 6121, Santa Ana, CA 92701
Tel: (714) 347-9150 Fax: (714) 347-9151
Area Supervisor **Thomas Lane** . . . . (714) 347-9150
E-mail: thomas.lane@atf.gov

Santa Maria (CA) Satellite Office (Criminal Enforcement)
1010 South Broadway, Suite J, Santa Maria, CA 93434
Tel: (805) 348-1820 Fax: (805) 348-9916
Group Supervisor (Acting) **Joshua Jackson** . . . . (805) 348-1820
E-mail: joshua.jackson@atf.gov

Santa Maria (CA) Satellite Office (IO)
1010 South Broadway, Suite J, Santa Maria, CA 93434
Tel: (805) 348-0027 Fax: (805) 348-9916
Investigator **Antonia Reza** . . . . (805) 348-0027
E-mail: antonia.reza@atf.gov

Louisville (KY) Field Division
600 Dr. Martin Luther King, Jr. Place,
Suite 500, Louisville, KY 40202
Tel: (502) 753-3400 Fax: (502) 753-3401
Areas Covered: KY, WV
● Special Agent-in-Charge **Stuart Lowrey** . . . . (502) 753-3400
Executive Assistant **Shwanda Alexander** . . . . (502) 753-3400
E-mail: shwanda.alexander@atf.gov
Assistant Special Agent-in-Charge **Tommy Estevan** . . . . . (502) 753-3400
E-mail: tommy.estevan@atf.gov
Director of Industry Operations **Adam Rogers** . . . . (502) 753-3400
Public Information Officer **George Huffman** . . . . (502) 753-3400

Ashland (KY) Field Office
1405 Greenup Avenue, Suite 232, Ashland, KY 41101
Tel: (270) 393-4801 Fax: (606) 325-5251
Resident Agent-in-Charge **(Vacant)** . . . . (270) 393-4801

Bowling Green (KY) Field Office
990 Wilkinson Place, Suite 205, Bowling Green, KY 42103
Tel: (270) 393-4756
Resident Agent-in-Charge **John Nokes** . . . . (270) 393-4755
E-mail: john.nokes@atf.gov

Bowling Green (KY) Satellite Office (Industry Operations)
2530 Scottsville Road, Room 26, Bowling Green, KY 42104
Fax: (270) 781-5543
Supervisor **Adam Rogers** . . . . (502) 753-3500
Fax: (502) 753-3501

Charleston (WV) Field Office
300 Summers Street, Suite 1400, Charleston, WV 25301
Tel: (304) 340-7800 Fax: (304) 340-7801
Resident Agent-in-Charge **Adam Black** . . . . (304) 340-7800

Charleston (WV) Satellite Office (Industry Operations)
300 Summers Street, Charleston, WV 25301
Tel: (304) 340-7820 Fax: (304) 340-7821

Supervisor **James Lentz** .... (304) 340-7820
E-mail: james.lentz@atf.gov

Clarksburg (WV) Field Office
111 Cambridge Place, Clarksburg, WV 26330
Tel: (304) 842-9830 Fax: (304) 842-9831

Resident Agent-in-Charge **Dewayne Haddix** .... (304) 842-9830

Lexington (KY) Field Office (Industry Operations)
2424 Sir Barton Way, Suite 250, Lexington, KY 40509
Tel: (502) 813-3725 Fax: (502) 813-3743

Area Supervisor **David Perry** .... (859) 219-4500

Lexington (KY) Field Office
2424 Sir Barton Way, Suite 200, Lexington, KY 40509
Tel: (502) 813-3700 Fax: (502) 813-3742

Resident Agent-in-Charge **Robert Maynare** .... (859) 219-4500

Lexington (KY) IV Satellite Office
2424 Sir Barton Way, Suite 200, Lexington, KY 40509

Resident Agent-in-Charge **William Baudhuin** .... (859) 219-4500

Louisville I (KY) Field Office
600 Dr. Martin Luther King, Jr. Place, Louisville, KY 40202
Tel: (502) 753-3450 Fax: (502) 753-3451

Louisville I Field Office Resident Agent-in-Charge
Brad Leberitt .... (502) 753-3450
Louisville II Field Office (Industry Operations)
Supervisor **Andrew Perdas** .... (502) 753-3500
Louisville III Field Office Group Supervisor
Kimberly K. Riddell .... (502) 753-3550
Fax: (502) 753-3551
Louisville IV Field Office Group Supervisor
Lawrence "Geoff" Brown .... (502) 753-3550

Wheeling (WV) Satellite Office
Riley Building, 53 - 14th Street, Room 200, Wheeling, WV 26003-3433
Tel: (304) 232-4170 Fax: (304) 233-9353

Resident Agent-in-Charge **Dewayne Haddix** .... (304) 232-4170
E-mail: dewayne.haddix@atf.gov

Miami (FL) Field Division
11410 NW 20 Street, Suite 201, Miami, FL 33178
Tel: (305) 597-4960 Fax: (305) 597-4801
Areas Covered: South FL, PR, VI

● Special Agent-in-Charge **Ari Shapira** .... (305) 597-4960
E-mail: ari.shapira@atf.gov
Assistant Special Agent-in-Charge **(Vacant)** .... (305) 597-4960
Director of Industry Operations **Mark Williams** .... (305) 597-4960
E-mail: mark.williams@atf.gov
Division Operations Officer **Melissa Davis** .... (305) 597-4960
Division Counsel **Robert J. Wilder** .... (305) 597-4960
E-mail: robert.wilder@atf.gov
Public Information Officer **Clara Himel** .... (305) 597-4960
E-mail: clara.himel@atf.gov

Puerto Rico Field Office
350 Carlos Chardon Street, Room 301, San Juan, PR 00918
Tel: (787) 773-3300 Fax: (787) 773-3301

Group 1 Supervisor **Jose Ruiz** .... (787) 773-3300
Group 2 Supervisor **Billy L. Wright** .... (787) 773-3300
E-mail: billy.l.wright@usdoj.gov
Group 3 Supervisor **Julio Torres** .... (787) 773-3300
E-mail: julio.torres@atf.gov

Nashville (TN) Field Division
5300 Maryland Way, Suite 200, Brentwood, TN 37027
Tel: (615) 565-1400 Fax: (615) 565-1401
Internet: www.atf.gov/field/nashville/index.html
Areas Covered: AL, TN

● Special Agent-in-Charge **Marcus S. Watson** .... (615) 565-1400
E-mail: marcus.s.watson@usdoj.gov
Assistant Special Agent-in-Charge **David Hyche** .... (615) 565-1400
Assistant Special Agent-in-Charge **(Vacant)** .... (615) 565-1400
Industry Operations Director **Steven A. Kolb** .... (615) 565-1400
Public Information Officer **Michael Knight** .... (615) 565-1400

Birmingham (AL) Field Office I
920 18th Street North, Room 201, Birmingham, AL 35203
Tel: (205) 583-5920 Fax: (205) 583-5921

Resident Agent-in-Charge **Alicia Jones** .... (205) 583-5920

Birmingham (AL) Field Office II (Industry Operations)
920 18th Street North, Room 237, Birmingham, AL 35203
Tel: (205) 583-5950 Fax: (205) 583-5951

Area Supervisor **M. Theresa Patrick** .... (205) 583-5950

Birmingham (AL) Field Office III
920 18th Street North, Room 214, Birmingham, AL 35203
Tel: (205) 583-5970 Fax: (205) 583-5971

Resident Agent-in-Charge **Lucas Iverson** .... (205) 583-5970

Chattanooga (TN) Field Office
Franklin Building, 5726 Marlin Road,
Suite 316, Chattanooga, TN 37411-4024
Tel: (423) 855-6422 Fax: (423) 855-6437

Resident Agent-in-Charge **Benjamin Gibbons** .... (423) 855-6422

Knoxville (TN) Field Office
710 Locust Street, Suite 514, Knoxville, TN 37902
Tel: (865) 582-3800 Fax: (865) 545-4512

Resident Agent-in-Charge **Keith Jordan** .... (865) 582-3800

Memphis (TN) Field Office I
225 North Humphreys Boulevard, Suite 2069, Memphis, TN 38120
Tel: (901) 334-5000 Fax: (901) 334-5620

Resident Agent in Charge **Christopher Beavers** .... (901) 334-5000

Memphis (TN) Field Office III
225 North Humphreys Boulevard, Suite 2069, Memphis, TN 38120
Tel: (901) 334-5600 Fax: (901) 334-5620

Resident Agent-in-Charge **(Vacant)** .... (901) 334-5000

Mobile (AL) Field Office
110 Beauregard Street, Suite 300, Mobile, AL 36602
Tel: (251) 405-5000 Fax: (251) 405-5010

Resident Agent-in-Charge **Michael A. Messinger** .... (251) 405-5000

Montgomery (AL) Field Office
Two North Jackson Street, Suite 404, Montgomery, AL 36104
Tel: (334) 206-6050 Fax: (334) 206-6051

Resident Agent-in-Charge **Jennifer Conway** .... (334) 206-6050

Nashville (TN) Field Office I
5300 Maryland Way, Suite 200, Brentwood, TN 37027
Tel: (615) 565-1410 Fax: (615) 565-1411

Group Supervisor **Frank Haera** .... (615) 565-1410
E-mail: frank.haera@atf.gov

Nashville (TN) Field Office II (Industry Operations)
5300 Maryland Way, Suite 200, Brentwood, TN 37027
Tel: (615) 565-1420 Fax: (615) 565-1412

Area Supervisor **Timothy Lang** .... (615) 565-1420

DEPARTMENTS

★ Presidential Appointment Requiring Senate Confirmation ☆ Presidential Appointment ☐ Schedule C Appointment ◇ Career Senior Foreign Service Appointment
● Career Senior Executive Service (SES) Appointment ○ Non-Career Senior Executive Service (SES) Appointment ■ Postal Career Executive Service

Nashville (TN) Field Office III (Intelligence)
5300 Maryland Way, Suite 200, Brentwood, TN 37027
Tel: (615) 565-1430 Fax: (615) 565-1401
Group Supervisor **Anthony "Wayne" Kilvay** . . . . (615) 565-1430

Nashville (TN) Field Office IV (Industry Operations)
5300 Maryland Way, Suite 200, Brentwood, TN 37027
Tel: (615) 565-1416 Fax: (615) 565-1412
Area Supervisor **Gregory Jackson** . . . . (615) 565-1416
E-mail: gregory.jackson@atf.gov

Nashville (TN) Field Office V
5300 Maryland Way, Suite 200, Brentwood, TN 37027
Tel: (615) 565-1410 Fax: (615) 565-1411
Group Supervisor **Marvin Longwood** . . . . (615) 565-1410

Newark (NJ) Field Division
One Garret Mountain Plaza, Suite 400, Woodland Park, NJ 07424
Tel: (973) 413-1179 Fax: (973) 413-1190
- • Special Agent In Charge **John Devito** . . . . (973) 413-1179

Assistant Special Agent in Charge **Scott Curley** . . . . (973) 413-1179
E-mail: scott.curley@atf.gov
Public Information Officer **Walter Kudron** . . . . (973) 247-3052
E-mail: walter.kudron@atf.gov
Director of Industry Operations **John Curtis** . . . . (973) 413-1179
Division Operation Officer **Peter Wagner** . . . . (973) 413-1179
E-mail: peter.wagner@atf.gov
Division Counsel **Lisa A. Jakubczyk** . . . . (973) 413-1179

New Jersey Group I (Criminal - Firearms)
Three Garret Mountain Plaza, Suite 202, Woodland Park, NJ 07424
Tel: (973) 247-3010 Fax: (973) 247-3011
Areas Covered: Northern and Central New Jersey
Supervisory Special Agent **Jason Zanaloss** . . . . (973) 247-3010

New Jersey Group II (Criminal - Arson and Explosives)
Three Garret Mountain Plaza, Suite 202, Woodland Park, NJ 07424
Tel: (973) 247-3020 Fax: (973) 247-3021
Areas Covered: New Jersey
Supervisory Special Agent **David Gibson** . . . . (973) 247-3020

New Jersey Group III (Industry Operations)
Three Garret Mountain Plaza, Suite 202, Woodland Park, NJ 07424
Tel: (973) 247-3030 Fax: (973) 247-3031
Areas Covered: All of Northern NJ
Group Supervisor **Maureen O'Rouke** . . . . (973) 247-3030
E-mail: maureen.orourke@atf.gov

New Jersey Group IV
Three Garret Mountain Plaza, Suite 202, Woodland Park, NJ 07424
Tel: (973) 413-1179
Group Supervisor **Michael Mohr** . . . . (973) 413-1179
E-mail: michael.mohr@atf.gov

Camden Field Office
Cherry Tree Corporate Center, 535 State Highway #38,
Suite 310, Cherry Hill, NJ 08002
Tel: (856) 488-2520 Fax: (856) 910-9245
Resident Agent in Charge **Thomas "Tom" Greco** . . . . (856) 488-2520

Atlantic City Satellite Office
English Creek Corporate Center, 500 Scarborough Drive,
Suite 303, Egg Harbor Township, NJ 08234
Tel: (609) 487-2110 Fax: (609) 487-2109
Resident Agent in Charge **Michael Gibbons** . . . . (609) 487-2110
E-mail: michael.gibbons@atf.gov

Trenton Field Office
Station Plaza III, 44 South Clinton Avenue,
Room 701, Trenton, NJ 08609-1227
Tel: (609) 989-2155 Fax: (609) 989-2358
Resident Agent in Charge **Joseph "Joe" Bodnar** . . . . (609) 989-2155

Trenton Satellite Office (Industry Operations)
Station Plaza III, 44 South Clinton Avenue, Trenton, NJ 08609-1227
Tel: (609) 989-2142 Fax: (609) 989-2358
Supervisory Inspector **Maureen O'Rouke** . . . . (609) 989-2142

New Orleans (LA) Field Division
One Galleria Boulevard, Suite 1700, Metairie, LA 70001
Tel: (504) 841-7000 Fax: (504) 841-7039
Areas Covered: AR, LA, MS
- • Special Agent-in-Charge **Dana K. Nichols** . . . . (504) 841-7000

Assistant Special Agent-in-Charge **William J. McCrary** . . . (504) 841-7000
Assistant Special Agent-in-Charge **Jeffrey R. Powell** . . . . . (504) 841-7000
E-mail: jeffrey.r.powell@usdoj.gov
Director of Industry Operations **Matt Wren** . . . . (504) 841-7000
Operations Officer **Kevin Moran** . . . . (504) 841-7000

Baton Rouge (LA) Field Office
5757 Corporate Boulevard, Suite 300, Baton Rouge, LA 70808
Tel: (225) 231-6620 Fax: (225) 231-6651
Resident Agent-in-Charge/Special Agent
Antonio Pittman . . . . (225) 231-6620

Gulfport (MS) Field Office
1319 26th Avenue, Suite 300, Gulfport, MS 39501
Tel: (228) 575-6501 Fax: (228) 575-6545
Resident Agent-in-Charge **Jason Denham** . . . . (228) 575-6501

Jackson (MS) Field Office
Federal Building, 100 West Capitol Street,
Suite 1403, Jackson, MS 39269
Tel: (601) 863-0900 Fax: (601) 863-0901
Resident Agent-in-Charge **Robert Haar** . . . . (601) 863-0900
Jackson II (Industry Operations) Area
Supervisor/Inspector **(Vacant)** . . . . (601) 863-0940
Fax: (601) 863-0931

Little Rock (AR) Field Office
425 West Capitol, Room 775, Little Rock, AR 72201
Tel: (501) 324-6181 Fax: (501) 324-5301
Resident Agent-in-Charge/Special Agent **Jeff Reed** . . . . . . (501) 324-6181
Area Supervisor/Inspector **Erik J. Longnecker** . . . . (501) 324-6457
E-mail: erik.j.longnecker@usdoj.gov Fax: (501) 324-6695

New Orleans (LA) Field Offices
One Galleria Boulevard, Suite 1800, Metairie, LA 70001
Fax: (985) 246-7038
New Orleans Group I Supervisor/Special Agent
Raymond "Ray" Connor . . . . (504) 841-7100
E-mail: raymond.connor@atf.gov Fax: (504) 841-7154
New Orleans Group II Supervisor (Firearms)/Special
Agent **Joe Belile** . . . . (504) 841-7140
Fax: (504) 841-7141
New Orleans Group III (Industry Operations) Area
Supervisor/Inspector **Angele Guient** . . . . (504) 841-7120
Fax: (504) 841-7159
New Orleans Group IV Supervisor
(Intelligence)/Special Agent **Mike Valle** . . . . (504) 841-7160
Fax: (504) 841-7189

Oxford (MS) Field Office
2109 University Avenue, Suite 202, Oxford, MS 38655
Tel: (662) 234-3751 Fax: (662) 236-4094
Resident Agent in Charge **Joe Frank** MS 38655 . . . . (662) 234-3751

★ Presidential Appointment Requiring Senate Confirmation ☆ Presidential Appointment ☐ Schedule C Appointment ◇ Career Senior Foreign Service Appointment
● Career Senior Executive Service (SES) Appointment ○ Non-Career Senior Executive Service (SES) Appointment ■ Postal Career Executive Service

Shreveport (LA) Field Office
400 Texas Street, Suite 500, Shreveport, LA 71101
Tel: (318) 424-6850 Fax: (318) 424-6871

Resident Agent-in-Charge **Kevin Smith** .... (318) 424-6850
E-mail: kevin.smith@atf.gov

New York (NY) Field Division
Financial Square, 32 Old Slip, Suite 3500, New York, NY 10005
Tel: (646) 335-9000 Fax: (646) 335-9001 E-mail: nydiv@atf.gov
Internet: www.atf.gov/field/newyork/index.html
Areas Covered: New York State

● Special Agent-in-Charge **Ashan M. Benedict** .... (646) 335-9000
Assistant Special Agent-in-Charge **James S. Higgins** .... (646) 335-9000
E-mail: james.higgins@atf.gov
Assistant Special Agent-in-Charge **Toby C. Taylor** .... (646) 335-9000
Director of Industry Operations **John Curtis** .... (646) 335-9000
E-mail: john.curtis@atf.gov
Public Information Officer **(Vacant)** .... (646) 335-9000
Division Counsel **Matthew Myerson** .... (646) 335-9000
E-mail: matthew.myerson@atf.gov
Organized Crime Drug Enforcement Task Force Coordinator **Kevin Kelleher** .... (646) 805-6324
88 10th Avenue, 3rd Floor, New York, NY 10011
E-mail: kevin.kelleher@atf.gov

Albany (NY) Field Office (Criminal)
North Pearl Street and Clinton Avenue,
Room 911, Albany, NY 12207-2202
Tel: (518) 431-4188 Fax: (518) 431-4183

Resident Agent-in-Charge **Brian Mein** .... (518) 431-4182

Buffalo (NY) I Field Office (Criminal)
598 Main Street, Suite 201, Buffalo, NY 14202
Tel: (716) 853-5070 Fax: (716) 853-5071

Resident Agent-in-Charge **Steven Dickey** .... (716) 853-5070

Buffalo (NY) II Field Office (Industry Operations)
598 Main Street, Suite 201, Buffalo, NY 14202
Tel: (716) 853-5160 Fax: (716) 853-5161

Area Supervisor **Edward Larouere** .... (716) 853-5160
E-mail: edward.larovere@atf.gov

Hudson Valley Field Office (Criminal)
1250 Waters Place, Suite 801, Bronx, NY 10461
Tel: (646) 335-9130 Fax: (646) 335-9131

Group Supervisor **(Vacant)** .... (646) 335-9130

Melville (NY) Field Office (Criminal)
155 Pinelawn Road, Suite 250 South, Melville, NY 11747
Tel: (631) 694-8372 Fax: (631) 249-8950
Areas Covered: Nassau County, Suffolk County

Resident Agent-in-Charge **Kenneth "Kenny" Crotty** .... (631) 694-8372
E-mail: kenneth.crotty@atf.gov

New York Group I (Criminal - Firearms)
300 Coffey Street, Brooklyn, NY 11231
Tel: (718) 552-1610 Fax: (718) 552-1611
Areas Covered: New York City Metropolitan Area

Supervisory Special Agent **John Chang** .... (718) 254-7845

New York Group II (Criminal - Firearms)
300 Coffey Street, Brooklyn, NY 11231
Tel: (718) 552-1620 Fax: (718) 552-1621
Areas Covered: New York City Metropolitan Area

Supervisory Special Agent **Jennifer Cicolani** .... (718) 552-1636
E-mail: jennifer.cicolani@atf.gov

New York Group III (Criminal - Arson and Explosives)
97-45 Queens Boulevard, 5th Floor, Rego Park, NY 11374
Tel: (646) 335-9130 Fax: (646) 335-9131
Areas Covered: New York City Metropolitan Area

Supervisory Special Agent **Brian DiGirolamo** .... (646) 335-9130
E-mail: bryan.digirolamo@atf.gov

New York Group IV (Criminal - Firearms)
241 - 37th Street, 3rd Floor, Brooklyn, NY 11232
Tel: (646) 335-9140 Fax: (646) 335-9141
Areas Covered: New York City Metropolitan Area

Supervisory Special Agent **(Vacant)** .... (646) 335-9140

New York Group V (Criminal - Firearms)
241 - 37th Street, 3rd Floor, Brooklyn, NY 11232
Tel: (646) 335-9150 Fax: (646) 335-9151
Areas Covered: New York City Metropolitan Area

Supervisory Special Agent **Andrew Boss** .... (646) 335-9150

New York Group VI (Industry Operations)
241 - 37th Street, 3rd Floor, Brooklyn, NY 11232
Tel: (646) 335-9060 Fax: (646) 335-9161
Areas Covered: Southern New York State

Supervisory Area Inspector **Merna Howard** .... (718) 650-4060

New York Group VII - (NY-NJ Regional Crime Gun Center)
241 - 37th Street, 3rd Floor, Brooklyn, NY 11232
Tel: (646) 335-9070 Fax: (646) 335-9071
Internet: www.atf.treas.gov/field/newyork/rcgc
Areas Covered: Divisionwide

Supervisory Special Agent **Kevin Kelleher** .... (646) 355-9070

Rochester (NY) Field Office (Criminal)
100 Chestnut Street, Suite 1100, Rochester, NY 14604
Tel: (585) 987-2100 Fax: (585) 987-2101

Resident Agent in Charge **(Vacant)** .... (585) 987-2100

Syracuse (NY) Field Office (Criminal)
100 South Clinton Street, Room 509, Syracuse, NY 13261
Tel: (315) 448-0889 Fax: (315) 448-0891

Resident Agent in Charge **Thomas Jusiauiec** .... (315) 448-0889

Philadelphia (PA) Field Division
The Curtis Center, 601 Walnut Street,
Suite 1000 E, Philadelphia, PA 19106
Tel: (215) 446-7800 Fax: (215) 446-7811
Areas Covered: Pennsylvania

● Special Agent-in-Charge **Donald G. Robinson** .... (215) 446-7800
Industry Operations Director **Juan Orellana** .... (215) 446-7800
Assistant Special Agent-in-Charge **Christopher Taylor** ... (215) 446-7800
E-mail: christopher.taylor@atf.gov
Public Information Officer **Amanda Hils** .... (215) 446-7800
E-mail: amanda.hils@atf.gov

Harrisburg (PA) Field Office
Market Square Plaza, 17 North Second Street,
Suite 1400, Harrisburg, PA 17101
Tel: (717) 231-3420 Fax: (717) 231-3401

Resident Agent-in-Charge **Eric Poole** .... (717) 231-3400
Area Supervisor **Michael Krivistky** .... (717) 231-3400

Lansdale (PA) Field Office (Industry Operations)
Century Plaza Building, 100 W. Main Street,
Suite 300-B, Lansdale, PA 19446-2022
Tel: (215) 362-1840 Fax: (215) 362-6532
Areas Covered: PA

Area Supervisor **Steve Konnovitch** .... (215) 362-1840

★ Presidential Appointment Requiring Senate Confirmation ☆ Presidential Appointment □ Schedule C Appointment ◇ Career Senior Foreign Service Appointment
● Career Senior Executive Service (SES) Appointment ○ Non-Career Senior Executive Service (SES) Appointment ■ Postal Career Executive Service

Philadelphia (PA) Field Office
Philadelphia, PA 19106

Group I (Firearms Trafficking) Supervisor **Jill Tucker** .... (215) 446-9610
U.S. Custom House, Fax: (215) 446-9611
2nd and Chestnut Street,
Suite 607, Philadelphia, PA 19106
E-mail: jill.tucker@atf.gov

Group II (Arson/Explosives) Supervisor
Mark Monaghan .... (215) 446-7860
U.S. Custom House, Fax: (215) 446-7861
Second and Chestnut Streets,
Suite 607, Philadelphia, PA 19106

Group V Supervisor **Steven Bartholomew** .... (215) 446-7840
U.S. Custom House, Fax: (215) 717-7841
Second and Chestnut Streets,
Room 607, Philadelphia, PA 19106

Group VI (Operation Cease Fire) Supervisor
John Bowman .... (215) 446-9640
U.S. Custom House, Fax: (215) 446-9641
Second and Chestnut Streets,
Room 607, Philadelphia, PA 19106

Group VII Supervisor **Brian Gallagher** .... (215) 446-9690
U.S. Custom House, Fax: (215) 446-9653
Second and Chestnut Streets,
Room 607, Philadelphia, PA 19106
E-mail: brian.gallagher@atf.gov

Pittsburgh (PA) Field Office
William S. Moorhead Federal Building,
1000 Liberty Avenue, Pittsburgh, PA 15222-4101
Tel: (412) 395-0540
Areas Covered: PA

Group I (Firearms) Supervisor **Louis Weiers** William S. Moorehead Federal Building, Suite 1414 .... (412) 395-0540
E-mail: louis.weiers@atf.gov Fax: (412) 395-0541

Group II (Arson/Explosives) Supervisor **Joseph Price**
William S. Moorehead Federal Building, Suite 1414 .... (412) 395-0540
E-mail: joseph.price@atf.gov Fax: (412) 395-0541

Group III (Industry Operations) Area Supervisor
Matthew Grimm William S. Moorehead Federal Building, Suite 1414 .... (412) 395-0600
Fax: (412) 395-0601

Reading (PA) Field Office
400 Washington Street, Room 500, Reading, PA 19601
Tel: (610) 208-5200 Fax: (610) 208-5201

Resident Agent-in-Charge **Eric Degree** .... (610) 208-5200
E-mail: eric.degree@atf.gov

Wilkes-Barre (PA) Area Office
Seven North Wilkes-Barre Boulevard,
Suite 271M, Wilkes Barre, PA 18702
Tel: (570) 820-2210 Fax: (570) 826-2225

Area Supervisor **Walter Glahn** .... (570) 820-2210

Phoenix (AZ) Field Division
201 East Washington Street, Suite 940, Phoenix, AZ 85004
Tel: (602) 776-5400 Tel: (602) 776-5480 (Industry Operations)
Fax: (602) 776-5429
Areas Covered: AZ, CO, NM, WY, UT

● Special Agent-in-Charge **John Durastanti** .... (602) 776-5400
E-mail: john.durastanti@atf.gov

Assistant Special Agent-in-Charge **Mark E. Murray** .... (602) 776-5400
E-mail: mark.murray@atf.gov

Assistant Special Agent-in-Charge
Gabriel "Gabe" Pinon .... (602) 776-5400
E-mail: gabriel.pinon@atf.gov

Assistant Special Agent-in-Charge **(Vacant)** .... (602) 776-5400

Industry Operations Director **Terry R. Dogan** .... (602) 776-5400

Division Operations
201 East Washington Street, Phoenix, AZ 85004
Tel: (602) 776-5400

Division Operations Officer **Kevin Simpson** .... (602) 776-5400

Division Operations *(continued)*

Las Cruces - Resident Agent in Charge **David Tabullo** .... (602) 776-5400
E-mail: david.tabullo@usdoj.gov

Phoenix I - Supervisory Special Agent
Larry Bettendorf .... (602) 776-5400

Phoenix II - Supervisory Special Agent **(Vacant)** .... (602) 776-5400

Phoenix IV (Intel) Supervisory Special Agent
Carrie Funke .... (602) 776-5400

Phoenix V (Arson) - Supervisory Special Agent
Larry Bettendorf .... (602) 776-5400

Phoenix VII - Supervisory Resident Agent in Charge
(Acting) **Jarrett McMaster** .... (602) 776-5400

Phoenix (AZ) Area Office (Industry Operations)
201 East Washington Street, Suite 940, Phoenix, AZ 85004
Tel: (602) 776-5480 Fax: (602) 776-5499
Areas Covered: AZ, NM

Area Supervisor **Christina Babcock** .... (602) 776-5480

Resident Agent in Charge (Tucson I) **Jeff Bell** .... (520) 297-2100
Fax: (520) 297-2638

Resident Agent in Charge (Tucson II)
Creighton Brandt .... (520) 297-2100
Fax: (520) 297-2638

Resident Agent in Charge (Tucson III)
Christina Babcock .... (520) 297-2100
Fax: (520) 297-2638

Resident Agent in Charge (Tucson IV)
Brian Biletnikoss .... (520) 297-2100

Resident Agent in Charge (Albuquerque I)
Joel Marquez .... (602) 777-6500
201 Third Street, NW, Albuquerque, NM 87102 Fax: (602) 777-6511

Resident Agent in Charge (Albuquerque II)
Elise Morse .... (602) 777-6500
201 Third Street, NW, Fax: (602) 777-6511
Suite 1550, Albuquerque, NM 87102
E-mail: elise.morse@atf.gov

Phoenix VI - Supervisory Special Agent in Charge
Albert Rivera .... (602) 776-5400

San Francisco (CA) Field Division
5601 Arnold Road, Suite 400, Dublin, CA 94568
Tel: (925) 557-2800 Fax: (925) 557-2805 E-mail: sffielddiv@atf.gov
Areas Covered: Northern CA, NV

● Special Agent-in-Charge **Jill A. Snyder** .... (925) 557-2800
E-mail: jill.a.snyder@usdoj.gov

Assistant Special Agent-in-Charge **Brice P. McCracken** .... (925) 557-2800
E-mail: brice.p.mccracken@usdoj.gov

Assistant Special Agent-in-Charge **Patrick T. Gorman** .... (925) 557-2800
E-mail: patrick.t.gorman@usdoj.gov

Director, Industry Operations **Roger Root** .... (925) 557-2800
E-mail: roger.m.root@usdoj.gov

Division Counsel **Melissa S. Delvecchio** .... (925) 557-2800

Assistant Chief Counsel **(Vacant)** .... (925) 557-2860

Public Information Officer **Alexandria A. Corneiro** .... (925) 202-8135
E-mail: alexandria.a.corneiro@usdoj.gov

Benicia Satellite Office (Industry Operations)
5430 Industrial Way, Benicia, CA 94510
Tel: (707) 742-6143 Fax: (707) 742-6190

Group Supervisor **Michael Scott** .... (707) 742-6143
E-mail: michael.scott@atf.gov

Dublin (CA) III (Industry Operations)
5601 Arnold Road, Suite 400, Dublin, CA 94568
Tel: (925) 557-2830 Fax: (925) 557-2831

Area Supervisor **Michael Scott** .... (925) 557-2830

Fresno (CA) Field Office
5200 North Palm, Suite 206, Fresno, CA 93704-2225
Tel: (925) 364-8570 Fax: (925) 364-8571

Resident Agent-in-Charge **Brice P. McCracken** .... (925) 364-8570

★ Presidential Appointment Requiring Senate Confirmation ☆ Presidential Appointment ☐ Schedule C Appointment ◇ Career Senior Foreign Service Appointment
● Career Senior Executive Service (SES) Appointment ○ Non-Career Senior Executive Service (SES) Appointment ■ Postal Career Executive Service

Fresno (CA) II (Industry Operations)
5200 North Palm Avenue, Room 204, Fresno, CA 93704-2225
Tel: (925) 364-8570
Area Supervisor **Wesley Beck** .... (925) 364-8570

Las Vegas (NV) Field Office
8965 South Eastern Avenue, Suite 200, Las Vegas, NV 89123
Tel: (702) 347-5910 Fax: (702) 347-5911
Resident Agent-in-Charge **Mark Bellucci** .... (702) 347-5910

Las Vegas (NV) III (Industry Operations)
8965 South Eastern Avenue, Suite 220, Las Vegas, NV 89123
Tel: (702) 347-5930 Fax: (702) 347-5931
Area Supervisor **(Vacant)** .... (702) 347-5930

Oakland (CA) Field Office
1301 Clay Street, Room 670S, Oakland, CA 94612-5217
Tel: (510) 267-2200 Fax: (510) 637-3445
Resident Agent-in-Charge **Thomas Cleary** .... (510) 267-2200

Reno (NV) Field Office
200 South Virginia Street, Suite 600, Reno, NV 89501
Tel: (775) 784-5251 Fax: (775) 784-5933
Resident Agent-in-Charge **(Vacant)** .... (775) 784-5251

Reno (NV) Office (Industry Operations)
200 South Virginia Street, Suite 600, Reno, NV 89501
Tel: (775) 784-5251 Fax: (775) 784-5933
Area Supervisor **(Vacant)** .... (775) 784-5251

Sacramento (CA) Field Office
1325 J Street, Suite 1520, Sacramento, CA 95814
Tel: (916) 498-5100 Fax: (925) 364-8501
Resident Agent-in-Charge **Russell Graham Barlowe** .... (916) 498-5100

Sacramento (CA) II (Industry Operations)
1325 J Street, Suite 1530, Sacramento, CA 95814-2928
Tel: (925) 364-8500 Fax: (925) 364-8531
Area Supervisor **Wesley Beck** .... (925) 364-8500

San Francisco (CA) (Metro Field Office)
450 Golden Gate, 15th Floor, San Francisco, CA 94102
Tel: (925) 364-8550 Fax: (925) 364-8551
Resident Agent in Charge **Josh Lusk** .... (415) 436-8020

San Jose (CA) Field Office
280 South First Street, Room 371, San Jose, CA 95113
Tel: (408) 882-5200 Fax: (408) 882-5201
Resident Agent-in-Charge **Thomas Cleary** .... (408) 882-5200

San Jose (CA) II (Industry Operations)
280 South First Street, Suite 371-B, San Jose, CA 95113
Tel: (408) 882-5250 Fax: (408) 882-5201
Area Supervisor **Michael Scott** .... (408) 882-5250

Stockton (CA) Field Office
3255 West March Lane, Suite 220, Stockton, CA 95219
Tel: (209) 954-9433 Fax: (209) 954-9456
Resident Agent in Charge **Jim Bauer** .... (209) 954-9433

Seattle (WA) Field Division
1521 1st Avenue South, Suite 600, Seattle, WA 98134
Tel: (206) 204-3205 Fax: (206) 204-3252
Areas Covered: AK, GU, HI, ID, OR, WA
● Special Agent In Charge **Darek Pleasants** .... (206) 204-3205
E-mail: darek.pleasants@atf.gov
Executive Assistant **(Vacant)** .... (206) 204-3205
Assistant Special Agent-in-Charge **Jonathan Blais** ...... (206) 204-3205
Assistant Special Agent-in-Charge **(Vacant)** .... (206) 204-3205

Seattle (WA) Field Division *(continued)*
Industry Operations Director **(Vacant)** .... (206) 204-3205
Public Information Officer **Jason R. Chudy** .... (206) 204-3205
E-mail: jason.chudy@atf.gov

Portland (OR) Field Office III
1201 NE Lloyd Boulevard, Suite 720, Portland, OR 97232-1208
Tel: (503) 331-7830 Fax: (503) 331-7831
Areas Covered: GU, HI, OR
Area Supervisor **Justin Lomax** .... (503) 331-7830

Seattle (WA) Field Office II (Industry Operations)
Jackson Federal Building, 915 Second Avenue,
Room 790, Seattle, WA 98174-1093
Tel: (206) 204-7693 Fax: (206) 204-9832
Areas Covered: AK, Western WA
Area Supervisor **Kent Sanchez** .... (206) 204-7693

Spokane (WA) Field Office II
1313 North Atlantic Street, Suite 4101, Spokane, WA 99201
Tel: (509) 324-7881 Fax: (509) 324-7874
Areas Covered: ID and Eastern WA
Area Supervisor **Linda Young** .... (509) 324-7881

Saint Paul (MN) Field Division
30 East Seventh Street, Suite 1900, St. Paul, MN 55101-4901
Tel: (651) 726-0200 Fax: (651) 726-0201 E-mail: stpauldiv@atf.gov
Areas Covered: MN, ND, SD, WI
● Special Agent-in-Charge **Kurt Thielhorn** .... (651) 726-0200
Assistant Special Agent-in-Charge **Joel L. Lee** .... (651) 726-0200
Assistant Special Agent-in-Charge **Kirk Howard** .... (651) 726-0200
E-mail: kirk.howard@atf.gov
Director of Industry Operations **Hans Hummel** .... (651) 726-0200
Public Information Officer **Ashlee J.L. Sherrill** .... (651) 726-0200
Division Operations Officer **Darren D. Hampton** .... (651) 726-0200

Fargo (ND) Field Office
657 Second Avenue North, Room 420, Fargo, ND 58102
Tel: (701) 293-2860 Fax: (701) 293-2861
Criminal Enforcement Resident Agent-in-Charge
Lowell Erickson .... (701) 293-2860
E-mail: lowell.erickson@atf.gov
Industry Operations Area Supervisor **(Vacant)** .... (651) 726-0220

Madison (WI) Field Office (Criminal Enforcement)
660 West Washington, City Station, Suite 306, Madison, WI 53703
Tel: (608) 441-5050 Fax: (608) 441-5057
Resident Agent-in-Charge **Jessie Summers** ...... (608) 441-5050 ext. 7

Milwaukee (WI) Field Office I (Criminal Enforcement)
1000 North Water Street, Suite 1700, Milwaukee, WI 53202
Tel: (414) 727-6170 Fax: (414) 727-6171
Resident Agent-in-Charge **John Adamson** .... (414) 727-6170

Milwaukee (WI) Area Office II (Industry Operations)
1000 North Water Street, Suite 1400, Milwaukee, WI 53202-6649
Tel: (414) 727-6200 Fax: (414) 727-6201
Area Supervisor **Wesley Beck** .... (414) 727-6200

Milwaukee (WI) Field Office III (Criminal)
1000 North Water Street, Suite 1400, Milwaukee, WI 53202
Resident Agent in Charge **John Biemeret** .... (414) 727-6190
E-mail: john.biemeret@atf.gov

Sioux Falls (SD) Field Office (Criminal Enforcement)
325 South First Avenue, Suite 201, Sioux Falls, SD 57104
Tel: (605) 782-8200 Fax: (605) 782-8219
Resident Agent-in-Charge **Kurt Wheeler** .... (605) 782-8200

★ Presidential Appointment Requiring Senate Confirmation ☆ Presidential Appointment ☐ Schedule C Appointment ◇ Career Senior Foreign Service Appointment
● Career Senior Executive Service (SES) Appointment ○ Non-Career Senior Executive Service (SES) Appointment ■ Postal Career Executive Service

Saint Paul (MN) Field Office I (Criminal Enforcement)
30 East Seventh Street, Suite 1900, St. Paul, MN 55101-4910
Tel: (651) 726-0300 Fax: (651) 726-0301
Resident Agent in Charge **(Vacant)** .... (651) 726-0300

Rapid City (SD) Satellite Office (Criminal Enforcement)
1825 Clearview Lane, Suite 201, Rapid City, SD 57701
Tel: (605) 343-3288 Fax: (605) 343-3509
Resident Agent-in-Charge **Kurt Wheeler** .... (605) 782-8200

Saint Paul (MN) Area Office II (Industry Operations)
30 East Seventh Street, Suite 1900, St. Paul, MN 55101-4901
Tel: (651) 726-0220 Fax: (651) 726-0221
Area Supervisor **Jeff Jenkins** .... (651) 726-0220

Saint Paul (MN) Field Office III (Intelligence)
30 East Seventh Street, Suite 1900, St. Paul, MN 55101-4910
Tel: (651) 726-0230 Fax: (651) 726-0231
Group Supervisor **Martin Siebenaler** .... (651) 726-0230

Saint Paul (MN) Field Office IV (Criminal Enforcement)
30 East Seventh Street, Suite 1900, St. Paul, MN 55101-4910
Resident Agent in Charge **Calvin Meyer** .... (651) 726-0260

Tampa (FL) Field Division
400 North Tampa Street, Suite 2100, Tampa, FL 33602
Tel: (813) 202-7300 Fax: (813) 202-7301
Areas Covered: Middle and North FL
● Special Agent-in-Charge **Daryl McCrary** .... (813) 202-7300
E-mail: daryl.mccrary@atf.gov
Assistant Special Agent in Charge **Craig Kailimai** .... (813) 202-7300
Assistant Special Agent-in-Charge **(Vacant)** .... (813) 202-7300
Director of Industry Operations **Aaron Gerber** .... (813) 202-7300
Division Operations Officer **Vincent Curry** .... (813) 202-7300
Public Information Officer **Mary Harmon-Elison** .... (813) 202-7300

Jacksonville (FL) Field Office
5210 Belfort Road, Suite 350, Jacksonville, FL 32256
Tel: (904) 380-5500 Fax: (904) 380-5475
Group I Supervisor **Eric Fox** .... (904) 380-5500
Group II Supervisor **Stephen Galloway** .... (904) 380-5500
E-mail: stephen.galloway@atf.gov
Group III Industry Operations Supervisor
Carolyn King .... (904) 380-5480

Orlando (FL) Field Office
3452 Lake Lynda Drive, Suite 450, Orlando, FL 32817
Tel: (407) 384-2411 Fax: (407) 384-2412
Group Supervisor **John Scanlon** .... (407) 384-2411

Orlando (FL) II Field Office (Industry Operations)
3452 Lake Lynda Drive, Suite 450, Orlando, FL 32817
Tel: (407) 384-2420 Fax: (407) 384-2421
Area Supervisor (Acting) **Suzanna Anderson** .... (407) 384-2420

Orlando (FL) III Field Office
135 West Central Boulevard, Suite 740, Orlando, FL 32801
Tel: (407) 254-4100 Fax: (407) 254-4101
Group Supervisor **Tim Gunning** .... (407) 254-4100
E-mail: tim.gunning@atf.gov

Pensacola (FL) Field Office
41 North Jefferson Street, Suite 200, Pensacola, FL 32501-5848
Tel: (850) 549-2500 Fax: (850) 549-2501
Resident Agent-in-Charge/Special Agent
George Bruno .... (850) 549-2517

Tallahassee (FL) Field Office
Bank of American Building, 315 South Calhoun Street, Suite 200, Tallahassee, FL 32301
Tel: (904) 380-5480 Fax: (850) 942-9665
Resident Agent-in-Charge/Special Agent **Todd Okray** .... (904) 380-5480
Industry Operations Area Supervisor **(Vacant)** .... (904) 380-5480

Tampa (FL) Field Office I
400 North Tampa Street, Suite 1000, Tampa, FL 33602
Tel: (813) 202-7310 Fax: (813) 202-7311
Tampa Group I Supervisor/Special Agent
Michael Coad .... (813) 202-7312
E-mail: michael.coad@atf.gov

Tampa (FL) Field Office II
400 North Tampa Street, Suite 2100, Tampa, FL 33602
Tel: (813) 612-2470 Fax: (813) 663-3923
Tampa Group II Area Supervisor (Industry Operations)
Mary Harmon-Elison .... (813) 612-2473

Tampa (FL) Field Office III
400 North Tampa Street, Suite 1000, Tampa, FL 33602
Tel: (813) 202-7330 Fax: (813) 202-7321
Tampa Group III Supervisor/Special Agent (Acting)
Robert Melton .... (813) 202-7350

Tampa (FL) Field Office IV
400 North Tampa Street, Suite 2100, Tampa, FL 33602
Tel: (813) 612-2470 Fax: (813) 663-3939
Tampa Group IV Supervisor/Special Agent
Tom Pietrowicz .... (813) 612-2472

Washington (DC) Field Division
90 K Street NE, Washington, DC 20002
Tel: (202) 648-8010 Fax: (202) 648-8001 E-mail: WashDiv@atf.gov
Areas Covered: DC, VA
● Special Agent In Charge **Thomas L. "Tom" Chittum** .... (202) 648-8010
Deputy Assistant Director **Michael Fizonczak** .... (202) 648-8010
Assistant Special Agent in Charge **R. Shawn Murrow** ... (202) 648-8010
Assistant Special Agent in Charge **Kirk H. Steward** ..... (202) 648-8010
E-mail: kirk.h.steward@usdoj.gov
Director of Industry Operations **Marjorie R. Randall** ..... (202) 648-8010
Division Operations Officer **Marjorie R. Randall** .... (202) 648-8010
Division Counsel **(Vacant)** .... (202) 648-8010
Public Information Officer **Lloyd Burton** .... (202) 648-8010

Richmond (VA) Field Office
1011 Bolder Spring Drive, Suite 300, Richmond, VA 23236
Tel: (804) 200-4200 Fax: (804) 200-4199
Areas Covered: VA
Industry Operations Area Supervisor
Kimberly Thompson .... (804) 200-4141
Criminal Enforcement Resident Agent-in-Charge
Scott Fulkerson .... (804) 200-4200

Office of Human Resources and Professional Development

Ariel Rios Federal Building, 99 New York Avenue, NE, Washington, DC 20226
Tel: (202) 648-8416 Fax: (202) 648-9732

ATF National Academy
Federal Law Enforcement Training Center, 1131 Chapel Crossing Road, Building 681, Glynco, GA 31524
Fax: (912) 267-2901
Chief **Kelly Brady** .... (912) 267-2251
Basic Training Program Branch Chief
Christopher Porreca .... (912) 554-4788
Logistics and Operations Branch Chief
Matthew White .... (912) 267-2261
Deputy Chief **Robert Kelly** .... (912) 267-2828

★ Presidential Appointment Requiring Senate Confirmation ☆ Presidential Appointment ☐ Schedule C Appointment ☆ Career Senior Foreign Service Appointment
● Career Senior Executive Service (SES) Appointment ○ Non-Career Senior Executive Service (SES) Appointment ■ Postal Career Executive Service

Office of Science and Technology (OST)
Ariel Rios Federal Building, 99 New York Avenue, NE, Washington, DC 20226
Tel: (202) 648-8390

Laboratory Services Division
National Laboratory Research Center, 6000 Ammendale Road, Ammendale, MD 20705-1250

Fire Research Laboratory
6000 Ammendale Road, Ammendale, MD 20705-1250
Tel: (202) 648-6200
Fire Research Laboratory Chief **John Allen** . . . . (240) 648-6200

Forensic Science Laboratory - Atlanta
Atlanta, GA 30345
Tel: (404) 417-2700
Forensic Science Laboratory- Atlanta Chief **Donal L. McClamroch** . . . . (404) 417-2702
2600 Century Parkway, NE, Room 410, Atlanta, GA 30345 Fax: (404) 414-2701

Forensic Science Laboratory - San Francisco
Walnut Creek, CA 94598
Tel: (925) 364-8413
Forensic Science Laboratory - San Francisco Chief **Bradley Cooper** . . . . (925) 280-3600
355 North Wiget Lane, Walnut Creek, CA 94598 Fax: (925) 280-3601

Forensic Science Laboratory - Washington
6000 Ammendale Road, Ammendale, MD 20705-1250
Tel: (202) 648-6100
Forensic Science Laboratory - Washington Chief **Julia Dolan** . . . . (240) 648-6100
E-mail: julia.dolan@atf.gov Fax: (240) 264-1495

Drug Enforcement Administration (DEA)
Lincoln Place-West, 700 Army Navy Drive, Arlington, VA 22202
Tel: (202) 307-4228
Tel: (800) 882-9539 (Narcotics License Registration Section)
Internet: www.dea.gov

OFFICE OF THE ADMINISTRATOR
Lincoln Place-West, 700 Army Navy Drive, Arlington, VA 22202
Fax: (202) 307-4540

Human Resources Division (HR)
Lincoln Place-West, 700 Army Navy Drive, Arlington, VA 22202

Office of Training (TR)
P.O. Box 1475, DEA Training Academy, Quantico, VA 22134-1475
Special Agent-in-Charge **James R. "Jay" Gregorius** . . . . (703) 632-5010
Assistant Special Agent-in-Charge/Domestic Training Section Chief **Wendy Woolcock** . . . . (703) 632-5310
International Training Section Chief **Thurman Peterson** . . . . (703) 632-5330

Intelligence Division (NC)
Lincoln Place-West, 700 Army Navy Drive, Arlington, VA 22202
Tel: (202) 307-3607

El Paso Intelligence Center (EPIC)
11339 SSG Simms Street, El Paso, TX 79908
Tel: (915) 760-2000 Internet: www.justice.gov/dea/ops/intel.shtml
Director (Acting) **K. Scott McRory** . . . . (915) 760-2011
Deputy Director (Acting) **Edward A. Regula** . . . . (915) 760-2007
E-mail: edward.a.regula@usdoj.gov
Executive Assistant **Miguel Dubet** . . . . (915) 760-2012

El Paso Intelligence Center *(continued)*
EPIC Division Counsel **Clark R. Fleming** . . . . (915) 760-2023
E-mail: clark.r.fleming@usdoj.gov
Information Management Section Chief **Prabhjot Bajwa** . . . . (915) 760-2180
Research and Analysis Section Chief **Raynaldo Cervantes** . . . . (915) 760-2301
Tactical Operations Section Chief **(Vacant)** . . . . (915) 760-2255
Watch Operations Section Chief (Acting) **Alfred Tanner** . . . . (915) 760-2221

Operations Division (OC)
Lincoln Place-West, 700 Army Navy Drive, Suite 12050, Arlington, VA 22202
Tel: (202) 307-7340
● Chief of Operations **Anthony D. Williams** . . . . (202) 307-7340
E-mail: anthony.d.williams@usdoj.gov
Executive Assistant **Patrick Kelly** . . . . (202) 307-4907

Aviation Division (OA)
2300 Horizon Drive, Fort Worth, TX 76177-5300
Tel: (817) 837-2000
Special Agent In Charge **Gary W. Hill** . . . . (817) 837-2004
E-mail: gary.w.hill@usdoj.gov

Division Offices

Atlanta Field Division
Richard B. Russell Federal Building, 75 Spring Street, SW, 8th Floor, Atlanta, GA 30303
Tel: (404) 893-7000 Fax: (404) 893-7110
Areas Covered: GA, NC, SC, TN
Special Agent-in-Charge **Daniel R. Salter** . . . . (404) 893-7100
E-mail: daniel.r.salter@usdoj.gov
Associate Special Agent in Charge **Robert Murphy** . . . . (404) 893-7100
E-mail: robert.murphy@usdoj.gov
Assistant Special Agent in Charge **Andrew T. Dimond** . . . . (678) 244-8400
E-mail: andrew.t.dimond@usdoj.gov
Assistant Special Agent in Charge **Phillip Scott Forbes** . . . . (404) 893-7100
Assistant Special Agent in Charge **(Vacant)** . . . . (404) 893-7000
Assistant Special Agent in Charge **David W. Stephens** . . . . (404) 638-7601
E-mail: david.w.stephens@usdoj.gov
Field Intelligence Manager **Robert N. Evans** . . . . (404) 893-7100
E-mail: robert.n.evans@usdoj.gov
Diversion Program Manager **David Hargroder** . . . . (404) 893-7000

Columbus (GA) Resident Office
1246 First Avenue, 4th Floor, Columbus, GA 31901
P.O. Box 1565, Columbus, GA 31902
Tel: (706) 649-7850 Fax: (706) 649-7872
Resident Agent-in-Charge **(Vacant)** . . . . (706) 649-7850

Macon (GA) Resident Office
3920 Arkwright Road, Suite 375, Macon, GA 31210
Tel: (478) 757-8754 Fax: (478) 471-1365
Resident Agent-in-Charge **Stephen B. Tinsley** . . . . (478) 757-8754

Savannah (GA) Resident Office
56 Park of Commerce Boulevard, Suite A, Savannah, GA 31405
Tel: (912) 447-1035 Fax: (912) 447-0231
Resident Agent-in-Charge **Michael Kersy** . . . . (912) 447-1035
Special Agent **(Vacant)** . . . . (706) 724-9021
DEA Post of Duty, 801 Broad Street, Suite 1115, Augusta, GA 30903 Fax: (706) 772-3870

Charlotte (NC) District Office
6324 Fairview Road, Suite 575, Charlotte, NC 28210
Tel: (704) 770-2050 Fax: (704) 770-2051
Assistant Special Agent-in-Charge **William F. Baxley, Jr.** . . . . (704) 770-2050

(continued on next page)

★ Presidential Appointment Requiring Senate Confirmation ☆ Presidential Appointment □ Schedule C Appointment ◇ Career Senior Foreign Service Appointment
● Career Senior Executive Service (SES) Appointment ○ Non-Career Senior Executive Service (SES) Appointment ■ Postal Career Executive Service

DEPARTMENTS

Charlotte (NC) District Office *(continued)*

Group Supervisor **Dustin T. Harmon** .... (828) 350-3440 ext. 222
Asheville Post of Duty, Fax: (828) 350-3454
151 Patton Avenue,
Suite 174, Asheville, NC 28801
E-mail: dustin.t.harmon@usdoj.gov

Greensboro (NC) Resident Office
1801 Stanley Road, Suite 201, Greensboro, NC 27407
Tel: (336) 547-4210 Fax: (336) 547-4215

Resident Agent-in-Charge **(Vacant)** .... (336) 547-4210

Raleigh (NC) Resident Office
4505 Falls of Neuse Road, Suite 200, Raleigh, NC 27609
Tel: (919) 790-3004 Fax: (919) 790-3011

Resident Agent-in-Charge **(Vacant)** .... (919) 790-3004

Wilmington (NC) Resident Office
Alton Lennon Federal Building, Two Princess Street,
Room 322, Wilmington, NC 28401
Tel: (910) 815-4513 Fax: (910) 815-4631

Resident Agent-in-Charge **Michael Franklin** .... (910) 815-4513

Columbia (SC) District Office
Strom Thurmond Federal Building, 1835 Assembly Street,
Room 1229, Columbia, SC 29201
Tel: (803) 765-5251 Fax: (803) 765-5410

Assistant Special Agent-in-Charge **E. Todd Spralling** .... (803) 765-5251

Charleston (SC) Resident Office
5900 Core Avenue, Suite 300, North Charleston, SC 29406
Tel: (843) 308-6660 Fax: (843) 308-6670

Resident Agent-in-Charge **(Vacant)** .... (843) 308-6660

Florence (SC) Resident Office
401 West Evans Street, Room 234, Florence, SC 29501
Tel: (843) 661-2171 Fax: (843) 679-3123

Resident Agent-in-Charge **(Vacant)** .... (843) 661-2171

Greenville (SC) Resident Office
403 Woods Lake Road, Suite 210, Greenville, SC 29607
Mail: P.O. Box 10915, Federal Station, Greenville, SC 29603
Tel: (864) 234-0237 Fax: (864) 234-5757

Resident Agent-in-Charge **Michael Rzepczynski** .... (864) 234-0237
E-mail: michael.rzepczynski@usdoj.gov

Nashville (TN) District Office
Estes Kefauver Building, FB-USCH, 801 Broadway,
Room 500, Nashville, TN 37203
Tel: (615) 736-5988 Fax: (615) 736-2221

Assistant Special Agent-in-Charge **(Vacant)** .... (615) 736-5988

Chattanooga (TN) Resident Office
Uptain Building, 5751 Uptain Road, Suite 417, Chattanooga, TN 37411
Tel: (423) 855-6600 Fax: (423) 855-6608

Resident Agent-in-Charge **(Vacant)** .... (423) 855-6600
Special Agent **(Vacant)** .... (706) 232-5104
DEA Rome Post of Duty, Fax: (706) 232-5162
Five Government Plaza, Rome, GA 30161

Knoxville (TN) Resident Office
1721 Midpark Drive, 3rd Floor, Knoxville, TN 37921
Tel: (865) 584-9364 Fax: (865) 584-8763

Resident Agent-in-Charge **Neil Morgenstem** .... (865) 584-9364

Memphis (TN) Resident Office
Morgan Keegan Tower, 50 North Front Street,
Suite 500, Memphis, TN 38103-1105
Tel: (901) 969-3500 Fax: (901) 544-3025

Resident Agent-in-Charge **(Vacant)** .... (901) 969-3500

Memphis (TN) Resident Office *(continued)*

Special Agent **(Vacant)** .... (731) 422-2696
Jackson DEA Post of Duty, Fax: (423) 854-9100
Ed Jones Federal Building,
1095 Highland Avenue, Suite 212, Jackson, TN 38301
Group Supervisor **Robert Bailess** .... (423) 854-9100 ext. 231
Johnson City DEA Post of Duty, 215 East Springbrook Drive,
Johnson City, TN 37601

Caribbean Division
Millennium Park Plaza, 15 Calle 2, Suite 710, Guaynabo, PR 00968
Tel: (787) 277-4700

Special Agent In Charge **Matthew Donahue** .... (787) 277-4700
E-mail: matthew.g.donahue@usdoj.gov

Chicago (IL) Division
1200 John C. Kluczynski Federal Building,
230 South Dearborn Street, Chicago, IL 60604
Tel: (312) 353-7875 Fax: (312) 846-7202
Areas Covered: IL, IN, MN, ND, WI

Special Agent-in-Charge **Brian M. McKnight** .... (312) 353-7875
E-mail: brian.m.mcknight@usdoj.gov
Assistant Special Agent-in-Charge **Marta Aiuffre** .... (312) 353-7875
Assistant Special Agent-in-Charge **Sheila Lyons** .... (312) 353-7875
E-mail: sheila.lyons@dea.gov
Assistant Special Agent-in-Charge **Donald Rospond** ..... (312) 353-7875
Assistant Special Agent-in-Charge **Sharon Santiago** ..... (312) 353-7875
Assistant Special Agent-in-Charge **Justin Williams** ...... (312) 353-7875
Security Officer **Michael Powers** .... (312) 353-7875
Training Officer **Chuck Soltys** .... (312) 353-1433
Fax: (312) 353-1900
Administrative Officer **John J. Biagioni** .... (312) 353-1434
E-mail: john.biagioni@usdoj.gov Fax: (312) 353-1500

Fargo (ND) Resident Office
One North Second Street, Suite 302, Fargo, ND 58102
Tel: (701) 476-5500

Resident Agent-in-Charge **Jeffrey Harford** .... (701) 476-5500
Bismarck (ND) Post of Duty Special Agent **(Vacant)** ..... (701) 476-5500
220 East Rosser, Bismarck, ND 58501

Rockford (IL) Resident Office
308 West State Street, Suite 475, Rockford, IL 61101
Tel: (815) 987-4494 Fax: (815) 987-4498

Resident Agent-in-Charge **(Vacant)** .... (815) 987-4494

Springfield (IL) Resident Office
2875 Via Verde Street, Springfield, IL 62703
Tel: (217) 585-2750 Fax: (217) 585-2753

Resident Agent-in-Charge **(Vacant)** .... (217) 585-2750

Indianapolis (IN) District Office
Minton-Capehart Federal Building, 575 North Pennsylvania Street,
Room 408, Indianapolis, IN 46204
Tel: (317) 226-7977 Fax: (317) 226-7703

Assistant Special Agent-in-Charge (Acting)
Gregory Westfall .... (317) 226-7977

Evansville (IN) Post of Duty
101 NW Martin Luther King, Jr. Boulevard,
Suite 261, Evansville, IN 47708
Tel: (812) 465-6457 Fax: (812) 465-6458

Group Supervisor **Douglas Freyburger** .... (812) 465-6457

Fort Wayne (IN) Post of Duty
1330 South Harrison, Room 154, Fort Wayne, IN 46802
Tel: (260) 420-4018 Fax: (260) 420-7028

Group Supervisor **Stephen T. Ribolla** .... (260) 420-4018
E-mail: stepehn.t.ribolla@usdoj.gov

Merrillville (IN) Resident Office
1571 East 85th Avenue, Suite 200, Merrillville, IN 46410
Tel: (219) 681-7000 Fax: (219) 681-7024
Resident Agent-in-Charge **Eric M. Stearns** . . . . (219) 681-7000

Milwaukee (WI) District Office
1000 North Water Street, Suite 1010, Milwaukee, WI 53202
Tel: (414) 336-7300 Fax: (414) 297-1169
Assistant Special Agent-in-Charge **Robert Bell** . . . . (414) 336-7300
Group Supervisor **(Vacant)** . . . . (414) 336-7300

Green Bay (WI) Resident Office
205 Doty Street, Suite 302, Green Bay, WI 54301
Tel: (920) 492-4907 Fax: (920) 492-4905
Resident Agent-in-Charge **Christopher Hoyt** . . . . (920) 492-4907

Madison (WI) Resident Office
740 Regent, Suite 200, Madison, WI 53715
Tel: (608) 264-5111 Fax: (608) 264-5116
Resident Agent-in-Charge **Dennis Hiorns** . . . . (608) 264-5111
E-mail: dennis.hiorns@usdoj.gov

Minneapolis-St. Paul (MN) District Office
330 Second Avenue, Suite 450, Minneapolis, MN 55401-2224
Tel: (612) 344-4100 Fax: (612) 348-1730
Assistant Special Agent-in-Charge **Daniel V. Moren** . . . . . (612) 344-4100

Dallas (TX) Division
10160 Technology Boulevard East, Dallas, TX 75220-4323
Tel: (214) 366-6900 Fax: (214) 366-6914
Areas Covered: OK, Northern TX
Special Agent-in-Charge **Clyde E. Shelley, Jr.** . . . . (214) 366-6917
E-mail: clyde.e.shelley@usdoj.gov

Fort Worth (TX) Resident Office
801 Cherry Street, Suite 700, Fort Worth, TX 76102-6192
Tel: (817) 639-2000 Fax: (817) 288-1005
Resident Agent-in-Charge **James R. Dehass** . . . . (817) 639-2023

Lubbock (TX) Resident Office
5214 68th Street, Suite 401, Lubbock, TX 79424
Tel: (806) 798-7189 Fax: (806) 794-3149
Resident Agent-in-Charge **William F. Kimbell** . . . . (806) 798-7189
E-mail: william.f.kimbell@usdoj.gov

Tyler (TX) Resident Office
909 ESE Loop 323, Suite 280, Tyler, TX 75701
Tel: (903) 579-2400 Fax: (903) 579-2412
Resident Agent-in-Charge **Arturo Cordova** . . . . (903) 579-2400
E-mail: arturo.cordova@dea.gov

Oklahoma City (OK) District Office
9900 Broadway, Oklahoma City, OK 73114-6305
Tel: (405) 475-7500 Fax: (405) 475-7577
Assistant Special Agent-in-Charge **Richard W. Salter** . . . . (405) 475-7500

McAlester (OK) Resident Office
100 Airport Road, McAlester, OK 74501
Tel: (918) 426-5020 Fax: (918) 423-2681
Resident Agent-in-Charge **Carl G. Stewart** . . . . (918) 426-5020

Tulsa (OK) Resident Office
7615 East 63rd Place, Suite 250, Tulsa, OK 74133
Tel: (918) 459-9600 Fax: (918) 459-2570
Resident Agent-in-Charge **David L. King** . . . . (918) 459-9600

Denver Division
12154 East Easter Avenue, Centennial, CO 80112
Tel: (720) 895-4040 Fax: (303) 799-1044 Fax: (303) 799-4751
Areas Covered: CO, MT, UT, WY
Special Agent-in-Charge **William T. McDermott** . . . . (720) 895-4040
E-mail: william.t.mcdermott@usdoj.gov
Assistant Special Agent-in-Charge **Deanne L. Rueter** . . . . (720) 895-4040
E-mail: deanne.l.reuter@usdoj.gov
Assistant Special Agent-in-Charge **Michael Cuento** . . . . . . (720) 895-4040
E-mail: michael.r.cuento@usdoj.gov
Group Supervisor **Donato E. Sikorski** . . . . (720) 895-4170
E-mail: Donato.e.sikorski@usdoj.gov
Administrative Officer **Marilyn C. Valdez** . . . . (720) 895-4140
E-mail: Marilyn.c.valdez@usdoj.gov
Public Information Officer **Randolph S. Ladd** . . . . (720) 895-4134
E-mail: randolph.s.ladd@usdoj.gov

Billings (MT) Resident Office
2970 King Avenue West, Billings, MT 59102
Tel: (406) 655-2900 Fax: (406) 651-1600
Resident Agent-in-Charge **Joseph C. Kirkland** . . . . (406) 655-2900
E-mail: joseph.c.kirkland@usdoj.gov

Cheyenne (WY) Resident Office
1205 Airport Parkway, Cheyenne, WY 82001
Tel: (307) 778-1500 Fax: (307) 778-1599
Resident Agent-in-Charge **David A. Tyree** . . . . (307) 778-1500

Colorado Springs (CO) Resident Office
111 South Tejon, Suite 306, Colorado Springs, CO 80903
Tel: (719) 262-3000 Fax: (719) 866-6053
Resident Agent-in-Charge **Timothy Scott** . . . . (719) 262-3000
E-mail: timothy.k.scott@usdoj.gov

Grand Junction (CO) Resident Office
2734 Crossroads Boulevard, Grand Junction, CO 81506
P.O. Box 2448, Grand Junction, CO 81501
Tel: (970) 683-3220 Fax: (970) 683-3222
Resident Agent-in-Charge **Steven L. Knight** . . . . (970) 683-3220
E-mail: steven.l.knight@usdoj.gov

Salt Lake City (UT) District Office
348 East South Temple, Salt Lake City, UT 84111
Tel: (801) 524-4156 Fax: (801) 524-5364
Assistant Special Agent-in-Charge **Brian S. Besser** . . . . . . (801) 524-4156

Detroit (MI) Division
Rick Finley Building, 431 Howard Street, Detroit, MI 48226-2507
Tel: (313) 234-4000 Fax: (313) 234-4141
Areas Covered: KY, MI, OH
Special Agent-in-Charge **Timothy J. Plancon** . . . . (313) 234-4000
E-mail: timothy.j.plancon@usdoj.gov
Education: Michigan State BA; Eastern Michigan MA
Assistant Special Agent-in-Charge **David Grant** . . . . (313) 234-4000
Assistant Special Agent-in-Charge **(Vacant)** . . . . (313) 234-4000
Assistant Special Agent-in-Charge **(Vacant)** . . . . (313) 234-4000
Assistant Special Agent-in-Charge **(Vacant)** . . . . (313) 234-4000

Grand Rapids (MI) Resident Office
330 Ionia, NW, Room 303, Grand Rapids, MI 49503
Tel: (616) 458-0616 Fax: (616) 458-3086
Resident Agent-in-Charge **Mike Rehg** . . . . (616) 458-0616

Flint (MI) Resident Office
432 N. Saginaw Street, 7th Floor, Flint, MI 48502
Tel: (810) 768-7600
Resident Agent-in-Charge **Don Grace** . . . . (810) 768-7600

Columbus (OH) District Office
500 South Front Street, Suite 612, Columbus, OH 43215
Tel: (614) 255-4163 Fax: (614) 469-5788
Resident Agent-in-Charge **Steve Verdow** . . . . (614) 255-4163

(continued on next page)

★ Presidential Appointment Requiring Senate Confirmation ☆ Presidential Appointment ☐ Schedule C Appointment ◇ Career Senior Foreign Service Appointment
● Career Senior Executive Service (SES) Appointment ○ Non-Career Senior Executive Service (SES) Appointment ■ Postal Career Executive Service

Columbus (OH) District Office *(continued)*

Assistant Special Agent-in-Charge
Mike Bulgrir Suite 750 .... (614) 255-4163

Cincinnati (OH) Resident Office
36 East Seventh Street, Suite 1900, Cincinnati, OH 45202
Tel: (513) 684-3671 Fax: (513) 684-3672
Resident Agent-in-Charge **Tim Reagan** .... (513) 684-3671

Cleveland (OH) Resident Office
1375 East Ninth Street, Suite 700, Cleveland, OH 44114
Tel: (216) 274-3600
Resident Agent-in-Charge **Keith Martin** .... (216) 274-3600
E-mail: keith.martin@usdoj.gov

Dayton (OH) Resident Office
One Prestige Place, Suite 450, Miamisburg, OH 45342
Tel: (937) 291-1988 Fax: (937) 291-0535
Resident Agent-in-Charge **Christopher Melink** .... (937) 291-1988

Toledo (OH) Resident Office
433 North Summitt Street, Suite 700, Toledo, OH 43604
Tel: (419) 259-6490 Fax: (419) 259-3725
Resident Agent-in-Charge **Jeremy Nissen** ...... (419) 259-6490 ext. 215

Youngstown (OH) Resident Office
10 East Commerce Street, Youngstown, OH 44503
Tel: (330) 729-7800 Fax: (330) 740-6969
Resident Agent-in-Charge **Silverio Balzano** .... (330) 729-7801

Louisville (KY) District Office
1006 Federal Building, 600 Dr. Martin Luther King Place,
Louisville, KY 40202
Tel: (502) 582-5908 Fax: (502) 582-5535
Assistant Special Agent-in-Charge **Thomas Gorman** ..... (502) 582-5234
Resident Agent in Charge **James Balcom** .... (502) 582-5908

Lexington (KY) Resident Office
997 Governors Lane, Suite 350, Lexington, KY 40513
Tel: (859) 977-6100
Resident Agent-in-Charge **(Vacant)** .... (859) 977-6100

London (KY) Resident Office
150 Hal Rogers Drive, London, KY 40744
Tel: (606) 862-4500 Fax: (606) 862-8296
Resident Agent-in-Charge **Daren L. Atkins** .... (606) 862-4500

El Paso (TX) Division

660 South Mesa Hills, Suite 2000, El Paso, TX 79912
Tel: (915) 832-6000 Fax: (915) 832-6001
Areas Covered: NM, Western TX
Special Agent-in-Charge **Kyle W. Williamson** .... (915) 832-6000
Security Officer **David Vega** .... (915) 832-6000
E-mail: david.vega@usdoj.gov
Training Officer **(Vacant)** .... (915) 832-6000

Alpine (TX) Resident Office
2500 North Highway 18, Suite D200, Alpine, TX 79830
Tel: (432) 837-6000 Fax: (432) 837-6060
Resident Agent-in-Charge **Wade C. Sparks** .... (432) 837-6000
E-mail: wade.c.sparks@usdoj.gov

Midland (TX) Resident Office
Dinero Plaza, 1004 North Big Spring, Room 225, Midland, TX 79701
Tel: (432) 686-4085 Fax: (432) 686-4090
Resident Agent-in-Charge **Robert E. Castaneda** .... (432) 686-4085

Albuquerque (NM) District Office
2660 Fritts Crossing SE, Albuquerque, NM 87106
Tel: (505) 452-4500 Fax: (505) 346-7454
Assistant Special Agent-in-Charge **Sean R. Waite** .... (505) 346-7425
E-mail: sean.r.waite@usdoj.gov

Las Cruces (NM) Resident Office
2290 East Griggs Avenue, Las Cruces, NM 88001
Tel: (575) 526-0700 Fax: (575) 524-0170
Resident Agent-in-Charge **Conan N. Becknell** .... (575) 526-0694
E-mail: conan.n.becknell@usdoj.gov

Houston (TX) Division

1433 West Loop S, Suite 600, Houston, TX 77027-9506
Tel: (713) 693-3000 Fax: (713) 693-3033
Areas Covered: Southern TX
Special Agent-in-Charge **William R. Glaspy** .... (713) 693-3001
Education: Southwestern BABA
Associate Special Agent-in-Charge **Sherod D. Jones** .... (713) 693-3045
E-mail: sherod.d.jones@usdoj.gov
Associate Special Agent-in-Charge **Steven S. Whipple** ... (713) 693-3009
E-mail: steven.s.whipple@usdoj.gov
Associate Special Agent-in-Charge **(Vacant)** .... (713) 693-3009
Media Contact **Wendell Campbell** .... (713) 693-3592
Recruiter **Douglas M. Irr** .... (713) 693-3149
Community Outreach Coordinator **Dawn Mathis** .... (713) 693-3152

Beaumont (TX) Resident Office
350 Magnolia, Suite 290, Beaumont, TX 77701-1899
Tel: (409) 981-7400 Fax: (409) 839-2551
Resident Agent-in-Charge **Timothy "Tim" Duriso** ...... (409) 981-7400
E-mail: timothy.w.duriso@usdoj.gov

Galveston (TX) Resident Office
2525 South Shore Harbour Boulevard, League City, TX 77573
Tel: (713) 693-2400 Fax: (281) 538-6226
Resident Agent-in-Charge **Luis M. Martinez** .... (713) 693-2401
E-mail: luis.m.martinuez@usdoj.gov

Laredo (TX) District Office
109 Shiloh Drive, Suite 500, Laredo, TX 78045
Tel: (956) 523-6000 Fax: (956) 523-6125
Assistant Special Agent-in-Charge **James R. Reed** ...... (956) 523-6106

McAllen (TX) District Office
1919 Austin Street, McAllen, TX 78501
Tel: (956) 992-8400 Fax: (956) 992-8495
Assistant Special Agent-in-Charge **Rudy Maldonado** .... (956) 992-8405

Brownsville (TX) Resident Office
1100 FM 802, Suite 200, Brownsville, TX 78521
Tel: (956) 504-7000 Fax: (956) 504-7008
Resident Agent-in-Charge **Andres L. Dominguez** .... (956) 504-7006
E-mail: andres.l.dominguez@usdoj.gov

Corpus Christi (TX) Resident Office
Wilson Plaza, 606 North Carancahua,
Suite 300, Corpus Christi, TX 78476
Tel: (361) 887-1200 Fax: (361) 887-1201
Resident Agent-in-Charge
William Brad "Brad" Baker .... (361) 887-1242
E-mail: william.b.baker@usdoj.gov

San Antonio (TX) District Office
10127 Morocco, Suite 200, San Antonio, TX 78216
Tel: (210) 442-5600 Fax: (210) 442-5617
Assistant Special Agent-in-Charge **Frank D. Sorianello** ... (210) 442-5702
E-mail: frank.d.sorianello@usdoj.gov

★ Presidential Appointment Requiring Senate Confirmation ☆ Presidential Appointment □ Schedule C Appointment ◇ Career Senior Foreign Service Appointment
● Career Senior Executive Service (SES) Appointment ○ Non-Career Senior Executive Service (SES) Appointment ■ Postal Career Executive Service

Austin (TX) Resident Office
9009 Mountain Ridge Drive, Suite A-300, Austin, TX 78759
Tel: (512) 344-4900 Fax: (512) 346-0825
Resident Agent-in-Charge **Scott E. Smith** .... (512) 344-4990
E-mail: scott.e.smith@usdoj.gov

Eagle Pass (TX) Resident Office
3381 US Highway South, Eagle Pass, TX 78852
Tel: (830) 752-4000 Fax: (830) 752-4040 Fax: (830) 752-4030 (Secure)
Resident Agent-in-Charge **Marlon Todd Harper** .... (830) 752-4001
E-mail: marlon.t.harper@usdoj.gov

Waco (TX) Resident Office
6801 Sanger Avenue, Suite 2000, Waco, TX 76710
Tel: (254) 297-0300 Fax: (254) 741-1434
Resident Agent-in-Charge **Donald L. York** .... (254) 297-0303

Los Angeles (CA) Division
Roybal Federal Building, 255 East Temple Street,
17th Floor, Los Angeles, CA 90012
Tel: (213) 621-6700 Fax: (213) 894-1769
Areas Covered: Southern CA, GU, HI, NV
Special Agent-in-Charge **David J. Downing** .... (213) 621-7032
E-mail: david.j.downing@usdoj.gov
Associate Special Agent-in-Charge **Steve Woodland** .... (213) 621-7033
Public Information Officer **Timothy J. Massino** .... (213) 621-6827
E-mail: timothy.j.massino@usdoj.gov
Security Officer **Nick Cappos** .... (213) 621-6741
Recruitment Coordinator **Alice Cubillos-Hall** .... (213) 621-6762
Fax: (213) 894-2490

Orange County Resident Office
1900 East First Street, Santa Ana, CA 92702
P.O. Box 385, Santa Ana, CA 92702
Tel: (714) 647-4900 Fax: (714) 647-4923
Resident Agent-in-Charge **Matthew Allen** .... (714) 647-4900

Ventura (CA) Resident Office
770 Paseo Camarillo, 3rd Floor, Camarillo, CA 93010
Tel: (805) 383-6454 Fax: (805) 383-6464
Resident Agent-in-Charge **William Torrance** .... (805) 383-6454

Honolulu (HI) District Office
300 Ala Moana Boulevard, Room 3147, Honolulu, HI 96813
P.O. Box 50163, Honolulu, HI 96850
Tel: (808) 541-1930 Fax: (808) 541-1936
Assistant Special Agent-in-Charge **Robin L. Dinlocker** ... (808) 541-1930
E-mail: robin.l.dinlocker@usdoj.gov

Guam Resident Office
Sirena Building, 108 Hernan Cortez Avenue,
Room 300, Hagatna, GU 96910
Tel: (671) 472-7281 Tel: (671) 472-7384 Fax: (671) 472-7426
Resident Agent-in-Charge **Michael Puralewski** .... (671) 472-7384

Las Vegas (NV) District Office
550 South Main Street, Suite A, Las Vegas, NV 89101
Tel: (702) 759-8000 Fax: (702) 759-8030
Assistant Special Agent-in-Charge **(Vacant)** .... (702) 759-8000

Reno (NV) Resident Office
8790 Double Diamond Parkway, Reno, NV 89521
Tel: (775) 327-8900 Fax: (775) 327-8950
Resident Agent-in-Charge **(Vacant)** .... (775) 327-8900

Riverside (CA) District Office
4470 Olivewood Avenue, Riverside, CA 92501-4155
Tel: (951) 328-6000 Fax: (951) 328-6060
Assistant Special Agent-in-Charge **Frank Pepper** .... (951) 328-6000

Louisville (KY) Division
Tel: (502) 582-5908
Special Agent In Charge **D. Christopher Evans** .... (502) 582-5908

Miami (FL) Division
2100 North Commerce Parkway, Weston, FL 33326
Tel: (954) 660-4500
Areas Covered: Nassau, Bahamas, FL
Special Agent-in-Charge **Adolphus P. Wright** .... (954) 660-4500
E-mail: adolphus.p.wright@usdoj.gov

Homestead (FL) Resident Office
3611 Alex Muxo Jr. Boulevard, Homestead, FL 33035
Tel: (305) 224-9851 Tel: (305) 224-9862
Resident Agent-in-Charge **Guillermo Aleman** .... (305) 224-9859

West Palm Beach (FL) District Office
444 West Railroad Avenue, Suite 500, West Palm Beach, FL 33401-6447
Tel: (561) 684-8000 Fax: (561) 684-8003
Assistant Special Agent-in-Charge **John J. McKenna** .... (561) 684-8010

Jacksonville (FL) District Office
4077 Woodcock Drive, Suite 210, Jacksonville, FL 32207
Tel: (904) 348-5225 Fax: (904) 348-7410
Assistant Special Agent-in-Charge **Chad W. Cook** .... (904) 348-5225

Gainesville (FL) Resident Office
235 South Main Street, Suite 202, Gainesville, FL 32601
Tel: (352) 371-2077 Fax: (352) 375-4356
Resident Agent-in-Charge **Ron Riddle** .... (352) 371-2077

Panama City (FL) Resident Office
3811 Frankford Avenue, Panama City, FL 32405
Tel: (850) 913-2700 Fax: (850) 913-2708
Resident Agent-in-Charge **David Lue** .... (850) 913-2700

Pensacola (FL) Resident Office
125 West Romana Street, Suite 330, Pensacola, FL 32501
Tel: (850) 469-9060 Fax: (850) 469-0755
Resident Agent-in-Charge **Marvin Gardner** .... (850) 469-9060

Tallahassee (FL) Resident Office
3384 Capitol Circle, NE, Tallahassee, FL 32308
Tel: (850) 350-7300 Fax: (850) 942-8420
Resident Agent-in-Charge **Pedro Guzman** .... (850) 350-7300

Orlando (FL) District Office
Heathrow Business Center, 300 International Parkway,
Suite 424, Heathrow, FL 32746
Tel: (407) 333-7000 Fax: (407) 333-7012
Assistant Special Agent-in-Charge **Jeffrey T. Walsh** ..... (407) 333-7050

Tampa (FL) District Office
4950 West Kennedy Boulevard, Suite 400, Tampa, FL 33609
Tel: (813) 287-5160 Fax: (813) 287-6499
Assistant Special Agent-in-Charge (Acting)
Eric Conaway .... (813) 287-4779

Fort Myers (FL) Resident Office
12730 New Brittany Boulevard, Suite 501, Fort Myers, FL 33907
Tel: (239) 275-3662 Fax: (239) 275-8945
Resident Agent-in-Charge **Mark Truessmann** .... (239) 275-3662

Port St. Lucie (FL) Resident Office
P.O. Box 880643, Port St. Lucie, FL 34986
Tel: (772) 873-3600 Fax: (772) 873-3606
Resident Agent-in-Charge **Sheldon J. Burkett** .... (772) 873-3600
E-mail: sheldon.j.burkett@usdoj.gov

★ Presidential Appointment Requiring Senate Confirmation ☆ Presidential Appointment ☐ Schedule C Appointment ◇ Career Senior Foreign Service Appointment
● Career Senior Executive Service (SES) Appointment ○ Non-Career Senior Executive Service (SES) Appointment ■ Postal Career Executive Service

DEPARTMENTS

New England Division

15 New Sudbury Street, Room E400, Boston, MA 02203-0402
Tel: (617) 557-2100 Fax: (617) 557-2135
Areas Covered: CT, ME, MA, NH, RI, VT

Special Agent-in-Charge **Brian Boyle** . . . . (617) 557-2116
E-mail: brian.d.boyle@usdoj.gov
Administrative Officer **Linda Karnafel** . . . . (617) 557-2103
E-mail: linda.karnafel@usdoj.gov
Assistant Administrative Officer **Diane Thompson** . . . . . . (617) 557-2486
E-mail: Diane.M.Thompson@usdoj.gov
Public Information Officer **Tim Desmond** . . . . (617) 557-2100

Bridgeport (CT) Resident Office

1000 Lafayette Boulevard, Room 404, Bridgeport, CT 06604
Tel: (203) 579-5591 Fax: (203) 579-5530

Resident Agent-in-Charge (Acting) **Brian Malagrida** . . . . . (203) 579-5591

Burlington (VT) Resident Office

55 Community Drive, Suite 101, South Burlington, VT 05403
Tel: (802) 951-2900 Fax: (802) 951-2970

Resident Agent-in-Charge **Kevin Black** . . . . (802) 951-2900

Hartford (CT) Resident Office

716 Brook Street, Suite 111, Hartford, CT 06067
Tel: (860) 257-2600 Fax: (860) 257-2616

Resident Agent-in-Charge **Uri Shafir** . . . . (860) 257-2600
E-mail: uri.shafir@dea.gov

Manchester (NH) District Office

324 South River Road, Bedford, NH 03110
Tel: (603) 628-7411 Fax: (603) 628-4788

Assistant Special Agent-in-Charge **Jon C. Delena** . . . . (603) 628-7411

New Bedford (MA) Resident Office

P.O. Box 3201, New Bedford, MA 02741-3201
Tel: (508) 996-4804 Fax: (508) 996-4829

Resident Agent-in-Charge **Kevin Eaton** . . . . (508) 996-4804

Portland (ME) Resident Office

1355 Congress Street, Suite D, Portland, ME 04102
Tel: (207) 780-3331 Fax: (207) 780-3413

Resident Agent-in-Charge **Michael W. Wardrop** . . . . (207) 780-3331

Providence (RI) Resident Office

Two International Way, Warwick, RI 02886
Tel: (401) 732-2550 Fax: (401) 739-3310

Resident Agent-in-Charge **Samuel Masiello** . . . . (401) 732-2550

Springfield (MA) Resident Office

1441 Main Street, Suite 1000, Springfield, MA 01103
Tel: (413) 306-6920 Fax: (413) 214-6396

Resident Agent-in-Charge **Daniel Pomeroy** . . . . (413) 785-0284

New Jersey Division

80 Mulberry Street, Second Floor, Newark, NJ 07102
Tel: (973) 776-1100 Fax: (973) 776-1111
Areas Covered: NJ

Special Agent-in-Charge **Valerie A. Nickerson** . . . . (973) 776-1200
E-mail: valerie.a.nickerson@usdoj.gov
Administrative Officer **Geralyn V. Magno** . . . . (973) 776-1112
E-mail: geralyn.magno@usdoj.gov
Public Information Officer **Timothy P. McMahon** . . . . (973) 776-1143
E-mail: timothy.p.mcmahon@usdoj.gov

Atlantic City (NJ) Resident Office

Executive Plaza, 2111 New Road, Suite 203, Northfield, NJ 08225
Tel: (609) 383-3322 Fax: (609) 383-0884

Resident Agent-in-Charge **Daniel Brown** . . . . (609) 383-3322
E-mail: daniel.brown@dea.gov

Camden (NJ) Resident Office

211 Boulevard Avenue, Maple Shade, NJ 08052
Tel: (856) 321-2420 Fax: (856) 321-2478

Resident Agent-in-Charge **Paris Pratt** . . . . (856) 321-2420

New Orleans (LA) Division

Three Lakeway Center, 3838 North Causeway Boulevard,
Suite 1800, Metairie, LA 70002
Tel: (504) 840-1100 Fax: (504) 840-1015
Areas Covered: AL, AR, LA, MS

● Special Agent-in-Charge **Stephen G. Azzam** . . . . (504) 840-1011
E-mail: stephen.g.azzam@usdoj.gov

Baton Rouge (LA) Resident Office

2237 South Acadian Thruway, Suite 306, Baton Rouge, LA 70808
Tel: (225) 389-0254 Fax: (225) 389-0772

Resident Agent-in-Charge **Brad Byerley** . . . . (225) 389-0254
Assistant Special Agent-in-Charge **Rene Rivera** . . . . (225) 389-0254
Assistant Special Agent-in-Charge **Susan M. Nave** . . . . . . (225) 389-0254

Lafayette (LA) Post of Duty

101 Feu Follet, Suite 200, Lafayette, LA 70508
Tel: (337) 706-3940 Fax: (337) 262-6770

Group Supervisor **Scott Wright** . . . . (337) 706-3940

Fayetteville (AR) Resident Office

179 East Colt Drive, Fayetteville, AR 72703
Tel: (479) 442-2618 Fax: (479) 442-2630

Resident Agent-in-Charge **Bryan Rurey** . . . . (479) 442-2618

Little Rock (AR) District Office

10825 Financial Parkway, Suite 200, Little Rock, AR 72211-3557
Tel: (501) 217-6500 Fax: (501) 217-6595

Assistant Special Agent-in-Charge **Justin C. King** . . . . (501) 217-6500
E-mail: justin.c.king@usdoj.gov

Fort Smith (AR) Post of Duty

30 South Sixth Street, Room B129A, Fort Smith, AR 72901
Tel: (479) 783-6300 Fax: (479) 783-7378

Group Supervisor **(Vacant)** . . . . (479) 783-6300

Shreveport (LA) Resident Office

401 Edwards Street, Suite 510, Shreveport, LA 71101
Tel: (318) 676-4080 Fax: (318) 676-4090

Resident Agent-in-Charge **Eric Watson** . . . . (318) 676-4080

Monroe (LA) Post of Duty

500 Natchitoches Street, Suite 200, West Monroe, LA 71291
Tel: (318) 651-7117 Fax: (318) 651-9137

Resident Agent-in-Charge **(Vacant)** . . . . (318) 676-7117

Jackson (MS) District Office

Dr. A. H. McCoy Federal Building, 100 West Capitol Street,
Suite 1213, Jackson, MS 39269
Tel: (601) 965-4400 Fax: (601) 965-4401

Assistant Special Agent-in-Charge
Daniel C. Comeaux . . . . (601) 965-4400
E-mail: daniel.c.comeaux@usdoj.gov

Gulfport (MS) Resident Office

2909 13th Street, Suite 500, Gulfport, MS 39501
Tel: (228) 863-2992 Fax: (228) 868-3112

Resident Agent-in-Charge **Terry Davis** . . . . (228) 863-2992

Oxford (MS) Resident Office

312 Heritage Drive, Suite 201, Oxford, MS 38655
Tel: (662) 232-3000 Fax: (662) 236-5119

Resident Agent-in-Charge **Warner Benson** . . . . (662) 232-3000

★ Presidential Appointment Requiring Senate Confirmation ☆ Presidential Appointment ☐ Schedule C Appointment ◇ Career Senior Foreign Service Appointment
● Career Senior Executive Service (SES) Appointment ○ Non-Career Senior Executive Service (SES) Appointment ■ Postal Career Executive Service

Montgomery (AL) District Office
2350 Fairlane Drive, Suite 200, Montgomery, AL 36116
Tel: (334) 273-7300 Fax: (334) 273-4780
Resident Agent-in-Charge **(Vacant)** .... (334) 273-7300

Birmingham (AL) Resident Office
920 18th Street North, Birmingham, AL 35203
Tel: (205) 321-1300 Fax: (205) 321-1301
Resident Agent-in-Charge **Clay Morris** .... (205) 321-1300
E-mail: clay.morris@dea.gov

Huntsville (AL) Post of Duty
101 Holmes Avenue, NE, Room B-3, Huntsville, AL 35801
Tel: (256) 519-6722 Fax: (256) 519-6724
Resident Agent-in-Charge **Clay Morris** .... (256) 519-6722
E-mail: clay.morris@dea.gov

Mobile (AL) Resident Office
900 Western America Circle, Suite 501, Mobile, AL 36609
Tel: (251) 441-5831 Fax: (251) 441-5289
Resident Agent-in-Charge **Donald DeSambo** .... (251) 441-5831

New York (NY) Division
99 Tenth Avenue, New York, NY 10011
Tel: (212) 337-3900 Fax: (212) 337-3978
Areas Covered: NY

• Special Agent-in-Charge (Acting) **Keith G. Kruskall** ..... (212) 337-2912
E-mail: keith.g.kruskall@usdoj.gov
• Associate Special Agent-in-Charge **Keith G. Kruskall** .... (646) 805-6916
E-mail: keith.g.kruskall@usdoj.gov
Associate Special Agent-in-Charge **John P. Reilly** .... (212) 274-4410
E-mail: john.p.reilly@usdoj.gov
• Associate Special Agent-in-Charge **(Vacant)** .... (212) 620-4919
• Associate Special Agent-in-Charge **(Vacant)** .... (212) 274-4458
• Unit Chief **Margaret Williams** .... (212) 274-4501
E-mail: margaret.williams@ic.fbi.gov Fax: (212) 337-3978
Security Specialist **Robert G. McAndrews** .... (212) 337-1799
E-mail: robert.g.mcandrews@usdoj.gov Fax: (212) 337-1880

Albany (NY) District Office
10 Hastings Drive, Latham, NY 12110
Tel: (518) 782-2001 Fax: (518) 782-2081
• Assistant Special Agent-in-Charge **David Zahn** .... (518) 782-2001
• Group Supervisor **Pat DeRubertis** .... (518) 431-4700
• Group Supervisor **Michael A Shelhamer** .... (518) 431-4700
E-mail: michael.a.shelhamer@usdoj.gov
• Group Supervisor **(Vacant)** .... (518) 431-4700

Buffalo (NY) Resident Office
535 Washington Street, Suite 500, Buffalo, NY 14203
Tel: (716) 846-6000 Fax: (716) 843-2143
• Resident Agent-in-Charge **John P. Flickinger** .... (716) 846-6060
E-mail: john.p.flickinger@usdoj.gov

Rochester (NY) Resident Office
Rochester, NY 14614
P.O. Box 14210, Rochester, NY 14614
Tel: (585) 263-3180 Fax: (585) 263-5870
• Resident Agent-in-Charge **Matthew Ramarge** .... (585) 263-3180

Long Island (NY) District Office
175 Pinelawn Road, Suite 205, Melville, NY 11747
Tel: (631) 420-4500 Fax: (631) 293-2048
• Assistant Special Agent-in-Charge **Kevin Larkin** .... (631) 420-4500
E-mail: kevin.larkin@usdoj.gov

Syracuse (NY) Resident Office
500 Plum Street, Suite 700, Syracuse, NY 13204
Tel: (315) 477-1700 Fax: (315) 468-2985
• Resident Agent-in-Charge **Edward J. Duffy** .... (315) 477-1700
E-mail: edward.j.duffy@usdoj.gov

Omaha (NE) Division
Tel: (402) 965-3600
Special Agent In Charge **Matthew R. Barden** .... (402) 493-8688

Philadelphia (PA) Division
William J. Green, Jr. Federal Building, 600 Arch Street, Room 10224, Philadelphia, PA 19106
Tel: (215) 861-3474 Fax: (215) 861-1979
Areas Covered: DE, PA
Special Agent-in-Charge **Jonathan A. Wilson** .... (215) 861-3437
E-mail: jonthan.a.wilson@usdoj.gov

Allentown (PA) Resident Office
504 West Hamilton Street, Suite 2500, Allentown, PA 18101
Tel: (610) 770-0940 Fax: (610) 435-6854
Resident Agent-in-Charge **Philip Bemel** .... (610) 770-0940

Harrisburg (PA) Resident Office
228 Walnut Street, Room 572, Harrisburg, PA 17101
P.O. Box 887, Harrisburg, PA 17108-0887
Tel: (717) 257-1620 Fax: (717) 257-1698
Resident Agent-in-Charge **Jeffrey Bielski** .... (717) 257-1621

Scranton (PA) Resident Office
235 North Washington Avenue, Room 205, Scranton, PA 18503
P.O. Box 751, Scranton, PA 18503-0751
Tel: (570) 496-1020 Fax: (570) 496-1025
Resident Agent-in-Charge **Mark Gabura** .... (570) 496-1020

Wilmington (DE) Resident Office
23 South Gate Boulevard, Suite 105, New Castle, DE 19720
Tel: (302) 395-4600 Fax: (302) 395-4661
Resident Agent-in-Charge **David B. Hughes** .... (302) 395-4600
E-mail: david.hughes@dea.gov

Pittsburgh (PA) District Office
1781 McKees Rocks Road, Mc Kees Rocks, PA 15136
Tel: (412) 777-6940 Fax: (412) 777-1820
Assistant Special Agent-in-Charge **David Batiste** .... (412) 777-6991

Phoenix (AZ) Division
3010 North Second Street, Suite 100, Phoenix, AZ 85012-3055
Tel: (602) 664-5600 Fax: (602) 664-5616
Areas Covered: AZ
Special Agent-in-Charge
Douglas W. "Doug" Coleman .... (602) 664-5601
E-mail: douglas.w.coleman@usdoj.gov

Yuma (AZ) Resident Office
780 East 39th Place, Yuma, AZ 85365-4905
Tel: (928) 344-9550 Fax: (928) 344-1444
Resident Agent-in-Charge **Darrion Eshmon** .... (928) 344-9550

Tucson (AZ) District Office
3285 East Hemisphere Loop, Tucson, AZ 85706-5014
Tel: (520) 573-5500 Fax: (520) 573-5632
Assistant Special Agent-in-Charge **Albert Laurita** .... (520) 573-5500

Nogales (AZ) Resident Office
141 Paseo De Yucatan, Rio Rico, AZ 85648
Tel: (520) 281-1727 Fax: (520) 281-1850
Resident Agent-in-Charge **Christopher Adduci** .... (520) 281-1727

Sierra Vista (AZ) Resident Office
1728 Paseo San Luis, Sierra Vista, AZ 85635-4610
Tel: (520) 458-3691 Fax: (520) 458-9770
Resident Agent-in-Charge **Michael Mam** .... (520) 458-3691

DEPARTMENTS

★ Presidential Appointment Requiring Senate Confirmation ☆ Presidential Appointment ☐ Schedule C Appointment ◇ Career Senior Foreign Service Appointment
● Career Senior Executive Service (SES) Appointment ○ Non-Career Senior Executive Service (SES) Appointment ■ Postal Career Executive Service

DEPARTMENTS

Saint Louis (MO) Division
317 South 16th Street, St. Louis, MO 63103
Tel: (314) 538-4600 Fax: (314) 538-4767
Areas Covered: Southern IL, IA, KS, MO, NE, SD

Special Agent-in-Charge **William J. Callahan III** .... (314) 538-4600
Education: Rutgers BA; John Jay Col MA
Assistant Special Agent-in-Charge **Larry J. Reavis, Jr.** .... (314) 538-4600
Assistant Special Agent-in-Charge **(Vacant)** .... (314) 538-4600

Cape Girardeau (MO) Resident Office
3065 William Street, Suite 501, Cape Girardeau, MO 63703
Tel: (573) 334-1534 Fax: (573) 335-4117
Resident Agent-in-Charge **Brian Barger** .... (573) 334-1534

Fairview Heights (IL) Resident Office
333 Salem Place, Suite 265, Fairview Heights, IL 62208
Tel: (618) 628-0025 Fax: (618) 628-0039
Resident Agent-in-Charge **Edgar Remspecher, Jr.** .... (618) 628-0025

Kansas City (KS) District Office
8600 Farley Street, Suite 200, Overland Park, KS 66212
Tel: (913) 825-4000 Fax: (913) 951-3681
Assistant Special Agent-in-Charge **Troy A. Derby** .... (913) 951-4006

Garden City (KS) Resident Office
2501 Campus Drive, Suite 900, Garden City, KS 67846
Tel: (620) 275-4373 Fax: (620) 275-5576
Resident Agent-in-Charge **Brian Inglis** .... (620) 275-4373
E-mail: brian.inglis@usdoj.gov

Springfield (MO) Resident Office
901 East St. Louis Street, Suite 301, Springfield, MO 65806
Tel: (417) 831-3948 Fax: (417) 831-0607
Resident Agent-in-Charge **Jay C. Forster** .... (417) 831-3948

Wichita (KS) Resident Office
1919 North Amidon, Suite 330, Wichita, KS 67203
Tel: (316) 838-2500 Fax: (316) 838-9123
Resident Agent-in-Charge **James R. Hall** .... (316) 838-2500

Omaha (NE) District Office
2707 North 108th Street, Suite D201, Omaha, NE 68164
Tel: (402) 965-3600 Fax: (402) 965-3700
Assistant Special Agent-in-Charge **Chad Robacker** ...... (402) 965-3600

Cedar Rapids (IA) Resident Office
Executive Plaza, 4403 First Avenue, SE,
Suite 200, Cedar Rapids, IA 52402
Tel: (319) 393-6075 Fax: (319) 393-7229
Resident Agent-in-Charge **Russell Colter** .... (319) 393-6075

Des Moines (IA) Resident Office
Federal Building, 210 Walnut Street, Room 937, Des Moines, IA 50309
Tel: (515) 284-4700 Fax: (515) 284-4927
Resident Agent-in-Charge **Matthew Roberts** .... (515) 284-4700

Sioux City (IA) Resident Office
320 Sixth Street, B-35, Sioux City, IA 51101
Tel: (712) 255-9128 Fax: (712) 258-1408
Resident Agent-in-Charge **Stephen Thomas** .... (712) 255-9128

Sioux Falls (SD) Resident Office
5000 South Broadband Lane, Suite 200, Sioux Falls, SD 57108
Tel: (605) 330-4421 Fax: (605) 330-4420
Resident Agent-in-Charge **Ronald Deist** .... (605) 330-4421

San Diego (CA) Division
4560 Viewridge Avenue, San Diego, CA 92123-1672
Tel: (858) 616-4100 Fax: (858) 616-4084
Areas Covered: CA (border area)
Special Agent-in-Charge **Karen I. Flowers** .... (858) 616-4100

Imperial County District Office
2425 La Brucherie Road, Imperial, CA 92251
Tel: (760) 355-0857 Fax: (760) 355-2946
Assistant Special Agent-in-Charge
Francisco Amavizca .... (760) 355-0857

Carlsbad (CA) Resident Office
5810 Newton Drive, Carlsbad, CA 92008
Tel: (760) 268-5700 Fax: (760) 268-5750
Resident Agent-in-Charge **Kevin Hatchett** .... (760) 268-5700

San Ysidro (CA) Resident Office
2255 Niels Bohr Circle, San Ysidro, CA 92173-3915
Tel: (619) 671-4500 Fax: (619) 671-4550
Resident Agent-in-Charge **Paul Abosamra** .... (619) 671-4500

San Francisco (CA) Division
450 Golden Gate Avenue, San Francisco, CA 94102
P.O. Box 36035, San Francisco, CA 94102
Tel: (415) 436-7860 Fax: (415) 436-7810
Areas Covered: Northern CA

Special Agent-in-Charge **Christopher Nielsen** .... (415) 436-7782
Secretary **Yolanda Ruiz** .... (415) 436-8682
E-mail: yolanda.ruiz@usdoj.gov
Assistant Special Agent-in-Charge **(Vacant)** .... (415) 436-8140
Assistant Special Agent-in-Charge **(Vacant)** .... (415) 436-7752
Assistant Special Agent-in-Charge **(Vacant)** .... (415) 436-7752
Divisional Training Coordinator **James Nuttall** .... (415) 436-8637
Primary Firearms Instructor **James Nuttall** .... (415) 436-8637

Bakersfield (CA) Resident Office
7400 Schirra Court, Bakersfield, CA 93313
Tel: (661) 396-3736 Fax: (661) 396-2630
Resident Agent-in-Charge **Bob P. Beris** .... (661) 396-3736
E-mail: bob.p.beris@usdoj.gov

Fresno (CA) Resident Office
2444 Main Street, Suite 240, Fresno, CA 93721
Tel: (559) 487-5402 Fax: (559) 487-5129
Resident Agent-in-Charge **Christopher Coleman** .... (559) 443-8102

Oakland (CA) Resident Office
1301 Clay Street, Suite 460 North, Oakland, CA 94612-5217
Tel: (510) 637-5600 Fax: (510) 637-5097
Resident Agent-in-Charge **Lesley C. Tomaich** .... (510) 634-5656

San Jose (CA) Resident Office
150 Almaden Blvd., Suite 500, San Jose, CA 95113
Tel: (408) 282-3400 Fax: (408) 282-3483
Resident Agent-in-Charge **Art Wiley** .... (408) 282-3420

Santa Rosa (CA) Resident Office
5770 Skyline Boulevard, Santa Rosa, CA 95492
Tel: (707) 837-2324 Fax: (707) 837-2321
Resident Agent-in-Charge **Ryan S. Sibbald** .... (707) 837-2330
E-mail: ryan.s.sibbald@usdoj.gov

Sacramento (CA) District Office
4328 Watt Avenue, Sacramento, CA 95821
Tel: (916) 480-7100 Fax: (916) 480-7207
Assistant Special Agent-in-Charge **Jerry Miller** .... (916) 480-7201

Seattle (WA) Division
300 Fifth Avenue, Suite 1300, Seattle, WA 98104
Tel: (206) 553-5443 Fax: (206) 553-1576
Areas Covered: AK, ID, OR, WA

● Special Agent-in-Charge **Keith Weiss** .... (206) 553-5443
Education: Portland State BS
Assistant Special Agent-in-Charge **Douglas James** ...... (206) 553-5443
Division Training Coordinator **Albert Brezicha** .... (206) 553-5443

★ Presidential Appointment Requiring Senate Confirmation ☆ Presidential Appointment ☐ Schedule C Appointment ◇ Career Senior Foreign Service Appointment
● Career Senior Executive Service (SES) Appointment ○ Non-Career Senior Executive Service (SES) Appointment ■ Postal Career Executive Service

Anchorage (AK) Resident Office
1630 East Tudor Road, Anchorage, AK 99507
101 12th Avenue, Box 18, Fairbanks, AK 99701 (Fairbanks Post of Duty)
Tel: (907) 455-1818 (Fairbanks Post of Duty) Tel: (907) 271-5033
Fax: (907) 455-1819 (Fairbanks Post of Duty) Fax: (907) 271-3097
Assistant Special Agent-in-Charge **Michael Root** .... (907) 271-5033

Bellingham (WA) Resident Office
1855 Barkley Blvd, Bellingham, WA 98226
Mail: P.O. Box 31610, Bellingham, WA 98228-3160
Tel: (360) 676-3100 Fax: (360) 676-3103
Resident Agent-in-Charge **Candice Flaherty** .... (360) 676-3100

Boise (ID) Resident Office
607 North Eighth Street, Suite 400, Boise, ID 83702
Tel: (208) 386-2100 Fax: (208) 386-9253
Resident Agent-in-Charge **William Lutz** .... (208) 386-2100

Spokane (WA) Resident Office
West 1124 Riverside, Suite L-300, Spokane, WA 99201
Tel: (509) 353-2964 Fax: (509) 353-2963
Assistant Special Agent-in-Charge **Tracy D. Simmons** ... (509) 353-2964
E-mail: tracy.d.simmons@usdoj.gov
Group Supervisor **Mark Haigh** .... (509) 353-2964

Tacoma (WA) Resident Office
1250 Pacific Avenue, Suite 850, Tacoma, WA 98407
Tel: (253) 383-7901 Fax: (253) 383-7974
Resident Agent-in-Charge **Ian McKenzie** .... (253) 383-7901

Yakima (WA) Resident Office
402 East Yakima Avenue, Suite 900, Yakima, WA 98901
Tel: (509) 454-4407 Fax: (509) 454-4413
Resident Agent-in-Charge **Jason Diaz** .... (509) 454-4407

Portland (OR) District Office
100 SW Main Street, Suite 500, Portland, OR 97204
Tel: (503) 721-6600 Fax: (503) 721-6602
Assistant Special Agent-in-Charge **Cam B. Straham** ..... (503) 721-6600

Eugene (OR) Resident Office
Federal Building, 211 East Seventh Avenue,
Room 420, Eugene, OR 97401
c/o Deschutes County Sheriff, 63333 Highway 20 West, Bend, OR 97701
(Bend Post of Duty)
Tel: (541) 385-8798 (Bend Post of Duty)
Tel: (541) 465-6861 (Eugene Resident Office)
Fax: (541) 385-9160 (Bend Post of Duty) Fax: (541) 465-6796
Resident Agent-in-Charge **William Kearney** .... (541) 465-6861

Medford (OR) Resident Office
1225 Crater Lake Avenue, Suite 201, Medford, OR 97504
Tel: (541) 776-4260 Fax: (541) 776-4263
Resident Agent-in-Charge (Acting) **Clark Wheeler** ...... (541) 776-4260

Salem (OR) Resident Office
2601 - 25th Street, SE, Suite 550, Salem, OR 97302
Tel: (503) 399-5902 Fax: (503) 399-5927
Resident Agent-in-Charge **Tyson "Frankie" Hodges** ..... (503) 399-5902

Washington (DC) Division
800 K Street, NW, Suite 500, Washington, DC 20530
Tel: (202) 305-8500 Fax: (202) 307-5760
Areas Covered: DC, MD, VA, WV
Special Agent-in-Charge (Acting) **Scott Hoernke** .... (202) 305-8120
E-mail: scott.hoernke@usdoj.gov
Assistant Special Agent-in-Charge **Kevin Carter** .... (202) 305-8103
Assistant Special Agent-in-Charge **Scott Hoernke** .... (202) 305-8103
E-mail: scott.hoernke@usdoj.gov
Assistant Special Agent-in-Charge **(Vacant)** .... (202) 305-8182
Assistant Special Agent-in-Charge **(Vacant)** .... (202) 305-8434

Charleston (WV) Resident Office
Union Square, Two Monongalia, Suite 300, Charleston, WV 25302-2349
Tel: (304) 347-5209 Fax: (304) 347-5212
Resident Agent-in-Charge **(Vacant)** .... (304) 347-5209

Baltimore (MD) District Office
200 St. Paul Place, Suite 2222, Baltimore, MD 21202
Tel: (410) 244-3500 Fax: (410) 244-3470
Assistant Special Agent-in-Charge **Don Hibberd** .... (410) 244-3430

Richmond (VA) District Office
111 Greencourt Road, Richmond, VA 23228
Tel: (804) 627-6300 Fax: (804) 627-6308
Assistant Special Agent-in-Charge **(Vacant)** .... (804) 627-6300

Norfolk (VA) Resident Office
Federal Office Building, 200 Granby Mall,
Suite 435, Norfolk, VA 23510-1811
Tel: (757) 314-2200 Fax: (757) 314-2247
Resident Agent-in-Charge **(Vacant)** .... (757) 314-2200

Roanoke (VA) Resident Office
105 West Franklin Road, Roanoke, VA 24011
Tel: (540) 857-2555 Fax: (540) 857-2569
Resident Agent-in-Charge **Jeffrey P. Wanner** .... (540) 857-2555

Federal Bureau of Investigation (FBI)
J. Edgar Hoover Building, 935 Pennsylvania Avenue, NW,
Washington, DC 20535-0001
Tel: (202) 324-3000 (Public Information) Internet: www.fbi.gov
Internet: www.fbi.gov/espanol/fbi-en-espanol (FBI in Spanish)

OFFICE OF THE DIRECTOR (DO)
J. Edgar Hoover Building, 935 Pennsylvania Avenue, NW,
Washington, DC 20535-0001

Regional Divisions

Albany (NY) Division
200 McCarty Avenue, Albany, NY 12209
Tel: (518) 465-7551 Fax: (518) 431-7463 E-mail: albany@fbi.gov
Internet: http://www.fbi.gov/albany/
Special Agent-in-Charge (Acting) **Charles Margiotta** .... (518) 465-7551
E-mail: cmargiotta@fbi.gov
Assistant Special Agent-in-Charge **Philip "Phil" Hale** .... (518) 431-7551
E-mail: philip.hale@ic.fbi.gov
Assistant Special Agent-in-Charge **Peter Magnetto** ...... (518) 431-7220
E-mail: peter.magnetto@ic.fbi.gov
Chief Division Counsel **Peter "Pete" Fitzgerald** .... (518) 465-7551
Law Enforcement and Media Relations Coordinator
(Vacant) .... (518) 465-7551
Training Coordinator **Carmello Ortiz** .... (518) 465-7551

Albuquerque (NM) Division
4200 Luecking Park Avenue, NE, Albuquerque, NM 87107
Tel: (505) 889-1300 Fax: (505) 889-1770 E-mail: aq.fbi@ic.fbi.gov
Internet: http://www.fbi.gov/albuquerque/
● Special Agent-in-Charge **James C. Langenberg** .... (505) 889-1300
E-mail: jclangenberg@fbi.gov
Assistant Special Agent-in-Charge **Bryan Finnegan** ...... (505) 889-1300
E-mail: bryan.finnegan@ic.fbi.gov
Assistant Special Agent-in-Charge **Derek Fuller** .... (505) 889-1300
E-mail: derek.fuller@ic.fbi.gov
Assistant Special Agent-in-Charge
Robert M. White, Sr. .... (505) 889-1300
E-mail: robert.white@ic.fbi.gov
Media Relations Coordinator **Frank Fisher** .... (505) 889-1438
E-mail: frank.fisher@ic.fbi.gov
Administrative Officer **Joelyn Rael** .... (505) 889-1300

(continued on next page)

★ Presidential Appointment Requiring Senate Confirmation ☆ Presidential Appointment ☐ Schedule C Appointment ◇ Career Senior Foreign Service Appointment
● Career Senior Executive Service (SES) Appointment ○ Non-Career Senior Executive Service (SES) Appointment ■ Postal Career Executive Service

DEPARTMENTS

Albuquerque (NM) Division *(continued)*

Security Officer **Mark Bracken** . . . . (505) 889-1300
E-mail: mark.bracken@ic.fbi.gov

Anchorage (AK) Division

101 East Sixth Avenue, Anchorage, AK 99501-2524
Tel: (907) 276-4441 Fax: (907) 265-8400 E-mail: anchoragefbi@ak.net
Internet: http://www.fbi.gov/anchorage/

● Special Agent-in-Charge **Jeffery Peterson** . . . . (907) 276-4441
E-mail: jepeterson@fbi.gov
Assistant Special Agent-in-Charge/Criminal
Antony A. Jung . . . . (907) 276-4441
Assistant Special Agent-in-Charge/National Security
Darrin T. Turpin . . . . (907) 276-4441
Chief Division Counsel **Richard W. Vanveldhuisen** . . . . . (907) 276-4441
E-mail: richard.vanveldhuisen@ic.fbi.gov

Atlanta (GA) Division

3000 Flowers Road South, Atlanta, GA 30341-3112
Tel: (770) 216-3000 Fax: (404) 679-6289 E-mail: atlanta@ic.fbi.gov
Internet: http://www.fbi.gov/atlanta/

● Special Agent-in-Charge **J.C. "Chris" Hacker** . . . . (404) 679-9000
E-mail: jchacker@fbi.gov
Assistant Special Agent-in-Charge
Matthew R. Alcoke . . . . (404) 679-9000
E-mail: mralcoke@fbi.gov
Assistant Special Agent-in-Charge
Ricardo Grave de Peralta . . . . (404) 679-9000
E-mail: ricardo.gravedeperalta@ic.fbi.gov
Assistant Special Agent-in-Charge (Acting)
Robert Mathews . . . . (404) 679-9000
E-mail: robert.mathews@ic.fbi.gov
Assistant Special Agent-in-Charge **Murang Pak** . . . . (404) 679-9000
E-mail: murang.pak@ic.fbi.gov
Education: North Florida 1993 BA; Michigan State 2016 MA
Senior Supervisory Intelligence Analyst
Ron H. Johnson . . . . (770) 216-3000

Baltimore (MD) Division

2600 Lord Baltimore Drive, Baltimore, MD 21244
Tel: (410) 265-8080 Fax: (410) 277-6677 E-mail: baltimore@fbi.gov
Internet: http://www.fbi.gov/baltimore/

● Special Agent-in-Charge **Gordon B. Johnson** . . . . (410) 265-8080
Executive Assistant **Sharon Berkeley** . . . . (410) 265-8080
Assistant Special Agent-in-Charge
Joseph D. Marasco . . . . (410) 265-8080
E-mail: joseph.marasco@ic.fbi.gov
Assistant Special Agent-in-Charge **Brian J. Nadeau** . . . . . (410) 265-8080
E-mail: brian.nadeau@ic.fbi.gov
Assistant Special Agent-in-Charge
Nicholas B. Savage . . . . (410) 265-8080
Media Relations Coordinator **David "Dave" Fitz** . . . . (410) 277-6689

Birmingham (AL) Division

1000 18th Street North, Birmingham, AL 35203
Tel: (205) 326-6166 Fax: (205) 279-1590
E-mail: birmingham@ic.fbi.gov Internet: http://www.fbi.gov/birmingham/

Special Agent-in-Charge **Johnnie Sharp** . . . . (205) 326-6166
E-mail: johnnie.sharp@ic.fbi.gov
Assistant Special Agent-in-Charge
Johnny J. Cooper II . . . . (205) 326-6166
E-mail: johnny.cooper@ic.fbi.gov
Assistant Special Agent-in-Charge **Todd Bobe** . . . . (205) 326-6166
Security Officer **Nate Rutledge** . . . . (205) 326-6166
Public Affairs Specialist **Paul E. Daymond** . . . . (205) 326-6166
E-mail: paul.daymond@ic.fbi.gov

Boston (MA) Division

201 Maple Street, Chelsea, MA 02150
Tel: (857) 386-2000 Fax: (617) 223-6327 E-mail: boston@fbi.gov
Internet: http://www.fbi.gov/boston/

Special Agent-in-Charge **Harold H. Shaw** . . . . (857) 386-2000
E-mail: harold.shaw@ic.fbi.gov
Education: Norwich BS

Boston (MA) Division *(continued)*

Assistant Special Agent-in-Charge **David R. Farrell** . . . . . . (857) 386-2000
E-mail: david.campbell@ic.fbi.gov
Assistant Special Agent-in-Charge **Randolph H. Jarvis** . . . (857) 386-2000
E-mail: randolph.jarvis@ic.fbi.gov
Assistant Special Agent-in-Charge
Peter F. Kowenhoven . . . . (857) 386-2000
E-mail: peter.kowenhoven@ic.fbi.gov
Assistant Special Agent-in-Charge **Steven Merrill** . . . . (857) 386-2000
E-mail: steven.merrill@ic.fbi.gov
Assistant Special Agent-in-Charge **Kevin R. White** . . . . . . (857) 386-2000
E-mail: krwhite@fbi.gov
Media Coordinator **Kristen Setera** . . . . (857) 386-2000
E-mail: kristen.setera@ic.fbi.gov
Community Outreach Specialist **Susan T. Durkin** . . . . (857) 386-2000
E-mail: susan.durkin@ic.fbi.gov
Administrative Officer **(Vacant)** . . . . (857) 386-2000
Senior Supervisory Intelligence Analyst
Gerald McMahon . . . . (857) 386-2000

Buffalo (NY) Division

One FBI Plaza, Buffalo, NY 14202-2698
Tel: (716) 856-7800 Fax: (716) 843-5288 E-mail: buffalo@ic.fbi.gov
Internet: http://www.fbi.gov/buffalo/

● Special Agent-in-Charge **Gary A. Loeffert** . . . . (716) 856-7800
E-mail: galoeffert@fbi.gov
Assistant Special Agent-in-Charge **Philip E. Frigm, Jr.** . . . . (716) 856-7800
E-mail: philip.frigm@ic.fbi.gov
Assistant Special Agent-in-Charge
Robert P. Guyton, Jr. . . . . (716) 856-7800
E-mail: robert.guyton@ic.fbi.gov

Charlotte (NC) Division

7915 Micosoft Way, Charlotte, NC 28273
Tel: (704) 672-6100 Fax: (704) 672-6595 E-mail: charlotte@fbi.gov
Internet: http://www.fbi.gov/charlotte/

Special Agent-in-Charge **John A. Strong** . . . . (704) 672-6100
E-mail: jastrong@fbi.gov
Assistant Special Agent-in-Charge **Keri E. Farley** . . . . (704) 672-6100
E-mail: keri.farley@ic.fbi.gov
Assistant Special Agent-in-Charge
Michael E. Stansbury . . . . (704) 672-6100
E-mail: michael.stansbury@ic.fbi.gov
Assistant Special Agent-in-Charge
Timothy M. Stranahan . . . . (704) 672-6100
E-mail: timothy.stranahan@ic.fbi.gov
Chief Division Counsel **Daniel J. Foore** . . . . (704) 672-6100
E-mail: daniel.foore@ic.fbi.gov
Private Sector Coordinator **Mark Aysta** . . . . (704) 280-7799
E-mail: mmaysta@fbi.gov
Public Affairs Specialist **Shelley Lynch** . . . . (704) 672-6766

Chicago (IL) Division

2111 West Roosevelt Road, Chicago, IL 60608
Tel: (312) 421-6700 Fax: (312) 829-5732 Fax: (312) 829-5738
E-mail: chicago@fbi.gov Internet: http://www.fbi.gov/chicago/

Special Agent-in-Charge **Jeffrey S. Sallet** . . . . (312) 421-6700
E-mail: jeffrey.sallet@ic.fbi.gov
Deputy Special Agent-in-Charge **Peter M. Angelini** . . . . . (312) 421-6700
E-mail: peter.angelini@ic.fbi.gov
Assistant Special Agent-in-Charge **Todd M. Carroll** . . . . . . (312) 421-6700
E-mail: todd.carroll@ic.fbi.gov
Assistant Special Agent-in-Charge **Jay Greenberg** . . . . . . (312) 421-6700
E-mail: jay.greenberg@ic.fbi.gov
Assistant Special Agent-in-Charge **Kevin S. Keithley** . . . . (312) 421-6700
E-mail: kevin.keithley@ic.fbi.gov
Assistant Special Agent-in-Charge **Larry L. Lapp** . . . . (312) 421-6700
E-mail: larry.lapp@ic.fbi.gov
Assistant Special Agent-in-Charge
Anthony Riedlinger . . . . (312) 421-6700
E-mail: anthony.riedlinger@ic.fbi.gov
Assistant Special Agent-in-Charge
Christopher Serdinak . . . . (312) 421-6700
E-mail: christopher.serdinak@ic.fbi.gov

★ Presidential Appointment Requiring Senate Confirmation ☆ Presidential Appointment ☐ Schedule C Appointment ◇ Career Senior Foreign Service Appointment
● Career Senior Executive Service (SES) Appointment ○ Non-Career Senior Executive Service (SES) Appointment ■ Postal Career Executive Service

Chicago (IL) Division *(continued)*

Chief Division Counsel **D.J. Rossini** .... (312) 421-6700
Senior Supervisory Intelligence Analyst
Matthew B. Wolfe .... (312) 421-6700
E-mail: matthew.wolfe@ic.fbi.gov

Cincinnati (OH) Division
2012 Ronald Reagan Drive, Cincinnati, OH 45236
Tel: (513) 421-4310 Fax: (513) 979-8450
Internet: http://www.fbi.gov/cincinnati/

Special Agent-in-Charge **Angela L. Byers** .... (513) 421-4310
E-mail: angela.byers@ic.fbi.gov
Education: Wheeling Jesuit
Assistant Special Agent-in-Charge **Joseph M. Deters** .... (513) 421-4310
E-mail: joseph.deters@ic.fbi.gov
Assistant Special Agent-in-Charge **Richard A. Mains** .... (513) 421-4310
E-mail: richard.mains@ic.fbi.gov
Assistant Special Agent-in-Charge **Herbert Stapleton** ... (513) 421-4310
Media Coordinator **Todd Lindgren** .... (513) 979-8347

Cleveland (OH) Division
1501 Lakeside Avenue East, Cleveland, OH 44114-1138
Tel: (216) 522-1400 Fax: (216) 622-6717
E-mail: cleveland.cv@ic.fbi.gov Internet: http://www.fbi.gov/cleveland/

Special Agent-in-Charge **Stephen D. Anthony** .... (216) 522-1400
E-mail: stephen.anthony@ic.fbi.gov
Education: John Carroll 1984 BA; Cleveland-Marshall 1987 JD
Assistant Special Agent in Charge **Jeffrey Fortunato** .... (216) 522-1400
E-mail: jeffrey.fortunato@ic.fbi.gov
Assistant Special Agent-in-Charge **Bryan P. Smith** ...... (216) 522-1400
Assistant Special Agent-in-Charge **Ganpat V. Wagh** ..... (216) 522-1400
E-mail: ganpat.wagh@ic.fbi.gov
Assistant Special Agent-in-Charge **Alvin M. Winston** .... (216) 522-1400
E-mail: alvin.winston@ic.fbi.gov
Administrative Officer **Eric M. Tranter** .... (216) 522-1400 ext. 6690
E-mail: eric.tranter@ic.fbi.gov
Media Coordinator **Vicki D. Anderson** .... (216) 522-1400

Columbia (SC) Division
151 Westpark Boulevard, Columbia, SC 29210-3857
Tel: (803) 551-4200 Fax: (803) 551-4324 E-mail: columbia@fbi.gov
Internet: http://www.fbi.gov/columbia/

Special Agent-in-Charge **Alphonso Norris III** .... (803) 551-4211
E-mail: alphonso.norris@ic.fbi.gov
Assistant Special Agent-in-Charge
Douglas Hemminghaus .... (803) 551-4241
E-mail: douglas.hemminghaus@ic.fbi.gov
Assistant Special Agent-in-Charge **Paul R. Davis** .... (803) 551-4221
E-mail: prdavis@fbi.gov
Chief Division Counsel (Acting) **Donald A. Wood** ...... (803) 551-4200
E-mail: donald.wood@ic.fbi.gov
Secretary **Rachel West** .... (803) 551-4212
Public Affairs Specialist **Denise M. Taiste** .... (803) 551-4352
E-mail: denise.taiste@ic.fbi.gov

Dallas (TX) Division
J. Gordon Shanklin Building, One Justice Way,
Suite 500, Dallas, TX 75220
Tel: (972) 559-5000 Fax: (972) 559-5600 E-mail: fbi.dallas@fbi.gov
Internet: http://www.fbi.gov/dallas/

Special Agent-in-Charge **Eric K. Jackson** .... (972) 559-5007
E-mail: eric.jackson@usdoj.gov
Assistant Special Agent-in-Charge **Michael Costanzi** .... (972) 559-5344
E-mail: michael.costanzi@ic.fbi.gov
Assistant Special Agent-in-Charge **Daniel Odom** .... (972) 559-5000
E-mail: daniel.odom@ic.fbi.gov
Assistant Special Agent-in-Charge **Patrick Reddan** ...... (972) 559-5350
E-mail: patrick.reddan@ic.fbi.gov
Assistant Special Agent-in-Charge **Aaron Tapp** .... (972) 559-5100
E-mail: aaron.tapp@ic.fbi.gov
Assistant Special Agent-in-Charge **Niambi Tillman** ...... (972) 559-5009
E-mail: niambi.tillman@ic.fbi.gov
Media Coordinator **Allison Mahan** .... (972) 559-5000

Denver (CO) Division
8000 East 36th Avenue, Denver, CO 80238
Tel: (303) 629-7171 Fax: (303) 575-7009 E-mail: denver@fbi.gov
Internet: http://www.fbi.gov/denver/

Special Agent-in-Charge **Dean Phillips** .... (303) 629-7171
Education: Air Force Acad 1988 BS;
Colorado (Colo Springs) 1996 MBA
Assistant Special Agent-in-Charge **Bradley Benavides** ... (303) 629-7171
Assistant Special Agent-in-Charge **Janeen Diguiseppi** ... (303) 629-7171
E-mail: janeen.diguiseppi@ic.fbi.gov
Assistant Special Agent-in-Charge **Michael Nordwall** .... (303) 629-7171
E-mail: michael.nordwall@ic.fbi.gov
Division Counsel **Robert J. Goffi** .... (303) 629-7171
Administrative Officer **Scott L. Gerlach** .... (303) 629-7171
E-mail: scott.gerlach@ic.fbi.gov
Chief Security Officer **Michael R. Mercer** .... (303) 629-7171
E-mail: michael.mercer@ic.fbi.gov
Media Coordinator **Amy E. Sanders** .... (303) 629-7171
E-mail: amy.sanders@ic.fbi.gov

Detroit (MI) Division
Patrick V. McNamara Federal Building, 477 Michigan Avenue,
26th Floor, Detroit, MI 48226
Tel: (313) 965-2323 Fax: (313) 965-4009 E-mail: detroit@fbi.gov
Internet: www.fbi.gov/detroit

Special Agent-in-Charge **Timothy R. Slater** .... (313) 965-2323
E-mail: trslater@fbi.gov
Assistant Special Agent-in-Charge **Jeffrey R. Downey** ... (313) 965-2323
E-mail: jeffrey.downey@ic.fbi.gov
Assistant Special Agent-in-Charge **Scott Mckee** .... (313) 965-2323
E-mail: scott.mckees@ic.fbi.gov
Assistant Special Agent-in-Charge **Maureen Reddy** ..... (313) 965-2323
E-mail: maureen.reddy@ic.fbi.gov
Assistant Special Agent-in-Charge
Felix A. Rivera-Esparra .... (313) 965-2323
E-mail: felix.rivera-esparra@ic.fbi.gov
Assistant Special Agent-in-Charge **Timothy T. Waters** ... (313) 965-2323
E-mail: timothy.waters@ic.fbi.gov
Secretary **Lynaye Soloniewicz** .... (313) 237-4001
E-mail: lynaye.soloniewicz@ic.fbi.gov
Media Coordinator **(Vacant)** .... (313) 965-1712

El Paso (TX) Division
660 South Mesa Hills, Suite 3000, El Paso, TX 79912-5533
Tel: (915) 832-5000 Fax: (915) 832-5259
Internet: http://www.fbi.gov/elpaso/

Special Agent-in-Charge **Emmerson Buie** .... (915) 832-5023
E-mail: emmerson.buie@ic.fbi.gov
Assistant Special Agent-in-Charge **Keith Byers** .... (915) 832-5000
E-mail: keith.byers@ic.fbi.gov
Assistant Special Agent-in-Charge **Karl Soete** .... (915) 832-5000
E-mail: ksoete@fbi.gov

Honolulu (HI) Division
91-1300 Enterprise Street, Kapolei, HI 96707
Tel: (808) 566-4300 Internet: http://www.fbi.gov/honolulu/

Special Agent-in-Charge **Sean L. Kaul** .... (808) 566-4300
E-mail: sean.kaul@ic.fbi.gov
Assistant Special Agent-in-Charge **Dean Chappell** .... (808) 566-4300
E-mail: dean.chappell@ic.fbi.gov
Assistant Special Agent-in-Charge **Tuan M. Nguyen** ..... (808) 566-4300
Administrative Officer **Kerry E. Hadaway** .... (808) 566-4300
E-mail: kerry.hadaway@ic.fbi.gov
Chief Division Counsel **Melissa Reynolds** .... (808) 566-4300
Financial Manager **Maria T. Elias** .... (808) 566-4300
Supervisory Information Technology Specialist
Edward A. Ricken .... (808) 566-4300
E-mail: edward.ricken@ic.fbi.gov
Media Coordinator **Matthew McDonald** .... (808) 566-4300

DEPARTMENTS

★ Presidential Appointment Requiring Senate Confirmation ☆ Presidential Appointment ☐ Schedule C Appointment ◇ Career Senior Foreign Service Appointment
● Career Senior Executive Service (SES) Appointment ○ Non-Career Senior Executive Service (SES) Appointment ■ Postal Career Executive Service

DEPARTMENTS

Houston (TX) Division
One Justice Park Drive, Houston, TX 77092
926277, Houston, TX 77292-6277
Tel: (713) 693-5000
Tel: (409) 832-8571 (Beaumont TX Resident Agency)
Tel: (979) 776-8894 (Bryan TX Resident Agency)
Tel: (281) 367-9433 (Conroe TX Resident Agency)
Tel: (361) 883-8671 (Corpus Christi TX Resident Agency)
Tel: (409) 935-7327 (Texas City TX Resident Agency)
Tel: (361) 582-0604 (Victoria TX Resident Agency) Fax: (713) 936-8999
E-mail: houston.texas@ic.fbi.gov Internet: http://www.fbi.gov/houston/

● Special Agent-in-Charge **Perrye K. Turner** .... (713) 693-5000
E-mail: perrye.turner@ic.fbi.gov
Education: Louisiana Tech U 1987 BS; Belhaven U 2006 MBA
Assistant Special Agent-in-Charge **Edward Michel** ...... (713) 693-5000
E-mail: edward.michel@ic.fbi.gov
Education: Tulane 1992 BA, 2017 MS
Assistant Special Agent-in-Charge **Deron Ogletree** ...... (713) 693-5000
E-mail: deron.ogletree@ic.fbi.gov
Assistant Special Agent-in-Charge **Mark N. Webster** .... (713) 693-5000
E-mail: mark.webster@ic.fbi.gov
Assistant Special Agent-in-Charge
Douglas A. Williams .... (713) 693-5000
Assistant Special Agent-in-Charge **(Vacant)** .... (713) 693-5000
Administrative Officer **Steven D. Volkman** .... (713) 693-5000
E-mail: steven.volkman@ic.fbi.gov
Community Outreach and Public Affairs Specialist
Christina Garza .... (713) 693-5000
E-mail: christina.garza@ic.fbi.gov
Media Representative **Shauna Dunlap** .... (713) 936-7638
E-mail: shauna.dunlap@ic.fbi.gov

Indianapolis (IN) Division
8825 Nelson B. Klein Parkway, Indianapolis, IN 46250
Tel: (317) 595-4000 Fax: (317) 845-7105 E-mail: indianapolis@fbi.gov
Internet: http://www.fbi.gov/indianapolis/

Special Agent-in-Charge
Bradley "Grant" Mendenhall .... (317) 595-4000
E-mail: bgmendenhall@fbi.gov
Education: Ball State 1986 BA
Assistant Special Agent-in-Charge **Gregory R. Massa** .... (317) 595-4000
E-mail: gregory.massa@ic.fbi.gov
Assistant Special Agent-in-Charge
Robert Alex Middleton .... (317) 595-4000
E-mail: robert.middleton@ic.fbi.gov
Assistant Special Agent-in-Charge **(Vacant)** .... (317) 595-4000
Administrative Officer **Christine R. Coning** .... (317) 595-4000
E-mail: christine.coning@ic.fbi.gov
Public Affairs Specialist **Christine "Chris" Bavender** .... (317) 845-7055
E-mail: christine.bavender@ic.fbi.gov

Jackson (MS) Division
1220 Echelon Parkway, Jackson, MS 39213
Tel: (601) 948-5000 Fax: (601) 713-7550 E-mail: fbijn@leo.gov
Internet: http://www.fbi.gov/jackson/

Special Agent-in-Charge **Christopher Freeze** .... (601) 948-5000
E-mail: christopher.freeze@ic.fbi.gov
Education: Lipscomb U 1989 BS, 2000 MA
Assistant Special Agent-in-Charge **Steven Jensen** .... (601) 948-5000
E-mail: Steven.jensen@ic.fbi.gov
Assistant Special Agent-in-Charge **Rodrigo Vargas** ...... (601) 948-5000
E-mail: rodrigo.vargas@ic.fbi.gov
Public Affairs Specialist **Brett Carr** .... (601) 948-5000
Division Counsel **Norman E. Comeaux** .... (601) 948-5000

Jacksonville (FL) Division
6061 Gate Parkway, Jacksonville, FL 32256
Tel: (904) 248-7000 Fax: (904) 248-7404 E-mail: jacksonville@fbi.gov
Internet: http://www.fbi.gov/jacksonville/

Special Agent-in-Charge **Charles P. Spencer** .... (904) 248-7000
Assistant Special Agent-in-Charge **Kacey Gabriel** .... (904) 248-7000
E-mail: kacey.gabriel@ic.fbi.gov
Assistant Special Agent-in-Charge **Carlton Peeples** ...... (904) 248-7000
E-mail: carlton.peeples@ic.fbi.gov

Kansas City (MO) Division
1300 Summit, Kansas City, MO 64105-1362
Tel: (816) 512-8200 Fax: (816) 512-8545 E-mail: kansascity@ic.fbi.gov
Internet: http://www.fbi.gov/kansascity/

Special Agent-in-Charge **Darrin E. Jones** .... (816) 512-8200
E-mail: darrin.jones@ic.fbi.gov
Assistant Special Agent-in-Charge **Shelley Doherty** ..... (816) 512-8200
Assistant Special Agent-in-Charge **Thomas F. Relford** ... (816) 512-8200
E-mail: thomas.relford@ic.fbi.gov
Assistant Special Agent-in-Charge **(Vacant)** .... (816) 512-8200
Chief Division Counsel **Robert Stuart** .... (816) 512-8200
Chief Security Officer **Sherri Steffensmeier** .... (816) 512-8200
E-mail: sherri.steffensmeier@ic.fbi.gov
Senior Supervisory Intelligence Analyst
Patricia J. Sola .... (816) 512-8200
E-mail: patricia.sola@ic.fbi.gov
Administrative Officer **Mariann Bozeman** .... (816) 512-8200
E-mail: mariann.bozeman@ic.fbi.gov

Knoxville (TN) Division
1501 Dowell Springs Boulevard, Knoxville, TN 37909
Tel: (865) 544-0751 Fax: (865) 602-7212 E-mail: knoxville@ifbi.gov
Internet: http://www.fbi.gov/knoxville/

Special Agent-in-Charge **Troy Sowers** .... (865) 544-0751
E-mail: tasowers@fbi.gov
Education: Wright State 1994 BS; Naval Postgrad 2013 MA
Assistant Special Agent-in-Charge (Acting)
Jeff Blanton .... (865) 544-0751
Education: Davidson 1989 BS
Assistant Special Agent-in-Charge **Ralph Tursi** .... (865) 544-0751
E-mail: rtursi@fbi.gov
Media Representative **(Vacant)** .... (865) 544-0751

Las Vegas (NV) Division
John Lawrence Bailey Building, 1787 West Lake Mead Boulevard,
Las Vegas, NV 89106
Tel: (702) 385-1281 Fax: (702) 584-5460 E-mail: lasvegas@ic.fbi.gov
Internet: http://www.fbi.gov/lasvegas/

Special Agent-in-Charge **Aaron C. Rouse** .... (702) 385-1281
E-mail: acrouse@fbi.gov
Assistant Special Agent-in-Charge **Ray E. Johnson** ...... (702) 385-1281
E-mail: ray.johnson@ic.fbi.gov
Assistant Special Agent-in-Charge **Frank S. Cucinotta** ... (702) 385-1281
Assistant Special Agent-in-Charge **Michael Hickok** ...... (702) 385-1281
E-mail: michael.hickok@ic.fbi.gov

Little Rock (AR) Division
24 Shackleford West Boulevard, Little Rock, AR 72211-3755
Tel: (501) 221-9100 Fax: (501) 228-8509
Internet: http://www.fbi.gov/littlerock/

● Special Agent-in-Charge **Diane Upchurch** .... (501) 221-9100
E-mail: diane.upchurch@ic.fbi.gov
Assistant Special Agent-in-Charge **L. Scott Reinhardt** ... (501) 221-9100
Assistant Special Agent-in-Charge **Jason Van Goor** ..... (501) 221-9100
E-mail: jvangoor@fbi.gov

Los Angeles (CA) Division
Federal Building, 11000 Wilshire Boulevard,
Suite 1700, Los Angeles, CA 90024-3602
Tel: (310) 477-6565 Fax: (310) 996-3359
Internet: http://www.fbi.gov/losangeles/

Assistant Director-in-Charge **Paul D. Delacourt** .... (310) 477-6565
E-mail: paul.delacourt@ic.fbi.gov
Education: Michigan BA; Wayne State U JD
Special Agent-in-Charge, Administrative Division
Danny Kennedy .... (310) 477-6565
E-mail: danny.kennedy@ic.fbi.gov
Special Agent-in-Charge, Administrative Division
Matthew S. Moon .... (310) 477-6565
E-mail: msmoon@fbi.gov
Special Agent-in-Charge, Counterintelligence and
Cyber Division **Jennifer Boone** .... (310) 477-6565
E-mail: jennifer.boone@ic.fbi.gov
Education: Georgetown BS, MA

★ Presidential Appointment Requiring Senate Confirmation ☆ Presidential Appointment ☐ Schedule C Appointment ◇ Career Senior Foreign Service Appointment
● Career Senior Executive Service (SES) Appointment ○ Non-Career Senior Executive Service (SES) Appointment ■ Postal Career Executive Service

Los Angeles (CA) Division *(continued)*

Special Agent-in-Charge, Counterterrorism Division
Ryan Young . . . . (310) 477-6565
E-mail: rtyoung@fbi.gov
Special Agent-in-Charge, Criminal Division
Voviette Morgan . . . . (310) 477-6565
E-mail: voviette.morgan@ic.fbi.gov
Special Agent in Charge, Intelligence Division
Stephen Woolery . . . . (310) 477-6565
Public Affairs Specialist **Laura Eimiller** . . . . (310) 996-3343
E-mail: laura.eimiller@ic.fbi.gov

Louisville (KY) Division

12401 Sycamore Station Place, Louisville, KY 40299-6198
Tel: (502) 263-6000 Fax: (502) 263-6245
Internet: http://www.fbi.gov/louisville/

Special Agent-in-Charge **James Robert Brown, Jr.** . . . . (502) 240-5944
E-mail: jrbrown@fbi.gov
Assistant Special Agent-in-Charge
Jeffrey "Jeff" Coburn . . . . (502) 240-5944
E-mail: jeffrey.coburn@ic.fbi.gov
Assistant Special Agent-in-Charge **Christie Curtis** . . . . (502) 263-6037
E-mail: christie.curtis@ic.fbi.gov
Chief Division Counsel **M. David Habich** . . . . (502) 263-6007

Memphis (TN) Division

Eagle Crest Building, 225 North Humphreys Boulevard,
Suite 3000, Memphis, TN 38120-2107
Tel: (901) 747-4300 Fax: (901) 747-9621
Internet: http://www.fbi.gov/memphis/

Special Agent-in-Charge **(Vacant)** . . . . (901) 747-4300
Assistant Special Agent-in-Charge **Jeremy N. Baker** . . . . (615) 232-7500
E-mail: jeremy.baker@ic.fbi.gov
Assistant Special Agent-in-Charge
Matthew E. Espenshade . . . . (615) 232-7500
E-mail: matthew.espenshade@ic.fbi.gov
Assistant Special Agent-in-Charge
William Chris Hoffman . . . . (901) 747-4300
E-mail: wchoffman@fbi.gov

Miami (FL) Division

2030 SW 145th Avenue, Miramar, FL 33027
Tel: (754) 703-2000 E-mail: miami@ic.fbi.gov
Internet: http://www.fbi.gov/miami/

Special Agent-in-Charge (Acting) **Thomas J. Jones** . . . . (754) 703-2000
E-mail: tjjones@fbi.gov
Assistant Special Agent-in-Charge
Michael A. Dalonzo . . . . (754) 703-2000
E-mail: michael.dalonzo@ic.fbi.gov
Assistant Special Agent-in-Charge **Justin Fleck** . . . . (754) 703-2000
E-mail: justin.fleck@ic.fbi.gov
Assistant Special Agent-in-Charge **Thomas J. Jones** . . . . (754) 703-2000
Assistant Special Agent-in-Charge
Xanthie C Mangum . . . . (754) 703-2000
E-mail: xanthi.mangum@ic.fbi.gov
Assistant Special Agent-in-Charge **Scott A. Rottman** . . . . (754) 703-2000
Education: Citadel 1992 BA; Webster 1998 MA
Assistant Special Agent-in-Charge **Denise M. Stemen** . . . . (754) 703-2000
Education: Ohio 1989 BS; Maryland University Col 2017 MA
Assistant Special Agent-in-Charge **Nancy A. Wood** . . . . (754) 703-2000
Administrative Officer **Helga R. Gonzalez** . . . . (754) 703-2000
E-mail: helga.gonzalez@ic.fbi.gov
Media Coordinator **Michael D. Leverock** . . . . (754) 703-2000
E-mail: michael.leverock@ic.fbi.gov
Public Affairs Specialist **James "Jim" Marshall** . . . . (754) 703-2000
E-mail: james.marshall@ic.fbi.gov

Milwaukee (WI) Division

3600 S. Lake Drive, St. Francis, WI 53235
Tel: (414) 276-4684 Fax: (414) 291-2400 E-mail: milwaukee@fbi.gov
Internet: http://www.fbi.gov/milwaukee/

Special Agent-in-Charge **R. Justin Tolomeo** . . . . (414) 276-4684
E-mail: rjtolomeo@fbi.gov
Education: Syracuse 1987 AB

Milwaukee (WI) Division *(continued)*

Assistant Special Agent-in-Charge **Robert Botsch** . . . . (414) 276-4684
E-mail: rjbotsch@fbi.gov
Assistant Special Agent-in-Charge (Acting) **Danny Day** . . . . (414) 276-4684
E-mail: danny.day@ic.fbi.gov
Community Outreach Specialist **Leonard C. Peace** . . . . (414) 276-4684
Public Affairs Coordinator **Leonard C. Peace** . . . . (414) 291-4892
E-mail: lcpeace@fbi.gov Fax: (414) 291-4291

Minneapolis (MN) Division

1501 Freeway Boulevard, Brooklyn Center, MN 55430
Tel: (763) 569-8000 Fax: (763) 569-8567 E-mail: minneapolis@fbi.gov
Internet: http://www.fbi.gov/minneapolis/

Special Agent-in-Charge **Jill Sanborn** . . . . (763) 569-8000
E-mail: jsanborn@fbi.gov
Assistant Special Agent-in-Charge **Robert C. Perry** . . . . (763) 569-8000
Assistant Special Agent-in-Charge **Joseph M. Rivers** . . . . (763) 569-8000
Assistant Special Agent-in-Charge **Ann Saunders** . . . . (763) 569-8000
Assistant Special Agent-in-Charge **Joe Weir** . . . . (763) 569-8000
Chief Division Counsel **Jeffrey Van Nest** . . . . (763) 569-8000
Associate Division Counsel **Michael Krause** . . . . (763) 569-8000
Media Coordinator **Michael J. Kulstad** . . . . (763) 569-8000

Mobile (AL) Division

200 North Royal Street, Mobile, AL 36602
Tel: (251) 438-3674 Fax: (251) 415-3235 E-mail: mobile@fbi.gov
Internet: http://www.fbi.gov/mobile/

● Special Agent-in-Charge **James E. Jewell** . . . . (251) 438-3674
E-mail: james.jewell@ic.fbi.gov
Education: Alabama 1987 BS; LSU 1993 MS
Assistant Special Agent-in-Charge **Rachel Byrd** . . . . (251) 438-3674
E-mail: rachel.byrd@ic.fbi.gov
Assistant Special Agent-in-Charge **Bret Kirby** . . . . (251) 438-3674
E-mail: bret.kirby@ic.fbi.gov
Assistant Special Agent-in-Charge **(Vacant)** . . . . (251) 438-3674
Administrative Officer **Lorraine Smith** . . . . (251) 438-3674
Law Enforcement Training Coordinator **(Vacant)** . . . . (251) 438-3674
Media Relations Coordinator **(Vacant)** . . . . (251) 415-3279

New Haven (CT) Division

600 State Street, New Haven, CT 06511-6505
Tel: (203) 777-6311 Fax: (203) 503-5155 E-mail: newhaven@fbi.gov
Internet: http://www.fbi.gov/newhaven/

● Special Agent-in-Charge **Brian C. Turner** . . . . (203) 777-6311
E-mail: bcturner@fbi.gov
Secretary **Robin E. Kudasik** . . . . (203) 503-5006
E-mail: rekudasik@fbi.gov
Assistant Special Agent-in-Charge **Robert Fuller** . . . . (203) 777-6311
E-mail: rfuller@fbi.gov
Assistant Special Agent-in-Charge **Michael S. Butsch** . . . . (203) 777-6311
E-mail: msbutsch@fbi.gov
Telecommunications Manager **Mark D. DeWolfe** . . . . (203) 503-5223
E-mail: mddewolfe@fbi.gov Fax: (203) 503-5098

New Orleans (LA) Division

2901 Leon C. Simon Drive, New Orleans, LA 70126
Tel: (504) 816-3000 Fax: (504) 816-3306 E-mail: neworleans@fbi.gov
Internet: http://www.fbi.gov/neworleans/

Special Agent-in-Charge **Eric J. Rommal** . . . . (504) 816-3000
Education: Maryland Eastern Shore 1990 BS
Assistant Special Agent-in-Charge
Andrew "Buck" Anderson . . . . (504) 816-3000
E-mail: andrew.anderson@ic.fbi.gov
Assistant Special Agent-in-Charge **Daniel Evans** . . . . (504) 816-3000
E-mail: daniel.evans2@ic.fbi.gov
Assistant Special Agent-in-Charge
Wendell "Drew" Watts . . . . (504) 816-3000
E-mail: drew.watts@ic.fbi.gov

DEPARTMENTS

★ Presidential Appointment Requiring Senate Confirmation ☆ Presidential Appointment ☐ Schedule C Appointment ◇ Career Senior Foreign Service Appointment
● Career Senior Executive Service (SES) Appointment ○ Non-Career Senior Executive Service (SES) Appointment ■ Postal Career Executive Service

DEPARTMENTS

New York (NY) Division
Jacob K. Javits Federal Building, 26 Federal Plaza, 23rd Floor, New York, NY 10278-0004
Tel: (212) 384-1000 Fax: (212) 384-4073 E-mail: ny1@fbi.gov
Internet: http://www.fbi.gov/newyork/

Assistant Director-in-Charge **William F. Sweeney, Jr. USN (Ret)** . . . . (212) 384-1000
Education: Villanova BA; Naval Postgrad MA
Special Agent In Charge, Administration **George J. Ennis, Jr.** . . . . (212) 384-1000
E-mail: george.ennis@ic.fbi.gov
Special Agent-in-Charge, Counterintelligence **Charles F. McGonigal** . . . . (212) 384-1000
E-mail: charles.mcgonigal@ic.fbi.gov
Special Agent-in-Charge, Counterterrorism **C. Bryan Paarmann** . . . . (212) 384-1000
E-mail: bryan.paarmann@ic.fbi.gov
Special Agent-in-Charge, Criminal Division **John J. Brosnan** . . . . (212) 384-1000
E-mail: jjbrosnan@fbi.gov
Special Agent in Charge, Intelligence Division **(Vacant)** . . . . (212) 384-1000
Special Agent In Charge, Special Operations/Cyber **Aristedes "Ari" Mahairas** . . . . (212) 384-1000
E-mail: aristedes.mahairas@ic.fbi.gov
Education: Baruch Col BA; New York Law JD
Media Coordinator **Adrienne Senatore** . . . . (212) 384-3123

Newark (NJ) Division
11 Centre Place, Newark, NJ 07102
Tel: (973) 792-3000 Fax: (973) 792-3035 E-mail: newark@fbi.gov
Internet: http://www.fbi.gov/newark/

Special Agent-in-Charge **Gregory W. Ehrie** . . . . (973) 792-3000
E-mail: gwehrie@fbi.gov
Assistant Special Agent-in-Charge **Michael Brodack** . . . . (973) 792-3000
E-mail: michael.brodack@ic.fbi.gov
Assistant Special Agent-in-Charge **Bradley W. Cohen** . . . . (973) 792-3000
E-mail: bwcohen@fbi.gov
Assistant Special Agent-in-Charge **Joseph Denahan** . . . . (973) 792-3000
E-mail: joseph.denahan@ic.fbi.gov
Assistant Special Agent-in-Charge **Wayne Jacobs** . . . . (973) 792-3000
E-mail: wayne.jacobs@ic.fbi.gov
Assistant Special Agent-in-Charge **Christopher Stangl** . . . (973) 792-3000
Assistant Special Agent-in-Charge **(Vacant)** . . . . (973) 792-3000
Information Technology Systems Supervisor **Tamika Anderson** . . . . (973) 792-3000
E-mail: tamika.anderson@ic.fbi.gov
Media Coordinator **(Vacant)** . . . . (973) 792-3020
Senior Supervisory Intelligence Analyst **Ian Cornell** . . . . (973) 792-3000
E-mail: icornell@fbi.gov
Administrative Officer **Dorisse Shakir-Ullah** . . . . (973) 792-3000
E-mail: DShakir-Ullah@fbi.gov

Norfolk (VA) Division
509 Resource Row, Chesapeake, VA 23320
Tel: (757) 455-0100 Fax: (757) 455-2647 E-mail: norfolk_fo@fbi.gov
Internet: http://www.fbi.gov/norfolk/

Special Agent-in-Charge **Martin W. Culbreth** . . . . (757) 455-0100
E-mail: martin.culbreth@ic.fbi.gov
Assistant Special Agent-in-Charge **Jesse Levine** . . . . (757) 455-0100
E-mail: jesse.levine@ic.fbi.gov
Assistant Special Agent-in-Charge **Jonathan F. Trimble** . . . . (757) 455-0100
E-mail: jonathan.trimble@ic.fbi.gov
Chief Division Counsel **Diane E. Maurice** . . . . (757) 455-0100
E-mail: diane.maurice@ic.fbi.gov

Oklahoma City (OK) Division
3301 West Memorial Drive, Oklahoma City, OK 73134
Tel: (405) 290-7770 Fax: (405) 290-3885 E-mail: oklahomacity@fbi.gov
Internet: http://www.fbi.gov/oklahomacity/

• Special Agent-in-Charge **Kathryn Peterson** . . . . (405) 290-7770
Assistant Special Agent-in-Charge **Raul Bujanda** . . . . (405) 290-7770
E-mail: raul.bujanda@ic.fbi.gov

Oklahoma City (OK) Division *(continued)*

Assistant Special Agent-in-Charge **Spencer L. Evans** . . . . (405) 290-7770
E-mail: slevans@fbi.gov
Assistant Special Agent-in-Charge **Dennis Passerman** . . . (405) 290-7770
E-mail: dennis.passerman@ic.fbi.gov

Omaha (NE) Division
4411 South 121st Court, Omaha, NE 68137-2112
Tel: (402) 493-8688 Fax: (402) 530-1523 E-mail: omaha@fbi.gov
Internet: http://www.fbi.gov/omaha/

Special Agent-in-Charge **Randall C. Thysse CPA** . . . . (402) 493-8688
E-mail: randall.thysse@ic.fbi.gov
Education: U St Thomas (MN) BA; Drake MBA
Assistant Special Agent-in-Charge **Kristi K. Johnson** . . . . (402) 493-8688
E-mail: kristi.johnson@ic.fbi.gov

Philadelphia (PA) Division
William J. Green, Jr. Federal Building, 600 Arch Street, 8th Floor, Philadelphia, PA 19106-1675
Tel: (215) 418-4000 Fax: (215) 418-4232 Fax: (215) 418-4013
E-mail: Philadelphia.complaints@ic.fbi.gov
Internet: http://www.fbi.gov/philadelphia/

Special Agent-in-Charge **Michael T. Harpster** . . . . (215) 418-4001
Assistant Special Agent-in-Charge **Tara Bloesch-McMahon** . . . . (215) 418-4650
E-mail: tara.mcmahon@ic.fbi.gov
Assistant Special Agent-in-Charge (Acting) **Kristen Komer** . . . . (215) 418-4005
Assistant Special Agent-in-Charge (Acting) **L.T. Seals** . . . . (215) 418-4003
Assistant Special Agent-in-Charge **Christian Zajac** . . . . (215) 418-4009
Assistant Special Agent-in-Charge **(Vacant)** . . . . (215) 418-4007
Senior Supervisory Intelligence Analyst **Caroline Barnes** . . . . (215) 418-4000
Supervisory IT Specialist **Joanna Viscome** . . . . (215) 418-4456
Administrative Officer **Anne Hanko** . . . . (215) 418-4250
Public Affairs Specialist **Carrie Adamowski** . . . . (215) 418-4135

Phoenix (AZ) Division
21711 North Seventh Street, Phoenix, AZ 85024
Tel: (623) 466-1999 Fax: (623) 466-1108 E-mail: phoenix@ic.fbi.gov
Internet: http://www.fbi.gov/phoenix/

Special Agent-in-Charge **Michael DeLeon** . . . . (623) 466-1999
E-mail: michael.deleon@ic.fbi.gov
Education: Lock Haven 1984 BA; Wilmington U 1997 MBA
Assistant Special Agent-in-Charge **Michael V. Caputo** . . . (623) 466-1999
E-mail: michael.caputo@ic.fbi.gov
Assistant Special Agent-in-Charge **Mark J. Cwynar** . . . . (623) 466-1999
E-mail: mark.cwynar@ic.fbi.gov
Assistant Special Agent-in-Charge **(Vacant)** . . . . (623) 466-1999
Information Technology Unit Manager **Richard "Rich" Stoddard** . . . . (623) 466-1999
E-mail: richard.stoddard@ic.fbi.gov
Security Officer **Giorgio Boscolo** . . . . (623) 466-1999
E-mail: giorgio.boscolo@ic.fbi.gov

Tucson Office
Assistant Special Agent-in-Charge **Steven Patterson** . . . . (520) 623-4306
E-mail: steven.patterson@ic.fbi.gov

Pittsburgh (PA) Division
3311 East Carson Street, Pittsburgh, PA 15203
Tel: (412) 432-4000 Fax: (412) 432-4188 E-mail: pittsburgh@fbi.gov
Internet: http://www.fbi.gov/pittsburgh/

Special Agent-in-Charge **Robert Allan Jones** . . . . (412) 432-4000
E-mail: rajones@fbi.gov
Education: Penn State 1986 BAA; Syracuse 1996 MS
Assistant Special Agent-in-Charge **B. Chad Yarbrough** . . . (412) 432-4000
E-mail: chad.yarbrough@ic.fbi.gov
Assistant Special Agent-in-Charge **Nicholas B. "Nick" Boshears** . . . . (412) 432-4000
E-mail: nicholas.boshears@ic.fbi.gov
Assistant Special Agent-in-Charge **Gregory Nelsen** . . . . (412) 432-4000
E-mail: gregory.nelsen@ic.fbi.gov

★ Presidential Appointment Requiring Senate Confirmation ☆ Presidential Appointment ☐ Schedule C Appointment ◇ Career Senior Foreign Service Appointment
● Career Senior Executive Service (SES) Appointment ○ Non-Career Senior Executive Service (SES) Appointment ■ Postal Career Executive Service

Portland (OR) Division
9109 NE Cascades Parkway, Portland, OR 97220
Tel: (503) 224-4181 Fax: (503) 460-8088 E-mail: portland@ic.fbi.gov
Internet: http://www.fbi.gov/portland/

● Special Agent-in-Charge **Loren "Renn" Cannon** . . . . (503) 224-4181
E-mail: lcannon@fbi.gov
Education: West Point 1990 BEc
Assistant Special Agent-in-Charge
George Chamberlin . . . . (503) 224-4181
E-mail: gechamberlin@fbi.gov
Assistant Special Agent-in-Charge **Steve A. Goldman** . . . (503) 224-4181
E-mail: sagoldman@fbi.gov
Assistant Special Agent-in-Charge **Steven Palmer** . . . . (503) 224-4181
E-mail: spalmer@fbi.gov
Administrative Officer **Natalie Voruz** . . . . (503) 224-4181
E-mail: navoruz@fbi.gov
Public Affairs Specialist **Beth Anne Steele** . . . . (503) 460-8099

Richmond (VA) Division
1970 East Parham Road, Richmond, VA 23228
P.O. Box 28060, Richmond, VA 23228
Tel: (804) 261-1044 Fax: (804) 627-4494
Internet: http://www.fbi.gov/richmond/

Special Agent-in-Charge **Adam Sidney Lee** . . . . (804) 261-1044
Note: Until November 31, 2018.
E-mail: aslee@fbi.gov
Assistant Special Agent-in-Charge
(Criminal/Administrative) **Thomas M. Chadwick** . . . . . . (804) 261-1044
E-mail: thomas.chadwick@ic.fbi.gov
Assistant Special Agent-in-Charge (NSB)
John Lenkart . . . . (804) 261-1044
E-mail: john.lenkart@ic.fbi.gov
Media Relations Coordinator **Dennette Rybiski** . . . . (804) 261-1044
E-mail: dennette.rybiski@ic.fbi.gov
Applicant Recruiter **Melissa Mallone Schuler** . . . . (804) 261-1044

Sacramento (CA) Division
4500 Orange Grove Avenue, Sacramento, CA 95841-4205
Tel: (916) 746-7000 Fax: (916) 977-2300 E-mail: sacramento@fbi.gov
Internet: http://www.fbi.gov/sacramento/

Special Agent-in-Charge **Sean Ragan** . . . . (916) 746-7000
E-mail: sean.ragan@ic.fbi.gov
Assistant Special Agent in Charge **Alyssa M. Doyle** . . . . . (916) 746-7000
E-mail: alyssa.doyle@ic.fbi.gov
Assistant Special Agent in Charge **Susan Ferensic** . . . . . . (916) 746-7000
E-mail: susan.ferensic@ic.fbi.gov
Assistant Special Agent in Charge **Tom F. Osborne** . . . . . . (916) 746-7000
E-mail: tom.osborne@ic.fbi.gov
Public Affairs Specialist **Gina Swankie** . . . . (916) 746-7000
E-mail: gina.swankie@ic.fbi.gov

Saint Louis (MO) Division
2222 Market Street, St. Louis, MO 63103-2516
Tel: (314) 589-2500 Fax: (314) 589-2636 E-mail: stlouis@fbi.gov
Internet: http://www.fbi.gov/stlouis/

Special Agent-in-Charge **Richard P. Quinn** . . . . (314) 589-2500
E-mail: richard.quinn@ic.fbi.gov
Assistant Special Agent-in-Charge **(Vacant)** . . . . (314) 589-2500
Assistant Special Agent-in-Charge **(Vacant)** . . . . (314) 589-2500
Public Affairs Specialist **Rebecca Wu** . . . . (314) 589-2500
E-mail: rebecca.wu@ic.fbi.gov

Salt Lake City (UT) Division
5425 West Amelia Earhart Drive, Salt Lake City, UT 84116
Tel: (801) 579-1400 Fax: (801) 579-6000 E-mail: saltlakecity@ic.fbi.gov
Internet: http://www.fbi.gov/saltlakecity/
Areas Covered: ID, MT, UT

Special Agent-in-Charge **Eric K. Barnhart** . . . . (801) 579-1400
E-mail: ekbarnhart@fbi.gov
Education: Wisconsin 1990 BA
Assistant Special Agent-in-Charge **Daniel Brady** . . . . (801) 579-1400
E-mail: daniel.brady@ic.fbi.gov

Salt Lake City (UT) Division *(continued)*

Assistant Special Agent-in-Charge **Earl Camp** . . . . (801) 579-1400
E-mail: earl.camp@ic.fbi.gov
Assistant Special Agent-in-Charge **Michael Hensle** . . . . . . (801) 579-1400
E-mail: michael.hensle@ic.fbi.gov
Media Coordinator **Sandra Yi Barker** . . . . (801) 579-6400

San Antonio (TX) Division
5740 University Heights, San Antonio, TX 78249
Tel: (210) 225-6741 Fax: (210) 650-6153 E-mail: sanantonio@ic.fbi.gov
Internet: www.fbi.gov/sanantonio

Special Agent-in-Charge **Christopher H. Combs** . . . . (210) 225-6741
E-mail: christopher.combs@ic.fbi.gov
Assistant Special Agent-in-Charge **James H. Smith III** . . . (210) 225-6741
E-mail: james.smith@ic.fbi.gov
Assistant Special Agent-in-Charge **Robert S. Krupa** . . . . . (210) 225-6741
E-mail: robert.krupa@ic.fbi.gov
Assistant Special Agent-in-Charge (Austin)
John W. Scata . . . . (512) 345-1111
E-mail: john.scata@ic.fbi.gov
Assistant Special Agent-in-Charge (McAllen)
Stephen E. Kam . . . . (210) 225-6741
E-mail: stephen.kam@ic.fbi.gov
Media Relations Coordinator **Michelle Lee** . . . . (210) 650-6333
Special Agent Recruiter **Eric Vasys** . . . . (210) 225-6741
Community Outreach Specialist **Roseanne Hughes** . . . . . (210) 650-6486

San Diego (CA) Division
10385 Vista Sorrento Parkway, San Diego, CA 92121
Tel: (858) 320-1800 Fax: (858) 499-7991
Internet: http://www.fbi.gov/sandiego/

Special Agent-in-Charge **John A. Brown** . . . . (858) 320-1800
E-mail: jabrown@fbi.gov
Assistant Special Agent-in-Charge **Daron Borst** . . . . (858) 320-1800
E-mail: daron.borst@ic.fbi.gov
Assistant Special Agent-in-Charge **Brian Gilhooly** . . . . (858) 320-1800
E-mail: brian.gilhooly@ic.fbi.gov
Assistant Special Agent-in-Charge **Johanna Hladun** . . . . . (858) 320-1800
E-mail: johanna.hladun@ic.fbi.gov
Assistant Special Agent-in-Charge **Robert Howe** . . . . (858) 320-1800
E-mail: robert.howe@ic.fbi.gov
Assistant Special Agent-in-Charge **Suzanne M. Turner** . . . (858) 320-1800
E-mail: suzanne.turner@ic.fbi.gov
Education: Notre Dame 1991 BA; Duke 2000 JD
Public Affairs Specialist **Davine Butler** . . . . (858) 320-8302
E-mail: dfbutler@fbi.gov

San Francisco (CA) Division
450 Golden Gate Avenue, 13th Floor, San Francisco, CA 94102-9523
P.O. Box 36015, San Francisco, CA 94102
Tel: (415) 553-7400 Fax: (415) 861-7674
Internet: http://www.fbi.gov/sanfrancisco/

Special Agent-in-Charge **John F. Bennett** . . . . (415) 553-7400
Assistant Special Agent-in-Charge
Lawrence D. Buckley . . . . (415) 553-7400
E-mail: lawrence.buckley@ic.fbi.gov
Assistant Special Agent-in-Charge **Craig Fair** . . . . (415) 553-7400
E-mail: craig.fair@ic.fbi.gov
Assistant Special Agent-in-Charge **Bertram R. Fairries** . . . (415) 553-7400
E-mail: bertram.fairries@ic.fbi.gov
Assistant Special Agent-in-Charge **Lisa Gentilcore** . . . . . . (415) 553-7400
E-mail: lisa.gentilcore@ic.fbi.gov
Assistant Special Agent-in-Charge
Malcolm K. Palmore . . . . (415) 553-7400
E-mail: m.palmore@ic.fbi.gov
Education: Naval Acad BS; Pepperdine MBA
Assistant Special Agent-in-Charge **Derek Fischel** . . . . (415) 553-7400
Assistant Special Agent-in-Charge **Marina A. Mayo** . . . . . (415) 553-7400
E-mail: marina.mayo@ic.fbi.gov
Assistant Special Agent-in-Charge **Stacey Moy** . . . . (415) 553-7400
E-mail: stacey.moy@ic.fbi.gov
Administrative Officer **(Vacant)** . . . . (415) 553-7400

DEPARTMENTS

★ Presidential Appointment Requiring Senate Confirmation ☆ Presidential Appointment □ Schedule C Appointment ◇ Career Senior Foreign Service Appointment
● Career Senior Executive Service (SES) Appointment ○ Non-Career Senior Executive Service (SES) Appointment ■ Postal Career Executive Service

DEPARTMENTS

San Juan (PR) Division
Federal Office Building, 150 Carlos Chardon Avenue,
Room 526, Hato Rey, PR 00918-1746
P.O. Box 366269, San Juan, PR 00936
Tel: (787) 754-6000 Fax: (787) 759-1587
Internet: http://www.fbi.gov/sanjuan/

Special Agent-in-Charge **Douglas A. Leff** . . . . (787) 754-6000
E-mail: douglas.leff@ic.fbi.gov
Education: St John's U (NY) 1992 JD
Assistant Special Agent-in-Charge **Angel M. Catalan** . . . . (787) 754-6000
Assistant Special Agent-in-Charge **John S. Morales** . . . . (787) 759-1508
Fax: (787) 759-5601
Assistant Special Agent-in-Charge
Judith Priegues-Lopez . . . . (787) 754-6000

Seattle (WA) Division
1110 Third Avenue, Seattle, WA 98101-2904
Tel: (206) 622-0460 Fax: (206) 262-2111
Internet: http://www.fbi.gov/seattle/

Special Agent-in-Charge (Acting) **Michael F. Paul** . . . . (206) 622-0460
E-mail: mfpaul@fbi.gov
Assistant Special Agent-in-Charge **Jodi Cohen** . . . . (206) 622-0460
E-mail: jodi.cohen@ic.fbi.gov
Assistant Special Agent-in-Charge **Michael Glasheen** . . . . (206) 622-0460
E-mail: michael.glasheen@ic.fbi.gov
Education: North Carolina State 1996 BA
Assistant Special Agent-in-Charge **Howard P. Yager** . . . . (206) 622-0460
E-mail: hpyager@fbi.gov
Education: SUNY (Stony Brook) BA; Dowling MBA

Springfield (IL) Division
900 East Linton Avenue, Springfield, IL 62703
Tel: (217) 522-9675 Fax: (217) 757-3558 E-mail: springfield@ic.fbi.gov
Internet: http://www.fbi.gov/springfield/

● Special Agent-in-Charge **Sean M Cox** . . . . (217) 522-9675
E-mail: sean.cox@ic.fbi.gov
Education: Mount Senario BSCrimJ
Assistant Special Agent-in-Charge **Jon Holloway** . . . . (217) 522-9675
E-mail: jon.holloway@ic.fbi.gov
Assistant Special Agent-in-Charge **Tracie Smith** . . . . (217) 522-9675

Tampa (FL) Division
5525 W. Gray Street, Tampa, FL 33609
Tel: (813) 253-1000 Fax: (813) 253-1456
E-mail: tampadivision@ic.fbi.gov Internet: http://www.fbi.gov/tampa/
Areas Covered: FL (Counties of Brevard, Charlotte, Collier, De Soto, Glades, Hardee, Hendry, Hernando, Hillsborough, Lee, Manatee, Orange, Osceola, Pasco, Pinellas, Polk, Sarasota, and Seminole)

Special Agent-in-Charge **Eric W. Sporre** . . . . (813) 253-1000
E-mail: eric.sporre@ic.fbi.gov
Education: Maryland 1991 BSB; Baltimore 1997 JD
Assistant Special Agent-in-Charge **Stephen Belongia** . . . . (813) 253-1000
E-mail: stephen.belongia@ic.fbi.gov
Assistant Special Agent-in-Charge **Kristin Rehler** . . . . (813) 253-1000
E-mail: kristin.rehler@ic.fbi.gov
Assistant Special Agent-in-Charge (Orlando)
Ronald Hopper . . . . (407) 875-9976
E-mail: ronald.hopper@ic.fbi.gov
Supervisory Information Technology Specialist
Daniel Sexton . . . . (813) 253-1213
E-mail: daniel.sexton@ic.fbi.gov
Administrative Officer **John Gustafson** . . . . (813) 253-1000
E-mail: john.gustafson@ic.fbi.gov
Media Coordinator **David "Dave" Couvertier** . . . . (813) 253-1033

Washington (DC) Field Office (WFO)
601 Fourth Street, NW, Washington, DC 20535-0002
Tel: (202) 278-2000 E-mail: washington@fbi.gov
Internet: http://www.fbi.gov/washingtondc/

Assistant Director-in-Charge **Nancy McNamara** . . . . (202) 278-2000
E-mail: nmcnamara@fbi.gov

Washington (DC) Field Office *(continued)*

Special Agent-in-Charge (Administration)
John P. Selleck . . . . (202) 278-3400
E-mail: jpselleck@fbi.gov
Special Agent-in-Charge (Counterintelligence)
Timothy M. Dunham . . . . (202) 278-3400
E-mail: tmdunham@fbi.gov
Special Agent-in-Charge (Counterterrorism) **(Vacant)** . . . . (202) 278-3400
E-mail: matthew.gorham@ic.fbi.gov
Special Agent-in-Charge (Criminal/Cyber)
Matthew J. DeSarno . . . . (202) 278-3400
Education: Richmond 1995 BA
Special Agent-in-Charge (Intelligence) **(Vacant)** . . . . (202) 278-3400
Public Information Officer and Supervisory Special Agent **(Vacant)** . . . . (202) 278-3519
Public Affairs Specialist **(Vacant)** . . . . (202) 278-2000
Public Affairs Specialist **(Vacant)** . . . . (202) 278-3519
Special Agent **(Vacant)** . . . . (202) 278-2000

Federal Bureau of Prisons (BOP)
Home Owners Loan Corporation Building,
320 First Street, NW, Washington, DC 20534
Tel: (202) 305-2500 (Nationwide Recruiting Information)
Tel: (800) 347-7744 Tel: (202) 307-3198 Internet: www.bop.gov

OFFICE OF THE DIRECTOR
Home Owners Loan Corporation Building, 320 First Street, NW, Suite 654, Washington, DC 20534
Fax: (202) 514-6878

National Institute of Corrections (NIC)
320 First Street, NW, Washington, DC 20534
Tel: (800) 995-6423 Fax: (202) 307-3361 Internet: www.nicic.gov

Information Center
11900 East Cornell Avenue, Unit C, Aurora, CO 80014
Tel: (800) 877-1461 Internet: http://nicic.gov/InformationCenter

Manager **Eric Bauer** . . . . (303) 338-6636
Systems Manager **(Vacant)** . . . . (303) 338-6643
Fax: (303) 338-6601

Human Resource Management Division
Home Owners Loan Corperation Building, 320 First Street, NW, Room 354, Washington, DC 20534
Fax: (202) 353-4954

Management and Specialty Training Center (MSTC)
11900 East Cornell Avenue, Unit C, Aurora, CO 80014
Tel: (303) 338-6540

Director **James W. Gray** . . . . (303) 338-6500
Deputy Director **Theresa K. Cozza-Rhodes** . . . . (303) 338-6500
Secretary **Kristy Farmer-Hudson** . . . . (303) 338-6512
Computer Services Manager **(Vacant)** . . . . (303) 338-6500
Controller **Duane Fisher** . . . . (303) 338-6500
Human Resources Manager **Tracy Doyle** . . . . (303) 338-6540
Instructional Systems Manager
Jackie Bryson-Thompson . . . . (303) 338-6500
Training Programs Manager **Carlos Lopez** . . . . (303) 338-6500

Staff Training Academy - Federal Law Enforcement Training Center (FLETC)
Federal Law Enforcement Training Center, Building 21,
1131 Chapel Crossing Road, Glynco, GA 31524
Tel: (912) 267-2100 Fax: (912) 554-4608

Director **Felipe Rodriguez, Jr.** . . . . (912) 267-2857
Secretary to the Director **Cynthia "Cindy" Kelsey** . . . . (912) 267-2719
Deputy Director **Kathleen McGowan-Cimino** . . . . (912) 267-2637

★ Presidential Appointment Requiring Senate Confirmation ☆ Presidential Appointment ☐ Schedule C Appointment ◇ Career Senior Foreign Service Appointment
● Career Senior Executive Service (SES) Appointment ○ Non-Career Senior Executive Service (SES) Appointment ■ Postal Career Executive Service

Regional Offices

Mid-Atlantic Region
302 Sentinel Drive, Suite 200, Annapolis Junction, MD 20701
Tel: (301) 317-3119 Fax: (301) 317-3119
Areas Covered: DE, DC, KY, MD, NC, TN, VA, WV

● Regional Director **Angela P. Dunbar** .... (301) 317-3100
Executive Assistant **Arnita V. Jones** .... (301) 317-3110
Deputy Regional Director **John Gilley** .... (301) 317-3108
Regional Counsel **Matthew Mellady** .... (301) 317-3120
Regional Comptroller **Kymberly Hines** .... (301) 317-3169
Correctional Service Administrator **Scott Pliler** .... (301) 317-3154
Correctional Programs Administrator **(Vacant)** .... (301) 317-3140
Discipline Hearing Administrator **Curtis Hise** .... (301) 317-3119
Diversity Management Administrator **Angela Lewis** .... (301) 317-3290
Facilities Administrator **Raphael Ramos** .... (301) 317-3247
Food Service Administrator **William O'Donnell** .... (301) 317-3155
Health Systems Administrator **Gretchen Ryles** .... (301) 317-3164
Human Resources Administrator **(Vacant)** .... (301) 317-3194
Correctional Service Specialist **Robert Carrasco** .... (301) 317-3156

Mid-Atlantic Region Residential Reentry Office
302 Sentinel Drive, Suite 200, Annapolis Junction, MD 20701
Tel: (301) 317-3100 Fax: (301) 317-3139
Areas Covered: DE, DC, KY, MD, NC, TN, VA, WV

Community Corrections Manager **(Vacant)** .... (301) 317-3207
Administrative Officer **(Vacant)** .... (301) 317-3101

Baltimore (MD) Residential Reentry Management Office
302 Sentinel Drive, Suite 200, Annapolis Junction, MD 20701
Tel: (301) 317-3281 Fax: (301) 317-3138

Community Corrections Manager (Acting) **Pierre LeCounte** .... (301) 317-3149
Community Corrections Assistant **(Vacant)** .... (301) 317-3142
Case Manager **(Vacant)** .... (301) 317-3192
Transitional Drug Abuse Contract Oversight Specialist **(Vacant)** .... (301) 317-3282
Psychology Treatment Program Coordinator **Christine Ganz** .... (301) 317-3168
Transitional Drug Abuse Treatment Oversight Specialist **Stacey Freeman** .... (301) 317-3198
Community Corrections Specialist **Lori Brown** .... (301) 317-3133
Contract Oversight Specialist **Phelicia Taplin** .... (301) 317-3283
Security Specialist **(Vacant)** .... (301) 317-3161
Fax: (301) 317-3159

Nashville (TN) Residential Reentry Management Office
U.S. Customs House, 701 Broadway, Suite 124, Nashville, TN 37203
Tel: (615) 736-5148 Fax: (615) 736-5147

Management Center Administrator **(Vacant)** .... (615) 736-5148
Contract Oversight Specialist **Linda Gallett** .... (615) 736-5148
Community Corrections Manager **Michelle Fulgum** .... (615) 736-5148
Residential Reentry Specialist **Kem Kyle** .... (615) 736-5148
Community Corrections Specialist **(Vacant)** .... (615) 736-5148

Raleigh (NC) Residential Reentry Management Office
Old NC Highway 75, Butner, NC 27509-1500
7000, Butner, NC 27509
Tel: (919) 575-2080 Fax: (919) 575-2073

Sector Administrator **Tom DiPaola** .... (919) 575-2080
Assistant Sector Administrator **(Vacant)** .... (919) 575-2080
Community Corrections Specialist **Patti Jacobson** .... (919) 575-2071
Contract Oversight Specialist **Gary O. Moore** .... (919) 575-2070
E-mail: gomoore@bop.gov
Contract Oversight Specialist **Pam Manowski** .... (919) 575-2077
Residential Reentry Specialist **Brandi Kaz** .... (919) 575-2072
Residential Reentry Specialist **Todd Meadows** .... (919) 575-2079
Residential Reentry Manager **(Vacant)** .... (919) 575-2076

Federal Correctional Complex - Hazelton (WV) (FCC Hazelton)
1640 Sky View Drive, Bruceton Mills, WV 26525
Tel: (304) 379-1500 (FCI) Tel: (304) 379-5000 (USP)
Tel: (304) 379-5039 E-mail: haf/execassistant@bop.gov (FCI)
E-mail: haz/execassistant@bop.gov (USP)

Complex Warden **Joe Coakley** .... (304) 379-1500
Warden (FCI) **Frederick Entzel, Jr.** .... (304) 379-1500
Warden (USP) **Joe Coakley** .... (304) 379-5000

Federal Correctional Complex - Petersburg (VA) (FCC PETERSBURG)
1100 River Road, Hopewell, VA 23860

Low Security Facility - Federal Correctional Institution - Petersburg (VA) (FCI Petersburg Low)
1100 River Road, Hopewell, VA 23860
Tel: (804) 733-7881 Fax: (804) 863-1510

● Warden **Eric D. Wilson** .... (804) 504-7200
Chief Correctional Supervisor **William Hicks** .... (804) 504-7200
Associate Warden **Allia Lewis** .... (804) 504-7200
Deputy Chief Correctional Supervisor **Toney Lee** .... (804) 733-7881

Medium Security Facility - Federal Correctional Institution - Petersburg (VA) (FCI Petersburg Medium)
1060 River Road, Hopewell, VA 23860
P.O. Box 90026, Petersburg, VA 23804-0026
Tel: (804) 504-7200 Fax: (804) 504-7204

● Warden **Eric D. Wilson** .... (804) 504-7200
Associate Warden **Richard Engel** .... (804) 733-7881
Associate Warden **Cristopher Maruka** .... (804) 504-7200
Associate Warden **Allia Lewis** .... (804) 504-7200
Associate Warden (Industries and Education) **(Vacant)** .... (804) 733-7881
Executive Assistant **(Vacant)** .... (804) 504-7200
Business Administrator **Corinna Van** .... (804) 504-7200
Food Administrator **Jeffry Greene** .... (804) 504-7200
Health Systems Administrator **Allison Chatman** .... (804) 733-7881
Satellite Operations Administrator **Tovia Thomas** .... (804) 504-7200
Education Supervisor **Dannerlyn Crosland** .... (804) 733-7881
Fax: (804) 863-1504
Facilities Manager **Dennis Forman** .... (804) 504-7200
Information Technology Manager **Darryl Strausser** .... (804) 504-7200
Safety Manager **(Vacant)** .... (804) 504-7200
Human Resources Manager **Crystal Banks** .... (804) 504-7200
Disciplinary Hearing Officer **(Vacant)** .... (804) 504-7200

Federal Correctional Institution - Ashland (KY) (FCI ASHLAND)
P.O. Box 888, Ashland, KY 41105-0888
Tel: (606) 928-6414 Fax: (606) 929-4399

Warden **Thomas B. Smith** .... (606) 928-6414 ext. 4000
Executive Assistant **(Vacant)** .... (606) 928-6414
Associate Warden (Operations and Programs) **Janisse Bishop** .... (606) 928-6414 ext. 4004
Chief Correctional Supervisor **David Root** .... (606) 928-6414 ext. 4025
Chief Psychologist **Brad Garner** .... (606) 928-6414 ext. 4150
Camp Administrator **(Vacant)** .... (606) 928-6414
Food Service Administrator **Frank Brewster** .... (606) 928-6414 ext. 4100
Health Services Administrator **Amanda Waugaman** .... (606) 928-6414 ext. 4110
Education Supervisor **(Vacant)** .... (606) 928-6414 ext. 4041
Employee Services Manager **Jennifer Smith** .... (606) 928-6414 ext. 4130
Facility Manager **Millard Gray** .... (606) 928-6414
UNICOR Factory Manager **David Martin** .... (606) 928-6414 ext. 4050
Inmate Systems Manager **Dan Snodgrass** .... (606) 928-6414 ext. 4140
Safety Manager **David Ash** .... (606) 928-6414 ext. 4165
Computer Specialist **Vadis Gauze** .... (606) 988-6414 ext. 4020

Federal Correctional Institution - Beckley (WV) (FCI BECKLEY)
1600 Industrial Park Road, P.O. Box 1280, Beaver, WV 25813
Tel: (304) 252-9758 Fax: (304) 256-4956

Warden **David Young** .... (304) 252-9758
Education Supervisor **Heather James** .... (304) 252-9758

DEPARTMENTS

★ Presidential Appointment Requiring Senate Confirmation ☆ Presidential Appointment ☐ Schedule C Appointment ◇ Career Senior Foreign Service Appointment
● Career Senior Executive Service (SES) Appointment ○ Non-Career Senior Executive Service (SES) Appointment ■ Postal Career Executive Service

Federal Correctional Institution - Butner (NC) (FCI BUTNER)
Old Highway 75, Butner, NC 27509
P.O. Box 1000, Butner, NC 27509-1000
Tel: (919) 575-5000 Fax: (919) 575-5023

Warden **Donna Smith** .... (919) 575-5000
Associate Warden **Tony Hiscocks** .... (919) 575-5000
Associate Warden **(Vacant)** .... (919) 575-5000
Attorney Advisor **Mike Bredenberg** .... (919) 575-3900
E-mail: mbredenberg@bop.gov
Business Administrator **Bernita Baldwin** .... (919) 575-5000
Camp Administrator **Gary Sailor** .... (919) 575-4541
Food Service Administrator **Ted Paluch** .... (919) 575-5000
Assistant Health Services Administrator **Terry Kilpatrick** .... (919) 575-5000
Deputy Captain Correctional Services Supervisor **Kelly Smith** .... (919) 575-5000
Complex Captain **(Vacant)** .... (919) 575-5000
Education Supervisor **Brian Neagle** .... (919) 575-5000
Complex Manager **Eric Weaver** .... (919) 575-5000
Employee Services Manager **(Vacant)** .... (919) 575-5000
Inmate Systems Manager **Candice Gregory** .... (919) 575-5000
E-mail: cgregory@bop.gov
Safety and Occupational Health Manager **(Vacant)** .... (919) 575-3900

Federal Correctional Institution - Cumberland (MD) (FCI CUMBERLAND)
14601 Burbridge Road, SE, Cumberland, MD 21502-8724
Tel: (301) 784-1000 Fax: (301) 784-1004

● Warden **Timothy Stewart** .... (301) 784-1000
Camp Administrator and Executive Assistant **Tracy Longacre** .... (301) 784-1000 ext. 1120
E-mail: tlongacre@bop.gov

Federal Correctional Institution - Gilmer (WV) (FCI Gilmer)
201 FCI Lane, Glenville, WV 26351
Tel: (304) 626-2500 Fax: (304) 626-2693
E-mail: gil/execassistant@bop.gov
Internet: http://www.bop.gov/locations/institutions/gil/

Warden **Jennifer Saad** .... (304) 626-2500
Education Supervisor **Miranda Yeager** .... (304) 626-2500

Federal Correctional Institution - Manchester (KY) (FCI MANCHESTER)
805 Fox Hollow Road, Manchester, KY 40962
P.O. Box 3000, Manchester, KY 40962
Tel: (606) 598-1900 Tel: (700) 965-4100 Fax: (606) 599-4115

● Warden **J.A. Barnhart** .... (606) 598-1900
Executive Assistant **Robert Bruner** .... (606) 598-1900
E-mail: MAN/ExecAssistant@bop.gov
Associate Warden (Industry and Education) **(Vacant)** .... (606) 598-1900
Associate Warden (Programs) **William Hutchings** .... (606) 598-1900
Associate Warden (Operations) **Brian English** .... (606) 598-1900
Business Administrator **Rachel Salinas** .... (606) 598-1900
Food Service Administrator **Keith Allen** .... (606) 598-1900
Health Services Administrator **Angel Wilson** .... (606) 598-1900
Chief Chaplain **Thomas Jahr** .... (606) 598-1900
Chief Correctional Supervisor **Jordan Treibley** .... (606) 598-1900
Chief Psychologist **Dr. Mary Williard** .... (606) 598-1900
Education Supervisor **Keith Pray** .... (606) 598-1900
Computer Services Manager **Corey Walterson** .... (606) 598-1900
Facilities Manager **Pam Clark** .... (606) 598-1900
Human Resources Manager **Jennifer Morris** .... (606) 598-1900
Supervisory Correctional Systems Specialist **William McManus** .... (606) 598-1900
Safety Manager **Rebecca Ebersole** .... (606) 598-1900
Clay Unit Manager **Jeff Ellifritz** .... (606) 598-1900
Knox Unit Manager **James Huff** .... (606) 598-1900
Laurel Unit Manager **Misty Ely** .... (606) 598-1900
Manchester/Oneida Unit Manager **Robert Bruner** .... (606) 598-1900
Whitley Unit Manager **Misty Ely** .... (606) 598-1900
Discipline Hearing Officer **William Sizemore** .... (606) 598-1900
Case Management Coordinator **Sheila Messer** .... (606) 598-1900

Federal Correctional Institution - McDowell (WV) (FCI McDowell)
101 Federal Drive, Welch, WV 24801
Tel: (304) 436-7300 Fax: (304) 436-7318
E-mail: mcd/execassistant@bop.gov

Warden **Barbara Rickard** .... (304) 436-7300
Education Supervisor **Tonya Norris** .... (304) 436-7300

Federal Correctional Institution - Memphis (TN) (FCI MEMPHIS)
1101 John A. Denie Road, Memphis, TN 38134-7690
Tel: (901) 372-2269 Fax: (901) 384-5462

● Warden **Myron L. Batts** .... (901) 372-2269
E-mail: mbatts@bop.gov
Executive Assistant **Jacklin Ash** .... (901) 372-2269
E-mail: mem/execassistant@bop.gov
Superintendent of Industries **(Vacant)** .... (901) 372-2269
Associate Warden (Operations) **Neil Robinson** .... (901) 372-2269
Associate Warden (Programs) **M. Alex Barbee** .... (901) 372-2269
Controller **(Vacant)** .... (901) 372-2269
Food Service Administrator **S. Crockett** .... (901) 372-2269
Health Services Administrator **Ella Taylor** .... (901) 372-2269
Chief Correctional Supervisor **James Jemison** .... (901) 372-2269
Education Supervisor **Melanie Blizzard** .... (901) 372-2269
Facilities Manager **LaDrone Parks-Harris** .... (901) 372-2269
Inmate Systems Manager/Case Management Coordinator **Sarah Smallwood** .... (901) 372-2269
Safety Manager **Debra Mayfield** .... (901) 372-2269
Employee Services Manager **Stacy Williams** .... (901) 372-2269
Computer Services Manager **Carolyn Livingston** .... (901) 372-2269

Federal Prison Camp - Millington (TN)
6696 Navy Road, Millington, TN 38053
Tel: (901) 872-2277

Camp Administrator **Tonya Hawkins** .... (901) 372-2269
Secretary **Chandra Reed** .... (901) 872-2277

Federal Correctional Institution - Morgantown (WV) (FCI MORGANTOWN)
446 Greenbag Road, Morgantown, WV 26507
P.O. Box 1000, Morgantown, WV 26507-1000
Tel: (304) 296-4416 Fax: (304) 284-3600

Warden **(Vacant)** .... (304) 296-4416
Associate Warden **Jay Fikes** .... (304) 296-4116
Business Administrator **Thomas Chandler** .... (304) 296-4416
Food Service Administrator **Steve Valvassori** .... (304) 296-4416
Health Services Administrator **(Vacant)** .... (304) 296-4416
Human Resources Administrator **Jamie Johnson** .... (304) 296-4416
Chief Correctional Supervisor **Bruce Bell** .... (304) 296-4416
Education Supervisor **Jessica Ware** .... (304) 296-4416
Employee Services Manager **Jamie Johnson** .... (304) 296-4416
Facilities Manager **Michael Romeo** .... (304) 296-4416
Case Management Coordinator **Marilyn Veltri** .... (304) 296-4416
Safety Manager **Jason Lintner** .... (304) 296-4416

Federal Medical Center - Butner (NC) (FMC BUTNER)
Old Oxford Highway 75, Butner, NC 27509
P.O. Box 1600, Butner, NC 27509
Tel: (919) 575-3900 Fax: (919) 575-4801

Complex Warden **J.C. Holland** .... (919) 575-3900
Associate Warden **E.A. Earwir** .... (919) 575-3900
Associate Warden **A.W. Rupska** .... (919) 575-3900
Complex Executive Assistant **(Vacant)** .... (919) 575-3900
E-mail: bux/execassistant@bop.gov

Federal Medical Center - Lexington (KY) (FMC LEXINGTON)
3301 Leestown Road, Lexington, KY 40511-8799
Tel: (859) 255-6812 Fax: (859) 253-8821

Note: This facility is for males only.

Warden **Francisco J. "Frank" Quintana** .... (859) 255-6812
Executive Assistant (Acting) **Jeffrey Toney** .... (859) 255-6812
Associate Warden (Clinical Programs) **Kevin Toney** .... (859) 255-6812

★ Presidential Appointment Requiring Senate Confirmation ☆ Presidential Appointment ☐ Schedule C Appointment ◇ Career Senior Foreign Service Appointment
● Career Senior Executive Service (SES) Appointment ○ Non-Career Senior Executive Service (SES) Appointment ■ Postal Career Executive Service

Federal Medical Center - Lexington (KY) *(continued)*

Associate Warden (Operations) **Renee Cosmore** . . . . (859) 255-6812
Associate Warden (Programs) **Jonathan Hemingway** . . . . (859) 255-6812
Attorney **Carlos Martinez** . . . . (859) 255-6812
Financial Administrator **Michael Kinsel** . . . . (859) 255-6812
Forensic Psychologist **Judith "Betsy" Campbell** . . . . (859) 255-6812
Forensic Psychologist **Alvin Wood** . . . . (859) 255-6812
Food Service Administrator **Kelvin Hibbard** . . . . (859) 255-6812
Health Services Administrator **Cecelia Bush** . . . . (859) 255-6812
Chief Correctional Supervisor **David Carpenter** . . . . (859) 255-6812
Education Supervisor **Jeffrey Toney** . . . . (859) 255-6812
Facilities Manager **Christopher Pauley** . . . . (859) 255-6812
Employee Services Manager **Joshua Hensley** . . . . (859) 255-6812
Inmate Systems Manager **Yvonne Hatfield** . . . . (859) 255-6812
Discipline Hearing Officer **William Sizemore** . . . . (606) 598-1900

Federal Prison Camp - Alderson (WV) (FPC ALDERSON)
Glen Ray Road, Box A, Alderson, WV 24910-0699
Tel: (304) 445-3300 Fax: (304) 445-3320

Warden **David R. Wilson** . . . . (304) 445-3300
Executive Assistant **Melissa Evans** . . . . (304) 445-3300
E-mail: mxevans@bop.gov
Associate Warden **Maria Arviza** . . . . (304) 445-3300
Food Services Administrator **Chad Reed** . . . . (304) 445-3300
Health Services Administrator **Dana Renick** . . . . (304) 445-3300
Chief Correctional Supervisor **(Vacant)** . . . . (304) 445-3300
Education Supervisor **Dorian Dickerson** . . . . (304) 445-3300
Employee Services Manager **Jesse Turner III** . . . . (304) 445-3300
E-mail: j4turner@bop.gov
Facilities Manager **Joseph Smith** . . . . (304) 445-3300
Inmate Systems Manager **Phil Fondale** . . . . (304) 445-3300
E-mail: pfondale@bop.gov
Safety Manager **Lisa Vandall** . . . . (304) 445-3300
E-mail: lvandall@bop.gov
Computer Services Manager **Kenneth Andrews** . . . . (304) 445-3300
E-mail: k3andrews@bop.gov

Low Security Correctional Institution - Butner (NC) (FCI Butner Low)
Old Oxford Highway 75, Butner, NC 27509-0999
P.O. Box 999, Butner, NC 27509-0999
Tel: (919) 575-5000 Fax: (919) 575-5023

Warden **Tracy W. John** . . . . (919) 575-5000
E-mail: tjohnn@bop.gov

U.S. Penitentiary - Big Sandy (KY) (USP Big Sandy)
1197 Airport Road, Inez, KY 41224
Tel: (606) 433-2400 Tel: (606) 433-2577
E-mail: bsy/execassistant@bop.gov

● Warden **Greg Kizziah** . . . . (606) 433-2400
Educational Supervisor **Chad Webb** . . . . (606) 433-2400

U.S. Penitentiary - Lee (VA) (USP Lee)
Lee County Industrial Park, Hickory Flats Road,
Pennington Gap, VA 24277
Tel: (276) 546-0150 Fax: (276) 546-9115
E-mail: lee/execassistant@bop.gov
Internet: http://www.bop.gov/locations/institutions/lee/

○ Warden **Charles Ratledge** . . . . (276) 546-0150
E-mail: cratledge@bop.gov
Education Supervisor **Lance Cole** . . . . (276) 546-0150

U.S. Penitentiary - McCreary (KY) (USP McCreary)
330 Federaly Way, Pine Knot, KY 42635
Tel: (606) 354-7000 Fax: (606) 354-7190
E-mail: mcr/execassistant@bop.gov

● Warden **Hector Joyner** . . . . (606) 354-7000

North Central Region
Gateway Complex, Tower II, 400 State Avenue,
8th Floor, Kansas City, KS 66101-2492
Tel: (913) 621-3939 Fax: (913) 551-1130
Areas Covered: CO, IL, IN, IA, KS, MI, MN, MO, NE, ND, SD, WI

● Regional Director **Sarah Revel** . . . . (913) 551-1000
Senior Deputy Regional Director **Amber L. Nelson** . . . . . . (913) 551-1032
E-mail: anelson@bop.gov
Executive Assistant **Elizabeth A. Pottios** . . . . (913) 551-1053
Regional Counsel **Rick Winter** . . . . (913) 551-1004
Administrative Officer **Shelley Winsor** . . . . (913) 551-1001
Affirmative Action **Deb Frandel** . . . . (913) 551-1144
Comptroller **Kim Cochrane** . . . . (913) 551-1041
Computer Services Administrator **Mike Prater** . . . . (913) 551-1070
E-mail: mprater@bop.gov
Correctional Programs **Melissa Bayless** . . . . (913) 551-1014
Correctional Services **Shawn Grant** . . . . (913) 551-1046
Facilities **Ty Bayless** . . . . (913) 551-1031
Food Services **Jason Langford** . . . . (913) 551-1008
Health Services **Terri Gregory** . . . . (913) 551-1158
Human Resources **Kelli C. Harpe** . . . . (913) 551-1131
E-mail: kcharpe@bop.gov

North Central Region Residential Reentry Office
Gateway Complex, Tower II, 400 State Avenue,
8th Floor, Kansas City, KS 66101-2492
Tel: (913) 551-1109 Fax: (913) 551-1076
Areas Covered: CO, IL, IA, KS, MN, MO, NE, ND, SD, WI

Sector Administrator **Michael Connelly** . . . . (913) 551-1139
E-mail: mconnelly@bop.gov

Chicago (IL) Residential Reentry Management Office
200 West Adams Street, Suite 2915, Chicago, IL 60606
Tel: (312) 886-2317 Fax: (312) 886-2118

Residential Reentry Manager **James Billingsley** . . . . (312) 886-2116

Detroit (MI) Residential Reentry Management Office
4026 E. Arkona Rd., Milan, MI 48160
Tel: (734) 439-7658 Fax: (734) 439-7671

Residential Reentry Manager **James Billingsley** . . . . (734) 439-7653
Residential Reentry Specialist **Clint Weaver** . . . . (734) 439-7658
Contract Oversight Specialist **Matt Call** . . . . (734) 439-7653

Kansas City (KS) Residential Reentry Management Office
Gateway Complex Tower II, 400 State Avenue,
8th Floor, Kansas City, KS 66101
Tel: (913) 551-1117

Community Corrections Specialist **Kendall James** . . . . (913) 551-1134
Community Corrections Manager **Melissa Acevedo** . . . . . (913) 551-1113
Community Corrections Specialist **(Vacant)** . . . . (913) 551-1116
Contract Oversight Specialist **Kris Robl** . . . . (913) 551-1118
Residential Reentry Specialist **Mike Earl** . . . . (913) 551-1114
Contract Oversight Specialist **Michelle Blake** . . . . (913) 551-1115

Minneapolis (MN) Residential Reentry Management Office
300 South Fourth Street, Suite 1210, Minneapolis, MN 55415
Tel: (612) 332-5030 Fax: (612) 332-5029

Residential Reentry Manager **Brenda Moore** . . . . (612) 332-5024

Saint Louis (MO) Residential Reentry Management Office
1222 Spruce Street, Suite 6.101, St. Louis, MO 63103
Tel: (314) 539-2376 Fax: (314) 539-2465

Residential Reentry Manager **Shai Foster** . . . . (314) 539-2367
E-mail: sfoster@bop.gov
Residential Reentry Contract Oversight Manager
Kathy Hueter . . . . (314) 539-2390
E-mail: mhueter@bop.gov

DEPARTMENTS

★ Presidential Appointment Requiring Senate Confirmation ☆ Presidential Appointment ☐ Schedule C Appointment ◇ Career Senior Foreign Service Appointment
● Career Senior Executive Service (SES) Appointment ○ Non-Career Senior Executive Service (SES) Appointment ■ Postal Career Executive Service

DEPARTMENTS

Federal Correctional Complex - Florence (CO) (FCC FLORENCE)
5880 State Highway 67 South, Florence, CO 81226

Federal Correctional Institution Florence (FCI Florence)
5880 State Highway 67 South, Florence, CO 81226
P.O. Box 6500, Florence, CO 81226
Tel: (719) 784-9100 Tel: (700) 739-4800 Fax: (719) 784-9504

Warden **Cathy Gotz** .... (719) 784-9100
Executive Assistant **Todd Chapman** .... (719) 784-9464
Associate Warden (Operations) **E. Hernandez** .... (719) 784-9100
Associate Warden (Programs) **E.A. Lennon** .... (719) 784-9100
Supervisory Attorney **Chris Synsvoll** .... (719) 784-9464
E-mail: csynsvoll@bop.gov
Food Services Administrator **Derek Jones** .... (719) 784-9454
Health Services Administrator **(Vacant)** .... (719) 784-9464
Education Supervisor **Jason Gunther** .... (719) 784-9464
Facilities Manager **Duane McMullen** .... (719) 784-9464
Human Resources Manager **Lauren Patch** .... (719) 784-9100
Inmate Systems Manager **Pete Mafnas** .... (719) 784-9464
Safety Manager **Lorie Guess** .... (719) 784-9100
Superintendent of Industries **(Vacant)** .... (719) 784-9100
UNICOR Factory Manager **Brian Tuttoilmondo** .... (719) 784-9100
UNICOR Quality Assurance Manager **Grant Versaw** .... (719) 784-9100
Security Officer **(Vacant)** .... (719) 784-9100

U.S. Penitentiary Florence - High (USP Florence High)
5880 State Highway 67 South, P.O. Box 7500, Florence, CO 81226
Tel: (719) 784-9464 Fax: (719) 784-5290

Warden **Joe Moorhead** .... (719) 784-9454

U.S. Penitentiary Florence - Administrative Maximum Facility (ADMAX)
5880 State Highway 67 South, P.O. Box 8500, Florence, CO 81226
Tel: (719) 784-9464 Fax: (719) 784-5290

Warden **Jack Fox** .... (719) 784-9464

Federal Correctional Complex - Terre Haute (IN) (FCI TERRE HAUTE)
4700 Bureau Road South, Terre Haute, IN 47802
Tel: (812) 244-4400 Fax: (812) 244-4791

• Complex Warden **Jeff Krueger** .... (812) 244-4400
E-mail: thp/warden@bop.gov
Education: Indiana State 1987 BS
Warden's Secretary **Cherie Chatman** .... (812) 244-4400
Associate Warden **Jason Cox** .... (812) 244-4400
Associate Warden **Bobby Gourdouze** .... (812) 244-4400
Associate Warden **Michael Underwood** .... (812) 238-1531
Federal Correctional Institute Warden **J.R. Bell** .... (812) 238-1531
FCI Warden's Secretary **Jennifer Ellis** .... (812) 238-1531
Captain **Gregory S. BonDurant** .... (812) 244-4400
Deputy Captain **William Hess** .... (812) 238-1537
Camp Administrator **Jenna N. Epplin** .... (812) 238-1531
E-mail: jepplin@bop.gov
Education Supervisor **Phil Woolston** .... (812) 238-1531
Health Services Administrator **Chris McCoy** .... (812) 244-4400
Human Resources Manager **Sandra Murphy** .... (812) 244-4400
Information Technology Manager **Trey Adams** .... (812) 244-4400
National Bus Center Manager **Chris McVay** .... (812) 238-1531
Safety Manager **Jeff Lamping** .... (812) 238-1531
E-mail: jlamping@bop.gov

Federal Correctional Institution - Englewood (CO) (FCI ENGLEWOOD)
9595 West Quincy Avenue, Littleton, CO 80123
Tel: (303) 985-1566 Fax: (303) 763-2553

Warden **(Vacant)** .... (303) 985-1566 ext. 1100
Executive Assistant **Beth Rickard** .... (303) 763-4305
Associate Warden (Programs)
Randal Mitchell .... (303) 985-1566 ext. 2367
Associate Warden (Operations) **(Vacant)** .... (303) 985-1566 ext. 2368
Chaplain **Matthew Berg** .... (303) 985-1566 ext. 1141
Food Service Administrator **(Vacant)** .... (303) 985-1566 ext. 1270

Federal Correctional Institution - Englewood (CO) *(continued)*

Health Systems Administrator
Michael "Mike" Hudson .... (303) 985-1566 ext. 1288
Chief Correctional Supervisor
Brian Duimond .... (303) 985-1566 ext. 1150
Education Supervisor **William McCormick** .... (303) 985-1566 ext. 1230
Camp and Jail Unit Manager **Beth Rickard** .... (303) 985-1566 ext. 1400
Computer Services Manager **Jesse Arellano** .... (303) 985-1566 ext. 4432
Employee Services Manager
Taffany Espinoza .... (303) 985-1566 ext. 1294
Facilities Manager **Steven Zerr** .... (303) 985-1566 ext. 1240
Safety Manager **(Vacant)** .... (303) 985-1566 ext. 1330
East Unit Manager **Gregory Staut** .... (303) 985-1566 ext. 1380
West Unit Manager **Steve Hansen** .... (303) 985-1566 ext. 1397
Case Management Coordinator **(Vacant)** .... (303) 985-1566 ext. 1135
Chief Psychologist **(Vacant)** .... (303) 985-1566 ext. 1315

Federal Correctional Institution - Greenville (IL) (FCI GREENVILLE)
100 U.S. Highway 40, Greenville, IL 62246
P.O. Box 4000, Greenville, IL 62246
Tel: (618) 664-6200 Fax: (618) 664-6372

• Warden **Thomas "Tom" Werlich** .... (618) 664-6200
E-mail: twerlich@bop.gov
Public Information Officer **(Vacant)** .... (618) 664-6200
Webmaster **Karen Landolt** .... (618) 664-6288
E-mail: klandolt@bop.gov
Education Supervisor **Stan Pickett** .... (618) 664-6200

Federal Correctional Institution - Milan (MI) (FCI MILAN)
East Arkona Road, Milan, MI 48160
Mail: P.O. Box 9999, Milan, MI 48160
Tel: (734) 439-1511 Fax: (734) 439-3608

Warden **Jason Terris** .... (734) 439-1511
Executive Assistant **Billy Eischen** .... (734) 439-4757
E-mail: mil/execassistant@bop.gov
Superintendent of Industries **(Vacant)** .... (734) 439-1511
Associate Warden (Programs) **Diana Easter** .... (734) 439-1511
Chaplain **Ki Nam Ko** .... (734) 439-1511
Chief of Health Programs **William Malatinski** .... (734) 439-1511
Chief Psychologist **Andrea Tobias** .... (734) 439-1511
Business Administrator **Sandy Rankin** .... (734) 439-1511
Detention Center Administrator **Billy Eischen** .... (734) 439-4757
Food Service Administrator **Elijah George** .... (734) 439-1511
Health Services Administrator **Jim Zestos** .... (734) 439-5419
Chief Correctional Supervisor **Anthony Bozeman** .... (734) 439-1511
Education Supervisor **Geoffrey Schlottman** .... (734) 439-1511
Trust Fund Supervisor **Elena Voggenreiter** .... (734) 439-1511
Computer Services Manager **Raymond Sisty** .... (734) 439-4753
Assistant Computer Services Manager
Mark Davenport .... (734) 439-4753
E-mail: mdavenport@bop.gov
Facilities Manager **Brian Smith** .... (734) 439-1511
Human Resources Manager **Ginger Auten** .... (734) 439-1511
E-mail: gauten@bop.gov
Inmate Systems Manager **Ian Healey** .... (734) 439-1511
UNICOR Factory Manager **Cody Maynard** .... (734) 439-1511
UNICOR Operational Accountant **Sarah Maynard** .... (734) 439-1511
Case Management Coordinator **Ian Healey** .... (734) 439-1511

Federal Correctional Institution - Oxford (WI) (FCI OXFORD)
Box 500, Oxford, WI 53952-0500
Tel: (608) 584-5511 Fax: (608) 584-6314

Warden **(Vacant)** .... (608) 584-5511
Executive Assistant/Public Information Officer
Rebecca Hensley .... (608) 584-5511
E-mail: oxf/execassistant@bop.gov
E-mail: rlhensley@bop.gov
Associate Warden (Operations) **Michael Lejeune** .... (608) 584-5511
Associate Warden (Programs) **Daniel Sullivan** .... (608) 584-5511
Captain **Corey A. Kirby** .... (608) 584-5511
Chaplain **Ryan Willis** .... (608) 584-5511

★ Presidential Appointment Requiring Senate Confirmation ☆ Presidential Appointment ☐ Schedule C Appointment ◇ Career Senior Foreign Service Appointment
● Career Senior Executive Service (SES) Appointment ○ Non-Career Senior Executive Service (SES) Appointment ■ Postal Career Executive Service

Federal Correctional Institution - Oxford (WI) *(continued)*

Psychology Services Chief **(Vacant)** . . . . . (608) 584-5511
Business Administrator **Bob Pahmeier** . . . . . (608) 584-5511
Food Service Administrator **Rebecca Pientok** . . . . . (608) 584-5511
Health Services Administrator **Melissa Laufenberg** . . . . . (608) 584-5511
Education Supervisor **Kyle Roberson** . . . . . (608) 584-5511
Inmate Services Supervisor **Rick Pease** . . . . . (608) 584-5511
Computer Services Manager **Dean MacKinnon** . . . . . (608) 584-5511
Correctional Systems Manager **John Numsen** . . . . . (608) 584-5511
E-mail: jnumsen@bop.gov
Facilities Manager **Kyle Hall** . . . . . (608) 584-5511
Safety Manager **Erin Penrose** . . . . . (608) 584-5511
Unit Manager **Al Broe** . . . . . (608) 584-5511
Unit Manager **Janis Braker** . . . . . (608) 584-5511
Unit Manager **(Vacant)** . . . . . (608) 584-5511
Case Management Coordinator **James Pfeifer** . . . . . (608) 584-5511
DAP Coordinator **Kurt Riem** . . . . . (608) 584-5511
E-mail: kriem@bop.gov
Contracting Officer **Robert Pahmeier** . . . . . (608) 584-5511
Personnel Officer **Doug Thompson** . . . . . (608) 584-5511

Federal Correctional Institution - Pekin (IL) (FCI PEKIN)
2600 South Second Street, Pekin, IL 61554
Mail: P.O. Box 5000, Pekin, IL 61555-5000 (Mailing Address for both Camp and Federal Correctional Institution Inmates)
P.O. Box 7000, Pekin, IL 61555 (Mailing Address for Staff)
Tel: (309) 346-8588 Fax: (309) 477-4670

Warden **Steve Kallis** . . . . . (309) 346-8588
E-mail: skallis@bop.gov

Federal Correctional Institution - Sandstone (MN) (FCI SANDSTONE)
2300 County Road 29, Sandstone, MN 55072-0999
Mail: P.O. Box 999, Sandstone, MN 55072 (Staff mail)
Tel: (320) 245-2262 Fax: (320) 245-0385

Warden **Rick Marques** . . . . . (320) 245-2262
Public Information Officer **Ernie Frie** . . . . . (320) 245-2262
Associate Warden **Eric Williams** . . . . . (320) 245-2262
Controller **Linda Peterson** . . . . . (320) 245-2262
Food Service Administrator **Anthony Eckert** . . . . . (320) 245-2262
Health Services Administrator **Heidi Voss** . . . . . (320) 245-6245
Chief Correctional Supervisor **Cleveland Swan** . . . . . (320) 245-2262
Education Supervisor **Laura Ping** . . . . . (320) 245-2262
Facilities Manager **Rodney Naab** . . . . . (320) 245-2262
Employee Services Manager **Rochelle Erickson** . . . . . (320) 245-2262
Safety Manager **Bernie Richards** . . . . . (320) 245-2262

Federal Correctional Institution - Waseca (MN) (FCI WASECA)
1000 University Drive, SW, Waseca, MN 56093
P.O. Box 1731, Waseca, MN 56093-0741
Tel: (507) 835-8972 Fax: (507) 837-4547

Warden **Annette Barnes** . . . . . (507) 835-8972
Education Supervisor
William "Billy" Kelsheimer . . . . . (507) 835-8972 ext. 3100

Federal Medical Center - Rochester (MN) (FMC ROCHESTER)
2110 East Center Street, Rochester, MN 55904
P.O. Box 4600, Rochester, MN 55903-4600
Tel: (507) 287-0674 Fax: (507) 424-7600

● Warden **David Paul** . . . . . (507) 287-0674
Associate Warden **Jaysen Relvas** . . . . . (507) 287-0674
Associate Warden **Bryan Birkholz** . . . . . (507) 287-0674
Supervisory Attorney **Kara Anderl** . . . . . (507) 287-0674

Federal Medical Center - Springfield (MO) (MCFP SPRINGFIELD)
1900 West Sunshine, Springfield, MO 65807
Tel: (417) 862-7041 Fax: (417) 837-1717

Warden **Michael D. Smith** . . . . . (417) 862-7041
Executive Assistant **Joe Davis** . . . . . (417) 862-7041 ext. 1214
Associate Warden (Health Services) **Sean Snider** . . . . . (417) 862-7041
Associate Warden (Operations) **Margaret Rehman** . . . . . (417) 862-7041

Federal Medical Center - Springfield (MO) *(continued)*

Associate Warden (Programs) **Matthew Marske** . . . . . (417) 862-7041
Attorney Advisor **Christina Scofield** . . . . . (417) 862-7041
E-mail: clongwell@bop.gov
Chief Correctional Supervisor **Gary Cooper** . . . . . (417) 862-7041
Chief Dental Officer **Allison Nelson** . . . . . (417) 862-7041
Chief of Psychiatry **Robert Serrazin** . . . . . (417) 862-7041
Chief of Psychology **Randy Brandt** . . . . . (417) 862-7041
Clinical Director **Scott Moose** . . . . . (417) 862-7041
Nursing Director **Janet Beyer** . . . . . (417) 862-7041
Food Services Administrator **Gary Swaney** . . . . . (417) 862-7041
Health Services Administrator **Rhonda Yarbrough** . . . . . (417) 862-7041
Computer Services Manager **John Jury** . . . . . (417) 862-7041
Employee Services Manager **Bradford Mackey** . . . . . (417) 862-7041
Facilities Manager **Jeremiah Johnston** . . . . . (417) 862-7041

Federal Prison Camp - Duluth (MN) (FPC DULUTH)
4464 Ralston Drive, Duluth, MN 55814
P.O. Box 1400, Duluth, MN 55814
Tel: (218) 722-8634 Fax: (218) 733-4701

Warden **Melissa Rios** . . . . . (218) 722-8634
Secretary **Stephanie Howe** . . . . . (218) 722-8634
E-mail: showe@bop.gov
Associate Warden **Ryan McCaffery** . . . . . (218) 722-8634
Business Administrator **Teresa Schaffer** . . . . . (218) 722-8634
Business Administrator **(Vacant)** . . . . . (218) 722-8634
Chaplain **Jessie Bell** . . . . . (218) 722-8634
Psychologist **Charlotte Francia** . . . . . (218) 722-8634
Food Service Administrator **Rod Bergsetd** . . . . . (218) 722-8634
Health Services Administrator **Keith Blanke** . . . . . (218) 722-8634
Chief Correctional Supervisor **(Vacant)** . . . . . (218) 722-8634
Corrections Systems Supervisor **John Witte** . . . . . (218) 722-8634
E-mail: jwitte@bop.gov
Education Program Manager **Andrew Lamarnad** . . . . . (218) 722-8634
Facilities Manager **Paul Wernke** . . . . . (218) 722-8634
Human Resource Manager **Carrie Foster** . . . . . (218) 722-8634
E-mail: cfoster@bop.gov
Inmate Systems Supervisor **Kim Stern** . . . . . (218) 722-8634
Douglas Unit Manager **Kyja Winger** . . . . . (218) 722-8634
E-mail: kwinger@bop.gov
St. Louis Unit Manager **Roger Pelawa** . . . . . (218) 722-8634
E-mail: rpelawa@bop.gov
Case Management Coordinator **John Witte** . . . . . (218) 722-8634
E-mail: jwitte@bop.gov

Federal Prison Camp - Yankton (SD) (FPC YANKTON)
P.O. Box 680, Yankton, SD 57078
Tel: (605) 665-3262 Fax: (605) 668-1113

Warden **Huriberto Tellez** . . . . . (605) 665-3262
Associate Warden **Billy Eichen** . . . . . (605) 665-3262
Pastoral Care **Doug Upton** . . . . . (605) 665-3262
Chief Psychologist **William Pierce** . . . . . (605) 665-3262
E-mail: wxpierce@bop.gov
Food Service Administrator **Tim Allen** . . . . . (605) 665-3262
Health Services Administrator **Christina Woehl** . . . . . (605) 665-3262
Chief Correctional Supervisor **Ernesto Recoder** . . . . . (605) 665-3262
Education Supervisor **Gurumindar Singh** . . . . . (605) 665-3262
Supervisory Inmate Systems Specialist **Robert Hale** . . . . . (605) 665-3262
Business Administrator **Jennifer Fink** . . . . . (605) 665-3262
E-mail: jfink@bop.gov
Facilities Manager **Fred Lyman** . . . . . (605) 665-3262
Human Resources Manager **Karen Edler** . . . . . (605) 665-3262
Safety Manager (Acting) **Cortland Wittenhagen** . . . . . (605) 665-3262
Unit Manager **Jill Sternhagen** . . . . . (605) 665-3262
Unit Manager **Anthony Edwards** . . . . . (605) 665-3262
E-mail: a3edwards@bop.gov
Case Management Coordinator **Lisa Allen** . . . . . (605) 665-3262
E-mail: lallen1@bop.gov
Trust Fund Supervisor **Alexander Fuentes** . . . . . (605) 665-3262
Computer Specialist **Kenneth Kulhavy** . . . . . (605) 665-3262

DEPARTMENTS

★ Presidential Appointment Requiring Senate Confirmation ☆ Presidential Appointment □ Schedule C Appointment ◇ Career Senior Foreign Service Appointment
● Career Senior Executive Service (SES) Appointment ○ Non-Career Senior Executive Service (SES) Appointment ■ Postal Career Executive Service

DEPARTMENTS

Metropolitan Correctional Center - Chicago (IL) (MCC CHICAGO)
71 West Van Buren Street, Chicago, IL 60605
Tel: (312) 322-0567 Fax: (312) 347-4012

Warden **Angela M. Owens** .... (312) 322-0567
Executive Assistant **Grant Heuett** .... (312) 322-0567 ext. 1508
Associate Warden (Operations) **Russell Heisner** .... (312) 322-0567 ext. 1524
Associate Warden (Programs) **James Dunn** .... (312) 322-0567 ext. 1526
Senior Attorney **Amy Standefer-Malott** .... (312) 322-0567 ext. 1432
Attorney **Zachary Zurek** .... (312) 322-0567 ext. 1503
Captain **Glenn MacDonald** .... (312) 322-0567 ext. 1433
Chaplain **Michael Leshon** .... (312) 322-0567 ext. 1489
Chief Psychologist **Jason Dana** .... (312) 322-0567 ext. 1469
Clinical Director **Brij Mohan** .... (312) 322-0567 ext. 1410
Business Administrator **Patrick Aston** .... (312) 322-0567 ext. 1514
Food Service Administrator **Michael Gilliam** .... (312) 322-0567 ext. 1451
Health Services Administrator **Zaida Ndife** .... (312) 322-0567 ext. 1401
Computer Services Manager **Ebbert Gene Greenwood** .... (312) 322-0567 ext. 1495
Education/Recreation Program Manager **Douglas Owens, Jr.** .... (312) 322-0567 ext. 1487
Employee Services Manager **Kenneth Davis** .... (312) 322-0567 ext. 1509
Facilities Manager **Matthew Flisk** .... (312) 322-0567 ext. 1445
Safety Manager **Anthony Rodriguez** .... (312) 322-0567 ext. 1430
Case Management Coordinator **Devon Campfield** .... (312) 322-0567 ext. 1480

U.S. Penitentiary - Leavenworth (KS) (USP LEAVENWORTH)
1300 Metropolitan, Leavenworth, KS 66048
Tel: (913) 682-8700 Fax: (913) 578-1010

● Warden **N.C. English** .... (913) 682-8700
Executive Assistant **Jacob Dyer** .... (913) 682-8700
Warden's Secretary **Cherise Berry** .... (913) 682-8700
E-mail: c1berry@bop.gov
Captain's Secretary **(Vacant)** .... (913) 682-8700
Associate Warden (Industries and Education) **(Vacant)** .... (913) 682-8700
Associate Warden (Programs) **Jason Streeval** .... (913) 682-8700
Associate Warden (Operations) **LaTrice Heyward** .... (913) 682-8700
Associate Warden's Secretary **Darrin Freeman** .... (913) 682-8700
Camp Administrator **Jacob Dyer** .... (913) 682-8700
Controller **Jennifer Langley** .... (913) 682-8700
E-mail: jlangley@bop.gov
Food Service Administrator **Victor Sears** .... (913) 682-8700
Health Services Administrator **Justin Blevins** .... (913) 682-8700
Chief Correctional Supervisor **Dennis Treadway** .... (913) 682-8700
Chief Psychologist **Joseph Bleier** .... (913) 682-8700
Computer Services Manager **Herman Moore** .... (913) 682-8700
Education Supervisor **Justin Welsh** .... (913) 682-8700
Employee Services Manager **Justin Bolin** .... (913) 682-8700
Facilities Manager **Kevin Gregory** .... (913) 682-8700
Case Management Coordinator **Mark Clark** .... (913) 682-8700
Legal Instruments Examiner **(Vacant)** .... (913) 682-8700
Recreation Supervisor **Troy Phipps** .... (913) 682-8700
Safety Manager **Billye Cordell** .... (913) 682-8700
Supervisory Chaplain **Lonnie Sutton** .... (913) 682-8700

U.S. Penitentiary - Marion (IL) (USP MARION)
4500 Prison Road, Marion, IL 62959
P.O. Box 2000, Marion, IL 62959
Tel: (618) 964-1441 Fax: (618) 964-2070

Warden **William P. True III** .... (618) 964-1441
Executive Assistant **(Vacant)** .... (618) 964-1441
Associate Warden **Jeffrey Powers** .... (618) 964-1441
Associate Warden **Todd Sloop** .... (618) 964-1441
Chaplain **Stephen Holem** .... (618) 964-1441
Chief Psychologist **Dr. Jay Munneke** .... (618) 964-1441
Psychologist **(Vacant)** .... (618) 964-1441
Food Administrator **Joshua Michaelis** .... (618) 964-1441
Health Systems Administrator **Mandie Bagwell** .... (618) 964-1441
E-mail: mbagwell@bop.gov
Chief Correctional Supervisor **Joseph Wadas** .... (618) 964-1441
Education Supervisor **Tammy Castellano** .... (618) 964-1441

U.S. Penitentiary - Marion (IL) *(continued)*

Computer Service Manager **Jay Bagwell** .... (618) 964-1441
E-mail: jbagwell@bop.gov
Facilities Manager **Mark Norris** .... (618) 964-1441
Safety Manager **Tim Gonzalez** .... (618) 964-1441
E-mail: tgonzalez@bop.gov
Unit Manager **(Vacant)** .... (618) 964-1441
Unit Manager **Sarah Byram** .... (618) 964-1441
Unit Manager **Rashaan Baskerville** .... (618) 964-1441
Case Management Coordinator **Michele Daun** .... (618) 964-1441
UNICOR **Shawn Whitecotton** .... (618) 964-1441
Disciplinary Hearing Officer **(Vacant)** .... (618) 964-1441
Personnel Officer **Chris Cullum** .... (618) 964-1441
E-mail: ccullum@bop.gov
Superintendent of Industry **(Vacant)** .... (618) 964-1441

Northeast Region
U.S. Custom House, Second and Chestnut Streets,
7th Floor, Philadelphia, PA 19106
Tel: (215) 521-7300 Fax: (215) 597-1893
Areas Covered: CT, ME, MA, NH, NJ, NY, OH, PA, RI, VT

● Regional Director **Michael Carvajal** .... (215) 521-7311
Executive Assistant **Kristie A. Breshears** .... (215) 521-7315
Deputy Regional Director **(Vacant)** .... (215) 521-7313
Legal Counsel **(Vacant)** .... (215) 521-7375
Comptroller **Kevin Kim** .... (215) 521-7420
E-mail: kkim@bop.gov
Affirmative Action Administrator **Tracey Kahoano** .... (215) 521-7395
E-mail: tkahoano@bop.gov
Computer Services Specialist **Darren Nguyen** .... (215) 521-7492
Correctional Programs Administrator **(Vacant)** .... (215) 521-7489
Correctional Programs Specialist **Tom Mulvey** .... (215) 521-7441
Correctional Services Administrator **(Vacant)** .... (215) 521-7450
Facilities Administrator **(Vacant)** .... (215) 521-7400
Food Services Administrator **Ronald Schreffler** .... (215) 521-7335
Health Services Administrator **Janet Bunts** .... (215) 521-7340
Human Resources Administrator **Camille Duchaussee** .... (215) 521-7360
E-mail: cxduchaussee@bop.gov

Cincinnati (OH) Residential Reentry Management Office
36 East Seventh Street, Suite 2107-A, Cincinnati, OH 45202-4458
Tel: (513) 684-2603 Fax: (513) 684-2590

Residential Reentry Manager **Christopher Paul** .... (513) 684-2603

New York (NY) Residential Reentry Management Office
80 29th Street, Brooklyn, NY 11232
Tel: (718) 840-4219 Fax: (718) 840-4207

Residential Reentry Specialist **Nicole Chisolm** .... (718) 840-4238
Community Corrections Specialist **(Vacant)** .... (718) 840-4219
Community Corrections Specialist **M. Reeder** .... (718) 840-4243
Contract Oversight Specialist **Maria E. Figueroa** .... (718) 840-4246
E-mail: mfigueroa@bop.gov
Residential Reentry Specialist **M. Reeder** .... (718) 840-4237
Residential Reentry Specialist **(Vacant)** .... (718) 840-4248

Philadelphia (PA) Residential Reentry Management Office
U.S. Custom House, Second and Chestnut Streets,
7th Floor, Philadelphia, PA 19106
Tel: (215) 521-7300 Fax: (215) 521-7486

Residential Reentry Manager **Chad Fultz** .... (215) 521-7465
Areas Covered: Eastern and Middle PA, NH, VT, CT, MA, ME, and RI.

Pittsburgh (PA) Residential Reentry Management Office
William S. Moorhead Federal Building, 1000 Liberty Avenue,
Room 1315, Pittsburgh, PA 15222
Tel: (412) 395-4740 Fax: (412) 395-4730

Residential Reentry Manager **Pamela Butler** .... (412) 395-4743
Residential Reentry Specialist **Raheem S. Garland** .... (412) 395-4740
Residential Reentry Specialist **Kathleen Gingell** .... (412) 395-4741
E-mail: kgingell@bop.gov

★ Presidential Appointment Requiring Senate Confirmation ☆ Presidential Appointment □ Schedule C Appointment ◇ Career Senior Foreign Service Appointment
● Career Senior Executive Service (SES) Appointment ○ Non-Career Senior Executive Service (SES) Appointment ■ Postal Career Executive Service

Pittsburgh (PA) Residential Reentry Management Office *(continued)*

Residential Reentry Specialist **(Vacant)** . . . . (412) 395-4744
Residential Reentry Specialist **(Vacant)** . . . . (412) 395-4740

Federal Correctional Institution - Allenwood [Medium Security] (FCI ALLENWOOD)
P.O. Box 2500, White Deer, PA 17887
Tel: (570) 547-7950 Fax: (570) 547-7751

Warden **Patricia Howard** . . . . (570) 547-7950
Executive Assistant **Christopher Brown** . . . . (570) 547-7950
Associate Warden (Industry) **(Vacant)** . . . . (570) 547-7950
Associate Warden (Programs) **Paul Gibson** . . . . (570) 547-7950
Chaplain **Brian Cieslukowski** . . . . (570) 547-7950
Food Services Administrator **Jacqueline Kennedy** . . . . . . (570) 547-7950
Health Services Administrator **James Potope** . . . . (570) 547-7950
Chief Corrections Supervisor **Lynn Hunter** . . . . (570) 547-7950
Education Supervisor **Nathaniel Yarnell** . . . . (570) 547-0963
Support Services Supervisor **Michael Constant** . . . . (570) 547-1990
Psychology Services Supervisor **Neal Kimble** . . . . (570) 547-0963
General Foreman **J. Tolliver** . . . . (570) 547-7950
Correctional Systems Manager **Brad Vegh** . . . . (570) 547-7950
Employee Services Manager **Tina Earnest** . . . . (570) 547-7950
Environment and Safety Manager **(Vacant)** . . . . (570) 547-0963
Unit Manager **Chris Angelini** . . . . (570) 547-7154
Case Management Coordinator **Kendahl Gainer** . . . . (570) 547-7950
Computer Services Manager **Kevin Gearheart** . . . . (570) 547-7950

Federal Correctional Institution - Berlin (NH) (FCI Berlin)
One Success Loop Road, Berlin, NH 03570
Tel: (603) 342-4000 Fax: (603) 342-4250
E-mail: ber/execassistant@bop.gov
Internet: http://www.bop.gov/locations/institutions/ber/

Warden **R. Hazelwood** . . . . (603) 342-4000
Education Supervisor **(Vacant)** . . . . (603) 342-4000

Federal Correctional Institution - Danbury (CT) (FCI DANBURY)
Route 37, Danbury, CT 06811-3099
Tel: (203) 743-6471 Tel: (700) 642-9441 Fax: (203) 312-5110

Warden **Herman Quay** . . . . (203) 743-6471
Executive Assistant **Lynne Kelly** . . . . (203) 743-6471
Associate Warden (Industry) **(Vacant)** . . . . (203) 743-6471
Associate Warden (Programs) **David E. Porter, Jr.** . . . . (203) 743-6471
Budget and Accounting Officer
Melonie Jaye Beacham . . . . (203) 743-6471
Food Service Administrator **William S. Rogers** . . . . (203) 743-6471
Health Services Administrator **Darin Daly** . . . . (203) 743-6471
Chief Correctional Supervisor **Thomas Peterson** . . . . (203) 743-6471
Education Supervisor **Tom Caravetta** . . . . (203) 743-6471
Special Investigative Supervisor **Mayland Langmaid** . . . . (203) 743-6471
Employee Services Manager **Michelle Tonic** . . . . (203) 743-6471
Facilities Manager **Bruce MacGregor** . . . . (203) 743-6471
Inmate Systems Manager **(Vacant)** . . . . (203) 743-6471
Safety Manager **Marvin Bundy** . . . . (203) 743-6471
E-mail: mbundy@bop.gov

Federal Correctional Institution - Elkton (OH) (FCI ELKTON)
8730 Scroggs Road, Elkton, OH 44432
P.O. Box 89, Elkton, OH 44415
Tel: (330) 420-6200 Fax: (330) 420-6436

Warden **Steven Merlak** . . . . (330) 420-6432
E-mail: smerlak@bop.gov
Computer Services Manager **Dave Beadnell** . . . . (330) 420-6200
E-mail: dbeadnell@bop.gov

Federal Correctional Institution - Fairton (NJ) (FCI FAIRTON)
P.O. Box 280, Fairton, NJ 08320
Tel: (856) 453-1177 Tel: (700) 298-1177 Fax: (856) 453-4015

Warden **Scott Young** . . . . (856) 453-1177
Fax: (856) 453-4186
Camp Administrator and Executive Assistant
Conrad Adameic . . . . (856) 453-1177

Federal Correctional Institution - Fairton (NJ) *(continued)*

Associate Warden (Operations) **Jeremy Nash** . . . . (856) 453-1177
Associate Warden (Programs) **Jamal Jamison** . . . . (856) 453-1177
Chief Correctional Supervisor **J.R. Morales** . . . . (856) 453-1177
Industries and Education Supervisor **Tammy Lynn** . . . . (856) 453-1177
Human Resources Manager **Nicole Tidwell** . . . . (856) 453-1177

DEPARTMENTS

Federal Correctional Institution - Fort Dix (NJ) (FCI FORT DIX)
P.O. Box 38, Joint Base McGuire-Dix-Lakehurst, NJ 08640
Tel: (609) 723-1100 Tel: (609) 724-0779 (East Facsimile)
Tel: (609) 723-2803 (West Facsimile)

Warden **David E. Ortig** . . . . (609) 723-1100 ext. 5100
Executive Assistant **Caryn Flowers** . . . . (609) 723-1100 ext. 5104
Warden's Secretary **Laura Coleman** . . . . (609) 723-1100 ext. 5101
E-mail: l1coleman@bop.gov
Associate Warden (Custody)
Marshall Grissom . . . . (609) 723-1100 ext. 6108
Associate Warden (Operations)
Kimberly Kodger . . . . (609) 723-1100 ext. 6108
Associate Warden (Programs)
Charles Smith . . . . (609) 723-1100 ext. 1103
Controller **George Steele** . . . . (609) 723-1100 ext. 5150
E-mail: gsteele@bop.gov
Staff Attorney **Christina Clark** . . . . (609) 723-1100 ext. 5388
E-mail: cmsaeha@bop.gov
Psychologist **Stacie Marantz** . . . . (609) 723-1100 ext. 1236
E-mail: smarantz@bop.gov
Food Service Administrator **Patrick Croker** . . . . (609) 723-1100 ext. 1243
Health Services Administrator
Travis Haczynski . . . . (609) 723-1100 ext. 1170
Recreation Supervisor **(Vacant)** . . . . (609) 723-1100 ext. 1320
Educational Supervisor **Brian Womack** . . . . (609) 723-1100 ext. 6728
UNICOR Associate Warden
Maurice Danzey . . . . (609) 723-1100 ext. 6107
UNICOR Computer Demanufacturing
Factory Manager **(Vacant)** . . . . (609) 723-1000 ext. 1358
Computer Service Manager **Jose Jimenez** . . . . . (609) 723-1100 ext. 1140
Correctional Services Manager **Andy Cruz** . . . . . (609) 723-1100 ext. 1109
Facilities Manager **(Vacant)** . . . . (609) 723-1100 ext. 6661
Human Resources Manager **Valerie Cross** . . . . . (609) 723-1100 ext. 5110
E-mail: vcross@bop.gov
Inmate Systems Manager **Edward Espinoza** . . . (609) 723-1100 ext. 6824
Safety Manager **Anthony Pizzo** . . . . (609) 723-1100 ext. 1477
Unit 1 Manager (East) **Raja Gilyard** . . . . (609) 723-1100 ext. 6824
Unit 2 Manager (East) **Robert Brinsom** . . . . (609) 723-1100 ext. 1321
Unit 3 Manager (East) **Benjamin O'Comb** . . . . . (609) 723-1100 ext. 1390
Unit 4 Manager (West) **Ralph Rodriguez** . . . . . . (609) 723-1100 ext. 6627
Unit 5 Manager (West) **(Vacant)** . . . . (609) 723-1100 ext. 6618
Unit 6 Manager (West) **(Vacant)** . . . . (609) 723-1100 ext. 6685
Case Management Coordinator (East)
Barbara Nevins . . . . (609) 723-1100 ext. 1199
E-mail: bnevins@bop.gov
Camp Unit Manager **Carlton Byrd** . . . . (609) 723-1100 ext. 4532
Trust Fund **Nakia Grimes** . . . . (609) 723-1100 ext. 5160
Disciplinary Hearing Officer **(Vacant)** . . . . (609) 723-1100 ext. 6815
Special Investigative Agent **(Vacant)** . . . . (609) 723-1100 ext. 6129
Contract Supervisor **Shannon Mutts** . . . . (609) 723-1100 ext. 5156

Federal Correctional Institution - Loretto (PA) (FCI LORETTO)
772 St. Joseph Street, Loretto, PA 15940
P.O. Box 1000, Loretto, PA 15940
Tel: (814) 472-4140 Fax: (814) 471-1660

Warden **Eric Bradley** . . . . (814) 472-4140
Associate Warden **Brent Taggart** . . . . (814) 472-4140
Business Administrator **Roberta Rodriguez** . . . . (814) 472-4140
E-mail: rrodriguez@bop.gov
Education: St Francis Col (PA) 1989 BS
Chief Psychologist **Matthew Robinowitz** . . . . (814) 472-4140
Food Service Administrator **Paul Homing** . . . . (814) 472-4140
Health Services Administrator **Norman Weidlich** . . . . (814) 472-4140
Chief Correctional Supervisor **Jason Berkihiser** . . . . (814) 472-4140
Education Supervisor **Ryan Barr** . . . . (814) 472-4140

(continued on next page)

★ Presidential Appointment Requiring Senate Confirmation ☆ Presidential Appointment □ Schedule C Appointment ◇ Career Senior Foreign Service Appointment
● Career Senior Executive Service (SES) Appointment ○ Non-Career Senior Executive Service (SES) Appointment ■ Postal Career Executive Service

DEPARTMENTS

Federal Correctional Institution - Loretto (PA) *(continued)*

Facilities Manager **John Noll** (814) 472-4140
Safety Manager **(Vacant)** (814) 472-4140
Unit Manager **Sean Miles** (814) 472-4140
Unit Manager **Kyle Bigart** (814) 472-4140
Case Management Coordinator **Heather Sposato** (814) 472-4140
Human Resources Manager **Chrystal Argenbright** (814) 472-4140 ext. 1418
E-mail: cargenbright@bop.gov
Computer Services **John Salyards** (814) 472-4140 ext. 1664

Federal Correctional Institution - McKean (PA) (FCI MCKEAN)

P.O. Box 5000, Bradford, PA 16701
Tel: (814) 362-8900

Warden (Acting) **Mark Williams** (814) 362-8900
Associate Operations Warden **J.F. Williams** (814) 362-8900
Associate Programs Warden **Mark Williams** (814) 362-8900
Business Administrator **Donna Moore** (814) 362-8900
Camp Administrator/Executive Assistant **Ian Healy** (814) 362-8900
Chief Correctional Supervisor **Michael Hall** (814) 362-8900
Food Service Administrator **Joby Rivera** (814) 362-8900
Health Services Administrator (Acting) **Scott Colson** (814) 362-8900
Human Resources Manager **Jennifer Sidon** (814) 362-8900
Education Supervisor **D.J. Whitmore** (814) 362-8900
Facilities Manager **Edward Fleeson** (814) 362-8900
Inmate Systems Manager **(Vacant)** (814) 362-8900
Safety Manager **Jason Tessena** (814) 362-8900
Unit A and B Manager **Emery Nelson** (814) 362-8900
Unit C and D Manager **(Vacant)** (814) 362-8900
Disciplinary Hearing Officer **(Vacant)** (814) 362-8900
Case Management Coordinator **Laura Lechien** (814) 362-8900
Camp Manager **Shaun Nink** (814) 362-8900
Computer Services Manager **Scott Colson** (814) 362-8900

Federal Correctional Institution - Otisville (NY) (FCI OTISVILLE)

Two Mile Drive, Otisville, NY 10963
P.O. Box 600, Otisville, NY 10963
Tel: (845) 386-6700 Fax: (845) 386-6703

• Warden **Barbara Von Blanckensee** (845) 386-6700 ext. 6701
Warden's Secretary **Amelia McDonald** (845) 386-6700 ext. 6702
Executive Assistant/Camp Administrator **Christopher Entzel** (845) 386-6700 ext. 6705
E-mail: otv/execassistant@bop.gov
Associate Warden (Operations) **Jorge L. Maldonado, Jr.** (845) 386-6700 ext. 6707
Education: Texas (El Paso)
Business Administrator **Coralee Glasspoole** (845) 386-6700 ext. 6802
Computer Services **William Gau** (845) 386-6700 ext. 6750
E-mail: bgau@bop.gov
Food Service Administrator **Charles Pavlov** (845) 386-6700 ext. 6884
Health Services Administrator **Bryan Walls** (845) 386-6700 ext. 6824
Chief Correctional Supervisor **Matthew Whinnery** (845) 386-6700 ext. 6753
Education Supervisor **Alicia Whinnery** (845) 386-6700 ext. 6763
Facilities Manager (Acting) **David Gottshall** (845) 386-6700 ext. 6777
Safety Manager **William Hugar** (845) 386-6700 ext. 6843
E-mail: whugar@bop.gov
Discipline Hearing Officer **(Vacant)** (845) 386-6700 ext. 6714
Employee Services Manager **Michelle Juerger** (845) 386-6700 ext. 6774
Case Management Coordinator **Gregory Salitis** (845) 386-6700 ext. 6711
Psychology Services **Adriana Restrepo** (845) 386-6700 ext. 6838
Religious Services **Rabbi A. Richter** (845) 386-6700 ext. 6808
Unit F/G **Ashley Cocho** (845) 386-6700 ext. 6867
Unit D/E **(Vacant)** (845) 386-6700 ext. 6860
Unit J **Kyle Lindsay** (845) 386-6700 ext. 6930

Federal Correctional Institution - Ray Brook (NY) (FCI RAY BROOK)

P.O. Box 300, Ray Brook, NY 12977
Tel: (518) 897-4000 Fax: (518) 897-4216

Warden **Mike Breckon** (518) 897-4000
Associate Warden (Operations) **Donna Attenhose** (518) 897-4031
Associate Warden (Programs) **Bruce Plumley** (518) 897-4030
Business Administrator **Travis W. Cayea** (518) 897-4058
Food Service Administrator **George Robinson** (518) 897-4120
Health Services Administrator **Kim Burdo** (518) 897-4101
Chief Correctional Supervisor **Patrick Delaney** (518) 897-4040
Education Supervisor **Scott Gladden** (518) 897-4160
Facilities Manager **Glen LaCroix** (518) 897-4130
Inmate Systems Manager **Doug Doty** (518) 897-4011
Safety Manager **Phil Hamel** (518) 897-4155
Discipline Hearing Officer **Michael Fulger** (518) 897-4020
Human Resources Manager **Valerie LaPoint** (518) 897-4070
Information Technology Manager **Daniel Bickford** (518) 897-4049

Federal Correctional Institution - Schuylkill (FCI SCHUYLKILL)

P.O. Box 700, Minersville, PA 17954
Tel: (570) 544-7100 Fax: (570) 544-7224

• Warden **Scott Finley** (570) 544-7100
Associate Warden (Programs) **Ken Gabrielson** (570) 544-7100
Associate Warden (Operations) **Michael Pacheco** (570) 544-7100
Business Administrator **Mark Rishel** (570) 544-7100
Executive Assistant **Ryan Miller** (570) 544-7100
Food Service Administrator **Suzanne Brown** (570) 544-7100
Health Services Administrator **Jeremy Simonson** (570) 544-7100
Chief Correctional Supervisor **Michael Miller** (570) 544-7100
Education Supervisor **Jennifer Reigel** (570) 544-7100
Facility Manager **Troy Hynicka** (570) 544-7100
Factory Manager **Gary Patraw** (570) 544-7100
Employee Services Manager **Lynn Dolo** (570) 544-7100
Case Management Coordinator **Pati Manbeck** (570) 544-7100

Federal Detention Center - Philadelphia (PA) (FDC PHILADELPHIA)

700 Arch Street, Philadelphia, PA 19106
Tel: (215) 521-4000 Fax: (215) 521-7220

Warden **David Ortiz** (215) 521-4000

Federal Medical Center - Devens (MA) (FMC DEVENS)

42 Patton Road, Devens, MA 01432
P.O. Box 880, Devens, MA 01432
Tel: (978) 796-1000 Fax: (978) 796-1118

Warden **Jeff Grondolsky** (978) 796-1000
Associate Warden (Medical) **Richard H. Russell** (978) 796-1000
Associate Warden (Operations) **(Vacant)** (978) 796-1000
Associate Warden (Programs) **(Vacant)** (978) 796-1000

Low Security Correctional Institution - Allenwood (FCI Allenwood Low)

P.O. Box 1500, White Deer, PA 17887
Tel: (570) 547-1990 Fax: (570) 547-0342

Warden **Douglas White** (570) 547-1990 ext. 4100
E-mail: dwhite@bop.gov
Associate Warden **Eric Rokosky** (570) 547-1990
Chaplain **Brian Cieslukowski** (570) 547-1990 ext. 4550
Psychology Services Chief **Neal Kimble** (570) 547-0963
Food Services Administrator **Jacqueline Kennedy** (570) 547-0963
Health Services Administrator **Bret Brosious** (570) 547-1990 ext. 4600
Chief Correctional Supervisor **(Vacant)** (570) 547-1990
Education Supervisor **Nathaniel Yarnell** (570) 547-1990
Inmate Systems Supervisor **Don Wasilko** (570) 547-1990
Trust Fund Supervisor **Michael Constant** (570) 547-1990
Employee Services Manager **Tina Earnest** (570) 547-7950
Facilities Manager **Vernon Morgan** (570) 547-0963 ext. 6250
Safety Manager **Kevin Seiler** (570) 547-0963
E-mail: kseiler@bop.gov
UNICOR Factory Manager **Greg Holmes** (570) 547-1990 ext. 5652

★ Presidential Appointment Requiring Senate Confirmation ☆ Presidential Appointment ☐ Schedule C Appointment ◇ Career Senior Foreign Service Appointment
● Career Senior Executive Service (SES) Appointment ○ Non-Career Senior Executive Service (SES) Appointment ■ Postal Career Executive Service

Low Security Correctional Institution - Allenwood *(continued)*

Brady Unit Manager **(Vacant)** . . . . . (570) 547-1990
Gregg Unit Manager **(Vacant)** . . . . . (570) 547-1990
Lycoming Unit Manager **Matt Rodarmel** . . . . . (570) 547-1990 ext. 4430
Union Unit Manager **Matt Rodarmel** . . . . . (570) 547-1990 ext. 4440
Case Management Coordinator
Bruce Beaver . . . . . (570) 547-1990 ext. 4400

Metropolitan Correctional Center - New York (NY) (MCC NEW YORK)

150 Park Row, New York, NY 10007-1779
Tel: (646) 836-6300 Fax: (646) 836-7751

• Warden **Lamine N'Diaye** . . . . . (646) 836-6423
Executive Assistant **Lee Plourde** . . . . . (646) 836-6496
Associate Warden (Operations) **Shirley Skipper-Scott** . . . (646) 836-6451
Associate Warden (Programs) **Kimo Elrahed** . . . . . (646) 836-6452
Supervisory Attorney **Adam Johnson** . . . . . (646) 836-6455
E-mail: a10johnson@bop.gov
Food Service Administrator **Rocco Lupo** . . . . . (646) 836-6344
Health Service Administrator **Hossam Georgy** . . . . . (646) 836-6445
Chief Correctional Supervisor **Douglas Bailey** . . . . . (646) 836-6448
Supervisor of Education **Thomas Volpini** . . . . . (646) 836-6472
Facilities Manager **Charles Bekgran** . . . . . (646) 836-7661
Safety Compliance Specialist **(Vacant)** . . . . . (646) 836-6374
Human Resources Manager **Barbara Latham** . . . . . (646) 836-6312
E-mail: blatham@bop.gov
Disciplinary Hearing Officer **John Banks** . . . . . (845) 386-6714
Computer Services Manager **Anil Kumar** . . . . . (646) 836-6459
E-mail: akumar@bop.gov Fax: (646) 836-7686
Computer Specialist **Elizabeth Rivera** . . . . . (646) 836-6323
E-mail: esilva@bop.gov Fax: (646) 836-7686

Metropolitan Detention Center - Brooklyn (NY) (MDC BROOKLYN)

80 29th Street, Brooklyn, NY 11232
Mail: P.O. Box 329001, Brooklyn, NY 11232 (Staff mail)
Tel: (718) 840-4200 Fax: (718) 840-5005

Warden **Herman Quay** . . . . . (718) 840-4200
Warden's Secretary **(Vacant)** . . . . . (718) 840-4200
Associate Warden (Administration) **Eleazar Garcia** . . . . . (718) 840-4200
E-mail: e8garcia@bop.gov
Associate Warden (Operations) **Martin Licom-Vitale** . . . . . (718) 840-4200
Associate Warden (Programs) **(Vacant)** . . . . . (718) 840-4200
Captain **Jonathan "J.J." White** . . . . . (718) 840-4200
Chief Psychologist **Corrine Ortega** . . . . . (718) 840-4200
Staff Psychologist **Ashley Jenkins** . . . . . (718) 840-4200
Food Service Administrator **Mary Lou Comer** . . . . . (718) 840-4200
Health Services Administrator **Gerard Traver** . . . . . (718) 840-4200
Education Supervisor **Michelle M. Gantt** . . . . . (718) 840-4200
Facilities Manager **(Vacant)** . . . . . (718) 840-4200
Employee Services Manager **Sandra Barns** . . . . . (718) 840-4200
Inmate Systems Manager
Samantha O'Brien-Lakeram . . . . . (718) 840-4200
Safety Manager **Andrew Butler** . . . . . (718) 840-4200
E-mail: abutler@bop.gov
Unit Manager (A/C/D) **(Vacant)** . . . . . (718) 840-4200
Unit Manager (B) **James Childeress** . . . . . (718) 840-4200
Unit Manager (E/H) **(Vacant)** . . . . . (718) 840-4200
Unit Manager (G/I) **(Vacant)** . . . . . (718) 840-4200
Unit Manager (J/K) **Jermaine Wilkins** . . . . . (718) 840-4200

U.S. Penitentiary - Allenwood (USP ALLENWOOD)

P.O. Box 3500, White Deer, PA 17887
Tel: (570) 547-0963 Fax: (570) 547-9201

Warden **Jean Beasley** . . . . . (570) 547-0963
Executive Assistant (Acting) **Nathan Mosier** . . . . . (570) 547-0963
Associate Warden (Operations) **Paul Gibson** . . . . . (570) 547-0963
Chief Correctional Supervisor **(Vacant)** . . . . . (570) 547-0963
Public Information Officer **(Vacant)** . . . . . (570) 547-0963
Business Manager **Nathan Mosier** . . . . . (570) 547-0963

U.S. Penitentiary - Canaan (PA) (USP Canaan)

3057 Easton Turnpike, Waymart, PA 18472
Tel: (570) 488-8000 Tel: (570) 488-8130
E-mail: caa/execassistant@bop.gov

Warden **Juan Baltazar** . . . . . (570) 488-8000
Education Supervisor **Tanya Kalix** . . . . . (570) 488-8000
Executive Assistant **Paul Gibson** . . . . . (570) 488-8000

U.S. Penitentiary - Lewisburg (PA) (USP LEWISBURG)

2400 Robert F. Miller Drive, Lewisburg, PA 17837
P.O. Box 1000, Lewisburg, PA 17837
Tel: (570) 523-1251 Fax: (570) 522-7745

• Warden **David J. Ebbert** . . . . . (570) 523-1251
Associate Warden (Operations) **Brian Lammer** . . . . . (570) 523-1251
Associate Warden (Programs) **Danon Colbert** . . . . . (570) 523-1251
Camp Administrator/Executive Assistant
Shawn Barlett . . . . . (570) 523-1251
Food Administrator **Patrick Ramirez** . . . . . (570) 523-1251
Health Services Administrator **Steve Brown** . . . . . (570) 523-1251
Chief Correctional Supervisor **Jay Rhodes** . . . . . (570) 523-1251
Education Supervisor **Christine Legrand** . . . . . (570) 523-1251
Facilities Manager **Kenneth Neuhard** . . . . . (570) 523-1251
Inmate Systems Manager and Case Management
Coordinator **Jessica Reibsome** . . . . . (570) 523-1251
Safety Manager **Ron Hicks** . . . . . (570) 523-1251
E-mail: rhicks@bop.gov
Personnel Officer **Donald Caribardi** . . . . . (570) 523-1251

South Central Region

344 Marine Forces Drive, Grand Prairie, TX 75051
Tel: (972) 730-8600 Fax: (972) 730-8809
Areas Covered: AR, LA, NM, OK, TX

• Regional Director **J.F. Coraway** . . . . . (972) 730-8600
Executive Assistant **(Vacant)** . . . . . (972) 730-8600
Administrative Officer to Regional Director
Michelle Tobin . . . . . (972) 730-8600
Deputy Regional Director **Andrew Ciolli** . . . . . (972) 730-8600
Western Sector Administrator for Residential Reentry
David Dwyer . . . . . (972) 730-8600
Legal Counsel **Jason Sickler** . . . . . (972) 730-8600
Comptroller **Art Sturges** . . . . . (972) 730-8600
Equal Employment Manager **M. Irizarry** . . . . . (972) 730-8600
Chaplaincy Services **(Vacant)** . . . . . (972) 730-8600
Computer Services **Ken Murell** . . . . . (972) 730-8600
Correctional Programs **Jefffrey L. Baney** . . . . . (972) 730-8600
Correctional Services **Alan Cohen** . . . . . (972) 730-8600
Facilities **Donald Hewellyn** . . . . . (972) 730-8600
Food Services **Julie Andino** . . . . . (972) 730-8600
Health Systems **Spencer Smith** . . . . . (972) 730-8600
E-mail: s6smith@bop.gov
Human Resources **Carmen Guajardo** . . . . . (972) 730-8600
E-mail: cguajardo@bop.gov
Psychology Services **(Vacant)** . . . . . (972) 730-8600
Regional Emergency Preparedness Officer
Patrick Wise . . . . . (972) 730-8600
Regional Reentry Affairs Coordinator **Linda Serrano** . . . . (972) 730-8600
Regional Trust Fund Administrator **(Vacant)** . . . . . (972) 730-8600

South Central Region Residential Reentry Office

344 Marine Forces Drive, Grand Prairie, TX 75051
Tel: (972) 730-8600 Fax: (972) 730-8809
Areas Covered: LA, NM, OK, TX

Regional Residential Reentry Administrator
David Dwyer . . . . . (972) 730-8600
Residential Reentry Specialist **(Vacant)** . . . . . (972) 730-8600
Community Transition Psychologist **(Vacant)** . . . . . (972) 730-8600
Transitional Drug Abuse Treatment Coordinator
Michael Nichols . . . . . (972) 730-8600
Transitional Drug Abuse Treatment Specialist
Christine Escobedo . . . . . (972) 730-8600
Transitional Drug Abuse Treatment Specialist
Stacie Rimmer . . . . . (972) 730-8600

(continued on next page)

★ Presidential Appointment Requiring Senate Confirmation ☆ Presidential Appointment ☐ Schedule C Appointment ◇ Career Senior Foreign Service Appointment
● Career Senior Executive Service (SES) Appointment ○ Non-Career Senior Executive Service (SES) Appointment ■ Postal Career Executive Service

DEPARTMENTS

South Central Region Residential Reentry Office *(continued)*

Transitional Drug Abuse Treatment Technician
Nikki Kinnick .... (972) 730-8600

Dallas (TX) Residential Reentry Management Office (CCM DALLAS)
344 Marine Forces Drive, Grand Prairie, TX 75051
Tel: (972) 730-8600 Fax: (972) 730-8838

Residential Reentry Manager **Luz Lujan** .... (214) 224-3517
Administrative Assistant **Teri Martin** .... (972) 730-8600
Residential Reentry Contract Oversight Specialist
Stacy Hollister .... (214) 224-3650
E-mail: shollister@bop.gov
Residential Reentry Contract Oversight Specialist
(Vacant) .... (214) 224-3519
Residential Reentry Specialist **Candice Girouard** .... (972) 730-8600
Residential Reentry Specialist **Gigi Mullins** .... (972) 730-8600
Residential Reentry Specialist **(Vacant)** .... (972) 730-8600

San Antonio (TX) Residential Reentry Management Office
727 East Durango, Room B-138, San Antonio, TX 78206
Tel: (210) 472-6225 Fax: (210) 472-6224

Residential Reentry Manager **LaTanya Robinson** .... (210) 472-6220
Deputy Residential Reentry Specialist
Angela Miller-Kelley .... (210) 472-4507
Residential Reentry Specialist **Martha Boyd** .... (210) 472-6275
Education: Hawaii Pacific 1993 BSBA
Residential Reentry Specialist **Enrique Cortez** .... (210) 472-6275
Residential Reentry Specialist **Erin Gostocmzik** .... (210) 472-6278
Residential Reentry Specialist **Maria Ortega** .... (210) 472-4504
Residential Reentry Specialist **Katy Solis** .... (210) 472-6277
E-mail: ksolis@bop.gov
Residential Reentry Specialist **Enrique Trevino** .... (210) 472-6279
E-mail: etrevino@bop.gov
Residential Reentry Specialist **(Vacant)** .... (210) 472-6319
Residential Reentry Specialist **(Vacant)** .... (210) 472-4500
Administrative Assistant **Susan Gonzales** .... (210) 472-6320
Case Manager **(Vacant)** .... (210) 472-4505
Case Manager **(Vacant)** .... (210) 472-6324
Contract Oversight Specialist **(Vacant)** .... (210) 472-6225

Federal Correctional Complex - Beaumont (TX) (FCC BEAUMONT)
5560 Knauth Road, Beaumont, TX 77705

Warden (Low Security) **Rachel Chapa** .... (409) 727-8172
P.O. Box 26025, Beaumont, TX 77720-6025 Fax: (409) 626-3500
E-mail: rchapa@bop.gov
Warden (Medium Security) **Dallas B. Jones** .... (409) 727-0101
P.O. Box 26045, Beaumont, TX 77720-6045 Fax: (409) 720-5000
E-mail: djones@bop.gov
Warden (U.S. Penitentiary - High Security) **(Vacant)** .... (409) 727-8188
P.O. Box 26035, Beaumont, TX 77720-6035 Fax: (409) 626-3700
E-mail: bmpiexecassistant@bop.gov

Federal Correctional Complex - Forrest City (AR) (FCC FORREST CITY)
P.O. Box 7000, Forrest City, AR 72336
Tel: (870) 494-4200 Fax: (870) 494-4496

● Warden **C. V. Rivera** .... (870) 494-4200 ext. 4207
Executive Assistant **Catalina Rodriguez** .... (870) 494-4200 ext. 4206

Federal Correctional Institution - Bastrop (TX) (FCI BASTROP)
1341 Highway 95 North, Bastrop, TX 78602
Mail: P.O. Box 730, Bastrop, TX 78602
Tel: (512) 321-3903 Fax: (512) 304-0117

Warden **Ronnie Myers** .... (512) 321-3903
Executive Assistant **Tom Barbee** .... (512) 321-3903
Associate Warden (Industries and Education) **(Vacant)** .... (512) 321-3903
Associate Warden (Programs) **Crystal Zerr** .... (512) 321-3903
Business Administrator **Gailene Gambol** .... (512) 321-3903
Food Service Administrator **Anthony Mendoza** .... (512) 321-3903
Health Services Administrator **Thomas Powell** .... (512) 321-3903
Satellite Operations Administrator **Tom Barbee** .... (512) 321-3903

Federal Correctional Institution - Bastrop (TX) *(continued)*

Chief Correctional Supervisor **John Grigsby** .... (512) 321-3903
Computer Services Manager **(Vacant)** .... (512) 321-3903
Education Supervisor **Shawn Mikeska** .... (512) 321-3903
Employee Services Manager **Sandra Paniagua** .... (512) 321-3903
Facilities Manager **Jamie Ehresman** .... (512) 321-3903
Safety Manager **(Vacant)** .... (512) 321-3903
UNICOR Business Manager **Marsha Flores** .... (512) 321-3903
UNICOR Factory Manager **Vance Hoffman** .... (512) 321-3903
UNICOR Quality Assurance Manager **Vince Bush** .... (512) 321-3903
Case Management Coordinator **Francene Helaire** .... (512) 321-3903
Supervisory Chaplain **Erich Stafford** .... (512) 321-3903

Federal Correctional Institution - Big Spring (TX) (FCI BIG SPRING)
1900 Simler Avenue, Big Spring, TX 79720-7799
Tel: (432) 466-2300

Warden **Jorge Castaneda** .... (432) 466-2300
Executive Assistant **Chris Willoughby** .... (432) 466-2300
Associate Warden **Scott Kellman** .... (432) 466-2300
Business Manager **Tommy Martinez** .... (432) 466-2300
Camp Administrator **Chris Willoughby** .... (432) 466-2300
Food Service Administrator **Javier Salinas** .... (432) 466-2300
Health Services Administrator **Teleasa Crnkovich** .... (432) 466-2300
Chief Correctional Supervisor **C.C. Ward** .... (432) 466-2300
Education Supervisor **Christopher Brammer** .... (432) 466-2300
E-mail: cbrammer@bop.gov
Computer Services Manager **Jeff Harwood** .... (432) 466-2300
E-mail: jharwood@bop.gov
Correctional Systems Manager **Kenneth Teters** .... (432) 466-2300
Human Resource Manager **Oscar Natividad** .... (432) 466-2402
E-mail: onatividad@bop.gov
Facilities Manager **Kenneth Patrick** .... (432) 466-2300
Safety Manager **(Vacant)** .... (432) 466-2300
Psychology Services **Dr. Anne Tubb** .... (432) 466-2300
E-mail: atubb@bop.gov
Religious Services Chaplain **Carlos Davantes** .... (432) 466-2300
Case Management Coordinator **Mack Word** .... (432) 466-2300
E-mail: mword@bop.gov

Federal Correctional Institution - El Reno (OK) (FCI EL RENO)
Highway 66 West, El Reno, OK 73036
P.O. Box 1000, El Reno, OK 73036-1000
Tel: (405) 262-4875 Fax: (405) 319-7626

● Warden **Thomas J. Scarantino** .... (405) 262-4875
Associate Warden (Industries) **(Vacant)** .... (405) 262-4875
Associate Warden (Programs) **Bradley Greilick** .... (405) 262-4875
Associate Warden (Operations) **Bannon Grady** .... (405) 262-4875
Business Administrator **Leah Rawlins** .... (405) 262-4875
Camp Administrator **Gene Albert** .... (405) 262-4875
Food Service Administrator **Shannon Colbert** .... (405) 262-4875
Health Services Administrator **Deborah Aynes** .... (405) 262-4875
Chief Correctional Supervisor **Matthew Jackson** .... (405) 262-4875
Education Supervisor **Scott McCutchan** .... (405) 262-4875
Human Resources Manager **Janice Humbertson** .... (405) 262-4875
Facilities Manager **Mike Herrell** .... (405) 262-4875
Farm Manager **Jeff Ropp** .... (405) 262-4875
Case Management Coordinator **Joel Rogalsky** .... (405) 262-4875
Safety Officer **Corey Ryans** .... (405) 262-4875
E-mail: cryans@bop.gov
Chief Psychologist **Amy Mayberry** .... (405) 262-4875
Chaplain **Jeffrey Wright** .... (405) 262-4875

Federal Correctional Institution - Fort Worth (TX) (FCI FORT WORTH)
3150 Horton Road, Fort Worth, TX 76119-5996
Tel: (817) 534-8400 Fax: (817) 413-3350

Warden **(Vacant)** .... (817) 413-3000
Executive Assistant **(Vacant)** .... (817) 413-3005
Associate Warden (Operations) **Albert Quintero** .... (817) 413-3001
Associate Warden (Programs) **Miguel Gonzalez** .... (817) 413-3002

★ Presidential Appointment Requiring Senate Confirmation ☆ Presidential Appointment ☐ Schedule C Appointment ◇ Career Senior Foreign Service Appointment
● Career Senior Executive Service (SES) Appointment ○ Non-Career Senior Executive Service (SES) Appointment ■ Postal Career Executive Service

Federal Correctional Institution - Fort Worth (TX) *(continued)*

Captain **Jamie Bengford** . . . . . (817) 413-3011
Chief Psychologist **Dr. Marti Carlson** . . . . . (817) 413-3013
E-mail: mcarlson@bop.gov
Business Administrator **(Vacant)** . . . . . (817) 413-3010
Case Management Coordinator **(Vacant)** . . . . . (817) 413-3148
Food Service Administrator **(Vacant)** . . . . . (817) 413-3150
Health Services Administrator **(Vacant)** . . . . . (817) 413-3400
Education Supervisor **Jennifer Tripp** . . . . . (817) 413-3082
Facility Manager **James Hawley** . . . . . (817) 413-3163
Human Resources Manager **(Vacant)** . . . . . (817) 413-3016
Safety Manager **Darnell Crawford** . . . . . (817) 413-3160
Computer Services Manager **Kathy Humphries** . . . . . (817) 413-3029

Federal Correctional Institution - La Tuna (FCI LA TUNA)

8500 Doniphan, Anthony, TX 79821
Mail: P.O. Box 1000, Anthony, TX 79821
Tel: (915) 791-9000 Fax: (915) 791-9858

Warden **Scott Nicklin** . . . . . (915) 791-9000 ext. 213
E-mail: snicklin@bop.gov
Executive Assistant **Johnny Chavez** . . . . . (915) 791-9000 ext. 215
Associate Warden (Operations) **Sandra Hijar** . . . . . (915) 564-2100
Associate Warden (Programs) **(Vacant)** . . . . . (915) 791-9000 ext. 314
Food Service Administrator (Acting)
Peter Kipriadis . . . . . (915) 791-9000 ext. 160
Health Services Administrator **Kelly Pierce** . . . . . (915) 791-9000 ext. 112
Industries Superintendent **(Vacant)** . . . . . (915) 791-9000 ext. 387
Chief Correctional Supervisor
Kenneth Hoover . . . . . (915) 791-9000 ext. 312
Education Supervisor **John Daley** . . . . . (915) 791-9000 ext. 350
Inmate Systems Specialist and Case
Management Coordinator **Scott Garland** . . . . . (915) 791-9000 ext. 244
Business Administrator **Anita Munoz** . . . . . (915) 791-9000 ext. 207
Facilities Manager **Carlos Gomez** . . . . . (915) 791-9000 ext. 372
Information Technology Manager
Joseph Waggoner . . . . . (915) 791-9000 ext. 158
Safety Manager **Delfino Cuellar** . . . . . (915) 791-9000 ext. 200
Psychology Services **Julia Landucci** . . . . . (915) 791-9000 ext. 254
Religious Services Chaplain **Carey Lane** . . . . . (915) 791-9000 ext. 275

Federal Correctional Institution - Oakdale (LA) (FCI OAKDALE)

P.O. Box 5050, Oakdale, LA 71463
Tel: (318) 335-4070 Tel: (318) 215-2500 Fax: (318) 215-2688

Warden **(Vacant)** . . . . . (318) 335-4070
Executive Assistant **(Vacant)** . . . . . (318) 335-4070
Associate Warden **Dean Peterson** . . . . . (318) 335-4070
Associate Warden **Paul Kelly** . . . . . (318) 335-4070
Associate Warden **Steve Merandino** . . . . . (318) 335-4070
Business Administrator **Lane West** . . . . . (318) 335-4070
Food Service Administrator **Cassandra Thomas** . . . . . (318) 335-4070
Health Services Administrator **Heather Howard** . . . . . (318) 335-4070
Industry Superintendent **(Vacant)** . . . . . (318) 335-4070
Chief Correctional Supervisor **(Vacant)** . . . . . (318) 335-4070
Education Supervisor **Charlotte Wilson** . . . . . (318) 335-4070
Employee Services Manager **Rickey Galloway** . . . . . (318) 335-4070
Facilities Manager **Charles Hoyt** . . . . . (318) 335-4070
Inmate Systems Manager **Milton Clayton** . . . . . (318) 335-4070
Safety Manager **Jeremy Wheat** . . . . . (318) 335-4070

Federal Correctional Institution - Seagoville (TX) (FCI SEAGOVILLE)

2113 North Highway 175, Seagoville, TX 75159
Tel: (972) 287-2911 Fax: (972) 287-5466

Warden **Martha Underwood** . . . . . (972) 287-2911 ext. 4003
E-mail: munderwood@bop.gov
Executive Assistant (Acting) **J. Hovden** . . . . . (972) 287-2911 ext. 4002
Associate Warden **D.J. Albert** . . . . . (972) 287-2911
Associate Warden (Operations)
Gerardo Rosalez . . . . . (972) 287-2911 ext. 4004
Chief Correctional Supervisor **M. Crittle** . . . . . (972) 287-2911 ext. 4009
Chief Psychologist **L. Carter** . . . . . (972) 287-2911 ext. 4411

Federal Correctional Institution - Seagoville (TX) *(continued)*

CMC/Inmate Systems Manager
Rhonda Kennedy . . . . . (972) 287-2911 ext. 4006
Computer Services Manager **(Vacant)** . . . . . (972) 287-2911 ext. 4042
Employee Services Manager **(Vacant)** . . . . . (972) 287-2911 ext. 4401
Education Supervisor **J. Hovden** . . . . . (972) 287-2911 ext. 4033
Facilities Manager **S. Jefferson** . . . . . (972) 287-2911 ext. 6777
Food Service Administrator **D. Lynn** . . . . . (972) 287-2911 ext. 4080
Health Services Administrator **A. Freeman** . . . . . (972) 287-2911 ext. 4411
Quality Assurance Manager **Richard Clark** . . . . . (972) 287-2911 ext. 4435
Safety Officer **(Vacant)** . . . . . (972) 287-2911 ext. 4430
Textile Factory Manager **(Vacant)** . . . . . (972) 287-2911 ext. 4434

Federal Correctional Institution - Texarkana (TX) (FCI TEXARKANA)

P.O. Box 9500, Texarkana, TX 75505-9500
Tel: (903) 838-4587 Tel: (903) 255-1100 Fax: (903) 223-4417

Warden **Linda Geter** . . . . . (903) 838-4587
Executive Assistant **(Vacant)** . . . . . (903) 838-4587
Associate Warden **Richard Luna** . . . . . (903) 838-4587
E-mail: rluna@bop.gov
Business Manager **Randy Garrison** . . . . . (903) 838-4587
Camp Administrator **(Vacant)** . . . . . (903) 838-4587
Food Service Administrator **Kathy Stockwell** . . . . . (903) 838-4587
Health Services Administrator **Mark Rayburn** . . . . . (903) 838-4587
Case Management Coordinator
Frances Blackman-Conston . . . . . (903) 838-4587
Chief Correctional Supervisor **(Vacant)** . . . . . (903) 838-4587
Education Supervisor **Matthew Clementz** . . . . . (903) 838-4587
Facilities Manager **Kevin Walker** . . . . . (903) 838-4587
Employee Services Manager **Shelly Chogoya** . . . . . (903) 838-4587
Safety Manager **Albert Hayden** . . . . . (903) 838-4587
Computer Services Manager **Isaac Kunz** . . . . . (903) 838-4587

Federal Correctional Institution - Three Rivers (TX) (FCI THREE RIVERS)

P.O. Box 4000, Three Rivers, TX 78071
Tel: (361) 786-3576 Fax: (361) 786-5069

Warden **Larry R. Shults** . . . . . (361) 786-3576
E-mail: lrshults@bop.gov
Executive Assistant **(Vacant)** . . . . . (361) 786-3576
Associate Warden (Operations) **Ruben S. Salinas** . . . . . (361) 786-3576
Associate Warden (Programs) **Stanley Lovett** . . . . . (361) 786-3576
Controller **Eva Farias** . . . . . (361) 786-3576
E-mail: efarias@bop.gov
Camp Administrator **(Vacant)** . . . . . (361) 786-3576
Food Service Administrator **Nathaniel Fomby** . . . . . (361) 786-3576
Health Services Administrator **Shane Terrell** . . . . . (361) 786-3576
Chief Correctional Supervisor **John Whitehouse** . . . . . (361) 786-3576
Computer Services Manager **Nicole Wilson** . . . . . (361) 786-3576
E-mail: nxwilson@bop.gov
Education Supervisor **Charles Lockey** . . . . . (361) 786-3576
Employee Services Manager **Pamela Dotson** . . . . . (361) 786-3576
E-mail: pdotson@bop.gov
Case Management Coordinator **Charles Hubbard** . . . . . (361) 786-3576
Safety Manager **Nicholas Barcomb** . . . . . (361) 786-3576
E-mail: nbarcomb@bop.gov

Federal Detention Center - Houston (TX) (FDC HOUSTON)

1200 Texas Avenue, Houston, TX 77002
Mail: P.O. Box 526245, Houston, TX 77052
Tel: (713) 221-5400 Fax: (713) 229-4200

Warden **Wayne Nolan Smith** . . . . . (713) 221-5400
Education Supervisor **Roberto Bustamante** . . . . . (713) 221-5400

Federal Correctional Institution Oakdale (LA) II (FCI OAKDALE II)

P.O. Box 5060, Oakdale, LA 71463-5060
Tel: (318) 335-4466 Tel: (318) 215-2000 Fax: (318) 215-2160

Warden **(Vacant)** . . . . . (318) 335-4466
Executive Assistant/Camp Administrator **(Vacant)** . . . . . (318) 335-4466
Associate Warden **Dean Peterson** . . . . . (318) 335-4466

(continued on next page)

★ Presidential Appointment Requiring Senate Confirmation ☆ Presidential Appointment □ Schedule C Appointment ◇ Career Senior Foreign Service Appointment
● Career Senior Executive Service (SES) Appointment ○ Non-Career Senior Executive Service (SES) Appointment ■ Postal Career Executive Service

Federal Correctional Institution Oakdale (LA) II *(continued)*

Associate Warden **Paul Kelly** .... (318) 335-4466
Associate Warden **Steve Merendino** .... (318) 335-4466
Business Administrator **Lane West** .... (318) 335-4466
Captain **Jeffrey Rex** .... (318) 335-4466
Chaplain **Olando Madrid** .... (318) 335-4466
Chief Psychologist **Barbara Moorehead** .... (318) 335-4466
Computer Services Manager **Joseph Pitre** .... (318) 335-4466
Education Supervisor **Charlotte Wilson** .... (318) 335-4466
Employee Services Manager **Rickey Galloway** .... (318) 335-4466
Facilities Manager **Charles Hoyt** .... (318) 335-4466
Food Service Administrator **Cassandra Thomas** .... (318) 335-4466
Health Services Administrator **Heather Howard** .... (318) 335-4466
Industries Supervisor **Cynthia Cotton** .... (318) 335-4466
Safety Manager **Jeremy Wheat** .... (318) 335-4466
Alexandria and Ville Platte Unit Manager
Alice Diaz-Hemandez .... (318) 335-4466
Oberlin Unit Manager **Ron Lee** .... (318) 335-4466
Case Management Coordinator **Antonia Ashford** .... (318) 335-4466

Federal Medical Center - Carswell (TX) (FMC CARSWELL)

Building 3000, J Street, Fort Worth, TX 76127
P.O. Box 27066, Fort Worth, TX 76127
Tel: (817) 782-4000 Fax: (817) 782-4875

● Warden **Jody R. Upton** .... (817) 782-4000

Federal Prison Camp - Bryan (TX) (FPC BRYAN)

1100 Ursuline, Bryan, TX 77805
P.O. Box 2197, Bryan, TX 77805
Tel: (979) 823-1879 Fax: (979) 821-3316

Warden **Marne Boyle** .... (979) 823-1879 ext. 3419
E-mail: mboyle@bop.gov
Secretary **Pam Carter** .... (979) 823-1879 ext. 3419
Associate Warden **Robert M. Haro** .... (979) 823-1879 ext. 3422
Controller **Linda Hill** .... (979) 823-1879 ext. 3440
Chief Psychologist **Dr. Ashley Noble** .... (979) 823-1879 ext. 3561
Chief Chaplain **Jordan May** .... (979) 823-1879 ext. 3526
Captain **(Vacant)** .... (979) 823-1879 ext. 3480
Food Service Administrator **Arthur Davila** .... (979) 823-1879 ext. 3602
Health Services Administrator
Cassidy Brown .... (979) 823-1879 ext. 3507
Education Supervisor **Erin Valentine** .... (979) 823-1879 ext. 3537
Employee Services Manager **(Vacant)** .... (979) 823-1879 ext. 3430
Fax: (979) 260-9539
Facilities Manager **Jeff Smith** .... (979) 823-1879 ext. 3620
Inmate Systems Manager **Richard Martinez** .... (979) 823-1879 ext. 3477
Fax: (979) 775-5765
Environmental and Safety Compliance
Administrator **Heather Matthews** .... (979) 823-1879 ext. 3462
Brazos Unit Manager **Kent Miles** .... (979) 823-1879 ext. 3700
Madison/RDAP Unit Manager
Roselyn Hammond .... (979) 823-1879 ext. 3732
Case Management Coordinator
Shannon Gibson .... (979) 823-1879 ext. 3740
Computer Services Manager **Ottia Sills** .... (979) 823-1879 ext. 3436
Trust Fund Supervisor **Mitch Luedecke** .... (979) 823-1879 ext. 3457

Federal Satellite Low La Tuna - El Paso (TX)

P.O. Box 1000, 8500 Doniphan Rd., Anthony, TX 88021
Tel: (915) 564-2100 Fax: (915) 564-2291

Warden **Scott Nicklin** .... (915) 791-9000 ext. 213
Associate Warden **Tim Vaught** .... (915) 791-9000 ext. 316
E-mail: t1vaught@bop.gov
Associate Warden **Sandra Hijar** .... (915) 791-9000 ext. 314
E-mail: shijar@bop.gov

Federal Transfer Center - Oklahoma City (OK) (FTC OKLAHOMA CITY)

7410 South MacArthur, P.O. Box 898802,
Oklahoma City, OK 73189-8802
Tel: (405) 682-4075 Fax: (405) 680-4043

Warden **John B. Fox** .... (405) 682-4075

Federal Transfer Center - Oklahoma City (OK) *(continued)*

Education Supervisor **Vicki Abner** .... (405) 682-4075

U.S. Penitentiary - Pollock (LA) (USP POLLOCK)

1000 Airbase Road, Pollock, LA 71467
P.O. Box 1000, Pollock, LA 71467
Tel: (318) 561-5300 Fax: (318) 561-5391

Warden **Calvin Johnson** .... (318) 561-5300

Correctional Institution - Cibola County (NM) (CI Cibola County)

2000 Cibola Loop, Milan, NM 87021
Tel: (505) 285-6991 Fax: (505) 285-6886 E-mail: cib/general@bop.gov
Note: CI Cibola County is a Contract Prison and is run by Corrections Corporation America.

Warden **Brian Koehn** .... (505) 285-6991

Correctional Institution - Giles W. Dalby (TX) (CI Giles W Dalby)

805 North Avenue F, Post, TX 79356
Tel: (806) 495-2175 Fax: (806) 495-3157 E-mail: dal/general@bop.gov
Note: CI Giles W. Dalby is a Contract Prison and is run by Management and Training Corporation.

Warden **Stephen McAdams** .... (806) 495-2175

Southeast Region

3800 Camp Creek Parkway SW, Building 2000, Atlanta, GA 30331-6226
Tel: (678) 686-1200 Fax: (678) 686-1229
Areas Covered: AL, FL, GA, MS, PR, SC, VI

● Regional Director **Jeffrey Allen "J.A." Keller** .... (678) 686-1201
Executive Assistant **Howard Johnson** .... (678) 686-1203
Deputy Regional Director **Jeff Lorenzini** .... (678) 686-1202
Comptroller **Sandra Alexander** .... (678) 686-1400
E-mail: salexander@bop.gov
Correctional Programs **Walter Wood** .... (678) 686-1350
Correctional Services **Lawrence Howard** .... (678) 686-1330
E-mail: lhoward@bop.gov
Discipline Hearing Administrator **James Moran** .... (678) 686-1333
Affirmative Employment Administrator **Keith Williams** .... (678) 686-1302
Facilities **(Vacant)** .... (678) 686-1230
Food Service Administrator **Scott Abrahims** .... (678) 686-1482
Regional Counsel **Craig Simmons** .... (678) 686-1281
Medical Services **Todd Crawford** .... (678) 686-1483
Personnel **Michele Cottingham** .... (678) 686-1300
E-mail: mcottingham@bop.gov
Psychology Services **Chad Lohman** .... (678) 686-1488

Southeast Region Residential Reentry Office

3800 Camp Creek Parkway SW, Building 2000, Atlanta, GA 30331
Tel: (678) 686-1200 Fax: (678) 686-1399
Areas Covered: AL, FL, GA, MS, PR, SC, VI

Regional Safety Specialist **Kimberly Willis-Barnes** .... (678) 686-1383

Atlanta (GA) Residential Reentry Management Office

715 McDonough Boulevard SE, Atlanta, GA 30315
Tel: (404) 635-5679 Fax: (404) 635-5390

Residential Reentry Manager **Michelle Taffe** .... (404) 635-5679
Transitional Services Specialist **Karen Donovan** .... (404) 635-5670
Transitional Services Manager **Cary Cruz** .... (404) 635-5677

Miami (FL) Residential Reentry Management Office

401 North Miami Avenue, Miami, FL 33128-1830
Fax: (305) 536-4024

Residential Reentry Manager **Carlos Rodriguez** .... (305) 536-5710
E-mail: crodriguez@bop.gov

Montgomery (AL) Residential Reentry Management Office

Building 1209, 820 Willow Street, Maxwell Air Force Base,
Montgomery, AL 36112
Tel: (334) 293-2360 Fax: (334) 293-2357

Residential Reentry Manager **David Potts** .... (334) 293-2355

★ Presidential Appointment Requiring Senate Confirmation ☆ Presidential Appointment □ Schedule C Appointment ◇ Career Senior Foreign Service Appointment
● Career Senior Executive Service (SES) Appointment ○ Non-Career Senior Executive Service (SES) Appointment ■ Postal Career Executive Service

Orlando (FL) Residential Reentry Management Office
6303 County Road 500, Wildwood, FL 34785
Tel: (352) 689-7390

Residential Reentry Manager **Darlene Tyler** .... (352) 689-7390
E-mail: dtyler@bop.gov

Federal Correctional Complex - Coleman (FL) (FCC COLEMAN)
846 NE 54th Terrace, Coleman, FL 33521-1029
Tel: (352) 689-3000 Fax: (352) 689-3013

Warden (Administrative) **Tamyra Jarvis** .... (352) 689-6000
Warden (Low Security) **Manuel "Manny" Ocasio** ...... (352) 689-4000
Deputy Warden (Medium Security) **Tamyra Jarvis** .... (352) 689-5000
Warden (USP1) **(Vacant)** .... (352) 689-6000
Warden (USP2) **Charles Lockett** .... (352) 689-3000

Federal Correctional Complex - Yazoo City (MS) (FCC YAZOO CITY)
P.O. Box 5666, Yazoo City, MS 39194
Tel: (662) 751-4800 (Low Security Federal Correction Institution)
Tel: (662) 716-1020 (Medium Security Federal Correctional Institution)
Fax: (662) 716-1036 E-mail: yaz/publicinformation@bop.gov

● Warden **Sharon Nash** .... (662) 716-1020
Chief Information Officer **(Vacant)** .... (662) 716-1020

Federal Correctional Institution - Aliceville (AL) (FCI Aliceville)
1107 Highway 14, Aliceville, AL 35442
Tel: (205) 373-5000 Fax: (205) 373-5020
E-mail: ali/execassistant@bop.gov
Internet: http://www.bop.gov/locations/institutions/ali/

Warden **Patricia Bradley** .... (205) 373-5000

Federal Correctional Institution - Bennettsville (SC) (FCI Bennettsville)
696 Muckerman Road, Bennettsville, SC 29512
Tel: (843) 454-8200 Fax: (843) 454-8219
E-mail: ben/execassistant@bop.gov

Warden **M. Travis Bragg** .... (843) 454-8200
Educational Supervisor **Roger Medlin** .... (843) 454-8200

Federal Correctional Institution - Edgefield (SC) (FCI EDGEFIELD)
501 Gary Hill Road, Edgefield, SC 29824
P.O. Box 723, Edgefield, SC 29824
Tel: (803) 637-1500 Fax: (803) 637-9840

Warden **Bonita Moseley** .... (803) 637-1301
Executive Assistant **Deborah Blakney** .... (803) 637-1303
Associate Warden (Programs) **Walter Vereen** .... (803) 637-1380
Associate Warden (Operations) **Nanette Barnes** .... (803) 637-1385
Camp Administrator **Deborah Blakney** .... (803) 637-1700

Federal Correctional Institution - Estill (SC) (FCI ESTILL)
100 Prison Road, Estill, SC 29918
P.O. Box 699, Estill, SC 29918
Tel: (803) 625-4607 Fax: (803) 625-5635

Warden **(Vacant)** .... (803) 625-4607
Executive Assistant and Camp Administrator **(Vacant)** .... (803) 625-4607 ext. 4003
Associate Warden (Programs) **David Crickard** .... (803) 625-4607
Associate Warden (Operations) **Jack Joyner** .... (803) 625-4607
Superintendent of Industries **(Vacant)** .... (803) 625-4607
Business Administrator **Christopher Mee** .... (803) 625-4607
Religious Services Chaplain **Mustapha Kulungu** .... (803) 625-4607
Captain **Ronald Gillard** .... (803) 625-4607
Food Services Administrator **Michael Potts** .... (803) 625-4607
Health Systems Administrator **Regina Bradley** .... (803) 625-4607
Education Supervisor **Justin Vaught** .... (803) 625-4607
Inmate Services Supervisor **Carlos Santiago** .... (803) 625-4607
Computer Services Manager **Timothy T. Hall** .... (803) 625-4607
E-mail: thall@bop.gov
Human Resources Manager **Virginia Hadwie** .... (803) 625-4656
Facility Manager **Lyman Pitman** .... (803) 625-4607

Federal Correctional Institution - Estill (SC) *(continued)*

Inmate Systems Manager **(Vacant)** .... (803) 625-4607
Safety Manager **David Bird** .... (803) 625-4607
E-mail: dbird@bop.gov
Case Management Coordinator **Jackie Brown** .... (803) 625-4607
Unit Manager (EF) **Cindy Rhodes** .... (803) 625-4607
Unit Manager (CD) **Steve Midock** .... (803) 625-4607
Unit Manager (AB) **Arthur Fredericks** .... (803) 625-4607

Federal Correctional Institution - Jesup (GA) (FCI JESUP)
2600 Highway 301 South, Jesup, GA 31599
Tel: (912) 427-0870 Fax: (912) 427-1125

Warden **Derrick Edge** .... (912) 427-0870 ext. 5350
Associate Warden (Industries) **Billy Smith** ..... (912) 427-0870 ext. 5717
Associate Warden (Operations) **Dave Crickard** .... (912) 427-0870 ext. 5318
Associate Warden (Programs) **L. A. Jones** ..... (912) 427-0870 ext. 5320
Controller **Joseph Eubanks** .... (912) 427-0870 ext. 5630
Food Service Administrator **Nicholas Stubbs** .... (912) 427-0870 ext. 5764
Health Services Administrator **Amanda Loveless** .... (912) 427-0870 ext. 5441
Executive Assistant/Camp Administrator **Nelson Ortiz** .... (912) 427-0870 ext. 6502
Chief Correctional Supervisor **Robert Baker** ... (912) 427-0870 ext. 5781
Education Supervisor **Kimberly Tirik** .... (912) 427-0870 ext. 5729
Computer Services Manager **Lance James** .... (912) 427-0870 ext. 5399
Employee Services Manager **Elizabeth Mann-Rodriguez** .... (912) 427-0870 ext. 5348
Facility Manager **Derek Bland** .... (912) 427-0870 ext. 5792
Inmate Systems Manager **Erin Chalfant** .... (912) 427-0870 ext. 5773
Safety Manager **Shawn Stanley** .... (912) 427-0870 ext. 5783
E-mail: sstanley@bop.gov
Disciplinary Hearing Officer **Scott Slater** ..... (912) 427-0870 ext. 5398

Federal Correctional Institution - Marianna (FL) (FCI MARIANNA)
3625 FCI Road, Marianna, FL 32446
Tel: (850) 526-2313 Fax: (850) 526-6359

Warden **Shannon Withers** .... (850) 526-2313
Associate Warden (Operations) **Myra Lowery** .... (850) 526-2313
Associate Warden (Programs) **Johnny Butts** .... (850) 526-2313
Captain **(Vacant)** .... (850) 526-2313
Chief Chaplain **Andrew Neamtu** .... (850) 526-2313
Chief Psychologist **Stephanie Rush** .... (850) 526-2313
Camp Administrator **Terri Whitehead** .... (850) 526-2313
E-mail: twhitehead@bop.gov
Food Services Administrator **(Vacant)** .... (850) 526-2313
Health Services Administrator **CDR Beatrice Lunsford-Williams** .... (850) 526-2313
Education Supervisor **Marilyn Franco** .... (850) 526-2313
Recreation Supervisor **Roland Speights** .... (850) 526-2313
Computer Services Manager **Ty Tidwell** .... (850) 526-2313
Facilities Manager **Todd Large** .... (850) 526-2313
Inmate Systems Manager **Ramona Hooks** .... (850) 526-2313
Safety Manager **J. Patrick Russ** .... (850) 526-2313
UNICOR Production Controller **Todd Lewis** .... (850) 482-2112
Apache/Creek Unit Manager **(Vacant)** .... (850) 526-2313
Mohawk/Navajo Unit Manager **Regina Williams** .... (850) 526-2313
Shawnee Unit Manager **Edward L. White** .... (850) 526-2313
Employee Services Department **Brenda Hoagland** .... (850) 526-2313
Public Information Officer **Terri Whitehead** .... (850) 526-2313

Federal Correctional Institution - Miami (FL) (FCI MIAMI)
15801 SW 137th Avenue, Miami, FL 33177
Tel: (305) 259-2100 Fax: (305) 259-2160

Warden **Bryan K. Dobbs** .... (305) 259-2150
Executive Assistant **Raymond Burgos** .... (305) 259-2244
Associate Warden (Operations and Programs) **Stevie Knight** .... (305) 259-2152
Warden's Secretary **Tomara Lamar** .... (305) 259-2149
Camp Administrator **Raymond Burgos** .... (305) 259-2244

(continued on next page)

★ Presidential Appointment Requiring Senate Confirmation ☆ Presidential Appointment □ Schedule C Appointment ◇ Career Senior Foreign Service Appointment
● Career Senior Executive Service (SES) Appointment ○ Non-Career Senior Executive Service (SES) Appointment ■ Postal Career Executive Service

DEPARTMENTS

Federal Correctional Institution - Miami (FL) *(continued)*

Controller **(Vacant)** .... (305) 259-2111
Food Service Administrator **Richard Everst** .... (305) 259-2198
Health Services Administrator **Rochelle Ford** .... (305) 259-2184
Chief Correctional Supervisor **Deborah Colon** .... (305) 259-2123
Education Supervisor **Jarmaine Knight** .... (305) 259-2193
Computer Services Manager **Orlando Valentin** .... (305) 259-2205
E-mail: ovalentin@bop.gov
Employee Services Manager **Emma Fernandez-Forbus** .... (305) 259-2240
Facilities Manager **Christopher Kaelin** .... (305) 259-2239
Case Management Coordinator/Inmate Systems Manager **Osimoo Izquierdo** .... (305) 259-2212
Safety Manager **(Vacant)** .... (305) 259-2264

Federal Correctional Institution - Talladega (AL) (FCI TALLADEGA)
565 East Renfroe Road, Talladega, AL 35160
Tel: (256) 315-4100 Fax: (256) 315-4495

● Warden **B. H. Ramomer** .... (256) 315-4307
Executive Assistant **Brian Best** .... (256) 315-4163
Associate Warden (Operations) **Derric Wilson** .... (256) 315-4134
Associate Warden (Programs) **Mich'elle Joseph** .... (256) 315-4132
Controller **M. Kenner** .... (256) 315-4143
Captain **Walter Watson** .... (256) 315-4112
Food Service Administrator **Orlando Jones** .... (256) 315-4184
Health Systems Administrator **Cecilia Hanson** .... (256) 315-4125
Operations Manager **(Vacant)** .... (256) 315-4195
Education Supervisor **Chris Williams** .... (256) 315-4346
Computer Services Manager **D. McKinney** .... (256) 315-4329
Human Resources Manager **Stephanie Ford** .... (256) 315-4128
Facilities Manager **Duston Warren** .... (256) 315-4166
Safety Officer **Mike Blount** .... (256) 315-4242
E-mail: mblount@bop.gov

Federal Correctional Institution - Tallahassee (FL) (FCI TALLAHASSEE)
501 Capital Circle, NE, Tallahassee, FL 32301-3572
Tel: (850) 878-2173 Fax: (850) 671-6105
E-mail: taladmi.lrg@gwmail.bop.gov

Warden **Craig E. Coil** .... (850) 878-2173
Associate Warden **Joetta Campbell** .... (850) 878-2173 ext. 1203
Associate Warden **Stacey Collins** .... (850) 878-2173 ext. 1212
Business Administrator **(Vacant)** .... (850) 878-2173 ext. 1217
Food Service Administrator **Deshaun China** .... (850) 878-2173 ext. 1370
Health Services Administrator **Jada Newell** .... (850) 878-2173 ext. 1407
Chief Correctional Supervisor **Dennis Holmes** .... (850) 878-2173 ext. 1314
Education Supervisor **Nicole McDowell** .... (850) 878-2173 ext. 1345
Employee Services Manager **Carlos Green** .... (850) 878-2173 ext. 1286
E-mail: cgreen@bop.gov
Employee Services Assistant **(Vacant)** .... (850) 878-2173 ext. 1409
Facilities Manager **Roger Hays** .... (850) 878-2173 ext. 1350
Human Resource Specialist **Christine Aldridge** .... (850) 878-2173 ext. 1408
Safety Manager **Matthew Decker** .... (850) 878-2173 ext. 1256
Supervisor of Industries **(Vacant)** .... (850) 878-2173 ext. 1303

Federal Correctional Institution - Williamsburg (SC) (FCI Williamsburg)
8301 Highway 521, Salters, SC 29590
Tel: (843) 387-9400 Fax: (843) 387-6961
E-mail: wil/execassistant@bop.gov
Internet: http://www.bop.gov/locations/institutions/wil/

Warden **Bryan Antonnelli** .... (843) 387-9400
Education Supervisor **T. Gordon** .... (843) 387-9400

Federal Detention Center - Miami (FL) (FDC MIAMI)
33 NE Fourth Street, Miami, FL 33132
P.O. Box 019118, Miami, FL 33101-9118
Tel: (305) 577-0010 Fax: (305) 536-7368

Warden **Roy Cheatham** .... (305) 577-0010
Primary Public Information Officer **Mercedes Feliciano** .... (305) 982-1311
Public Information Officer **Marco Cuero** .... (305) 982-1311
Public Information Officer/Administrator **Mercedes Feliciano** .... (305) 982-1311
Safety Manager **Carlos Nardo** .... (305) 577-0010
Fax: (305) 982-1379

Federal Prison Camp - Montgomery (AL) (FPC MONTGOMERY)
Maxwell Air Force Base, Montgomery, AL 36112
Tel: (334) 293-2100 Tel: (700) 221-2100 Fax: (334) 293-2329

Warden **Dennis W. Stamper** .... (334) 293-2100
E-mail: dwstamper@bop.gov
Associate Warden **(Vacant)** .... (334) 293-2100
Budget/Accounting Officer **Donna Houston** .... (334) 293-2100
E-mail: dhouston@bop.gov
Chaplain **Chris Douglas** .... (334) 293-2100
Psychologist **Dr. Juliana Dodd** .... (334) 293-2100
E-mail: jdodd@bop.gov
Food Service Administrator **Steve Moore** .... (334) 293-2100
Health Services Administrator **(Vacant)** .... (334) 293-2100
Chief Correctional Supervisor **(Vacant)** .... (334) 293-2100
Education Supervisor **Elizabeth Baskin** .... (334) 293-2100
Facilities Manager **Milton Graham** .... (334) 293-2100
Personnel Officer **Estelle Hunter** .... (334) 293-2100
E-mail: ebhunter@bop.gov
Safety Manager **Eddie Baldwin** .... (334) 293-2100
E-mail: ebaldwin@bop.gov
UNICOR Laundry Plant Manager **Joseph Pemberton** .... (334) 293-2100
Unit Manager **Barry Briggs** .... (334) 293-2100
Unit Manager **(Vacant)** .... (334) 293-2100
Case Management Coordinator **Scott Sutton** .... (334) 293-2100
SCSS **Anthony Barnes** .... (334) 293-2100

Federal Prison Camp - Pensacola (FL) (FPC PENSACOLA)
110 Raby Avenue, Pensacola, FL 32509-5127
Tel: (850) 458-7201 Fax: (850) 458-7291

Warden **William L. Woods** .... (850) 458-7201
Associate Warden **Kerry Kemble** .... (850) 458-7202
Business Administrator **Michelle Jackson** .... (850) 457-1911
Chaplain **Brian Wright** .... (850) 457-1911
Psychologist **Mandy Ramsey** .... (850) 457-1911
Food Service Administrator **Sonia Joseph Ganzy** .... (850) 457-1911
Health Systems Administrator **(Vacant)** .... (850) 457-1911
Chief Correctional Supervisor **Matthew Hawley** .... (850) 457-1911
Education Supervisor **William Griffin** .... (850) 457-1911
Computer Services Manager **Jameise Smasal** .... (850) 457-1911
Facilities Manager **(Vacant)** .... (850) 457-1911
Human Resource Manager **Kari Nelson** .... (850) 457-1911
E-mail: kmnelson@bop.gov
Safety Manager **Michael Carly** .... (850) 457-1911
Unit Manager **Eric Mamula** .... (850) 457-1911
Case Management Coordinator **Jennifer Fultz** .... (850) 457-1911

Metropolitan Detention Center - Guaynabo (PR) (MDC GUAYNABO)
P.O. Box 2008, Catano, PR 00963-2008
Tel: (787) 749-4480 Fax: (787) 775-7824

● Warden **Angel L. Adan** .... (787) 749-4480 ext. 7801
E-mail: aadan@bop.gov
Warden's Secretary **Michelle Ayala** .... (787) 749-4480 ext. 7802
E-mail: m1ayala@bop.gov
Associate Warden (Custody) **Victor Morino** .... (787) 749-4480 ext. 7804
Associate Warden (Operations) **Miguel A. Medina** .... (787) 749-4480 ext. 7811
Associate Warden (Programs) **Stephanie Canilla** .... (787) 749-4480 ext. 7805

★ Presidential Appointment Requiring Senate Confirmation ☆ Presidential Appointment □ Schedule C Appointment ◇ Career Senior Foreign Service Appointment
● Career Senior Executive Service (SES) Appointment ○ Non-Career Senior Executive Service (SES) Appointment ■ Postal Career Executive Service

Metropolitan Detention Center - Guaynabo (PR) *(continued)*

Attorney Advisor **Jorge L. Matos** . . . . (787) 749-4480 ext. 7807
E-mail: jlmatos@bop.gov
Controller **(Vacant)** . . . . (787) 749-4480 ext. 7874
Chaplain **Juan Cintron** . . . . (787) 749-4480 ext. 7970
Food Service Administrator **Martin Lopez** . . . . . (787) 749-4480 ext. 7915
Health Services Administrator
Tania M. Macias . . . . (787) 749-4480 ext. 7920
Chief Correctional Supervisor
Victor Moreno . . . . (787) 749-4480 ext. 7830
Education Supervisor **Rebecca Layer** . . . . (787) 749-4480
Executive Assistant **Frances Rivera** . . . . (787) 749-4480 ext. 7940
E-mail: farivera@bop.gov Fax: (787) 775-7951
Facilities Manager **Richard Funk** . . . . (787) 749-4480 ext. 7865
Inmate Systems Manager **(Vacant)** . . . . (787) 749-4480 ext. 7963
Safety Manager **Karl Nickels** . . . . (787) 749-4480 ext. 7985
E-mail: knickels@bop.gov
Captain **Victor Moreno** . . . . (787) 749-4480 ext. 7830
E-mail: vmoreno@bop.gov
Computer Services Manager **Patrick Kaough** . . . (787) 749-4480 ext. 7825
E-mail: pkaough@bop.gov

U.S. Penitentiary - Atlanta (GA) (USP ATLANTA)

601 McDonough Boulevard, SE, Atlanta, GA 30315-0182
Tel: (404) 635-5100 Fax: (404) 331-2137

Warden **D. Herman** . . . . (404) 635-5100
Executive Assistant **D. Baysore** . . . . (404) 635-5100
Associate Warden (Industry and Education)
William E. Mackelburg . . . . (404) 635-5100
Associate Warden (Operations) **F. Valerie** . . . . (404) 635-5100
Associate Warden (Programs) **(Vacant)** . . . . (404) 635-5100
Camp Administrator **D. Baysore** . . . . (404) 635-5100
Captain **Davis Silva** . . . . (404) 635-5100
Chaplain **Perry White** . . . . (404) 635-5100
Chief Psychologist **Dr. Pinnix-Hall** . . . . (404) 635-5100
Computer Specialist **(Vacant)** . . . . (404) 635-5100
Controller **Jeremy Mullins** . . . . (404) 635-5100
Education Supervisor **(Vacant)** . . . . (404) 635-5100
Education Technician **(Vacant)** . . . . (404) 635-5100
Facilities Manager **J. Moore** . . . . (404) 635-5100
Food Service Administrator **(Vacant)** . . . . (404) 635-5100
Health Systems Administrator **Tara Hollinger** . . . . (404) 635-5100
Human Resource Manager **Sharon Benefield** . . . . (404) 635-5100
Correctional Systems Manager **D. Newbould** . . . . (404) 635-5100
Jail Administrator **Steven Cardona** . . . . (404) 635-5100
Safety Manager **Duanne McQueen** . . . . (404) 635-5100
Special Investigative Agent **Gersion Rivera** . . . . (404) 635-5100

Correctional Institution - Adams County (MS) (CI Adams County)

20 Hobo Fork Road, Natchez, MS 39120
Tel: (601) 304-2500 Fax: (601) 446-5224 E-mail: acc/general@bop.gov

Note: CI Adams County is a Contract Prison and is run by Corrections Corporation of America.

Warden **Stephen Julian** . . . . (601) 304-2500

Correctional Institution - McRae (GA) (CI McRae)

112 Jim Hammock Drive, McRae, GA 31055
Tel: (229) 868-7778 Fax: (229) 868-7640 E-mail: mca/general@bop.gov

Note: CI McRae is a Contract Prison and is run by Corrections Corporation America.

Warden **Stacey Stone** . . . . (229) 868-7778

Western Region

7338 Shoreline Drive, Stockton, CA 95219
Tel: (209) 956-9700
Areas Covered: AK, AZ, CA, HI, ID, MT, NV, OR, UT, WA, WY

● Regional Director **Mary M. Mitchell** . . . . (209) 956-9700
Deputy Regional Director **Steve Lake** . . . . (209) 956-9700
Executive Assistant **Melinda Clark** . . . . (209) 956-9700

Western Region *(continued)*

Legal Counsel **Dennis Wong** . . . . (209) 956-9700
E-mail: dwong@bop.gov
Affirmative Action **Crystal Rufus** . . . . (209) 956-9700
E-mail: crufus@bop.gov
Comptroller **Kristen Boone** . . . . (209) 956-9700
Computer Services **Eric Luke** . . . . (209) 956-9700
E-mail: eluke@bop.gov
Correctional Programs Administrator **Todd Javernick** . . . . (209) 956-9700
Correctional Services Administrator **Dave O. Carl** . . . . (209) 956-9700
Correctional Systems Specialist **Doug Davis** . . . . (209) 956-9700
E-mail: edavis@bop.gov
Discipline Hearing Administrator **Ismael Hernandez** . . . . (209) 956-9700
Facilities Administrator **Aaron Wilkerson** . . . . (209) 956-9700
Food Service Administrator **Juan Salazar** . . . . (209) 956-9700
Health Systems Administrator **Gloria Rodrigues** . . . . (925) 833-7500
Human Resource Administrator **Jeannie Bratschi** . . . . (209) 956-9700
E-mail: jbratschi@bop.gov
Senior Human Resource Specialist **(Vacant)** . . . . (209) 956-9700

Western Region Residential Reentry Program

7338 Shoreline Drive, Stockton, CA 95219
Tel: (209) 956-9700
Areas Covered: AK, AZ, CA, GU, HI, ID, MT, NV, OR, UT, WA, WY, Saipan

Reentry Affairs Administrator **Kim Beakey** . . . . (209) 956-9700

Long Beach (CA) Residential Reentry Management Office

1299 Seaside Avenue, San Pedro, CA 90731
Tel: (310) 732-5179 Fax: (310) 732-5291

Residential Reentry Manager **Wes Mayhew** . . . . (310) 732-5179

Phoenix (AZ) Residential Reentry Management Office

230 North First Avenue, Suite 405, Phoenix, AZ 85003
Tel: (602) 514-7075 Fax: (602) 514-7076
Internet: http://www.bop.gov/locations/ccm/cph/

Residential Reentry Manager **(Vacant)** . . . . (602) 514-7095
Residential Reentry Specialist **Ada Taylor** . . . . (602) 514-7096
Residential Reentry Specialist **Thomas Conbar** . . . . (602) 514-7094
Residential Reentry Specialist **Tricia Sparks** . . . . (602) 514-7081

Sacramento (CA) Residential Reentry Management Office

501 I Street, Suite 9-400, Sacramento, CA 95814
Tel: (916) 930-2002 Fax: (916) 930-2008 E-mail: csc/ccm@bop.gov

Residential Reentry Manager **(Vacant)** . . . . (916) 930-2002 (SIU)

Salt Lake City (UT) Residential Reentry Management Office

324 South State Street, Suite 228, Salt Lake City, UT 84111
Tel: (801) 524-4212 Fax: (801) 524-3112
Areas Covered: MT, NV, UT, WY

Community Corrections Manager **(Vacant)** . . . . (801) 524-4212

Seattle (WA) Residential Reentry Management Office

2425 South 200th Street, SeaTac, WA 98198
Tel: (206) 870-1011 Fax: (206) 870-1012

Residential Reentry Manager **(Vacant)** . . . . (206) 870-1088

Federal Correctional Complex - Tucson (AZ) (FCC TUCSON)

9300 South Wilmot Road, Tucson, AZ 85756
Tel: (520) 663-5000 Fax: (520) 663-5024 Fax: (520) 663-5158 (Records)

Warden (FCI) **Robbie Rhodes** . . . . (520) 574-7100
Associate Warden **Thahesha Jusino** . . . . (520) 663-5000
Associate Warden **Charles E. Harding** . . . . (520) 574-7100
E-mail: ceharding@bop.gov
Associate Warden **Shawn Salmonson** . . . . (520) 663-5000
Associate Warden **Ronell Prioleau** . . . . (520) 663-5000
Executive Assistant/Camp Administrator **(Vacant)** . . . . (520) 663-5000
Business Administrator **(Vacant)** . . . . (520) 574-7100
Chief Psychologist **James Hayden** . . . . (520) 663-5000
Food Service Administrator **Michael Howard** . . . . (520) 574-7100
Health Services Administrator **Shannon England** . . . . (520) 663-5000
Chief Correctional Supervisor **Darrin McWhorter** . . . . (520) 663-5000

(continued on next page)

★ Presidential Appointment Requiring Senate Confirmation ☆ Presidential Appointment □ Schedule C Appointment ◇ Career Senior Foreign Service Appointment
● Career Senior Executive Service (SES) Appointment ○ Non-Career Senior Executive Service (SES) Appointment ■ Postal Career Executive Service

Federal Correctional Complex - Tucson (AZ) *(continued)*

Deputy Captain **(Vacant)** .... (520) 574-7100
Education Supervisor **Timothy Amico** .... (520) 663-5000
Facilities Manager **Chadwick Schickel** .... (520) 663-5000
Supervisory Correctional Systems Specialist
Lora Molinar .... (520) 663-5000
Personnel Officer **Jason Ludwick** .... (520) 663-5000
Safety Manager **(Vacant)** .... (520) 663-5000 ext. 5190

Federal Correctional Complex - Victorville (CA) (FCC VICTORVILLE)

13777 Air Expressway Boulevard, Victorville, CA 92394

Complex Department Heads

Business Administrator **Rhae Lynn Helms** .... (760) 246-2455
Chaplain **M. Northway** .... (760) 530-5700 ext. 5905
Clinical Director **Ross Quinn** .... (760) 530-5700 ext. 5985
Chief Psychologist **M'Liss Doman** .... (760) 530-5895
Computer Services Manager **Troy Sandum** .... (760) 246-2563
E-mail: tsandum@bop.gov
Education Supervisor **Sandra John** .... (760) 246-2508
Employee Services Manager **Shirley Cain** .... (760) 530-5953
Facilities Manager **David Dittemore** .... (760) 530-5874
Health Services Administrator **Randall Gillian** .... (760) 530-5912
Safety Manager **Kelvin Brown, Sr.** .... (760) 530-5944

Federal Correctional Institution I - Victorville (CA) (FCI VICTORVILLE I)

P.O. Box 5400, Adelanto, CA 92301
Tel: (760) 246-2400 Fax: (760) 246-2461

Warden **Cynthia Swain** .... (760) 246-2401
Secretary **Norma Moreno** .... (760) 246-2402
E-mail: nmoreno@bop.gov
Associate Warden (Industries and Education)
Kevin Young .... (760) 246-2630
Tel: (760) 246-2600
Associate Warden **Estela Derr** .... (760) 246-2477
Captain **John Gabby** .... (760) 246-2479
Deputy Case Management Coordinator
Melissa Quijada .... (760) 246-2441
Unit Manager A/B **Cresie Lyons** .... (760) 246-2547
Unit Manager C/D **Will Ramirez** .... (760) 246-2400 ext. 1058
Unit Manager E/F **(Vacant)** .... (760) 246-2400 ext. 1078
Information Technology Specialist **Ryan McCarty** .... (760) 246-2492
E-mail: rmccarty@bop.gov
Information Technology Specialist **Rufus Jenkins** .... (760) 246-2562
Information Technology Specialist **T. J. Schaaf** .... (760) 246-2466
E-mail: tschaaf@bop.gov

Federal Correctional Institution II - Victorville (CA) (FCI VICTORVILLE II)

P.O. Box 5400, Adelanto, CA 92301
Tel: (760) 530-5700 Fax: (760) 530-5706

Warden **Michael Carroll** .... (760) 530-5710
Warden's Secretary **J. Randall** .... (760) 530-5709
Associate Warden **H. Barron** .... (760) 530-5919
Associate Warden **F. Garrido** .... (760) 530-5917
Captain **E Ricolcol** .... (760) 530-5741
Deputy Case Management Coordinator **Karrie Langel** .... (760) 530-5918
E-mail: klangel@bop.gov
Unit Manager A/B **C. Sylvester** .... (760) 530-5780
Unit Manager C/D **Maria Orozco** .... (760) 530-5786
Unit Manager E/F **Morgan Miccio** .... (760) 530-5813

U.S. Penitentiary - Victorville (CA) (USP Victorville)

P.O. Box 5400, Adelanto, CA 92301
Tel: (760) 530-5000 Fax: (760) 530-5103

Warden **David Shinn** .... (760) 530-5100
Warden's Secretary **Alicia Harris** .... (760) 530-5101
Associate Warden **Chris Ulrich** .... (760) 530-5107
Associate Warden **F. Keilman** .... (760) 530-5108
Executive Assistant **Jeff Pino** .... (760) 530-5102

U.S. Penitentiary - Victorville (CA) *(continued)*

Captain **T. Lillard** .... (760) 530-5135
Case Management Coordinator **(Vacant)** .... (760) 530-5122
Unit Manager 1/3 **Edward Perez** .... (760) 530-5047
Unit Manager 4/6 **Farrah Sliver** .... (760) 530-5020

Federal Correctional Institution - Dublin (CA) (FCI DUBLIN)

5701 Eighth Street - Camp Parks, Dublin, CA 94568
Tel: (925) 833-7500 Fax: (925) 833-7555

Warden **Dr. Wiley Jenkins** .... (925) 833-7510
E-mail: wzjenkins@bop.gov
Public Information Officer **Sally Swarts** .... (925) 833-7529
E-mail: sswarts@bop.gov
Warden's Secretary **Celeste Magana** .... (925) 833-7511
E-mail: cmagana@bop.gov Fax: (925) 833-7555
Associate Warden (Operations) **Dr. Tamara Mischel** .... (925) 833-7514
Associate Warden (Programs) **John T. LeMaster** .... (925) 833-7515
Chaplain **Margaret Ashforth** .... (925) 833-7500 ext. 384
Controller **Laura Weaver** .... (925) 833-7577
E-mail: lxweaver@bop.gov
General Counsel **(Vacant)** .... (209) 956-9732
Case Management Coordinator **Monica Taylor** .... (925) 833-7517
Food Service Administrator **Julie Hyde** .... (925) 833-7526
Health Services Administrator
Jessica Figlenski .... (925) 833-7500 ext. 214
E-mail: jfiglenski@bop.gov
Chief Correctional Supervisor **(Vacant)** .... (925) 833-7569
Education Supervisor **Loanne Tran** .... (925) 833-7500 ext. 529
Computer Services Manager **Timothy Hosker** .... (925) 833-7509
E-mail: thosker@bop.gov
Facility Manager **Doug Ricks** .... (925) 833-7519
Safety Manager **(Vacant)** .... (925) 833-7500 ext. 387
UNICOR Call Center Manager **Darlene Ingham** .... (925) 833-7538
E-mail: darlene.ingham2@usdoj.gov
Camp Unit Manager **Kimberly Luke** .... (925) 833-7500 ext. 541
Unit A/B Manager **Christine Moore** .... (925) 833-7500 ext. 541
Unit C/D/E/F Manager **Shikha Dosanj** .... (925) 833-7500 ext. 260
Human Resources Manager **Renee Aragonez** .... (925) 833-7522
E-mail: raragonez@bop.gov
Security Officer **(Vacant)** .... (925) 833-7500 ext. 620
Psychology Chief **Dr. Francis "Frank" Davis** .... (925) 833-7500 ext. 373
E-mail: fdavis@bop.gov
Supervisory Correctional Systems Specialist
Alicia Gonzaga .... (925) 833-7500 ext. 365
E-mail: agonzaga@bop.gov

Federal Correctional Institution - Herlong (CA) (FCI Herlong)

PO Box 900, Herlong, CA 96113
Tel: (530) 827-8000 Fax: (530) 827-8024

Warden **Paul Thompson** .... (530) 827-8101
E-mail: HER/Warden@bop.gov
Executive Assistant **David Alatary** .... (530) 827-8102
E-mail: HER/ExecAssistant@bop.gov
Associate Warden **Jessica Sage PsyD** .... (530) 827-8107
E-mail: HER/AW-Operations@bop.gov
Associate Warden **Herbert Koger** .... (530) 827-8108
E-mail: her/aw-operations@bop.gov
Chief Correctional Supervisor **Roger Reed** .... (530) 827-8000
Chief Psychologist **Stephanie Owens PsyD** .... (530) 827-8000 ext. 4280
Chaplain **Joseph Hammiel** .... (530) 827-8000
Note: On leave.
Food Service Administrator **Michael Ratkey** .... (530) 827-8000
Educational Supervisor **Carl Johnson** .... (530) 827-8000 ext. 4270
E-mail: cbjohnson@bop.gov
Computer Services Manager **David Law** .... (530) 827-8000
E-mail: HER/ComputerServices@bop.gov
Facilities Manager **Gregory Lux** .... (530) 827-8000 ext. 4325
Human Resource Manager **Nancy Simpson** .... (530) 827-8000 ext. 4118
E-mail: HER/HumanResources@bop.gov
Safety Manager **Matt Murphy** .... (530) 827-8000 ext. 4300
Unit Manager **Mike Nimmo** .... (530) 827-8000
Unit Manager **Elizabeth Sotomayor** .... (530) 827-8000

★ Presidential Appointment Requiring Senate Confirmation ☆ Presidential Appointment ☐ Schedule C Appointment ◇ Career Senior Foreign Service Appointment
● Career Senior Executive Service (SES) Appointment ○ Non-Career Senior Executive Service (SES) Appointment ■ Postal Career Executive Service

Federal Correctional Institution - Mendota (CA) (FCI Mendota)
33500 West California Avenue, Mendota, CA 93640
Tel: (559) 274-4000 Fax: (559) 274-4223
E-mail: men/execassistant@bop.gov

Warden **Rafael Zuniga** .... (559) 274-4000
Associate Warden **Brent Watson** .... (559) 274-4000

Federal Correctional Institution - Lompoc (CA) (FCI LOMPOC)
3901 Klein Road, Lompoc, CA 93436
Tel: (805) 735-2771

● Warden **Steve Langford** .... (805) 735-2771 ext. 3413
Secretary **Veronica Floyd** .... (805) 735-2771 ext. 3285
E-mail: LOX/ExecAssistant@bop.gov
Associate Warden (Operations) **R. L. Rhodes** ... (805) 736-4154 ext. 5060
Budget and Accounting Officer
Doris Fredieu .... (805) 736-4154 ext. 5130
Chaplain **Michael Neal** .... (805) 735-2771 ext. 3546
Chief Psychologist **Catherine Spitz** .... (805) 735-2271 ext. 3528
Clinical Director **(Vacant)** .... (805) 735-2771 ext. 3200
Food Service Administrator **Art Navarro** .... (805) 735-2771 ext. 3400
Education Supervisor **Matt Brown** .... (805) 735-2771 ext. 3454
Recreation Supervisor **Jacky Blair** .... (805) 735-2771 ext. 3477
Facilities Manager **Randy L. McCarty** .... (805) 735-2771 ext. 3305
Human Resource Manager **Chong Boley** .... (805) 736-4154 ext. 5100
E-mail: cboley@bop.gov
Safety Manager **William O'Brien** .... (805) 735-2771 ext. 3380
Case Management Coordinator
Stephanie Candela .... (805) 735-2771 ext. 3501
E-mail: smcandela@bop.gov
Computer Services Manager **Jonathan Simo** .... (805) 735-2771
E-mail: jsimo@bop.gov

Federal Correctional Institution - Phoenix (AZ) (FCI PHOENIX)
37900 North 45th Avenue, Phoenix, AZ 85086-7008
Tel: (623) 465-9757 Tel: (700) 762-8000 Fax: (623) 465-5199

Warden **(Vacant)** .... (623) 465-9757
Associate Warden **Mark Butierrez** .... (623) 465-9757
Associate Warden **Leslie Jones** .... (623) 465-9757
Associate Warden **(Vacant)** .... (623) 465-9757
Associate Warden **(Vacant)** .... (623) 465-9757
Attorney Advisor **David Huband** .... (623) 465-9757
Business Administrator **Valerie Murpha** .... (623) 465-9757
Captain **Edward Gramh** .... (623) 465-9757
Chief Psychologist **Cynthia Mathieu** .... (623) 465-9757
Education Supervisor **Andre Thomas** .... (623) 465-9757
Employee Services Manager **(Vacant)** .... (623) 465-9757
Facilities Manager **(Vacant)** .... (623) 465-9757
Food Service Administrator **Frank Jacobs** .... (623) 465-9757
Health Systems Administrator **LCDR Daniel Miller** .... (623) 465-9757
Computer Services Manager **Nellie Estraga** .... (623) 465-9757
Correctional Systems Manager **Aimee Arthur-Wastell** .... (623) 465-9757

Federal Correctional Institution - Safford (AZ) (FCI SAFFORD)
1529 West US Highway 366, Safford, AZ 85546
P.O. Box 820, Safford, AZ 85548
Tel: (928) 428-6600 Fax: (928) 348-1355

Warden **Felipe Martinez, Jr.** .... (928) 428-6600 ext. 1106
Secretary **Ronda Abalos** .... (928) 428-6601 ext. 1106
E-mail: rabalos@bop.gov
Associate Warden
Francisco "Fred" Moreno .... (928) 428-6600 ext. 1108
Controller **(Vacant)** .... (928) 348-1343
Chaplain **(Vacant)** .... (928) 428-6600
Food Administrator **(Vacant)** .... (928) 348-1356
Health Systems Administrator **Jeffrey Richardson** .... (928) 348-1359
UNICOR Superintendent **(Vacant)** .... (928) 348-1361
Chief Correctional Supervisor **Angela Smith** .... (928) 428-6600
Education Supervisor **Angela Gilber** .... (928) 348-1348
Chief Mechanical Services **Ben Fajardo** .... (928) 348-1609
Computer Services **Don Paul** .... (928) 348-1341
Psychology Services **(Vacant)** .... (928) 348-1357
Personnel Officer **Sandra Mendez** .... (928) 348-1337

Federal Correctional Institution - Safford (AZ) *(continued)*

Safety Officer **Steve Warren** .... (928) 348-1335
Inmate Systems Manager **Gaira Germaine** .... (928) 348-1346
Unit/Case Management **(Vacant)** .... (928) 428-6600
Unit/Case Management **Chad Shilliday** .... (928) 428-6600

Federal Correctional Institution - Sheridan (OR) (FCI SHERIDAN)
27072 Ballston Road, Sheridan, OR 97378-9601
P.O. Box 8000, Sheridan, OR 97378
Tel: (503) 843-4442 Fax: (503) 843-6645

● Warden **Josias Salazar** .... (503) 843-6701
Warden's Secretary **Tanya Bishop** .... (503) 843-6702
E-mail: SHE/ExecAssistant@bop.gov
E-mail: tbishop@bop.gov
Associate Warden (Programs) **(Vacant)** .... (503) 843-6704
Associate Warden (Operations) **Andrew Cooper** .... (503) 843-6703
Business Administrator **Brenda Herron** .... (503) 843-6398
Executive Assistant and Satellite Operations
Administrator **Amberly Newman** .... (503) 843-6711
Tel: (503) 843-7010
Food Service Administrator **Terry Uhrinak** .... (503) 843-6416
Health Services Administrator **Rosita Leen** .... (503) 843-6441
Chief Correctional Supervisor **James Galbreth** .... (503) 843-4442
Chief, Psychology Services **Cynthia Campanga PhD** .... (503) 843-6466
E-mail: clenning@bop.gov
Education Supervisor **Sue Cain** .... (503) 843-6381
E-mail: scain@bop.gov
Computer Services Manager **Jeff Hevener** .... (503) 843-6366
Facilities Manager **David Childress** .... (503) 843-6345
FPC Unit Manager **Sean Price** .... (503) 843-6720
Human Resources Manager **Sonja Garcia** .... (503) 843-6425
Safety Manager **Brice Ingram** .... (503) 843-6770
Unit Manager **Brian Russell** .... (503) 843-6566
Unit Manager **(Vacant)** .... (503) 843-6579
Case Management Coordinator **Lisa Pauly** .... (503) 843-6431
Discipline Hearing Officer **Daniel Cortez, Jr.** .... (503) 843-6378
E-mail: dcortezjr@bop.gov

Federal Correctional Institution - Terminal Island (CA) (FCI TERMINAL ISLAND)
1299 Seaside Avenue, Terminal Island, CA 90731
Tel: (310) 831-8961 Tel: (310) 793-1160 Fax: (310) 732-5325

Warden **Felicia Ponce** .... (310) 831-8961
Associate Warden (Operations) **Israel Jacquez** .... (310) 831-8961
Associate Warden (Programs) **Gabriel Gutierrez** .... (310) 831-8961
Business Administrator **Claudia Pinzon** .... (310) 831-8961
Food Service Administrator **Leon Flint** .... (310) 831-8961
Health Services Administrator **Mahesh Patel** .... (310) 831-8961
Chief Psychologist **Michael Wydo** .... (310) 831-8961
Chief Correctional Supervisor **James Hundt** .... (310) 831-8961
Education Supervisor **Reynold Bills** .... (310) 831-8961
Computer Service Manager **Teresa Legaspi** .... (310) 831-8961
Facilities Manager **Grant Stine** .... (310) 831-8961
Safety Manager **Robert Caternolo** .... (310) 831-8961
Human Resources Manager **Melisa Hess** .... (310) 831-8961

Federal Detention Center - Honolulu (HI) (FDC Honolulu)
351 Elliott Street, Honolulu, HI 96819
Tel: (808) 838-4200 Fax: (808) 838-4507
E-mail: hon/execassistant@bop.gov
Internet: http://www.bop.gov/locations/institutions/hon/

Warden **Hiro Kobayashi** .... (808) 838-4200
Education Supervisor **K. Germeson** .... (808) 838-4200

Federal Detention Center - SeaTac (WA) (FDC SEATAC)
2425 South 200th Street, SeaTac, WA 98198
P.O. Box 13901, Seattle, WA 98198
Tel: (206) 870-5701 Fax: (206) 870-5717

Warden **Daniel Sproul** .... (206) 870-5701
E-mail: dsproul@bop.gov

(continued on next page)

DEPARTMENTS

★ Presidential Appointment Requiring Senate Confirmation ☆ Presidential Appointment ☐ Schedule C Appointment ◇ Career Senior Foreign Service Appointment
● Career Senior Executive Service (SES) Appointment ○ Non-Career Senior Executive Service (SES) Appointment ■ Postal Career Executive Service

Federal Detention Center - SeaTac (WA) *(continued)*

Secretary **Shanna C. McCuiston** .... (206) 870-5702
E-mail: smccuiston@bop.gov
Computer Services Manager **Richard Dedrick** .... (206) 870-5721
Employee Services Manager **Tina Britton** .... (206) 870-5742
Fax: (206) 870-5732

Metropolitan Correctional Center - San Diego (CA) (MCC SAN DIEGO)
808 Union Street, San Diego, CA 92101-6078
Tel: (619) 232-4311 Tel: (700) 890-0000 Fax: (619) 595-0390

Warden **Louis Williams II** .... (619) 232-4311
Associate Warden (Operations) **Robert Garcia** .... (619) 232-4311
Associate Warden (Programs) **Arthur Douglas** .... (619) 232-4311
Senior Counsel **Theresa Talplacido** .... (619) 232-4311
Captain **(Vacant)** .... (619) 232-4311
Business Administrator **Carmen O'Brien** .... (619) 232-4311
Education Supervisor **Aaron Cathey** .... (619) 232-4311
Food Service Administrator **(Vacant)** .... (619) 232-4311
Health Services Administrator **Melanie Paredes** .... (619) 232-4311
Clinical Director **Jamal Gwathney** .... (619) 232-4311
Computer Services Manager **George Wiley** .... (619) 232-4311
Correctional Systems Supervisor **Michael Bucio** .... (619) 232-4311
Correctional Systems Supervisor **Camilo Zuniga** .... (619) 232-4311
E-mail: czuniga@bop.gov
Facilities Manager **Kyle Ball** .... (619) 232-4311
Human Resources Manager **Craig Allen** .... (619) 232-4311
Safety Manager **Joseph Hendrickson** .... (619) 232-4311
Case Management Coordinator **Ezequiel Echevette** ...... (619) 232-4311
Trustfund Supervisor **Abraham Patino** .... (619) 232-4311

Metropolitan Detention Center - Los Angeles (CA) (MDC LOS ANGELES)
535 North Alameda Street, Los Angeles, CA 90012
Tel: (213) 485-0439 Fax: (213) 253-9510

• Warden **Louis J Milusnie** .... (213) 485-0439 ext. 5101
Associate Warden (Operations)
Sherrielyn Beauchamp .... (213) 485-0439 ext. 5102
Associate Warden (Programs) **Bret Dorethy** .... (213) 485-0439 ext. 5104
Business Administrator **(Vacant)** .... (213) 485-0439 ext. 5146
Chief Correctional Supervisor
Timmy Vaught .... (213) 485-0439 ext. 5134
Education Supervisor **Enoch Jackson** .... (213) 485-0439 ext. 5161
Food Services Administrator **Daniel Couick** .... (213) 485-0439 ext. 5118
Health Services Administrator
Omar Muhammad .... (213) 485-0439 ext. 5351
Human Resources Manager **(Vacant)** .... (213) 485-0439 ext. 5173
Facilities Manager **Fran Morin** .... (213) 485-0439 ext. 5128
Inmate Systems Manager
Veronica Eberhardt .... (213) 485-0439 ext. 5139
Safety Manager **Demetrio Alford** .... (213) 485-0439 ext. 5174
E-mail: dalford@bop.gov
Supervisory Attorney **Eliezer Ben-Shmuel** .... (213) 485-0439 ext. 5428
E-mail: eben-shmuel@bop.gov
Psychology Services **Lisa Hope DrMed** .... (213) 485-0439 ext. 5437
Supervisory Chaplain **Syed Ahmed** .... (213) 485-0439 ext. 5473
Computer Services Manager **Manuel Yanez** .... (213) 485-0439 ext. 5156

U.S. Penitentiary - Atwater (CA) (USP Atwater)
One Federal Way, Atwater, CA 95301
Tel: (209) 386-0257 Fax: (209) 386-4635
E-mail: atw/execassistant@bop.gov
Internet: http://www.bop.gov/locations/institutions/atw/

Warden **Andre Matevousian** .... (209) 386-0257
Executive Assistant **Deborah Cassity** .... (209) 386-0257
E-mail: dcassity@bop.gov
E-mail: ATW/ExecAssistant@bop.gov

U.S. Penitentiary - Lompoc (CA) (USP LOMPOC)
3901 Klein Boulevard, Lompoc, CA 93436
Tel: (805) 735-2771

Warden **Steve Langford** .... (805) 735-2771 ext. 3413

U.S. Penitentiary - Lompoc (CA) *(continued)*

Executive Assistant **(Vacant)** .... (805) 735-2771 ext. 3415
E-mail: lox/execassistant@bop.gov
Secretary **Veronica Floyd** .... (805) 735-2771 ext. 3285
Associate Warden (Operations)
Scott Nichols .... (805) 735-2771 ext. 3412
Associate Warden (Programs)
Ronald Muñoz .... (805) 735-2771 ext. 3414
Camp Administrator **Katina Heckard** .... (805) 735-2771 ext. 3415
E-mail: katina.heckard@bop.gov
Food Service Administrator **Art Navarro** ...... (805) 735-2771 ext. 3400
Health Services Administrator **(Vacant)** .... (805) 735-2771 ext. 3535
Captain **Christian Levin** .... (805) 735-2771 ext. 3471
Education Supervisor **Matt Brown** .... (805) 735-2771 ext. 3454
Employee Services Manager **Chong Boley** ..... (805) 736-4145 ext. 5100
E-mail: cboley@bop.gov
Facilities Manager **Randy L. McCarty** .... (805) 735-2771 ext. 3305
Safety Manager **William O'Brien** .... (805) 735-2771 ext. 3380
E-mail: wobrien@bop.gov
Discipline Hearing Officer
William Chetwood .... (805) 735-2771 ext. 3496
Supervisory Investigative Agent
Victor Gonzalez .... (805) 735-2771 ext. 3539
Computer Services Manager **Jonathan Simo** .... (805) 735-2771
E-mail: jsimo@bop.gov

Correctional Institution - Taft (CA) (CI Taft)
1500 Cadet Road, Taft, CA 93268
Tel: (661) 763-2510 Fax: (661) 765-3034 E-mail: taf/general@bop.gov
Note: CI Taft is a Contract Prison and is run by Management and Training Corporation.

Warden **Craig Apker** .... (661) 763-2510
Educational Supervisor **(Vacant)** .... (661) 763-2510

United States Marshals Service (USMS)

United States Marshals Headquarters, 2604 Jefferson Davis Highway, Alexandria, VA 22301
Mail: United States Marshals Service Headquarters, Washington, DC 20530-1000
Tel: (202) 307-9100 (Communications Center)
Tel: (202) 336-0162 (Public Affairs After hours)
E-mail: us.marshals@usdoj.gov Internet: www.usmarshals.gov

OFFICE OF THE DIRECTOR

United States Marshals Headquarters, 2604 Jefferson Davis Highway, Alexandria, VA 22301
Fax: (703) 603-7021

Office of the Deputy Director

Directorate of Operations

Justice Prisoner and Alien Transportation System (JPATS)
1251 Northwest Briar Cliff Parkway, Suite 300, Kansas City, MO 64116
Tel: (816) 467-1900 Tel: (405) 680-3400 (Prisoner Transportation)
Fax: (816) 467-1980 Internet: https://www.usmarshals.gov/jpats/

• Assistant Director **Shannon Brown** .... (816) 467-1900
E-mail: shannon.brown@usdoj.gov

Tactical Operations Division
2604 Jefferson Davis Highway, Alexandria, VA 22301

• Assistant Director **Roberto Robinson** .... (703) 740-0919
E-mail: roberto.robinson@usdoj.gov
Deputy Assistant Director **(Vacant)** .... (202) 616-2822
Special Operations Group Commander **Eric Kessel** ...... (318) 640-4560
E-mail: eric.kessel@usdoj.gov

★ Presidential Appointment Requiring Senate Confirmation ☆ Presidential Appointment □ Schedule C Appointment ◇ Career Senior Foreign Service Appointment
● Career Senior Executive Service (SES) Appointment ○ Non-Career Senior Executive Service (SES) Appointment ■ Postal Career Executive Service

District Offices

Alabama - Northern District
1729 Fifth Avenue North, Room 240, Birmingham, AL 35203
Tel: (205) 307-7335 Fax: (205) 776-6220

★ U.S. Marshal **Chester Martin Keely** . . . . (205) 307-7335
E-mail: martin.keely@usdoj.gov
Education: Samford BGS; Birmingham JD
Chief Deputy U.S. Marshal **Cliff Labarge** . . . . (205) 776-6210
E-mail: cliff.labarge@usdoj.gov
Supervisory Deputy U.S. Marshal (Operations)
Don Snider . . . . (205) 776-6215
Fax: (205) 776-6206
Administrative Officer **Jill Ellis** . . . . (205) 307-7335
E-mail: jill.ellis3@usdoj.gov
Administrative Support Specialist **Natalie Harrison** . . . . . . (205) 776-6223
E-mail: natalie.harrison@usdoj.gov
Criminal Program Specialist **(Vacant)** . . . . (205) 731-0100 ext. 235
Criminal Program Specialist **(Vacant)** . . . . (205) 776-6221
Investigative Research Analyst
Gaytan Glover . . . . (205) 731-0100 ext. 221
Budget Analyst **Sandrieka Moore** . . . . (205) 776-6232
E-mail: sandrieka.moore@usdoj.gov

Huntsville (AL) Office
101 Holmes Avenue, NE, Room 210, Huntsville, AL 35801
Tel: (256) 534-4520 Fax: (256) 539-8574

Deputy U.S. Marshal **Mark Mobley** . . . . (256) 534-4529 ext. 2
Deputy U.S. Marshal **Ron Whelpley** . . . . (256) 534-4529 ext. 1
E-mail: ron.whelpley@usdoj.gov
Deputy U.S. Marshal **Curtis Yates** . . . . (256) 534-4520 ext. 4
E-mail: curtis.yates@usdoj.gov

Alabama - Middle District
One Church Street, Suite A-100, Montgomery, AL 36104
Tel: (334) 223-7401 Fax: (334) 223-7726

★ U.S. Marshal **Jesse Seroyer, Jr.** . . . . (334) 954-3717
E-mail: jesse.seroyer@usdoj.gov
Chief Deputy U.S. Marshal **Thomas Hession** . . . . (334) 223-3090
E-mail: thomas.hession@usdoj.gov
Supervisory Deputy U.S. Marshal **Ashley Hefelfinger** . . . . (334) 223-3111
E-mail: ashley.hefelfinger@usdoj.gov
Administrative Officer **June Rylant** . . . . (334) 223-3100
E-mail: june.rylant@usdoj.gov

Alabama - Southern District
113 St. Joseph Street, Room 413, Mobile, AL 36602
Tel: (251) 690-2841 Fax: (251) 694-4285

★ U.S. Marshal **Mark F. Sloke** . . . . (251) 690-2900
Note: On August 28, 2018 the United States Senate confirmed Mark F Sloke to be a United States Marshal for the Southern District of Alabama.
Education: South Alabama BA
Chief Deputy U.S. Marshal **Vernon Johnson** . . . . (251) 690-2931
E-mail: vernon.johnson@usdoj.gov
Supervisory Deputy U.S. Marshal (Operations)
Timothy Garrett . . . . (251) 690-2939
E-mail: timothy.garrett2@usdoj.gov
Supervisory Deputy U.S. Marshal (Enforcement)
Sean Carney . . . . (251) 690-2841
E-mail: sean.carney@usdoj.gov
Deputy U.S. Marshal **Delvin Brown** . . . . (251) 690-2841
E-mail: delvin.brown4@usdoj.gov
Deputy U.S. Marshal **Michael Clemmons** . . . . (251) 690-2841
E-mail: michael.clemmons@usdoj.gov
Deputy U.S. Marshal **Joshua Devine** . . . . (251) 690-2841
E-mail: joshua.devine@usdoj.gov
Deputy U.S. Marshal **Nolan Dice** . . . . (251) 690-2011
E-mail: nolan.dice@usdoj.gov
Deputy U.S. Marshal **Jordan Futo** . . . . (251) 690-2841
E-mail: jordan.futo@usdoj.gov
Deputy U.S. Marshal **Lawanda Hewitt** . . . . (251) 690-2841
E-mail: lawanda.hewitt@usdoj.gov

Alabama - Southern District *(continued)*

Deputy U.S. Marshal **William McAdam** . . . . (251) 690-2841
E-mail: william.mcadam@usdoj.gov
Deputy U.S. Marshal **Reid Van Bogart** . . . . (251) 690-2841
E-mail: reid.van.bogart@usdoj.gov
Deputy U.S. Marshal **Alejandro Negron** . . . . (251) 690-2841
E-mail: alejandro.negron@usdoj.gov
Deputy U.S. Marshal **Nate Matthews** . . . . (251) 690-2841
Sex Offender Investigative Coordinator
Edward Eversman . . . . (251) 690-2769
E-mail: edward.eversman@usdoj.gov
Judicial Security Inspector **Scott R. Page** . . . . (251) 690-2770
E-mail: scott.page@usdoj.gov
Administrative Officer **Angela D. Garriz** . . . . (251) 690-2841
E-mail: angela.garriz@usdoj.gov
Administrative Support Assistant **(Vacant)** . . . . (251) 690-2841
Criminal Program Specialist **Bernadette Allen** . . . . (251) 690-2841
E-mail: bernadette.allen@usdoj.gov
Budget Analyst **Philomenia Klopner** . . . . (251) 690-2841
E-mail: philomenia.y.klopner@usdoj.gov
Operational Supervisor **Marc Howard** . . . . (251) 690-2841

Alaska District
Federal Building and U.S. Courthouse, 222 West Seventh Avenue #28, Room 170, Anchorage, AK 99513
Tel: (907) 271-5154 Fax: (907) 271-3674

★ U.S. Marshal **Robert William "Rob" Heun** . . . . (907) 271-5154
E-mail: rob.heun@usdoj.gov
Education: West Point 1977 BS
Chief Deputy U.S. Marshal **David Long** . . . . (907) 271-3543
E-mail: david.long@usdoj.gov
Supervisory Deputy U.S. Marshal **John Olson** . . . . (907) 271-1229
E-mail: john.olson@usdoj.gov
Deputy U.S. Marshal **Bryson Barnes** . . . . (907) 271-5154
E-mail: bryson.barnes@usdoj.gov
Deputy U.S. Marshal **Mick Bunn** . . . . (907) 271-5154
E-mail: mick.bunn@usdoj.gov
Deputy U.S. Marshal **Kevin S. Guinn** . . . . (907) 271-5154
E-mail: kevin.guinn@usdoj.gov
Deputy U.S. Marshal **Rochelle L. Liedike** . . . . (907) 271-5154
E-mail: rochelle.liedike@usdoj.gov
Deputy U.S. Marshal **Gilbert Morales** . . . . (907) 271-5154
E-mail: gilbert.morales@usdoj.gov
Deputy U.S. Marshal **Katie Willson** . . . . (907) 271-3501
Deputy U.S. Marshal **(Vacant)** . . . . (907) 271-5154
Deputy U.S. Marshal and District Pilot
James "Sonny" Caudill . . . . (907) 271-5154
E-mail: james.caudill@usdoj.gov
Court Security Inspector **James "Jimmy" Johnson** . . . . . (907) 271-1229
E-mail: jimmy.johnson@usdoj.gov
Administrative Officer **Tanya Lauseher** . . . . (907) 271-5159
Asset Forfeiture Analyst **(Vacant)** . . . . (907) 271-5154
Budget Analyst **(Vacant)** . . . . (907) 271-4375
Criminal Program Specialist **(Vacant)** . . . . (907) 271-4374
Senior Inspector Sex Offender Investigations
Lisa Norbert . . . . (907) 271-5154
E-mail: lisa.norbert@usdoj.gov
Task Force Supervisor **Randy Coyne** . . . . (907) 271-5154
E-mail: randy.coyne@usdoj.gov
Warrant Supervisor **Randy Coyne** . . . . (907) 271-5154
E-mail: randy.coyne@usdoj.gov

Fairbanks (AK) Office
U.S. Courthouse and Federal Building, 101 - 12th Avenue, #6, Room 336, Fairbanks, AK 99701
Tel: (907) 456-0246 Fax: (907) 456-0383

Supervisory Deputy U.S. Marshal
Andrew "Andy" Mazerik . . . . (907) 456-0246
E-mail: andy.mazerik@usdoj.gov
Deputy U.S. Marshal **Scott Ireton** . . . . (907) 456-0246
E-mail: scott.ireton@usdoj.gov
Deputy U.S. Marshal **(Vacant)** . . . . (907) 456-0380

DEPARTMENTS

Arizona District

Sandra Day O'Connor U.S. Courthouse, 401 West Washington Street, Suite 270, SPC 64, Phoenix, AZ 85003-2159
Tel: (602) 382-8767 Fax: (602) 258-1857
Internet: https://www.usmarshals.gov/district/az/

★ U.S. Marshal **David P. Gonzales** .... (602) 382-8767
Education: Arizona 1997 BS
Secretary **(Vacant)** .... (602) 382-8767
Chief Deputy U.S. Marshal **(Vacant)** .... (602) 761-2002
Assistant Chief Deputy U.S. Marshal **(Vacant)** .... (602) 382-2010
Supervisory Deputy of Operations **Jerome Fairweather** .... (602) 382-8781
Supervisory Deputy for Civil **(Vacant)** .... (602) 761-2641
Fax: (602) 382-8760
Criminal Desk **Joann Sandoval-Tirado** .... (602) 761-2653
E-mail: joann.sandoval@usdoj.gov
Investigations Desk **April Rowley** .... (602) 761-2632
Operations Support Specialist **(Vacant)** .... (928) 213-0045
Supervisory Deputy U.S. Marshal - Warrants **(Vacant)** .... (602) 761-2631
Judicial Security Inspector Deputy U.S. Marshal **Jennifer Harkins** .... (602) 761-2411
E-mail: jennifer.harkins@usdoj.gov
Deputy U.S. Marshal **Jeff Parris** .... (602) 382-8764
E-mail: jeff.parris@usdoj.gov
Deputy U.S. Marshal **Pat Willhite** .... (602) 382-8755
E-mail: pat.willhite@usdoj.gov
Deputy U.S. Marshal **(Vacant)** .... (602) 382-8773
Deputy U.S. Marshal **(Vacant)** .... (602) 382-8757
Deputy U.S. Marshal **(Vacant)** .... (602) 382-8766
Deputy U.S. Marshal **(Vacant)** .... (602) 382-8775
Deputy U.S. Marshal **(Vacant)** .... (602) 382-8777
Program Analyst **(Vacant)** .... (602) 382-8767
Detention Enforcement Officer **Troy Hookom** .... (602) 382-8785
E-mail: troy.hookom@usdoj.gov
Detention Enforcement Officer **(Vacant)** .... (602) 382-8785
Asset Forfeiture Supervisor **(Vacant)** .... (602) 382-8722
Computer Specialist **James Dugger** .... (602) 382-8768
E-mail: james.dugger@usdoj.gov
Budget Analyst **(Vacant)** .... (602) 382-8713
Program Analyst **Cynthia Abril** .... (602) 382-8716
Purchasing Officer **(Vacant)** .... (602) 382-8711

Flagstaff (AZ) Office

123 North San Francisco Street, Room 101, Flagstaff, AZ 86001
Tel: (928) 213-0045 Fax: (928) 213-0152

Supervisory Deputy U.S. Marshal **(Vacant)** .... (928) 213-0453
Senior Deputy U.S. Marshal **(Vacant)** .... (928) 213-0045

Tucson (AZ) Office

Evo A. DeConcini Courthouse, 405 West Congress Street, Suite 2300, Tucson, AZ 85701
Tel: (520) 879-6900 Fax: (520) 879-6920

Assistant Chief Deputy U.S. Marshal **(Vacant)** .... (520) 209-0900
Supervisory Deputy U.S. Marshal (District Court Operations) **(Vacant)** .... (520) 879-6951
Supervisory Deputy U.S. Marshal (Enforcement) **Michael Lavin** .... (520) 879-6941
E-mail: michael.lavin@usdoj.gov
Supervisory Deputy U.S. Marshal (Enforcement) **Ron Schlagel** .... (520) 879-6931
E-mail: ron.schlagel@usdoj.gov
Supervisory Deputy U.S. Marshal (Magistrate Court Operations) **Jose Valenzuela, Jr.** .... (520) 879-6972
E-mail: jose.valenzuela@usdoj.gov
Supervisory Deputy U.S. Marshal (Prisoner Operations) **(Vacant)** .... (520) 879-6921
Deputy U.S. Marshal **Audra Bidegain** .... (520) 879-6936
Deputy U.S. Marshal **Ricardo Camacho** .... (520) 879-6968
E-mail: ricardo.camancho@usdoj.gov
Deputy U.S. Marshal **Matthew Crossman** .... (520) 879-6913
E-mail: matthew.crossman@usdoj.gov
Deputy U.S. Marshal **Hector Dominguez** .... (520) 879-6963
E-mail: hector.dominguez@usdoj.gov

Tucson (AZ) Office *(continued)*

Deputy U.S. Marshal **Frederick Freeman** .... (520) 879-6971
E-mail: frederick.freeman@usdoj.gov
Deputy U.S. Marshal **Daniel Hernandez** .... (520) 879-6915
E-mail: daniel.hernandez@usdoj.gov
Deputy U.S. Marshal **Eugene Honce** .... (520) 879-6965
E-mail: eugene.honce@usdoj.gov
Deputy U.S. Marshal **Carlos Najera** .... (520) 879-6912
E-mail: carlos.najera@usdoj.gov
Deputy U.S. Marshal **Art Olivas** .... (520) 879-6978
E-mail: arthur.olivas@usdoj.gov
Deputy U.S. Marshal **Brian Teston** .... (520) 879-6987
E-mail: brian.teston@usdoj.gov
Deputy U.S. Marshal **James Thursby** .... (520) 879-6917
E-mail: james.thursby@usdoj.gov
Deputy U.S. Marshal **Michael Villegas** .... (520) 879-6923
E-mail: michael.villegas@usdoj.gov
Deputy U.S. Marshal **(Vacant)** .... (520) 879-6997
Criminal Investigator **James Bennett** .... (520) 879-6995
E-mail: james.bennett2@usdoj.gov
Criminal Investigator **Bryan Bia** .... (520) 879-6986
E-mail: bryan.bia@usdoj.gov
Criminal Investigator **David Bland** .... (520) 879-6976
E-mail: david.bland@usdoj.gov
Criminal Investigator **Patrick Conover** .... (520) 879-6958
E-mail: patrick.conover@usdoj.gov
Criminal Investigator **Cesar Cordova** .... (520) 879-6900
E-mail: cesar.cordova@usdoj.gov
Criminal Investigator **Allan Magno** .... (520) 879-6926
E-mail: allan.magno@usdoj.gov
Criminal Investigator **George Martinez** .... (520) 879-6967
E-mail: george.martinez@usdoj.gov
Criminal Investigator **Oscar Pintor** .... (520) 879-6989
E-mail: oscar.pintor@usdoj.gov
Criminal Investigator **Jennifer Rippey** .... (520) 879-6908
E-mail: jennifer.rippey@usdoj.gov
Criminal Investigator **Tresa Rodriguez** .... (520) 879-6984
E-mail: tresa.rodriguez@usdoj.gov
Criminal Investigator **(Vacant)** .... (520) 879-6956
Criminal Investigator **(Vacant)** .... (520) 879-6983
Criminal Investigator **(Vacant)** .... (520) 879-6969
Lead Detention Enforcement Officer **Beatriz Gonzalez** ... (520) 879-6997
E-mail: beatriz.gonzalez@usdoj.gov
Detention Enforcement Officer **Rafael Gonzalez** .... (520) 879-6997
Detention Enforcement Officer **(Vacant)** .... (520) 879-6964
Judicial Security Inspector **Rich Tracy** .... (520) 209-0956
E-mail: rich.tracy@usdoj.gov
Contract Oversight Specialist **(Vacant)** .... (520) 879-6925
Criminal Program Specialist **Adria Fernandez** .... (520) 879-6952
E-mail: adria.fernandez@usdoj.gov
Criminal Program Specialist **Olga Ravago** .... (520) 879-6955
E-mail: olga.ravago@usdoj.gov
Investigative Research Analyst **Sylvia Stoddard** .... (520) 879-6934
Investigative Research Specialist **(Vacant)** .... (520) 879-6933
Investigative Research Specialist **(Vacant)** .... (520) 879-6933
Records Examiner and Analyst **(Vacant)** .... (520) 879-6932
Lead Administrative Support Assistant **(Vacant)** .... (520) 209-0952
Administrative Support Specialist **Myriam Estrada** ..... (520) 209-0921
E-mail: myriam.estrada@usdoj.gov
Administrative Support Assistant **(Vacant)** .... (520) 209-0959
Deputy U.S. Marshal **(Vacant)** .... (520) 879-6947

Yuma (AZ) Office

John M. Roll United States Courthouse, 98 West First Street, Yuma, AZ 85364
Tel: (928) 783-6337 Fax: (928) 783-6356

Supervisory Deputy U.S. Marshal **Tom Smith** .... (928) 373-6582
Supervisory Deputy U.S. Marshal **Jennifer Wells** .... (928) 783-6337
E-mail: jennifer.wells@usdoj.gov
Deputy U.S. Marshal **Jesus Cordova** .... (928) 783-6337
E-mail: jesus.cordova@usdoj.gov
Deputy U.S. Marshal **Joshua Finniss** .... (928) 783-6337
E-mail: joshua.finniss@usdoj.gov

★ Presidential Appointment Requiring Senate Confirmation ☆ Presidential Appointment □ Schedule C Appointment ◇ Career Senior Foreign Service Appointment
● Career Senior Executive Service (SES) Appointment ○ Non-Career Senior Executive Service (SES) Appointment ■ Postal Career Executive Service

Yuma (AZ) Office *(continued)*

Deputy U.S. Marshal **Steven Lipscomb** . . . . (928) 783-6337
E-mail: steven.lipscomb@usdoj.gov
Deputy U.S. Marshal **William McAvoy** . . . . (928) 783-6337
E-mail: william.mcavoy@usdoj.gov
Deputy U.S. Marshal **Efrain Velazquez** . . . . (928) 373-6584
E-mail: efrain.velazquez@usdoj.gov
Deputy U.S. Marshal **(Vacant)** . . . . (928) 373-6584
Deputy U.S. Marshal **Matthew B. Waring** . . . . (928) 373-6584
E-mail: matthew.waring@usdoj.gov
Detention Enforcement Officer
Carlos Garabito . . . . (928) 783-6337 ext. 224
E-mail: carlos.garabito@usdoj.gov
Administrative Support Specialist
Javier Hernandez . . . . (928) 783-6337 ext. 277
E-mail: javiert.hernandez@usdoj.gov
Criminal Program Specialist **Joan Demott** . . . . . . (928) 783-6337 ext. 228
E-mail: joan.demott@usdoj.gov
Operational Support Specialist **Kira Shurtleff** . . . . (928) 783-6337 ext. 228
E-mail: kira.shurtleff@usdoj.gov

Arkansas - Eastern District

U.S. Courthouse, 600 West Capitol Avenue,
Room 445, Little Rock, AR 72201
Tel: (501) 324-6256 Fax: (501) 324-6252

★ U.S. Marshal (Acting) **Jay L. Tuck** . . . . (501) 324-6256
E-mail: jay.tuck@usdoj.gov
Chief Deputy U.S. Marshal **David Rahbany** . . . . (501) 324-6256
E-mail: david.rahbany@usdoj.gov
Supervisory Deputy U.S. Marshal **(Vacant)** . . . . (501) 324-6256
Deputy U.S. Marshal **Kevin Sanders** . . . . (501) 324-6256
E-mail: kevin.sanders@usdoj.gov
Deputy U.S. Marshal **Reagan Stephens** . . . . (501) 324-6256
E-mail: reagan.stephens@usdoj.gov
Deputy U.S. Marshal **Jay L. Tuck** . . . . (501) 324-6256
E-mail: jay.tuck@usdoj.gov
Deputy U.S. Marshal **Charles "Chuck" Uchtman** . . . . (501) 324-6256
E-mail: chuck.uchtman@usdoj.gov
Deputy U.S. Marshal **(Vacant)** . . . . (501) 324-6256
Deputy U.S. Marshal **(Vacant)** . . . . (501) 324-6256
Deputy U.S. Marshal **(Vacant)** . . . . (501) 324-6256
Court Security Inspector **(Vacant)** . . . . (501) 324-6256
Asset Forfeiture Investigator **(Vacant)** . . . . (501) 324-6256
Administrative Officer **Beverly Kaplon** . . . . (501) 324-6256
E-mail: beverly.kaplon@usdoj.gov
Administrative Staff **Diane Darbonne** . . . . (501) 324-6256
E-mail: diane.darbonne@usdoj.gov
Administrative Staff **Michelle Haskins** . . . . (501) 324-6256
E-mail: michelle.haskins@usdoj.gov

Jonesboro (AR) Office

311 Federal Building, 615 South Main Street, Jonesboro, AR 72403
Tel: (870) 972-4611

Deputy U.S. Marshal **Bob Clark** . . . . (870) 972-4611
E-mail: bob.clark@usdoj.gov

Pine Bluff (AR) Office

100 East Eighth Street, Room 316, Pine Bluff, AR 71601
Tel: (870) 536-0098 Fax: (870) 536-0079

Deputy U.S. Marshal **(Vacant)** . . . . (870) 536-0098

Arkansas - Western District

Judge Isaac C. Parker Federal Building, 30 South Sixth Street,
Room 243, Fort Smith, AR 72901-2410
Tel: (479) 783-5215 Fax: (479) 782-4204

★ U.S. Marshal **Harold Michael "Mike" Oglesby** . . . . (479) 783-5215
E-mail: harold.oglesby@usdoj.gov
Chief Deputy U.S. Marshal **Dewaine Allen** . . . . (479) 783-5215
E-mail: dewaine.allen@usdoj.gov
Supervisory Deputy U.S. Marshal **Timothy Greer** . . . . (479) 783-5215
E-mail: timothy.greer@usdoj.gov
Deputy U.S. Marshal **Jeffrey D. Landers** . . . . (479) 783-5215
E-mail: jeff.landers@usdoj.gov

Arkansas - Western District *(continued)*

Deputy U.S. Marshal **Cory Thomas** . . . . (479) 783-5215
E-mail: cory.thomas@usdoj.gov
Deputy U.S. Marshal **(Vacant)** . . . . (479) 783-5215
Administrative Officer **Karen Rehing** . . . . (479) 783-5215

El Dorado (AR) Office

101 South Jackson Street, Room 202, El Dorado, AR 71730
Tel: (870) 863-4734 Fax: (870) 863-7726

Deputy U.S. Marshal **Lance Hancock** . . . . (870) 863-4734 ext. 222
E-mail: lance.hancock@usdoj.gov
Deputy U.S. Marshal **Mel Carver** . . . . (870) 863-4734 ext. 221

Fayetteville (AR) Office

35 East Mountain Street, Room 516, Fayetteville, AR 72701
Tel: (479) 442-6141 Fax: (479) 443-1674

Deputy U.S. Marshal **Ben Rennels** . . . . (479) 442-6141
Deputy U.S. Marshal **(Vacant)** . . . . (479) 442-6141
Deputy U.S. Marshal **(Vacant)** . . . . (479) 442-6141

Hot Springs (AR) Office

100 Reserve Street, Room 352, Hot Springs, AR 71901
Tel: (501) 623-9547 Fax: (501) 321-9613

Deputy U.S. Marshal **(Vacant)** . . . . (501) 623-9547 ext. 222
Deputy U.S. Marshal **(Vacant)** . . . . (501) 623-9547 ext. 223

Texarkana (AR) Office

500 Stateline Road, Texarkana, AR 75501
Tel: (870) 774-9922

Deputy U.S. Marshal **Matthew Bremer** . . . . (870) 774-9922 ext. 226
E-mail: matthew.bremer@usdoj.gov

California - Central District

350 W. 1st Street, Suite 3001, Los Angeles, CA 90012-4798
Tel: (213) 620-7676 Fax: (213) 894-2078

★ U.S. Marshal **David Mark Singer** . . . . (213) 894-2485
Education: Cal State (Long Beach) BSCrimJ, MPA
Executive Assistant **Tyree Rios** . . . . (213) 620-8331
E-mail: tyree.rios@usdoj.gov
Chief Deputy U.S. Marshal **Michael Peerson** . . . . (213) 894-2485
E-mail: michael.peerson@usdoj.gov
Assistant Chief Deputy U.S. Marshal
Joseph "Joe" Exner . . . . (213) 894-2485
E-mail: joseph.exner@usdoj.gov
Assistant Chief Deputy U.S. Marshal **Janelle Hohke** . . . . . (213) 894-2485
Systems Administrator **Patrick Tsai** . . . . (213) 894-2485
E-mail: patrick.tsai@usdoj.gov

Riverside (CA) Office

3470 12th Street, Room G-122, Riverside, CA 92501
Tel: (951) 276-6120 Fax: (951) 276-6101

Supervisory Deputy U.S. Marshal **Joe Lewis** . . . . (951) 276-6120

Santa Ana (CA) Office

411 West Fourth Street, Santa Ana, CA 92701-4516
Tel: (714) 338-4610 Fax: (714) 338-4601

Supervisory Deputy U.S. Marshal **(Vacant)** . . . . (714) 338-4610

California - Eastern District

5-600 U.S. Courthouse, 501 I Street, Sacramento, CA 95814
Tel: (916) 930-2030 Fax: (916) 930-2050

★ U.S. Marshal (Acting) **Karen Thomas** . . . . (916) 930-2030
E-mail: karen.thomas@usdoj.gov
Chief Deputy U.S. Marshal **Karen Thomas** . . . . (916) 930-2032
E-mail: karen.thomas@usdoj.gov
Supervisory Deputy U.S. Marshal **Anne Gaskins** . . . . (916) 930-2034
E-mail: anne.gaskins@usdoj.gov
Deputy U.S. Marshal **Jared Belcher** . . . . (916) 930-2044
E-mail: jared.belcher@usdoj.gov
Deputy U.S. Marshal **G. Kevin Biernat** . . . . (916) 930-2037
E-mail: kevin.biernat@usdoj.gov

(continued on next page)

DEPARTMENTS

★ Presidential Appointment Requiring Senate Confirmation ☆ Presidential Appointment □ Schedule C Appointment ◇ Career Senior Foreign Service Appointment
● Career Senior Executive Service (SES) Appointment ○ Non-Career Senior Executive Service (SES) Appointment ■ Postal Career Executive Service

DEPARTMENTS

California - Eastern District *(continued)*

Deputy U.S. Marshal **Philip "Joe" McKeough** .... (916) 930-2041
E-mail: philip.mckeough@usdoj.gov
Deputy U.S. Marshal **Brandon McMullen** .... (916) 930-2030
E-mail: brandon.mcmullen@usdoj.gov
Deputy U.S. Marshal **Kelly Pope** .... (916) 930-2214
E-mail: kelly.pope@usdoj.gov
Deputy U.S. Marshal **(Vacant)** .... (916) 930-2052
Deputy U.S. Marshal **(Vacant)** .... (916) 930-2046
Administrative Officer **(Vacant)** .... (916) 930-2033

Fresno (CA) Office

U.S. Courthouse, 2500 Tulare Street, Suite 3501, Fresno, CA 93721
Tel: (559) 487-5600 Fax: (559) 487-5616

Supervisory Deputy U.S. Marshal **Gilbert Rodriguez** .... (559) 487-5551
E-mail: gilbert.rodriguez@usdoj.gov
Assistant Chief Deputy U.S. Marshal **(Vacant)** .... (559) 487-5550
Deputy U.S. Marshal **Joseph "Joe" Faranda** .... (559) 487-5600
E-mail: joseph.faranda@usdoj.gov
Deputy U.S. Marshal **Anne Gaskins** .... (559) 487-5600
E-mail: anne.gaskins@usdoj.gov
Deputy U.S. Marshal **Stephen Drayton** .... (559) 487-5600
E-mail: stephen.drayton@usdoj.gov
Deputy U.S. Marshal **Edward Zucker** .... (559) 487-5600
E-mail: edward.zucker@usdoj.gov
Detention Officer **Mark Yang** .... (559) 487-5600
E-mail: mark.yang@usdoj.gov
Deputy U.S. Marshal **(Vacant)** .... (559) 487-5600
Deputy U.S. Marshal **(Vacant)** .... (559) 487-5600

California - Northern District

U.S. Courthouse, 450 Golden Gate Avenue,
Room 20-6888, San Francisco, CA 94102
Tel: (415) 436-7677 Fax: (415) 436-7622

★ U.S. Marshal **Donald Martin O'Keefe** .... (415) 436-7688
E-mail: donald.o'keefe@usdoj.gov
Education: Notre Dame de Namur 1995 BS;
U San Francisco 1999 MPA
Chief Deputy U.S. Marshal **Christopher Johannsen** ..... (415) 436-7689
Assistant Chief Deputy U.S. Marshal **Jay Bieber** .... (415) 436-7689
E-mail: jay.bieber@usdoj.gov
Supervisory Deputy U.S. Marshal **Frank Conroy** .... (415) 436-7674
E-mail: frank.conroy@usdoj.gov
Supervisory Deputy U.S. Marshal **Jason Ferrell** .... (415) 436-7658
E-mail: jason.ferrell@usdoj.gov
Supervisory Deputy U.S. Marshal
Michael "Mike" Dyke .... (415) 436-7680
E-mail: michael.dyke@usdoj.gov
Administrative Officer **Judith Tejada** .... (415) 436-7632
E-mail: judith.tejada@usdoj.gov

Oakland (CA) Office

1301 Clay Street, Room 150C, Oakland, CA 94612-5217
Tel: (510) 637-3650

Supervisory Deputy U.S. Marshal
Christopher "Chris" Hanson .... (510) 637-3650
E-mail: christopher.hanson@usdoj.gov

San Jose (CA) Office

280 South First Street, Room 2100, San Jose, CA 95113
Tel: (408) 535-5484

Supervisory Deputy U.S. Marshal **Marc Harwell** .... (408) 808-3950
E-mail: marc.harwell@usdoj.gov

California - Southern District

U.S. Courthouse Annex, 333 West Broadway,
Suite 100, San Diego, CA 92101-8930
Tel: (619) 557-6620 Fax: (619) 557-5215

★ U.S. Marshal **Steven Clayton Stafford** .... (619) 557-6620
E-mail: steven.stafford@usdoj.gov
Education: Northeastern BSCrimJ

California - Southern District *(continued)*

Chief Deputy U.S. Marshal (Acting) **Keith Johnson** ..... (619) 557-6620
E-mail: keith.johnson@usdoj.gov
Assistant Chief Deputy U.S. Marshal **Greg Doss** .... (619) 557-6620
E-mail: greg.doss@usdoj.gov
Assistant Chief Deputy U.S. Marshal **(Vacant)** .... (619) 557-6620
Supervisory Deputy U.S. Marshal **Paul Beal** .... (619) 557-6620
E-mail: paul.beal@usdoj.gov
Supervisory Deputy U.S. Marshal **John Buckley** .... (619) 557-6620
E-mail: john.buckley@usdoj.gov
Supervisory Deputy U.S. Marshal **Steve Jurman** .... (619) 557-6620
E-mail: steve.jurman@usdoj.gov
Supervisory Deputy U.S. Marshal **Kenneth Lavigna** ..... (619) 557-6620
E-mail: kenneth.lavigna@usdoj.gov
Supervisory Deputy U.S. Marshal **Kipp Foreman** .... (619) 557-6620
E-mail: kipp.foreman@usdoj.gov
Supervisory Deputy U.S. Marshal
Joseph O'Callaghan .... (619) 557-6620
E-mail: joseph.o'callaghan@usdoj.gov
Supervisory Deputy U.S. Marshal **Matthew Peters** ...... (619) 557-6620
E-mail: matthew.peters@usdoj.gov
Supervisory Deputy U.S. Marshal
Joe Ruiz de Chavez .... (619) 557-6620
E-mail: joseph.ruiz.de.chavez@usdoj.gov
Supervisory Deputy U.S. Marshal **Jaime Schimmel** ..... (619) 557-6620
E-mail: jaime.schimmel@usdoj.gov
Supervisory Deputy U.S. Marshal **Dexter Vilain** .... (619) 557-6620
E-mail: dexter.vilain@usdoj.gov

El Centro (CA) Office

2003 West Adams Avenue, Suite 210, El Centro, CA 92243
Tel: (760) 353-9790 Fax: (760) 370-3945

Supervisory Deputy U.S. Marshal **Scott Hilbert** .... (760) 353-9790
Supervisory Deputy U.S. Marshal **Ryan Raimo** .... (760) 353-9790
E-mail: ryan.raimo@usdoj.gov

Colorado District

U.S. Courthouse, 901 19th Street, Suite 300, Denver, CO 80294
Tel: (303) 335-3400 Fax: (303) 335-3366

★ U.S. Marshal **David A. Weaver** .... (303) 335-3400
E-mail: david.weaver@usdoj.gov
Chief Deputy U.S. Marshal **Michael Bunk** .... (303) 335-3400
Assistant Chief Deputy U.S. Marshal **(Vacant)** .... (303) 335-3400
Supervisory Deputy U.S. Marshal **Royce Namoca** .... (303) 335-3400
E-mail: royce.namoca@usdoj.gov
Administrative Officer **Shae Haley** .... (303) 335-3400
E-mail: shae.haley@usdoj.gov

Connecticut District

U.S. Courthouse, 141 Church Street - Mezzanine,
New Haven, CT 06510-2030
Tel: (203) 773-2107 Fax: (203) 773-2419

★ U.S. Marshal (Acting) **Brian Taylor** .... (203) 773-2107 ext. 3001
E-mail: brian.taylor@usdoj.gov
Chief Deputy U.S. Marshal **Lawrence Bobnick** .... (203) 773-2107
E-mail: lawrence.bobnick@usdoj.gov
Supervisory Deputy U.S. Marshal **Brian O'Neill** .... (203) 773-2107
E-mail: brian.oneill@usdoj.gov
Deputy U.S. Marshal **Michael Upchurch** .... (203) 773-2107
E-mail: michael.upchurch@usdoj.gov
Deputy U.S. Marshal **Michael Curra** .... (203) 773-2107
E-mail: michael.curra@usdoj.gov
Deputy U.S. Marshal **Mark Benjamin** .... (203) 773-2107
E-mail: mark.benjamin@usdoj.gov
Deputy U.S. Marshal **Matthew Moore** .... (203) 773-2107
E-mail: matthew.moore@usdoj.gov
Asset Forfeiture Program Coordinator
Lisa Staffieri .... (203) 773-2107 ext. 3012
E-mail: lisa.staffieri@usdoj.gov
Asset Forfeiture Program Coordinator
(Vacant) .... (203) 773-2107 ext. 3009
Inspector, Court Security **(Vacant)** .... (203) 773-2107
Warrant Coordinator **Matthew Duffy** .... (203) 773-2107
E-mail: matthew.duffy@usdoj.gov

★ Presidential Appointment Requiring Senate Confirmation ☆ Presidential Appointment ☐ Schedule C Appointment ◇ Career Senior Foreign Service Appointment
● Career Senior Executive Service (SES) Appointment ○ Non-Career Senior Executive Service (SES) Appointment ■ Postal Career Executive Service

Connecticut District *(continued)*

Warrant Coordinator **(Vacant)** .... (806) 240-3245
Administrative Officer **(Vacant)** .... (203) 773-2107 ext. 3007
Administrative Support Assistant **(Vacant)** ..... (203) 773-2107 ext. 3000
Budget Analyst **Christopher Grimes** .... (203) 773-2107 ext. 3004
E-mail: christopher.grimes@usdoj.gov
Criminal Clerk **James Hilaire** .... (203) 773-2107 ext. 3006
E-mail: james.hilaire@usdoj.gov

Bridgeport (CT) Office

Federal Building and U.S. Courthouse, 915 Lafayette Boulevard,
Room 211, Bridgeport, CT 06604
Tel: (203) 579-5897 Fax: (203) 579-5612

Supervisory Deputy U.S. Marshal **(Vacant)** .... (203) 579-5899
Deputy U.S. Marshal **Sarah Calgreen** .... (203) 579-5892
E-mail: sarah.calgreen@usdoj.gov
Deputy U.S. Marshal **Adam Mackey** .... (203) 579-5897
E-mail: adam.mackey@usdoj.gov
Deputy U.S. Marshal **Michael J. Moore** .... (203) 579-5532
E-mail: michael.moore@usdoj.gov
Deputy U.S. Marshal **(Vacant)** .... (203) 579-5589
Senior Inspector **James Masterson** .... (203) 579-5589
E-mail: james.masterson@usdoj.gov

Hartford (CT) Office

Federal Building and U.S. Courthouse, 450 Main Street,
Suite 317, Hartford, CT 06103
Tel: (860) 240-3245 Fax: (860) 240-3248

Supervisory Deputy U.S. Marshal **Abhay Dave** .... (860) 240-3228
E-mail: abhay.dave@usdoj.gov
Deputy U.S. Marshal **John Iverson** .... (860) 240-3245
E-mail: john.iverson@usdoj.gov
Deputy U.S. Marshal **Fred Gengler** .... (860) 240-3216
E-mail: fred.gengler@usdoj.gov
Deputy U.S. Marshal **Kevin Perreault** .... (860) 240-3246
E-mail: kevin.perreault@usdoj.gov
Deputy U.S. Marshal **Frank Roche** .... (860) 240-3245
E-mail: frank.roche@usdoj.gov
Deputy U.S. Marshal **John Stevens** .... (860) 240-3048
E-mail: john.stevens@usdoj.gov

Delaware District

1100 U.S. Courthouse, 844 King Street, Wilmington, DE 19801-3519
Tel: (302) 573-6176 Fax: (302) 573-6218

★ U.S. Marshal **Michael C. "Mike" McGowan** .... (302) 573-6176
E-mail: michael.mcgowan@usdoj.gov
Education: Delaware; Wilmington U MPA
Chief Deputy U.S. Marshal **Tyler S. Kellner** .... (302) 573-6176
E-mail: tyler.kellner@usdoj.gov
Supervisory Deputy U.S. Marshal **William G. David** ..... (302) 573-6176
E-mail: william.david@usdoj.gov
Supervisory Deputy U.S. Marshal **Shateim Mills** .... (302) 573-6176
E-mail: shateim.mills@usdoj.gov
Deputy U.S. Marshal **Toby Conrad** .... (302) 573-6176
E-mail: toby.conrad@usdoj.gov
Deputy U.S. Marshal **Robert E. Henderson** .... (302) 573-6176
E-mail: robert.henderson@usdoj.gov
Deputy U.S. Marshal **Brian Powers** .... (302) 573-6176
E-mail: brian.powers@usdoj.gov
Deputy U.S. Marshal **Jeffrey Zimmer** .... (302) 573-6176
E-mail: jeffrey.zimmer@usdoj.gov
Judicial Security Inspector **Barbara Fahey** .... (302) 573-6176
E-mail: barbara.fahey@usdoj.gov
Administrative Officer **Leslie S. Jamison** .... (302) 573-6176
E-mail: leslie.jamison@usdoj.gov
Budget Analyst **Mindy Coverdale-Moss** .... (302) 573-6176
E-mail: mindy.coverdale-moss@usdoj.gov
Criminal Program Specialist **(Vacant)** .... (302) 573-6176

District of Columbia District

U.S. Courthouse, 333 Constitution Avenue, NW,
Room 1500, Washington, DC 20001
Tel: (202) 353-0600 Fax: (202) 273-5036

★ U.S. Marshal (Acting) **Robert F. Turner** .... (202) 353-0600
E-mail: robert.turner@usdoj.gov
Education: Cal State (Chico) 1994 BA;
Charter Oak State 2014 BSCrimJ
Chief Deputy U.S. Marshal **(Vacant)** .... (202) 353-0600
Assistant Chief Deputy U.S. Marshal **Lamont Ruffin** ..... (202) 353-0600
E-mail: lamont.ruffin@usdoj.gov
Supervisory Deputy U.S. Marshal (Criminal
Investigations) **Linwood "Chuck" Battle** .... (202) 353-0600
E-mail: linwood.battle@usdoj.gov
Supervisory Deputy U.S. Marshal (General Operations)
Gina Chambliss .... (202) 353-0600
E-mail: gina.chambliss@usdoj.gov
Supervisory Deputy U.S. Marshal (Prisoner Logistics
and Services) **Henry D. Alvarado** .... (202) 353-0600
E-mail: henry.alvarado@usdoj.gov
Supervisory Deputy U.S. Marshal **Craig Shelton** .... (202) 353-0600
E-mail: craig.shelton@usdoj.gov

District of Columbia Superior Court

500 Indiana Avenue, NW, Room C-250, Washington, DC 20001
Tel: (202) 616-8600 Fax: (202) 616-8666

★ U.S. Marshal **Michael A. Hughes** .... (202) 616-8604
E-mail: michael.hughes@usdoj.gov
Education: Montclair State U 1990; American U 2007 MPA
Chief Deputy U.S. Marshal **(Vacant)** .... (202) 616-8600
Assistant Chief Deputy U.S. Marshal **Phillip Patterson** ... (202) 307-9269
E-mail: phillip.patterson@usdoj.gov
Assistant Chief Deputy U.S. Marshal **(Vacant)** .... (202) 616-8600
Supervisory Deputy U.S. Marshal **Ronnie Bolls** .... (202) 616-8555
E-mail: ronald.bolls@usdoj.gov
Supervisory Deputy U.S. Marshal **Rafael Ortega** .... (202) 616-8600
E-mail: rafael.ortega@usdoj.gov
Supervisory Deputy U.S. Marshal **John Russotti** .... (202) 616-2294
E-mail: john.russotti@usdoj.gov
Supervisory Deputy U.S. Marshal **Todd Singleton** .... (202) 616-8600
E-mail: todd.singleton@usdoj.gov
Supervisory Deputy U.S. Marshal **Kevin Spencer** .... (202) 616-1962
E-mail: kevin.spencer2@usdoj.gov
Supervisory Deputy U.S. Marshal **John Waters** .... (202) 616-8600
E-mail: john.waters@usdoj.gov
Supervisory Deputy U.S. Marshal **(Vacant)** .... (202) 616-8550
Supervisory Deputy U.S. Marshal **(Vacant)** .... (202) 616-8600
Supervisory Deputy U.S. Marshal **(Vacant)** .... (202) 616-8550
Supervisory Deputy U.S. Marshal **(Vacant)** .... (202) 616-8600

Florida - Middle District

U.S. Courthouse, 801 North Florida Avenue,
4th Floor, Tampa, FL 33602
Tel: (813) 483-4200 Fax: (813) 274-6487

★ U.S. Marshal **William Berger, Sr.** .... (813) 483-4201
E-mail: william.berger@usdoj.gov
Education: St Thomas U BA, MA; Nova Southeastern 2003 JD
Chief Deputy U.S. Marshal **Thomas Figmik** .... (813) 483-4200
E-mail: thomas.figmik@usdoj.gov
Assistant Chief Deputy U.S. Marshal **Dexter Sylvester** ... (813) 483-4200
E-mail: dexter.sylvester@usdoj.gov
Supervisory Deputy U.S. Marshal **Mike McClung** .... (813) 483-4245
Supervisory Deputy U.S. Marshal **(Vacant)** .... (813) 483-4222
Administrative Officer **Amy Warner** .... (813) 483-4218
E-mail: amy.warner@usdoj.gov

Fort Myers (FL) Office

2110 First Street, Room 1-116, Fort Myers, FL 33901
Tel: (239) 337-0002 Fax: (239) 337-7849

Supervisory Deputy U.S. Marshal **Ryan Barry** .... (239) 337-0002
E-mail: ryan.barry@usdoj.gov

★ Presidential Appointment Requiring Senate Confirmation ☆ Presidential Appointment □ Schedule C Appointment ◇ Career Senior Foreign Service Appointment
● Career Senior Executive Service (SES) Appointment ○ Non-Career Senior Executive Service (SES) Appointment ■ Postal Career Executive Service

Jacksonville (FL) Office
300 North Hogan Street, Suite 2-450, Jacksonville, FL 32202
Tel: (904) 301-6687

Supervisory Deputy U.S. Marshal **Penelope Knox** . . . . (904) 301-6670
E-mail: penelope.knox@usdoj.gov

Orlando (FL) Office
401 N. Central Boulevard, Suite 2300, Orlando, FL 32801-0230
Tel: (407) 316-5500 Fax: (407) 316-5510

Supervisory Deputy U.S. Marshal **Anthony Santoro** . . . . . (407) 316-5500

Florida - Northern District
U.S. Courthouse, 111 North Adams Street,
Room 277, Tallahassee, FL 32301
Tel: (850) 942-8400 Fax: (850) 942-8388

★ U.S. Marshal **Robert "Don" Ladner, Jr.** . . . . (850) 942-8400
E-mail: don.ladner@usdoj.gov
Education: St Leo Col BA; Naval Postgrad MA
Chief Deputy U.S. Marshal **Scott Wilson** . . . . (850) 942-8400
Supervisory Deputy U.S. Marshal **Paul J. Joanos** . . . . (850) 942-8400
E-mail: paul.joanos2@usdoj.gov
Assistant Chief Deputy U.S. Marshal (Enforcement)
Greg Lajedal . . . . (850) 942-8400
Assistant Chief Deputy U.S. Marshal (Enforcement)
Andrew Williams . . . . (850) 942-8400
E-mail: andrew.williams@usdoj.gov
Deputy U.S. Marshal **Chase Goller** . . . . (850) 942-8400
E-mail: chase.goller@usdoj.gov
Deputy U.S. Marshal **Kerry Phillips** . . . . (850) 942-8400
E-mail: kerry.phillips@usdoj.gov
Deputy U.S. Marshal **Matt Rongey** . . . . (850) 942-8400
Deputy U.S. Marshal **Marty Horne** . . . . (850) 942-8400
E-mail: marty.horne@usdoj.gov
Deputy U.S. Marshal **Whitney Horne** . . . . (850) 942-8400
E-mail: whitney.horne@usdoj.gov
District Judicial Security Inspector
Christopher Barther . . . . (850) 942-8400
E-mail: christopher.barther@usdoj.gov
Investigative Research Specialist **Robyn Dixon** . . . . (850) 942-8400
Seizure/Forfeiture Specialist **Julie White** . . . . (850) 942-8400
E-mail: julie.white@usdoj.gov
Administrative Officer **Jan Bell** . . . . (850) 942-8400
E-mail: jan.bell@usdoj.gov
Budget Analyst **Kathy Sparman** . . . . (850) 942-8400
Criminal Program Specialist **(Vacant)** . . . . (850) 942-8394

Gainesville (FL) Office
401 SE First Avenue, Room 255, Gainesville, FL 32601
Tel: (352) 378-2082 Fax: (352) 372-1421

Supervisory Deputy U.S. Marshal **John Hallman** . . . . (352) 378-2082
E-mail: john.hallman@usdoj.gov
Deputy U.S. Marshal **Don McAfee** . . . . (352) 378-2082
E-mail: don.mcafee@usdoj.gov
Deputy U.S. Marshal **Adam Myers** . . . . (352) 240-0430
E-mail: adam.myers@usdoj.gov
Deputy U.S. Marshal **(Vacant)** . . . . (352) 378-2082
Administrative Assistant **Jennifer Tallarico** . . . . (352) 378-2082
E-mail: jennifer.tallarico@usdoj.gov

Panama City (FL) Office
30 West Government Street, Panama City, FL 34201
Tel: (850) 763-0771 Fax: (850) 763-0643

Deputy U.S. Marshal **John Farrish** . . . . (850) 763-6449
E-mail: john.farrish@usdoj.gov
Deputy U.S. Marshal **Christopher "Chris" Mask** . . . . (850) 763-0771
E-mail: christopher.mask@usdoj.gov
Administrative Assistant **Jennifer Greene** . . . . (850) 763-0771
E-mail: jennifer.greene@usdoj.gov

Pensacola (FL) Office
U.S. Courthouse, One North Palafox Street, Pensacola, FL 32595
Tel: (850) 469-8270 Fax: (850) 432-2741

Supervisory Deputy U.S. Marshal **Allen Upson** . . . . (850) 469-8270
E-mail: allen.upson@usdoj.gov
Deputy U.S. Marshal **Nichole Dugan** . . . . (850) 469-8270
E-mail: nichole.dugan@usdoj.gov
Deputy U.S. Marshal **Cody Medlock** . . . . (850) 469-8270
E-mail: cody.medlock@usdoj.gov
Deputy U.S. Marshal **Tom Little** . . . . (850) 469-8270
E-mail: tom.little@usdoj.gov
Deputy U.S. Marshal **Carl LoPresti** . . . . (850) 469-8276
E-mail: carl.lopresti@usdoj.gov
Deputy U.S. Marshal **Jennifer Lucht** . . . . (850) 469-8270
E-mail: jennifer.lucht@usdoj.gov
Deputy U.S. Marshal **Rafael Obrochta** . . . . (850) 469-8270
E-mail: rafael.obrochta@usdoj.gov
Deputy U.S. Marshal **(Vacant)** . . . . (850) 469-8270
Deputy U.S. Marshal **(Vacant)** . . . . (850) 469-8270
Investigative Research Specialist **Donna Cato** . . . . (850) 469-8270

Florida - Southern District
400 North Miami Avenue, 6th Floor, Miami, FL 33128
Tel: (786) 433-6340 Fax: (305) 536-5907

★ U.S. Marshal **Gadyaces S. Serralta** . . . . (786) 433-6340
E-mail: gadyaces.serralta@usdoj.gov
Chief Deputy U.S. Marshal **Keith Kluttz** . . . . (786) 433-6342
E-mail: keith.kluttz@usdoj.gov
Assistant Chief Deputy U.S. Marshal **Manny Puri** . . . . (786) 433-6500
51 SW First Avenue, Room 900, Miami, FL 33130
E-mail: manny.puri2@usdoj.gov
Assistant Chief Deputy Northern Division **Glen Wilner** . . . (954) 356-7256
E-mail: glen.wilner@usdoj.gov
Deputy-in-Charge **John Karlovitch** . . . . (561) 467-2347
500 Orange Avenue, Fort Pierce, FL 34950
E-mail: john.karlovitch@usdoj.gov
Supervisor **Wayne Pickering** . . . . (561) 832-7195
701 Clematis Street, Room 215, West Palm Beach, FL 33042
E-mail: wayne.pickering@usdoj.gov
Supervisor **Sabrina Livingston** . . . . (954) 356-7578
299 East Broward Boulevard, Room 312, Fort Lauderdale, FL 33301
Asset Seizure Supervisor **Jacqueline Vazquez** . . . . (786) 433-6391
51 SW First Avenue, Room 900, Miami, FL 33130
E-mail: jacqueline.vazquez@usdoj.gov
Court Security Supervisor **(Vacant)** . . . . (786) 433-6635
Prisoner/Fugitive Operations Supervisor **Joe Godsk** . . . . . (786) 433-6603
Prisoner/Fugitive Operations Supervisor
Robert Rodriguez . . . . (786) 433-6340
Administrative Officer **Madeleine Rivera** . . . . (786) 433-6610
E-mail: madeleine.rivera@usdoj.gov

Georgia - Middle District
U.S. Courthouse, 475 Mulberry Street,
4th Floor, Macon, GA 31201
P.O. Box 7, Macon, GA 31202
Tel: (478) 752-8280 Fax: (478) 752-8214
Internet: https://www.usmarshals.gov/district/ga-m/

★ U.S. Marshal **John Cary Bittick** . . . . (478) 752-8280
E-mail: john.bittick@usdoj.gov
Education: Mercer BA
Chief Deputy U.S. Marshal **Will Hawkins** . . . . (478) 752-8280
E-mail: will.hawkins@usdoj.gov
Supervisory Deputy U.S. Marshal **Brad Wood** . . . . (478) 752-8280
E-mail: brad.wood@usdoj.gov
Senior Deputy U.S. Marshal/Criminal
Investigator/Judicial Security Inspector
Rondell Davis . . . . (478) 752-8280
E-mail: rondell.davis@usdoj.gov
Senior Deputy U.S. Marshal/Criminal Investigator
Tom Patton . . . . (478) 752-8280
E-mail: tom.patton@usdoj.gov
Deputy U.S. Marshal/Criminal Investigator
Thad Binford . . . . (478) 752-8280
E-mail: thad.binford@usdoj.gov

★ Presidential Appointment Requiring Senate Confirmation ☆ Presidential Appointment □ Schedule C Appointment ◇ Career Senior Foreign Service Appointment
● Career Senior Executive Service (SES) Appointment ○ Non-Career Senior Executive Service (SES) Appointment ■ Postal Career Executive Service

Georgia - Middle District *(continued)*

Deputy U.S. Marshal/Criminal Investigator **Ken Britt** . . . . . (478) 752-8280
E-mail: ken.britt@usdoj.gov
Deputy U.S. Marshal/Criminal Investigator
Lataria Cheatham . . . . . (478) 752-8280
E-mail: lataria.cheatham@usdoj.gov
Deputy U.S. Marshal/Criminal Investigator **Don Haney** . . . (478) 752-8280
E-mail: don.haney@usdoj.gov
Deputy U.S. Marshal/Criminal Investigator **(Vacant)** . . . . . (478) 752-8280
Deputy U.S. Marshal/Criminal Investigator
Chris Wright . . . . . (478) 752-8280
E-mail: christopher.wright@usdoj.gov
Deputy U.S. Marshal/Criminal Investigator **(Vacant)** . . . . . (478) 752-8280
Deputy U.S. Marshal/Criminal Investigator **(Vacant)** . . . . . (478) 752-8280
Investigative Research Specialist **Theresa Christian** . . . . . (478) 752-8280
Administrative Officer **Melody Young** . . . . . (478) 752-8280
E-mail: melody.young@usdoj.gov
Budget Analyst **Gena Goodwin** . . . . . (478) 752-8280
E-mail: gena.goodwin@usdoj.gov
Criminal Program Specialist **Tomeko Bryant** . . . . . (478) 752-8280

Albany (GA) Office

U.S. Post Office and Courthouse, 201 West Broad Avenue,
Room 133, Albany, GA 31701
Tel: (229) 430-8436

Deputy U.S. Marshal-in-Charge (Acting)
Stephenie Usher . . . . . (229) 430-8436
E-mail: stephenie.usher@usdoj.gov
Deputy U.S. Marshal/Criminal Investigator
Elorm Blake . . . . . (229) 430-8436
E-mail: elorm.blake@usdoj.gov
Deputy U.S. Marshal/Criminal Investigator
Rodger Hormell . . . . . (229) 430-8436
E-mail: rodger.hormell@usdoj.gov
Deputy U.S. Marshal/Criminal Investigator
Antry Pearson . . . . . (229) 430-8436
E-mail: antry.pearson@usdoj.gov
Deputy U.S. Marshal/Criminal Investigator
Joshua Perreira . . . . . (229) 430-8436
E-mail: joshua.perreira@usdoj.gov
Operational Support Specialist **Kimberley Kvistad** . . . . . (229) 430-8436
Supervisory Deputy U.S. Marshal **(Vacant)** . . . . . (229) 430-8436

Columbus (GA) Office

U.S. Courthouse, 120 12th Street, Columbus, GA 31901
Tel: (706) 649-7822

Deputy U.S. Marshal **Stephen Hall** . . . . . (706) 649-7822
E-mail: stephen.hall@usdoj.gov
Supervisory Deputy U.S. Marshal **Robert Greene** . . . . . (706) 649-7822
E-mail: robert.greene@usdoj.gov
Deputy in Charge/Criminal Investigator
Lane Yarbrough . . . . . (706) 649-7822
E-mail: lane.yarbrough@usdoj.gov
Deputy U.S. Marshal/Criminal Investigator
William "Will" Bowen . . . . . (706) 649-7822
E-mail: william.bowen@usdoj.gov
Deputy U.S. Marshal/Criminal Investigator **(Vacant)** . . . . . (706) 649-7822

Georgia - Northern District

Richard B. Russell Federal Building, 75 Ted Turner Drive S.W.,
Suite 1600, Atlanta, GA 30303
Tel: (404) 331-6833 Fax: (404) 331-3139

★ U.S. Marshal **Beverly Joyce Harvard** . . . . . (404) 331-6833
E-mail: beverly.harvard@usdoj.gov
Education: Morris Brown 1972 BA; Georgia State 1980 MS
★ U.S. Marshal-Designate **Michael S. Yeager** . . . . . (404) 331-6833
Chief Deputy U.S. Marshal **Dawn Anderson** . . . . . (404) 331-6833
E-mail: dawn.anderson@usdoj.gov
Assistant Chief Deputy U.S. Marshal **Daniel Hall** . . . . . (404) 331-6833
E-mail: daniel.hall@usdoj.gov
Administrative Officer **Maureen Chestnut** . . . . . (404) 730-9245
E-mail: maureen.chestnut@usdoj.gov

Georgia - Southern District

U.S. Courthouse, 125 Bull Street, Room 333, Savannah, GA 31401
Tel: (912) 652-4212 Fax: (912) 652-4064

★ U.S. Marshal **David L. Lyons** . . . . . (912) 652-4212
E-mail: david.lyons@usdoj.gov
Education: Tennessee (Chattanooga) BS; Central Michigan MA;
Woodrow Wilson Law JD
Chief Deputy U.S. Marshal
James T. "Tom" Morefield . . . . . (912) 652-4212
E-mail: tom.morefield@usdoj.gov
Supervisory Deputy U.S. Marshal **Keith Sampsell** . . . . . (912) 652-4212
E-mail: keith.sampsell@usdoj.gov
Supervisory Deputy U.S. Marshal **Ramiro Suarez** . . . . . (912) 652-4212
E-mail: ramiro.suarez@usdoj.gov

Augusta (GA) Office

600 James Brown Boulevard, Augusta, GA 30901
Tel: (706) 724-5040 Fax: (706) 724-5041

Criminal Investigator **Brandon Williams** . . . . . (706) 724-5040
Education: Arizona 2001 JD
Criminal Investigator **(Vacant)** . . . . . (706) 724-5040
Criminal Investigator **(Vacant)** . . . . . (706) 724-5040
Criminal Investigator **(Vacant)** . . . . . (706) 724-5040

Brunswick (GA) Office

801 Gloucester Street, Room 213, Brunswick, GA 31520
Tel: (912) 264-8429 Fax: (912) 264-8434

Criminal Investigator **Jason Parnell** . . . . . (912) 264-8429
E-mail: jason.parnell@usdoj.gov
Criminal Investigator **(Vacant)** . . . . . (912) 264-8429
Criminal Investigator **(Vacant)** . . . . . (912) 264-8429

Statesboro (GA) Office

P.O. Box 81, Statesboro, GA 30459
Tel: (912) 489-4735 Fax: (912) 489-4862

Criminal Investigator **(Vacant)** . . . . . (912) 489-4735

Guam and Northern Mariana Islands District

520 West Soledad Avenue, Room 344, Hagatna, GU 96910
Tel: (671) 477-7827 Fax: (671) 473-9195

★ U.S. Marshal **Frank G. Leon Guerrero** . . . . . (671) 473-9101
E-mail: frank.leonguerrero@usdoj.gov
Education: U Guam 1997 BA
Chief Deputy U.S. Marshal **Chuck Ellis** . . . . . (671) 473-9122
E-mail: chuck.ellis@usdoj.gov
Sex Offender Investigation Coordinator
John C. Untalan, Jr. . . . . . (671) 473-9157
E-mail: john.untalan2@usdoj.gov
Judicial Security Inspector **Tanya Muna** . . . . . (671) 473-9104
E-mail: tanya.muna@usdoj.gov
Deputy U.S. Marshal **Alfred A. "Jake" Celes II** . . . . . (671) 473-9105
E-mail: Alfred.Celes@usdoj.gov
Deputy U.S. Marshal **Carlos D. Griffith** . . . . . (671) 473-9106
E-mail: carlos.griffith@usdoj.gov
Deputy U.S. Marshal **Marciano Patricio** . . . . . (671) 473-9103
E-mail: marciano.patricio@usdoj.gov
Deputy U.S. Marshal **David Punzalan** . . . . . (671) 473-9153
E-mail: david.punzalan@usdoj.gov
Deputy U.S. Marshal **(Vacant)** . . . . . (671) 473-9104
Administrative Officer **Elaine J. Gogue** . . . . . (671) 473-9166
E-mail: elaine.gogue@usdoj.gov
Education: U Guam BS
Administrative Support Assistant **Therese Quinata** . . . . . (671) 473-9174
E-mail: therese.quinata@usdoj.gov
Budget Analyst **(Vacant)** . . . . . (671) 473-9176
FSA Property Custodian **Tina B. Diras** . . . . . (671) 473-9169
E-mail: tina.diras@usdoj.gov

DEPARTMENTS

★ Presidential Appointment Requiring Senate Confirmation ☆ Presidential Appointment ☐ Schedule C Appointment ◇ Career Senior Foreign Service Appointment
● Career Senior Executive Service (SES) Appointment ○ Non-Career Senior Executive Service (SES) Appointment ■ Postal Career Executive Service

Northern Mariana Islands Office
Horiguchi Building, Garapan Village Beach Road,
1st Floor, Saipan, MP 96950-0570
P.O. Box 500570, Saipan, MP 96950-0570
Tel: (670) 236-2954 Fax: (670) 236-2956

Supervisory Deputy U.S. Marshal **Don Hall** .... (670) 236-2954
E-mail: don.hall@usdoj.gov
Deputy U.S. Marshal **John Vega** .... (670) 236-2953
E-mail: john.vega@usdoj.gov
Education: U Guam 2010 BSCrimJ
Deputy U.S. Marshal **(Vacant)** .... (670) 236-2955

Hawaii District
Prince Jonah Kuhio Kalanianaole Federal Building,
300 Ala Moana Boulevard, Room 2800, Honolulu, HI 96850
Tel: (808) 541-3000 Tel: (800) 336-0102 (National Command Center)
Fax: (808) 541-3056 (Administration)
Fax: (808) 541-3015 (General Operations)
Internet: https://www.usmarshals.gov/district/hi/

★ U.S. Marshal **Charles L. Goodwin** .... (808) 541-3000
E-mail: charles.goodwin@usdoj.gov
Education: Penn State BA; Woodrow Wilson Law JD
Chief Deputy U.S. Marshal **Gary H. Yandell** .... (808) 541-3000
E-mail: gary.yandell@usdoj.gov
Supervisory Deputy U.S. Marshal **Russ Jacobs** .... (808) 541-3000
E-mail: russell.jacobs@usdoj.gov
Supervisory Deputy U.S. Marshal **Justin Leong** .... (808) 541-3000
E-mail: justin.leong@usdoj.gov
Deputy U.S. Marshal **James "Brent" Cooper** .... (808) 541-3000
E-mail: james.cooper@usdoj.gov
Deputy U.S. Marshal **Thomas Decker** .... (808) 541-3000
E-mail: thomas.decker@usdoj.gov
Deputy U.S. Marshal **Harvey Scott Fuata** .... (808) 541-3000
E-mail: harvey.fuata@usdoj.gov
Deputy U.S. Marshal **Gabriel Ganibe** .... (808) 541-3000
E-mail: gabriel.ganibe@usdoj.gov
Deputy U.S. Marshal **Dexter Gapusan** .... (808) 541-3000
E-mail: dexter.gapusan@usdoj.gov
Deputy U.S. Marshal **Anton "Tony" Hopkins** .... (808) 292-4956
E-mail: anton.hopkins@usdoj.gov
Deputy U.S. Marshal **Eric Kalima** .... (808) 541-3000
E-mail: eric.kalima@usdoj.gov
Deputy U.S. Marshal **Troy Medeiros** .... (808) 541-3000
E-mail: troy.medeiros@usdoj.gov
Deputy U.S. Marshal **Gin Ortiz** .... (808) 436-3000
E-mail: gin.ortiz@usdoj.gov
Deputy U.S. Marshal **Angelique Poe** .... (808) 541-3000
E-mail: angelique.poe@usdoj.gov
Deputy U.S. Marshal **Stanley Sales** .... (808) 541-3000
E-mail: stanley.sales@usdoj.gov
Deputy U.S. Marshal **Nolan Sasaki** .... (808) 541-3000
E-mail: nolan.sasaki@usdoj.gov
Administrative Officer **Channing T. Iwamuro** .... (808) 541-3000
E-mail: channing.iwamuro@usdoj.gov
Deputy U.S. Marshal **(Vacant)** .... (808) 541-3000
Deputy U.S. Marshal **(Vacant)** .... (808) 541-3000
Budget Analyst **(Vacant)** .... (808) 541-3000
Criminal Program Specialist **Sharon Kanakaole** .... (808) 541-3000
DAFC Coordinator **(Vacant)** .... (808) 541-3000
Judicial Security Inspector **Fred Edwards** .... (808) 541-3000
E-mail: fred.edwards@usdoj.gov

Idaho District
Federal Building and U.S. Courthouse,
550 West Fort Street, Boise, ID 83724
Tel: (208) 334-1298 Fax: (208) 334-9383

★ U.S. Marshal **Brian Todd Underwood** .... (208) 334-1298
E-mail: brian.underwood@usdoj.gov
Education: Idaho State 1998 BS
Chief Deputy U.S. Marshal (Acting) **Paul Baxter** .... (208) 334-1298
Supervisory Deputy U.S. Marshal
Peter "Pete" Thompson .... (208) 334-1298
E-mail: peter.thompson@usdoj.gov

Idaho District *(continued)*

Deputy U.S. Marshal **Vance Kosir** .... (208) 334-1298
E-mail: vance.kosir@usdoj.gov
Court Security **George Matthews** .... (208) 334-9679
Administrative Officer **Heidi Moore** .... (208) 334-9495
E-mail: heidi.moore@usdoj.gov

Coeur d'Alene (ID) Office
Federal Building and U.S. Court House,
205 North Fourth Street, Coeur d'Alene, ID 83814
Tel: (208) 667-6840

Deputy U.S. Marshal **Alex Claunts** .... (208) 667-6840 ext. 210
E-mail: alex.claunts@usdoj.gov
Deputy U.S. Marshal **Glenn Morgan** .... (208) 667-6840 ext. 211
E-mail: glenn.morgan@usdoj.gov

Pocatello (ID) Office
U.S. Court House, 801 East Sherman, Pocatello, ID 83201
Tel: (208) 478-4186

Supervisory Deputy U.S. Marshal **Darrin Lambert** .... (208) 478-4191
E-mail: darrin.lambert@usdoj.gov

Illinois - Central District
Paul Finley Building and U.S. Courthouse, 600 East Monroe Street,
Room 333, Springfield, IL 62701
Tel: (217) 492-4430 Fax: (217) 492-5053 (Administration)
Fax: (217) 492-4428 (Operations)
Fax: (217) 492-4840 (Seized Assets, Warrants)

★ U.S. Marshal **Brendan Heffner** .... (217) 492-4430
E-mail: brendan.heffner@usdoj.gov
Education: Illinois State BS
Chief Deputy U.S. Marshal **Brent L. Broshow** .... (217) 492-4467
E-mail: brent.broshow@usdoj.gov
Supervisory Deputy U.S. Marshal **Brett Jackson** .... (309) 208-6384
Areas Covered: Warrants

E-mail: brett.jackson@usdoj.gov
Supervisory Deputy U.S. Marshal **Doug Sparks** .... (217) 492-4227
Areas Covered: Operations

E-mail: douglas.sparks@usdoj.gov
Deputy U.S. Marshal **Karl Hein** .... (217) 492-4229
E-mail: karl.hein@usdoj.gov
Deputy U.S. Marshal **Craig Kmett** .... (217) 492-5008
E-mail: craig.kmett@usdoj.gov
Deputy U.S. Marshal **(Vacant)** .... (217) 492-4435
Administrative Officer **Billie Sparrell** .... (217) 492-5052
Fax: (217) 492-4534
Administrative Support Assistant/Criminal Program
Specialist **(Vacant)** .... (217) 492-5000
Financial Specialist **(Vacant)** .... (217) 492-4535
Seizure and Forfeiture Specialist **(Vacant)** .... (217) 492-5001
Senior Systems Administrator **Michael Jagels** .... (217) 492-4835
E-mail: michael.jagels@usdoj.gov
Judicial Security Inspector **J. Glen Williams** .... (217) 492-5006
E-mail: glen.williams@usdoj.gov

Peoria (IL) Office
Federal Building, 100 NE Monroe Street,
Room 42, Peoria, IL 61602
Tel: (309) 671-7053 Fax: (309) 671-7845

Supervisory Deputy U.S. Marshal **Doug Sparks** .... (309) 671-7156
E-mail: douglas.sparks@usdoj.gov
Deputy U.S. Marshal **Brent Cranford** .... (309) 671-7185
E-mail: brent.cranford@usdoj.gov
Deputy U.S. Marshal **Shawn Langley** .... (309) 671-7042
E-mail: shawn.langley@usdoj.gov
Deputy U.S. Marshal **(Vacant)** .... (309) 671-7158
Deputy U.S. Marshal **(Vacant)** .... (309) 671-7244
Deputy U.S. Marshal **(Vacant)** .... (309) 671-7184
Administrative Support Assistant **(Vacant)** .... (309) 671-7157

★ Presidential Appointment Requiring Senate Confirmation ☆ Presidential Appointment ☐ Schedule C Appointment ◇ Career Senior Foreign Service Appointment
● Career Senior Executive Service (SES) Appointment ○ Non-Career Senior Executive Service (SES) Appointment ■ Postal Career Executive Service

Rock Island (IL) Office
211 - 19th Street, Room G18, Rock Island, IL 61201
Tel: (309) 793-5796 Fax: (309) 793-5808

Deputy U.S. Marshal-in-Charge **Scott Shepherd** .... (309) 793-5794
E-mail: scott.shepherd@usdoj.gov
Deputy U.S. Marshal **(Vacant)** .... (309) 793-5795

Urbana (IL) Office
201 South Vine Street, Room 15, Urbana, IL 61801
Tel: (217) 344-9935 Fax: (217) 344-9972

Supervisory Deputy U.S. Marshal **Brett Jackson** .... (217) 344-9945
E-mail: brett.jackson@usdoj.gov
Deputy U.S. Marshal **Mark Aughenbaugh** .... (217) 344-9963
E-mail: mark.aughenbaugh@usdoj.gov
Deputy U.S. Marshal **Danielle J. Hale** .... (217) 344-9958
E-mail: danielle.hale@usdoj.gov
Deputy U.S. Marshal **(Vacant)** .... (217) 344-9968
Deputy U.S. Marshal **(Vacant)** .... (217) 344-9951

Illinois - Northern District
Dirksen Federal Building, 219 South Dearborn Street,
Room 2444, Chicago, IL 60604
Tel: (312) 353-5290 Fax: (312) 353-4132

★ U.S. Marshal (Acting) **Jason R. Wojdylo** .... (312) 353-5043
E-mail: jason.wojdylo@usdoj.gov
Chief Deputy U.S. Marshal **(Vacant)** .... (312) 353-4979
Supervisory Deputy U.S. Marshal **(Vacant)** .... (312) 353-5291
Supervisory Deputy U.S. Marshal (Asset Seizure)
Cynthia Villarruel .... (312) 353-5291
E-mail: cynthia.villarruel@usdoj.gov
Supervisory Deputy U.S. Marshal (Lock-Up)
Christopher Shaw .... (312) 353-5290
E-mail: christopher.shaw@usdoj.gov
Supervisory Deputy U.S. Marshal (Warrants)
Belkis Sandoval .... (312) 353-6363
E-mail: belkis.sandoval@usdoj.gov
Assistant Chief Deputy U.S. Marshal (Acting)
Ken Robinson .... (312) 353-7192
E-mail: ken.robinson@usdoj.gov
Senior Judicial Security Inspector **Richard Walenda** .... (312) 353-5290
E-mail: richard.walenda@usdoj.gov
Judicial Security Inspector **Paul Banos** .... (312) 353-5290
E-mail: paul.banos@usdoj.gov
Administrative Officer **David Shereyk** .... (312) 353-7034
E-mail: david.shereyk@usdoj.gov

Illinois - Southern District
U.S. Courthouse, 750 Missouri Avenue, East St. Louis, IL 62201
Tel: (618) 482-9336 Fax: (618) 482-9235

★ U.S. Marshal **Bradley A. Maxwell** .... (618) 482-9339
Education: Comm Col Air Force AAS; Park U BA
Chief Deputy U.S. Marshal **Karen Simons** .... (618) 482-9421
E-mail: karen.simons@usdoj.gov
Supervisory Deputy U.S. Marshal **Christopher Boyce** .... (618) 482-9321
Supervisory Deputy U.S. Marshal **Thomas Woods** .... (618) 482-9236
E-mail: thomas.woods@usdoj.gov
Supervisory Deputy U.S. Marshal **(Vacant)** .... (618) 439-7701
Deputy U.S. Marshal **Donald Berry** .... (618) 482-9137
E-mail: donald.berry@usdoj.gov
Deputy U.S. Marshal **James Brigham** .... (618) 482-9159
E-mail: james.brigham@usdoj.gov
Deputy U.S. Marshal **James Jackson III** .... (618) 482-9087
E-mail: james.jackson@usdoj.gov
Deputy U.S. Marshal **Roderick Johnson** .... (618) 482-9239
E-mail: roderick.johnson@usdoj.gov
Deputy U.S. Marshal **Chad Uhl** .... (618) 482-9085
E-mail: chad.uhl@usdoj.gov
Deputy U.S. Marshal **(Vacant)** .... (618) 482-9086
Deputy U.S. Marshal **(Vacant)** .... (618) 482-9089
Deputy U.S. Marshal **(Vacant)** .... (618) 482-9337
Deputy U.S. Marshal **(Vacant)** .... (618) 482-9487
Purchasing Agent **Phyllis Gonzalez** .... (618) 482-9140
E-mail: phyllis.gonzalez@usdoj.gov

Illinois - Southern District *(continued)*

Criminal Program Specialist **(Vacant)** .... (618) 482-9336
Administrative Officer **Wendy Winston** .... (618) 482-9065
E-mail: wendy.winston@usdoj.gov
Accounting Technician **Aaron Thompson** .... (618) 482-9337
Court Security Inspector **Jeffrey Larson** .... (618) 482-9048
E-mail: jeff.larson@usdoj.gov
Investigative Research Specialist **(Vacant)** .... (618) 482-9065
Detention Enforcement Officer **(Vacant)** .... (618) 482-9492

Benton (IL) Office
301 West Main Street, Benton, IL 62812
Tel: (618) 439-6442 Fax: (618) 439-4482

Supervisory Deputy U.S. Marshal **Tana Curtwright** .... (618) 439-7701
Deputy U.S. Marshal **Kevin Castleman** .... (618) 439-7703
E-mail: kevin.castleman@usdoj.gov
Deputy U.S. Marshal **Clark Meadows** .... (618) 439-7704
E-mail: clark.meadows@usdoj.gov
Deputy U.S. Marshal **Jim Robertson** .... (618) 439-7704
E-mail: jim.robertson@usdoj.gov
Operations Support Specialist **Lynn Steh** .... (618) 439-7700

Indiana - Northern District
5400 Federal Plaza, Suite 1200, Hammond, IN 46320
Tel: (219) 852-6776 Fax: (219) 852-6771

★ U.S. Marshal (Acting) **Todd L. Nukes** .... (219) 852-6776
Note: On May 15, 2018, the nomination Todd L. Nukes to be United States Marshal for the Northern District of Indiana was sent to the Senate. Mr. Nukes is currently acting in this position.
E-mail: todd.nukes@usdoj.gov
Education: Ball State BSCrim
Chief Deputy U.S. Marshal (Acting)
Melanie Thompson .... (219) 852-6776
Supervisory Deputy U.S. Marshal **Melanie Thompson** .... (219) 852-6776
E-mail: melanie.thompson@usdoj.gov
Deputy U.S. Marshal **Timothy Craigin** .... (219) 852-6776
E-mail: timothy.craigin@usdoj.gov
Deputy U.S. Marshal **Khari Davis** .... (219) 852-6776
E-mail: khari.davis@usdoj.gov
Deputy U.S. Marshal **Lauren Holly** .... (219) 852-6776
E-mail: lauren.holly@usdoj.gov
Deputy U.S. Marshal **Edward Payne** .... (219) 852-6776
E-mail: ed.payne@usdoj.gov
Deputy U.S. Marshal **Derek Rubarts** .... (219) 852-6776
E-mail: derek.rubarts@usdoj.gov
Deputy U.S. Marshal **(Vacant)** .... (219) 852-6776
Deputy U.S. Marshal **(Vacant)** .... (219) 852-6776
Detention Enforcement Officer **Chris Knudsen** .... (219) 852-6776
Administrative Officer **Rita Anthony** .... (219) 852-6776
E-mail: rita.anthony@usdoj.gov
Administrative Assistant **(Vacant)** .... (219) 852-6776
Budget Analyst **Lorraine Ward** .... (219) 852-6776
Operational Support Specialist **Tamar DeCosta** .... (219) 852-6776

Fort Wayne (IN) Office
1300 South Harrison Street, Room 1147, Fort Wayne, IN 46802
Tel: (260) 423-4667 Fax: (260) 424-8753

Deputy U.S. Marshal **Eric Anderson** .... (260) 423-4667
E-mail: eric.anderson@usdoj.gov
Deputy U.S. Marshal **Michael Minnick** .... (260) 423-4667
E-mail: michael.minnick@usdoj.gov
Deputy U.S. Marshal **John Simpson** .... (260) 423-4667
E-mail: john.simpson@usdoj.gov
Deputy U.S. Marshal **David Veasey** .... (260) 423-4667
E-mail: david.veasey@usdoj.gov
Investigative Research Specialist **Manny Gonzalez** .... (260) 423-4667

South Bend (IN) Office
204 South Main Street, Room 233, South Bend, IN 46601
Tel: (574) 236-8291 Fax: (574) 236-8815

Supervisory Deputy U.S. Marshal
Pamela D. Mozdzierz .... (574) 236-8291
E-mail: pamela.mozdzierz@usdoj.gov

(continued on next page)

★ Presidential Appointment Requiring Senate Confirmation ☆ Presidential Appointment □ Schedule C Appointment ◇ Career Senior Foreign Service Appointment
● Career Senior Executive Service (SES) Appointment ○ Non-Career Senior Executive Service (SES) Appointment ■ Postal Career Executive Service

South Bend (IN) Office *(continued)*

Deputy U.S. Marshal **William Boothe** .... (574) 236-8291
E-mail: william.boothe@usdoj.gov
Deputy U.S. Marshal **Alex Lubarsky** .... (574) 236-8291
Deputy U.S. Marshal **Rodney Shields** .... (574) 236-8291
E-mail: rodney.shields@usdoj.gov
Deputy U.S. Marshal **Amos Workman** .... (574) 236-8291
E-mail: amos.workman@usdoj.gov
Deputy U.S. Marshal **Curtis Dawson** .... (574) 236-8291
E-mail: curtis.dawson@usdoj.gov
Senior Inspector **Laura McKesson** .... (574) 236-8291
E-mail: laura.mckesson@usdoj.gov

Indiana - Southern District

179 Birch Bayh Federal Building and U.S. Courthouse,
46 East Ohio Street, Room 179, Indianapolis, IN 46204
Tel: (317) 226-6566 Fax: (317) 226-7695

★ U.S. Marshal **Joseph D. McClain** .... (317) 226-6566
E-mail: joseph.mcclain@usdoj.gov
Chief Deputy U.S. Marshal **William "Buz" Brown** ...... (317) 226-6566
E-mail: buz.brown@usdoj.gov
Administrative Officer **Lisa R. Black** .... (317) 226-5411
E-mail: lisa.black@usdoj.gov
Operational Supervisor **(Vacant)** .... (317) 226-0253
Warrants Supervisor **John Beeman** .... (317) 226-6059
E-mail: john.beeman@usdoj.gov
Senior Deputy U.S. Marshal **John Pappas** .... (317) 614-0006
E-mail: john.pappas@usdoj.gov
Deputy U.S. Marshal - SOIC **Robert Jackson** .... (317) 226-6570
E-mail: rob.jackson@usdoj.gov
Warrants Supervisor **Megan Sullivan** .... (317) 226-7115
E-mail: megan.sullivan@usdoj.gov
Judicial Security Inspector **Garrett Hawk** .... (317) 226-7789
E-mail: garrett.hawk@usdoj.gov
Administrative Support Assistant/Criminal
Clerk/Service of Process **Sherita Byrdsong** .... (317) 614-0011
E-mail: sherita.byrdsong@usdoj.gov
Financial Specialist **Diana Dickerson** .... (317) 226-6569
District Asset Forfeiture Coordinator **Nneka Greene** ..... (317) 226-6123
E-mail: nneka.greene@usdoj.gov
Investigative Research Specialist (Warrants)
Jarmila "Joi" Howard .... (317) 226-0254
E-mail: joi.howard@usdoj.gov

Evansville (IN) Office

101 NW Martin Luther King Boulevard,
Room 332, Evansville, IN 47708
Tel: (812) 465-6437 Fax: (812) 465-6473

Deputy U.S. Marshal **Jon Albright** .... (812) 465-6437
E-mail: jonathan.albright@usdoj.gov
Deputy U.S. Marshal **Christopher Baldelli** .... (812) 465-6437
Operations Supervisory Deputy U.S. Marshal
Ryan Filson .... (812) 465-6437

New Albany (IN) Office

121 West Spring Street, Room 229, New Albany, IN 47150
Tel: (812) 948-5235 Fax: (812) 948-5207

Deputy U.S. Marshal **Kevin Ferran** .... (812) 948-5235
E-mail: kevin.ferran@usdoj.gov

Terre Haute (IN) Office

30 North Seventh Street, Room 218, Terre Haute, IN 47807
Tel: (812) 232-5058 Fax: (812) 232-3561

Deputy U.S. Marshal **Greg Snyder** .... (812) 232-5058
Deputy U.S. Marshal **David Lewis** .... (812) 232-5058

Iowa - Northern District

111 Seventh Avenue SE, Box 7, Cedar Rapids, IA 52401
Tel: (319) 362-4411 Fax: (319) 362-7098

★ U.S. Marshal **Kenneth James Runde** .... (319) 362-4411
E-mail: kenneth.runde@usdoj.gov
Education: Pepperdine 1975 AA; Wisconsin 1982 BA

Iowa - Northern District *(continued)*

★ U.S. Marshal-Designate **Douglas J. Strike** .... (319) 362-4411
Chief Deputy U.S. Marshal **Myron McDaniel** .... (319) 362-4411
E-mail: myron.mcdaniel@usdoj.gov
Deputy U.S. Marshal **Nicholas Bonifazi** .... (319) 362-4411
E-mail: nicholas.bonifazi@usdoj.gov
Deputy U.S. Marshal **Christopher Kegley** .... (319) 362-4411
E-mail: christopher.kegley@usdoj.gov
Deputy U.S. Marshal **Tyrus Lester** .... (319) 362-4411
E-mail: tyrus.lester@usdoj.gov
Deputy U.S. Marshal **Jeffrey "Jeff" Lour** .... (319) 362-4411
E-mail: jeff.lour@usdoj.gov
Deputy U.S. Marshal **Pedro "Pete" Lozano** .... (319) 362-4411
E-mail: pedro.lozano@usdoj.gov
Deputy U.S. Marshal **Richard Manning** .... (319) 362-4411
E-mail: richard.manning@usdoj.gov
Deputy U.S. Marshal **Earl Plattner** .... (319) 362-4411
E-mail: earl.plattner@usdoj.gov
Administrative Officer **Mellissa Brockes** .... (319) 362-4411
E-mail: mellissa.brockes@usdoj.gov
Management and Program Analyst **Gail Arndt** .... (319) 362-4411
Criminal Program Specialist **Lance Akery** .... (319) 362-4411
E-mail: lance.akery@usdoj.gov
Administrative Support Assistant **Joshua Hammitt** ...... (319) 362-4411
E-mail: joshua.hammitt@usdoj.gov

Sioux City (IA) Office

320 Sixth Street, Room 308, Sioux City, IA 51101
Tel: (712) 252-3077 Fax: (712) 252-3300

Deputy U.S. Marshal **David Hubbell** .... (712) 252-3077
E-mail: david.hubbell@usdoj.gov
Deputy U.S. Marshal **Brandon Johnson** .... (712) 252-3077
E-mail: brandon.johnson@usdoj.gov
Deputy U.S. Marshal **Charles McCormick** .... (712) 252-3077
E-mail: charles.mccormick@usdoj.gov
Deputy U.S. Marshal **Peter Zellmer** .... (712) 252-3077
E-mail: peter.zellmer@usdoj.gov
Deputy U.S. Marshal **(Vacant)** .... (712) 252-3077
Deputy U.S. Marshal **(Vacant)** .... (712) 252-3077
Deputy U.S. Marshal **(Vacant)** .... (712) 252-3077
Operations Support Specialist **Lanae Minten** .... (712) 252-3077
E-mail: lanae.minten@usdoj.gov

Iowa - Southern District

U.S. Courthouse, 123 East Walnut Street,
Room 343A, Des Moines, IA 50309
Tel: (515) 284-6240 Fax: (515) 284-6204
Fax: (515) 323-2800 (Criminal Division)

★ U.S. Marshal **Ted G. Kamatchus** .... (515) 284-6240
E-mail: ted.kamatchus@usdoj.gov
Chief Deputy U.S. Marshal **Robert Otto** .... (515) 284-6423
E-mail: robert.otto@usdoj.gov
Supervisory Deputy U.S. Marshal **Michael Powell** .... (515) 323-2854
E-mail: michael.powell@usdoj.gov
Deputy U.S. Marshal **Justin Barlow** .... (515) 284-6240
E-mail: justin.barlow@usdoj.gov
Deputy U.S. Marshal **Justin Buell** .... (515) 284-6240
E-mail: justin.buell@usdoj.gov
Deputy U.S. Marshal **Scott Cannon** .... (515) 284-6240
E-mail: scott.cannon@usdoj.gov
Deputy U.S. Marshal **Nick Gries** .... (515) 323-2883
E-mail: nicholas.gries@usdoj.gov
Deputy U.S. Marshal **Luke Peters** .... (515) 323-2880
E-mail: luke.peters@usdoj.gov
Deputy U.S. Marshal **Robert Schulte** .... (515) 323-2887
E-mail: robert.schulte@usdoj.gov
Deputy U.S. Marshal **David Zimmer** .... (515) 323-2899
E-mail: david.zimmer@usdoj.gov
Deputy U.S. Marshal **(Vacant)** .... (515) 323-2889
Deputy U.S. Marshal **(Vacant)** .... (515) 323-2893
Administrative Officer **Rita Mason** .... (515) 323-2884
E-mail: rita.mason@usdoj.gov
Criminal Program Specialist **Jeanne O'Keefe** .... (515) 323-2944
E-mail: jeanne.okeefe@usdoj.gov

★ Presidential Appointment Requiring Senate Confirmation ☆ Presidential Appointment ☐ Schedule C Appointment ◇ Career Senior Foreign Service Appointment
● Career Senior Executive Service (SES) Appointment ○ Non-Career Senior Executive Service (SES) Appointment ■ Postal Career Executive Service

Iowa - Southern District *(continued)*

Computer Specialist **Christopher Newcomb** . . . . (515) 323-2882
E-mail: chris.newcomb@usdoj.gov
Judicial Security Inspector **James Batey** . . . . (515) 323-6166
E-mail: james.batey@usdoj.gov
Information and Resources Specialist **Steve Svendsen** . . . (515) 284-6240
E-mail: steve.svendsen@usdoj.gov

Council Bluffs (IA) Office

8 South Sixth Street, Room 344, Council Bluffs, IA 51501
Tel: (712) 322-2034 Fax: (712) 322-2024

Deputy U.S. Marshal **Corey Sherven** . . . . (712) 322-2034
E-mail: corey.sherven@usdoj.gov

Davenport (IA) Office

131 East Fourth Street, Room 300, Davenport, IA 52801
Tel: (563) 884-7667 Fax: (563) 884-7660

Supervisory Deputy U.S. Marshal **Sean O'Neal** . . . . (563) 884-7659
Deputy U.S. Marshal **Terry Bumann** . . . . (563) 884-7663
E-mail: terry.bumann@usdoj.gov
Deputy U.S. Marshal **Joe McCaffry** . . . . (563) 884-7667
E-mail: joe.mccaffry@usdoj.gov
Deputy U.S. Marshal **William Weier** . . . . (563) 884-7661
E-mail: william.weier@usdoj.gov
Deputy U.S. Marshal **(Vacant)** . . . . (563) 884-7667
Operations Support **(Vacant)** . . . . (563) 884-7667

Kansas District

Robert Dole Courthouse, 500 State Avenue,
Suite 380, Kansas City, KS 66101
Tel: (913) 551-6727 Fax: (913) 551-6535

★ U.S. Marshal **Ronald Lee Miller** . . . . (913) 551-6727
Education: Central Missouri 1972 BA; Wichita State 1975 MA
Chief Deputy U.S. Marshal **Craig Beam** . . . . (913) 551-6727
E-mail: craig.beam@usdoj.gov
Supervisory Deputy U.S. Marshal **Jerry Viera** . . . . (913) 551-6727
E-mail: jerry.viera@usdoj.gov
Supervisory Deputy U.S. Marshal **Michael Thibault** . . . . . (913) 551-6727
E-mail: michael.thibault@usdoj.gov
Inspector **Sean Franklin** . . . . (913) 551-6727
E-mail: sean.franklin@usdoj.gov
Inspector **(Vacant)** . . . . (913) 551-6727
Deputy U.S. Marshal **Jovan Archuleta** . . . . (913) 551-6727
E-mail: jovan.archuleta@usdoj.gov
Deputy U.S. Marshal **David Dane** . . . . (913) 551-6727
E-mail: david.dane@usdoj.gov
Deputy U.S. Marshal **Brady Flannigan** . . . . (913) 551-6727
E-mail: brady.flannigan@usdoj.gov
Deputy U.S. Marshal **Roland Hoffer** . . . . (913) 551-6727
E-mail: roland.hoffer@usdoj.gov
Deputy U.S. Marshal **Zachary Howard** . . . . (913) 551-6727
E-mail: zachary.howard@usdoj.gov
Deputy U.S. Marshal **Christopher Johnson** . . . . (913) 551-6727
E-mail: christopher.johnson@usdoj.gov
Deputy U.S. Marshal **Jeremy Pineau** . . . . (913) 551-6727
E-mail: jeremy.pineau@usdoj.gov
Deputy U.S. Marshal **Jason Pizza** . . . . (913) 551-6727
E-mail: jason.pizza@usdoj.gov
Deputy U.S. Marshal **John Volk** . . . . (913) 551-6727
E-mail: john.volk@usdoj.gov
Deputy U.S. Marshal **Christopher Wallace** . . . . (913) 551-6727
E-mail: christopher.wallace@usdoj.gov

Topeka (KS) Office

Federal Building, 444 SE Quincy Street,
Suite 456, Topeka, KS 66683
Tel: (785) 295-2775 Fax: (785) 295-2548

Supervisory Deputy U.S. Marshal **Jeffrey Andrew** . . . . . . (785) 295-2775
E-mail: jeffrey.andrew@usdoj.gov
Deputy U.S. Marshal **Mark Aicega** . . . . (785) 295-2775
E-mail: mark.aicega@usdoj.gov
Deputy U.S. Marshal **Zane Hake** . . . . (785) 295-2775
E-mail: zane.hake@usdoj.gov

Topeka (KS) Office *(continued)*

Deputy U.S. Marshal **Nathan Staab** . . . . (785) 295-2775
E-mail: nathan.staab@usdoj.gov

Wichita (KS) Office

Federal Courthouse, 401 North Market Street,
Suite 207, Wichita, KS 67202
Tel: (316) 269-6479 Fax: (316) 269-6480

Supervisory Deputy U.S. Marshal **Troy Oberly** . . . . (316) 269-6479
E-mail: troy.oberly@usdoj.gov
Deputy U.S. Marshal **Michael Caraway** . . . . (316) 269-6479
E-mail: michael.caraway@usdoj.gov
Deputy U.S. Marshal **Jacob Hilton** . . . . (316) 269-6479
E-mail: jacob.hilton@usdoj.gov
Deputy U.S. Marshal **Lesley Kal** . . . . (316) 269-6479
E-mail: lesley.kal@usdoj.gov
Deputy U.S. Marshal **Keith Lane** . . . . (316) 269-6479
E-mail: keith.lane@usdoj.gov
Deputy U.S. Marshal **Blake Lemer** . . . . (316) 269-6479
E-mail: blake.lemer@usdoj.gov
Deputy U.S. Marshal **Josh Moff** . . . . (316) 269-6479
E-mail: joshua.moff@usdoj.gov
Deputy U.S. Marshal **Quentin Terrel** . . . . (316) 269-6479
E-mail: quentin.terrel@usdoj.gov
Deputy U.S. Marshal **(Vacant)** . . . . (316) 269-6479
Inspector **David Stevens** . . . . (316) 269-6479
E-mail: david.stevens@usdoj.gov

Kentucky - Eastern District

Federal Building, 101 Barr Street, Room 162, Lexington, KY 40507
Tel: (859) 233-2513 Fax: (859) 233-2517

★ U.S. Marshal **BG Norman E. Arflack ARNG (Ret)** . . . . . . (859) 233-2601
E-mail: norman.arflack@usdoj.gov
Education: Eastern Kentucky; Shippensburg MPA; Army War Col
Chief Deputy U.S. Marshal (Acting) **Eric Marcotte** . . . . . . (859) 233-2629
E-mail: eric.marcotte@usdoj.gov
Supervisory Deputy U.S. Marshal (Enforcement)
Gordon Hotchkiss . . . . (859) 410-8034
E-mail: gordon.hotchkiss2@usdoj.gov
Supervisory Deputy U.S. Marshal (Operational)
Robert Kostenbader . . . . (859) 233-2600
E-mail: robert.kostenbader@usdoj.gov
Deputy U.S. Marshal **Jonathan Baus** . . . . (859) 233-2513 ext. 234
E-mail: jonathan.baus@usdoj.gov
Deputy U.S. Marshal **Roger Daniel** . . . . (859) 410-8024
E-mail: roger.daniel@usdoj.gov
Deputy U.S. Marshal **Jeffrey Kelly** . . . . (859) 233-2513 ext. 241
E-mail: jeffrey.kelly@usdoj.gov
Deputy U.S. Marshal **Kenneth "Kenny" Vanover** . . . . (859) 410-8021
E-mail: kenneth.vanover@usdoj.gov
Deputy U.S. Marshal **Gary Heiden** . . . . (859) 233-2513 ext. 234
E-mail: gary.heiden@usdoj.gov
Court Security Inspector **Donnie Ray** . . . . (859) 233-2513 ext. 227
E-mail: donnie.ray@usdoj.gov
Administrative Officer **Sandra K. King** . . . . (859) 410-8029
E-mail: sandy.king@usdoj.gov
Criminal Administrative Support Assistant
(Vacant) . . . . (859) 233-2513 ext. 244
DAFC **Missy Berryhill** . . . . (859) 410-8028
E-mail: missy.berryhill2@usdoj.gov
Data Analyst **Lydia Fuller** . . . . (859) 410-8028
E-mail: lydia.fuller@usdoj.gov
Data Analyst **Jennifer Reynolds** . . . . (859) 410-8030
E-mail: jennifer.reynolds@usdoj.gov
Management Program Analyst **Melissa Smith** . . . . (859) 410-8035
E-mail: melissa.smith6@usdoj.gov
Purchasing Agent **Susan Moore** . . . . (859) 410-8026
E-mail: susan.moore@usdoj.gov
AFI **Eric Marcotte** . . . . (859) 685-4844
E-mail: eric.marcotte@usdoj.gov
Investigative Research Specialist **(Vacant)** . . . . (859) 410-8040 ext. 244
Civil Administrative Support Assistant
Kellyann Thompson . . . . (859) 233-2513 ext. 221

★ Presidential Appointment Requiring Senate Confirmation ☆ Presidential Appointment ☐ Schedule C Appointment ◇ Career Senior Foreign Service Appointment
● Career Senior Executive Service (SES) Appointment ○ Non-Career Senior Executive Service (SES) Appointment ■ Postal Career Executive Service

Ashland (KY) Office
1405 Greenup Avenue, Ashland, KY 41101
Tel: (606) 329-2587 Fax: (606) 329-2559

Deputy U.S. Marshal **Michael Blackburn** .... (606) 329-2587
E-mail: michael.blackburn@usdoj.gov

Covington (KY) Office
U.S. Courthouse, 35 West Fifth Street, Covington, KY 41012
Tel: (859) 392-7918 Fax: (859) 392-7924

Deputy U.S. Marshal **Paul Fetchik** .... (859) 392-7918
E-mail: paul.fetchik@usdoj.gov
Deputy U.S. Marshal **Brian Hilsinger** .... (859) 392-7918
E-mail: brian.hilsinger@usdoj.gov
Deputy U.S. Marshal **Zachary Thompson** .... (859) 392-7918
E-mail: zachary.thompson@usdoj.gov

Frankfort (KY) Office
330 West Broadway, Room 326, Frankfort, KY 40602
Tel: (502) 223-5608 Fax: (502) 223-2745

Note: This office is staffed as needed.

Deputy U.S. Marshal **Gary Heiden** .... (502) 223-5608
E-mail: gary.heiden@usdoj.gov

London (KY) Office
Federal Building, Third and Main, London, KY 40741
Tel: (606) 864-6993 Fax: (606) 878-9310

Deputy U.S. Marshal **Eric Delahoussaye** .... (606) 864-6993
E-mail: eric.delahoussaye@usdoj.gov
Deputy U.S. Marshal **Jonathan Baus** .... (606) 864-6993
E-mail: jonathan.baus@usdoj.gov
Deputy U.S. Marshal **Daniel Garland** .... (606) 864-6993
E-mail: daniel.garland@usdoj.gov
Deputy U.S. Marshal **Todd Hansford** .... (606) 864-6993
E-mail: todd.hansford@usdoj.gov
Supervisory Deputy U.S. Marshal (Operational)
Rick Kelley .... (606) 864-6993
E-mail: rick.kelley@usdoj.gov

Pikeville (KY) Office
Federal Building, 110 Main Street, Pikeville, KY 41502
Tel: (606) 437-6537 Fax: (606) 432-8457

Deputy U.S. Marshal **Matthew Wilson** .... (606) 437-6537

Kentucky - Western District
114 U.S. Courthouse, 601 West Broadway Street,
Louisville, KY 40202-2278
Tel: (502) 588-8000 Fax: (502) 588-8005

★ U.S. Marshal-Designate **Gary B. Burman** .... (502) 588-8010
Education: Louisville BA
Chief Deputy U.S. Marshal **Brian A. Parrish** .... (502) 588-8020
E-mail: brian.parrish@usdoj.gov
Supervisory Deputy U.S. Marshal **Jennifer Fitzgerald** ... (502) 588-8040
E-mail: jennifer.fitzgerald@usdoj.gov
Supervisory Deputy U.S. Marshal **David Hale** .... (502) 588-8080
E-mail: david.hale@usdoj.gov

Louisiana - Eastern District
500 Camp Street, Room 724, New Orleans, LA 70130
Tel: (504) 589-6079 Fax: (504) 589-4028

★ U.S. Marshal **Scott Patrick Illing** .... (504) 589-3683
Education: Southeastern Louisiana BA
Chief Deputy U.S. Marshal **(Vacant)** .... (504) 589-3627

Louisiana - Middle District
Russell B. Long Federal Building and U.S. Courthouse, 777 Florida Street, Room G48, Baton Rouge, LA 70801
Tel: (225) 389-0364 Fax: (225) 389-0370

★ U.S. Marshal (Acting) **Randall "Randy" Breckwoldt** .... (225) 389-0364
E-mail: randall.breckwoldt@usdoj.gov
★ U.S. Marshal-Designate **William Travis Brown, Jr.** ...... (225) 389-0364
Education: LSU BSCrimJ

Louisiana - Middle District *(continued)*

Chief Deputy U.S. Marshal (Acting) **Brian Lucio** .... (225) 382-2168
E-mail: brian.lucio@usdoj.gov
Supervisory Deputy U.S. Marshal
Clayton McDonough .... (225) 382-2156
E-mail: clayton.mcdonough@usdoj.gov
Deputy U.S. Marshal **(Vacant)** .... (225) 382-2003
Deputy U.S. Marshal **(Vacant)** .... (225) 382-2023
Criminal Investigator **Jeff Bowie** .... (225) 382-2026
E-mail: jeff.bowie@usdoj.gov
Criminal Investigator **Bobby Bradstreet** .... (225) 389-0364
E-mail: robert.bradstreet@usdoj.gov
Criminal Investigator **Mark Canning** .... (225) 382-2022
E-mail: mark.canning@usdoj.gov
Criminal Investigator **Daniel Lang** .... (225) 382-0364
E-mail: daniel.lang@usdoj.gov
Criminal Investigator **Josh Reich** .... (225) 382-2023
E-mail: joshua.reich@usdoj.gov
Criminal Investigator **(Vacant)** .... (225) 382-0280
Investigative Research Specialist **Barbara Junius** .... (225) 382-2034
E-mail: barbara.junius@usdoj.gov
Warrant Supervisor **Brian Lucio** .... (225) 382-2010
E-mail: brian.lucio@usdoj.gov
Judicial Security Inspector **Mike Attaway** .... (225) 389-0359
E-mail: mike.attaway@usdoj.gov
Administrative Officer **Alison Alsept** .... (225) 382-2169
E-mail: alison.alsept@usdoj.gov
Criminal Program Specialist **(Vacant)** .... (225) 382-0304
Budget Analyst **Jenevia Johnson** .... (225) 382-2031
E-mail: jjohnson12@usms.doj.gov

Louisiana - Western District
U.S. Courthouse, 300 Fannin Street, Suite 1202,
Shreveport, LA 71101-6304
Tel: (318) 934-4300 Fax: (318) 676-4295

★ U.S. Marshal **Henry Lee Whitehorn, Sr.** .... (318) 934-4300
E-mail: henry.whitehorn@usdoj.gov
Education: LSU (Shreveport) 1986 BA; Grambling State 1989 MS
Chief Deputy U.S. Marshal
Quintella Downs-Bradshaw .... (318) 934-4300
E-mail: quintella.downs@usdoj.gov
Supervisory Deputy U.S. Marshal (Operations)
Donnie Turner .... (318) 934-4304
E-mail: donnie.turner@usdoj.gov
Supervisory Deputy U.S. Marshal (Warrants)
Christopher "Chris" Turner .... (318) 934-4304
E-mail: christopher.turner@usdoj.gov
Administrative Officer **James McLain** .... (318) 934-4300
E-mail: james.mclain@usdoj.gov
Senior Systems Analyst **Dennis K. Austin** .... (318) 676-4296
E-mail: dennis.austin@usdoj.gov

Lafayette (LA) Office
800 Lafayette, Suite 1100, Lafayette, LA 70501
Tel: (337) 262-6666 Fax: (337) 262-6846

Supervisory Deputy U.S. Marshal **(Vacant)** .... (337) 262-6666
Senior Inspector/Court Security **(Vacant)** .... (337) 262-6666

Maine District
156 Federal Street, Suite 180, Portland, ME 04101
Tel: (207) 780-3365 Fax: (207) 780-3230

★ U.S. Marshal **Theodor G. Short** .... (207) 780-3355
E-mail: theodor.short@usdoj.gov
Education: Husson BSCrimJ
Chief Deputy U.S. Marshal **Sean Willitts** .... (207) 780-3355
E-mail: sean.willitts@usdoj.gov
Supervisory Deputy U.S. Marshal **Dean Knightly** .... (207) 780-3355
E-mail: dean.knightly@usdoj.gov
Deputy U.S. Marshal **Jesse Belanger** .... (207) 780-3355
E-mail: jesse.belanger@usdoj.gov
Deputy U.S. Marshal **Spencer Christie** .... (207) 780-3355
E-mail: spencer.christie@usdoj.gov
Deputy U.S. Marshal **Sean Joyce** .... (207) 780-3355
E-mail: sean.joyce@usdoj.gov

Maine District *(continued)*

Deputy U.S. Marshal **Mike Tenuta** .... (207) 780-3355
E-mail: michael.tenuta@usdoj.gov
Deputy U.S. Marshal **(Vacant)** .... (207) 780-3355
Deputy U.S. Marshal **(Vacant)** .... (207) 780-3355
Deputy U.S. Marshal **(Vacant)** .... (207) 780-3355
Purchasing Agent **Tina M. Moore** .... (207) 780-3355
E-mail: tina.moore@usdoj.gov
Administrative Officer **Lisa Caron** .... (207) 780-3355
E-mail: lisa.caron@usdoj.gov
Criminal Program Specialist **Kathy Perron** .... (207) 780-3355
Forfeiture Specialist **(Vacant)** .... (207) 780-3355

Bangor (ME) Office

Federal Building, 202 Harlow Street, Room 322, Bangor, ME 04401
Tel: (207) 945-0416 Fax: (207) 945-0419

Supervisory Deputy U.S. Marshal **Alexander Patnode** ... (207) 945-0416
E-mail: alexander.patnode@usdoj.gov
Senior Deputy U.S. Marshal **Tom Britt** .... (207) 945-0416
E-mail: tom.britt@usdoj.gov
Administrative Support Clerk **Lorie Wing** .... (207) 945-0416
E-mail: lorie.wing@usdoj.gov

Maryland District

Garmatz Federal Courthouse Building, 101 West Lombard Street,
Suite 6115, Baltimore, MD 21201
Tel: (410) 962-2220 Fax: (410) 962-3780

★ U.S. Marshal **Johnny Lewis Hughes** .... (410) 962-2519
E-mail: johnny.hughes@usdoj.gov
Chief Deputy U.S. Marshal **Jack Leo** .... (410) 962-2256
E-mail: jack.leo@usdoj.gov
Assistant Chief Deputy U.S. Marshal **Steven D. Akers** ... (410) 962-7562
E-mail: steve.akers@usdoj.gov
Greenbelt (MD) Office Supervisory Deputy U.S. Marshal **Sean Wolcoff** .... (301) 344-8406
U.S. Courthouse, 6500 Cherrywood Lane,
Suite 170, Greenbelt, MD 20770
E-mail: sean.wolcoff@usdoj.gov
Prisoner Operations Supervisory Deputy U.S. Marshal **Sterling Johnson** .... (410) 962-3533
E-mail: sterling.johnson@usdoj.gov
Warrants Supervisory Deputy U.S. Marshal **Tom McDaniel** .... (410) 779-7331
E-mail: tom.mcdaniel@usdoj.gov
Administrative Officer **Annabelle Perez** .... (410) 779-7345
E-mail: annabelle.perez@usdoj.gov
Management and Program Analyst **(Vacant)** .... (410) 962-7564

Massachusetts District

John Joseph Moakley U.S. Courthouse, One Courthouse Way,
Suite 500, Boston, MA 02210
Tel: (617) 748-2500 Fax: (617) 748-2539

★ U.S. Marshal **John Gibbons** .... (617) 748-2500
E-mail: john.gibbons2@usdoj.gov
Education: American International 1978 BA, 1979
Chief Deputy U.S. Marshal **Kenneth Nunes** .... (617) 748-2500
E-mail: kenneth.nunes@usdoj.gov
Assistant Chief Deputy U.S. Marshal **Jeffrey Bohn** ...... (617) 748-2500
E-mail: jeff.bohn@usdoj.gov
Assistant Chief Deputy U.S. Marshal **John Wickham** .... (617) 748-2500
E-mail: john.wickham@usdoj.gov
Supervisory Deputy U.S. Marshal **Donald Freeman** ..... (617) 748-2500
E-mail: donald.freeman@usdoj.gov
Supervisory Deputy U.S. Marshal **Kevin Neal** .... (617) 748-2500
E-mail: kevin.neal2@usdoj.gov
Supervisory Deputy U.S. Marshal **(Vacant)** .... (617) 748-2500
Administrative Officer **George Farren** .... (617) 748-2516
E-mail: george.farren@usdoj.gov

Springfield (MA) Office

Federal Building and Courthouse, 300 State Street,
Springfield, MA 01105-2926
Tel: (413) 504-1051

Supervisory Deputy U.S. Marshal **Daniel Spellacy** ...... (413) 504-1051
E-mail: daniel.spellacy@usdoj.gov

Worcester (MA) Office

Donahue Federal Building, 595 Main Street, Worcester, MA 01608
Tel: (508) 368-7300

Supervisory Deputy U.S. Marshal **Katherine Wilson** ..... (508) 368-7300

Michigan - Eastern District

Federal Building and U.S. Courthouse, 231 West Lafayette Boulevard,
3rd Floor, Detroit, MI 48226
Tel: (313) 234-5600 Fax: (313) 234-5632

★ U.S. Marshal (Acting) **Mark Jankowski** .... (313) 234-5600
E-mail: mark.jankowski2@usdoj.gov
Chief Deputy U.S. Marshal **Mark Jankowski** .... (313) 234-5600
E-mail: mark.jankowski2@usdoj.gov
Assistant Chief Deputy U.S. Marshal **(Vacant)** .... (313) 234-5600

Michigan - Western District

110 Michigan Street, NW, Room 744, Grand Rapids, MI 49503
Tel: (616) 456-2438 Fax: (616) 456-2446

★ U.S. Marshal (Acting) **Bruce A. Nordin** .... (616) 456-2438
E-mail: bruce.nordin@usdoj.gov
Chief Deputy **Bruce A. Nordin** .... (616) 456-2438
E-mail: bruce.nordin@usdoj.gov
Supervisory Deputy U.S. Marshal **Joseph Guzman** ..... (616) 456-2438
E-mail: joseph.guzman@usdoj.gov

Kalamazoo (MI) Office

410 West Michigan Avenue, Room 154, Kalamazoo, MI 49006
Tel: (269) 349-8700 Tel: (269) 349-9867 Fax: (269) 349-0906

Deputy U.S. Marshal **Mark Holloway** .... (269) 349-3053
Deputy U.S. Marshal **(Vacant)** .... (269) 349-1869

Lansing (MI) Office

315 West Allegan Street, Room 154, Lansing, MI 48933
Tel: (517) 377-1571 Fax: (517) 377-1575

Deputy U.S. Marshal **Scott Masteller** .... (517) 377-1571
E-mail: scott.masteller@usdoj.gov
Deputy U.S. Marshal **(Vacant)** .... (517) 377-1571

Marquette (MI) Office

Federal Building, 202 West Washington Street,
Room 233, Marquette, MI 49855
P.O. Box 698, Marquette, MI 49855
Tel: (906) 226-8812 Fax: (906) 226-7733

Deputy U.S. Marshal **Joshua Ramey** .... (906) 226-8812
E-mail: joshua.ramey@usdoj.gov
Deputy U.S. Marshal **(Vacant)** .... (906) 226-8812

Minnesota District

300 South Fourth Street, Room 402, Minneapolis, MN 55415
Tel: (612) 664-5900 Fax: (612) 664-5955

★ U.S. Marshal (Acting) **Daniel Elbers** .... (612) 664-5905
E-mail: dan.elbers@usdoj.gov
★ U.S. Marshal-Designate **Ramona L. "Mona" Dohman** ... (612) 664-5900
Education: Alexandria Tech 1982 AA; Metropolitan State U 1998 BA;
U St Thomas (MN) 2003 MA
Chief Deputy U.S. Marshal **Daniel Elbers** .... (612) 664-5906
E-mail: dan.elbers@usdoj.gov
Assistant Chief Deputy U.S. Marshal **(Vacant)** .... (612) 664-5970
Supervisory Deputy U.S. Marshal **Rich Pederson** .... (612) 644-5931
E-mail: richard.pederson@usdoj.gov
Supervisory Deputy U.S. Marshal (Warrants) **Michael A. Fuller** .... (612) 664-5900
E-mail: michael.fuller@usdoj.gov
Deputy U.S. Marshal **(Vacant)** .... (612) 664-5960

(continued on next page)

DEPARTMENTS

★ Presidential Appointment Requiring Senate Confirmation ☆ Presidential Appointment ☐ Schedule C Appointment ◇ Career Senior Foreign Service Appointment
● Career Senior Executive Service (SES) Appointment ○ Non-Career Senior Executive Service (SES) Appointment ■ Postal Career Executive Service

Minnesota District *(continued)*

Deputy U.S. Marshal **(Vacant)** .... (612) 664-5921
Administrative Officer **Sharon Eliason** .... (612) 664-5909
E-mail: sharon.eliason@usdoj.gov
Judicial Security Division Inspector **Tom Knutson** .... (612) 664-5910
E-mail: tom.knutson@usdoj.gov
Prisoner Operations Supervisor **(Vacant)** .... (612) 664-5970

Saint Paul (MN) Office

316 North Robert Street, Room 670, St. Paul, MN 55101
Tel: (651) 848-1435 Fax: (651) 848-1440

Supervisory Deputy U.S. Marshal **Rich Pederson** .... (651) 848-1435
Deputy U.S. Marshal **(Vacant)** .... (651) 848-1435

Mississippi - Northern District

911 Jackson Avenue, Room 348, Oxford, MS 38655
Tel: (662) 234-6661 Fax: (662) 234-0219

★ U.S. Marshal **Daniel R. McKittrick** .... (662) 234-6661
Education: Mississippi Col BS
Chief Deputy U.S. Marshal **Jeff Woodfin** .... (662) 234-6661
E-mail: jeff.woodfin@usdoj.gov
Supervisory Deputy U.S. Marshal **Michael Quarles** .... (662) 234-6661
E-mail: michael.quarles@usdoj.gov
Deputy U.S. Marshal **Charles Force** .... (662) 332-6661
E-mail: charles.force@usdoj.gov
Deputy U.S. Marshal **James E. "Bo" Rambo** .... (662) 234-6661
E-mail: james.rambo@usdoj.gov
Deputy U.S. Marshal **(Vacant)** .... (662) 234-6661
Deputy U.S. Marshal **(Vacant)** .... (662) 234-6661
Deputy U.S. Marshal **(Vacant)** .... (662) 234-6661
Deputy U.S. Marshal **(Vacant)** .... (662) 234-6661
Asset Forfeiture Unit Deputy U.S. Marshal **Jill Strauss** .... (662) 234-6661
E-mail: jill.strauss@usdoj.gov
Sex Offender Unit Deputy U.S. Marshal
Richard "Charles" Upchurch .... (662) 234-6661
E-mail: charles.upchurch@usdoj.gov
Administrative Officer **(Vacant)** .... (662) 234-2323
Purchasing Agent **(Vacant)** .... (662) 234-6661
Budget Analyst **(Vacant)** .... (662) 234-6661
Investigative Research Specialist **Carole Arnold** .... (662) 234-6661
Judicial Security Inspector **Gregory Loftin** .... (662) 234-6661
E-mail: gregory.loftin@usdoj.gov

Aberdeen (MS) Office

Federal Building, 301 West Commerce Street,
Room 360, Aberdeen, MS 39730
Tel: (662) 369-4892 Fax: (662) 369-6936

Deputy U.S. Marshal **Joseph Stephens** .... (662) 369-4892
E-mail: joseph.stephens@usdoj.gov
Deputy U.S. Marshal **Corey Rikard** .... (662) 369-4892

Greenville (MS) Office

Federal Building, Main and Poplar Streets,
Room 343, Greenville, MS 38701
Tel: (662) 332-5680 Fax: (662) 335-4703

Deputy U.S. Marshal **William Donald** .... (662) 332-5680
E-mail: william.donald@usdoj.gov
Deputy U.S. Marshal **Robert Lugg** .... (662) 332-5680

Mississippi - Southern District

501 East Court Street, Suite 1.150, Jackson, MS 39201
Tel: (601) 608-6800 Fax: (601) 965-4245

★ U.S. Marshal **George White** .... (601) 608-6800
E-mail: george.white@usdoj.gov Fax: (601) 965-4245
Education: Alcorn State 2009 BS
★ U.S. Marshal-Designate **Mark B. Shepherd** .... (601) 608-6800
Fax: (601) 965-4245
Chief Deputy U.S. Marshal **(Vacant)** .... (601) 608-6800
Supervisory Deputy U.S. Marshal **James McIntosh** .... (601) 608-6804
E-mail: james.mcintosh@usdoj.gov
Deputy U.S. Marshal **Chris Baker** .... (601) 608-6822

Mississippi - Southern District *(continued)*

Deputy U.S. Marshal **Howard Sanford** .... (601) 608-6807
E-mail: howard.sanford@usdoj.gov
Deputy U.S. Marshal **Jeremy Stilwell** .... (601) 608-6800
Deputy U.S. Marshal **Shermaine Sullivan** .... (601) 608-6817
Deputy U.S. Marshal **(Vacant)** .... (601) 608-6812
Deputy U.S. Marshal **(Vacant)** .... (601) 608-6810
Deputy U.S. Marshal **(Vacant)** .... (601) 608-6810
Deputy U.S. Marshal **(Vacant)** .... (601) 608-6821
Judicial Security Division Inspector
Brandon Pritchard .... (601) 965-4444
Administrative Officer **Linda M. Shepherd** .... (601) 608-6850
E-mail: linda.shepherd@usdoj.gov

Gulfport (MS) Office

Federal Building, 2012 15th Street, Room 302, Gulfport, MS 39501
Tel: (228) 563-1505 Fax: (228) 563-1511

Supervisory Deputy U.S. Marshal **Brian Dial** .... (228) 563-1505
E-mail: brian.dial@usdoj.gov
Deputy U.S. Marshal **Steven Davis** .... (228) 563-1505
E-mail: steven.davis@usdoj.gov
Deputy U.S. Marshal **Ivy Jenkins** .... (228) 563-1505
Deputy U.S. Marshal **(Vacant)** .... (228) 563-1505
Deputy U.S. Marshal **(Vacant)** .... (228) 563-1505

Hattiesburg (MS) Office

Federal Building, 701 North Main Street,
Room 331, Hattiesburg, MS 39401
Tel: (601) 582-8464

Deputy U.S. Marshal **Stephen Newell** .... (601) 582-8464
E-mail: stephen.newell@usdoj.gov
Deputy U.S. Marshal **(Vacant)** .... (601) 582-8464
Deputy U.S. Marshal **Marcus Bass** .... (601) 582-8464
E-mail: marcus.bass@usdoj.gov

Missouri - Eastern District

Thomas Eagleton Courthouse, 111 South 10th Street,
Room 2-319, St. Louis, MO 63102-1125
Tel: (314) 539-2212 Fax: (314) 539-2225

★ U.S. Marshal **John D. Jordan** .... (314) 539-2212
Note: On August 28, 2018 the United States Senate confirmed John D. Jordan to be a United States Marshal for the Eastern District of Missouri.
E-mail: john.jordan@usdoj.gov
Chief Deputy U.S. Marshal **Virgil Rickey** .... (314) 539-2212
Assistant Chief Deputy U.S. Marshal
Robert O'Connor .... (314) 539-2212
E-mail: robert.oconnor@usdoj.gov
Supervisory Deputy U.S. Marshal **Cory Harris** .... (314) 539-2212
Administrative Officer **Geraldine Webb** .... (314) 539-2212

Cape Girardeau (MO) Office

555 Independence Street, Suite 2100, Cape Girardeau, MO 63701
Tel: (573) 986-4747 Fax: (573) 986-4770

Supervisory Deputy U.S. Marshal **Charlie Doerge** .... (573) 986-4750
Fax: (573) 986-4752

Missouri - Western District

400 East Ninth Street, Suite 3740, Kansas City, MO 64106
Tel: (816) 512-2000 Fax: (816) 512-2005

★ U.S. Marshal **Mark S. James** .... (816) 512-2000
E-mail: mark.james@usdoj.gov
Education: Central Missouri BS; National Defense Intelligence Col MS
Chief Deputy U.S. Marshal **Scott Seeling** .... (816) 512-2000
E-mail: scott.seeling@usdoj.gov
Supervisory Deputy U.S. Marshal **Shane VanMeter** .... (816) 512-2000
E-mail: shane.vanmeter@usdoj.gov
Administrative Officer **Kateri Flory** .... (816) 512-2000
E-mail: kateri.flory@usdoj.gov

★ Presidential Appointment Requiring Senate Confirmation ☆ Presidential Appointment ☐ Schedule C Appointment ◇ Career Senior Foreign Service Appointment
● Career Senior Executive Service (SES) Appointment ○ Non-Career Senior Executive Service (SES) Appointment ■ Postal Career Executive Service

Montana District
James F. Battin United States Courthouse, 2601 2nd Avenue North, Suite 2300, Billings, MT 59101
Tel: (406) 247-7030 Fax: (406) 247-7035

★ U.S. Marshal **Rodney Ostermiller** . . . . . (406) 247-7030
E-mail: rod.ostermiller@usdoj.gov
Education: Montana State BS; Golden Gate MPA; Champlain MBA
Chief Deputy U.S. Marshal **(Vacant)** . . . . . (406) 247-7030
Supervisory Deputy U.S. Marshal **Tim Hornung** . . . . . (406) 247-7030
E-mail: timothy.hornung@usdoj.gov
Administrative Officer **Carol L. Rash** . . . . . (406) 247-7030
E-mail: carol.rash@usdoj.gov

Nebraska District
Roman L. Hruska U.S. Courthouse, 111 South 18th Plaza, Suite B06, Omaha, NE 68102
Tel: (402) 221-4782 Fax: (402) 221-3006

★ U.S. Marshal **Scott E. Kracl** . . . . . (402) 221-4782
E-mail: scott.kracl@usdoj.gov
Education: Bellevue U BSCrimJ
Chief Deputy U.S. Marshal **Jaime Galindo** . . . . . (402) 221-4782
E-mail: jaime.galindo@usdoj.gov
Administrative Officer **Jane A. Loeck** . . . . . (402) 221-4782
E-mail: jane.loeck@usdoj.gov
Administrative Support Assistant **(Vacant)** . . . . . (402) 221-4782
Asset Forfeiture Coordinator **Chris A. Newton** . . . . . (402) 221-4782
Criminal Program Specialist **Kamela Skinner** . . . . . (402) 221-4782
E-mail: kamela.skinner@usdoj.gov
Management and Program Analyst **Kellie A. Strain** . . . . (402) 221-4782
Purchasing Agent **(Vacant)** . . . . . (402) 221-4782
Supervisory Deputy U.S. Marshal **Bill D. Bitting** . . . . . (402) 221-4782
E-mail: bill.bitting@usdoj.gov
Supervisory Deputy U.S. Marshal **(Vacant)** . . . . . (402) 221-4782
Deputy U.S. Marshal **Thadd W. Baird** . . . . . (402) 221-4782
E-mail: thadd.baird@usdoj.gov
Deputy U.S. Marshal **Shane Knopp** . . . . . (402) 221-4782
E-mail: shane.knopp@usdoj.gov
Deputy U.S. Marshal **Rovance Lewis** . . . . . (402) 224-4782
E-mail: rovance.lewis@usdoj.gov
Deputy U.S. Marshal **Jay Mason** . . . . . (402) 221-4782
E-mail: jay.mason@usdoj.gov
Deputy U.S. Marshal **Chad Reynoldson** . . . . . (402) 221-4782
E-mail: chad.reynoldson@usdoj.gov
Deputy U.S. Marshal **Steven Walter** . . . . . (402) 221-4782
E-mail: steven.walter@usdoj.gov
Deputy U.S. Marshal **(Vacant)** . . . . . (402) 221-4782
Deputy U.S. Marshal/Criminal Investigator **John M. Huggins** . . . . . (402) 221-4782
E-mail: john.huggins@usdoj.gov
Education: Southeast Missouri State BBA; Washington U (MO) MBA
Deputy U.S. Marshal/Criminal Investigator **Daniel Potter** . . . . . (402) 221-4782
E-mail: dan.potter@usdoj.gov
Deputy U.S. Marshal/Criminal Investigator **Chris L. White** . . . . . (402) 221-4782
E-mail: chris.white@usdoj.gov
Deputy U.S. Marshal/Criminal Investigator **(Vacant)** . . . . . (402) 221-4782
Deputy U.S. Marshal/Criminal Investigator **(Vacant)** . . . . . (402) 221-4782
Deputy U.S. Marshal/Criminal Investigator **(Vacant)** . . . . . (402) 221-4782
Deputy U.S. Marshal/Criminal Investigator/Court Security Inspector **W. Chris West** . . . . . (402) 221-4677
E-mail: chris.west@usdoj.gov

Lincoln (NE) Office
Federal Building, 100 Centennial Mall North, Room 552, Lincoln, NE 68508
Tel: (402) 742-7021 Fax: (402) 742-7077

Supervisory Deputy U.S. Marshal **William Iverson** . . . . . (402) 742-7021
E-mail: william.iverson@usdoj.gov
Administrative Operations Assistant **Mark Long** . . . . . (402) 742-7021
E-mail: mark.long3@usdoj.gov
Deputy U.S. Marshal/Criminal Investigator **Allen E. Jewitt, Jr.** . . . . . (402) 742-7021
E-mail: allen.jewitt@usdoj.gov

Lincoln (NE) Office *(continued)*
Deputy U.S. Marshal **Aaron Crooks** . . . . . (402) 742-7021
E-mail: aaron.crooks@usdoj.gov
Deputy U.S. Marshal **(Vacant)** . . . . . (402) 742-7021
Deputy U.S. Marshal **(Vacant)** . . . . . (402) 742-7021

Nevada District
Lloyd D. George Federal Building & U.S. Courthouse, 333 Las Vegas Boulevard, South, Suite 2058, Las Vegas, NV 89101
Tel: (702) 388-6355 Fax: (702) 388-6703

★ U.S. Marshal **Gary Schofield** . . . . . (702) 388-6355
E-mail: gary.schofield@usdoj.gov
Education: Thomas Edison State BS; Alaska (Fairbanks) MS
Chief Deputy U.S. Marshal **Doyle Decker** . . . . . (702) 388-6356
E-mail: doyle.decker@usdoj.gov
Supervisory Deputy U.S. Marshal **Michael Banez** . . . . . (702) 388-6356
E-mail: michael.banez@usdoj.gov
Supervisory Deputy U.S. Marshal **Melinda Kormos** . . . . . (702) 388-6355
E-mail: melinda.kormos@usdoj.gov
Supervisory Deputy U.S. Marshal **Nathan Powell** . . . . . (702) 388-6356
E-mail: nathan.powell@usdoj.gov
Deputy U.S. Marshal **Rudy Lara** . . . . . (702) 388-6356
E-mail: rudy.lara@usdoj.gov
Deputy U.S. Marshal **(Vacant)** . . . . . (702) 388-6356
Court Security Inspector **Reuben Bugtong** . . . . . (702) 388-6356
E-mail: reuben.bugtong@usdoj.gov
Task Force Supervisor **(Vacant)** . . . . . (702) 388-6356
Data Analyst **Peter Tomas** . . . . . (702) 388-6355

Reno (NV) Office
Bruce R. Thompson Federal Building, 400 South Virginia Street, Room 201, Reno, NV 89501
Tel: (775) 686-5780 Fax: (775) 686-5794

Supervisory Deputy U.S. Marshal **Tyrone Kilpatrick** . . . . . (775) 686-5780
E-mail: tyrone.kilpatrick@usdoj.gov
Deputy U.S. Marshal **Rhonda Adams** . . . . . (775) 686-5780
E-mail: rhonda.adams@usdoj.gov
Deputy U.S. Marshal **Eric Beyersdorf** . . . . . (775) 686-5780
E-mail: eric.beyersdorf@usdoj.gov
Deputy U.S. Marshal **Daryl Hollenbach** . . . . . (775) 686-5780
Deputy U.S. Marshal **Quinn Pardo** . . . . . (775) 686-5780
E-mail: quinn.pardo@usdoj.gov
Deputy U.S. Marshal **(Vacant)** . . . . . (775) 686-5780

New Hampshire District
Warren Rudman Courthouse, 55 Pleasant Street, Suite 207, Concord, NH 03301
Tel: (603) 225-1632 Fax: (603) 225-1633

★ U.S. Marshal **Enoch "Nick" Willard** . . . . . (603) 225-1632
E-mail: enoch.willard@usdoj.gov
Education: New Hampshire Tech AS
Chief Deputy U.S. Marshal **Brenda Mikelson** . . . . . (603) 225-1632
Supervisory Deputy U.S. Marshal **Eugene Robinson** . . . . (603) 225-1635
Deputy U.S. Marshal **Daniel Ciancilo** . . . . . (603) 226-7302
Deputy U.S. Marshal **Chris Deaton** . . . . . (603) 226-7757
E-mail: chris.deaton@usdoj.gov
Deputy U.S. Marshal **Daniel Dempsey** . . . . . (603) 225-7379
E-mail: daniel.dempsey@usdoj.gov
Deputy U.S. Marshal **Mark Lewis** . . . . . (603) 226-7372
E-mail: mark.lewis@usdoj.gov
Deputy U.S. Marshal **Gregory Murano** . . . . . (603) 225-1595
E-mail: gregory.murano@usdoj.gov
Deputy U.S. Marshal **Joseph Vetanze** . . . . . (603) 226-7765
E-mail: joseph.vetanze@usdoj.gov
Deputy U.S. Marshal **Jeffrey White, Jr.** . . . . . (603) 226-7376
E-mail: jeffrey.white@usdoj.gov
Judicial Security Inspector **(Vacant)** . . . . . (603) 225-1636
Administrative Officer **Barbara Gatti** . . . . . (603) 225-1443
E-mail: barbara.gatti@usdoj.gov
Administrative Assistant **Wanda Dechaine** . . . . . (603) 225-1630
E-mail: wanda.dechaine@usdoj.gov
Administrative Officer **Kimberly Dow** . . . . . (603) 225-1646
E-mail: kimberly.dow@usdoj.gov

(continued on next page)

DEPARTMENTS

New Hampshire District *(continued)*

District Asset Forfeiture Specialist **Kathleen Renaud** .... (603) 226-7375
E-mail: kathleen.renaud@usdoj.gov

New Jersey District

Martin Luther King, Jr. Courthouse, 50 Walnut Street, Room 2009, Newark, NJ 07102
Tel: (973) 645-2404 Fax: (973) 693-4142

★ U.S. Marshal **Juan Mattos, Jr.** .... (973) 645-2404
E-mail: juan.mattos@usdoj.gov
Education: Jersey City State; Monmouth U MA

Chief Deputy U.S. Marshal **John M. Svinos** .... (973) 645-2404 ext. 250
E-mail: john.svinos@usdoj.gov

Administrative Officer **Robert Freyland** .... (973) 645-2626
E-mail: robert.freyland@usdoj.gov

Administrative Support Specialist **Elizabeth Baskerville** .... (973) 645-2404 ext. 247
E-mail: elizabeth.baskerville@usdoj.gov

Camden (NJ) Office

P.O. Box 288, Camden, NJ 08101
Tel: (856) 757-5024 Fax: (856) 757-5161

Supervisor **Chad W. Grant** .... (856) 757-5024
E-mail: chad.grant@usdoj.gov

Trenton (NJ) Office

402 East State Street, Trenton, NJ 08608
Tel: (609) 989-2069 Fax: (609) 989-2145

Supervisor (Acting) **Michael Lewandowski** .... (609) 989-2069
E-mail: michael.lewandowski@usdoj.gov

New Mexico District

U.S. Courthouse, 333 Lomas, NW, Suite 180, Albuquerque, NM 87102
Tel: (505) 346-6400 Fax: (505) 346-6417

★ U.S. Marshal **Sonya K. Chavez** .... (505) 346-6400
E-mail: sonya.chavez@usdoj.gov
Education: New Mexico State BA; New Mexico MA

Chief Deputy U.S. Marshal **(Vacant)** .... (505) 346-6400

Supervisory Deputy U.S. Marshal **Vincent Gambone** .... (505) 462-2368
E-mail: vincent.gambone@usdoj.gov

Judicial Security Inspector **Jennifer Simonetty** .... (505) 462-2339
E-mail: jennifer.simonetty@usdoj.gov

Asset Forfeiture Criminal Investigator **Mitch Varley** ...... (505) 346-6400
E-mail: mitch.varley@usdoj.gov

Administrative Officer **Randy Rettinger** .... (505) 462-2302
E-mail: randy.rettinger@usdoj.gov

New York - Eastern District

225 Cadman Plaza East, Room G-20, Brooklyn, NY 11201
Tel: (718) 260-0400 Fax: (718) 260-0436 Fax: (718) 260-0431

★ U.S. Marshal (Acting) **Bryan Mullee** .... (718) 260-0401
E-mail: bryan.mullee@usdoj.gov
Education: St John's U (NY) 1990 BS; Brooklyn Law 1996 JD

Chief Deputy U.S. Marshal **Bryan Mullee** .... (718) 260-0402
E-mail: bryan.mullee@usdoj.gov
Education: St John's U (NY) 1990 BS; Brooklyn Law 1996 JD

Assistant Chief Deputy U.S. Marshal **James Elcik** .... (718) 260-0403
E-mail: james.elcik@usdoj.gov

Assistant Chief Deputy U.S. Marshal **Juan Tavarez** ...... (718) 260-0407
E-mail: juan.tavarez@usdoj.gov

System Administrator **Raymond Ng** .... (718) 260-0433
E-mail: raymond.ng@usdoj.gov

New York - Northern District

Federal Building, 100 South Clinton Street, 10th Floor, Syracuse, NY 13261
Tel: (315) 473-7601 Fax: (315) 473-7600

★ U.S. Marshal **David L. McNulty** .... (315) 473-7601
E-mail: david.mcnulty@usdoj.gov

Chief Deputy U.S. Marshal **(Vacant)** .... (315) 473-7612

Supervisory Deputy U.S. Marshal **(Vacant)** .... (315) 473-7613

New York - Northern District *(continued)*

Deputy U.S. Marshal **Christopher Amoia** .... (315) 473-7630
E-mail: christopher.amoia@usdoj.gov

Deputy U.S. Marshal **(Vacant)** .... (315) 473-7627

Deputy U.S. Marshal **Mark Jenkusky** .... (315) 473-7621
E-mail: mark.jenkusky@usdoj.gov

Deputy U.S. Marshal **Greg Morawiec** .... (315) 473-7618
E-mail: gregory.morawiec@usdoj.gov

Deputy U.S. Marshal **Jim Nichols** .... (315) 473-7617
E-mail: james.nichols@usdoj.gov

Deputy U.S. Marshal **(Vacant)** .... (315) 473-7601

Deputy U.S. Marshal **(Vacant)** .... (315) 473-7623

Deputy U.S. Marshal **(Vacant)** .... (315) 473-7601

Deputy U.S. Marshal **(Vacant)** .... (315) 473-7629

Administrative Officer **Barbara D. Wright** .... (315) 473-7603
E-mail: barbara.wright@usdoj.gov

Deputy U.S. Marshal **(Vacant)** .... (315) 473-7620

Fiscal Officer **Steven Seaman** .... (315) 473-7670
E-mail: steven.seaman@usdoj.gov

Investigative Research Specialist **(Vacant)** .... (315) 473-7608

Property Manager **(Vacant)** .... (315) 473-7601

Criminal Clerk **(Vacant)** .... (315) 473-7670

Civil Clerk **Jacqueline Cleary** .... (315) 473-7669
E-mail: jacqueline.cleary@usdoj.gov

Albany (NY) Office

James T. Foley Courthouse, 445 Broadway, Albany, NY 12207
Tel: (518) 472-5401 Tel: (315) 473-7601 (24 Hours)
Fax: (518) 472-5400

Supervisory Deputy U.S. Marshal **Brandon LaMora** ..... (518) 472-5413
E-mail: brandon.lamora@usdoj.gov

Deputy U.S. Marshal **Alex Baker** .... (518) 472-5401
E-mail: alexander.baker@usdoj.gov

Deputy U.S. Marshal **Joseph Graziane** .... (518) 472-5401
E-mail: joseph.graziane@usdoj.gov

Deputy U.S. Marshal **Ken Mead** .... (518) 472-5416
E-mail: kenneth.mead@usdoj.gov

Deputy U.S. Marshal **Michael Tracey** .... (518) 472-5420
E-mail: michael.tracey@usdoj.gov

Deputy U.S. Marshal **William C. O'Toole** .... (518) 472-5430
E-mail: william.otoole@usdoj.gov

Deputy U.S. Marshal **Mark Voellm** .... (518) 472-5425
E-mail: mark.voellm@usdoj.gov

Deputy U.S. Marshal **Michael Woerner** .... (518) 472-5427
E-mail: michael.woerner@usdoj.gov

Deputy U.S. Marshal **(Vacant)** .... (518) 472-5426

Deputy U.S. Marshal **(Vacant)** .... (518) 472-5421

Administrative Assistant **(Vacant)** .... (518) 472-5401

Detention Officer **(Vacant)** .... (518) 472-5417

Binghamton (NY) Office

U.S. Courthouse and Federal Building, 15 Henry Street, Room 228, Binghamton, NY 13902
Tel: (607) 773-2723 Tel: (315) 732-2123 (24 Hours)
Fax: (607) 773-2726

Deputy U.S. Marshal **(Vacant)** .... (607) 773-2723

Utica (NY) Office

Federal Building, 10 Broad Street, Room 213, Utica, NY 13501
Tel: (315) 793-8109 Tel: (315) 732-2123 (24 Hours)
Fax: (315) 793-8196

Deputy U.S. Marshal **Jamie Farrington** .... (315) 793-8109
E-mail: jamie.farrington@usdoj.gov

New York - Southern District

500 Pearl Street, 4th Floor, New York, NY 10007
Tel: (212) 331-7200 Fax: (212) 637-6130

★ U.S. Marshal **Michael Greco** .... (212) 331-7100
E-mail: michael.greco@usdoj.gov
Education: Excelsior 2012 AA

Chief Deputy U.S. Marshal **Eric B. Timberman** .... (212) 331-7200 ext. 7102
E-mail: eric.timberman@usdoj.gov

★ Presidential Appointment Requiring Senate Confirmation ☆ Presidential Appointment □ Schedule C Appointment ◇ Career Senior Foreign Service Appointment
● Career Senior Executive Service (SES) Appointment ○ Non-Career Senior Executive Service (SES) Appointment ■ Postal Career Executive Service

New York - Western District
Robert H. Jackson United States Courthouse,
2 Niagara Square, Buffalo, NY 14202
Tel: (716) 348-5300 Fax: (716) 551-5505

★ U.S. Marshal **Charles F. Salina** .... (716) 348-5300
E-mail: charles.salina@usdoj.gov
Education: SUNY (Oswego)
Chief Deputy U.S. Marshal **David Goldman** .... (716) 348-5300
Supervisory Deputy U.S. Marshal **Michael Malcolm** .... (716) 348-5300
E-mail: michael.malcolm@usdoj.gov
Supervisory Deputy U.S. Marshal **Rebecca Smith** .... (716) 348-5300
Deputy U.S. Marshal **Scott Baryza** .... (716) 348-5300
E-mail: scott.baryza@usdoj.gov
Deputy U.S. Marshal **Lee Eckenrode** .... (716) 348-5300
E-mail: lee.eckenrode@usdoj.gov
Deputy U.S. Marshal **Mark Fialkiewicz** .... (716) 348-5300
E-mail: mark.fialkiewicz@usdoj.gov
Deputy U.S. Marshal **Kenneth Gordon** .... (716) 348-5300
E-mail: kenneth.gordon@usdoj.gov
Deputy U.S. Marshal **Michael Malcolm** .... (716) 348-5300
E-mail: michael.malcolm@usdoj.gov
Deputy U.S. Marshal **Brent Novak** .... (716) 348-5300
E-mail: brent.novak@usdoj.gov
Deputy U.S. Marshal **Kenneth Pirone** .... (716) 348-5300
E-mail: ken.pirone@usdoj.gov
Deputy U.S. Marshal **Richard Rooney** .... (716) 348-5300
E-mail: richard.rooney@usdoj.gov
Deputy U.S. Marshal **Doug Wilson** .... (716) 348-5300
E-mail: doug.wilson@usdoj.gov
Deputy U.S. Marshal **(Vacant)** .... (716) 348-5300
Deputy U.S. Marshal **(Vacant)** .... (716) 348-5300
Deputy U.S. Marshal **(Vacant)** .... (716) 348-5300
Administrative Officer **Jennifer Pearson** .... (716) 348-5300
68 Court Street, Room 129, Buffalo, NY 14202
E-mail: jennifer.pearson@usdoj.gov
Criminal Program Specialist **(Vacant)** .... (716) 348-5300
Criminal Program Specialist **(Vacant)** .... (716) 348-5300
68 Court Street, Room 129, Buffalo, NY 14202
Property Management Specialist **(Vacant)** .... (716) 348-5300
68 Court Street, Room 129, Buffalo, NY 14202
Administrative Support Specialist **(Vacant)** .... (716) 348-5300
DAFC **Beata Hosking** .... (716) 348-5300
E-mail: beata.hosking@usdoj.gov
Management and Program Analyst **Jennifer Pearson** .... (716) 348-5300

Rochester (NY) Office
U.S. Courthouse, 100 State Street, Room 2240, Rochester, NY 14614
Tel: (585) 263-5787 Fax: (585) 263-6741

Supervisory Deputy U.S. Marshal **(Vacant)** .... (585) 263-5850
Deputy U.S. Marshal **(Vacant)** .... (585) 263-5787
Deputy U.S. Marshal **Mark Leveque** .... (585) 263-5787
E-mail: mark.leveque@usdoj.gov
Deputy U.S. Marshal **Shane Marshall** .... (585) 263-5787
Deputy U.S. Marshal **Carlton Smith** .... (585) 263-5787
Deputy U.S. Marshal **Rebecca Smith** .... (585) 263-5787
E-mail: rebecca.smith@usdoj.gov
Deputy U.S. Marshal **(Vacant)** .... (585) 263-5787 ext. 229
Deputy U.S. Marshal **(Vacant)** .... (585) 263-5787 ext. 224
Deputy U.S. Marshal **(Vacant)** .... (585) 263-5787 ext. 226
Deputy U.S. Marshal **(Vacant)** .... (585) 263-6765
Operational Support Specialist
Steven Pascuzzi .... (585) 263-5787 ext. 221

North Carolina - Eastern District
550 Federal Building, 310 New Bern Avenue, Raleigh, NC 27601
Tel: (919) 856-4153 Fax: (919) 856-4812

★ U.S. Marshal (Acting) **Robert Pettit** .... (919) 856-4153
E-mail: robert.pettit@usdoj.gov
Chief Deputy U.S. Marshal **Robert Pettit** .... (919) 856-4153 ext. 6151
E-mail: robert.pettit@usdoj.gov
Supervisory Deputy U.S. Marshal **(Vacant)** .... (919) 856-4153
Administrative Officer **Lisa Vajdl** .... (919) 856-4153
E-mail: lisa.vajdl@usdoj.gov
Education: Brenau U BS; Pfeiffer U MBA

Elizabeth City (NC) Office
306 East Main Street, Elizabeth City, NC 27909
P.O. Box 787, Elizabeth City, NC 27909
Tel: (252) 338-1439 Fax: (252) 338-5770

Deputy U.S. Marshal **James K. "Kelly" Jones** .... (252) 338-1422
E-mail: james.jones@usdoj.gov

Fayetteville (NC) Office
301 Federal Building, 301 Green Street, Fayetteville, NC 28302
Tel: (910) 483-0550 Fax: (910) 483-2628

Deputy U.S. Marshal **Daniel Tubman** .... (910) 483-0550
E-mail: daniel.tubman@usdoj.gov

Greenville (NC) Office
Federal Building, 201 South Evans Street, Greenville, NC 27858
Tel: (252) 752-0901 Fax: (252) 752-7030

Supervisory Deputy U.S. Marshal **Howard Turner** .... (252) 752-1054
E-mail: howard.turner@usdoj.gov

New Bern (NC) Office
413 Middle Street, New Bern, NC 28560
Tel: (252) 638-2705 Fax: (252) 638-1073

Deputy U.S. Marshal **John Payne** .... (252) 638-2705
E-mail: john.payne@usdoj.gov

Wilmington (NC) Office
Two Princess Street, Room 223, Wilmington, NC 28401
Tel: (910) 815-4707 Fax: (910) 815-4706

Deputy U.S. Marshal **Brian Tyndall** .... (910) 815-4707
E-mail: brian.tyndall@usdoj.gov

North Carolina - Middle District
U.S. Courthouse, 324 West Market Street,
Room 234, Greensboro, NC 27401
Tel: (336) 332-8700 Fax: (336) 332-8750

U.S. Marshal **Steven L. Gladden** .... (336) 332-8700
E-mail: steve.gladden@usdoj.gov
Supervisory Deputy U.S. Marshal **Thomas Patrick** .... (336) 332-8700
E-mail: thomas.patrick@usdoj.gov
Supervisory Deputy U.S. Marshal **Michael Potter** .... (336) 332-8700
E-mail: michael.potter@usdoj.gov
Chief Deputy U.S. Marshal **Chris Atwater** .... (336) 332-8700
E-mail: chris.atwater@usdoj.gov
Deputy U.S. Marshal **Michael Browning** .... (336) 332-8700
E-mail: michael.browning@usdoj.gov
Deputy U.S. Marshal **Ryan King** .... (336) 332-8700
E-mail: ryan.king2@usdoj.gov
Deputy U.S. Marshal **Byron Pelote** .... (336) 332-8700
E-mail: byron.pelote@usdoj.gov
Deputy U.S. Marshal **Michael Penland** .... (336) 332-8700
E-mail: michael.penland@usdoj.gov
Deputy U.S. Marshal **Luis Ramirez** .... (336) 332-8700
E-mail: luis.ramirez2@usdoj.gov
Deputy U.S. Marshal **Joshua Shuba** .... (336) 332-8700
E-mail: joshua.shuba@usdoj.gov
Deputy U.S. Marshal **Michael Sprague** .... (336) 332-8700
E-mail: michael.sprague@usdoj.gov
Detention Enforcement Officer **Ingra R. Smith** .... (336) 332-8700
E-mail: ingra.smith@usdoj.gov
Judicial Security Inspector **Steve Underwood** .... (336) 332-8700
E-mail: steve.underwood2@usdoj.gov
Administrative Officer **Brantley Williams** .... (336) 332-8700
E-mail: brantley.williams@usdoj.gov
Administrative Support Assistant **(Vacant)** .... (336) 332-8700
Budget Analyst **Angela C. Wilson** .... (336) 332-8700
E-mail: angela.wilson@usdoj.gov
Criminal Program Specialist **Jessica Williams** .... (336) 332-8700
Purchasing Agent **Teresa Brookshire** .... (336) 332-8700
E-mail: teresa.brookshire@usdoj.gov

★ Presidential Appointment Requiring Senate Confirmation ☆ Presidential Appointment ☐ Schedule C Appointment ◇ Career Senior Foreign Service Appointment
● Career Senior Executive Service (SES) Appointment ○ Non-Career Senior Executive Service (SES) Appointment ■ Postal Career Executive Service

Durham (NC) Office
U.S. Courthouse, 323 East Chapel Hill Street, Durham, NC 27702
Tel: (919) 541-5452

Deputy U.S. Marshal **Donald Johnson** .... (919) 541-5452
E-mail: donald.johnson@usdoj.gov

Winston-Salem (NC) Office
Federal Building, 251 North Main Street,
Room 304, Winston-Salem, NC 27101
Tel: (336) 631-5166

Deputy U.S. Marshal **Arthur Gandy** .... (336) 631-5101
E-mail: arthur.gandy@usdoj.gov
Deputy U.S. Marshal **Joel McCready** .... (336) 631-5101
E-mail: joel.mccready@usdoj.gov
Deputy U.S. Marshal **Jason Morton** .... (336) 631-5101
E-mail: jason.morton@usdoj.gov

North Carolina - Western District
Charles R. Jonas Federal Building, 401 West Trade Street,
Charlotte, NC 28202
U.S. Courthouse, 100 Otis Street, Asheville, NC 28802 (Asheville Office)
Tel: (704) 350-8000 Tel: (828) 771-7400 (Asheville Office)
Fax: (704) 344-6523 Fax: (828) 271-4578 (Asheville Office)

★ U.S. Marshal **Gregory Allyn Forest** .... (704) 350-8000
E-mail: gregory.forest@usdoj.gov
Education: North Carolina Charlotte BSCrimJ
Chief Deputy U.S. Marshal **Mark A. Chapman** .... (704) 350-8000

North Dakota District
Quentin Burdick U.S. Courthouse, 655 First Avenue North,
Suite 110, Fargo, ND 58102-4932
Tel: (701) 297-5760 Fax: (701) 297-7305

★ U.S. Marshal **Dallas L. Carlson** .... (701) 297-5760
E-mail: dallas.carlson@usdoj.gov
Education: Dickinson State U BA; North Dakota Lake Region AA
Chief Deputy U.S. Marshal **Dan Orr** .... (701) 530-2460
E-mail: dan.orr@usdoj.gov
Administrative Officer **Cindy Fontaine** .... (701) 530-2460
E-mail: cindy.fontaine@usdoj.gov

Ohio - Northern District
U.S. Courthouse, 801 West Superior Avenue,
Suite 12-100, Cleveland, OH 44113-1853
Tel: (216) 522-2150 Fax: (216) 522-7908

★ U.S. Marshal **Peter J. Elliott** .... (216) 522-2150
E-mail: peter.elliott@usdoj.gov
Education: Capital U BA
Chief Deputy U.S. Marshal **(Vacant)** .... (216) 522-2150
Assistant Chief Deputy U.S. Marshal **Ronald Carter** .... (216) 522-2150
Administrative Officer **Denise Bortnick** .... (216) 522-2150
E-mail: denise.bortnick@usdoj.gov

Ohio - Southern District
U.S. Courthouse, 85 Marconi Boulevard,
Room 460, Columbus, OH 43215
Tel: (614) 469-5540 Fax: (614) 469-2298

★ U.S. Marshal **Peter C. "Pete" Tobin** .... (614) 469-5540
E-mail: peter.tobin@usdoj.gov
Chief Deputy U.S. Marshal **Patrick J. Sedoti** .... (614) 469-5540
E-mail: pat.sedoti@usdoj.gov

Oklahoma - Eastern District
Fifth and Okmulgee Streets, Muskogee, OK 74401
P.O. Box 738, Muskogee, OK 74402
Tel: (918) 687-2523 Fax: (918) 687-2526

★ U.S. Marshal-Designate **Frank M. Coffman** .... (918) 687-2523
Education: Oklahoma State BS; Northeastern State MS
Chief Deputy U.S. Marshal **Tony L. Overstreet** .... (918) 687-2523
Supervisory Deputy U.S. Marshal **Lloyd Vellek** .... (918) 687-2523
E-mail: lloyd.vellek@usdoj.gov

Oklahoma - Eastern District *(continued)*

Supervisory Deputy U.S. Marshal (Warrants)
Dustin Ramsey .... (918) 687-2523
E-mail: dustin.ramsey@usdoj.gov
Judicial Security Inspector U.S. Marshal
Thomas Wayerski .... (918) 687-2523
E-mail: thomas.wayerski@usdoj.gov
Criminal Investigator Deputy U.S. Marshal
Jeffrey Lundy .... (918) 687-2523
E-mail: jeffrey.lundy@usdoj.gov
Deputy U.S. Marshal **Billy Banks** .... (918) 687-2523
E-mail: billy.banks@usdoj.gov
Deputy U.S. Marshal **Brian Gilliam** .... (918) 687-2523
Deputy U.S. Marshal **Misty Stewart** .... (918) 687-2523
E-mail: misty.stewart@usdoj.gov
Deputy U.S. Marshal **(Vacant)** .... (918) 687-2523
Deputy U.S. Marshal - Sex Offender Investigations
Coordinator **Ryan J. Hilton** .... (918) 687-2523
E-mail: ryan.hilton@usdoj.gov
Administrative Officer **Aimee Karnes** .... (918) 687-2523
E-mail: aimee.karnes@usdoj.gov
Asset Forfeiture Contracts **(Vacant)** .... (918) 687-2523
Criminal Program Specialist **Julie Henning** .... (918) 687-2523
E-mail: julie.henning@usdoj.gov
Budget Analyst **(Vacant)** .... (918) 687-2523

Oklahoma - Northern District
333 West Fourth Street, Room 2050, Tulsa, OK 74103
P.O. Box 1097, Tulsa, OK 74101-1097
Tel: (918) 581-7738 Fax: (918) 581-7735

★ U.S. Marshal **Clayton D. Johnson** .... (918) 581-7738
E-mail: clayton.johnson@usdoj.gov
Chief Deputy U.S. Marshal **Carroll Allbery** .... (918) 581-7738
Supervisory Deputy U.S. Marshal **Lyle Brown** .... (918) 581-7738
Deputy U.S. Marshal **(Vacant)** .... (918) 581-7738
Deputy U.S. Marshal **(Vacant)** .... (918) 581-7738
Deputy U.S. Marshal **(Vacant)** .... (918) 581-7738
Deputy U.S. Marshal **(Vacant)** .... (918) 581-7738
Fugitive Task Force Coordinator **John Gage** .... (918) 581-7738
E-mail: john.gage@usdoj.gov
Judicial Security Division Inspector **(Vacant)** .... (918) 581-7738
Criminal Program Specialist **Mary J. Layfield** .... (918) 581-7738
Security Officer in Charge **(Vacant)** .... (918) 581-7738
Warrants Coordinator **John Gage** .... (918) 581-7738
Seizure and Forfeiture Specialist
Pamela B. Johnson .... (918) 581-7858
E-mail: pamela.johnson@usdoj.gov
Budget Analyst **Angela Liter** .... (918) 581-7738
E-mail: angela.liter@usdoj.gov
Administrative Officer **Michelle McLaughlin** .... (918) 581-7738
E-mail: michelle.mclaughlin@usdoj.gov

Oklahoma - Western District
200 NW Fourth Street, 2nd Floor, Oklahoma City, OK 73102
Tel: (405) 231-4206 Fax: (405) 231-5597

★ U.S. Marshal **Johnny Lee Kuhlman** .... (405) 231-4206
E-mail: johnny.kuhlman@usdoj.gov
Education: Southern Nazarene 2002 BS
Chief Deputy U.S. Marshal
Johnny Ray Williams .... (405) 231-4206 ext. 102
Administrative Officer **Katherine Brock** .... (405) 231-4209 ext. 110
E-mail: katherine.brock@usdoj.gov

Oregon District
401 U.S. Courthouse, 1000 SW Third Avenue, Portland, OR 97204-2902
Tel: (503) 326-2209 Fax: (503) 326-3145

★ U.S. Marshal **Russel Edwin Burger** .... (503) 326-2209
E-mail: russel.burger@usdoj.gov
Education: Oregon State BABA
Chief Deputy U.S. Marshal **(Vacant)** .... (503) 326-2209
Supervisory Deputy U.S. Marshal (Warrants) **(Vacant)** .... (503) 326-5777
Assistant Chief Deputy U.S. Marshal **(Vacant)** .... (503) 326-2209
Inspector - Judicial Security **Karl Knobbs** .... (503) 326-5007

★ Presidential Appointment Requiring Senate Confirmation ☆ Presidential Appointment ☐ Schedule C Appointment ◇ Career Senior Foreign Service Appointment
● Career Senior Executive Service (SES) Appointment ○ Non-Career Senior Executive Service (SES) Appointment ■ Postal Career Executive Service

Oregon District *(continued)*

Operations Supervisor **Thadd W. Baird** . . . . . (503) 326-7806
VOTF Supervisor **Eric Wahlstrom** . . . . . (503) 326-3695
E-mail: eric.wahlstrom@usdoj.gov
Deputy U.S. Marshal **Barbara Alfano** . . . . . (503) 326-5709
E-mail: barbara.alfano@usdoj.gov
Deputy U.S. Marshal **Jordan Bury** . . . . . (503) 326-4163
E-mail: jordan.bury@usdoj.gov
Deputy U.S. Marshal **Troy Gangwisch** . . . . . (503) 326-4177
E-mail: troy.gangwisch@usdoj.gov
Deputy U.S. Marshal **Karrie Holden** . . . . . (503) 326-3532
E-mail: karrie.holden@usdoj.gov
Deputy U.S. Marshal **Don Holdon** . . . . . (503) 326-7048
E-mail: donald.holdon@usdoj.gov
Deputy U.S. Marshal **Jonathan Lobell** . . . . . (503) 326-5472
E-mail: jonathan.lobell@usdoj.gov
Deputy U.S. Marshal **Pat McGarrah** . . . . . (503) 326-5473
E-mail: pat.mcgarrah@usdoj.gov
Deputy U.S. Marshal **John Moody** . . . . . (503) 326-3491
E-mail: john.moody@usdoj.gov
Deputy U.S. Marshal **Brian Petty** . . . . . (503) 326-5176
E-mail: brian.petty@usdoj.gov
Deputy U.S. Marshal **James Stratton** . . . . . (503) 326-7808
E-mail: james.stratton@usdoj.gov
Deputy U.S. Marshal **(Vacant)** . . . . . (503) 326-3470
Deputy U.S. Marshal **(Vacant)** . . . . . (503) 326-2996
Deputy U.S. Marshal **(Vacant)** . . . . . (503) 326-3157
Deputy U.S. Marshal **(Vacant)** . . . . . (503) 326-3903
Detention Officer **Jesse Lindgren** . . . . . (503) 326-3462
E-mail: jesse.lindgren@usdoj.gov
Warrant Administration **Erin Bennett-Howard** . . . . . (503) 326-3939
E-mail: erin.bennett-howard@usdoj.gov
Senior Inspector - Asset Forfeiture Division
Larry Gloth . . . . . (503) 727-1058
E-mail: larry.gloth@usdoj.gov
Seizure and Forfeiture Specialist **Sheila Meyer** . . . . . (503) 326-4194
E-mail: sheila.meyer@usdoj.gov
Administrative Officer **Brett Caillier** . . . . . (503) 326-4184
E-mail: brett.caillier@usdoj.gov
System Administrator **(Vacant)** . . . . . (503) 326-5178
Management and Program Analyst **Rebecca Cook** . . . . . (503) 326-3126
E-mail: rebecca.cook@usdoj.gov
Budget Analyst **(Vacant)** . . . . . (503) 326-7807
Criminal Clerk **Rufus Black** . . . . . (503) 326-2318
E-mail: rufus.black@usdoj.gov
Purchasing Agent **(Vacant)** . . . . . (503) 326-3531

Eugene (OR) Office
405 East Eighth Avenue, Suite 1200, Eugene, OR 97401
Tel: (541) 465-6701

Supervisory Deputy U.S. Marshal **Bryon Carroll** . . . . . (541) 465-6701
Deputy U.S. Marshal **Michael Bryant** . . . . . (541) 465-6965
E-mail: michael.bryant2@usdoj.gov
Deputy U.S. Marshal **Bryce Collins** . . . . . (541) 465-6568
E-mail: bryce.collins@usdoj.gov
Deputy U.S. Marshal **Eric Kinney** . . . . . (541) 465-6701
E-mail: eric.kinney@usdoj.gov
Deputy U.S. Marshal **Kara Kinney** . . . . . (541) 465-6766
E-mail: kara.kinney@usdoj.gov
Deputy U.S. Marshal **Andrew Simpson** . . . . . (541) 465-6851
E-mail: andrew.simpson@usdoj.gov

Medford (OR) Office
Federal Building and U.S. Courthouse, 310 West Sixth Street, Room 131, Medford, OR 97501
Tel: (541) 776-4277

Supervisory Deputy U.S. Marshal
Timothy Sundheim . . . . . (541) 776-4277 ext. 1000
E-mail: timothy.sundheim@usdoj.gov
Deputy U.S. Marshal **Rodney Lowe** . . . . . (541) 776-4277 ext. 1007
E-mail: rodney.lowe@usdoj.gov
Deputy U.S. Marshal **Brad Sholer** . . . . . (541) 776-4277 ext. 1001
E-mail: brad.sholer@usdoj.gov

Pennsylvania - Eastern District
U.S. Courthouse, 601 Market Street, Room 2110, Philadelphia, PA 19106
Tel: (215) 597-7272 Fax: (215) 597-1688

★ U.S. Marshal **David Blake Webb** . . . . . (215) 597-1852
E-mail: david.webb@usdoj.gov
★ U.S. Marshal-Designate **Eric S. Gartner** . . . . . (215) 597-1852
Education: Earlham BA; Delaware MA; Air Command Col MA; National War Col MS
Secretary **Maryann Shelinsky** . . . . . (215) 597-1687
E-mail: maryann.shelinsky@usdoj.gov
Chief Deputy U.S. Marshal **James Burke** . . . . . (215) 597-9688
E-mail: james.burke@usdoj.gov
Assistant Chief Deputy U.S. Marshal **Gary Hipple** . . . . . (215) 597-0753
E-mail: gary.hipple@usdoj.gov
Supervisory Deputy U.S. Marshal (JSI)
Michael P. Green . . . . . (267) 232-4100
E-mail: michael.green@usdoj.gov
Supervisory Deputy U.S. Marshal (Criminal Squad)
David Sprague . . . . . (215) 597-0023
E-mail: david.sprague@usdoj.gov
Supervisory Deputy U.S. Marshal **(Vacant)** . . . . . (610) 433-4307
1700 U.S. Courthouse, 504 Hamilton Street West, Allentown, PA 18101
Deputy U.S. Marshal **Chris Alegado** . . . . . (267) 232-4125
E-mail: christopher.alegado@usdoj.gov
Deputy U.S. Marshal **David Austin** . . . . . (267) 232-4117
E-mail: david.austin@usdoj.gov
Deputy U.S. Marshal **Christopher Berdos** . . . . . (267) 232-4112
E-mail: christopher.berdos@usdoj.gov
Deputy U.S. Marshal **Dawn M. Cardinal** . . . . . (267) 232-4121
E-mail: dawn.cardinal@usdoj.gov
Deputy U.S. Marshal **Richard Castle** . . . . . (267) 232-4131
E-mail: richard.castle@usdoj.gov
Deputy U.S. Marshal **Steve Eckman** . . . . . (267) 232-4161
E-mail: steven.eckman@usdoj.gov
Deputy U.S. Marshal **Joseph Franchi** . . . . . (267) 232-4097
E-mail: joseph.franchi@usdoj.gov
Deputy U.S. Marshal **Thomas Gabriel** . . . . . (267) 232-4124
E-mail: thomas.gabriel@usdoj.gov
Deputy U.S. Marshal **Niklaus "Nik" Hannevig** . . . . . (610) 433-2176
E-mail: niklaus.hannevig@usdoj.gov
Deputy U.S. Marshal **Enrico L. Ilagan** . . . . . (267) 232-4124
E-mail: enrico.ilagan@usdoj.gov
Deputy U.S. Marshal **Johannes Jarkowsky** . . . . . (267) 232-4127
E-mail: johannes.jarkowsky@usdoj.gov
Deputy U.S. Marshal **Kenny King** . . . . . (215) 597-7272
E-mail: kenneth.king@usdoj.gov
Deputy U.S. Marshal **Michael Longo** . . . . . (267) 232-4120
E-mail: michael.longo@usdoj.gov
Deputy U.S. Marshal **Gregory Marks** . . . . . (267) 232-4119
E-mail: gregory.marks@usdoj.gov
Deputy U.S. Marshal **Rob Miller** . . . . . (267) 232-4156
E-mail: robert.miller@usdoj.gov
Deputy U.S. Marshal **Stanley Sawyer** . . . . . (267) 232-4130
E-mail: stanley.sawyer@usdoj.gov
Deputy U.S. Marshal **William O'Shaughnessy** . . . . . (267) 232-4118
E-mail: william.oshaughnessy@usdoj.gov
Deputy U.S. Marshal **Jeffery Sharp** . . . . . (267) 232-4118
E-mail: jeffery.sharp@usdoj.gov
Deputy U.S. Marshal **James Toland** . . . . . (267) 232-4128
E-mail: James.Toland@usdoj.gov
Deputy U.S. Marshal **Christopher Wuyts** . . . . . (215) 232-4121
E-mail: christopher.wuyts@usdoj.gov
Deputy U.S. Marshal **Victor Yepez** . . . . . (267) 232-4155
E-mail: victor.yepez@usdoj.gov
Deputy U.S. Marshal **(Vacant)** . . . . . (267) 232-4129
Deputy U.S. Marshal **(Vacant)** . . . . . (267) 232-4094
Deputy U.S. Marshal **(Vacant)** . . . . . (267) 232-4158
Deputy U.S. Marshal **(Vacant)** . . . . . (215) 560-1663
Deputy U.S. Marshal (Warrants) **Roger Bomenblit** . . . . . (215) 597-4234
E-mail: roger.bomenblit@usdoj.gov
Deputy U.S. Marshal (Warrants) **Daniel Donnelly** . . . . . (215) 597-4253
E-mail: daniel.donnelly@usdoj.gov
Deputy U.S. Marshal (Warrants) **Shawn Eck** . . . . . (610) 433-3973
E-mail: shawn.eck@usdoj.gov
Deputy U.S. Marshal (Warrants) **(Vacant)** . . . . . (215) 597-4241

(continued on next page)

★ Presidential Appointment Requiring Senate Confirmation ☆ Presidential Appointment ☐ Schedule C Appointment ◇ Career Senior Foreign Service Appointment
● Career Senior Executive Service (SES) Appointment ○ Non-Career Senior Executive Service (SES) Appointment ■ Postal Career Executive Service

Pennsylvania - Eastern District *(continued)*

Deputy U.S. Marshal (JSI) **(Vacant)** .... (267) 232-4099
Deputy U.S. Marshal and Threat Coordinator
Mark D. Dunaway .... (267) 232-4095
E-mail: mark.dunaway@usdoj.gov
Deputy U.S. Marshal (PII) **(Vacant)** .... (267) 232-4093
Detention Enforcement Officer **Gabriel Rodriguez** ...... (215) 597-9468
Detention Enforcement Officer **(Vacant)** .... (215) 597-7272
Administrative Officer **Daniel A. Orr** .... (215) 597-1685
E-mail: danny.orr@usdoj.gov
Budget Analyst **Joseph "Joe" Gohn** .... (267) 232-4149
E-mail: joseph.gohn@usdoj.gov
Civil, National Asset Seizure and Forfeiture (NASAF)
Supervisor **Patrick Ennis** .... (215) 597-1683
E-mail: patrick.ennis@usdoj.gov
Civil, NASAF Deputy **(Vacant)** .... (215) 597-0024
Civil Administrative **(Vacant)** .... (267) 232-4146
NASAF Administrative **Cheryl Lee** .... (267) 232-4153
E-mail: cheryl.lee@usdoj.gov
Criminal Squad Administrative **Miriam Burnstein** ..... (215) 597-9443
Criminal Squad Administrative **Kayla Crane** .... (215) 597-8562
E-mail: kayla.crane@usdoj.gov
Forfeiture Support Associates Administrative
Marie Gohn .... (267) 232-4147
E-mail: marie.gohn@usdoj.gov
Prison Operations Supervisor
William O'Shaughnessy .... (215) 597-3507
Warrant Squad Supervisor **Robert Clark** .... (215) 597-4203
E-mail: robert.clark@usdoj.gov
Warrant Squad Deputy **(Vacant)** .... (215) 597-4236
Warrant Squad Deputy **Christian Tumolo** .... (215) 597-4235
E-mail: christian.tumolo@usdoj.gov
Warrant Squad Administrative **Sandra Becker** .... (215) 597-4204
E-mail: sandy.becker@usdoj.gov

Pennsylvania - Middle District

Federal Building, 235 North Washington Avenue,
Room 215, Scranton, PA 18501
Tel: (570) 346-7277 Fax: (570) 346-7342

★ U.S. Marshal **Martin John Pane** .... (570) 346-7277
Education: Mansfield 1987 BA
Chief Deputy U.S. Marshal **James Nelson** .... (570) 346-7277
E-mail: james.nelson@usdoj.gov
Assistant Chief Deputy U.S. Marshal **(Vacant)** .... (570) 346-7277
Supervisory Deputy U.S. Marshal **Christopher Kane** ..... (570) 346-7277
E-mail: chris.kane@usdoj.gov
Administrative Officer **Cathy McGarny** .... (570) 346-7277
E-mail: cathy.mcgarny@usdoj.gov

Harrisburg (PA) Office

Federal Building, 228 Walnut Street, Room 1004, Harrisburg, PA 17108
P.O. Box 11668, Harrisburg, PA 17108
Tel: (717) 221-2212 Fax: (717) 221-4412
Supervisory Deputy U.S. Marshal **Brad Reiff** .... (717) 221-2212

Williamsport (PA) Office

240 West Third Street, Williamsport, PA 17701
Tel: (570) 323-7245 Fax: (570) 323-7268
Supervisory Deputy U.S. Marshal (Acting) **Brad Reiff** .... (570) 323-7245

Pennsylvania - Western District

U.S. Courthouse Building, 700 Grant Street,
Room 2360, Pittsburgh, PA 15219
Tel: (412) 644-3351 Fax: (412) 644-4769

★ U.S. Marshal (Acting) **Michael D. Baughman** .... (412) 355-2456
Note: On June 11, 2018 the nomination for Michael D. Baughman to be a United States Marshal for the Western District of Pennsylvania was sent to the Senate. Mr. Baughman is currently acting in the position. This nomination is currently pending in the Senate.
E-mail: mike.baughman@usdoj.gov
Chief Deputy U.S. Marshal **Michael D. Baughman** ...... (412) 644-6747
Administrative Officer **James Bailey** .... (412) 644-4531
E-mail: james.bailey2@usdoj.gov

Puerto Rico District

200 Federal Building, 150 Carlos Chardon Avenue,
San Juan, PR 00918-1740
Tel: (787) 766-6000 Fax: (787) 766-6211

★ U.S. Marshal (Acting) **Orlando Rivera** .... (787) 754-4018
E-mail: orlando.rivera@usdoj.gov
Program Management Specialist **Yaritza Diaz** .... (787) 754-4245
Chief Deputy U.S. Marshal **Antonio Torres** .... (787) 754-4023
E-mail: antonio.torres@usdoj.gov
Assistant Chief Deputy U.S. Marshal
Arnaldo H. Rodriguez .... (787) 754-4048
E-mail: arnaldo.rodriguez@usdoj.gov
Supervisory Deputy U.S. Marshal **Gustavo Rodriguez** ... (787) 754-6000
E-mail: gustavo.rodriguez@usdoj.gov
Supervisory Deputy U.S. Marshal **Javier Villanueva** ..... (787) 754-4450
E-mail: javier.villanueva@usdoj.gov
Supervisory Deputy U.S. Marshal **(Vacant)** .... (787) 754-6000
Deputy U.S. Marshal **John Coleman** .... (787) 766-6000
E-mail: john.coleman@usdoj.gov
Deputy U.S. Marshal **Pedro Fortier** .... (787) 766-6000
E-mail: pedro.fortier@usdoj.gov
Deputy U.S. Marshal **Carlos Fuentes** .... (787) 766-6000
E-mail: carlos.fuentes@usdoj.gov
Deputy U.S. Marshal **Roberto Gonzalez** .... (787) 766-6000
E-mail: roberto.gonzalez@usdoj.gov
Deputy U.S. Marshal **George Rodriguez** .... (787) 766-6000
E-mail: george.rodriguez@usdoj.gov
Deputy U.S. Marshal **Shelia San Miguel** .... (787) 766-6000
Criminal Investigator/Deputy U.S. Marshal
Christian Cepeda .... (787) 754-4167
E-mail: christian.cepeda@usdoj.gov
Criminal Investigator/Deputy U.S. Marshal
Luis B. Perez .... (787) 754-4120
E-mail: luis.perez2@usdoj.gov
Criminal Investigator/Deputy U.S. Marshal
Jose Román .... (787) 754-4233
E-mail: jose.román@usdoj.gov
Criminal Investigator **Andrés E. Jimenez** .... (787) 766-6000
E-mail: andres.jimenez@usdoj.gov
Criminal Investigator **Raul Camacho** .... (787) 766-6000
E-mail: raul.camacho@usdoj.gov
Criminal Investigator **Jose Carreras** .... (787) 766-6000
E-mail: jose.carreras@usdoj.gov
Criminal Investigator **Felix Carrion** .... (787) 766-6000
E-mail: felix.carrion@usdoj.gov
Criminal Investigator **Benjamin Fountain** .... (787) 766-6000
E-mail: benjamin.fountain@usdoj.gov
Criminal Investigator **Gabriel Moreno** .... (787) 766-6000
E-mail: gabriel.moreno@usdoj.gov
Criminal Investigator **Miguel Tejeda** .... (787) 766-6000
Administrative Officer **Robert Gonzalez-Arturet** .... (787) 754-4028
E-mail: robert.gonzalez2@usdoj.gov
Detention Manager Inspector **Griselle Mirabal** .... (787) 766-6000
E-mail: griselle.mirabal@usdoj.gov
Detention Officer **Eduardo Burgos** .... (787) 754-4243
E-mail: eduardo.burgos@usdoj.gov
Detention Officer **(Vacant)** .... (787) 754-4243
Detention Officer **(Vacant)** .... (787) 754-4243
Judicial Security Inspector **Alexis Powell** .... (787) 754-4109
E-mail: alex.powell@usdoj.gov
Judicial Security Inspector **Manuel Varela** .... (787) 754-4312
E-mail: manuel.varela@usdoj.gov
Criminal Clerk **Waldemar Lorenzo** .... (787) 754-4205
E-mail: waldemar.lorenzo@usdoj.gov
District Asset Forfeiture Coordinator **Lizette Delpin** ..... (787) 766-6000
Seizure and Forfeiture Specialist **(Vacant)** .... (787) 754-4113
Budget Analyst **Gilberto Serrano** .... (787) 754-4046
E-mail: gilberto.serrano@usdoj.gov
Contract Specialist **Roberto Schmidt** .... (787) 754-4047
E-mail: roberto.schmidt@usdoj.gov
Investigative Research Specialist
William Meadows-Marquiz .... (787) 754-4254
Property Manager **Yaritza Diaz** .... (787) 754-4067

★ Presidential Appointment Requiring Senate Confirmation ☆ Presidential Appointment ☐ Schedule C Appointment ◇ Career Senior Foreign Service Appointment
● Career Senior Executive Service (SES) Appointment ○ Non-Career Senior Executive Service (SES) Appointment ■ Postal Career Executive Service

Puerto Rico District *(continued)*

Prisoner Support/Administrative Specialist
Anais Velez-Perez (787) 754-4415
E-mail: anais.velez-perez@usdoj.gov

Rhode Island District

John O. Pastore Federal Building, Two Exchange Terrace, Providence, RI 02903
P.O. Box 1524, Providence, RI 02901-1524
Tel: (401) 528-5300 Fax: (401) 528-5307

★ U.S. Marshal **Jamie A. Hainsworth** (401) 528-5300
E-mail: jamie.hainsworth@usdoj.gov
Education: Roger Williams

★ U.S. Marshal-Designate **Wing Chau** (401) 528-5300
Education: Comm Col Rhode Island AS; Rhode Island Col BS

Chief Deputy U.S. Marshal **David G. Remington** (401) 528-5303
E-mail: david.remington@usdoj.gov

Supervisory Deputy U.S. Marshal **Robert J. Charette** (401) 528-5305
E-mail: robert.charette@usdoj.gov

Deputy U.S. Marshal **Justin Carvalho** (401) 528-5320
E-mail: justin.carvalho@usdoj.gov

Deputy U.S. Marshal **Elden DaSilva** (401) 528-5326
E-mail: elden.dasilva@usdoj.gov

Deputy U.S. Marshal **John Edson** (401) 528-5306
E-mail: john.edson@usdoj.gov

Deputy U.S. Marshal **Justin Engen** (401) 528-5476
E-mail: justin.engen@usdoj.gov

Deputy U.S. Marshal **Brenton Moore** (401) 528-5324
E-mail: brenton.moore@usdoj.gov

Deputy U.S. Marshal **Joseph Murphy** (401) 528-5326
E-mail: joseph.murphy@usdoj.gov

Deputy U.S. Marshal **(Vacant)** (401) 528-5323

Deputy U.S. Marshal **(Vacant)** (401) 528-5323

Administrative Officer **Karen W. Green** (401) 528-5308
E-mail: karen.green@usdoj.gov

Administrative Support Specialist **(Vacant)** (401) 528-5298

Budget Analyst **Linda Ramos** (401) 528-5304
E-mail: linda.ramos@usdoj.gov

Criminal Investigator **Justin Carvalho** (401) 528-5324

Detention Enforcement Officer **John Cinquegrana** (401) 528-5473

Investigative Research Specialist **Karen A. Lundgren** (401) 528-5327

Judicial Security Inspector **William T. Francis** (401) 528-4196
E-mail: william.francis@usdoj.gov

Property Custodian **Dianna Prete** (401) 528-5470
E-mail: dianna.prete@usdoj.gov

Senior Inspector **Erick Brown** (401) 528-5300

Supervisory Criminal Investigator **Charles J. Wyant** (401) 528-5300

South Carolina District

U.S. Courthouse, 901 Richland Street, Suite 1300, Columbia, SC 29201
Tel: (803) 765-5821 Fax: (803) 765-5824

★ U.S. Marshal **Thomas M. Griffin, Jr.** (803) 765-5866
E-mail: thomas.griffin@usdoj.gov
Education: South Carolina BS

Chief Deputy U.S. Marshal
Richard T. "Rick" Long, Jr. (803) 765-5825

Assistant Chief Deputy U.S. Marshal **(Vacant)** (803) 253-3575

Supervisory Deputy U.S. Marshal (Operations)
Johnny Goodwin (803) 765-5821
E-mail: johnny.goodwin@usdoj.gov

Supervisory Deputy U.S. Marshal (Warrants)
Rodney Duckett (803) 253-3298
E-mail: rodney.duckett@usdoj.gov

Deputy U.S. Marshal **John Alexander** (803) 765-5821

Deputy U.S. Marshal **James "Jim" Brewton** (803) 765-5821

Deputy U.S. Marshal **Brent Daniels** (803) 765-5821
E-mail: brent.daniels@usdoj.gov

Deputy U.S. Marshal **Gerald Hotchkiss** (803) 765-5821
E-mail: gerald.hotchkiss@usdoj.gov

Deputy U.S. Marshal **Jonathan Lorenzen** (803) 765-5821
E-mail: jonathan.lorenzen@usdoj.gov

Deputy U.S. Marshal **Amanda Lyons** (803) 765-5821
E-mail: amanda.lyons@usdoj.gov

South Carolina District *(continued)*

Deputy U.S. Marshal **Rohn Morales** (803) 765-5821
E-mail: rohn.morales@usdoj.gov

Deputy U.S. Marshal **John Radney** (803) 765-5921
E-mail: john.radney@usdoj.gov

Deputy U.S. Marshal **Christopher Taylor** (803) 765-5821
E-mail: christopher.taylor@usdoj.gov

Deputy U.S. Marshal **(Vacant)** (803) 765-5821

Deputy U.S. Marshal **(Vacant)** (803) 765-5821

Deputy U.S. Marshal and Sexual Offender Investigation
Coordinator **Derek Miller** (803) 253-3963
E-mail: derek.miller@usdoj.gov

Administrative Assistant **Brenda Strickland** (803) 253-3308

Budget Analyst **Mary Harper** (803) 765-5610
E-mail: mary.harper@usdoj.gov

Criminal Program Specialist **Pam Schwartz** (803) 765-5823
E-mail: pamela.schwartz@usdoj.gov

District Asset Forfeiture Coordinator **Sonya Adams** (803) 765-5868

Accounting Technician **Sheron Bauldrick** (803) 765-5338

Criminal Program Specialist **(Vacant)** (803) 765-3965

Criminal/Civil Administrative Support Assistant
Jacqui Moses (803) 253-3855

Criminal/Civil Administrative Support Assistant
Judy Williams (803) 765-5822
E-mail: judy.williams@usdoj.gov

Fugitive Task Force Investigative Research Analyst
(Vacant) (803) 253-3966

Judicial Security Inspector **(Vacant)** (803) 253-3569

Anderson (SC) Office

315 South McDuffie Street, Anderson, SC 29622
Tel: (864) 224-0927 Fax: (864) 224-2129

Deputy U.S. Marshal-in-Charge **(Vacant)** (864) 224-0927

Charleston (SC) Office

Hollings Judicial Center, 81 Broad Street, Charleston, SC 29403
Tel: (843) 727-4255 Fax: (843) 727-4423
Fax: (803) 727-4103 (Warrants)

Supervisory Deputy U.S. Marshal **(Vacant)** (843) 727-4255

Deputy U.S. Marshal **Russell H. Channell** (843) 727-4255
E-mail: russell.channell@usdoj.gov

Deputy U.S. Marshal **Ellen DePatie** (843) 727-4255
E-mail: ellen.depatie@usdoj.gov

Deputy U.S. Marshal **Jimmy Dyches** (843) 727-4255
E-mail: jimmy.dyches@usdoj.gov

Deputy U.S. Marshal **Kaitlyn Kent** (843) 727-4255

Deputy U.S. Marshal **Rob Roe** (843) 727-4255
E-mail: robert.roe@usdoj.gov

Deputy U.S. Marshal **Dennis Suszko** (843) 727-4255
E-mail: dennis.suszko@usdoj.gov

Deputy U.S. Marshal **Tim Zayac** (843) 727-4255
E-mail: tim.zayac@usdoj.gov

Deputy U.S. Marshal **(Vacant)** (843) 727-4255

Operational Support Assistant **Kathy Roberts** (843) 727-4255

Florence (SC) Office

McMillan Federal Building, 401 West Evans Street, Room 341, Florence, SC 29503
Tel: (843) 662-0750 Fax: (843) 662-0794

Supervisory Deputy U.S. Marshal
Joseph Rick "Joe" Tessari (843) 662-0750
E-mail: joseph.tessari@usdoj.gov

Deputy U.S. Marshal **Roberto Carrillo** (843) 662-0750
E-mail: roberto.carrillo@usdoj.gov

Deputy U.S. Marshal **Bradley Dorn** (843) 662-0750
E-mail: brad.dorn@usdoj.gov

Deputy U.S. Marshal **Brian A. Jordan** (843) 662-0750
E-mail: brian.jordan@usdoj.gov

Deputy U.S. Marshal **William "Trey" Laffin** (843) 662-0750
E-mail: william.laffin@usdoj.gov

Deputy U.S. Marshal **Janet Ward** (843) 662-0750
E-mail: janet.ward@usdoj.gov

Administrative Assistant **(Vacant)** (843) 662-0750

DEPARTMENTS

★ Presidential Appointment Requiring Senate Confirmation ☆ Presidential Appointment ☐ Schedule C Appointment ◇ Career Senior Foreign Service Appointment
● Career Senior Executive Service (SES) Appointment ○ Non-Career Senior Executive Service (SES) Appointment ■ Postal Career Executive Service

DEPARTMENTS

Greenville (SC) Office
Federal Building, 300 East Washington Street,
Room 232, Greenville, SC 29603
Tel: (864) 232-1566 Fax: (864) 370-9752

Supervisory Deputy U.S. Marshal **Johnson Bond** . . . . (864) 232-1566
E-mail: johnson.bond@usdoj.gov Fax: (864) 370-3276
Deputy U.S. Marshal **Bo Barrett** . . . . (864) 232-1566
Deputy U.S. Marshal **Patrick Campbell** . . . . (864) 232-1566
Deputy U.S. Marshal **William Cook** . . . . (864) 232-1566
E-mail: william.cook@usdoj.gov
Deputy U.S. Marshal **David Cranford** . . . . (864) 232-1566
Deputy U.S. Marshal **Doug Leslie** . . . . (864) 232-1566
Deputy U.S. Marshal **Anne McPoland** . . . . (864) 232-1566
Deputy U.S. Marshal **Leon Pernell** . . . . (864) 232-1566
Deputy U.S. Marshal **Patrick Pruitt** . . . . (864) 232-1566
E-mail: patrick.pruitt@usdoj.gov
Deputy U.S. Marshal **Douglas Skutka** . . . . (864) 232-1566
Deputy U.S. Marshal **Joseph Rick "Joe" Tessari** . . . . (864) 232-1566
Administrative Support Assistant **(Vacant)** . . . . (864) 232-1566

South Dakota District
216 Federal Building, 400 South Phillips Avenue, Sioux Falls, SD 57104
Tel: (605) 330-4351 Fax: (605) 330-4586

★ U.S. Marshal **Daniel Mosteller** . . . . (605) 330-4351
E-mail: daniel.mosteller@usdoj.gov
Education: South Dakota BS
Chief Deputy U.S. Marshal **Scott Rolstad** . . . . (605) 330-4351
E-mail: scott.rolstad@usdoj.gov
Supervisory Deputy U.S. Marshal **Shelly Metzger** . . . . (605) 330-4351
E-mail: shelly.metzger@usdoj.gov

Aberdeen (SD) Office
102 SE Fourth Avenue, Room 409, Aberdeen, SD 57401
Tel: (605) 226-1794 Fax: (605) 226-1793

Supervisory Deputy U.S. Marshal **Cole Johnson** . . . . (605) 226-1794
Note: Occupied only during term of court
E-mail: cole.johnson@usdoj.gov

Pierre (SD) Office
459 U.S. Courthouse, 225 South Pierre Street, Pierre, SD 57501
P.O. Box 397, Pierre, SD 57501
Tel: (605) 224-8396 Fax: (605) 224-0214

Supervisory Deputy U.S. Marshal
Stephen Houghtaling . . . . (605) 224-8396
E-mail: stephen.houghtaling@usdoj.gov

Rapid City (SD) Office
323 U.S. Courthouse, 515 Ninth Street, Rapid City, SD 57701
Tel: (605) 342-6331 Fax: (605) 342-7161

Supervisory Deputy U.S. Marshal **Jane A. Koball** . . . . (605) 342-6331
E-mail: jane.koball@usdoj.gov

Tennessee - Eastern District
Howard Baker Courthouse, 800 Market Street,
Suite 320, Knoxville, TN 37902
Tel: (865) 545-4182 Fax: (865) 545-4187

★ U.S. Marshal **David Glenn Jolley** . . . . (865) 545-4182
E-mail: david.jolley@usdoj.gov
Education: Mid Tennessee State BS
Chief Deputy U.S. Marshal **Frank Castiglia** . . . . (865) 545-4182
E-mail: frank.castiglia@usdoj.gov
Supervisory Deputy U.S. Marshal **Kent C. Miller** . . . . (865) 545-4182
E-mail: kent.c.miller@usdoj.gov
Supervisory Deputy U.S. Marshal **Brad Quillen** . . . . (865) 545-4182
E-mail: brad.quillen@usdoj.gov
Deputy U.S. Marshal **Dustin Anderson** . . . . (865) 545-4182
E-mail: dustin.anderson@usdoj.gov
Deputy U.S. Marshal **Claude "Matt" Byrum** . . . . (865) 545-4182
E-mail: claude.byrum@usdoj.gov
Deputy U.S. Marshal **Gregory "Greg" Dahl** . . . . (865) 545-4182
E-mail: gregory.dahl@usdoj.gov

Tennessee - Eastern District *(continued)*

Deputy U.S. Marshal **Becky Gambill** . . . . (865) 545-4182
E-mail: becky.gambill@usdoj.gov
Deputy U.S. Marshal **Brad Redmond** . . . . (865) 545-4182
E-mail: bradley.redmond@usdoj.gov
Deputy U.S. Marshal **John Sanchez** . . . . (865) 545-4182
E-mail: john.sanchez@usdoj.gov
Deputy U.S. Marshal **Matthew "Matt" Sikes** . . . . (865) 545-4182
E-mail: matthew.sikes@usdoj.gov
District Asset Forfeiture Coordinator
Heather Harrington . . . . (865) 545-4182
E-mail: heather.harrington@usdoj.gov
Forfeiture Support Associate **Barbara "Sue" Norris** . . . . (865) 545-4182
E-mail: bnorris1@usms.doj.gov
Judicial Security Inspector **Richie Bradley** . . . . (865) 545-4182
E-mail: richie.bradley@usdoj.gov
Sex Offender Investigation Coordinator
Derrick Swenson . . . . (865) 545-4182
E-mail: derrick.swenson@usdoj.gov
Senior Systems Administrator **(Vacant)** . . . . (865) 545-4182
Administrative Officer **Doug Brooks** . . . . (865) 545-4182
E-mail: doug.brooks@usdoj.gov
Administrative Support Specialist **Charles Maurer** . . . . . (865) 545-4182
E-mail: charles.maurer@usdoj.gov
Financial Specialist **Thomas "Tom" Golacinski** . . . . (865) 545-4182
E-mail: thomas.golacinski@usdoj.gov
Criminal Program Specialist **Ronald Coots** . . . . (865) 545-4182
E-mail: ronald.coots@usdoj.gov
Management/Program Manager **Eileen Darden** . . . . (865) 545-4182
E-mail: eileen.darden@usdoj.gov

Chattanooga (TN) Office
U.S. Courthouse, 900 Georgia Avenue,
Room 340, Chattanooga, TN 37401
Tel: (423) 752-5115 Fax: (423) 752-5119

Supervisory Deputy U.S. Marshal **John Bieber** . . . . (423) 752-5115
E-mail: john.bieber@usdoj.gov
Deputy U.S. Marshal **Bradley "Brad" Fearn** . . . . (423) 752-5115
E-mail: bradley.fearn@usdoj.gov
Deputy U.S. Marshal **Michael Fugate** . . . . (423) 752-5115
E-mail: michael.fugate@usdoj.gov
Deputy U.S. Marshal **Edward "Ted" Gregory** . . . . (423) 752-5115
E-mail: edward.gregory@usdoj.gov
Deputy U.S. Marshal **Jason Ladd** . . . . (423) 752-5115
E-mail: jason.ladd@usdoj.gov
Deputy U.S. Marshal **James Miller III** . . . . (423) 752-5115
E-mail: james.miller4@usdoj.gov
Deputy U.S. Marshal **Paul Salayko** . . . . (423) 752-5115
E-mail: paul.salayko@usdoj.gov
Deputy U.S. Marshal **Joshua Scarborough** . . . . (423) 752-5115
E-mail: joshua.scarborough@usdoj.gov
Deputy U.S. Marshal **Bronco Sullivan** . . . . (423) 752-5115
E-mail: bronco.sullivan@usdoj.gov
Deputy U.S. Marshal **(Vacant)** . . . . (423) 752-5115
Administrative **Brandy Hanson** . . . . (423) 752-5115
E-mail: brandy.hanson@usdoj.gov

Greeneville (TN) Office
220 West Depot, Suite 100, Greeneville, TN 37744
Tel: (423) 638-3391 Fax: (423) 638-4971

Supervisory Deputy U.S. Marshal **Toby Deaton** . . . . (423) 638-3391
E-mail: toby.deaton@usdoj.gov
Deputy U.S. Marshal **Benjamin Caldwell** . . . . (423) 638-3391
E-mail: Benjamin.caldwell@usdoj.gov
Deputy U.S. Marshal **Chris Dockter** . . . . (423) 638-3391
E-mail: christopher.dockter@usdoj.gov
Deputy U.S. Marshal **Paul Glassmyer** . . . . (423) 638-3391
E-mail: paul.glassmyer@usdoj.gov
Deputy U.S. Marshal **Michael "Mike" McCoy** . . . . (423) 638-3391
E-mail: michael.mccoy3@usdoj.gov
Deputy U.S. Marshal **Jason Tarwater** . . . . (423) 638-3391
E-mail: jason.tarwater@usdoj.gov
Administrative **Sharon Maxey** . . . . (423) 328-3391
E-mail: sharon.maxey@usdoj.gov

★ Presidential Appointment Requiring Senate Confirmation ☆ Presidential Appointment □ Schedule C Appointment ◇ Career Senior Foreign Service Appointment
● Career Senior Executive Service (SES) Appointment ○ Non-Career Senior Executive Service (SES) Appointment ■ Postal Career Executive Service

Tennessee - Middle District
110 Ninth Avenue South, Room A750, Nashville, TN 37203
Tel: (615) 736-5417 Fax: (615) 736-5134

★ U.S. Marshal **Louise W. Kelton** (615) 736-5417
E-mail: louise.kelton@usdoj.gov
Education: Tennessee State; Cumberland U MPSA
★ U.S. Marshal-Designate **Denny Wade King** (615) 736-5417
Education: Bethel U BSCrimJ; Walters State Comm Col AS
Chief Deputy U.S. Marshal **John Shell** (615) 736-5417
E-mail: john.shell@usdoj.gov
Supervisory Deputy U.S. Marshal **Jeffrey Dill** (615) 736-5417
E-mail: jeff.dill@usdoj.gov
Deputy U.S. Marshal **Brian E. Biermann** (615) 736-5417
Deputy U.S. Marshal **Christopher Burtt** (615) 736-5417
E-mail: christopher.burtt@usdoj.gov
Deputy U.S. Marshal **MIchael Etheridge** (615) 736-5417
E-mail: michael.etheridge@usdoj.gov
Deputy U.S. Marshal **Cordell Frazier** (615) 736-5417
E-mail: cordell.frazier@usdoj.gov
Deputy U.S. Marshal **Victor Gribben** (615) 736-5417
E-mail: victor.gribben@usdoj.gov
Deputy U.S. Marshal **John Hargis** (615) 736-5417
E-mail: john.hargis@usdoj.gov
Deputy U.S. Marshal **Bryon Osborne** (615) 736-5417
E-mail: bryon.osborne@usdoj.gov
Deputy U.S. Marshal **Patrick Pruter** (615) 736-5417
E-mail: pat.pruter@usdoj.gov
Deputy U.S. Marshal **Adrian Romaniuk** (615) 736-5417
E-mail: adrian.romaniuk@usdoj.gov
Deputy U.S. Marshal **Robin Romaniuk** (615) 736-5417
District Asset Forfeiture Coordinator **Harold Higgins** (615) 736-5417
E-mail: harold.higgins2@usdoj.gov
Judicial Security Inspector **Thomas L. Wehby** (615) 736-5417
E-mail: thomas.wehby@usdoj.gov
Administrative Officer **Marnie Lehew** (615) 736-5417
E-mail: marnie.lehew@usdoj.gov
Data Analyst **Katrina Burch** (615) 736-5417
Data Analyst **(Vacant)** (615) 736-5417
Financial Analyst **Latitia Machado** (615) 736-5417
E-mail: latitia.machado@usdoj.gov
Records Examiner **(Vacant)** (615) 736-5417
Sex Offender Investigation Coordinator **Marty Magnon** (615) 736-5417
E-mail: marty.magnon@usdoj.gov
Task Force Coordinator **(Vacant)** (615) 736-5417

Tennessee - Western District
Clifford Davis Federal Building, 167 North Main Street, Room 1072, Memphis, TN 38103
Tel: (901) 544-3304 Fax: (901) 544-4111

★ U.S. Marshal **Jeffrey T. Holt** (901) 544-3304
E-mail: jeffrey.holt@usdoj.gov
Education: Tennessee (Martin) 1977 BSCrimJ
★ U.S. Marshal-Designate **Barrett W. Rich** (901) 544-3304
Education: Bethel Col (TN) BSM; Nashville JD
Chief Deputy U.S. Marshal **Eddie Laster** (901) 544-3304
E-mail: Eddie.Laster@usdoj.gov
Operations Supervisory Deputy U.S. Marshal **George Mavromatis** (901) 544-3304
E-mail: george.mavromatis@usdoj.gov
Warrant Supervisory Deputy U.S. Marshal **Owen R. Woods** (901) 544-3304
E-mail: owen.woods@usdoj.gov
Deputy U.S. Marshal **Thomas A. Ballard** (901) 544-3304
E-mail: thomas.ballard@usdoj.gov
Deputy U.S. Marshal **Joseph Beidl** (901) 544-3304
E-mail: joseph.beidl@usdoj.gov
Deputy U.S. Marshal **Michael Bowling** (901) 544-3304
E-mail: Michael.Bowling@usdoj.gov
Deputy U.S. Marshal **Seth Bruce** (901) 544-3304
E-mail: seth.bruce@usdoj.gov
Deputy U.S. Marshal **Jessica DeBoer** (901) 544-3304
E-mail: jessica.deboer@usdoj.gov
Deputy U.S. Marshal **James Edge** (901) 544-3304
E-mail: james.edge@usdoj.gov

Tennessee - Western District *(continued)*

Deputy U.S. Marshal **Shane Fisher** (901) 544-3304
E-mail: shane.fisher@usdoj.gov
Deputy U.S. Marshal **Jon Massa** (901) 544-3304
E-mail: jon.massa@usdoj.gov
Deputy U.S. Marshal **Michael McCord** (901) 544-3304
E-mail: michael.mccord@usdoj.gov
Deputy U.S. Marshal **Trayon Murray** (901) 544-3304
E-mail: trayon.murray@usdoj.gov
Deputy U.S. Marshal **Brian Sanders** (901) 544-3304
E-mail: brian.sanders@usdoj.gov
Deputy U.S. Marshal **Kyle Singleton** (901) 544-3304
E-mail: kyle.singleton@usdoj.gov
Deputy U.S. Marshal **Hunter Sykes** (901) 544-3304
E-mail: Hunter.Sykes@usdoj.gov
Deputy U.S. Marshal **Darrel Weldon** (901) 544-3304
E-mail: Darrel.weldon@usdoj.gov
Deputy U.S. Marshal for Sexual Offender Investigations **(Vacant)** (901) 544-3304
Judicial Security Inspector **Joshua Russell** (901) 969-4219
E-mail: joshua.russell@usdoj.gov
Senior Inspector **Michael Patton** (901) 544-4221
E-mail: michael.patton@usdoj.gov
Administrative Officer **Toxis St. Clair** (901) 544-4287
E-mail: toxis.st.clair@usdoj.gov

Jackson (TN) Office
111 South Highland Avenue, Room 214, Jackson, TN 38301
Tel: (731) 427-4661 Fax: (731) 427-8934

Deputy U.S. Marshal **Shane Brown** (731) 427-4661
Deputy U.S. Marshal **Russell Kinard** (731) 427-4661
E-mail: russell.kinard@usdoj.gov
Deputy U.S. Marshal **William Love** (731) 427-4661
Deputy U.S. Marshal **Paul Melson** (731) 427-4661

Texas - Eastern District
U.S. Courthouse, 211 West Ferguson Street, Room 307, Tyler, TX 75702
Tel: (903) 590-1370 Fax: (903) 590-1379
Internet: https://www.usmarshals.gov/district/tx-e/

★ U.S. Marshal **Thomas J. Smith** (903) 590-1370
E-mail: robert.hobbs@usdoj.gov
★ U.S. Marshal-Designate **John M. Garrison** (903) 590-1370
Chief Deputy U.S. Marshal **Steve Tiller** (903) 590-1370
E-mail: steve.tiller@usdoj.gov
Assistant Chief Deputy U.S. Marshal **(Vacant)** (903) 590-1370
Supervisory Deputy U.S. Marshal **Christopher Hicks** (903) 590-1370
E-mail: christopher.hicks@usdoj.gov
Deputy U.S. Marshal **Victor Paul Barry** (903) 590-1370
E-mail: victor.barry@usdoj.gov
Deputy U.S. Marshal **Matt Bunnell** (903) 590-1370
E-mail: matt.bunnell@usdoj.gov
Deputy U.S. Marshal **Brian Leach** (903) 590-1370
E-mail: brian.leach@usdoj.gov
Deputy U.S. Marshal **(Vacant)** (903) 590-1370
Deputy U.S. Marshal **(Vacant)** (903) 590-1370
Deputy U.S. Marshal **(Vacant)** (903) 590-1370
Judicial Security Inspector Deputy U.S. Marshal **(Vacant)** (903) 590-1370
Senior Inspector U.S. Marshal **(Vacant)** (903) 590-1370
Administrative Officer **Melinda Holcomb** (903) 590-1370
E-mail: melinda.holcomb@usdoj.gov
Administrative (Criminal) **(Vacant)** (903) 590-1370
DAFC **Denise Reynolds** (903) 590-1370
E-mail: denise.reynolds@usdoj.gov
Asset Forfeiture Contractor **(Vacant)** (903) 590-1370
Budget Analyst **Karen Clopton** (903) 590-1370
E-mail: karen.clopton@usdoj.gov

DEPARTMENTS

★ Presidential Appointment Requiring Senate Confirmation ☆ Presidential Appointment ☐ Schedule C Appointment ◇ Career Senior Foreign Service Appointment
● Career Senior Executive Service (SES) Appointment ○ Non-Career Senior Executive Service (SES) Appointment ■ Postal Career Executive Service

DEPARTMENTS

Beaumont (TX) Office
Federal Building, 300 Willow Street, Room 116, Beaumont, TX 77701
Tel: (409) 839-2581 Fax: (409) 839-2585

Supervisory Deputy U.S. Marshal **Rhonda Sowell** ...... (409) 839-2581
E-mail: rhonda.sowell@usdoj.gov
Deputy U.S. Marshal **Christopher Christian** .... (409) 839-2581
E-mail: christopher.christian@usdoj.gov
Deputy U.S. Marshal **Vincent Doan** .... (409) 839-2581
E-mail: vince.doan@usdoj.gov
Deputy U.S. Marshal **James Fulcher** .... (409) 839-2581
E-mail: james.fulcher@usdoj.gov
Deputy U.S. Marshal **James McNeely** .... (409) 839-2581
E-mail: james.mcneely@usdoj.gov
Deputy U.S. Marshal **Eugene Rachal** .... (409) 839-2581
Deputy U.S. Marshal **(Vacant)** .... (409) 839-2581
Administrative **Stacey Plummer** .... (409) 839-2581
Administrative **Shannon Woods** .... (409) 839-2581

Lufkin (TX) Office
104 North Third Street, Lufkin, TX 75901
Tel: (936) 634-9733 Fax: (936) 634-9741

Note: This office is staffed only when court is in session by marshals from the Beaumont office.

Deputy U.S. Marshal **(Vacant)** .... (903) 935-5737

Marshall (TX) Office
U.S. Courthouse, 100 East Houston Street, Marshall, TX 75672
Tel: (903) 935-5737 Fax: (903) 938-9033

Deputy U.S. Marshal **Justin Pierce** .... (903) 935-5737
E-mail: justin.pierce@usdoj.gov

Plano (TX) Office
7940 Preston Road, Room 107, Plano, TX 75024
Tel: (214) 705-9850 Fax: (214) 705-1380

Deputy in Charge **Jake Herrington** .... (214) 705-9850
E-mail: jake.herrington@usdoj.gov
Deputy U.S. Marshal **Paul Denton** .... (214) 705-9850
E-mail: paul.denton@usdoj.gov
Deputy U.S. Marshal **Mark Freeman** .... (214) 705-9850
E-mail: mark.freeman@usdoj.gov
Deputy U.S. Marshal **Osvaldo Ortiz** .... (214) 705-9850
E-mail: osvaldo.ortiz2@usdoj.gov
Deputy U.S. Marshal **David Ramirez** .... (214) 705-9850
E-mail: david.ramirez@usdoj.gov
Administrative Officer **Kathleen Goldynia** .... (214) 705-9850
E-mail: kathleen.goldynia@usdoj.gov

Sherman (TX) Office
U.S. Courthouse, 101 East Pecan Street,
Room 302, Sherman, TX 75090
Tel: (903) 868-2379 Fax: (903) 868-9398

Supervisory Deputy U.S. Marshal **Melinda Robinson** .... (903) 868-2379
E-mail: melinda.robinson2@usdoj.gov
Deputy U.S. Marshal **Kenny Abel** .... (903) 868-2379
E-mail: kenny.abel@usdoj.gov
Deputy U.S. Marshal **Jack Bass** .... (903) 868-2379
E-mail: jack.bass@usdoj.gov
Deputy U.S. Marshal **(Vacant)** .... (903) 868-2379
Deputy U.S. Marshal **(Vacant)** .... (903) 868-2379
Asset Forfeiture Financial Investigator
Dustin Williams .... (903) 868-2379
E-mail: dustin.williams@usdoj.gov
Administrative **(Vacant)** .... (903) 868-2379

Texarkana (TX) Office
U.S. Courthouse, Fifth and State Line, Room 209, Texarkana, TX 75504
Tel: (903) 793-8782 Fax: (903) 792-2286

Deputy U.S. Marshal **Andrew Leach** .... (903) 793-8782 ext. 22
E-mail: andrew.leach@usdoj.gov
Deputy U.S. Marshal **Darrell Williams** .... (903) 793-8782 ext. 23
E-mail: darrell.williams@usdoj.gov
Administrative Officer **(Vacant)** .... (903) 793-8782 ext. 24

Texas - Northern District
Earle Cabell Federal Building, 1100 Commerce Street,
Room 1657, Dallas, TX 75242-1698
Tel: (214) 767-0836 Fax: (214) 767-4974
Internet: https://www.usmarshals.gov/district/tx-n/

★ U.S. Marshal **Richard E. "Rick" Taylor, Jr.** .... (214) 767-0836
E-mail: rick.taylor@usdoj.gov
Education: National-Louis 1997 BSM;
Cal State (Northridge) 2007 MPA
Chief Deputy U.S. Marshal (Acting) **Trent Touchstone** ... (214) 767-0836
E-mail: trent.touchstone@usdoj.gov
Assistant Chief Deputy U.S. Marshal (Acting)
Wendell Thompson .... (214) 767-0836
E-mail: wendell.thompson@usdoj.gov
Administrative Officer **John Aragon** .... (214) 767-0836
E-mail: john.aragon@usdoj.gov

Texas - Southern District
U.S. Courthouse, 515 Rusk Avenue, 10th Floor, Room 10002,
Houston, TX 77002
Tel: (713) 718-4800 Fax: (713) 718-4849

★ U.S. Marshal **Gary Blankinship** .... (713) 718-4800
E-mail: gary.blankinship@usdoj.gov
Chief Deputy U.S. Marshal **Richard Hunter** .... (956) 618-4800
E-mail: richard.hunter@usdoj.gov
Assistant Chief Deputy (Warrants) **Marianne Matus** ..... (713) 718-4800
E-mail: marianne.matus@usdoj.gov
Prisoner Movement/Civil Supervisor **Isaac Karam** .... (713) 718-4800
Warrant Supervisor **Richard Baker** .... (713) 718-4259
Warrant Supervisor/Commander **Arthur Fernandez** ...... (713) 718-4259
E-mail: arthur.fernandez@usdoj.gov
Administrative Officer **Ann Hephner** .... (713) 718-4800
E-mail: ann.hephner@usdoj.gov
Public Affairs Officer **Alfredo Perez** .... (713) 718-4259
Purchasing Agent **Noel Bautista** .... (713) 718-4800
E-mail: noel.bautista@usdoj.gov

Brownsville (TX) Office
600 East Harrison, Room 104, Brownsville, TX 78520
Tel: (956) 548-2519 Fax: (956) 548-2534

Assistant Chief Deputy U.S. Marshal **John Allen** .... (956) 548-2519
E-mail: john.allen@usdoj.gov
Supervisory Deputy (Enforcement) **(Vacant)** .... (956) 548-2519
Supervisory Deputy (Operations) **George Ramirez** ...... (956) 548-2519
E-mail: george.ramirez@usdoj.gov

Corpus Christi (TX) Office
1133 North Shoreline Boulevard, Suite 109,
Corpus Christi, TX 78401-2349
Tel: (361) 888-3154 Fax: (361) 888-3174

Assistant Chief Deputy U.S. Marshal **Russell O'Riley** .... (361) 888-3154
E-mail: russell.oriley@usdoj.gov
Supervisory Deputy (Enforcement) **Carlos Alvarado** ..... (361) 888-3154
E-mail: carlos.alvarado@usdoj.gov
Supervisory Deputy (Operations) **(Vacant)** .... (361) 888-3154

Galveston (TX) Office
601 Rosenberg, Room 502, Galveston, TX 77550
Tel: (409) 684-9421 Fax: (409) 766-3707

Assistant Chief Deputy U.S. Marshal (Acting)
Marianne Matus .... (409) 684-9421
E-mail: marianne.matus@usdoj.gov
Supervisory Deputy U.S. Marshal **George Hephner** ..... (409) 684-9421
E-mail: george.hephner@usdoj.gov

Laredo (TX) Office
1300 Victoria Street, Suite 1197, Laredo, TX 78040
Tel: (956) 794-1060 Fax: (956) 726-2335

Assistant Chief Deputy U.S. Marshal **Russell O'Riley** .... (409) 684-9421
Supervisory Deputy (Enforcement) **Kevin Labrador** ...... (956) 794-1060
E-mail: kevin.labrador@usdoj.gov
Supervisory Deputy (Enforcement) **(Vacant)** .... (956) 794-1060

★ Presidential Appointment Requiring Senate Confirmation ☆ Presidential Appointment □ Schedule C Appointment ◇ Career Senior Foreign Service Appointment
● Career Senior Executive Service (SES) Appointment ○ Non-Career Senior Executive Service (SES) Appointment ■ Postal Career Executive Service

Laredo (TX) Office *(continued)*

Supervisory Deputy (Operations) **Robert Julien** . . . . (956) 794-1060
E-mail: robert.julien@usdoj.gov
Supervisory Deputy (Operations) **Carlos Palos** . . . . (956) 794-1060
E-mail: carlos.palos@usdoj.gov

McAllen (TX) Office

1701 West Business Highway 83, Suite 1125, McAllen, TX 78501
Tel: (956) 618-8025 Fax: (956) 618-8029

Assistant Chief Deputy U.S. Marshal (Acting)
Daniel Flores . . . . (956) 618-8025
E-mail: daniel.flores@usdoj.gov
Supervisory Deputy (Enforcement) **John Allen** . . . . (956) 618-8025
E-mail: john.allen@usdoj.gov
Supervisory Deputy (Enforcement) **Dagoberto Lopez** . . . . (956) 618-8025
E-mail: dagoberto.lopez@usdoj.gov
Supervisory Deputy (Operations) **Baldo Montano** . . . . (956) 618-8025
E-mail: baldo.montano@usdoj.gov
Supervisory Deputy (Operations) **(Vacant)** . . . . (956) 618-8025

Victoria (TX) Office

312 South Main Street, Room 326, Victoria, TX 77902
Tel: (361) 578-4932 Fax: (361) 576-0065

Assistant Chief Deputy U.S. Marshal **Russell O'Riley** . . . . (361) 578-4932
Supervisory Deputy (Enforcement) **Alfredo Lujan** . . . . (361) 578-4932
E-mail: alfredo.lujan@usdoj.gov
Supervisory Deputy (Operations) **(Vacant)** . . . . (361) 578-4932

Texas - Western District

John H. Wood Federal Courthouse, 655 East Durango Boulevard, Room 235, San Antonio, TX 78206
Tel: (210) 472-6540 Fax: (210) 472-4134
Internet: https://www.usmarshals.gov/district/tx-w/

★ U.S. Marshal **MajGen Susan Lewellyn Pamerleau** . . . . . (210) 472-6540
Education: Wyoming BA; Golden Gate MPA
Administrative Support Specialist
Elaine Anaya-Ortiz . . . . (210) 472-6540
E-mail: elaine.anaya-ortiz@usdoj.gov
Education: Texas (San Antonio) BA
Chief Deputy U.S. Marshal **(Vacant)** . . . . (210) 472-6540
Assistant Chief Deputy U.S. Marshal **(Vacant)** . . . . (210) 472-6540
Assistant Chief Deputy U.S. Marshal **(Vacant)** . . . . (210) 472-6540
Supervisory Deputy U.S. Marshal **Preston Browning** . . . . (210) 472-6540
E-mail: preston.browning2@usdoj.gov
Supervisory Deputy U.S. Marshal **Mark McPherson** . . . . . (210) 472-6540
E-mail: mark.mcpherson@usdoj.gov
Deputy U.S. Marshal **Vincent "Vinnie" Bellino** . . . . (210) 472-6540
E-mail: vincent.bellino@usdoj.gov
Deputy U.S. Marshal **Christopher Bozeman** . . . . (210) 472-6540
E-mail: christopher.bozeman@usdoj.gov
Deputy U.S. Marshal **John Gonzalez** . . . . (210) 472-6540
E-mail: john.gonzalez@usdoj.gov
Deputy U.S. Marshal **Edward Hernandez** . . . . (210) 472-6540
E-mail: edward.hernandez@usdoj.gov
Deputy U.S. Marshal **Michael "Mike" Parsley** . . . . (210) 472-6540
E-mail: michael.parsley@usdoj.gov
Deputy U.S. Marshal **Matthew Rector** . . . . (210) 472-6540
E-mail: matthew.rector@usdoj.gov
Deputy U.S. Marshal **Nicholas Rose** . . . . (210) 472-6540
E-mail: nicholas.rose@usdoj.gov
Deputy U.S. Marshal **Edgar Santana** . . . . (210) 472-6540
E-mail: edgar.santana@usdoj.gov
Deputy U.S. Marshal **Alan Schrecongost** . . . . (210) 472-6540
E-mail: alan.schrecongost@usdoj.gov
Deputy U.S. Marshal **Kristopher Waterman** . . . . (210) 472-6540
E-mail: kristopher.waterman@usdoj.gov
Deputy U.S. Marshal **(Vacant)** . . . . (210) 472-6540
Deputy U.S. Marshal **(Vacant)** . . . . (210) 472-6540
Deputy U.S. Marshal **(Vacant)** . . . . (210) 472-6540
Deputy U.S. Marshal **(Vacant)** . . . . (210) 472-6540
Detention Enforcement Officer **(Vacant)** . . . . (210) 472-6540
Judicial Security Inspector **(Vacant)** . . . . (210) 472-6540
Protective Intelligence Investigator **(Vacant)** . . . . (210) 472-6540

Texas - Western District *(continued)*

Senior Inspector **(Vacant)** . . . . (210) 472-5633
Administrative Officer **Sherry Poligala** . . . . (210) 271-2529
E-mail: sherry.poligala@usdoj.gov
Accounting Technician **Ana Santana** . . . . (210) 472-6540
Budget Analyst **Joanna Zuniga** . . . . (210) 472-6540
E-mail: joanna.zuniga@usdoj.gov
Criminal Program Specialist **Charla Mora** . . . . (210) 472-6540
Investigative Research Specialist **(Vacant)** . . . . (210) 271-2555
Management and Program Analyst **Julissa Falconi** . . . . . . (210) 472-6540
Program Analyst **(Vacant)** . . . . (210) 472-6540
Purchasing Agent **Anna Marmolejo** . . . . (210) 472-5636
E-mail: anna.marmolejo@usdoj.gov
Seizure and Forfeiture Specialist **(Vacant)** . . . . (210) 472-6540
Senior Computer Specialist **James Cobarruvias** . . . . (210) 472-6540
E-mail: james.cobarruvias@usdoj.gov
Supervisory Property Management Specialist **(Vacant)** . . . (210) 472-6685
Property Management Specialist **Heidi Schroeder** . . . . . (210) 472-6540

Alpine (TX) Office

803 North Second Street, Alpine, TX 79830
Tel: (432) 837-7295 Fax: (432) 837-1629

Deputy U.S. Marshal **Kenneth Roberts** . . . . (432) 837-7295

Austin (TX) Office

316 U.S. Courthouse, 200 West Eighth Street, Suite 316, Austin, TX 78701
Tel: (512) 916-5393 Fax: (512) 916-5405

Supervisory Deputy U.S. Marshal **Hector Gomez** . . . . (512) 916-5393
E-mail: hector.gomez@usdoj.gov
Supervisory Deputy U.S. Marshal **Darren Sartin** . . . . (512) 916-5393
E-mail: darren.sartin@usdoj.gov
Deputy U.S. Marshal **Adam Campbell** . . . . (512) 916-5393
E-mail: adam.campbell@usdoj.gov
Deputy U.S. Marshal **Marvin Conley** . . . . (512) 916-5393
E-mail: marvin.conley@usdoj.gov
Deputy U.S. Marshal **Aaron Greenwood** . . . . (512) 916-5393
E-mail: aaron.greenwood@usdoj.gov
Deputy U.S. Marshal **James Johnson** . . . . (512) 916-5393
E-mail: james.johnson@usdoj.gov
Deputy U.S. Marshal **Yolanda Pesina** . . . . (512) 916-5393
E-mail: yolanda.pesina@usdoj.gov
Deputy U.S. Marshal **Brian Sheely** . . . . (512) 916-5393
E-mail: brian.sheely@usdoj.gov
Deputy U.S. Marshal **(Vacant)** . . . . (512) 916-5393
Deputy U.S. Marshal **(Vacant)** . . . . (512) 916-5393
Operations Support Specialist **Sasha Guerra** . . . . (512) 916-5393
E-mail: sasha.guerra@usdoj.gov
Operations Support Specialist **(Vacant)** . . . . (512) 916-5393

Del Rio (TX) Office

A106 U.S. Courthouse, 111 East Broadway, Del Rio, TX 78840
Tel: (830) 703-2075 Fax: (830) 703-2084

Supervisory Deputy U.S. Marshal **Christian Casson** . . . . . (830) 703-2075
E-mail: christian.casson@usdoj.gov
Supervisory Deputy U.S. Marshal **Kevin Scott** . . . . (830) 703-2075
E-mail: kevin.scott@usdoj.gov
Supervisory Deputy U.S. Marshal **(Vacant)** . . . . . . (830) 703-2075 ext. 200
Criminal Investigator **Michael Caro** . . . . (830) 703-2075
E-mail: michael.caro@usdoj.gov
Deputy U.S. Marshal **Steven Fernandez** . . . . (830) 703-2075
E-mail: steven.fernandez@usdoj.gov
Deputy U.S. Marshal **Keith Lawson** . . . . (830) 703-2075
E-mail: keith.lawson@usdoj.gov
Deputy U.S. Marshal **Adrian Pena** . . . . (830) 703-2075
E-mail: adrian.pena@usdoj.gov
Deputy U.S. Marshal **Korey Reichert** . . . . (830) 703-2075
E-mail: korey.reichert@usdoj.gov
Deputy U.S. Marshal **Vicente Rodriguez** . . . . (830) 703-2075
E-mail: vicente.rodriguez@usdoj.gov
Investigative Research Specialist **Lilian Galindo** . . . . (830) 703-2075
Administrative Support Assistant **Sylvia Cuevas** . . . . (830) 703-2075
E-mail: sylvia.cuevas@usdoj.gov

(continued on next page)

★ Presidential Appointment Requiring Senate Confirmation ☆ Presidential Appointment ☐ Schedule C Appointment ◇ Career Senior Foreign Service Appointment
● Career Senior Executive Service (SES) Appointment ○ Non-Career Senior Executive Service (SES) Appointment ■ Postal Career Executive Service

Del Rio (TX) Office *(continued)*

Administrative Support Assistant **Pamela Geis** . . . . (830) 703-2075
E-mail: pamela.geis@usdoj.gov
Administrative Support Assistant **Samuel Lopez** . . . . . . (830) 703-2075
E-mail: sam.lopez@usdoj.gov
Criminal Program Specialist **Rosie Perez** . . . . (830) 703-2075
E-mail: rose.perez@usdoj.gov

El Paso (TX) Office

305 U.S. Courthouse, 511 East San Antonio, El Paso, TX 79901
Tel: (915) 534-6779 Tel: (915) 534-6018 (Warrants) Fax: (915) 534-6777
Fax: (915) 534-6262 (Warrants)

Assistant Chief Deputy U.S. Marshal **(Vacant)** . . . . (915) 534-6779
Supervisory Deputy U.S. Marshal **Adrian Aranda** . . . . (915) 534-6779
E-mail: adrian.aranda@usdoj.gov
Supervisory Deputy U.S. Marshal **Jesus Solorzano** . . . . . (915) 534-6779
E-mail: jesus.solorzano@usdoj.gov
Supervisory Deputy U.S. Marshal **Javier Velasco** . . . . (915) 534-6779
E-mail: javier.velasco@usdoj.gov
Supervisory Deputy U.S. Marshal **(Vacant)** . . . . (915) 534-6779
Deputy U.S. Marshal **Karla Almazan** . . . . (915) 534-6779
E-mail: karla.almazan@usdoj.gov
Deputy U.S. Marshal **Miguel Alvarado** . . . . (915) 534-6779
Deputy U.S. Marshal **Emiliano Baca** . . . . (915) 534-6779
E-mail: emiliano.baca@usdoj.gov
Deputy U.S. Marshal **John Botello, Jr.** . . . . (915) 534-6779
Deputy U.S. Marshal **Yvette Castro** . . . . (915) 534-6779
E-mail: yvette.castro@usdoj.gov
Deputy U.S. Marshal **Mayra Contreras** . . . . (915) 534-6779
E-mail: mayra.contreras@usdoj.gov
Deputy U.S. Marshal **Steve Douglas** . . . . (915) 534-6779
E-mail: steven.douglas@usdoj.gov
Deputy U.S. Marshal **Damian Fernandez** . . . . (915) 534-6779
E-mail: damian.fernandez@usdoj.gov
Deputy U.S. Marshal **Greg Haley** . . . . (915) 534-6779
E-mail: greg.haley@usdoj.gov
Deputy U.S. Marshal **Salvador Martinez** . . . . (915) 534-6779
E-mail: salvador.martinez2@usdoj.gov
Deputy U.S. Marshal **David Ogaz** . . . . (915) 534-6779
E-mail: david.ogaz@usdoj.gov
Deputy U.S. Marshal **Josh Paulson** . . . . (915) 534-6779
E-mail: joshua.paulson@usdoj.gov
Deputy U.S. Marshal **Emir Perez** . . . . (915) 534-6779
E-mail: emir.perez@usdoj.gov
Deputy U.S. Marshal **Lee Rosas** . . . . (915) 534-6779
E-mail: lee.rosas@usdoj.gov
Deputy U.S. Marshal **Anthony Rossi** . . . . (915) 534-6779
E-mail: anthony.rossi@usdoj.gov
Deputy U.S. Marshal **Kenneth Schmidt** . . . . (915) 534-6779
E-mail: kenneth.schmidt@usdoj.gov
Deputy U.S. Marshal **Juan Trujillo** . . . . (915) 534-6779
E-mail: juan.trujillo@usdoj.gov
Deputy U.S. Marshal **Mike Uehara** . . . . (915) 534-6779
E-mail: michael.uehara@usdoj.gov
Deputy U.S. Marshal **Salvador Vazquez, Jr.** . . . . (915) 534-6779
E-mail: salvador.vazquez@usdoj.gov
Deputy U.S. Marshal **(Vacant)** . . . . (915) 534-6779
Deputy U.S. Marshal **(Vacant)** . . . . (915) 534-6779
Deputy U.S. Marshal **(Vacant)** . . . . (915) 534-6779
Deputy U.S. Marshal **(Vacant)** . . . . (915) 534-6779
Deputy U.S. Marshal **(Vacant)** . . . . (915) 534-6779
Deputy U.S. Marshal **(Vacant)** . . . . (915) 534-6779
Deputy U.S. Marshal **(Vacant)** . . . . (915) 534-6779
Deputy U.S. Marshal **(Vacant)** . . . . (915) 534-6779
Deputy U.S. Marshal **(Vacant)** . . . . (915) 534-6779
Deputy U.S. Marshal **(Vacant)** . . . . (915) 534-6779
Deputy U.S. Marshal **(Vacant)** . . . . (915) 534-6779
Deputy U.S. Marshal **(Vacant)** . . . . (915) 534-6779
Detention Enforcement Officer **Jose Perez-Rivera** . . . . . . (915) 534-6779
E-mail: jose.perez-rivera@usdoj.gov
Criminal Investigator **Daniel Galvan** . . . . (915) 534-6779
E-mail: daniel.galvan@usdoj.gov
Criminal Investigator **David Ochoa** . . . . (915) 534-6779
E-mail: david.ochoa@usdoj.gov

El Paso (TX) Office *(continued)*

Criminal Investigator **Michael Sharboneau** . . . . (915) 534-6779
E-mail: michael.sharboneau@usdoj.gov
Administrative Support Assistant **Inez Cage** . . . . (915) 534-6779
E-mail: inez.cage@usdoj.gov
Administrative Support Assistant **Minerva Mercado** . . . . . (915) 534-6779
E-mail: minerva.mercado@usdoj.gov
Administrative Support Assistant **(Vacant)** . . . . (915) 534-6779
Administrative Support Assistant **(Vacant)** . . . . (915) 534-6779
Administrative Support Assistant **(Vacant)** . . . . (915) 534-6779
Investigative Research Specialist **Betty Cabrera** . . . . (915) 534-6779
Investigative Research Specialist **Darlene Medina** . . . . (915) 534-6779
Prisoner Support Specialist **Maria Fuentez** . . . . (915) 534-6779
Property Management Specialist **Rejane Hinkle** . . . . (915) 534-6779
Purchasing Agent **Sal Bretado** . . . . (915) 534-6779
E-mail: sal.bretado@usdoj.gov
Seizure and Forfeiture Specialist
Esther Gonzales-Flores . . . . (915) 534-6779

Midland (TX) Office

George H.W. Bush and George W. Bush U.S. Courthouse, 200 East Wall, Room 213, Midland, TX 79701
P.O. Box 593, Midland, TX 79701
Tel: (432) 686-4100 Fax: (432) 686-4105

Supervisory Deputy U.S. Marshal **(Vacant)** . . . . (432) 686-4100
Deputy U.S. Marshal **Monica Almengor** . . . . (432) 686-4100
E-mail: monica.almengor@usdoj.gov
Deputy U.S. Marshal **George Butcher** . . . . (432) 686-4100
E-mail: george.butcher@usdoj.gov
Deputy U.S. Marshal **Cynthia Myers** . . . . (432) 686-4100
E-mail: cynthia.myers@usdoj.gov
Deputy U.S. Marshal **John Pennington** . . . . (432) 686-4100
E-mail: john.pennington@usdoj.gov
Deputy U.S. Marshal **Thomas Reese** . . . . (432) 686-4100
E-mail: thomas.reese@usdoj.gov
Deputy U.S. Marshal **Brent Sheets** . . . . (432) 686-4100
E-mail: brent.sheets@usdoj.gov
Deputy U.S. Marshal **(Vacant)** . . . . (432) 686-4100
Deputy U.S. Marshal **(Vacant)** . . . . (432) 686-4100
Deputy U.S. Marshal **(Vacant)** . . . . (432) 686-4100
Operations Support Specialist **(Vacant)** . . . . (432) 686-4100
Criminal Program Specialist **(Vacant)** . . . . (432) 686-4100

Pecos (TX) Office

Post Office Building, 410 South Cedar,
Room 204, Pecos, TX 79772
Tel: (432) 445-5495 Fax: (432) 445-4308

Supervisory Deputy U.S. Marshal **(Vacant)** . . . . (432) 445-5495
Deputy U.S. Marshal **Adrian Bolanos** . . . . (432) 445-5495
E-mail: adrian.bolanos@usdoj.gov
Deputy U.S. Marshal **Chad Hasz** . . . . (432) 445-5495
E-mail: chad.hasz@usdoj.gov
Deputy U.S. Marshal **Joe Sorge** . . . . (432) 445-5495
E-mail: joseph.sorge@usdoj.gov
Deputy U.S. Marshal **(Vacant)** . . . . (432) 445-5495
Administrative Support Specialist **Hilda Woods** . . . . (432) 445-5495

Waco (TX) Office

800 Franklin Avenue, Suite 200, Waco, TX 76701
Tel: (254) 750-1570 Fax: (254) 750-1575

Supervisory Deputy U.S. Marshal **(Vacant)** . . . . (254) 750-1570
Deputy U.S. Marshal **Anton Slavich** . . . . (254) 750-1570
E-mail: anton.slavich@usdoj.gov
Deputy U.S. Marshal **(Vacant)** . . . . (915) 534-6779
Deputy U.S. Marshal **(Vacant)** . . . . (254) 750-1570
Deputy U.S. Marshal **(Vacant)** . . . . (254) 750-1570

★ Presidential Appointment Requiring Senate Confirmation ☆ Presidential Appointment ☐ Schedule C Appointment ◇ Career Senior Foreign Service Appointment
● Career Senior Executive Service (SES) Appointment ○ Non-Career Senior Executive Service (SES) Appointment ■ Postal Career Executive Service

Utah District
351 South West Temple, Suite 4.200, Salt Lake City, UT 84101
Tel: (801) 524-5693 Fax: (801) 524-4359

★ U.S. Marshal **Dr. Matthew D. Harris** . . . . (801) 524-5693
E-mail: matthew.harris@usdoj.gov
Education: Kutztown 1995 BSPA; John Jay Col 2001 MPA; Northcentral Tech 2012 PhD
Chief Deputy U.S. Marshal **Brandon Holt** . . . . (801) 524-5693
E-mail: brandon.holt@usdoj.gov
Supervisory Deputy U.S. Marshal **Derryl Spencer** . . . . . (801) 524-5693
E-mail: derryl.spencer@usdoj.gov
Supervisory Deputy U.S. Marshal **Dan Juergens** . . . . . (801) 524-5693
E-mail: dan.juergens@usdoj.gov
Deputy U.S. Marshal **Brett Glissmeyer** . . . . (801) 524-5693
E-mail: brett.glissmeyer@usdoj.gov
Deputy U.S. Marshal **(Vacant)** . . . . (801) 524-5693

Vermont District
U.S. Federal Building, 11 Elmwood Avenue,
Room 601, Burlington, VT 05401
P.O. Box 946, Burlington, VT 05402-0946
Tel: (802) 951-6271 Fax: (802) 951-6378

★ U.S. Marshal (Acting) **John Hall** . . . . (802) 951-6271
★ U.S. Marshal-Designate **Bradley Jay LaRose** . . . . . . (802) 951-6271
Education: Champlain BSLE, AS
Chief Deputy U.S. Marshal **(Vacant)** . . . . (802) 951-6271
Supervisory Deputy U.S. Marshal **Insup Shin** . . . . . . (802) 951-6202
E-mail: insup.shin@usdoj.gov
Criminal Investigator **John P. Curtis** . . . . (802) 951-6271
E-mail: john.curtis@usdoj.gov
Criminal Investigator **Max Galusha** . . . . (802) 951-6271
E-mail: max.galusha@usdoj.gov
Deputy U.S. Marshal **Michael Barron** . . . . (802) 951-6271
E-mail: michael.barron@usdoj.gov
Deputy U.S. Marshal **Christopher Kopac** . . . . (802) 951-6271
E-mail: christopher.kopac@usdoj.gov
Deputy U.S. Marshal **Brandon Wilson** . . . . (802) 951-6271
E-mail: brandon.wilson@usdoj.gov
Deputy U.S. Marshal **(Vacant)** . . . . (802) 951-6271
Inspector **(Vacant)** . . . . (802) 951-6271
Inspector **(Vacant)** . . . . (802) 951-6204
Administrative Officer **(Vacant)** . . . . (802) 951-9202

Brattleboro (VT) Office
P.O. Box 37, Brattleboro, VT 05301
Tel: (802) 257-1464
Deputy U.S. Marshal **(Vacant)** . . . . (802) 257-1464

Virgin Islands District
Ron DeLugo Federal Building and U.S. Courthouse, Veterans Drive,
Charlotte Amalie, Room 115, St. Thomas, VI 00802
P.O. Box 9018, Charlotte Amalie, St. Thomas, VI 00801
Tel: (340) 774-2743 Fax: (340) 776-1105

★ U.S. Marshal **James Edward "Jim" Clark** . . . . . (340) 774-2743 ext. 234
E-mail: jim.clark2@usdoj.gov
Administrative Officer **(Vacant)** . . . . (340) 774-2743 ext. 227
Chief Deputy U.S. Marshal **(Vacant)** . . . . (340) 774-2743 ext. 225

Virginia - Eastern District
Albert V. Bryan, Sr., U.S. Courthouse,
401 Courthouse Square, Alexandria, VA 22314-5795
Tel: (703) 837-5500 Fax: (703) 837-5546

★ U.S. Marshal **Robert W. "Bobby" Mathieson** . . . . . (703) 837-5500
E-mail: robert.mathieson@usdoj.gov
Education: St Leo U 1988
★ U.S. Marshal-Designate **Nick Edward Proffitt** . . . . . (703) 837-5500
Education: Embry-Riddle BS
Chief Deputy U.S. Marshal **(Vacant)** . . . . (703) 837-5500
Assistant Chief/Deputy U.S. Marshal **Brian Thomas** . . . . . (804) 545-8542
E-mail: brian.thomas@usdoj.gov
Supervisory Deputy U.S. Marshal **(Vacant)** . . . . (703) 837-5500

Virginia - Eastern District *(continued)*

Deputy U.S. Marshal **Charles Bradley** . . . . (703) 837-5500
E-mail: charles.bradley@usdoj.gov
Deputy U.S. Marshal **Keith Burgos** . . . . (703) 837-5500
E-mail: keith.burgos@usdoj.gov
Deputy U.S. Marshal **James Knapp** . . . . (703) 837-5500
E-mail: james.knapp2@usdoj.gov
Deputy U.S. Marshal **John Noel** . . . . (703) 837-5500
E-mail: john.noel@usdoj.gov
Deputy U.S. Marshal **Amanda Shields** . . . . (703) 837-5500
E-mail: amanda.shields@usdoj.gov
Deputy U.S. Marshal **Carl Staley** . . . . (703) 837-5500
E-mail: carl.staley@usdoj.gov
Deputy U.S. Marshal **James Turner** . . . . (703) 837-5500
E-mail: james.turner@usdoj.gov
Criminal Program Specialist **(Vacant)** . . . . (703) 837-5538
Investigative Research Specialist **(Vacant)** . . . . . . (703) 837-5500
Program Analyst **Ronda Patterson** . . . . (703) 837-5525
E-mail: ronda.patterson@usdoj.gov
Property Management Specialist **Andrew Russell** . . . . . (703) 837-5500
E-mail: andrew.russell@usdoj.gov
Purchasing Specialist **Karen Norton** . . . . (703) 837-5517
E-mail: karen.norton@usdoj.gov
Administrative Officer **Wendy Putnam** . . . . (703) 837-5518
E-mail: wendy.putnam@usdoj.gov
Budget Analyst **Yolanda Sylvia** . . . . (703) 837-5500
Deputy U.S. Marshal **(Vacant)** . . . . (703) 451-2001
Deputy U.S. Marshal **(Vacant)** . . . . (703) 837-5500
Detention Officer **(Vacant)** . . . . (703) 837-5500
Administrative Support Assistant **Maiya Morales** . . . . . (703) 837-5512
E-mail: maiya.morales@usdoj.gov

Norfolk (VA) Office
U.S. Courthouse, 600 Granby Street, Norfolk, VA 23510
Tel: (757) 963-5963

Chief Deputy U.S. Marshal **(Vacant)** . . . . (703) 837-5500
Supervisory Deputy U.S. Marshal **(Vacant)** . . . . (757) 963-5963
Supervisory Deputy U.S. Marshal **(Vacant)** . . . . (757) 963-5963
Deputy U.S. Marshal **Timothy Alley** . . . . (757) 963-5963
E-mail: timothy.alley@usdoj.gov
Deputy U.S. Marshal **Sherri Annan** . . . . (757) 963-5963
E-mail: sherri.annan@usdoj.gov
Deputy U.S. Marshal **Carter Davis** . . . . (757) 963-5963
E-mail: carter.davis@usdoj.gov
Deputy U.S. Marshal **Jerold Rozier** . . . . (757) 963-5963
E-mail: jerold.rozier@usdoj.gov
Deputy U.S. Marshal **Jason Silvia** . . . . (757) 963-5963
E-mail: jason.silvia@usdoj.gov
Deputy U.S. Marshal **Robert Wilhite** . . . . (757) 963-5963
E-mail: robert.wilhite@usdoj.gov
Deputy U.S. Marshal **Patrick Yetzer** . . . . (757) 963-5963
E-mail: patrick.yetzer@usdoj.gov
Administrative Clerk **James Wilkins** . . . . (757) 963-5963
E-mail: james.wilkins@usdoj.gov
Deputy U.S. Marshal **(Vacant)** . . . . (757) 963-5963
Deputy U.S. Marshal **(Vacant)** . . . . (757) 963-5963
Deputy U.S. Marshal **(Vacant)** . . . . (757) 963-5963
Civil Processing Clerk **(Vacant)** . . . . (757) 963-5963
Detention Officer **(Vacant)** . . . . (757) 963-5963
Deputy U.S. Marshal **(Vacant)** . . . . (757) 963-5963

Richmond (VA) Office
74 Broad Street, Suite 2800, Richmond, VA 23219
Tel: (804) 545-8501

Supervisory Deputy U.S. Marshal **Robert Mathison** . . . . (804) 545-8501
Deputy U.S. Marshal **Lisa Berger** . . . . (804) 545-8501
E-mail: lisa.berger@usdoj.gov
Deputy U.S. Marshal **James Gurley** . . . . (804) 545-8501
E-mail: james.gurley@usdoj.gov
Deputy U.S. Marshal **Adam Hundley** . . . . (804) 545-8501
E-mail: adam.hundley@usdoj.gov
Deputy U.S. Marshal **Kevin R. Trevillian** . . . . (804) 545-8501
E-mail: kevin.trevillian@usdoj.gov

(continued on next page)

DEPARTMENTS

★ Presidential Appointment Requiring Senate Confirmation ☆ Presidential Appointment ☐ Schedule C Appointment ◇ Career Senior Foreign Service Appointment
● Career Senior Executive Service (SES) Appointment ○ Non-Career Senior Executive Service (SES) Appointment ■ Postal Career Executive Service

DEPARTMENTS

Richmond (VA) Office *(continued)*

Deputy U.S. Marshal **(Vacant)** .... (804) 545-8501
Deputy U.S. Marshal **(Vacant)** .... (804) 545-8501
Deputy U.S. Marshal **(Vacant)** .... (804) 545-8501
Civil Clerk **(Vacant)** .... (804) 545-8501
Criminal Clerk **Sonya Moseley** .... (804) 545-8501
E-mail: sonya.moseley@usdoj.gov

Virginia - Western District

Federal Office Building, 210 Franklin Road, SW,
Room 247, Roanoke, VA 24011
P.O. Box 2280, Roanoke, VA 24009
Tel: (540) 857-2230 Fax: (540) 857-2032

★ U.S. Marshal (Acting) **Richard B. Sellers** .... (540) 857-2230
Chief Deputy U.S. Marshal **Richard B. Sellers** .... (434) 293-2230
255 West Main Street, Charlottesville, VA 22901
Supervisory Deputy U.S. Marshal **Wade Hepburn** .... (540) 857-2230
E-mail: wade.hepburn@usdoj.gov
Administrative Officer **Sean Verlik** .... (540) 857-2320
E-mail: sean.verlik@usdoj.gov
Criminal Program Specialist **(Vacant)** .... (540) 857-2231

Abingdon (VA) Sub-Office

180 West Main Street, Abingdon, VA 24210
Tel: (276) 628-9402 Fax: (276) 628-8650

Supervisory Deputy U.S. Marshal
Matthew Davis .... (276) 628-1398 ext. 501
E-mail: matthew.davis@usdoj.gov
Deputy U.S. Marshal **Woodrow McGlothlin** .... (276) 628-9402 ext. 506
Deputy U.S. Marshal **Jim Satterwhite** .... (276) 628-9402 ext. 502
E-mail: jim.satterwhite@usdoj.gov
Deputy U.S. Marshal **Byron Schiesz** .... (276) 628-9402
E-mail: byron.schiesz@usdoj.gov

Charlottesville (VA) Sub-Office

255 West Main Street, Charlottesville, VA 22901
Tel: (434) 293-6612 Fax: (434) 293-3299

Supervisory Deputy U.S. Marshal **Steve Carter** .... (434) 293-6612
E-mail: steve.carter@usdoj.gov
Deputy U.S. Marshal **(Vacant)** .... (434) 293-6612

Washington - Eastern District

Thomas S. Foley U.S. Courthouse, 920 West Riverside Avenue,
Room 200, Spokane, WA 99201
P.O. Box 1463, Spokane, WA 99210-1463
Tel: (509) 368-3600 Fax: (509) 353-2766

★ U.S. Marshal **Craig Ellis Thayer** .... (509) 368-3600
E-mail: craig.thayer@usdoj.gov
Education: Gonzaga BS, JD
Chief Deputy U.S. Marshal **Kevin Kilgore** .... (509) 368-3600
E-mail: kevin.kilgore@usdoj.gov
Deputy U.S. Marshal/ Asset Forfeiture Financial
Investigator **Jerome Brown** .... (509) 353-0533
E-mail: jerome.brown@usdoj.gov
Deputy U.S. Marshal **David Brod** .... (509) 353-2781
E-mail: david.brod@usdoj.gov
Deputy U.S. Marshal **Scott Hershey** .... (509) 353-2788
E-mail: scott.hershey@usdoj.gov
Deputy U.S. Marshal **Martin J. Kridler** .... (509) 353-0615
E-mail: martin.kridler@usdoj.gov
Deputy U.S. Marshal **(Vacant)** .... (509) 353-2781
Deputy U.S. Marshal **(Vacant)** .... (509) 353-2781
Deputy U.S. Marshal (K9) **Hank Shafer** .... (509) 353-0624
E-mail: hank.shafer@usdoj.gov
Supervisory Criminal Investigator **Robert L. Doty** .... (509) 368-3600
Supervisory Officer In Charge **(Vacant)** .... (509) 368-3600
Supervisory Criminal Investigator **(Vacant)** .... (509) 353-0617
Judicial Security Inspector **Ben Haraseth** .... (509) 353-7011
E-mail: benjamin.haraseth@usdoj.gov
Administrative Officer **Jacqueline P. Gabert** .... (509) 368-3600
E-mail: jacqueline.gabert@usdoj.gov
Criminal Program Specialist **Debbie Anderson** .... (509) 353-0623

Washington - Eastern District *(continued)*

Investigative Research Specialist **Reagan Havey** .... (509) 353-0706
Management and Program Analyst **(Vacant)** .... (509) 353-0534
Administrative Support Specialist **Mary McGoldrick** .... (509) 368-3600
E-mail: mary.mcgoldrick@usdoj.gov
Administrative Support Specialist **Vicky Lynn Peters** .... (509) 368-3610
E-mail: victoria.peters@usdoj.gov

Richland (WA) Office

Federal Building, 825 Jadwyn Avenue,
Room G-69, Richland, WA 99352-3586
P.O. Box 1026, Richland, WA 99352-1026
Tel: (509) 946-9423 Fax: (509) 946-8893

Deputy U.S. Marshal **Julio Hernandez** .... (509) 946-9423
Deputy U.S. Marshal **Darrick Swick** .... (509) 946-9423
Deputy U.S. Marshal **(Vacant)** .... (509) 946-9423
Deputy U.S. Marshal **(Vacant)** .... (509) 946-9423
Administrative Support Specialist **Tricia Moore** .... (509) 368-3600
E-mail: tricia.moore@usdoj.gov

Yakima (WA) Office

402 East Yakima Avenue, Suite 210, Yakima, WA 98901
Tel: (509) 575-5917 Fax: (509) 575-5812

Supervisory Deputy U.S. Marshal **(Vacant)** .... (509) 575-5917
Deputy U.S. Marshal **Arik Coleman** .... (509) 575-5917
E-mail: arik.coleman@usdoj.gov
Deputy U.S. Marshal **Bradley LeCompte** .... (509) 575-5917
Deputy U.S. Marshal **Christopher Smith** .... (509) 575-5917
Deputy U.S. Marshal **(Vacant)** .... (509) 575-5917
Operations Support Specialist **(Vacant)** .... (509) 575-5917

Washington - Western District

700 Stewart Street, Suite 9000, Seattle, WA 98101-1271
Tel: (206) 370-8600 Fax: (206) 370-8670

★ U.S. Marshal (Acting) **Jacob Green** .... (206) 370-8601
E-mail: jacob.green@usdoj.gov
Chief Deputy U.S. Marshal **(Vacant)** .... (206) 370-8602
Supervisory Deputy U.S. Marshal **(Vacant)** .... (206) 370-8606
Administrative Officer **(Vacant)** .... (206) 370-8650

Tacoma (WA) Office

1170 U.S. Courthouse, 1717 Pacific Avenue, Tacoma, WA 98402
Tel: (253) 302-8680 Fax: (253) 302-8668

Supervisory Deputy U.S. Marshal **(Vacant)** .... (206) 370-8607

West Virginia - Northern District

U.S. Post Office, 500 W. Pike Street, Clarksburg, WV 26301
P.O. Box 2807, Clarksburg, WV 26302
Tel: (304) 623-0486 Fax: (304) 623-5708

★ U.S. Marshal **J. C. Raffety** .... (304) 623-0486
E-mail: j.c.raffety@usdoj.gov
Education: Illinois State 1970 BS; Pittsburgh 1978 MPA
Chief Deputy U.S. Marshal **Alex P. Neville** .... (304) 623-0486
E-mail: alex.neville@usdoj.gov
Supervisory Deputy U.S. Marshal **Terry Moore** .... (304) 623-0486
E-mail: terry.moore@usdoj.gov
Deputy U.S. Marshal **Phillip Efaw** .... (304) 623-0486
E-mail: phillip.efaw@usdoj.gov
Deputy U.S. Marshal **Wesley Frederick** .... (304) 623-0486
E-mail: wesley.frederick@usdoj.gov
Deputy U.S. Marshal **John D. Hare** .... (304) 623-0486
E-mail: john.hare@usdoj.gov
Deputy U.S. Marshal **Dustin Hotsinpiller** .... (304) 623-0486
E-mail: dustin.hotsinpiller@usdoj.gov
Deputy U.S. Marshal **Joseph "Joe" McCarty** .... (304) 623-0486
E-mail: joseph.mccarty@usdoj.gov
Deputy U.S. Marshal **Joseph "Joe" Nichols** .... (304) 623-0486
E-mail: joseph.nichols@usdoj.gov
Deputy U.S. Marshal **Derek Patrick** .... (304) 623-0486
E-mail: derek.patrick@usdoj.gov
Budget Analyst **Sharon Pernell** .... (304) 623-0486
E-mail: sharon.pernell@usdoj.gov

★ Presidential Appointment Requiring Senate Confirmation ☆ Presidential Appointment □ Schedule C Appointment ◇ Career Senior Foreign Service Appointment
● Career Senior Executive Service (SES) Appointment ○ Non-Career Senior Executive Service (SES) Appointment ■ Postal Career Executive Service

West Virginia - Northern District *(continued)*

Criminal Investigative Specialist **Erica Martin** .... (304) 623-0486
Seizure and Forfeiture Specialist **Kimberly Landes** ...... (304) 623-0486
E-mail: kimberly.landes@usdoj.gov
Administrative Officer **Rhonda Kirby** .... (304) 623-0486
E-mail: rhonda.kirby@usdoj.gov

Elkins (WV) Office
Jennings Randolph Federal Center, 300 Third Street,
Room 317, Elkins, WV 26241
P.O. Box 1454, Elkins, WV 26241
Tel: (304) 636-0332 Fax: (304) 636-6712
Deputy U.S. Marshal **(Vacant)** .... (304) 623-0486

Martinsburg (WV) Office
217 W. King St., Martinsburg, WV 25401
Tel: (304) 267-7179 Fax: (304) 267-9369
Supervisory Deputy U.S. Marshal **Cole Barnhart** .... (304) 267-7179
E-mail: cole.barnhart@usdoj.gov
Deputy U.S. Marshal **(Vacant)** .... (304) 267-7179
Deputy U.S. Marshal **Jon LaLiberte** .... (304) 267-7179
E-mail: jon.laliberte@usdoj.gov
Deputy U.S. Marshal **Michael Ulrich** .... (304) 267-7179
E-mail: michael.ulrich@usdoj.gov
Deputy U.S. Marshal **Alphonso Wideman** .... (304) 267-7179
E-mail: alphonso.wideman@usdoj.gov

Wheeling (WV) Office
Federal Building, 1125-1141 Chapline Street,
Room 407, Wheeling, WV 26003
P.O. Box 726, Wheeling, WV 26003
Tel: (304) 232-2980 Fax: (304) 232-0410
Deputy U.S. Marshal **Sara Ahrens** .... (304) 232-2980
E-mail: sara.ahrens@usdoj.gov
Deputy U.S. Marshal **Chad Simpson** .... (304) 232-2980
E-mail: chad.simpson@usdoj.gov
Deputy U.S. Marshal **Don Walker** .... (304) 232-2980
E-mail: don.walker@usdoj.gov
Deputy U.S. Marshal **Vinnie Viola** .... (304) 267-7179
E-mail: vinnie.viola@usdoj.gov

West Virginia - Southern District
Robert C. Byrd U.S. Courthouse, 300 Virginia Street East,
Room 3602, Charleston, WV 25301
Tel: (304) 347-5136 Fax: (304) 347-5394
★ U.S. Marshal **Michael T. Baylous** .... (304) 347-5140
E-mail: michael.baylous@usdoj.gov
Education: West Virginia BA; Marshall AA
Chief Deputy U.S. Marshal **Timothy Goode** .... (304) 347-5136
E-mail: timothy.goode@usdoj.gov
Supervisory Deputy U.S. Marshal **Jeremy Honaker** ..... (304) 347-5651
E-mail: jeremy.honaker@usdoj.gov
Supervisory Deputy U.S. Marshal **Madonna Pursell** ..... (304) 347-5652
E-mail: madonna.pursell@usdoj.gov
Deputy U.S. Marshal **Patrick Hernandez** .... (304) 347-5136
E-mail: patrick.hernandez@usdoj.gov
Deputy U.S. Marshal **Scott Hill** .... (304) 347-5662
E-mail: scott.hill@usdoj.gov
Deputy U.S. Marshal **James Ingram** .... (304) 347-5136
E-mail: james.ingram@usdoj.gov
Deputy U.S. Marshal **Marcus Roth** .... (304) 347-5660
E-mail: marcus.roth@usdoj.gov
Deputy U.S. Marshal **Eric Tipton** .... (304) 347-5383
E-mail: eric.tipton@usdoj.gov
Sex Offender Investigations Coordinator/Deputy U.S.
Marshal **William L. Seckman** .... (304) 347-5136
E-mail: william.seckman@usdoj.gov
Budget Analyst **Melinda K. Brown** .... (304) 347-5582
E-mail: melinda.brown@usdoj.gov
Administrative Officer **Christopher C. Thompson** ...... (304) 347-5135
E-mail: christopher.thompson@usdoj.gov
Civil Program Assistant **Jody M. Wills** .... (304) 347-5553

West Virginia - Southern District *(continued)*

Court Security Inspector **Christopher T. Lair** .... (304) 347-5136
E-mail: christopher.lair@usdoj.gov
Asset Forfeiture Specialist **Laura Adkins** .... (304) 347-5582
E-mail: laura.adkins@usdoj.gov

Beckley (WV) Office
Robert C. Byrd U.S. Courthouse, 110 Heber Street,
Suite G-56, Beckley, WV 25801-4501
Tel: (304) 253-1519 Fax: (304) 253-1382
Deputy U.S. Marshal **Shane Osgood** .... (304) 253-1519
E-mail: shane.osgood@usdoj.gov
Deputy U.S. Marshal **Frederick Lamey** .... (304) 253-1519
E-mail: frederick.lamey@usdoj.gov
Deputy U.S. Marshal **(Vacant)** .... (304) 253-1519

Bluefield (WV) Office
2114 Federal Building, 601 Federal Street, Bluefield, WV 24701
Tel: (304) 327-6000 Fax: (304) 325-9778
Deputy U.S. Marshal **Karen A. Long** .... (304) 347-5136
E-mail: karen.long@usdoj.gov

Huntington (WV) Office
201 U.S. Courthouse and Federal Building,
845 Fifth Avenue, Huntington, WV 25701
Tel: (304) 529-5560 Fax: (304) 529-5130
Deputy U.S. Marshal **John LaJeunesse** .... (304) 529-5560
E-mail: john.lajeunesse@usdoj.gov
Deputy U.S. Marshal **James Mounts** .... (304) 529-5560
E-mail: james.mounts@usdoj.gov
Deputy U.S. Marshal **Justin Mounts** .... (304) 529-5560
E-mail: justin.mounts@usdoj.gov

Wisconsin - Eastern District
Federal Courthouse, 517 East Wisconsin Avenue,
Suite 711, Milwaukee, WI 53202
Tel: (414) 297-3707 Fax: (414) 297-1825
★ U.S. Marshal **Kevin Anthony Carr** .... (414) 297-3707
E-mail: kevin.carr@usdoj.gov
Education: Concordia U (WI) 1997 BA
Chief Deputy U.S. Marshal **Thomas P. Conlon** .... (414) 297-3707
E-mail: thomas.conlon@usdoj.gov
Supervisory Deputy U.S. Marshal **Jeremy Loesch** .... (414) 297-3707
Supervisory Deputy U.S. Marshal **Gary Enos** .... (414) 297-3707
E-mail: gary.enos@usdoj.gov
Criminal Investigator **Joshua Bissey** .... (414) 297-3707
E-mail: joshua.bissey@usdoj.gov
Criminal Investigator **Robert Bressers** .... (414) 297-3707
E-mail: robert.bressers@usdoj.gov
Criminal Investigator **Rodney Clauss** .... (414) 297-3707
E-mail: rodney.clauss@usdoj.gov
Criminal Investigator **Kasey Doty** .... (414) 297-3707
E-mail: kasey.doty@usdoj.gov
Criminal Investigator **Kristina Haven** .... (414) 297-3707
Criminal Investigator **April Hemstad** .... (414) 297-3707
E-mail: april.hemstad@usdoj.gov
Criminal Investigator **Shane Hitchler** .... (414) 297-3707
E-mail: shane.hitchler@usdoj.gov
Criminal Investigator **Scott Keller** .... (414) 297-3707
E-mail: scott.keller@usdoj.gov
Criminal Investigator **Brian Nodes** .... (414) 297-3707
E-mail: brian.nodes@usdoj.gov
Criminal Investigator **(Vacant)** .... (414) 297-3707
Court Security Inspector **Robert O'Connor** .... (414) 297-3707
Administrative Officer **Dion Hill** .... (414) 297-3707
E-mail: dion.hill3@usdoj.gov
Administrative Support Assistant **(Vacant)** .... (414) 297-3707
Budget Analyst **Yamilet Mendez-West** .... (414) 297-3707
E-mail: yamilet.mendez-west@usdoj.gov
District Asset Forfeiture Coordinator
Christopher Eden .... (414) 297-3707
Seizure and Forfeiture Specialist **(Vacant)** .... (414) 297-3707
Investigative Research Specialist **Lindsay Vahravian** ..... (414) 297-3707

(continued on next page)

★ Presidential Appointment Requiring Senate Confirmation ☆ Presidential Appointment □ Schedule C Appointment ◇ Career Senior Foreign Service Appointment
● Career Senior Executive Service (SES) Appointment ○ Non-Career Senior Executive Service (SES) Appointment ■ Postal Career Executive Service

DEPARTMENTS

Wisconsin - Eastern District *(continued)*

Purchasing Agent **(Vacant)** .... (414) 297-3707

Wisconsin - Western District

Federal Courthouse, 120 North Henry Street,
Room 440, Madison, WI 53703
Tel: (608) 661-8300 Fax: (608) 661-8304

★ U.S. Marshal-Designate **Kim Gaffney** .... (608) 661-8300
Chief Deputy U.S. Marshal **Jeff Michaelis** .... (608) 661-8300
E-mail: jeff.michaelis@usdoj.gov
Supervisory Deputy U.S. Marshal **Lucien Chastain** ...... (608) 301-6007
E-mail: lucien.chastain@usdoj.gov
Supervisory Deputy U.S. Marshal **(Vacant)** .... (608) 661-8300
Deputy U.S. Marshal **Lucas Balde** .... (608) 661-8300
E-mail: lucas.balde@usdoj.gov
Deputy U.S. Marshal **Kent Halverson** .... (608) 661-8300
E-mail: kent.halverson@usdoj.gov
Deputy U.S. Marshal **Emily Krueger** .... (608) 661-8300
E-mail: emily.krueger@usdoj.gov
Deputy U.S. Marshal **Brad Meng** .... (608) 661-8300
E-mail: brad.meng@usdoj.gov
Deputy U.S. Marshal **Michael Pritchard** .... (608) 661-8300
E-mail: michael.pritchard@usdoj.gov
Deputy U.S. Marshal **(Vacant)** .... (608) 661-8300
Deputy U.S. Marshal (SOIC) **Patrick Kirchenwitz** .... (608) 661-8300
E-mail: patrick.kirchenwitz@usdoj.gov
Judicial Security Inspector **Dale Emmerton** .... (608) 661-8300
E-mail: dale.emmerton2@usdoj.gov
Administrative Systems Administrator **Roland Perez** ..... (608) 661-8225
E-mail: roland.perez@usdoj.gov
Administrative Officer **Dionne Smith** .... (608) 661-8300
E-mail: dionne.smith@usdoj.gov
Budget Analyst **Diana Forsberg** .... (608) 661-8300
E-mail: diana.forsberg@usdoj.gov
Criminal Program Specialist **(Vacant)** .... (608) 661-8300

Wyoming District

J.C. O'Mahoney Federal Building, 2120 Capitol Avenue,
Room 1100, Cheyenne, WY 82001
Tel: (307) 772-2196 Fax: (307) 772-2735

★ U.S. Marshal **(Vacant)** .... (307) 772-2196
Chief Deputy U.S. Marshal **Gary Brewer** .... (307) 772-2952
Supervisory Deputy U.S. Marshal **Jason Griess** .... (307) 772-2265
E-mail: jason.griess@usdoj.gov
Deputy U.S. Marshal **Justin Cline** .... (307) 772-2198
E-mail: justin.cline@usdoj.gov
Deputy U.S. Marshal **Justin Stephenson** .... (307) 772-2198
E-mail: justin.stephenson@usdoj.gov
Deputy U.S. Marshal **Jon Goodman** .... (307) 772-2198
E-mail: jon.goodman@usdoj.gov
Deputy U.S. Marshal **Robert MacMaster** .... (307) 772-2198
E-mail: robert.macmaster@usdoj.gov
Deputy U.S. Marshal **Ross P. Mueske** .... (307) 772-2198
E-mail: ross.mueske@usdoj.gov
Sex Offender Investigations Coordinator/Deputy U.S.
Marshal **Dennis Conmay** .... (307) 772-2198
E-mail: dennis.conmay@usdoj.gov
Administrative Officer **Christine E. Butterfield** .... (307) 772-2926
E-mail: chris.butterfield@usdoj.gov Fax: (307) 772-2271
Financial Specialist **Dana Murrell** .... (307) 772-2510
E-mail: dana.murrell@usdoj.gov
Investigative Research Specialist **(Vacant)** .... (307) 772-2257
Judicial Security Inspector **Douglas Lineen** .... (307) 772-2927
E-mail: douglas.lineen@usdoj.gov
Administrative Support Assistant **Amanda McCartney** ... (307) 772-2668
E-mail: amanda.neubeck@usdoj.gov

Casper (WY) Office

111 South Wolcott Street, Room 128, Casper, WY 82601
Tel: (307) 261-5411 Fax: (307) 261-5410

Deputy U.S. Marshal **Brian Hoose** .... (307) 261-5405
E-mail: brian.hoose@usdoj.gov
Supervisory Deputy U.S. Marshal **(Vacant)** .... (307) 261-5417

Casper (WY) Office *(continued)*

Deputy U.S. Marshal **Matthew Berg** .... (307) 262-5400
E-mail: matthew.berg@usdoj.gov
Deputy U.S. Marshal **Zachary Cantrell** .... (307) 262-5418
E-mail: zachary.cantrell@usdoj.gov
Deputy U.S. Marshal **Del Ramsey** .... (307) 262-5412
E-mail: del.ramsey@usdoj.gov

Lander (WY) Office

125 Sunflower, Lander, WY 82520
Tel: (307) 332-8696 Fax: (307) 332-8646

Supervisory Deputy U.S. Marshal **Carl Von Rein** .... (307) 332-8696
E-mail: carl.vonrein@usdoj.gov
Deputy U.S. Marshal **(Vacant)** .... (307) 332-1384
Deputy U.S. Marshal **(Vacant)** .... (307) 332-8696

Yellowstone National Park (WY) Office

Yellowstone National Park (WY) Office, Building 13-A UpperMammoth,
P.O. Box 588, Yellowstone National Park, WY 82190
Tel: (307) 344-6517 Fax: (307) 344-6515

Deputy U.S. Marshal **Travis Mangum** .... (307) 344-7775

United States Department of Labor

Contents

United States Department of Labor (DOL)

Description: The Department of Labor promotes the welfare of wage-earners in the United States through the administration of federal labor laws. The department guarantees safe and healthful working conditions, a minimum hourly wage, overtime pay, unemployment insurance, worker's compensation, and freedom from employment discrimination. In addition, the department protects workers' pension rights, provides job training programs, works to strengthen free collective bargaining, and both collects and tracks statistics on employment, prices and other national economic measurements.

DEPARTMENTS

200 Constitution Avenue, NW, Washington, DC 20210
Tel: (202) 693-6000 Tel: (866) 487-2365 (Personnel Locator)
Tel: (202) 691-5200 (Bureau of Labor Statistics Hotline)
Tel: (202) 693-0101 (Contracts and Compliance)
Tel: (202) 693-4650 (Public Information)
Tel: (202) 693-5540 (Freedom of Information/Privacy Act)
Tel: (800) 347-3756 (Fraud, Waste and Abuse Hotline)
Tel: (703) 235-1452 (Mine Safety and Health Act)
Tel: (800) 746-1553 (Mine Safety and Health Act - To report mine accidents) Tel: (800) 746-1554 (Mine Safety and Health Act - To anonymously report mine safety and health concerns) TTY: (877) 889-5627 (Public Information)
E-mail: open@dol.gov Internet: www.dol.gov
Internet: www.dol.gov/open (Open Government Directive)
Internet: http://www.mynextmove.org/
Internet: http://ogesdw.dol.gov (Online Enforcement Database)
Internet: www.veterans.gov (Veterans Employment Resources)

OFFICE OF THE SECRETARY

200 Constitution Avenue, NW, Room S-2018, Washington, DC 20210
Tel: (202) 693-6000 Fax: (202) 693-6111

Office of Administrative Law Judges (OALJ)

TechWorld, 800 K Street, NW, Suite 400N, Washington, DC 20001-8002
Tel: (202) 693-7300 Fax: (202) 693-7365 Internet: www.oalj.dol.gov

District Judges

Boston (MA) Office

Thomas P. O'Neill Federal Building, 10 Causeway Street, Room 411, Boston, MA 02222
Tel: (617) 223-9355 Fax: (617) 223-4254
E-mail: oalj.bo@internetmci.com

District Chief Judge **Colleen A. Geraghty** . . . . (617) 223-9355
E-mail: geraghty.colleen@dol.gov
Paralegal Specialist **Deneen Davis** . . . . (617) 223-9355
E-mail: davis.deneen@dol.gov
Administrative Officer **Darcy Rossman** . . . . (617) 223-9325
E-mail: rossman.darcy.s@dol.gov
Judge **Jonathan Calianos** . . . . (617) 223-9355
E-mail: calianos.jonathan@dol.gov
Education: St Anselm 1988 BA; Creighton 1992 JD
Judge **Timothy J. McGrath** . . . . (617) 223-9355
E-mail: mcgrath.timothy@dol.gov
Attorney Advisor **Lynne Cutaiar** . . . . (617) 223-9355
E-mail: cutaiar.lynne@dol.gov
Law Clerk **Heather M. LaCount** . . . . (617) 223-9355
E-mail: lacount.heather.m@dol.gov
Law Clerk **(Vacant)** . . . . (617) 223-9355
Legal Assistant **Kristian Hinojosa** . . . . (617) 223-9355
E-mail: hinojosa.kristian@dol.gov

Cherry Hill (NJ) Office

Two Executive Campus, Suite 450, Cherry Hill, NJ 08002
Tel: (856) 486-3800 Fax: (856) 486-3806

District Chief Judge (Acting) **Lystra A. Harris** . . . . (856) 486-3800
E-mail: harris.lystra@dol.gov
Judge **Lauren C. Boucher-Lakin** . . . . (856) 486-3800
Judge **Scott Richard Morris** . . . . (856) 486-3800
E-mail: morris.scott.r@dol.gov
Judge **Adele H. Odegard** . . . . (856) 486-3800
E-mail: odegard.adele@dol.gov
Judge **Theresa C. Timlin** . . . . (856) 486-3800
E-mail: timlin.theresa@dol.gov
Administrative Specialist
Constance M. "Connie" Stiles . . . . (856) 486-3800 ext. 115
E-mail: stiles.constance@dol.gov

Cincinnati (OH) Office

36 East Seventh Street, Suite 2525, Cincinnati, OH 45202
Tel: (513) 684-3252 Fax: (513) 684-6108

District Chief Judge (Acting) **John P. Sellers III** . . . . (513) 684-3252
E-mail: sellers.john.p@dol.gov
Education: Cincinnati 1982 JD; NYU 1987 LLM
Judge **Steven D. Bell** . . . . (513) 684-3252
E-mail: bell.steven.d@dol.gov
Judge **Jason A. Golden** . . . . (513) 684-3252
E-mail: golden.jason.a@dol.gov
Judge **Joseph E. Kane** . . . . (513) 684-3252
E-mail: kane.joseph@dol.gov
Judge **Peter B. Silvain, Jr.** . . . . (513) 684-3252
E-mail: silvainjr.peter@dol.gov
Judge **Larry A. Temin** . . . . (513) 684-3252
E-mail: temin.larry.a@dol.gov

Covington (LA) Office

5100 Village Walk, Suite 200, Covington, LA 70433
Tel: (985) 809-5173 Fax: (985) 893-7351

District Chief Judge **Lee J. Romero, Jr.** . . . . (985) 809-5173 ext. 225
E-mail: romero.lee@dol.gov
Judge **Tracy Allen Daly** . . . . (985) 809-5173
E-mail: daly.tracy.a@dol.gov
Judge **Clement J. Kennington** . . . . (985) 809-5173 ext. 221
E-mail: kennington.clement@dol.gov
Judge **Larry W. Price** . . . . (985) 809-5173 ext. 227
E-mail: price.larry@dol.gov
Judge **Patrick Rosenow** . . . . (985) 809-5173 ext. 223
E-mail: rosenow.patrick@dol.gov

Newport News (VA) Office

11870 Merchants Walk, Suite 204, Newport News, VA 23606
Tel: (757) 591-5140 Fax: (757) 591-5150

District Chief Judge **Paul C. Johnson, Jr.** . . . . (757) 591-5142
Judge **Alan L. Bergstrom** . . . . (757) 591-5142
E-mail: bergstrom.alan@dol.gov
Judge **Monica F. Markley** . . . . (757) 591-5142
E-mail: markley.monica.f@dol.gov
Judge **Dana Rosen** . . . . (757) 591-5142

★ Presidential Appointment Requiring Senate Confirmation ☆ Presidential Appointment □ Schedule C Appointment ◇ Career Senior Foreign Service Appointment
● Career Senior Executive Service (SES) Appointment ○ Non-Career Senior Executive Service (SES) Appointment ■ Postal Career Executive Service

DEPARTMENTS

Pittsburgh (PA) Office
1000 Liberty Avenue, Suite 1800, Pittsburgh, PA 15222
Tel: (412) 644-5754 Fax: (412) 644-5005

District Chief Judge (Acting) **Drew A. Swank** . . . . (412) 644-5754
E-mail: swank.drew.a@dol.gov

San Francisco (CA) Office
90 Seventh Street, Suite 4-800, San Francisco, CA 94103-1516
Tel: (415) 625-2200 Fax: (415) 625-2201
Areas Covered: AK, AZ, CA, HI, NM, OR, UT, WA, Guam, Saipan

District Chief Judge **Jennifer Gee** . . . . (415) 625-2200
E-mail: gee.jennifer@dol.gov
Education: UC Berkeley 1971 BA; Boalt Hall 1974 JD
Judge **Steven B. Berlin** . . . . (415) 625-2200
Judge **Richard Manuel Clark** . . . . (415) 625-2200
Judge **J. Christopher Larsen** . . . . (415) 625-2200
Judge **Evan H. Nordby** . . . . (415) 625-2200
Judge **(Vacant)** . . . . (415) 625-2200

OFFICE OF THE DEPUTY SECRETARY (ODS)
200 Constitution Avenue, NW, Room S2018, Washington, DC 20210
Tel: (202) 693-6002 Fax: (202) 693-6143

Office of the Assistant Secretary for Administration and Management (OASAM)
200 Constitution Avenue, NW, Room S-2203, Washington, DC 20210
Fax: (202) 693-4055 Internet: www.dol.gov/oasam

Deputy Assistant Secretary for Operations (DASO)
200 Constitution Avenue, NW, Room S2203, Washington, DC 20210

Regional Offices

Atlanta (GA) Regional Office
61 Forsyth Street, SW, Atlanta, GA 30303
Tel: (404) 302-5800 Fax: (404) 302-5882

Regional Administrator **Michelle M. Driscoll** . . . . (404) 302-5800
Sam Nunn Atlanta Federal Center, 10300 SW 72nd Street, Room 6B65, Miami, FL 33173
E-mail: driscoll.michelle.m@dol.gov
Regional Administrative Services Officer
Rebecca Browning Room 6B25 . . . . (404) 302-5819
E-mail: browning.rebecca@dol.gov Fax: (404) 302-5886
Human Resources Officer **Cindy Williams** . . . . (972) 850-4441
E-mail: williams.cindy@dol.gov
Civil Rights Officer **(Vacant)** . . . . (404) 302-5878
Sam Nunn Atlanta Federal Center, 10300 SW 72nd Street, Room 6B25, Miami, FL 33173
Finance and Administrative Services Director
Ada Brightwell . . . . (404) 302-5829
Safety and Health Officer **Jeffrey Thompson** . . . . (404) 302-5810
E-mail: thompson.jeffrey@dol.gov
Information Technology Manager
Ray Kelly Suite 6B30 . . . . (404) 302-5805
E-mail: kelly.ray@dol.gov

Boston (MA)/New York (NY) Regional Office
John F. Kennedy Federal Building, 25 Sudbury Street, Room E-215, Boston, MA 02203
Tel: (617) 788-2800 (Boston) Tel: (646) 264-5050 (New York)
Fax: (617) 788-2836

Regional Administrator **Mark L. Vrooman** . . . . (617) 788-2888
E-mail: vrooman.mark.l@dol.gov
Executive Assistant **Christian Flores** . . . . (617) 788-2818
Regional Administrative Services Officer
Glen M. Tynan . . . . (617) 788-2807
15 Sudbury Street, Boston, MA 02203
E-mail: tynan.glen.m@dol.gov
Director of Administrative Services
Francesca Sullivan Room E215 . . . . (617) 788-2809
E-mail: sullivan.francesca.e@dol.gov
Civil Rights Officer **(Vacant)** . . . . (617) 788-2800

Boston (MA)/New York (NY) Regional Office *(continued)*

Finance Officer **Edmund Ward** . . . . (617) 788-2819
Human Resource Officer **Robert Spencer** . . . . (617) 788-2802
Labor Relations Officer **John Martorana** . . . . (617) 788-2805
Training Officer **Greg Ramos** . . . . (646) 264-5013
Information Technology Specialist **John Sheehan** . . . . (617) 788-2822
E-mail: sheehan.john@dol.gov
Information Technology Manager **Laurence Vasile** . . . . . . (646) 264-5001
E-mail: vasile.laurence@dol.gov
Safety and Health Manager **Kathy Benzi** . . . . (617) 788-2825
E-mail: benzi.katherine@dol.gov

Chicago (IL) Regional Office
Kluczynski Federal Building, 230 South Dearborn Street, Room1004, Chicago, IL 60604
Tel: (312) 353-8373 Fax: (312) 886-3219

Regional Administrator **Jon Sebastian** . . . . (312) 353-8373
E-mail: sebastian.jon@dol.gov

Dallas (TX) Regional Office
Federal Building, 525 South Griffin Street, Suite 744, Dallas, TX 75202-5001
Tel: (972) 850-4401 Fax: (972) 850-4410

Regional Administrator **Kelley Pettit** . . . . (972) 850-4401
E-mail: pettit.kelley@dol.gov
Acquisition Services Director **Charlie DeCeasar** . . . . (972) 850-4411
E-mail: deceasar.charlie@dol.gov
Education: Roosevelt 1982 BGS
Finance and Administrative Services Director
Richard Perez . . . . (972) 850-4402
Information Technology Manager **Janet Travers** . . . . (972) 850-4461
E-mail: travers.janet@dol.gov
Safety and Health Manager
CMSgt Terry D. Goines USAF . . . . (972) 850-4472
E-mail: goines.terry.d@dol.gov
Supervisor for Administrative Services
Florence Jackson . . . . (972) 850-4415
E-mail: jackson.florence@dol.gov
Human Resources Director **Davida Guy** . . . . (972) 850-4401
E-mail: guy.davida@dol.gov
Regional Freedom of Information Act Coordinator
Denise Childress . . . . (972) 850-4401
E-mail: childress.denise@dol.gov
Director of Safety, Technology and Emergency Management **Frances Memmolo** . . . . (972) 850-4401
E-mail: memmolo.frances@dol.gov

Philadelphia (PA) Regional Office
The Curtis Center, 170 South Independence Mall West, Suite 600E, Philadelphia, PA 19106-3315
Tel: (215) 861-5030 Fax: (215) 861-5087

Regional Administrator **Crystal Guy** . . . . (215) 861-5030
E-mail: guy.crystal@dol.gov
Administrative Officer **Lucy Buzzone** . . . . (215) 861-5030
E-mail: buzzone.lucy@dol.gov
Regional Administrative Services Supervisor
Christian Callender . . . . (215) 861-5083
E-mail: callender.christian@dol.gov
Human Resources Director **Connie Jones-Pearson** . . . . . . (215) 861-5030
E-mail: jones-pearson.connie@dol.gov
Director of Technology and Administrative Services
Robert Lazarski . . . . (215) 861-5030
Director, Safety and Health **Donald "Don" Tillotson** . . . . (215) 861-5030
E-mail: tillotson.donald@dol.gov

San Francisco (CA) Regional Office
90 Seventh Street, Suite 12-300, San Francisco, CA 94103
Tel: (415) 625-2370 Fax: (415) 625-2427
Areas Covered: AK, AZ, CA, GU, HI, ID, NV, OR, WA, Saipan

Regional Administrator **Bonnie Macaraig** . . . . (415) 625-2371
Fax: (415) 975-4914
Regional Administrative Services Officer **Sean Ryan** . . . . . (415) 625-2381
E-mail: ryan.sean@dol.gov
Financial Management Director **Paul Cardenas** . . . . (415) 625-2388

★ Presidential Appointment Requiring Senate Confirmation ☆ Presidential Appointment □ Schedule C Appointment ◇ Career Senior Foreign Service Appointment
● Career Senior Executive Service (SES) Appointment ○ Non-Career Senior Executive Service (SES) Appointment ■ Postal Career Executive Service

San Francisco (CA) Regional Office *(continued)*

Regional Human Resources Officer **Lourdes Devigal** . . . . (415) 625-2396
E-mail: devigal.lourdes@dol.gov
Safety, Technology and Emergency Management
Director **Ferdinand Ralleta** . . . .(415) 625-2371
E-mail: ralleta.ferdinand@dol.gov
Acquisition Services Branch Chief **Mary Fronck** . . . . (415) 625-2432
Financial Chief **Joseph Maciel** . . . . (415) 625-2374
Support Services Assistant **Cheryl Maze** . . . .(415) 625-2371
E-mail: maze.cheryl@dol.gov
Executive Assistant **Andrea Gabossy** . . . . (415) 625-2373

Office of Congressional and Intergovernmental Affairs (OCIA)

200 Constitution Avenue, NW, Room S2006, Washington, DC 20210
Tel: (202) 693-4600 Fax: (202) 693-4641

Secretary's Regional Representatives (SRR)

Chicago (IL) Regional Office
Kluczynski Federal Building, 230 South Dearborn Street,
Suite 3192, Chicago, IL 60604
Tel: (312) 353-4591 Fax: (312) 353-8679
Areas Covered: IA, IL, KY, IN, MI, MN, MO, OH, TN, WI
□ Secretary's Regional Representative **(Vacant)** . . . . (312) 353-4591
Fax: (312) 353-8679

Denver (CO) Regional Office
Cesar E. Chavez Memorial Building, 1244 Speer Boulevard,
Suite 536, Denver, CO 80204
Tel: (303) 844-1256 Fax: (303) 844-1257
Areas Covered: AL, AR, CO, LA, KS, MI, NE, NM, OK, TX
□ Secretary's Regional Representative **(Vacant)** . . . . (303) 844-1256

San Francisco (CA) Regional Office
90 Seventh Street, Floor 2, Suite 650, San Francisco, CA 94103
Tel: (415) 625-2420 Fax: (415) 625-2330
Areas Covered: AS, AZ, CA, GU, HI, NV, UT, Northern Mariana Islands
□ Secretary's Regional Representative **(Vacant)** . . . .(213) 894-4980

New York (NY) Regional Office
201 Varick Street, Room 601, New York, NY 10014-4811
Tel: (212) 337-2387 Fax: (212) 337-2386
Areas Covered: CT, DC, DE, FL, GA, MA, MD, ME, NH, NC, NJ, NY, PA, PR, RI, SC, VA, VI, VT, WV
□ Secretary's Regional Representative **(Vacant)** . . . .(212) 337-2387

Seattle (WA) Regional Office
300 Fifth Avenue, Room 1275, Seattle, WA 98104
Fax: (206) 757-6745
Areas Covered: AK, ID, OR, MT, ND, SD, WY, WA
□ Secretary's Regional Representative **(Vacant)** . . . . (206) 757-6743

Office of Inspector General (OIG)

200 Constitution Avenue, NW, Room S5502, Washington, DC 20210
Tel: (202) 693-5100 Fax: (202) 693-5114 Internet: www.oig.dol.gov

Office of Audit

200 Constitution Avenue, NW, Room S5512, Washington, DC 20210
Fax: (202) 693-5169 Internet: www.oig.dol.gov/auditreports.htm

Atlanta (GA) Regional Office
Atlanta Federal Center, 61 Forsyth Street, SW,
Room 6T20, Atlanta, GA 30303-3104
Tel: (404) 665-4360 Fax: (404) 665-4361
Regional Inspector General (Acting) **Dwight Gates** . . . . . .(404) 665-4362

Chicago (IL) Regional Office
Kluczynski Federal Building, 230 South Dearborn Street,
Room 744, Chicago, IL 60604-1782
Tel: (312) 353-2416 Fax: (312) 353-2328
Audit Director **Nicholas G. Christopher** . . . . (312) 353-2416

Dallas (TX) Regional Office
A. Maceo Smith Federal Building, 525 South Griffin Street,
Room 415, Dallas, TX 75202-5096
Tel: (972) 850-4000 Fax: (972) 850-4001
Director **Michael Kostrzewa** . . . .(972) 850-4003
E-mail: kostrzewa.michael@oig.dol.gov
Manager **Douglas Case** . . . . (972) 850-4014
Assistant Manager **Mary Stepney** . . . .(972) 850-4012
E-mail: stepney.mary@oig.dol.gov
Audit Technician **(Vacant)** . . . .(972) 850-4004

New York (NY) Regional Office
201 Varick Street, Room 871, New York, NY 10014-4811
Tel: (646) 264-3500 Fax: (646) 264-3501
Audit Director **Mark L. Schwartz** . . . .(646) 264-3500 ext. 43511
E-mail: schwartz.mark@oig.dol.gov
Audit Technician **(Vacant)** . . . . (646) 264-3500

Philadelphia (PA) Regional Office
Public Ledger Building, 150 South Independence Mall West,
Suite 1072, Philadelphia, PA 19106
Tel: (215) 446-3710 Fax: (215) 446-3727
Audit Director **Stephen Fowler** . . . .(215) 446-3701
E-mail: fowler.stephen@oig.dol.gov
Program Analyst **Theresa Remolde** . . . . (215) 446-3710
E-mail: remolde.theresa@oig.dol.gov

San Francisco (CA) Regional Office
90 Seventh Street, Suite 2-750, San Francisco, CA 94103
Tel: (415) 625-2700 Fax: (415) 625-2711
Audit Director **Ray Armada** . . . .(415) 625-2713
E-mail: rarmada@oig.dol.gov
Audit Manager **Heather Atkins** . . . .(415) 625-2715
E-mail: atkins.heather@oig.dol.gov
Audit Director **(Vacant)** . . . . (415) 625-2716
Audit Manager **Jon Ling** . . . .(415) 625-2717
E-mail: ling.jon@oig.dol.gov
Auditor **Steve Chang** . . . . (415) 625-2707
Auditor **(Vacant)** . . . . (415) 625-2704
Auditor **Angela Stewart** . . . . (415) 625-2709
E-mail: astewart@oig.dol.gov
Auditor **Kathy Vochatzer** . . . .(415) 625-2701
E-mail: kvochatzer@oig.dol.gov
Auditor **(Vacant)** . . . . (415) 625-2707
Auditor **(Vacant)** . . . . (415) 625-2705
Senior Analyst **Catherine Christian** . . . . (415) 625-2708
E-mail: christian.catherine@oig.dol.gov
Program Analyst **(Vacant)** . . . .(415) 625-2710

Office of Labor Racketeering and Fraud Investigations (OLRFI)

200 Constitution Avenue, NW, Room S5014, Washington, DC 20210
Tel: (202) 693-7034 Fax: (202) 693-7035

Atlanta (GA) Regional Office
Atlanta Federal Center, 61 Forsyth Street, SW,
Suite 6T1, Atlanta, GA 30303
Tel: (404) 665-4350 Fax: (404) 665-4347
Areas Covered: AL, FL, GA, KY, MS, NC, SC, TN
Special Agent-in-Charge **Rafiq Ahmad** . . . .(404) 665-4350
E-mail: ahmad.rafiq@oig.dol.gov
Assistant Special Agent-in-Charge **Brian McGamery** . . . . .(404) 665-4352

★ Presidential Appointment Requiring Senate Confirmation ☆ Presidential Appointment □ Schedule C Appointment ◇ Career Senior Foreign Service Appointment
● Career Senior Executive Service (SES) Appointment ○ Non-Career Senior Executive Service (SES) Appointment ■ Postal Career Executive Service

Miami (FL) Resident Office
510 Shotgun Road, Sunrise, FL 33326
Tel: (954) 236-5554 Fax: (954) 987-2837

Assistant Special Agent-in-Charge
Matthew Broadhurst . . . . (954) 236-5554 ext. 13
E-mail: broadhurst.matthew@oig.dol.gov

Chicago (IL) Regional Office
Kluczynski Federal Building, 230 South Dearborn Street, Room 756, Chicago, IL 60604
Tel: (312) 353-0509 Fax: (312) 886-2880
Areas Covered: IL, IN, IA, KS, MI, MN, MO, NE, OH, WI

Special Agent-in-Charge **James Vanderberg** . . . . (312) 353-0509
Assistant Special Agent-in-Charge **Irene Lindow** . . . . (312) 353-0509
E-mail: lindow.irene@oig.dol.gov
Assistant Special Agent in Charge **Daniel Loza** . . . . (312) 353-0509
E-mail: loza.daniel@oig.dol.gov
Criminal Investigator **Brooks Abramson** . . . . (312) 353-0509
Criminal Investigator **Lee Dahlgren** . . . . (312) 353-0509
E-mail: dahlgren.lee@oig.dol.gov
Criminal Investigator **Carmen Gomez** . . . . (312) 353-0509
Criminal Investigator **Anne Houston** . . . . (312) 353-0509
E-mail: houston.anne@oig.dol.gov
Criminal Investigator **Dana Johnson** . . . . (312) 353-0509
E-mail: johnson.dana@oig.dol.gov
Criminal Investigator **Jonathan McKean** . . . . (312) 353-0509
Criminal Investigator **Sean Moore** . . . . (312) 353-0509
Criminal Investigator **Angel Pena** . . . . (312) 353-0509
E-mail: pena.angel@oig.dol.gov
Criminal Investigator **Kathryn Schwass** . . . . (312) 353-0509
Criminal Investigator **(Vacant)** . . . . (312) 353-0509
Investigative Analyst **Felecia McGee Crawford** . . . . (312) 353-0509
E-mail: mcgee-crawford.felecia@oig.dol.gov
Investigative Research Specialist
Janet Parker . . . . (312) 353-0509 ext. 4219

Cleveland (OH) Resident Office
1240 East Ninth Street, Room 821, Cleveland, OH 44199
Tel: (216) 615-4870 Fax: (216) 615-4879

Criminal Investigator **Jeffrey Buttolph** . . . . (216) 615-4870
Criminal Investigator **Barry Hyland** . . . . (216) 615-4870

Columbus (OH) Resident Office
200 North High Street, Room 605, Columbus, OH 43216
Mail: P.O. Box 15596, Columbus, OH 43216
Tel: (614) 469-2004 Fax: (614) 469-2260

Criminal Investigator **Brian Acklin** . . . . (614) 469-2004
Criminal Investigator **Larry Bailey** . . . . (614) 469-2004

Detroit (MI) Resident Office
Federal Building & U.S. Courthouse, 211 West Fort Street, Room 1304, Detroit, MI 48226
Tel: (313) 226-3100 Fax: (313) 226-6245

Assistant Special Agent-in-Charge **James Mead** . . . . (313) 226-3100
Criminal Investigator **Steve Bognar** . . . . (313) 226-3100
Criminal Investigator **Andrew Donohue** . . . . (313) 226-3100
Criminal Investigator **Shanika Sanders** . . . . (313) 226-3100
Criminal Investigator **Gregory Waterson** . . . . (313) 226-3100

Minneapolis (MN) Resident Office
One Federal Drive, Suite 1340, Fort Snelling, MN 55111

Criminal Investigator **Anne Thomas** . . . . (202) 439-3286

Saint Louis (MO) Resident Office
Robert A. Young Building, 1222 Spruce Street, Suite 2.102F, St. Louis, MO 63013
Tel: (314) 539-3962 Fax: (314) 539-3964

Criminal Investigator **Brenton Hudelston** . . . . (314) 539-3962
Criminal Investigator **Christopher Roberson** . . . . (314) 539-3962
Criminal Investigator **(Vacant)** . . . . (314) 539-3962

Dallas (TX) Regional Office
525 S. Griffin Street, Room 414, Dallas, TX 75202-9927
Tel: (972) 850-4050 Fax: (972) 850-4002
Areas Covered: AR, CO, LA, MT, NM, ND, OK, SD, TX, UT, WY

Special Agent-in-Charge **Steve Grell** . . . . (972) 850-4050
Intelligence Analyst **(Vacant)** . . . . (972) 850-4060

Baton Rouge (LA) Resident Office
5353 Essen Lane, Suite 219, Baton Rouge, LA 70809
Tel: (225) 757-7755 Fax: (225) 757-7757

Assistant Special Agent-in-Charge
Casey Howard . . . . (713) 988-7627 ext. 22

Denver (CO) Resident Office
1244 Speer Boulevard, Suite 3210, Denver, CO 80204
Tel: (303) 844-1250 Fax: (303) 844-1252

Senior Special Agent **Betty Roberts** . . . . (303) 844-1250

Houston (TX) Resident Office
525 Griffin Street, Dallas, TX 75202
Tel: (713) 988-7844 Fax: (713) 981-4940

Assistant Special Agent-in-Charge
Casey Howard . . . . (713) 988-7627 ext. 22

Kansas City (MO) Resident Office
P.O. Box 26125, Kansas City, MO 64196-6125
Two Perishing Square Building, 2300 Main Street, Suite 1040, Kansas City, MO 64108
Tel: (816) 285-7240 Fax: (816) 285-7239

Assistant Special Agent-in-Charge **Sean P. Kilcoyne** . . . . . (816) 285-7240
E-mail: kilcoyne.sean@oig.dol.gov
Criminal Investigator **John D. Cress** . . . . (816) 285-7240
Criminal Investigator **Staci Gurin** . . . . (816) 285-7240
Criminal Investigator **Wayne Hakes** . . . . (816) 285-7240
E-mail: hakes.wayne@oig.dol.gov
Criminal Investigator **Jay Roberts** . . . . (816) 285-7240
E-mail: roberts.jay@oig.dol.gov
Intelligence Research Specialist **Rebecca Bright** . . . . (816) 285-7240

Division of Advanced Technology and Analytics
200 Constitution Avenue, NW, Room S-5014, Washington, DC 20210

Special Agent In Charge **Christopher Cooper** . . . . (202) 693-7034
E-mail: cooper.christopher@oig.dol.gov

Division of Investigations and Administration
200 Constitution Avenue, NW, Room S-5014, Washington, DC 20210

Los Angeles (CA) Regional Office
100 North Barranca Street, Suite 520, West Covina, CA 91791
Tel: (626) 858-1720 Fax: (626) 858-1727

Special Agent-in-Charge **Abel Salinas** . . . . (626) 858-1728
E-mail: salinas.abel@oig.dol.gov
Assistant Special Agent-in-Charge **Quentin Heiden** . . . . . (626) 858-1726
E-mail: heiden.quentin@oig.dol.gov
Special Agent **Michael Blas** . . . . (626) 859-2246
E-mail: blas.michael@oig.dol.gov
Special Agent **(Vacant)** . . . . (626) 858-1720
Special Agent **Manuel Gonzales** . . . . (626) 858-1725
E-mail: mgonzales@oig.dol.gov
Special Agent **Cory Oravecz** . . . . (626) 858-1723
E-mail: oravecz.cory@oig.dol.gov
Special Agent **Cynthia Penilla** . . . . (626) 858-1724
Special Agent **Marcus Valle** . . . . (626) 858-1720
E-mail: valle.marcus@oig.dol.gov

Las Vegas (NV) Resident Office
600 Las Vegas Boulevard South, Suite 510, Las Vegas, NV 89101
Tel: (702) 366-9644 Fax: (702) 388-6373

Special Agent **James Buck** . . . . (702) 366-9644 ext. 12
Special Agent **Michael Kwak** . . . . (702) 366-9644 ext. 14
E-mail: kwak.michael@oig.dol.gov

San Francisco (CA) Resident Office
90 Seventh Street, Suite 2-700, San Francisco, CA 94103
Tel: (415) 625-2681 Fax: (415) 625-2689
Areas Covered: AK, AS, AZ, CA, GU, HI, ID, NV, OR, UT, WA, Trust Territory of the Pacific Islands

Special Agent-in-Charge **Abel Salinas** . . . . (415) 625-2681
E-mail: salinas.abel@oig.dol.gov
Assistant Special Agent-in-Charge **Alfredo Nodal** . . . . (415) 625-2684
E-mail: nodal.alfredo@oig.dol.gov
Special Agent **Chris Collins** . . . . (415) 625-2681
E-mail: collins.john@oig.dol.gov
Special Agent **Juan Ferrer** . . . . (415) 625-2691
E-mail: ferrer.juan@oig.dol.gov
Investigative Analyst **Medy Reyes** . . . . (415) 625-2692
E-mail: mreyes@oig.dol.gov
Management Services Specialist **(Vacant)** . . . . (415) 625-2699

Seattle (WA) Resident Office - Program Fraud
300 Fifth Avenue, Seattle, WA 98104
Tel: (206) 757-6620 Fax: (206) 757-6627

Investigative Analyst **(Vacant)** . . . . (206) 757-6623
Special Agent **Marc Montague** . . . . (206) 757-6621
Special Agent **Keven Standley** . . . . (206) 757-6622
E-mail: standley.keven@oig.dol.gov
Assistant Special Agent-in-Charge **(Vacant)** . . . . (206) 757-6620

New York (NY) Regional Office
201 Varick Street, Room 891, New York, NY 10014-4811
Tel: (646) 264-3550 Fax: (646) 264-3502
Areas Covered: CT, ME, MA, NH, NJ, NY, PR, RI, VT, VI

Special Agent-in-Charge (Acting) **Peter Nozka** . . . . (646) 264-3550
Assistant Special Agent-in-Charge **Peter Nozka** . . . . (646) 264-3550
Assistant Special Agent-in-Charge **Shannon Woolard** . . . (646) 264-3550

Atlantic City (NJ) Resident Office
6601 Ventnor Avenue, Suite 109, Ventnor City, NJ 08406
Tel: (609) 487-2579 Fax: (609) 487-6941

Assistant Special Agent-in-Charge
Jonathan Mellone . . . . (908) 301-8100 ext. 8103
200 Sheffield Street, Fax: (908) 233-0268
Suite 309, Mountainside, NJ 07092

Boston (MA) Resident Office
12 New England Executive Park, Burlington, MA 01803
Tel: (781) 238-7940 Fax: (781) 238-7941

Assistant Special Agent-in-Charge **Nikitas Splagounis** . . . (781) 238-7940

Buffalo (NY) Resident Office
138 Delaware Avenue, First Floor, Buffalo, NY 14202
Tel: (716) 843-5700 Fax: (716) 551-5563

Special Agent **Jonathan Mellone** . . . . (716) 843-5700

Mountainside (NJ) Resident Office
200 Sheffield Street, Mountainside, NJ 07092
Tel: (908) 301-8100 Fax: (908) 233-0268

Assistant Special Agent-in-Charge
Jonathan Mellone . . . . (908) 301-8100 ext. 8103

Philadelphia (PA) Regional Office
The Public Ledger Building, 150 South Independence Mall West, Suite 1072, Philadelphia, PA 19106
Tel: (215) 446-3755 Fax: (215) 446-3754
Areas Covered: DE, DC, MD, PA, VA (Western District), WV

Special Agent-in-Charge **Richard Deer** . . . . (215) 446-3755
Assistant Special Agent-in-Charge **Marc Walker** . . . . (215) 446-3755

Pittsburgh (PA) Resident Office
Federal Building, 1000 Liberty Avenue, Room 1401, Pittsburgh, PA 15222
Tel: (412) 395-4495 Fax: (412) 395-5018

Assistant Special Agent-in-Charge **Richard Deer** . . . . (540) 857-2133
Special Agent **Jeremy Metcalf** . . . . (412) 395-4495
Special Agent **Stephen Wilburn** . . . . (412) 395-4495

Pittsburgh (PA) Resident Office *(continued)*

Special Agent **(Vacant)** . . . . (412) 395-4495

Roanoke (VA) Resident Office
310 First Street, SW, Suite 410, Roanoke, VA 24011
Tel: (540) 857-2133 Fax: (540) 857-2655

Assistant Special Agent-in-Charge **Richard Deer** . . . . (540) 857-2133
Special Agent **Stephen Wilburn** . . . . (540) 857-2133
Special Agent **Jeffrey Carter** . . . . (540) 857-2133

Washington (DC) Regional Office
375 E Street SW, Suite 11-300, Washington, DC 20024-3221
Tel: (202) 515-2605 Fax: (202) 515-2601
Areas Covered: DC, MD, VA (Eastern District); all investigations involving high ranking Department of Labor officials, labor racketeering violations, and Department of Labor program fraud

Special Agent-in-Charge **Robin Blake** . . . . (202) 515-2611
Assistant Special Agent-in-Charge **Derek Pickle** . . . . (202) 515-2608
Assistant Special Agent-in-Charge **Troy Springer** . . . . (202) 515-2607
Program Support Specialist **Juliet Coipuram** . . . . (202) 515-2620

Office of the Solicitor (SOL)
200 Constitution Avenue, NW, Washington, DC 20210
Tel: (202) 693-5260 Fax: (202) 693-5278 Internet: www.dol.gov/sol

Deputy Solicitor for Regional Enforcement
200 Constitution Avenue, NW, Room S2002, Washington, DC 20210

Region 1 - Boston (MA)
John F. Kennedy Federal Building, 25 Sudbury Street, Room E-375, Boston, MA 02203
Tel: (617) 565-2500 Fax: (617) 565-2142

● Regional Solicitor **Michael D. Felsen** . . . . (617) 565-2500
E-mail: felsen.michael@dol.gov
Deputy Regional Solicitor **Christine Eskilson** . . . . (617) 565-2500
E-mail: eskilson.christine@dol.gov

Region 2 - New York (NY)
201 Varick Street, Room 983, New York, NY 10014-4811
Tel: (646) 264-3650 Fax: (646) 264-3660

● Regional Solicitor **Jeffrey S. Rogoff** . . . . (646) 264-3650
E-mail: rogoff.jeffrey@dol.gov
Deputy Regional Solicitor (Acting)
Kathryn L. Stewart . . . . (646) 264-3652
Counsel for Civil Rights **Sudwiti Chandra** . . . . (646) 264-3650
Counsel for ERISA **Michael R. Hartman** . . . . (646) 264-3650
Counsel for OSHA **Diane C. Sherman** . . . . (646) 264-3650
E-mail: sherman.diane@dol.gov
Counsel for Wage and Hour **Molly Knopp Biklen** . . . . (646) 264-3650
E-mail: biklen.molly@dol.gov
Education: Columbia 2004 JD
Management Analyst **Gaby Markey** . . . . (646) 264-3650

Region 3 - Philadelphia (PA)
The Curtis Center, 170 South Independence Mall West, Suite 630E, Philadelphia, PA 19106
Tel: (215) 861-5121 Fax: (215) 861-5162

● Regional Solicitor **Oscar L. Hampton III** . . . . (215) 861-5120
E-mail: hampton.oscar@dol.gov
Deputy Regional Solicitor **Richard "Buck" Buchanan** . . . (215) 861-5127
E-mail: buchanan.richard@dol.gov
Management Analysis **Patricia "Tricia" Sanders** . . . . (215) 861-5121
E-mail: sanders.patricia@dol.gov
Counsel for BLBA **(Vacant)** . . . . (215) 861-5132
Counsel for ESA **Adam Welsh** . . . . (215) 861-5121
E-mail: welsh.adam@dol.gov
Counsel for ERISA **Jodeen Hobbs** . . . . (215) 861-5159
E-mail: hobbs.jodeen@dol.gov
Counsel for MSHA **(Vacant)** . . . . (215) 861-5132
Counsel for OSHA **Michael Doyle** . . . . (215) 861-5128
E-mail: doyle.michael@dol.gov

★ Presidential Appointment Requiring Senate Confirmation ☆ Presidential Appointment ☐ Schedule C Appointment ◇ Career Senior Foreign Service Appointment
● Career Senior Executive Service (SES) Appointment ○ Non-Career Senior Executive Service (SES) Appointment ■ Postal Career Executive Service

DEPARTMENTS

Arlington (VA) Branch Office
201 12th Street South, Suite 500, Arlington, VA 22002-5414
Tel: (202) 693-9393 Fax: (202) 693-9392

Associate Regional Solicitor **Samantha N. Thomas** . . . . (703) 693-9388
E-mail: thomas.samantha.n@dol.gov
Education: CUNY 2009 JD
Counsel for Wage and Hour **Samantha N. Thomas** . . . . (703) 693-9373
E-mail: thomas.samantha.n@dol.gov
Education: CUNY 2009 JD
Counsel for MSHA **Robert S. Wilson** . . . . (703) 693-9389
E-mail: wilson.robert.s@dol.gov

Region 4 - Atlanta (GA)
Sam Nunn Atlanta Federal Center, 61 Forsyth Street, SW, Suite 7T10, Atlanta, GA 30303
Tel: (404) 302-5440 Fax: (404) 302-5438

● Regional Solicitor **Stanley E. Keen** . . . . (404) 302-5435
E-mail: keen.stanley@dol.gov
Deputy Regional Solicitor **Tremelle I. Howard-Fishburne** . . . . (404) 302-5435
Counsel for Civil Rights **Channah S. Broyde** . . . . (404) 302-5440
E-mail: broyde.channah@dol.gov
Counsel for ERISA **Robert M. Lewis, Jr.** . . . . (404) 302-5440
Counsel for MSHA **Uche N. Egemonye** . . . . (404) 302-5440
Counsel for OSHA **Karen E. Mock** . . . . (404) 302-5440
E-mail: mock.karen@dol.gov
Counsel for Wage and Hour **Robert L. Walter** . . . . (404) 302-5440

Nashville (TN) Branch Office
Castner Knott Building, 618 Church Street, Suite 230, Nashville, TN 37219-2440
Tel: (615) 781-5328 Fax: (615) 781-5321

Associate Regional Solicitor **Theresa Ball** . . . . (615) 781-5330 ext. 222
E-mail: ball.theresa@dol.gov
Supervisory Legal Assistant **Pamela "Pam" Reedus** . . . . (615) 781-5328

Region 5 - Chicago (IL)
Kluczynski Federal Building, 230 South Dearborn Street, Room 844, Chicago, IL 60604
Tel: (312) 886-5260 Fax: (312) 353-5698

● Regional Solicitor **Christine Heri** . . . . (312) 353-8885
E-mail: heri.christine@dol.gov
Deputy Regional Solicitor **Richard Kordys** . . . . (312) 353-8885

Cleveland (OH) Branch Office
A.J. Celebrezze Federal Building, 1240 East Ninth Street, Room 881, Cleveland, OH 44199
Tel: (216) 522-3870 Fax: (216) 522-7172

Associate Regional Solicitor **Benjamin T. Chinni** . . . . (216) 522-3870
E-mail: chinni.benjamin@dol.gov

Kansas City (MO) Branch Office
2300 Main Street, Suite 1020, Kansas City, MO 64108
Tel: (816) 285-7260 Fax: (816) 285-7287

Associate Regional Solicitor **H. Alice Jacks** . . . . (816) 285-7260

Region 6 - Dallas (TX)
Federal Building, 525 South Griffin Street, Suite 501, Dallas, TX 75202-5001
Tel: (972) 850-3100 Fax: (972) 850-3101

● Regional Solicitor **James E. Culp** . . . . (972) 850-3192
E-mail: culp.james@dol.gov
Deputy Regional Solicitor **Connie M. Ackermann** . . . . (972) 850-3100
E-mail: ackermann.connie@dol.gov
Counsel for Civil Rights **Robert C. Beal** . . . . (972) 850-3100
E-mail: beal.robert@dol.gov
Counsel for ERISA **Robert A. Goldberg** . . . . (972) 850-3100
Counsel for OSHA **Madeleine T. Le** . . . . (972) 850-3100
E-mail: le.madeleine@dol.gov
Counsel for MSHA **Mary K. Cobb** . . . . (972) 850-3100
Counsel for Wage and Hour **Margaret T. Cranford** . . . . (972) 850-3100
E-mail: cranford.margaret@dol.gov

Region 6 - Dallas (TX) *(continued)*

Management Analyst **Rina Rucker** Suite 707 . . . . (972) 850-3146
Fax: (972) 850-4420

Denver (CO) Branch Office
Cesar E. Chavez Memorial Building, 1244 Speer Boulevard, Suite 515, Denver, CO 80204
Tel: (303) 884-1745 Fax: (303) 844-1753

Associate Regional Solicitor **John T. P. Rainwater** . . . . (303) 884-1745
E-mail: rainwater.john@dol.gov
Counsel for OSHA **Timothy Williams** . . . . (303) 884-1745
E-mail: williams.timothy@dol.gov
Counsel for Wage and Hour **Lydia Tzagoloff** . . . . (303) 884-1745
E-mail: tzagoloff.lydia@dol.gov
Legal Assistant **Paula Bachowski** . . . . (303) 884-1745
E-mail: bachowski.paula@dol.gov

Region 9 - San Francisco (CA)
90 Seventh Street, Suite 3-700, San Francisco, CA 94103
Tel: (415) 625-7740 Fax: (415) 625-7772

● Regional Solicitor **Janet M. Herold** . . . . (415) 625-7754
E-mail: herold.janet.m@dol.gov
Deputy Regional Solicitor **Susan Gillett Kumli** . . . . (415) 625-7760
E-mail: kumli.susan@dol.gov
Counsel for Civil Rights **Ian Eliasoph** . . . . (415) 625-7740
E-mail: eliasoph.ian@dol.gov
Counsel for Employment Standards **David M. Kahn** . . . . (415) 625-7740
E-mail: kahn.david.m@dol.gov
Counsel for ERISA **Marc Pilotin** . . . . (415) 625-7740
Education: Berkeley Law 2009 JD
Counsel for MSHA and OSHA **Susan Gillett Kumli** . . . . (415) 625-7740
E-mail: kumli.susan@dol.gov
Management Analyst **(Vacant)** . . . . (415) 625-7740

Los Angeles (CA) Branch Office
World Trade Center, 350 South Figueroa Street, Suite 370, Los Angeles, CA 90071-1202
Tel: (213) 894-4980 Fax: (213) 894-2064

Associate Regional Solicitor **Daniel J. Chasek** . . . . (213) 894-2681
E-mail: chasek.daniel@dol.gov
Attorney **Susan Seletsky** . . . . (213) 894-4983
E-mail: seletsky.susan@dol.gov

Seattle (WA) Branch Office
300 Fifth Avenue, Suite 1120, Seattle, WA 98104-2397
Tel: (206) 757-6762 Fax: (206) 757-6761

Associate Regional Solicitor **Bruce L. Brown** . . . . (206) 757-6762
E-mail: brown.bruce@dol.gov
Management Analyst **Claire Barba** . . . . (206) 757-6762
Legal Assistant **Tammie R. Holper** . . . . (206) 757-6762
Civil Rights Counsel (Acting) **Jeremiah Miller** . . . . (206) 757-6762
E-mail: miller.jeremiah@dol.gov

Office of Federal Contract Compliance Programs (OFCCP)

200 Constitution Avenue, NW, Room C3325, Washington, DC 20210
Tel: (202) 693-0101 Fax: (202) 693-1304 Internet: www.dol.gov/ofccp

Regional Offices

Mid-Atlantic Regional Office

The Curtis Center, 170 South Independence Mall West, Suite 650 South, Philadelphia, PA 19106-3317
Tel: (215) 861-5765 Fax: (215) 861-5769
E-mail: OFCCP-MA-PreAward@dol.gov
Areas Covered: DE, DC, MD, PA, VA, WV

● Regional Director **Michele Hodge** . . . . (215) 861-5765
E-mail: hodge.michele@dol.gov
Deputy Regional Director **Donna M. Felder** . . . . (215) 861-5765
E-mail: felder.donna@dol.gov
Regional Operations Director **Evan Szarenski** . . . . (215) 861-5765
E-mail: szarenski.evan@dol.gov

★ Presidential Appointment Requiring Senate Confirmation ☆ Presidential Appointment □ Schedule C Appointment ◇ Career Senior Foreign Service Appointment
● Career Senior Executive Service (SES) Appointment ○ Non-Career Senior Executive Service (SES) Appointment ■ Postal Career Executive Service

Baltimore (MD)/Washington D.C. District Office
Two Hopkins Place, Suite 600, Baltimore, MD 21201
Tel: (410) 962-6480 Fax: (410) 962-6481

District Director **Tom Wells** .... (410) 962-6480
E-mail: wells.tom@dol.gov
Assistant District Director **Tanya Bennett** .... (410) 962-6480
E-mail: bennett.tanya@dol.gov
Assistant District Director **Maurice Richard** .... (410) 962-6480
E-mail: richard.maurice@dol.gov

Philadelphia (PA) District Office
Robert Nix Federal Building, Ninth & Market Streets,
Room 311, Philadelphia, PA 19107
Tel: (215) 597-4121 Fax: (215) 597-9447

District Director **Edward J. Rogers** .... (215) 597-4121
E-mail: rogers.edward@dol.gov
Assistant District Director **Marlene Y. Williams** .... (215) 597-4121
E-mail: williams.marlene@dol.gov
Assistant District Director **(Vacant)** .... (215) 597-4121

Pittsburgh (PA) District Office
William S. Moorhead Federal Building, 1000 Liberty Avenue,
Room 2103, Pittsburgh, PA 15222
Tel: (412) 395-6300 Fax: (412) 395-5408

District Director **Tracie Brown** .... (412) 395-6300
E-mail: brown.tracie@dol.gov
Assistant District Director **Natalie Allen** .... (412) 395-6300
E-mail: allen.natalie@dol.gov
Assistant District Director **(Vacant)** .... (412) 395-6300

Richmond (VA) District Office
Federal Building, 400 North Eighth Street,
Room 466, Richmond, VA 23219
Mail: P.O. Box 10128, Richmond, VA 23240
Tel: (804) 888-6714 Fax: (804) 888-6715

District Director **Rodney Hawkins** .... (804) 888-6714
Assistant District Director **Dianna Adams** .... (804) 888-6714
E-mail: adams.dianna@dol.gov
Assistant District Director **Heidi Lacy** .... (804) 888-6714
E-mail: lacy.heidi@dol.gov

Midwest Regional Office
230 South Dearborn Street, Room 570, Chicago, IL 60604
Tel: (312) 596-7010 Fax: (312) 596-7036
Areas Covered: IL, IN, IA, KS, MI, MN, MO, NE, OH, WI

● Regional Director **(Vacant)** .... (312) 596-7010
Deputy Regional Director **Carmen Navarro** .... (312) 596-7010
E-mail: navarro.carmen@dol.gov

Chicago (IL) District Office
230 South Dearborn Street, Suite 434, Chicago, IL 60604
Tel: (312) 596-7045 Fax: (312) 596-7085

District Director **Michael Thomas** .... (312) 596-7045
Assistant District Director **Shelley J. Gordon** .... (312) 596-7045
E-mail: gordon.shelley@dol.gov
Assistant District Director **Jamayan Watkins** .... (312) 596-7045
E-mail: watkins.jamayan@dol.gov
Assistant District Director **Adam Young** .... (312) 596-7045
E-mail: young.adam@dol.gov

Columbus (OH) District Office
New Federal Building, 200 North High Street,
Room 409, Columbus, OH 43215-2488
Tel: (614) 469-5831 Fax: (614) 469-6606

District Director (Acting) **Phyllis Lipkin** .... (614) 469-5831
E-mail: lipkin.phyllis@dol.gov
Assistant District Director **Veronica Minnefield** .... (614) 469-5831
E-mail: minnefield.veronica@dol.gov

Omaha (NE) Area Office
Central Park Plaza, 222 South 15th Street,
Suite 504B, Omaha, NE 68102
Tel: (402) 221-3381 Fax: (402) 221-3379

Area Director **Maxine Manus** .... (402) 221-3381
E-mail: manus.maxine@dol.gov
Assistant District Director **Walker Plank** .... (402) 221-3381
E-mail: plank.walker@dol.gov

Detroit (MI) District Office
211 West Fort Street, Suite 1320, Detroit, MI 48226
Tel: (313) 442-3360 Fax: (313) 226-3254

District Director **Phyllis Lipkin** .... (313) 442-3360
E-mail: lipkin.phyllis@dol.gov
Assistant District Director **(Vacant)** .... (313) 442-3360
Assistant District Director **Hoan Luong** .... (313) 442-3360
E-mail: luong.hoan@dol.gov

Grand Rapids (MI) Area Office
Gerald R. Ford Federal Building, 110 Michigan Street NW,
Suite 228, Grand Rapids, MI 49503
Tel: (616) 456-4760 Fax: (616) 456-4761

Area Director **Phyllis Lipkin** .... (616) 456-4760

Indianapolis (IN) District Office
46 East Ohio Street, Suite 419, Indianapolis, IN 46204-1946
Tel: (317) 226-5860 Fax: (317) 226-5878

District Director (Acting) **Maxine Manus** .... (317) 226-5860
E-mail: manus.maxine@dol.gov
Assistant District Director **David Smith** .... (317) 226-5860
E-mail: smith.david@dol.gov

Kansas City (MO) District Office
2300 Main Street, Suite 1030, Kansas City, MO 64108
Tel: (816) 502-0370 Fax: (816) 502-0371

District Director **Maxine Manus** .... (816) 502-0370
E-mail: manus.maxine@dol.gov
Assistant District Director **Tracie Gregurich** .... (816) 502-0370
E-mail: gregurich.tracie@dol.gov

St. Louis (MO) Area Office
Robert Young Federal Building, 1222 Spruce Street,
Room 10.207, St. Louis, MO 63103
Tel: (314) 539-6394 Fax: (314) 539-6399

Area Director **Maxine Manus** .... (816) 502-0370
E-mail: manus.maxine@dol.gov
Area Assistant Director **Karen Johnson-Robinson** .... (314) 539-6394

Milwaukee (WI) District Office
Henry S. Reuss Federal Plaza, 310 West Wisconsin Avenue,
Suite 1115, Milwaukee, WI 53203
Tel: (414) 297-3822 Fax: (414) 297-4038

District Director (Acting) **Henrietta Brinson** .... (414) 297-3821
E-mail: brinson.henrietta@dol.gov
Assistant District Director **Timothy P. Roark** .... (414) 297-3821
E-mail: roark.timothy@dol.gov

Minneapolis (MN) District Office
920 Second Avenue South, Suite 575, Minneapolis, MN 55402
Tel: (612) 370-3177 Fax: (612) 370-3178

District Director (Acting) **Henrietta Brinson** .... (612) 370-3177
E-mail: brinson.henrietta@dol.gov
Assistant District Director **Nathaniel Jackson** .... (612) 370-3177
E-mail: jackson.nathaniel@dol.gov

Northeast Regional Office
201 Varick Street, Room 750, New York, NY 10014-4811
Tel: (646) 264-3170 Fax: (646) 264-3009
E-mail: ofccp-ne-preaward@dol.gov
Areas Covered: CT, ME, MA, NH, NJ, NY, PR, RI, VT, VI

Regional Director **Diana S. Sen** .... (646) 264-3170
E-mail: sen.diana@dol.gov

(continued on next page)

★ Presidential Appointment Requiring Senate Confirmation ☆ Presidential Appointment □ Schedule C Appointment ◇ Career Senior Foreign Service Appointment
● Career Senior Executive Service (SES) Appointment ○ Non-Career Senior Executive Service (SES) Appointment ■ Postal Career Executive Service

DEPARTMENTS

Northeast Regional Office *(continued)*

Deputy Regional Director (Acting)
Stephen "Steve" Sunshine .... (646) 264-3170
E-mail: sunshine.stephen@dol.gov
Planning and Support Director **Norvilla Millington** ...... (646) 264-3163
E-mail: millington.norvilla@dol.gov

Boston (MA) District Office
John F. Kennedy Federal Building, 25 Sudbury Street,
Room E-235, Boston, MA 02203
Tel: (617) 624-6780 Fax: (617) 624-6702

District Director **Rhonda Aubin-Smith** .... (617) 624-6780
E-mail: aubin-smith.rhonda@dol.gov
Assistant District Director **Mandi Costa** .... (617) 624-6780
E-mail: costa.mandi@dol.gov
Assistant District Director **Adriana Lopez** .... (617) 624-6780
E-mail: lopez.adriana@dol.gov

Hartford (CT) District Office
William R. Cotter Federal Building, 135 High Street,
Room 219, Hartford, CT 06103-1595
Tel: (860) 240-4277 Fax: (860) 240-4280

District Director **Mary Ellen Bentivogli** .... (860) 244-8600
E-mail: bentivogli.mary@dol.gov Fax: (860) 244-8633
Assistant District Director **Tracey Mills** .... (860) 244-8600
E-mail: mills.tracey@dol.gov
Assistant District Director **(Vacant)** .... (860) 244-8600

Mountainside (NJ) District Office
200 Sheffield Street, Room 102, Mountainside, NJ 07092-2314
Tel: (908) 317-6969 Fax: (908) 317-6962

District Director **Pranita Raghavan** .... (908) 317-6969
E-mail: raghavan.pranita@dol.gov

New York (NY) District Office
Jacob K. Javits Federal Building, 26 Federal Plaza,
Room 36-116, New York, NY 10278-0002
Tel: (212) 264-7743 Fax: (212) 264-8166

District Director **Konrad Batog** .... (212) 264-7743
E-mail: batog.konrad@dol.gov
Assistant District Director **Manuel Garcia** .... (212) 264-7742
Assistant District Director **Eunsook Kim** .... (212) 264-7742
E-mail: kim.eunsook@dol.gov
Assistant District Director **Rubayyi Salaam** .... (212) 264-7742
E-mail: salaam.rubayyi@dol.gov

Buffalo (NY) Area Office
Olympic Tower, 300 Pearl Street, Suite 175, Buffalo, NY 14202
Tel: (716) 464-5353 Fax: (716) 464-5341

District Director **Mary Ellen Bentivogli** .... (716) 842-2979
E-mail: bentivogli.mary@dol.gov

Caribbean Field Station
Plaza Las Americas Tower, 525 F. D. Roosevelt Avenue,
Suite 1202, San Juan, PR 00918
Tel: (787) 771-1461 Fax: (787) 771-1461
Areas Covered: PR, VI

District Director **Konrad Batog** .... (212) 264-7743
Assistant District Director **Manuel Garcia** .... (212) 264-7742
E-mail: garcia.manuel@dol.gov

Pacific Regional Office
90 Seventh Street, Suite 18-300, San Francisco, CA 94103
Tel: (415) 625-7800 Fax: (415) 625-7799
Areas Covered: AK, AZ, CA, GU, HI, ID, NV, OR, WA

• Regional Director (Acting) **Jane Suhr** .... (415) 625-7800
E-mail: suhr.jane@dol.gov
Deputy Regional Director **Jane Suhr** .... (415) 625-7800
E-mail: suhr.jane@dol.gov

Pacific Regional Office *(continued)*

Planning and Support Division Director (Acting)
Hea Jung Atkins .... (415) 625-7829
E-mail: atkins.heajung@dol.gov
Regional Operations Division Director
Luis N. Rodriguez .... (415) 625-7800
E-mail: rodriguez.luis.n@dol.gov

Los Angeles (CA) District Office
1640 South Sepulveda Boulevard, Suite 440, Los Angeles, CA 90025
Tel: (310) 268-1201 Fax: (310) 268-1620

District Director **(Vacant)** .... (310) 268-1201
Assistant District Director **Agnes Huang** .... (310) 268-1201
E-mail: huang.agnes@dol.gov

Orange (CA) Area Office
770 The City Drive, Suite 5700, Orange, CA 92868
Tel: (714) 621-1631 Fax: (714) 621-1640

Area Director **Hector Sanchez** .... (714) 621-1631

Greater San Francisco Bay District Office
90 Seventh Street, Suite 18-300, San Francisco, CA 94103
Tel: (415) 625-7828 Fax: (415) 625-7792

District Director (Acting) **Luis N. Rodriguez** .... (415) 625-7828
E-mail: rodriguez.luis.n@dol.gov

Phoenix (AZ) District Office
230 North First Avenue, Suite 503, Phoenix, AZ 85003-1725
Tel: (602) 514-4660 Fax: (602) 514-4698

District Director **Marvin Jordan** .... (602) 514-4660
E-mail: jordan.marvin@dol.gov
Assistant District Director **(Vacant)** .... (602) 514-4660

San Diego (CA) District Office
550 West C Street, Suite 900, San Diego, CA 92101
Tel: (619) 557-7400 Fax: (619) 557-7490

District Director **Sean Ratliff** .... (619) 557-7400
E-mail: ratliff.sean@dol.gov
Assistant District Director **(Vacant)** .... (619) 557-7400

San Jose (CA) District Office
96 North 3rd Street, Suite 410, San Jose, CA 95112-7709
Tel: (408) 283-5480 Fax: (408) 283-5467

District Director (Acting) **Lynda Sakseangvirat** .... (408) 283-5480
E-mail: sakseangvirat.lynda@dol.gov
Assistant District Director **(Vacant)** .... (408) 283-5480

Hawaii (HI) Area Office
Prince Jonah Kuhio Kalanianaole Federal Building,
300 Ala Moana Boulevard, Room 7-227, Honolulu, HI 96850
Mail: P.O. Box 50149, Honolulu, HI 96850
Tel: (808) 541-2933 Fax: (808) 541-2904

Area Director **Brian Mikel** .... (808) 541-2937

Seattle (WA) District Office
300 Fifth Avenue, Suite 1100, Seattle, WA 98104
Tel: (206) 398-8005 Fax: (206) 224-3100

District Director (Acting) **Leigh Jones** .... (206) 504-5013
E-mail: jones.leigh@dol.gov
Assistant District Director **Quanda Evans** .... (206) 504-5015
E-mail: evans.quanda@dol.gov

Portland (OR) Area Office
620 SW Main Street, Suite 411, Portland, OR 97205
Tel: (503) 326-4112 Fax: (503) 326-5746

Area Director **Brenda Terreault** .... (503) 326-4112

★ Presidential Appointment Requiring Senate Confirmation ☆ Presidential Appointment □ Schedule C Appointment ◇ Career Senior Foreign Service Appointment
● Career Senior Executive Service (SES) Appointment ○ Non-Career Senior Executive Service (SES) Appointment ■ Postal Career Executive Service

Southeast Regional Office
Atlanta Federal Center, 61 Forsyth Street, SW,
Suite 7B75, Atlanta, GA 30303
Tel: (404) 893-4545 Fax: (404) 893-4546
Areas Covered: AL, FL, GA, KY, MS, NC, SC, TN

● Regional Director **Samuel Maiden** .... (404) 893-4545
E-mail: maiden.samuel@dol.gov
Deputy Regional Director **George Dorsey** .... (404) 893-4545
E-mail: dorsey.george@dol.gov
Director of Regional Compliance **(Vacant)** .... (404) 893-4545
Director of Regional Operations **Jonide Corbin** .... (404) 893-4545
E-mail: corbin.jonide@dol.gov
Personnel and Support Director **(Vacant)** .... (404) 893-4545

Atlanta (GA) District Office
61 Forsyth Street, SW, Suite 17T50, Atlanta, GA 30303
Tel: (404) 893-4575 Fax: (404) 893-4576

District Director **Sybil Shy-Demmons** .... (404) 893-4575
Assistant District Director **William Glisson** .... (404) 893-4575
E-mail: glisson.william@dol.gov
Assistant District Director **(Vacant)** .... (404) 893-4575
Assistant District Director **(Vacant)** .... (404) 893-4575

Jacksonville (FL) Area Office
400 West Bay Street, Room 939, Jacksonville, FL 32202-4242
Tel: (904) 351-0551 Fax: (904) 351-0560

District Director **Miguel A. Rivera, Jr.** .... (904) 351-0551
Fax: (904) 351-0560
Assistant District Director **Charles Robinson** .... (904) 351-0551

Birmingham (AL) District Office
Medical Forum Building, Jefferson Civic Center, 950 22nd Street, North,
Room 660, Birmingham, AL 35203
Tel: (205) 731-0820 Fax: (205) 731-3466

District Director **Alvin Mitchell** .... (205) 731-0820
E-mail: mitchell.alvin@dol.gov
Assistant District Director **Christopher Williams** .... (205) 731-0826

Jackson (MS) Area Office
100 West Capitol Street, Suite 721, Jackson, MS 39269
Tel: (601) 965-4668 Fax: (601) 965-4726

Area Director **Katie Course** .... (601) 965-4668

Charlotte (NC) District Office
3800 Arco Corporate Drive, Suite 465, Charlotte, NC 28273
Tel: (704) 749-3380 Fax: (704) 749-3381

District Director **Pamela Quinn** .... (704) 749-3380
E-mail: quinn.pamela@dol.gov
Assistant District Director **William Crews** .... (704) 749-3380
E-mail: crews.william@dol.gov

Columbia (SC) District Office
Strom Thurmond Federal Building, 1835 Assembly Street,
Room 608, Columbia, SC 29201
Tel: (803) 251-4680 Fax: (803) 251-4690

Assistant District Director **(Vacant)** .... (803) 251-4680

Raleigh (NC) Area Office
4407 Bland Road, Suite 270, Raleigh, NC 27609
Tel: (919) 790-8248 Fax: (919) 790-8297

Area Director (Acting) **Pamela Quinn** .... (919) 790-8248
Assistant Area Director **George Rouse** .... (919) 790-8248

Nashville (TN) District Office
1321 Murfreesboro Road, Suite 301, Nashville, TN 37217
Tel: (615) 781-5395 Fax: (615) 781-5399

District Director **Michelle Hernandez** .... (615) 781-5395
Assistant District Director **Valerie McClelland** .... (615) 781-5395
E-mail: mcclelland.valerie@dol.gov

Memphis (TN) Area Office
Davis Federal Building, 167 North Main Street,
Room 101, Memphis, TN 38103
Tel: (901) 544-3458 Fax: (901) 544-4259

Area Director **Alvin Mitchell** .... (901) 544-3458
Assistant Area Director **(Vacant)** .... (901) 544-3458

Orlando (FL) District Office
Enterprise Building, 1001 Executive Center Drive,
Suite 100, Orlando, FL 32803
Tel: (407) 648-6181 Fax: (407) 648-6084

District Director **Miguel A. Rivera, Jr.** .... (407) 648-6181
E-mail: rivera.miguel@dol.gov
Assistant District Director **(Vacant)** .... (407) 648-6181
Assistant District Director **Dawn Hayn** .... (407) 648-6181
E-mail: hayn.dawn@dol.gov

Miami (FL) Area Office
Brickell Plaza Federal Building, 909 SE First Avenue,
Room 722, Miami, FL 33131
Tel: (305) 536-5670 Fax: (305) 536-5675

District Director **Miguel A. Rivera, Jr.** .... (305) 536-5670
Assistant District Director **Jacqueline Ortiz-Baerga** ..... (305) 536-5670
E-mail: ortiz-baerga.jacqueline@dol.gov

Southwest and Rocky Mountain Regional Office (SWARM)
A. Maceo Smith Federal Building, 525 South Griffin Street,
Room 840, Dallas, TX 75202-5007
Tel: (972) 850-2550 Fax: (972) 850-2552
Areas Covered: AR, CO, LA, MT, NM, ND, OK, SD, TX, UT, WY

● Regional Director **Melissa L. Speer** .... (972) 850-2550
● Deputy Regional Director **Aida Collins** .... (972) 850-2550
E-mail: collins.aida@dol.gov
● Director of Regional Operations **Ronald Sullivan** .... (972) 850-2550
E-mail: sullivan.ronald@dol.gov
Secretary **Lisa McBride** .... (972) 850-2550
E-mail: mcbride.lisa@dol.gov

Dallas (TX) District Office
525 South Griffin Street, Room 512, Dallas, TX 75202-5096
Tel: (972) 850-2650 Fax: (972) 850-2651

District Director **Ellen Boyd** .... (972) 850-2650
Assistant District Director **(Vacant)** .... (972) 850-2650

Denver (CO) District Office
1244 Speer Boulevard, Denver, CO 80202
Tel: (720) 264-3200 Fax: (720) 264-3211

District Director **Nicole Huggins** .... (720) 264-3200
E-mail: huggins.nicole@dol.gov
Assistant District Director **(Vacant)** .... (720) 264-3200

Houston (TX) District Office
2320 La Branch, Suite 1103, Houston, TX 77004
Tel: (713) 718-3800 Fax: (713) 718-3818

District Director **Karen Hyman** .... (713) 718-3800
E-mail: hyman.karen@dol.gov
Assistant District Director **LaToya Smith** .... (713) 718-3800
E-mail: smith.latoya@dol.gov

New Orleans (LA) District Office
F. Edward Hebert Building, 600 South Maestri Place,
Suite 728, New Orleans, LA 70130
Tel: (504) 589-6575 Fax: (504) 589-6576

District Director **Rachel Woods** .... (504) 589-6575
E-mail: woods.rachel@dol.gov

★ Presidential Appointment Requiring Senate Confirmation ☆ Presidential Appointment ☐ Schedule C Appointment ◇ Career Senior Foreign Service Appointment
● Career Senior Executive Service (SES) Appointment ○ Non-Career Senior Executive Service (SES) Appointment ■ Postal Career Executive Service

DEPARTMENTS

San Antonio (TX) District Office
800 Dolorosa Street, Room 340, San Antonio, TX 78207
Tel: (210) 472-5835 Fax: (210) 472-5842

District Director **Dinorah Boykin** .... (210) 472-5835
E-mail: boykin.dinorah@dol.gov

Assistant District Director **James Shinn** .... (210) 472-5835
E-mail: shinn.james@dol.gov

Office of Labor-Management Standards (OLMS)

200 Constitution Avenue, NW, Room N5603, Washington, DC 20210
Fax: (202) 693-1206 Internet: www.dol.gov/olms

Office of Field Operations

• Director **Stephen Willertz** .... (202) 693-1182
E-mail: willertz.stephen@dol.gov Fax: (202) 693-1343

Office of Labor-Management Standards - Central Regional Office

310 West Wisconsin Avenue, Room 1160W, Milwaukee, WI 53203
Tel: (414) 297-1504 Fax: (414) 297-1685

• Regional Director **Daniel LaFond** .... (414) 297-1504
E-mail: lafond.daniel@dol.gov

Chicago (IL) District Office
Kluczynski Federal Building, 230 South Dearborn Street, Room 774, Chicago, IL 60604
Tel: (312) 596-7160 Fax: (312) 596-7174
Areas Covered: IL (counties of Coles, Edgar, Macoupin, Montgomery, Pike, Scott, Shelby, and all counties north thereof); IN (counties of Blackford, Carroll, Cass, Grant, Jay, Miami, Tippecanoe, Warren, and all counties north thereof)

District Director **Michael Purcell** .... (312) 596-7167
E-mail: purcell.michael@dol.gov

Cincinnati (OH) District Office
36 East Seventh Street, Suite 2550, Cincinnati, OH 45202
Tel: (513) 684-6840 Fax: (513) 684-6845
Areas Covered: IN (Counties of Clinton, Delaware, Fountain, Howard, Madison, Montgomery, Randolph, Vermillion, and all counties South thereof), KY, OH (Athens, Darke, Fayette, Greene, Montgomery, Pickaway, Vinton, and all counties South thereof)

District Director **Brian Pifer** .... (513) 684-6840 ext. 224
E-mail: pifer.brian@dol.gov

Supervisory Investigator **Megan Ireland** .... (513) 684-3307

Cleveland (OH) District Office
A.J. Celebrezze Federal Building, 1240 East Ninth Street, Room 831, Cleveland, OH 44199
Tel: (216) 357-5455 Fax: (216) 357-5425
Areas Covered: OH (Counties of Allen, Ashland, Ashtabula, Auglaize, Belmont, Carroll, Champaign, Clark, Clermont, Columbiana, Coshocton, Crawford, Cuyahoga, Defiance, Delaware, Erie, Fairfield, Franklin, Fulton, Geauga, Guernsey, Hancock, Hardin, Harrison, Henry, Hocking, Holmes, Huron, Jefferson, Knox, Lake, Licking, Logan, Lorain, Lucas, Madison, Mahoning, Marion, Medina, Mercer, Miami, Monroe, Morgan, Morrow, Muskingum, Noble, Ottawa, Paulding, Perry, Portage, Putnam, Richland, Sandusky, Seneca, Shelby, Stark, Summit, Trumbull, Tuscarawas, Union, Van Wert, Washington, Wayne, Williams, Wood, and Wyandot)

District Director **Brian Pifer** .... (216) 357-5455
E-mail: pifer.brian@dol.gov

Detroit (MI) District Office
211 West Fort Street, Suite 1313, Detroit, MI 48226
Tel: (313) 226-6200 Fax: (313) 226-4391
Areas Covered: MI

District Director (Acting) **Thomas Murray** .... (313) 226-6200
E-mail: murray.thomas@dol.gov
Education: Marquette 2002 BS

Milwaukee (WI) District Office
Federal Building and U.S. Courthouse, 310 West Wisconsin Avenue, Suite 1160, Milwaukee, WI 53203
Tel: (414) 297-1501 Fax: (414) 297-1685
Areas Covered: MN, ND, SD, WI

District Director (Acting) **Thomas Murray** .... (414) 297-1501
E-mail: murray.thomas@dol.gov
Education: Marquette 2002 BS

Supervisory Investigator **Thomas Murray** .... (414) 297-1212
Education: Marquette 2002 BS

Minneapolis (MN) Resident Office
920 Second Avenue South, Room 450, Minneapolis, MN 55402
Tel: (612) 370-3111 Fax: (612) 370-3107

Director **Ian Burg** .... (612) 370-3111
E-mail: burg.ian@dol.gov

Office of Labor-Management Standards - Northeastern Regional Office

The Curtis Center, 170 South Independence Mall West, Suite 760 West, Philadelphia, PA 19106-3315
Tel: (215) 861-4818 Fax: (215) 861-4819

• Regional Director (Acting) **Kevin Kennedy** .... (215) 861-4818
E-mail: kennedy.kevin@dol.gov

Boston (MA) District Office
John F. Kennedy Federal Building, Room E-365, Boston, MA 02203
Tel: (617) 624-6690 Fax: (617) 624-6606
Areas Covered: CT, ME, MA, NH, RI, VT

District Director **Jonathan Russo** .... (617) 624-6690
E-mail: russo.jonathan@dol.gov

Buffalo (NY) District Office
130 South Elmwood Avenue, Suite 510, Buffalo, NY 14202
Tel: (716) 842-2900 Fax: (716) 842-2901 E-mail: dololms@buffalo.com

District Director **Jonathan Russo** .... (716) 842-2900
E-mail: russo.jonathan@dol.gov

Supervisory Investigator **Jennifer Rudewicz** .... (716) 842-4270

New York (NY) District Office
201 Varick Street, Room 878, New York, NY 10014-4811
Tel: (646) 264-3190 Fax: (646) 264-3191
Areas Covered: NJ, Southeastern NY, PR and USVI

District Director **Andriana Vamvakas** .... (646) 264-3190
E-mail: vamvakas.andriana@dol.gov

Supervisory Investigator **Joy Mitchell** .... (646) 264-3192

Philadelphia (PA) District Office
The Curtis Center, 170 South Independence Mall West, Room 760-West, Philadelphia, PA 19106-3310
Tel: (215) 861-4818 Fax: (215) 861-4819
Areas Covered: DE, PA (all counties east of Cameron, Centre, Fulton, Huntingdon and Potter Counties)

District Director **Kevin Kennedy** .... (215) 861-4818
E-mail: kennedy.kevin@dol.gov

Supervisory Investigator **Megan Underwood** .... (215) 861-4829

Pittsburgh (PA) District Office
1000 Liberty Avenue, Room 1411, Pittsburgh, PA 15222
Tel: (412) 395-6925 Fax: (412) 395-5409
Areas Covered: PA (25 Western counties: Bedford, Blair, Clearfield, Elk, McKean, and all counties west thereof), WV

District Director **Kevin Kennedy** .... (412) 395-5443
E-mail: kennedy.kevin@dol.gov

Office of Labor-Management Standards - Southern Regional Office

600 South Maestri Place, New Orleans, LA 70130
Tel: (504) 589-6174 Fax: (504) 589-7174

Regional Director **Daniel B. Cherry** .... (504) 589-6174
E-mail: cherry.daniel@dol.gov

Atlanta (GA) District Office

Sam Nunn Atlanta Federal Center, 61 Forsyth Street, SW, Room 16T10, Atlanta, GA 30303
Tel: (404) 562-2083 Fax: (404) 562-2087
Areas Covered: FL, GA, SC, PR, VI

District Director **Horace C. "Craig" Neel** .... (404) 562-2090
E-mail: neel.horace@dol.gov

Dallas (TX) District Office

A. Maceo Smith Federal Building, 525 S. Griffin Street, Room 300, Dallas, TX 75202
Tel: (972) 850-2500 Fax: (972) 850-2501
Areas Covered: AR, OK, TX

District Director **Michelle Hussar** .... (972) 850-2500
E-mail: hussar.michelle@dol.gov

Nashville (TN) District Office

233 Cumberland Bend Drive, Suite 110, Nashville, TN 37228
Tel: (615) 736-5906 Fax: (615) 736-7148
Areas Covered: AL, NC, TN

District Director **Horace C. "Craig" Neel** .... (615) 736-5906
E-mail: neel.horace@dol.gov
Supervisory Investigator **Donna Jolyn Underwood** ..... (615) 736-5906

Birmingham (AL) Resident Investigator Office

950 North 22nd Street, Suite 601, Birmingham, AL 35203
Tel: (205) 731-0239 Fax: (205) 731-0305

District Director **Horace C. "Craig" Neel** .... (205) 731-0239
E-mail: neel.horace@dol.gov

New Orleans (LA) District Office

600 South Maestri Place, Room 604, New Orleans, LA 70130
Tel: (504) 589-6174 Fax: (504) 589-7174
Areas Covered: AL (Baldwin, Mobile counties), AR, LA, MS, TX (Houston Area, San Antonio)

District Director **Michelle Hussar** .... (504) 589-6174
E-mail: hussar.michelle@dol.gov
Supervisory Investigator **Tara Thibodaux** .... (504) 589-6174

Fort Lauderdale (FL) Resident Investigator Office

One East Broward Boulevard, Fort Lauderdale, FL 33301
Tel: (954) 356-6850 Fax: (954) 356-6852
Areas Covered: FL

Supervisory Investigator **Takiia L. Anderson** .... (404) 562-2083
61 Forsyth Street, SW, Fax: (404) 562-2087
Suite 8B85, Atlanta, GA 30303
E-mail: anderson.takiia@dol.gov

Tampa (FL) Resident Investigator Office

500 Zack Street, Suite 213, Tampa, FL 33602
Tel: (813) 288-2031 Fax: (813) 288-2032

Supervisory Investigator **Takiia L. Anderson** .... (404) 562-2083
61 Forsyth Street, SW, Fax: (404) 562-2087
Suite 8B85, Atlanta, GA 30303
E-mail: anderson.takiia@dol.gov

Washington (DC) District Office

375 E Street SW, Suite 11-200, Washington, DC 20024-3221
Tel: (202) 513-7300 Fax: (202) 513-7301
Areas Covered: DC, MD, VA

District Director **Mark Wheeler** .... (202) 513-7316
E-mail: wheeler.mark@dol.gov
Supervisory Investigator **Christian Saenz** .... (202) 513-7320

Office of Labor-Management Standards - Western Regional Office

1244 Speer Boulevard, Room 1000, Denver, CO 80204
Tel: (816) 502-0284 Fax: (816) 503-8590

Director **Jena de Mers Raney** Suite 415 .... (720) 264-3232
E-mail: raney.jena@dol.gov Fax: (720) 264-3230

Denver (CO) District Office

1999 Broadway, Suite 1150, Denver, CO 80202-5712
Tel: (720) 264-3232 Fax: (720) 264-3230
Areas Covered: CO, MT, NM, UT, WY

District Director **Emily Prosise** .... (720) 264-3232
E-mail: prosise.emily@dol.gov

Los Angeles (CA) District Office

915 Wilshire Boulevard, Suite 910, Los Angeles, CA 90017-3446
Tel: (213) 534-6405 Fax: (213) 534-6413
Areas Covered: AS, AZ, Southern CA, HI, Guam, NV (Clark County), Wake Island

District Director **Edgar Oquendo** Room 910 .... (213) 534-6405
E-mail: oquendo.edgar@dol.gov
Supervisory Investigator **Pearl Moenahele** .... (808) 664-8497
E-mail: moenahele.pearl@dol.gov

Honolulu (HI) Resident Office

300 Ala Moana Boulevard, Room 5-121, Honolulu, HI 96850
Tel: (808) 541-2705 Fax: (808) 541-2719

Director **Pearl Moenahele** .... (808) 541-2705
E-mail: moenahele.pearl@dol.gov
Investigator **Pearl Moenahele** .... (808) 541-2705

Phoenix (AZ) Resident Office

Federal Building and Courthouse, North First Avenue, Room 501, Phoenix, AZ 85003
Tel: (480) 266-0325 Fax: (602) 514-7102

District Director **Edgar Oquendo** .... (213) 891-6965
E-mail: oquendo.edgar@dol.gov

Saint Louis (MO) District Office

Robert A. Young Federal Building, 1222 Spruce Street, Room 9-109E, St. Louis, MO 63103
Tel: (314) 539-2667 Fax: (314) 539-2626
Areas Covered: IA, IL (Calhoun, Clark, Cumberland, Effingham, Fayette, Green, Macoupin, Montgomery, and all counties South thereof), KS, MO, NE

District Director **Emily Prosise** .... (314) 539-2667
1222 Spruce Street, Room 9.109E, St. Louis, MO 63013
E-mail: prosise.emily@dol.gov

Kansas City (MO) Resident Office

Two Pershing Square Building, 1244 Speer Boulevard, Suite 1000, Denver, CO 80204
Tel: (816) 502-0290 Fax: (816) 502-0288

Director **Christiane Abendroth** .... (314) 539-2667
Robert A. Young Federal Building, 1222 Spruce Street, Room 9.109E, St. Louis, MO 63103
E-mail: abendroth.christiane@dol.gov

San Francisco (CA) District Office

90 Seventh Street, Suite 2-825, San Francisco, CA 94103
Tel: (415) 625-2661 Fax: (415) 625-2662
Areas Covered: CA (Inyo, Kings, Monterey, Tulare, and all counties North thereof), HI, NV, AS, GU, Wake Island

District Director **Bruce Edgington** .... (415) 625-2671
E-mail: edgington.bruce@dol.gov
Supervisory Investigator **Kenric Michel** .... (415) 625-2676

★ Presidential Appointment Requiring Senate Confirmation ☆ Presidential Appointment ☐ Schedule C Appointment ◇ Career Senior Foreign Service Appointment
● Career Senior Executive Service (SES) Appointment ○ Non-Career Senior Executive Service (SES) Appointment ■ Postal Career Executive Service

Seattle (WA) District Office
300 Fifth Avenue, Suite 1290, Seattle, WA 98104-2429
Tel: (206) 398-8099 Fax: (206) 398-8090
Areas Covered: AK, ID, OR, WA

District Director **Bruce Edgington** . . . . (206) 398-8099
E-mail: edgington.bruce@dol.gov
Supervisory Investigator **Chad Markham** . . . . (206) 504-5364

Office of Public Affairs (OPA)
200 Constitution Avenue, NW, Room S2514, Washington, DC 20210
Tel: (202) 693-4676 Fax: (202) 693-5057

Regional Offices

Region 1/2 - Boston (MA) and New York (NY)
John F. Kennedy Federal Building, 25 Sudbury Street,
Room 525-A, Boston, MA 02203
Tel: (617) 565-2072

Regional Director of Public Affairs **Ted Fitzgerald** . . . . . . (617) 565-2072
E-mail: fitzgerald.edmund@dol.gov Fax: (617) 565-2076

Region 3 - Philadelphia (PA)
170 South Independence Mall West, Suite 633 East,
Philadelphia, PA 19106-3315
Tel: (215) 861-5100

Regional Director of Public Affairs
Lenore "Leni" Uddyback-Fortson . . . . (215) 861-5102
E-mail: uddyback-fortson.lenore@dol.gov Fax: (215) 861-5103

Region 4 - Atlanta (GA)
Atlanta Federal Center, 61 Forsyth Street, SW,
Suite 6B75, Atlanta, GA 30303
Tel: (678) 237-0630

Regional Director of Public Affairs **Michael D'Aquino** . . . (678) 237-0630
E-mail: d'aquino.michael@dol.gov

Region 5 - Chicago (IL)
230 South Dearborn Street, Room 3192, Chicago, IL 60604-1505
Tel: (312) 353-6976

Regional Director of Public Affairs **Scott Allen** . . . . (312) 353-6976
230 South Dearborn Street, Fax: (312) 353-6631
3192, Chicago, IL 60604
E-mail: allen.scott@dol.gov

Region 6 - Dallas (TX)
525 S. Griffin Street, Room 734, Dallas, TX 75202
Tel: (972) 850-4708 Fax: (972) 850-4711

Regional Director of Public Affairs
Chauntra D. Rideaux . . . . (972) 850-4708
Federal Building, 525 South Griffin Street,
Suite 734, Dallas, TX 75202-5001
E-mail: rideaux.chauntra.d@dol.gov

Region 9 - San Francisco (CA)
90 Seventh Street, Suite 2-650, San Francisco, CA 94103
Tel: (415) 625-2633 Tel: (415) 625-2632 Fax: (415) 625-2632

Regional Director of Public Affairs **Leo F. Kay** . . . . (415) 625-2633
E-mail: kay.leo.f@dol.gov

Office of Workers' Compensation Programs (OWCP)
200 Constitution Avenue, NW, Washington, DC 20210
Tel: (202) 343-5580 Fax: (202) 343-5974 Internet: www.dol.gov/owcp

Regional Offices

Mid-Atlantic Region
The Curtis Center, 170 South Independence Mall West,
Suite 780 West, Philadelphia, PA 19106-3313
Tel: (267) 687-4089 Fax: (215) 861-5400
Areas Covered: DE, DC, MD, PA, VA, WV

Regional Director **Kellianne Conaway** . . . . (267) 687-4089
E-mail: conaway.kellianne@dol.gov

Midwest Region
Kluczynski Federal Building, 230 South Dearborn Street,
Room 800, Chicago, IL 60604
Tel: (312) 789-2800 Fax: (312) 596-7148
Areas Covered: IA, IL, IN, KS, MI, MN, MO, NE, OH, WI

Regional Director (Acting) **Annette M. Prindle** . . . . (312) 789-2800
E-mail: prindle.annette@dol.gov

Northeast Region
201 Varick Street, Room 740, New York, NY 10014-4811

Regional Director **Zev Sapir** . . . . (212) 863-0800
E-mail: sapir.zev@dol.gov

Pacific Region
90 Seventh Street, Suite 15100F, San Francisco, CA 94103
Tel: (866) 692-7487 Tel: (415) 625-7500 Fax: (415) 625-7470
Areas Covered: AZ, CA, HI, NV, GU, Trust Territories of the Pacific

Regional Director **Christy A. Long** . . . . (415) 241-3489
E-mail: long.christy@dol.gov

Southeast Region
400 West Bay Street, Suite 943, Jacksonville, FL 32202-4242
Areas Covered: AL, FL, GA, KY, MS, NC, SC, TN

Regional Director **Magdalena "Maggie" Fernandez** . . . . (904) 357-4776
E-mail: fernandez.magdalena@dol.gov

Southwest Region
One Denver Federal Center, Building 53, Denver, CO 80225-1601
Tel: (303) 462-6407
Areas Covered: AR, CO, IA, KS, LA, MO, MT, NE, ND, NM, OK, SD, TX, UT, WY

● Regional Director **Dean W. Woodard** . . . . (214) 749-4148
525 South Griffin Street, Dallas, TX 75202-5001
E-mail: woodard.dean@dol.gov
Education: Oklahoma 1977 AB, 1993 ScM; North Texas 2009 PhD
Deputy Regional Director **John L. Sullivan** . . . . (303) 462-6410

Division of Coal Mine Workers' Compensation (DCMWC)
200 Constitution Avenue, NW, Washington, DC 20210
Fax: (202) 693-1398 E-mail: dcmwc-public@dol.gov

Charleston (WV) District Office- Federal Black Lung Program
Charleston Federal Center, 500 Quarrier Street,
Suite 110, Charleston, WV 25301
Tel: (800) 347-3749 (Claims) Tel: (304) 347-7100 Fax: (304) 347-7115
Areas Covered: WV (Counties of Boone, Cabell, Fayette, Kanawha, Lincoln, Logan, McDowell, Mingo, Putnam, Raleigh, Wayne, Wyoming)

District Director **Carolyn King** . . . . (304) 344-5121 ext. 760000

★ Presidential Appointment Requiring Senate Confirmation ☆ Presidential Appointment □ Schedule C Appointment ◇ Career Senior Foreign Service Appointment
● Career Senior Executive Service (SES) Appointment ○ Non-Career Senior Executive Service (SES) Appointment ■ Postal Career Executive Service

Parkersburg (WV) Sub-District Office - Federal Black Lung Program
Parkersburg Federal Building, 425 Juliana Street,
Suite 3116, Parkersburg, WV 26101
Tel: (800) 347-3751 (Claims) Tel: (304) 420-6385 Fax: (304) 420-6389
Areas Covered: WV (Counties of Barbour, Berkeley, Braxton, Brooke, Calhoun, Clay, Doddridge, Gilmer, Grant, Greenbrier, Hampshire, Hancock, Hardy, Harrison, Jackson, Jefferson, Lewis, Marion, Marshall, Mason, Mercer, Mineral, Monongalia, Monroe, Morgan, Nicholas, Ohio, Pendleton, Pleasants, Pocahontas, Preston, Randolph, Ritchie, Roane, Summers, Taylor, Tucker, Tyler, Upshur, Webster, Wetzel, Wirt, Wood)
Supervisor **Tami Brown** .... (304) 420-6385

Columbus (OH) District Office - Federal Black Lung Program
1160 Dublin Road, Suite 300, Columbus, OH 43215
Tel: (800) 347-3771 (Claims) Tel: (614) 469-5227 Fax: (614) 469-2276
Areas Covered: IL, IN, MI, MN, OH, WI
District Director **Tami Brown** .... (614) 469-5227
Fax: (614) 469-2276

Denver (CO) District Office - Federal Black Lung Program
P.O. Box 25603, Denver, CO 80225-0603
Building 53, One Denver Federal Center,
Suite D2212, Denver, CO 80225-0603
Tel: (800) 366-4612 (Black Lung Inquiries) Tel: (720) 264-3100
Fax: (720) 264-3110
Areas Covered: AK, AS, AZ, AR, CA, CO, GU, HI, ID, IA,KS, LA, MO, MT, NE, NV, NM, ND, the North Mariana Islands, OK, OR, SD, TX, UT, WA, WY
District Director **Theresa Hobbs** .... (720) 264-3102

Greensburg (PA) District Office - Federal Black Lung Program
Wellington Square, 1225 South Main Street,
Suite 405, Greensburg, PA 15601
Tel: (800) 347-3753 (Claims) Tel: (724) 836-7230 Fax: (724) 836-2822
Areas Covered: Part B&C claims in MD and PA (Counties of Allegheny, Armstrong, Beaver, Butler, Clarion, Crawford, Erie, Fayette, Forest, Greene, Lawrence, Mercer, Venango, Warren, Washington, Westmoreland); Part B claims acquired from the Social Security Administration in CT, DE, DC, ME, MD, MA, NH, NJ, NY, PR, RI, VT
District Director **Colleen Smalley** .... (724) 836-7230

Johnstown (PA) District Office - Federal Black Lung Program
Greater Johnstwon Technology Park, One Tech Park Drive,
Suite 250, Johnstown, PA 15901
Tel: (814) 619-7777 Fax: (814) 619-7790
Areas Covered: PA (Counties of Adams, Bedford, Berks, Blair, Bucks, Cambria, Cameron, Centre, Chester, Clearfield, Clinton, Cumberland, Dauphin, Delaware, Elk, Franklin, Fulton, Huntington, Indiana, Jefferson, Juniata, Lancaster, Lebanon, Lycoming, McKean, Mifflin, Montgomery, Montour, Northumberland, Perry, Philadelphia, Potter, Snyder, Somerset, Tioga, Union, York), VA
District Director **Colleen Smalley** .... (814) 619-7777
E-mail: smalley.colleen@dol.gov

Pikeville (KY) District Office - Federal Black Lung Program
164 Main Street, Suite 508, Pikeville, KY 41501
Tel: (800) 366-4599 (Claims) Tel: (606) 218-9300 Fax: (606) 432-3574
Areas Covered: KY
District Director **Sheila Singleton** .... (606) 218-9203
E-mail: singleton.sheila@dol.gov

Mount Sterling (KY) Sub-District Office
402 Campbell Way, Mount Sterling, KY 40353
Tel: (800) 366-4628 (Claims) Tel: (859) 498-9700 Fax: (859) 498-5787
Areas Covered: AL, FL, GA, MS, NC, SC, TN
Office Manager **Vicky Ashby** .... (859) 497-8528

Division of Energy Employees' Occupational Illness Compensation

200 Constitution Avenue, NW, Room C3321, Washington, DC 20210
Fax: (202) 693-1465

Cleveland (OH) Office
1001 Lakeside Drive, Suite 350, Cleveland, OH 44114
Tel: (216) 802-1300
Areas Covered: CT, DE, DC, IL, IN, ME, MD, MA, MI, MN, NH, NJ, OH, PA, PR, RI, VT, VA, VI, WV, WI
District Director **Karen R. Spence** .... (216) 802-1312
E-mail: spence.karen@dol.gov

Denver (CO) Office
PO Box 25601, Denver, CO 80225-0601
Tel: (720) 264-3060 Fax: (720) 264-3099
Areas Covered: AR, CO, IA, KS, LA, MO, MT, NE, NM, ND, OK, SD, UT, TX, WY
District Director **Ronnie R. Sanchez** .... (720) 264-3125
Assistant District Director **Kathryn Jimmerson** .... (720) 264-3060

Jacksonville (FL) Office
400 West Bay Street, Suite 722, Jacksonville, FL 32202-4242
Mail: 8306, London, KY 40742-8306
Tel: (904) 357-4795 Fax: (904) 357-4704
Areas Covered: AL, FL, GA, LA, KY, MS, NC, SC, TN
District Director **James "Jim" Bibeault** .... (904) 357-4795
E-mail: bibeault.james@dol.gov

Seattle (WA) Office
719 Second Avenue, Suite 601, Seattle, WA 98104
Tel: (206) 373-6750 Fax: (206) 373-6798
Areas Covered: AK, AR, CA, HI, ID, Marshall Islands, NV, NM, OR, WA
District Director **Joleen Smith** .... (206) 373-6751
E-mail: smith.joleen@dol.gov

Division of Federal Employees' Compensation (DFEC)

District Office 1 – Boston (MA)
John F. Kennedy Federal Building, Room E-260, Boston, MA 02203
Mail: USDOL - FECP, P.O. Box 8300, London, KY 40742-8300
Tel: (857) 264-4600 Fax: (857) 264-4602
Areas Covered: CT, ME, MA, NH, RI, VT
District Director **Mark Foley** .... (857) 264-4600

District Office 2 – New York (NY)
201 Varick Street, Room 740, New York, NY 10014
Mail: USDOL -2 FECP, P.O. Box 8300, London, KY 40742-8300
Tel: (646) 264-3000
Tel: (866) 692-7487 (Automated 24-hour Information Line)
Areas Covered: NJ, NY, PR, VI
District Director **Rholanda Basnight** .... (212) 863-0800

District Office 3 – Philadelphia (PA)
The Curtis Center, 170 South Independence Mall West,
Suite 715-E, Philadelphia, PA 19106-3308
Mail: USDOL - FECP, P.O. Box 8300, London, KY 40742-8300
Tel: (267) 687-4160 Fax: (215) 861-5453
Areas Covered: DE, PA, WV
District Director **Angelo Randazzo** .... (267) 687-4093

District Office 6 – Jacksonville (FL)
Charles E. Bennett Federal Building, 400 West Bay Street,
Suite 826, Jacksonville, FL 32202-4242
USDOL - FECP, P.O. Box 8300, London, KY 40742-8300
Tel: (904) 366-0100 Fax: (904) 357-4773
Areas Covered: AL, FL, GA, KY, MS, NC, SC, TN
District Director **Tisha Carter** .... (904) 366-0100
Assistant District Director **(Vacant)** .... (904) 366-0100

(continued on next page)

★ Presidential Appointment Requiring Senate Confirmation ☆ Presidential Appointment ☐ Schedule C Appointment ◇ Career Senior Foreign Service Appointment
● Career Senior Executive Service (SES) Appointment ○ Non-Career Senior Executive Service (SES) Appointment ■ Postal Career Executive Service

District Office 6 – Jacksonville (FL) *(continued)*

Office Manager **(Vacant)** .... (904) 366-0100
Regional Administrative Officer **(Vacant)** .... (904) 357-4735
Fax: (904) 357-4742

District Office 9 – Cleveland (OH)
A.J. Celebreeze Federal Building, 1240 East Ninth Street, Room 851, Cleveland, OH 44199
Mail: USDOL - FECP, P.O. Box 8300, London, KY 40742-8300
Fax: (216) 357-5378
Areas Covered: IN, MI, OH
District Director **Lana Betton** .... (216) 902-5600

District Office 10 – Chicago (IL)
Kluczynski Federal Building, 230 South Dearborn Street, 8th Floor, Chicago, IL 60604
Mail: USDOL - FECP, PO Box 8300, London, KY 40742-8300
Tel: (312) 789-2800 Fax: (312) 596-7145
Areas Covered: IL, MN, WI
District Director **James F. Polcyn** .... (312) 789-2800

District Office 11 – Kansas City (MO)
U.S. Department of Labor, DFEC Central Mailroom, P.O. Box 83, London, KY 40742-8300
Two Pershing Square Building, 2300 Main Street, Suite 1090, Kansas City, MO 64108
Tel: (816) 268-3040 Fax: (816) 502-0314
Areas Covered: IA, KS, MO, NE
District Director **Jack Mercer** .... (816) 268-3040

District Office 12 – Denver (CO)
One Denver Federal Center, Building 53, Denver, CO 80225-0602
P.O. Box 25602, Denver, CO 80225-0602
Fax: (720) 264-3124
Areas Covered: CO, MT, ND, SD, UT, WY
District Director **Nigel Strozier** .... (720) 202-2500

District Office 13 – San Francisco (CA)
90 Seventh Street, Suite 15-300, San Francisco, CA 94103
Mail: P.O. Box 193769, San Francisco, CA 94119-3769
Tel: (415) 241-3300 Fax: (415) 625-7450
Areas Covered: AZ, CA, HI, NV
District Director **Susan Pearlman** .... (415) 241-3300
Assistant District Director **(Vacant)** .... (415) 241-3300

District Office 14 – Seattle (WA)
300 Fifth Avenue, Suite 1050, Seattle, WA 98104
Mail: USDOL FECP, P.O. Box 8300, London, KY 40742-8300
Tel: (206) 470-3100 Fax: (206) 398-8151
Areas Covered: AK, ID, OR, WA
District Director **Marcus Tapia** .... (206) 470-3100

District Office 16 – Dallas (TX)
525 South Griffin Street, Room 100, Dallas, TX 75202-5001
Mail: USDOL FECP, P.O. Box 8300, London, KY 40742-8300
Fax: (214) 749-2321
Areas Covered: LA, OK, TX
District Director **Gloria Taylor** .... (214) 749-2320

District Office 25 – Washington (DC)
800 North Capitol Street, NW, Room 800, Washington, DC 20211
USDOL - FECP, P.O. Box 8300, London, KY 40742-8300
Tel: (202) 513-6800 Tel: (866) 692-7487 (Interactive Voice Response)
Fax: (202) 513-6806
Areas Covered: DC, MD, VA; all areas outside the U.S., its possessions, territories, and trust territories; and all special claims
District Director **Abbas Sadiq** .... (202) 513-6800

Division of Longshore and Harbor Workers' Compensation

200 Constitution Avenue, NW, Room C4315, Washington, DC 20210
Tel: (202) 693-0038

Region I – Boston (MA)
John F. Kennedy Federal Building, Room E-260, Boston, MA 02203
Tel: (617) 624-6750 Fax: (617) 624-6603
Areas Covered: CT, ME, MA, NH, RI, VT
District Director **David Groeneveld** .... (617) 624-6750

Region II – New York (NY)
201 Varick Street, Room 740, New York, NY 10014-4811
Mail: P.O. Box 249, New York, NY 10014-0249
Tel: (646) 264-3010 Fax: (646) 264-3002
Areas Covered: NJ, NY, PR, VI
District Director **David Abeijon** .... (646) 264-3010

Region III – Philadelphia (PA)
Areas Covered: DE, DC, MD, PA, VA, WV

Norfolk (VA) Longshore District Office
Federal Office Building, 200 Granby Mall, Room 212, Norfolk, VA 23510-1879
Tel: (757) 441-3071 Fax: (757) 441-6909
District Director **Theresa Magyar** .... (757) 452-6504

Region IV – Atlanta (GA)
Areas Covered: AL, FL, GA, KY, NC, SC, TN

Jacksonville (FL) Longshore District Office
400 West Bay Street, Suite 63A, Box 28, Jacksonville, FL 32202-4242
Tel: (904) 357-4788 Fax: (904) 357-4787
District Director **(Vacant)** .... (904) 357-4788

Region VI – Dallas (TX)
Areas Covered: AR, LA, MS, NM, OK, TX

Houston (TX) Longshore District Office
1919 Smith Street, Suite 890, Houston, TX 77002
Tel: (713) 651-4650 Fax: (713) 651-4651
Areas Covered: IL, IN, IA, KS, MI, MN, MO, NE, NM, OH, OK, WI, TX
District Director **David Widener** .... (713) 943-1605

New Orleans (LA) Longshore District Office
600 South Maestri Place, Suite 617, New Orleans, LA 70130
Mail: P.O. Box 30728, New Orleans, LA 70190-0728
Tel: (504) 589-2671 Fax: (504) 589-3969
Areas Covered: AR, LA, MS
District Director **David A. Duhon** .... (504) 589-2671

Region IX – San Francisco (CA)
90 Seventh Street, Suite 15100, San Francisco, CA 94103
Tel: (415) 625-7669 Fax: (415) 625-7470
Areas Covered: AZ, CA, GU, HI, NV
District Director **R. Todd Bruininks** .... (415) 625-7669

Honolulu (HI) Longshore District Office
Prince Jonah Kuhio Kalanianaole Federal Building, 300 Ala Moana Boulevard, Room 5-135, Honolulu, HI 96850
Mail: 90 Seventh Street, Suite 15100, San Francisco, CA 94103
Tel: (808) 541-1983 Fax: (808) 541-1758
District Director **R. Todd Bruininks** .... (415) 625-7669

Long Beach (CA) Longshore District Office
501 West Ocean Boulevard, Suite 6230, Long Beach, CA 90802
Tel: (562) 980-3577 Fax: (562) 980-3587
District Director **Marco Adame** .... (562) 980-3577

Region X – Seattle (WA)
300 Fifth Avenue, Suite 1050L, Seattle, WA 98104
Tel: (206) 504-5287 Fax: (206) 467-1073
Areas Covered: AK, CO, ID, MT, ND, OR, SD, UT, WA, WY
District Director **R. Todd Bruininks** .... (415) 625-7669

Wage and Hour Division (WHD)

200 Constitution Avenue, NW, Washington, DC 20210
Tel: (202) 693-0051 Fax: (202) 693-1406 Internet: www.dol.gov/whd

Regional Offices

Midwest Region

Kluczynski Federal Building, 230 South Dearborn Street,
Room 530, Chicago, IL 60604-1591
Tel: (312) 596-7180 Fax: (312) 596-7205
Areas Covered: IL, IN, IA, KS, MI, MN, MO, NE, OH, WI
Regional Administrator **Michael A. Lazzeri** .... (312) 596-7186
E-mail: lazzeri.michael@dol.gov
Deputy Regional Administrator **Dieera Fitzgerald** .... (312) 596-7186
E-mail: fitzgerald.dieera@dol.gov
Regional Operation Management **Ingrid Wenner** .... (312) 596-7186
E-mail: wenner.ingrid@dol.gov

Chicago (IL) District Office
Kluczynski Federal Building, 230 South Dearborn Street,
Room 412, Chicago, IL 60604-1595
Tel: (312) 596-7230 Fax: (312) 596-7251
District Director **Thomas Gauza** .... (312) 596-7230
E-mail: gauza.thomas@dol.gov
Assistant District Director **Robert Lisec** .... (312) 596-7230
E-mail: lisec.robert@dol.gov
Assistant District Director **(Vacant)** .... (312) 596-7230

Springfield (IL) Area Office
3161 West White Oaks Drive, Suite 203, Springfield, IL 62704
Tel: (217) 793-5028 Fax: (217) 793-5198
Assistant District Director **(Vacant)** .... (217) 793-5028
Assistant District Director **(Vacant)** .... (217) 793-5028

Columbus (OH) District Office
Federal Building, 200 North High Street,
Room 646, Columbus, OH 43215
Tel: (614) 469-5678 Fax: (614) 469-5428
District Director **George Victory** .... (614) 469-5678
E-mail: victory.george@dol.gov
Assistant District Director **John R. Dudash** .... (614) 469-5678
E-mail: dudashjr.john@dol.gov

Cincinnati (OH) Area Office
550 Main Street, Room 10-409, Cincinnati, OH 45202
Tel: (513) 684-2908 Fax: (513) 684-2906
Assistant District Director **(Vacant)** .... (513) 684-2908

Cleveland (OH) Area Office
A. J. Celebrezze Federal Building, 1240 East Ninth Street,
Room 817, Cleveland, OH 44199-2054
Tel: (216) 357-5400 Fax: (216) 357-5422
Assistant District Director **Brian Woodruff** .... (216) 357-5400
E-mail: woodruff.brian@dol.gov
Assistant District Director **(Vacant)** .... (216) 357-5400

Des Moines (IA) District Office
Federal Building, 210 Walnut Street, Room 643, Des Moines, IA 50309
Tel: (515) 284-4625 Fax: (515) 284-7171
District Director **(Vacant)** .... (515) 284-4625
Assistant District Director **(Vacant)** .... (515) 284-4625
Assistant District Director **Adam Wombacher** .... (515) 284-4625
E-mail: wombacher.adam@dol.gov

Omaha (NE) Area Office
222 South 15 Street, Suite 504A, Omaha, NE 68102
Tel: (402) 221-4682 Fax: (402) 221-3719
Areas Covered: Western two thirds of KS, NE
Assistant District Director **Richard Tesarek** .... (402) 221-4682
E-mail: tesarek.richard@dol.gov

Detroit (MI) District Office
211 West Fort Street, Room 517, Detroit, MI 48226
Tel: (313) 309-4500 Fax: (313) 226-3072
District Director **Timolin Mitchell** .... (313) 309-4500
E-mail: mitchell.timolin@dol.gov
Assistant District Director **(Vacant)** .... (313) 226-1447

Grand Rapids (MI) District Office
800 Monroe Avenue, NW, Suite 315, Grand Rapids, MI 49503
Tel: (616) 456-2004 Fax: (616) 456-2258
Assistant District Director **Mary O'Rourke** .... (616) 456-2004
E-mail: orourke.mary@dol.gov Fax: (616) 456-2258

Troy (MI) Area Office
5700 Crooks Road, Room 310, Troy, MI 48098
Fax: (313) 226-3439 Tel: (313) 226-7447
Assistant District Director **(Vacant)** .... (313) 226-7447

Indianapolis (IN) District Office
135 North Pennsylvania Street, Suite 700, Indianapolis, IN 46204
Tel: (317) 226-6801 Fax: (317) 226-5177
District Director **Patricia Lewis** .... (317) 226-6801
E-mail: lewis.patricia@dol.gov

South Bend (IN) Area Office
2420 Viridian Drive, Suite 160E, South Bend, IN 46628
Tel: (574) 236-8331 Fax: (574) 236-8819
Assistant District Director **(Vacant)** .... (574) 236-8331

Kansas City (KS) District Office
Gateway Tower II, 400 State Avenue, Suite 1010, Kansas City, KS 66101
Tel: (913) 551-5721 Fax: (913) 551-5730
District Director **(Vacant)** .... (913) 551-5721
Assistant District Director **Aracelis Scarbrough** .... (913) 551-5721
E-mail: scarbrough.aracelis@dol.gov

Wichita (KS) Area Office
United States Courthouse B-58, 401 North Market Street,
Wichita, KS 67202
Tel: (316) 269-7166 Fax: (316) 269-7163
Assistant District Director **(Vacant)** .... (316) 269-7166

Minneapolis (MN) District Office
Tri Tech Office Center, 331 Second Avenue, South,
Room 920, Minneapolis, MN 55401-2233
Tel: (612) 370-3341 Fax: (612) 370-3372
District Director **David King** .... (612) 370-3341
E-mail: king.david@dol.gov
Assistant District Director **Ann Buysman** .... (612) 370-3341
E-mail: buysman.ann@dol.gov

Milwaukee (WI) Area Office
310 West Wisconsin Avenue, Suite 1170, Milwaukee, WI 53203
Tel: (414) 297-1590 ext. 308 Fax: (414) 297-3591
Assistant District Director **(Vacant)** .... (414) 297-1590

Saint Louis (MO) District Office
Robert A. Young Federal Building, 1222 Spruce Street,
Room 9.102B, St. Louis, MO 63103
Tel: (314) 539-2706 Fax: (314) 539-2723
Areas Covered: Eastern half of MO
District Director **Norma Cervi** .... (314) 539-2706
E-mail: cervi.norma@dol.gov
Assistant District Director **(Vacant)** .... (314) 539-2706

Northeast Region
170 South Independence Mall, Suite 850-W, Philadelphia, PA 19106-3317
Tel: (215) 861-5800 Fax: (215) 861-5840
Areas Covered: CT, DE, DC, ME, MD, MA, NH, NJ, NY, PA, PR, RI, VA, VI, WV

● Regional Administrator **Mark Watson, Jr.** . . . . (267) 687-4040
E-mail: watsonjr.mark@dol.gov
Deputy Regional Administrator **James Kolpack** . . . . (267) 687-4034
E-mail: kolpack.james@dol.gov
Deputy Regional Administrator **Maria Rosado** . . . . (646) 587-5310
170 South Independence Mall West, Philadelphia, PA 19106-3315
E-mail: rosado.maria@dol.gov

Albany (NY) District Office
Leo O'Brien Federal Building, Clinton Avenue and North Pearl Street, Room 822, Albany, NY 12207
Tel: (518) 431-6460 Fax: (518) 431-4281

District Director **Jay Rosenblum** . . . . (518) 431-6460
E-mail: rosenblum.jay@dol.gov
Assistant District Director **Michael Milazzo** . . . . (518) 431-6470
E-mail: milazzo.michael@dol.gov

Baltimore (MD) District Office
Two Hopkins Plaza, Suite 601, Baltimore, MD 21201
Tel: (410) 962-6211 Fax: (410) 962-9512

District Director **Mark Lara** . . . . (410) 962-2240 ext. 11
E-mail: lara.mark@dol.gov
Assistant District Director **Joseph Corbin** . . . . (410) 962-3223
E-mail: corbin.joseph@dol.gov

Hyattsville (MD) Area Office
6525 Belcrest Road, Suite 560, Hyattsville, MD 20782
Tel: (301) 436-6767

Assistant District Director **Bruce Dory** . . . . (301) 436-6767
E-mail: dory.bruce@dol.gov

Arlington (VA) Area Office
2300 Claredon Boulevard, Suite 1330, Arlington, VA 22201

Assistant District Director **Christopher Silva** . . . . (703) 235-1182
E-mail: silva.christopher@dol.gov

Boston (MA) District Office
John F. Kennedy Federal Building, Room 525, Boston, MA 02203
Tel: (617) 624-6700 Fax: (617) 624-6701

District Director **Carlos Matos** . . . . (617) 624-6728
E-mail: matos.carlos@dol.gov
Assistant District Director **Roberto Quintana** . . . . (617) 624-6700
E-mail: quintana.roberto@dol.gov

Caribbean District Office
T-Mobile Center, B-7 Tabonuco Street, Suite 1104, Guaynabo, PR 00968
Tel: (787) 775-1924 Fax: (787) 775-1906

District Director **Jose R. Vazquez** . . . . (787) 775-1924
E-mail: vazquez.jose.r@dol.gov
Assistant District Director **David Marin** . . . . (787) 775-1924
E-mail: marin.david@dol.gov

Hartford (CT) District Office
William R. Cotter Federal Building, 135 High Street, Room 210, Hartford, CT 06103-1198
Tel: (860) 240-4160 Fax: (860) 240-4029

District Director **David Gerrain** . . . . (860) 240-4160
E-mail: gerrain.david@dol.gov

New Haven (CT) Area Office
150 Court Street, Room 208, New Haven, CT 06510
Tel: (203) 773-2249 Fax: (203) 773-2380

Assistant District Director **Nancy DiPietro** . . . . (203) 773-2249
E-mail: dipietro.nancy@dol.gov

Providence Field Office
The Federal Center, 380 Westminster Street, Room 546, Providence, RI 02903
Tel: (401) 528-4431

Assistant District Director **Donald Epifano** . . . . (401) 528-4431
E-mail: epifano.donald@dol.gov

Long Island (NY) District Office
Parkway Plaza, 1400 Old Country Road, Suite 410, Westbury, NY 11590
Tel: (516) 338-1890 Fax: (516) 338-8901

District Director **Irv Miljoner** . . . . (516) 338-1890
E-mail: miljoner.irv@dol.gov
Assistant District Director **Francisco Marchan** . . . . (516) 338-1890
E-mail: marchan.francisco@dol.gov
Assistant District Director **(Vacant)** . . . . (516) 338-1890

Manchester (NH) District Office
1155 Elm Street, Suite 501, Manchester, NH 03101
Tel: (603) 666-7716 Fax: (603) 666-7600

District Director **Daniel Cronin** . . . . (603) 666-7716
E-mail: cronin.daniel@dol.gov

Bangor (ME) Field Station
Federal Building, 202 Harlow Street, Room 234, Bangor, ME 04401
Mail: P.O. Box 1356, Bangor, ME 04401
Tel: (207) 945-0330 Fax: (207) 945-0332

District Director **Daniel Cronin** . . . . (603) 666-7716
1155 Elm Street, Suite 111, Manchester, NH 03101
E-mail: cronin.daniel@dol.gov

Burlington (VT) Field Station
11 Elmwood Avenue, Room 111, Burlington, VT 05402-5224
Mail: P.O. Box 5224, Burlington, VT 05402-5224
Tel: (802) 951-6283

District Director **Daniel Cronin** . . . . (603) 666-7716
1155 Elm Street, Suite 111, Manchester, NH 03101
E-mail: cronin.daniel@dol.gov

Portland (ME) Field Station
100 Middle Street Plaza, Portland, ME 04101
Tel: (207) 780-3344 Fax: (207) 780-3787

District Director **Daniel Cronin** . . . . (603) 666-7716
1155 Elm Street, Suite 111, Manchester, NH 03101
E-mail: cronin.daniel@dol.gov

New York (NY) District Office
26 Federal Plaza, Suite 3700, New York, NY 10278
Tel: (212) 264-8185 Fax: (212) 264-9548

District Director **David An** . . . . (212) 264-8185
E-mail: an.david@dol.gov
Assistant District Director **Deborah "Debbie" Lau** . . . . . . (212) 264-8185
E-mail: lau.debbie@dol.gov
Assistant District Director **Dinah Solivan** . . . . (718) 254-9410
Two Metrotech Center, 100 Myrtle Avenue, 7th Floor, Brooklyn, NY 11201
E-mail: solivan.dinah@dol.gov
Assistant District Director **(Vacant)** . . . . (212) 264-8185

Queens (NY) Area Office
68-60 Austin Street, Room 601, Forest Hills, NY 11375
Tel: (718) 834-2090

Director **(Vacant)** . . . . (718) 834-2090

Northern New Jersey District Office (Newark)
200 Sheffield Street, Suite 102, Mountainside, NJ 07092
Tel: (908) 317-8611 Fax: (908) 317-8620

District Director **John Warner** . . . . (908) 317-8611
Assistant District Director **Daniele Eller** . . . . (908) 317-8611
E-mail: eller.daniele@dol.gov
Assistant District Director **Paula Ruffin** . . . . (908) 317-8611
E-mail: ruffin.paula@dol.gov

★ Presidential Appointment Requiring Senate Confirmation ☆ Presidential Appointment □ Schedule C Appointment ◇ Career Senior Foreign Service Appointment
● Career Senior Executive Service (SES) Appointment ○ Non-Career Senior Executive Service (SES) Appointment ■ Postal Career Executive Service

Philadelphia (PA) District Office
1617 John F Kennedy Blvd, Suite 1780, Philadelphia, PA 19103
Tel: (215) 597-4950 Fax: (215) 597-4949

District Director **James Cain** .... (215) 597-4950
E-mail: cain.james@dol.gov
Assistant District Director **Maribel Rivera-Lopez** .... (215) 597-4950
E-mail: rivera-lopez.maribel@dol.gov

Pittsburgh (PA) District Office
William S. Moorhead Federal Building, 1000 Liberty Avenue,
Room 1416, Pittsburgh, PA 15222
Tel: (412) 395-4996 Fax: (412) 395-5772

District Director **John DuMont** .... (412) 395-4996
E-mail: dumont.john@dol.gov
Assistant District Director **Brian Heeter** .... (412) 395-4996
E-mail: heeter.brian@dol.gov
Assistant District Director **(Vacant)** .... (412) 395-4996

Charleston (WV) Area Office
500 Quarrier Street, Room 120, Charleston, WV 25301
Tel: (304) 347-5206 Fax: (304) 347-5467

Assistant District Director **Catherine Glencoe** .... (304) 347-5206
E-mail: glencoe.catherine@dol.gov

Richmond (VA) District Office
Richmond Federal Building, 400 North Eighth Street,
Room 416, Richmond, VA 23240-4815
Tel: (804) 771-2995 Fax: (804) 771-8127

District Director **Carmen Otero-Infante** .... (804) 771-2995
E-mail: otero-infante.carmen@dol.gov
Assistant District Director **Roberto Melendez** .... (804) 771-2995
E-mail: melendez.roberto@dol.gov
Assistant District Director **(Vacant)** .... (804) 771-2995

Southern New Jersey District Office (Lawrenceville)
Building 5, 3131 Princeton Pike, Room 216, Lawrenceville, NJ 08648
Tel: (609) 538-8310 Fax: (609) 538-8314

District Director **Charlene Rachor** .... (609) 989-2247
E-mail: rachor.charlene@dol.gov
Assistant District Director **John R. Kelly** .... (609) 538-8312
E-mail: kelly.john.r@dol.gov
Assistant District Director **Steven Risko** .... (609) 538-8312
E-mail: risko.steven@dol.gov

Wilkes-Barre (PA) District Office
Stegmaier Building, Seven North Wilkes-Barre Boulevard,
Suite 373M, Wilkes Barre, PA 18702
Tel: (570) 826-6316 Fax: (570) 821-4186

District Director **Alfonso "Al" Gristina** .... (570) 826-6316 ext. 101
E-mail: gristina.alfonso@dol.gov
Assistant District Director **(Vacant)** .... (570) 826-6316
Assistant District Director **(Vacant)** .... (570) 826-6316

Southeast Region

Sam Nunn Atlanta Federal Center, 61 Forsyth Street, SW,
Suite 7M40, Atlanta, GA 30303
Tel: (678) 237-0480 Tel: (866) 487-2365 (Information)
Fax: (404) 893-4524
Areas Covered: AL, FL, GA, KY, MS, NC, SC, TN

• Regional Administrator (Acting) **Betty R. Campbell** ..... (678) 237-0480
E-mail: campbell.betty@dol.gov
Deputy Regional Administrator **(Vacant)** .... (678) 237-0498
Director of Operations **Jose Medina** .... (404) 893-4525
E-mail: medina.jose@dol.gov

Atlanta (GA) District Office
Atlanta Federal Building, 61 Forsyth Street, SW,
Room 7M10, Atlanta, GA 30303
Tel: (678) 237-0525 Fax: (404) 893-4601

District Director **Eric Williams** .... (678) 237-0525
E-mail: williams.eric@dol.gov

Atlanta (GA) District Office *(continued)*

Assistant District Director **Sung Kim Chu** .... (678) 237-0525
Harris Tower, 233 Peachtree Street NE,
Suite 650, Atlanta, GA 30303
E-mail: chu.sung@dol.gov
Assistant District Director **(Vacant)** .... (404) 893-4600

Savannah (GA) Area Office
Oglethorpe Office Park, 450 Mall Boulevard,
Suite D, Savannah, GA 31406
Tel: (912) 652-4221 Fax: (912) 652-4992

Assistant District Director **Larry Benjamin** .... (912) 652-4221
E-mail: benjamin.larry@dol.gov

Birmingham (AL) District Office
The Forum Building, 950 North 22nd Street,
Room 605, Birmingham, AL 35203
Tel: (205) 536-8570 Fax: (205) 397-7101

District Director **Kenneth "Ken" Stripling** .... (205) 536-8570
E-mail: stripling.kenneth@dol.gov
Assistant District Director **(Vacant)** .... (205) 536-8570

Jackson (MS) Area Office
100 West Capitol Street, Suite 725, Jackson, MS 39269
Fax: (601) 965-5408

Assistant District Director **Audrey Hall** .... (601) 965-4347
E-mail: hall.audrey@dol.gov

Mobile (AL) Area Office
1119 Government Street, Mobile, AL 36609
Tel: (251) 441-5311

Assistant District Director **Patricia Chambers** .... (251) 441-5311
E-mail: chambers.patricia@dol.gov

Montgomery (AL) Area Office
4001 Carmichael Road, Suite 215, Montgomery, AL 36106
Tel: (334) 223-7641

Assistant District Director **Yvette Davis** .... (334) 223-7641
E-mail: davis.yvette@dol.gov

Columbia (SC) District Office
Federal Building, 1872 Assembly Street,
Room 1072, Columbia, SC 29201
Tel: (803) 765-5981 ext. 3436 Fax: (803) 253-3003

District Director **Jamie Benefiel** .... (803) 765-5981
E-mail: benefiel.jamie@dol.gov
Assistant District Director **(Vacant)** .... (803) 765-5981

Jacksonville (FL) District Office
400 West Bay Street, 9th Floor, Room 956, Box 017,
Jacksonville, FL 32202-4242
Tel: (904) 359-9292 Fax: (904) 359-9279

District Director **Daniel "Dan" White** .... (904) 359-9292
E-mail: white.daniel@dol.gov

Orlando (FL) Area Office
1001 Executive Center Drive, Suite 103, Orlando, FL 32803
Tel: (407) 648-6471 Fax: (407) 648-6094

Assistant District Director **Wildali Dejesus** .... (407) 648-6471
E-mail: dejesus.wildali@dol.gov

Tallahassee (FL) Area Office
Building D, 325 John Knox Road, Suite 102, Tallahassee, FL 32303
Tel: (850) 942-8341 Fax: (850) 942-8342

Assistant District Director **Cynthia Hickman** .... (850) 942-8341
E-mail: hickman.cynthia@dol.gov

Louisville (KY) District Office
Romono Mazzooi Federal Buiilding, 600 Dr. Martin Luther King Jr. Place,
Room 352, Louisville, KY 40202
Tel: (502) 582-5226 Fax: (502) 582-6890

District Director **Karen Garnett** .... (502) 582-5226
E-mail: garnett.karen@dol.gov

(continued on next page)

★ Presidential Appointment Requiring Senate Confirmation ☆ Presidential Appointment ☐ Schedule C Appointment ◇ Career Senior Foreign Service Appointment
● Career Senior Executive Service (SES) Appointment ○ Non-Career Senior Executive Service (SES) Appointment ■ Postal Career Executive Service

DEPARTMENTS

Louisville (KY) District Office *(continued)*

Assistant District Director **(Vacant)** . . . . (502) 582-5226

Miami (FL) District Office
10300 Southwest 72nd Street, Suite 255, Miami, FL 33173
Tel: (305) 598-6607
Tel: (305) 598-6607 (24-hour General Information Recording)
Fax: (305) 279-8393

District Director **Tony Pham** . . . . (305) 598-6607
E-mail: pham.tony@dol.gov
Assistant District Director **(Vacant)** . . . . (305) 596-9874

Fort Lauderdale (FL) Area Office
510 Shotgun Road, Suite 140, Sunrise, FL 33326
Tel: (954) 356-6896 Fax: (954) 356-7920

Assistant District Director **Nury Vergara** . . . . (954) 356-6896
E-mail: vergara.nury@dol.gov

West Palm Beach (FL) Area Office
1818 South Australian Avenue, Room 251, West Palm Beach, FL 33401

Assistant District Director **Norman Mann** . . . . (561) 640-0474
E-mail: mann.norman@dol.gov

Nashville (TN) District Office
1321 Murfreesboro Road, Suite 204, Nashville, TN 37217
Tel: (615) 781-5343 Fax: (615) 781-5347

District Director **Nettie Lewis** . . . . (615) 781-5344
E-mail: lewis.nettie@dol.gov

Knoxville (TN) Area Office
John J. Duncan Federal Building, 710 Locust Street,
Room 101, Knoxville, TN 37902
Tel: (865) 545-4619 Fax: (865) 545-4623

Assistant District Director **(Vacant)** . . . . (865) 545-4619

Memphis (TN) Area Office
Federal Office Building, 167 North Main Street,
Room 484, Memphis, TN 38103
Tel: (901) 544-3418 Fax: (901) 544-4237

Assistant District Director **(Vacant)** . . . . (901) 544-3418

Raleigh (NC) District Office
Somerset Park Building, 4407 Bland Road,
Suite 260, Raleigh, NC 27609
Tel: (919) 790-2742
Tel: (919) 790-2741 (24-hour General Information Recording)
Fax: (919) 790-2843

District Director **Richard Blaylock** . . . . (919) 790-2742
E-mail: blaylock.richard@dol.gov
Assistant District Director **(Vacant)** . . . . (919) 790-2742

Charlotte (NC) Area Office
3800 Arco Corporate Drive, Suite 460, Charlotte, NC 28273
Tel: (704) 749-3360 Fax: (704) 749-3361

Assistant District Director **Caryl Stribling** . . . . (704) 749-3360
E-mail: stribling.caryl@dol.gov
Assistant District Director **(Vacant)** . . . . (704) 749-3360

Tampa (FL) District Office
Austin Laurel Building, 4905 West Laurel Avenue,
Suite 300, Tampa, FL 33607-3838
Tel: (813) 288-1242 Fax: (813) 288-1240

District Director **James M. Schmidt** . . . . (813) 288-1242
E-mail: schmidt.james@dol.gov
Assistant District Director **David King** . . . . (813) 288-1242
E-mail: king.david@dol.gov
Assistant District Director **Nicolas Ratmiroff** . . . . (813) 288-1242
E-mail: ratmiroff.nicolas@dol.gov
Assistant District Director
Jim "Jimmy" Rogers . . . . (813) 288-1242 ext. 36
E-mail: rogers.jim@dol.gov

Southwest Region

A. Maceo Smith Federal Building, 525 South Griffin Street,
Room 800, Dallas, TX 75202-5001
Tel: (972) 850-2600 Fax: (972) 850-2601
Areas Covered: AR, CO, LA, MT, NM, ND, OK, SD, TX, UT, WY

Regional Administrator (Acting) **Lee Ann Dunbar** . . . . . . (972) 850-2600
E-mail: dunbar.lee@dol.gov
Deputy Regional Administrator **Lee Ann Dunbar** . . . . (972) 850-2600
E-mail: dunbar.lee@dol.gov
Regional Director of Enforcement **Naixa Franquiz** . . . . . . (214) 749-2017
E-mail: franquiz.naixa@dol.gov
Regional Operations Manager **Donnette Holder** . . . . (214) 749-2010
E-mail: holder.donnette@dol.gov

Albuquerque (NM) District Office
Chavez Federal Building, 500 Gold Avenue,
Suite 12000, Albuquerque, NM 87103-0907
Mail: P.O. Box 907, Albuquerque, NM 87102
Tel: (505) 248-6100 Fax: (505) 248-6108

District Director **Evelyn Sanchez** . . . . (505) 248-2670
E-mail: sanchez.evelyn@dol.gov
Assistant District Director **Theodore Trujillo** . . . . (505) 248-2671
E-mail: trujillo.theodore@dol.gov

El Paso (TX) Area Office
Richard White Federal Building, 700 East San Antonio Street,
Room B400, El Paso, TX 79901
Tel: (915) 534-6426 Fax: (915) 534-6429

Assistant District Director (Acting) **Evelyn Sanchez** . . . . . (915) 534-6426
E-mail: sanchez.evelyn@dol.gov

Lubbock (TX) Area Office
1205 Texas Avenue, Room 410, Lubbock, TX 79401
Tel: (806) 472-7666 Fax: (806) 472-7207

Assistant District Director **Ryan Martin** . . . . (806) 472-6459
E-mail: martin.ryan@dol.gov

Dallas (TX) District Office
The Offices at Brookhollow, 1701 East Lamar Boulevard, Box 22,
Suite 270, Arlington, TX 76006-7303
Tel: (817) 861-2150 Fax: (817) 861-5085

District Director **Curtis L. Poer** . . . . (817) 861-2150
Assistant District Director **Gary L. Edwards** . . . . (214) 804-8006
E-mail: edwards.gary@dol.gov
Assistant District Director **Shayne Tackett** . . . . (214) 804-8037
E-mail: tackett.shayne@dol.gov
Assistant District Director **Sherry Trout** . . . . (214) 804-8008
E-mail: trout.sherry@dol.gov
Assistant District Director **Jesus Valdez** . . . . (214) 804-8009
E-mail: valdez.jesus@dol.gov

Denver (CO) District Office
1999 Broadway, Suite 710, Denver, CO 80202-5712
Tel: (720) 264-3250 Fax: (720) 264-3255

District Director **Charles L. "Chad" Frasier** . . . . (720) 264-2806
E-mail: frasier.charles@dol.gov
Assistant District Director **Jason Helme** . . . . (720) 264-2807
E-mail: helme.jason@dol.gov
Assistant District Director **David Skinner** . . . . (720) 264-2830
E-mail: skinner.david@dol.gov
Assistant District Director **Janet A. Wilson** . . . . (720) 264-2808
E-mail: wilson.janet@dol.gov

Houston (TX) District Office
8701 South Gessner, Suite 1164, Houston, TX 77074
Tel: (713) 339-5500 Fax: (713) 339-5590

District Director **Robin R. Mallett** . . . . (713) 773-5355
E-mail: mallett.robin@dol.gov
Assistant District Director **Velma Garcia** . . . . (713) 773-5367
E-mail: garcia.velma@dol.gov
Assistant District Director **Rebecca Hanks** . . . . (713) 773-5357
E-mail: hanks.rebecca@dol.gov
Assistant District Director **Annie Robson** . . . . (713) 773-5358
E-mail: robson.annie@dol.gov

★ Presidential Appointment Requiring Senate Confirmation ☆ Presidential Appointment ☐ Schedule C Appointment ◇ Career Senior Foreign Service Appointment
● Career Senior Executive Service (SES) Appointment ○ Non-Career Senior Executive Service (SES) Appointment ■ Postal Career Executive Service

Clear Lake City (TX) Area Office
17625 El Camino Real, Suite 482, Houston, TX 77058
Fax: (281) 488-0690 Tel: (281) 280-7131

District Director **Adrian Samaniego** .... (281) 280-7140
E-mail: samaniego.adrian@dol.gov
Assistant District Director **Kristen McQueen** .... (281) 280-7145
E-mail: mcqueen.kristen@dol.gov

Little Rock (AR) District Office
Danville Building 2, 10810 Executive Center Drive,
Suite 220, Little Rock, AR 72211
Tel: (501) 223-9114 Fax: (501) 223-8734

District Director **Hanz Grunauer** .... (501) 221-4607
E-mail: grunauer.hanz@dol.gov
Assistant District Director **Reed Trone** .... (501) 221-4608
E-mail: trone.reed@dol.gov

McAllen (TX) District Office
1101 East Hackberry Avenue, Suite 400, McAllen, TX 78501
Tel: (956) 682-4631 Fax: (956) 682-5783

District Director **Nathan Barrow** .... (956) 632-3910
E-mail: barrow.nathan@dol.gov
Assistant District Director **Elsa Gonzalez** .... (956) 632-3914
E-mail: gonzalez.elsa@dol.gov

Corpus Christi (TX) Area Office
Wilson Plaza, 606 North Carancahua,
Suite 413, Corpus Christi, TX 78401
Tel: (361) 888-3152 Fax: (361) 888-3153

Assistant District Director **Vicente "Vince" Leija** .... (361) 885-3210
E-mail: leija.vicente@dol.gov

New Orleans (LA) District Office
F. Edward Hebert Building, 600 South Maestri Place,
Room 615, New Orleans, LA 70130
Tel: (504) 589-6171 Fax: (504) 589-4751

District Director **Troy Mouton** .... (504) 299-1491
E-mail: mouton.troy@dol.gov
Assistant District Director **Jason Brister** .... (504) 463-5042
E-mail: brister.jason@dol.gov
Assistant District Director **Charlotta Williams** .... (504) 299-1492
E-mail: williams.charlotta@dol.gov

Oklahoma City (OK) District Office
215 Dean A. McGee Avenue, Room 318, Oklahoma City, OK 73102
Tel: (405) 231-4158 Fax: (405) 231-4545

District Director **Michael Speer** .... (405) 595-3460
E-mail: speer.michael@dol.gov
Assistant District Director **Michael Lonesky** .... (405) 595-3461
E-mail: lonesky.michael@dol.gov

Tulsa (OK) Area Office
224 South Boulder Avenue, Room 320, Tulsa, OK 74103
Tel: (918) 581-6303 Fax: (918) 496-6791

Assistant District Director **Matthew Helm** .... (918) 270-5720
E-mail: helm.matthew@dol.gov

Salt Lake City (UT) District Office
60 East South Temple Street, Suite 575, Salt Lake City, UT 84111
Tel: (801) 257-6561 Fax: (801) 524-5722

District Director **Joseph Doolin** .... (801) 257-6565
E-mail: doolin.joseph@dol.gov
Assistant District Director **Kevin Hunt** .... (801) 257-6567
E-mail: hunt.kevin@dol.gov
Assistant District Director **Kathy Milton** .... (801) 257-6575
E-mail: milton.kathy@dol.gov

San Antonio (TX) District Office
Northchase I Office Building, 10127 Morocco Street,
Suite 140, San Antonio, TX 78216
Tel: (210) 308-4515 Fax: (210) 308-4518

District Director **Cynthia Ramos** .... (210) 308-2308
E-mail: ramos.cynthia@dol.gov

San Antonio (TX) District Office *(continued)*

Assistant District Director **Erica Holder** .... (210) 308-2312
E-mail: holder.erica@dol.gov

Austin (TX) District Office
300 East Eighth Street, Room 865, Austin, TX 78701
Tel: (512) 236-2560 Fax: (512) 236-2561

District Director **Nicole Sellers** .... (512) 236-2568
E-mail: sellers.nicole@dol.gov
Assistant District Director **Rosalinda Haro** .... (512) 236-2569
E-mail: haro.rosalinda@dol.gov
Assistant District Director **Rosalinda Huffman** .... (512) 236-2571
E-mail: huffman.rosalinda@dol.gov

DEPARTMENTS

Western Region
90 7th Street, Suite 13-1000, San Francisco, CA 94103
Tel: (415) 625-7700 Fax: (415) 625-7699
Areas Covered: AK, AZ, CA, GU, HI, ID, NV, OR, Trust Territory of the Pacific Islands, WA

• Regional Administrator **Ruben Rosalez** .... (415) 625-7700
E-mail: rosalez.riben@dol.gov
Management Analyst **(Vacant)** .... (415) 625-7700
Deputy Regional Administrator **Juan Coria** .... (415) 625-7700
E-mail: coria.juan@dol.gov
Director of Enforcement **Richard Longo** .... (415) 625-7700
Director of Operations **Celeste Hill** .... (415) 625-7700
Deputy Director of Operations **Adriana Iglesias** .... (415) 625-7700
E-mail: iglesias.adriana@dol.gov
Regional Wage Specialist **Kwok-Wai Lau** .... (415) 625-7700
E-mail: lau.kwok-wai@dol.gov

Las Vegas (NV) District Office
600 Las Vegas Boulevard South, Suite 550, Las Vegas, NV 89101
Tel: (702) 928-1240 Fax: (702) 928-1241

District Director **Gaspar Montanez** .... (702) 928-1250

Los Angeles (CA) District Office
915 Wilshire Boulevard, Suite 1060, Los Angeles, CA 90017-3446
Tel: (213) 894-6375 Fax: (213) 894-6845

District Director **Kimchi Bui** .... (213) 894-6375
E-mail: bui.kimchi@dol.gov
Assistant District Director **Susan Bacon** .... (213) 894-6375
E-mail: bacon.susan@dol.gov
Assistant District Director **Eduardo Huerta** .... (213) 894-6375
E-mail: huerta.eduardo@dol.gov
Assistant District Director **Francisco Ocampo** .... (213) 894-6375
E-mail: ocampo.francisco@dol.gov

Fresno (CA) Area Office
395 W. Street, Suite 102, Clovis, CA 93691
Tel: (559) 487-5317

Assistant District Director **Nora Pedraza** .... (559) 487-5317
E-mail: pedraza.nora@dol.gov

Phoenix (AZ) District Office
230 North First Avenue, Suite 402, Phoenix, AZ 85003-1725
Tel: (602) 514-7100 Fax: (602) 514-7103

District Director **Eric Murray** .... (602) 514-7100
E-mail: murray.eric@dol.gov
Assistant District Director **(Vacant)** .... (602) 514-7100
Assistant District Director **Susan P. Nern** .... (602) 514-7100
E-mail: nern.susan@dol.gov

Tucson (AZ) Area Office
300 West Congress Street, Suite 4-H, Tucson, AZ 85701-1390
Tel: (520) 670-4899 Fax: (520) 670-4641

Assistant District Director **(Vacant)** .... (520) 670-4899

Portland (OR) District Office
620 SW Main Street, Suite 423, Portland, OR 97205-3028
Tel: (503) 326-3057 Fax: (503) 326-5951

District Director **Thomas Silva** .... (503) 326-3057
E-mail: silva.thomas@dol.gov

★ Presidential Appointment Requiring Senate Confirmation ☆ Presidential Appointment ☐ Schedule C Appointment ◇ Career Senior Foreign Service Appointment
● Career Senior Executive Service (SES) Appointment ○ Non-Career Senior Executive Service (SES) Appointment ■ Postal Career Executive Service

DEPARTMENTS

Sacramento (CA) District Office
2800 Cottage Way, Suite W-1836, Sacramento, CA 95825-1886
Tel: (916) 978-6123 Fax: (916) 978-6125

District Director **Cesar Avila** . . . . . (916) 978-6123
E-mail: avila.cesar@dol.gov
Assistant District Director **(Vacant)** . . . . . (916) 978-6123
Assistant District Director (Fresno) **Patricia Canites** . . . . . (559) 487-5317
395 W. Street, Suite 105, Clovis, CA 93691 Fax: (559) 487-5497
E-mail: canites.patricia@dol.gov

San Diego (CA) District Office
550 Corporate Center, 550 West C Street,
Suite 990, San Diego, CA 92101
Tel: (619) 557-5110 Fax: (619) 557-5146

District Director **Rodolfo Cortez** . . . . . (619) 557-5110
E-mail: cortez.rodolfo@dol.gov
Assistant District Director **Troy Washington** . . . . . (619) 557-5110
E-mail: washington.troy@dol.gov
Assistant District Director **(Vacant)** . . . . . (619) 557-5110

Orange (CA) Area Office
770 The City Drive South, Suite 5710, Orange, CA 92868-4954
Tel: (714) 621-1650 Fax: (714) 621-1655

Assistant District Director **(Vacant)** . . . . . (714) 489-6032

San Francisco (CA) District Office
90 7th Street, Suite 12-100, San Francisco, CA 94103
Tel: (415) 625-7720 Fax: (415) 625-7735

Assistant District Director **Alberto Raymond** . . . . . (415) 625-7720
Assistant District Director **Alberto Raymond** . . . . . (415) 625-7720
E-mail: raymond.alberto@dol.gov
Assistant District Director **Celeste Hale** . . . . . (415) 625-7720
E-mail: hale.celeste@dol.gov

Honolulu (HI) District Office
300 Ala Moana Boulevard, Suite 7225, Honolulu, HI 96850-7225
Tel: (808) 541-1361 Fax: (808) 541-1695

District Director **Terence Trotter** . . . . . (808) 541-1361
E-mail: trotter.terence@dol.gov
Assistant District Director **Min Kirk** . . . . . (808) 541-1361
E-mail: kirk.min@dol.gov

Guam Area Office
520 West Soledad Avenue, Hagatna, GU 96910-4950
Tel: (671) 473-9178 Fax: (671) 473-9189

Assistant District Director **Patrick Candoleta** . . . . . (671) 473-9178
E-mail: candoleta.patrick@dol.gov

San Jose (CA) District Office
96 North 3rd Street, Suite 400, San Jose, CA 95112-7709
Tel: (408) 291-7730 Fax: (408) 291-7731

Assistant District Director **Lilita Hom** . . . . . (408) 291-7730
E-mail: hom.lilita@dol.gov
District Director **Susana Blanco** . . . . . (408) 291-7730
E-mail: blanco.susana@dol.gov

Seattle (WA) District Office
300 Fifth Avenue, Suite 1130, Seattle, WA 98104-2397
Tel: (206) 398-8039 Fax: (206) 224-4111

District Director **Jeanette Aranda** . . . . . (206) 398-8039
E-mail: aranda.jeanette@dol.gov
Assistant District Director **Tuan Huynh** . . . . . (206) 398-8039
E-mail: huynh.tuan@dol.gov
Assistant District Director **Manuel Lucero** . . . . . (206) 398-8039
E-mail: lucero.manuel@dol.gov

West Covina (CA) District Office
100 North Barranca Street, Suite 850, West Covina, CA 91791-1638
Tel: (626) 966-0478 Fax: (626) 966-5539

District Director **Daniel Pasquil** . . . . . (626) 966-0478
E-mail: pasquil.daniel@dol.gov
Assistant District Director **Gayane Aleksanian** . . . . . (626) 966-0478
E-mail: aleksanian.gayane@dol.gov

West Covina (CA) District Office *(continued)*

Assistant District Director **Paul Chang** . . . . . (626) 966-0478
E-mail: chang.paul@dol.gov
Education: Cal State (Los Angeles) 1996 BA, 2009 MSPA
Assistant District Director **(Vacant)** . . . . . (626) 966-0478

Bureau of Labor Statistics (BLS)

Postal Square Building, Two Massachusetts Avenue, NE,
Room 2850, Washington, DC 20212
Tel: (202) 691-7705 (Hotline) Internet: www.bls.gov
Internet: www.bls.gov/data (Published Datasets)

Office of Field Operations (OFO)

2 Massachusetts Avenue, NE, Washington, DC 20212
Fax: (202) 691-5811

Boston (MA)/New York (NY) Region
John F. Kennedy Federal Building, Room E-310, Boston, MA 02203
Tel: (617) 565-2327 Fax: (617) 565-4182 Internet: www.bls.gov/ro1
Areas Covered: CT, ME, MA, NH, NY, PR, RI, VT, VI

Regional Commissioner **Deborah A. Brown** . . . . . (617) 565-2331
E-mail: brown.deboraha@bls.gov Fax: (617) 565-4183
Compensation Programs Assistant Regional Commissioner **Michael Foley** . . . . . (617) 565-2315
E-mail: foley.michael@dol.gov
Federal-State Cooperative Programs Assistant Regional Commissioner **Jim Sibley** . . . . . (617) 565-2333
Price Programs Assistant Regional Commissioner **Joyce A. Sweeney** . . . . . (617) 565-2358
E-mail: sweeney.joyce@dol.gov
Regional Economist **Tim Consedine** . . . . . (617) 565-2324
Administrative Officer **LaFleur Gonsalves** . . . . . (617) 565-2332
E-mail: gonsalves.lafleur@dol.gov Fax: (617) 565-4183

Mid-Atlantic Region
The Curtis Center, 170 South Independence Mall West,
Suite 610E, Philadelphia, PA 19106-3305
Tel: (215) 861-5600 Fax: (215) 861-5703 E-mail: eai_ec@bls.gov
Internet: www.bls.gov/ro3
Areas Covered: DE, DC, MD, NJ, PA, VA, WV

Regional Commissioner **Sheila Watkins** . . . . . (215) 861-5600
E-mail: watkins.sheila@bls.gov
Secretary/Administrative Specialist **Donna Marie Parker** . . . . . (215) 861-5601
E-mail: parker.donna@bls.gov
Compensation Programs Assistant Regional Commissioner **(Vacant)** . . . . . (215) 861-5695
Federal-State Programs Assistant Regional Commissioner **Frank V. Waligorski** . . . . . (215) 861-5633
Price Programs Assistant Regional Commissioner **Maureen McDevitt-Greene** . . . . . (215) 861-5650
E-mail: greene.maureen@bls.gov
Economic Analysis and Information **Kara Markley** . . . . . (215) 861-5603
E-mail: markley.kara@bls.gov
Regional Network Administrator **Joseph Piotti** . . . . . (215) 861-5621
The Curtis Center, 170 South Independence Mall West,
Suite 610E, Philadelphia, PA 19106-3315
Administrative Officer **Kathleen Sullivan** . . . . . (215) 861-5656

Midwest Region
Kluczynski Federal Building, 230 South Dearborn Street,
9th Floor, Room 960, Chicago, IL 60604
Tel: (312) 353-7200 Tel: (312) 353-1880 (CPI Hotline)
Fax: (312) 353-1886 E-mail: blsinfochicago@bls.gov
Internet: www.bls.gov/ro5
Areas Covered: IL, IN, IA, MI, MN, NE, ND, OH, SD, WI

Regional Commissioner **Charlene Peiffer** . . . . . (312) 353-7200
E-mail: peiffer.charlene@bls.gov
Regional Economist **Paul Laporte** . . . . . (312) 353-1138
E-mail: laporte.paul@bls.gov

★ Presidential Appointment Requiring Senate Confirmation ☆ Presidential Appointment ☐ Schedule C Appointment ◇ Career Senior Foreign Service Appointment
● Career Senior Executive Service (SES) Appointment ○ Non-Career Senior Executive Service (SES) Appointment ■ Postal Career Executive Service

Midwest Region *(continued)*

Federal-State Cooperative Programs Assistant Regional Commissioner **Charles Jirik** . . . . . (312) 353-7200
E-mail: jirik.chuck@bls.gov
Education: Illinois (Chicago) BS

Price Programs Assistant Regional Commissioner **Bryan Droste** . . . . . (312) 353-7200
E-mail: droste.bryan@bls.gov

Wage Programs Assistant Regional Commissioner **Julia Wilson** . . . . . (312) 353-7200

Administrative Officer **LaWanda "La" Fitten** . . . . . (312) 353-7200

Electronic Data Interchange (EDI) Manager **Jeffrey Bates** . . . . . (312) 353-7200

Regional LAN Administrator **Dan Tolson** . . . . . (312) 353-7200
E-mail: tolson.dan@bls.gov Fax: (312) 353-1103

New York Regional Office for Economic Analysis and Information

201 Varick Street, Room 808, New York, NY 10014-4811
Tel: (646) 264-3600 Fax: (212) 337-2532 E-mail: businfonyc@bls.gov
Internet: www.bls.gov/ro2/home.htm

Regional Network Administrator **Eustace Browne** . . . . . (212) 337-2490
E-mail: browne.eustace@bls.gov Fax: (212) 337-2411

Chief Regional Economist **Martin Kohli** . . . . . (646) 264-3620
E-mail: kohli.martin@bls.gov

Administrative Specialist **Hermenia Jewth** . . . . . (212) 337-2470
E-mail: jewth.hermenia@bls.gov

Southeast Region

Sam Nunn Atlanta Federal Center, 61 Forsyth Street, SW, Suite 7T50, Atlanta, GA 30303
Tel: (404) 893-8300 Fax: (404) 893-8308 Internet: www.bls.gov/ro4
Areas Covered: AL, FL, GA, KY, MS, NC, SC, TN

Regional Commissioner **Janet S. Rankin** . . . . . (404) 893-8300
E-mail: rankin.janet@bls.gov

Federal-State Cooperative Programs Assistant Regional Commissioner **Eddie L. Green** . . . . . (404) 893-1961
E-mail: green.eddie@bls.gov

National Compensation Programs Assistant Regional Commissioner **Charles Eberle III** . . . . . (404) 893-1921

Price Programs Assistant Regional Commissioner **Victoria G. Lee** . . . . . (404) 893-1978
E-mail: lee.victoria@bls.gov

Administrative Officer **Deborah Woodard** . . . . . (404) 893-8302

Regional Economist **Tim Ewing** . . . . . (404) 893-4222

Southwest Region

A. Maceo Smith Federal Building, 525 Griffin Street, Room 221, Dallas, TX 75202
Tel: (972) 850-4800 Fax: (972) 850-4804 Internet: www.bls.gov/ro6
Areas Covered: AR, CO, KS, LA, MO, MT, NM, OK, TX, UT, WY

Assistant Commissioner for Regional Operations **Stanley W. Suchman** . . . . . (972) 850-4882
E-mail: suchman.stan@bls.gov

Administrative Officer **Mary Lane Moore** . . . . . (972) 850-4886
E-mail: moore.marylane@bls.gov

Regional Economist **Cheryl Abbot** . . . . . (972) 850-4805

Compensations Branch Assistant Regional Commissioner **Fonda Ivy** . . . . . (972) 850-4850
E-mail: ivy.fonda@bls.gov

Federal/State Programs Assistant Regional Commissioner **Susan Mendez** . . . . . (972) 850-4809

Price Branch Assistant Regional Commissioner **Michael Hirniak** . . . . . (972) 850-4860

Kansas City (MO) Office

Two Perishing Place, 2300 Main Street, Suite 1190, Kansas City, MO 64108-2426
Tel: (816) 285-7018 Fax: (816) 426-6537 Internet: www.bls.gov/ro7

Assistant Commissioner for Regional Operations **Stanley W. Suchman** . . . . . (816) 285-7018
E-mail: suchman.stanley@bls.gov

Western Region

90 Seventh Street, Suite 14-100, San Francisco, CA 94103
Tel: (415) 625-2245 Fax: (415) 625-2350 E-mail: BLSinfoSF@bls.gov
Internet: https://www.bls.gov/regions/west/
Areas Covered: AK, American Samoa, AZ, CA, GU, HI, ID, NV, OR, Trust Territory of the Pacific Islands, WA

Regional Commissioner **Richard Holden** . . . . . (415) 625-2245

Assistant Regional Commissioner, Compensation Division **Christopher Rosenlund** . . . . . (415) 625-2313
E-mail: rosenlund.chris@dol.gov

Assistant Regional Commissioner, Federal-State Programs **Dennis Reid** . . . . . (415) 625-2260

Assistant Regional Commissioner, Price Programs Division **Sam Pence** . . . . . (415) 625-2288
E-mail: pence.sam@dol.gov

Chief, Economic Analysis and Information Branch **Amar Mann** . . . . . (415) 625-2285
E-mail: mann.amar@dol.gov

Administrative Officer **Nancy Gonzalez** . . . . . (415) 625-2322
E-mail: gonzalez.nancy@dol.gov

DEPARTMENTS

Employee Benefits Security Administration (EBSA)

200 Constitution Avenue, NW, Washington, DC 20210
Tel: (202) 693-8300 Fax: (202) 219-5526 Internet: www.dol.gov/ebsa

Regional Offices

Atlanta (GA) Regional Office

Atlanta Federal Center, 61 Forsyth Street, SW, Room 7B54, Atlanta, GA 30303
Tel: (404) 302-3900 Fax: (404) 302-3975
Areas Covered: AL, FL, GA, MS, NC, SC, TN, PR

● Regional Director **Isabel Colon** . . . . . (404) 302-3900
E-mail: colon.isabel@dol.gov Fax: (404) 302-3975

Miami (FL) District Office

1000 South Pine Island Road, Suite 100, Plantation, FL 33324
Tel: (954) 424-4022 Fax: (954) 424-0548

District Supervisor **Norman Rivera** . . . . . (954) 424-4022
E-mail: rivera.norman@dol.gov

Boston (MA) Regional Office

John F. Kennedy Federal Building, 25 Sudbury Street, Room 575, Boston, MA 02203
Tel: (617) 565-9600 Fax: (617) 565-9666
Areas Covered: CT, ME, MA, NH, Central and Western NY, RI, VT

● Regional Director (Acting) **Carol Hamilton** . . . . . (617) 565-9600
E-mail: hamilton.carol@dol.gov

Chicago (IL) Regional Office

John C. Kluczynksi Federal Building, 230 South Dearborn Street, Suite 2160, Chicago, IL 60604-1505
Tel: (312) 353-0900 Fax: (312) 353-1023
Areas Covered: Northern IL, Northern IN, WI

● Regional Director **Jeffrey Monhart** . . . . . (312) 353-0140
E-mail: monhart.jeff@dol.gov

Deputy Regional Director **Donna Seermon** . . . . . (312) 353-5511
E-mail: seermon.donna@dol.gov

Associate Regional Director **Chris Davis** . . . . . (312) 886-0497
E-mail: davis.chris@dol.gov

Supervisory Benefits Advisor **Cindy Saba** . . . . . (312) 886-0587

Cincinnati (OH) Regional Office

1885 Dixie Highway, Suite 210, Fort Wright, KY 41011-2664
Tel: (859) 578-4680 Fax: (859) 578-4688
Areas Covered: Southern IN, KY, MI, OH

Regional Director **L. Joe Rivers** . . . . . (859) 578-4680

★ Presidential Appointment Requiring Senate Confirmation ☆ Presidential Appointment ☐ Schedule C Appointment ◇ Career Senior Foreign Service Appointment
● Career Senior Executive Service (SES) Appointment ○ Non-Career Senior Executive Service (SES) Appointment ■ Postal Career Executive Service

DEPARTMENTS

Dallas (TX) Regional Office
Federal Building, 525 South Griffin Street,
Room 900, Dallas, TX 75202-5025
Tel: (972) 850-4500 Fax: (214) 767-1055
Areas Covered: AR, LA, NM, OK, TX

Regional Director **Deborah Perry** .... (972) 850-4500

Kansas City (MO) Regional Office
2300 Main Street, Suite 1100, Kansas City, MO 64108
Tel: (816) 285-1800 Fax: (816) 285-1888
Areas Covered: CO, Southern IL, IA, KS, MN, MO, MT, NE, ND, SD, WY

● Regional Director **James Purcell** .... (816) 285-1810
Education: Rockhurst U BSBA

Saint Louis (MO) District Office
1222 Spruce Street, Room 6. 310, St. Louis, MO 63103-2818
Tel: (314) 539-2693 Fax: (314) 539-2697

District Supervisor **(Vacant)** .... (816) 285-1863

Los Angeles (CA) Regional Office
1055 East Colorado Boulevard, Suite 200, Pasadena, CA 91106-2357
Tel: (626) 229-1000 Fax: (626) 229-1098
Areas Covered: AZ, Southern CA, HI, American Samoa, Guam, Wake Island

Regional Director **Crisanta Johnson** .... (626) 229-1000
Supervisory Benefits Advisor **Marites AbadSantos** ..... (626) 229-1070
Local Area Network Administrator **Bonnie Horowitz** .... (626) 229-1018
E-mail: horowitz.bonnie@dol.gov

New York (NY) Regional Office
33 Whitehall Street, Suite 1200, New York, NY 10004
Tel: (212) 607-8600 Fax: (212) 607-8681
Areas Covered: Northern NJ (Bergen, Essex, Hudson, Hunterdon, Mercer, Middlesex, Monmouth, Morris, Passaic, Somerset, Sussex, Union, Waren); Eastern NY (Bronx, Columbia, Dutchess, Greene, Kings, Nassau, New York, Orange, Putnam, Queens, Richmond, Rockland, Suffolk, Sullivan, Ulster, and Westchester Counties)

● Regional Director (Acting) **Thomas Licetti** .... (212) 607-8600
E-mail: licetti.thomas@dol.gov

Philadelphia (PA) Regional Office
The Curtis Center, 170 South Independence Mall West,
Suite 870W, Philadelphia, PA 19106-3317
Tel: (215) 861-5300 Fax: (215) 861-5347
Areas Covered: DE, DC, MD, Southern NJ, PA, VA, WV

● Regional Director (Acting) **Michael Schloss** .... (215) 861-5300
E-mail: schloss.michael@dol.gov
Education: Yeshiva 1983 BA; Cardozo 1987 JD
Administrative Officer **Stephanie Evans** .... (215) 861-5308
E-mail: evans.stephanie@dol.gov

Washington (DC) District Office
Silver Spring Metro Center, 1335 East-West Highway,
2nd Floor, Suite 200, Silver Spring, MD 20910
Tel: (202) 693-8700 Fax: (202) 693-8736

District Supervisor **Elizabeth Bond** .... (202) 693-8700

San Francisco (CA) Regional Office
90 Seventh Street, Suite 11-300, San Francisco, CA 94103
Tel: (415) 625-2481 Fax: (415) 625-2450
Areas Covered: AK, Northern CA, ID, NV, OR, UT, WA

● Regional Director (Acting) **Klaus Placke** .... (415) 625-2481
E-mail: placke.klaus@dol.gov
Deputy Regional Director **Klaus Placke** .... (415) 625-2481
E-mail: placke.klaus@dol.gov
Associate Regional Director for Technical Review and Analysis **Chris Swanson** .... (415) 625-2481
E-mail: swanson.chris@dol.gov

San Francisco (CA) Regional Office *(continued)*

Group Supervisor **Robert Paine** .... (415) 625-2481
E-mail: paine.robert@dol.gov
Group Supervisor **Heather Hesik** .... (415) 625-2481
E-mail: hesik.heather@dol.gov
Group Supervisor **(Vacant)** .... (415) 625-2481
Group Supervisor **(Vacant)** .... (415) 625-2481
Administrative Officer **Chuanbi Li** .... (415) 625-2481
E-mail: li.chuanbi@dol.gov
Supervisory Benefits Advisor **Sarah K. Holt** .... (415) 625-2481

Seattle (WA) District Office
300 Fifth Avenue, Suite 1110, Seattle, WA 98104
Tel: (206) 757-6781 Fax: (206) 757-6662

District Supervisor **Tonya Hanson** .... (206) 757-6781
E-mail: hanson.tonya@dol.gov
Group Supervisor **Tonya Hanson** .... (206) 757-6781
E-mail: hanson.tonya@dol.gov
Supervisory Benefits Advisor **William "Bill" Pierron** .... (206) 757-6781
E-mail: pierron.bill@dol.gov

Employment and Training Administration (ETA)
200 Constitution Avenue, NW, Room S2307, Washington, DC 20210
Tel: (202) 693-2772 Fax: (202) 693-2726 Internet: www.doleta.gov
Internet: www.myskillsmyfuture.org

DEPUTY ASSISTANT SECRETARY

Office of Management and Administrative Services (OMAS)
200 Constitution Avenue, NW, Room N4653, Washington, DC 20210
Tel: (202) 693-2800 Fax: (202) 693-2857

Office of Regional Management (ORM)
200 Constitution Avenue, NW, Room C-4517, Washington, DC 20210
Tel: (202) 693-3690

Region 1 – Boston (MA)
John F. Kennedy Federal Building, Room E-350, Boston, MA 02203
Tel: (617) 788-0170 Fax: (617) 788-0101 E-mail: ro1-ra-bos@dol.gov
Areas Covered: CT, ME, MA, NH, NJ, NY, PR, RI, VI, VT

● Regional Administrator (Acting) **Timothy S. Martin** ..... (617) 788-0170
E-mail: martin.timothy@dol.gov
Executive Assistant (Acting) **Keeva Davis** .... (617) 788-0157
Office State Systems Regional Director **Timothy S. Martin** .... (617) 788-0170
E-mail: martin.timothy@dol.gov
Office of Special Initiatives and Demonstration Chief **Heather E. Graham** .... (617) 788-0163
E-mail: graham.heather@dol.gov
Financial Management and Administrative Services Division Chief **Jon Lirag** .... (617) 788-0159
E-mail: lirag.ernesto@dol.gov
Workforce Investment Division Chief (Acting) **Christina Eckenroth** .... (617) 788-0133
E-mail: eckenroth.christina@dol.gov
Workforce Security Chief **Barbara D'Amore** .... (617) 788-0115
E-mail: damore.barbara@dol.gov
Demonstration Grants Division Chief **(Vacant)** .... (617) 788-0170

Region 2 – Philadelphia (PA)
The Curtis Center, 170 South Independence Mall West,
Suite 825 East, Philadelphia, PA 19106-3315
Tel: (215) 861-5204 Fax: (215) 861-5260
Internet: www.doleta.gov/regions/reg02
Areas Covered: DE, DC, MD, PA, VA, WV

● Regional Administrator **Leo Miller** .... (215) 861-5202
Executive Secretary **(Vacant)** .... (215) 861-5202

★ Presidential Appointment Requiring Senate Confirmation ☆ Presidential Appointment ☐ Schedule C Appointment ◇ Career Senior Foreign Service Appointment
● Career Senior Executive Service (SES) Appointment ○ Non-Career Senior Executive Service (SES) Appointment ■ Postal Career Executive Service

Region 2 - Philadelphia (PA) *(continued)*

Executive Assistant **Jeff Gabriel** .... (215) 861-5229
Director, Office of Special Initiatives and Demonstrations **Eric Nelson** .... (215) 861-5221
E-mail: nelson.eric@dol.gov
Director, Office of State Systems **Jennifer Raymond** .... (215) 861-5204
Regional Director, Office of Apprenticeship
Tom Bydlon .... (215) 861-4830
Fax: (215) 861-4833
Division of Financial Management and Administrative Services Chief **Jennifer Friedman** .... (215) 861-5298
E-mail: friedman.jennifer@dol.gov

Region 3 - Atlanta (GA)
61 Forsyth Street, SW, Room 6M12, Atlanta, GA 30303
Tel: (404) 302-5300 Fax: (404) 302-5382
Areas Covered: AL, FL, GA, KY, MS, NC, SC, TN

● Regional Administrator **Les Range** .... (404) 302-5332
E-mail: range.les@dol.gov
Executive Assistant **Sherrill Michell Robinson** .... (404) 302-5300
Regional Director, Apprenticeship Training, Employer and Labor Services Office **Garfield G. Garner** .... (404) 302-5478
E-mail: garner.garfield@dol.gov
Regional Director, Office of Job Corps **(Vacant)** .... (404) 302-5400
Director, Division of Financial Management and Administrative Services **Lane Boseman** .... (404) 302-5309
E-mail: Boseman.Lane@dol.gov
Director, Office of Special Initiatives and Demonstrations **David L. Bridges** .... (404) 302-5341
E-mail: Bridges.David.L@dol.gov
Director, Office of State Systems **Winston Tompoe** ..... (404) 302-5355
E-mail: tompoe.winston@dol.gov
Webmaster **Carlos Camacho Colon** .... (404) 302-5308
E-mail: camachocolon.carlos@dol.gov

Foreign Labor Certification National Processing Center - Atlanta
Harris Tower, 233 Peachtree Street NE,
Suite 410, Atlanta, GA 30303
Tel: (404) 893-0101 (Customer Service) Fax: (404) 893-4644
Internet: www.foreignlaborcert.doleta.gov

Director of Operations **Isabel Myers** .... (404) 893-6066
E-mail: myers.isabel@dol.gov
Director of Administration **(Vacant)** .... (404) 893-5358
Certifying Officer **Brandt Carter** .... (404) 893-0101
E-mail: carter.brandt@dol.gov
Certifying Officer **Didra Goodlow** .... (404) 893-0101
E-mail: goodlow.didra@dol.gov
Certifying Officer **Gema Hall** .... (404) 893-0128
E-mail: hall.gema@dol.gov
Certifying Officer **Melanie Shay** .... (404) 893-0101
E-mail: shay.melanie@dol.gov
Certifying Officer **(Vacant)** .... (404) 893-0101
Supervisory Program Analyst **(Vacant)** .... (404) 893-0101

Region 4 - Dallas (TX)
Federal Building, 525 Griffin Street, Suite 317, Dallas, TX 75202
Tel: (972) 850-4600 Fax: (972) 850-4605
Internet: www.doleta.gov/regions/reg04
Areas Covered: AR, CO, LA, MT, ND, NM, OK, SD, TX, UT, WY

● Regional Administrator **Nicholas "Nick" Lalpuis** .... (972) 850-4612
E-mail: lalpuis.nicholas@dol.gov
Executive Assistant **Rebecca Sarmiento** .... (972) 850-4642
Director, Office of Special Initiatives and Demonstrations **Greg Goodwin** .... (972) 850-4611
E-mail: goodwin.greg@dol.gov
Director, Office of State Systems **Frank Stluka** .... (972) 850-4622
E-mail: stluka.frank@dol.gov
Director, Division of Financial Management and Administrative Services **Kristy Woodard** .... (972) 850-4661
E-mail: woodard.kristy@dol.gov

Region 5 - Chicago (IL)
Kluczynski Federal Building, 230 South Dearborn Street,
Chicago, IL 60604-1505
Tel: (312) 596-5400 Fax: (312) 596-5401 E-mail: ro5-ra-chi@dol.gov
Internet: www.doleta.gov/regions/reg05
Areas Covered: IL, IN, IA, KS, MI, MN, MO, NE, OH, WI

● Regional Administrator **Christine Quinn** Room 638 ..... (312) 596-5403
E-mail: quinn.christine@dol.gov
● Deputy Regional Administrator
Rosaura "Rose" Zibert .... (312) 596-5525
E-mail: zibert.rosaura@dol.gpv
Director, Office of State Systems **(Vacant)** Room 623 .... (312) 596-5532
Director, Apprenticeship Training, Employer and Labor Services Office **Dean Guido** Room 656 .... (312) 596-5502
E-mail: guido.dean@dol.gov
Director, Division of Financial Management and Administrative Services **Tom DiLisio** Room 628 .... (312) 596-5454
E-mail: dilisio.thomas@dol.gov
Director, Office of Job Corps
Milagros Steele Room 676 .... (312) 596-5474
Director, Office of Special Initiatives and Demonstrations **(Vacant)** .... (312) 596-5525

Foreign Labor Certification National Processing Center - Chicago
536 South Clark Street, 9th Floor, Chicago, IL 60605-1509
Tel: (312) 886-8000 Fax: (312) 886-1688

Director **Shane Barbour** .... (312) 886-8000
E-mail: barbour.shane@dol.gov

Region 6 - San Francisco (CA)
90 Seventh Street, Suite 17-300, San Francisco, CA 94103
Mail: P.O. Box 193767, San Francisco, CA 94119-3767
Tel: (415) 625-7901 Fax: (415) 625-7903 E-mail: ro-ra-sf@dol.gov
Areas Covered: AK, AS, AZ, CA, GU, HI, ID, NV, OR, WA, Outer Pacific

● Regional Administrator (Acting) **John Bailey** .... (415) 625-7900
Regional Director, Office of Apprenticeship
Patti Garcia .... (415) 625-2230
Fax: (415) 625-2235
Regional Director, Office of Special Initiatives and Demonstrations **Haven Bays** .... (415) 625-7951
E-mail: bays.haven@dol.gov
Regional Director, Office of State Systems **(Vacant)** ..... (415) 625-7921
Program Manager, Division of Financial, Management and Administrative Services **Steve Malliaras** .... (415) 625-7951
E-mail: malliaras.steve@dol.gov

★ Presidential Appointment Requiring Senate Confirmation ☆ Presidential Appointment ☐ Schedule C Appointment ◇ Career Senior Foreign Service Appointment
● Career Senior Executive Service (SES) Appointment ○ Non-Career Senior Executive Service (SES) Appointment ■ Postal Career Executive Service

DEPARTMENTS

Mine Safety and Health Administration (MSHA)

201 12th Street South, Suite 4C317, Arlington, VA 22002-5414
Tel: (202) 693-9414
Tel: (800) 746-1553 (MSHA 24 hour Hotline to report accidents)
Tel: (800) 746-1554 (MSHA 24 hour Hotline to anonymously report safety and health concerns) Fax: (202) 693-9401 Internet: www.msha.gov

OFFICE OF THE ASSISTANT SECRETARY

1100 Wilson Boulevard, Arlington, VA 22209-3939
Tel: (202) 693-9414 Fax: (202) 693-9401

Directorate of Educational Policy and Development (DEPD)

201 12th Street South, Arlington, VA 22002-5414
Fax: (202) 693-9571

Educational Field and Small Mine Services (EFSMS)

Eastern Field Office
1301 Airport Road, Beaver, WV 25813
Fax: (304) 256-3319

Assistant Regional Manager **Glen Poe** .... (304) 256-3223
E-mail: poe.glen@dol.gov

Western Field Office
P.O. Box 25367, DFC, Denver, CO 80225-0367
Fax: (303) 231-5550

Assistant Regional Manager **Eric C. Johnson** ..... (303) 231-5434 ext. 3
E-mail: johnson.eric.c@dol.gov

National Mine Health and Safety Academy

1301 Airport Road, Beaver, WV 25813
Tel: (304) 256-3100 Fax: (304) 256-3324
Internet: www.msha.gov/programs/epd2.htm

Superintendent **Michael Faughnan** .... (304) 256-3200
Instructional Materials Department Chairman
Tiffany Blair .... (304) 256-3283
Instructional Services Department Chairman **(Vacant)** .... (304) 256-3211
Mining Technology Department Chairman
Terry Phillips .... (304) 256-3213
E-mail: phillips.terry@dol.gov
Technical Information Center and Library Director
(Vacant) .... (304) 256-3531
Administrative Officer **Stephanie Sullivan** .... (304) 256-3231

Directorate of Program Evaluation and Information Resources (DPEIR)

1100 Wilson Boulevard, Arlington, VA 22209-3939
Tel: (202) 693-9750 Fax: (202) 693-9751

Information Technology Center

Denver Federal Center, 6th and Kipling,
2nd Street, Building 25, Denver, CO 80225
Mail: P.O. Box 25367, Denver, CO 80225-0367
Tel: (303) 231-5475 Fax: (303) 231-5542

Chief **Julie "Joy" DeNiro** .... (303) 231-5475
E-mail: deniro.julie@dol.gov
Administrative Officer **Sandra Turner** .... (303) 231-5412
Applications Management Division Chief
Mary Nettles .... (303) 231-5475
E-mail: nettles.mary@dol.gov
Network Operations Division Chief **(Vacant)** .... (303) 231-5932
Support Services Division Chief **Mark Siler** .... (303) 231-5475

Injury and Employment Information Office

1999 Broadway, Denver, CO 80202-5712
Fax: (303) 231-5515

Chief **Sherie Wycoff** .... (303) 231-5515
E-mail: wycoff.sherie@dol.gov

Directorate of Technical Support (DTS)

1100 Wilson Boulevard, Arlington, VA 22209-3939
Tel: (202) 693-9470 Fax: (202) 693-9471

Approval and Certification Center

765 Technology Drive, Triadelphia, WV 26059
Tel: (304) 547-0400 Fax: (304) 547-2044

Chief **Dennis Ferlich** .... (304) 547-2044
E-mail: ferlich.dennis@dol.gov
Applied Engineering Division Chief
Wesley Shumaker .... (304) 547-2034
E-mail: shumaker.wesley@dol.gov
Center Operations Division Chief
David "Dave" Diegmiller .... (304) 547-2041
E-mail: diegmiller.david@dol.gov
Electrical Safety Division Chief **Kevin Dolinar** .... (304) 547-2030
E-mail: dolinar.kevin@dol.gov
Mechanical and Engineering Safety Division Chief
Richard Skrabak .... (304) 547-2058
E-mail: skrabak.richard@dol.gov
Quality Assurance and Material Testing Division Chief
John P. Faini .... (304) 547-2038
E-mail: faini.john@dol.gov

Safety and Health Technology Center

Cochrans Mill Road, Building 151, Pittsburgh, PA 15236

Chief **George Gardner** .... (412) 386-6276
E-mail: gardner.george@dol.gov

Office of Coal Mine Safety and Health (CMSH)

201 12th Street South, Suite 4C317, Arlington, VA 22002-5414
Fax: (202) 693-9517 Internet: www.msha.gov

District 2

319 Paintersville Road, Hunker, PA 15639
Tel: (724) 925-5150 Fax: (724) 925-6190
Areas Covered: Bituminous coal mining regions in PA (Central and Western PA)

District Manager **Russell J. Riley** .... (724) 925-5150 ext. 112
E-mail: riley.russell@dol.gov
Secretary **Deb Moberg** .... (724) 925-5150 ext. 110
Inspection Division Assistant District Manager
Michael Kelley .... (724) 925-5150
E-mail: kelley.michael@dol.gov
Technical Division Assistant District Manager
Steven E. Womack .... (724) 925-5150
E-mail: womack.steven@dol.gov
Programs Specialist **Gretchen Horrell** .... (724) 925-5150 ext. 157
E-mail: horrell.gretchen@dol.gov

Clearfield (PA) Field Office
230 Hammermill Road, Clearfield, PA 16830
Tel: (814) 765-9627 Fax: (814) 765-9635

Supervisor **Robert E. Roland** .... (814) 765-9627 ext. 11
E-mail: roland.robert@dol.gov

Frackville (PA) Field Office
426 Schuylkill Mall, Frackville, PA 17931
Tel: (570) 874-8980 Fax: (570) 648-4579

Supervisor **Patrick Boylan** .... (570) 874-8980
E-mail: boylan.patrick@dol.gov
Supervisor **Thomas J. "Tom" Yencho** .... (570) 874-8980
E-mail: yencho.thomas@dol.gov
Supervisor **(Vacant)** .... (570) 874-8980

Indiana (PA) Field Office
1265 Wayne Avenue, Box 310-A, Indiana, PA 15701
Tel: (724) 465-5591 Fax: (724) 465-4903

Supervisor **Daniel "Dan" Mansell** .... (724) 465-5591 ext. 11
E-mail: Mansell.Daniel@dol.gov

★ Presidential Appointment Requiring Senate Confirmation ☆ Presidential Appointment ☐ Schedule C Appointment ◇ Career Senior Foreign Service Appointment
● Career Senior Executive Service (SES) Appointment ○ Non-Career Senior Executive Service (SES) Appointment ■ Postal Career Executive Service

Johnstown (PA) Field Office
Richland Square III, 1397 Eisenhower Boulevard,
Suite 100, Johnstown, PA 15904
Tel: (814) 266-0008 Fax: (814) 266-0015

Supervisor **Dennis Zeanchock** .... (814) 266-0008 ext. 24
E-mail: zeanchock.dennis@dol.gov

Kittanning (PA) Field Office
245 Butler Road, Suite 7, Kittanning, PA 16201
Tel: (724) 548-5611 Fax: (724) 543-6535

Supervisor **Richard A. Gray** .... (724) 548-5611
E-mail: gray.richard.a@dol.gov

Ruff Creek (PA) Field Office
259 Dunn Station Road, Prosperity, PA 15329
Tel: (724) 627-5558 Fax: (724) 627-4119

Work Group 1 Supervisor **Thomas J. Bochna** ... (724) 627-5558 ext. 235
E-mail: bochna.thomas@dol.gov
Work Group 2 Supervisor **David J. Severini** .... (724) 627-5558 ext. 230
E-mail: severini.david@dol.gov

District 3
604 Cheat Road, Morgantown, WV 26508
Tel: (304) 225-6800 Fax: (304) 225-2256
Areas Covered: MD, OH, Northern WV

• District Manager **Carlos T. Mosley** .... (304) 225-6801
E-mail: mosley.carlos@dol.gov
Inspection Programs Assistant District Manager
Gregory W. Fetty .... (304) 225-6809
Technical Programs Assistant District Manager
John Hayes .... (304) 225-6811
Purchasing, Travel, Property Officer, GSA Fleet
Coordinator **(Vacant)** .... (304) 225-6807
Staff Assistant **Michael Stark** .... (304) 225-6851
E-mail: stark.michael@dol.gov
Supervisory Management Analyst
Kimberly A. Cordwell .... (304) 225-6805
Workers' Compensation Program Coordinator
Donna M. Weston .... (304) 225-6806
E-mail: weston.donna@dol.gov
Program Analyst **Mary Harbaugh** .... (304) 225-6804
E-mail: harbaugh.mary@dol.gov Fax: (304) 225-2257
Webmaster/Information Technology Specialist
David DesLauriers .... (304) 225-6851
E-mail: deslauriers.david@dol.gov

Bridgeport (WV) Field Office
105 Platinum Drive, Suite B, Bridgeport, WV 26330
Tel: (304) 842-0610 Fax: (304) 842-0613

Supervisor **Steve Stankus** .... (304) 842-0610
E-mail: stankus.steven@dol.gov
Supervisor **Chad Currence** .... (304) 842-0610
E-mail: currence.chad@dol.gov

McHenry (MD) Field Office
1550 Deep Creek Drive, McHenry, MD 21541
Tel: (301) 387-8295 Fax: (301) 387-4575

Supervisor **Allen Rohrbaugh** .... (301) 387-8295
E-mail: rohrbaugh.allen@dol.gov

Morgantown (WV) Field Office
604 Cheat Road, Morgantown, WV 26508
Tel: (304) 225-6800 Fax: (304) 225-2256

Supervisor **Richard "Rick" Show** .... (304) 225-6841
E-mail: show.richard@dol.gov

Saint Clairsville (OH) Field Office
50985 National Road, Saint Clairsville, OH 43950
Tel: (740) 695-2297 Fax: (740) 695-2315

Supervisor, Work Group 1 **Thomas E. McCort** .... (740) 695-2297
E-mail: mccort.thomas.e@dol.gov
Supervisor, Work Group 2 **Larry Johnson** .... (740) 695-2297

District 4
100 Bluestone Road, Mount Hope, WV 25880
Tel: (304) 877-3900 Fax: (304) 877-9206
Areas Covered: Southern West Virginia (counties of Boone, Braxton, Clay, Fayette, Greenbrier, Kanawha, Monroe, Nicholas, Pocahontas, Putnam, Raleigh, Summers, and Webster)

District Manager **David "Scott" Mandeville** .... (304) 877-3900 ext. 112
E-mail: mandeville.david@dol.gov
Assistant District Manager **David S. Morris** ..... (304) 877-3900 ext. 113
E-mail: morris.david@dol.gov
Assistant District Manager
Lincoln L. Selfe, Jr. .... (304) 877-3900 ext. 106
E-mail: selfe.lincoln@dol.gov
Staff Assistant **Joseph Presley** .... (304) 877-3900 ext. 115
E-mail: presley.joseph@dol.gov
IT Specialist **Edith "Cathy" Hedrick** .... (304) 877-3900 ext. 179
E-mail: hedrick.edith@dol.gov

Madison (WV) Field Office
1664 Pond Fork Road, Madison, WV 25130
Tel: (304) 369-1502 Fax: (304) 369-5013

Supervisor **(Vacant)** .... (304) 369-1502
Supervisor **Terry Price** .... (304) 369-1502
E-mail: price.terry@dol.gov

Mount Carbon (WV) Field Office
P.O. Box 38, Mount Carbon, WV 25139
Tel: (304) 442-5145 Fax: (304) 442-2896

Supervisor **(Vacant)** .... (304) 442-5145
Supervisor **Martin Carver** .... (304) 442-5145
E-mail: carver.martin@dol.gov

Mount Hope (WV) Field Office
100 Bluestone Road, Mount Hope, WV 25880
Tel: (304) 877-3900 ext. 150 Fax: (304) 877-2965

Supervisor **Sabian VanDyke** .... (304) 877-3900 ext. 119
E-mail: vandyke.sabian@dol.gov
Supervisor **Fred D. Wills** .... (304) 877-3900 ext. 150
E-mail: wills.fred@dol.gov

Summersville (WV) Field Office
Joo Building, 818-D Arbuckle Road, Summersville, WV 26651
Tel: (304) 872-4001 Fax: (304) 872-0021

Supervisor **Gary Harris** .... (304) 872-4001
E-mail: harris.gary.w@dol.gov
Supervisor **(Vacant)** .... (304) 872-4001

District 5
Wise County Plaza, 2nd Floor, Norton, VA 24273
Mail: P.O. Box 560, Norton, VA 24273
Tel: (276) 679-0230 Fax: (276) 679-1663
Areas Covered: VA

District Manager (Acting) **Lincoln L. Selfe, Jr.** .... (276) 679-0230
E-mail: selfe.lincoln@dol.gov
Inspection Division Assistant District Manager
James A. Kiser .... (276) 679-0230
E-mail: kiser.james@dol.gov
Management and Program Supervisor
Terry R. Sheffield .... (276) 679-0230
E-mail: sheffield.terry@dol.gov
Purchasing Agent **Stephanie Meade** .... (276) 679-0230
E-mail: meade.stephanie@dol.gov

Norton (VA) Field Office
Wise County Plaza, 2nd Floor, Norton, VA 24273
Mail: P.O. Box 560, Norton, VA 24273
Tel: (276) 679-0264 Fax: (276) 679-1663

Work Group 1 Supervisor **Jeffrey C. Webb** .... (276) 679-0264
E-mail: webb.jeffrey@dol.gov
Work Group 2 Supervisor **Scott M. Beverly** .... (276) 679-0264
E-mail: beverly.scott@dol.gov
Work Group 3 Supervisor **Michael B. Colley** .... (276) 679-0264
E-mail: colley.michael@dol.gov

DEPARTMENTS

★ Presidential Appointment Requiring Senate Confirmation ☆ Presidential Appointment □ Schedule C Appointment ◇ Career Senior Foreign Service Appointment
● Career Senior Executive Service (SES) Appointment ○ Non-Career Senior Executive Service (SES) Appointment ■ Postal Career Executive Service

DEPARTMENTS

Pikeville (KY) Field Office
100 Fae Ramsey Lane, Pikeville, KY 41501-2158
Tel: (606) 432-0944 Fax: (606) 432-6964

Supervisor **Silas Adkins** .... (606) 432-0944
E-mail: adkins.silas@dol.gov
Supervisor **Danny Deel** .... (606) 432-0944
E-mail: deel.danny@dol.gov

Vansant (VA) Field Office
P.O. Box M, Oakwood, VA 24631-1011
Fax: (276) 498-1647

Work Group 1 Supervisor **Paul E. Smith** .... (276) 498-1758
E-mail: smith.paul.e@dol.gov
Work Group 2 Supervisor **Carl Kline** .... (276) 498-1758

Whitesburg (KY) Field Office
704 Highway 2034, Whitesburg, KY 41858-1277
Tel: (606) 633-4882 Fax: (606) 633-9277

Supervisor **Greg Ison** .... (606) 633-4882
E-mail: ison.gregory@dol.gov
Supervisor **David Ison** .... (606) 633-4882
E-mail: ison.david@dol.gov

District 7
3837 South U.S. Highway 25E, Barbourville, KY 40906
Tel: (606) 546-5123 Fax: (606) 546-5245
Areas Covered: Northern GA, Central and Southeastern KY, NC, SC, TN, Puerto Rico and the U.S. Virgin Islands.

Work Group 1 Supervisor **Edward Boylen** .... (205) 424-0247
E-mail: boylen.edward@dol.gov
Work Group 2 Supervisor **Jacky H. Shubert** .... (205) 424-0247
E-mail: shubert.jacky@dol.gov
District Manager **Jim W. Langley** .... (606) 546-5123
E-mail: langley.jim@dol.gov
Assistant District Manager **Dennis J. Cotton** .... (606) 546-5123
E-mail: cotton.dennis@dol.gov
Assistant District Manager **Samuel R. Creasy** .... (606) 546-5123
E-mail: creasy.samuel@dol.gov
Staff Assistant **Steven L. Sorke** .... (606) 546-5123
Management Analyst **Loretta Roark** .... (606) 546-5123
Purchasing Agent **Charles A. Thaler** .... (606) 546-5123
E-mail: thaler.charles@dol.gov
Information Technology Specialist **Jason Middleton** .... (606) 546-5123
E-mail: middleton.jason@dol.gov

Barbourville (KY) Field Office
3837 South U.S. Highway 25E, Barbourville, KY 40906
Tel: (606) 546-5123 Fax: (606) 546-6394

Supervisor **William C. Clark** .... (606) 546-5123
E-mail: clark.william@dol.gov
Supervisor **Kevin D. Bruner, Sr.** .... (606) 546-5123
E-mail: bruner.kevin@dol.gov

Harlan (KY) Field Office
133 Readymix Road, Harlan, KY 40831
Tel: (606) 573-3400 Fax: (606) 573-1774

Supervisor **Leland E. Stewart** .... (606) 573-3400
Supervisor **William Brad Sears** .... (606) 573-3400
E-mail: sears.william@dol.gov

Hazard (KY) Field Office
145 Reynolds Lane, Hazard, KY 41701
Tel: (606) 439-2396 Fax: (606) 439-1851

Supervisor **Marvin Hoskins** .... (606) 439-2396
E-mail: hoskins.marvin@dol.gov

Jacksboro (TN) Field Office
136 Mountain Perkins Lane, Suite 1, Jacksboro, TN 37757
Tel: (423) 562-8484 Fax: (423) 562-1067

Supervisor **Kevin D. Bruner, Sr.** .... (423) 562-8484
E-mail: bruner.kevin@dol.gov

Martin (KY) Field Office
1102 Left Beaver, Martin, KY 41649
Tel: (606) 285-3281 Fax: (606) 285-0255

Supervisor **Billy Buchanan** .... (606) 285-3281
E-mail: Buchanan.Billy@dol.gov
Supervisor **Craig Plumley** .... (606) 285-3281
E-mail: plumley.craig@dol.gov

District 8
2300 Willow Street, Suite 200, Vincennes, IN 47591
Tel: (812) 882-7617 Fax: (812) 882-7622
Areas Covered: IL, IN, IA, MI, MN, bituminous coal mining regions in MO (Northern MO), WI

District Manager **Ronald W. Burns** .... (812) 882-7617
E-mail: burns.ronald@dol.gov
Assistant District Manager **Mary Jo Bishop** .... (812) 882-7617
E-mail: bishop.maryjo@dol.gov
Assistant District Manager **(Vacant)** .... (812) 882-7617

Litchfield (IL) Field Office
11006 US Route 66, Litchfield, IL 62056
Tel: (217) 324-4545 Fax: (217) 324-4555

Supervisor **Bradley Smith** .... (217) 324-4545
E-mail: smith.bradley.e@dol.gov
Mine Inspector **Michael Riggs** .... (217) 324-4545
E-mail: riggs.michael@dol.gov

Marion (IL) Field Office
8223 Express Drive, Marion, IL 62959
Tel: (618) 997-0584 Fax: (618) 997-0592

Group 1 Supervisor **Robert Bretzman** .... (618) 997-0584
E-mail: bretzman.robert@dol.gov
Group 2 Supervisor **(Vacant)** .... (618) 997-0584

Vincennes (IN) Field Office
2300 Willow Street, Suite 200, Vincennes, IN 47591
Tel: (812) 895-0512 Fax: (812) 895-0536

Group 1 Supervisor **George Heacock** .... (812) 895-0512
E-mail: heacock.george@dol.gov
Group 2 Supervisor **Anthony DiLorenzo** .... (812) 895-0512
E-mail: dilorenzo.anthony@dol.gov

District 9
P.O. Box 25367, DFC, Denver, CO 80225-0367
Tel: (303) 231-5458 Fax: (303) 231-5553
Areas Covered: AK, AZ, CO, KS, LA, MT, NM, ND, OK, UT, TX, WA, WY

District Manager **Richard A. Gates** .... (303) 231-5458
E-mail: gates.richard@dol.gov
Supervisor **Kendell Whitman** .... (918) 423-5966
E-mail: whitman.kendell@dol.gov
Assistant District Manager, Inspection Programs
(Vacant) .... (303) 231-5558
Assistant District Manager, Technical Programs
James Preece .... (303) 231-5563
E-mail: preece.james@dol.gov
Staff Assistant **Ronnie Free** .... (303) 231-5560
E-mail: free.ronnie@dol.gov
IT Specialist **Dario Ronzone** .... (303) 231-5577
E-mail: ronzone.dario@dol.gov

Farmington (NM) Field Office
800 East 30th Street, Building 5, Suite B, Farmington, NM 87401
Tel: (505) 327-1220 Fax: (505) 327-3082

Supervisor **Jeff "Bill" Scott** .... (505) 327-1220
E-mail: scott.jeff@dol.gov

Craig (CO) Field Office
415 Green Street, Craig, CO 81625
P.O. Box 1305, Craig, CO 81625
Tel: (970) 824-4943 Fax: (970) 824-8220

Supervisor **Richard L. Eddy** .... (970) 824-4943
E-mail: eddy.richard@dol.gov

★ Presidential Appointment Requiring Senate Confirmation ☆ Presidential Appointment ☐ Schedule C Appointment ◇ Career Senior Foreign Service Appointment
● Career Senior Executive Service (SES) Appointment ○ Non-Career Senior Executive Service (SES) Appointment ■ Postal Career Executive Service

Delta (CO) Field Office
675 Industrial Boulevard, Delta, CO 81416-1811
Tel: (970) 874-7637 Fax: (970) 874-4592

Supervisor **Gary Polson** .... (970) 874-7637
E-mail: polson.gary@dol.gov

Gillette (WY) Field Office
620 North Highway 14-16, Unit S, Gillette, WY 82716
Tel: (307) 682-1142 Fax: (307) 686-6345

Supervisor **Wayne Johnson** .... (307) 682-1142
E-mail: johnson.wayne@dol.gov

Price (UT) Field Office
45 East 1375 South, Price, UT 84501-3035
Tel: (435) 637-3051 Fax: (435) 637-4528

Supervisor **Cord Cristando** .... (435) 637-3051 ext. 134
E-mail: cristando.cord@dol.gov
Supervisor **Donnie Durrant** .... (435) 637-3051 ext. 133
E-mail: durrant.donald@dol.gov

McAlester (OK) Field Office
509 South Third Street, McAlester, OK 74502-5819
Tel: (918) 423-5966 Fax: (918) 426-5989

District 10
100 YMCA Drive, Madisonville, KY 42431-9019
Tel: (270) 821-4180 Fax: (270) 825-0949
Areas Covered: Western KY

District Manager **Robert A. "Tony" Simms** .... (270) 821-4180
E-mail: simms.robert@dol.gov
Inspection Supervisor **David West** .... (270) 821-4180 ext. 1229

Beaver Dam (KY) Field Office
1101 Town Square Drive, Beaver Dam, KY 42320
Tel: (270) 274-9628 Fax: (270) 274-9629

Work Group 1 Supervisor **William Cook III** .... (270) 274-9628
E-mail: cook.william@dol.gov

Madisonville (KY) Field Office
100 YMCA Drive, Madisonville, KY 42431-9019
Tel: (270) 821-4180 Fax: (270) 825-0949

Work Group 1 Supervisor
Abel "Abe" DeLeon .... (270) 821-4180 ext. 1227
Work Group 2 Supervisor **Alan Frederick** .... (270) 821-4180 ext. 1243
E-mail: frederick.alan@dol.gov
Work Group 1 Member **Trent Clark** .... (270) 821-4180 ext. 1259
Work Group 1 Member **James A. Jordan** .... (270) 821-4180 ext. 1263
Work Group 1 Member **Brian Perdue** .... (270) 821-4180
Work Group 1 Member **Chrystal Vanover** .... (270) 821-4180 ext. 1249
Work Group 1 Member **Mike Billingham** .... (270) 821-4180 ext. 1271
Work Group 1 Member **(Vacant)** .... (270) 821-4180
Work Group 1 Member **(Vacant)** .... (270) 821-4180 ext. 1259
Work Group 2 Member **Ray Cartwright** .... (270) 821-4180
E-mail: cartwright.ray@dol.gov
Work Group 2 Member **Jeffrey Eli** .... (270) 821-4180
Work Group 2 Member **Joshua Orr** .... (270) 821-4180 ext. 1278
Work Group 2 Member **Mark Stamper** .... (270) 821-4180 ext. 1275
Work Group 2 Member **(Vacant)** .... (270) 821-4180
Work Group 2 Member **Jeremy Walker** .... (270) 821-4180 ext. 1260

Morganfield (KY) Field Office
112 East Main Street, Morganfield, KY 42437
Tel: (270) 389-3134 Fax: (270) 389-9814

Work Group 1 Supervisor **Curtis Hardison** .... (270) 389-3134 ext. 102
E-mail: hardison.curtis@dol.gov

District 12
1301 Airport Road, Beaver, WV 25813
Tel: (304) 253-5237
Areas Covered: Southern West Virginia (counties of Cabell, Lincoln, Logan, McDowell, Mercer, Mingo, Wayne, and Wyoming)

District Manager **Brian Dotson** .... (304) 732-6410
E-mail: dotson.brian@dol.gov
Assistant District Manager, Inspections **Charles Bigley** .... (304) 253-5237
E-mail: bigley.charles@dol.gov
Assistant District Manager, Technical Support
Larry E. Bailey .... (304) 256-3536
E-mail: bailey.larry.e@dol.gov

Logan (WV) Field Office
100 Chalet Village Drive, Logan, WV 25601
Tel: (304) 752-5315 Fax: (304) 752-2335

Supervisor **Kenneth Butcher** .... (304) 752-5315
E-mail: butcher.kenneth@dol.gov
Supervisor **Lawrence Mendez** .... (304) 752-5315
E-mail: mendez.lawrence@dol.gov
Supervisor **Herman Miller** .... (304) 752-5315
E-mail: miller.herman@dol.gov

Pineville (WV) Field Office
P.O. Box 650, Pineville, WV 24874
Tel: (304) 732-8010 Fax: (304) 732-6135

Supervisor **Nicholas Christian** .... (304) 732-6410
E-mail: christian.nicholas@dol.gov
Supervisor **Rodney Lusk** .... (304) 732-6410
E-mail: lusk.rodney@dol.gov

Princeton (WV) Field Office
110 Gott Road, Princeton, WV 24740
Tel: (304) 425-8161 Fax: (304) 425-7552

Supervisor **Gerald Cook, Sr.** .... (304) 425-8161
E-mail: cook.gerald@dol.gov

Office of Metal and Nonmetal Mine Safety and Health
201 12th Street South, Arlington, VA 22002-5414
Tel: (202) 693-9600 Fax: (202) 693-9601

North Central District
Federal Building and U.S. Courthouse, 515 West First Street, Suite 333, Duluth, MN 55802-1302
Tel: (218) 720-5448 Fax: (218) 720-5650
Areas Covered: IL, IN, IA, MI, MN, OH, WI

District Manager **Christopher "Chris" Hensler** .... (218) 720-5448
E-mail: hensler.christopher@dol.gov
Assistant District Manager **Gerald D. Holeman** .... (218) 720-5448
E-mail: holeman.gerald@dol.gov
Assistant District Manager **Scott Johnson** .... (218) 720-5448
E-mail: johnson.scott@dol.gov
Supervisory Management/Program Analyst **Carol Frink** .... (218) 720-5448
E-mail: frink.carol@dol.gov
Supervisory Special Investigator
Wilbert Koskiniemi, Jr. .... (218) 720-5448
E-mail: koskiniemi.wilbert@dol.gov
Staff Assistant **(Vacant)** .... (218) 720-5448
Conference Litigation Representative **Daniel Goyen** .... (218) 720-5448
E-mail: goyen.daniel@dol.gov
Conference Litigation Representative **George F. Schorr** .... (218) 720-5448
E-mail: schorr.george@dol.gov
Health Specialist **Stephen D. Cotie** .... (218) 720-5448
E-mail: cotie.stephen@dol.gov
Safety Specialist **Kenneth L. Bickel** .... (218) 720-5448
E-mail: bickel.kenneth@dol.gov
Safety Specialist **(Vacant)** .... (218) 720-5448

DEPARTMENTS

★ Presidential Appointment Requiring Senate Confirmation ☆ Presidential Appointment □ Schedule C Appointment ◇ Career Senior Foreign Service Appointment
● Career Senior Executive Service (SES) Appointment ○ Non-Career Senior Executive Service (SES) Appointment ■ Postal Career Executive Service

Duluth (MN) Field Duty Station
Federal Bldg. and U.S. Courthouse, 515 West First Street,
Suite 333, Duluth, MN 55802-1302
Tel: (218) 720-5448 Fax: (218) 720-5650

Supervisor **William Soderlind** (218) 262-5205
E-mail: soderlind.william@dol.gov

Fort Dodge (IA) Field Office
1615 Central Avenue, Fort Dodge, IA 50501
Tel: (515) 955-5383 Fax: (515) 955-2646

Supervisor **Anthony Runyon** (515) 955-5383
E-mail: runyon.anthony@dol.gov

Hibbing (MN) Field Office
522 East Howard Street, Room 201A, Hibbing, MN 55746
Tel: (218) 262-5205 Fax: (218) 262-1296

Supervisor **Richard V. Boeckermann** (218) 262-5205
E-mail: boeckermann.richard@dol.gov

Lansing (MI) Field Office
315 West Allegan Street, Room 230, Lansing, MI 48933
Tel: (517) 377-1751 Fax: (517) 377-1598

Supervisor **George Colby** (517) 377-1751
E-mail: colby.george@dol.gov

Marquette (MI) Field Office
Orlich Office Complex, 1901 West Ridge Street,
Suite 8, Marquette, MI 49855
Tel: (906) 228-6805 Fax: (906) 228-3871

Supervisor **James Hautamaki** (906) 228-6805
E-mail: Hautamaki.James@dol.gov

Mooresville (IN) Field Office
100 Town Center Road South, Suite F, Mooresville, IN 46158
Tel: (317) 831-2602 Fax: (317) 831-2631

Supervisor **Donnie Lewis** (317) 821-0358
E-mail: lewis.donnie@dol.gov

Peru (IL) Field Office
2200 Marquette Road, Suite 110, Peru, IL 61354
Tel: (815) 223-0697 Fax: (815) 223-6501

Supervisor **James P. Kirk** (815) 223-0697
E-mail: kirk.james.p@dol.gov

Northeastern District
Thornhill Industrial Park, 178 Thornhill Road,
Suite 100, Warrendale, PA 15086
Tel: (724) 772-2334 Fax: (724) 772-0260
Areas Covered: CT, DE, DC, ME, MD, MA, NH, NJ, NY, OH, PA, RI, VA, VT, WV

District Manager **Peter J. Montali** (724) 772-2334
E-mail: montali.peter@dol.gov
Secretary **Linda Columbus** (724) 772-2334
E-mail: columbus.linda@dol.gov
Assistant District Manager **Kevin Abel** (724) 772-2334

Albany (NY) Field Office
24 Computer Drive West, Suite 101, Albany, NY 12205
Tel: (518) 489-0573 Fax: (518) 489-3661

Supervisor **James Logan** (518) 489-0573
E-mail: logan.james@dol.gov

Geneva (NY) Field Office
636 West Washington Street, Geneva, NY 14456
Tel: (315) 789-0522 Fax: (315) 781-3214

Supervisor **Edward Knoll** (315) 789-0522
E-mail: knoll.edward@dol.gov

Hebron (OH) Field Office
96 Integrity Drive, Suite F, Hebron, OH 43025
Fax: (740) 928-0931

Supervisor **Carl Graham** (740) 928-0479
E-mail: graham.carl@dol.gov

Manchester (NH) Field Office
222 International Drive, Suite 10, Portsmouth, NH 03801
Tel: (603) 666-7691 Fax: (603) 666-7609

Supervisor **Robert A. Dow, Jr.** (603) 666-7691
E-mail: dow.robert@dol.gov

Staunton (VA) Field Office
148 Parkersburg Turnpike, Staunton, VA 24401
Tel: (540) 887-9682 Fax: (540) 887-9685

Supervisor **Joseph Bosley** (540) 887-9682

Warrendale (PA) Field Office
Thornhill Industrial Park, 178 Thornhill Road,
Suite 100, Warrendale, PA 15086
Tel: (724) 772-2336 Fax: (724) 772-0260

Supervisor **Rodney "Ronnie" Rice** (724) 772-2336
E-mail: rice.rodney@dol.gov

Wyomissing (PA) Field Office
Executive Plaza, 2001 State Hill Road,
Suite 3, Wyomissing, PA 19610
Tel: (610) 372-2761 Fax: (610) 320-5259

Supervisor **William MacDonald** (610) 372-2761
E-mail: macdonald.william@dol.gov

Rocky Mountain District
Denver Federal Center, 6th and Kipling, 2nd Street, Building 25,
Dock E-18, Denver, CO 80225
Mail: P.O. Box 25367, DFC, Denver, CO 80225-0367
Tel: (303) 231-5465 Fax: (303) 231-5468
Areas Covered: AZ, CO, KS, MT, NE, ND, SD, UT, WY

District Manager **David L. Weaver** (303) 231-5465
E-mail: weaver.david@dol.gov
Assistant District Manager **Brad Breland** (303) 231-5579
E-mail: breland.brad@dol.gov
Assistant District Manager **Dustan Crelly** (303) 231-5465
E-mail: crelly.dustan@dol.gov
Supervisory Management Program Analyst
Samsara Sorrells (303) 231-5465
E-mail: sorrells.samsara@dol.gov

Denver (CO) Field Office
Denver Federal Center, 6th and Kipling, 2nd Street, Building 25,
Room E-18, Denver, CO 80225
Mail: P.O. Box 25367, DFC, Denver, CO 80225-0367
Tel: (303) 231-5469 Fax: (303) 231-5468

Supervisory Mine Safety and Health Inspector
Shane Julien (303) 231-5469
E-mail: julien.shane@dol.gov

Green River (WY) Field Office
50 Shoshone Avenue, Suite A, Green River, WY 82935
Tel: (307) 875-6300 Fax: (307) 875-6301

Supervisory Mine Safety and Health Inspector
Steve Pilling (307) 875-6300
E-mail: pilling.steve@dol.gov

Helena (MT) Field Office
10 West 15th Street, Suite 2100, Helena, MT 59626
Tel: (406) 441-1180 Fax: (406) 441-1182

Supervisory Mine Safety and Health Inspector
Curtis Petty (406) 441-1180
E-mail: petty.curtis@dol.gov

Mesa (AZ) Field Office
63 East Main Street, Suite 303, Mesa, AZ 85201
Tel: (480) 649-5452 Fax: (480) 649-5662

Supervisory Mine Safety and Health Inspector
James Eubanks (480) 649-5452
E-mail: eubanks.james@dol.gov

★ Presidential Appointment Requiring Senate Confirmation ☆ Presidential Appointment □ Schedule C Appointment ◇ Career Senior Foreign Service Appointment
● Career Senior Executive Service (SES) Appointment ○ Non-Career Senior Executive Service (SES) Appointment ■ Postal Career Executive Service

Rapid City (SD) Field Office
2455 West Chicago Street, Rapid City, SD 57702
Tel: (605) 348-2076 Fax: (605) 348-2077

Supervisory Mine Safety and Health Inspector
James M. Peck . . . . (605) 348-2076
E-mail: peck.james@dol.gov

Salt Lake City (UT) Field Office
125 South State Street, Room 2425, Salt Lake City, UT 84138
Tel: (801) 524-3450 Fax: (801) 524-3453

Supervisory Mine Safety and Health Inspector
Steven Polgar . . . . (801) 567-9993
E-mail: polgar.steven@dol.gov

Topeka (KS) Field Office
Federal Building, 444 SE Quincy, Room 245, Box 38,
Topeka, KS 66683-3581
Tel: (785) 295-2636 Fax: (785) 295-2666

Supervisory Mine Safety and Health Inspector
Robert Small . . . . (785) 295-2636
E-mail: small.robert@dol.gov

South Central District

Earle Cabell Federal Building, 1100 Commerce Street,
Room 462, Dallas, TX 75242-0499
Tel: (214) 767-8401 Fax: (214) 767-8405
Areas Covered: AR, LA, MO, NM, OK, TX

District Manager **Michael A. Davis** . . . . (214) 767-8401
E-mail: davis.michael@dol.gov
Assistant District Manager **William O'Dell** . . . . (214) 767-8401
E-mail: odell.william@dol.gov
Assistant District Manager **(Vacant)** . . . . (214) 767-8401
Supervisory Management/Program Analyst
Elizabeth "Lisa" Monsivais . . . . (214) 767-8401
Supervisory Special Investigator **(Vacant)** . . . . (214) 767-8401
Conference Litigation Representative **Brett Barrick** . . . . . . (214) 767-8405
E-mail: barrick.brett@dol.gov
Conference Litigation Representative **Jim DoByns** . . . . (214) 767-8405
E-mail: dobyns.jim@dol.gov
Conference Litigation Representative **Maria Rich** . . . . (214) 767-8401
E-mail: rich.maria@dol.gov
Safety Specialist **Nicholas A. "Nick" Gutierrez** . . . . (214) 767-8401
E-mail: gutierrez.nick@dol.gov
Safety Specialist **David Hamm** . . . . (214) 767-8401
E-mail: hamm.david@dol.gov
Industrial Hygienist **(Vacant)** . . . . (214) 767-8401
IT Specialist **Mark Bradshaw** . . . . (214) 767-8401
E-mail: bradshaw.mark@dol.gov
Health Specialist **Robert Dreyer** . . . . (214) 767-8401
E-mail: dreyer.robert@dol.gov
Staff Assistant **Elwood "Mac" Burriss** . . . . (214) 767-8401
E-mail: burriss.elwood@dol.gov

Albuquerque (NM) Field Office
Two Park Central Tower, 300 San Mateo Boulevard, NE,
Suite 407, Albuquerque, NM 87108
Tel: (505) 346-6775 Fax: (505) 346-6776

Supervisor **Bradley Peay** . . . . (505) 346-6775
E-mail: Peay.Bradley@dol.gov

Carlsbad (NM) Field Office
114 South Halagueno Street, Room 129, Carlsbad, NM 88220-3354
Tel: (575) 887-6074 Fax: (505) 885-2477

Supervisor **Darwin Bratcher** . . . . (575) 887-6074
E-mail: bratcher.darwin@dol.gov

Dallas (TX) Field Office
1100 Commerce Street, Room 452, Dallas, TX 75242-0499
Tel: (214) 767-8430 Fax: (214) 767-8456

Supervisor **Laurence M. Dunlap** . . . . (214) 767-8430
E-mail: dunlap.laurence@dol.gov

Broussard Field Office
817-A Albertson Parkway, Broussard, LA 70518
Tel: (337) 839-0263

Supervisor **Joseph Olivier** . . . . (337) 839-0263
E-mail: olivier.joseph@dol.gov

Little Rock (AR) Field Office
700 West Capitol Street, Room 2420, Little Rock, AR 72201
Tel: (501) 324-5281 Tel: (501) 324-5358 Fax: (501) 324-5394

Supervisor **Michael R. Van Dorn** . . . . (501) 324-5281
E-mail: vandorn.michael@dol.gov

Norman (OK) Field Office
West Oaks Building C, 2227 West Lindsey Street,
Suite 1450, Norman, OK 73069-4053
Tel: (405) 360-7691 Fax: (405) 360-8093

Supervisor **Wesley Hackworth** . . . . (405) 360-7691
E-mail: hackworth.wesley@dol.gov

Rolla (MO) Field Office
1404 Independence Road, Rolla, MO 65401
Tel: (573) 364-8282 Tel: (573) 364-6898 Fax: (573) 364-0305

Supervisor-North Field Office **Robert Seelke** . . . . (573) 364-8282
E-mail: seelke.robert@dol.gov
Supervisor-South Field Office **Lawrence Sherrill** . . . . (573) 364-8282
E-mail: sherrill.lawrence@dol.gov

San Antonio (TX) Field Office
North Park Corporate Center, 17319 San Pedro Avenue,
Suite 110, San Antonio, TX 78232
Tel: (210) 403-5943 Tel: (210) 403-5944 Fax: (210) 403-5946

Supervisor **Homer "Hap" Pricer** . . . . (210) 403-5943
E-mail: pricer.homer@dol.gov

Southeastern District

1030 London Drive, Suite 400, Birmingham, AL 35211
Tel: (205) 290-7294 Fax: (205) 290-7299
Areas Covered: AL, FL, GA, KY, MS, NC, PR, SC, TN, VA, VI

District Manager **Samuel Pierce** . . . . (205) 290-7296 ext. 223
E-mail: pierce.samuel@dol.gov
Assistant District Manager **Doniece L. Schlick** . . . . (205) 290-7294
E-mail: schlick.doniece@dol.gov
Assistant District Manager **Brian Thompson** . . . . (205) 290-7294
E-mail: thompson.brian@dol.gov
Conference Litigation Representative **Anthony Burke** . . . . (863) 533-5390
1662 Park Avenue, Bartow, FL 33830-3139
E-mail: burke.anthony@dol.gov
Conference Litigation Representative
Brandon Russell . . . . (205) 290-7296 ext. 281
E-mail: russell.brandon@dol.gov
Conference Litigation Representative
James R. Shaffer . . . . (205) 290-7296 ext. 228
E-mail: shaffer.james@dol.gov
Conference Litigation Representative **(Vacant)** . . . (205) 290-7296 ext. 228
Health Specialist **Patrick Sharp** . . . . (205) 290-7296 ext. 227
Health Specialist **(Vacant)** . . . . (205) 290-7296 ext. 231
Safety Specialist **Michael A. Evans** . . . . (205) 290-7296 ext. 225
E-mail: evans.michael@dol.gov
Staff Assistant **Judith Etterer** . . . . (205) 290-7296
E-mail: etterer.judith@dol.gov
Supervisory Management and Program
Analyst **Michael Giddens** . . . . (205) 290-7294 ext. 226
Supervisory Special Investigator
LeRoy Lockett . . . . (205) 290-7294 ext. 237
E-mail: lockett.leroy@dol.gov

Bartow (FL) Field Office
1662 Park Avenue, Bartow, FL 33830-3139
Tel: (863) 533-5390 Fax: (863) 533-1464

Supervisor **Curtis Roth** . . . . (863) 533-5390
E-mail: roth.curtis@dol.gov

DEPARTMENTS

★ Presidential Appointment Requiring Senate Confirmation ☆ Presidential Appointment ☐ Schedule C Appointment ◇ Career Senior Foreign Service Appointment
● Career Senior Executive Service (SES) Appointment ○ Non-Career Senior Executive Service (SES) Appointment ■ Postal Career Executive Service

Birmingham (AL) Field Office
1030 London Drive, Suite 400, Birmingham, AL 35211
Tel: (205) 290-7601 Fax: (205) 290-7345

Supervisor **Rory Smith** .... (205) 290-7601

Columbia (SC) Field Office
Strom Thurmond Federal Building, 1872 Assembly Street, Room 365, Columbia, SC 29201
Tel: (803) 765-5802 Fax: (803) 765-5805

Supervisor **Jeffrey Phillips** .... (803) 765-5802
E-mail: phillips.jeffrey@dol.gov

Franklin (TN) Field Office
377 Riverside Drive, Suite 104, Franklin, TN 37064
Tel: (615) 790-0562 Fax: (615) 790-9745

Supervisor **James Hollis** .... (615) 790-0562
E-mail: hollis.james.m@dol.gov

Knoxville (TN) Field Office
4712 Western Avenue, Knoxville, TN 37921-3303
Tel: (865) 545-4626 Fax: (865) 545-4673

Supervisor **Ryan O'Boyle** .... (865) 545-4626
E-mail: oboyle.ryan@dol.gov

Lexington (KY) Field Office
152 West Zandale Drive, Suite 102, Lexington, KY 40503
Tel: (859) 276-1384 Fax: (859) 276-1470

Supervisor **Darren Conn** .... (859) 276-1384
E-mail: conn.darren@dol.gov

Macon (GA) Field Office
Building C, 640 North Avenue, Suite 300, Macon, GA 31211-1494
Tel: (478) 477-7611 Fax: (478) 477-7482

Supervisor **Felix "Walter" DeLoach** .... (478) 477-7611
E-mail: deloach.felix@dol.gov

Sanford (NC) Field Office
Moore Business Park, 225 Commercial Court, Suite 1, Sanford, NC 27330
Tel: (919) 774-8113 Fax: (919) 775-5954

Supervisor **Stanley Stevenson** .... (919) 774-8113
E-mail: stevenson.stanley@dol.gov

San Juan (PR) Field Office
GSA Center, 651 Federal Drive, Suite 384-06, Guaynabo, PR 00965
Tel: (787) 749-4343 Fax: (787) 749-4300

Supervisor **Luis Valentin** .... (787) 749-4343
E-mail: valentin.luis@dol.gov

Western District
991 Nut Tree Road, Second Floor, Vacaville, CA 95687
Tel: (707) 447-9844 Fax: (707) 447-9816
Areas Covered: AK, CA, HI, ID, NV, OR, WA

District Manager **(Vacant)** .... (707) 447-9844 ext. 3025
Assistant District Manager **Kevin Hirsch** .... (707) 447-9844
E-mail: Hirsch.Kevin@dol.gov
Assistant District Manager **John Pereza** .... (707) 447-9844 ext. 3028
E-mail: pereza.john@dol.gov
Supervisory Management and Program Analyst **Patricia Borer** .... (707) 447-7864
E-mail: borer.patricia@dol.gov

Albany (OR) Field Office
321 First Avenue, Room 1A, Albany, OR 97321
Tel: (541) 924-8495 Fax: (541) 924-8499

Supervisor **Randy Cardwell** .... (541) 924-8495
E-mail: Cardwell.Randy@dol.gov

Anchorage (AK) Field Office
Anchorage Federal Building/U.S. Courthouse Annex, 222 West 7th Avenue, Room A35, Anchorage, AK 99513
Tel: (907) 271-1250 Fax: (907) 271-1252

Supervisor **Robert Wood** .... (907) 271-1250
E-mail: wood.robert@dol.gov

Boise (ID) Field Office
Lake Point Centre 1, 300 East Mallard Drive, Suite 150, Boise, ID 83706
Tel: (208) 334-1835 Fax: (208) 334-1838

Supervisor **Ron Jacobsen** .... (208) 334-1835
E-mail: jacobsen.ronald@dol.gov

Elko (NV) Field Office
567 West Silver Street, Suite 401, Elko, NV 89801
Tel: (775) 753-4732 Fax: (775) 778-0930

Supervisory Mine Safety and Health Inspector **Gary Hebel** .... (775) 753-4732

Henderson (NV) Field Office
150 N. Stephanie Street, Suite 151, Henderson, NV 89074
Tel: (702) 558-4656 Fax: (702) 294-0893

Supervisory Mine Safety and Health Inspector **Bart Wrobel** .... (702) 558-4665

Kent (WA) Field Office
South 204th Street, Suite 180, Kent, WA 98032
Tel: (253) 395-9585 Fax: (253) 395-5157

Supervisor **Melvin "Keith" Palmer** .... (253) 395-9585
E-mail: palmer.melvin@dol.gov

Redlands (CA) Field Office
720 Carnegie Drive, Room 100, San Bernardino, CA 92408
Tel: (909) 890-1987 Fax: (909) 890-1557

Supervisor **Stephen Cain** .... (909) 890-1557
E-mail: cain.stephen@dol.gov

Vacaville (CA) Field Office
991 Nut Tree Road, First Floor, Vacaville, CA 95687
Tel: (707) 447-9842 Fax: (707) 447-9432

Supervisor **Troy VanWey** .... (707) 447-9842
E-mail: vanwey.troy@dol.gov

Occupational Safety and Health Administration (OSHA)
200 Constitution Avenue, NW, Room S2315, Washington, DC 20210
Tel: (202) 693-2772 Tel: (202) 693-1999 (Communications)
Tel: (800) 321-6742 (Emergency and Accident Reporting Hotline)
Fax: (202) 693-1635 Internet: www.osha.gov

Directorate of Technical Support and Emergency Management
200 Constitution Avenue, NW, Washington, DC 20210
Tel: (202) 693-2300 Fax: (202) 693-1644

Cincinnati (OH) Technical Center
435 Elm Street, Suite 500, Cincinnati, OH 45202
Tel: (513) 684-3721 Fax: (513) 684-2630

Director **Robert T. Williams** .... (513) 684-3721 ext. 101
Oracle Developer **Ram Moola** .... (513) 684-3721

Engineering Support
Engineering Support Manager, Supervisory Electronics Engineer **John Schneider** .... (513) 684-3721
Lead Electronics Technician **Leonard Zielinski** .... (513) 684-3721

Program Support
Program Support Manager, Supervisory Management and Program Analyst **Donna Lake** .... (513) 684-3721

★ Presidential Appointment Requiring Senate Confirmation ☆ Presidential Appointment □ Schedule C Appointment ◇ Career Senior Foreign Service Appointment
● Career Senior Executive Service (SES) Appointment ○ Non-Career Senior Executive Service (SES) Appointment ■ Postal Career Executive Service

Regional Offices

Occupational Safety and Health Administration - Region 1

John F. Kennedy Federal Building, Room E-340, Boston, MA 02203
Tel: (617) 565-9860 Fax: (617) 565-9827
Areas Covered: CT, ME, MA, NH, RI

- ● Regional Administrator (Acting) **Jeffrey "Jeff" Erskine** ... (617) 565-9860
  E-mail: erskine.jeff@dol.gov
- Deputy Regional Administrator **Jeffrey "Jeff" Erskine** ... (617) 565-9860
  E-mail: erskine.jeff@dol.gov
- Consultation and State Programs, Assistant Regional Administrator **Timothy Irving** ... (617) 565-9807
  E-mail: irving.timothy@dol.gov
- Enforcement Programs and Technical Support, Assistant Regional Administrator **Amee Bhatt** ... (617) 565-9859
  E-mail: bhatt.amee@dol.gov
- Program Planning and Support, Assistant Regional Administrator **Stacy McGuire** ... (617) 565-9840

Augusta (ME) Area Office

E.S. Muskie Federal Building, 40 Western Avenue, Room G 26, Augusta, ME 04330
Tel: (207) 626-9160 Fax: (207) 622-8213

Area Director **Mary Ann Medeiros** ... (207) 626-9160
E-mail: medeiros.maryann@dol.gov

Bangor (ME) District Office

382 Harlow Street, Room 240, Bangor, ME 04401
Tel: (207) 941-8177 Fax: (207) 941-8179

Team Leader **(Vacant)** ... (207) 941-8177

Boston (MA) Area Office - North

Shattuck Office Center, 138 River Road, Suite 102, Andover, MA 01810
Tel: (978) 837-4455 Fax: (978) 837-4455

Area Director **Anthony Covello** ... (978) 837-4460
E-mail: covello.anthony@dol.gov

Boston (MA) Area Office - South

639 Granite Street, 4th Floor, Braintree, MA 02184
Tel: (617) 565-6924 Fax: (617) 565-6923

Area Director **Kenneth Shedden** ... (617) 565-6924
E-mail: shedden.kenneth@dol.gov

Bridgeport (CT) Area Office

Clark Building, 1057 Broad Street, 14th Floor, Bridgeport, CT 06604
Tel: (203) 579-5581 Fax: (203) 579-5516

Area Director **Steven Biasi** ... (203) 579-5581
E-mail: biasi.steve@dol.gov

Concord (NH) Area Office

J.C. Cleveland Federal Building, 53 Pleasant Street, Room 3901, Concord, NH 03301
Tel: (603) 225-1629 Fax: (603) 225-1580

Area Director **Rosemarie Ohar-Cole** ... (603) 225-1629

Hartford (CT) Area Office

35 High Street, Suite 361, Hartford, CT 06103
Tel: (860) 240-3152 Fax: (860) 240-3155

Area Director **Warren Simpson** ... (860) 240-3152
E-mail: simpson.warren@dol.gov

Providence (RI) Area Office

The Federal Center, 380 Westminster Mall, Room 543, Providence, RI 02903
Tel: (401) 528-4669 Fax: (401) 528-4663

Area Director **Patrick Griffin** ... (401) 528-4669
E-mail: griffin.patrick@dol.gov

Springfield (MA) Area Office

1441 Main Street, Room 550, Springfield, MA 01103
Tel: (413) 785-0123 Fax: (413) 785-0136

Area Director **Mary E. Hoye** ... (413) 785-0123
E-mail: hoye.mary@dol.gov

Occupational Safety and Health Administration - Region 2

201 Varick Street, Room 670, New York, NY 10014-4811
Tel: (212) 337-2378 Fax: (212) 337-2371
Areas Covered: NJ, NY, PR, VI

- ● Regional Administrator **Robert D. Kulick** ... (212) 337-0118
  E-mail: kulick.robert@dol.gov
- Deputy Regional Administrator **Steve Kaplan** ... (212) 337-2326
  E-mail: kaplan.steve@dol.gov
- Federal Enforcement Operations Assistant **Warren Simpson** ... (212) 337-2338
- Consultation, Administrative, Programs and State Plans **Babette Velev** ... (212) 337-2330
- Technical Support Assistant Regional Administrator **Laura Kenny** ... (212) 337-2348
  E-mail: kenny.laura@dol.gov
- Training Outreach Partnerships Assistant Regional Administrator **Mike Levy** ... (212) 337-2378
  E-mail: levy.mike@dol.gov
- Labor Liaison **(Vacant)** ... (212) 337-2350

Albany (NY) Area Office

401 New Karner Road, Suite 300, Albany, NY 12205-3809
Tel: (518) 464-4338 Fax: (518) 464-4337

Area Director **Robert Garvey** ... (518) 464-4338
E-mail: garvey.robert@dol.gov

Avenel (NJ) Area Office

1030 St. Georges Avenue, Plaza 35, Suite 205, Avenel, NJ 07001
Tel: (732) 750-3270 Fax: (732) 750-4737

Area Director **Patricia Jones** ... (732) 750-3270
E-mail: jones.patricia@dol.gov

Buffalo Area Office

130 South Elmwood Avenue, Suite 500, Buffalo, NY 14202-2465
Tel: (716) 551-3053 Fax: (716) 551-3126

Area Director **Michael "Mike" Scime** ... (716) 551-3053
E-mail: scime.mike@dol.gov

Hasbrouck Heights (NJ) Area Office

500 Route 17 South, 2nd Floor, Room 204, Hasbrouck Heights, NJ 07604
Tel: (201) 288-1700 Fax: (201) 288-7315

Area Director **Lisa Levy** ... (201) 288-1700
E-mail: levy.lisa@dol.gov

Long Island Area Office

1400 Old Country Road, Suite 208, Westbury, NY 11590
Tel: (516) 334-3344 Fax: (516) 334-3326

Area Director **Anthony Ciuffo** ... (516) 334-3344
E-mail: ciuffo.anthony@dol.gov

Queens (NY) District Office

45-15 Marathon Parkway, Little Neck, NY 11362
Tel: (718) 279-9060 Fax: (718) 279-9057

Area Director **Kay Gee** ... (212) 620-3200
E-mail: gee.kay@dol.gov
Assistant Area Director **Lois Wallace** ... (718) 279-9060
E-mail: wallace.lois@dol.gov

Manhattan (NY) Area Office

201 Varick Street, Room 908, New York, NY 10014-4811
Tel: (212) 620-3200 Fax: (212) 620-4121

Area Director **Kay Gee** ... (212) 620-3200
E-mail: gee.kay@dol.gov

★ Presidential Appointment Requiring Senate Confirmation ☆ Presidential Appointment ☐ Schedule C Appointment ◇ Career Senior Foreign Service Appointment
● Career Senior Executive Service (SES) Appointment ○ Non-Career Senior Executive Service (SES) Appointment ■ Postal Career Executive Service

DEPARTMENTS

Marlton (NJ) Area Office
Marlton Executive Park, Building 2, 701 Route 73 South, Suite 120, Marlton, NJ 08053
Tel: (856) 596-5200 Fax: (856) 596-5201

Area Director **Paula Dixon-Roderick** .... (856) 596-5200
E-mail: dixon-roderick.paula@dol.gov

Parsippany (NJ) Area Office
299 Cherry Hill Road, Suite 103, Parsippany, NJ 07054
Tel: (973) 263-1003 Fax: (973) 299-7161

Area Director **Kris Hoffmann** .... (973) 263-1003
E-mail: hoffman.kris@dol.gov

Puerto Rico Area Office
BBV Plaza Building, 1510 F. D. Roosevelt Avenue, Suite 5B, Guaynabo, PR 00968
Tel: (787) 277-1560 Fax: (787) 277-1567

Area Director **William Bridges** .... (787) 277-1560 ext. 2021
E-mail: bridges.william@dol.gov

Syracuse (NY) Area Office
3300 Vickery Road, North Syracuse, NY 13212
Tel: (315) 451-0808 Fax: (315) 451-1351

Area Director **Chris Adams CIH, CSP** .... (315) 451-0808

Tarrytown (NY) Area Office
660 White Plains Road, 4th Floor, Tarrytown, NY 10591-5107
Tel: (914) 524-7510 Fax: (914) 524-7515

Area Director **Diana Cortez** .... (914) 524-7510
E-mail: cortez.diana@dol.gov

Occupational Safety and Health Administration - Region 3

The Curtis Center, 170 South Independence Mall West, Suite 740-W, Philadelphia, PA 19106-3309
Tel: (215) 861-4900 Fax: (215) 861-4904
Areas Covered: DE, DC, MD, PA, VA, WV

● Regional Administrator **Richard Mendelson** .... (215) 861-4900
E-mail: mendelson.richard@dol.gov
Deputy Regional Administrator **Michael J. Rivera** .... (215) 861-4900
E-mail: rivera.michael@dol.gov
Assistant Regional Administrator, Administrative Programs **(Vacant)** .... (215) 861-4900
Assistant Regional Administrator, Cooperative and State Programs **(Vacant)** .... (215) 861-4900
Assistant Regional Administrator, Enforcement Programs **Thomas C. Carle** .... (215) 861-4900
E-mail: carle.tom@dol.gov
Whistleblower Program Supervisory Investigator **(Vacant)** .... (215) 861-4900
Librarian **(Vacant)** .... (215) 861-4900

Allentown (PA) Area Office
Stabler Corporate Center, 3477 Corporate Parkway, Suite 120, Center Valley, PA 18034-8235
Tel: (267) 429-7542 Fax: (267) 429-7567

Area Director **Jean G. Kulp** .... (267) 429-7542
E-mail: kulp.jean@dol.gov

Baltimore-Washington Area Office
1099 Winterson Road, Suite 140, Linthicum, MD 21090-2218
Tel: (410) 865-2055 Fax: (410) 865-2068

Area Director **Nadira Janack** .... (410) 865-2055
E-mail: janack.nadira@dol.gov

Charleston (WV) Area Office
405 Capitol Street, Suite 407, Charleston, WV 25301-1727
Tel: (304) 347-5937 Fax: (304) 347-5275

Area Director **Prentice Cline** .... (304) 347-5937
E-mail: cline.prentice@dol.gov

Erie (PA) Area Office
1128 State Street, Suite 200, Erie, PA 16501-1920
Tel: (814) 874-5150 Fax: (814) 874-5151

Area Director **Brendan Claybaugh** .... (814) 874-5150
E-mail: claybaugh.brendan@dol.gov

Harrisburg (PA) Area Office
43 Kline Plaza, Harrisburg, PA 17104-1529
Tel: (717) 782-3902 Fax: (717) 782-3746

Area Director **David Olah** .... (717) 782-3902
E-mail: olah.david@dol.gov

Norfolk (VA) Area Office
Federal Office Building, 200 Granby Mall, Room 614, Norfolk, VA 23510-1819
Tel: (757) 441-3820 Fax: (757) 441-3594

Area Director **Stan Dutko** .... (757) 441-3820

Philadelphia (PA) Area Office
The Wanamaker Building, 100 Penn Square East, 12th Floor, Philadelphia, PA 19107
Tel: (215) 597-4955 Fax: (215) 597-1956

Area Director **(Vacant)** .... (215) 597-4955

Pittsburgh (PA) Area Office
William Moorhead Federal Building, 1000 Liberty Avenue, Room 905, Pittsburgh, PA 15222
Tel: (412) 395-4903 Fax: (412) 395-6380

Area Director **Christopher Robinson** .... (412) 395-4903
E-mail: robinson.christopher@dol.gov

Wilkes-Barre (PA) Area Office
Stegmaier Building, Seven North Wilkes-Barre Boulevard, Suite 410, Wilkes Barre, PA 18702-5241
Tel: (570) 826-6538 Fax: (570) 821-4170

Area Director **Mark L. Stelmack** .... (570) 826-6538
E-mail: stelmack.mark@dol.gov

Wilmington (DE) Area Office
Mellon Bank Building, 919 Market Street, Suite 900, Wilmington, DE 19801-3319
Tel: (302) 573-6518 Fax: (302) 573-6532

Area Director **Erin G. Patterson** .... (302) 573-6518
E-mail: patterson.erin.g@dol.gov

Occupational Safety and Health Administration - Region 4

Atlanta Federal Center, 61 Forsyth Street, SW, Room 6T50, Atlanta, GA 30303
Tel: (678) 237-0400
Areas Covered: AL, FL, GA, KY, MS, NC, SC, TN

● Regional Administrator **Kurt A. Petermeyer** .... (678) 237-0400
E-mail: petermeyer.kurt@dol.gov
Deputy Regional Administrator **(Vacant)** .... (678) 237-0400
Deputy Regional Administrator **(Vacant)** .... (678) 237-0400
Administrative Programs Assistant Regional Administrator **Italo Alfieri** .... (678) 237-0400
E-mail: alfieri.italo@dol.gov
Enforcement Programs Assistant Regional Administrator **Billie A. Kizer** .... (678) 237-0400
E-mail: kizer.billie@dol.gov
Cooperative and State Programs Assistant Regional Administrator **Americo Pagan** .... (678) 237-0400
E-mail: pagan.americo@dol.gov

Atlanta East Area Office
2296 Henderson Mill Road, NE, Suite 200, Atlanta, GA 30345
Tel: (770) 493-6644 Fax: (770) 493-7725

Area Director **William Flucher** .... (770) 493-6644

★ Presidential Appointment Requiring Senate Confirmation ☆ Presidential Appointment ☐ Schedule C Appointment ◇ Career Senior Foreign Service Appointment
● Career Senior Executive Service (SES) Appointment ○ Non-Career Senior Executive Service (SES) Appointment ■ Postal Career Executive Service

Atlanta West Area Office
The Meridian, 1995 North Place, SE, Room 525, Atlanta, GA 30339
Tel: (770) 984-8700 Fax: (770) 984-8855

Area Director **Christi Griffin** .... (770) 984-8700
E-mail: griffin.christi@dol.gov

Birmingham (AL) Area Office
Medical Forum Building, 950 North 22nd Street,
Room 150, Birmingham, AL 35203
Tel: (205) 731-1534 Fax: (205) 731-0504

Area Director **Ramona Morris** .... (205) 731-1534
E-mail: morris.ramona@dol.gov

Columbia (SC) Area Office
Strom Thurmond Federal Building, 1835 Assembly Street,
Room 1472, Columbia, SC 29201-2453
Tel: (803) 765-5904 Fax: (803) 765-5591

Area Director **Kimberly Morton** .... (803) 765-5904
E-mail: morton.kim@dol.gov

Fort Lauderdale (FL) Area Office
1000 South Pine Island Road, Plantation, FL 33324
Tel: (954) 424-0242 Fax: (954) 424-3073

Area Director **Condell Eastmond** .... (954) 424-0242
E-mail: eastmond.condell@dol.gov

Jackson (MS) Area Office
3780 I-55 North, Suite 210, Jackson, MS 39211-6323
Tel: (601) 965-4606 Fax: (601) 965-4610

Area Director (Acting) **Courtney Bohannon** .... (601) 965-4606
E-mail: bohannon.courtney@dol.gov

Jacksonville (FL) Area Office
Ribault Building, 1851 Executive Center Drive,
Suite 227, Jacksonville, FL 32207
Tel: (904) 232-2895 Fax: (904) 232-1294

Area Director **Brian Sturtecky** .... (904) 232-2895
E-mail: sturtecky.brian@dol.gov

Mobile (AL) Area Office
1141 Montlimar Drive, Suite 1006, Mobile, AL 36609
Tel: (251) 441-6131 Fax: (251) 441-6396

Area Director **Joseph Roesler** .... (251) 441-6131
E-mail: roesler.joseph@dol.gov

Nashville (TN) Area Office
51 Century Boulevard, Suite 340, Nashville, TN 37214
Tel: (615) 232-3803 Fax: (615) 232-3827

Area Director **William C. Cochran** .... (615) 232-3803
E-mail: cochran.william@dol.gov

Raleigh (NC) Area Office
Somerset Park, 4407 Bland Road, Suite 210, Raleigh, NC 27609
Tel: (919) 790-8096 Fax: (919) 790-8224

Area Director **Kimberly Morton** .... (919) 790-8096
E-mail: morton.kim@dol.gov

Savannah (GA) Area Office
450 Mall Boulevard, Suite J, Savannah, GA 31406-1418
Tel: (912) 652-4393 Fax: (912) 652-4329

Area Director **Margo Westmoreland** .... (912) 652-4393
E-mail: westmoreland.margo@dol.gov

Tampa (FL) Area Office
5807 Breckenridge Parkway, Suite A, Tampa, FL 33610-4249
Tel: (813) 626-1177 Fax: (813) 626-7015

Area Director **Leslie Grove** .... (813) 626-1177
E-mail: grove.les@dol.gov

Occupational Safety and Health Administration - Region 5

Kluczynski Federal Building, 230 South Dearborn Street,
Room 3244, Chicago, IL 60604
Tel: (312) 353-2220 Fax: (312) 353-7774
Areas Covered: IL, IN, MI, MN, OH, WI

● Regional Administrator
Kenneth Nishiyama "Ken" Atha .... (312) 353-2220
E-mail: atha.ken@dol.gov
Education: Mount Senario BSCrimJ

Deputy Regional Administrator **William Donovan** .... (312) 353-2220
E-mail: donovan.william@dol.gov

Deputy Regional Administrator **Nancy Hauter** .... (312) 353-2220
E-mail: hauter.nancy@dol.gov

Administrative Programs Assistant Regional Administrator **Janette Schroeder** .... (312) 353-2220
E-mail: schroeder.janette@dol.gov

Cooperative/State Programs Assistant Regional Administrator **Darnell Crenshaw** .... (312) 353-2220
E-mail: crenshaw.darnell@dol.gov

Enforcement Programs Assistant Regional Administrator **Gary Lescallett** .... (312) 353-2220

Whistleblower Protection Program Assistant Regional Administrator **Mary Ann Howe** .... (312) 353-2220
E-mail: howe.mary@dol.gov

Training Coordinator **Darnell Crenshaw** .... (312) 353-2220
E-mail: crenshaw.darnell@dol.gov

Librarian **Susan Thompson** .... (312) 886-6291
E-mail: thompson.susan@dol.gov

Webmaster **Nelson Rodriguez** .... (312) 886-7024
E-mail: rodriguez.nelson@dol.gov

Appleton (WI) Area Office
1648 Tri Park Way, Appleton, WI 54914
Tel: (920) 734-4521 Fax: (920) 734-2661

Area Director **Robert Bonack** .... (920) 734-4521
E-mail: bonack.robert@dol.gov

Chicago (IL) South Area Office
8505 West 183rd Street, Suite C, Tinley Park, IL 60487
Tel: (708) 342-2840 Fax: (708) 444-0042

Area Director **Kathy Webb** .... (708) 342-2840
E-mail: webb.kathy@dol.gov

Chicago (IL) North Area Office
701 Lee Street, Suite 950, Des Plaines, IL 60016
Tel: (847) 803-4800 Fax: (847) 390-8220

Area Director **Angeline Loftus** .... (847) 803-4800

Cincinnati (OH) Area Office
36 Triangle Park Drive, Cincinnati, OH 45246
Tel: (513) 841-4132 Fax: (513) 841-4114

Area Director **Kenneth Montgomery** .... (513) 841-4132
E-mail: montgomery.ken@dol.gov

Cleveland (OH) Area Office
6593 Oak Tree Boulevard, Suite 203, Independence, OH 44131-6964
Tel: (216) 447-4194 Fax: (216) 520-1624

Area Director **Howard Eberts** .... (216) 447-4194
E-mail: eberts.howard@dol.gov

Columbus (OH) Area Office
Federal Building, 200 North High Street,
Room 620, Columbus, OH 43215
Tel: (614) 469-5582 Fax: (614) 469-6791

Area Director **Larry D. Johnson** .... (614) 469-5582
E-mail: johnson.larry@dol.gov

DEPARTMENTS

★ Presidential Appointment Requiring Senate Confirmation ☆ Presidential Appointment ☐ Schedule C Appointment ◇ Career Senior Foreign Service Appointment
● Career Senior Executive Service (SES) Appointment ○ Non-Career Senior Executive Service (SES) Appointment ■ Postal Career Executive Service

DEPARTMENTS

Eau Claire (WI) Area Office
1310 West Clairemont Avenue, Eau Claire, WI 54701
Tel: (715) 832-9019 Fax: (715) 832-1147

Area Director **Mark Hysell** . . . . (715) 832-9019
E-mail: hysell.mark@dol.gov

Fairview Heights (IL) Area Office
11 Executive Drive, Suite 11, Fairview Heights, IL 62208
Tel: (618) 632-8612 Fax: (618) 632-5712

Area Director **Aaron Priddy** . . . . (618) 632-8612
E-mail: priddy.aaron@dol.gov

Indianapolis (IN) Area Office
Federal Building/Courthouse, 46 East Ohio Street,
Room 453, Indianapolis, IN 46204-1946
Tel: (317) 226-7290 Fax: (317) 226-7292

Area Director **Vanessa Martin** . . . . (317) 226-7290
E-mail: martin.vanessa@dol.gov

Lansing (MI) Area Office
315 West Allegan Street, Suite 207, Lansing, MI 48933
Tel: (517) 487-4996 Fax: (517) 487-4997

Area Director **(Vacant)** . . . . (517) 487-4996

Madison (WI) Area Office
4802 East Broadway, Madison, WI 53716
Tel: (608) 441-5388 Fax: (608) 441-5400

Area Director **Ann Grevenkamp** . . . . (608) 441-5388
E-mail: grevenkamp.ann@dol.gov

Milwaukee (WI) Area Office
310 West Wisconsin Avenue, Room 1180, Milwaukee, WI 53203
Tel: (414) 297-3315 Fax: (414) 297-4299

Area Director **Christine "Chris" Zortman** . . . . (414) 297-3315
E-mail: zortman.chris@dol.gov

North Aurora (IL) Area Office
365 Smoke Tree Plaza, North Aurora, IL 60542
Tel: (630) 896-8700 Fax: (630) 892-2160

Area Director **Jacob Scott** . . . . (630) 896-8700
E-mail: scott.jacob@dol.gov

Peoria (IL) Area Office
1320 West Commerce Drive, Suite 800, Peoria, IL 61615
Tel: (309) 589-7033 Fax: (309) 589-7326

Area Director **Barry Salerno** . . . . (309) 589-7033
E-mail: salerno.barry@dol.gov

Toledo (OH) Area Office
Federal Building, 420 Madison Avenue,
Suite 600, Toledo, OH 43604
Tel: (419) 259-7542 Fax: (419) 259-6355

Area Director **Kimberly Nelson** . . . . (419) 259-7542
E-mail: nelson.kimberly@dol.gov

Occupational Safety and Health Administration - Region 6

A. Maceo Smith Federal Building, 525 South Griffin Street,
Room 602, Dallas, TX 75202
Tel: (972) 850-4145 Fax: (972) 850-4149
Areas Covered: AR, LA, NM, OK, TX

• Regional Administrator (Acting) **Eric S. Harbin** . . . . (972) 850-4182
E-mail: harbin.eric@dol.gov
Deputy Regional Administrator **Dorinda J. Folse** . . . . (972) 850-4196
E-mail: folse.dorinda@dol.gov
Administrative Programs Assistant Regional Administrator **Christina Myers** . . . . (972) 850-4136
Cooperative and State Programs Assistant Regional Administrator **Joshua Flesher** . . . . (972) 850-4186
E-mail: flesher.josh@dol.gov

Occupational Safety and Health Administration - Region 6 *(continued)*

Enforcement Programs Assistant Regional Administrator **Jeffrey B. Lewis** . . . . (972) 850-4177

Austin (TX) Area Office
La Costa Green Building, 1033 La Posada,
Suite 375, Austin, TX 78752-3832
Tel: (512) 374-0271 Fax: (512) 374-0086

Area Director **Ryan C. Perkins** . . . . (512) 374-0271 ext. 225
E-mail: perkins.ryan@dol.gov
Assistant Area Director **Michael Jarvis** . . . . (512) 374-0271 ext. 229
E-mail: jarvis.michael@dol.gov
Assistant Area Director **Elizabeth R. Slatten** . . . (512) 374-0271 ext. 227
E-mail: slatten.elizabeth@dol.gov

Baton Rouge (LA) Area Office
9100 Bluebonnet Center Boulevard, Suite 201, Baton Rouge, LA 70809
Tel: (225) 298-5458 Fax: (225) 298-5457

Area Director **(Vacant)** . . . . (225) 298-5458 ext. 222
Assistant Area Director **Roderic Chube** . . . . (225) 298-5458 ext. 113
E-mail: chube.roderic@dol.gov
Assistant Area Director **Jason Coffey** . . . . (225) 298-5458 ext. 132
E-mail: coffey.jason@dol.gov
Assistant Area Director **(Vacant)** . . . . (225) 298-5458

Corpus Christi (TX) Area Office
Wilson Plaza, 606 North Carancahua,
Suite 700, Corpus Christi, TX 78401
Tel: (361) 888-3420 Fax: (361) 888-3424

Area Director **Travis G. Clark** . . . . (361) 888-3420 ext. 225
E-mail: clark.travis@dol.gov
Assistant Area Director **Luis Ramos-Morales** . . . (361) 888-3420 ext. 224
E-mail: ramos-morales.luis@dol.gov
Assistant Area Director **Michele Shield** . . . . (361) 888-3420 ext. 228
E-mail: shield.michele@dol.gov

Dallas (TX) Area Office
1100 East Campbell Road, Suite 250, Dallas, TX 75228
Tel: (972) 952-1330 Fax: (972) 952-1338

Area Director **Basil Singh** . . . . (972) 952-1330 ext. 223
E-mail: singh.basil@dol.gov
Assistant Area Director **Noel Buitrago** . . . . (972) 952-1338 ext. 248
E-mail: buitrago.noel@dol.gov
Assistant Area Director **Gregory Wynn** . . . . (972) 952-1330 ext. 243
E-mail: wynn.greg@dol.gov

El Paso (TX) Area Office
4849 North Mesa, Suite 200, El Paso, TX 79912
Tel: (915) 534-6251 Fax: (915) 534-6259

Area Director **Diego Alvarado** . . . . (915) 534-6251 ext. 224
E-mail: alvarado.diego@dol.gov
Assistant Area Director **David Arrey** . . . . (915) 534-6251 ext. 224
E-mail: arrey.david@dol.gov

Fort Worth (TX) Area Office
North Star II, 8713 Airport Freeway,
Suite 302, Fort Worth, TX 76180-7610
Tel: (817) 428-2470 Fax: (817) 581-7723

Area Director **Jack A. Rector** . . . . (817) 581-7303 ext. 227
E-mail: rector.jack@dol.gov
Assistant Area Director **Gary Files** . . . . (817) 428-2470 ext. 226
E-mail: files.gary@dol.gov

Houston (TX) North Area Office
690 S. Loop 336, Suite 400, Caldwell, TX 77304
Tel: (936) 760-3800 Fax: (281) 591-1459

Area Director **Joann Figueroa** . . . . (936) 760-3800 ext. 121
E-mail: figueroa.joann@dol.gov
Assistant Area Director
Stephen J. "Steve" DeVine . . . . (936) 760-3800 ext. 122
E-mail: devine.steve@dol.gov

★ Presidential Appointment Requiring Senate Confirmation ☆ Presidential Appointment ☐ Schedule C Appointment ◇ Career Senior Foreign Service Appointment
● Career Senior Executive Service (SES) Appointment ○ Non-Career Senior Executive Service (SES) Appointment ■ Postal Career Executive Service

Houston (TX) North Area Office *(continued)*

Assistant Area Director **David Squires** . . . . (936) 760-3800 ext. 123
E-mail: squires.david@dol.gov

Houston (TX) South Area Office
17625 El Camino Real, Suite 400, Houston, TX 77058
Tel: (281) 286-0583 Fax: (281) 286-6352

Area Director **Mark R. Briggs** . . . . (281) 286-0583 ext. 225
E-mail: briggs.mark@dol.gov
Assistant Area Director **(Vacant)** . . . . (281) 286-0583 ext. 223
Assistant Area Director, Process Safety Management Team **Mhekeba J. Hager** . . . . (281) 286-0583 ext. 222
E-mail: hager.mhekeba@dol.gov
Area Supervisor **James Lawrence** . . . . (281) 286-0583 ext. 224
E-mail: lawrence.james@dol.gov

Little Rock (AR) Area Office
Danville Building 2, 10810 Executive Center Drive, Suite 206, Little Rock, AR 72211
Tel: (501) 224-1841 Fax: (501) 224-4431

Area Director **Carlos M. Reynolds** . . . . (501) 224-1841 ext. 221
E-mail: reynolds.carlos@dol.gov
Assistant Area Director **Roosevelt Shavers** . . . . (501) 224-1841 ext. 237
E-mail: shavers.roosevelt@dol.gov
Assistant Area Director **(Vacant)** . . . . (501) 224-1841 ext. 228

Lubbock (TX) District Office
1205 Texas Avenue, Room 806, Lubbock, TX 79401
Tel: (806) 472-7681 Fax: (806) 472-7686

Area Director **Elizabeth Routh** . . . . (806) 472-7681
E-mail: routh.elizabeth@dol.gov
Assistant Area Director **Jose "Joe" Hernandez, Jr.** . . . . (806) 472-7681 ext. 225

Oklahoma City (OK) Area Office
5104 North Francis Ave, Suite 200, Oklahoma City, OK 73118
Tel: (405) 278-9560 Fax: (405) 278-9572

Area Director **David A. Bates** . . . . (405) 278-9560 ext. 222
E-mail: bates.david@dol.gov
Assistant Area Director **Meghan Christie** . . . . . . (405) 278-9560 ext. 233
E-mail: christie.meghan@dol.gov
Assistant Area Director **Steven Kirby** . . . . (405) 278-9560 ext. 232
E-mail: kirby.steven@dol.gov
Assistant Area Director **Carmen Martinez** . . . . . . (405) 278-9560 ext. 223
E-mail: martinez.carmen@dol.gov

San Antonio (TX) District Office
Fountainhead Tower, 8200 W. Interstate 10, Suite 605, San Antonio, TX 78230-3877
Tel: (210) 472-5040 Fax: (210) 472-5045

Area Director **Alejandro Porter** . . . . (210) 472-5040 ext. 225
E-mail: porter.alejandro@dol.gov

Occupational Safety and Health Administration - Region 7

City Center Square, 2300 Main Street, Suite 1010, Kansas City, MO 64105
Tel: (816) 283-8745 Fax: (816) 283-0545
Areas Covered: IA, KS, MO, NE

● Regional Administrator **Kimberly Stille** . . . . (816) 283-8745
E-mail: stille.kim@dol.gov
Education: Mount Mercy 1983 BA; Iowa State 1987 MA
Deputy Regional Administrator **Bonita Winingham** . . . . . . (816) 283-8745
E-mail: winingham.bonita@dol.gov
Administrative Support **Dee Cantu** . . . . (816) 283-8745
E-mail: cantu.dee@dol.gov
Compliance Assistance **Glenn Taylor** . . . . (816) 283-8745
E-mail: taylor.glenn@dol.gov
Enforcement Programs **Brian Drake** . . . . (816) 283-8745
E-mail: drake.brian@dol.gov

Des Moines (IA) Area Office
Federal Building, 210 Walnut Street, Room 815, Des Moines, IA 50309
Tel: (515) 284-4794 Fax: (515) 284-4058

Area Director **Larry Davidson** . . . . (515) 284-4794

Kansas City (MO) Area Office
6200 Connecticut Avenue, Suite 100, Kansas City, MO 64120
Tel: (816) 483-9531 Fax: (816) 483-5167

Area Director **Karena Lorek** . . . . (816) 483-9531
E-mail: lorek.karena@dol.gov

Omaha (NE) Area Office
Overland Wolf Building, 6910 Pacific Street, Room 100, Omaha, NE 68106
Tel: (402) 553-0171 Fax: (402) 551-1288

Area Director **Jeffery R. "Jeff" Funke** . . . . (402) 553-0171
E-mail: funke.jeff@dol.gov

Saint Louis (MO) Area Office
911 Washington, Room 420, St. Louis, MO 63101
Tel: (314) 425-4249 Fax: (314) 425-4289

Area Director **Bill McDonald** . . . . (314) 425-4249
E-mail: mcdonald.bill@dol.gov

Wichita (KS) Area Office
271 West Third Street North, Room 400, Wichita, KS 67202
Tel: (316) 269-6644 Fax: (316) 269-6185

Area Director **Ryan Hodge** . . . . (316) 269-6644
E-mail: hodge.ryan@dol.gov

Occupational Safety and Health Administration - Region 8

Cesar Chavez Memorial Building, 1244 Speer Boulevard, Suite 551, Denver, CO 80204
Tel: (720) 264-6550 Fax: (720) 264-6585
Areas Covered: CO, MT, ND, SD, UT, WY

● Regional Administrator (Acting) **Rita Lucero** . . . . (720) 264-6551
E-mail: lucero.rita@dol.gov
Deputy Regional Administrator (Acting) **Dave Nelson** . . . (720) 264-6571
E-mail: nelson.dave@dol.gov
Federal-State Operations Assistant Regional Administrator (Acting) **Megan Meagher** . . . . (720) 264-6566
E-mail: meagher.megan@dol.gov
Program Planning and Support Assistant Regional Administrator **(Vacant)** . . . . (720) 264-6565
Technical Support Assistant Regional Administrator **Cory Wilson** . . . . (720) 264-6559
E-mail: wilson.cory@dol.gov

Billings (MT) Area Office
2900 Fourth Avenue North, Suite 303, Billings, MT 59101
Tel: (406) 247-7494 Fax: (406) 247-7499

Area Director **Arthur "Art" Hazen** . . . . (406) 247-7494
E-mail: hazen.arthur@dol.gov

Bismarck (ND) Area Office
521 East Main Avenue, Suite 200, Bismarck, ND 58501
Tel: (701) 250-4521 Fax: (701) 250-4520

Area Director **Eric Brooks** . . . . (701) 250-4521
E-mail: brooks.eric@dol.gov

Denver (CO) Area Office
1391 Speer Boulevard, Suite 210, Denver, CO 80204-2552
Tel: (303) 844-5285 Fax: (303) 844-6676

Area Director **Herbert "Herb" Gibson** . . . . (303) 844-5285
E-mail: gibson.herb@dol.gov

★ Presidential Appointment Requiring Senate Confirmation ☆ Presidential Appointment ☐ Schedule C Appointment ◇ Career Senior Foreign Service Appointment
● Career Senior Executive Service (SES) Appointment ○ Non-Career Senior Executive Service (SES) Appointment ■ Postal Career Executive Service

Englewood (CO) Area Office
7935 East Prentice Avenue, Suite 209, Englewood, CO 80111-2714
Tel: (303) 843-4500 Fax: (303) 843-4515

Area Director **Dave Nelson** . . . . (303) 843-4500
E-mail: nelson.dave@dol.gov

Occupational Safety and Health Administration - Region 9

90 Seventh Street, Suite 18100, San Francisco, CA 94103
Tel: (415) 625-2547 Fax: (415) 625-2534
Areas Covered: AZ, CA, GU, HI, NV, American Samoa, Trust Territories of the Pacific

• Regional Administrator **Barbara Y. Goto** . . . . (415) 625-2547
E-mail: goto.barbara@dol.gov
Deputy Regional Administrator **James Wulff** . . . . (415) 625-2547
E-mail: wulff.james@dol.gov
Enforcement Programs Assistant Regional Administrator **Paul Leary** . . . . (415) 625-2547
E-mail: leary.paul@dol.gov
Administrative Programs Assistant Regional Administrator **James Dement** . . . . (415) 625-2547
E-mail: dement.james@dol.gov
Cooperative and State Programs Assistant Regional Administrator **Patricia Gaydos** . . . . (415) 625-2547
E-mail: gaydos.patricia@dol.gov

Occupational Safety and Health Administration - Region 10

300 Fifth Avenue, Suite 1280, Seattle, WA 98104
Tel: (206) 757-6700 Fax: (206) 757-6705
Areas Covered: AK, ID, OR, WA

• Regional Administrator (Acting) **Barbara Y. Goto** . . . . (206) 757-6700
E-mail: goto.barbara@dol.gov

Anchorage (AK) Area Office
222 West 7th Avenue, Box 22, Anchorage, AK 99513
Tel: (907) 271-5152 Fax: (907) 271-4238

Area Director **(Vacant)** . . . . (907) 271-5152

Bellevue (WA) Area Office
520 112th Avenue N.E., Suite 200, Bellevue, WA 98004
Tel: (425) 450-5480 Fax: (425) 450-5483

Area Director **Jacob Ewer** . . . . (425) 450-5481 ext. 25
E-mail: ewer.jacob@dol.gov

Boise (ID) Area Office
1387 S. Vinnell Way, Suite 218, Boise, ID 83709
Tel: (208) 321-2960 Fax: (208) 321-2966

Area Director **David Kearns** . . . . (208) 321-2960
E-mail: kearns.david@dol.gov

Portland (OR) Area Office
911 NE 11th Avenue, Suite 649, Portland, OR 97232
Tel: (503) 231-2017 Fax: (503) 231-2329

Area Director **Cecil Tipton** . . . . (503) 326-2017
E-mail: tipton.cecil@dol.gov

Veterans' Employment and Training Service (VETS)

200 Constitution Avenue, NW, S1325, Washington, DC 20210
Tel: (202) 693-4700 Internet: www.dol.gov/vets
Internet: www.veterans.gov Internet: www.americanheroesatwork.gov

Regional Offices

Atlanta Region

Sam Nunn Atlanta Federal Center, 61 Forsyth Street, SW, Suite 6T85, Atlanta, GA 30303
Tel: (404) 665-4330 Fax: (404) 562-2313
Areas Covered: AL, FL, GA, KY, MS, NC, SC, TN

Regional Administrator **John Savage** . . . . (404) 665-4330
Deputy Regional Administrator **Matthew M. Heaney** . . . . (404) 665-4330
Veterans' Program Specialist **Vivian D. Blair** . . . . (404) 665-4330
Veterans' Program Specialist **Ramon "Luis" Burgos** . . . . (404) 665-4330
Veterans' Program Specialist **Trey Robinson** . . . . (404) 665-4330
Veterans' Program Specialist **Michael J. Long** . . . . (404) 665-4330
Administrative Officer **Travis L. Robinson** . . . . (404) 665-4330
E-mail: robinson.travis.l@dol.gov
Senior Investigator **(Vacant)** . . . . (404) 665-4330
Veterans' Employment Coordinator **Matthew A. Grob** . . . (404) 665-4330
E-mail: grob.matthew.a@dol.gov

Alabama
649 Monroe Street, Room 2218, Montgomery, AL 36131-6300
Tel: (334) 242-8116 Fax: (334) 265-8927

Director **Larry Stewart** . . . . (334) 242-8116
Assistant Director **Misty Bass** . . . . (334) 242-8116
E-mail: bass.misty@dol.gov
Assistant Director **Maxwell L. "Max" Williams** . . . . (334) 242-8116
E-mail: williams.maxwell.l@dol.gov
Veterans' Program Analyst **(Vacant)** . . . . (334) 242-8116

Florida
600 S. Calhoun Street, Suite 154, Tallahassee, FL 32399
P.O. Box 1527, Tallahassee, FL 32399
Tel: (850) 717-0765 Fax: (850) 245-7186

Director **Bernadette Walsh** . . . . (850) 245-7199
E-mail: walsh.bernadette@dol.gov
Assistant Director **Michelle Allen** . . . . (850) 717-0765
E-mail: allen.michelle.c@dol.gov
Assistant Director **Chantal Escoto** . . . . (850) 717-0765
215 Market Street, Fax: (850) 245-7186
Suite 300, Jacksonville, FL 32202-2851
P.O. Box 17747, Jacksonville, FL 32245-7747
E-mail: escoto.chantal@dol.gov
Assistant Director **Angela Mauldin** . . . . (813) 930-7889
201 14th Avenue S.E., Ruskin, FL 33570 Fax: (855) 484-6947
E-mail: mauldin.angela@dol.gov
Assistant Director **Craig Spry** . . . . (727) 608-2495
13805 58th Street North, Fax: (727) 328-3392
Suite 2-144, Clearwater, FL 33760
P.O. Box 12528, St. Petersburg, FL 33731
E-mail: spry.craig@dol.gov
Assistant Director **Thomas Richardson** . . . . (727) 608-2495
13805 58th Street North, Clearwater, FL 33760
P.O. Box 12528, St. Petersburg, FL 33731
Veterans' Program Specialist **(Vacant)** . . . . (850) 717-0765
Veterans' Program Specialist **(Vacant)** . . . . (813) 930-7889
9350 Bay Plaza Boulevard, Fax: (855) 484-6947
Suite 121, Tampa, FL 33619
Veterans' Program Specialist **(Vacant)** . . . . (850) 245-7199

Georgia
148 Andrew Young International Boulevard, Suite 225, Atlanta, GA 30303
Tel: (404) 232-3870 Fax: (404) 232-3874

Director **(Vacant)** . . . . (404) 232-3870
Assistant Director **Marion Crosby** . . . . (404) 232-3872
E-mail: crosby.marion.t@dol.gov

★ Presidential Appointment Requiring Senate Confirmation ☆ Presidential Appointment ☐ Schedule C Appointment ◇ Career Senior Foreign Service Appointment
● Career Senior Executive Service (SES) Appointment ○ Non-Career Senior Executive Service (SES) Appointment ■ Postal Career Executive Service

Georgia *(continued)*

Assistant Director
Betty Jackson CARE Building, Suite 203 . . . . (404) 232-3876
E-mail: jackson.betty.j@dol.gov
Assistant Director **(Vacant)** . . . . (404) 232-3877

Kentucky
275 East Main Street, 2nd Floor, West - 2WA, Frankfort, KY 40621-2339
Tel: (502) 564-7062 Fax: (502) 564-1476
Director **Donietta L. Hawkey** . . . . (502) 564-7062
E-mail: Hawkey.Donietta.L@dol.gov
Education: Mid-Continent BA; Trident International MBA
Assistant Director **(Vacant)** . . . . (502) 564-7062

Mississippi
1235 Echelon Parkway, Jackson, MS 39215
P.O. Box 1699, Jackson, MS 39215-1699
Tel: (601) 321-6078 Fax: (601) 321-6187
Director **Benjamin "Ben" McCaffrey** . . . . (601) 321-6078
E-mail: mccaffery.benjamin@dol.gov
Veterans' Program Specialist **Robert Smith** . . . . (601) 321-6235
E-mail: smith.robert@dol.gov

North Carolina
313 Chapanoke Road, Suite 140, Raleigh, NC 27603
P.O. Box 27625, Raleigh, NC 27611-7625
Tel: (919) 814-0250 Fax: (919) 914-0360
Director **Lane Dyer** . . . . (919) 814-0250
E-mail: dyer.lane@dol.gov
Assistant Director **J'Metria Amderson** . . . . (919) 814-0250
Assistant Director **Michael Robinson** . . . . (919) 814-0250
Veterans' Program Assistant **(Vacant)** . . . . (919) 814-0250
Information Program Assistant **(Vacant)** . . . . (919) 814-0250

South Carolina
Lem Harper Building, 631 Hampton Street,
Suite 141, Columbia, SC 29201
P.O. Box 1755, Columbia, SC 29202-1755
Tel: (803) 737-7650 Fax: (803) 737-7656
Director **Robert Trahan** . . . . (803) 737-7650
E-mail: trahan.robert@dol.gov Fax: (803) 737-7656
Assistant Director **(Vacant)** . . . . (803) 737-4893
1550 Gadsden Street, Fax: (803) 737-4423
Room 133, Columbia, SC 29201
Assistant Director **(Vacant)** . . . . (803) 737-7650
Veterans' Program Specialist **(Vacant)** . . . . (803) 737-7649

Tennessee
665 Mainstream Drive, Room 1.313, Clarksville, TN 37243
Tel: (615) 736-7680 Fax: (615) 741-4241
Director **Wendy Harrison** . . . . (615) 736-7680
E-mail: harrison.wendy.d@dol.gov
Assistant Director **Brett Abernathy** . . . . (615) 736-7680
E-mail: abernathy.brett@dol.gov
Assistant Director **(Vacant)** . . . . (615) 736-7680
Fax: (615) 741-4241
Veterans' Program Specialist **(Vacant)** . . . . (615) 736-7680

Boston Region
John F. Kennedy Federal Building, Room E-315, Boston, MA 02203
Tel: (617) 565-2080 Fax: (617) 565-2082
Areas Covered: CT, ME, MA, NH, NJ, NY, PR, RI, VI, VT
Regional Administrator **Michael J. Colman** . . . . (617) 565-2080
E-mail: colman.michael.j@dol.gov
Deputy Regional Administrator **Nuno A. Medeiros** . . . . . . (617) 565-2080
E-mail: medeiros.nuno.a@dol.gov
Senior Veterans' Program Specialist
Charlotte Brindley . . . . (617) 565-2080
E-mail: brindley.charlotte@dol.gov
Veterans' Program Specialist **John Vincent Sabella** . . . . . (617) 565-2080
E-mail: sabella.johnvincent@dol.gov

Boston Region *(continued)*
Veterans' Program Specialist **Yendis Colon** . . . . (617) 565-2080
E-mail: colon.yendis@dol.gov
Veterans' Employment Coordinator **Paul M. Furbush II** . . . (617) 565-2080
E-mail: furbush.paul.m@dol.gov
Senior Investigator **James N. Downey** . . . . (617) 565-2080
E-mail: downey.james.n@dol.gov
Administrative Officer **(Vacant)** . . . . (617) 565-2080

Connecticut
200 Folly Brook Boulevard, Wethersfield, CT 06109
Tel: (860) 263-6490 Fax: (860) 263-6498
State Director **Lisa C. Jones** . . . . (860) 263-6490
E-mail: jones.lisa.c@dol.gov
Assistant Director **Heather Suddaby** . . . . (860) 263-6490
E-mail: suddaby.heather.a@dol.gov
Veterans Program Assistant **(Vacant)** . . . . (860) 263-6490

Maine
5 Mollison Way, Suite 104, Lewiston, ME 04240
Tel: (207) 753-9089 Fax: (207) 783-5304
State Director **Debbie J. Kelly** . . . . (207) 753-9089
E-mail: kelly.debbie.j@dol.gov

Massachusetts
C. F. Hurley Building, 19 Staniford Street,
1st Floor, Boston, MA 02114
Tel: (617) 626-6699 Fax: (617) 727-2330
State Director **Anthony "Tony" Laterza** . . . . (617) 626-6699
E-mail: laterza.anthony@dol.gov
Assistant Director **Chris E. Brown** . . . . (617) 626-6699
E-mail: brown.chris.e@dol.gov
Assistant Director **Karen J. Frias** . . . . (617) 626-6699
E-mail: frias.karen.j@dol.gov
Veterans Program Assistant **Christine "Tina" Beech** . . . . . (617) 626-6699
E-mail: beech.christine@dol.gov

New Hampshire
45 South Fruit Street, Room 336, Concord, NH 03301
Tel: (603) 225-1424 Fax: (603) 225-1545
State Director **Donna M. Nobrega** . . . . (603) 225-1424
E-mail: nobrega.donna.m@dol.gov
Veterans Program Specialist **(Vacant)** . . . . (603) 225-1424

New Jersey
1 John Fitch Plaza, 10th Floor, Trenton, NJ 08625 (PO Box 058)
Tel: (609) 292-2930 Fax: (609) 292-9070
Director **(Vacant)** . . . . (609) 292-2930
Assistant Director **(Vacant)** . . . . (609) 292-2930
Assistant Director **Anthony J. Sordini** . . . . (609) 292-2930
Assistant Director **Terray E. Wood** . . . . (609) 292-2930
E-mail: wood.terray.e@dol.gov
Veterans Program Specialist **(Vacant)** . . . . (609) 292-2930
Veterans' Program Assistant **(Vacant)** . . . . (609) 292-2930

New York
Building 12, Harriman State Campus, Room 518, Albany, NY 12240-0099
Fax: (518) 435-0833
State Director **COL Eric J. Hesse USA (Ret)** . . . . (518) 457-7465
E-mail: hesse.eric.j@dol.gov
Assistant Director **Anthony Alicea** . . . . (315) 772-0837
11042 Mount Belvedere Boulevard, Fax: (315) 772-7720
Room128, Fort Drum, NY 13602
E-mail: alicea.anthony@dol.gov
Assistant Director **Alexander "Alex" Ciccarone** . . . . (518) 457-7465
E-mail: ciccarone.alex@dol.gov
Assistant Director **Edward L. Diaz** . . . . (718) 613-3677
Nine Bond Street, Room 302, Brooklyn, NY 11201
E-mail: diaz.edward.l@dol.gov

(continued on next page)

★ Presidential Appointment Requiring Senate Confirmation ☆ Presidential Appointment □ Schedule C Appointment ◇ Career Senior Foreign Service Appointment
● Career Senior Executive Service (SES) Appointment ○ Non-Career Senior Executive Service (SES) Appointment ■ Postal Career Executive Service

DEPARTMENTS

New York *(continued)*

Assistant Director **Marlon Ramirez** .... (718) 613-3677
Nine Bond Street, Fax: (718) 613-3685
Room 4511, Brooklyn, NY 11201
PO Box 668, New York, NY 10014-0668
E-mail: ramirez.marlon@dol.gov
Assistant Director **Kristi E. Schmidt** .... (518) 457-7465
E-mail: schmidt.kristi.e@dol.gov
Veterans' Program Assistant **(Vacant)** .... (518) 457-7465

Puerto Rico and Virgin Islands
National Plaza Building, 431 Ponce de León Avenue,
Suite 12, Hato Rey, PR 00917
Tel: (787) 625-3137 ext. 2530 Fax: (787) 945-7471
Areas Covered: PR, VI
Director **Miguel Gonzalez** .... (787) 625-3137
E-mail: gonzalez.miguel@dol.gov
Veterans' Program Specialist **Dennis Torres** .... (787) 625-3137
E-mail: torres.dennis.m@dol.gov

Rhode Island
Dr. John E. Donley Rehabilitation Center,
249 Blackstone Boulevard, Providence, RI 02906
Tel: (401) 243-1281 Fax: (401) 243-1240
Director **James J. White** .... (401) 243-1281
E-mail: white.james.j@dol.gov
Veterans' Program Assistant **(Vacant)** .... (401) 243-1281

Vermont
63 Pearl Street, Suite 207, Burlington, VT 05401
Mail: P.O. Box 603, Montpelier, VT 05601
Tel: (802) 828-2057 Fax: (802) 828-2069
Director **Mark Audy** .... (802) 652-0324
E-mail: audy.mark.a@dol.gov Fax: (802) 863-7538
Program Assistant **(Vacant)** .... (802) 828-2057

Chicago Region
230 South Dearborn Street, Room 1064, Chicago, IL 60604
Tel: (312) 353-0970 Fax: (312) 886-1184
Areas Covered: IL, IN, IA, KS, MI, MN, MO, NE, OH, WI
Regional Administrator **Heather Higgins** .... (312) 353-0970
E-mail: higgins.heather@dol.gov
Deputy Regional Administrator **Patricia Mayfield** .... (312) 353-0971
230 South Dearborn Street, Room 1064, Chicago, IL 60604-1505
E-mail: mayfield.patricia@dol.gov
Regional Veterans' Employment Coordinator
Eric K. Asmussen .... (312) 353-6489
Supervisor Veterans' Program Specialist
Travis S. Siggers .... (312) 886-0692
E-mail: siggers.travis.s@dol.gov
Veterans' Program Specialist **Anthony Spraggins** .... (312) 886-6972
E-mail: spraggins.anthony@dol.gov
Veterans' Program Specialist **(Vacant)** .... (312) 353-0972
Veterans' Program Specialist **(Vacant)** .... (312) 353-4933
230 South Dearborn Street, Room 1064, Chicago, IL 60604-1505
Management Services Assistant **Calvin Lane** .... (312) 886-0694
E-mail: lane.calvin@dol.gov

Illinois
33 South State Street, 8th Floor, Room N811, Chicago, IL 60605
Tel: (312) 793-3433 Fax: (312) 793-4795
Director **Robert Mikyska** .... (312) 793-3433
E-mail: Mikyska.robert.j@dol.gov
Assistant Director **Sheneen L. Ammons** .... (312) 793-3433
E-mail: ammons.sheneen.l@dol.gov
Assistant Director **Adriane D. Easte** .... (312) 793-3433
E-mail: easte.adriane.d@dol.gov
Assistant Director **Jose I. Ponce** .... (312) 793-3433
E-mail: ponce.jose.i@dol.gov
Assistant Director **(Vacant)** .... (312) 793-3433
Veterans' Program Assistant **Bianca Elmore** .... (312) 793-3433
E-mail: elmore.bianca@dol.gov

Indiana
10 North Senate Avenue, Room SE 103, Indianapolis, IN 46204
Tel: (317) 232-6804 Fax: (317) 232-5720
Director **Steven P. Potter** .... (317) 232-6804
E-mail: potter.p.steven@dol.gov
Assistant Director **David Rowell** .... (317) 232-6803
E-mail: rowell.david@dol.gov
Assistant Director **(Vacant)** .... (317) 232-4188
Veterans' Program Assistant **Donald Mains** .... (317) 232-6805
E-mail: mains.donald@dol.gov

Iowa
1000 East Grand Avenue, 1st Floor, Des Moines, IA 50319
Fax: (515) 281-9063
Director **Anthony J. Smithhart** 2nd Floor .... (515) 281-9062
E-mail: smithhart.anthony@dol.gov
Assistant Director
Steven J. "Steve" Olsen 2nd Floor .... (515) 281-9061
E-mail: olsen.steven.j@dol.gov

Kansas
900 South Kansas Avenue, Suite 305, Topeka, KS 66612-1220
Tel: (785) 783-8263 Fax: (785) 783-8542
Director **Theo Coney** .... (785) 783-8264
E-mail: coney.theathria@dol.gov
Assistant Director **(Vacant)** .... (785) 783-8263
Veterans' Program Specialist **Levi Perkins** .... (785) 783-8263
E-mail: perkins.levi.c@dol.gov

Michigan
Victor Office Center, 201 North Washington Square,
1st Floor, Lansing, MI 48913
Tel: (517) 373-7094 Fax: (517) 373-1117
Director **Stacey G. Cooper** .... (517) 373-7094
E-mail: cooper.stacey.g@dol.gov
Assistant Director **Christina Bartholomew** .... (517) 373-7094
E-mail: bartholomew.christina@dol.gov
Veterans' Program Assistant **Ethan McCallum** .... (517) 373-7094
E-mail: McCallum.Ethan.J@dol.gov

Minnesota
1st Bank Building, 332 Minnesota Street,
Suite W1372, St. Paul, MN 55101-1351
Tel: (651) 259-7511 Fax: (651) 282-2711
Director **David Seay** .... (651) 259-7511
E-mail: seay.david@dol.gov
Assistant Director **(Vacant)** .... (651) 259-7512
Veterans' Program Assistant **Anthony "Tony" Franz** .... (651) 259-7512
E-mail: franz.anthony@dol.gov

Missouri
421 East Dunklin Street, Jefferson City, MO 65101-3138
Tel: (573) 751-3921 Fax: (573) 751-6710
Director **William A. "Bill" Benzel** .... (573) 751-3921
E-mail: benzel.william@dol.gov
Assistant Director **Jeremy Amick** .... (573) 751-3921
E-mail: amick.jeremy@dol.gov
Assistant Director **Shawn C. Johnson** .... (573) 751-3921
E-mail: johnson.shawn@dol.gov

Nebraska
P.O. Box 94600, Lincoln, NE 68509-4600
550 South 16th Street, Room 206, Lincoln, NE 68508
Tel: (402) 471-9833 Fax: (402) 471-2092
Director **Cecilia Coatney** .... (402) 471-9837
E-mail: coatney.cecilia.k@dol.gov
Veterans' Program Assistant **(Vacant)** .... (402) 471-9833

★ Presidential Appointment Requiring Senate Confirmation ☆ Presidential Appointment ☐ Schedule C Appointment ◇ Career Senior Foreign Service Appointment
● Career Senior Executive Service (SES) Appointment ○ Non-Career Senior Executive Service (SES) Appointment ■ Postal Career Executive Service

Ohio
4020 East Fifth Avenue, Room M-153, Columbus, OH 43219-1618
P.O. Box 1618, Columbus, OH 43219
Tel: (614) 466-2768 Fax: (614) 752-5007

Director **Darrin Adams** .... (614) 466-2768
E-mail: adams.darrin.m@dol.gov
Assistant Director **Richard "Rich" Gelin** .... (614) 466-2768
2026 South Avenue, Youngstown, OH 44502
E-mail: gelin.richard@dol.gov
Assistant Director **(Vacant)** .... (614) 466-2768
Assistant Director **Nelson "Pat" Patrick** .... (614) 466-2768
E-mail: nelson.patrick@dol.gov
Veterans' Program Assistant **Dorinda Johnston** .... (614) 466-2768
E-mail: johnston.dorinda@dol.gov

Wisconsin
201 East Washington Avenue, Room G109, Madison, WI 53703
Mail: P.O. Box 8310, Madison, WI 53708-8310
Tel: (608) 266-3110 Fax: (608) 261-6710

Director **Patrick J. Kilgore** .... (608) 266-3110
E-mail: kilgore.patrick.j@dol.gov
Assistant Director **Michael D. Beck** .... (608) 266-8600
E-mail: beck.michael.d@dol.gov
Veterans' Program Assistant **(Vacant)** Room G-201A .... (608) 266-8600

Dallas Region
Federal Building, 525 South Griffin Street,
Room 858, Dallas, TX 75202-5096
Tel: (972) 850-4715 Fax: (972) 850-4716
Areas Covered: AR, CO, LA, MT, ND, NM, OK, SD, TX, UT, WY

Regional Administrator **Robert Creel** .... (972) 850-4715
E-mail: creel.robert@dol.gov
Deputy Regional Administrator **George J. Riedel** .... (972) 850-4719
E-mail: riedel.george.j@dol.gov
Veterans Program Specialist **Terri Cook** .... (972) 850-4721
E-mail: cook.terri@dol.gov
Veterans Program Specialist **Rebekah Haydin** .... (972) 850-4720
E-mail: haydin.rebekah@dol.gov
Veterans' Program Specialist **Demond L. Hassell** .... (972) 850-4723
E-mail: hassell.demond.l@dol.gov
Supervisory Veterans' Program Specialist
David A. Vogt .... (972) 850-4724
E-mail: vogt.david@dol.gov
Supervisory Investigator **Kimberly R. Spakes** .... (972) 850-4722
E-mail: spakes.kimberly.r@dol.gov

Arkansas
Arkansas Department of Workforce Services, Two Capital Mall,
Room 237, Little Rock, AR 72201
P.O. Box 128, Little Rock, AR 72203
Fax: (501) 682-3752

Director **Roy Schultz** .... (501) 682-3785
E-mail: schultz.roy@dol.gov
Assistant Director **John Donovan** .... (501) 682-3786
E-mail: donovan.john@dol.gov

Colorado
633 17th Street, 9th Floor, Denver, CO 80202
Tel: (303) 318-8827 Fax: (303) 844-2017

Director **Brian Gault** .... (303) 318-8371
E-mail: gault.brian.d@dol.gov
Assistant Director **David Palmer** .... (719) 226-8031
2864 S. Circle Drive, Fax: (719) 226-8032
Suite 375, Colorado Springs, CO 80906
E-mail: palmer.david@dol.gov
Assistant Director **Jovita Martinez** .... (303) 318-8827
E-mail: martinez.jovita@dol.gov
Veterans' Program Analyst **Terri R. Register** .... (303) 318-8371
E-mail: register.terri.r@dol.gov

Louisiana
1001 North 23rd Street, Room 184, Baton Rouge, LA 70802
Mail: P.O. Box 94094, Baton Rouge, LA 70804-9094
Tel: (225) 342-4692 Fax: (225) 342-3152

Director **Billy Miller** .... (225) 342-4692
E-mail: miller.billy@dol.gov
Assistant Director **(Vacant)** .... (337) 262-6714
Veterans' Program Specialist **(Vacant)** .... (225) 389-0440
Senior Investigator **Woody Lambert** .... (225) 342-4692
E-mail: lambert.woody@dol.gov

Montana
715 Front Street, Room 578, Helena, MT 59601
P.O. Box 1728, Helena, MT 59604
Tel: (406) 447-3233 Fax: (406) 447-3213

Director **Thomas L. Finch, Jr.** .... (406) 447-3233
E-mail: finch.thomas.l@dol.gov
Veterans' Program Assistant **Scott Mitchell** .... (406) 447-3233
E-mail: mitchell.scott@dol.gov

New Mexico
401 Broadway Boulevard Northeast, Albuquerque, NM 87102
Mail: P.O. Box 25085, Albuquerque, NM 87102-2301
Fax: (505) 242-6179

Director **Spencer Weaver** .... (505) 346-7502
E-mail: weaver.spencer.l@dol.gov
Veterans' Program Analyst **Sandra Epenesa** .... (505) 346-7503
E-mail: epenesa.sandra@dol.gov

North Dakota
1000 East Divide Avenue, Bismarck, ND 58501
Fax: (701) 328-2890

Director **Gerald H. "Jerry" Meske** .... (701) 250-4337
E-mail: meske.gerald@dol.gov
Veterans' Program Assistant **(Vacant)** .... (701) 250-4337

Oklahoma
2401 North Lincoln Boulevard, Room 304-2, Oklahoma City, OK 73105
P.O. Box 52003, Oklahoma City, OK 73152-2003
Tel: (405) 231-5088 Tel: (405) 557-7189 Fax: (405) 557-7123

Director **Kenneth "Ken" Allen** .... (405) 231-5088
E-mail: allen.kenneth@dol.gov
Assistant Director **Lucius Drawhorn** .... (405) 231-5088
E-mail: drawhorn.lucius@dol.gov
Veterans' Program Assistant **Donna D. Winklesky** ...... (405) 231-5088
E-mail: winklesky.donna@dol.gov

South Dakota
420 South Roosevelt Street, Aberdeen, SD 57401-5131
Mail: P.O. Box 4730, Aberdeen, SD 57402-4730
Tel: (605) 626-2325 Fax: (605) 626-2359

Director **Sarah Bierman** .... (605) 626-2325
E-mail: bierman.sarah@dol.gov
Veterans' Program Specialist **Nicole Renner** .... (605) 626-2325
E-mail: renner.nicole.m@dol.gov

Texas
TWC Building, 1117 Trinity Street, Room 516-T, Austin, TX 78701
Mail: P.O. Box 1468, Austin, TX 78767
Tel: (512) 463-2814 Fax: (512) 475-2999

Director **Brian C. Schroepfer** .... (512) 463-2207
E-mail: schroepfer.brian.c@dol.gov
Assistant Director **Steven L. Day** .... (512) 463-2056
301 West 13th Street, Suite 407, Fort Worth, TX 76102-4699
P.O. Box 591, Fort Worth, TX 76102-0591
E-mail: day.steven.l@dol.gov
Assistant Director **Frances DeSoto** .... (210) 582-1629
Workforce Solutions Alamo - Walzem, Fax: (210) 822-6068
4615 Walzem Road,
Suite 100, San Antonio, TX 78218-1610
E-mail: desoto.frances@dol.gov

(continued on next page)

★ Presidential Appointment Requiring Senate Confirmation ☆ Presidential Appointment ☐ Schedule C Appointment ◇ Career Senior Foreign Service Appointment
● Career Senior Executive Service (SES) Appointment ○ Non-Career Senior Executive Service (SES) Appointment ■ Postal Career Executive Service

DEPARTMENTS

Texas *(continued)*

Assistant Director **Philip Q. Estep** . . . . (512) 463-2816
E-mail: estep.philip.q@dol.gov
Assistant Director **Jason Evans** . . . . (512) 463-2815
E-mail: evans.jason@dol.gov
Assistant Director **Janice Maupin-Anderson** . . . . (512) 463-2065
E-mail: maupinanderson.jan@dol.gov
Veterans' Program Specialist **(Vacant)** . . . . (512) 463-2056
Veterans' Program Assistant **(Vacant)** . . . . (512) 463-2814
4615 Walzem Road, San Antonio, TX 78218-1610

Utah

140 East 300 South, Suite 209, Salt Lake City, UT 84111-2333
Tel: (801) 524-5703 Fax: (801) 524-3099

Director **Howard Dale Brockbank** . . . . (801) 524-5703
E-mail: brockbank.howard@dol.gov
Veterans' Program Specialist **Karen Williams** . . . . (801) 524-5703
E-mail: williams.karen@dol.gov

Wyoming

100 West Midwest Avenue, Casper, WY 82602-2429
Mail: P.O. Box 2760, Casper, WY 82602-2760
Tel: (307) 261-5454 Tel: (307) 235-3281 Tel: (307) 235-3282
Fax: (307) 235-3272

Director **Laura J. Jeffrey** . . . . (307) 777-7631
1510 East Pershing Boulevard, Fax: (307) 777-5298
Second Floor, Room 2019, Cheyenne, WY 82001
E-mail: jeffrey.laura.j@dol.gov
Veterans' Program Assistant **(Vacant)** . . . . (307) 261-5454

Philadelphia Region

170 South Independence Mall West, Suite 770 West,
Philadelphia, PA 19106-3310
Fax: (215) 861-5389
Areas Covered: DE, DC, MD, PA, VA, WV, NJ, NY, PR, VI

Regional Administrator **Timothy P. "Tim" Crowley** . . . . . (215) 861-5390
E-mail: crowley.timothy.p@dol.gov
Deputy Regional Administrator **Marcus K. Wardlaw** . . . . (215) 861-5390
E-mail: wardlaw.marcus.k@dol.gov
Veterans Program Specialist **Carolyn Applewhite** . . . . (215) 861-5390
E-mail: applewhite.carolyn@dol.gov
Veterans Program Specialist **LaCarole Faulkner** . . . . (215) 861-5390
E-mail: faulkner.lacarole@dol.gov
Veterans Program Specialist **Virginia M. Youst** . . . . (215) 861-5390
E-mail: youst.virginia@dol.gov
Senior Investigator **Paul Marone** . . . . (215) 861-5390
E-mail: marone.paul@dol.gov

Delaware

Annex Building, 4425 North Market Street, Wilmington, DE 19802
Tel: (302) 761-8138 Fax: (302) 761-4676

Director **David B. Rich** . . . . (302) 761-8139
E-mail: rich.david@dol.gov
Veterans Program Assistant **James E. Williams** . . . . (302) 761-8138
E-mail: williams.james.e@dol.gov

District of Columbia

4058 Minnesota Avenue, N.E., Suite 4007, Washington, DC 20019
Tel: (202) 671-2179 Fax: (202) 671-1503

Director **Lane V. Williams** . . . . (202) 671-2143
E-mail: williams.lane.v@dol.gov
Assistant Director **Omar A. Williams** . . . . (202) 671-2120
E-mail: williams.omar.a@dol.gov

Maryland

1100 North Eutaw Street, Room 201, Baltimore, MD 21201
Tel: (410) 767-2110 Fax: (410) 333-5136

Director **Kristoffer M. Evans** . . . . (410) 767-2110
E-mail: evans.kristoffer.m@dol.gov
Assistant Director **Willis E. Gay** . . . . (410) 767-2110
Veterans' Program Assistant **(Vacant)** . . . . (410) 767-2111

Maryland *(continued)*

Veterans Program Specialist **(Vacant)** . . . . (301) 393-8253
14 North Potomac Street, Fax: (301) 393-2654
Suite 100, Hagerstown, MD 21740

Pennsylvania

Labor and Industry Building, 651 Boas Street,
Room 1106, Harrisburg, PA 17121
Fax: (717) 783-2631

Director **Randall Wright** . . . . (717) 787-5834
E-mail: wright.randall@dol.gov
Assistant Director **Dennis M. Ero** . . . . (814) 445-4161 ext. 239
Somerset Job, 218 North Kimberly Avenue, Fax: (814) 445-3913
Somerset, PA 15501-4161
E-mail: ero.dennis@dol.gov
Assistant Director **David Cummiskey** . . . . (717) 787-5834
E-mail: cummiskey.david.p@dol.gov
Assistant Director **Vincent DeMedici** . . . . (717) 787-5834
E-mail: demedici.vincent@dol.gov
Assistant Director **Billy Lanham** . . . . (717) 783-8113
E-mail: lanham.billy.g@dol.gov

Virginia

707 East Main Street, Room 118, Richmond, VA 23219
Fax: (804) 786-4548

Director **Patrick Hecker** . . . . (804) 786-7269
E-mail: hecker.patrick@dol.gov
Assistant Director **Aleshia V. Thomas-Miller** . . . . (703) 813-1314
5520 Cherokee Avenue, Fax: (703) 813-1338
Suite 16-, Alexandria, VA 22312
E-mail: miller.aleshia.v@dol.gov
Assistant Director **Tony E. Cropper** . . . . (757) 629-4721
861 Glenrock Road, Fax: (757) 455-0415
Suite 100, Norfolk, VA 23502
E-mail: cropper.tony.e@dol.gov
Assistant Director **Patricia Sykes** . . . . (804) 786-5436
E-mail: sykes.patricia@dol.gov

West Virginia

Building 3, 1900 Kanawha Blvd E, Suite 400,
Charleston, WV 25305-0112
Tel: (304) 558-4001 Fax: (304) 344-4591

Director **Cheryl A. Stiles** . . . . (304) 558-4001
Veterans' Program Specialist **Jeffrey Schoolcraft** . . . . (304) 558-4001
E-mail: schoolcraft.jeffrey@dol.gov
Veterans Program Specialist
(Vacant) Capitol Complex, Room 112F . . . . (304) 558-4001

San Francisco Region

90 Seventh Street, Suite 2-600, San Francisco, CA 94103
Tel: (415) 625-7670 Fax: (415) 625-7677
Areas Covered: AK, WA, ID, OR, AZ, CA, HI, NV

Regional Administrator **Alfred L. Kwok** . . . . (415) 625-7673
Deputy Regional Administrator **Nancy J. Sanders** . . . . . . (415) 625-7671
E-mail: sanders.nancy@dol.gov
Supervisory Veterans' Program Specialist
Barrett S. Watkins . . . . (415) 625-7672
E-mail: watkins.barrett.s@dol.gov
Veterans' Program Specialist **Rebecca M. Klein** . . . . (415) 625-7675
71 Stevenson Street, Suite 705, San Francisco, CA 94105
E-mail: klein.rebecca.m@dol.gov
Veterans' Program Specialist **Pamela Young** . . . . (415) 625-7673
E-mail: young.pamela@dol.gov
Veterans' Program Specialist **Roloando C. Calvo** . . . . (415) 625-7680
E-mail: calvo.rolando.c@dol.gov
Veterans' Program Specialist **Timothy Hall** . . . . (415) 625-7674
E-mail: hall.timothy@dol.gov
Veterans' Employment Coordinator
LTC Tony D. Forbes USA . . . . (415) 625-7676
E-mail: Forbes.Tony.D@dol.gov
Senior Investigator **Rebecca M. Klein** . . . . (415) 625-7675
E-mail: klein.rebecca.m@dol.gov

Alaska
3301 Eagle Street, Suite 101, Anchorage, AK 99503
Fax: (907) 754-3436

Director **Aaron A. Gustafson** . . . . (907) 754-3438
E-mail: gustafson.aaron.a@dol.gov
Assistant Director **(Vacant)** . . . . (907) 754-3437
Veterans Program Assistant **(Vacant)** . . . . (907) 465-2723

Arizona
1400 West Washington Street, Suite 123, Phoenix, AZ 85005
P.O. Box 6123-SC760E, Phoenix, AZ 85005
Tel: (602) 542-2516 Fax: (602) 542-4103

Director **Jesus A. Arrieta** . . . . (602) 542-2516
E-mail: arrieta.jesus.a@dol.gov
Assistant Director **DeeAnna Bratton** . . . . (602) 542-2515
E-mail: bratton.deeanna@dol.gov
Veterans Program Assistant **(Vacant)** . . . . (602) 542-2516

California
2450 E. Lincoln Avenue, Anaheim, CA 92806
P.O. Box 826880, Sacramento, CA 94280-0001
Tel: (916) 654-8282 Fax: (916) 654-9469

Director **Jason Keller** . . . . (916) 654-8282
E-mail: keller.jason.r@dol.gov
Assistant Director **Raymond Carrillo** . . . . (916) 654-8282
E-mail: carrillo.raymond@dol.gov
Assistant Director **Jeffery Chao** . . . . (626) 282-0220
933 South Glendora Avenue, Fax: (626) 282-0540
West Covina, CA 91790
E-mail: chao.jeffery@dol.gov
Assistant Director **Linda Cole** Room 201 . . . . (707) 648-5569
E-mail: jacobe.linda@dol.gov Fax: (707) 648-0102
Assistant Director **Nancy Ise** . . . . (714) 687-4845
2450 East Lincoln Avenue, Fax: (714) 518-2391
Anaheim, CA 92806-4175
E-mail: ise.nancy@dol.gov
Assistant Director **(Vacant)** . . . . (925) 602-5032
4071 Port Chicago Highway, Fax: (925) 602-1585
Suite 250, Concord, CA 94520
Assistant Director **Cristino M. Medina** . . . . (916) 654-8180
E-mail: medina.cristino.m@dol.gov
Assistant Director **Maarla K. Milligan** . . . . (619) 266-4299
4389 Imperial Ave, San Diego, CA 92113 Fax: (619) 264-3407
E-mail: milligan.maarla.k@dol.gov
Assistant Director **Joseph Moran** . . . . (760) 639-3761
1949 Avenida del Oro, Fax: (760) 639-3892
Suite 114, Oceanside, CA 92056
E-mail: moran.joseph@dol.gov
Assistant Director **Jose N. Sanchez** . . . . (714) 687-4847
13160 Mindanao Way, Fax: (714) 687-0502
Suite 105, Marina del Rey, CA 90292-7904
E-mail: sanchez.jose.n@dol.gov
Assistant Director **Brandon C. Webb** . . . . (916) 654-8178
E-mail: webb.brandon.c@dol.gov
Tel: (916) 657-0763
Veterans Program Assistant **Wendy Andersen** . . . . (707) 648-5569
E-mail: andersen.wendy@dol.gov Fax: (707) 648-0102

Hawaii/Guam
Keelikolani Building, 830 Punchbowl Street,
Room 315, Honolulu, HI 96813
P.O. Box 3680, Honolulu, HI 96811
Tel: (808) 522-8216 Fax: (808) 586-9258

Director **BrigGen Ann Greenlee ANG** . . . . (808) 522-8216
E-mail: greenlee.ann.m@dol.gov
Assistant Director **Bridget Komine** . . . . (808) 586-8827
E-mail: komine.bridget@dol.gov

Idaho
317 West Main Street, Boise, ID 83735
Tel: (208) 332-8946 Fax: (208) 334-6389

Director **Pamela K. Langley** . . . . (208) 332-8946

Idaho *(continued)*

Assistant Director **Brent M. Ferro** . . . . (208) 332-8947
E-mail: ferro.brent.m@dol.gov

Nevada
2800 East St. Louis Avenue, Las Vegas, NV 89104
Fax: (702) 486-6426

Director **Doreen A. Owens** . . . . (702) 486-2883
E-mail: owens.doreen.a@dol.gov
Assistant Director **James A. "Jim" Scheppard** . . . . (702) 486-0539
E-mail: scheppard.james.a@dol.gov Fax: (702) 486-6426

Oregon
Employment Division Building, 875 Union Street, NE,
Room 303, Salem, OR 97311-0100
77959 Southwest Mohawk Street, Tualatin, OR 97062
Tel: (503) 947-1490 (Salem) Tel: (503) 612-4328 (Tualatin)
Fax: (503) 947-1492 (Salem) Fax: (503) 612-4250 (Tualatin)

Director **Tonja M. Pardo** . . . . (503) 947-1490
E-mail: pardo.tonja@dol.gov
Assistant Director **Eddie Abrams** . . . . (503) 947-1490
1433 SW Sixth Avenue, Portland, OR 97201
E-mail: abrams.eddie@dol.gov
Assistant Director **(Vacant)** . . . . (503) 947-1490
1433 SW Sixth Avenue, Portland, OR 97201
Veterans Program Assistant **(Vacant)** . . . . (503) 947-1490

Washington
1570 Irving Street Southwest, Tumwater, WA 98512
Tel: (360) 507-9739 Fax: (360) 507-9957

Director **Shannon L. Langley** . . . . (360) 507-9740
E-mail: langley.shannon.l@dol.gov
Assistant Director **Rachel Bailey** . . . . (360) 507-9741
E-mail: bailey.rachel@dol.gov
Assistant Director **Terry Jones** . . . . (360) 507-9742
E-mail: jones.terry@dol.gov
Veterans Program Assistant **(Vacant)** . . . . (360) 407-4636

Women's Bureau (WB)
200 Constitution Avenue, NW, Washington, DC 20210
Tel: (202) 693-6710 Fax: (202) 693-6725
Fax: (202) 693-6746 (Alternate) Internet: www.dol.gov/wb

Regional Offices

Region 1
John F. Kennedy Federal Building, Room 525 A, Boston, MA 02203
Tel: (617) 565-1988 Fax: (617) 565-1986
Areas Covered: CT, ME, MA, NH, RI, VT

Regional Administrator **Jacqueline R. Cooke** . . . . (617) 565-1988
E-mail: cooke.jacqueline@dol.gov
Program Analyst **Angela M. Rizzolo** . . . . (617) 565-1988
E-mail: rizzolo.angela@dol.gov
Program Assistant **Barbara C. Stadig** . . . . (617) 565-1988
E-mail: stadig.barbara@dol.gov

Region 2
201 Varick Street, Room 602, New York, NY 10014-4811
Tel: (646) 264-3789 Fax: (646) 264-3794
Areas Covered: NJ, NY, PR, VI

Regional Administrator (Acting)
Joan Harrigan-Farrelly . . . . (646) 264-3789
E-mail: farrelly.joan@dol.gov
Program Analyst **Mallory Trachtenberg** . . . . (646) 264-3789
E-mail: trachtenberg.mallory@dol.gov
Program Analyst **(Vacant)** . . . . (646) 264-3789

DEPARTMENTS

Region 3

The Curtis Center, 170 South Independence Mall West,
Suite 631E, Philadelphia, PA 19106-3317
Tel: (215) 861-4860 Fax: (215) 861-4867
Areas Covered: DE, DC, MD, PA, VA, WV

Regional Administrator (Acting) **Rose Holandez** .... (215) 861-4860
E-mail: holandez.rose@dol.gov
Senior Program Analyst **(Vacant)** .... (215) 861-4860

Region 4

Samuel Nunn Federal Center, 61 Forsyth Street, SW,
Suite 6875, Atlanta, GA 30303
Tel: (404) 562-2336 Fax: (404) 562-2413
Areas Covered: AL, FL, GA, KY, MS, NC, SC, TN

Regional Administrator **Paulette Lewis** .... (404) 562-2336
Program Assistant **Viola J. Fountain** .... (404) 562-2336
E-mail: fountain.viola@dol.gov
Program Analyst **(Vacant)** .... (404) 562-2336

Region 5

Kluczynski Federal Building, 230 South Dearborn Street,
Room 1022, Chicago, IL 60604
Tel: (312) 353-6985 Fax: (312) 353-6986
Areas Covered: IL, IN, MI, MN, OH, WI

Regional Administrator **Grace Protos** .... (312) 353-6985 ext. 4
E-mail: protos.grace@dol.gov
Program Analyst **Deborah Pascal** .... (312) 353-6985 ext. 2
E-mail: pascal.deborah@dol.gov
Program Analyst **(Vacant)** .... (312) 353-6985

Region 6

Federal Building, 525 South Griffin Street,
Room 735, Dallas, TX 75202
Tel: (972) 850-4700 Fax: (972) 850-4706
Areas Covered: AR, LA, NM, OK, TX

Regional Administrator **Charmaine Davis** .... (972) 850-4700 ext. 1
E-mail: davis.charmaine@dol.gov
Program Analyst **Dolores Bischof** .... (972) 850-4700 ext. 2
E-mail: bischof.dolores@dol.gov
Program Analyst **Valerie Davis** .... (972) 850-4700 ext. 3
E-mail: davis.valerie@dol.gov

Region 7

2300 Main Street, Suite 1050, Kansas City, MO 64108
Tel: (816) 285-7234 Fax: (816) 285-7237
Areas Covered: IA, KS, MO, NE

Regional Administrator (Acting) **Grace Protos** .... (816) 285-7234
E-mail: protos.grace@dol.gov
Program Analyst **Olivia Schuckman** .... (816) 285-7234
E-mail: schuckman.olivia@dol.gov
Program Analyst **Carla Tillmon** .... (816) 285-7234
E-mail: tillmon.carla@dol.gov

Region 8

1999 Broadway, Suite 1620, Denver, CO 80202-6550
Tel: (303) 844-1286 Fax: (303) 844-1283
Areas Covered: CO, MT, ND, SD, UT, WY

Regional Administrator **(Vacant)** .... (303) 844-1286
Program Analyst
Marzette Bedford-Billinghurst .... (303) 844-1286 ext. 2
E-mail: bedford-billinghurst.marzette@dol.gov
Program Analyst **(Vacant)** .... (303) 844-1286 ext. 3

Region 9

90 Seventh Street, Suite 2-650, San Francisco, CA 94103
Tel: (415) 625-2638 Fax: (415) 625-2641
Areas Covered: AZ, CA, GU, HI, NV

Regional Administrator **Kelly Jenkins-Pultz** .... (415) 625-2640
E-mail: jenkins-pultz.kelly@dol.gov
Education: St Mary's Col (MD) 1985 BA;
George Washington 1991 MA
Program Analyst **(Vacant)** .... (415) 625-2638

Region 10

300 Fifth Avenue, Suite 1230, Seattle, WA 98104
Tel: (206) 757-6740 Fax: (206) 757-6739
Areas Covered: AK, ID, OR, WA

Regional Administrator **Betty Lock** .... (206) 757-6740
E-mail: lock.betty@dol.gov
Program Analyst **Manuelita Ybarra** .... (206) 757-6740
E-mail: ybarra.manuelita@dol.gov
Program Analyst **(Vacant)** .... (206) 757-6740

United States Department of State

Contents

DEPARTMENTS

DEPARTMENTS

United States Department of State (DOS)

Description: The Department of State advises the President in the formulation and execution of foreign policy by determining and analyzing facts relating to American interests overseas. To promote the long-range security and well-being of the United States, the department negotiates treaties and agreements with foreign nations and speaks for the country in the United Nations and other international organizations and conferences.

Harry S. Truman Building, 2201 C Street, NW, Washington, DC 20520
Tel: (202) 647-4000 (Personnel Locator)
Tel: (703) 875-6037 (Acquisition Information)
Tel: (202) 647-6575 (Public Information)
Tel: (202) 261-8314 (Freedom of Information/Privacy Act)
Tel: (202) 261-8484 (Freedom of Information/Privacy Act [Alternate])
Tel: (202) 647-5225 (American Travelers' Hotline)
Tel: (202) 647-3320 (Inspector General's Hotline)
Tel: (877) 487-2778 (National Passport Information Center)
Tel: (202) 647-0518 (Passport Information Inquiries)
Tel: (202) 663-1225 (US Visa Information Inquiries - General)
Tel: (202) 663-1541 (US Visa Information Inquiries - Immigrant Visa Preference Dates) Internet: www.state.gov
Internet: www.state.gov/open (Open Government Initiative)
Internet: www.usa.gov (Official US Government Website)

OFFICE OF THE SECRETARY (S)

Harry S. Truman Building, 2201 C Street, NW, Washington, DC 20520
Tel: (202) 647-9572 Fax: (202) 647-2283
Internet: www.state.gov/secretary

Commissions

International Boundary Commission, U.S. and Canada – United States Section (IBC)

1717 H Street, NW, Suite 845, Washington, DC 20006
Tel: (202) 736-9102 Fax: (202) 254-4562
E-mail: commission@washington.ijc.org
Internet: www.internationalboundarycommission.org

☆ U.S. Commissioner **Kyle K. Hipsley** .... (202) 736-9102
E-mail: hipseyk@ibcusca.org
Deputy Commissioner **John T. Moore** .... (202) 736-9029
Records Management Officer **Tracy Morrison** .... (202) 736-9101

Central Region Field Office
17786 Highway 59, NE, Thief River Falls, MN 56701
Mail: P.O. Box 29, Thief River Falls, MN 56701
Tel: (218) 681-5248 E-mail: ibcmn@wiktel.com
Engineering Technician **Bryan C. Cloutier** .... (218) 681-5248

Eastern Region Field Office
1 Military Street, Houlton, ME 04760
Mail: P.O. Box 459, Houlton, ME 04730
Tel: (207) 532-2111
Engineering Technician **Graig Hill** .... (207) 532-2111

Western Region Field Office
1600 Stuckey Road, Great Falls, MT 59406
Mail: P.O. Box 7007, Great Falls, MT 59406
Tel: (406) 727-9341
Engineering Technician **Phil Hargrove** .... (406) 727-9341

International Boundary and Water Commission, United States and Mexico – United States Section (IBWC)

4171 North Mesa, Suite C-100, El Paso, TX 79902-1441
Tel: (915) 832-4100 Tel: (800) 262-8857 Fax: (915) 832-4191
Internet: www.ibwc.gov/home.html

☆ U.S. Commissioner (Acting) **Jose A. Nuñez** .... (915) 832-4100
E-mail: jose.nunez@ibwc.gov
Education: Texas (El Paso) BSCE
Special Administrative Assistant **Lisa Holguin** .... (915) 832-4765
E-mail: lisa.holguin@ibwc.gov
Equal Opportunity Specialist **Frances Castro** .... (915) 832-4112

Foreign Affairs Office
Foreign Affairs Officer **Sally Spener** .... (915) 832-4175
E-mail: sally.spener@ibwc.gov

Human Resources Office
Director **Fred Graf** .... (915) 832-4114
E-mail: fred.graf@ibwc.gov

Legal Affairs Office
Chief Counsel [Chief FOIA Officer, Designated Agency Ethics Official (DAEO)]
Matthew A. "Matt" Myers, Sr. .... (915) 832-4728
E-mail: matthew.myers@ibwc.gov
Education: Virginia 1980 BA, 1988 JD; Judge Advocate Gen 1999 LLM

Public Affairs Office
Public Affairs Officer **Lori Kuczmanski** .... (915) 832-4106
E-mail: lori.kuczmanski@ibwc.gov

Administration Department
4171 North Mesa, El Paso, TX 79902-1441
Fax: (915) 832-4195
Chief Administrative Officer / Chief Information Officer **Diana C. Forti** .... (915) 832-4123
E-mail: diana.forti@ibwc.gov

Acquisition Division
4171 North Mesa, El Paso, TX 79902-1441
Supervisory Procurement Analyst **(Vacant)** .... (915) 832-4119

Asset Management
Logistics Management Specialist **(Vacant)** .... (915) 832-4138

Budget Division
4171 North Mesa, El Paso, TX 79902-1441
Budget Officer **Albert Moehlig** .... (915) 832-4158
E-mail: albert.moehlig@ibwc.gov

Finance and Accounting Division
Accounting Officer **Dorinda Morgan** .... (915) 832-4132

Information Management Division
Supervisory IT Specialist **Zenon Mora** .... (915) 832-4755
E-mail: z.mora@ibwc.gov
IT Specialist **Karen Cross** .... (915) 832-4127
E-mail: karen.cross@ibwc.gov

★ Presidential Appointment Requiring Senate Confirmation ☆ Presidential Appointment ☐ Schedule C Appointment ◇ Career Senior Foreign Service Appointment
● Career Senior Executive Service (SES) Appointment ○ Non-Career Senior Executive Service (SES) Appointment ■ Postal Career Executive Service

DEPARTMENTS

Engineering Department
4171 North Mesa, El Paso, TX 79902-1441
Fax: (915) 832-4195
Principal Engineer (Acting) **Padinare Unnikrishna** ...... (915) 832-4749

Master Planning Office
Supervisory Program Analyst **Vivian Gonzales** .... (915) 832-4113

Operations Department
4171 North Mesa, El Paso, TX 79902-1441
Fax: (915) 832-4195
Principal Engineer **(Vacant)** .... (915) 832-4118

Amistad Dam and Power Plant
670 Texas Spur 349, Del Rio, TX 78840-0425
Tel: (830) 775-2437 (Amistad Dam)
Tel: (830) 774-5519 (Amistad Power Plant) Fax: (830) 775-5956
Area Operations Manager **Elsayyid Ibrahim** .... (830) 734-1545

Falcon Dam and Power Plant
1 Reservoir Road, Falcon Heights, TX 78545-0001
Tel: (956) 848-5211 (Falcon Dam)
Tel: (956) 848-5265 (Falcon Power Plant) Fax: (956) 848-5426
Area Operations Manager **Ramon Navarro** .... (956) 848-5265

Lower Rio Grande Flood Control Project
325 Golf Course Road, Mercedes, TX 78570-9677
Tel: (956) 565-3150 Fax: (956) 565-1575
Area Operations Manager **Juan F. Uribe, Jr.** .... (956) 565-3150 ext. 224

Nogales International Wastewater Treatment Plant
865 Rio Rico Industrial Park, Rio Rico, AZ 85648
Mail: P.O. Box 4063, Rio Rico, AZ 85648-4063
Tel: (520) 281-1832 Fax: (520) 281-1565
Area Operations Manager **John M. Light** .... (520) 281-1832

Presidio Flood Control Project
P.O. Box 848, Presidio, TX 79845-0848
Tel: (432) 229-3751 Fax: (432) 229-4636
Area Operations Manager **Hector Delgado** .... (432) 229-3752

San Diego Project
2225 Dairy Mart Road, San Ysidro, CA 92173-2840
Tel: (619) 662-7600 Fax: (619) 662-7607
Area Operations Manager **Carlos Peña, Jr.** .... (619) 662-7600

Upper Rio Grande Project Office (URGP)
2616 West Paisano Drive, El Paso, TX 79922-1629
Tel: (915) 351-1030 Fax: (915) 351-1511
Area Operations Manager (Acting) **Jose Luis Sierra** ..... (915) 351-1030
Supervisor, American Dam and Canal Extension Project **Guy Hernandez** .... (915) 351-1030

Las Cruces Field Office
504 South Miranda, Las Cruces, NM 88005-2824
Tel: (575) 541-7050 Fax: (575) 541-7051
Area Operations Manager **Flavio Apodaca** .... (575) 541-7050

Zacarias Dominguez Field Office
P.O. Box 8, Fort Hancock, TX 79839-0008
Tel: (915) 832-4131 Fax: (915) 769-3780
Supervisor (Acting) **Esteban Olivas** .... (915) 832-4718

Yuma Project
2995 South Pacific Avenue, Yuma, AZ 85365-3510
Tel: (928) 782-1598 Fax: (928) 782-1043
Area Operations Manager **Anna C. Morales** .... (928) 782-1598

International Joint Commission, Canada and United States – United States Section (IJC)
1717 H Street, NW, Suite 801, Washington, DC 20006
Tel: (202) 736-9000 Fax: (202) 632-2006
E-mail: commission@washington.ijc.org Internet: www.ijc.org

★ Chair **Lana B. Pollack** .... (202) 736-9000
Education: Michigan 1965 BA, 1970 MA
★ Chair-Designate **Jane L. Corwin** .... (202) 736-9000
Education: SUNY (Albany) 1985 BA; Pace 1990 MBA
★ U.S. Commissioner **Richard M. "Rich" Moy** .... (202) 736-9000
Education: Montana BA, MA; Missouri PhD
★ U.S. Commissioner-Designate **Robert C. Sisson** .... (202) 736-9000
★ U.S. Commissioner **(Vacant)** .... (202) 736-9000
★ U.S. Commissioner-Designate **Lance V. Yohe** .... (202) 736-9000
Education: Concordia Col Moorhead MN BS

U.S. Section Staff
1717 H Street, NW, Washington, DC 20006
Tel: (202) 736-9000 Fax: (202) 632-2006
Senior Advisor **David C. "Dave" Hermann** .... (202) 736-9103
E-mail: hermannd@washington.ijc.org
Engineering Advisor **Dr. Mark F. Colosimo** .... (202) 736-9021
Engineering Advisor **Dr. Mark Gabriel** .... (202) 736-9007
Environmental Advisor **Victor Serveiss** .... (202) 736-9017
E-mail: serveissv@washington.ijc.org
Legal Advisor [Designated Agency Ethics Official (DAEO)] **Susan E. Daniel** .... (202) 736-9011
E-mail: daniels@washington.ijc.org
Strategic Policy Advisor **(Vacant)** .... (202) 674-0054
Advisor **(Vacant)** .... (202) 550-6897
Geographic Information Systems Coordinator **Michael Laitta** .... (202) 736-9022
E-mail: laittam@washington.ijc.org
Network Specialist **Talante Henderson** .... (202) 736-9003
E-mail: hendersont@washington.ijc.org
Public Information Officer **Frank Bevacqua** .... (202) 736-9024
E-mail: bevacquaf@washington.ijc.org
Education: Michigan 1978 BA
Writer-Communications Specialist **Kevin Bunch** .... (202) 632-2014
E-mail: bunchk@washington.ijc.org
Secretary **Charles Alden Lawson** .... (202) 736-9008
E-mail: lawsonc@washington.ijc.org
Special Assistant **Antionette Cade** .... (202) 736-9023
E-mail: cadea@washington.ijc.org
Special Assistant **Brian A. Maloney** .... (202) 736-9009
E-mail: maloneyb@washington.ijc.org
Administrative Officer **Alice Ross** .... (202) 736-9013
E-mail: rossa@washington.ijc.org
Administrative Officer **(Vacant)** .... (202) 736-9013
Administrative Specialist **Valerie Hoopes** .... (202) 736-9001
E-mail: hoopesv@washington.ijc.org
General Clerk **(Vacant)** .... (202) 736-9001

Great Lakes Regional Office
100 Ouellette Avenue, 8th Floor, Windsor, Ontario N9A 6T3, Canada
Mail: P.O. Box 32869, Detroit, MI 48232
Tel: 1 (519) 257-6700 Tel: (313) 226-2170 Fax: 1 (519) 257-6740
Director **David Burden** 1 (519) 257-6715
E-mail: burdend@windsor.ijc.org
Public Information Officer **Sally Cole-Misch** 1 (519) 257-6733
E-mail: colemischs@windsor.ijc.org

★ Presidential Appointment Requiring Senate Confirmation ☆ Presidential Appointment ☐ Schedule C Appointment ◇ Career Senior Foreign Service Appointment
● Career Senior Executive Service (SES) Appointment ○ Non-Career Senior Executive Service (SES) Appointment ■ Postal Career Executive Service

Under Secretary for Management (M)
Harry S. Truman Building, 2201 C Street, NW,
Room 7207, Washington, DC 20520
Tel: (202) 647-1500 Fax: (202) 647-0168 E-mail: M_Staff@state.gov
Internet: www.state.gov/m

Bureau of Administration (A)
Harry S. Truman Building, 2201 C Street, NW,
Room 6529, Washington, DC 20520
Fax: (202) 647-1558 Internet: www.state.gov/m/a

Deputy Assistant Secretary for Logistics Management (A/LM)
1700 North Lynn Street, Rosslyn, VA 22209
Fax: (703) 875-4731

Office of Logistics Operations (A/LM/OPS)
1701 North Fort Myer Drive, Room 527, Arlington, VA 22209
Mail: Room 527, Mail Stop SA-6, Washington, DC 20522-0605

U.S. Despatch Agency - Baltimore (MD)
2200 Broening Highway, Suite 125, Baltimore, MD 21224
Tel: (410) 631-0043 Fax: (410) 631-0058
Despatch Agent **Nicky A. Frantz** .... (410) 631-0044
E-mail: frantzna@state.gov
Deputy Despatch Agent **Colleen Menser** .... (410) 631-0044

U.S. Despatch Agency - Miami (FL)
7789 Northwest 48th Street, Suite 250, Miami, FL 33166
Tel: (305) 640-4574 Fax: (305) 715-3502
Despatch Agent **Maureen L. Gabbard** .... (305) 640-4574

U.S. Despatch Agency - New York (NY)
555 U.S. Route One South, Iselin, NJ 08830-3013
Tel: (732) 855-8880 Fax: (732) 855-8899
Despatch Agent **Bernard Thompson** .... (732) 855-8880

U.S. Despatch Agency - Seattle (WA)
2800 South 192nd Street, Room 108, Seattle, WA 98188-5163
Tel: (206) 764-3805 Fax: (206) 764-6660
Despatch Agent **Raymond F. Schoenberg** .... (206) 764-3805
E-mail: schoenbergrf@state.gov

Bureau of Consular Affairs (CA)
600 19th Street, NW, Room 12.100, Washington, DC 20006
Fax: (202) 647-0341 E-mail: ca-staffers-mailbox@state.gov
Internet: travel.state.gov

Deputy Assistant Secretary for Passport Services (CA/PPT)
600 19th Street, NW, SA-17, Washington, DC 20006
Tel: (877) 487-2778 (National Passport Information Center Automated Information and Customer Service Representatives)
TTY: (888) 874-7793 (National Passport Information Center Automated Information and Customer Service Representatives) Fax: (202) 647-9622

National Passport Center
207 International Drive, Portsmouth, NH 03801-2900
Tel: (877) 487-2778 (Information) Fax: (603) 334-0596
Director **Karen Pizza** .... (603) 334-0115
E-mail: pizzaka@state.gov

Arkansas (AR) Passport Center
191 Office Park Drive, Hot Springs, AR 71913-5496
Tel: (877) 487-2778 (Information) Fax: (501) 622-2442
Director **Joseph Gately** .... (520) 733-8006
E-mail: gatelyjf@state.gov

Boston (MA) Passport Agency
Thomas P. O'Neill Federal Building, 10 Causeway Street,
Room 247, Boston, MA 02222-1094
Tel: (877) 487-2778 (Information/Appointments) Fax: (617) 878-0912
Regional Director **Michael Wood** .... (617) 878-0920
E-mail: woodmt@state.gov

Charleston (SC) Passport Center
Building 643, 1269 Holland Street, Charleston, SC 29405
Director **Timothy "Tim" Wiesnet** .... (843) 746-1883
E-mail: wiesnett@state.gov

Chicago (IL) Passport Agency
101 West Congress Parkway, Ninth Floor, Chicago, IL 60605-1074
Tel: (877) 487-2778 (Information/Appointments)
Regional Director **Sean Loftus** .... (312) 341-6743
E-mail: loftussm@state.gov

Connecticut (CT) Passport Agency
850 Canal Street, Stamford, CT 06902
Tel: (877) 487-2778 (Information/Appointments)
Director **Steven Christian** .... (877) 487-2778
E-mail: christians@state.gov

Colorado Passport Agency
Cherry Creek Place III Corporate Center, 3151 South Vaughn Way,
Suite 600, Aurora, CO 80014
Tel: (877) 487-2778 (Information/Appointments)
Regional Director **(Vacant)** .... (303) 696-3037

Honolulu (HI) Passport Agency
Prince Jonah Kuhio Kalanianaole Federal Building,
300 Ala Moana Boulevard, Suite I-330, Honolulu, HI 96850
Tel: (877) 487-2778 (Information/Appointments)
Regional Director **Steven Mullen** .... (808) 544-6060
E-mail: mullensj@state.gov

Houston (TX) Passport Agency
Mickey Leland Federal Building, 1919 Smith Street,
Fourth Floor, Houston, TX 77002-8049
Tel: (877) 487-2778 (Information/Appointments)
Regional Director **Kathe Harrell** .... (713) 655-5919
E-mail: harrellkl@state.gov

Los Angeles (CA) Passport Agency
Federal Office Building, 11000 Wilshire Boulevard,
Suite 1000, Los Angeles, CA 90024-3615
Tel: (877) 487-2778 (Information/Appointments) Fax: (310) 575-5729
Regional Director **Christine M. Kagarise** .... (310) 575-5710
E-mail: KagariseCM@state.gov

Miami (FL) Passport Agency
1501 Biscayne Boulevard, Suite 210, Miami, FL 33132
Tel: (877) 487-2778 (Information/Appointments)
Regional Director **Ryan Dooley** .... (305) 810-0710
E-mail: dooleyrm@state.gov

Minneapolis Passport Agency
United States Federal Office Building,
212 3rd Avenue South, Minneapolis, MN 55401
Director **Jennifer J. Danover** .... (612) 656-5172
E-mail: danoverjj@state.gov

New Orleans (LA) Passport Center
One Canal Place, 365 Canal Street, Suite 1300,
New Orleans, LA 70130-6508
Tel: (877) 487-2778 (Information/Appointments)
Regional Director **Stacey Porter** .... (504) 412-2620
E-mail: portersb@state.gov

New York (NY) Passport Agency
Greater New York Federal Building, 376 Hudson Street,
10th Floor, New York, NY 10014
Tel: (877) 487-2778 (Information/Appointments)
Regional Director **Michael Hoffman** .... (212) 206-3010
E-mail: hoffmanm@state.gov

★ Presidential Appointment Requiring Senate Confirmation ☆ Presidential Appointment □ Schedule C Appointment ◇ Career Senior Foreign Service Appointment
● Career Senior Executive Service (SES) Appointment ○ Non-Career Senior Executive Service (SES) Appointment ■ Postal Career Executive Service

DEPARTMENTS

DEPARTMENTS

Philadelphia (PA) Passport Agency
U.S. Custom House, 200 Chestnut Street,
Room 103, Philadelphia, PA 19106-2970
Tel: (877) 487-2778 (Information/Appointments)

Regional Director **Orlando L. Rivera** .... (215) 931-4510
E-mail: riveraol@state.gov

San Francisco (CA) Passport Agency
450 Golden Gate Avenue, Suite #3-2501, San Francisco, CA 94102
Tel: (877) 487-2778 (Information/Appointments)

Regional Director **David A. Tyler** .... (415) 538-2710
E-mail: tylerda@state.gov

Seattle (WA) Passport Agency
Fifth and Yesler Building, 300 5th Avenue,
Suite 600, Seattle, WA 98104
Tel: (877) 487-2778 (Information/Appointments)

Regional Director **S. Teresa Bobotek** .... (206) 808-5710
E-mail: bobotekt@state.gov

Washington (DC) Passport Agency
600 19th Street, NW, Washington, DC 20006
Tel: (877) 487-2778 (Information/Appointments) Fax: (202) 955-0108

Regional Director **Lindsay Nicole Henderson** .... (202) 485-8102
E-mail: hendersonln@state.gov

Special Issuance Agency (CA/PPT/SIA)
600 19th Street, NW, Washington, DC 20006
Fax: (202) 955-0182

Director **Jennifer Dewitt Walsh** .... (202) 485-8202
E-mail: walshjd3@state.gov

El Paso (TX) Passport Agency
303 North Oregon Street, El Paso, TX 79901

Director **(Vacant)** .... (915) 496-2001

Deputy Assistant Secretary for Visa Services (CA/VO)
Tel: (202) 663-1225 (US Visa Information Inquiries - General)
Tel: (202) 663-1541 (US Visa Information Inquiries - Immigrant Visa Preference Dates) Tel: (606) 526-7500 (US Visa Information Inquiries - Visa Lottery Information) Fax: (202) 647-0341

Kentucky Consular Center (KCC)
3505 U.S. Highway North, Williamsburg, KY 40769
Tel: (606) 526-7500 E-mail: KCCDV@state.gov

Director **Christopher "Chris" Beard** .... (606) 526-7667

National Visa Center
32 Rochester Avenue, Portsmouth, NH 03801
Tel: (603) 334-0700 Fax: (603) 334-0759 E-mail: nvcinquiry@state.gov

Director **Conn J. Schrader** .... (603) 334-0927
E-mail: schradercj@state.gov

Bureau of Diplomatic Security (DS)
Harry S. Truman Building, 2201 C Street, NW,
Room 6316, Washington, DC 20520
Internet: www.state.gov/m/ds

Principal Deputy Assistant Secretary for Diplomatic Security/Diplomatic Security Service (DS/DSS)
1801 North Lynn Street, 23rd Floor, Arlington, VA 22209

Deputy Assistant Secretary and Assistant Director for Domestic Operations (DS/DO)
1801 North Lynn Street, 23rd Floor, Arlington, VA 22209
Fax: (571) 345-3844

Office of Field Office Management (DS/DO/FLD)

Boston (MA) Field Office
Thomas P. O'Neill Federal Building, 10 Causeway Street,
Suite 1001, Boston, MA 02222-1078
Tel: (617) 565-8200 (24-Hour) Fax: (617) 565-8222
Areas Covered: ME, MA, NH, RI, VT

Special Agent-in-Charge **William B. Gannon** .... (617) 565-8201
E-mail: gannonwb@state.gov

Portsmouth (NH) Resident Office
249 Corporate Drive, Portsmouth, NH 03801
Fax: (603) 610-2406

Resident Agent-in-Charge **David Tauber** .... (603) 319-3600

St. Albans (VT) Resident Office
50 South Main Street, St. Albans, VT 05478
Fax: (802) 527-6613

Resident Agent-in-Charge **Brian A. Sultzbaugh** .... (802) 527-6609
E-mail: sultzbaughba@state.gov

Chicago (IL) Field Office
Kluczynski Federal Building, 230 South Dearborn,
Suite 2318, Chicago, IL 60604
Fax: (312) 886-7895
Areas Covered: IL, IN, IA, KS, KY, MI, MN, MO, NE, ND, OH, SD, WI

Special Agent-in-Charge **Benjamin W. "Ben" Sides** .... (312) 353-6163

Detroit (MI) Resident Office
211 West Fort Street, Suite 300, Detroit, MI 48226
Fax: (313) 234-2902

Resident Agent-in-Charge **Robert M. Picco** .... (313) 234-2956

Minneapolis (MN) Resident Office
330 Second Avenue South, Suite 845, Minneapolis, MN 55401
Fax: (612) 659-7551

Resident Agent-in-Charge **Daniel R. Bleakmore** .... (612) 659-7060

St. Louis (MO) Resident Office
Robert A. Young Federal Building, 1222 Spruce Street,
Room 6.102, St. Louis, MO 63103
Fax: (314) 539-2746

Resident Agent-in-Charge **William G. "Bill" Embry** ..... (314) 539-2721
E-mail: embrywg@state.gov

Houston (TX) Field Office
Mickey LeLand Federal Building, 1919 Smith Street,
Suite 2100, Houston, TX 77002
Fax: (281) 228-5670
Areas Covered: OK, TX

Special Agent-in-Charge **Michael V. Perkins** .... (713) 654-0401
Assistant Special Agent-in-Charge **Teresa A. Teno** .... (713) 654-0401
E-mail: tenota@state.gov

★ Presidential Appointment Requiring Senate Confirmation ☆ Presidential Appointment ☐ Schedule C Appointment ◇ Career Senior Foreign Service Appointment
● Career Senior Executive Service (SES) Appointment ○ Non-Career Senior Executive Service (SES) Appointment ■ Postal Career Executive Service

Dallas (TX) Resident Office
Earle Cabell Federal Building, 1100 Commerce Street,
Room 749, Dallas, TX 75242
Tel: (214) 767-0700 Fax: (214) 767-3544

Resident Agent-in-Charge **Ryan Tanner** . . . . (214) 767-0702

Los Angeles (CA) Field Office (DS/FLD/LAFO)
Roybal Federal Building, 255 East Temple Street,
Room 1273, Los Angeles, CA 90012
Tel: (213) 894-3290 Fax: (213) 894-0914
Internet: https://www.state.gov/m/ds
Areas Covered: AZ, Southern CA, HI, Southern NV (Las Vegas metropolitan area), NM

Special Agent-in-Charge **Michael E. Bishop** . . . .(213) 894-4610
E-mail: bishopme@state.gov

Honolulu (HI) Resident Office
PJKK Federal Building, 300 Ala Moana Boulevard, Honolulu, HI 96850
Fax: (808) 522-8037

Resident Agent-in-Charge **Marc A. Weinstock** . . . .(808) 522-8020
E-mail: weinstockma@state.gov

San Diego (CA) Resident Office
555 West Beech Street, Suite 222, San Diego, CA 92101
Tel: (619) 557-6194 Fax: (619) 557-5919

Resident Agent-in-Charge **Jason T. Kephart** . . . . (619) 557-6194
E-mail: kephartjt@state.gov
Education: Roger Williams BA; Salve Regina U MBA

West Los Angeles (CA) Satellite Office
Federal Building and U.S. Post Office, 11000 Wilshire Boulevard,
Suite 1109, Los Angeles, CA 90024-3683
Tel: (310) 235-7937 Fax: (310) 235-7932

Supervisory Special Agent **Dean M. Phillip** . . . .(310) 235-7937
E-mail: phillipdm@state.gov

Tucson (AZ) Resident Office
300 West Congress Street, Suite 4K, Tucson, AZ 85701
Fax: (520) 670-4850

Resident Agent-in-Charge **(Vacant)** . . . . (520) 670-4841

Miami (FL) Field Office
1645 Biscayne Boulevard, Suite 310, Miami, FL 33132
Fax: (305) 810-5816
Areas Covered: AL, AR, FL, GA, LA, MS, SC, TN, PR

Special Agent-in-Charge **Frederick R. "Fred" Stolper** . . . (305) 810-5850
E-mail: stolperfr@state.gov
Education: Southern Illinois 1983

Atlanta (GA) Resident Office
10 Tenth Street, NE, Suite 160, Atlanta, GA 30309
Tel: (404) 879-0134 Fax: (404) 879-0149

Resident Agent-in-Charge **Raymond "Ray" Kyliavas** . . . . (404) 879-0134
E-mail: kyliavasr@state.gov

New Orleans (LA) Resident Office
365 Canal Street, Suite 1130, New Orleans, LA 70130
Fax: (504) 589-2028

Resident Agent-in-Charge **Michael N. Wray** . . . .(504) 589-2010

San Juan (PR) Resident Office
La Torre De Plaza, 525 F. D. Roosevelt Avenue,
Suite 1115, Hato Rey, PR 00918
Fax: (787) 771-3693

Resident Agent-in-Charge **Rick Hayes** . . . .(787) 766-5704

New York (NY) Field Office
Two Executive Drive, Suite 300, Fort Lee, NJ 07024-3309
Fax: (201) 944-5106
Areas Covered: CT, DE, NJ, NY, PA

Special Agent-in-Charge **Timothy W. "Tim" Dumas** . . . . (201) 346-8100
E-mail: dumastw@state.gov
Education: Illinois 1994 BA

Assistant Special Agent-in-Charge **Tanya Sears** . . . .(201) 346-8100

Philadelphia (PA) Resident Office
William J. Green, Jr. Federal Building, 600 Arch Street,
Room 3218, Philadelphia, PA 19106
Fax: (215) 861-3369

Resident Agent-in-Charge **Michael Davis** . . . .(215) 861-3370

San Francisco (CA) Field Office
235 Pine Street, Suite 900, San Francisco, CA 94104
Fax: (415) 705-1187
Areas Covered: AK, Northern CA, CO, ID, MT, NV (except Las Vegas metropolitan area), OR, UT, WA, WY

Special Agent-in-Charge **Matthew Perlman** . . . .(415) 705-1176

Denver (CO) Resident Office
8101 East Prentice Avenue, Suite 550, Greenwood Village, CO 80111
Fax: (303) 486-7011

Resident Agent-in-Charge **Angela Brenner** . . . .(303) 486-7010
E-mail: brennera@state.gov
Education: Colorado 1999 BA

Seattle (WA) Resident Office
300 Fifth Avenue, Suite 800, Seattle, WA 98104

Resident Agent-in-Charge **Robert "Rob" Holbrook** . . . . . (206) 393-0740
E-mail: holbrookrw@state.gov

Washington (DC) Field Office (DS/FLD/WFO)
2222 Gallows Road, Dunn Loring, VA 22027
Tel: (571) 226-9300 Fax: (571) 226-9382
Areas Covered: DC, MD, NC, VA, WV

Special Agent-in-Charge **Edwin Guard** . . . .(571) 226-9313
E-mail: guarde@state.gov
Education: George Mason 1981 BA

Charleston (SC) Satellite Office (DS/WFO/CHRO)
Building 643, 1269 Holland Street, Room 228, Charleston, SC 29405
Fax: (843) 746-1910

Resident Agent-in-Charge **(Vacant)** . . . .(843) 746-1906

Greensboro (NC) Resident Office
1801 Stanley Street, Suite 2003, Greensboro, NC 27407
Fax: (336) 547-4298

Resident Agent-in-Charge **David Monroe** . . . .(336) 547-4292
E-mail: monroedm@state.gov

Office of Foreign Missions (M/OFM)
Harry S. Truman Building, 2201 C Street, NW,
Room 2236, Washington, DC 20520
Tel: (202) 647-3417 Fax: (202) 736-4145
E-mail: ofminfo@state.gov E-mail: ofmassistants@state.gov
E-mail: ofm-pr@state.gov (Public Affairs) Internet: www.state.gov/ofm

Chicago (IL) Regional Office
Ralph H. Metcalfe Federal Building, 77 West Jackson Boulevard,
Suite 2122, Chicago, IL 60604
Tel: (312) 353-5762 Fax: (312) 353-5768
E-mail: OFMCGCustomerService@state.gov
Note: The New York and Chicago Regional Offices are collectively referred to as the Northern Area Office.

Area Director (Resident in New York)
Brooke E. Knobel . . . . (646) 282-2811

DEPARTMENTS

★ Presidential Appointment Requiring Senate Confirmation ☆ Presidential Appointment ☐ Schedule C Appointment ◇ Career Senior Foreign Service Appointment
● Career Senior Executive Service (SES) Appointment ○ Non-Career Senior Executive Service (SES) Appointment ■ Postal Career Executive Service

Houston (TX) Regional Office
8701 South Gessner Road, Suite 906, Houston, TX 77074
Tel: (713) 272-2865 Fax: (713) 272-2866
E-mail: OFMHOCustomerService@state.gov
Internet: https://www.state.gov/ofm/ro/ho/

Regional Director **Robin E. Blunt** .... (713) 272-2865

Los Angeles (CA) Regional Office
10940 Wilshire Boulevard, Suite 1550, Los Angeles, CA 90024
Tel: (310) 235-6292 Fax: (310) 235-6297
E-mail: OFMLACustomerService@state.gov
Internet: https://www.state.gov/ofm/ro/la/index.htm

Regional Director
Christina J. "C.J." Hernandez .... (310) 235-6292 ext. 304
E-mail: hernandezcj@state.gov
Assistant Regional Director **Wes Evans** .... (310) 235-6292 ext. 305
E-mail: evansw@state.gov
Program Manager **Tarik A. Obeidi** .... (310) 235-6292 ext. 301
E-mail: obeidita@state.gov
Education: Cal State (Fullerton) 1994 BS; American U 1997 MIS
Program Officer **Fahima Danishgar** .... (310) 235-6292 ext. 304
E-mail: danishgarf@state.gov
Foreign Missions Specialist **Yeji L. Shin** .... (310) 235-6292 ext. 303
E-mail: shinyl@state.gov
Administrative Assistant **Christine Miller** .... (310) 235-6292 ext. 308

Miami (FL) Regional Office
95 Merrick Way, Suite 505, Coral Gables, FL 33134
Tel: (305) 442-4943 Fax: (305) 442-4973 E-mail: OFMMiami@state.gov
E-mail: OFMMICustomerService@state.gov
Internet: https://www.state.gov/ofm/ro/mi/index.htm

Director **Frances Crespo** .... (305) 442-4943 ext. 26
Program Manager **Miguel A. Morales** .... (305) 442-4943 ext. 25
Program Officer **Maria V. Suhr** .... (305) 442-4943 ext. 22

New York (NY) Regional Office
799 United Nations Plaza, 8th Floor, New York, NY 10017-3505
Tel: (646) 282-2825 Fax: (212) 826-4508
E-mail: ofmnewyork@state.gov E-mail: ofmnycustomerservice@state.gov
Internet: https://www.state.gov/ofm/ro/ny/index.htm
Note: The New York and Chicago Regional Offices are collectively referred to as the Northern Area Office.

Area Director **Brooke E. Knobel** .... (646) 282-2811

San Francisco (CA) Regional Office
235 Pine Street, Suite 1600, San Francisco, CA 94104
Tel: (415) 744-2910 Fax: (415) 744-2913
E-mail: OFMSFCustomerService@state.gov
Internet: https://www.state.gov/ofm/ro/sf/index.htm
Areas Covered: AK, Northern CA, GU, HI, ID, MT, Northern NV, ND, OR, SD, WA, WY

Regional Director **Clayton Stranger** .... (415) 744-2910
Associate Regional Director, Client Relations
Matthew Davis .... (415) 744-2910 ext. 25
Program Specialist **Armond Oliver** .... (415) 744-2910 ext. 21

Under Secretary for Public Diplomacy and Public Affairs (R)

Harry S. Truman Building, 2201 C Street, NW,
Room 5932, Washington, DC 20520
Tel: (202) 647-9199 Fax: (202) 647-9140
E-mail: r_staffassistants@state.gov Internet: www.state.gov/r

Bureau of Public Affairs (PA)
2201 C Street, NW, Room 6634, Washington, DC 20520
Tel: (202) 647-6575 (Public Information/Inquiries) Fax: (202) 647-3344
Internet: www.state.gov/r/pa

Deputy Spokesperson

Foreign Press Centers (PA/FPC)
National Press Building, 529 - 14th Street. NW,
Suite 800, Washington, DC 20045
Tel: (202) 504-6300 E-mail: FPCOwner@state.gov Internet: fpc.state.gov

Director of Centers **Benjamin Weber** .... (202) 504-6317

New York (NY) Foreign Press Center
799 U.N. Plaza, 10th Floor, New York, NY 10017
Tel: (646) 282-2830 Fax: (646) 282-2847 Internet: fpc.state.gov

Director **Kathleen M. "Kathy" Eagen** .... (646) 282-2837
E-mail: eagenkm2@state.gov
Education: Georgetown 1995 BS
Deputy Director **Melissa N. Waheibi** .... (646) 282-2831
E-mail: waheibimn@state.gov
East Asia and Pacific Islands
Daphne Z. Stavropoulos .... (646) 282-2835
E-mail: stavropoulosdz2@state.gov
Education: George Washington 2000 BA; Columbia 2003 MA
Eastern Europe / Western Hemisphere/ Middle East and North Africa Media Relations Officer
Shana Kieran .... (646) 282-2836
E-mail: kieransl2@state.gov
Western Europe Media Relations Officer
Melissa N. Waheibi .... (646) 282-2831
E-mail: waheibimn@state.gov

United States Embassies, Consulates, and Diplomatic Missions

AFRICA

U.S. Embassy in Angola

American Embassy - Luanda, Angola, Rua Houari Boumedienne No. 32, Miramar, Luanda, Angola
Tel: 244 222-641-000 Fax: 244 222-641-232

Office of the U.S. Ambassador to Angola
American Embassy - Luanda, Angola,
Rua Houari Boumedienne No. 32, C.P. 6468,
Miramar, Luanda, Angola
Mail: Department of State, 2550 Luanda Place, Dulles, VA 20189-2550

★ Ambassador **Ambassador Nina Maria Fite** 244 222-641-000
E-mail: fitenm@state.gov
Education: Carnegie Mellon BArch; Thunderbird Global MBA; Indust'l Col Armed Forces 2011 MS
Office Management Specialist to the Ambassador
Angela White McKnight 244 222-641-000
E-mail: whitemcknightal@state.gov
Deputy Chief of Mission
Mitchell Peter "Mitch" Benedict 244 222-641-000
E-mail: benedictmp@state.gov
Office Management Specialist to the Deputy Chief of Mission **Aurelie Florian** 244 222-641-000
E-mail: floriana@state.gov
Community Liaison Officer **Holly Whitt** 244 222-64-1000

Office of the U.S. Ambassador to Angola *(continued)*

Consular Affairs Officer **Samuel Worland-Esquith** 244 222-641-000
E-mail: worland-esquiths@state.gov
E-mail: consularluanda@state.gov
Equal Employment Opportunity Officer
Mballe M. Nkembe 244 222-641-000
E-mail: nkembemm@state.gov
Financial Management Officer **Dedrick Roberts** 244 222-641-000
General Services Officer **Siza Ntshakala** 244 222-641-000
E-mail: NtshakalaSC@state.gov
Information Management Officer
Abraham Adjei-Gbenda 244 222-641-000
E-mail: adjei-gbendaa@state.gov
Information Systems Security Officer
Ibrahim Hassan 244 222-641-000
Management Officer **Jeffrey Bournes** 244 222-641-000
Political/Economic Officer **Lance B. Kinne** 244 222-641-000
E-mail: kinnelb@state.gov
Public Affairs Officer (Acting) **Nafeesah Allen** 244 222-641-000
E-mail: PASInboxluanda@state.gov
E-mail: allenn@state.gov
Regional Security Officer **Duane Gordon** 244 222-641-000

Agency for International Development [Angola]
Rua N'Kwamme N'Krumah, 31 Edificio Maianga,
4th and 5th Floor, Luanda, Angola
Mail: Department of State, 2550 Luanda Place, Dulles, VA 20189-2550
Tel: 244 222-641-000 Fax: 244 222-641-262
E-mail: info.usaid.angola@usaid.gov Internet: www.usaid.gov/angola

Mission Director (Acting) **Donald Clark** 244 222-641-000

Agricultural Section (Foreign Agricultural Service) [Angola]
American Embassy - Luanda, Angola,
Rua Houari Boumedienne No. 32, C.P. 6468,
Miramar, Luanda, Angola
Tel: 244 222 641 1058

Agricultural Officer (Resident in Pretoria)
James J. "Jim" Higgiston 27 (12) 431-4057
877 Pretorius Street, Arcadia 0083, Pretoria, 0001, South Africa
E-mail: james.higgiston@fas.usda.gov

Commercial Section (Foreign Commercial Service) [Angola]
American Embassy - Luanda, Angola, Rua Houari Boumedienne No. 32,
Miramar, Luanda, Angola
Tel: 244 222 64 1000 Fax: 244 222 64 1232
E-mail: luandacommercial@state.gov E-mail: Office.Luanda@trade.gov

Senior Commercial Officer **Everett G. Wakai** 244 641-603
E-mail: everett.wakai@trade.gov

Federal Aviation Administration (Resident in Dakar) [Angola]
American Embassy - Dakar, Senegal, 45 Avenue Jean XXIII and rue
Kleber, Boite Postal 49, Dakar, Senegal
Mail: FAA AMEMB Dakar, Senegal, 2130 Dakar Place,
Washington, DC 20521-2130
Tel: 221 33-829-2100 Fax: 221 33-823-9286

FAA Representative **Grady Stone** 221 33-829-2180

Office of the Defense Attaché [Angola]
American Embassy - Luanda, Angola, Rua Houari Boumedienne No. 32,
Miramar, Luanda, Angola
Mail: American Embassy - Luanda, Angola, Department of State,
2550 Luanda Place, Dulles, VA 20189-2550
Tel: 244 222-447-028 Fax: 244 222-348-217

Defense Attaché **COL Matthew Sousa USA** 244 222-447-028

U.S. Embassy in Benin
American Embassy, 35 Rue Caporal Bernard Anani,
01 B.P. 2012 Cotonou, Benin
Tel: 229 21-30-06-50 Fax: 229 21-30-03-84
E-mail: usembassycot@state.gov

Office of the U.S. Ambassador to Benin
American Embassy, 35 Rue Caporal Bernard Anani,
01 B.P. 2012 Cotonou, Benin
Mail: American Embassy, Department of State,
2120 Cotonou Place, Washington, DC 20521-2120

★ Ambassador **Ambassador Lucy Tamlyn** 229 21-30-06-50
Note: On July 31, 2018, President Donald J. Trump nominated Lucy Tamlyn to be Ambassador to the Central African Republic. This nomination is pending in the Senate.
E-mail: tamlynl@state.gov
Education: St John's Col (MD) BLA; Columbia MA
★ Ambassador-Designate **Patricia A. "Trish" Mahoney** 229 21-30-06-50
E-mail: mahoneypa@state.gov
Education: Harvard BA; Hawaii MA; National War Col 2009 MSS
Chargé d'Affaires **Laura Phipps Hruby** 229 21-30-06-50
E-mail: hrubylp@state.gov
Education: Georgetown BS
Office Management Specialist to the Ambassador
(Acting) **Michelle L. Arter** 229 21-30-06-50
E-mail: arterml@state.gov
Deputy Chief of Mission **Laura Phipps Hruby** 229 21-30-06-50
E-mail: hrubylp@state.gov
Education: Georgetown BS
Consular Officer **Timothy J. Foley** 229 21-30-06-50
Economic Officer **(Vacant)** 229 21-30-06-50
Management Officer **Scott A. Blomquist** 229 21-30-06-50
E-mail: blomquistsa@state.gov
Community Liaison Officer **Genicia Broughton** 229 21-30-06-50
Financial Management Officer **Thea Wargowsky** 229 21-30-06-50
General Services Officer **Sarah E. Kahnt** 229 21-30-06-50
E-mail: kahntse@state.gov
Information Management Officer **Maximo Marte** 229 21-30-06-50
Information Systems Security Officer
Mikolaj M. Slomka 229 21-30-06-50
E-mail: slomkamm@state.gov
Political/Economic Officer **Marisa N. Cohrs** 229 21-30-06-50
Political/Military Officer **Francesco Barbacci** 229 21-30-06-50
Public Affairs Officer **Kanishka Gangopadhyay** 229 21-30-06-50
Assistant Public Affairs Officer
Christopher "Chris" Schirm 229 21-30-06-50
Regional Security Officer **Ryan Pack** 229 21-30-06-50
E-mail: packrm@state.gov

Agency for International Development [Benin]
American Embassy - Cotonou, Benin, 35 Rue Caporal Bernard Anani,
B.P. 2012, Cotonou, Benin
Mail: American Embassy - Cotonou, Benin, Department of State,
2120 Cotonou Place, Washington, DC 20521-2120
Tel: 229 21-30-05-00 Fax: 229 21-30-12-60
Internet: www.usaid.gov/benin

Country Representative **Jonathan Richter** 229 21-30-05-00
E-mail: jrichter@usaid.gov

Federal Aviation Administration (Resident in Dakar) [Benin]
American Embassy - Dakar, Senegal, 45 Rue Kleber,
2nd Floor, Boite Postal 49 Dakar, Senegal
Mail: FAA AMEMB Dakar, Senegal, Department of State,
Washington, DC 20521-2130
Tel: 221 823-6753 Fax: 221 823-9286

FAA Representative **Grady Stone** 221 221-33-829-2180

★ Presidential Appointment Requiring Senate Confirmation ☆ Presidential Appointment □ Schedule C Appointment ◇ Career Senior Foreign Service Appointment
● Career Senior Executive Service (SES) Appointment ○ Non-Career Senior Executive Service (SES) Appointment ■ Postal Career Executive Service

Office of the Defense Attaché (Resident in Abidjan) [Benin]
American Embassy - Abidjan, Cote d'Ivoire, 5 Rue Jesse Owens,
01 B.P. 1712, Abidjan, Cote d'Ivoire
Mail: Department of State, 2010 Abidjan Place,
Washington, DC 20510-2010
Tel: 225 22-49-40-00 Fax: 225 20-22-32-59

Defense Attaché **LtCol Christopher Ginther USMC** 225 22-49-40-00

Peace Corps [Benin]
35 Rue Caporal Bernard Anani, 01 B.P. 2012 Cotonou, Benin
Mail: Department of State, 2120 Cotonou Place,
Washington, DC 20521-2120
Tel: 229 31-38-93 Fax: 229 31-01-92
Internet: www.peacecorps.gov/benin

Country Director **Gordon Brown** 229 31-38-93

U.S. Embassy in Botswana

American Embassy - Gaborone, Botswana,
P.O. Box 90, Gaborone, Botswana
Tel: 267 395-3982 (Monday-Friday, 7:30AM - 5:00PM)
Tel: 267 395-7111 (After Hours) Fax: 267 318-0232
E-mail: consulargaborone@state.gov

Office of the U.S. Ambassador to Botswana

American Embassy - Gaborone, Botswana,
P.O. Box 90, Gaborone, Botswana
Mail: American Embassy, 2170 Gaborone Place,
Department of State, Dulles, VA 20189

★ Ambassador-Designate **Craig Lewis Cloud** 267 395-3982
E-mail: cloudcl@state.gov
Education: North Carolina State 1986 BS

Chargé d'Affaires **Kali C. Jones** 267 395-3982
E-mail: joneskc@state.gov
Education: Howard U 1992 BA; Tulane MSPH, 1996 JD
Office Management Specialist to the Ambassador **(Vacant)** .... 267 395-3982 ext. 5261

Deputy Chief of Mission **Kali C. Jones** .... 267 395-3982 ext. 5270
E-mail: joneskc@state.gov
Education: Howard U 1992 BA; Tulane MSPH, 1996 JD
Office Management Specialist to the Deputy Chief of Mission **Ginger G. Richter** .... (267) 395-3982
E-mail: richtergg@state.gov

Community Liaison Officer **T. C. Scarborough** 267 395-3982
E-mail: scarboroughtc@state.gov
Education: Trident International

Consular Officer **Carina Canaan** .... 267 395-3982 ext. 5325
E-mail: canaancr@state.gov

Economic/Commercial Officer **James Gardiner** .... 267 395-3982 ext. 5325

Environment, Science, and Technology Officer **Donald L. "Don" Brown** .... 267 395-3982 ext. 2257
E-mail: browndl4@state.gov Fax: 267 395-6504

Financial Management Officer **Benjamin A. Swanson** ... (267) 395-3982
E-mail: swansonba@state.gov
Education: Bethel U 2001 BS

General Service Officer **Erik Liederbach** .... (267) 395-3982

Information Management Officer **Mark Jennings** .... 267 395-3982 ext. 5274

Information Systems Security Officer **Mark Jennings** 267 395-3982

Management Officer **James "Jim" Bredeck** .... 267 395-3982 ext. 5336
E-mail: bredeckjm@state.gov

Political Officer **Elizabeth O'Rourke** 267 395-3982

Political/Economic Officer **Daniel M. Renna** 267 395-3982
E-mail: rennadm@state.gov
Education: Yeshiva 1994 BA; George Washington 1997 MA

Public Affairs Officer **Ineke Margaret Stoneham** .... 267 395-3982 ext. 2468

Regional Security Officer **Kieran McCambridge** .... 267 395-3982 ext. 5259

Agency for International Development [Botswana]
American Embassy - Gaborone, Botswana,
P.O. Box 90, Gaborone, Botswana
E-mail: tkwape@usaid.gov Internet: www.usaid.gov/botswana

Country Representative **Alyson McFarland** 27 (12) 452-2000
E-mail: amcfarland@usaid.gov

Agricultural Section (Foreign Agricultural Service) (Resident in Pretoria) [Botswana]
American Embassy - Pretoria, South Africa,
877 Pretorius Street, Arcaidia 0083, P.O. Box 9536, Pretoria, 0001, South Africa
Mail: American Embassy - Pretoria, Department of State,
Washington, DC 20521-9300
Tel: 27 (12) 431-4057 Fax: 27 (12) 342-2264

Agricultural Officer **James J. "Jim" Higgiston** 27 (12) 431-4057
E-mail: james.higgiston@fas.usda.gov

Drug Enforcement Administration (Resident in Pretoria) [Botswana]
American Embassy - Pretoria, South Africa,
877 Pretorius Street, Arcadia 0083, P.O. Box 9536, Pretoria, 0001, South Africa
Fax: 27 (12) 362-5007

DEA Officer **Sean P. Yauger** 27 (12) 431-4735
E-mail: yaugersp@state.gov

Federal Aviation Administration (Resident in Dakar) [Botswana]
American Embassy - Dakar, Senegal, 45 Rue Kleeber,
2nd Floor, Boite Postal 49 Dakar, Senegal
Mail: FAA AMEMB Dakar, Senegal, Department of State,
Washington, DC 20521-2130
Tel: 221 823-6753 Fax: 221 823-9286

FAA Representative **Grady Stone** 221 33-829-2180

Office of the Defense Attaché [Botswana]
P.O. Box 90, Gaborone, Botswana
Mail: American Embassy - Gaborone, Botswana,
Department of State, Washington, DC 20521-2170
Tel: 267 395-3982

Defense Attaché **LtCol Christopher J. "Chris" Dorough USAF** .... 267 3953982 ext. 5244

Office of Defense Cooperation [Botswana]
American Embassy - Gaborone, Botswana,
P.O. Box 90, Gaborone, Botswana
Mail: American Embassy - Gaborone, Botswana,
Department of State, Washington, DC 20521-2170
Tel: 267 395-3982 Fax: 267 395-6947

Defense Cooperation Officer **COL Christopher P. "Chris" Folk USA** 267 395-3982

Peace Corps [Botswana]
American Embassy - Gaborone, Botswana,
P.O. Box 90, Gaborone, Botswana
Tel: 267 393-3639 E-mail: info@bw.peacecorps.gov
Internet: www.peacecorps.gov/botswana

Country Director **(Vacant)** 267 395-6947

Voice of America - International Broadcasting Bureau [Botswana]
American Embassy - Gaborone, Botswana,
P.O. Box 90, Gaborone, Botswana
Mail: American Embassy - Gaborone, Botswana,
Department of State, Washington, DC 20521-2170
Tel: 267 260-0986 Fax: 267 260-0988

VOA Officer **Charles Shepard** 267 260-0986

★ Presidential Appointment Requiring Senate Confirmation ☆ Presidential Appointment □ Schedule C Appointment ◇ Career Senior Foreign Service Appointment
● Career Senior Executive Service (SES) Appointment ○ Non-Career Senior Executive Service (SES) Appointment ■ Postal Career Executive Service

U.S. Embassy in Burkina Faso

American Embassy - Ouagadougou, Burkina Faso,
Secteur 15, Ouaga 2000, Avenue Sembène Ousmane, Rue 15.873,
Ouagadougou, Burkina Faso 01
Tel: 226 25-49-53-00 Fax: 226 25-49-56-23
E-mail: amembouaga@state.gov
E-mail: consularouaga@state.gov (Consular Issues)

Office of the U.S. Ambassador to Burkina Faso

American Embassy - Ouagadougou, Burkina Faso,
Secteur 15, Ouaga 2000, Avenue Sembène Ousmane, Rue 15.873,
Ouagadougou, Burkina Faso 01
Mail: American Embassy - Ouagadougou, Department of State,
2440 Ouagadougou Place, Washington, DC 20521-2440

★ Ambassador **Ambassador Andrew Robert Young** 226 25-49-53-00
E-mail: youngar@state.gov
Education: UC Berkeley AB; Johns Hopkins MA
Office Management Specialist to the Ambassador
Abigail Veronneau 226 25-49-53-00
E-mail: veronneauae@state.gov
Deputy Chief of Mission **Shannon Nagy Cazeau** 226 25-49-53-00
E-mail: cazeausn@state.gov
Education: Alaska (Fairbanks) BA; Pittsburgh MA
Office Management Specialist to the Deputy Chief
of Mission **Laura M. Piper** 226 25-49-53-00
E-mail: piperlm@state.gov
Education: BYU 1996 BA; U Washington 2010 MBA
Consular Officer **Rafael Andrade** 226 25-49-53-00
E-mail: andrader@state.gov
Community Liaison Officer **Shauna Marshall** 226 25-49-53-00
Economic/Commercial Officer **John C. Corrao** 226 25-49-53-00
E-mail: corraojc@state.gov
Equal Employment Opportunity Officer
Doni M. Phillips 226 25-49-53-00
E-mail: phillipsdm@state.gov
Education: Bryn Mawr 1989 AB; Wyoming 1994 JD
Financial Management Officer **Craig Kennedy** 226 25-49-53-00
Education: U Washington 1983
General Services Officer **Charles N. "Chuck" Kinn** 226 25-49-53-00
E-mail: kinncn@state.gov
Information Management Officer
Michael J. Beaupain 226 25-49-53-00
E-mail: beaupainmj@state.gov
Information Program Officer **(Vacant)** 226 25-49-53-00
Legal Attaché (Resident in Ghana)
Fritzgerald S. Kennely 233 0-30-274-1000
E-mail: kennelyfs@state.gov
Management Officer **Perry A. Gresham** 226 25-49-53-00
E-mail: greshampa@state.gov
Political Officer **Victoria Cedeno** 226 25-49-53-00
E-mail: cedenovm@state.gov
Public Affairs Officer **Matthew W. Long** 226 25-49-53-00
E-mail: longmw@state.gov
Education: Duke 1989 BA
Regional Security Officer **Rosendo Cedeno** 226 25-49-53-00

Agency for International Development [Burkina Faso]

Internet: https://www.usaid.gov/burkina-faso
Country Representative
Christian "Chris" La Pietra-Fung 226 5049-5300
E-mail: clapietrafung@usaid.gov

Federal Aviation Administration (Resident in Dakar) [Burkina Faso]

American Embassy - Dakar, Senegal, 45 Rue Kleeber,
2nd Floor, Boite Postal 49 Dakar, Senegal
Mail: FAA AMEMB Dakar, Senegal, Department of State,
Washington, DC 20521-2130
Tel: 221 823-6753 Fax: 221 823-9286

FAA Representative **Grady Stone** 221 33-829-2180

Office of the Defense Attaché [Burkina Faso]

American Embassy - Abidjan, Cote d'Ivoire, 5 Rue Jesse Owens,
01 B.P. 1712, Abidjan, Cote d'Ivoire
Mail: American Embassy - Abidjan, Department of State,
Washington, DC 20521-2010
Defense Attaché **Andrew Visser** 226 25-49-53-00

U.S. Embassy in Burundi

American Embassy - Bujumbura, Burundi,
No. 50 Avenue des Etats-Unis, 110-01-02 Bujumbura, Burundi
Tel: 257 22 207 000 Fax: 257 22 222 926 Internet: bi.usembassy.gov

Office of the U.S. Ambassador to Burundi

American Embassy - Bujumbura, Burundi,
No. 50 Avenue des Etats-Unis, 110-01-02 Bujumbura, Burundi
Mail: American Embassy - Bujumbura,
2100 Bujumbura Place, Washington, DC 20521-2100

★ Ambassador **Ambassador Anne S. Casper** 257 22 207 000
E-mail: casperas@state.gov
Education: Tufts BA; Johns Hopkins MA; National War Col MS
Office Management Specialist to the Ambassador
Julia Harrison 257 22 207 000
Deputy Chief of Mission **Jennifer Langston Duval** 257 22 207 317
E-mail: duvaljl@state.gov
Office Management Specialist to the Deputy Chief of
Mission **(Vacant)** 257 22 207 000
Community Liaison Officer **Lindsay McKeon** 257 22 207 000
Economic Officer **(Vacant)** 257 22-207-000
Consular Officer (Acting) **Kristen E. Weaver** 257 22 207 304
E-mail: weaverke@state.gov
Education: Santa Clara U 1997 BA; Stanford 1999 MA
Equal Employment Opportunity Officer
Susan B. L'Ecuyer 257 22 207 305
Education: Arkansas State 1990 BA
Facilities Management Officer (Acting) **Floyd Beech** 257 22 207 306
Financial Management Officer **Karen Heimsoth** 257 22 207 306
General Services Officer (Acting) **Peter Maher** 257 22 207 234
Education: Boston Col 1972 BA; Francis King Carey Law 1985 JD
Information Management Officer
Mehari O. Tesfamicael 257 22 207 308
E-mail: tesfamicaelmo@state.gov
Information Program Officer **(Vacant)** 257 22 207 000
Information Systems Security Officer
Mehari O. Tesfamicael 257 22 207 000
E-mail: tesfamicaelmo@state.gov
Legal Attaché **(Vacant)** 257 22 207 000
Management Officer **Otis L. Harrison, Jr.** 257 22 207 000
E-mail: harrisonol@state.gov
Political and Economic Officer **William Echols** 257 22 207 264
Public Affairs Officer **Ashley White** 257 22 207 304
Regional Security Officer **Anand Arockiasamy** 257 22 207 305
E-mail: ArockiasamyA@state.gov

Agency for International Development [Burundi]

American Embassy - Bujumbura, Burundi,
No. 50 Avenue des Etats-Unis, 110-01-02 Bujumbura, Burundi
Fax: 254 (20) 862-2680 E-mail: bujumburausaid@state.gov
Internet: www.usaid.gov/burundi

USAID Representative **Timothy Born** 254 (20) 862-2000
E-mail: tborn@usaid.gov

Drug Enforcement Administration (Resident in Cairo) [Burundi]

American Embassy - Cairo, Egypt, 5 Latin America Street,
Garden City, Cairo, Egypt
Mail: American Embassy - Sanaa, Yemen,
6330 Sanaa Place, Washington, DC 20521-6330
Tel: 20 (2) 2797-3300 Fax: 20 (2) 2797-3200

DEA Officer **Leon M. Palmer** 20 (2) 2797-3300

★ Presidential Appointment Requiring Senate Confirmation ☆ Presidential Appointment □ Schedule C Appointment ◇ Career Senior Foreign Service Appointment
● Career Senior Executive Service (SES) Appointment ○ Non-Career Senior Executive Service (SES) Appointment ■ Postal Career Executive Service

Federal Aviation Administration (Resident in Dakar) [Burundi]
American Embassy - Dakar, Senegal, 45, Rue Kleeber, Boite Postal 49, Dakar, Senegal
Mail: FAA AMEMB Dakar, Senegal, Department of State, Washington, DC 20521-2130
Tel: 221 823-6753 Fax: 221 823-9286

FAA Representative **Grady Stone** 221 33-879-4835

Office of the Defense Attaché [Burundi]
American Embassy - Bujumbura, Burundi, No. 50 Avenue des Etats-Unis, 110-01-02 Bujumbura, Burundi
Mail: American Embassy - Bujumbura, 2100 Bujumbura Place, Washington, DC 20521-2100
Tel: 257 22 207 209

Defense Attaché **Serge Mettes** 257 22 207 309

U.S. Embassy in Cameroon

American Embassy - Yaoundé, Cameroon, 6.050 Avenue Rosa Parks, B.P. 817, Yaoundé, Cameroon
Tel: 237 2200-1500 Fax: 237 2200-1500

Office of the U.S. Ambassador to Cameroon

American Embassy - Yaoundé, Cameroon, 6.050 Avenue Rosa Parks, B.P. 817, Yaoundé, Cameroon
Mail: Department of State, 2520 Yaoundé Place, Washington, DC 20521-2520

★ Ambassador **Ambassador Peter Henry Barlerin** 237 2220-1500
E-mail: barlerinph@state.gov
Education: Middlebury BA; Maryland MA
Office Management Specialist to the Ambassador **Lori L. Enders** 237 2220-1500

Deputy Chief of Mission **Vernelle Trim FitzPatrick** 237 2220-1500
E-mail: trimvx@state.gov
Education: Davidson BA; George Washington MA
Office Management Specialist to the Deputy Chief of Mission **Debra Clark-Ware** 237 2220-1500
E-mail: clark-wared@state.gov

Consular Section Chief **Michael Fitzpatrick** 237 2220-1500
Fax: 237 223-0581

Community Liaison Officer **Ashley Tikkanen** 237 2220-1500
Financial Management Officer **Kimberly Maine** 237 2200-1500
General Services Officer **Monica Barreto** 237 2220-1500
Fax: 237 223-4373
Information Management Officer **Bridget Tambe** 237 2220-1500
Information Program Officer **Tai Kyung "T.K." Park** 237 2220-1500
Information Systems Officer **Franklin "Frank" Lum** 237 2220-1500
Information Systems Security Officer **Franklin "Frank" Lum** 237 2220-1500
Management Officer **(Vacant)** 237 2220-1500
Fax: 237 222-5517
Political/Economic Officer **(Vacant)** 237 2220-1500
Fax: 237 222-1890
Public Affairs Officer **S. Lee McManis** .... 237 2220-1500 ext. 4162
Fax: 237 222-6765
Regional Security Officer **(Vacant)** 237 2220-1500

Agency for International Development [Cameroon]
6.050 Avenue Rosa Parks, B.P. 817, Yaoundé, Cameroon
Internet: www.usaid.gov/cameroon

Field Office Director **Mounkaila Billo** 237 2200-1500
E-mail: mbillo@usaid.gov

Federal Aviation Administration (Resident in Dakar) [Cameroon]
American Embassy - Dakar, Senegal, 45, Rue Kleeber, Boite Postal 49, 2nd Floor, Dakar, Senegal
Mail: FAA AMEMB Dakar, Senegal, Department of State, Washington, DC 20521-2130
Tel: 221 823-6753 Fax: 221 823-9286

FAA Representative **Grady Stone** 221 33-829-2180

Office of the Defense Attaché [Cameroon]
American Embassy - Yaoundé, Cameroon, Rue Nachtigal, B.P. 817, Yaoundé, Cameroon
Mail: Department of State, 2520 Yaoundé Place, Washington, DC 20521-2520
Tel: 237 2220-1500 Fax: 237 222-5189

Defense Attaché **(Vacant)** 237 2220-1500

Peace Corps [Cameroon]
American Embassy - Yaounde, Cameroon, Rue Nachtigal, B.P. 817, Yaoundé, Cameroon
Mail: Department of State, 2520 Yaounde Place, Washington, DC 20521-2520
Tel: 237 2220-1500 Fax: 237 221-5398 E-mail: info@cm.peacecorps.gov
Internet: www.peacecorps.gov/cameroon

Country Director **Mark Orlic** 237 2220-1500
E-mail: morlic@peacecorps.gov

Douala Branch Office
Department of State, 2520 Yaounde Place, Washington, DC 20521-2520
Tel: 237 3342-5331 Fax: 237 3342-7790

Director **Sita Liane Chakrawarti** 237 3342-5331
E-mail: ChakrawartiSL@State.gov

U.S. Embassy in Cabo Verde

American Embassy - Praia, Cabo Verde, Rua Abilio Macedo 6, Praia, Cabo Verde
Tel: 238 260-8900 Fax: 238 261-1355 Internet: cv.usembassy.gov

Office of the U.S. Ambassador to Cabo Verde

American Embassy - Praia, Cabo Verde, Rua Abilio Macedo 6, Praia, Cabo Verde
Mail: American Embassy - Praia, Department of State, 2460 Praia Place, Washington, DC 20521-2460

★ Ambassador **(Vacant)** 238 260-8900
Chargé d'Affaires **Marissa Denise Scott** 238 260-8900
E-mail: scottm@state.gov
Education: Dillard BA
Office Management Specialist to the Ambassador **(Vacant)** 238 260-8929
Deputy Chief of Mission **Marissa Denise Scott** 238 260-8900
E-mail: scottm@state.gov
Education: Dillard BA
Consular Affairs Officer **Stephen F. Le Compte** 238 260-8900
Vice-Consul **Gabrielle Chwazik-Gee** 238 260-8900
Community Liaison Officer **Jeanae Davidson** 238 260-8900
General Service Officer **Jeffrey J. "Jeff" Duarte** 238 260-8900
E-mail: duartejj@state.gov
Education: UMass (Dartmouth) 1983 BS; Chapman 1988 MS; New Mexico 1995 MA; Texas (Dallas) 2003 MBA
Information Management Officer **Derek Mikiewicz** 238 260-8900
Information Systems Security Officer **(Vacant)** 238 260-8900
Management Officer **Jeffrey J. "Jeff" Duarte** 238 260-8900
E-mail: duartejj@state.gov
Education: UMass (Dartmouth) 1983 BS; Chapman 1988 MS; New Mexico 1995 MA; Texas (Dallas) 2003 MBA
Political/Economic Officer **Amelia R. Runyon** 238 260-8900
Public Affairs Officer **Jaclyn A. Cole** 238 260-8900
Education: Howard U 2005 BA; Yale 2007 MA
Regional Security Officer **Michael Davidson** 238 260-8900

Federal Aviation Administration (Resident in Dakar) [Cabo Verde]
American Embassy - Dakar, Senegal, 45, Rue Kleeber, Boite Postal 49, 2nd Floor, Dakar, Senegal
Mail: FAA AMEMB Dakar, Department of State, 2130 Dakar Place, Washington, DC 20521-2130
Tel: 221 823-6753 Fax: 221 823-9286

FAA Representative **Grady Stone** 221 33-879-48-35

★ Presidential Appointment Requiring Senate Confirmation ☆ Presidential Appointment □ Schedule C Appointment ◇ Career Senior Foreign Service Appointment
● Career Senior Executive Service (SES) Appointment ○ Non-Career Senior Executive Service (SES) Appointment ■ Postal Career Executive Service

Office of the Defense Attaché (Resident in Dakar) [Cabo Verde]
American Embassy - Dakar, Senegal, 45, Rue Kleeber, Boite Postal 49, Dakar, Senegal
Mail: American Embassy - Dakar, Department of State, 2130 Dakar Place, Washington, DC 20521-2130
Tel: 221 823-4296 Fax: 221 822-2991
Defense Attaché **LTC Scott H. Morgan USA** 221 33-829-2100

U.S. Embassy in the Central African Republic

American Embassy - Bangui, Central African Republic, Avenue David Dacko, B.P. 924, Bangui, Central African Republic
Tel: 236 21-61-02-00 Fax: 236 21-61-44-94

Office of the U.S. Ambassador to the Central African Republic

American Embassy - Bangui, Central African Republic, Avenue David Dacko, B.P. 924, Bangui, Central African Republic
Mail: American Embassy - Bangui, Department of State, Washington, DC 20521-2060
E-mail: banguiconsular@state.gov

★ Ambassador-Designate **Ambassador Lucy Tamlyn** 236 21-61-02-00
E-mail: tamlynl@state.gov
Education: St John's Col (MD) BLA; Columbia MA
Chargé d'Affaires **David P. Brownstein** 236 21-61-02-00
E-mail: brownsteindp@state.gov
Education: Williams 1992; National Intelligence U 2012
Office Management Specialist to the Ambassador **Veronica Scruggs** 236 21-61-02-00
Deputy Chief of Mission **David P. Brownstein** 236 21-61-02-00
E-mail: brownsteindp@state.gov
Education: Williams 1992; National Intelligence U 2012
Political/Economic Officer **Lilieth R. Whyte** . . . 236 21-61-02-22 ext. 3255
E-mail: whytelr@state.gov
General Services Officer **Eric Wild** 236 61-02-00
Information Management Officer **Rydell C. Fletcher** 236 21-61-02-00
Management Officer **Olga Tunga** . . . . 236 21-61-02-00 ext. 3295
Public Affairs Officer **Michelle Zjhra** 236 21-61-02-00
Regional Security Officer **Paul Benvie** 236 21-61-02-00

U.S. Embassy in Chad

American Embassy - N'Djamena, Chad, Rond-Point de Chagoua, B.P. 413, N'Djamena, Chad
Tel: 235 2251-5017

Office of the U.S. Ambassador to Chad

American Embassy - N'Djamena, Chad, Rond-Point de Chagoua, B.P. 413, N'Djamena, Chad
Mail: American Embassy, Department of State, 2410 N'Djamena Place, Washington, DC 20520-2410

★ Ambassador **(Vacant)** 235 2251-5017
Chargé d'Affaires **Richard K. Bell** 235 2251-5017
E-mail: bellrk@state.gov
Office Management Specialist to the Ambassador **Carol Hazzard** 235 2251-5017
Deputy Chief of Mission **Chahrazed Sioud** 235 2251-5017
E-mail: sioudcx@state.gov
Office Management Specialist to the Deputy Chief of Mission **(Vacant)** 235 2251-5017
Consular Officer **(Vacant)** 235 2251-5017
Community Liaison Officer **(Vacant)** 235 2251-5017
Economic/Commercial Officer **(Vacant)** 235 2251-5017
Financial Management Officer **Daniel Dagley** 235 2251-5017
E-mail: dagleydl@state.gov
General Services Officer **(Vacant)** 235 2251-5017
Information Management Officer **(Vacant)** 235 2251-5017
Information Program Officer **Thomas Morris** 235 2251-5017
Management Officer **Philip "Phil" Kern** 235 2251-5017
E-mail: kernpr@state.gov
Political/Economic Officer **C. Amanda Cranmer** 235 2251-5017
Public Affairs Officer **Grant Phillipp** . . . . 235 2251-5019 ext. 24661
E-mail: phillippgg@state.gov

Office of the U.S. Ambassador to Chad *(continued)*

Regional Security Officer **James Falgoust** 235 2251-5017
E-mail: falgoustjj@state.gov

Agency for International Development [Chad]
Internet: https://www.usaid.gov/chad
Country Representative **Leslie E. "Les" McBride** 235 2251-5017
E-mail: mcbridele@state.gov
Education: U Washington BA

Federal Aviation Administration (Resident in Dakar) [Chad]
American Embassy - Dakar, Senegal, 45, Rue Kleeber, Boite Postal 49, 2nd Floor, Dakar, Senegal
Mail: FAA AMEMB Dakar, Senegal, Department of State, Washington, DC 20521-2130
Tel: 221 823-6753 Fax: 221 823-9286
FAA Representative **Grady Stone** 221 33-829-2180

Office of the Defense Attaché [Chad]
American Embassy - N'Djamena, Chad, Rond-Point de Chagoua, B.P. 413, N'Djamena, Chad
Mail: American Embassy - N'Djamena, Chad, Department of State, 2410 N'Djamena Place, Washington, DC 20521-2410
E-mail: ndjamena_detcmd@state.gov
Defense Attaché **Joseph Edward Williams** 235 2251-5017

U.S. Embassy in the Democratic Republic of the Congo

American Embassy, Kinshasa, Democratic Republic of the Congo, 310 Avenue des Aviateurs, Commune de la Gombe, Kinshasa, Democratic Republic of Congo
Tel: 243 81-556-0151 Fax: 243 81-55-60-175
E-mail: usembassykinshasa@state.gov

Office of the U.S. Ambassador to the Democratic Republic of the Congo

American Embassy, Kinshasa, Democratic Republic of the Congo, 310 Avenue des Aviateurs, Commune de la Gombe, Kinshasa, Democratic Republic of Congo
Mail: American Embassy Kinshasa, 2220 Kinshasa PL, Washington, DC 20521-2220

★ Ambassador **Ambassador Michael A. "Mike" Hammer** 243 81-556-0151
E-mail: hammerma@state.gov
Education: Georgetown BS; Fletcher Law & Diplomacy MALD; National War Col MS
Office Management Specialist to the Ambassador **(Vacant)** 243 81-556-0151
◇ Deputy Chief of Mission **Jennifer Conn Haskell** 243 81-556-0151
E-mail: haskellj@state.gov
Education: Oregon 1982 BA; Thunderbird Global 1988 MBA
Office Management Specialist to the Deputy Chief of Mission **JoAnn M. Liner** 243 81-556-0151
Consular Section Chief **Cedra Eaton** 243 81-556-0151
E-mail: eatoncd@state.gov
Community Liaison Officer **Jennifer Aitken-Wietecha** 243 81-556-0151
E-mail: aitken-wietechajm@state.gov
Cultural Affairs Officer **Jessica Chesbro** 243 81-556-0151
E-mail: chesbrojk@state.gov
Economic Officer **Dovas A. Saulys** 243 81-556-0151
E-mail: saulysda@state.gov Fax: 243 81-556-0169
Equal Employment Officer **Travis Smalls** 243 81-556-0151
Financial Management Officer **Alan R. Royston** 243 81-556-0151
E-mail: roystonar@state.gov
General Service Officer **Steve Hazel** 243 81-556-0151
E-mail: hazels@state.gov
Human Resources Officer **(Vacant)** 243 81-556-0151
Information Management Officer **Elton Sankoh** 243 81-556-0151
E-mail: sankoheu@state.gov
Information Program Officer **(Vacant)** 243 81-556-0151
Information Systems Security Officer **(Vacant)** 243 81-556-0151

(continued on next page)

DEPARTMENTS

★ Presidential Appointment Requiring Senate Confirmation ☆ Presidential Appointment ☐ Schedule C Appointment ◇ Career Senior Foreign Service Appointment
● Career Senior Executive Service (SES) Appointment ○ Non-Career Senior Executive Service (SES) Appointment ■ Postal Career Executive Service

DEPARTMENTS

Office of the U.S. Ambassador to the Democratic Republic of the Congo *(continued)*

Management Officer **Erin M. Butler** 243 81-556-0151
E-mail: butlerem@state.gov
Political Officer **Aaron B. Sampson** 243 81-556-0151
E-mail: sampsonab@state.gov
Public Affairs Officer **Yolonda Kerney** 243 81-556-0151
E-mail: kerneyyv@state.gov
Regional Security Officer **Robert Little** 243 81-556-0151
E-mail: littlera@state.gov

Agency for International Development [Democratic Republic of the Congo]
198 Isiro Avenue, Commune de la Gombe, Kinshasa,
Democratic Republic of Congo
Mail: US AID, American Embassy - Kinshasa,
Unit 31550, APO, AE 09828
Fax: 243 880-3274 Internet: www.usaid.gov/democratic-republic-congo

◇ Mission Director **Paul Sabatine** 243 81-700-5701
E-mail: psabatine@state.gov
Education: Catholic U 1990 BA; Mount Angel Sem 1996 MA; George Washington 1999 MBA

Centers for Disease Control [Democratic Republic of the Congo]
198 Isiro Avenue, Commune de la Gombe, Kinshasa,
Democratic Republic of Congo
Mail: American Embassy Kinshasa, 2220 Kinshasa PL,
Washington, DC 20521-2220

Country Director **Raimi Ewetola** 243 81-556-0151
E-mail: rewetola@cdc.gov

Federal Aviation Administration (Resident in Dakar) [Democratic Republic of the Congo]
American Embassy - Dakar, Senegal, 45, Rue Kleeber, Boite Postal 49,
2nd Floor, Dakar, Senegal
Mail: FAA AMEMB Dakar, Senegal, Department of State,
Washington, DC 20521-2130
Tel: 221 823-6753 Fax: 221 823-9286

FAA Representative **Grady Stone** 221 33-879 4835

Office of the Defense Attaché [Democratic Republic of the Congo]
Defense Attaché and Senior Defense Official
LTC Cheryl Korver USA 243 81-556-0151
E-mail: korvercr@state.gov

U.S. Embassy in the Republic of the Congo
70-83 Section D, Maya-Maya Boulvard, Brazzaville, Republic of Congo
Tel: 242 06612-2000 Internet: cg.usembassy.gov

Office of the U.S. Ambassador to the Republic of the Congo – Brazzaville Embassy Office
70-83 Section D, Maya-Maya Boulvard, Brazzaville, Republic of Congo

★ Ambassador **Ambassador Todd Philip Haskell** 242 06612-2000
E-mail: haskelltt@state.gov
Education: Georgetown 1984 BSFS
Office Management Specialist to the Ambassador **Nadia C. Shepherd** . . . . 242 06612-2000 ext. 2025
E-mail: shepherdnc@state.gov
Deputy Chief of Mission
Matthew V. Cassetta . . . . 242 06612-2000 ext. 2058
E-mail: CassettaMV@state.gov
Community Liaison Officer **Amber Fijolek** 242 06612-2000
Consular Officer **Regis Prevot** . . . . 242 06612-2000 ext. 2012
Economic Officer **Elizabeth E. "Beth" Gee** 242 06612-2000
Facilities Management Officer **Sharla A. Magana** 242 06612-2000
E-mail: maganasa@state.gov
General Services Officer **Daniel C. Muffley** 242 06612-2000
E-mail: muffleydc@state.gov
Human Resources Officer (Resident in Kinshasa)
(Vacant) 242 06612-2000
Information Management Officer
Stephen O. Martins . . . . 242 06612-2000 ext. 2145
Information Systems Officer **(Vacant)** 242 06612-2000

Office of the U.S. Ambassador to the Republic of the Congo – Brazzaville Embassy Office *(continued)*

Management Officer **Daniel J. Horning** . . . . . . 242 06612-2000 ext. 2019
Political Officer **Benjamin David "Ben" Mossberg** 242 06612-2000
Public Affairs Officer **Jacqueline D. Mourot** 242 06612-2000
E-mail: MourotJD@state.gov
Regional Security Officer **James Nangle** . . . . . 242 06612-2000 ext. 2110

Federal Aviation Administration (Resident in Dakar) [Republic of Congo]
American Embassy - Dakar, Senegal, 45, Rue Kleeber, Boite Postal 49,
2nd Floor, Dakar, Senegal
Mail: FAA AMEMB Dakar, Senegal, Department of State,
Washington, DC 20521-2130
Tel: 221 823-6753 Fax: 221 823-9286

FAA Representative **Grady Stone** 221 33-879 4835

U.S. Embassy in Côte d'Ivoire
American Embassy - Abidjan, Cote d'Ivoire,
Riviera Golf, 01 B.P. 1712, Abidjan, 01, Cote d'Ivoire
Tel: 225 22-49-40-00 Fax: 225 22-49-43-23

Office of the U.S. Ambassador to Côte d'Ivoire
American Embassy - Abidjan, Cote d'Ivoire,
Riviera Golf, 01 B.P. 1712 Abidjan, 01, Cote d'Ivoire
Mail: American Embassy - Abidjan, 2010 Abidjan Place,
Dulles, VA 20189-2010

★ Ambassador **(Vacant)** 225 22-49-40-00
◇ Charge d'Affaires **Katherine A. Brucker** 225 22-49-40-00
E-mail: bruckerka2@state.gov
Education: Tulane 1982 BA; Thunderbird International 1993 MIM; Indust'l Col Armed Forces 2012 MS
Office Management Specialist to the Ambassador
(Vacant) 225 22-49-40-00
◇ Deputy Chief of Mission (Acting)
Paul Douglas Yeskoo 225 22-49-40-00
E-mail: yeskoopd@state.gov
Education: Wheaton (IL) 1981 BA
Office Management Specialist to the Deputy Chief of Mission **Linda D. Goodman** 225 22-49-40-00
E-mail: goodmanld@state.gov
Education: Argosy U 2013 BS
Community Liaison Officer **Susan E. McCarthy** 225 22-49-40-00
Consular Officer **Glenn E. Fedzer** 225 22-49-40-00
E-mail: fedzerge2@state.gov Fax: 225 20-22-45-23
Political/Economic Officer **David Mosby** 225 22-49-40-00
E-mail: mosbydg@state.gov
Financial Management Officer **Misun Pak Fedzer** 225 22-49-40-00
General Services Officer **Roland Dixon** 225 22-49-40-00
Human Resources Officer **Jonathan D. Cebra** 225 20-21-09-79
E-mail: cebrajd@state.gov
Information Management Officer **Linda L. Pohl** 225 22-49-40-00
E-mail: pohllI@state.gov
Information Program Officer **Hugh Thompson** 225 22-49-40-00
Information Systems Security Officer **Linda L. Pohl** 225 22.49.40.00
E-mail: pohlll@state.gov
◇ Management Officer **Michael A. Chung** 225 20-21-09-79
E-mail: chungm@state.gov Fax: 225 20-21-52-75
Public Affairs Officer **Daniel "Dan" Langenkamp** 225 22-44-40-00
E-mail: langenkampdb@state.gov Fax: 225 22-44-53-96
E-mail: abjpress@state.gov
Regional Security Officer **William D. McCarthy** 225 22-49-40-00

Agency for International Development [Côte d'Ivoire]
American Embassy - Abidjan, Cote d'Ivoire,
Riviera Golf, 01 B.P. 1712, Abidjan, 01, Cote d'Ivoire
Internet: www.usaid.gov/cote-divoire

Development Counselor **(Vacant)** 225 22 49 41 32

★ Presidential Appointment Requiring Senate Confirmation ☆ Presidential Appointment ☐ Schedule C Appointment ◇ Career Senior Foreign Service Appointment
● Career Senior Executive Service (SES) Appointment ○ Non-Career Senior Executive Service (SES) Appointment ■ Postal Career Executive Service

Federal Aviation Administration (Resident in Dakar) [Côte d'Ivoire]
American Embassy - Dakar, Senegal, 45, Rue Kleeber, Boite Postal 49, 2nd Floor, Dakar, Senegal
Mail: FAA AMEMB Dakar, Senegal, Department of State, Washington, DC 20521-2130
Tel: 221 823-9753 Fax: 221 823-9286

FAA Representative **Grady Stone** 221 33-829-2180

Office of the Defense Attaché [Côte d'Ivoire]
American Embassy - Abidjan, 2010 Abidjan Place, Washington, DC 20521-2010
American Embassy - Abidjan, Cote d'Ivoire, Riviera Golf, 01 B.P. 1712, Abidjan, 01, Cote d'Ivoire
Tel: 225 22-49-40-00 Fax: 225 20-22-32-59

Defense Attaché **LtCol Christopher Ginther USMC** 225 22-49-40-00

U.S. Embassy in Djibouti

American Embassy - Djibouti, B.P. 185, Plateau du Serpent, Boulevard Marechal Joffre, Djibouti, Djibouti
Tel: 253 21-45-30-00 Fax: 253 21-45-31-29

Office of the U.S. Ambassador to Djibouti

American Embassy - Djibouti, B.P. 185, Plateau du Serpent, Boulevard Marechal Joffre, Djibouti, Djibouti
Mail: Department of State, 2150 Djibouti Place, Washington, DC 20521-2150

★ Ambassador **Ambassador Lawrence Edward "Larry" André, Jr.** 253 21-45-30-00
E-mail: andrele@state.gov
Education: Claremont McKenna BA; Thunderbird International 1988 MBA
Office Management Specialist to the Ambassador **Olivia J. Lindenberg** 253 21-45-30-00
E-mail: lindenbergo@state.gov
Deputy Chief of Mission **Joseph Alexander "Alex" Hamilton** 253 21-45-30-00
Office Management Specialist to the Deputy Chief of Mission **(Vacant)** 253 21-45-30-00
Consular Officer **Devin J. Kennington** 253 21-45-30-00
E-mail: kenningtondj@state.gov
Community Liaison Officer **(Vacant)** 253 21-45-30-00
Economic Officer **Merry Walker** 253 21-45-30-00
Equal Employment Opportunity Officer **Danelle Ragoonanan-Storph** 253 21-45-30-00
E-mail: ragoonanan-storphdi@state.gov
Financial Management Officer **(Vacant)** 253 21-45-30-00
General Services Officer **Edith Davis** 253 21-45-30-00
Information Management Officer **Didier Diakite** 253 21-45-30-00
E-mail: mdidierdiakite@state.gov
Information Systems Security Officer **William J. "Bill" Manuel** 253 21-45-30-00
Management Officer **Barbara S. Keary** 253 21-45-30-00
E-mail: kearybs@state.gov
Military Liaison Officer/Office of Defense Cooperation Chief **MAJ Trish A. Basile USA** 253 21-45-30-00
E-mail: basileta@state.gov
Political Officer **Chuma Nnawulezi** 253 21-45-30-00
Public Affairs Officer **Jessica R. Banuls** 253 21-45-30-00
E-mail: banulsjr@state.gov
Regional Security Officer **Gregory G. "Greg" Mitchell** 253 21-45-30-00
E-mail: mitchellgg@state.gov

Agency for International Development [Djibouti]
American Embassy - Djibouti, B.P. 185, Plateau du Serpent, Boulevard Marechal Joffre, Djibouti, Djibouti
Mail: 2150 Djibouti Place, Washington, DC 20521-2150
Fax: 253 2145-3129 E-mail: djiboutimail@usaid.gov
Internet: www.usaid.gov/djibouti

USAID Representative **Rabihah Mateen** 253 2145-3204
E-mail: rmateen@usaid.gov

Federal Aviation Administration (Resident in Dakar) [Djibouti]
American Embassy - Dakar, Senegal, 45, Rue Kleeber, Boite Postal 49, 2nd Floor, Dakar, Senegal
Mail: FAA AMEMB Dakar, Senegal, Department of State, Washington, DC 20521-2130
Tel: 221 823-6753 Fax: 221 823-9286

FAA Representative **Grady Stone** 221 33-829-2180

Office of the Defense Attaché [Djibouti]
Defense Attaché **John Tully** 253 21-45-30-00
E-mail: tullyjm@state.gov

U.S. Embassy in Equatorial Guinea

Malabo II Highway, Malabo, Equatorial Guinea
Tel: 240 333-09-57-41 Fax: 240 333-098894
E-mail: malabopublic@state.gov

Office of the U.S. Ambassador to Equatorial Guinea

Malabo II Highway, Malabo, Equatorial Guinea
Tel: 240 333-09-57-41 Fax: 240 333-098894
E-mail: malabopublic@state.gov Internet: gq.usembassy.gov

★ Ambassador **Ambassador Julie Anne Furuta-Toy** 240 333-09-57-41
E-mail: furutatoyja@state.gov
Education: UC Riverside BA; Indiana MA; Indust'l Col Armed Forces MA
★ Ambassador-Designate **Susan N. Stevenson** 240 333-09-57-41
E-mail: stevensonsn@state.gov
Education: Pennsylvania 1988 BS
Office Management Specialist to the Ambassador **Gail Lewis** 240 333-09-57-41
Deputy Chief of Mission **Jarahn D. Hillsman** 240 333-09-57-41
Community Liaison Officer **Dina Rotenberg** 240 333-09-57-41
Consul **Bryan S. Schiller** 240 333-09-57-41
E-mail: schillerbs@state.gov
Defense Attaché **(Vacant)** 240 333-09-57-41
Political/Economic Officer **Samuel J. "Sam" Rotenberg** 240 333-09-57-41
E-mail: rotenbergsj@state.gov
Management Officer **Theresa A. Sondjo** 240 333-09-57-41
Financial Management Officer **Theresa A. Sondjo** 240 333-09-57-41
General Services Officer **Daniel James Beauchamp** 240 333-09-57-41
Information Management Officer **Joseph J. Hromatka** 240 333-09-57-41
E-mail: hromatkajj@state.gov
Information Systems Security Officer **Joseph J. Hromatka** 240 333-09-57-41
E-mail: hromatkajj@state.gov
Regional Security Officer **Jose Mercado** 240 333-09-57-41
Education: East Carolina 2001 MA
Public Affairs Officer **Jason D. Seymour** 240 333-09-57-41
E-mail: seymourjd@state.gov

U.S. Embassy in Eritrea

U.S. Embassy - Asmara, Eritrea, 179 Alaa Street, P.O. Box 211, Asmara, Eritrea
Tel: 291 (1) 12-00-04 Fax: 291 (1) 12-75-84

Office of the U.S. Ambassador to Eritrea

U.S. Embassy - Asmara, Eritrea, 179 Alaa Street, P.O. Box 211, Asmara, Eritrea
Mail: Department of State, 7170 Asmara Place, Washington, DC 20521-7170
Tel: 291 (1) 12-00-04 Fax: 291 (1) 12-75-84 Internet: er.usembassy.gov

★ Ambassador **(Vacant)** 291 (1) 12-00-04
◇ Chargé d'Affaires **Natalie E. Brown** 291 (1) 12-00-04
Office Management Specialist to the Chargé d'Affaires **Debra R. DeBose** 291 (1) 12-00-04
Fax: 291 (1) 12-22-68
Deputy Chief of Mission **Stephen B. "Steve" Banks** 291 (1) 12-00-04
E-mail: bankssb@state.gov

(continued on next page)

★ Presidential Appointment Requiring Senate Confirmation ☆ Presidential Appointment □ Schedule C Appointment ◇ Career Senior Foreign Service Appointment
● Career Senior Executive Service (SES) Appointment ○ Non-Career Senior Executive Service (SES) Appointment ■ Postal Career Executive Service

DEPARTMENTS

Office of the U.S. Ambassador to Eritrea *(continued)*

Consular Affairs Officer **Jolanta Mikiewicz** 291 (1) 12-00-04
Community Liaison Officer **Kedir Nasser** 291 (1) 12-00-04
Information Management Officer **Marc Alfano** 291 (1) 12-00-04
E-mail: alfanomc@state.gov
Education: William & Mary 2004 BS
Information Systems Security Officer **Marc Alfano** 291 (1) 12-00-04
E-mail: alfanomc@state.gov
Education: William & Mary 2004 BS
Management Officer **Elizabeth K. Thompson** 291 (1) 12-37-20
E-mail: thompsonek@state.gov Fax: 291 (1) 12-68-80
Political/Economic Officer **Violeta Talandis**...........291 (1) 12-00-04
Public Affairs Officer **Violeta Talandis** 291 (1) 12-00-04
Regional Security Officer
Charles E. "Chuck" Diamond, Jr. 291 (1) 12-00-04

Federal Aviation Administration (Resident in Dakar) [Eritrea]
American Embassy - Dakar, Senegal,
45 Avenue Jean XXIII and rue Kleber, Boite Postal 49,
2nd Floor, Dakar, Senegal
Mail: FAA AMEMB Dakar, Senegal, 2130 Dakar Place,
Washington, DC 20521-2130
Tel: 221 33-829-2100 Fax: 221 33-823-9286

FAA Representative **Grady Stone** 221 33-829-2180

U.S. Embassy in Eswatini

Corner of MR 103 and Cultural Center Drive, Ezulwini, Mbabane, Eswatini
Tel: 268 2417-9000 Fax: 268 2416-3344 Internet: sz.usembassy.gov
Note: King Mswati III changed the name of the country from Swaziland to Eswatini in April 2018.

Office of the U.S. Ambassador to Eswatini

American Embassy - Mbabane, Swaziland,
Corner of MR 103 and Cultural Center Drive, Ezulwini, Mbabane, Eswatini
Mail: American Embassy - Mbabane, 2350 Mbabane Place,
Dulles, VA 20189-2350
E-mail: USEmbassyMbabane@state.gov

★ Ambassador **Ambassador Lisa J. Peterson** 268 2417-9000
E-mail: petersonlj@state.gov
Office Management Specialist to the Ambassador
Ursula M. Eley 268 2417-9000
E-mail: eleyum@state.gov
Deputy Chief of Mission **Michael R. Lombardo** 268 2417-9000
E-mail: lombardomr@state.gov
Office Management Specialist to the Deputy Chief of Mission **Ursula M. Eley** 268 2417-9000
E-mail: eleyum@state.gov
Consular Officer **Jeff Rotering** 268 2417-9000
E-mail: roteringj@state.gov
Community Liaison Officer **Jenny Jeffress**.............268 2417-9000
Financial Management Officer **Marc Trahan** 268 2417-9000
General Services Officer **Marjorie Rapp** 268 2417-9000
E-mail: gsombabane@state.gov
Information Management Officer **Noah P. Dietrich**.......268 2417-9000
E-mail: dietrichnp@state.gov
Information Program Officer **(Vacant)** 268 2417-9000
Information Systems Officer **Ken Kapoor** 268 2417-9000
Information Systems Security Officer **Noah P. Dietrich** ... 268 2417-9000
E-mail: dietrichnp@state.gov
Management Officer **Marc Trahan** 268 2417-9000
Political/Economic Officer **Michael C. "Mich" Coker** 268 2417-9000
E-mail: cokermc@state.gov
Public Affairs Officer **Joia A. Starks** 268 2417-9000
E-mail: starksja@state.gov
Regional Security Officer **Michael B. "Mike" Jeffress** ... 268 2417-9000
E-mail: jeffressmb@state.gov

Agricultural Section (Foreign Agricultural Service) (Resident in Pretoria) [Eswatini]
American Embassy - Pretoria, South Africa, 877 Pretorius Street,
Arcadia 0083, Pretoria, 0001, South Africa
P.O. Box 9536, Pretoria, 0001, South Africa
Mail: American Embassy - Pretoria, Department of State,
Washington, DC 20521-9300
Tel: 27 (12) 431-4057 Fax: 27 (12) 342-2264
Agricultural Officer **James J. "Jim" Higgiston**.......27 (12) 431-4057
E-mail: james.higgiston@fas.usda.gov

Centers for Disease Control [Eswatini]
Central Bank Building, Corner of MR 103 and Cultural Center Drive,
Ezulwini, Mbabane, Eswatini
Mail: American Embassy - Mbabane, 2350 Mbabane Place,
Dulles, VA 20189-2350
CDC Representative **Dr. Caroline A. Ryan** 27 (12) 346-0170

Drug Enforcement Administration (Resident in Pretoria) [Eswatini]
American Embassy - Pretoria, South Africa, 877 Pretorius Street,
Arcadia 0083, Pretoria, 0001, South Africa
Mail: American Embassy - Pretoria, South Africa,
Department of State, Washington, DC 20521-9300
DEA Officer **Sean P. Yauger**........................27 (12) 431-4735
E-mail: yaugersp@state.gov

Federal Aviation Administration (Resident in Dakar) [Eswatini]
American Embassy - Dakar, 45 Rue Kleeber, Boite Postal 49,
2nd Floor, Dakar, Senegal
Mail: FAA AMEMB Dakar, Senegal, Department of State,
Washington, DC 20521-2130
Tel: 221 823-6753 Fax: 221 823-9286
FAA Representative **Grady Stone** 221 33-879 48 35

Office of the Defense Attaché (Resident in Pretoria) [Eswatini]
American Embassy - Pretoria, South Africa, 877 Pretorius Street,
Acadia 0083, P.O. Box 9536, Pretoria, 0001, South Africa
Mail: American Embassy - Pretoria, Department of State,
Washington, DC 20521-9300
Tel: 27 (12) 342-4000 Fax: 27 (12) 431-6161
Defense Attaché **CAPT Steven A. Morgenfeld USN** ... 27 (12) 431-4180

Peace Corps [Eswatini]
Corner of MR 103 and Cultural Center Drive, Ezulwini, Mbabane, Eswatini
Mail: American Embassy - Mbabane, 2350 Mbabane Place,
Dulles, VA 20189-2350
Internet: www.peacecorps.gov/swaziland
Country Director **Glenda N. Green** 268 2417-9000

U.S. Embassy in Ethiopia

American Embassy - Addis Ababa, Ethiopia,
Entoto Street, P.O. Box 1014, Addis Ababa, Ethiopia
Tel: 251 (11) 130-6000 Fax: 251 (11) 124-24-01

Office of the U.S. Ambassador to Ethiopia

American Embassy - Addis Ababa, Ethiopia,
Entoto Street, P.O. Box 1014, Addis Ababa, Ethiopia
Mail: American Embassy - Addis Ababa, Ethiopia,
Department of State, Washington, DC 20521-2030

★ Ambassador
Ambassador Michael Arthur "Mike" Raynor 251 (11) 130-60-00
E-mail: raynorma@state.gov
Education: Lafayette 1984 BA; Columbia MIA
Office Management Specialist to the Ambassador
Katie Koehler 251 (11) 130-60-00
E-mail: koehlerke@state.gov Fax: 251 (11) 555-07-74
◇ Deputy Chief of Mission **Troy Damian Fitrell** 251 (11) 130-60-00
E-mail: fitrelltd@state.gov
Office Management Specialist to the Deputy Chief of Mission **Lisa Burkholder** 251 (11) 130-60-00
Consular Affairs Officer **(Vacant)** 251 (11) 11-130-6000

★ Presidential Appointment Requiring Senate Confirmation ☆ Presidential Appointment □ Schedule C Appointment ◇ Career Senior Foreign Service Appointment
● Career Senior Executive Service (SES) Appointment ○ Non-Career Senior Executive Service (SES) Appointment ■ Postal Career Executive Service

Office of the U.S. Ambassador to Ethiopia *(continued)*

Community Liaison Officer **Christine A. Lusk** 251 (11) 130-60-00
E-mail: LuskCA@state.gov Fax: 251 (11) 524-24-03
Community Liaison Officer **Fritz von Schlegell** 251 (11) 130-60-00
Fax: 251 (11) 524-24-03
Economic Officer **Helena P. Schrader** 251 (11) 130-60-00
E-mail: schraderhp@state.gov
Economic/Commercial Officer **(Vacant)** 251 (11) 130-60-00
Financial Management Officer **Javier Pareja** 251 (11) 130-60-00
E-mail: parejaj@state.gov
General Service Officer **Paul Pousette** 251 (11) 130-60-00
Human Resources Officer **Mekdim Zewde** 251 (11) 130-60-00
E-mail: zewdem@state.gov
Information Management Officer
Wesley E. Pendergist 251 (11) 130-60-68
E-mail: pendergistwe@state.gov
Information Program Officer **Armando Muir** 251 (11) 130-60-00
Information Systems Officer **Joshua Kase** 251 (11) 130-60-00
Legal Attaché **Daniel Choldin** 251 (11) 130-6000
E-mail: choldindl@state.gov
Management Officer **(Vacant)** 251 (11) 517-43-01
Political/Economic Counselor **David W. Renz** 251 (11) 130-60-00
E-mail: renzdx@state.gov
Public Affairs Officer **(Vacant)** 251 (11) 130-72-74
E-mail: pasaddis@state.gov Fax: 251 (11) 555-17-48
Regional Environment Officer
Christopher M. "Chris" Nyce 251 (11) 130-6777
E-mail: nycec@state.gov
Regional Security Officer **Yvon Guillaume** 251 (11) 130-60-00
E-mail: guillaumey2@state.gov
E-mail: RSOAddisAbaba@state.gov

Agency for International Development [Ethiopia]
American Embassy - Addis Ababa, Ethiopia,
Entoto Street, P.O. Box 1014, Addis Ababa, Ethiopia
Mail: American Embassy - Addis Ababa, Ethiopia,
Department of State, Washington, DC 20521-2030
Tel: 251 (11) 130-60-02 Fax: 251 (11) 124-2438
E-mail: aidethiopia@usaid.gov Internet: www.usaid.gov/ethiopia

Mission Director **Leslie Reed** 251 (11) 130-60-01
E-mail: lreed@usaid.gov

Agricultural Section (Foreign Agricultural Service) [Ethiopia]
American Embassy - Addis Ababa, Ethiopia,
Entoto Street, P.O. Box 1014, Addis Ababa, Ethiopia
Tel: 251 (11) 130-6777 E-mail: agaddisababa@fas.usda.gov

Counselor for Agricultural Affairs **Rachel Bickford** . . . 251 (11) 130-6777
E-mail: rachel.bickford@fas.usda.gov
Education: Rochester 1996 BA; George Washington 2000 MA

Centers for Disease Control [Ethiopia]
American Embassy - Addis Ababa, Ethiopia,
Entoto Street, P.O. Box 1014, Addis Ababa, Ethiopia
Mail: American Embassy - Addis Ababa, Ethiopia,
Department of State, Washington, DC 20521-2030
Tel: 251 11-130-6001 Fax: 251 (11) 465-95-67
E-mail: cdcaethiopia@etcdc.com

Country Director **Jeffrey "Jeff" Hanson** 251 (11) 130-6943
E-mail: jeff.hanson@cdc.hhs.gov

Commercial Section (Foreign Commercial Service) [Ethiopia]
Senior Commercial Officer
Christopher "Chris" Wilken 251 (11) 130-6683
E-mail: Christopher.Wilken@trade.gov
Education: Manhattanville 2005 BA; Johns Hopkins 2010 MA

Federal Aviation Administration (Resident in Dakar) [Ethiopia]
American Embassy - Dakar, Senegal, 45, Rue Kleeber, Boite Postal 49,
2nd Floor, Dakar, Senegal
Mail: FAA AMEMB Dakar, Senegal, Department of State,
Washington, DC 20521-2130
Tel: 221 823-6753 Fax: 221 823-9286

FAA Representative **Grady Stone** 221 33-879-4835

Office of the Defense Attaché [Ethiopia]
American Embassy - Addis Ababa, Ethiopia,
Entoto Street, P.O. Box 1014, Addis Ababa, Ethiopia
Mail: American Embassy - Addis Ababa, Ethiopia,
Department of State, Washington, DC 20521-2030
Tel: 251 11-130-7006 Fax: 251 (11) 124-24-45
E-mail: mausembassy@state.gov

Defense Attaché **LTC Michael McCullough USA** 251 (11) 1307006

Peace Corps [Ethiopia]
American Embassy - Addis Ababa, Ethiopia,
Entoto Street, P.O. Box 1014, Addis Ababa, Ethiopia
Fax: 251 (11) 320-03-16 E-mail: ethiopia@peacecorps.gov
Internet: www.peacecorps.gov/ethiopia

Country Director **Brannon Brewer** 251 (11) 320-03-16
E-mail: bbrewer@peacecorps.gov

U.S. Embassy in Gabon

Sablière B.P. 4000, Libreville, Gabon
Tel: 241 01-45-71-00 Internet: ga.usembassy.gov

Office of the U.S. Ambassador to Gabon

American Embassy - Libreville, Gabon,
Sablière B.P. 4000, Libreville, Gabon
Mail: Department of State, 2270 Libreville Place,
Washington, DC 20521-2270
E-mail: usembassylibreville@state.gov
Note: The U.S. Ambassador to Gabon serves concurrently as the U.S. Ambassador to Sao Tome and Principe.

★ Ambassador **Ambassador Joel Danies** 241 01-45-71-00
E-mail: daniesj@state.gov
Education: Maryland 1979 BA; National War Col 2010 MS
Office Management Specialist to the Ambassador
Courtney W. Canchola 241 01-45-71-00
E-mail: CancholaCW@state.gov
Deputy Chief of Mission **Randall Todd Merideth** 241 01-45-71-00
E-mail: meridethrt@state.gov
Education: Gustavus Adolphus 1987 BA
Community Liaison Officer **Cody Clayborne** 241 01-45-71-00
Consular Affairs Officer **Natalie Peterson** 241 01-45-71-00
Financial Management Officer **Meredith Spivey** 241 01-45-71-00
E-mail: spiveymm@state.gov
General Services Officer **Tessa Henry** 241 01-45-71-00
Education: Tufts 2010 BA; Harvard 2017 MA
Information Management Officer **Zeze Onivogui** 241 01-45-71-00
E-mail: onivoguiz@state.gov
Information Systems Officer **Joshua Rice** 241 01-45-71-00
Education: Wright State 2002 BS
Information Systems Security Officer **Joshua Rice** 241 01-45-71-00
Education: Wright State 2002 BS
Economic Officer **(Vacant)** 241 01-45-71-00
Management Officer **Keiji D. Turner** 241 01-45-71-00
Political/Economic Officer **Diana Costa** 241 01-45-71-00
Public Affairs Officer **Melissa Cotton** 241 01-45-71-00
Regional Security Officer **Christopher McVay** 241 01-45-71-00

Office of the Defense Attaché [Gabon]
Sablière B.P. 4000, Libreville, Gabon
Mail: Department of State, 2270 Libreville Place,
Washington, DC 20521-2270
Tel: 241 762003 Fax: 241 745507

Defense Attaché **Charles Barton** 241 762003

★ Presidential Appointment Requiring Senate Confirmation ☆ Presidential Appointment □ Schedule C Appointment ◇ Career Senior Foreign Service Appointment
● Career Senior Executive Service (SES) Appointment ○ Non-Career Senior Executive Service (SES) Appointment ■ Postal Career Executive Service

DEPARTMENTS

U.S. Embassy in The Gambia

Fajara, Kairaba Ave., P.M.B. 19, Banjul, Gambia
Tel: 220 439-2856 Fax: 220 439-2475 Internet: gm.usembassy.gov

Office of the U.S. Ambassador to The Gambia

American Embassy - Banjul, The Gambia, Fajara, Kairaba Ave., P.M.B. 19, Banjul, Gambia
Mail: American Embassy - Banjul, The Gambia, Department of State, Washington, DC 20521-2070

★ Ambassador
Ambassador Carolyn Patricia "Pat" Alsup 220 439-2858
E-mail: alsupcp@state.gov
Education: Wellesley BA; Harvard MBA; Indust'l Col Armed Forces 2008 MS

★ Ambassador-Designate
Richard Carlton "Carl" Paschall III 220 439-2856
E-mail: paschallrc@state.gov
Education: North Carolina 1991 BA; National Defense U 2013 MS

Chargé d'Affaires **Shelly A. Seaver** 220 439-2858
E-mail: seaversa@state.gov
Education: Emory
Office Management Specialist to the Ambassador
(Vacant) 220 439-2856

Deputy Chief of Mission **Shelly A. Seaver** 220 439-2858
E-mail: seaversa@state.gov
Education: Emory

Community Liaison Officer **Cindy Tillman** 220 439-2856
Consular Section Chief **Caitlin J. Tumulty** 220 439-2856
E-mail: tumultycj@state.gov
Financial Management Officer **Susan C. N'Garnim** 220 439-2856
E-mail: ngarnimsc@state.gov
General Services Officer **Doreen C. Farnitano** 220 439-2856
Information Management Officer **(Vacant)** 220 439-2856
Information Systems Officer **(Vacant)** 220 439-2856
Information Systems Security Officer **(Vacant)** 220 439-2856
Management Officer **Erik M. Hall** 220 439-2856
Political/Economic Officer **Youliana P. Sadowski** 220 439-2856
Public Affairs Officer **Kathryn Edwards** .... 220 439-2856 ext. 2168
E-mail: edwardsk@state.gov
Regional Security Officer **Robert E. Tillman** 220 439-2856

Federal Aviation Administration (Resident in Dakar) [The Gambia]

American Embassy - Dakar, Senegal, 45, Rue Kleeber, Boite Postal 49, 2nd Floor, Dakar, Senegal
Mail: FAA AMEMB - Dakar, Senegal, Department of State, Washington, DC 20521-2130
Tel: 221 823-6753 Fax: 221 823-9286

FAA Representative **Grady Stone** 221 33-829-2180

Office of the Defense Attaché (Resident in Dakar) [The Gambia]

American Embassy - Dakar, Senegal, 45, Rue Kleeber, Boite Postal 49, Dakar, Senegal
Mail: American Embassy - Dakar, Senegal, Department of State, Washington, DC 20521-2130
Tel: 221 829-2100

Defense Attaché **LTC Scott H. Morgan USA** 221 829-2100

U.S. Embassy in Ghana

American Embassy - Accra, Ghana, No. 24, Fourth Circular Road, Cantonments Accra, Ghana
Tel: 233 (30) 274-1000 Fax: 233 (30) 741-389
Internet: gh.usembassy.gov

Office of the U.S. Ambassador to Ghana

American Embassy - Accra, Ghana, No. 24, Fourth Circular Road, Cantonments Accra, Ghana
P.O. Box 194, Accra, Ghana
Mail: Department of State, 2020 Accra Place, Washington, DC 20521-2020

★ Ambassador
Ambassador Stephanie Sanders Sullivan 233 (30) 274-1000
Note: On September 6, 2018, the Senate confirmed Stephanie Sullivan to be Ambassador to Ghana.
E-mail: sullivanss@state.gov
Education: Brown U BA; National War Col MS

◇ Chargé d'Affaires **Christopher John Lamora** 233 (30) 274-1000
E-mail: lamoracj@state.gov
Education: Georgetown 1991 BA
Office Management Specialist to the Ambassador
(Vacant) 233 (30) 274-1000

◇ Deputy Chief of Mission
Christopher John Lamora 233 (30) 274-1000
E-mail: lamoracj@state.gov
Education: Georgetown 1991 BA
Office Management Specialist to the Deputy Chief of Mission **LaVonya M. Hayward** 233 (30) 274-1000
E-mail: haywardlm@state.gov

Community Liaison Officer **Shana Tongren** 233 (30) 274-1000
E-mail: tongrensh@state.gov
Consular Section Chief **Jayne Allison Howell** 233 (30) 274-1000
E-mail: howellja@state.gov
Consular Officer **Keith Murphy** 233 (30) 274-1000
Economic Officer **(Vacant)** 233 (30) 274-1000
Equal Employment Officer **Allison Gildon** 233 (30) 274-1000
E-mail: gildonam@state.gov
Financial Management Officer **(Vacant)** 233 (30) 274-1000
General Services Officer **Alexandra S. Aitken** 233 (30) 274-1000
E-mail: aitkenas@state.gov
Information Management Officer **Jarrod M. Frahm** 233 (30) 274-1000
E-mail: frahmjm@state.gov
Information Program Officer **Joseph Ohikuare** 233 (30) 274-1000
Information Systems Officer **Michael Halls** 233 (30) 274-1000
Information Systems Security Officer
Michael Halls 233 (30) 274-1000
International Broadcasting Bureau Officer
Kathryn Peterson 233 (30) 274-1000
Legal Attaché **Fritzgerald S. Kennely** 233 (30) 274-1000
E-mail: kennelyfs@state.gov
Management Officer **Michelle E. Wollam** 233 (30) 274-1000
E-mail: wollamme@state.gov
Political Officer **Thomas H. Lyons** 233 (30) 274-1000
E-mail: lyonsth@state.gov
Political/Economic Officer **(Vacant)** 233 (30) 274-1000
Public Affairs Officer **Roberto "Rob" Quiroz II** 233 (30) 274-1150
E-mail: quirozr2@state.gov Fax: 233 (30) 274-1692
Cultural Attaché **Sarah Shabbir** 233 (30) 274-1150
Press Attaché **Sara Veldhuizen Stealy** 233 (30) 274-1150
E-mail: stealysv@state.gov
Regional Security Officer
Jeffrey S. "Jeff" Rusinek 233 (30) 274-1000
E-mail: rusinekjs@state.gov

Agency for International Development [Ghana]

American Embassy - Accra, Ghana, E45/3 Independence Avenue, Accra, Ghana
Mail: Department of State, 2020 Accra Place, Washington, DC 20521-2020
Tel: 233 (30) 274-1200 Fax: 233 (30) 2-741-365
E-mail: ghanaweb@usaid.gov Internet: www.usaid.gov/ghana

Mission Director **Sharon Lee Cromer** 233 (30) 274-1200
E-mail: scromer@usaid.gov
Education: Barnard 1980; Georgetown JD

★ Presidential Appointment Requiring Senate Confirmation ☆ Presidential Appointment ☐ Schedule C Appointment ◇ Career Senior Foreign Service Appointment
● Career Senior Executive Service (SES) Appointment ○ Non-Career Senior Executive Service (SES) Appointment ■ Postal Career Executive Service

Agency for International Development [Ghana] *(continued)*

◇ Regional Mission Director, West Africa
Daniel Moore 233 (30) 274-1200
E-mail: dmoore@usaid.gov
Education: Willamette BSc; UC Davis MSc

Agricultural Section (Foreign Agricultural Service) [Ghana]
American Embassy - Accra, Ghana, No. 24, Fourth Circular Road, Cantonments Accra, Ghana
Tel: 233 (30) 2741-421 Fax: 233 (30) 741-478
E-mail: agaccra@fas.usda.gov

Agricultural Counselor **Charles Rush** 233 (30) 2741-421
E-mail: charles.rush@fas.usda.gov
Attaché **Daniel Archibald** 233 (30) 2741-421

Commercial Section (Foreign Commercial Service) [Ghana]
Ridge Roundabout, P.O. Box GP 194, Accra, Ghana
Mail: Department of State, 2020 Accra Place, Washington, DC 20521-2020
Fax: 233 (30) 274-1401 E-mail: office.accra@trade.gov
Internet: http://www.export.gov/ghana/

Senior Commercial Officer **Tyrena Holley** 233 (30) 274-1086
E-mail: tyrena.holley@trade.gov
Education: UC Davis 1977 BA

Department of Homeland Security - U.S. Citizenship and Immigration Services [Ghana]
American Embassy - Accra, Ghana, 6th and 10th Lanes, OSU, P.O. Box 194, Accra, Ghana
Mail: Department of State, 2020 Accra Place, Washington, DC 20521-2020
E-mail: uscis.accra@uscis.dhs.gov

Immigration Attaché **Fatou Sidibe** 233 (30) 274-1000

Federal Aviation Administration (Resident in Dakar) [Ghana]
American Embassy - Dakar, Senegal, 45 Avenue Jean XXIII and rue Kleber, Boite Postal 49, 2nd Floor, Dakar, Senegal
Mail: FAA AMEMB Dakar, Senegal, Department of State, Washington, DC 20521-2130
Tel: 221 823-6753 Fax: 221 823-9286

FAA Representative **Grady Stone** 221 33-829-2180

Office of the Defense Attaché [Ghana]
American Embassy - Accra, Ghana, No. 24, Fourth Circular Road, Cantonments Accra, Ghana
Mail: Department of State, 2020 Accra Place, Washington, DC 20521-2020

Defense Attaché **Joseph Lee** 233 (30) 274-1000

Peace Corps [Ghana]
Peace Corps, No. 26 West Cantonments, P.O. Box AN 5796, Accra, Ghana
Mail: Department of State, 2020 Accra Place, Washington, DC 20521-2020
Tel: 233 (30) 274-4600 Fax: 233 (30) 277-4383
Internet: www.peacecorps.gov/ghana

Country Director **Carla Ellis** 233 (30) 274-4600
E-mail: cellis@peacecorps.gov

U.S. Embassy in Guinea
Transversale No. 2, B.P. 603, Centre Administratif de Koloma, Commune de Ratoma, Conakry, Guinea
Tel: 224 6510-4000 Fax: 224 6510-4297 Internet: gn.usembassy.gov

Office of the U.S. Ambassador to Guinea
American Embassy - Conakry, Guinea, Transversale No. 2, B.P. 603, Centre Administratif de Koloma, Commune de Ratoma, Conakry, Guinea
Mail: Department of State, 2110 Conakry Place, Washington, DC 20521-2110

★ Ambassador **Ambassador Dennis B. Hankins** 224 6510-4000
Note: On August 16, 2018, President Donald J. Trump nominated Dennis Hankins to be Ambassador to Mali. This nomination is pending in the Senate.
E-mail: hankinsdb@state.gov
Education: Georgetown 1981 BSFS; National War Col 1999 MA
★ Ambassador-Designate **Simon A. Henshaw** 224 6510-4000
E-mail: henshaws@state.gov
Education: UMass (Amherst) 1983 BA; National War Col 2004 MS
Office Management Specialist to the Ambassador
Althena Aikens 224 6510-4000
E-mail: aikensax@state.gov
Deputy Chief of Mission **Hugues P. Ogier** 224 6510-4000
E-mail: ogierhp@state.gov
Office Management Specialist to the Deputy Chief of Mission **(Vacant)** 224 6510-4000
Consular Officer **Jennifer L. Schools** 224 6510-4000
E-mail: schoolsjl@state.gov
Education: Texas 1979 BA; Texas (Dallas) 1981 (Attended)
Community Liaison Officer **(Vacant)** 224 6510-4000
Economic/Commercial Officer **John Stark** 224 6510-4000
Equal Employment Opportunity Officer
Kevin Kabumoto 224 6510-4000
E-mail: kabumotokc@state.gov
Financial Management Officer **(Vacant)** 224 6510-4000
General Services Officer **(Vacant)** 224 6510-4000
Information Management Officer
William B. "Bill" Hagan 224 6510-4000
E-mail: haganwb@state.gov
Information Systems Security Officer **Michelle Judy** 224 6510-4000
Management Officer **Femi Akinyemi** 224 6510-4000
E-mail: AkinyemiFO@state.gov
Political/Economic Section Chief **Kevin Kabumoto** 224 6510-4081
E-mail: kabumotokc@state.gov
Political Officer **Chukwudi J. Nwadibia** 224 6510-4000
E-mail: nwadibiacj@state.gov
Public Affairs Officer **Dawn Dowling** 224 6510-4176
E-mail: dowlingdm@state.gov Fax: 224 30-41-29-21
Regional Security Officer **Duane Mitchell** 224 6510-4000

Agency for International Development [Guinea]
American Embassy - Guinea, Transversale No. 2, B.P. 603, Centre Administratif de Koloma, Commune de Ratoma, Conakry, Guinea
Tel: 224 3046-8715 Fax: 224 3046-8714 Internet: www.usaid.gov/guinea

Mission Director **Jeff Bryan** 224 3046-8715
E-mail: jbryan@usaid.gov
Education: James Madison 1991 BA; Texas A&M 2000 MA

Federal Aviation Administration (Resident in Dakar) [Guinea]
American Embassy - Dakar, Senegal, 45, Rue Kleeber, Boite Postal 49, 2nd Floor, Dakar, Senegal
Mail: FAA AMEMB Dakar, Senegal, Department of State, Washington, DC 20521-2130
Tel: 221 823-6753 Fax: 221 823-9286

FAA Representative **Grady Stone** 221 33-829-2180

Office of the Defense Attaché [Guinea]
Department of State, 2110 Conakry Place, Washington, DC 20521-2110

Defense Attaché **LTC Kristopher "Kris" Kvam USA** 224 6510-4000

★ Presidential Appointment Requiring Senate Confirmation ☆ Presidential Appointment □ Schedule C Appointment ◇ Career Senior Foreign Service Appointment
● Career Senior Executive Service (SES) Appointment ○ Non-Career Senior Executive Service (SES) Appointment ■ Postal Career Executive Service

Peace Corps [Guinea]
Transversale No. 2, B.P. 603, Centre Administratif de Koloma, Commune de Ratoma, Conakry, Guinea
Mail: Department of State, 2110 Conakry Place,
Washington, DC 20521-2110
Internet: www.peacecorps.gov/guinea
Country Director **Brian Cavanagh** 224 622350240

U.S. Embassy in Kenya
American Embassy - Nairobi, Kenya, United Nations Avenue, P.O. Box 606 Village Market, 00621 Nairobi, Kenya
Tel: 254 (20) 363-6000 Fax: 254 (20) 363-6157
Internet: ke.usembassy.gov

Office of the U.S. Ambassador to Kenya
American Embassy - Nairobi, Kenya, United Nations Avenue, P.O. Box 606 Village Market, 00621 Nairobi, Kenya
Mail: American Embassy - Nairobi, Kenya, Unit 64100,
APO, AE 09831-4100

★ Ambassador **Ambassador Robert F. Godec, Jr.** 254 (20) 363-6056
E-mail: godecrf@state.gov
Education: Virginia BA; Yale MA

★ Ambassador-Designate **Kyle McCarter** 254 (20) 363-6000
Education: Oral Roberts BS

Office Management Specialist to the Ambassador **Anni Pirinen Valme** 254 (20) 363-6056

◇ Deputy Chief of Mission **Mirembe L. Nantongo** 254 (20) 363-6057
E-mail: nantongoml@state.gov

Office Management Specialist to the Deputy Chief of Mission **Ana Maria Prieto-Danaher** 254 (20) 363-6057
E-mail: prietodanahera@state.gov

Community Liaison Officer **(Vacant)** 254 (20) 363-6000

Consul General **Glen C. Keiser** 254 (20) 363-6037
E-mail: keisergc@state.gov

Economic Officer **Mario A. Fernandez** 254 (20) 363-6051
E-mail: fernandezma@state.gov

Facilities Management Officer **Mike Dzingleski** 254 (20) 363-6085
E-mail: Dzingleskim@state.gov

Financial Management Officer **Brian Alistair "Alistair" Cooke** 254 (20) 363-6000

General Services Officer **Michael "Mike" Pace** 254 (20) 363-6085
E-mail: pacem@state.gov

Human Resources Officer **Sebron Toney** 254 (20) 363-6157

Information Management Officer **James E. "Eddie" Barclay** 254 (20) 363-6004
E-mail: barclayje@state.gov

Information Program Officer **Aaron Luffman** 254 (20) 363-6000
E-mail: luffmana@state.gov
Education: Graceland U 1998 BA

Information Systems Officer **Jahiro Demian "Demian" Lamadrid** 254 (20) 363-6000
E-mail: lamadridjd@state.gov

Information Systems Security Officer **Dipesh Patel** ... 254 (20) 363-6000

Management Officer **James E. "Jim" Vanderpool** ... 254 (20) 363-6555
E-mail: vanderpoolje@state.gov

Political Officer **Eric W. Kneedler** 254 (20) 363-6177

Public Affairs Officer **Paul S. Watzlavick** 254 (20) 363-6202
E-mail: watzlavickps@state.gov
Education: Texas 1986 BA, 1998 MPP; Marine War Col 2015 MS

Regional Security Officer **Lance M. Bailey** 254 (20) 363-6301
E-mail: baileylm@state.gov

Agency for International Development - East Africa Regional Mission [Kenya]
American Embassy - Nairobi, Kenya, P.O. Box 30261, Nairobi, Kenya
Mail: American Embassy - Nairobi, Kenya, Unit 64102,
APO, AE 09831-4102
Tel: 254 (20) 862-2000 Fax: 254 (20) 862-2680
E-mail: eastafrica-info@usaid.gov Internet: www.usaid.gov/kenya
Internet: www.usaid.gov/east-africa-regional

Note: This Mission is responsible for both Kenya and the East Africa Region.

Mission Director **Mark Andrew Meassick** 254 (20) 862-2000
E-mail: mmeassick@usaid.gov
Education: Wake Forest BA; UMass (Amherst) MBA, MEd

Agricultural Section (Foreign Agricultural Service) [Kenya]
American Embassy - Nairobi, Kenya, United Nations Avenue, P.O. Box 606 Village Market, 00621 Nairobi, Kenya
Mail: American Embassy - Nairobi, Kenya, Unit 8900, Box #4301,
DPO, AE 09831
Tel: 254 (20) 363-6340 Fax: 254 (20) 363-6349
E-mail: agnairobi@usda.gov Internet: www.fas.usda.gov/regions/kenya

Agricultural Counselor **Kevin Sage-EL** 254 (20) 363-6413
E-mail: Kevin.Sage-EL@fas.usda.gov

Centers for Disease Control [Kenya]
American Embassy - Nairobi, Kenya, United Nations Avenue, P.O. Box 606 Village Market, 00621 Nairobi, Kenya
Mail: American Embassy - Nairobi, Kenya, Unit 64112,
APO, AE 09831-4112
Tel: 254 (20) 271-3008 Fax: 254 (20) 271-4745

Director **Kevin M. De Cock** 254 (20) 286185
E-mail: kmd2@cdc.gov
Education: Bristol U 1974 MD

Commercial Service (Foreign Commercial Service) [Kenya]
American Embassy - Nairobi, Kenya, Unit 64100, APO, AE 09831-4100
American Embassy - Nairobi, Kenya, United Nations Avenue, P.O. Box 606 Village Market, 00621 Nairobi, Kenya
Tel: 254 (20) 363-6059 Internet: www.export.gov/kenya

Senior Commercial Officer **James Rigassio** .... 254 (20) 363-6000 ext. 6424
E-mail: James.Rigassio@trade.gov

Department of Homeland Security [Kenya]
American Embassy - Nairobi, Kenya, United Nations Avenue, P.O. Box 606 Village Market, 00621 Nairobi, Kenya
Mail: American Embassy - Nairobi, Kenya, Unit 64116,
APO, AE 09831-4116
Tel: 254 (20) 363-6102 Fax: 254 (20) 363-6103

Customs and Border Protection Officer-in-Charge **Kevin Martinson** 254 (20) 363-6112

Citizenship and Immigration Services Officer-in-Charge **(Vacant)** 254 (20) 363-6112

Transportation Security Administration Officer-in-Charge **Gary Seffel** 254 (20) 363-6112

Federal Aviation Administration (Resident in Dakar) [Kenya]
American Embassy - Dakar, Senegal, Avenue Jean XXIII and Rue Kleber, Boite Postal 49, Dakar, Senegal
Mail: Department of State/FAA, 2130 Dakar Place,
Washington, DC 20521-2130
Tel: 221 823-6753 Fax: 221 823-9286

FAA Representative **Grady Stone** 221 33-829-48-35

Federal Bureau of Investigation [Kenya]
American Embassy - Nairobi, Kenya, Unit 64100, APO, AE 09831-4100
American Embassy - Nairobi, Kenya, United Nations Avenue, P.O. Box 606 Village Market, 00621 Nairobi, Kenya
Tel: 254 (20) 363-6264

Legal Attaché **Andrea Dobranski** 254 (20) 363-6264

Library of Congress [Kenya]
American Embassy - Nairobi, Kenya, United Nations Avenue, P.O. Box 606 Village Market, 00621 Nairobi, Kenya
Mail: LOC-Nairobi, Unit 64110, APO, AE 09831-4110
Tel: 254 (20) 363-6300 Fax: 254 (20) 363-6321

Field Director **Edward Miner** 254 (20) 363-6146
E-mail: nairobi@loc.gov

★ Presidential Appointment Requiring Senate Confirmation ☆ Presidential Appointment ☐ Schedule C Appointment ◇ Career Senior Foreign Service Appointment
● Career Senior Executive Service (SES) Appointment ○ Non-Career Senior Executive Service (SES) Appointment ■ Postal Career Executive Service

Office of the Defense Attaché [Kenya]
American Embassy - Nairobi, Kenya, United Nations Avenue, P.O. Box 606 Village Market, 00621 Nairobi, Kenya
Mail: American Embassy - Nairobi, Kenya, Unit 64115, APO, AE 09831-4115
Tel: 254 (20) 363-6041 Fax: 254 (20) 363-6396
E-mail: daonairobi@hotmail.com
Defense Attaché
COL Gregory "Greg" Broecker USA 254 (20) 363-6041

Peace Corps [Kenya]
American Embassy - Nairobi, Kenya, P.O. Box 30158, Nairobi, Kenya
Mail: American Embassy - Nairobi, Kenya, Unit 64107, APO, AE 09831-4107
Tel: 254 (20) 444-8692 Fax: 254 (20) 444-5175
Internet: www.peacecorps.gov/kenya
Note: Peace Corps suspended its volunteer activities in Kenya in July 2014.
Country Director **(Vacant)** 254 (20) 444-8694

U.S. Embassy in Lesotho
254 Kingsway Road, Maseru, 100, Lesotho
Tel: 266 22-312-666 Fax: 266 22-310-116 Internet: ls.usembassy.gov

Office of the U.S. Ambassador to Lesotho
American Embassy - Maseru, Lesotho, 254 Kingsway Road, Maseru, 100, Lesotho
Mail: Department of State, 2340 Maseru Place, Washington, DC 20521-2340
E-mail: infomaseru@state.gov
★ Ambassador **Ambassador Rebecca Eliza Gonzales** 266 22-312-666
E-mail: gonzalezr@state.gov
Education: George Washington BA, MBA; Eisenhower National Security and Resource Strategy MS
Office Management Specialist to the Ambassador
Serita Hansen 266 22-312-666
Deputy Chief of Mission **Daniel S. Katz** 266 22-312-666
E-mail: katzds@state.gov
Education: Rutgers; American U MIR
Community Liaison Officer **Daryl Peterson** 266 22-312-666
Consular Officer **Melissa A. Ledesma-Leese** 266 22-312-666
Political/Economic Officer **Matthew Jamrisko** 266 22-312-666
General Services Officer **Nicole T. Shire** 266 22-312-666
Information Management Officer
Alexander N. "Alex" Ueki 266 22-312-666
Management Officer **Jacob M. Rocca** 266 22-312-666
◇ Public Affairs Officer **Melissa A. Jones** 266 22-312-666
Regional Security Officer **Dennis Jones** 266 22-312-666
PEPFAR Coordinator **Aubrey Casey** 266 22-312-666

Agricultural Section (Foreign Agricultural Service) (Resident in Pretoria) [Lesotho]
American Embassy - Pretoria, South Africa, 877 Pretorius Street, P.O. Box 0083, Arcadia, Pretoria, 0001, South Africa
Mail: Department of State, 9300 Pretoria Place, Washington, DC 20521-9300
Tel: 27 (12) 431-4057 Fax: 27 (12) 342-2264
Agricultural Officer **James J. "Jim" Higgiston** 27 (12) 431-4057
E-mail: james.higgiston@fas.usda.gov

Centers for Disease Control [Lesotho]
American Embassy - Maseru, Lesotho, 254 Kingsway Road, Maseru, 100, Lesotho
Country Director **Andy Pelletier** 266 22-312-666

Federal Aviation Administration (Resident in Dakar) [Lesotho]
American Embassy - Dakar, Senegal, 45 Avenue Jean XXIII and rue Kleber, 2nd Floor, Boite Postal 49 Dakar, Senegal
Mail: FAA AMEMB Dakar, Senegal, Department of State, Washington, DC 20521-2130
Tel: 221 823-6753 Fax: 221 823-9286
FAA Representative **Grady Stone** 221 33-829-2180

Office of the Defense Attaché (Resident in Pretoria) [Lesotho]
American Embassy - Pretoria, South Africa, 877 Pretorius Street, Arcadia 0083, Pretoria, 0001, South Africa
P.O. Box 9536, Pretoria, 0001, South Africa
Mail: Department of State, 9300 Pretoria Place, Washington, DC 20521-9300
Tel: 27 (12) 431-4000 Fax: 27 (12) 431-6161
Defense Attaché **CAPT Steven A. Morgenfeld USN** ... 27 (12) 431-4180

Peace Corps [Lesotho]
Makaoteng Estate, Intersection of Pioneer Rd & Pope John Paul II Rd, Maseru, Lesotho
Mail: Department of State, 2340 Maseru Place, Washington, DC 20521-2340
Tel: 266 2231-3871 E-mail: info@ls.peacecorps.gov
Internet: www.peacecorps.gov/lesotho
Country Director **Leon Kayego** 266 22-313-871
E-mail: lkayego@peacecorps.gov

U.S. Embassy in Liberia
502 Benson Street, P.O. Box 98, Monrovia, Liberia
Tel: 231 776-777-000 Fax: 231 776-777-370

Office of the U.S. Ambassador to Liberia
American Embassy - Monrovia, Liberia, 502 Benson Street, P.O. Box 98, Monrovia, Liberia
Mail: American Embassy - Monrovia, Department of State, Washington, DC 20521-8800
★ Ambassador **Ambassador Christine Ann Elder** 231 776-777-000
E-mail: elderca@state.gov
Education: Kentucky BA; George Washington MA
Office Management Specialist to the Ambassador
Linda C. Richardson 231 776-777-000
E-mail: richardsonlc@state.gov
◇ Deputy Chief of Mission **Alyson L. Grunder** 231 776-777-000
E-mail: grunderal2@state.gov
Education: Yale 1982 BA
Office Management Specialist to the Deputy Chief of Mission **Angela F. Simonson-Hijarunguru** 231 776-777-000
E-mail: Simonson-Hijarunguru@state.gov
Community Liaison Officer **Istvan Rozanich** 231 776-777-000
Consular Officer **Jay Sorensen** 231 776-777-000
Economic Officer **Richard C. "Rick" Merrin** 231 776-777-000
E-mail: merrinrc@state.gov
Education: Malone Col BA; Ohio State JD, MBA; Naval War 2018 MNSSS
Financial Management Officer **Joselito C. Rivera** 231 776-777-000
Education: Baruch Col 2002 BBA
General Services Officer **Robert B. Burnett** 231 776-777-000
E-mail: burnettrb@state.gov
Human Resources Officer **Kathleen V. Hare** 231 776-777-000
E-mail: harekv@state.gov
Information Management Officer
Scott M. McKnight 231 776-777-000
E-mail: mcknightsm@state.gov
Information Program Officer **(Vacant)** 231 776-777-000
Information Systems Officer **(Vacant)** 231 776-777-000
Information Systems Security Officer **(Vacant)** 231 776-777-000
Management Officer **Richard C. Nicholson** 231 776-777-000
E-mail: nicholsonrc@state.gov
Political/Economic Officer **Meghan M. Moore** 231 776-777-000
E-mail: mooremm2@state.gov
E-mail: Monrovia-Commercial@state.gov
Education: USC BA; UCLA MA
Public Affairs Officer **Selim Ariturk** 231 77-677-7428
E-mail: ariturks@state.gov
E-mail: MonroviaPD@state.gov
Education: Chicago 2000 AB; Johns Hopkins 2005 MA
Regional Security Officer **David Brown** 231 776-777-000

★ Presidential Appointment Requiring Senate Confirmation ☆ Presidential Appointment ☐ Schedule C Appointment ◇ Career Senior Foreign Service Appointment
● Career Senior Executive Service (SES) Appointment ○ Non-Career Senior Executive Service (SES) Appointment ■ Postal Career Executive Service

DEPARTMENTS

Agency for International Development [Liberia]
American Embassy - Monrovia, Liberia, 111 United Nations Drive, Mamba Point, P.O. Box 10-0098, Monrovia, Liberia
Mail: American Embassy - Monrovia, Department of State, Washington, DC 20521-8800
Tel: 231 77-677-7000 Fax: 231 777-010-370
Internet: www.usaid.gov/liberia

Mission Director **Anthony S. "Tony" Chan** 231 777-054-825
E-mail: achan@usaid.gov
Education: UCLA PhD

Agricultural Section (Foreign Agriculture Service) (Resident in Accra) [Liberia]
American Embassy - Monrovia, Liberia, 502 Benson Street, P.O. Box 98, Monrovia, Liberia
Tel: 233 (30) 2-741-421 Fax: 233 (30) 2-741-000

Agricultural Counselor **Charles Rush** 233 302 741-421
E-mail: charles.rush@fas.usda.gov

Drug Enforcement Administration (Resident in Lagos) [Liberia]
U.S. Consulate General - Lagos, Nigeria, 2 Walter Carrington Crescent, Victoria Island Broad Street, Lagos, Nigeria
Tel: 234 (1) 261-0050

DEA Officer **Eric Hill** 234 (1) 261-0050

Federal Aviation Administration (Resident in Dakar) [Liberia]
American Embassy - Dakar, Senegal, 45 Avenue Jean XXIII and rue Kleber, Boite Postal 49, 2nd Floor, Dakar, Senegal
Tel: 221 823-6753 Fax: 221 823-9286

FAA Officer **Grady Stone** 221 33-829-2180

Office of the Defense Attaché [Liberia]
American Embassy - Monrovia, Liberia, 111 United Nations Drive, P.O. Box 10-0098, Monrovia, Liberia
Mail: American Embassy - Monrovia, Department of State, Washington, DC 20521-8800
Tel: 231 77-677-7156

Defense Attaché **LTC Marc Saphir USA** 231 77-677-7156

Peace Corps [Liberia]
American Embassy - Monrovia, Liberia, 502 Benson Street, P.O. Box 98, Monrovia, Liberia
Internet: www.peacecorps.gov/liberia

Country Director **(Vacant)** 231 (0) 777-867-861

U.S. Embassy in Madagascar

Lot 207 A - Andranoro - Antehiroka, 105 Antananarivo, Madagascar
Tel: 261 (20) 23-480-00 Fax: 261 (20) 23-480-35
Internet: mg.usembassy.gov

Office of the U.S. Ambassador to Madagascar

American Embassy - Antananarivo, Madagascar, Lot 207 A - Andranoro - Antehiroka, 105 Antananarivo, Madagascar
Mail: Department of State, 2040 Antananarivo Place, Washington, DC 20521-2040

★ Ambassador-Designate **Michael P. Pelletier** 261 (20) 23-480-00
E-mail: pelletiermp@state.gov
Education: Georgetown 1986 BSFS; Columbia 1991 MIA

Chargé d'Affaires **Stuart Raymond Wilson** 261 (20) 23-480-00
E-mail: wilsonsr@state.gov
Education: Georgetown 1998 MNSSS

Office Management Specialist to the Ambassador
Nadia Ravelomanana 261 (20) 23-480-00
E-mail: ravelomanananv@state.gov

Deputy Chief of Mission
Stuart Raymond Wilson 261 (20) 23-480-00
E-mail: wilsonsr@state.gov
Education: Georgetown 1998 MNSSS

Office Management Specialist to the Deputy Chief of Mission **Kathleen A. Edgin** 261 (20) 23-480-00
E-mail: edginka@state.gov

Office of the U.S. Ambassador to Madagascar *(continued)*

Consul **Vu X. Le** 261 (20) 23-480-00
E-mail: levx@state.gov

Community Liaison Officer **(Vacant)** 261 (20) 23-480-00

Financial Management Officer **Kam Gordon** 261 (20) 23-480-00

General Services Officer **Amy Monsarrat** 261 (20) 23-480-00
E-mail: monsarratar@state.gov

Information Management Officer **Kane Mason** 261 (20) 23-480-00

Information Program Officer **(Vacant)** 261 (20) 23-480-00

Information Systems Security Officer **Kane Mason** ... 261 (20) 23-480-00

Legal Attaché (Resident in Pretoria) **J. Patrick Farris** ... 27 (12) 431-4511
E-mail: farrisjp@state.gov

Management Officer **Ann Marie Everitt** 261 (20) 23-480-00
E-mail: everitta@state.gov

Chief Political/Economic and Commercial Officer
Kelly Hapka 261 (20) 23-480-00
E-mail: hapkaka@state.gov

Public Affairs Officer **Nicole C. Bayer** 261 (20) 23-480-00
E-mail: bayernc@state.gov

Regional Security Officer **David C. Renauldi** 261 (20) 23-480-00
E-mail: renauldidc@state.gov

Agency for International Development [Madagascar]
USAID Madagascar - ZITAL Tower, ZI Taloumis Ankorondrano, P.O. Box 5253, 6th Floor, 101 Antananarivo, Madagascar
Mail: USAID/Madagascar, Department of State, 2040 Antananarivo Place, Washington, DC 20521-2040
Tel: 261 (20) 23-480-00 Fax: 261 (20) 23-480-44
E-mail: info.madagascar@usaid.gov Internet: www.usaid.gov/madagascar

◇ Mission Director **John Dunlop** 261 (20) 22-539-20
E-mail: jdunlop@usaid.gov
Education: UC San Diego 1990 BA; Johns Hopkins 1995 MPH

Agricultural Section (Foreign Agricultural Service) (Resident in Pretoria) [Madagascar]

Agricultural Officer **James J. "Jim" Higgiston** 27 (12) 431-4057
E-mail: james.higgiston@fas.usda.gov

Drug Enforcement Administration (Resident in Pretoria) [Madagascar]
American Embassy - Pretoria, South Africa, 877 Pretorius Street, Arcadia 0083, 0001 Pretoria, South Africa
P.O. Box 9536, Pretoria, 0001, South Africa
Tel: 27 (12) 342-1048

DEA Officer **Sean P. Yauger** 27 (12) 431-4735
E-mail: yaugersp@state.gov

Federal Aviation Administration (Resident in Dakar) [Madagascar]
American Embassy - Dakar, Senegal, 45 Rue Kleeber, Boite Postal 49, 2nd Floor, Dakar, Senegal
Mail: FAA AMEMB Dakar, Senegal, Department of State, Washington, DC 20521-2130
Tel: 221 823-6753 Fax: 221 823-9286

FAA Representative **Grady Stone** 221 33-829-2180

Office of the Defense Attaché [Madagascar]
American Embassy - Madagascar, Lot 207 A - Andranoro - Antehiroka, 105 Antananarivo, Madagascar

Defense Attaché **CDR Jason A. Neal USN** 261 (20) 23-480-00

Peace Corps [Madagascar]
American Embassy - Madagascar, 14-16 Rue Rainitovo, Antananarivo, Madagascar
Tel: 261 (20) 22-212-57 Internet: www.peacecorps.gov/madagascar

Country Director **Vanessa Dickey** 261 (20) 22-221-57

★ Presidential Appointment Requiring Senate Confirmation ☆ Presidential Appointment ☐ Schedule C Appointment ◇ Career Senior Foreign Service Appointment
● Career Senior Executive Service (SES) Appointment ○ Non-Career Senior Executive Service (SES) Appointment ■ Postal Career Executive Service

U.S. Embassy in Malawi

P.O. Box 30016, 16 Jomo Kenyatta Road, Lilongwe, 3, Malawi
Tel: 265 1-773-166 Fax: 265 1-770-471 Internet: mw.usembassy.gov

Office of the U.S. Ambassador to Malawi

American Embassy - Lilongwe, Malawi, P.O. Box 30016,
16 Jomo Kenyatta Road, Lilongwe, 3, Malawi
Mail: Department of State, 2280 Lilongwe Place,
Washington, DC 20521-2280

★ Ambassador **Ambassador Virginia E. Palmer** 265 1-773-166
E-mail: palmerve@state.gov
Education: Georgetown BSFS; Virginia MA

★ Ambassador-Designate **Robert K. "Rob" Scott** 265 1-773-166
E-mail: scottrk@state.gov
Education: Lawrence U BA; American U MA

Office Management Specialist to the Ambassador
Lauren Bradley 265 1-773-166
Fax: 265 1-772-316

Deputy Chief of Mission **Andrew R. Herrup** 265 1-773-166
E-mail: herrupar@state.gov
Education: UCLA 1991 JD

Office Management Specialist to the Deputy Chief of Mission **Elizabeth Al Sulaimani** 265 1-773-166

Consular Officer **Karen Abban** 265 1-773-166
E-mail: abbank@state.gov

Community Liaison Officer **Allison W. Corbitt** 265 1-773-166

Facilities Management Officer **Shantel Barker** 265 1-773-166

Financial Management Officer **Catherine Truong** 265 1-773-166
E-mail: truongc@state.gov
Education: Beloit 2002 BA; UC San Diego 2008

General Services Officer **Scott Dargus** 265 1-773-166

Information Management Officer **Sean Stapleton** 265 1-773-166
E-mail: stapletonsc@state.gov

Information Systems Security Officer **Sean Stapleton** 265 1-773-166
E-mail: stapletonsc@state.gov

Management Officer **Kenneth G. Dupree** 265 1-773-166
E-mail: dupreekg@state.gov

Political Officer **Tamara Shie** 265 773-166

Economic/Commercial Officer **Joel Hansen** 265 1-773-166
Education: North Dakota State 1996 BS; UC San Diego 2008

Public Affairs Officer **Douglas "Doug" Johnston** 265 1-772-222
E-mail: lilongwepao@state.gov Fax: 265 1-771-142
Education: U Bergen 1998

Regional Security Officer **Timothy "Tim" Corso** 265 1-773-166

Agency for International Development [Malawi]

American Embassy - Lilongwe, Malawi,
P.O. Box 30016, Lilongwe, 3, Malawi
Mail: Department of State, 2280 Lilongwe Place,
Washington, DC 20521-2280
Tel: 265 1-772-455 Fax: 265 1-773-183 Internet: www.usaid.gov/malawi

Mission Director **Littleton "Lit" Tazewell** 265 1-772-455
E-mail: ltazewell@usaid.gov
Education: William & Mary 1991 LLM; London School Econ (UK) 1992 LLM

Agricultural Section (Foreign Agricultural Service) (Resident in Nairobi) [Malawi]

American Embassy - Nairobi, Kenya, United Nations Avenue, P.O. Box 606 Village Market, 00621 Nairobi, Kenya
Mail: American Embassy - Nairobi, Kenya, Unit 8900, Box #4301, DPO, AE 09831
Tel: 254 (20) 363-6340 Fax: 254 (20) 363-6349

Agricultural Counselor **Kevin Sage-EL** 254 (20) 363-6340

Centers for Disease Control [Malawi]

American Embassy - Lilongwe, Malawi,
16 Jomo Kenyatta Road, 3 Lilongwe, Malawi
P.O Box 30016, 3 Lilongwe, Malawi
Mail: 2280 Lilongwe Place, Washington, DC 20521-2280
Tel: 265 1-775-188 Fax: 265 1-775-848

CDC Country Director **Francis "Andew" Auld** 265 1-775-188

Office of the Defense Attaché [Malawi]

Defense Attaché (Resident in Harare)
(Vacant) .... 263 (4) 250-593 ext. 212

Peace Corps [Malawi]

American Embassy - Lilongwe, Malawi,
P.O. Box 30016, Lilongwe, 3, Malawi
Mail: Department of State, 2280 Lilongwe Place,
Washington, DC 20521-2280
Tel: 265 1-757-157 Fax: 265 1-751-008
Internet: www.peacecorps.gov/malawi

Country Director **Carol Spahn** 265 1-757-157
E-mail: cspahn@peacecorps.gov

U.S. Embassy in Mali

ACI 2000, Rue 243, Porte 297, Bamako, Mali
Tel: 223 2070-2300 Fax: 223 2070-2479 Internet: ml.usembassy.gov

Office of the U.S. Ambassador to Mali

American Embassy - Bamako, Mali, ACI 2000, Rue 243, Porte 297, Bamako, Mali
Mail: Department of State, 2050 Bamako Place,
Washington, DC 20521-2050

★ Ambassador **Ambassador Paul A. Folmsbee** 223 2070-2300
E-mail: folmsbeepa@state.gov
Education: Tabor 1982 BA; Oklahoma MA

★ Ambassador-Designate
Ambassador Dennis B. Hankins 223 2070-2300
E-mail: hankinsdb@state.gov
Education: Georgetown 1981 BSFS; National War Col 1999 MA

Office Management Specialist to the Ambassador
Maria D. "Fina" Valentine 223 2070-2300
E-mail: valentinemd@state.gov

Deputy Chief of Mission
Gregory Lawrence "Greg" Garland 223 2070-2300
E-mail: garlandgl@state.gov

Office Management Specialist to the Deputy Chief of Mission **Margaret M. Gray** 223 2070-2300

Consular Section Chief **Andrew J. Partin** 223 2070-2300
E-mail: PartinAJ@state.gov

Community Liaison Officer **Robert Taylor** 223 2070-2300

Economic/Commercial Officer **Rebecca Taylor** 223 2070-2300

Equal Employment Opportunity Officer **Joyce E. Otero** 223 2070-2300
E-mail: OteroJE@state.gov

Financial Management Officer **Michael Jackson** 223 2070-2300

General Services Officer **Ani A. Akinbiyi** 223 2070-2300
E-mail: AKINBIYIAA@state.gov

Information Management Officer
Wilson R. Keverenge 223 2070-2300
E-mail: KeverengeWR@state.gov

Information Systems Security Officer **Scott Patterson** 223 2070-2300

Management Officer **Leslie A. Moeller** 223 2070-2300
E-mail: moellerla@state.gov
Education: Cornell 2004 BS; Chicago 2018 MLA

Political/Economic Officer **John D. Dunham** 223 2070-2300
E-mail: DunhamJD@state.gov

Public Affairs Officer **Wendy K. Barton** .... 223 2070-2300 ext. 2422
E-mail: BartonW@state.gov

Regional Security Officer (Acting)
Randall J. "Randy" Smith 223 2070-2300
Education: West Chester BEc; Princeton 2000 MA

Agency for International Development [Mali]

American Embassy - Bamako, Mali, ACI 2000, Rue 243, Porte 297, Bamako, Mali
Mail: American Embassy - Bamako, Mali,
Department of State, Washington, DC 20521-2050
Tel: 223 2070-2300 Fax: 223 2023-6832 E-mail: bamakoinfo@usaid.gov
Internet: www.usaid.gov/mali

◇ Mission Director **Scott Dobberstein** 223 2070-2300
E-mail: sdobberstein@usaid.gov
Education: St Olaf 1984 BA; Georgetown 1989 MIR

★ Presidential Appointment Requiring Senate Confirmation ☆ Presidential Appointment □ Schedule C Appointment ◇ Career Senior Foreign Service Appointment
● Career Senior Executive Service (SES) Appointment ○ Non-Career Senior Executive Service (SES) Appointment ■ Postal Career Executive Service

Federal Aviation Administration (Resident in Dakar) [Mali]
American Embassy - Dakar, Senegal, 45 Avenue Jean XXIII and rue Kleber, 2nd Floor, Boite Postal 49 Dakar, Senegal
Mail: FAA AMEMB Dakar, Senegal, Department of State, Washington, DC 20521-2130
Tel: 221 823-6753 Fax: 221 823-9286

FAA Representative **Grady Stone** 221 33-829-2180

Office of the Defense Attaché [Mali]
American Embassy - Bamako, Mali, Rue Rochester NY and Rue Mohamed V, Boite Postal 34 Bamako, Mali
Mail: Department of State, 2050 Bamako Place, Washington, DC 20521-2050
Tel: 223 2070-2300

Defense Attaché **Paul S. Cazier** .... 223 2070-2300 ext. 2570

U.S. Embassy in Mauritania

Nouadhibou Road, Avenue Al Quds, NOT PRTZ, Nouakchott, Mauritania
Tel: 222 525-2660 Fax: 222 525-1592 Internet: mr.usembassy.gov

Office of the U.S. Ambassador to Mauritania

American Embassy - Nouakchott, Mauritania, Nouadhibou Road, Avenue Al Quds, NOT PRTZ, Nouakchott, Mauritania
Mail: American Embassy - Nouakchott, 2340 Nouakchott Place, Department of State, Washington, DC 20521-2430

★ Ambassador **Ambassador Michael James Dodman** 222 525-2660
E-mail: dodmanmj@state.gov
Education: Georgetown BS; Boston U MA; Princeton MPP
Office Management Specialist to the Ambassador **Leilani S. Dimatulac** 222 525-2660
Deputy Chief of Mission **Anne E. Linnee** 222 525-26-60
E-mail: linneeae@state.gov
Education: Minnesota 1995 BA
Office Management Specialist to the Deputy Chief of Mission **Adriana A. Durisova** 222 525-2660
Consular Officer **(Vacant)** .... 222 525-26-60 ext. 4553
E-mail: consularNKC@state.gov
Community Liaison Officer **(Vacant)** 222 525-2660
Financial Management Officer **Hare I. O'Donnell** 222 45-25-2660
General Services Officer **Benson Siwek** 222 525-2660
Information Management Officer **(Vacant)** 222 525-26-60
Information Systems Security Officer **Shahnawaz "Shahn" Shaikh** 222 525-26-60
Information Systems Officer **Richard Kirlin** 222 525-26-60
Legal Attaché **(Vacant)** 222 525-26-60
Management Officer **Laurent M. "Larry" Dagenais** 222 525-26-60
E-mail: dagenaislm@state.gov
Political Officer **Ousmane Cisse** .... 222 525-26-60 ext. 4553
Political/Economic Officer **(Vacant)** 222 525-2660
Public Affairs Officer **Kimberly A. Pease** .... 222 525-2660 ext. 4774
Regional Security Officer **Frank P. Ebel** 222 525-26-60
E-mail: ebelfp@state.gov

Agency for International Development [Mauritania]
American Embassy - Nouakchott, Mauritania, Nouadhibou Road, Avenue Al Quds, NOT PRTZ, Nouakchott, Mauritania
Internet: www.usaid.gov/mauritania

Note: Mauritania is currently a non-presence country for USAID; however, USAID West Africa Regional Office funds a variety of activities in Mauritania addressing youth, health and food security issues.

Program Coordinator **Lisa Washington-Sow** .... 222 525-2660 ext. 4441
E-mail: lwashington-sow@usaid.gov

Federal Aviation Administration (Resident in Dakar) [Mauritania]
American Embassy - Dakar, Senegal, 45 Avenue Jean XXIII and rue Kleber, 2nd Floor, Boite Postal 49 Dakar, Senegal
Mail: FAA AMEMB Dakar, Senegal, Department of State, Washington, DC 20521-2130
Tel: 221 823-6753 Fax: 221 823-9286

FAA Representative **Grady Stone** 221 33-829-2180

Office of the Defense Attaché [Mauritania]
Nouadhibou Road, Avenue Al Quds, NOT PRTZ, Nouakchott, Mauritania
Mail: 2430 Nouakchott Place, Washington, DC 20521-2430
Tel: 222 525-2660 Fax: 222 525-1592

Defense and Army Attaché **Gabe Austin** 222 525-2660

U.S. Embassy in Mauritius and Seychelles

Rogers House, P.O. Box 544, John Kennedy Street, Port Louis, Mauritius
Tel: 230 202-4400 Fax: 230 208-9534 Internet: mu.usembassy.gov

Office of the U.S. Ambassador to Mauritius and Seychelles

American Embassy - Port Louis, Mauritius, Rogers House, P.O. Box 544, John Kennedy Street, 4th Floor, Port Louis, Mauritius
Mail: Department of State, 2450 Port Louis Place, Washington, DC 20521-2450
E-mail: usembass@intnet.mu

★ Ambassador **Ambassador David Dale Reimer** 230 202-4400
E-mail: reimerd@state.gov Fax: 230 208-9768
Education: Goshen BA; Pittsburgh MIA
Office Management Specialist to the Ambassador **Cynthia L. "Cyndi" Kesavan** 230 202-4400
E-mail: kesavancl@state.gov
Deputy Chief of Mission **Melanie Anne Zimmerman** 230 202-4400
E-mail: ZimmermanMA@state.gov
Office Management Specialist to the Deputy Chief of Mission **Kim Hoffman** 230 202-4400
Consular Officer **Jennifer A. Barr** 230 202-4400
Community Liaison Officer **(Vacant)** 230 202-4400
Economic/Commercial Officer **Paul A. Stempel** 230 202-4400
Financial Management Officer **Bupendra Hutheram** 230 202-4400
General Services Officer **Alan W. Eaton** 230 202-4400
E-mail: eatonaw@state.gov
Information Management Officer **Steven "Steve" McFall** 230 202-4400
Management Officer **Patrick Caley McCormick** 230 202-4400
E-mail: McCormickPC@state.gov
Political Officer **Edward E "Ed" Daizovi** 230 202-4400
Political/Military Officer **(Vacant)** 230 202-4400
Public Affairs Officer **Tedde Thompson** 230 202-4444
Fax: 230 212-2808
Regional Security Officer **Richard "Rich" Fisher** 230 202-4400

Office of the Defense Attaché (Resident in Madagascar) [Mauritius]

Defense Attaché **CDR Jason A. Neal USN** 261 (20) 22-212-57

U.S. Embassy in Mozambique

Avenida Kenneth Kaunda 193, Maputo, Mozambique
Tel: 258 (21) 49-27-97 Fax: 258 (21) 49-01-14
Internet: mz.usembassy.gov

Office of the U.S. Ambassador to Mozambique

American Embassy - Maputo, Mozambique, Avenida Kenneth Kaunda 193, P.O. Box 783, Maputo, Mozambique
Mail: Department of State, 2330 Maputo Place, Washington, DC 20521-2330

★ Ambassador **Ambassador H. Dean Pittman** 258 (21) 49-27-97
E-mail: pittmanhd@state.gov
Education: Millsaps BA; Johns Hopkins MIA
★ Ambassador-Designate **Dennis Walter Hearne** 258 (21) 49-27-97
E-mail: hearnedw@state.gov
Education: Wake Forest BA, 1982 BA; National War Col MS
Office Management Specialist to the Ambassador **Cecilia W. Wylie** 258 (21) 49-27-97
◇ Deputy Chief of Mission **Bryan David Hunt** 258 (21) 49-27-97
E-mail: huntbd@state.gov
Education: American U BA
Office Management Specialist to the Deputy Chief of Mission **Bernadette A. Failla** 258 (21) 49-27-97

★ Presidential Appointment Requiring Senate Confirmation ☆ Presidential Appointment □ Schedule C Appointment ◇ Career Senior Foreign Service Appointment ● Career Senior Executive Service (SES) Appointment ○ Non-Career Senior Executive Service (SES) Appointment ■ Postal Career Executive Service

Office of the U.S. Ambassador to Mozambique *(continued)*

Consular Section Chief **John Sarraf** 258 (21) 49-27-97
E-mail: consularmaputo@state.gov Fax: 258 (21) 49-04-48
Community Liaison Officer
Omolola A. Oguntomilade 258 (21) 49-27-97
Political/Economic Officer **Christopher Friefeld** 258 (21) 49-27-97
Financial Management Officer
Yang Zhang Monteiro 258 (21) 49-27-97
General Services Officer
Katherine A. "Kate" Reilly 258 (21) 49-27-97
E-mail: reillyka@state.gov
Information Management Officer
Richard Scott Trezise 258 (21) 49-27-97
Management Officer **Matthew C. "Matt" Austin** 258 (21) 49-27-97
Equal Employment Opportunity Officer
Alice Caruso 258 (21) 49-27-97
Public Affairs Officer **David Feldmann** 258 (21) 49-19-16
Fax: 258 (21) 49-19-18
Regional Security Officer **David Root** 258 (21) 49-27-97
Information Systems Officer
Alexandra P. Sweeney 258 (21) 49-27-97
E-mail: sweeneyap@state.gov
Information Systems Security Officer **(Vacant)** 258 (21) 49-27-97

Agency for International Development [Mozambique]
JAT Complex, Rua 1231, No. 41 Bairro Central C., Maputo, Mozambique
Tel: 258 (21) 352-000 Fax: 258 (21) 352-100
Internet: www.usaid.gov/mozambique

◇ Mission Director **Jennifer Adams** 258 (21) 352-000
E-mail: jeadams@usaid.gov
Education: Johns Hopkins BA; Sussex (UK) MA; Cambridge (UK) 1989 PhD

Agricultural Section (Foreign Agricultural Service) [Mozambique]
American Embassy - Maputo, Mozambique,
Avenida Kenneth Kaunda 193, P.O. Box 783, Maputo, Mozambique
Tel: 258 (21) 49- 2797 ext. 3016 Fax: 258 (21) 490-114

Agricultural Officer (Resident in Pretoria)
James J. "Jim" Higgiston 27 (12) 431-4057
877 Pretorius Street, Arcadia 0083, Pretoria, 0001, South Africa
E-mail: james.higgiston@fas.usda.gov

Commercial Section (Foreign Commercial Service) [Mozambique]
American Embassy - Maputo, Mozambique,
Avenida Kenneth Kaunda 193, Maputo, Mozambique
E-mail: maputocommercial@state.gov

Senior Commercial Officer **Tamarind Murrietta** 258 (21) 35-54-18
E-mail: Tamarind.Murrietta@trade.gov
Education: King's Col (UK) MIR

Federal Aviation Administration (Resident in Dakar) [Mozambique]
American Embassy - Dakar, Senegal, 45 Rue Kleber, Boite Postal 49, 2nd Floor, Dakar, Senegal
Mail: FAA AMEMB Dakar, Senegal, Department of State, Washington, DC 20521-2130
Tel: 221 823-6753 Fax: 221 823-9286

FAA Representative **Grady Stone** 221 33-829-4835

Office of the Defense Attaché [Mozambique]
American Embassy - Maputo, Mozambique,
Avenida Kenneth Kaunda 193, Maputo, Mozambique
Mail: American Embassy - Maputo, Mozambique, Department of State, Washington, DC 20521-2330
Tel: 258 (21) 49-27-97 Fax: 258 (21) 49-01-14

Defense Attaché **LTC Robert Ramsey USA** 258 (21) 49-27-97

Peace Corps [Mozambique]
American Embassy - Maputo, Mozambique,
Avenida Kenneth Kaunda 193, Maputo, Mozambique
Mail: Peace Corps, Department of State,
2330 Maputo Place, Washington, DC 20521-2330
Tel: 258 (21) 49-90-82 Fax: 258 (21) 49-68-70
E-mail: webmaster@mz.peacecorps.gov
Internet: www.peacecorps.gov/mozambique

Country Director **Sanjay Mathur** 258 (21) 49-90-82
E-mail: smathur@peacecorps.gov

U.S. Embassy in Namibia
14 Lossen Street, Private Bag 12029, Ausspannplatz Windhoek, Namibia
Tel: 264 (61) 295-8500 Tel: 264 (61) 295-8603
Internet: na.usembassy.gov

Office of the U.S. Ambassador to Namibia
American Embassy - Windhoek, Namibia, Ausplan Building,
14 Lossen Street, Private Bag 12029, Ausspannplatz Windhoek, Namibia
Mail: American Embassy - Windhoek, Namibia,
Department of State, Washington, DC 20521-2540

★ Ambassador **Ambassador Lisa A. Johnson** 264 (61) 295-8500
E-mail: johnsonla@state.gov
Education: Stanford AB; Columbia MA; National War Col MS
Office Management Specialist to the Ambassador
Becky Keily 264 (61) 295-8500
E-mail: keilyb@state.gov
Deputy Chief of Mission **Peter W. Lord** 264 (61) 295-8500
E-mail: lordpw@state.gov
Office Management Specialist to the Deputy Chief of Mission **Janice Morris** 264 (61) 295-8500
Consular Officer **Katherine Cantrell** 264 (61) 295-8500
E-mail: cantrellke@state.gov
Community Liaison Officer **Emily Schlink** 264 (61) 295-8500
E-mail: schlinkee@state.gov
Economic/Commercial Officer **Caroline Dow** 264 (61) 295-8500
E-mail: dowc@state.gov
E-mail: econ_comm_windhoek@state.gov
Financial Management Officer **Paul R. Kenul** 264 (61) 295-8500
General Services Officer **Mark Schlink** 264 (61) 295-8500
E-mail: schlinkmj@state.gov
Information Management Officer
Mutasim U. Rahman 264 (61) 295-8500
Education: NJIT 2006 BS
Information Systems Security Officer
Mutasim U. Rahman 264 (61) 295-8500
Education: NJIT 2006 BS
Labor Officer (Resident in Johannesburg)
John Barbian 27 (11) 644-8000
U.S. Consulate General - Johannesburg,
Department of State, Washington, DC 20521-2500
Management Officer
Christiana M. "Christy" Foreman 264 (61) 295-8500
Political/Economic Officer **Maria Kirsten Blees** 264 (61) 295-8500
Political Officer **Mark Hitchcock** 264 (61) 295-8500
E-mail: HitchcockMJ@state.gov
Education: Boalt Hall 2009
Public Affairs Officer **Eric T. Atkins** 264 (61) 295-8500
E-mail: atkinset@state.gov Fax: 264 (61) 232-476
Regional Security Officer **Denis G. O'Sullivan** 264 (61) 295-8500
E-mail: o'sullivandg@state.gov

Agency for International Development [Namibia]
American Embassy - Windhoek, Namibia,
Ausplan Building, 14 Lossen Street, Private Bag 12029,
Ausspannplatz Windhoek, Namibia
Mail: American Embassy - Windhoek, Namibia,
Department of State, Washington, DC 20521-2540
Tel: 264 (61) 273-700 Fax: 264 (61) 227-006
Internet: www.usaid.gov/namibia

Country Representative
Dr. Paul R "Randy" Kolstad PhD 264 (61) 273-700
E-mail: rkolstad@usaid.gov
Education: UC Berkeley 1989 BA; Johns Hopkins 1998 PhD

★ Presidential Appointment Requiring Senate Confirmation ☆ Presidential Appointment ☐ Schedule C Appointment ◇ Career Senior Foreign Service Appointment
● Career Senior Executive Service (SES) Appointment ○ Non-Career Senior Executive Service (SES) Appointment ■ Postal Career Executive Service

DEPARTMENTS

Agricultural Section (Foreign Agricultural Service) (Resident in Pretoria) [Namibia]
American Embassy - Pretoria, South Africa, 877 Pretorius Street, Arcadia 0083, P.O. Box 9536, Pretoria, 0001, South Africa
Mail: American Embassy–Pretoria, South Africa, Department of State, Washington, DC 20521-9300
Tel: 27 (12) 431-4057 Fax: 27 (12) 342-2264

Agricultural Officer **James J. "Jim" Higgiston** 27 (12) 431-4057
E-mail: james.higgiston@fas.usda.gov

Drug Enforcement Administration [Namibia]
American Embassy - Pretoria, South Africa, 877 Pretorius Street, Arcadia 0083, P.O. Box 9536, Pretoria, 0001, South Africa

DEA Officer (Resident in Pretoria) **Sean P. Yauger** 27 (12) 431-4735
E-mail: yaugersp@state.gov

Federal Aviation Administration (Resident in Dakar) [Namibia]
American Embassy - Dakar, Senegal, 45 Avenue Jean XXIII and rue Kleber, 2nd Floor, Boite Postal 49 Dakar, Senegal
Mail: FAA AMEMB Dakar, Senegal, Department of State, Washington, DC 20521-2130
Tel: 221 823-6753 Fax: 221 823-9286

FAA Representative **Grady Stone** 221 33-829-2180

Office of the Defense Attaché [Namibia]
American Embassy - Windhoek, Namibia, Ausplan Building, 14 Lossen Street, Private Bag 12029, Ausspannplatz Windhoek, Namibia

Defense Attaché **LtCol John Lacy USAF** 264 (61) 221-601

Peace Corps [Namibia]
14 Lossen Street, Private Bag 12029, Ausspannplatz Windhoek, Namibia
Mail: Department of State, Washington, DC 20521-2540
Tel: 264 (61) 221-601 Internet: www.peacecorps.gov/namibia

Country Director **Kevin W. Fleming** 264 (61) 226-525
E-mail: kfleming@peacecorps.gov

U.S. Embassy in Niger

BP 11201, Niamey, Niger
Tel: 227 20-73-31-61 Fax: 227 20-73-55-60 Internet: ne.usembassy.gov

Office of the U.S. Ambassador to Niger

BP 11201, Niamey, Niger
Mail: American Embassy - Niamey, Niger, 2420 Niamey Place, Washington, DC 20521-2420
Tel: 227 20-73-31-61 Fax: 227 20-73-55-60
E-mail: niameypasn@state.gov Internet: ne.usembassy.gov

★ Ambassador **Ambassador Eric P. Whitaker** 227 20-73-31-61
E-mail: whitakerep@state.gov
Education: Illinois BS, MS; Pittsburgh MPA; Princeton MPP
Office Management Specialist to the Ambassador **Adriana "M." Snydstrup** 227 20-73-31-61
E-mail: snydstrupam@state.gov

Deputy Chief of Mission **Earl Jay "Jay" Zimmerman** 227 20-73-31-61
Education: Juniata BA; North Carolina MPH
Office Management Specialist to the Deputy Chief of Mission **Therese Davis** 227 20-73-31-61

Consular Officer **(Vacant)** 227 20-73-31-61

Community Liaison Officer **Wilhelm Nassmacher** 227 20-73-31-61
E-mail: NassmacherWA@state.gov

Economic Officer **Carl-Heinz "Jason" Wemhoener-Cuite** 227 20-73-31-61
E-mail: wemhoener-cuitej@state.gov

Financial Management Officer **(Vacant)** 227 20-73-31-61

General Services Officer **Traci L. Goins** 227 20-73-31-61

Information Management Officer **Venod V. Kerns** 227 20-73-31-61
E-mail: kernsvv@state.gov

Information Systems Security Officer **(Vacant)** 227 20-73-31-61

Legal Attaché **John Barrett** 227 20-73-31-61

Management Officer **Melisa Doherty** 227 20-73-31-61

Political Officer **Wendy L. Nassmacher** 227 20-73-31-61

Office of the U.S. Ambassador to Niger *(continued)*

Public Affairs Officer **Cynthia H. Faby** 227 20-73-31-69
E-mail: fabych@state.gov Fax: 227 20-73-55-60

Regional Security Officer **Horacio Ortega** 227 20-73-31-61

Agency for International Development [Niger]
American Embassy - Niamey, Niger, 2420 Niamey Place, Washington, DC 20521-2420
Internet: www.usaid.gov/niger

Country Representative **Lorraine Sherman** 227 20 72 26 61
E-mail: lsherman@usaid.gov

Federal Aviation Administration (Resident in Dakar) [Niger]
American Embassy - Dakar, Senegal, 45 Avenue Jean XXIII and rue Kleber, Boite Postal 49, 2nd Floor, Dakar, Senegal
Mail: FAA AMEMB Dakar, Senegal, Department of State, Washington, DC 20521-2130
Tel: 221 823-6753 Fax: 221 823-9286

FAA Representative **Grady Stone** 221 33-879-4835

Office of the Defense Attaché [Niger]
USDAO, American Embassy - Niamey, 2420 Niamey Place, Washington, DC 20521-2420
Tel: 227 20-72-26-61 Fax: 227 20-72-31-46

Defense Attaché **Ryan Campbell** 225 20-21-09-79

U.S. Embassy in Nigeria

Plot 1075 Diplomatic Drive, Central District Area, Abuja, Nigeria
Tel: 234 (9) 461-4000 Fax: 234 (9) 461-4306 Internet: ng.usembassy.gov

Office of the U.S. Ambassador to Nigeria

U.S. Embassy - Abuja, Nigeria, Plot 1075 Diplomatic Drive, Central District Area, Abuja, Nigeria
Mail: Department of State, 8320 Abuja Place, Washington, DC 20521-8320

★ Ambassador **Ambassador William Stuart "Stuart" Symington IV** 234 (9) 461-4000
E-mail: symingtonws@state.gov
Education: Brown U 1974 BA; Columbia JD
Office Management Specialist to the Ambassador **Carol R. Johnson** 234 (9) 461-4000
E-mail: johnsoncr5@state.gov

◇ Deputy Chief of Mission **David J. Young** 234 (9) 461-4000
E-mail: youngdj@state.gov
Education: Missouri 1984 BA; Boston U 1987 MDiv, 1988 MA
Office Management Specialist to the Deputy Chief of Mission **Alasha Black** 234 (9) 461-4000

Community Liaison Officer **Guadalupe E. Galindo** 234 (9) 461-4000
E-mail: galindoge@state.gov

Consular Section Chief **(Vacant)** 234 (9) 461-4000
E-mail: ConsularAbuja@state.gov

Economic Officer **Susan P. Garro** 234 (9) 461-4000
E-mail: garrosp@state.gov

Facilities Management Officer **Caroll E. Webb** 234 (9) 461-4000

Financial Management Officer **N. Scott Einhorn** 234 (9) 461-4000

General Services Officer **(Vacant)** 234 (9) 461-4000

Human Resources Officer **(Vacant)** 234 (9) 461-4000

Information Management Officer **Dante J. Bostic** 234 (9) 461-4000

Information Program Officer **Nestor Ezekwesili** 234 (9) 461-4000

Information Systems Officer **Melvin Coleman** 234 (9) 461-4000

Information Systems Security Officer **(Vacant)** 234 (9) 461-4000

Legal Attaché **Paula Parkinson** 234 (9) 461-4000

Management Officer **Kay Crawford** 234 (9) 461-4000
E-mail: crawfordk@state.gov
Education: Chicago BA

Political Officer **David Mathew Purl** 234 (9) 461-4000

◇ Public Affairs Officer **Aruna S. G. Amirthanayagam** 234 (9) 461-4000

Regional Security Officer **William I. Mellott** 234 (9) 461-4000
E-mail: mellottwi@state.gov

★ Presidential Appointment Requiring Senate Confirmation ☆ Presidential Appointment □ Schedule C Appointment ◇ Career Senior Foreign Service Appointment
● Career Senior Executive Service (SES) Appointment ○ Non-Career Senior Executive Service (SES) Appointment ■ Postal Career Executive Service

Agency for International Development [Nigeria]
U.S. Embassy - Abuja, Nigeria, 7 Membilla Street,
Off Aso Drive, Maitama District, Abuja, Nigeria
Mail: Department of State, 8320 Anuja Place,
Washington, DC 20521-8320
Fax: 234 (9) 234-2930 Internet: www.usaid.gov/nigeria

◇ Mission Director **Stephen M. Haykin** 234 (803) 900-9300
E-mail: shaykin@usaid.gov
Education: Evergreen State BA; Georgetown MA

Office of the Defense Attaché [Nigeria]
U.S. Embassy - Abuja, Nigeria, 7 Mambilla Street,
Off Aso Drive, Maitama District, Abuja, Nigeria
Mail: Department of State, 8320 Abuja Place,
Washington, DC 20521-8320
Tel: 234 (9) 461-4000 Fax: 234 (9) 461-4305

Defense Attaché **Jason B. Nicholson** 234 (9) 461-4000

Lagos Consulate General
U.S. Consulate General - Lagos, Nigeria, 2 Walter Carrington Crescent,
Victoria Island, Broad Street, Lagos, Nigeria
Mail: U.S. Consulate General - Lagos, Nigeria,
Department of State, Washington, DC 20521-8300
Tel: 234 (1) 460-3400 Fax: 234 (1) 460-3717

◇ Consul General **Francis John "John" Bray, Jr.** 234 (1) 460-3400
E-mail: BrayFJ@state.gov
Office Management Specialist to the Consul
General **Ademola Adejuwon** 234 (1) 460-3400
Consular Officer **Alice F. Seddon** 234 (1) 460-3400
E-mail: lagosacs@state.gov Fax: 234 (1) 261-2218
General Services Officer **Luberta Abraham** 234 (1) 460-3400
E-mail: abrahaml@state.gov
Information Program Officer **Louis R. Baluyut** 234 (1) 460-3400
Information Systems Officer **Mike Khattak** 234 (1) 460-3400
Legal Attaché **Mark Grimm** 234 (1) 460-3400
Management Officer **(Vacant)** 234 (1) 460-3400
Political/Economic Officer **Osman N. Tat** 234 (1) 460-3400
Public Affairs Officer **Darcy F. Zotter** 234 (1) 460-3400
E-mail: zotterdf@state.gov
Regional Security Officer **Vincent Carpenter** 234 (1) 460-3400

Agricultural Section (Foreign Agricultural Service) [Nigeria]
U.S. Consulate General - Lagos, Nigeria, 2 Walter Carrington Crescent,
Victoria Island, Broad Street, Lagos, Nigeria
Mail: Lagos Consulate General, Department of State,
Washington, DC 20521-8300
Tel: 234 (1) 460-3577 E-mail: aglagos@fas.usda.gov

Agricultural Counselor **Jude Akhidenor** 234 (1) 460-3577
E-mail: jude.akhidenor@fas.usda.gov

Commercial Section (Foreign Commercial Service) [Nigeria]
U.S. Commercial Service, Nigeria, U.S. Consulate General Lagos,
2 Eleke Crescent, Victoria Island, Lagos, Nigeria
Mail: Lagos Consulate General, Department of State,
Washington, DC 20521-8300
Tel: 234 (1) 460-3400 Fax: 234 (1) 261-0544
E-mail: Lagos.Office.Box@trade.gov Internet: export.gov/nigeria

Senior Commercial Officer **Brent Omdahl** . . . 234 (1) 460-3400 ext. 3498
E-mail: brent.omdahl@trade.gov
Education: BYU 1991 BA; Tufts 1994 MA

Drug Enforcement Administration [Nigeria]
U.S. Consulate General - Lagos, Nigeria, 2 Walter Carrington Crescent,
Victoria Island, Broad Street, Lagos, Nigeria
Mail: Lagos Consulate General, Department of State,
Washington, DC 20521-8300
Fax: 234 (1) 261-7874

DEA Officer **Eric Hill** 234 (1) 460-3400

U.S. Embassy in Rwanda
2657 Avenue de la Gendarmerie, B.P. 28 Kigali, Rwanda
Tel: 250 252-596-400 Fax: 250 252-580-325 Internet: rw.usembassy.gov

Office of the U.S. Ambassador to Rwanda
Embassy of the United States of America - Kigali, Rwanda,
2657 Avenue de la Gendarmerie, B.P. 28 Kigali, Rwanda
Mail: Department of State, 2210 Kigali Place,
Washington, DC 20521-2210
E-mail: kigaliembassy@state.gov

★ Ambassador
Ambassador Peter Hendrick Vrooman 250 252-596-400
E-mail: vroomanp@state.gov
Education: Harvard AB;
Eisenhower National Security and Resource Strategy 2011 MS
Office Management Specialist to the Ambassador
(Vacant) 250 252-596-400
Deputy Chief of Mission **Richard C. Michaels** 250 252-596-400
E-mail: michaelsrc@state.gov
Education: Georgetown 1995 BSFS; Stanford 1998 MA
Office Management Specialist to the Deputy Chief of
Mission **Natasha Greer** 250 252-596-400
Consular Affairs Officer **Bethany "Beth" Milton** 250 252-596-400
E-mail: miltonb@state.gov
Community Liaison Officer **Brook Sahn** 250 252-596-400
Economic/Commercial Officer **Matthew Steed** 250 252-596-400
Financial Management Officer **Jimmey Aucoin, Jr.** 250 252-596-400
General Services Officer **James H. Coddington** 250 252-596-400
E-mail: coddingtonjh@state.gov
Information Management/Information Program
Officer **Roger W. Johnson** 250 252-596-400
E-mail: johnstonrw@state.gov
Information Systems Officer **Rithy Keng** 250 252-596-400
E-mail: kengr@state.gov
Management Officer **Robert F. Hommowun** 250 252-596-652
E-mail: hommowunrf@state.gov
Political Officer **Dennis Test** 250 252-596-400
Political/Economic Officer
Elizabeth M. "Beth" Smith 250 252-596-400
E-mail: smithbm@state.gov
Education: NYU BA; Fordham MEd
Public Affairs Officer **Marissa K. Rollens** 250 252-596-400
E-mail: rollensmk@state.gov
Education: Rice 2006 BA; Michigan 2008 MPP
Regional Security Officer **Timothy Feeney** 250 252-596-400
E-mail: feeneytb@state.gov

Agency for International Development [Rwanda]
Embassy of the United States of America - Kigali, Rwanda,
2657 Avenue de la Gendarmerie, B.P. 28 Kigali, Rwanda
Mail: American Embassy - Kigali, Rwanda,
Department of State, Washington, DC 20521-2210
Tel: 250 252-596-400 E-mail: kigali@usaid.gov
Internet: www.usaid.gov/rwanda

Mission Director **Leslie Marbury** 250 252-596-400
E-mail: lmarbury@usaid.gov

Drug Enforcement Administration (Resident in Cairo) [Rwanda]
American Embassy - Cairo, Egypt, Unit 64900, Box 11, APO, AE 09839
American Embassy - Cairo, Egypt, Eight Kamal El Din Salah Street,
Garden City, Cairo, Egypt
Tel: 20 (2) 2797-3300 Fax: 20 (2) 2797-3200

DEA Officer **Leon M. Palmer** 20 (2) 2797-3300

Federal Aviation Administration (Resident in Dakar) [Rwanda]
American Embassy - Dakar, Senegal, 45 Avenue Jean XXIII and rue
Kleber, Boite Postal 49 Dakar, Senegal
Mail: FAA AMEMB Dakar, Senegal, Department of State,
Washington, DC 20521-2130
Tel: 221 823-6753 Fax: 221 823-9286

FAA Representative **Grady Stone** 221 33-829-2180

★ Presidential Appointment Requiring Senate Confirmation ☆ Presidential Appointment ☐ Schedule C Appointment ◇ Career Senior Foreign Service Appointment
● Career Senior Executive Service (SES) Appointment ○ Non-Career Senior Executive Service (SES) Appointment ■ Postal Career Executive Service

Office of the Defense Attaché [Rwanda]
Embassy of the United States of America - Kigali, Rwanda,
2657 Avenue de la Gendarmerie, B.P. 28 Kigali, Rwanda
Mail: American Embassy - Kigali, Rwanda,
Department of State, Washington, DC 20521-2210
Tel: 250 252-596-400 Fax: 250 252-596-591

Defense Attaché **Jason Farmer** 250 252-596-400

Peace Corps [Rwanda]
Embassy of the United States of America - Kigali, Rwanda,
2657 Avenue de la Gendarmerie, B.P. 28 Kigali, Rwanda
Internet: www.peacecorps.gov/rwanda E-mail: rw01-info@peacecorps.gov

Country Director **Keith Hackett** 250 252-580-390
E-mail: khackett@peacecorps.gov

U.S. Embassy in Senegal

B.P. 49, Route des Almadies, Dakar, Senegal
Tel: 221 33-879-4000 Fax: 221 33-879-4100 Internet: sn.usembassy.gov

Office of the U.S. Ambassador to Senegal

American Embassy - Dakar, Senegal, B.P. 49, Route des Almadies, Dakar, Senegal
Mail: American Embassy - Dakar, Senegal,
2130 Dakar Place, Dulles, VA 20189-2130

★ Ambassador
Ambassador Tulinabo Salama "Tuli" Mushingi 221 33-879-4000
E-mail: mushingits@state.gov
Education: Howard U MA; Georgetown 1989 PhD
Office Management Specialist to the Ambassador
Beverley A. Crane 221 33-879-4000
E-mail: craneba@state.gov

◇ Deputy Chief of Mission **Martina T. Boustani** 221 33-879-4000
E-mail: boustanimt@state.gov
Education: U Tubingen BA; Michigan MA; Pennsylvania MA
Office Management Specialist to the Deputy Chief of Mission **(Vacant)** 221 33-879-4000

Consular Affairs Officer **Patricia Neary** 221 33-879-4000
E-mail: nearyp@state.gov

Community Liaison Officer **Larry Parks** 221 33-879-4000

Economic Officer **Heath Bailey** 221 33-879-4000
Education: BYU 1996 BA, 1999 JD

Economic/Commercial Officer **Jonathan Scott** 221 33-879-4000
E-mail: scottjc@state.gov

Facilities Management Officer **Edwin F. Wirz** 221 33-879-4000
E-mail: wirzef@state.gov
Education: Illinois 1977 BS

Financial Management Officer **Susan C. N'Garnim** 221 33-879-4000
E-mail: ngarnimsc@state.gov

General Services Officer **Wayne D. Hemmings** 221 33-879-4000
E-mail: hemmingswd@state.gov

Information Management Officer **Edgar Ruiz** 221 33-879-4000

Information Programs Officer **Kelly Richardson** 221 33-879-4000

Information Systems Officer **Dale Jones** 221 33-879-4000

Information Systems Security Officer **Dale Jones** 221 33-879-4000

Legal Attaché **Keith Bethke, Jr.** 221 33-879-4000

Management Officer **Todd R. Whatley** 221 33-879-4000
E-mail: WhatleyTR@state.gov
Education: Oklahoma BA, 2000 MBA

Political Officer **John Ice** 221 33-879-4000

Public Affairs Officer **Matthew "Matt" Miller** 221 33-879-4000

Regional Security Officer **Christopher Tremann** 221 33-879-4000
E-mail: TremannCX@state.gov

Agency for International Development [Senegal]
American Embassy - Dakar, Senegal, Avenue Jean XXIII and rue Kleber, B.P. 49, Dakar, Senegal
Mail: 2130 Dakar Place, Washington, DC 20521-2130
E-mail: usaid-senegal@usaid.gov Internet: www.usaid.gov/senegal

◇ Mission Director **Lisa Franchett** 221 33-879-4000
E-mail: lfranchett@usaid.gov

Agricultural Section (Foreign Agricultural Service) [Senegal]
American Embassy - Dakar, Senegal - USAID Annex,
Avenue Jean XXIII and rue Kleber, Boit Postal 49 Dakar, Senegal
Tel: 221 33-879-4000 ext. 4901 Fax: 221 33-820-5673
E-mail: agdakar@fas.usda.gov

Agricultural Officer **Joshua "Josh" Lagos** ... 221 33-879-4000 ext. 4901
E-mail: Joshua.Lagos@fas.usda.gov

Agricultural Attaché **Jasmine Osinski** .... 221 33-879-4000 ext. 4901
E-mail: jasmine.junk@fas.usda.gov

Drug Enforcement Administration [Senegal]
DEA Officer **Kevin Adams** 221 33-879-4000

Federal Aviation Administration [Senegal]
American Embassy - Dakar, Senegal,
45 Avenue Jean XXIII and rue Kleber, Boite Postal 49,
2nd Floor, Dakar, Senegal
Mail: FAA AMEMB Dakar, Senegal, 2130 Dakar Place,
Dulles, VA 20189-2130
Tel: 221 33-829-2100 Fax: 221 33-823-9286

FAA Representative **Grady Stone** 221 33-829-2180

Office of the Defense Attaché [Senegal]
American Embassy - Dakar, Senegal, Avenue Jean XXIII and rue Kleber, Boit Postal 49 Dakar, Senegal
Mail: 2130 Dakar Place, Washington, DC 20521-2130

Defense Attaché **LTC Scott H. Morgan USA** 221 33-879-4000

Office of Defense Cooperation [Senegal]
American Embassy - Dakar, Senegal, Avenue Jean XXIII and rue Kleber, Boite Postal 49 Dakar, Senegal
Mail: 2130 Dakar Place, Washington, DC 20521-2130

ODC Officer **LTC Scott H. Morgan USA** 221 33-879-4000

Peace Corps [Senegal]
Allées Papa Guèye Fall, B.P. 2534, Dakar, Senegal
Mail: American Embassy - Dakar, Senegal,
Department of State, Washington, DC 20521-2130
Tel: 221 33-859-7575 Fax: 221 33-859-7580
Internet: www.peacecorps.gov/senegal

Country Director **Cheryl Gregory Faye** 221 33-859-7575
E-mail: cfaye@peacecorps.gov

U.S. Embassy in Sierra Leone

Southridge - Hill Station, Freetown, Sierra Leone
Tel: 232 99-105-500 Fax: 232 99-105-355 Internet: sl.usembassy.gov

Office of the U.S. Ambassador to Sierra Leone

American Embassy - Freetown, Southridge - Hill Station, Freetown, Sierra Leone
Mail: American Embassy - Freetown, Department of State,
Washington, DC 20521-2160

★ Ambassador **Ambassador Maria E. Brewer** 232 99-105-500
E-mail: brewerme@state.gov
Education: Valparaiso 1995 BA; National Defense U MS

★ Ambassador-Designate **Lynne M. Tracy** 232 99-105-500
E-mail: tracylm@state.gov
Education: Georgia 1986 BA; Akron 1994 JD
Office Management Specialist to the Ambassador
Sheila A. Palmer 232 99-105-500
E-mail: palmersa@state.gov

Deputy Chief of Mission **Tomekah L. Burl** 232 99-105-500
Education: Columbia BA
Office Management Specialist to the Deputy Chief of Mission **Anita Beamon-Freeman** 232 99-105-500
E-mail: beamonfreemanar@state.gov

Community Liaison Officer **Sherlyn Howlett** 232 99-105-500

Consular Section Chief **Lynn "M." Vacca** ..... 232 99-105-500 ext. 5080
E-mail: consularfreetown@state.gov
E-mail: vaccalm@state.gov

Economic/Commercial Officer **Derrin Smith** ... 232 99-105-500 ext. 5120
E-mail: freetown-econ@state.gov

★ Presidential Appointment Requiring Senate Confirmation ☆ Presidential Appointment ☐ Schedule C Appointment ◇ Career Senior Foreign Service Appointment
● Career Senior Executive Service (SES) Appointment ○ Non-Career Senior Executive Service (SES) Appointment ■ Postal Career Executive Service

Office of the U.S. Ambassador to Sierra Leone *(continued)*

Facilities Management Officer **(Vacant)** 232 99-105-500
General Services Officer **Mpaza Kapembwa** 232 99-105-500
Information Management Officer **Charles L. Scarlett** 232 99-105-500
E-mail: scarlettcl@state.gov
Information Systems Security Officer
Charles L. Scarlett 232 99-105-500
E-mail: scarlettcl@state.gov
Management Officer **Salma Rahman** 232 99-105-500
Political Officer **Carlton A. Philadelphia** 232 99-105-500
E-mail: philadelphiaca@state.gov
Public Affairs Officer **Emily R. Green** 232 99-105-500
E-mail: PASFreetown@state.gov
Regional Security Officer **Ken A. Bomongcag** 232 99-105-500
E-mail: bomongcagka@state.gov

Agency for International Development [Sierra Leone]
American Embassy - Freetown, Southridge - Hill Station, Freetown, Sierra Leone
Internet: www.usaid.gov/sierra-leone

Mission Director **Jeff Bryan** 232 99-105-500
E-mail: jbryan@usaid.gov
Education: James Madison 1991 BA; Texas A&M 2000 MA

Drug Enforcement Administration (Resident in Lagos) [Sierra Leone]
American Embassy - Lagos, Nigeria, 2 Louis Farrakan Crescent, Lagos, Nigeria
Tel: 234 (1) 261-0050

DEA Officer **Eric Hill** 234 (1) 261-0050

Federal Aviation Administration (Resident in Dakar) [Sierra Leone]
American Embassy - Dakar, Senegal, 45 Rue Kleeber, 2nd Floor, Boite Postal 49 Dakar, Senegal
Mail: FAA AMEMB Dakar, Senegal, Department of State, Washington, DC 20521-2130
Tel: 221 823-6753 Fax: 221 823-9286

FAA Representative **Grady Stone** 221 33-829-2180

Office of the Defense Attaché [Sierra Leone]
Department of State, 2110 Conakry Place, Washington, DC 20521-2110

Defense Attaché **LTC Kimberly Lee USA** 232 99-105-500

U.S. Mission to Somalia

American Embassy - Nairobi, Kenya, United Nations Avenue, P.O. Box 606 Village Market, 00621 Nairobi, Kenya
Tel: 254 (20) 363-6000 Fax: 254 (20) 363-6157
Internet: so.usmission.gov

Note: The U.S. Mission to Somalia is currently based at the U.S. Embassy in Nairobi, Kenya. However, some functions of the Mission are now being carried out in Mogadishu, Somalia.

Office of the U.S. Ambassador to Somalia

American Embassy - Nairobi, Kenya, United Nations Avenue, P.O. Box 606 Village Market, 00621 Nairobi, Kenya

★ Ambassador
Ambassador Donald Y. "Don" Yamamoto 254 (20) 363-6000
E-mail: yamamotod@state.gov
Education: Columbia AB, MA; National War Col MS
Office Management Specialist to the Ambassador
Stephanie Hill 254 (20) 363-6000
Deputy Chief of Mission **Martin A. "Marty" Dale** ... 254 (20) 363-6000
E-mail: dalema@state.gov
Education: Simpson (IA) BA; Bowling Green State MA
Legal Attaché **Jesse Dodson** 234 (9) 461-4000
E-mail: dodsonjc@state.gov
Management Officer (Mogadishu)
Marialice Burford de Castillo 254 (20) 363-6000
E-mail: burfordm@state.gov
Management Officer (Nairobi) **James Holtsnider** 254 (20) 363-6000
Political/Economic Section Chief
Andrea J. Tomaszewicz 254 (20) 363-6000
E-mail: tomaszewiczaj@state.gov
Education: Rensselaer Poly 1994 BS; George Washington 2001 MA

Office of the U.S. Ambassador to Somalia *(continued)*

Public Affairs Officer **Janet E. Deutsch** 254 (20) 363-6000
E-mail: deutschje@state.gov
E-mail: somaliapublicaffairs@state.gov
Regional Security Officer **(Vacant)** 254 (20) 363-6000

Agency for International Development [Somalia]
PO Box 629, Village Market, 00621 Nairobi, Kenya
E-mail: usaidsomalia-info@usaid.gov Internet: www.usaid.gov/somalia

◇ Mission Director **Alexander Dickie** 254 (20) 862-2000
Education: Texas A&M BSc; Fax: 254 (20) 862-2680
New Mexico State MSc; Utah State PhD

U.S. Embassy in South Africa

877 Pretorius Street, Arcadia 0083, Pretoria, 0001, South Africa
Tel: 27 (12) 431-4000 Fax: 27 (12) 342-2299
E-mail: embassypretoria@state.gov Internet: za.usembassy.gov

Office of the U.S. Ambassador to South Africa

American Embassy - Pretoria, South Africa, 877 Pretorius Street, Arcadia 0083, Pretoria, 0001, South Africa
P.O. Box 9536, Pretoria, 0001, South Africa
Mail: American Embassy - Pretoria, South Africa, Department of State, 9300 Pretoria Place, Washington, DC 20521-9300

★ Ambassador-Designate **Lana J. Marks** 27 (12) 431-4000
Education: U Witwatersrand
◇ Chargé d'Affaires **Jessica E. "Jessye" Lapenn** 27 (12) 431-4000
E-mail: lapennj@state.gov
Office Management Specialist to the Ambassador
(Vacant) 27 (12) 431-4880
◇ Deputy Chief of Mission
Jessica E. "Jessye" Lapenn 27 (12) 431-4000
E-mail: lapennj@state.gov
Office Management Specialist to the Deputy Chief of Mission **(Vacant)** 27 (12) 431-4850
Community Liaison Officer **Kate Dooley** 27 (12) 431-4000
◇ Economic Officer **Alan R. Tousignant** 27 (12) 431-4340
E-mail: TousignantAR@state.gov
Environment, Science and Technology Officer
Roberta Burns 27 (12) 431-4345
Facilities Management Officer **Ronald Saunders** 27 (12) 431-4000
Financial Management Officer **Rajiv N.M.N. Malik** 27 (12) 431-4339
General Services Officer
Geraldine Gray Thibodeau 27 (12) 431-4000
E-mail: ThibodeauGG@state.gov
Human Resources Officer **Paul S. Dever** 27 (12) 431-4000
E-mail: DeverPS@state.gov
Information Management Officer
Jeffrey S. "Jeff" Myers 27 (12) 431-4000
Information Program Officer **A. Bryan Thibodeau** 27 (12) 431-4219
Fax: 27 (12) 431-4695
Information Security Officer **Jose A. Rivera** 27 (12) 431-4000
Information Systems Security Officer **(Vacant)** 27 (12) 431-4000
Legal Attaché **Stephen Hart** 27 (12) 431-4511
Management Officer **Matthew Alan "Matt" Weiller** ... 27 (12) 431-4230
E-mail: weillerma2@state.gov
Education: Georgetown 1987 MSFS
Political Officer **Ian J. McCary** 27 (12) 431-4170
E-mail: mccaryij@state.gov Fax: 27 (12) 431-4612
Public Affairs Officer **(Vacant)** 27 (12) 431-4210
Fax: 27 (12) 431-4529
Regional Security Officer **Ivan A. Wray** 27 (12) 431-4388

★ Presidential Appointment Requiring Senate Confirmation ☆ Presidential Appointment □ Schedule C Appointment ◇ Career Senior Foreign Service Appointment
● Career Senior Executive Service (SES) Appointment ○ Non-Career Senior Executive Service (SES) Appointment ■ Postal Career Executive Service

DEPARTMENTS

Agency for International Development - Southern Africa Regional Mission [South Africa]
100 Totius Street, Groenkloof X6, P.O. Box 43, Pretoria, 0027, South Africa
Mail: American Embassy–Pretoria, South Africa, Department of State, Washington, DC 20521-9300
Tel: 27 (12) 452-2000 Fax: 27 (12) 460-3177
E-mail: pretoriainfo@usaid.gov
Internet: https://www.usaid.gov/southern-africa-regional

◇ Mission Director **John Groarke** 27 (12) 452-2000
E-mail: jgroarke@usaid.gov
Education: NYU BA; London School Econ (UK); Pennsylvania 1988 JD

Deputy Mission Director **Rebecca O. Krzywda** 27 (12) 452-2000
E-mail: rkrzywda@usaid.gov

Agricultural Section (Foreign Agricultural Service) [South Africa]
American Embassy - Pretoria, South Africa, 877 Pretorius Street, Arcadia 0083, Pretoria, 0001, South Africa
P.O. Box 9536, Pretoria, 0001, South Africa
Mail: American Embassy - Pretoria, South Africa, Department of State, 9300 Pretoria Place, Washington, DC 20521-9300
Tel: 27 (12) 431-4057 Fax: 27 (12) 342-2264
E-mail: agpretoria@fas.usda.gov

Agricultural Officer **James J. "Jim" Higgiston** 27 (12) 431-4057
E-mail: james.higgiston@fas.usda.gov

Senior Attaché **Laura Geller** 27 (12) 431-4057
E-mail: laura.geller@fas.usda.gov

Attaché **Kyle Bonsu** 27 (12) 431-4057
E-mail: Kyle.Bonsu@fas.usda.gov

Centers for Disease Control [South Africa]
American Embassy - Pretoria, South Africa, 877 Pretorius Street, Arcadia 0083, Pretoria, 0001, South Africa
P.O. Box 9536, Pretoria, 0001, South Africa
Mail: American Embassy - Pretoria, South Africa, Department of State, Washington, DC 20521-7140
Tel: 27 (12) 346-4286

CDC Officer **Dr. Amy Herman-Roloff** 27 (12) 346-0170

Commercial Section (Foreign Commercial Service) (Resident in Johannesburg) [South Africa]
American Embassy - Pretoria, South Africa, 877 Pretorius Street, Arcadia 0083, 0001 Pretoria, South Africa
Mail: American Embassy - Pretoria, South Africa, Department of State, Washington, DC 20521-7140
Internet: export.gov/southafrica

Minister Counselor **Pamela Ward** 27 (11) 290-3316
E-mail: pamela.ward@trade.gov

Department of Homeland Security - U.S. Immigration and Customs Enforcement [South Africa]
American Embassy - Pretoria, South Africa, 877 Pretorius, Arcadia 0083, Pretoria, 0001, South Africa
Mail: American Embassy - Pretoria, South Africa, Department of the State - Embassy Customs, 9300 Pretoria Place, Washington, DC 20521-9300
Tel: 27 (12) 342-8062 Tel: 27 (12) 431-4747

Regional Attaché, Homeland Security Investigations **Steve Martin** 27 (12) 431-4733
Education: Cal State (Long Beach) 1987 BA

Drug Enforcement Administration [South Africa]
American Embassy - Pretoria, South Africa, 877 Pretorius Street, Arcadia 0083, 0001 Pretoria, South Africa
Mail: American Embassy - Pretoria, South Africa, Department of State, Washington, DC 20521-9300
Fax: 27 (12) 362-5007

DEA Officer **Sean P. Yauger** 27 (12) 431-4735
E-mail: yaugersp@state.gov

Federal Aviation Administration (Resident in Dakar) [South Africa]
American Embassy - Dakar, Senegal, 45 Avenue Jean XXIII and rue Kleber, Boite Postal 49, 2nd Floor, Dakar, Senegal
Mail: FAA AMEMB Daker, Senegal, Department of State, Washington, DC 20521-2130
Tel: 221 823-6753 Fax: 221 823-9286

FAA Representative **Grady Stone** 221 33-829-2180

Office of the Defense Attaché [South Africa]
American Embassy - Pretoria, South Africa, 877 Pretorius Street, Arcadia 0083, Pretoria, 0001, South Africa
P.O. Box 9536, Pretoria, 0001, South Africa
Mail: American Embassy - Pretoria, South Africa, Department of State, 9300 Pretoria Place, Washington, DC 20521-9300
Tel: 27 (12) 431-4180 Fax: 27 (12) 431-6161

Defense Attaché **CAPT Steven A. Morgenfeld USN** . . . 27 (12) 431-4180

Peace Corps [South Africa]
American Embassy - Pretoria, South Africa, 877 Pretorius Street, Arcadia 0083, 0001 Pretoria, South Africa
Internet: www.peacecorps.gov/south-africa

Country Director **J. Ronald "Ron" Campbell** 27 (12) 344-4255

Cape Town Consulate General
U.S. Consulate General - Cape Town, South Africa, 2 Reddam Avenue, Westlake 7945, Postnet Suite 50, Private Bag X 26, Tokai, Cape Town, South Africa 7966
Mail: U.S. Consulate General - Cape Town, Department of State, Washington, DC 20521-2480
Tel: 27 (21) 702-7300 Fax: 27 (21) 702-7493
E-mail: consularcapetown@state.gov

◇ Consul General **Virginia M. Blaser** 27 (21) 702-7442
E-mail: blaservm@state.gov
Education: Southern Methodist BA
Office Management Specialist to the Consul General **Jacqueline M. Justin** 27 (21) 421-4280
E-mail: justinjm@state.gov

Consular Officer **Thomas Bills** 27 (21) 421-4280
Fax: 27 (21) 425-3014

Community Liaison Officer **Victoria Whitney** 27 (21) 421-4280

Economic Officer **Andrea Cameron** 27 (21) 421-4280

Financial Management Officer **Rajiv N.M.N. Malik** 27 (21) 702-7300

General Services Officer **Jamison Pixley** 27 (21) 702-7300
E-mail: PixleyJF@state.gov

Information Program Officer **Gregory A. Strozier, Jr.** . . . . 27 (21) 421-4280 ext. 2211
E-mail: StrozierGA@state.gov

Management Officer **Brian A. Randall** . . . . 27 (21) 421-4280 ext. 2333
E-mail: randallba@state.gov Fax: 27 (21) 418-1989

Political Officer **Charles A. Lobdell** 27 (21) 421-4280
E-mail: LobdellCA@state.gov
Education: Notre Dame 1987 BA; St Thomas U 1995 JD

Political/Economic Officer **(Vacant)** 27 (21) 421-4280

Public Affairs Officer **Ellen Masi** . . . . 27 (21) 421-4280 ext. 2863
E-mail: masieb@state.gov Fax: 27 (21) 425-2536

Regional Security Officer **Robert "Eli" Whitney** . . . . 27 (21) 421-4280 ext. 2242

Commercial Section (Foreign Commercial Service) [South Africa]
Montecarlo Building, Herrengracht, Foreshore, 4th Floor, Cape Town, South Africa
Mail: U.S. Commercial Service, Department of State, 2480 Cape Town Place, Washington, DC 20521-2480
Tel: 27 (21) 702-7300 Fax: 27 (21) 702-7402
E-mail: capetownoffice@trade.gov

Senior Commercial Specialist **Jaisvir Sewpaul** 27 (21) 702-7379
E-mail: jaisvir.sewpaul@trade.gov

★ Presidential Appointment Requiring Senate Confirmation ☆ Presidential Appointment □ Schedule C Appointment ◇ Career Senior Foreign Service Appointment
● Career Senior Executive Service (SES) Appointment ○ Non-Career Senior Executive Service (SES) Appointment ■ Postal Career Executive Service

Durban Consulate General

U.S. Consulate General - Durban, South Africa, Old Mutual Centre, 303 West Street, 31st Floor, Durban, 4001, South Africa
Mail: U.S. Consulate General - Durban, Department of State, Washington, DC 20521-2490
Tel: 27 (31) 305-7600 Fax: 27 (31) 305-7691
E-mail: consulardurban@state.gov
Internet: za.usembassy.gov/embassy-consulates/durban

Consul General **Sherry Zalika Sykes** ... 27 (31) 305-7600
E-mail: sykessz@state.gov
Office Management Specialist to the Consul General **(Vacant)** ... 27 (31) 305-7600
Consular Officer **Sandra Cortina** ... 27 (31) 305-7600 ext. 104
Economic/Political Officer **Hala Rharrit** ... 27 (31) 305-7600
E-mail: RharritH@state.gov
Information Program Officer/Information Systems Security Officer **Troy A. Jackson** ... 27 (31) 305-7600
Management Officer **Thomas R. Debor** ... 27 (31) 305-7600 ext. 116
E-mail: debortr@state.gov
Public Affairs Officer **Felix Salazar** ... 27 (31) 305-7600 ext. 211
Regional Security Officer **Keith Sims** ... 27 (31) 305-7650

Johannesburg Consulate General

U.S. Consulate General - Johannesburg, South Africa, 1 Sandton Drive, Sandhurst, 2196 Johannesburg, South Africa
Mail: U.S. Consulate General - Johannesburg, Department of State, Washington, DC 20521-2500
Tel: 27 (11) 290-3000 Fax: 27 (11) 884-0396
E-mail: consularjohannesburg@state.gov

◇ Consul General **Michael A. McCarthy** ... 27 (11) 290-3000
Office Management Specialist to the Consul General **(Vacant)** ... 27 (11) 290-3000
Consular Officer **Elizabeth Power** ... 27 (11) 290-3000
E-mail: powerec@state.gov
General Services Officer **Jennifer B. Johnson** ... 27 (11) 290-3000
Information Program Officer **Eric Peterson** ... 27 (11) 290-3000
Information Systems Officer **Darrin Brown** ... 27 (11) 290-3000
Management Officer **Silje Grimstad** ... 27 (11) 290-3000
E-mail: grimstadsm@state.gov
Political/Labor Officer **John Barbian** ... 27 (11) 290-3000
E-mail: BarbianJW@state.gov
Public Affairs Officer **Anthony "Tony" Deaton** ... 27 (11) 290-3000
E-mail: deatonaa@state.gov
Regional Security Officer **Joshua Bauer** ... 27 (11) 290-3000
E-mail: BauerJP@state.gov

Commercial Section (Foreign Commercial Service) [South Africa]

U.S. Foreign Commercial Service, 15 Chaplin Road, Illovo, Corner of Oxford Road, Johannesburg, 2196, South Africa
Mail: U.S. Consulate General - Johannesburg, Department of State, Washington, DC 20521-2500
Tel: 27 (11) 290-3192 Fax: 27 (11) 884-0253
E-mail: Office.Johannesburg@trade.gov

◇ Minister Counselor **Pamela Ward** ... 27 (11) 290-3316
E-mail: pamela.ward@trade.gov
◇ Senior Commercial Officer **Brian McCleary** ... 27 (11) 290-3227
E-mail: brian.mccleary@trade.gov

U.S. Embassy in South Sudan

U.S. Embassy, Kololo Road, Juba, South Sudan
Tel: (202) 216-6279 E-mail: usembassyjuba@state.gov
Internet: ss.usembassy.gov

Office of the U.S. Ambassador to South Sudan

U.S. Embassy, Kololo Road, Juba, South Sudan

★ Ambassador
Ambassador Thomas J. "Tom" Hushek ... 249 183-774701
E-mail: hushektj@state.gov
Education: Wisconsin BA; Columbia MA
Office Management Specialist to the Ambassador **Marites Eustaquio** ... (202) 216-6279 ext. 216

Office of the U.S. Ambassador to South Sudan *(continued)*

◇ Deputy Chief of Mission **Stephen G. "Steve" Fakan** ... 249 183-774701
E-mail: fakansg@state.gov
Education: American U BA
Consular Officer **Denise Knapp** ... 249 1-870-2-2000
Information Management Officer **Harold Griffin** ... (202) 216-6279 ext. 216
Information Program Officer **(Vacant)** ... (202) 216-6279
Management Officer **Danielle Wood** ... 249 1-870-2-2000
Public Affairs Officer **Mark Weinberg** ... 249 1-870-2-2000
E-mail: jubapas@state.gov
Political Officer **Francesca Lichauco** ... 249 1-870-2-2000
E-mail: lichaucofg@state.gov
Economic Officer **Philip Cummings** ... 249 1-870-2-2000
Regional Security Officer **Kenneth "Ken" Davis** ... 249 1-870-2-2000
General Services Officer **Chris Berkey** ... 249 1-870-2-2000

Agency for International Development [South Sudan]

U.S. Embassy, Kololo Road, Juba, South Sudan
Internet: www.usaid.gov/south-sudan

◇ Mission Director **James M. "Jim" Hope** ... 249 1-870-2-2000
E-mail: jhope@usaid.gov
Education: American U BA; Yale MA
◇ Deputy Mission Director **Elise M. Jensen** ... 249 1-870-2-2000
E-mail: ejensen@usaid.gov

Federal Aviation Administration (Resident in Dakar) [South Sudan]

FAA Representative **Grady Stone** ... 221 33-829-48-35

U.S. Embassy in Sudan

Kilo 10, Soba, Khartoum, Sudan
Mail: P.O. Box 699, APO, AE 09829
Tel: 249 187-0-22000 Fax: 249 183-774137 Internet: sd.usembassy.gov

Office of the U.S. Ambassador to Sudan

American Embassy - Khartoum, Sudan, Kilo 10, Soba, Khartoum, Sudan
Mail: P.O. Box 699, APO, AE 09829

★ Ambassador **(Vacant)** ... 249 187-0-22000
◇ Chargé d'Affaires **Steven C. Koutsis** ... 249 187-0-22000
E-mail: koutsissc@state.gov
Education: Boston U 1979 BA
Office Management Specialist to the Ambassador **Pamela Lee-Pow Ayoung** ... 249 187-0-22000
Deputy Chief of Mission **Ellen B. Thorburn** ... 249 187-0-22000
E-mail: thorburneb@state.gov
Education: Michigan State BA; Pittsburgh JD; George Washington JD
Office Management Specialist to the Deputy Chief of Mission **(Vacant)** ... 249 187-0-22000
Community Liaison Officer **Rhonda Hester** ... 249 187-0-22000
Consular Officer **Susan Dunathan** ... 249 187-0-22000
Facilities Management Officer **Scott McFadden** ... 249 187-0-22000
E-mail: mcfaddens@state.gov
Financial Management Officer **Zulal Vincent** ... 249 187-0-22000
General Service Officer **John B. Everman** ... 249 187-0-22000
E-mail: evermanjb@state.gov
Information Management Officer **(Vacant)** ... 249 187-0-22000
Information Program Officer **(Vacant)** ... 249 187-0-22000
Information Systems Officer **(Vacant)** ... 249 187-0-22000
Management Officer **Timothy "Tim" Bashor** ... 249 187-0-22000
Political Officer **Wallace R. Bain** ... 249 187-0-22000
E-mail: bainwr@state.gov
Public Affairs Officer **Keith Hughes** ... 249 187-0-22000
Regional Security Officer **Corynn L. Stratton** ... 249 187-0-22000

Agency for International Development [Sudan]

P.O. Box 699, APO, AE 09829
Internet: www.usaid.gov/sudan

◇ Mission Director **Marcia Musisi-Nkambwe** ... 249 187-0-22000
E-mail: mmusisi-nkambwe@usaid.gov

★ Presidential Appointment Requiring Senate Confirmation ☆ Presidential Appointment ☐ Schedule C Appointment ◇ Career Senior Foreign Service Appointment
● Career Senior Executive Service (SES) Appointment ○ Non-Career Senior Executive Service (SES) Appointment ■ Postal Career Executive Service

Office of Defense Attaché [Sudan]
P.O. Box 699, APO, AE 09829
Defense Attaché **LTC Mark Choate USA** 249 (12) 377-4701

U.S. Embassy in Tanzania

686 Old Bagamoyo Road, P.O. Box 9130, Dar es Salaam, Tanzania
Tel: 255 (22) 229-4000 Fax: 255 (22) 229-4970
Internet: tz.usembassy.gov

Office of the U.S. Ambassador to Tanzania

American Embassy - Dar es Salaam, Tanzania, 686 Old Bagamoyo Road, P.O. Box 9123, Dar es Salaam, Tanzania
Mail: Department of State, 2140 Dar es Salaam Place, Washington, DC 20521-2140

★ Ambassador **(Vacant)** 255 (22) 229-4000
◇ Chargé d'Affaires **Inmi Kim Patterson** 255 (22) 229-4000
E-mail: pattersonik@state.gov
Office Management Specialist to the Ambassador **(Vacant)** 255 (22) 229-4000
Deputy Chief of Mission (Acting) **Steven Sinnott** 255 (22) 229-4000
Office Management Specialist to the Deputy Chief of Mission **Leza L. Olson** 255 (22) 229-4000
Community Liaison Officer **(Vacant)** 255 (22) 229-4000
Consular Officer **Laura Chamberlin** 255 (22) 229-4000
Financial Management Officer **David Hamiel** 255 (22) 229-4000
General Services Officer **Marcus Fallion** 255 (22) 229-4000
Information Management Officer **Gregg Church** 255 (22) 229-4000
Management Officer **(Vacant)** 255 (22) 229-4000
Political/Economic Section Chief **John L. Espinoza** ... 255 (22) 229-4000
E-mail: espinozajl@state.gov
Education: Bard 1994 BA
Public Affairs Officer **Brinille E. Ellis** 255 (22) 229-4000
Regional Security Officer **Jessica M. Moore** 255 (22) 229-4000

Agency for International Development [Tanzania]
American Embassy - Dar Es Salaam, Tanzania, 686 Old Bagamoyo Road, P.O. Box 9130, Dar es Salaam, Tanzania
Mail: Department of State, 2140 Dar es Salaam Place, Washington, DC 20521-2140
Tel: 255 (22) 229-4490 Fax: 255 (22) 266-8421
Internet: www.usaid.gov/tanzania

◇ Mission Director **Andrew "Andy" Karas** 255 (22) 229-4490
E-mail: akaras@usaid.gov

Agricultural Section (Foreign Agricultural Service) [Tanzania]
Agricultural Counselor (Resident in Nairobi) **Kevin Sage-EL** 254 (20) 363-6413

Centers for Disease Control and Prevention [Tanzania]
American Embassy - Dar es Salaam, Tanzania, 686 Old Bagamoyo Road, P.O. Box 9123, Dar es Salaam, Tanzania
Tel: 255 (22) 212-1440

Director **Maestro Evans** 255 (22) 212-1440
National Institute for Medical Research HQ, Lithuli Road, Dar es Salaam, Tanzania

Commercial Section (Foreign Commercial Service) [Tanzania]
American Embassy - Dar es Salaam, Tanzania, 686 Old Bagamoyo Road, P.O. Box 9123, Dar es Salaam, Tanzania
Mail: Department of State, 2140 Dar es Salaam Place, Washington, DC 20521-2140
Internet: export.gov/tanzania

Senior Commercial Officer **Patricia M. Wagner** 255 (22) 229-4340
E-mail: patricia.wagner@trade.gov Fax: 255 (22) 229-4970

Office of the Defense Attaché [Tanzania]
American Embassy, Dar es Salaam, Tanzania, 686 Old Bagamoyo, Dar es Salaam, Tanzania
P.O. Box 9123, Dar es Salaam, Tanzania

Defense Attaché **LTC Michael Lee USA** 255 (22) 229-4000

Federal Aviation Administration (Resident in Dakar) [Tanzania]
American Embassy - Dakar, Senegal, 45 Avenue Jean XXIII and rue Kleber, Boite Postal 49, 2nd Floor, Dakar, Senegal
Mail: Department of State, 2130 Dakar Place, Washington, DC 20521-2130
Tel: 221 823-4296 Fax: 221 823-9286

FAA Representative **Grady Stone** 221 33-829-2180

Peace Corps [Tanzania]
36A Zambia Road, P.O. Box 9123, Dar es Salaam, Tanzania
Mail: Department of State, 2140 Dar es Salaam Place, Washington, DC 20521-2140
Tel: 255 (22) 266-7172 Fax: 255 (22) 266-8354
Internet: www.peacecorps.gov/tanzania

Country Director **Nelson Cronyn** 255 (22) 266-7372
E-mail: ncronyn@peacecorps.gov

U.S. Embassy in Togo

4332 Boulevard Gnassingbe Eyadema, B.P. 852, Lomé, Togo
Tel: 228 261-5470 Fax: 228 261-5501 Internet: tg.usembassy.gov

Office of the U.S. Ambassador to Togo

4332 Boulevard Gnassingbe Eyadema, B.P. 852, Lomé, Togo
Mail: American Embassy - Lome, Department of State, 2300 Lome Place, Washington, DC 20521-2300

★ Ambassador **Ambassador David R. Gilmour** 228 226-5470
E-mail: GilmourDR@state.gov
★ Ambassador-Designate **Eric W. Stromayer** 228 261-5470
E-mail: stromayerew@state.gov
Education: Northwestern 1982 BA; Johns Hopkins 1986 MA
Office Management Specialist to the Ambassador **Dionne Sims** 228 261-5470
Deputy Chief of Mission **Michael Ralph DeTar** 228 261-5470
E-mail: detarmr@state.gov
Consular Officer **Brian Sells** 228 261-5470
E-mail: sellsba@state.gov
Community Liaison Officer **Jacqueline "Jackie" Pryor** ... 228 261-5470
Financial Management Officer **Frida Sells** 228 261-5470
E-mail: sellsfm@state.gov
Political/Economic Officer **(Vacant)** 228 221-29-91
Economic Officer **Ryan Ballow** 228 221-29-91
E-mail: ballowrd@state.gov
General Services Officer **Jonathan Nwosu** 228 261-5470
Information Management Officer **Howard E. Stugard** 228 261-5470
E-mail: StugardHE@state.gov
Information Systems Security Officer **John Volk** 228 261-5470
E-mail: volkjg@state.gov
Management Officer **Lisa A. Derrickson** 228 261-5470
E-mail: derricksonla@state.gov
Public Affairs Officer **Michael Pryor** 228 261-5470
Fax: 228 261-5469
Regional Security Officer **Christopher "Chris" Knysch** 228 261-5470
E-mail: KnyschCL@state.gov

Federal Aviation Administration (Resident in Dakar) [Togo]
American Embassy - Dakar, 45 Avenue Jean XXIII and rue Kleber, Boite Postal 49, 2nd Floor, Dakar, Senegal
Mail: FAA American Embassy - Dakar, Department of State, Washington, DC 20521-2130
Tel: 221 823-6753 Fax: 221 823-9286

FAA Representative **Grady Stone** 228 33-829-2180

Office of the Defense Attaché (Resident in Accra) [Togo]
American Embassy – Accra, Department of State, Washington, DC 20521-2010
Tel: 233 (30) 2741-150

Defense Attaché **Joseph Lee** 233 (30) 2741-150

★ Presidential Appointment Requiring Senate Confirmation ☆ Presidential Appointment ☐ Schedule C Appointment ◇ Career Senior Foreign Service Appointment
● Career Senior Executive Service (SES) Appointment ○ Non-Career Senior Executive Service (SES) Appointment ■ Postal Career Executive Service

Peace Corps [Togo]
Department of State, 2300 Lome Place, Washington, DC 20521-2300
Fax: 228 22 21 06 14 E-mail: info@tg.peacecorps.gov
Internet: www.peacecorps.gov/togo
Country Director **Victor Luboyeski** 228 221-0614

U.S. Embassy in Uganda
1577 Ggaba Road, P.O. Box 7007, Kampala, Uganda
Tel: 256 312-306-001 Fax: 256 (41) 425-9794
Internet: ug.usembassy.gov

Office of the U.S. Ambassador to Uganda
American Embassy - Kampala, Uganda, 1577 Ggaba Road,
P.O. Box 7007, Kampala, Uganda
Mail: American Embassy - Kampala, Uganda,
Department of State, Washington, DC 20521-2190

★ Ambassador **Ambassador Deborah Ruth Malac** 256 312-306-001
E-mail: malacdr@state.gov
Education: Furman 1977 BA; Virginia 1981 MA; National Defense U 2002 MS
Office Management Specialist to the Ambassador **Renuka R. "Renee" MacEwen** 256 312-306-001
E-mail: macewenrr@state.gov
◇ Deputy Chief of Mission **Colette A. Marcellin** 256 312-306-001
E-mail: MarcellinCA@state.gov
Office Management Specialist to the Deputy Chief of Mission **Peter Kennett** 256 312-306-001
Community Liaison Officer **George Cornick** 256 312-306-001
Consular Officer **Eugene "Gene" Arnold** 256 312-306-001
Education: Northeast Missouri State; Evangel Col
Economic Officer **Seth Miller** 256 312-306-001
Education: Miami 1995 BBA; Johns Hopkins 2003 MA; Maryland 2010 MBA
Financial Management Officer **Douglas R. Boudreau** ... 256 312-306-001
E-mail: boudreaudr@state.gov
General Services Officer **Lisa Coles** 256 312-306-001
Information Management Officer **James "Jim" Fox** 256 312-306-001
Information Program Officer **(Vacant)** 256 312-306-001
Information Systems Officer **Michael Bostic** 256 312-306-001
Information Systems Security Officer **James "Jim" Fox** 256 312-306-001
Management Officer **Daniel G. Brown** 256 312-306-001
Political Officer **Kimberly Harrington** 256 312-306-001
Political/Economic Officer **Rebecca K. Hunter** 256 312-306-001
E-mail: hunterrk@state.gov
Public Affairs Officer **Ronald E. "Ron" Hawkins, Jr.** 256 312-306-001
E-mail: hawkinsre@state.gov
Education: American U 1995 BA, 1997 MIA
Regional Security Officer **Michael L. Cygrymus** 256 312-306-001

Agency for International Development [Uganda]
American Embassy - Kampala, Uganda, Plot 1577 Ggaba Road,
P.O. Box 7007, Kampala, Uganda
Mail: American Embassy - Kampala, Uganda,
Department of State, Washington, DC 20521-2190
Tel: 256 0414-306-001 Internet: www.usaid.gov/uganda

◇ Mission Director **Joakim Parker** 256 0414-306-001
E-mail: jparker@usaid.gov
Education: Stanford; Hastings; U West Indies (Trinidad & Tobago)

Drug Enforcement Administration (Resident in Cairo) [Uganda]
American Embassy - Cairo, 5 Latin America Street,
Garden City, Cairo, Egypt
Mail: American Embassy - Cairo, Unit 64900, APO, AE 09839-4900
Tel: 20 (2) 2795-3300 Fax: 20 (2) 2797-3200
DEA Officer **Leon M. Palmer** 20 (2) 2795-3300

Federal Aviation Administration (Resident in Dakar) [Uganda]
American Embassy - Dakar, Senegal, 45 Rue Kleeber,
2nd Floor, Boite Postal 49 Dakar, Senegal
Mail: FAA American Embassy - Dakar, Senegal,
Department of State, Washington, DC 20521-2130
Tel: 221 823-6753 Fax: 221 823-9286
FAA Representative **Grady Stone** 221 33-829-2180

Office of Defense Attaché [Uganda]
American Embassy - Kampala, Plot 1577 Ggaba Road,
P.O. Box 7007, Kampala, Uganda
Mail: American Embassy - Kampala, Department of State,
Washington, DC 20521-2190
Defense Attaché **COL Edward J. "EJ" Dupont USA** ... 256 312-306-001

Peace Corps [Uganda]
American Embassy - Kampala, Uganda, 1577 Ggaba Road,
P.O. Box 7007, Kampala, Uganda
E-mail: info@ug.peacecorps.gov Internet: www.peacecorps.gov/uganda
Country Director **Sean Cantella** 256 31-711-1200

U.S. Embassy in Zambia
Eastern End of Kabulonga Road, Ibex Hill,
P.O. Box 320065, Lusaka, Zambia
Tel: 260 (21) 1357-000 Fax: 260 (21) 1357-224
Internet: zm.usembassy.gov

Office of the U.S. Ambassador to Zambia
American Embassy - Lusaka, Zambia,
Eastern End of Kabulonga Road, Ibex Hill,
P.O. Box 320065, Lusaka, Zambia
Mail: Department of State, 2310 Lusaka Place,
Washington, DC 20521-2310

★ Ambassador **Ambassador Daniel Lewis "Dan" Foote** 260 (21) 1357-000
E-mail: footedl@state.gov
Education: Columbia 1986 BA
Office Management Specialist to the Ambassador **Jackie Valenzuela** 260 (21) 1357-000
E-mail: valenzuelalj@state.gov
◇ Deputy Chief of Mission **Christopher M. "Chris" Krafft** 260 (21) 1357-000
E-mail: krafftcm@state.gov
Office Management Specialist to the Deputy Chief of Mission **Tracy L. Chandonnet** 260 (21) 1357-000
Consular Section Chief **Brandon Baron** 260 (21) 1357-000
Community Liaison Officer **Sienna Baron** 260 (21) 1357-000
Economic Officer **Brandon Wilson** 260 (21) 1357-000
Equal Employment Opportunity Officer **(Vacant)** 260 (21) 1357-000
Financial Management Officer **Gabriel Del Bosque** ... 260 (21) 1357-000
General Services Officer **John McDonald** 260 (21) 1357-000
Information Management Officer **Daniel A. Siebert** ... 260 (21) 1357-000
E-mail: siebertda@state.gov
Information Systems Security Officer **Benjamin Hubbard** 260 (21) 1357-000
Management Officer **James "Sean" Kennedy** 260 (21) 1357-000
E-mail: kennedyjs@state.gov
Education: Stanford 1996 BA; UC Berkeley 2006 MSW
Political/Economic Officer **Doreen Bailey** 260 (21) 1357-000
Political Officer **David Reynolds** 260 (21) 1357-000
Public Affairs Officer **Sean J. McIntosh** 260 (21) 1357-000
COMESA Building, Fax: 260 (21) 1226-523
PA Section, Ben Bella Road,
P.O. Box 32053, Lusaka, Zambia
E-mail: mcintoshsj@state.gov
Education: Stanford 2002 AB; Chicago 2004 MPP
Regional Security Officer **Jason Willis** 260 (21) 1357-000
Education: Hillsborough Comm 2005 AA; American U 2006 BA

★ Presidential Appointment Requiring Senate Confirmation ☆ Presidential Appointment ☐ Schedule C Appointment ◇ Career Senior Foreign Service Appointment
● Career Senior Executive Service (SES) Appointment ○ Non-Career Senior Executive Service (SES) Appointment ■ Postal Career Executive Service

Agency for International Development [Zambia]
Subdivision 694/Stand 100, Ibex Hill Road,
P.O. Box 320373, Lusaka, 10101, Zambia
Mail: Department of State, 2310 Lusaka Place,
Washington, DC 20521-2310
Tel: 260 (21) 1-357-000 Fax: 260 (21) 1-357-041
E-mail: infozambia@usaid.gov Internet: www.usaid.gov/zambia

Mission Director **Patrick K. "Pat" Diskin** 260 (21) 1-357-000
E-mail: pdiskin@usaid.gov

Agricultural Section (Foreign Agricultural Service) (Resident in Pretoria) [Zambia]
Agricultural Counselor **James J. "Jim" Higgiston** 27 (12) 431-4057
E-mail: james.higgiston@fas.usda.gov

Centers for Disease Control [Zambia]
American Embassy - Lusaka, Zambia,
Eastern End of Kabulonga Road, Ibex Hill,
P.O. Box 320065, Lusaka, Zambia
Mail: Department of State, 2310 Lusaka Place,
Washington, DC 20521-2310
Tel: 260 (21) 1250-955 Fax: 260 (21) 1252-225

Country Director **Sundeep Gupta** 260 (21) 1257-515

Commercial Section (Foreign Commercial Service) [Zambia]
American Embassy - Lusaka, Zambia,
Eastern End of Kabulonga Road, Ibex Hill,
P.O. Box 320065, Lusaka, Zambia
Mail: Department of State, 2310 Lusaka Place,
Washington, DC 20521-2310
Tel: 260 (21) 1250-955 Fax: 260 (21) 1252-225
E-mail: commerciallusaka@state.gov

Senior Commercial Specialist (Resident in Cape Town) **Jaisvir Sewpaul** .... 27 (21) 702-7300 ext. 7379
E-mail: jaisvir.sewpaul@trade.gov

Federal Aviation Administration (Resident in Dakar) [Zambia]
American Embassy - Dakar, Senegal, 45, Rue Kleeber, Boite Postal 49,
2nd Floor, Dakar, Senegal
Mail: FAA AMEMB Dakar, Senegal, Department of State,
Washington, DC 20521-2130

FAA Representative **Grady Stone** 221 33-879-48-35

Office of the Defense Attaché [Zambia]
American Embassy - Lusaka, Zambia,
Eastern End of Kabulonga Road, Ibex Hill,
P.O. Box 320065, Lusaka, Zambia
Mail: Department of State, 2310 Lusaka Place,
Washington, DC 20521-2310
Tel: 260 (21) 1250-955 Fax: 260 (21) 1252-225

Defense Attaché **LtCol Anthony Sidoti USAF** 260 (21) 1250-955

Peace Corps [Zambia]
c/o American Embassy - Lusaka, Zambia,
P.O. Box 50707, 71A Kabulonga Road,
Lusaka Kabulonga, Lusaka, Zambia
Mail: Department of State, 2310 Lusaka Place,
Washington, DC 20521-2310
Tel: 260 (21) 1260-377 Fax: 260 (21) 1260-685
E-mail: pczambia@peacecorps.gov Internet: www.peacecorps.gov/zambia

Country Director **Bradford "Brad" Favor** 260 (21) 1260-636

U.S. Embassy in Zimbabwe

American Embassy - Harare, Zimbabwe,
172 Herbert Chitepo Avenue, P.O. Box 3340, Harare, Zimbabwe
Tel: 263 (4) 250-593 Fax: 263 (4) 796-488 Internet: zw.usembassy.gov

Office of the U.S. Ambassador to Zimbabwe
American Embassy - Harare, Zimbabwe,
172 Herbert Chitepo Avenue, P.O. Box 3340, Harare, Zimbabwe
Mail: Department of State, 2180 Harare Place,
Washington, DC 20521-2180

★ Ambassador **Ambassador Brian A. Nichols** ... 263 (4) 250593 ext. 4630
E-mail: nicholsba@state.gov
Education: Tufts
Office Management Specialist to the Ambassador **Michael D. Raney** .... 263 (4) 250-593 ext. 4630
E-mail: raneymd@state.gov

Deputy Chief of Mission **Jennifer L. Savage** ... 263 (4) 250-593 ext. 201
E-mail: SavageJL@state.gov
Office Management Specialist to the Deputy Chief of Mission **(Vacant)** 263 (4) 250-593

Consular Officer **Amy Diaz** .... 263 (4) 250-593 ext. 206
E-mail: consularharare@state.gov Fax: 263 (4) 722618

Community Liaison Officer **Tiffany Monnett** 263 (4) 250-593

Economic Officer **Yvonne M. Gonzales** 263 (4) 250-593
E-mail: gonzalesym@state.gov

Financial Management Officer (Acting) **Brian J. Peterson** 263 (4) 250-593
E-mail: petersonbj@state.gov

General Services Officer **Lolita Jones** 263 (4) 250-593

Information Management Officer **Frank R. Jones** .... 263 (4) 250-593 ext. 234

Information Program Officer **Eric C. Finkenbiner** .... 263 (4) 250-593 ext. 234

Information Systems Security Officer **Eric C. Finkenbiner** .... 263 (4) 250-593 ext. 234

Management Officer **Mathew A. "Matt" Spivak** .... 263 (4) 250-593 ext. 270
E-mail: spivakma@state.gov

Political Officer **Yvonne M. Gonzales** 263 (4) 250-593
E-mail: gonzalesym@state.gov

Political/Economic Officer **Christopher N. "Chris" Hunnicutt** 263 (4) 250-593
E-mail: hunnicuttcn@state.gov
Education: North Carolina 2004 BA, 2010 MBA

Public Affairs Officer **David J. "Dave" McGuire** 263 (4) 758-800
E-mail: mcguiredj@state.gov Fax: 263 (4) 758-802
Education: Providence 1994 BA; Tennessee 2000 MA

Regional Security Officer **Patrick G. Bellinger** .... 263 (4) 250-593 ext. 261
E-mail: bellingerpg@state.gov

Agency for International Development [Zimbabwe]
USAID, 1-3 Pascoe Avenue, Belgravia, Harare, Zimbabwe
Mail: Department of State, 2180 Harare Place,
Washington, DC 20521-2180
Tel: 263 (4) 252401 Internet: www.usaid.gov/zimbabwe

◇ Mission Director **Stephanie Funk** .... 263 (4) 252-590 ext. 204
E-mail: sfunk@usaid.gov

Deputy Mission Director **Michael Richard McCord** 263 (4) 252401
Education: San Diego State 1988 BA; Oregon 1996 JD

Agricultural Section (Foreign Agricultural Service) (Resident in Pretoria) [Zimbabwe]
American Embassy - Pretoria, South Africa,
877 Pretorius Street, Arcadia 0083, P.O. Box 9536, Pretoria, 0001,
South Africa
Mail: American Embassy - Pretoria, South Africa,
Department of State, Washington, DC 20521-9300
Tel: 27 (12) 431-4057 Fax: 27 (12) 342-2264

Agricultural Officer **James J. "Jim" Higgiston** 27 (12) 431-4057
E-mail: james.higgiston@fas.usda.gov

★ Presidential Appointment Requiring Senate Confirmation ☆ Presidential Appointment ☐ Schedule C Appointment ◇ Career Senior Foreign Service Appointment
● Career Senior Executive Service (SES) Appointment ○ Non-Career Senior Executive Service (SES) Appointment ■ Postal Career Executive Service

Federal Aviation Administration (Resident in Dakar) [Zimbabwe]
American Embassy - Dakar, Senegal, Avenue Jean XXIII and rue Kleber, 2nd Floor, Boite Postal 49 Dakar, Senegal
Mail: FAA AMEMB Dakar, Senegal, Department of State, Washington, DC 20521-2130
Tel: 221 823-6753 Fax: 221 823-9286

FAA Representative **Grady Stone** 221 33-829-2180

Office of the Defense Attaché [Zimbabwe]
American Embassy - Harare, Zimbabwe, 172 Herbert Chitepo Avenue, P.O. Box 3340, Harare, Zimbabwe
Mail: Department of State, 2180 Harare Place, Washington, DC 20521-2180
Tel: 263 (4) 250-593

Defense Attaché
LTC Jeffrey Schroeder USA .... 263 (4) 250-593 ext. 212

U.S. Mission to the United Nations Environment Programme and United Nations Center for Human Settlements

American Embassy - Nairobi, Kenya, United Nations Avenue, P.O. Box 606 Village Market, 00621 Nairobi, Kenya
Mail: American Embassy - Nairobi, Kenya, Unit 64111, APO, AE 09831-4111
Tel: 254 (20) 363-6304 Fax: 254 (20) 363-6427

U.S. Representative/United Nations Environment Program Officer **Lori Peterson Dando** 254 (20) 363-6304
E-mail: dandolp@state.gov

Deputy U.S. Representative **Ozge Drinkard** 254 (20) 363-6304
E-mail: drinkardo@state.gov

Deputy U.S. Representative **(Vacant)** 254 (20) 363-6304

U.S. Mission to the African Union (USAU)

American Embassy - Addis Ababa, Ethiopia, Entoto Street, P.O. Box 1014, Addis Ababa, Ethiopia
Tel: 251 (11) 130-7001 Fax: 251 (11) 124-2459
E-mail: usau-info@state.gov Internet: www.usau.usmission.gov

★ U.S. Representative to the African Union
Ambassador Mary Beth Leonard 251 (11) 130-7001
E-mail: leonardmb@state.gov
Education: Boston U BA; Johns Hopkins 1988 MA; Naval War 2004

Office Management Specialist to the Ambassador
(Vacant) 251 (11) 130-7001

Deputy Chief of Mission **Jessica Lynn Davis Ba** 251 (11) 130-7001
E-mail: davisbajl@state.gov

Economic Officer **Pren-Tsiliyah Boa-Guehe** 251 (11) 130-7001
E-mail: boa-guehep@state.gov

Peace and Security Adviser **Kevin W. Warthon** 251 (11) 130-7001
E-mail: warthonkw@state.gov

Political Officer **T. Michael Wyrick** 251 (11) 130-7001
E-mail: wyricktm@state.gov
Education: Thunderbird Global 2014 MBA

Political/Public Diplomacy Officer
Christopher Meade 251 (11) 130-7001
E-mail: meadec@state.gov

THE AMERICAS

U.S. Embassy in Argentina

American Embassy - Buenos Aires, Argentina, Colombia 4300, 1425 Buenos Aires, Argentina
Tel: 54 (11) 5777-4533 Fax: 54 (11) 5777-4240

Office of the U.S. Ambassador to Argentina

American Embassy - Buenos Aires, Argentina, Colombia 4300, 1425 Buenos Aires, Argentina
Mail: American Embassy - Buenos Aires, Unit 3130, DPO, AA 34034
E-mail: buenosairesconsulate@state.gov

★ Ambassador **Ambassador Edward Charles Prado** ... 54 (11) 5777-4533
E-mail: pradoec@state.gov
Education: Texas 1969 BA, 1972 JD

Office of the U.S. Ambassador to Argentina *(continued)*

Office Management Specialist to the Ambassador
Melissa Cruz 54 (11) 5777-4533

◇ Deputy Chief of Mission
Thomas E. "Tom" Cooney 54 (11) 5777-4321
E-mail: cooneyte@state.gov
Education: Cornell BS; South Carolina MIB

Office Management Specialist to the Deputy Chief of Mission (Acting) **Judith Zavala** 54 (11) 5777-4567
Education: St Leo U 2016 MBA

Consular Section Chief **Mark A. Leoni** 54 (11) 5777-4310
E-mail: leonima@state.gov

Consular Officer **Robert S. Neus** 54 (11) 5777-4533
E-mail: neusrs@state.gov

Community Liaison Officer **Erika Soulier** 54 (11) 5777-4625

◇ Economic Officer **Timothy M. "Tim" Stater** 54 (11) 5777-4747
E-mail: statertm@state.gov

Environment, Science, and Technology Officer
Michael "Mike" Garcia 54 (11) 5777-4747
Fax: 54 (11) 5777-4212

Financial Management Officer **Pedro V. Palugyai** 54 (11) 5777-4603
E-mail: palugyaipv@state.gov

General Services Officer **Blake Butler** 54 (11) 5777-4421

Human Resources Officer **Theresa Gillespie** 54 (11) 5777-4414
E-mail: gillespiete@state.gov

Information Management Officer **William D. Griffin** ... 54 (11) 5777-4376
E-mail: griffinwd@state.gov

Information Program Officer **Brian Viggiano** 54 (11) 5777-4533
E-mail: viggianobf@state.gov

Information Systems Officer **Katina L. Caldwell** 54 (11) 5777-4533
E-mail: caldwellkl@state.gov

Information Systems Security Officer
Brian Viggiano 54 (11) 5777-4533
E-mail: viggianobf@state.gov

Legal Attaché **Murry T. Streetman** 54 (11) 5777-4300

Management Officer **Jeremey M. "Jerry" Neitzke** ... 54 (11) 5777-4413
E-mail: neitzkej@state.gov

Military Liaison Officer **(Vacant)** 54 (11) 5777-4388

Political Officer **Albert J. Kraaimoore** 54 (11) 5777-4656
E-mail: kraaimooreaj@state.gov

Public Affairs Officer **Silvio I. Gonzalez** 54 (11) 5777-4405
E-mail: gonzalezsi@state.gov Fax: 54 (11) 5777-4229
Education: American U 2000 MA

Regional Security Officer **Mathieu Souliere** 54 (11) 5777-4298
E-mail: soulieremj@state.gov

Agricultural Section (Foreign Agricultural Service) [Argentina]
American Embassy - Buenos Aires, Argentina, Colombia 4300, C1425GMN Buenos Aires, Argentina
Mail: American Embassy - Buenos Aires, Unit 3130, DPO, AA 34034
Tel: 54 (11) 5777-4627 Fax: 54 (11) 5777-4216
E-mail: agbuenosaires@fas.usda.gov
Internet: ar.usembassy.gov/embassy/fas

Agricultural Counselor **M. Melinda Meador** 54 (11) 5777-4627
E-mail: melinda.meador@fas.usda.gov

Animal and Plant Health Inspection Service [Argentina]
American Embassy - Buenos Aires, Colombia 4300, 1425 Buenos Aires, Argentina
Mail: American Embassy - Buenos Aires, Unit 3130, DPO, AA 34034
Tel: 54 (11) 5777-4624 Fax: 54 (11) 4706-2303

APHIS Officer **(Vacant)** 54 (11) 5777-4624

Commercial Section (Foreign Commercial Service) [Argentina]
Colombia 4300, 1425 Buenos Aires, Argentina
Mail: 3130 Buenos Aires Place, Washington, DC 20521-3130
Tel: 54 (11) 5777-4367 Fax: 54 (11) 5777-4203
E-mail: office.buenosaires@trade.gov Internet: export.gov/argentina

Senior Commercial Officer **Rick de Lambert** 54 (11) 5777-4367
E-mail: rick.delambert@trade.gov

Department of Homeland Security - Transportation Security Administration [Argentina]

TSA Representative **Julio De Jesus** 54 (11) 5777-4533

★ Presidential Appointment Requiring Senate Confirmation ☆ Presidential Appointment □ Schedule C Appointment ◇ Career Senior Foreign Service Appointment
● Career Senior Executive Service (SES) Appointment ○ Non-Career Senior Executive Service (SES) Appointment ■ Postal Career Executive Service

Drug Enforcement Administration [Argentina]
Colombia 4300, 1425 Buenos Aires, Argentina
Mail: American Embassy - Buenos Aires, Unit 3130, DPO, AA 34034
Tel: 54 (11) 5777-4275
DEA Country Attaché **Steven G. Genevish** 54 (11) 5777-4716

Federal Aviation Administration (Resident in Brazil) [Argentina]
American Embassy - Brasilia, Brazil, Avenida das Nações,
Quadra 801, Lote 3 Brasilia, 70403-900, Brazil
Mail: American Embassy - Brasilia, Brazil, Unit 3500, APO, AA 34030
Fax: 55 (61) 3312-7295
FAA Senior Representative
Paul Leandro Friedman 55 (61) 3312-7293
E-mail: paul.friedman@faa.gov

Office of the Defense Attaché [Argentina]
American Embassy - Buenos Aires, Argentina,
Colombia 4300, C1425GMN Buenos Aires, Argentina
Mail: American Embassy - Buenos Aires, Unit 3130, DPO, AA 34034
Tel: 54 (11) 5777-4845 Fax: 54 (11) 5777-0197
Defense Attaché **COL Ed W. "Eddie" Ortiz USA** 54 (11) 5777-4381
Education: Sacred Heart (PR) 1992 BB; South Florida 2005 MA

U.S. Embassy in The Bahamas

42 Queen Street, P.O. Box N-8197, Nassau, Bahamas
Tel: 1 (242) 322-1181 Fax: 1 (242) 356-7174 Internet: bs.usembassy.gov

Office of the U.S. Ambassador to The Bahamas

American Embassy - Nassau, Bahamas, 42 Queen Street,
P.O. Box N-8197, Nassau, Bahamas
Mail: 3370 Nassau Place, Washington, DC 20521-3370
Tel: 1 (242) 328-2206 (After-hours Line)
★ Ambassador-Designate
Douglas F. "Papa Doug" Manchester . . . . 1 (242) 322-1181 ext. 4204
Education: San Diego State BS
Chargé d'Affaires **Stephanie L. Bowers** 1 (242) 328-2206
E-mail: bowerss@state.gov
Office Management Specialist to the Ambassador **(Vacant)** . . . . 1 (242) 322-1181 ext. 4204
Fax: 1 (242) 356-0222
Deputy Chief of Mission (Acting)
Penny Rechkemmer . . . . 1 (242) 322-1181 ext. 4205
Office Management Specialist to the Deputy Chief of Mission **Stephanie Quinones** 1 (242) 322-1181
Community Liaison Officer **Tracey Kelly** 1 (242) 322-1181
Consul **Angelina M. Wilkinson** . . . . 1 (242) 322-1181 ext. 4483
Fax: 1 (242) 328-7858
Financial Management Officer **Lia Fischer Neal** 1 (242) 322-1181
General Services Officer
Michael J. "Mike" Fundahn 1 (242) 322-1181
E-mail: fundahnmj@state.gov
Education: Olympic 1983 AS; Hawaii 1992 BA, 1992 MBA
Information Management Officer
Ted A. Cross . . . . 1 (242) 322-1181 ext. 4222
Information Program Officer **Laura Lasala** 1 (242) 322-1181
Information Systems Officer **(Vacant)** 1 (242) 322-1181
Information Systems Security Officer **Laura Lasala** 1 (242) 322-1181
Legal Attaché **Jeffrey Seawell** 1 (242) 322-1181
Management Officer (Acting)
Michael J. "Mike" Fundahn . . . . 1 (242) 322-1181 ext. 4285
E-mail: fundahnmj@state.gov
Education: Olympic 1983 AS; Hawaii 1992 BA, 1992 MBA
Narcotics Affairs Officer **Jamie Martin** . . . . . . 1 (242) 322-1181 ext. 4212
Fax: 1 (242) 356-0918
Political/Economic Officer **Douglas Lee Sun** 1 (242) 322-1181
Public Affairs Officer
Penny Rechkemmer . . . . 1 (242) 322-1181 ext. 4213
Regional Security Officer
Peter Kapoukakis . . . . 1 (242) 322-1181 ext. 4125

Agricultural Trade Office - Caribbean Basin
USDA/Agricultural Trade Office, 909 SE First Avenue,
Suite 720, Miami, FL 33131
Tel: (305) 536-5300 Fax: (305) 536-7577
E-mail: atocaribbeanbasin@fas.usda.gov
Director **Richard J. Battaglia** . . . . (305) 536-5300
E-mail: richard.battaglia@fas.usda.gov

Department of Homeland Security - U.S. Customs and Border Protection [Bahamas]
American Embassy - Nassau, Bahamas, Queen Street,
P.O. Box N-8197, Nassau, Bahamas
Mail: 3370 Nassau Place, Dulles, VA 20189
Tel: 1 (242) 322-1181 Fax: 1 (242) 377-6139
Customs Officer **Jeffrey Mara** 1 (242) 377-7126

Drug Enforcement Administration [Bahamas]
American Embassy - Nassau, Bahamas, Queen Street,
P.O. Box N-8197, Nassau, Bahamas
Mail: 3370 Nassau Place, Dulles, VA 20189
Tel: 1 (242) 322-1700 Fax: 1 (242) 322-8882
DEA Officer Country Attaché **Mark Webb** . . . . 1 (242) 322-1181 ext. 330

Federal Aviation Administration (Resident in Florida) [Bahamas]
FAA Representative **Alex D. Rodriguez** . . . . (202) 267-0426
2895 SW 145 Avenue, Miramar, FL 33027
E-mail: alex.d.rodriguez@faa.gov

Internal Revenue Service (Resident in Mexico City) [Bahamas]
American Embassy - Mexico City, Mexico,
Paseo de la Reforma 305M, Mexico City, D.F. 06500, Mexico
Mail: American Embassy - Mexico City, P.O. Box 3087,
Laredo, TX 78044-3087
Tel: 52 (55) 5080-2000 Fax: 52 (55) 5080-2882
IRS Representative **George Peralta** . . . . 52 (55) 5080-2000 ext. 2901

U.S. Coast Guard Liaison Office [Bahamas]
American Embassy - Nassau, Bahamas, Queen Street,
P.O. Box N-8197, Nassau, Bahamas
Mail: 3370 Nassau Place, Dulles, VA 20189
Tel: 1 (242) 322-1181 Fax: 1 (242) 328-7694
Coast Guard Liaison **(Vacant)** . . . . 1 (242) 322-1181 ext. 4215

U.S. Navy Liaison Office [Bahamas]
American Embassy - Nassau, Bahamas, Queen Street,
P.O. Box N-8197, Nassau, Bahamas
Mail: American Embassy Nassau/NLO,
PSC 1012 General Delivery, FPO, AA 34058
Tel: 1 (242) 322-8587 Fax: 1 (242) 328-7694
Naval Liaison **(Vacant)** . . . . 1 (242) 322-1181 ext. 4216

U.S. Embassy in Barbados, the Eastern Caribbean, and the Organisation of Eastern Caribbean States

American Embassy, Wildey Business Park, Wildey, Saint Michael,
Barbados 14006
Tel: 1 (246) 227-4000 Fax: 1 (246) 227-4088 Internet: bb.usembassy.gov

Office of the U.S. Ambassador to Barbados - Eastern Caribbean

American Embassy, Wildey Business Park, Wildey, Saint Michael,
Barbados 14006
Mail: American Embassy - Bridgetown,
CMR 1014, APO, AA 34055
★ Ambassador
Ambassador Linda Swartz Taglialatela 1 (264) 227-4000
E-mail: TaglialatelaLS@state.gov
Education: SUNY (Oneonta) BA; Virginia Tech MBA
★ Ambassador-Designate
Leandro P. "Lee" Rizzuto, Jr. 1 (264) 227-4000
Office Management Specialist to the Ambassador
Marsha K. Philipak-Chambers 1 (246) 227-4000

★ Presidential Appointment Requiring Senate Confirmation ☆ Presidential Appointment □ Schedule C Appointment ◇ Career Senior Foreign Service Appointment
● Career Senior Executive Service (SES) Appointment ○ Non-Career Senior Executive Service (SES) Appointment ■ Postal Career Executive Service

Office of the U.S. Ambassador to Barbados - Eastern Caribbean
(continued)

◇ Deputy Chief of Mission **Joaquin F. Monserrate** 1 (246) 227-4000
E-mail: monserratejf@state.gov
Education: Georgetown 1988 BA
Office Management Specialist to the Deputy Chief of Mission **Paula Constantino** 1 (246) 227-4000
Principal Officer, Grenada **Stephen Frahm** 1 (473) 444-1173
U.S. Embassy Grenada, Lance Aux Epines, Saint George's, Grenada
E-mail: frahmst@state.gov
Consul General **Tina D. Onufer** 1 (246) 227-4000
E-mail: onufertd@state.gov Fax: 1 (246) 431-0179
Community Liaison Officer **Karen J. Ostlund** 1 (246) 227-4000
E-mail: ostlundkj@state.gov
Economic Officer **(Vacant)** 1 (246) 227-4000
Equal Employment Opportunity Officer **(Vacant)** 1 (246) 227-4000
Financial Management Officer **Adam Dorosz** 1 (246) 227-4000
General Services Officer **James Rush** 1 (246) 227-4000
Information Management Officer **Joseph L. "Joe" Constantino** 1 (246) 227-4000
E-mail: CostantinoJL@state.gov
Information Systems Officer **Rodney "Rod" Bolles MBA** 1 (246) 227-4000
Education: U Phoenix 2004 BS, MBA
Information Systems Security Officer **Rodney "Rod" Bolles MBA** 1 (246) 227-4000
Education: U Phoenix 2004 BS, MBA
Legal Attaché **Scott MacCracken** 1 (246) 227-4000
Management Officer **Chris Hanson** 1 (246) 227-4000
Military Liaison Officer **CDR Elizabeth Booker USCG** 1 (246) 227-4000
Fax: 1 (246) 427-1668
Narcotics Affairs Section Officer **Jeannette M. Juricic** 1 (246) 227-4000
E-mail: juricicjm@state.gov
Political/Economic Officer **Shante J. Moore** 1 (246) 227-4000
Education: Kansas State 1996; Georgetown 2000 MSFS
Public Affairs Officer **James Rodriguez** 1 (246) 227-4000
E-mail: bridgetownpublicaffairs@state.gov Fax: 1 (246) 227-4177
Cultural Affairs Assistant **Sophia Lewis** 1 (246) 227-4000
Cultural Affairs Assistant (Exchanges) **Lisa Howell** ... 1 (246) 227-4000
Regional Security Officer **Robert Gousie** 1 (246) 227-4000

Agency for International Development [Barbados]
American Embassy, Wildey Business Park, Wildey, Saint Michael, Barbados 14006
Internet: www.usaid.gov/barbados
◇ Mission Director **Christopher M. "Chris" Cushing** 1 (246) 227-4118
E-mail: ccushing@usaid.gov

Drug Enforcement Administration [Barbados]
American Embassy - Bridgetown, Barbados,
Canadian Imperial Bank of Commerce Building,
Broad Street, Bridgetown, Barbados
Mail: American Embassy Bridgetown, CMR 1014, APO, AA 34055
Tel: 1 (246) 227-4000 Fax: 1 (246) 429-5246
DEA Country Attaché **Mark McHugh** 1 (246) 227-4000

Peace Corps (Resident in Saint Lucia) [Barbados]
American Embassy - Bridgetown, CMR 1014, APO, AA 34055
Tel: 1 (758) 453-6373 Internet: www.peacecorps.gov/eastern-caribbean
Country Director **Mary Kate Lowndes** 1 (758) 453-6373

U.S. Embassy in Belize
American Embassy - Belmopan, Belize,
Floral Park Road, Belmopan, Cayo, Belize
Tel: 501 822-4011 Fax: 501 822-4012 E-mail: embbelize@state.gov
Internet: bz.usembassy.gov

Office of the U.S. Ambassador to Belize
American Embassy - Belmopan, Belize,
Floral Park Road, Belmopan, Cayo, Belize
Mail: American Embassy - Belmopan, Belize, Unit 3050, DPO, AA 34025
★ Ambassador **(Vacant)** 501 822-4011
Chargé d'Affaires **Keith R. Gilges** 501 822-4011
E-mail: gilgeskr@state.gov
Education: William & Mary 1990 BA; U Hong Kong (Japan) 1998 MSc
Office Management Specialist to the Ambassador **(Vacant)** 501 822-4011
Deputy Chief of Mission (Acting) **Deborah B. "Debbie" Lingwood** 501 822-4011
E-mail: lingwooddb@state.gov
Education: Bryn Mawr BA; Georgetown MA
Office Management Specialist to the Deputy Chief of Mission **(Vacant)** 501 822-4011
Consul **Yomaris MacDonald** 501 822-4011
Community Liaison Officer **Kimberly Singleton** 501 822-4011
Financial Management Officer **Anthony "Tony" Zaccagnino** 501 822-4011
General Services Officer **Paul Martinek** 501 822-4011
Information Management Officer **Jerry A. Lopez** 501 822-4011
E-mail: lopezja@state.gov
Management Officer (Acting) **William L. Rada** 501 822-4011
E-mail: radawl@state.gov
Military Liaison Officer **LTC Eldridge "Raj" Singleton USA** 501 822-4011
Fax: 501 822-4012
Political Officer **Bryn West** 501 822-4011
Political/Economic Section Chief **Beverly E. Mather-Marcus** 501 822-4011
E-mail: mather-marcusbe@state.gov
Public Affairs Officer **Natella Svistunova** 501 822-4011
Regional Security Officer **Erica D. Smith** 501 (2) 25-2009

Agricultural Section (Foreign Agricultural Service) (Resident in Guatemala City) [Belize]
American Embassy - Guatemala City, Guatemala,
7-01 Avenida de la Reforma, Zone 10 Guatemala City, Guatemala 01010
Mail: American Embassy - Guatemala City, Unit 3305, APO, AA 34024
Tel: 502 2332-4030 Fax: 502 2331-8293
E-mail: agguatemala@fas.usda.gov
Agricultural Counselor **Richard "Todd" Drennan** 502 2332-4030

Drug Enforcement Administration [Belize]
American Embassy - Belmopan, Belize,
Floral Park Road, Belmopan, Cayo, Belize
Mail: American Embassy - Belmopan, Belize, Unit 7405, APO, AA 34025
Tel: 501 822-4011 Fax: 501 822-4012
DEA Officer **Andreas B. Dyer** 501 822-4011

Federal Aviation Administration (Resident in Panama) [Belize]
Senior FAA Representative **Carl N. Johnson** 507 317-5046

Internal Revenue Service (Resident in Mexico City) [Belize]
American Embassy - Mexico City, Paseo de la Reforma 305,
Colonia Cuauhtemoc, Apartado Postal 88-BIF, Mexico City, D.F. 06500, Mexico
Mail: American Embassy - Mexico City, Mexico, P.O. Box 3087, Laredo, TX 78044-3087
Tel: 52 (55) 5080-2000 Fax: 52 (55) 5080-2882
IRS Officer **George Peralta** .... 52 (55) 5080-2000 ext. 2901

★ Presidential Appointment Requiring Senate Confirmation ☆ Presidential Appointment □ Schedule C Appointment ◇ Career Senior Foreign Service Appointment
● Career Senior Executive Service (SES) Appointment ○ Non-Career Senior Executive Service (SES) Appointment ■ Postal Career Executive Service

DEPARTMENTS

Office of the Defense Attaché (Resident in Tegucigalpa) [Belize]
American Embassy - Tegucigalpa, Honduras, Avenida La Paz,
Apartado Postal Number 3453, Tegucigalpa, Honduras
Mail: USDAO, Unit 2942, APO, AA 34022
Tel: 504 2236-9320 Fax: 504 2236-5645 E-mail: usdaoho@datum.hn

Defense Attaché **(Vacant)** .... 504 2236-9320 ext. 4582

Peace Corps [Belize]
6130 Iguana Street Extension, Belmopan, Cayo, Belize
Mail: American Embassy - Belmopan, Belize, Unit 7404, APO, AA 34025
Tel: 501 822-4011 Fax: 501 822-4012 E-mail: cd@bz.peacecorps.gov
Internet: www.peacecorps.gov/belize

Country Director **Melanie Emerson** 501 822-1771

U.S. Consulate General in Bermuda

U.S. Consulate General - Hamilton, Bermuda, Crown Hill,
16 Middle Road, Devonshire, DV 03, Bermuda
Tel: 1 (441) 295-1342 Fax: 1 (441) 295-1592
E-mail: hamiltonconsulate@state.gov

Bermuda Consulate General
U.S. Consulate General - Hamilton, Bermuda, Crown Hill,
16 Middle Road, Devonshire, DV 03, Bermuda
Mail: 5300 Hamilton Place, Washington, DC 20521-5300

◇ Consul General **Constance M. "Connie" Dierman** 1 (441) 295-1342
E-mail: diermance@state.gov
Office Management Specialist to the Consul General **Cindy S. Almeida** 1 (441) 295-1342
Deputy Principal Officer **Derek Schilling Worman** .... 1 441-295-1342 ext. 229
E-mail: wormands@state.gov
Consular Section Chief **Marcy S. Brown** .... 1 441-295-1342 ext. 226
Community Liaison Officer **Sara Lowther** 1 (441) 295-1342
Economic/Management/Political Officer **Derek Schilling Worman** .... 1 (441) 295-1342 ext. 229
E-mail: wormands@state.gov
Information Systems Security Officer **Derek Schilling Worman** 1 (441) 295-1342
E-mail: wormands@state.gov
Regional Security Officer (Resident in New York) **Kenneth Greenblatt** 1 (441) 295-1342
Affiliation: Regional Security Officer, United States Mission to the United Nations, United States Department of State
799 United Nations Plaza, New York, NY 10017-3505
Tel: (212) 415-4158

Agricultural Trade Office - Caribbean Basin
USDA/Agricultural Trade Office, 909 SE 1st Avenue,
Suite 720, Miami, FL 33131
Tel: (305) 536-5300 Fax: (305) 536-7577
E-mail: atocaribbeanbasin@fas.usda.gov

Director **Richard J. Battaglia** .... (305) 536-5300
E-mail: richard.battaglia@fas.usda.gov

Department of Homeland Security - U.S. Customs and Border Protection [Bermuda]
Civil Air Terminal, Two Kindley Field Road, Saint George's, Bermuda
Mail: 5300 Hamilton Place, Washington, DC 20521-5300
Tel: 1 (441) 293-0353 Fax: 1 (441) 293-1509

Officer in Charge **William Cletus** .... (441) 293-0353

U.S. Embassy in Bolivia

American Embassy - La Paz, Bolivia, 2780 Arce Avenue, La Paz, Bolivia
Tel: 591 (2) 216-8000 Fax: 591 (2) 216-8111

Office of the U.S. Ambassador to Bolivia
American Embassy - La Paz, Bolivia, 2780 Arce Avenue,
P.O. Box 425, La Paz, Bolivia
Mail: American Embassy - La Paz, Bolivia, APO, AA 34032
Tel: 591 (2) 216-8000 Fax: 591 (2) 216-8111 Internet: bo.usembassy.gov

★ Ambassador **(Vacant)** 591 (2) 216-8000

Office of the U.S. Ambassador to Bolivia *(continued)*

◇ Charge d'Affaires **Bruce Williamson** 591 (2) 216-8700
E-mail: williamsonb@state.gov
Education: Yale 1978 BA; Harvard JD
Office Management Specialist to the Charge d'Affaires **Marcia Gutierrez** 591 (2) 216-8700
Deputy Chief of Mission **Marianne C. Scott** 591 (2) 216-8214
Fax: 591 (2) 216-8787
Office Management Specialist to the Deputy Chief of Mission **Amy A. Balog** 591 (2) 216-8700
Consular Officer **Michael D. "Mike" Ose** 591 (2) 216-8666
Fax: 591 (2) 216-8808
Community Liaison Officer **(Vacant)** 591 (2) 216-8242
Financial Management Officer **Charles "Chuck" McShane** 591 (2) 216-8132
E-mail: mcshanec@state.gov
Education: St Cloud State 1993 BSAcc
General Services Officer **Ana P. Baide** 591 (2) 216-8174
Human Resources Officer **Karen Rodriguez** 591 (2) 216-8028
Fax: 591 (2) 216-8787
Information Management Officer **Brian W. Jetter** 591 (2) 216-8087
E-mail: jetterbw@state.gov Fax: 591 (2) 216-8111
Information Program Officer **Richard E. "Ric" Mangus, Jr.** 591 (2) 216-8249
E-mail: mangusre@state.gov
Information Systems Officer **(Vacant)** 591 (2) 216-8249
Information Systems Security Officer **Brian W. Jetter** 591 (2) 216-8249
E-mail: jetterbw@state.gov
Management Officer **Donald R. Coleman** 591 (2) 216-8214
E-mail: colemandr@state.gov Fax: 591 (2) 216-8787
Military Liaison Officer **(Vacant)** 591 (2) 216-8223
Fax: 591 (2) 216-8889
Political/Economic Officer **Rolf A. Olson** 591 (2) 216-8745
Fax: 591 (2) 216-8625
Public Affairs Officer **Emily Kenealy** 591 (2) 216-8222
Fax: 591 (2) 216-8622
Regional Security Officer **Kristi A. Sarosik** 591 (2) 216-8903
E-mail: SarosikKA@state.gov Fax: 591 (2) 216-8259

Agricultural Section (Foreign Agricultural Service) (Resident in Lima) [Bolivia]
American Embassy - Lima, Peru, Enclada Avenue, Cuadra 17,
Monterrico, Lima, 33, Peru
Mail: American Embassy - FAS, Unit 3785, APO, AA 34031-5000
Tel: 51 (1) 434-3042 Fax: 51 (1) 434-3043 E-mail: aglima@fas.usda.gov

Agricultural Counselor **Casey Bean** 51 (1) 549-2491
E-mail: casey.bean@fas.usda.gov
Education: Maryland BS; Rhode Island MEc

Department of Homeland Security - U.S. Immigration and Customs Enforcement (Resident in Brasilia) [Bolivia]
American Embassy - Brasilia D.F., Brazil, Das Nacoes Avenue,
Quadra 801, Lote 3, 70403-900 Brasilia, Brazil
Mail: American Embassy - Brasilia, Brazil, Unit 3500, APO, AA 34030
Tel: 55 (61) 3312-7000 Fax: 55 (61) 3312-7338

ICE Attaché **Robert Fuentes** 55 (61) 3312-7000

Federal Aviation Administration (Resident in Brazil) [Bolivia]
American Embassy - Brasilia, Brazil, Avenida das Nações,
Quadra 801, Lote 3 Brasilia, 70403-900, Brazil
Mail: American Embassy - Brasilia, Brazil, Unit 3500, APO, AA 34030
Fax: 55 (61) 3312-7295

FAA Senior Representative **Paul Leandro Friedman** 55 (61) 3312-7580
E-mail: paul.friedman@faa.gov

★ Presidential Appointment Requiring Senate Confirmation ☆ Presidential Appointment ☐ Schedule C Appointment ◇ Career Senior Foreign Service Appointment
● Career Senior Executive Service (SES) Appointment ○ Non-Career Senior Executive Service (SES) Appointment ■ Postal Career Executive Service

Internal Revenue Service (Resident in Mexico City) [Bolivia]
American Embassy - Mexico City, Mexico,
Paseo de la Reforma 305M, Colonia Cuahtemoc,
Room 116, Mexico City, D.F. 06500, Mexico
Mail: American Embassy - Mexico City, Mexico, P.O. Box 3087,
Laredo, TX 78044-3087
Tel: 52 (55) 5080-2000 Fax: 52 (55) 5080-2882
IRS Officer **George Peralta** 52 (55) 5080-2000

Office of the Defense Attaché [Bolivia]
American Embassy - La Paz, Bolivia, 2780 Arce Avenue, La Paz, Bolivia
Mail: American Embassy - La Paz, Bolivia, USDAO Unit 3912,
APO, AA 34032
Tel: 591 (2) 216-8469 Fax: 591 (2) 216-8886
Defense Attaché **Col David W. Diehl USAF** 591 (2) 216-8469

Cochabamba Consular Agency
U.S. Consular Agency - Cochabamba, Bolivia,
564 Oquendo Avenue, Torres Soffer, Office 601,
6th Floor, Cochabamba, Bolivia
Mail: U.S. Consular Agency - Cochabamba,,
c/o American Embassy - La Paz, Bolivia, APO, AA 34032
Tel: 591 (4) 411-6313 Fax: 591 (4) 425-6714
E-mail: cochabambavpp@state.gov
Consular Agent **(Vacant)** 591 (2) 216-8666

Santa Cruz Consular Agency
U.S. Consular Agency - Santa Cruz, Bolivia, 146 Avenue Roque Aguilera,
3er. Anillo, Santa Cruz, Bolivia
Mail: U.S. Consular Agency - Santa Cruz,
c/o American Embassy - La Paz, Bolivia, APO, AA 34032
Tel: 591 (3) 351-3477 Fax: 591 (3) 351-3478
E-mail: santacruzvpp@state.gov
Consular Agent **Nicole Martinez** 591 (2) 216-8666

U.S. Embassy in Brazil
American Embassy - Brasilia, Brazil, Avenida das Nacoes,
Lote 3, Brasilia, D.F. 70403-900, Brazil
Tel: 55 (61) 3312-7000 Tel: 55 (61) 3225-9136 E-mail: ircbsb@state.gov

Office of the U.S. Ambassador to Brazil
American Embassy - Brasilia, Brazil, Avenida das Nações,
Quadra 801, Lote 3 Brasilia, 70403-900, Brazil
Mail: American Embassy - Brasilia, Brazil, Unit 3500, APO, AA 34030
★ Ambassador **(Vacant)** 55 (61) 3312-7588
◇ Chargé d'Affaires **William W. "Bill" Popp** 55 (61) 3312-7000
E-mail: poppww@state.gov
Education: Westminster (MO) 1995 BA;
George Washington 1997 MIA; National War Col 2013 MS
Office Management Specialist to the Ambassador
Alma R. Pratt 55 (61) 3312-7000
◇ Deputy Chief of Mission **William W. "Bill" Popp** 55 (61) 3312-7445
E-mail: poppww@state.gov
Education: Westminster (MO) 1995 BA;
George Washington 1997 MIA; National War Col 2013 MS
Office Management Specialist to the Deputy Chief
of Mission **Michael "Mike" Johns** 55 (61) 3312-7445
Education: BYU 2008 BBA
◇ Consular Affairs Officer
Douglas A. "Doug" Koneff 55 (61) 3312-7053
E-mail: KoneffD@state.gov
Education: Cornell 1983 BA
Community Liaison Officer **Veronica Sheriff** 55 (61) 3312-7000
E-mail: sheriffv@state.gov
Education: Ball State BS, MBA
◇ Economic Counselor **Valerie L. Belon** 55 (61) 3312-7180
E-mail: belonvl@state.gov
Education: Princeton 1987 BA; UCLA 1990 MBA; Stanford 1999 MA
Environment, Science and Technology Officer
Pablo Valdez 55 (61) 3312-7000
E-mail: ValdezPM2@state.gov
Education: Stanford 1992; Texas MPP

Office of the U.S. Ambassador to Brazil *(continued)*
Facilities Management Officer **Zachary N. Gernes** 55 (61) 3312-7000
E-mail: gerneszn@state.gov
Education: Marquette 2004 BSME
Financial Management Officer **Bryan Ermatinger** 55 (61) 3312-7000
E-mail: ermatingerb@state.gov
Education: Weber State 1985 BAcc
General Services Officer
Judith Hinshaw "Judy" Semilota 55 (61) 3312-7068
E-mail: semilotajh@state.gov
Human Resources Officer **Cristina Stokes** 55 (61) 3312-7000
E-mail: StokesC@state.gov
Information Program Officer **Alberto Barrero** 55 (61) 3312-7000
E-mail: BarreroA@state.gov
Information Management Officer **Blanca M. Neve** 55 (61) 3312-7280
E-mail: nevebm@state.gov
Information Systems Officer **Ronald Foreman** 55 (61) 3312-7277
Legal Attaché **David Brassanini** 55 (61) 3312-7312
E-mail: brassaninid@state.gov
◇ Management Officer **Panfilo Marquez** 55 (61) 3312-7022
E-mail: MarquezP@state.gov
Military Liaison Officer **Rick Ursery** 55 (61) 3248-8200
◇ Political Officer **Kristin M. Kane** 55 (61) 3312-7438
E-mail: kanekm@state.gov
◇ Public Affairs Officer **Erik Anders Holm-Olsen** 55 (61) 3312-7361
E-mail: holm-olsene@state.gov
Education: Brown U 1984 BA; William & Mary 1987 JD
Regional Security Officer **Jason H. Smith** 55 (61) 3312-7397

Agency for International Development [Brazil]
American Embassy - Brasilia, Brazil, Avenida das Nacoes,
Lote 3, Brasilia, D.F. 70403-900, Brazil
Mail: American Embassy - Brasilia, Brazil, Unit 2500, APO, AA 34030
Tel: 55 (61) 3312-7248 Fax: 55 (61) 3312-7648
E-mail: brazil.info@usaid.gov Internet: www.usaid.gov/brazil
◇ Country Representative **Michael J. Eddy** 55 (61) 3312-7237
E-mail: meddy@usaid.gov

Agricultural Section (Foreign Agricultural Service) [Brazil]
American Embassy - Brasilia, Brazil, Avenida das Nações,
Quadra 801, Lote 3 Brasilia, 70403-900, Brazil
Tel: 55 (61) 3312-7101 Fax: 55 (61) 3312-7659
E-mail: agbrasilia@usda.gov
Agricultural Counselor **Oliver Flake** 55 (61) 3312-7101
E-mail: oliver.flake@fas.usda.gov
Education: BYU BS; Arizona State MS

Belo Horizonte Commercial Section (Foreign Commercial Service)
Av. Contorno 4520, 8th Floor, 30110-028 Belo Horizonte, Brazil
Tel: 55 (31) 3213-1571 Fax: 55 (31) 3213-1575
◇ Deputy Senior Commercial Officer (Resident in São
Paulo) **Alyce Camille "Camille" Richardson** 55 (11) 3250-5429
E-mail: camille.richardson@trade.gov

Commercial Section (Foreign Commercial Service) [Brazil]
American Embassy - Brasilia, Brazil, Avenida das Nacoes,
Lote 3, Brasilia, D.F. 70403-900, Brazil
Mail: American Embassy - Brasilia, Brazil, Unit 3500, APO, AA 34030
Tel: 55 (61) 312-7418 Fax: 55 (61) 312-7656
E-mail: office.brasilia@trade.gov
Senior Commercial Officer **(Vacant)** 55 (11) 5186-7401
Fax: 55 (11) 5186-7382
Senior Commercial Specialist **Daniele Andrews** 55 (61) 3312-7458
E-mail: daniele.andrews@trade.gov

Department of Agriculture - Animal and Plant Health Inspection Service [Brazil]
APHIS Attaché **John F. Gilmore** 55 (61) 3312-7589
E-mail: john.f.gilmore@aphis.usda.gov

★ Presidential Appointment Requiring Senate Confirmation ☆ Presidential Appointment □ Schedule C Appointment ◇ Career Senior Foreign Service Appointment
● Career Senior Executive Service (SES) Appointment ○ Non-Career Senior Executive Service (SES) Appointment ■ Postal Career Executive Service

Department of Homeland Security - U.S. Immigration and Customs Enforcement [Brazil]
American Embassy - Brasilia, Brazil, Avenida das Nações,
Quadra 801, Lote 3 Brasilia, 70403-900, Brazil
Mail: American Embassy - Brasilia, Brazil, Unit 3500, APO, AA 34030
Tel: 55 (61) 3312-7000 Fax: 55 (61) 3312-7338

ICE Attaché **Robert Fuentes** 55 (61) 3312-7000

Department of Justice - Drug Enforcement Administration [Brazil]
American Embassy - Brasilia, Brazil, Avenida das Nações,
Quadra 801, Lote 3 Brasilia, 70403-900, Brazil
Mail: American Embassy - Brasilia, Brazil, Unit 3500, APO, AA 34030
Tel: 55 (61) 3312-7000 Fax: 55 (61) 3312-7657

DEA Country Attaché **Lawrence Reichner** 55 (61) 3312-7118

Federal Aviation Administration [Brazil]
FAA Senior Representative
Paul Leandro Friedman 55 (61) 8116-5291
E-mail: paul.friedman@faa.gov

Office of the Defense Attaché [Brazil]
Defense Attache **Lorenzo Harris** 55 (61) 3312-7000

Porto Alegre Consulate
1889 Avenida Assis Brasil - Passo dAreia, Porto Alegre, Brazil
Tel: 55 (51) 3345-6000 E-mail: portoalegreimprensa@state.gov

Principal Officer/Consul General **Julia L. Harlan** 55 (51) 3345-6000
E-mail: harlanjl@state.gov
Office Management Specialist to the Consul General **Evelyn Haddad** 55 (51) 3345-6000
Deputy Principal Officer/Consular Officer **David William Franz** 55 (51) 3345-6000
E-mail: franzdw@state.gov
Community Liaison Officer **(Vacant)** 55 (51) 3345-6000
Financial Management Officer **Christopher D. "Chris" Waugh** 55 (61) 3312-7000
E-mail: waughcd@state.gov
Education: Maryland 2004 BS
Information Program Officer **Sean Gilligan** 55 (51) 3345-6000
Management Officer/General Services Officer **Mark Hernandez** 55 (51) 3345-6000
Political/Economic Officer **Aline Vecchia** 55 (51) 3345-6000
Public Affairs Officer **John Jacobs** 55 (51) 3345-6000
Regional Security Officer **John Mazzuchi** 55 (51) 3345-6000

Recife Consulate General
Rua Goncalves Maia, 163, Boa Vista, 50070-060 Recife, Brazil PE
Mail: Unit 3503, APO, AA 34030
Tel: 55 (81) 3416-3050 Fax: 55 (81) 3231-1906
Internet: br.usembassy.gov/embassy-consulates/recife

Consul General **John Morgan Barrett** 55 (81) 3416-3050
E-mail: barrettjm@state.gov
Commercial Officer **Geoffrey Bogart** 55 (81) 3416-3075
E-mail: geoffrey.bogart@trade.gov
Community Liaison Officer **Kathryn Cathey** 55 (81) 3416-3050
E-mail: catheykk@state.gov
Consular Affairs Officer **Michael Catley** 55 (81) 3416-3050
General Services Officer **Bernardo Diaz** 55 (81) 3416-3050
Information Programs Officer/Information Systems Security Officer **David Wolf-Hudson** 55 (81) 3416-3050
E-mail: wolf-hudsonkd@state.gov
Management Officer **Daniel Hughes** 55 (81) 3416-3050
Political/Economic Officer **Catherine Griffith** 55 (81) 3416-3050
Public Affairs Officer **Daniel A. Stewart** 55 (81) 3416-3050
E-mail: stewartda@state.gov
Regional Security Officer **Andrew Sellhorn** 55 (81) 3416-3050

Rio de Janeiro Consulate General
U.S. Consulate General - Rio de Janeiro, Brazil,
Avenida Presidente Wilson 147 Castelo, 20030-020 Rio de Janeiro, Brazil RJ
Mail: U.S. Consulate General - Rio de Janeiro, Unit 3501, APO, AA 34030
Tel: 55 (21) 3823-2000 Fax: 55 (21) 3823-2003

Consul General **Scott I. Hamilton** 55 (21) 3823-2000
E-mail: hamiltonsi2@state.gov
Education: Oxford (UK) 1986 BA; Harvard 1989 JD; National War Col 2013 MS
Office Management Specialist to the Consul General **Madeleine A. Palomino** 55 (21) 3823-2806
E-mail: PalominoMA@state.gov
Consular Officer **Rebecca A. Pasini** 55 (21) 3823-2000
E-mail: pasinira@state.gov
General Services Officer **Laura A. Quinn** 55 (21) 3823-2000
E-mail: quinnla@state.gov
Information Program Officer **Mark R. Hall** 55 (21) 3823-2000
Information Systems Security Officer **Dustin Washburn** 55 (21) 3823-2000
Management Officer **Jill Thompson** 55 (21) 3823-2000
Political/Economic Officer **Kathryn Hoffman** 55 (21) 3823-2000
Education: Johns Hopkins; Harvard 2002 MPA
Public Affairs Officer **Viraj M. Lebailly** 55 (21) 3823-2000
E-mail: lebaillyvm@state.gov
Education: Trinity Col (CT) 1999 BA; Yale 2001 MA
Regional Security Officer **Etienne Singleton** 55 (21) 3823-2000

Commercial Section (Foreign Commercial Service) [Brazil]
U.S. Consulate General - Rio de Janeiro, Brazil,
Avenue Presidente Wilson, 147, Rio de Janeiro, 20030-020, Brazil
Mail: U.S. Consulate General - Rio de Janeiro, Unit 3501, APO, AA 34030
Tel: 55 (21) 3823-2000 Fax: 55 (21) 2240-9738

Principal Commercial Officer **Marianne Drain** 55 (21) 3823-2000
E-mail: marianne.drain@trade.gov
Education: U Washington 1996 BA

Library of Congress [Brazil]
U.S. Consulate General - Rio de Janeiro, Brazil,
Avenida Presidente Wilson 147 Castelo, 20030-020 Rio de Janeiro, Brazil RJ
Mail: U.S. Consulate General - Rio de Janeiro, Unit 3501, APO, AA 34030
Tel: 55 (21) 3823-2320 Fax: 55 (21) 3822-2333 E-mail: rio@loc.gov
Internet: www.loc.gov/acq/ovop/rio

Field Director **Pamela Howard-Reguindin** 55 (21) 3823-2320
E-mail: pamelahr@loc.gov

Office of the Defense Attaché [Brazil]
U.S. Consulate General - Rio de Janeiro, Brazil,
Avenue President Wilson, 147, Rio de Janeiro, 20030-020, Brazil
Mail: U.S. Consulate General - Rio de Janeiro, Unit 3501, APO, AA 34030
Tel: 55 (21) 3823-2463

Defense Attaché **(Vacant)** 55 (21) 3823-2000

São Paulo Consulate General
U.S. Consulate General - São Paulo, Brazil, Rua Henri Dunant, 500, Chácara Santo Antônio, São Paulo, 04709-110, Brazil
Mail: U.S. Consulate General - São Paulo, P.O. Box 2489, Unit 3502, APO, AA 34030
Tel: 55 (11) 3250-5000 Fax: 55 (11) 3250-5099

◇ Consul General **Adam M. Shub** 55 (11) 3250-5000
E-mail: shubam@state.gov
Education: Columbia 1979 BA; NYU 1985 MBA
Office Management Specialist to the Consul General **Beatriz O. Beroud** 55 (11) 3250-5000
E-mail: BeroudBO@state.gov
◇ Consular Officer **David D. Potter** 55 (11) 3250-5000
E-mail: potterdd@state.gov
Community Liaison Officer **(Vacant)** 55 (11) 3250-5000

★ Presidential Appointment Requiring Senate Confirmation ☆ Presidential Appointment ☐ Schedule C Appointment ◇ Career Senior Foreign Service Appointment
● Career Senior Executive Service (SES) Appointment ○ Non-Career Senior Executive Service (SES) Appointment ■ Postal Career Executive Service

São Paulo Consulate General *(continued)*

Financial Management Officer **Aaron C. Olsa** 55 (11) 3250-5000
E-mail: OlsaAC@state.gov
Education: Iowa 1994 BA

General Services Officer **Kate Higgins** 55 (11) 3250-5000

Information Program Officer **Joseph A. Moreno** 55 (11) 3250-5000
E-mail: morenoja2@state.gov
Education: Southern Illinois 2008

Information Systems Officer **Joseph A. Moreno** 55 (11) 3250-5000
E-mail: morenoja2@state.gov
Education: Southern Illinois 2008

Management Officer **Aaron C. Olsa** 55 (11) 3250-5000
E-mail: OlsaAC@state.gov
Education: Iowa 1994 BA

Political/Economic Officer
Maxwell J. "Max" Hamilton 55 (11) 3250-5000
E-mail: hamiltonmj@state.gov
Education: Georgetown 2004; Harvard 2008 MPP

Public Affairs Officer **Stephen M. Stark** 55 (11) 3250-5000
E-mail: starksm@state.gov

Regional Security Officer **Mike Escott** 55 (11) 3250-5000

Agricultural Trade Office [Brazil]
U.S. Consulate General - São Paulo, Brazil,
Alameda Santos, 2224- São Paulo, j.11, Brazil
Mail: U.S. Consulate General - São Paulo, P.O. Box 8063,
APO, AA 34030
Tel: 55 (11) 3250-5400 Fax: 55 (11) 3250-5499
E-mail: atosaopaulo@fas.usda.gov

Director **Chanda Beckman Berk** 55 (11) 5186-7400
E-mail: chanda.berk@fas.usda.gov

Commercial Section (Foreign Commercial Service) [Brazil]
U.S. Commercial Office (Trade Center), c/o U.S. Consulate General,
Rua Estados, Unidos 1812 São Paulo, 01427-002, Brazil
Mail: U.S. Commercial Office (Trade Center), P.O. Box 8063,
APO, AA 34030
Tel: 55 (11) 3897-4000 Fax: 55 (11) 3085-2744

◇ Deputy Senior Commercial Officer
Alyce Camille "Camille" Richardson 55 (11) 3250-5172
E-mail: camille.richardson@trade.gov

Department of Justice - Drug Enforcement Administration [Brazil]
Rua Henri Dunant, 500, Chácara Santo Antônio, São Paulo, 04709-110,
Brazil
Mail: U.S. Consulate General - São Paulo, P.O. Box 2489, Unit 3502,
APO, AA 34030
Tel: 55 (11) 3250-5000

DEA Attaché **Jacqueline Ramirez** 55 (11) 3250-5000

Internal Revenue Service (Resident in Mexico City) [Brazil]
American Embassy - Mexico City, Mexico,
Paseo de la Reforma 305M, Mexico City, D.F. 06500, Mexico
Mail: American Embassy - Mexico City, Mexico, P.O. Box 3087,
Laredo, TX 78044-3087
Tel: 52 (55) 5080-2000 Fax: 52 (55) 5080-2882

IRS Officer **George Peralta** .... 52 (55) 5080-2000 ext. 2901

U.S. Embassy in Canada
American Embassy - Ottawa, Ontario, Canada,
490 Sussex Drive, Ottawa, Ontario K1N 1G8, Canada
Tel: 1 (613) 688-5335 Fax: 1 (613) 688-3080

Office of the U.S. Ambassador to Canada
American Embassy - Ottawa, Ontario, Canada,
490 Sussex Drive, Ottawa, Ontario K1N 1G8, Canada
Mail: American Embassy - Ottawa, Ontario, P.O. Box 5000,
Ogdensburg, NY 13669-0430
E-mail: comments@usembassycanada.gov

★ Ambassador
Ambassador Kelly G. Knight Craft ...... 1 (613) 688-5335 ext. 5200
Education: Kentucky BA

Office of the U.S. Ambassador to Canada *(continued)*

Office Management Specialist to the
Ambassador **Chad Lee Wilton** .... 1 (613) 688-5335 ext. 5200
Education: Occidental 1990; Stanford 1993

Deputy Chief of Mission **(Vacant)** 1 (613) 688-5335

Office Management Specialist
to the Deputy Chief of Mission
Christina "Chris" Temen .... 1 (613) 688-5335 ext. 5203
E-mail: temenc2@state.gov

◇ Consul General **Michael A. Barkin** .... 1 (613) 688-5335 ext. 5299
E-mail: barkinma@state.gov
Education: Emory BA; Princeton MPP; NYU JD

Consular Section Officer
Daniela A. DiPierro .... 1 (613) 688-5335 ext. 5304
E-mail: dipierroda@state.gov

Community Liaison Officer **Tara Joos** .... 1 (613) 688-5335 ext. 5274

◇ Economic Officer **Stuart A. Dwyer** .... 1 (613) 688-5335 ext. 5214
E-mail: dwyersa@state.gov

Environment, Science and Technology Officer
(Vacant) 1 (613) 688-5335

Equal Employment Opportunity Officer
Kundai Mashingaidze 1 (613) 688-5210
E-mail: mashingaidzek@state.gov Fax: 1 (613) 688-3087
Education: USC 2007 MBA

Facilities Management Officer **Michael P. Duprez** 1 (613) 688-5335

Financial Management Officer
Laura A. Danylin .... 1 (613) 688-5335 ext. 5389
E-mail: danylinla@state.gov

General Services Officer **Ryan R. Ruta** ...... 1 (613) 688-5335 ext. 5250
E-mail: rutarr@state.gov

Human Resources Officer
Jeffrey T. "Jeff" Ogren .... 1 (613) 688-5335 ext. 5265
Fax: 1 (613) 688-3055

Information Management Officer
Latifa Bousaidi Taylor .... 1 (613) 688-5335 ext. 5276

Information Program Officer
William K. "Will" Broughton 1 (613) 688-5335
E-mail: broughtonwk@state.gov

Information Systems Officer **(Vacant)** 1 (613) 688-5347

Information Systems Security Officer
(Vacant) .... 1 (613) 688-5335 ext. 5278

Legal Attaché **Kevin Vorndran** .... 1 (613) 688-5335 ext. 5383

Management Officer
Leslie S. "Les" Degraffenried .... 1 (613) 688-5335 ext. 5260
E-mail: degraffenriedls@state.gov
Education: Texas 1979 BA; Baylor 1982 JD

Political Officer **(Vacant)** .... 1 (613) 688-5335 ext. 5325

Political/Military Officer **(Vacant)** 1 (613) 688-5335

◇ Public Affairs Officer
Stacy Elizabeth White .... 1 (613) 688-5335 ext. 5417
E-mail: whites@state.gov

Regional Security Officer **David Hall** .... 1 (613) 688-5335 ext. 5262

Agricultural Section (Foreign Agricultural Service) [Canada]
American Embassy - Ottawa, Ontario, Canada,
490 Sussex Drive, Ottawa, Ontario K1N 1G8, Canada
Mail: American Embassy - Ottawa, Ontario, P.O. Box 5000,
Ogdensburg, NY 13669-0430
Tel: 1 (613) 688-5267 E-mail: agottawa@fas.usda.gov

Minister-Counselor for Agricultural Affairs
Holly S. Higgins 1 (613) 688-5267
E-mail: holly.higgins@fas.usda.gov

Commercial Section (Foreign Commercial Service) [Canada]
American Embassy - Ottawa, Ontario, Canada,
490 Sussex Drive, Ottawa, Ontario K1N 1G8, Canada
Mail: U.S. Embassy–Commercial Service (MS 35), P.O. Box 5000,
Ogdensburg, NY 13669
Tel: 1 (613) 688-5217 Fax: 1 (613) 238-5999
E-mail: office.ottawa@trade.gov

◇ Senior Commercial Officer
Christopher R. Quinlivan 1 (613) 688-5217
E-mail: christopher.quinlivin@trade.gov

(continued on next page)

Commercial Section (Foreign Commercial Service) [Canada] *(continued)*

Deputy Senior Commercial Officer
Janee Pierre-Louis 1 (613) 688-5222
E-mail: janee.pierre-louis@trade.gov
Senior Commercial Specialist **Lucy Latka** 1 (613) 688-5219
E-mail: lucy.latka@trade.gov

Department of Homeland Security - U.S. Immigration and Customs Enforcement [Canada]
American Embassy - Ottawa, Ontario, Canada,
490 Sussex Drive, Ottawa, Ontario K1N 1G8, Canada
Mail: American Embassy - Ottawa, Ontario, P.O. Box 5000,
Ogdensburg, NY 13669-0430
Tel: 1 (613) 688-5335 Fax: 1 (613) 238-5720

Customs Officer **Melissa Ruiz** .... 1 (613) 688-5335 ext. 5467
E-mail: melissa.ruiz@ice.dhs.gov

Drug Enforcement Administration [Canada]
American Embassy - Ottawa, Ontario, Canada,
490 Sussex Drive, Ottawa, Ontario K1N 1G8, Canada
Mail: American Embassy - Ottawa, Ontario, P.O. Box 5000,
Ogdensburg, NY 13669-0430
Tel: 1 (613) 688-5335 Fax: 1 (613) 238-5720
E-mail: ottawadea@state.gov

DEA Officer **(Vacant)** .... 1 (613) 688-5335 ext. 5309

Office of the Defense Attaché [Canada]
American Embassy - Ottawa, Ontario, Canada,
490 Sussex Drive, Ottawa, Ontario K1N 1G8, Canada
Mail: American Embassy - Ottawa, Ontario, P.O. Box 5000,
Ogdensburg, NY 13669-0430
Tel: 1 (613) 688-5335

Defense Attaché **Col Thad Hunkins USAF** ... 1 (613) 688-5335 ext. 5401
E-mail: hunkinsta@state.gov

Calgary Consulate General
U.S. Consulate General - Calgary, Alberta, Canada,
615 Macleod Trail, SE, 10th Floor, Calgary, Alberta, Canada T2G 4T8
Mail: U.S. Consulate General - Calgary, State Department,
Washington, DC 20521-5490
Tel: 1 (403) 266-8962 Tel: 1 (403) 444-5203 (Public Affairs)
Fax: 1 (403) 264-6630
Internet: ca.usembassy.gov/embassy-consulates/calgary

Consul General **Lucia C. Piazza** 1 (403) 444-5299
E-mail: piazzalc@state.gov
Education: New Hampshire 2001 BA; National Defense U 2015 MS
Consular Affairs Officer **Matt Whitton** 1 (403) 444-5215
General Services Officer **Jason Azevedo** 1 (403) 444-5219
Management Officer **Jason Azevedo** 1 (403) 444-5227
Political/Economic Officer **Susan Riggs** 1 (403) 266-8962

Commercial Section (Foreign Commercial Service) [Canada]
615 Macleod Trail, SE, Calgary, Alberta, Canada T2G 4T8
E-mail: office.calgary@trade.gov

Principal Commercial Officer **Thomas Hanson** .... (403) 265-2116
E-mail: thomas.hanson@trade.gov
Commercial Specialist **Crystal Roberts** .... (403) 265-2116
E-mail: crystal.roberts@trade.gov
Commercial Specialist **Connie Haider** .... (403) 265-2116
E-mail: connie.haider@trade.gov
Commercial Specialist **(Vacant)** .... (403) 265-2116
Commercial Specialist **(Vacant)** .... (403) 265-2116

Halifax Consulate General
U.S. Consulate General - Halifax, Canada, 1969 Upper Water Street,
Purdy's Wharf Tower II, Suite 904, Halifax, Nova Scotia,
Canada NS B3J 3R7
Mail: P.O. Box 5000, Ogdensburg, NY 13669-0430
Tel: 1 (902) 429-2480 Tel: 1 (902) 429-2485 (Public Affairs)
Fax: 1 (902) 423-6861

Consul General **Kevin D. Skillin** 1 (902) 423-3047
E-mail: skillinkd@state.gov
Education: Pittsburgh; Princeton; Marine War Col 2018 MSS

Halifax Consulate General *(continued)*

Consular Officer **Andrea J. Wiktowy** 1 (902) 423-3047
E-mail: wiktowyaj@state.gov
Education: St Andrews 1999 MA; Catholic U 2003 JD

Commercial Section (Foreign Commercial Service) [Canada]
U.S. Consulate General - Halifax, Canada,
1969 Upper Water Street, Halifax, Nova Scotia, Canada NS B3J 3R7
Mail: P.O. Box 5000, Ogdensburg, NY 13669-0430
Tel: 1 (902) 429-2482 Fax: 1 (902) 429-7690
E-mail: halifax.office.box@trade.gov

Commercial Specialist **(Vacant)** .... 1 (902) 429-2482 ext. 2992

Montreal Consulate General
U.S. Consulate General - Monteal, Quebec, Canada,
1155 Rue St. Alexandre, Montreal, Quebec, Canada H3B 3Z1
Mail: U.S. Consulate General - Montreal, P.O. Box 847,
Champlain, NY 12919-0847
Tel: 1 (514) 398-9695 Fax: 1 (514) 398-0973

Consul General **Robert W. Thomas** 1 (514) 398-9695
E-mail: thomasrw@state.gov Fax: 1 (514) 398-9430
Office Management Specialist to the Consul General **Cynthia L. Kraemer** 1 (514) 398-9695
E-mail: kraemercl@state.gov
Consular Affairs Officer **Cheryl Bodek** 1 (514) 398-9695
E-mail: bodekc@state.gov Fax: 1 (514) 398-9748
Human Resources Officer (Resident in Ottawa) **Jeffrey T. "Jeff" Ogren** .... 1 (613) 688-5335 ext. 5265
Information Program Officer/Information Systems Security Officer **Jonathan M. Keesling** 1 (514) 398-9695
Management Officer **Lenton K. Davies** 1 (514) 398-0973
Political/Economic Officer **Mary Elizabeth Nameth** ... 1 (514) 398-9695
Public Affairs Officer **Katherine A. "Katie" Caro** 1 (514) 398-9695
E-mail: caroka@state.gov
Education: Emory 2003 BA
Regional Security Officer **Kevin M. Perry** 1 (514) 908-3666
E-mail: perrykm@state.gov

Commercial Section (Foreign Commercial Service) [Canada]
U.S. Consulate General - Monteal, Quebec, Canada,
1155 Rue St. Alexandre, Montreal, Quebec, Canada H3B 3Z1
Tel: 1 (514) 398-9695 ext. 2220 Fax: 1 (514) 398-0711
E-mail: office.montreal@trade.gov

Principal Commercial Officer
Catherine Cathy Feig .... 1 (514) 398-9695 ext. 2220
E-mail: Cathy.Feig@trade.gov
Education: Baylor BA; George Washington MA

Quebec Consulate General
U.S. Consulate General - Quebec City, Quebec, Canada,
2 Rue de la Terrasse-Dufferin, C.P. 939, Québec City, Quebec,
Canada G1R 4T9
Mail: U.S. Consulate General - Quebec City, P.O. Box 1547,
Champlain, NY 12919-1547
Tel: 1 (418) 692-2095 Fax: 1 (418) 692-4640

Consul General **Allison Areias-Vogel** 1 (418) 692-4007
E-mail: areiasav@state.gov
Consular Officer **Michael Hackett** 1 (418) 692-2474

Toronto Consulate General
U.S. Consulate General - Toronto, Ontario, Canada,
360 University Avenue, Toronto, Ontario, Canada M5G 1S4
Mail: U.S. Consulate General - Toronto, P.O. Box 135,
Lewiston, NY 14092-0135
Tel: 1 (416) 595-1700 Fax: 1 (416) 595-1090

Consul General
Gregory S. "Greg" Stanford .... 1 (416) 595-1700 ext. 288
E-mail: stanfordgs@state.gov
Office Management Specialist to the Consul General **(Vacant)** .... 1 (416) 595-1700 ext. 288
Consular Affairs Officer **Sonya M. Tsiros** 1 (416) 595-1700
E-mail: tsirossm@state.gov Fax: 1 (416) 595-5466
Community Liaison Officer **Karie L. Skiles** 1 (416) 595-1700

★ Presidential Appointment Requiring Senate Confirmation ☆ Presidential Appointment □ Schedule C Appointment ◇ Career Senior Foreign Service Appointment
● Career Senior Executive Service (SES) Appointment ○ Non-Career Senior Executive Service (SES) Appointment ■ Postal Career Executive Service

Toronto Consulate General *(continued)*

General Services Officer **Jaclyn Luo** 1 (416) 595-1700
Information Programs Officer
J. Douglas "Doug" Farrington 1 (416) 595-1700
E-mail: farringtonjd@state.gov
Legal Attaché **Courtland Rae** 1 (416) 595-1700
Management Officer **Caren A. Brown** 1 (416) 595-1700
E-mail: brownca@state.gov
Political Officer **(Vacant)** 1 (416) 595-1700
Political and Economic Officer **Andrea Gorog** 1 (416) 595-1700
E-mail: goroga@state.gov
Public Affairs Officer **Anne Lee Seshadri** .... 1 (416) 595-1700 ext. 216
E-mail: seshadrial@state.gov
Regional Security Officer **Milan Bankovic** 1 (416) 595-1700
E-mail: bankovicm@state.gov

Commercial Section (Foreign Commercial Service) [Canada]
U.S. Consulate General - Toronto, Ontario, Canada,
480 University Avenue, Suite 602, Toronto, Ontario M5G 1V2, Canada
Mail: U.S. Consulate General - Toronto, P.O. Box 135,
Lewiston, NY 14092-0135
Tel: 1 (416) 595-5412 Fax: 1 (416) 595-5419
E-mail: office.toronto@trade.gov

Principal Commercial Officer **Eric Crowley** ... 1 (416) 595-5412 ext. 221
E-mail: eric.crowley@trade.gov

Department of Homeland Security - U.S. Immigration and Customs Enforcement [Canada]
U.S. Consulate General - Toronto, Ontario, Canada,
360 University Avenue, Toronto, Ontario, Canada M5G 1S4
Mail: U.S. Consulate General - Toronto, P.O. Box 135,
Lewiston, NY 14092-0135
Tel: 1 (416) 595-1700 Fax: 1 (416) 595-0051

Customs Officer **Ronald O. Marcell** 1 (905) 676-2563

Vancouver Consulate General
U.S. Consulate General - Vancouver, British Columbia,
1095 West Pender Street, 19th Floor, Vancouver, British Columbia,
Canada V6E 2M6
Mail: U.S. Consulate General - Vancouver, BC, P.O. Box 5002,
Point Roberts, WA 98281-5002
Tel: 1 (604) 685-4311 Tel: 1 (604) 689-3937 (Public Affairs)
Fax: 1 (604) 685-5285

◇ Consul General
Katherine Simonds "Kathy" Dhanani 1 (604) 685-4311
E-mail: dhananiks@state.gov
Education: Kenyon 1981 BA; MIT 1985 MS
Office Management Specialist to the Consul
General **Carla L. Calhoun** 1 (604) 685-4311
E-mail: calhouncl@state.gov
Consular Officer **Sarah E. Welborne** 1 (604) 685-4311
E-mail: welbornese@state.gov
Information Program Officer **Jeni Rae Watson** 1 (604) 685-4311
Information Systems Security Officer
Jeni Rae Watson 1 (604) 685-4311
Economic Officer **Charles Park** 1 (604) 685-4311
Legal Attaché **Sherri Onks** 1 (604) 685-4311
Management Officer **Annaliese J. Heiligenstein** 1 (604) 685-5285
Political/Economic Officer **Adam J. Hantman** 1 (604) 685-4311
E-mail: hantmanaj@state.gov
Political Officer **(Vacant)** 1 (604) 685-4311
Public Affairs Officer **Kathey-Lee A. Galvin** 1 (604) 685-4311
Regional Security Officer **Casey Cross** 1 (604) 685-4311
E-mail: crossca@state.gov
Education: Texas 2002 BA

Commercial Section (Foreign Commercial Service) [Canada]
U.S. Consulate General - Vancouver, British Columbia,
1095 West Pender Street, Vancouver, British Columbia, Canada V6E 2M6
Mail: U.S. Consulate General - Vancouver, BC, P.O. Box 5002,
Point Roberts, WA 98281-5002
Tel: 1 (604) 685-3382 Fax: 1 (604) 687-6095

Senior Commercial Specialist **(Vacant)** 1 (604) 685-3382

Winnipeg Consulate General
201 Portage Avenue, Suite 860, Winnipeg, Manitoba, Canada R3B 3K6
Mail: American Embassy - Ottawa, Ontario, P.O. Box 5000,
Ogdensburg, NY 13669-0430
Tel: 1 (204) 940-1800 Fax: 1 (204) 940-1809

Consul/Principal Officer **Anthony "Tony" Pagliai** 1 (204) 940-1800

U.S. Embassy in Chile

American Embassy - Santiago, Chile, Avenue Andres Bello 2800,
Las Condes, Santiago, Chile
Tel: 56 (2) 330-3000 Fax: 56 (2) 330-3710 E-mail: infousa@state.gov

Office of the U.S. Ambassador to Chile
American Embassy - Santiago, Chile, Avenue Andres Bello 2800,
Las Condes, Santiago, Chile
Mail: Unit 3460, Box 142, DPO, AA 34033-0142

★ Ambassador **Ambassador Carol Zelis Perez** 56 (2) 330-3000
Note: On August 1, 2018, President Donald J. Trump nominated Carol Perez to be Director General of the Foreign Service. This nomination is currently pending in the Senate.
E-mail: perezcz@state.gov
Education: Hiram 1975 BA; George Washington MA
Office Management Specialist to the Ambassador
(Vacant) 56 (2) 330-3000
◇ Deputy Chief of Mission **J. Baxter Hunt** 56 (2) 330-3000
E-mail: huntjb@state.gov
Office Management Specialist to the Deputy Chief
of Mission **Alina Montano** 56 (2) 330-3000
Education: National U 2013 MA
Community Liaison Officer **(Vacant)** 56 (2) 330-3000
Consul General **(Vacant)** 56 (2) 330-3000
Economic/Political Counselor **Lawrence J. Petroni** 56 (2) 330-3000
E-mail: PetroniLF@state.gov
Financial Management Officer **Robert Watson** 56 (2) 330-3000
General Services Officer **Edward Waters** 56 (2) 330-3000
E-mail: watersel@state.gov
Information Management Officer
Timothy "Tim" Teas 56 (2) 330-3000
E-mail: teast@state.gov
Information Security Officer **(Vacant)** 56 (2) 330-3000
Information Systems Security Officer **(Vacant)** 56 (2) 330-3000
Legal Attaché **Ben Perez-Martinez** 56 (2) 330-3000
Management Officer **Carla J. Fleharty** 56 (2) 330-3000
E-mail: flehartycj@state.gov
Military Group Commander
Col. Rodney Fauth USAF 56 (2) 330-3000
Public Affairs Officer **Eric V. Catalfamo** 56 (2) 330-3000
E-mail: catalfamoev@state.gov Fax: 56 (2) 330-3160
Cultural Affairs Officer **David Fogelson** 56 (2) 330-3000
E-mail: FogelsonD@state.gov
Information Officer **Nicole Gallagher** 56 (2) 330-3000
Regional Security Officer **Michael A. Limpantsis** 56 (2) 330-3000
E-mail: limpantsism@state.gov

Agricultural Section (Foreign Agricultural Service) [Chile]
American Embassy - Santiago, Chile, Avenue Andres Bello 2800,
Las Condes, Santiago, Chile
Mail: American Embassy - Santiago, Chile, APO, AA 34033
Tel: 56 (2) 330-3704 Fax: 56 (2) 330-3203
E-mail: agsantiago@fas.usda.gov

Agricultural Attaché **Marcela Rondón** 56 (2) 330-3704
E-mail: marcela.rondon@fas.usda.gov

Animal and Plant Health Inspection Service [Chile]
American Embassy - Santiago, Chile, Avenue Andres Bello 2800,
Las Condes, Santiago, Chile
Mail: American Embassy - Santiago, Chile, APO, AA 34033
Tel: 56 (2) 330-3480 Fax: 56 (2) 335-6442

APHIS Officer **Robert S. "Sam" Johnson** 56 (2) 330-3427
E-mail: robert.s.johnson@aphis.usda.gov

★ Presidential Appointment Requiring Senate Confirmation ☆ Presidential Appointment ☐ Schedule C Appointment ◇ Career Senior Foreign Service Appointment
● Career Senior Executive Service (SES) Appointment ○ Non-Career Senior Executive Service (SES) Appointment ■ Postal Career Executive Service

Commercial Section (Foreign Commercial Service) [Chile]
American Embassy - Santiago, Chile, Avenue Andres Bello 2800,
Las Condes, Santiago, Chile
Mail: American Embassy - Santiago, Chile, APO, AA 34033
Tel: 56 (2) 330-3316 Fax: 56 (2) 330-3172
E-mail: office.santiago@trade.gov Internet: export.gov/chile

◇ Senior Commercial Counselor **James M. McCarthy** 56 (2) 330-3310
E-mail: james.mccarthy@trade.gov

Federal Aviation Administration (Resident in Brazil) [Chile]
American Embassy - Brasilia, Brazil, Avenida das Nações,
Quadra 801, Lote 3 Brasilia, 70403-900, Brazil
Mail: American Embassy - Brasilia, Brazil, Unit 3500, APO, AA 34030
Fax: 55 (61) 3312-7295

FAA Senior Representative
Paul Leandro Friedman 55 (61) 8116-5291
E-mail: paul.friedman@faa.gov

Internal Revenue Service (Resident in Mexico City) [Chile]
American Embassy - Mexico City, Mexico,
Paseo de la Reforma 305, Mexico City, D.F. 06500, Mexico
Mail: (IRS) U.S. Logistics Center, 225 Vermillion Road,
Brownsville, TX 78520-0900
Tel: 52 (55) 5080-2000 Fax: 52 (55) 5080-2882

IRS Officer **George Peralta** .... 52 (55) 5080-2000 ext. 2901

Office of the Defense Attaché [Chile]
American Embassy - Santiago, Chile, Avenue Andres Bello 2800,
Las Condes, Santiago, Chile
Mail: American Embassy - Santiago, Chile,
American Embassy - Santiago, Unit 3460, APO, AA 34033
Fax: 56 (2) 330-3710 E-mail: dao.stgo@rdc.cl

Defense and Navy Attaché **Capt John Morris USN** 56 (2) 330-3000
Air Force Attaché **Col Jaime Gomez, Jr. USAF** 56 (2) 330-3000
Army Attaché **COL Charles Nolan USA** 56 (2) 330-3000

Office of Naval Research [Chile] (ONR)
American Embassy - Santiago, Chile, Avenue Andres Bello 2800,
Las Condes, Santiago, Chile
Mail: Unit 3460, Box 142, DPO, AA 34033-0142
E-mail: latinamerica@onrifo.navy.mil

Regional Director **(Vacant)** 56 (2) 330-3154

U.S. Embassy in Colombia

American Embassy - Bogota, Colombia,
Carrera 45 No. 24B-27, Bogota, Colombia
Tel: 57 (1) 275-2000 Fax: 57 (1) 275-4600

Office of the U.S. Ambassador to Colombia

American Embassy - Bogota, Colombia,
Carrera 45 No. 24B-27, Bogota, Colombia
Mail: American Embassy - Bogota, Colombia, APO, AA 34038
Tel: 57 (1) 275-2000 Fax: 57 (1) 275-4600 Internet: co.usembassy.gov

★ Ambassador **Ambassador Kevin M. Whitaker** 57 (1) 275-2000
E-mail: whitakerkm@state.gov
Education: Virginia BA

★ Ambassador-Designate
Ambassador Joseph E. Macmanus 57 (1) 275-2000
E-mail: macmanusje@state.gov
Education: Notre Dame 1975 BA; SUNY (Buffalo) MLS
Office Management Specialist to the Ambassador
(Vacant) 57 (1) 275-2000

◇ Deputy Chief of Mission **Philip Laidlaw** 57 (1) 275-2000
E-mail: laidlawpg@state.gov
Education: Wake Forest 1989 BSc; National War Col 2011 MNSSS
Office Management Specialist to the Deputy Chief
of Mission **Paula M. Monaghan** 57 (1) 275-2000
E-mail: monaghanpm@state.gov

Community Liaison Officer **Anne Grabins** 57 (1) 275-2000
E-mail: GrabinsAM@state.gov

◇ Consul General **J. Richard Walsh** 57 (1) 275-2000
E-mail: walshrj@state.gov

Office of the U.S. Ambassador to Colombia *(continued)*

Consular Affairs Officer **Jeffrey Miles** 57 (1) 275-2000
Economic Officer **Jacqueline Ward** 57 (1) 275-2000
Facilities Management Officer **(Vacant)** 57 (1) 275-2000
Financial Management Officer **Kevin Bohne** 57 (1) 275-2000
E-mail: bohnekx@state.gov
General Services Officer **Eric Kramp** 57 (1) 275-2000
E-mail: krampej@state.gov
Human Resources Officer **Dolores Jacobson** 57 (1) 275-2000
Information Management Officer **Perry Romeo** 57 (1) 275-2000
E-mail: romeopm@state.gov
Information Program Officer **Rick Schmude** 57 (1) 275-2000
Information Security Officer **Alex Peterson** 57 (1) 275-2000
Information Systems Security Officer **Alex Dennis** 57 (1) 275-2000
Labor Officer **Randall Hicks** 57 (1) 275-2000
Legal Attaché **Andres Quintero** 57 (1) 275-2000
Management Officer **Calvin Watlington** 57 (1) 275-2000
Education: Baruch Col 1980 BBA; George Mason 1994 JD
Military Liaison Officer
CAPT Jason D. Weddle USN 57 (1) 275-2000

◇ Narcotics Affairs Officer
Christopher A. "Chris" Landberg 57 (1) 275-2000
E-mail: landbergca@state.gov
Education: Wisconsin; Harvard

Political Officer **Jennifer "Jen" Davis-Paguada** 57 (1) 275-2000

◇ Public Affairs Officer **Abigail L. Dressel** 57 (1) 275-2000
E-mail: dresselal@state.gov Fax: 57 (1) 315-2208
Education: George Washington 2001 BA

Regional Security Officer **(Vacant)** 57 (1) 275-2000

Agency for International Development [Colombia]
American Embassy - Bogota, Colombia,
Diagonal 22D Bis No. 47-51, Bogota, Colombia
Mail: American Embassy - Bogota, Colombia, APO, AA 34038
Fax: 57 (1) 315-3528 E-mail: colombiausaidwebinfo@usaid.gov
Internet: www.usaid.gov/colombia

◇ Director **Lawrence J. "Larry" Sacks** 57 (1) 275-2000
E-mail: lsacks@usaid.gov

Deputy Director **Aman S. Djahanbani** 57 (1) 275-2000
E-mail: adjahanbani@usaid.gov

Agricultural Section (Foreign Agricultural Service) [Colombia]
American Embassy - Bogota, Colombia,
Carrera 45 No. 24B-27, Bogota, Colombia
Mail: American Embassy - Bogota, Colombia, APO, AA 34038
Tel: 57 (1) 275-4623 E-mail: agbogota@fas.usda.gov

◇ Agricultural Counselor **Michael Conlon** 57 (1) 275-2033
E-mail: michael.conlon@fas.usda.gov

Animal and Plant Health Inspection Service [Colombia]
American Embassy - Bogota, Colombia,
Carrera 45 No. 24B-27, Bogota, Colombia
Mail: American Embassy - Bogota, APO, AA 34038
Tel: 57 (1) 315-2192 Fax: 57 (1) 315-2191

◇ APHIS Attaché **Marc Clayton Gilkey** 57 (1) 315-2192
E-mail: marc.c.gilkey@aphis.usda.gov

Commercial Section (Foreign Commercial Service) [Colombia]
American Embassy - Bogota, Colombia,
Carrera 45 No. 24B-27, Bogota, Colombia
Mail: American Embassy - Bogota, Colombia,
U.S. Commercial Service, Unit 5120, APO, AA 34038
Tel: 57 (1) 383-2519 Fax: 57 (1) 315-2171
E-mail: office.bogota@trade.gov Internet: http://export.gov/colombia/

Senior Commercial Officer **(Vacant)** 57 (1) 275-2519

Department of Homeland Security - U.S. Immigrations and Customs Enforcement [Colombia]
American Embassy - Bogota, Colombia,
Carrera 45 No. 24B-27, Bogota, Colombia
Mail: American Embassy - Bogota, APO, AA 34038

Customs Officer **Luis Sierra** 57 (1) 275-2000

Department of Justice - Drug Enforcement Administration [Colombia]
American Embassy - Bogota, Colombia,
Carrera 45 No. 24B-27, Bogota, Colombia
Mail: American Embassy - Bogota, Colombia, APO, AA 34038
Fax: 57 (1) 315-2197
Country Attaché **Richard M. Dobrich** 57 (1) 275-2000

Federal Aviation Administration (Resident in Panama) [Colombia]
FAA Senior Representative **Carl N. Johnson** 507 317-5046

Internal Revenue Service [Colombia]
American Embassy - Bogota, Colombia,
Carrera 45 No. 24B-27, Bogota, Colombia
Mail: American Embassy - Bogota, APO, AA 34038
Attaché **Emmanuel Gomez** 57 (1) 275-2000

International Criminal Investigative Training Assistance Program (ICITAP)
American Embassy - Bogota, Colombia,
Carrera 45 No. 24B-27, Bogota, Colombia
Mail: American Embassy - Bogota, APO, AA 34038
Fax: 57 (1) 315-2197
Project Manager **Carl Risheim** 57 (1) 275-2000

Office of the Defense Attaché [Colombia]
American Embassy - Bogota, Colombia,
Carrera 45 No. 24B-27, Bogota, Colombia
Mail: American Embassy - Bogota, Colombia, APO, AA 34038
Fax: 57 (1) 315-2197
Defense Attaché **LTC Robert Wagner USA** 57 (1) 275-2000

Cartagena Branch Office
#26-78 Piso 5, Cra 13B, Cartagena, Colombia
Tel: 57 (5) 664-9369
Regional Security Officer **Julia E. Hawley** 57 (5) 664-9369
E-mail: HawleyJE@state.gov

U.S. Embassy in Costa Rica

American Embassy - San Jose, Costa Rica,
Calle 120 Avenida O, Apartado 920-1200, Pavas, San Jose, Costa Rica
Tel: 506 2519-2000 Fax: 506 2519-2305

Office of the U.S. Ambassador to Costa Rica

American Embassy - San Jose, Costa Rica,
Calle 120 Avenida O, Apartado 920-1200, Pavas, San Jose, Costa Rica
Mail: American Embassy - San Jose, Costa Rica, Unit 2501,
APO, AA 34020

★ Ambassador **Ambassador Sharon Day** 506 2519-2000
Office Management Specialist to the Ambassador
Silvia Hanigan 506 2519-2000
◇ Deputy Chief of Mission **Gloria F. Berbena** 506 220-2304
E-mail: berbenagf@state.gov Fax: 506 220-2305
Education: UC Davis BA
Office Management Specialist to the Deputy Chief of Mission **Sherrill Fortinberry** 506 2519-2000
Community Liaison Officer **Paola Gaviria** 506 2519-2000
Consul General **Mary Francis Fisk-Telchi** 506 2519-2000
E-mail: fisktelchimf@state.gov
Regional Environmental Officer
Heidi Hakone Jovanovic 506 2519-2000
E-mail: JovanovicHH@state.gov
Financial Management Officer **Melissa Huth** 506 2519-2000
E-mail: huthm@state.gov
General Services Officer **Mark Whitehead** 506 2519-2000
Information Management Officer **Jerry Davis** 506 2519-2000
Information Systems Officer **Gerald O'Neil** 506 2519-2000
Information Systems Security Officer **Mark Reed** 506 2519-2000
Management Officer **Anne Marie Moore** 506 2519-2000
E-mail: mooream@state.gov
Narcotics Affairs Officer **Christopher Harris** 506 2519-2305

Office of the U.S. Ambassador to Costa Rica *(continued)*
Chief, Office of Defense Representative
CDR Brent R. Bergan USCG 506 2519-2000
Political/Economic Section Chief
Anthony A. Pahigian 506 2519-2000
E-mail: PahigianAA@state.gov
Education: Wesleyan U 1982 BA; Maryland 1987 MA
Public Affairs Officer **Addie Schroeder** 506 2519-2000
Fax: 506 232-7944
Regional Security Officer **Joseph J. "Jeff" Howard** 506 2519-2000
E-mail: howardjj@state.gov
Education: Kentucky 1994 BA; US Army Command 2011

Agricultural Section (Foreign Agricultural Service) [Costa Rica]
American Embassy - San Jose, Costa Rica, Unit 2507,
APO, AA 34020-9507
American Embassy - San Jose, Costa Rica,
Calle 120 Avenida O, Apartado 920-1200, Pavas, San Jose, Costa Rica
Tel: 506 2519-2333 Fax: 506 2519-2475 E-mail: agsanjose@fas.usda.gov
Agricultural Counselor **Anita Katial** 506 2519-2333
E-mail: anita.katial@fas.usda.gov

Animal and Plant Health Inspection Service [Costa Rica]
De la Casa de Oscar Arias Rohrm,
100 metros norte, 75 metros este (casa a mano derecha),
Rohrmoser, San Jose, Costa Rica
Mail: American Embassy - San Jose, Costa Rica, Unit 2522,
APO, AA 34020-9522
Tel: 506 290-42-97 Fax: 506 296-35-56
Area Director **Jeffery "Jeff" Austin** 506 2519-2237
E-mail: jeffery.austin@aphis.usda.gov

Commercial Section (Foreign Commercial Service) (Resident in San Salvador) [Costa Rica]
American Embassy - San Salvador, El Salvador,
Boulevard Santa Elena, Antiguo Cuscatlan, San Salvador, El Salvador
Mail: Unit 3116, APO, AA 34023
Tel: 503 2501-2999 Fax: 503 2501-3067 Internet: export.gov/costarica
Regional Senior Commercial Officer **Eric B. Wolff** 506 2519-2293
E-mail: eric.wolff@trade.gov

Drug Enforcement Administration [Costa Rica]
American Embassy - San Jose, Costa Rica, Calle 120 Avenida O, Pavas,
Apartado 920-1200, San Jose, Costa Rica
Mail: American Embassy - San Jose, Costa Rica, Unit 2501,
APO, AA 34020
Tel: 506 2519-2000
Country Attaché **Alan S. Burkhead** 506 2519-2000
E-mail: burkheadas@state.gov

Federal Aviation Administration (Resident in Panama) [Costa Rica]
American Embassy - Panama City, Panama,
Building 783, Demetrio Basilio Lakas Avenue,
Clayton, Panama City, 5, Panama
Mail: American Embassy - Panama City, Panama, Unit 0945,
APO, AA 34002
FAA Representative **Carl N. Johnson** 507 317-5046

Internal Revenue Service (Resident in Mexico City) [Costa Rica]
American Embassy - Mexico City, Mexico,
Paseo de la Reforma 305, Mexico City, D.F. 06500, Mexico
Mail: (IRS) U.S. Logistics Center, 225 Vermillion Road,
Brownsville, TX 78520-0900
Tel: 52 (55) 5080-2000 Fax: 52 (55) 5080-2882
IRS Officer **George Peralta** .... 52 (55) 5080-2000 ext. 2901

Peace Corps [Costa Rica]
American Embassy - San Jose, Costa Rica, Calle 120 Avenida O, Pavas,
Apartado 920-1200, San Jose, Costa Rica
Mail: American Embassy - San Jose, Costa Rica, Unit 2501,
APO, AA 34020
Tel: 506 2231-4122 Internet: www.peacecorps.gov/costa-rica
Country Director **Anne Braghetta** 506 2231-4122

★ Presidential Appointment Requiring Senate Confirmation ☆ Presidential Appointment ☐ Schedule C Appointment ◇ Career Senior Foreign Service Appointment
● Career Senior Executive Service (SES) Appointment ○ Non-Career Senior Executive Service (SES) Appointment ■ Postal Career Executive Service

U.S. Embassy in Cuba

American Embassy - Havana, Cuba, Calzada between L and M Streets, Vedado, Havana, Cuba
Tel: 53 (7) 839-4100 Fax: 53 (7) 839-4141

Office of the U.S. Ambassador to Cuba

American Embassy - Havana, Cuba, Calzada between L and M Streets, Vedado, Havana, Cuba
Mail: Department of State, 3200 Havana Place, Washington, DC 20521-3200

★ Ambassador **(Vacant)** 53 (7) 839-4100
◇ Chargé d'Affaires **Mara Tekach** 53 (7) 839-4100
E-mail: tekachm@state.gov
Education: Wharton 1982 BS; Columbia 1987 MA, EdD
Office Management Specialist to the Chargé d'Affaires **(Vacant)** 53 (7) 839-4100
Deputy Chief of Mission **Mara Tekach** 53 (7) 839-4140
E-mail: tekachm@state.gov
Education: Wharton 1982 BS; Columbia 1987 MA, EdD
Office Management Specialist to the Deputy Chief of Mission **(Vacant)** 53 (7) 839-4100
Consul General **Steven S. Giegerich** 53 (7) 839-4100
E-mail: giegerichss@state.gov
Community Liaison Officer **(Vacant)** 53 (7) 839-4100
Facilities Management Officer **Brian Pendergast** 53 (7) 839-4100
Financial Management Officer **Crystal Trainor** 53 (7) 839-4100
Education: Virginia Tech 2001 BS; Maryland 2007 MBA, 2007 MS
General Services Officer **Paul Nichols** 53 (7) 839-4100
E-mail: nicholspm@state.gov
Human Resources Officer **Crystal Trainor** 53 (7) 839-4100
Education: Virginia Tech 2001 BS; Maryland 2007 MBA, 2007 MS
Information Management Officer **(Vacant)** 53 (7) 839-4100
Information Program Officer **(Vacant)** 53 (7) 839-4100
Information Systems Officer **Kasey D. Snyder** 53 (7) 839-4100
E-mail: snyderkd@state.gov
Information Systems Security Officer **(Vacant)** 53 (7) 839-4100
Management Officer **Crystal Trainor** 53 (7) 839-4100
Education: Virginia Tech 2001 BS; Maryland 2007 MBA, 2007 MS
Political/Economic Officer **(Vacant)** 53 (7) 839-4100
Public Affairs Officer **(Vacant)** 53 (7) 839-4100
Regional Security Officer **Marco Ayub** 53 (7) 839-4100
Political Affairs Officer **Todd D. Anderson** 53 (7) 839-4100
E-mail: andersontd@state.gov

Federal Aviation Administration (Resident in Florida) [Cuba]

2895 SW 145 Avenue, Miramar, FL 33027
FAA Representative **Alex D. Rodriguez** .... (202) 267-0426

Department of Homeland Security - U.S. Citizenship and Immigration Services [Cuba]

American Embassy - Havana, Cuba, Calzada between L and M Streets, Vedado, Havana, Cuba
Mail: Immigration Service, Havana, 3200 Havana Place, Washington, DC 20521-3200
E-mail: havanauscis@uscis.dhs.gov
Officer-in-Charge **Marilyn Rebatta** 53 (7) 839-4107

U.S. Consulate General in Curaçao

U.S. Consulate General - Curacao, Netherlands Antilles, J. B. Gorsiraweg #1, P.O. Box 158, Willemstad, Curaçao
Mail: U.S. Consulate General - Curacao, N.A., Department of State, 3160 Curacao Place, Washington, DC 20521-3160
Tel: 599 (9) 461-3066 Fax: 599 (9) 461-6489
E-mail: infocuracao@state.gov Internet: cw.usconsulate.gov

◇ Consul General **Margaret D. "Nini" Hawthorne** 599 (9) 461-3066
E-mail: HawthorneMD@state.gov
Consular Section Chief **Derek R. Kolb** 599 (9) 4611060
E-mail: kolbdr@state.gov
Education: Oklahoma 2005 BA; UC San Diego 2009 MPIA
Political/Economic Officer **Christian R. Olsen** 599 (9) 4611060
E-mail: olsencr@state.gov
Education: William & Mary 2003 BA; Maryland Law 2012 JD

U.S. Consulate General in Curaçao *(continued)*

Information Management Officer **Matthew T. Mullins** 599 (9) 461-3066
E-mail: mullinsmt@state.gov
Education: Miami U (OH) 2002 BS; Baltimore 2009 BA; Maryland 2012 MPP
Financial Management Officer **Anthony "Tony" Zaccagnino** 599 (9) 461-3066
Legal Attaché **Khaimraj "Yudi" Bhagwandin** 599 (9) 461-3066
Management Officer **Jeffrey Hanley** 599 (9) 461-3066
Public Affairs Officer **Christian R. Olsen** 599 (9) 461-3066
E-mail: olsencr@state.gov
Education: William & Mary 2003 BA; Maryland Law 2012 JD
Regional Security Officer (Resident in Cartagena, Colombia) **Julia E. Hawley** 57 (5) 664-9369

Agricultural Trade Office - Caribbean Basin

USDA Agricultural Trade Office, 909 SE First Avenue, Suite 720, Miami, FL 33131
Tel: (305) 536-5300 Fax: (305) 536-7577
E-mail: atocaribbeanbasin@fas.usda.gov
Director **Richard J. Battaglia** .... (305) 536-5300
E-mail: richard.battaglia@fas.usda.gov

Drug Enforcement Administration [Curaçao]

U.S. Consulate General - Curacao, Netherlands Antilles, J. B. Gorsiaweg #1, Willemstad, Curaçao
Mail: U.S. Consulate General - Curacao, N.A., Department of State, Washington, DC 20521-3160
Tel: 599 (9) 4616985 Fax: 599 (9) 4613192
DEA Officer **J. Gregory Garza** 599 (9) 4616985

Federal Aviation Administration (Resident in Florida) [Curaçao]

2895 SW 145 Avenue, Suite 221, Miramar, FL 33027
Tel: (954) 641-6700
FAA Representative **Alex D. Rodriguez** .... (202) 267-0426

U.S. Embassy in the Dominican Republic

American Embassy - Santo Domingo, Dominican Republic, Avenida República de Colombia #57, Santo Domingo, Dominican Republic
Tel: 1 (809) 567-7775 Fax: 1 (809) 686-7437

Office of the U.S. Ambassador to the Dominican Republic

American Embassy - Santo Domingo, Dominican Republic, Avenida República de Colombia #57, Santo Domingo, Dominican Republic
Mail: American Embassy - Santo Domingo, Unit 5500, APO, AA 54041
Tel: 1 (809) 567-7775 Fax: 1 (809) 686-7437 Internet: do.usembassy.gov

★ Ambassador **Ambassador Robin S. Bernstein** 1 (809) 567-7775
Education: American U BA; George Washington MBA
Office Management Specialist to the Ambassador **George Baciu** 1 (809) 567-7775
E-mail: baciug@state.gov
Education: American Military U 2013 BA
◇ Deputy Chief of Mission **Robert E. Copley** 1 (809) 567-7775
E-mail: copleyre@state.gov
Office Management Specialist to the Deputy Chief of Mission **Janie M. Carpenter** 1 (809) 567-7775
Community Liaison Officer **Laura Jett** 1 (809) 567-7775
Consul General **Shane I. Myers** 1 (809) 567-7775
E-mail: myerssi@state.gov
Education: Rutgers 1995 BA; Norwich 2007 MA
Cultural Attaché **(Vacant)** 1 (809) 567-7775
Financial Management Officer **Margarita Halle** 1 (809) 567-7775
General Services Officer **Phillip Anthony "Phil" de Souza** 1 (809) 567-7775
Human Resources Officer **Jared P. Webber** 1 (809) 567-7775
Information Management Officer **Carrie Fox-Myers** 1 (809) 567-7775
Information Program Officer **Francisco Cordero** 1 (809) 567-7775
Information Systems Officer **Steve Vasiladiotis** 1 (809) 567-7775

★ Presidential Appointment Requiring Senate Confirmation ☆ Presidential Appointment ☐ Schedule C Appointment ◇ Career Senior Foreign Service Appointment
● Career Senior Executive Service (SES) Appointment ○ Non-Career Senior Executive Service (SES) Appointment ■ Postal Career Executive Service

Office of the U.S. Ambassador to the Dominican Republic *(continued)*

Legal Attaché **Nelson Delgado** 1 (809) 567-7775
Fax: 1 (809) 686-4913

Management Officer **James Arlen "Arlen" Holt** 1 (809) 567-7775
Fax: 1 (809) 731-4280

Narcotics Affairs Officer **Timothy Peltier** 1 (809) 567-7775

Political/Economic Officer **Katharine Beamer** 1 (809) 567-7775
E-mail: beamerk@state.gov

Public Affairs Officer **Chase Beamer** 1 (809) 567-7775
Fax: 1 (809) 381-0066

Regional Security Officer **Dominic Gagliardi** 1 (809) 567-7775

Agency for International Development [Dominican Republic]
American Embassy - Santo Domingo, Dominican Republic,
Avenida República de Colombia #57, Santo Domingo,
Dominican Republic
Mail: American Embassy - Santo Domingo, Unit 5500, APO, AA 54041
Tel: 1 (809) 567-7775 Fax: 1 (809) 221-0444 E-mail: drinfo@usaid.gov
Internet: www.usaid.gov/dominican-republic

◇ Mission Director **Arthur W. "Art" Brown** 1 (809) 567-7775
E-mail: artbrown@usaid.gov
Education: Virginia BA; Johns Hopkins MBA

Agricultural Section (Animal and Plant Health Inspection Service) [Dominican Republic]
Avenue Pedro Henriquez Urena 133,
Edificio Empressarial Reyna 1, La Esperilla,
4th Floor, Santo Domingo, Dominican Republic
Mail: American Embassy - Santo Domingo, Unit 5500, APO, AA 54041
Tel: 1 (809) 368-7775

APHIS Area Director **David Midgarden** 1 (809) 368-7017
E-mail: david.g.midgarden@aphis.usda.gov

Agricultural Section (Foreign Agricultural Service) [Dominican Republic]
Avenue Pedro Henriquez Urena 133,
Edificio Empressarial Reyna 1, La Esperilla,
4th Floor, Santo Domingo, Dominican Republic
Mail: American Embassy - Santo Domingo, Unit 5500, APO, AA 54041
Tel: 1 (809) 567-7775 E-mail: agsantodomingo@fas.usda.gov

Senior Agricultural Attaché **Elizabeth Autry** 1 (809) 567-7775

Agricultural Attaché **Lisa Ahramjian** 1 (809) 567-7775

Centers for Disease Control and Prevention [Dominican Republic]

Public Health Attaché **Nelson Arboleda** .... (202) 647-4000

Commercial Section (Foreign Commercial Service) [Dominican Republic]
Avenue Pedro Henriquez Urena 133,
Edificio Empressarial Reyna 1, La Esperilla,
5th Floor, Santo Domingo, Dominican Republic
Mail: American Embassy - Santo Domingo, Unit 5500, APO, AA 54041
Tel: 1 (809) 567-7775 ext. 7249 Fax: 1 (809) 540-1267
E-mail: office.santodomingo@trade.gov

Senior Commercial Officer **Bryan Larson** .... 1 (809) 567-7775 ext. 7249
E-mail: bryan.larson@trade.gov
Education: Colorado 1991 BA; American U 1995 MA

Department of Homeland Security [Dominican Republic]
American Embassy - Santo Domingo, Dominican Republic,
Avenida República de Colombia #57, Santo Domingo,
Dominican Republic
Mail: American Embassy - Santo Domingo, Unit 5500, APO, AA 54041
Tel: 1 (809) 731-4390 Fax: 1 (809) 731-4350
E-mail: usins.adm@codetel.net.do

U.S. Citizenship and Immigration Service (USCIS) - Officer in Charge **(Vacant)** ...... 1 (809) 221-2171 ext. 4470

U.S. Immigration and Customs Enforcement (ICE) - Attaché **Cesar Cabrera** .... 1 (809) 731-4390 ext. 4470

Drug Enforcement Administration [Dominican Republic]
American Embassy - Santo Domingo, Dominican Republic,
Avenida República de Colombia #57, Santo Domingo,
Dominican Republic
Mail: American Embassy - Santo Domingo, Unit 5500, APO, AA 54041
Tel: 1 (809) 221-2171 ext. 4381

DEA Country Attaché **John F. Kanig** .... 1 (809) 221-2171 ext. 4460

Federal Aviation Administration (Resident in Panama) [Dominican Republic]

FAA Representative **Carl N. Johnson** 507 317-5046

Internal Revenue Service (Resident in Mexico City) [Dominican Republic]
American Embassy - Mexico City, Mexico,
Paseo de la Reforma 305, Mexico City, D.F. 06500, Mexico
Mail: (IRS) U.S. Logistics Center, 225 Vermillion Road,
Brownsville, TX 78520-0900
Tel: 52 (55) 5080-2000 Fax: 52 (55) 5080-2882

IRS Officer **George Peralta** .... 52 (55) 5080-2000 ext. 2901

Office of the Defense Attaché [Dominican Republic]
American Embassy - Santo Domingo, Dominican Republic,
Avenida República de Colombia #57, Santo Domingo,
Dominican Republic
Mail: American Embassy - Santo Domingo, Unit 5500, APO, AA 54041
Tel: 1 (809) 221-2171 ext. 4220 Fax: 1 (809) 687-5222

Defense Attaché **LtCol Jeffrey M. Opsitos USMC** .... 1 (809) 731-2171 ext. 4215

Peace Corps [Dominican Republic]
Avenida Bolivar #451, Gazcue, Santo Domingo, Dominican Republic
Mail: Unit 5500, APO, AA 54041
Tel: 1 (809) 685-4102 Fax: 1 (809) 686-3241
E-mail: info@do.peacecorps.gov
Internet: www.peacecorps.gov/dominican-republic

Country Director **Kristin Kaper** 1 (809) 685-4102

Puerto Plata Consular Agency
Abraxa Bookstore Bldg., Villanueva Street at the Corner of Juan Bosch,
2nd Floor, Puerto Plata, Dominican Republic
Mail: U.S. Consular Agency - Puerto Plata, Unit 5500, APO, AA 54041
Tel: 1 (809) 586-4204 Fax: 1 (809) 586-8015
E-mail: puertoplataconsularagency@state.gov

Consular Agent **(Vacant)** 1 (809) 586-4204

U.S. Embassy in Ecuador
American Embassy - Quito, Ecuador, Avigiras E12-170 y Eloy Alfaro,
Quito, Ecuador
Tel: 593 2-398-5000 Fax: 593 2-398-1000

Office of the U.S. Ambassador to Ecuador
American Embassy - Quito, Ecuador, Avigiras E12-170 y Eloy Alfaro,
Quito, Ecuador
Mail: American Embassy - Quito, Ecuador, DPO, AA 34039

★ Ambassador **Ambassador Todd Crawford Chapman** ... 593 2-398-5000
E-mail: chapmantc@state.gov
Education: Duke 1983 BA; Military Intelligence Col

★ Ambassador-Designate **Michael J. "Mike" Fitzpatrick** ... 593 2-398-5000
E-mail: fitzpatrickmj@state.gov
Education: Georgetown 1981 BA; Columbia 1985 MIA

Office Management Specialist to the Ambassador **(Vacant)** 593 2-398-5000

◇ Deputy Chief of Mission **Robin D. Meyer** 593 2-398-5000
E-mail: meyerrd@state.gov

Office Management Specialist to the Deputy Chief of Mission **Evelyn King** 593 2-398-5000

Consul General **(Vacant)** 593 2-398-5000

Consular Officer **Alexander "Alex" Delorey** 593 2-398-5000

Community Liaison Officer **Christopher Welch** 593 2-398-5000

Economic Section Chief **Michael Taylor** 593 2-398-5000

Equal Employment Opportunity Officer **(Vacant)** 593 2-398-5000

(continued on next page)

★ Presidential Appointment Requiring Senate Confirmation ☆ Presidential Appointment ☐ Schedule C Appointment ◇ Career Senior Foreign Service Appointment
● Career Senior Executive Service (SES) Appointment ○ Non-Career Senior Executive Service (SES) Appointment ■ Postal Career Executive Service

DEPARTMENTS

Office of the U.S. Ambassador to Ecuador *(continued)*

Financial Management Officer **Edward P. Luchessi** 593 2-398-5000
E-mail: luchessiep@state.gov
General Services Officer **James Kuebler** 593 2-398-5000
Information Management Officer
Daniel L. "Dan" Sweet 593 2-398-5000
E-mail: sweetdl@state.gov
Information Program Officer **Jeffrey Smith** 593 2-398-5000
Information Systems Security Officer
James "Jim" Fieser 593 2-398-5000
Legal Attache **(Vacant)** 593 2-398-5000
Management Officer **Scott D. McDonald** 593 2-398-5000
E-mail: mcdonaldsd@state.gov
Political Section Chief **Kristen L. Pisani** 593 2-398-5000
E-mail: pisanikl@state.gov
Public Affairs Officer **Susan E. Bridenstine** 593 2-398-5256
E-mail: bridenstinese@state.gov
Regional Security Officer **Roger Skavdahl** 593 2-398-5000

Agricultural Section (Foreign Agricultural Service) [Ecuador]
American Embassy - Quito, Ecuador, Avigiras E12-170 y Eloy Alfaro, Quito, Ecuador
Tel: 593 2-398-5323 Fax: 593 (22) 985-031
E-mail: agquito@fas.usda.gov
Agricultural Counselor (Resident in Lima)
(Vacant) .... 51 (1) 434-3000 ext. 2613

Commercial Section (Foreign Commercial Service) [Ecuador]
Servicio U.S. AID, Avenida Colombia 1573 y Queseras del Medio, Quito, Ecuador
Mail: American Embassy - Quito, Ecuador, APO, AA 34039
Tel: 593 2-398-5000 E-mail: ecuadorcommercial@state.gov
Internet: export.gov/ecuador
Commercial Assistant **Sofia Zarate** 593 2-398-5000
E-mail: ZarateSC@state.gov

Department of Homeland Security - U.S. Immigration and Customs Enforcement [Ecuador]
American Embassy - Quito, Ecuador, Avigiras E12-170 y Eloy Alfaro, Quito, Ecuador
Mail: American Embassy - Quito, Ecuador, DPO, AA 34039
Tel: 593 2-398-5000
DHS Officer **Yvette Searight** 593 2-398-5000

Department of Justice - Drug Enforcement Administration [Ecuador]
American Embassy - Quito, Ecuador, Avigiras E12-170 y Eloy Alfaro, Quito, Ecuador
Mail: American Embassy - Quito, Ecuador, DPO, AA 34039
Tel: 593 2-398-5000
DEA Officer **Gene Hawk** 593 2-398-5000

Federal Aviation Administration (Resident in Brazil) [Ecuador]
American Embassy - Brasilia, Brazil, Avenida das Nações,
Quadra 801, Lote 3 Brasilia, 70403-900, Brazil
Mail: American Embassy - Brasilia, Brazil, Unit 3500, APO, AA 34030
Fax: 55 (61) 3312-7295
FAA Senior Representative
Paul Leandro Friedman 55 (61) 3312-7293
E-mail: paul.friedman@faa.gov

Internal Revenue Service (Resident in Mexico City) [Ecuador]
American Embassy - Mexico City, Mexico,
Paseo de la Reforma 305, Mexico City, D.F. 06500, Mexico
Mail: (IRS) U.S. Logistics Center, 225 Vermillion Road, Brownsville, TX 78520-0900
Tel: 52 (55) 5080-2000 Fax: 52 (55) 5080-2882
IRS Officer **George Peralta** .... 52 (55) 5080-2000 ext. 2901

Office of the Defense Attaché [Ecuador]
American Embassy - Quito, Ecuador, Avigiras E12-170 y Eloy Alfaro, Quito, Ecuador
Mail: American Embassy - Quito, Ecuador, APO, AA 34039
Tel: 593 2-398-5000
Defense Attaché **Col Christopher T. Anthony USAF** 593 2-398-5000
E-mail: christopher.t.anthony.mil@mail.mil

Peace Corps [Ecuador]
American Embassy - Quito, Ecuador, Avigiras E12-170 y Eloy Alfaro, Quito, Ecuador
Mail: American Embassy - Quito, Ecuador, APO, AA 34039
Tel: 593 2-398-5000 E-mail: solicitud@ec.peacecorps.gov
Internet: www.peacecorps.gov/ecuador
Country Director **Michael Donald** 593 2-227-6300
Education: UC Davis BS

Guayaquil Consulate General
U.S. Consulate General - Guayaquil, Ecuador,
Calle Santa Ana y Av. José Rodriguez,
Bonin, Guayaquil, Ecuador
Mail: U.S. Consulate General - Guayaquil,
Unit 5350, DPO, AA 34039
Tel: 593 4-371-7000 Fax: 593 4-371-7045
Consul General **Andrew Kenneth Sherr** 593 4-371-7000
E-mail: SherrAK@state.gov
Consular Officer **Gabriel Kaypaghian** 593 4-371-7000
Community Liaison Officer **Sara Ripley** 593 4-371-7000
E-mail: ripleysa@state.gov
General Services Officer **Jane Denham** 593 4-371-7000
E-mail: denhamjl@state.gov
Information Program Officer **David Jefferson** 593 4-371-7000
E-mail: jeffersond@state.gov
Information Systems Security Officer **Rene Lainez** 593 4-371-7000
Management Officer **Peter Covington** 593 4-371-7000
Political/Economic Officer **Emily E. Hennell** 593 4-371-7000
E-mail: hennellee@state.gov
Public Affairs Officer **Erin N. Markley** 593 4-371-7000
E-mail: pas_guayaquil@state.gov
Regional Security Officer **Karin Terry** 593 4-371-7000

Department of Justice - Drug Enforcement Administration [Ecuador]
Calle Santa Ana y Av. José Rodriguez,
Bonin, Guayaquil, Ecuador
Mail: Unit 5350, DPO, AA 34039
Tel: 593 (44) 232-3570
DEA Officer **David Zahn** 593 (44) 232-3570

U.S. Embassy in El Salvador

American Embassy - San Salvador, El Salvador,
Boulevard Santa Elena, Antiguo Cuscatlan, San Salvador, El Salvador
Tel: 503 2501-2999 Fax: 503 2501-2150

Office of the U.S. Ambassador to El Salvador

American Embassy - San Salvador, El Salvador,
Boulevard Santa Elena, Antiguo Cuscatlan, San Salvador, El Salvador
Mail: American Embassy - San Salvador, Unit 3116, APO, AA 34023
★ Ambassador **Ambassador Jean Elizabeth Manes** 503 2501-2999
E-mail: manesje@state.gov
Education: Liberty 1992 BS; American U 1996 MIA
★ Ambassador-Designate **Ronald D. Johnson** 503 2501-2999
Education: National Intelligence U MS
Office Management Specialist to the Ambassador
Kathryn Coster 503 2501-2003
Fax: 503 2501-2001
Deputy Chief of Mission **Mark C. Johnson** 503 2501-2004
Fax: 503 2278-3345
Office Management Specialist to the Deputy Chief of Mission **Jean Smith** 503 2501-2004
Consul General **Brendan J. O'Brien** 503 2501-2999
Community Liaison Officer **Kimberly Mike** 503 2501-2099
Cultural Affairs Officer **Brent Israelsen** 503 2501-2999

★ Presidential Appointment Requiring Senate Confirmation ☆ Presidential Appointment □ Schedule C Appointment ◇ Career Senior Foreign Service Appointment
● Career Senior Executive Service (SES) Appointment ○ Non-Career Senior Executive Service (SES) Appointment ■ Postal Career Executive Service

Office of the U.S. Ambassador to El Salvador *(continued)*

Economic Officer **Mary Brett Rogers-Springs** 503 2501-2050
Fax: 503 2298-2336
Financial Management Officer **Bradley H. Doebel** 503 2501-2200
General Services Officer **Debra L. Shea** 503 2501-2801
Fax: 503 2501-2158
Information Management Officer **Armando Asencio** 503 2501-2362
Fax: 503 2501-2153
Information Program Officer **Matthew Jurach** 503 2501-2363
Information Systems Officer **(Vacant)** 503 2501-2364
Information Systems Security Officer
Armando Asencio 503 2501-2999
Labor Officer **John Szypula** 503 2501-2030
Fax: 503 2228-1857
Legal Attaché **Tyler McCurdy** 503 2501-2999
Management Officer **M. Holly Peirce** 503 2501-2291
Fax: 503 2289-4591
Narcotics Affairs Officer **Gregory Campbell** 503 2501-2999
Political Officer **Amy E. Archibald** 503 2501-2025
E-mail: archibaldae@state.gov Fax: 503 2228-1857
Public Affairs Officer **Tobias A. Bradford** 503 2501-2483
E-mail: bradfordta@state.gov Fax: 503 2278-6015
Regional Security Officer **Wade W. Burton** 503 2501-2999

Agency for International Development [El Salvador]
American Embassy - San Salvador, El Salvador,
Boulevard Santa Elena, Antiguo Cuscatlan, San Salvador, El Salvador
Mail: American Embassy - San Salvador, Unit 3110, APO, AP 34023
Tel: 503 2501-2999 Fax: 503 2501-3401
Internet: www.usaid.gov/el-salvador

◇ Mission Director **Peter Ryan Natiello** .... 503 2278-4444 ext. 1440
E-mail: pnatiello@usaid.gov
Education: Columbia 1990 MIA

Agricultural Section (Foreign Agricultural Service) (Resident in Guatemala City) [El Salvador]
American Embassy - San Salvador, El Salvador,
Boulevard Santa Elena, Antiguo Cuscatlan, San Salvador, El Salvador
E-mail: agsansalvador@fas.usda.gov

Agricultural Counselor (Resident in Guatemala City)
Richard "Todd" Drennan 502 2332-4030

Commercial Section (Foreign Commercial Service) [El Salvador]
American Embassy - San Salvador, El Salvador,
Boulevard Santa Elena, Antiguo Cuscatlan, San Salvador, El Salvador
Mail: Unit 3116, APO, AA 34023
Tel: 503 2501-2999 Fax: 503 2501-3067
E-mail: office.sansalvador@trade.gov Internet: export.gov/elsalvador

Senior Commercial Officer **Rachel Kreissl** 503 2501-3211
E-mail: rachel.kreissl@trade.gov

Department of Homeland Security - U.S. Citizenship and Immigration Services [El Salvador]
American Embassy - San Salvador, El Salvador,
Boulevard Santa Elena, Antiguo Cuscatlan, San Salvador, El Salvador
Mail: Unit 3116, APO, AA 34023
Tel: 503 2278-4444 ext. 2619

CIS Officer **Claudia Guevara** 503 2501-2234

Department of Justice - Drug Enforcement Administration [El Salvador]
American Embassy - San Salvador, El Salvador,
Boulevard Santa Elena, Antiguo Cuscatlan, San Salvador, El Salvador
Mail: American Embassy - San Salvador, Unit 3116, APO, AA 34023
Tel: 503 2501-2436 Fax: 503 2278-6012

DEA Country Attaché **Zachary Bell** 503 2501-2438

Federal Aviation Administration (Resident in Panama) [El Salvador]
American Embassy - Panama City, Panama,
Building 783, Demetrio Basilio Lakas Avenue,
Clayton, Panama City, 5, Panama
Mail: American Embassy - Panama City, Panama, Unit 0945, APO, AA 34002

FAA Representative **Carl N. Johnson** 507 317-5046

Internal Revenue Service (Resident in Mexico) [El Salvador]
American Embassy - Mexico City, Mexico,
Paseo de la Reforma 305, Mexico City, D.F. 06500, Mexico
Mail: (IRS) U.S. Logistics Center, 225 Vermillion Road, Brownsville, TX 78520-0900
Tel: 52 (55) 5080-2000 Fax: 52 (55) 5080-2882

IRS Officer **George Peralta** .... 52 (55) 5080-2000 ext. 2901

Office of the Defense Attaché [El Salvador]
American Embassy - San Salvador, El Salvador,
Boulevard Santa Elena, Antiguo Cuscatlan, San Salvador, El Salvador
Mail: American Embassy - San Salvador, Unit 3108, APO, AA 34023
Tel: 503 2228-2017 Fax: 503 2278-1037

Defense Attaché **Elliot Harris** 503 2228-2386
Commander of the Cooperative Security Location
(Vacant) 503 2333-1700

U.S. Embassy in Guatemala

American Embassy - Guatemala City, Guatemala,
Avenida Reforma 7-01, Zone 10, 01010 Guatemala City, Guatemala
Tel: 502 2326-4000 Fax: 502 2326-4654 Internet: gt.usembassy.gov

Note: Construction of a new U.S. Embassy in Guatemala is underway. The project is expected to be completed in 2022.

Office of the U.S. Ambassador to Guatemala
American Embassy - Guatemala City, Guatemala,
Avenida Reforma 7-01, Zone 10, 01010 Guatemala City, Guatemala
Mail: American Embassy - Guatemala City, APO, AA 34024

★ Ambassador **Ambassador Luis E. Arreaga** 502 2326-4000
E-mail: arreaga-rodaslx@state.gov
Education: Wisconsin (Milwaukee) BA, 1976 MM, 1981 PhD
Office Management Specialist to the Ambassador
Katherine M. McGifford 502 2326-4200
E-mail: mcgiffordkm@state.gov
◇ Deputy Chief of Mission
David Andrew Hodge .... 502 2331-1541 ext. 4201
E-mail: hodgeda@state.gov
Office Management Specialist to the Deputy Chief of Mission **Mayra Yissel Ahern** 502 2331-1541
E-mail: ahernmy@state.gov
◇ Consular Section Chief **Kent C. Brokenshire** 502 2326-4000
E-mail: brokenshirekc@state.gov Fax: 502 2326-4674
E-mail: consularguatem@state.gov
Education: Duke BA; Stanford MA; National War Col 2007 MSS
Community Liaison Officer **Mieke Gooch** 502 2326-4323
Equal Employment Officer **Robert Bunge** 502 2326-4000
Financial Management Officer **Kevin Perkins** 502 2331-1541
General Services Officer **Frederick "Fred" Olivo** 502 2331-1541
Information Management Officer **(Vacant)** 502 2326-4000
Information Program Officer **(Vacant)** 502 2331-1541
Information Systems Officer/Information Systems Security Officer
Douglas B. "Doug" Huyett .... 502 2331-1541 ext. 4215
E-mail: huyettdb@state.gov
Labor Officer **Andrew Hamrick** .... 502 2331-1541 ext. 4635
Management Officer **Bevan Benjamin** .... 502 2331-1541 ext. 4530
Military Liaison Officer
COL Steven D. Stanley USA .... 502 2331-1541 ext. 4212
E-mail: stanleysd@state.gov
Narcotics Affairs Officer **Hugo A. Guevara** .... 502 2331-1541 ext. 4450
E-mail: guevaraha@state.gov
Political/Economic Officer **Shawn E. Flatt** ..... 502 2331-1541 ext. 4634
E-mail: flattse@state.gov Fax: 502 2334-8474

(continued on next page)

★ Presidential Appointment Requiring Senate Confirmation ☆ Presidential Appointment ☐ Schedule C Appointment ◇ Career Senior Foreign Service Appointment
● Career Senior Executive Service (SES) Appointment ○ Non-Career Senior Executive Service (SES) Appointment ■ Postal Career Executive Service

Office of the U.S. Ambassador to Guatemala *(continued)*

Public Affairs Officer
Stephen J. Posivak, Jr. .... 502 2331-1541 ext. 4250
E-mail: posivaksj@state.gov Fax: 502 2332-1549
Regional Security Officer **Vasilli A. Alafogiannis** 502 2331-1541
E-mail: alafogiannisva@state.gov
Education: Whitman BA; American U

Agency for International Development [Guatemala]
Edificio Plaza Uno, 1a. Calle 7-66, Zona 9, Guatemala City, Guatemala
Mail: American Embassy - Guatemala City, APO, AA 34024
Tel: 502 2422-4000 Fax: 502 2422-4592
Internet: www.usaid.gov/guatemala

◇ Mission Director **John A. Beed** 502 2422-4000
E-mail: jbeed@usaid.gov
Education: Tulane 1985 BA; Florida State MA
◇ Deputy Mission Director **Tanya Urquieta** 502 2422-4000
E-mail: turquieta@usaid.gov

Agricultural Section (Foreign Agricultural Service) [Guatemala]
American Embassy - Guatemala City, Guatemala,
Avenida Reforma 7-01, Zone 10, 01010 Guatemala City, Guatemala
Mail: American Embassy - Guatemala City, Unit 3305, APO, AA 34024
Tel: 502 2334-8439 Fax: 502 2331-8293
E-mail: agguatemala@fas.usda.gov

Agricultural Counselor **Richard "Todd" Drennan** 502 2332-4030
E-mail: drennanrt@state.gov
E-mail: todd.drennan@fas.usda.gov

Animal and Plant Health Inspection Service [Guatemala]
4a. Avenida 12-62, Zona 10, Guatemala City, Guatemala
Mail: American Embassy - Guatemala City, APO, AA 34024
Tel: 502 2389-4600

APHIS Officer **Roberto Pantaleon** 502 2389-4615
E-mail: Roberto.Pantaleon@aphis.usda.gov

Commercial Section (Foreign Commercial Service) [Guatemala]
American Embassy - Guatemala City, Guatemala,
Avenida Reforma 7-01, Zone 10, 01010 Guatemala City, Guatemala
Mail: American Embassy - Guatemala City, APO, AA 34024
Tel: 502 2326-4000 Fax: 502 2331-7373
E-mail: office.guatemala@trade.gov

Senior Commercial Officer **Nicole DeSilvis** .... 502 2334-3147 ext. 4261
E-mail: Nicole.DeSilvis@trade.gov
Education: Millersville; Temple JD

Department of Homeland Security - Immigration and Customs Enforcement [Guatemala]
American Embassy - Guatemala City, Guatemala,
Avenida Reforma 7-01, Zone 10, 01010 Guatemala City, Guatemala
Mail: American Embassy - Guatemala City, Unit 3305, APO, AA 34024
Tel: 502 2331-1541 Fax: 502 2339-2472

Attaché (Acting) **Ricardo Ramirez** 502 2331-1541

Department of Homeland Security – U.S. Citizenship and Immigration Services [Guatemala]
Tel: 502 2326-4000 E-mail: Guatemala.USCIS@uscis.dhs.gov

Field Office Director **Suzanne Sinclair-Smith** 502 2326-4000

Department of Justice - Drug Enforcement Administration [Guatemala]
American Embassy - Guatemala City, Guatemala,
Avenida Reforma 7-01, Zone 10, 01010 Guatemala City, Guatemala
Mail: American Embassy - Guatemala City, APO, AA 34024

Country Attaché **Adam Marcus** 502 2326-4000

Federal Aviation Administration (Resident in Panama) [Guatemala]
American Embassy - Panama City, Panama,
Building 783, Demetrio Basilio Lakas Avenue,
Clayton, Panama City, 5, Panama
Mail: American Embassy - Panama City, Panama, Unit 0945,
APO, AA 34002

FAA Representative **Carl N. Johnson** 507 317-5046

Internal Revenue Service (Resident in Mexico City) [Guatemala]
American Embassy - Mexico City, Mexico,
Paseo de la Reforma 305, Mexico City, D.F. 06500, Mexico
Mail: (IRS) U.S. Logistics Center, 225 Vermillion Road,
Brownsville, TX 78520-0900
Tel: 52 (55) 5080-2000 Fax: 52 (55) 5080-2882

IRS Officer **George Peralta** .... 52 (55) 5080-2000 ext. 2901

Office of the Defense Attaché [Guatemala]
American Embassy - Guatemala City, Guatemala Avenida Reforma 7,
Guatemala City, Guatemala
Mail: American Embassy - Guatemala City, APO, AA 34024
Tel: 502 2331-1541 Fax: 502 2339-4301

Senior Defense Official
COL Steven D. Stanley USA .... 502 2331-1541 ext. 4224
E-mail: stanleysd@state.gov

Peace Corps [Guatemala]
8a. Calle 6-55, Zona 9, Guatemala City, Guatemala
Mail: American Embassy - Guatemala City, APO, AA 34024
Tel: 502 2334-8263 Fax: 502 2334-4121
E-mail: guatemaladesk@peacecorps.gov
Internet: www.peacecorps.gov/guatemala

Country Director **(Vacant)** 502 2334-8263

U.S. Embassy in Guyana

100 Young and Duke Streets, Kingston, Georgetown, Guyana
Tel: 592 225-4900 Fax: 592 225-8497 Internet: gy.usembassy.gov

Office of the U.S. Ambassador to Guyana

100 Young and Duke Streets, Kingston, Georgetown, Guyana
Mail: American Embassy, Department of State,
3170 Georgetown Place, Washington, DC 20521-3170

★ Ambassador **Ambassador Perry L. Holloway** 592 225-4900
E-mail: hollowaypl@state.gov
Education: Wofford 1983 BA; South Carolina MIB;
Indust'l Col Armed Forces MNR
★ Ambassador-Designate **Sarah-Ann Lynch** 592 225-4900
Education: Mount Holyoke BA; Tufts MALD; National War Col MS
Office Management Specialist to the Ambassador
Dawn D. Leavitt 592 225-4900
E-mail: leavittdd@state.gov
Deputy Chief of Mission **Terry Steers-Gonzalez** 592 225-4900
E-mail: steers-gonzalezt@state.gov
Office Management Specialist to the Deputy Chief of
Mission **Kimberly McDowell** 592 225-4900
Community Liaison Officer **(Vacant)** 592 225-4900
Consular Section Chief **Jerome N. "Jay" Epping** 592 225-4900
E-mail: eppingjn@state.gov
Economic/Commercial Officer **(Vacant)** 592 225-4900
Equal Employment Opportunity Officer
Amanda Cauldwell 592 225-4900
Financial Management Officer **John W. Osborne** 592 225-4900
General Services Officer **Kevin M. Phillips** 592 225-4900
E-mail: PhillipsKM2@state.gov
Legal Attaché **(Vacant)** 592 225-4900
Information Management Officer **Dannie L. McDowell** 592 225-4900
Information Program Officer **(Vacant)** 592 225-4900
Information Systems Security Officer
Dannie L. McDowell 592 225-4900
Management Officer **Curtis T. "Curt" Whittaker** 592 225-4900
E-mail: whittakerct@state.gov
Education: BYU 1986 BA; San José State 1991;
George Washington 2000 MA
Military Liaison Officer **LCDR Michael A. White USN** 592 225-4900
Public Affairs Officer **Amanda Cauldwell** 592 225-4900
Political/Economic Section Chief
Raymond "Ray" Slanina 592 225-4900
Education: Trinity U 1994 BS; U Redlands 2014 MBA
Regional Security Officer **Josiah T. Keener** 592 225-4900

★ Presidential Appointment Requiring Senate Confirmation ☆ Presidential Appointment □ Schedule C Appointment ◇ Career Senior Foreign Service Appointment
● Career Senior Executive Service (SES) Appointment ○ Non-Career Senior Executive Service (SES) Appointment ■ Postal Career Executive Service

Agency for International Development (Resident in Barbados) [Guyana]
American Embassy - Georgetown, Guyana,
99-100 Young and Duke Streets, Georgetown, Guyana
Mail: Department of State, 3170 Georgetown Place,
Washington, DC 20521-3170
Tel: 592 225-7315 Fax: 592 225-7316 Internet: www.usaid.gov/guyana

◇ Mission Director
Christopher M. "Chris" Cushing .... 592 225-7315 ext. 4216
E-mail: ccushing@usaid.gov

Centers for Disease Control [Guyana]
100 Young and Duke Streets, Kingston, Georgetown, Guyana
Country Director **Douan Kirivong** 592 223-6502

Peace Corps [Guyana]
American Embassy - Guyana, 99-100 Young and Duke Streets, Georgetown, Guyana
Mail: American Embassy, Department of State, 3170 Georgetown Place, Washington, DC 20521-3170
Tel: 592 225-5072 Fax: 592 225-3202
E-mail: pcgy_desk@gy.peacecorps.gov
Internet: www.peacecorps.gov/guyana
Country Director **Kury W. Cobham** 592 225-5072

U.S. Embassy in Haiti

American Embassy - Port-au-Prince, Haiti,
Tabarre 41, Boulevard 15 Octobre, Port-au-Prince, Haiti
Mail: American Embassy - Port-au-Prince, Haiti,
Department of State, Washington, DC 20521-3400

Office of the U.S. Ambassador to Haiti

American Embassy - Port-au-Prince, Haiti,
Tabarre 41, Boulevard 15 Octobre, Port-au-Prince, Haiti
Mail: American Embassy - Port-au-Prince, Haiti,
Department of State, Washington, DC 20521-3400
Tel: 509 2-229-8000 Fax: 509 2-229-8028 Internet: ht.usembassy.gov

★ Ambassador **Ambassador Michele Jeanne Sison** 509 2-229-8000
E-mail: sisonmj@state.gov
Education: Wellesley 1981 BA; London School Econ (UK) (Attended)
Office Management Specialist to the Ambassador
Kam Ting Wong 509 2-229-8000
E-mail: wongkt@state.gov

◇ Deputy Chief of Mission **Robin D. Diallo** 509 2-229-8000
Office Management Specialist to the Deputy Chief of
Mission **Tiffany Sims** 509 2-229-8000
Consul General (Acting) **Maureen Smith** 509 2-229-8000
Community Liaison Officer **(Vacant)** 509 2-229-8000
Economic/Commercial Officer **Linessa J. Wahid** 509 2-229-8000
E-mail: wahidlj@state.gov
Equal Employment Opportunity Officer
Michelle Milardo 509 2-229-8000
Financial Management Officer **Javier A. Araujo** 509 2-229-8000
General Services Officer **Faybein Moy** 509 2-229-8000
E-mail: moyf@state.gov
Human Resources Officer **(Vacant)** 509 2-229-8000
Information Management Officer
Jeffrey L. "Jeff" Cook 509 2-229-8000
E-mail: cookjl@state.gov
Information Program Officer **(Vacant)** 509 2-229-8000
Information Systems Officer **Byrum M. Stevens** 509 2-229-8000
E-mail: stevensbm@state.gov
Information Systems Security Officer **Shawn Owens** 502 2-229-8000
Management Officer **Beverly D. Rochester** 509 2-229-8000
E-mail: RochesterBD@state.gov
Military Liaison Officer **CDR Michael Bennett USCG** ... 509 2-229-8000
Narcotics Affairs Officer **Nicholas Hilgert** 509 2-229-8000
Political Officer **Melinda Crowley** 509 2-229-8000
Public Affairs Officer **Jeanne Clark** 509 2-229-8000
Regional Security Officer **Mario Reta** 509 2-229-8000
Education: Houston 1992 BA

Agency for International Development [Haiti]
American Embassy - Port-au-Prince, Haiti,
Tabarre 41, Boulevard 15 Octobre, Port-au-Prince, Haiti
Mail: American Embassy - Port-au-Prince, Haiti,
Department of State, Washington, DC 20521-3400
Tel: 509 2-229-8000 Fax: 509 2-229-8066 Internet: www.usaid.gov/haiti

◇ Mission Director **Jene Clark Thomas** 509 2-229-8028
E-mail: jethomas@usaid.gov

Animal and Plant Health Inspection Service [Haiti]
American Embassy - Port-au-Prince, Haiti,
Tabarre 41, Boulevard 15 Octobre, Port-au-Prince, Haiti
Mail: American Embassy - Port-au-Prince, Haiti,
Department of State, Washington, DC 20521-3400
Tel: 509 2-229-8077 Fax: 509 2-229-8091
APHIS Officer **(Vacant)** 509 2-229-8077

Drug Enforcement Administration [Haiti]
American Embassy - Port-au-Prince, Haiti,
Tabarre 41, Boulevard 15 Octobre, Port-au-Prince, Haiti
Mail: American Embassy - Port-au-Prince, Haiti,
Department of State, Washington, DC 20521-3400
Tel: 509 2-229-8000
DEA Country Attaché **Vincent Williams** 509 2-229-8000

Federal Aviation Administration (Resident in Florida) [Haiti]
2895 SW 145 Avenue, Miramar, FL 33027
FAA Representative **Alex D. Rodriguez** .... (202) 267-0426

Department of Homeland Security - Citizenship and Immigration Services [Haiti]
American Embassy - Port-au-Prince, Haiti,
Tabarre 41, Boulevard 15 Octobre, Port-au-Prince, Haiti
Mail: American Embassy - Port-au-Prince, Haiti,
Department of State, Washington, DC 20521-3400
Tel: 509 2-229-8000
DHS Officer **Margarette Nicolas** 509 2-229-8000

Internal Revenue Service (Resident in Mexico City) [Haiti]
(IRS) U.S. Logistics Center, 225 Vermillion Road,
Brownsville, TX 78520-0900
American Embassy - Mexico City, Mexico,
Paseo de la Reforma 305, Mexico City, D.F. 06500, Mexico
Tel: 52 (55) 5080-2000 Fax: 52 (55) 5080-2882
IRS Officer **George Peralta** .... 52 (55) 5080-2000 ext. 2901

Office of the Defense Attaché [Haiti]
American Embassy - Port-au-Prince, Haiti,
Tabarre 41, Boulevard 15 Octobre, Port-au-Prince, Haiti
Mail: American Embassy - Port-au-Prince, Haiti,
Department of State, Washington, DC 20521-3400
Tel: 509 2-229-8000
Defense Attaché **CDR Michael Bennett USCG** 509 2-229-8000

U.S. Embassy in Honduras

American Embassy - Tegucigalpa, Honduras,
Avenida La Paz, Apartado Postal No. 3453, Tegucigalpa, Honduras
Tel: 504 2236-9320 Fax: 504 2236-9037 Internet: hn.usembassy.gov

Office of the U.S. Ambassador to Honduras

American Embassy - Tegucigalpa, Honduras,
Avenida La Paz, Apartado Postal No. 3453, Tegucigalpa, Honduras
Mail: American Embassy - Tegucigalpa, Honduras, APO, AA 34022

★ Ambassador-Designate
Francisco Luis "Paco" Palmieri 504 2236-9320
E-mail: palmierifl@state.gov
Education: Princeton 1983 AB; National War Col 2006 MSS

◇ Chargé d'Affaires **Heide B. Fulton** 504 2236-9320
Office Management Specialist to the
Ambassador **(Vacant)** .... 504 2236-9320 ext. 4268

◇ Deputy Chief of Mission **Heide B. Fulton** ..... 504 2236-9320 ext. 4768

(continued on next page)

★ Presidential Appointment Requiring Senate Confirmation ☆ Presidential Appointment ☐ Schedule C Appointment ◇ Career Senior Foreign Service Appointment
● Career Senior Executive Service (SES) Appointment ○ Non-Career Senior Executive Service (SES) Appointment ■ Postal Career Executive Service

DEPARTMENTS

Office of the U.S. Ambassador to Honduras *(continued)*

Office Management Specialist to the Deputy Chief of Mission **(Vacant)** . . . . . 504 2236-9320 ext. 4768
Consul General **Dana D. Deree** . . . . . 504 2236-9320 ext. 4400
E-mail: dereed2@state.gov Fax: 504 2238-4357
Education: Harding 1993 BA, 1995 BA, 1995 MEd
Community Liaison Officer **Julie Rickey** 504 2236-9037
Corps of Engineers Chief **(Vacant)** . . . . . 504 2236-9320 ext. 4934
Economic Officer **Lisa D. Miller** . . . . . 504 2236-9320 ext. 4178
Fax: 504 2236-6836
Financial Management Officer **Carl Clifton Scott** 504 2236-9320
E-mail: scottcc@state.gov
Education: Morehouse Col 2000 MA
General Services Officer **Joseph Vasquez** . . . . . 504 2236-9320 ext. 4876
Fax: 504 2236-5245
Information Management Officer **Marcelo M. Coronel** . . . . . 504 2236-9320 ext. 4243
Information Program Officer **Larry Helmich** . . . . . 504 2236-9320 ext. 4202
Information Systems Officer **Bonita L. Johnson** . . . . . 504 2236-9320 ext. 4710
Information Systems Security Officer **Bonita L. Johnson** 504 2236-9320
Joint Task Force-Bravo Liaison Officer **Albert Marckwardt** . . . . . 504 2236-9320 ext. 4812
Human Rights and Labor Attaché **Jason A. Smith** . . . . . 504 2236-9320 ext. 4820
Legal Attaché **(Vacant)** 504 2236-9320
Management Officer **Charles H. Morrill** . . . . . 504 2236-9320 ext. 4781
E-mail: morrillch@state.gov
Narcotics Affairs Section Officer **Rodrigo Garza** . . . . . 504 2236-9320 ext. 4291
Political Counselor **Elizabeth McGee Bailey** . . . 504 2236-4320 ext. 4820
Fax: 504 2238-4446
Public Affairs Officer **(Vacant)** . . . . . 504 2236-9320 ext. 4139
Fax: 504 2236-9309
Press Attaché **(Vacant)** . . . . . 504 2236-9320 ext. 4528
Cultural Affairs Officer **(Vacant)** 504 2236-9320
Regional Security Officer **Philip W. Nazelrod** . . . . . 504 2236-9320 ext. 4771

Agency for International Development [Honduras]
American Embassy - Tegucigalpa, Honduras,
Avenida La Paz, Apartado Postal No. 3453, Tegucigalpa, Honduras
Mail: American Embassy - Tegucigalpa, Honduras, APO, AA 34022
Tel: 504 2236-9320 Fax: 504 2236-7776
Internet: www.usaid.gov/honduras
Mission Director **Fernando Cossich** 504 2236-9320
E-mail: fcossich@usaid.gov

Agricultural Section (Foreign Agricultural Service) [Honduras]
American Embassy - Tegucigalpa, Honduras,
Avenida La Paz, Apartado Postal No. 3453, Tegucigalpa, Honduras
Tel: 504 2236-6944 Fax: 504 2236-8342
E-mail: agtegucigalpa@fas.usda.gov
Agricultural Counselor (Resident in Guatemala City) **Richard "Todd" Drennan** 502 2332-4030

Commercial Section (Foreign Commercial Service) [Honduras]
American Embassy - Tegucigalpa, Honduras,
Avenida La Paz, Apartado Postal No. 3453, Tegucigalpa, Honduras
Internet: www.export.gov/honduras
Regional Senior Commercial Officer (Resident in San Jose) **Eric B. Wolff** 506 2519-2293
E-mail: eric.wolff@trade.gov

Department of Homeland Security - U.S. Immigration and Customs Enforcement [Honduras]
American Embassy - Tegucigalpa, Honduras,
Avenida La Paz, Apartado Postal No. 3453, Tegucigalpa, Honduras
Mail: American Embassy - Tegucigalpa, Honduras, APO, AA 34022
Tel: 504 2236-9320 Fax: 504 2236-9107
Customs Officer **Victor Curley** . . . . . 504 2236-9320 ext. 4500

Drug Enforcement Administration [Honduras]
American Embassy - Tegucigalpa, Honduras,
Avenida La Paz, Apartado Postal No. 3453, Tegucigalpa, Honduras
Mail: American Embassy - Tegucigalpa, Honduras, APO, AA 34022
Tel: 504 2236-9320 Fax: 504 2236-9781
DEA Country Attaché **Alvaro Agrelo** . . . . . 504 2236-9320 ext. 4889

Office of the Defense Attaché [Honduras]
American Embassy - Tegucigalpa, Honduras,
Avenida La Paz, Apartado Postal No. 3453, Tegucigalpa, Honduras
Mail: American Embassy - Tegucigalpa, Honduras, APO, AA 34022
Tel: 504 2236-9320 Fax: 504 2236-5645
Defense Attaché **COL Hector E. Paz USA** . . . . . 504 2236-9320 ext. 4582

Office of Security Cooperation [Honduras] (OSC)
American Embassy - Tegucigalpa, Honduras,
Avenida La Paz, Apartado Postal No. 3453, Tegucigalpa, Honduras
Chief **COL John Groves USA** 504 2236-9320

U.S. Embassy in Jamaica
142 Old Hope Road, Kingston, 6, Jamaica
Tel: 1 (876) 702-6000 Fax: 1 (876) 702-6348 Internet: jm.usembassy.gov

Office of the U.S. Ambassador to Jamaica
American Embassy - Kingston, Jamaica,
142 Old Hope Road, Kingston, 6, Jamaica
Mail: American Embassy Kingston, 3210 Kingston Place, Washington, DC 20521-3210
★ Ambassador-Designate **Donald R. "Don" Tapia** 1 (876) 702-6000
Education: St Leo U BA, MBA
◇ Chargé d'Affaires **Eric Khant** 1 (876) 702-6000
E-mail: khante@state.gov
Office Management Specialist to the Ambassador **(Vacant)** 1 (876) 702-6000
◇ Deputy Chief of Mission **Eric Khant** 1 (876) 702-6000
E-mail: khante@state.gov
Office Management Specialist to the Deputy Chief of Mission **Linda Loth** 1 (876) 702-6000
Community Liaison Officer **James "Cory" Chambers** 1 (876) 702-6000
E-mail: chambersjc@state.gov
◇ Consul General **Mark Wayne Seibel** 1 (876) 702-6000
Financial Management Officer **Thomas F. Doherty, Jr.** 1 (876) 702-6000
General Services Officer **Dean L. Hobson** 1 (876) 702-6000
E-mail: hobsondl@state.gov
Human Resources Officer **Dennie R. Ege** 1 (876) 702-6000
Information Management Officer **Scott D. Ternus** 1 (876) 702-6000
E-mail: ternussd@state.gov
Information Systems Officer **Andrew O. Ash** 1 (876) 702-6000
Information Systems Security Officer **Anthony "Tony" Shands** 1 (876) 702-6000
Legal Attaché **(Vacant)** 1 (876) 702-6000
Management Officer **Marcus A. McChristian** 1 (876) 702-6000
E-mail: McChristianMA@state.gov
Military Liaison Officer **Darryl C. Clary USCG** 1 (876) 702-6000
E-mail: daryl.c.clary@uscg.mil
Narcotics Affairs Section Officer **Garth T. Hall** 1 (876) 702-6000
E-mail: hallgt@state.gov
Political/Economic Officer **Alexander W. Sokoloff** 1 (876) 702-6000
E-mail: SokoloffAW@state.gov
Education: Georgetown 1980 BS; Johns Hopkins 1982 MA
Public Affairs Officer **Jeremiah Knight** 1 (876) 702-6000
E-mail: knightj@state.gov Fax: 1 (876) 702-6001
Regional Security Officer **Michael "Mike" Rohlfs** 1 (876) 702-6001

Agency for International Development [Jamaica]
142 Old Hope Road, Kingston, 6, Jamaica
Tel: 1 (876) 702-6444 Fax: 1 (876) 702-6385
Internet: www.usaid.gov/jamaica
◇ Mission Director **Jason Fraser** 1 (876) 702-6444
E-mail: jfraser@usaid.gov
Education: Bates 1994 BA; Columbia 1998 MIA, 1998 JD

★ Presidential Appointment Requiring Senate Confirmation ☆ Presidential Appointment ☐ Schedule C Appointment ◇ Career Senior Foreign Service Appointment
● Career Senior Executive Service (SES) Appointment ○ Non-Career Senior Executive Service (SES) Appointment ■ Postal Career Executive Service

Agricultural Section (Foreign Agricultural Service) (Resident in Santo Domingo) [Jamaica]
American Embassy - Santo Domingo, Dominican Republic,
Calles Cesar Nicolas Penson and Leopoldo Navarro, Santo Domingo, Dominican Republic
Mail: American Embassy - Santo Domingo, Unit 5500, APO, AA 34041
Tel: 1 (876) 702-6142 Fax: 1 (876) 702-6397
Senior Agricultural Attaché (Resident in Santo Domingo) **Elizabeth Autry** 1 (809) 227-0112

Animal and Plant Health Inspection Service [Jamaica]
One Stop Export Complex, Norman Manley International Airport,
Two Haining Road, Kingston, 5, Jamaica
Mail: American Embassy - Kingston, 3210 Kingston Place,
Washington, DC 20521-3210
Tel: 1 (876) 924-8741 Fax: 1 (876) 924-8742
Internet: http://kingston.usembassy.gov/aphis.html
APHIS Officer **Lloyd Garcia** 1 (876) 924-8741

Commercial Section (Foreign Commercial Service) (Resident in Santo Domingo) [Jamaica]
Avenue Pedro Henriquez Urena 133, Edificio Empressarial Reyna 1,
La Esperilla, Santo Domingo, Dominican Republic
Mail: Unit 5500, APO, AA 54041
Tel: 1 (809) 221-2121 Fax: 1 (809) 540-1267
E-mail: santo.domingo.office.box@mail.doc.gov
Senior Regional Commercial Officer
Bryan Larson .... 1 (809) 567-7775 ext. 7249
E-mail: bryan.larson@trade.gov
Education: Colorado 1991 BA; American U 1995 MA

Department of Justice - Drug Enforcement Administration [Jamaica]
142 Old Hope Road, Kingston, 6, Jamaica
Mail: American Embassy Kingston, 3210 Kingston Place,
Washington, DC 20521-3210
Tel: 1 (876) 929-4956
DEA Officer **Dolan Greenridge** 1 (876) 929-4956
E-mail: dolan.o.greenidge@usdoj.gov

Federal Aviation Administration (Resident in Washington, D.C.) [Jamaica]
American Embassy Kingston, 3210 Kingston Place,
Washington, DC 20521-3210
Fax: (202) 267-5032
FAA Representative **Allan B. Hurr** .... (202) 385-8887

Internal Revenue Service (Resident in Mexico City) [Jamaica]
American Embassy - Mexico City, Mexico,
Paseo de la Reforma 305, Mexico City, D.F. 06500, Mexico
Mail: American Embassy - Mexico City, Mexico, P.O. Box 3087,
Laredo, TX 78044-3087
Tel: 52 (55) 5080-2000 Fax: 52 (55) 5080-2882
IRS Officer **George Peralta** .... 52 (55) 5080-2000 ext. 2901

Office of the Defense Attaché [Jamaica]
American Embassy - Kingston, 3210 Kingston Place,
Washington, DC 20521-3210
142 Old Hope Road, Kingston, 6, Jamaica
Tel: 1 (876) 935-6021 Fax: 1 (876) 926-6743
Defense Attaché **LTC Pablo Raggio USA** 1 (876) 382-9030
E-mail: pablo.a.raggio.mil@mail.mil

Peace Corps [Jamaica]
Peace Corps, 8 Worthington Avenue, Kingston, 5, Jamaica
Mail: American Embassy Kingston, 3210 Kingston Place,
Washington, DC 20521-3210
Tel: 1 (876) 929-0495 Fax: 1 (876) 929-3015
Internet: www.peacecorps.gov/jamaica
Country Director **Paul Sully** 1 (876) 929-0495
E-mail: psully@peacecorps.gov

Cayman Islands Consular Agency
Smith Road Center, 150 Smith Road, Georgetown,
Unit 202B, Grand Cayman, Cayman Islands
PO Box 12204, KY1-1010, Grand Cayman, Cayman Islands
Tel: 1 (345) 945-8173 Fax: 1 (345) 945-8192
E-mail: caymanacs@state.gov
Consular Agent **Gary Montemayor** 1 (345) 945-8173

Montego Bay Consular Agency
Whitter Village, Ironshore, Montego Bay, St James,
Unit EU-1, Jamaica
Mail: U.S. Consular Agency - Montego Bay, Jamaica,
3210 Kingston Place, Washington, DC 20521-3210
Tel: 1 (876) 953-0620 Fax: 1 (876) 953-3898
E-mail: mobayacs@state.gov
Consular Agent **Lisa Hyde** 1 (876) 983-0620

U.S. Embassy in Mexico
Paseo de la Reforma 305, Mexico City, D.F. 06500, Mexico
Tel: 52 (55) 5080-2000 Fax: 52 (55) 5080-2005
Internet: mx.usembassy.gov

Office of the U.S. Ambassador to Mexico
American Embassy - Mexico City, Mexico, Paseo de la Reforma 305,
Col. Cuauhtemoc, Mexico City, 06500, Mexico
Mail: American Embassy - Mexico City, Mexico, P.O. Box 9000,
Brownsville, TX 78520-0900
★ Ambassador **(Vacant)** 52 (55) 5080-2100
Fax: 52 (55) 5207-0091
◇ Chargé d'Affaires **John S. Creamer** 52 (55) 5080-2200
E-mail: creamerjs@state.gov
Education: Georgetown BA, JD; National Defense U MS
Office Management Specialist to the Ambassador **(Vacant)** 52 (55) 5080-2100
◇ Deputy Chief of Mission **John S. Creamer** 52 (55) 5080-2200
E-mail: creamerjs@state.gov
Education: Georgetown BA, JD; National Defense U MS
Office Management Specialist to the Deputy Chief of Mission **(Vacant)** 52 (55) 5080-2200
◇ Consul General **Eric A. Fichte** 52 (55) 5080-2000
E-mail: fichtee@state.gov
Office Management Specialist to the Consul General **Reyna M. Ramirez** 52 (55) 5080-2000
E-mail: ramirezr@state.gov
Consular Affairs Officer **(Vacant)** 52 (55) 5080-2000
Community Liaison Officer **Britta White** 52 (55) 5080-2000
◇ Economic Section Officer **Karen Choe-Fichte** 52 (55) 5080-2850
E-mail: choe-fichtek@state.gov
Environment, Science and Technology Officer **(Vacant)** .... 52 (55) 5080-2000 ext. 2112
Facilities Management Officer
Thomas "Tom" Bauer 52 (55) 5080-2000
Equal Employment Opportunity Officer **(Vacant)** 52 (55) 5080-2444
Financial Attaché **(Vacant)** 52 (55) 5080-2740
Financial Management Officer **(Vacant)** 52 (55) 5080-2000
General Services Officer **Rebecca Landis** 52 (55) 5080-2774
E-mail: landisrl@state.gov
Human Resources Officer **Alboino L. Deulus** 52 (55) 5080-2000
Information Management Officer
Frederick M. "Fred" Armand 52 (55) 5080-2220
E-mail: armandfm@state.gov
Information Program Officer **David Kent** 52 (55) 5080-2220
Information Systems Officer
Francisco "Frank" Alonso 52 (55) 5080-2615
E-mail: alonsof@state.gov
Information Systems Security Officer **(Vacant)** 52 (55) 5080-2615
Legal Attaché **Carlos Cases** .... 52 (55) 5080-2000 ext. 2177
◇ Management Officer **Thomas R. Favret** 52 (55) 5080-2300
E-mail: favrettr@state.gov
Education: Catholic U 1980 BA; National Defense U 2015 MS
◇ Management Counselor **Marco A. Sims** 52 (55) 5080-2000
E-mail: simsma@state.gov
Education: Chicago 1989 BA, 1992 MBA, 1992 MIR

(continued on next page)

★ Presidential Appointment Requiring Senate Confirmation ☆ Presidential Appointment ☐ Schedule C Appointment ◇ Career Senior Foreign Service Appointment
● Career Senior Executive Service (SES) Appointment ○ Non-Career Senior Executive Service (SES) Appointment ■ Postal Career Executive Service

DEPARTMENTS

Office of the U.S. Ambassador to Mexico *(continued)*

Military Liaison Officer
COL Shawn D. Fritz USA .... 52 (55) 5080-2000 ext. 4201
Narcotics Affairs Section Officer
Tobin J. Bradley .... 52 (55) 5080-2000 ext. 2986
Political Officer **(Vacant)** .... 52 (55) 5080-2000 ext. 4445
Fax: 52 (55) 5080-2247
Public Affairs Officer **Susan M. Elbow** 52 (55) 5080-2253
Education: Smith BA; Rochester MA; JFK School Govt MPA
Cultural Affairs Officer **James Wolfe** 52 (55) 5080-2253
Spokesperson **Jessica Simon** 52 (55) 5080-2253
Education: Tufts 1995; Georgetown 2001 MSFS
Regional Security Officer **(Vacant)** .... 52 (55) 5080-2000 ext. 4411

Agency for International Development [Mexico]
American Embassy - Mexico City, Mexico, Paseo de la Reforma 305, Col. Cuauhtemoc, Mexico City, 06500, Mexico
Mail: American Embassy - Mexico City, Mexico, P.O. Box 9000, Brownsville, TX 78520-0900
Tel: 52 (55) 5080-2000 Fax: 52 (55) 5080-2000 ext. 4864
Internet: www.usaid.gov/mexico

Mission Director **Elizabeth B. Warfield** .... 52 (55) 5080-2257 ext. 2954
E-mail: ewarfield@usaid.gov
Education: Fletcher Law & Diplomacy MALD
◇ Deputy Mission Director **Margaret Enis Spears** 52 (55) 5080-2257
E-mail: mspears@usaid.gov

Agricultural Section (Foreign Agricultural Service) [Mexico]
American Embassy - Mexico City, Mexico, Paseo de la Reforma 305, Col. Cuauhtemoc, Mexico City, 06500, Mexico
Mail: American Embassy - Mexico City, Mexico, P.O. Box 9000, Brownsville, TX 78520-0900
Tel: 52 (55) 5080-2532 Fax: 52 (55) 5080-2130

◇ Minister-Counselor for Agricultural Affairs
Melinda D. Sallyards 52 (55) 5080-2532
E-mail: melinda.sallyards@fas.usda.gov

Agricultural Trade Office [Mexico]
Jaime Balmes 8-201, Col. Los Morales Polanco, Mexico City, 11510, Mexico
Mail: American Embassy - Mexico City, Mexico, P.O. Box 9000, Brownsville, TX 78520-0900
E-mail: atomexico@fas.usda.gov Internet: www.mexico-usda.com.mx

Director **Erich Kuss** 52 (55) 5080-2000
E-mail: erich.kuss@fas.usda.gov
Deputy Director **Rhiannon Elms** 52 (55) 5080-2000
Education: West Virginia 2006 BA

Animal and Plant Health Inspection Service [Mexico]
c/o American Embassy - Mexico City, Mexico,
Sierra Nevada 115, Col. Lomas de Chapultepec, Mexico City, C.P. 11000, Mexico
American Embassy - Mexico City, Mexico, P.O. Box 9000, 78520 Mexico City, 0900, Mexico
Mail: (APHIS) U.S. Logistics Center, 225 Vermillion Road, Brownsville, TX 78520-0900
Tel: 52 (55) 1997-1500 Fax: 52 (55) 1997-1540

Director **(Vacant)** 52 (55) 5080-5421

Bureau of Alcohol, Tobacco, Firearms and Explosives [Mexico]
American Embassy - Mexico City, Mexico,
Paseo de la Reforma 305, Mexico City, 06500, Mexico
Mail: American Embassy - Mexico City, Mexico, P.O. Box 9000, Brownsville, TX 78520-0900
Tel: 52 (55) 5080-2827/2055/2782 Fax: 52 (55) 5533-5478

ATF Officer **Craig Saier** .... 52 (55) 5080-2000 ext. 2832

Commercial Section (Foreign Commercial Service) [Mexico]
American Embassy - Mexico City, Mexico, Paseo de la Reforma 305, Col. Cuauhtemoc, Mexico City, 06500, Mexico
Mail: American Embassy - Mexico City, Mexico, P.O. Box 9000, Brownsville, TX 78520-0900
Tel: 52 (55) 5080-2000 ext. 5207 Fax: 52 (55) 5566-1115
Internet: export.gov/mexico

◇ Senior Commercial Officer **Brian C. Brisson** 52 (55) 5080-2006
E-mail: brian.brisson@trade.gov
Education: Notre Dame 1985 BA; Michigan MPP
◇ Deputy Senior Commercial Officer
Isabella G. Cascarano 52 (55) 5080-2029
E-mail: Isabella.Cascarano@trade.gov

Drug Enforcement Administration [Mexico]
American Embassy - Mexico City, Mexico,
Paseo de la Reforma 305, Mexico City, 06500, Mexico
Mail: American Embassy - Mexico City, Mexico, P.O. Box 9000, Brownsville, TX 78520-0900
Tel: 52 (55) 5080-2000 ext. 4636 Fax: 52 (55) 5080-2531

DEA Officer **John Niedzialek** .... 52 (55) 5080-2000 ext. 4636

Department of Homeland Security - U.S. Citizenship and Immigration Services [Mexico]
American Embassy - Mexico City, Mexico,
Paseo de la Reforma 305, Col. Cuauhtemoc,
Room 118, Mexico City, 06500, Mexico
Mail: American Embassy - Mexico City, Mexico, P.O. Box 9000, Brownsville, TX 78520-0900
Tel: 52 (55) 5080-2000 Fax: 52 (55) 5080-2313

District Director **Brett Lassen** .... 52 (55) 5080-2000 ext. 2416

Department of Homeland Security - U.S. Customs and Border Protection [Mexico]
American Embassy - Mexico City, Mexico,
Paseo de la Reforma 305, Mexico City, 06500, Mexico
Mail: American Embassy - Mexico City, Mexico, P.O. Box 9000, Brownsville, TX 78520-0900
Tel: 52 (55) 5080-2000 Fax: 52 (55) 5525-5977

Customs Officer **Carlos Gonzalez** 52 (55) 5080-2452

Department of Homeland Security - U.S. Immigration and Customs Enforcement [Mexico]
Immigration and Customs Officer
Timothy "Tim" Tubbs 52 (55) 5080-2000

Internal Revenue Service [Mexico]
American Embassy - Mexico City, Mexico, Paseo de la Reforma 305, Room 114, Mexico City, 06500, Mexico
Mail: American Embassy - Mexico City, Mexico, P.O. Box 3087, Laredo, TX 78044-3087
Tel: 52 (55) 5080-2000 Fax: 52 (55) 5080-2882

Attaché **George Peralta** .... 52 (55) 5080-2000 ext. 2901

Office of the Defense Attaché [Mexico]
American Embassy - Mexico City, Mexico,
Paseo de la Reforma 305, Mexico City, 06500, Mexico
Mail: American Embassy - Mexico City, Mexico, P.O. Box 9000, Brownsville, TX 78520-0900
Tel: 52 (55) 5080-2000 Fax: 52 (55) 5080-2448

Defense Attaché **COL Edward Monroe Bonfoy III USA** .... 52 (55) 5080-2000 ext. 4558
E-mail: bonfoeyem@state.gov
Education: Virginia 1989 BA; New Mexico 2001 MA

Peace Corps [Mexico]
Av. Universidad 202 Ote., Col. San Javier, 76020 Querétaro, Mexico
Tel: 52 (442) 238-6900 Internet: www.peacecorps.gov/mexico
Fax: 52 (442) 238-6903

Country Director **(Vacant)** 52 (442) 238-6900

★ Presidential Appointment Requiring Senate Confirmation ☆ Presidential Appointment ☐ Schedule C Appointment ◇ Career Senior Foreign Service Appointment
● Career Senior Executive Service (SES) Appointment ○ Non-Career Senior Executive Service (SES) Appointment ■ Postal Career Executive Service

DEPARTMENTS

Ciudad Juarez Consulate General

U.S. Consulate General - Ciudad Juarez, Mexico,
Paseo de la Victoria #3650, Fracc. Partido Senecú,
Ciudad Juarez, Chihuahua, Mexico C.P. 32543
Mail: U.S. Consulate General - Ciudad Juarez, P.O. Box 10545,
El Paso, TX 79995-0545
Tel: 52 (656) 227-3000 Fax: 52 (656) 616-9056

Consul General **John Stephen Tavenner** 52 (656) 227-3000
E-mail: tavennerj@state.gov
Education: Texas Tech JD; Thunderbird International MIM
◇ Deputy Consul General **Eric Scott Cohan** 52 (656) 227-3000
E-mail: cohanes@state.gov
◇ Consular Officer **Eric Scott Cohan** 52 (656) 227-3000
E-mail: cohanes@state.gov
Community Liaison Officer **(Vacant)** 52 (656) 227-3000
General Services Officer **David Urbia** 52 (656) 227-3000
Information Program Officer
Thomas "Tom" Murray 52 (656) 227-3000
E-mail: murrayt@state.gov
Information Systems Officer **Brian H. Metso** 52 (656) 227-3000
Management Officer **Nathan Boyack** 52 (656) 227-3000
E-mail: boyacknj@state.gov
Political/Economic Officer **Molly Flores** 52 (656) 227-3000
Public Affairs Officer **Brian M. Straight** 52 (656) 227-3449
E-mail: straightbm@state.gov
E-mail: cdjwfnoticias@state.gov
Regional Security Officer **Kevin K. Hamilton** 52 (656) 227-3000
Education: Kentucky BS

Department of Homeland Security - U.S. Citizenship and Immigration Services [Mexico]

U.S. Consulate General - Ciudad Juarez, Mexico,
Avenue Lopez Mateos 924 Norte, 32000 Ciudad Juarez, Mexico
Mail: U.S. Consulate General - Ciudad Juarez, P.O. Box 10545,
El Paso, TX 79995-0545
Tel: 52 (656) 227-3451 Fax: 52 (656) 611-5284
E-mail: cdj.uscis@uscis.dhs.gov

Field Office Director **Miguel "Mike" Chavez** 52 (656) 227-3451

Drug Enforcement Administration [Mexico]

U.S. Consulate General - Ciudad Juarez, Mexico,
Avenue Lopez Mateos 924 Norte, 32000 Ciudad Juarez, Mexico
Mail: U.S. Consulate General - Ciudad Juarez, P.O. Box 10545,
El Paso, TX 79995-0545

DEA Attaché **Miguel Flores** 52 (656) 227-3000

Guadalajara Consulate General

U.S. Consulate General - Guadalajara, Mexico,
Progresso 175, Guadalajara, Jalisco, Mexico C.P. 44160
Mail: U.S. Consulate General - Guadalajara, P.O. Box 9001,
Brownsville, TX 78520-0901
Tel: 52 (33) 3268-2100 Fax: 52 (33) 3825-1951

Consul General (Acting) **Matthew C. Hurley** 52 (33) 3268-2100
E-mail: hurleymc@state.gov
Education: Catholic U; Dayton JD
Consular Section Chief **Matthew C. Hurley** 52 (33) 3268-2100
E-mail: hurleymc@state.gov
Education: Catholic U; Dayton JD
General Services Officer **Sean Buckley** 52 (33) 3268-2100
Information Management Officer/Information
Program Officer **Mark D. Raglin** 52 (33) 3268-2100
Legal Attaché **Michael Dreher** 52 (33) 3268-2100
Management Officer **Ramon E. Best** 52 (33) 3268-2100
E-mail: bestre@state.gov
Political/Economic Officer **Jeffrey P. Cernyar** 52 (33) 3268-2100
E-mail: cernyarjp@state.gov
Public Affairs Officer **Caroline Nohr** 52 (33) 3268-2100
Regional Security Officer **Brian Cooke** 52 (33) 3268-2100

Animal and Plant Health Inspection Service [Mexico]

U.S. Consulate General - Guadalajara, Mexico,
Progresso 175, 44100 Guadalajara, Jalisco, Mexico
Mail: U.S. Consulate General - Guadalajara, (APHIS) P.O. Box 9001,
Brownsville, TX 78520-9001
Tel: 52 (33) 3641-8310

APHIS Officer **Paul G. McGowan** 52 (33) 3641-8310

Commercial Section (Foreign Commercial Service) [Mexico]

U.S. Consulate General - Guadalajara, Mexico,
Progresso 175, 44100 Guadalajara, Jalisco, Mexico
Mail: U.S. Consulate General - Guadalajara, (FCS) P.O. Box 9001,
Brownsville, TX 78520-0901
Tel: 52 (33) 3615-1140 Fax: 52 (33) 3615-7665

Principal Commercial Officer **(Vacant)** 52 (33) 3615-1140

Drug Enforcement Administration [Mexico]

U.S. Consulate General - Guadalajara, Mexico,
Progresso 175, 44100 Guadalajara, Jalisco, Mexico
Mail: U.S. Consulate General - Guadalajara, (DEA) P.O. Box 9001,
Brownsville, TX 78520-0901
Tel: 52 (33) 3268-2100

DEA Officer **Rene Amarillas** 52 (33) 3268-2100

Vallarta Consular Agency

U.S. Consular Agency - Puerto Vallarta, Mexico,
Paseo de los Cocoteros #85, Sur Paradise Plaza, Interior Local L-7,
Puerto Vallarta, Nayarit, Mexico C.P. 63732
Mail: U.S. Consulate General - Guadalajara, P.O. Box 9001,
Brownsville, TX 78520-0901
Tel: 52 33-32682100 E-mail: conagencypuertov@state.gov

Consular Agent **Kelly A. Trainor de Oceguera** 52 33-32682100

Hermosillo Consulate General

Consulado Americano, Monterrey 141 entre las calles,
Rosales y Galeana, Col. Esqueda, C.P. 83260 Hermosillo, Sonora, Mexico
Mail: U.S. Consulate - Hermosillo, P.O. Box 1689,
Nogales, AZ 85628-1689
Tel: 52 (662) 289-3500 Fax: 52 (662) 217-1890

Consul General **Elia E. Tello** 52 (662) 289-3500
E-mail: telloee@state.gov
Consular Affairs Officer **Anthony W. Clare** 52 (662) 289-3500
Information Program Officer **(Vacant)** 52 (662) 289-3500
Management Officer **Carolyn K. Calderon** 52 (662) 289-3500
Regional Security Officer **Craig S. Belcher** 52 (662) 289-3500

Department of Homeland Security - U.S. Immigration and Customs Enforcement [Mexico]

Consulado Americano, Monterrey 141 entre las calles,
Rosales y Galeana, Col. Esqueda, C.P. 83000 Hermosillo, Sonora, Mexico
Mail: U.S. Consulate - Hermosillo, P.O. Box 1689,
Nogales, AZ 85628-1689
Tel: 52 (662) 212-3971 Fax: 52 (662) 212-4034

Customs Officer (Acting) **Oscar Diaz** 52 (662) 217-1109

Drug Enforcement Administration [Mexico]

DEA Officer **Jacob W. Gilliam** 52 (662) 289-3500

Matamoros Consulate General

U.S. Consulate - Matamoros, Mexico, Calle Primera #2002,
Col. Jardin, Matamoros, Tamaulipas, Mexico 87330
Mail: U.S. Consulate - Matamoros, P.O. Box 9004,
Brownsville, TX 78520-0904
Tel: 52 (868) 812-4402 Fax: 52 (868) 812-2171
E-mail: matamorosacs@state.gov

Consul General **Neda A. Brown** 52 (868) 812-4402
E-mail: brownna@state.gov
Education: Bennett 2001 BA; Fletcher Law & Diplomacy 2003 MALD
Consular Officer **Elizabth Alarid** 52 (868) 812-4402
Information Program Officer/Information Systems
Security Officer **Eric W. Burkett** 52 (868) 812-4402

(continued on next page)

Matamoros Consulate General *(continued)*

Management Officer **Claudia M. Coleman** 52 (868) 812-4402
Regional Security Officer **Joseph R. Wysowaty** 52 (868) 812-4402
E-mail: wysowatyj@state.gov
Political/Economic Officer **Jose A. Gutierrez** 52 (868) 812-4402

Merida Consulate General

U.S. Consulate - Merida, Mexico, Calle 60 No. 338-K por 29 y 31 Col. Alcala Martin, C.P., 97050 Merida, 97050, Yucatan, Mexico
Mail: U.S. Consulate - Merida, P.O. Box 9003, Brownsville, TX 78520-0903
Tel: 52 (999) 942-5700 Fax: 52 (999) 942-5758

Consul General **Courtney A. Beale** 52 (999) 942-5700
E-mail: bealeca@state.gov
Education: Georgetown 2002 BSFS; Princeton 2014 MPP
Consular Officer **Lioudmila Millman** 52 (999) 942-5700
Equal Employment Officer **(Vacant)** 52 (999) 942-5700
General Services Officer/Management Officer
Irene Arino De La Rubia 52 (999) 942-5700
Information Program Officer **Michael S. Durfee** 52 (999) 942-5700
Regional Security Officer **Christopher M. Keenan** 52 (999) 942-5700

Drug Enforcement Administration [Mexico]

U.S. Consulate - Merida, Mexico, Calle 60 No. 338-K por 29 y 31 Col. Alcala Martin, C.P., 97050 Merida, 97050, Yucatan, Mexico
Mail: U.S. Consulate - Merida, (DEA) P.O. Box 9003, Brownsville, TX 78520-0903
Tel: 52 (999) 942-5700 Fax: 52 (999) 942-5777

DEA Officer **Ramon De La Garza** 52 (999) 942-5700

Monterrey Consulate General

U.S. Consulate General - Monterrey, 150 Avenida Alfonso Reyes, 69196 Santa Catarina, Nuevo Leon, Mexico
Tel: 52 (81) 8047-3100 Fax: 52 (81) 8342-5433
E-mail: monterreyacs@state.gov

◇ Consul General **William H. Duncan** 52 (81) 8047-3100
E-mail: duncanw@state.gov
Consular Officer **Daniel B. King** 53 (41) 8047-3100
Fax: 52 (81) 8343-9399
Community Liaison Officer **Shavon McNeary** 53 (41) 8047-3100
Political/Economic Officer **Heidy Servin-Baez** 53 (41) 8047-3100
E-mail: ServinBaezH@state.gov Fax: 52 (81) 8342-0177
General Services Officer **John Thompson** 53 (41) 8047-3100
Information Program Officer **Stephen Stockdale** 52 (81) 8047-3100
Legal Attaché **Christopher Watkins** 52 (81) 8047-3100
Management Officer **Myrna Ortiz-Kerr** 52 (81) 8047-3100
Public Affairs Officer **Ruth N. Urry** 52 (81) 8047-3100
E-mail: urryrn@state.gov Fax: 52 (81) 8342-7970
Regional Security Officer **John Hicks** 52 (81) 8047-3100

Agricultural Section (Foreign Agricultural Service) - Agricultural Trade Office [Mexico]

150 Avenida Alfonso Reyes, 69196 Santa Catarina, Nuevo Leon, Mexico
Tel: 52 (81) 8047-3232 E-mail: atomonterrey@fas.usda.gov

Director **Orestes Vasquez** 52 (81) 8047-3266

Commercial Section (Foreign Commercial Service) [Mexico]

U.S. Consulate General - Monterrey, Mexico, Avenue Constitucion 411 Poniente, 64000 Monterrey, Nuevo Leon, Mexico
Mail: U.S. Consulate General - Monterrey, (FCS) P.O. Box 9002, Brownsville, TX 78520-0902
Tel: 52 (81) 8047-3450 Fax: 52 (81) 8047-3188

Principal Commercial Officer **Eric Olson** 52 (81) 8047-3223

Department of Homeland Security - U.S. Citizenship and Immigration Services [Mexico]

U.S. Consulate General - Monterrey, Mexico, Avenue Constitucion 411 Poniente, 64000 Monterrey, Nuevo Leon, Mexico
Mail: U.S. Consulate General - Monterrey, (INS) P.O. Box 9002, Brownsville, TX 78520-0902
Tel: 52 (81) 8345-2120 Fax: 52 (81) 8343-0543

CIS Officer in Charge **Joel Miramontes** ..... 52 (81) 8345-2120 ext. 448

Department of Homeland Security - U.S. Customs and Border Protection [Mexico]

U.S. Consulate General - Monterrey, Mexico, Avenue Constitucion 411 Poniente, 64000 Monterrey, Nuevo Leon, Mexico
Mail: U.S. ConGen- Monterrey, (U.S. Customs Service) P.O. Box 9002, Brownsville, TX 78520-0902
Tel: 52 (81) 8345-2120 Fax: 52 (81) 8343-2708

Customs Attaché **Dionicio Delgado** .... 52 (81) 8345-2120 ext. 425

Drug Enforcement Administration [Mexico]

U.S. Consulate General - Monterrey, Mexico, Avenue Constitucion 411 Poniente, 64000 Monterrey, Nuevo Leon, Mexico
Mail: U.S. Consulate General - Monterrey, (DEA) P.O. Box 9002, Brownsville, TX 78520-0902
Tel: 52 (81) 8345-2120 Fax: 52 (81) 8342-0177

DEA Officer **Mark Ayoob** 52 (81) 8345-2120

Nogales Consulate General

U.S. Consulate - Nogales, Mexico, Calle San Jose S/N, Fraccionamiento los Alamos, Nogales, Sonora, Mexico C.P. 84065
Mail: U.S. Consulate Nogales, P.O. Box 1729, Nogales, AZ 85628
Tel: 52 (631) 311-8150 Fax: 52 (631) 313-4652

Consul General **Virginia Louise Staab** 52 (631) 311-8150
E-mail: staabvl@state.gov
Consular Officer **James M. Harvey** 52 (631) 311-8150
E-mail: harveyjm@state.gov
Equal Employment Officer **Clifton Funkhouser** 52 (631) 311-8150
E-mail: funkhousercm@state.gov
General Services/Management Officer
Charles A. Matack 52 (631) 311-8150
Information Program Officer **Avril S. Brewster** 52 (631) 311-8150
E-mail: brewsteras@state.gov
Regional Security Officer **Pablo J. Rojas** 52 (631) 311-8150
Political/Economic Officer **(Vacant)** 52 (631) 311-8150

Nuevo Laredo Consulate General

U.S. Consulate - Nuevo Laredo Mexico, Paseo Colon 1901, Colonia Madero, 88260 Nuevo Laredo, Tamaulipas, Mexico
Mail: U.S. Consulate - Nuevo Laredo, Box 3089, Laredo, TX 78044-3089
Tel: 52 (867) 714-0512 Fax: 52 (867) 714-7984

Consul General
Kathryn L. "Kate" Flachsbart .... 52 (867) 714-0017 ext. 100
E-mail: flachsbartkl@state.gov
Education: Georgetown 1997 BSFS
Office Management Specialist to the Consul
General **Sonia Guerra** 52 (867) 714-0512
Consular Officer **Jennifer Becker** .... 52 (867) 714-0512 ext. 105
Information Management Officer
Jesus Alejandro .... 52 (867) 714-0512 ext. 129
E-mail: alejandroj@state.gov
General Services Officer/Management
Officer **William Harrison** .... 52 (867) 714-0512 ext. 129
Regional Security Officer **Paul Sanchez** 52 (867) 714-0512
Political Officer **Chad Wesen** 52 (867) 714-0512

★ Presidential Appointment Requiring Senate Confirmation ☆ Presidential Appointment ☐ Schedule C Appointment ◇ Career Senior Foreign Service Appointment
● Career Senior Executive Service (SES) Appointment ○ Non-Career Senior Executive Service (SES) Appointment ■ Postal Career Executive Service

Tijuana Consulate General

U.S. Consulate General, Paseo de las Culturas s/n,,
Mesa de Otay, 22425 Tijuana, Mexico
Mail: U.S. Consulate General - Tijuana, P.O. Box 439039,
San Diego, CA 92143-9039
Tel: 52 (664) 977-2000 Fax: 52 (664) 622-7417

◇ Consul General **Sue Ellen Saarnio** 52 (664) 622-7497
E-mail: saarniose@state.gov
Education: Macalester 1980 BA
Office Management Specialist to the Consul General **Myrtha Quiros** 52 (664) 977-2000
E-mail: quirosml@state.gov
Deputy Principal Officer/Consular Officer **Cynthia A. Haley** 52 (664) 622-7413
Community Liaison Officer **Michelle Unger** 52 (664) 622-7400
Equal Employment Officer **Shella Biallas** 52 (664) 622-7400
General Services Officer **William M. Morgan** 52 (664) 622-7400
Information Program Officer **Robert H. "Bob" Weed** 52 (664) 622-7653
E-mail: weedrh@state.gov
Legal Attaché **Enrique Corral** 52 (664) 977-2000
Management Officer **Glenn Lewis** 52 (664) 622-7619
Political and Economic Affairs Section Chief **Bridget M. Premont** 52 (664) 977-2000
E-mail: premontbm@state.gov
Public Affairs Officer **(Vacant)** 52 (664) 622-7639
Regional Security Officer **Anna M. Kephart** 52 (664) 622-7464

Department of Homeland Security - U.S. Immigration and Customs Enforcement [Mexico]

U.S. Consulate General - Tijuana, Mexico,
Tapachula 96, Mexico City, B.C.N. 22420, Mexico
Mail: U.S. Consulate General - Tijuana, P.O. Box 439039,
San Diego, CA 92143-9039
Tel: 52 (664) 622-7400 Fax: 52 (664) 622-7607

Senior ICE Representative **(Vacant)** 52 (664) 622-7400

Drug Enforcement Administration [Mexico]

U.S. Consulate General - Tijuana, Mexico,
Tapachula 96, Mexico City, B.C.N. 22420, Mexico
Mail: U.S. Consulate General - Tijuana, P.O. Box 439039,
San Diego, CA 92143-9039
Tel: 52 (664) 622-7400 Fax: 52 (664) 622-5019

DEA Officer **Manuel "Manny" Castanon** 52 (664) 622-7452

U.S. Embassy in Nicaragua

Km. 5 1/2 Carretera Sur., Managua, Nicaragua
Tel: 505 (2) 252-7100 Fax: 505 (2) 2252-7250 Internet: ni.usembassy.gov

Office of the U.S. Ambassador to Nicaragua

American Embassy - Managua, Nicaragua,
Km. 5 1/2 Carretera Sur., Managua, Nicaragua
Mail: American Embassy - Managua, Nicaragua, APO, AA 34021

★ Ambassador **Ambassador Kevin K. Sullivan** 505 (2) 252-7100
E-mail: sullivankk@state.gov
Education: Georgetown BA; Princeton MPP
◇ Chargé d'Affaires **Chad Parker Cummins** 505 (2) 252-7100
E-mail: cumminscp@state.gov
Education: Westmont 1991 BA; American U 1995 MA; National War Col 2015 MS
Office Management Specialist to the Ambassador **Vivian W. Richter** 505 (2) 252-7100
E-mail: richtervw@state.gov
◇ Deputy Chief of Mission **Chad Parker Cummins** 505 (2) 252-7100
E-mail: cumminscp@state.gov
Education: Westmont 1991 BA; American U 1995 MA; National War Col 2015 MS
Office Management Specialist to the Deputy Chief of Mission **Lawrence Johnson** 505 (2) 252-7100
Community Liaison Officer **(Vacant)** 505 (2) 252-7100
Consul General (Acting) **Joachim Van Brandt** 505 (2) 252-7100
E-mail: vanbrandtj@state.gov
Education: Maryland 2004 BA

Office of the U.S. Ambassador to Nicaragua *(continued)*

Economic/Commercial Officer **Trevor Gudie** 505 (2) 252-7100
E-mail: gudiet@state.gov
Financial Management Officer **Boubacar Ide** 505 (2) 252-7100
E-mail: ideb@state.gov
General Services Officer **(Vacant)** 505 (2) 252-7100
Human Resources Officer **Philip D. Wilson** 505 (2) 252-7100
E-mail: wilsonpd@state.gov
Information Management Officer **Jack H. Carollo** 505 (2) 252-7100
E-mail: carollojh@state.gov
Information Program Officer **(Vacant)** 505 (2) 252-7100
Information Systems Officer **Joseph Fagg** 505 (2) 252-7100
E-mail: faggjd@state.gov
Information Systems Security Officer **(Vacant)** 505 (2) 252-7100
Management Officer **Carolyn N. Cooley** 505 (2) 252-7100
Narcotics Affairs Officer **(Vacant)** 505 (2) 252-7100
Political Officer **Jonathan T. Austin** 505 (2) 252-7100
E-mail: AustinJT@state.gov
Public Affairs Officer **(Vacant)** . . . . . 505 (2) 252-7100 ext. 7598
Fax: 505 (2) 252-7260
Regional Security Officer **Roger K. Vansanford** 505 (2) 252-7100
E-mail: vansanfordrk@state.gov

Agency for International Development [Nicaragua]

American Embassy - Managua, Nicaragua,
Km. 5 1/2 Carretera Sur., Managua, Nicaragua
Mail: American Embassy - Managua, Nicaragua, APO, AA 34021
Tel: 505 (2) 252-7100 Fax: 505 (2) 252-7324
Internet: www.usaid.gov/nicaragua

Mission Director **Theodore "Ted" Gehr** 505 (2) 252-7806
E-mail: tgehr@usaid.gov
Education: Oregon

Agricultural Section (Foreign Agricultural Service) [Nicaragua]

American Embassy - Managua, Nicaragua,
Km. 5 1/2 Carretera Sur., Managua, Nicaragua
E-mail: agmanagua@fas.usda.gov
Internet: nicaragua.usembassy.gov/fas.html

Agricultural Counselor (Resident in San Jose) **Anita Katial** 506 2519-2000
E-mail: anita.katial@fas.usda.gov

Drug Enforcement Administration [Nicaragua]

American Embassy - Managua, Nicaragua,
Km. 5 1/2 Carretera Sur., Managua, Nicaragua
Mail: American Embassy - Managua, Nicaragua, APO, AA 34021
Tel: 505 (2) 252-7100 Fax: 505 (2) 252-7260

DEA Officer **James Rodriguez** 505 (2) 252-7100

Federal Aviation Administration (Resident in Panama) [Nicaragua]

American Embassy - Panama City, Panama,
Building 783, Demetrio Basilio Lakas Avenue,
Clayton, Panama City, 5, Panama
Mail: American Embassy - Panama City, Panama, Unit 0945,
APO, AA 34002

FAA Representative **Carl N. Johnson** 507 317-5046

Internal Revenue Service (Resident in Panama City) [Nicaragua]

American Embassy - Panama City, Panama,
Building 783, Demetrio Basilio Lakas Avenue,
Clayton, Panama City, 5, Panama
Mail: American Embassy - Panama City, Panama, Unit 0945,
APO, AA 34002

IRS Officer **Carlos Orozco** 507 317-5159

Office of the Defense Attaché [Nicaragua]

American Embassy - Managua, Nicaragua,
Km. 5 1/2 Carretera Sur., Managua, Nicaragua
Mail: American Embassy - Managua, Nicaragua, APO, AA 34021
Tel: 505 (2) 252-7100 Fax: 505 (2) 252-7620

Defense Attaché **COL Darren Lynn USA** 505 (2) 252-7100

DEPARTMENTS

★ Presidential Appointment Requiring Senate Confirmation ☆ Presidential Appointment ☐ Schedule C Appointment ◇ Career Senior Foreign Service Appointment
● Career Senior Executive Service (SES) Appointment ○ Non-Career Senior Executive Service (SES) Appointment ■ Postal Career Executive Service

DEPARTMENTS

Peace Corps [Nicaragua]
American Embassy - Managua, Nicaragua,
Km. 5 1/2 Carretera Sur., Managua, Nicaragua
Mail: American Embassy - Managua, Nicaragua, APO, AA 34021
Tel: 505 (2) 252-7100 Fax: 505 (2) 252-7660
Internet: www.peacecorps.gov/nicaragua

Country Director **Howard T. Lyon** 505 (2) 252-7100
E-mail: hlyon@peacecorps.gov

U.S. Embassy in Panama

Building 783, Demetrio Basilio Lakas Avenue,
Clayton, Panama City, 5, Panama
Tel: 507 317-5000 Fax: 507 317-5568 E-mail: panamaweb@state.gov

Office of the U.S. Ambassador to Panama
American Embassy - Panama City, Panama,
Building 783, Demetrio Basilio Lakas Avenue,
Clayton, Panama City, 5, Panama
Mail: American Embassy - Panama City, Panama, Unit 0945,
APO, AA 34002

★ Ambassador **(Vacant)** 507 317-5000
◇ Chargé d'Affaires **Roxanne J. Cabral** 507 317-5000
E-mail: cabralrj@state.gov
Education: Vanderbilt BA; Johns Hopkins MPH
Office Management Specialist to the Ambassador
Dominique S. Emery 507 317-5000
E-mail: emeryds@state.gov
Deputy Chief of Mission (Acting) **Elias S. Baumann** 507 317-5000
E-mail: baumannes@state.gov
Office Management Specialist to the Deputy Chief of
Mission **Mary M. Navarro** 507 317-5000
Community Liaison Officer **Dawn German** 507 317-5000
Consul General **Adrienne L. Harchik** 507 317-5000
E-mail: harchikal@state.gov
Economic Officer **Isabel E. Rioja-Scott** 507 317-5000
E-mail: rioja-scottie@state.gov
Education: Pennsylvania 2001 BA
Financial Management Officer **Jenny Potter** 507 317-5000
General Services Officer **Matthew J. Miller** 507 317-5000
E-mail: millermj@state.gov
Information Management Officer **Jaime Scarpatti** 507 317-5000
Information Program Officer **Leonel Ruiz** 507 317-5000
Information Systems Officer **Gonzalo Saldias** 507 317-5000
Information Systems Security Officer **(Vacant)** 507 317-5000
Legal Attaché **Rafael Ruiz** 507 317-5000
Management Officer (Acting) **Matthew J. Miller** 507 317-5000
E-mail: millermj@state.gov
Narcotics Affairs Officer **David Foran** 507 317-5000
Political Officer **Ryan Rowlands** 507 317-5000
E-mail: rowlandsr@state.gov
Political/Economic Officer **(Vacant)** 507 317-5000
Public Affairs Officer **Francisco Paco Perez** 507 317-5000
E-mail: perezfp@state.gov
Regional Security Officer **Thomas Rhodes** 507 317-5000

Agricultural Section (Foreign Agricultural Service) [Panama]
American Embassy - Panama City, Panama,
Building 783, Demetrio Basilio Lakas Avenue,
Clayton, Panama City, 5, Panama
Tel: 507 317-5064 E-mail: agpanamacity@fas.usda.gov

Agricultural Counselor (Resident in San Jose)
Anita Katial 506 2519-2000
E-mail: anita.katial@fas.usda.gov

Animal and Plant Health Inspection Service [Panama]
American Embassy - Panama City, Panama,
Apartado 6959, Panama City, 5, Panama
Mail: American Embassy - Panama City, Panama, Unit 0945,
APO, AA 34002
Tel: 507 207-7000 Fax: 507 232-6647

APHIS Officer **Dr. Antonio Arroyave** 507 207-7043

Commercial Section (Foreign Commercial Service) [Panama]
American Embassy - Panama City, Panama,
Apartado 6959, Panama City, 5, Panama
Mail: American Embassy - Panama City, Panama, Unit 0945,
APO, AA 34002
Tel: 507 207-7000 Fax: 507 317-5573 Internet: export.gov/panama

Senior Commercial Officer **Laura Gimenez** 507 317-5388
E-mail: laura.gimenez@trade.gov

Department of Homeland Security - U.S Immigration and Customs Enforcement
American Embassy - Panama City, Panama,
Apartado 6959, Panama City, 5, Panama
Mail: American Embassy - Panama City, Panama, Unit 0945,
APO, AA 34002
Tel: 507 207-7000 Fax: 507 225-7084

Immigration Attaché **Stephen Kleppe** 507 207-7000

Department of Homeland Security - U.S. Customs and Border Protection [Panama]
American Embassy - Panama City, Panama,
Apartado 6959, Panama City, 5, Panama
Mail: American Embassy - Panama City, Panama, Unit 0945,
APO, AA 34002
Tel: 507 207-7000 Fax: 507 227-1713

Customs Attaché **Michael Vargas** 507 207-7000
Education: U Phoenix BS

Drug Enforcement Administration [Panama]
American Embassy - Panama City, Panama,
Apartado 6959, Panama City, 5, Panama
Mail: American Embassy - Panama City, Panama, Unit 0945,
APO, AA 34002
Tel: 507 207-7000 Fax: 507 227-1964

DEA Attaché **Michael J. Sanders** 507 207-7000

Federal Aviation Administration [Panama]
FAA Representative **Carl N. Johnson** 507 317-5046

Internal Revenue Service [Panama]
American Embassy - Panama City, Panama,
Building 783, Demetrio Basilio Lakas Avenue,
Clayton, Panama City, 5, Panama
Mail: American Embassy - Panama City, Panama, Unit 0945,
APO, AA 34002

IRS Officer **Carlos Orozco** 507 317-5159

Office of the Defense Attaché [Panama]
American Embassy - Panama City, Panama,
Apartado 6959, Panama City, 5, Panama
Mail: American Embassy - Panama City, Panama, Unit 0945,
APO, AA 34002
Tel: 507 207-7000 Fax: 507 225-2453

Defense Attaché **CAPT Matthew Turner USN** 507 207-7000

Peace Corps [Panama]
American Embassy - Panama City, Panama,
Apartado 6959, Panama City, 5, Panama
Mail: American Embassy - Panama City, Panama, Unit 0945,
APO, AA 34002
Tel: 507 269-2100 Fax: 507 269-2123
Internet: www.peacecorps.gov/panama

Country Director **Diane Carazas** 507 269-2100

★ Presidential Appointment Requiring Senate Confirmation ☆ Presidential Appointment ☐ Schedule C Appointment ◇ Career Senior Foreign Service Appointment
● Career Senior Executive Service (SES) Appointment ○ Non-Career Senior Executive Service (SES) Appointment ■ Postal Career Executive Service

U.S. Embassy in Paraguay

1776 Mariscal Lopez Avenue, Castilla Postal 402, Asuncion, Paraguay
Tel: 595 (21) 213-715 Fax: 595 (21) 213-728
E-mail: paraguayusembassy@state.gov Internet: py.usembassy.gov

Office of the U.S. Ambassador to Paraguay

American Embassy - Asuncion, Paraguay, 1776 Mariscal Lopez Avenue, Casilla Postal 402, Asuncion, Paraguay
Mail: American Embassy - Asuncion, Paraguay, Unit 4700, APO, AA 34036-0001

★ Ambassador **Ambassador M. Lee McClenny** 595 (21) 213-715
E-mail: mcclennyml@state.gov
Education: U Washington BA
Office Management Specialist to the Ambassador **(Vacant)** 595 (21) 213-715
◇ Deputy Chief of Mission **Hugo F. Rodriguez, Jr.** 595 (21) 213-715
E-mail: rodriguezh@state.gov
Office Management Specialist to the Deputy Chief of Mission **(Vacant)** 595 (21) 213-715
Community Liaison Officer **Kathryn Morse** 595 (21) 213-715
Consular Section Chief **Karen K. Wiebelhaus** 595 (21) 213-715
E-mail: wiebelhauskk@state.gov
Drug Enforcement Administration Attaché **Eric B. Barnard** 595 (21) 213-715
Economic/Commercial Officer **Charles L. Wheeler** 595 (21) 213-715
E-mail: WheelerCL@state.gov
Financial Management Officer **Ronald Jay "Jay" Kryk** 595 (21) 213-715
E-mail: krykrj@state.gov
General Services Officer **Virgile G. Borderies** 595 (21) 213-715
E-mail: borderiesvg@state.gov
Information Management Officer **Darrell H. Chapman** 595 (21) 213-715
E-mail: chapmandh@state.gov
Education: Virginia Tech 1990 BS
Information Programs Officer **Cuba L. Edwards** 595 (21) 213-715
Information Systems Officer **Kevin R. Lee** 595 (21) 213-715
E-mail: leekr@state.gov
Information Systems Security Officer **Adam Duboise** 595 (21) 213-715
Legal Attaché **(Vacant)** 595 (21) 213-715
Management Officer **Miriam Elise "Elise" Tokumasu Da Silva** 595 (21) 213-715
E-mail: tokumasume1@state.gov
Political and Economic Section Chief **Michael Shane "Shane" Hough** 595 (21) 213-715
E-mail: houghms@state.gov
Public Affairs Officer **Kathleen Marie "Kathy" Guerra** 595 (21) 213-715
E-mail: guerrakm@state.gov Fax: 595 (21) 212-312
Regional Security Officer **Federico Casso** 595 (21) 213-715

Agency for International Development [Paraguay]

Juan de Salazar 364 c/ Artigas, Asuncion, Paraguay
Mail: American Embassy - Asuncion, Paraguay, Unit 4734, APO, AA 34036-0000
Fax: 595 (21) 213-732 E-mail: usaidparaguay@usaid.gov
Internet: www.usaid.gov/paraguay

◇ Country Representative (Acting) **Wayne R. Nilsestuen** 595 (21) 220-715
Education: Wisconsin 1972 MA, 1972 MPA

Agricultural Section (Foreign Agricultural Service) (Resident in Buenos Aires) [Paraguay]

American Embassy - Buenos Aires, Argentina, Colombia 4300, 1425 Buenos Aires, Argentina
Mail: American Embassy - Buenos Aires, Unit 4325, APO, AA 34034
Tel: 54 (11) 5777-4627 Fax: 54 (11) 5777-4216
E-mail: agbuenosaires@fas.usda.gov
Internet: ar.usembassy.gov/embassy/fas

Agricultural Counselor **M. Melinda Meador** 54 (11) 5777-4841
E-mail: melinda.meador@fas.usda.gov

Federal Aviation Administration (Resident in Brazil) [Paraguay]

FAA Senior Representative **Paul Leandro Friedman** 55 (61) 8116-5291
E-mail: paul.friedman@faa.gov

Internal Revenue Service (Resident in Mexico City) [Paraguay]

American Embassy - Mexico City, Mexico, Paseo de la Reforma 305M, Mexico City, D.F. 06500, Mexico
Mail: American Embassy - Mexico City, Mexico, P.O. Box 3087, Laredo, TX 78044-3087
Tel: 52 (55) 5080-2000 Fax: 52 (55) 5080-2882

IRS Officer **George Peralta** . . . . 52 (55) 5080-2000 ext. 2901

Office of Defense Cooperation [Paraguay]

American Embassy - Asuncion, Paraguay, 1776 Mariscal Lopez Avenue, Castilla Postal 402, Asuncion, Paraguay
Mail: American Embassy - Asuncion, Paraguay, Unit 4742, APO, AA 34036-0000
Tel: 595 (21) 213-715 Fax: 595 (21) 213-728

Defense Cooperation Officer **Col. Corey Michael Tejchma USA** 595 (21) 213-715

Office of the Defense Attaché [Paraguay]

American Embassy - Asuncion, Paraguay, 1776 Mariscal Lopez Avenue, Castilla Postal 402, Asuncion, Paraguay
Mail: American Embassy - Asuncion, Paraguay, Unit 4736, APO, AA 34036-0000
Tel: 595 (21) 213-715 Fax: 595 (21) 213-728

Defense Attaché **Col. Corey Michael Tejchma USA** . . . 595 (21) 213-715

Peace Corps [Paraguay]

American Embassy - Asuncion, Paraguay, 1776 Mariscal Lopez Avenue, Castilla Postal 402, Asuncion, Paraguay
Mail: American Embassy - Asuncion, Paraguay, Unit 4744, APO, AA 34036-0000
Tel: 595 (21) 600-155 Fax: 595 (21) 606-650
Internet: www.peacecorps.gov/paraguay

Country Director **Kate Raftery** 595 (21) 600-155
Education: Central Conn State U 1973 BA

U.S. Embassy in Peru

Avenida La Encalada Cuadra 17, s/n Surco, Lima, 33, Peru
Tel: 51 (1) 618-2000 Fax: 51 (1) 618-2397 Internet: pe.usembassy.gov

Office of the U.S. Ambassador to Peru

American Embassy - Lima, Peru, Avenida La Encalada cuadra 17, s/n, Surco, Lima, 33, Peru
Mail: American Embassy - Lima, Peru, APO, AA 34031-5000
Tel: 51 (1) 618-2000 Fax: 51 (1) 618-2397
E-mail: lima_webmaster@state.gov Internet: pe.usembassy.gov

★ Ambassador **Ambassador Krishna R. "Kris" Urs** 385 (52) 6182000
E-mail: urskr@state.gov
Education: Georgetown 1980 BSFS; Texas 1985 MEc
Office Management Specialist to the Ambassador **Mikkela Thompson** 385 (52) 6182000
◇ Deputy Chief of Mission **Mark A. Wells** 385 (52) 6182000
E-mail: wellsm@state.gov
Office Management Specialist to the Deputy Chief of Mission **Lizbeth Gonzales** 385 (52) 6182000
Community Liaison Officer **Megan Kuhn** 385 (52) 6182000
◇ Consul General **Denison Kyle Offutt** 385 (52) 6182000
E-mail: offuttdk@state.gov
Economic Affairs Officer **James "Jim" Potts** 385 (52) 618-2000
E-mail: econlima@state.gov
Equal Employment Opportunity Officer **(Vacant)** 385 (52) 618-2000
Fax: 51 (1) 561-2034
Facilities Management Officer **Richard Marrs** 51 (1) 618-2000
Financial Management Officer **James "Jim" Wickersham** 385 (52) 618-2000
E-mail: WickershamJD@state.gov
General Services Officer **Carla Gonneville** 385 (52) 618-2000
E-mail: GonnevilleCA@state.gov Fax: 51 (1) 226-1205

(continued on next page)

★ Presidential Appointment Requiring Senate Confirmation ☆ Presidential Appointment ☐ Schedule C Appointment ◇ Career Senior Foreign Service Appointment
● Career Senior Executive Service (SES) Appointment ○ Non-Career Senior Executive Service (SES) Appointment ■ Postal Career Executive Service

DEPARTMENTS

Office of the U.S. Ambassador to Peru *(continued)*

Human Resources Officer **Mark I. Mishkin** 51 (1) 618-2000
E-mail: mishkinmi@state.gov
Information Management Officer **Paul J. Echaniz** 385 (52) 618-2000
E-mail: EchanizPJ@state.gov
Education: Boston U 1995 MS
Information Programs Officer **Nathan McDaniel** 385 (52) 618-2000
Information Systems Officer **Joshua J. Walde** 385 (52) 618-2000
E-mail: WaldeJJ@state.gov
Information Systems Security Officer **Ricardo Perez** 51 (1) 618-2000
Management Officer **Leo F. Voytko, Jr.** 51 (1) 618-2443
E-mail: VoytkoLF@state.gov Fax: 51 (1) 434-1302
Narcotics Affairs Officer **Alberto Rodriguez** 385 (52) 618-2000
Political Affairs Officer **(Vacant)** 385 (52) 618-2000
Public Affairs Officer **Judith Ravin** 385 (52) 618-2000
E-mail: ravinj@state.gov Fax: 51 (1) 434-1299
Regional Security Officer
Donald E. Gonneville . . . . 385 (52) 618-2000 ext. 2497
E-mail: GonnevilleDE@state.gov

Agency for International Development [Peru]
Agency for International Development, Avenida La Encalada Cuadra 17, s/n Monterrico, Surco, Lima, 33, Peru
Mail: American Embassy - Lima, Peru, APO, AA 34031-5000
Tel: 51 (1) 618-1200 Fax: 51 (1) 618-1350 Internet: www.usaid.gov/peru

Mission Director **Lawrence Rubey** 51 (1) 618-1220
E-mail: lrubey@usaid.gov
Education: Northwestern BA; Boston U MA; Michigan State PhD

Agricultural Section (Foreign Agricultural Service) [Peru]
American Embassy - Lima, Peru, Avenida La Encalada Cuadra 17, s/n Surco, Lima, 33, Peru
Mail: American Embassy - Lima, Peru, APO, AA 34031-5000
Tel: 51 (1) 434-3042 Fax: 51 (1) 434-3043 E-mail: aglima@fas.usda.gov

Agricultural Counselor **Michael Riedel** 51 (1) 434-3042
E-mail: michael.riedel@fas.usda.gov
Education: Western Michigan 1994 BA; George Washington 2000 MA

Animal and Plant Health Inspection Service [Peru]
American Embassy, Avenida La Encalada Cuadra 17, s/n Surco, Lima, 33, Peru
Fax: 51 (1) 434-1302

APHIS Regional Officer **Russell A. Duncan** 51 (1) 618-2732
E-mail: Russell.A.Duncan@aphis.usda.gov

Commercial Section (Foreign Commercial Service) [Peru]
American Embassy - Lima, Peru, Avenida La Encalada cuadra 17, s/n Surco, Lima, 33, Peru
Mail: U.S. Commercial Service, American Embassy, Unit 3780, APO, AA 34031
Tel: 51 (1) 434-3040 Fax: 51 (1) 434-3041 E-mail: office.lima@trade.gov
Internet: export.gov/peru

Senior Commercial Officer **Val Eugene Huston** 51 (1) 618-2442
E-mail: val.huston@trade.gov

Department of Homeland Security - U.S. Citizenship and Immigration Services [Peru]
American Embassy - Lima, Peru, Avenida La Encalada Cuadra 17, s/n Surco, Lima, 33, Peru
Mail: American Embassy - Lima, Peru, APO, AA 34031-5000
Tel: 51 (1) 549-2653 Fax: 51 (1) 434-2483

Immigration Attaché **William Lujan** 51 (1) 549-2653

Drug Enforcement Administration [Peru]
Drug Enforcement Officer **Carlos L. Mitchem** 51 (1) 618-2000
Fax: 51 (1) 434-3054

Federal Aviation Administration (Resident in Brazil) [Peru]
American Embassy - Brasilia, Brazil, Avenida das Nações, Quadra 801, Lote 3 Brasilia, 70403-900, Brazil
Mail: American Embassy - Brasilia, Brazil, Unit 3500, APO, AA 34030
Fax: 55 (61) 3312-7295

FAA Senior Representative
Paul Leandro Friedman 55 (61) 8116-5291
E-mail: paul.friedman@faa.gov

Internal Revenue Service (Resident in Mexico City) [Peru]
American Embassy - Mexico City, Mexico, Paseo de la Reforma 305M, Mexico City, D.F. 06500, Mexico
Mail: American Embassy - Mexico City, Mexico, P.O. Box 3087, Laredo, TX 78044-3087
Tel: 52 (55) 5080-2000 Fax: 52 (55) 5080-2882

IRS Officer **George Peralta** . . . . 52 (55) 5080-2000 ext. 2901

Office of the Defense Attaché [Peru]
American Embassy - Lima, Peru, Avenida La Encalada cuadra 17, s/n Surco, Lima, 33, Peru
Mail: American Embassy - Lima, Peru, APO, AA 34031-5000
Tel: 51 (1) 549-2421 Fax: 51 (1) 434-0117

Naval and Defense Attaché **Scott Johnson** 51 (1) 549-2421

Peace Corps [Peru]
Avenida La Encalada Cuadra 17, s/n Surco, Lima, 33, Peru
Mail: American Embassy - Peru, APO, AA 34031-5000
Tel: 51 (1) 434-3000 Fax: 51 (1) 434-3037
Internet: www.peacecorps.gov/peru

Country Director **Parmer Heacox** 51 (1) 434-3000
E-mail: pheacox@peacecorps.gov

U.S. Embassy in Suriname

165 Kristalstraat, Paramaribo, Suriname
Tel: 597 556-700 Fax: 597 410972 Internet: sr.usembassy.gov

Office of the U.S. Ambassador to Suriname

American Embassy - Paramaribo, Suriname, 165 Kristalstraat, Paramaribo, Suriname
Mail: American Embassy - Paramaribo, Suriname, 3390 Paramaribo Place, Washington, DC 20521-3390

★ Ambassador **Karen Lynn Williams** 597 556-700
Note: On November 8, 2018, Karen Williams was sworn in as Ambassador to Suriname.
Education: Drury Col BA; National War Col 2006 MNSSS
Chargé d'Affaires **Graham L. Webster** 597 556-700
E-mail: webstergl@state.gov
Education: Florida International BS; Florida MA
Office Management Specialist to the Ambassador
Joy Blake 597 556-700
Deputy Chief of Mission **Graham L. Webster** 597 556-700
E-mail: webstergl@state.gov
Education: Florida International BS; Florida MA
Community Liaison Officer **Jai Shamdasani** 597 556-700
Consular Section Officer **Rob M. Pastore** 597 556-700
E-mail: pastorerm@state.gov
Economic Officer **(Vacant)** 597 556-700
General Services Officer **Kory A. Strickland** 597 556-700
Information Management Officer **Veronica Johnson** 597 556-700
Education: St Mary's U (TX) 2001 MBA
Information Program Officer **(Vacant)** 597 556-700
Information Systems Security Officer **(Vacant)** 597 556-700
Management Officer **Michelle M. Mason** 597 556-700
Education: Chaminade 1998 BS; Fax: 597 410972
American InterContinental 2005 MEd
Political Officer **Christy Doherty** 597 556-700
Political/Economic Officer **Timothy J. "Joe" Relk** 597 556-700
E-mail: relktj@state.gov
Public Affairs Officer **Patrick Geraghty** 597 556-700
Regional Security Officer **Steven Johnston** 597 556-700

★ Presidential Appointment Requiring Senate Confirmation ☆ Presidential Appointment ☐ Schedule C Appointment ◇ Career Senior Foreign Service Appointment
● Career Senior Executive Service (SES) Appointment ○ Non-Career Senior Executive Service (SES) Appointment ■ Postal Career Executive Service

Agricultural Section (Foreign Agricultural Service) (Resident in Caracas) [Suriname]
American Embassy - Caracas, Venezuela, Calle F con Calle Suapure, Colinas de Valle Arriba, P.O. Box 62291, Caracas, 1060-A, Venezuela
Mail: American Embassy - Caracas, Venezuela, APO, AA 34037
Tel: 58 (212) 907-8333 Fax: 58 (212) 907-8542

Agricultural Officer **(Vacant)** 58 (212) 907-8332

Drug Enforcement Administration (Resident in Curacao) [Suriname]
U.S. Consulate General - Curacao, Netherlands Antilles, J. B. Gorsiraweg #1, Willemstad, Curaçao
Mail: U.S. Consulate General - Curacao, N.A., Department of State, Washington, DC 20521-3160
Tel: 599 (9) 4616985 Fax: 599 (9) 4613192

DEA Officer **J. Gregory Garza** 599 (9) 4616985

Federal Aviation Administration (Resident in Florida) [Suriname]
American Embassy - Paramaribo, Suriname, 165 Kristalstraat, Paramaribo, Suriname
Fax: (954) 641-6706

FAA Representative **Alex D. Rodriguez** .... (202) 267-0426

Internal Revenue Service (Resident in Mexico City) [Suriname]
American Embassy - Mexico City, Mexico, Paseo de la Reforma 305, Mexico City, D.F. 06500, Mexico
Mail: American Embassy - Mexico City, Mexico, P.O. Box 3087, Laredo, TX 78044-3087
Tel: 52 (55) 5080-2000 Fax: 52 (55) 5080-2882

IRS Officer **(Vacant)** .... 52 (55) 5080-2000 ext. 2901

Office of the Defense Attaché (Resident in Brazil) [Suriname]
American Embassy - Brasilia, Brazil, Avenida das Nações, Quadra 801, Lote 3 Brasilia, 70403-900, Brazil
Mail: American Embassy - Brasilia, Brazil, Unit 3500, APO, AA 34030
Tel: 55 (61) 3312-7000 Fax: 55 (61) 3312-7676

Defense Attaché **LCDR Paolo Carcavallo USN** 55 (61) 3312-7000

U.S. Embassy in Trinidad and Tobago

15 Queen's Park West, P.O. Box 752, Port of Spain, Trinidad and Tobago
Tel: 1 (868) 622-6371 Fax: 1 (868) 822-5905 Internet: tt.usembassy.gov

Office of the U.S. Ambassador to Trinidad and Tobago

American Embassy - Port of Spain, Trinidad and Tobago, 15 Queen's Park West, P.O. Box 752, Port of Spain, Trinidad and Tobago
Mail: Department of State, 3410 Port of Spain Place, Washington, DC 20521-3410

★ Ambassador
Ambassador Joseph N. "Joe" Mondello 1 (868) 622-6371-6
Education: Hofstra 1962 BA; New England 1969 JD
Office Management Specialist to the Ambassador
Monica L. Morse 1 (868) 622-6371-6

Deputy Chief of Mission **John W. McIntyre** 1 (868) 622-6371-6
E-mail: mcintyrejw@state.gov
Education: Wisconsin 1993 BA; Kansas 1996 MPA
Office Management Specialist to the Deputy Chief of Mission **Monica L. Morse** 1 (868) 622-6371-6

Consular Officer **Timothy C. Swanson** 1 (868) 622-6371-6
Community Liaison Officer **(Vacant)** 1 (868) 622-6371-6
Economic/Commercial Officer
Matthew Ciesielski 1 (868) 622-6371-6
E-mail: CiesielskiMM@state.gov Fax: 1 (868) 622-2444
Financial Management Officer **(Vacant)** 1 (868) 622-6371-6
General Services Officer **Hyun Yoon** 1 (868) 622-6371-6
Information Management Officer
Glenn S. Shellahamer 1 (868) 622-6371-6
E-mail: ShellahamerGS@state.gov
Information Systems Security Officer
Glenn S. Shellahamer 1 (868) 622-6371-6
E-mail: ShellahamerGS@state.gov
Legal Attaché **Robert Price** 1 (868) 622-6371-6
Management Officer **Mary K. Gunn** 1 (868) 622-6371-6
Fax: 1 (868) 622-2571

Office of the U.S. Ambassador to Trinidad and Tobago *(continued)*

Military Liaison Officer
COL Claudia Carrizales USA 1 (868) 822-5943
E-mail: claudia.j.carrizales.mil@mail.mil
Political/Economic Officer **Kyle Fonay** 1 (868) 622-6371-6
E-mail: fonaykw@state.gov
Public Affairs Officer **Adam J. "AJ" Jagelski** 1 (868) 622-5979
E-mail: JagelskiAJ@state.gov Fax: 1 (868) 628-7944
Regional Security Officer **Robert Byrd** 1 (868) 622-6371-6

Agricultural Trade Office - Caribbean Basin
Caribbean Basin Agricultural Trade Office, Brickell Plaza Federal Building, 909 SE 1st Avenue, Suite 720, Miami, FL 33131
Tel: (305) 536-5300 Fax: (305) 536-7577
E-mail: atocaribbeanbasin@fas.usda.gov

Director **Richard J. Battaglia** .... (305) 536-5300
E-mail: richard.battaglia@fas.usda.gov

Commercial Section (Foreign Commercial Service) (Resident in Santo Domingo) [Trinidad and Tobago]
Avenue Pedro Henriquez Urena 133, Edificio Empressarial Reyna 1, La Esperilla, Santo Domingo, Dominican Republic
Mail: Unit 5500, APO, AA 54041
E-mail: office.santodomingo@trade.gov

Senior Regional Commercial Officer
Bryan Larson .... 1 (809) 567-7775 ext. 7249
E-mail: bryan.larson@trade.gov
Education: Colorado 1991 BA; American U 1995 MA

Department of Homeland Security - Customs and Border Protection [Trinidad and Tobago]
American Embassy - Port of Spain, Trinidad and Tobago, 15 Queen's Park West, P.O. Box 752, Port of Spain, Trinidad and Tobago
Tel: 1 (868) 622-6371

Customs Attaché **Arthlyn Samuel** 1 (868) 625-6604

Federal Aviation Administration (Resident in Florida) [Trinidad and Tobago]
11410 NW 20th Street, Suite 250, Miami, FL 33172

FAA Representative **Alex D. Rodriguez** .... (202) 267-0426

Office of the Defense Attaché (Resident in Caracas) [Trinidad and Tobago]
Calle con Supaure, Colinas de valle arriba, Caracas, DF 1080, Venezuela
Tel: 58 (212) 975-9620

Defense Attaché **José Estrada** 58 (212) 975-9620

U.S. Embassy in Uruguay

American Embassy - Montevideo, Uruguay, Lauro Muller 1776, 11200 Montevideo, Uruguay
Tel: 598 (2) 1770-2000 Fax: 598 (2) 1770-2128
Internet: uy.usembassy.gov

Office of the U.S. Ambassador to Uruguay

American Embassy - Montevideo, Uruguay, Lauro Muller 1776, 11200 Montevideo, Uruguay
Mail: American Embassy - Montevideo, Uruguay, Unit 3360, DPO, AA 34035
Tel: 598 (2) 1770-2000 Fax: 598 (2) 1770-2128
E-mail: webmastermvd@pd.state.gov Internet: uy.usembassy.gov

★ Ambassador
Ambassador Kelly A. Keiderling-Franz 598 (2) 1770-2000
E-mail: keiderlingka@state.gov
Education: Georgetown BS; National Defense U MS

★ Ambassador-Designate
Kenneth S. "Kenn" George 598 (2) 1770-2000
Education: Washington and Lee BA; Texas MBA
Office Management Specialist to the Ambassador
Enriqueta "Kittie" Tamayo 598 (2) 1770-2300
E-mail: tamayoe@state.gov

(continued on next page)

Office of the U.S. Ambassador to Uruguay *(continued)*

Deputy Chief of Mission
Nicholas Joseph Giacobbe, Jr. 598 (2) 1770-2301
E-mail: giacobbenj@state.gov
Office Management Specialist to the Deputy Chief of Mission **Adrienne L. Gersnoviez-Frybarger** ... 598 (2) 1770-2301
E-mail: gersnoviez-frybarger@state.gov
Consul **Leslie A. Linnemeier** 598 (2) 1770-2315
Community Liaison Officer **Kirsten L. Labion** 598 (2) 1770-2442
E-mail: montevideoclo@state.gov
Community Liaison Officer **(Vacant)** 598 (2) 1770-2302
E-mail: montevideoclo@state.gov
Economic and Commercial Officer
Michael J. Schreuder 598 (2) 1770-2495
E-mail: schreudermj@state.gov
Regional Financial Management Officer (Resident in Florida) **(Vacant)** .... (954) 630-1167
General Services Officer **Karen Doig** 598 (2) 1770-2367
Information Management Officer (Acting)
Richard Barsanti 598 (2) 1770-2780
E-mail: barsantir@state.gov
Information Program Officer **Richard Barsanti** 598 (2) 1770-2780
E-mail: barsantir@state.gov
Information Systems Officer (Acting)
Richard Barsanti 598 (2) 1770-2185
E-mail: barsantir@state.gov
Management Officer **David J. Kloesel** 598 (2) 1770-2369
E-mail: kloeseldj@state.gov
Political/Economic Officer **Lance K. Hegerle** 598 (2) 1770-2320
E-mail: hegerlelk@state.gov Fax: 598 (2) 418-8581
Public Affairs Officer (Acting) **Nicholas J. Sesnak** ... 598 (2) 1770-2374
E-mail: sesnaknj@state.gov Fax: 598 (2) 410-9775
Education: Cal Poly San Luis Obispo 2004 BA; Oregon State 2006 MA
Regional Security Officer (Acting)
Natalie M. Baker 598 (2) 1770-2319
Education: Miami U (OH) 2009 BA; Hawaii Pacific 2012 MA
Webmaster **Juan F. Casal** 598 (2) 1770-2161
E-mail: casaljf@state.gov
Information Systems Security Officer
Dennis J. Maldonado 598 (2) 1770-2780
E-mail: maldonadodj@state.gov

Agricultural Section (Foreign Agricultural Service) (Resident in Buenos Aires) [Uruguay]
American Embassy - Buenos Aires, Argentina,
Colombia 4300, 1425 Buenos Aires, Argentina
Mail: American Embassy - Buenos Aires, Unit 3130, DPO, AA 34034
Tel: 54 (11) 5777-4533 Fax: 54 (11) 5777-4216
E-mail: agbuenosaires@usda.gov

Agricultural Counselor **M. Melinda Meador** 54 (11) 5777-4841
E-mail: melinda.meador@fas.usda.gov

Animal and Plant Health Inspection Service (APHIS) (Resident in Brasilia) [Uruguay]
American Embassy - Montevideo, Uruguay,
Lauro Muller 1776, 11200 Montevideo, Uruguay
Tel: 55 (61) 3312-7019 Fax: 55 (61) 3312-7659

Area Director **(Vacant)** 55 (61) 3312-7589

Department of Homeland Security - U.S. Immigration and Customs Enforcement (Resident in Buenos Aires) [Uruguay]
American Embassy - Montevideo, Uruguay,
Lauro Muller 1776, 11200 Montevideo, Uruguay
Tel: 54 (11) 5777-4483 Fax: 54 (11) 5777-4489

Customs Attaché **David Emond** 54 (11) 5777-4482

Drug Enforcement Administration [Uruguay]
American Embassy - Montevideo, Uruguay,
Lauro Muller 1776, 11200 Montevideo, Uruguay
Tel: 598 (2) 1770-2332

Country Attaché **Nelson Vargas, Jr.** 598 (2) 1770-2529
E-mail: nelson.vargas2@usdoj.gov
Education: St Joseph's Col (NY) 1999 BS

Federal Aviation Administration (Resident in Brazil) [Uruguay]
American Embassy - Montevideo, Uruguay,
Lauro Muller 1776, 11200 Montevideo, Uruguay
Tel: 55 (61) 3312-7580 Fax: 55 (61) 3312-7295

FAA Senior Representative
Paul Leandro Friedman 55 (61) 8116-5291
E-mail: paul.friedman@faa.gov

Internal Revenue Service (Resident in Mexico City) [Uruguay]
American Embassy - Mexico City, Mexico,
Paseo de la Reforma 305, Mexico City, D.F. 06500, Mexico
Mail: (IRS) U.S. Logistics Center, 225 Vermillion Road, Brownsville, TX 78520-0900
Tel: 52 (55) 5080-2000 Fax: 52 (55) 5080-2882

IRS Officer **George Peralta** .... 52 (55) 5080-2000 ext. 2901

Office of the Defense Attaché [Uruguay]
American Embassy - Montevideo, Uruguay,
Lauro Muller 1776, 11200 Montevideo, Uruguay
Mail: American Embassy - Montevideo, Uruguay, Unit 3360, DPO, AA 34035
Tel: 598 (2) 413-1617 Fax: 598 (2) 413-1619

Army Attaché **Col Lawrence E. Pravecek USAF** 598 (2) 1770-2324
E-mail: lawrence.e.pravecek.mil@mail.mil

Office of Defense Cooperation [Uruguay]
American Embassy - Montevideo, Uruguay,
Lauro Muller 1776, 11200 Montevideo, Uruguay
Mail: American Embassy - Montevideo, Uruguay, Unit 3360, DPO, AA 34035
Tel: 598 (2) 418-8163 Fax: 598 (2) 411-8678

Senior Defense Official/Defense Attaché
Col Lawrence E. Pravecek USAF 598 (2) 1770-2346
E-mail: lawrence.e.pravecek.mil@mail.mil

U.S. Embassy in Venezuela

Calle F con Calle Suapure, Colinas de Valle Arriba, P.O. Box 62291, Caracas, 1060-A, Venezuela
Tel: 58 (212) 975-6411 Fax: 58 (212) 907-8106
Internet: ve.usembassy.gov

Office of the U.S. Ambassador to Venezuela

American Embassy - Caracas, Venezuela,
Calle F con Calle Suapure, Urb. Colinas de Valle Arriba, Caracas, 1080, Venezuela
Mail: American Embassy - Caracas, Venezuela, DPO, AA 34037

★ Ambassador **(Vacant)** 58 (212) 975-6411
☆ Chargé d'Affaires
James Broward "Jimmy" Story 58 (212) 975-6411
E-mail: storyjb@state.gov
Education: South Carolina 1993 BA; Georgetown 1997 MSFS
Office Management Specialist to the Chargé d'Affaires **LeShawn Mapp** 58 (212) 975-6411
E-mail: MappLT@state.gov
Deputy Chief of Mission
James Broward "Jimmy" Story 58 (212) 975-6411
E-mail: storyjb@state.gov
Education: South Carolina 1993 BA; Georgetown 1997 MSFS
Office Management Specialist to the Deputy Chief of Mission **Heidi J. Sierra** 58 (212) 975-6411
E-mail: sierrahj@state.gov
Education: National U 2010 BA
Consul General (Acting)
William R. "Reb" Dowers 58 (212) 975-6411
E-mail: dowerswr@state.gov
Consular Officer **Christopher J. Pistulka** 58 (212) 975-6411
E-mail: pistulkacj@state.gov
Community Liaison Officer **Michelle Lawton** 58 (212) 975-6411
Economic Officer **Anthony Eterno** 58 (212) 975-6411
E-mail: eternoar@state.gov
Financial Management Officer **Jeffrey Smith** 58 (212) 975-6411
General Services Officer **Malene Carr** 58 (212) 975-6411

★ Presidential Appointment Requiring Senate Confirmation ☆ Presidential Appointment ☐ Schedule C Appointment ◇ Career Senior Foreign Service Appointment
● Career Senior Executive Service (SES) Appointment ○ Non-Career Senior Executive Service (SES) Appointment ■ Postal Career Executive Service

Office of the U.S. Ambassador to Venezuela *(continued)*

Information Management Officer (Acting)
Bruce G. Sherry 58 (212) 975-6411
E-mail: sherrybg@state.gov
Information Program Officer **Scott S. Alper** 58 (212) 975-6411
E-mail: alperss@state.gov
Education: Penn State BA; George Mason MA
Information Systems Officer (Acting)
Jeffrey D. Hiatt 58 (212) 975-6411
E-mail: hiattjd@state.gov
Information Systems Security Officer **(Vacant)** 58 (212) 682-6411
Legal Attaché **(Vacant)** 58 (212) 975-6411
Fax: 58 (212) 975-9629
◇ Management Officer **Christopher A. Lambert** 58 (212) 975-6411
E-mail: lambertca@state.gov Fax: 58 (212) 975-9429
◇ Political Officer **Willard Tenney Smith** 58 (212) 975-6411
E-mail: smithwt@state.gov
Education: BYU 1985; Texas 1992; Indust'l Col Armed Forces 2011
◇ Public Affairs Officer **Rebecca B. Thompson** 58 (212) 907-8550
E-mail: thompsonrb@state.gov Fax: 58 (212) 907-8243
E-mail: CaracasPress@state.gov
Regional Security Officer (Acting) **Marlon Grullon** . . . 58 (212) 975-6411
Fax: 58 (212) 975-8972

Agricultural Section (Foreign Agricultural Service) [Venezuela]
American Embassy - Caracas, Venezuela,
Calle F con Calle Suapure, Urb. Colinas de Valle Arriba, Caracas, 1080, Venezuela
Mail: American Embassy - Caracas, Venezuela, APO, AA 34037
Tel: 58 (212) 907-8333 Fax: 58 (212) 907-8542
E-mail: agcaracas@fas.usda.gov
Agricultural Attaché **(Vacant)** 58 (212) 907-8332

Department of Homeland Security - U.S. Immigration and Customs Enforcement [Venezuela]
American Embassy - Caracas, Venezuela,
Calle F con Calle Suapure, Urb. Colinas de Valle Arriba, Caracas, 1080, Venezuela
Mail: American Embassy - Caracas, Venezuela, APO, AA 34037
Tel: 58 (212) 975-9110 Fax: 58 (212) 975-6556
Customs Attaché **(Vacant)** . . . . . (3) 975-9110

Drug Enforcement Administration [Venezuela]
American Embassy - Caracas, Venezuela,
Calle F con Calle Suapure, Urb. Colinas de Valle Arriba, Caracas, 1080, Venezuela
Mail: American Embassy - Caracas, Venezuela, APO, AA 34037
Tel: 58 (212) 975-8910 Fax: 58 (212) 975-9146
DEA Country Attaché **Marc Ando** 58 (212) 975-6411

Federal Aviation Administration (Resident in Florida) [Venezuela]
American Embassy - Caracas, Venezuela,
Calle F con Calle Suapure, Urb. Colinas de Valle Arriba, Caracas, 1080, Venezuela
Fax: 55 (61) 3312-7295
FAA Representative **Alex D. Rodriguez** . . . . . (202) 267-0426

Internal Revenue Service (Resident in Mexico City) [Venezuela]
American Embassy - Mexico City, Mexico,
Paseo de la Reforma 305, Mexico City, D.F. 06500, Mexico
Mail: (IRS) U.S. Logistics Center, 225 Vermillion Road, Brownsville, TX 78520-0900
Tel: 52 (55) 5080-2000 Fax: 52 (55) 5080-2882
IRS Officer **George Peralta** . . . . . 52 (55) 5080-2000 ext. 2901

Office of the Defense Attaché [Venezuela]
American Embassy - Caracas, Venezuela,
Calle F con Calle Suapure, Urb. Colinas de Valle Arriba, Caracas, 1080, Venezuela
Mail: American Embassy - Caracas, Venezuela, APO, AA 34037
Tel: 58 (212) 975-9620 Fax: 58 (212) 975-6542
Defense Attaché **José Estrada** 58 (212) 975-9620

U.S. Mission to the International Civil Aviation Organization (ICAO)

999 Robert-Bourassa Blvd, Suite 1410, Montreal, Quebec, Canada H3C 5J9
Mail: U.S. Mission to ICAO, P.O. Box 847, Champlain, NY 12919-0847
Tel: 1 (514) 954-8304 Fax: 1 (514) 954-8021 E-mail: usa@icao.int
Internet: icao.usmission.gov

★ U.S. Representative
Ambassador Thomas L. "Tom" Carter 1 (514) 954-8304
Education: U Memphis BS; Georgetown MA
Office Management Specialist to the U.S. Representative **Kevin M. Wood** 1 (514) 954-8306
Deputy Chief of Mission **Charlie H. Ashley III** 1 (514) 954-8304
E-mail: ashleych@state.gov
Air Navigation Commissioner and Alternate U.S. Representative **James Mark "Mark" Reeves** 1 (514) 954-8304
Civil Aviation Assistant **Belinde Riedler** 1 (514) 954-8304
E-mail: RiedlerB@state.gov

CENTRAL AND SOUTH ASIA

U.S. Embassy in Afghanistan

American Embassy - Kabul, Afghanistan,
The Great Masood Road, Kabul, Afghanistan
Tel: 93 (0)700-10-8000 Fax: 93 (0)700-108-564

Office of the U.S. Ambassador to Afghanistan
American Embassy - Kabul, Afghanistan,
The Great Masood Road, Kabul, Afghanistan
Mail: Department of State, 6180 Kabul Place, Washington, DC 20521-6180

★ Ambassador **Ambassador John R. Bass** . . . . . 93 (0)700-10-8000
E-mail: bassjr@state.gov
Education: Syracuse BA
Office Management Specialist to the Ambassador
Theresa Gibson . . . . . 93 (0)700-10-8000
◇ Deputy Chief of Mission **Karen B. Decker** . . . . . 93 (0)700-10-8000
E-mail: deckerk@state.gov
Education: Georgetown 1987 BSFS
Office Management Specialist to the Deputy Chief of Mission **Paulette Sides** . . . . . 93 (0)700-10-8000
◇ Assistant Chief of Mission
James P. "Jim" DeHart . . . . . 93 (0)700-10-8000
E-mail: dehartjp@state.gov
Education: Gonzaga BA; George Washington MIA
Community Liaison Officer **Elaine Fields** . . . . . 93 (0)700-10-8000
E-mail: fieldsex@state.gov
Consul General **Carson Wu** . . . . . 93 (0)700-10-8000
Economic Officer **Douglas Alan "Doug" Morris** . . . . . 93 (0)700-10-8000
E-mail: morrisda@state.gov
Deputy Economic Officer **Eric M. Frater** . . . . . 93 (0)700-10-8000
E-mail: fraterem@state.gov
Equal Employment Officer **(Vacant)** . . . . . 93 (0)700-10-8000
Facilities Management Officer **James Milletary** . . . . . 93 (0)700-10-8000
E-mail: milletaryj@state.gov
Financial Management Officer **Kevin M. Doyle** . . . . . 93 (0)700-10-8000
E-mail: doylekm@state.gov
General Services Officer **Charles Hughes** . . . . . 93 (0)700-10-8000
E-mail: hughesc2@state.gov
Human Resources Officer **Jami Papa** . . . . . 93 (0)700-10-8000
Information Management Officer **Mark J. Davis** . . . . . 93 (0)700-10-8000
Information Program Officer
James W. "Jim" Bayer . . . . . 93 (0)700-10-8000
Education: Virginia 2002 MS
Information Security Officer **John L. Nave** . . . . . 93 (0)700-10-8000
E-mail: navejl@state.gov
Information Systems Security Officer
Steven A. "Steve" Pearson . . . . . 93 (0)700-10-8000
E-mail: pearsons@state.gov
Legal Attaché **Mark S. McKinnie** . . . . . 93 (0)700-10-8000
E-mail: mckinniems@state.gov

(continued on next page)

★ Presidential Appointment Requiring Senate Confirmation ☆ Presidential Appointment □ Schedule C Appointment ◇ Career Senior Foreign Service Appointment
● Career Senior Executive Service (SES) Appointment ○ Non-Career Senior Executive Service (SES) Appointment ■ Postal Career Executive Service

Office of the U.S. Ambassador to Afghanistan *(continued)*

◇ Management Officer **Lawrence G. "Larry" Richter** . . . 93 (0)700-10-8000
E-mail: richterlg@state.gov
Education: Wheaton (IL) 1981 BA

Narcotics Affairs Officer **Marc L. Shaw** . . . . 93 (0)700-10-8000
E-mail: shawml@state.gov
Education: Emory 1997 BEc; Johns Hopkins MA

Deputy Narcotics Affairs Officer
Christopher "Chris" Andino . . . . 93 (0)700-10-8000
E-mail: andinocl@state.gov
Education: Virginia 2003 BA

Political Officer **David Burger** . . . . 93 (0)700-10-8000
Education: Virginia 1989 BA, 1990 MA

Political/Military Officer **Raymond "Ray" Hotz** . . . . . . 93 (0)700-10-8000
Education: High Point 1986 BS; Northern Illinois 1991 MBA

◇ Public Affairs Officer **William A. "Will" Ostick** . . . . . . 93 (0)700-10-8000
E-mail: ostickwa@state.gov
E-mail: kabulpressoffice@state.gov
Education: Georgia 1988 ABJ

Regional Security Officer **(Vacant)** . . . . 93 (0)700-10-8000

Agency for International Development [Afghanistan]

Great Masood Road, Kabul, Afghanistan
Mail: AID, Department of State, 6180 Kabul Place,
Washington, DC 20521-6180
Tel: (301) 490-1042 E-mail: kblaiddocinformation@usaid.gov
Internet: https://www.usaid.gov/afghanistan

◇ Mission Director **Herbert "Herbie" Smith** . . . . 93 (0)700-10-8000
E-mail: hsmith@usaid.gov
Education: Delaware BA; American U MA

Deputy Mission Director
Tamra Halmrast-Sanchez . . . . 93 (0)700-10-8000
E-mail: thalmrast-sanchez@usaid.gov

Deputy Mission Director **(Vacant)** . . . . 93 (0)700-10-8000

Deputy Mission Director **Jeffery P. Cohen** . . . . 93 (0)700-10-8000
E-mail: jcohen@usaid.gov

Agricultural Section (Foreign Agricultural Service) (Resident in Dubai) [Afghanistan]

American Consulate General -, Al Seef Road - Bur Dubai, Dubai,
United Arab Emirates

Counselor **Kurt F. Seifarth** 971 (4) 309-4902

Commercial Section (Foreign Commercial Service) [Afghanistan]

Senior Commercial Officer **(Vacant)** . . . . (301) 490-1042 ext. 8498
Fax: (703) 524-2649

Drug Enforcement Administration [Afghanistan]

Great Masood Road, Kabul, Afghanistan
Mail: DEA, Department of State, 6180 Kabul Place,
Washington, DC 20521-6180

DEA Officer **Yong Kim** . . . . 93 (0)700-10-8000

Office of the Defense Attaché [Afghanistan]

Great Masood Road, Kabul, Afghanistan
Mail: Defense Attache, Department of State,
6180 Kabul Place, Washington, DC 20521-6180

Defense Attaché **COL Darren R. Smith USA** . . . . 93 (0)700-10-8000

U.S. Embassy in Bangladesh

American Embassy - Diplomatic Enclave, Madani Avenue,
Baridhara, Dhaka, Bangladesh
Tel: 880 (2) 5566-2000 Fax: 880 (2) 5566-2910
E-mail: dhakapa@state.gov

Office of the U.S. Ambassador to Bangladesh

American Embassy - Diplomatic Enclave, Madani Avenue,
Baridhara, Dhaka, Bangladesh
Mail: Department of State, 6120 Dhaka Place,
Washington, DC 20521-6120

★ Ambassador
Ambassador Marcia Stephens Bloom Bernicat . . . 880 (2) 5566-2000
E-mail: bernicatms@state.gov
Education: Lafayette 1975 BA; Georgetown 1980 MS

★ Ambassador **Ambassador Earl Robert Miller** 880 (2) 5566-2000
Note: On October 11, 2018, the Senate confirmed Earl Miller to be Ambassador to Bangladesh.
E-mail: millerer@state.gov
Education: Michigan BA; Marine Corps Command Col
Office Management Specialist to the Ambassador
Erné Guzman 880 (2) 5566-2000

◇ Deputy Chief of Mission **Joel Richard Reifman** 880 (2) 5566-2000
E-mail: reifmanjr@state.gov
Office Management Specialist to the Deputy Chief of Mission **(Vacant)** 880 (2) 5566-2000

Consular Officer **Donald F. Mulligan** 880 (2) 5566-2000
E-mail: mulligandf@state.gov

Economic Officer **Chad S. Peterson** 880 (2) 5566-2000
E-mail: petersoncs@state.gov
Education: DePauw 1992 BA; Boston U 1994 MA;
London School Econ (UK) 2002 PhD

Equal Employment Officer **Jennifer Garcia** 880 (2) 5566-2000

Information Management Officer **Gaspar Guzman** . . . 880 (2) 5566-2000
E-mail: guzmang@state.gov

Information Program Officer **Gerard Abamonte** 880 (2) 5566-2000

Information Systems Officer **Mohamed Farah** 880 (2) 5566-2000

Information Systems Security Officer **(Vacant)** 880 (2) 5566-2000

Management Officer **Dawn F. Scott** 880 (2) 5566-2000
Community Liaison Officer **Shateel Bin Salah** 880 (2) 5566-2000
Financial Management Officer
Fredericak Carreon 880 (2) 5566-2000
General Services Officer
Gwendolyn G. Llewellyn 880 (2) 5566-2000
Human Resource Officer **William Nix** 880 (2) 5566-2000

Legal Attaché **James Price** 880 (2) 5566-2000

Public Affairs Officer **Nicholas Papp** 880 (2) 5566-2000

Regional Medical Officer **(Vacant)** 880 (2) 5566-2000

Regional Security Officer **William Noone** 880 (2) 5566-2000

Political/Economic/Commercial Officer
William E. "Bill" Moeller III 880 (2) 5566-2000
E-mail: moellerwe@state.gov
Education: Syracuse 1984 BA; Columbia 1990 MIA

Agency for International Development [Bangladesh]

American Embassy - Diplomatic Enclave, Madani Avenue,
Baridhara, Dhaka, Bangladesh
Mail: Department of State, 6120 Dhaka Place,
Washington, DC 20521-6120
Tel: 880 (2) 5566-2000 E-mail: idhaka@usaid.gov
Internet: https://www.usaid.gov/bangladesh

◇ Mission Director **Derrick S. Brown** 880 (2) 5566-2000
E-mail: derrick@usaid.gov
E-mail: idhaka@usaid.gov
Education: Alabama State BS; Maryland MS

★ Presidential Appointment Requiring Senate Confirmation ☆ Presidential Appointment ☐ Schedule C Appointment ◇ Career Senior Foreign Service Appointment
● Career Senior Executive Service (SES) Appointment ○ Non-Career Senior Executive Service (SES) Appointment ■ Postal Career Executive Service

Agricultural Section (Foreign Agricultural Service) [Bangladesh]
American Embassy - Diplomatic Enclave, Madani Avenue, Baridhara, Dhaka, Bangladesh
Mail: Department of State, 6120 Dhaka Place, Washington, DC 20521-6120
Tel: 880 (2) 883-7155 Fax: 880 (2) 882-0207
E-mail: agdhaka@fas.usda.gov

Counselor for Agricultural Affairs (Resident in New Delhi) **Jeanne Bailey** 91 (11) 2419-8769
E-mail: jeanne.bailey@fas.usda.gov
Agricultural Attaché **Mark A. Myers** 880 (2) 883-7155
E-mail: mark.myers@fas.usda.gov

Federal Aviation Administration (Resident in New Delhi) [Bangladesh]
American Embassy - New Delhi, Shanti Path, Chanakyapuri, New Delhi, 110 021, India
Mail: Department of State, 9000 New Delhi Place, Washington, DC 20521-9000
Fax: 91 (11) 2419-0003

FAA Representative **Thomas M. "Tom" Miller** 91 (11) 2419-8403

Office of the Defense Attaché [Bangladesh]
American Embassy - Diplomatic Enclave, Madani Avenue, Bairdhara, Dhaka, Bangladesh
Mail: Department of State, 6120 Dhaka Place, Washington, DC 20521-6120

Defense Attaché **Kyle Marcrum** 880 (2) 5566-2000

U.S. Embassy in India

American Embassy - New Delhi, India, Shanti Path, Chanakyapuri, 110021 New Delhi, India
Tel: 91 (11) 2419-8000 Fax: 91 (11) 2419-0017
E-mail: ndwebmail@state.gov Internet: in.usembassy.gov

Office of the U.S. Ambassador to India

American Embassy - New Delhi, India, Shanti Path, Chanakyapuri, New Delhi, 110 021, India
Mail: Department of State, 9000 New Delhi Place, Washington, DC 20521-9000

★ Ambassador
Ambassador Kenneth Ian "Ken" Juster 91 (11) 2419-8000
Education: Harvard 1976 AB, 1980 MPP, 1980 JD
Office Management Specialist to the Ambassador
Teresa A. Bills 91 (11) 2419-8000
E-mail: billsta@state.gov

◇ Deputy Chief of Mission **MaryKay Loss Carlson** 91 (11) 2419-8000
E-mail: carlsonml@state.gov
Education: Georgetown 1985 MA; National War Col 2007 MNSSS
Office Management Specialist to the Deputy Chief of Mission **Roland Elliott** 91 (11) 2419-8000

◇ Consular Affairs Officer **Joseph M. Pomper** 91 (11) 2419-8000
E-mail: pomperjm@state.gov
Education: Brandeis AB; Johns Hopkins 1982 MA; Tulane JD

Community Liaison Officer **Karime Kasey** 91 (11) 2419-8000
E-mail: kaseyk@state.gov

◇ Economic, Environmental, Science and Technology Officer **J. Robert "Rob" Garverick** 91 (11) 2419-8000
E-mail: garverickjr@state.gov
Education: Kent State 1986 BA; George Washington 1989 MBA; National Defense U 2014 MSS

Facilities Management Officer **Mark Schroeppel** 91 (11) 2419-8000
E-mail: SchroeppelM@state.gov

Financial Management Officer **Fred J. Mauren** 91 (11) 2419-8000
E-mail: maurenf@state.gov

General Services Officer **Lynn A. Nelson** 91 (11) 2419-8000
E-mail: nelsonl@state.gov

Human Resources Officer **Heather Grant** 91 (11) 2419-8000

Information Management Officer
George M. Navadel 91 (11) 2419-8000
E-mail: navadelgm@state.gov

Office of the U.S. Ambassador to India *(continued)*

Information Program Officer
Raemona Willis-Middlebrooks 91 (11) 2419-8000
E-mail: willis-middlebrooksr@state.gov

Information Systems Officer **Mark Allen** 91 (11) 2419-8000

Information Systems Security Officer
Sekou X. Dembele 91 (11) 2419-8000
E-mail: DembeleSX@state.gov

Legal Attaché **(Vacant)** 91 (11) 2419-8000

Management Officer **Michael B. Phillips** 91 (11) 2419-8000
E-mail: phillipsmb@state.gov

◇ Political Affairs Officer **Lesslie C. "Les" Viguerie** 91 (11) 2419-8000
E-mail: viguerielc@state.gov
Education: George Washington 1982 BA; Catholic U 1985 JD

◇ Public Affairs Officer **David Kennedy** 91 (11) 2419-8000
Education: Harvard 1983 AB; George Washington MA; UMass (Amherst) MBA

◇ Cultural Affairs Officer **Conrad W. Turner** 91 (11) 2419-8000
E-mail: turnercw@state.gov
Education: Haverford 1981 BA; Bryn Mawr 1990 MA

Spokesperson **Jinnie Lee** 91 (11) 2419-8000
Education: Wellesley 1999 BA; Princeton 2012 MPP

Regional Security Officer
Gregary J. "Greg" Levin 91 (11) 2419-8000
E-mail: levingj@state.gov

Agency for International Development [India]
American Embassy - New Delhi, India, Shanti Path, Chanakyapuri, New Delhi, 110 021, India
Mail: American Embassy, Department of State, 9000 New Delhi Place, Washington, DC 20521-9000
Tel: 91 (11) 2419-8000 Fax: 91 (11) 2419-8612
E-mail: indiaprogramsupport@usaid.gov
Internet: https://www.usaid.gov/india

◇ Mission Director **Mark Anthony White** 91 (11) 2419-8000
Education: Xavier (OH) BS; North Carolina MPH

Agricultural Section (Foreign Agricultural Service) [India]
American Embassy - New Delhi, India, Shanti Path, Chanakyapuri, New Delhi, 110 021, India
Mail: American Embassy, Department of State, 9000 New Delhi Place, Washington, DC 20521-9000
Tel: 91 (11) 2419-8769 Fax: 91 (11) 2419-8530
E-mail: agnewdelhi@fas.usda.gov

◇ Counselor for Agricultural Affairs **Jeanne Bailey** 91 (11) 2419-8769
E-mail: jeanne.bailey@fas.usda.gov

Centers for Disease Control [India]
Centers for Disease Control Officer
Dr. Kayla Laserson 91 (11) 2419-8000
E-mail: klaserson@cdc.gov

Commercial Section (Foreign Commercial Service) [India]
New Delhi American Center, 24, Kasturba Gandhi Marg, New Delhi, 110001, India
Mail: American Embassy, Department of State, 9000 New Delhi Place, Washington, DC 20521-9000
Tel: 91 (11) 2347-2000 Fax: 91 (11) 2331-5172
E-mail: office.newdelhi@trade.gov Internet: export.gov/india

◇ Senior Commercial Officer (Acting)
Mary Aileen "Aileen" Nandi 91 (11) 2347-2000
E-mail: aileen.nandi@trade.gov
Education: Richmond BA; Georgetown MA

Deputy Senior Commercial Officer (Acting)
Gregory Taevs 91 (11) 2347-2194
E-mail: gregory.taevs@trade.gov
Education: Cal State (Long Beach) MBA

★ Presidential Appointment Requiring Senate Confirmation ☆ Presidential Appointment ☐ Schedule C Appointment ◇ Career Senior Foreign Service Appointment
● Career Senior Executive Service (SES) Appointment ○ Non-Career Senior Executive Service (SES) Appointment ■ Postal Career Executive Service

DEPARTMENTS

Department of Homeland Security - U.S. Citizenship and Immigration Services [India]
American Embassy - New Delhi, India,
Shanti Path, Chanakyapuri, New Delhi, 110 021, India
Mail: American Embassy, Department of State,
9000 New Delhi Place, Washington, DC 20521-9000
Tel: 91 (11) 2419-8000 Fax: 91 (11) 2419-0017

Field Office Director **Kenneth J. Sherman** 91 (11) 2419-8000
E-mail: shermankj@state.gov

Department of Homeland Security - U.S. Customs and Border Protection [India]
American Embassy - New Delhi, India,
Shanti Path, Chanakyapuri, 110021 New Delhi, India
E-mail: CBPNewDelhiInquiry@State.gov

Attaché **Erik D. Aubin** 91 (11) 2419-8640
E-mail: aubined@state.gov

Department of Homeland Security - U.S. Immigration and Customs Enforcement [India]
American Embassy - New Delhi, India,
Shanti Path, Chanakyapuri, 110021 New Delhi, India
Mail: 9000 New Delhi Place, Washington, DC 20521-9000
Tel: 91 (11) 2419-8000 Fax: 91 (11) 2419-0017

Attaché (Acting) **Udaykiran Devineni** 91 (11) 2419-8000
E-mail: DevineniU@state.gov

Department of Justice - Drug Enforcement Administration [India]
American Embassy - New Delhi, India,
Shanti Path, Chanakyapuri, New Delhi, 110 021, India
Mail: American Embassy, Department of State,
9000 New Delhi Place, Washington, DC 20521-9000
Tel: 91 (11) 2419-8000 Fax: 91 (11) 2419-0017

DEA Officer **Mark Frederick** 91 (11) 2419-8000

Federal Aviation Administration [India]
American Embassy - New Delhi, India,
Shanti Path, Chanakyapuri, New Delhi, 110 021, India
Fax: 91 (11) 2419-0003

FAA Representative **Thomas M. "Tom" Miller** 91 (11) 2419-8403

Library of Congress [India]
American Embassy - New Delhi, India,
Shanti Path, Chanakyapuri, New Delhi, 110 021, India
Mail: LOC-New Delhi, Department of State,
9000 New Delhi Place, Washington, DC 20521-9000
Tel: 91 (11) 2331-6841 Fax: 91 (11) 2419-0017
E-mail: newdelhi@loc.gov Internet: www.loc.gov/acq/ovop/delhi

Field Director **Laila Mulgaokar** 91 (11) 2331-6841
E-mail: newdelhi@loc.gov

Office of the Defense Attaché [India]
American Embassy - New Delhi, India,
Shanti Path, Chanakyapuri, New Delhi, 110 021, India
Mail: American Embassy, Department of State,
9000 New Delhi Place, Washington, DC 20521-9000
Tel: 91 (11) 2419-8000 Fax: 91 (11) 2419-0017

Senior Defense Official and Defense Attaché
BG David E. Brigham USA 91 (11) 2419-8000
Education: Norwich 1988 BS

Office of Defense Cooperation [India]
American Embassy - New Delhi, India,
Shanti Path, Chanakyapuri, New Delhi, 110 021, India
Mail: American Embassy, Department of State,
9000 New Delhi Place, Washington, DC 20521-9000
Tel: 91 (11) 2419-8415 Fax: 91 (11) 2419-0005

Chief **CAPT Robert F. Ogden USN** 91 (11) 2419-8415
E-mail: ogdenrf@state.gov

Chennai Consulate General
U.S. Consulate General - Chennai, India,
Gemini Circle, 220 Anna Salai, Chennai, 600006, India
Mail: Department of State, 6260 Chennai Place,
Washington, DC 20521-6260
Tel: 91 (44) 2857-4000 Fax: 91 (44) 2811-2020
E-mail: chennaic@state.gov

◇ Consul General **Robert G. Burgess** 91 (44) 2857-4000
E-mail: burgessrg@state.gov
Education: Colorado Col BA; Hastings JD;
National War Col 2012 MNSSS
Office Management Specialist to the Consul
General **Holly A. Wazelle** 91 (44) 2857-4000
E-mail: wazelleha@state.gov Fax: 91 (44) 2811-2022
Consular Section Chief **C. Kent May** 91 (44) 2857-4000
E-mail: mayck@state.gov Fax: 91 (44) 2811-2027
Community Liaison Officer **Kelsey Lyle** 91 (44) 2857-4000
Equal Employment Opportunity Officer
Holly A. Wazelle 91 (44) 2857-4000
E-mail: wazelleha@state.gov
General Service Officer **Andrew Holtz** 91 (44) 2857-4000
Information Program Officer
William C. "Bill" Bridgeland 91 (44) 2857-4000
E-mail: bridgelandwc@state.gov
Information Systems Security Officer **Pildong Choi** ... 91 (44) 2857-4000
E-mail: choip@state.gov
Management Officer **Alan E. Greenfield** 91 (44) 2857-4000
E-mail: greenfieldae@state.gov
Economic Officer **Joseph S. Bernath** 91 (44) 2875-4480
Political Officer **Johanna L. Fernando** 91 (44) 2875-4480
E-mail: fernandojl@state.gov
Public Affairs Officer **Lauren H. Lovelace** 91 (44) 2857-4000
E-mail: lovelacelh@state.gov Fax: 91 (44) 2811-2050
Regional Security Officer **Joseph W. Jung** 91 (44) 2857-4000
E-mail: jungjw@state.gov
Spokesperson **Alexis S. Wolff** 91 (44) 2857-4000
E-mail: wolffas@state.gov

Commercial Section (Foreign Commercial Service) [India]
U.S. Consulate General - Chennai, India,
Gemini Circle, 220 Anna Salai, Chennai, 600006, India
Mail: Department of State, 6260 Chennai Place,
Washington, DC 20521-6260
Tel: 91 (44) 2857-4477 Fax: 91 (44) 2857-4212
E-mail: office.chennai@trade.gov

◇ Principal Commercial Officer **James "Jim" Fluker** ... 91 (44) 2857-4477
E-mail: james.fluker@trade.gov

Hyderabad Consulate General
U.S. Consulate General - Hyderabad, India,
1-8-323, Chiran Fort Lane, Begumpet, Secunderabad, Hyderabad, India
Tel: 91 (40) 4625-8222

◇ Consul General **Katherine B. Hadda** 91 (40) 4625-8222
E-mail: haddakb2@state.gov
Office Management Specialist to the Consul
General **Melissa Bitter** 91 (40) 4625-8222
E-mail: bitterm@state.gov
Consular Section Chief **Eric M. Alexander** 91 (40) 4625-8222
E-mail: alexanderem@state.gov
Information Program Officer **Terrence Cooney** 91 (40) 4625-8222
Information Systems Security Officer
Terrence Cooney 91 (40) 4625-8222
General Services Officer **(Vacant)** 91 (40) 4625-8222
Management Officer **Paebo Kurian** 91 (40) 4625-8222
E-mail: kurianp@state.gov
Political/Economic Officer **Seth C. Peavey** 91 (40) 4625-8222
E-mail: peaveysc@state.gov
Public Affairs Officer **John D. "Drew" Giblin** 91 (40) 4625-8222
E-mail: giblinjd@state.gov
Education: Richmond 2003 BA; Chicago 2004 MA
Regional Security Officer **Arthur "Nick" Stankey** ... 91 (40) 4625-8222

★ Presidential Appointment Requiring Senate Confirmation ☆ Presidential Appointment □ Schedule C Appointment ◇ Career Senior Foreign Service Appointment
● Career Senior Executive Service (SES) Appointment ○ Non-Career Senior Executive Service (SES) Appointment ■ Postal Career Executive Service

Kolkata Consulate General (Calcutta Consulate General)
U.S. Consulate General - Calcutta, India,
38A, J.L.Nehru Road, Kolkata, 700071, West Bengal, India
Mail: U.S. Consulate General, Department of State,
6250 Calcutta Place, Dulles, VA 20189-6250
Tel: 91 (33) 3984-6300 Fax: 91 (33) 2288-1616

Consul General **Patricia L. "Patti" Hoffman** 91 (33) 3984-6300
E-mail: hoffmanpl@state.gov
Education: Columbia BA; Bristol U MIR; National War Col MNSSS
Office Management Specialist to the Consul General **Cassandra L. Lewis** 91 (33) 3984-6300
Consular Section Chief **Lee A. Calkins** 91 (33) 3984-6300
E-mail: calkinsla@state.gov
American Citizen Services: kolkataacs@state.gov
Consular Officer **Shoshauna A. Clark** 91 (33) 3984-6300
E-mail: clarksa@state.gov
Consular Officer **Julie A. Espinosa** 91 (33) 3984-6300
Consular Officer **Madelyn A. Mahon** 91 (33) 3984-6300
Information Programs Officer **Clinton E. Frith** 91 (33) 3984-6300
E-mail: frithce@state.gov
Management Officer **Rodney D. Cunningham** 91 (33) 3984-6300
E-mail: cunninghamrd@state.gov
General Services Officer **Sheena R. Hall** 91 (33) 3984-6300
Political/Economic Officer **Prasenjit R. Gupta** 91 (33) 3984-6300
E-mail: guptap@state.gov
Public Affairs Officer **James A. "Jamie" Dragon** 91 (33) 3984-6300
38A, Jawaharlal Nehru Road, Kolkata, 700071, India
E-mail: dragonja@state.gov
Assistant Public Affairs Officer **Jay B. Treloar** 91 (33) 3984-6300
38A, Jawaharlal Nehru Road, Kolkata, 700071, India
E-mail: TreloarJB@state.gov
Education: Georgetown 2010 MS
Regional Security Officer **Corbin V. Ellison** 91 (33) 3984-6300
5/1 Ho Chi Minh Sarani, Kolkata, 700071, India
E-mail: ellisoncv@state.gov

Commercial Section (Foreign Commercial Service) [India]
38A, Jawaharlal Nehru Road, Kolkata, 700071, India
Mail: U.S. Consulate General, 6250 Calcutta Place,
Dulles, VA 20189-6250
Tel: 91 (33) 3984-6300 Fax: 91 (33) 2288-1207
E-mail: office.kolkata@trade.gov

Principal Commercial Officer **Jonathan Ward** 91 (33) 3984-6353
E-mail: Jonathan.Ward@trade.gov
Education: Wisconsin 1988 BS, 1997 MBA

Mumbai Consulate General
U.S. Consulate General - Mumbai, India,
C-49, G-Block, Bandra Kurla Complex, Mumbai, 400051, India
Mail: U.S. Consulate General, Department of State,
6240 Mumbai Place, Washington, DC 20521-6240
Tel: 91 (22) 2672-4000 Fax: 91 (22) 2672-4755

Consul General **Edgard D. Kagan** 91 (22) 2672-4000
E-mail: kaganed@state.gov
Education: Yale 1989 BA
Office Management Specialist to the Consul General **Abena Owusu-Afriyie** 91 (22) 2672-4000
E-mail: owusu-afriyiea@state.gov
Deputy Principal Officer **Jennifer Adriana Larson** 91 (22) 2672-4000
E-mail: larsonja@state.gov
◇ Consular Officer **Robert L. Batchelder** 91 (22) 2672-4000
E-mail: batchelderrl@state.gov
Education: Colorado 1991 BA; Thunderbird International 1993 MIM
Community Liaison Officer **Julio Rodriguez** 91 (22) 2672-4000
Political/Economic Officer
Christopher G. "Chris" Grossman 91 (22) 2672-4000
E-mail: grossmancg@state.gov
General Services Officer **Shankar Rao** 91 (22) 2672-4000
E-mail: raos@state.gov
Information Program Officer **Emmanuel Obasi** 91 (22) 2672-4000
Information Systems Officer **(Vacant)** 91 (22) 2672-4000
Management Officer **Clay C. Allen** 91 (22) 2672-4000
E-mail: allenca@state.gov

Mumbai Consulate General *(continued)*

Public Affairs Officer **Victoria L. Sloan** 91 (22) 2672-4000
E-mail: sloanvl@state.gov
Information Officer/Spokesperson
Heidi Hattenbach 91 (22) 2672-4000
E-mail: hattenbachhs@state.gov
Regional Security Officer **Kevin R. Irvine** 91 (22) 2672-4000

Agricultural Section (Foreign Agricultural Service) [India]
U.S. Consulate General - Mumbai, India,
C-49, G-Block, Bandra Kurla Complex, Mumbai, 400051, India
Fax: 91 (22) 2672-4755 E-mail: agmumbai@fas.usda.gov

Senior Attaché **Tiffany Landry** 91 (22) 2672-4863

Commercial Section (Foreign Commercial Service) [India]
The American Center, Sundeep Building, 4, New Marine Lines,
5th Floor, Mumbai, India
Mail: U.S. Consulate General, Department of State,
6240 Mumbai Place, Washington, DC 20521-6240
Tel: 91 (22) 2672-4000 Fax: 91 (22) 2672-4400
E-mail: office.mumbai@trade.gov

Principal Commercial Officer **Gregory Taevs** 91 (22) 2672-4215
E-mail: gregory.taevs@trade.gov
Education: Cal State (Long Beach) MBA

U.S. Embassy in Kazakhstan
Rakhymzhan Koshkarbayev Avenue, No. 3., Astana, Kazakhstan 010010
Tel: 7 (7172) 70-21-00 Fax: 7 (7172) 54-09-14
Internet: kz.usembassy.gov

Office of the U.S. Ambassador to Kazakhstan
Rakhymzhan Koshkarbayev Avenue, No. 3., Astana, Kazakhstan 010010
Mail: Department of State, 7030 Almaty Place,
Washington, DC 20521-7030
E-mail: astanainfo@state.gov

★ Ambassador-Designate
Ambassador William H. "Will" Moser 7 (7172) 70-21-00
E-mail: moserwh@state.gov
Education: North Carolina 1977 BA
◇ Chargé d'Affaires **Theodore J. "Ted" Lyng** 7 (7172) 70-21-00
E-mail: lyngtj@state.gov
Education: Cornell 1983 BA; Columbia 1985 MA
Office Management Specialist to the Ambassador
Terri John 7 (7172) 70-21-00
Deputy Chief of Mission (Acting)
Christian M. Wright 7 (7172) 70-21-00
E-mail: wrightcm@state.gov
Office Management Specialist to the Deputy Chief of Mission **Renata Wojtasiewicz** 7 (7172) 70-21-00
E-mail: WojtasiewiczR@state.gov
Consular Affairs Officer **Andrew L. Flashberg** 7 (7172) 70-21-00
E-mail: flashbergal@state.gov
Community Liaison Officer **(Vacant)** 7 (7172) 70-21-00
Economic Officer **Shelbie Legg** 7 (7172) 70-21-00
E-mail: leggsc@state.gov
Equal Employment Opportunity Officer
Bradford C. "Brad" Hopewell 7 (7172) 70-21-00
E-mail: hopewellbc@state.gov
Environment, Science, and Technology Officer
Konstantin Dubrovsky 7 (7172) 70-21-00
E-mail: DubrovskyK@state.gov
Information Management Officer **Angelo Dorto** 7 (7172) 70-21-00
E-mail: dortoam@state.gov
Information Program Officer **Angelo Dorto** 7 (7172) 70-21-00
E-mail: dortoam@state.gov
Information Systems Officer **(Vacant)** 7 (7172) 70-21-00
Legal Attaché **Michael Malsch** 7 (7172) 70-21-00
Management Officer **Robert E. "Bob" Miller** 7 (7172) 70-21-00
Financial Management Officer **Jonathan Earle** 7 (7172) 70-21-00
E-mail: earleje@state.gov
General Services Officer
William M. "Bill" Crummey III 7 (7172) 70-21-00
E-mail: crummeywm@state.gov

(continued on next page)

★ Presidential Appointment Requiring Senate Confirmation ☆ Presidential Appointment □ Schedule C Appointment ◇ Career Senior Foreign Service Appointment
● Career Senior Executive Service (SES) Appointment ○ Non-Career Senior Executive Service (SES) Appointment ■ Postal Career Executive Service

DEPARTMENTS

Office of the U.S. Ambassador to Kazakhstan *(continued)*

Office of Military Cooperation Chief
LTC Thomas Higginson USA 7 (7172) 70-21-00
Political Officer **Paul I. Jukic** 7 (7172) 70-21-00
E-mail: jukicpi@state.gov
Public Affairs Officer **Christian M. Wright** 7 (7172) 70-21-00
E-mail: wrightcm@state.gov
Regional Security Officer **Robert "Rob" Roulston** 7 (7172) 70-21-00
E-mail: roulstonrj@state.gov

Agency for International Development [Kazakhstan]
Internet: https://www.usaid.gov/kazakhstan
Country Director **Ryan M. Weddle** 7 (7172) 70-21-00
E-mail: rweddle@usaid.gov

Agricultural Section (Foreign Agricultural Service) [Kazakhstan]
Rakhymzhan Koshkarbayev Avenue, No. 3., Astana, Kazakhstan 010010
Tel: 7 (7172) 70-22-68 ext. 2268 Fax: 7 (7172) 70-22-87
Agricultural Officer (Resident in Moscow)
Deanna Ayala 7 (495) 728-5222
E-mail: deanna.ayala@fas.usda.gov

Defense Threat Reduction Agency [Kazakhstan] (DTRA)
Rakhymzhan Koshkarbayev Avenue, No. 3., Astana, Kazakhstan 010010
Office Director **Brian Stephan** 7 (7172) 70-21-00

Department of Homeland Security - U.S. Customs and Border Protection [Kazakhstan]
Building 3, Rakhymzhan Koshkarbayev Avenue, No. 3., Astana, Kazakhstan 010010
Mail: Department of State, 7030 Almaty Place, Washington, DC 20521-7030
Tel: 7 (7172) 70-2100
Customs Attaché **Andrew Chilcoat** 7 (7172) 70-2100

Federal Aviation Administration (Resident in Moscow) [Kazakhstan]
Rakhymzhan Koshkarbayev Avenue, No. 3., Astana, Kazakhstan 010010
Tel: 7 (495) 728-5000
FAA Senior Representative **Andrew McKee** . . . . (301) 490-1042 ext. 7815

Office of the Defense Attaché [Kazakhstan]
Building 3, Rakhymzhan Koshkarbayev Avenue, No. 3., Astana, Kazakhstan 010010
Mail: Department of State, 7030 Almaty Place, Washington, DC 20521-7030
Tel: 7 (7272) 63-3921 Fax: 7 (7272) 50-7620
Defense Attaché **COL David Wiseman USA** 7 (7172) 70-2100

Almaty Consulate General
Samal-2, 97 Zholdasbekov Street, Almaty, Kazakhstan 050051
Tel: 7 (7272) 50-76-12 E-mail: uscgalmatyinvitation@state.gov
Consul General **Eric S. Meyer** 7 (7272) 50-76-12
E-mail: meyeres@state.gov
Education: UC Berkeley BA; Georgetown MBA
Office Management Specialist to the Consul General **Diana Flewelling** 7 (7272) 50-76-12
E-mail: flewellingd@state.gov
Consular Officer **Martin Ryan** 7 (7272) 50-76-12
Community Liaison Officer **Emily Larsen** 7 (7272) 50-76-12
Economic Officer **Charles "CJ" Perego** 7 (7272) 50-76-12
E-mail: PeregoCJ@state.gov
General Services Officer **Michael Pitts** 7 (7272) 50-76-12
E-mail: pittsmk@state.gov
Management Officer **Keely Kilburg** 7 (7272) 50-76-12
E-mail: KilburgKZ@state.gov
Political Officer **Erik Ryan** 7 (7272) 50-76-12
Education: Arkansas (Little Rock) 2004 BS
Public Affairs Officer **(Vacant)** 7 (7272) 50-76-12
Regional Security Officer **Scott Berman** 7 (7272) 50-76-12

Agency for International Development - Central Asia Regional Mission
41 Kazibek Bi Street, B Wing, Almaty, Kazakhstan 480100
Mail: American Embassy - Almaty, Kazakhstan, Department of State, 7030 Almaty Place, Washington, DC 20521-7030
Tel: 7 (7272) 50-76-12 Fax: 7 (7272) 50-76-35
Internet: https://www.usaid.gov/central-asia-regional
Areas Covered: Kazakhstan, Kyrgyzstan, Tajikistan, Turkmenistan, Uzbekistan
◇ Regional Mission Director **Christopher Edwards** 7 (7272) 50-7612
E-mail: chedwards@usaid.gov

Commercial Section (Foreign Commercial Service) [Kazakhstan]
EBO Almaty, 97 Zholdasbekov Street, Almaty, Kazakhstan 050059
Mail: Department of State, 7030 Almaty Place, Washington, DC 20521-7030
Tel: 7 (7272) 50-7612 ext. 6490 Fax: 7 (7272) 50-07-77
Internet: export.gov/kazakhstan
Senior Commercial Officer
Dean R. Matlack . . . . 7 (7272) 50-7612 ext. 6488
E-mail: dean.matlack@trade.gov

U.S. Embassy in the Kyrgyz Republic

171 Prospect Mira, 720016 Bishkek, Kyrgyzstan
Tel: 996 (312) 597-000 Fax: 996 (312) 597-744
Internet: kg.usembassy.gov

Office of the U.S. Ambassador to the Kyrgyz Republic

American Embassy - Bishkek, Kyrgyzstan, 171 Prospect Mira, 720016 Bishkek, Kyrgyzstan
Mail: Department of State, 7040 Bishkek Place, Washington, DC 20521-7040
★ Ambassador **Ambassador Donald Lu** 996 (312) 597-000
E-mail: lud@state.gov
Education: Princeton 1988 BA, 1991 MA
Office Management Specialist to the Ambassador **(Vacant)** 996 (312) 597-000
Deputy Chief of Mission **Brian K. Stimmler** 996 (312) 597-000
E-mail: stimmlerbk@state.gov
Education: BYU BA; Princeton PhD
Office Management Specialist to the Deputy Chief of Mission **Nicole Owens** 996 (312) 597-000
Community Liaison Officer **Keysha Evans** 996 (312) 597-000
Consular Section Chief
Juan Carlos "J.C." Campos 996 (312) 597-000
E-mail: consularbishkek@state.gov
Financial Management Officer **Rebecca Reis** 996 (312) 597-000
E-mail: reisr@state.gov
General Services Officer **Michael Scheer** 996 (312) 597-000
Human Resources Officer **Ola B. Criss** 996 (312) 597-000
E-mail: crissob@state.gov
Education: George Washington 1982 PhD
Information Management Officer **Kenya Owens** 996 (312) 597-000
Management Officer **Lyngrid S. Rawlings** 996 (312) 597-000
E-mail: rawlingsls@state.gov
Political/Economic Officer
Thomas "Tom" Selinger 996 (312) 597-000
E-mail: sellingertb@state.gov
Education: Duke 1988 BA
Public Affairs Officer **(Vacant)** 996 (312) 597-000
Regional Security Officer
Matthew A. "Matt" Wolsey 996 (312) 597-000
E-mail: wolseyma@state.gov
International Narcotics and Law Enforcement Affairs Director **Sandeep K. Paul** 996 (312) 597-000
E-mail: paulsk@state.gov

★ Presidential Appointment Requiring Senate Confirmation ☆ Presidential Appointment ☐ Schedule C Appointment ◇ Career Senior Foreign Service Appointment
● Career Senior Executive Service (SES) Appointment ○ Non-Career Senior Executive Service (SES) Appointment ■ Postal Career Executive Service

Agency for International Development [Kyrgyz Republic]
American Embassy - Bishkek, Kyrgyzstan,
171 Prospect Mira, 720016 Bishkek, Kyrgyzstan
Mail: Department of State, 7040 Bishkek Place,
Washington, DC 20521-7040
Tel: 996 (312) 55-12-41 Internet: https://www.usaid.gov/kyrgyz-republic

Mission Director **Dr. Gary B. Linden PhD** 996 (312) 55-12-41
E-mail: glinden@usaid.gov
Education: Pomona BA; Texas MA, PhD

Federal Aviation Administration (Resident in Moscow) [Kyrgyz Republic]
American Embassy/FAA, 8 Bolshoy Devyatinsky Pereulok,
121099 Moscow, Russia
Mail: American Embassy/FAA, PSC 77, APO, AE 09721
Tel: 7 (495) 728-5000

FAA Senior Representative **Andrew McKee** 7 (495) 728-5000

Office of the Defense Attaché [Kyrgyz Republic]
American Embassy - Bishkek, 171 Prospect Mira, 720016 Bishkek, Kyrgyzstan
Mail: Department of State, 7040 Bishkek Place,
Washington, DC 20521-7040
Tel: 996 (312) 55-12-41

Defense and Air Attaché **Donald Perry** 996 (312) 55-12-41

Peace Corps [Kyrgyz Republic]
American Embassy - Bishkek, Kyrgyzstan,
171 Prospect Mira, 720016 Bishkek, Kyrgyzstan
Mail: Department of State, 7040 Bishkek Place,
Washington, DC 20521-7040
Fax: 996 (312) 65-03-62 E-mail: info-kg@peacecorps.gov
Internet: www.peacecorps.gov/kyrgyz-republic

Country Director (Acting) **Jeremy Parker** 996 (312) 65-09-89

U.S. Embassy in Nepal

Maharajgunj, Kathmandu, Nepal
Tel: 977 (1) 423-4000 Fax: 977 (1) 400-7272
E-mail: usembktm@state.gov Internet: https://np.usembassy.gov/

Office of the U.S. Ambassador to Nepal

American Embassy - Kathmandu/Nepal,
Maharajgunj, Kathmandu, Nepal
Mail: American Embassy - Kathmandu, Nepal,
Department of State, Washington, DC 20521-6190

★ Ambassador **Ambassador Randy William Berry** 977 (1) 423-4000
E-mail: berryrw@state.gov
Education: Bethany (KS) 1987 BEd
Office Management Specialist to the Ambassador
Ann E. Rehme 977 (1) 423-4000
E-mail: rehmeae@state.gov

◇ Deputy Chief of Mission
Michael C. "Mike" Gonzales 977 (1) 423-4000
E-mail: gonzalesmc@state.gov
Education: Occidental BA; American U MA
Office Management Specialist to the Deputy Chief of Mission **(Vacant)** 977 (1) 423-4000

Community Liaison Officer **Emily J. Warren** 977 (1) 423-4000
Consular Officer **Michael E. Mussi** 977 (1) 423-4000
E-mail: mussime@state.gov Fax: 977 (1) 400-7281
Financial Management Officer
Robert C. "Bob" Meister 977 (1) 423-4000
General Services Officer **Scott N. McDow** 977 (1) 423-4000
E-mail: McDowS@state.gov
Information Management Officer **(Vacant)** 977 (1) 423-4000
Information Program Officer **Brandon S. Lee** 977 (1) 423-4000
Information Systems Security Officer **(Vacant)** 977 (1) 423-4000
Management Officer **Todd K. Tiffany** 977 (1) 423-4000
E-mail: tiffanytk@state.gov
Military Liaison Officer/Office of Defense Cooperation Chief
MAJ Jonathan R. Swoyer USA 977 (1) 423-4000
E-mail: swoyerjr@state.gov

Office of the U.S. Ambassador to Nepal *(continued)*

Political/Economic Officer **Clinton S. "Tad" Brown** ... 977 (1) 423-4000
E-mail: browncs@state.gov
Education: National War Col
Political/Military Officer **Richard Hoge** 977 (1) 423-4000
E-mail: hoger@state.gov
Public Affairs Officer **Paul S. Thomas** 977 (1) 423-4000
Education: Colorado 2003 BA
Regional Security Officer **Daniel J. "Dan" Messelt** 977 (1) 423-4000
E-mail: messeltdj@state.gov
Regional Environmental Officer for South Asia
Sara L. Litke 977 (1) 423-4000
E-mail: litkesl@state.gov

Agency for International Development [Nepal]
American Embassy - Kathmandu/Nepal,
Maharajgunj, Kathmandu, Nepal
Mail: American Embassy - Kathmandu, Nepal,
Department of State, Washington, DC 20521-6190
Fax: 977 (1) 400-7285 Internet: www.usaid.gov/nepal

◇ Mission Director **Amy Tohill-Stull** 977 (1) 423-4260
E-mail: atohill-stull@usaid.gov
Education: Purdue BA; American U MID

Federal Aviation Administration (Resident in New Delhi) [Nepal]
American Embassy - New Delhi, Shanti path, Chanakyapuri,
New Delhi, 110 021, India
Mail: Department of State, 9000 New Delhi Place,
Washington, DC 20521-9000
Fax: 91 (11) 2419-0003

FAA Representative **Thomas M. "Tom" Miller** 91 (11) 2419-8403

Office of the Defense Attaché [Nepal]
American Embassy - Kathmandu/Nepal,
Maharajgunj, Kathmandu, Nepal
Mail: American Embassy - Kathmandu, Nepal,
Department of State, Washington, DC 20521-6190
Tel: 977 (1) 400-7200 Fax: 977 (1) 400-7272

Defense Attaché **LTC Gregory D. Pipes USA** 977 (1) 400-7200
E-mail: pipesgd@state.gov

Peace Corps [Nepal]
American Embassy - Kathmandu/Nepal,
Maharajgunj, Kathmandu, Nepal
E-mail: EMA_nepal@peacecorps.gov Internet: www.peacecorps.gov/nepal

Country Director **Nelson Chase** 977 (1) 401-6027
E-mail: nchase@peacecorps.gov

U.S. Embassy in Pakistan

Diplomatic Enclave, Ramna 5, Islamabad, Pakistan
Tel: 92 (51) 201-4000 Tel: 92 (51) 233-8071 Internet: pk.usembassy.gov

Office of the U.S. Ambassador to Pakistan

American Embassy - Islamabad, Pakistan, Diplomatic Enclave,
Ramna 5, Islamabad, Pakistan
Mail: Unit 62200, Box 1048, APO, AE 09812-2200

★ Ambassador **(Vacant)** 92 (51) 201-4000
E-mail: haledm2@state.gov

◇ Chargé d'Affaires **Ambassador Paul Wayne Jones** ... 92 (51) 201-4000
E-mail: jonespw2@state.gov
Education: Cornell BA; Virginia MPA; Naval War MNSSS
Office Management Specialist to the Ambassador
Judith L. "Judy" Reed 92 (51) 201-4000
E-mail: reedjl1@state.gov

◇ Deputy Chief of Mission
Ambassador John F. Hoover 92 (51) 201-4000
E-mail: hooverjf@state.gov
Education: Princeton BA
Office Management Specialist to the Deputy Chief of Mission **Eunhee Jeong** 92 (51) 201-4000
E-mail: jeonge@state.gov

(continued on next page)

★ Presidential Appointment Requiring Senate Confirmation ☆ Presidential Appointment ☐ Schedule C Appointment ◇ Career Senior Foreign Service Appointment
● Career Senior Executive Service (SES) Appointment ○ Non-Career Senior Executive Service (SES) Appointment ■ Postal Career Executive Service

Office of the U.S. Ambassador to Pakistan *(continued)*

◇ Consular Affairs Officer
Joshua W. "Josh" Glazeroff 92 (51) 201-4000
E-mail: glazeroffj@state.gov
Education: Harvard 1992 BA; Brown U 1996 MAT

Community Liaison Officer **Cindy Russell** 92 (51) 201-4000

Economic Officer **Michael A. Sullivan** 92 (51) 201-4000
E-mail: sullivanma2@state.gov
Education: Tennessee 1987 BA; George Washington 1994 MA; National War Col 2016 MS

Equal Employment Opportunity Officer
Tracy Thomas 92 (51) 201-4000

Facilities Management Officer **Eric B. Millson** 92 (51) 201-4000
E-mail: millsoneb@state.gov

Financial Management Officer **Sharon Yang** 92 (51) 201-4000

General Services Officer
Christopher M. "Chris" Newton 92 (51) 201-4000
E-mail: newtoncm2@state.gov
Education: Baylor BA, MA

Human Resources Officer **Mira Piplani** 92 (51) 201-4000
E-mail: piplanim@state.gov

Information Management Officer
Mari Jane Womack 92 (51) 201-4000
E-mail: womackmj@state.gov

Information Program Officer **Steven L. White** 92 (51) 201-4000
E-mail: whitesl@state.gov

Information Systems Officer **Krishnan S. Sridhar** 92 (51) 201-4000
E-mail: sridharks@state.gov

Information Systems Security Officer **Omer Orozco** ... 92 (51) 201-4000
E-mail: orozcoo@state.gov

Legal Attaché **Marvis Taylor** 92 (51) 201-4000

Management Officer **Mark Perry** 92 (51) 201-4000
E-mail: perrymx@state.gov

Narcotics Affairs Officer **Jason A. Donovan** 92 (51) 201-4000
E-mail: donovanj@state.gov

Political Officer **Theodore J. "Ted" Craig** 92 (51) 201-4000
E-mail: craigtj@state.gov
Education: Colorado Col 1987 BA; Johns Hopkins 1990 MA

◇ Public Affairs Officer
Christopher "Chris" Fitzgerald 92 (51) 201-4000
Education: Columbia 1982
Press Attaché/Spokesperson
Richard William Snelsire 92 (51) 201-4000
E-mail: snelsirerw@state.gov
E-mail: infoisb@state.gov
Education: Ohio 1988 MA

Regional Security Officer **Daniel "Dan" Cronin** 92 (51) 201-4000
E-mail: cronind@state.gov
Education: Maryland 1993 BS

Agency for International Development [Pakistan]
American Embassy - Islamabad, Pakistan, Diplomatic Enclave,
Ramna 5, Islamabad, Pakistan
Mail: Unit 62200, Box 1048, APO, AE 09812-2200
Fax: 92 (51) 262-3567 E-mail: infopakistan@usaid.gov
Internet: www.usaid.gov/pakistan

◇ Mission Director **Jerry Paul Bisson** 92 (51) 208-2000
E-mail: jbisson@usaid.gov
Education: Vermont BS; SUNY (Syracuse) 1982 MS

Agricultural Section (Foreign Agricultural Service) [Pakistan]
Unit 62200, Box 1048, APO, AE 09812-2200
Tel: 92 (51) 208-2275 Fax: 92 (51) 227-8142
E-mail: agislamabad@fas.usda.gov

Agricultural Officer **Casey Bean** 92 (51) 208-2275
E-mail: casey.bean@fas.usda.gov
Education: Maryland BS; Rhode Island MEc

Commercial Section (Foreign Commercial Service) [Pakistan]
American Embassy - Islamabad, Pakistan, Diplomatic Enclave,
Ramna 5, Islamabad, Pakistan
Mail: Unit 62200, Box 51, APO, AE 09812-2200
Tel: 92 (51) 208-0000 Fax: 92 (51) 282-3981
Internet: www.export.gov/pakistan

Senior Commercial Officer (Resident in Karachi)
(Vacant) 92 (21) 3527-5000

Drug Enforcement Administration [Pakistan]
American Embassy - Islamabad, Pakistan, Diplomatic Enclave,
Ramna 5, Islamabad, Pakistan
Mail: American Embassy - Islamabad, Pakistan, Unit 62215,
APO, AE 09812-2200

DEA Officer **Gavin Kersellius** 92 (51) 201-4000

Federal Aviation Administration (Resident in New Delhi) [Pakistan]
American Embassy - New Delhi, India,
Shanti Path, Chanakyapuri, New Delhi, 110 021, India
Mail: Department of State, 9000 New Delhi Place,
Washington, DC 20521-9000
Fax: 91 (11) 2419-0003

FAA Representative **Thomas M. "Tom" Miller** 91 (11) 2419-8403

Library of Congress [Pakistan]
American Embassy - Islamabad, Pakistan, Diplomatic Enclave,
Ramna 5, Islamabad, Pakistan
Mail: Unit 62200, Box 1048, APO, AE 09812-2200
Tel: 92 (51) 201-4000 ext. 4037 Tel: 92 (51) 2082529
E-mail: islamabad@loc.gov Internet: www.loc.gov/acq/ovop/islamabad

Field Director (Acting) **Fehl Cannon** .... 92 (51) 201-4000 ext. 4037
E-mail: fcan@loc.gov

Office of the Defense Attaché [Pakistan]
American Embassy - Islamabad, Pakistan, Diplomatic Enclave,
Ramna 5, Islamabad, Pakistan
Mail: American Embassy - Islamabad, Pakistan, Box 13, Unit 62200,
APO, AE 09812-2200

Defense Attaché **Peter "Pete" Rowell** 92 (51) 201-4000

Office of the Defense Representative [Pakistan] (ODR-P)
Diplomatic Enclave, Ramna 5, Islamabad, Pakistan

Chief **(Vacant)** 92 (51) 201-4000

Karachi Consulate General
U.S. Consulate General - Karachi, Pakistan,
3,4,5 New TPX Area, Mai Kolachi Road, Karachi, Pakistan
Mail: U.S. Consulate General-Karachi, Pakistan, Unit 62400,
APO, AE 09814-2400
Tel: 92 (21) 3527-5000 Fax: 92 (21) 3561-2413

◇ Consul General **JoAnne Wagner** 92 (21) 3527-5000
E-mail: wagnerj@state.gov
Education: National War Col MNSSS; Saint Louis U JD
Office Management Specialist to the Consul
General **Wendy Bieber** 92 (21) 3527-5000
E-mail: bieberwm@state.gov

◇ Deputy Consul General **John E. Warner** 92 (21) 3527-5000
E-mail: warnerje@state.gov

Consular Officer **John H. Gimbel IV** 92 (21) 3527-5000
E-mail: gimbelj@state.gov

Economic Officer **(Vacant)** 92 (21) 3527-5000

Political/Economic Officer **Jimmy Mauldin** 92 (21) 3527-5000

Financial Management Officer (Resident in
Islamabad) **Sharon Yang** 92 (51) 208-02-308

General Services Officer **Brian Robinson** 92 (21) 3527-5000

Information Program Officer **Richard Livingston** 92 (21) 3527-5000
E-mail: livingstonrp@state.gov

Information Security Officer **Marc Nelson** 92 (21) 3527-5000

Information Systems Security Officer
Richard Livingston 92 (21) 3527-5000
E-mail: livingstonrp@state.gov

Management Officer **Brian E. Kressin** 92 (21) 3527-5000
E-mail: kressinbe@state.gov

★ Presidential Appointment Requiring Senate Confirmation ☆ Presidential Appointment ☐ Schedule C Appointment ◇ Career Senior Foreign Service Appointment
● Career Senior Executive Service (SES) Appointment ○ Non-Career Senior Executive Service (SES) Appointment ■ Postal Career Executive Service

Karachi Consulate General *(continued)*

Public Affairs Officer **Jason Green** . . . 92 (21) 3527-5000
Education: SUNY (Purchase) 2004 BFA; Southern Illinois 2006 JD
Regional Security Officer **Shane Dixon** . . . 92 (21) 3527-5000
E-mail: dixonsl@state.gov

Lahore Consulate General
U.S. Consulate - Lahore, Pakistan, 50, Sharah-e-Abdul Hameed Bin Badees (Old Empress Road), (near Shimla Hill Rotary), Lahore, Pakistan 54000
Mail: U.S. Consulate - Lahore, Pakistan, Unit 62216, APO, AE 09812-2216
Tel: 92 (42) 3603-4000 Fax: 92 (42) 3603-4200

Consul General **Colleen E. Crenwelge** . . . 92 (42) 603-4000
E-mail: crenwelgece@state.gov
Education: Texas A&M BA
Office Management Specialist to the Consul General **(Vacant)** . . . 92 (42) 603-4000
Consular Section Chief **Jamie Sutter** . . . 92 (42) 3603-4000
Economic Officer **Theodore A. "Ted" Meinhover** . . . 92 (42) 603-4000
E-mail: meinhoverta@state.gov
Education: U Indonesia 2006; Minnesota 2007 BA
General Services Officer **Robert C. "Chris" Wolf** . . . 92 (42) 603-4000
E-mail: wolfrc@state.gov
Information Management Officer **(Vacant)** . . . 92 (42) 603-4000
Information Systems Officer **John C. Prukop** . . . 92 (42) 603-4000
E-mail: prukopjc@state.gov
Management Officer **Darian L. Arky** . . . 92 (42) 603-4000
E-mail: arkydl@state.gov
Political Officer **(Vacant)** . . . 92 (42) 603-4000
Political/Economic Officer **Ann L. Mason** . . . 92 (42) 603-4000
E-mail: masonal@state.gov
Public Affairs Officer **Michael D. Guinan** . . . 92 (42) 603-4000
E-mail: GuinanMD@state.gov
Regional Security Officer **Matthew C. McCormack** . . . 92 (42) 603-4000
E-mail: mccormackmc@state.gov

Commercial Section (Foreign Commercial Service) [Pakistan]
50, Sharah-e-Abdul Hameed Bin Badees (Old Empress Road), (near Shimla Hill Rotary), Lahore, Pakistan 54000
Mail: U.S. Consulate - Lahore, Pakistan, Unit 62216, APO, AE 09812-2216
Tel: 92 (42) 603-4000 Fax: 92 (42) 603-4229

Commercial Specialist **Aftab Qamar** . . . 92 (42) 603-4000
E-mail: aftab.qamar@mail.doc.gov

Peshawar Consulate General
U.S. Consulate - Peshawar, Pakistan, 11 Hospital Road, Peshawar Cantt, AC Peshawar, Pakistan
Mail: U.S. Consulate - Peshawar, Pakistan, Unit 62217, APO, AE 09812-2217
Tel: 92 (91) 526-8800 Fax: 92 (91) 527-6712
E-mail: info_pesh@state.gov

◇ Consul General **Jonathan L. Shrier** . . . 92 (91) 526-8800
E-mail: shrierj@state.gov
Education: Dartmouth 1985 AB; London School Econ (UK) 1986 MSc; U London 2005 MBA; Indust'l Col Armed Forces 2010 MS
Information Security Officer **Ali M. Nikooazm** . . . 92 (91) 526-8800
E-mail: NikooazmAM@state.gov
Management Officer **Robert P. Peck** . . . 92 (91) 526-8800
Political/Economic Officer **Kira L. Zaporski** . . . 92 (91) 526-8800
E-mail: zaporskikl@state.gov
Education: Wisconsin JD
Public Affairs Officer **Ajay S. Rao** . . . 92 (91) 526-8800
E-mail: raoas@state.gov
Regional Security Officer **Bernard J. Green** . . . 92 (91) 526-8800
E-mail: greenbj@state.gov

U.S. Embassy in Sri Lanka
210 Galle Road, Colombo, 3, Sri Lanka
Tel: 94 (11) 249-8500 Fax: 94 (11) 243-7345 Internet: lk.usembassy.gov

Office of the U.S. Ambassador to Sri Lanka
American Embassy - Colombo, Sri Lanka, 210 Galle Road, P.O. Box 106, Colombo, 3, Sri Lanka
Mail: Department of State, 6100 Colombo Place, Washington, DC 20521-6100
Note: The U.S. Ambassador to Sri Lanka serves concurrently as the U.S. Ambassador to the Republic of Maldives.

★ Ambassador **Ambassador Alaina B. Teplitz** . . . 94 (11) 249-8500
E-mail: teplitzab@state.gov
Education: Georgetown 1991 BSFS
Office Management Specialist to the Ambassador **Deveater "Dee" Henry** . . . 94 (11) 249-8500
◇ Deputy Chief of Mission **Robert B. Hilton** . . . 94 (11) 249-8500
E-mail: hiltonrb@state.gov
Education: Michigan BA; Army War Col 2012 MSS
Office Management Specialist to the Deputy Chief of Mission **Carolyn S. Murphy** . . . 94 (11) 249-8500
Community Liaison Officer **(Vacant)** . . . 94 (11) 249-8500
Consular Officer **Phillip J. VanHorn** . . . 94 (11) 249-8500
Fax: 94 (11) 243-6943
Commercial Officer **Partha Mazumdar** . . . 94 (11) 249-8500
E-mail: mazumdarp@state.gov
Economic Officer **Partha Mazumdar** . . . 94 (11) 249-8500
E-mail: mazumdarp@state.gov
Financial Management Officer **Steven B. Bennett** . . . 94 (11) 249-8500
E-mail: bennettsb@state.gov
General Services Officer **Thomas A. "Tab" Bryant** . . . 94 (11) 249-8500
E-mail: bryantta@state.gov
Information Management Officer **Kevin R. Bruner** . . . 94 (11) 249-8500
Information Program Officer **Devin Hendriksen** . . . 94 (11) 249-8500
E-mail: hendriksendm@state.gov
Information Systems Security Officer **Devin Hendriksen** . . . 94 (11) 249-8500
E-mail: hendriksendm@state.gov
Management Officer **Michael Cragun** . . . 94 (11) 249-8500
E-mail: cragunm@state.gov Fax: 94 (11) 247-1091
Political Officer **Patrick Tillou** . . . 94 (11) 249-8500
E-mail: tilloupa@state.gov
Education: Duke 1997; Michigan 1999 JD
Public Affairs Officer **Nancy VanHorn** . . . 94 (11) 249-8100
Fax: 94 (11) 244-9070
Regional Security Officer **Jason P. "Jay" Williams** . . . 94 (11) 249-8500
E-mail: williamsj@state.gov

Agency for International Development [Sri Lanka]
44 Galle Road, Colombo, 3, Sri Lanka
Mail: Department of State, 6100 Colombo Place, Washington, DC 20521-6100
Tel: 94 (11) 249-8000 Fax: 94 (11) 247-2850 E-mail: infosl@usaid.gov
Internet: www.usaid.gov/sri-lanka

◇ Mission Director **Reed Aeschliman** . . . 94 (11) 249-8000
E-mail: raeschliman@usaid.gov

Agricultural Section (Foreign Agricultural Service) [Sri Lanka]
◇ Counselor for Agricultural Affairs (Resident in New Delhi) **Jeanne Bailey** . . . 91 (11) 2419-8769
E-mail: jeanne.bailey@fas.usda.gov

Department of Homeland Security - U.S. Customs and Border Protection [Sri Lanka]
U.S. Customs Attaché **Robert Shih** . . . 94 (11) 249-8500

Federal Aviation Administration (Resident in New Delhi) [Sri Lanka]
American Embassy - New Delhi, India, Shanti Path, Chanakyapuri, New Delhi, 110 021, India
Mail: Department of State, 9000 New Delhi Place, Washington, DC 20521-9000
Fax: 91 (11) 2419-0003

FAA Representative **Thomas M. "Tom" Miller** . . . 91 (11) 2419-8403

★ Presidential Appointment Requiring Senate Confirmation ☆ Presidential Appointment □ Schedule C Appointment ◇ Career Senior Foreign Service Appointment
● Career Senior Executive Service (SES) Appointment ○ Non-Career Senior Executive Service (SES) Appointment ■ Postal Career Executive Service

International Broadcasting Bureau [Sri Lanka]
American Embassy - Colombo, Sri Lanka,
210 Galle Road, Colombo, 3, Sri Lanka
Mail: Department of State, 6100 Colombo Place,
Washington, DC 20521-6100
Tel: 94 (11) 225-5931 Fax: 94 (11) 225-5822

IBB Officer **(Vacant)** 94 (11) 225-5931

Office of the Defense Attaché [Sri Lanka]
American Embassy - Colombo, Sri Lanka,
210 Galle Road, Colombo, 3, Sri Lanka
Mail: Department of State, 6100 Colombo Place,
Washington, DC 20521-6100
Tel: 94 (11) 249-8500 Fax: 94 (11) 243-7345

Defense Attaché **LTC Douglas C. Hess USA** 94 (11) 249-8500

U.S. Embassy in Tajikistan

109-A Ismoli Somoni Avenue, Dushanbe, 734019, Tajikistan
Tel: 992 (372) 29-2000 Fax: 992 (372) 29-2050
Internet: tj.usembassy.gov

Office of the U.S. Ambassador to Tajikistan

American Embassy - Dushanbe, Tajikistan,
109-A Ismoli Somoni Avenue, Dushanbe, 734019, Tajikistan
Mail: American Embassy - Dushanbe, Tajikistan,
Department of State, Washington, DC 20521-7090
Tel: 992 (372) 29-2000 Fax: 992 (372) 29-2050
E-mail: usembassydushanbe@state.gov Internet: tj.usembassy.gov

★ Ambassador-Designate **John Mark Pommersheim** ... 992 (372) 29-2000
E-mail: pommersheimjm@state.gov
Education: Bucknell BS; Columbia MA

Chargé d'Affaires **Kevin T. Covert** 992 (372) 29-2000
E-mail: covertkt@state.gov

Office Management Specialist to the Ambassador
Genevieve L. Shapiro 992 (372) 29-2000
E-mail: shapirog@state.gov

Deputy Chief of Mission **Kevin T. Covert** 992 (372) 29-2000
E-mail: covertkt@state.gov

Office Management Specialist to the Deputy Chief of Mission **(Vacant)** 992 (372) 29-2000

Consular Officer **Beth M. Andonov** 992 (372) 29-2000
E-mail: andonovbm@state.gov

Community Liaison Officer **Victoria Griffith** 992 (372) 29-2000
E-mail: clodushanbe@state.gov

Economic Officer **(Vacant)** 992 (372) 29-2000

Financial Management Officer
Shelton Crawford Bowers 992 (372) 29-2000
E-mail: bowerssc@state.gov

General Services Officer **Chad Pittman** 992 (372) 29-2000

Human Resources Officer **Brenda M. Wells** 992 (372) 29-2000
E-mail: wellsbm2@state.gov

Information Management Officer
Walter H. Yates III 992 (372) 21-0348
E-mail: yateswh@state.gov

Information Program Officer **Jeffrey Patricelli** 992 (372) 29-2000
E-mail: patricellija@state.gov

Legal Attaché **(Vacant)** 992 (372) 29-2000

Management Officer **Keith F. Sanders** 992 (372) 29-2000
E-mail: sanderskf@state.gov

Political/Economic Officer
Andrew G. "Drew" Bury 992 (372) 29-2000
E-mail: buryag@state.gov
Education: Emory 2008 BA

Political Officer **G. Brandon Sherwood** 992 (372) 29-2000
E-mail: sherwoodgb@state.gov

Public Affairs Officer **Lucy Jilka** 992 (372) 29-2000
E-mail: jilkalm@state.gov

Regional Security Officer
Christopher "Chris" Cicoria 992 (372) 29-2000
Education: St Thomas Aquinas 2001 BS

Agency for International Development [Tajikistan]
American Embassy - Dushanbe, Tajikistan,
109-A Ismoli Somoni Avenue, Dushanbe, 734019, Tajikistan
Tel: 992 (372) 29-2608 Internet: www.usaid.gov/tajikistan

Country Director **Katherine Crawford** 992 (372) 29-2601
E-mail: kacrawford@usaid.gov

Drug Enforcement Administration [Tajikistan]

DEA Officer **Scott Oringderff** 992 (372) 29-2000
E-mail: oringderffse@state.gov

Federal Aviation Administration (Resident in Moscow) [Tajikistan]
Eight Bolshoy Devyatinsky Pereulok, 121099 Moscow, Russia

FAA Senior Representative **Andrew McKee** 7 (495) 728-5125

Office of the Defense Attaché [Tajikistan]
American Embassy - Dushanbe, Tajikistan,
Department of State, Washington, DC 20521-7090
109-A Ismoli Somoni Avenue, Dushanbe, 734019, Tajikistan
Tel: 992 (372) 29-2000 Fax: 992 (372) 29-2050

Defense Attaché
COL Daniel "Dan" Zeytoonian USA 992 (372) 29-2000

U.S. Embassy in Turkmenistan

American Embassy - Ashgabat, Turkmenistan,
9 1984 Street (formerly Pushkin Street), Ashgabat, Turkmenistan 744000
Tel: 993 (12) 94-00-45 Fax: 993 (12) 94-26-14
Internet: tm.usembassy.gov

Note: On October 5, 2015, the Department of State began construction on a new U.S. Embassy facility in Ashgabat that will replace the Embassy's current facilities. The project is expected to be completed in 2018.

Office of the U.S. Ambassador to Turkmenistan

American Embassy - Ashgabat, Turkmenistan,
9 1984 Street (formerly Pushkin Street), Ashgabat, Turkmenistan 744000
Mail: Department of State, 7070 Ashgabat Place,
Washington, DC 20521-7070

★ Ambassador **Ambassador Allan P. Mustard** 993 (12) 94-00-45
E-mail: mustarda@state.gov
Education: Grays Harbor 1975 AS; U Washington 1978 BS; Illinois 1982 MS

Office Management Specialist to the Ambassador
Nancy J. Walraven 993 (12) 94-00-45

◇ Deputy Chief of Mission
Andrea R. Brouillette-Rodriguez 993 (12) 94-00-45
Education: Barry BS; Tulane MA

Office Management Specialist to the Deputy Chief of Mission **Lisa Cantonwine** 993 (12) 94-00-45
E-mail: cantonwinelm@state.gov

Community Liaison Officer **(Vacant)** 993 (12) 94-00-45

Consular Section Officer **Monique A. Nowicki** 993 (12) 94-00-45
E-mail: nowickima@state.gov Fax: 993 (12) 94-26-14
E-mail: consularashgab@state.gov

Economic Officer **Courtney J. Brasier** 993 (12) 94-00-45
Education: Michigan State 2004 BA; Maryland 2011 MPP

Financial Management Officer **Mary Jo Long** 993 (12) 94-00-45

General Services Officer **Michelle Braunstein** 993 (12) 94-00-45

Information Management Officer **Steven Long** 993 (12) 94-00-45

Information Program Officer **(Vacant)** 993 (12) 94-00-45

Information Systems Officer **(Vacant)** 993 (12) 94-00-45

Management Officer **Ethan Curbow** 993 (12) 94-00-45

Office of Military Cooperation Chief
LtCol Dimitri N. Kesi USAF 993 (12) 94-00-45

Political/Economic Section Chief
Joseph "Joe" Boski 993 (12) 94-00-45
E-mail: boskij@state.gov

Political Officer **(Vacant)** 993 (12) 94-00-45

Public Affairs Officer **Dr. Bridget F. Gersten PhD** 993 (12) 47-35-03
Education: U Ca' Foscari (Italy) BA; Arizona MA; Arizona State PhD

Cultural Affairs Officer **Sarah M. Belousov** 993 (12) 47-35-03
Fax: 993 (12) 47-35-29

Information Officer **Joshua deLara** 993 (12) 47-35-03

★ Presidential Appointment Requiring Senate Confirmation ☆ Presidential Appointment ☐ Schedule C Appointment ◇ Career Senior Foreign Service Appointment
● Career Senior Executive Service (SES) Appointment ○ Non-Career Senior Executive Service (SES) Appointment ■ Postal Career Executive Service

Office of the U.S. Ambassador to Turkmenistan *(continued)*

Regional Security Officer **Michael Don Chapple** 993 (12) 94-00-45
E-mail: chapplemd@state.gov

Agency for International Development [Turkmenistan]
Department of State, 7070 Ashgabat Place, Washington, DC 20521-7070
American Embassy - Ashgabat, Turkmenistan,
9 Pushkin Street, Ashgabat, Turkmenistan 744000
Tel: 993 (12) 45-61-30 Fax: 993 (12) 45-47-62
Internet: www.usaid.gov/turkmenistan

Country Director **Mischere Kawas** 993 (12) 46-61-30
E-mail: mkawas@usaid.gov

Agricultural Section (Foreign Agricultural Service) (Resident in Ankara) [Turkmenistan]
American Embassy - Ankara, Turkey, 110 Ataturk Boulevard, Ankara, Turkey
Mail: American Embassy - Ankara, Turkey, PSC 93, Box 5000, APO, AE 09823
Tel: 90 (312) 468-6110 Fax: 90 (312) 467-0019

Agricultural Officer **Christine Strossman** 90 (312) 468-6110
E-mail: christine.strossman@fas.usda.gov

Commercial Section (Foreign Commercial Service) (Resident in Ankara) [Turkmenistan]
American Embassy - Ankara, Turkey, 110 Ataturk Boulevard, Ankara, Turkey
Mail: American Embassy - Ankara, Turkey, PSC 93, Box 5000, APO, AE 09823
Tel: 90 (312) 455-5555 Fax: 90 (312) 457-7302

◇ Commercial Officer **William "Bill" Czajkowski** 90 (312) 457-7278
E-mail: william.czajkowski@trade.gov

Federal Aviation Administration (Resident in Moscow) [Turkmenistan]
Eight Bolshoy Devyatinsky Pereulok, 121099 Moscow, Russia
Mail: American Embassy/FAA, PSC 77, APO, AE 09721
Fax: 7 (495) 728-5350

FAA Senior Representative **Andrew McKee** 7 (495) 728-5125

Office of the Defense Attaché [Turkmenistan]
American Embassy - Ashgabat, Turkmenistan,
9 Pushkin Street, Ashgabat, Turkmenistan 744000
Mail: Department of State, 7070 Ashgabat Place, Washington, DC 20521-7070
Tel: 993 (12) 94-00-45 Fax: 993 (12) 39-26-14

Defense Attaché **Karla Daniels** 993 (12) 94-00-45

U.S. Embassy in Uzbekistan

American Embassy - Tashkent, Uzbekistan,
3 Moyqo'rq'on, 5th Block, Yunusobod District, Tashkent, 100093, Uzbekistan
Tel: 998 (71) 120-54-50 Fax: 998 (71) 120-63-35
E-mail: TashkentInfo@state.gov Internet: uz.usembassy.gov

Office of the U.S. Ambassador to Uzbekistan

American Embassy - Tashkent, Uzbekistan,
3 Moyqo'rq'on, 5th Block, Yunusobod District, Tashkent, 100093, Uzbekistan
Mail: Department of State, 7110 Tashkent Place, Washington, DC 20521-7110

★ Ambassador-Designate
Daniel N. "Dan" Rosenblum 998 (71) 120-54-50
E-mail: rosenblumdn@state.gov

◇ Chargé d'Affaires **Alan D. Meltzer** 998 (71) 120-54-50
E-mail: meltzerad@state.gov
Education: Haverford 1985 BA; Virginia 1988 JD

Office Management Specialist to the Ambassador (Acting) **Christopher "Chris" Call** 998 (71) 120-54-50
E-mail: callc@state.gov

◇ Deputy Chief of Mission **Alan D. Meltzer** 998 (71) 120-54-50
E-mail: meltzerad@state.gov
Education: Haverford 1985 BA; Virginia 1988 JD

Office of the U.S. Ambassador to Uzbekistan *(continued)*

Office Management Specialist to the Deputy Chief of Mission (Acting) **Diane Edge** 998 (71) 120-54-50
E-mail: edged@state.gov

Community Liaison Officer **Lauren McCaughey** 998 (71) 120-5450
E-mail: McCaugheyLG@state.gov

Consular Section Chief **Hadi K. Deeb** 998 (71) 120-54-44
E-mail: deebhk@state.gov
Tel: 998 (71) 140-2215
Consular Section: ConsularTashkent@state.gov
Immigrant Visa Unit: TashkentIV@state.gov

Financial Management Officer **Irina Itkin** 998 (71) 120-54-50
E-mail: ltkinI@state.gov

General Services Officer **Jason Halleck** 998 (71) 120-54-50
E-mail: HalleckJD@state.gov

Information Management Officer **Mahmood Khattak** 998 (71) 120-54-50
E-mail: KhattakMH@state.gov

Information Systems Officer **Munkhtur Enkhbold** ... 998 (71) 120-54-50
E-mail: EnkhboldM@state.gov

Management Officer **Jason A. Brenden** 998 (71) 120-54-50
E-mail: brendenja@state.gov

Political/Economic Officer **Deborah "Debby" Robinson** 998 (71) 120-54-50

Public Affairs Officer **John Brown** 998 (71) 120-54-50
E-mail: BrownJS2@state.gov

Regional Security Officer **Brendan McCaughey** 998 (71) 120-5450
E-mail: McCaugheyBE@state.gov

Export Control and Related Border Security Program Advisor **Nick Cavellero** 998 (71) 120-54-50
E-mail: CavelleroNA@state.gov

Agency for International Development [Uzbekistan]
American Embassy - Tashkent, Uzbekistan,
3 Moyqo'rq'on, 5th Block, Yunusobod District, Tashkent, 100093, Uzbekistan
Mail: Department of State, 7110 Tashkent Place, Washington, DC 20521-7110
Tel: 998 (71) 140-2486 Fax: 998 (71) 120-6309
Internet: www.usaid.gov/uzbekistan

Country Director **Gary Robbins** 998 (71) 140-2486
E-mail: grobbins@usaid.gov

Defense Threat Reduction Office [Uzbekistan] (DTRO)
Department of State, 7110 Tashkent Place, Washington, DC 20521-7110
American Embassy - Tashkent, Uzbekistan,
3 Moyqo'rq'on, 5th Block, Yunusobod District, Tashkent, 100093, Uzbekistan

Chief **(Vacant)** 998 (71) 120-54-50

Federal Aviation Administration (Resident in Moscow) [Uzbekistan]
Eight Bolshoy Devyatinsky Pereulok, 121099 Moscow, Russia
Mail: American Embassy - Moscow, Russia, PSC 77, FAA, APO, AE 09721
Fax: 7 (495) 728-5350

FAA Senior Representative **Andrew McKee** 7 (495) 728-5125

Office of the Defense Attaché [Uzbekistan]
Department of State, 7110 Tashkent Place, Washington, DC 20521-7110
American Embassy - Tashkent, Uzbekistan,
3 Moyqo'rq'on, 5th Block, Yunusobod District, Tashkent, 100093, Uzbekistan
Tel: 998 (71) 120-54-50

Defense Attaché **Dale Slade** 998 (71) 120-54-50
E-mail: sladedk@state.gov

★ Presidential Appointment Requiring Senate Confirmation ☆ Presidential Appointment □ Schedule C Appointment ◇ Career Senior Foreign Service Appointment
● Career Senior Executive Service (SES) Appointment ○ Non-Career Senior Executive Service (SES) Appointment ■ Postal Career Executive Service

DEPARTMENTS

EAST ASIA AND PACIFIC

U.S. Embassy in Australia

American Embassy - Canberra A.C.T.,
Moonah Place, Canberra, ACT 2600, Australia
Tel: 61 (2) 6214-5600 Fax: 61 (2) 6214-5970
E-mail: askembassycanberra@state.gov

Office of the U.S. Ambassador to Australia

American Embassy - Canberra A.C.T.,
Moonah Place, Canberra, ACT 2600, Australia
Mail: American Embassy - Canberra, APO, AP 96549

★ Ambassador-Designate **Arthur B. Culvahouse, Jr.** 61 (2) 6214-5600
Education: Tennessee 1970 BS; NYU 1973 JD
Chargé d'Affaires **James A. Carouso** 61 (2) 6214-5600
E-mail: carousoja@state.gov
Education: Hamilton 1978 BA
Office Management Specialist to the Ambassador **Susan L. "Sue" Heckman** 61 (2) 6214-5601
E-mail: heckmansl@state.gov
Deputy Chief of Mission (Acting) **Michael G. Heath** . . . 61 (2) 6214-5843
E-mail: heathmg@state.gov
Office Management Specialist to the Deputy Chief of Mission **Rachel Watson** 61 (2) 6214-5843
Community Liaison Officer **Tracie Kania** 61 (2) 6214-5600
E-mail: kaniatl@state.gov
Consular Officer **(Vacant)** 61 (2) 6214-5854
Economic Officer (Acting) **Michael R. Roberts** 61 (2) 6214-5759
Environment, Science and Technology Officer **Andrew Riplinger** 61 (2) 6214-5810
E-mail: riplingeraj@state.gov
Equal Employment Officer **(Vacant)** 61 (2) 6214-5662
Facilities Management Officer **Therman Campbell** 61 (2) 6214-5600
Financial Management Officer **Calvin D. Levo** 61 (2) 6214-5887
E-mail: levocd1@state.gov
General Services Officer **Michael Warren** 61 (2) 6214-5703
Human Resources Officer (Acting) **Jeramee Rice** 61 (2) 6214-5723
Education: Union U 1999 BS; London School Econ (UK) 2002 MSc
Information Management Officer (Acting) **Marqui Neder** 61 (2) 6214-5901
E-mail: nederm@state.gov
Information Program Officer (Acting) **Andrew Calvin** 61 (2) 6214-5662
Information Systems Officer (Acting) **Martin Milner** . . . 61 (2) 6214-5912
Information Systems Security Officer **Wendall Anderson** 61 (2) 6214-5912
Legal Attaché **Thomas Schultz** 61 (2) 6214-5731
Management Officer **John C. Dockery** 61 (2) 6214-5990
E-mail: dockeryjc@state.gov
Political Officer **John T. Hennessey-Niland** 61 (2) 6214-5884
E-mail: hennessey-nilandj@state.gov
Education: Tufts 1985 BA; Fletcher Law & Diplomacy 1987 MALD
Public Affairs Officer **Gavin A. Sundwall** 61 (2) 6214-5770
E-mail: sundwallga@state.gov Fax: 61 (2) 6273-3051
Regional Security Officer **Scott Messick** 61 (2) 6214-5733
E-mail: messicksm@state.gov

Agricultural Section (Foreign Agricultural Service) [Australia]

American Embassy - Canberra A.C.T.,
Moonah Place, Canberra, ACT 2600, Australia
Mail: American Embassy - Canberra, APO, AP 96549
Tel: 61 (2) 6214-5854 Fax: 61 (2) 6273-1656
E-mail: agcanberra@fas.usda.gov

Agricultural Officer **Rey Santella** 61 (2) 6214-5854
E-mail: Rey.Santella@fas.usda.gov

Commercial Section (Foreign Commercial Service) (Resident in Sydney) [Australia]

MLC Centre, 19-29 Martin Place, Level 59, Sydney, New South Wales 2000, Australia
Mail: U.S. Commercial Service, PSC 280, Unit 11024, APO, AP 96554
Tel: 61 (2) 9373-9204 Fax: 61 (2) 9221-0573
Internet: www.export.gov/australia

Senior Commercial Officer **(Vacant)** 61 (2) 9373-9201

Commercial Section (Foreign Commercial Service) (Resident in Sydney) [Australia] *(continued)*

Deputy Senior Commercial Officer **(Vacant)** 61 (3) 9526-5923

Federal Aviation Administration (Resident in Tokyo) [Australia]

American Embassy - New Delhi, India,
Shanti Path, Chanakyapuri, 110021 New Delhi, India
Fax: 81 (3) 3582-5974

Senior FAA Representative **Nathan "Nate" Purdy** 81 (3) 3224-5511

Office of the Defense Attaché [Australia]

American Embassy - Canberra A.C.T.,
Moonah Place, Canberra, ACT 2600, Australia
Mail: American Embassy - Canberra, APO, AP 96549
Tel: 61 (2) 6214-5807 Fax: 61 (2) 6273-5232

Defense and Air Attaché **Col Raymond Powell USAF** 61 (2) 6214-5732

Melbourne Consulate General

U.S. Consulate General - Melbourne, 553 Street Kilda Road, P.O. Box 6722, Melbourne, Victoria 3004, Australia
Mail: U.S. Consulate General - Melbourne, Unit 11011, APO, AP 96551-0002
Tel: 61 (3) 9526-5900 Fax: 61 (3) 9510-4646

Consul General **Michael F. Kleine** 61 (3) 9526-5921
E-mail: kleinemf@state.gov
Education: Duke 1990 BA, 1993 JD; National War Col 2013 MS
Office Management Specialist to Consul General **Alison Millard** 61 (3) 9526-5921
Consular Section Officer **Cecilia Coleman** 61 (3) 9526-5962
Fax: 61 (3) 9525-0769
Information Management Officer **(Vacant)** 61 (3) 9526-5933
Information Program Officer **Billy McGowan** 61 (3) 9526-5933
Information Systems Security Officer **Billy McGowan** 61 (3) 9526-5900
Management Officer **Leah M. Thorstenson** 61 (3) 9526-5958
E-mail: thorstensonlm@state.gov
Education: Clemson 2004 BS; Thunderbird Global 2011 MBA
Political/Economic Officer **Michele Woonacott** 61 (3) 9526-5992
Public Affairs Officer **David Edginton** 61 (3) 9526-5920

Perth Consulate General

U.S. Consulate General - Perth, 16 Saint George's Terrace, 4th Floor, Perth, Western Australia 6000, Australia
Mail: U.S. Consulate General - Perth, APO, AP 96530
Tel: 61 (8) 6144-5100 Fax: 61 (8) 9231-9444
E-mail: usrsaustralia@state.gov

Consul General **Rachel L. Cooke** 61 (8) 6144-5100
E-mail: cookerl@state.gov
Deputy Principal Officer **Margaret Mason** 61 (8) 6144-5100
Office Management Specialist to the Consul General **Marianne Primrose** 61 (8) 6144-5100
E-mail: primrosemh@state.gov
Consular Section Officer **Craig Dennison** 61 (8) 6144-5100
Economic Section **Gina Soos** 61 (8) 6144-5100
E-mail: soosrm@state.gov
General Services Officer **Wendy Hipworth** 61 (8) 6144-5100
Information Systems Officer **Eric Jarrett** 61 (8) 6144-5100
Management Officer **Justin Bytheway** 61 (8) 6144-5100
E-mail: bythewayjs@state.gov
Education: BYU 2008 BA
Political Officer **Kyle Regan** 61 (8) 6144-5100
Political/Economic Officer **Joe V. James** 61 (8) 6144-5100
E-mail: jamesjv@state.gov
Public Affairs Officer **Lisa Marino** 61 (8) 6144-5100
E-mail: marinolm@state.gov
Regional Security Officer **Lee Richards** 61 (8) 6144-5100

★ Presidential Appointment Requiring Senate Confirmation ☆ Presidential Appointment □ Schedule C Appointment ◇ Career Senior Foreign Service Appointment
● Career Senior Executive Service (SES) Appointment ○ Non-Career Senior Executive Service (SES) Appointment ■ Postal Career Executive Service

Sydney Consulate General
U.S. Consulate General - Sydney, MLC Centre, 19-29 Martin Place, Level 10, Sydney, New South Wales 2000, Australia
Mail: U.S. Consulate General - Sydney, PSC 280, Unit 11026, APO, AP 96554-0002
Tel: 61 (2) 9373-9200 Fax: 61 (2) 9373-9125

Consul General **Sharon Hudson-Dean** 61 (2) 9373-9104
E-mail: hudsondeans@state.gov
Education: Georgetown BA; Johns Hopkins MA
Office Management Specialist to the Consul General **Beth Albrecht** 61 (2) 9373-9104
E-mail: albrechtba@state.gov
Consular Affairs Officer **Linda Daetwyler** 61 (2) 9373-9200
E-mail: daetwylerle@state.gov
Equal Employment Officer **(Vacant)** 61 (2) 9373-9104
General Services Officer
Christopher "Chris" Crawford 61 (2) 9373-9200
E-mail: crawfordca@state.gov
Information Program Officer **Bruce A. Waddell** 61 (2) 9373-9135
E-mail: waddellba@state.gov
Information Systems Officer **(Vacant)** 61 (2) 9373-9200
Information Systems Security Officer
Bruce A. Waddell 61 (2) 9373-9200
E-mail: waddellba@state.gov
Legal Attaché **Timothy J. "Tim" O'Malley** 61 (2) 9373-9200
Management Officer **Jeramee Rice** 61 (2) 9373-9111
Education: Union U 1999 BS; London School Econ (UK) 2002 MSc
Political/Economic Officer **Andrea Aquilla** 61 (2) 9373-9108
Public Affairs Officer **Donald G. Maynard** 61 (2) 9373-9221
E-mail: maynarddg@state.gov
Regional Security Officer **Abdul Malik** 61 (2) 9373-9191

Commercial Section (Foreign Commercial Service) [Australia]
U.S. Consulate General - Sydney, New South Wales, Australia, MLC Centre, 19-29 Martin Place, Level 10, Sydney, New South Wales 2000, Australia
Mail: U.S. Consulate General - Sydney, PSC 280, Unit 11026, APO, AP 96554-0002
Tel: 61 (2) 9373-9205 Fax: 61 (2) 9221-0573
E-mail: Office.Australia@trade.gov Internet: export.gov/australia

Senior Commercial Officer **(Vacant)** 61 (2) 9373-9201

Department of Homeland Security - Transportation Security Administration [Australia]
U.S. Consulate General - Sydney, New South Wales, Australia, MLC Centre, 19-29 Martin Place, 59th Floor, Sydney, New South Wales 2000, Australia
Mail: U.S. Consulate General - Sydney, PSC 280, Unit 11026, APO, AP 96554-0002
Tel: 61 (2) 9373-9152 Fax: 61 (2) 9221-0598

TSA Officer **Eric Yatar** 61 (2) 9373-9152

U.S. Embassy in Brunei Darussalam
Simpang 336-52-16-9, Jalan Duta, Bandar Seri Begawan, Brunei Darussalam BS8675
Tel: 673 238-4616 Fax: 673 238-4604
E-mail: amembassy_bsb@state.gov

Office of the U.S. Ambassador to Brunei Darussalam
Simpang 336-52-16-9, Jalan Duta, Bandar Seri Begawan, Brunei Darussalam BS8675
Mail: American Embassy - Bandar Seri Begawan, 4020 Bandar Seri Begawan Place, Dulles, VA 20189
E-mail: amembassy_bsb@state.gov

★ Ambassador-Designate
Ambassador Matthew John "Matt" Matthews 673 238-4616
E-mail: matthewsmj@state.gov
Education: Oregon BA; Johns Hopkins 1985 MA
Chargé d'Affaires **Scott Edward Woodard** 673 238-4616
E-mail: woodards@state.gov
Education: DePauw BA; Virginia MA

Office of the U.S. Ambassador to Brunei Darussalam *(continued)*

Office Management Specialist to the Ambassador
Victoria A. Douvres 673 238-4616
E-mail: douvresva@state.gov
Deputy Chief of Mission **Scott Edward Woodard** 673 238-4616
E-mail: woodards@state.gov
Education: DePauw BA; Virginia MA
Office Management Specialist to the Deputy Chief of Mission **(Vacant)** 673 238-4616
Financial Management Officer (Resident in Singapore)
Yuting Shao 65 6476-9100
E-mail: shaoy2@state.gov
Information Management Officer **William N. Price** 673 238-4616
E-mail: pricewn@state.gov
Management Officer **Eric C. Moore** 673 238-4616
E-mail: mooreec@state.gov
Education: Minnesota 1992 BA
Consular/Political/Economic Officer **Paul Estrada** 673 238-4616
E-mail: estradapr@state.gov
Political/Economic Officer **(Vacant)** 673 238-4616
Public Affairs Officer **Eric C. Moore** 673 238-4616
E-mail: mooreec@state.gov
Education: Minnesota 1992 BA
Regional Security Officer **Nadim F. Abdush-Shahid** 673 238-4616

Agricultural Section (Foreign Agricultural Service) (Resident in Kuala Lumpur) [Brunei]
American Embassy - Kuala Lumpur, Malaysia, 376 Jalan Tun Razak, 50400 Kuala Lumpur, Malaysia
Mail: American Embassy - Kuala Lumpur, APO, AP 96535-8152
Tel: 60 (3) 2168-5082 Fax: 60 (3) 2168-5023

Agricultural Officer **Joani Dong** 60 (3) 2168-5082

Department of Homeland Security - U.S. Immigration and Customs Enforcement (Resident in Singapore) [Brunei]
American Embassy - Singapore, FPO, AP 96534-0001
Tel: 65 6476-9425 Fax: 65 6476-9188

Customs Officer **Calvin Webb** 65 6476-9425

Federal Aviation Administration (Resident in Singapore) [Brunei]
American Embassy, 27 Napier Road, Singapore, 258508, Singapore
Mail: American Embassy - Singapore, PSC 470 FAA IAO, FPO, AP 96534-0001
Tel: 65 6543-1466 Fax: 65 6543-1952

FAA Representative **James "Jim" Spillane** 65 6543-1466
E-mail: james.spillane@faa.gov

Office of the Defense Attaché (Resident in Singapore) [Brunei]
American Embassy - Singapore, FPO, AP 96534-0001
Tel: 65 6476-9392 Fax: 65 6476-9277 E-mail: singaporedao@state.gov

Defense Attaché
CAPT So Won Silas "Silas" Ahn USN 65 6476-9392

Office of Defense Cooperation [Brunei]
American Embassy - Singapore, FPO, AP 96534-0001

Defense Cooperation Officer **Lucas Barlow** 673 238-4616

U.S. Embassy in Burma
American Embassy - Rangoon, Burma, 110 University Avenue (GPO 521), Kamayut Township, Yangon, Myanmar
Tel: 95 (1) 536509 Fax: 95 (1) 511069

Office of the U.S. Ambassador to Burma
American Embassy - Rangoon, Burma, 110 University Avenue (GPO 521), Kamayut Township, Yangon, Myanmar
Mail: American Embassy - Rangoon, Burma, Box B, APO, AP 96546

★ Ambassador **Ambassador Scot Alan Marciel** 95 1-536-509
E-mail: marcielsa@state.gov
Education: UC Davis BA; Fletcher Law & Diplomacy 1983 MA
Office Management Specialist to the Ambassador
Johanna G. "Jo" Villemarette 95 (1) 536509
E-mail: villemarettejg@state.gov

(continued on next page)

DEPARTMENTS

Office of the U.S. Ambassador to Burma *(continued)*

◇ Deputy Chief of Mission **George N. Sibley** 95 (1) 536509
E-mail: sibleygn@state.gov
Education: Oberlin 1977 BA
Office Management Specialist to the Deputy Chief of Mission **Ethan Tidwell** 95 (1) 536509
Education: Andrews 2002 BA
Consular Section Chief **Kristofor Graf** 95 (1) 536509
Community Liaison Officer **Jeremy Giacoletto-Stegall** . . . 95 (1) 536509
Education: Wyoming BA; Comm Col Air Force AS
Economic Officer **(Vacant)** 95 (1) 536509
Financial Management Officer **Gia Parker** 95 (1) 536509
General Services Officer **Daniel J. "Dan" Tarapacki** 95 (1) 536509
Fax: 95 (1) 650306
Information Management Officer **Sheik W. Huie** 95 (1) 536509
E-mail: huiesw@state.gov
Information Program Officer **Erik D. McCulley** 95 (1) 536509
E-mail: mcculleyed@state.gov
Information Security Officer **Russell Walker** 95 (1) 536509
Information Systems Security Officer **Erik D. McCulley** . . . 95 (1) 536509
E-mail: mcculleyed@state.gov
Legal Attaché **(Vacant)** 95 (1) 536509
Management Officer **Gustav Goger, Jr.** 95 (1) 536509
Political Officer **William "Bill" Flens** 95 (1) 536509
E-mail: flensw@state.gov
Political/Economic Section Chief **William "Bill" Flens** 95 (1) 536509
E-mail: flensw@state.gov
Public Affairs Officer **John Groch** 95 (1) 536509
Fax: 95 (1) 650306
Regional Security Officer **Noah Ross** 95 (1) 536509

Agency for International Development [Burma]
American Embassy - Rangoon, Burma, Box B, APO, AP 96546
Internet: www.usaid.gov/burma

◇ Mission Director **Teresa L. McGhie** 95 (1) 536509
E-mail: tmcghie@usaid.gov
Education: Utah State BA; American U JD

Agricultural Section (Foreign Agricultural Service) [Burma]
American Embassy - Yangon, Myanmar, 110 University Avenue, Kamayut Township, Yangon, Myanmar
Mail: Box B, APO, AP 96546-0002
Tel: 95 (1) 536-509 ext. 4356 Fax: 95 (1) 511-069
E-mail: agrangoon@fas.usda.gov

Agricultural Attaché **Rachel Nelson** . . . . 95 (1) 536-509 ext. 4356
E-mail: rachel.nelson@fas.usda.gov

Commercial Section (Foreign Commercial Service) [Burma]
American Embassy - Rangoon, Burma,
110 University Avenue (GPO 521), Kamayut Township, Yangon, Myanmar

Senior Commercial Officer **John M. Fleming** 95 (1) 536-509
E-mail: john.fleming@trade.gov

Drug Enforcement Administration [Burma]
Drug Enforcement Administration Attaché **Michael Brown** 95 (1) 536509

Federal Aviation Administration (Resident in Singapore) [Burma]
American Embassy, 27 Napier Road, Singapore, 258508, Singapore
Mail: American Embassy - Singapore,
PSC 470 FAA IAO, FPO, AP 96534-0001
Tel: 65 6543-1466 Fax: 65 6543-1952

FAA Representative **James "Jim" Spillane** 65 6543-1466
E-mail: james.spillane@faa.gov

Office of the Defense Attaché [Burma]
American Embassy - Rangoon, Burma,
110 University Avenue (GPO 521), Kamayut Township, Yangon, Myanmar
Mail: American Embassy - Rangoon, Burma, Box B, APO, AP 96546
Tel: 95 (1) 536509

Defense Attaché **COL Craig J. Tippins USA** 95 (1) 536509

U.S. Embassy in Cambodia
American Embassy - Phnom Penh, Cambodia,
#1, Street 96, Phnom Penh, Cambodia
Tel: 855 23-728-000 Fax: 855 23-728-600

Office of the U.S. Ambassador to Cambodia
American Embassy - Phnom Penh, Cambodia,
#1, Street 96, Phnom Penh, Cambodia
Mail: American Embassy - Phnom Penh, Cambodia, Box P, APO, AP 96546

★ Ambassador **Ambassador William A. Heidt** 855 27-728-000
E-mail: heidtwa@state.gov
★ Ambassador-Designate **W. Patrick Murphy** 855 23-728-000
E-mail: murphywp@state.gov
Education: Vermont 1985 BA; Johns Hopkins 1991 MA; National War Col 2009 MS
Office Management Specialist to the Ambassador **Hana Tezera** 855 23-728-000
Deputy Chief of Mission **Michael Anthony Newbill** 855 23-728-000
E-mail: newbillma@state.gov
Office Management Specialist to the Deputy Chief of Mission **Craig Abernathy** 855 23-728-000
Consular Section Chief **Nophawan "Nikk" Sookmeewiriya** 855 23-728-000
E-mail: sookmeewiriyan@state.gov
Community Liaison Officer **Brian Koren** 855 23-728-000
Financial Management Officer **James R. Barber** 855 23-728-000
General Services Officer **Brendan Harley** 855 23-728-000
Information Management Officer **Chandra P. Masdar** 855 23-728-000
E-mail: masdarcp@state.gov
Legal Attaché **John Wilson** 237 28-000
Management Officer **Gary D. Anderson** 855 23-728-000
E-mail: andersongd2@state.gov
Political/Economic Section Chief **Daniel Kronenfeld** 855 23-728-000
Public Affairs Officer **Arend C. Zwartjes** 855 23-728-000
Fax: 855 23-217-637
Regional Security Officer **Timothy Pittman** . . . . 855 23-726-000 ext. 169

Agency for International Development [Cambodia]
American Embassy - Phnom Penh, Cambodia,
16, Street 228, Phnom Penh, Cambodia
Mail: American Embassy - Phnom Penh, Cambodia, Box P, APO, AP 96546
Tel: 855 23-728-000 Fax: 855 23-430-263 E-mail: icambodia@usaid.gov
Internet: www.usaid.gov/cambodia

◇ Mission Director (Acting) **Veena Reddy** 855 23-728-000
E-mail: vreddy@usaid.gov

Federal Aviation Administration (Resident in Singapore) [Cambodia]
American Embassy - Singapore, 27 Napier Road, Singapore, 258508, Singapore
Mail: American Embassy - Singapore,
PSC 470 FAA IAO, FPO, AP 96534-0001
Tel: 65 6543-1466 Fax: 65 6543-1952

FAA Representative **James "Jim" Spillane** 65 6543-1466
E-mail: james.spillane@faa.gov

Office of the Defense Attaché [Cambodia]
American Embassy - Phnom Penh, Cambodia,
16, Street 228, Phnom Penh, Cambodia
Mail: American Embassy - Phnom Penh, Cambodia, Box P, APO, AP 96546
Fax: 855 23-728-200 E-mail: USDAOCambodia@state.gov

Defense and Army Attaché **Col. Michael P. Stelzig USA** . . . . 855 23-216-436 ext. 275

Office of Defense Cooperation [Cambodia]
Number 18, Street 228, Phnom Penh, Cambodia
Mail: ODC Cambodia, Unit 8166, Box P, APO, AP 96546-0001
Tel: 855 23-216-436 Fax: 855 23-218-136
E-mail: ODCCambodia@state.gov

Chief **(Vacant)** 855 23-216-438

★ Presidential Appointment Requiring Senate Confirmation ☆ Presidential Appointment ☐ Schedule C Appointment ◇ Career Senior Foreign Service Appointment
● Career Senior Executive Service (SES) Appointment ○ Non-Career Senior Executive Service (SES) Appointment ■ Postal Career Executive Service

Peace Corps [Cambodia]
American Embassy - Phnom Penh, Cambodia,
#1, Street 96, Phnom Penh, Cambodia
Internet: www.peacecorps.gov/cambodia
Country Director **Paula Albertson** 855 23-222-901

U.S. Embassy in China

American Embassy - Beijing, China, No. 55 An Jia Lou Road, Beijing, China 100600
Tel: 86 (10) 8531-3000 Fax: 86 (10) 8531-4200

Office of the U.S. Ambassador to China

American Embassy - Beijing, China, No. 55 An Jia Lou Road, Beijing, China 100600
Mail: American Embassy - Beijing, China, PSC 461, Box 50, FPO, AP 96521-0002

★ Ambassador **Ambassador Terry E. Branstad** 86 (10) 8531-3000
Education: Iowa 1969 BA; Drake 1974 JD
☐ Chief of Staff **Steven W. Churchill** 86 (10) 8531-3000
Office Management Specialist to the Ambassador
Andrea Miller 86 (10) 8531-3000
Deputy Chief of Mission
Robert W. "Rob" Forden 86 (10) 8531-3000
E-mail: fordenrw@state.gov
Education: UC Santa Cruz 1981 BA; Fletcher Law & Diplomacy 1986
Office Management Specialist to the Deputy Chief of Mission **Aleksandra Pitner** 86 (10) 8531-3000
E-mail: pitnerau@state.gov
◇ Consul General **Henry H. Hand** 86 (10) 8531-3000
E-mail: handhh@state.gov Fax: 86 (10) 6532-4153
◇ Consular Officer **Jewell Elizabeth Evans** 86 (10) 8531-3000
E-mail: beijingacs@state.gov Fax: 86 (10) 6532-4153
E-mail: evansje@state.gov
Community Liaison Officer **Chris Pedersen** 86 (10) 8531-3000
Education: Northwestern 1998 BA; Embry-Riddle 2010 MAS
Economic Section Chief
Matthew D. "Matt" Murray 86 (10) 8531-3000
Fax: 86 (10) 8531-4949
Environment, Science, Technology and Health Officer **Travis Warner** 86 (10) 8531-4258
E-mail: beijingusembassyesth@state.gov Fax: 86 (10) 8531-3939
Education: Kansas 2006 BA; Chicago 2014 PhD
Facilities Management Officer **Gil Serrao** 86 (10) 6531-3000
Financial Management Officer
Jeffrey B. "Jeff" Scearce 86 (10) 8531-3000
E-mail: scearcejb@state.gov
General Services Officer **Rick Johnson** 86 (10) 8531-3000
Human Resources Officer **Terry Pitner** 86 (10) 8531-3000
Information Management Officer
Shane W. Krohne 86 (10) 8531-3000
E-mail: krohnesw@state.gov
Information Program Officer **William L. Nguyen** 86 (10) 8531-3000
Information Systems Officer **David A. Penuel** 86 (10) 8531-3000
E-mail: penuelda@state.gov
Information Systems Security Officer
Robert E. "Rob" Weber 86 (10) 8531-3000
E-mail: weberre@state.gov
Legal Attache **Robert Stewart** 86 (10) 8531-3000
◇ Management Officer
Katherine Anne Munchmeyer 86 (10) 8531-3000
E-mail: munchmeyerka@state.gov Fax: 86 (10) 8531-3181
Education: Wellesley 1987 BS
◇ Political Section Chief **William H. "Bill" Klein** 86 (10) 8531-3000
E-mail: kleinwh@state.gov Fax: 86 (10) 8531-4966
◇ Public Affairs Officer **Frank J. Whitaker** 86 (10) 8531-4200
E-mail: WhitakerFJ@state.gov Fax: 86 (10) 8531-4200
Regional Security Officer **K. Andrew Wroblewski** 86 (10) 8531-3000
E-mail: wroblewskika@state.gov Fax: 86 (10) 8531-3165
Education: Kansas BA

Agency for International Development [China]
American Embassy - Beijing, China, No. 55 An Jia Lou Road, Beijing, China 100600
Internet: https://www.usaid.gov/china E-mail: beijingusaid@state.gov
◇ Development Counselor **Miles F. Toder** 86 (10) 8531-3855
E-mail: mtoder@usaid.gov

Agricultural Section (Foreign Agricultural Service) [China]
American Embassy - Beijing, China, No. 55 An Jia Lou Road, Beijing, China 100600
Mail: American Embassy - Beijing, China, PSC 461, Box 50, FPO, AP 96521-0002
Tel: 86 (10) 8531-3600 Fax: 86 (10) 8531-3636
E-mail: agbeijing@fas.usda.gov Internet: www.usdachina.com/beijing
◇ Agricultural Minister-Counselor
Bobby J. Richey, Jr. 86 (10) 8531-3600
E-mail: bobby.richey@fas.usda.gov

Agricultural Trade Office [China]
American Embassy - Beijing, China, PSC 461, Box 50, FPO, AP 96521-0002
Tel: 86 (10) 8531-3950 Fax: 86 (10) 8531-3050
E-mail: atobeijing@fas.usda.gov
Internet: www.usdachina.com/Beijing-ATO
Director **Mark Ford** 86 (10) 8531-3950
E-mail: mark.ford@fas.usda.gov

Animal and Plant Health Inspection Service [China]
International Club Building, 6th Floor, Beijing, China 100600
Mail: APHIS c/o U.S. Embassy - Beijing, China, PSC 461, Box 50, FPO, AP 96521-0002
Tel: 86 (10) 8531-3030 Fax: 86 (10) 8531-3033
APHIS Area Director **Silvia Kreindel** 86 (10) 8531-4524
E-mail: silvia.kreindel@aphis.usda.gov

Commercial Section (Foreign Commercial Service) [China]
American Embassy - Beijing, China, PSC 461, Box 50, FPO, AP 96521-0002
55 An Jia Lou road, Beijing, 100600, Chaoyang District, China
Tel: 86 (10) 8531-3557 Fax: 86 (10) 8531-3701
E-mail: office.beijing@trade.gov Internet: export.gov/china
◇ Senior Commercial Officer **Cynthia A. Griffin** 86 (10) 8531-3557
E-mail: cindy.griffin@trade.gov
◇ Deputy Senior Commercial Officer **Scott Shaw** 86 (10) 8531-3053
E-mail: scott.shaw@trade.gov

Drug Enforcement Administration [China]
North Tower, Beijing Kerry Center, 20th Floor, Room 2008, Beijing, 100020, China
Mail: American Embassy - Beijing, China, PSC 461, Box 50, FPO, AP 96521-0002
Tel: 86 (10) 8529-6880 Fax: 86 (10) 8529-6885
Drug Enforcement Administration Representative
Lance Ho 86 (10) 8529-6880

Federal Aviation Administration [China]
31 Technical Club Co., Ltd., 15 Guang Hua Li, Chao Yang District, Beijing, China 100020
Mail: American Embassy - Beijing, China, PSC 461, Box 50, FPO, AP 96521-0002
Tel: 86 (10) 8531-3987 Fax: 86 (10) 8531-4600
FAA Representative **Chris Collins** 86 (10) 8531-3987

Office of the Defense Attaché [China]
American Embassy - Beijing, China, No. 55 An Jia Lou Road, Beijing, China 100600
Mail: American Embassy - Beijing, China, PSC 461, Box 50, FPO, AP 96521-0002
Tel: 86 (10) 8531-3000 E-mail: daobej@state.gov
Defense Attaché
CAPT Thomas Henderschedt USN 86 (10) 8531-3000

★ Presidential Appointment Requiring Senate Confirmation ☆ Presidential Appointment ☐ Schedule C Appointment ◇ Career Senior Foreign Service Appointment
● Career Senior Executive Service (SES) Appointment ○ Non-Career Senior Executive Service (SES) Appointment ■ Postal Career Executive Service

Department of Homeland Security - Transportation Security Administration [China]
Silver Tower, 12th Floor, Room 1201, Beijing, China 100020
Tel: 86 (10) 6410-6621 Fax: 86 (10) 6410-6620

TSA Attaché **Friend L. Walker** 86 (10) 6410-6621

Department of Homeland Security - U.S. Citizenship and Immigration Services [China]
Kerry Center, South Tower, 23rd Floor, Beijing, China 100600
Tel: 86 (10) 8529-6740 Fax: 86 (10) 8529-6779

Officer-in-Charge **James Chiang** 86 (10) 8529-6740

Department of Homeland Security - U.S. Immigration and Customs Enforcement [China]
Silver Tower, 17th Floor, Room 1701, Beijing, China 100020
Tel: 86 (10) 6410-9223 Fax: 86 (10) 6500-3032
E-mail: customs@eastnet.com.cn

Customs Officer **Kai Wah Chan** 86 (10) 6410-9223

Chengdu Consulate General

U.S. Consulate General - Chengdu, China,
4 Lingshiguan Road, Chengdu, 610041, Sichuan, China
Mail: U.S. Consulate General - Chengdu, China, PSC 461, Box 85, FPO, AP 96521-0002
Tel: 86 (28) 8558-3992 Fax: 86 (28) 8558-3520

Consul General **James D. "Jim" Mullinax** 86 (28) 8558-3992
E-mail: mullinaxjd@state.gov
Office Management Specialist to the Consul General **Sandra D. Polley** 86 (28) 8558-3992
E-mail: polleysd@state.gov
Consular Section Chief **Clark Ledger** 86 (28) 8558-3992
E-mail: ledgerc@state.gov
General Services Officer **Geoffrey N. "Geoff" Benelisha** 86 (28) 8558-3992
E-mail: benelishagn@state.gov
Information Management Officer (Resident in Beijing) **Shane W. Krohne** 86 (10) 8531-3000
E-mail: krohnesw@state.gov
Information Program Officer **(Vacant)** 86 (28) 8558-3992
Management Officer **Mason Yu** 86 (28) 8558-3992
E-mail: yum@state.gov
Economic and Political Section Chief **Ory S. Abramowicz** 86 (28) 8558-3992
E-mail: abramowiczos@state.gov
Public Affairs Officer **Keith A. Lommel** 86 (28) 8558-3792
E-mail: lommelka@state.gov Fax: 86 (28) 8557-7540
Regional Security Officer **Nathan Kim** 86 (28) 8558-3992

Agricultural Trade Office [China]
Western Tower, No. 19 4th Section, South Renmin Road, Suite 1222, Chengdu, China 610041
Tel: 86 (28) 8526-8668 Fax: 86 (28) 8526-8118
E-mail: atochengdu@fas.usda.gov Internet: www.usdachina.com/chendu

Director **Yvonne McDowell** 86 (28) 8558-3992
E-mail: Yvonne.McDowell@fas.usda.gov

Commercial Section (Foreign Commercial Service) [China]
U.S. Consulate General - Chengdu, China, 4 Lingshiguan Road, Renmin Nanlu Section 4, Chengdu, 610041, Sichuan, China
Tel: 86 (28) 8558-3992 Fax: 86 (28) 8558-9221

Senior Commercial Officer **Francis M. "Chip" Peters** 86 (28) 8598-6661
E-mail: francis.peters@trade.gov

Guangzhou Consulate General

U.S. Consulate General - Guangzhou, China,
43 Hua Jiu Road, Guangzhou, 510623, China
Mail: U.S. Department of State, 4090 Guangzhou Place, Washington, DC 20521-4090
Tel: 86 (20) 3814-5000 Fax: 86 (20) 3814-5001

◇ Consul General **James M. "Jim" Levy** 86 (20) 3814-5000
E-mail: levyjm@state.gov
Education: Yale

Guangzhou Consulate General *(continued)*

Office Management Specialist to the Consul General **Jennifer L. Khov** 86 (20) 3814-5000
E-mail: khovjl@state.gov
Consular Section Chief **Jeremy A. Cornforth** 86 (20) 3814-5000
Economic/Political Section Chief **Christopher Smith** 86 (20) 3814-5000
General Services Officer **(Vacant)** 86 (20) 3814-5000
Information Program Officer **Michael C. Tagge** 86 (20) 3814-5000
E-mail: taggemc@state.gov
Management Officer **Jason W. Sheets** 86 (20) 3814-5000
Public Affairs Officer **Alan Clark** 86 (20) 3814-5000
Education: New Orleans 1994 BA
Regional Security Officer **Alex B. Reinshagen** 86 (20) 3814-5000
E-mail: reinshagenab@state.gov

Agricultural Trade Office [China]
U.S. Consulate General - Guangzhou, China,
43 Hua Jiu Road, Guangzhou, 510623, China
Mail: ATO - U.S. Consulate Guangzhou, PSC 461, Box 100, FPO, AP 96521-0002
Tel: 86 (20) 3814-5453 Fax: 86 (20) 3814-5310
E-mail: atoguangzhou@fas.usda.gov
Internet: www.usdachina.com/guangzhou

Director **Levin Flake** 86 (20) 3814-5453
E-mail: levin.flake@fas.usda.gov

Commercial Section (Foreign Commercial Service) [China]
U.S. Consulate General - Guangzhou, PSC 461, Box 100, FPO, AP 96521-0002
U.S. Consulate General - Guangzhou, China,
43 Hua Jiu Road, Guangzhou, 510623, China
Tel: 86 (20) 3814-5000 Fax: 86 (20) 3814-5310
E-mail: office.guangzhou@trade.gov

Principal Commercial Officer **Elizabeth M. "Betsy" Shieh** 86 (20) 3814-5564
E-mail: elizabeth.shieh@trade.gov

Department of Homeland Security - U.S. Citizenship and Immigration Services [China]
U.S. Consulate General - Guangzhou, PSC 461, Box 100, FPO, AP 96521-0002
U.S. Consulate General - Guangzhou, China,
43 Hua Jiu Road, Guangzhou, 510623, China
Tel: 86 (20) 3814 5880 Fax: 86 (20) 3814 5883
E-mail: CIS.Guangzhou@uscis.dhs.gov

Officer-in-Charge **(Vacant)** 86 (20) 3814 5880

Shanghai Consulate General

U.S. Consulate General - Shanghai, China,
1469 Huai Hai Zhong Lu, Shanghai, 200031, China
Mail: AmConGen Shanghai, PSC 461, Box 200, FPO, AP 96521-0200
Tel: 86 (21) 6433-6880 Fax: 86 (21) 6121-2182

◇ Consul General **Sean B. Stein** 86 (21) 6433-6880
E-mail: steinsb@state.gov
Education: Georgetown 1993 BA
Office Management Specialist to the Consul General **Alison Sierra** 86 (21) 6433-6880
Deputy Principal Officer **Gwendolyn J. "Gwen" Cardno** 86 (21) 6433-6880
E-mail: cardnogj@state.gov
Consular Officer **William J. Weissman** 86 (21) 6433-6880
E-mail: weissmanwj@state.gov Fax: 86 (21) 6471-1148
General Services Officer **Vicki S. Ting** 86 (21) 6433-6880
E-mail: tingvs@state.gov
Information Program Officer **Calos Fong** 86 (21) 6433-6880
Information Systems Officer **(Vacant)** 86 (21) 6433-6880
Information Systems Security Officer **Kenneth A. Kobilarcik** 86 (21) 6433-6880
E-mail: Kobilarcik@state.gov
Management Officer **John Hartman** 86 (21) 6433-6880
Education: Naval Acad 1990; UMass (Amherst) 2003 MBA Fax: 86 (21) 6474-6869

★ Presidential Appointment Requiring Senate Confirmation ☆ Presidential Appointment □ Schedule C Appointment ◇ Career Senior Foreign Service Appointment
● Career Senior Executive Service (SES) Appointment ○ Non-Career Senior Executive Service (SES) Appointment ■ Postal Career Executive Service

Shanghai Consulate General *(continued)*

Political/Economic Section Chief **Nancy W. Leou** 86 (21) 6433-6880
E-mail: LeouNW@state.gov Fax: 86 (21) 6433-4122
Public Affairs Officer **Pauline Kao** 86 (21) 6279-7662
Fax: 86 (21) 6279-7603
Regional Security Officer **Sean McClanahan** 86 (21) 6433-6880

Agricultural Trade Office [China]
Shanghai Center, 1376 Nanjing West Road,
Suite 331, Shanghai, 200040, China
Mail: ATO Shanghai, AMCONGEN Shanghai, PSC 461, Box 200,
FPO, AP 96521-0002
Tel: 86 (21) 6279-8622 Fax: 86 (21) 6279-8336
E-mail: atoshanghai@fas.usda.gov Internet: www.usdachina.com/shanghai

Director **Ryan C. Scott** 86 (21) 6279-8622
E-mail: ryan.scott@fas.usda.gov

Commercial Section (Foreign Commercial Service) [China]
U.S. Consulate General - Shanghai, China, PSC 461, Box 200,
FPO, AP 96521-0002
U.S. Consulate General - Shanghai, China, Shanghai Center,
1376 Nanjing West Road, Suite 631, Shanghai, 200040, China
Tel: 86 (21) 6279-7630 Fax: 86 (21) 6279-7639

◇ Principal Commercial Officer **Jonathan Heimer** 86 (21) 6279-7638
E-mail: jonathan.heimer@trade.gov
Education: Union Col (NY) 1985 BA; Michigan 1990 JD

Shenyang Consulate General
U.S. Consulate General - Shenyang, China, 5214th Wei Road,
Heping District, Shenyang, 110003, China
Mail: U.S. Consulate General - Shenyang, China, PSC 461, Box 45,
FPO, AP 96521-0002
Tel: 86 (24) 2322-1198 Fax: 86 (24) 2322-2374

Consul General **Gregory C. "Greg" May** 86 (24) 2322-1198
E-mail: maygc@state.gov Fax: 86 (24) 2322-1942
Office Management Specialist to the Consul General **George Tarry** 86 (24) 2322-0848
E-mail: tarrygr@state.gov
Consular Officer **Bradly J. "Brad" Roberson** 86 (24) 2322-1198
E-mail: robersonbj@state.gov Fax: 86 (24) 2323-1465
General Services Officer **Baylor M. Duncan** 86 (24) 2322-1198
Information Program Officer **Joseph Plunkett** 86 (24) 2322-1198
Information Systems Security Officer **Heath Call** 86 (24) 2322-1198
Education: Thomas Edison State 2011 AA
Management Officer **J. Dennis Robertson** 86 (24) 2322-1198
E-mail: robertsonjd@state.gov
Political/Economic Section Chief **Rashad N. Jones** 86 (24) 2322-1198
Fax: 86 (24) 2322-1942
Economic Officer **Samuel Yee** 86 (24) 2322-1198
Public Affairs Officer **Daniel A. "Dan" Phelps** 86 (24) 2322-2976
E-mail: phelpsda@state.gov Fax: 86 (24) 2322-1505
E-mail: ShenyangPA@state.gov
Regional Security Officer **William Burns** 86 (24) 2322-1198
Political/Economic Section Chief **(Vacant)** 86 (24) 2322-1198
Fax: 86 (24) 2322-1942
Political Officer **Matthew Yi** 86 (24) 2322-1198
Fax: 86 (24) 2322-1942

Agricultural Trade Office [China]
North Media International Tower, No. 167 Qing Nian Street,
Suite 1903, Shenyang, China 110014
Tel: 86 (24) 2318-1380 Fax: 86 (24) 2318-1332
E-mail: atoshenyang@fas.usda.gov
Internet: www.usdachina.com/shengyan

Director **Roseanne Freese** 86 (24) 2318-1380
E-mail: roseanne.freese@fas.usda.gov

Commercial Section (Foreign Commercial Service) [China]
U.S. Consulate General - Shenyang, China, 52 Shi Si Wei Lu,
Heping Qu, Shenyang, Liaoning 110013, China
Mail: U.S. Consulate General - Shenyang, China, PSC 461, Box 45,
FPO, AP 96521-0002
Tel: 86 (24) 2322-1198 Fax: 86 (24) 2322-2206
E-mail: office.shenyang@trade.gov

Principal Commercial Officer **Taylor Moore** 86 (24) 2322-1198
E-mail: taylor.moore@trade.gov

Wuhan Consulate General
U.S. Consulate General - Wuhan, China, 568 Jianshe Avenue,
Jianghan District, Room 4701, Wuhan, 430022, China
Tel: 86 (27) 8555-7791 Fax: 86 (27) 8555-7761
E-mail: usconsulatewuhan@state.gov

Consul General **B. Jamison "Jamie" Fouss** 86 (27) 8555-7791
E-mail: foussbj@state.gov
Consular Officer **Terry D. Mobley** 86 (27) 8555-7791
E-mail: mobleytd@state.gov
Principal Commercial Officer **Henley Jones** 86 (27) 8555-7791
E-mail: Henley.Jones@trade.gov
Education: Kansas 1984 BChE; Stuttgart (Germany) 1986; George Washington 1991 MBA
Community Liaison Officer **Wakami Chu** 86 (27) 8555-7791
Management Officer **Kevin Fisher** 86 (27) 8555-7791
Economic/Political Section Chief **Jonathan Adams** 86 (27) 8555-7791
Public Affairs Officer **Michael R. Dubray** 86 (27) 8555-7791
E-mail: dubraymr@state.gov
Regional Security Officer **Troy Hively** 86 (27) 8555-7791
E-mail: hivelyte@state.gov

U.S. Embassy in Fiji, Kiribati, Nauru, Tonga, and Tuvalu
American Embassy - Suva, Fiji, 158 Prince's Road, Suva, Fiji Islands
Tel: 679 331-4466 Fax: 679 330-5106

Office of the U.S. Ambassador to Fiji, Kiribati, Nauru, Tonga, and Tuvalu
American Embassy - Suva, Fiji, 158 Prince's Road, Suva, Fiji Islands
Mail: American Embassy - Suva, Fiji, Department of State, 4290 Suva Place, Washington, DC 20521-4290
Note: The U.S. Ambassador to Fiji serves concurrently as U.S. Ambassador to the following countries: the Republic of Kiribati, the Republic of Nauru, the Kingdom of Tonga, and Tuvalu.

★ Ambassador-Designate **Joseph J. "Joe" Cella** 679 331-4466
Education: Hillsdale BA
Chargé d'Affaires
Michael Benjamin "Mike" Goldman 679 331-4466
E-mail: goldmanmb@state.gov
Office Management Specialist to the Ambassador **(Vacant)** 679 331-4466
Deputy Chief of Mission
Michael Benjamin "Mike" Goldman 679 331-4466
E-mail: goldmanmb@state.gov
Office Management Specialist to the Deputy Chief of Mission **(Vacant)** 679 331-4466
Consular Section Chief **Robert "Robbie" Reeves** 679 331-4466
Community Liaison Officer **Danielle DePorter** 679 331-4466
Economic Officer **(Vacant)** 679 331-4466
Equal Employment Opportunity Officer **Shawn K. Gray** 679 331-4466
Financial Management Officer **Beth Abraham** 679 331-4466
General Services Officer **Eric T. Vogel** 679 331-4466
E-mail: vogelet@state.gov
Education: Georgia Tech 2007 BS
Information Program Officer **Steven Rawlins** 679 331-4466
E-mail: rawlinss@state.gov
Education: Utah 2009 BS
Information Management Officer **David W. Robinson** 679 331-4466
E-mail: robinsondw2@state.gov
Information Systems Officer/Information Systems Security Officer **David W. Robinson** 679 331-4466
E-mail: robinsondw2@state.gov

(continued on next page)

★ Presidential Appointment Requiring Senate Confirmation ☆ Presidential Appointment □ Schedule C Appointment ◇ Career Senior Foreign Service Appointment
● Career Senior Executive Service (SES) Appointment ○ Non-Career Senior Executive Service (SES) Appointment ■ Postal Career Executive Service

Office of the U.S. Ambassador to Fiji, Kiribati, Nauru, Tonga, and Tuvalu *(continued)*

Management Officer **Ronald D. "Ron" Perkel** 679 331-4466
E-mail: perkelrd@state.gov
Political/Economic Officer **Charles M. Bennett** 679 331-4466
Public Affairs Officer **Rebecca Archer-Knepper** 679 331-4466
Education: USC 2000 BA; London School Econ (UK) 2006 BSc
Regional Security Officer **Shawn K. Gray** 679 331-4466

Department of Homeland Security - Transportation Security Administration (Resident in Sydney) [Fiji]
U.S. Consulate General - Sydney, New South Wales, Australia,
MLC Centre, 19-29 Martin Place, 59th Floor, Sydney, New South Wales 2000, Australia
Mail: U.S. Consulate General - Sydney, PSC 280, Unit 11026,
APO, AP 96554-0002
Tel: 61 (2) 9373-9152 Fax: 61 (2) 9221-0598
TSA/CASLO Officer **Eric Yatar** 61 (2) 9373-9152

Federal Aviation Administration (Resident in Tokyo) [Fiji]
American Embassy - Tokyo, 1-10-5 Akasaka,
Minato-ku, Tokyo, Japan 107-8420
Mail: American Embassy - Tokyo, Japan, Unit 45004, Box 207,
APO, AP 96337-5004
Tel: 81 (3) 3224-5511 Fax: 81 (3) 3582-5974
FAA Representative **Nathan "Nate" Purdy** 81 (3) 3224-5511

Office of the Defense Attaché [Fiji]
American Embassy - Suva, Fiji, 158 Prince's Road, Suva, Fiji Islands
Mail: American Embassy - Suva, Fiji, Department of State, 4290 Suva Place, Washington, DC 20521-4290
Tel: 679 331-4466 Fax: 679 331-2603
Defense Attaché **CDR Constantine Panayiotou USN** 679 331-4466

Peace Corps [Fiji]
24 Saint-Fort Street, Suva, Fiji Islands
Mail: Private Mail Bag, Suva, Fiji, Department of State, 4290 Suva Place, Washington, DC 20521-4290
Tel: 679 331-7505 Fax: 679 331-7517 E-mail: fj01-info@peacecorps.gov
Internet: www.peacecorps.gov/fiji
Country Director **Dennis McMahon** 679 331-7505

U.S. Consulate General in Hong Kong and Macau

U.S. Consulate General - Hong Kong, China,
26 Garden Road, Central Hong Kong, Hong Kong
Tel: 852 2523-9011 Fax: 852 2845-1598 Internet: hk.usconsulate.gov

Hong Kong and Macau Consulate General
U.S. Consulate General - Hong Kong, China,
26 Garden Road, Central Hong Kong, Hong Kong
Mail: Consulate General - Hong Kong, Unit 8000, Box 5000,
FPO, AP 96521
◇ Consul General **Ambassador Kurt Walter Tong** 852 2523-9011
E-mail: tongkw@state.gov
Education: Princeton 1987 BA
Office Management Specialist to the Consul General
Shelby J. Martin 852 2523-9011
E-mail: martinsj@state.gov
◇ Deputy Consul General **Thomas M. Hodges** 852 2523-9011
E-mail: hodgestm@state.gov
Consular Section Chief **Brendan Mullarkey** 852 2523-9011
E-mail: mullarkeybp@state.gov Fax: 852 2147-5790
Community Liaison Officer **Brittanie Maffeo** 852 2523-9011
Economic/Political Section Chief **Dante Paradiso** 852 2523-9011
E-mail: paradisodx@state.gov
Education: Yale 1992 BA; UCLA 2000 JD
Financial Management Officer **Auburn Parker** 852 2523-9011
General Services Officer **Todd Harry Lundgren** 852 2523-9011
E-mail: lundgrenth@state.gov
Information Management Officer
Jeffrey "Jeff" Shrader 852 2523-9011

Hong Kong and Macau Consulate General *(continued)*
Information Program Officer **(Vacant)** 852 2523-9011
Information Systems Officer **Timothy A. Hinman** 852 2523-9011
E-mail: hinmanta@state.gov
Legal Attaché **Joshua Kim** 852 2523-9011
Management Officer **Arlene Barilec** 852 2523-9011
E-mail: barilecar@state.gov
Education: Columbia
Public Affairs Officer **Darragh T. Paradiso** 852 2523-9011
E-mail: paradisodt@state.gov
Education: Princeton MPP
Regional Security Officer **Andrew J. Loftus** 852 2523-9011
E-mail: loftusaj@state.gov

Agricultural Trade Office [Hong Kong]
Foreign Agricultural Service - St. John's Building, 33 Garden Road, 18th Floor, Central Hong Kong, Hong Kong
Mail: ATO - U.S. Consulate Hong Kong, Unit 8000, Box 5000,
FPO, AP 96521
Tel: 852 2841-2350 Fax: 852 2845-0943
E-mail: atohongkong@fas.usda.gov
Director **Alicia Hernandez** 852 2841-2350
E-mail: alicia.hernandez@fas.usda.gov

Animal and Plant Health Inspection Service (Resident in Beijing) [Hong Kong]
12-21 China World Trade Center, No. 1 Jianguomenwai Avenue,
Beijing, 100600, China
Mail: APHIS c/o U.S. Embassy - Beijing, China, PSC 461, Box 50,
FPO, AP 96521-0002
Tel: 86 (10) 8531-3030 Fax: 86 (10) 8531-3033
APHIS Officer **Murali Bandla** 86 (10) 8531-4524

Commercial Section (Foreign Commercial Service) [Hong Kong]
American Consulate General - FCS, 26 Garden Road, Central Hong Kong, Hong Kong
Mail: U.S. Consulate General - Hong Kong, FCS, Unit 8000, Box 5000,
FPO, AP 96521
Tel: 852 2521-1467 Fax: 852 2845-9800
E-mail: office.hongkong@trade.gov Internet: export.gov/hongkong
Senior Commercial Officer
James "Jim" Cunningham 852 2521-5753
E-mail: jim.cunningham@trade.gov
Deputy Senior Commercial Officer **Geoffrey Parish** 852 2521-1467
E-mail: Geoffrey.Parish@trade.gov
Education: Emerson 1996 BSc; Cambridge (UK) 2003 MBA

Department of Homeland Security - U.S. Immigration and Customs Enforcement [Hong Kong]
U.S. Consulate General - Hong Kong, China,
26 Garden Road, Central Hong Kong, Hong Kong
Mail: U.S. Consulate General - Hong Kong, PSC 461, Box 15,
FPO, AP 96521-0006
Tel: 852 2524-1136
Customs Officer **Christopher Pater** 852 2524-1136

Department of Justice - Drug Enforcement Administration [Hong Kong]
U.S. Consulate General - Hong Kong, China,
26 Garden Road, Central Hong Kong, Hong Kong
Mail: U.S. Consulate General - Hong Kong, PSC 461, Box 16,
FPO, AP 96521-0006
Tel: 852 2523-9011
DEA Officer **Phillip "Chad" Esch** 852 2523-9011

Federal Aviation Administration (Resident in Beijing) [Hong Kong]
15 Guang Hua Ki, Jian Guo Men Wai, Chao Yang District, Beijing, China 100020
Mail: American Embassy - Beijing, China, PSC 461, Box 50,
FPO, AP 96521-0002
Tel: 86 (10) 8531-3987 Fax: 86 (10) 8531-4600
FAA Representative **Chris Collins** 86 (10) 8531-3987

★ Presidential Appointment Requiring Senate Confirmation ☆ Presidential Appointment □ Schedule C Appointment ◇ Career Senior Foreign Service Appointment
● Career Senior Executive Service (SES) Appointment ○ Non-Career Senior Executive Service (SES) Appointment ■ Postal Career Executive Service

Internal Revenue Service [Hong Kong]
U.S. Consulate General - Hong Kong, China,
26 Garden Road, Central Hong Kong, Hong Kong
Mail: Consulate General - Hong Kong, PSC 461, Box 20,
FPO, AP 96521-0006
Tel: 852 2179-5972
IRS Officer **David Lum** 852 2841-2361

Office of the Defense Attaché [Hong Kong]
Defense Attaché **William G. Miller** 852 2523-9011

U.S. Embassy in Indonesia
Medan Merdeka Selatan 5, Jakarta, Indonesia
Tel: 62 (21) 3435-9000 Fax: 62 (21) 385-2259 Internet: id.usembassy.gov

Office of the U.S. Ambassador to Indonesia
American Embassy - Jakarta, Indonesia,
Medan Merdeka Selatan 5, Jakarta, Indonesia
Mail: American Embassy - Jakarta, Indonesia, Unit 8129, Box 1,
FPO, AP 96520-0001
E-mail: irc@usembassyjakarta.org

★ Ambassador
Ambassador Joseph R. Donovan, Jr. 62 (21) 3435-9000
E-mail: donovanjr@state.gov
Education: Georgetown 1973 BSFS; Naval Postgrad 1993 MA
Office Management Specialist to the Ambassador
Jodee R. Peterson 62 (21) 3435-9800

◇ Deputy Chief of Mission
Heather Catherine Variava 62 (21) 3435-9000
E-mail: VariavaHC@state.gov
Education: Georgetown BSFS; Missouri MA; Sussex (UK) MA; National War Col 2012 MNSSS
Office Management Specialist to the Deputy Chief of Mission **Brian H. Wainscott** 62 (21) 3435-9800
E-mail: wainscottbh@state.gov

Consul General **Kimberly C. Kelly** 62 (21) 3435-9051
E-mail: kellykc@state.gov
Community Liaison Officer **Deanna M. Gobert** 62 (21) 3435-9255
Economic Officer **Andrew Shaw** 62 (21) 3435-9094
E-mail: shawa@state.gov Fax: 62 (21) 3435-9971
Environment, Science and Technology Officer
Jai L. Nair 62 (21) 3435-9068
Equal Employment Opportunity Officer
James Cerven 62 (21) 3435-9083
E-mail: cervenj@state.gov
Education: Michigan 2004 JD
Facilities Management Officer **Walt R. O'Banion** 62 (21) 3435-9000
E-mail: obanionwr@state.gov
Financial Management Officer **Gregory E. Sanford** 62 (21) 3435-9031
E-mail: sanfordge@state.gov
General Services Officer
Christopher "Chris" Bergaust 62 (21) 3435-9026
E-mail: bergaustc@state.gov
Human Resources Officer **Kathryn D. Morgan** 62 (21) 3435-9000
Information Management Officer
Osman M. Koclar 62 (21) 3435-9301
Information Program Officer **(Vacant)** 62 (21) 3435-9039
Information Systems Officer
Yerusalem Woldeselassie 62 (21) 3435-9090
E-mail: woldeselassiey@state.gov
Legal Attaché **Joseph Callahan** 62 (21) 3435-9000
◇ Management Officer **James R. Dayringer** 62 (21) 3435-9011
E-mail: dayringerjr@state.gov Fax: 62 (21) 3435-9940
Political Officer **David Robert Greenberg** 62 (21) 3435-9280
◇ Public Affairs Officer **Susan Marie Shultz** 62 (21) 3435-9502
E-mail: shultzsm@state.gov Fax: 62 (21) 381-0243
Press Attaché/Spokesperson **Rakesh Surampudi** 62 (21) 3435-9000
E-mail: surampudir@state.gov
Regional Security Officer **Brendan M. Murray** 62 (21) 3435-9013
E-mail: murraybm@state.gov
Regional Affairs Officer **Jerry Woolsey** 62 (21) 3435-9000
E-mail: woolseyjm@state.gov

Office of the U.S. Ambassador to Indonesia *(continued)*
Narcotics Affairs Officer
Gregory "Greg" Wiegand 62 (21) 3435-9000
E-mail: wiegandgs@state.gov

Agency for International Development [Indonesia]
American Embassy - Jakarta, Indonesia,
Medan Merdeka Selatan 5, Jakarta, Indonesia
Mail: American Embassy - Jakarta, Indonesia, Box 4, Unit 8135,
APO, AP 96520-8135
Tel: 62 (21) 3435-9300 Fax: 62 (21) 380-6694
Internet: www.usaid.gov/indonesia
Mission Director (Acting) **Dr. David Hoffman PhD** 62 (21) 3435-9300
Education: Stanford 1995 BA, 1995 BS; UC Berkeley 2000 PhD

Agricultural Section (Foreign Agricultural Service) [Indonesia]
American Embassy - Jakarta, Indonesia,
Medan Merdeka Selatan 5, Jakarta, Indonesia
Mail: American Embassy - Jakarta, Indonesia, Box 1, Unit 8129,
APO, AP 96520-8129
Tel: 62 (21) 3435-9161 Fax: 62 (21) 3435-9920
E-mail: agjakarta@fas.usda.gov Internet: www.usdaindonesia.org
Agricultural Officer
Christopher P. "Chris" Rittgers 62 (21) 3435-9161
E-mail: chris.rittgers@fas.usda.gov

Commercial Section (Foreign Commercial Service) [Indonesia]
Wisma Metropolitan II, Jendral Sudirman Kav. 29-31,
3rd Floor Jl., Jakarta, Indonesia 12920
Mail: U.S. Commercial Service, Box 1, Unit 8129 FCS, FPO, AP 96520
Tel: 62 (21) 526-2850 Fax: 62 (21) 526-2855
E-mail: office.jakarta@trade.gov Internet: export.gov/indonesia
Senior Commercial Officer
Rosemary Gallant .... 62 (21) 526-2850 ext. 3001
E-mail: rosemary.gallant@trade.gov

Department of Homeland Security - U.S. Immigration and Customs Enforcement [Indonesia]
American Embassy - Jarkata, Indonesia, Box 2, Unit 8133,
APO, AP 96520-8133
Customs Officer **James Klink** 62 (21) 3435-9783

Federal Aviation Administration (Resident in Singapore) [Indonesia]
American Embassy, 27 Napier Road, Singapore, Singapore 258508
Mail: American Embassy - Singapore,
PSC 470 FAA IAO, FPO, AP 96534-0001
Tel: 65 6543-1466 Fax: 65 6543-1952
FAA Representative **James "Jim" Spillane** 65 6543-1466
E-mail: james.spillane@faa.gov

Library of Congress [Indonesia]
Library of Congress, Jakarta Regional Office for Southeast Asia, Jakarta, Indonesia
Mail: LOC-Jakarta, American Embassy, Box 1, Unit 8129,
FPO, AP 96520-0001
Tel: 62 (21) 314-4944 Fax: 62 (21) 314-4945 Internet: www.locjkt.or.id
Field Director **Carol L. Mitchell PhD** 62 (21) 310-2127
E-mail: jakarta@loc.gov

Office of the Defense Attaché [Indonesia]
American Embassy - Jakarta, Indonesia,
Medan Merdeka Selatan 5, Jakarta, Indonesia
Mail: American Embassy - Jakarta, Indonesia, Box 1, Unit 8134,
APO, AP 96520-8134
Tel: 62 (21) 3435-9725 Fax: 62 (21) 3435-9921
Defense Attaché **Michael Spake** 62 (21) 3435-9725

DEPARTMENTS

★ Presidential Appointment Requiring Senate Confirmation ☆ Presidential Appointment □ Schedule C Appointment ◇ Career Senior Foreign Service Appointment
● Career Senior Executive Service (SES) Appointment ○ Non-Career Senior Executive Service (SES) Appointment ■ Postal Career Executive Service

Office of Defense Cooperation [Indonesia]
American Embassy - Jakarta, Indonesia,
Medan Merdeka Selatan 5, Jakarta, Indonesia
Mail: American Embassy - Jarkata, Indonesia, Box 2, Unit 8133,
APO, AP 96520-8133
Tel: 62 (21) 3435-9601 Fax: 62 (21) 384-3339

Office of Defense Cooperation **Brady Crosier** 62 (21) 3435-9601

Surabaya Consulate General
U.S. Consulate General - Surabaya, Indonesia, Jalan Citra Raya,
Niaga No. 2, Surabaya, Indonesia 60217
Mail: U.S. Consulate General - Surabaya, Box 1, Unit 8131,
APO, AP 96520-0002
Tel: 62 (31) 297-5300 Fax: 62 (31) 297-5301
E-mail: consurabaya@state.gov

Consul General **Mark McGovern** 62 (31) 297-5300
E-mail: mcgovernmg@state.gov
Office Management Specialist to the Consul
General **Mary Anne Green** 62 (31) 297-5300
Community Liaison Officer **Julie Ramirez** 62 (31) 297-5300
Consular Section Officer **Sadie Dworak** 62 (31) 297-5300
E-mail: dworakse@state.gov
Political/Economic Officer
Brian Jungwiwattanaporn 62 (31) 297-5300
E-mail: jungwiwattanapornb@state.gov
Education: Boston U 1999 BA; Johns Hopkins 2009 MA
General Services Officer **(Vacant)** 62 (31) 297-5300
Information Management Officer
Douglas "Doug" McDonald 62 (31) 297-5300
Education: UNLV 1978 BS
Management Officer **Seth Cornell** 62 (31) 297-5300
Political Officer **(Vacant)** 62 (31) 297-5300
Public Affairs Officer **Christine Getzler Vaughan** 62 (31) 297-5300
Regional Security Officer **Abraham Ramirez** 62 (31) 297-5300
Education: Cal State (San Bernardino) BS; American Military U MS

Medan Consulate
U.S. Consulate - Medan, Indonesia, Uni Plaza Building 4th Floor,
West Tower, Jl. Let. Jend. MT. Haryono A-1, Medan, Indonesia 10110
Tel: 62 (61) 451-9000 Fax: 62 (61) 455-9033 E-mail: sumatra@state.gov

Principal Officer and Consul **Juha P. Salin** 62 (61) 451-9000
Deputy Principal Officer and Deputy Consul
Jessica E. Panchatha 62 (61) 451-9000
E-mail: panchathaje@state.gov
Education: George Washington 2001 BA

Bali Consular Agency
U.S. Consular Agency - Bali, Indonesia,
Jalan Hayam Wuruk 188, Denpasar, 80235, Bali, Indonesia
Mail: U.S. Consular Agency - Bali, Indonesia, Box 1, APO, AP 96520
Tel: 62 (361) 233-605 Fax: 62 (361) 222-426 E-mail: cabali@state.gov

Consular Agent **Joseph Curtin** 62 (361) 233-605

U.S. Embassy in Japan

10-5 Akasaka 1-chome, Minato-ku, Tokyo, 107-8420, Japan
Tel: 81 (3) 3224-5000 Fax: 81 (3) 3505-1862 Internet: jp.usembassy.gov

Office of the U.S. Ambassador to Japan
American Embassy - Tokyo, Japan, 10-5 Akasaka 1-chrome,
Minato-ku, Tokyo, 107-8420, Japan
Mail: Unit 45004, Box 258, APO, AP 96337-5004

★ Ambassador
Ambassador William Francis "Bill" Hagerty IV 81 (3) 3224-5000
E-mail: hagertywf@state.gov
Education: Vanderbilt BS, JD
Office Management Specialist to the Ambassador
David W. Mandis 81 (3) 3224-5000
E-mail: mandisdw@state.gov
Deputy Chief of Mission **Joseph M. "Joe" Young** 81 (3) 3224-5000
E-mail: youngjm@state.gov
Office Management Specialist to the Deputy Chief
of Mission **Joyce S. Ogier** 81 (3) 3224-5000

Office of the U.S. Ambassador to Japan *(continued)*

Community Liaison Officer **Rohini M. Johnson** 81 (3) 3224-5000
◇ Consul General **Stuart M. Hatcher** 81 (3) 3224-5000
E-mail: hatchersm@state.gov
Consular Section Officer **Timothy G. Smith** 81 (3) 3224-5000
E-mail: smithtg@state.gov
Economic Officer **Nicholas M. Hill** 81 (3) 3224-5000
E-mail: hillnm@state.gov Fax: 81 (3) 3224-5019
Education: Bowdoin 1981 BA;
Georgetown MIA; National War Col MS
Environment, Science and Technology Officer
Michael F. Cavanaugh 81 (3) 3224-5000
E-mail: cavanaughmf@state.gov
Facilities Management Officer
Steven G. "Steve" Kisling 81 (3) 3224-5000
E-mail: kislings@state.gov
Financial Attaché **Matthew Poggi** 81 (3) 3224-5000
E-mail: poggima@state.gov
Financial Management Officer **Li Gong** 81 (3) 3224-5000
General Services Officer **Alma M. Johnson** 81 (3) 3224-5000
Human Resources Officer **Michael T. Greer** 81 (3) 3224-5000
E-mail: greermt@state.gov
Education: BYU MS; Texas MBA
Information Management Officer **Kevin Rubesh** 81 (3) 3224-5000
Information Program Officer **Christina Bergen** 81 (3) 3224-5000
Information Systems Officer **Brian Hering** 81 (3) 3224-5000
Information Systems Security Officer **Derek Hester** 81 (3) 3224-5000
Legal Attaché **Jeffrey Green** 81 (3) 3224-5000
◇ Management Officer **Matthew D. Smith** 81 (3) 3224-5000
E-mail: smithmd2@state.gov
Education: Hofstra 1990 BA; Naval War 2013 MNSP
Military Liaison Officer **Jackelyn Kang** 81 (3) 3224-5000
Political Officer **Daniel A. Rochman** 81 (3) 3224-5000
E-mail: rochmanda@state.gov
Education: Michigan 1986 BA; Johns Hopkins 1991 MA
Public Affairs Officer **Carolyn B. Glassman** 81 (3) 3224-5000
E-mail: glassmancb@state.gov Fax: 81 (3) 5562-9282
Regional Security Officer **Wiiliam Densmore** 81 (3) 3224-5000
E-mail: densmorewe@state.gov
Political/Military Officer **Aaron Snipe** 81 (3) 3224-5000

Agency for International Development [Japan]
American Embassy - Tokyo, Japan, 10-5 Akasaka 1-chome,
Minato-ku, Tokyo, 107-8420, Japan
Mail: American Embassy - Tokyo, Japan, Unit 45004, Box 258,
APO, AP 96337-0001
Tel: 81 (3) 3224-5015 Fax: 81 (3) 3224-5010

Senior Development Counselor **(Vacant)** 81 (3) 3224-5015

Agricultural Section (Foreign Agricultural Service) [Japan]
American Embassy - Tokyo, Japan, 10-5 Akasaka 1-chome,
Minato-ku, Tokyo, 107-8420, Japan
Mail: American Embassy - Tokyo, Japan, Unit 9800, Box 475,
APO, AP 96303
Tel: 81 (3) 3224-5102 Fax: 81 (3) 3589-0793
Internet: www.usdajapan.org

◇ Agricultural Minister-Counselor **Gary W. Meyer** 81 (3) 3224-5102
E-mail: gary.meyer@fas.usda.gov

Agricultural Trade Office [Japan]
Tameike Tokyu Building, 1-14 Akasaka 1-chome, Minato-ku,
8th Floor, Tokyo, 107-0052, Japan
Mail: ATO Tokyo c/o U.S. Embassy, Unit 9800, Box 591, APO, AP 96303
Tel: 81 (3) 3224-5115 Fax: 81 (3) 3582-6429
E-mail: atotokyo@fas.usda.gov

Director **Morgan A. Perkins** 81 (3) 3224-5115
E-mail: morgan.perkins@fas.usda.gov
Deputy Director **Barrett Bumpas** 81 (3) 3224-5115
E-mail: barrett.bumpas@fas.usda.gov
Education: Texas Tech 2008 BA

★ Presidential Appointment Requiring Senate Confirmation ☆ Presidential Appointment ☐ Schedule C Appointment ◇ Career Senior Foreign Service Appointment
● Career Senior Executive Service (SES) Appointment ○ Non-Career Senior Executive Service (SES) Appointment ■ Postal Career Executive Service

Animal and Plant Health Inspection Service [Japan]
American Embassy - Tokyo, Japan, 10-5 Akasaka 1-chome, Minato-ku, Tokyo, 107-8420, Japan
Mail: American Embassy - Tokyo, Japan, Unit 45004, Box 226, APO, AP 96337-0001
Tel: 81 (3) 3224-5000 Fax: 81 (3) 3224-5291

APHIS Officer **(Vacant)** 81 (3) 3224-5453

Commercial Section (Foreign Commercial Service) [Japan]
Commercial Service American Embassy - Tokyo, Japan, 1-10-5, Akasaka, Minato-ku, Tokyo, 107-8420, Japan
Mail: U.S. Commercial Service, Unit 45005, Box 204, APO, AP 96337-5004
Tel: 81 (3) 3224-5060 Fax: 81 (3) 3589-4235
E-mail: office.tokyo@trade.gov Internet: www.export.gov/japan

◇ Senior Commercial Officer **Edwin "Keith" Kirkham** ... 81 (3) 3224-5050
E-mail: keith.kirkham@trade.gov
Education: Indiana 1985 BA; Michigan State 1987 MPA

Deputy Senior Commercial Officer **Stephen "Steve" Knode** 81 (3) 3224-5060
E-mail: steve.knode@trade.gov
Education: Denison BA; Cornell MBA

Department of Homeland Security - Transportation Security Administration [Japan]
American Embassy - Tokyo, Japan, 10-5 Akasaka 1-chome, Minato-ku, Tokyo, 107-8420, Japan
Mail: Unit 45004, Box 258, APO, AP 96337-5004

TSA Attaché **Martin W. "Marty" Robinson** 81 (3) 3224-5000
E-mail: martin.robinson@tsa.dhs.gov

Department of Homeland Security - U.S. Customs and Border Protection [Japan]
American Embassy - Tokyo, Japan, 10-5 Akasaka 1-chome, Minato-ku, Tokyo, 107-8420, Japan
Mail: American Embassy - Tokyo, Japan, Unit 45004, Box 221, APO, AP 96337-5004
Tel: 81 (3) 3224-5000 Fax: 81 (3) 3224-5426

Customs Attaché **Brendon O'Hearn** 81 (3) 3224-5400
E-mail: brendan.ohearn@dhs.gov

Drug Enforcement Administration [Japan]
American Embassy - Tokyo, Japan, 1-10-5, Akasaka, Minato-ku, Tokyo, 107-8420, Japan
Mail: American Embassy - Tokyo, Japan, Unit 45004, Box 211, APO, AP 96337-0001
Tel: 81 (3) 3224-5000 Fax: 81 (3) 3505-1862

DEA Country Attaché **Kasey K. Kanekoa** 81 (3) 3224-5000

Federal Aviation Administration [Japan]
American Embassy - Tokyo, Japan, 10-5 Akasaka 1-chome, Minato-ku, Tokyo, 107-8420, Japan
Mail: American Embassy - Tokyo, Japan, Unit 45004, Box 207, APO, AP 96337-0001
Tel: 81 (3) 3224-5511 Fax: 81 (3) 3582-5974

FAA Representative **Nathan "Nate" Purdy** 81 (3) 3224-5511

Office of the Defense Attaché [Japan]
American Embassy - Tokyo, Japan, 10-5 Akasaka 1-chome, Minato-ku, Tokyo, 107-8420, Japan
Mail: American Embassy - Tokyo, Japan, Unit 45004, Box 222, APO, AP 96337-0001
Tel: 81 (3) 3224-5000 Fax: 81 (3) 3505-1862

Defense Attaché **CAPT Manuel A. Picon USN** 81 (3) 3224-5000
E-mail: PiconMA@state.gov

U.S. Department of Energy [Japan]
American Embassy - Tokyo, Japan, 10-5 Akasaka 1-chome, Minato-ku, Tokyo, 107-8420, Japan
Mail: American Embassy - Tokyo, Japan, Unit 45004, Box 219, APO, AP 96337-0001
Tel: 81 (3) 3224-5000 Fax: 81 (3) 3505-1862

DOE Officer **Ross Matzkin-Bridger** 81 (3) 3224-5000
Education: George Washington 2006 BA; Georgetown 2010 MSFS

Naha, Okinawa, Consulate General
U.S. Consulate General - Naha, Okinawa, Japan, 2-1-1 Toyama Urasoe City, Okinawa, Japan 901-2104
Mail: U.S. Consulate General - Naha, Okinawa, PSC 556, Box 840, Un, FPO, AP 96386-0840
Tel: 81 (988) 76-4211 Fax: 81 (988) 76-4243

Consul General **Robert T. Koepcke** 81 (988) 76-4211
E-mail: koepckert@state.gov

Deputy Principal Officer **Hilary Dauer** 81 (988) 76-4211

Consular Affairs Officer **Bernard Uadan** 81 (988) 76-4211

Information Systems Officer **Timothy W. Martin** 81 (988) 76-4211
E-mail: martintw@state.gov

Information Program Officer **John E. Buhler** 81 (988) 76-4211
E-mail: buhlerje@state.gov

Management Officer **Timothy W. Martin** 81 (988) 76-4211
E-mail: martintw@state.gov

Political/Economic Officer **Hilary Dauer** 81 (988) 76-4211

Public Affairs Officer **Richard Roberts** 81 (988) 76-4211

Regional Security Officer **Timothy W. Martin** 81 (988) 76-4211

Osaka-Kobe Consulate General
U.S. Consulate General - Osaka-Kobe, Japan, 11-5 Nishitenma 2-chome, Kita-ku, Osaka, 530-8543, Japan
Mail: U.S. Consulate General - Osaka-Kobe, Unit 45004, Box 239, APO, AP 96337-5004
Tel: 81 (6) 6315-5900 Fax: 81 (6) 6315-5915

◇ Consul General **Karen D. Kelley** 81 (6) 6315-5900
E-mail: kelleyk@state.gov Fax: 81 (6) 6315-5930
Education: Syracuse 1979 BA

Consular Affairs Officer **Celia C. Thompson** 81 (6) 6315-5900
E-mail: thompsoncc2@state.gov

Information Program Officer/Information Systems Security Officer **Michael Yoho** 81 (6) 6315-5900

Management Officer **Michael Tapley** 81 (6) 6315-5900
E-mail: tapleymn@state.gov

Political and Economic Section Chief **Colin W. Fishwick** 81 (6) 6315-5900

Regional Security Officer **Scott Williams** 81 (6) 6315-5900

Agricultural Trade Office [Japan]
U.S. Consulate General - Osaka-Kobe, Japan 11-5 Nishitenma, 2-chrome, Kita-ku, Osaka, 530-8543, Japan
Mail: American Trade Office ATO Osaka, Unit 45005, Box 239, APO, AP 96337-5004
Tel: 81 (6) 6315-5904 Fax: 81 (6) 6315-5906
E-mail: atoosaka@fas.usda.gov

Director (Resident in Tokyo) **Morgan A. Perkins** 81 (3) 3505-6050

Commercial Section (Foreign Commercial Service) [Japan]
U.S. Commercial Service Osaka, 2-11-5 Nishitenma, Kita-Ku, Osaka, 530-8543, Japan
Mail: U.S. Commercial Service Osaka, Unit 45004, Box 239, APO, AP 96337-5004
Tel: 81 (6) 6315-5957 Fax: 81 (6) 6315-5963
E-mail: office.osaka-kobe@trade.gov

Principal Commercial Officer **Jay Biggs** 81 (6) 6315-5953
E-mail: Jay.Biggs@trade.gov
Education: American U MA

DEPARTMENTS

★ Presidential Appointment Requiring Senate Confirmation ☆ Presidential Appointment ☐ Schedule C Appointment ◇ Career Senior Foreign Service Appointment
● Career Senior Executive Service (SES) Appointment ○ Non-Career Senior Executive Service (SES) Appointment ■ Postal Career Executive Service

Kansai American Center
U.S. Consulate General - Osaka-Kobe, Japan, 11-5 Nishitenma 2-chome, Kita-ku, Osaka, 530-8543, Japan
Mail: U.S. Consulate General - Osaka-Kobe, Unit 45004, Box 239, APO, AP 96337-5004
Tel: 81 (6) 6315-5965 Fax: 81 (6) 6315-5999 E-mail: osakapd@state.gov

Public Affairs Officer and Center Director **Brooke Spelman** 81 (6) 6315-5965
Fax: 81 (6) 6361-5987

Sapporo Consulate General
U.S. Consulate General - Sapporo, Japan, Kita 1- Jo Nishi 28-chome, Chuo-ku, Sapporo, 064-0821, Japan
Mail: U.S. Consulate General - Sapporo, Japan, Unit 45004, Box 276, APO, AP 96337-5004
Tel: 81 (11) 641-1115 Fax: 81 (11) 643-1283

Principal Officer **Rachel Brunette-Chen** 81 (11) 641-1115
E-mail: BrunetteChenR@state.gov
Consular/Economic/Management Officer **Justin Tull** 81 (11) 641-1115
Political Officer **(Vacant)** 81 (11) 641-1115
Public Affairs Officer **Ryan S. Ingrassia** 81 (11) 641-1115
E-mail: ingrassiars@state.gov
Education: USC BFA; Georgetown MSFS

Fukuoka Consulate
U.S. Consulate - Fukuoka, Japan, 5-26 Ohori 2-chome, Chou-ku, Fukuoka, 810-0052, Japan
Mail: U.S. Consulate - Fukuoka, Japan, Unit 45004, Box 242, APO, AP 96337-0001
Tel: 81 (92) 751-9331 Fax: 81 (92) 713-9222

Principal Officer **Joy Michiko Sakurai** 81 (92) 751-9331
Management Officer **Dominic So** 81 (92) 751-9331
Political/Economic Officer **Thomas Whitney** 81 (92) 751-9331

Fukuoka American Center
8F, 2-2-67 Tenjin, Chuo-ku, Fukuoka, 810-0001, Japan
Mail: U.S. Consulate - Fukuoka, Japan, Unit 45004, Box 242, APO, AP 96337-5004
Tel: 81 (92) 733-0246 Fax: 81 (92) 716-6152

Public Affairs Officer and Center Director **Vanessa Zenji** 81 (92) 761-6661

Nagoya Consulate
Nagoya International Center Building, U.S. Consulate - Nagoya, Japan, 1-47-1 Nagono, Nakamuraku, Sixth Floor, Nagoya, 450-0001, Japan
Mail: U.S. Consulate - Nagoya c/o AMEMB Toyko, Unit 45004, Box 280, APO, AP 96337-5004
Tel: 81 (52) 581-4501 Fax: 81 (52) 581-3190

Principal Officer **Gary E. Schaefer** 81 (52) 581-4501
Consular Officer **(Vacant)** 81 (52) 581-4501

Department of Homeland Security - U.S. Customs and Border Protection [Japan]
Nagoya International Center Building, 6F, 1-47-1, Nakamuraku, Nagoya, Nagoya, 450-0001, Japan
Mail: U.S. Consulate - Nagoya c/o AMEMB Tokyo, Unit 45004, Box 280, APO, AP 96337-5004
Tel: 81 (52) 581-4501 Fax: 81 (52) 581-3190

Customs Attaché **Michael J. Meuse** 81 (534) 581-4501

Nagoya American Center
Nagoya Kokusai Center Building 6F, 47-1 Nagono 1-chome, Nakamura-ku, Nagoya, 450-0001, Japan
Mail: U.S. Consulate - Nagoya c/o AMEMB Tokyo, Unit 45004, Box 215, APO, AP 96337-5004
Tel: 81 (52) 581-8631 Fax: 81 (52) 581-3190

Public Affairs Officer **(Vacant)** 81 (52) 581-8631

Yokohama Language and Area Training Center (FSI Yokohama)
U.S. Consulate - Yokohama, Japan, 152-3 Yamate-Cho, Naka-ku, 231-0862 Yokohama, Japan
Tel: 81 (45) 622-6514 Fax: 81 (45) 622-6516

Director **Carmela A. Conroy** 81 (45) 622-6514
E-mail: conroyca@state.gov
Education: U Washington 1984 BA, 1990 JD; Naval War 2004 MA

U.S. Embassy in Korea

188 Sejong-daero, Jongno-gu, Seoul, 03141, South Korea
Tel: 82 (2) 397-4114 Fax: 82 (2) 738-8845 Internet: kr.usembassy.gov

Office of the U.S. Ambassador to Korea
American Embassy - Seoul, Korea, 188 Sejong-daero, Jongno-gu, Seoul, 03141, South Korea
Mail: American Embassy - Seoul, Korea, Unit 15550, APO, AP 96205-5550

★ Ambassador **Ambassador Harry B. Harris, Jr.** 82 (2) 397-4114
Education: Naval Acad 1978; Harvard MPA; Georgetown MA
Office Management Specialist to the Ambassador **(Vacant)** 82 (2) 397-4114
◇ Deputy Chief of Mission **Robert Glenn "Rob" Rapson** 82 (2) 397-4114
E-mail: rapsonrg@state.gov
Education: Penn State BA
Office Management Specialist to the Deputy Chief of Mission **Lindy Ransom** 82 (2) 397-4114
E-mail: ransoml@state.gov
Community Liaison Officer **Jan T. Von Schleh** 82 (2) 397-4114
E-mail: vonschlehjt@state.gov
◇ Consul General **Angela M. Kerwin** 82 (2) 397-4114
E-mail: kerwinam@state.gov
Education: Penn State BS; Dickinson Law JD; Army War Col MSS
◇ Economic Officer **Pushpinder S. Dhillon** 82 (2) 397-4400
E-mail: dhillonps@state.gov
Environment, Science and Technology Officer **(Vacant)** 82 (2) 397-4114
Facilities Management Officer **(Vacant)** 82 (2) 397-4114
Financial Management Officer **Robert Gresbrink** 82 (2) 397-4114
E-mail: gresbrinkr@state.gov
General Services Officer **Charles T. "Chuck" Clegg** 82 (2) 397-4114
Human Resources Officer **Gregory "Greg" Von Schleh** 82 (2) 397-4114
E-mail: vonschlehg@state.gov
Education: CityU Seattle 2003
Information Management Officer **Elaine S. Tiang-Chu** 82 (2) 397-4114
E-mail: tiangchues@state.gov
Information Program Officer **Gene L. Thompson** 82 (2) 397-4114
E-mail: thompsong@state.gov
Information Systems Officer **David Foster** 82 (2) 397-4114
◇ Management Officer **Christopher J. "Chris" Del Corso** 82 (2) 397-4114
E-mail: delcorsocj@state.gov
Political Officer **Lucy Chang** 82 (2) 397-4114
E-mail: changl@state.gov
Public Affairs Officer **Dale G. Kreisher** 82 (2) 397-4114
E-mail: kreisherdg@state.gov
Education: Akron 1986 BA; Harvard MPP
Regional Security Officer **David Walsh** 82 (2) 397-4114
E-mail: walshda@state.gov

Agricultural Section (Foreign Agricultural Service) [Korea]
188 Sejong-daero, Jongno-gu, Seoul, 03141, South Korea
Mail: American Embassy - Seoul, Korea, Unit 15550, APO, AP 96205-5550
Tel: 82 (2) 397-4297 Fax: 82 (2) 738-7147
E-mail: agseoul@fas.usda.gov

◇ Agricultural Officer **Ronald P. "Ron" Verdonk** 82 (2) 397-4297
E-mail: ron.verdonk@fas.usda.gov
Senior Attaché **Peter Olson** 82 (2) 397-4297
E-mail: peter.olson@fas.usda.gov
Attaché **Amanda Hinkle** 82 (2) 397-4297
E-mail: amanda.hinkle@fas.usda.gov

★ Presidential Appointment Requiring Senate Confirmation ☆ Presidential Appointment ☐ Schedule C Appointment ◇ Career Senior Foreign Service Appointment
● Career Senior Executive Service (SES) Appointment ○ Non-Career Senior Executive Service (SES) Appointment ■ Postal Career Executive Service

Agricultural Trade Office [Korea]
Leema Building, 146-1, Susong-dong, Chongro-ku,
Room 303, Seoul, 110-755, South Korea
Mail: Agricultural Trade Office - A. E., Seoul, Unit 15550,
APO, AP 96205-5550
Tel: 82 (2) 6951-6848 Fax: 82 (2) 720-7921
E-mail: atoseoul@fas.usda.gov Internet: www.atoseoul.com

Director **Lynne Larrabee** 82 (2) 397-4188
E-mail: lynne.larrabee@fas.usda.gov

Animal and Plant Health Inspection Service [Korea]
Leema Building, 146-1, Susong-dong, Chongro-ku,
Room 303, Seoul, 110-755, South Korea
Mail: American Embassy - Seoul, Korea, Unit 15550,
APO, AP 96205-5550
Tel: 82 (2) 725-5495

APHIS Attaché **Kelan R. Evans** 82 (2) 6951-6857
E-mail: evanskr3@state.gov
Education: Missouri BS

Commercial Section (Foreign Commercial Service) [Korea]
American Embassy - Seoul, Korea, 32 Sejong-Ro,
Chongro-ku, Seoul, 110-710, South Korea
Mail: American Embassy - Seoul, Korea, Unit 15550,
APO, AP 96205-5550
Tel: 82 (2) 397-4535 Fax: 82 (2) 739-1628
E-mail: office.seoul@trade.gov Internet: www.export.gov/southkorea

Senior Commercial Officer **Gregory "Greg" Briscoe** 82 (2) 397-4208
E-mail: Gregory.Briscoe@trade.gov

Deputy Commercial Officer **Robert W. Dunn** 82 (2) 397-4356
E-mail: robert.dunn@trade.gov

Department of Homeland Security - U.S. Citizenship and Immigration Services [Korea]
American Embassy - Seoul, Korea, 188 Sejong-daero,
Jongno-gu, Seoul, 03141, South Korea
Mail: American Embassy - Seoul, Korea, Unit 15550,
APO, AP 96205-5550
Tel: 82 (2) 397-4279 Fax: 82 (2) 720-7419

Field Office Director (Acting) **Matthew P. Mumper** 82 (2) 397-4282

Department of Justice - Drug Enforcement Administration [Korea]
American Embassy - Seoul Korea, 32 Sejong-Ro,
Chongro-ku, Seoul, 110-710, South Korea
Mail: American Embassy - Seoul, Korea, Unit 15550,
APO, AP 96205-5550
Tel: 82 (2) 397-4114 Fax: 82 (2) 738-8845

DEA Attaché **Howard Shu** 82 (2) 397-4114

Federal Aviation Administration (Resident in Tokyo) [Korea]
American Embassy - Tokyo/FAA, 1-10-5, Akasaka,
Minato-ku, Tokyo, 107-8420, Japan
Mail: American Embassy - Tokyo/FAA,
Unit 45004, Box 207, APO, AP 96337-5004
Fax: 81 (3) 3582-5974

FAA Representative **Nathan "Nate" Purdy** 81 (3) 3224-5511

Federal Bureau of Investigation [Korea]
American Embassy - Seoul, Korea, 32 Sejong-Ro,
Chongro-ku, Seoul, 110-710, South Korea
Mail: American Embassy - Seoul, Korea, Unit 15550,
APO, AP 96205-5550
Tel: 82 (2) 397-4243

Legal Attaché **Kyung Jin Kim** 82 (2) 397-4243

Homeland Security Investigations [Korea] (HSI)
American Embassy - Seoul Korea, 188 Sejong-daero,
Jongno-gu, Seoul, 03141, South Korea
Mail: American Embassy - Seoul, Korea, Unit 15550,
APO, AP 96205-5550
Tel: 82 (2) 397-4524 Fax: 82 (2) 736-6850

HSI Attaché **Donald Bruckschen** 82 (2) 397-4524

Office of the Defense Attaché [Korea]
American Embassy - Seoul Korea, 188 Sejong-daero,
Jongno-gu, Seoul, 03141, South Korea
Mail: American Embassy - Seoul, Korea, Unit 15550,
APO, AP 96205-5550
Tel: 82 (2) 397-4040 Fax: 82 (2) 725-5262

Defense Attaché **COL John C. Lee USA** 82 (2) 397-4040

Busan Consulate
Lotte Gold Rose Building #150-3, Unit 612, Yangjung-dong, Busanjin-gu,
6th Floor, Pusan, South Korea
Tel: 82 (2) 397-6834

Consul **Daniel C. Gedacht** 82 (2) 397-6834
E-mail: gedachtdc@state.gov
Education: Clark U; American U; Korea U

Department of Homeland Security - Customs and Border Protection (CBP) [Korea]
American Embassy - Seoul, Korea, 188 Sejong-daero,
Jongno-gu, Seoul, 03141, South Korea
E-mail: cbp.seoul.inquiries@cbp.dhs.gov

CBP Attaché **Edward V. Bayron** 82 (2) 397-4114

U.S. Embassy in Laos
Thadeua Road, Km 9, Ban Somvang Thai,
Hatsayfong District, Vientiane, Laos
Tel: 856 (21) 48-7000 Fax: 856 (21) 26-7190 Internet: la.usembassy.gov

Office of the U.S. Ambassador to Laos
American Embassy - Vientiane, Laos,
Thadeua Road, Km 9, Ban Somvang Thai,
Hatsayfong District, Vientiane, Laos
E-mail: webmastervientiane@state.gov

★ Ambassador **Ambassador Rena Bitter** 856 (21) 26-7000
E-mail: bitterr@state.gov
Education: Northwestern BS; Southern Methodist JD
Office Management Specialist to the Ambassador
Stacey Phengvath 856 (21) 26-7207
E-mail: phengvaths@state.gov

Deputy Chief of Mission **Colin T. Crosby** 856 (21) 26-7207
E-mail: crosbyc@state.gov
Education: Ohio 1995 BA; Princeton 2008 MPP
Office Management Specialist to the Deputy Chief of Mission **(Vacant)** 856 (21) 26-7000

Consular Officer **Steven R. Carroll** 856 (21) 26-7228
E-mail: carrollsr@state.gov

Community Liaison Officer **Juan Carlos** 856 (21) 26-7000

Economic Officer **Joseph John "Joe" Narus** 856 (21) 26-7156

General Services Officer **James C. Bennett** 856 (21) 26-7179
E-mail: bennettjc@state.gov

Information Management Officer **Eddie Barrington** 856 (21) 26-7175

Information Program Officer **Jordan Smock** 856 (21) 26-7175
E-mail: smockjw@state.gov

Information Systems Security Officer
Jordan Smock 856 (21) 48-7000
E-mail: smockjw@state.gov

Management Officer **Brian B. Himmelsteib** 856 (21) 26-7221
E-mail: himmelsteibbb@state.gov

Narcotics Affairs Officer **(Vacant)** 856 (21) 26-7013

Political/Economic Officer
Machutmi "Machut" Shishak 856 (21) 26-7000
E-mail: shishakm@state.gov

Public Affairs Officer **Nolan Barkhouse** 856 (21) 26-7214
E-mail: barkhousene@state.gov Fax: 856 (21) 26-7160

Regional Security Officer **Eugene Kim** 856 (21) 26-7197

★ Presidential Appointment Requiring Senate Confirmation ☆ Presidential Appointment □ Schedule C Appointment ◇ Career Senior Foreign Service Appointment
● Career Senior Executive Service (SES) Appointment ○ Non-Career Senior Executive Service (SES) Appointment ■ Postal Career Executive Service

Federal Aviation Administration (Resident in Singapore) [Laos]
American Embassy, 27 Napier Road, 258508 Singapore, Singapore
Mail: American Embassy - Singapore,
PSC 470 FAA IAO, FPO, AP 96507
Tel: 65 6543-1466 Fax: 65 6543-1952

FAA Representative **James "Jim" Spillane** 65 6543-1466
E-mail: james.spillane@faa.gov

DEPARTMENTS

U.S. Embassy in Malaysia

376 Jalan Tun Razak, 50400 Kuala Lumpur, Malaysia
Tel: 60 (3) 2168-5000 Fax: 60 (3) 2142-2207 Internet: my.usembassy.gov

Office of the U.S. Ambassador to Malaysia

American Embassy - Kuala Lumpur, Malaysia,
376 Jalan Tun Razak, 50400 Kuala Lumpur, Malaysia
Mail: American Embassy - Kuala Lumpur, APO, AP 96535-8152

★ Ambassador **Ambassador Kamala Shirin Lakhdhir** ... 60 (3) 2168-5000
E-mail: lakhdhirks@state.gov
Office Management Specialist to the Ambassador
Shirley Kowalenko 60 (3) 2168-5000
Deputy Chief of Mission **Dean R. Thompson** 60 (3) 2168-5000
E-mail: thompsondr@state.gov
Education: Wittenberg 1989 BA; Maryland 1993 MPM; National War Col 2011 MNSSS
Office Management Specialist to the Deputy Chief of Mission **(Vacant)** 60 (3) 2168-5000
Community Liaison Officer
Jewel L. Turner .... 60 (3) 2168-5000 ext. 5046
Consular Section Chief **Matthew E. Keene** 60 (3) 2168-5000
E-mail: KLConsular@state.gov Fax: 60 (3) 2148-5801
Economic Officer **Nathaniel S. Turner** ...... 60 (3) 2168-5000 ext. 5153
Fax: 60 (3) 2168-4952
Equal Employment Opportunity Officer
Michael P. Casey 60 (3) 2168-5050
Fax: 60 (3) 2148-4035
Financial Management Officer (Acting)
Francis M. "Frank" Conte 60 (3) 2168-5000
Education: St Vincent's Col BS
General Services Officer **Dianne K. Syrvalin** 60 (3) 2168-5000
Fax: 60 (3) 2168-4948
Information Management Officer **(Vacant)** 60 (3) 2168-5000
Information Systems Officer **Joy K. Bhattacharyya** 60 (3) 2168-5000
Information Systems Security Officer
Joy K. Bhattacharyya 60 (3) 2168-5000
Legal Attaché **David C. Smith** 60 (3) 2168-5000
Management Officer **Luther Eric "Eric" Lindberg** 60 (3) 2168-5000
Fax: 60 (3) 2168-4961
Political Officer **Sally Behrhorst** .... 60 (3) 2168-5000 ext. 4946
E-mail: behrhorstsp@state.gov Fax: 60 (3) 2142-5165
Public Affairs Officer **Bradley Hurst** 60 (3) 2168-5000
Fax: 60 (3) 2148-9192
Regional Security Officer
Brian D. Cummings .... 60 (3) 2168-5000 ext. 5111
Fax: 60 (3) 2148-2207

Agricultural Section (Foreign Agricultural Service) [Malaysia]
American Embassy - Kuala Lumpur, Malaysia,
376 Jalan Tun Razak, 50400 Kuala Lumpur, Malaysia
Mail: American Embassy - Kuala Lumpur, APO, AP 96535-8152
Tel: 60 (3) 2168-5082 Fax: 60 (3) 2168-5023
E-mail: agkualalumpur@fas.usda.gov

Agricultural Officer **Joani Dong** 60 (3) 2168-5082
E-mail: joani.dong@fas.usda.gov

Commercial Section (Foreign Commercial Service) [Malaysia]
U.S. Commercial Service, 376 Jalan Tun Razak, 50450 Kuala Lumpur, Malaysia
Mail: U.S. Commercial Service, American Embassy - Kuala Lumpur, APO, AP 96535-8152
Tel: 60 (3) 2168-5000 Fax: 60 (3) 2142-1866
E-mail: office.kualalumpur@trade.gov Internet: export.gov/malaysia

Senior Commercial Officer **Catherine P. Spillman** 60 (3) 2168-4869
E-mail: Catherine.Spillman@trade.gov

Department of Homeland Security - U.S. Immigration and Customs Enforcement [Malaysia]
American Embassy - Singapore, FPO, AP 96534-0001
Customs Attaché **Marcus S. Phill** 60 (3) 2168-5000

Drug Enforcement Administration [Malaysia]
American Embassy - Kuala Lumpur, Malaysia,
376 Jalan Tun Razak, 50400 Kuala Lumpur, Malaysia
Mail: American Embassy - Kuala Lumpur, APO, AP 96535-8152
Tel: 60 (3) 2168-5000 ext. 4957 Fax: 60 (3) 2148-9508

Country Attaché **Joseph R. Lipp** .... 60 (3) 2168-5000 ext. 4957

Federal Aviation Administration (Resident in Singapore) [Malaysia]
American Embassy, 27 Napier Road, Singapore, 258508, Singapore
Mail: American Embassy - Singapore,
PSC 470 FAA IAO, FPO, AP 96507
Tel: 65 6543-1466 Fax: 65 6543-1952

FAA Representative **James "Jim" Spillane** 65 6543-1466
E-mail: james.spillane@faa.gov

Office of the Defense Attaché [Malaysia]
American Embassy - Kuala Lumpur, Malaysia,
376 Jalan Tun Razak, 50400 Kuala Lumpur, Malaysia
Mail: American Embassy - Kuala Lumpur, APO, AP 96535-8152
Tel: 60 (3) 2168-5000 ext. 5133 Fax: 60 (3) 2142-1579

Defense Attaché **CAPT Brent D. Sadler USN** 60 (3) 2168-5000

Office of Defense Cooperation [Malaysia]
American Embassy - Kuala Lumpur, 376 Jalan Tun Razak, 50400 Kuala Lumpur, Malaysia
Tel: 60 (3) 2168-4827 Fax: 60 (3) 2141-1080 E-mail: klodc@state.gov

Chief **LTC Sukhdev S. Purewal USA** 60 (3) 2168-4827

U.S. Embassy in the Marshall Islands

Mejen Weto, Ocean Side, Majuro, Marshall Islands 96960
Tel: 692 247-4011 Fax: 692 247-4012 Internet: mh.usembassy.gov

Office of the U.S. Ambassador to the Marshall Islands

American Embassy - Majuro, Marshall Islands,
Mejen Weto, Ocean Side, Majuro, Marshall Islands 96960
Mail: PO Box 1379, Majuro, Marshall Islands 96960

★ Ambassador **Ambassador Karen Brevard Stewart** 692 247-4011
E-mail: stewartkb@state.gov
Education: Wellesley BA; National War Col 1998 MS
Office Management Specialist to the Ambassador **(Vacant)** .... 692 247-4011 ext. 228
Deputy Chief of Mission
Katherine M. Reimondez .... 692 247-4011 ext. 242
E-mail: reimondezkm@state.gov
Office Management Specialist to the Ambassador **(Vacant)** .... 692 247-4011 ext. 228
Consular Officer **Daniel B. Dolan** 692 247-4011
General Services/Information Management Officer **Laurel C. Bonds** .... 692 247-4011 ext. 229
E-mail: bondslc@state.gov
Management Officer **Katherine M. Reimondez** 692 247-4011
Political/Economic Officer **Daniel B. Dolan** 692 247-4011
Public Affairs Officer **Katherine M. Reimondez** 692 247-4011
Regional Security Officer **Laurel C. Bonds** 692 247-4011
E-mail: bondslc@state.gov
Disaster Assistance Coordinator **(Vacant)** 692 247-4011

★ Presidential Appointment Requiring Senate Confirmation ☆ Presidential Appointment ☐ Schedule C Appointment ◇ Career Senior Foreign Service Appointment
● Career Senior Executive Service (SES) Appointment ○ Non-Career Senior Executive Service (SES) Appointment ■ Postal Career Executive Service

U.S. Embassy in the Federated States of Micronesia

American Embassy - Kolonia, 1286 U.S. Embassy Place, Kolonia, Pohnpei, Micronesia 96941
Tel: 691 320-2187 Fax: 691 320-2186 E-mail: koloniaacs@state.gov

Office of the Ambassador to the Federated States of Micronesia

American Embassy - Kolonia, 1286 U.S. Embassy Place, Kolonia, Pohnpei, Micronesia 96941
P.O. Box 1286, Kolonia, Pohnpei, Micronesia 96941
Tel: 691 320-2187 Fax: 691 320-2186 E-mail: koloniaacs@state.gov

★ Ambassador
Ambassador Robert Annan "Bob" Riley III 691 320-2187
E-mail: rileyra@state.gov
Education: Yale 1979 BA
Office Management Specialist to the Ambassador
Emerlynn Shed 691 320-2187
E-mail: shedek@state.gov
Deputy Chief of Mission **Heather Coble** 691 320-2187
E-mail: cobleh@state.gov
Office Management Specialist to the Deputy Chief of Mission **Emerlynn Shed** 691 320-2187
E-mail: shedek@state.gov
Community Liaison Officer **(Vacant)** 691 320-2187
Consular Officer **Anthony W. "Tony" Alexander** 691 320-2187
E-mail: alexanderaw@state.gov
Education: Cal State (Long Beach) 1986 BSE
Economic Officer **Anthony W. "Tony" Alexander** 691 320-2187
E-mail: alexanderaw@state.gov
Education: Cal State (Long Beach) 1986 BSE
Financial Management Officer (Resident in Manila)
Joseph C. Johnson 63 (2) 301-2000
PSC 500, Box 1, FPO, AP 96515-1000
E-mail: johnsonjc2@state.gov
General Services Officer **Scott Anderson** 691 320-2187
E-mail: andersonsl@state.gov
Human Resources Officer **(Vacant)** 691 320-2187
Information Management Specialist **Robert Boylan** 691 320-2187
E-mail: boylanrj@state.gov
Information Systems Security Officer **(Vacant)** 691 320-2187
Management Officer **Kevin J. Harris** 691 320-2187
E-mail: harriskj2@state.gov
Political Military Specialist **Lynn D. Pangelinan** 691 320-2187
E-mail: pangelinanld@state.gov
Public Affairs Specialist **Abigail Kim** 691 320-2187
E-mail: kimaa@state.gov
Regional Security Officer (Resident in Manila) (Acting) **Ryan Smith** .... 63 (2) 301-2000 ext. 6337
American Embassy - Manila, Philippines, PSC 500 Box 1, FPO, AP 96515-1000 Fax: 63 (2) 523-1296
E-mail: smithrt1@state.gov

Federal Aviation Administration (Resident in Tokyo) [Federated States of Micronesia]

American Embassy - Tokyo/FAA, 1-10-5, Akasaka, Minato-ku, Tokyo, 107-8420, Japan
Mail: American Embassy - Tokyo/FAA, Unit 45004, Box 207, APO, AP 96337-5004
Tel: 81 (3) 3224-5511

FAA Representative **Nathan "Nate" Purdy** 81 (3) 3224-5511

U.S. Embassy in Mongolia

Denver Street #3, 11th Micro-District, Ulaanbaatar, 14190, Mongolia
Tel: 976 7007-6001 Fax: 976 7007-6174 Internet: mn.usembassy.gov

Office of the U.S. Ambassador to Mongolia

American Embassy - Ulaanbaatar, Mongolia, Denver Street #3, 11th Micro-District, Ulaanbaatar, 14190, Mongolia

★ Ambassador-Designate **Michael Stanley Klecheski** 976 7007-6001
E-mail: klecheskims@state.gov
Education: Georgetown BSFS; Columbia MA, MPhil

Office of the U.S. Ambassador to Mongolia *(continued)*

◇ Chargé d'Affaires **Manuel P. "Manny" Micaller** 976 7007-6001
E-mail: micallermp@state.gov
Education: Johns Hopkins 1994 BA; George Washington 2008 MBA
Office Management Specialist to the Chargé d'Affaires **Snezhina Sandlin** 976 7007-6001
E-mail: SandlinSD@state.gov
Deputy Chief of Mission (Acting)
Kurt W. Aufderheide 976 7007-6001
E-mail: AufderheideKW@state.gov
Office Management Specialist to the Deputy Chief of Mission **Snezhina Sandlin** 976 7007-6001
E-mail: SandlinSD@state.gov
Consular Officer **Jason P. Spellberg** 976 7007-6001
E-mail: SpellbergJP@state.gov
Commercial/Economic Officer **John McDaniel** 976 7007-6001
Community Liaison Officer **(Vacant)** 976 7007-6001
E-mail: CLOUlaanbaatar@state.gov
Environment, Science, Technology and Health Officer
Onejin Wu 976 7007-6001
Financial Management Officer **Marcus Boyle** 976 7007-6001
General Services Officer **William J. Miskelly** 976 7007-6001
E-mail: MiskellyWJ@state.gov
Information Management Officer **Randall D. Loy** 976 7007-6001
E-mail: loyrd@state.gov
Information Program Officer **(Vacant)** 976 7007-6001
Information Systems Officer/Information Systems Security Officer **Randall D. Loy** 976 7007-6001
E-mail: loyrd@state.gov
Management Officer **Marcus Boyle** 976 7007-6001
Military Liaison Officer **MAJ Nathan Pooler USA** 976 7007-6001
Political Officer **Kurt W. Aufderheide** 976 7007-6001
E-mail: AufderheideKW@state.gov
Political/Military Officer **(Vacant)** 976 7007-6001
Public Affairs Officer **Cristoph Mark** 976 7007-6001
E-mail: markca@state.gov
Regional Security Officer
William Bartley "Bart" Sandlin 976 7007-6001
E-mail: sandlinw@state.gov

Agricultural Section (Foreign Agricultural Service) [Mongolia]

Agricultural Officer (Resident in Beijing) **(Vacant)** 86 (10) 8531-3600

Agricultural Trade Office (Resident in Beijing) [Mongolia]

Director (Resident in Beijing) **Mark Ford** 86 (10) 8531-3950

Animal and Plant Health Inspection Service (Resident in Beijing) [Mongolia]

12-21 China World Trade Center, No. 1 Jianguomenwai Avenue, Beijing, 100600, China
Mail: APHIS c/o U.S. Embassy - Beijing, China, PSC 461, Box 50, FPO, AP 96521-0002
Tel: 86 (10) 8531-3030 Fax: 86 (10) 8531-3033

APHIS Officer **Murali Bandla** 86 (10) 8531-4524

Drug Enforcement Administration [Mongolia]

Drug Enforcement Officer (Resident in Beijing)
Lance Ho
Affiliation: Drug Enforcement Administration Representative, Drug Enforcement Administration [China], Office of the U.S. Ambassador to China, United States Department of State
North Tower, Beijing Kerry Center, 20th Floor, Room 2008, Beijing, 100020, China
Tel: 86 (10) 8529-6880

Department of Homeland Security - U.S. Immigration and Customs Enforcement [Mongolia]

31 Technical Club Co., Limited, 15 Guang Hua Li, Chao Yang District, Beijing, China 100020

Customs Officer (Resident in Beijing)
Kai Wah Chan 86 (10) 6532-3831

★ Presidential Appointment Requiring Senate Confirmation ☆ Presidential Appointment ☐ Schedule C Appointment ◇ Career Senior Foreign Service Appointment
● Career Senior Executive Service (SES) Appointment ○ Non-Career Senior Executive Service (SES) Appointment ■ Postal Career Executive Service

DEPARTMENTS

Federal Aviation Administration (Resident in Beijing) [Mongolia]
31 Technical Club Co., Limited, 15 Guang Hua Li, Chao Yang District, Beijing, China 100020
Mail: American Embassy - Beijing, PSC 461, Box 50, FPO, AP 96521-0002
Tel: 86 (10) 8531-3987 Fax: 86 (10) 8531-4600
FAA Representative **Chris Collins** 86 (10) 8531-3987

Office of the Defense Attaché [Mongolia]
American Embassy - Ulaanbaatar, Mongolia, Micro Region 11, Big Ring Road, Ulaanbaatar, Mongolia
Mail: American Embassy - Ulaanbaatar, Mongolia, PSC 461, Box 300, FPO, AP 96521-0002
Defense and Army Attaché **Michael B. Dorschner** 976 7007-6001

Peace Corps [Mongolia]
Chingel Tey District, 6 Subdistrict, Block 95, Entrance 3, Ulaanbaatar, Mongolia
Mail: American Embassy - Ulaanbaatar, Mongolia, PSC 461, Box 300, FPO, AP 96521-0002
Tel: 976 (11) 311-518 Fax: 976 (11) 311-520
E-mail: uspc@magicnet.mn Internet: www.peacecorps.gov/mongolia
Country Director **Kimberly "Kim" Mansaray** 976 (11) 311-518
Education: Lock Haven

U.S. Embassy in New Zealand

29 Fitzherbert, Thorndon, Wellington, New Zealand
Tel: 64 (4) 462-6000 Fax: 64 (4) 499-0490 Internet: nz.usembassy.gov

Office of the U.S. Ambassador to New Zealand

American Embassy - Wellington, New Zealand, 29 Fitzherbert Terrace, Thorndon, P.O. Box 1190, Wellington, New Zealand
Mail: American Embassy - Wellington, New Zealand, PSC 467, Box 1, APO, AP 96531-1034
Note: The U.S. Ambassador to New Zealand serves concurrently as the U.S. Ambassador to Samoa.

★ Ambassador **Ambassador Scott Philip Brown** 64 (4) 462-6142
Education: Tufts 1981 BA; Boston Col 1985 JD
Office Management Specialist to the Ambassador
Virginia Krause 64 (4) 462-6142
◇ Deputy Chief of Mission **Susan Butler Niblock** 64 (4) 462-6101
E-mail: niblocks@state.gov
Community Liaison Officer **Gaby Puleo** 64 (4) 462-6000
Economic Officer **Andrew Covington** 64 (4) 462-6000
Management Officer **Peter A. Schroeder** 64 (4) 462-6131
General Services Officer **Gavin Elliott** 64 (4) 462-6046
E-mail: wellington.gso@state.gov
Information Management Officer **Anup Y. Shah** 64 (4) 462-6115
E-mail: shahay@state.gov
Political/Economic Officer **Demian Smith** 64 (4) 462-6063
E-mail: smithd3@state.gov
E-mail: protocolwellington@state.gov
Education: William & Mary 2000 BA; National Defense U 2009 MS
Public Affairs Officer **Dolores Prin** 64 (4) 462-6082
E-mail: publicaffairsusnz@state.gov
Regional Security Officer **Matt Reilly** 64 (4) 462-6013

Commercial Section (Foreign Commercial Service) (Resident in Sydney) [New Zealand]
U.S. Commercial Service American Embassy - Wellington, 29 Fitzherbert, Thorndon, Wellington, New Zealand
Mail: U.S. Commercial Service, PSC 467, Box 1, FPO, AP 96531-1034
Tel: 64 (4) 462-6002 Fax: 64 (4) 473-0770
Senior Commercial Officer **(Vacant)** 61 (2) 9373-9205
U.S. Consulate General - Sydney, New South Wales, Australia, 19-29 Martin Place, 59th Floor, Sydney, New South Wales 2000, Australia

Federal Aviation Administration (Resident in Singapore) [New Zealand]
American Embassy - Wellington, New Zealand, 29 Fitzherbert Terrace, Thorndon, P.O. Box 1190, Wellington, New Zealand
Tel: 86 (10) 8532-1761 ext. 206 Fax: 86 (10) 8532-1758
FAA Representative **Nathan "Nate" Purdy** ...... 65 6469-2057 ext. 206

Office of the Defense Attaché [New Zealand]
American Embassy - Wellington, New Zealand, 29 Fitzherbert Terrace, Thorndon, P.O. Box 1190, Wellington, New Zealand
Mail: PSC 467, Box 1, APO, AP 96531-1034
Tel: 64 (4) 462-6074 Fax: 64 (4) 472-3537
Defense Attaché
COL James G. "Jamie" McAden USA 64 (4) 462-6073

Auckland Consulate General
U.S. Consulate General - Auckland, New Zealand, Citibank Building, 23, Customs Street East, Level 3, 92022 Auckland, New Zealand
Mail: PSC 467, Box 99, APO, AP 96531-1034
Tel: 64 (9) 303-2724 Fax: 64 (9) 366-0870
Consul General **Katelyn M. Choe** 64 (9) 303-2724
Education: Columbia
Office Management Specialist to the Consul General
Agnes Rounds 64 (9) 303-2724
Consular Affairs Officer **April C. Scarrow** ..... 64 (9) 303-2724 ext. 222
Education: North Texas 1995
Information Systems Security Officer **Sean McLeod** 64 (9) 303-2724
Management Officer **Sean McLeod** 64 (9) 303-2724
Political Officer **(Vacant)** 64 (9) 303-2724
Political/Economic Officer **Craig Halbmaier** 64 (9) 303-2724
Public Affairs Officer **Natalie Wilkins** 64 (9) 303-2724

U.S. Embassy in Papua New Guinea

Douglas Street, P.O. Box 1492, Port Moresby, NCD 121, Papua New Guinea
Tel: 675 321-1455 Fax: 675 320-0637 Internet: pg.usembassy.gov

Office of the U.S. Ambassador to Papua New Guinea

American Embassy - Port Moresby, Papua New Guinea, Douglas Street, P.O. Box 1492, Port Moresby, NCD 121, Papua New Guinea
Mail: Department of State, 4240 Port Moresby Place, Washington, DC 20521-4240
Note: The U.S. Ambassador to Papua New Guinea serves concurrently as U.S. Ambassador to the Solomon Islands and as U.S. Ambassador to the Republic of Vanuatu.

★ Ambassador **Ambassador Catherine I. Ebert-Gray** 675 321-1455
E-mail: ebert-grayci@state.gov
Education: Wisconsin BA; Eisenhower National Security and Resource Strategy MS
Office Management Specialist to the Ambassador
(Vacant) 675 321-1455
Deputy Chief of Mission **Bernard E. "Bernie" Link** 675 321-1455
E-mail: linkbe@state.gov
Education: Virginia 1992 JD
Office Management Specialist to the Deputy Chief of Mission **(Vacant)** .... 675 321-1455 ext. 2104
Community Liaison Officer **Yvette D. Perica** 675 321-1455
Consular Section Chief **Michael "Mike" Mitchell** 675 321-1455
E-mail: ConsularPortMoresby@state.gov Fax: 675 321-1593
Economic Officer **Wendy Kolls** 675 321-1455
E-mail: EconPortMoresby@state.gov
E-mail: kollswa@state.gov
Financial Management Officer (Resident in Australia)
Calvin D. Levo 61 (2) 6214-5887
E-mail: levocd1@state.gov
Affiliation: Financial Management Officer, Office of the U.S. Ambassador to Australia, U.S. Embassy in Australia, United States Department of State
American Embassy - Canberra, APO, AP 96549
Tel: 61 (2) 6214-5887
E-mail: levocd1@state.gov
General Services Officer **Tara A. Logan** 675 321-1455

★ Presidential Appointment Requiring Senate Confirmation ☆ Presidential Appointment ☐ Schedule C Appointment ◇ Career Senior Foreign Service Appointment
● Career Senior Executive Service (SES) Appointment ○ Non-Career Senior Executive Service (SES) Appointment ■ Postal Career Executive Service

Office of the U.S. Ambassador to Papua New Guinea *(continued)*

Information Management Officer **Richard Burns** 675 321-1455
Information Systems Security Officer
Patrick J. Kennedy 675 321-1455
Management Officer **J. Frederick "Fred" Miller** 675 321-1455
Political Officer **Christine E. Buzzard** 675 321-1455
E-mail: buzzardcm@state.gov
E-mail: PoliticalPortMoresby@state.gov
Public Affairs Officer **Beverly Thacker** 675 321-1455
E-mail: PDPortMoresby@state.gov
Regional Security Officer **Guillermo Morales** 675 321-1455
E-mail: PortMoresbyRSO@state.gov

Federal Aviation Administration (Resident in Tokyo) [Papua New Guinea]
American Embassy - Tokyo, Japan, 1-10-5 Akasaka,
Minato-ku, Tokyo, Japan 107-8420
Mail: American Embassy - Tokyo, Japan, Unit 45004, Box 207,
APO, AP 96337-5004
Tel: 81 (3) 3224-5511 Fax: 81 (3) 3582-5974

FAA Representative **Nathan "Nate" Purdy** 81 (3) 3224-5511
E-mail: nate.purdy@faa.gov

Office of the Defense Attaché (Resident in Fiji) [Papua New Guinea]
Defense Attaché **CDR Constantine Panayiotou USN** 675 321-1455
Affiliation: Defense Attaché, Office of the Defense Attaché [Fiji], Office of the U.S. Ambassador to Fiji, Kiribati, Nauru, Tonga, and Tuvalu, United States Department of State
American Embassy - Suva, Fiji, 158 Prince's Road, Suva, Fiji Islands
Tel: 679 331-4466

U.S. Embassy in the Philippines

1201 Roxas Boulevard, Manila, 1000, Philippines
Tel: 63 (2) 301-2000 Fax: 63 (2) 301-2017 Internet: ph.usembassy.gov

Office of the U.S. Ambassador to the Philippines

American Embassy, 1201 Roxas Boulevard, P.O. Box 151,
Ermita, Manila, 1000, Philippines
Mail: American Embassy - Manila, Philippines, PSC 500 Box 1,
FPO, AP 96515-1000
E-mail: manila1@pd.state.gov

★ Ambassador **Ambassador Sung Y. Kim** 63 (2) 301-2000
Education: Pennsylvania 1982 BA; Loyola U (Chicago) JD; London School Econ (UK) LLM
Office Management Specialist to the Ambassador
Joanne Ingalls 63 (2) 301-2000
◇ Deputy Chief of Mission **John C. Law** 63 (2) 301-2000
E-mail: lawj@state.gov Fax: 63 (2) 522-1163
Office Management Specialist to the Deputy Chief of Mission **Marilou B. Endermuhle** 63 (2) 301-2000
E-mail: endermuhlemb@state.gov
◇ Consul General **Russel J. Brown** 63 (2) 301-2000
E-mail: brownrj@state.gov Fax: 63 (2) 526-7736
Community Liaison Officer **Kathryn R. Epperson** 63 (2) 301-2000
E-mail: eppersonkr@state.gov
Economic Counselor **Lynne Gadkowski** 63 (2) 301-2280
E-mail: gadkowskilb@state.gov
Education: Cornell 1998 BA; London School Econ (UK) 2007 MPA
Facilities Management Officer **(Vacant)** 63 (2) 301-2000
Financial Management Officer **(Vacant)** 63 (2) 301-2000
General Services Officer **John Benton "Jay" Parker** ... 63 (2) 301-2000
E-mail: parkerjb@state.gov Fax: 63 (2) 804-0008
Human Resources Officer **Rosario "Cherry" Larsen** 63 (2) 301-2000
Information Management Officer **Ryan Boera** 63 (2) 301-2000
E-mail: boerar@state.gov
Tel: 63 (2) 523-1173
Education: North Carolina Wilmington 1993; North Carolina State 1999; National Defense U 2014
Information Program Officer **James W. Gallup** 63 (2) 301-2000
Information Systems Officer **Eric S. Covington** 63 (2) 301-2000
E-mail: covingtones@state.gov
Information Systems Security Officer
Kenneth W. "Ken" Phipps 63 (2) 301-2000
E-mail: phippskw@state.gov

Office of the U.S. Ambassador to the Philippines *(continued)*

International Broadcasting Bureau Representative
William S. Martin 63 (45) 982-3442
Legal Attaché **Lamont C. Siller** 63 (2) 301-2000
E-mail: sillerlc@state.gov
◇ Management Officer **Amy Hart Vrampas** 63 (2) 301-2000
E-mail: vrampasah@state.gov Fax: 63 (2) 301-2443
Political Officer **David Whiting** .... 63 (2) 301-2000 ext. 2263
E-mail: whitingd@state.gov Fax: 63 (2) 301-2473
Public Affairs Officer **Philip W. Roskamp** .... 63 (2) 301-2000 ext. 2363
E-mail: roskamppw@state.gov Fax: 63 (2) 301-2453
Education: Georgetown 1997 BSFS; Texas 2002 JD
Cultural Affairs Officer
Matthew T. "Matt" Keener .... 63 (2) 301-2000 ext. 2363
Fax: 63 (2) 301-2453
Regional Security Officer **Michael C. Ranger** 63 (2) 523-1296
Assistant Regional Security Officer
Ryan Smith .... 63 (2) 301-2000 ext. 6337
E-mail: smithrt1@state.gov
Tel: 63 (2) 523-1296

Agency for International Development [Philippines]
Annex 2 Building, U.S. Embassy, 1201 Roxas Boulevard, Manila, 1000, Philippines
Mail: U.S.A.I.D, PSC 502 Box 1, FPO, AP 96515-1200
Tel: 63 (2) 301-6000 Fax: 63 (2) 301-6213 E-mail: infoph@usaid.gov
Internet: www.usaid.gov/philippines

◇ Mission Director **Lawrence Hardy II** .... (703) 897-6183
E-mail: lhardy@usaid.gov
Education: Harvard BA; UC Berkeley MBA

Agricultural Section (Foreign Agricultural Service) [Philippines]
F.A.S., PSC 500 Box 31, FPO, AP 96515-1000
1201 Roxas Boulevard, Manila, 1000, Philippines
E-mail: agmanila@fas.usda.gov

Agricultural Counselor **Ralph Bean** 63 (2) 301-6503
E-mail: ralph.bean@fas.usda.gov

Animal and Plant Health Inspection Service [Philippines]
1201 Roxas Boulevard, Manila, 1000, Philippines
Tel: 63 (2) 840-3197 Fax: 63 (2) 830-2376

Attaché **George Andrew "Andy" Ball** 63 (2) 840-3197
E-mail: george.a.ball@aphis.usda.gov

Commercial Section (Foreign Commercial Service) [Philippines]
Ayala Life-FGU Center, 6811 Ayala Avenue,
25th Floor, Makati City, Philippines
Mail: FCS, PSC 500 Box 34, FPO, AP 96515-1000
Tel: 63 (2) 301-2000 Fax: 63 (2) 521-0416
E-mail: businessphilippines@trade.gov
Internet: www.export.gov/philippines

Senior Commercial Officer **Diane Jones** 63 (2) 301-2000
E-mail: diane.jones@trade.gov
Commercial Officer **Yuri Arthur** 63 (2) 301-2000
E-mail: yuri.arthur@trade.gov

Department of Homeland Security - Transportation Security Administration [Philippines]
American Embassy, 1201 Roxas Boulevard, Manila, 1000, Philippines
Mail: FAA, PSC 500 Box 21, FPO, AP 96515-1000
Tel: 63 (2) 301-2000 Fax: 63 (2) 524-2129

TSA Officer **Eustacio C. Berganos** 63 (2) 301-2000
E-mail: berganosea@state.gov

Department of Homeland Security - U.S. Citizenship and Immigration Services [Philippines]
American Embassy - Manila, Philippines,
1201 Roxas Boulevard, Manila, 1000, Philippines
Mail: INS, PSC 500 Box 22, FPO, AP 96515-1000
Tel: 63 (2) 301-2000 Fax: 63 (2) 522-4362

Officer-in-Charge **Thomas E. Curley** 63 (2) 301-2000
E-mail: curleyte@state.gov

★ Presidential Appointment Requiring Senate Confirmation ☆ Presidential Appointment ☐ Schedule C Appointment ◇ Career Senior Foreign Service Appointment
● Career Senior Executive Service (SES) Appointment ○ Non-Career Senior Executive Service (SES) Appointment ■ Postal Career Executive Service

DEPARTMENTS

DEPARTMENTS

Department of Homeland Security - U.S. Immigration and Customs Enforcement [Philippines]
1201 Roxas Boulevard, Manila, 1000, Philippines
Mail: PSC 500, Box 1, FPO, AP 96515-1000
Tel: 63 (2) 301-2000
ICE Attaché **Ransom J. Avilla** 63 (2) 301-2000

Drug Enforcement Administration [Philippines]
1201 Roxas Boulevard, Manila, 1000, Philippines
Tel: 63 (2) 301-2000
Country Attaché **Mark O. Juvrud** 63 (2) 301-2000
E-mail: juvrudmo@state.gov

Office of the Defense Attaché [Philippines]
American Embassy, 1201 Roxas Boulevard, Manila, 1000, Philippines
Mail: D.A.O., PSC 500 Box 19, FPO, AP 96515-1000
Tel: 63 (2) 301-2000 Fax: 63 (2) 522-4361
Defense Attaché **Col Brian E. Bell USAF** 63 (2) 301-2000
E-mail: bellbe@state.gov
Tel: 63 (2) 522-1774

Peace Corps [Philippines]
PNB Financial Center, Bay Side Diosdado Macapagal Avenue,
6th Floor, Pasay City, Philippines
Tel: 63 (2) 833-6420 Fax: 63 (2) 833-6425
E-mail: info@ph.peacecorps.gov
Internet: www.peacecorps.gov/philippines
Country Director **(Vacant)** 63 (2) 833-6420

Social Security Administration [Philippines]
Social Security Division, Veterans Affairs Regional Office,
1201 Roxas Boulevard, 0930 Manila, Philippines
Tel: 63 (2) 301-2000 ext. 9 Fax: 63 (2) 708-9723
E-mail: fbu.manila@ssa.gov
Division Chief **Darrin K. Morgan** . . . . 63 (2) 301-2000 ext. 2564
E-mail: darrin.morgan@ssa.gov

Asian Development Bank - Manila
#6 ADB Avenue, Mandaluyong City, Ninth Floor, Suite Seven,
1550 Metro Manila, Philippines
Mail: Asian Development Bank, PSC 500 Box 29, FPO, AP 96515-1000
Tel: 63 (2) 632-6050 Fax: 63 (2) 636-2444 E-mail: phco@adb.org
Internet: www.adb.org
★ U.S. Executive Director (Acting) **Eli H. Miller** . . . . (202) 622-1906
E-mail: eli.miller@treasury.gov
U.S. Alternate Executive Director **Michael Strauss** 63 (2) 632-6051

Commercial Section (Foreign Commercial Service) at Asian Development Bank
Ayala Life-FGU Center, 6811 Ayala Avenue,
25th Floor, Makati City, Philippines
Mail: Asian Development Bank, PSC 500 Box 33, FPO, AP 96515-1000
Tel: 63 (2) 301-2000 E-mail: office.manilaadb@trade.gov
Internet: export.gov/adb
Senior Commercial Officer **Gregory Harris** 63 (2) 516-5093

U.S. Embassy in the Republic of Palau
Omsangel/Beklelachieb, Airai, Palau 96940
Tel: 680 587-2920 Fax: 680 587-2911
E-mail: usembassykoror@palaunet.com Internet: pw.usembassy.gov

Office of the U.S. Ambassador to the Republic of Palau
Omsangel/Beklelachieb, Airai, Palau 96940
★ Ambassador **Ambassador Amy Jane Hyatt** 680 587-2920
E-mail: hyattaj@state.gov
Education: SUNY (Binghamton) BA; Stanford 1981 JD; National War Col MS
Deputy Chief of Mission **Jennifer J. Nehez** 680 587-2920
E-mail: nehezjj@state.gov
Consul Assistant **Marjorie T. Towai** 680 587-2920
E-mail: towaimt@state.gov

Office of the U.S. Ambassador to the Republic of Palau *(continued)*
Political/Economic Assistant **Jocelyne Isechal** 680 587-2920
E-mail: isechalj@state.gov
Management Officer **Jennifer J. Nehez** 680 587-2920
E-mail: nehezjj@state.gov

Federal Aviation Administration (Resident in Tokyo) [Republic of Palau]
American Embassy - Tokyo/FAA, 1-10-5, Akasaka,
Minato-ku, Tokyo, 107-8420, Japan
Mail: American Embassy - Tokyo/FAA,
Unit 45004, Box 207, APO, AP 96337-5004
Fax: 81 (3) 3582-5974
FAA Representative **Nathan "Nate" Purdy** 81 (3) 3224-5511

U.S. Embassy in Samoa
ACC Building, Matafele, 5th Floor, Apia, Samoa
Tel: 685 21-631 Fax: 685 22-030 Internet: ws.usembassy.gov

Office of the U.S. Ambassador to Samoa
ACC Building, Matafele, Apia, Samoa
Mail: PSC 467, Box 1, APO, AP 96531-1001
Tel: 685 21-631 Fax: 685 22-030 Internet: ws.usembassy.gov
Note: The U.S. Ambassador to New Zealand serves concurrently as the U.S. Ambassador to Samoa.
★ Ambassador (Resident in Wellington)
Ambassador Scott Philip Brown 64 (4) 462-6142
American Embassy - Wellington, New Zealand,
PSC 467, Box 1, APO, AP 96531-1034
Education: Tufts 1981 BA; Boston Col 1985 JD
Chargé d'Affaires **Antone C. "Tony" Greubel** 685 21-631
E-mail: greubelac@state.gov
Consular Affairs Officer (Resident in Auckland) **April C. Scarrow** . . . . 64 (9) 303-2724 ext. 222
Education: North Texas 1995
General Services Officer (Resident in Wellington)
Gavin Elliott 64 (4) 462-6046
E-mail: wellington.gso@state.gov
Management Officer (Resident in Wellington)
Peter A. Schroeder 64 (4) 462-6131
Public Affairs Officer (Resident in Wellington)
Dolores Prin 64 (4) 462-6082
Regional Security Officer (Resident in Wellington)
Matt Reilly 64 (4) 462-6013

Federal Aviation Administration (Resident in Tokyo) [Samoa]
American Embassy - Tokyo, Japan, 1-10-5 Akasaka,
Minato-ku, Tokyo, Japan 107-8420
Mail: American Embassy - Tokyo, Japan, Unit 45004, Box 207,
APO, AP 96337-5004
Tel: 81 (3) 3224-5511 Fax: 81 (3) 3582-5974
FAA Representative **Nathan "Nate" Purdy** 81 (3) 3224-5511

Office of the Defense Attaché (Resident in Wellington) [Samoa]
American Embassy - Wellington, New Zealand, 29 Fitzherbert Terrace,
Thorndon, Wellington, New Zealand
Mail: PSC 467, Box 1, APO, AP 96531-1034
Tel: 64 (4) 462-6074 Fax: 64 (4) 472-3537
Defense Attaché
COL James G. "Jamie" McAden USA 64 (4) 462-6073

★ Presidential Appointment Requiring Senate Confirmation ☆ Presidential Appointment ☐ Schedule C Appointment ◇ Career Senior Foreign Service Appointment
● Career Senior Executive Service (SES) Appointment ○ Non-Career Senior Executive Service (SES) Appointment ■ Postal Career Executive Service

U.S. Embassy in Singapore

American Embassy - Singapore, 27 Napier Road, Singapore, 258508, Singapore
Tel: 65 6476-9100 Fax: 65 6476-9340
E-mail: singaporeusembassy@state.gov Internet: sg.usembassy.gov

Office of the U.S. Ambassador to Singapore

American Embassy - Singapore, 27 Napier Road, Singapore, 258508, Singapore
Mail: American Embassy - Singapore, FPO, AP 96507

★ Ambassador **(Vacant)** 65 6476-9167
◇ Chargé d'Affaires **Stephanie F. Syptak-Ramnath** 65 6476-9433
E-mail: syptak-ramnathsf@state.gov
Education: Georgetown 1992 BSFS
Office Management Specialist to the Ambassador **(Vacant)** 65 6476-9167
◇ Deputy Chief of Mission **Stephanie F. Syptak-Ramnath** 65 6476-9433
E-mail: syptak-ramnathsf@state.gov
Education: Georgetown 1992 BSFS
Office Management Specialist to the Deputy Chief of Mission **Allie Hutton** 291 6476-9230
Consul **Paul Herman** 65 6476-9422
E-mail: singaporecon@state.gov Fax: 65 6476-9232
Community Liaison Officer **Tracy Blair** 65 6476-9100
Financial Management Officer **Yuting Shao** 65 6476-9100
E-mail: shaoy2@state.gov
General Services Officer **Darren P. Bologna** 65 6476-9234
E-mail: bolognadp@state.gov Fax: 65 6476-9342
Information Management Officer **Michael R. Wheeler** 65 6476-9369
E-mail: wheelermr@state.gov Fax: 65 6476-9340
Information Program Officer **Ryan Key** 65 6476-9100
Information Security Officer **Edith Vargas** 65 6476-9100
Legal Attaché **Vincent Lucero** 65 6476-9100
Management Officer **Tor R. Petersen** 65 6476-9036
E-mail: petersentr@state.gov Fax: 65 6476-9040
Political/Economic Officer **Melissa A. Brown** 65 6476-9100
Public Affairs Officer **Camille Dawson** 65 6476-9265
E-mail: DawsonCP@state.gov Fax: 65 6476-9035
Regional Security Officer **Bryan Scruggs** 65 6476-9447
E-mail: scruggsb@state.gov Fax: 65 6476-9040

Agricultural Section (Foreign Agricultural Service) [Singapore]

American Embassy - Singapore, PSC 470 (Agriculture), FPO, AP 96507
Tel: 65 6476-9120 Fax: 65 6476-9157 E-mail: agsingapore@fas.usda.gov

Agricultural Officer (Resident in Kuala Lumpur) **Joani Dong** 60 (3) 2168-5000

Commercial Section (Foreign Commercial Service) [Singapore]

U.S. Commercial Service, PSC 470, FCS, FPO, AP 96507
Tel: 65 6476-9037 Fax: 65 6476-9080
E-mail: office.singapore@trade.gov Internet: export.gov/singapore

◇ Regional Senior Commercial Officer **Margaret A. "Maggie" Hanson-Muse** 65 6476-9401
E-mail: mhansonm@trade.gov
Education: Brandeis 1978 BA; Columbia 1983 MBA

Department of Homeland Security - U.S. Immigration and Customs Enforcement [Singapore]

American Embassy - Singapore, FPO, AP 96507
Tel: 65 6476-9425 Fax: 65 6476-9188 E-mail: casx@pacific.net.sg

Customs Officer **Calvin Webb** 65 6476-9425

Federal Aviation Administration [Singapore]

American Embassy - Singapore, PSC 470 - FAA IAO, FPO, AP 96507
Tel: 65 6543-1466 Fax: 65 6543-1952

FAA Senior Representative **James "Jim" Spillane** 65 6543-1466
E-mail: james.spillane@faa.gov

Office of the Defense Attaché [Singapore]

American Embassy - Singapore, FPO, AP 96507
Tel: 65 6476-9392 Fax: 65 6476-9277 E-mail: singaporedao@state.gov

Defense and Naval Attaché **CAPT So Won Silas "Silas" Ahn USN** 65 6476-9392

Office of Defense Cooperation [Singapore]

American Embassy - Singapore, FPO, AP 96507
Tel: 65 6476-9336 Fax: 65 6476-9483 E-mail: singaporeodc@san.osd.mil

Defense Cooperation Officer **Col Curtis Walker USAF** 65 6476-9336

American Institute in Taiwan (AIT)

American Institute in Taiwan - Taipei Office, Number Seven, Lane 134, Xinyi Road, Section Three, Taipei, 10659, Taiwan
Tel: 886 (2) 2162-2000 Fax: 886 (2) 2162-2251 Internet: www.ait.org.tw

Note: The American Institute in Taiwan will be moving to a new office complex in Neihu District, Tapei in summer 2018.

◇ Director **William "Brent" Christensen** 886 (2) 2162-2000
E-mail: christensenwb@state.gov
Education: BYU BA; George Washington MA; Oregon Health DMD
Office Management Specialist to the Director **(Vacant)** 886 (2) 2162-2000
Deputy Director **Raymond F. "Ray" Greene** 886 (2) 2162-2000
Education: Maryland BA, MPM; International Christian (Attended)
Office Management Specialist to the Deputy Director **Yvonne Sandor** 886 (2) 2162-2000
E-mail: sandory@state.gov
Community Liaison Officer **Carla C. Hitchcock** 886 (2) 2162-2000
E-mail: hitchcockcc@state.gov
Consular Officer **Lara K. Harris** 886 (2) 2162-2000
E-mail: harrislk@state.gov Fax: 886 (2) 2162-2239
Economic Officer **Jeffrey D. Horwitz** 886 (2) 2162-2000
Equal Employment Opportunity Officer **Katie Ortiz** 886 (2) 2162-2000
Financial Management Officer **Jing W. Edwards** 886 (2) 2162-2000
E-mail: edwardsj@state.gov
General Services Officer **Ryan E. McKean** 886 (2) 2162-2000
E-mail: mckeanre@state.gov
Human Resources Officer (Acting) **Eliza F. Al-Laham** 886 (2) 2162-2000
E-mail: allahamef@state.gov
Information Management Officer **John Voxakis** 886 (2) 2162-2000
E-mail: voxakisja@state.gov
Information Program Officer **John T. Lee** 886 (2) 2162-2000
E-mail: leejt@state.gov
Information Systems Security Officer **Derek M. Bibler** 886 (2) 2162-2000
E-mail: biblerdm@state.gov
Legal Attaché **(Vacant)** 886 (2) 2162-2000
Management Officer **Brian Reynolds** 886 (2) 2162-2000
E-mail: reynoldsbr@state.gov
Political Officer **Christian M. Marchant** 886 (2) 2162-2000
E-mail: marchantcm@state.gov
Public Affairs Officer **Jesse Starr Curtis** 886 (2) 2162-2000
E-mail: curtisjs@state.gov
Cultural Affairs Officer **Eric B. Aldrich** 886 (2) 2162-2000
E-mail: aldricheb@state.gov
Education: Chicago BA; Yale MPH
Spokesperson **Amanda J. Mansour** 886 (2) 2162-2000
Education: Columbia 2004 BA
Regional Security Officer **Tony Hornik-Tran** 886 (2) 2162-2000
E-mail: horniktrant@state.gov

Washington Headquarters [Taiwan]

American Institute in Taiwan - Washington Headquarters, 1700 North Moore Street, Suite 1700, Arlington, VA 22209
Tel: (703) 525-8474 Fax: (703) 841-1385

Chair **Ambassador James Francis Moriarty** .... (703) 525-8474
Education: Dartmouth BA
Managing Director **John Jacob Norris, Jr.** .... (703) 525-8474
E-mail: norrisjj@state.gov

DEPARTMENTS

★ Presidential Appointment Requiring Senate Confirmation ☆ Presidential Appointment ☐ Schedule C Appointment ◇ Career Senior Foreign Service Appointment
● Career Senior Executive Service (SES) Appointment ○ Non-Career Senior Executive Service (SES) Appointment ■ Postal Career Executive Service

Agricultural Section (Foreign Agriculture Service) [Taiwan]
American Institute in Taiwan - Taipei Office, Number Seven, Lane 134, Xinyi Road, Section Three, Taipei, 10659, Taiwan
Tel: 886 (2) 2162-2316 Fax: 886 (2) 2162-2238
E-mail: agtaipei@fas.usda.gov

Chief **Mark A. Petry** 886 (2) 2705-6536
E-mail: mark.petry@fas.usda.gov
Education: Purdue 1996 BS, 1998 MS; Michigan State 2013 MS
Deputy Chief **Andrew Anderson-Sprecher** 886 (2) 2162-2316

Agricultural Trade Office [Taiwan]
Number 136, Renai Road, Section Three,
7th Floor, Room 704, Taipei, Taiwan 106
Tel: 886 (2) 2705-6536 Fax: 886 (2) 2706-4885
E-mail: atotaipei@fas.usda.gov
Internet: www.ait.org.tw/en/agricultural-trade-office.html

Agricultural Trade Officer **Chris Frederick** 886 (2) 2705-6536

American Center
International Trade Building, 333 Keelung Road, Section One,
21st Floor, Room 2101, Taipei, Taiwan 110
Tel: 886 (2) 2723-3959 Fax: 886 (2) 2725-2934
E-mail: aitarc@mail.ait.org.tw

Director **Eric B. Aldrich** 886 (2) 2723-3959
E-mail: aldricheb@state.gov
Education: Chicago BA; Yale MPH

Animal and Plant Health Inspection Service Office [Taiwan]
American Institute in Taiwan - Taipei Office, Number Seven, Lane 134, Xinyi Road, Section Three, Taipei, 10659, Taiwan
Tel: 886 (2) 2162-2000 Fax: 886 (2) 2162-2251

APHIS Officer **Russell T. "Russ" Caplen** 886 (2) 2162-2221

Commercial Section (Foreign Commercial Service) [Taiwan]
International Trade Building, 333 Keelung Road, Section One,
32nd Floor, Room 3207, Taipei, Taiwan 110
Tel: 886 (2) 2720-1550 Fax: 886 (2) 2757-7162
E-mail: office.taipei@trade.gov Internet: http://export.gov/taiwan/

Senior Commercial Officer
Helen Peterson .... 886 (2) 2720-1550 ext. 382
E-mail: helen.peterson@trade.gov

Kaohsiung Branch Office
5F, No.88, Chenggong 2nd Road, Qianzhen District, Kaohsiung, 80661, Taiwan 800
Tel: 886 (7) 335-5006 Fax: 886 (7) 338-0551
Internet: www.ait.org.tw/offices/kaohsiung

Branch Chief **Matthew "Matt" O'Connor** 886 (7) 335-5006
Deputy Branch Chief **Suzanne Yueh Wong** 886 (7) 335-5006
Consular Officer **Suzanne Yueh Wong** 886 (7) 335-5006
Economic Officer **Suzanne Yueh Wong** 886 (7) 335-5006
Management Officer **(Vacant)** 886 (7) 335-5006
Political Officer **(Vacant)** 886 (7) 335-5006
Public Affairs Officer **Peter McSharry** 886 (7) 335-5006
E-mail: mcsharryp@state.gov
Education: Wesleyan U BA; Fletcher Law & Diplomacy 2000 MALD

Commercial Section (Foreign Commercial Service) [Taiwan]
5F, No.88, Chenggong 2nd Road, Qianzhen District,
5th Floor, Kaohsiung, 80661, Taiwan 800
E-mail: office.kaohsiung@trade.gov

Principal Commercial Officer **(Vacant)** .... 886 (7) 335-5006 ext. 6118

U.S. Embassy in Thailand
120 Wireless Road, Bangkok, 10330, Thailand
Tel: 66 2205-4000 Fax: 66 2205-4306 Internet: th.usembassy.gov

Office of the U.S. Ambassador to Thailand
American Embassy - Bangkok, Thailand,
120 Wireless Road, Bangkok, 10330, Thailand
Mail: American Embassy - Bangkok, Thailand, APO, AP 96546

★ Ambassador **(Vacant)** 66 2205-4000
◇ Chargé d'Affaires **Peter M. Haymond** 66 2205-4000
E-mail: haymondp@state.gov
Education: BYU BA; Fletcher Law & Diplomacy PhD
Office Management Specialist to the Ambassador
Mark A. Friedbauer 66 2205-4000
E-mail: friedbauerma@state.gov
◇ Deputy Chief of Mission **Peter M. Haymond** 66 2205-4000
E-mail: haymondp@state.gov
Education: BYU BA; Fletcher Law & Diplomacy PhD
Office Management Specialist to the Deputy Chief of Mission **Antonette Schroeder** 66 2205-4000
Community Liaison Officer **Layla Shaw** 66 2205-4000
◇ Consul General **Timothy M. Scherer** 66 2205-4000
E-mail: scherertm@state.gov
Economic Officer **Douglas Joseph Apostol** 66 2205-4000
E-mail: nemroffc@state.gov
Education: Stanford 1979 BA; Harvard 1983 JD; Tufts 1983 MA; National Defense U 2014 MNR
Facilities Management Officer **Paul Schaefer** 66 2-205-4306
Financial Management Officer **Mary Jo Rasing** 66 2205-4000
E-mail: rasingmj@state.gov
General Services Officer **John T. Stremel** 66 2205-4000
E-mail: stremeljt@state.gov
Human Resources Officer **Jill E. Perry** 66 2-205-4000
E-mail: perryje@state.gov
Global Financial Services Director **Ralph A. Hamilton** 66 2205-4000
E-mail: hamiltonra@state.gov
Information Management Officer **Jeffrey J. Schroeder** 66 2205-4000
Information Programs Officer **(Vacant)** 66 2205-4000
Information Systems Officer **(Vacant)** 66 2205-4000
Information System Security Officer **Brad J. Naessens** 66 2205-4000
E-mail: naessensbj@state.gov
Legal Attaché **John M. Schachnovsky** 66 2205-4000
E-mail: schachnovskyjm@state.gov
Management Officer (Acting) **John T. Stremel** 66 2205-4000
E-mail: stremeljt@state.gov
Narcotics Affairs Officer **Jenny Malheiro** 66 2205-4000
E-mail: malheiroj@state.gov
Political Officer **Henry M. Rector** 66 2205-4000
Public Affairs Officer **J. Robert "Bob" Post** 66 2205-4000
E-mail: postjr@state.gov
Regional Security Officer **Peter M. Riva** 66 2205-4000
E-mail: rivapm@state.gov

Agency for International Development - Regional Development Mission for Asia [Thailand] (USAID/RDMA)
Athenee Tower, 63 Wireless Road, 25th Floor, Bangkok, 10330, Thailand
E-mail: info-rdma@usaid.gov
Internet: https://www.usaid.gov/asia-regional
Areas Covered: Burma, China, Laos, Thailand, and Vietnam

◇ Mission Director (Acting)
Richard J. "Dick" Goughnour 66 2-257-3000
E-mail: rgoughnour@usaid.gov
Education: Minnesota BABA
Deputy Mission Director **Todd Sorenson** 66 2205-4000
E-mail: tsorenson@usaid.gov
Education: Drake 1988 BS

Agricultural Section (Foreign Agricultural Service) [Thailand]
American Embassy - Bangkok, Thailand,
120 Wireless Road, Bangkok, 10330, Thailand
Mail: American Embassy - Bangkok, Thailand, APO, AP 96546
Fax: 66 2255-2907 E-mail: agbangkok@fas.usda.gov

Agricultural Counselor **Russell "Russ" Nicely** 66 2205-5106

★ Presidential Appointment Requiring Senate Confirmation ☆ Presidential Appointment ☐ Schedule C Appointment ◇ Career Senior Foreign Service Appointment
● Career Senior Executive Service (SES) Appointment ○ Non-Career Senior Executive Service (SES) Appointment ■ Postal Career Executive Service

Agricultural Section (Foreign Agricultural Service) [Thailand] *(continued)*

Agricultural Attaché **Paul Welcher** 66 2205-5106

Animal and Plant Health Inspection Service [Thailand]

APHIS Attaché **Elia P. "Lou" Vanechanos** 66 2205-5989
E-mail: elia.p.vanechanos@aphis.usda.gov

Commercial Section (Foreign Commercial Service) [Thailand]

American Embassy - The Commercial Service, Diethelm Tower A,
93/1 Wireless Road, 3rd Floor, Suite 302, Bangkok, 10330, Thailand
Mail: Box 51, APO, AP 96546-0001
Tel: 66 2205-5090 Fax: 66 2255-2915 E-mail: office.bangkok@trade.gov
Internet: export.gov/thailand

◇ Senior Commercial Officer (Acting)
Stephen J. Anderson 66 2205-5280
E-mail: Stephen.Anderson@trade.gov
Education: Oberlin 1979 BA; MIT MS, 1987 PhD

Commercial Attaché **Stephen J. Anderson** 66 2205-5263
E-mail: Stephen.Anderson@trade.gov
Education: Oberlin 1979 BA; MIT MS, 1987 PhD

Senior Commercial Specialist **Kitisorn Sookpradist** 66 2205-5279
E-mail: kitisorn.sookpradist@trade.gov

United States Trade and Development Agency [Thailand]

American Embassy - The Commercial Service, Diethelm Tower A,
93/1 Wireless Road, Bangkok, 10330, Thailand
Mail: Box 51, APO, AP 96546-0001
Tel: 66 2205-5090 Fax: 66 2255-2915

Regional Manager for Asia **Brandon Megorden** 66 2205-5262
E-mail: bmegorden@ustda.gov

Department of Homeland Security - Transportation Security Administration [Thailand]

American Embassy - Bangkok, Thailand,
120 Wireless Road, Bangkok, 10330, Thailand
Mail: American Embassy - Bangkok, Thailand, APO, AP 96546
Tel: 66 2205-4148 Fax: 66 2253-2422

TSA Officer **Annmarie Lontz** . . . . . 66 2205-4148 ext. 2387

Department of Homeland Security - U.S. Citizenship and Immigration Services [Thailand]

Diethelm Tower B, 93/1 Wireless Road,
Suite 114/1, Bangkok, Thailand
Mail: American Embassy - Bangkok, Thailand, APO, AP 96546
Tel: 66 2205-4000 Fax: 66 2650-7770

CIS Officer **Donald J. Monica** 66 2205-4000

Department of Homeland Security - U.S. Immigration and Customs Enforcement [Thailand]

American Embassy - Bangkok, Thailand,
120 Wireless Road, Bangkok, 10330, Thailand
Mail: American Embassy - Bangkok, Thailand, APO, AP 96546
Tel: 66 2205-5015 Fax: 66 2253-4448

U.S. Customs Attaché **(Vacant)** 66 2205-5015

Department of Justice - Drug Enforcement Administration [Thailand]

Regional Director **Jesse Fong** 66 2205-4000

Department of Justice - Intellectual Property Law Enforcement [Thailand]

Intellectual Property Law Enforcement Coordinator
Catharine Hartzenbusch 66 2205-4000

Federal Aviation Administration (Resident in Singapore) [Thailand]

American Embassy, 27 Napier Road, Singapore, 258508, Singapore
Mail: American Embassy - Singapore, PSC 470 FAA IAO,
FPO, AP 96507
Tel: 65 6543-1466 Fax: 65 6543-1952

FAA Representative **James "Jim" Spillane** 65 6476-9320
E-mail: james.spillane@faa.gov

Office of the Defense Attaché [Thailand]

American Embassy - Bangkok, Thailand,
120 Wireless Road, Bangkok, 10330, Thailand
Mail: American Embassy - Bangkok, Thailand, APO, AP 96546
Tel: 66 2205-4000 Fax: 66 2254-2990 E-mail: daobangkok@state.gov

Defense Attaché **Col Albert "Al" Fitts USAF** 66 2205-4000

Peace Corps [Thailand]

American Embassy - Bangkok, Thailand,
120 Wireless Road, Bangkok, 10330, Thailand
Internet: www.peacecorps.gov/thailand
E-mail: thailand_info@peacecorps.gov

Country Director **Gene Nixon** 66 2-2430140

Chiang Mai Consulate General

U.S. Consulate General - Chiang Mai, Thailand,
387 Wichayanond Road, Chiang Mai, Thailand 50300
Mail: U.S. Consulate General - Chiang Mai, Box C, APO, AP 96546
Tel: 66 5310-7700 Fax: 66 5325-2633

Consul General **Jennifer A. Harhigh** 66 5310-7700
E-mail: harhighja@state.gov

Consular Officer **Daniel Jacobs-Nhan** 66 5310-7700
E-mail: jacobs-nhanda@state.gov

Management Officer **Nathan D. Austin** 66 5310-7700

Political/Economic Officer **Vi L. Jacobs-Nhan** 66 5310-7700
E-mail: jacobs-nhanvl@state.gov

Regional Security Officer **Ben Rathsack** 66 5310-7700

U.S. Embassy in Timor-Leste

Avenida de Portugal, Praia dos Coqueiros, Dili, East Timor
Tel: 670 332-4684 Fax: 670 331-3206 Internet: tl.usembassy.gov

Office of the U.S. Ambassador to Timor-Leste

Avenida de Portugal, Praia dos Coqueiros, Dili, East Timor
Mail: U.S. Embassy - Dili, East Timor,
8250 Dili Place, Washington, DC 20521-8250

★ Ambassador **Ambassador Kathleen M. Fitzpatrick** 670 332-4684
E-mail: fitzpatrickkm@state.gov
Education: Dayton BA; Georgetown MA; National War Col MS

Office Management Specialist to the Ambassador **Shawn White** . . . . . 670 332-4684 ext. 2171

Deputy Chief of Mission
Daniel R. "Dan" Bischof . . . . . 670 390-332-4684 ext. 2028
E-mail: bischofdr@state.gov

Office Management Specialist to the Deputy Chief of Mission **(Vacant)** 670 332-4684

Community Liaison Officer **(Vacant)** 670 332-4684

Consular Officer **Tye Sundlee** . . . . . 670 332-4684 ext. 2034
Education: Willamette BA; Georgetown 2015 MBA

Financial Management Officer **Melanie Parris** 670 332-4684

General Services Officer **Chris Pritchett** 66 2205-4000
E-mail: pritchettcd@state.gov
Education: Georgia Tech BS, 2009 MS; Seoul National (Korea) 2010

Information Management Officer
Dominic "Doc" Meyer . . . . . 670 332-4684 ext. 2060

Information Systems Security Officer
Richard L. "Rick" Derousse 670 332-4684

Legal Attaché **Theodore Merritt** 670 332-4684

Management Officer
William Joseph "Joe" Childers . . . . . 670 332-4684 ext. 2143
Fax: 670 331-3206

Political/Economic Officer **Tye Sundlee** . . . . . 670 332-4684 ext. 2034
Education: Willamette BA; Georgetown 2015 MBA

(continued on next page)

★ Presidential Appointment Requiring Senate Confirmation ☆ Presidential Appointment □ Schedule C Appointment ◇ Career Senior Foreign Service Appointment
● Career Senior Executive Service (SES) Appointment ○ Non-Career Senior Executive Service (SES) Appointment ■ Postal Career Executive Service

Office of the U.S. Ambassador to Timor-Leste *(continued)*

Public Affairs Officer **Courtney Woods** 670 332-4684
Regional Security Officer **Lech D. Kazmirski** 670 332-4684
E-mail: kazmirskild@state.gov

Agency for International Development [Timor-Leste]
Avenida de Portugal, Praia dos Coqueiros, Dili, East Timor
Tel: 670 332-2211 Fax: 670 332-2216
E-mail: usaid-timor-leste-info@usaid.gov
Internet: https://www.usaid.gov/timor-leste

Mission Director **Diana Putman** 670 332-2211
E-mail: dputman@usaid.gov
Education: Bryn Mawr BA; Army War Col MSS

Office of Defense Cooperation [Timor-Leste]
Avenida de Portugal, Praia dos Coqueiros, Dili, East Timor
Mail: U.S. Embassy - Dili, East Timor,
8250 Dili Place, Washington, DC 20521-8250
Tel: 670 332-4684 ext. 2103 Fax: 670 331-3206

Chief **Pete Roongsang** . . . . 670 332-4684 ext. 2103

U.S. Embassy in Vietnam

American Embassy - Hanoi, Vietnam, 7 Lang Ha Street, Ba Dinh District, Hanoi, Vietnam
Tel: 84 24-3850-5000 E-mail: hanoiac@state.gov
Internet: vn.usembassy.gov

Office of the U.S. Ambassador to Vietnam

American Embassy - Hanoi, Vietnam, 7 Lang Ha Street, Ba Dinh District, Hanoi, Vietnam
Mail: Department of State, 4550 Hanoi Place,
Washington, DC 20521-4550

★ Ambassador
Ambassador Daniel Joseph "Dan" Kritenbrink 84 24-3850-5000
E-mail: kritenbrinkdj@state.gov
Education: Nebraska (Kearney) BA; Virginia MA
Office Management Specialist to the Ambassador
Kim M. Tesone 84 24-3850-5000
E-mail: tesonek@state.gov
Deputy Chief of Mission **Caryn R. McClelland** 84 24-3850-5166
E-mail: mcclellandcr@state.gov
Office Management Specialist to the Deputy Chief of Mission **Rhonda Sheppard** 84 24-3850-5166
Consular Section Chief **Adam M. Center** 84 24-831-4590
Community Liaison Officer **Tammy Dewan** 84 24-3850-5000
Economic Officer **Robert R. Gabor** 84 24-3850-5000
E-mail: gaborrr@state.gov
E-mail: econvietnam@state.gov
Environment, Science, Technology and Health Officer
Jason McInerney 84 24-3850-5000
Financial Management Officer
Tyrone "Ty" Campbell 84 24-3850-5000
General Services Officer **Michael Warfield** 84 24-3850-5000
Human Resources Officer
Thomas F. "Tom" Zeitler 86 (10) 8531-3000
E-mail: zeitlertf@state.gov
Information Management Officer **Todd Cheng** 84 24-3850-5000
Information Systems Officer **(Vacant)** 84 24-3850-5000
Management Officer **Daniel F. "Dan" McCullough** 84 24-3850-5000
Public Affairs Officer **Molly L. Stephenson** 84 24-831-4580
Rose Garden Tower, 6 Ngoc Khann Street,
3rd Floor, Hanoi, Vietnam
Political Officer **Noah S. Zaring** 84 24-3850-5000
E-mail: zaringns@state.gov
Education: Grinnell 1993 BA; Johns Hopkins 1997 MA; National War Col 2016 MNSSS
Regional Security Officer **Alan Chipman** 84 24-3850-5000

Agricultural Section (Foreign Agricultural Service) [Vietnam]
American Embassy - Hanoi, Vietnam, 7 Lang Ha Street, Ba Dinh District, Hanoi, Vietnam
Mail: Department of State, 4550 Hanoi Place,
Washington, DC 20521-4550
Tel: 84 24-3850-5000 ext. 6106 Fax: 84 24-3850-5130
E-mail: aghanoi@fas.usda.gov

◇ Agricultural Counselor
Robert Henry Hanson . . . . 84 24-3850-5000 ext. 6106
E-mail: robert.hanson@fas.usda.gov
Agricultural Attaché
Benjamin "Ben" Petlock . . . . 84 24-3850-5000 ext. 6106
E-mail: benjamin.petlock@fas.usda.gov

Animal and Plant Health Inspection Service (Resident in Beijing) [Vietnam]
International Club Buiding, 6th Floor, Beijing, China 100600
Mail: APHIS c/o U.S. Embassy - Beijing, China, PSC 461, Box 50, FPO, AP 96521-0002
Tel: 86 (10) 8531-3030 Fax: 86 (10) 8531-3033

APHIS Officer **Murali Bandla** 86 (10) 8531-4524

Centers for Disease Control [Vietnam]
American Embassy - Hanoi, Vietnam, 7 Lang Ha Street, Ba Dinh District, Hanoi, Vietnam
Mail: PSC 461, Box 100, FPO, AP 96521-0002
Tel: 84 24-831-4580

Country Director **Anthony Mounts** 84 24-831-4580

Commercial Section (Foreign Commercial Service) [Vietnam]
American Embassy - Hanoi, Vietnam, 7 Lang Ha Street, Ba Dinh District, Hanoi, Vietnam
Mail: Department of State, 4550 Hanoi Place,
Washington, DC 20521-4550
Tel: 84 24-3850-5199 Fax: 84 24-3850-5064
E-mail: office.hanoi@trade.gov Internet: export.gov/vietnam

Senior Commercial Officer **Eric Hsu** 84 24-3850-5199
E-mail: eric.hsu@trade.gov
Education: Chicago BA
Commercial Officer **James "Jim" Curtis** 84 24-3850-5169
E-mail: James.Curtis@trade.gov
Education: James Madison 1992 BS; Maryland 2009 MBA

Department of Homeland Security - U.S. Immigration and Customs Enforcement [Vietnam]
American Embassy - Hanoi, Vietnam, 7 Lang Ha Street, Ba Dinh District, Hanoi, Vietnam
Mail: PSC 461, Box 400, FPO, AP 96521-0002
Tel: 84 24-772-1500 Fax: 84 (4) 772-1510

ICE Attaché **Cory Dunne** 84 24-772-1500

Drug Enforcement Administration [Vietnam]
American Embassy - Hanoi, Vietnam, 7 Lang Ha Street, Ba Dinh District, Hanoi, Vietnam
Mail: PSC 461, Box 100, FPO, AP 96521-0002
Tel: 84 24-772-1500 Fax: 84 24-772-1510

Drug Enforcement Administration Attaché
Daniel "Dan" Holcomb 84 24-772-1500

Federal Aviation Administration (Resident in Singapore) [Vietnam]
American Embassy - Singapore, 27 Napier Street, Singapore, 258508, Singapore
Mail: American Embassy - Singapore, PSC 470 FAA IAO,
FPO, AP 96534-0001
Tel: 65 6543-1466 Fax: 65 6543-1952

FAA Representative **James "Jim" Spillane** 65 6543-1466
E-mail: james.spillane@faa.gov

★ Presidential Appointment Requiring Senate Confirmation ☆ Presidential Appointment □ Schedule C Appointment ◇ Career Senior Foreign Service Appointment
● Career Senior Executive Service (SES) Appointment ○ Non-Career Senior Executive Service (SES) Appointment ■ Postal Career Executive Service

Defense POW/MIA Accounting Agency, Task Element Vietnam
53 Tran Phu, Ba Dinh District, Hanoi, Vietnam
Mail: PSC 461, Box 100, FPO, AP 96521-0002
Tel: 84 24-734-3929 Fax: 84 24-734-3930

Defense POW/MIA Accounting Agency Officer
(Vacant) 84 24-734-3929

Office of the Defense Attaché [Vietnam]
American Embassy - Hanoi, Vietnam, 7 Lang Ha Street, Ba Dinh District, Hanoi, Vietnam
Mail: PSC 461, Box 400, FPO, AP 96521-0002
Tel: 84 24-772-1500 Fax: 84 24-831-3239

Defense Attaché **Tuan Ton** 84 24-772-1500

Agency for International Development [Vietnam]
Tung Shing Square Building, USAID/Vietnam Program Office, 2 Ngo Quyen Street, 15th Floor, Hanoi, Vietnam
Mail: PSC 461, Box 400, FPO, AP 96521-0002
Tel: 84 (4) 3935-1260 Fax: 84 (4) 3935-1265
Internet: www.usaid.gov/vietnam E-mail: usaidvietnam@usaid.gov

◇ Mission Director **Michael J. Greene** 84 (4) 935-1260
E-mail: mgreene@usaid.gov

Ho Chi Minh City Consulate General
U.S. Consulate General - Ho Chi Minh City, Vietnam, 4 Le Duan Boulevard, District 1, Ho Chi Minh City, Vietnam
Mail: U.S. Consulate General–Ho Chi Minh City, PSC 461, Box 500, FPO, AP 96521-0002
Tel: 84 28-3520-4200 Fax: 84 28-3520-4244

◇ Consul General **Mary E. Tarnowka** 84 28-3520-4200
E-mail: tarnowkame@state.gov
Office Management Specialist to the Consul General **Elaine M. Benedict** 84 28-3520-4200
E-mail: benedictem@state.gov
Deputy Principal Officer **Timothy "Tim" Liston** 84 28-3520-4200
◇ Countrywide Consular Coordinator
Hale Colburn VanKoughnett 84 28-3520-4200
E-mail: vankoughnetthc@state.gov
Consular Section Chief
Gregory Jon "Greg" Adamson 84 28-3520-4200
E-mail: adamsongj@state.gov
Community Liaison Officer **Helena Mae Saele** 84 28-3520-4200
Economic Officer **Emily Fleckner** 84 28-3520-4200
General Services Officer **Shanthini Watson** 84 28-3520-4200
Information Programs Officer
Samuel "Sam" Axelrod 84 28-3520-4200
Management Officer **Anne Baker** 84 28-3520-4200
Education: Georgetown 1994 BA
Political Officer **Justin Brown** 84 28-3520-4200
Saigon Center Building, 65 Le Loi Boulevard, 9th Floor, Ho Chi Minh City, Vietnam
Public Affairs Officer **Matthew Ference** 84 28-3520-4200
Regional Security Officer **Aria Lu** 84 28-3520-4200

Agricultural Section (Foreign Agricultural Service) [Vietnam]
Office of Agricultural Affairs, US Consulate General - Ho Chi Minh City, 7160 Ho Chi Minh Place, Dulles, VA 20189-7160
Tel: 84 28-3520-4630 Fax: 84 28-3520-4636
E-mail: atohochiminh@fas.usda.gov

Senior Attaché **Gerald Smith** 84 28-3520-4630
E-mail: Gerald.Smith@fas.usda.gov

Commercial Section (Foreign Commercial Service) [Vietnam]
U.S. Consulate General - Ho Chi Minh City, Vietnam, Saigon Center 9F, Le Loi Boulevard, District 1, Ho Chi Minh City, Vietnam
Mail: U.S. Commercial Service, PSC 461, Box 500, FPO, AP 96251
Fax: 84 28-3520-4681

Principal Commercial Officer
Douglas N. "Doug" Jacobson 84 28-3520-4680
E-mail: doug.jacobson@trade.gov
Education: Texas 1983 BA; Washington U (MO) 1987 DMD; Washington College of Law 1990 JD

Commercial Section (Foreign Commercial Service) [Vietnam] *(continued)*

Commercial Officer **Joshua Leibowitz** 84 28-3520-4680
E-mail: joshua.leibowitz@trade.gov

U.S. Mission to the Association of Southeast Asian Nations (USASEAN)
Jl. Medan Merdeka Selatan 5, 10110 Jakarta, Indonesia
Tel: 62 (21) 3435-9000 Fax: 62 (21) 385-7189
Internet: asean.usmission.gov E-mail: usasean@state.gov

★ Ambassador **(Vacant)** 62 (21) 3435-9000
Chargé d'Affaires
Ambassador Piper Anne Wind Campbell 62 (21) 3435-9000
E-mail: campbellp@state.gov
Education: Georgetown 1988 BSFS; Harvard 1999 MPA
Office Management Specialist to the Chargé d'Affaires **Sonia Vinson** 62 (21) 3435-9000
E-mail: vinsonsa@state.gov
Deputy U.S. Representative **Jane Ellen Bocklage** 62 (21) 3435-9000
E-mail: bocklageje@state.gov
Economic Officer **(Vacant)** 62 (21) 3435-9000
Political Officer **Jacob Chriqui** 62 (21) 3435-9000
E-mail: chriquij@state.gov
Education: Rollins BA; Middlebury MA
Political/Economic Officer **Dec Ly** 62 (21) 3435-9000
Public Affairs Officer **Brian K. Ferinden** 62 (21) 3435-9000
E-mail: ferindenb@state.gov
Education: Florida 1988 BA; Rutgers 1995 MFA
◇ Regional Senior Commercial Officer
Margaret A. "Maggie" Hanson-Muse 65 6476-9037
E-mail: margaret.hanson-muse@trade.gov
Education: Brandeis 1978 BA; Columbia 1983 MBA
Director, US-ASEAN Connect **Peter D. Thorin** 62 (21) 3435-9000
E-mail: thorinpd@state.gov
Education: U Washington 1989 BA, 1993 MPA

EUROPE AND EURASIA

U.S. Embassy in Albania
American Embassy - Tirana, Albania, 103 Tirana Rruga Elbasanit, Tirana, Albania
Tel: 355 (4) 2247-285 Fax: 355 (4) 2232-222

Office of the U.S. Ambassador to Albania
American Embassy - Tirana, Albania, 103 Tirana Rruga Elbasanit, Tirana, Albania
Mail: Department of State, 9510 Tirana Place, Dulles, VA 20189

★ Ambassador-Designate
Kathleen A. "Kathy" Kavalec 355 (4) 2247-285
E-mail: kavalecka@state.gov
Education: UC Berkeley 1982 AB; Georgetown 1984 MSFS
Chargé d'Affaires **Leyla L. Moses-Ones** 355 (4) 2247-285
E-mail: onesll@state.gov
Education: Georgetown
Office Management Specialist to the Ambassador
(Vacant) 355 (4) 2247-285
Deputy Chief of Mission **Leyla L. Moses-Ones** 355 (4) 2247-285
E-mail: onesll@state.gov
Education: Georgetown
Office Management Specialist to the Deputy Chief of Mission
Martha Hood .... 355 (4) 2247-285 ext. 1220
Consular Affairs Officer **Daniel D. Koski** 355 (4) 2247-285
E-mail: koskidd@state.gov
Community Liaison Officer **Rachel Cormier** 355 (4) 2247-285
Economic Officer **Jeffrey "Jeff" Bowan** 355 (4) 2247-285
E-mail: bowanjd@state.gov
Facilities Management Officer **Sonequa Braddy** 355 (4) 2247-285
Financial Management Officer **Jason Beck** 355 (4) 2247-285
General Services Officer **Sally B. Lewis** 355 (4) 2247-285

(continued on next page)

DEPARTMENTS

★ Presidential Appointment Requiring Senate Confirmation ☆ Presidential Appointment ☐ Schedule C Appointment ◇ Career Senior Foreign Service Appointment
● Career Senior Executive Service (SES) Appointment ○ Non-Career Senior Executive Service (SES) Appointment ■ Postal Career Executive Service

DEPARTMENTS

Office of the U.S. Ambassador to Albania *(continued)*

Information Management Officer **Justan E. Neels** 355 (4) 2247-285
E-mail: neelsje@state.gov
Education: Southern Illinois 2004 BS; South Florida 2015 PhD; Florida Tech 2007 MS

Information Program Officer **Justan E. Neels** 355 (4) 2247-285
E-mail: neelsje@state.gov
Education: Southern Illinois 2004 BS; South Florida 2015 PhD; Florida Tech 2007 MS

Information Systems Officer **Justan E. Neels** 355 (4) 2247-285
E-mail: neelsje@state.gov
Education: Southern Illinois 2004 BS; South Florida 2015 PhD; Florida Tech 2007 MS

Information Systems Security Officer **Justan E. Neels** 355 (4) 2247-285
E-mail: neelsje@state.gov
Education: Southern Illinois 2004 BS; South Florida 2015 PhD; Florida Tech 2007 MS

Management Officer **Lori A. Johnson** 355 (4) 2247-285

Political/Economic Officer **(Vacant)** 355 (4) 2247-285

Political Officer **Carson Relitz Rocker** 355 (4) 2247-285
E-mail: relitzrockerc@state.gov

Public Affairs Officer **Brian P. Beckmann** 355 (4) 2247-285
E-mail: pastirana@state.gov
E-mail: beckmannbp@state.gov
Education: Gustavus Adolphus 2004 BA; George Washington 2007 MPP

Regional Security Officer **Janet Meyer** 355 (4) 2247-285
Education: Texas A&M 1997 BA

Agency for International Development [Albania]
American Embassy - Tirana, Albania, Tirana Rruga Elbasanit 103, Tirana, Albania
Mail: Department of State, 9510 Tirana Place, Washington, DC 20521-9510
Tel: 355 (4) 2247-285 Fax: 355 (4) 223-3520
E-mail: tirana-webcontact@usaid.gov Internet: www.usaid.gov/albania

Country Representative **Mikaela Meredith** ... 355 (4) 2247-285 ext. 3232
E-mail: mmeredith@usaid.gov
Education: Union Col (NY) 1986; Columbia 1988 MA

Agricultural Section (Foreign Agricultural Service) (Resident in Rome) [Albania]
American Embassy - Rome, Italy, Via Veneto 119/A, 00187 Rome, Italy
Mail: American Embassy - Rome, Italy, Unit 9500, Box 13, FPO, AE 09624-0013
Tel: 39 (06) 4674-2396 Fax: 39 (06) 4788-7008

Agricultural Officer **Frederick H. "Fred" Giles** 39 (06) 4674-2396
E-mail: frederick.giles@fas.usda.gov

Federal Aviation Administration (Resident in Moscow) [Albania]
Eight Bolshoy Devyatinsky Pereulok, 121099 Moscow, Russia
Mail: American Embassy, PSC 77, APO, AE 09721
Fax: 7 (495) 728-5350

FAA Senior Representative **Andrew McKee** 7 (495) 728-5125

Office of the Defense Attaché [Albania]
American Embassy - Tirana, Tirana Rruga Elbasanit 103, Tirana, Albania
Mail: Department of State, 9510 Tirana Place, Washington, DC 20521-9510
Tel: 355 (4) 2247-285 Fax: 355 (4) 2232-222

Defense Attaché **CDR James Hilton USN** 355 (4) 2247-285

Office of Defense Cooperation [Albania]
American Embassy - Tirana, Tirana Rruga Elbasanit 103, Tirana, Albania
Mail: Department of State, 9510 Tirana Place, Washington, DC 20521-9510
Tel: 355 (4) 2247-285 Fax: 355 (4) 2232-222

ODC Attaché **(Vacant)** 355 (4) 2247-285

Peace Corps [Albania]
E-mail: information@al.peacecorps.gov

Country Director **Kate Becker** 355 (4) 2365033

U.S. Embassy in Armenia
American Embassy - Yerevan, Armenia, One American Avenue, 375082 Yerevan, Armenia
Tel: 374 (10) 46-47-00 Fax: 374 (10) 46-47-42

Office of the U.S. Ambassador to Armenia
American Embassy - Yerevan, Armenia, One American Avenue, 375082 Yerevan, Armenia
Mail: Department of State, 7020 Yerevan Place, Washington, DC 20521-7020

★ Ambassador **(Vacant)** 374 (10) 46-47-00

◇ Chargé d'Affaires **Rafik K. Mansour** 374 (10) 46-47-00
E-mail: mansourrk@state.gov
Education: UC Irvine BA, BS; National War Col MNSSS
Office Management Specialist to the Ambassador **Tiffany Byrd** 374 (10) 46-47-00

◇ Deputy Chief of Mission **Rafik K. Mansour** 374 (10) 46-47-00
E-mail: mansourrk@state.gov
Education: UC Irvine BA, BS; National War Col MNSSS
Office Management Specialist to the Deputy Chief of Mission **Graciela L. "Grace" Tift** 374 (10) 46-47-00
E-mail: tiftgl@state.gov

Consular Section Officer **Erin Eussen** 374 (10) 46-47-00
E-mail: eussenek@state.gov

Community Liaison Officer **Nancy Harper** 374 (10) 46-47-00

Economic Officer **Raphael Sambou** 374 (10) 46-47-00
E-mail: sambour@state.gov

Financial Management Officer **Magdalena Galus** 374 (10) 46-47-00
E-mail: galusma@state.gov

General Services Officer **Dana Al-Ebrahim** 374 (10) 46-47-00

Information Management Officer **Steven "Steve" Labocki** 374 (10) 46-47-00

Information Programs Officer **Brian E. Wilson** 374 (10) 46-47-00

Information Systems Officer **Terrence Andrews** 374 (10) 46-47-00

Information Systems Security Officer **Steven "Steve" Labocki** 374 (10) 46-47-00

Management Officer **Andres Valdes** 374 (10) 46-47-00

Narcotics Affairs Section Officer **Shannon D. Behaj** 374 (10) 46-47-00

Political/Economic Officer **Matthew "Matt" Eussen** 374 (10) 46-47-00
E-mail: eussenm@state.gov

Public Affairs Officer **Robert Anderson** 374 (10) 49-46-91
E-mail: YerevanUSPress@state.gov

Regional Security Officer **Amanda Philpot** 374 (10) 46-47-00

Legal Attaché **(Vacant)** 374 (10) 46-47-00

Agency for International Development [Armenia]
American Embassy - Yerevan, Armenia, One American Avenue, 375082 Yerevan, Armenia
Mail: Department of State, 7020 Yerevan Place, Washington, DC 20521-7020
Tel: 374 (10) 46-47-00 Fax: 374 (10) 46-47-28
Internet: www.usaid.gov/armenia

◇ Mission Director **Deborah Lynn Grieser** 374 (10) 46-47-00
E-mail: dgrieser@usaid.gov

Agricultural Section (Foreign Agricultural Service) (Resident in Moscow) [Armenia]

Agricultural Officer **Deanna Ayala** 7 (495) 728-5222
E-mail: deanna.ayala@fas.usda.gov

Federal Aviation Administration (Resident in Moscow) [Armenia]
Eight Bolshoy Devyatinsky Pereulok, 121099 Moscow, Russia
Mail: American Embassy, PSC 77, APO, AE 09721
Fax: 7 (495) 728-5350

FAA Senior Representative **Andrew McKee** 7 (495) 728-5125

★ Presidential Appointment Requiring Senate Confirmation ☆ Presidential Appointment ☐ Schedule C Appointment ◇ Career Senior Foreign Service Appointment
● Career Senior Executive Service (SES) Appointment ○ Non-Career Senior Executive Service (SES) Appointment ■ Postal Career Executive Service

Office of the Defense Attaché [Armenia]
American Embassy - Yerevan, Armenia,
One American Avenue, 375082 Yerevan, Armenia
Mail: USDAO Yerevan, American Embassy - Yerevan,
7020 Yerevan Place, Washington, DC 20521-7020
Tel: 374 (10) 52-46-61 ext. 4621 Fax: 374 (10) 151-550
Defense Attaché **COL Bruce A. Murphy USA** 374 (10) 54-21-32

Office of Defense Cooperation [Armenia]
American Embassy - Yerevan, Armenia,
One American Avenue, 375082 Yerevan, Armenia
Tel: 374 (10) 46-47-00 Fax: 374 (10) 46-47-42
Chief **(Vacant)** 374 (10) 46-47-00

Peace Corps [Armenia]
Peace Corps, Charentsi Street 33, Yerevan, Armenia
Mail: Department of State, 7020 Yerevan Place,
Washington, DC 20521-7020
Tel: 374 (10) 513-500 Fax: 374 (10) 55-79-91
E-mail: pcarmenia@peacecorps.gov
Internet: www.peacecorps.gov/armenia
Country Director **(Vacant)** .... 374 (10) 52-44-50 ext. 102

U.S. Embassy in Austria

American Embassy - Vienna, Austria, Boltzmanngasse 16,
A-1090 Vienna, Austria
Tel: 43 (1) 31339-0 Fax: 43 (1) 310-06-82
E-mail: viennausembassy@state.gov

Office of the U.S. Ambassador to Austria

American Embassy - Vienna, Austria, Boltzmanngasse 16,
A-1090 Vienna, Austria

★ Ambassador **Ambassador Trevor D. Traina** 43 (1) 31339-0
Education: Princeton BA; Haas 1996 MBA
Office Management Specialist to the Ambassador **Patricia A. "Tricia" Wingerter** .... 43 (1) 31339-0 ext. 2414
E-mail: WingerterTA@state.gov
Deputy Chief of Mission **Robin L. Dunnigan** 43 (1) 31339-0
E-mail: dunniganrl@state.gov
Office Management Specialist to the Deputy Chief of Mission **Christine Melendez-Beck** 43 (1) 31339-0
Consul General **Gregory A. "Greg" Floyd** 43 (1) 31339-0
E-mail: floydga@state.gov Fax: 43 (1) 512-5835
Education: UC Santa Barbara 1991 BS; Hastings 1991 JD
Community Liaison Officer **(Vacant)** 43 (1) 31339-0
Economic Officer **John Speaks** 43 (1) 31339-0
Facilities Management Officer **James Horner** 43 (1) 31339-0
Financial Management Officer **Cynthia Rafferty** 43 (1) 31339-0
Education: Delaware 1998 BS; Rutgers (Camden) 2005 MBA
General Services Officer **Mikael McCowan** 43 (1) 31339-0
Human Resources Officer **Thomas W. Komons** 43 (1) 31339-0
Information Management Officer **Mark A. Wilson** 43 (1) 31339-0
Information Programs Officer **Arthur Saunders** 43 (1) 31339-0
Information Systems Officer **Samuel S. Berardi** 43 (1) 31339-0
Information Systems Security Officer **Josef J. Schmidt** 43 (1) 31339-0
E-mail: schmidtjj@state.gov
Legal Attaché **Theodore Callimanis** 43 (1) 31339-0
E-mail: callimanist@state.gov
E-mail: callimanist@state.gov
◇ Management Officer **Erica A. Renew** 43 (1) 31339-0
E-mail: renewea@state.gov Fax: 43 (1) 31339-2510
Political Officer **Elisabeth Rosenstock-Siller** 43 (1) 31339-0
◇ Political/Economic Officer **Stephen A. "Steve" Hubler** 43 (1) 31339-0
E-mail: hublersa@state.gov
Public Affairs Officer **Daniel S. Mattern** 43 (1) 31339-0
Fax: 43 (1) 313-39-2057
Regional Security Officer **David Lyons** 43 (1) 31339-0

Agricultural Section (Foreign Agricultural Service) [Austria]
American Embassy - Vienna, Austria, Boltzmanngasse 16,
A-1090 Vienna, Austria
E-mail: agvienna@fas.usda.gov
Agricultural Officer (Resident in Berlin) **Kelly Stange** 49 (30) 8305-1150
E-mail: kelly.stange@fas.usda.gov

Animal and Plant Health Inspection Service [Austria]
American Embassy - Vienna, Austria, Boltzmanngasse 16,
A-1091 Vienna, Austria
Mail: American Embassy - Vienna, Austria,
Department of State, Washington, DC 20521-9900
Tel: 43 (1) 31339-2950 Fax: 43 (1) 31339-3287
APHIS Officer **(Vacant)** 43 (1) 31339-2951

Commercial Section (Foreign Commercial Service) [Austria]
American Embassy - Vienna, Austria, Boltzmanngasse 16,
A-1091 Vienna, Austria
Mail: American Embassy - Vienna, Austria,
Department of State, Washington, DC 20521-9900
Tel: 43 (1) 31339-2297 Fax: 43 (1) 310-69-17
E-mail: office.vienna@trade.gov Internet: www.export.gov/austria
Commercial Officer **Julia Rauner Guerrero** 43 (1) 31339-2296
E-mail: julia.rauner@trade.gov
Education: Santa Clara U 1986 BA; American U 1988 MA

Department of Homeland Security - U.S. Immigration and Customs Enforcement [Austria]
American Embassy - Vienna, Austria, Boltzmanngasse 16,
A-1091 Vienna, Austria
Mail: American Embassy - Vienna, Austria,
Department of State, Washington, DC 20521-9900
Tel: 43 (1) 31339-2111 Fax: 43 (1) 313-39-2430
Customs Officer **Sarah Bay** 43 (1) 31339-2111

Drug Enforcement Administration [Austria]
Gartenbaupromenade 2, 24th Floor, A-1010 Vienna, Austria
Mail: American Embassy - Vienna, Austria,
Department of State, Washington, DC 20521-9900
Tel: 43 (1) 31339-7551 Fax: 43 (1) 513-82-87
DEA Officer **(Vacant)** 43 (1) 31339-7548

Federal Aviation Administration (Resident in Paris) [Austria]
American Embassy/FAA, AEU-PAR, 2, Avenue Gabriel, 75382 Paris, Cedex 08, France
Mail: American Embassy/FAA, PSC 116, Box A-215, APO, AE 09777
Tel: 33 (1) 43 12 22 25 Fax: 33 (1) 43 12 25 05
FAA Senior Representative **Ian H. Ross** 33 (1) 43 12 22 25

Office of the Defense Attaché [Austria]
American Embassy - Vienna, Austria, Boltzmanngasse 16,
A-1091 Vienna, Austria
Mail: American Embassy - Vienna, Austria,
Department of State, Washington, DC 20521-9900
Tel: 43 (1) 31339-0 Fax: 43 (1) 310-69-18
Defense Attaché **COL David Knych USA** 43 (1) 31339-2277
Office of Defense Cooperation Chief **LTC Marek Stobbe USA** 43 (1) 31339-2277

DEPARTMENTS

★ Presidential Appointment Requiring Senate Confirmation ☆ Presidential Appointment ☐ Schedule C Appointment ◇ Career Senior Foreign Service Appointment
● Career Senior Executive Service (SES) Appointment ○ Non-Career Senior Executive Service (SES) Appointment ■ Postal Career Executive Service

DEPARTMENTS

U.S. Embassy in Azerbaijan

American Embassy - Baku, Azerbaijan,
111 Azadlig avenue, AZ 1007 Baku, Azerbaijan
Tel: 994 (12) 488-3300 Fax: 994 (12) 488-3300

Office of the U.S. Ambassador to Azerbaijan

American Embassy - Baku, Azerbaijan,
111 Azadlig avenue, AZ 1007 Baku, Azerbaijan
Mail: American Embassy - Baku, Azerbaijan,
7050 Baku Place, Washington, DC 20521-7050

★ Ambassador-Designate
Earle D. "Lee" Litzenberger 994 (12) 488-3300
E-mail: litzenbergered@state.gov
Education: Middlebury 1979 BA; Army War Col 2006 MS
◇ Chargé d'Affaires **William Robert "Will" Gill, Jr.** 994 (12) 488-3300
E-mail: gillwr@state.gov
Office Management Specialist to the Ambassador
Laurie L. Bateman 994 (12) 488-3300
E-mail: batemanll@state.gov
◇ Deputy Chief of Mission
William Robert "Will" Gill, Jr. 994 (12) 488-3300
E-mail: gillwr@state.gov
Office Management Specialist to the Deputy Chief of Mission **Kevan Tavakoli** 994 (12) 488-3300
Consular Section Chief **Jeremy Little** 994 (12) 488-3300
E-mail: consularbaku@state.gov
Community Liaison Officer **(Vacant)** 994 (12) 488-3300
Economic Officer **Carter W. Wilbur** 994 (12) 488-3300
E-mail: wilburcw@state.gov
Financial Management Officer **Chris Green** 994 (12) 488-3300
General Services Officer **Lucy Reyno** 994 (12) 488-3300
Information Management Officer
Harry S. Johnson 994 (12) 488-3300
Information Program Officer **Greg Dustman** 994 (12) 488-3300
Information Systems Officer **Yan Li** 994 (12) 488-3300
Legal Attaché **(Vacant)** 994 (12) 488-3300
Management Officer **Jonathan R. Bayat** 994 (12) 488-3300
E-mail: bayatj@state.gov
Political Officer **Bridgette L. Walker** 994 (12) 488-3300
Public Affairs Officer **Heidi E. Smith** 994 (12) 488-3300
Cultural Affairs Officer **Amy Petersen** 994 (12) 488-3300
Information Officer **Ray Nayler** 994 (12) 488-3300
Regional Security Officer **Scott Kimpton** 994 (12) 488-3300

Agency for International Development [Azerbaijan]

The Landmark Building, 96 Nizami Street, AZ1010 Baku, Azerbaijan
Tel: 994 (12) 498-1835 Internet: www.usaid.gov/azerbaijan

Mission Director **Jaidev Singh** 994 (12) 498-1835
E-mail: jsingh@usaid.gov
Education: Panjab U (India) 1990 MBA; Kentucky 1992 MA; U Washington 2001 PhD

Agricultural Section (Foreign Agricultural Service) (Resident in Ankara) [Azerbaijan]

American Embassy - Ankara, Turkey, 110 Ataturk Boulevard, Ankara, Turkey
Mail: American Embassy - Ankara, Turkey, PSC 93, Box 5000, APO, AE 09823
Tel: 90 (312) 468-6129 Fax: 90 (312) 467-0056

Agricultural Officer **Christine Strossman** 90 (312) 468-6129
E-mail: christine.strossman@fas.usda.gov

Drug Enforcement Administration (Resident in Ankara) [Azerbaijan]

American Embassy - Ankara, Turkey, 110 Ataturk Boulevard, Ankara, Turkey
Mail: American Embassy - Ankara, Turkey, PSC 93, Box 5000, APO, AE 09823
Tel: 90 (312) 455-5555

DEA Officer **(Vacant)** 90 (312) 455-5555

Federal Aviation Administration (Resident in Moscow) [Azerbaijan]

Eight Bolshoy Devyatinsky Pereulok, 121099 Moscow, Russia
Mail: American Embassy, PSC 77, APO, AE 09721
Fax: 7 (495) 728-5350

FAA Senior Representative **Andrew McKee** 7 (495) 728-5125

Office of the Defense Attaché [Azerbaijan]

American Embassy - Baku, Azerbaijan,
Azadlig Prospekti 83, AZ 10007 Baku, Azerbaijan
Mail: American Embassy - Baku, Azerbaijan,
7050 Baku Place, Washington, DC 20521-7050

Defense Attaché **Col Adam Kavlick USAF** 994 (12) 488-3300

U.S. Embassy in Belarus

American Embassy - Minsk, Belarus, 46 Starovilenskaya Street, Minsk, 220002, Belarus
Tel: 375 (172) 10-12-83 Fax: 375 (172) 34-78-53
E-mail: usembassyminsk@state.gov

Office of the U.S. Ambassador to Belarus

American Embassy - Minsk, Belarus, 46 Starovilenskaya Street, Minsk, 220002, Belarus
Mail: American Embassy - Minsk, Belarus,
Department of State, Washington, DC 20521-7010

★ Ambassador **(Vacant)** 375 (172) 10-1283
Chargé d'Affaires **Jenifer H. Moore** 375 (172) 10-1283
E-mail: moorejh@state.gov
Education: Georgia Tech BS, MS, MPP
Office Management Specialist to the Ambassador
(Vacant) 375 (172) 10-1283
Deputy Chief of Mission **Jenifer H. Moore** 375 (172) 10-1283
E-mail: moorejh@state.gov
Education: Georgia Tech BS, MS, MPP
Office Management Specialist to the Deputy Chief of Mission **(Vacant)** 375 (172) 10-1283
Community Liaison Officer **Jessica W. Drollette** 375 (172) 10-12-83
E-mail: drollettejw@state.gov
Consul **Aleta Kovensky** 375 (172) 10-1283
E-mail: kovenskya@state.gov
Financial Management Officer
John T. "Jack" Hardman 375 (172) 10-1283
E-mail: hardmanjt@state.gov
General Services Officer
James "Jimmy" Landherr 375 (172) 10-1283
E-mail: LandherrJE@state.gov
Information Management Officer
Jonathan A. Reed 375 (172) 10-12-83
Information Program Officer **(Vacant)** 375 (172) 10-12-83
Management Officer **John T. "Jack" Hardman** 375 (172) 10-1283
E-mail: hardmanjt@state.gov
Political/Economic Officer **P. Christopher McCabe** ... 375 (172) 10-1283
Economic Officer **Peter Sloan** 375 (172) 10-1283
Public Affairs Officer **Elisabeth "Betsy" Lewis** 375 (172) 17-04-81
Fax: 375 (172) 11-03-84
Regional Security Officer (Resident in Lithuania)
Andres Barcenas 370 (5) 266-5621
E-mail: barcenasaa@state.gov

Agency for International Development [Belarus]

American Embassy - Minsk, 46 Starovilenskaya Street, Minsk, 220002, Belarus
Mail: American Embassy - Minsk, Belarus,
Department of State, Washington, DC 20521-7010
Tel: 375 (172) 10-1283 Fax: 375 (172) 11-3032
Internet: www.usaid.gov/belarus

Country Director **Victoria Mitchell Avdiu** 375 (172) 10-1283
E-mail: vmitchellavdiu@usaid.gov

★ Presidential Appointment Requiring Senate Confirmation ☆ Presidential Appointment □ Schedule C Appointment ◇ Career Senior Foreign Service Appointment
● Career Senior Executive Service (SES) Appointment ○ Non-Career Senior Executive Service (SES) Appointment ■ Postal Career Executive Service

Agricultural Section (Foreign Agricultural Service) (Resident in Moscow) [Belarus]
American Embassy - Moscow, Russia, Novinskiy Bul'var 19/23, Moscow, Russia
Mail: American Embassy - Moscow, Russia, APO, AE 09721
Tel: 7 (495) 728-5222 Fax: 7 (495) 728-5133
E-mail: agmoscow@fas.usda.gov

Agricultural Officer **Deanna Ayala** 7 (495) 728-5222
E-mail: deanna.ayala@fas.usda.gov

Drug Enforcement Administration (Resident in Vienna) [Belarus]
Gartenbaupromenade 2, 24th Floor, A-1010 Vienna, Austria
Mail: American Embassy - Vienna, Austria,
Department of State, Washington, DC 20521-9900

DEA Officer **(Vacant)** 43 (1) 31339-7548

Federal Aviation Administration (Resident in Moscow) [Belarus]
American Embassy, Eight Bolshoy Devyatinsky Pereulok,
121099 Moscow, Russia
Mail: American Embassy, PSC 77 FAA, APO, AE 09721
Fax: 7 (495) 728-5350

FAA Senior Representative **Andrew McKee** 7 (495) 728-5125

Office of the Defense Attaché (Resident in Kiev) [Belarus]
10 Yuria Kotsubynskoho, 01901 Kiev, Ukraine

Defense Attaché
Col Thomas Quinn "Quinn" Wofford USAF 380 (44) 521-5000

Office of the Legal Attaché (Resident in Kiev) [Belarus]
American Embassy - Kiev, Ukraine, 10 Yuria Kotsubynskoho, 01901 Kiev, Ukraine
Mail: American Embassy - Kiev, Ukraine,
5850 Kiev Place, Washington, DC 20521-5850

Legal Attaché **Laura Kriegbaum** 380 (44) 521-5000

U.S. Embassy in Belgium

American Embassy - Brussels, Belgium,
27 Boulevard du Regent, B-10 Brussels, Belgium
Tel: 32 (2) 811-4000 Fax: 32 (2) 811-4500

Office of the U.S. Ambassador to Belgium

American Embassy - Brussels, Belgium,
27 Boulevard du Regent, B-1000 Brussels, Belgium
Mail: American Embassy - Brussels, Belgium, PSC 82, Box 133,
DPO, AE 09710

★ Ambassador **Ambassador Ronald J. "Ron" Gidwitz** 32 (2) 811-4000
Education: Brown U 1967 BA
Office Management Specialist to the Ambassador
Susan K. Christy 32 (2) 508-2444
E-mail: christysk@state.gov Fax: 32 (2) 508-2160

◇ Deputy Chief of Mission
Matthew Robert "Matt" Lussenhop 32 (2) 508-2446
E-mail: lussenhopm@state.gov
Office Management Specialist to the Deputy Chief of Mission **Laura Query** 32 (2) 508-2446

Consul General **(Vacant)** 32 (2) 508-2382

Consular Officer **Joshua Fischel** 32 (2) 508-2382
E-mail: fischelj@state.gov

Community Liaison Officer **Tracy Scully** 32 (2) 508-2111
E-mail: scullyta@state.gov

Facilities Management Officer **Keith Reling** 32 (2) 811-4000

Financial Management Officer **David H. Howard** 32 (2) 508-2111
E-mail: howarddh@state.gov

General Services Officer
Gregory A. "Greg" MacDonald 32 (2) 508-2111
E-mail: macdonaldga@state.gov

Human Resources Officer **Anthony Blenke** 32 (2) 811-4000
E-mail: blenkea@state.gov

Information Management Officer
Leonardo "Leo" Oporto 32 (2) 508-2200
E-mail: oportolg@state.gov

Information Program Officer **(Vacant)** 32 (2) 508-2111

Office of the U.S. Ambassador to Belgium *(continued)*

Information Systems Officer **Kurtis Potts** 32 (2) 508-2111
E-mail: pottsk@state.gov

Information Systems Security Officer **Brian Boyer** 32 (2) 508-2111

Legal Attache **Gibson M. Wilson** 32 (2) 508-2408

◇ Management Officer **Michael C. Mullins** 32 (2) 508-2350
E-mail: mullinsmc@state.gov
Education: Amherst BA; Brown U MA

Political/Economic Counselor
Joseph F. "Joe" Trimble 32 (2) 508-2448
E-mail: trimblejf@state.gov Fax: 32 (2) 513-5333
Education: Texas A&M 1992 BA

Public Affairs Officer **Carla Ann Benini** 32 (2) 508-2408
E-mail: beninica@state.gov Fax: 32 (2) 513-4278

Regional Security Officer **Daniel J. "Dan" Weber** 32 (2) 508-2370
American Embassy - Paris, 2 Avenue Gabriel, 75382 Paris, Cedex 08, France
E-mail: weberdj@state.gov

Agricultural Section (Foreign Agricultural Service) [Belgium]
American Embassy - Brussels, Belgium,
27 Boulevard du Regent, B-1000 Brussels, Belgium
E-mail: aguseubrussels@fas.usda.gov

◇ Agricultural Counselor **Bruce J. Zanin** 32 (2) 811-4000
E-mail: bruce.zanin@fas.usda.gov

Commercial Section (Foreign Commercial Service) [Belgium]
U.S. Embassy - Commercial Section, 27 Boulevard du Regent,
BE-1000 Brussels, Belgium
Mail: American Embassy - Brussels, Belgium, PSC 82, Box 002,
DPO, AE 09710
Tel: 32 (2) 811 4600 Fax: 32 (2) 512-3644
E-mail: office.brussels@trade.gov Internet: http://export.gov/belgium/

◇ Senior Commercial Officer
Mitchell Gregory "Mitch" Larsen 32 (2) 811 5269
E-mail: mitch.larsen@trade.gov

Department of Homeland Security - Transportation Security Administration [Belgium]
American Embassy - Brussels, Belgium,
27 Boulevard du Regent, B-1000 Brussels, Belgium
Tel: 32 (2) 508-2708 Fax: 32 (2) 230-0642

TSA Representative **David Gordner** 32 (2) 508-2708

Drug Enforcement Administration [Belgium]
American Embassy - Brussels, Belgium,
27 Boulevard du Regent, B-1000 Brussels, Belgium
Mail: American Embassy - Brussels, Belgium, PSC 82, Box 107,
APO, AE 09710
Tel: 32 (2) 508-2420 Fax: 32 (2) 511-2725

DEA Officer **Scott Andrew Albrecht** 32 (2) 508-2420
E-mail: albrechtsa@state.gov

Federal Aviation Administration [Belgium]
American Embassy/FAA, AEU-BRU, 27 Boulevard du Regent,
B-1000 Brussels, Belgium
Mail: American Embassy/FAA, PSC 82, Box 106,
AEU-BRU, APO, AE 09710
Tel: 32 (2) 508-2700 Fax: 32 (2) 230-2597

FAA Senior Representative, Brussels
Maria DiPasquantonio 32 (2) 811-4038

Office of the Defense Attaché [Belgium]
American Embassy - Brussels, Belgium,
27 Boulevard du Regent, B-1000 Brussels, Belgium
Mail: American Embassy - Brussels, Belgium, PSC 82, Box 112,
APO, AE 09710
Tel: 32 (2) 508-2505 Fax: 32 (2) 508-2153

Defense Attaché **COL Peter J. Scammell USA** 32 (2) 508-2505
E-mail: scammellpj@state.gov

★ Presidential Appointment Requiring Senate Confirmation ☆ Presidential Appointment ☐ Schedule C Appointment ◇ Career Senior Foreign Service Appointment
● Career Senior Executive Service (SES) Appointment ○ Non-Career Senior Executive Service (SES) Appointment ■ Postal Career Executive Service

Office of Defense Cooperation [Belgium]
American Embassy - Brussels, Belgium,
27 Boulevard du Regent, B-1000 Brussels, Belgium
Mail: American Embassy - Brussels, Belgium, PSC 82, Box 139, APO, AE 09710
Tel: 32 (2) 508-2650 Fax: 32 (2) 514-5666

Defense Cooperation Officer **Kenneth "Ken" Gjone** 32 (2) 508-2650
E-mail: gjonekd@state.gov

U.S. Embassy in Bosnia and Herzegovina

American Embassy - Sarajevo, Bosnia-Herzegovina,
1 Robert C. Frasure Street, 71000 Sarajevo, Bosnia and Herzegovina
Tel: 387 (33) 704-000 Fax: 387 (33) 659-722

Office of the U.S. Ambassador to Bosnia-Herzegovina

American Embassy - Sarajevo, Bosnia-Herzegovina,
1 Robert C. Frasure Street, 71000 Sarajevo, Bosnia and Herzegovina
Mail: American Embassy - Sarajevo, 7130 Sarajevo Place, Department of State, Washington, DC 20521-7130

★ Ambassador
Ambassador Maureen Elizabeth Cormack 387 (33) 704-000
E-mail: cormackm@state.gov
Education: Illinois BA; Chicago 1989 MA

★ Ambassador-Designate **Eric G. Nelson** 387 (33) 704-000
E-mail: nelsoneg@state.gov
Education: Rice 1983 BSChE; Texas 1988 MBA
Office Management Specialist to the Ambassador
Urszula I. Horn 387 (33) 704-000
E-mail: hornu@state.gov

◇ Deputy Chief of Mission **Ellen Jacqueline Germain** ... 387 (33) 704-000
E-mail: germainej@state.gov
Office Management Specialist to the Deputy Chief of Mission **Kimberly McKeown** 387 (33) 704-000
E-mail: mckeownka@state.gov

Consul **Scott A. Norris** 387 (33) 704-000

Community Liaison Officer **Kristen Loehr** 387 (33) 704-000
E-mail: loehrk@state.gov

Economic Officer **John M. Ashworth** 387 (33) 704-000
E-mail: ashworthjm@state.gov
Education: Wake Forest 2001 BA

Environment, Science, and Technology Officer (Resident in Budapest) **Katia Bennett** 420 (2) 27-022-000
E-mail: bennettk@state.gov

Financial Management Officer **Todd Bate-Poxon** 387 (33) 704-000
E-mail: batepoxont@state.gov Fax: 387 (33) 215-590

General Service Officer **(Vacant)** 387 (33) 704-000

Information Management Officer
Edward D. "Dwaine" Jefferson 387 (33) 704-000
E-mail: jeffersoned@state.gov

Information Programs Officer
Brig "Hilmar" Anderson 387 (33) 704-000

Information Systems Officer
Scott "Victor" Torbeck 387 (33) 704-000
E-mail: torbeckvs@state.gov

Information Systems Security Officer
Michael "Mike" Bala 387 (33) 704-000

Legal Attaché **John Bivona** 387 (33) 704-000
E-mail: bivonaja@state.gov

Management Officer **Michael J. McKeown** 387 (33) 704-000
E-mail: mckeownmj@state.gov

Political Officer **Craig Conway** 387 (33) 704-000

Public Affairs Officer **Leah Pease** 387 (33) 619-592
Fax: 387 (33) 619-593

Regional Security Officer **Matthew L. Golbus** 387 (33) 704-000
E-mail: golbusm@state.gov

Agency for International Development [Bosnia-Herzegovina]
39 Hamdije Cemerlica, 71000 Sarajevo, Bosnia and Herzegovina
Mail: USAID, c/o American Embassy - Sarajevo, 7130 Sarajevo Place, Department of State, Washington, DC 20521-7130
Tel: 387 (33) 70-40-00 Fax: 387 (33) 611-973
E-mail: usaidsarajevo@usaid.gov Internet: www.usaid.gov/bosnia

Mission Director **Peter Duffy** 387 (33) 70-40-00
E-mail: pduffy@usaid.gov

Agricultural Section (Foreign Agriculture Service) [Bosnia-Herzegovina]
American Embassy - Sarajevo, Bosnia-Herzegovina,
1 Robert C. Frasure Street, 71000 Sarajevo, Bosnia and Herzegovina
Tel: 387 (33) 61-184-755 Fax: 387 (33) 704-425
E-mail: agsarajevo@fas.usda.gov

Agricultural Attaché (Resident in Rome)
Frederick H. "Fred" Giles 39 (06) 4674-2396
E-mail: frederick.giles@fas.usda.gov

Commercial Section (Foreign Commercial Service) [Bosnia-Herzegovina]
Fra Andjela Zvizdovica 1, Unis Towers, Alipasina 43, 10th Floor, 71000 Sarajevo, Bosnia and Herzegovina
Mail: American Embassy - Sarajevo, Department of State, Washington, DC 20521-7130
Tel: 387 (33) 445-700 Fax: 387 (33) 659-722
Internet: www.export.gov/bosniaandherzegovina

Regional Senior Commercial Officer (Resident in Romania) **Gregory "Greg" O'Connor** 40 (21) 200-3376
E-mail: Greg.O'Connor@trade.gov

Department of Homeland Security - U.S. Immigration and Customs Enforcement (Resident in Vienna) [Bosnia-Herzegovina]
American Embassy - Vienna, Austria, Boltzmanngasse 16, A-1091 Vienna, Austria
Mail: American Embassy - Vienna, Austria, Department of State, Washington, DC 20521-9900
Tel: 43 (1) 31339-0 Fax: 43 (1) 313-39-2430

Customs Officer **Sarah Bay** 43 (1) 31339-2111

Federal Aviation Administration (Resident in Moscow) [Bosnia-Herzegovina]
American Embassy, Eight Bolshoy Devyatinsky Pereulok, 121099 Moscow, Russia
Mail: Unit 5430, DPO, AE 09721
Tel: 7 (495) 728-5125 Fax: 7 (495) 728-5350

FAA Senior Representative **Andrew McKee** 7 (495) 728-5125

Office of the Defense Attaché [Bosnia-Herzegovina]
American Embassy - Sarajevo, 7130 Sarajevo Place, Department of State, Washington, DC 20521-7130
Tel: 387 (33) 445-700 Fax: 387 (33) 659-722

Defense Attaché **COL Mark Karas USA** 387 (33) 445-700

Office of Defense Cooperation Chief
LTC Corey N. Shea USA 387 (33) 445-700
E-mail: sheacn@state.gov

Banja Luka Branch Office
American Embassy Branch Office - Bosnia-Herzegovina, Jovana Ducica 5, Banja Luka, Bosnia and Herzegovina
Mail: U.S. Embassy Branch Office - Banja Luka, Department of State, Washington, DC 20521-7130
Tel: 387 (51) 211-500 Fax: 387 (51) 211-775

Director **Corey Gonzalez** 387 (33) 445-700
Education: Maryland 2005 MA

Political/Economic Officer **Sutton Meagher** 387 (51) 211-500
E-mail: meaghersa@state.gov

Mostar Branch Office
American Embassy Branch Office - Mostar, Bosnia-Herzegovina, Husnije Repca 3, 88 000, Mostar, Bosnia and Herzegovina
Mail: U.S. Embassy Branch Office - Mostar, Department of State, Washington, DC 20521-7130
Tel: 387 (36) 580-580 Fax: 387 (36) 580-581

Consular Officer (Resident in Sarajevo)
Scott A. Norris 387 (33) 445-700

Financial Management Officer
Todd Bate-Poxon .... 387 (33) 445-700 ext. 2030
E-mail: batepoxont@state.gov

Political Officer **(Vacant)** 387 (33) 445-700

★ Presidential Appointment Requiring Senate Confirmation ☆ Presidential Appointment ☐ Schedule C Appointment ◇ Career Senior Foreign Service Appointment
● Career Senior Executive Service (SES) Appointment ○ Non-Career Senior Executive Service (SES) Appointment ■ Postal Career Executive Service

U.S. Embassy in Bulgaria

American Embassy - Sofia, Bulgaria, 16 Kozyak Street, Sofia, 1408, Bulgaria
Tel: 359 (2) 937-5100 Fax: 359 (2) 937-5320
E-mail: sofia@usembassy.bg

Office of the U.S. Ambassador to Bulgaria

American Embassy - Sofia, Bulgaria, 16 Kozyak Street, Sofia, 1408, Bulgaria
Mail: American Embassy - Sofia, Bulgaria, Department of State, 5740 Sofia Place, Washington, DC 20521-5740

★ Ambassador **Ambassador Eric Seth Rubin** 359 (2) 937-5100
E-mail: rubines@state.gov
Education: Yale 1983 BA
Office Management Specialist to the Ambassador **Deborah R. Mahoney** 359 (2) 937-5100

◇ Deputy Chief of Mission **Justin P. Friedman** 359 (2) 937-5100
E-mail: friedmanj@state.gov
Education: UC Berkeley 1985 BA; Columbia 1990 MA; National War Col 2009 MS
Office Management Specialist to the Deputy Chief of Mission **Kathleen Olson** 359 (2) 937-5100

Consul General **Viki Thomson** 359 (2) 937-5100
Fax: 359 (2) 937-5209

Community Liaison Officer **Jennifer Snodgrass** 359 (2) 937-5100
Education: Ottawa U

Financial Management Officer **Mark M. Bliss** 359 (2) 937-5100

General Services Officer **Bridget Bittle** 359 (2) 937-5100
Fax: 359 (2) 939-5790

General Services Officer **Paul Swider** 359 (2) 937-5100
Fax: 359 (2) 939-5790

Human Resources Officer **Mark M. Bliss** 359 (2) 937-5100

Information Management Officer **Maurio Lopez** 359 (2) 937-5100
E-mail: lopezm@state.gov

Information Systems Officer **Robert Levay** 359 (2) 937-5100

Information Systems Security Officer **Tracy Calhon** 359 (2) 937-5100
Education: Louisiana (Monroe) 1999 BBA; Webster 2013 MBA

Legal Attache **Jack Liao** 359 (2) 937-5100

Management Officer **Andrew D. McClearn** 359 (2) 937-5100
Fax: 359 (2) 937-5231

Political/Economic Counselor **David McCormick** 359 (2) 937-5100

Public Affairs Officer **(Vacant)** 359 (2) 937-5100
Fax: 359 (2) 937-5326

Regional Security Officer **Robert F. Kelty** 359 (2) 937-5100
E-mail: keltyrf@state.gov
Tel: 359 (2) 937-5328

Agricultural Section (Foreign Agricultural Service) [Bulgaria]

American Embassy - Warsaw, Poland, Aleje Ujazdowskie 29/31, Warsaw, Poland 00-540
Tel: 359 (2) 937-5774 Fax: 359 (2) 939-5744
E-mail: agsofia@fas.usda.gov
Areas Covered: Bulgaria, Moldova, Romania

Agricultural Attaché (Resident in Warsaw) **John Slette** 48 (22) 5042336

Commercial Section (Foreign Commercial Service) [Bulgaria]

American Embassy - Sofia, Bulgaria, 16 Kozyak Street, Sofia, 1408, Bulgaria
Mail: American Embassy - Sofia, Bulgaria, Department of State, 5740 Sofia Place, Washington, DC 20521-5740
Tel: 359 (2) 939-5784 Fax: 359 (2) 939-5735
E-mail: office.sofia@trade.gov Internet: www.export.gov/bulgaria

Senior Commercial Officer **Miguel Hernández** 359 (2) 939-5745
E-mail: Miguel.Hernandez@trade.gov
Education: UC Berkeley BA; Columbia MIA

Drug Enforcement Administration (Resident in Bucharest) [Bulgaria]

DEA Attaché **Stephen Borowski** 359 (2) 937-5100

Office of the Defense Attaché [Bulgaria]

American Embassy - Sofia, Bulgaria, 16 Kozyak Street, Sofia, 1408, Bulgaria
Mail: American Embassy - Sofia, Bulgaria, Department of State, 5740 Sofia Place, Washington, DC 20521-5740
Tel: 359 (2) 937-5100 Fax: 359 (2) 937-5461

Defense Attaché **Col James W. Crowhurst USAF** 359 (2) 937-5100
Education: Air Force Acad 1987 BA; Webster 1996 MA; Air Command Col 2000; Air War Col 2004

Office of Defense Cooperation [Bulgaria]

American Embassy - Sofia, Bulgaria, 16 Kozyak Street, Sofia, 1408, Bulgaria
Mail: American Embassy - Sofia, Bulgaria, Department of State, 5740 Sofia Place, Washington, DC 20521-5740
Tel: 359 (2) 939-5662 Fax: 359 (2) 939-5680

Chief **LTC Kelly G. MacDonald USA** 359 (2) 939-5662

U.S. Embassy in Croatia

American Embassy - Zagreb, Croatia, Thomasa Jeffersona 2, 10010 Zagreb, Croatia
Tel: 385 (1) 661-2200 Fax: 385 (1) 661-2373

Office of the U.S. Ambassador to Croatia

American Embassy - Zagreb, Croatia, Thomasa Jeffersona 2, 10010 Zagreb, Croatia
Mail: Department of State, 5080 Zagreb Place, Washington, DC 20521-5080

★ Ambassador **Ambassador W. Robert Kohorst** 385 (1) 661-2200
Education: Dayton 1975 BSAcc; Michigan 1978 JD
Office Management Specialist to the Ambassador **Stacy L. Elliott** 385 (1) 661-2200
E-mail: elliottsl@state.gov Fax: 385 (1) 665-8939

Deputy Chief of Mission **Victoria J. Taylor** 385 (1) 661-2200
E-mail: taylorvj@state.gov
Education: Pennsylvania 2002 BA; London School Econ (UK) 2003 MSc
Office Management Specialist to the Deputy Chief of Mission **Kimberly M. "Kim" Carter** 385 (1) 661-2200
Fax: 385 (1) 665-8939

Community Liaison Officer **Ellen Fihlman** 385 (1) 661-2200

Consular Officer **David J. Jendrisak** 385 (1) 661-2200
E-mail: jendrisakdj@state.gov
Education: Kent State 1991 BA; Ohio 1995 MA

Economic Officer **(Vacant)** 385 (1) 661-2200

Financial Management Officer **Trishita Maula** 385 (1) 661-2200

General Services Officer **Matthew D. Warin** 385 (1) 661-2200
E-mail: warinmd@state.gov

Information Management Officer **Thomas P. Pitts** 385 (1) 661-2200
E-mail: pittstp@state.gov

Information Program Officer **Julio C. Herrera** 385 (1) 661-2200

Information Systems Officer **Shawn A. Wistrom** 385 (1) 661-2200
E-mail: wistromsa@state.gov
Education: Michigan BS; San José State 2004 MLIS

Information Systems Security Officer **Thomas P. Pitts** 385 (1) 661-2200
E-mail: pittstp@state.gov

Management Officer **Matthew J. Garrett** 385 (1) 661-2200
E-mail: garrettmj@state.gov Fax: 385 (1) 661-2370

Political Officer **(Vacant)** 385 (1) 661-2200

Political and Economic Officer **Sarah L. Groen** 385 (1) 661-2200
E-mail: groensl@state.gov

Public Affairs Officer **Wylita L. Bell** 385 (1) 661-2200
E-mail: bellwl@state.gov Fax: 385 (1) 665-8936

Regional Security Officer **Roger Thyen** 385 (1) 661-2200
E-mail: thyenr@state.gov

DEPARTMENTS

★ Presidential Appointment Requiring Senate Confirmation ☆ Presidential Appointment ☐ Schedule C Appointment ◇ Career Senior Foreign Service Appointment
● Career Senior Executive Service (SES) Appointment ○ Non-Career Senior Executive Service (SES) Appointment ■ Postal Career Executive Service

DEPARTMENTS

Agricultural Section (Foreign Agricultural Service) [Croatia]
American Embassy - Zagreb, Croatia, Thomasa Jeffersona 2,
10010 Zagreb, Croatia
Tel: 385 (1) 661-2467 Fax: 385 (1) 665-8950
E-mail: agzagreb@state.gov

Agricultural Attaché (Resident in Rome)
Frederick H. "Fred" Giles 39 (06) 4674-2396
E-mail: frederick.giles@fas.usda.gov

Commercial Section (Foreign Commercial Service) [Croatia]
American Embassy - Zagreb, Croatia, Thomasa Jeffersona 2,
10010 Zagreb, Croatia
Mail: Department of State, 5080 Zagreb Place,
Washington, DC 20521-5080
Tel: 385 (1) 661-2224 Fax: 385 (1) 661-2446
Internet: www.export.gov/croatia E-mail: office.zagreb@trade.gov

Regional Senior Commercial Officer (Resident in Romania) **Gregory "Greg" O'Connor** 40 (21) 200 3372
E-mail: greg.o'connor@trade.gov

Senior Commercial Specialist **Damjan Bencic** 385 (1) 661-2186
E-mail: damjan.bencic@trade.gov

Federal Aviation Administration (Resident in Moscow) [Croatia]
Eight Bolshoy Devyatinsky Pereulok, 121099 Moscow, Russia
Mail: American Embassy, PSC 77, APO, AE 09721
Fax: 7 (495) 728-5350

FAA Senior Representative **Andrew McKee** 7 (495) 728-5125

Office of the Defense Attaché [Croatia]
American Embassy - Zagreb, Croatia, Thomasa Jeffersona 2,
10010 Zagreb, Croatia
Mail: Department of State, 5080 Zagreb Place,
Washington, DC 20521-5080
Tel: 385 (1) 661-2200 Fax: 385 (1) 665-8945

Defense Attaché **COL Robert S. Mathers USA** 385 (1) 661-2200

Office of Defense Cooperation [Croatia]
American Embassy - Zagreb, Croatia, Thomasa Jeffersona 2,
10010 Zagreb, Croatia
Mail: Department of State, 5080 Zagreb Place,
Washington, DC 20521-5080
Tel: 385 (1) 661-2223 Fax: 385 (1) 378-6535

Military Liaison Officer
LtCol Matthew Denny USAF 385 (1) 661-2223

U.S. Embassy in Cyprus

U.S. Embassy - Nicosia, Cyprus, Metochiou and Ploutarchou Streets,
Engomi, Nicosia, Cyprus
Tel: 357 22-393939 Fax: 357 22-780944
E-mail: consularnicosia@state.gov

Office of the U.S. Ambassador to Cyprus

U.S. Embassy - Nicosia, Cyprus, Metochiou and Ploutarchou Streets,
Engomi, 2407 Nicosia, Cyprus
Mail: U.S. Embassy - Nicosia, Cyprus, PSC 815, FPO, AE 09836-0001

★ Ambassador **Ambassador Kathleen Ann Doherty** 357 22-393939
E-mail: dohertyka@state.gov
Education: Colgate BA; London School Econ (UK) 1990 MSc

★ Ambassador-Designate
Ambassador Judith Gail "Judy" Garber 357 22-393939
E-mail: garberjg@state.gov
Education: Georgetown 1983 BSFS
Office Management Specialist to the Ambassador
Katherine Ramirez 357 22-393939

Deputy Chief of Mission
Nathaniel Pabody "Chip" Dean 357 22-393939
E-mail: deannp@state.gov
Office Management Specialist to the Deputy Chief of Mission **Deirdre E O'Leary** 357 22-393939
E-mail: olearyde@state.gov
Education: Loyola U (New Orleans) 1999

Community Liaison Officer **Michelle Hathaway** 357 22-393939

Office of the U.S. Ambassador to Cyprus *(continued)*

Consular Officer **Dr. Newton J. Gaskill** 357 22-393939
E-mail: gaskillnj@state.gov
Education: Weber State 1990 BA; Texas 1992 MA, 2003 PhD

Economic/Commercial Officer **(Vacant)** 357 22-393939
Fax: 357 22-393923

Financial Management Officer **Kaul Ashok** 357 22-393939

General Services Officer
Thomas L. "Tom" Czerwinski 357 22-393-939
E-mail: czerwinskitl@state.gov
Education: Emory 2003 BA; Texas 2008 MPAff

Information Management Officer **(Vacant)** 357 22-393939

Information Program Officer **Truong Nguyen** 357 22-393939

Management Officer **Robert A. "Bob" Collins** 357 22-393939

Political/Economic Officer **Daniel Wartko** 357 22-393939
Education: SUNY (Buffalo) 1990 BA; George Washington 1993 MIR

Public Affairs Officer **Glen Davis** 357 22-393939
Fax: 357 22-393931

Regional Security Officer **Daniel M. "Dan" Childs** 357 22-393939
Fax: 357 22-393467

Agency for International Development (Resident In Kiev) [Cyprus]
U.S. Embassy - Nicosia, Cyprus, Metochiou and Ploutarchou Streets,
Engomi, 2407 Nicosia, Cyprus
Internet: www.usaid.gov/cyprus

Mission Director **Susan Kosinski Fritz** 380 (44) 521-5000
E-mail: sfritz@usaid.gov
Education: Rutgers 1986 BA; American U 1989 MPA

Drug Enforcement Administration [Cyprus]
U.S. Embassy - Nicosia, Cyprus, Metochiou and Ploutarchou Streets,
Engomi, Nicosia, Cyprus
Mail: U.S. Embassy - Nicosia, Cyprus, PSC 815, FPO, AE 09836-0001
Tel: 357 22-393939 Fax: 357 22-393471

DEA Country Attaché **Joseph Hathaway** 357 22-393939

Federal Aviation Administration (Resident in Moscow) [Cyprus]
FAA Senior Representative **Andrew McKee** 7 (495) 728-5125

Office of the Defense Attaché [Cyprus]
U.S. Embassy - Nicosia, Cyprus, Metochiou and Ploutarchou Streets,
Engomi, Nicosia, Cyprus
Mail: U.S. Embassy - Nicosia, Cyprus, PSC 815, FPO, AE 09836-0001
Tel: 357 22-393939 Fax: 357 22-393468

Defense Attaché **COL Andrew "Andy" Mack USA** 357 22-393939

U.S. Embassy in The Czech Republic

American Embassy - Prague, Czech Republic (Int'l),
Trziste 15, 11801 Prague, Czechia
Tel: 420 (2) 57-022-000 Fax: 420 (2) 57-022-809
E-mail: praguewebmaster@state.gov

Office of the U.S. Ambassador to the Czech Republic

American Embassy - Prague, Czech Republic (Int'l),
Trziste 15, 11801 Prague, Czechia
Mail: American Embassy - Prague, Czech Republic,
Department of State, Washington, DC 20521-5630

★ Ambassador
Ambassador Stephen B. "Steve" King 420 (2) 57-022-000
Education: Western Illinois BA, 1967 MA
Office Management Specialist to the Ambassador
Janice C. Green 420 (2) 57-022-000

◇ Deputy Chief of Mission **Kelly Adams-Smith** 420 (2) 57-022-000
Office Management Specialist to the Deputy Chief of Mission **Janelle Walker** 420 (2) 57-022-000

Consul General **Kimberly K. "Kim" Atkinson** 420 (2) 57-022-000
E-mail: atkinsonkk@state.gov

Community Liaison Officer **Heath Cox** 420 (2) 57-022-000
E-mail: coxhf@state.gov

Economic Officer
Michael Patrick "Patrick" Ellsworth 420 (2) 57-022-000

★ Presidential Appointment Requiring Senate Confirmation ☆ Presidential Appointment ☐ Schedule C Appointment ◇ Career Senior Foreign Service Appointment
● Career Senior Executive Service (SES) Appointment ○ Non-Career Senior Executive Service (SES) Appointment ■ Postal Career Executive Service

Office of the U.S. Ambassador to the Czech Republic *(continued)*

Environment, Science, and Technology Officer
(Vacant) . . . 420 (2) 57-022-000
Equal Employment Opportunity Officer **(Vacant)** . . . 420 (2) 57-022-000
Financial Management Officer **Jennie Young** . . . 420 (2) 57-022-000
General Services Officer **Aaron Burge** . . . 420 (2) 57-022-000
E-mail: burgeap@state.gov
Education: Maryland
Information Management Officer
Jason Krautkramer . . . 420 (2) 57-022-000
Legal Attaché **(Vacant)** . . . 420 (2) 724-162-483
Management Officer **Alexander K. "Alex" Hardin** . . . 420 (2) 57-022-000
E-mail: hardinak2@state.gov
Education: Ohio Wesleyan 1996 BA
Political Officer **James Tira** . . . 420 (2) 57-022-000
Political/Economic Counselor **John David Nylin** . . . 420 (2) 57-022-000
E-mail: nylinjd@state.gov
Education: UC Davis 1991 BA; UC San Diego 1997 MPIA
Public Affairs Officer **Joann Marie Lockard** . . . 420 (2) 57-022-000
Fax: 420 (2) 57-535-240
Regional Security Officer **Hunter Martin** . . . 420 (2) 57-022-000

Agricultural Section (Foreign Agricultural Service) [Czech Republic]
Trziste 15, 11801 Prague, Czechia
Tel: 420 257-022-026 Fax: 420 257-022-803 E-mail: agprague@usda.gov

Agricultural Officer (Resident in Berlin)
Kelly Stange . . . 49 (30) 8305-1150

Commercial Section (Foreign Commercial Service) [Czech Republic]
American Embassy - Prague, Czech Republic,
(International) Trziste 15, 11801 Prague, Czechia
Mail: Department of State, 5630 Prague Place,
Washington, DC 20521-5630
Tel: 420 (2) 57-022-434 Fax: 420 (2) 57-022-810
E-mail: office.prague@trade.gov Internet: www.export.gov/czechrepublic

Senior Commercial Officer **(Vacant)** . . . 420 (2) 57-022-434

Federal Aviation Administration (Resident in Moscow) [Czech Republic]
FAA Senior Representative **Andrew McKee** . . . 7 (495) 7285125

International Broadcasting Bureau [Czech Republic]
American Embassy - Prague, Czech Republic,
Department of State, Washington, DC 20521-5630
American Embassy - Prague, Czech Republic,
Vinohradska 1, 11801 Prague, Czechia
Tel: 420 (2) 21-123-776 Fax: 420 (2) 21-123-774

International Broadcasting Bureau Officer
Adam Gartner . . . 420 (2) 21-123-773
E-mail: atgartne@bbg.gov

Office of the Defense Attaché [Czech Republic]
American Embassy - Prague, Czech Republic,
Department of State, Washington, DC 20521-5630
American Embassy - Prague, Czech Republic,
(International) Trziste 15, 11801 Prague, Czechia
Tel: 420 (2) 57-022-000 Fax: 420 (2) 57-532-718

Defense Attaché **Mark Wootan** . . . 420 (2) 57-530-663

Office of Defense Cooperation [Czech Republic]
American Embassy - Prague, Czech Republic,
Trziste 15, 11801 Prague, Czechia

Chief **Michael Cushwa** . . . 420 (2) 57-022-000

U.S. Embassy in Denmark

American Embassy - Copenhagen, Denmark,
Dag Hammarskjolds Alle 24, 2100 Copenhagen, Denmark
Tel: 45 33 417100 Fax: 45 35 430223 E-mail: mail@usembassy.dk

Office of the U.S. Ambassador to Denmark, the Faroe Islands, and Greenland
American Embassy - Copenhagen, Denmark,
Dag Hammarskjolds Alle 24, 2100 Copenhagen, Denmark
Mail: American Embassy - Copenhagen, Denmark, PSC 73,
APO, AE 09716

★ Ambassador **Ambassador Carla Sands** . . . 45 35 553144
Office Management Specialist to the Ambassador
Llywelyn C. Graeme . . . 45 3341 7100
E-mail: graemelc@state.gov
◇ Deputy Chief of Mission **Laura A. Lochman** . . . 45 3341 7100
E-mail: lochmanla@state.gov
Office Management Specialist to the Deputy Chief of
Mission **Beverly M. Fenwick** . . . 45 33 417333
E-mail: fenwickbm@state.gov
Consular Officer **Krystina L. Rabassa** . . . 45 33 417100
E-mail: rabassakl@state.gov
Education: Michigan 1998
Community Liaison Officer **Tarek Abu Sham** . . . 45 33 417345
E-mail: abushamt@state.gov
Community Liaison Officer **Johnny Fagler** . . . 45 33 417345
Economic Officer **Aaron L. Feit** . . . 45 334 7335
E-mail: feital@state.gov
Education: Michigan 1997 BA
Environment, Science and Technology Officer
Stephen S. Wheeler . . . 45 3341 7383
E-mail: wheelerss@state.gov
Education: Cal Poly San Luis Obispo; South Carolina MIB
Equal Employment Opportunity Officer
Theresa Nielsen . . . 45 33 417371
General Services Officer **Adrienne Fagler** . . . 45 33 417100
E-mail: faglerag@state.gov
Information Management Officer **Scott Tatu** . . . 45 3341 7388
E-mail: tatusf@state.gov
Information Program Officer **Scott Tatu** . . . 45 33 417100
E-mail: tatusf@state.gov
Information Systems Security Officer **(Vacant)** . . . 45 3341 7388
Management Officer
B. Alexander "Zander" Lipscomb . . . 45 3341 7499
E-mail: lipscombab@state.gov Fax: 45 35 269611
Narcotics Affairs Officer **(Vacant)** . . . 45 33 417100
Political/Economic Officer **Steven R. "Steve" Bitner** . . . 45 3341 7334
E-mail: BitnerSR@state.gov
Political Officer **Sung Choi** . . . 45 3341 7371
Public Affairs Officer **Daniel J. Ernst** . . . 45 3341 7245
E-mail: ernstdj@state.gov
Regional Security Officer **Joseph A. "Joe" Schulter** . . . 45 33417389
Public Diplomacy Officer **William J. O'Connor** . . . 45 3341 7245

Agricultural Section (Foreign Agricultural Service) (Resident in The Hague) [Denmark]
American Embassy - The Hague, Netherlands,
Lange Voorhut 102, NL-25 The Hague, 4 EJ, Netherlands
Mail: American Embassy - The Hague, Netherlands, PSC 71, Box 1000,
APO, AE 09715
Fax: 31 (70) 365-7681

Agricultural Officer **Susan B. Phillips** . . . 31 (70) 310-2300
Education: Wisconsin 1985 BS; Kansas State 1991 MSA

Commercial Section (Foreign Commercial Service) [Denmark]
American Embassy - Copenhagen, Denmark,
Dag Hammarskjolds Alle 24, 2100 Copenhagen, Denmark
Mail: American Embassy - Copenhagen, Denmark, PSC 73,
APO, AE 09716
Tel: 45 33 41 73 15 Fax: 45 35 420175
Internet: www.export.gov/denmark

Senior Commercial Specialist **Bjarke Frederiksen** . . . 45 33 417403
E-mail: bjarke.frederiksen@trade.gov

★ Presidential Appointment Requiring Senate Confirmation ☆ Presidential Appointment ☐ Schedule C Appointment ◇ Career Senior Foreign Service Appointment
● Career Senior Executive Service (SES) Appointment ○ Non-Career Senior Executive Service (SES) Appointment ■ Postal Career Executive Service

Department of Homeland Security - U.S. Immigration and Customs Enforcement [Denmark]
American Embassy - Copenhagen, Denmark,
Dag Hammarskjolds Alle 24, 2100 Copenhagen, Denmark
Fax: 45 35 430223

ICE Attaché **(Vacant)** 45 33 553144

Drug Enforcement Administration [Denmark]
DEA Officer **Christopher J. Urben** 45 35 553144
E-mail: urbencj@state.gov

Federal Aviation Administration (Resident in Moscow) [Denmark]
American Embassy, Eight Bolshoy Devyatinsky Pereulok,
121099 Moscow, Russia
Mail: Unit 5430, DPO, AE 09721
Fax: 7 (495) 728-5350

FAA Senior Representative **Andrew McKee** 7 (495) 728-5125

Federal Bureau of Investigation [Denmark]
American Embassy - Copenhagen, Denmark,
Dag Hammarskjolds Alle 24, 2100 Copenhagen, Denmark
Mail: American Embassy - Copenhagen, Denmark, PSC 73, APO, AE 09716
Tel: 45 33 417100 Fax: 45 35 269611

Legal Attaché **Dick A. Robles** 45 35 553144

Office of the Defense Attaché [Denmark]
American Embassy - Copenhagen, Denmark,
Dag Hammarskjolds Alle 24, 2100 Copenhagen, Denmark
Mail: American Embassy - Copenhagen, Denmark, PSC 73, APO, AE 09716
Tel: 45 35 553144 Fax: 45 35 422516

Defense Attaché, Naval Attaché and Naval Air Attaché
CAPT James F. Gibson, Jr. USN 45 35 553144
E-mail: gibsonjf@state.gov
Army Attaché **LTC Ali N. Omur USA** 45 35 553144

Office of Defense Cooperation [Denmark]
American Embassy - Copenhagen, Denmark,
Dag Hammarskjolds Alle 24, 2100 Copenhagen, Denmark
Mail: American Embassy - Copenhagen, Denmark, PSC 73, APO, AE 09716
Tel: 45 35 662100 Fax: 45 35 663510

Defense Cooperation Officer **(Vacant)** 45 35 662100
Commander, Detachment 1 **Scott A. Schneider** 45 35 662100

U.S. Embassy in Estonia

American Embassy - Tallinn, Estonia, Kentmanni 20, 15099 Tallinn, Estonia
Tel: 372 668-8100 Fax: 372 668-8134 E-mail: usasaatkond@state.gov

Office of the U.S. Ambassador to Estonia

American Embassy - Tallinn, Estonia, Kentmanni 20, 15099 Tallinn, Estonia
Mail: Department of State, 4530 Tallinn Place,
Washington, DC 20521-4530

★ Ambassador **(Vacant)** 372 668-8100
◇ Chargé d'Affaires **Ambassador Clifford G. Bond** 372 668-8100
E-mail: bondcg@state.gov
Education: Georgetown 1970 BSFS;
London School Econ (UK) 1971 MSc
Office Management Specialist to the Ambassador
(Vacant) 372 668-8103
◇ Deputy Chief of Mission **Elizabeth K. Horst** 372 668-8100
E-mail: horstek@state.gov
Office Management Specialist to the Deputy Chief of Mission **Jillian "Jill" Stirling** 372 668-8139
Consul **Carlo Boehm** 372 668-8111
Fax: 372 668-8267
Community Liaison Officer **Lyn Dunn** 372 668-8100

Office of the U.S. Ambassador to Estonia *(continued)*

Environment, Science and Technology Officer (Resident in Copenhagen) **(Vacant)** 45 3341 7383
American Embassy - Copenhagen, Denmark, PSC 73, APO, AE 09716
Equal Employment Opportunity Officer
Sandra K. Jacobs 372 668-8111
Economic/Commercial Officer **Nichole Johnson** 372 668-8100
General Services Officer **Melania Rita Arreaga** 372 668-8100
E-mail: arreagamr@state.gov
Information Management Officer
Stephen Cunningham 372 668-8100
Information Systems Officer
Kenneth Alex "Alex" Schreiner 372 668-8100
Legal Attaché **Michael Kolessar** 372 668-8100
E-mail: kolessarm@state.gov
Management Officer **Melania Rita Arreaga** 372 668-8105
E-mail: arreagamr@state.gov
Political/Economic Officer **John Daniel Spykerman** 372 668-8100
Public Affairs Officer **Edward "Ed" Dunn** 372 668-8124
Fax: 372 668-8253
Regional Security Officer **Omar Facuse** 372 668-8100

Agricultural Section (Foreign Agricultural Service) (Resident in Warsaw) [Estonia]
American Embassy - Warsaw, Poland, Aleje Ujazdowskie 29/31, Warsaw, Poland 00-540
Mail: American Embassy - Warsaw, Poland,
Department of State, 5010, Washington, DC 20521-5010
Tel: 48 (22) 504-2336 Fax: 48 (22) 504-2320

Agricultural Officer **John Slette** 48 (22) 504-2336

Commercial Section (Foreign Commercial Service) (Resident in Finland) [Estonia]
American Embassy - Helsinki, Finland,
Itanen Puistotie 14B, 00140 Helsinki, Finland
Tel: 358 (9) 616-25342 Internet: www.export.gov/estonia

Senior Commercial Officer **Aaron M. Held** 358 (9) 616-250
E-mail: Aaron.Held@trade.gov

Department of Homeland Security - U.S. Secret Service [Estonia]
Kentmanni 20, 15099 Tallinn, Estonia

Secret Service Attaché **(Vacant)** 372 668-8100

Federal Aviation Administration (Resident in Moscow) [Estonia]
American Embassy, Eight Bolshoy Devyatinsky Pereulok,
121099 Moscow, Russia
Mail: Unit 5430, DPO, AE 09721
Fax: 7 (495) 728-5350

FAA Senior Representative **Andrew McKee** 7 (495) 728-5125

Office of the Defense Attaché [Estonia]
American Embassy - Tallinn, Estonia, Kentmanni 20, 15099 Tallinn, Estonia
Mail: Department of State, 4530 Tallinn Place,
Washington, DC 20521-4530
Tel: 372 668-8200 Fax: 372 668-8257

Defense Attaché **Povilas Strazdas** 372 668-8200
Office of Defense Cooperation Chief **Jason Gresh** 372 668-8200
Naval Operations Assistant
LCDR Jon J. Hagadorn USN 372 668-8200

U.S. Embassy in Finland

American Embassy, Itainen Puistotie 14-A, 00140 Helsinki, Finland
Tel: 358 (9) 616-250 Fax: 358 (9) 6162-5135 Internet: fi.usembassy.gov

Office of the U.S. Ambassador to Finland

American Embassy, Itainen Puistotie 14-A, 00140 Helsinki, Finland
E-mail: webmaster@usembassy.fi

★ Ambassador
Ambassador Robert Frank "Bob" Pence 358 (9) 616-250
Education: Maryland 1967 BA; American U 1971 JD, 1997 MA, 1999 MA; Yale 2003 MPhil, 2005 MA

★ Presidential Appointment Requiring Senate Confirmation ☆ Presidential Appointment ☐ Schedule C Appointment ◇ Career Senior Foreign Service Appointment
● Career Senior Executive Service (SES) Appointment ○ Non-Career Senior Executive Service (SES) Appointment ■ Postal Career Executive Service

Office of the U.S. Ambassador to Finland *(continued)*

Office Management Specialist to the Ambassador
Rosi Smith 358 (9) 616250
Education: Champlain 2017 BS

◇ Deputy Chief of Mission **Donna Ann Welton** 358 (9) 616250
E-mail: weltonda2@state.gov

Office Management Specialist to the Deputy Chief of Mission **Seiyefa S. "Seifa" Hauptmann** 358 (9) 616-250
E-mail: hauptmannss@state.gov

Consul **Jeremy R. Wisemiller** 358 (9) 616250

Community Liaison Officer **Erin Cassidy** 358 (9) 616-250

General Services Officer **Monica Madrid** 358 (9) 616-250

Information Management Officer
Michael J. Schultheis 358 (9) 616250
E-mail: schultheismj@state.gov

Information Systems Officer **Herman Linnen II** 358 (9) 616-250
E-mail: linnenh@state.gov

Information Systems Security Officer **(Vacant)** 358 (9) 616-250

Management Officer **Lisa Laurette Ficek** 358 (9) 616250
E-mail: ficekll@state.gov
Education: Creighton 1993 BA; Marquette 1994 MA; Kansas MBA

Political/Economic Officer **Shawn Waddoups** 358 (9) 616250
E-mail: waddoupss@state.gov

Public Affairs Officer **Thomas J. "T.J." Grubisha** 358 (9) 616250
E-mail: grubishatj@state.gov Fax: 358 (9) 61625110

Regional Security Officer **Jonathan Poole** 358 (9) 616250

Agricultural Section (Foreign Agricultural Service) (Resident in The Hague) [Finland]
American Embassy - The Hague, Netherlands,
John Adams Park 1, 2244 BZ Wassenaar, Netherlands
Mail: PSC 115, Box 038, APO, AE 09715
Tel: 31 (70) 310-2299 Fax: 31 (70) 365-7681

Agricultural Officer **Susan B. Phillips** 31 (70) 310-2300
Education: Wisconsin 1985 BS; Kansas State 1991 MSA

Commercial Section (Foreign Commercial Service) [Finland]
American Embassy - Helsinki, Finland,
Itainen Puistotie 14-B, FIN-00140 Helsinki, Finland
Mail: American Embassy - PSC 78, Box H, APO, AE 09723
Tel: 358 (9) 616-250 Tel: 358 (9) 616-25130
E-mail: office.helsinki@trade.gov Internet: export.gov/finland

Senior Commercial Officer **Aaron M. Held** 358 (9) 616-250
E-mail: Aaron.Held@trade.gov

Federal Aviation Administration (Resident in Moscow) [Finland]
American Embassy, Eight Bolshoy Devyatinsky Pereulok,
121099 Moscow, Russia
Fax: 7 (495) 728-5350

FAA Senior Representative **Andrew McKee** 7 (495) 728-5125

Office of the Defense Attaché [Finland]
American Embassy - Helsinki, Finland, APO, AE 09723
American Embassy, Itainen Puistotie 14-A, 00140 Helsinki, Finland
Tel: 358 (9) 616-250 Fax: 358 (9) 171-396

Defense Attaché **Col Keith N. Felter, Jr. USAF** 358 (9) 616250

U.S. Embassy in France

American Embassy - Paris, France, 2 Avenue Gabriel,
75382 Paris, Cedex 08, France
Tel: 33 (1) 4312-2222 Fax: 33 (1) 4266-9783 Internet: fr.usembassy.gov

Office of the U.S. Ambassador to France

American Embassy - Paris, France, 2 Avenue Gabriel,
75382 Paris, Cedex 08, France
Mail: American Embassy - Paris, France, PSC 116, A128,
APO, AE 09777

★ Ambassador **Ambassador Jamie D. McCourt** 33 (1) 4312-2700
Note: Ambassador McCourt serves concurrently as ambassador to Monaco.
Education: Georgetown BS; Maryland JD; MIT MS

Office of the U.S. Ambassador to France *(continued)*

Office Management Specialist to the Ambassador
Virginia R. Neumann 33 (1) 4312-2802
E-mail: neumannvr@state.gov

◇ Deputy Chief of Mission **Henry Thomas Wooster** 33 (1) 4312-2800
E-mail: woosterht@state.gov
Education: Yale 1989 MA

Office Management Specialist to the Deputy Chief of Mission **John Natter** 33 (1) 4312-2800
E-mail: natterjh@state.gov

Community Liaison Officer **Lacey Anderson** 33 (1) 4312-2155
Education: Central Missouri State 2011 BS

◇ Consul General **Robert F. "Bob" Hannan** 33 1-4312-2222
E-mail: hannanrf@state.gov
Education: Georgetown 1984 BSFS; Indust'l Col Armed Forces 2010 MS

◇ Economic Affairs Officer **Kristina A. Kvien** 33 (1) 4312-2654
E-mail: kvienka@state.gov
Education: Occidental 1987 BA; Army War Col 2014 MS

Environmental, Scientific and Technological Officer
John Hall Griffith 33 (1) 4312-2654

Equal Employment Opportunity Officer **(Vacant)** 33 (1) 4312-2222

Facilities Management Officer **Tom Nave** 33 (1) 4266-9783

Financial Management Officer **Rick Simpson** 33 (1) 4312-2222

General Services Officer **Scott M. Simpson** 33 (1) 4312-2222
E-mail: simpsons@state.gov

Human Resources Officer **Marielle H. Martin** 33 (1) 4312-2222

Information Management Officer
Richard Scott "Scott" Hewitt 33 (1) 4312-2141
E-mail: hewittrs@state.gov

Information Program Officer
Frederick E. "Rick" Ogg 33 (1) 4312-2222
E-mail: oggfe@state.gov

Information Systems Officer **Wenyi Shu** 33 (1) 4312-2222

Information Systems Security Officer **David Conn** 33 (1) 4312-2222

Legal Attaché **Eric C. Schramm** 33 (1) 4312-2400
E-mail: schrammec@state.gov

◇ Management Officer **Frank Joseph Ledahawsky** 33 (1) 4312-2009

◇ Political Affairs Officer **Brian C. Aggeler** 33 (1) 4312-2783
E-mail: aggelerbc@state.gov

◇ Public Affairs Officer **Angela Price Aggeler** 33 (1) 4312-4901
E-mail: aggelerap@state.gov Fax: 33 (1) 4312-2401

Regional Security Officer
Andriy R. "Andy" Koropeckyj 33 (1) 4312-2796
E-mail: koropeckyjar@state.gov
Education: Indiana 1988 MA

Africa Regional Services (Bureau of African Affairs)
14, boulevard Haussmann, 75009 Paris, France
Embassy of the United States Africa Regional Services,
18, avenue Gabriel, 75382 Paris, Cedex 08, France
Mail: American Embassy - Paris, France, Africa Regional Services,
Unit 9200, Box NEO, DPO, AE 09777
Tel: 33 (1) 43-12-22-22 Fax: 33 (1) 4312-7188 E-mail: ars@state.gov
Internet: fr.usembassy.gov/ars-paris

Director **Christopher Snipes** 33 (1) 43-12-22-22

Agricultural Section (Foreign Agricultural Service) [France]
American Embassy - Paris, France, 2 Avenue Gabriel,
75382 Paris, Cedex 08, France
Mail: American Embassy - Paris, France, Unit 9200, Box 44,
DPO, AE 09777
Tel: 33 (1) 4312-2277 Fax: 33 (1) 4312-2662
E-mail: agparis@fas.usda.gov Internet: www.usda-france.fr

Counselor for Agricultural Affairs
Kathryn A. "Kate" Snipes 33 (1) 4312-2329
E-mail: kate.snipes@fas.usda.gov

American Battle Monuments Commission [France]

● Chief Operating Officer **John Wessels** 33 (1) 40 75 27 62
E-mail: wesselsj@abmc.gov
Education: Carnegie Mellon 1985 BS

★ Presidential Appointment Requiring Senate Confirmation ☆ Presidential Appointment □ Schedule C Appointment ◇ Career Senior Foreign Service Appointment
● Career Senior Executive Service (SES) Appointment ○ Non-Career Senior Executive Service (SES) Appointment ■ Postal Career Executive Service

American Citizens Services [France]
2, avenue Gabriel, 75382 Paris, Cedex 08, France
Mail: American Embassy - Paris, France, PSC 116 E-009, APO, AE 09777
Tel: 33 (1) 4312-4876 E-mail: citizeninfo@state.gov

Chief **Laura L. Biedebach** 33 (1) 4312-4603
E-mail: biedebachll@state.gov

Commercial Section (Foreign Commercial Service) [France]
American Embassy - Paris, France, 2 Avenue Gabriel, 75382 Paris, Cedex 08, France
Mail: American Embassy - Paris, France, PSC 116, B-101, APO, AE 09777
Tel: 33 (1) 4312-7083 Fax: 33 (1) 4312-7012
E-mail: office.paris@trade.gov Internet: export.gov/france

Senior Commercial Officer **Stephen "Steve" Alley** 33 (1) 4312-7083
E-mail: steve.alley@trade.gov
First Secretary - DSCO **John Howell** 33 (1) 4312-7196
E-mail: john.howell@trade.gov
Commercial Officer **Joel Reynoso** 33 (1) 4312-7083

Drug Enforcement Administration [France]
2 Avenue Gabriel, 75382 Paris, Cedex 08, France
Mail: PSC 116, APO, AE 09777
Tel: 33 (1) 4312-7420

DEA Officer **Richard Bachour** 33 (1) 4312-7420

Federal Aviation Administration [France]
American Embassy/FAA, AEU-PAR, 2, Avenue Gabriel, 75382 Paris, Cedex 08, France
Mail: American Embassy/FAA, PSC 116, Box A-215, APO, AE 09777
Tel: 33 (1) 43 12 22 25 Fax: 33 (1) 43 12 25 05

FAA Senior Representative **Ian H. Ross** 33 (1) 43 12 22 25

Office of the Defense Attaché [France]
American Embassy - Paris, France, 2 Avenue Gabriel, 75382 Paris, Cedex 08, France
Mail: American Embassy - Paris, France, PSC 116, B-207, APO, AE 09777
Tel: 33 (1) 4312-2669 Fax: 33 (1) 4742-9183

Defense Attaché **COL David K. Chapman USA** 33 (1) 4312-2682
Education: Citadel BA; Troy State MA; National Defense U MNSSS

Department of Homeland Security - Transportation Security Administration [France]
American Embassy - Paris, France, 2 Avenue Gabriel, 75382 Paris, Cedex 08, France
Mail: American Embassy - Paris, France, PSC 116, Box A-113, APO, AE 09777
Tel: 33 (1) 4637-3182 Fax: 33 (1) 6312-2505

TSA Officer **James Duncan** 33 (1) 4312-2629

Department of Homeland Security - U.S. Immigration and Customs Enforcement [France]
American Embassy - Paris, France, 2 Avenue Gabriel, 75382 Paris, Cedex 08, France
Mail: American Embassy - Paris, France, PSC 116, D-320, APO, AE 09777
Tel: 33 (1) 4312-7400

Customs Officer **Steve Andres** 33 (1) 4312-7355

Marseille Consulate General
U.S. Consulate General - Marseille, France, Place Varian Fry, 13286 Marseille, France
Mail: U.S. Consulate General - Marseille, PSC 116 (MAR), APO, AE 09777
Tel: 33 01-43-12-48-85 Fax: 33 (4) 9155-0947

Consul General **Simon R. Hankinson** 33 01-43-12-48-85
E-mail: hankinsonsr@state.gov
Office Management Specialist to the Consul General **Stacy K. Teyssier** 33 01-43-12-48-85
Consular Officer **Seth Snyder** 33 01-43-12-48-85

Strasbourg Consulate General
U.S. Consulate General - Strasbourg, France, 14, Ave. d'Alsace, 67082 Strasbourg, Cedex, France
Mail: U.S. Consulate General, PSC 116 (Strasbourg), APO, AE 09777
Tel: 33 1-43 -124-880 Fax: 33 (3) 8824-0695

Consul General **Kara Cherise McDonald** . . . . 33 1-43 -124-880
E-mail: mcdonaldkc@state.gov

Bordeaux Consulate
American Presence Post - Bordeaux, 89, quai des Chardons, 33000 Bordeaux, Cedex, France
Mail: American Embassy - Paris, France, PSC 116, A128, APO, AE 09777
Tel: 33 1 43 12 48 65 Fax: 33 (5) 5651-6197
E-mail: usabordeaux@state.gov

Principal Officer **Daniel E. Hall** 33 1 43 12 48 65

Lyon Consulate
U.S. Consulate General, 1, quai Jules Courmont, 69002 Lyon, France
Mail: American Embassy - Paris, France, PSC 116, A128, APO, AE 09777
Tel: 33 1 43 12 48 60 Fax: 33 (4) 72 41 71 81
E-mail: usalyon@state.gov

Principal Officer **Rebecca Kimbrell** 33 1 43 12 48 60

Rennes Consulate
30, Quai Duguay-Trouin, 35000 Rennes, France
Mail: American Embassy - Paris, France, PSC 116, A128, APO, AE 09777
Tel: 33 (2) 1 43 12 48 70 Fax: 33 (2) 9935-0092
E-mail: usarennes@state.gov

Consul **(Vacant)** 33 (2) 1 43 12 48 70

Toulouse Consulate
25 Allee Jean-Jaures, 2nd Floor, 31000 Toulouse, France
Mail: American Embassy - Paris, France, PSC 116, A128, APO, AE 09777
Tel: 33 (5) 1 43 12 48 75 Fax: 33 (5) 3441-1619
E-mail: usatoulouse@state.gov

Consul **(Vacant)** 33 (5) 1 43 12 48 75

U.S. Embassy in Georgia
American Embassy - Tbilisi, Georgia, 11 George Balanchine Street, Tbilisi, 0131, Georgia
Tel: 995 (32) 227-70-00 Fax: 995 (32) 253-23-10
Internet: ge.usembassy.gov

Office of the U.S. Ambassador to Georgia
American Embassy - Tbilisi, Georgia, 11 George Balanchine Street, Tbilisi, 0131, Georgia
Mail: Department of State, 7060 Tbilisi Place, Washington, DC 20521-7060

★ Ambassador **(Vacant)** 995 (32) 227-70-00
◇ Chargé d'Affaires **Elizabeth Helen Rood** 995 (32) 227-70-00
E-mail: roodeh@state.gov
Office Management Specialist to the Ambassador **(Vacant)** 995 (32) 227-70-00
Deputy Chief of Mission (Acting) **Jeffrey K. "Jeff" Reneau** 995 (32) 227-70-00
E-mail: reneaujk@state.gov
Education: Georgetown BA; Harvard MEd
Office Management Specialist to the Deputy Chief of Mission **Cheryl Michaels** 995 (32) 227-70-00
Education: Thunderbird Global 2007 MBA; U Phoenix 2010 MS
Community Liaison Officer **Jennifer Gunnoe** 995 (32) 227-70-00
Consular Section Chief **Jeanette M. Rebert** 995 (32) 227-70-00
E-mail: rebertjm@state.gov
Education: Georgetown 1997 BSFS, 2001 MSFS
Financial Management Officer **Gregory B. "Greg" Keller** 995 (32) 227-70-00
E-mail: kellergb@state.gov

★ Presidential Appointment Requiring Senate Confirmation ☆ Presidential Appointment ☐ Schedule C Appointment ◇ Career Senior Foreign Service Appointment
● Career Senior Executive Service (SES) Appointment ○ Non-Career Senior Executive Service (SES) Appointment ■ Postal Career Executive Service

Office of the U.S. Ambassador to Georgia *(continued)*

General Services Officer **John Etcheverry** 995 (32) 227-70-00
E-mail: etcheverryjc@state.gov
Information Management Officer **David D. Ray** 995 (32) 227-70-00
E-mail: raydd@state.gov
Information Program Officer **Patrick T. Tran** 995 (32) 227-70-00
Information Security Officer
Arthur J. "Art" Mendez 995 (32) 227-70-00
E-mail: mendezaj@state.gov
Information Systems Security Officer
Patrick T. Tran 995 (32) 227-70-00
Legal Attaché **Diep Shoemaker** 995 (32) 227-70-00
Management Officer **Jason D. Kalbfleisch** 995 (32) 227-70-00
E-mail: kalbflieschj@state.gov
Education: Michigan State 1995 BS
Political/Economic Officer
Elizabeth F. "Liz" Zentos 995 (32) 227-70-00
E-mail: zentosef@state.gov
Public Affairs Officer **Jeffrey K. "Jeff" Reneau** 995 (32) 227-70-00
E-mail: reneaujk@state.gov Fax: 995 (32) 93 17 69
Education: Georgetown BA; Harvard MEd
Regional Security Officer **Nicolas P. Keefe** 995 (32) 227-70-00
E-mail: keefenp@state.gov

Agency for International Development [Georgia]
American Embassy - Tbilisi, Georgia, 11 George Balanchine Street, Tbilisi, 0131, Georgia
Mail: Department of State, 7060 Tbilisi Place, Washington, DC 20521-7060
Tel: 995 (32) 254 40 00 Fax: 995 (32) 254-41-45
Internet: www.usaid.gov/georgia

◇ Mission Director **Peter A. Wiebler** 995 (32) 54 40 00
E-mail: pwiebler@usaid.gov

Agricultural Section (Foreign Agricultural Service) [Georgia]
American Embassy - US Department of Agriculture, 11 George Balanchine Street, 0131 Ankara, Turkey
Tel: 995 (32) 227-7934 Fax: 995 (32) 227-7709
E-mail: dzirkvadzed@state.gov

Agricultural Officer (Resident in Ankara)
Christine Strossman 90 (312) 468-6129
E-mail: christine.strossman@fas.usda.gov

Commercial Section (Foreign Commercial Service) (Resident in Ankara) [Georgia]
American Embassy - Ankara, Turkey, 110 Ataturk Boulevard, Ankara, Turkey
Mail: PCS 93, Box 5000, APO, AE 09823
Tel: 90 (312) 455-5555 Fax: 90 (312) 457-7302

◇ Senior Commercial Officer
William "Bill" Czajkowski 90 (312) 457-7278
E-mail: william.czajkowski@trade.gov

Drug Enforcement Administration (Resident in Ankara) [Georgia]
American Embassy - Ankara, Turkey, 110 Ataturk Boulevard, Ankara, Turkey
Mail: American Embassy - Ankara, Turkey, PSC 93, Box 5000, APO, AE 09823
Tel: 90 (312) 455-5555 Fax: 90 (312) 467-0019

DEA Officer **(Vacant)** 90 (312) 455-5555

Federal Aviation Administration (Resident in Moscow) [Georgia]
Eight Bolshoy Devyatinsky Pereulok, 121099 Moscow, Russia
Mail: American Embassy, PSC 77, APO, AE 09721
Fax: 7 (495) 728-5350

FAA Senior Representative **Andrew McKee** 7 (495) 728-5125

Department of Justice - Narcotics Affairs Section [Georgia]
American Embassy - Tbilisi, Georgia, 11 George Balanchine Street, Tbilisi, 0131, Georgia
Mail: American Embassy - Georgia, Department of State, 7060 Tbilisi Place, Washington, DC 20521-7060
Tel: 995 (32) 98 99 67 Fax: 995 (32) 93 37 59

Narcotics Affairs Section Officer
Michael McMahon 995 (32) 98 99 67

Office of the Defense Attaché [Georgia]
American Embassy - Tbilisi, Georgia, 11 George Balanchine Street, Tbilisi, 0131, Georgia
Mail: Department of State, 7060 Tbilisi Place, Washington, DC 20521-7060
Tel: 995 (32) 98 99 67 Fax: 995 (32) 99 87 48

Defense Attaché
COL Jeffrey "Jeff" Hartman USA 995 (32) 98 99 67
Office of Defense Cooperation Chief
LTC John J. Myers USA 995 (32) 98 99 67
Defense Threat Reduction Agency Eurasia Chief
COL James Ron Hogan USA 995 (32) 98 99 67

Peace Corps [Georgia]
American Embassy - Tbilisi, Georgia, 25 Atoneli Street, Tbilisi, 0105, Georgia
Mail: Department of State, 7060 Tbilisi Place, Washington, DC 20521-7060
Tel: 995 (32) 2-24-12-20 E-mail: info@ge.peacecorps.gov
Internet: www.peacecorps.gov/georgia

Country Director **Stephen Meade Smith** 995 (32) 98 99 67

U.S. Embassy in Germany

American Embassy - Berlin, Germany, Clayallee 170, 14191 Berlin, Germany
Tel: 49 (30) 8305-0 Fax: 49 (30) 238-6290

Office of the U.S. Ambassador to Germany

American Embassy - Berlin, Germany, Clayallee 170, 14191 Berlin, Germany
Mail: American Embassy - Berlin, Germany, PSC 12017, APO, AE 09265

★ Ambassador **Ambassador Richard A. "Ric" Grenell** 49 (30) 8305-0
Education: Evangel Col BA; Harvard 1998 MPA
Office Management Specialist to the Ambassador
Solveig Caren Reeker 49 (30) 8305-0
E-mail: reekersc@state.gov
◇ Deputy Chief of Mission **Robin S. Quinville** 49 (30) 8305-0
E-mail: quinvillers@state.gov
Education: Columbia MA, MPhil
Office Management Specialist to the Deputy Chief of Mission **(Vacant)** 49 (30) 8305-0
Consular Section Chief **Kelly Scott "Scott" Cecil** 49 (30) 8305-0
American Embassy Consular Section - Berlin, Germany, Clayallee 170, 14195 Berlin, Germany
Community Liaison Officer **Carmen N. Andrews** 49 (30) 8305-0
◇ Economic Officer **Woodward Clark Price** 49 (30) 8305-0
E-mail: pricewc@state.gov
Education: Chicago 1984 BA; Johns Hopkins 1989 MS
Facilities Management Officer **Michael A. Itinger** 49 (30) 8305-0
Financial Management Officer **William Bill Haley** 49 (30) 8305-0
E-mail: haleywf2@state.gov
General Services Officer **Cheryl A. Moore** 49 (30) 8305-0
Human Resources Officer **Robert C. Ruehle** 49 (30) 8305-0
E-mail: ruehlerc@state.gov
Information Management Officer **Laura R. Leinow** 49 (30) 8305-0
Information Program Officer
Andrew L. "Andy" Jaeger 49 (30) 8305-0
E-mail: jaegeral@state.gov
Information Systems Officer
Stephen P. "Steve" McCain 49 (30) 8305-0
E-mail: mccainsp@state.gov
Information Systems Security Officer **Joel R. Rigby** 49 (30) 8305-0
E-mail: rigbyj@state.gov
Legal Attaché **Donald Schultz** 49 (30) 8305-0

(continued on next page)

★ Presidential Appointment Requiring Senate Confirmation ☆ Presidential Appointment ☐ Schedule C Appointment ◇ Career Senior Foreign Service Appointment
● Career Senior Executive Service (SES) Appointment ○ Non-Career Senior Executive Service (SES) Appointment ■ Postal Career Executive Service

Office of the U.S. Ambassador to Germany *(continued)*

◇ Management Officer **Eric A. Flohr** 49 (30) 8305-0
E-mail: flohrea@state.gov
Education: Franklin & Marshall 1986 BA; American U 1991 MA

◇ Political Affairs Officer **Eugenia M. Sidereas** 49 (30) 8305-0
E-mail: sidereasem@state.gov
Deputy Political Affairs Officer **Genevieve Libonati** . . . 49 (30) 8305-0
E-mail: libonatig@state.gov
Education: Catholic U 1992 BA; Chicago 1999 MA

◇ Public Affairs Officer **Christina Maria Huth Higgins** 49 (30) 8305-0
E-mail: higginscm@state.gov

Regional Security Officer **Todd R. Ziccarelli** 49 (30) 8305-0
E-mail: ziccarellitr@state.gov

Agricultural Section (Foreign Agricultural Service) [Germany]
American Embassy Consular Section - Berlin, Germany,
Clayallee 170, 14195 Berlin, Germany
Mail: American Embassy - Berlin, Germany, PSC 120, APO, AE 09265
Tel: 49 (30) 8305-1150 Fax: 49 (30) 8431-1935
E-mail: agberlin@fas.usda.gov

Agricultural Counselor **Kelly Stange** 49 (30) 8305-1150
E-mail: kelly.stange@fas.usda.gov

Commercial Section (Foreign Commercial Service) [Germany]
American Embassy - Berlin, Germany,
Clayallee 170, 14191 Berlin, Germany
Mail: Commercial Service - U.S. Embassy Berlin, PSC 120, Box 1000, APO, AE 09265
Tel: 49 (30) 8305-2940 Fax: 49 (30) 8305-1949
E-mail: office.berlin@trade.gov Internet: export.gov/germany

◇ Regional Senior Commercial Officer
John M. McCaslin 49 22-625-4374
E-mail: John.McCaslin@trade.gov

◇ Deputy Senior Commercial Officer **John P. Fay** 49 (30) 30.8305.1940
E-mail: john.fay@trade.gov

Federal Aviation Administration (Resident in Paris) [Germany]
American Embassy/FAA, AEU-PAR, 2, Avenue Gabriel, 75382 Paris, Cedex 08, France
Mail: American Embassy/FAA, PSC 116, Box A-215, APO, AE 09777
Tel: 33 (1) 43 12 22 25 Fax: 33 (1) 43 12 25 05

FAA Senior Representative, Paris **Ian H. Ross** 33 (1) 43 12 22 25

Office of the Defense Attaché [Germany]
American Embassy - Berlin, Germany,
Clayallee 170, 14191 Berlin, Germany
Mail: American Embassy - Berlin, Germany, PSC 120, APO, AE 09265

Defense Attaché **Terry Anderson** 49 (30) 8305-0

Office of Defense Cooperation [Germany]
American Embassy - Berlin, Germany,
Clayallee 170, 14191 Berlin, Germany
Fax: 49 (30) 8305-2445

Chief **Col Paul A. Tombarge USAF** 49 (30) 8305-2278
E-mail: tombargepa@state.gov

Deputy Chief **Chris A. Charveron** 49 (30) 8305-2040
E-mail: charveronca@state.gov
Education: Millikin 1979 BIE

Düsseldorf Consulate General
U.S. Consulate General - Düsseldorf, Germany,
Willi-Becker-Allee 10, 40227 Düsseldorf, Germany
Tel: 49 (211) 7888927 Fax: 49 (211) 788-8936
E-mail: PADuesseldorf@state.gov (Public Affairs)

Consul General **Fiona Evans** 49 (211) 47061-24
E-mail: evansf@state.gov
Education: Tufts 1997 BA, 2000 MALD
Office Management Specialist to the Consul General **Nicole Leick** 49 (211) 47061-24
E-mail: leicknx@state.gov

International Relations Officer Generalist (IROG)
Benjamin B. "Ben" Chapman 49 (211) 47061 25
E-mail: chapmanbb@state.gov
Education: American U BA, MS

Commercial Section (Foreign Commercial Service) [Germany]
U.S. Consulate General - Düsseldorf, Germany,
Willi-Becker-Allee 10, 40227 Düsseldorf, Germany
Tel: 49 (211) 737767-0 Fax: 49 (211) 737767-67
E-mail: office.dusseldorf@trade.gov

Principal Commercial Officer **Ken Walsh** 49 (211) 737767-0
E-mail: ken.walsh@trade.gov

Frankfurt Consulate General
U.S. Consulate General - Frankfurt Am Main, Germany,
Gießener Strasse 30, 60435 Frankfurt am Main, Germany
Mail: PSC 115, APO, AE 09213-0115
Tel: 49 (69) 7535-0 Fax: 49 (69) 7535-5410

◇ Consul General **Patricia A. Lacina** 49 (69) 7535-2222
E-mail: lacinapa@state.gov
Education: Cal State (Sacramento) 1987 MA
Office Management Specialist to the Consul General
Jennifer A. Koon 49 (69) 45350
E-mail: koonja@state.gov

◇ Deputy Principal Officer **David S. Elmo** 49 (69) 7535-2221
E-mail: elmods@state.gov
Education: Fordham 1984 BS; Webster 1988 MS; Army War Col 2001 MS; Columbia 1991 MS

◇ Consular Section Chief
Mary Emma "Mea" Arnold 49 (69) 7535-2510
E-mail: arnoldme@state.gov
E-mail: germanyacs@state.gov

Community Liaison Officer **Jonette C. Vaughan** 49 (69) 75350
E-mail: vaughanjc@state.gov

Equal Employment Officer **Allison Ebert** 49 (69) 75350

General Services Officer **Marissa M. Gurfield** 49 (69) 75350
E-mail: gurfieldmm@state.gov

Information Management Officer
Jeanette D. Garner 49 (69) 7535-2550
E-mail: garnerjd@state.gov

Information Program Officer **Joseph S. Conners** 49 (69) 75350
E-mail: connersj@state.gov

Information Systems Officer **Zekarias Gebeyehou** 49 (69) 75350
E-mail: gebeyehouz@state.gov

Information Systems Security Officer **Hervé Irion** 49 (69) 75350
E-mail: irionh@state.gov

Legal Attaché **Casey R. Harrington** 49 (69) 7535-3870

◇ Management Officer **Michelle Ann Burton** 49 (69) 7535-5440
E-mail: burtonma@state.gov
Education: North Dakota State 1994 BS

Political/Economic Section Chief
Nimesh N. "Nick" Parikh 49 (69) 7535-2221
E-mail: parikhn@state.gov

Public Affairs Officer **Carrie K. Lee** 49 (69) 7535-8831
Fax: 49 (69) 7535-8842

Regional Security Officer **Kerry K. Crockett** 49 (69) 7535-2408

Commercial Section (Foreign Commercial Service) [Germany]
U.S. Consulate General - Frankfurt, PSC 115, APO, AE 09213-0115
U.S. Consulate General - Frankfurt Am Main, Germany,
Platenstrasse 1, Dornbusch, 60323 Frankfurt am Main, Germany
Tel: 49 (69) 7535-3120 Fax: 49 (69) 7535-3171
E-mail: office.frankfurt@trade.gov

◇ Principal Commercial Officer
Cynthia "Cindy" Biggs 49 (69) 7535–3169
E-mail: cindy.biggs@trade.gov

Department of Homeland Security - U.S. Customs and Border Protection [Germany]

Customs Officer **(Vacant)** 49 (69) 7535-0

Hamburg Consulate General

U.S. Consulate General - Hamburg, Germany,
Alsterufer 27/28, 20354 Hamburg, Germany
Mail: U.S. Consulate General - Hamburg,
Department of State, 5180 Hamburg Place, Washington, DC 20521-5180
Tel: 49 (40) 411-71100 Fax: 49 (40) 411-71222
E-mail: hamburgpa@state.gov

Consul General **Richard T. "Rick" Yoneoka** 49 (40) 411-71100
E-mail: yoneokar@state.gov
Education: Tufts 1992 BA; London School Econ (UK) 1995 MS
Political/Economic Officer **Laura Hammond** 49 (40) 411-71207
Regional Security Officer (Resident in Berlin)
Brad Pittson 49 (30) 8305-0
Education: Citadel 2003 BA

Leipzig Consulate General

U.S. Consulate General - Leipzig, Wilhelm-Seyfferth-Str. 4,
04107 Leipzig, Germany
Mail: U.S. Consulate General - Leipzig, PSC 120, Box 1000,
APO, AE 09265
Tel: 49 (341) 213-840 Fax: 49 (341) 213-8475
E-mail: LeipzigUSConsulate@state.gov

Consul General **Timothy Eydelnant** 49 (341) 213-840
E-mail: eydelnantt@state.gov
Office Management Specialist to the Consul General
Birgit Kaemmer 49 (341) 213-84-0
Information Systems Security Officer (Resident in
Berlin) **Joel R. Rigby** 49 (30) 8305-0
E-mail: rigbyj@state.gov
Political/Economic Officer **Emily Y. Norris** 49 (341) 213-84-0
E-mail: norrisey@state.gov
Education: Princeton 2009 BA
Regional Security Officer **Sean Berk** 49 (30) 8305-0
E-mail: berksr@state.gov
Education: La Salle U 2005 BA; Villanova 2012 MA

Munich Consulate General

U.S. Consulate General - Munich, Germany,
Königinstrasse 5, 80539 Munich, Germany
Tel: 49 (89) 2888-0 Fax: 49 (89) 280-9998

Consul General **Meghan E. Gregonis** 49 (89) 2888-736
E-mail: gregonisme@state.gov
Office Management Specialist to the Consul
General **Caroline A. Bennett** 49 (89) 2888-736
E-mail: bennettca@state.gov
Consular Officer **Richard J. Faillace** 49 (89) 2888-0
E-mail: faillacerj@state.gov
Information Programs Officer **Kevin R. Kiah** 49 (89) 2888-634
E-mail: kiahkr@state.gov
Management Officer **Hunter B. Chen** 49 (89) 2888-745
E-mail: chenhb@state.gov
Political/Economic Officer **Lu Zhou** 49 (89) 2888-0
E-mail: zhoul@state.gov
Public Affairs Officer **Stephen F. Ibelli** 49 (89) 2888-0
E-mail: ibellisf@state.gov
Regional Security Officer **Claude Poole** 49 (89) 2888-648
E-mail: poolec@state.gov

Commercial Section (Foreign Commercial Service) [Germany]

U.S. Consulate General - Munich, Germany,
Königinstrasse 5, 80539 Munich, Germany
Tel: 49 (89) 2888-748 Fax: 49 (89) 285-261
E-mail: office.munich@trade.gov

Commercial Officer **Erik Hunt** 49 (89) 2888-643
E-mail: erik.hunt@trade.gov

U.S. Embassy in Greece

American Embassy - Athens, Greece, 91 Vasilissis Sophias Avenue,
10160 Athens, Greece
Tel: 30 (21) 0721-2951 Fax: 30 (21) 0645-6282
Internet: gr.usembassy.gov

Office of the U.S. Ambassador to Greece

American Embassy - Athens, Greece, 91 Vasilissis Sophias Avenue,
10160 Athens, Greece
Mail: American Embassy - Athens, Greece, PSC 108,
DPO, AE 09842-0108

★ Ambassador
Ambassador Geoffrey R. "Geoff" Pyatt 30 (21) 0720-2378
E-mail: pyattgr@state.gov
Education: UC Irvine 1985 BA; Yale 1987 MA
Office Management Specialist to the Ambassador
Lori A. McLean 30 (21) 0720-2378
E-mail: McLeanLA@state.gov
◇ Deputy Chief of Mission **Kate Marie Byrnes** 30 (21) 0720-2342
Note: On November 7, 2018, President Donald J. Trump announced his intention to nominate Kate Byrnes to be ambassador to Macedonia.
E-mail: ByrnesKM2@state.gov
Education: Georgetown BS, MA
Office Management Specialist to the Deputy Chief
of Mission **Margaret Johnson** 30 (21) 0720-2342
E-mail: JohnsonM2@state.gov
Consul **(Vacant)** 30 (21) 0720-2810
Co-Community Liaison Officer
Christine D. Gardner 30 (21) 0720-4826
E-mail: GardnerCD@state.gov
Co-Community Liaison Officer
Sylvia J. Rogers-Romero 30 (21) 0720-2239
E-mail: RogersSJ@state.gov
Economic Officer **William Henry "Chip" Laitinen** . . . 30 (21) 0720-2304
E-mail: laitinenwh@state.gov
Equal Employment Opportunity Officer
Brigid J. Ryan 30 (21) 0720-2551
E-mail: RyanBJ1@state.gov
Education: Maryland JD
Facilities Management Officer **Daniel P. Hess** 30 (21) 0720-2144
E-mail: HessDP2@state.gov
Financial Management Officer **Wagih H. Ibrahim** 30 (21) 0720-4727
E-mail: IbrahimWH@state.gov
General Services Officer **Elizabeth A. Keene** 30 (21) 0720-4703
E-mail: keeneea@state.gov
Human Resources Officer **Erfana S. Dar** 30 (21) 0720-4726
E-mail: DarES@state.gov
Information Management Officer
Curtis M. Presson 30 (21) 0720-2347
E-mail: PressonCM@state.gov
Information Program Officer **Shane W. Child** 30 (21) 0720-2340
E-mail: ChildSW@state.gov
Information Systems Officer **Dwayne E. Singleton** . . . 30 (21) 0720-2247
E-mail: SingletonDE@state.gov
Information Systems Security Officer
Kevin R. Handy 30 (21) 0720-2851
E-mail: HandyKR@state.gov
Legal Attaché **Aristos Papadacos** 30 (21) 0720-2455
E-mail: Aristos.Papadacos@ic.fbi.gov
Management Officer **James Kent "Kent" Stiegler** . . . 30 (21) 0720-4723
E-mail: stieglerjk2@state.gov
Political Officer **Amy C. Carlon** 30 (21) 0720-2385
E-mail: CarlonAC@state.gov
Political/Military Officer **Julia I. Jacoby** 30 (21) 0720-2391
E-mail: JacobyJI@state.gov
Public Affairs Officer **Monica L. Cummings** 30 (21) 0720-4782
E-mail: CummingsML@state.gov
Press Attaché **Eshel William "Bill" Murad** 30 (21) 0720-4780
E-mail: MuradEW@state.gov
Regional Security Officer **Raymond Bassi** 30 (21) 0720-2855
E-mail: BassiR@state.gov

★ Presidential Appointment Requiring Senate Confirmation ☆ Presidential Appointment □ Schedule C Appointment ◇ Career Senior Foreign Service Appointment
● Career Senior Executive Service (SES) Appointment ○ Non-Career Senior Executive Service (SES) Appointment ■ Postal Career Executive Service

DEPARTMENTS

Agricultural Section (Foreign Agricultural Service) (Resident in Rome) [Greece]
American Embassy - Rome, Italy, Via Veneto 119/A, 00187 Rome, Italy
Mail: American Embassy - Rome, Italy, PSC 59, Box 13, APO, AE 09624
Tel: 39 (06) 46741 Fax: 39 (06) 488-2672

Agricultural Attaché **Frederick H. "Fred" Giles** 39 (06) 4674-2396
E-mail: frederick.giles@fas.usda.gov

Commercial Section (Foreign Commercial Service) [Greece]
American Embassy - Athens, Greece, 91 Vasilissis Sophias Avenue, 10160 Athens, Greece
Mail: American Embassy - Athens, Greece, PSC 108, APO, AE 09842-0108
E-mail: office.athens@trade.gov Internet: export.gov/greece

Senior Commercial Officer **Keith L. Silver** 30 (21) 0720-4817
E-mail: keith.silver@trade.gov
Education: New England Col 1990 BA; Tufts 1995 MA

Drug Enforcement Administration [Greece]
American Embassy - Athens, Greece, 91 Vasilissis Sophias Avenue, 10160 Athens, Greece
Mail: American Embassy - Athens, Greece, PSC 108, APO, AE 09842-0108
Tel: 30 (21) 0720-2785

DEA Officer **John Livanis** 30 (21) 0721-4831
E-mail: LivanisJ@state.gov

Department of Homeland Security - U.S. Citizenship and Immigration Services [Greece]
American Embassy - Athens, Greece, 91 Vasilissis Sophias Avenue, 10160 Athens, Greece
Mail: American Embassy - Athens, Greece, PSC 108, APO, AE 09842-0108

CIS Officer **James Fletcher** 30 (21) 0721-2780
E-mail: James.C.Fletcher@uscis.dhs.gov

Federal Aviation Administration (Resident in Paris) [Greece]
American Embassy/FAA, AEU-PAR, 2, Avenue Gabriel, 75382 Paris, Cedex 08, France
Mail: American Embassy/FAA, PSC 116, Box A-215, APO, AE 09777
Tel: 33 (1) 4312-2225 Fax: 33 (1) 4312-2505

FAA Representative **Ian H. Ross** 33 (1) 4312-2225
E-mail: RossIH@state.gov

Office of the Defense Attaché [Greece]
American Embassy - Athens, Greece, 91 Vasilissis Sophias Avenue, 10160 Athens, Greece
Mail: American Embassy - Athens, Greece, PSC 108, APO, AE 09842-0108
Tel: 30 (21) 0720-2212 Fax: 30 (21) 0725-0373

Defense Attaché **CAPT Robert H. Palm USN** 30 (21) 0720-2205
E-mail: PalmRH@state.gov

Thessaloniki Consulate General
U.S. Consulate General - Thessaloniki, Greece, 43 Tsimiski Street, 7th Floor, 546 23 Thessaloniki, Greece
Mail: U.S. Consulate General - Thessaloniki, PSC 108, Box 37, DPO, AE 09842-0108
Tel: 30 (231) 024-2905 Fax: 30 (231) 024-2927

Principal Officer **Gregory W. "Greg" Pfleger** 30 (231) 024-3102
E-mail: pflegergw@state.gov

Political Officer **Gregory W. "Greg" Pfleger** 30 (231) 024-3102
E-mail: pflegergw@state.gov

U.S. Embassy to the Holy See
Via Sallustiana, 49, 00187 Rome, Italy
Tel: 39 (06) 4674-1 Fax: 39 (06) 4674 3412 Internet: va.usembassy.gov

Office of the U.S. Ambassador to the Holy See
Via Sallustiana, 49, 00187 Rome, Italy
Mail: American Embassy - The Holy See, PSC 59, Box 66, APO, AE 09624

★ Ambassador
Ambassador Callista Louise Gingrich 39 (06) 4674-3425
Education: Luther Col 1988 BA
Office Management Specialist to the Ambassador
(Vacant) 39 (06) 4674-3425

Deputy Chief of Mission **Louis L. Bono** 39 (06) 4674-3428
E-mail: bonoll@state.gov
Office Management Specialist to the Deputy Chief of Mission **Jelena Lazovic** 39 (06) 4674-3425

Political/Military Officer **(Vacant)** 39 (06) 4674-3439
Fax: 39 (06) 5730-0682

Political and Economic Chief
Aud-Frances McKernan 39 (06) 4674-3437

Political/Economic Officer
Amal Moussaoui Haynes 39 (06) 4674-3425

Political Officer **Emmett Sapp** 39 (06) 4674-1

Public Affairs Officer **Theodore E. Diehl** 39 (06) 4674-3431
E-mail: diehlte@state.gov
Education: U Pacific BA; San Francisco State U MA

Regional Security Officer (Resident in Rome)
Justin J. Otto 39 (06) 4674-2175
American Embassy - Rome, Italy, PSC 59, Box 100, APO, AE 09624 — Fax: 39 (06) 488-2672
E-mail: ottojj@state.gov

U.S. Embassy in Hungary
Szabadsag ter 7-9, Granite Tower, H-1054 Budapest, Hungary
Tel: 36 (1) 475-4400 Fax: 36 (1) 475-4248 Internet: hu.usembassy.gov

Office of the U.S. Ambassador to Hungary
Szabadsag ter 12, H-1054 Budapest, Hungary
Mail: Department of State, 5270 Budapest Place, Washington, DC 20521-5270

★ Ambassador **Ambassador David B. Cornstein** 36 (1) 475-4400
Education: Lafayette BA; NYU MBA
Office Management Specialist to the Ambassador
(Vacant) 36 (1) 475-4634

◇ Deputy Chief of Mission **David J. Kostelancik** 36 (1) 475-4776
E-mail: kostelancikdj@state.gov
Education: Northwestern 1986 BA; Michigan 1989 MA; National Defense U 2008 MS
Office Management Specialist to the Deputy Chief of Mission **Jessica Haynie** 36 (1) 475-4776
E-mail: hayniej@state.gov

Consular Section Chief **Christopher J. Vogt** 36 (1) 475-4164
Education: Maryland BS; Johns Hopkins MS — Fax: 36 (1) 475-4188

Community Liaison Officer **Diane Baker** 36 (1) 475-4038

Economic Officer **(Vacant)** 36 (1) 475-4400

Environment, Science and Technology Officer
Katia Bennett 36 (1) 475-4956
E-mail: bennettk@state.gov

Financial Management Officer **Marcela Curtis** 36 (1) 475-4330

General Services Officer **(Vacant)** 36 (1) 475-4896

Information Management Officer **Richard K. Clark** 36 (1) 475-4211

Information Program Officer **Rickye Webb** 36 (1) 475-4210

Information Systems Security Officer **Rickye Webb** 36 (1) 475-4210

Legal Attaché **David Snyder** 36 (1) 475-4017

Management Officer
Jay Douglas "Douglas" Dykhouse 36 (1) 475-4353
Fax: 36 (1) 475-4520

Political and Economic Section Chief
Mark Tervakoski 36 (1) 475-4670
Education: Maryland 2000 BASc; Oxford (UK) 2003 MPhil — Fax: 36 (1) 475-4280

★ Presidential Appointment Requiring Senate Confirmation ☆ Presidential Appointment □ Schedule C Appointment ◇ Career Senior Foreign Service Appointment
● Career Senior Executive Service (SES) Appointment ○ Non-Career Senior Executive Service (SES) Appointment ■ Postal Career Executive Service

Office of the U.S. Ambassador to Hungary *(continued)*

Public Affairs Officer **James G. Land** 36 (1) 475-4292
E-mail: landjg@state.gov Fax: 36 (1) 475-4712
Regional Security Officer **Brian Blackman** 36 (1) 475-4916

Agency for International Development [Hungary]
Szabadsag ter 12, H-1054 Budapest, Hungary
Mail: Department of State, 5270 Budapest Place,
Washington, DC 20521-5270
Tel: 36 (1) 475-4604 Fax: 36 (1) 302-0693

AID Officer **Ivana Vuco** 36 (1) 475-4422
E-mail: ivuco@usaid.gov

Agricultural Section (Foreign Agricultural Service) [Hungary]
American Embassy, Szabadsag ter 12, H-1054 Budapest, Hungary
Mail: Department of State, 5270 Budapest Place,
Washington, DC 20521-5270
Tel: 36 (1) 475-4162 Fax: 36 (1) 475-4676
E-mail: agbudapest@fas.usda.gov

Agricultural Counselor (Resident in Berlin)
Kelly Stange 49 (30) 8305-1158
American Embassy Consular Section - Berlin, Germany,
Clayallee 170, 14195 Berlin, Germany
E-mail: kelly.stange@fas.usda.gov

Commercial Section (Foreign Commercial Service) [Hungary]
Bank Center Building, Szabadsag ter 7-9, Granite Tower,
1st Floor, H-1054 Budapest, Hungary
Mail: Department of State, 5270 Budapest Place,
Washington, DC 20521-5270
Tel: 36 (1) 475-4090 Fax: 36 (1) 475-4205
E-mail: office.budapest@trade.gov Internet: export.gov/hungary

Senior Commercial Officer
Jennifer Kane-Zabolotskaya 36 (1) 475-4090
E-mail: jennifer.kane@trade.gov

Federal Aviation Administration (Resident in Moscow) [Hungary]
FAA Representative **Andrew McKee** 7 (495) 728-5125

Office of the Defense Attaché [Hungary]
Szabadsag ter 12, H-1054 Budapest, Hungary
Mail: Department of State, 5270 Budapest Place,
Washington, DC 20521-5270
Tel: 36 (1) 475-4648 Fax: 36 (1) 475-4223

Defense and Army Attaché **Donald Baker** 36 (1) 475-4648

U.S. Embassy in Iceland

Laufasvegur 21, IS-101, Reykjavik, Iceland
Tel: 354 595 2200 Tel: 354 562-9118 Internet: is.usembassy.gov

Office of the U.S. Ambassador to Iceland

American Embassy, Laufasvegur 21, IS-101, Reykjavik, Iceland
Mail: American Embassy - Reykjavik, PSC 1003, Box 40,
FPO, AE 09728-0340
Tel: 354 595 2200 Fax: 354 562-9118

★ Ambassador-Designate **Dr. Jeffrey Ross Gunter** 354 595 2200
Education: UC Berkeley AB; USC MD
◇ Chargé d'Affaires **Jill Marie Esposito** 354 562-2206
E-mail: espositojm@state.gov
Office Management Specialist to the Ambassador
(Vacant) 354 595 2200
◇ Deputy Chief of Mission **Jill Marie Esposito** 354 562-2206
E-mail: espositojm@state.gov
Office Management Specialist to the Deputy Chief of
Mission **Joanne Juliano** 354 595 2200
E-mail: julianojm@state.gov
Community Liaison Officer **(Vacant)** 354 595 2200
Consular Officer **(Vacant)** 354 595 2200
Economic/Commercial Officer **John P. Kill** 354 595 2200
Environment, Science and Technology Officer **(Vacant)** 354 595 2200
General Services Officer **(Vacant)** 354 595 2200
Information Management Officer **John A. Miller** 354 595 2200

Office of the U.S. Ambassador to Iceland *(continued)*

Information Program Officer **John R. Muskat** 354 595 2200
Information Systems Security Officer **John R. Muskat** 354 595 2200
Management Officer **Janice C. Anderson** 354 595 2200
Political Officer **Emily Cintora** 354 595 2200
Public Affairs Officer **Oscar Avila** 354 595 2200
Fax: 354 552-9529
Regional Security Officer **John Cerri** 354 595 2200

Agricultural Section (Foreign Agricultural Service) (Resident in The Hague) [Iceland]
American Embassy - The Hague, Netherlands,
John Adams Park 1, 2244 BZ Wassenaar, Netherlands
Mail: PSC 115, Box 038, APO, AE 09715

Agricultural Counselor **Susan B. Phillips** American
Embassy - The Hague, Netherlands 31 (70) 310-2300
Education: Wisconsin 1985 BS; Fax: 31 (70) 365-7681
Kansas State 1991 MSA

Federal Aviation Administration (Resident in Moscow) [Iceland]
American Embassy, Eight Bolshoy Devyatinsky Pereulok,
121099 Moscow, Russia
Mail: Unit 5430, DPO, AE 09721
Fax: 7 (495) 728-5350

FAA Senior Representative **Andrew McKee** 7 (495) 728-5125

U.S. Embassy in Ireland

42 Elgin Road, Ballsbridge, Dublin, Ireland 4
Tel: 353 (1) 668-8777 Fax: 353 (1) 668-2896 Internet: ie.usembassy.gov

Office of the U.S. Ambassador to Ireland

American Embassy - Dublin, Ireland, 42 Elgin Road,
Ballsbridge, Dublin, Ireland
Mail: American Embassy - Dublin, Ireland,
5290 Dublin Place, Washington, DC 20521-5290

★ Ambassador-Designate **Edward F. Crawford** 353 (1) 668-8777
Education: John Carroll
Chargé d'Affaires **Lonnie Reece "Reece" Smyth** 353 (1) 668-8777
E-mail: smythlr@state.gov
Office Management Specialist to the Ambassador
(Vacant) 353 (1) 668-8777
Deputy Chief of Mission (Acting) **L. Kirk Wolcott** 353 (1) 668-8777
E-mail: wolcottlk@state.gov
Office Management Specialist to the Deputy Chief
of Mission **Cindy Thompson** 353 (1) 668-8777
Consular Affairs Officer **Mary Virginia Hantsch** 353 (1) 668-8777
Community Liaison Officer **Erika Furey** 353 (1) 668-8777
E-mail: fureye@state.gov
Financial Management Officer
Jonathan M. Dennehy 353 (1) 668-8777
E-mail: dennehyjm@state.gov
General Services Officer **(Vacant)** 353 (1) 668-8777
Information Management Officer
Laura A. Campbell 353 (1) 668-8777
Information Program Officer **Doug Surette** 353 (1) 668-8777
Management Officer **Adham Zibas Loutfi** 353 (1) 668-8777
E-mail: loutfiaz@state.gov Fax: 353 (1) 668-7734
Political Officer **Faith Colvin** 353 (1) 668-8777
Political/Economic Officer **Timothy Forsyth** 353 (1) 668-8777
E-mail: forsythtl@state.gov
Public Affairs Officer **L. Kirk Wolcott** .... 353 (1) 668-8777 ext. 2104
E-mail: wolcottlk@state.gov Fax: 353 (1) 668-9184
Regional Security Officer **David P. Malone** 353 (1) 668-8777

Agricultural Section (Foreign Agricultural Service) (Resident in London) [Ireland]
American Embassy - London, England,
33 Nine Elms Lane, London, SW11 7US, United Kingdom
Tel: 44 (20) 7894-0464 E-mail: aglondon@fas.usda.gov

Agricultural Officer **Stanley S. "Stan" Phillips** 44 (20) 7894-0464
E-mail: stan.phillips@fas.usda.gov

DEPARTMENTS

★ Presidential Appointment Requiring Senate Confirmation ☆ Presidential Appointment ☐ Schedule C Appointment ◇ Career Senior Foreign Service Appointment
● Career Senior Executive Service (SES) Appointment ○ Non-Career Senior Executive Service (SES) Appointment ■ Postal Career Executive Service

DEPARTMENTS

Commercial Section (Foreign Commercial Service) [Ireland]
American Embassy - Dublin, Ireland, 42 Elgin Road,
Ballsbridge, Dublin, Ireland 4
Mail: American Embassy - Dublin, Ireland,
5290 Dublin Place, Washington, DC 20521-5290
Tel: 353 (1) 237-5850 Fax: 353 (1) 667-4754 Internet: export.gov/ireland
E-mail: office.dublin@trade.gov

◇ Senior Commercial Officer (Resident in Stockholm)
Sandillo N. "Dillon" Banerjee 46 (8) 783-5346
E-mail: dillon.banerjee@trade.gov
Education: William & Mary 1990 BA; American U 1994 MA

Department of Homeland Security - U.S. Immigration and Customs Enforcement (Resident in London)
Attaché **James R. "Jim" Mancuso** 44 (20) 7499-9000
E-mail: MancusoJR@state.gov

Department of Homeland Security - U.S. Customs and Border Protection [Ireland]
Customs Officer **Zachary "Clay" Thomas** 353 (1) 668-8777

Federal Aviation Administration (Resident in Paris) [Ireland]
American Embassy/FAA, AEU-PAR, 2, Avenue Gabriel, 75382 Paris,
Cedex 08, France
Mail: PSC 116, APO, AE 09777
Fax: 33 (1) 4312-2505
FAA Senior Representative **Ian H. Ross** 33 (1) 4312-2225

Office of the Defense Attaché [Ireland]
American Embassy - Dublin, Ireland, 42 Elgin Road,
Ballsbridge, Dublin, Ireland
Mail: American Embassy - Dublin, Ireland,
5290 Dublin Place, Washington, DC 20521-5290
Tel: 353 (1) 668-8777 ext. 2200 Fax: 353 (1) 668-8698
Defense Attaché **Andrew Martin** .... 353 (1) 668-8777 ext. 2200

U.S. Embassy in Italy
Via Vittorio Veneto 119/A, 00187 Rome, Italy
Tel: 39 (06) 46741 Fax: 39 (06) 488-2672 Internet: it.usembassy.gov

Office of the U.S. Ambassador to Italy
American Embassy - Rome, Italy, Via Vittorio Veneto 119/A-00187,
Rome, Italy
Mail: American Embassy - Rome, Italy, PSC 59, Box 100 (F),
APO, AE 09624
E-mail: romepressoffice@state.gov

★ Ambassador
Ambassador Lewis M. "Lew" Eisenberg 39 (06) 4674-2210
Note: Ambassador Eisenberg serves concurrently as ambassador to San Marino.
E-mail: eisenberglm@state.gov
Education: Dartmouth 1964 BA; Cornell 1966 MBA
Office Management Specialist to the Ambassador
Abigail Erickson 39 (06) 4674-2210
E-mail: ericksonae@state.gov
◇ Deputy Chief of Mission **Kelly C. Degnan** 39 (06) 4674-2210
E-mail: degnankc@state.gov
Education: Northwestern BA
Office Management Specialist to the Deputy Chief of Mission **Meghan McGivern** 39 (06) 4674-2210
◇ Consul General **Michael J. Jacobsen** 39 (06) 4674-2210
E-mail: jacobsenmj@state.gov
Community Liaison Officer **Lauren Benson** 39 (06) 4674-2210
Cultural Affairs Officer **Rodney D. Ford** 39 (06) 46741
Education: Emory 1993 BA; Georgia State 2001 MA;
National Defense U 2017 MS
Economic Affairs Officer **Jean Ellen Preston** 39 (06) 4674-2107
E-mail: prestonj@state.gov
Environment, Science and Technology Officer
Caron De Mars 39 (06) 4674-2691
E-mail: demarsce1@state.gov Fax: 39 (06) 4674-2398
Equal Employment Opportunity Officer **(Vacant)** 39 (06) 4674-2210

Office of the U.S. Ambassador to Italy *(continued)*

Facilities Management Officer **Dennis E. Nice** 39 (06) 4674-1
E-mail: nicede@state.gov
Financial Management Officer
James W. "Jim" Paravonian 39 (06) 4674-2210
E-mail: paravonianjw@state.gov
General Services Officer **Jerome P. Hohman** 39 (06) 4674-2210
E-mail: hohmanjp@state.gov
Human Resources Officer **Cassandra Hamblin** 39 (06) 46741
E-mail: hamblinc@state.gov
Information Management Officer
John "Troy" Conway 39 (06) 4674-2157
E-mail: conwayjt@state.gov
Information Program Officer **Janet G. Stevenson** 39 (06) 4674-2379
E-mail: stevensonjg@state.gov Fax: 39 (06) 4674-2701
Information Systems Officer **Tacla Boohaker** 39 (06) 4674-2210
E-mail: boohakertr@state.gov
Information Systems Security Officer **Marvin A. Biteng** ... 39 (06) 46741
Legal Attaché **Kieran Ramsey** 39 (06) 46741
◇ Management Officer **Martin P. Hohe** 39 (06) 4674-2210
E-mail: hohemp@state.gov
Military Liaison Officer **(Vacant)** 39 (06) 4674-2161
◇ Public Affairs Officer **Beth L. Poisson** 39 (06) 4674-2368
E-mail: poissonbl@state.gov Fax: 39 (06) 4674-2478
Education: Georgetown 1980 BA;
Johns Hopkins 1987 MA
Press Attaché
Lillian Germaine deValcourt-Ayala 39 (06) 4674-2426
E-mail: devalcourtlg@state.gov
E-mail: romepressoffice@state.gov
◇ Political Affairs Officer **James E. "Jim" Donegan** ... 39 (06) 4674-2106
E-mail: doneganje2@state.gov
Political-Military Officer **Jason Baird Grubb** 39 (06) 4674-2106
E-mail: grubbjb@state.gov
Regional Security Officer **Justin J. Otto** 39 (06) 4674-2175
E-mail: ottojj@state.gov

Agricultural Section (Foreign Agricultural Service) [Italy]
American Embassy - Rome, Italy, Via Veneto 119/A, 00187 Rome, Italy
Mail: American Embassy - Rome, Italy, Unit 9500, Box 13,
FPO, AE 09624-0013
Tel: 39 (06) 4674-2396 Fax: 39 (06) 4788-7008
E-mail: agrome@fas.usda.gov
Agricultural Attaché **Frederick H. "Fred" Giles** 39 (06) 4674-2396
E-mail: frederick.giles@fas.usda.gov

Commercial Section (Foreign Commercial Service) [Italy]
American Embassy - Rome, Italy, Via Vittorio Veneto 119/A,
00187 Rome, Italy
Mail: American Embassy - Rome, Italy, PSC 59, Box 30, APO, AE 09624
Tel: 39 (06) 4674-2202 Fax: 39 (06) 4674-2113
Internet: http://export.gov/italy/
◇ Senior Commercial Officer **Todd Avery** 39 (06) 4674-2824
E-mail: todd.avery@trade.gov
Deputy Senior Commercial Officer
Matthew Hilgendorf 39 (06) 4674-2105
E-mail: Matthew.Hilgendorf@trade.gov
Education: American U 1993 BA

Department of Homeland Security - U.S. Citizenship and Immigration Services [Italy]
American Embassy - Rome, Italy, Via Veneto 119/A, Rome, Italy
Mail: American Embassy - Rome, Italy, PSC 59, Box 37, APO, AE 09624
Tel: 39 (06) 4674-2586 Fax: 39 (06) 4674-2920
CIS Officer **Joseph Langois** 39 (06) 4674-2586

Department of Homeland Security - U.S. Immigration and Customs Enforcement [Italy]
American Embassy - Rome, Italy, Via Veneto 119/A, Rome, Italy
Mail: American Embassy - Rome, Italy, PSC 59, Box 19, APO, AE 09624
Tel: 39 (06) 46741 Fax: 39 (06) 488-2672
Customs Officer **Armando Astorga** 39 (06) 4674-2475

★ Presidential Appointment Requiring Senate Confirmation ☆ Presidential Appointment ☐ Schedule C Appointment ◇ Career Senior Foreign Service Appointment
● Career Senior Executive Service (SES) Appointment ○ Non-Career Senior Executive Service (SES) Appointment ■ Postal Career Executive Service

Department of Justice - Drug Enforcement Administration [Italy]
American Embassy - Rome, Italy, Via Vittorio Veneto 119/A, 00187 Rome, Italy
Mail: American Embassy - Rome, Italy, PSC 59, Box 100 (F), APO, AE 09624
Tel: 39 (06) 4674-2319
DEA Country Attaché **Scott Seeley Hacker** 39 (06) 4674-2319

Federal Aviation Administration (Resident in Paris) [Italy]
FAA Senior Representative **Ian H. Ross** 33 (1) 4312-2225

Office of the Defense Attaché [Italy]
American Embassy - Rome, Italy, Via Veneto 119/A, Rome, Italy
Mail: American Embassy - Rome, Italy, PSC 59, Box 20, APO, AE 09624
Tel: 39 (06) 4674-2524
Defense Attaché **CAPT Timothy Trampenau USN** . . . 39 (06) 4674-2524

Florence Consulate General
U.S. Consulate General - Florence, Italy, Lungarno Amerigo Vespucci 38, Firenze, 50123 Florence, Italy
Mail: U.S. Consulate General - Florence, Italy, PSC 59, Box 100(F), APO, AE 09624
Tel: 39 (055) 266-951 Fax: 39 (055) 284-088
Consul General/Principal Officer
Benjamin V. Wohlauer 39 (055) 266-951
E-mail: wohlauerbv@state.gov
Deputy Principal Officer
Christopher Thomas "Chris" Polillo 39 (055) 266-951
E-mail: polilloc@state.gov
Consular/Management Officer
Christopher Thomas "Chris" Polillo 39 (055) 266-951
E-mail: polilloc@state.gov

Milan Consulate General
U.S. Consulate General - Milan, Italy, Via Principe Amedeo 2/10, 20121 Milan, Italy
Mail: U.S. Consulate General - Milan, Italy, PSC 59, Box 60 (MI), APO, AE 09624
Tel: 39 (02) 290-351 Fax: 39 (02) 290-354-40
◇ Consul General **Elizabeth Lee Martinez** 39 (02) 290-351
E-mail: martinezel@state.gov
Education: Miami U (OH) BA; George Washington 1983 MIA
Office Management Specialist to Consul General
Monica M. Lam 39 (02) 290-351
Consular Section Officer **Charles J. Hamilton** 39 (02) 290-351
E-mail: hamiltoncj@state.gov
Community Liaison Officer **Elisabeth Merrill** 39 (02) 290-351
Economic Officer **Adam J. Leff** 39 (02) 290-351
E-mail: leffaj@state.gov
General Services Officer **Patrick Merrill** 39 (02) 290-351
Information Program Officer **Carlos M. Zapata** 39 (02) 290-351
E-mail: zapatacm@state.gov
Information Systems Security Officer
Carlos M. Zapata 39 (02) 290-351
E-mail: zapatacm@state.gov
Management Officer **Juan T. "Jay" Avecilla** 39 (02) 290-351
E-mail: avecillajt@state.gov
Political Officer **John R. Crosby** 39 (02) 290-351
E-mail: crosbyjr@state.gov
Public Affairs Officer **Kim M. Natoli** 39 (02) 2903-5400
E-mail: natolikm@state.gov Fax: 39 (02) 2900-1165
Regional Security Officer **Jamal Horry** 39 (02) 2903-5287
E-mail: horryja@state.gov

Commercial Section (Foreign Commercial Service) [Italy]
Via Principe Amedeo 2/10, 20121 Milan, Italy
Mail: Foreign Commercial Service, Box M, PSC 59, APO, AE 09624
Tel: 39 (02) 626 88 500 Fax: 39 (02) 659 65 61
E-mail: office.milan@trade.gov
Principal Commercial Officer **Tanya Cole** 39 (02) 88 500
E-mail: tanya.cole@trade.gov
Education: UCLA BS; Westminster U (UK) MA; Harvard

Naples Consulate General
U.S. Consulate General - Naples, Italy, Piazza della Repubblica, 80122 Naples, Italy
Mail: U.S. Consulate General - Naples, Italy, PSC 813, Box 18, FPO, AE 09619-0002
Tel: 39 (081) 583-8111 Fax: 39 (081) 761-1869
◇ Consul General **Mary Ellen Countryman** 39 (081) 583-8245
E-mail: countrymanme@state.gov
Consular Affairs Officer **Lena Levitt** 39 (081) 583-8111
Information Program Officer
Norman Gem B. Ellasos 39 (06) 4674-2379
E-mail: ellasosngb@state.gov Fax: 39 (06) 4674-2701
Management Officer **Richard N. Reilly** 39 (081) 583-8241
E-mail: reillyrn@state.gov
Political/Economic Officer **Dana Murray** 39 (081) 583-8258
Public Affairs Officer
Guy Shawn "Shawn" Baxter 39 (081) 583-8111
E-mail: baxtergs@state.gov Fax: 39 (081) 664-207
Regional Security Officer **Joseph B. Murphy** 39 (081) 583-8111

U.S. Embassy in Kosovo

Dragodan-Arberia, Nazim Hikmet 30, Pristina, Kosovo, Serbia
Mail: US Office Pristina - Department of State, 9520 Pristina Place, Washington, DC 20521-9520
Tel: 381 (38) 59-59-3000 Fax: 381 (38) 549-890
E-mail: papristina@state.gov Internet: xk.usembassy.gov

Office of the U.S. Ambassador to Kosovo
Dragodan-Arberia, Nazim Hikmet 30, Pristina, Kosovo, Serbia
★ Ambassador **Philip S. "Phil" Kosnett** 381 (38) 59-59-3000
Note: On September 6, 2018, the Senate confirmed Philip Kosnett to be Ambassador to Kosovo.
E-mail: kosnettps@state.gov
Education: Harvard 1982 AB
◇ Chargé d'Affaires **Colleen E. Hyland** 381 (38) 5959-3000
E-mail: hylandce2@state.gov
Education: Mount Holyoke BA; Naval War 2013 MNSSS
Office Management Specialist to the Ambassador
Michele L. Stovall 381 (38) 5959-3000
E-mail: stovallml@state.gov
◇ Deputy Chief of Mission **Colleen E. Hyland** 381 (38) 5959-3000
E-mail: hylandce2@state.gov
Education: Mount Holyoke BA; Naval War 2013 MNSSS
Office Management Specialist to the Deputy Chief of Mission **Sara Pfeffer SHRM-CP** 381 (38) 5959-3000
E-mail: PfefferSJ@state.gov
Education: Metro State U Denver 2001 BS
Community Liaison Officer **(Vacant)** 381 (38) 5959-3000
Consular Affairs Officer
James P. "Jimmy" Finan 381 (38) 5959-3000
Education: West Point 1998 BS; Columbia 2007 MIA
Economic Officer **Lori Michaelson** 381 (38) 5959-3000
E-mail: michaelsonlj@state.gov
Education: American U BA, 2003 MPA
Financial Management Officer **(Vacant)** 381 (38) 5959-3000
General Services Officer **(Vacant)** 381 (38) 5959-3000
Information Management Officer **Andreas Welch** 381 (38) 5959-3000
Information Program Officer
Christopher L. Fields 381 (38) 5959-3735
Information Systems Officer **Joshua T. Miller** 381 (38) 5959-3000
Information Systems Security Officer **(Vacant)** 381 (38) 5959-3000
Management Officer **John K. Madden** 381 (38) 5959-3000
E-mail: maddenjk@state.gov
Education: Harding 1987 BA; Arkansas 1991 JD
Political/Economic Chief **Jessica Long** 381 (38) 5959-3000
Education: Rice
◇ Public Affairs Officer **Richard Mei, Jr.** 381 (38) 5959-3000
Regional Security Officer **Troy Larson** 381 (38) 5959-3000

DEPARTMENTS

Agency for International Development [Kosovo]
Dragodan-Arberia, Nazim Hikmet 30, Pristina, Kosovo, Serbia
Mail: US Office Pristina - Department of State,
9520 Pristina Place, Washington, DC 20521-9520
Tel: 381 (38) 5959-2000 Fax: 381 (38) 249493
E-mail: kosovousaidinfo@usaid.gov Internet: www.usaid.gov/kosovo

Mission Director **Lisa Magno** 381 (38) 243673
E-mail: lmagno@usaid.gov
Deputy Mission Director **(Vacant)** 381 (38) 243673

Office of the Defense Attaché [Kosovo]
Defense Attaché
Col Jeffrey H. "Jeff" Fischer USAF 381 (38) 5959-3000

Peace Corps [Kosovo]
Dragodan-Arberia, Nazim Hikmet 30, Pristina, Kosovo, Serbia
Internet: www.peacecorps.gov/kosovo E-mail: kosovopc@peacecorps.gov

Country Director **Darlene Grant** 381 (38) 712-770
E-mail: dgrant@peacecorps.gov
Education: Tennessee 1994 PhD

U.S. Embassy in Latvia

1 Samnera Velsa Street, Riga, LV-1510, Latvia
Tel: 371 6710-7000 Fax: 371 6710-7050 Internet: lv.usembassy.gov

Office of the U.S. Ambassador to Latvia

American Embassy - Riga, Latvia, 1 Samnera Velsa Street, Riga, LV-1510, Latvia
Mail: American Embassy, PSC 78, Box Riga, APO, AE 09723
Tel: 371 6710-7000 Fax: 371 6710-7050
E-mail: us.embassy.riga@gmail.com

★ Ambassador **Ambassador Nancy Bikoff Pettit** 371 6710-7000
E-mail: pettitnb@state.gov
Office Management Specialist to the Ambassador
(Vacant) 371 6710-7000
Deputy Chief of Mission **Paul Evans Poletes** 371 6710-7000
Office Management Specialist to the Deputy Chief of Mission **Leslie Leedy Stroope** 371 6710-7000
Consular Chief **Anne Debevoise** 371 6710-7000
E-mail: askconsular@usriga.lv
Community Liaison Officer **Michael Thomas** 371 6710-7000
General Services Officer **John E. Langer** 371 6710-7000
Information Management Officer **(Vacant)** 371 6710-7000
Information Programs Officer **Walter Pinkevich** 371 6710-7000
Information Systems Officer **(Vacant)** 371 6710-7000
Legal Attaché **Russell L. Hunt** 371 6710-7000
Management Officer **Glenn Tosten** 371 6710-7000
E-mail: tosteng@state.gov
Education: Hampden-Sydney BA; U London
Military Liaison Officer/Defense Cooperation Office Chief **(Vacant)** 371 6710-7000
Political/Economic Officer **Lyn Debevoise** 371 6710-7000
Public Affairs Officer **Chad M. Twitty** 371 6710-7000
Regional Security Officer **Erik Winterhalter** 371 6710-7000

Agricultural Section (Foreign Agricultural Service) (Resident in Warsaw) [Latvia]
American Embassy - Warsaw, Poland, Aleje Ujazdowskie 29/31, Warsaw, Poland 00-540
Mail: American Embassy - Warsaw, Poland,
Department of State, 5010, Washington, DC 20521-5010
Tel: 48 (22) 504-2336 Fax: 48 (22) 504-2320

Agricultural Counselor **John Slette** 48 (22) 504-2336

Commercial Section (Foreign Commercial Service) [Latvia]
American Embassy - Riga, Latvia, 1 Samnera Velsa Street, Riga, LV-1510, Latvia
Tel: 371 6703-6200 Fax: 371 6782-0047 Internet: www.export.gov/latvia

Commercial Assistant **Guntars Vicmanis** 371 6710-7141
E-mail: vicmanisg@state.gov

Defense Attaché Office [Latvia]
Defense Attaché **LtCol Alexandra K. Nielsen USMC** 371 6710-7000

U.S. Embassy in Lithuania

Akmenu 6, 2600 Vilnius, Lithuania
Tel: 370 (5) 266-5500 Fax: 370 (5) 266-5510 Internet: lt.usembassy.gov

Office of the U.S. Ambassador to Lithuania

American Embassy - Vilnius, Lithuania,
Akmenu 6, LT-03106 Vilnius, Lithuania
Mail: American Embassy - Vilnius, Lithuania, PSC 78, Box V, APO, AE 09723
Tel: 370 (5) 266-5500 Fax: 370 (5) 266-5510
E-mail: webemailvilnius@state.gov

★ Ambassador **Ambassador Anne Hall** 370 (5) 266-5500
E-mail: halla@state.gov
Education: Maine 1981 BA; Texas 1987 MA, MPAff
Office Management Specialist to the Ambassador
Suzonne M. Woytovech 370 (5) 266-5500
E-mail: woytovechsm@state.gov
◇ Deputy Chief of Mission **Marcus R. Micheli** 370 (5) 266-5500
E-mail: michelimr@state.gov
Education: Reed BA; Naval War MA; Columbia MA
Office Management Specialist to the Deputy Chief of Mission **Libbie Wride** 370 (5) 266-5500
Consular Officer **David W. Warner** 370 (5) 266-5500
Community Liaison Officer **Elaine Chambliss** 370 (5) 266-0330
Economic Officer **(Vacant)** 370 (5) 266-5500
General Services Officer **Nicholas "Nick" Reynolds** ... 370 (5) 266-5500
Education: Colorado 2007 BA; Boston U 2009 MBA; Liaoning Province 2016
Information Management Officer **Jing Wright** 370 (5) 266-5500
Information Program Officer **(Vacant)** 370 (5) 266-5500
Information Systems Officer **Jing Wright** 370 (5) 266-5500
Information Systems Security Officer
Melissa Morris 370 (5) 266-5500
Management Officer
Christopher W. "Chris" Volciak 370 (5) 266-5500
Political/Economic Officer **Heidi "Rebecca" Grutz** 370 (5) 266-5500
E-mail: grutzhr@state.gov
Education: Columbia BA, JD
Public Affairs Officer **Heather E. Steil** 370 (5) 266-0330
The American Center, Fax: 370 (5) 212-0445
Pranciskonu 3/6, 2001, Vilnius, Lithuania
E-mail: webemailvilnius@state.gov
Regional Security Officer **Andres Barcenas** 370 (5) 266-5621
E-mail: barcenasaa@state.gov

Agricultural Section (Foreign Agricultural Service) (Resident in Warsaw) [Lithuania]
American Embassy - Warsaw, Poland, Aleje Ujazdowskie 29/31, 00-540 Warsaw, Poland
Mail: American Embassy - Warsaw, Poland,
Department of State, Washington, DC 20521-5010
Tel: 48 (22) 504-2336 Fax: 48 (22) 504-2320

Agricultural Officer **John Slette** 48 (22) 504-2336

Commercial Section (Foreign Commercial Service) [Lithuania]
American Embassy - Vilnius, Akmenu 6, 2600 Vilnius, Lithuania
Mail: American Embassy - Vilnius, Lithuania, PSC 78, Box V, APO, AE 09723
Tel: 370 (5) 266-5500 Fax: 370 (5) 266-5510
Internet: www.export.gov/lithuania

Commercial Specialist **Jonas Vasilevicius** 370 (5) 266-5500
E-mail: vasileviciusj@state.gov

Department of Homeland Security - U.S. Citizenship and Immigration Services (Resident in Copenhagen) [Lithuania]
American Embassy - Copenhagen, Denmark,
PCS 73, APO, AE 09716
Tel: 45 35 553144 Fax: 45 35 430223

CIS Officer **Gilbert L. Jacobs** 45 33 553144

★ Presidential Appointment Requiring Senate Confirmation ☆ Presidential Appointment ☐ Schedule C Appointment ◇ Career Senior Foreign Service Appointment
● Career Senior Executive Service (SES) Appointment ○ Non-Career Senior Executive Service (SES) Appointment ■ Postal Career Executive Service

Department of Homeland Security - U.S. Immigration and Customs Enforcement (Resident in Frankfurt) [Lithuania]
U.S. Consulate General - Frankfurt Am Main, Germany,
Gießener Strasse 30, 60435 Frankfurt am Main, Germany
Mail: PSC 115, APO, AE 09213-0115
Tel: 49 (69) 7535-0

Customs Officer **Matthew Brodman** 49 (69) 7535-0
U.S. Consulate General - Frankfurt Am Main, Germany, PCS 115, APO, AE 09213-0115

Drug Enforcement Administration (Resident in Copenhagen) [Lithuania]
American Embassy, Copenhagen, Denmark,
PSC-73, 09716 Copenhagen, Denmark
Tel: 45 35 430223

DEA Officer **Christopher J. Urben** 45 35 553144

Federal Aviation Administration (Resident in Moscow) [Lithuania]
American Embassy, Eight Bolshoy Devyatinsky Pereulok,
121099 Moscow, Russia
Tel: 7 (495) 728-5125 Fax: 7 (495) 728-5350

FAA Senior Representative **Andrew McKee** 7 (495) 728-5125

Office of the Defense Attaché [Lithuania]
American Embassy - Vilnius, Lithuania,
Akmenu 6, 2600 Vilnius, Lithuania
Mail: American Embassy - Vilnius, Lithuania, PSC 78, Box V,
APO, AE 09723
Tel: 370 (5) 266-5500 Fax: 370 (5) 266-5510

Defense Attaché **LTC Scott Thompson USA** 370 (5) 266-5500

Office of the Defense Cooperation [Lithuania]
American Embassy - Vilnuis, Lithuania, PSC 78,
Box V, APO, AE 09723
Tel: 370 (5) 266-5500

ODC Officer **Col Christopher R. Chambliss USAF** ... 370 (5) 266-5500
Fax: 370 (5) 266-5510

U.S. Embassy in Luxembourg
22 Boulevard, Emmanuel-Servais, Luxembourg, L-2535, Luxembourg
Tel: 352 46 01 23 Fax: 352 46 14 01 Internet: lu.usembassy.gov

Office of the U.S. Ambassador to Luxembourg
American Embassy - Luxembourg, 22 Boulevard, Emmanuel-Servais,
Luxembourg, L-2535, Luxembourg
Mail: American Embassy - Luxembourg, Unit 1410,
APO, AE 09126-1410

★ Ambassador
Ambassador James Randolph "Randy" Evans 352 46 01 23
Education: West Georgia Col 1980 BA; Georgia 1983 JD
Office Management Specialist to the Ambassador
Kelly A. Gerstbacher 352 46 01 23
E-mail: gerstbacherka@state.gov

Deputy Chief of Mission **Robert E. "Rob" Hurlbert** 352 46 01 23
E-mail: hurlbertre@state.gov
Education: Syracuse 1975; Babson 1976 MBA

Office Management Specialist to the Deputy Chief of Mission **Marie E. Pursley** 352 46 01 23 03
E-mail: pursleyme@state.gov

Community Liaison Officer **Catherine Schopp MBA** 352 46 01 23
Education: Grand Valley State 2008 BS; Colorado State 2014 MBA

Consular Officer **Chinwe Obianwu** 352 46 01 23
Fax: 352 46 19 39

General Services Officer **Joseph R. Knupp** 352 46 01 23
E-mail: knuppjr@state.gov Fax: 352 22 00 28

Information Management Officer
James L. "Jim" Madril 352 46 01 23
E-mail: madriljl@state.gov

Information Systems Security Officer **Brian Anderson** 352 46 01 23

Legal Attaché (Resident in Brussels)
Gibson M. Wilson 32 (2) 508-2551
American Embassy - Brussels, Belgium,
PSC 82, Box 002, APO, AE 09710

Office of the U.S. Ambassador to Luxembourg *(continued)*

Management Officer **Paul G. Rey** 352 46 01 23
E-mail: reypx@state.gov

Political/Economic Officer **Kristin M. "Kristi" Roberts** 352 46 01 23
Education: U Washington 2000 BA, 2003 JD

Political/Military Officer **Jennifer Van Ette** 352 46 01 23
E-mail: vanettejk@state.gov

Public Affairs Officer **Daniel Michael Pattarini** 352 46 01 23

Regional Security Officer **Paul Hendricks** 352 46 01 23

Agricultural Section (Foreign Agricultural Service) (Resident in Brussels) [Luxembourg]

◇ Agricultural Officer **Bruce J. Zanin** 32 (2) 811-4154
E-mail: bruce.zanin@fas.usda.gov

Commercial Section (Foreign Commercial Service) (Resident in Brussels) [Luxembourg]
American Embassy - Brussels, Belgium,
27 Boulevard du Regent, B-1000 Brussels, Belgium
Mail: American Embassy - Brussels, Belgium, PSC 82, Box 002,
APO, AE 09710
Tel: 32 (2) 508-2425 Fax: 32 (2) 512-3644

◇ Senior Commercial Officer
Mitchell Gregory "Mitch" Larsen 32 (2) 508-2425
E-mail: mitch.larsen@trade.gov

Department of Homeland Security - Transportation Security Administration (Resident in Brussels) [Luxembourg]
U.S. Embassy - Brussels, PSC 82, Box 002, APO, AE 09710
American Embassy - Brussels, Belgium,
American Embassy - Brussels, Belgium, 15 Rue de la Loi,
3rd Floor, B-10, B-1040 Brussels, Belgium
Tel: 32 (2) 508-2708 Fax: 32 (2) 230-0642

TSA Representative **David Gordner** 32 (2) 508-2708

Department of Homeland Security - U.S. Customs and Border Protection (Resident in The Hague) [Luxembourg]

Customs Officer **Patrick Ott** 352 46 01 23 00

Drug Enforcement Administration (Resident in Brussels) [Luxembourg]
American Embassy - Brussels, Belgium,
27 Boulevard du Regent, B-1000 Brussels, Belgium
Mail: American Embassy - Brussels, Belgium, PSC 82, Box 002,
APO, AE 09710
Tel: 32 (2) 508-2420 Fax: 32 (2) 512-9914

DEA Officer **Scott Andrew Albrecht** 32 (2) 508-2420
E-mail: albrechtsa@state.gov

Federal Aviation Administration (Resident in Brussels) [Luxembourg]
American Embassy/FAA, AEU-BRU, 27 Boulevard du Regent,
B-1000 Brussels, Belgium
Mail: American Embassy/FAA, PSC 82, Box 002,
AEU-BRU, APO, AE 09710
Fax: 32 (2) 811-5295

FAA Senior Representative, Brussels
Maria DiPasquantonio 32 (2) 811-4038

Office of the Defense Attaché [Luxembourg]

Defense Attaché **COL M Brant Stephenson USA** 352 46 01 23

Office of Defense Cooperation (Resident in Brussels) [Luxembourg]
American Embassy - Brussels, Belgium,
27 Boulevard du Regent, B-1000 Brussels, Belgium
Mail: American Embassy - Brussels, Belgium, PSC 82, Box 002,
APO, AE 09710
Tel: 32 (2) 508-2650 Fax: 32 (2) 514-5666

Defense Cooperation Officer **Kenneth "Ken" Gjone** 32 (2) 508-2650
E-mail: gjonekd@state.gov

★ Presidential Appointment Requiring Senate Confirmation ☆ Presidential Appointment □ Schedule C Appointment ◇ Career Senior Foreign Service Appointment
● Career Senior Executive Service (SES) Appointment ○ Non-Career Senior Executive Service (SES) Appointment ■ Postal Career Executive Service

U.S. Embassy in Macedonia

Samoilova 21, 1000 Skopje, Macedonia
Tel: 389 (2) 310-2000 Fax: 389 (2) 310-2499 Internet: mk.usembassy.gov

Office of the U.S. Ambassador to Macedonia

American Embassy - Skopje, Macedonia,
Samoilova 21, 1000 Skopje, Macedonia
Mail: Department of State, 7120 Skopje Place,
Washington, DC 20521-7120
Tel: 389 (2) 310-2000 Fax: 389 (2) 310-2499

★ Ambassador **Ambassador Jess Lippincott Baily** 389 (2) 310-2000
E-mail: bailyjl@state.gov
Education: Yale 1982 BA; Columbia 1985 MA
★ Ambassador-Designate **Kate Marie Byrnes** 389 (2) 310-2000
Education: Georgetown BS, MA
Office Management Specialist to the Ambassador
(Vacant) 389 (2) 310-2000
◇ Deputy Chief of Mission
Micaela A. Schweitzer-Bluhm 389 (2) 310-2000
E-mail: schweitzerbluhmma@state.gov
Office Management Specialist to the Deputy Chief of Mission **Dina D. Obey** 389 (2) 310-2000
E-mail: obeydd@state.gov
Consular Section Officer **Thomas Scott Brown** 389 (2) 310-2000
Community Liaison Officer **Julie Boyett** 389 (2) 310-2000
Financial Management Officer **Sirli Hill** 389 (2) 310-2000
E-mail: hillsp@state.gov
General Services Officer **Mark Obey** 389 (2) 310-2000
E-mail: obeym@state.gov
Information Management Officer **Rick Melton** 389 (2) 310-2000
Information Program Officer
Christopher A. "Chris" Fink 389 (2) 310-2000
E-mail: finkca@state.gov
Education: Simpson (IA) 2006 BA
Information Systems Security Officer
Christopher A. "Chris" Fink 389 (2) 310-2000
E-mail: finkca@state.gov
Education: Simpson (IA) 2006 BA
Management Officer **Michael Konstantino** 389 (2) 310-2000
E-mail: konstantinomm@state.gov
Military Liaison Officer **Jeffrey Vansickle** 389 (2) 310-2000
E-mail: vansicklejb@state.gov
Political/Economic Officer **Shannon E. Runyon** 389 (2) 310-2000
E-mail: runyonse@state.gov
Education: Chicago 1983 AB; Thunderbird Global 1993 MIM
Public Affairs Officer **Laura Brown** 389 (2) 310-2000
Regional Security Officer **Jared Thurman** 389 (2) 310-2000
E-mail: thurmanjm@state.gov

Agency for International Development [Macedonia]

American Embassy - Skopje, Macedonia,
Samoilova 21, 1000 Skopje, Macedonia
Fax: 389 (2) 310 2000 Internet: www.usaid.gov/macedonia

◇ Country Representative **David C. Atteberry** 389 (2) 310-231
E-mail: datteberry@usaid.gov

Department of Homeland Security - U.S. Immigration and Customs Enforcement (Resident in Vienna) [Macedonia]

Customs Officer **Sarah Bay** 43 (1) 31339-2111

Drug Enforcement Administration (Resident in Athens) [Macedonia]

American Embassy - Athens, Greece, 91 Vasilissis Sophias Boulevard,
10160 Athens, Greece
Mail: PSC 108, APO, AE 09842-0108
Tel: 30 (21) 720-2785

DEA Officer **John Livanis** 30 (21) 0721-4831
E-mail: LivanisJ@state.gov

Federal Aviation Administration (Resident in Moscow) [Macedonia]

American Embassy/FAA, Eight Bolshoy Devyatinsky Pereulok,
121099 Moscow, Russia
Mail: American Embassy/FAA, PSC 77, APO, AE 09721
Tel: 7 (495) 728-5000

FAA Senior Representative **Andrew McKee** 7 (495) 728-5125

Office of the Defense Attaché [Macedonia]

American Embassy - Skopje, Macedonia,
Bul. Ilinden b.b., 1000 Skopje, Macedonia
Mail: Unit 7120, Box 1000, APO, AE 09737-1000

Defense Attaché
COL Thomas M. "Tom" Butler USA 389 (2) 310-2000

Peace Corps [Macedonia]

Bul. Ilinden b.b., 1000 Skopje, Macedonia
Mail: 7120 Skopje Place, Washington, DC 20521-7120
Tel: 389 (2) 3090-012 E-mail: info@mk.peacecorps.gov
Internet: www.peacecorps.gov/macedonia

Country Director **Mark Hannafin** 389 (2) 310-2000
E-mail: mhannafin@usaid.gov
Education: Hobart & William Smith 1990 BA; Tufts 1999 MALD

U.S. Embassy in Malta

Ta' Qali National Park, Attard, Floriana, Malta ATD 4000
Tel: 356 2561-4000 Fax: 356 2124-3229 Internet: mt.usembassy.gov

Office of the U.S. Ambassador to Malta

American Embassy - Valletta, Malta, Ta' Qali National Park,
Attard, Floriana, Malta ATD 4000
Mail: American Embassy - 5800 Valletta Place,
Washington, DC 20521-5800
E-mail: usembmalta@state.gov

★ Ambassador-Designate **Christine J. Toretti** 356 2561-4142
Education: Virginia 1981 BS
Chargé d'Affaires **Mark A. Schapiro** 356 2561-4143
E-mail: schapiroma@state.gov
Education: Brown U
Office Management Specialist to the Ambassador
Erin McCoy 356 2561-4142
Deputy Chief of Mission **Mark A. Schapiro** 356 2561-4143
E-mail: schapiroma@state.gov
Education: Brown U
Office Management Specialist to the Deputy Chief of Mission **Tiffany Inglee** 356 2561-4142
E-mail: ingleetm@state.gov
Community Liaison Officer **Jennifer Luce** 356 2561-4000
Consular Section Chief **Joan Flynn** 356 2561-4146
General Services Officer **Nathan Johnson** 356 2561-4145
Information Management Officer **Teja Dontamsetti** 356 2561-4155
Information Systems Security Officer
Teja Dontamsetti 356 2561-4118
Legal Attaché **Kieran Ramsey** 356 2561-4154
Management Officer **Hormazd Kanga** 356 2561-4145
E-mail: kangahj@state.gov
Political/Economic Section Chief
Marjorie Marji Christian 356 2561-4167
E-mail: christianmc@state.gov
Education: Missouri 2005 BSChE, 2007 MBA
Public Affairs Officer **Ryan M. Janda** 356 2561-4152
E-mail: jandarm@state.gov
Regional Security Officer **Gregory Brenneman** 356 2561-4138
E-mail: BrennemanGR@state.gov

Agricultural Section (Foreign Agricultural Service) (Resident in Rome) [Malta]

American Embassy - Rome, Italy, Via Vittorio Veneto 119/A,
00187 Rome, Italy
Mail: American Embassy - Rome, Italy, PSC 59, Box 13, APO, AE 09624
Tel: 39 (06) 4674-2396 Fax: 39 (06) 4788-7088
E-mail: agrome@fas.usda.gov

Agricultural Officer **Frederick H. "Fred" Giles** 39 (06) 4674-2396
E-mail: frederick.giles@fas.usda.gov

Federal Aviation Administration (Resident in Paris) [Malta]

American Embassy/FAA, AEU-PAR, 2, Avenue Gabriel, 75382 Paris,
Cedex 08, France
Mail: PSC 116, Box A-215, APO, AE 09777
Tel: 33 (1) 4312-2225 Fax: 33 (1) 4312-2505

FAA Representative **Ian H. Ross** 33 (1) 4312-2225

★ Presidential Appointment Requiring Senate Confirmation ☆ Presidential Appointment ☐ Schedule C Appointment ◇ Career Senior Foreign Service Appointment
● Career Senior Executive Service (SES) Appointment ○ Non-Career Senior Executive Service (SES) Appointment ■ Postal Career Executive Service

Office of the Defense Attaché [Malta]
American Embassy - Valletta, Malta, Development House,
Saint Anne Street, 3rd Floor, Floriana, Malta
Mail: American Embassy - Valletta, Malta,
Department of State, Washington, DC 20521-5800
Tel: 356 2561-4161
Defense and Naval Attaché **CDR Carlos Plazas USN** 356 2561-4161

U.S. Embassy in Moldova

Strada Alexei Mateevici 103, 2009 Chisinau, Moldova
Tel: 373 (22) 408-300 Fax: 373 (22) 233-044 Internet: md.usembassy.gov

Office of the U.S. Ambassador to Moldova

American Embassy - Chisinau, Moldova,
Strada Alexei Mateevici #103, 2009 Chisinau, Moldova
Mail: Department of State, 7080 Chisinau Place,
Washington, DC 20521-7080
E-mail: ircchisinau@state.gov Internet: md.usembassy.gov

★ Ambassador **Ambassador Dereck J. Hogan** 373 (22) 408-300
E-mail: hogandj@state.gov
Education: Pittsburgh BA; Princeton MPA
Office Management Specialist to the Ambassador
Megan Walton 373 (22) 408-300
E-mail: waltonm@state.gov
Education: BYU (HI) 2005 BA
Deputy Chief of Mission
Henry "Martin" McDowell 373 (22) 408-300
E-mail: mcdowellhm@state.gov
Education: Alabama 1992 BA, 1996 MAIS; Charles U DPhil
Office Management Specialist to the Deputy Chief of Mission **James J. Zellinger** 373 (22) 408-300
E-mail: zellingerjj@state.gov
Education: St Xavier 1999 BA; U Salzburg 1999; Aalborg U 2005 MA
Consular Officer **Amy Reardon** 373 (22) 408-300
Community Liaison Officer **Brooke McLaughlin** 373 (22) 408-300
E-mail: mclaughlinbl@state.gov
Economic/Commercial Officer **Charles Vetter** 373 (22) 408-300
Political/Economic Officer **Anne S. Coleman-Honn** ... 373 (22) 408-486
E-mail: colemanas@state.gov
Education: William & Mary; Col of Europe (Belgium)
Financial Management Officer **D. Trent Dabney** 373 (22) 408-300
E-mail: dabneydt@state.gov
General Services Officer **Mark R. Jorgensen** 373 (22) 408-300
E-mail: jorgensenmr@state.gov
Information Management Officer **(Vacant)** 373 (22) 408-300
Information Systems Officer **Michael "Mike" Walls** ... 373 (22) 408-300
Information Systems Security Officer
Michael Quinlan 373 (22) 408-300
Management Officer **Andrew Berdy** 373 (22) 408-300
E-mail: berdya@state.gov
Public Affairs Officer **Aaron D. Honn** 373 (22) 408-300
E-mail: honnad@state.gov
Regional Security Officer **Kurt J. Finley** 373 (22) 408-300
E-mail: finleykj@state.gov

Agency for International Development [Moldova]
American Embassy - Chisinau, Moldova,
Strada Banulescu-Bodini, N.R. 57/1, E.T. 5, 2005 Chisinau, Moldova
Mail: USAID - Department of State, 7080 Chisinau Place,
Washington, DC 20521-7080
Tel: 373 (22) 201-800 Fax: 373 (22) 201-800
E-mail: chisinau_reception@usaid.gov Internet: www.usaid.gov/moldova
AID Officer **Karen Hilliard** 373 (22) 201-800
E-mail: khilliard@usaid.gov
Education: Northern Illinois 1979; U Mexico 1984 MPA, 1986 PhD

Federal Aviation Administration (Resident in Moscow) [Moldova]
American Embassy/FAA, Eight Bolshoy Devyatinsky Pereulok,
121099 Moscow, Russia
Mail: American Embassy/FAA, PSC 77, APO, AE 09721
Fax: 7 (495) 728-5350
FAA Senior Representative **Andrew McKee** 7 (495) 728-5125

Office of the Defense Attaché [Moldova]
American Embassy - Chisinau, Moldova,
Strada Alexei Mateevici 103, 2009 Chisinau, Moldova
Mail: DAO - Department of State, 7080 Chisinau Place,
Washington, DC 20521-7080
Tel: 373 (22) 40-83-00 Fax: 373 (22) 233-044
Defense Attaché **LTC Jeffrey Muir USA** 373 (22) 40-83-00

U.S. Embassy in Montenegro

Dzona Dzeksona 2, 81000 Podgorica, Montenegro
Tel: 382 (20) 410-500 Fax: 382 (20) 241-358 Internet: me.usembassy.gov

Office of the U.S. Ambassador to Montenegro

Dzona Dzeksona 2, 81000 Podgorica, Montenegro
Mail: U.S. Consulate Podgorica, 5570 Podgorica Place,
Washington, DC 20521-5570
E-mail: podgorica@state.gov

★ Ambassador **Judy R. Reinke** 382 (20) 410-500
Note: On October 15, 2018, the Senate Judy Reinke was sworn in as Ambassador to Montenegro.
Education: Smith 1980 AB; Princeton 1983 MPAff
Chargé d'Affaires **Judy Haiguang Kuo** 382 (20) 410-500
E-mail: kuojh@state.gov
Office Management Specialist to the Ambassador
Katherine E. "Kathy" Pelzer 382 (20) 410-500
Deputy Chief of Mission **Judy Haiguang Kuo** 382 (20) 410-500
E-mail: kuojh@state.gov
Consular Section Chief **April Hayne** 382 (20) 410-500
Community Liaison Officer **Christopher V. Pelzer** 382 (20) 410-500
Economic/Commercial Officer
Brendan Kyle Hatcher 382 (20) 410-500
E-mail: hatcherbk@state.gov
General Services Officer **Paul H. Saaranen** 382 (20) 410-500
Information Management Officer **Cem B. Asci** 382 (20) 410-500
Information Systems Security Officer
Thomas "Tommy" Binning 381 (11) 410-500
E-mail: binningt@state.gov
Education: Arizona State 1999 BA
International Narcotics and Law Enforcement Resident Legal Advisor **Erik Larson** 382 (20) 410-500
Management Officer **Michael H. Scanlon** 382 (20) 410-500
Political/Economic Section Chief **Lewis Gitter** 382 (20) 410-500
E-mail: gitterl@state.gov
Public Affairs Officer **Jeffrey "Jeff" Adler** 382 (20) 410-500
Regional Security Officer **Keith Easter** 382 (20) 410-500

Office of the Defense Attaché [Montenegro]
Defense Attaché **LTC Michael Tarquinto USA** 382 (20) 410-500

U.S. Embassy in the Netherlands

John Adams Park 1, 2244 BZ Wassenaar, Netherlands
Tel: 31 (70) 310-2209 Fax: 31 (70) 310-2207 Internet: nl.usembassy.gov

Office of the U.S. Ambassador to the Netherlands

John Adams Park 1, 2244 BZ Wassenaar, Netherlands

★ Ambassador **Ambassador Peter "Pete" Hoekstra** 31 (70) 310-2209
Education: Hope 1975 BA; Michigan 1977 MBA
Office Management Specialist to the Ambassador
Timothy W. "Tim" Markley 31 (70) 310-2209
E-mail: markleytw@state.gov
◇ Deputy Chief of Mission **Shawn P. Crowley** 31 (70) 310-2209
E-mail: crowleysp@state.gov
Office Management Specialist to the Deputy Chief of Mission **Amy Yribar** 31 (70) 310-2209
E-mail: yribaram@state.gov
Community Liaison Officer **Natalie Billick** 31 (70) 310-2209
General Services Officer **James Oden** 31 (70) 310-2209
E-mail: odenj@state.gov
Information Management Officer **(Vacant)** 31 (70) 310-2209
Information Program Officer **Brandon White** 31 (70) 310-2209
Information Systems Security Officer **(Vacant)** 31 (70) 310-2209

(continued on next page)

★ Presidential Appointment Requiring Senate Confirmation ☆ Presidential Appointment ☐ Schedule C Appointment ◇ Career Senior Foreign Service Appointment
● Career Senior Executive Service (SES) Appointment ○ Non-Career Senior Executive Service (SES) Appointment ■ Postal Career Executive Service

Office of the U.S. Ambassador to the Netherlands *(continued)*

Management Officer **Robert L. "Bob" Kingman** 31 (70) 310-2209
E-mail: kingmanrl@state.gov
Legal Attaché **William "Bill" Stern** 31 (70) 310-2209
Political/Economic Officer
Steven R. "Steve" Butler 31 (70) 310-2209
E-mail: butlersr@state.gov
Public Affairs Officer **Sherry C. Keneson-Hall** 31 (70) 310-2440
E-mail: Keneson-HallSC@state.gov
Regional Security Officer **Vanessa C. Freeman** 31 (70) 310-2209
E-mail: freemanvc@state.gov

Agricultural Section (Foreign Agricultural Service) [The Netherlands]
John Adams Park 1, 2244 BZ Wassenaar, Netherlands
Tel: 31 (70) 310-9209 Fax: 31 (70) 365-7681
E-mail: agthehague@fas.usda.gov

Agricultural Officer **Susan B. Phillips** 31 (70) 310-2300
E-mail: susan.phillips@fas.usda.gov
Education: Wisconsin 1985 BS; Kansas State 1991 MSA

Animal and Plant Health Inspection Service [The Netherlands]
Fax: 31 (70) 252-417019

APHIS Officer **Heather S. Coady** 31 (70) 252-412973
E-mail: heather.s.coady@aphis.usda.gov

Commercial Section (Foreign Commercial Service) [The Netherlands]
Tel: 31 (70) 310-2417 Fax: 31 (70) 363-2985
E-mail: Office.Netherlands@trade.gov Internet: export.gov/netherlands

Head of Section **Alan Ras** 31 (70) 310-2418
E-mail: alan.ras@trade.gov

Drug Enforcement Administration [The Netherlands]
DEA Officer **Michael L. Maxwell** 31 (70) 310-2209

Department of Homeland Security - U.S. Immigration and Customs Enforcement [The Netherlands]
Immigration Officer **Kumar C. Kibble** 31 (70) 353-1533
E-mail: kibblek@state.gov
Customs Officer **Patrick Ott** 31 (70) 310-2209

Federal Aviation Administration (Resident in Brussels) [The Netherlands]
American Embassy - Brussels, Belgium,
15 Rue de la Loi, B-1040 Brussels, Belgium
Tel: 44 (20) 7408-8094 Fax: 44 (20) 7894-0173

FAA Representative **Maria DiPasquantonio** 32 (2) 811-4038
Fax: 32 (2) 230-0642

Office of the Defense Attaché [The Netherlands]
Tel: 31 (70) 310-9209 Fax: 31 (70) 310-9252

Defense Attaché **Robert Buzzell** 31 (70) 310-2255
Chief, Office of Defense Cooperation
Col Trevor Nitz USAF 31 (70) 310-2282
E-mail: ODCTheHague@state.gov

Amsterdam Consulate General

U.S. Consulate General - Amsterdam, Netherlands,
Museumplein 19, 1071 DJ Amsterdam, Netherlands
Mail: PSC 115, Box 038, APO, AE 09715
Tel: 31 (20) 575 5330 Fax: 31 (20) 575-5310

Consul General **Joseph A. "Joe" Parente** 31 (20) 575 5330
E-mail: parenteja@state.gov
Education: UNLV BA
Office Management Specialist to Consul General
Eline J. Van Duren 31 (20) 575 5330
E-mail: vandurenej@state.gov
Consular Officer **Rosalyn Wiese** 31 (20) 575 5330
E-mail: wiesern@state.gov
Regional Security Officer **Gavin F. Hurst** 31 (20) 575 5330
E-mail: hurstgf@state.gov

U.S. Embassy in Norway

Morgedalsvegen 36, 0378 Oslo, Norway
Tel: 47 21-30-85-40 Fax: 47 22-43-07-77 Internet: no.usembassy.gov

Office of the U.S. Ambassador to Norway
American Embassy, Morgedalsvegen 36, 0378 Oslo, Norway
Mail: American Embassy - Oslo, PSC 69, Box 1000, APO, AE 09707

★ Ambassador
Ambassador Kenneth J. "Ken" Braithwaite 47 21-30-85-40
Education: Naval Acad 1984 BS; Pennsylvania MGA
Office Management Specialist to the Ambassador
Christine du Plessis de Richelieu 47 21-30-85-40
E-mail: duplessisc@state.gov
◇ Deputy Chief of Mission **Richard H. Riley** 47 21-30-85-40
E-mail: rileyrh@state.gov
Education: Georgia BBA; Harvard MBA; National Defense U MS
Office Management Specialist to the Deputy Chief of Mission **Sarah G. Gowen** 47 21-30-85-40
E-mail: gowensg@state.gov
Community Liaison Officer **Joshua Maak** 47 21-30-85-40
Consular Officer **William Whitaker** 47 21-30-85-40
E-mail: whitakerww@state.gov
Economic Officer **Kristin L. Westphal** 47 21-30-85-40
E-mail: westphalkl@state.gov
Financial Management Officer **Monte Parker** 47 21-30-85-40
General Services Officer **Chris F. Pierson** 47 21-30-85-40
Education: Naval Acad 1981 BS
Information Management Officer **Jon C. Peterson** 47 21-30-85-40
E-mail: petersonjc@state.gov
Information Systems Officer **(Vacant)** 47 21-30-85-40
Information Systems Security Officer
Joshua A. Chastain 47 21-30-85-40
E-mail: chastainja@state.gov
Management Officer
Alfred Thomas "Tom" Canahuate 47 21-30-85-40
E-mail: canahuateat@state.gov
Political/Economic Officer **Maureen Haggard** 47 21-30-85-40
E-mail: haggardme@state.gov
◇ Public Affairs Officer **Ann Barrows McConnell** 47 21-30-85-40
E-mail: mcconnellab@state.gov Fax: 47 22-44-04-36
Regional Security Officer **Kenneth D. Lindberg** 47 21-30-85-40
E-mail: lindbergk@state.gov

Agricultural Section (Foreign Agricultural Service) (Resident in The Hague) [Norway]
American Embassy - The Hague, Netherlands,
John Adams Park 1, 2244 BZ Wassenaar, Netherlands
Mail: PSC 115, Box 038, APO, AE 09715
Tel: 31 (70) 310-2209 Fax: 31 (70) 365-7681

Agricultural Counselor **Susan B. Phillips** 31 (70) 310-2300
Education: Wisconsin 1985 BS; Kansas State 1991 MSA

Commercial Section (Foreign Commercial Service) [Norway]
American Embassy, Morgedalsvegen 36, 0378 Oslo, Norway
Mail: American Embassy - Oslo, PSC 69, Box 1000, APO, AE 09707
Tel: 47 21-30-88-66 Fax: 47 22-55-88-03 E-mail: office.oslo@trade.gov
Internet: export.gov/norway

Commercial Officer **Vidar Keyn** 47 21-30-88-34
E-mail: vidar.keyn@trade.gov

Federal Aviation Administration (Resident in Moscow) [Norway]
American Embassy, Eight Bolshoy Devyatinsky Pereulok,
121099 Moscow, Russia
Mail: Unit 5430, DPO, AE 09721
Fax: 7 (495) 728-5350

FAA Senior Representative **Andrew McKee** 7 (495) 728-5125

Federal Bureau of Investigation (Resident in Copenhagen) [Norway]
American Embassy - Copenhagen, Denmark,
Dag Hammaarskjölds Alle 24, 2100 Copenhagen, Denmark
Mail: American Embassy - Copenhagen, Denmark, PSC 73, APO, AE 09716
Tel: 45 33-26-96-11 Fax: 45 35-43-02-23

Legal Attaché **Dick A. Robles** 45 35-55-31-44

★ Presidential Appointment Requiring Senate Confirmation ☆ Presidential Appointment ☐ Schedule C Appointment ◇ Career Senior Foreign Service Appointment
● Career Senior Executive Service (SES) Appointment ○ Non-Career Senior Executive Service (SES) Appointment ■ Postal Career Executive Service

Office of the Defense Attaché [Norway]
American Embassy, Morgedalsvegen 36, 0378 Oslo, Norway
Mail: American Embassy - Oslo, PSC 69, Box 1000, APO, AE 09707
Tel: 47 21-30-85-50 Fax: 47 22-44-37-34 E-mail: usdao@online.no

Defense and Naval Attaché
CAPT Gary A. Rogeness USN 47 21-30-85-50
Army Attaché **COL Renee Underwood USA** 47 21-30-85-50
Air Attaché **Col Aaron W. Steffens USAF** 47 21-30-85-50
Education: Air Force Acad 1992 BS; Air Command Col 2006 MS; Air War Col 2013 MS

Office of Defense Cooperation [Norway]
American Embassy, Morgedalsvegen 36, 0378 Oslo, Norway
Mail: American Embassy - Oslo, PSC 69, Box 1000, APO, AE 09707
Tel: 47 21-30-85-50 Fax: 47 22-44-98-92

Chief **Lt. Col. Richard Rosenstein USMC** 47 21-30-89-45

U.S. Embassy in Poland

Aleje Ujazdowskie 29/31, Warsaw, Poland 00-540
Tel: 48 (22) 504-2000 Tel: 48 (22) 504-2226 Internet: pl.usembassy.gov

Office of the U.S. Ambassador to Poland

American Embassy - Warsaw, Poland, Aleje Ujazdowskie 29/31, Warsaw, Poland 00-540
Mail: American Embassy - Warsaw, Poland,
Department of State, 5010, Washington, DC 20521-5010

★ Ambassador **Ambassador Georgette Mosbacher** 48 (22) 504-2000
Education: Indiana BS
Office Management Specialist to the Ambassador
Veronica A. Peters 48 (22) 504-2900
◇ Deputy Chief of Mission **Eric F. Green** 48 (22) 504-2400
E-mail: greene@state.gov
Education: Grinnell 1985 BA; Yale 1988 MA
Office Management Specialist to the Deputy Chief of Mission **Joanna Dylewicz** 48 (22) 504-2400
E-mail: DylewiczJM@state.gov
◇ Consul General **Patrick W. "Pat" Walsh** 48 (22) 504-2156
E-mail: walshpw@state.gov
Community Liaison Officer **Kristen Banks** 48 (22) 504-2357
Economic Officer **John L. Armstrong** 48 (22) 504-2000
E-mail: armstrongjl3@state.gov
Facilities Management Officer **Gerald Toomey** 48 (22) 504-2000
Financial Management Officer **David Orton** 48 (22) 504-2410
General Services Officer **Tod Earl Duran** 48 (22) 504-2460
E-mail: durante@state.gov
Human Resources Officer **Richard Marsh** 48 (22) 504-2239
Education: Comm Col Air Force 1998 AA Fax: 48 (22) 504-2265
Information Management Officer
Gregory W. "Greg" Liddle 48 (22) 504-2710
E-mail: liddlegw@state.gov
Education: Illinois Tech 1995 BS; Wheaton (IL) 1995 BA
Information Programs Officer
James B. "Jim" Cavanaugh 48 (22) 504-2343
E-mail: cavanaughjb@state.gov
Information Systems Officer **Mark D. Wecker** 48 (22) 504-2626
E-mail: weckermd@state.gov
Information Systems Security Officer
Mark D. Wecker 48 (22) 504-2626
E-mail: weckermd@state.gov
Legal Attaché **Justin Kolenbrander** 48 (22) 504-2000
Management Officer **Matthew L. Shields** 48 (22) 504-2222
E-mail: shieldsml@state.gov
Political Officer **Yuriy R. Fedkiw** 48 (22) 504-2631
E-mail: fedkiwyr@state.gov
Education: Wittenberg 1999 BA
◇ Public Affairs Officer **Frank Jonathan Finver** 48 (22) 504-2380
E-mail: finverfj@state.gov Fax: 48 (22) 504-2364
Cultural Attaché **Daniel O. Hastings** 48 (22) 504-2000
E-mail: hastingsdo@state.gov
E-mail: culture_warsaw@state.gov
Press Attaché **Alice Chu** 48 (22) 504-2000
E-mail: warsawmedia@state.gov
Regional Security Officer **Roy Stillman** 48 (22) 504-2107
E-mail: stillmanr@state.gov

Agricultural Section (Foreign Agricultural Service) [Poland]
American Embassy - Warsaw, Poland, Aleje Ujazdowskie 29/31, Warsaw, Poland 00-540
Mail: American Embassy - Warsaw, Poland,
Department of State, 5010, Washington, DC 20521-5010
Fax: 48 (22) 504-2320

Agricultural Attaché **John Slette** 48 (22) 504-2336

Commercial Section (Foreign Commercial Service) [Poland]
Al Jerozolimskie 56C, Warsaw, Poland 00-803
Mail: American Embassy - Warsaw, Poland,
Department of State, 5010, Washington, DC 20521-5010
Tel: 48 (22) 625-4374 Fax: 48 (22) 621-6327
E-mail: office.warsaw@trade.gov Internet: www.export.gov/poland

Commercial Counselor **Charles R. Ranado** 48 (22) 625-4374
E-mail: Charles.Ranado@trade.gov

Federal Aviation Administration (Resident in Paris) [Poland]
American Embassy/FAA, AEU-PAR, 2, Avenue Gabriel, 75382 Paris, Cedex 08, France
Mail: PSC 116, APO, AE 09777
Fax: 33 (1) 4312-2505

FAA Senior Representative **Ian H. Ross** 33 (1) 4312-2225

Office of the Defense Attaché [Poland]
American Embassy - Warsaw, Poland, Aleje Ujazdowskie 29/31, Warsaw, Poland 00-540
Mail: American Embassy - Warsaw, Poland,
Department of State, 5010, Washington, DC 20521-5010
Fax: 48 (22) 504-2640 E-mail: daowarsaw@state.gov

Defense Attaché **John Downey** 48 (22) 504-2677
E-mail: downeyja@state.gov

Krakow Consulate General
U.S. Consulate General - Krakow, Poland,
Ulica Stolarska 9, 31043 Krakow, Poland
Mail: U.S. Consulate General - Krakow, Poland,
Department of State, Washington, DC 20521-5040
Tel: 48 (12) 424-5100 Fax: 48 (12) 424-5103
E-mail: krakowniv@state.gov
Internet: pl.usembassy.gov/embassy-consulate/krakow

◇ Consul General **Begzat Bix "Bix" Aliu** 48 (12) 424-5180
E-mail: aliubb@state.gov
Education: Army War Col MSS
Consular Chief **Kathryn Porter** 48 (12) 424-5184
Financial Management Officer **Shelly Zia** 48 (12) 424-5187
General Services Officer **Shelly Zia** 48 (12) 424-5187
Information Program Officer/Information Security Officer **Shelly Zia** 48 (12) 424-5187
Management Officer **Shelly Zia** 48 (12) 424-5187
Political/Economic Officer **Thomas "Tom" Zia** 48 (12) 424-5181
Public Affairs Officer **Amy B. Steinmann** 48 (12) 424-5184
E-mail: steinmannab@state.gov
Education: Delaware 2004 BA; American U 2005 MA
Regional Security Officer **Anthony Campagna** 48 (12) 424-5100

U.S. Embassy in Portugal

Avenida das Forcas Armadas, 1600-081 Lisbon, Portugal
Tel: 351 (21) 727-3300 Fax: 351 (21) 726-9109
Internet: pt.usembassy.gov

Office of the U.S. Ambassador to Portugal

American Embassy - Lisbon, Portugal,
Avenida das Forcas Armadas, 1600-081 Lisbon, Portugal
Mail: American Embassy - Lisbon, Portugal, PSC 83, DPO, AE 09726-9998
E-mail: lisbonweb@state.gov

★ Ambassador **Ambassador George Edward Glass** 351 (21) 727-3300
Education: Oregon BS

(continued on next page)

★ Presidential Appointment Requiring Senate Confirmation ☆ Presidential Appointment ☐ Schedule C Appointment ◇ Career Senior Foreign Service Appointment
● Career Senior Executive Service (SES) Appointment ○ Non-Career Senior Executive Service (SES) Appointment ■ Postal Career Executive Service

DEPARTMENTS

Office of the U.S. Ambassador to Portugal *(continued)*

Office Management Specialist to the Ambassador
Jennifer Clemente MBA 351 (21) 727-3300
E-mail: clementej@state.gov
Education: Col Santa Fe 2003 AA; Eckerd 2005 BA; Florida Atlantic 2010 MBA

◇ Deputy Chief of Mission **Herro K. Mustafa** 351 (21) 727-3300
E-mail: mustafahk@state.gov
Office Management Specialist to the Deputy Chief of Mission **Jennifer Martin** 351 (21) 727-3300

Consul General **Angela Dalrymple** 351 (21) 727-3300
E-mail: dalrympleav@state.gov Fax: 351 (21) 727-2354

Community Liaison Officer **Jennifer Alamo** 351 (21) 727-3300
E-mail: alamojm@state.gov

Financial Management Officer **Liv Kilpatrick** 351 (21) 727-3300
E-mail: kilpatrickli@state.gov

General Services Officer **Nancy Rhodes** 351 (21) 727-3300
E-mail: rhodesnl2@state.gov

Information Management Officer
Joseph C. "Joe" Dalrymple 351 (21) 727-3300
E-mail: dalrymplejc@state.gov

Information Program Officer
David J. "Dave" Spadacino 351 (21) 727-3300
E-mail: spadacinodj@state.gov

Information Systems Officer **Daniel Murry** 351 (21) 727-3300

Legal Attaché (Resident in Madrid) **Roque Tolentino** 34 91-587-2350
American Embassy - Madrid, Spain, PSC 61, DPO, AE 09642 Fax: 34 91-587-2303

Management Officer **Martin B. "Marty" Schwartz** . . . 351 (21) 727-3300
E-mail: schwartzmb@state.gov

Political/Economic Officer **Peter Donald Andreoli** 351 (21) 727-3300
E-mail: andreolipd@state.gov
Education: Naval Acad 1997 BS

Public Affairs Officer **Todd K. Miyahira** 351 (21) 770-2436
E-mail: miyahiratk@state.gov Fax: 351 (21) 727-6791

Regional Security Officer **Jennifer Babic** 351 (21) 727-3300
E-mail: babicj2@state.gov

Commercial Section (Foreign Commercial Service) [Portugal]
American Embassy - Lisbon, Portugal,
Avenida das Forcas Armadas, 1600-081 Lisbon, Portugal
Mail: American Embassy - Lisbon, Portugal, PSC 83, DPO, AE 09726-9998
Tel: 351 (21) 770-2528 Fax: 351 (21) 726-8914
Internet: www.export.gov/portugal

Commercial Counselor **Rafael Patiño** 351 (21) 770-2526
E-mail: rafael.patino@trade.gov
Education: UC Irvine 1993 BA, 1996 MBA

Drug Enforcement Administration [Portugal]
American Embassy - Lisbon, Portugal,
Avenida das Forcas Armadas, 1600-081 Lisbon, Portugal
Mail: Unit 5320 Box 181, DPO, AE 09726
Tel: 351 (21) 770-2260 Tel: 351 (21) 726-6676

Special Agent **Matthew Coleman** 351 (21) 770-2263

Federal Aviation Administration (Resident in Paris) [Portugal]
American Embassy/FAA, AEU-PAR, 2, Avenue Gabriel, 75382 Paris, Cedex 08, France
Mail: American Embassy/FAA, PSC 116, Box A-215, APO, AE 09777
Tel: 33 (1) 43 12 22 25 Fax: 33 (1) 43 12 25 05

FAA Representative **Ian H. Ross** 359 (52) 43 12 22 22

Office of the Defense Attaché [Portugal]
American Embassy - Lisbon, Portugal,
Avenida das Forcas Armadas (Sete Rios), 1600 Lisbon, Portugal
Mail: American Embassy - Lisbon, Portugal, PSC 83, APO, AE 09726-9998
Tel: 351 (21) 770-2246 Fax: 351 (21) 727-1142

Defense Attaché **Col Glenn LeMasters USAF** 351 (21) 770-2227

Office of Defense Cooperation [Portugal]
American Embassy - Lisbon, Portugal,
Avenida das Forcas Armadas, 1600-081 Lisbon, Portugal
Mail: American Embassy - Lisbon, Portugal, PSC 83, DPO, AE 09726-9998
Tel: 351 (21) 770-2270 Fax: 351 (21) 726-8913

Chief **Scott Worthington** 351 (21) 770-2227
E-mail: WorthingtonSD@state.gov

Ponta Delgada Consulate
U.S. Consulate - Ponta Delgada, Sao Miguel, Azores,
Príncipe de Mónaco, 6-2 F, 9500 Ponta Delgada, Sao Miguel, Azores, Portugal
Mail: U.S. Consulate - Ponta Delgada, PSC 76, Box 3000, APO, AE 09720-0002
Tel: 351 (296) 308 330 Fax: 351 (296) 287-216
E-mail: conspontadelgada@state.gov E-mail: pontadelgadaweb@state.gov

Principal Officer **Jason Chue** 351 (296) 308 330
E-mail: chuej@state.gov
Education: Columbia 2001 JD

U.S. Embassy in Romania

4-6, Dr. Liviu Librescu Blvd, District 1 Bucharest, 015118, Romania
Tel: 40 (21) 200-3300 Tel: 40 (21) 200-3442 Internet: ro.usembassy.gov

Office of the U.S. Ambassador to Romania
American Embassy - Bucharest, Romania,
4-6, Dr. Liviu Librescu Blvd, District 1 Bucharest, 015118, Romania
Mail: American Embassy - Bucharest, Romania, Department of State, 5260 Bucharest Place, Washington, DC 20521-5260

★ Ambassador **Ambassador Hans G. Klemm** 40 (21) 200-3300
E-mail: klemmhg@state.gov
Education: Indiana 1980 BA; Stanford 1996 AM

★ Ambassador-Designate **Adrian Zuckerman** 40 (21) 200-3300
Education: MIT 1979 SB; New York Law 1983 JD
Office Management Specialist to the Ambassador
(Vacant) 40 (21) 200-3300

◇ Deputy Chief of Mission
Abigail Misciagno "Abby" Rupp 40 (21) 200-3300
E-mail: ruppam@state.gov
Office Management Specialist to the Deputy Chief of Mission **Reyna M. Font** 40 (21) 200-3300

Consul General **Sharon M. Umber** 40 (21) 200-3300
E-mail: umbersm@state.gov

Community Liaison Officer **Lauren Pickle** 40 (21) 200-3300

Economic Officer **Ernest J. Abisellan** 40 (21) 200-3300
E-mail: abisellanej@state.gov

Financial Management Officer **George Meray** 40 (21) 200-3300

General Services Officer **Trenton B. Douthett** 40 (21) 200-3300
E-mail: douthetttb@state.gov
Education: Naval Acad 1996 BS; Ohio State 2006 JD

Human Resources Officer **Katherine Pate** 40 (21) 200-3300
E-mail: pateke@state.gov

Information Management Officer
Ronald M. Yonashiro 40 (21) 200-3300
E-mail: yonashirorm@state.gov

Information Program Officer **Travis J. Nissen** 40 (21) 200-3300
E-mail: nissentj@state.gov

Information Systems Officer/Information Systems Security Officer **Syed Gardezi** 40 (21) 200-3300
E-mail: gardezisr@state.gov

Legal Attaché **David M. Varner** 40 (21) 200-3300

Management Officer **Bradley E. "Brad" Page** 40 (21) 200-3300
E-mail: pagebe2@state.gov

Political Officer **David Allen Schlaefer** 40 (21) 200-3300
E-mail: schlaeferda2@state.gov

Public Affairs Officer **Merry Miller** 40 (21) 200-3300
Cultural Officer **Scott A. Reese** 40 (21) 200-3300
E-mail: ReeseSA@state.gov

Regional Security Officer **Patrick J. Keegan** 40 (21) 200-3300
E-mail: keeganpj@state.gov

U.S. Secret Service Attaché **Donald B. Witham** 40 (21) 200-3300

★ Presidential Appointment Requiring Senate Confirmation ☆ Presidential Appointment ☐ Schedule C Appointment ◇ Career Senior Foreign Service Appointment
● Career Senior Executive Service (SES) Appointment ○ Non-Career Senior Executive Service (SES) Appointment ■ Postal Career Executive Service

Agricultural Section (Foreign Agricultural Service) [Romania]
American Embassy - Bucharest, Romania,
4-6, Dr. Liviu Librescu Blvd, District 1 Bucharest, 015118, Romania
Tel: 40 (21) 200-3374 Fax: 40 (21) 200-3442
E-mail: agbucharest@fas.usda.gov

Regional Agricultural Attaché (Resident in Warsaw)
John Slette 48 (22) 504-2336

Commercial Section (Foreign Commercial Service) [Romania]
American Embassy - Bucharest, Romania, Strada Tudor Arghezi 7-9, Sector 1, Bucharest, Romania
Mail: U.S. Commercial Service, Department of State, 5260 Bucharest Place, Washington, DC 20521-5260
Tel: 40 (21) 200-3372 Fax: 40 (21) 316-0690
E-mail: office.bucharest@trade.gov Internet: www.export.gov/romania

Regional Senior Commercial Officer
Gregory "Greg" O'Connor 40 (21) 200-3372
E-mail: Greg.O'Connor@trade.gov

Drug Enforcement Administration [Romania]
DEA Attaché **Stephen Borowski** 40 (21) 200-3300

Federal Aviation Administration (Resident in Moscow) [Romania]
FAA Senior Representative **Andrew McKee** 7 (495) 728-5125

Office of the Defense Attaché [Romania]
American Embassy - Bucharest, Romania, Strada Tudor Arghezi 7-9, Bucharest, Romania
Mail: American Embassy - Bucharest, Romania, Department of State, 5260 Bucharest Place, Washington, DC 20521-5260
Tel: 40 (21) 210-4042 Fax: 40 (21) 210-0395

Defense Attaché **Col Scott Weston USAF** 40 (21) 200-3300

Office of Defense Cooperation [Romania]
American Embassy - Bucharest, Romania, Strada Tudor Arghezi 7-9, Sector 1, Bucharest, Romania

Chief **Steven Klingman** 40 (21) 200-3300

U.S. Embassy in Russia

Bolshoy Deviatinsky, Pereulok No. 8, Moscow, 121099, Russia
Tel: 7 (495) 728-5000 Fax: 7 (495) 728-5090 Internet: ru.usembassy.gov

Office of the U.S. Ambassador to Russia

American Embassy - Moscow, Russia, Bolshoy Deviatinsky, Pereulok No. 8, Moscow, 121099, Russia
Mail: Unit 5430, DPO, AE 09721

★ Ambassador
Ambassador Jon Meade Huntsman, Jr. 7 (495) 728-5000
Education: Pennsylvania 1987 BA
Office Management Specialist to the Ambassador
Laura M. Birner 7 (495) 728-5180
E-mail: birnerlm@state.gov

◇ Deputy Chief of Mission **Anthony F. Godfrey** 7 (495) 728-5190
E-mail: godfreyaf@state.gov
Education: UC Davis
Office Management Specialist to the Deputy Chief of Mission **Nghi Cosgrove** 7 (495) 728-5190
E-mail: cosgrovenghi@state.gov
Education: George Mason BA; VCU

Community Liaison Officer **Seth Langer** 7 (495) 728-5000

Consular Section Chief **Michael L. Yoder** 7 (495) 728-5217
Education: Indiana 1979 BA; Georgia 1983 MFA
Fax: 7 (495) 728-5358

◇ Economic Affairs Section Chief
Andrew G. Chritton 7 (495) 728-5000
E-mail: chrittonag@state.gov

Environment, Science and Technology and Health Officer **Mateo M. Ayala** 7 (495) 728-5324
E-mail: ayalamm@state.gov
Education: Alberta 1994 BA; Texas 1996 MBA; McGill (Canada) 1997 MBA

Office of the U.S. Ambassador to Russia *(continued)*

Facilities Management Officer
Thomas M. "Tom" Murphy 7 (495) 728-5000
E-mail: murphytm@state.gov

Financial Management Officer **Tahwanda Lambert** 7 (495) 728-5056

General Services Officer **Jason Haskins** 7 (495) 728-5248

Human Resources Officer **Susan M. Carl** 7 (495) 728-5248
E-mail: carlsm@state.gov

Information Management Officer **Robert A. Hall** 7 (495) 728-5300
E-mail: hallra@state.gov

Information Program Officer **(Vacant)** 7 (495) 728-5330

Information Systems Officer **(Vacant)** 7 (495) 728-5000

Information Systems Security Officer **Philip Harris** 7 (495) 728-5835

Labor Officer **(Vacant)** 7 (495) 728-5349

Legal Attaché **Stephen Iwan** 7 (495) 728-5000

◇ Management Officer **John Marsh Kuschner** 7 (495) 728-5185
E-mail: kuschnerjm@state.gov

Political Officer **(Vacant)** 7 (495) 728-5341

Public Affairs Officer **Thomas M. "Tom" Leary** 7 (495) 728-5926
E-mail: learytm@state.gov
Spokesperson **Andrea R. Kalan** 7 (495) 728-5000
E-mail: kalanar@state.gov
Education: Southern Methodist 1992 BA; Ohio State 1996 MA

Regional Security Officer **Stephen "Steve" Sexton** 7 (495) 728-6040

Agricultural Section (Foreign Agricultural Service) [Russia]
American Embassy - Moscow, Russia, 8 Devyatinsky Pereulok, 121099 Moscow, Russia
Mail: Unit 5430, DPO, AE 09721
Tel: 7 (495) 728-5222 Fax: 7 (495) 728-5133
E-mail: agmoscow@fas.usda.gov

◇ Agricultural Officer **Deanna Ayala** 7 (495) 728-5222
E-mail: deanna.ayala@fas.usda.gov

Agricultural Trade Office - Moscow [Russia]
American Embassy - Moscow, Russia, 8 Devyatinsky Pereulok, 121099 Moscow, Russia
Mail: Unit 5430, DPO, AE 09721
Tel: 7 (495) 728-5560 Fax: 7 (495) 728-5069
E-mail: atomoscow@fas.usda.gov

Director **David Leishman** 7 (495) 728-5560

Commercial Section (Foreign Commercial Service) [Russia]
23/38 Bolshaya Molchanovka, 121069 Moscow, Russia
Mail: Unit 5430, DPO, AE 09721
Tel: 7 (495) 728-5580 Fax: 7 (495) 728-5585
E-mail: office.moscow@trade.gov Internet: http://export.gov/russia/

Senior Commercial Officer (Acting)
Heather R. Byrnes 7 (495) 728-5474
E-mail: Heather.Byrnes@trade.gov
Education: Georgetown 1991 BA

Deputy Senior Commercial Officer **(Vacant)** 7 (495) 728-5364

Department of Energy [Russia]
American Embassy - Moscow, Russia, 8 Bolshoy Devyatinsky Pereulok, 121099 Moscow, Russia
Tel: 7 (495) 728-5220 Fax: 7 (495) 728-5360

Director **Heather Bell** 7 (495) 728-5220

Drug Enforcement Administration [Russia]
American Embassy - Moscow, Russia, Eight Bolshoy Devyatinsky Pereulok, 121099 Moscow, Russia
Mail: Unit 5430, DPO, AE 09721
Tel: 7 (495) 728-5218 Fax: 7 (495) 728-5059

Attaché **Michael Rusciano** 7 (495) 728-5218

Federal Aviation Administration [Russia]
American Embassy, Eight Bolshoy Devyatinsky Pereulok, 121099 Moscow, Russia
Mail: Unit 5430, DPO, AE 09721
Tel: 7 (495) 728-5125 Fax: 7 (495) 728-5350

FAA Senior Representative **Andrew McKee** 7 (495) 728-5125
E-mail: andrew.s.mckee@faa.gov

DEPARTMENTS

★ Presidential Appointment Requiring Senate Confirmation ☆ Presidential Appointment ☐ Schedule C Appointment ◇ Career Senior Foreign Service Appointment
● Career Senior Executive Service (SES) Appointment ○ Non-Career Senior Executive Service (SES) Appointment ■ Postal Career Executive Service

Department of Homeland Security - U.S. Citizenship and Immigration Services [Russia]
American Embassy - Moscow, Russia,
Novinsky Boulevard 19/23, 121099 Moscow, Russia
Mail: Unit 5430, DPO, AE 09721
Tel: 7 (495) 728-5236 Fax: 7 (495) 728-5083

CIS Officer **Emery Moore** 7 (495) 728-4551

Department of Homeland Security - U.S. Immigration and Customs Enforcement [Russia]
American Embassy - Moscow, Russia,
Novinsky Boulevard 19/23, 121099 Moscow, Russia
Mail: Unit 5430, DPO, AE 09721
Tel: 7 (495) 728-5050 Fax: 7 (495) 728-5140

Customs Attaché **Jason Cassidy** 7 (495) 728-5215

National Aeronautics and Space Administration [Russia]
American Embassy - Moscow, Russia,
Novinsky Boulevard 19/23, 121099 Moscow, Russia

NASA Russia Representative **Justin Tilman** 7 (495) 728-5829
Tel: 7 (495) 728-5127

Office of the Defense Attaché [Russia]
American Embassy - Moscow, Russia,
8 Devyatinsky Pereulok, 121099 Moscow, Russia
Mail: Unit 5430, DPO, AE 09721
Tel: 7 (495) 728-5123 Fax: 7 (495) 728-5183

Senior Defense Official and Defense Attaché
BG Garrick M. Harmon USA 7 (495) 728-5317

U.S. Secret Service [Russia]
American Embassy - Moscow, Russia,
Novinsky Boulevard 19/23, 121099 Moscow, Russia

Agent-in-Charge **Keith Jones** 7 (495) 728-5000

Vladivostok Consulate General
U.S. Consulate General - Vladivostok, Russia,
Ulitsa Pushkinskaya 32, Vladivostok, 690001, Russia
Mail: 5880 Vladivostok Place, Department of State,
Washington, DC 20521-5880
Tel: 7 (423) 230-00-70 Fax: 7 (423) 249-93-72 E-mail: pavlad@state.gov

Consul General **Michael C. Keays** 7 (423) 30-00-70
E-mail: keaysmc@state.gov
Consular Affairs Officer **Mary Pellegrini** 7 (423) 230-00-79
Fax: 7 (423) 230-00-91
General Services Officer **(Vacant)** 7 (423) 230-00-70
Information Systems Officer **(Vacant)** 7 (423) 230-00-70
Information Systems Security Officer **Dong Lee** 7 (423) 230-00-70
Management Officer **Doug Rose** 7 (423) 230-00-70
Education: Wisconsin 1989 BA; U St Thomas (MN) 2004 MIM
Political/Economic Affairs Officer **Benjamin Parisi** 7 (423) 230-00-70
E-mail: parisib@state.gov
Public Affairs Officer **Darren Thies** 7 (423) 230-00-70
E-mail: thiesdt@state.gov Fax: 7 (423) 230-00-95
Regional Security Officer **Alice E. Lookofsky** 7 (423) 230-00-70
E-mail: lookofskyae@state.gov
Education: Kentucky 2000 BA; Georgetown 2003

Yekaterinburg Consulate General
American Consulate General - Yekaterinburg, Ulitsa Gogolya 15A,
P.O. Box 620151, Yekaterinburg, Russia
Mail: U.S. Consulate General - Yekaterinburg,
5890 Yekaterinburg Place, Washington, DC 20521-5890
Tel: 7 (343) 379-3001 Fax: 7 (343) 379-4515
E-mail: uscgyekat@state.gov

Consul General **Paul M. Carter, Jr.** 7 (343) 379-3001
E-mail: carterpm@state.gov
Education: Catholic U 1981 BA; Indiana PhD
Consular Officer **(Vacant)** 7 (343) 379-3001
Information Systems Officer **(Vacant)** 7 (343) 379-3001
Information Systems Security Officer **(Vacant)** 7 (343) 379-3001
Management Officer **Richard A. Woodhouse** 7 (343) 379-3001
E-mail: woodhousera@state.gov

Yekaterinburg Consulate General *(continued)*

Political/Economic Officer **(Vacant)** 7 (343) 379-3001
Public Affairs Officer **Peter A. Burba** 7 (343) 379-3001
E-mail: burbapa@state.gov
Regional Security Officer **Joseph Burkhead** 7 (343) 379-3001
E-mail: burkheadjd@state.gov

Commercial Section (Foreign Commercial Service) (Resident in Moscow) [Russia]
Senior Commercial Officer **(Vacant)** 7 (495) 728-5474

U.S. Embassy in Serbia

American Embassy - Belgrade, 92 Bulevar kneza Aleksandra
Karadjordjevica, 11040 Belgrade, Serbia
Tel: 381 (11) 706-4000 Fax: 381 (11) 706-4005
Internet: rs.usembassy.gov

Office of the U.S. Ambassador to Serbia

American Embassy - Belgrade, 92 Bulevar kneza Aleksandra
Karadjordjevica, 11040 Belgrade, Serbia
Mail: American Embassy - Belgrade, 5070 Belgrade Place,
Washington, DC 20521-5070

★ Ambassador **Ambassador Kyle Randolph Scott** 381 (11) 706-4000
E-mail: scottkr@state.gov
Office Management Specialist to the Ambassador
Sandra Shaffer 381 (11) 706-4000
◇ Deputy Chief of Mission **Kurt D. Donnelly** 381 (11) 706-4000
E-mail: donnellykd@state.gov
Office Management Specialist to the Deputy Chief
of Mission **Yvette Foster** 381 (11) 706-4000
Consular Affairs Section Chief **Karen N. Mims** 381 (11) 706-4000
E-mail: mimskn@state.gov
Education: Virginia 1997 BA; Pennsylvania 2006 PhD
Community Liaison Officer **Stephany Rapier** 381 (11) 706-4000
Economic Officer **Carolina Hidea** 381 (11) 706-4000
Financial Management Officer
Spencer A. Maguire 381 (11) 706-4000
E-mail: maguiresa@state.gov
Education: Syracuse 1997 BA; Kansas 2005 MPA;
Roger Williams 2007 JD
General Services Officer **Kimberly A. Keck** 381 (11) 706-4000
E-mail: keckka@state.gov
ICASS Chair **(Vacant)** 381 (11) 706-4000
Information Management Officer **John E. Combs** 381 (11) 706-4000
Information Program Officer **Joshua Kim** 381 (11) 706-4000
Information Systems Officer **Joshua Kim** 381 (11) 706-4000
Management Officer **Phathanie S. Chapman** 381 (11) 706-4000
E-mail: chapmanps@state.gov
Political Officer **David Lindgren Gehrenbeck** 381 (11) 706-4000
Public Affairs Officer
Timothy M. "Tim" Standaert 381 (11) 706-4000
E-mail: standaerttm@state.gov
Regional Security Officer **Adam M. Schrandt** 381 (11) 706-4000

Agency for International Development [Serbia]
American Embassy - Belgrade, 92 Bulevar kneza Aleksandra
Karadjordjevica, 11040 Belgrade, Serbia
Mail: American Embassy - Belgrade, 5070 Belgrade Place,
Washington, DC 20521-5070
Fax: 381 (11) 361-8267 Internet: www.usaid.gov/serbia

◇ Mission Director **Osvaldo M. "Mike" de la Rosa** 381 (11) 706-4000
E-mail: mdelarosa@usaid.gov
Education: Georgia Tech 1981 BS;
London School Econ (UK) 1990 MSc; National Defense U 2012 MS

★ Presidential Appointment Requiring Senate Confirmation ☆ Presidential Appointment □ Schedule C Appointment ◇ Career Senior Foreign Service Appointment
● Career Senior Executive Service (SES) Appointment ○ Non-Career Senior Executive Service (SES) Appointment ■ Postal Career Executive Service

Agricultural Section (Foreign Agricultural Service) [Serbia]
American Embassy - Sofia, Bulgaria, 16 Kozyak Street, Sofia, 1408, Bulgaria
Mail: American Embassy - Sofia, Bulgaria, Department of State, 5740 Sofia Place, Washington, DC 20521-5740
Tel: 381 (11) 706-4403 E-mail: agbelgrade@fas.usda.gov

Agricultural Attaché (Resident in Rome) **Frederick H. "Fred" Giles** 381 (11) 706-4403
E-mail: frederick.giles@fas.usda.gov

Commercial Section (Foreign Commercial Service) [Serbia]
American Embassy - Belgrade, 92 Bulevar kneza Aleksandra Karadjordjevica, 11040 Belgrade, Serbia
Mail: American Embassy - Belgrade, 5070 Belgrade Place, Washington, DC 20521-5070
Internet: export.gov/serbia

Senior Commercial Officer **Suzanne Platt** 381 (11) 706-4072
E-mail: Suzanne.Platt@trade.gov
Education: Virginia 2003 BA; Johns Hopkins 2008 MA

Department of Homeland Security - U.S. Immigration and Customs Enforcement (Resident in Vienna) [Serbia]
Customs Attaché **Sarah Bay** 43 (1) 31339-2111

Office of the Defense Attaché [Serbia]
American Embassy - Belgrade, 92 Bulevar kneza Aleksandra Karadjordjevica, 11040 Belgrade, Serbia
Mail: American Embassy - Belgrade, 5070 Belgrade Place, Washington, DC 20521-5070

Defense Attaché **COL Douglas M. Faherty USA** 381 (11) 706-4000
E-mail: fahertydm@state.gov

U.S. Embassy in Slovakia

Hviezdoslavovo Namestie 5, 81102 Bratislava, Slovakia
Tel: 421 (2) 5443-3338 Fax: 421 (2) 5441-8861
Internet: sk.usembassy.gov

Office of the U.S. Ambassador to Slovakia

American Embassy - Bratislava, Slovakia, Hviezdoslavovo Namestie 5, 814 99 Bratislava, Slovakia
Mail: American Embassy - Bratislava, Slovakia, 5840 Bratislava Place, Washington, DC 20521-5840

★ Ambassador **Ambassador Adam H. Sterling** 421 (2) 5922-3421
E-mail: sterlingah@state.gov
Education: Grinnell BA; JFK School Govt MPP

Office Management Specialist to the Ambassador **Diane O'Guerin** 421 (2) 5922-3421
E-mail: oguerindp@state.gov

Deputy Chief of Mission **Natasha S. Franceschi** 421 (2) 5922-3323
E-mail: franceschins@state.gov
Education: Swarthmore 1996; Fletcher Law & Diplomacy 2000 MALD

Office Management Specialist to the Deputy Chief of Mission **Dorsey DuPont** 421 (2) 5922-3323
E-mail: dupontdj@state.gov

Consular Section Chief **Matthew C. "Matt" Pierson** 421 (2) 5443-3338
Fax: 421 (2) 5441-8861

Community Liaison Officer **(Vacant)** 421 (2) 5922 3199

Economic Officer **Liam Sullivan** 421 (2) 5922-3412
E-mail: sullivanll@state.gov

General Services Officer **Scott Gallaway** 421 (2) 5922-3308
E-mail: gallawaysa@state.gov Fax: 421 (2) 5922-3044

Information Management Officer **Freddy R. Mendez** 421 (2) 5922-3075
E-mail: mendezfr@state.gov

Information Program Officer **Alex B. Kim** 421 (2) 5922-3280
E-mail: kimab@state.gov

Legal Attaché (Resident in Prague) **Paul H. Haertel** 420 (2) 724-162-483
American Embassy - Prague, Department of State, Washington, DC 20521-5630
E-mail: haertelph@state.gov

Office of the U.S. Ambassador to Slovakia *(continued)*

Management Officer (Acting) **Scott Gallaway** 421 (2) 5922-3227
E-mail: gallawaysa@state.gov Fax: 421 (2) 5441-5148

Political/Economic Officer **Ralan Lucas Hill** 421 (2) 5922-3291
Education: Tufts BSChE; Cal State (Dominguez) MA

Public Affairs Officer **David M. Duerden** 421 (2) 5922-3159
E-mail: duerdendm@state.gov
Education: Ricks 2001 AS; BYU 2005 BA; U London 2005 MA

Regional Security Officer **Anthony Dylan "Dylan" Ragan** 421 (2) 5922-3051
E-mail: raganad@state.gov Fax: 421 (2) 5922-3382

Agricultural Section (Foreign Agricultural Service) (Resident in Berlin) [Slovakia]
American Embassy - Bratislava, Slovakia, Hviezdoslavovo Namestie 5, 814 99 Bratislava, Slovakia
Tel: 48 (22) 504-2000 Fax: 48 (22) 504-2320

Agricultural Counselor **Kelly Stange** 49 (30) 8305-1150

Commercial Section (Foreign Commercial Service) (Resident in Austria) [Slovakia]
American Embassy - Bratislava, Slovakia, Hviezdoslavovo Namestie 5, 81102 Bratislava, Slovakia
Mail: American Embassy - Bratislava, Slovakia, Department of State, 5840 Bratislava Place, Washington, DC 20521-5840
Tel: 421 (2) 5922-3222 Fax: 421 (2) 5922-3345
E-mail: office.bratislava@trade.gov

Commercial Officer **Marián Volent** 421 (2) 5922 3510
E-mail: marian.volent@trade.gov

Drug Enforcement Administration (Resident in Vienna) [Slovakia]
Gartenbaupromenade 2, 4th Floor, A-1010 Vienna, Austria
Mail: Department of State, 9900 Vienna Place, Washington, DC 20521-9900
Tel: 43 (1) 313-39 Fax: 43 (1) 310-0682

DEA Officer **(Vacant)** 43 (1) 3-1339-7548

Federal Aviation Administration (Resident in Moscow) [Slovakia]
FAA Senior Representative, Paris **Andrew McKee** 7 (495) 728-5125

Office of the Defense Attaché [Slovakia]
American Embassy - Bratislava, Slovakia, Hviezdoslavovo Namestie 5, 81102 Bratislava, Slovakia
Mail: Department of State, 5840 Bratislava Place, Washington, DC 20521-5840
Tel: 421 (2) 5922-3061 Fax: 421 (2) 5441-8856

Defense Attaché **LTC Jonathan Dunn USA** 421 (2) 5922-3061
E-mail: dunnjs@state.gov

Office of Defense Cooperation [Slovakia]
American Embassy - Bratislava, Slovakia, Hviezdoslavovo namestie 5, 811 Bratislava, 02, Slovakia
Mail: Department of State, 5840 Bratislava Place, Washington, DC 20521-5840
Tel: 421 (2) 4445-3456 Fax: 421 (2) 4445-9627

Chief **LTC Walter E. Richter USA** 421 (2) 4445-3454
E-mail: walter.e.richter2.mil@mail.mil

U.S. Embassy in Slovenia

Presernova 31, 1000 Ljubljana, Slovenia
Tel: 386 (1) 200-5500 Fax: 386 (1) 200-5555 Internet: si.usembassy.gov

Office of the U.S. Ambassador to Slovenia

American Embassy - Ljubljana, Slovenia, Presernova 31, 1000 Ljubljana, Slovenia
Mail: American Embassy - Ljubljana, Slovenia, 7140 Ljubljana Place, Washington, DC 20521-7140
E-mail: usembassyljubljana@state.gov

★ Ambassador-Designate **Lynda "Lindy" Blanchard** 386 (1) 200-5500
Education: Auburn BS

Chargé d'Affaires **Gautam A. Rana** 386 (1) 200-5500
E-mail: ranaga@state.gov

(continued on next page)

★ Presidential Appointment Requiring Senate Confirmation ☆ Presidential Appointment ☐ Schedule C Appointment ◇ Career Senior Foreign Service Appointment
● Career Senior Executive Service (SES) Appointment ○ Non-Career Senior Executive Service (SES) Appointment ■ Postal Career Executive Service

DEPARTMENTS

Office of the U.S. Ambassador to Slovenia *(continued)*

Office Management Specialist to the Ambassador
(Vacant) 386 (1) 200-5500
Deputy Chief of Mission **Gautam A. Rana** 386 (1) 200-5500
E-mail: ranaga@state.gov
Office Management Specialist to the Deputy Chief of Mission **Kristy A. Ejjalty** 386 (1) 200-5500
E-mail: ejjaltyka@state.gov
Consular Officer **Amy L. Lorenzen** 386 (1) 200-5500
E-mail: lorenzenal@state.gov
Community Liaison Officer **Samantha A. Martin** 386 (1) 200-5500
Economic Officer **William D. Baker** 386 (1) 200-5500
Financial Management Officer **Valerie J. Martin** 386 (1) 200-5500
E-mail: martinvj@state.gov
General Service Officer **Julia A. Stanley** 386 (1) 200-8200
E-mail: stanleyja3@state.gov
Information Management Officer/Information Systems Security Officer **Patricia A. Rainey** 386 (1) 200-5500
E-mail: raineypa@state.gov
Legal Attaché **Amy L. Shuman** 386 (1) 200-5500
Management Officer **Valerie J. Martin** 386 (1) 200-5500
E-mail: martinvj@state.gov
Political/Economic Officer **Laura E. Anderson** 386 (1) 200-5500
E-mail: andersonle@state.gov
Political/Military Officer **James C. Peranteau** 386 (1) 200-5500
Education: Wisconsin (Milwaukee) 2015 BA; Georgetown 2017 MS
Public Affairs Officer **Jean B. Leedy** 386 (1) 200-5500
E-mail: leedyjb@state.gov Fax: 386 (1) 426-4284
Regional Security Officer **David M. Gallagher** 386 (1) 200-5500
E-mail: gallagherdm1@state.gov

Agricultural Section (Foreign Agricultural Service) (Resident in Berlin) [Slovenia]
American Embassy Consular Section - Berlin, Germany, Clayallee 170, 14195 Berlin, Germany
Mail: American Embassy - Berlin, Germany, PSC 120, APO, AE 09265
Tel: 49 (30) 8305-1150 Fax: 49 (30) 8431-1935

Agricultural Officer **Kelly Stange** 49 (30) 8305-1150
E-mail: kelly.stange@fas.usda.gov

Commercial Section (Foreign Commercial Service) [Slovenia]
American Embassy - Ljubljana, Slovenia, Presernova 31, 1000 Ljubljana, Slovenia
Mail: American Embassy - Ljubljana, Slovenia, 7140 Ljubljana Place, Washington, DC 20521-7140
Fax: 386 (1) 200-5650 Internet: www.export.gov/slovenia/index.asp

Commercial Officer **Matjaz Kavcic** 386 (1) 200-5537

Federal Aviation Administration (Resident in Moscow) [Slovenia]
American Embassy, Eight Bolshoy Devyatinsky Pereulok, 121099 Moscow, Russia
Mail: Unit 5430, DPO, AE 09721
Fax: 7 (495) 728-5350

FAA Senior Representative **Andrew McKee** 7 (495) 728-5125

Office of the Defense Attaché [Slovenia]
American Embassy - Ljubljana, Slovenia, Presernova 31, 1000 Ljubljana, Slovenia
Mail: American Embassy - Ljubljana, Slovenia, Department of State, Washington, DC 20521-7140
Tel: 386 (1) 200-5500 Fax: 386 (1) 200-5555

Defense Attaché **LTC Krist G. Thodoropoulos USA** ... 386 (1) 200-5500
E-mail: thodoropouloskg@state.gov

Office of the Defense Cooperation [Slovenia]
American Embassy - Liubljana, Slovenia, Presernova 31, 1000 Ljubljana, Slovenia
Mail: American Embassy - Liubljana, Slovenia, Department of State, Washington, DC 20521-7140
Tel: 386 (1) 471 2873

Chief **LTC Steven J. Pena USA** .... (52) 200-5500

U.S. Embassy in Spain
Serrano 75, 28006 Madrid, Spain
Tel: 34 91-587-2200 Fax: 34 91-587-2303 Internet: es.usembassy.gov

Office of the U.S. Ambassador to Spain
American Embassy - Madrid, Spain, Serrano 75, 28006 Madrid, Spain
Mail: American Embassy - Madrid, Spain, PSC 61, DPO, AE 09642

★ Ambassador
Ambassador Richard "Duke" Buchan III 34 91-587-2200
Note: Ambassador Buchan serves concurrently as ambassador to Andorra.
Education: North Carolina BA; Harvard MBA
Office Management Specialist to the Ambassador
Maria Alejandra "Alejandra" Ferreira-Sachero 34 91-587-2394
◇ Deputy Chief of Mission **Benjamin G. Ziff** 34 91-587-2200
E-mail: ziffbg@state.gov
Education: Cal State (Long Beach) 1985 BA; Tufts 1987 MALD; National War Col 2004 MS
Office Management Specialist to the Deputy Chief of Mission **Claudia Ellingwood** 34 91-587-2200
Community Liaison Officer **Annette Ortiz** 34 91-587-2200
Consul General **Liza Petrush** 34 91-587-2200
Economic Officer **Thomas E. Reott** 34 91-587-2200
E-mail: reottte@state.gov
Education: Miami U (OH) 1988 BS; Fletcher Law & Diplomacy 1999 MIA
Environment, Science and Technology Officer
Frank P. Talluto 34 91-587-2200
Facilities Management Officer **Alicia Dasso** 34 91-587-2200
Financial Management Officer **Satish Nair** 34 91587-2200
General Services Officer **Juan Carlos Ospina** 34 91-587-2229
Human Resources Officer **Karen Klaver** 34 91-587-2200
Information Management Officer
Rodney "Rod" Burney 34 91-587-2200
Information Systems Officer/Information Systems Security Officer **Dianna Rosa** 34 91-587-2200
Information Program Officer **Cynthia Segura** 34 91-548-9250
Legal Attaché **Roque Tolentino** 34 91-587-2200
◇ Management Officer **David W. Simons** 34 91-587-2200
Political Officer **Scott Higgins** 34 91-587-2200
Education: Colorado 1992 BA; South Carolina State 2000 MBA
◇ Public Affairs Officer **Stewart D. Tuttle, Jr.** 34 91-587-2500
E-mail: tuttlesd@state.gov Fax: 34 91-576-8464
Education: BYU 1993 JD
Cultural Affairs Officer **Ana Duque-Higgins** 34 91-587-2200
Education: North Carolina BA; South Carolina MBA
Information Officer **David Connell** 34 91-587-2200
Regional Affairs Officer **(Vacant)** 34 91-587-2200
Regional Security Officer **Fernando J. Matus** 34 91-587-2200
E-mail: matusfj@state.gov

Agricultural Section (Foreign Agricultural Service) [Spain]
American Embassy - Madrid, Spain, Serrano 75, 28006 Madrid, Spain
Mail: American Embassy - Madrid, Spain, APO, AE 09642
Tel: 34 915-872-555 Fax: 34 915-872-556
E-mail: agmadrid@fas.usda.gov

Agricultural Counselor **Jennifer Clever** 34 915-872-555
E-mail: jennifer.clever@fas.usda.gov

Commercial Section (Foreign Commercial Service) [Spain]
American Embassy - Madrid, Spain, Serrano 75, 28006 Madrid, Spain
Mail: American Embassy - Madrid, Spain, APO, AE 09642
Tel: 34 91564-8976 Fax: 34 91563-0859
E-mail: office.madrid@trade.gov Internet: export.gov/spain

Senior Commercial Officer (Acting) **Ricardo Pelaez** 34 91-308-1529
E-mail: ricardo.pelaez@trade.gov
Education: Kent State 1997 BA; Cleveland State 2002 MBA
Senior Commercial Officer **Cameron Werker** 34 91564-8976
E-mail: Cameron.Werker@trade.gov
Education: Colorado State 1991 BS
Deputy Commercial Officer **(Vacant)** 34 91-308-1527
International Trade Specialist **Carmen Adrada** 34 91-308-1542
E-mail: carmen.adrada@trade.gov

★ Presidential Appointment Requiring Senate Confirmation ☆ Presidential Appointment ☐ Schedule C Appointment ◇ Career Senior Foreign Service Appointment
● Career Senior Executive Service (SES) Appointment ○ Non-Career Senior Executive Service (SES) Appointment ■ Postal Career Executive Service

Commercial Section (Foreign Commercial Service) [Spain] *(continued)*

International Trade Specialist **Helen Crowley** 34 91-308-1548
E-mail: helen.crowley@trade.gov
International Trade Specialist **Jesus Garcia** 34 91-308-1578
E-mail: jesus.garcia@trade.gov
International Trade Specialist **Carlos Perezminguez** 34 91-308-1598
E-mail: carlos.perezminguez@trade.gov

Department of Homeland Security - Transportation Security Administration [Spain]
American Embassy - Madrid, Spain, Serrano 75, 28006 Madrid, Spain
Mail: American Embassy - Madrid, Spain, PSC 61, Box 0047, APO, AE 09642
Tel: 34 91587-2300 Fax: 34 91587-2301

TSA Chief **(Vacant)** 34 91-587-2300

Department of Homeland Security - U.S. Immigration and Customs Enforcement [Spain]
American Embassy - Madrid, Spain, Serrano 75, 28006 Madrid, Spain
Mail: American Embassy - Madrid, Spain, PSC 61, DPO, AE 09642

Chief **(Vacant)** 34 91-587-2200

Drug Enforcement Administration [Spain]
American Embassy - Madrid, Spain, Serrano 75, 28006 Madrid, Spain
Mail: American Embassy - Madrid, Spain, APO, AE 09642
Tel: 34 91587-2200 Fax: 34 91587-2303

Special Agent **Daniel Saavedra** 34 91-587-2200

Federal Aviation Administration (Resident in Paris) [Spain]
American Embassy/FAA, AEU-PAR, 2, Avenue Gabriel, 75382 Paris, Cedex 08, France
Mail: American Embassy/FAA, PSC 116, Box A-215, APO, AE 09777
Tel: 33 (1) 4312-2225 Fax: 33 (1) 4312-2505

FAA Senior Representative, London **Ian H. Ross** 33 (1) 4312-2225

Office of the Defense Attaché [Spain]
American Embassy - Madrid, Spain, Serrano 75, 28006 Madrid, Spain
Mail: American Embassy - Madrid, Spain, APO, AE 09642
Tel: 34 91587-2200 Fax: 34 91587-2303

Defense and Naval Attaché
CAPT Brett Fullerton USN 34 91-587-2200

Office of Defense Cooperation [Spain]
American Embassy - Madrid, Spain, Serrano 75, 28006 Madrid, Spain
Mail: American Embassy - Madrid, Spain, APO, AE 09642
Tel: 34 91543-2800 Fax: 34 91543-3207

Defense Cooperation Office Chief **Carlos Ortiz** 34 91-543-2800

Barcelona Consulate General
U.S. Consulate General - Barcelona, Spain,
Paseo Reina Elisenda de Montcada, 23, 08034 Barcelona, Spain
Mail: U.S. Consulate General–Barcelona, Spain, PSC 61, Box 0005, DPO, AE 09642
Tel: 34 93280-2227 Fax: 34 93-280-61-75

Consul General **Robert J. "Bob" Riley** 34 93-280-2227
E-mail: rileyrj@state.gov
Education: Notre Dame 1984 BA; Michigan 1987 JD
Consular Officer **Ehren S. Schimmel** 34 93-280-2227
Consul for Regional Affairs **Samir George** 34 93-280-2227
Political/Management Officer **Saul Mercado** 34 93-280-2227
E-mail: mercados1@state.gov
Public Affairs Officer **(Vacant)** 34 93-280-2227
Fax: 34 93-205-5857

Fuengirola (Malaga) Consular Agency
U.S. Consular Agency - Fuengirola, Avda. Juan Gomez "Juanito" 8,
Edificio Lucia - 1C, Fuengirola, 29640 Malaga, Spain
Mail: U.S. Consular Agency–Fuengirola, Malaga,
c/o American Embassy - Madrid, DPO, AE 09642
Tel: 34 95247-4891 Fax: 34 95246-5189 E-mail: malagacons@state.gov

Consular Agent **Roberta G. Aaron** 34 952-47-48-91

Las Palmas Consular Agency
U.S. Consular Agency - Las Palmas, Spain, Los Martinez de Escoba 3,
Oficina 7, 35007 Las Palmas, Spain
Mail: U.S. Consular Agency - Las Palmas, Spain,
c/o American Embassy - Spain, DPO, AE 09642
Tel: 34 92827-1259 Fax: 34 92822-5863
E-mail: laspalmascons@state.gov

Consular Agent **Ana Maria Quintana** 34 928-271-259

Palma de Mallorca Consular Agency
U.S. Consular Agency - Palma de Mallorca, Spain,
Edificio Reina Constanza, c/o Porto Pi, 8-9D, 07015 Palma de Mallorca, Spain
Mail: U.S. Consular Agency - Palma de Mallorca,
c/o American Embassy - Spain, DPO, AE 09642
Tel: 34 97140-3707 Fax: 34 97140-3971 E-mail: pmagency@state.gov

Consular Agent **Kimberly Marshall** 34 971-725-051

Seville Consular Agency
U.S. Consular Agency - Seville, Spain, Plaza Nueva 8-8 duplicado,
2ª planta, E2, Nº 4, 41001 Seville, Spain
Mail: U.S. Consular Agency - Seville, Spain,
c/o American Embassy - Spain, DPO, AE 09642
Tel: 34 95421-8751 Fax: 34 95422-0791 E-mail: sevillecons@state.gov

Consular Agent **Raynold von Samson-Himmelstjern** ... 34 95421-8571
Education: Pittsburgh MBA

U.S. Embassy in Sweden

Dag Hammarskjölds Väg 31, S-115, 89 Stockholm, Sweden
Tel: 46 (8) 783-5300 Fax: 46 (8) 661-1964 Internet: se.usembassy.gov

Office of the U.S. Ambassador to Sweden

Embassy of the United States of America - Stockholm,
Dag Hammarskjölds Väg 31, 89 Stockholm, Sweden
Mail: Embassy of the United States of America, Department of State,
5750 Stockholm Place, Washington, DC 20521-5750

★ Ambassador-Designate **Kenneth A. "Ken" Howery** 46 (8) 783-5300
Education: Stanford 1998 BA
◇ Chargé d'Affaires **David E. Lindwall** 46 (8) 783-5300
E-mail: lindwallde@state.gov
Office Management Specialist to the Ambassador
(Vacant) 46 (8) 783-5300
Deputy Chief of Mission (Acting)
Kristin L. Rockwood 46 (8) 783-5300
E-mail: rockwoodkl@state.gov
Education: Thunderbird Global MBA
Office Management Specialist to the Deputy Chief
of Mission **Maria Elena Alcazar-Schensted** 46 (8) 783-5300
Consul **Patrick I. Tanimura** 46 (8) 783-5300
E-mail: tanimurapi@state.gov Fax: 46 (8) 660-5879
Community Liaison Officer **Meredith Olson** 46 (8) 783-5300
Customs Attaché **John E. Connors** 46 (8) 783-5300
Economic Officer **Paul Stahle** 46 (8) 783-5300
Financial Management Officer **Monte Parker** 46 (8) 783-5300
General Services Officer **Stephen C. Macleod** 46 (8) 783-5300
Information Management Officer **Nathan A. Holder** 46 (8) 783-5300
E-mail: holderna@state.gov
Education: West Virginia State U 1998 BS; Marshall 2002 MS
Information Program Officer **(Vacant)** 46 (8) 783-5300
Legal Attaché **Douglas Olson** 46 (8) 783-5300
Management Officer **Kristin L. Rockwood** 46 (8) 783-5300
E-mail: rockwoodkl@state.gov
Education: Thunderbird Global MBA
Political Officer **Christopher H. Dorn** 46 (8) 783-5300
E-mail: dornch@state.gov
Education: British Columbia Tech 1986 BS; Columbia 1988 MS, 1991 JD
Political/Economic Officer **Paul F. Narain** 46 (8) 783-5300
E-mail: narainpf@state.gov
Education: Johns Hopkins BA; Tufts MALD

(continued on next page)

★ Presidential Appointment Requiring Senate Confirmation ☆ Presidential Appointment □ Schedule C Appointment ◇ Career Senior Foreign Service Appointment
● Career Senior Executive Service (SES) Appointment ○ Non-Career Senior Executive Service (SES) Appointment ■ Postal Career Executive Service

Office of the U.S. Ambassador to Sweden *(continued)*

Public Affairs Officer **Williams S. "Bill" Martin** 46 (8) 783-5300
E-mail: martinws@state.gov Fax: 46 (8) 665-3303
Education: Duke 1983 BA; Vanderbilt 1987 JD; Johns Hopkins 1991 MA

Regional Security Officer **Jamie Palagi** 46 (8) 783-5300

Agricultural Section (Foreign Agricultural Service) (Resident in The Hague) [Sweden]
American Embassy - The Hague, Netherlands,
John Adams Park 1, 2244 BZ Wassenaar, Netherlands
Mail: PSC 115, Box 038, APO, AE 09715
Fax: 31 (70) 365-7681 Internet: www.export.gov/sweden

Agricultural Counselor **Susan B. Phillips** 31 (70) 310-2300
Education: Wisconsin 1985 BS; Kansas State 1991 MSA

Commercial Section (Foreign Commercial Service) [Sweden]
Embassy of the United States of America - Stockholm,
Dag Hammarskjölds Väg 31, S-115, 89 Stockholm, Sweden
Mail: Embassy of the United States of America,,
Department of State, Washington, DC 20521-5750
Tel: 46 (8) 783-5346 Fax: 46 (8) 660-9181
E-mail: office.stockholm@trade.gov Internet: www.export.gov/sweden

Regional Senior Commercial Officer
Sandillo N. "Dillon" Banerjee 46 (8) 783-5346
E-mail: dillon.banerjee@trade.gov
Education: William & Mary 1990 BA; American U 1994 MA

Drug Enforcement Administration (Resident in Copenhagen) [Sweden]
American Embassy - Copenhagen, Denmark,
Dag Hammarskjölds Alle 24, 2100 Copenhagen, Denmark
Tel: 45 35 55 31 44

DEA Attaché **Christopher J. Urben** 45 35 55-31-44

Federal Aviation Administration (Resident in Moscow) [Sweden]
American Embassy, Eight Bolshoy Devyatinsky Pereulok,
121099 Moscow, Russia
Mail: Unit 5430, DPO, AE 09721
Fax: 7 (495) 728-5350

FAA Senior Representative **Andrew McKee** 7 (495) 728-5125

Office of the Defense Attaché [Sweden]
Embassy of the United States of America - Stockholm,
Dag Hammarskjölds Väg 31, S-115, 89 Stockholm, Sweden
Mail: Embassy of the United States of America, Department of State,
5750 Stockholm Place, Washington, DC 20521-5750
Tel: 46 (8) 783-5300 Fax: 46 (8) 662-8046

Defense Attaché **Col Charles Metrolis USAF** 46 (8) 783-5300

U.S. Embassy in Switzerland

Sulgeneckstrasse 19, CH-3007 Bern, Switzerland
Tel: 41 (31) 357-7011 Fax: 41 (31) 357-7320 Internet: ch.usembassy.gov

Office of the U.S. Ambassador to Switzerland

American Embassy - Bern, Switzerland,
Sulgeneckstrasse 19, CH-3007 Bern, Switzerland
Mail: Department of State, 5110 Bern Place, Washington, DC 20521-5110

★ Ambassador
Ambassador Edward T. "Ed" McMullen, Jr. 41 (31) 357-7011
Note: Ambassador McMullen serves concurrently as ambassador to Liechtenstein.
Education: Hampden-Sydney BA
Office Management Specialist to the Ambassador
Theresa R. Dowling 41 (31) 357-7011
E-mail: dowlingtr@state.gov

Deputy Chief of Mission **Tara Feret Erath** 41 (31) 357-7011
E-mail: erathtf@state.gov
Office Management Specialist to the Deputy Chief of Mission **Diane G. Corbin** 41 (31) 357-7011
E-mail: corbindg@state.gov

Community Liaison Officer **(Vacant)** 41 (31) 357-7011

Office of the U.S. Ambassador to Switzerland *(continued)*

Consular General **Brianna E. Powers** 41 (31) 357-7011
E-mail: powersbe@state.gov
Tel: 41 (31) 357-7280

Economic Officer **Thomas W. "Toby" Wolf** 41 (31) 357-7011
E-mail: wolftw@state.gov

General Services Officer **Leslie Abitz** 41 (31) 357-7011
E-mail: abitzla@state.gov

Information Management Officer **Neeru Lal** 41 (31) 357-7011

Information Programs Officer **Lubomir D. Velkov** 41 (31) 357-7011
E-mail: velkovld@state.gov

Information Systems Security Officer
Lubomir D. Velkov 41 (31) 357-7011
E-mail: velkovld@state.gov

Legal Attaché **William Peterson** 41 (31) 357-7340
Fax: 41 (31) 357-7268

Management Officer **Kelia Cummins** 41 (31) 357-7011
E-mail: cumminske@state.gov

Political Officer **Desiree A. Baron** 41 (31) 357-7424
E-mail: baronda@state.gov

Political/Economic Officer **Scott E. Sommers** 41 (31) 357-7011
E-mail: sommersse@state.gov

Regional Security Officer **Todd Healey** 41 (31) 357-7011
E-mail: healeyte@state.gov

Public Affairs Officer **Tanya A. Ward** 41 (31) 357-7238
Fax: 41 (31) 357-7379

Federal Aviation Administration (Resident in Paris) [Switzerland]
American Embassy/FAA, AEU-PAR, 2, Avenue Gabriel, 75382 Paris, Cedex 08, France
Mail: PSC 116, APO, AE 09777
Fax: 33 (1) 4312-2505

FAA Senior Representative **Ian H. Ross** 33 (1) 4312-2225

Office of the Defense Attaché [Switzerland]
American Embassy - Bern, Switzerland,
Jubilaeumstrasse 93, 3005 Bern, Switzerland
Mail: Department of State, 5110 Bern. Place,
Washington, DC 20521-5110
Tel: 41 (31) 357-7011 Fax: 41 (31) 357-7381

Defense Attaché **Col John T. Aalborg, Jr. USAF** 41 (31) 357-7011
E-mail: AalborgJT@state.gov

U.S. Embassy in Turkey

110 Ataturk Boulevard, Kavaklidere, 06100 Ankara, Turkey
Tel: 90 (312) 455-5555 Fax: 90 (312) 467-0019
Internet: tr.usembassy.gov

Office of the U.S. Ambassador to Turkey

American Embassy - Ankara, Turkey, 110 Ataturk Boulevard,
Kavaklidere, 06100 Ankara, Turkey
Mail: American Embassy - Ankara, Turkey, PSC 93, Box 5000,
APO, AE 09823

★ Ambassador **(Vacant)** 90 (312) 544-5555
Fax: 90 (312) 467-2532

◇ Chargé d'Affaires **Jeffrey M. "Jeff" Hovenier** 90 (312) 455-5555
E-mail: hovenierjm@state.gov
Education: BYU 1988 BA; Georgetown 1990 MA
Office Management Specialist to the Chargé d'Affaires **Tara A. Bell** 90 (312) 455-5555
E-mail: bellta@state.gov

◇ Deputy Chief of Mission (Acting)
Scott D. Weinhold 90 (312) 455-5555
E-mail: weinholds@state.gov
Education: Virginia 1989 BA
Office Management Specialist to the Deputy Chief of Mission **(Vacant)** 90 (312) 455-5555

◇ Consul **Amber Michele Baskette** 90 (312) 455-5555
E-mail: basketteam@state.gov Fax: 90 (312) 468-6131

Community Liaison Officer **Jamie Weinhold** 90 (312) 455-5555
Fax: 90 (312) 457-7425

Economic Officer **Erika Olson** 90 (312) 455-5555
Fax: 90 (312) 457-7048

★ Presidential Appointment Requiring Senate Confirmation ☆ Presidential Appointment ☐ Schedule C Appointment ◇ Career Senior Foreign Service Appointment
● Career Senior Executive Service (SES) Appointment ○ Non-Career Senior Executive Service (SES) Appointment ■ Postal Career Executive Service

Office of the U.S. Ambassador to Turkey *(continued)*

Facilities Management Officer **Onder Durmus** 90 (312) 455-5555
E-mail: durmuso@state.gov
Financial Management Officer **Courtney B. Houk** 90 (312) 455-5555
E-mail: houkcb@state.gov
General Services Officer **Robert F. Doyle** 90 (312) 455-5555
E-mail: doylerf@state.gov Fax: 90 (312) 457-7391
Human Resources Officer **Elizabeth Zelle** 90 (312) 455-5555
Information Management Officer
Charles A. "Chuck" O'Malley 90 (312) 455-7555
E-mail: omalleyca@state.gov
Information Program Officer **Keith Houk** 90 (312) 455-5555
E-mail: houkk@state.gov
Information Systems Officer **(Vacant)** 90 (312) 455-7555
Information Systems Security Officer
Matthew S. Sacks 90 (312) 455-5555
Labor Officer **Amanda "Amy" Lillis** 90 (312) 455-5555
E-mail: lillisaj@state.gov Fax: 90 (312) 457-7115
Education: Lewis & Clark 2004 BA;
George Mason 2014 MA
Legal Attaché **Zrinka Dilber** 90 (312) 455-5555
Management Officer **Jason Meeks** 90 (312) 455-5555
E-mail: meeksjp@state.gov Fax: 90 (312) 457-7048
Political Officer **Denise M. Marsh** 90 (312) 455-5555
E-mail: marshdm@state.gov Fax: 90 (312) 457-7115
Political/Military Officer **Eric R. Mehler** 90 (312) 455-5555
E-mail: mehlerer@state.gov
◇ Public Affairs Officer **Scott D. Weinhold** 90 (312) 455-5555
E-mail: weinholds@state.gov Fax: 90 (312) 457-7376
Education: Virginia 1989 BA
Regional Security Officer **Peter A. Dinoia** 90 (312) 455-5555
E-mail: dinoiapa@state.gov

Agricultural Section (Foreign Agricultural Service) [Turkey]
American Embassy - Ankara, Turkey, 110 Ataturk Boulevard, Ankara, Turkey
Mail: American Embassy - Ankara, Turkey, PSC 93, Box 5000, APO, AE 09823
Tel: 90 (312) 468-6129 Fax: 90 (312) 467-0056
E-mail: agankara@fas.usda.gov

Agricultural Officer **Christine Strossman** 90 (312) 468-6129
E-mail: christine.strossman@fas.usda.gov
Attaché **Elizabeth Leonardi** 90 (312) 468-6129
E-mail: elizabeth.leonardi@fas.usda.gov
Attaché **Christine Mumma** 90 (312) 468-6129
E-mail: Christine.Mumma@fas.usda.gov
Education: Tufts 2009 BA; Wisconsin 2013 JD

Commercial Section (Foreign Commercial Service) [Turkey]
American Embassy - Ankara, Turkey, 110 Ataturk Boulevard, Ankara, Turkey
Mail: American Embassy - Ankara, Turkey, PSC 93, Box 5000, APO, AE 09823
Tel: 90 (312) 455-5555 Fax: 90 (312) 457-7302

◇ Senior Commercial Officer
William "Bill" Czajkowski 90 (312) 457-7278
E-mail: william.czajkowski@trade.gov
Commercial Attaché **Katja Kravetsky** 90 (312) 457-7188
E-mail: katja.kravetsky@trade.gov
Education: Georgetown 1991 BS; Arizona 1994 MA
Commercial Officer **Shari Stout** 90 (312) 457-7167
E-mail: shari.stout@trade.gov
Budget Analyst **Sema Okurer** 90 (312) 457-457-7289
E-mail: sema.okurer@trade.gov

Drug Enforcement Administration [Turkey]
DEA Officer **(Vacant)** 90 (312) 455-5555

Federal Aviation Administration (Resident in Moscow) [Turkey]
FAA Senior Representative **Andrew McKee** 7 (495) 728-5125

Office of the Defense Attaché [Turkey]
American Embassy - Ankara, Turkey, 110 Ataturk Boulevard, Ankara, Turkey
Mail: American Embassy - Ankara, Turkey, PSC 93, Box 5000, APO, AE 09823
Defense Attaché **(Vacant)** 90 (312) 422-6880

Istanbul Consulate General
U.S. Consulate General - Istanbul, Turkey, Kaplicalar Mevki Sok NO:2, Istinye, Istanbul, Turkey
Mail: U.S. Consulate General–Istanbul, Turkey, PSC 97, Box 0002, APO, AE 09827-0002
Tel: 90 (212) 335-9000 Fax: 90 (212) 335-9019

Consul General **Jennifer L. Davis** 90 (212) 335-9000
E-mail: davisjl5@state.gov
Education: North Carolina 1994 BA, 1997 JD; Oxford (UK) 2001 LLM
Office Management Specialist to the Consul
General **Rebecca A. "Becca" Nassar** 90 (212) 335-9000
E-mail: nassarra1@state.gov
Deputy Principal Officer **Barbara M. Thomas** 90 (212) 335-9000
E-mail: thomasbm@state.gov
Community Liaison Officer **Kristin Izzo** 90 (212) 335-9000
Consular Officer **Deborah Campbell** 90 (212) 335-9000
Education: Florida Atlantic BA, MA
Financial Management Officer **Robin S. Clune** 90 (212) 335-9000
E-mail: CluneRS@state.gov
Education: Colorado (Colo Springs) 2005 BA
General Services Officer **Dean Peterson** 90 (212) 335-9000
Information Programs Officer **(Vacant)** 90 (212) 335-9000
Information Systems Officer **Colin R. Hankey** 90 (212) 335-9000
E-mail: hankeycr@state.gov
Legal Attaché **Joy A. Hess** 90 (212) 335-9000
E-mail: hessja@state.gov
Education: Kent State 2000 BA
Management Officer **Susan L. Unruh** 90 (212) 335-9000
E-mail: unruhsl@state.gov Fax: 90 (212) 335-9107
Political/Economic Officer **(Vacant)** 90 (212) 335-9000
Public Affairs Officer **Stephanie R. Kuck** 90 (212) 335-9059
E-mail: kucksr@state.gov Fax: 90 (212) 335-9093
Regional Security Officer **Anton G. Kort** 90 (212) 335-9000
E-mail: kortag@state.gov

Agricultural Section (Foreign Agricultural Service) [Turkey]
U.S. Consulate General - Istanbul, Turkey, Kaplicalar Mevki Sok NO:2, Istinye, Istanbul, Turkey
Fax: 90 (212) 335-9077

Agricultural Officer (Resident in Ankara)
Christine Strossman 90 (312) 455-5555
E-mail: christine.strossman@fas.usda.gov

Commercial Section (Foreign Commercial Service) [Turkey]
U.S. Consulate General - Istanbul, Turkey, 104-108 Mesrutiyet Caddesi, Tepebasi, Istanbul, Turkey
Mail: U.S. Consulate General–Istanbul, Turkey, PSC 97, Box 0002, APO, AE 09827-0002
Tel: 90 (212) 335-9040 Fax: 90 (212) 335-9103

Principal Commercial Officer **John F. Coronado** 90 (212) 335-9302
E-mail: john.coronado@trade.gov

Adana Consulate
U.S. Consulate - Adana, Turkey, Guzelevler Mahallesi, Girne Bulvari, NO: 212, Yuregir Adana, Turkey
Mail: U.S. Consulate - Adana, Turkey, PSC 94, APO, AE 09824
Tel: 90 (322) 455-4100 Fax: 90 (322) 455-4141
E-mail: Webmaster_Adana@state.gov

Principal Officer/Consul General
Alejandro H. "Hoot" Baez 90 (322) 455-4100
Education: Southern Methodist BA; Texas A&M MA; Lancaster (UK)
Consular Officer **Kara B. Babrowski** 90 (322) 455-4100
E-mail: babrowskikb@state.gov
Economic Officer **Kara B. Babrowski** 90 (322) 455-4100
E-mail: babrowskikb@state.gov

(continued on next page)

★ Presidential Appointment Requiring Senate Confirmation ☆ Presidential Appointment ☐ Schedule C Appointment ◇ Career Senior Foreign Service Appointment
● Career Senior Executive Service (SES) Appointment ○ Non-Career Senior Executive Service (SES) Appointment ■ Postal Career Executive Service

Adana Consulate *(continued)*

Information Program Officer **Durwood L. Young** 90 (322) 455-4100
E-mail: youngdl@state.gov
Management Officer **Maureen P. Vahey** 90 (322) 455-4100
E-mail: vaheymp@state.gov
Political Officer **Rebecca Doffing** 90 (322) 455-4100
Education: Boston U 2008 BA
Public Affairs Officer **Jenny Curatola** 90 (322) 455-4100
Regional Security Officer **Brian A. Tanner** 90 (322) 455-4100
E-mail: tannerba@state.gov

Izmir Consular Agency

U.S. Consular Agency - Izmir, Turkey, Izmir, Turkey
Mail: U.S. Consular Agency - Izmir, Turkey, PSC 88, Box 5000, APO, AE 09821
Tel: 90 (232) 464-8755 Fax: 90 (232) 464-8916

Consular Agent **Guliz Balsari** 90 (232) 464-8755

Commercial Section (Foreign Commercial Service) [Turkey]

U.S. Commercial Service, Ataturk Caddesi, No. 126,
Kat: 5th Floor, Pasaport Izmir, 35210, Turkey
Mail: U.S. Commercial Service, PSC 88, Box 5000, APO, AE 09821
Tel: 90 (232) 441-2446 Fax: 90 (232) 489-0267
E-mail: office.izmir@trade.gov

Commercial Specialist **Berrin Erturk** 504 2441-2446
E-mail: berrin.erturk@trade.gov

U.S. Embassy in Ukraine

4 A.I. Sikorsky St., 04112 Kiev, Ukraine
Tel: 380 (44) 521-5000 Fax: 380 (44) 521-5155
Internet: ua.usembassy.gov

Office of the U.S. Ambassador to Ukraine

American Embassy - Kiev, Ukraine, 4 A.I. Sikorsky St., 04112 Kiev, Ukraine
Mail: Department of State, 5850 Kiev Place, Washington, DC 20521-5850

★ Ambassador
Ambassador Marie L. "Masha" Yovanovitch 380 (44) 521-5000
Education: Princeton 1980 BA; National War Col 2001 MS
Office Management Specialist to the Ambassador
Dianne Wampler 380 (44) 521-5000
E-mail: wamplerd@state.gov
◇ Deputy Chief of Mission **Pamela M. Tremont** 380 (44) 521-5000
Office Management Specialist to the Deputy Chief of Mission **(Vacant)** 380 (44) 521-5000
Community Liaison Officer **AmyLyn Reynolds** 380 (44) 521-5000
Consul General **Kimberly A. "Kim" McDonald** 380 (44) 521-5000
Economic Officer **John P. "J.P." Schutte** 380 (44) 521-5000
E-mail: schuttejp@state.gov
Financial Management Officer **Jeanie Clayton** 380 (44) 521-5000
General Services Officer **Joey E. "Joe" Klinger** 380 (44) 521-5000
E-mail: klingerje@state.gov
Information Management Officer **Bethany McDow** ... 380 (44) 521-5000
E-mail: mcdowbj@state.gov
Education: National Intelligence U
Information Program Officer **Inna Moody** 380 (44) 521-5000
E-mail: moodyi@state.gov
Education: Webster 2010 BS
Information Systems Officer **M. Blaine Tyson** 380 (44) 521-5000
E-mail: tysonmb@state.gov
Information Systems Security Officer **(Vacant)** 380 (44) 521-5000
Legal Attaché **Laura Kriegbaum** 380 (44) 521-5000
Management Officer **Matthew A. Werner** 380 (44) 521-5000
E-mail: wernerma@state.gov
Political Officer **David A. Holmes** 380 (44) 521-5000
E-mail: holmesda@state.gov
◇ Public Affairs Officer
David Michael "Mike" Reinert 380 (44) 521-5000
E-mail: reinertdm@state.gov
Cultural Affairs Officer **Sean O'Hara** 380 (44) 521-5000
Press Attaché **Raymond A. "Ray" Castillo** 380 (44) 521-5000
E-mail: CastilloRA@state.gov
Education: Middlebury 1986 BA; George Washington 1990 MA

Office of the U.S. Ambassador to Ukraine *(continued)*

Regional Security Officer
Nicholas A. "Nick" Collura 380 (44) 521-5000
E-mail: collurana@state.gov
Education: Hilbert BA; Naval War MA

Agency for International Development [Ukraine]

USAID (Regional Mission to Ukraine, Belarus and Moldova), 19 Nyzhniy Val Street, 04071 Kiev, Ukraine
Mail: Department of State, 5850 Kiev Place, Washington, DC 20521-5850
Tel: 380 (44) 521-5000 Fax: 380 (44) 521-5245
E-mail: kyvinfo@usaid.gov Internet: www.usaid.gov/ukraine

Mission Director **Susan Kosinski Fritz** 380 (44) 462-5678
E-mail: sfritz@usaid.gov
Education: Rutgers 1986 BA; American U 1989 MPA

Agricultural Section (Foreign Agricultural Service) [Ukraine]

USDA/FAS/American Embassy - Kiev, Ukraine, 4 Hlybochytska Street, 5th Floor, 04050 Kiev, Ukraine
Mail: Department of State, 5850 Kiev Place, Washington, DC 20521-5850
Tel: 380 (44) 521-5496 Fax: 380 (44) 521-5038

Attaché **Dwight Wilder** 380 (44) 521-5496
E-mail: dwight.wilder@fas.usda.gov
Attaché **Robin Gray** 380 (44) 521-5496
E-mail: robin.gray@fas.usda.gov
Education: South Dakota State 1980 BA; George Washington 1987 MS

Commercial Section (Foreign Commercial Service) [Ukraine]

U.S. Foreign Commercial Service, 4 Hlybochytska Street, 5th Floor, 04050 Kiev, Ukraine
Mail: Department of State, 5850 Kiev Place, Washington, DC 20521-5850
Fax: 380 (44) 521-5727 E-mail: office.kyiv@trade.gov
Internet: export.gov/ukraine

◇ Regional Senior Commercial Officer
Michael A. Lally 380 (44) 521-5539
E-mail: michael.lally@trade.gov
Senior Commercial Officer **Martin Claessens** 380 (44) 521-5465
E-mail: Martin.Claessens@trade.gov
Commercial Officer **Charles Phillips** 380 (44) 521-5465
E-mail: charles.phillips@trade.gov

Federal Aviation Administration (Resident in Moscow) [Ukraine]

Eight Bolshoy Devyatinsky Pereulok, 121099 Moscow, Russia
Mail: American Embassy/FAA, PSC 77, APO, AE 09721
Fax: 7 (495) 728-5350

FAA Senior Representative **Andrew McKee** 7 (495) 728-5125

Office of the Defense Attaché [Ukraine]

American Embassy - Kiev, Ukraine, 10 Yuria Kotsubynskoho, 01901 Kiev, Ukraine
Mail: Department of State, 5850 Kiev Place, Washington, DC 20521-5850

Senior Defense Official and Defense Attaché
Col Thomas Quinn "Quinn" Wofford USAF 380 (44) 521-5000

Peace Corps [Ukraine]

Peace Corps, 48 B Khmelnytskoho Street, 01030 Kiev, Ukraine
Mail: Department of State, 5850 Kiev Place, Washington, DC 20521-5850
Tel: 380 (44) 391-6620 Fax: 380 (44) 391-6621
Internet: www.peacecorps.gov/ukraine

Country Director **Denny Robertson** 380 (44) 391-6620
E-mail: drobertson@peacecorps.gov
Education: Michigan; Michigan State MA

★ Presidential Appointment Requiring Senate Confirmation ☆ Presidential Appointment ☐ Schedule C Appointment ◇ Career Senior Foreign Service Appointment
● Career Senior Executive Service (SES) Appointment ○ Non-Career Senior Executive Service (SES) Appointment ■ Postal Career Executive Service

U.S. Embassy in the United Kingdom

American Embassy - London, England,
33 Nine Elms Lane, London, SW11 7US, United Kingdom
Tel: 44 (20) 7499-9000 Internet: uk.usembassy.gov

Office of the U.S. Ambassador to the United Kingdom

American Embassy - London, England, U.K.,
33 Nine Elms Lane, London, SW11 7US, England, United Kingdom
Tel: 44 (20) 7499-9000 Internet: uk.usembassy.gov

★ Ambassador **Ambassador Robert Wood "Woody" Johnson IV** 44 (20) 7499-9000
Education: Arizona 1972 BA
Office Management Specialist to the Ambassador **Elizabeth Roberts-Strang** 44 (20) 7894 0214
E-mail: roberts-strangea@state.gov

◇ Deputy Chief of Mission **Ambassador Lewis A. Lukens** 44 (20) 7499-9000
E-mail: lukensla@state.gov
Education: Princeton BA, 2003 MPP
Office Management Specialist to the Deputy Chief of Mission **Laura Reddy** 44 (20) 7499-9000
E-mail: reddyl@state.gov

◇ Consular Affairs Officer **Karen L. Ogle** 44 (20) 7499-9000
E-mail: oglekl@state.gov Fax: 44 (20) 7495-5012

Community Liaison Officer **Sherri Zimmerman** 44 (20) 7499-9000

◇ Economic Officer **Gregory S. "Greg" Burton** 44 (20) 7499-9000
E-mail: burtongs@state.gov Fax: 44 (20) 7409-1637
Education: Dickinson Col BA; Fordham MA; National War Col 2008 MS

Environment, Science and Technology Officer **Dena Brownlow** 44 (20) 7499-9000

Facilities Management Officer **William Knight** 44 (20) 7499-9000

Financial Management Officer **John Bredin** 44 (20) 7499-9000
E-mail: bredinjs@state.gov

General Services Officer **Thomas Clifford "Clifford" Reed** 44 (20) 7499-9000
E-mail: reedtc@state.gov

Human Resources Officer **Ann E. Gabrielson** 44 (20) 7499-9000
E-mail: gabrielsonae@state.gov

Information Management Officer **Francoise Blais** 44 (20) 7499-9000

Information Program Officer **Eric Rose** 44 (20) 7499-9000

Information Systems Officer **James Donegan** 44 (20) 7499-9000

Information Systems Security Officer **James Swineford** 44 (20) 7499-9000
E-mail: swinefordj@state.gov

Labor Officer **(Vacant)** 44 (20) 7499-9000

◇ Management Officer **Virginia Idelle "Ginger" Keener** 44 (20) 7499-9000
E-mail: keenervi2@state.gov Fax: 44 (20) 7629-9124

◇ Political Officer **Jennifer D. Gavito** 44 (20) 7499-9000
E-mail: gavitojd@state.gov
Education: American U 1997 BA

◇ Public Affairs Officer **Courtney E. Austrian** 44 (20) 7499-9000
E-mail: austriance@state.gov Fax: 44 (20) 7629-8288
Education: Swarthmore 1987 BA; National War Col 2010 MS

Regional Security Officer **Thomas "Tom" McDonough** 44 (20) 7499-9000

Agricultural Section (Foreign Agricultural Service) [United Kingdom]

American Embassy- London, 33 Nine Elms Lane, London, SW11 7US, England, United Kingdom
Mail: Unit 8400, Box 48, DPO, AE 09498-0048
Tel: 44 (20) 7891-3313 E-mail: aglondon@fas.usda.gov

◇ Agricultural Officer **Stanley S. "Stan" Phillips** 44 (20) 7891-3313
E-mail: stan.phillips@fas.usda.gov

Commercial Section (Foreign Commercial Service) [United Kingdom]

U.S. Commercial Service, American Embassy,
33 Nine Elms Lane, London, SW11 7US, England, United Kingdom
Tel: 44 (20) 7891 3419 E-mail: office.london@trade.gov
Internet: export.gov/unitedkingdom

◇ Senior Commercial Officer **John Simmons** 44 (20) 7891 3419

Commercial Section (Foreign Commercial Service) [United Kingdom] *(continued)*

Deputy Senior Commercial Officer **James D. "Jim" Lindley** 44 (20) 7891 3424
E-mail: james.lindley@trade.gov
Education: Southern Methodist 1995 BS; Texas 1999 MPA

Department of Homeland Security - Transportation Security Administration [United Kingdom]

American Embassy - London, England, U.K.,
33 Nine Elms Lane, London, SW11 7US, England, United Kingdom
Mail: American Embassy - London, England, U.K., PSC 801, Box 40, FPO, AE 09498-4040
Tel: 44 (20) 7499-9000 ext. 2410 Fax: 44 (20) 7491-1128

TSA/CASLO Officer **Demetrios Lambropoulos** .... 44 (20) 7499-9000 ext. 2410

Department of Homeland Security - U.S. Immigration and Customs Enforcement

American Embassy - London, England, U.K.,
33 Nine Elms Lane, London, SW11 7US, England, United Kingdom
Mail: American Embassy - London, England, U.K., PSC 801, Box 40, FPO, AE 09498-4040
Tel: 44 (20) 7499-9000

Attaché **James R. "Jim" Mancuso** 44 (20) 7499-9000
E-mail: MancusoJR@state.gov

Department of Homeland Security - U.S. Customs and Border Protection [United Kingdom]

American Embassy - London, England, U.K.,
33 Nine Elms Lane, London, SW11 7US, England, United Kingdom
Mail: American Embassy - London, England, U.K., PSC 801, Box 52, FPO, AE 09498-4040
Tel: 44 (20) 7499-9000

Customs Officer **Gregory "Greg" Olsavsky** 44 (20) 7499-9000

Department of Homeland Security - U.S. Secret Service [United Kingdom]

American Embassy - London, England, U.K., PSC 801, Box 64, FPO, AE 09498-4040
American Embassy - London, England, U.K.,
33 Nine Elms Lane, London, SW11 7US, England, United Kingdom
Tel: 44 (20) 7499-9000

Secret Service Officer **Eric Whatley** 44 (20) 7499-9000

Drug Enforcement Administration [United Kingdom]

American Embassy - London, England, U.K.,
33 Nine Elms Lane, London, SW11 7US, England, United Kingdom
Mail: American Embassy - London, England, U.K., PSC 801, Box 8, FPO, AE 09498-4040
Tel: 44 (20) 7499-9000

DEA Officer **Justin May** 44 (20) 7499-9000

Federal Aviation Administration (Resident in Paris) [United Kingdom]

American Embassy/FAA, AEU-PAR, 2, Avenue Gabriel, 75382 Paris, Cedex 08, France
Mail: PSC 116, APO, AE 09777
Fax: 33 (1) 4312-2505

FAA Senior Representative **Ian H. Ross** 33 (1) 4312-2225

Federal Bureau of Investigation [United Kingdom]

American Embassy - London, England, U.K.,
33 Nine Elms Lane, London, SW11 7US, England, United Kingdom
Mail: American Embassy - London, England, U.K., PSC 801, Box 55, FPO, AE 09498-4040
Tel: 44 (20) 7499-9000 Fax: 44 (20) 7499-7944

Legal Attaché **(Vacant)** 44 (20) 7499-9000

★ Presidential Appointment Requiring Senate Confirmation ☆ Presidential Appointment □ Schedule C Appointment ◇ Career Senior Foreign Service Appointment
● Career Senior Executive Service (SES) Appointment ○ Non-Career Senior Executive Service (SES) Appointment ■ Postal Career Executive Service

London Regional Media Hub (Media Outreach Center) (MOC)
American Embassy - London, England,
33 Nine Elms Lane, London, SW11 7US, United Kingdom
Tel: 44 (20) 7499-9000 Fax: 44 (20) 7629-9124
E-mail: londonhub@state.gov
Internet: www.state.gov/r/pa/ime/londonmediahub

Director **Jared S. Caplan** 44 (20) 7499-9000
E-mail: caplanjs@state.gov
Education: Georgetown

Office of the Defense Attaché [United Kingdom]
American Embassy - London, England, U.K.,
33 Nine Elms Lane, London, SW11 7US, England, United Kingdom
Mail: American Embassy - London, England, U.K., PSC 801, Box 54, FPO, AE 09498-4040

Defense Attaché **(Vacant)** 44 (20) 7894-0726
E-mail: DAOLondon@state.gov

Office of Defense Cooperation [United Kingdom]
American Embassy - London, England, U.K.,
33 Nine Elms Lane, London, SW11 7US, England, United Kingdom
Mail: American Embassy - London, England, U.K., PSC 801, Box 55, FPO, AE 09498-4040
Tel: 44 (20) 7894-0737 Fax: 44 (20) 7894-0730

Defense Cooperation Officer **Allen Roberts** 44 (20) 7894-0737

Belfast, Northern Ireland, Consulate General
U.S. Consulate General - Belfast, Northern Ireland, U.K.,
Danesfort House, 223 Stranmillis Road, Belfast, BT9 5GR, Northern Ireland, United Kingdom
Mail: U.S. Consulate General - Belfast, PSC 801, Box 40, APO, AE 09498-4040
Tel: 44 (28) 9038-6100 Fax: 44 (28) 9068-1301

Consul General **Elizabeth Kennedy "Liz" Trudeau** . . . 44 (28) 9038-6100
E-mail: trudeauek@state.gov
Consular Officer **Aaron Karnell** 44 (28) 9038-6100
Management Officer **Richard Saunders** 44 (28) 9038-6100
E-mail: saundersrm1@state.gov
Political/Economic Officer **Bernadette E. Roberts** 44 (28) 9038-6100
E-mail: robertsbe@state.gov
Public Affairs Officer **(Vacant)** 44 (28) 9038-6100
Regional Security Officer **(Vacant)** 44 (28) 9038-6100

Commercial Section (Foreign Commercial Service) [United Kingdom]
U.S. Consulate General, Belfast, Northern Ireland, Danesfort House, 223 Stranmillis Road, Belfast, BT9 5GR, Northern Ireland, United Kingdom
Mail: U.S. Commercial Service, PSC 801 - Box 40, APO, AE 09498-4040
Tel: 44 (28) 9038-6100 Fax: 44 (28) 9068-1301

Senior Commercial Officer **(Vacant)** 44 (28) 9038-6100

Edinburgh, Scotland, Consulate General
U.S. Consulate General - Edinburgh, Scotland, U.K.,
3 Regent Terrace, Edinburgh, EH7 5BW, Scotland, United Kingdom
Mail: U.S. Consulate General - Edinburgh, PSC 801, Box 40, FPO, AE 09498-4040
Tel: 44 (131) 556-8315 Fax: 44 (131) 557-6023
E-mail: edinburgh-info@state.gov

Principal Officer **Ellen Y. Wong** 44 (131) 556-8315
E-mail: wongey@state.gov
Education: Princeton BA; Johns Hopkins MA

U.S. Mission to the European Office of the United Nations and Other International Organizations in Geneva

Mission Permanente Des Etats-Unis, Route de Pregny 11, Chambesy, 1292 Geneva, Switzerland
Mail: US Mission to the European Office of the UN, Department of State, Washington, DC 20521-5120
Tel: 41 (22) 749-4111 Fax: 41 (22) 749-4892
E-mail: genevausmission@state.gov

★ U.S. Permanent Representative-Designate **Andrew P. Bremberg** 41 (22) 749-4111
Education: Franciscan U BA; Catholic U JD
◇ Chargé d'Affaires **Mark Joseph Cassayre** 41 (22) 749-4111
E-mail: cassayremj@state.gov
Education: UC Santa Barbara 1994 BA; HEI (Switzerland) 1998 MA
Office Management Specialist to the U.S. Representative **(Vacant)** 41 (22) 749-4111
Deputy Chief of Mission **Theodore Allegra** 41 (22) 749-4111
E-mail: allegratx@state.gov
Education: Colorado BA; Denver JD; Georgetown MLL
Office Management Specialist to the Deputy Chief of Mission **Kimberly Lowecke** 41 (22) 749-4302
U.S. Representative to the Executive Board of the World Health Organization.-Designate **Dr. Brett P. Giroir** 41 (22) 749-4111
Education: Harvard 1982 BS; Texas Southwestern Medical 1986 MD
★ U.S. Representative to the United Nations Human Rights Council **(Vacant)** 41 (22) 749-4111
Note: On June 19, 2018, the State Department announced that the United States is withdrawing from the U.N. Human Rights Council.
U.S. Deputy Representative to the United Nations Human Rights Council **Jason R. Mack** 41 (22) 749-4111
Note: On June 19, 2018, the State Department announced that the United States is withdrawing from the U.N. Human Rights Council.
E-mail: mackjr@state.gov
Community Liaison Officer **Kerry Fraatz** 41 (22) 749-4111
E-mail: fraatzkm@state.gov
Community Liaison Officer **Maureen Rieras** 41 (22) 749-4111
Economic Officer **William Glover "Bill" Lehmberg** . . . 41 (22) 749-4628
Environment, Science and Technology Officer **(Vacant)** 41 (22) 749-4309
Facilities Management Officer **David H. Bodycoat** 41 (22) 749-4618
E-mail: BodycoatDH@state.gov
Financial Management Officer **Daniel Driggers** 41 (22) 749-4545
Fax: 41 (22) 749-4671
General Services Officer **Richard Johns** 41 (22) 749-4111
Information Management Officer **Aaron Bascue** 41 (22) 749-4306
E-mail: bascueax@state.gov
Information Program Officer **Philip J. Wilkin** 41 (22) 749-4111
E-mail: wilkinpj@state.gov
Information Systems Officer **Ruben Solis** 41 (22) 749-4744
E-mail: solisr@state.gov
Information Systems Security Officer **Johnathon McCombs** 41 (22) 749-4111
Legal Attaché **(Vacant)** 41 (22) 749-4316
Management Officer **Andrew D. Siegel** 41 (22) 749-4524
E-mail: SiegelAD@state.gov Fax: 41 (22) 749-4491
Education: Virginia 1985 JD
◇ Political Officer **Howard T. Solomon** 41 (22) 749-4618
E-mail: solomonht@state.gov
◇ Public Affairs Officer **Thomas Joseph Nicholas Pierce** 41 (22) 749-4360
Fax: 41 (22) 749-4314
Regional Security Officer **Terrie B. Lora** 41 (22) 749-4479
E-mail: loratb@state.gov
Education: U Washington 1994

★ Presidential Appointment Requiring Senate Confirmation ☆ Presidential Appointment ☐ Schedule C Appointment ◇ Career Senior Foreign Service Appointment
● Career Senior Executive Service (SES) Appointment ○ Non-Career Senior Executive Service (SES) Appointment ■ Postal Career Executive Service

U.S. Mission to the World Trade Organization

Office of the U.S. Trade Representative,
Geneva, Switzerland, 11 route de Pregny,
1292 Chambesy, Geneva, Switzerland
Mail: Office of the USTR - Geneva, 5120 Geneva Place,
Washington, DC 20521-5120
Tel: 41 (22) 749-5214 Fax: 41 (22) 749-5308
Internet: http://geneva.usmission.gov/us-mission-wto

★ Deputy U.S. Trade Representative/U.S. Ambassador to the World Trade Organization **Ambassador Dennis C. Shea** 41 (22) 749-5246
E-mail: dennis.c.shea@ustr.eop.gov
Education: Harvard 1983 AB, 1983 AM, 1986 JD
Office Management Specialist to the Ambassador **(Vacant)** 41 (22) 749-5246

● Deputy Chief of Mission/Deputy Permanent Representative of the U.S. to the World Trade Organization **Christopher S. "Chris" Wilson** 41 (22) 749-5243
Education: Georgetown 1984 BSFS

Management Officer **Elizabeth Faulkner** 41 (22) 749-5253

Agricultural Section (Foreign Agricultural Service) [World Trade Organization]
U.S. Trade Representative - Geneva, Switzerland, 11 route de Pregny,
1292 Chambesy, Geneva, Switzerland
Mail: U.S. Trade Representative - Geneva,
5120 Geneva Place, Washington, DC 20521-5120
Tel: 41 (22) 749-5247

◇ Minister-Counselor **W. Garth Thorburn** 41 (22) 749-5247
E-mail: garth.thorburn@fas.usda.gov

Senior Agricultural Attaché **(Vacant)** 41 (22) 749-5247

Agricultural Attaché **Jeffrey "Jeff" Albanese** 41 (22) 749-5247
E-mail: jeffrey.albanese@fas.usda.gov

U.S. Delegation to the Conference on Disarmament

U.S. Mission Building, Route de Pregny 11,
1292 Chambesy, Geneva, Switzerland
Mail: U.S. Delegation to the CD, Geneva,
Department of State, Washington, DC 20521-5120
Tel: 41 (22) 749-4822 Fax: 41 (22) 749-4833
E-mail: genevacddelegation@state.gov
Internet: https://geneva.usmission.gov/disarmament/

★ U.S. Representative to the Conference on Disarmament/Special Representative of the President of the U.S. for Non-proliferation of Nuclear Weapons **Ambassador Robert A. Wood** 41 (22) 749-4822
E-mail: woodra@state.gov

Deputy U.S. Representative **Cynthia Plath** 41 (22) 749-4825
E-mail: plathc@state.gov
Education: UC Santa Barbara 1997 BA; San Francisco State U 2002 MA

U.S. Mission to the European Union (USEU)

Zinnerstraat - 13, Rue Zinner, B-1000 Brussels, Belgium
Mail: USEU, PSC 82, Box 002, APO, AE 09710
Tel: 32 (2) 811-4100 Fax: 32 (2) 811-4500 E-mail: useupa@state.gov
Internet: http://useu.usmission.gov

★ U.S. Representative to the European Union **Ambassador Gordon D. Sondland** 32 (2) 508-2750
Education: U Washington (Attended)
Office Management Specialist to the U.S. Representative **(Vacant)** 32 (2) 508-2752

◇ Deputy Chief of Mission **Mark W. Libby** 32 (2) 508-2752
E-mail: libbymw@state.gov
Office Management Specialist to the Deputy Chief of Mission **Denise Bouthillier** 32 (2) 508-2752

Minister Counselor for Consular Affairs **(Vacant)** 32 (2) 508-2222

◇ Minister Counselor for Economic Affairs **J. David Lippeatt** 32 (2) 508-2787
E-mail: lippeattjd@state.gov Fax: 32 (2) 511-20-92
Education: Stanford 1986 BA; Texas 1994 MPA

U.S. Mission to the European Union *(continued)*

Counselor for International Narcotics and Law Enforcement Affairs Officer **(Vacant)** 32 (2) 508-2672

◇ Minister Counselor for Management Affairs **Michael C. Mullins** 32 (2) 811-4100
E-mail: mullinsmc@state.gov
Education: Amherst BA; Brown U MA

◇ Minister Counselor for Political Affairs **Virginia E. Murray** 32 (2) 508-2773
E-mail: murrayve@state.gov
Education: Duke 1985 BA; Maryland University Col 1997 MIB

◇ Public Affairs Officer **Christina Louise Tomlinson** 32 (2) 508-2774
E-mail: tomlinsonc@state.gov
E-mail: useupa@state.gov
Education: BYU 1990 BA

Community Liaison Officer **(Vacant)** 32 (2) 811-4100

Information Systems Security Officer **Brian Boyer** 32 (2) 811-4100

Facilities Management Officer **Keith Reling** 32 (2) 811-4100

Regional Security Officer **Daniel J. "Dan" Weber** 32 (2) 811-4100
E-mail: weberdj@state.gov

Legal Attaché **Jason A. Biros** 32 (2) 811-4100
E-mail: birosja@state.gov
Education: Princeton BA; London School Econ (UK) MA; Columbia JD

Agency for International Development [European Union]
USEU, Zinnerstraat - 13, Rue Zinner, B-1000 Brussels, Belgium
Mail: USEU, PSC 82, Box 212, APO, AE 09710
Tel: 32 (2) 508-2636 Fax: 32 (2) 512-7066

USAID Representative **Marc Ellingstad** 32 (2) 508-2636

Agricultural Section (Foreign Agricultural Service) [European Union]
27 Boulevard du Regent, B-1000 Brussels, Belgium
Tel: 32 (2) 811-4247 Fax: 32 (2) 811-5560
E-mail: aguseubrussels@fas.usda.gov Internet: www.usda-eu.org

◇ Agricultural Counselor **Bruce J. Zanin** 32 (2) 811-4154
E-mail: bruce.zanin@fas.usda.gov

Animal and Plant Health Inspection Service [European Union]
USEU, Zinnerstraat - 13, Rue Zinner, B-1000 Brussels, Belgium
Mail: USEU, PSC 82, Box 214, APO, AE 09710
Tel: 32 (2) 508-2849 Fax: 32 (2) 511-0918

USDA-APHIS-IS Minister-Counselor, Principal Animal and Plant Health Officer **(Vacant)** 32 (2) 508-2849

Commercial Section (Foreign Commercial Service) [European Union]
USEU, Zinnerstraat - 13, Rue Zinner, B-1000 Brussels, Belgium
Mail: USEU/FCS, PSC 82, Box 206, APO, AE 09710
Tel: 32 (2) 508-2746 Fax: 32 (2) 513-1228
Internet: export.gov/europeanunion

Senior Commercial Officer **John David Breidenstine** 32 (2) 811 53 74
E-mail: john.breidenstine@trade.gov
Education: Davidson 1984 BA

Deputy Senior Commercial Officer **Yasue Pai** 32 (2) 811 53 28
E-mail: yasue.pai@trade.gov

Deputy Senior Commercial Officer **(Vacant)** 32 (2) 811 43 65

Department of Homeland Security - U.S. Immigration and Customs Enforcement [European Union]
USEU, Zinnerstraat - 13, Rue Zinner, B-1000 Brussels, Belgium
Mail: USEU, PSC 82, Box 201, APO, AE 09724
Tel: 32 (2) 508-2770 Fax: 32 (2) 513-1818

Department of Homeland Security Attaché **Erik R. Barnett** 32 (2) 508-2771
Education: Arizona BA; Cal Western 1993 JD

Department of Justice [European Union]
USEU, Zinnerstraat - 13, Rue Zinner, B-1000 Brussels, Belgium
Mail: USEU, PSC 82, Box 205, APO, AE 09710
Tel: 32 (2) 508-2365 Fax: 32 (2) 512-0069

Justice Counselor **(Vacant)** 32 (2) 508-2667

★ Presidential Appointment Requiring Senate Confirmation ☆ Presidential Appointment □ Schedule C Appointment ◇ Career Senior Foreign Service Appointment
● Career Senior Executive Service (SES) Appointment ○ Non-Career Senior Executive Service (SES) Appointment ■ Postal Career Executive Service

Drug Enforcement Administration [European Union]
Zinnerstraat - 13, Rue Zinner, B-1000 Brussels, Belgium
Fax: 32 (2) 512-9914
Assistant Regional Director **David Spencer** 32 (2) 508-2407

U.S. Mission to International Organizations in Vienna (UNVIE)

Wagramerstrasse 17-19, A-1220 Vienna, Austria
Mail: 9950 UNVIE Place, Washington, DC 20521-9950
Tel: 43 (1) 31339-0 Fax: 43 (1) 367-07-64 E-mail: pavienna@state.gov
Internet: http://vienna.usmission.gov

★ U.S. Representative and U.S. Representative to the International Atomic Energy Agency **Ambassador Jackie Wolcott** 43 (1) 31339-4801
Education: Bowling Green State 1976 BA
Office Management Specialist to the Ambassador **(Vacant)** 43 (1) 31339-4801
◇ Deputy Chief of Mission **Nicole Dayan Shampaine** 43 (1) 31339-4802
E-mail: shampainend@state.gov Fax: 43 (1) 31339-4873
Education: Stanford
Office Management Specialist to the Deputy Chief of Mission **Steven Abels** 43 (1) 31339-4802
Counselor for Arms Control **Erik C. Martini** 43 (1) 31339-4797
E-mail: martinie@state.gov Fax: 43 (1) 31339-4795
◇ Counselor for International Atomic Energy Agency Affairs **Keith Mims Anderton** 43 (1) 31339-0
E-mail: andertonkm@state.gov
Education: Princeton 1982 AB; Harvard 1985 MA, 1993 PhD
Counselor for United Nations Affairs **Michele Dastin-Van Rijn** 43 (1) 31339-4728
E-mail: DastinMJ@state.gov Fax: 43 (1) 31339-4772
Education: UC Berkeley 1988 BA; Columbia 1992 MA
Facilities Manager **James Homer** 43 (1) 31339-74-3501
Financial Management Officer **Cynthia Rafferty** 43 (1) 313339-74-3501
Education: Delaware 1998 BS; Rutgers (Camden) 2005 MBA
Information Management Officer **Mark A. Wilson** 43 (1) 31339-2371
Information Program Officer **Arthur Saunders** 43 (1) 31339-74-3501
Information Systems Officer **Samuel S. Berardi** . . . 43 (1) 31339-74-3501
◇ Management Officer **Erica A. Renew** 43 (1) 31339-4730
E-mail: renewea@state.gov Fax: 43 (1) 31339-4765
Public Affairs Officer **Justen A. Thomas** 43 (1) 31339-4726
E-mail: ThomasJA@state.gov Fax: 43 (1) 31339-4772
Education: Wisconsin 2003 BA; Bristol U 2005 MS
Regional Security Officer **David Lyons** 43 (1) 31339-2221
Political/Economic Officer **(Vacant)** 43 (1) 31339-4730

Animal and Plant Health Inspection Service [International Organizations in Vienna]
APHIS Attaché **(Vacant)** 43 (1) 31339-2951

U.S. Mission to the North Atlantic Treaty Organization (USNATO)

U.S. Mission to NATO, Boulevard Leopold III, 1110 Brussels, Belgium
Mail: U.S. Mission to NATO, PSC 81, APO, AE 09724
Tel: 32 (2) 811-4000 Fax: 32 (2) 811-4500
E-mail: usnatopublicaffairs@state.gov Internet: http://nato.usmission.gov

★ U.S. Permanent Representative **Ambassador Kathryn Ann Bailey "Kay Bailey" Hutchison** 32 (2) 811-4000
Education: Texas 1962 BA, 1967 JD
Office Management Specialist to the Ambassador **Kathryn M. Martin** 32 (2) 811-4000
E-mail: martinkm@state.gov
◇ Deputy Permanent Representative/Deputy Chief of Mission **Douglas D. Jones** 32 (2) 811-4000
Office Management Specialist to the Deputy Chief of Mission **Amanda Frantz** 32 (2) 811-4000
U.S. Military Representative to the Military Committee **VADM John N. Christenson USN** 32 (2) 811-4000
Education: Naval Acad 1981; Naval War 1993 MNSSS

U.S. Mission to the North Atlantic Treaty Organization *(continued)*

Deputy U.S. Military Representative to the Military Committee **RDML Roy I. Kitchener USN** 32 (2) 811-4000
Education: Unity 1984 BA; Naval Postgrad 1992 MA
General Services Officer **Karl Schuler** 32 (2) 811-4000
Information Management Officer **Leonardo "Leo" Oporto** 32 (2) 811-4000
E-mail: oportolg@state.gov
Information Program Officer **Lisa Kurtz** 32 (2) 811-4000
E-mail: kurtzla@state.gov
Information Systems Officer **Garland E. Saunders** 32 (2) 811-4000
E-mail: saundersge@state.gov
Information Systems Security Officer **Brian Boyer** 32 (2) 811-4000
Management Officer **Charles "Chuck" Fanshaw** 32 (2) 811-4000
Political Officer **John J. "Jack" Hillmeyer** 32 (2) 811-4000
E-mail: hillmeyerjj@state.gov
Public Affairs Officer **John E. Johnson** 32 (2) 811-4000
E-mail: johnsonje@state.gov
Education: U Washington 1995 BA
Regional Security Officer **Dominic Caruso** 32 (2) 811-4000
E-mail: carusodc@state.gov
Senior Civilian Defense Representative and Defense Advisor **Richard B. Landolt** 32 (2) 811-4000
Education: Florida 1981 BA; Naval Postgrad MS

U.S. Mission to the Organization for Economic Cooperation and Development (USOECD)

USOECD, 18, avenue Gabriel, 75008 Paris, France
Mail: USOECD, American Embassy - Paris, France, PSC 116, A128, APO, AE 09777
Tel: 33 (1) 43 12 74 26 Fax: 33 (1) 43 12 74 07
Internet: http://usoecd.usmission.gov

★ U.S. Permanent Representative-Designate **Pamela M. Bates** 33 (1) 43 12 74 26
E-mail: batespm@state.gov
Education: Bowdoin AB; Johns Hopkins MA; Wharton MBA
◇ Chargé d'Affaires **Andrew Bauer Haviland** 33 (1) 43 12 74 26
E-mail: havilandab@state.gov
Office Management Specialist to the Ambassador **Lindsey Bowman** 33 (1) 43 12 74 26
◇ Deputy U.S. Permanent Representative/Deputy Chief of Mission (Acting) **Melissa Jane Kehoe** 5057 . . . . . 33 (1) 43 12 7417
E-mail: kehoemj@state.gov
Office Management Specialist to the Deputy Chief of Mission **Lindsey Bowman** 33 (1) 43 12 74 26
APHIS Senior International Organizations Coordinator **Dr. Alejandro B. Thiermann** 33 (1) 43 12 74 26
E-mail: alejandro.b.thiermann@aphis.usda.gov
Anti-Bribery and Middle East and North Africa Advisor **(Vacant)** 5105 . . . . 33 (1) 43 12 74 26
Department of Energy Attaché **Michael P. Apicelli** . . . 33 (1) 43 12 74 31
E-mail: apicellimp@state.gov
Labor, Education, and Gender Advisor **Michael Gunzburger** 5106 . . . . 33 (1) 43 12 7460
Energy and Resources Advisor **Margo Pogorzelski** 5077 . . . . 33 (1) 43 12 7460
E-mail: pogorzelskiml@state.gov
Energy and Resources Advisor **Brian L. Shelbourn** . . . 33 (1) 43 12 7460
USOECD, 19 Rue de Franqueville, 5077, 75016 Paris, France
Economic Advisor **Cyprien Bechler** 33 (1) 43 12 7417
External Relations Advisor **Douglas G. "Doug" Carey** 33 (1) 43 12 7439
Information Program Officer **Frederick E. "Rick" Ogg** 33 (1) 43 12 74 26
E-mail: oggfe@state.gov
Governance and Anticorruption Advisor **Thomas Nathan Anderson** 33 (1) 43 12 7439
Macroeconomic and Financial Affairs Advisor **Alexander Ted Bryan** 33 (1) 43 12 7417
Management Officer **Sumera Ashruf** 5065 . . . . 33 (1) 43 12 74 26
Public Diplomacy Advisor **(Vacant)** 5051 . . . . 33 (1) 43 12 7417
Fax: 33 (1) 43 12 74 07

U.S. Mission to the Organization for Economic Cooperation and Development *(continued)*

Public Affairs Advisor **Youssef Erkouni** 33 (1) 43 12 7460
E-mail: usoecdpao@state.gov
Regional Security Officer **(Vacant)** 33 (1) 43 12 74 26
Science and Environment Advisor **Seth Vaughn** 33 (1) 43 12 7430
Trade and Agriculture Advisor
Elizabeth Hosinski 5104 . . . . 33 (1) 43 12 7427
Secretary of the Delegation **(Vacant)** 33 (1) 43 12 7417
USAID Counselor and U.S. Representative to the OECD Development Assistance Committee
Nadereh C. Lee 33 (1) 43 12 7434
E-mail: nlee@usaid.gov

U.S. Mission to the Organization for the Prohibition of Chemical Weapons (OPCW)

Johan de Wittlaan 32, 2517 JR The Hague, Netherlands
Mail: PSC 115, Box 038, APO, AE 09715
Tel: 31 (70) 416-3300 Tel: 31 (70) 416-3535
E-mail: mediabr@opcw.org (Media and Public Affairs Branch)
Internet: www.opcw.org Internet: www.cwc.gov

★ U.S. Representative
Ambassador Kenneth Damian "Ken" Ward 31 (70) 351-8130
E-mail: wardke@state.gov Fax: 31 (70) 355-4271
Deputy U.S. Representative **Bettina D. Gorczynski** 31 (70) 351-8130
E-mail: GorczynskiBD@state.gov

U.S. Mission to the Organization for Security and Cooperation in Europe (USOSCE)

U.S. Mission to the OSCE, Wagramerstrasse 17-19, 1220 Vienna, Austria
American Embassy - Vienna, Austria, Department of State, Washington, DC 20521-9850
Tel: 43 (1) 31339-0 Internet: http://osce.usmission.gov

★ U.S. Representative-Designate
The Honorable James S. "Jim" Gilmore III 43 (1) 31339-0
Education: Virginia 1971 BA, 1977 JD
◇ Chargé d'Affaires **Harry Russell Kamian** 43 (1) 31339-0
E-mail: kamianhr@state.gov
Office Management Specialist to the Ambassador
(Vacant) 43 (1) 31339-0
Deputy Chief of Mission (Acting)
Gregory Paul "Greg" Macris 43 (1) 31339-0
E-mail: macrisg@state.gov
Education: James Madison 1986 BBA
Office Management Specialist to the Deputy Chief of Mission **Claudette Bergeron** 43 (1) 31339-0
E-mail: bergeronc@state.gov
◇ U.S. Co-Chair of the Minsk Group **Andrew J. Schofer** . . . 43 (1) 31339-0
E-mail: schoferja@state.gov
Education: Yale 1985 BA; Columbia 1989 MA
Community Liaison Officer **Meghann Daigle** 43 (1) 31339-0
Defense Attaché **(Vacant)** 43 (1) 31339-0
Facilities Manager **James Horner** 43 (1) 31339-0
Financial Management Officer **Cynthia Rafferty** 43 (1) 31339-0
Education: Delaware 1998 BS; Rutgers (Camden) 2005 MBA
General Services Officer **Mikael McCowan** 43 (1) 31339-0
Information Management Officer **Mark A. Wilson** 43 (1) 31339-0
Information Systems Security Officer
Josef J. Schmidt 43 (1) 31339-0
E-mail: schmidtjj@state.gov
◇ Management Officer **Erica A. Renew** 43 (1) 31339-0
E-mail: renewea@state.gov
Political Officer **Gregory Paul "Greg" Macris** 43 (1) 31339-0
E-mail: macrisg@state.gov
Education: James Madison 1986 BBA
Public Affairs Officer **Elaine A. Paplos** 43 (1) 31339-0
E-mail: pa-usosce@state.gov
Regional Security Officer **David Lyons** 43 (1) 31339-0
Chief Arms Control Delegate
Christopher J. "Chris" Panico 43 (1) 31339-0

U.S. Mission to the United Nations Agencies for Food and Agriculture (FODAG)

U.S. Mission to the UN Agencies in Rome, via Boncompagni 2, Rome, Italy
Mail: U.S. Mission to the U.N. (FODAG), PSC 59, Box 31, APO, AE 09624
Tel: 39 (06) 4674-3500 Fax: 39 (06) 4674-3535
E-mail: usunrome@state.gov Internet: http://usunrome.usmission.gov

★ U.S. Permanent Representative-Designate **Kip Tom** 39 (06) 4674-3500
◇ Chargé d'Affaires **Thomas M. "Tom" Duffy** 39 (06) 4674-3500
E-mail: duffytm@state.gov
Education: Notre Dame 1985 BA; King's Col (UK) 1989 MA; Naval War 1994
Office Management Specialist to the Ambassador
(Vacant) 39 (06) 4674-3502
◇ Deputy U.S. Permanent Representative/Deputy Chief of Mission **Thomas M. "Tom" Duffy** 39 (06) 4674-3513
E-mail: duffytm@state.gov Fax: 39 (06) 4674-3517
Education: Notre Dame 1985 BA; King's Col (UK) 1989 MA; Naval War 1994
Office Management Specialist to the Deputy Chief of Mission **Terentia "Terry" Stefani** 39 (06) 4674-3502
First Secretary, Alternate Permanent U.S. Representative and Political/Economic Section Chief **Emily Katkar** 39 (06) 4674-3506
E-mail: katkarel@state.gov
Tel: 39 (06) 4674-3516
First Secretary, Alternate Permanent U.S. Representative and Political/Economic Officer
Sandrine Goffard 39 (06) 4674-3528
E-mail: goffardss@state.gov
Tel: 39 (06) 4674-3535
Second Secretary, Alternate Permanent U.S. Representative and Political/Economic Officer
Daleya Uddin 39 (06) 4674-3505
E-mail: uddinsd@state.gov
Alternate Permanent U.S. Representative and Agricultural Specialist
Maria Adelaide D'Arcangelo 39 (06) 4674-3508
E-mail: darcangelom@state.gov Fax: 39 (06) 4674-3518
Alternate Permanent U.S. Representative and Senior Humanitarian Advisor **William S. Berger** 39 (06) 4674-3515
E-mail: bergerws@state.gov Fax: 39 (06) 4674-3518
Alternate Permanent U.S. Representative and Management Officer **(Vacant)** 39 (06) 4674-3528
Fax: 39 (06) 4674-3516
Alternate Permanent U.S. Representative and Public Affairs Officer **Jodi R. Breisler** 39 (06) 4674-3521
E-mail: brieslerjr@state.gov Fax: 39 (06) 4674-3516
Education: Minnesota 1999 BA; Edinburgh (Scotland) 2002 MSc; Columbia 2004 MA
Alternate Permanent U.S. Representative and Political Officer **(Vacant)** 39 (06) 4674-3528
Fax: 39 (06) 4674-3516
Alternate Permanent U.S. Representative and United States Agency for International Development Counselor **Marcus A. Johnson, Jr.** 39 (06) 4674-3512
E-mail: marcusjohnson@usaid.gov Fax: 39 (06) 4674-3518
Education: VCU 1989 BFA; George Mason 1994 MPA; National Defense U 2014 MS
Alternate Permanent U.S. Representative and United States Agency for International Development Humanitarian Program Specialist
Hang Nguyen 39 (06) 4674-3510
E-mail: nguyenhk@state.gov Fax: 39 (06) 4674-3518
Alternate Permanent U.S. Representative and United States Agency for International Development Finance and Oversight Specialist
Elizabeth Petrovski 39 (06) 4674-3509
E-mail: petrovskiea@state.gov Fax: 39 (06) 4674-3518
Alternate Permanent U.S. Representative and United States Agency for International Development Regional Legal Advisor **(Vacant)** 39 (06) 4674-2263
United States Agency for International Development Advisor **Fabrizio Moscatelli** 39 (06) 4674-3544
E-mail: moscatellif@state.gov

★ Presidential Appointment Requiring Senate Confirmation ☆ Presidential Appointment ☐ Schedule C Appointment ◇ Career Senior Foreign Service Appointment
● Career Senior Executive Service (SES) Appointment ○ Non-Career Senior Executive Service (SES) Appointment ■ Postal Career Executive Service

Agricultural Section (Foreign Agricultural Service) [United Nations Agencies for Food and Agriculture]
Via Veneto 119/A, 00187 Rome, Italy
Mail: U.S. Mission to the U.N. (FODAG), PSC 59, Box 31, APO, AE 09624
Tel: 39 (06) 4674-3507 Fax: 39 (06) 4674-3520
E-mail: agromefodag@usda.gov

Counselor (Acting) **Bryce Quick** 39 (06) 4674-3507
E-mail: Bryce.Quick@fas.usda.gov
Education: BYU 1990 BA

□ Minister-Counselor **Tommie Williams** 39 (06) 4674-3507
Education: Georgia BA; Georgia Southern MA

U.S. Mission to the United Nations Educational, Scientific, and Cultural Organization (UNESCO)

UNESCO c/o American Embassy - Paris, France,
2 Avenue Gabriel, 75382 Paris, Cedex 08, France
Mail: UNESCO c/o U.S. Embassy - Paris, France, Box A.203, APO, AE 09777
Tel: 33 (1) 4524-7456 Fax: 33 (1) 4524-7458
Internet: http://www.unesco.usmission.gov E-mail: parisunesco@state.gov

Note: On October 12, 2017, the Department of State announced that the U.S. will withdraw from UNESCO effective December 31, 2018. At that time, the U.S. will seek to establish a permanent observer mission to the organization.

★ U.S. Permanent Representative to UNESCO **(Vacant)** . . . 33 (1) 4312-2620
Office Management Specialist to the Ambassador **(Vacant)** 33 (1) 4524-7416
Deputy Chief of Mission **(Vacant)** 33 (1) 4312-2029
Office Management Specialist to the Deputy Chief of Mission **Robin Taylor** 33 (1) 4524-7481
E-mail: taylorr@state.gov
Information Management Officer **Richard Scott "Scott" Hewitt** 33 (1) 4312-2222
E-mail: hewittrs@state.gov
Political Officer **(Vacant)** 33 (1) 4312-2029
Public Affairs Officer **(Vacant)** 33 (1) 4312-2029
Regional Security Officer **Marian Cotter** 33 (1) 4524-7456
Education: Wisconsin BA; Georgetown MA

MIDDLE EAST AND NORTH AFRICA

U.S. Embassy in Algeria

American Embassy - Algiers, Algeria,
4 Chemin Cheikh Bachir El-Ibrahimi, Algiers, 16000, Algeria
Mail: American Embassy - Algiers, Algeria, Department of State, 6030 Algiers Place, Washington, DC 20521-6030
Tel: 213 770-08-2000 Fax: 213 60-7355 Internet: dz.usembassy.gov

Office of the U.S. Ambassador to Algeria

American Embassy - Algiers, Algeria,
4 Chemin Cheikh Bachir El-Ibrahimi, Algiers, 16000, Algeria
Mail: American Embassy - Algiers, Algeria, Department of State, 6030 Algiers Place, Washington, DC 20521-6030

★ Ambassador **Ambassador John P. Desrocher** 213 770-08-2000
E-mail: desrocherjp@state.gov
Education: Georgetown BS
Office Management Specialist to the Ambassador **Rebecca Robinson** 213 770-08-2000
Deputy Chief of Mission **Lawrence M. Randolph** 213 770-08-2000
E-mail: randolphlm@state.gov
Office Management Specialist to the Deputy Chief of Mission **Susan B. Hinton** 213 770-08-2000
E-mail: hintonsb@state.gov
Community Liaison Officer **Christophe J. Paccard** 213 770-08-2000
Consular Officer **Marwa Zeini** 213 770-08-2000
E-mail: ZeiniMM@state.gov
Economic Officer **(Vacant)** 213 770-08-2000
Financial Management Officer **Eric G. Flaxman** 213 770-08-2000
E-mail: flaxmaneg@state.gov

Office of the U.S. Ambassador to Algeria *(continued)*

General Services Officer **John Volkoff** 213 770-08-2000
E-mail: volkoffj@state.gov
Information Management Officer **Herman A. Llorin** 213 770-08-2000
E-mail: llorinha@state.gov
Information Program Officer **(Vacant)** 213 770-08-2000
Information Systems Officer **Veronica E. Thomas** 213 770-08-2000
E-mail: thomasve@state.gov
Information Systems Security Officer **Veronica E. Thomas** 213 770-08-2000
E-mail: thomasve@state.gov
Legal Attaché **(Vacant)** 213 770-08-2000
Management Officer **Ginger M. Campbell** 213 770-08-2000
E-mail: campbellgm@state.gov
Political/Economic Chief **David G. Wisner** 213 770-08-2000
E-mail: wisnerdg@state.gov
Public Affairs Officer **Ruben Harutunian** 213 770-08-2000
E-mail: HarutunianR@state.gov
Regional Security Officer **Michael Vannett** 213 770-08-2000
E-mail: VannettMF@state.gov

Agricultural Section (Foreign Agricultural Service) [Algeria]
American Embassy - Algiers, Algeria,
4 Chemin Cheikh Bachir El-Ibrahimi, Algiers, 16000, Algeria
E-mail: agalgiers@fas.usda.gov

Attaché **Justina Torry** 213 770 08-2111
E-mail: justina.torry@fas.usda.gov

Commercial Section (Foreign Commercial Service) [Algeria]
American Embassy - Algiers, Algeria,
4 Chemin Cheikh Bachir El-Ibrahimi, Algiers, 16000, Algeria
Tel: 213 770-08-2035 Fax: 213 (21) 69-3132 Internet: export.gov/algeria

Senior Commercial Officer **Nathan Seifert** 213 770 224 890
E-mail: Nathan.Seifert@trade.gov

Office of the Defense Attaché [Algeria]
American Embassy - Algiers, Algeria, 4 Chemin Cheikh Bachir El-Ibrahimi, B.P. 408 (Alger Gare), Algiers, 16000, Algeria
Mail: American Embassy - Algiers, Algeria, Department of State, Washington, DC 20521-6030
Tel: 213 770-08-2000 Fax: 213 (21) 69-39-79
E-mail: usdaoalgiers@state.gov

Defense Attaché **COL Don D. Robertson USA** 213 770-08-2000
Defense Cooperation Chief **Maj Marshall Klitzke USAF** 213 770-08-2000
E-mail: KlitzkeMW@state.gov

Federal Aviation Administration (Resident in Moscow) [Algeria]
Eight Bolshoy Devyatinsky Pereulok, 121099 Moscow, Russia

FAA Representative **Andrew McKee** 7 916-222-6735

U.S. Embassy in Bahrain

American Embassy - Manama, Bahrain, Building No. 979 Road 3119, Block 331, Zinj District, Manama, Bahrain

Office of the U.S. Ambassador to Bahrain

American Embassy - Manama, Bahrain, Building No. 979 Road 3119, Block 331, Zinj District, Manama, Bahrain
Mail: American Embassy (Manama, Bahrain), FPO, AE 09834-5100
Tel: 973 1724-2700 Tel: 973 1724-5126 (After Hours)
Fax: 973 1727-2594 Internet: bh.usembassy.gov

★ Ambassador **Ambassador Justin Hicks Siberell** 973 1724-2700
E-mail: siberelljh@state.gov
Education: UC Berkeley BA
Office Management Specialist to the Ambassador **Tammy Lubulu** 973 1724-2787
E-mail: LubuluTT@state.gov
Deputy Chief of Mission **Aimee Cutrona** 973 1724-2773
E-mail: cutronaa@state.gov
Office Management Specialist to the Deputy Chief of Mission **Jocelyn Lacy** 973 1724-2773
Community Liaison Officer **Sarah Bowers** 973 1724-2700

★ Presidential Appointment Requiring Senate Confirmation ☆ Presidential Appointment □ Schedule C Appointment ◇ Career Senior Foreign Service Appointment
● Career Senior Executive Service (SES) Appointment ○ Non-Career Senior Executive Service (SES) Appointment ■ Postal Career Executive Service

Office of the U.S. Ambassador to Bahrain *(continued)*

Consular Section Officer/Consul General
Jeffrey Austin 973 1724-2770
Fax: 973 1725-6242
Financial Management Officer **Marina A. O'Connell** 973 1724-2700
E-mail: oconnellma@state.gov
General Services Officer **Agnes Lopez** 973 1724-2700
Information Management Officer **Joshua Rush** 973 1724-2777
Information Program Officer **Paul Berry** 973 1724-2769
Information Systems Security Officer **Delbreco Coney** 973 1724-2777
E-mail: coneydl@state.gov
Legal Attaché **Terry M. Parish** 973 1724-2700
Management Officer **Christian Lynch** 973 1724-2881
Fax: 973 1727-5418
Political/Economic Officer **Anne Bennett** 973 1724-2700
Political/Military Officer **Michael James** 973 1724-2700
Public Affairs Officer **Thomas Tanner** 973 1724-2717
Fax: 973 1727-0547
Regional Security Officer
David A. "Dave" Noonan .... 973 1724-2761 ext. 3082
E-mail: noonand@state.gov

Office of Military Cooperation [Bahrain]
PSC 451, Box 270, FPO, AE 09834-5100
Tel: 973 1727-2784 Fax: 973 1727-6046 E-mail: omcbah@state.gov

Defense Cooperation Officer
Col Stephen H. Bissonnette USAF 973 1724-2829
Education: Connecticut 1988 BSME; Embry-Riddle 1999 MAS; Naval War 2002 MA; Air War Col 2010 MA

U.S. Embassy in Egypt

American Embassy - Cairo, Egypt, 5 Tawfik Diab Street, Garden City, Cairo, Egypt
Tel: 20 (2) 2797-3300 Fax: 20 (2) 2797-3200

Office of the U.S. Ambassador to Egypt
American Embassy - Cairo, Egypt, 5 Tawfik Diab Street, Garden City, Cairo, Egypt
Mail: American Embassy - Cairo, Egypt, Unit 64900, APO, AE 09839-4900

★ Ambassador **(Vacant)** 20 (2) 2797-3300
◇ Chargé d'Affaires **Thomas H. "Tom" Goldberger** 20 (2) 2797-3300
E-mail: goldbergerth@state.gov
Office Management Specialist to the Ambassador
(Vacant) 20 (2) 2797-3300
Fax: 20 (2) 2797-2000
◇ Deputy Chief of Mission **Dorothy C. Shea** 20 (2) 2797-3300
E-mail: shead@state.gov
Education: Virginia 1988 BA; Georgetown 1991 MSFS; National War Col 2011 MS
Office Management Specialist to the Deputy Chief of Mission **Virginia E. Baldwin** 20 (2) 2797-3300
E-mail: baldwinve@state.gov
◇ Consul General **Lisa A. Vickers** 20 (2) 2797-3300
E-mail: vickersla@state.gov Fax: 20 (2) 2797-2472
E-mail: consularcairo@state.gov
Education: U Pacific 1986 BA
Community Liaison Officer **Tazmeen A. Sallay** 20 (2) 2797-3300
E-mail: sallayta@state.gov
◇ Economic Officer **James A. "Jim" Boughner** 20 (2) 2797-3300
E-mail: boughnerja@state.gov
Economic/Political Officer **(Vacant)** 20 (2) 2797-3300
Fax: 20 (2) 2797-2181
Equal Employment Opportunity Officer **(Vacant)** 20 (2) 2797-3300
Facilities Management Officer **Gary Hein** 20 (2) 2797-3300
Financial Management Officer **James O. Inder** 20 (2) 2797-3300
General Services Officer **Michael "Mike" Okamura** 20 (2) 2797-3300
E-mail: okamuram@state.gov
Human Resources Officer **Natasha Burney** 20 (2) 2797-3300
E-mail: burneynn@state.gov
Education: Syracuse 1991 BA; Rollins 1997 MBA
Information Management Officer
Elizabeth M. Slater 20 (2) 2797-3411

Office of the U.S. Ambassador to Egypt *(continued)*

Information Program Officer **(Vacant)** 20 (2) 2797-3300
Information Services Officer **James M. Sallay** 20 (2) 2797-3300
Information Systems Security Officer
James M. Sallay 20 (2) 2797-3300
Legal Attaché **Mark Green** 20 (2) 2797-3300
Fax: 20 (2) 2797-2932
◇ Management Officer **Wayne Amory McDuffy** 20 (2) 2797-3300
E-mail: mcduffywa2@state.gov Fax: 20 (2) 2795-2875
Education: Harvard 1983 BA
◇ Public Affairs Officer **Helen Grace LaFave** 20 (2) 2797-3474
E-mail: lafavehg@state.gov Fax: 20 (2) 2797-3591
Education: Smith 1985 AB; William & Mary 1987 AM; National War Col 2011 MS
Regional Security Officer **Paul D. Brown** 20 (2) 2797-3300
E-mail: brownpd@state.gov Fax: 20 (2) 2797-2828
Political Section Chief **Mustafa M. Popal** 20 (2) 2797-3300
E-mail: popalmm@state.gov
Political/Military Officer **(Vacant)** 20 (2) 2797-3300

Agency for International Development [Egypt]
1A Nady El Etisalat Street, New Maadi, 11435 Cairo, Egypt
Mail: American Embassy - Cairo, Egypt, Unit 64900, APO, AE 09839-4900
Tel: 20 (2) 2522-7000 Fax: 20 (2) 2516-4628
Internet: www.usaid.gov/egypt

◇ Mission Director **Sherry Faith Carlin** 20 (2) 2522-7000
E-mail: scarlin@usaid.gov Fax: 20 (2) 2516-5628
◇ Deputy Mission Director **Rebecca A. Latorraca** 20 (2) 2522-7000
E-mail: rlatorraca@usaid.gov
Education: Lawrence U 1984 BA; American U 1992 MA

Agricultural Section (Foreign Agricultural Service) [Egypt]
Sa'awan Street, Bahar Hemyar Zone, Sanaa, Yemen
Mail: American Embassy - Cairo, Egypt, Unit 64900, APO, AE 09839-4900
Tel: 20 (2) 2797-2388 Fax: 20 (2) 2796-3989
E-mail: agcairo@fas.usda.gov

◇ Agricultural Counselor **Ali Abdi** 20 (2) 2797-2388
E-mail: ali.abdi@fas.usda.gov
Senior Attaché **Mariano Beillard** 20 (2) 2797-2388
Attaché **Bret Tate** 20 (2) 2797-2388

Commercial Section (Foreign Commercial Service) [Egypt]
Eight Kamal El Din Salah Street, Garden City, Cairo, Egypt
Mail: American Embassy - Cairo, Egypt, Unit 64900, Box 11, APO, AE 09839
Tel: 20 (2) 2797-2689 Fax: 20 (2) 2795-8368
E-mail: office.cairo@trade.gov Internet: www.export.gov/egypt

◇ Senior Commercial Officer **James "Jim" Sullivan** 20 (2) 2797-2340
E-mail: jim.sullivan@trade.gov
Deputy Commercial Officer **(Vacant)** 20 (2) 2797-2610
Commercial Officer **Mohmoud Chikh-Alli** 20 (2) 2797-2426
E-mail: mohmoud.chikh-ali@trade.gov

Drug Enforcement Administration [Egypt]
5 Tawfik Diab Street, Garden City, Cairo, Egypt
Mail: American Embassy - Cairo, Egypt, Unit 64900, APO, AE 09839-4900
Tel: 20 (2) 2797-3300 Fax: 20 (2) 2797-3200

DEA Officer **Leon M. Palmer** 20 (2) 2797-3300
E-mail: palmerlm@state.gov

Federal Aviation Administration (Resident in Abu Dhabi) [Egypt]
American Embassy/FAA, Embassies District (Airport Road) Street #4, 09825 Abu Dhabi, United Arab Emirates
PSC 82, Box 002, AEU-BRU Abu Dhabi, United Arab Emirates
Fax: 971 (2) 414-2588

FAA Senior Representative **Robert Roxbrough** 971 (2) 414-2438

★ Presidential Appointment Requiring Senate Confirmation ☆ Presidential Appointment ☐ Schedule C Appointment ◇ Career Senior Foreign Service Appointment
● Career Senior Executive Service (SES) Appointment ○ Non-Career Senior Executive Service (SES) Appointment ■ Postal Career Executive Service

Office of Defense Attaché [Egypt]
Eight Kamal El Din Salah Street, Garden City, Cairo, Egypt
Mail: American Embassy - Cairo, Egypt, Unit 64900,
APO, AE 09839-4900
Tel: 20 (2) 2797-3300 Fax: 20 (2) 2797-3049
Defense Attaché **(Vacant)** 20 (2) 2797-3300

Library of Congress, Cairo [Egypt]
American Embassy - Cairo, Egypt, 5 Tawfik Diab Street,
Garden City, Cairo, Egypt
Mail: Unit 64900, APO, AE 09839-4900
Tel: 20 (2) 2797-2206 Fax: 20 (2) 2796-0233
Internet: www.loc.gov/acq/ovop/cairo
Field Director **William Kopycki** 20 (2) 2797-2206
E-mail: cairo@loc.gov

Alexandria Consulate General
Helnan Palestine, Montazah Gardens, Alexandria, Egypt
Mail: Unit 64900, Box X, APO, AE 09839-4900
Tel: 20 (3) 538-5800 E-mail: alexpa@fan.gov
◇ Consul General **Nancy Lynn Corbett** 20 (3) 538-5800
E-mail: corbettnl@state.gov
Office Management Specialist to the Consul General
Karine Freihales 20 (3) 538-5800
Deputy Principal Officer **(Vacant)** 20 (3) 538-5800
General Services Officer **Tarek Abdelhamid** 20 (3) 538-5800
Management Officer **Omar Ahmed Ali** 20 (3) 538-5800
E-mail: alioa@state.gov
Political/Economic Officer **John Winstead** 20 (3) 538-5800
Public Affairs Officer **Minta Madeley** 20 (3) 538-5800
E-mail: madeleyme@state.goy
Regional Security Officer **Ryan Renuart** 20 (3) 538-5800

U.S. Embassy in Iraq
Al-Kindi Street, International Zone, Baghdad, Iraq
Tel: 964 760-030-3000 Internet: iq.usembassy.gov

Office of the U.S. Ambassador to Iraq
American Embassy, Al-Kindi Street, International Zone, Baghdad, Iraq
Mail: APO, AE 09316
Tel: 964 760-030-3000 Internet: iq.usembassy.gov
★ Ambassador **Ambassador Douglas Alan Silliman** . . . 964 760-030-3000
E-mail: sillimanda@state.gov
Education: Baylor 1982 BA; George Washington MA
★ Ambassador-Designate
Ambassador Matthew H. Tueller 964 760-030-3000
Education: BYU BA; Harvard MPP
Office Management Specialist to the Ambassador
Emily Weston 964 760-030-3000
◇ Deputy Chief of Mission **Joey R. Hood** 964 760-030-3000
E-mail: hoodjr@state.gov
Office Management Specialist to the Deputy Chief
of Mission **Malgorzata Gosia Lamot** 964 760-030-3000
E-mail: lamotgx@state.gov
Community Liaison Officer **Emily Genung** 964 760-030-3000
Consul General **James A. Jimenez** 964 760-030-3000
E-mail: jimenezj@state.gov
◇ Economic Officer **Gabriel Escobar** 964 760-030-3000
E-mail: escobarg@state.gov
Education: Barnard 1988 BA; Columbia 1990
Equal Employment Opportunity Officer
Charles Hendrix 964 760-030-3000
Facilities Management Officer **Maurice Pettiford** 964 760-030-3000
E-mail: pettifordmb@state.gov
Financial Attaché **John L. Sullivan** 964 760-030-3000
E-mail: john.sullivan@treasury.gov
Education: George Washington 2004 BA
Financial Management Officer **Donna Edmonds** 964 760-030-3000
General Services Officer
Lawrence P. "Larry" Lane 964 760-030-3000
E-mail: lanelp@state.gov
Education: Wisconsin 1991 BA; UC Berkeley 2004
Human Resources Officer **Lora West** 964 760-030-3000

Office of the U.S. Ambassador to Iraq *(continued)*
Information Management Officer **Doyle R. Lee** 964 760-030-3000
E-mail: leedr@state.gov
Information Programs Officer **(Vacant)** 964 760-030-3000
Information Systems Officer **Michael Adams** 964 760-030-3000
Information Systems Security Officer **Keith Griggs** 964 760-030-3000
E-mail: griggskl@state.gov
International Narcotics and Law Enforcement
Director **(Vacant)** 964 760-030-3000
◇ Senior Coordinator, Office of Refugee and Internally
Displaced Persons Affairs **Stephen P. O'Dowd** 964 760-030-3000
E-mail: o'dowdsp@state.gov
Education: Hamilton 1981 BA;
Eisenhower National Security and Resource Strategy 2013 MS
Labor Officer **(Vacant)** 964 760-030-3000
Legal Attaché **Bryan Finnegan** 964 760-030-3000
E-mail: bryan.finnegan@ic.fbi.gov
◇ Management Officer **Michelle A. LaBonte** 964 760-030-3000
E-mail: labontema@state.gov
Political Affairs Section Chief **Apar S. Sidhu** 964 760-030-3000
E-mail: sidhuas@state.gov
Political/Military Officer **Claire K. Kaneshiro** 964 760-030-3000
E-mail: kaneshirock@state.gov
◇ Public Affairs Officer **John Stuart Kincannon** 964 760-030-3000
E-mail: kincannonj@state.gov
Regional Security Officer **Julie S. Cabus** 964 760-030-3000
E-mail: cabusjs@state.gov
Education: Susquehanna 1995 BA
Senior Deputy Regional Security Officer
Mark A. Sullo 964 760-030-3000
E-mail: sullom@state.gov

Agency for International Development [Iraq]
APO, AE 09316
Internet: www.usaid.gov/iraq
◇ Mission Director **Dana R. Mansuri** . . . . (202) 216-6276
E-mail: dmansuri@usaid.gov
Education: U Washington 1982 BA;
American Grad International Mgmt 1986 MIB
◇ Deputy Mission Director **William M. Patterson** . . . . . . (202) 216-6276
E-mail: wpatterson@usaid.gov

Agricultural Section (Foreign Agricultural Service) (Resident in Cairo) [Iraq]
American Embassy, Al-Kindi Street, International Zone, Baghdad, Iraq
Tel: 964 (1) 240-553-0581 ext. 2051 E-mail: baghdadag@state.gov
◇ Agricultural Counselor **Ali Abdi** 20 (2) 2797-2388
E-mail: Ali.Abdi@fas.usda.gov

Federal Aviation Administration (Resident in Abu Dhabi) [Iraq]
Federal Aviation Administration Representative
Robert Roxbrough 971 (2) 414-2438

Office of Security Cooperation [Iraq] (OSC-I)
Chief **MG Sean M. Jenkins USA** 964 760-030-3000
Deputy Chief **BrigGen Craig D. Wills USAF** 964 760-030-3000
Command Sergeant Major
CSM Edison M. Rebuck USA 964 760-030-3000

Basrah Consulate General
APO, AE 09375
Tel: (301) 985-8635 E-mail: basrahprotocol@state.gov
Note: On September 28, 2018, the Department of State suspended operations at the Basrah Consulate and all personnel have been evacuated. Embassy Baghdad is providing full consular services to for those in and around Basrah.
Consul General **Tim T. "Timmy" Davis** . . . . (301) 985-8635
E-mail: davistt@state.gov
Education: Alabama
Office Management Specialist to the Consul General
Kristina Lorenger . . . . (301) 985-8635
Deputy Principal Officer
Benjamin A. "Ben" Rockwell . . . . (301) 985-8635
Education: George Washington
Consular Officer **(Vacant)** . . . . (301) 985-8635

★ Presidential Appointment Requiring Senate Confirmation ☆ Presidential Appointment ☐ Schedule C Appointment ◇ Career Senior Foreign Service Appointment
● Career Senior Executive Service (SES) Appointment ○ Non-Career Senior Executive Service (SES) Appointment ■ Postal Career Executive Service

Basrah Consulate General *(continued)*

Economic Officer **Joseph E. "Joe" Salazar** . . . . (301) 985-8635
Economic and Commercial Officer
Daniel N. "Dan" Daley . . . . (301) 985-8635
E-mail: daleydn@state.gov
Education: Michigan AB; Johns Hopkins MA
Facilities Management Officer **Frank Anthony** . . . . (301) 985-8635
General Services Officer **Dan Trif** . . . . (301) 985-8635
Information Management Officer **(Vacant)** . . . . (301) 985-8635
Information Program Officer
William "Bill" Geschwind . . . . (301) 985-8635
E-mail: GeschwindWF@state.gov
Information Systems Security Officer
Kon Keng "Keng" Chen . . . . (301) 985-8635
Management Officer **David H. Liboff** . . . . (301) 985-8635
E-mail: liboffd@state.gov
Political Officer **Arthur J. Bell** . . . . (301) 985-8635
Political/Economic Officer **(Vacant)** . . . . (301) 985-8635
Public Affairs Officer **Tina Ziegenhain** . . . . (301) 985-8635
Regional Security Officer **Keith F. Spain** . . . . (301) 985-8635
E-mail: spainkf@state.gov
Education: Monterey Inst 2002 MA

Erbil Consulate General

American Embassy, Al-Kindi Street, International Zone, Baghdad, Iraq
Tel: (240) 264-3467

◇ Consul General **Steven H. Fagin** . . . . (240) 264-3467
E-mail: faginsh2@state.gov
Education: Williams BA; Michigan MA
Office Management Specialist to Consul General
Tamara McDaniel . . . . (240) 264-3467
Deputy Principal Officer
Steven Guy Matthew "Steve" Gillen . . . . (240) 264-3467
Consular Affairs Officer **Catherine Clum** . . . . (240) 264-3467
Defense Attaché **(Vacant)** . . . . (240) 264-3467
General Services Officer **Dwayne T. McDavid** . . . . (240) 264-3467
E-mail: McDavidDT@state.gov
Information Management Officer
Thomas E. "Tom" Stock 964 240-553-0589
E-mail: stockte@state.gov
Information Program Officer
Thomas E. "Tom" Stock 964 240-553-0589
E-mail: stockte@state.gov
Legal Attaché **Fernando Motta** . . . . (240) 264-3467
Economic Officer **(Vacant)** . . . . (240) 264-3467
Management Officer **Christopher G. "Chris" Pixley** . . . . . (240) 264-3467
E-mail: pixleycg@state.gov
Narcotics Affairs Officer **(Vacant)** . . . . (240) 264-3467
Political/Economic Officer **Silvia Eiriz** . . . . (240) 264-3467
Public Affairs Officer **Kimberly M. "Kim" Strollo** . . . . . . (240) 264-3467
E-mail: erbilpublicaffairs@state.gov
Regional Security Officer **Hoyt J. "Jessy" Alexander** . . . (240) 264-3467
Special Representative for Minority Assistance
Programs in Iraq **Max Primorac** . . . . (240) 264-3467
E-mail: mprimorac@usaid.gov
Education: Franklin & Marshall BA; Chicago MA
Information Systems Security Officer **Kari Faflik** 964 240-553-0589

U.S. Embassy in Israel

14 David Flusser, 9378322 Jerusalem, Israel
Tel: 972 (2) 630-4000 Internet: il.usembassy.gov

Note: On October 18, 2018, Secretary of State Mike Pompeo announced the planned merger of the US Embassy in Jerusalem and the US Consulate General in Jerusalem.

Office of the U.S. Ambassador to Israel

★ Ambassador **Ambassador David Melech Friedman** . . . 972 (2) 630-4000
Education: Columbia 1978 BA; NYU 1981 JD
Office Management Specialist to the Ambassador
Stela Sears 972 (2) 630-4000

Tel Aviv Branch Office

71 Hayarkon Street, 6343229 Tel Aviv, Israel
Tel: 972 (3) 519-7575 Fax: 972 (3) 517-3227

◇ Deputy Chief of Mission **Leslie Meredith Tsou** 972 (3) 5197580
E-mail: tsoul@state.gov
Education: Georgetown
Office Management Specialist to the Deputy Chief
of Mission **Sandra L. McInturff** 972 (3) 5197583
E-mail: mcinturffsl@state.gov
□ Senior Advisor **Aryeh Lightstone** 972 (3) 519-7575
Community Liaison Officer **Ana G. Townsend** 972 (3) 519-7575
E-mail: townsendag@state.gov
Education: Wayland Baptist 2006 BBA
◇ Consul General **Paul Michael Fitzgerald** 972 (3) 5197671
E-mail: fitzgeraldpm@state.gov Fax: 972 (3) 5160315
◇ Economic Officer **Eugene "Gene" Young** 972 (3) 5197364
E-mail: younge@state.gov
Facilities Management Officer **Kato Smith** 972 (3) 519-7575
Financial Management Officer **(Vacant)** 972 (3) 519-7575
General Services Officer **Eric J. Mendenhall** 972 (3) 519-7575
E-mail: mendenhallej@state.gov
Human Resources Officer **Erika Zielke** 972 (3) 519-7575
E-mail: zielkeeb@state.gov
Information Management Officer **David A. Douthit** 972 (3) 5197380
E-mail: douthitda@state.gov
Information Program Officer **Dongni D. Alcantara** 972 (3) 519-7585
E-mail: alcantaradd@state.gov
Information Systems Officer
Gwendolyn "Gwen" Sell 972 (3) 519-7520
Information Systems Security Officer **Tam Nguyen** 972 (3) 519-7575
Legal Attaché **Cary Gleicher** 972 (3) 5197481
E-mail: gleichercx@state.gov
◇ Management Officer **Jonathan A. Schools** 972 (3) 5197307
E-mail: schoolsja@state.gov Fax: 972 (3) 5108382
Political Officer **Michael G. Snowden** 972 (3) 5197566
E-mail: snowdenmg@state.gov
◇ Public Affairs Officer **Terry R. Davidson** 972 (3) 5103821
E-mail: davidsontr@state.gov
Regional Security Officer **Hartaje K. "Teji" Thiara** 972 (3) 519-7602
E-mail: thiaratk@state.gov
Education: Cal State (Chico) 1991 BA; USC 1997 MPA
Environment, Science, Technology, and Health
Officer **Christopher R. Green** 972 (3) 519-7575
Education: Texas 1990 BA; St Mary's U (TX) 1995 MA, 1995 JD

Agency for International Development - West Bank and Gaza

71 Hayarkon Street, 63903 Tel Aviv, Israel
Tel: 972 (3) 511-4848 Fax: 972 (3) 511-4888 E-mail: wbgpro@usaid.gov
Internet: https://www.usaid.gov/west-bank-and-gaza

◇ Mission Director **Monica Stein-Olson** 972 (3) 511-4848
E-mail: mstein-olson@usaid.gov

Agricultural Section (Foreign Agricultural Service) [Israel]

71 HaYarkon Street, 63903 Tel Aviv, Israel
Tel: 972 (3) 519-7588 Fax: 972 (3) 510-2565
E-mail: agtelaviv@fas.usda.gov

◇ Agricultural Counselor (Resident in Cairo) **Ali Abdi** 20 (2) 2797-2388
E-mail: Ali.Abdi@fas.usda.gov

Commercial Section (Foreign Commercial Service) [Israel]

American Embassy - Tel Aviv, Unit 7228, Box 21, APO, AE 09830
Tel: 972 (3) 519-8500 Fax: 972 (3) 510-8530
E-mail: office.telaviv@trade.gov Internet: export.gov/israel

◇ Senior Commercial Officer **Ireas Cook** 972 (3) 519-8510
E-mail: ireas.cook@trade.gov
Deputy Senior Commercial Officer
Susan Hettleman 972 (3) 519-8509
E-mail: susan.hettleman@trade.gov

★ Presidential Appointment Requiring Senate Confirmation ☆ Presidential Appointment □ Schedule C Appointment ◇ Career Senior Foreign Service Appointment
● Career Senior Executive Service (SES) Appointment ○ Non-Career Senior Executive Service (SES) Appointment ■ Postal Career Executive Service

DEPARTMENTS

Office of the Defense Attaché [Israel]
71 Hayarkon Street, Tel Aviv, Israel
Tel: 972 (3) 519-7333 Fax: 972 (3) 516-7605
E-mail: telavivdao@state.gov

Senior Defense Official and Defense Attaché
BrigGen Corey J. Martin USAF, USAF 972 (3) 5197333
Education: Air Force Acad 1991 BS; Webster 1999 MA

U.S. Consulate General in Jerusalem

U.S. Consulate General - Jerusalem, 18 Agron Road, 91002 Jerusalem, Israel
Mail: U.S. Consulate General - Jerusalem, Unit 7228, Box 0039, APO, AE 09830
Tel: 972 (2) 622-7230 Fax: 972 (2) 622-3551
E-mail: uscongenjerusalem@state.gov Internet: jru.usconsulate.gov

Note: On October 18, 2018, Secretary of State Mike Pompeo announced the planned merger of the US Embassy in Jerusalem and the US Consulate General in Jerusalem.

Consul General **Karen Hideko Sasahara** 972 (2) 622-7284
E-mail: sasaharakh@state.gov Fax: 972 (2) 624-9462
Education: Wisconsin (Milwaukee) BA; George Washington MA; Southern Methodist JD
Office Management Specialist to the Consul General **(Vacant)** 972 (2) 622-7230
Deputy Consul General **Michael P. "Mike" Hankey** 972 (2) 622-7285
E-mail: hankeym@state.gov
Education: George Washington 2000 BA; Indiana 2007 MEd
Consular Section Chief **Aaron Hellman** 972 (2) 622-7226
E-mail: hellmana2@state.gov Fax: 972 (2) 627-2233
Community Liaison Officer **Noemi Hellman** 972 (2) 622-6930
Fax: 972 (2) 623-5636
Economic Chief **James J. Turner** 972 (2) 622-7281
Fax: 972 (2) 625-3186
Financial Management Officer **Francisco Lloret** 972 (2) 622-7128
E-mail: lloretfl@state.gov Fax: 972 (2) 622-3550
General Services Officer **Bryan Lance** 972 (2) 649-3001
Information Management Officer **James H. May** 972 (2) 622-7299
E-mail: mayjh@state.gov Fax: 972 (2) 624-0771
Information Program Officer **Travis Waites** 972 (2) 622-7299
E-mail: waitestj@state.gov
Information Systems Officer **Paul Fano** 972 (2) 622-6940
E-mail: fanopv@state.gov
Education: Marygrove 2002 BAS; Michigan (Dearborn) 2011 MBA
International Broadcasting Bureau Officer **(Vacant)** 972 (2) 622-7230
Legal Attaché **Chung Chang** 972 (2) 622-7230
Management Officer **Andrea S. Baker** 972 (2) 622-7299
Fax: 972 (2) 624-0771
Narcotics Affairs Officer **Margaret H. Nardi** 972 (2) 622-7230
E-mail: nardimh@state.gov
Political Officer **David B. Berns** 972 (2) 622-7282
E-mail: bernsdb@state.gov Fax: 972 (2) 624-9462
Public Affairs Officer **Christopher W. Hodges** 972 (2) 622-6909
E-mail: hodgescw@state.gov Fax: 972 (2) 624-0939
Regional Security Officer **Paul J. Fiffick** 972 (2) 622-7230
E-mail: fiffickpj2@state.gov

U.S. Agency for International Development - West Bank and Gaza (Resident in Tel Aviv)
71 HaYarkon Street, Tel Aviv, Israel
Tel: 972 (3) 511-4848 Fax: 972 (3) 511-4888 E-mail: wbgpro@usaid.gov
Internet: www.usaid.gov/west-bank-and-gaza

◇ Mission Director **Monica Stein-Olson** 972 (3) 511-4848
E-mail: mstein-olson@usaid.gov

Commercial Section (Foreign Commercial Service) - West Bank
U.S. Consulate General, Unit 7228, Box 0039, APO, AE 09830
Tel: 972 (2) 625-5201 Fax: 972 (2) 623-5132
E-mail: office.jerusalem@trade.gov Internet: export.gov/westbank

◇ Senior Commercial Officer (Resident in Tel Aviv)
Ireas Cook 972 (3) 519-8510
E-mail: ireas.cook@trade.gov
Senior Commercial Specialist **Assad Barsoum** 972 (2) 625-4742
E-mail: assad.barsoum@trade.gov

Commercial Section (Foreign Commercial Service) - West Bank *(continued)*

Commercial Specialist **Issa Noursi** 972 (2) 625-5201
E-mail: issa.noursi@trade.gov

Office of the United States Security Coordinator for Israel and the Palestinian Authority (USSC)
U.S. Security Coordinator **LTG Eric P. Wendt USA** 972 (2) 622-6926

U.S. Embassy in Jordan

Abdoun, Al-Umawyeen St., Amman, Jordan
Tel: 962 (6) 590-6000 Fax: 962 (6) 592-0163 Internet: jo.usembassy.gov

Office of the U.S. Ambassador to Jordan
American Embassy - Amman, Jordan, Abdoun, Al-Umawyeen St., Amman, Jordan
Mail: American Embassy - Amman, Jordan, Unit 70200, Box 1, APO, AE 09892-0200
Tel: 962 (6) 590-6000 Fax: 962 (6) 592-0163 Internet: jo.usembassy.gov

★ Ambassador **(Vacant)** 962 (6) 590-6000
◇ Chargé d'Affaires **Paul Ramsey Malik** 962 (6) 590-6000
E-mail: malikp@state.gov
Office Management Specialist to the Ambassador **(Vacant)** 962 (6) 590-6636
◇ Deputy Chief of Mission (Acting) **Jim Barnhart, Jr.** ... 962 (6) 590-6000
E-mail: jbarnhart@usaid.gov
Education: Furman 1985 BA; Johns Hopkins MA; Georgia State PhD
Office Management Specialist to the Deputy Chief of Mission **Dazzie Derlene "Derlene" Mazyck** 962 (6) 590-6635
E-mail: mazyckdd@state.gov
Consul General (Acting) **Darren I. Wang** 962 (6) 590-6700
E-mail: wangdi@state.gov
Community Liaison Officer **Mary Kay Cunningham** ... 962 (6) 590-6200
Fax: 962 (6) 592-4102
Economic Officer **(Vacant)** 962 (6) 590-6558
Financial Management Officer **Maureen M. Danzot** ... 962 (6) 590-6688
E-mail: DanzotMM@state.gov Fax: 962 (6) 592-7653
Education: Chaminade 1993 BBA
General Services Officer **Elizabeth A. Sewall** 962 (6) 590-6657
E-mail: sewallea@state.gov Fax: 962 (6) 592-0121
Human Resources Officer **Bernt B. Johnson** 962 (6) 590-6000
E-mail: johnsonbb@state.gov
Information Management Officer **Walter C. Cunningham** 962 (6) 590-6505
E-mail: cunninghamwc@state.gov Fax: 962 (6) 592-0159
Information Program Officer **John Jackson** 962 (6) 590-6413
Fax: 962 (6) 592-1276
Information Systems Officer **(Vacant)** 962 (6) 590-6244
Information Systems Security Officer **Aaron C. Lassman** 962 (6) 590-6000
E-mail: lassmanac@state.gov
Legal Attaché **John Connell** 962 (6) 590-6413
◇ Management Officer **John M. Kowalski** 962 (6) 590-6036
E-mail: kowalskijm@state.gov
Political Officer **Nikolas Granger** 962 (6) 590-6591
E-mail: grangerne@state.gov
Public Affairs Officer **Adrienne B. Nutzman** 962 (6) 590-6578
E-mail: nutzmanab@state.gov
Education: Wheaton (IL) 1995 BA; Florida State 1996 MIA
Regional Security Officer **Paul R. Houston** 962 (6) 590-6555
E-mail: houstonpr@state.gov

Agency for International Development [Jordan]
American Embassy - Amman, Jordan, P.O. Box 354, Amman, 11118, Jordan
Mail: American Embassy - Amman, Jordan, Unit #70206, APO, AE 09892-0206
Tel: 962 (6) 590-6000 Fax: 962 (6) 592-0143
Internet: www.usaid.gov/jordan

◇ Mission Director **Jim Barnhart, Jr.** 962 (6) 590-6000
E-mail: jbarnhart@usaid.gov
Education: Furman 1985 BA; Johns Hopkins MA; Georgia State PhD

★ Presidential Appointment Requiring Senate Confirmation ☆ Presidential Appointment □ Schedule C Appointment ◇ Career Senior Foreign Service Appointment
● Career Senior Executive Service (SES) Appointment ○ Non-Career Senior Executive Service (SES) Appointment ■ Postal Career Executive Service

Commercial Section (Foreign Commercial Service) [Jordan]
Commercial Section, American Embassy, Unit 70200, Box 15,
APO, AE 09892-0200
Tel: 962 (6) 590-6632 Fax: 962 (6) 592-0146
E-mail: office.amman@trade.gov Internet: export.gov/jordan

Commercial Officer **Fred W. Aziz** 962 (6) 590-6632
E-mail: fred.aziz@trade.gov
Senior Commercial Specialist **Muna Farkouh** 962 (6) 590-6057
E-mail: muna.farkouh@trade.gov
Commercial Specialist **Ala'a Qaqish** 962 (6) 590-6053
E-mail: ala.qaqish@trade.gov

Office of the Defense Attaché [Jordan]
American Embassy - Amman, Jordan, P.O. Box 354, Amman, 11118, Jordan
Mail: American Embassy - Amman, Jordan,
DAO, Unit 70207, APO, AE 09892-0207
Tel: 962 (6) 590-6646 Fax: 962 (6) 592-0160

Defense Attaché **COL Richard J. Quirk USA** 962 (6) 590-6647
E-mail: quirkrj@state.gov

Peace Corps [Jordan]
American Embassy - Amman, Jordan, P.O. Box 354, Amman, 11118, Jordan
Mail: American Embassy - Amman, Jordan,
Peace Corps, APO, AE 09892-0200
Tel: 962 (6) 461-9144 Fax: 962 (6) 461-9351
Internet: www.peacecorps.gov/jordan
Note: In March 2015, the Peace Corps suspended its volunteer activities in Jordan.

Country Director **(Vacant)** 962 (6) 461-9144

U.S. Embassy in Kuwait

Bayan, Area 14, Al-Masjed Al-Aqsa Street,
P.O. Box 77, Safat, 13001 Kuwait City, Kuwait
Tel: 965 2259-1001 Fax: 965 2538-0282 Internet: kw.usembassy.gov

Office of the U.S. Ambassador to Kuwait

American Embassy - Kuwait City, Kuwait,
Bayan, Area 14 Al-Masjed Al-Aqsa Street,
P.O. Box 77, Safat, 13001 Kuwait City, Kuwait
Mail: American Embassy - Kuwait City, Kuwait, Unit 69000,
APO, AE 09880-9000
E-mail: paskuwaitm@state.gov

★ Ambassador
Ambassador Lawrence Robert "Larry" Silverman ... 965 2539-5307
E-mail: silvermanlr@state.gov
Education: Duke 1980 MA
Office Management Specialist to the Ambassador
Carol A. Bourne 965 2539-5307
E-mail: bourneca2@state.gov

◇ Deputy Chief of Mission **Larry L. Memmott** 965 2539-5307
E-mail: memmottll@state.gov
Education: Utah BA
Office Management Specialist to the Deputy Chief of Mission **Giovanni Missmar** 965 2539-5307
E-mail: MissmarG@state.gov

Community Liaison Officer **Nicole B. Jubeck** 965 2259-1001
Consular Officer **Timothy F. Ponce** 965 2539-5307
E-mail: poncetf@state.gov Fax: 965 539-2484
Economic Officer **Joseph M. "Joe" Ripley** 965 2539-5307
E-mail: ripleyjm@state.gov
Financial Management Officer **(Vacant)** 965 2539-5307
General Services Officer **Craig Coombs** 965 2539-5307
E-mail: coombsgc@state.gov Fax: 965 539-0974
Information Management Officer (Acting)
Robert S. Hong 965 2539-5307
E-mail: hongrs@state.gov
Information Program Officer **Stephen A. Lavarn** 965 2259-1001
E-mail: lavarnsa@state.gov
Information Systems Officer **Robert S. Hong** 965 2259-1001
E-mail: hongrs@state.gov
Information Systems Security Officer **Drake O. Crane** 965 2259-1001

Office of the U.S. Ambassador to Kuwait *(continued)*

Legal Attaché **Rebekah J. Tuthill** 965 2259-1001
E-mail: tuthillrj@state.gov
Management Officer **Kevin A. Weishar** 965 2539-5307
E-mail: weisharka2@state.gov
Military Liaison Officer **David P. San Clemente** 965 2539-5307
E-mail: sanclemented@state.gov
Political Officer **Daniel F. McNicholas** 965 2539-5307
E-mail: mcnicholasdf@state.gov
Public Affairs Officer **Ravi S. Candadai** 965 2539-5307
E-mail: candadairs@state.gov Fax: 965 538-0294
Regional Security Officer **Robert B. Kimbrough** 965 2539-5307
E-mail: kimbroughrb@state.gov

Agricultural Section (Foreign Agricultural Service) (Resident in Dubai) [Kuwait]
World Trade Center, Agricultural Trade Office - Dubai, U.A.E.,
P.O. Box 9343, 21st Floor, Dubai, United Arab Emirates
Mail: U.S. Consulate General - Dubai, U.A.E.,
Department of State, Washington, DC 20521-6020
Tel: 971 (4) 309-4902 Fax: 971 (4) 354-7279 E-mail: atodubai@state.gov

Counselor **Kurt F. Seifarth** 971 (4) 309-4902

Commercial Section (Foreign Commercial Service) [Kuwait]
U.S. Commercial Service, Al-Masjeed Al-Aqsa Street, Plot 14, Block14,
Bayan, Kuwait City, Kuwait
Mail: U.S. Commercial Service, Unit 69000, Box 10,
APO, AE 09880-9000
Tel: 965 2259-1014 Fax: 965 2259-1271
E-mail: office.kuwaitcity@trade.gov Internet: export.gov/kuwait

Senior Commercial Officer **Jeffrey "Jeff" Hamilton** 965 2259-1354
E-mail: jeff.hamilton@trade.gov

Department of Homeland Security - U.S. Customs and Border Protection [Kuwait]
American Embassy - Kuwait City, Kuwait,
Bayan, Area 14, Al-Masjed Al-Aqsa Street,
P.O. Box 77, Safat, 13001 Kuwait City, Kuwait
Mail: American Embassy - Kuwait City, Kuwait, Unit 69000,
APO, AE 09880-9000
Tel: 965 2539-5307

Customs Attaché **Erick Osteen** 965 2539-5307
E-mail: osteenea@state.gov

Federal Aviation Administration (Resident in Abu Dhabi) [Kuwait]
American Embassy - Abu Dhabi, United Arab Emirates, Al-Sudan Street,
P.O. Box 4009, Abu Dhabi, United Arab Emirates
Mail: American Embassy - Abu Dhabi, United Arab Emirates,
6010 Abu Dhabi Place, Washington, DC 20521-6010
Fax: 971 (2) 414-2588

FAA Senior Representative **Robert Roxbrough** 971 (2) 414-2438

International Broadcasting Bureau [Kuwait]
American Embassy - Kuwait City, Kuwait,
Bayan, Area 14, Al-Masjed Al-Aqsa Street,
P.O. Box 77, Safat, 13001 Kuwait City, Kuwait
Mail: American Embassy - Kuwait City, Kuwait, Unit 69000,
APO, AE 09880-9000
Tel: 965 601-5071 Fax: 965 601-5072

Station Manager **Gunter Schwabe** 965 2456-2752
E-mail: gschwabe@bbg.gov

★ Presidential Appointment Requiring Senate Confirmation ☆ Presidential Appointment □ Schedule C Appointment ◇ Career Senior Foreign Service Appointment
● Career Senior Executive Service (SES) Appointment ○ Non-Career Senior Executive Service (SES) Appointment ■ Postal Career Executive Service

U.S. Embassy in Lebanon

P.O. Box 70-840 Antelias, Beirut, Lebanon
Tel: 961 (4) 542-600 Fax: 961 (4) 544-136 Internet: lb.usembassy.gov

Office of the U.S. Ambassador to Lebanon

American Embassy - Antelias, P.O. Box 70-840 Antelias, Beirut, Lebanon
Mail: American Embassy - Beirut, 6070 Beirut Place,
Washington, DC 20521-6070

★ Ambassador
Ambassador Elizabeth Holzhall Richard 961 (4) 542-600
E-mail: richardeh2@state.gov
Education: Southern Methodist BA, JD; National War Col MS
Office Management Specialist to the Ambassador
Janice "Jan" Forman 961 (4) 542-600
◇ Deputy Chief of Mission **Edward "Ed" White** 961 (4) 542-600
Office Management Specialist to the Deputy Chief of Mission **(Vacant)** 961 (4) 542-600
Community Liaison Officer **Ashley Melichar** 961 (4) 542-600
Consular Chief **Rosemary R. Macray** 961 (4) 504-037
E-mail: MacrayRR@state.gov
Education: Florida BS; Oklahoma MA
Economic Officer **Jennifer T. Mergy** 961 (4) 542-600
E-mail: mergyj@state.gov
Economic/Commercial Officer **(Vacant)** 961 (4) 544-860
Financial Management Officer **Rebecca Edwards** 961 (4) 542-600
General Services Officer **Carolee Williamson** 961 (4) 543-600
Information Management Officer **Leul Fassil** 961 (4) 543-600
Information Systems Officer **(Vacant)** 961 (4) 542-600
Information Systems Security Officer **Mam Jobe** 961 (4) 542-600
Legal Attaché **Anish Shukla** 961 (4) 542-600
Management Officer **Michelle N. Ward** 961 (4) 542-600
E-mail: wardmn2@state.gov Fax: 961 (4) 544-604
Narcotics Affairs Officer **Wesley W. Robertson** 961 (4) 542-600
Political Officer **(Vacant)** 961 (4) 542-600
Political/Economic Officer **Hans F. Wechsel** 961 (4) 542-600
E-mail: wechselhf@state.gov
Public Affairs Officer **Ellen Peterson** 961 (4) 542-600
E-mail: petersonet2@state.gov Fax: 961 (4) 544-861
Regional Security Officer **David C. Hartinger** 961 (4) 542-600
E-mail: hartingerd@state.gov

Agency for International Development [Lebanon]

American Embassy, Awkar, Lebanon
Mail: American Embassy - Beirut, 6070 Beirut Place,
Washington, DC 20521-6070
Tel: 961 (4) 542-600 Fax: 961 (4) 544-254 E-mail: usaidbeirut@state.gov
Internet: www.usaid.gov/lebanon

◇ Mission Director **Anne Elizabeth Patterson** 961 (4) 542-600
E-mail: apatterson@usaid.gov

Agricultural Section (Foreign Agricultural Service) (Resident in Cairo) [Lebanon]

Eight Kamal El Din Salah Street, Garden City, Cairo, Egypt
Mail: American Embassy - Cairo, Egypt, Unit 64900,
APO, AE 09839-4900
Tel: 20 (2) 2797-2388 Fax: 20 (2) 2796-3989
E-mail: agcairo@fas.usda.gov

◇ Agricultural Counselor **Ali Abdi** 20 (2) 2797-2388
E-mail: Ali.Abdi@fas.usda.gov
Senior Attaché **Mariano Beillard** 20 (2) 2797-2388

Federal Aviation Administration (Resident in Abu Dhabi) [Lebanon]

American Embassy/FAA, Embassies District (Airport Road) Street #4,
09825 Abu Dhabi, United Arab Emirates
PSC 82, Box 002, AEU-BRU Abu Dhabi, United Arab Emirates
Fax: 971 (2) 414-2588

FAA Senior Representative **Robert Roxbrough** 971 (2) 414-2438

Office of Defense Attaché [Lebanon]

American Embassy - Antelias, Beirut, Lebanon
Mail: American Embassy - Beirut, 6070 Beirut Place,
Washington, DC 20521-6070
Tel: 961 (4) 543-600 Fax: 961 (4) 544-136

Defense Attaché **COL Daniel Mouton USA** 961 (4) 543-600
E-mail: usdaobeirut@state.gov

Office of Defense Cooperation [Lebanon]

American Embassy, Antelias, P.O. Box 70-840, Beirut, Lebanon
Mail: American Embassy - Beirut, Department of State,
6070 Beirut Place, Washington, DC 20521-6070
Tel: 961 (4) 543-600

Military Liaison Officer/Defense Cooperation Office Chief **Phil Messer** 961 (4) 542-600

U.S. Embassy in Libya

Zone Nord-Est Les Berges du Lac, 1053 Tunis, Tunisia
Tel: 216 7110-7216 Fax: 216 7110-7090 Internet: ly.usembassy.gov
Note: In 2015, the U.S. Embassy in Tripoli temporarily relocated to Tunis, Tunisia and is known as the "Libya External Office."

Office of the U.S. Ambassador to Libya

E-mail: tripolipao@state.gov (General Information and Public Affairs)

★ Ambassador **(Vacant)** 216 7110-7216
Chargé d' Affaires **Donald A. Blome** 216 7110-7216
Note: On August 16, 2018, President Donald J. Trump nominated Donald Blome to be Ambassador to Tunisia. This nomination is pending in the Senate.
E-mail: BlomeDA@state.gov
Education: Michigan BA, JD
Office Management Specialist to the Ambassador
Christine M. Marks 216 7110-7216
E-mail: markscm@state.gov
Deputy Chief of Mission **Natalie Ashton Baker** 216 7110-7216
Consular Officer **(Vacant)** 216 7110-7216
Community Liaison Officer **(Vacant)** 216 7110-7216
Economic Officer **Ryan Steffenhagen** 216 7110-7216
Financial Management Officer **(Vacant)** 216 7110-7216
General Services Officer **(Vacant)** 216 7110-7216
Information Management Officer **Roger W. Powe** 216 7110-7216
E-mail: powerw@state.gov
Information Systems Officer **(Vacant)** 216 7110-7216
Legal Attaché **Michael L. Wagner** 216 7110-7216
Management Officer **Joy Yamamura** 216 7110-7216
Political/Economic Officer **Fareed A. Abdullah** 216 7110-7216
E-mail: abdullahfa@state.gov
Political Officer **Birgitta S. Hoggren** 216 7110-7216
Public Affairs Officer **Allison J. Lee** 216 7110-7216
Regional Security Officer **Shannon S. Conrad** 216 7110-7216
E-mail: conradss@state.gov

Office of the Defense Attaché [Libya]

Defense Attaché **(Vacant)** 216 7110-7216

U.S. Embassy in Morocco

Km 5.7 Avenue Mohammed VI, 10170 Rabat, Morocco
Tel: 212 (53) 7-637-200 Fax: 212 (53) 7-637-201
Internet: ma.usembassy.gov

Office of the U.S. Ambassador to Morocco

American Embassy - Rabat, Morocco, Km 5.7 Avenue Mohammed VI, 10170 Rabat, Morocco
Mail: American Embassy - Rabat, Morocco,
PSC 74, APO, AE 09718
Tel: 212 (53) 7-637-200 Fax: 212 (53) 7-637-201
E-mail: ircrabat@usembassy.ma Internet: ma.usembassy.gov

★ Ambassador-Designate **David T. Fischer** 212 (53) 7-637-200
Education: Parsons Col BA
◇ Chargé d'Affaires **Stephanie A. Miley** 212 (53) 7-637-200
E-mail: mileysa@state.gov

★ Presidential Appointment Requiring Senate Confirmation ☆ Presidential Appointment ☐ Schedule C Appointment ◇ Career Senior Foreign Service Appointment
● Career Senior Executive Service (SES) Appointment ○ Non-Career Senior Executive Service (SES) Appointment ■ Postal Career Executive Service

Office of the U.S. Ambassador to Morocco *(continued)*

Office Management Specialist to the Ambassador
Cheryl L. Helm 212 (53) 7-637-200
E-mail: helmcl@state.gov
Deputy Chief of Mission (Acting) **Manu Bhalla** 212 (53) 7-637-200
E-mail: bhallam@state.gov
Office Management Specialist to the Deputy Chief of Mission **(Vacant)** 212 (53) 7-637-200
Consul General **(Vacant)** 212 (53) 7-637-200
Community Liaison Officer **(Vacant)** 212 (53) 7-637-200
Cultural Affairs Officer **Erica N. Thibault** 212 (53) 7-637-200
Economic/Commercial Officer **April Cohen** 212 (53) 7-637-200
E-mail: cohena@state.gov
Equal Employment Opportunity Officer
Stephanie Hutchison 212 (53) 7-637-200
Financial Management Officer **Newman Waters** 212 (53) 7-637-200
General Services Officer **Patrick D. Fenning** 212 (53) 7-637-200
E-mail: fenningpd@state.gov
Human Resources Officer **Melissa Bruni** 212 (53) 7-637-200
Information Management Officer
Jonathan E. Daves-Brody 212 (53) 7-637-200
E-mail: davesbrodyje@state.gov
Information Program Officer **James E. Forrest** 212 (53) 7-637-200
Information Systems Officer **Anis Bayna** 212 (53) 7-637-200
Information Systems Security Officer **(Vacant)** 212 (53) 7-637-200
Legal Attache **Timothy Stone** 212 (53) 7-637-200
Regional Attache, Department of Homeland Security **Robert McLaughlin** 212 (53) 7-637-200
Management Officer **Daley C. O'Neil** 212 (53) 7-63-7568
E-mail: o'neildc@state.gov
Political Officer **Andrew T. MacDonald** 212 (53) 7-637-200
E-mail: macdonaldat@state.gov
Education: Davidson 2003 BA; Georgetown 2011 MBA
Public Affairs Officer **Brian J. George** 212 (53) 7-637-200
E-mail: georgebj@state.gov Fax: 212 (53) 766-82-84
Regional Security Officer **John M. Lagasse** 212 (53) 7-637-200
E-mail: lagassejm@state.gov
Narcotics Affairs Officer **Thomas E. Brown** 212 (53) 7-637-200

Agency for International Development [Morocco]
American Embassy - Rabat, Morocco, PSC 74, APO, AE 09718
Tel: 212 (53) 763-20-00 Fax: 212 (53) 37 63 20
Internet: https://www.usaid.gov/morocco
Mission Director **Daniel Cabet** 212 (53) 763-20-00
E-mail: dcabet@usaid.gov

Agricultural Section (Foreign Agricultural Service) [Morocco]
American Embassy - Rabat, Morocco, 2 Avenue de Marrakech, Rabat, Morocco
Mail: American Embassy - Rabat, Morocco, PSC 74, APO, AE 09718
Tel: 212 (53) 763-7505 Fax: 212 (53) 776-54-93
E-mail: agrabat@fas.usda.gov
Agricultural Attaché **Morgan Haas** 212 (53) 763-7505

Federal Aviation Administration (Resident in Moscow) [Morocco]
FAA Representative **Andrew McKee** 7 (495) 728-5125

Office of Defense Cooperation [Morocco]
American Embassy - Rabat, Morocco, 2 Avenue de Marrakech, Rabat, Morocco
Mail: American Embassy - Rabat, Morocco, PSC 74, APO, AE 09718
Defense Cooperation Officer **Greg R. Mitchell** 212 (53) 7-637-200

Office of the Defense Attaché [Morocco]
American Embassy - Rabat, Morocco, 2 Avenue de Marrakech, Rabat, Morocco
Mail: American Embassy - Rabat, Morocco, PSC 74, APO, AE 09718
Tel: 212 (53) 776-22-65 Fax: 212 (53) 776-56-61
Defense Attaché **Andrew Hamann** 212 (53) 776-22-65

Peace Corps [Morocco]
1 Zankat Benzerte, Rabat, Morocco
Mail: American Embassy - Rabat, Morocco, PSC 74, APO, AE 09718
Fax: 212 (53) 768-37-99 Internet: www.peacecorps.gov/morocco
Director **Steven Leo "Steve" Driehaus** 212 (53) 768-37-80
E-mail: sdriehaus@peacecorps.gov
Education: Miami U (OH) 1988 BA; Indiana 1995 MPA

Casablanca Consulate General
U.S. Consulate General - Casablanca, Morocco, 8 Boulevard Moulay Youssef, Casablanca, Morocco
Mail: U.S. Consulate General - Casablanca, PSC 74, Box 24, APO, AE 09718
Tel: 212 (52) 2-64-20-00 Fax: 212 (52) 2-20-41-27
Consul General **Jennifer L. Rasamimanana** 212 (52) 2-64-20-00
Office Management Specialist to the Consul General **Melissa L. McCreery** 212 (52) 2-64-20-00
E-mail: mccreeryml@state.gov
Consular Officer **John Edward Caveness** 212 (52) 2-64-20-00
E-mail: cavenessje@state.gov
Community Liaison Officer **(Vacant)** 212 (52) 2-64-20-00
Economic Officer **Ashton Robison** 212 (52) 2-64-20-00
E-mail: robisonae@state.gov
Education: St Edward's 2013 BA; American U 2015 MA
Equal Employment Opportunity Officer **(Vacant)** 212 (52) 2-64-20-00
General Services Officer **Bernard D. Coffey** 212 (52) 2-64-20-00
E-mail: coffeybd@state.gov
Information Program Officer **Adnan F. Blaibel** 212 (52) 2-64-20-00
E-mail: blaibelaf@state.gov
Labor Officer **Richard A. "Andy" Allen** 212 (52) 2-64-20-00
Management Officer **Vincent Mut-Tracy** 212 (52) 2-64-20-00
Political Officer **Richard A. "Andy" Allen** 212 (52) 2-64-20-00
Public Affairs Officer **Stephen C. Kochuba** 212 (52) 2-22-14-60
Dar America 10 Place Bel Air, Casablanca, Morocco
E-mail: kochubasc@state.gov
E-mail: daramerica@state.gov
Regional Security Officer
Christopher T. "Chris" O'Brien 212 (52) 2-64-20-00
E-mail: obrienct@state.gov

Commercial Section (Foreign Commercial Service) [Morocco]
U.S. Consulate General - Casablanca, Morocco, 8 Blvd. Moulay Youssef, Casablanca, Morocco
Mail: U.S. Consulate General - Casablanca, PSC 74, Box 24, APO, AE 09718
Tel: 212 522-64-20-23 Fax: 212 522-22-02-59
E-mail: office.casablanca@trade.gov Internet: export.gov/morocco
Commercial Counselor **Nathalie Scharf** 212 522-64-21-29
E-mail: Nathalie.Scharf@trade.gov
Education: Cal State (Northridge) 1991 BA; Washburn 1995 JD; Tulane 1996 MCL

U.S. Embassy in Oman
Jamiat Al Dowal Al Arabiya, Shatti Al Qurum, Muscat, Oman
Tel: 968 2464-3400 Fax: 968 2464-3740 Internet: om.usembassy.gov

Office of the U.S. Ambassador to Oman
Building 32, Jamiat Al Dowal Al Arabiya, Shatti Al Qurum, Muscat, Oman
Mail: Unit 73000, APO, AE 09890-3000
U.S. Embassy Oman - Postal Code No. 115, Madinat Al Sultan Q, Muscat, Oman
★ Ambassador **Ambassador Marc Jonathan Sievers** 968 2464-3400
E-mail: sieversmj@state.gov Fax: 968 2469-3885
Education: Utah 1978 BA; Columbia 1980 MIA
Office Management Specialist to the Ambassador
Stephen Rogerson 968 2464-3400
E-mail: rogersonsh@state.gov
Deputy Chief of Mission **Stephanie Lynne Hallett** 968 2464-3400
E-mail: hallettsl@state.gov

(continued on next page)

★ Presidential Appointment Requiring Senate Confirmation ☆ Presidential Appointment □ Schedule C Appointment ◇ Career Senior Foreign Service Appointment
● Career Senior Executive Service (SES) Appointment ○ Non-Career Senior Executive Service (SES) Appointment ■ Postal Career Executive Service

DEPARTMENTS

Office of the U.S. Ambassador to Oman *(continued)*

Office Management Specialist to the Deputy Chief of Mission **Michele Balthazaar** 968 2464-3400
E-mail: BalthazaarMS@state.gov
Community Liaison Officer **Becky Henderson** 968 2464-3400
E-mail: clomuscat@state.gov
Consular Officer **Sean Hanifen** 968 2464-3400
E-mail: hanifensm@state.gov
Financial Management Officer **Benjamin Bohman** 968 2464-3400
E-mail: BohmanB@state.gov
General Services Officer **Keith Thrasher** 968 2464-3689
E-mail: thrasherka@state.gov Fax: 968 2469-9778
Human Resources Officer **Hilde L. Pearson** 968 2464-3400
E-mail: PearsonHL@state.gov
Education: Xavier (OH) 1992 BA
Information Management Officer **Bruce Chaplin** 968 2464-3400
E-mail: chaplinbr@state.gov
Information Program Officer **Lyle Howard** 968 2464-3400
E-mail: howardlj@state.gov
Information Systems Officer **Manuel Dipre** 968 2464-3400
E-mail: dipremc@state.gov
Legal Attaché **Craig Rose** 968 2464-3400
E-mail: rosecp@state.gov
Management Officer **Judes E. DeBaere** 968 2464-3400
E-mail: debaereje@state.gov
Political/Military Officer **Cooper Wimmer** 968 2464-3400
E-mail: wimmercj@state.gov
Political/Economic Officer **Jamal Al-Mussawi** 968 2464-3413
E-mail: al-mussawija@state.gov
Public Affairs Officer
Michelle Yvette Outlaw .... 968 2464-3400 ext. 3630
E-mail: OutlawMY@state.gov Fax: 968 2464-3777
Regional Security Officer **David Heddleston** 968 2464-3400
E-mail: heddlestondm@state.gov
Political Officer **Kabeer Parwani** 968 2464-3400
E-mail: ParwaniK@state.gov

Agricultural Section (Foreign Agricultural Service) (Resident in Dubai) [Oman]
American Consulate General, Al Seef Road - Bur Dubai, Dubai, United Arab Emirates
Mail: U.S. Consulate General - Dubai, U.A.E., Department of State, Washington, DC 20521-6020
Tel: 971 (4) 309-4902 Fax: 971 (4) 354-7279 E-mail: atodubai@state.gov

Counselor **Kurt F. Seifarth** .... 971 (4) 309-4000 ext. 4177

Commercial Section (Foreign Commercial Service) [Oman]
American Embassy - Muscat, Oman, P.O. Box 202, Code No. 115, Medinat Al-Sultan Qaboos, Muscat, Oman
Mail: American Embassy - Muscat, Oman, Unit 73000, APO, AE 09890-3000
Tel: 968 24643-400 Fax: 968 24604-316
E-mail: muscatcommercial@state.gov Internet: export.gov/oman

Economic/Commercial Officer
Andrew "Andy" Barwig 968 24643-400
E-mail: BarwigAW@state.gov
Commercial Assistant **Raji Daniel** 968 2464-3784
E-mail: danielr@state.gov Fax: 968 2469-3432

Federal Aviation Administration (Resident in Abu Dhabi) [Oman]
American Embassy - Abu Dhabi, United Arab Emirates, Al-Sudan Street, P.O. Box 4009, Abu Dhabi, United Arab Emirates
Mail: American Embassy - Abu Dhabi, United Arab Emirates, 6010 Abu Dhabi Place, Washington, DC 20521-6010
Fax: 971 (2) 414-2588

FAA Senior Representative **Robert Roxbrough** 971 (2) 414-2438

Office of the Defense Attaché [Oman]
American Embassy - Muscat, Oman, P.O. Box 202, Code No. 115, Medinat Qaboos, Muscat, Oman
Mail: American Embassy - Muscat, Oman, Unit 73000, APO, AE 09890-3000
Tel: 968 24643-400 Fax: 968 24699-779

Defense Attaché **Eric Larson** 968 2464-3400
E-mail: larsonej@state.gov

U.S. Embassy in Qatar

Al-Luqta District, 22nd February Street, Doha, Qatar
Tel: 974 4496-6000 Fax: 974 4488-4298 Internet: qa.usembassy.gov

Office of the U.S. Ambassador to Qatar
American Embassy - Doha, Qatar, Al-Luqta District, 22nd February Street, Doha, Qatar
Mail: American Embassy - Doha, Qatar, Department of State, 6130 Doha Place, Washington, DC 20521-6130
P.O. Box 2399, Doha, Qatar
E-mail: pasdoha@state.gov

★ Ambassador-Designate
Ambassador Mary Catherine "Molly" Phee 974 4496-6000
Education: Indiana 1985 BA; Fletcher Law & Diplomacy 1989 MALD
◇ Chargé d'Affaires **William Kevin Grant** 974 4496-6000
E-mail: grantwk@state.gov
Education: Pennsylvania 1974 BA
Office Management Specialist to the Ambassador
(Vacant) 974 4496-6000
◇ Deputy Chief of Mission **Phillip R. Nelson** 974 4496-6000
E-mail: nelsonpr@state.gov
Office Management Specialist to the Deputy Chief of Mission **Elizabeth C. Marker** 974 4496-6000
E-mail: markerec@state.gov
Consular Officer **John J. Ibarra** 974 4496-6000
E-mail: ibarraj@state.gov Fax: 974 4488-4176
Community Liaison Officer **Jennifer Kaaoush** 974 4496-6000
Education: Monterey Peninsula 2014 ABA; American Public 2016 BBA; Cabrillo 2009 AA
Economic Officer **(Vacant)** 974 4496-6000
Financial Management Officer (Acting) **Ronald Dailey** ... 974 4496-6000
E-mail: daileyr@state.gov
General Services Officer **Benjamin Bandoh** 974 4496-6000
Information Management Officer **Jeffrey Yolangco** 974 4496-6000
Information Program Officer
Richard W. Middleton CISSP, CISM 974 4496-6000
E-mail: middletonrw@state.gov
Education: South Carolina 1996 BA
Information Systems Officer **(Vacant)** 974 4496-6000
Information Systems Security Officer
Richard W. Middleton CISSP, CISM 974 4496-6000
E-mail: middletonrw@state.gov
Education: South Carolina 1996 BA
Legal Attaché **Maher Dimachkie** 974 4496-6000
Management Officer **Margaret C. Sula** 974 4496-6000
E-mail: sulamc2@state.gov
Political Affairs Officer **(Vacant)** 974 4496-6000
Political/Economic Officer **Thomas M. Rosenberger** 974 4496-6000
Public Affairs Officer **Carissa Gonzales** 974 4496-6000
Fax: 974 4488-4173
Regional Security Officer **Andrew G. Simpson** 974 4496-6000

Agricultural Section (Foreign Agricultural Service) (Resident in Dubai) [Qatar]
Agricultural Trade Office - Dubai, U.A.E. World Trade Center, P.O. Box 9343, 21st Floor, Dubai, United Arab Emirates
Mail: U.S. Consulate General - Dubai, U.A.E., Department of State, Washington, DC 20521-6020
Tel: 971 (4) 309-4902 Fax: 971 (4) 354-7279
E-mail: atodubai@fas.usda.gov E-mail: atodubai@state.gov

Counselor **Kurt F. Seifarth** .... 971 (4) 309-4902 ext. 4177
E-mail: kurt.seifarth@fas.usda.gov

★ Presidential Appointment Requiring Senate Confirmation ☆ Presidential Appointment ☐ Schedule C Appointment ◇ Career Senior Foreign Service Appointment
● Career Senior Executive Service (SES) Appointment ○ Non-Career Senior Executive Service (SES) Appointment ■ Postal Career Executive Service

Commercial Service Section [Qatar]
American Embassy - Doha, Qatar, Al-Luqta District,
22nd February Street, Doha, Qatar
Mail: American Embassy - Doha, Qatar, Department of State,
6130 Doha Place, Washington, DC 20521-6130
P.O. Box 2399, Doha, Qatar
Tel: 974 4496 6000 Fax: 974 4488-4163 Internet: export.gov/qatar

Senior Commercial Officer **Ilona Shtrom** 974 4496-6739
E-mail: ilona.shtrom@trade.gov

Federal Aviation Administration (Resident in Abu Dhabi) [Qatar]
American Embassy - Doha, Qatar, Al-Luqta District,
22nd February Street, Doha, Qatar
Tel: 971 (2) 41-4142-438 Fax: 971 (2) 41-4142-588

FAA Senior Representative **Robert Roxbrough** 971 (2) 414-2438

Office of the Defense Attaché [Qatar]
American Embassy - Doha, Qatar, Al-Luqta District,
22nd February Street, Doha, Qatar
Mail: American Embassy - Doha, Qatar, Department of State,
6130 Doha Place, Washington, DC 20521-6130
Fax: 974 4488-4298

Defense Attaché **(Vacant)** 974 4496-6000

U.S. Embassy in Saudi Arabia

Collector Road M, Riyadh Diplomatic Quarter, 11693 Riyadh,
Saudi Arabia
Tel: 966 (11) 488-3800 Tel: 966 (11) 488-7360
Internet: sa.usembassy.gov

Office of the U.S. Ambassador to Saudi Arabia

American Embassy - Riyadh, Saudi Arabia, Collector Road M,
Riyadh Diplomatic Quarter, 11693 Riyadh, Saudi Arabia
Mail: American Embassy, Unit 61307, APO, AE 09803-1307
Tel: 966 (11) 488-3800 Fax: 966 (11) 488-7360
Internet: sa.usembassy.gov

★ Ambassador-Designate
GEN John P. Abizaid USA (Ret) 966 (11) 488-3800
Education: West Point 1973 BS; Harvard 1981 AM

◇ Chargé d'Affaires **Christopher P. "Chris" Henzel** 966 (11) 488-3800
Note: On September 28, 2018, President Donald J. Trump nominated Christopher Henzel to be Ambassador to Yemen. This nomination is pending in the Senate.
E-mail: henzelcp@state.gov
Education: Col Holy Cross BA; National War Col MS

Office Management Specialist to the Ambassador
(Vacant) 966 (11) 488-3800

◇ Deputy Chief of Mission **Martina A. Strong** 966 (11) 488-3800
E-mail: strongma@state.gov

Office Management Specialist to the Deputy Chief of Mission **Cristina Moreau** 966 (11) 488-3800
E-mail: MoreauCG@state.gov

Community Liaison Officer **Brigitte Campbell** 966 (11) 488-3800
E-mail: campbellb@state.gov

◇ Consul General **Sean Murphy** 966 (11) 488-3800
Education: McGill (Canada) 1986 MA

◇ Economic Officer **(Vacant)** 966 (11) 488-3800

Equal Employment Opportunity Officer
David E. Merrell 966 (11) 488-3800

Facilities Management Officer **Jeffrey Lucas** 966 (11) 498-2480

Financial Management Officer **Kim Harmon** 966 (11) 488-3800

Financial Management Officer **R. Shelton Haynie** 966 (11) 488-3800
E-mail: haynier@state.gov

General Services Officer
Douglas L. "Doug" Demaggio 966 (11) 498-2480
E-mail: demaggiodl@state.gov

Human Resources Officer **Dinka Masic** 966 (11) 488-3800
E-mail: MasicD@state.gov

Information Management Officer **Ross Campbell** 966 (11) 488-3800

Information Program Officer **(Vacant)** 966 (11) 488-3800

Information Systems Officer **Stacey L. Hopkins** 966 (11) 435-7006
E-mail: hopkinss@state.gov

Office of the U.S. Ambassador to Saudi Arabia *(continued)*

Information Systems Security Officer
Joseph Brown 966 (11) 435-7006
Education: Columbia Southern 2010 BBA, 2014 MS

Legal Attaché **Terry Parrish** 966 (11) 488-3800

Management Officer **Debra Smoker-Ali** 966 (11) 488-3800
E-mail: SmokerAliDL@state.gov
Education: Purdue 1980 BS

Political Officer **Neil W. Hop** 966 (11) 488-3800
E-mail: hopnw@state.gov

Political/Military Officer **Alexander L. Barrasso** 966 (11) 488-3800
E-mail: BarrassoAL@state.gov

Public Affairs Officer **Brian A. Shott** 966 (11) 488-3800
E-mail: shottba@state.gov Fax: 966 (11) 488-3989

Regional Security Officer **Timothy "Tim" Laas** 966 (11) 488-3800
E-mail: LaasTE@state.gov

Agricultural Section (Foreign Agricultural Service) [Saudi Arabia]
Agricultural Trade Office c/o American Embassy - Riyadh,
Diplomatic Quarter, P.O. 94309, Riyadh, 11693, Saudi Arabia
Mail: Unit 61307, APO, AE 09803-1307
Tel: 966 (11) 482-2197 Fax: 966 (11) 482-4364
E-mail: agriyadh@fas.usda.gov

Attaché **Alan Hallman** 966 (11) 482-2197
E-mail: alan.hallman@fas.usda.gov

Commercial Section (Foreign Commercial Service) [Saudi Arabia]
American Embassy - Riyadh, Saudi Arabia,
P.O. Box 94309, Riyadh, 11693, Saudi Arabia
Mail: American Embassy, Unit 61307, APO, AE 09803-1307
Tel: 966 (11) 488-3800 Fax: 966 (11) 488-3237
E-mail: office.riyadh@trade.gov Internet: www.export.gov/saudiarabia

◇ Senior Commercial Officer
Nasir A. Abbasi .... 966 (11) 488-3800 ext. 4603
E-mail: nasir.abbasi@trade.gov

Department of Homeland Security - U.S. Immigration and Customs Enforcement [Saudi Arabia]

Customs Attaché **George Guzman** 966 (11) 488-3800
E-mail: george.guzman@dhs.gov

Drug Enforcement Administration (Resident in Cairo) [Saudi Arabia]
American Embassy - Cairo, Egypt, 5 Tawfik Diab Street,
Garden City, Cairo, Egypt
Mail: Unit 64900, APO, AE 09839-4900

DEA Officer **Leon M. Palmer** 966 (11) 488-3800
E-mail: palmerlm@state.gov

Office of the Defense Attaché [Saudi Arabia]
American Embassy - Riyadh, Saudi Arabia,
P.O. Box 94309, Riyadh, 11693, Saudi Arabia
Mail: American Embassy, Unit 61307, APO, AE 09803-1307
Tel: 966 (11) 488-3800 Fax: 966 (11) 488-7809

Defense Attaché
COL Ulises "Uli" Calvo USA .... 966 (11) 488-3800 ext. 4683
E-mail: CalvoUV@state.gov

Dhahran Consulate General

U.S. Consulate General - Dhahran, Saudi Arabia,
Between Aramco Headquarters and King Abdulaziz Airbase,
P.O. Box 38955, Dhahran, Saudi Arabia 31942
Mail: U.S. Consulate General - Dhahran, Unit 66803,
APO, AE 09858-6803
Tel: 966 (13) 330-3200 Fax: 966 (13) 330-0464

Consul General **Rachna Sachdeva Korhonen** 966 (13) 330-3200
E-mail: KorhonenRS@state.gov Fax: 966 (13) 330-0464

Office Management Specialist to the Consul General **(Vacant)** 966 (13) 330-3200

Consular Officer **Vito DiPaola** 966 (13) 330-3200
E-mail: DiPaolaVG@state.gov Fax: 966 (11) 330-6816

General Services Officer **Dante Legaspi** 966 (13) 330-3200

Information Program Officer
Michael T. "Mike" Jackson 966 (13) 330-3200

(continued on next page)

★ Presidential Appointment Requiring Senate Confirmation ☆ Presidential Appointment ☐ Schedule C Appointment ◇ Career Senior Foreign Service Appointment
● Career Senior Executive Service (SES) Appointment ○ Non-Career Senior Executive Service (SES) Appointment ■ Postal Career Executive Service

Dhahran Consulate General *(continued)*

Management Officer **Justin Steckley** 966 (13) 330-3200
Political/Economic Officer **Eric C. Williams** 966 (13) 330-3200
Political Officer **(Vacant)** 966 (13) 330-3200
Public Affairs Officer **John Paul Orak** 966 (13) 330-3200
E-mail: orakjp@state.gov
Education: Col Charleston 2003 BA; American U 2005 MIA
Regional Security Officer **Jesse Valdez** 966 (13) 330-3200

Commercial Section (Foreign Commercial Service) [Saudi Arabia]
American Consulate General - Dhahran, Saudi Arabia,
Between Aramco Headquarters and King Abdulaziz Airbase,
P.O. Box 38955, Dhahran, Saudi Arabia 31942
Mail: American Consulate General, Unit 66803, APO, AE 09858-6803
Tel: 966 (13) 330-3200 Fax: 966 (13) 330-2190
E-mail: officedhahran@trade.gov

Principal Commercial Officer **Gary Rand** ... 966 (13) 330-3200 ext. 3014
E-mail: gary.rand@trade.gov

Jeddah Consulate General
U.S. Consulate General - Jeddah Saudi Arabia, Palestine Road,
Ruwais, P.O. Box 149, Jeddah, 21411, Saudi Arabia
Mail: U.S. Consulate General, Unit 62112, APO, AE 09811-2112
Tel: 966 (12) 667-0080 Fax: 966 (12) 669-3074

◇ Consul General **Ryan M. Gliha** 966 (13) 667-0080
E-mail: GlihaRM@state.gov Fax: 966 (12) 669-2991
Education: Arizona State 1998 BA;
Pennsylvania 2002 MA
Office Management Specialist to the Consul
General **Pablo J. Paganini** 966 (12) 667-0080
E-mail: paganinipj@state.gov
Education: Montgomery Col 2001 AA
Consul Officer
William Johann "Johann" Schmonsees 966 (12) 667-0080
E-mail: schmonseeswj@state.gov Fax: 966 (12) 669-3078
Political and Economic Officer **Paul Loh** 966 (12) 667-0080
E-mail: lohpa@state.gov
General Services Officer
Christopher C. "Chris" Clemmens 966 (12) 691-0192
E-mail: clemmenscc@state.gov Fax: 966 (12) 682-1452
Information Program Officer **Farakh Khan** 966 (12) 488-3800
Information Systems Security Officer
Michael Sanders 966 (12) 488-3800
Management Officer **Michael L. Longhauser** 966 (12) 667-0080
E-mail: LonghauserML@state.gov
Political Officer **(Vacant)** 966 (12) 667-0080
Public Affairs Officer **Angie C. Smith** 966 (12) 667-0080
E-mail: smithac@state.gov Fax: 966 (12) 660-6367
Education: Chicago 2000 MA
Press Officer and Spokesperson
Gledisa Sanxhaku 966 (12) 667-0080
E-mail: sanxhakug@state.gov
Education: Pennsylvania 2012 BA, 2014 MPA
Regional Security Officer **Kevin O'Connor** 966 (12) 667-0080

Commercial Section (Foreign Commercial Service) [Saudi Arabia]
U.S. Commercial Service - Jeddah, Saudi Arabia,
Al-Malik Road, Beautat Business Park,
P.O. Box 149, Jeddah, 21411, Saudi Arabia
Mail: U.S. Consulate General - Jeddah, Unit 62112, APO, AE 09811-2112
Tel: 966 (12) 667-0080 Fax: 966 (12) 664-4148
E-mail: office.jeddah@trade.gov

Principal Commercial Officer
Timothy Cannon .... 966 (12) 667-0080 ext. 4215
E-mail: timothy.cannon@trade.gov

U.S. Embassy in Syria

Abou Roumaneh, Al Mansur Street, #2, P.O. Box 29, Damascus, Syria
Tel: 963 (11) 3391-4444 Fax: 963 (11) 3391-3999
Internet: sy.usembassy.gov

Note: As of February 6, 2012, the Department of State has suspended operations of U.S. Embassy Damascus. All American personnel have departed the country.

Office of the U.S. Ambassador to Syria
American Embassy - Damascus, Syria,
Abou Roumaneh, Al Mansur Street, #2, P.O. Box 29, Damascus, Syria
Mail: American Embassy - Damascus, Syria,
Department of State, Washington, DC 20521-6110

★ Ambassador **(Vacant)** 963 (11) 3391-4444

Federal Aviation Administration (Resident in Abu Dhabi) [Syria]
American Embassy - Abu Dhabi, United Arab Emirates, Al-Sudan Street,
P.O. Box 4009, Abu Dhabi, United Arab Emirates
Mail: American Embassy - Abu Dhabi, United Arab Emirates,
6010 Abu Dhabi Place, Washington, DC 20521-6010
Tel: 971 (2) 414-2438

FAA Senior Representative **Robert Roxbrough** 971 (2) 414-2438

U.S. Embassy in Tunisia

Zone Nord-Est Les Berges du Lac, 1053 Tunis, Tunisia
Tel: 216 71-107-000 Fax: 216 71-107-090 Internet: tn.usembassy.gov

Office of the U.S. Ambassador to Tunisia
American Embassy - Tunis,Tunisia, Zone Nord-Est Les Berges du Lac,
1053 Tunis, Tunisia
Mail: American Embassy - Tunis, Tunisia,
Department of State, Washington, DC 20521-6360
E-mail: tuniswebsitecontact@state.gov

★ Ambassador **Ambassador Daniel H. Rubinstein** 216 71-107-000
E-mail: rubinsteindh@state.gov
Education: UC Berkeley 1989 BA
★ Ambassador-Designate **Donald A. Blome** 216 71-107-000
E-mail: BlomeDA@state.gov
Education: Michigan BA, JD
Office Management Specialist to the Ambassador
Sharon E. Rogers 216 71-107-000
E-mail: rogersse@state.gov
◇ Deputy Chief of Mission
Benjamin W. "Ben" Moeling 216 71-107-000
E-mail: moelingbw@state.gov
Office Management Specialist to the Deputy Chief of
Mission **Maho Fischer** 216 71-107-000
E-mail: fischerm@state.gov
Consular Section Chief **Brooke G. Kidd** 216 71-107-000
E-mail: kiddbg@state.gov
Community Liaison Officer **(Vacant)** 216 71-107-000
Economic Officer **Jonathan S. Fischer** 216 71-107-000
Financial Management Officer **(Vacant)** 216 71-107-000
General Services Officer **Judith C. Spanberger** 216 71-107-000
E-mail: spanbergerjc@state.gov
Information Management Officer
Thomas S. "Tom" Kirk 216 71-107-000
Information Program Officer **Raymond Marcero** 216 71-107-000
Information Systems Officer **Enrico C. Walker** 216 71-107-000
E-mail: walkerec@state.gov
Information Systems Security Officer **Stanley Acosta** ... 216 71-107-000
Legal Attaché **Bruce D. Sweeny** 216 71-107-000
E-mail: sweenybd@state.gov
Management Officer **Catherine Connell** 216 71-107-000
Director of International Narcotics and Law
Enforcement Affairs **Matilda Frances Gawf** 216 71-107-000
E-mail: gawfm@state.gov
Political Officer **Jonathan R. Peccia** 216 71-107-000
E-mail: pecciajr@state.gov
Political/Economic Officer **(Vacant)** 216 71-107-000
Public Affairs Officer **Gabrielle M. Price** 216 71-107-000
E-mail: pricegm@state.gov
Education: Georgetown 1996 BS, BSFS
Cultural Affairs Officer **Sara M. Ferchichi** 216 71-107-000
E-mail: ferchichism@state.gov
Regional Security Officer **Brian K. Wood** 216 71-107-000

★ Presidential Appointment Requiring Senate Confirmation ☆ Presidential Appointment ☐ Schedule C Appointment ◇ Career Senior Foreign Service Appointment
● Career Senior Executive Service (SES) Appointment ○ Non-Career Senior Executive Service (SES) Appointment ■ Postal Career Executive Service

Agency for International Development [Tunisia]
American Embassy - Tunis, Tunisia, Zone Nord-Est Les Berges du Lac, 1053 Tunis, Tunisia
Internet: www.usaid.gov/tunisia

Country Representative **Peter Riley** 216 71-107-000
E-mail: priley@usaid.gov
Education: Harvard 1983 BA; Tufts 1989 MA

Agricultural Section (Foreign Agricultural Service) [Tunisia]
Zone Nord-Est Les Berges du Lac, 1053 Tunis, Tunisia
Tel: 216 71-107-486 ext. 2083 Fax: 216 71-107-101
E-mail: agtunis@fas.usda.gov

Agricultural Attaché (Resident in Rabat)
Morgan Haas . . . . 212 (53) 776-22-65 ext. 2083

American Battle Monuments Commission [Tunisia]
American Embassy - Tunis, Tunisia, Zone Nord-Est des Berges du Lac, Nord de Tunis, 1053 Tunis, Tunisia
Mail: American Embassy - Tunis, Tunisia, Department of State, Washington, DC 20521-6360
Tel: 216 7174-7767 Fax: 216 7174-7051

North Africa American Cemetery and Memorial
Superintendent **Foued Bouaziz** 216 71-747-767

Commercial Section (Foreign Commercial Service) [Tunisia]
American Embassy - Tunis, Tunisia, 144 Avenue de la Liberte, 1002 Tunis, Belvedere, Tunisia
Mail: American Embassy - Tunis, Tunisia, Department of State, Washington, DC 20521-6360
Tel: 216 71-107-000 Fax: 216 71-107-090
Internet: www.export.gov/tunisia

Commercial Attaché **Aysa Miller** 216 71-107-460
Education: U Washington 2004 BBA; Johns Hopkins 2010 MA

Federal Aviation Administration (Resident in Moscow)
FAA Representative **Andrew McKee** 7 (495) 728-5125

Office of Counterterrorism and Countering Violent Extremism [Tunisia]
Zone Nord-Est des Berges du Lac, Nord de Tunis, 1053 Tunis, Tunisia
Tel: 39 71-107-000

Director **(Vacant)** 39 71-107-000

Office of the Defense Attaché [Tunisia]
American Embassy - Tunis, Tunisia, 144 Avenue de la Liberte, 1002 Tunis, Belvedere, Tunisia
Mail: American Embassy - Tunis, Tunisia, Department of State, Washington, DC 20521-6360

Defense Attaché (Acting) **Brian Kurzeja** 216 71-107-000
E-mail: KurzejaB@state.gov
Chief, Office of Security Cooperation
COL R. Reed Anderson USA 216 71-107-000

U.S. Embassy in the United Arab Emirates

Al-Sudan Street, P.O. Box 4009, Abu Dhabi, United Arab Emirates
Tel: 971 (2) 414-2200 Fax: 971 (2) 414-2575 Internet: ae.usembassy.gov

Office of the U.S. Ambassador to the United Arab Emirates

American Embassy - Abu Dhabi, United Arab Emirates, Al-Sudan Street, P.O. Box 4009, Abu Dhabi, United Arab Emirates
Mail: American Embassy - Abu Dhabi, United Arab Emirates, 6010 Abu Dhabi Place, Washington, DC 20521-6010

★ Ambassador-Designate **John Rakolta, Jr.** 971 (2) 414-2200
Education: Marquette 1970 BSCE
◇ Chargé d'Affaires **Steven C. "Steve" Bondy** 971 (2) 414-2200
E-mail: bondysc@state.gov
Education: Delaware 1984 BA, 1986 MA
Office Management Specialist to the Ambassador **(Vacant)** . . . . 971 (2) 414-2200 ext. 2431

Office of the U.S. Ambassador to the United Arab Emirates *(continued)*

◇ Deputy Chief of Mission
Steven C. "Steve" Bondy . . . . 971 (2) 414-2200 ext. 2460
E-mail: bondysc@state.gov
Education: Delaware 1984 BA, 1986 MA
Office Management Specialist to the Deputy Chief of Mission **(Vacant)** . . . . 971 (2) 414-2200 ext. 2460
Consular Section Chief
Jeffrey P. Lodinsky . . . . 971 (2) 414-2200 ext. 2657
Fax: 971 (2) 414-2241
Community Liaison Officer **Laura Vargas** . . . . 971 (2) 414-2200 ext. 2675
Financial Management Officer
Wendy Kahler . . . . 971 (2) 414-2200 ext. 2389
E-mail: kahlerwa@state.gov
General Service Officer **John A. Marten** . . . . 971 (2) 414-2200 ext. 2667
E-mail: martenja@state.gov
Human Resources Officer **Natalie R. Koza** . . . . 971 (2) 414-2200 ext. 2224
E-mail: kozanr@state.gov Fax: 971 (2) 414-2215
Information Management Officer
Robert Glunt . . . . 971 (2) 414-2200 ext. 2380
Information Program Officer
Arun R. Jagga . . . . 971 (2) 414-2200 ext. 2397
Information Systems Officer/Information Systems Security Officer **Ligang Chen** 971 (2) 414-2200
E-mail: chenl3@state.gov
Legal Attaché **Stephen Gaudin** . . . . 971 (2) 414-2200 ext. 2408
E-mail: gaudinsj@state.gov
◇ Management Counselor **William Steuer** . . . . 971 (2) 414-2200 ext. 2613
E-mail: steuerw@state.gov
Education: Texas State (San Marcos) 1989
Political/Economic Officer **(Vacant)** . . . . 971 (2) 414-2200 ext. 2231
Public Affairs Officer **Scott Bolz** . . . . 971 (2) 414-2200 ext. 2332
E-mail: bolzsc@state.gov Fax: 971 (2) 414-2603
Regional Security Officer **Chris Berry** 971 (2) 414-2200

Commercial Section (Foreign Commercial Service) [United Arab Emirates]
P.O. Box 4009, Abu Dhabi, United Arab Emirates
Mail: American Embassy - Abu Dhabi, United Arab Emirates, 6010 Abu Dhabi Place, Washington, DC 20521-6010
Tel: 971 (2) 414-2200 ext. 2518 Fax: 971 (2) 414-2228

Regional Senior Commercial Officer
Thomas Bruns . . . . 971 (2) 414-2200 ext. 2518
E-mail: thomas.bruns@trade.gov
Education: Thunderbird Global 2005 MBA

Federal Aviation Administration [United Arab Emirates]
American Embassy - Abu Dhabi, United Arab Emirates, Al-Sudan Street, P.O. Box 4009, Abu Dhabi, United Arab Emirates
Fax: 971 (2) 414-2588

FAA Senior Representative
Robert Roxbrough . . . . 971 (2) 414-2200 ext. 2438
E-mail: roxbroughrj@state.gov

Office of the Defense Attaché [United Arab Emirates]
American Embassy - Abu Dhabi, United Arab Emirates, Al-Sudan Street, P.O. Box 4009, Abu Dhabi, United Arab Emirates
Mail: American Embassy - Abu Dhabi, United Arab Emirates, 6010 Abu Dhabi Place, Washington, DC 20521-6010
Tel: 971 (2) 414-2200 ext. 2347 Fax: 971 (2) 414-2259

Senior Defense Official and Defense Attaché **BG Miguel A. Correa USA** . . . . 971 (2) 414-2200 ext. 2347

Dubai Consulate General
121777, Dubai, United Arab Emirates
Corner of Sheikh Khalifa Bin Zayed Road and Al Seef Road, Al Seef Road - Bur Dubai, Dubai, United Arab Emirates
Tel: 971 (4) 309-4000 Fax: 971 (4) 354-7531
E-mail: webmasterdubai@state.gov

◇ Consul General **Philip A. "Phil" Frayne** 971 (4) 309-4000
E-mail: fraynepa@state.gov
Education: Columbia 1981 BA; Johns Hopkins 1986 MA
◇ Deputy Principal Officer **Martin Kelly** 971 (4) 309-4000
E-mail: kellym@state.gov

(continued on next page)

Dubai Consulate General *(continued)*

Office Management Specialist to the Consul General **Gayle Shayman** .... 971 (4) 309-4000 ext. 4012
Community Liaison Officer **Susan Johnson** .... 971 (2) 414-2200 ext. 4155
Consular Officer **Richard E. Swart** .... 971 (4) 309-4000 ext. 4945
Economic/Political Officer **Dale R. Carden** ... 971 (4) 309-4000 ext. 4025
General Services Officer **Robert Barney** ..... 971 (4) 309-4000 ext. 4910
Information Program Officer **Nijay P. Saini** ... 971 (4) 309-4000 ext. 4187
E-mail: saininp@state.gov
Legal Attaché **Ryan Lewis** .... 971 (4) 309-4000 ext. 4066
E-mail: lewisrt@state.gov
Management Officer **Lynn C. Virgil** .... 971 (4) 309-4000 ext. 4091
Public Affairs Officer **Christine Dal Bello** ... 971 (4) 309-4000 ext. 4108
Regional Security Officer **Mark D. Hartfield** .... 971 (4) 309-4000 ext. 4930

Agricultural Section (Foreign Agricultural Service) [United Arab Emirates]

World Trade Center, Agricultural Trade Office - Dubai, United Arab Emirates, P.O. Box 9343, 21st Floor, Dubai, United Arab Emirates
Mail: U.S. Consulate General - Dubai, United Arab Emirates, 6020 Dubai Place, Washington, DC 20521-6020
E-mail: atodubai@fas.usda.gov E-mail: atodubai@state.gov

Counselor **Kurt F. Seifarth** .... 971 (4) 309-4902 ext. 4177
E-mail: kurt.seifarth@fas.usda.gov

Commercial Section (Foreign Commercial Service) [United Arab Emirates]

U.S. Consulate General - Dubai, United Arab Emirates, Dubai International Trade Center, P.O. Box 9343, 21st Floor, Dubai, United Arab Emirates
Mail: U.S. Consulate General - Dubai, United Arab Emirates, 6020 Dubai Place, Washington, DC 20521-6020

Principal Commercial Officer **Shakir Farsakh** .... 971 (4) 309-4000 ext. 4963
E-mail: shakir.farsakh@trade.gov
Education: Wesleyan U 1984 BA; Johns Hopkins 1986 MA

Department of Homeland Security - U.S. Immigration and Customs Enforcement [United Arab Emirates]

Customs Officer **Leo B. Akers** .... 971 (4) 309-4000 ext. 4018
E-mail: akerslb@state.gov

U.S. Embassy in Yemen

Palestine Road, Ruwais, P.O. Box 149, Jeddah, 21411, Saudi Arabia
Tel: 966 (12) 667-0080 Fax: 966 (12) 669-3074
Internet: ye.usembassy.gov

Note: On February 11, 2015, the Department of State suspended operations at Embassy Sanaa and all personnel have been evacuated. The ambassador and key staff are operating the Yemen Affairs Unit at the U.S. Consulate in Jeddah, Saudi Arabia.

Office of the U.S. Ambassador to Yemen

Palestine Road, Ruwais, P.O. Box 149, Jeddah, 21411, Saudi Arabia

★ Ambassador **Ambassador Matthew H. Tueller** 966 (12) 667-0080
Note: On November 8, 2018, President Donald J. Trump announced his intention to nominate Matthew Tueller to be ambassador to Iraq.
E-mail: tuellermh@state.gov
Education: BYU BA; Harvard MPP
★ Ambassador-Designate **Christopher P. "Chris" Henzel** 966 (12) 667-0080
E-mail: henzelcp@state.gov
Education: Col Holy Cross BA; National War Col MS
Office Management Specialist to the Ambassador **Mary Grey** 966 (12) 667-0080
Deputy Chief of Mission **Junaid Mazhar "Jay" Munir** 966 (12) 667-0080
E-mail: munirjm@state.gov
Education: Yale 1988 BA; Harvard 2001 JD
Economic Officer **Michael Pennell** 966 (12) 667-0080
E-mail: pennellm@state.gov

Office of the U.S. Ambassador to Yemen *(continued)*

Financial Management Officer **(Vacant)** 966 (12) 667-0080
General Services Officer **(Vacant)** 966 (12) 667-0080
Management Officer **(Vacant)** 966 (12) 667-0080
Political/Economic Officer **Michael Pennell** 966 (12) 667-0080
E-mail: pennellm@state.gov
◇ Public Affairs Officer **Adnan A. Siddiqi** 966 (12) 667-0080
Education: Columbia 1980 BA, 1981 MIA
Regional Security Officer **Joshua S. Godbois** 966 (12) 667-0080
E-mail: GodboisJS2@state.gov

Federal Aviation Administration (Resident in Brussels) [Yemen]

American Embassy - Abu Dhabi, United Arab Emirates, Al-Sudan Street, P.O. Box 4009, Abu Dhabi, United Arab Emirates
Mail: American Embassy - Abu Dhabi, United Arab Emirates, 6010 Abu Dhabi Place, Washington, DC 20521-6010
Fax: 971 (2) 414-2588

FAA Senior Representative **Robert Roxbrough** 971 (2) 414-2438

Office of the Defense Attaché [Yemen]

American Embassy - Sanaa, Yemen, Sa'awan Street, Himyar Zone, P.O. Box 22347, Sanaa, Yemen
Mail: American Embassy - Sanaa, Yemen, Department of State, Washington, DC 20521-6330

Defense Attaché **John J. Zavage** 966 (12) 667-0080

★ Presidential Appointment Requiring Senate Confirmation ☆ Presidential Appointment □ Schedule C Appointment ◇ Career Senior Foreign Service Appointment
● Career Senior Executive Service (SES) Appointment ○ Non-Career Senior Executive Service (SES) Appointment ■ Postal Career Executive Service

United States Department of Transportation

DEPARTMENTS

Contents

United States Department of Transportation (DOT)

Description: The Department of Transportation establishes the nation's overall transportation policy. Within the department there are ten administrations that have jurisdiction over highway planning, development, and construction; motor carrier safety; urban mass transit; railroads; aviation; and the safety of waterways, ports, highways, and oil and gas pipelines.

1200 New Jersey Avenue, SE, Washington, DC 20590-9898
Tel: (202) 366-4542 (Freedom of Information)
Tel: (800) 424-9071 (Inspector General's Hotline)
Tel: (202) 366-4000 (Personnel Locator)
Tel: (202) 366-4263 (Procurement Information)
Tel: (202) 366-4570 (Publications Information)
Internet: www.transportation.gov
Internet: www.usa.gov (Official US Government Website)
Internet: http://ntl.bts.gov (National Transportation Library)

OFFICE OF THE SECRETARY

West Building, 1200 New Jersey Avenue, SE,
9th Floor, Washington, DC 20590-9898
Tel: (202) 366-4000 Fax: (202) 366-7202
Internet: www.transportation.gov/office-of-secretary

Office of the Deputy Secretary

1200 New Jersey Avenue, SE, 9th Floor, Room W91-307,
Washington, DC 20590-9898
Fax: (202) 366-3937

Office of the Assistant Secretary for Research and Technology (OST-R)

1200 New Jersey Avenue, SE, Washington, DC 20590-9898
Tel: (202) 366-3492 Tel: (800) 853-1351 Fax: (202) 366-3759

Assistant Secretary-Designate
Diana Furchtgott-Roth East Building, 3rd Floor ...... (202) 366-3492
Education: Swarthmore BA; Oxford (UK) MPhil

○ Senior Advisor to the Secretary
Keith Nelson East Building, 3rd Floor .... (202) 366-3492
E-mail: keith.nelson@dot.gov

Executive Assistant **(Vacant)** .... (202) 366-4158

Senior Advisor **Tim Wang** .... (202) 366-0637

Transportation Safety Institute (TSI)

6500 South MacArthur Boulevard, Oklahoma City, OK 73169
Mail: P.O. Box 25082, Oklahoma City, OK 73125-5050
Tel: (800) 858-2107 E-mail: tsi@dot.gov Internet: www.rita.dot.gov/tsi/

Director **Kevin C. Womack PE, MASCE** .... (405) 954-7312
E-mail: kevin.womack@dot.gov
Education: Oregon State 1980 BS; Pennsylvania 1985 MSE; Oregon State 1989 PhD

Senior Advisor for Transportation Safety and Security Training Policy and Programs **Christine Lawrence** ..... (405) 954-7198
E-mail: christine.lawrence@dot.gov

John A. Volpe National Transportation Systems Center

55 Broadway, Cambridge, MA 02142
Tel: (617) 494-2224 Fax: (617) 494-3530 Internet: www.volpe.dot.gov

Office of the Director

55 Broadway, Cambridge, MA 02142

● Director **Anne D. Aylward** .... (617) 494-2191
Education: Radcliffe 1969 AB; MIT 1975 MPL

Chief Counsel **Monica Conyngham Esq.** .... (617) 494-2731

Office of the Director *(continued)*

Financial Manager (Acting) **Susan M. Connors** .... (617) 494-2478

Departmental Office of Civil Rights (DOCR)

1200 New Jersey Avenue, SE, Room W78, Washington, DC 20590-9898
Tel: (202) 366-4648 Fax: (202) 366-5575
Fax: (202) 366-7717 (Alternate)

Atlanta (GA) Case Management Branch

1701 Columbia Avenue, Room 110-G, College Park, GA 30337
Tel: (404) 305-6667
Areas Covered: AL, FL, GA, KY, MS, NC, PR, SC, TN

Branch Chief **Angela Williams** .... (202) 366-6297
E-mail: angela.williams@dot.gov

Cambridge (MA) Case Management Branch

RTV-8A, 55 Broadway, Room 947, S-341, Cambridge, MA 02142
Tel: (617) 494-3051 Tel: (866) 355-2629 TTY: (617) 494-3472
Fax: (617) 494-2941
Areas Covered: CT, MA, ME, NH, NJ, NY, PA, RI, VI, VT

Branch Chief **Angela Williams** .... (202) 366-6297
E-mail: angela.williams@dot.gov

Chicago (IL) Case Management Branch

2300 East Devon Avenue, Room 406, S-344, Des Plaines, IL 60018-4696
Tel: (847) 294-8600 Tel: (847) 355-7154 TTY: (866) 355-7154
Fax: (847) 294-8605
Areas Covered: IA, IL, IN, KS, MI, MN, MO, NE, OH, WI

Branch Chief **Angela Williams** .... (202) 366-6297
E-mail: angela.williams@dot.gov

Dallas/Fort Worth (TX) Case Management Branch

2601 Meacham Boulevard, Fort Worth, TX 76137-4298
Tel: (817) 222-5275 TTY: (817) 222-4083 Tel: (866) 355-5312
Fax: (817) 222-4084
Areas Covered: AR, CO, LA, MT, ND, NM, OK, SD, TX, UT, WY

Branch Chief **Angela Williams** .... (202) 366-6297
2300 East Devon Avenue, Room 406, Mail Stop S-344,
Des Plaines, IL 60018
E-mail: angela.williams@dot.gov

Equal Opportunity Complaints and Investigations Division

1200 New Jersey Avenue, SE, Room W-78, Washington, DC 20590-9898
Tel: (202) 366-9370 Tel: (866) 355-7147 TTY: (202) 855-1000 (Voice)
TTY: (202) 855-1234 (Text) Fax: (202) 366-4659
Areas Covered: AK, American Samoa, AZ, CA, DE, DC, Guam, HI, ID, MD, NV, OR, Pacific Islands, VA, WA, WV

Associate Director (Acting) **Beverly Onwubere** .... (202) 366-5988
E-mail: beverly.onwubere@dot.gov

Program Assistant **Patricia Fields** .... (202) 366-9370
E-mail: patricia.fields@dot.gov Fax: (202) 493-2065

★ Presidential Appointment Requiring Senate Confirmation ☆ Presidential Appointment □ Schedule C Appointment ◇ Career Senior Foreign Service Appointment
● Career Senior Executive Service (SES) Appointment ○ Non-Career Senior Executive Service (SES) Appointment ■ Postal Career Executive Service

DEPARTMENTS

Office of Inspector General (OIG)

West Building, 1200 New Jersey Avenue, SE,
Washington, DC 20590-9898
Tel: (202) 366-1959 Fax: (202) 366-3912 Internet: www.oig.dot.gov

Regional Offices

Atlanta (GA) Regional Office
Atlanta Federal Center, 61 Forsyth Street SW,
Suite 17T60, Atlanta, GA 30303-3104
Tel: (404) 562-3850 Fax: (404) 562-3849

Aviation Safety Audits Director **Tina Nystead** .... (404) 562-3770
Special Agent-in-Charge for Investigations
Marlies T. Gonzalez .... (404) 562-3850
Assistant Special Agent-in-Charge for Investigations
(Vacant) .... (404) 562-3850

Baltimore (MD) Regional Office
10 South Howard Street, Suite 4500, Baltimore, MD 21201
Tel: (410) 962-3612 Fax: (410) 962-7469

Program Director
George Banks City Crescent Building .... (410) 962-3612

Chicago (IL) Regional Office
200 West Adams, Chicago, IL 60606
Tel: (312) 353-0106 Fax: (312) 353-7032

Special Agent-in-Charge for Investigations
Thomas J. Ullom .... (312) 353-0106 ext. 111

Fort Worth (TX) Regional Office
Lanham Federal Building, 819 Taylor Street,
Room 13A42, Fort Worth, TX 76102
Tel: (817) 978-3236 Fax: (817) 978-3092

Program Director **Kerry Barras** .... (817) 978-3236

New York (NY) Regional Office
201 Varick Street, Room 1161, New York, NY 10014
Tel: (212) 337-1280 Fax: (212) 620-3252

Audit Manager **George Lavaco** .... (212) 337-1280
E-mail: george.lavaco@oig.dot.gov
Special Agent-in-Charge, Investigations **(Vacant)** .... (212) 337-1250
Fax: (212) 620-3220

Oklahoma City (OK) Regional Office
Building 30, 6500 South MacArthur Boulevard,
Room 100, Oklahoma City, OK 73169
Tel: (405) 954-3718 Fax: (405) 954-3034 Internet: www.oig.dot.gov

Audits Program Manager/Supervisory Auditor **(Vacant)** ... (405) 954-5116
Senior Auditor **Maria Lynn Dowds** .... (405) 954-5109
E-mail: maria.dowds@oig.dot.gov
Senior Auditor **Tim D. Roberts** .... (405) 954-5115
E-mail: tim.roberts@oig.dot.gov

San Francisco (CA) Regional Office
50 United Nation Plaza, Suite 5300, San Francisco, CA 94102
Tel: (415) 522-4902 Fax: (415) 522-4901

Program Director **Marshall Jackson** .... (415) 522-4902
E-mail: marshall.jackson@oig.dot.gov
Special Agent-in-Charge for Investigations **Lisa Glazzy** ... (415) 744-2511
E-mail: lisa.glazzy@oig.dot.gov

Seattle (WA) Regional Office
Jackson Federal Building, 915 Second Avenue,
Room 1840, Seattle, WA 98174-1001
Tel: (206) 220-7754 Fax: (206) 220-7758

Audit Program Director **Darren L. Murphy** .... (206) 255-1929
E-mail: darren.l.murphy@oig.dot.gov

Office of Investigations

West Building, 1200 New Jersey Avenue, SE,
Washington, DC 20590-9898
Tel: (202) 366-1967 Fax: (202) 366-3912
Internet: www.oig.dot.gov/investigations

Cambridge (MA) Regional Office of Investigations
Kendall Square, 55 Broadway, JRI-1, Room 1055, Cambridge, MA 02142
Tel: (617) 494-2701 Fax: (617) 494-2845

Special Agent-in-Charge **(Vacant)** .... (617) 494-2701

Los Angeles (CA) - Regional Investigations
17785 Center Court Drive, North, Suite 350, Cerritos, CA 90703-9327
Tel: (562) 467-5360 (Investigations) Fax: (562) 467-5377

Special Agent-in-Charge **William Swallow** .... (562) 467-5360
Assistant Special Agent-in-Charge **Brendan Culley** ...... (562) 467-5360

Miami (FL) Resident Office - Investigations
510 Shotgun Road, Suite 220, Sunrise, FL 33326
Tel: (954) 382-6645 Fax: (954) 382-6654

Special Agent-in-Charge for Investigations
Marlies T. Gonzalez .... (954) 382-6645

Philadelphia (PA) Regional Office - Investigations
Parkview Tower, 1150 First Avenue, Suite 380-B,
King of Prussia, PA 19406
Tel: (610) 337-2725 Fax: (610) 337-2810

Special Agent-in-Charge **Douglas Shoemaker** .... (212) 337-1250
201 Varick Street, New York, NY 10014

Federal Aviation Administration (FAA)

800 Independence Avenue, SW, Washington, DC 20591
Tel: (866) 835-5322 Tel: (202) 267-9165 (Freedom of Information)
Tel: (202) 267-3117 (Library Services - Reference and Research)
Tel: (202) 267-9895 (Privacy Act Information)
Tel: (202) 267-9532 (Safety Hotline - DC Metropolitan Area)
Tel: (800) 255-1111 (Safety Hotline - Continental US, Alaska and Hawaii)
Fax: (202) 267-3505 Fax: (202) 267-3507 (Alternate)
Internet: www.faa.gov

OFFICE OF THE ADMINISTRATOR

800 Independence Avenue, SW, Room 1010, Washington, DC 20591
Fax: (202) 267-5047

Air Traffic Organization (ATO)

800 Independence Avenue, SW, Room 1019, Washington, DC 20591
Tel: (202) 267-7111 Fax: (202) 267-5085 Internet: www.ato.faa.gov

Air Traffic Services

Federal Building, 10B, 600 Independence Avenue, SW,
Washington, DC 20591
Tel: (202) 267-0634 Fax: (202) 267-1265

Terminal Services

Central Terminal Service Area (CTSA)
2601 Meacham Boulevard, Fort Worth, TX 76193
Tel: (817) 222-5500 Fax: (817) 222-5966

Manager **Tony Mello** .... (817) 222-4008
Tactical Manager **(Vacant)** .... (817) 222-4010

Western Service Area South
1601 Lind Avenue, SW, Renton, WA 98057-4099

Director of Operations **Ronald Fincher** .... (425) 203-4044
Administrative Officer **Jerry Guerrero** .... (425) 203-4054
Fax: (425) 203-4045

★ Presidential Appointment Requiring Senate Confirmation ☆ Presidential Appointment □ Schedule C Appointment ◇ Career Senior Foreign Service Appointment
● Career Senior Executive Service (SES) Appointment ○ Non-Career Senior Executive Service (SES) Appointment ■ Postal Career Executive Service

System Operations Services

800 Independence Avenue, SW, Room 1002W, Washington, DC 20591
Fax: (202) 267-5456

Flight Services Program Operations Office (FSPO)

1575 Eye Street, NW, Room 8100, Washington, DC 20005
Fax: (202) 385-7539

Area Offices

Alaska Flight Services Information Area Group
222 West Seventh Avenue, Box 14, Anchorage, AK 99513-7587
Tel: (907) 271-5464 Fax: (907) 271-2850

Manager of Information Office
James M. Miller Anchorage FS Area .... (907) 271-5464
P.O. Box 14, Anchorage, AK 99513-7587
Safety and Operations Branch Manager **(Vacant)** .... (907) 271-5467
Secretary **(Vacant)** .... (907) 271-5464

Continental United States (CONUS) Flight Services Information Area Group
901 Locust Street, Kansas City, MO 64106-2641
Fax: (816) 329-2575

Air Traffic Control Specialist **James L. "Jim" Harvey** ... (816) 329-2544

System Operations Air Traffic Control System Command Center Office

800 Independence Avenue, SW, Washington, DC 20591
Fax: (703) 904-4461

Tactical Operations Northeast - US Group
Manager **Warren Strickland** .... (718) 553-2623
4205 Johnson Avenue, Ronkonkoma, NY 11779
Senior Advisor **William "Bill" Burns** .... (718) 553-2624
159-30 Rockaway Boulevard, Fax: (718) 995-5664
Room 435, Jamaica, NY 11434
Executive Assistant **Margaret Shea** .... (718) 553-4532
159-30 Rockaway Boulevard, Fax: (718) 995-5907
Room 434, Jamaica, NY 11434

Tactical Operations Southeast - US Group
Manager **Mike Richardson** .... (404) 305-6246
Integration and Efficiency Specialist **Tim Helms** .... (404) 305-6567
Marine Representative **(Vacant)** .... (404) 305-6907
I and E Specialist System Operations **Ron Krebs** .... (404) 305-6547
Administrative Officer **Dorcas Allen** .... (404) 305-6200

Tactical Operations Southwest - US Group
10101 Hillwood Parkway, Fort Worth, TX 76177

Manager **Ronald "Ron" Schneider** .... (202) 267-6553
Administrative Officer **Alexandra Strebeck** .... (817) 222-4010

Tactical Operations Western Pacific - US Group
Manager **Bill Whitford** .... (425) 203-4031

Technical Operations

FAA National Headquarters, 800 Independence Avenue, SW,
Mail Stop AJW-0, Washington, DC 20591
Tel: (202) 267-3366 Fax: (202) 267-6060

Area Offices

Central Service Area (CSA)
2601 Meacham Boulevard, Fort Worth, TX 76137

Director **(Vacant)** .... (202) 267-3366
Engineering Services Manager **Jeff Tague** .... (817) 222-4035
Technical Services Manager **Carl Piccolo** .... (817) 222-4501
Technical Services Manager **Howard T. Manning** .... (817) 222-4785
Technical Operations Area Director **Denise Knight** ...... (817) 222-4000

Eastern Service Area (ESA)
1701 Columbia Avenue, College Park, GA 30337
Fax: (404) 305-6215

Director **Mary K. Sherer** .... (404) 305-6242

Eastern Service Area *(continued)*

Deputy Director **Sherry Taylor** .... (404) 305-6214
E-mail: sherry.taylor@faa.gov
Executive Advisor **Katrina Lawson** .... (404) 305-6217
Administrative Officer **Stacie Sinclair** .... (404) 305-6210
E-mail: stacie.sinclair@faa.gov
Management Program Analyst **Lori DeWulf** .... (404) 305-6239
E-mail: lori.dewulf@faa.gov

Engineering Services
Manager **(Vacant)** .... (202) 267-3366
Management and Program Assistant
Maria Decorla-Souza .... (718) 553-4805
E-mail: maria.decorla-souza@faa.gov Fax: (718) 995-5682
Communications Engineering Group Manager
David McClain .... (404) 305-7061
E-mail: david.mcclain@faa.gov
Engineering Support Group Manager **David Patrick** ...... (404) 305-7091
En Route/FSS Engineering Group Manager
Mark Beekman .... (404) 305-7051
Infrastructure Engineering Group Manager
James Garrett .... (404) 305-7081
NAVAIDS Engineering Group Manager
Jeffrey A. Jones .... (404) 305-7071
Terminal Surveillance/Weather Engineering Group
Manager **David Lebby** .... (404) 305-7041

Western Service Area Office (WSAO)
1601 Lind Avenue, SW, Renton, WA 98057-4099
Tel: (206) 231-2420 Fax: (425) 203-4055

Western Service Area Manager **Gary Grant** .... (907) 271-2250
Western Service Area Manager **Dave Washino** .... (206) 231-2420
Executive Advisor **Mandy West** .... (206) 231-2356
E-mail: mandy.west@faa.gov
Technical Services Manager **Kevin Zirger** .... (206) 231-2420
Technical Services Manager **Randall L. Gubert** .... (510) 745-3470
FAA Oakland ARTCC, 5125 Central Avenue,
2nd Floor, Room 4, Tech Ops, Fremont, CA 94536
Seattle District Manager **Kelly Dodge** .... (253) 351-3315
FAA Seattle ARTCC, Fax: (425) 804-2969
3101 Auburn Way S,
Room 340, TO District Manager, Auburn, WA 98092
Denver District Manager **Terri MacKendrick** .... (303) 684-5002
FAA Denver District Office, 1921 Corporate Center Circle,
Suite 3-D, Longmont, CO 80501
Salt Lake City District Manager **Michael Tebbs** .... (801) 320-2250
Building 1, FAA Salt Lake City ARTCC, Fax: (801) 320-2074
2150 W 700 N,
Room 1, Salt Lake City, UT 84116
Oakland District Manager **Steve Aguirre** .... (916) 859-6038
11025 Trade Center Drive, Fax: (916) 366-4414
Room 125, Rancho Cordova, CA 95670
Los Angeles District Manager **Donell Johnson** .... (310) 725-6940
15000 Aviation Boulevard, Room 4006, Tech Ops District Mgr.,
Lawndale, CA 90261
Los Angeles District Manager **Joe Haj-Eid** .... (310) 725-6933
15000 Aviation Boulevard, Lawndale, CA 90261
Honolulu District Manager **Douglas A. Klauck** .... (808) 840-6401
760 Worchester Avenue, Room 1102, Honolulu, HI 96818
Anchorage District Manager **(Vacant)** .... (206) 231-2420

★ Presidential Appointment Requiring Senate Confirmation ☆ Presidential Appointment ☐ Schedule C Appointment ◇ Career Senior Foreign Service Appointment
● Career Senior Executive Service (SES) Appointment ○ Non-Career Senior Executive Service (SES) Appointment ■ Postal Career Executive Service

Office of the Deputy Administrator (ODA)

Associate Administrator for Aviation Safety (AVR)

800 Independence Avenue, SW, Room 1000W, Washington, DC 20591
Fax: (202) 267-9675

Aircraft Certification Service (AIR)

800 Independence Avenue, SW, Room 800E, Washington, DC 20591
Tel: (202) 267-8235 Fax: (202) 267-5364

Flight Standards Service (AFS)

FAA National Headquarters, 800 Independence Avenue, SW, Washington, DC 20591
Tel: (202) 267-3651 Fax: (202) 267-5230

- ● Executive Director **John S. Duncan** Room 821 .... (202) 267-8237
- ● Deputy Executive Director, Flight Standards Field Operations **Michael J. "Mike" Zenkovich** .... (817) 222-5661
  FAA Southwest Regional Office, 2601 Meacham Boulevard, Room 626, Fort Worth, TX 76137-4298
  Education: Henderson State 1979 BSc
- ● Deputy Executive Director, Flight Standards Policy Oversight (Acting) **John Barbagallo** Room 821 .... (202) 267-1023
  E-mail: john.barbagallo@faa.gov

Chief of Staff **Robert Carty** .... (202) 267-7676
Senior Technical Advisor **Christopher MacWhorter** ..... (540) 454-0587
Senior Technical Advisor **(Vacant)** .... (817) 222-5234
10101 Hillwood Parkway, Ste 400, 6S-657-A, Fort Worth, TX 76177

Flight Standards International Field Offices

Dallas/Ft. Worth International Field Office
Centre Port Business Park, Dallas/Fort Worth International Field Office, 14800 Trinity Boulevard, Suite 300, Fort Worth, TX 76155
Tel: (817) 684-6700 Fax: (817) 684-6784
Areas Covered: Mexico

Manager **Christopher J. "Chris" Collins** .... (214) 277-0301
E-mail: chris.collins@faa.gov

Miami International Field Office
2895 SW 145th Avenue, Suite 221, Miramar, FL 33027
Tel: (954) 641-6700 Tel: (954) 641-6718 Fax: (954) 641-6720
Fax: (954) 641-6727
Areas Covered: Caribbean and South American countries

Manager **James R. Jelinski** .... (954) 641-6701
E-mail: james.r.jelinski@faa.gov
Aviation Safety Technician **Martha B. Acosta** .... (954) 641-6775
Administrative Officer **Beatriz F. Ruiz** .... (954) 641-6702
E-mail: beatriz.f.ruiz@faa.gov

New York International Field Office
1 Aviation Plaza, 159-30 Rockaway Boulevard, Jamaica, NY 11434-4809
Tel: (718) 995-5447 Fax: (718) 995-5496
Areas Covered: JFK, EWR, LGA, PHL, Eastern Canada, Europe, Africa, Middle East, Iceland and Greenland.

Manager **Nicholas Tsokris** .... (718) 995-5450
E-mail: nicholas.tsokris@faa.gov
Administrative Officer **Anthony Troia** .... (718) 995-5433
Operations **(Vacant)** .... (718) 995-5450

Los Angeles International Field Office
15000 Aviation Boulevard, Lawndale, CA 90261
Tel: (310) 725-7330 Fax: (310) 725-6859
Areas Covered: Australia, Cook Islands, Fiji, French Polynesia, Japan, Korea, Kiribati, New Caledonia, New Zealand, Philippines, Tahiti, Tonga Islands, Taiwan, Solomon Islands, Vanuatu and Western Samoa.

Manager **(Vacant)** .... (310) 725-7330

Assistant Administrator for Policy, International Affairs and Environment (APL)

800 Independence Avenue, SW, Room 900W, Washington, DC 20591
Fax: (202) 267-5800

International Offices

Africa, Europe and Middle East Office
American Embassy/FAA, 37-40 Boulevard du Regent, AEU-1, B-1000 Brussels, Belgium
Mail: American Embassy/FAA, PSC 82, Box 106, APO, AE 09710
Fax: 32 (2) 230-2597
Areas Covered: Africa (Algeria, Angola, Benin, Botswana, Burkina Faso, Burundi, Cameroon, Cape Verde, Central African Republic, Chad, Comoros, Congo, Cote d'Ivoire, Democratic Republic of the Congo, Djibouti, Equatorial Guinea, Eritrea, Ethiopia, Gabon, The Gambia, Ghana, Guinea, Guinea-Bissau, Kenya, Lesotho, Liberia, Madagascar, Malawi, Mali, Mauritania, Mauritius, Morocco, Mozambique, Namibia, Nigeria, Rwanda, Sao Tome and Principe, Senegal, Seychelles, Sierra Leone, Somalia, South Africa, Sudan, Swaziland, Tanzania, Togo, Tunisia, Uganda, Western Sahara, Zambia, Zimbabwe), Europe (Albania, Andorra, Austria, Belgium, Bosnia and Herzegovina, Bulgaria, Croatia, Czech Republic, Denmark, Estonia, Finland, the Former Soviet Union, France, Germany, Greece, The Holy See, Hungary, Iceland, Ireland, Italy, Latvia, Liechtenstein, Lithuania, Luxembourg, Former Republic of Macedonia, Macedonia, Malta, Monaco, Netherlands, Norway, Poland, Portugal, Romania, San Marino, Serbia and Montenegro, Slovakia, Slovenia, Spain, Sweden, Switzerland, Turkey, United Kingdom), Middle East (Afghanistan, Bahrain, Cyprus, Egypt, Iran, Iraq, Israel, Jordan, Kuwait, Lebanon, Libya, Oman, Qatar, Saudi Arabia, Syria, United Arab Emirates, Yemen)

Director **Catherine M. "Kate" Lang** 32 (2) 811-5159
E-mail: catherine.m.lang@faa.gov
Education: Briar Cliff Col BA; Loyola U (Chicago) MPS

Africa, Europe, and Middle East Staff
600 Independence Avenue, SW, 6th Floor, Suite 6E1500, Washington, DC 20591
Tel: (202) 267-1000

Africa, Europe and Middle East Manager **Jennifer Arquilla** Room 6E22SS .... (202) 267-8621

FAA Senior Representative, Abu Dhabi
American Embassy/FAA, Embassies District (Airport Road) Street #4, 09825 Abu Dhabi, United Arab Emirates
PSC 82, Box 002, AEU-BRU Abu Dhabi, United Arab Emirates
Tel: 971 (2) 414-2438 Fax: 971 (2) 414-2588
Areas Covered: Bahrain, Egypt, Iran, Israel, Jordan, Kuwait, Lebanon, Libya, Oman, Palestine, Qatar, Saudi Arabia, Syria, United Arab Emirates, Yemen

FAA Senior Representative, Abu Dhabi **Robert Roxbrough** 971 (2) 414-2438
Administrative Assistant **Mary Nagy** 971 (2) 414-2438

FAA Senior Representative, Brussels
American Embassy/FAA, AEU-BRU, 37-40 Boulevard du Regent, B-1000 Brussels, Belgium
Mail: American Embassy/FAA, PSC 82, Box 106, APO, AE 09710
Fax: 32 (2) 811-5295
Areas Covered: Belgium, Luxembourg, Turkey, European Union

FAA Senior Representative, Brussels **Maria DiPasquantonio** 32 (2) 811-4038
Administrative Assistant **Amelita Weber** 32 (2) 811-5159

★ Presidential Appointment Requiring Senate Confirmation ☆ Presidential Appointment ☐ Schedule C Appointment ◇ Career Senior Foreign Service Appointment
● Career Senior Executive Service (SES) Appointment ○ Non-Career Senior Executive Service (SES) Appointment ■ Postal Career Executive Service

FAA Senior Representative, Dakar, Senegal
American Embassy/FAA, Avenue Jean XXIII, angle Rue Kleber, AEU-DKR, Boite Postal 49 Dakar, Senegal
Mail: American Embassy/FAA, Department of State, 2130 Dakar Place, AEU-DKR, Washington, DC 20521-2130
Tel: 221 33-823-6753 Fax: 221 33-823-9286
Areas Covered: Angola, Benin, Botswana, Burkina Faso, Burundi, Cameroon, Cape Verde, Central African Republic, Chad, Comoros, Cote d'Ivoire, Democratic Republic of the Congo, Djibouti, Equatorial Guinea, Ethiopia, Gabon, Gambia, Ghana, Guinea, Guinea-Bissau, Kenya, Lesotho, Liberia, Madagascar, Malawi, Mali, Mauritania, Mauritius, Mozambique, Namibia, Niger, Nigeria, Republic of the Congo, Rwanda, Sao Tome and Principe, Senegal, Seychelles, Sierra Leone, Somalia, South Africa, Sudan, Swaziland, Tanzania, Togo, Uganda, Zambia, Zimbabwe

Senior FAA Representative **Grady Stone** 221 33-829-4835
Staff Assistant **Oumou Bengeloune** 221 33-829-2180
E-mail: oumou.bengeloune@faa.gov

FAA Senior Representative, Paris
American Embassy/FAA, 2, Avenue Gabriel, AEU-PAR, 75382 Paris, Cedex 08, France
Mail: FAA, Unit 9200, DPO, AE 09777
Tel: 33 (1) 43 12 22 22 Fax: 33 (1) 42 66 97 83
Areas Covered: Algeria, Andorra, Austria, Bulgaria, Cyprus, Czech Republic, France, Germany, Greece, Holy See, Hungary, Italy, Ireland, Malta, Monaco, Morocco, Poland, Portugal, Romania, San Marino, Slovak Republic, Spain, Switzerland, Tunisia, Turkey, United Kingdom

FAA Senior Representative, Paris **Ian H. Ross** 33 (1) 43 12 22 25
Staff Assistant **Gracianne Nicolas** 33 (1) 43 12 22 25
E-mail: gracianne.nicolas@faa.gov

FAA Senior Representative, Moscow
American Embassy, Novinsky Bulvar 19/23, AEU-MOW, Moscow, Russia 121099
Mail: American Embassy/FAA, PSC 82 Box 002, APO, AE 09724
Tel: 7 (495) 728-5125 Fax: 7 (495) 728-5350
Areas Covered: Albania, Armenia, Azerbaijan, Belarus, Bosnia-Herzegovina, Croatia, Denmark, Estonia, Finland, Georgia, Iceland, Kazakhstan, Kyrgyzstan, Macedonia, Moldova, Norway, Russia, Sweden, Slovenia, Tajikistan, Turkmenistan, Ukraine, Uzbekistan

FAA Senior Representative, Moscow **(Vacant)** 7 (495) 728-5125

Asia-Pacific Area Office
FAA National Headquarters, 800 Independence Avenue, SW, Suite 6E1100, Washington, DC 20591
Tel: (202) 267-1000 Fax: (202) 267-5032
Areas Covered: Asia (Bangladesh, Bhutan, Brunei, Cambodia, China, Hong Kong, India, Indonesia, Japan, North Korea, South Korea, Laos, Macau, Malaysia, Maldives, Mongolia, Myanmar [Burma], Nepal, Pakistan, Philippines, Singapore, Sri Lanka, Taiwan, Thailand, Vietnam), and Pacific (Australia, Cook Islands, Fiji, French Polynesia, Kiribati, Nauru, New Caledonia, New Zealand, Niue, Papua New Guinea, Samoa, Solomon Islands, Tonga, Tuvalu, Vanuatu, Wallis and Futuna)

Asia Pacific Office Director **Carey Fagan** 65 6476-9475
E-mail: carey.fagan@faa.gov Fax: 65 64769458

Asia-Pacific Staff
800 Independence Avenue, SW, Suite 6E1500, Washington, DC 20591

Asia Pacific Manager
(Vacant) 6th Floor, Room 6E21PN .... (202) 267-1000

FAA Senior Representative, Beijing
U.S. Embassy-Beijing, No.55 An Jia Lou, Beijing, China 100600
Mail: American Embassy - Beijing, PSC 461, Box 50, APC-BEI, FPO, AP 96521-0002
Tel: 86 (10) 8531-4289 Fax: 86 (10) 8531-4600
Areas Covered: China, Hong Kong, Macau, Mongolia

FAA Senior Representative, Beijing **(Vacant)** 86 (10) 8531-3987

FAA Representative, New Delhi
American Embassy - New Delhi, Shantipath, Chanakyapuri, New Delhi, India 110021
Tel: 91 (11) 2419-4654 Fax: 91 (11) 2419-0003
Areas Covered: South Asia (Afghanistan, Bangladesh, Bhutan, India, Maldives, Nepal, Pakistan, Sri Lanka).

FAA Representative, New Delhi
Thomas M. "Tom" Miller 91 (11) 2419-8403
Staff Assistant **(Vacant)** 91 (11) 2419-4654

FAA Representative, Singapore
American Embassy, 27 Napier Road, Singapore, 258508, Singapore
Mail: American Embassy - Singapore, Box FAA/IAO, FPO, AP 96507
Tel: 65 6476-9170 Fax: 65 6476-9458
Areas Covered: Southeast Asia (Brunei, Burma, Cambodia, East Timor, Indonesia, Laos, Malaysia, New Zealand, Singapore, Thailand, Vietnam) and Australia

FAA Representative, Singapore **James "Jim" Spillane** 65 6476-9031
E-mail: james.spillane@faa.gov

FAA Senior Representative, Tokyo
American Embassy - Tokyo/FAA, 1-10-5, Akasaka, Minato-ku, Tokyo, Japan 107-8420
Mail: American Embassy - Tokyo/FAA, Unit 45004, Box 207, APO, AP 96337-5004
Tel: 81 (3) 3224-5514 Fax: 81 (3) 3582-5974
Areas Covered: Australia, Japan, New Zealand, Papua New Guinea and the Pacific Island countries and territories, Philippines, Taiwan; Cook Islands, Fiji, Kiribati, Nauru, Samoa, Solomon Islands, Tonga, Tuvalu, Vanuatu, Wallis and Futuna, North Korea, South Korea, Marshall Islands, Federated States of Micronesia, Palau

Senior FAA Representative, Tokyo
Nathan "Nate" Purdy 81 (3) 3224-5511
Staff Assistant **Yukari Suto** 81 (3) 3224-5514
E-mail: yukari.soto@faa.gov

Western Hemisphere Office
800 Independence Avenue, SW, Suite 6E1500, Washington, DC 20591
Tel: (202) 267-1000 Fax: (202) 267-7198

Western Hemisphere Manager **Christopher A. Barks** ..... (507) 317-5370
E-mail: christopher.barks@faa.gov
Education: Minnesota 1993 BA; Georgetown 1997 MA

FAA Senior Representative, Caribbean
HQ U.S. Southern Command, Interagency Directorate (J9), 9301 NW 33rd Street, Doral, FL 33172
Tel: (202) 267-1000
Areas Covered: Caribbean (Barbados, Guyana, Haiti, Jamaica, Suriname, Trinidad and Tobago, French Guiana, St. Maarten, Aruba, Curacao), Bahamas, Bermuda, Cuba, Venezuela, Dependent Territories (British Virgin Islands, Turks and Caicos, Cayman Islands, Guadeloupe, Martinique)

FAA Senior Representative **Alex D. Rodriguez** .... (661) 265-8360
E-mail: alex.d.rodriguez@faa.gov

FAA Senior Representative, Panama City
American Embassy/FAA, Embajada de los Estados Unidos Edificio 783, Ave. Demetrio B. Lakas Clayton, Panama City, Panama
Tel: 507 317-5000 Fax: 507 207-7401
Areas Covered: Mexico, Central America, (Belize, Costa Rica, El Salvador, Guatemala, Honduras, Nicaragua), Panama, Colombia, Dominican Republic

FAA Senior Representative **Carl N. Johnson** 507 317-5046

DEPARTMENTS

FAA Senior Representative, Sao Paulo
U.S. Consulate, Rua Henry Dunant 700,
Chacara Santo Antonio, 04709-110 São Paulo, Brazil
Tel: 55 (11) 5186-7398 Fax: 55 (11) 3312-7295
Areas Covered: Argentina, Bolivia, Brazil, Chile, Ecuador, Paraguay, Peru, Uruguay
FAA Senior Representative, Brazil
Paul Leandro Friedman 55 (61) 8116-5291
E-mail: paul.friedman@faa.gov

National Engagement and Regional Administration
800 Independence Avenue, SW, Washington, DC 20591
Tel: (202) 267-9011 Fax: (202) 267-5193

Mike Monroney Aeronautical Center
6500 South MacArthur Boulevard, Oklahoma City, OK 73169-6901
Mail: P.O. Box 25082, Mike Monroney Aeronautical Center, Oklahoma City, OK 73125-4901
● Director **Michelle Coppedge** .... (405) 954-4521
E-mail: michelle.coppedge@faa.gov
Deputy Director **Kevin O'Connor** .... (405) 954-4521
3500 South MacArthur Boulevard, Oklahoma City, OK 73169
Quality Systems and Business Resources Manager
Kim Sheppard .... (405) 954-3527
National Airspace Systems Engineering Division
Manager **Tony Delavega** .... (405) 954-3647
E-mail: tony.delavega@faa.gov
Regulatory Support Division Manager **Van L. Kerns** ..... (405) 954-4431
E-mail: van.l.kerns@faa.gov Fax: (405) 954-0245
Security and Investigations Division Manager
Lesha Sloan-Thompson .... (405) 954-7650
Budget and Performance Program Director
Toni Haught .... (405) 954-4338
E-mail: toni.haught@faa.gov
Enterprise Services **Robyn M. Burk** .... (405) 954-8980
E-mail: robyn.burk@faa.gov
FAA Logistics Center Program Director **Randall Burke** ... (405) 954-4358
Facility Management Program Director
Charles Sullivan .... (405) 954-4572
Flight Inspection Services Program Director
David H. Boulter .... (202) 267-0222
E-mail: david.h.boulter@faa.gov
Office of Acquisition Services Program Director
Michael Yort .... (405) 954-7700
Civil Rights **Joyce Davis** .... (817) 222-5009
10101 Hillwood Parkway, Room 230, Fort Worth, TX 76177
E-mail: joyce.davis@faa.gov
Public Affairs Officer **Roland Herwig** .... (405) 954-7500
E-mail: roland.herwig@faa.gov
Aeronautical Center Counsel **A. Lester Haizlip** .... (405) 954-3296
● Director, Civil Aerospace Medical Institute
Melchor J. Antuñano .... (405) 954-1000
E-mail: melchor.j.antunano@faa.gov
Education: U Nacional Autónoma (Mexico) 1985 MD; Wright State 1987 MS
Management Program Analyst, Small Business Development Program Group **Gerald A. Lewis** .... (405) 954-7704
E-mail: gerald.a.lewis@faa.gov Fax: (405) 954-0034
AAC Regional Human Resource Services Director
Nicole Gage .... (405) 954-3501
E-mail: nicole.gage@faa.gov
Director, Civil Aviation Registry **Joe D. Smith** .... (405) 954-4331

FAA Academy
6500 South MacArthur Boulevard, Oklahoma City, OK 73169
Fax: (386) 446-7133
Director **Keith Deberry** .... (405) 954-8700
E-mail: keith.deberry@faa.gov

Alaskan Region
222 West Seventh Avenue, Room 14, Anchorage, AK 99513-7587
Tel: (907) 271-5645 Fax: (907) 271-5113
Areas Covered: AK
● Regional Administrator (Acting) **Richard Van Allman** ... (907) 271-5649

Alaskan Region *(continued)*
Deputy Regional Director **Deke Abbott** .... (907) 271-5215
E-mail: deke.abbott@faa.gov
Regional Counsel **Howard Martin** .... (907) 271-5269
E-mail: howard.martin@faa.gov
Equal Employment Opportunity Officer
Charles Luddington .... (907) 271-5291
E-mail: charles.luddington@faa.gov

Airports Division
222 West Seventh Avenue, Anchorage, AK 99513-7587
Tel: (907) 271-5438 Fax: (907) 271-2851
Internet: www.faa.gov/airports_airtraffic/airports/regional_guidance/alaskan
Director (Acting) **Kristi Warden** .... (907) 271-5438
E-mail: kristi.warden@faa.gov
Deputy Director **Kristi Warden** .... (907) 271-5438

Aviation Medical Division
222 West Seventh Avenue, Anchorage, AK 99513-7587
Tel: (907) 271-5431 Fax: (907) 271-3769
Regional Flight Surgeon **Dr. Marcel Dionne MD** .... (907) 271-5431

Aviation Security and Investigations Division
222 West Seventh Avenue, Anchorage, AK 99513-7587
Tel: (907) 271-5557 Fax: (907) 271-4933
Point of Contact **Kim Cole** .... (907) 271-4408

Flight Standards Division
222 West Seventh Avenue, Anchorage, AK 99513-7587
Tel: (907) 271-5514 Fax: (907) 271-1665
Manager **Clint Wease** .... (907) 271-5514
Assistant Manager **Wes Mooty** .... (907) 271-5910
Fax: (907) 271-1665
Operations Curriculum Branch Manager **(Vacant)** .... (718) 553-4830
Systems Safety Analysis Branch Manager **(Vacant)** .... (907) 271-5910
Technical Standards Branch Manager **(Vacant)** .... (907) 271-5215

Human Resource Management Division
222 West Seventh Avenue, Anchorage, AK 99513-7587
Tel: (907) 271-5471 Fax: (907) 271-4809
Manager **Nancy Owens-Curtis** .... (907) 271-5471
Human Resource Specialist **Valerie Honeman** .... (907) 271-5476
E-mail: valerie.honeman@faa.gov
Personnel Services Manager **(Vacant)** .... (907) 271-5371

NAS Implementation Center
222 West Seventh Avenue, Anchorage, AK 99513-7587
Tel: (907) 271-5351 Fax: (907) 271-2853
Communications Manager **Margaret Oswald** .... (907) 271-3824
E-mail: margaret.oswald@faa.gov
Enroute Manager **(Vacant)** .... (907) 271-5218
NAV-AIDS/Landings Manager **(Vacant)** .... (907) 271-3814
Operations Manager **(Vacant)** .... (907) 271-5359
Telecommunications Manager
Michael "Mike" Holland .... (907) 271-5345
E-mail: michael.holland@faa.gov
Terminal Installation Manager **Warren Gool** .... (907) 271-2436

Western Logistics Service Area
222 West Seventh Avenue, Anchorage, AK 99513-7587
Tel: (907) 271-5429 Fax: (907) 271-5214
Manager **(Vacant)** .... (907) 271-5429
Acquisition and Real Estate Branch Manager **(Vacant)** ... (907) 271-5848
Real Estate Manager **Alice Salzman** .... (907) 271-5876
E-mail: alice.salzman@faa.gov

★ Presidential Appointment Requiring Senate Confirmation ☆ Presidential Appointment ☐ Schedule C Appointment ◇ Career Senior Foreign Service Appointment
● Career Senior Executive Service (SES) Appointment ○ Non Career Senior Executive Service (SES) Appointment ■ Postal Career Executive Service

Central Region
DOT Regional Headquarters, 901 Locust Street,
Kansas City, MO 64106-2641
Tel: (816) 329-3050 Fax: (816) 329-3055
Areas Covered: IA, KS, MO, NE

● Regional Administrator **John Speckin** .... (816) 329-3053
E-mail: john.speckin@faa.gov

Regional Runway Safety Program Office
901 Locust Street, Kansas City, MO 64106-2641
Fax: (816) 329-3043

Program Manager **Tom Frakes** .... (816) 329-3044
E-mail: tom.frakes@faa.gov
Regional Counsel **(Vacant)** .... (816) 329-3764
Administrative Officer **Sebrina Sirna** .... (816) 329-3767
E-mail: sebrina.sirna@faa.gov Fax: (816) 329-3771
Public Affairs Officer **Anthony T. "Tony" Molinaro** ..... (847) 294-7427
E-mail: tony.molinaro@faa.gov Fax: (847) 294-7852

Airports Division
901 Locust Street, Kansas City, MO 64106-2641
Tel: (816) 329-2600 Fax: (816) 329-2610

Director **James A. "Jim" Johnson** .... (816) 329-2600
Deputy Director **Rodney Joel** .... (816) 329-2631
E-mail: rodney.joel@faa.gov
Administrative Officer **Angela "Angie" Muder** .... (816) 329-2620
E-mail: angela.muder@faa.gov
Planning and Engineering Branch Manager **Ed Hyatt** ..... (816) 329-2605

Aerospace Medicine Division
901 Locust Street, Kansas City, MO 64106-2641
Tel: (816) 329-3250 Fax: (816) 329-3266

Regional Flight Surgeon **Dr. Daniel Berry** .... (816) 329-3250
E-mail: daniel.berry@faa.gov
Deputy Regional Flight Surgeon **James R. Elliott** .... (816) 329-3250
Fax: (816) 329-3266

Flight Standards Division
901 Locust Street, Kansas City, MO 64106-2641
Tel: (816) 329-3200 Fax: (816) 329-3208

Manager **Ricardo "Rick" Domingo** .... (816) 329-3200
Assistant Manager **David Sequeira** .... (425) 227-2570
1601 Lind Avenue, SW, Room 560, Renton, WA 98057-4099
Deputy Assistant Manager **(Vacant)** .... (816) 329-3200
Manager, Resource and Program Management Branch
(Acting) **Andrew Estrada** .... (816) 329-3219
Manager, Technical Air Carrier Support Branch
Marita Burgess .... (816) 329-3223
Manager, Safety Analysis and Evaluation
Jack Swensen .... (816) 329-3225
Manager, NextGen Branch **Eric Parker** .... (816) 329-3277

Human Resource Management Division
901 Locust Street, Kansas City, MO 64106-2641
Fax: (816) 329-2653

Manager **(Vacant)** .... (816) 329-2685
Assistant Manager **(Vacant)** .... (816) 329-2660
Management and Program Analyst **Monica Hufford** .... (816) 329-2692
E-mail: monica.hufford@faa.gov
Manager, Personnel Service Branch **Chester Brock** ...... (816) 329-2685
E-mail: chester.brock@faa.gov
Manager, Labor and Employee Relations Branch
Clifton Lovelace .... (816) 329-2652

Information Technology Division
901 Locust Street, Kansas City, MO 64106-2641
Fax: (816) 329-2430

Information Technology Branch Manager
Kenneth "Ken" Jones .... (816) 329-2444
E-mail: ken.jones@faa.gov

Logistics Division
901 Locust Street, Kansas City, MO 64106-2641
Tel: (817) 222-4345 Fax: (816) 329-3136

Manager **(Vacant)** .... (817) 222-4345
Acquisition and Office Services Branch Manager
(Vacant) .... (816) 329-3119
Logistics Liaison **(Vacant)** .... (817) 222-4345

Security and Hazardous Materials Division
901 Locust Street, Kansas City, MO 64106-2641
Tel: (816) 329-3700 Fax: (816) 329-3753

Manager **(Vacant)** .... (817) 222-5700
2601 Meacham Boulevard, Fort Worth, TX 76137 Fax: (817) 222-5990
Manager, Hazardous Materials Branch (Acting)
Gary Mohr .... (817) 222-5700
2601 Meacham Boulevard, Fort Worth, TX 76137
E-mail: gary.mohr@faa.gov
Investigations and LEAP Division Manager
Hope Hernandez .... (817) 222-5701
2601 Meacham Boulevard, Fort Worth, TX 76137
E-mail: hope.hernandez@faa.gov
Manager, Personnel Security and Identification Media
Division **Tyrone Chatter** .... (847) 294-7758
2300 East Devon Avenue, Room 209, Des Plaines, IL 60018
E-mail: tyrone.chatter@faa.gov
Management Program Analyst **Leslie D. Grounds** .... (817) 222-5752
2601 Meacham Boulevard, Room 470, Fort Worth, TX 76137-4298

Executive Support Staff
901 Locust Street, Kansas City, MO 64106-2641
Tel: (816) 329-3050 Fax: (816) 329-3055

Regional Executive Manager **(Vacant)** .... (816) 329-3050
Administrative Specialist **Jamie Marrs** .... (816) 329-3052
E-mail: jamie.marrs@faa.gov
Freedom of Information Act Coordinator
Judy A. Shipp .... (817) 222-5440
Administrative Assistant **Cindy Cigich** .... (816) 329-3050

Executive Operations Staff (OCS)
901 Locust Street, Kansas City, MO 64106-2641
Fax: (816) 329-3069

Emergency Preparedness Special Projects
Gordon Evans .... (816) 329-3011
E-mail: gordon.evans@faa.gov
State Aviation Director's Liaison **(Vacant)** .... (816) 329-2963

Eastern Region
1 Aviation Plaza, 159-30 Rockaway Boulevard, Jamaica, NY 11434-4809
Tel: (718) 553-3375
Areas Covered: DE, DC, MD, NJ, NY, PA, VA, WV

● Regional Administrator
Jennifer E. "Jenny" Solomon .... (202) 267-7954
Regional Executive Manager **Maria Stanco** .... (718) 553-3000
Building Services Team Manager **Jim Hamill** .... (718) 553-2612
Building Services Specialist **Thomas Beckford** .... (718) 553-4988
Regional Emergency Preparedness Officer
James F. Robinson .... (718) 553-3076

Office of the Regional Counsel (ORC)
Regional Counsel **Mary M. McCarthy** .... (718) 553-3259

Aerospace Medicine Division
Regional Flight Surgeon **Dr. Harriet Lester MD** .... (718) 553-3300
Deputy Regional Flight Surgeon
Dominick S. Zito MD .... (718) 553-3300
E-mail: dominick.zito@faa.gov
Management and Program Analyst **Carol Cruise** .... (718) 553-3302
Substance Abuse Program Manager **Janet Wright** .... (404) 305-6164

Airports Division
Director **Steven M. "Steve" Urlass** .... (718) 553-3333
Deputy Director **David Fish** .... (718) 553-3331
Management Assistant **Audrey Carter** .... (718) 553-3333
E-mail: audrey.carter@faa.gov

(continued on next page)

★ Presidential Appointment Requiring Senate Confirmation ☆ Presidential Appointment ☐ Schedule C Appointment ◇ Career Senior Foreign Service Appointment
● Career Senior Executive Service (SES) Appointment ○ Non-Career Senior Executive Service (SES) Appointment ■ Postal Career Executive Service

DEPARTMENTS

Airports Division *(continued)*

Administrative Officer **Karen Smoczkiewicz** . . . . (718) 553-3332
E-mail: karen.smoczkiewicz@faa.gov
Manager, Planning, Programming and Capacity Branch
Patricia Henn . . . . (718) 553-3335
E-mail: patricia.henn@faa.gov
Manager, Safety and Standards Branch
Mahendra Raghubeer . . . . (718) 553-3352
E-mail: mahendra.raghubeer@faa.gov

Executive Operations Staff
Manager **Jacqueline Marcello** . . . . (718) 553-2558
Administrative and Program Specialist
Judy Tramantano-Gray . . . . (718) 553-4164
E-mail: judy.tramantano-gray@faa.gov
Building Services Team Leader **James Hamill** . . . . (718) 553-2612
Executive Operations Team Coordinator **Steven Jones** . . . (718) 553-3049
E-mail: steven.jones@faa.gov

Flight Standards Division
Manager **Lawrence Fields** . . . . (718) 553-3200
Management and Program Analyst
Barbara Skawinska . . . . (718) 553-4510
E-mail: barbara.skawinska@faa.gov
Assistant Manager **(Vacant)** . . . . (718) 553-3201
Secretary **(Vacant)** . . . . (718) 553-3375
Program Management Branch Manager **Joyce Dyer** . . . . . . (718) 553-3205
E-mail: joyce.dyer@faa.gov
Technical Branch Manager **Steven Trupkin** . . . . (718) 553-3240

Human Resource Management Division
Director **Keith E. Johnson** . . . . (718) 553-3113
Personnel Services Branch Manager **Ryan Gill** . . . . (718) 553-3459
E-mail: ryan.gill@faa.gov
Labor Relations/Employee Development Branch
Manager **Sandra Peets** . . . . (718) 553-3160
E-mail: sandra.peets@faa.gov Fax: (718) 977-6707
Administrative Officer **(Vacant)** . . . . (718) 553-3375

Information Technology Division
Manager **Gary Solomon** . . . . (718) 553-4157
E-mail: gary.solomon@faa.gov

Eastern Logistics Service Area
Office Manager/Liaison **Diana Rizzuto** . . . . (718) 553-4983
Fax: (718) 995-5684
Staff Assistant **(Vacant)** . . . . (718) 553-3073
Team Leader, Acquisition Management **(Vacant)** . . . . (718) 553-3079

Security and Hazardous Materials Division
Director **Aaron Sinder** . . . . (781) 238-7711
1200 District Avenue, Room 105, Burlington, MA 01803
E-mail: aaron.sinder@faa.gov
Deputy Director **(Vacant)** . . . . (718) 553-2595
Administrative Officer **Rosa Umana** . . . . (718) 553-3124
E-mail: rosa.umana@faa.gov
Hazardous Materials Branch Manager **(Vacant)** . . . . (718) 553-2596
Investigations Branch Manager **(Vacant)** . . . . (718) 553-3126

Great Lakes Region
2300 East Devon Avenue, Des Plaines, IL 60018
Tel: (847) 294-7294 Fax: (847) 294-7971
Areas Covered: IL, IN, MI, MN, ND, OH, SD, WI

● Regional Administrator (Acting)
Rebecca Byers MacPherson . . . . (847) 294-7294
Education: Tulane JD
Deputy Regional Administrator **Christina Drouet** . . . . (847) 294-7294
E-mail: christina.drouet@faa.gov
Education: Illinois 1979 BS; Illinois Tech 2007 MPA
Civil Rights Officer **Joyce Davis** . . . . (817) 222-5009
10101 Hillwood Parkway, Fax: (847) 294-7356
Room 230, Fort Worth, TX 76177
E-mail: joyce.davis@faa.gov
Regional Chief Counsel **Jeffrey "Jeff" Klang** . . . . (847) 294-7109
E-mail: jeffrey.klang@faa.gov Fax: (847) 294-7498

Aerospace Medicine Division
2300 East Devon Avenue, Des Plaines, IL 60018
Tel: (847) 294-7491 Fax: (847) 294-7808
Regional Flight Surgeon **Joseph "Joey" Helmes** . . . . (847) 294-7773

Airports Division
2300 East Devon Avenue, Room 312, Des Plaines, IL 60018
Tel: (847) 294-7272 Fax: (847) 294-7036
Director **Susan Mowery-Schalk** . . . . (847) 294-7272

Des Plaines, Chicago, Illinois
Manager **Deb Bartell** . . . . (847) 294-7335

Minneapolis-Saint. Paul International Airport Minneapolis, Minnesota
6020 28th Avenue South, Minneapolis, MN 55450-2700
Division Manager **Andy Peek** . . . . (612) 253-4631
2300 East Devon Avenue, Des Plaines, IL 60018

Romulus, Detroit, Michigan
11677-B S Wayne Road, Romulus, MI 48174
Manager **John L. Mayfield, Jr.** . . . . (734) 229-2900

Flight Standards Division
2300 East Devon Avenue, Des Plaines, IL 60018
Tel: (847) 294-7252 Fax: (847) 294-7661
Manager **James E. Gardner** . . . . (847) 294-7252

Human Resource Management Office
2300 East Devon Avenue, Des Plaines, IL 60018
Tel: (847) 294-7730 Fax: (847) 294-8535
Director **Debra Larson** . . . . (847) 294-7730

Information Technology Branch
2300 East Devon Avenue, Des Plaines, IL 60018
Tel: (847) 294-7224 Fax: (847) 294-7776
Manager **John Swaney CISSP** Room 369 . . . . (847) 294-7224
E-mail: john.swaney@faa.gov

Logistics Division
2300 East Devon Avenue, Des Plaines, IL 60018
Tel: (847) 294-7166 Fax: (847) 294-7270
Acquisitions Manager **(Vacant)** . . . . (847) 294-7166

Public Affairs Division
2300 East Devon Avenue, Des Plaines, IL 60018
Tel: (847) 294-7427 Fax: (847) 294-7852
Public Affairs Officer
Anthony T. "Tony" Molinaro Room 432 . . . . (847) 294-7339
E-mail: tony.molinaro@faa.gov

New England Region
12 New England Executive Park, Burlington, MA 01803
Tel: (781) 238-7020 Fax: (781) 238-7005
Areas Covered: CT, ME, MA, NH, RI, VT

● Regional Administrator **(Vacant)** . . . . (907) 271-5645
Deputy Regional Administrator (Acting)
Julie Seltsam-Wilps . . . . (781) 238-7389
E-mail: julie.a.seltsam@faa.gov
Administrative Specialist **Catherine Miller** . . . . (781) 238-7024
E-mail: catherine.miller@faa.gov
Regional Counsel **Mary M. McCarthy** . . . . (781) 238-7042
E-mail: mary.m.mccarthy@faa.gov
National Aviation Education Program Manager
James Brough . . . . (781) 238-7027
E-mail: james.brough@faa.gov
Web Developer **JoAnn Napolitano** . . . . (781) 238-7399
E-mail: webmasterane@faa.gov
Senior Advisor **Julie Seltsam-Wilps** . . . . (781) 238-7389

★ Presidential Appointment Requiring Senate Confirmation ☆ Presidential Appointment □ Schedule C Appointment ◇ Career Senior Foreign Service Appointment
● Career Senior Executive Service (SES) Appointment ○ Non-Career Senior Executive Service (SES) Appointment ■ Postal Career Executive Service

Human Resource Management Office
12 New England Executive Park, Burlington, MA 01803-5299
Fax: (781) 238-7283

Director and Human Resource Management Officer
April Gauthier . . . . . (781) 238-7253
E-mail: april.gauthier@faa.gov
Compensation and Staffing Specialist **Eileen Celli** . . . . . (781) 238-7256
E-mail: eileen.celli@faa.gov
Federal Personnel Payroll System Manager
Kerry Ferreira . . . . . (781) 238-7259
E-mail: kerry.ferreira@faa.gov
Human Resources Specialist **Cheryl Johnson** . . . . . (781) 238-7261
E-mail: cheryl.johnson@faa.gov
Team Lead **Katrina Newlin** . . . . . (781) 238-7266
E-mail: katrina.newlin@faa.gov
Administrative Officer **Linda Cucchiara** . . . . . (781) 238-7251
E-mail: linda.cucchiara@faa.gov

Airports Division
12 New England Executive Park, Burlington, MA 01803-5299
Fax: (781) 238-7608

Director (Acting) **Gail Lattrell** . . . . . (781) 238-7600
E-mail: gail.lattrell@faa.gov
Deputy Director **Gail Lattrell** . . . . . (781) 238-7615
Environmental Program Manager **Richard Doucette** . . . . . (781) 238-7602
E-mail: richard.doucette@faa.gov
Boston Airport District Office Manager
Kelly Slusarski . . . . . (781) 238-7600
E-mail: kelly.slusarski@faa.gov
Safety and Standards Branch Manager **(Vacant)** . . . . . (781) 238-7620

Aerospace Medical Division
12 New England Executive Park, Burlington, MA 01803-5299
Fax: (781) 238-7306

Regional Flight Surgeon (Acting)
Dr. Stephen Goodman MD . . . . . (781) 238-7300
E-mail: stephen.goodmanmd@faa.gov Fax: (781) 238-7306

Flight Standards Division
12 New England Executive Park, Burlington, MA 01803-5299
Fax: (781) 238-7245

Assistant Division Manager **Edward "Ed" Reinecker** . . . . (781) 238-7206
Associate Division Manager **Beth Babb** . . . . . (781) 238-7201
Program Management Branch Manager **(Vacant)** . . . . . (781) 238-7020
Safety and Analysis Branch Manager
Nicholas Gregoriades . . . . . (781) 553-3205

Logistics Division
12 New England Executive Park, Burlington, MA 01803-5299
Fax: (781) 238-7654

Real Estate and Utilities Group, ALO-620 Manager
Larry Robinson . . . . . (781) 238-7656
E-mail: larry.robinson@faa.gov
Real Estate and Utilities Frontline Manager, ALO-620
Inger Brown . . . . . (781) 238-7656
E-mail: inger.brown@faa.gov
Real Estate and Utilities Frontline Manager, ALO-620
Jaime Reyes . . . . . (781) 238-7656

Security and Investigations Division
12 New England Executive Park, Burlington, MA 01803-5299
Fax: (781) 238-7716

Internal Security Manager **(Vacant)** . . . . . (781) 238-7711

Executive Operations Staff
12 New England Executive Park, Burlington, MA 01803-5299
Fax: (781) 238-7380

Manager **(Vacant)** . . . . . (781) 238-7020
Information Technology Manager **David Wierzbicki** . . . . . (781) 238-7478
E-mail: david.wierzbicki@faa.gov

Northwest Mountain Region
2200 South 216th Street, Des Moines, WA 98198
Tel: (206) 231-2393
Areas Covered: CO, ID, MT, OR, UT, WA, WY

Regional Administrator (Acting) **David C. Suomi** . . . . . (206) 231-2393
1601 Lind Avenue, SW, Suite 500, Renton, WA 98057-4099
E-mail: david.suomi@faa.gov
Deputy Regional Administrator (Acting)
Shelly Larson . . . . . (206) 231-2393
E-mail: shelly.larson@faa.gov
Regional Counsel **Dwight Williams** . . . . . (425) 227-2007
1601 Lind Avenue, SW, Fax: (425) 227-1007
Suite 570, Renton, WA 98057-4099
E-mail: dwight.williams@faa.gov
Western Service Area Quality Assurance Group Team
Manager **Brian Schimpf** . . . . . (206) 231-2055
1601 Lind Avenue, SW, Suite 580, Renton, WA 98057-4099
Civil Rights Director **Kelly Boodell** . . . . . (206) 231-2044
1601 Lind Avenue, SW, Fax: (425) 227-1009
Suite 240, Renton, WA 98057-4099
E-mail: kelly.boodell@faa.gov
Regional Public Affairs Manager **W. Allen Kenitzer** . . . . . (425) 227-2015
1601 Lind Avenue, SW, Fax: (425) 227-1233
Suite 520, Renton, WA 98057-4099
Air Force Representative **(Vacant)** . . . . . (425) 227-2947
1601 Lind Avenue, SW, Fax: (425) 227-1114
Suite 314, Renton, WA 98057-4099
Army Representative **Deanna Bridenback** . . . . . (425) 227-2955
1601 Lind Avenue, SW, Suite 314, Renton, WA 98057-4099
E-mail: deanna.bridenback@faa.gov
Marine Representative **(Vacant)** . . . . . (425) 227-1384
Navy Representative **Tom Cawley** . . . . . (425) 227-2740
1601 Lind Avenue, SW, Fax: (425) 227-1114
Suite 314, Renton, WA 98057-4099
E-mail: tom.cawley@faa.gov
Computer Specialist **Mike McDonnell** . . . . . (425) 227-2963
E-mail: mike.mcdonnell@faa.gov
NAVREP **Jason Anton** . . . . . (425) 227-2665

Aerospace Medicine Division
1601 Lind Avenue, SW, Suite 100, Renton, WA 98057-4099
Tel: (425) 227-2300 Fax: (425) 227-1300

Regional Flight Surgeon **Brett Wyrick MPH, DO** . . . . . (425) 227-2300
Fax: (425) 227-1300

Airports Division
1601 Lind Avenue, SW, Suite 315, Renton, WA 98057-4099
Tel: (425) 227-2600 Fax: (425) 227-1600

Denver, Colorado
26805 East 68th Ave, Denver, CO 80249
Tel: (303) 342-1254 Fax: (303) 342-1260

Manager **John Bauer** . . . . . (303) 342-1259

Helena, Montana
2725 Skyway Drive, Helena, MT 59602

Manager **Dave Stelling** . . . . . (406) 449-5271

Seattle, Washington
Manager **Joelle Briggs** . . . . . (206) 231-4126

Flight Standards Division
1601 Lind Avenue, SW, Suite 560, Renton, WA 98057-4099
Tel: (425) 227-2200 Fax: (425) 227-1200

Manager **Ricardo "Rick" Domingo** . . . . . (425) 227-2200
Assistant Manager **Wayne P. Fry** . . . . . (425) 227-2200
Flight Standards District Office Manager
David "Dave" Menzimer Suite 260 . . . . . (425) 227-2567
Fax: (425) 227-1810
Resource Management Branch Manager **(Vacant)** . . . . . (425) 227-2234
Seattle Aircraft Evaluation Group Manager **(Vacant)** . . . . . (425) 917-6601
Fax: (425) 227-1270

(continued on next page)

DEPARTMENTS

★ Presidential Appointment Requiring Senate Confirmation ☆ Presidential Appointment □ Schedule C Appointment ◇ Career Senior Foreign Service Appointment
● Career Senior Executive Service (SES) Appointment ○ Non-Career Senior Executive Service (SES) Appointment ■ Postal Career Executive Service

DEPARTMENTS

Flight Standards Division *(continued)*

Technical Standards Branch Manager
Jody M. Radcliffe . . . . (425) 227-2871
E-mail: jody.m.radcliffe@faa.gov

Human Resources Division
1601 Lind Avenue, SW, Suite 320, Renton, WA 98057-4099
Tel: (425) 227-2010 Fax: (425) 227-1010

Manager **Leslie McBroom** . . . . (425) 227-2017
E-mail: leslie.mcbroom@faa.gov
Employment Services Branch Manager **(Vacant)** . . . . (425) 227-2441
Labor and Employee Relations Branch Manager
Tom Schloetter . . . . (425) 227-2033
E-mail: tom.schloetter@faa.gov

Information Technology Division
1601 Lind Avenue, SW, Renton, WA 98057-4099
Tel: (425) 227-2440 Fax: (425) 227-1040

Manager **Chris Guinotte** . . . . (425) 227-2553
E-mail: chris.guinotte@faa.gov

Logistics Division
1601 Lind Avenue, SW, Renton, WA 98057-4099
Tel: (425) 227-2050 Fax: (425) 227-1055

Western Logistics Service Manager **(Vacant)** . . . . (425) 227-2050
Materiel and Personal Property Group Manager
Doreen Boschee . . . . (425) 227-2941
E-mail: doreen.boschee@faa.gov
Real Estate and Utilities Group Manager
Damon McGruder . . . . (425) 227-2155

Terminal Planning
Landmark Building, 1601 Lind Avenue, SW, Renton, WA 98057-4099
Tel: (425) 203-4793

Manager **(Vacant)** . . . . (202) 385-8546

Western Flight Procedures Office
1601 Lind Avenue, SW, Renton, WA 98057-4099
Tel: (425) 917-6720 Fax: (425) 227-2269

Manager **David G. "Dave" Parker** . . . . (425) 917-6720
E-mail: david.g.parker@faa.gov
Lead **Beverly Tulip** . . . . (425) 917-6720
Fax: (405) 954-9962
Lead **Rachelle Dailey** . . . . (425) 917-6720
Fax: (405) 954-9962

Southern Region
1701 Columbia Avenue, College Park, GA 30337
Mail: P.O. Box 20636, Atlanta, GA 30320-0631
Tel: (404) 305-5000 Fax: (404) 305-5010
Areas Covered: AL, FL, GA, KY, MS, NC, PR, SC, TN, VI

● Regional Administrator **Michael C. O'Harra** . . . . (404) 305-5000
Deputy Regional Administrator **Pearlis Johnson** . . . . (404) 305-5000
Regional Counsel **(Vacant)** . . . . (404) 305-5200
Civil Rights Staff Manager **(Vacant)** . . . . (404) 305-5250
Regional Operations Center Manager **(Vacant)** . . . . (404) 305-5180
External Communications Manager
Kathleen B. Bergen . . . . (404) 305-5100
E-mail: kathleen.bergen@faa.gov
Executive Operations **Valerie Thompson** . . . . (404) 305-5851
Air Force Representative **(Vacant)** . . . . (404) 305-6901
Army Representative **Jeff Martuscelli** . . . . (404) 305-6915
Marine Corps Representative **(Vacant)** . . . . (404) 305-5000
Navy Representative **(Vacant)** . . . . (404) 305-6906

Aerospace Medicine Division
Regional Flight Surgeon **Dr. Susan Northrup** . . . . (404) 305-6150
Deputy Flight Surgeon **Dr. John Barson** . . . . (404) 305-6150

Airports Division
Manager **Steven Hicks** . . . . (404) 305-6700
Regional Airports Programs **(Vacant)** . . . . (404) 305-6702

Atlanta, Georgia
Manager (Acting) **Aimee McCormick** . . . . (404) 305-7143

Jackson, Mississippi
100 West Cross Street, Jackson, MS 39208
Manager **Rans Black** . . . . (601) 664-9892

Memphis, Tennessee
2600 Thousand Oaks Boulevard, Memphis, TN 38118
Manager **Phillip Braden** . . . . (901) 322-8181

Orlando, Florida
5950 Hazeltine National Drive, Orlando, FL 32822
Manager **Bart Vernace** . . . . (407) 812-6331 ext. 127

Flight Standards Division
Manager **Thomas Winston** . . . . (404) 305-6000
Assistant Manager **(Vacant)** . . . . (404) 305-6000

Human Resource Management Division
Manager **Q. Scott Brackett** . . . . (404) 305-5300

Logistics Division
Logistics Services Area Manager **Roger Lilley** . . . . (404) 305-5700
E-mail: roger.lilley@faa.gov
Acquisitions Group Manager **Troy Slezak** . . . . (404) 305-5771
Materiel and Personal Property Manager
William Nelmes . . . . (404) 305-5796
E-mail: william.nelmes@faa.gov
Real Estate and Utilities Group Manager **Inger Brown** . . . (404) 305-5784

Security and Hazardous Materials Division
Manager **(Vacant)** . . . . (404) 305-6750
Hazardous Materials Branch Manager **(Vacant)** . . . . (404) 305-6750
Investigations and Internal Security Branch Manager
Barbara Grimes . . . . (404) 305-6771
E-mail: barbara.grimes@faa.gov
Atlanta Hazardous Material Division Manager
Deborah Kennedy . . . . (404) 305-6831
E-mail: deborah.kennedy@faa.gov Fax: (404) 305-6754

Southwest Region
2601 Meacham Boulevard, Fort Worth, TX 76137-4298
Tel: (817) 222-5000 Tel: (817) 222-5006 (Operations Center)
Fax: (817) 222-5944
Areas Covered: AR, LA, NM, OK, TX

● Regional Administrator **Terry Biggio** . . . . (817) 222-5001
E-mail: terry.biggio@faa.gov Fax: (817) 222-5042
Deputy Regional Administrator **(Vacant)** . . . . (817) 222-5000
Regional Counsel **Kimberly "Kim" Toler** . . . . (614) 280-6144
E-mail: kimberly.toler@hud.gov Fax: (817) 222-5092
Budget and Resource Program Lead **Angela Majar** . . . . (817) 222-5491
Fax: (817) 222-5891
Civil Rights Manager **Joyce Davis** . . . . (817) 222-5009
E-mail: joyce.davis@faa.gov Fax: (817) 225-5724
Public Affairs Officer **Lynn Lunford** . . . . (817) 222-4455
Management and Program Analyst
Sandra E. Freeman . . . . (817) 222-5440

Aerospace Medicine Division
2601 Meacham Boulevard, Fort Worth, TX 76137
Tel: (817) 222-5300 Fax: (817) 222-5965

Regional Flight Surgeon **G. J. Salazar** . . . . (817) 222-5478
Deputy Regional Flight Surgeon
Denise L. Baisden MD . . . . (817) 222-5300

Airports Division
2601 Meacham Boulevard, Fort Worth, TX 76137
Tel: (817) 222-5600

Manager **Ignacio Flores** . . . . (817) 222-5600
Planning and Programming Branch Manager
Cameron Bryan . . . . (817) 222-5610
E-mail: cameron.bryan@faa.gov Fax: (817) 222-5985

★ Presidential Appointment Requiring Senate Confirmation ☆ Presidential Appointment ☐ Schedule C Appointment ◇ Career Senior Foreign Service Appointment
● Career Senior Executive Service (SES) Appointment ○ Non-Career Senior Executive Service (SES) Appointment ■ Postal Career Executive Service

Airports Division *(continued)*

Safety and Standards Branch Manager
Joseph G. Washington .... (817) 222-5620
E-mail: joe.washington@faa.gov Fax: (817) 222-5984

Louisiana/New Mexico Airports Development Office
Manager **Lacey Spriggs** .... (817) 222-5640
E-mail: lacey.spriggs@faa.gov Fax: (817) 222-5988
Assistant Manager **John Michener** .... (817) 222-5010
E-mail: john.michener@faa.gov

Arkansas/Oklahoma Airports Development Office
Manager **Glenn A. Boles** .... (817) 222-5630
Fax: (817) 222-5987

Texas Airports Development Office
Manager **Edward N. Agnew** .... (817) 222-5650
E-mail: ed.agnew@faa.gov Fax: (817) 222-5989

Flight Standards Division
2601 Meacham Boulevard, Fort Worth, TX 76137
Tel: (817) 222-5200
Division Manager **Nicholas "Nick" Reyes** .... (817) 222-5200
E-mail: nicholas.reyes@faa.gov Fax: (817) 222-5286
Assistant Division Manager **Dennis J. Hill** .... (817) 222-5206
E-mail: dennis.j.hill@faa.gov
Leadership Development Team, Mentor/Coach
Debra Z. Joiner .... (817) 562-3213
Fort Worth AEG Manager **Mark C. Fletcher** .... (817) 222-5269
Planning and Program Management Manager
Tracy Leese .... (817) 222-5225

Human Resource Management Division
2601 Meacham Boulevard, Fort Worth, TX 76137
Manager **Doug Lane** .... (817) 222-5810
Fax: (817) 222-5948
Employment Branch Manager **Faith V. Downes** .... (817) 222-5844
E-mail: faith.v.downes@faa.gov
Labor/Employee Relations and Workforce Development Branch Manager **Gina Alcala** .... (817) 222-5815

Logistics Division
2601 Meacham Boulevard, Fort Worth, TX 76137
Tel: (817) 222-4350
Manager **Keith J. Moore** .... (817) 222-4301
Education: Lehigh 1983 BS Fax: (817) 222-5956
Regional Acquisitions Manager **Lawrence Ayers** .... (817) 222-4330
E-mail: lawrence.ayers@faa.gov
Frontline Manager **Carolyn J. Holman** .... (817) 222-4377
Materiel and Personal Property Group Manager
Lawana S. Kadel .... (817) 222-4345
Real Estate and Utilities Branch Manager
James M. Nelson .... (817) 222-4238

Security and Hazardous Materials Division
2601 Meacham Boulevard, Fort Worth, TX 76137
Tel: (817) 222-5700
Manager **(Vacant)** .... (817) 222-5700
Hazardous Materials Branch Manager **Gary Mohr** .... (817) 222-5720
E-mail: gary.mohr@faa.gov
Internal Security and Investigations Branch Manager
Hope Hernandez .... (817) 222-5777

Information Technology Branch
2601 Meacham Boulevard, Fort Worth, TX 76137
Manager **Roy LaBuff** .... (210) 308-3359
E-mail: roy.labuff@faa.gov Fax: (817) 222-5954

Military Representatives
2601 Meacham Boulevard, Fort Worth, TX 76137
Air Force Representative **(Vacant)** .... (817) 222-5000
Army Representative **LTC Robert Wegner USA** .... (817) 222-5921
E-mail: robert.wegner@faa.gov
Navy Representative **Arjuna Fields** .... (817) 222-5931

Western Pacific Region
15000 Aviation Boulevard, Lawndale, CA 90261
Mail: P.O. Box 92007, Los Angeles, CA 90009
Tel: (310) 725-3550
Tel: (206) 231-2089 (24-hour accident and incident response)
Fax: (310) 725-6811 Internet: www.faa.gov/airports/western_pacific
Areas Covered: AZ, CA, HI, NV, Guam, American Samoa and former U.S. trust territories, including Federated States of Micronesia, Republic of Palau, Republic of the Marshall Islands
● Regional Administrator **Dennis E. Roberts** .... (310) 725-3550
Education: Central Missouri State BS, MS Fax: (310) 725-6811
Deputy Regional Administrator **Tamara Swann** .... (310) 725-3550
Regional Executive Manager **(Vacant)** .... (310) 725-3550
Administrative Officer **(Vacant)** .... (310) 725-3550
Regional Counsel **Adam Runkel** .... (425) 227-2914
1601 Lind Avenue, SW, Room 6007H, Renton, WA 98057-4099
Civil Rights Staff Manager **(Vacant)** .... (310) 725-3943
Special Programs Staff Manager **Keith Lusk** .... (310) 725-3808
Media Relations **(Vacant)** .... (310) 725-3580

Airports Division
Manager **Robin K. Hunt** .... (310) 725-3654
Manager **Mark McClardy** .... (310) 725-3600
Planning and Programs Branch Manager **Mia Ratcliff** .... (310) 725-3610
E-mail: mia.ratcliff@faa.gov
Safety and Standards Branch Manager
Brian Armstrong .... (310) 725-3620

Los Angeles, California
Manager **Dave Cushing** .... (310) 725-3644

San Francisco, California
Airports District Office Manager (Acting) **David Fish** .... (650) 827-7601
Assistant ADO Manager **(Vacant)** .... (650) 827-7602

Honolulu, Hawaii
300 Ala Moana Boulevard, Room 7-128, Honolulu, HI 96850
Tel: (808) 312-6028 Fax: (808) 312-6048
Manager **(Vacant)** .... (808) 312-6028

Phoenix, Arizona
3800 Central Avenue, Room 1025, Phoenix, AZ 85012
Manager **Michael N. "Mike" Williams** .... (602) 792-1064
Assistant Manager **(Vacant)** .... (602) 792-1065

Aerospace Medicine Division
Regional Flight Surgeon **Dr. Stephen Griswold MD** .... (310) 725-3750
Fax: (310) 725-6835
Deputy Regional Flight Surgeon **Marvin Jackson** .... (310) 725-3824
Fax: (847) 294-8566
Flight Surgeon **Dr. Stephen Lenchner MD** .... (310) 725-3750
Supervisory Program Analyst **(Vacant)** .... (310) 725-3770
Drug Abatement Program (Internal) **(Vacant)** .... (310) 725-3550

Flight Standards Division
Manager **Thuan Nguyen** .... (310) 725-7200
Planning and Resource Management Branch Manager
Judy Ekmalian .... (310) 725-7210

Human Resource Management Division
Manager **(Vacant)** .... (310) 725-7800
Administrative Officer **Marilyn Alvarez** .... (310) 725-7802
E-mail: marilyn.alvarez@faa.gov Fax: (310) 725-6380
Employment Services and Benefits Branch Manager
Karen Pecchia .... (310) 725-7830
E-mail: karen.pecchia@faa.gov
Labor/Employment Relations, Training Manager
Aletha Hicks-Moffatt .... (310) 725-7820
Human Resources Specialist **Deidra Mitchell** .... (310) 725-7874
E-mail: deidra.mitchell@faa.gov

Information Resource Division
Manager **(Vacant)** .... (310) 725-6700

DEPARTMENTS

★ Presidential Appointment Requiring Senate Confirmation ☆ Presidential Appointment □ Schedule C Appointment ◇ Career Senior Foreign Service Appointment
● Career Senior Executive Service (SES) Appointment ○ Non-Career Senior Executive Service (SES) Appointment ■ Postal Career Executive Service

DEPARTMENTS

Logistics Service Area
Manager **Angela Layman** .... (425) 227-1150
E-mail: angela.layman@faa.gov
Small Business Senior Analyst **Frederick L. "Fred" Dendy** .... (202) 267-7454
E-mail: fred.dendy@faa.gov
Logistic Management Program Analyst **Betsy Tiedemann** .... (310) 725-7510

Security and Hazardous Materials Division
Division Manager **(Vacant)** .... (310) 725-3550
Hazardous Materials Branch Manager **(Vacant)** .... (310) 725-3701

Los Angeles Aircraft Certification Office
3960 Paramount Boulevard, Lakewood, CA 90712-4137
Manager **Kevin Hull** .... (562) 627-5202
E-mail: kevin.hull@faa.gov
Airframe Branch Manager **Greg DiLibero** .... (562) 627-5220
E-mail: greg.dilibero@faa.gov
Flight Test Branch Manager **Joe Hashemi** .... (562) 627-5360
E-mail: joe.hashemi@faa.gov
Manufacturing Inspection Branch Manager **Wanda Kimura** .... (562) 627-5290
E-mail: wanda.kimura@faa.gov
Propulsion Branch Manager **(Vacant)** .... (562) 627-5240
Systems and Equipment Branch Manager **(Vacant)** .... (562) 627-5330
Technical and Administrative Support Staff Manager **Haifa Haj-Eid** .... (562) 627-5300
Senior Engineer **Hank Tong** .... (562) 627-5373

Military Representatives
Air Force Representative **Lenore Marentette** .... (425) 227-2947
Army Representative **Deanna Bridenback** .... (310) 725-3550
Navy Representative **Anthony F. Smith** .... (425) 227-2740

Federal Highway Administration (FHWA)

Southeast Federal Center Building, 1200 New Jersey Avenue, SE, Washington, DC 20590-9898
Tel: (202) 366-0537 (Personnel Locator)
Tel: (202) 366-0660 (Public Information/Publications Information)
Tel: (202) 366-0534 (Freedom of Information/Privacy Act)
Internet: www.fhwa.dot.gov
Internet: https://www.fhwa.dot.gov/foia/err.cfm (Legal Documents Homepage)

OFFICE OF THE ADMINISTRATOR

Southeast Federal Center Building, 1200 New Jersey Avenue, SE, Washington, DC 20590-9898
Fax: (202) 366-3244

Field Services

Field Services - North

Leo W. O'Brien Federal Building, Ste 715, Albany, NY 12207
Fax: (410) 962-3655
Areas Covered: CT, IA, IL, IN, MA, ME, MI, MN, MO, NH, NJ, NY, OH, PA, RI, VT, WI, WV
● Director **Robert E. "Bob" Arnold** .... (518) 431-8873
Fax: (202) 366-3225
Counsel **Sharon Vaughn-Fair** .... (410) 962-2544

Federal-Aid Division Offices

Connecticut Division Office
628-2 Hebron Avenue, Suite 303, Glastonbury, CT 06033-5007
Tel: (860) 659-6703 Fax: (860) 659-6724
E-mail: connecticut.fhwa@dot.gov Internet: www.fhwa.dot.gov/ctdiv
Division Administrator **Amy D. Jackson-Grove** .... (860) 659-6703
E-mail: amy.jackson-grove@dot.gov

Connecticut Division Office *(continued)*
Assistant Division Administrator **Michelle Hilary** .... (860) 494-7571
E-mail: michelle.hilary@dot.gov
Financial Manager **Debra P. "Debbie" Ramirez** .... (860) 494-7569

Engineering and Operations
Engineering Team Leader **David W. Nardone** .... (860) 494-7559

Program Development Team
Team Leader **Kurt Salmoiraghi** .... (860) 494-7561
E-mail: kurt.salmoiraghi@dot.gov

Illinois Division Office
3250 Executive Park Drive, Springfield, IL 62703-4514
Tel: (217) 492-4640 Fax: (217) 492-4621 E-mail: illinois.fhwa@dot.gov
Internet: www.fhwa.dot.gov/ildiv
Division Administrator **Catherine A. "Kay" Batey** .... (217) 492-4640
E-mail: catherine.batey@dot.gov

Assistant Division Administrator
Assistant Division Administrator **Glenn D. Fulkerson** .... (217) 492-4641
E-mail: glenn.fulkerson@dot.gov

Administrative Team
Administrative Officer **(Vacant)** .... (217) 492-4640

Infrastructure and Technology Team
Bridge Engineer **Dan Brydl** .... (217) 492-4632
E-mail: dan.brydl@dot.gov

Finance and Logistics Team
Financial Manager **Chris Hall** .... (217) 492-4610
E-mail: christopher.j.hall@dot.gov

Field Engineering
Field Engineering Manager **Michael W. "Mike" Smart** .... (217) 492-4613

Engineering Team A
Engineering Team Leader **Omar Qudus** .... (217) 492-4634
E-mail: omar.qudus@dot.gov
Transportation Engineer (Chicago Urban Satellite Office) **William Chris Byars** .... (312) 886-1606

Engineering Team B
Engineering Team Leader **Mike Staggs** .... (217) 492-4630
E-mail: mike.staggs@dot.gov

Planning and Program Development
Planning and Program Development Manager **Jon-Paul Kohler** .... (217) 492-4988

Mobility and Safety Team
Mobility and Safety Engineer **Alan Ho** .... (217) 492-4622
E-mail: alan.ho@dot.gov

Planning, Environment and Right of Way Team
Planning, Environment and Right-of-Way Team Leader **Jerry D. "JD" Stevenson** .... (217) 492-4638
E-mail: jerry.stevenson@dot.gov
Metropolitan Planning Specialist (Chicago Urban Satellite Office) **John M. Donovan** .... (312) 353-4048

Indiana Division Office
Minton Capehart Federal Building, 575 North Pennsylvania Street, Room 254, Indianapolis, IN 46204-1576
Tel: (317) 226-7475 Fax: (317) 226-7341 E-mail: indiana.fhwa@dot.gov
Internet: www.fhwa.dot.gov/indiv
Division Administrator **Mayela Sosa** .... (317) 226-7476
E-mail: mayela.sosa@dot.gov
Education: Texas 2005 MS
Assistant Division Administrator **(Vacant)** .... (317) 226-7483
Division Emergency Coordinator **Karen Stippich** .... (317) 226-7122

★ Presidential Appointment Requiring Senate Confirmation ☆ Presidential Appointment ☐ Schedule C Appointment ◇ Career Senior Foreign Service Appointment
● Career Senior Executive Service (SES) Appointment ○ Non-Career Senior Executive Service (SES) Appointment ■ Postal Career Executive Service

Financial Management Team
Finance Manager Team Leader **Adam Makuley** . . . . (317) 226-7482

Performance Management Team
Performance Management Team Leader
Keith Hoernschemeyer . . . . (317) 226-7490

Planning, Environment, Air Quality, and Right-of-Way Team (PEAR)
PEAR Team Leader **Janice Osadczuk** . . . . (317) 226-7486
E-mail: janice.osadczuk@dot.gov

Project Delivery Team
Project Delivery Team Leader **Jay DuMontelle** . . . . (317) 226-7491

Iowa Division Office
105 Sixth Street, Ames, IA 50010-6337
Tel: (515) 233-7300 Fax: (515) 233-7499
E-mail: iowa.fhwa@fhwa.dot.gov Internet: www.fhwa.dot.gov/iadiv

Division Administrator **Karen Bobo** . . . . (515) 233-7300
E-mail: karen.bobo@dot.gov
Assistant Division Administrator **Mark A. Johnson** . . . . . . (515) 233-7317
E-mail: marka.johnson@dot.gov
Financial Manager **Diana Watts** . . . . (515) 233-7330

Program Delivery Team
Program Delivery Team Leader
Andrew "Andy" Wilson . . . . (515) 233-7306

Planning and Development Team
Planning and Development Team Leader **Sean Litteral** . . . (515) 233-7321

Maine Division Office
Edmund S. Muskie Federal Building, 40 Western Avenue,
Room 614, Augusta, ME 04330-6394
Tel: (207) 622-8350 Fax: (207) 626-9133
E-mail: maine.fhwa@fhwa.dot.gov Internet: www.fhwa.dot.gov/mediv

Division Administrator **Todd D. Jorgensen** . . . . . (207) 512-4911 ext. 106
E-mail: todd.jorgensen@dot.gov
Assistant Division Administrator
Cheryl "Sherry" Martin . . . . (207) 622-4912 ext. 105
E-mail: cheryl.martin@dot.gov
Administrative Operations Assistant **Simona Petrick** . . . . . (207) 512-4915
E-mail: Simona.Petrick@dot.gov

Finance Team
Financial Manager **Christopher Trenholm** . . . . . . (207) 622-8350 ext. 110

Engineering Team
Engineering Team Leader **Brian Lawrence** . . . . (207) 512-4920

Program Delivery
Planning and Development Manager
Carlos Pena . . . . (207) 622-4917 ext. 117

Massachusetts Division Office
55 Broadway, 10th Floor, Mail Code RTV-8C, Cambridge, MA 02142
Tel: (617) 494-3657 Fax: (617) 494-3355
E-mail: massachusetts.fhwa@dot.gov Internet: www.fhwa.dot.gov/madiv

Division Administrator **Jeff H. McEwen PE** . . . . (617) 494-3657
Assistant Division Administrator
Kenneth S. "Ken" Miller PE . . . . (617) 494-2164
E-mail: kenneth.miller@dot.gov
Director of Project Delivery **John McVann** . . . . (617) 494-2521

Financial Management
Financial Manager **Amy Sullivan** . . . . (617) 494-2014
E-mail: amy.sullivan@dot.gov
Financial Specialist **Hermiose Dornevil** . . . . (617) 494-3278

Project Delivery Team
Technical Services / Construction Quality Engineer
Gregory J. Doyle . . . . (617) 494-3279
Field Operations Specialist Team Leader
Joshua "Josh" Grzegorzewsk . . . . (617) 494-2791
Division Bridge Team Leader **Olu Adeyemi** . . . . (617) 494-2462

Program Development
Team Leader **Nelson Hoffman** . . . . (617) 494-3275

Michigan Division Office
Federal Building, 315 West Allegan Street,
Room 201, Lansing, MI 48933
Tel: (517) 377-1844 Fax: (517) 377-1804
E-mail: michigan.fhwa@dot.gov Internet: www.fhwa.dot.gov/midiv

Division Administrator **Russell L. Jorgenson** . . . . (517) 377-1844
E-mail: russell.jorgenson@dot.gov
Assistant Division Administrator **Theodore G. Burch** . . . . (517) 702-1835
E-mail: theodore.burch@dot.gov

Engineering and Operations Unit
Engineering and Operations Manager **(Vacant)** . . . . (517) 702-1825

Executive Coordination Unit
Executive Coordination Unit Manager **Mike Ivey** . . . . (517) 702-1824

Program Development Team
Program Development Unit Team Leader and Bridge
Engineer **Mark Lewis** . . . . (517) 702-1846
Senior Transportation Planner - Ann Arbor, Bay City,
Detroit, Midland, Port Huron, Saginaw **Andy Pickard** . . . (517) 702-1827

Minnesota Division Office
380 Jackson Street, Suite 500, Suite 500, St. Paul, MN 55101-4802
Tel: (651) 291-6100 Fax: (651) 291-6000
E-mail: minnesota.fhwa@fhwa.dot.gov Internet: www.fhwa.dot.gov/mndiv

Division Administrator **Arlene Kocher** . . . . (651) 291-6100
E-mail: arlene.kocher@dot.gov
Assistant Division Administrator **David J. Scott** . . . . (651) 291-6103
E-mail: david.scott@dot.gov

Field Operations Team
Field Operations Team Leader **William "Bill" Lohr** . . . . . . (651) 291-6119

Technical Services Team
Technical Services Team Leader **Kris Riesenberg** . . . . (651) 291-6114

Financial and Administration Team
Financial Manager Team Leader **Sheri T. Koch** . . . . (651) 291-6113

Missouri Division Office
3220 West Edgewood, Jefferson City, MO 65109
Tel: (573) 636-7104 Fax: (573) 636-9283
E-mail: missouri.fhwa@fhwa.dot.gov Internet: www.fhwa.dot.gov/modiv

Division Administrator **Kevin W. Ward** . . . . (573) 636-7104
Assistant Division Administrator **(Vacant)** . . . . (573) 636-7104

Program Development Team
Team Leader **Raegan M. Ball** . . . . (573) 638-2620
Financial Specialist **Sandra "Sandy" Moeller** . . . . (573) 638-2623

Program Implementation Team
Team Leader **James "Jim" Stevenson** . . . . (573) 638-2610
Bridge Engineer **Ken Foster** . . . . (573) 638-2613
State/National Pavement and Materials Engineer
Mike McGee . . . . (573) 638-2608
Transportation Engineer **Brian Nevins** . . . . (573) 638-2624
Transportation Engineer (Kansas City/NW Region)
Kevin Irving . . . . (573) 638-2612
Transportation Engineer (NE/SE Regions)
Felix R. Gonzalez . . . . (573) 638-2622

New Hampshire Division Office
James C. Cleveland Federal Building, 53 Pleasant Street,
Suite 2200, Concord, NH 03301
Tel: (603) 228-0417 Fax: (603) 228-2829
E-mail: newhampshire.fhwa@fhwa.dot.gov
Internet: www.fhwa.dot.gov/nhdiv

Division Administrator **Patrick A. Bauer** . . . . (603) 410-4872
E-mail: patrick.bauer@dot.gov

(continued on next page)

★ Presidential Appointment Requiring Senate Confirmation ☆ Presidential Appointment ☐ Schedule C Appointment ◇ Career Senior Foreign Service Appointment
● Career Senior Executive Service (SES) Appointment ○ Non-Career Senior Executive Service (SES) Appointment ■ Postal Career Executive Service

DEPARTMENTS

New Hampshire Division Office *(continued)*

Assistant Division Administrator
Cynthia "Cindy" Vigue .... (603) 410-4874
E-mail: cindy.vigue@dot.gov
Finance Manager **Karen R. Damiani** .... (603) 410-4846
Computer Specialist **Mark Demers** .... (603) 410-4854
E-mail: mark.demers@dot.gov

Planning and Development
Planning and Development Supervisor **Leigh Levine** .... (603) 410-4844
Environmental Program Manager **Jamie Sikora** .... (603) 410-4870
E-mail: jamie.sikora@dot.gov
Civil Rights Program Manager
Wanda Hughley-Culbertson .... (603) 228-0417
E-mail: wanda.hughley-culbertson@dot.gov

Engineering and Operations
Engineering and Operations Supervisor **Yamilee Volcy** .... (603) 228-0417

New Jersey Division Office
840 Bear Tavern Road, Suite 202, Trenton, NJ 08628-1019
Tel: (609) 637-4200 Fax: (609) 538-4919
Internet: www.fhwa.dot.gov/njdiv

Division Administrator **Robert J. Clark** .... (609) 637-4210
E-mail: robert.clark@dot.gov
Assistant Division Administrator
Dr. Valeriya Remezova .... (609) 637-4211
E-mail: valeriya.remezova@dot.gov
Director of Engineering **Roger S. Lall** .... (609) 637-4209

Planning and Program Development
Program Development Manager **(Vacant)** .... (609) 637-4200

Project and Program Delivery Team
Project and Program Delivery Manager **John H. Miller** .... (609) 637-4235

Technical Services Team
Technical Programs Manager **Matt Zeller** .... (609) 637-4230
E-mail: matthew.zeller@dot.gov

Finance Team
Finance Manager **Steve Hanson** .... (609) 637-4215
Finance Specialist **Jennifer Poinsett** .... (609) 637-4220

New York Division Office
Leo W. O'Brien Federal Building, 11A Clinton Avenue,
Suite 719, Albany, NY 12207
Tel: (518) 431-4127 Fax: (518) 431-4121 E-mail: fhwa.newyork@dot.gov
Internet: www.fhwa.dot.gov/nydiv

● Division Administrator (Acting) **Michael Canavan** .... (518) 431-8879
E-mail: michael.canavan@dot.gov
Chief Operating Officer **Michael Canavan** .... (518) 431-8879
Engineer Coordinator **Joan P. Walters** .... (518) 431-8868
E-mail: joan.walters@dot.gov
Senior Advisor **John Formosa** .... (212) 668-2205
Administrative Assistant **Alejandra Arce** .... (518) 431-4127
Fax: (518) 431-4121

Office of Finance and Administration
Director of Finance and Administration
James E. Griffin .... (518) 431-8884
Administrative Coordinator and Program Analyst
Paul Hesse .... (518) 431-8888

Office of Program Management
Director of Program Management **Anna Price** .... (518) 431-8858
E-mail: anna.price@dot.gov
Operations, Performance Management, and Safety
Team Leader **Randy Warden** .... (401) 528-4031
Senior Transportation Management Engineer
Arthur T. O'Connor .... (212) 668-2206
Planning/Environment Team Leader
Dr. Valeriya Remezova .... (518) 431-8862

Office of Engineering
Director of Engineering
Christopher W. "Chris" Gatchell .... (518) 431-8883
E-mail: chris.gatchell@dot.gov

Ohio Division Office
200 North High Street, Room 328, Columbus, OH 43215-2408
Tel: (614) 280-6896 Fax: (614) 280-6876 E-mail: ohio.fhwa@dot.gov
Division Administrator **Laura S. "Laurie" Leffler** .... (614) 280-6896
E-mail: laurie.leffler@dot.gov
Assistant Division Administrator **Robert L. Griffith** .... (614) 280-6896
E-mail: robert.griffith@dot.gov
Program Management Analyst **Stuart Hembree** .... (614) 280-6894
E-mail: stuart.hembree@dot.gov

Financial and Administrative Team
Financial Manager **Jessica M. Patterson** .... (614) 280-6858

Office of Program Development
Director, Office of Program Development
Jeffrey "Jeff" Blanton .... (614) 280-6824
200 North High Street, Columbus, OH 43215

Special Programs Team
Special Programs Team Leader **Eric Ross** .... (614) 280-6839

Planning and Environmental Team
Planning and Environmental Team Leader
Leigh Oesterling .... (614) 280-6837

Office of Engineering and Operations
Director **David J. Snyder** .... (614) 280-6852

Field Operations Team
Field Operations Team Leader **Rachel LeVee** .... (614) 280-6890
Transportation Engineer, District 5 and 6 **(Vacant)** .... (614) 280-6896
Transportation Engineer, District 4, 10 and 11
Daniel Brodhag .... (614) 280-6849
Transportation Engineer, District 3 and 12
Naureen Dar .... (614) 280-6846

Technical Programs Team
Technical Programs Team Leader **Eric Ross** .... (614) 280-6839

ADL Positions
ADL STIC Program Coordinator **Sara Lowry** .... (614) 280-6835
ADL HAIS Computer Specialist
Joseph "Joe" Watson .... (614) 280-6829
E-mail: joe.watson@dot.gov

Pennsylvania Division Office
228 Walnut Street, Room 508, Harrisburg, PA 17101-1720
Tel: (717) 221-3461 Fax: (717) 221-3494
E-mail: pennsylvania.fhwa@fhwa.dot.gov
Internet: www.fhwa.dot.gov/padiv/index.htm
Division Administrator **Alicia Nolan** .... (720) 963-3003
E-mail: alicia.nolan@dot.gov
Assistant Division Administrator (Acting)
Katherine "Kathy" Sugnet .... (720) 963-3737
E-mail: kathy.sugnet@fhwa.dot.gov

Administrative Team
Administrative Officer
Douglas A. "Doug" Broughton .... (717) 221-3461
E-mail: doug.broughton@dot.gov
Financial Manager/Team Leader **Christine D. Perez** .... (717) 221-4555
Civil Rights Specialist **Khan Mitchell** .... (717) 221-3705
E-mail: khan.mitchell@dot.gov

Project Management and Engineering
Director **Anthony L. "Tony" Mento PE** .... (717) 221-3412
Engineering Coordinator **Pete Nanov PE** .... (717) 221-3461

★ Presidential Appointment Requiring Senate Confirmation ☆ Presidential Appointment □ Schedule C Appointment ◇ Career Senior Foreign Service Appointment
● Career Senior Executive Service (SES) Appointment ○ Non-Career Senior Executive Service (SES) Appointment ■ Postal Career Executive Service

Program Development
Director, Program Development
Keith M. Lynch 5th Floor .... (717) 221-4545

Technical Services
Director **Roger L. Ryder** .... (717) 221-3461
E-mail: roger.ryder@dot.gov
Pavement/Materials Engineer
Jennifer A. Albert PhD, PE .... (717) 221-2238
Senior Bridge Engineer **Jonathan Buck** .... (717) 221-3461

Rhode Island Division Office
380 Westminster Mall, Suite 601, Providence, RI 02903
Tel: (401) 528-4541 Fax: (401) 528-4542
E-mail: rhodeisland.fhwa@dot.gov
Internet: www.fhwa.dot.gov/ridiv/index.cfm

Division Administrator **Carlos C. Machado** .... (401) 528-4544
Financial Manager **Linda Burke** .... (401) 528-4543
E-mail: linda.burke@dot.gov

Program Delivery Team
Area Engineer (Construction) **John D. Nickelson PE** .... (401) 528-4551
E-mail: john.nickelson@dot.gov

Program Development Team
Program Development Supervisor **(Vacant)** .... (401) 528-4541
Administrative Operations Assistant **Audry Bendigo** ..... (401) 528-4541
E-mail: audry.bendigo@dot.gov

Vermont Division Office
Federal Building, 87 State Street, Room 216, Montpelier, VT 05602
Mail: P.O. Box 568, Montpelier, VT 05601-0568
Tel: (802) 828-4423 Fax: (802) 828-4424 E-mail: vermont.fhwa@dot.gov
Internet: www.fhwa.dot.gov/vtdiv

Division Administrator **Matthew R. Hake** .... (802) 828-4570
E-mail: matthew.hake@dot.gov
Assistant Division Administrator **Lawrence Dwyer** ...... (802) 828-4423
E-mail: lawrence.dwyer@dot.gov

Project Delivery
Project Delivery Team Leader and Program Analyst
Matthew DiGiovanni .... (802) 224-1368
Construction and Maintenance Engineer
Larkin Wellborn .... (802) 828-4576

Program Development
Team Leader and Finance Manager **Patrick Kirby** .... (802) 828-4568

Wisconsin Division Office
525 Junction Road, Suite 8000, Madison, WI 53717
Tel: (608) 829-7500 Fax: (608) 662-2121
E-mail: wisconsin.fhwa@dot.gov Internet: www.fhwa.dot.gov/widiv

Division Administrator **Michael A. "Mike" Davies PE** ... (608) 829-7505
E-mail: michael.davies@dot.gov
Assistant Division Administrator **Timothy C. Marshall** ... (608) 829-7506
E-mail: Timothy.Marshall@dot.gov

Program and Projects Team
Major Projects Environmental Manager
Bethaney Bacher-Gresock .... (608) 662-2119
Major Projects Engineer **(Vacant)** .... (608) 829-7523
Senior Field Operations Engineer **Anna M. Varney** ...... (608) 829-7514
Project Team Leader/ Traffic and Operations
Daniel Holt .... (608) 829-7515
Program and Projects Team Director
Tracey Blankenship .... (608) 829-7510
Field Operations Engineer **Peter "Pete" Garcia** .... (608) 829-7513
Field Operations Engineer
Gregory J. "Greg" Newhouse .... (608) 829-7521

Programs Team
Division Bridge Engineer **Joe Balice** .... (608) 829-7528
Safety/Design Engineering **David Jolicoeur** .... (608) 829-7520
Field Operations Engineer **Gary Martindale** .... (608) 829-7512

Programs Team *(continued)*
sdPOM Oversight Manager **David "Dave" Platz** .... (608) 829-7509
Program Improvement Specialist
Peter "Pete" Eakman .... (608) 829-7516

Systems Planning and Performance Team
Team Leader **Mary Forlenza** .... (608) 829-7517
Right of Way Specialist [Civil Rights] **Joel Batha** .... (608) 829-7519
E-mail: joel.batha@dot.gov
Environmental Program Manager **Ian Chidister** .... (608) 829-7503
Transportation Planner **Michael "Mitch" Batuzich** ...... (608) 829-7523
Community Planner **Matthew "Matt" Spiel** .... (608) 829-7518

Finance Team
Financial Specialist **Timothy "Tim" Klecker** .... (608) 829-7511

West Virginia Division Office
Geary Plaza, 700 Washington Street, East,
Suite 200, Charleston, WV 25301-1604
Tel: (304) 347-5928 Fax: (304) 347-5103
E-mail: westvirginia.fhwa@fhwa.dot.gov
Internet: www.fhwa.dot.gov/wvdiv

Division Administrator **Edward Stephen** .... (304) 347-5121
154 Court Street, Charleston, WV 25301
Assistant Division Administrator **Barbara M. Breslin** .... (304) 347-5929
E-mail: barbara.breslin@dot.gov

Administrative Team

Finance Team
Finance Manager **Karen A. Holmes** .... (304) 347-5930
154 Court Street, Charleston, WV 25301

Project Delivery Team
Team Lead **Henry "Ed" Compton** .... (304) 347-5434
E-mail: henry.compton@dot.gov

Program Delivery Team
Director of Planning and Environment
Jason E. Workman .... (304) 347-5271
154 Court Street, Charleston, WV 25301

Headquarters and Shared Resources
Information Technology Spec (HQ) **Tony Helton** .... (304) 347-5270
E-mail: tony.helton@dot.gov

Program Management
Program Management Analyst **(Vacant)** .... (304) 347-5928

Field Services-South
61 Forsyth Street, SW, Suite 17T26, Atlanta, GA 30303-3104
Fax: (404) 562-3701
Areas Covered: AL, AR, DE, DC, FL, GA, KS, KY, LA, MD, MS, NC, OK, PR, SC, TN, TX, VA, VI

• Director **Derrell E. Turner** .... (404) 562-3571
E-mail: derrell.turner@dot.gov
Education: Alabama BSCE
Assistant Chief Counsel **Gloria J. Hardiman-Tobin** ...... (404) 562-3678

Federal-Aid Division Offices

Alabama Division Office
9500 Wynlakes Place, Montgomery, AL 36117-8515
Tel: (334) 274-6350 Fax: (334) 274-6352 E-mail: alabama.fhwa@dot.gov

Division Administrator **Mark D. Bartlett** .... (334) 274-6350
Assistant Division Administrator **Brian Hogge** .... (334) 274-6341
E-mail: brian.hogge@dot.gov

Finance
Financial Manager (Team Leader)
Kadian Hollenquest .... (334) 274-6349
Administrative Officer **(Vacant)**

★ Presidential Appointment Requiring Senate Confirmation ☆ Presidential Appointment ☐ Schedule C Appointment ◇ Career Senior Foreign Service Appointment
● Career Senior Executive Service (SES) Appointment ○ Non-Career Senior Executive Service (SES) Appointment ■ Postal Career Executive Service

DEPARTMENTS

Project Delivery
Project Delivery (Team Leader) **Jeffrey "Jeff" Shelley** . . . (334) 274-6362
E-mail: jeff.shelley@dot.gov

Planning and Program Management
Planning and Program Management (Team Leader)
Clint Andrews . . . (334) 274-6345

Arkansas Division Office
Federal Office Building, 700 West Capitol Avenue,
Suite 3130, Little Rock, AR 72201-3298
Tel: (501) 324-5625 Fax: (501) 324-6423 E-mail: arkansas.fhwa@dot.gov
Internet: www.fhwa.dot.gov/ardiv

Division Administrator **Angel L. Correa** . . . (501) 324-5625
E-mail: angel.correa@dot.gov
Assistant Division Administrator
Peter A. "Pete" Jilek . . . (501) 324-6437
E-mail: pete.jilek@dot.gov
Financial Manager **Brenda Washington** . . . (501) 324-5628
Financial Specialist **Genese C. Harris** . . . (501) 324-5627
Administrative Specialist **Danya L. Steele** . . . (501) 324-6439
E-mail: danya.steele@dot.gov
IT Specialist **(Vacant)** . . . (501) 324-5625

Field Operations Team
Field Operations Engineer (Team Leader)
Scott P. Bowles . . . (501) 324-6441
Safety Operations Engineer **Joseph T. Heflin** . . . (501) 324-6443

Planning and Air Quality Team
Team Leader **Amy Hardin Heflin** . . . (501) 324-6435
Right-Of-Way Officer and Planner [Civil Rights]
David T. Blakeney . . . (501) 324-6438

Delaware Division
1201 College Park Road, Suite 102, Dover, DE 19904
Tel: (302) 734-5323 Fax: (302) 734-3066

Division Administrator **Mary Ridgeway** . . . (302) 734-3819
E-mail: mary.ridgeway@dot.gov

Finance Team

Project Delivery Team
Team Supervisor **Caroline Trueman** . . . (302) 734-1946
Bridge Engineer **(Vacant)** . . . (302) 734-2835
Safety and Mobility Engineer **Patrick Kennedy** . . . (302) 734-5326
Senior Area Engineer **Daniel Montag** . . . (302) 734-1719
Information Technology Specialist **Gary Tabor** . . . (410) 779-7135
31 Hopkins Plaza, Baltimore, MD 21201
E-mail: gary.tabor@dot.gov

Program Development Team
Team Supervisor **Ryan O'Donoghue** . . . (302) 734-2745
E-mail: ryan.odonoghue@dot.gov
Planning Specialist **Lindsay Donnellon** . . . (302) 734-4018
Civil Rights Specialist **William C. Jones** . . . (302) 735-5564
E-mail: william.jones@dot.gov
Environmental Specialist **Rebecca Ledebohm** . . . (302) 734-2378
10 South Howard Street, Baltimore, MD 21201

District of Columbia Division Office
1990 K Street, NW, Suite 510, Washington, DC 20006-1103
Tel: (202) 219-3570 Fax: (202) 493-7040 E-mail: dc.fhwa@fhwa.dot.gov
Internet: www.fhwa.dot.gov/dcdiv

Division Administrator **Joseph Christopher Lawson** . . . (202) 493-7030
E-mail: Christopher.Lawson@dot.gov
Assistant Division Administrator **Tanya A. Emam** . . . (202) 219-3570
E-mail: Tanya.Emam@dot.gov
Civil Rights Manager **Janine Ashe** . . . (202) 493-7026
E-mail: janine.ashe@dot.gov

Program Delivery Team
Team Leader (Acting) **Carlos Castro** . . . (202) 493-7034
Environmental Engineer **Michael "Mike" Hicks** . . . (202) 219-3513
Bridge Engineer **Carlos Castro** . . . (302) 734-2617

Finance & Administrative Team
Financial Manager **Charlena Young** . . . (202) 219-3512

Florida Division Office
3500 Financial Plaza, Suite 400, Tallahassee, FL 32312-5902
George C. Young Federal Building & Courthouse,
400 West Washington Street, Room 4200, Orlando, FL 32801
Tel: (850) 553-2201 (Tallahassee Office Number)
Tel: (407) 867-6400 (Orlando Office Number)
Fax: (850) 942-9691 (Tallahassee Fax Number)
Fax: (850) 942-8308 (Tallahassee Fax Number)
Fax: (407) 867-6418 (Orlanda Fax Number)
E-mail: florida.fhwa@fhwa.dot.gov Internet: www.fhwa.dot.gov/fldiv

● Division Administrator **James S. Christian** . . . (512) 536-5911
E-mail: james.christian@dot.gov
Chief Operating Officer **David C. Hawk** . . . (850) 553-2203
E-mail: david.hawk@dot.gov

Office of Finance and Administration
Office of Finance and Administration Director
Kenneth W. "Ken" Harvey . . . (850) 553-2212
E-mail: ken.harvey@fhwa.dot.gov
Financial Manager **Martha Solorzano** . . . (850) 553-2238
E-mail: martha.solorzano@dot.gov

Office of Project Delivery
Associate Division Administrator for Project Delivery
Nicholas "Nick" Finch . . . (407) 867-6410
E-mail: nick.finch@dot.gov
Major Projects Oversight Manager **Andrew DeTizio** . . . (407) 867-6411
E-mail: andrew.detizio@dot.gov
Program Operations Engineer **Chad Thompson** . . . (850) 553-2239
E-mail: chad.thompson@dot.gov

Office of Project Development
Office of Project Development Director
Karen Brunelle . . . (850) 553-2218
E-mail: karen.brunelle@dot.gov
Realty Officer **Brian Telfair** . . . (850) 553-2228
E-mail: brian.telfair@dot.gov
Environmental Team Leader **(Vacant)** . . . (850) 553-2201
Planning Team Leader **Cathy Kendall** . . . (850) 553-2225
E-mail: cathy.kendall@dot.gov

Office of Technical Services
Director **Khoa Nguyen** . . . (850) 553-2204
E-mail: Khoa.Nguyen@dot.gov
ITS/Traffic Operations Engineer **Frank Corrado** . . . (850) 553-2247
E-mail: Frank.Corrado@dot.gov
Senior Structures Engineer **(Vacant)** . . . (850) 553-2201
Structures Engineer **Hector R. Laureano** . . . (407) 867-6427
Bridge Engineer **Rafiq Darji** . . . (850) 553-2242
Safety Engineer **Kevin Burgess** . . . (850) 553-2229

Georgia Division Office
61 Forsyth Street, SW, Suite 17T100, Atlanta, GA 30303-3104
Fax: (404) 562-3703 E-mail: georgia.fhwa@fhwa.dot.gov
Internet: www.fhwa.dot.gov/gadiv

Division Administrator (Acting) **Moises Marrero** . . . (404) 562-3630
E-mail: moises.marrero@dot.gov
Assistant Division Administrator **William C. Farr** . . . (404) 562-3635
E-mail: william.farr@dot.gov

Finance
Financial Team Leader **Russell Wright** . . . (404) 562-4283
Administrative Program Assistant **Steven Staud** . . . (404) 562-3633
E-mail: steven.staud@dot.gov
Administrative Officer **Maria Sandoval** . . . (404) 562-3663
E-mail: maria.sandoval@dot.gov

Program Development
Program Development Director **Steve Luxenberg** . . . (404) 562-3650

Project Delivery
Project Delivery Team Leader **Alvin Gutierrez** . . . (404) 562-3632

★ Presidential Appointment Requiring Senate Confirmation ☆ Presidential Appointment ☐ Schedule C Appointment ◇ Career Senior Foreign Service Appointment
● Career Senior Executive Service (SES) Appointment ○ Non-Career Senior Executive Service (SES) Appointment ■ Postal Career Executive Service

Kansas Division Office
6111 SW 29th Street, Suite 100, Topeka, KS 66614-4271
Tel: (785) 273-2600 Fax: (785) 273-2620 E-mail: kansas.fhwa@dot.gov
Internet: www.fhwa.dot.gov/ksdiv

Division Administrator **Richard E. "Rick" Backlund** ..... (785) 273-2600
E-mail: richard.backlund@dot.gov
Assistant Division Administrator **Norbert Muñoz** .... (785) 273-2627
E-mail: norbert.munoz@dot.gov

Project Delivery
Project Delivery Team Leader **James R. Simerl** .... (785) 273-2629

Program Development
Finance Manager and Team Leader
Matthew G. McDonald .... (785) 273-2600

Kentucky Division Office
John C. Watts Federal Building, 330 West Broadway,
Room 264, Frankfort, KY 40601
Tel: (502) 223-6720 Fax: (502) 223-6735
E-mail: kentucky.fhwa@dot.gov Internet: www.fhwa.dot.gov/kydiv

Division Administrator **Thomas L. Nelson, Jr.** .... (502) 223-6720
E-mail: thomas.nelson@dot.gov
Assistant Division Administrator
Steven R. "Steve" Mills .... (502) 223-6723
E-mail: steve.mills@dot.gov
Administrative Officer **(Vacant)** .... (502) 223-6720

Finance and Program Management Team
Finance Manager -Team Leader **Steven Jacobs** .... (502) 223-6731

Program Delivery Team
Transportation Specialist - Team Leader
John Ballantyne .... (502) 223-6747

Engineering and Operations Team
Team Leader **David Whitworth** .... (502) 223-6741

Maryland Division Office
George Fallon Federal Building, 31 Hopkins Plaza,
Room 840, Baltimore, MD 21210
Tel: (410) 962-4440 Fax: (410) 962-4054
E-mail: maryland.fhwa@fhwa.dot.gov

Division Administrator **Gregory K. Murrill** .... (410) 779-7130
E-mail: gregory.murrill@dot.gov
Assistant Division Administrator **Bill Wade** .... (410) 779-7131
E-mail: bill.wade@dot.gov

ADA / Administration and Finance Team
Civil Rights Specialist **Francisco "Edwin" Gonzalez** .... (410) 779-7150
E-mail: francisco.gonzalez@dot.gov
Administrative Coordinator **Dennis Jones** .... (410) 779-7133
E-mail: dennis.jones@dot.gov
Financial Specialist **Brenda Sullivan** .... (410) 779-7137
Program Management Analyst **Marisela Tavarez** .... (410) 779-7151

Technology Services / ROW / Planning Team
Technology Services/Planning Team Leader
Azmat Hussain .... (410) 779-7161
Transportation Management Engineer **Breck Jeffers** ..... (410) 779-7153
Planning Program Manager **Kwame Arhin** .... (410) 779-7158
Community Planner **Lindsay Donnellon** .... (410) 779-7157
Bridge Engineer **Tahir Chaudhry** .... (410) 779-7162

Project Delivery/Environment Team
Project Delivery/Environment Team Leader
Jitesh Parikh .... (410) 779-7136
Senior Area Engineer **Phillip Bello** .... (410) 464-8214
E-mail: phillip.bello@dot.gov
Senior Area Engineer **Lourdes Castaneda** .... (410) 779-7142
E-mail: lourdes.castaneda@dot.gov
Area Engineer **Blair Jones** .... (410) 779-7149
E-mail: blair.jones@dot.gov

Project Delivery/Environment Team *(continued)*
Area Engineer **Keilyn Perez** .... (410) 779-7141
E-mail: keilyn.perez@dot.gov
Area Engineer **Daniel Suarez** .... (410) 779-7159
E-mail: daniel.suarez@dot.gov
Area Engineer **(Vacant)** .... (302) 734-2745
1201 College Park Road, Dover, DE 19904
Environmental Manager **Jeanette Mar** .... (410) 779-7152
Environmental Specialist **Joy Liang** .... (410) 779-7148
E-mail: joy.liang@dot.gov

Louisiana Division Office
5304 Flanders Drive, Suite A, Baton Rouge, LA 70808-4348
Tel: (225) 757-7600 Fax: (225) 757-7601
E-mail: louisiana.fhwa@fhwa.dot.gov
Internet: www.fhwa.dot.gov/ladiv/index.htm

Division Administrator **Charles W. "Wes" Bolinger** ..... (225) 757-7602
E-mail: charles.bolinger@dot.gov
Assistant Division Administrator **Todd A. Jeter** .... (225) 757-7612
E-mail: todd.jeter@dot.gov

Program Delivery Team
Program Delivery Team Leader **Mary Stringfellow** ...... (225) 757-7610

Project Delivery Team
Project Delivery Team Leader **Joshua Cunningham** ..... (225) 757-7615

Mississippi Division Office
McCoy Federal Building, 100 West Capitol Street,
Suite 1062, Jackson, MS 39269
Tel: (601) 965-4215 Fax: (601) 965-4231
E-mail: mississippi.fhwa@dot.gov Internet: www.fhwa.dot.gov/msdiv

Division Administrator **(Vacant)** .... (601) 965-4216
Assistant Division Administrator
Donald E. "Don" Davis .... (601) 965-4146
E-mail: donald.davis@dot.gov

Financial Management Team
Financial Management Team Leader **Eric Griffith** .... (601) 965-4224

Field Operations Team
Field Operations Team Leader **Christy Poon-Atkins** ..... (601) 965-4222

Project Development Team
Team Leader **Shundreka Givan** .... (601) 965-4217

North Carolina Division Office
310 New Bern Avenue, Suite 410, Raleigh, NC 27601
Tel: (919) 856-4346 Fax: (919) 747-7030
E-mail: northcarolina.fhwa@dot.gov

Division Administrator
John F. Sullivan III PE .... (919) 856-4346 ext. 122
E-mail: john.sullivan@dot.gov
Assistant Division Administrator
Edward T. Parker .... (919) 856-4346 ext. 121
E-mail: edward.parker@dot.gov

Office of Administration
Financial Manager **Audrey Davis** .... (919) 747-7003
Executive/Financial Assistant **(Vacant)** .... (919) 856-4346 ext. 120
Student Intern (Financial Specialist)
Kevin Washington .... (919) 747-7029

Quality Coordinator
Quality Coordinator **Donna Dancausse** .... (919) 747-7016

Civil Rights
Civil Rights Program Manager **Lynise DeVance** .... (919) 747-7010
E-mail: lynise.devance@dot.gov

Preconstruction and Environment
Preconstruction and Environment Director
Clarence Coleman PE .... (919) 747-7014
E-mail: clarence.coleman@dot.gov

DEPARTMENTS

★ Presidential Appointment Requiring Senate Confirmation ☆ Presidential Appointment ☐ Schedule C Appointment ◇ Career Senior Foreign Service Appointment
● Career Senior Executive Service (SES) Appointment ○ Non-Career Senior Executive Service (SES) Appointment ■ Postal Career Executive Service

DEPARTMENTS

Operations
Operations Engineer **Bradley "Brad" Hibbs** . . . . (919) 747-7006
Major Projects and Transportation Engineer (Divisions 5-6) **Jim Martin PE** . . . . (919) 747-7008

Planning and Program Development
Planning and Program Development Manager
George Hoops PE . . . . (919) 747-7022

Alternate Duty Location
Office of Bridge Technology – Bridge Safety Engineer
Thomas "Tom" Drda . . . . (919) 747-7011

Oklahoma Division Office
5801 North Broadway Extension, Suite 300, Oklahoma City, OK 73118
Tel: (405) 254-3300 Fax: (405) 254-3302
E-mail: oklahoma.fhwa@fhwa.dot.gov Internet: www.fhwa.dot.gov/okdiv

Division Administrator **Basharat Siddiqi** . . . . (405) 254-3300
E-mail: basharat.siddiqi@dot.gov
Assistant Division Administrator **Louisa Ward** . . . . (405) 254-3300
E-mail: louisa.ward@dot.gov

Operations, Technology and Program Development Team
Operations, Technology and Program Development Team Leader **(Vacant)** . . . . (405) 254-3300

Administrative, Program Support, and Technical Services Team
Administrative, Program Support, and Technical Services Team Leader **Carl P. Selby** . . . . (405) 254-3320
E-mail: carl.selby@dot.gov

Puerto Rico and Virgin Islands Division Office
350 Torre Chardon, Carlos Chardon Street,
Suite 210, San Juan, PR 00918-2161
Tel: (787) 766-5600 Fax: (787) 766-5924
E-mail: PuertoRico.fhwa@dot.gov Internet: www.fhwa.dot.gov/prdiv

Division Administrator **James S. Christian** . . . . (512) 536-5911
E-mail: james.christian@dot.gov
Associate Division Administrator **Michael Avery** . . . . (787) 771-2510

Bridge
Bridge Engineer **Hector R. Laureano** . . . . (407) 867-6427
400 West Washington Street, Orlando, FL 32801

Civil Rights and Right of Way
Civil Rights and Right of Way (Acting)
Carey Shepherd . . . . (850) 553-2206
E-mail: carey.shepherd@dot.gov

Environment
Senior Environmental Specialist **Luis D. Lopez** . . . . (407) 867-6420
E-mail: Luis.D.Lopez@dot.gov

Finance and Administrative Team
Programs Delivery Team Leader **Michael Figueroa** . . . . . . (787) 771-2512
Financial Specialist **Sandra Fuentes** . . . . (787) 766-2540
Senior Administrative Assistant **Nilda Morales** . . . . (787) 771-2513
E-mail: nilda.morales.ctr@dot.gov
Territorial Program Manager **(Vacant)** . . . . (787) 766-5600

Field Operations Team
Team Leader (Acting) **Andrés Alvarez** . . . . (787) 771-2523

Planning

South Carolina Division Office
Strom Thurmond Federal Building, 1835 Assembly Street,
Suite 1270, Columbia, SC 29201
Tel: (803) 765-5411 Fax: (803) 253-3989
E-mail: southcarolina.fhwa@dot.gov

Division Administrator **Emily O. Lawton** . . . . (803) 765-5411
E-mail: emily.lawton@dot.gov
Assistant Division Administrator
Stephen R. "Steve" Ikerd . . . . (803) 253-3885
E-mail: stephen.ikerd@dot.gov

South Carolina Division Office *(continued)*

Administrative Officer **Alma "Jeannie" Moore** . . . . (803) 253-3876
E-mail: alma.moore@dot.gov

Program Specialists
Financial Manager **Bryan Smith** . . . . (803) 765-5331

Tennessee Division Office
Building 200, 404 BNA Drive, Suite 508, Nashville, TN 37217
Tel: (615) 781-5770 Fax: (615) 781-5773
E-mail: tennessee.fhwa@dot.gov Internet: www.fhwa.dot.gov/tndiv

Division Administrator **Pamela M. Kordenbrock** . . . . (615) 781-5770
E-mail: pamela.kordenbrock@dot.gov
Assistant Division Administrator **Sabrina S. David** . . . . . . (615) 781-5770
E-mail: sabrina.david@dot.gov

Field Operations and Finance Team
Team Leader **Gerald L. Varney** . . . . (615) 781-5765
Financial Manager **Frank K. Vickers** . . . . (615) 781-5768
Area Engineer, Region 3 ADHS Coordinator
Thor Steffen . . . . (615) 781-5763

Technical Programs Team
Technical Programs Team Leader **(Vacant)** . . . . (615) 781-5762
Administrative Operations Assistant **(Vacant)** . . . . (615) 781-5787

Technical Services Team
Team Leader **Pamela Heimsness** . . . . (615) 781-5774

Planning and Program Development Team
Team Leader **Theresa Claxton** . . . . (615) 781-5772
E-mail: theresa.claxton@dot.gov

Texas Division Office
Federal Office Building, 300 East Eighth Street,
Room 826, Austin, TX 78701
Tel: (512) 536-5900 Fax: (512) 536-5990
E-mail: texas.fhwa@fhwa.dot.gov Internet: www.fhwa.dot.gov/txdiv

● Division Administrator **Achille "Al" Alonzi** . . . . (512) 536-5902
E-mail: al.alonzi@dot.gov
Education: Worcester Polytech 1990 BS
Chief Operating Officer (COO) **Marcus D. Wilner** . . . . . . (505) 690-6153

Planning and Program Development
Director, Program Development
Michael T. "Mike" Leary . . . . (512) 536-5940
E-mail: michael.leary@dot.gov

District Operations
Director of Operations **Carl M. Highsmith** . . . . (512) 536-5950
District Engineer (South) **(Vacant)** . . . . (512) 536-5900

Technical Programs
Director of Technical Programs **Melanie Twehues** . . . . . . (512) 536-5953

Finance and Administration
Director of Finance and Administration
Donny E. Hamilton, Jr. . . . . (916) 498-5066
E-mail: donny.hamilton@dot.gov
Financial Manager **Jack Bales** . . . . (512) 536-5909
E-mail: jack.bales@dot.gov
Financial Analyst **Steve Christian** . . . . (512) 536-5911
Administrative Officer **Robert Goodacre** . . . . (512) 536-5919
E-mail: robert.goodacre@dot.gov

Virginia Division Office
400 North Eighth Street, Room 750, Richmond, VA 23219
Tel: (804) 775-3320 Fax: (804) 775-3356 E-mail: virginia.fhwa@dot.gov
Internet: www.fhwa.dot.gov/vadiv

Division Administrator **Jessie L. Yung** . . . . (804) 775-3333
E-mail: jessie.yung@dot.gov
Assistant Division Administrator
Richard Wayne Fedora . . . . (804) 775-3344
E-mail: r.wayne.fedora@dot.gov

★ Presidential Appointment Requiring Senate Confirmation ☆ Presidential Appointment ☐ Schedule C Appointment ◇ Career Senior Foreign Service Appointment
● Career Senior Executive Service (SES) Appointment ○ Non-Career Senior Executive Service (SES) Appointment ■ Postal Career Executive Service

Virginia Division Office *(continued)*

Director of Program Development
Edward "Ed" Sundra .... (804) 775-3353
E-mail: ed.sundra@dot.gov

Administrative Services
Administrative Officer **Robbie Scott** .... (804) 775-3334
E-mail: robbie.scott@dot.gov
Administrative Operations Assistant **Reinette Fed** .... (804) 775-3323
E-mail: reinette.fed@dot.gov

Civil Rights
Civil Rights Program Manager **Mohamed Dumbuya** .... (804) 775-3339
E-mail: mohamed.dumbuya@dot.gov

Program Delivery Team
Program Delivery Team Leader **Gilberto De León PE** .... (804) 775-3362

Structures and Bridge Team
Structure and Bridge Team Leader **Rodolfo Maruri PE** ... (804) 775-3353

Major Projects
Senior Major Projects Engineer **Tarsem Lal PE** .... (804) 775-3345

TPM, Research, LPA Team
Senior TPM and Research Engineer
Lorenzo Casanova PE .... (804) 775-3361
LPA and ITS Engineer **Iris Rodriguez-Pagan** .... (804) 775-3340

Safety
Highway Safety Engineer and Emergency Coordinator
Karen King PE .... (804) 775-3363

Financial Management Team
Financial Manager **Jacqueline Gillispie** .... (804) 775-3360

Planning and Environment Team
Planning and Environment Team Leader
John Simkins .... (804) 775-3347
E-mail: john.simkins@dot.gov

Realty
Right-of-Way Officer **Janice Williams** .... (804) 775-3327

Field Services- Mid-America

4749 Lincoln Mall Drive, Matteson, IL 60443
Director **John G. Rohlf** .... (708) 283-3507
Fax: (708) 283-3501
Assistant Chief Counsel **Glenn R. Harris** ...... (708) 283-3561 ext. 3561

Field Services-West

12300 West Dakota Avenue, Suite 310, Lakewood, CO 80228
Fax: (801) 967-5522
Areas Covered: AK, AZ, CA, CO, HI, ID, MT, ND, NE, NM, NV, OR, SD, UT, WA, WY
• Director **Peter W. Osborn** .... (720) 963-3730
E-mail: peter.osborn@dot.gov Fax: (518) 431-4121
Education: Rhode Island 1989 BSCE; Northwestern 1993 MSCE
Assistant Chief Counsel **Lawrence Porter P. Hanf** .... (720) 963-3095

Federal-Aid Division Offices

Alaska Division Office
709 West Ninth Street, Room 851, Juneau, AK 99802-1648
Mail: P.O. Box 21648, Juneau, AK 99802-1648
Tel: (907) 586-7418 Fax: (907) 586-7420 E-mail: alaska.fhwa@dot.gov
Internet: www.fhwa.dot.gov/akdiv
Division Administrator **Sandra A. Garcia-Aline** .... (907) 586-7180
E-mail: sandra.garcia-aline@dot.gov
Assistant Division Administrator **Kathleen Graber** ...... (907) 586-7458
E-mail: kathleen.graber@dot.gov
Assistant Division Administrator **(Vacant)** .... (907) 586-7418

Engineering and Operations Team
Team Leader **Simons Latunde-Addey** .... (907) 586-7464
Pavement, Material, Safety **Al Fletcher** .... (907) 586-7245

Finance and Program Development Team
Financial Manager **Julie A. Jenkins** .... (907) 586-7476
Environment Program Manager **Tim Haugh** .... (907) 586-7430
E-mail: tim.haugh@dot.gov
Transportation Planner **John Lohrey** .... (907) 586-7428
PO Box 21648, Juneau, AK 99802

DEPARTMENTS

Arizona Division Office
4000 North Central Avenue, Suite 1500, Phoenix, AZ 85012-3500
Tel: (602) 379-3646 Fax: (602) 382-8998 E-mail: arizona.fhwa@dot.gov
Division Administrator **Karla S. Petty PE** .... (602) 379-3676
E-mail: karla.petty@dot.gov
Education: West Virginia Tech 1983 BS
Assistant Division Administrator (Acting)
Anthony Sarhan PE .... (602) 382-8989
E-mail: anthony.sarhan@dot.gov

Finance and Administrative Team
Finance Manager **Roman Moreno** .... (602) 382-8981

Planning, Environment, Air Quality, and Realty (PEAR) Team
Program Management Team Leader **Alan Hansen** .... (602) 382-8964
E-mail: alan.hansen@dot.gov

Project Delivery Team
Project Delivery Team Leader
Thomas "Tom" Deitering .... (602) 382-8971

Regional IT Support
Systems Administrator **Raquel Bonner** .... (602) 382-8977
E-mail: raquel.bonner.ctr@dot.gov

System Performance Team
System Performance Team Leader **Jennifer H. Brown** ... (602) 382-8961

California Division Office
650 Capitol Mall, Suite 4-100, Sacramento, CA 95814-4708
Tel: (916) 498-5001 TTY: (916) 498-5064 Fax: (916) 498-5008
E-mail: california.fhwa@dot.gov Internet: www.fhwa.dot.gov/cadiv
• Division Administrator (HDA-CA)
Vincent "Vince" Mammano .... (916) 498-5015
E-mail: vincent.mammano@dot.gov
Executive Administrative Assistant **(Vacant)** .... (916) 498-5001
Associate Division Administrator **Monica L. Gourdine** ... (213) 894-4560
Administrative Assistant-Associate DA
Emmanuel Rodriguez .... (213) 894-4500
E-mail: emmanuel.rodriguez@dot.gov
Administrative Officer/Team Leader
Kara Magdaleno .... (916) 498-5774 ext. 256
Chief Operating Officer (Acting)
Paul D. Schneider .... (916) 498-5014 ext. 222
IT and Computer Specialist **John Kinyon** .... (916) 498-5764 ext. 287
Tribal Transportation Coordinator **Anthony Spann** ...... (916) 498-5001

Project Delivery
Director **Matthew T. "Matt" Schmitz** .... (916) 498-5850
E-mail: matthew.schmitz@dot.gov

Performance Management
Director **Aimee Kratovil** .... (916) 498-5866
E-mail: aimee.kratovil@dot.gov

Financial Services
Director **Rodney Whitfield** .... (916) 498-5001

Planning and Environment
Director **Tashia Clemons** .... (916) 498-5001
Planning Team Leader **(Vacant)** .... (916) 498-5001

Technical Services
Director **Maiser A. Khaled** .... (916) 498-5020

★ Presidential Appointment Requiring Senate Confirmation ☆ Presidential Appointment ☐ Schedule C Appointment ◇ Career Senior Foreign Service Appointment
● Career Senior Executive Service (SES) Appointment ○ Non-Career Senior Executive Service (SES) Appointment ■ Postal Career Executive Service

California South Office (CALSOUTH)
888 South Figueroa Street, Suite 750, Los Angeles, CA 90017-5467
Tel: (213) 202-3950 Fax: (213) 202-3961

CalSouth Deputy Office Director (Team Leader)
Hector Santiago .... (213) 894-4468
E-mail: hector.santiago@dot.gov
Community Planner **Michael A. "Mike" Morris, Jr.** .... (916) 498-5887
E-mail: michael.morris@dot.gov
Senior ITS Engineer (Technical Services)
Lawrence J. "Jesse" Glazer .... (213) 894-6352
E-mail: jesse.glazer@dot.gov
Senior Transportation Engineer and Project Delivery
Josue M. "Jay" Yambo .... (213) 894-5351
Senior Transportation Engineer and Project Delivery
District 7 **(Vacant)** .... (213) 202-3950

Colorado Division Office
12300 West Dakota Avenue, Suite 180, Lakewood, CO 80228
Tel: (720) 963-3000 E-mail: colorado.fhwa@dot.gov
Internet: www.fhwa.dot.gov/codiv/

Division Administrator **John M. Cater** .... (720) 963-3003
E-mail: jcater@fhwa.dot.gov
Assistant Division Administrator **Vershun Tolliver** .... (720) 963-3030
E-mail: vershun.tolliver@dot.gov
Financial Manager and Team Leader **Andre Compton** .... (720) 963-3034

Program Development Team
Urban Planner and Team Leader **William "Bill" Haas** .... (720) 963-3016

Program Delivery Team (Region1 and 3)
Program Delivery Team Leader (CDOT Region 1 and 3) **(Vacant)** .... (720) 963-3000

Program Delivery Team (Region 2,4, and 5)
Program Delivery Team Leader (CDOT Region 2,4, and 5) **Randy Jensen** .... (720) 963-3031
E-mail: randy.jensen@dot.gov

Hawaii Division Office
Prince Jonah Kuhio Kalanianaole Federal Bldg.,
300 Ala Moana Blvd., Rm. 3-306, Honolulu, HI 96850
Box 50206, Honolulu, HI 96850
Tel: (808) 541-2700 Fax: (808) 541-2704 E-mail: hawaii.fhwa@dot.gov
Internet: www.fhwa.dot.gov/hidiv/

Division Administrator **Ralph J. Rizzo** .... (808) 541-2312
E-mail: ralph.j.rizzo@dot.gov
Assistant Division Administrator **Richelle Takara** .... (808) 541-2309
E-mail: richelle.takara@dot.gov
Tel: (808) 541-2311

Finance and Administrative Team
Financial Manager **Michael Nadeau** .... (808) 541-2307
E-mail: michael.nadeau@dot.gov

Programs and Project Development Team
Team Leader **Kaha'a Rezantes** .... (808) 541-2314

Idaho Division Office
3050 Lakeharbor Lane, Suite 126, Boise, ID 83703-6243
Fax: (208) 334-1691 E-mail: Idaho.fhwa@dot.gov
Internet: www.fhwa.dot.gov/iddiv/index.htm

Division Administrator **Peter J. Hartman** .... (208) 334-9180 ext. 118
E-mail: peter.hartman@dot.gov
Assistant Division Administrator
Gus Shanine .... (208) 334-9180 ext. 119
E-mail: gus.shanine@dot.gov

Field Operations Team
Field Operations Engineer/Team Leader
John A. Perry .... (208) 334-9180 ext. 116

Environmental Program Team
Environmental Program Manager/Program Implementation Team Leader
Brent Inghram .... (208) 334-9180 ext. 114
E-mail: brent.inghram@dot.gov

Finance and Administration Team
Transportation Finance Manager/Team Leader
Randy Rhuman .... (208) 334-9180 ext. 121

Montana Division Office
585 Shepard Way, Suite 2, Helena, MT 59602
Tel: (406) 441-3900 Fax: (406) 449-5314 E-mail: montana.fhwa@dot.gov

Division Administrator **Kevin L. McLaury** .... (406) 441-3901
E-mail: kevin.mclaury@dot.gov

Finance and Program Management Team
Supervisor **Brian Hasselbach** .... (406) 441-3908
Financial Manager - Functional Lead
Judy Broadwater .... (406) 441-3922

Field Operations Team
Supervisor **Christopher W. Riley** .... (406) 441-3913

Nebraska Division Office
Federal Building, 100 Centennial Mall North,
Room 220, Lincoln, NE 68508-3803
Tel: (402) 742-8460 Fax: (402) 742-8480
Internet: www.fhwa.dot.gov/nediv

Division Administrator **Joseph A. "Joe" Werning** .... (402) 742-8461
E-mail: joseph.werning@dot.gov

Assistant Division Administrator
Assistant Division Administrator **Douglas S. Atkin** .... (402) 742-8462
E-mail: doug.atkin@dot.gov

Engineering and Operations Team
Engineering and Operations Team Leader
Mary Burroughs .... (402) 742-8477

Finance and Administrative Services Team
Transportation Finance Manager **James A. Lockwood** .... (402) 742-8468
Administrative Assistant **Sue Petracek** .... (402) 742-8470
E-mail: sue.petracek@dot.gov

Program Delivery Team
Program Delivery Team Leader **Melissa Maiefski** .... (402) 742-8473

Nevada Division Office
705 North Plaza Street, Suite 220, Carson City, NV 89701
Tel: (775) 687-1204 Fax: (775) 687-3803
E-mail: nevada.fhwa@fhwa.dot.gov
Internet: www.fhwa.dot.gov/nvdiv/nevada.html

Division Administrator **Susan "Sue" Klekar** .... (775) 687-1204
E-mail: susan.klekar@dot.gov
Assistant Division Administrator **Greg Novak** .... (775) 687-1204
E-mail: greg.novak@dot.gov
Administrative Assistant **Pamela Angelo** .... (775) 687-1207

Financial Management Team
Financial Manager **Tylor Finley** .... (775) 687-5336
Financial Specialist **(Vacant)** .... (775) 687-8581

Field Operations Team
Field Operations Team Leader **Jacob R. Waclaw** .... (775) 687-5320

Program Development Team
Environmental Program Manager **Abdelmoez Abdalla** .... (775) 687-1231

★ Presidential Appointment Requiring Senate Confirmation ☆ Presidential Appointment □ Schedule C Appointment ◇ Career Senior Foreign Service Appointment
● Career Senior Executive Service (SES) Appointment ○ Non-Career Senior Executive Service (SES) Appointment ■ Postal Career Executive Service

New Mexico Division Office

4001 Office Court Drive, Suite 801, Santa Fe, NM 87507
Tel: (505) 820-2021 Fax: (505) 820-2040
E-mail: newmexico.fhwa@dot.gov Internet: www.fhwa.dot.gov/nmdiv

Division Administrator **J. Don Martinez** . . . . (505) 820-2022
E-mail: johndon.martinez@fhwa.dot.gov
Assistant Division Administrator **(Vacant)** . . . . (505) 820-2023

Transportation Operations

Transportation Operations Engineer **Frank Lozano** . . . . (505) 820-2031
E-mail: frank.lozano@dot.gov

Planning and Program Development

Planning and Program Management Team Leader **Rodolfo Monge-Oviedo** . . . . (505) 820-2037
E-mail: rodolfo.monge-oviedo@dot.gov
Safety/Pavement Engineer **Luis Melgoza** . . . . (505) 820-2028
ROW Officer **Greg Heitmann** . . . . (505) 820-2027
Civil Rights Specialist **Lisa Neie** . . . . (505) 820-2036
E-mail: lisa.neie@dot.gov
Transportation Finance Manager **Monica Gourd** . . . . (505) 820-2024
Finance Specialist **Dolores Gallegos** . . . . (505) 820-2026

North Dakota Division Office

4503 Coleman Street, Suite 205, Bismarck, ND 58503-0567
Tel: (701) 250-4204 Fax: (701) 250-4395
E-mail: northdakota.fhwa@fhwa.dot.gov

Division Administrator **Wendall Meyer** . . . . (701) 221-9460
E-mail: wendall.meyer@dot.gov

Engineering and Operations Team

Engineering and Operations Team Supervisor (Acting) **Stephanie Hickman** . . . . (701) 221-9462

Technical Services Team

Technical Service Team Supervisor **Sandy Zimmer** . . . . . . (701) 221-9469
E-mail: sandy.zimmer@dot.gov

Oregon Division Office

The Equitable Center, 530 Center Street, NE,
Suite 100, Salem, OR 97301-3740
Tel: (503) 399-5749 Fax: (503) 399-5838
E-mail: oregon.fhwa@fhwa.dot.gov
Internet: www.fhwa.dot.gov/ordiv/index.cfm

Division Administrator **Phillip A. Ditzler** . . . . (503) 316-2540
Assistant Division Administrator **Thomas D. "Tom" Goldstein** . . . . (503) 316-2545
E-mail: thomas.goldstein@dot.gov
Environmental Program Manager **Michelle Eraut** . . . . (503) 316-2559

Field Operations

Senior Field Operations Engineer/Team Leader **Mike Morrow** . . . . (503) 316-2552

Finance and Administration

Financial Program Manager/Team Leader **Linda Swann** . . . . (503) 316-2546

Technical Services

Team Leader **Timothy Rogers PE** . . . . (503) 316-2564
Local Programs Manager **Satvinder Sandhu** . . . . (503) 316-2560
E-mail: satvinder.sandhu@dot.gov

South Dakota Division Office

116 East Dakota Avenue, Suite A, Pierre, SD 57501-3110
Tel: (605) 224-8033 Fax: (605) 224-8307
E-mail: southdakota.fhwa@fhwa.dot.gov
Internet: www.fhwa.dot.gov/sddiv/index.cfm

Division Administrator **Robert Kirk Fredrichs** . . . . (605) 776-1001
E-mail: kirk.fredrichs@dot.gov

Technical Services

Supervisory Transportation Finance Manager **Carla A. Remmich** . . . . (605) 776-1003

Technical Services *(continued)*

ITS Specialist **Bruce Hunt** . . . . (605) 776-1002
Staff Assistant **(Vacant)** . . . . (605) 224-8033
Special Projects Engineer **Ronald W. McMahon** . . . . (605) 776-1009

Utah Division Office

2520 West 4700 South, Suite 9A, Salt Lake City, UT 84129-1847
Tel: (801) 955-3500 Fax: (801) 955-3539 E-mail: hdaut@dot.gov
Internet: www.fhwa.dot.gov/utdiv/utah.htm

Division Administrator **Ivan Marrero** . . . . (801) 955-3501
E-mail: Ivan.Marrero@dot.gov
Assistant Division Administrator **Brigitte A. Mandel** . . . . . (801) 955-3502
E-mail: brigitte.mandel@dot.gov
Program Assistant **Debra Sauers** . . . . (801) 955-3521
E-mail: debra.sauers@dot.gov
Financial Manager **Trevor Hart** . . . . (801) 955-3519

Program Development

Program Development Team Leader **Steven A. Call** . . . . . (801) 955-3513

Project Delivery

Civil Rights Program Manager and Project Delivery Team Leader **Russell Robertson** . . . . (801) 955-3512

Shared Resources

4000 North Central Avenue, Phoenix, AZ 85012-3500

IT Network Manager **Raquel Bonner** . . . . (602) 382-8977
E-mail: raquel.bonner.ctr@dot.gov

Washington Division Office

Evergreen Plaza, 711 South Capitol Way,
Suite 501, Olympia, WA 98501-1284
Tel: (360) 753-9480 Fax: (360) 753-9889
E-mail: washington.fhwa@dot.gov Internet: www.fhwa.dot.gov/wadiv

Division Administrator **Daniel M. Mathis** . . . . (360) 753-9413
E-mail: daniel.mathis@dot.gov
Assistant Division Administrator **Melinda L. Roberson** . . . . (360) 753-9554
Major Projects Oversight Manager **Anthony Sarhan PE** . . . . (206) 220-7538

Financial Management Team

Team Leader **Rick Judd** . . . . (360) 753-9485
Administrative Assistant **Teri Goodwillie** . . . . (360) 753-9480

Technical Services Team

Transportation Mobility Engineer **(Vacant)** . . . . (360) 753-9408

Field Operations Team

Team Leader **Susan M. Wimberly PE** . . . . (360) 753-9414

Program Development Team

Transportation Planning Program Manager/ Team Leader **Sidney W. "Sid" Stecker** . . . . (360) 753-9555
Planning and Freight Program Manager **Sharleen A. Bakeman** . . . . (360) 753-9418
Environmental Specialist/Biologist **Cindy Callahan** . . . . . . (360) 753-9480

Liaisons and Trainees

RC Safety Engineer **Dick B. Albin PE** . . . . (360) 534-9312

Wyoming Division Office

2617 East Lincolnway, Suite D, Cheyenne, WY 82001-5671
Tel: (307) 772-2101 Fax: (307) 772-2011 E-mail: hdawy@dot.gov
Internet: www.fhwa.dot.gov/wydiv

Division Administrator **Bryan R. Cawley** . . . . (202) 366-1333

Engineering and Operations

Supervisor and Environmental Engineer **Shaun Cutting** . . . . (307) 771-2942

Technical Services

Supervisor, Financial Manager **Cindy Thompsen** . . . . (307) 771-2948
E-mail: cindy.jerkins@dot.gov

DEPARTMENTS

★ Presidential Appointment Requiring Senate Confirmation ☆ Presidential Appointment □ Schedule C Appointment ◇ Career Senior Foreign Service Appointment
● Career Senior Executive Service (SES) Appointment ○ Non-Career Senior Executive Service (SES) Appointment ■ Postal Career Executive Service

DEPARTMENTS

Resource Centers

31 Hopkins Plaza, Baltimore, MD 21201
E-mail: fhwatechnicalservices@dot.gov
Internet: www.fhwa.dot.gov/resourcecenter

FHWA Resource Center Director **Bernetta Collins** ...... (512) 536-5978
Program Assistant **William Alquist** .... (720) 963-3266

Resource Center at Atlanta

Atlanta Federal Center, 61 Forsyth Street, SW,
Suite 17T26, Atlanta, GA 30303-3104
Tel: (404) 562-3570 Fax: (404) 562-3700

Civil Rights Team Manager (Acting) **Patrick Gomez** ..... (404) 562-3570
E-mail: patrick.gomez@dot.gov
Construction and Project Management Team Manager
G. Rob Elliott .... (404) 895-6080
Operations Technical Service Team Manager
Grant Zammit .... (404) 274-5058

Resource Center at Baltimore

City Crescent Building, 10 South Howard Street,
Suite 4000, Baltimore, MD 21201
Tel: (410) 962-0093 Fax: (410) 962-3419

Air Quality Specialist **Kevin Black** .... (410) 962-2177
Fax: (410) 962-3655
Air Quality Specialist **Paul Heishman** .... (410) 962-2362
Fax: (410) 962-4319
Air Quality Modeling Specialist **(Vacant)** .... (410) 962-0069
Fax: (410) 962-3655
Civil Rights Specialist
Sandra "Sandy" Talbert-Jackson .... (410) 962-0116
E-mail: sandy.talbert-jackson@dot.gov Fax: (410) 962-3419
Community Planner **Jocelyn Jones** .... (410) 962-2486
Fax: (410) 962-3419
Construction and Project Management Engineer
Kathryn Weisner .... (202) 823-2267
Environmental Program Specialist **Keith Moore** .... (410) 962-0051
Fax: (410) 962-3419
Community Planner **Brian Betlyon** .... (410) 962-0086
Fax: (410) 962-3419
Financial Management Specialist **Jeffrey Blais** .... (410) 962-0720
Geotechnical and Hydraulic Engineering Team
Manager **Gregory "Greg" Punske** .... (512) 534-6165
Management Assistant **Susie Tingler** .... (410) 962-3187
E-mail: susie.tingler@dot.gov
Operations Specialist **Richard Denney** .... (410) 962-4796
Fax: (410) 962-4586
Pavement and Materials Technical Service Team
Manager **Michael Arasteh** .... (410) 962-0678
Fax: (410) 962-3655
Program Assistant **Marlene Eichner** .... (410) 962-1890
Fax: (410) 962-4586
Program Assistant **Melvin Harris** .... (410) 962-2773
Fax: (410) 962-4586
Safety Engineer **John McFadden** .... (410) 962-0982
Fax: (410) 962-3419
Safety Engineer **David Petrucci** .... (410) 962-2372
Fax: (410) 962-3419
Safety Engineer **Keith Sinclair** .... (410) 962-3742
Fax: (410) 962-3419
Senior Geotechnical Engineer **Justice Maswoswe** ...... (410) 962-2460
Fax: (410) 962-4586
Senior Pavement and Materials Engineer
Andrew Mergenmeier .... (410) 962-0091
Fax: (410) 962-3655
Senior Structural Engineer **Waider Wong** .... (410) 962-9252
Fax: (410) 962-4586
SHRP2 Pavement Renewal Engineer
Stephen J. Cooper .... (410) 962-0629
Fax: (410) 962-3655
Support Services Coordinator **(Vacant)** .... (410) 962-7971
Fax: (410) 962-3655

Resource Center at Lakewood (CO)

12300 West Dakota Avenue, Suite 340, Lakewood, CO 80228
Tel: (720) 963-3250 Fax: (720) 963-3232

Environment, Air Quality and Realty Technical Service
Team Manager **Lisa Hanf** .... (720) 963-3210
E-mail: lisa.hanf@dot.gov
Hydraulics Technical Service Team Manager **(Vacant)** .... (720) 963-3200
Geotechnical Technical Service Team Manager
(Vacant) .... (720) 963-3244
Freight and Transportation Performance Team Manager
Lisa Randall .... (404) 895-6080
E-mail: lisa.randall@dot.gov
Financial Management Specialist **(Vacant)** .... (720) 963-3250
Transportation Planner **Larry Anderson** .... (720) 963-3268

Resource Center at Matteson (IL)

One Prairie Office Center, 4749 Lincoln Mall Drive,
Suite 600, Matteson, IL 60443
Tel: (708) 283-3500 Fax: (708) 283-3501

Safety and Highway Design Technical Service Team
Manager **Patrick Hasson** .... (708) 359-5079
Civil Rights Specialist **(Vacant)** .... (708) 283-3519
Financial Specialist **Arturo Perez** .... (708) 283-3511
Information Technology Specialist **Ray Murphy** .... (224) 415-1449
E-mail: ray.murphy@dot.gov

Resource Center at San Francisco

201 Mission Street, Suite 1700, San Francisco, CA 94105
Tel: (415) 744-3103 Fax: (415) 744-2620

Public Affairs Specialist **(Vacant)** .... (415) 744-3103

Office of Federal Lands Highway Programs (HFL-1)

Southeast Federal Center Building, 1200 New Jersey Avenue, SE,
Room E61-316, Washington, DC 20590-9898
Tel: (202) 366-9494 Fax: (202) 366-7495
E-mail: federallands.fhwa@fhwa.dot.gov Internet: http://flh.fhwa.dot.gov

Field Offices

Central Federal Lands Highway Division

12300 West Dakota Avenue, Lakewood, CO 80228
Tel: (720) 963-3500 Tel: (888) 739-1055 Fax: (720) 963-3379
E-mail: cfl.fhwa@fhwa.dot.gov Internet: www.cflhd.gov
Areas Covered: AZ, CA, CO, HI, KS, NE, NV, NM, ND, OK, SD, TX, UT, WY

● Division Director (Acting) **Curtis R. Scott** .... (720) 963-3558
E-mail: curtis.scott@dot.gov
Transportation Specialist **Ronald E. "Ron" Williams** .... (720) 963-3450

Office of Project Delivery

Director of Project Delivery **(Vacant)** .... (720) 963-3500

Construction Engineering Branch

Supervisory Highway Engineer **Gene Dodd** .... (720) 963-3414
Supervisory Highway Engineer **(Vacant)** .... (360) 619-7717

Project Development Engineering Branch

Chief of Engineering (Acting) **Brian Kozy** .... (202) 366-4596

Project Management Engineering Branch

Branch Chief **Gary Strike** .... (720) 963-3464

Office of Program Administration

Director of Program Administration
Judy Salomonson .... (720) 963-3463
E-mail: judy.salomonson@dot.gov

Administrative Programs

Administrative Program Coordinator/Executive Officer
(Vacant) .... (720) 963-3500

★ Presidential Appointment Requiring Senate Confirmation ☆ Presidential Appointment ☐ Schedule C Appointment ◇ Career Senior Foreign Service Appointment
● Career Senior Executive Service (SES) Appointment ○ Non-Career Senior Executive Service (SES) Appointment ■ Postal Career Executive Service

Planning and Programs Branch
Branch Chief **(Vacant)** .... (720) 963-3729

Eastern Federal Lands Highway Division
21400 Ridgetop Circle, Suite 300, Sterling, VA 20166-6511
Tel: (703) 404-6201 Fax: (703) 404-6217 E-mail: efl.fhwa@fhwa.dot.gov
Internet: www.efl.fhwa.dot.gov
Areas Covered: AL, AR, CT, DE, DC, FL, GA, IL, IN, IA, KY, LA, ME, MD, MA, MI, MN, MS, MO, NH, NJ, NY, NC, OH, PA, RI, SC, TN, VT, VA, WV, WI

- ● Division Director **Monique R. Evans** .... (202) 493-3074
  E-mail: monique.evans@dot.gov
- Assistant Chief Counsel **Milton Hsieh** .... (703) 404-6206
- Chief of Business Operations **Kurt Dowden** .... (571) 434-1598
  E-mail: kurt.dowden@dot.gov
- Chief of Engineering **Laurin Lineman** .... (703) 404-6261
- Technical Services Engineer **Libby O'Brien** .... (703) 404-6201
- Construction Engineer **Thomas J. "Tom" Scott, Jr.** .... (703) 404-6270
- Bridge Engineer **Hratch "Rich" Pakhchanian** .... (703) 404-6246
- Administration Program Manager **Elizabeth Garrido** .... (703) 404-6201
- Planning and Programs Manager **Holly E. Bell** .... (703) 404-6293
- Project Management Engineer **Scott R. Whittemore** .... (703) 404-6332
- Highway Design Engineer **Marc Carruthers** .... (571) 434-1594

Western Federal Lands Highway Division
610 East Fifth Street, HFL-17, Vancouver, WA 98661-3801
Tel: (360) 619-7700 Tel: (866) 890-6230 Fax: (360) 619-7846
E-mail: wfl.fhwa@dot.gov Internet: www.wfl.fhwa.dot.gov
Areas Covered: AK, ID, MT, OR, WA
Director **Ricardo Suarez PE** .... (720) 963-3448

Office of Program Administration
Director **(Vacant)** .... (360) 619-7966

Administrative Programs
Administrative Service Team Manager
Brandon Brokaw .... (360) 619-7729
Finance Manager **William Crandell** .... (360) 619-7589
Administrative Specialist **(Vacant)** .... (360) 619-7802
Supply Management Specialist **Dyan Van Brunt** .... (360) 619-7755

Acquisitions Team
Acquisition Team/Contract Development Engineer
Elizabeth M. Firestone .... (360) 619-7931
E-mail: elizabeth.firestone@dot.gov

Information Technology Services Team
Technology Development Engineer **Amit Armstrong** .... (360) 619-7668
E-mail: amit.armstrong@dot.gov

Planning and Programs Branch
Planning and Programs Branch Chief **(Vacant)** .... (360) 619-7922
Program Coordination Team Leader **(Vacant)** .... (360) 619-7922

Office of Project Delivery
Director of Project Delivery **(Vacant)** .... (360) 619-7700

Construction Branch
Construction Branch Chief **Richard J. Barrows** .... (360) 619-7704
Management and Program Analyst **Lynn Hertz** .... (360) 619-7624
Program Coordination Engineer **(Vacant)** .... (360) 619-7819
Contract Administration Specialist **Susan M. Yenne** .... (360) 619-7601
E-mail: susan.yenne@dot.gov
Civil Engineer **P. Marty Flores** .... (360) 619-7972
Idaho - Montana Construction Operations Engineer
James Rathke .... (360) 619-7582
National Park Service Construction Operations
Engineer **Howe T. Crockett** .... (360) 619-7750
Oregon Construction Operations Engineer
Charles "Chuck" Dissen .... (360) 619-7979
Washington Construction Operations Engineer
Craig Sanders .... (360) 619-7985
Engineer Systems Coordinator **Juan P. Aguirre** .... (360) 619-7745

Project Development Engineering Branch
Design Quality and Safety Engineer
Stephen Chapman .... (360) 619-7801
E-mail: stephen.chapman@dot.gov
Highway Design Engineer **Edwin M. "Ted" Wood, Jr.** .... (360) 619-7715
Highway Safety Engineer **Victoria "Tori" Brinkly** .... (360) 619-7885

Technical Services Branch
Hydraulics Engineer Team Leader **Sven Leon** .... (360) 619-7964

DEPARTMENTS

Federal Motor Carrier Safety Administration (FMCSA)
West Building, 1200 New Jersey Avenue, SE,
6th Floor, Washington, DC 20590-9898
Tel: (800) 832-5660 Fax: (202) 366-3224 Internet: www.fmcsa.dot.gov

OFFICE OF THE ADMINISTRATOR (OA)
West Building, 1200 New Jersey Avenue, SE,
6th Floor, Washington, DC 20590-9898
Fax: (202) 366-3224

Field Offices

Alabama Division Office
520 Cotton Gin Road, Montgomery, AL 36117-2018
Tel: (334) 290-4954 Fax: (334) 290-4944
Division Administrator **Kenneth Price** .... (334) 290-4954
Transportation Assistant **Frank Benefield** .... (334) 290-4954
E-mail: frank.benefield@dot.gov

Alaska Division Office
Frontier Building, 3601 C Street, Suite 260, Anchorage, AK 99503
Tel: (907) 271-4068 Fax: (907) 271-4069
Division Administrator **Tracey Lewellyn** .... (907) 271-4068
E-mail: tracey.lewellyn@dot.gov
Transportation Assistant **(Vacant)** .... (907) 271-4068
Safety Investigator **Lloyd Coleman** .... (907) 271-4068

Arizona Division Office
One Arizona Center, 400 East Van Buren Street,
Suite 401, Phoenix, AZ 85004-2258
Tel: (602) 379-6851 Fax: (602) 379-3627
Division Administrator **Matthew Fix** .... (602) 379-6851 ext. 302
Transportation Assistant **Gregory Cannady** .... (602) 379-6851 ext. 302
E-mail: gregory.cannady@dot.gov

Arkansas Division Office
Federal Building, 700 West Capitol Avenue,
Room 2527, Little Rock, AR 72201
Tel: (501) 324-5050 Fax: (501) 324-6562
Division Administrator **Kevin Breedlove** .... (501) 324-6595
E-mail: kevin.breedlove@dot.gov

Connecticut Division Office
628-2 Hebron Avenue, Suite 302, Glastonbury, CT 06033
Tel: (860) 659-6700 Fax: (860) 659-6725
Division Administrator **Christopher Henry** .... (860) 659-6702
E-mail: christopher.henry@dot.gov
Federal Program Specialist **Ed Brickner** .... (860) 657-1816
Transportation Assistant **Lisa J. Daniel** .... (860) 659-6700
E-mail: lisa.daniel@dot.gov
State Program Specialist **David West** .... (860) 659-6700
Motor Carrier Safety Specialist **Catherine Bordzol** .... (860) 659-1819
Motor Carrier Safety Specialist **Ernest Galante** .... (860) 657-1818

★ Presidential Appointment Requiring Senate Confirmation ☆ Presidential Appointment ☐ Schedule C Appointment ◇ Career Senior Foreign Service Appointment
● Career Senior Executive Service (SES) Appointment ○ Non-Career Senior Executive Service (SES) Appointment ■ Postal Career Executive Service

DEPARTMENTS

Colorado Division Office
12300 West Dakota Avenue, Suite 130, Lakewood, CO 80228
Tel: (720) 963-3130 Fax: (720) 963-3131
Division Administrator **Steven Kleszczynski** . . . . (720) 963-3130

Delaware Division Office
College Business Park, 1203 College Park Drive,
Suite 102, Dover, DE 19904-8703
Fax: (302) 346-5101
Division Administrator **Philip "Phil" Strohm** . . . . (302) 734-3966
E-mail: philip.strohm@dot.gov
Federal Program Specialist **Nancy Vaughn** . . . .(302) 734-3973
Safety Investigator **Robin Callaway** . . . .(302) 734-3968
Transportation Assistant **Corinne Osborn** . . . . (302) 734-8173
E-mail: corinne.osborn@dot.gov

District of Columbia Division Office
1990 K Street, NW, Suite 510, Washington, DC 20006
Fax: (202) 219-3545
Division Administrator **Joe Shea** . . . .(202) 219-3550
E-mail: joe.shea@dot.gov
Federal Program Manager **Bernard McWay** . . . . (202) 219-3549
Transportation Assistant **Carla Williams** . . . . (202) 219-3559
E-mail: carla.williams@dot.gov
Regional Traffic Safety Program Manager
Angelique Cancino-Wolfe . . . . (202) 366-9358

Florida Division Office
3500 Financial Plaza, Suite 200, Tallahassee, FL 32312-5902
Tel: (850) 942-9338 Fax: (850) 942-9680
Division Administrator **Jeff Sanderson** . . . . (850) 942-9338
E-mail: jeff.sanderson@dot.gov
Federal Programs Manager **Diana Morales** . . . .(850) 942-9338
State Programs Manager **Michael Davis** . . . . (850) 942-9338

Georgia Division Office
Two Crown Center, 1745 Phoenix Boulevard,
Suite 380, Atlanta, GA 30349
Tel: (678) 284-5130 Fax: (678) 284-5146
Division Administrator **Clinton Seaymour** . . . .(678) 284-5130
State Programs Manager **Clay Greene** . . . .(678) 284-5130
E-mail: clay.greene@dot.gov
Transportation Assistant **(Vacant)** . . . .(678) 284-5130

Hawaii Division Office
Prince Jonah Kuhio Kalanianaole Federal Building,
300 Ala Moana Boulevard, Room 3-239, Honolulu, HI 96850
Mail: P.O. Box 50226, Honolulu, HI 96850
Tel: (808) 541-2790 Fax: (808) 541-2702
Division Administrator
Stephen J. "Steve" McCormick . . . .(808) 541-2790

Idaho Division Office
3200 North Lakeharbor Lane, Suite 161, Boise, ID 83703
Tel: (208) 334-1842 Fax: (208) 334-1046
Division Administrator **Richard York** . . . .(208) 334-1842
E-mail: richard.york@dot.gov
Transportation Assistant **Karen Salas** . . . . (208) 334-1842
E-mail: karen.salas@dot.gov

Illinois Division Office
3250 Executive Park Drive, Springfield, IL 62703
Tel: (217) 492-4608 Fax: (217) 492-4986
Division Administrator **Dan Meyer** . . . . (217) 492-4608
E-mail: dan.meyer@dot.gov
State Programs Specialist **Scott Thompson** . . . .(217) 492-4604
Hazardous Materials Specialist **(Vacant)** . . . . (618) 302-1535
Transportation Assistant **Kate Joyce** . . . . (217) 492-4612

Indiana Division Office
Minton-Capehart Federal Building, 575 North Pennsylvania Street,
Room 261, Indianapolis, IN 46204-1520
Tel: (317) 226-7474 Fax: (317) 226-5657
Division Administrator **Kenneth D. Strickland** . . . . (317) 226-7474
E-mail: kenneth.strickland@dot.gov
Federal Programs Specialist **(Vacant)** . . . .(317) 226-7474
State Programs Specialist **Daniel J. Beaver** . . . . (317) 226-7474

Iowa Division Office
105 Sixth Street, Ames, IA 50010-6337
Tel: (515) 233-7400 Fax: (515) 233-7494
Division Administrator **Shirley Maguire** . . . .(515) 233-7400
Federal Programs Specialist
Christopher Soder . . . . (515) 233-7400 ext. 412
State Program Specialist **Jeremy Dugger** . . . .(515) 233-7400 ext. 410
E-mail: jeremy.dugger@dot.gov
Transportation Assistant **Denise McDonald** . . . . (515) 233-7400

Kansas Division Office
1303 SW First American Place, Topeka, KS 66604
Tel: (785) 271-1260 Fax: (877) 547-0378
Division Administrator **Jeffrey Ellett** Suite 200 . . . .(785) 271-1260
E-mail: jeff.ellett@dot.gov
Federal Program Specialist **Michelle Long** . . . . (785) 271-1260
State Program Specialist
Michael Christopher Suite 200 . . . . (785) 271-1260
Transportation Assistant **Kay Morgan** Suite 200 . . . .(785) 271-1260
E-mail: kay.morgan@dot.gov

Kentucky Division Office
John C. Watts Federal Building and U.S. Courthouse, 330 West Broadway,
Room 124, Frankfort, KY 40601
Tel: (502) 223-6779 Fax: (502) 223-6767
Division Administrator **Linda H. Goodman** . . . . (502) 223-6779
E-mail: linda.goodman@dot.gov
Federal Programs Manager **Sean Anderson** . . . .(502) 223-6766
State Programs Manager **(Vacant)** . . . . (502) 223-6779
Safety Investigator **William Rein** . . . . (502) 223-6776
Safety Investigator **Lolita Kendrick** . . . . (502) 223-6776
Safety Investigator **Paul M. Stewart** . . . . (502) 223-6772
Transportation Assistant **Serena Shelton** . . . . (502) 223-6769

Louisiana Division Office
5304 Flanders Drive, Suite A, Baton Rouge, LA 70808
Tel: (225) 757-7640 Fax: (225) 757-7636
E-mail: Louisiana.fhwa@dot.gov
Division Administrator **William Norris** . . . .(225) 757-7640 ext. 248
E-mail: william.norris@dot.gov

Maine Division Office
Edmund S. Muskie Federal Building, 40 Western Avenue,
Room 411, Augusta, ME 04330
Tel: (207) 622-8358 Fax: (207) 622-8477
Division Administrator **Eric Adair** . . . . (207) 622-8358 ext. 121
E-mail: eric.adair@dot.gov
Transportation Assistant **(Vacant)** . . . .(207) 622-8358
Safety Investigator **Dennis Anderson** . . . .(207) 622-8358
Safety Investigator **Ross Michaud** . . . .(207) 622-8358
Program Specialist **Cheryl Quirion** . . . . (207) 622-8358
Program Specialist **Alan Vitcavage** . . . . (207) 622-8358

Maryland Division Office
City Crescent Building, 10 South Howard Street,
Suite 2710, Baltimore, MD 21201-2526
Tel: (410) 962-2889 Fax: (410) 962-3916
Division Administrator **(Vacant)** . . . .(410) 962-2889
State Program Manager **Richard Johnson** . . . . (410) 962-2889
E-mail: richard.johnson@dot.gov

Massachusetts Division Office
50 Mall Road, Suite 212, Burlington, MA 01803
Tel: (781) 425-3210 Fax: (781) 425-3225

Division Administrator **Richard R. Bates** .... (781) 425-3213
E-mail: richard.bates@dot.gov
State Program Specialist **Matthew Poirier** .... (781) 425-3212
Federal Program Manager **Steven Hanley** .... (781) 425-3210
Program Analyst **Erin Silva** .... (781) 425-3210
Special Agents **Jason Alfred** .... (781) 425-3218
Special Agents **Robert Comire, Jr.** .... (781) 425-3217
Special Agents **Patty Lavoie** .... (781) 425-3215
Special Agents **Terrence McSweeney** .... (781) 425-3210
Special Agents **Robert Soojian** .... (781) 425-3210
Special Agents **Charles Tarr** .... (781) 425-3210
Special Agents **(Vacant)** .... (781) 425-3216
Special Agents **(Vacant)** .... (781) 425-3219
Transportation Assistant **Kerry Diggins** .... (781) 425-3210

Michigan Division Office
USDOT FMCSA, 315 West Allegan Street,
Room 219, Lansing, MI 48933
Tel: (517) 853-5990 Fax: (517) 377-1868

Division Administrator **Patrick Muinch** .... (517) 853-5990 ext. 111
E-mail: patrick.muinch@dot.gov
Federal Program Manager **Matthew Fabry** ...... (517) 853-5990 ext. 103
Hazardous Materials Specialist
Cindy Hedman .... (517) 853-5997 ext. 205
State Program Manager **John P. Wallace** .... (517) 853-5990 ext. 104

Minnesota Division Office
Galtier Plaza, 380 Jackson Street, Suite 500, St. Paul, MN 55101-2904
Tel: (651) 291-6150 Fax: (651) 291-6001

Division Administrator **Matthew Marrin** .... (651) 291-6150
E-mail: matthew.marrin@dot.gov
Federal Program Manager **Charles St. Martin** .... (651) 291-6150
Program Analyst **Kathleen Childs** .... (651) 291-6150
Safety Investigator **James Harmon** .... (651) 291-6150
Safety Investigator **Brandon Sadler** .... (651) 291-6150
Safety Investigator **Mark Strazzinski** .... (651) 291-6150
Transportation Assistant **Charlene Davis-Winslow** ...... (651) 291-6153
E-mail: charlene.davis@dot.gov Fax: (651) 291-6001

Mississippi Division Office
100 West Capitol Street, Suite 1049, Jackson, MS 39269
Tel: (601) 965-4219 Fax: (601) 965-4674

Division Administrator **(Vacant)** .... (601) 965-4219

Missouri Division Office
3219 Emerald Lane, Suite 500, Jefferson City, MO 65109-6863
Tel: (573) 636-3246 Fax: (573) 636-8901

Division Administrator **Julie Lane** .... (573) 636-3246
E-mail: julie.lane@dot.gov
Federal Program Manager **Hope Maddox** .... (573) 636-1034
State Programs Manager **Chris Luebbert** .... (573) 636-3246 ext. 222

Montana Division Office
2880 Skyway Drive, Helena, MT 59602
Tel: (406) 449-5304 Fax: (406) 449-5318

Division Administrator **Bruce D. Holmes** .... (406) 449-5304 ext. 107
E-mail: bruce.holmes@dot.gov
Federal Program Specialist **Jesus Jan** .... (406) 449-5304 ext. 106
E-mail: jesus.jan@dot.gov
Safety Investigator **Edith Diaz-Hansen** .... (406) 449-5304 ext. 101
Safety Investigator **Tim Tenley** .... (406) 449-5304 ext. 105
State Programs Manager **Ann Svendsen** .... (406) 449-5304 ext. 104
Safety Investigator **Curtis Weidow** .... (406) 449-5304 ext. 105
Transportation Assistant **Tami Ross** .... (406) 449-5304 ext. 100
E-mail: tami.ross@dot.gov

Nebraska Division Office
100 Centennial Mall North, Room 406, Lincoln, NE 68508
Tel: (402) 437-6630 Fax: (402) 437-5837

Division Administrator **Elyse A. Mueller** .... (402) 437-5980
Federal Program Specialist **Kyle Zimmer** .... (402) 437-5963
State Program Specialist **Diane K. Podany** .... (402) 437-5979
Safety Investigator **Larry Bennett** .... (402) 437-6630
Safety Investigator **(Vacant)** .... (402) 437-5982
Safety Investigator **(Vacant)** .... (402) 437-5983
Transportation Assistant **Cheri Brinkman** .... (402) 437-6630
E-mail: cheri.brinkman@dot.gov

Nevada Division Office
705 North Plaza Street, Suite 204, Carson City, NV 89701
Tel: (775) 687-5335 Fax: (775) 687-8353

Division Administrator **William E. Bensmiller** .... (775) 687-5335
E-mail: william.bensmiller@dot.gov
State Program Specialist **Adrian Cerros** .... (775) 687-5335
Safety Investigator **Savbas Garcia** .... (702) 497-4705
Safety Investigator **Michael Schlarmann** .... (775) 687-5335
E-mail: michael.schlarmann@dot.gov
Transportation Assistant **(Vacant)** .... (775) 687-5335

New Hampshire Division Office
70 Commercial Street, Suite 102, Concord, NH 03301-7502
Tel: (603) 228-3112 Fax: (603) 223-0390
E-mail: newhampshiremc.motorcarrier@igate.dot.gov

Division Administrator **Steven Piwowarski** ..... (603) 228-3112 ext. 103
Division Program Specialist **Tom Kelly** .... (603) 228-3112 ext. 104
State Program Specialist **Tim White** .... (202) 267-0208
Federal Program Manager
Christopher "Chris" Gray .... (603) 228-3112 ext. 105
E-mail: christopher.gray@dot.gov
Safety Investigator **Michael "Mike" Sebor** ..... (603) 228-3112 ext. 106
E-mail: michael.sebor@dot.gov
Transportation Assistant **Wendy Fragala** .... (603) 228-3112 ext. 101

New Jersey Division Office
Five Independence Way, #125, Princeton, NJ 08540
Tel: (609) 275-2604 Fax: (609) 275-5107

Division Administrator **Christopher Rotondo** .... (609) 275-4380
E-mail: chris.rotondo@dot.gov
Transportation Assistant **Joanne Ciriaco** .... (609) 275-2604
E-mail: joanne.ciriaco@dot.gov
Safety Investigator **Matthew Golden** .... (609) 275-4831
Safety Investigator **Patricia Lees** .... (609) 275-4382
E-mail: patricia.lees@dot.gov
Safety Investigator **Gordon McCutcheon** .... (609) 275-4383
E-mail: gordon.mccutcheon@dot.gov
Federal Program Supervisor **Edgar Albisurez** .... (609) 275-2609
Federal Program Manager **Douglas Dougherty** .... (609) 275-4832
State Program Manager **Joseph Costello** .... (609) 275-2607
Safety Specialist **Lawrence Higgins** .... (609) 275-4833
Safety Specialist **Timothy O'Donnell** .... (609) 275-4834
E-mail: timothy.odonnell@dot.gov
Safety Specialist **Stacy Ropp** .... (609) 275-4384
E-mail: stacy.ropp@dot.gov
Safety Specialist **Uerequenia Pereira** .... (609) 275-4835
E-mail: uerequenia.pereira@dot.gov
Safety Specialist **Ashley Sullivan** .... (609) 275-4385
E-mail: ashley.sullivan@dot.gov
Safety Specialist **Selby P. Jones** .... (609) 275-4381
E-mail: selby.jones@dot.gov
Program Analyst **Andrea D'Antignac** .... (609) 275-4831
E-mail: andrea.dantignac@dot.gov

New Mexico Division Office
2440 Louisiana Boulevard NE, Suite 520, AFC-5,
Albuquerque, NM 87110-4316
Tel: (505) 346-7858 Fax: (505) 346-7859

Division Administrator **Cyndee Teetzen** .... (505) 346-2595
State Program Manager **Teresa Murray** .... (505) 346-7868

(continued on next page)

DEPARTMENTS

★ Presidential Appointment Requiring Senate Confirmation ☆ Presidential Appointment ☐ Schedule C Appointment ◇ Career Senior Foreign Service Appointment
● Career Senior Executive Service (SES) Appointment ○ Non-Career Senior Executive Service (SES) Appointment ■ Postal Career Executive Service

New Mexico Division Office *(continued)*

Border Supervisor **Rodolfo Marrufo** .... (505) 589-4656
Border Inspector **Steve Babbey** .... (505) 589-4656
E-mail: steve.babbey@dot.gov
Border Inspector **Jose Contreras** .... (505) 589-4656
Border Inspector **Luis Garcia** .... (505) 589-4656
Border Inspector **Francisco Monsivais** .... (505) 346-7858
E-mail: francisco.monsivais@dot.gov
Border Inspector **John Paul Picasso** .... (505) 589-4656
Border Inspector **Jesus Soto** .... (505) 589-4656
E-mail: jesus.soto@dot.gov
Federal Program Manager **Kevin Shurwan** .... (505) 346-7858
Safety Specialist **Sonia Leon** .... (505) 346-7865
Safety Investigator **Amanda Espy** .... (505) 346-7858
Transportation Assistant **(Vacant)** .... (505) 346-7858

New York Division Office

Leo W. O'Brien Federal Building, Clinton Avenue and North Pearl Street, Room 815, Albany, NY 12207
Tel: (518) 431-4145 Fax: (518) 431-4140

Division Administrator **Brian K. Temperine** ..... (518) 431-4145 ext. 111
E-mail: brian.temperine@dot.gov
Field Office Supervisor **Laura Lawton** .... (518) 431-4145 ext. 118
State Programs Specialist **John Weeks** .... (518) 431-4145 ext. 113
Hazardous Materials Specialist
Brandon Bulkley .... (518) 431-4145 ext. 112
Transportation Assistant **Allison Oswald** .... (518) 431-4145 ext. 115
E-mail: allison.oswald@dot.gov

Buffalo (NY) Office

Niagara Center, 130 South Elmwood Avenue,
Suite 524, Buffalo, NY 14202
Tel: (716) 551-4701 Fax: (716) 551-3312

Field Office Supervisor
William "Bill" Kacprowicz .... (716) 551-4701 ext. 237
Safety Auditor **Franklin Castle** .... (716) 551-4701 ext. 228
E-mail: frank.castle@dot.gov
Safety Investigator **Timothy Grimley** .... (716) 551-4701 ext. 226
Safety Investigator
Dorothea Keighron-Schroeder .... (716) 551-4701 ext. 224
Safety Investigator **Keith Kloesz** .... (716) 551-4701 ext. 227
E-mail: keith.kloesz@dot.gov
Safety Investigator **Steven Raschella** .... (716) 226-2971
E-mail: steven.raschella@dot.gov
Safety Investigator **Keith Field** .... (315) 350-0764
Safety Investigator **Melvin Williams** .... (315) 415-2832

New York (NY) Office

One Bowling Green, Room 420, New York, NY 10004
Tel: (212) 668-2130 Fax: (212) 668-2133

Field Office Supervisor **Doris Eusebio** .... (212) 668-2134
One Bowling Green, Room 420, New York, NY 10004-1415
E-mail: doris.eusebio@dot.gov
Safety Investigator **Jeffrey Wood** .... (212) 668-2063
E-mail: jeffrey.wood@dot.gov
Safety Investigator **Elaine Chan** .... (212) 668-2131
Safety Investigator **Joseph Dunn** .... (212) 668-2132
E-mail: joseph.dunn@dot.gov
Safety Investigator **Bernard Iacampo** .... (212) 668-2135
Safety Investigator **Cheron Marks** .... (212) 668-5823
E-mail: cheron.marks@dot.gov
Safety Investigator **Donald T. O'Connor** .... (212) 668-2131
E-mail: donald.o'connor@dot.gov
Program Assistant **Robert Davis** .... (716) 551-4701 ext. 231
Niagara Center, 130 S Elmwood Avenue, Fax: (716) 551-3312
Suite 524, Buffalo, NY 14202
Program Assistant **Vidalina Deleon-Zysk** .... (212) 668-2130

North Carolina Division Office

310 New Bern Avenue, Room 468, Raleigh, NC 27601
Tel: (919) 856-4378 Fax: (919) 856-4369

Division Administrator **Jon R. McCormick** ..... (919) 856-4365 ext. 365
State Program Manager **(Vacant)** .... (919) 856-4378

North Dakota Division

1471 Interstate Loop, Bismarck, ND 58503-0567
Tel: (701) 250-4346 Fax: (701) 250-4389

Division Administrator **Jeffrey P. Jensen** .... (701) 250-4346

Ohio Division Office

200 North High Street, Room 609, Columbus, OH 43215
Tel: (614) 280-5657 Fax: (614) 280-6875

Division Administrator **Linda Gilliam** .... (614) 280-6870
E-mail: linda.gilliam@dot.gov
State Program Manager
Keith R. Willoughby .... (614) 280-5657 ext. 6863
Federal Program Manager **Shelia D. Lucas** .... (614) 280-5657 ext. 6873
Hazardous Material Specialist
Andrea L. "Annie" Carpenter .... (614) 280-6865
Program Assistant
Cynthia I. "Cindy" Rader .... (614) 280-5657 ext. 6862
E-mail: cynthia.rader@dot.gov
Safety Investigator **Ana M. Curry** .... (614) 280-5657 ext. 6864
Safety Investigator **Tonya Neal** .... (614) 280-5657
Safety Investigator **Jimmie Perkins** .... (614) 280-5657 ext. 6865
Information Technology Specialist
Jeffrey Stoughton .... (614) 280-5657 ext. 6868

Oklahoma Division Office

300 North Meridian, Suite 106-S, Oklahoma City, OK 73107-6560
Tel: (405) 605-6047 Fax: (405) 605-6176

Division Administrator **Jerry "Mac" Kirk** .... (405) 605-6047
Safety Program Manager **Larry Ramsey** .... (405) 605-6047
E-mail: larry.ramsey@dot.gov
Safety Investigator **Joe Hardridge** .... (405) 605-6047
E-mail: joe.hardridge@dot.gov
Safety Investigator **Sandra Primm** .... (405) 605-6047
Safety Investigator **Doug Vollgraff** .... (405) 605-6047
E-mail: doug.vollgraff@dot.gov
Federal Program Specialist **(Vacant)** .... (405) 605-6047
Transportation Assistant **Seanna Case** .... (405) 605-6047
E-mail: seanna.case@dot.gov

Oregon Division Office

The Equitable Center, 530 Center Street, NE,
Suite 440, Salem, OR 97301
Tel: (503) 399-5775 Fax: (503) 316-2580

Division Administrator **Andrew E. Eno** .... (503) 399-5775
E-mail: andrew.eno@dot.gov
Federal Program Manager **Warren L. Simpson** .... (503) 399-5775
State Program Manager **David Rios** .... (503) 399-5775
Hazardous Materials Specialist **Janelle L. Brewster** ..... (503) 399-5775

Pennsylvania Division Office

215 Limekiln Road, Suite 200, New Cumberland, PA 17070
Tel: (717) 614-4060 Fax: (717) 614-4066 E-mail: mcpaoff@dot.gov

Division Administrator **Timothy A. Cotter** .... (717) 614-4060
E-mail: tim.cotter@dot.gov
Special Agent **Donald Orye** .... (717) 614-4060
Special Agent **Daniel Woodruff** .... (717) 614-4060
E-mail: daniel.woodruff@dot.gov
State Program Specialist **James J. Cusick** .... (717) 614-4060
Transportation Assistant **Rebecca Kueger** .... (717) 614-4060

King of Prussia (PA) Field Office

1150 First Avenue, Suite 380A, King of Prussia, PA 19406
Tel: (610) 992-8680 Fax: (610) 992-8685

Federal Program Specialist **Francis T. Ross** .... (610) 992-8680
E-mail: francis.ross@dot.gov
Special Agent **Mark J. Milligan** .... (610) 992-8680
E-mail: mark.milligan@dot.gov
Special Agent **Terrence M. Rink** .... (610) 992-8680
E-mail: terrence.rink@dot.gov
Special Agent **Jeff Tudor** .... (610) 992-8680
Transportation Assistant **Lois Holody** .... (610) 992-8680
E-mail: lois.holody@dot.gov

★ Presidential Appointment Requiring Senate Confirmation ☆ Presidential Appointment ☐ Schedule C Appointment ◇ Career Senior Foreign Service Appointment
● Career Senior Executive Service (SES) Appointment ○ Non-Career Senior Executive Service (SES) Appointment ■ Postal Career Executive Service

Pittsburgh (PA) Field Office
Federal Building, 1000 Liberty Avenue,
Room 1300, Pittsburgh, PA 15222
Tel: (412) 395-6935 Fax: (412) 395-5078

Federal Program Specialist **Todd C. Yusavage** ..... (412) 395-6935 ext. 5
E-mail: todd.yusavage@dot.gov
Special Agent **Thomas J. Paulmeier** .... (412) 395-6935 ext. 2
E-mail: thomas.paulmeier@dot.gov
Special Agent **(Vacant)** .... (412) 395-6935

Puerto Rico Division Office
Torre Chardón, 350 Chardón Street, Suite 207, Hato Rey, PR 00918
Tel: (787) 766-5985 Fax: (787) 766-5015

State Director **(Vacant)** .... (787) 766-5985

Rhode Island Division Office
20 Risho Avenue, Suite E, East Providence, RI 02914
Tel: (401) 431-6010 Fax: (401) 431-6019

Division Administrator **Kevin P. Carter** .... (401) 431-6015
E-mail: kevin.carter@dot.gov
Federal Program Manager **Stacy Johnson** .... (401) 431-6013
E-mail: stacy.johnson@dot.gov
Safety Investigator **(Vacant)** .... (401) 431-6010
State Program Manager **Daniel C. "Dan" Cusumano** .... (401) 431-6014
E-mail: dan.cusumano@dot.gov

South Carolina Division Office
Strom Thurmond Federal Building, 1835 Assembly Street,
Suite 1253, Columbia, SC 29201-2430
Tel: (803) 765-5414 Fax: (803) 765-5413

Division Administrator **Christopher M. Hartley** .... (803) 765-5414
Federal Program Manager **Carlean Glover** .... (803) 765-5414
E-mail: carlean.glover@dot.gov
State Program Manager **(Vacant)** .... (803) 765-5414

South Dakota Division Office
1410 East Highway 14, Suite B, Pierre, SD 57501-3110
Tel: (605) 224-8202 Fax: (605) 224-1766

Division Administrator **Mark D. Gilmore** .... (605) 224-8202 ext. 222
E-mail: mark.gilmore@dot.gov
Division Program Manager **(Vacant)** .... (605) 224-8202
Transportation Assistant **Susan Gregory** .... (605) 224-8202 ext. 221
E-mail: susan.gregory@dot.gov

Tennessee Division Office
640 Grassmere Park, Suite 111, Nashville, TN 37211
Tel: (615) 781-5781 Fax: (615) 781-5755

Division Administrator **Jon A. Dierberger** .... (615) 781-5781
E-mail: jon.dierberger@dot.gov
State Programs Specialist **Jeff Cooper** .... (615) 781-5781
Safety Program Manager **Lisa Rouse** .... (615) 781-5781
Safety Specialist **(Vacant)** .... (615) 781-5781
Safety Specialist **(Vacant)** .... (615) 781-5781
Safety Specialist **(Vacant)** .... (615) 781-5781
Safety Specialist **(Vacant)** .... (615) 781-5781
Safety Specialist **(Vacant)** .... (615) 781-5781
Hazardous Materials Specialist **(Vacant)** .... (502) 223-6779
Transportation Assistant **Shanita Randolph** .... (615) 781-5781

Texas Division Office
903 San Jacinto Boulevard, Room 101, Austin, TX 78701
Tel: (512) 916-5440 Fax: (512) 916-5482

Division Administrator **Joanne A. Cisneros** .... (512) 916-5440
Assistant Division Administrator **Mike Lamm** .... (512) 536-5981
E-mail: mike.lamm@dot.gov
Transportation Assistant **Sandra Bernal** .... (512) 916-5440
E-mail: sandra.bernal@dot.gov
State Program Manager **Rodney Baumgartner** .... (512) 916-5440
E-mail: rodney.baumgartner@dot.gov
Federal Program Specialist **Jeff Langloss** .... (512) 916-5440
Federal Program Specialist **Julio C. Manjarrez** .... (512) 916-5440

Texas Division Office *(continued)*

Transportation Assistant **Brian Hetzel** .... (512) 916-5440
E-mail: brian.hetzel@dot.gov

El Paso Field Office
8370 Burham, Suite 100, El Paso, TX 79907
Tel: (915) 593-8574 Fax: (915) 594-8857

Operations Supervisor **(Vacant)** .... (915) 593-8574

Laredo Field Office
5810 San Bernardo, 2nd Floor, Suite 290, Laredo, TX 78041
Tel: (956) 712-1385 Fax: (956) 723-1479

Operations Supervisor **Santos Pecina** .... (956) 712-1385
Operations Supervisor **Oscar Garza** .... (956) 447-5608

Utah Division Office
2520 West 4700 South, Suite 9B, Salt Lake City, UT 84118-1847
Tel: (801) 288-0360 Fax: (801) 963-0086

Division Administrator **(Vacant)** .... (801) 288-0360 ext. 202
Federal Program Specialist **Kim O'Kelly** .... (801) 288-0360
Safety Investigator **Carrie Baker** .... (801) 288-0360 ext. 203
Safety Investigator **Nicole Cardwell** .... (801) 288-0360 ext. 206
E-mail: nicole.cardwell@dot.gov
Safety Investigator **(Vacant)** .... (801) 288-0360 ext. 205
Transportation Assistant **Shana Hatch** .... (801) 288-0360
State Program Specialist **David Blauer** .... (801) 270-4528

Vermont Division Office
Federal Building, 87 State Street, Room 305, Montpelier, VT 05602
Mail: P.O. Box 338, Montpelier, VT 05601
Tel: (802) 828-4480 Fax: (802) 828-4581
Areas Covered: VT, Quebec

Division Administrator **Ture A. Nelson III** .... (802) 828-4480
E-mail: ture.nelson@dot.gov
Safety Program Manager **Joe Arduca** .... (802) 828-4480
Safety Investigator **Donald J. Banach** .... (802) 828-4480
E-mail: donald.banach@dot.gov
Safety Investigator **Breanna Kline** .... (802) 828-4480
E-mail: breanna.kline@dot.gov
Transportation Assistant **Denise Woodward** .... (802) 828-4480

Virginia Division Office
400 North Eighth Street, Suite 780, Richmond, VA 23219-4827
Tel: (804) 771-8585 Fax: (804) 771-8670

Division Administrator **Craig A. Feister** .... (804) 771-8585
Federal Program Specialist **Leland McLennan** .... (804) 771-8585
State Program Specialist **William Anderson** .... (804) 771-8585
Hazardous Material Specialist **Anthony J. Kryfka** .... (804) 771-8585

Washington Division Office
2424 Heritage Court, SW, Suite 302, Olympia, WA 98502
Tel: (360) 753-9875 Fax: (360) 753-9024

Division Administrator **Jeffrey "Jeff" James** ... (360) 753-9875 ext. 208
State Program Manager **Donald "Don" Ross** .... (360) 753-9429

West Virginia Division Office
Geary Plaza, 700 Washington Street, East,
Suite 205, Charleston, WV 25301-1620
Tel: (304) 347-5935 Fax: (304) 347-5617

Division Administrator **Michael W. "Mike" Myers** ...... (304) 347-5401

Wisconsin Division Office
567 D'Onofrio Drive, Suite 101, Madison, WI 53719-2844
Tel: (608) 662-2010 Fax: (608) 829-7540 E-mail: mcwioff@dot.gov

Division Administrator **Mark G. Oesterle** .... (608) 829-7532
E-mail: mark.oesterle@dot.gov
Federal Programs Manager **Jeff Kwilinski** .... (608) 662-2010
Hazardous Materials Specialist **Michael E. Mannikko** .... (920) 380-0012
Safety Investigator **Barbara N. Koehler** .... (715) 342-5992
Safety Investigator **Grant Barnes** .... (608) 662-2010

(continued on next page)

Wisconsin Division Office *(continued)*

State Program Manager **Mark B. Gessler** .... (608) 829-7539
Transportation Assistant **Marlene A. Skuldt** .... (608) 662-2010
E-mail: marlene.skuldt@dot.gov

Wyoming Division Office
1637 Stillwater, Suite F, Cheyenne, WY 82009
Tel: (307) 772-2305 Fax: (307) 772-2905

Division Administrator **John Mulcare** .... (307) 772-2305 ext. 106
E-mail: john.mulcare@dot.gov
Federal Program Manager **Eric Ramirez** .... (307) 772-2305 ext. 107
Special Agent **Edward Winans** .... (307) 772-2305 ext. 105
Special Agent **Juel Leuis** .... (307) 772-2904
Transportation Assistant **Ashley Wheeler** .... (307) 772-2305
E-mail: ashley.wheeler@dot.gov

California Division Office
1325 J Street, Suite 1540, Sacramento, CA 95814
Tel: (916) 930-2760 Fax: (916) 930-2778
Areas Covered: Northern Division (Monterey-Fresno Counties to OR border); Southern Division (Monterey-Fresno Counties to Mexico border)

Division Administrator **Steven Mattioli** .... (916) 930-2760
E-mail: steve.mattioli@dot.gov
Field Office Supervisor **Afshin Coleman** .... (916) 930-2760
E-mail: afshin.coleman@dot.gov
Safety Investigator **Terrance Early** .... (916) 930-2760
State Program Manager **Gregor "Greg" Bragg** .... (916) 930-2760
E-mail: gregor.bragg@dot.gov
Hazardous Materials Specialist
Donald "Don" Tomlinson .... (916) 930-2760
Transportation Assistant **(Vacant)** .... (916) 930-2760

California Field Office - Calexico
1778 Carr Road, Suite 3A, Calexico, CA 92231
Tel: (760) 768-7300 Fax: (760) 768-6423

Border Office Supervisor **Isabel Lopez** .... (760) 768-7300

California Field Office - Ontario
3401 Centre Lake Drive, Suite 550A, Ontario, CA 91761
Tel: (909) 937-2949 Fax: (909) 390-5642

Field Office Supervisor **Amy Hope** .... (909) 937-2949
E-mail: amy.hope@dot.gov
Household Goods Specialist **Marcos Anguiano** .... (909) 937-2949
E-mail: marcos.anguiano@dot.gov
Household Goods Specialist **Eduardo Suarez** .... (909) 937-2949
Transportation Assistant **Michelle Randle-Mitchell** ...... (909) 937-2949

California Field Office - Otay Mesa
2297 Niels Bohr Court, Suite 204, San Diego, CA 92154
Tel: (619) 710-8400 Fax: (619) 710-2804

Border Office Supervisor **Lynda Holst** .... (619) 710-8400

Service Centers (SC)

Eastern Service Center
802 Cromwell Park Drive, Suite N, Glen Burnie, MD 21061
Tel: (443) 703-2240 Fax: (443) 703-2253
Areas Covered: CT, DE, DC, ME, MD, MA, NH, NJ, NY, PA, PR, RI, VT, VA, WV

• Regional Field Administrator **Curtis L. Thomas** .... (443) 703-2240
E-mail: curtis.thomas@dot.gov
Education: South Carolina State 1982 BS; Webster 1999 MS
Eastern Field Administrator **Taft Kelly** .... (443) 703-2265
E-mail: taft.kelly@dot.gov
Administrative Officer **Lolita Salley** .... (443) 703-2243
E-mail: lolita.salley@dot.gov
Enforcement Program Manager **Lee S. Zimmerman** ..... (443) 703-2264
E-mail: lee.zimmerman@dot.gov
Attorney **Cynthia Campise** .... (443) 703-2255
E-mail: cynthia.campise@dot.gov
Attorney **Anthony G. Lardieri** .... (443) 703-2248
E-mail: anthony.lardieri@dot.gov
Education: Loyola U (Maryland) 1990 BA; Baltimore 1993 JD

Eastern Service Center *(continued)*

Enforcement Program Specialist **Robert King** .... (443) 703-2266
E-mail: robert.king2@dot.gov
Enforcement Program Specialist
John J. "Jay" Vasconez .... (443) 703-2259
E-mail: jay.vasconez@dot.gov
Enforcement Program Specialist (NE)
Stephanie Haller .... (443) 703-2262
E-mail: stephanie.haller@dot.gov
Enforcement Program Specialist (NE)
Kathryn Narducci .... (610) 992-8686
E-mail: kathryn.narducci@dot.gov
Enforcement Technician **Alise Griffith** .... (443) 703-2256
New Entrant (NE) Coordinator
Carolyn Temperine .... (518) 431-4145 ext. 270
E-mail: carolyn.temperine@dot.gov
Executive Assistant **Tanesha Wilson** .... (443) 703-2240
Hazardous Material Manager **Suzanne Ellis** .... (443) 695-9008
Paralegal **Ashley Drexel** .... (443) 703-2255
E-mail: ashley.barreto.ctr@dot.gov
Administrative Program Assistant **Cynthia Johnson** ..... (443) 703-2256
Administrative Program Assistant **William Jones** .... (443) 703-2240
Financial Specialist **Arnaud Kalameu** .... (443) 703-2245
E-mail: arnaud.kalameu@dot.gov

Midwestern Service Center
Midwestern Service Center, 4749 Lincoln Mall Drive, Suite 300A, Matteson, IL 60443
Tel: (708) 283-3577 Fax: (708) 283-3579
Areas Covered: IL, IN, IA, KS, MI, MN, MO, NE, OH, WI

Service Center Director **DaVina Farmer** .... (708) 283-3577
Field Administrator **Max Strathman** .... (708) 283-3577
Administrative Officer **Victoria Lopez** .... (708) 283-3518
E-mail: victoria.lopez@dot.gov
State Program Manager **Garth Lantz** .... (219) 741-0789
Computer Specialist **(Vacant)** .... (708) 283-3575
Enforcement Program Manager **Donnell Mosley** .... (708) 283-3571
Enforcement Program Clerk **Lennette Henderson** ...... (708) 283-3589
Enforcement Program Technician **Crystal Hunter** .... (708) 283-3555
Enforcement Program Specialist **Christina Baker** .... (708) 679-3703
Enforcement Program Specialist **James Dearing** .... (708) 679-3704
Financial Management Specialist **Freddie Rayon** .... (708) 283-3527
Hazardous Materials Program Manager **Arthur Fleener** ... (708) 283-3572
Highway Safety Program Manager **Paul Gozman** .... (708) 679-3703
Highway Safety Program Manager **William Honan** ...... (708) 283-3551
Medical Program Specialist **Leslie Payne** .... (708) 283-3569
Paralegal **Gayle Kick** .... (708) 283-3506
E-mail: gayle.kick@dot.gov
Attorney **Peter Hines** .... (708) 283-3577
E-mail: peter.hines@dot.gov
Trial Attorney **Stacy Luedtke** .... (708) 283-3515
Administrative Assistant **(Vacant)** .... (708) 283-3577

Southern Service Center
1800 Century Boulevard, NE, Suite 1700, Atlanta, GA 30345-3220
Tel: (404) 327-7360 Fax: (404) 327-7349
Areas Covered: AL, AR, FL, GA, KY, LA, MS, NM, NC, OK, SC, TN, TX

Service Center Director **Pamela Rice** .... (404) 327-7350
E-mail: pamela.rice@dot.gov
Southern Regional Field Administrator **Darrell Ruban** .... (404) 327-7379
E-mail: darrell.ruban@dot.gov
Driver Qualifications Specialist **Lloyd Goldsmith** .... (404) 327-7400
E-mail: lloyd.goldsmith@dot.gov
Hazardous Materials Specialist **David Ford** .... (404) 327-7374
Financial Management Specialist **James Thomas** .... (404) 327-7388

★ Presidential Appointment Requiring Senate Confirmation ☆ Presidential Appointment ☐ Schedule C Appointment ◇ Career Senior Foreign Service Appointment
● Career Senior Executive Service (SES) Appointment ○ Non-Career Senior Executive Service (SES) Appointment ■ Postal Career Executive Service

Western Service Center
Golden Hills Office Centre, 12600 West Colfax Avenue,
Suite B-300, Lakewood, CO 80215-3755
Tel: (303) 407-2350 Fax: (303) 407-2339
Areas Covered: AK, AZ, CA, CO, HI, ID, MT, NV, NM, ND, OR, SD, TX, UT, WA, WY

Western Regional Field Administrator **William Paden** .... (303) 407-2350
Field Administrator **Terry D. Wolf** .... (916) 930-2776
Service Center Director **Lorraine Ehret** .... (303) 407-2350
State Programs Manager **Wendy LB Cunningham** .... (360) 596-4342
Administrative Officer **Cassandra Vigil** .... (303) 407-2371
E-mail: cassandra.vigil@dot.gov
Enforcement Program Manager **Arturo Ramirez** .... (303) 407-2361
Enforcement Program Specialist **(Vacant)** .... (303) 407-2350
New Entrance Program Manager **Daniel Perez** .... (619) 710-8406
Hazardous Materials Specialist **James O. Simmons** .... (303) 407-2368
Information Technical Specialist **(Vacant)** .... (303) 407-2350
Trial Attorney **Nancy Jackson** .... (303) 407-2363
E-mail: nancy.jackson@dot.gov
Trial Attorney **Jedd Miloud** .... (303) 407-2362
E-mail: jedd.miloud@dot.gov
Operations Research Analyst **Caroline Poyurs** .... (206) 231-2984

Federal Railroad Administration (FRA)

1200 New Jersey Avenue, SE, Washington, DC 20590-9898
Tel: (202) 366-4000 (Personnel Locator)
Tel: (202) 493-6039 (Freedom of Information)
Tel: (202) 493-0489 (Privacy Act Information)
Tel: (202) 493-6024 (Public Affairs) Fax: (202) 493-6009
Internet: www.fra.dot.gov

OFFICE OF THE ADMINISTRATOR

West Building, 1200 New Jersey Avenue, SE,
Washington, DC 20590-9898
Tel: (202) 493-6014 Fax: (202) 493-6009

Regional Offices

Region I
55 Broadway, Suite 1077, Cambridge, MA 02142
Tel: (617) 494-2302 Tel: (800) 724-5991 Fax: (617) 494-2967
Areas Covered: CT, ME, MA, NH, NJ, NY, RI, VT

Regional Administrator **Les Fiorenzo** .... (617) 494-3484
E-mail: les.fiorenzo@dot.gov
Deputy Regional Administrator **Michelle Muhlanger** .... (617) 494-2630
E-mail: michelle.muhlanger@dot.gov
Deputy Regional Administrator **Janet A. Lee** .... (617) 494-3990
Administrative Officer **Kristine Simpson** .... (617) 494-2215
IT Specialist **Patrick Devine** .... (617) 494-3988
E-mail: patrick.devine@dot.gov
Chief Inspector **Patrick Corcoran** .... (401) 828-2482
Chief Inspector **Edward Flynn** .... (617) 494-2302
Chief Inspector **Richard F. Thomas** .... (617) 494-2302
Chief Inspector **Gary White** .... (732) 570-5352

Region II
Baldwin Tower, 1510 Chester Pike, Suite 660, Crum Lynne, PA 19022
Tel: (610) 521-8200 Tel: (800) 724-5992 Fax: (610) 521-8225
Areas Covered: DE, DC, MD, OH, PA, VA, WV

Regional Administrator **David L. Kannenberg** .... (610) 521-8216
E-mail: david.kannenberg@dot.gov
Deputy Regional Administrator **Mikel Cipollini** .... (610) 521-8210
E-mail: mikel.cipollini@dot.gov
Deputy Regional Administrator **Louis Tomassone, Jr.** .... (610) 521-8220
E-mail: louis.tomassone@dot.gov
Crossing and Trespasser Regional Manager
Evelyn Hendricks .... (610) 521-8200
Administrative Officer **Barbara E. Pilny** .... (610) 521-8205
E-mail: barbara.pilny@dot.gov
Chief Inspector **Patrick L. Boyd** .... (610) 521-8200

Region II *(continued)*

Hazardous Materials Inspector **Marc A. Dougherty** .... (610) 521-8200
Hazardous Materials Inspector **Clifton Rineheart** .... (610) 521-8200
Grade Crossing Inspector **Douglas Jolley** .... (610) 521-8200
Hazardous Materials Specialist **Joel B. Roberts** .... (610) 521-8200
Motive Power and Equipment Inspector
Kenneth "Kenny" Pugh .... (610) 521-8200
Chief Inspector **James M. Cassatt, Jr.** .... (610) 521-8200
Operating Practices Inspector **Jimmy D. Gee** .... (610) 521-8200
Signal and Train Control Specialist
Lawrence J. "Larry" Kuhn .... (610) 521-8200
Track Inspector **John M. Wilcha** .... (610) 521-8200
Computer Specialist **Phillip E. Hunt** .... (610) 521-8207
E-mail: phillip.hunt@dot.gov
Motive Power and Equipment Specialist
Thomas R. Delano .... (610) 521-8200
Operating Practices Specialist **Mark M. Pruden** .... (610) 521-8200
Track Specialist **Christopher F. Schulte** .... (610) 521-8200
Track Specialist **Shane Stiffler** .... (610) 521-8200
Signal and Train Control Inspector **Chuck Sumoski** .... (610) 521-8200
Chief Inspector **James M. Hoffnagle** .... (610) 521-8200
Motive Power and Equipment Inspector **Jeffrey Apple** .... (610) 521-8200
Motive Power and Equipment Inspector
Joseph J. Sokolsky .... (610) 521-8200
Motive Power and Equipment Inspector
Richard Timberman .... (610) 521-8200
Signal and Train Control Inspector **James T. Hurley** .... (610) 521-8200
Operating Practices Inspector **(Vacant)** .... (610) 521-8200

Charleston (WV) Field Inspectors
Hazardous Materials Inspector **Dannie B. McCourt** .... (610) 521-8200
Chief Inspector **Terrence L. "Terry" Allums** .... (304) 586-3206
Operating Practices Inspector **(Vacant)** .... (610) 521-8200
Operating Practices Inspector **Kurt Erickson** .... (610) 521-8200
Signal and Train Control Inspector **Dean A. Hudnall** .... (610) 521-8200
Track Inspector **Paul E. Smailes** .... (610) 521-8200
Motive Power and Equipment Inspector **Jason Jeffries** .... (610) 521-8200
Operating Practices Inspector **Joseph "J.D." Clay** .... (610) 521-8200

Cincinnati (OH) Field Inspectors
Hazardous Material Inspector **Gary Kearney** .... (610) 521-8200

Cleveland (OH) Field Inspectors
Hazardous Materials Inspector **Anthony P. Schneider** .... (610) 521-8200
Track Inspector **Chad Broski** .... (610) 521-8200
Signal and Train Control Inspector **Terry M. Ellis** .... (610) 521-8200
Operating Practices Inspector **Karrie-Ann L. DiNigro** .... (610) 521-8200

Columbus (OH) Field Inspectors
Signal and Train Control Inspector **Robert K. Hancock** .... (610) 521-8200
Track Inspector **C. Joe Hurm** .... (610) 521-8200
Motive Power and Equipment Inspector
Thomas M. Tumbry .... (610) 521-8200
Grade Crossing Inspector **James Wes McQuinn** .... (610) 521-8200

Harrisburg (PA) Field Inspectors
Motive Power and Equipment Inspector
David Graubard .... (610) 521-8200
Track Inspector **Jon Todd Kraholik** .... (610) 521-8200
Track Inspector **William H. Wilson** .... (610) 521-8200
Operating Practices Inspector **Michael R. Bull** .... (610) 521-8200
Signal and Train Control Inspector **(Vacant)** .... (610) 521-8200

Newark (DE) Field Inspectors
Motive Power and Equipment Inspector
Jack Buchanan, Jr. .... (610) 521-8200

Norfolk (VA) Field Inspectors
Hazardous Materials Inspector **Timothy D. Brown** .... (610) 521-8200

Pittsburgh (PA) Field Inspectors
Hazardous Materials Inspector **John T. Johnson** .... (610) 521-8200

(continued on next page)

★ Presidential Appointment Requiring Senate Confirmation ☆ Presidential Appointment ☐ Schedule C Appointment ◇ Career Senior Foreign Service Appointment
● Career Senior Executive Service (SES) Appointment ○ Non-Career Senior Executive Service (SES) Appointment ■ Postal Career Executive Service

DEPARTMENTS

Pittsburgh (PA) Field Inspectors *(continued)*

Hazardous Materials Inspector **Timothy R. Rowan** ...... (610) 521-8200
Motive Power and Equipment Inspector
Patrick M. Doepfer ...... (610) 521-8200
Motive Power and Equipment Inspector
Dennis D. Steinbugl ...... (610) 521-8200
Operating Practices Inspector **Larry L. Ross** ...... (610) 521-8200
Signal and Train Control Inspector **Thomas M. Henry** ...... (610) 521-8200
Track Inspector **James R. Ruff** ...... (610) 521-8200

Richmond (VA) Field Inspectors

Motive Power and Equipment Inspector **Ervin White** ...... (610) 521-8200
Track Inspector **Kirk I. Munro** ...... (610) 521-8200
Operating Practices Inspector **John F. Ranschaert** ...... (610) 521-8200
Signal and Train Control Inspector **Louis S. Farley** ...... (610) 521-8200

Roanoke (VA) Field Inspectors

Chief Inspector **(Vacant)** ...... (540) 890-5298
Crossing and Trespassing Manager **Rodney C. Whaley** ...... (610) 521-8200
Track Inspector **Ronald T. McCormick** ...... (610) 521-8200
Motive Power and Equipment Inspector
Timothy N. Lynch ...... (610) 521-8200

Toledo (OH) Field Inspectors

Motive Power and Equipment Inspector
Robert A. Heinzman ...... (610) 521-8200
Track Inspector **Nathan Vance** ...... (610) 521-8200
Hazardous Material Inspector **Gary R. Longo** ...... (610) 521-8200
Operating Practices Inspector **Jordan Gibson** ...... (610) 521-8200

Region III

Atlanta Federal Center, 61 Forsyth Street, SW,
Suite 16T20, Atlanta, GA 30303-3104
Tel: (404) 562-3800 Tel: (800) 724-5993 Fax: (404) 562-3830
Areas Covered: AL, FL, GA, KY, MS, NC, SC, TN

Regional Administrator **Carmen Patriarca** ...... (404) 562-3800
E-mail: carmen.patriarca@dot.gov
Deputy Regional Administrator **Melvin Strong** ...... (404) 562-3800
E-mail: melvin.strong@dot.gov
Chief Inspector **Roger Francis** ...... (404) 562-3800
Computer Specialist **Mixon Cowart** ...... (404) 562-3800
Motive Power and Equipment Specialist
Adam Marshall ...... (404) 562-3800
Operating Practices Specialist **James Palley** ...... (404) 562-3800
Signal and Train Control Specialist
Raymond D. Lucas ...... (404) 562-3800
Track Specialist **Lance Hawks** ...... (404) 562-3817

Atlanta (GA) Field Inspectors

Hazardous Materials Inspector **Nancy Hunter** ...... (404) 562-3800
Motive Power and Equipment Inspector
Richard F. Thomas ...... (404) 562-3800
Operating Practices Inspector **Marlo R. Owens** ...... (404) 562-3800
Grade Crossing Manager **Elizabeth "Liz" Hudd** ...... (404) 562-3800
E-mail: elizabeth.hudd@dot.gov
Operating Practices Inspector **Steve Young** ...... (404) 562-3800
Signal and Train Control Inspector **Donnie P. Johnson** ...... (404) 562-3800
Grade Crossing Manager **Thomas Drake** ...... (404) 562-3800
E-mail: thomas.drake@dot.gov
Track Inspector **Corwyn Foster** ...... (404) 562-3800

Birmingham (AL) Field Inspectors

61 Forsyth Street, SW, Suite 16T20, Atlanta, GA 30303-3104

Hazardous Materials Inspector **Kevin Cash** ...... (404) 562-3800
Motive Power and Equipment Inspector **(Vacant)** ...... (404) 562-3800
Operating Practices Inspector **Michael Chambliss** ...... (404) 562-3800
Signal and Train Control Inspector **(Vacant)** ...... (404) 502-5800
Track Inspector **(Vacant)** ...... (404) 562-3800

Charleston and Columbia (SC) Field Inspectors

61 Forsyth Street, SW, Suite 16T20, Atlanta, GA 30303-3104

Hazardous Materials Inspector **David J. Snyder** ...... (404) 562-3800

Charleston and Columbia (SC) Field Inspectors *(continued)*

Operating Practices Inspector **Angela M. Smith** ...... (404) 562-3800
E-mail: angela.smith@dot.gov
Signal and Train Control Inspector
Ricky A. Lindstrom ...... (404) 562-3800
Track Inspector **(Vacant)** ...... (404) 562-3800

Charlotte (NC) Field Inspectors

61 Forsyth Street, SW, Suite 16T20, Atlanta, GA 30303-3104

Deputy Administrator **(Vacant)** ...... (404) 562-3800
Chief Inspector **Gregory Drakulic** ...... (404) 562-3800
Hazardous Materials Inspector **David A. Schwake** ...... (404) 562-3800
Signal and Train Control Inspector **Shaun Barrett** ...... (404) 562-3800

Jacksonville (FL) Field Inspectors

61 Forsyth Street, SW, Suite 16T20, Atlanta, GA 30303-3104

Chief Inspector **Richard J. Rusnak** ...... (404) 562-3800
Hazardous Materials Inspector **Kenneth Barefield** ...... (404) 562-3800
Motive Power and Equipment Inspector
Don Humphries ...... (404) 562-3800
Operating Practices Inspector **Arlie Sears** ...... (404) 562-3800
Signal and Train Control Inspector
Johnothon Humphrey ...... (404) 562-3800
Track Inspector **Ben Johnston** ...... (404) 562-3800

Knoxville (TN) Field Inspectors

61 Forsyth Street, SW, Suite 16T20, Atlanta, GA 30303-3104

Hazardous Materials Inspector **Gary Burke** ...... (404) 562-3800
Motive Power and Equipment Inspector **Nathan Rose** ...... (404) 562-3800
Signal and Train Control Inspector **Hugh Schwartz** ...... (404) 562-3800
E-mail: hugh.schwartz@dot.gov

Lakeland (FL) Field Inspectors

61 Forsyth Street, SW, Suite 16T20, Atlanta, GA 30303-3104

Motive Power and Equipment Inspector **John Lowery** ...... (404) 562-3800
Operating Practices Inspector **James Turpen** ...... (404) 562-3800
Signal and Train Control Inspector **Russell Hunter** ...... (404) 562-3800
E-mail: russell.hunter@dot.gov
Track Inspector **Dillon Nondo** ...... (404) 562-3800

Louisville/Lexington (KY) Field Inspectors

61 Forsyth Street, SW, Suite 16T20, Atlanta, GA 30303-3104

Hazardous Materials Inspector **Roy Shuler** ...... (404) 562-3800
Motive Power and Equipment Inspector **(Vacant)** ...... (404) 562-3800
Operating Practices Inspector **Barry Stamper** ...... (404) 562-3800
Track Inspector **(Vacant)** ...... (404) 562-3800

Memphis (TN) Field Inspectors

61 Forsyth Street, SW, Suite 16T20, Atlanta, GA 30303-3104

Motive Power and Equipment Inspector
Cedric Killebrew ...... (404) 562-3802
Hazardous Materials Inspector **Dion LeSure** ...... (404) 562-3800
Operating Practices Inspector **Debbie Gladden** ...... (404) 562-3800

Mississippi Field Inspectors

61 Forsyth Street, SW, Suite 16T20, Atlanta, GA 30303-3104

Chief Inspector **Frank Matthews** ...... (404) 562-3800
Motive Power and Equipment Inspector **Tye Ames** ...... (404) 562-3800
Track and Signal Inspector **Craig Harrell** ...... (404) 562-3800

Mobile (AL) Field Inspectors

Motive Power and Equipment Inspector **John Shiver** ...... (404) 562-3800
Track Inspector **Jeremy Motes** ...... (404) 562-3800

Nashville (TN) Field Inspectors

Chief Inspector **(Vacant)** ...... (404) 562-3800
Motive Power and Equipment Inspector **(Vacant)** ...... (404) 562-3800
Signal and Train Control Inspector **C. Leon Horton** ...... (404) 562-3800
Track Inspector **Joseph R. Grady** ...... (404) 562-3800

★ Presidential Appointment Requiring Senate Confirmation ☆ Presidential Appointment ☐ Schedule C Appointment Career Senior Foreign Service Appointment
● Career Senior Executive Service (SES) Appointment ○ Non-Career Senior Executive Service (SES) Appointment ■ Postal Career Executive Service

Raleigh (NC) Field Inspectors
Hazardous Material Inspector **Richard L. Ingram, Sr.** . . . . (404) 562-3800
Operating Practices Inspector **Joe Corcoran** . . . . (404) 562-3800

Region IV
200 West Adams Street, Suite 310, Chicago, IL 60606
Tel: (312) 353-6203 Fax: (312) 886-9634
Areas Covered: IL, IN, MI, MN, WI
Regional Administrator **Michael Turnbull** . . . . (312) 353-6203
E-mail: michael.turnbull@dot.gov
Deputy Regional Administrator
Michael Bodoh . . . . (312) 353-6203 ext. 112
E-mail: michael.bodoh@dot.gov
Deputy Regional Administrator **Kirk Gill** . . . . (312) 353-6203 ext. 117
Administrative Officer **Julia Boyd** . . . . (312) 353-6203 ext. 111
E-mail: julia.boyd@dot.gov
Chief Inspector **(Vacant)** . . . . (312) 353-6203 ext. 148
Chief Inspector **Ronald Damron** . . . . (312) 353-6203 ext. 120
Highway Crossing Manager **Tammy Wagner** . . . . (312) 353-6203 ext. 149
Computer Specialist **Dierre Massie** . . . . (312) 886-9634 ext. 136
E-mail: dierre.massie@dot.gov
Hazardous Materials Specialist **Alan Budleski** . . . (312) 353-6203 ext. 137
Motive Power and Equipment Specialist
Thomas Wozniak . . . . (312) 353-6203 ext. 118
Operating Practices Specialist
Patrick Damron . . . . (312) 353-6203 ext. 119
Signal and Train Control Specialist
Jeffrey Thomas . . . . (312) 353-6203 ext. 121
Track Specialist **John Bullock** . . . . (312) 353-6203 ext. 116

Region V
4100 International Plaza, Suite 450, Fort Worth, TX 76109-4820
Fax: (817) 862-2204
Areas Covered: AR, LA, NM, OK, TX
Regional Administrator **Vence Haggard** . . . . (817) 862-2200
E-mail: vence.haggard@dot.gov
Deputy Regional Administrator **Gregory Migely** . . . . (817) 862-2218
E-mail: gregory.migely@dot.gov
Deputy Regional Administrator
John "Jack" Stolarczyk . . . . (817) 862-2220
Project Manager - BNSF **C. Wayne Lane** . . . . (817) 862-2211
Hazardous Materials Inspector **Russell Canant** . . . . (405) 454-6037
Hazardous Materials Inspector **Tremelle Sykes** . . . . (817) 561-9541
Hazardous Materials Specialist **Robert Franco** . . . . (817) 862-2244
Motive Power and Equipment Inspector **Lonnie Hill** . . . . . . (817) 862-2223
Motive Power and Equipment Inspector **Stacy Stokes** . . . . (806) 655-2219
Motive Power and Equipment Specialist **Doug Bryan** . . . . (817) 539-0295
Operating Practices Inspector **Thomas Woodhams** . . . . . . (504) 232-6601
Operating Practices Specialist **Steve Dupont** . . . . (817) 862-2219
Signal and Train Control Inspector
Ted "Teddy" Bourgeois . . . . (225) 265-2951
Signal and Train Control Specialist **David Lindberg** . . . . . (817) 862-2207
Track Inspector **Patrick Doepser** . . . . (918) 609-5046
Track Inspector **Kenneth Long** . . . . (940) 648-2209
Track Inspector **David Roberts** . . . . (817) 862-2229
Track Inspector **Nick Roppolo** . . . . (504) 391-1984
Track Inspector **Darius Mack** . . . . (505) 565-2261
Track Specialist **Robert Faaborg** . . . . (817) 862-2243
E-mail: robert.faaborg@dot.gov
Administrative Officer **Cynthia Batchelor** . . . . (817) 862-2240
E-mail: cynthia.batchelor@dot.gov
Administrative Assistant **Sharon Banks** . . . . (817) 862-2232
E-mail: sharon.banks@dot.gov
Administrative Assistant **Paula Reed** . . . . (817) 862-2216
E-mail: paula.reed@dot.gov
Administrative Assistant **Rhonda Simpson** . . . . (817) 862-2225
E-mail: rhonda.simpson@dot.gov
Computer Specialist **Kim Flippo** . . . . (817) 862-2238
E-mail: kim.flippo@dot.gov
Program Assistant **Veronica Gomez** . . . . (817) 862-2214

El Paso (TX) Field Office
4050 Rio Bravo, Suite 210, El Paso, TX 79902
Tel: (915) 534-6445 Fax: (915) 534-6444
Hazardous Materials Inspector **Raymond "Ray" Diehl** . . . (915) 855-0411
Motive Power and Equipment Inspector **Dan Lucero** . . . . . (915) 534-6445
Operating Practices Safety Inspector **(Vacant)** . . . . (915) 534-6445
Signal and Train Control Inspector **(Vacant)** . . . . (915) 534-6445

Houston (TX) Field Inspectors
Federal Building, 2320 LaBranch Street,
Room 2102, Houston, TX 77004
Tel: (713) 718-3716 Fax: (713) 718-3633
Chief Inspector **Kenneth "Ken" Werres** . . . . (713) 718-3645
Regional Manager, Highway-Rail Safety **Carolyn Cook** . . . (512) 282-8412
E-mail: carolyn.cook@dot.gov
Hazardous Materials Inspector **Leroy Gonzales** . . . . (281) 859-4901
E-mail: leroy.gonzales@dot.gov
Hazardous Materials Inspector **Douglas Johnson** . . . . (281) 829-2596
Operating Practices Inspector **Stephen Dupont** . . . . (817) 235-0849
Operating Practices Safety Inspector
Dan "Danny" Holmes . . . . (713) 213-2026
Operating Practices Safety Inspector **(Vacant)** . . . . (281) 259-7142
Track Safety Inspector **Adam A. Giovando** . . . . (713) 463-5923
Administrative Assistant **Maxine Williams** . . . . (713) 718-3716
E-mail: maxine.williams@dot.gov

San Antonio (TX) Field Inspectors
Chief Inspector **Nathan Wallace** . . . . (210) 654-6703
E-mail: nathan.wallace@dot.gov
Hazardous Materials Inspector **Billy J. Steel** . . . . (210) 499-4224
Motor Power and Equipment Inspector **Scott Moser** . . . . . (830) 438-6536
Track Safety Inspector **David F. Casaceli** . . . . (210) 402-0756

Shreveport (LA) Field Inspectors
Assistant Grade Crossing and Trespassers
Richard Washington . . . . (318) 364-7229

Region VI
901 Locust Street, Suite 464, Kansas City, MO 64106
Tel: (816) 329-3840 Tel: (800) 724-5996 Fax: (816) 329-3867
Areas Covered: CO, IA, KS, MO, NE
Regional Administrator **Steven J. Fender** . . . . (816) 329-3840
Deputy Regional Administrator **Gabriel "Gabe" Neal** . . . . (816) 329-3840
E-mail: gabe.neal@dot.gov
Deputy Regional Administrator **Arthur "Art" Johnson** . . . (816) 329-3840
E-mail: arthur.johnson@dot.gov
Administrative Officer **Julie Benoit** . . . . (816) 329-3840
E-mail: julie.benoit@dot.gov
Grade Crossing and Trespasser Manager
William Cleveland . . . . (816) 329-3840
Grade Crossing and Trespasser Manager
Howard Gillespie . . . . (816) 407-9651
Grade Crossing and Trespasser Manager
Steven Jankowski . . . . (816) 407-9651
Railroad Operating Safety Manager **Michael Corum** . . . . . (816) 320-2239
Chief Inspector **Mark Culver** . . . . (816) 329-3847
Chief Inspector **Matt Flynn** . . . . (816) 329-3840
Chief Inspector **Mark Williams** . . . . (816) 329-3840
Chief Inspector **(Vacant)** . . . . (816) 329-3840
Hazardous Materials Inspector **Pam Gingerich** . . . . (816) 329-3840
Hazardous Materials Specialist **Russell McNamara** . . . . . . (816) 329-3840
Information Technology Specialist **Linda Hyrne** . . . . (816) 329-3840
E-mail: linda.hyrne@dot.gov
Motive Power and Equipment Inspector **Joseph Berry** . . . (816) 966-0594
Safety Specialist **Timothy Coronado** . . . . (816) 329-3840
Motive Power and Equipment Inspector **Randy Mohr** . . . . (816) 873-3596
Operating Practices Inspector **(Vacant)** . . . . (816) 296-7425
Operating Practices Inspector **Mary Shaver** . . . . (816) 436-7319
Signal and Train Control Inspector **Bruce Miller** . . . . (816) 587-7228
Signal and Train Control Specialist **Larry Stubrud** . . . . . . (816) 329-3840
Track Inspector **(Vacant)** . . . . (816) 758-4072
Track Inspector **Timothy M. Hecker** . . . . (816) 329-3840

(continued on next page)

DEPARTMENTS

★ Presidential Appointment Requiring Senate Confirmation ☆ Presidential Appointment ☐ Schedule C Appointment ◇ Career Senior Foreign Service Appointment
● Career Senior Executive Service (SES) Appointment ○ Non-Career Senior Executive Service (SES) Appointment ■ Postal Career Executive Service

Region VI *(continued)*

Track Inspector Specialist **Eric Van Buskirk** .... (816) 329-3840

Saint Louis (MO) District Office

1222 Spruce Street, St. Louis, MO 63103-2818
Tel: (816) 329-3840 Fax: (816) 329-3867

Note: All employees based in this office are telecommuters.

Chief Inspector **Mark Culver** .... (314) 539-2850
Hazardous Materials Inspector **(Vacant)** .... (618) 249-6142
Motive Power and Equipment Inspector **Fred Buck** ...... (636) 922-0153
Operating Practices Inspector **Dave Mouldon** .... (314) 288-7433
Operating Practices Inspector **Larry Piper** .... (314) 539-2850
Signal and Train Control Inspector **(Vacant)** .... (573) 358-5424
Track Inspector **(Vacant)** .... (314) 539-2850

Denver (CO) Field Office

12300 West Dakota Avenue, Suite 120, Lakewood, CO 80228
Tel: (720) 963-3080 Tel: (800) 724-5996 Fax: (720) 963-3081

Chief Inspector **Mark Williams** .... (720) 963-3080

North Platte (NE) Field Office

Federal Building, 300 East Third Street,
Room 328, North Platte, NE 69101

Track Inspector **(Vacant)** .... (402) 889-3396

Wichita (KS) Field Inspectors

Operating Practices Inspector **Eugene See** .... (303) 249-1451
Signal and Train Control Inspector **Luong Le** .... (620) 837-5613
Track Safety Specialist **Rick Bruce** .... (316) 322-8732

Region VII

801 I Street, Suite 466, Sacramento, CA 95814
Tel: (916) 498-6540 Fax: (916) 498-6546
Areas Covered: AZ, CA, NV, UT

Regional Administrator **James M. Jordan** .... (916) 498-6547
E-mail: james.jordan@dot.gov
Deputy Regional Administrator **Kevin Fitzgerald** .... (916) 414-2323
Deputy Regional Administrator **Mark Adamczak** .... (909) 937-7241
3401 Centre Lake Drive, Suite 480, Ontario, CA 91761
E-mail: mark.adamczak@dot.gov
Administrative Officer **Felicia Brown** .... (916) 414-2326
E-mail: felicia.brown@dot.gov
Administrative Assistant **(Vacant)** .... (916) 498-6540
Administrative Assistant **Sandi Smith** .... (916) 414-2315
E-mail: sandi.smith@dot.gov
Administrative Specialist **(Vacant)** .... (916) 414-2332
Grade Crossing Inspector **(Vacant)** .... (916) 498-6540
Grade Crossing Inspector **(Vacant)** .... (916) 498-6540
Chief Inspector **Anthony Smialek** .... (916) 414-2330
Hazardous Materials Specialist **Ernie Sirotek** .... (916) 414-2328
Hazardous Materials Inspector **Gary Flores** .... (916) 414-2314
Hazardous Materials Inspector **Russell Kelly** .... (925) 778-2540
Motive, Power and Equipment Specialist **Mikell Fox** ..... (916) 414-2331
Operating Practices Specialist **Scott Woolstenhulme** .... (916) 414-2324
Operating Practices Inspector **Wayne Burris** .... (559) 297-7682
Signal and Train Control Specialist **Chad Tisdale** .... (916) 414-2317
Signal and Train Control Inspector **Jason Evans** .... (916) 498-6540
Track Specialist **James McVicker** .... (916) 414-2325
Track Inspector **Timothy "Tim" Pendleton** .... (916) 349-9167
Computer Specialist **Steven Pahota** .... (916) 414-2327
E-mail: steven.pahota@dot.gov

Ontario (CA) Field Office

3401 Centrelake Drive, Suite 480, Ontario, CA 91761
Tel: (909) 937-0749

Hazardous Materials Inspector **Jonah Lennear** .... (909) 937-0749
Signal and Train Control Inspector **Anthony Loya** .... (909) 937-0749
Track Inspector **Paul Martinez** .... (909) 937-0749

Region VIII

Columbia Bank Building, 500 East Broadway,
Suite 240, Vancouver, WA 98660
Tel: (360) 696-7536 Fax: (360) 696-7548
Areas Covered: AK, ID, MT, ND, OR, SD, WA, WY (Except Albany, Carbon, Goshen, Laramie, and Platte Counties)

Regional Administrator **Mark S. Daniels** .... (360) 696-7536
E-mail: mark.daniels@dot.gov
Deputy Regional Administrator **Eldon Offutt** .... (360) 696-7536
E-mail: eldon.offutt@dot.gov
Administrative Officer **Jennifer Springer** .... (360) 696-7536
E-mail: jennifer.springer@dot.gov
Chief Inspector **(Vacant)** .... (360) 696-7536
Hazardous Materials Safety Inspector **Loren Hudon** ..... (360) 696-7536
Motive Power and Equipment Safety Inspector
Brandon King .... (360) 696-7536
Operating Practices Safety Inspector **Jeff Russell** .... (360) 696-7536
Signal and Train Control Safety Inspector
Stanley "Stan" Versnick III .... (360) 696-7536
Track Safety Inspector **Edwin Page** .... (360) 696-7536
Grade Crossing and Trespass Manager **Chris Adams** ..... (360) 696-7536
Hazardous Materials Specialist **Kenneth Holgard** .... (406) 657-6642
Motive Power and Equipment Specialist
Zacarias Biagtan .... (360) 696-7536
Information Technology Specialist **Mike Zinni** .... (360) 696-7536
E-mail: michael.zinni@dot.gov
Operating Practices Specialist **Edward McCullough** ..... (360) 696-7536
Signal and Train Control Specialist **Scott J. Johnson** .... (360) 696-7536
Industrial Hygienist **Jenika Major** .... (360) 696-7536
Investigative Reports Analyst **Jeffrey P. Stewart** .... (360) 696-7536
Program Assistant **Gail Gruber** .... (360) 696-7536
E-mail: gail.gruber@dot.gov

Billings (MT) Field Office

2929 Third Avenue North, Suite 505, Billings, MT 59101
Tel: (406) 657-6642 Fax: (406) 657-6644

Chief Inspector **William Naylor** .... (406) 657-6642
Hazardous Materials Safety Specialist **(Vacant)** .... (406) 657-6642
Motive Power and Equipment Safety Inspector
Michael Blackwell .... (406) 657-6642
Signal and Train Control Safety Inspector
Scott J. Johnson .... (406) 657-6642
Track Safety Inspector **Anthony Moler** .... (406) 657-6642
Program Assistant **Renee Buzzetti** .... (406) 657-6642
E-mail: renee.buzzetti@dot.gov

Bismarck (ND) Field Office

Civic Square Plaza, 521 East Main Avenue,
Suite 150, Bismarck, ND 58501
Tel: (701) 250-4714 Fax: (701) 250-4630

Chief Inspector **Michael Bachmeier** .... (701) 250-4714
Motive Power and Equipment Safety Inspector
Brian Ramey .... (701) 250-4714
South Dakota Operating Practices Safety Inspector
Raymond Lindsey .... (605) 290-9969
Signal and Train Control Safety Inspector
Brandon Snyder .... (701) 250-4714
Track Safety Inspector **Todd Anderson** .... (701) 250-4714
E-mail: todd.anderson@dot.gov
Track Safety Inspector **Quinn Ligon** .... (701) 578-4021
E-mail: quinn.ligon@dot.gov
Grade Crossing and Trespass Manager
Cheryl Bonebreak .... (701) 509-9779
E-mail: cheryl.bonebrake@dot.gov

Pocatello (ID) Field Office

416 Fourth Avenue South, Pocatello, ID 83201

Hazardous Materials Safety Inspector **Ellias Hire** .... (360) 869-6277
Motive Power and Equipment Safety Inspector
Don Jonuska .... (208) 400-0051
Operating Practices Safety Inspector **Jeff Deakins** .... (360) 448-0264
Signal and Train Control Safety Inspector
James Curlee .... (208) 215-4417

★ Presidential Appointment Requiring Senate Confirmation ☆ Presidential Appointment ☐ Schedule C Appointment ◇ Career Senior Foreign Service Appointment
● Career Senior Executive Service (SES) Appointment ○ Non-Career Senior Executive Service (SES) Appointment ■ Postal Career Executive Service

Pocatello (ID) Field Office *(continued)*

Track Safety Inspector **Tim Presser** . . . . (208) 241-9458

Seattle (WA)/Area Field Inspectors

Chief Inspector **Scott Barrett** . . . . (360) 264-7216
Hazardous Materials Safety Inspector
Randall Boyington . . . . (360) 921-0574
Motive Power and Equipment Safety Inspector
Christopher Lewis . . . . (360) 979-6354
Motive Power and Equipment Safety Inspector
Howard Gehrke . . . . (360) 696-7536
Operating Practices Inspector **Stacey Thompson** . . . . (360) 515-8591
Operating Practices Safety Inspector **John Mayser** . . . . (208) 220-9572
Signal and Train Control Inspector **Mike Spurlock** . . . . (206) 316-6612
Track Safety Inspector **Paul Gangstad** . . . . (206) 669-2064

Spokane (WA)/Area Field Inspectors

Motive Power and Equipment Safety Inspector
William J. McCain . . . . (509) 481-3361
Operating Practices Safety Inspector **Lynann Rainville** . . . (509) 380-3893
Signal and Train Control Safety Inspector
Bryan Morris . . . . (509) 590-6012
Track Safety Inspector **(Vacant)** . . . . (360) 921-1186
Operating Practices Safety Inspector (Pasco, WA)
(Vacant) . . . . (509) 828-5612

Federal Transit Administration (FTA)

East Building, 1200 New Jersey Avenue, SE, Washington, DC 20590-9898
Tel: (202) 366-4000 (Personnel Locator)
Tel: (202) 366-4043 (Public Information)
Tel: (202) 366-0234 (Publications Information)
Tel: (202) 366-4865 (Freedom of Information/Privacy Act)
Fax: (202) 366-3472 Internet: www.transit.dot.gov/

OFFICE OF THE ADMINISTRATOR

East Building, 1200 New Jersey Avenue, SE,
5th Floor, Suite E-57, Washington, DC 20590-9898
Tel: (202) 366-4040 Fax: (202) 366-9854

★ Administrator-Designate **Thelma Drake** . . . . (202) 366-4040

Regional Offices

Region I

Kendall Square, 55 Broadway, Room 922, Cambridge, MA 02142
Tel: (617) 494-1784 Fax: (617) 494-2865
Areas Covered: CT, ME, MA, NH, RI, VT

● Regional Administrator **(Vacant)** . . . . (617) 494-1784
Deputy Regional Administrator **Peter Butler** . . . . (617) 494-2729
E-mail: peter.butler@dot.gov
Regional Counsel **Charles H. Dyer** . . . . (617) 494-2409
E-mail: charles.dyer@dot.gov
Planning and Program Development Office Director
Kristin Wood . . . . (617) 494-2729
Program Management and Oversight Office Director
Matthew Keamy . . . . (617) 494-3038
Civil Rights Officer **Margaret A. Griffin** . . . . (617) 494-2397
E-mail: margaret.griffin@dot.gov
General Engineer **Marilyn Scheffler** . . . . (617) 494-4914

Region II

One Bowling Green, Suite 429, New York, NY 10004-1415
Tel: (212) 668-2170 Fax: (212) 668-2136 TTY: (212) 668-2170
Areas Covered: CT, NJ, NY

● Regional Administrator **Stephen Goodman** . . . . (212) 668-2170
Education: Manhattan Col BSCE
Deputy Regional Administrator **Anthony G. Carr** . . . . (212) 668-2175
E-mail: anthony.carr@dot.gov
Regional Counsel **Michael L. Culotta** . . . . (212) 668-2178
E-mail: michael.culotta@dot.gov

Region II *(continued)*

Operations and Program Management Office Director
Darreyl Davis . . . . (212) 668-2176
Planning and Program Development Office Director
Donald Burns . . . . (212) 668-2170
Regional Civil Rights Officer **(Vacant)** . . . . (212) 668-2179
Regional LAN Liaison **James A. Goveia** . . . . (212) 668-2325
Administrative Officer **Douglas Stephen** . . . . (212) 668-2170
E-mail: douglas.stephen@dot.gov

Lower Manhattan Recovery Office (LMRO)

One Bowling Green, Room 436, New York, NY 10004
Tel: (212) 668-1770

Director (Acting) **Hans PointduJour** . . . . (212) 668-2500
E-mail: hans.pointdujour@dot.gov

Region III

1760 Market Street, Suite 500, Philadelphia, PA 19103
Tel: (215) 656-7100 Fax: (215) 656-7260
Areas Covered: DE, DC, MD, PA, VA, WV

● Regional Administrator
Theresa "Terry" Garcia Crews . . . . (215) 656-7263
E-mail: theresa.garciacrews@dot.gov
Education: Arizona BS
Special Assistant **Gail McFadden-Roberts** . . . . (215) 656-7255
Deputy Regional Administrator
Anthony "Tony" Tarone . . . . (215) 656-7072
E-mail: tony.tarone@dot.gov
Regional Counsel **Monique Galloway** . . . . (215) 656-7258
E-mail: monique.galloway@dot.gov
Education: Texas Southern 2003 JD; Temple 2008 MLaw
Civil Rights Officer **Lynn Bailey** . . . . (215) 656-7121
E-mail: lynn.bailey@dot.gov
Planning and Program Development Director
Kathleen Zubrzycki . . . . (215) 656-7262
Program Management and Oversight Director
Anthony "Tony" Cho . . . . (215) 656-7250
Administrative Program Assistant
Deborah "Debi" Epps . . . . (215) 656-7247
Administrative Program Assistant **Audra J. Ouellette** . . . . (215) 656-7052
Administrative Officer **Deborah E. Brown** . . . . (215) 656-7110
E-mail: deborah.brown@dot.gov
Education: VCU BS, MBA

Region IV

230 Peachtree Street, N.W., Suite 1400, Atlanta, GA 30303
Tel: (404) 865-5600 Fax: (404) 865-5605
Areas Covered: AL, FL, GA, KY, MS, NC, PR, SC, TN, VI

● Regional Administrator **Yvette G Taylor PhD** . . . . (404) 865-5610
Deputy Regional Administrator **Dudley Whyte** . . . . (404) 865-5629
Regional Counsel **Micah Miller** . . . . (404) 865-5625
E-mail: micah.miller@dot.gov
Oversight Director **Margarita Sandberg** . . . . (404) 865-5626
Planning and Program Development Office Director
Keith Melton PE . . . . (404) 865-5632
Education: Texas (Arlington) 1983 BSCE
Administrative Officer **Fredaricka Tolen** . . . . (404) 865-5613
E-mail: fredaricka.tolen@dot.gov
Civil Rights Officer **Doretha "Dee" Foster** . . . . (404) 865-5471
E-mail: doretha.foster@dot.gov
Program Analyst **Rhonda King-Lakeman** . . . . (404) 865-5620
Program Specialist **Roxanne Ledesma** . . . . (404) 865-5633

Region V

200 West Adams Street, Suite 320, Chicago, IL 60606
Tel: (312) 353-2789 Fax: (312) 886-0351
Areas Covered: IL, IN, MI, MN, OH, WI

● Regional Administrator **Kelley Brookins** . . . . (312) 353-2789
E-mail: kelley.brookins@dot.gov
Regional Counsel **Kathryn Loster** . . . . (312) 353-3869
Civil Rights Officer **Marjorie Hughes** . . . . (312) 353-4025
E-mail: marjorie.espina@dot.gov

(continued on next page)

★ Presidential Appointment Requiring Senate Confirmation ☆ Presidential Appointment □ Schedule C Appointment ◇ Career Senior Foreign Service Appointment
● Career Senior Executive Service (SES) Appointment ○ Non-Career Senior Executive Service (SES) Appointment ■ Postal Career Executive Service

DEPARTMENTS

Region V *(continued)*

Deputy Regional Administrator **(Vacant)** . . . (312) 353-2789
Planning and Program Development Director
Jason "Jay" Ciavarella . . . (312) 353-1653
Financial Management and Program Oversight Director
Vanessa Adams . . . (312) 886-0309
Program Management and Project Oversight Director
Melody Hopson . . . (312) 886-1611

Region VI

819 Taylor Street, Room 8A36, Fort Worth, TX 76102
Tel: (817) 978-0550 Fax: (817) 978-0575
Areas Covered: AR, LA, NM, OK, TX

● Regional Administrator **Robert C. Patrick** . . . (817) 978-0550
E-mail: robert.patrick@dot.gov
Education: Southern Illinois BSBA
Deputy Regional Administrator **Gail Lyssy** . . . (817) 978-0550
E-mail: gail.lyssy@dot.gov
Education: Texas A&M 1985 BS
Regional Counsel **Eldridge Onco** . . . (817) 978-0550
E-mail: eldridge.onco@dot.gov
Planning and Program Development Office Director
Donald Koski . . . (817) 978-0550
Program Management and Oversight Office
Laura Wallace . . . (817) 978-0550
Administrative Officer **Margaret Lee** . . . (817) 978-0550
E-mail: margaret.ake@dot.gov
LAN Manager **(Vacant)** . . . (817) 978-0563

Region VII

901 Locust Street, State 404, Kansas City, MO 64106-2328
Tel: (816) 329-3920 Fax: (816) 329-3921
Areas Covered: IA, KS, MO, NE

● Regional Administrator **Mokhtee Ahmad** . . . (816) 329-3920
E-mail: mokhtee.ahmad@dot.gov
Education: Oklahoma 1967 BSc; Iowa State 1969 BSE
Deputy Regional Administrator **Mark Bechtel** . . . (816) 329-3920
Regional Counsel **John Lynch** . . . (816) 329-3920
E-mail: john.lynch@dot.gov
Program Management Specialist **Jessica Gladstone** . . . (816) 329-3920
E-mail: jessica.gladstone@dot.gov
Civil Rights Officer **(Vacant)** . . . (816) 329-3920
Operations and Program Management Team Leader
William Kalt . . . (816) 329-3920
E-mail: william.kalt@dot.gov
Planning and Program Development Team Leader
(Vacant) . . . (816) 329-3920
Environmental Protection Specialist **Beth Held** . . . (816) 329-3920
E-mail: beth.held@dot.gov
Transportation Program Specialist **Logan Daniels** . . . (816) 329-3920
E-mail: logan.daniels@dot.gov
Administrative Program Assistant and Webmaster
Austi Barnett . . . (816) 329-3920
E-mail: austi.barnett@dot.gov

Region VIII

12300 West Dakota Avenue, Suite 310, Lakewood, CO 80228
Tel: (303) 362-2400 Fax: (303) 292-5904
Areas Covered: CO, MT, ND, SD, UT, WY

● Regional Administrator **Cindy Terwilliger** . . . (303) 362-2410
E-mail: cindy.terwilliger@dot.gov
Deputy Regional Administrator
David L. "Dave" Beckhouse . . . (303) 362-2411
Regional Counsel (Acting) **Eldridge Onco** . . . (817) 978-0550
E-mail: eldridge.onco@dot.gov
Regional Civil Rights Officer (Acting) **Morgan Hecht** . . . (303) 362-2400
E-mail: morgan.hecht@dot.gov
Planning and Program Development Team Leader
Darin Allan . . . (303) 362-2386
Operations and Management Team Leader
Tiffany Gallegos . . . (303) 362-2400
E-mail: tiffany.gallegos@dot.gov
Community Planner **Kristin Kenyon** . . . (303) 362-2391

Region VIII *(continued)*

General Engineer **(Vacant)** . . . (303) 362-2390
Administrative Officer **Terry Gonzales** . . . (303) 362-2401
E-mail: terry.gonzales@dot.gov
State and Tribal Programs Coordinator
Jennifer Stewart . . . (303) 362-2395
Transportation Program Specialist **Kevin Osborn** . . . (303) 362-2400
Transportation Program Specialist, Finance
Cheryl J. "C. J." Schlis . . . (303) 362-2402
Transportation Program Specialist **Ranae Tunison** . . . (303) 362-2397
Transportation Program Specialist **Melanie Choquette** . . . (303) 362-2388

Region IX

90 Seventh Street, Suite 15-300, San Francisco, CA 94103-6701
Tel: (415) 734-9490 Fax: (415) 734-9489
Areas Covered: AZ, CA, GU, HI, NV; American Samoa, Northern Mariana Islands

● Regional Administrator (Acting) **Edward Carranza, Jr.** . . . (415) 734-9455
E-mail: edward.carranza@dot.gov
Deputy Regional Administrator **Edward Carranza, Jr.** . . . (415) 734-9455
E-mail: edward.carranza@dot.gov
Regional Counsel **Martia Fox** . . . (415) 734-9459
Assistant Regional Counsel **Minming Wu Morri** . . . (415) 734-9479
Planning and Program Development Director **(Vacant)** . . . (415) 734-9490
Program Management and Oversight Director
Bernardo O. Bustamante . . . (415) 734-9454
Program Management Specialist **Patricia Valentine** . . . (415) 734-9474
E-mail: patricia.valentine@dot.gov
Program Management Assistant **Elba Lira-Martinez** . . . (415) 734-9463
E-mail: elba.lira-martinez@dot.gov
Civil Rights Officer **Lynette Little** . . . (415) 734-9464

Los Angeles Metropolitan Office
888 South Figueroa Street, Suite 1850, Los Angeles, CA 90017-5467
Tel: (213) 202-3950 Fax: (213) 202-3961
Areas Covered: Los Angeles metropolitan area

Director **Raymond Tellis** . . . (213) 202-3956

Region X

Jackson Federal Building, 915 Second Avenue,
Suite 3142, Seattle, WA 98174-1095
Tel: (206) 220-7954 TTY: (206) 220-7961 Fax: (206) 220-7959
Areas Covered: AK, ID, OR, WA

● Regional Administrator **Linda Gehrke** . . . (206) 220-7954
E-mail: linda.gehrke@dot.gov
Deputy Regional Administrator **Kenneth Feldman** . . . (206) 220-7954
E-mail: kenneth.feldman@dot.gov
Legal Counsel **Francis Eugenio** . . . (206) 220-7954
E-mail: francis.eugenio@dot.gov

★ Presidential Appointment Requiring Senate Confirmation ☆ Presidential Appointment ☐ Schedule C Appointment ◇ Career Senior Foreign Service Appointment
● Career Senior Executive Service (SES) Appointment ○ Non-Career Senior Executive Service (SES) Appointment ■ Postal Career Executive Service

Maritime Administration (MARAD)

West Building, 1200 New Jersey Avenue, SE,
2nd Floor, Washington, DC 20590-9898
Tel: (202) 366-5812 (Public Information)
Tel: (202) 366-5746 (Freedom of Information/Privacy Act)
Tel: (202) 366-5807 (Publications Information)
Tel: (800) 996-2723 (Automated Information Hotline)
Internet: www.marad.dot.gov

OFFICE OF THE ADMINISTRATOR

West Building, 1200 New Jersey Avenue, SE,
2nd Floor, Washington, DC 20590-9898
Tel: (202) 366-1719 Fax: (202) 366-3890

United States Merchant Marine Academy (USMMA)

300 Steamboat Road, Kings Point, NY 11024
Tel: (516) 726-5800 Fax: (516) 773-5582 Internet: www.usmma.edu

Administration

● Superintendent **(Vacant)** .... (516) 726-5800
Deputy Superintendent
RDML Susan Dunlap USMS, USN (Ret) .... (516) 726-5816
E-mail: dunlaps@usmma.edu
Education: Northwestern 1984 BA; Naval War MNSSS
Executive Officer **John Demers** .... (516) 726-5817
Commandant of Midshipmen (Acting)
Capt. Mikel E. "Mike" Stroud USMS .... (516) 726-5664
Education: Wyoming 1987 BS
Academic Dean and Provost
Col John R. Ballard USMC (Ret) .... (516) 726-5836
Education: Catholic U 1994 PhD; Cal State (Dominguez) 1987 MA; Naval Acad 1979 BS
Assistant Academic Dean, Academic Programs
Dianne Taha .... (516) 726-5835
E-mail: tahad@usmma.edu
Counsel to the Academy **(Vacant)** .... (516) 726-5661
Director, Admissions **Cdr. Michael Bedryk USMS** .... (516) 773-5641
Director, Athletics **Maureen "Mo" White** .... (516) 726-5590
Education: Providence; Connecticut
Director, Human Resources **(Vacant)** .... (516) 726-5814
Director, Information Technology **(Vacant)** .... (516) 726-5800
Fax: (516) 773-5612
Director, Institutional Research **Dr. Lori Townsend** .... (516) 726-5653
Director, Music **Robert Nixon** .... (516) 726-5653
Director, Offshore Sailing **(Vacant)** .... (516) 773-5478
Director, Public Affairs **(Vacant)** .... (516) 726-5814
Director, Registrar **Lisa Jerry** .... (516) 726-5653
Director, Resource Management **David Socolof** .... (516) 726-5814
Director, Waterfront Activities and Sailing Master
(Vacant) .... (516) 726-6034
Fax: (516) 773-5344
Assistant Supervisor of Plant Assessment **(Vacant)** .... (516) 726-5814
Head, Department of Marine Engineering
Capt Joseph Poliseno USMS .... (516) 726-5732
Head, Department of Marine Transportation
George Edenfield .... (516) 726-5874
Education: US Merchant Marine Acad 1979 BS
Head, Department of Public Works **Dan LaPointe** .... (516) 726-5620
Head, Office of Procurement **Maximilian Diah** .... (516) 726-6152
E-mail: diahm@usmma.edu
Chief, Public Safety **Jeffery Thomas** .... (516) 726-5620
Fax: (516) 773-5328
Operations Officer **(Vacant)** .... (516) 726-5700
Personnel Officer **Raymond A. Venkersammy** .... (516) 726-6181
E-mail: venkersammyr@usmma.edu
Public Information Officer **Veronica Barry** .... (516) 726-6048
Risk Management Officer **Kelly Butruch** .... (516) 726-6174
Education: St Francis Col (NY) 1992 BA; John Jay Col 2001 MPA
Chaplain **Jerry Durham** .... (516) 773-5347
Chief Librarian - Schuyler Otis Bland Memorial Library **Donna Selvaggio** .... (516) 726-5747

Administration *(continued)*

Diversity Recruitment Specialist **(Vacant)** .... (516) 726-5645

Training and Development (TD)

Director, Academic Center for Excellence
CDR(Ret.) Paul Acquaro USN (Ret) .... (516) 726-5961

Associate Administrator for Intermodal Systems Development

West Building, 1200 New Jersey Avenue, SE,
2nd Floor, Washington, DC 20590-9898
Fax: (202) 366-6988

Office of Gateways (OG)

1200 New Jersey Avenue, SE, Mail Stop 201,
Washington, DC 20590-9898
Tel: (202) 366-0720 Fax: (202) 366-6988

Eastern Gulf/Lower Mississippi Gateway Office

500 Poydras Street, Room 1223, New Orleans, LA 70130
Tel: (504) 589-2000 Fax: (504) 589-6593
Areas Covered: Mexico: Campeche; Chiapas; Durango; Northern Zacatecas; Nuevo León; Quitana Roo; San Luis Potosi; Tabasco; Tamaulipas; Veracruz; Yucatan **Areas Covered:** United States: Alabama; Arkansas; Louisiana; Mississippi; Tennessee; Western Panhandle of Florida
Director **James J. Murphy** .... (504) 589-6658

Ship Operations Field Office (SOFO)

550 Fannin Street, Beaumont, TX 77701
Tel: (409) 284-1427
Supervisory Marine Surveyor **Billy F. Greer** .... (409) 284-1427

Division of Gulf Operations

Director **Deepak Varshney** .... (504) 589-4600
Education: Michigan BS; Maryland MS; Naval War MA
Program Analysis **Dean Baldus** .... (504) 589-6557
E-mail: dean.baldus@dot.gov Fax: (504) 589-6593
Supervisory Marine Surveyor **Robert Babin** .... (504) 589-6556
Fax: (504) 589-6593
Finance Officer **Michelle Barthelemy** .... (504) 589-6562

Beaumont (TX) Reserve Fleet

2600 Amoco Road, Beaumont, TX 77705
Tel: (409) 722-3433 Fax: (409) 720-5230
Fleet Superintendent **John M. Hickey** .... (409) 722-3433 ext. 227

Great Lakes Gateway Office (GLGO)

P.O. Box 1156, Chicago, IL 60690
Tel: (312) 353-1032
Areas Covered: Canada: Ontario; Quebec **Areas Covered:** United States: Areas surrounding the Great Lakes/ St. Lawrence Seaway System - Minnesota, Wisconsin, Illinois, Indiana, Michigan, Ohio, Pennsylvania, and New York.
Director **Floyd Miras** .... (312) 353-1032
E-mail: floyd.miras@dot.gov

Mid-Atlantic Gateway Office

Building 4D, 7737 Hampton Boulevard,
Room 211, Norfolk, VA 23505-1204
Fax: (757) 440-0812
Areas Covered: United States: Maryland; North Carolina; Virginia; West Virginia
Director **(Vacant)** .... (202) 366-0706

DEPARTMENTS

★ Presidential Appointment Requiring Senate Confirmation ☆ Presidential Appointment ☐ Schedule C Appointment ◇ Career Senior Foreign Service Appointment
● Career Senior Executive Service (SES) Appointment ○ Non-Career Senior Executive Service (SES) Appointment ■ Postal Career Executive Service

Fort Eustis (VA) Field Office – James River Reserve Fleet
Building 2606, James River Reserve Fleet,
End of Harrison Road, Joint Base Langley-Eustis, VA 23604
Mail: James River Reserve Fleet, Drawer C,
Joint Base Langley-Eustis, VA 23604
Tel: (757) 887-3233 Fax: (757) 887-1188

Fleet Superintendent **Martin Walker** .... (757) 887-3233 ext. 11
Deputy Superintendent **George "Andy" Diggs** .... (757) 887-3233
E-mail: george.diggs@dot.gov
High Voltage Electrical Supervisor
Keith Wiehrs .... (757) 887-3233 ext. 18
Mechanical Supervisor **Aaron Relford** .... (757) 887-3233 ext. 22
Deck Operations Supervisor **(Vacant)** .... (757) 887-3233
Fleet Administrative Officer **James Holden** .... (757) 887-3233
E-mail: james.holden@dot.gov
Environmental Program Specialist
Bonnie McClutchy .... (757) 887-3233 ext. 13
Safety and Occupational Health Specialist
Timothy Witham .... (757) 887-3233 ext. 15
E-mail: timothy.witham@dot.gov

Office of Program Excellence and Quality Assurance
Building 4-D, 7737 Hampton Boulevard,
Room 211, Norfolk, VA 23505-1204
Fax: (757) 440-0812

Advisor **Mayank "Nuns" Jain** .... (757) 322-5801

North Atlantic Gateway Office
One Bowling Green, Room 418, New York, NY 10004-1415
Tel: (212) 668-2064 Fax: (212) 668-3382
Areas Covered: Canada: New Brunswick; New Foundland; Nova Scotia; Prince Edward Island **Areas Covered:** United States: Connecticut; Maine; Massachusetts; New Hampshire; New Jersey; New York; Rhode Island; Vermont

Director
CAPT Jeffrey "Jeff" Flumignan USNR (Ret) .... (212) 668-2064
Education: US Merchant Marine Acad 1986 BS; Naval War 2003 MSS
Deputy Director **(Vacant)** .... (212) 668-2064

Northern California Gateway Office
1301 Clay Street, Suite 140N, Oakland, CA 94612
Tel: (510) 457-2590 (Main Office Number)
Tel: (510) 457-2588 (Administration) Fax: (510) 267-0746
Areas Covered: United States: Northern California (North of Point Conception), Nevada, Utah

Director **John Hummer** .... (510) 457-2570
Fax: (510) 267-0747
Ship Operations and Maintenance Officer
Henry D. Ryan .... (510) 457-2577
Staff Shipping Representative **Simon Tao** .... (510) 457-2579
Division Team Lead, Field Engineer **Kathy Jannett** ...... (510) 457-2571

Benicia (CA) Field Office
Suisun Bay Reserve Fleet, 2595 Lake Herman Road, Benicia, CA 94510
Tel: (707) 745-0487 Fax: (707) 745-2508

Fleet Program Manager **Joseph A. Pecoraro** .... (707) 745-0487

Pacific Northwest/Alaska Gateway Office
Henry M. Jackson Federal Building, 915 Second Avenue,
31st Floor, Room 3196, Seattle, WA 98174-1095
Areas Covered: Canada: Alberta, British Columbia, Manitoba, Saskatchewan

United States: Alaska, Idaho, Oregon, Washington

Director **CAPT Robert Loken USN (Ret)** .... (206) 220-7717
Fax: (206) 220-7715

South Atlantic Gateway Office
51 SW First Avenue, Suite 1305, Miami, FL 33130
Tel: (305) 530-6420 Fax: (305) 530-6422
Areas Covered: United States: Florida with the exception of anything west of the Apalachicola River; Georgia; Puerto Rico; South Carolina; U.S. Virgin Islands

Director **Frances "Fran" Bohnsack** .... (305) 530-6420
Tel: (786) 837-4382

Southern California Gateway Office
Glenn M. Anderson Federal Building, 501 West Ocean Boulevard,
Room 5190, Long Beach, CA 90802
Tel: (415) 744-2924 Tel: (415) 310-8062 Fax: (415) 744-2298
Areas Covered: United States: Arizona; Southern California, south of Point Conception **Areas Covered:** Mexico: Aguascalientes; Baja California; Baja California Sur; Colima; Guanajuato; Guerrero; Hidalgo; Jalisco; México (State of); México City, D.F; Michoacán; Morelos; Nayarit; Oaxaca; Puebla; Queretaro; Sinaloa; Sonora; Southern Zacatecas; Tlaxcala

Director **Eric Shen** .... (202) 308-8968

Inland Waterways Gateway Office
Robert A. Young Federal Building, 1222 Spruce Street,
Suite 2.202F, St. Louis, MO 63103-2818
Fax: (314) 539-6787
Areas Covered: United States: Iowa; Kansas; Kentucky; Missouri; Montana; Nebraska; North Dakota; South Dakota; Pennsylvania all areas west of Pittsburgh; Southern Illinois; Southern Minnesota; Wyoming

Director **Branden Criman** .... (314) 539-6783

Western Gulf Gateway Office
8701 South Gessner Road, Ste 1235, Houston, TX 77074
Areas Covered: Mexico: Chihuahua, Coahuila

United States: Colorado, New Mexico, Oklahoma, Texas

Director **Brian P. Hill** Suite 1235 .... (713) 272-2864
Fax: (713) 272-2882

National Highway Traffic Safety Administration (NHTSA)

West Building, 1200 New Jersey Avenue, SE,
Washington, DC 20590-9898
Tel: (202) 366-4000 (Personnel Locator)
Tel: (202) 366-9550 (Public Information)
Tel: (202) 366-1658 (Publications Information)
Tel: (202) 366-2870 (Freedom of Information/Privacy Act)
Tel: (800) 424-9393 (Auto Safety Hot Line - Continental US)
Tel: (888) 327-4236 (Auto Safety Hot Line - DC Metropolitan Area)
TTY: (800) 424-9153 Internet: www.nhtsa.gov/
Internet: http://www.distraction.gov/

OFFICE OF THE ADMINISTRATOR

West Building, 1200 New Jersey Avenue, SE,
Washington, DC 20590-9898
Tel: (202) 366-1836 Fax: (202) 366-2106

Traffic Injury Control (TIC)

West Building, 1200 New Jersey Avenue, SE,
Washington, DC 20590-9898
Fax: (202) 366-7149

Associate Administrator for Regional Operations and Program Delivery

West Building, 1200 New Jersey Avenue, SE,
Room W46-304, Washington, DC 20590-9898
Fax: (202) 366-7394

Region 1

Volpe National Transportation Systems Center,
Kendall Square (RTV-8E), 55 Broadway, Cambridge, MA 02142
Tel: (617) 494-3427 Fax: (617) 494-3646 E-mail: region1@nhtsa.dot.gov
Areas Covered: CT, ME, MA, NH, RI, VT

Regional Administrator **Arthur Kinsman** .... (617) 494-3427
E-mail: arthur.kinsman@dot.gov
Deputy Regional Administrator **Gabriel Cano** .... (617) 494-3427
E-mail: gabriel.cano@dot.gov

Region 2

245 Main Street, Suite 210, White Plains, NY 10601-2442
Tel: (914) 682-6162 Fax: (914) 682-6239 E-mail: region2@dot.gov
Areas Covered: NJ, NY, PA, PR, VI

Regional Administrator (Acting)
Michael "Mike" Geraci .... (914) 682-6162
E-mail: michael.geraci@dot.gov
Deputy Regional Administrator **Richard Simon** .... (914) 682-6162
E-mail: richard.simon@dot.gov

Region 3

31 Hopkins Plaza, Room 902, Baltimore, MD 21201
Tel: (410) 962-0090 Fax: (410) 962-2770 E-mail: nhtsa@dot.gov
Areas Covered: DE, DC, KY, MD, NC, VA, WV

Regional Administrator **Elizabeth A. Baker PhD** .... (410) 962-0090
E-mail: beth.baker@dot.gov

Region 4

Atlanta Federal Center, 61 Forsyth Street, SW,
Suite 17T30, Atlanta, GA 30303-3104
Tel: (404) 562-3739 Fax: (404) 562-3763 E-mail: region4@dot.gov
Areas Covered: AL, FL, GA, SC, TN

Regional Administrator **Carmen Hayes** .... (404) 562-3739
E-mail: carmen.hayes@dot.gov
Deputy Regional Administrator **Alex Cabral** ... (404) 562-3739 ext. 3766
E-mail: alex.cabral@dot.gov

Region 5

4749 Lincoln Mall Drive, Suite 300B, Matteson, IL 60443
Tel: (708) 503-8822 Fax: (708) 503-8991 E-mail: region5@nhtsa.dot.gov
Areas Covered: IL, IN, MI, MN, OH, WI

Regional Administrator **(Vacant)** .... (708) 503-8822
Secretary **Cynthia Davis** .... (708) 503-8822

Region 6

Lanham Federal Building, 819 Taylor Street, Room 8A38,
Fort Worth, TX 76102-6177
Tel: (817) 978-3653 Fax: (817) 978-8339 E-mail: region6@dot.gov
Areas Covered: LA, MS, NM, OK, TX, Indian Nations

Regional Administrator **(Vacant)** .... (817) 978-3653
Deputy Regional Administrator **Brian Jones** .... (817) 978-3656
E-mail: brian.jones@dot.gov

Region 7

901 Locust Street, Room 466, Kansas City, MO 64106-2641
Tel: (816) 329-3900 Fax: (816) 329-3910 E-mail: region7@dot.gov
Areas Covered: AR, IA, KS, MO, NE

Regional Administrator **Susan L. de Courcy** .... (816) 329-3900
E-mail: susan.decourcy@dot.gov
Deputy Regional Administrator **Jeff Halloran** .... (816) 329-3900
E-mail: jeff.halloran@dot.gov
Administrative Assistant **Sharon Blackmon** .... (816) 329-3900
E-mail: sharon.blackmon@dot.gov

Region 8

12300 West Dakota Avenue, Suite 140, Lakewood, CO 80228-2583
Tel: (720) 963-3100 Fax: (720) 963-3124 E-mail: region8@nhtsa.dot.gov
Areas Covered: CO, MT, ND, SD, UT, WY

Regional Administrator **Gina Espinosa-Salcedo** .... (720) 963-3100

Region 9

John E. Moss Federal Building, 650 Capitol Mall,
Suite 5-400, Sacramento, CA 95814-4708
Tel: (916) 498-5058 Fax: (916) 498-5047
Areas Covered: AZ, CA, HI, American Samoa, Guam, Northern Mariana Islands

Regional Administrator
Christopher J. "Chris" Murphy .... (916) 479-2199
Education: Cal State (Bakersfield) 1985 BS
Deputy Regional Administrator **Karen Coyle** .... (916) 498-5060
Regional Program Manager **Edward "Ed" Gebing** ...... (916) 498-5055
Regional Program Manager **Brian Huynh** .... (916) 498-5051
Regional Program Manager **Jady Ramirez** .... (916) 498-5054
Regional Program Manager **Rosalind Tianco** .... (916) 498-5050
Law Enforcement Liaison **(Vacant)** .... (415) 744-4217
Secretary **Jack Wright** .... (916) 498-5058

Region 10

915 Second Avenue, Suite 3140, Seattle, WA 98174-1079
Fax: (206) 220-7651
Areas Covered: AK, ID, MT, OR, WA

Regional Administrator **Greg T. Fredericksen** .... (206) 220-7641
E-mail: greg.fredericksen@dot.gov

DEPARTMENTS

★ Presidential Appointment Requiring Senate Confirmation ☆ Presidential Appointment □ Schedule C Appointment ◇ Career Senior Foreign Service Appointment
● Career Senior Executive Service (SES) Appointment ○ Non-Career Senior Executive Service (SES) Appointment ■ Postal Career Executive Service

DEPARTMENTS

Pipeline and Hazardous Materials Safety Administration (PHMSA)

East Building, 1200 New Jersey Avenue, SE,
2nd Floor, Washington, DC 20590-9898
Internet: www.phmsa.dot.gov

OFFICE OF THE ADMINISTRATOR (OA)

East Building, 1200 New Jersey Avenue, SE,
2nd Floor, Suite E27-300, Washington, DC 20590-9898
Fax: (202) 366-3666

Associate Administrator for Hazardous Materials Safety (OHS)

East Building, 1200 New Jersey Avenue, SE,
2nd Floor, Washington, DC 20590-9898
Tel: (800) 867-4922 (Hazardous Materials Information Center)
Fax: (202) 366-5713 E-mail: phmsa.hmhazmatsafety@dot.gov
Internet: www.phmsa.dot.gov/hazmat

Field Operations

1200 New Jersey Avenue, SE, Washington, DC 20590-9898

Office of Field Services Support

1200 New Jersey Avenue, SE, Washington, DC 20590-9898
Tel: (202) 366-4700 Fax: (202) 366-7435

Central Region

901 Locust Street, Suite 462, Kansas City, MO 64106-2641
Tel: (847) 294-8580 Fax: (847) 294-8590
Areas Covered: IL, IN, IA, KY, MI, MN, MO, NE, ND, OH, SD, WI

Director (Acting) **Lisa Davies O'Donnell** .... (202) 366-1109
Enforcement Director **Tyler Patterson** .... (847) 294-8580
Chief Investigator **Tiffany Ziemer** .... (847) 294-8580
Senior Investigator **(Vacant)** .... (847) 294-8580
Hazmat Coordinator **Neal Suchak** .... (847) 294-8580
Investigator **Timothy Buffum** .... (202) 366-4700
Investigator **Michael Jennens** .... (847) 294-8580
Investigator **Terry Pollard** .... (202) 366-4700
Investigator **Daniel "Dan" Richards** .... (202) 366-4700
Investigator **Theodore "Ted" Turner III** .... (202) 366-4700

Eastern Region

820 Bear Tavern Road, Suite 306, West Trenton, NJ 08628
Tel: (609) 771-7890 Fax: (609) 989-2277
Areas Covered: CT, DC, DE, ME, MD, MA, NH, NJ, NY, PA, RI, VT, VA, WV

Director **Vincent Mercadante** .... (609) 771-7890
Chief Investigator **Mitchell Brown** .... (609) 771-7890
E-mail: mitchell.brown@dot.gov
Senior Investigator **Anthony Lima** .... (609) 771-7890
E-mail: anthony.lima@dot.gov
Senior Investigator **Charles Odum** .... (609) 771-7890
E-mail: charles.odum@dot.gov
Administrative Support Assistant **Carolyn Callaghan** .... (609) 771-7890
E-mail: carolyn.callaghan@dot.gov
Transportation Specialist **Anthony Murray** .... (609) 771-7894
E-mail: anthony.murray@dot.gov
Investigator **Margaret Carson** .... (609) 771-7890
Investigator **Andrew Cooke** .... (609) 771-7890
Investigator **Robinson Cox** .... (609) 771-7890
Investigator **Patrick Durkin** .... (609) 771-7890
Investigator **Jorg Kaltenegger** .... (609) 771-7890
Investigator **Katelin Maits** .... (609) 771-7890
Investigator **Jessica Snyder** .... (609) 771-7890
Investigator **David Williamson** .... (609) 771-7890

Southern Region

233 Peachtree Street, NE, Suite 600 (DHM-46), Atlanta, GA 30303
Tel: (404) 832-1140 Fax: (404) 832-1168
Areas Covered: AL, FL, GA, KY, MS, NC, PR, SC, TN

Regional Director **John Heneghan** .... (202) 366-0656
Senior Investigator **Robert D. Digiacomandrea** .... (404) 832-1140
Chief Investigator **(Vacant)** .... (404) 832-1140
Investigator **Robert "Bob" Burns** .... (404) 832-1140
Investigator **Randy Dick** .... (404) 832-1140
Investigator **Ernest Quail** .... (404) 832-1140
Investigator **Edward Rastetter** .... (404) 832-1140
Investigator **Stuart Streck** .... (404) 832-1145
Investigator **Kimberly Yoder** .... (202) 366-4700
Public Outreach Coordinator **Clayton Hatfield** .... (404) 832-1140
E-mail: clayton.hatfield@dot.gov
Community Liaison **Arthur Buff** .... (770) 841-3483
E-mail: arthur.buff@dot.gov
Community Liaison **James Kelly** .... (404) 990-1848
E-mail: james.kelly@dot.gov
Administrative Support Assistant **Janetta Whatley** .... (404) 832-1140
E-mail: janetta.whatley@dot.gov

Southwest Region

8701 South Gessner Road, Suite 1110, Houston, TX 77074
Tel: (713) 272-2820 Fax: (713) 272-2821
Areas Covered: AR, CO, KS, LA, NM, OK, TX

Director **Matt Ripley** .... (713) 272-2820
E-mail: matt.ripley@dot.gov
Secretary **Antwela Cato** .... (713) 272-2820
E-mail: antwela.cato@dot.gov
Chief Investigator **Robert Strollo** .... (713) 272-2820
E-mail: robert.strollo@dot.gov
Investigator **Johnny Benavidez** .... (713) 272-2820
Investigator **Alan Carson** .... (713) 272-2820
E-mail: alan.carson@dot.gov
Investigator **Shawn Daniels** .... (713) 272-2820
E-mail: shawn.daniels@dot.gov
Investigator **Dollie DeWalt** .... (713) 272-2820
E-mail: dollie.dewalt@dot.gov
Investigator **(Vacant)** .... (713) 272-2820
Investigator **Thomas "Tom" Lynch** .... (713) 272-2820
E-mail: tom.lynch@dot.gov
Investigator **Ryan Rigdon** .... (713) 272-2820
Investigator **Walter Rucker** .... (713) 272-2820
E-mail: walter.rucker@dot.gov
Investigator **Chevella Smith** .... (713) 272-2820
E-mail: chevella.smith@dot.gov
Investigator **David Smith** .... (713) 272-2820
Transportation Specialist **Mike Roberts** .... (713) 272-2820

Western Region

3401 Centrelake Drive, Suite 550B, Ontario, CA 91761
Tel: (909) 937-3279 Fax: (909) 390-5142
Areas Covered: AK, AZ, CA, CO, GU, HI, ID, MT, NV, OR, UT, WA, WY

Director **Marc Nichols** .... (909) 937-3279
E-mail: marc.nichols@dot.gov
Chief **Kameron Walch** .... (909) 937-7222
Senior Investigator **(Vacant)** .... (909) 937-3279
Hazardous Materials Investigator **William Arrington** .... (909) 937-7232
Hazardous Materials Investigator
April Charnota Suite 550 B .... (909) 660-0737
Hazardous Materials Investigator **Patrick Lease** .... (224) 612-0617
Hazardous Materials Investigator **Dale Lewis** .... (909) 937-7235
Hazardous Materials Investigator **Rene Silva** .... (909) 937-7225
Hazardous Materials Investigator **Joe Vega** .... (360) 701-2840
Senior Administrative Assistant **Brandi Woods** .... (909) 937-7222
E-mail: brandi.woods.ctr@dot.gov
Transportation Specialist **Brandon Westbrook** .... (925) 917-5695
Transportation Specialist **Jack "Earl" Whitley** .... (909) 937-7228

★ Presidential Appointment Requiring Senate Confirmation ☆ Presidential Appointment ☐ Schedule C Appointment ◇ Career Senior Foreign Service Appointment
● Career Senior Executive Service (SES) Appointment ○ Non-Career Senior Executive Service (SES) Appointment ■ Postal Career Executive Service

Associate Administrator for Pipeline Safety (OPS)

East Building, 1200 New Jersey Avenue, SE,
2nd Floor, Washington, DC 20590-9898
Tel: (202) 366-4595 Fax: (202) 366-4566
E-mail: phmsa.pipelinesafety@dot.gov
Internet: www.phmsa.dot.gov/pipeline

Regional Offices (RO)

Central Regional Office (CRO)
901 Locust Street, Room 480, Kansas City, MO 64106-2641
Tel: (816) 329-3800 Fax: (816) 329-3831
Areas Covered: IA, IL, IN, KS, MI, MN, MO, NE, ND, OH, SD, WI

Regional Director **Allan Beshore** .... (816) 329-3829
E-mail: allan.beshore@dot.gov
Chicago District Representative **Joseph Elmer** .... (219) 661-8586
Fax: (219) 661-8587
Ohio District Representative
Gerhardt "Gery" Bauman .... (740) 587-0275
Operations Supervisor **David Barrett** .... (816) 329-3800
Operations Supervisor **Jim Bunn** .... (816) 329-3800
Operations Supervisor **Karen Butler** .... (952) 447-4884
Operations Supervisor **Gregory "Greg" Ochs** .... (816) 329-3814
General Engineer **Eric Del Toro** .... (816) 329-3800
General Engineer **Darren Hamilton** .... (816) 329-3807
General Engineer **Gabe Hodill** .... (816) 329-3823
General Engineer **Darren Lemmerman** .... (763) 444-9282
General Engineer **Angela Pickett** .... (816) 329-3800
General Engineer **Hans Shieh** .... (816) 329-3805
General Engineer **Nathan Solem** .... (816) 329-3800
General Engineer **Dane Spillers** .... (217) 626-1780
General Engineer **Russell "Russ" Spruill** .... (816) 329-3803
General Engineer **Cathy Washabaugh** .... (816) 329-3800
General Engineer **(Vacant)** .... (816) 329-3826
General Engineer **(Vacant)** .... (816) 329-3807
General Engineer **(Vacant)** .... (816) 329-3809
Community Assistance and Technical Services (CATS)
Karen Lynch .... (202) 366-6855
Community Assistance and Technical Services (CATS)
(Vacant) .... (816) 329-3811

Eastern Regional Office
Mountain View Office Park, 820 Bear Tavern Road,
Suite 306, West Trenton, NJ 08628
Tel: (609) 771-7800 Fax: (609) 989-2277
Areas Covered: CT, DE, DC, ME, MD, MA, NH, NJ, NY, OH, PA, RI, VT, VA, WV

Regional Director **Robert Burrough** .... (609) 771-7800
E-mail: robert.burrough@dot.gov
General Engineer **Wayne Chan** .... (609) 771-7821
E-mail: wayne.chan@dot.gov
General Engineer **Christopher D'Souza** .... (609) 771-7812
E-mail: chris.d'souza@dot.gov
General Engineer **Barbara Dahlinger** .... (609) 771-7813
E-mail: barbara.dahlinger@dot.gov
General Engineer **Steven Giarratano** .... (609) 771-7822
E-mail: steven.giarratano@dot.gov
General Engineer **James Pfeifle** .... (609) 771-7818
E-mail: james.pfeifle@dot.gov
General Engineer **Marta Riendeau** .... (609) 771-7807
E-mail: marta.riendeau@dot.gov
General Engineer **Al Schoen** .... (609) 989-2239
E-mail: al.schoen@dot.gov
General Engineer **Matthew Valerio** .... (609) 989-2171
E-mail: matthew.valerio@dot.gov
General Engineer - CATS **Alex J. Dankanich** .... (609) 989-2171
E-mail: alex.dankanich@dot.gov
General Engineer - CATS **Karen Gentile** .... (609) 989-2171
E-mail: karen.gentile@dot.gov

New England Remote Office
DOT/RSPA/OPS/Eastern Region, New England Remote Office,
105 Nahant Street, Suite 4, Lynn, MA 01903
Tel: (781) 599-9909 Fax: (781) 592-0337
New England Field Representative **Robert Smallcomb** ... (781) 599-9909
E-mail: robert.smallcomb@dot.gov

Pittsburgh Remote Office
DOT/RSPA/OPS/Eastern Region, Pittsburgh Remote Office,
234 Forsythe Road, Valencia, PA 16059
Tel: (724) 898-3705
Pittsburgh Field Representative
Michael S. Yazemboski .... (724) 898-3705

Southern Regional Office
233 Peachtree Street, NE, Suite 600, Atlanta, GA 30303
Tel: (404) 832-1147 Fax: (404) 832-1169
Areas Covered: AL, AR, FL, GA, KY, MS, NC, PR, SC, TN

Regional Director **James Urisko** .... (404) 832-1147
E-mail: james.urisko@dot.gov
Operations Supervisor **Michael A. Schwarzkopf** .... (404) 832-1158
E-mail: michael.schwarzkopf@dot.gov
Senior Engineer and Project Manager **Derick Turner** .... (404) 832-1156
Senior Engineer **John Dallas Rea** .... (404) 832-1154
General Engineer **Donald Murphy** .... (404) 832-1147
General Engineer **Chris Taylor** .... (404) 832-1147
General Engineer **Vasilios Tzamos** .... (404) 832-1147
General Engineer/CATS **Joseph Mataich** .... (404) 832-1159
Program Assistant **Nancy Chai** .... (404) 832-1147
E-mail: nancy.chai@dot.gov

Southwest Regional Office
8701 South Gessner Road, Suite 1110, Houston, TX 77074
Tel: (713) 272-2859 Fax: (713) 272-2831
Areas Covered: AZ, LA, NM, OK, TX

Regional Director **(Vacant)** .... (713) 272-2859
Program Assistant **Cynthia Lewis** .... (713) 272-2842
E-mail: cynthia.lewis@dot.gov
Staff Engineer/Inspector **Alexander Ashe, Jr.** .... (713) 272-2885
Staff Engineer/Inspector **Basim Bacenty** .... (713) 272-2838
Staff Engineer/Inspector **Terri J. Binns** .... (713) 272-2825
Staff Engineer/Inspector **Frank Causey** .... (713) 272-2863
Staff Engineer/Inspector **David Eng** .... (713) 272-2861
Staff Engineer/Inspector **Jocelyn Kerl** .... (713) 272-2846
Staff Engineer/Inspector **Victor Lopez** .... (713) 272-2848
Staff Engineer/Inspector **Mohammed Mahmood** .... (713) 272-2830
Staff Engineer/Inspector **Jon Manning** .... (713) 272-2856
Staff Engineer/Inspector **Noah Matthews** .... (713) 272-2857
Staff Engineer/Inspector **Juan A. Mendoza** .... (713) 272-2824
Staff Engineer/Inspector **Gene Roberson** .... (713) 272-2851
Staff Engineer/Inspector **Jason Terry** .... (713) 272-2854
Staff Engineer/Inspector **David York** .... (713) 272-2834
Staff Engineer/Inspector **(Vacant)** .... (713) 272-2853
Staff Engineer/Inspector **(Vacant)** .... (713) 272-2859
Staff Engineer/Inspector **(Vacant)** .... (713) 272-2844
Staff Engineer/Inspector **(Vacant)** .... (713) 272-2826
Staff Engineer/Inspector **(Vacant)** .... (713) 272-2850
Community Assistance and Technical Services (CATS)
William "Bill" Lowry .... (713) 272-2845
Community Assistance and Technical Services (CATS)
James Prothro .... (713) 272-2832
Accident Investigator **(Vacant)** .... (713) 272-2859
Accident Investigator **(Vacant)** .... (713) 272-2833
Accident Investigator **(Vacant)** .... (713) 272-2862
Contractor Program Assistant **Sheila White** .... (713) 272-2831
E-mail: sheila.white.ctr@dot.gov

Louisiana District Office
18258 John Broussard Road, Prairieville, LA 70769
Staff Engineer/Inspector **Aaron "Buddy" Sheets** .... (225) 677-8495

★ Presidential Appointment Requiring Senate Confirmation ☆ Presidential Appointment □ Schedule C Appointment ◇ Career Senior Foreign Service Appointment
● Career Senior Executive Service (SES) Appointment ○ Non-Career Senior Executive Service (SES) Appointment ■ Postal Career Executive Service

DEPARTMENTS

Western Regional Office
12300 West Dakota Avenue, Suite 110, Lakewood, CO 80228
Tel: (720) 963-3160 Fax: (720) 963-3161
Areas Covered: AK, AZ, CA, CO, HI, ID, MT, NV, OR, UT, WA, WY

Regional Director **(Vacant)** .... (720) 963-3160
Senior Engineer/Project Manager **Huy Nguyen** .... (720) 963-3174
Engineer/Inspector **Claude E. Allen** .... (720) 963-3190
Engineer/Inspector **Brent C. Brown** .... (720) 963-3189
Engineer/Inspector **Jeff Stahoviak** .... (720) 963-3192
Engineer/Inspector **(Vacant)** .... (720) 963-3184
Community Assistance and Technical Services (CATS)
Ross Reineke .... (720) 963-3182
Community Assistance and Technical Services (CATS)
Thomas "Tom" Finch .... (720) 963-3175
Program Assistant **Kristi Bonnett** .... (720) 963-3160
E-mail: kristi.bonnett@dot.gov

Alaska Project Office
222 West Seventh Avenue, Suite 200, Anchorage, AK 99513
Mail: P.O. Box 37, Anchorage, AK 99513
Tel: (907) 271-6517 Fax: (907) 271-6581

General Engineer **Michael Chard** .... (907) 271-6517
General Engineer **Robert Guisinger** .... (907) 271-6520
General Engineer **David Hassell** .... (907) 271-6519
General Engineer **Donald T. "Tom" Johnson** .... (907) 271-4934
General Engineer **Adelheid "Heidi" Marlowe** .... (907) 271-5261

Billings (MT) Satellite Office
725 Middlemas Road, Helena, MT 59602
Engineer **Michael Petronis** .... (713) 272-2859

Saint Lawrence Seaway Development Corporation (SLSDC)

1200 New Jersey Avenue, SE, Suite W32-300,
Washington, DC 20590-9898 (Mailing Address)
55 M Street, SE, Suite 930, Washington, DC 20003 (Physical Address)
Tel: (202) 366-0091 (Freedom of Information/Privacy Act)
Fax: (202) 366-7147 Internet: www.seaway.dot.gov
Internet: www.greatlakes-seaway.com (Great Lakes Saint Lawrence Seaway System)

OFFICE OF THE ADMINISTRATOR

1200 New Jersey Avenue, SE, Suite W32-300,
Washington, DC 20590-9898
Tel: (202) 366-0091 Fax: (202) 366-7147

Office of the Associate Administrator (OAA)

P.O. Box 520, 180 Andrews Street, Massena, NY 13662-0520
Tel: (315) 764-3200 Fax: (315) 764-3235

● Associate Administrator/Resident Manager
Thomas A. Lavigne .... (315) 764-3251
E-mail: thomas.lavigne@dot.gov
Education: Clarkson U BCE, MCE
Financial Management and Administration Office
Director/Chief Financial Officer **Nancy C. Scott** .... (315) 764-3273
Human Resources Officer **Deborah Perkins** .... (315) 764-3230
E-mail: deborah.perkins@dot.gov
Engineering and Maintenance Office Director
Jeffrey Scharf .... (315) 764-3200
E-mail: jeffrey.scharf@dot.gov
Executive Officer **Michael Howard** .... (315) 764-3200
Education: Trident International 2008 BBA
Lock Operations and Marine Services Office Director
Christopher Guimond .... (315) 764-3200
E-mail: christopher.guimond@dot.gov
Chief of Security **Josef D. Walker** .... (315) 764-3218
E-mail: josef.walker@dot.gov

Office of the Associate Administrator *(continued)*

Manager of Equal Employment Opportunity,
Labor Relations and Human Development
Julie A. Kuenzler .... (315) 764-3200
E-mail: julie.kuenzler@dot.gov

★ Presidential Appointment Requiring Senate Confirmation ☆ Presidential Appointment □ Schedule C Appointment ◇ Career Senior Foreign Service Appointment
● Career Senior Executive Service (SES) Appointment ○ Non-Career Senior Executive Service (SES) Appointment ■ Postal Career Executive Service

United States Department of the Treasury

Contents

United States Department of the Treasury (TREAS)

Description: The Department of the Treasury formulates and recommends economic, financial, tax and fiscal policies, and manages the public debt. The department serves as chief financial agent for the United States, collecting taxes and manufacturing currency and coins.

1500 Pennsylvania Avenue, NW, Washington, DC 20220
Tel: (202) 622-2000 Tel: (202) 622-0530 (Procurement Information)
Tel: (202) 622-2960 (Press Inquiries)
Tel: (202) 622-2040 (Automated Press Releases by Facsimile)
Tel: (202) 622-0930 (Freedom of Information/Privacy Act)
Tel: (202) 622-1090 (Inspector General's Waste, Fraud and Abuse Hotline - DC Metropolitan Area) Tel: (800) 359-3898 (Inspector General's Waste, Fraud and Abuse Hotline - Continental US, Alaska and Hawaii)
Tel: (800) 306-2822 (Foreign Assets Control Office Hotline)
Tel: (202) 622-0896 (Tour Information)
Fax: (202) 622-6415 Internet: https://home.treasury.gov/
Internet: www.treasury.gov/open (Open Government Directive Website)
Internet: www.usa.gov (Official US Government Website)

OFFICE OF THE SECRETARY (OS)

1500 Pennsylvania Avenue, NW, Washington, DC 20220
Tel: (202) 622-2000 (General Information) Fax: (202) 622-0073

Office of the Deputy Secretary (ODS)

1500 Pennsylvania Avenue, NW, Washington, DC 20220
Fax: (202) 622-0073

Office of Tax Policy

1500 Pennsylvania Avenue, NW, Washington, DC 20220
Tel: (202) 622-0050 Fax: (202) 622-0605

Alcohol and Tobacco Tax and Trade Bureau (TTB)

1310 G Street, NW, Washington, DC 20220
Tel: (202) 453-2000 Internet: www.ttb.gov

Office of the Administrator

1310 G Street, NW, Suite 300 East, Washington, DC 20220
Tel: (202) 453-2000

Office of the Chief Counsel (OCC)

1310 G Street, NW, Suite 300 West, Washington, DC 20220
Fax: (202) 453-2987

Assistant Chief Counsel (Field Operations) - Cincinnati (OH)

8002 Federal Office Building, 550 Main Street, Cincinnati, OH 45202-3222
Tel: (513) 684-3225 Fax: (202) 453-2446

Assistant Chief Counsel **Caroline F. "Carrie" May** . . . . . . (513) 684-3225
E-mail: caroline.may@ttb.gov
Legal Assistant **Diane Barnhill** . . . .(513) 684-3225
E-mail: diane.barnhill@ttb.gov

OFFICE OF DOMESTIC FINANCE

1500 Pennsylvania Avenue, NW, Room 3312, Washington, DC 20220
Tel: (202) 622-1703 Fax: (202) 622-0265

Fiscal Service

1500 Pennsylvania Avenue, NW, Room 2118, Washington, DC 20220
Tel: (202) 622-8951 Fax: (202) 622-0962

Bureau of the Fiscal Service (BFS)

Liberty Center Building, 401 14th Street, SW, Washington, DC 20227
Internet: www.fiscal.treasury.gov

Office of the Commissioner

401 14th Street, SW, Washington, DC 20227
Tel: (202) 874-7000 Fax: (202) 874-6743

Information Resources

401 14th Street, SW, Washington, DC 20227
Fax: (202) 874-8866

Platform Operations Directorate

3700 East-West Highway, Hyattsville, MD 20782
Fax: (202) 874-8551

Kansas City Regional Operations Center (KROC)

4241 Northeast 34th Street, Kansas City, MO 64117
Tel: (816) 414-2100 Fax: (816) 414-3614

Director **Carlos Antonio Usera** . . . . (816) 414-3601
E-mail: carlos.usera@fiscal.treasury.gov
Education: West Point 1978 BSE; Clemson 1987 MSIE
Computer Operations Manager **(Vacant)** . . . . (816) 414-3611 ext. 3602

Payment Management

Liberty Center, 401 14th Street, SW, Washington, DC 20227-0003
Tel: (202) 874-6790 Fax: (202) 874-7184

Regional Financial Centers (RFC)

Kansas City (MO) Bureau of the Fiscal Service

P.O. Box 12599-0599, Kansas City, MO 64116-0599
Tel: (816) 414-2100 Fax: (816) 414-2192

● Director **Gary M. Beets** . . . . (816) 414-2000
E-mail: gary.beets@fiscal.treasury.gov
Deputy Director **Susan Robinson** . . . . (816) 414-2000
Education: Central Missouri State BS
Customer Service Branch Manager **Julie Nielsen** . . . . (816) 414-2050
E-mail: thomas.nelson@fiscal.treasury.gov
Financial Support Services Branch Manager
Francie Abbott . . . .(816) 414-2100
E-mail: francie.abbott@fiscal.treasury.gov Fax: (816) 414-2180
Information Systems and Support Branch Manager
Cynthia Sheppard . . . .(816) 414-2300
E-mail: cynthia.sheppard@fiscal.treasury.gov
Payment Management Operations Manager
Toni Mussorici . . . . (816) 414-2200

★ Presidential Appointment Requiring Senate Confirmation ☆ Presidential Appointment ☐ Schedule C Appointment ◇ Career Senior Foreign Service Appointment
● Career Senior Executive Service (SES) Appointment ○ Non-Career Senior Executive Service (SES) Appointment ■ Postal Career Executive Service

Philadelphia (PA) Bureau of the Fiscal Service (PFC)
13000 Townsend Road, Philadelphia, PA 19154
P.O. Box 51317, Philadelphia, PA 19115-6317
Tel: (215) 516-8000 Fax: (215) 516-8010
E-mail: philly@fiscal.treasury.gov

• Director **Elizabeth A. "Betty" Belinsky** .... (215) 516-8002
E-mail: elizabeth.belinsky@fiscal.treasury.gov
Deputy Director **Ed Wesley Johnson** .... (215) 516-8100
Executive Assistant **Bridget Williams-Kreckmann** ...... (215) 516-8000
E-mail: bridget.wms-kreckmann@fiscal.treasury.gov
Executive Assistant **(Vacant)** .... (215) 516-8106
Customer Service Branch Manager **Lisa Andre** .... (215) 516-8022
Electronic Operations Branch Manager **Phillip Tropea** .... (215) 516-8067
E-mail: phillip.tropea@fiscal.treasury.gov
Operations Support and Control Branch Manager
Monique Wooden-Goodwin .... (215) 516-8036
Payment and Mail Operations Branch Manager
Cheryl Russell .... (215) 516-8107

Bureau of Engraving and Printing (BEP)

Bureau of Engraving and Printing, 14th and C Streets, SW,
Washington, DC 20228
Tel: (202) 874-4000 (General Information)
Tel: (877) 874-4114 (General Inquiries)
Tel: (866) 874-2330 (Washington D.C. Public Tour Information)
Tel: (866) 865-1194 (Fort Worth, TX Public Tour Information)
Tel: (866) 575-2361 (Mutilated Currency Division) Fax: (202) 874-3177
E-mail: moneyfactory.info@bep.gov (General Information)
E-mail: mcdstatus@bep.gov (Mutilated/Damaged Currency Redemption)
Internet: www.moneyfactory.gov

OFFICE OF THE DIRECTOR

Bureau of Engraving and Printing, Main Building,
14th and C Streets, SW, Washington, DC 20228
Fax: (202) 874-3879

Eastern Currency Facility (ECF)

Bureau of Engraving and Printing, Main Building,
14th and C Streets, SW, Washington, DC 20228
Fax: (202) 874-2034

• Associate Director (Manufacturing)
Charlene E. Williams Room 104-16M .... (202) 874-3993
E-mail: charlene.williams@bep.gov
Deputy Associate Director **(Vacant)** .... (202) 874-2277
14th and C Streets, SW, Room 702-26A, Washington, DC 20228

Office of Engraving (OE)
Bureau of Engraving and Printing Annex,
14th and C Streets, SW, Washington, DC 20228
Fax: (202) 874-4690

Chief **Scott Green** Room 702-26A .... (202) 874-7873
Assistant Chief **Bradley Donovan** Room 702-14A .... (202) 874-4000
Engraving Accountability and Plate Vault Operations
Manager **Deborah Hill** Room 407-10A .... (202) 874-6703
Engraving and Pre-press Manager **Ross Morres** .... (202) 927-4801
Plate Manufacturing Manager **Justin Draheim** .... (202) 927-2795

Office of Operations Support
Chief **Linda Korbol** Bureau of Engraving and Printing
Main Building, Room 104-4M .... (202) 874-1597
ECF Operations Analysis Division Manager
Michael O'Leary .... (202) 874-2477
Bureau of Engraving and Printing Annex, 14th and C Streets, SW,
Room 315A, Washington, DC 20228
Warehouse and Materials Distribution Division
Manager **Lemuel Talley, Jr.** Bureau of Engraving
and Printing Annex, Room 315-122A .... (202) 874-2119

Office of Security Manufacturer
14th and C Streets, SW, Washington, DC 20228
Fax: (202) 874-2958

Chief **David Hatch** .... (202) 874-2385
Bureau of Engraving and Printing Main Building,
14th and C Streets, SW, Room 306-5M, Washington, DC 20228
Deputy Chief **(Vacant)** Bureau of Engraving and
Printing Main Building, Room 306-5M .... (202) 874-2385
Currency Overprinting Inspection Division Manager
Robert Bernhard Bureau of Engraving and Printing
Main Building, Room A205-M .... (202) 874-3081
Federal Reserve Vault and Packing Branch Manager
Brian McCray Bureau of Engraving and Printing
Annex, Room 300-M-3 .... (202) 874-2251
Inspection Division Manager **Phillip Jackson** .... (202) 874-2351
Intaglio Printing Division Manager **Robert Smith**
Bureau of Engraving and Printing Main Building,
Room 306-M .... (202) 874-2653
Miscellaneous Production Division Manager
Douglas Gandy Bureau of Engraving and Printing
Main Building, Room 306-15M .... (202) 874-2555
Fax: (202) 874-2958
Offset Printing Division Manager **David Smeltzer** .... (202) 874-1982
Program Manager **Ronald Armstrong** Room 420-03M ... (202) 874-2653

Western Currency Facility (WCF)

9000 Blue Mound Road, Fort Worth, TX 76131
Fax: (817) 847-3703

• Associate Director of Manufacturing
Charlene E. Williams Room A215 .... (817) 847-3880
E-mail: charlene.williams@bep.gov
Currency Manufacturing Office Chief
(Vacant) Room A-251 .... (817) 847-3979
Fax: (817) 847-3998
Human Resources Management Division Manager
Theresa Emery Room A-139 .... (817) 847-3933
Mechanical Exam Operations Manager
Terry L. Scott Room P153 .... (817) 847-3835
Operations Support Division Chief
Marcelo Dijamco Room T-236 .... (817) 847-3936
Security Support Division Manager
Thomas L. Klug Room A145 .... (817) 847-3927
E-mail: thomas.klug@bep.gov
Offset Operations Branch Manager
Vernon Hathaway Room PE109 .... (817) 847-3718
Product Security Branch Manager
Kimberly Simpson Room SE212 .... (817) 847-3778

★ Presidential Appointment Requiring Senate Confirmation ☆ Presidential Appointment □ Schedule C Appointment ◇ Career Senior Foreign Service Appointment
● Career Senior Executive Service (SES) Appointment ○ Non-Career Senior Executive Service (SES) Appointment ■ Postal Career Executive Service

Internal Revenue Service (IRS)

1111 Constitution Avenue, NW, Washington, DC 20224-0002
Tel: (866) 591-0860 (Freedom of Information/Privacy Act)
Tel: (202) 317-4000 (Media Relations)
Tel: (800) 829-3676 (Tax Forms and Publications)
Tel: (800) 829-1040 (Taxpayer Assistance and Information)
Tel: (800) 829-4477 (Teletax Refund Information) TTY: (800) 829-4059
Internet: www.irs.gov

OFFICE OF THE COMMISSIONER

1111 Constitution Avenue, NW, Washington, DC 20224-0002
Tel: (202) 317-7070

Communications and Liaison (CL)

1111 Constitution Avenue, NW, Washington, DC 20224-0002
Tel: (202) 317-6890 Fax: (202) 622-5067

Office of Communications

1111 Constitution Avenue, NW, Washington, DC 20224-0002

Field Media Relations (FMR)

Chief **William M. Cressman** .... (215) 861-1550
600 Arch Street, Room 7420, Philadelphia, PA 19106 Fax: (215) 861-1632
E-mail: william.m.cressman@irs.gov

Area I Manager **Chris D. Kerns** .... (513) 263-3078
550 Main Street, Cincinnati, OH 45202 Fax: (513) 263-3756
E-mail: chris.d.kerns@irs.gov

Area II Manager **(Vacant)** .... (414) 231-2251
310 West Wisconsin Avenue, Mail Stop 1020MIL, Milwaukee, WI 53203 Fax: (414) 231-2248

Area III Manager **(Vacant)** .... (510) 637-2800
1301 Clay Street, Room 1630S, Oakland, CA 94612

Area IV Manager (Spanish Media) **Maritza R. Michaud** .... (954) 423-7630
7850 SW 6th Court, Mail Stop 6020, Plantation, FL 33324-3202 Fax: (954) 423-7631
E-mail: maritza.michaud@irs.gov

Office of the National Taxpayer Advocate (NTA)

1111 Constitution Avenue, NW, Washington, DC 20224-0002
Fax: (202) 317-6100 Fax: (202) 317-4097

IRS Campuses

Andover (MA) Center

310 Lowell Street, Andover, MA 01810
Tel: (978) 805-0745

Local Taxpayer Advocate Manager **(Vacant)** .... (978) 805-0745

Accounts Management Field Director **Patrick J. Bazick** .... (404) 338-7767
E-mail: patrick.j.bazick@irs.gov Fax: (978) 474-5711

Compliance Field Director **(Vacant)** .... (978) 805-0745

Secretary **Trina Simard** .... (978) 805-0745
Note: On detail.

Brookhaven (NY) Center

1040 Waverly Avenue, Holtsville, NY 11742
Tel: (631) 654-6686 Fax: (855) 818-5701

Local Taxpayer Advocate Manager **Christopher "Chris" Morell** .... (631) 654-6687

Site Coordinator **Thomas Nicolazzi** .... (631) 977-4115

Wage and Investment Center Director - Field Accounts Management (Acting) **Carl Ochs** .... (631) 977-4091

Small Business/Self Employed Service Center Director - Field Compliance (Acting) **Patricia Demaio** .... (631) 977-4091

Small Business/Self Employed Communications Manager **Christine Hicks-Nash** .... (631) 977-3669
E-mail: christine.hicks-nash@irs.gov

Cincinnati (OH) Center

201 River Center, Covington, KY 41011
Tel: (859) 669-5385

Campus Exam/AUR Director **James E. Rogers, Jr.** ..... (859) 669-7110
200 West Fourth Street, Covington, KY 41011 Fax: (859) 669-5387
E-mail: james.rogers@irs.gov

Accounts Management Field Director **(Vacant)** .... (859) 669-5385
200 West Fourth Street, MS 5900G, Covington, KY 41011

Submission Processing Field Director **James E. Rogers, Jr.** .... (859) 669-7110
200 West Fourth Street, MS 5900G, Covington, KY 41011 Fax: (859) 669-5387
E-mail: james.rogers@irs.gov

Taxpayer Advocate Service Manager **Deana Johnson** .... (859) 669-4240
201 West River Center, MS 11G, Mail Stop 11G, Covington, KY 41011 Fax: (859) 669-5405

Memphis (TN) Center

5333 Getwell Road, Mail Stop 5, Memphis, TN 38118
Tel: (901) 546-2225 Fax: (901) 546-2140

Accounts Management Field Director (Acting) **Paul Morgan** .... (901) 546-2225

Local Taxpayer Advocate Manager **Donna Wess** .... (901) 395-1901
E-mail: donna.wess@irs.gov

Memphis Examination Campus Director **Dennis Krings** Mail Stop 8 .... (901) 546-2017

Ogden (UT) Center

1973 North Rulon White Boulevard, M/S 1000, Ogden, UT 84404
Tel: (801) 620-6366 Fax: (855) 873-0298

Submission Processing Field Director **Denise M. Lage** ... (801) 620-6366

Accounts Management Director **Mary Ann Thompson** ... (801) 620-5201
E-mail: mary.a.thompson@irs.gov

Director, Examination **Ivy McChesney** .... (801) 612-4401

Local Taxpayer Advocate Manager **Ann R. Brunetti** ..... (801) 620-3000

Philadelphia (PA) Center

2970 Market Street, Mail Stop 2, Philadelphia, PA 19104
Tel: (267) 466-2427 Fax: (855) 822-1226

Local Taxpayer Advocate **Brenda Lackey** .... (267) 466-2355

Local Taxpayer Advocate Service

Alabama - Taxpayer Advocate Service Office

801 Tom Martin Drive, Room 151, Birmingham, AL 35211
Tel: (205) 912-5634 Fax: (855) 822-2207

Taxpayer Advocate **Clifford Whitely** .... (205) 912-5634

Taxpayer Advocate Group Manager **Drema Knapp-Morrison** .... (205) 912-5630
Fax: (855) 822-2207

Secretary **Ursula Fullilove** .... (205) 912-5634

Senior Program Analyst **Kelly S. Farris** .... (205) 912-5355

Alaska - Taxpayer Advocate Service Office

949 East 36th Avenue, Stop A-405, Anchorage, AK 99508-4361
Tel: (907) 786-9777 Fax: (907) 271-6157

Local Taxpayer Advocate/Commissioner's Representative **(Vacant)** .... (907) 271-6877

Arizona - Taxpayer Advocate Service Office

4041 N. Central Avenue, Phoenix, AZ 85012
Tel: (602) 636-9500

Local Taxpayer Advocate Manager **Caroline E. Ware** .... (602) 636-9500

Management Assistant **(Vacant)** .... (602) 636-9500
Fax: (855) 829-5330

Arkansas - Taxpayer Advocate Service Office

700 West Capitol Avenue, Mail Stop 1005, Little Rock, AR 72201
Tel: (501) 396-5978 Fax: (501) 396-5768

Local Taxpayer Advocate Manager **Bill J. Wilde** .... (501) 396-5820

DEPARTMENTS

★ Presidential Appointment Requiring Senate Confirmation ☆ Presidential Appointment ☐ Schedule C Appointment ◇ Career Senior Foreign Service Appointment
● Career Senior Executive Service (SES) Appointment ○ Non-Career Senior Executive Service (SES) Appointment ■ Postal Career Executive Service

Delaware - Taxpayer Advocate Service Office
1352 Marrows Road, Suite 203, Newark, DE 19711
Tel: (302) 286-1654 Fax: (302) 286-1643
Local Taxpayer Advocate Manager (Acting)
Yvette Jackson . . . . (302) 286-1654
Administrative Officer **(Vacant)** . . . . (302) 286-1555

Florida - Taxpayer Advocate Service Office (North)
400 West Bay Street, Stop TAS, Jacksonville, FL 32202
Tel: (904) 665-1000 Fax: (904) 665-1802
Taxpayer Advocate **Stephen D. Halker** . . . . (904) 665-0523

Florida - Taxpayer Advocate Service Office (South)
7850 SW Sixth Court, Plantation, FL 33324
Tel: (954) 423-7677 Fax: (954) 423-7680
Taxpayer Advocate **Theresa Luccotti-Bildik** . . . . (954) 423-7677
Senior Program Analyst **Linda Berkman** . . . . (954) 423-7677
Fax: (954) 423-7685

Georgia - Taxpayer Advocate Service Office
401 West Peachtree Street, NW, Room 510, Atlanta, GA 30308
Tel: (404) 338-8099 Fax: (404) 338-8096
Local Taxpayer Advocate **Starvis Smith** . . . . (404) 338-0899

Hawaii - Taxpayer Advocate Service Office
300 Ala Moana Boulevard, #50089, Room 1-214, Mail Stop H405, Honolulu, HI 96850
Tel: (808) 566-2950 Fax: (808) 566-2986
Local Taxpayer Advocate **Gayvial D. James** . . . . (808) 566-2950

Idaho - Taxpayer Advocate Service Office
550 West Fort Street, Boise, ID 83724-0041
Tel: (208) 387-2827 Fax: (208) 334-1977
Local Taxpayer Advocate Manager
Jane Knowles . . . . (208) 387-2827 ext. 272

Illinois - Taxpayer Advocate Service Office
230 South Dearborn Street, MS 1005CHI, Chicago, IL 60604
Tel: (312) 292-3800 Fax: (855) 833-6443
Local Taxpayer Advocate **Andrew VanSingel** . . . . (312) 292-3800

Indiana - Taxpayer Advocate Service Office
575 North Pennsylvania Steet, Indianapolis, IN 46204
Tel: (317) 685-7840 Fax: (855) 827-2637
Local Taxpayer Advocate Manager **(Vacant)** . . . . (317) 685-7840

Kansas City - Taxpayer Advocate Service Office
333 West Pershing Road, Stop 1005 S-2, Kansas City, MO 64108
Tel: (816) 499-4041 Fax: (816) 499-7887
Local Taxpayer Advocate **Desiree Frierson** . . . . (816) 499-4327

Kentucky - Taxpayer Advocate Service Office
600 Dr. Martin Luther King, Jr. Place,
Suite 325, Louisville, KY 40202
Fax: (502) 912-5040
Local Taxpayer Advocate **Robert Nicks** . . . . (502) 912-5050

Louisiana - Taxpayer Advocate Service Office
Mail Stop 2, New Orleans, LA 70112
Tel: (504) 558-3001 Tel: (877) 777-4778 Fax: (504) 558-3348
Local Taxpayer Advocate Manager **Andis Agusto** . . . . (504) 202-9614
Communication and Liaison Disclosure Officer
Lea Crusberg . . . . (281) 721-8130
Houston, TX 77002 Fax: (281) 721-7007
E-mail: lea.c.crusberg@irs.gov
Government Liaison **Steven St. Cyr** . . . . (504) 558-3068
Fax: (504) 558-3483

Maine - Taxpayer Advocate Service Office
68 Sewall Street, Room 416, Augusta, ME 04330
Tel: (207) 480-6094 Fax: (207) 480-6093
Local Taxpayer Advocate Manager
Deborah A. Weaver . . . . (207) 480-6094
Senior Commissioner's Representative **Diane Fredette** . . . (207) 480-6052
Fax: (207) 353-8402

Massachusetts - Taxpayer Advocate Service Office
JFK Building, 15 New Sudbury Street,
Room 725, Boston, MA 02203
Tel: (617) 316-2690 Fax: (617) 316-2700
Local Taxpayer Advocate Manager **Bob Allen** . . . . (617) 316-2625

Michigan - Taxpayer Advocate Service Office
McNamara Federal Building, 477 Michigan Avenue,
Room 1745, Stop 7, Detroit, MI 48226
Tel: (313) 628-3670 Fax: (313) 628-3669
Local Taxpayer Advocate Manager **Pamara Blount** . . . . . . (313) 628-3670

Minnesota - Taxpayer Advocate Service Office
30 East 7th Street, Suite 817, St. Paul, MN 55101
Tel: (651) 312-7999 Fax: (651) 312-7872
Local Taxpayer Advocate
Maximilian Mixon Esq., LLM . . . . (651) 312-7999

Mississippi - Taxpayer Advocate Service Office
100 West Capitol Street, Stop 31, Jackson, MS 39269
Tel: (601) 292-4800 Fax: (855) 822-2212
Local Taxpayer Advocate Manager **Cathy Herrington** . . . . (601) 292-4806

Missouri - Taxpayer Advocate Service Office
1222 Spruce Street, Mail Stop 1005-STL, St. Louis, MO 63103
Tel: (314) 612-4610 Fax: (314) 612-4628
Local Taxpayer Advocate **Peggy A. Guinn** . . . . (314) 612-4371
Government Liaison - IRS **Tina Haas** . . . . (314) 612-4410

Kansas City Area Office
P.O. Box 24551, Kansas City, MO 64131
Tel: (816) 291-9000 Fax: (816) 292-6000
Local Taxpayer Advocate Manager **Desiree Frierson** . . . . . (816) 291-9001
Submission Processing Center Director **(Vacant)** . . . . (816) 325-3000

Montana - Taxpayer Advocate Service Office
10 West 15th Street, Helena, MT 59626-0023
Tel: (406) 444-8668
Local Taxpayer Advocate **Karen L. Alvear** . . . . (406) 444-8668

Nebraska - Taxpayer Advocate Service Office
1616 Capitol Avenue, Omaha, NE 68102-4923
Tel: (402) 233-7272 TTY: (800) 829-4059 Fax: (402) 233-7471
Fax: (855) 833-8232 (e-Fax)
Local Taxpayer Advocate Manager (Acting)
Darci Smith Suite 182 . . . . (402) 233-7272

Nevada - Taxpayer Advocate Service Office
110 City Parkway, Las Vegas, NV 89106
Tel: (702) 868-5179 Fax: (885) 820-5132
Local Taxpayer Advocate Manager **Deborah Mata** . . . . . . (702) 868-5179

New Jersey - Taxpayer Advocate Service Office
955 South Springfield Avenue, 1st Floor, Springfield, NJ 07081
Tel: (973) 921-4043 Fax: (973) 921-4355
Local Taxpayer Advocate **Soh-Yung E. Son** . . . . (973) 921-4376

New Mexico - Taxpayer Advocate Service
5338 Montgomery Boulevard, NE, Mail Stop 1005 ALB,
Albuquerque, NM 87109
Tel: (505) 837-5631 Fax: (505) 837-5519
Local Taxpayer Advocate Manager **(Vacant)** . . . . (505) 837-5631

★ Presidential Appointment Requiring Senate Confirmation ☆ Presidential Appointment ☐ Schedule C Appointment ◇ Career Senior Foreign Service Appointment
● Career Senior Executive Service (SES) Appointment ○ Non-Career Senior Executive Service (SES) Appointment ■ Postal Career Executive Service

North Dakota - Taxpayer Advocate Service Office
657 Second Avenue North, Room 412, Fargo, ND 58102
Tel: (701) 237-8342 Fax: (855) 829-6044
Local Taxpayer Advocate Manager
Elizabeth "Lizzie" Buckle .... (701) 237-8342

Oklahoma - Taxpayer Advocate Service Office
55 North Robinson Street, Room 138, Mail Stop 1005 OKC, Oklahoma City, OK 73102
Tel: (405) 297-4055 Fax: (405) 297-4056
Local Taxpayer Advocate **Delphine A. Hensley** .... (405) 297-4055

Oregon - Taxpayer Advocate Service Office
1220 SW Third Avenue, Portland, OR 97204
Local Taxpayer Advocate **David Vawser** .... (503) 265-3582
Senior Commissioner's Representative
Judi L. Nicholas .... (206) 220-5010

Pennsylvania - Taxpayer Advocate Service Office

Philadelphia - Taxpayer Advocate Service Office
600 Arch Street, Room 7426, Philadelphia, PA 19106
Tel: (267) 941-6623 Fax: (267) 941-6725
Local Taxpayer Advocate Manager **Brenda Lackey** ...... (267) 941-6624

Pittsburgh - Taxpayer Advocate Service Office
1000 Liberty Avenue, Room 1400, Pittsburgh, PA 15222
Tel: (412) 404-9098 Fax: (855) 821-2125
Local Taxpayer Advocate **Dawn M. Hoppe** .... (412) 404-9098

Rhode Island - Taxpayer Advocate Service
380 Westminster Street, Providence, RI 02903
Tel: (401) 528-1921 Fax: (401) 528-1890
Local Taxpayer Advocate **Timothy "Tim" McLaughin** ... (401) 528-1921
Senior Commissioner's Representative **Nancy J. Zitoli** ... (617) 316-2544
Commissioner's Representative **(Vacant)** .... (401) 525-1865
Commissioner's Representative **Edward Vasconcellos** ... (401) 826-4740
Administrative Officer **Jerry Bassett** .... (401) 826-4772

South Carolina - Taxpayer Advocate Service Office
1835 Assembly Street, Room 466, Columbia, SC 29201
Tel: (803) 312-7901 Fax: (803) 312-7885
Local Taxpayer Advocate Manager **Janet Nesmith** ...... (803) 312-7901

South Dakota - Taxpayer Advocate Service Office
115 Fourth Avenue, SE, Suite 413, Aberdeen, SD 57401-4360
Tel: (605) 377-1600 Fax: (855) 829-6038
Local Taxpayer Advocate Manager
Matthew R. Fonder .... (605) 377-1606

Texas - Taxpayer Advocate Service Office

Austin Local Taxpayer Advocate
300 East Eighth Street, Austin, TX 78701
Tel: (512) 460-8300 Fax: (512) 499-5687
Local Taxpayer Advocate Manager **Roberto Lira** .... (512) 460-8300

Austin - Taxpayer Advocate Service Office
3651 South Interregional Highway, Mail Stop 1005, Austin, TX 78741
Tel: (512) 460-8300 Fax: (512) 460-8267
Local Taxpayer Advocate Manager **(Vacant)** .... (512) 460-4650
Submission Processing Director **Dagoberto Gonzalez** ... (512) 460-7002

Houston Area Taxpayer Advocate Service Office
1919 Smith Street, Room 1630, Mail Stop 1005, Houston, TX 77002
Tel: (346) 227-6750 Fax: (713) 209-3708
Local Taxpayer Advocate Manager **Gina Smith** .... (346) 227-6750

North Texas Local Taxpayer Advocate Service Office
1114 Commerce Street, MC 1005 DAL, Dallas, TX 75242
Local Taxpayer Advocate **William "Bill" Roberts** .... (214) 413-6520

Utah - Taxpayer Advocate Service Office

Salt Lake City Area Taxpayer Advocate Service Office
50 South 200 East, MS 1005, Salt Lake City, UT 84111
Tel: (801) 799-6958 Fax: (855) 832-7121
Local Taxpayer Advocate **Tamara Angeloff** .... (801) 799-6962

Vermont - Taxpayer Advocate Service Office
128 Lakeside Avenue, Suite 204, Burlington, VT 05401-5908
Tel: (802) 859-1052 Fax: (855) 836-9628
Taxpayer Advocate **Robert H. Fett** .... (802) 859-1052
Education: Syracuse BA

Virginia - Taxpayer Advocate Service Office
400 North Eighth Street, Room 916, Richmond, VA 23219
Tel: (804) 916-3501 Fax: (804) 916-3535
Area 2 Director (Greensboro)/Area Taxpayer Advocate Manager **Erica Shaffor** .... (336) 690-6117
Local Taxpayer Advocate Manager **Sherry Stadler** ...... (804) 916-3500

West Virginia - Taxpayer Advocate Service Office
700 Market Street, Suite 303, Parkersburg, WV 26101
Tel: (304) 420-8695 Fax: (855) 755-5453
Local Taxpayer Advocate Manager **Larry A. Hostottle** ... (304) 420-8659
Management Assistant **Carolyn L. Arnold** .... (304) 420-8654
E-mail: carolyn.arnold@irs.gov

Wyoming - Taxpayer Advocate Service Office
5353 Yellowstone Road, Cheyenne, WY 82009
Mail: P.O. Box 2941, Cheyenne, WY 82003-2941
Tel: (307) 633-0800 Fax: (307) 633-0918
Local Taxpayer Advocate Manager **Ann M. Logan** ...... (307) 823-6827

Operations Support (OS)
1111 Constitution Avenue, NW, Washington, DC 20224-0002
Tel: (202) 317-3950 Fax: (202) 622-6408

Office of the Chief Financial Officer (OCFO)
1111 Constitution Avenue, NW, Washington, DC 20224-0002
Tel: (202) 317-6400 Fax: (202) 317-6772

Financial Management Unit
1111 Constitution Avenue, NW, Washington, DC 20224-0002
Tel: (202) 803-9729

Beckley Finance Center
P.O. Box 9002, Beckley, WV 25802
Tel: (304) 256-3033 Fax: (304) 254-3544
Director **(Vacant)** .... (304) 254-5926

Office of the Chief Information Officer
1111 Constitution Avenue, NW, Washington, DC 20224-0002
Tel: (202) 317-5000 Fax: (866) 753-9924

Operations
1111 Constitution Avenue, NW, Room 3137, Washington, DC 20224-0002
Tel: (202) 317-6800

Enterprise Operations
1111 Constitution Avenue, NW, Room 3137, Washington, DC 20224-0002

Detroit (MI) Enterprise Computing Center
985 Michigan Avenue, Detroit, MI 48226-1128
Tel: (313) 234-1062 Fax: (313) 234-1364
Director, Program Planning **(Vacant)** .... (313) 234-2458
Secretary **(Vacant)** .... (313) 234-1040

DEPARTMENTS

★ Presidential Appointment Requiring Senate Confirmation ☆ Presidential Appointment ☐ Schedule C Appointment ◇ Career Senior Foreign Service Appointment
● Career Senior Executive Service (SES) Appointment ○ Non-Career Senior Executive Service (SES) Appointment ■ Postal Career Executive Service

Enterprise Computing Center - Operations Division (ECC)
250 Murall Drive, Mail Stop 1000, Kearneysville, WV 25430
Tel: (304) 264-7111 Fax: (304) 264-7013

Director **Claud Parsons** .... (304) 264-7111
Staff Assistant **Debra I. Delo** .... (681) 260-3692
E-mail: debra.i.delo@irs.gov
Mainframe Operations Branch Chief **Don Palmer** .... (901) 707-6069
Enterprise Configuration Management & Processing Validation Branch Chief **Donna Mann** .... (317) 685-7628
E-mail: donna.mann@irs.gov
Operations Scheduling Branch Chief **Sean Keefe** .... (681) 260-3687
Project Responsibilities Management Branch Chief **Paula Williams** .... (804) 916-3676
E-mail: paula.williams@irs.gov
Test Administration Branch Chief **(Vacant)** .... (304) 264-7111
Unix Server Systems Branch Chief **Laura Whipple** .... (816) 499-4598
E-mail: laura.whipple@irs.gov
Wintel Server Systems Branch Chief **Randall Davis** .... (949) 575-6241
E-mail: randall.davis@irs.gov
Secretary **Rhonda Sterling** .... (313) 234-1040

Information Technology Command Center - Operations Division
250 Murall Drive, Kearneysville, WV 25430
Tel: (304) 264-7113 Fax: (304) 264-7013

Director (Acting) **Candice Joines** .... (240) 613-4727
Executive Assistant **(Vacant)** .... (304) 264-7113
Secretary **(Vacant)** .... (304) 264-7113
End to End Project Branch Chief **(Vacant)** .... (240) 613-3519
Incident and Problem Management Branch Chief **(Vacant)** .... (304) 264-7346
Mainframe Monitoring and Triage Branch Chief **(Vacant)** .... (901) 546-3293
Secretary **Roxanne Washington** .... (304) 264-5713
Service Operations Command Center Branch Chief **Sheila Washington** .... (304) 264-7781
Systems Monitoring Branch Chief **Madelyn S. Walker** .... (512) 460-8680
E-mail: madelyn.s.walker@irs.gov
SVR Network Monitor/Triage Branch Chief **Sheila Washington** .... (304) 264-7781
Secretary **Theresa Mendoza** .... (512) 460-7557

Strategy and Modernization
1111 Constitution Avenue, NW, Room 3137, Washington, DC 20224-0002

Services and Enforcement (SE)
1111 Constitution Avenue, NW, Washington, DC 20224-0002
Tel: (202) 317-4263 Fax: (202) 622-8393

Criminal Investigation (CI)
1111 Constitution Avenue, NW, Washington, DC 20224-0002
Tel: (202) 317-3200 Fax: (202) 622-2703

Field Operations
1111 Constitution Avenue, NW, Washington, DC 20224-0002

Northern Area Field Operations
600 Arch Street, Suite 7408, Philadelphia, PA 19106
Tel: (215) 969-9516

Director **(Vacant)** .... (202) 317-3541
1111 Constitution Avenue NW, Washington, DC 20224-0002

Southern Area Field Operations
1111 Constitution Avenue, NW, Washington, DC 20224-0002
Tel: (404) 338-8600

• Director **Jim Lee** .... (202) 317-3934
E-mail: jim.lee@ci.irs.gov

Western Area Field Operations
24000 Avila Road, Suite 3506, Laguna Niguel, CA 92677

• Director **Toni Weirauch** .... (202) 317-3200

Strategy
1111 Constitution Avenue, NW, Washington, DC 20224-0002
Fax: (202) 622-7613

National Criminal Investigation Training Academy
Building 67, Federal Law Enforcement Training Center, Brunswick, GA 31524
Tel: (912) 267-2123 Fax: (912) 267-2399

Director **Domenic A. McClinton** .... (912) 267-2123

Large Business and International Division (LBID)
801 9th Street, NW, Fourth Floor, Washington, DC 20220-0012
Tel: (202) 515-4400 Fax: (202) 515-4437

Deputy Commissioner
999 North Capitol St., NE, Washington, DC 20003

• Deputy Commissioner (Acting) **Nikole C. Flax** .... (202) 317-8836
E-mail: nikole.c.flax@irs.gov

Central Compliance Practice Area
1301 Clay Street, Oakland, CA 94612
Fax: (202) 283-8313

• Director (Acting) **Paul Curtis** .... (949) 575-6237
801 9th Street, NW, Room M3-443, Washington, DC 20001
E-mail: paul.curtis@irs.gov
Executive Assistant **(Vacant)** .... (202) 515-4400
55 North Robinson Street, Oklahoma City, OK 73102
Director of Field Operations, North Central **(Vacant)** .... (202) 515-4400
4050 Alpha Road, Dallas, TX 75244-4203
Senior Manager **Mary Greco** .... (206) 220-5662
Areas Covered: Groups in CA, CO, WA Fax: (866) 334-4848
950 Second Avenue, Seattle, WA 98174
Senior Manager **Walter Hong** .... (781) 876-1095
Areas Covered: Groups in CT, MA, NJ, NY, PA Fax: (781) 876-1095
One Montvale Avenue, Stoneham, MA 02180-3559
Senior Manager **Robin P. Ruegg** .... (651) 312-7697
Areas Covered: Groups in LA, MN, MO, OK, TX Fax: (651) 312-7789
1550 American Boulevard, Suite E, Bloomington, MN 55425
Senior Manager **Eduardo Umbricht** .... (346) 227-6615
Director of Field Operations, South Central **Margie Maxwell** .... (512) 490-0249
12309 North Mopac Expressway, Austin, TX 30341-4002
Senior Manager (Acting) **Kyle Enns** .... (918) 384-4744
Fountains Business Center, 319 Fountains Parkway, Fairview Heights, IL 62208-2059
Senior Manager **Daniel J. "Dan" LaFortune** .... (405) 982-6651
4050 Alpha Road, MS 4300 DAL, Dallas, TX 75244-4201
Senior Manager (Acting) **Ingrid Mathis** .... (346) 227-6610
Senior Manager **Evelyn Johnson** .... (346) 227-6655
Senior Manager **Jessica R. Samuel** .... (651) 726-1525
Areas Covered: Groups in MN, ND, SD Fax: (651) 270-0268
US Bank Financial Center, 1550 American Boulevard, Bloomington, MN 55425

Eastern Compliance Practice Area
999 North Capitol St., NE, Washington, DC 20003
Tel: (732) 452-8101 Fax: (732) 452-8140

Director (Acting) **Cheryl A. Teifer** .... (904) 661-3124
400 West Bay Street, Jacksonville, FL 32202
Executive Assistant **Brenda Jackson** .... (321) 441-2475
850 Trafalgar Court, Mail Stop 4366, Maitland, FL 32751 Fax: (321) 441-2583
Senior Manager **Keith Garrison** .... (470) 719-6759
Director of Field Operations Great Lakes **Judith A. "Judy" McNamara** .... (630) 493-5172
2001 Butterfield Road, Downers Grove, IL 60515
Senior Manager **Renee Banks** .... (301) 566-3962
Senior Manager **Robert Budney** .... (630) 493-5447
2001 Butterfield Road, Downers Grove, IL 60515
Senior Manager **Diane L. Flouro** .... (262) 513-3413
Senior Manager **James J. O'Hara** .... (732) 452-8130
101 Wood Avenue South, Iselin, NJ 08830

★ Presidential Appointment Requiring Senate Confirmation ☆ Presidential Appointment ☐ Schedule C Appointment ◇ Career Senior Foreign Service Appointment
● Career Senior Executive Service (SES) Appointment ○ Non-Career Senior Executive Service (SES) Appointment ■ Postal Career Executive Service

Eastern Compliance Practice Area *(continued)*

Senior Manager **Donna Zeppiero** .... (501) 396-5911
Fax: (501) 396-5764

Director of Field Operations Southeast
Cheryl A. Teifer .... (904) 665-1223
Senior Manager **Catherine Brooks** .... (470) 719-6553
Senior Manager **Mark Furtak** .... (321) 441-2500
850 Trafalgar Court, Maitland, FL 32751 Fax: (321) 441-2583
Senior Manager **Janet Phillips** .... (732) 452-8101
7850 SW Sixth Court, Plantation, FL 33324 Fax: (954) 423-7829

Northeastern Compliance Practice Area
290 Broadway, 12th Floor, New York, NY 10007

● Director (Acting) **Barbara L. Harris** Floor 12 .... (212) 298-2130
Executive Assistant **Luciene Wright** .... (917) 421-8435
Director of Field Operations North-Atlantic
Darlena Billops-Hill .... (203) 492-8765
150 Court Street, New Haven, CT 06510-2022
Senior Manager **Guy DiSpigna** .... (917) 421-8430
Areas Covered: Groups in NY.
110 West 44th Street, New York, NY 10036
Senior Manager (Acting) **Mark Weinberg** .... (646) 259-8403
Areas Covered: Specialty Program in NY
Senior Manager **Deborah Mullen** .... (781) 876-1016
One Montvale Avenue, Stoneham, MA 02180-3559
Senior Manager **Phyllis Newman** .... (212) 298-2165
Areas Covered: Groups in NY Fax: (212) 298-2279
Senior Manager **(Vacant)** .... (202) 515-4400
150 Court Street, New Haven, CT 06510-2022
Senior Manager **(Vacant)** .... (202) 515-4400
Areas Covered: Groups in NY
110 West 44th Street, New York, NY 10036
Director of Field Operations Mid-Atlantic
Nancy Wiltshire .... (202) 317-8819
999 North Capitol St., NE, Washington, DC 20003
Senior Manager **Renee Bowers** .... (716) 961-5057
Areas Covered: Groups in NY Fax: (716) 961-5057
130 South Elmwood, Buffalo, NY 14202
Senior Manager **Quinton "Jack" Ferguson** .... (757) 213-3840
200 Granby Street, Room 539, Norfolk, VA 23510
Senior Manager **Karen M. Hawkins** .... (484) 636-0481
601 South Henderson Road, Suite 200, King of Prussia, PA 19406
Senior Manager (Acting) **Adanel Vega** .... (908) 301-2171
600 Arch Street, Philadelphia, PA 19106

Western Compliance Practice Area
1301 Clay Street, Oakland, CA 94612
Tel: (630) 493-5900 Fax: (630) 493-5910

● Director (Acting) **Paul Curtis** .... (949) 575-6237
E-mail: paul.curtis@irs.gov
Executive Assistant **Nanette Hamilton** .... (408) 283-1845
55 South Market Street, San Jose, CA 95113
Senior Manager **Asma Latif** .... (949) 575-6035
Director for Field Operations West **Eric Slack** .... (630) 493-5900
Senior Manager **H. Nicholas "Nick" Photakis** .... (818) 543-2390
225 West Broadway, Fax: (818) 543-1578
Suite 200, Glendale, CA 91204
Senior Manager (Acting) **Jacqueline Torres** .... (415) 837-6370
450 Golden Gate Avenue, San Francisco, CA 94102
Senior Manager **Erwin D. Walker** .... (818) 543-2230
225 West Broadway, Fax: (818) 543-2851
Suite 200, Glendale, CA 91204
Senior Manager **Martha "Marty" Walker** .... (206) 946-8070
915 Second Avenue, Seattle, WA 98174
Director of Field Operations Southwest (Acting)
Nora Beltran .... (415) 837-6294
Areas Covered: Responsible for groups located in AZ, CA, NM, NV, UT
24000 Avila Road, Laguna Niguel, CA 92677
Senior Manager **Alyson Brennam** .... (801) 799-6856
Senior Manager **Thomas V. "Tom" Collins** .... (801) 626-0726
Senior Manager **Kevin McAlpin** .... (213) 372-4178
300 North Los Angeles Street, Los Angeles, CA 90012
Senior Manager **Michael S. Pratt** .... (718) 876-1160
One Montvale Avenue, Stoneham, MA 02180-3559

Small Business and Self-Employed Division (SB/SE)
1111 Constitution Avenue, NW, Room 3406, Washington, DC 20224-0002
Fax: (202) 317-6815

Area Offices

Boston Area SB/SE Office
15 New Sudbury Street, Mail Stop 11300, Boston, MA 02203-0002
Mail: P.O. Box 9112, Stop 11300, Boston, MA 02203
Fax: (617) 316-2200
Area Director **(Vacant)** .... (202) 317-6500

Central Examination Area Office
600 Arch Street, Room 7408, Philadelphia, PA 19106
Tel: (267) 941-6246
Area Director **John H. Imhoff, Jr.** .... (267) 941-6159
Education: Notre Dame BBA

Chesterfield (MO) Area SB/SE Office
1122 Town and Country Commons, Chesterfield, MO 63017
Tel: (636) 255-1599 Fax: (636) 940-6427
Territory Manager (St. Louis), Small Business/Self-Employed and International
Victoria Gally .... (636) 255-1599

Florida Area SB/SE Office
400 West Bay Street, Jacksonville, FL 32202
Tel: (904) 665-0501 Fax: (904) 665-1840
Commissioner's Representative **(Vacant)** .... (904) 665-0506
Government Liaison and Deputy Associate Director of Disclosure **Deborah Wan** .... (904) 665-0525
E-mail: deborah.wan@irs.gov
Small Business/Self-Employed Examination Area Director **Pat Shore** .... (904) 665-0501

Maitland (FL) Area SB/SE Office
850 Trafalgar Court, Suite 200, Maitland, FL 32751
Small Business/Self-Employed Compliance Territory Manager **Alysia Burgman** .... (321) 441-2420

Miami (FL) Area SB/SE Office
51 Southwest First Avenue, Miami, FL 33130
Tel: (305) 982-5001 Fax: (305) 982-5412
Small Business/Self-Employed Compliance Territory Manager **Shalon Anderson** .... (954) 423-7149
7850 Southwest Sixth Court, Plantation, FL 33324
Administrative Assistant **(Vacant)** .... (305) 982-5001

South Florida Area SB/SE Office
7850 SW Sixth Court, Plantation, FL 33324
Tel: (954) 423-7300
Small Business/Self-Employed Taxpayer Education and Communication (TEC) Territory Manager
Craig McLaughlin .... (954) 423-7748
E-mail: craig.mclaughlin@irs.gov Fax: (954) 423-7342
Small Business/Self-Employed Collection Territory Manager **Shalon Anderson** .... (954) 423-7149
Small Business/Self-Employed Collection Territory Manager **Atehawung Taku** .... (954) 423-7311
Fax: (954) 423-7309
Administrative Assistant **Karen Lewallen** .... (954) 423-7300
E-mail: karen.lewallen@irs.gov

Tampa (FL) Area SB/SE Office
3848 West Columbus Drive, Suite A, Tampa, FL 33607-5768
Tel: (813) 348-1831
Small Business/Self-Employed Compliance Territory Manager 1 **Tom Hellier** .... (813) 348-1831
Small Business/Self-Employed Bank Secrecy Act Policy and Operations **Tom Ludwig** .... (813) 348-1831

DEPARTMENTS

★ Presidential Appointment Requiring Senate Confirmation ☆ Presidential Appointment ☐ Schedule C Appointment ◇ Career Senior Foreign Service Appointment
● Career Senior Executive Service (SES) Appointment ○ Non-Career Senior Executive Service (SES) Appointment ■ Postal Career Executive Service

DEPARTMENTS

Gulf States Collection Area Office
12309 North Mopac Expressway, Austin, TX 30341-4002
Area Director **Quinton B. Smith** .... (615) 250-5795
E-mail: quinton.b.smith@irs.gov

Gulf States Examination Area Office
4050 Alpha Road, 14th Floor, Dallas, TX 75244-4203
Fax: (972) 308-7008
Area Director **Leslye Baronich** .... (202) 317-4263
4050 Alpha Road, Farmers Branch, TX 75244-4201

Southwest Stakeholder Liaison Field Office
1919 Smith Street, Houston, TX 77002
Tel: (281) 721-7021 Fax: (713) 209-3946
Area Manager, Southwest Area Small Business/Self-Employed Stake Holder Liaison (SB/SE) Office **Janell Warren** .... (713) 209-3814
E-mail: janell.warren@irs.gov

Hawaii Area SB/SE Office
300 Ala Moana Boulevard, Honolulu, HI 96850
Tel: (808) 566-2705 Fax: (808) 539-2860
Administrative Officer **Donna A. Park** .... (808) 566-2860
E-mail: donna.a.park@irs.gov

Laguna Niguel Area SB/SE Office
24000 Avila Road, Mail Stop 5000, Laguna Niguel, CA 92677
Tel: (949) 389-4257 Fax: (877) 477-9193
Technical Services Director **John Tuzynski** .... (949) 389-4257
E-mail: john.tuzynski@irs.gov

Louisiana Area SB/SE Office
1555 Poydras Street, New Orleans, LA 70112
Fax: (504) 558-3366
Territory Manager (New Orleans), Small Business Self-Employed Compliance **(Vacant)** .... (504) 202-3181

Midwest Area Collection Office
230 South Dearborn Street, MS 1000, Chicago, IL 60604
Area Director **Rena Skeen** .... (312) 292-4400

Minnesota Area SB/SE Office
430 North Wabasha Street, St. Paul, MN 55101
Tel: (651) 312-8082 Fax: (651) 312-7775
Area Director - Compliance **Sara Sphinx** .... (651) 312-7777

Nevada Area SB/SE Office
110 City Parkway, Las Vegas, NV 89106
Tel: (702) 868-5005 Fax: (702) 455-1450
Territory Manager **Robert "Bob" Carey** .... (702) 868-5191

North Atlantic Collection Area Office
290 Broadway, 5th Floor, New York, NY 10007
Tel: (212) 298-2413 Fax: (212) 436-1044
Area Director - Collection **Timothy S. Sherrill** .... (212) 298-2401
110 West 44th Street, 9th Floor, New York, NY 10036 Fax: (212) 298-2438
E-mail: timothy.s.sherrill@irs.gov
Stakeholder Liaison **Lillian Davenport** .... (212) 298-2405

South Atlantic Area SB/SE Office
77 K Street NE, Room 5100, Washington, DC 20002
Area Director **Nikki Johnson** .... (202) 317-4263

Southwest Area SB/SE Office
300 North Los Angeles Street, Los Angeles, CA 90012
Fax: (866) 435-7034
Area Director **Shelly Foster** .... (202) 317-4263

IRS Area Offices

Connecticut
135 High Street, Mail Stop 209, Hartford, CT 06103
Tel: (860) 594-9200
Area Director - Stakeholders, Partnerships, Education and Communication **(Vacant)** .... (860) 594-9200
936 Silas Deane Highway, Wethersfield, CT 06109
Area Manager (East) - Small Business/Self-Employed **(Vacant)** .... (860) 594-9200
936 Silas Deane Highway, Wethersfield, CT 06109
Field Assistance, Area 1, Wage and Investment Area Director **(Vacant)** .... (860) 594-9200
310 Lowell Street, MS 114, Andover, MA 01810
Local Taxpayer Advocate (CT) **Kristy Moquin** .... (860) 594-9200

New Hampshire
80 Daniel Street, Portsmouth, NH 03802
Tel: (516) 576-7201 Fax: (603) 433-0742
Senior Commissioner Representative **Christopher A. "Chris" Palin** .... (212) 298-2083
E-mail: chris.a.palin@irs.gov
SB/SE Collection Territory Manager **Shahid A. Babar** ... (603) 594-4077
E-mail: shahid.a.babar@irs.gov
Local Taxpayer Advocate Manager **Terri J. Polvino** ...... (603) 570-0598
Supervisory Internal Revenue Agent **Frank Torres** .... (603) 594-1304
Administrative Officer **Lisa Pastore** .... (516) 576-7201

New York - Manhattan Area Office
290 Broadway, 12th Floor, New York, NY 10007
Tel: (212) 436-1000 Fax: (212) 298-2199
Areas Covered: CT, ME, MA, MI, NH, NJ, NY, OH, PA, RI, VT
Senior Commissioner's Representative **Christopher A. "Chris" Palin** .... (212) 298-2083
E-mail: chris.a.palin@irs.gov
Administrative Officer **Tammy Y. Turner** .... (212) 298-2359
E-mail: tammy.y.turner@irs.gov
Territory 5 Manager - Wage and Investment - CARE - Field Assistance Area 1 Customer Assistance-Relationship and Education (CARE) **James M. Duffy** Ground Floor .... (212) 436-1397
Fax: (212) 436-1467
Area Counsel - Large and Mid-Size Business - International Division **(Vacant)** .... (212) 436-1000
Special Agent In Charge - Criminal Investigation **James D. Robnett** 4th Floor .... (212) 436-1633
Local Taxpayer Advocate **Elizabeth Blazey Pennell** ..... (212) 436-1000

Upstate New York Area Office
130 South Elmwood, Buffalo, NY 14202
Tel: (716) 961-5393 Fax: (855) 834-7726
Local Taxpayer Advocate Manager (Albany) **Sharen Moore** .... (518) 427-5413
Clinton Avenue and North Pearl Street, Albany, NY 12207 Fax: (518) 427-5494

North Carolina
4905 Koger Boulevard, Greensboro, NC 27407
Tel: (336) 574-6024 Fax: (336) 378-2069
Territory Manager (Greensboro) Field Assistance **Steven F. Owens** .... (336) 574-6024
Local Taxpayer Advocate Manager **Tina Juncewicz** ..... (336) 574-6024
Wage and Investment SPEC Director, Area 1 (Acting) **Dennis Krings** .... (336) 574-6024

Ohio
550 Main Street, Cincinnati, OH 45202
Tel: (513) 263-3260 Fax: (513) 263-3257
Taxpayer Advocate Service Manager (Acting) **Nancy Eyman** .... (513) 263-3260
Administrative Officer **Timothy J. Comer** .... (513) 263-3399
E-mail: timothy.j.comer@irs.gov

★ Presidential Appointment Requiring Senate Confirmation ☆ Presidential Appointment □ Schedule C Appointment ◇ Career Senior Foreign Service Appointment
● Career Senior Executive Service (SES) Appointment ○ Non-Career Senior Executive Service (SES) Appointment ■ Postal Career Executive Service

Ohio *(continued)*

Employee Plans Determinations Manager, Tax Exempt/Government Entities Operating Division
Andrew "Andy" Fedders .... (513) 263-3260

Tax Exempt/Exempt Organizations Determinations Manager, Government Entities Operating Division
(Vacant) .... (513) 263-3404
Fax: (513) 263-4554

Cleveland (OH) Area Office
1240 East Ninth Street, Cleveland, OH 44199
Tel: (216) 522-7134 Fax: (216) 522-2947

Taxpayer Advocate Service Manager
Debbie Y. Kennamer .... (216) 522-8241

Tennessee
801 Broadway, Room 481, MDP-1, Nashville, TN 37203
Fax: (615) 250-5735

Area 3 Director, Appeals Field Operations East
(Vacant) .... (615) 250-5601
810 Broadway, Suite 300, Nashville, TN 37203

Local Taxpayer Advocate Manager **(Vacant)** .... (615) 250-6015

Office of the Comptroller of the Currency (OCC)

400 7th St. SW, Mail Stop 3E-218, Washington, DC 20219
Tel: (202) 649-6800
Tel: (800) 613-6743 (Customer Assistance Group/Complaint Hotline)
Internet: www.occ.gov

OFFICE OF THE COMPTROLLER

400 7th St. SW, Washington, DC 20219
Tel: (202) 649-6400
Tel: (800) 613-6743 (Customer Assistance Group and Complaint Hotline)

Note: The Comptroller may continue to serve until reappointed or replaced.

District Offices (DO)

Central District Office

440 South LaSalle Street, Suite 2700, Chicago, IL 60605
Tel: (312) 360-8800 TTY: (312) 360-8827 Fax: (312) 435-0951

Areas Covered: IL, IN, Eastern and Northwestern IA, Northern KY, MI, MN, Eastern MO, ND, OH, WI

Deputy Comptroller **Blake Paulson** .... (312) 360-8802
Education: South Dakota BSBA

Assistant Deputy Comptroller, Specialties/Operations
(Vacant) .... (312) 360-8800

Associate Deputy Comptroller **Brian L. James** .... (312) 360-8849

Associate Deputy Comptroller **Benjamin Lemanski** .... (312) 360-8849

Community Affairs Liaison **Paul Ginger** .... (312) 360-8876

Community Affairs Liaison **Timothy "Tim" Herwig** .... (312) 660-8713

Licensing Manager **John O'Brien** .... (312) 360-8866

Risk and Operations Officer **Jason Joy** .... (312) 360-8803

Field Offices

Champaign (IL)
Harris Center, 3001 Research Road, Suite E2, Champaign, IL 61822-1081
Tel: (217) 402-8186 Fax: (217) 352-5671

Assistant Deputy Comptroller **Mark Drafahl** .... (217) 402-8209

Chicago (IL) Downers Grove
2001 Butterfield Road, Downers Grove, IL 60515

Assistant Deputy Comptroller **Nathan Perry** .... (331) 777-8249

Chicago (IL) Schaumburg
1700 East Golf Road, Suite 800, Schaumburg, IL 60173
Tel: (847) 598-4501 Fax: (847) 413-1427

Assistant Deputy Comptroller **(Vacant)** .... (847) 598-4501

Chicago (IL) South
2001 Butterfield Road, Suite 400, Downers Grove, IL 60515
Tel: (331) 777-8300 Fax: (630) 963-1738

Assistant Deputy Comptroller **(Vacant)** .... (331) 777-8300

Cincinnati (OH)
Westlake Center, 4555 Lake Forest Drive, Suite 520, Cincinnati, OH 45242-3760
Tel: (513) 769-6601 Fax: (513) 769-6723

Assistant Deputy Comptroller **Mark Ridlen** .... (513) 337-9484

Assistant Deputy Comptroller **(Vacant)** .... (513) 769-6601

Columbus (OH)
655 Metro Place South, Suite 625, Dublin, OH 43017
Tel: (614) 356-3703 Fax: (614) 766-6545

Assistant Deputy Comptroller **Julie Blake** .... (614) 356-3704

Assistant Deputy Comptroller **(Vacant)** .... (614) 356-3703

Cleveland (OH)
200 Public Square, Suite 1610, Cleveland, OH 44114
Tel: (216) 416-0600 Fax: (216) 274-1261

Assistant Deputy Comptroller **Allyn Adams** .... (216) 416-0658
E-mail: allyn.adams@occ.treas.gov

Assistant Deputy Comptroller **Joseph "Joe" Wachtel** ... (216) 416-0600
E-mail: joe.wachtel@occ.treas.gov

Detroit (MI)
Omni Office Center, 26877 Northwestern Highway, Suite 411, Southfield, MI 48033-8418
Tel: (248) 727-2910 Fax: (248) 355-4162

Assistant Deputy Comptroller **Allyn Adams** ..... (248) 355-1110 ext. 223

Assistant Deputy Comptroller **Joseph "Joe" Wachtel** ... (248) 727-2910

Indianapolis (IN)
8777 Purdue Road, Suite 105, Indianapolis, IN 46268-3104
Tel: (317) 616-2402 Fax: (317) 872-0957

Assistant Deputy Comptroller **Jill Hoyle** .... (317) 616-2402

Evansville (IN)
21 SE Third Street, Suite 901, Evansville, IN 47708
Tel: (812) 774-4400 Fax: (812) 428-0369

Assistant Deputy Comptroller **Jill Hoyle** .... (812) 774-4400

Louisville (KY)
Ormsby III Building, 10200 Forest Green Boulevard, Louisville, KY 40223
Tel: (502) 429-3422 Fax: (502) 429-0339

Assistant Deputy Comptroller **Joseph A. Lorbeske** .... (502) 883-7054

Milwaukee (WI)
High Pointe Office Center, 1200 North Mayfair Road, Suite 200, Wauwatosa, WI 53226-3282
Tel: (414) 203-5001 Fax: (414) 456-1785

Assistant Deputy Comptroller **Mark Zeihen** .... (414) 203-5001

Iron Mountain (MI)
2906 North Stephenson Avenue, Suite One, Iron Mountain, MI 49801
Tel: (906) 779-7320 Fax: (906) 779-3880

Assistant Deputy Comptroller **Mark Zeihen** .... (906) 779-7320

Minneapolis (MN)
Campbell Mithun Tower, 222 South Ninth Street, Suite 800, Minneapolis, MN 55402
Tel: (612) 355-1465 Fax: (612) 332-3373

Assistant Deputy Comptroller **Douglas Boser** .... (612) 355-1465

(continued on next page)

DEPARTMENTS

★ Presidential Appointment Requiring Senate Confirmation ☆ Presidential Appointment ☐ Schedule C Appointment ◇ Career Senior Foreign Service Appointment
● Career Senior Executive Service (SES) Appointment ○ Non-Career Senior Executive Service (SES) Appointment ■ Postal Career Executive Service

DEPARTMENTS

Minneapolis (MN) *(continued)*

Assistant Deputy Comptroller **Jay Branger** . . . . . (612) 355-1465
Assistant Deputy Comptroller **Sandra Holenko** . . . . . (612) 355-1465

Alexandria (MN)
123 3rd Avenue East, Suite 400, Alexandria, MN 56308
Tel: (320) 759-3972 Fax: (320) 763-4782
Assistant Deputy Comptroller **Sandra Holenko** . . . . . (320) 759-3972

Fargo (ND)
3211 Fiechtner Drive, SW, Fargo, ND 58103-2394
Tel: (701) 552-4602 Fax: (701) 237-5116
Assistant Deputy Comptroller **Jay Branger** . . . . . (701) 552-4603

Peoria (IL)
211 Fulton Street, Suite 604, Peoria, IL 61602
Tel: (309) 407-7481 Fax: (309) 676-6764
Assistant Deputy Comptroller **Brandon Marriott** . . . . . (309) 407-7481

Saint Louis (MO)
500 North Broadway, Suite 1700, St. Louis, MO 63102
Tel: (314) 236-2333 Fax: (314) 436-8580
Assistant Deputy Comptroller **Mary Beth Farrell** . . . . . (314) 236-2333

Northeastern District Office

340 Madison Avenue, 5th Floor, New York, NY 10173
Tel: (212) 790-4000 Fax: (212) 790-4098 Internet: www.occ.treas.gov
Areas Covered: CT, DE, DC, GA, KY, ME, MD, MA, MI, MN, NC, NH, NJ, NY, OH, PA, SC, RI, VT, VI, WI, WV

Deputy Comptroller **Kristin A. Kiefer** . . . . . (212) 790-4001
Education: St Cloud State BS; UC Berkeley MBA
Secretary **Helen McGovern** . . . . . (212) 790-4002
E-mail: helen.mcgovern@occ.treas.gov
District Counsel **Jonathan Rushdoony** . . . . . (212) 790-4010
E-mail: jonathan.rushdoony@occ.treas.gov

Field Offices

Boston (MA)
99 Summer Street, Suite 1400, Boston, MA 02110-1213
Tel: (857) 415-3400 Fax: (617) 482-6864
Assistant Deputy Comptroller **Michael Moriarty** . . . . . (857) 415-3400
Assistant Deputy Comptroller **(Vacant)** . . . . . (857) 415-3400

Charlotte (NC)
212 South Tryon Street, Suite 700, Charlotte, NC 28281
Tel: (704) 350-8300 Fax: (704) 350-8337
Assistant Deputy Comptroller **Scotty Duncan** . . . . . (704) 350-8300

New Jersey (NJ)
343 Thornall Street, Suite 610, Edison, NJ 08837
Tel: (732) 635-2070 Fax: (732) 635-2087
Assistant Deputy Comptroller **Thomas Angstadt** . . . . . (732) 635-2070
Assistant Deputy Comptroller **Melinda Bosworth** . . . . . (732) 635-2070

New York (NY)
340 Madison Avenue, 4th Floor, New York, NY 10173
Tel: (212) 790-4025 Tel: (212) 790-4020 Fax: (212) 790-4083
Assistant Deputy Comptroller **Matthew Johnson** . . . . . (212) 790-4020
Assistant Deputy Comptroller **Edward Dowling** . . . . . (212) 790-4025

New York National Trust Banks
340 Madison Avenue, Ninth Floor, New York, NY 10173
Tel: (212) 790-4044 Fax: (212) 790-4083
Assistant Deputy Comptroller **Michael F. Rea** . . . . . (212) 790-4044

Philadelphia (PA)
1150 Northbrook Drive, Suite 303, Trevose, PA 19053
Tel: (215) 494-7700 Fax: (215) 357-7954
Assistant Deputy Comptroller **Emmit Odom** . . . . . (215) 494-7700

Philadelphia (PA) *(continued)*
Assistant Deputy Comptroller **Julie A. Pleimling** . . . . . (215) 494-7700

Wilkes-Barre (PA) (Satellite Office)
60 Public Square, Suite 602, Wilkes Barre, PA 18701
Tel: (570) 825-9117 Fax: (570) 825-0814
Assistant Deputy Comptroller **Julie A. Pleimling** . . . . . (570) 825-9117
Assistant Deputy Comptroller **Emmit Odom** . . . . . (570) 825-9117

Pittsburgh (PA)
Corporate One Office Park, Building 2, 4075 Monroeville Boulevard, Suite 300, Monroeville, PA 15146-2529
Tel: (412) 702-0400 Fax: (412) 856-6863
Assistant Deputy Comptroller **Robert Ortiz** . . . . . (412) 702-0400

Roanoke (VA)
4419 Pheasant Ridge Road, Suite 300, Roanoke, VA 24014
Tel: (540) 759-3800 Fax: (540) 776-7615
Assistant Deputy Comptroller **Jeff King** . . . . . (540) 759-3800

Syracuse (NY)
5000 Brittonfield Parkway, Suite 102, East Syracuse, NY 13057
Tel: (315) 728-7000 Fax: (315) 431-2830
Assistant Deputy Comptroller **Jesse Anderson** . . . . . (315) 431-2820

Washington DC
400 7th St. SW, Washington, DC 20219
Tel: (202) 649-6510 Fax: (202) 649-7919
Assistant Deputy Comptroller **Linda Nichols** . . . . . (202) 649-6510

Southern District Office

500 North Akard Street, Suite 1600, Dallas, TX 75201
Tel: (214) 720-0656 TTY: (214) 720-7086 Fax: (214) 720-7000
Areas Covered: AL, AR, FL, GA, Southern KY, LA, MS, OK, TN, TX

Deputy Comptroller **Troy Thornton** . . . . . (214) 720-7005
E-mail: troy.thornton@occ.treas.gov
Associate Deputy Comptroller **Carter Messick** . . . . . (214) 720-2835
Associate Deputy Comptroller **Kent Stone** . . . . . (214) 720-2812
District Counsel **Randall M. Ryskamp** . . . . . (214) 720-7012
E-mail: randy.ryskamp@occ.treas.gov
Licensing Manager **Karen Bryant** . . . . . (214) 720-7087
Fax: (214) 720-7098 Fax: (214) 720-7002
Risk and Operations Officer **Oscar Harvey** . . . . . (214) 720-7082

Field Offices

Atlanta (GA)
Three Ravina Drive, Suite 550, Atlanta, GA 30346
Tel: (770) 280-4438 Fax: (770) 390-0979
Assistant Deputy Comptroller **Jason Sisack** . . . . . (770) 280-4400
Assistant Deputy Comptroller **Deborah Thompson** . . . . . (770) 280-4400

Birmingham (AL)
3595 Grandview Parkway, Suite 655, Birmingham, AL 35243
Tel: (205) 510-7050 Fax: (205) 298-8635
Assistant Deputy Comptroller
Thomas "Tom" Herslebs . . . . . (205) 510-7050

Dallas (TX)
225 East John Carpenter Freeway, Suite 900, Irving, TX 75062-2270
Tel: (972) 277-9500 Fax: (972) 409-9614
Assistant Deputy Comptroller **Terry Richter** . . . . . (903) 252-3800
Assistant Deputy Comptroller **Nanalie Andress** . . . . . (972) 409-9614

Fort Worth (TX)
9003 Airport Freeway, Suite 275, North Richland Hills, TX 76180-9127
Tel: (817) 918-3941 Fax: (817) 281-5512
Assistant Deputy Comptroller
Chaunce "Hub" Thompson . . . . . (817) 918-3941
Fax: (817) 281-5512

★ Presidential Appointment Requiring Senate Confirmation ☆ Presidential Appointment □ Schedule C Appointment ◇ Career Senior Foreign Service Appointment
● Career Senior Executive Service (SES) Appointment ○ Non-Career Senior Executive Service (SES) Appointment ■ Postal Career Executive Service

Houston (TX)
1301 McKinney Street, Suite 1410, Houston, TX 77010-3031
Tel: (713) 336-4200 Fax: (713) 336-4201
Assistant Deputy Comptroller **David Elsenbrock** . . . . (713) 336-4200

Little Rock (AR)
Ozark National Life Building, 10201 West Markham,
Suite 105, Little Rock, AR 72205-2180
Tel: (501) 707-6400 Fax: (501) 225-2711
Assistant Deputy Comptroller (Acting)
Rosalyn Anthony . . . . (615) 238-9000

Longview (TX)
1800 West Loop 281, Suite 306, Longview, TX 75604-2516
Tel: (903) 252-3800 Fax: (903) 759-4515
Assistant Deputy Comptroller **Colleen Welch** . . . . (903) 252-3800

Lubbock (TX)
5225 South Loop 289, Suite 108, Lubbock, TX 79424-1319
Tel: (806) 412-4112 Fax: (806) 798-1129
Assistant Deputy Comptroller **Amy Kline** . . . . (806) 412-4112

Miami (FL)
9850 Northwest 41st Street, Suite 260, Miami, FL 33178-2987
Tel: (305) 702-3210 Fax: (305) 715-9716
Areas Covered: North to Vero Beach, South to Key West, West to Naples
Assistant Deputy Comptroller **Brett Bouchard** . . . . (305) 702-3210
Assistant Deputy Comptroller **Elizabeth Ferradas** . . . . (305) 702-3210

Nashville (TN)
320 Seven Springs Way, Suite 310, Brentwood, TN 37027-4537
Tel: (615) 238-9000 Fax: (615) 337-6283
Assistant Deputy Comptroller **Wendell Walker** . . . . (615) 238-9000

New Orleans (LA)
3838 North Causeway Boulevard, Suite 2890, Metairie, LA 70002-8105
Tel: (504) 434-3970 Fax: (504) 828-9087
Assistant Deputy Comptroller **David Clay** . . . . (504) 434-3970

Oklahoma City (OK)
Harvey Parkway Building, 301 NW 63rd Street,
Suite 490, Oklahoma City, OK 73116-7909
Tel: (405) 529-5701 Fax: (405) 848-8085
Assistant Deputy Comptroller **Brian Wall** . . . . (405) 529-5701

San Antonio (TX)
10101 Reunion Place Boulevard, Suite 402, San Antonio, TX 78216-4165
Tel: (210) 780-7000 Fax: (210) 349-1862
Assistant Deputy Comptroller **NS "Scott" Ward III** . . . . . . (210) 780-7000
Assistant Deputy Comptroller (Acting)
Melody Gregerson . . . . (210) 780-7000

Tampa (FL)
4042 Park Oaks Blvd., Suite 240, Tampa, FL 33610-9538
Tel: (813) 284-3180 Fax: (813) 664-0902
Assistant Deputy Comptroller **Marilyn Bueno** . . . . (813) 284-3180
E-mail: marilyn.bueno@occ.treas.gov

Jacksonville (FL)
8375 Dix Ellis Trail, Suite 403, Jacksonville, FL 32256-8281
Tel: (904) 248-4205 Fax: (904) 363-3870
Assistant Deputy Comptroller **Marilyn Bueno** . . . . (904) 248-4205

Tulsa (OK)
8282 South Memorial Drive, Suite 300, Tulsa, OK 74133
Tel: (918) 505-4500 Fax: (918) 459-0446
Assistant Deputy Comptroller **Scott Williams** . . . . (918) 505-4500
Fax: (918) 459-0446

Western District Office
1225 17th Street, Suite 300, Denver, CO 80202
Tel: (720) 475-7600 Fax: (720) 475-7693
Areas Covered: AK, AZ, CA, CO, HI, IA, ID, KS, MN, MO, MT, NE, NV, NM, OR, SD, UT, WA, WY
Deputy Comptroller **Kay E. Kowitt** . . . . (720) 475-7600
E-mail: kay.kowitt@occ.treas.gov
Education: Oregon BBA
Associate Deputy Comptroller **Thomas Jorn** . . . . (720) 475-7600
Associate Deputy Comptroller
Benjamin "Ben" Rudolph . . . . (720) 475-7600
Community Affairs Officer **Beth Castro** . . . . (818) 539-8909
E-mail: beth.castro@occ.treas.gov
Community Affairs Officer **Michael "Mike" Nield** . . . . . . (913) 401-4436
E-mail: michael.nield@occ.treas.gov
Community Affairs Officer **Katherine Holmes** . . . . (720) 475-7670
E-mail: katherine.holmes@occ.treas.gov
District Counsel **Jimmy Singh** . . . . (720) 475-7600
E-mail: jimmy.singh@occ.treas.gov
District Risk and Operations Officer **Karen Boehler** . . . . . (720) 475-7600
Training Officer **Rebecca Espitia** . . . . (312) 660-8724

Field Offices

Denver (CO)
1225 17th Street, Suite 450, Denver, CO 80202
Tel: (720) 475-7500 Fax: (720) 475-7590
Assistant Deputy Comptroller **Kurt Raney** . . . . (720) 475-7500
Assistant Deputy Comptroller **Gary TeKolste** . . . . (720) 475-7500

Des Moines (IA)
1089 Jordan Creek Parkway, Suite 230, West Des Moines, IA 50266
Tel: (515) 829-3630 Fax: (515) 224-4309
Areas Covered: Des Moines is a Satellite Office of Omaha, NE.
Assistant Deputy Comptroller **Jolene Schack** . . . . (515) 829-3630

Kansas City (KS)
7101 College Boulevard, Suite 1600, Overland Park, KS 66210
Tel: (913) 401-4303 Fax: (571) 293-4002
Assistant Deputy Comptroller **Kevin Johnson** . . . . (913) 401-4303
Assistant Deputy Comptroller **Douglas Pittman** . . . . (913) 401-4303

Los Angeles (CA)
550 North Brand Boulevard, Suite 500, Glendale, CA 91203-1985
Tel: (818) 539-8909 Fax: (703) 857-8547
Assistant Deputy Comptroller **Richard Dixon** . . . . (818) 539-8909

Omaha (NE)
13710 FNB Parkway, Suite 110, Omaha, NE 68154-5298
Tel: (402) 513-4197 Fax: (402) 293-4900
Assistant Deputy Comptroller **Jolene Schack** . . . . (402) 513-4197

San Francisco (CA)
One Front Street, Suite 1000, San Francisco, CA 94111
Tel: (415) 805-3000 Fax: (415) 291-8584
Assistant Deputy Comptroller **Johnny Stanley** . . . . (415) 805-3000

Santa Ana (CA)
1551 North Tustin Avenue, Suite 1050, Santa Ana, CA 92705
Tel: (714) 796-4700 Fax: (714) 796-4710
Assistant Deputy Comptroller **Lawrence Carter** . . . . (714) 796-4700

Seattle (WA)
101 Stewart Street, Suite 1010, Seattle, WA 98101
Tel: (206) 829-2602 Fax: (206) 441-4634
Assistant Deputy Comptroller **Norman McIntyre** . . . . (206) 829-2602

Sioux Falls (SD)
4900 South Minnesota Avenue, Suite 300, Sioux Falls, SD 57108
Tel: (605) 809-4134 Fax: (605) 336-7769
Assistant Deputy Comptroller **Tom Sutcliffe** . . . . (605) 809-4134

★ Presidential Appointment Requiring Senate Confirmation ☆ Presidential Appointment □ Schedule C Appointment ◇ Career Senior Foreign Service Appointment
● Career Senior Executive Service (SES) Appointment ○ Non-Career Senior Executive Service (SES) Appointment ■ Postal Career Executive Service

Wichita (KS)
2959 North Rock Road, Suite 510, Wichita, KS 67226
Tel: (316) 361-5101 Fax: (571) 293-4005
Assistant Deputy Comptroller **Keith Osborne** .... (316) 361-5101

Large Banks

OCC National Bank Examiners - Bank of America Corporation
101 South Tryon Street, NC1-002-31-15, Charlotte, NC 28255-0002
315 Montgomery Street, Mezzanine Level, CA5-704-MZ-09,
San Francisco, CA 94104-1521
Tel: (704) 386-1011 Fax: (704) 386-8874
Tel: (415) 622-3399 (San Francisco office)
Fax: (415) 622-3214 (San Francisco office)
Examiner-in-Charge (Acting) **Kathryn Drumwright** ..... (980) 386-1011

OCC National Bank Examiners - BlackRock Institutional Trust Co.
One Front Street, San Francisco, CA 94111
Senior National Bank Examiner **Rachel Bayless** .... (415) 291-8358

OCC National Bank Examiners - Capital One Financial
1680 Capital One Drive, McLean, VA 22102
Fax: (301) 433-6224
Examiner-in-Charge **Michael "Tim" McDonald** .... (703) 720-1581

OCC National Bank Examiners - Citigroup, Inc.
880 Third Avenue, 5th Floor, New York, NY 10022-4730
Tel: (212) 527-1020 Fax: (212) 527-1047
Examiner-in-Charge **Greg Sullivan** .... (212) 527-1020
Fax: (212) 527-1047

OCC National Bank Examiners - RBS Citizens Inc.
One Citizens Plaza, Suite 610, Providence, RI 02903
Examiner-in-Charge **Bethany "Beth" Dugan** .... (617) 737-2528
Education: West Virginia BA, MBA

OCC National Bank Examiners - HSBC Bank North America Inc.
HSBC Bank USA, National Association, 10 East 40th Street,
14th Floor, New York, NY 10016
Tel: (212) 525-7376
Examiner-in-Charge **Ronald "Ron" Frake** .... (212) 525-7376

OCC National Bank Examiners - J.P. Morgan Chase and Company
1114 Avenue of the Americas, Suite 3900, New York, NY 10036-7780
Tel: (212) 899-1222 Fax: (301) 333-7031
Examiner-in-Charge **Mark Richardson** .... (212) 899-1292
Fax: (301) 433-9012

OCC National Bank Examiners - Morgan Stanley
750 Seventh Avenue, 31st Floor, New York, NY 10019
Fax: (212) 762-0619
Examiner-in-Charge **Thomas E. McQuade** .... (212) 762-0710

OCC National Bank Examiners - KeyCorp
127 Public Square, Mezzanine Level, Mail Stop OH-01-27-MZ 02,
Cleveland, OH 44114-1306
Tel: (216) 689-5785 Fax: (216) 689-5995
Examiner-in-Charge **Robert Barnes** .... (216) 689-5714

OCC National Bank Examiners - TD Banknorth Group, Inc.
2059 Springdale Road, Cherry Hill, NJ 08003
Tel: (856) 470-3768 Fax: (856) 470-3843
Examiner-in-Charge **Carlos Hernandez** .... (856) 552-2557
Education: San José State BA Fax: (856) 552-2560

OCC National Bank Examiners - The PNC Financial Services Group, Inc.
OCC, Two PNC Plaza, 620 Liberty Avenue,
Mail Stop P2-PTPP-20-3, Pittsburgh, PA 15222-2719
Tel: (412) 762-2738 Fax: (412) 762-5239
Examiner-in-Charge **Ron Pasch** .... (412) 762-2738
Education: Wisconsin (River Falls) BA

OCC National Bank Examiners - UnionBanCal Corporation
Union Bank of California, 400 California Street,
3rd Floor, San Francisco, CA 94104-1332
Tel: (415) 765-2545 Fax: (415) 765-2213
Examiner-in-Charge **Carolyn G. DuChene** .... (415) 765-2545

OCC National Bank Examiners - U.S. Bancorp
U.S. Bancorp Center, 800 Nicollet Mall,
Mail Stop BC-MN-H170, Minneapolis, MN 55402-4302
Tel: (612) 303-4091 Fax: (612) 303-4023
Examiner-in-Charge **Serena Christenson** .... (612) 303-4054

OCC National Bank Examiners - Wells Fargo and Company
343 Sansome Street, Suite 1150, MAC A0163-110,
San Francisco, CA 94163-0001
Tel: (415) 396-5896 Fax: (415) 398-5046
Examiner-in-Charge (Acting) **Tanya Smith** .... (415) 396-5896

OCC Large Bank Examiners - Charlotte Office
212 South Tryon Street, Suite 500, Charlotte, NC 28281
Tel: (704) 347-3670 Fax: (704) 350-8422
Examiner-in-Charge **(Vacant)** .... (704) 350-8400

OCC Large Bank Examiners - London Office
Box 20, 24 Grosvenor Square, London, England W1A 1AE,
United Kingdom
Mail: American Embassy - London, England, U.K., PSC 801, Box 20,
FPO, AE 09498-4020
Tel: 44 (20) 7894-0197 Fax: 44 (20) 7491-0077
Examiner-in-Charge (Acting) **Mark Malsbury** 44 (20) 74894-0197

OCC Large Bank Examiners - New Jersey Office
343 Thornall Street, Suite 620, Edison, NJ 08837
Tel: (732) 650-3400 Fax: (732) 603-2465
Examiner-in-Charge **(Vacant)** .... (732) 603-2450

United States Mint (USMint)

801 9th Street, NW, Washington, DC 20220
Tel: (202) 756-6468 Tel: (800) 872-6468 (Customer Service)
Tel: (800) 872-4653 (American Eagle Marketing Division Hotline)
Internet: www.usmint.gov

OFFICE OF THE DIRECTOR

801 9th Street, NW, Washington, DC 20220
Fax: (202) 756-6160
Note: The Director may continue to serve until reappointed or replaced.

Manufacturing Department

801 9th Street, NW, Washington, DC 20220
Fax: (202) 756-6500

U.S. Mint - Denver (CO)

320 West Colfax, Denver, CO 80204
Tel: (303) 405-4600 Fax: (303) 405-4604
Superintendent (Acting) **Randy Johnson** .... (303) 405-4601
E-mail: randy.johnson@usmint.treas.gov
Deputy Plant Manager **(Vacant)** .... (303) 405-4635
Financial Management Division Chief **Tanya Mueller** .... (303) 405-4647
Coining Division Chief **Rudy Beiler** .... (303) 405-4891
Die Manufacturing Division **Gary Hall** .... (303) 405-4672
Environmental Safety, Health and Energy Division
Aubrey Pharo .... (303) 405-4827
Quality and Technical Support Division Chief
Robert Coleman .... (303) 405-4684
Personnel Division Chief **(Vacant)** .... (303) 405-4775
Plant Engineering Division Chief **Deborah Roberts** ..... (303) 405-4825
Police Division Chief **Rob Telfor** .... (303) 405-4875

★ Presidential Appointment Requiring Senate Confirmation ☆ Presidential Appointment ☐ Schedule C Appointment ◇ Career Senior Foreign Service Appointment
● Career Senior Executive Service (SES) Appointment ○ Non-Career Senior Executive Service (SES) Appointment ■ Postal Career Executive Service

U.S. Mint - Denver (CO) *(continued)*

Information Technology Division **Rick Early** . . . . (303) 405-4704
E-mail: rick.early@usmint.treas.gov
Procurement Officer **Michael "Mike" Carriveau** . . . . (303) 405-4629
E-mail: michael.carriveau@usmint.treas.gov

U.S. Mint - Philadelphia (PA)

151 North Independence Mall East, Philadelphia, PA 19106
Tel: (215) 408-0367 Fax: (215) 408-2700

● Plant Manager **(Vacant)** . . . . (215) 408-0367
Deputy Plant Manager **James Nicolo** . . . . (215) 408-0146
E-mail: james.nicolo@usmint.treas.gov
Administrative Services Division Chief **(Vacant)** . . . . (215) 408-0103
Finance Manager **Leonard Allison** . . . . (215) 408-0138
Traffic Manager **Thomas Browne** . . . . (215) 408-0201
Coining Division Chief **Norman Patterson** . . . . (215) 408-0380
E-mail: norman.patterson@usmint.treas.gov
Die Manufacturing Division Chief **Dave Puglia** . . . . (215) 408-0335
Engraving Division Chief (Acting) **Ronald E. Harrigal** . . . (202) 354-7649
Human Resource Division Chief (Acting)
Cindy Waddle
Information Technology Manager **Quincy Dutchin** . . . . . . (215) 408-0126
E-mail: quincy.dutchin@usmint.treas.gov
Numismatic Division Chief **Vincent Frese** . . . . (215) 408-0561
E-mail: vincent.frese@usmint.treas.gov
Facilities Management and Engineering Division Chief
Franz Felix . . . . (215) 408-0153
Procurement Division Chief **(Vacant)** . . . . (215) 408-0160
Supply Division Chief **Steven Lewis** . . . . (215) 408-0290
Exhibits and Public Services Staff Chief
Timothy Grant . . . . (215) 408-0110
E-mail: timothy.grant@usmint.treas.gov
Management Analysis Staff Chief **(Vacant)** . . . . (215) 408-0280
Safety Officer **Debra Davis** . . . . (215) 408-0274
E-mail: debra.davis@usmint.treas.gov
Police Officer Field Chief **Robert Bankhead** . . . . (215) 408-0367
E-mail: robert.bankhead@usmint.treas.gov
Supervisory Quality Assurance Specialist **Eric Larsen** . . . . (215) 408-0310
E-mail: eric.larsen@usmint.treas.gov

U.S. Mint - San Francisco (CA)

155 Hermann Street, San Francisco, CA 94102
Tel: (415) 575-8000 Fax: (415) 575-7765

● Superintendent **David Jacobs** . . . . (415) 575-7761
E-mail: david.jacobs@usmint.treas.gov
● Executive Assistant **Lynn Black** . . . . (415) 575-7761
E-mail: lynn.black@usmint.treas.gov
● Deputy Superintendent **Paul Lewis** . . . . (415) 575-7631
E-mail: paul.lewis@usmint.treas.gov
● Information Technology Manager **Robert Fonnesbeck** . . . (415) 575-7749
E-mail: robert.fonnesbeck@usmint.treas.gov Fax: (415) 575-7664
● Financial Manager **Ginger Moralez** . . . . (415) 575-7912
E-mail: ginger.moralez@usmint.treas.gov Fax: (415) 575-7652
● Security Division Chief **John Abbey** . . . . (415) 575-7611
E-mail: john.abbey@usmint.treas.gov Fax: (415) 575-7613
● Labor Officer **Michael Hunt** . . . . (415) 575-7835
E-mail: michael.hunt@usmint.treas.gov
● Personnel Officer **Vergus Davis** . . . . (415) 575-7844
E-mail: vergus.davis@usmint.treas.gov
● Safety and Occupational Health Manager
Susanne Turner . . . . (415) 575-7681
E-mail: susanne.turner@usmint.treas.gov Fax: (415) 575-7688

U.S. Mint - West Point (NY)

Route 218, P.O. Box 37, West Point, NY 10996
Tel: (845) 446-6200 Fax: (845) 446-6258

Supervisor **Ellen McCullom** . . . . (845) 446-6201
E-mail: ellen.mccullom@usmint.treas.gov
Deputy Supervisor **Thomas "Tom" DiNardi** . . . . (845) 446-6205
Assay and Quality Control Division Chief
Jeanette Grogan . . . . (845) 446-6248
Information Technology Manager **Mark Riegner** . . . . (845) 446-1713
Plant Engineering Division Chief **Luigi DiCocco** . . . . (845) 446-6240

U.S. Mint - West Point (NY) *(continued)*

Police Chief **John Brawdy** . . . . (845) 446-6234
E-mail: john.brawdy@usmint.treas.gov

Protection Directorate

801 9th Street, NW, Washington, DC 20220
Fax: (202) 756-6398

U.S. Bullion Depository

P.O. Box 965, Fort Knox, KY 40121
Tel: (502) 942-1194 Fax: (502) 942-2153

Field Chief, Officer-in-Charge **Kathi Posey** . . . . (502) 942-1847

★ Presidential Appointment Requiring Senate Confirmation ☆ Presidential Appointment □ Schedule C Appointment ◇ Career Senior Foreign Service Appointment
● Career Senior Executive Service (SES) Appointment ○ Non-Career Senior Executive Service (SES) Appointment ■ Postal Career Executive Service

United States Department of Veterans Affairs

Contents

United States Department of Veterans Affairs (VA)

Description: The Department of Veterans Affairs operates a number of programs that benefit veterans and their families. These include compensation payments for disability or death related to military service, as well as pensions, education, rehabilitation, and home loan guarantees. The Department also manages the National Cemetery Administration and provides nursing homes, clinics, and medical centers for veterans.

810 Vermont Avenue, NW, Washington, DC 20420
Tel: (800) 827-1000 (Benefits and Customer Service) Tel: (800) 488-8244 (Fraud, Waste and Abuse Hotline - Continental US, Puerto Rico, and the Virgin Islands) Tel: (800) 749-8387 (Medical Care and Other Benefits)
Tel: (800) 273-8255 ext. 1 (Veterans Crisis Line)
Internet: www.va.gov Internet: www.vets.gov (Veteran Online Services)
Internet: www.usa.gov (Official US Government Website)

OFFICE OF THE SECRETARY

810 Vermont Avenue, NW, Washington, DC 20420
Tel: (202) 461-4800 Fax: (202) 495-5463
E-mail: open@va.gov (Open Government Directive)
Internet: www.va.gov/open (Open Government Directive)

General Counsel (GC)

810 Vermont Avenue, NW, Washington, DC 20420
Tel: (202) 461-4995 Fax: (202) 273-6671 Internet: www.va.gov/ogc

Offices of Chief Counsel in the Districts

Continental - East
1500 East Woodrow Wilson Boulevard, Jackson, MS 39216
Tel: (601) 364-1261 Fax: (601) 364-1263
Areas Covered: AR, LA, MS
● Chief Counsel **Sonya Cromwell** .... (601) 882-2885
E-mail: sonya.cromwell@va.gov

Continental - West
155 Van Gordon Street, Suite 551, Lakewood, CO 80228
Mail: P.O. Box 25126, Denver, CO 80225
Tel: (303) 914-5810 Fax: (303) 914-5849
Areas Covered: CO, MT, OK, TX, UT, WY
Chief Counsel **Jeffrey Stacey** .... (303) 914-5810
E-mail: jeffrey.stacey@va.gov

Houston (TX) Office of Regional Counsel
6900 Almeda Road, Houston, TX 77030-4200
Tel: (713) 383-2784 Fax: (713) 383-2783
Regional Counsel **Kevin Curtis** .... (713) 383-2784
E-mail: kevin.curtis@va.gov

Midwest - East
441 Wolf Ledges Parkway, Suite 403, Akron, OH 44311
Fax: (330) 258-8105
Areas Covered: IN, MI, OH
● Chief Counsel **Dennis M. McGuire** .... (614) 388-7039
E-mail: dennis.mcguire@va.gov
Supervisory Attorney **Arlene T. Shively** .... (330) 252-2482
E-mail: arlene.shively@va.gov

Detroit (MI) Office of Chief Counsel
477 Michigan Avenue, Detroit, MI 48226
Tel: (313) 471-3649 Fax: (313) 471-3655
● Regional Counsel **Dennis M. McGuire** .... (313) 471-3649
E-mail: dennis.mcguire@va.gov

Indianapolis (IN) Office of Chief Counsel
575 North Pennsylvania Street, Room 309, Indianapolis, IN 46204
Tel: (317) 916-3775 Fax: (317) 226-6297
Deputy Chief Counsel **Kristi Glavich** .... (317) 916-3775

Midwest - West
Building 1, 5000 South Fifth Avenue, Room G131, Hines, IL 60141-3030
P.O. Box 1427, Hines, IL 60141
Tel: (708) 202-2216 Fax: (708) 202-2239
Areas Covered: IA, IL, KS, MI (Upper Peninsula), MN, MO, ND, NE, SD, WI
● Chief Counsel **(Vacant)** .... (708) 202-2216
Deputy Chief Counsel **Lisa Yee** .... (708) 202-2216
Assistant Chief Counsel **Mike Newman** .... (414) 902-5047
Milwaukee, WI 53202

Saint Louis (MO) Office of Chief Counsel
One Jefferson Barracks Drive, St. Louis, MO 63125-4185
Tel: (314) 845-5050 Fax: (314) 845-5057
● Deputy Chief Counsel **Michael Anfang** .... (314) 845-5050
Education: Wisconsin BA, JD
Paralegal Specialist **Pamela Wilburn** .... (314) 845-5050

North Atlantic - North
Building 14, 800 Poly Place, Brooklyn, NY 11209
Tel: (718) 630-2900 Fax: (718) 630-2917
Areas Covered: CT, DE, MA, ME, NH, NJ, NY, PA, RI, VT
● Chief Counsel **Daniel "Dan" Rattray** .... (716) 862-8853
120 LeBrun Road, Buffalo, NY 14215
E-mail: daniel.rattray@va.gov

Boston (MA) Office of Regional Counsel
VA Medical Center, 200 Springs Road, Bedford, MA 01730
Tel: (781) 687-3600 Fax: (781) 687-3626
Regional Counsel **(Vacant)** .... (781) 687-3600

Buffalo (NY) Office of Chief Counsel
120 LeBrun Road, Buffalo, NY 14215
Tel: (716) 862-8853 Fax: (716) 862-6545
Chief Counsel **Daniel "Dan" Rattray** .... (716) 862-8853
E-mail: daniel.rattray@va.gov

Philadelphia (PA) Office of Deputy Chief Counsel
P.O. Box 13399, Philadelphia, PA 19101
Tel: (215) 381-3167 Fax: (215) 318-3147
● Deputy Chief Counsel **James C. Sinwell** .... (412) 822-1584
E-mail: james.sinwell@va.gov
Information Technology Specialist
Conchita Sanders Woodard .... (215) 842-2000 ext. 2150
E-mail: conchita.woodard@va.gov

Pittsburgh (PA) Office of Deputy Chief Counsel
1010 Delafield Road, Pittsburgh, PA 15215
Tel: (412) 822-1580 Fax: (412) 822-1588
Deputy Chief Counsel **James C. Sinwell** .... (412) 822-1584
E-mail: james.sinwell@va.gov

★ Presidential Appointment Requiring Senate Confirmation ☆ Presidential Appointment ☐ Schedule C Appointment ◇ Career Senior Foreign Service Appointment
● Career Senior Executive Service (SES) Appointment ○ Non-Career Senior Executive Service (SES) Appointment ■ Postal Career Executive Service

DEPARTMENTS

North Atlantic - South
251 North Main Street, Room 826, Winston-Salem, NC 27155
Tel: (336) 631-5014 Fax: (336) 631-5041
Areas Covered: DC, MD, NC, VA, WV

Chief Counsel **Daniel "Dan" Rattray** .... (336) 631-5035
E-mail: daniel.rattray@va.gov
Deputy Chief Counsel **Julie Zimmer** .... (540) 597-1701
E-mail: julie.zimmer@va.gov

Pacific - North
VA Medical Center, 4150 Clement Street,
Building 210, San Francisco, CA 94121
Tel: (415) 750-2288 Fax: (415) 750-2255
Areas Covered: AK, CA (Northern), HI, ID, NV, OR, WA, Pacific Territories, Manila RP.

Chief Counsel **Brent Pope** .... (415) 750-2288
E-mail: brent.pope@va.gov
Education: Saint Louis U 1987 BA, 1990 JD

Pacific - South
Building 24, 650 East Indian School Road, Phoenix, AZ 85012
Tel: (602) 212-2091 Fax: (602) 212-2144
Areas Covered: AZ, CA (Southern), NM

Chief Counsel **Mark Romaneski** .... (602) 212-2091
E-mail: mark.romaneski@va.gov

Southeast - North
3322 West End Avenue, Suite 509, Nashville, TN 37203
Tel: (615) 695-4633 Fax: (615) 695-4634
Areas Covered: AL, GA, KY, SC, TN

● Chief Counsel [Designated Agency Ethics Official (DAEO)] **Tammy L. Kennedy** .... (615) 695-4633
E-mail: tammy.kennedy@va.gov

Atlanta (GA) Office of Deputy Chief Counsel
1700 Clairmont Road, Decatur, GA 30033-4032
Tel: (404) 929-5851 Fax: (404) 929-5870

Chief Counsel **Tammy L. Kennedy** .... (615) 695-4633
3322 West End Avenue, Nashville, TN 37203
E-mail: tammy.kennedy@va.gov
Deputy Chief Counsel **Bradley Flippin** .... (615) 695-4633
3322 West End Avenue, Nashville, TN 37203
Deputy Chief Counsel **Sophia Haynes** .... (615) 695-4633
3322 West End Avenue, Nashville, TN 37203

Southeast - South
140 Fountain Parkway, Suite 520, St. Petersburg, FL 33716
Tel: (727) 540-3900
Areas Covered: FL, PR, USVI

● Chief Counsel **(Vacant)** .... (727) 540-3900

Inspector General (IG)
810 Vermont Avenue, NW, Washington, DC 20420
Tel: (202) 461-4720 Tel: (800) 488-8244 (Inspector General's Hotline)
Tel: (202) 461-4683 (Press inquiries) Fax: (202) 565-8667
Fax: (202) 495-5861 (Inspector General's Hotline)
E-mail: vaoighotline@va.gov (Hotline) Internet: www.va.gov/oig

Office of Audits and Evaluations
810 Vermont Avenue, NW, Washington, DC 20420
Fax: (202) 565-8103

Atlanta (GA) Audit Operations Division
1700 Clairmont Road, 4th Floor, Decatur, GA 30033-4032
Tel: (404) 929-5921 Fax: (404) 929-5929

Division Director **(Vacant)** .... (404) 929-5921

Bedford (MA) Audit Operations Division
Building 12, 200 Springs Road, Room 118, Bedford, MA 01730
Tel: (781) 687-3120 Fax: (781) 687-3131

Director **Dr. Irene J. Barnett PhD, CFE** .... (781) 687-3120
Education: St Francis U BA; Kent State PhD

Chicago (IL) Audit Operations Division
5000 South Fifth Avenue, Hines, IL 60141
P.O. Box 1399, Hines, IL 60141
Tel: (708) 202-2667 Fax: (708) 202-2770

Director **Herman Woo** .... (708) 202-2670
E-mail: herman.woo@va.gov

Kansas City (MO) Audit Operations Division
800 East 101st Terrace, Suite 100, Kansas City, MO 64131
Tel: (816) 997-6931 Fax: (816) 997-6954

Division Director **(Vacant)** .... (816) 997-6931

Los Angeles (CA) Audit Operations Division
Building 258, 11301 Wilshire Boulevard,
Room 330, Los Angeles, CA 90073
Tel: (310) 268-4335 Fax: (310) 268-4827

Division Director **Janet C. Mah** .... (310) 268-4336
E-mail: janet.mah@va.gov
Audit Manager **Corina Riba** .... (310) 268-4330
E-mail: corina.riba@va.gov
Audit Manager **Andrea Sandoval** .... (213) 253-2677 ext. 24902
E-mail: andrea.sandoval3@va.gov Fax: (213) 253-5155

Seattle (WA) Audit Operations Division
Jackson Federal Building, 915 Second Avenue, Box 409,
Room 3098, Seattle, WA 98174
Fax: (206) 220-6650

Division Director **Matthew "Matt" Rotter** .... (206) 220-6651
E-mail: matthew.rotter@va.gov
Information Technology Specialist **John Towery** .... (253) 254-8811
E-mail: john.towery@va.gov
Program Assistant **Rosa Meadors** .... (206) 220-6658
E-mail: rosa.meadors@va.gov

Office of Investigations (OI)
810 Vermont Avenue, NW, Washington, DC 20420
Tel: (202) 461-4702 Fax: (202) 565-7630
Internet: www.va.gov/oig/about/investigations.asp

Central Field Office (CFO)
Building 16, Fifth Avenue and Roosevelt Road,
Room 112, Hines, IL 60141
Mail: P.O. Box 1454, Hines, IL 60141-1454
Tel: (708) 202-2676 Fax: (708) 202-2358
Areas Covered: CO, IL, IN, IA, KS, MI, MO, MN, NE, ND, OH, SD, WI

Special Agent-in-Charge (Acting) **Gregg Hirstein** .... (708) 202-2676
Investigative and Administrative Coordinator **(Vacant)** .... (708) 202-2676
Supervisor Information Technology Support Division **Rhena Williams MCP, MCSE, MCSA** .... (708) 202-5191
E-mail: rhena.williams@va.gov Fax: (708) 202-2770
Education: Indiana Northwest 1988 AAS, 1988 BST; U Phoenix 2002 MBA

Cleveland (OH) Resident Agency
VA Regional Office, 1240 East Ninth Street,
Room 1619, Cleveland, OH 44199
Tel: (216) 522-7606 Fax: (216) 522-8344

Resident Agent-in-Charge **Gavin McClaren** .... (216) 522-7606 ext. 1

Denver (CO) Resident Agency
Ptarmigan Place, West Tower, 3773 Cherry Creek North Drive,
Suite 540, Denver, CO 80209
Tel: (303) 331-7674 Fax: (303) 331-7824

Resident Agent-in-Charge **Randy Rupp** .... (330) 331-7674

Kansas City (MO) Resident Agency
800 East 101st Terrace, Kansas City, MO 64131
Tel: (816) 997-6972 Fax: (816) 997-6954

Resident Agent-in-Charge **Greg Billingsley** .... (816) 997-6975

Mid-Atlantic Field Office
VA OIG, 1722 I Street, NW, Washington, DC 20006
Tel: (202) 530-9193
Areas Covered: DC, MD, NC, Western PA, SC, VA, WV

Special Agent-in-Charge **Kim Lampkins** .... (202) 530-9193
E-mail: kim.lampkins@va.gov

Columbia (SC) Resident Agency
6437 Garners Ferry Road, Columbia, SC 29209
Tel: (803) 695-6707 Fax: (803) 695-6708

Resident Agent-in-Charge **Scott Bailey** .... (803) 695-6707
Investigative Assistant **(Vacant)** .... (803) 647-5822

Nashville (TN) Resident Agency
110 Ninth Avenue, South, Room A-104, Nashville, TN 37203
Fax: (615) 695-6173

Resident Agent-in-Charge **Brian Celatka** .... (615) 695-6170
Investigative Assistant **Emily Wiest** Room A-309 .... (615) 695-6172

Pittsburgh (PA) Resident Agency
VA Pittsburgh Healthcare Systems VAMC (646/003-H),
Pittsburgh Resident Agency, 7180 Highland Drive, Pittsburgh, PA 15206
Tel: (412) 688-6000

Resident Agent **Tim Barry** .... (412) 688-6000

Northeast Field Office
20 Washington Place, Third Floor, Newark, NJ 07102
Tel: (973) 297-3338 Fax: (973) 297-3345
Areas Covered: CT, DE, ME, MA, NH, NJ, NY, Eastern PA, RI, VT

Resident Agent-in-Charge **Donna Neves** .... (603) 222-5865
275 Chestnut Street, Manchester, NH 03101
Resident Agent-in-Charge **Gerard Poto** .... (973) 297-3340

Boston (MA) Resident Agency
Building 12, 200 Springs Road, Room 124, Bedford, MA 01730
Tel: (781) 687-3157

Resident Agent in Charge **Sean Smith** .... (781) 687-3148

Buffalo (NY) Resident Agency
130 South Elmwood Avenue, Suite 475, Room 601,
Buffalo, NY 14202-2478
Fax: (716) 551-3381

Resident Agent **Jeffrey Stachowiak** .... (716) 857-5012

New York (NY) Resident Agency
Building 3, 423 East 23rd Street, 2nd Floor, New York, NY 10010-5011
Tel: (212) 951-6850 Fax: (212) 951-5959

Resident Agent in Charge **Christopher Wagner** .... (212) 951-5449

South Central Field Office
4040 North Central Expressway, Suite 500, Dallas, TX 75204
Tel: (214) 253-3360 Fax: (214) 253-3376
Areas Covered: AR, LA, MS, OK, TX

Special Agent-in-Charge **James W. "Jim" Werner** ...... (214) 253-3361
Resident Agent-in-Charge **Patrick Roche** .... (214) 253-3363

Houston (TX) Resident Agency
6900 Almeda Road, Room 1073, Houston, TX 77030
Tel: (713) 383-2793 Fax: (713) 383-2795

Resident Agent **James Ross** .... (713) 383-2791

Little Rock (AR) Resident Office
2200 Fort Roots Drive, North Little Rock, AR 72114-1756
Tel: (501) 257-3446 Fax: (501) 257-3444

Resident Agent **Jeremiah Reppert** .... (501) 257-4494

Jackson (MS) Resident Agency
Jackson VA Regional Office, 1600 East Woodrow Wilson Drive,
Jackson, MS 39216
Tel: (601) 364-7289 Fax: (601) 364-7290

Resident Agent-in-Charge **John R. Ramsey** .... (601) 364-7289
E-mail: john.ramsey@va.gov
Education: Georgia State 1997 BS; George Washington 2000 MS

Southeast Field Office
P.O. Box 446, Bay Pines, FL 33744
Tel: (727) 319-1215 Fax: (727) 398-9542
Areas Covered: FL, GA, PR, TN

Special Agent In Charge **Lamont "Monty" Stokes** ..... (727) 319-1214
Assistant Special Agent in Charge **Scott Keller** .... (727) 319-1244
Investigative and Administrative Coordinator
Linda K. Knop .... (727) 319-1215
E-mail: linda.knop@va.gov
Special Agent **Doug Williams** .... (727) 319-1217

Atlanta (GA) Resident Agency
1700 Clairmont Road, Suite 4.500, Decatur, GA 30033
Tel: (404) 929-5950 Fax: (404) 929-5947

Resident Agent-in-Charge **Gilbert "Gil" Humes** .... (404) 929-5980
Special Agent **Tracy Brumfield** .... (404) 929-5955
Special Agent **Priva Guillory** .... (404) 929-5952
Special Agent **Angela Picou** .... (404) 929-5952
Special Agent **Kendrick Stoudmire** .... (404) 929-5951
Investigative Assistant **Cevessia Prude** .... (404) 929-5954

Tallahassee (FL) Resident Agency
1844 Fiddler Court, Suite A, Tallahassee, FL 32308
Tel: (850) 656-1145 Fax: (850) 656-3962

Special Agent **Daniel Henson** .... (850) 877-0729
Special Agent **Eric Lindquist** .... (850) 656-1145
Special Agent **Frederick Fernandes** .... (850) 402-1454
Fax: (850) 656-3962

West Palm Beach (FL) Resident Agency
7721 North Military Trail, Suite 5, West Palm Beach, FL 33410-6400
Tel: (561) 882-7461 Fax: (561) 422-5666

Special Agent-in-Charge **David Spilker** .... (561) 422-2340
Special Agent **Travis Hunter** .... (561) 308-9577
Fax: (561) 882-7462
Special Agent **Kenneth Velazquez** .... (561) 422-5535
Special Agent **Greg Wentz** .... (561) 422-5699
Investigative Assistant **Lisa Baker** .... (561) 422-7768

Western Field Office
Building 258, 11301 Wilshire Boulevard,
Room 330, Los Angeles, CA 90073
P.O. Box 241516, Los Angeles, CA 90024
Tel: (310) 268-4269 Fax: (310) 268-4832
Areas Covered: AZ, CA, NV, NM, UT

Special Agent-in-Charge **Douglas J. Carver** .... (310) 268-4269
E-mail: douglas.carver@va.gov

Las Vegas (NV) Resident Agency
1750 North Buffalo Drive, Las Vegas, NV 89128
Tel: (702) 791-9106 Fax: (702) 878-8100

Resident Agent **Gregory Fitzgerald** .... (702) 791-9106
E-mail: gregory.fitzgerald@va.gov

Phoenix (AZ) Resident Agency
3333 North Central Avenue, Suite 1063, Phoenix, AZ 85012
P.O. Box 34142, Phoenix, AZ 85067-4142
Tel: (602) 627-3252 Fax: (602) 627-3259

Resident Agent **Richard Cady** .... (602) 627-3252

★ Presidential Appointment Requiring Senate Confirmation ☆ Presidential Appointment ☐ Schedule C Appointment ◇ Career Senior Foreign Service Appointment
● Career Senior Executive Service (SES) Appointment ○ Non-Career Senior Executive Service (SES) Appointment ■ Postal Career Executive Service

San Diego (CA) Resident Agency
5120 Shoreham Place, Suite 200, San Diego, CA 92122
P.O. Box 22070, San Diego, CA 92192-2070
Tel: (858) 404-8301 Fax: (858) 202-0677
Resident Agent **Rebeccalynn Staples-Devine** .... (858) 404-8301

Northwestern Field Office
Federal Building, 1301 Clay Street, Suite 1610N, Oakland, CA 94612-5209
P.O. Box 70732, Oakland, CA 94613-0732
Tel: (510) 637-6361 Fax: (510) 637-6366
Areas Covered: CA, HI, ID, MT, OR
Special Agent In Charge **Michael Seitler** .... (510) 637-6361

Seattle (WA) Resident Agency
915 Second Avenue, Box 409, Suite 990, Seattle, WA 98174
Tel: (206) 220-6656 Fax: (206) 220-4466
Resident Agent **Robert Sproull** .... (206) 220-6655

Spokane (WA) Resident Agency
904 West Riverside Avenue, Suite 420, Spokane, WA 99201
Tel: (509) 353-0638 Fax: (509) 353-0640
Resident Agent **Robert Sproull** .... (509) 353-0638

Office of the Deputy Secretary (DS)
810 Vermont Avenue, NW, Washington, DC 20420
Tel: (202) 461-4817

Office of Human Resources and Administration
810 Vermont Avenue, NW, Washington, DC 20420
Internet: www.va.gov/employee

Human Resources Management (OHRM)
810 Vermont Avenue, NW, Washington, DC 20420
Tel: (202) 461-7765 Fax: (202) 273-5790 Internet: www.va.gov/ohrm

Veteran Employment Services Office (VESO)
810 Vermont Avenue, NW, Washington, DC 20420
E-mail: vesovets@va.gov Internet: vaforvets.va.gov
Director (Acting) **John Brown** .... (202) 461-7959

Office of Management (OM)
810 Vermont Avenue, NW, Washington, DC 20420
Tel: (202) 461-6703 Fax: (202) 273-6892 Internet: www.va.gov/om

Office of Finance
810 Vermont Avenue, NW, Washington, DC 20420
Tel: (202) 461-6180 Fax: (202) 273-6794

VA Debt Management Center - St. Paul (MN)
11930, St. Paul, MN 55111-0930
Tel: (612) 713-6415 Fax: (612) 970-5688 E-mail: dmc.ops@va.gov
Internet: www.va.gov/debtman
• Director **Joseph "Joe" Schmitt** .... (612) 843-6552
P.O. Box 11930, St. Paul, MN 55111-0930
Education: National U 1999 BS, 2007 EMBA

VA Financial Services Center - Austin (TX) (FSC)
1615 Woodward Street, Austin, TX 78772
Tel: (877) 353-9791 Fax: (512) 460-5425
Internet: https://www.va.gov/finance/fsc.asp
• Director **Terry Riffel** .... (877) 353-9791
E-mail: terry.riffel@va.gov
Deputy Director **Jared Martin** .... (877) 353-9791
Program Specialist **Jacqueline Carr** .... (202) 461-6631
810 Vermont Avenue, NW, Washington, DC 20420
Data Analytics Chief **David Fuller** .... (877) 353-9791
810 Vermont Avenue, NW, Washington, DC 20420
E-mail: david.fuller@va.gov
Education: Northwest Christian 1993 BA; St Mary's U (TX) 2003 MS

Office of Public and Intergovernmental Affairs (OPIA)
810 Vermont Avenue, NW, Suite 900, Washington, DC 20420
Tel: (202) 461-7500 Fax: (202) 495-5228
E-mail: va.media.relations@va.gov Internet: https://www.va.gov/opa/

Public and Intergovernmental Affairs
810 Vermont Avenue, NW, Washington, DC 20420
Tel: (202) 461-7500 Tel: (202) 461-7600 (Media Requests)

Field Operations
810 Vermont Avenue, NW, Room 911, Washington, DC 20420
Tel: (202) 461-7600

Continental District - North
155 Van Gordon Street, Suite 500, Lakewood, CO 80228
P.O. Box 25126, Denver, CO 80225
Tel: (303) 914-5855 Fax: (303) 914-5874
Areas Covered: CO; ID: Pocatello; IA, IL: E. Moline, Marion & Mound City; IN: Evansville; KS; MN; MO; MT: NE; ND; SD; UT; WI: Superior; WY
Director **Paul Sherbo** .... (303) 914-5855
E-mail: paul.sherbo@va.gov
Public Affairs Specialist **Elaine Buehler** .... (303) 914-5855
E-mail: elaine.buehler@va.gov

Continental District - South
2301 East Lamar Boulevard, Suite 350, Arlington, TX 76006
Tel: (817) 385-3720 Fax: (817) 385-3726
Areas Covered: AR, LA, MS, OK, TX
District Director **Jessica Jacobsen** .... (817) 385-3720
E-mail: jessica.jacobsen@va.gov
Deputy Director **(Vacant)** .... (817) 385-3720
Public Affairs Specialist **Lana Shuman** .... (817) 385-3720
E-mail: lana.shuman@va.gov

North Atlantic District (NAD)
245 West Houston Street, New York, NY 10014-4805
Tel: (212) 807-3429 Fax: (212) 807-4030
Areas Covered: CT, DE, DC, MD, ME, MA, NC, NH, NJ, NY, PA, RI, VA, VT, WV
Regional Director **James A. "Jim" Blue** .... (212) 807-3429
E-mail: james.blue@va.gov
Deputy Director **(Vacant)** .... (202) 461-7859
810 Vermont Avenue, NW, Washington, DC 20420
Public Affairs Specialist **(Vacant)** .... (212) 807-3429

Midwest District
2122 West Taylor Street, Suite 320, Chicago, IL 60612
Tel: (312) 980-4235 Fax: (312) 706-6671
Areas Covered: IL except E. Moline, Marion, Mound City; IN except Evansville; MI; OH; WI except Superior
District Director **Craig W. Larson** .... (312) 980-4235
E-mail: craig.larson@va.gov
Public Affairs Specialist **(Vacant)** .... (312) 980-4235
Public Affairs Specialist **Bess Griseto** .... (312) 980-4235
E-mail: bessie.griseto@va.gov

Pacific District
Building 506, 11301 Wilshire Boulevard, Los Angeles, CA 90073
Mail: P.O. Box 84041, Los Angeles, CA 90073
Tel: (310) 268-4207 Fax: (310) 268-4835
Areas Covered: AK; AZ; CA; HI; ID; NM; NV; OR; WA; Manila, Philippines
District Director **Jessica Baxter** .... (310) 467-5298
E-mail: jessica.baxter1@va.gov
Education: American U 2004 BA; George Washington 2007 MPA

★ Presidential Appointment Requiring Senate Confirmation ☆ Presidential Appointment ☐ Schedule C Appointment ◇ Career Senior Foreign Service Appointment
● Career Senior Executive Service (SES) Appointment ○ Non-Career Senior Executive Service (SES) Appointment ■ Postal Career Executive Service

Southeast District
1700 Clairmont Road, Decatur, GA 30033-4032
Tel: (404) 929-5880 Fax: (404) 929-5878
Areas Covered: AL, FL, GA, KY, PR, SC, TN, VI

District Director
Janice M. "Jan" Northstar .... (404) 929-5880 ext. 5881
E-mail: jan.northstar@va.gov
Education: CUNY 1987 BA
Deputy Director **Candace Hull** .... (404) 929-5880
E-mail: candace.hull@va.gov
Public Affairs Specialist **Erika Ruthman** .... (404) 929-5880
E-mail: erika.ruthman@va.gov
Program Assistant **(Vacant)** .... (404) 929-5880

National Cemetery Administration (NCA)

810 Vermont Avenue, NW, ATTN: 43A2, Washington, DC 20420
Tel: (202) 632-8035 Internet: www.cem.va.gov
Internet: gravelocator.cem.va.gov

OFFICE OF THE UNDER SECRETARY FOR MEMORIAL AFFAIRS (MA)

810 Vermont Avenue, NW, Washington, DC 20420
Fax: (202) 273-6709

Principal Deputy Under Secretary for Memorial Affairs

810 Vermont Avenue, NW, Washington, DC 20420

Memorial Service Networks (MSN)

Memorial Service Network 1 – Philadelphia (PA) Office
5000 Wissahickon Avenue, Suite 787, Philadelphia, PA 19144
Tel: (215) 381-3787 Fax: (215) 381-3444

● Executive Director **(Vacant)** .... (215) 381-3013
Financial Program Administrator **(Vacant)** ..... (215) 381-3787 ext. 4046
Agronomist **Stephen Ercolino** .... (215) 381-3787 ext. 4045
Contract Liaison **(Vacant)** .... (215) 381-3787 ext. 4050
Contracting Officer **Iris Chen** .... (215) 381-3787 ext. 4635
E-mail: iris.chen1@va.gov
Chief of Operations **Maria Garza** .... (215) 381-3787 ext. 4053
Human Resources Program Analyst
Alice Easterday .... (215) 381-3787 ext. 4051
E-mail: alice.easterday@va.gov
Program Specialist and Engineering
Technician **Samuel R. Ruggieri** .... (215) 381-3787 ext. 4646
Program Assistant **Mary W. Hampton** .... (215) 381-3787 ext. 4044
Management Analyst **Linda Melvin** .... (215) 381-3787 ext. 4052
E-mail: linda.melvin@va.gov
Purchasing Agent **(Vacant)** .... (215) 381-3787 ext. 4590

Memorial Service Network 2 – Atlanta (GA) Office
1700 Clairmont Road, Decatur, GA 30033
Tel: (404) 929-5899 Fax: (404) 929-5900

● Director of Operations **James R. Taft** .... (404) 929-5899

Memorial Service Network 3 – Denver (CO) Office
155 Van Gordon Street, Suite 510, Lakewood, CO 80228
P.O. Box 25126, Denver, CO 80225
Tel: (303) 914-5700 Fax: (303) 914-5715

● Director **Steven P. "Steve" Best** .... (303) 914-5700
E-mail: steven.best@va.gov
Chief Operation Officer **Sara J. Elton** .... (303) 914-5708
E-mail: sara.elton@va.gov
Information Technology Program Analyst
Elton C. Wooten .... (303) 914-5709
E-mail: elton.wooten@va.gov
Program Specialist **Albert Kuczak** .... (303) 914-5707
E-mail: albert.kuczak@va.gov

Memorial Service Network 4 – Indianapolis (IN) Office
Minton-Capehart Federal Building, 575 North Pennsylvania Street, 495, Indianapolis, IN 46204
Tel: (317) 916-3790 Fax: (317) 226-0206

● Director **Joshua M. "Josh" de Leon** .... (317) 916-3790
E-mail: joshua.deleon@va.gov

Memorial Service Network 5 – Oakland (CA) Office
Oakland Federal Building, 1301 Clay Street,
Suite 1230N, Oakland, CA 94612-5209
Tel: (510) 637-6270 Fax: (510) 637-6273

● Executive Director **Bradley G. Phillips** .... (510) 637-6280
Program Specialist **Kenneth C. Johnson** .... (510) 637-6279
E-mail: kenneth.johnson1@va.gov
Chief of Operations **James A. Spaulding** .... (510) 637-6284
Agronomist **Michael Gaussa** .... (510) 637-6277
Budget Administrator **Amanda Randle** .... (510) 637-6275
Chief Engineer **Clifford J. Schem** .... (510) 637-6281
Engineering Technician **Judith Rogers** .... (510) 637-6278
Program Analyst **Benedict G. Calpo** .... (510) 637-6276
E-mail: bcalpo@va.gov
Program Specialist (Human Resource Liaison)
Ronny Alvarez .... (510) 637-6283
E-mail: ronny.alvarez@va.gov
Human Resources Specialist **Ronny Alvarez** .... (510) 637-6282

National Cemeteries (NC)

Alabama

Fort Mitchell National Cemetery
553 Highway 165, Fort Mitchell, AL 36856-0553
Tel: (334) 855-4731 Fax: (334) 855-4740
Internet: www.cem.va.gov/cems/nchp/ftmitchell.asp
Cemetery Administrator **Col Eldon A. Woodie USAF** ... (334) 855-2184
Education: North Carolina 1981 BS; National Col 1986 MPA

Mobile National Cemetery
1202 Virginia Street, Mobile, AL 36604
Mail: c/o Barrancas National Cemetery,
80 Hovey Road, Pensacola, FL 32508
Tel: (251) 690-2858 Tel: (850) 453-4846 Fax: (850) 453-4635
Internet: www.cem.va.gov/CEM/cems/nchp/mobile.asp
Director **Craig Lachance** .... (850) 453-4846

Alaska

Fort Richardson National Cemetery
Building 58-512, Davis Highway,
Joint Base Elmendorf-Richardson, AK 99505
Mail: P.O. Box 5-498, Joint Base Elmendorf-Richardson, AK 99505
Tel: (907) 384-7075 Fax: (907) 384-7111
Internet: www.cem.va.gov/cems/nchp/ftrichardson.asp
Cemetery Administrator **Virginia M. Walker** .... (907) 384-7075

Sitka National Cemetery
Sawmill Creek Road, Sitka, AK 99835
Mail: P.O. Box 5-498, Joint Base Elmendorf-Richardson, AK 99505
Tel: (907) 384-7075 Fax: (907) 384-7111
Internet: www.cem.va.gov/cems/nchp/sitka.asp
Cemetery Administrator **Virginia M. Walker** .... (907) 384-7075

Arizona

National Memorial Cemetery of Arizona
23029 North Cave Creek Road, Phoenix, AZ 85024
Tel: (602) 505-8532 Fax: (480) 513-1412
Internet: www.cem.va.gov/CEM/cems/nchp/nmca.asp
Director **Jerry Rainey** .... (480) 513-3600

★ Presidential Appointment Requiring Senate Confirmation ☆ Presidential Appointment ☐ Schedule C Appointment ◇ Career Senior Foreign Service Appointment
● Career Senior Executive Service (SES) Appointment ○ Non-Career Senior Executive Service (SES) Appointment ■ Postal Career Executive Service

Prescott National Cemetery
500 Highway 89 North, Prescott, AZ 86301
Tel: (480) 513-3600 Fax: (480) 513-1412
Internet: www.cem.va.gov/CEM/cems/nchp/prescott.asp
Director **Jerry Rainey** .... (480) 513-3600

Arkansas

Fort Smith National Cemetery
522 Garland Avenue and South Sixth Street, Fort Smith, AR 72901
Tel: (479) 783-5345 Fax: (479) 785-4189
Internet: www.cem.va.gov/CEM/cems/nchp/ftsmith.asp
Director **Gerald Lyons** .... (479) 783-5345

Little Rock National Cemetery
2523 Confederate Boulevard, Little Rock, AR 72206
Tel: (501) 324-6401 Fax: (501) 324-7182
Internet: www.cem.va.gov/cems/nchp/littlerock.asp
Director **Gerald Lyons** .... (479) 783-5345

California

Fort Rosecrans National Cemetery
P.O. Box 6237, San Diego, CA 92166
Tel: (619) 553-2084 Fax: (619) 553-6593
Internet: www.cem.va.gov/CEM/cems/nchp/ftrosecrans.asp
Director **Rex Kern** .... (619) 553-2084

Golden Gate National Cemetery
1300 Sneath Lane, San Bruno, CA 94066
Tel: (650) 589-7737 Fax: (650) 873-6578
Internet: www.cem.va.gov/CEM/cems/nchp/goldengate.asp
Director **Kathleen McCall** .... (650) 589-7737

Los Angeles National Cemetery
950 South Sepulveda Boulevard, Los Angeles, CA 90049
Tel: (310) 268-4494 Fax: (310) 268-3257
Director **Thomas Ruck** .... (310) 268-4494
E-mail: thomas.ruck@va.gov

Riverside National Cemetery
22495 Van Buren Boulevard, Riverside, CA 92518
Tel: (951) 653-8417 Fax: (951) 653-5233
Internet: www.cem.va.gov/cems/nchp/riverside.asp
Director **Peter Young** .... (951) 653-8417
Assistant Director **(Vacant)** .... (951) 653-8417

San Francisco National Cemetery
c/o Golden Gate National Cemetery, 1300 Sneath Lane, San Bruno, CA 94066
Tel: (650) 589-7737 Fax: (650) 873-6578
Internet: www.cem.va.gov/CEM/cems/nchp/sanfrancisco.asp
Director **Kathleen McCall** .... (650) 589-7737

San Joaquin Valley National Cemetery
32053 West McCabe Road, Santa Nella, CA 95322
Tel: (209) 854-1040 Fax: (209) 854-3944
Director **Margaret Agnes** .... (209) 854-1040 ext. 107

Colorado

Fort Logan National Cemetery
4400 West Kenyon Avenue, Denver, CO 80236
Tel: (303) 761-0117 Fax: (303) 781-9378
Internet: www.cem.va.gov/cems/nchp/ftlogan.asp
Director **Mat S. Williams** .... (303) 761-0117

Fort Lyon National Cemetery
15700 Country Road HH, Building 401, Las Animas, CO 81054
Tel: (303) 761-0117 Fax: (303) 781-9378
Internet: www.cem.va.gov/cems/nchp/ftlyon.asp
Director **Mat S. Williams** .... (303) 761-0117

Florida

Barrancas National Cemetery
80 Hovey Road, Pensacola, FL 32508
Tel: (850) 453-4846 Fax: (850) 453-4635
Internet: www.cem.va.gov/CEM/cems/nchp/barrancas.asp
Director **Craig Lachance** .... (850) 453-4846

Cape Canaveral National Cemetery
5525 U.S. Highway 1, Mims, FL 32754
Tel: (321) 383-2638
Director **Don Murphy** .... (321) 383-2638

Florida National Cemetery
6502 SW 102nd Avenue, Bushnell, FL 33513
Tel: (352) 793-7740 Fax: (352) 793-9560
Internet: www.cem.va.gov/cems/nchp/florida.asp
Director **Kurt W. Rotar** .... (352) 793-7740

Bay Pines National Cemetery
P.O. Box 477, Bay Pines, FL 33744
Tel: (727) 319-6479 Fax: (727) 398-9520
Internet: www.cem.va.gov/cems/nchp/baypines.asp
Director **Kurt W. Rotar** .... (352) 793-7740

Jacksonville National Cemetery
4083 Lannie Road, Jacksonville, FL 32218-1247
Tel: (904) 766-5222 Fax: (904) 766-5980
Director **Alphaeus L. Richburg** .... (904) 766-5975
Education: Central Texas Col 1995 AA; Southern Illinois 2000 BS

Saint Augustine National Cemetery
104 Marine Street, St. Augustine, FL 32084
Mail: 6502 SW 102nd Avenue, Bushnell, FL 33513
Tel: (904) 766-5222 Fax: (904) 766-5980
Internet: www.cem.va.gov/cems/nchp/staugustine.asp
Director **Alphaeus L. Richburg** .... (904) 766-5222
Education: Central Texas Col 1995 AA; Southern Illinois 2000 BS

Tallahassee National Cemetery
5015 Apalachee Parkway, Tallahassee, FL 32311
Tel: (850) 402-8941 Fax: (850) 402-4099
Director **Raymond Miller** .... (850) 402-8941

Georgia

Georgia National Cemetery
2025 Mount Carmel Church Lane, Canton, GA 30114
Tel: (866) 236-8159 Tel: (770) 479-9300 Fax: (770) 479-9311
Internet: www.cem.va.gov/CEM/cems/nchp/georgia.asp
Director **Margaret Helgerson** .... (866) 236-8159

Marietta National Cemetery
500 Washington Avenue, Marietta, GA 30060
Tel: (770) 428-5631 Fax: (770) 479-9311
Internet: www.cem.va.gov/CEM/cems/nchp/marietta.asp
Cemetery Administrator **Margaret Helgerson** .... (770) 428-5631

Hawaii

National Memorial Cemetery of the Pacific
2177 Puowaina Drive, Honolulu, HI 96813-1729
Tel: (808) 532-3720 Fax: (808) 532-3756
Internet: www.cem.va.gov/CEM/cems/nchp/nmcp.asp
Director **James Horton** .... (808) 532-3720

★ Presidential Appointment Requiring Senate Confirmation ☆ Presidential Appointment ☐ Schedule C Appointment ◇ Career Senior Foreign Service Appointment
● Career Senior Executive Service (SES) Appointment ○ Non-Career Senior Executive Service (SES) Appointment ■ Postal Career Executive Service

Illinois

Abraham Lincoln National Cemetery
20953 West Hoff Road, Elwood, IL 60421
Tel: (815) 423-9958 Fax: (815) 423-5824
Internet: www.cem.va.gov/cems/nchp/abrahamlincoln.asp

Director **Quincy Whitehead** . . . . (815) 423-9958
Administrative Officer **Matthew Ulrich** . . . . (815) 423-9958

Alton National Cemetery
600 Pearl Street, Alton, IL 62003
Mail: Jefferson Barracks National Cemetery, 2900 Sheridan Rd., St. Louis, MO 63125
Tel: (314) 845-8320 Fax: (314) 845-8355
Internet: www.cem.va.gov/cems/nchp/alton.asp

Director **Jeffrey S. Barnes** . . . . (314) 845-8320

Camp Butler National Cemetery
5063 Camp Butler Road, Springfield, IL 62707-9722
Tel: (217) 492-4070 Fax: (217) 492-4072
Internet: www.cem.va.gov/CEM/cems/nchp/campbutler.asp

Director **Kevin Miller** . . . . (217) 492-4070
Program Support Assistant **(Vacant)** . . . . (217) 492-4070

Danville (IL) National Cemetery
1900 East Main Street, Danville, IL 61832
Tel: (217) 554-4550 Fax: (217) 554-4803
Internet: www.cem.va.gov/CEM/cems/nchp/danvilleil.asp

Director **Quincy Whitehead** . . . . (217) 554-4550
Supervisor **(Vacant)** . . . . (217) 554-4550

Mound City National Cemetery
Jefferson Barracks National Cemetery, 2900 Sheridan Rd., St. Louis, MO 63125
141 State Highway 37, Mound City, IL 62963
Tel: (618) 748-9107 Fax: (314) 845-8355
Internet: www.cem.va.gov/CEM/cems/nchp/moundcity.asp

Director **Jeffrey S. Barnes** . . . . (314) 845-8320

Rock Island National Cemetery
Building 118, Rock Island Arsenal, Rock Island, IL 61299
Tel: (309) 782-2094 Fax: (309) 782-2097
Internet: www.cem.va.gov/CEM/cems/nchp/rockisland.asp

Director **Sue Nan Jehlen** . . . . (309) 782-2094
E-mail: suenan.jehlen@va.gov

Quincy National Cemetery
36th and Maine Streets, Quincy, IL 62301
Mail: Building 118, Rock Island Arsenal, Rock Island, IL 61299
Tel: (309) 782-2094 Fax: (309) 782-2097
Internet: www.cem.va.gov/CEM/cems/nchp/quincy.asp

Director **Sue Nan Jehlen** . . . . (309) 782-2094
E-mail: suenan.jehlen@va.gov

Indiana

Crown Hill National Cemetery
700 West 38th Street, Indianapolis, IN 46208
Mail: 1700 East 38th Street, Marion, IN 46953
Tel: (765) 674-0284 Fax: (765) 674-4521
Internet: www.cem.va.gov/CEM/cems/nchp/crownhill.asp

Director (Acting) **Thomas Kulich** . . . . (765) 674-0284

Marion National Cemetery
1700 East 38th Street, Marion, IN 46953
Tel: (765) 674-0284 Fax: (765) 674-4521
Internet: www.cem.va.gov/CEM/cems/nchp/marion.asp

Director **Douglas Ledbetter** . . . . (765) 674-0284

New Albany National Cemetery
1943 Ekin Avenue, New Albany, IN 47150
Tel: (812) 948-5234 Fax: (502) 893-6612
Internet: www.cem.va.gov/cems/nchp/newalbany.asp

Director **Michael Niklarz** . . . . (859) 885-5727

Iowa

Keokuk National Cemetery
1701 J Street, Keokuk, IA 52632
Mail: Building 118, Rock Island Arsenal, Rock Island, IL 61299
Tel: (309) 782-2094 Fax: (309) 782-2097
Internet: www.cem.va.gov/CEM/cems/nchp/keokuk.asp

Director **Sue Nan Jehlen** . . . . (309) 782-2094
E-mail: suenan.jehlen@va.gov

Kansas

Ft. Leavenworth National Cemetery
395 Biddle Boulevard, Fort Leavenworth, KS 66027
Mail: P.O. Box 1694, Leavenworth, KS 66048
Tel: (913) 727-1376 Tel: (913) 758-4106 Fax: (913) 758-4136
Internet: http://www.cem.va.gov/cems/nchp/ftleavenworth.asp

Director **Peter "Pete" Sardo** . . . . (913) 946-1540

Fort Scott National Cemetery
900 East National Avenue, Fort Scott, KS 66701
Tel: (620) 223-2840 Fax: (620) 223-2505
Internet: http://www.cem.va.gov/cems/nchp/ftscott.asp

Director **Peter "Pete" Sardo** . . . . (913) 758-1540
P.O. Box 1694, Leavenworth, KS 66048

Leavenworth National Cemetery
150 Muncie Road, Leavenworth, KS 66048
Tel: (913) 758-4105 Tel: (913) 758-4106 Fax: (913) 758-4136
Internet: http://www.cem.va.gov/cems/nchp/leavenworth.asp

Director **Peter "Pete" Sardo** . . . . (913) 946-1540

Kentucky

Camp Nelson National Cemetery
6980 Danville Road, Nicholasville, KY 40356
Tel: (859) 885-5727 Fax: (859) 887-4860
Internet: www.cem.va.gov/CEM/cems/nchp/campnelson.asp

Director **Michael Niklarz** . . . . (859) 885-5727
Program Assistant **Katie Caudill** . . . . (859) 885-5727
E-mail: katie.caudill@va.gov

Cave Hill National Cemetery
701 Baxter Avenue, Louisville, KY 40204
Tel: (502) 893-3852 Fax: (502) 893-6612
Internet: www.cem.va.gov/cems/nchp/cavehill.asp

Director **Michael Niklarz** . . . . (859) 885-5727

Danville (KY) National Cemetery
277 North First Street, Danville, KY 40442
Camp Nelson National Cemetery, 6980 Danville Road, Nicholasville, KY 40356
Tel: (859) 885-5727 Fax: (859) 887-4860
Internet: www.cem.va.gov/nchp/danvilleky.htm

Director **Michael Niklarz** . . . . (859) 885-5727
Program Assistant **Katie Caudill** . . . . (859) 885-5727
E-mail: katie.caudill@va.gov

Lebanon National Cemetery
20 Highway 208, Lebanon, KY 40033
Tel: (270) 692-3390 Fax: (270) 692-0018
Internet: www.cem.va.gov/cems/nchp/lebanon.asp

Director **Michael Niklarz** . . . . (859) 885-5727

Lexington National Cemetery
833 West Main Street, Lexington, KY 40508
Camp Nelson National Cemetery, 6980 Danville Road, Nicholasville, KY 40356
Tel: (859) 885-5727 Fax: (859) 887-4860
Internet: www.cem.va.gov/CEM/cems/nchp/lexington.asp

Director **Michael Niklarz** .... (859) 885-5727
Program Assistant **Katie Caudill** .... (859) 885-5727
E-mail: katie.caudill@va.gov

Mill Springs National Cemetery
Nancy, KY 42544
Camp Nelson National Cemetery, 6980 Danville Road, Nicholasville, KY 40356
Tel: (859) 885-5727 Fax: (859) 887-4860
Internet: www.cem.va.gov/CEM/cems/nchp/millsprings.asp

Director **Michael Niklarz** .... (859) 885-5727
Program Assistant **Katie Caudill** .... (859) 885-5727
E-mail: katie.caudill@va.gov

Zachary Taylor National Cemetery
4701 Brownsboro Road, Louisville, KY 40207
Tel: (502) 893-3852 Fax: (502) 893-6612
Internet: www.cem.va.gov/cems/nchp/zacharytaylor.asp

Director **Michael Niklarz** .... (859) 885-5727

Louisiana

Alexandria National Cemetery
209 East Shamrock Street, Pineville, LA 71360
Tel: (318) 449-1793
Internet: www.cem.va.gov/CEM/cems/nchp/alexandriava.asp

Director **Maurice A. Roan, Sr.** .... (225) 654-1988

Baton Rouge National Cemetery
220 North 19th Street, Baton Rouge, LA 70806
Tel: (225) 654-3767 Fax: (225) 654-3728
Internet: www.cem.va.gov/CEM/cems/nchp/batonrouge.asp

Director **Maurice A. Roan, Sr.** .... (225) 654-3767
20978 Port Hickey Road, Zachary, LA 70791

Port Hudson National Cemetery
20978 Port Hickey Road, Zachary, LA 70791
Fax: (225) 654-1989
Internet: www.cem.va.gov/CEM/cems/nchp/porthudson.asp

Director **Maurice A. Roan, Sr.** .... (225) 654-1988

Maine

Togus National Cemetery
VA Medical and Regional Office Center, Togus, ME 04330
Massachusetts National Cemetery, Bourne, MA 02532
Tel: (508) 563-7113 (Information via Massachusetts National Cemetery)
Internet: www.cem.va.gov/CEM/cems/nchp/togus.asp

Director **Richard Wallace** .... (508) 563-7113
Massachusetts National Cemetery, Bourne, MA 02532 Fax: (508) 564-9946
Education: Park U 2006 BS; American Military U 2012 MA

Maryland

Baltimore National Cemetery
5501 Frederick Avenue, Baltimore, MD 21228
Tel: (410) 644-9696 Fax: (410) 644-1563
Internet: www.cem.va.gov/cems/nchp/baltimore.asp

Director **Michael Brophy** .... (410) 644-9696 ext. 4001
Program Assistant **Donna Drones** .... (410) 644-9696 ext. 4002

Annapolis National Cemetery
800 West Street, Annapolis, MD 21401
Tel: (410) 644-9696 Fax: (410) 644-1563
Internet: www.cem.va.gov/cems/nchp/annapolis.asp

Director **Michael Brophy** .... (410) 644-9696
c/o Baltimore National Cemetery, 5501 Frederick Avenue, Baltimore, MD 21228
E-mail: michael.brophy@va.gov

Congressional Cemetery
1801 E Street, SE, Washington, DC 20003
Internet: www.cem.va.gov/cems/lots/congressional.asp

Director **Michael Brophy** .... (410) 644-9696

Loudon Park National Cemetery
3443 Frederick Avenue, Baltimore, MD 21228
Tel: (410) 644-9696 Fax: (410) 644-1563
Internet: www.cem.va.gov/cems/nchp/loudonpark.asp

Director **Michael Brophy** .... (410) 644-9696
c/o Baltimore National Cemetery, 5501 Frederick Avenue, Baltimore, MD 21228

Point Lookout Confederate Cemetery
Point Lookout State Park, P.O. Box 48, Scotland, MD 20687
Tel: (410) 644-9696 Fax: (410) 644-1563
Internet: www.cem.va.gov/cems/lots/point_lookout.asp

Director **Michael Brophy** .... (410) 644-9696
5501 Frederick Avenue, Baltimore, MD 21228
E-mail: michael.brophy@va.gov

Massachusetts

Massachusetts National Cemetery
Bourne, MA 02532
Tel: (508) 563-7113 Fax: (508) 564-9946
Internet: www.cem.va.gov/CEM/cems/nchp/massachuetts.asp

Director **Richard Wallace** .... (508) 563-7113
Education: Park U 2006 BS; American Military U 2012 MA

Michigan

Fort Custer National Cemetery
15501 Dickman Road, Augusta, MI 49012
Tel: (269) 731-4164 Fax: (269) 731-2428
Internet: www.cem.va.gov/CEMs/nchp/ftcuster.asp

Director **Lance Steven Pridemore** .... (269) 731-4164

Minnesota

Fort Snelling National Cemetery
7601 - 34th Avenue South, Minneapolis, MN 55450-1199
Tel: (612) 726-1127 Fax: (612) 725-2059 Fax: (612) 726-9119
Internet: www.cem.va.gov/CEM/cems/nchp/ftsnelling.asp

Director **John Knapp** .... (612) 726-1127
Assistant Director **Donn Christy** .... (612) 762-1127
Budget Analyst **Michael "Mike" Mulvihill** .... (612) 726-1127
Program Support Assistant **Alda Munoz** .... (612) 467-4619
E-mail: alda.munoz@va.gov

Mississippi

Biloxi National Cemetery
400 Veterans Avenue, Biloxi, MS 39531
P.O. Box 4968, Biloxi, MS 39535
Tel: (228) 388-6668 Fax: (228) 594-1021
Internet: www.cem.va.gov/CEM/cems/nchp/biloxi.asp

Director **Graham Wright III** .... (228) 388-6668

★ Presidential Appointment Requiring Senate Confirmation ☆ Presidential Appointment ☐ Schedule C Appointment ◇ Career Senior Foreign Service Appointment
● Career Senior Executive Service (SES) Appointment ○ Non-Career Senior Executive Service (SES) Appointment ■ Postal Career Executive Service

Corinth National Cemetery
1551 Horton Street, Corinth, MS 38834
Memphis National Cemetery, 3568 Townes Avenue, Memphis, TN 38122
Tel: (901) 386-8311 Fax: (901) 382-0750
Internet: www.cem.va.gov/CEM/cems/nchp/corinth.asp
Director **Amanda Rhodes-Wharton** .... (901) 386-8311 ext. 221

Natchez National Cemetery
41 Cemetery Road, Natchez, MS 39120
Tel: (601) 445-4981 Fax: (601) 445-8815
Internet: www.cem.va.gov/cems/nchp/natchez.asp
Director **Maurice A. Roan, Sr.** .... (601) 445-4981
Associate Director **Skip Solomon** .... (225) 654-1988
Tel: (601) 445-4981

Missouri

Jefferson Barracks National Cemetery
2900 Sheridan Road, St. Louis, MO 63125
Tel: (314) 845-8320 Fax: (314) 845-8355
Internet: www.cem.va.gov/CEM/cems/nchp/jeffersonbarracks.asp
Director **Jeffrey S. Barnes** .... (314) 845-8320

Jefferson City (MO) National Cemetery
1024 East McCarty Street, Jefferson City, MO 65101
Jefferson Barracks National Cemetery, 2900 Sheridan Road, St. Louis, MO 63125
Tel: (314) 845-8320 Fax: (314) 845-8355
Internet: www.cem.va.gov/CEM/cems/nchp/jeffersoncity.asp
Director **Jeffrey S. Barnes** .... (314) 845-8320 ext. 4101

Springfield National Cemetery
1702 East Seminole Street, Springfield, MO 65804
Tel: (417) 881-9499 Fax: (417) 881-7862
Internet: www.cem.va.gov/CEM/cems/nchp/springfield.asp
Director **Gary Edmondson** .... (417) 881-9499
E-mail: gary.edmondson@va.gov

Montana

Yellowstone National Cemetery
55 Buffalo Trail Road, Laurel, MT 59044
Tel: (406) 647-2746
Director **Adrian Benton** .... (406) 647-2746

Nebraska

Fort McPherson National Cemetery
12004 South Spur 56A, Maxwell, NE 69151-1031
Tel: (308) 582-4433 Tel: (888) 737-2800 Fax: (308) 582-4616
Internet: www.cem.va.gov/cems/nchp/ftmcpherson.asp
Director **Cindy M. Van Bibber** .... (308) 582-4433

Omaha National Cemetery
14250 Schram Road, Omaha, NE 69138
Tel: (402) 253-3949
Director **Cindy M. Van Bibber** .... (402) 253-3949

New Jersey

Beverly National Cemetery
916 Bridgeboro Road, Beverly, NJ 08010
Tel: (215) 504-5610 Fax: (215) 504-5611
Internet: www.cem.va.gov/cems/nchp/beverly.asp
Director **Gregory Whitney** .... (215) 504-5610
Program Support Clerk/Cemetery Representative
Michael Sasse .... (215) 504-5610

Finn's Point National Cemetery
456 Ft. Mott Road, Pennsville, NJ 08070
Mail: 916 Bridgeboro Road, Beverly, NJ 08010
Tel: (215) 504-5610 Fax: (215) 504-5611
Internet: www.cem.va.gov/cems/nchp/finnspoint.asp
Director **Gregory Whitney** .... (215) 504-5610

New Mexico

Fort Bayard National Cemetery
P.O. Box 189, Fort Bayard, NM 88036
Tel: (915) 564-0201 Fax: (915) 564-3746
Internet: www.cem.va.gov/cems/nchp/ftbayard.asp
Director **James P. Sanders** .... (915) 564-0201

Santa Fe National Cemetery
501 North Guadalupe Street, Santa Fe, NM 87501
Tel: (505) 988-6400 Fax: (505) 988-6497
Internet: www.cem.va.gov/CEM/cems/nchp/santafe.asp
Director **Jared Howard** .... (505) 988-6400 ext. 105

New York

Bath National Cemetery
San Juan Avenue, Bath, NY 14810
Tel: (607) 664-4853 Fax: (607) 664-4761
Internet: www.cem.va.gov/CEM/cems/nchp/bath.asp
Director **Duane Mendenhall** .... (607) 664-4806

Calverton National Cemetery
210 Princeton Boulevard, Calverton, NY 11933-1031
Tel: (631) 727-5410 Fax: (631) 369-4397
Internet: www.cem.va.gov/CEM/cems/nchp/calverton.asp
Director **Michael G. Picerno** .... (631) 727-5410 ext. 1131
Assistant Director **Steve Callagy** .... (631) 727-5410 ext. 1129

Cypress Hills National Cemetery
625 Jamaica Avenue, Brooklyn, NY 11208
Mail: Long Island National Cemetery, 2040 Wellwood Avenue, Farmingdale, NY 11735
Tel: (631) 454-4949 Fax: (631) 694-5422
Internet: www.cem.va.gov/cem/cems/nchp/cypresshills.asp
Director **Roderick Thomas** .... (631) 454-4949 ext. 2118
Assistant Director **Craig Arsell** .... (631) 454-4949
E-mail: craig.arsell@va.gov

Gerald B. H. Solomon Saratoga National Cemetery
200 Duell Road, Schuylerville, NY 12871-1721
Tel: (518) 581-9128 Fax: (518) 583-6975
Internet: www.cem.va.gov/CEM/cems/nchp/geraldbhsolomonsaratoga.asp
Director **William Scott Lamb** .... (518) 581-9128 ext. 207
Maintenance and Operations Foreman
Willard "Bill" Nelson .... (518) 583-3482 ext. 210
Program Analyst **Joseph Gilheany** .... (518) 581-9128 ext. 203

Long Island National Cemetery
2040 Wellwood Avenue, Farmingdale, NY 11735
Tel: (631) 454-4949 Fax: (631) 694-5422
Internet: www.cem.va.gov/cem/cems/listcem.asp
Director **Roderick Thomas** .... (631) 454-4949 ext. 2118
Assistant Director **Craig Arsell** .... (631) 454-4949
E-mail: craig.arsell@va.gov

Woodlawn National Cemetery
1825 Davis Street, Elmira, NY 14901
Tel: (607) 732-5411 Fax: (607) 732-1769
Internet: www.cem.va.gov/CEM/cems/nchp/woodlawn.asp
Director **Duane Mendenhall** .... (607) 664-4806

★ Presidential Appointment Requiring Senate Confirmation ☆ Presidential Appointment ☐ Schedule C Appointment ◇ Career Senior Foreign Service Appointment
● Career Senior Executive Service (SES) Appointment ○ Non-Career Senior Executive Service (SES) Appointment ■ Postal Career Executive Service

North Carolina

New Bern National Cemetery
1711 National Avenue, New Bern, NC 28560
Tel: (252) 637-2912 Fax: (252) 637-7145
Internet: www.cem.va.gov/CEM/cems/nchp/newbern.asp

Director (Acting) **O'Neal Cunningham** . . . . (704) 636-2661
501 Statesville Boulevard, Salisbury, NC 28144

Raleigh National Cemetery
501 Rock Quarry Road, Raleigh, NC 27610
Tel: (252) 637-2912 Fax: (252) 637-7145
Internet: www.cem.va.gov/CEM/cems/nchp/raleigh.asp

Director (Acting) **O'Neal Cunningham** . . . . (704) 636-2661
501 Statesville Boulevard, Salisbury, NC 28144

Salisbury National Cemetery
501 Statesville Boulevard, Salisbury, NC 28144
Tel: (704) 636-2661 Fax: (704) 636-1115
Internet: www.cem.va.gov/CEM/cems/nchp/salisbury.asp

Director (Acting) **O'Neal Cunningham** . . . . (704) 636-2661

Wilmington National Cemetery
2011 Market Street, Wilmington, NC 28403
Tel: (252) 637-2912 Fax: (252) 637-7145
Internet: www.cem.va.gov/CEM/cems/nchp/wilmington.asp

Director (Acting) **O'Neal Cunningham** . . . . (704) 636-2661
501 Statesville Boulevard, Salisbury, NC 28144

Ohio

Dayton National Cemetery
4400 West Third Street, Dayton, OH 45428
Tel: (937) 268-2221 Fax: (937) 268-2225
Internet: www.cem.va.gov/CEM/cems/nchp/dayton.asp

Director **Douglas Ledbetter** . . . . (937) 268-2221
Administrative Assistant to the Director
Daniel Barford . . . . (937) 268-2221 ext. 2001

Ohio Western Reserve National Cemetery
10175 Rawiga Road, Rittman, OH 44270-0008
P.O. Box 8, Rittman, OH 44270-0008
Tel: (330) 335-3069 Fax: (330) 335-5087
Internet: www.cem.va.gov/cems/nchp/ohiowesternreserve.asp

Director **Mark Polen** . . . . (330) 335-3069

Oklahoma

Fort Gibson National Cemetery
1423 Cemetery Road, Fort Gibson, OK 74434
Tel: (918) 478-2334 Tel: (918) 478-9825 Fax: (918) 478-2661
Internet: www.cem.va.gov/CEM/cems/nchp/ftgibson.asp

Director **William Rhoades** . . . . (918) 478-2334

Fort Sill National Cemetery
2648 NE Jake Dunn Road, Elgin, OK 73538-9762
Tel: (580) 492-3200 Fax: (580) 492-3208
Internet: www.cem.va.gov/cems/nchp/ftsill.asp

Director **William Rhoades** . . . . (918) 478-2334

Oregon

Eagle Point National Cemetery
2763 Riley Road, Eagle Point, OR 97524
Tel: (541) 826-2511 Fax: (541) 826-2888
Internet: www.cem.va.gov/cems/nchp/eaglepoint.asp

Director **Andrew D. Matthews** . . . . (541) 826-2511
E-mail: andrew.matthews@va.gov

Roseburg National Cemetery
1770 West Harvard Street, Roseburg, OR 97470
Tel: (541) 677-3152 Fax: (541) 677-3044
Internet: www.cem.va.gov/cems/nchp/roseburg.asp

Director **Andrew D. Matthews** . . . . (541) 677-3152
E-mail: andrew.matthews@va.gov

Willamette National Cemetery
11800 SE Mt. Scott Boulevard, Portland, OR 97086-6937
Tel: (503) 273-5250 Fax: (503) 273-5251 Fax: (503) 273-5332
Internet: www.cem.va.gov/cems/nchp/willamette.asp

Director **George A. Allen** . . . . (503) 273-5250

Pennsylvania

Indiantown Gap National Cemetery
Indiantown Gap Road, R.R. 2, Box 484, Annville, PA 17003-9618
Tel: (717) 865-5254 Fax: (717) 865-5256
Internet: www.cem.va.gov/CEM/cems/nchp/indiantowngap.asp

Director **James R. Metcalfe II** . . . . (717) 865-5254

Philadelphia National Cemetery
Haines Street and Limekiln Pike, Philadelphia, PA 19138
Tel: (215) 504-5610 Fax: (215) 504-5611
Internet: www.cem.va.gov/cems/nchp/philadelphia.asp

Director **Gregory Whitney** . . . . (215) 504-5610

Washington Crossing National Cemetery
830 Highland Road, Newtown, PA 18940

Director **Gregory Whitney** . . . . (215) 504-5610

Puerto Rico

Puerto Rico National Cemetery
National Cemetery Avenue, #50, Bayamon, PR 00961-3887
Tel: (787) 798-8400 Tel: (787) 798-8413 Fax: (787) 785-7281
Internet: www.cem.va.gov/cems/nchp/puertorico.asp

Director **Juan D. Nieves** . . . . (787) 798-8413

South Carolina

Beaufort National Cemetery
1601 Boundary Street, Beaufort, SC 29902-3947
Tel: (843) 524-3925 Fax: (843) 524-8538
Internet: www.cem.va.gov/CEM/cems/nchp/beaufort.asp

● Director **Sonny R. Peppers** . . . . (843) 524-3925 ext. 105

Florence National Cemetery
803 East National Cemetery Road, Florence, SC 29506
Tel: (843) 669-8783 Fax: (843) 662-8318
Internet: www.cem.va.gov/CEM/cems/nchp/florence.asp

Director **Carolyn Howard** . . . . (843) 669-8783

Fort Jackson National Cemetery
4170 Percival Road, Columbia, SC 29229
Tel: (803) 699-2246 Tel: (866) 577-5248 (Toll-free) Fax: (803) 699-3086

Director **Gene Linxwiler** . . . . (803) 699-2246

South Dakota

Black Hills National Cemetery
20901 Pleasant Valley Drive, Sturgis, SD 57785-0640
Tel: (605) 347-3830 Tel: (800) 743-1070 ext. 7299 Fax: (605) 720-7298
Internet: www.cem.va.gov/CEM/cems/nchp/blackhills.asp

Director **Adrian Benton** . . . . (605) 347-3830
E-mail: adrian.benton@va.gov

★ Presidential Appointment Requiring Senate Confirmation ☆ Presidential Appointment □ Schedule C Appointment ◇ Career Senior Foreign Service Appointment
● Career Senior Executive Service (SES) Appointment ○ Non-Career Senior Executive Service (SES) Appointment ■ Postal Career Executive Service

Fort Meade National Cemetery
Old Stone Road, Sturgis, SD 57785
Tel: (605) 347-3830 Fax: (605) 720-7298
Internet: www.cem.va.gov/CEM/cems/nchp/ftmeade.asp

Director **Adrian Benton** . . . . (605) 347-3830
c/o Black Hills National Cemetery, 20901 Pleasant Valley Drive, Sturgis, SD 57785-0640

Hot Springs National Cemetery
500 North Fifth Street, Hot Springs, SD 57747
Tel: (605) 347-3830 Fax: (605) 720-7298
Internet: www.cem.va.gov/CEM/cems/nchp/hotsprings.asp

Director **Adrian Benton** . . . . (605) 347-3830
c/o Black Hills National Cemetery, 20901 Pleasant Valley Drive, Sturgis, SD 57785-0640

Tennessee

Chattanooga National Cemetery
1200 Bailey Avenue, Chattanooga, TN 37404
Tel: (423) 855-6590 Fax: (423) 855-6597

Cemetery Director **Charles Rudy Arnold** . . . . . . (423) 855-6590 ext. 5801

Knoxville National Cemetery
939 Tyson Street, NW, Knoxville, TN 37917
Chattanooga National Cemetery, 1200 Bailey Avenue, Chattanooga, TN 37404
Tel: (423) 855-6590 Fax: (423) 855-6597

Director **Charles Rudy Arnold** . . . . . . (423) 855-6590 ext. 5801

Memphis National Cemetery
3568 Townes Avenue, Memphis, TN 38122
Tel: (901) 386-8311 Fax: (901) 382-0750
Internet: www.cem.va.gov/cems/nchp/memphis.asp

Director **Amanda Rhodes-Wharton** . . . . . . (901) 386-8311 ext. 221

Mountain Home National Cemetery
Mountain Home, TN 37684
P.O. Box 8, Mountain Home, TN 37684
Tel: (423) 979-3535 Fax: (423) 979-3521
Internet: www.cem.va.gov/CEM/cems/nchp/mountainhome.asp

Director **Jeny Walker** . . . . (423) 979-3535

Nashville National Cemetery
1420 Gallatin Road, South, Madison, TN 37115-4619
Tel: (615) 860-0086 Tel: (615) 860-0230 Fax: (615) 860-8691
Internet: www.cem.va.gov/CEM/cems/nchp/nashville.asp

Director **Charles Rudy Arnold** . . . . . . (423) 855-6590 ext. 5801

Texas

Dallas-Fort Worth National Cemetery
2000 Mountain Creek Parkway, Dallas, TX 75211
Tel: (214) 467-3374 Fax: (214) 467-3316
Internet: www.cem.va.gov/cems/nchp/dallasftworth.asp

Director **Larry Williams** . . . . . . (214) 467-3374 ext. 205

Fort Bliss (TX) National Cemetery
P.O. Box 6342, Fort Bliss, TX 79906
Tel: (915) 564-0201 Fax: (915) 564-3746
Internet: www.cem.va.gov/CEM/cems/nchp/ftbliss.asp

Director **James Porter** . . . . (915) 564-0201

Fort Sam Houston National Cemetery
1520 Harry Wurzbach Road, San Antonio, TX 78209
Tel: (210) 820-3891 Fax: (210) 820-3445
Internet: www.cem.va.gov/cems/nchp/ftsamhouston.asp

Director **Elfreda "Freda" Robinson** . . . . . . (210) 820-3891
Assistant Director **Aubrey David** . . . . . . (210) 820-3891
Office Manager **Brenda Hoster** . . . . . . (210) 820-3891

Houston National Cemetery
10410 Veterans Memorial Drive, Houston, TX 77038
Tel: (281) 447-8686 Fax: (281) 447-0580
Internet: www.cem.va.gov/CEM/cems/nchp/houston.asp

Director **Mat S. Williams** . . . . (281) 447-8686
Fax: (281) 447-0580

Virginia

Alexandria National Cemetery
1450 Wilkes Street, Alexandria, VA 22314
Mail: Quantico National Cemetery, P.O. Box 10, Triangle, VA 22172
Tel: (703) 221-2183 Fax: (703) 221-2185
Internet: www.cem.va.gov/cems/nchp/alexandriava.asp

Director **James P. Sanders** . . . . . . (703) 221-2183 ext. 100

Balls Bluff National Cemetery
Route 7, Leesburg, VA 22075
Culpeper National Cemetery, 305 U.S. Avenue, Culpeper, VA 22701-4619
Tel: (703) 221-2183 Fax: (540) 825-6684
Internet: www.cem.va.gov/CEM/cems/nchp/ballsbluff.asp

Director **Matthew Priest** . . . . . . (703) 221-2183 ext. 100

City Point National Cemetery
Tenth Avenue and Davis Street, Hopewell, VA 23860
Mail: Fort Harrison National Cemetery, 8620 Varina Road, Richmond, VA 23231
Tel: (804) 795-2031 Tel: (804) 795-2278 Fax: (804) 795-1064
Internet: www.cem.va.gov/CEM/cems/nchp/citypoint.asp

Cemetery Administrator **Janice Hill** . . . . . . (757) 723-7104

Cold Harbor National Cemetery
6038 Cold Harbor Road, Mechanicsville, VA 23111
Tel: (804) 795-2031 Tel: (804) 795-2278 Fax: (804) 795-1064
Internet: www.cem.va.gov/CEM/cems/nchp/coldharbor.asp

Cemetery Administrator **Janice Hill** . . . . . . (757) 723-7104

Culpeper National Cemetery
305 U.S. Avenue, Culpeper, VA 22701-4619
Tel: (540) 825-0027 Fax: (540) 825-6684
Internet: www.cem.va.gov/cems/nchp/culpeper.asp

Cemetery Administrator **Matthew Priest** . . . . . . (703) 221-2183

Danville (VA) National Cemetery
721 Lee Street, Danville, VA 24541
Mail: 501 Statesville Boulevard, Salisbury, NC 28144
Tel: (704) 636-2661 Fax: (704) 636-1115
Internet: www.cem.va.gov/nchp/danvilleva.htm

Director **(Vacant)** . . . . (704) 636-2661

Fort Harrison National Cemetery
8620 Varina Road, Richmond, VA 23231
Tel: (804) 795-2031 Tel: (804) 795-2278 Fax: (804) 795-1064
Internet: www.cem.va.gov/CEM/cems/nchp/ftharrison.asp

Cemetery Administrator **Janice Hill** . . . . . . (757) 723-7104

Glendale National Cemetery
8301 Willis Church Road, Richmond, VA 23231
Tel: (804) 795-2031 Tel: (804) 795-2278 Fax: (804) 795-1064
Internet: www.cem.va.gov/CEM/cems/nchp/glendale.asp

Cemetery Administrator **Janice Hill** . . . . . . (757) 723-7104

Hampton National Cemetery
Cemetery Road at Marshall Avenue, Hampton, VA 23669
Tel: (757) 723-7104 Tel: (757) 728-3131 Fax: (757) 728-3144
Internet: www.cem.va.gov/cems/nchp/hampton.asp

Director **Janice Hill** . . . . (757) 723-7104

DEPARTMENTS

★ Presidential Appointment Requiring Senate Confirmation ☆ Presidential Appointment ☐ Schedule C Appointment ◇ Career Senior Foreign Service Appointment
● Career Senior Executive Service (SES) Appointment ○ Non-Career Senior Executive Service (SES) Appointment ■ Postal Career Executive Service

DEPARTMENTS

Quantico National Cemetery
18424 Joplin Road, Triangle, VA 22172
Mail: P.O. Box 10, Triangle, VA 22172
Tel: (703) 221-2183 Fax: (703) 221-2185
Internet: www.va.gov/CEM/cems/nchp/quantico.asp
Director **James P. Sanders** .... (703) 221-2183 ext. 100

Richmond National Cemetery
1701 Williamsburg Road, Richmond, VA 23231
Tel: (804) 795-2031 Tel: (804) 795-2278 Fax: (804) 795-1064
Internet: www.cem.va.gov/CEM/cems/nchp/richmond.asp
Cemetery Administrator **Janice Hill** .... (757) 723-7104

Seven Pines National Cemetery
400 East Williamsburg Road, Sandston, VA 23150
Tel: (804) 795-2031 Tel: (804) 795-2278 Fax: (804) 795-1064
Internet: www.cem.va.gov/CEM/cems/nchp/sevenpines.asp
Cemetery Administrator **Janice Hill** .... (757) 723-7104

Staunton National Cemetery
901 Richmond Avenue, Staunton, VA 24401
Tel: (540) 825-0027 Fax: (540) 825-6684
Internet: www.cem.va.gov/cems/nchp/staunton.asp
Cemetery Administrator **Matthew Priest** .... (703) 221-2138

Winchester National Cemetery
401 National Avenue, Winchester, VA 22601
Tel: (540) 825-0027 Fax: (540) 825-6684
Internet: www.cem.va.gov/cems/nchp/winchester.asp
Cemetery Administrator **Matthew Priest** .... (703) 221-2183

Washington

Tahoma National Cemetery
18600 SE 240th Street, Kent, WA 98042-4868
Tel: (425) 413-9614 Fax: (425) 413-9618
Internet: www.cem.va.gov/CEM/cems/nchp/tahoma.asp
Director **Thomas Yokes** .... (425) 413-9614 ext. 4110
Budget Analyst **Donnetta Coleman** .... (425) 413-9614 ext. 4100
E-mail: donnetta.coleman@va.gov

West Virginia

Grafton National Cemetery
West Virginia National Cemetery, 1431 Walnut Street, Grafton, WV 26354
Tel: (304) 265-2044 Fax: (304) 265-4336
Internet: www.cem.va.gov/CEM/cems/nchp/grafton.asp
Director **Brian Barnes** .... (304) 265-2044

West Virginia National Cemetery
42 Veterans Memorial Lane, Grafton, WV 26354
Tel: (304) 265-2044 Fax: (304) 265-4336
Internet: www.cem.va.gov/cem/cems/nchp/westvirginia.asp
Director **Brian Barnes** .... (304) 265-2044

Wisconsin

Wood National Cemetery
Building 1301, 5000 West National Avenue, Milwaukee, WI 53295-3000
Tel: (414) 382-5300 Fax: (414) 382-5321
Internet: www.cem.va.gov/cems/nchp/wood.asp
Director **Quincy Whitehead** .... (414) 382-5301
Assistant Director **Don Owens** .... (414) 382-5300

Veterans Benefits Administration (VBA)
811 Vermont Avenue NW, Washington, DC 20420
Mail: 810 Vermont Avenue, NW, Washington, DC 20420
Internet: www.vba.va.gov

OFFICE OF THE UNDER SECRETARY FOR BENEFITS
810 Vermont Avenue, NW, Washington, DC 20420
Fax: (202) 275-3591

Office of Field Operations (OFO)
810 Vermont Avenue, NW, (20F), Washington, DC 20420
Tel: (202) 461-9340 Internet: www.benefits.va.gov/benefits/offices.asp

Continental District
Areas Covered: AR, CO, LA, MS, MT, OK, TX, UT, WY

Denver (CO) Regional Office
155 Van Gordon Street, Lakewood, CO 80228
Mail: P.O. Box 25126, Denver, CO 80225
Tel: (800) 827-1000 E-mail: denver.query@vba.va.gov
Internet: www.benefits.va.gov/denver
Areas Covered: CO, WY
● Regional Office Director **Melanie Renaye Murphy** ...... (303) 914-5800
Education: San Francisco State U BA
Management Analyst **Robert Ryan** .... (303) 914-5800
Assistant Director **Christopher Holly** .... (303) 914-5800
Chief Counsel **Jeffrey Stacey** .... (303) 914-5810
E-mail: jeffrey.stacey@va.gov
Service Center Manager **Katie Claussen** .... (303) 914-5956
Support Services Chief **Dean Tayloe** .... (303) 914-5887
E-mail: dean.tayloe@va.gov
Human Resources Management Liaison **John Zodrow** ... (303) 914-5510
Loan Guaranty Officer **Andrew Post** .... (303) 914-5623
Vocational Rehabilitation and Employment Officer
James Ziruolo .... (303) 914-5550
Information Security Officer **Tom Regen** .... (303) 914-5889

Cheyenne (WY) Regional Medical Center and VBA Satellite Regional Office
2360 East Pershing Boulevard, Cheyenne, WY 82001-5392
Tel: (307) 778-7550 Fax: (307) 778-7336
● Medical Center Director **Paul L. Roberts USA (Ret)** .... (307) 778-7550
District Counsel **Alexander Radich** .... (307) 778-7332
E-mail: alexander.radich@va.gov
Fiscal Services Division Director **Renee Remines** .... (307) 778-7339
Personnel Officer **Kay S. Peterson** .... (307) 778-3740
Business Service Line Chief **Ken Bush** .... (307) 778-7302

Fort Harrison (MT) Regional Office
3687 Veterans Drive, Fort Harrison, MT 59636
P.O. Box 188, Fort Harrison, MT 59636
Tel: (406) 442-6410 Fax: (406) 495-2009
E-mail: ftharrison.query@vba.va.gov
Internet: www.benefits.va.gov/fortharrison
Regional Office Director **(Vacant)** .... (801) 326-2400
550 Foothill Drive, Salt Lake City, UT 84158 Fax: (801) 326-2409
Assistant Director **Michael Crouse** .... (406) 442-6410
District Counsel **(Vacant)** .... (406) 495-2077
Veterans Service Center Manager **Koryn Arnold** .... (406) 495-2024
E-mail: koryn.arnold@vba.va.gov
Fiscal Service Officer **(Vacant)** .... (406) 442-6410 ext. 7729
Vocational Rehabilitation and Counseling Psychologist
(Vacant) .... (406) 495-2010

Houston (TX) Regional Office
6900 Almeda Road, Houston, TX 77030
Tel: (800) 827-1000 Internet: www.benefits.va.gov/Houston
● Regional Office Director **(Vacant)** .... (800) 827-1000

★ Presidential Appointment Requiring Senate Confirmation ☆ Presidential Appointment □ Schedule C Appointment ◇ Career Senior Foreign Service Appointment
● Career Senior Executive Service (SES) Appointment ○ Non-Career Senior Executive Service (SES) Appointment ■ Postal Career Executive Service

Houston (TX) Regional Office *(continued)*

Assistant Director **J. M. Hedge** ....(800) 827-1000
E-mail: james.hedge@va.gov
Assistant Director **Richmond H. "Dick" Laisure** ....(800) 827-1000
Education: Embry-Riddle BS; Troy U MS, Ed.S.
Regional Counsel **Kevin Curtis** ....(800) 827-1000
E-mail: kevin.curtis@va.gov
Loan Guaranty Officer **John Heil** ....(800) 827-1000
Support Services Division Chief **Mikea Morin** ....(800) 827-1000
E-mail: mikea.morin@va.gov
Veterans Service Center Manager **Emile Dufrene** ....(800) 827-1000
Vocational Rehabilitation and Employment Division
Chief **Kelly Shupak** ....(800) 827-1000
E-mail: kelly.shupak@va.gov
Lead IT Specialist **Veron Joseph** ....(800) 827-1000
E-mail: veron.joseph@va.gov
Supervisory Information Technology Specialist
Steven Sunseri ....(800) 827-1000
E-mail: steven.sunseri@va.gov
Telecommunications Specialist **Jerry Henton** ....(800) 827-1000
E-mail: jerry.henton@va.gov

Jackson (MS) Regional Office

1600 East Woodrow Wilson Avenue, Jackson, MS 39216
Tel: (601) 364-7010 Fax: (601) 364-7007
E-mail: jackson.query@vba.va.gov Internet: www.benefits.va.gov/jackson
Areas Covered: MS

● Director **Darryl R. Brady** ....(601) 364-7010
E-mail: darryl.brady@va.gov
Assistant Director **Tammy Fowler** ....(601) 364-7010
Education: New Orleans BBA; Alabama MBA
Management Analyst **(Vacant)** ....(601) 364-7002
● Chief Counsel **Sonya Cromwell** ....(601) 364-1467
E-mail: sonya.cromwell@va.gov
Support Services Division Chief **Demeria Williams** .....(601) 364-7040
Information Security Officer **Carolyn Pryer** ....(601) 364-7117
Public Affairs Officer **Vincent Paul Norris** ....(601) 364-7002
E-mail: paul.norris1@va.gov
Training Manager **Bobbie Carter** ....(601) 364-7274
Vocational Rehabilitation and Employment Officer
Chloe Freeman ....(601) 364-7164
Veterans Service Center Manager **(Vacant)** ....(601) 364-7009
Human Resource Liaison **Mamie Doyle** ....(601) 364-7008
E-mail: mamie.doyle@va.gov

Muskogee (OK) Regional Office

125 South Main Street, Muskogee, OK 74401-7025
Tel: (918) 781-7500 E-mail: dir.vbamus@va.gov
Internet: www.benefits.va.gov/muskogee
Areas Covered: OK: payment of benefits for compensation, pension, vocational rehabilitation; Western US: education assistance programs.

● Regional Office Director **C. Jason McClellan** ....(918) 781-7500
E-mail: c.mcclellan@va.gov
Assistant Director **Linda LoPinto** ....(918) 781-7500
E-mail: linda.lopinto@va.gov
Assistant Director **Judy Sikes** ....(918) 781-7500
E-mail: judy.sikes@va.gov
Division Chief, Disability Assistance **Tim Clark** ....(918) 781-7600
E-mail: tim.clark@va.gov
Division Chief, Education **Pam Stephens** ....(918) 781-7800
Division Chief, Education Call Center
Mary Ann McMullen ....(918) 781-7800
Division Chief, Human Resources **Leah Bracken** ....(918) 781-7556
E-mail: leah.bracken@va.gov
Division Chief, Support Services **Eddie Keefe** ....(918) 781-7550
E-mail: eddie.keefe@va.gov
Division Chief, Vocational Rehabilitation and
Employment **Kathryn "Kathy" Harmon** ....(918) 781-7540
Senior Staff Assistant **Ed Jacobs Nichols** ....(918) 781-7500
Information Resources Management Systems Officer
Lee Munson ....(918) 781-7700
Information Security Officer **Mark Ingold** ....(918) 781-7520
Fax: (918) 781-7509

Muskogee (OK) Regional Office *(continued)*

Information Security Officer **Ronald Thomas** ....(918) 781-7520
Fax: (918) 781-7509
Webmaster **Lee Munson** ....(918) 781-7700

New Orleans (LA) Regional Office

1250 Poydras Street, Suite 200, New Orleans, LA 70113
Tel: (800) 827-1000 (Information) Fax: (504) 252-4665
E-mail: neworleans.query@vba.va.gov
Internet: www.benefits.va.gov/neworleans
Areas Covered: LA

● Regional Office Director **Mark Bologna** ....(504) 619-4590
E-mail: mark.bologna@va.gov
Assistant Director **Debbie Biagioli** ....(504) 619-4590
E-mail: debbie.biagioli@va.gov
Financial Manager **Ava Nicholas** ....(504) 619-4412
Veterans Service Center Manager **Steve Kelly** ....(504) 619-4494
E-mail: steve.kelly@va.gov
HRM Liaison **(Vacant)** ....(504) 619-4543
Vocational Rehabilitation and Employment Officer
Jesse Julias ....(504) 619-4361

North Little Rock (AR) Regional Office

Building 65, 2200 Fort Roots Drive, North Little Rock, AR 72114-1756
Tel: (501) 370-3700 Fax: (501) 370-3831
E-mail: littlerock.query@va.gov Internet: www.benefits.va.gov/littlerock
Areas Covered: AR; Texarkana, TX

● Regional Office Director **Lisa Breun Moreland** ....(501) 370-3700
E-mail: lisa.breun@va.gov
Education: Loyola U (New Orleans) 1992 BA, 1992 MBA
Assistant Director **Linda Parker** ....(501) 370-3700
E-mail: linda.parker4@va.gov
Veterans Service Center Manager **Tamelia Morrow** ....(501) 370-3710
E-mail: tamelia.morrow@va.gov
Assistant Veterans Service Center Manager
Laura Jones ....(501) 370-3710
E-mail: laura.jones1@va.gov
Assistant Veterans Service Center Manager
Jason Ware ....(501) 370-3710
E-mail: jason.ware@va.gov
Management Analyst and Public Affairs Officer
Kim Godeaux ....(501) 370-3850
E-mail: kim.godeaux@va.gov
Support Services Chief **Steven Bogle** ....(501) 370-3703
E-mail: steven.bogle@va.gov
Vocational Rehabilitation and Employment Officer
Trena Hyde ....(501) 370-3780

Salt Lake City (UT) Regional Office

VA Hospital Campus, 550 Foothill Drive,
Room 305, Salt Lake City, UT 84158
Mail: P.O. Box 581900, Salt Lake City, UT 84158-1900
Tel: (801) 326-2400 E-mail: saltlake.query@va.gov
Internet: www.benefits.va.gov/saltlakecity

● Regional Office Director **(Vacant)** ....(801) 326-2400
Assistant Director **Michael Crouse** ....(801) 326-2400
Assistant Director **(Vacant)** ....(801) 326-2442
Secretary **Erin Kinder** ....(801) 326-2400
Regional Counsel **Letna Miller** ....(303) 914-5810
155 Van Gordon Street, Lakewood, CO 80228
E-mail: letna.miller@va.gov
Support Services Division Chief **Karla Lowry** ....(801) 326-1800
E-mail: karla.lowry@va.gov
Vocational Rehabilitation and Employment Officer
Jean Chadwick Room 302 ....(801) 326-2431
Veterans Service Center Manager
Kimberly Albers Room 200 ....(801) 326-2313
E-mail: kimberly.albers@va.gov
Veterans Care Manager **Corina Boyd** ....(801) 708-8000
E-mail: corina.boyd@va.gov
Fiduciary Hub Manager **(Vacant)** ....(801) 708-7300
Human Resources Liaison **Theresa Michal** ....(801) 326-2440
E-mail: theresa.michal@va.gov

(continued on next page)

★ Presidential Appointment Requiring Senate Confirmation ☆ Presidential Appointment ☐ Schedule C Appointment ◇ Career Senior Foreign Service Appointment
● Career Senior Executive Service (SES) Appointment ○ Non-Career Senior Executive Service (SES) Appointment ■ Postal Career Executive Service

Salt Lake City (UT) Regional Office *(continued)*

Management Analyst **Rodney LaPlant** . . . . (801) 326-8204
E-mail: rodney.laplant@va.gov
Management Analyst **(Vacant)** . . . . (801) 326-2408

Waco (TX) Regional Office

One Veterans Plaza, 701 Clay Avenue, Waco, TX 76799
Tel: (254) 299-9850 Internet: www.benefits.va.gov/waco
Areas Covered: 164 counties in North, West, and Central TX – northern two thirds of the state

• Regional Office Director **John S. Limpose** . . . . (254) 299-9850
E-mail: john.limpose@va.gov
Education: Wooster 1983 BA
Assistant Director **Darlene Jones** . . . . (254) 299-9850
E-mail: darlene.jones3@va.gov
Assistant Director **Pandi S. Van Houten** . . . . (254) 299-9850
E-mail: pandi.van.houten@va.gov
Staff Assistant **Sherry Zahirniak** . . . . (254) 299-9405
E-mail: sherry.zahirniak@va.gov
Regional Counsel **(Vacant)** . . . . (254) 297-5300
Veterans Service Center Manager **(Vacant)** . . . . (254) 299-9110
Support Services Division Chief **Brian Hoeldtke** . . . . (254) 299-9410
E-mail: brian.hoeldtke@va.gov
Support Services Division Assistant Chief **(Vacant)** . . . . . . (254) 299-9410
Finance Chief **Nancy Owen** . . . . (254) 299-9410
Vocational Rehabilitation and Employment Officer
Carolyn Williams . . . . (254) 299-9810
E-mail: carolyn.williams9@va.gov

Midwest District

Areas Covered: IA, IL, IN, KS, KY, MI, MN, MO, ND, NE, OH, SD, WI

• Area Director **Thomas J. "Tom" Murphy** . . . . (314) 253-4310
Education: Colorado Christian 1999 BS;
Colorado (Colo Springs) 2001 MBA

Chicago (IL) Regional Office

2122 West Taylor Street, Chicago, IL 60612
Tel: (312) 980-4203 TTY: (800) 829-4833 Fax: (312) 706-6668
Internet: www.benefits.va.gov/chicago

• Regional Office Director **Hughes S. Turner** . . . . (312) 980-4203
Assistant Director **Anna McBarron** . . . . (312) 980-4203
• Regional Counsel **Tim Morgan** . . . . (312) 980-4207
E-mail: tim.morgan@va.gov
Facility Chief Information Officer **Mitchell D. Wilson** . . . . (312) 980-4211
E-mail: mitchell.wilson@va.gov Fax: (312) 706-6672
Information Security Officer **Jose D. Diaz** . . . . (312) 980-4215
E-mail: jose.diaz4@va.gov
Support Services Officer **Nikia Carter** . . . . (312) 980-4217
Vocational Rehabilitation and Counseling Officer
Herbert Morris . . . . (312) 980-4458
E-mail: herbert.morris@va.gov
Service Center Manager **Ruth Grezlik** . . . . (312) 980-4307
E-mail: ruth.grezlik@va.gov

Cleveland (OH) Regional Office

A. J. Celebrezze Federal Building, 1240 East Ninth Street, Cleveland, OH 44199
Tel: (216) 522-3600 Fax: (216) 522-3518
E-mail: cleveland.query@vba.va.gov Internet: benefits.va.gov/cleveland

• Regional Office Director **Anthony "Tony" Milons** . . . . . . (216) 522-3530
Education: Chicago State BA; Keller Grad School MBA
Assistant Director **Charles Moore** . . . . (216) 522-3530
Assistant Director **Todd J. Weber** . . . . (216) 522-3530
E-mail: todd.weber@va.gov
Education: Toledo BA, JD
Chief Counsel **Dennis M. McGuire** . . . . (614) 388-7039
Building 1, 10000 Brecksville Road, Fax: (440) 717-2883
5th Floor, Brecksville, OH 44141
E-mail: dennis.mcguire@va.gov
Support Services Division Chief **John Hibbler** . . . . (216) 522-2600
Education: Ohio State BSBA; Fax: (216) 522-3389
Cleveland State MBA

Cleveland (OH) Regional Office *(continued)*

Home Loan Guaranty Officer **Jennifer Toth** . . . . (216) 522-3614
Education: Kent State BBA Fax: (216) 522-3101
Vocational Rehabilitation and Employment Officer
Ashley Adomaites . . . . (216) 522-2583
E-mail: ashley.adomaites@va.gov
Education: Kent State 1994 BSEd, 1996 MEd
Veterans Services Center Manager **Ted Ebert** . . . . (216) 522-4950
Fax: (216) 522-8262
Information Resource Management Chief
Christine Wilson . . . . (216) 522-3565
E-mail: christine.wilson@va.gov Fax: (216) 522-3603
National Call Center Manager **Ashley Boykins** . . . . (216) 522-3530
Education: Wilberforce BS

Des Moines (IA) Regional Office

Federal Building, 210 Walnut Street, Des Moines, IA 50309
Tel: (800) 827-1000 (Information)
Internet: www.benefits.va.gov/desmoines
Areas Covered: IA

Customer Support Services Division Chief
Kathleen Taylor . . . . (515) 323-7515
Fax: (515) 323-7428
Regional Office Director **Bruce Voigt** . . . . (515) 323-7500
Fax: (515) 323-7407
Training Administrator **Nancy Orth** . . . . (515) 323-7449
E-mail: nancy.orth@va.gov
Veterans Service Center Manager **Athena Delgado** . . . . . . (515) 323-7465
Human Resources Management Liaison
Kristine Vance . . . . (515) 323-7505
Fax: (515) 323-7407
Vocational Rehabilitation and Employment Officer
Randal Beyer . . . . (515) 323-7557
E-mail: randal.beyer@va.gov
Staff Assistant **Rodney Derringer** . . . . (515) 323-7504
E-mail: rodney.derringer@va.gov

Detroit (MI) Regional Office

Patrick V. McNamara Federal Building,
477 Michigan Avenue, Detroit, MI 48226
Tel: (313) 471-3600 Fax: (313) 471-3633
E-mail: detroit.query@vba.va.gov Internet: benefits.va.gov/detroit

• Regional Office Director **Terri Beer** . . . . (313) 471-3600
E-mail: terri.beer@va.gov
Assistant Director **(Vacant)** . . . . (313) 471-3600
Regional Counsel **(Vacant)** . . . . (313) 471-3644
Veterans Service Center Manager **Keith Sekuterski** . . . . . . (313) 471-3701
E-mail: keith.sekuterski@va.gov
Support Services Chief **LaShawn Carr** . . . . (313) 471-3610
Human Resource Liaison **Michele Blunk** . . . . (313) 471-3607
E-mail: michele.blunk@va.gov
Vocational Rehabilitation and Employment Officer
John McCarthy . . . . (313) 471-3801
Webmaster **(Vacant)** . . . . (313) 471-3627
Change Management Agent **(Vacant)** . . . . (313) 471-3600

Fargo (ND) Regional Office

2101 Elm Street, Fargo, ND 58102
Tel: (800) 827-1000 Fax: (701) 451-4690
E-mail: fargo.query@vba.va.gov Internet: www.benefits.va.gov/fargo
Areas Covered: MN (Counties of Becker, Beltrami, Clay, Clearwater, Kittson, Lake of the Woods, Mahnomen, Marshall, Norman, Otter Tail, Pennington, Polk, Red Lake, Roseau, Wilkin), ND

• Director **Shawn Bohn** . . . . (605) 336-3230 ext. 9150
2501 West 22nd Street, Sioux Falls, SD 57105
Associate Director **(Vacant)** . . . . (701) 239-3700
Veterans Service Center Manager **Paula Heitmann** . . . . . . (701) 451-4601
E-mail: paula.conard@va.gov
Chief of Information Technology
Raymond A. Nelson . . . . (701) 232-3241 ext. 3854
E-mail: raymond.nelson2@va.gov
Information Security Officer
Robert A. "Bob" Berg . . . . (701) 232-3241 ext. 3853
E-mail: bob.berg@va.gov

★ Presidential Appointment Requiring Senate Confirmation ☆ Presidential Appointment ☐ Schedule C Appointment ◇ Career Senior Foreign Service Appointment
● Career Senior Executive Service (SES) Appointment ○ Non-Career Senior Executive Service (SES) Appointment ■ Postal Career Executive Service

Fargo (ND) Regional Office *(continued)*

Vocational Rehabilitation and Employment Officer
Margie Polak .... (800) 827-1000

Indianapolis (IN) Regional Office
Minton-Capehart Federal Building, 575 North Pennsylvania Street, Indianapolis, IN 46204
Tel: (317) 916-3400 Fax: (317) 916-3818
E-mail: indianapolis.query@vba.va.gov
Internet: www.benefits.va.gov/indianapolis

● Regional Office Director **Michael R. Stephens** .... (317) 916-3400
E-mail: michael.stephens2@va.gov
Assistant Director **Michael A. Scheibel** .... (317) 916-3404
Management Analyst **Lisa Goebel** .... (317) 916-3405
E-mail: lisa.goebel@vba.va.gov
Human Resources Liaison **Sonya Wilson** .... (317) 916-3409
Support Services Division Chief **Horace Jordan** .... (317) 916-3761
Veterans Service Center Manager **Teria Dowdy** .... (317) 916-3414
Education: Alverno 2002 MA
Assistant Veterans Service Center Manager
Angela Thomas .... (317) 916-3492
Vocational Rehabilitation and Employment Officer
(Vacant) .... (317) 916-3485
Webmaster **Kyle E. Schmidt** .... (317) 916-3830
E-mail: kyle.e.schmidt@va.gov

Lincoln (NE) Regional Office
3800 Village Drive, Lincoln, NE 68501
Mail: P.O. Box 85816, Lincoln, NE 68501
Tel: (800) 827-1000 E-mail: lincoln.query@vba.va.gov
Internet: www.benefits.va.gov/lincoln
Areas Covered: NE

Regional Office Director **Kerrie L. Witty** .... (402) 420-4225
Assistant Director **Jason Rogers** .... (402) 420-4225
Secretary to the Director **Peggy Brown** .... (402) 420-4301
Human Resources Liaison **Rebecca Norris** .... (402) 420-4225
Support Services Division Chief **Joe Hlavac** .... (402) 420-4225
E-mail: joe.hlavac@va.gov
Vocational Rehabilitation and Counseling Officer
Dorothy McKenzie .... (402) 420-4225
Fiduciary Hub Manager **Courtney Morehead** .... (800) 827-1000
Veteran Service Center Manager **(Vacant)** .... (402) 420-4239

Milwaukee (WI) Regional Office
5400 West National Avenue, Milwaukee, WI 53214
Tel: (800) 827-1000 Fax: (414) 902-9400
Internet: www.benefits.va.gov/Milwaukee

● Regional Office Director **Duane Honeycutt** .... (414) 902-5001
E-mail: duane.honeycutt1@va.gov
Assistant Director **Keri Brezgel** .... (414) 902-5158
E-mail: keri.brezgel@va.gov
Assistant Director **Jesse Severe** .... (414) 902-5005
E-mail: jesse.severe@va.gov
Education: Wartburg Col 1996 BA; Iowa 2001 MA; Brandeis 2017 MA
Executive Assistant **Jenn Wagner** .... (414) 902-5003
Information Resource Management Chief
Elizabeth Henry .... (312) 980-4211
2122 West Taylor Street, Chicago, IL 60612
Information Systems Officer **Ronald Cox** .... (414) 902-5613
E-mail: ronald.cox@va.gov
SSD Officer **Mary Hankes** .... (414) 902-5626
Training Manager **Lindsay Bertrandt** .... (414) 902-5171
Management Analyst **Timothy Sullivan** .... (414) 902-1051
Pension Maintenance Center Manager **Chris Fischer** ..... (414) 902-5108
E-mail: chris.fischer@va.gov
Veterans Service Center Manager **Barbara Nehls** .... (414) 902-5045
E-mail: barbara.nehls@va.gov
Vocational Rehabilitation and Employment Officer
David Crosby .... (414) 902-5116
Fiduciary Hub Manager **Denise Niemczyk-Mullins** ..... (414) 292-2651
Education: Wisconsin (Stevens Point) BA

Wichita (KS) Regional Office
5500 East Kellogg Drive, Wichita, KS 67218-1698
Tel: (800) 827-1000 Fax: (316) 651-2970
E-mail: wichita.query@vba.va.gov Internet: www.benefits.va.gov/wichita

Director **(Vacant)** .... (316) 651-3602
Management Analyst **Tara Cisneros** .... (316) 685-2221 ext. 56791
Veterans Services Manager **Aimee Rogers** .... (316) 685-6838
Vocational Rehabilitation and Counseling
Officer **Heather Shade** .... (316) 685-2221 ext. 56842

Saint Louis (MO) Regional Office
9700 Page Avenue, St. Louis, MO 63132
Tel: (314) 253-4310 Fax: (314) 253-4135
E-mail: stlouis.query@vba.va.gov Internet: www.benefits.va.gov/stlouis

Regional Office Director **Mitzi Marsh** .... (314) 253-4310
E-mail: mitzi.marsh@va.gov
Education: Peru State 1988 BASc
Assistant Director **Stanton Nickens** .... (314) 253-4310
E-mail: stanton.nickens@va.gov
Assistant Director **Stacey Bonnett** .... (314) 253-4310
Regional Counsel **(Vacant)** .... (314) 845-5050
Education Officer **Valkyrie Nordman** .... (314) 253-4336
Support Services Division Chief **Angela Nash** .... (314) 253-4486
Vocational Rehabilitation and Employment Division
Chief **Corliss De La Garza** .... (314) 253-4402
Veterans Service Center Manager **Gary Moore** .... (314) 253-4370
Human Resources Management Liaison **Susan Dobbs** ... (314) 253-4426
Call Center Personnel **Georgia "Doreen" Jones** .... (314) 253-4218

Saint Paul (MN) Regional Office
1 Federal Drive, St. Paul, MN 55111-4050
Tel: (612) 970-5200 Fax: (612) 970-5415
Internet: www.benefits.va.gov/stpaul E-mail: stpaul.query@va.gov

● Director **Kimberly A. "Kim" Graves** .... (612) 970-5200
Education: Nebraska BA, MPA
Assistant Director **Kay L. Anderson** .... (612) 970-5200
E-mail: kay.anderson@va.gov
Assistant Director **Donna Meyer-Hickel** .... (612) 970-5200
Loan Guaranty Officer **Kimberly "Kim" Girard** .... (612) 970-5500
Support Services Division Chief **Ronald Sackett** .... (612) 970-5200
E-mail: ronald.sackett@va.gov
Vocational Rehabilitation and Employment Officer
Linda Steffensmeier .... (612) 970-5440
E-mail: linda.steffensmeier@vba.va.gov
Pension Management Center Manager **Joanna Yanez** .... (612) 713-8900
Veterans Service Center Manager **Jessica Gillette** .... (612) 970-5300
Human Resources Management Liaison Unit Specialist
Krysten Ehlert .... (612) 970-5468

Sioux Falls (SD) Regional Office
2501 West 22nd Street, Sioux Falls, SD 57105
Mail: Sioux Falls, SD 57105
Tel: (800) 827-1000 (Veterans Assistance) Fax: (605) 333-5316
Internet: www.benefits.va.gov/siouxfalls

Director **Shawn Bohn** .... (605) 333-6839
Regional Counsel **Starla Larson-Pfeifer** .... (605) 333-6853
E-mail: starla.larson-pfeifer@va.gov
Regional Counsel **Sarah Theophilus** .... (605) 333-6853
E-mail: sarah.theophilus@va.gov
Veterans Service Center Manager **Aaron Filsinger** .... (605) 333-6825
Vocational Rehabilitation and Employment Officer
Margie Polak .... (800) 827-1000

North Atlantic District
Areas Covered: CT, DC, DE, MA, MD, ME, NC, NH, NJ, NY, PA, RI, VA, VT, WV

DEPARTMENTS

★ Presidential Appointment Requiring Senate Confirmation ☆ Presidential Appointment □ Schedule C Appointment ◇ Career Senior Foreign Service Appointment
● Career Senior Executive Service (SES) Appointment ○ Non-Career Senior Executive Service (SES) Appointment ■ Postal Career Executive Service

Baltimore (MD) Regional Office
George H. Fallon Federal Building, 31 Hopkins Plaza,
Baltimore, MD 21201-0001
Tel: (800) 827-1000 Tel: (410) 230-4510 Fax: (410) 230-4516
E-mail: baltimore.query@va.gov Internet: www.benefits.va.gov/baltimore
Areas Covered: MD

● Regional Office Director **Antione Waller** .... (410) 230-4510
Education: Salisbury State U 1984 BA
Assistant Director **Kenesha Britton** .... (410) 230-4510
Education: Benedict 2003 BS; Webster 2006 MA
Regional Counsel **Daniel "Dan" Rattray** .... (410) 605-7600
E-mail: daniel.rattray@va.gov
Service Center Manager **Lisa Green** .... (410) 230-4529
Human Resource Liaison **Tracey Edwards-Fields** .... (410) 230-4510
Vocational Rehabilitation and Counseling Officer
(Acting) **Chantile L. Stovall** .... (410) 230-4550
Information Technology Chief **Christopher Elbrecht** .... (410) 230-4521
Information Security Officer **Michelle Ashton** .... (410) 230-4510
Chief Support Services Officer **Alfred Brown** .... (800) 827-1000

Boston (MA) Regional Office
John F. Kennedy Federal Building, 15 New Sudbury Street,
Room 1600, Boston, MA 02203
Tel: (617) 303-4250 Tel: (800) 827-1000 TTY: (800) 829-4833
Tel: (617) 303-4251 (Human Resource Management)
Tel: (781) 687-3600 (Regional Counsel, Bedford, MA)
Tel: (617) 303-1385 (Veterans Service Center Manager)
Tel: (617) 303-5533 (Vocational Rehabilitation and Counseling Office)
Fax: (617) 303-5561 E-mail: boston.query@vba.va.gov
Internet: www.benefits.va.gov/boston

● Regional Office Director **Bradley G. "Brad" Mayes** .... (617) 303-4250
Education: Southern IL Edwardsville BSEc
● Assistant Director **Ena Lima** .... (617) 303-4250
Education: Hobart & William Smith BA
Vocational Rehabilitation and Employment Officer
Jennifer Hersey .... (617) 303-4250
E-mail: jennifer.hersey@va.gov
Education: Wellesley BS; UMass (Boston) MEd

Buffalo (NY) Regional Office
130 South Elmwood Avenue, Buffalo, NY 14202-2478
Tel: (716) 857-3450 Fax: (716) 551-3072
E-mail: vavbabuf/ro/dir@vba.va.gov Internet: www.benefits.va.gov/buffalo

● Regional Office Director **Donna P. Mallia** .... (716) 857-3450
Assistant Director **Nicholas "Nick" Pamperin** .... (716) 857-3450
Regional Counsel (Acting) **Bradley Shaughnessy** .... (716) 862-8853
120 LeBrun Rd., Buffalo, NY 14215 Fax: (716) 862-6545
Management Analyst **Ronald Piaseczny** .... (716) 857-3450
Education: SUNY (Buffalo) 1999 BA; Widener 2002 JD;
SUNY (Buffalo) 2004 BA, 2007 MA
Veterans Service Center Manager **Antoinette Zingale** .... (716) 857-3030
Support Services Chief **Monica Benz** .... (716) 857-3015
E-mail: monica.benz@va.gov
Human Resources Management Section Chief
Timothy Griffin .... (716) 857-3020
Vocational Rehabilitation and Employment Division
Chief **Susan Fitzgibbons** .... (716) 857-3370
E-mail: susan.fitzgibbons@va.gov
Education Officer **Kim Wagner** .... (716) 857-3140
E-mail: kim.wagner@va.gov
Assistant Education Officer **Jennifer Cassidy** .... (716) 857-3140
E-mail: jennifer.cassidy@va.gov
Assistant Education Officer **Clarice Gist** .... (716) 857-3140

Hartford (CT) Regional Office
PO BOX 310909, Newington, CT 06131-0909
Tel: (860) 666-7300 Fax: (860) 667-1062
E-mail: hartford.query@vba.va.gov
Internet: www.vba.va.gov/ro/hartford/index.htm

Regional Office Director **Suzanne DeNeau-Galley** .... (860) 666-7300
E-mail: suzanne.denaeu@va.gov
Veterans Service Center Manager **Sarah Classy** .... (860) 666-7355

Hartford (CT) Regional Office *(continued)*

Vocational Rehabilitation and Employment Officer
James Lester .... (860) 666-7379
Human Resources Advisor **Johnna A. Roche** .... (860) 666-7377
E-mail: johnna.roche@va.gov
Support Services Chief **Jeffrey Ramia** .... (860) 666-7312

Huntington (WV) Regional Office
640 Fourth Avenue, Huntington, WV 25701-1340
Tel: (304) 399-9340 Fax: (304) 399-9355
E-mail: huntington.query@vba.va.gov
Internet: https://www.benefits.va.gov/huntington/
Areas Covered: WV (except Counties of Brooke, Hancock, Marshall, and Ohio)

Regional Office Director **Shannon Kelley** .... (304) 399-9340
Education: Ohio 1991 BS; Cleveland-Marshall 2001 JD
Service Center Manager **John Hewitt** .... (304) 399-9340
Staff Assistant **Amanda Penn** .... (304) 399-9204
Vocational Rehabilitation Officer **David Wirtz** .... (304) 399-9300
Education: Carroll Col (MT) 2010 BA; Utah State 2012 MS
Support Services Division Chief **Ron Bonecutter** .... (304) 399-9327
E-mail: ron.bonecutter@va.gov
Human Resources Management Liaison
Christopher Lowe .... (304) 399-9219

Manchester (NH) Regional Office
Norris Cotton Federal Building, 275 Chestnut Street,
Manchester, NH 03101
Tel: (603) 222-5700 Tel: (800) 827-1000 (Veterans Benefits)
Fax: (603) 222-5766 E-mail: manchester.query@va.gov
Internet: www.benefits.va.gov/manchester
Areas Covered: NH

Regional Office Director **Bradley G. "Brad" Mayes** .... (603) 222-5700
Education: Southern IL Edwardsville BSEc
Assistant Director **Ena Lima** .... (603) 222-5700
Education: Hobart & William Smith BA
Management Analyst **(Vacant)** .... (802) 295-9363 ext. 5324
Veterans Service Center Manager
Pamela "Pam" Tebo-Piccione .... (603) 222-5711
E-mail: pam.tebo-piccione@va.gov
Assistant Loan Guaranty Officer (CT, ME, MA, NH,
NY, RI, VT) **Kenneth "Ken" Beaudoin** .... (603) 222-5800
Vocational Rehabilitation and Employment Officer
(NH, VT) **Jennifer Hersey** .... (603) 222-5752
E-mail: jennifer.hersey@va.gov
Education: Wellesley BS; UMass (Boston) MEd
Support Services Division Chief **Michael Yensz** .... (603) 222-5760
E-mail: michael.yensz@va.gov
Support Services Specialist **Barbara Payne** .... (603) 222-5700 ext. 5710
E-mail: barbara.payne@va.gov

Newark (NJ) Regional Office
20 Washington Place, Newark, NJ 07102
Tel: (800) 827-1000 Internet: www.benefits.va.gov/newark

Regional Office Director **Lillie Nuble** .... (973) 297-3348
Veterans Service Center Manager **Michael Bucolo** .... (973) 297-3232
Chief, Support Services Division **Barbara Sapp** .... (973) 297-3315
Vocational Rehabilitation and Employment Officer
Daniel Umlauf .... (973) 297-3221

New York (NY) Regional Office
245 West Houston Street, New York, NY 10014
Tel: (800) 827-1000 Fax: (212) 807-4024
E-mail: newyork.query@vba.va.gov
Internet: www.benefits.va.gov/newyork

● Regional Office Director **Sue A. Malley** .... (212) 807-3055
Assistant Director **Adam Swantz** .... (212) 807-3055
Chief Counsel **George J. Bums** .... (718) 630-2900
800 Poly Place, Fax: (718) 630-2917
Buildingl 14, Brooklyn, NY 11209
E-mail: george.burns@va.gov
Systems Administrator **Brian Mincy** .... (212) 807-3080
E-mail: brian.mincy@va.gov

★ Presidential Appointment Requiring Senate Confirmation ☆ Presidential Appointment ☐ Schedule C Appointment ◇ Career Senior Foreign Service Appointment
● Career Senior Executive Service (SES) Appointment ○ Non-Career Senior Executive Service (SES) Appointment ■ Postal Career Executive Service

New York (NY) Regional Office *(continued)*

Public Affairs District Director
James A. "Jim" Blue Suite 3156 .... (212) 807-3429
E-mail: james.blue@va.gov Fax: (212) 807-4030
Veterans' Benefits and Services Division Manager
Joe Corretjer .... (212) 807-3412
VSC Assistant Chief **Dene Davis** .... (212) 807-3415
Human Resources Liaison **Thomas Collins** .... (212) 807-3050
E-mail: thomas.collins@va.gov
Vocational Rehabilitation and Employment Officer
D'Laija S. Francis-Abdullah .... (212) 807-3030
Support Services Division Chief **Adelaide De Falco** ..... (212) 807-3080
E-mail: adelaide.defalco@va.gov

Philadelphia (PA) VA Regional Office and Insurance Center
5000 Wissahickon Avenue, Philadelphia, PA 19144-4867
Mail: P.O. Box 8079, Philadelphia, PA 19101
Tel: (215) 842-2000 (Regional Office)
Tel: (800) 827-1000 (Information) Tel: (800) 669-8477 (Insurance)
Tel: (215) 823-5800 (VA Medical Center) Fax: (215) 381-3549
E-mail: VAinsurance@vba.va.gov (Insurance Center)
Internet: www.benefits.va.gov/philadelphia

● Director (Acting) **Duane Honeycutt** .... (215) 381-3100
E-mail: duane.honeycutt@va.gov
Assistant Director **Jennifer Parkin** .... (215) 381-3001
Education: Rutgers BS
Assistant Director **Rashetta D. Smith** .... (215) 381-3001
National Call Center Manager **Laura Wright** .... (215) 842-2000
Education: Indiana (PA) BA
Veterans Service Center Manager **James Brewer** .... (215) 842-2000
Public Affairs Officer **Erica Dunbar** .... (215) 842-2000

Pittsburgh (PA) Regional Office
William S. Moorhead Federal Building,
1000 Liberty Avenue, Pittsburgh, PA 15222-4097
Tel: (412) 395-6002 E-mail: pittsburgh.query@vba.va.gov
Internet: www.benefits.va.gov/pittsburgh

● Regional Office Director **Jennifer Vandermolen** .... (412) 395-6008
E-mail: jennifer.vandermolen@va.gov
Assistant Director **(Vacant)** .... (412) 395-6008
Secretary **(Vacant)** .... (412) 395-6008
Support Services Division Chief (Acting)
Scott Shields .... (412) 395-6171
E-mail: scott.shields@va.gov
Vocational Rehabilitation and Employment Officer
Elizabeth Lucas .... (412) 395-6067
Human Resources Management Liaison **William Cox** .... (412) 395-6004
Information Resources Manager **Jonathan Dixon** .... (412) 395-6029
Veterans Services Center Manager **Cythnia McJunkin** ... (412) 395-6080
Veterans Services Center Assistant Manager
Laura Waszil .... (412) 395-6080

Providence (RI) Regional Office
The Federal Center, 380 Westminster Street, Providence, RI 02903
Tel: (401) 223-3600 Fax: (401) 223-3604
E-mail: providence.query@vba.va.gov

Regional Office Director **Edward "EJ" McQuade** .... (401) 223-3600
Regional Counsel **(Vacant)** .... (401) 223-3620
Information Security Officer **Rick Ciampa** .... (401) 223-3778
Vocational Rehabilitation and Counseling
Officer **Nicole Robert** .... (401) 223-3600 ext. 1333
Support Services Division Chief **Kathy Livesley** .... (401) 347-1325
Veterans Services Center Manager **Rachel Fuhrman** ..... (401) 223-3629
Human Resources Specialist **Katherine Schreck** .... (401) 347-1325
E-mail: katherine.schreck1@va.gov
Disability Rating Activity Site **Kenneth Gareau** .... (401) 223-3613

Roanoke (VA) Regional Office
Poff Building, 210 Franklin Road, SW, Roanoke, VA 24011
Tel: (540) 597-1120 Fax: (540) 597-1785
E-mail: roanoke.query@vba.va.gov
Internet: www.benefits.va.gov/Roanoke

● Regional Office Director **Robert T. "Rob" Reynolds** .... (540) 857-1471
E-mail: robert.reynolds@va.gov
Support Services Chief **Valentine "Tina" Saunders** ..... (540) 857-1130
E-mail: valentine.saunders@va.gov
Assistant Director **Kathleen R. Sullivan** .... (540) 857-1121
E-mail: kathleen.sullivan@va.gov
Education: Cleveland State 1990 MBA
Deputy Chief Counsel **Amanda Shaw** .... (540) 597-1693
E-mail: amanda.shaw@va.gov
Education: Harvard 1992 AB; Washington and Lee 1996 JD
Finance Officer **Lori Malzi** .... (540) 597-1120
Human Resources Liaison (Acting)
Jacob S. "Jake" Riske .... (540) 597-1769
Education: North Carolina 2012 BA; North Carolina Charlotte 2015 JD
Home Loan Guaranty Officer **Cynthia "Cindy" Smith** ... (540) 597-1500
Public Contact Team Leader **David "Matt" Clarke** ...... (540) 597-1229
Veterans Service Center Manager
Anthony D. Coltrane .... (540) 597-1120
Education: U Central Texas; Indiana Wesleyan MBA
Vocational Rehabilitation and Employment Officer
Karen DeSeguirant .... (540) 597-1670
E-mail: karen.deseguirant@vba.va.gov
Building Manager **Daniel "Dan" Jones** .... (540) 597-1134
Fax: (540) 597-1787

Togus Regional Benefit Office
1 VA Center, Augusta, ME 04330
Tel: (800) 827-1000 Fax: (207) 621-4898
E-mail: togus.query@vba.va.gov Internet: www.benefits.va.gov/togus

Regional Office Director **Julie L. Carie** .... (207) 623-8411 ext. 5179
Education: Metropolitan State U BS; Concordia U (MN) 2006 MM
Vocational Rehabilitation and Employment
Chief **Jeffrey Jones** .... (207) 623-8411 ext. 4871
E-mail: jeffrey.jones6@va.gov
Staff Assistant **(Vacant)** .... (207) 623-8411 ext. 5522
Support Service Chief **Tracy Sinclair** .... (207) 623-8411 ext. 5221
E-mail: tracy.sinclair@va.gov
Executive Secretary **Rosemary Adams** .... (207) 623-8411 ext. 4903

National Capital Regional Benefit Office
1722 I Street, NW, Washington, DC 20421-1111
Tel: (800) 827-1000 Fax: (202) 530-9326
E-mail: washingtondc.query@vba.va.gov
Internet: www.benefits.va.gov/washington
Areas Covered: DC, MD (Counties of Prince Georges and Montgomery), VA (Counties of Fairfax and Arlington; Cities of Alexandria, Fairfax and Falls Church), all foreign countries except Mexico, Central and South America, the Caribbean, Canada, the Philippines and other Pacific locations under the jurisdiction of Honolulu, HI

● Regional Office Director **Antione Waller** .... (202) 530-9400
Education: Salisbury State U 1984 BA
Assistant Director **Kenesha Britton** .... (202) 530-9400
Education: Benedict 2003 BS; Webster 2006 MA
Veterans Service Center Officer **Lisa Green** .... (202) 530-9000
Vocational Rehabilitation and Employment Officer
Chantile L. Stovall .... (202) 530-9150

White River Junction Regional Office
215 North Main Street, White River Junction, VT 05009-0001
Tel: (802) 295-9363 Fax: (802) 291-6299
Internet: www.benefits.va.gov/whiteriverjunction
Areas Covered: VT, Canada

Regional Office Director
Bradley G. "Brad" Mayes .... (802) 295-9363 ext. 5322
Education: Southern IL Edwardsville BSEc

★ Presidential Appointment Requiring Senate Confirmation ☆ Presidential Appointment ☐ Schedule C Appointment ◇ Career Senior Foreign Service Appointment
● Career Senior Executive Service (SES) Appointment ○ Non-Career Senior Executive Service (SES) Appointment ■ Postal Career Executive Service

Winston-Salem (NC) Regional Office
251 North Main Street, Winston-Salem, NC 27155
Tel: (336) 251-0703 Fax: (336) 631-5154
Internet: www.benefits.va.gov/WinstonSalem/

- • Regional Office Director **Mark M. Bilosz** .... (800) 827-1000
- Assistant Director **Leigh Ann Skeens Wilson** .... (800) 827-1000
  Education: Emory & Henry BA
- Assistant Director **Brian K. Ward** .... (800) 827-1000
- Veterans Service Center Manager **Kimberley Schillhammer** .... (800) 827-1000
- Human Resources Liaison **Sabrina Smith** .... (800) 827-1000
- Information Resources Management Supervisor **Allen Branson** .... (800) 827-1000
  Education: High Point 1996 BS
- Loan Guaranty Eligibility Center Chief **(Vacant)** .... (800) 827-1000
- Support Services Center Division Chief **Lisa Bowman** ... (800) 827-1000
  E-mail: lisa.bowman@va.gov
- Vocational Rehabilitation and Employment Officer **Carolyn A. Lightfoot** .... (800) 827-1000
  E-mail: carolyn.lightfoot@va.gov

Pacific District
Areas Covered: AK, AZ, CA, HI, ID, NM, NV, OR, WA, The Philippines

Albuquerque (NM) Regional Office
500 Gold Avenue, SW, Albuquerque, NM 87102
Tel: (800) 827-1000 E-mail: albuquerque.query@vba.va.gov
Internet: https://www.benefits.va.gov/albuquerque/
Areas Covered: NM

- Regional Office Director **Chris Norton** .... (800) 827-1000
  E-mail: chris.norton@va.gov
- Veterans Service Center Manager **Timothy Love** .... (800) 827-1000
- Vocational Rehabilitation Officer **Kathryn Nelson** .... (800) 827-1000

Anchorage (AK) Regional Office
1201 North Muldoon Road, Anchorage, AK 99504
Tel: (907) 257-5420 Fax: (907) 257-6750
E-mail: anchorage.query@vba.va.gov
Internet: www.benefits.va.gov/anchorage

- Regional Office Director **(Vacant)** .... (801) 326-2400
- Assistant Director **Carol Roane** .... (907) 257-5420
- Assistant Director **Michael Rohrbach** .... (907) 257-5420
  Education: South Florida
- Veteran Service Center Manager **Chad Pomelow** .... (907) 433-1002
  E-mail: chad.pomelow@va.gov
- Loan Guaranty Division Chief **(Vacant)** .... (907) 257-4745
  Fax: (907) 257-6792
- Vocational Rehabilitation and Employment Officer **Aaron Pugh** .... (406) 495-2010
  3687 Veterans Drive, Fort Harrison, MT 59636

Boise (ID) Regional Office
444 West Fort Street, Boise, ID 83702-4513
Tel: (800) 827-1000 Fax: (208) 429-2280
E-mail: boise.query@vba.va.gov Internet: www.benefits.va.gov/boise

- Regional Office Director **Kathryn Malin** .... (800) 827-1000
- District Counsel **Briana Buban** .... (800) 827-1000
  E-mail: briana.buban@va.gov
- Support Services Officer **Raymond Bales** .... (800) 827-1000
  E-mail: raymond.bales@va.gov
- Veterans Service Center Manager **Kevin Schneider** .... (800) 827-1000
- Vocational Rehabilitation and Employment Officer **Michael Duke** .... (800) 827-1000

Honolulu (HI) Regional Office
P.O. Box 29020, Honolulu, HI 96820-9989
Tel: (800) 827-1000 Fax: (808) 433-0478
Internet: https://www.benefits.va.gov/honolulu/
Areas Covered: AS, GU, HI, Wake and Midway Islands, Trust Territories of the Pacific Islands

- Regional Office Director **Karen M. Gooden** .... (808) 433-0106
- Program Analyst **Aiko Ortega-Shibuya** .... (808) 433-0501

Los Angeles (CA) Regional Office
Federal Building, 11000 Wilshire Boulevard, Los Angeles, CA 90024
Tel: (800) 827-1000 Fax: (310) 235-6640
E-mail: losangeles.query@vba.va.gov
Internet: www.benefits.va.gov/losangeles
Areas Covered: CA (Counties of Inyo, Kern, Los Angeles, San Bernardino, San Luis Obispo, Santa Barbara, and Ventura)

- • Director **(Vacant)** .... (310) 235-7696
- Assistant Director **Emmett O'Meara** .... (310) 235-7696
  E-mail: emmett.omeara@va.gov
- Regional Counsel **(Vacant)** .... (800) 827-1000
  1050 East Southern Avenue, Tempe, AZ 85282
- Support Services Division Chief **(Vacant)** .... (310) 235-7441
- Vocational Rehabilitation and Employment Officer **Woodrow Anthony Roeback** .... (310) 235-7722
  E-mail: woodrow.roeback@va.gov
- Veterans Services Center Manager **Jamie Cannon** .... (310) 235-7688
  E-mail: jamie.cannon@va.gov
- Information Security Officer **Richard Tercero** .... (310) 882-1091
- Information Technology Supervisor **Shayan Shahabi** .... (310) 235-7951

Manila Regional Office
1501 Roxas Boulevard, Pasay City, 1302, Philippines
Tel: 63 (2) 550-8387 Fax: 63 (2) 550-3944
Internet: www.benefits.va.gov/manila

- • Regional Office Director (Acting) **Mary Souza** 63 (2) 5503888
- Associate Director **Mary Souza** 63 (2) 550-3870
- Chief Information Officer **Roel M. Crucillo** 63 (2) 550-3839
  E-mail: roel.crucillo@va.gov Fax: 63 (2) 523-1347

Oakland (CA) Regional Office
Oakland Federal Building, 1301 Clay Street,
Suite 1400N, Oakland, CA 94612-5209
Tel: (800) 827-1000 Tel: (510) 637-6000 Fax: (510) 637-6111
Internet: www.benefits.va.gov/oakland/

- • Regional Office Director **Wendy Torres** .... (510) 637-6000
  E-mail: wendy.torres@va.gov
- Assistant Director **Michele Kwok** .... (510) 637-6000
  E-mail: michele.kwok@va.gov
- Veterans Service Center Manager **Mary Beth Markey** .... (510) 637-6059
- Fiscal Resource Manager **Zeferino Murillo** .... (510) 637-6395
- Human Resource Liaison **Blanca Herrera** .... (510) 637-6000
  E-mail: hrm.vbaoak@va.gov
- Information Resource Manager **Clint Walker** .... (510) 637-6130
  E-mail: clint.walker3@va.gov
- Vocational Rehabilitation and Employment Officer **Rodney Hackney** .... (510) 637-6215
  E-mail: rodney.hackney@va.gov
- Information Security Officer **Ashley Reede** .... (510) 637-6004

Phoenix (AZ) Regional Office
3333 North Central Avenue, Phoenix, AZ 85012
Tel: (800) 827-1000 Fax: (602) 627-2745
Internet: www.benefits.va.gov/phoenix/
Areas Covered: AZ, NV, NM, CA

- • Regional Office Director **Chris Norton** .... (602) 627-2740
  E-mail: chris.norton@va.gov
- Assistant Director **Sergio Chao** .... (602) 627-2740
- Federal Chief Information Officer **Luke Bader** .... (602) 627-2828
  E-mail: luke.bader@va.gov Fax: (602) 627-2838

Portland (OR) Regional Office
100 SW Main Street, Floor 2, Portland, OR 97204
Tel: (503) 412-4530 Fax: (503) 412-4744
E-mail: vbadirectorportlandro@va.gov
Internet: www.benefits.va.gov/portland
Areas Covered: OR, WA (Counties of Clark, Klickitat, Skamania)

- • Regional Office Director **(Vacant)** .... (503) 412-4530
- Assistant Director **Carol Roane** .... (503) 412-4530
- Assistant Director **Michael Rohrbach** .... (503) 412-4530
  Education: South Florida
- Regional Counsel **(Vacant)** .... (503) 412-4580
  Fax: (503) 412-4789

★ Presidential Appointment Requiring Senate Confirmation ☆ Presidential Appointment ☐ Schedule C Appointment ◇ Career Senior Foreign Service Appointment
● Career Senior Executive Service (SES) Appointment ○ Non-Career Senior Executive Service (SES) Appointment ■ Postal Career Executive Service

Portland (OR) Regional Office *(continued)*

Veterans Service Center Manager **Kevin D. Kalama** . . . . . . (503) 412-4746
E-mail: kevin.d.kalama@va.gov
Vocational Rehabilitation and Employment Officer
Chris Olson . . . . (503) 412-4577
E-mail: chris.olson@va.gov

Reno (NV) Regional Office
5460 Reno Corporate Drive, Reno, NV 89511
Tel: (800) 827-1000 (General Information) Fax: (775) 321-4708
E-mail: reno.query@vba.va.gov Internet: www.benefits.va.gov/reno
Areas Covered: CA (Counties of Alpine, Lassen, Modoc, Mono); NV

Regional Office Director **Shelia Jackson** . . . . (775) 321-4700
E-mail: shelia.jackson1@va.gov
Staff Assistant **(Vacant)** . . . . (775) 321-4700
Veterans Service Center Manager **(Vacant)** . . . . (775) 321-4700
Vocational Rehabilitation Officer
Leah C. Augustine-Veal . . . . (702) 224-6808

San Diego (CA) Regional Office
8810 Rio San Diego Drive, San Diego, CA 92108-1622
Tel: (619) 400-5400 Tel: (800) 827-1000 (Benefits Information)
Tel: (800) 733-8387 (CHAMPVA)
Tel: (800) 827-0648 (Debt Management Center)
Tel: (888) 442-4551 (Education) Tel: (800) 749-8387 (Gulf War Hotline)
Tel: (800) 697-6947 (Headstones and Markers)
Tel: (800) 669-8477 (Life Insurance) TTY: (800) 829-4833
Tel: (800) 871-8387 (VA Online Bulletin Board) Fax: (619) 400-5418
E-mail: sandiego.query@va.gov Internet: www.benefits.va.gov/sandiego
Areas Covered: CA (Counties of Imperial, Orange, Riverside, San Diego)

● Regional Office Director **Patrick C. "Pat" Prieb** . . . . (619) 400-5400
E-mail: pat.prieb@va.gov
Regional Office Assistant Director
Gary D. Chesterton . . . . (619) 400-5400
Regional Office Assistant Director
Andrea M. Lapinski . . . . (619) 400-5400
Human Resources Liaison **Robyn Logsdon** . . . . (619) 400-5402
Support Services Chief **Kevin McGrew** . . . . (619) 400-5537
Fax: (619) 400-5508
Network Support Center Manager **Emily Marshall** . . . . (619) 400-5300
Fax: (619) 400-5460
Veterans Service Center Manager **Stacey Bonnett** . . . . . . (619) 400-5598
Vocational Rehabilitation and Employment Manager
Ashley Johnson . . . . (619) 400-5479

Seattle (WA) Regional Office
Jackson Federal Building, 915 Second Avenue, Seattle, WA 98174
Fax: (206) 220-6143 Internet: www.benefits.va.gov/seattle

● Regional Office Director **Pritz K. Navaratnasingam** . . . . . (206) 341-8225
E-mail: pritz.navaratnasingam@va.gov
● Assistant Director **Cesar Romero** . . . . (206) 341-8225
E-mail: cesar.romero@va.gov
● Assistant Director **Michael Fernandez** . . . . (206) 341-8225
● Security Information Officer **Casey D. Longacre** . . . . (206) 341-8227
E-mail: casey.longacre@vba.va.gov
Regional Counsel **Rex Cray** . . . . (206) 220-6102
E-mail: rex.cray@va.gov
Education: Oregon 1973 JD
● Veteran Service Center Manager **Stephen Strope** . . . . (206) 341-8225
E-mail: Stephen.Strope@va.gov
● Support Services Division Officer **Mary A. Yates** . . . . (206) 341-8225
E-mail: mary.yates@va.gov
● Human Resources Liaison **Sara Carter** . . . . (206) 220-6125
Chief Information Officer **Chris Melary** . . . . (206) 220-6124 ext. 3500
● Vocational Rehabilitation and Employment Officer
David Boyd . . . . (206) 314-8228
E-mail: david.boyd1@va.gov
Employee Development Specialist **Rachael Rehburg** . . . . . (206) 220-6274
Special Mission Project Officer **James Smith** . . . . (206) 965-3469

Southeast District
Areas Covered: AL, FL, GA, MS, PR, SC, TN

Atlanta (GA) Regional Office
1700 Clairmont Road, Decatur, GA 30033-4032
P.O. Box 100026, Decatur, GA 30031-7021
Tel: (404) 929-5818 Fax: (404) 929-5819
E-mail: atlanta.query@vba.va.gov Internet: www.benefits.va.gov/atlanta

● Director **Al Bocchicchio** . . . . (404) 929-5818
E-mail: al.bocchicchio@va.gov
Education: LaSalle Col (Canada) 1990 BA
Assistant Director **(Vacant)** . . . . (404) 929-5830
Assistant Director **Patrick Zondervan** . . . . (404) 929-5818
Regional Counsel (TN) **Tammy L. Kennedy** . . . . (404) 929-5851
E-mail: tammy.kennedy@va.gov
Education Officer **Angela Seelhammer** . . . . (404) 929-3144
E-mail: angela.seelhammer@vba.va.gov
Information Security Officer **John Hazell** . . . . (404) 929-5826
Loan Guaranty Officer (GA, NC, SC, TN)
Randy Rudeseal . . . . (404) 929-5400
Public Affairs Officer **Velda McCoy** . . . . (404) 929-5825
E-mail: velda.mccoy@va.gov
Vocational Rehabilitation and Counseling Officer
Amy Thompson . . . . (404) 929-3152
E-mail: amy.thompson@va.gov
Services Center Manager **Stephanie DiBello** . . . . (404) 929-5555
Training Manager **Velda McCoy** . . . . (404) 929-5818
E-mail: velda.mccoy@va.gov
Congressional Liaison **Sharon McGill** . . . . (404) 929-5818
Human Resources Liaison **Sharon Key** . . . . (404) 929-5844
E-mail: hrsv@vba.va.gov Fax: (404) 929-5848
Management and Program Analyst
Howard "Chris" Baker . . . . (404) 929-5827
Management Analyst **David N. "Seth" Jones** . . . . (404) 929-5825
Management and Program Analyst **Ellen Shaheed** . . . . . . (404) 929-5818
Education: Columbia Southern 2010 BS;
Keller Grad School 2012 MBA

Columbia (SC) Regional Office
6437 Garners Ferry Road, Columbia, SC 29209
E-mail: columbia.query@va.gov Internet: www.benefits.va.gov/Columbia

● Regional Office Director **Leanne D. Weldin** . . . . (803) 647-2351
E-mail: leanne.weldin@va.gov
Secretary **Jonathan Bruce II** . . . . (803) 647-2351
Secretary **Lauren Baldwin** . . . . (803) 647-2352
Assistant Director **Charles Kimberger** . . . . (803) 647-2351
E-mail: charles.kimberger@va.gov
Assistant Director **Woody Middleton** . . . . (803) 647-2351
Regional Counsel **Edith Lewis** . . . . (803) 647-5839
VA Medical Center, 6439 Garners Ferry Road, Columbia, SC 29209
National Call Center Manager **Wayne Oswald** . . . . (803) 647-2351
Support Services Chief **Reubin Bookert** . . . . (803) 647-2351
Veterans Service Center Manager **James Ard** . . . . (803) 647-2351
E-mail: james.ard@va.gov
Vocational Rehabilitation and Employment Officer
Paul G. Knight . . . . (803) 647-2400
Management Analyst **Christopher Colvin** . . . . (803) 647-2351
Human Resources Liaison **Anita Dimitrof-Bass** . . . . (803) 647-2356
Supervisory Computer Specialist **Mark Wells** . . . . (803) 647-2351

Louisville (KY) Regional Office
321 West Main Street, Suite 390, Louisville, KY 40202
Tel: (502) 566-4500 Fax: (502) 566-5032
E-mail: louisville.query@vba.va.gov Internet: benefits.va.gov/louisville

● Regional Office Director **(Vacant)** . . . . (502) 566-4500
Assistant Director **Michael C. Fairchild** . . . . (502) 566-4500
E-mail: michael.fairchild@va.gov
Human Resource Liaison **Billy Bunch** . . . . (502) 566-4505
Regional Counsel **Brent Asseff** . . . . (502) 566-4454
● Support Services Division Chief **Michael Clock** . . . . (502) 566-4440
● Veterans Service Center Manager
Laura Kurezi-Rogers . . . . (502) 566-4301
E-mail: laura.kurezi-rogers@va.gov
Vocational Rehabilitation and Education Officer
(Vacant) . . . . (502) 566-4444
Fiduciary Hub Manager **Brian Martin** . . . . (502) 566-4444

DEPARTMENTS

DEPARTMENTS

Montgomery (AL) Regional Office
345 Perry Hill Road, Montgomery, AL 36109
Tel: (800) 827-1000 Fax: (334) 213-3351
E-mail: montgomery.query@va.gov
Internet: www.benefits.va.gov/montgomery
Areas Covered: AL: all benefits; FL panhandle: rehabilitation benefits only

- ● Regional Office Director **Cory A. Hawthorne** .... (334) 213-3400
- Assistant Director **Lauren Cox** .... (334) 213-3400
- Human Resources Liaison **Carol T. Carter** .... (334) 213-3410
  E-mail: carol.carter@va.gov
- Veterans Service Center Manager **(Vacant)** .... (334) 213-3458
  - Veterans Service Center Assistant Manager **(Vacant)** .... (334) 213-3458
  - Veterans Service Center Assistant Manager **Dorian Jenkins** .... (334) 213-3458
- Information Security Officer **James Hudson** .... (334) 213-3406
- Assistant Public Affairs Officer and Management Analyst **Kia Wallace** .... (334) 213-3448
- Support Services Officer **Priscilla Humphrey-Parker** .... (334) 213-3405
  E-mail: priscilla.humphrey-parker@va.gov
- Vocational Rehabilitation and Employment Officer **Jamie Bozeman** .... (334) 396-1986
  Education: Auburn 1999 BS, 2000 MS
- Management Analyst **Ebony Black** .... (334) 213-3448
- Webmaster **Kia Wallace** .... (334) 213-3403

Nashville (TN) Regional Office
110 9th Avenue South, Nashville, TN 37203
Tel: (615) 695-6005 Tel: (800) 827-1000 Fax: (615) 695-6008
E-mail: dir.vbanas@va.gov Internet: www.benefits.va.gov/nashville

- ● Regional Office Director (Acting) **Travis E. Kraft** .... (615) 695-6005
- Assistant Regional Director **Travis E. Kraft** .... (615) 695-6005
- ● Regional Counsel **(Vacant)** .... (615) 695-6236
  3322 West End Avenue, Suite 509, Nashville, TN 37203
- Veterans Service Center Manager **Angela Odom** .... (615) 695-6236
- Fiscal Officer **Michel Casey** .... (615) 695-6320
- Vocation Rehabilitation and Employment Officer **Shari "Tonna" Mustian** .... (615) 695-6151
- Human Resources Management Liaison **Susan "Katie" Galaz** .... (615) 695-6004
- Human Resources Management Liaison **Lisa M. Simpson** .... (615) 695-6005
- Human Resources Management Liaison **Darlene "DJ" Wiggins** .... (615) 695-6003
- Chief Information Officer **Mace Salinas** .... (615) 695-6274

Saint Petersburg (FL) Regional Office
9500 Bay Pines Boulevard, Saint Petersburg, FL 33708
Mail: P.O. Box 1437, Saint Petersburg, FL 33731
Tel: (727) 319-5900 Tel: (727) 319-5995 Fax: (727) 319-7761
E-mail: stpete.query@va.gov Internet: www.benefits.va.gov/stpetersburg

- ● Director **Julianna M. Boor** .... (727) 319-5900
  E-mail: julianna.boor@va.gov
- Assistant Director **Emily Wilson** .... (727) 319-5900
- Assistant Director **Craig Sergott** .... (727) 319-5900
- Chief Counsel **(Vacant)** .... (727) 540-3912
  P.O. Box 5005, Bay Pines, FL 33744 Fax: (727) 398-9384
- Service Center Chief **Christine Moorby** .... (727) 319-5900
- Support Services Division Chief **Kathy Bernheim** .... (727) 319-5900
- Loan Guaranty Officer **Donny Flores** .... (727) 319-5900
- Vocational Rehabilitation and Counseling Officer **Kim Lloyd** .... (727) 319-5900
  Education: Florida MS

San Juan (PR) Regional Office
50 Carretera 165, Guaynabo, PR 00968-8024
Tel: (787) 772-7302 Fax: (787) 772-7458
Internet: www.benefits.va.gov/sanjuan

- ● Director **Bernard Johnson** .... (787) 772-7302
  - Staff Assistant **Adelaida Figueroa** .... (787) 772-7302
    E-mail: adelaida.figueroa@va.gov
    Education: Inter American BA

San Juan (PR) Regional Office *(continued)*

- Assistant Director **Abner Concepcion** .... (787) 772-7302
  E-mail: abner.concepcion@va.gov
- Senior Attorney **Ana M. Margarida Julia** .... (787) 641-4350
  E-mail: ana.margaridajulia@va.gov
- Human Resources Management Liaison **William Penneman** .... (787) 772-7308
  E-mail: william.penneman@va.gov
- Information Security Officer **Edgardo Rivera** .... (787) 772-7301
  E-mail: edgardo.rivera1@va.gov
  Education: Excelsior BA
- Information Technology Specialist **Gerardo Fernandez** .... (787) 772-7323
  E-mail: gerardo.fernandez@va.gov Fax: (787) 772-7461
  Education: Inter American MA
  - Program Support Services Division Specialist **Benjamin Bruno** .... (787) 772-7336
    E-mail: benjamin.bruno@va.gov Fax: (787) 772-7460
- Supervisory Information Technology Specialist **Nelson de la Rosa** .... (787) 772-7325
  E-mail: nelson.delarosa@va.gov Fax: (787) 772-7461
  Education: Poly U Puerto Rico MA
- Support Services Chief **Margarita Castillo** .... (787) 772-7330
  Fax: (787) 772-7461
- Veterans Service Center Manager (Acting) **Jannice Toledo** .... (787) 772-7302
- Vocation Rehabilitation and Employment Officer **Bonnie Thomas** .... (787) 772-7302

Veterans Health Administration (VHA)
810 Vermont Avenue, NW, Washington, DC 20420
Internet: www.va.gov/health

OFFICE OF THE UNDER SECRETARY FOR HEALTH
810 Vermont Avenue, NW, Washington, DC 20420
Tel: (202) 461-7000 Fax: (202) 495-6156

Office of the Principal Deputy Under Secretary for Health (OPDUSH)
810 Vermont Avenue, NW, Room 806, Washington, DC 20420
Fax: (202) 273-7090

Office of the Deputy Under Secretary for Health for Operations and Management (DUSHOM)
810 Vermont Avenue, NW, Washington, DC 20420

Health Operations and Management – Veterans Integrated Service Networks (VISNs)
810 Vermont Avenue, NW, Washington, DC 20420
Fax: (202) 273-7090

VISN 1 - VA New England Healthcare System
Building 61, 200 Springs Road, Bedford, MA 01730
Tel: (781) 687-4821 Fax: (781) 687-3470
Internet: www.newengland.va.gov

- Network Director **Ryan S. Lilly** .... (781) 687-4821
  Education: West Virginia 1999 MPA
- Deputy Network Director **Barrett Franklin MS, CCE** .... (781) 687-4821
- Chief Financial Officer **Cody Couch** .... (781) 687-4953
- Chief Information Officer **(Vacant)** .... (781) 687-4857
- Network Communications Officer **Maureen P. Heard** .... (781) 687-4742
  E-mail: maureen.heard@va.gov
  Education: Defense Language 1980; Maryland University Col 1987 BA
- Network Contract Manager **(Vacant)** .... (781) 687-4993
  - Senior Procurement Analyst and Small Business Liaison **(Vacant)** .... (774) 826-1635

★ Presidential Appointment Requiring Senate Confirmation ☆ Presidential Appointment ☐ Schedule C Appointment ◇ Career Senior Foreign Service Appointment
● Career Senior Executive Service (SES) Appointment ○ Non-Career Senior Executive Service (SES) Appointment ■ Postal Career Executive Service

VISN 1 - VA New England Healthcare System *(continued)*

Chief Medical Officer (Acting)
Dr. Lisa Lehmann MD, PhD, MSc .... (781) 687-4874
Education: Cornell BA; Johns Hopkins MD, PhD; Harvard MSc
Webmaster **Jean Dumais** .... (781) 687-4879
E-mail: jean.dumais@va.gov
Small Business Liaison **John Young** .... (401) 455-4908
E-mail: john.young2@va.gov

Connecticut

VA Connecticut Healthcare System

950 Campbell Avenue, West Haven, CT 06516
Tel: (203) 932-5711 Fax: (203) 937-3868
Internet: www.connecticut.va.gov

• Director **Gerald F. Culliton** .... (203) 937-3888
Associate Director **John Callahan** .... (203) 937-3888
Education: Rhode Island 1980 BSPh
Associate Director for Patient Care Services
Linda Accordino .... (203) 937-3888
Chief of Staff **Dr. Michael Ebert MD** .... (203) 937-3825
E-mail: michael.ebert@va.gov

Newington (CT) Division

555 Willard Avenue, Newington, CT 06111
Tel: (860) 666-6951 Fax: (860) 667-6764

Assistant Director **Ross Hildonen** .... (860) 666-6951 ext. 6837
Education: Westfield State U 2008 BA, 2011 MPA

West Haven (CT) Division

950 Campbell Avenue, West Haven, CT 06516
Tel: (203) 937-3888 Fax: (203) 937-3868

DSS Site Manager **Ann Wernicke** .... (203) 932-5711 ext. 4892
Assistant Director **(Vacant)** .... (203) 937-3888
Assistant Chief of Staff **George F. Fuller MD, FAAFP** .... (203) 937-3825
E-mail: george.fuller@va.gov
Education: Fairfield; Uniformed Services MD
Library Technician **Jennifer Martin** .... (203) 932-5711 ext. 2857

Maine

VA Maine Healthcare System (Maine VA Healthcare System)

1 VA Center, Augusta, ME 04330
Tel: (207) 623-8411 ext. 5200 Internet: www.maine.va.gov

• Director (Interim) **Dan Dücker** .... (207) 623-5710
Education: Northern Iowa 1987 BA; South Carolina 1992 MEd; Army War Col 2010 MSS
Assistant Director **Russell Armstead** .... (207) 623-5710
Associate Director for Patient/Nursing
Services **Amy Gartley RN** .... (207) 623-8411 ext. 5419
Education: Maine 1991 BSN; Thomas Col (ME) 2004 MBA
Chief of Staff **Stephen Sears** .... (207) 623-5757
E-mail: stephen.sears3@va.gov
Education: Dartmouth MD; Johns Hopkins MPH
Facilities Management Chief **Edwin Lee** .... (207) 623-8411 ext. 5285
Education: Maine 1990 BSME
Chief Information Officer/Information
Management Service Chief **Joseph Davis** .... (207) 623-8411 ext. 4884
Prosthetics Section Chief **Kim Michaud** .... (207) 623-5769
E-mail: kim.michaud@va.gov
VA Police Chief **Michael Emmons** .... (207) 623-8411 ext. 5333
E-mail: michael.emmons@va.gov
Voluntary Services Chief **Jonathan Barczyk** ... (207) 623-8411 ext. 5286
E-mail: jonathan.barczyk@va.gov
Education: Michigan State 2008 BS; U Freiburg 2007
Geriatrics and Extended Care Service Line
Manager **(Vacant)** .... (207) 623-8411 ext. 4317
Fax: (207) 621-7305
Social Work Executive **Lee Lyford** .... (207) 623-8411 ext. 5672

Massachusetts

VA Boston Healthcare System

150 South Huntington Avenue, Boston, MA 02130 (Jamaica Plain Division)
Tel: (617) 232-9500 Tel: (508) 583-4500 Fax: (617) 323-7700
Internet: www.boston.va.gov

• Director **Vincent W. Ng** .... (857) 203-6000
E-mail: vincent.ng@va.gov
Education: U Washington 1977 BS; Trinity U 1979 MBA
Chief Information Officer **Kenny Brehaut** .... (774) 826-2524
Librarian **Elaine Alligood** .... (857) 364-5778
E-mail: elaine.alligood@va.gov
Education: Maryland 1974

VA Central Western Massachusetts Healthcare System

421 North Main Street, Leeds, MA 01605
Tel: (413) 584-4040 Fax: (413) 582-3121
Internet: www.centralwesternmass.va.gov

• Director **COL John Patrick Collins USA (Ret)** .... (413) 582-3000
Education: Providence 1982 BS; Northeastern 1984 MBA; Baylor 1992 MHCA; Oklahoma 2001 MEd; National Defense U 2005 MNR
Secretary to the Director **Lynn Boldac** .... (413) 582-3000
Associate Director **Andrew T. McMahon** .... (413) 582-3000
Education: Maryland BS; Boston U 2007 MSM; UMass (Amherst) 2017 MPH
Associate Director of Patient Care Services
Marie Annette Robinson-McLaughlin RN, MSN, ACNS-BC .... (413) 582-3000
Chief of Staff **Dr. Seth Kupferschmid MD** .... (413) 582-3000
Education: Icahn School of Medicine 1995 MD
Acquisition Manager (Acting)
William Ziemek .... (413) 584-4040 ext. 3006
Dental **Amit Sharma** .... (413) 584-4040 ext. 2300
Education Coordinator **Cathy Tenerowicz** ..... (413) 584-4040 ext. 2065
E-mail: cathy.tenerowicz@va.gov
Education Program Manager **(Vacant)** .... (413) 584-4040
Nursing **Elvira Loncto** .... (413) 584-4040 ext. 2240
E-mail: elvira.loncto@va.gov
Pathology and Laboratory Medicine **Robin Lazorik** ...... (413) 582-3018
Pharmacy **Claudine Wega** .... (413) 582-3028
E-mail: claudine.wega@va.gov
Police and Security Chief **Brian McLain** .... (413) 582-3029
Primary Care and Ambulatory Care Manager **(Vacant)** ... (413) 582-3153
Psychology Supervisor **Dana Weaver** .... (413) 584-4040 ext. 3022
E-mail: dana.weaver@va.gov
Radiology **Dr. John Hubbard MD** .... (413) 582-3018
Rehabilitation Medicine **Sandra Diamond** ..... (413) 584-4040 ext. 2260
Social Work Supervisor (Acting)
Bethany Graziadei .... (413) 584-4040 ext. 2616
E-mail: bethany.graziadei@va.gov
Librarian **Jessie Casella** .... (413) 584-4040 ext. 2432
Fax: (413) 582-3039
Public Affairs Officer **Dennis Ramstein** .... (413) 582-3005

Edith Nourse Rogers Memorial Veterans Hospital (Bedford VA Medical Center)

Edith Nourse Rogers Memorial Veterans Hospital,
200 Springs Road, Bedford, MA 01730
Tel: (781) 687-2000 Fax: (781) 687-2101 Internet: www.bedford.va.gov

Director **Dr. Joan Clifford DNP, RN, FACHE, NEA-BC** ... (781) 687-2201
Education: Salem State U 1979 BSN; Emmanuel (MA) 2001 MSM; MGH Inst 2016 DNP
Associate Director **Edward "Ed" Koetting** .... (781) 687-2202
Education: Northwood 1996 BAcc; Columbia Col (MO) 2002 BS; William Woods 2006 MBA
Nurse Executive and Associate Director for Patient
Services **Mary Anderson RN, MSN** .... (781) 687-2083
Education: Southern Maine BSN; St Joseph's U MSN
Chief Information Officer **(Vacant)** .... (781) 687-4880
Chief Medical Officer **(Vacant)** .... (781) 687-2867
Chief of Staff
Dr. Daniel R. "Dan" Berlowitz MD, MPH .... (781) 687-2203
E-mail: dan.berlowitz@va.gov
Education: Albert Einstein Medical MD; Boston U MPA

DEPARTMENTS

★ Presidential Appointment Requiring Senate Confirmation ☆ Presidential Appointment ☐ Schedule C Appointment ◇ Career Senior Foreign Service Appointment
● Career Senior Executive Service (SES) Appointment ○ Non-Career Senior Executive Service (SES) Appointment ■ Postal Career Executive Service

New Hampshire

VA Medical Center Manchester, New Hampshire (VAMC Manchester)

718 Smyth Road, Manchester, NH 03104
Tel: (603) 624-4366 Fax: (603) 626-6576
Internet: www.manchester.va.gov

Director **Alfred A. Montoya, Jr. MHA** . . . . (603) 624-4366 ext. 6000
Education: Wayland Baptist BEd; Walden MHCA
Secretary to the Director (Acting)
Margaret Bieler . . . . (603) 624-4366 ext. 6004
Associate Director **Kevin Forrest FACHE** . . . . . . (603) 624-4366 ext. 6001
Education: New Hampshire 1989 BS; UMass (Lowell) MS
Associate Director Patient/Nursing Services
Dr. Bernadette Y. Jao DNP, MSN, RN-BC . . . . (603) 624-4366
Education: U City Manila BSN; U Phoenix MSN; Old Dominion DNP
Chief of Staff (Acting)
Dr. Paul Zimmerman DDS . . . . (603) 624-4366 ext. 6519
Education: Ohio State DDS
Chief Information Officer **John Foote** . . . . (603) 624-4366 ext. 6618
E-mail: john.foote@va.gov
Webmaster **Jean Dumais** . . . . (781) 687-4879
200 Springs Road, Bedford, MA 01730
E-mail: jean.dumais@va.gov

Rhode Island

Providence (RI) VA Medical Center

830 Chalkstone Avenue, Providence, RI 02908-4799
Tel: (401) 273-7100 Fax: (401) 457-1430
Internet: www.providence.va.gov

• Director **Dr. Susan A. MacKenzie PhD** . . . . (401) 457-3042
E-mail: susan.mackenzie@va.gov
Education: Northeastern BSHS, MPA, 2002 PhD
Chief of Staff **Dr. Satish Sharma MD** . . . . (401) 457-3040
E-mail: satish.sharma@va.gov
Associate Director for Operations
Erin Clare Sears MSW, MBA . . . . (401) 457-3041
Education: Colorado BA; Art Inst Boston MSW; Salve Regina U MBA
Associate Director for Patient Care
Matthiew "Matt" Goulet . . . . (401) 273-7100 ext. 5364
Education: Norwich 1999 BA, 2012 MS
Director of Quality Management **(Vacant)** . . . . . (401) 273-7100 ext. 3087
Telecommunications Specialist **Leonard Bourgeois** . . . . . . (401) 457-3084
E-mail: leonard.bourgeois@va.gov
Public Affairs Officer **Winfield S. Danielson III** . . . . (401) 457-3369
E-mail: winfield.danielsoniii@va.gov
Education: Connecticut 1992 BA; Colorado 1997 MA
Chief Information Officer **Dawn Pedchenko** . . . (401) 273-7100 ext. 1418
E-mail: dawn.pedchenko2@va.gov
Education: Roger Williams 1992 BS

Vermont

White River Junction (VT) VA Medical Center

215 North Main Street, White River Junction, VT 05009-0001
Tel: (802) 295-9363 Fax: (802) 296-6354 Internet: www.whiteriver.va.gov

• Director (Acting) **Dr. Brett Rusch MD** . . . . (802) 295-9363 ext. 5400
Education: Wisconsin BS, MD
Associate Director **Becky Rhoads** . . . . (802) 295-9363 ext. 5410
Education: Vermont 2004 BA; Northeastern 2008 AuD
Associate Director, Patient Care and Nursing Services
Laura Miraldi RN, MSN . . . . (802) 296-5127
Education: Hunter; Vermont MSN
Chief of Staff (Acting) **Dr. Brett Rusch MD** . . . (802) 295-9363 ext. 5420
Education: Wisconsin BS, MD
Acquisitions Officer **Randall Tinard** . . . . (802) 295-9363 ext. 5790
Chief Information Officer **Matt Rafus** . . . . (802) 295-9363 ext. 6288
E-mail: matthew.raful@va.gov
Contracts Officer **Jeffrey Reed** . . . . (802) 295-5102 ext. 6336
E-mail: jeffrey.reed@va.gov
General Counsel **Neil Nulty** . . . . (802) 295-9363 ext. 5800
E-mail: neil.nulty@va.gov
Public Affairs Officer **Joseph "Joe" Anglin** . . . (802) 295-9363 ext. 5880
E-mail: joseph.anglin@va.gov
Librarian **Loretta Grikis** . . . . (802) 295-9363 ext. 5236

VISN 2 - VA Health Care Upstate New York

Building 7, 113 Holland Avenue, Albany, NY 12208
Tel: (518) 626-7300 Fax: (518) 626-7333 Internet: www.visn2.va.gov

• Network Director **Dr. Joan E. McInerney MD** . . . . (718) 741-4134
Education: Stern MBA; Naval Postgrad MA
Deputy Network Director (Interim)
Thomas W. Sharpe . . . . (518) 626-7317
Chief Financial Officer **Thomas W. Sharpe** . . . . (518) 626-7322
Chief Medical Officer **Dr. Michael Rader MD** . . . . (518) 626-7301
Education: CCNY 1971 BS; SUNY Downstate Med 1975 MD
Network Contract Manager **Cherie Widger-Kresge** . . . . . . (716) 862-6388
E-mail: cherie.widger-kresge@va.gov Fax: (716) 862-8893
Administrative Officer **Angela Taylor** . . . . (518) 626-7317
E-mail: angie.taylor@med.va.gov

Bath (NY) VA Medical Center

76 Veterans Avenue, Bath, NY 14810-0842
Tel: (607) 664-4000 Fax: (607) 664-4861 Internet: www.bath.va.gov

• Director (Interim) **Bruce Tucker** . . . . (607) 664-4722
Associate Director **Richard Salgueiro FACHE** . . . . (607) 664-4854
Education: Suffolk BSB; George Washington MHSA
Associate Director for Patient Care/Nursing Services
Michelle Santos Martinez . . . . (607) 664-4515
Chief of Staff **Dr. Susan Herson** . . . . (607) 664-4770
Education: Cornell BS; New York Medical MD
Chief of Police **Joseph Day** . . . . (607) 664-4763
Manager (Behavioral VA Healthcare)
Sharon McKinley . . . . (607) 664-4513
E-mail: sharon.mckinley@va.gov
Co-Manager (Behavioral VA Healthcare) **Bruce Tucker** . . . (607) 664-4314
E-mail: bruce.tucker@va.gov
Acquisitions and Material Management Logistics
Manager **Randy Metz** . . . . (607) 664-4754
E-mail: randy.metz@va.gov
VA Medical Care Manager **Bruce Tucker** . . . . (607) 664-4603
E-mail: bruce.tucker@va.gov
Public Affairs Officer **Brandon Gardner** . . . . (607) 664-4799
E-mail: brandon.gardner@va.gov

Canandaigua (NY) VA Medical Center

400 Fort Hill Avenue, Canandaigua, NY 14424
Tel: (585) 394-2000 Fax: (585) 393-8328
Internet: www.canandaigua.va.gov
Areas Covered: NY (Counties of Livingston, Monroe, Ontario, Seneca, and Wayne)

• Director (Acting) **Bruce Tucker** . . . . (585) 393-7208
E-mail: bruce.tucker@va.gov
Associate Medical Center Director
Kenneth P. Piazza MHSA, CPHQ . . . . (585) 393-7648
Education: George Washington MHSA
Associate Director for Patient and Nursing Services
COL Lisa A. Lehning USA, RN, MSN, CNS . . . . (585) 393-8175
Education: Georgetown 1990 BSN; U Washington 2005 MSN
Chief of Staff **Joanne J. Malina MD** . . . . (585) 393-7202
E-mail: joanne.malina@va.gov
Education: Texas BSES; Texas Southwestern Medical MD
Chief of Police and Security **Joseph Day** . . . . (585) 393-7402
Fax: (585) 393-7404
Chief Information Officer/Information Systems
Manager **Scott DeCaro** . . . . (585) 393-8260
Fax: (585) 393-8351

Albany (NY) Stratton VA Medical Center (Samuel S. Stratton VA Medical Center)

113 Holland Avenue, Albany, NY 12208
Tel: (518) 626-5000 Fax: (518) 626-6735 Internet: www.albany.va.gov

• Director **Darlene A. DeLancey MT (ASCP)** . . . . (518) 626-6731
E-mail: darlene.delancey@va.gov
Education: SUNY (Albany) BS, MS
Marketing, Development and Public Relations Director
Peter Richard Potter, I . . . . (518) 626-5522
E-mail: peter.potter@va.gov
Education: SUNY (Albany) 1993 BA
Facility Education Manager **Dr. Martha Farber MD** . . . . . . (518) 626-7318
Education: SUNY Downstate Med MD

★ Presidential Appointment Requiring Senate Confirmation ☆ Presidential Appointment ☐ Schedule C Appointment ◇ Career Senior Foreign Service Appointment
● Career Senior Executive Service (SES) Appointment ○ Non-Career Senior Executive Service (SES) Appointment ■ Postal Career Executive Service

Albany (NY) Stratton VA Medical Center *(continued)*

Police Chief **Thomas Gibbons** . . . . . (518) 626-5000
Fax: (518) 626-6758

Syracuse (NY) VA Medical Center
800 Irving Avenue, Syracuse, NY 13210
Tel: (315) 425-4400 Tel: (315) 425-2422 (Public Affairs)
Fax: (315) 425-4375 Internet: www.syracuse.va.gov

● Medical Director
Dr. Judy Hayman FACHE . . . . . (315) 425-4892 ext. 56789
Education: Fairleigh Dickinson PhD

Chief of Staff **Asif Ali** . . . . . (315) 425-4400 ext. 54888

Associate Director for Patient/Nursing Services **Cheryl Czajkowski** . . . . . (315) 425-4400 ext. 53757
Education: SUNY (Upstate Med) BSN; Walden MSN

Education Representative **Tracy Morris** . . . . . (315) 425-4400 ext. 52813
E-mail: tracy.morris@va.gov

Chief of Police **Benjamin Robertson** . . . . . (315) 425-4400 ext. 54684

Patient Representative **Coleen Lancette** . . . . . (315) 425-4345 ext. 54345
E-mail: coleen.lancette@va.gov

Public Affairs Officer **Robert Mclean** . . . . . (315) 425-2422
E-mail: robert.mclean@va.gov

VA Western New York Health Care System
3495 Bailey Avenue, Buffalo, NY 14215
Tel: (716) 834-9200 Tel: (585) 297-1000 Internet: www.buffalo.va.gov

Associate Medical Center Director **Royce Calhoun** . . . . . (716) 862-8526
Education: Colorado MHA; D'Youville BSAcc

Chief of Staff **Grace L. Stringfellow MD** . . . . . (716) 862-8530

Public Affairs Officer **Evangeline Conley** . . . . . (716) 862-8753
E-mail: evangeline.conley@va.gov

Facility Education Coordinator **Laura Russillio** . . . . . (716) 862-6091

VA Police Chief (Acting) **Stephen Coville II** . . . . . (716) 862-8747
E-mail: stephen.coville@va.gov

VISN 2 - New York/New Jersey VA Health Care Network
Building 16, 130 West Kingsbridge Road, Bronx, NY 10468
Tel: (718) 741-4110 Fax: (718) 741-4141 Internet: www.nynj.va.gov

● Network Director **Dr. Joan E. McInerney MD** . . . . . (718) 741-4131
E-mail: joan.mcinerney@va.gov
Education: Stern MBA; Naval Postgrad MA

Deputy Executive Director, Office of Information and Technology Operations **Darlene Delaney** . . . . . (718) 630-2850

Chief Financial Officer **Thomas W. Sharpe** . . . . . (718) 741-4110

Chief Information Officer **Linda Bund** . . . . . (718) 741-4110

Chief Medical Officer **(Vacant)** . . . . . (718) 741-4110

Network Contract Manager **Yolanda Borges** . . . . . (718) 741-4591
E-mail: yolanda.borges@va.gov

Small Business Contracting Officer **Kenneth Mullins** . . . (718) 741-4677
E-mail: kenneth.mullins@va.gov

Small Business Contracting Officer
Myrmetrius Pringle . . . . . (845) 831-2000 ext. 4128
E-mail: myrmetrius.pringle@va.gov

New Jersey

VA New Jersey Health Care System
385 Tremont Avenue, East Orange, NJ 07018-1095
Tel: (973) 676-1000 Tel: (908) 647-0180 (Lyons) Fax: (973) 676-4226
Internet: www.newjersey.va.gov

● Director **Vincent F. Immiti MBA, FACHE** . . . . . (973) 676-1000 ext. 1211

Administrative Officer **Mary Jo Apice** . . . . . (973) 676-1000 ext. 1211
E-mail: maryjo.apice@va.gov

Associate Director **Mara Davis** . . . . . (908) 647-1000 ext. 1212
Education: Brooklyn 1987 BA; Adelphi 1989 MSW; Baruch Col 2011 MPA

Associate Director
John A. Griffith USA (Ret) . . . . . (973) 676-1000 ext. 1212
Education: Rutgers BSN; Central Michigan MHCA

Associate Director for Patient and Nursing Services **Patrick J. Troy RN** . . . . . (973) 676-1000 ext. 1355

Chief of Staff **Beverly R. Delaney** . . . . . (973) 676-1000 ext. 1213

Deputy Chief of Staff **(Vacant)** . . . . . (973) 676-1000 ext. 1214

VA New Jersey Health Care System *(continued)*

Chief Information Officer/Information Resources Management Chief
Kamesha Scarlett . . . . . (908) 647-0180 ext. 4904
151 Knollcroft Road, Lyons, NJ 07939
E-mail: kamesha.scarlett@va.gov

Police and Security Chief
Jose Gonzalez . . . . . (973) 676-1000 ext. 1297 (East Orange, NJ)
E-mail: jose.gonzalez@va.gov Fax: (973) 395-7166
Lyons, NJ: (908) 647-0180 4117

Quality Manager **Linda Moward RN** . . . . . (973) 676-1000 ext. 2266
E-mail: linda.moward@va.gov

Compliance Officer **Cynthia A. Pride RN** . . . . . (973) 676-1000 ext. 3363
E-mail: cynthia.pride@va.gov

Chief Librarian **(Vacant)** . . . . . (973) 676-1000 ext. 4413

Chief Librarian (Lyons Campus) **(Vacant)** . . . . . (908) 647-0180 ext. 4413
151 Knollcroft Road, Lyons, NJ 07939

Education Coordinator **John Phillips** . . . . . (973) 676-1000 ext. 1912
E-mail: john.phillips@va.gov Fax: (973) 395-7148

New York

James J. Peters VA Medical Center
130 West Kingsbridge Road, Bronx, NY 10468
Tel: (718) 584-9000 Fax: (718) 741-4269 Internet: www.bronx.va.gov

● Director **Dr. Erik Langhoff MD, PhD** . . . . . (718) 584-9000 ext. 6513
E-mail: erik.langhoff@va.gov

Associate Director
Rosemary Cancel-Santiago . . . . . (718) 584-9000 ext. 6659

Associate Director for Patient Care Services/Nurse Executive
Kathleen M. Capitulo RN, FAAN . . . . . (718) 584-9000 ext. 6519

Associate Director, Clinical Operations
Sylvia M. Barchue RN . . . . . (718) 584-9000

Chief of Staff **Sarah Garrison** . . . . . (718) 584-9000 ext. 6522

Public Affairs Officer **James Connell** . . . . . (718) 584-9000 ext. 6620
E-mail: jim.connell@va.gov

Librarian **Judy L. Steever** . . . . . (718) 741-4229
E-mail: judy.steever@va.gov

VA New York (NY) Harbor Healthcare System
VA New York Harbor Health Care System,
423 East 23rd Street, New York, NY 10010
Tel: (212) 686-7500 Fax: (212) 951-3487 Internet: www.nyharbor.va.gov

● Director **Martina A. Parauda** . . . . . (212) 951-3240
E-mail: martina.parauda@va.gov

Executive Chief of Staff **Dr. Patrick C. Malloy MD** . . . . . (212) 951-3264

Associate Chief of Staff (Acting)
Lincoln E. Bartholomew . . . . . (212) 686-7500 ext. 2202

Associate Healthcare System Director for Patient Services and Chief Nurse Executive
Cynthia Caroselli RN . . . . . (212) 686-7500 ext. 6805

Associate Director, Facilities and Human Resources
Kathy Gaine . . . . . (718) 630-3521

Associate Director, Finance and Information Management **Jodie A. Jackson** . . . . . (212) 686-7500 ext. 5465

Librarian, Brooklyn Campus **(Vacant)** . . . . . (718) 630-3815

Librarian, Manhattan Campus **Peter Cole** . . . . . (212) 686-7500 ext. 7687

Northport (NY) VA Medical Center
79 Middleville Road, Northport, NY 11768-2290
Tel: (631) 261-4400 Fax: (631) 754-7905 Internet: www.northport.va.gov

Director (Acting) **Dr. Cathy Cruise MD** . . . . . (631) 261-4400 ext. 2747
Education: Virginia 1986 BS; NYU 1991 MD

Librarian **Wendy Isser** . . . . . (631) 261-4400 ext. 2966
Fax: (631) 754-7992

Learning Systems Coordinator
Dale Gradel RN . . . . . (631) 261-4400 ext. 7738
Fax: (631) 754-7998

Police Service Chief **Nicholas "Nick" Squicciarini** . . . . . (631) 754-7924
E-mail: nicholas.squicciarini@va.gov Fax: (631) 266-6013

★ Presidential Appointment Requiring Senate Confirmation ☆ Presidential Appointment □ Schedule C Appointment ◇ Career Senior Foreign Service Appointment
● Career Senior Executive Service (SES) Appointment ○ Non-Career Senior Executive Service (SES) Appointment ■ Postal Career Executive Service

VA Hudson Valley Health Care System
2094 Albany Poast Road, Montrose, NY 10548
Mail: 2094 Albany Post Road, P.O. Box 100, Montrose, NY 10548
Tel: (914) 737-4400 Fax: (914) 788-4244
Internet: http://www.hudsonvalley.va.gov/

Castle Point (NY) Campus
41 Castle Point Road, Wappingers Falls, NY 12590
Tel: (845) 831-2000 Fax: (845) 838-5193
Areas Covered: NY Dutchess, Orange and Sullivan Counties

● Director **Margaret B. Caplan** . . . . (845) 831-2000 ext. 5400
E-mail: margaret.oshea@va.gov
Education: Virginia Tech 1981 BA; Catholic U MLS
Associate Director **Dawn M. Schaal** . . . .(845) 831-2000 ext. 5401
Associate Director of Patient Care
Beverly Duncklee . . . . (845) 831-2000 ext. 5159
Chief of Staff **Dr. Elisa Jacqueline Valencia-Sanchez MD, FAAFP, CMD** . . . . (845) 831-2000 ext. 5471
E-mail: Elisa.ValenciaSanchez@va.gov
Public Affairs Officer
Renee Giordano LCSW . . . . (845) 831-2000 ext. 5234
E-mail: Renee.Giordano@va.gov

Franklin Delano Roosevelt Campus (FDR Montrose Campus)
2094 Albany Post Road, P.O. Box 100, Montrose, NY 10548
Tel: (914) 737-4400 Fax: (914) 788-4244
Areas Covered: NY: Westchester, Rockland, and Putnam Counties

● Director **Margaret B. Caplan** . . . . (914) 737-4400 ext. 2400
E-mail: margaret.oshea@va.gov
Education: Virginia Tech 1981 BA; Catholic U MLS
Associate Director **Dawn M. Schaal** . . . .(914) 737-4400 ext. 2401
Associate Director of Patient Care
Beverly Duncklee . . . . (914) 737-4400 ext. 2486
Chief of Staff **Dr. Elisa Jacqueline Valencia-Sanchez MD, FAAFP, CMD** . . . . (914) 737-4400 ext. 2471
E-mail: Elisa.ValenciaSanchez@va.gov
Facility Chief Information Officer **Angel Pagan** . . . .(914) 788-4828
E-mail: angel.pagan@va.gov
Tel: (845) 831-2000 6319
Public Affairs Officer
Renee Giordano LCSW . . . . (914) 737-4400 ext. 2255
E-mail: Renee.Giordano@va.gov

VISN 4 - VA Capitol Healthcare Network

323 North Shore Drive, Suite 400, Pittsburgh, PA 15212
Fax: (412) 822-3295 Internet: www.visn4.va.gov
Areas Covered: PA, and counties within DE, NJ, NY, OH and WV

● Network Director **Dr. Michael D. Adelman** . . . . (412) 822-3314
E-mail: michael.adelman@va.gov
Education: Allegheny BS; Pittsburgh 1981 MD
Executive Assistant **Jo Petro** . . . .(412) 822-3315
E-mail: Josephine.Petro@va.gov
Deputy Network Director **Charles R. Thilges** . . . .(412) 822-3313
Chief Financial Officer **Beth Howard** . . . .(412) 822-3322
Chief Information Officer **Mark Haxton** . . . .(412) 822-3310
Chief Logistics Officer **James McKinley** . . . . (570) 830-7020
E-mail: james.mckinley@va.gov
Chief Medical Officer **Timothy R. Burke MD** . . . . (412) 822-3309
E-mail: timothy.burke@va.gov
Education: Pittsburgh 1996 MD
Network Contract Manager **Benjamin "Ben" Iachiani** . . . (412) 822-3314
E-mail: benjamin.iachaini@va.gov
Small Business Contracting Officer **(Vacant)** . . . . (412) 822-3775
Communications Manager and Public Affairs Officer
David E. Cowgill . . . .(412) 822-3318
E-mail: david.cowgill@va.gov Fax: (412) 954-4841
Quality Management Officer **Moira M. Hughes** . . . .(412) 822-3294

Delaware

Wilmington (DE) VA Medical Center
1601 Kirkwood Highway, Wilmington, DE 19805
Tel: (800) 461-8262 Tel: (302) 994-2511 Fax: (302) 633-5516
Internet: www.wilmington.va.gov

● Director **Vincent R. "Vince" Kane** . . . .(302) 633-5201
Associate Director of Operations
Kimberly "Kim" Butler MPH . . . . (302) 994-2511 ext. 5202
Associate Director for Patient Care Services
Kathleen Craige MSN, RN-BC, NEA-BC . . . . (302) 994-2511 ext. 5201
Education: Penn State BSN; Drexel MSN Fax: (302) 633-5591
Chief of Staff (Interim) **George L. Tzanis** . . . . . (302) 994-2511 ext. 5202
Education: Temple 1986 BA; Penn State (Hershey) 1995 MD

Pennsylvania

Coatesville (PA) Veterans Affairs Medical Center
1400 Black Horse Hill Road, Coatesville, PA 19320-2096
Tel: (610) 384-7711 Fax: (610) 383-0207
Internet: www.coatesville.va.gov

● Director **Carla Acre Sivek** . . . . (610) 380-4303
Chief of Staff **Dr. Michael F. Gliatto MD** . . . . (610) 383-0219
Public Affairs Specialist **Kirk Fernitz** . . . . (610) 384-7711 ext. 4348
E-mail: Kirk.Fernitz@va.gov
Librarian **(Vacant)** . . . .(610) 384-7711 ext. 4288

Corporal Michael J. Crescenz VA Medical Center (Corporal Michael J. Crescenz VAMC)
3900 Woodland Avenue, Philadelphia, PA 19104
Tel: (215) 823-5800 Fax: (215) 823-6007
Internet: www.philadelphia.va.gov

● Director **Daniel D. "Dan" Hendee MHA, FACHE** . . . . (215) 823-5857
Education: Eastern Michigan 1982 BA; Detroit 1989 MHSA
Secretary **Matt Harding** . . . .(215) 823-5857
Director of Public Affairs **Fern Billet** . . . .(215) 823-5916
E-mail: fern.billet@va.gov
Associate Director for Clinical Operations
Patricia O'Kane . . . . (215) 823-5856
Education: Bryn Mawr MSS
Associate Director for Operations (Interim)
Nancy Hofstetter . . . .(215) 823-5858
Associate Director for Patient Care Services/Chief Nursing Officer
Coy L. Smith RN, MSN, NEA-BC, FACHE . . . .(215) 823-5896
Chief of Staff **Dr. John J. Kelly MD** . . . .(215) 823-5859
Librarian **Priscilla Stevenson** . . . . (215) 823-6699

Erie (PA) VA Medical Center
135 East 38th Street, Erie, PA 16504
Tel: (814) 868-8661 Fax: (814) 860-2135 Internet: www.erie.va.gov

Director **John A. Gennaro FACHE, MHSA** . . . . (814) 860-2576
Education: Saint Xavier Col BA, MBA
Chief of Staff **Dr. David M. Lavin** . . . .(814) 860-2581

James E. Van Zandt Altoona (PA) VA Medical Center
2907 Pleasant Valley Boulevard, Altoona, PA 16602-4377
Tel: (814) 943-8164 Tel: (814) 940-6404 (Public Affairs)
Fax: (814) 940-7898 Internet: www.altoona.va.gov

● Director **Sigrid D. Andrew** . . . . (814) 943-8164 ext. 7031
Education: Wilmington U BSN; Maryland MHCA
Associate Director
Dr. Derek Coughenour PT, DPT, MPM . . . . . .(814) 943-8164 ext. 7031
Education: Penn State 2000 BS; Pittsburgh 2003 DPT; Carnegie Mellon 2012 MPM
Associate Director for Patient/Nursing Services (Acting) **Debra Meyers** . . . . (814) 943-8164 ext. 7133
Chief Information Officer **(Vacant)** . . . . (814) 943-8164 ext. 7030
Chief of Staff (Interim) **Dr. R. Samuel Magee MD** . . . . . .(814) 943-8164
Education: Air Force Acad (Portugal) 1984 BS; Cal State (Sacramento) 1996 MEc
Contracting Officer **Michael Koontz** . . . . (814) 943-8164 ext. 7234
Librarian Technician **Maureen Novella** . . . . (814) 943-8164 ext. 7156
Education Program Specialist **Jeff Lesko** . . . . . . (814) 943-8164 ext. 7421
E-mail: jeff.lesko@va.gov

★ Presidential Appointment Requiring Senate Confirmation ☆ Presidential Appointment ☐ Schedule C Appointment ◇ Career Senior Foreign Service Appointment
● Career Senior Executive Service (SES) Appointment ○ Non-Career Senior Executive Service (SES) Appointment ■ Postal Career Executive Service

James E. Van Zandt Altoona (PA) VA Medical Center *(continued)*

Police Services Chief **Paul Blanchard** . . . . (814) 943-8164 ext. 7258
E-mail: paul.blanchard@va.gov

Lebanon (PA) VA Medical Center
1700 South Lincoln Avenue, Lebanon, PA 17042-7597
Tel: (717) 272-6621 Fax: (717) 228-5907 Internet: www.lebanon.va.gov

• Director **Robert W. "Bob" Callahan, Jr.** . . . . . . (717) 272-6621 ext. 5904
Education: St Mary's Col (MD) BS
Associate Director **Jeffrey A. Beiler II** . . . . (717) 228-6621 ext. 4000
Education: Cedarville U 1993 BA; Kutztown 1999 MBA
Associate Director, Patient Care Services
Margaret Wilson RN . . . . (717) 272-6621 ext. 5223
Chief of Staff
COL Stuart A. Roop MC, USA, FCCP . . . . . . (717) 272-6621 ext. 5929
Education: West Point 1988 BS; Uniformed Services 1996 MD
Chief Information Officer **Andru Ditzler** . . . . (717) 228-6111
E-mail: andru.ditzler@va.gov Fax: (717) 228-6092
Director, Quality Management
Laine Hellein RN . . . . (717) 272-6621 ext. 4407
Education Chief **Jose Tores RN** . . . . (717) 272-6621 ext. 4432
Fax: (717) 228-5905
Library Service Chief **Kristine Scannell** . . . . . . (717) 272-6621 ext. 4746
E-mail: kristine.scannell@va.gov
Police Office Chief **Grover Royal** . . . . (717) 228-5911
E-mail: grover.royal@va.gov Fax: (717) 228-6139
Contracting Officer **Seth Custer** . . . . (717) 228-6197
E-mail: seth.custer@va.gov
Public and Community Relations Manager
Douglas Etter . . . . (717) 228-6079
E-mail: douglas.etter@va.gov Fax: (717) 228-5907

VA Butler Healthcare
325 New Castle Road, Butler, PA 16001-2480
Tel: (724) 287-4781 Fax: (724) 282-4408 Internet: www.butler.va.gov
Areas Covered: OH (Mahoning County), PA (Counties of Armstrong, Butler, Clarion, Lawrence, Mercer)

• Director **MAJ Jon R. Lasell, Jr. USA** . . . . (878) 271-6681
Education: Prairie View A&M BS; Baylor MS
Associate Director **Rebecca Hubscher MSW, MBA** . . . . . (878) 271-6681
Education: Carlow Col MS; Pittsburgh MSW; Waynesburg Col MBA
Nurse Executive and Associate Director of Patient Care Services **Sharon Coyle RN, MSN, MBA** . . . . (878) 271-6682
Education: Duquesne BSN; Waynesburg Col MBA, MSN
Chief of Staff (Acting) **JoAnne Suffoletto** . . . . (878) 271-6680
Manager Information Systems/Chief Information Officer **Kirk Hastings** . . . . (724) 477-5042
Purchasing Officer **Richard Anzelone** . . . . (724) 285-2271
Supervisory Police Officer **Thomas Bennett** . . . . (724) 477-5002
Events Planner **Amanda Kurtz** . . . . (724) 282-5583
Education Coordinator **James "Jim" Bilanich** . . . . (724) 477-5024
Fax: (724) 477-5061
Library Technician **MaryAnn Wagner** . . . . (724) 287-4781
E-mail: maryann.wagner@va.gov

VA Pittsburgh (PA) Healthcare System
University Drive C, Oakland Division, Pittsburgh, PA 15240
Tel: (412) 360-6000 Fax: (412) 360-6789
Internet: www.pittsburgh.va.gov

• Director **Karin L. McGraw FACHE, MSN** . . . . (412) 360-6391
E-mail: karin.mcgraw@va.gov
Education: West Virginia 1979 BSN; Bellarmine U 1992 MS
Special Assistant to Director
Margaret "Peggy" Donahoe . . . . (412) 360-6391
E-mail: margaret.donahoe@va.gov
Deputy Director **Barbara Forsha MSN, RN** . . . . (412) 360-6391
Secretary to Deputy Director **Rosemary Shaw** . . . . (412) 360-6101
E-mail: rosemary.shaw@va.gov
Chief of Staff **Dr. Ali Sonel** . . . . (412) 360-6102
E-mail: ali.sonel@va.gov
Associate Director **Lovetta O. Ford LCSW** . . . . (412) 822-3325
Education: West Virginia BS, 1991 MS
Associate Director, Patient Care Services
Ira Richmond . . . . (412) 360-6103

VA Pittsburgh (PA) Healthcare System *(continued)*

Education Director **JoAnne Suffoletto** . . . . (412) 360-6591
E-mail: joanne.suffoletto@va.gov Fax: (412) 360-6595
Security Chief **Scott Engel** . . . . (412) 360-6483
E-mail: scott.engel@va.gov Fax: (412) 360-6860
Information Security Officer [Chief Information Officer] **Judith "Judy" Buccini** . . . . (412) 822-3270
E-mail: judith.buccini@va.gov Fax: (412) 822-3366

Wilkes-Barre (PA) VA Medical Center
1111 East End Boulevard, Wilkes Barre, PA 18711-0026
Tel: (570) 824-3521 Tel: (877) 928-2621 Fax: (570) 821-7278
Internet: www.wilkes-barre.va.gov

Medical Center Director **Russell E. Lloyd** . . . . (570) 821-7204
Executive Assistant **William Klaips** . . . . (570) 830-7042
Associate Director **Joseph F. Sharon** . . . . (570) 821-7206
Chief of Staff **Mirza Z. Ali MD** . . . . (570) 821-7207
E-mail: mirza.ali@va.gov
Chief, Primary Care Services
Bina Ahmed MD . . . . (570) 824-3521 ext. 4253
Associate Chief of Staff for Research and Development **Michael J. Surdy PharmD** . . . . (570) 824-3521 ext. 4995
Associate Director for Nursing Services
Valerie M. Boytin RN, MSN . . . . (570) 821-7238
ACOS, Mental Health and Behavioral Medicine Service
Marcia Flugsrud-Breckenridge . . . . (570) 824-3521 ext. 7931
Chief, Business Office, Health Administrative Service **David Brown** . . . . (570) 824-3521 ext. 4643
Geriatrics and Extended Care Service Associate Chief **Linda Zaneski RN** . . . . (570) 824-3521 ext. 7803
Imaging Service Chief
Dr. Joseph Rienzi MD . . . . (570) 824-3521 ext. 7861
Facilities Management Service Chief
Christopher English . . . . (570) 824-3521 ext. 7350
Fiscal Service Chief **David Cichocki** . . . . (570) 824-3521 ext. 7211
Human Resources Service Chief
Dawn DeMorrow . . . . (570) 824-3521 ext. 4963
E-mail: dawn.demorrow@va.gov
Medical and Rehabilitation Service Chief
Nabeela Mian . . . . (570) 824-3521 ext. 7600
E-mail: nabeela.mian@va.gov
Nutrition and Food Services Chief
Gina Foltz . . . . (570) 824-3521 ext. 7442
Pharmacy Service Chief **Donna Tigue** . . . . (570) 824-3521 ext. 7114
Police Service Chief **Albert Felker** . . . . (570) 824-3521 ext. 5112
E-mail: albert.felker@va.gov
Social Work Service Chief (Acting)
Leonard McNabb . . . . (570) 824-3521 ext. 4368
Staff Development Service Chief
Susan Lewis . . . . (570) 824-3521 ext. 4172
Surgical Service Chief
Dr. Ghazali A. Chaudry MD . . . . (570) 824-3521 ext. 7557
Voluntary Service Chief **Debra Schlosser** . . . . . (570) 830-7022 ext. 7448
Librarian **(Vacant)** . . . . (570) 824-3521 ext. 7422
Webmaster **(Vacant)** . . . . (570) 824-3521 ext. 7248

West Virginia

Louis A. Johnson VA Medical Center
1 Medical Center Drive, Clarksburg, WV 26301
Tel: (304) 623-3461 Internet: www.clarksburg.va.gov
Areas Covered: Harrison and surrounding counties and Community Based Outpatient Clinics (CBOCs) at Braxton, Monongalia, Tucker and Wood Counties.

• Director **Glenn R. Snider, Jr. MD, FACP** . . . . (304) 623-7602
Associate Director **Terry Massey** . . . . (304) 623-7604
Chief of Staff **Dr. Pramoda Devabhaktuni MD** . . . . (304) 623-7606
Library Technician **Annette Webb** . . . . (304) 623-3461 ext. 3435
E-mail: annette.webb@va.gov

★ Presidential Appointment Requiring Senate Confirmation ☆ Presidential Appointment □ Schedule C Appointment ◇ Career Senior Foreign Service Appointment
● Career Senior Executive Service (SES) Appointment ○ Non-Career Senior Executive Service (SES) Appointment ■ Postal Career Executive Service

VISN 5 - Capitol Health Care Network

849 International Drive, Suite 275, Linthicum, MD 21090
Tel: (410) 691-1131 Fax: (410) 684-3189 Internet: www.va.gov/visn5

- ● Network Director (Acting) **Dr. Raymond Chung MD** .... (410) 691-1131
- Deputy Network Director **Guy B. Richardson FACHE** .... (410) 691-1131
- Chief Financial Officer **Daniel Luttrell** .... (410) 691-1135
- Chief Information Officer **James Nichols** ..... (304) 263-0811 ext. 4021
  VA Medical Center, Rte. 9, Fax: (304) 262-4859
  Martinsburg, WV 25401
- Chief Logistics Officer **William Pritchett** .... (410) 691-1131
- Chief Medical Officer **(Vacant)** .... (410) 691-1131
- Network Contract Manager **Scott Sands** .... (410) 691-1131
  - Small Business Liaison **Alison Klein** .... (304) 623-3461 ext. 4143
    E-mail: Alison.Klein@va.gov
- Quality Management Officer **Jeffrey D. Lee RN** .... (410) 691-1131
- Human Resources **William Coy** .... (410) 691-1291
  E-mail: william.coy@va.gov
- Strategic Planner **Kimberly D. Marvin** .... (410) 691-1131
  E-mail: kimberly.marvin@va.gov
- Webmaster **Kim Taylor** .... (304) 263-0811 ext. 4309
  E-mail: kimberly.taylor@va.gov

District of Columbia

Washington (DC) VA Medical Center
50 Irving Street, NW, Washington, DC 20422
Tel: (202) 745-8000 Fax: (202) 745-8530
Internet: www.washingtondc.va.gov

- ● Director **COL Michael S. Heimall USA** .... (202) 745-8350
  E-mail: michael.heimall@va.gov
- Deputy Medical Center Director **(Vacant)** .... (202) 745-8000
- Chief of Staff **Dr. Charles Faselis MD** .... (202) 745-8225
  Education: U Athens MD
- Chief Information Officer **Dennis Wells** .... (202) 745-8000
  Education: Naval Acad 1982 BS; San Diego State 1989 MA
- Assistant Director **Stanley L. Staton USA (Ret)** .... (202) 745-8000
  Education: St Leo U BA; U Phoenix MBA
- Chief of Human Resource Management Service
  Shannon Carroll .... (202) 745-8605
  E-mail: shannon.carroll@va.gov
- Chief of Pharmacy Services (Acting) **Ivan P. Cephas** .... (202) 745-8000
- Nurse Executive **Denise L. Boehm MSN, RN** .... (202) 745-8000
  Education: Carlow U BSN, MSNE
- Nurse Manager, Medical Intensive Care Unit **(Vacant)** .... (202) 745-8000
- Director of Public Affairs and Community Relations
  Gloria Hairston .... (202) 745-4037
  E-mail: gloria.hairston@va.gov

VA Maryland Health Care System

10 North Greene Street, Baltimore, MD 21201
Internet: www.maryland.va.gov

- ● Director **VADM Adam M. Robinson, Jr. USN (Ret), MD, MBA, FACS, CPE** .... (410) 605-7016
  E-mail: adam.robinson@va.gov
  Education: South Florida MBA; Indiana (Indianapolis) MD
- Chief of Staff **Dr. Sandra "Sandie" Marshall MD** ...... (410) 605-7019
  E-mail: sandie.marshall@va.gov
- Deputy Chief of Staff and Chief Medical Officer
  (Vacant) .... (410) 605-7019
- Associate Director for Finance **(Vacant)** .... (410) 642-1012
- Associate Director for Operations **Frederick P. Soetje** .... (410) 605-7017
  Education: Long Island 1987 (Attended);
  Massachusetts Pharmacy 1990 BSPh;
  Maryland University Col 2006 MHCA
- Associate Director for Patient Care Services/Chief
  Nurse Executive **Sheila Bryson-Eckroade** .... (410) 605-7041
  E-mail: sheila.bryson-eckroade@va.gov
  Education: North Carolina Greensboro BSN, MSN

Baltimore (MD) VA Medical Center
10 North Greene Street, Baltimore, MD 21201
Tel: (410) 605-7000 Fax: (410) 605-7900

- Police Security Chief **Troy Brown** .... (410) 605-7305
  Fax: (410) 605-7880

Perry Point (MD) VA Medical Center
Building 5, Perry Point, MD 21902
Tel: (410) 642-2411 Fax: (410) 642-1165

- Site Manager **(Vacant)** .... (410) 642-1012

West Virginia

Martinsburg (WV) VA Medical Center
510 Butler Avenue, Martinsburg, WV 25405
Tel: (304) 263-0811 Fax: (304) 262-7433
Internet: www.martinsburg.va.gov
Areas Covered: MD (Counties of Allegany, Frederick, Garrett and Washington), PA (Counties of Franklin and Fulton), VA (Counties of Clarke, Fauquier, Frederick, Loudoun, Page, Rappahannock, Rockingham, Shenandoah and Warren), WV (Counties of Berkeley, Grant, Hampshire, Hardy, Jefferson, Mineral, Morgan and Pendleton)

- ● Director **Timothy J. Cooke** .... (304) 263-0811 ext. 4000
- Associate Medical Center Director **(Vacant)** .... (304) 263-0811 ext. 4004
- Associate Director, Patient Care Services
  Sandra C. Sullivan .... (304) 263-0811 ext. 3656
- Chief of Learning Resources
  Agnes Llewellyn .... (304) 263-0811 ext. 3821
  E-mail: agnes.llewellyn@va.gov
- Chief of Police **Robin Hardy** .... (304) 263-0811 ext. 4100
- Chief of Staff **Dr. Richard Siemens MD, JD** .... (304) 263-0811
- Patient Representative **Phillip Garvey** .... (304) 263-0811 ext. 3068
- Public Affairs Officer **Michael McAleer** .... (304) 263-0811 ext. 4013
- Webmaster **(Vacant)** .... (304) 263-0811 ext. 4079

VISN 6 - VA Mid-Atlantic Healthcare Network

The Durham Centre, 300 West Morgan Street,
Suite 700, Durham, NC 27701
Tel: (919) 956-5541 Fax: (919) 956-7152 Internet: www.visn6.va.gov

- ● Network Director **DeAnne M. Seekins MBA** .... (919) 956-5541
- Deputy Network Director **(Vacant)** .... (919) 956-5541
- Chief Information Officer **Milton Harrison** .... (919) 956-5541
- Chief Medical Officer **Dr. Mark E. Shelhorse MD** ...... (919) 956-5541
  Education: Augusta 1977 BS; Medical Col (GA) 1981 MD
- Communications Officer **(Vacant)** .... (919) 956-5541
- Network Contract Manager **David Weller** .... (757) 728-3113
  - Senior Procurement Analyst **(Vacant)** .... (757) 728-3113
  - Procurement Analyst **(Vacant)** .... (757) 315-3984
- Webmaster **Mark Thompson** .... (919) 956-5541
  E-mail: mark.thompson@va.gov

North Carolina

Charles George VA Medical Center- Asheville, NC (Charles George VAMC)
1100 Tunnel Road, Asheville, NC 28805
Tel: (828) 298-7911 Internet: www.asheville.va.gov

- ● Medical Center Director
  Stephanie A. Young .... (828) 298-7911 ext. 5224
  Fax: (828) 299-2563
- Associate Director **Robert D. Evans** .... (828) 298-7911 ext. 5212
- Executive Nurse and Associate Director for
  Patient Care Services **David Przestrzelski** .... (828) 298-7911 ext. 5449
- Chief of Staff (Acting) **Paul Riggs** .... (828) 298-7911 ext. 5221
- Information Resource Management
  Director/Chief Information Officer
  Carla McLendon .... (828) 298-7911 ext. 5698
  E-mail: carla.mclendon@va.gov Fax: (828) 299-5888
- Designated Learning Officer and
  Chief, Learning Resources Service
  Charles Cooley .... (828) 298-7911 ext. 5517
  Fax: (828) 299-2500
- Chief of Police **Anthony Laush** .... (828) 298-7911 ext. 2915
  E-mail: anthony.laush2@va.gov
- Public Affairs Officer **Scott Pittillo** .... (828) 298-7911 ext. 4446
  E-mail: scott.pittillo@va.gov

★ Presidential Appointment Requiring Senate Confirmation ☆ Presidential Appointment ☐ Schedule C Appointment ◇ Career Senior Foreign Service Appointment
● Career Senior Executive Service (SES) Appointment ○ Non-Career Senior Executive Service (SES) Appointment ■ Postal Career Executive Service

DEPARTMENTS

Durham (NC) VA Health Care System
508 Fulton Street, Durham, NC 27705-3875
Tel: (919) 286-0411 Fax: (919) 286-6805 Internet: www.durham.va.gov

● Director **Paul S. Crews MPH, CPHQ, FACHE** .... (919) 286-0411
E-mail: paul.crews@va.gov
Education: Southwest Texas State 2000 BHCA; Texas A&M 2002 MPH
Administrative Assistant to the Director **Abby Parker** ... (919) 286-0411
Education: Columbia Col (MO) 2012 BA; Liberty 2016 MA Fax: (919) 286-6805
Associate Director **Kevin Amick** .... (919) 286-0411
Education: Old Dominion BS; Strayer U 2010 MBA
Assistant Director (Acting) **Dan Fields** .... (919) 286-0411
Chief of Staff **Kenneth C. Goldberg MD** .... (919) 286-6907
E-mail: kenneth.goldberg@va.gov
Associate Chief of Staff for Education **(Vacant)** .... (919) 286-6909
Fax: (919) 416-5890
Associate Director for Patient Care Services/Chief Nurse Executive (Acting)
Marri "Nicki" Fryar MBA, MHA, BSN, RN .... (919) 286-0411
Education: North Carolina Central 1992 BSN; Pfeiffer U 2007 MBA; Pfeiffer Col 2007 MHA
Chief Information Officer **Seginald Bryant** .... (919) 416-5812
Education: Cincinnati 2003 BS
Chief, Library Services **Jeffrey Kager** .... (919) 286-6929
E-mail: jeff.kager@va.gov
Education: SUNY Col (Buffalo) 1979 BS, 1983 MLS
Police and Security Service Chief **Dean Dockus** .... (919) 286-6872
E-mail: dean.dockus@va.gov

Fayetteville (NC) VA Medical Center
2300 Ramsey Street, Fayetteville, NC 28301
Tel: (910) 488-2120 Fax: (910) 822-7927
Internet: www.fayettevillenc.va.gov

● Director **COL James A. Laterza USA (Ret)** ... (910) 488-2120 ext. 7401
Education: Cameron 1989 BA; Central Michigan 1993 MA
Associate Director **Donna Fagan** .... (910) 488-2120 ext. 7100
Associate Director, Patient Care Services
Debra Young .... (910) 488-2120 ext. 7997
Chief of Staff
Dr. Gregory A. Antoine MD, FACS .... (910) 488-2120 ext. 7061
Education: SUNY (Buffalo) 1976 MD
Public Affairs Officer **Jeffery "Jeff" Melvin** ... (910) 488-2120 ext. 5991
E-mail: jeffery.melvin2@va.gov
Chief Information Officer/Information Resources Management Service Chief
Mark Grady .... (910) 488-2120 ext. 7444

W. G. "Bill" Hefner VA Medical Center- Salisbury, NC (Salisbury NC VA Medical Center)
1601 Brenner Avenue, Salisbury, NC 28144
Tel: (704) 638-9000 Fax: (704) 638-3395 Fax: (704) 638-3346
Internet: www.salisbury.va.gov

● Medical Center Director **Joseph "Joe" Vaughn** .... (704) 638-3344
Education: U Phoenix BS; Mississippi State MBA
Associate Medical Center Director
Linette L. Baker MPA .... (704) 638-9000
Education: Southern Illinois BVEd; Oklahoma 1997 MPA
Executive Nurse and Associate Director for Patient Care Services
Elizabeth A. Stroup .... (704) 638-9000 ext. 12980
Education: Iowa 2003 BSN; Clarkson Col 2008 MSN
Chief of Staff **Subbarao Pemmaraju** .... (704) 638-3353 ext. 3353
E-mail: subbarao.pemmaraju2@va.gov
Education: North Carolina MHA
Chief Information Officer **Deborah Clark** ...... (704) 638-9000 ext. 4847
E-mail: deborah.clark@va.gov
Medical Librarian **Nancy Martino** .... (704) 638-9000 ext. 4064
Kernersville Health Care Center
Administrator **Brent J. Erickson** .... (336) 515-5000 ext. 21299
Charlotte Health Care Center Administrator
(Vacant) .... (704) 329-1300 ext. 3111

Virginia

Hampton (VA) VA Medical Center
100 Emancipation Drive, Hampton, VA 23667
Tel: (757) 722-9961 Fax: (757) 728-7000 Internet: www.hampton.va.gov

● Director **James Ronald "Ron" Johnson FACHE** .... (757) 722-9961
E-mail: james.johnson1ca475@va.gov
Education: William & Mary; Medical Col (VA) MD
Executive Assistant **Sheila Bailey** .... (757) 722-9961 ext. 3077
Associate Director for Operations
Dr. Taquisa K. Simmons PhD .... (757) 728-3101
Education: Norfolk State BS, MSW; Regent U PhD
Associate Director for Patient Care Services
Crystal Lindaman .... (757) 722-9961
Chief of Staff **Dr. Priscilla Hankins MD** .... (757) 728-3102

Hunter Holmes McGuire VA Medical Center- Richmond, VA
1201 Broad Rock Boulevard, Richmond, VA 23249
Tel: (804) 675-5000 Fax: (804) 675-5585 Internet: www.richmond.va.gov

● Director (Acting) **Alan Lombardo** .... (804) 675-5501
Education: Slippery Rock U 1998 BS; Shenandoah 2002 MS; Baylor 2011 MHA
Public Affairs Director **Darlene Edwards** .... (804) 675-5242
E-mail: darlene.edwards@va.gov
Librarian **Susana Hernandez-Kurtulus** .... (804) 675-5000 ext. 3223

Salem (VA) VA Medical Center
1970 Roanoke Boulevard, Salem, VA 24153
Tel: (540) 982-2463 Fax: (540) 983-1096 Internet: www.salem.va.gov

Director **Rebecca J. "Becky" Stackhouse**
FACHE, MA .... (540) 982-2463 ext. 2100
Education: Central Michigan 1991 MA
Associate Director **Allen R. Moye** .... (540) 982-2463 ext. 2102
Secretary to the Director
Eva Goldfield-Strausbaugh .... (540) 982-2463 ext. 2100
Chief of Staff **Dr. Anne Hutchins** .... (540) 982-2463
E-mail: anne.hutchins@va.gov
Chief of Human Resources **Brian T. Zeman** .... (540) 982-2463 ext. 2102
Associate Director, Patient/Nursing Service
(Acting) **Pamela McAnally MSN, RN** .... (540) 982-2463 ext. 2401
E-mail: pamela.mcanally@va.gov
Chief Information Officer/Information
Resource Management Chief **James Knox** ... (540) 982-2463 ext. 2058
Fax: (540) 855-3409
Public Affairs Officer **Anne Benois** .... (540) 855-3460
Chief Librarian **Jaime Blankenship** .... (540) 982-2463

West Virginia

Beckley (WV) VA Medical Center
200 Veterans Avenue, Beckley, WV 25801
Tel: (304) 255-2121 Fax: (304) 256-5495 Internet: www.beckley.va.gov

● Director **Stacy J. Vasquez** .... (304) 255-2121 ext. 4100
Associate Director
John D. Stout MBA, USMC (Ret) .... (304) 255-2121 ext. 4159
Education: Mississippi 1999 BA; Naval Postgrad 2004 MBA
Associate Director for Patient Care Services/Nurse Executive
Debra Lynn Legg .... (304) 255-2121 ext. 4499
Fax: (304) 256-5495
Chief of Staff **Dr. Mark Harris MD, MC, USA (Ret)** ..... (304) 255-2121
Chief Information Officer
William B. "Bill" Shepperd, Jr. .... (304) 255-2121 ext. 4962
E-mail: william.shepperd@med.va.gov
Public Affairs Officer **Sara Yoke** .... (304) 255-2121 ext. 4883
E-mail: sara.yoke@va.gov
Purchasing Officer **Steve McGraw** .... (304) 255-2121 ext. 4135
Librarian **Lois Watson** .... (304) 255-2121 ext. 4342
E-mail: lois.watson@va.gov
Supervisory Information Technology
Specialist **Sherry Gregg** .... (304) 255-2121 ext. 4124
E-mail: sherry.gregg@va.gov

★ Presidential Appointment Requiring Senate Confirmation ☆ Presidential Appointment ☐ Schedule C Appointment ◇ Career Senior Foreign Service Appointment
● Career Senior Executive Service (SES) Appointment ○ Non-Career Senior Executive Service (SES) Appointment ■ Postal Career Executive Service

DEPARTMENTS

Hershel "Woody" Williams VA Medical Center (Huntington VAMC)
1540 Spring Valley Drive, Huntington, WV 25704
Tel: (304) 429-6755 Fax: (304) 429-7570
Internet: www.huntington.va.gov

- ● Director **J. Brian Nimmo** .... (304) 429-6741 ext. 2271
  E-mail: brian.nimmo@va.gov
- Associate Director **(Vacant)** .... (304) 429-6741 ext. 2272
- Associate Director for Patient Care Services (Acting) **Carrie L. Hensley** .... (304) 429-6741 ext. 2100
  Fax: (304) 429-7576
- Chief of Staff **Jeffery B. Breaux MD** .... (304) 429-6741 ext. 2275
  E-mail: jeffery.breaux@va.gov
- Associate Chief of Staff, Ambulatory Care **James S. Duthie** .... (304) 429-6741 ext. 2122
- Chief, Financial Operations **Cindy Dyer** .... (304) 429-6741 ext. 2420
  Fax: (304) 429-7567
- Chief, Engineering Services **John Klim** .... (304) 429-6741 ext. 2373
  E-mail: john.klim2@va.gov
- Chief Information Officer **Brandon Richmond** .... (304) 429-6741 ext. 3284
- Chief Learning Officer **Melissa Johnson** ...... (304) 429-6741 ext. 2497
- Veterans Justice Outreach Specialist **Tammy Miller** ...... (304) 429-6741
- Veterans Outreach Specialist **Krista White** .... (304) 429-6741

VISN 7 - VA Southeast Network

3700 Crestwood Parkway NW, Suite 220,
Suite 500, Duluth, GA 30096
Tel: (678) 924-5700 Fax: (678) 924-5757 Internet: www.southeast.va.gov

- ● Network Director **Leslie B. Wiggins** .... (678) 924-5700
  E-mail: leslie.wiggins@va.gov
  Education: Ohio State; Indiana; Indiana Wesleyan 1997
  Staff Assistant to the Director **Benita Miller** .... (678) 924-5700
- Deputy Network Director **(Vacant)** .... (678) 924-5702
- Chief Financial Officer **Brenda Schmitz** .... (706) 924-5700
- Chief Medical Officer **Ajay K. "Aj" Dhawan** .... (678) 924-5700
- Chief Nursing Officer **(Vacant)** .... (678) 924-5700
- Patient Safety Officer **Robin Anderson** .... (678) 924-5703
  E-mail: robin.anderson@va.gov
- Quality Management Officer **Heather Miller** .... (678) 924-5723
- Network Contract Manager **Prudence Howard** .... (706) 823-3943
  E-mail: prudence.howard@va.gov
  Small Business Contracting Officer **(Vacant)** .... (404) 321-6111 ext. 7652
- Health System Specialist **(Vacant)** .... (678) 924-5725

Alabama

Birmingham (AL) VA Medical Center
700 South 19th Street, Birmingham, AL 35233
Tel: (205) 933-8101 Internet: www.birmingham.va.gov
Areas Covered: Tertiary Care: AL, Western GA; Primary/Secondary Care: Northern AL

- Director **Thomas C. Smith III FACHE** .... (205) 558-4726
- Associate Director **Mary S. Mitchell** .... (205) 558-4801
- Assistant Director **Kelvin Owens** .... (205) 558-4801
- Associate Director for Patient/Nursing Services **Cynthia D. Cleveland DNP, RN, NE-BC** .... (205) 933-8101
- Chief of Staff **Dr. Oladipo A. Kukoyi** .... (205) 933-8101 ext. 4711
  Education: Alabama Birmingham 1999 MD
- Chief Information Officer **Antonia "Toni" Mohamed** .... (205) 933-8101 ext. 7070
  E-mail: antonia.mohamed@va.gov
- Public Affairs Director **Jeffrey A. Hester** .... (205) 558-4744
  E-mail: jeffrey.hester@va.gov

Central Alabama Veterans Health Care System (CAVHCS)
Montgomery VA Medical Center - West Campus,
215 Perry Hill Road, Montgomery, AL 36109
Montgomery VA Medical Center - East Campus,
2400 Hospital Road, Tuskegee, AL 36083
Tel: (334) 272-4670 (Montgomery Office)
Tel: (334) 727-0550 (Tuskegee Office)
Internet: www.centralalabama.va.gov
Areas Covered: South and Central AL, Southwest GA

- ● Director **Linda Boyle** .... (334) 272-4670 ext. 4421
  Secretary **Barbara Green** .... (334) 272-4670
- Associate Director, Operations **(Vacant)** .... (334) 272-4670
- Associate Director, Patient Care Services **Carolyn Caver-Gordon RN** .... (334) 272-4670
- Associate Director **Thomas Huettemann** .... (334) 272-4670
  Education: Troy U MPA
- Assistant Director **(Vacant)** .... (334) 260-4194
- Chief of Staff (Acting) **Dr. Robert R. Norvel MD, EMBA** .... (334) 272-4670 ext. 4096
  Education: Alcorn State 1988 BS; Mississippi Medical 1993 MD; Alabama EMBA
- Chief of Police (Acting) **Elvis Walton** .... (334) 272-4670

Tuscaloosa (AL) VA Medical Center
3701 Loop Road East, Tuscaloosa, AL 35404
Tel: (205) 554-2000 Internet: www.tuscaloosa.va.gov

- ● Director **LTC John Merkle FACHE, USA (Ret)** .... (205) 554-2000 ext. 2201
  E-mail: john.merkle@va.gov
  Education: John Carroll 1988 BSBA; St Martin's Col 1997 MBA; Baylor 2000 MHA
- Associate Director **Amir Farooqi** .... (205) 554-2000 ext. 2203
  Education: Texas 1997; Texas Woman's 2001 MS
  Administrative Assistant to the Associate Director **Henry L. Hudson** .... (205) 554-2000 ext. 4083
- Associate Director for Nursing and Patient Care Services **David L. Carden** .... (205) 554-2000 ext. 2215
  Education: Auburn 1981 BSN; Tulane 1989 MPH; Baylor 1998 MHA
- Chief of Staff (Acting) **Carlos Berry** .... (205) 554-2000 ext. 2209
- Chief Information Officer **Bryant Lewis** .... (205) 554-2000 ext. 2825
  Tel: (205) 554-2000 2080
- Executive Assistant **Jay D. Moyer** .... (205) 554-3782

Georgia

Atlanta (GA) VA Health Care System
1670 Clairmont Road, Decatur, GA 30033
Tel: (404) 321-6111 Internet: www.atlanta.va.gov

- ● Director (Interim) **Ajay K. "Aj" Dhawan** ...... (404) 321-6111 ext. 7601
- Associate Director (Interim) **Christian "Lance" Davis** ... (404) 728-7602
- Assistant Director **Alvin "Al" Rosado** .... (404) 321-6111 ext. 7602
- Nursing and Patient Services Associate Director (Acting) **David L. Carden** .... (404) 321-6111 ext. 6260
  Education: Auburn 1981 BSN; Tulane 1989 MPH; Baylor 1998 MHA
- Chief of Staff **Dr. David James Bower MD** .... (404) 728-7604
  E-mail: david.bower@va.gov
  Education: Emory MD
- Chief Information Officer (Acting) **Andrea Yates** .... (404) 321-6111
- Quality Manager Coordinator **Robert Morgan** .... (404) 321-6111 ext. 7653
- Compliance Officer **(Vacant)** .... (404) 321-6111 ext. 2297
- Equal Employment Opportunity Officer **Tiffany Marshall** .... (404) 321-6111 ext. 6960
- Information Privacy Officer **Shirley Hobsen** ... (404) 321-6111 ext. 2749
  Fax: (404) 728-7658
- Information Security Officer **Autry Curry** ...... (404) 321-6111 ext. 6735
- Public Affairs Officer **Gregory "Greg" Kendall** .... (404) 417-5385
  E-mail: gregory.kendall@va.gov
- Veterans Justice Outreach Specialist **Katherine Andrade** .... (404) 321-6111
- Veterans Justice Outreach Specialist **Tyson Lynch** .... (404) 321-6111

★ Presidential Appointment Requiring Senate Confirmation ☆ Presidential Appointment ☐ Schedule C Appointment ◇ Career Senior Foreign Service Appointment
● Career Senior Executive Service (SES) Appointment ○ Non-Career Senior Executive Service (SES) Appointment ■ Postal Career Executive Service

Charlie Norwood VA Medical Center (Augusta VA Medical Center)
One Freedom Way, Augusta, GA 30904-6285
Tel: (706) 733-0188 Fax: (706) 823-3934
Internet: http://www.augusta.va.gov

- ● Director **Dr. Robin E. Jackson PhD** .... (706) 733-0188 ext. 2101
- Associate Director for Patient Care/Nursing Services **Michelle Cox-Henley MSN, RN** .... (706) 733-0188
- Associate Director **COL Robert Reeder USA (Ret)** .... (706) 733-0188 ext. 2104
- Assistant Director **John "JD" Stenger** .... (706) 733-0188
- Chief of Staff **(Vacant)** .... (706) 733-0188 ext. 2108
- Police Service Chief **Thomas Howe** .... (706) 733-0188 ext. 3200
  E-mail: thomas.howe@va.gov Fax: (706) 823-1744
- Chief Information Officer **Ricky Hedgepeth** .... (706) 481-6750
  E-mail: ricky.hedgepeth@va.gov Fax: (706) 481-6771
- Public Affairs Officer **Jason Tudor** .... (706) 823-1733
  E-mail: jason.tudor@va.gov
- Librarian **Billy Houke** .... (706) 733-0188 ext. 7513
  E-mail: billy.houke@va.gov

Carl Vinson VA Medical Center Dublin, Georgia (Dublin VA Medical Center)
1826 Veterans Boulevard, Dublin, GA 31021
Tel: (478) 272-1210 Fax: (478) 277-2717 Internet: www.dublin.va.gov

- ● Director (Interim) **Dr. Brent A. Thelen** .... (478) 272-1210
  Education: Southern Illinois 1992 BS; Central Michigan 1999 MS
- Associate Director **Gerald "Jay" DeWorth** .... (478) 277-2701
- Associate Director, Patient Care Services **Connie Hampton** .... (478) 277-2730
  Education: Alabama 2010 DNP Fax: (478) 274-5510
- Deputy Chief of Staff (Interim) **Ijeoma Kene-Ewulu** .... (478) 272-1210
- Customer Service Manager **Keith Griffin** .... (478) 272-1210 ext. 3278
- Public Affairs Officer **Scott Whittington** .... (478) 274-5440
  Fax: (478) 274-5875
- Information Management Business Manager **Mark Coarant** .... (478) 274-1210 ext. 3589
- Police/Security Chief **Roderick McNeil** .... (478) 277-2766
  Fax: (478) 277-2772

South Carolina

Ralph H. Johnson VA Medical Center (Ralph H. Johnson VAMC)
109 Bee Street, Charleston, SC 29401-5799
Tel: (843) 577-5011 Tel: (888) 878-6884 Fax: (843) 937-6100
Internet: www.charleston.va.gov

- ● Director **Scott R. Isaacks MBA** .... (843) 789-7200
  Education: Miami BA; Tennessee MBA
- Chief Information Officer **LaBon Hardy** .... (843) 577-5011 ext. 7400
  E-mail: labon.hardy@va.gov
- Librarian **Jeanette Augenstein** .... (843) 577-5011 ext. 7274

William Jennings Bryan Dorn VA Medical Center (Dorn VA)
William Jennings Bryan Dorn VA Medical Center,
6439 Garners Ferry Road, Columbia, SC 29209-1639
Tel: (803) 776-4000 Fax: (803) 695-6739
Internet: www.columbiasc.va.gov

- ● Director **David L. Omura FAPTA, FACHE** CHE .... (803) 695-7980
  E-mail: david.omura@va.gov
  Education: Boston U MS; Florida MHA; MGH Inst DPT
- Assistant Director (Acting) **Angelia Scott** CHE .... (803) 776-4000 ext. 7981
- Chief of Staff **COL Bernard L. DeKoning USA (Ret)** .... (803) 695-7982
  Education: Illinois (Chicago) BS; Rush MD
- Associate Director for Patient Care and Nursing Services **Ruth Mustard RN, MSN** .... (803) 695-6778
  E-mail: ruth.mustard@va.gov
- Chief Information Officer **Stephen Chalfant** .... (803) 776-4000 ext. 6312
  E-mail: stephen.chalfant@va.gov

VISN 8 - Sunshine Healthcare Network

140 Fountain Parkway, Suite 600, St. Petersburg, FL 33716
Tel: (727) 575-8069 Fax: (727) 575-8114 Internet: www.visn8.va.gov

- ● Network Director **Miguel H. LaPuz MD, MBA** .... (727) 575-8069
  E-mail: miguel.lapuz2@va.gov

VISN 8 - Sunshine Healthcare Network *(continued)*

- Deputy Network Director (Acting) **Verana Richardson** .... (727) 575-8056
- Chief Financial Officer **James Pasquith** .... (727) 575-8053
- Chief Information Officer (Acting) **Michael Hickman** .... (330) 724-2416
  E-mail: michael.hickman@va.gov
- Chief Medical Officer **Dr. Edward P. Cutolo, Jr. MD** .... (727) 575-8029
  Education: Johns Hopkins BA; South Florida MD
- Chief Operations Officer **(Vacant)** .... (727) 575-8069
- Primary Care and Specialty Care Manager **(Vacant)** .... (727) 575-8064
- Network Contract Manager **Stephen M. Elliott** .... (813) 972-7515
  - Small Business Liaison **Nicholas Milone** .... (813) 631-2830
    E-mail: nicholas.milone@va.gov

Florida

Bay Pines (FL) VA Healthcare System
P.O. Box 5005, Bay Pines, FL 33744
10000 Bay Pines Boulevard, Bay Pines, FL 33744
Tel: (727) 398-6661 ext. 15501 Fax: (727) 398-9442
E-mail: vhabaypublicaffairs@va.gov Internet: www.baypines.va.gov

- ● Director **Paul M. Russo FACHE, RD** .... (727) 398-9300
  Education: RIT MS
- Deputy Director **Kristine "Kris" Brown** .... (727) 398-9301
- Associate Director for Patient and Nursing Services **Teresa Kumar** .... (727) 398-6661 ext. 4319
- Associate Director **Jonathan Benoit** .... (727) 398-6661 ext. 15501
  Education: North Florida 2009 BS; Central Florida 2012 MS
- Chief of Staff **Dr. Dominique Thuriere MD** .... (727) 398-9302
- Chief Fiscal Officer **(Vacant)** .... (727) 398-6661
- Chief Librarian **Diana Akins** .... (727) 398-6661 ext. 5566
- Chief of Police **Edward Avila** .... (727) 398-6661 ext. 5162
  Fax: (727) 395-9510
- Information Security Officer **Gina Rhodes** .... (727) 398-6661 ext. 1153
- Information Systems Service **Scott Cummins** .... (727) 398-6661 ext. 4800
- Public Affairs Officer **Jason W. Dangel** .... (727) 398-6661 ext. 15031
  E-mail: jason.dangel@va.gov
- Webmaster **Christopher Adams** .... (727) 398-6661 ext. 5329

James A. Haley VA Medical Center
James A. Haley Veterans Hospital, 13000 Bruce B. Downs Boulevard, Tampa, FL 33612
Tel: (813) 972-2000 Fax: (813) 972-7673 Internet: www.tampa.va.gov

- ● Director **Joe D. Battle** .... (813) 972-7536
  Education: Alabama 1981 BS
- Deputy Director (Acting) **Melissa Sundin** .... (813) 972-7626
  Education: West Virginia BS
- Associate Director **Ken Turner PE, CEM, MBA** .... (813) 972-3012
  Education: Citadel 1993 BS; South Carolina 2006 ME; Strayer U 2013 MBA
- Assistant Director **Suzanne M. Tate RN** .... (813) 972-5160
  E-mail: suzanne.tate@va.gov
  Education: Purdue; Indiana MHA
- Associate Director, Patient Care/Nursing Services **Laureen Doloresco RN** .... (813) 979-3654
  E-mail: laureen.doloresco@va.gov
- Chief of Staff (Acting) **Dr. Colleen E. Jakey MD, FACS** .... (813) 972-7537
  E-mail: colleen.jakey@va.gov
  Education: Philadelphia Col Pharmacy 1991 BS; Maryland 1995 MD
- Chief Information Officer **Jose G. Seymour** .... (813) 903-4868
  E-mail: jose.seymour@va.gov Fax: (813) 910-3041
- Patient Safety Center Director **Laura B. Smith** .... (813) 972-2000 ext. 6073
- Librarian **Priscilla L. Stephenson** .... (813) 972-2000 ext. 7531
- IT Specialist (IRMS) **Jose G. Seymore** .... (813) 972-2000 ext. 3973

Miami (FL) VA Healthcare System
1201 NW 16th Street, Miami, FL 33125-2106
Tel: (305) 575-7000 Tel: (305) 575-3399 (Office of Public Affairs)
Fax: (305) 575-3266 Internet: www.miami.va.gov

- ● Director **David J. VanMeter MHA** .... (305) 575-7000 ext. 3124
  Education: Kentucky 2001 BA, 2003 MHCA

(continued on next page)

DEPARTMENTS

Miami (FL) VA Healthcare System *(continued)*

Chief of Staff
Dr. Vincent A. DeGennaro MD . . . . (305) 575-7000 ext. 3157
Associate Director **Loyman R. Marin** . . . . (305) 575-7000 ext. 3203
Education: Nova Southeastern 2008 MBA
Associate Director for Patient Care Services
Marcia Lysaght RN . . . . (305) 575-7000 ext. 4224
Librarian **Monica Bamio-Aparicio** . . . . (305) 575-4376
Fax: (305) 575-3118
Public Affairs Officer **Shane Suzuki** . . . . (305) 575-7303
E-mail: shane.suzuki@va.gov
Education: U Washington 2009 BA, 2011 MC

North Florida/South Georgia Veterans Health System
1601 SW Archer Road, Gainesville, FL 32608-1197
Tel: (352) 376-1611 Tel: (800) 324-8387 Fax: (352) 374-6113
Internet: www.northflorida.va.gov

Malcom Randall VA Medical Center
1601 SW Archer Road, Gainesville, FL 32608-1197
Tel: (352) 376-1611 Tel: (800) 324-8387 Fax: (352) 374-6113

• Director **Thomas J. "Tom" Wisnieski** . . . . (352) 548-6027
E-mail: thomas.wisnieski@va.gov
Staff Assistant to the Director **(Vacant)** . . . . (352) 374-6027
Deputy Director **Wende Dottor** . . . . (352) 548-6012
Associate Director for Patient
Care Services (Acting)
Karen L. Spada MSN, MPH, FNP . . . . (352) 548-6000 ext. 106050
Assistant Director **Chad Adams** . . . . (352) 548-6000 ext. 105386
Chief of Staff (Acting) **Ilona Schmalfuss** . . . (352) 548-6000 ext. 104205
Associate Chief of Staff for Education
Josepha Cheong . . . . (352) 374-7486
Fax: (352) 374-6168
Chief of Surgical Services **Dr. William Zingarelli MD** . . . . (352) 374-6013
Information Resources Management Service Chief
(Vacant) . . . . (352) 248-0959
Fax: (352) 379-4171
Librarian **Cornelia Camerer** . . . . (352) 376-1611 ext. 6312
Fax: (352) 374-6148
Police Service Chief **Wayne E. NeSmith** . . . . . . (352) 376-1611 ext. 6155
Fax: (352) 379-4171

Lake City VA Medical Center
619 South Marion Avenue, Lake City, FL 32025-5808
Tel: (386) 755-3016 Fax: (386) 758-6005

• Director **Thomas J. "Tom" Wisnieski** . . . . (386) 755-3016 ext. 2000
E-mail: thomas.wisnieski@va.gov
Deputy Director **Nancy Reissener** . . . . (386) 755-3016 ext. 2000
Associate Director
Maureen M. Wilkes FACHE . . . . (386) 755-3016 ext. 2000
Education: Florida BSN, MSN
Logistics Service Chief **(Vacant)** . . . . (386) 755-3016 ext. 2093
Dental Service Associate Chief
Steven Keir DDS . . . . (386) 755-3016 ext. 2160
E-mail: steven.keir@va.gov
Internal Medicine Section, Associate Chief of
Medical Services **P. Raj** . . . . (386) 755-3016 ext. 2662
E-mail: p.raj@va.gov
Purchase and Contract Section Chief
Susan Little . . . . (386) 755-3016 ext. 2095
E-mail: susan.little@va.gov
Librarian **(Vacant)** . . . . (386) 755-3016

Orlando VA Medical Center
13800 Veterans Way, Orlando, FL 32827
Tel: (407) 631-1000 Internet: www.orlando.va.gov

• Director **Timothy W. Liezert FACHE** . . . . (407) 631-1000
E-mail: timothy.liezert@va.gov
Associate Director **Cory P. Price FACHE** . . . . (407) 631-0001
Education: Embry-Riddle 1997 BS; Webster 2012 MHA
Chief of Staff
COL Lisa L. Zacher USA (Ret), MD, FACP . . . . (407) 631-1000
Education: South Dakota Mines 1985 BChem; South Dakota 1989 MD
Associate Director for Patient Care Services **(Vacant)** . . . . (407) 631-1000

Orlando VA Medical Center *(continued)*

Assistant Director **Dan Herrera** . . . . (407) 631-1000
E-mail: dan.herrera@va.gov
Education: Montana State 1986 BS

West Palm Beach (FL) VA Medical Center
7305 North Military Trail, West Palm Beach, FL 33410-6400
Tel: (561) 422-8262 Fax: (561) 422-8613
Internet: www.westpalmbeach.va.gov

• Director **Donna M. Katen-Bahensky** . . . . (561) 422-8431
Education: Missouri BA, MS
Executive Assistant **Allison Perry** . . . . (561) 422-8602
Associate Director (Acting) **Maria T. Nguyen MPH** . . . . . (561) 422-8605
Education: Ohio State BSc, MPH
Assistant Director (Acting) **Julia Spence** . . . . (561) 422-8605
Education: Alderson-Broaddus; Baylor MBA;
Baylor Col Dentistry MHCA
Staff Assistant to Associate Director **(Vacant)** . . . . (561) 422-8606
Associate Director for Patient Care Services
Lyumma Archeval RN . . . . (561) 422-6901
Education: Pontifical Catholic (Puerto Rico) MSN
Chief of Staff (Acting) **CAPT Ronald K. Williams DO** . . . (561) 422-8603
Education: Hofstra BA; New York Inst Tech DO
Chief of Staff for Primary Care **Darin Rubin** . . . . (561) 422-8431
E-mail: darin.rubin@va.gov
Deputy Chief of Staff **Haresh N Patel** . . . . (561) 422-5579
Procurement Business Division Chief **(Vacant)** . . . . (561) 422-6511
Dental Chief **(Vacant)** . . . . (561) 422-6573
Facilities Management Services Chief
Damian Mindley . . . . (561) 422-6669
Education: Morgan State 2003 BSEE
Fiscal Chief **(Vacant)** . . . . (561) 882-6735
Human Resources Chief **Shelley Combs** . . . . (561) 422-5543
Information Resources Management Service Chief
James Barton . . . . (561) 422-6801
E-mail: james.barton@va.gov
Logistic Chief **Stacey Wallace** . . . . (561) 422-6509
Mental Health and Behavioral Sciences Chief **(Vacant)** . . . (561) 422-7252
Pathology Chief **Dr. Sundara Sridhar MD** . . . . (561) 422-6822
Pharmacy Service Chief **Nick Beckey** . . . . (561) 422-7205
Physical Medicine and Rehabilitation Services Chief
Ramon Cuevas-Trisan . . . . (561) 422-5732
E-mail: ramon.cuevas-trisan@va.gov
Media Production Chief **Joanne Deithorn** . . . . (561) 422-6551
E-mail: joanne.deithorn@va.gov
Education: RIT 1989 BA
Social Work Section Chief **Kerri L. Boyd** . . . . (561) 422-6845
Education: Florida State 1999 MSW
Voluntary Services Chief **Mary Phillips** . . . . (561) 422-7372
Quality Management Coordinator
Donnalee Relyea RN . . . . (561) 422-7355
Education: SUNY (Farmingdale)
Veterans Justice Outreach Specialist **Jana Shiffert** . . . . . . (561) 422-7101

Puerto Rico

VA Caribbean Healthcare System
10 Casia Street, San Juan, PR 00921-3201
Tel: (787) 641-7582 Fax: (787) 641-4557 Internet: www.caribbean.va.gov

• Director (Acting) **Dr. Antonio Sanchez**
MD, MHSA, FACHE . . . . (787) 641-7582 ext. 35913
E-mail: antonio.sanchez@va.gov
Education: Puerto Rico MD, MHSA
Deputy Director **George Velez** . . . . (787) 641-5980
Associate Director **Jaime E. Marrero** . . . . (787) 641-7582 ext. 35914
Education: Puerto Rico 1990 BME
Associate Director of Patient Care Services
Iris S. Hernandez . . . . (787) 641-7582 ext. 35955
Education: Puerto Rico BSN, MS
Chief of Staff **Dr. Antonio Sanchez MD,**
MHSA, FACHE . . . . (787) 641-7582 ext. 35934
E-mail: antonio.sanchez@va.gov
Education: Puerto Rico MD, MHSA
Deputy Chief of Staff
Dr. William Acevedo . . . . (787) 641-7582 ext. 35935

★ Presidential Appointment Requiring Senate Confirmation ☆ Presidential Appointment ☐ Schedule C Appointment ◇ Career Senior Foreign Service Appointment
● Career Senior Executive Service (SES) Appointment ○ Non-Career Senior Executive Service (SES) Appointment ■ Postal Career Executive Service

VA Caribbean Healthcare System *(continued)*

Compliance Officer **Luz Torres** .... (787) 641-7582 ext. 12566
E-mail: luz.torres@va.gov
Public Affairs Officer **Axel R. Román** .... (787) 641-7582 ext. 31932
E-mail: axel.roman@va.gov
Webmaster **Carlos Molina-Ramos** .... (787) 641-7582 ext. 19116
E-mail: carlos.molina-ramos@va.gov

VISN 9 - MidSouth Healthcare Network

1801 West End Avenue, Suite 600, Nashville, TN 37203
Tel: (615) 695-2200 Fax: (615) 695-2210 Internet: www.visn9.va.gov

● Network Director **Cynthia Breyfogle FACHE** .... (615) 695-2200
E-mail: cynthia.breyfogle@va.gov
Education: Drury U 1984 BSBA; Webster 1990 MA
Chief Financial Officer **Lynn Marie Heathcoat** .... (615) 695-2200
Chief Information Officer **Harold McDavid** .... (615) 695-2200
E-mail: harold.mcdavid@va.gov
Chief Medical Officer
Dr. Richard J. Kaufmann MD, FACS .... (615) 695-2203
Network Contract Manager **(Vacant)** .... (615) 695-2200
Deputy Network Contract Manager
Susan "Sue" Nagel .... (615) 225-6964
E-mail: susan.nagel@va.gov Fax: (615) 225-5431
Small Business Analyst **Susan "Sue" Nagel** .... (615) 225-3402
E-mail: susan.nagel@va.gov

Kentucky

Lexington VA Health Care System

1101 Veterans Drive, Lexington, KY 40502
2250 Leestown Road, Lexington, KY 40511
Tel: (859) 233-4511 Fax: (859) 281-4911 Internet: www.lexington.va.gov

● Director **Emma M. Metcalf RN** .... (859) 281-4901
Secretary **Monica Burke** .... (859) 281-4901
Associate Director
James E. "Jim" Belmont, Jr. FACHE ...... (859) 233-4511 ext. 4901
Associate Director, Patient Care Services
Mary Kelly McCullough MSN, RN, NE-BC .... (859) 281-4511 ext. 4229
Education: Mid Tennessee State 1990 ADN
Chief of Staff **Dr. Patricia Breeden MD** .... (859) 281-4902
Web Master **(Vacant)** .... (859) 281-4973
Fax: (859) 281-4994

Robley Rex VA Medical Center (Louisville VA Medical Center)

800 Zorn Avenue, Louisville, KY 40206-1499
Tel: (502) 287-4000 Fax: (502) 287-6225 Internet: www.louisville.va.gov

● Director (Interim) **Eileen Kingston RN** .... (502) 287-5500
E-mail: eileen.kingston@va.gov
Chief of Staff **Marylee Rothschild MD, MPH** .... (502) 287-6203
E-mail: marylee.rothschild@va.gov
Deputy Chief of Staff **Dr. Andrea Yancey MD** .... (502) 287-4000
Associate Director for Operations
Larry D. Roberts .... (502) 287-4000 ext. 55507
Education: Morehead State 2004 MBA
Associate Director, Patient Care Services
Dr. Debbie Hunt MD .... (502) 287-4198
Chief Information Officer **Augustine Bittner** .... (502) 287-6977
E-mail: augustine.bittner@va.gov

Tennessee

Memphis (TN) VA Medical Center

1030 Jefferson Avenue, Memphis, TN 38104-2193
Tel: (901) 523-8990 Fax: (901) 577-7241 Internet: www.memphis.va.gov
Areas Covered: 55 counties in west TN, northeast AR, north MS, southwest KY, and the boot heel of MO

● Director and Chief Executive Officer
COL David K. Dunning USA (Ret), MPA .... (901) 577-7200
Education: Furman 1987 BA
Assistant Director (Acting) **Tommy D. Ambrose** .... (901) 577-7201
Associate Director for Patient Care Services
Karen Gillette .... (901) 577-7454

Memphis (TN) VA Medical Center *(continued)*

Communications and Public Affairs Officer
Willie M. Logan .... (901) 523-8990 ext. 5453
E-mail: willie.logan@va.gov
Chief of Staff **Dr. Thomas C. Ferguson MD** .... (901) 577-7202
Deputy Chief of Staff **Dr. Gail K. Berntson MD** .... (901) 577-7202
Associate Chief of Staff/Education **Jim Lewis** .... (901) 577-7207
Fax: (901) 448-8231
Chief Logistics Officer **David S. Reesman** .... (901) 577-7227
Chief Information Officer
Roy Eckelbarger III .... (901) 523-8990 ext. 7209
Librarian **(Vacant)** .... (901) 523-8990 ext. 5884
Chief Financial Manager **Kristi Depperman** .... (901) 523-8990 ext. 5837
Police Chief (Acting) **Terrell Owens** .... (901) 577-7294
Fax: (901) 577-7256

Mountain Home VA Healthcare System

P.O. Box 4000, Mountain Home, TN 37684
Tel: (423) 926-1171 Fax: (423) 979-3572
Internet: www.mountainhome.va.gov/index.asp
Areas Covered: Southeastern KY, Eastern TN, Southwestern VA

● Director **Col Dean B. Borsos USAF (Ret)** ..... (423) 926-1171 ext. 7102
Education: Ohio 1989 MHSA, 1987 BS
Associate Director
Daniel B. "Dan" Snyder MBA .... (423) 926-1171 ext. 7104
Associate Director for Patient Care/Nursing Services
(Acting) **Deborah Eddy** .... (423) 926-1171
Education: East Tennessee State BS, MSN
Chief of Staff
Dr. David S. Hecht MD, MBA .... (423) 926-1171 ext. 7116
Public Affairs Officer **Kristen Schabert** .... (423) 979-3446
E-mail: kristen.schabert@va.gov
Education: Austin Peay State 2004 BS
Information Resource Management Chief **Karen Perry** ... (423) 979-1401
E-mail: karen.perry@va.gov
Police and Security Service Chief
Jerry Shelton .... (423) 926-1171 ext. 7194
E-mail: jerry.shelton@va.gov Fax: (423) 975-6117

Tennessee Valley Healthcare System

1310 24th Avenue, South, Nashville, TN 37212-2637
Tel: (615) 327-4751 Internet: www.tennesseevalley.va.gov

● Director **CAPT Jennifer Vedral-Baron NC, USN** .... (615) 225-2530
Education: North Florida 1986 BSN; Florida 1996 MA
Deputy Health System Director (Murfreesboro)
(Vacant) .... (615) 327-4751
Deputy Health System Director (Nashville)
Suzanne L. Jené .... (615) 327-4751
Education: Point Park U BS; DeVry U MBA
Associate Director **Ronnie Smith** .... (615) 873-6972
Assistant Director **Marianne M. Myers** .... (615) 225-2563
Education: Mid Tennessee State BS, MA
Associate Director for Patient Care Services
Cynthia L. Johnson .... (615) 873-6943
Chief of Staff **John H. Nadeau** .... (615) 873-6969
Chief Information Officer **Paul Hardy** .... (615) 327-4751
Education Service Chief **(Vacant)** .... (615) 873-6758
Police Chief **Jon Maggard** .... (615) 873-6968
E-mail: jon.maggard@va.gov
Public Affairs Officer **Chris Vadnais** .... (615) 873-7734
E-mail: chris.vadnais@va.gov
Education: New York Inst Tech 2008 MA

VISN 10 - VA Healthcare System Serving Ohio, Indiana and Michigan

11500 Northlake Drive, Suite 200, Cincinnati, OH 45249
Tel: (513) 247-4621 Fax: (513) 247-4620 Internet: www.visn10.va.gov
Note: VISN 10 is the result of the integration of VISNs 10 and 11 as part of the MyVA transformation plan.

● Network Director (Acting)
Denise M. Deitzen FNP, FACHE .... (734) 222-4366
Education: Michigan State 1986 BSN; Grand Valley State 1992 MSN
Deputy Network Director **Ronald Stertzbach** .... (513) 247-4631
Chief Financial Officer **Sandy Selvidge** .... (513) 247-4627

(continued on next page)

★ Presidential Appointment Requiring Senate Confirmation ☆ Presidential Appointment ☐ Schedule C Appointment ◇ Career Senior Foreign Service Appointment
● Career Senior Executive Service (SES) Appointment ○ Non-Career Senior Executive Service (SES) Appointment ■ Postal Career Executive Service

DEPARTMENTS

VISN 10 - VA Healthcare System Serving Ohio, Indiana and Michigan *(continued)*

Chief Information Officer **(Vacant)** .... (440) 838-6070
Chief Medical Officer **Dr. Peter Dews III MD** .... (734) 222-4300
Education: Wayne State U MD
Network Contract Manager **Terry Spitzmiller** .... (513) 553-3701
E-mail: terry.spitzmiller@va.gov
Deputy Director of Contracting **Marie Smith** .... (937) 262-3384
E-mail: marie.smith@va.gov
Education: Columbia Col (CA) 2006 BS

Satellite Office
P.O. Box 134002, Ann Arbor, MI 48113-4002
Tel: (734) 222-4300 Fax: (734) 222-4340

Chief Financial Officer **Sandra Selvidge** .... (513) 247-4633
Chief Logistics Officer **Jodi Cokl** .... (513) 247-4290
Education: Cleary U BS; U Phoenix MBA
Chief Information Officer
General Kearney CISSP, CHSP, CSP .... (734) 222-4300
E-mail: general.kearney@va.gov
Education: Park U 1987 BSHS; La Verne 1992 MSB; Jones International 2009 MBA
Chief Medical Officer **Dr. Peter Dews III MD** .... (734) 222-4300
Education: Wayne State U MD
Quality Management Officer **Jane Johnson** .... (734) 222-4300

Indiana

Veteran Health Indiana (Richard L. Roudebush VA Medical Center)
1481 West 10th Street, Indianapolis, IN 46202-2884
Tel: (317) 554-0000 Fax: (317) 988-3370
Internet: www.indianapolis.va.gov

● Director **J. Brian Hancock MD, FACEP** .... (317) 988-2206
Education: Rush MD Fax: (317) 988-5322
Associate Director **Laura Ruzick FACHE** .... (317) 988-2207
Education: Xavier (OH) 1980 BS; Lewis U 1983 BSN, 2001 MBA
Associate Director for Patient Care Services (Acting)
Margaret R. "Margie" Lanza RN, CGRN .... (317) 988-3102
Education: Cincinnati 1986 BSN; Northern Kentucky 2012 MSN Fax: (317) 988-5322
Assistant Director **Cathy G. Lee-Sellers** .... (317) 988-2207
E-mail: cathy.lee-sellers@va.gov Fax: (317) 988-5322
Education: VCU BS
Chief of Staff (Interim) **Dr. Imtiaz Munshi MD** .... (317) 988-2160
E-mail: imtiaz.munshi@va.gov Fax: (317) 988-5322
Education: Brooklyn 1987 BA; SUNY Downstate Med 1991 MD; UMass (Amherst) 2006 MBA
Deputy Chief of Staff (Interim) **Loretta M. VanEvery** .... (317) 988-2160
Fax: (317) 988-5322
Chief Information Officer **Steve Stoner** .... (317) 988-4247
E-mail: steve.stoner@va.gov
Public Affairs Officer **Peter Scovill** .... (317) 988-2310
Education Service Chief **Dr. Dione Farria MD** .... (317) 988-2104
Fax: (317) 988-2838
Police Service Chief (Acting)
Ronald "Ron" Scanland .... (317) 988-2211
E-mail: ronald.scanland@va.gov Fax: (317) 988-5374
Librarian **Linda Bennett** .... (317) 988-2333
E-mail: linda.bennett@va.gov Fax: (317) 988-3176

VA Northern Indiana Health Care System (VANIHCS)
2121 Lake Avenue, Fort Wayne, IN 46805-5100 (Fort Wayne Campus)
1700 East 38th Street, Marion, IN 46953 (Marion Campus)
Tel: (260) 460-1310 Fax: (260) 460-1336
Internet: www.northernindiana.va.gov

● Director **COL Michael E. Hershman USA (Ret)** .... (260) 460-1310 (Fort Wayne)
Education: Lehigh BA; Baylor 1996 MHCA
Associate Director of Operations **Jay Miller** ... (765) 674-3321 ext. 72503
Associate Director, Patient Care Services
Audrey L. Frison .... (260) 426-5431 ext. 71413
Assistant Director **John Shealey** .... (765) 674-3321 ext. 73251
Chief of Staff **Wayne McBride** .... (260) 460-1311
Information Technology Management Chief
Joe Grey .... (260) 674-3321 ext. 76100

VA Northern Indiana Health Care System *(continued)*

Contracting Officer **Nikki Horther** .... (260) 426-5431 ext. 71593
E-mail: nikki.horther@va.gov

Michigan

Adela E. Lutz VA Medical Center (Saginaw VA Medical Center)
1500 Weiss Street, Saginaw, MI 48602
Tel: (989) 497-2500 Fax: (989) 321-4903 Internet: www.saginaw.va.gov

● Director (Acting) **Dr. Barbara Bates** .... (989) 497-2500 ext. 11500
E-mail: barbara.bates@va.gov
Associate Director **Christopher Cauley** ...... (989) 497-2500 ext. 13013
Associate Director for Patient Care Services
Steven Haag .... (989) 497-2500 ext. 11420
Chief of Staff (Acting) **Dr. Thomas Campana** .... (989) 497-2500
E-mail: thomas.campana@va.gov
Employee Development Specialist
Supervisor **Patti Pasionek** .... (989) 497-2500 ext. 11875
Fax: (989) 321-4902
Police Service Chief **(Vacant)** .... (989) 497-2500 ext. 13201
Fax: (989) 321-4921
Contracting Officer **(Vacant)** .... (989) 321-4805

VA Ann Arbor Healthcare System
2215 Fuller Road, Ann Arbor, MI 48105
Tel: (734) 769-7100 Fax: (734) 845-3245 Internet: www.annarbor.va.gov

● Director **Ginny L. Creasman** .... (734) 845-5458
E-mail: ginny.creasman@va.gov
Staff Assistant to the Director **(Vacant)** .... (734) 845-3403
Associate Chief of Staff for Education
Dr. Monica L. Lypson MD .... (734) 845-5180
Associate Director (Acting) **Christopher Cauley** .... (734) 845-5455
Associate Director for Patient Care
Stacey Breedveld MSN, RN .... (734) 845-3410
Assistant Director **Kevin D. Swallow MPA** .... (734) 845-3303
Public Affairs/Marketing Manager **(Vacant)** .... (734) 845-5043
Chief Information Officer **Rob Whitehurst** .... (734) 845-3805
E-mail: rob.whitehurst@va.gov Fax: (734) 845-5921
Chief Librarian **Sara Peth** .... (734) 845-5408
E-mail: sara.peth@va.gov
Chief of Staff **Mark S. Hausman, Jr.** .... (734) 845-3400
Police Chief **Gregory Allen** .... (734) 845-3405
E-mail: gregory.allen2@va.gov
Contracting Specialist **John Beard** .... (734) 222-6173
E-mail: john.beard@va.gov

Battle Creek (MI) VA Medical Center
5500 Armstrong Road, Battle Creek, MI 49037
Tel: (269) 966-5600 Tel: (888) 214-1247 Fax: (269) 223-5483
Internet: www.battlecreek.va.gov

● Director **James Doelling** .... (269) 966-5600 ext. 35212
Education: Duquesne 1988 BSN; Springfield (MA) 2005 MS
Associate Director **Edward G. Dornoff** .... (269) 966-5600 ext. 35213
Associate Director for Patient Care Services
Kimberly Zipper .... (269) 966-5600 ext. 35233
Information Management Service Chief **Daniel Garay** .... (269) 966-5600
Fax: (269) 966-5486
Chief of Staff **Dr. Ketan Shah MD** .... (269) 966-5600 ext. 35212
Librarian **Linda Polardino** .... (269) 966-5600 ext. 36490
E-mail: linda.polardino@va.gov
Webmaster **(Vacant)** .... (269) 966-5600 ext. 35218
Contracting Officer
Christopher "Chris" Gundy .... (269) 966-5600 ext. 36450
E-mail: christopher.gundy@va.gov

John D. Dingell VA Medical Center
4646 John R Street, Detroit, MI 48201
Tel: (313) 576-1000 TTY: (700) 576-3380 Fax: (313) 576-1991
Internet: www.detroit.va.gov

● Director **Dr. Pamela J. Reeves MD** .... (313) 576-1212
E-mail: pamela.reeves@va.gov
Education: Western Michigan BS; Michigan MD
Associate Director **Michelle S. Werner** .... (313) 576-4421
Education: Eastern Michigan BS

John D. Dingell VA Medical Center *(continued)*

Associate Director for Patient Care Services
Belinda Brown-Tezera APRN, MSN, MBA, FNP . . . . (313) 576-1000 ext. 61855
Education: Georgia State MSN; U Phoenix MBA

Chief of Staff
Dr. Scott A. Gruber MD, PhD, MBA . . . . (313) 576-1000 ext. 63327
E-mail: scott.gruber@va.gov
Education: Johns Hopkins BES; SUNY Downstate Med MD; Minnesota PhD

Business Practice Chief
Vanassa Owens-Warren MS . . . . (313) 576-1000 ext. 65393
Fax: (313) 576-1197

Education and Training Section Chief
Tina Nudell . . . . (313) 576-1000 ext. 63834

Human Resources Chief **Andre Gray** . . . . (313) 576-1000 ext. 63540
Fax: (313) 576-1150

Information Resource Management Chief
Jonathan Small . . . . (313) 576-1000 ext. 65169
E-mail: jonathan.small@va.gov Fax: (313) 576-1270

Protection and Support Service Chief
Vantrese McMillian . . . . (313) 576-1000 ext. 64818

Associate Chief of Staff/Education and Designated Educational Officer
Dr. Maryjean Schenk MD, MPH, MS . . . . (313) 576-4911
E-mail: maryjean.schenk@va.gov Fax: (313) 576-1048
Education: Grand Valley State 1977 BSChem; Wayne State Col 1983 MD

Information Security Officer
Toysan Jennings . . . . (313) 576-1000 ext. 65235
Education: Baker Col 2012

Webmaster **Elizabeth Ellison** . . . . (313) 576-1000 ext. 63798
E-mail: elizabeth.ellison@va.gov

Contracting Officer **Gregory Stevens** . . . . (313) 756-4281
E-mail: gregory.stevens@va.gov

Ohio

VA Central Ohio Healthcare System

420 North James Road, Columbus, OH 43219
Tel: (614) 257-5200 Fax: (614) 257-5460 Internet: www.columbus.va.gov

● Medical Center Director **COL Vivian Hutson USA** . . . . (614) 257-5450
Education: Cornell 1986 BS; Webster 1991 MA; Baylor 1998 MHA
Secretary **Holly Love** . . . . (614) 257-5450
Fax: (614) 257-5460

Associate Director **Jamie L. Kuhne MSW, LISW-S** . . . . (614) 257-5454
Education: Iowa 2002 BA, 2005 MSW

Chief Information Officer **Chris Baxter** . . . . (614) 388-7000
E-mail: chris.baxter@va.gov

Public Affairs Officer **Carl Higginbotham** . . . . (614) 257-5455
E-mail: carl.higginbotham@va.gov

Chillicothe (OH) VA Medical Center

17273 State Route 104, Chillicothe, OH 45601
Tel: (740) 773-1141 Fax: (740) 772-7102
Internet: www.chillicothe.va.gov

● Associate Director (Acting) **Christina White** . . . . (740) 773-1141 ext. 7001
Education: Butler 2007 MBA, 2007 PharmD

Chief of Staff **Deborah M. Meesig MD** . . . . (740) 773-1141 ext. 7254
E-mail: deborah.meesig@va.gov
Education: Ohio State 1981 MD; Capital U 2006 JD

Chief Information Officer **Shauna Ford** . . . . (740) 773-1141 ext. 7189

Associate Director (Acting) **Justin Peters** . . . . (740) 773-1141 ext. 7001
Education: Bowling Green State MSPH

Associate Medical Center Director for Patient Care Services **Cindy Norton-Roush** . . . . (740) 773-1141 ext. 7365

Acquisition and Materiel Management Chief
Scott Royse . . . . (740) 773-1141 ext. 6352

Librarian **Tina Fore** . . . . (740) 773-1141 ext. 7650

Webmaster **(Vacant)** . . . . (740) 773-1141 ext. 7189

Cincinnati (OH) VA Medical Center

3200 Vine Street, Cincinnati, OH 45220-2288
Tel: (513) 861-3100 Fax: (513) 475-6500 Internet: www.cincinnati.va.gov

Director **Mark Murdock MHSA, FACHE** . . . . (513) 861-3100
Education: Park U 1985 BS; Xavier (OH) 1993 MSHA

Associate Director **Gregory "Greg" Goins FACHE** . . . . (513) 475-6301
Education: Western Washington BA; Ohio State MBA

Nurse Executive **Katheryn Cook RN** . . . . (513) 475-6302
Education: Northern Kentucky BSN; Bellarmine U MS

Director of Community Outreach Division
Sally Hammitt . . . . (513) 977-6800
Fax: (513) 475-6991

Chief of Staff **Dr. Elizabeth Brill MD** . . . . (513) 475-6302
Fax: (513) 475-6525

Chief Information Officer **Brian Zeitz** . . . . (513) 475-6314
Education: Southern Illinois 1988 BS; Arkansas 1991 MS; Air Force Inst Tech 2005 MS Fax: (513) 475-6578

Public Relations Officer **(Vacant)** . . . . (513) 487-6056
Fax: (513) 475-6525

Webmaster **Michelle Haverland** . . . . (513) 475-6314
E-mail: vhacinwebmasters@va.gov Fax: (513) 475-6578

Police Service Chief **David Bartos** . . . . (513) 475-6331
E-mail: david.bartos@va.gov Fax: (513) 475-6646

Librarian **Sandra Mason** . . . . (513) 475-6315
E-mail: sandra.mason@va.gov Fax: (513) 475-6454

Dayton (OH) VA Medical Center

4100 West Third Street, Dayton, OH 45428
Tel: (937) 268-6511 Fax: (937) 262-2179 Internet: www.dayton.va.gov

● Director **Jill K Dietrich JD, MBA, FACHE** . . . . (937) 262-2114
Education: Indiana 2002 BA; Case Western 2007 MBA, 2007 JD

Chief Information Officer/Information Resource Management Chief **(Vacant)** . . . . (937) 268-6511 ext. 1229
Fax: (937) 262-2170

Police Service Chief **Earl F. Burkhart** . . . . (937) 268-6511 ext. 3968
E-mail: earl.burkhart@va.gov Fax: (937) 267-5359

Librarian Technician
Kathy L. "Lorraine" Balsbaugh . . . . (937) 268-6511 ext. 2379
E-mail: lorraine.balsbaugh@va.gov

Louis Stokes VA Medical Center

10701 East Boulevard, Cleveland, OH 44106 (Wade Park Campus)
Mail: 10000 Brecksville Road, Brecksville, OH 44141 (Brecksville Campus)
Tel: (216) 791-3800 (Wade Park Campus)
Tel: (440) 526-3030 (Brecksville Campus)
Fax: (440) 838-6017 (Brecksville Campus)
Internet: www.cleveland.va.gov

● Director **Susan Fuehrer MBA** . . . . (216) 791-3800 ext. 4000
E-mail: susan.fuehrer@va.gov
Education: New Hampshire 1986 BA; Case Western 1990 MA

Deputy Director **Andrew Pacyna** . . . . (216) 791-3800 ext. 4000

Associate Director for Patient Care Services/Nurse Executive
Innette Sarduy DNP, MPH, RN, NEA-BC . . . . (216) 791-3800 ext. 5100
Education: Rush BSN; South Florida MPH; Miami DNP

Chief of Staff **(Vacant)** . . . . (216) 791-3800 ext. 3030

Chief of Library Services **Simran Singh** . . . . (440) 526-3030 ext. 6242

Mental Health Care Line VISN 10 Manager
(Vacant) . . . . (440) 526-3030 ext. 6716

VISN 12 - VA Great Lakes Health Care System

Four Westbrook Corporate Tower, 11301 West Cermak Road, Suite 810, Westchester, IL 60154
Tel: (708) 492-3900 Fax: (708) 492-3948 Internet: www.visn12.va.gov/

Network Director **Renee Oshinski** . . . . (708) 492-3900
Executive Assistant **Kathleen Kennedy** . . . . (708) 492-3910

Chief Financial Officer **Kalpana Mehta** . . . . (708) 492-3955

Chief Information Officer **Jeffrey Fears** . . . . (708) 492-3987
E-mail: jeff.fears@va.gov

Chief Medical Officer **Dr. Praveen Mehta MD** . . . . (708) 492-3909

Quality Management Officer **Shavetta R. Williams** . . . . (708) 492-3900
Education: Chamberlain U BSN; Trident International MS

(continued on next page)

DEPARTMENTS

★ Presidential Appointment Requiring Senate Confirmation ☆ Presidential Appointment ☐ Schedule C Appointment ◇ Career Senior Foreign Service Appointment
● Career Senior Executive Service (SES) Appointment ○ Non-Career Senior Executive Service (SES) Appointment ■ Postal Career Executive Service

VISN 12 - VA Great Lakes Health Care System *(continued)*

Chief Logistics Officer **Robby Schopen** .... (414) 844-8410
E-mail: robby.schopen2@va.gov
Webmaster **Andrea Harden** .... (708) 492-3990
E-mail: andrea.harden@va.gov

Illinois

VA Illiana Health Care System (VAIHCS)
1900 East Main Street, Danville, IL 61832-5198
Tel: (217) 554-3000 Fax: (217) 554-4552 Internet: www.danville.va.gov

• Director **Kelley A. Sermak** .... (217) 554-5073

Jesse Brown VA Medical Center
820 South Damen Avenue, Chicago, IL 60612
Tel: (312) 569-8387 Fax: (312) 569-6188 Internet: www.chicago.va.gov

• Director **Marc A. Magill** .... (312) 569-6101
E-mail: marc.magill@va.gov
Education: Millikin BS; Trinity U MSHA
Chief of Staff **(Vacant)** .... (312) 569-6102
Librarian **Barbara Haynes-Donati** .... (312) 569-8387

Edward Hines, Jr. (IL) VA Hospital
Edward Hines, Jr. Hospital, 5000 South Fifth Avenue,
Hines, IL 60141-5000
Tel: (708) 202-8387 Fax: (708) 202-2720 E-mail: director@hines.va.gov
Internet: www.hines.va.gov
Areas Covered: Northern and Central IL; Northwest IN

• Director **COL Steven E. Braverman USA (Ret)** .... (708) 202-2153
Education: Virginia 1983 BA; Vanderbilt 1987 MD;
National Defense U 2005 MS
Staff Assistant to Director **Jane Moen** .... (708) 202-5640
Associate Director **Candace Ifabiyi** .... (708) 202-8387 ext. 22453
Associate Director for Patient Care Services/Nurse
Executive **Marianne Locke RN, MSN** .... (708) 202-5003
Assistant Director **Michelle Schlup** .... (708) 202-5635
Chief Information Officer (Acting)
Jonathan J. Jackson MS .... (708) 202-5538
Chief of Staff **Elaine Adams** .... (708) 202-1231

Captain James A. Lovell Federal Health Care Center (Lovell FHCC)
3001 Green Bay Road, North Chicago, IL 60064
Tel: (847) 688-1900 Tel: (800) 393-0865 Internet: www.lovell.fhcc.va.gov

Director
CAPT Robert G. Buckley USN, MD, MPH, FACEP .... (224) 610-3002
Education: Cal State (Fullerton) 1983 BChem; Northwestern 1987;
San Diego State 1998 MPH
Deputy Director and Commanding Officer
CAPT Gregory Thier USN .... (224) 610-3001
Education: Georgia 1992
Executive Officer
CAPT Andrew Mario Archila MSC, USN .... (224) 610-1551
Education: Houston 1997 BS, 1999 DO; CUNY 2007 MBA
Associate Director, Clinical Support Services
Dr. Piyush Vyas MD .... (224) 610-5576
Education: Medical Col Baroda MD
Associate Director, Dental Services
CAPT Grace Lumaban Key USPHS .... (224) 610-5576
Education: Pittsburgh 1997 DMD
Associate Director, Facility Support **Judy T. Finley** ...... (224) 610-3343
Education: Hinds Com Col ASN; Southern Mississippi BSN;
Union U MBA
Associate Director, Fleet Medicine
CDR Cynthia S. Sikorski MSC, USN .... (847) 688-1900
Education: Thomas Jefferson MD; Uniformed Services 2009 MPH
Associate Director, Geriatrics, Extended Care and
Mental Health (Acting) **Stephanie James** .... (847) 688-1900
Associate Director, Inpatient Services/Navy Nurse
Executive **CAPT Deborah A. Kumaroo MSC, USN** .... (224) 610-5576
Education: Central Florida BSN
Associate Director, Nursing Practice/Senior VA Nurse
Executive **Dr. Sarah Fouse PhD** .... (224) 610-3717
Education: Alverno BSN; Wisconsin (Milwaukee) PhD

Captain James A. Lovell Federal Health Care Center *(continued)*

Associate Director, Primary Care
CDR David You MSC, USN .... (224) 610-5576
Education: Augustana (IL) BA; Loyola U (Chicago) MD
Associate Director, Specialty Care
CDR Josephine Nguyen MC, USN .... (847) 688-1900
Education: Naval Acad 1999 BS; Stanford 2003 MD;
Dartmouth 2017 MS
Chief Medical Executive **Dr. Frank Maldonado MD** ..... (224) 610-3701
Command Master Chief
CMDCM(SW) Jonathan Crisafulli USN .... (224) 610-3002
Education Program Director **Lt. Alison Siepker** .... (224) 610-3499
Informatics Program Chief **Paul Lam** .... (224) 610-5700
E-mail: paul.lam@va.gov
Police and Safety Chief (Acting) **Michael Unthank** ...... (224) 610-1776
Fax: (224) 610-3776
Veterans Justice Outreach Specialist **LaTia Russell** ...... (847) 688-1900

Michigan

Oscar G. Johnson VA Medical Center (Iron Mountain VAMC)
325 East H Street, Iron Mountain, MI 49801
Tel: (906) 774-3300 Fax: (906) 779-3114
Internet: www.ironmountain.va.gov

• Director **James W. Rice** .... (906) 774-3300 ext. 32000
Associate Director **Drew A. DeWitt FACHE** ... (906) 774-3300 ext. 32013
Chief of Staff **Dr. Marie A. DeWitt MD** ...... (906) 774-3300 ext. 32010
Education: Michigan MD
Public Affairs Officer **Bradley Nelson** .... (906) 774-3300 ext. 32001
Education Coordinator
Tammy Schill-Pavlat .... (906) 774-3300 ext. 32009
Police Service Chief **Patrick Palmquist** ...... (906) 774-3300 ext. 32030
Fax: (906) 779-3188

Wisconsin

Clement J. Zablocki VA Medical Center
5000 West National Avenue, Milwaukee, WI 53295
Tel: (414) 384-2000 Tel: (888) 469-6614 Fax: (414) 382-5370
Internet: www.milwaukee.va.gov

• Director
Dr. Daniel S. Zomchek PhD, FACHE ...... (414) 384-2000 ext. 41025
E-mail: daniel.zomchek@va.gov
Education: Loyola U (Chicago) 1998 BA;
Bowling Green State 2003 PhD
Deputy Medical Center Director
James McLain .... (414) 384-2000 ext. 41024
Assistant Medical Center Director
Christina P. Orr .... (414) 384-2000 ext. 41024
Public Affairs Officer **Gary Kunich** .... (414) 382-5363
E-mail: gary.kunich@va.gov Fax: (414) 389-4251
Learning Resources and Education Program
Manager **(Vacant)** .... (414) 384-2000 ext. 42345
Chief of Police **Timothy "Tim" Jantz** .... (414) 384-2000
E-mail: timothy.jantz@va.gov Fax: (414) 382-5319

Tomah (WI) VA Medical Center
500 East Veterans Street, Tomah, WI 54660
Tel: (608) 372-3971 Fax: (608) 372-1692 Internet: www.tomah.va.gov

• Director **Victoria P. Brahm RN** .... (608) 372-1777
E-mail: victoria.brahm@va.gov
Executive Secretary **(Vacant)** .... (608) 372-1777
Lead Police Officer **Rex Sweet** .... (608) 372-3971 ext. 61244
Fax: (608) 372-1107
Education Coordinator **Debra Young** .... (608) 372-3971 ext. 61128
Fax: (608) 372-1183
Information Technology Service Line
Coordinator **Brendan Smith** .... (608) 372-3971 ext. 61124
Fax: (608) 372-1111

William S. Middleton Memorial Veterans Hospital (Madison VAMC)
2500 Overlook Terrace, Madison, WI 53705-2286
Tel: (608) 256-1901 Fax: (608) 280-7155 Internet: www.madison.va.gov

• Director **John Rohrer** .... (608) 280-7091
Fax: (608) 280-7096

★ Presidential Appointment Requiring Senate Confirmation ☆ Presidential Appointment ☐ Schedule C Appointment ◇ Career Senior Foreign Service Appointment
● Career Senior Executive Service (SES) Appointment ○ Non-Career Senior Executive Service (SES) Appointment ■ Postal Career Executive Service

William S. Middleton Memorial Veterans Hospital *(continued)*

Associate Director **(Vacant)** .... (608) 280-7092
Assistant Director **Abraham C. Rabinowitz** .... (608) 280-7090
Chief of Pharmacy
Andrew Wilcox PharmD .... (608) 256-1901 ext. 11028
E-mail: andrew.wilcox@va.gov Fax: (608) 280-7279
Chief of Staff **Alan J. Bridges DrMed** .... (608) 280-7094
E-mail: alan.bridges@va.gov Fax: (608) 280-7096
Education: Illinois (Peoria) 1983 MD
Associate Director of Patient Care Services
David E. Murray .... (608) 280-7080
Fax: (608) 280-7086
Information Resource Management Chief
Randall Margenau .... (608) 280-7010
E-mail: randall.margenau@va.gov Fax: (608) 280-7089
Organizational Improvement Manager **Rebecca Strini** .... (608) 280-7264
Fax: (608) 280-7096
Police Service Chief **Jerry Pierce** .... (608) 256-1901 ext. 17115
E-mail: jerry.pierce@va.gov Fax: (608) 280-7096
Public Affairs Officer **Paul Rickert** .... (608) 280-7030
Fax: (608) 280-7105
Patient Advocate **Chad Casey** .... (608) 256-1901 ext. 17182
Patient Advocate **Megan Devault** .... (608) 256-1901 ext. 17182
Webmaster **Tim Donovan** .... (608) 256-1901 ext. 12053
Fax: (608) 280-7096

VISN 15 - VA Heartland Network

1201 Walnut Street, Suite 800, Kansas City, MO 64106
Fax: (816) 221-0930 Internet: www.visn15.va.gov/

Network Director **Dr. William Patterson MD** .... (816) 701-3000
Deputy Network Director
Michael Moore PhD, PhD, FACHE .... (816) 701-3074
Chief Financial Officer **Marcus Jackson** ...... (816) 701-3000 ext. 3025
Chief Information Officer **George Parry** .... (816) 701-3000 ext. 3048
E-mail: georg.parry@va.gov
Chief Medical Officer **Kanan J. Chatterjee MD, MBA** ... (816) 701-3000
Network Contract Manager **William "Bill" Strobel** ...... (913) 946-1147
E-mail: william.strobel@va.gov
Small Business Liaison **Kay R. Brundage** .... (913) 946-1108
E-mail: kay.brundage@va.gov
Events Planner **(Vacant)** .... (816) 701-3034

Illinois

Marion (IL) VA Medical Center
2401 West Main Street, Marion, IL 62959
Tel: (618) 997-5311 Fax: (618) 993-4155 Internet: www.marion.va.gov

● Director **Jo-Ann M. Ginsberg MSN, RN** ..... (618) 997-5311 ext. 54300
Education: Hunter BSN, MSN
Associate Director **Seth W. Barlage** .... (618) 997-5311 ext. 54101
Associate Director, Patient Care/Nursing
Services (Interim) **Roberta L. Patterson** .... (618) 997-5311 ext. 54207
Chief of Staff **Dr. Garrett S. Lynchard**
MD, FACC, FACP .... (618) 993-5311 ext. 73608
Public Affairs Officer **Kevin Harris** .... (618) 997-5311 ext. 54381
Contracting Officer **Timothy "Tim" Daly** .... (765) 677-6112
E-mail: timothy.daly2@va.gov

Kansas

VA Eastern Kansas Health Care System
2200 Gage Boulevard, Topeka, KS 66622
4101 Fourth Street Trafficway, Leavenworth, KS 66048
Tel: (913) 682-2000 (Leavenworth VAMC)
Tel: (785) 350-3111 (Topeka VAMC) Fax: (785) 350-4336
Internet: www2.va.gov/directory/guide/facility.asp?id=70
Internet: http://www.leavenworth.va.gov/
Internet: http://www.topeka.va.gov/

● Director **A. Rudy Klopfer FACHE** .... (785) 350-4307
E-mail: rudy.klopfer@va.gov
Executive Assistant to the Director **Stacey Askew** ...... (785) 350-4512
Assistant Director (Acting) **Jennifer Price** .... (785) 350-4306
Tel: (913) 682-2000

Dwight D. Eisenhower VA Medical Center
4101 South Fourth Street, Trafficway, Leavenworth, KS 66048
Tel: (913) 682-2000 Fax: (913) 758-4107
Internet: www.leavenworth.va.gov

● Director **A. Rudy Klopfer FACHE** .... (913) 682-2000 ext. 2008

Robert J. Dole Veterans Affairs Medical Center
VA Medical and Regional Office Center,
5500 East Kellogg Drive, Wichita, KS 67218
Tel: (316) 685-2221 Fax: (316) 651-3666 Internet: www.wichita.va.gov

● Director **Ricky A. Ament** .... (316) 685-2221 ext. 53601
Education: Virginia Tech 1982 BS; Central Michigan 1987 MS
Associate Director **Dana D. Foley** .... (316) 685-2221 ext. 53100
Education: Oklahoma State PhD
Associate Director of Patient
Care/Nurse Executive (Interim)
Julianna Cotton MSN, RN .... (316) 685-2221 ext. 53728
● Assistant Director (Acting)
Sharon Lien USAF (Ret) .... (316) 685-2221 ext. 56702
Chief of Staff
Dr. Robert V. Cummings MD, USAF (Ret) .... (316) 651-3731
E-mail: robert.cummings@va.gov
Education: Hahnemann
Chief Information Officer **Tony Sines** .... (316) 685-2221 ext. 53695
E-mail: tony.sines@va.gov
Information Security Officer **Rolando Trevino** .... (316) 681-5585
E-mail: rolando.trevino@va.gov
Education Services Supervisor
Tammy Huneycutt .... (316) 685-2221 ext. 53809
Chief of Police **William Howard** .... (316) 685-2221 ext. 53206
Fiscal Service Chief (Acting)
Jennifer Dowell .... (316) 685-2221 ext. 52720
Education: Kansas State 2001 MAcc

Missouri

Harry S. Truman Memorial Veterans' Hospital (Columbia MO VA Medical Center)
800 Hospital Drive, Columbia, MO 65201
Tel: (573) 814-6000 Fax: (573) 814-6309
Internet: www.columbiamo.va.gov

● Director **David Isaacks** .... (573) 814-6300
E-mail: david.isaacks@va.gov
Information Management Director **Michael H. Gracie** .... (573) 814-6525
E-mail: michael.gracie@va.gov Fax: (573) 814-6502
Nurse Educator **Nancy Day** .... (573) 814-6515
Education Specialist **Sara Hake** .... (573) 814-6000 ext. 4071
Fax: (573) 814-6591
Police Section Chief **David Agee** .... (573) 814-6320

John J. Pershing VA Medical Center
1500 North Westwood Boulevard, Poplar Bluff, MO 63901
Tel: (573) 686-4151 Fax: (573) 778-4559
Internet: www.poplarbluff.va.gov

● Director **Patricia L Hall PhD** .... (573) 778-4690
E-mail: patricia.tenhaff2@va.gov
Chief of Staff **(Vacant)** .... (573) 778-4691
Associate Chief of Staff for Primary Care
Yogesh Bhatt MD .... (573) 778-4760
E-mail: yogesh.bhatt@va.gov
Associate Chief of Staff for Specialty Care
Balamurugan Krishnan .... (573) 778-4760
Financial Manager **Kristy Williams** .... (573) 686-4151
E-mail: kristy.roberts@va.gov
Chief Information Officer **Michael Gustin** .... (785) 350-3111 ext. 54437
Chief of Police **Dale Garrett** .... (573) 778-4209
Fax: (573) 778-4559

Kansas City (MO) VA Medical Center
4801 East Linwood Boulevard, Kansas City, MO 64128-2295
Tel: (816) 861-4700 Fax: (816) 922-4755
Internet: www.kansascity.va.gov

● Director **Kathleen R. Fogarty** .... (816) 922-2046
E-mail: kathleen.fogarty@va.gov

(continued on next page)

★ Presidential Appointment Requiring Senate Confirmation ☆ Presidential Appointment ☐ Schedule C Appointment ◇ Career Senior Foreign Service Appointment
● Career Senior Executive Service (SES) Appointment ○ Non-Career Senior Executive Service (SES) Appointment ■ Postal Career Executive Service

Kansas City (MO) VA Medical Center *(continued)*

Associate Director
Paula Roychaudhuri FACHE . . . . (816) 861-4700 ext. 56888
Education: Kansas 2005 MHSA
Assistant Director
Angela J. Nix MHA, MBA, RHIA . . . . (816) 861-4700 ext. 52046
Education: Louisiana (Lafayette) 2003 BS; Houston (Clear Lake) 2008 MBA
Chief of Staff **Dr. Ahmad Batrash MD, FACP** . . . . (816) 922-2010
Public Relations Officer **(Vacant)** . . . .(816) 861-4700 ext. 52627
Librarian **Elizabeth "Liz" Burns** . . . .(816) 861-4700 ext. 52315
E-mail: liz.burns@va.gov
Veterans Justice Outreach Specialist
Kelly Winship . . . . (816) 861-4700 ext. 56155

Saint Louis (MO) VA Medical Center
915 North Grand, St. Louis, MO 63106-1621
Tel: (314) 652-4100 Fax: (314) 289-6557 Internet: www.stlouis.va.gov

● Director **Keith Repko** . . . . (314) 289-7651
E-mail: keith.repko@va.gov
Deputy Director **Desmond McMullan MBA** . . . . (314) 289-7651
Associate Director **Fabian Grabski** . . . . (314) 289-7651
Associate Director, Nursing Services
Patricia Hendrickson . . . . (314) 289-7651
Chief of Staff **Dr. Michael D. Crittenden MD** . . . . (314) 289-7651
Chief Information Officer **Steve Warmbold** . . . . (314) 289-6480
E-mail: steve.warmboldt@va.gov
Public Affairs Manager **Marcena Gunter** . . . . (314) 289-6379
E-mail: marcena.gunter@va.gov
Tel: (314) 894-6530
Librarian **Robert "Mason" Baldwin** . . . . (314) 652-4100
E-mail: robert.baldwin4@va.gov
Clinical Engineer **Wesley Sargent** . . . . (314) 652-4100
Information Security Officer **(Vacant)** . . . . (314) 652-4100
Security Chief **William Shirah** . . . .(314) 289-6325
Fax: (314) 289-7603
Training Administrative Officer
Julia King MHA, RN, NEA-BC . . . .(314) 289-6385
#1 Jefferson Barracks Drive, St. Louis, MO 63125-4199 Fax: (314) 289-7904
E-mail: julia.king@va.gov

VISN 16 - South Central VA Health Care Network
Plaza 1, 715 South Pear Orchard Road, Ridgeland, MS 39157-4807
Tel: (601) 206-6900 Fax: (601) 206-7018 Internet: www.visn16.va.gov

● Network Director **Skye McDougall PhD** . . . .(601) 206-6979
E-mail: skye.mcdougall@va.gov
Deputy Network Director (Acting)
Shannon C. Novotny . . . . (601) 206-6980
E-mail: shannon.novotny@va.gov
Health Systems Specialist/Network Director
LaWanda W. Parks . . . . (601) 206-6976
Education: Tougaloo BA; Alabama Birmingham MHA
Chief Financial Officer **Cynthia Jwainat** . . . . (601) 206-6910
Chief Medical Officer (Interim) **Dr. John P. Areno MD** . . . (601) 206-6973
Education: LSU Health Sciences Ctr 1991 MD
Deputy Chief Medical Officer **Dr. Amy W. Smith** . . . . . (601) 206-6973
E-mail: amy.smith212ba9@va.gov
Chief Operating Officer **Shannon C. Novotny** . . . . (601) 206-6980
Human Resources Manager (Acting) **Michael Palmier** . . . (501) 257-1898
Information Security Manager **Jose C. Arriola** . . . . (713) 794-7983
Quality Management Officer **Tom Drago** . . . . (601) 206-7027
Chief Learning Officer **(Vacant)** . . . . (601) 206-6932

Arkansas

Central Arkansas Veterans Healthcare System
4300 West Seventh Street, Little Rock, AR 72205
Tel: (501) 257-1000 Fax: (501) 257-5404 Internet: www.littlerock.va.gov

● Director **Dr. Margie A. Scott** . . . . (501) 257-5400
Deputy Director (Acting) **Patricia A. Bryant** . . . . (501) 257-1344
Associate Director **Cyril O. Ekeh** . . . . (501) 257-5400
Associate Director for Patient Care Services/Nurse Executive **Salena Wright-Brown** . . . . (501) 257-6151

Central Arkansas Veterans Healthcare System *(continued)*

Chief of Staff **Catina McClain** . . . . (501) 257-5300
Public Affairs Officer **Chris Durney** . . . . (501) 257-5393
E-mail: public.affairs2@va.gov
Education: Slippery Rock U 1984 BComm
Chief of Police **Timothy Kildea** . . . . (501) 257-3050
Education: Excelsior 2000 BS Fax: (501) 257-3051
Webmaster **Maurice Brooks** . . . . (501) 257-1555

Veterans Health Care System of the Ozarks
1100 North College Avenue, Fayetteville, AR 72703
Tel: (479) 443-4301 Fax: (479) 444-5089
Internet: www.fayettevillear.va.gov

● Director (Interim) **Kelvin L. Parks MA** . . . . (479) 444-5058
Education: Crichton 2002 BS; Webster 2009 MA
Associate Director (Acting) **Birch G. Wright** . . . . (479) 444-5058
Education: Arkansas MPA
Associate Director, Patient Care Services
Amy Huycke RN, MS . . . . (479) 444-3025
Chief of Staff **Dr. Mark Worley MD** . . . . (479) 444-5050
E-mail: mark.worley@va.gov
Chief Information Officer **Sara McCoy** . . . .(479) 443-4301 ext. 65395
E-mail: sara.mccoy2@va.gov Fax: (479) 587-5899
Primary Care Administrator **Dr. Ricky Kine** . . . . (479) 444-5001
Information Technology Chief **Scott Lozen** . . . . (479) 444-4040
E-mail: scott.lozen@va.gov Fax: (479) 587-5985
Webmaster **Jerry Bailey** . . . . (479) 444-5883
E-mail: jerry.bailey@med.va.gov

Louisiana

Alexandria VA Health Care System (AVAHCS)
VA Medical Center, P.O. Box 69004, Alexandria, LA 71306-9004
Tel: (318) 473-0010 Fax: (318) 483-5029
Internet: www.alexandria.va.gov

● Director **Peter C. Dancy, Jr. FACHE** . . . . (318) 466-2205
E-mail: peter.dancy@va.gov
Associate Director **Lisa M. Hamilton** . . . . (318) 466-2206
Information Resource Management Service Chief
Louis J. Santin . . . . (318) 466-4192
Information Security Officer **Lydia White** . . . .(318) 466-2080
Associate Director for Patient Care Services
James Lawhorn, Jr. . . . . (318) 466-2558
Chief of Staff **Dr. Harlan "Mark" Guidry MD, MPH** . . . . (318) 466-2202
Education: Texas BS; Texas (Galveston) DM
Public Affairs Officer and Chief of Voluntary Services
Tammie Arnold . . . . (318) 466-2061
E-mail: tammie.arnold@va.gov
Webmaster **Tammie Arnold** . . . . (318) 466-2061
E-mail: tammie.arnold@va.gov

Southeast Louisiana Veterans Health Care System (SLVHCS)
1601 Perdido Street, New Orleans, LA 70146
P.O. Box 61011, New Orleans, LA 70161-1011
Tel: (504) 412-3700 Tel: (800) 935-8387 Fax: (504) 565-4835
Internet: www.neworleans.va.gov

● Director **Fernando O. Rivera MBA, FACHE** . . . . (504) 565-4830
E-mail: fernando.rivera@va.gov
Education: New Orleans, MBA
Special Assistant to the Director **Licinda Collins** . . . .(504) 565-4848
Deputy Director (Acting) **Dr. Stephanie Repasky** . . . . (504) 565-4845
Associate Director for Patient/Nursing Services
Brinda Williams-Morgan . . . . (504) 565-4963
Associate Director **Dr. Stephanie Repasky** . . . . (504) 565-1433
E-mail: stephanie.repasky@va.gov Fax: (504) 558-1429
Chief of Staff **Dr. Ralph Schapira MD** . . . . (504) 565-4870
Associate Chief of Staff for Quality and Performance Improvement **Denise Overby-Reyes** . . . .(504) 565-4937
Clinical Information Management Service Line Director **Darryl Dragon** . . . . (504) 565-4881
Medicine Service Line Director **Michael Landry** . . . . (504) 565-4918
Education: Tulane MD
Mental Health Service Line Director **Dean Robinson** . . . . (504) 412-3685
Pathology and Laboratory Medicine Service Line Director **Giovanni Lorusso** . . . . (504) 565-4972

★ Presidential Appointment Requiring Senate Confirmation ☆ Presidential Appointment ☐ Schedule C Appointment ◇ Career Senior Foreign Service Appointment
● Career Senior Executive Service (SES) Appointment ○ Non-Career Senior Executive Service (SES) Appointment ■ Postal Career Executive Service

Southeast Louisiana Veterans Health Care System *(continued)*

Radiology Service Line Director **Robert Perret** .... (504) 545-4922
Surgery Service Line Director
Dr. James Smith MD, FACS .... (504) 565-4911
Business Operations Director **Michael Brown** .... (504) 558-1431
Chief Financial Officer **Patricia Smith** .... (504) 558-3657
Public Affairs Officer **Amanda Jones** .... (504) 565-4852
Logistics Management Service Chief (Acting)
Jennifer Loudermilk .... (504) 558-3616
Ambulatory and Primary Care Service **(Vacant)** .... (504) 565-4883
Facilities Management (Acting) **Nacelyn Lombard** .... (504) 553-5977
E-mail: nacelyn.lombard@va.gov

Overton Brooks VA Medical Center (Shreveport VA Medical Center)
510 East Stoner Avenue, Shreveport, LA 71101-4295
Tel: (318) 221-8411 Fax: (318) 990-5552
Internet: www.shreveport.va.gov

● Director **Richard L. Crockett** .... (318) 990-5133
Education: Rockhurst U 2013 MBA
Chief of Staff (Interim) **Don Pirraglia** .... (318) 990-4986
Education: Wagner 1986 BS
Education and Training Chief **Robert Lukeman MD** ..... (318) 990-5002
Health Information Management Chief
Cathy Gillyard .... (318) 221-8411 ext. 6480
E-mail: cathy.gillyard@va.gov
Police Chief **Gary Alderman** .... (318) 221-8411 ext. 5250
Librarian **(Vacant)** .... (318) 990-5181

Mississippi

VA Gulf Coast Veterans Health Care System – Biloxi (MS)
400 Veterans Avenue, Biloxi, MS 39531-2410
Tel: (228) 523-5000 Fax: (228) 523-5719

● Medical Center Director **Bryan C. Matthews MBA** ...... (228) 523-5766
Education: Maryland BA; U Phoenix MHCM
Associate Director (Acting) **Adam G. Bearden** .... (850) 912-2202
Education: Loyola U (New Orleans) 1991 MBA
Associate Director for Outpatient Operations
Adam G. Bearden .... (850) 912-2202
Education: Loyola U (New Orleans) 1991 MBA
Associate Director for Patient Care Services/Nurse
Executive **M. Christopher Saslo ARNP-BC, FAANP** ... (228) 523-4679
Education: Marywood U 1990 BSN; La Salle U 1995 MSN; Florida Atlantic 2007 DNSc
Assistant Director **(Vacant)** .... (850) 912-2202
Chief of Staff
Dr. Reginald Labossiere MD, FACP .... (432) 263-7361 ext. 7112
Public Affairs Chief **Mary Kay Gominger** .... (228) 523-5945
Education: Southern Mississippi 1979 MS Fax: (228) 523-4967
Librarian **Maggie Altman** .... (228) 523-4931
E-mail: mary.altman@va.gov
Information Management Service Chief **David Wagner** ... (228) 523-4520
E-mail: david.wagner@va.gov
Lead Psychologist (Interim) **Kimberly Tartt-Godbolt** .... (228) 523-5000
Education: Alabama Birmingham 2000 BS; Argosy U 2003 MA, 2007 PsyD
Veterans Justice Outreach Specialist **Kathy Monson** ..... (228) 523-5000
Veterans Justice Outreach Specialist **David Nelsen** ...... (228) 523-5000
Veterans Justice Outreach Specialist **Lysbeth Spence** .... (228) 523-5000

G. V. "Sonny" Montgomery VA Medical Center
1500 East Woodrow Wilson Drive, Jackson, MS 39216-5116
Tel: (601) 362-4471 Fax: (601) 364-1456 Internet: www.jackson.va.gov

● Director **Dr. David M. Walker** .... (601) 364-1435
E-mail: david.walker@va.gov
Special Assistant to Director
Shawana Jones .... (601) 362-4471 ext. 55498
Associate Director (Acting) **Kai D. Mentzer** ... (601) 362-4471 ext. 51204
Education: Arizona 2010 BSBA
Associate Director of Patient Care Services
Eva M. Santoyo .... (601) 362-4471 ext. 55672
Assistant Director **Patricia A. Lane** .... (601) 362-4471 ext. 3977
Education: Frostburg State U BSC; Maryland Baltimore MSSW
Chief of Staff **Susan Roberts** .... (601) 364-1432

G. V. "Sonny" Montgomery VA Medical Center *(continued)*

Administrative Assistant to the Nurse Executive
Thantween Rucker-White .... (601) 364-1334
Public Relations Director **Susan Varcie** .... (601) 368-4477
Information Resource Management Chief
Rachel Stokes .... (601) 364-1385
E-mail: Rachel.stokes@va.gov
Information Security Officer
Lance Boyington .... (601) 362-4471 ext. 56030

Oklahoma

Eastern Oklahoma VA Health Care System (Muskogee VA)
1011 Honor Heights Drive, Muskogee, OK 74401
Tel: (918) 577-3000 Fax: (918) 577-3648
Internet: www.muskogee.va.gov

● Director **Mark E. Morgan FACHE, MHA** .... (918) 577-3645
E-mail: mark.morgan@va.gov
Education: Florida BA; North Carolina MHA
Associate Director
Jonathan M. Plasencia MBA, FACHE .... (918) 577-3642
Education: UC San Diego 2006 BA; UC Irvine 2013 MBA
Chief of Staff (Acting) **Michael Prior** .... (918) 577-3650
E-mail: michael.prior2@va.gov
Associate Director for Patient Care Services (Acting)
Carol Rueter .... (918) 577-3759
Fax: (918) 577-3763
Education Service Chief **Susan Hays** .... (918) 577-3754
Education: Northeastern State 1997 BS; Oklahoma 1998 MS
Information Management Chief **Mark Carr** .... (918) 577-3933
E-mail: mark.carr@va.gov

Oklahoma City (OK) VA Medical Center
921 NE 13th Street, Oklahoma City, OK 73104
Tel: (405) 456-1000 Fax: (405) 456-1560 Internet: www.oklahoma.va.gov

● Director **Kristopher Wade Vlosich** .... (405) 456-3301
E-mail: kristopher.vlosich@va.gov
Education: Texas Tech 2002 BA, 2004 MBA
Secretary to the Director **Joyce Wilson** .... (405) 456-3300
Librarian **(Vacant)** .... (405) 456-1622
Education Coordinator **Mark Hooten** .... (405) 456-4382
Information Technology Chief **Robert Finigan** .... (405) 456-5748
Fax: (405) 456-1535
Police Service Chief **Claude Rivers** .... (405) 456-5592
Fax: (405) 456-5919

Texas

Michael E. DeBakey VA Medical Center (DeBakey VA Medical Center)
2002 Holcombe Boulevard, Houston, TX 77030
Tel: (713) 791-1414 Fax: (713) 794-7038 Internet: www.houston.va.gov

● Director **Francisco Vazquez** .... (713) 794-7531
E-mail: francisco.vazquez@va.gov
Deputy Director
Karandeep "Kenny" Sraon MBBS, MBA, FACHE .... (713) 794-8923
Education: Loyola U (Chicago) MBA
Associate Director **Anthony L. Dawson FACHE, MHA** ... (713) 794-7531
Education: Jackson State U 1983 BS; Mississippi 1986 BS; Xavier (OH) 1989 MSHA
Chief of Staff **Jagadeesh S. Kalavar MD** .... (713) 794-7011
E-mail: jagadeesh.kalavar@va.gov
Deputy Chief of Staff **Dr. James W. Scheurich MD** ... (713) 794-7436
Education: Baylor Col Medicine 1979 MD
Associate Director for Patient Care Services
Kelly A. Irving .... (713) 794-7475
Public Affairs Officer **Maureen Dyman** .... (713) 794-7349
E-mail: vhahoupublicaffairs@va.gov
Social Media Specialist/Webmaster **Nikki Verbeck** .... (713) 794-7349
E-mail: nikki.verbeck@va.gov

★ Presidential Appointment Requiring Senate Confirmation ☆ Presidential Appointment □ Schedule C Appointment ◇ Career Senior Foreign Service Appointment
● Career Senior Executive Service (SES) Appointment ○ Non-Career Senior Executive Service (SES) Appointment ■ Postal Career Executive Service

VISN 17 - Heart of Texas Health Care Network

2301 E. Lamar Boulevard, Suite 650, Arlington, TX 76006
Tel: (817) 652-1111 Fax: (817) 385-3700
Internet: www.heartoftexas.va.gov

- ● Network Director **Jeffery L. "Jeff" Milligan** .... (817) 652-1111
  Education: U Memphis BSEE; Baylor MHCA
- Deputy Network Director **Mark Doskocil FACHE** .... (817) 385-3764
  Education: Iowa 1978 BS; Pittsburgh 1981 MPH
- Associate Director for Health Care Recruitment **Russell Peal** .... (817) 652-1111
  E-mail: Russell.Peal@va.gov
- Chief Financial Officer **Michael Kuchyak** .... (817) 652-1111
- Chief Health Information Officer **Brian H. Foresman** .... (210) 694-6231
- Chief Medical Officer **Dr. Wendell Jones MD** .... (817) 652-1111
  E-mail: wendell.jones@va.gov
- Network Contract Manager **(Vacant)** .... (817) 385-3779
  - Small Business Contracting Officer **(Vacant)** .... (214) 857-0023

Texas

Amarillo VA Health Care System

6010 Amarillo Boulevard, West, Amarillo, TX 79106
Tel: (806) 355-9703 Fax: (806) 354-7860 Internet: www.amarillo.va.gov

- ● Director **COL Michael L. Kiefer USA (Ret), FACHE, MHA** ..... (806) 354-7801
  Education: Lehigh 1986 BA; Baylor 1994 MHA
- Associate Director **Elizabeth Lowery MA** ..... (806) 355-9703 ext. 7006
- Chief Information Officer **(Vacant)** .... (806) 355-9703 ext. 7012
- Chief Nurse **Louise Osteen RN** .... (806) 355-9703 ext. 4141
  Education: Walden MSN
- Chief of Staff **Dr. Sameh Moawad** .... (806) 355-9703 ext. 7004
- Acquisition and Material Management Service Chief **Karen Bradshaw** .... (806) 355-9703 ext. 7836
  E-mail: karen.bradshaw@va.gov
- Admission and Referral Service Chief **Franke Robertson** .... (806) 355-9703
  E-mail: franke.robertson@va.gov
- Ambulatory Care Service Chief **Dr. Bauer Horton** .... (806) 355-9703 ext. 7674
- Chaplain Service Chief **Joseph Kutin** .... (806) 355-9703 ext. 7114
  E-mail: joseph.kutin@va.gov
- Community and Patient Relations Chief **Barbara Moore** .... (806) 354-3737
- Education Service Chief **(Vacant)** .... (806) 355-9703 ext. 7343
  Fax: (806) 356-3802
- Engineering Service Chief **Ryan Schwitzer** .... (806) 355-9703 ext. 7426
- Environmental Management Service Chief **Kathy O'Dell** .... (806) 355-9703 ext. 7376
  E-mail: kathy.odell@va.gov
- Fiscal Service Chief **Ruth Lee** .... (806) 355-9703 ext. 7370
- Health Administration Service Chief **T.J. "Tommy" Bowerman** .... (806) 355-9703 ext. 7289
  E-mail: tommy.bowerman@va.gov Fax: (806) 354-7876
- Human Resources Chief **Zephfina Wyatt** ...... (806) 355-9703 ext. 7329
  E-mail: zephfina.wyatt@va.gov
- Laboratory and Pathology Service Chief **(Vacant)** .... (806) 355-9703 ext. 7170
- Medical Service Chief **Dr. Anjali Kherdekar** ... (806) 355-9703 ext. 7871
- Mental Health Service Chief **Michael Lambert MD** .... (806) 355-9703 ext. 7147
  E-mail: michael.lambert4@va.gov
- Nutrition and Food Service Chief **Annette Jenks** .... (806) 355-9703 ext. 7383
- Occupational Health and Rehab Medicine Chief **(Vacant)** .... (806) 355-9703 ext. 7245
- Performance Improvement Chief **Ginger Mitchell** .... (806) 355-9703 ext. 7007
- Pharmacy Service Chief **John Gulde** .... (806) 355-9703 ext. 7291
  E-mail: john.gulde@va.gov
- Police Service Chief **George Loomis** .... (806) 355-9703 ext. 7062
  E-mail: george.loomis@va.gov
- Prosthetics and Sensory Aids Service Chief **(Vacant)** .... (806) 355-9703 ext. 7500
- Radiology Service Chief **Arturo Lira** .... (806) 355-9703 ext. 7896
- Surgery Service Chief **(Vacant)** .... (806) 355-9703 ext. 7207

Central Texas VA Health Care System

1901 Veterans Memorial Drive, Temple, TX 76504
Tel: (254) 778-4811 Fax: (254) 743-2338
Internet: www.centraltexas.va.gov

- ● Director **Christopher R. Sandles MBA, FACHE** .... (254) 743-2306
  Education: Texas Tech BB, MHA
- Associate Director for Patient Care Services **Bryan W. Sisk** .... (254) 743-2385
- ● Associate Director **Andrew T. Garcia** .... (254) 743-2332
- Chief of Staff **Dr. Olawale O. Fashina MD** .... (254) 743-2323
  E-mail: olawale.fashina@va.gov
- Public Affairs Officer **Deborah Meyer** .... (254) 743-2376
  E-mail: deborah.meyer@va.gov
  Tel: (254) 534-0304
- Chief Librarian **Roger Hunceker** .... (254) 743-0533

Olin E. Teague VA Medical Center

1901 Veterans Memorial Drive, Temple, TX 76504
Tel: (254) 778-4811 Tel: (800) 423-2111 Tel: (254) 743-2338

- ● Director **(Vacant)** .... (254) 743-2306
- Assistant Director for Operations **(Vacant)** .... (254) 743-2332

Doris Miller VA Medical Center

4800 Memorial Drive, Waco, TX 76711
Tel: (254) 752-6581 Fax: (254) 756-5215 Tel: (800) 423-2111
Internet: http://www.centraltexas.va.gov/locations/Waco.asp

- ● Director (Acting) **Russell E. Lloyd** .... (254) 743-2306
  E-mail: russell.lloyd@va.gov
- Assistant Director for Operations **Amy L. Maynard** ...... (254) 297-3158

El Paso VA Health Care System

5001 North Piedras Street, El Paso, TX 79930-4211
Tel: (915) 564-6100 Tel: (800) 672-3782 Fax: (915) 564-7920
Internet: www.elpaso.va.gov

- ● Director **COL Michael L. Amaral USA (Ret)** .... (915) 564-7904
  Education: Norwich BS; Baylor MS
- Associate Director **Jamie Park** .... (915) 564-7901
- Nurse Executive **Lenore S. Enzel RNC, NE-BC, CLNC** ... (915) 564-7908
  Education: CUNY 1976 BSN; Hawaii 1992 MSN
- Chief of Staff **Brian H. Foresman** .... (915) 564-7911
- Information Resource Management Service Chief **LCDR Byron Moss USN (Ret)** .... (915) 564-7938
  E-mail: byron.moss@va.gov
- Voluntary Service Officer **Thomas Sotomayor** .... (915) 564-7882
- Management Analyst **(Vacant)** .... (915) 564-6100 ext. 7576

North Texas VA Health Care System

4500 South Lancaster Road, Dallas, TX 75216
Internet: www.northtexas.va.gov

Dallas (TX) VA Medical Center

4500 South Lancaster Road, Dallas, TX 75216
Tel: (214) 742-8387 Internet: www.northtexas.va.gov

- ● Director **Dr. Stephen R. Holt MD, MPH** .... (214) 857-1112
  Education: Uniformed Services MD
- Associate Director **Kendrick D. Brown** .... (214) 857-1143
- Assistant Director **Eric D. Jacobsen** .... (214) 857-1144
  Education: Texas 1996; Trinity U 1999 MS
- Associate Director, Patient Care Services **Gwendella C. Robinson** .... (214) 857-4910
- Chief of Staff **Jeffrey L Hastings** .... (214) 857-1150
- Associate Chief of Staff for Education **Cynthia Foslein-Nash** .... (214) 857-1152
- Information Technology Chief/Chief Information Officer **Odell Brown** .... (214) 857-2042
- Police Service Chief **Raul de Velasco, Jr.** .... (214) 857-0419
- Public Affairs Officer **Jeffrey Clapper** .... (214) 857-1155
- Webmaster **(Vacant)** .... (214) 857-1158
  E-mail: ntxpublicaffairs@va.gov

Sam Rayburn Memorial Veterans Center
1201 East Ninth Street, Bonham, TX 75418-4091
Tel: (903) 583-2111 Fax: (903) 583-6692
Internet: www.northtexas.va.gov/locations/Bonham.asp

● Operations Manager **Elizabeth Dannel** .... (903) 583-6210
E-mail: elizabeth.dannel@va.gov

South Texas VA Health Care System (STVHCS)
7400 Merton Minter Boulevard, San Antonio, TX 78229-4404
Tel: (210) 617-5140 Fax: (210) 617-5167
Internet: www.southtexas.va.gov

● Director **Robert M. Walton** .... (210) 617-5140
Education: Texas BSEE; Long Island MPA
Associate Director **Lisa J. Simoneau FACHE, PMP** ..... (210) 617-5300
Education: Randolph-Macon Woman's 1989 BA; Florida Atlantic 1999 MPA
Associate Director for Patient Care Services and Nurse Executive **Valerie Rodriguez-Yu** .... (210) 617-5300
Education: Texas Health Science BSN; U Phoenix 2008 MSN
Deputy Associate Director for Patient Care Services **COL Yolanda Ruiz-Isales USA** .... (210) 617-5300 ext. 14841
Education: Puerto Rico 1983 BSN; LSU (New Orleans) 1993 MN; Indust'l Col Armed Forces 2006 MS
Chief of Staff **Dr. Julianne Flynn MD** .... (210) 617-5140
Deputy Chief of Staff **Calvin Leuschen** .... (210) 617-5177
Assistant Director **Trisha M. Lodde** .... (210) 617-5140
Public Affairs Officer **Nenette C. Madla** .... (210) 617-5274
E-mail: nenette.madla@va.gov

Kerrville (TX) VA Medical Center
3600 Memorial Boulevard, Kerrville, TX 78028
Tel: (830) 792-2112 Fax: (830) 792-2480

Administrative Officer **Lance Maley** .... (830) 792-2472
E-mail: lance.maley@va.gov

Texas Valley Coastal Bend VA Health Care System
2701 S 77 Sunshine Strip, Harlingen, TX 78550
Tel: (956) 291-9000 Tel: (956) 430-9303 (Media Inquiries)
Internet: www.texasvalley.va.gov/

Director (Acting) **Homero S. Martinez III** .... (956) 291-9332
Education: Wayland Baptist 2000 BAS; Touro 2007 MBA
Associate Director (Acting) **Charles Harpel** .... (956) 291-9331
Chief of Staff (Acting) **Dr. Eric D. Kendle** .... (956) 291-9333
Nurse Executive and Associate Director for Patient Care Services (Acting) **Rolando Ramos** .... (956) 291-9249
Education: Texas (Brownsville) MSN
Patient Advocate **Hugo Martinez** .... (956) 430-9303
E-mail: hugo.martinez@va.gov
Education: Columbia Southern 2011 BASc
Veterans Justice Outreach Specialist **Yasisca Pujols** ...... (210) 617-5140
Veterans Justice Outreach Specialist **Jenesis Shaw MS, LPC** .... (210) 617-5140
Education: Texas A&M (Corpus Christi) 2006 BS, 2006 MS

West Texas VA Health Care System
300 Veterans Boulevard, Big Spring, TX 79720-5500
Tel: (432) 263-7361 Fax: (432) 264-4878 Internet: www.bigspring.va.gov

● Director **Kalautie S. JangDhari MPH** .... (432) 263-7361
E-mail: kalautie.jangdhari@va.gov
Education: Tennessee BS; Meharry Medical MSPH
Associate Director **Manuel Davila** .... (432) 264-4813
Education: Walden 2010 PhD; U Phoenix 2006 MBA
Chief of Staff (Acting) **Dr. Darcie Chitwood DO** .... (432) 264-4812
Associate Director of Patient Care Services/Chief Nurse Executive **Rebekah Friday** .... (432) 263-7361
Dental Service Chief **Gloria King** .... (432) 264-4815
Fiscal Chief **(Vacant)** .... (432) 264-4896
Logistics Chief **Carlla McCullough** .... (432) 264-4890
Pathology and Laboratory Medicine Service Chief **(Vacant)** .... (432) 263-7361 ext. 7231
Pharmacy Service Chief **Larry Thompson** .... (432) 264-4836
Physical Medicine and Rehabilitation Service Chief **Kristin Arnoldy** .... (432) 263-7361 ext. 7216
Psychiatry Service Chief **Dr. Connie Ponce** .... (432) 263-7361 ext. 7301

VISN 19 - Rocky Mountain Network
Mountain Towers, 4100 East Mississippi Avenue, Suite 510, Glendale, CO 80246
Tel: (303) 756-9279 Tel: (866) 301-9626 Fax: (303) 756-9243
Internet: www.visn19.va.gov

● Network Director **Ralph T. Gigliotti** .... (303) 202-8165
E-mail: ralph.gigliotti2@va.gov
Deputy Network Director **Sunaina Kumar** .... (303) 202-8165
Chief Financial Officer **Eliott Vanderstek** .... (303) 756-9279
Chief Information Officer **(Vacant)** .... (303) 756-9279
Chief Medical Officer **Dr. Leigh Anderson** .... (303) 202-8165
Webmaster **Kirk Prince** .... (303) 756-9279
E-mail: kirk.prince@va.gov
Small Business Liaison **Dan O. Freeman** .... (303) 712-5703

Colorado

VA Eastern Colorado Health Care System (VA ECHCS)
1055 Clermont Street, Denver, CO 80220
Tel: (303) 399-8020 Fax: (303) 393-2861 Internet: www.denver.va.gov

● Director **Sallie Houser-Hanfelder FACHE** .... (720) 723-6511
E-mail: sallie.houser-hanfelder@va.gov
Education: Texas A&M 1978 BS; East Texas State 1986 MS
Deputy Director **Duane Gill** .... (720) 723-6509
Education: Eastern Kentucky 2003 BA; Indiana Wesleyan 2006 MA
Associate Director, Patient Care Services **Keith Harmon** .... (720) 723-6510
Associate Director **Joshua Pridgen** .... (720) 723-6508
Associate Director **Richard J. Tremaine** .... (720) 399-8020 ext. 2324
Chief of Staff **Harold Dillon** .... (720) 723-6541
Deputy Chief of Staff **Clifford L. Parmley** .... (720) 723-6539
Quality Management Director **Lori Lee** .... (303) 399-8020 ext. 2032
Police Service Chief **Jon Heikka** .... (303) 393-2812
E-mail: jon.heikka@va.gov
Chief Information Officer **Don Huckaby** .... (303) 393-5289
E-mail: donald.huckaby@va.gov
Privacy Officer **Jeffrey Day** Room BA-121 ..... (303) 399-8020 ext. 2080
E-mail: jeffrey.day@va.gov
Veterans Justice Outreach Specialist **Michael Jay** .... (303) 399-8020
Veterans Justice Outreach Specialist **Nathan Viton** ...... (303) 399-8020
Nurse Recruiter **Shelli Kriley** .... (303) 202-7921
Regional Manager for Southern Colorado **Kimberly C. Hoge** .... (719) 327-5660
Education: Southern Mississippi 1992 BS; Southern U A&M 1995 MS

VA Western Colorado Health Care System
2121 North Avenue, Grand Junction, CO 81501
Tel: (970) 242-0731 Tel: (866) 206-6415 Fax: (970) 244-1303
Internet: www.grandjunction.va.gov

● Director **Michael Todd Kilmer** .... (970) 263-5034
E-mail: michael.kilmer@va.gov
Education: U Washington 2001 BS, 2004 MSW
Special Assistant to the Director **Cindi Ackerman-Castro** .... (970) 242-0731 ext. 2182
E-mail: cindi.ackerman-castro@va.gov
Associate Medical Center Director **(Vacant)** .... (970) 244-1334
Associate Director/Facility Planner **Patrick S. Marbas** .... (970) 263-2806
Chief of Staff **Srinivas Ginjupalli** .... (970) 242-0731 ext. 5064
Nurse Executive **Molly Bruner** .... (970) 242-0731
Infection Control Nurse **Susan Christian** ...... (970) 242-0731 ext. 2485
Information Technology Service Chief **Lyndon Fogg** .... (970) 242-0731 ext. 2595
Customer Relations, Patient Advocate **Timothy Johnson** .... (970) 263-2826
Librarian **(Vacant)** .... (970) 242-0731 ext. 2254
Veterans Justice Outreach Specialist **Rainy Reaman** ..... (970) 242-0731

Montana

VA Montana Healthcare System
3687 Veterans Drive, Fort Harrison, MT 59636
Tel: (406) 442-6410 Fax: (406) 447-7916 Internet: www.montana.va.gov

● Director **Kathy W. Berger** .... (406) 447-7301
E-mail: kathy.berger@va.gov

(continued on next page)

DEPARTMENTS

VA Montana Healthcare System *(continued)*

Assistant Director **Kirby Ostler** .... (406) 373-3940
Associate Director **Anthony Giljum** .... (406) 447-7301
Education: New Mexico Tech 1993 BS
Associate Director of Patient Care Services
Nina Morris .... (406) 447-7536
Chief of Staff
William Howard Campbell FACHE, MD, MBA .... (406) 447-7301
E-mail: william.campbell@va.gov
Education: Loyola U (Chicago) 1982 MD; Jacksonville U 1990 MBA
Deputy Chief of Staff **Marilyn LaJoie** .... (406) 447-7301
Chief Financial Officer **(Vacant)** .... (406) 442-7729
Chief Information Officer **Paul Gauthier** ...... (406) 442-6410 ext. 7673
Acquisition and Materiel Chief **Brian Nelson** .... (406) 447-7731
E-mail: brian.nelson2@va.gov
Police Service Chief **Charles White** .... (406) 442-6410 ext. 7660
Education Coordinator **Robert Nazzarini** ...... (406) 442-6410 ext. 7533
Congressional Liaison **Christina Lundstrom** .... (406) 442-7302
Fax: (406) 447-7916
Librarian **Kathy Williamson** .... (406) 447-7301
Fax: (406) 447-7916
Webmaster **James Shaw** .... (406) 447-7680

Utah

VA Salt Lake City Health Care System

500 Foothill Drive, Salt Lake City, UT 84148
Tel: (801) 582-1565 Fax: (801) 584-1289
Internet: www.saltlakecity.va.gov

• Director **Shella D. Stovall RN** .... (801) 582-1565 ext. 1211
E-mail: shella.stovall@va.gov
Education: Westminster (UT) 1989 BSN; U Phoenix 1993
Associate Director **Warren E. Hill** .... (801) 582-1565 ext. 1500
Associate Director, Quality and Safety
Systems **(Vacant)** .... (801) 582-1565 ext. 4608
Associate Director, Patient Care Services
Linda Pimenta .... (801) 582-1565 ext. 2447
Education: New Hampshire Tech 1995 ADN;
New Hampshire 2005 BSN; Maryville U 2014 DNP
Chief of Staff **Karen H. Gribbin MD** .... (801) 582-1565 ext. 1505
E-mail: karen.gribbin@va.gov
Associate Chief of Staff and Education
Grant W. Cannon MD, FACP .... (801) 582-1565 ext. 4301
E-mail: grant.cannon@va.gov
• Chief Information Officer **Lisa Leonelli** .... (801) 582-1565 ext. 5442
E-mail: lisa.leonelli@va.gov
Chief of Police **Ronald Beard** .... (801) 582-1565 ext. 2480
Head Librarian **Peter Schenk** .... (801) 582-1565 ext. 1209
Training Coordinator **Deborah Henry** .... (801) 582-1565 ext. 2256
Veterans Justice Outreach Specialist
Amy Earle .... (801) 582-1565 ext. 6327
Veterans Justice Outreach Specialist
Jessica Mann .... (801) 582-1565 ext. 6337
Nurse Recruiter **Amber D. Brennan** .... (801) 582-1565 ext. 1128

Wyoming

Cheyenne (WY) VA Medical Center and Regional Office Center

2360 East Pershing Boulevard, Cheyenne, WY 82001-5392
Tel: (800) 827-1000 Fax: (307) 778-7336 Internet: www.cheyenne.va.gov

• Director **Charles Kates** .... (307) 778-7550
Chief of Staff **Dr. James Gray MD** .... (307) 778-7550
E-mail: james.gray@va.gov
Education: Harding 1966 BS; Missouri 1971 MD
Chief, Learning Resources **Charles P. Cooley** .... (307) 778-7321
Chief, Police and Security **(Vacant)** .... (307) 778-7315

Sheridan (WY) VA Medical Center

1898 Fort Road, Sheridan, WY 82801
Tel: (307) 672-3473 Fax: (307) 675-7030 Internet: www.sheridan.va.gov

• Director **Pamela S. Crowell** .... (307) 675-3675
Associate Director **Donald Todd Mcgraw** .... (307) 675-3676
Chief of Staff **Eric Crawford** .... (307) 675-3674
E-mail: eric.crawford@va.gov

Sheridan (WY) VA Medical Center *(continued)*

Associate Chief of Staff, Mental Health Program
(Acting) **Dr. Vivianne Tran** .... (307) 675-3176
E-mail: vivianne.tran@va.gov
Associate Director, Patient Care Services and Nurse
Executive **Andrea Henderson** .... (307) 675-3646
E-mail: andrea.henderson2@va.gov
Associate Chief of Staff, Primary Care Program
(Vacant) .... (307) 675-3576
Facilities Management Service Chief **Sean Saltzman** .... (307) 675-3419
Library Section Chief **Teri Bagley** .... (307) 675-3661
Police Chief **Michael Penny** .... (307) 675-3602
Chief Information Officer **Troy Nissen** .... (307) 675-7383
Public Affairs Officer **Kristina Miller** .... (307) 675-3959
Education Coordinator/Events Planner **(Vacant)** .... (307) 675-3888
Veterans Justice Outreach Specialist **Karl Jantz** .... (307) 672-3383

VISN 20 - Northwest Health Network

P.O. Box 1035, Portland, OR 97207
Tel: (360) 619-5925 Fax: (360) 737-1405
Internet: www.visn20.med.va.gov

• Network Director **Michael J. Murphy FACHE** .... (360) 619-5925
E-mail: michaelmurphy6@va.gov
Deputy Network Director **John A. Mendoza** .... (360) 619-5925
Administrative Support Assistant **Amber Pilcher** ...... (360) 619-5939
Capital Asset Manager **Anne-Marie Naficy** .... (360) 619-5925
Chief Financial Officer **Adam Merryweather** .... (360) 567-4651
Chief Information Officer **James Horner** .... (360) 619-5961
Chief Logistics Officer **John Wilson** .... (360) 619-5938
E-mail: john.wilson@va.gov
Chief Medical Officer (Acting) **Nicholas Popochny** ..... (208) 422-1102
Network Contract Manager **Col Scott Benza USAF** ..... (360) 852-9850
E-mail: scott.benza@va.gov
Small Business Liaison **Marc A. Frederick** .... (253) 888-4913
E-mail: marc.frederick@va.gov
Small Business Liaison **(Vacant)** .... (360) 816-2783

Alaska

Alaska VA Healthcare System

1201 North Muldoon Road, Anchorage, AK 99504
Tel: (907) 257-4700 Fax: (907) 257-6774 Internet: www.alaska.va.gov

• Director **Dr. Timothy Ballard MD, MS** .... (907) 257-5460
Education: Air Force Acad 1988 BS; Uniformed Services 1992 MD; Cincinnati 2008 MS
Chief Financial Officer **Jennifer Price** .... (907) 257-4700
Executive Assistant to Director **Eric Wallis** .... (907) 257-5460
Associate Director **Thomas A. Steinbrunner FACHE** .... (907) 257-5460
Chief, Domiciliary Care for Homeless Veterans
Karen MacClain .... (907) 273-4055
E-mail: karen.macclain@va.gov Fax: (907) 273-4085
Chief, Health Care Homeless Veteran Services
John Pendrey .... (907) 273-4051
E-mail: john.pendrey@va.gov
Associate Director, Nursing and Patient Care Services
Francisco Hurtado RN, BSN, MHA .... (907) 257-5460
Chief of Staff **Dr. Cynthia A. Joe MD** .... (907) 257-5460
E-mail: cynthia.joe@va.gov
Executive Assistant to Chief of Staff
Mike Woodyard .... (907) 257-5460
Associate Chief of Staff for Social, Mental and
Behavioral Health **Ronald Poole** .... (907) 257-4766
E-mail: ronald.poole@va.gov
Audiology Service Chief **Michelle Fornelli** .... (907) 257-4916
Dental Service Chief **William Musick** .... (907) 257-4940
E-mail: william.musick@va.gov Fax: (907) 257-4953
Fiscal Service Chief **Jennifer Price** .... (907) 257-7466
Fax: (907) 929-3101
Information Technology Operations Systems Chief
Kathy Fanning .... (907) 257-5426
E-mail: kathy.fanning@va.gov Fax: (907) 257-6793
Human Resource Management Service Chief
Paul Bauer .... (907) 257-4750
Fax: (907) 257-6787

★ Presidential Appointment Requiring Senate Confirmation ☆ Presidential Appointment □ Schedule C Appointment ◇ Career Senior Foreign Service Appointment
● Career Senior Executive Service (SES) Appointment ○ Non-Career Senior Executive Service (SES) Appointment ■ Postal Career Executive Service

Alaska VA Healthcare System *(continued)*

Integrated Care Service Chief **Delynn James** . . . . (907) 257-6922
E-mail: delynn.james@va.gov Fax: (907) 770-2075
Laboratory Section Chief and Radiology Chief
Judith "Judie" Jordan . . . . (907) 257-6973
Radiology: (907) 257-7490 Fax: (907) 257-6703 (Laboratory)
Library Service Chief **Jarmila Henderson** . . . . (907) 257-4924
E-mail: jarmila.henderson@va.gov
Facilities Management Chief **Doug Lofgren** . . . . (907) 257-7463
National Cemetery Chief **Virginia M. Walker** . . . . (907) 384-7075
Fax: (907) 384-7111
Pharmacy Service Chief **Benjamin "Ben" Jensen** . . . . . . (907) 257-4805
Tel: (907) 257-4833 Fax: (907) 257-6755
Primary Care Chief **Kristen Sorrells** . . . . (907) 257-4939
E-mail: kristen.sorrells@va.gov Fax: (907) 257-6724
Prosthetics and Sensory Aids Service Chief (Acting)
Robert "Rocky" Reynolds . . . . (907) 257-4930
Fax: (907) 257-6980
Quality Management Service Chief **John Dee** . . . . (907) 257-5445
Fax: (907) 257-6759
Surgical Service Chief (Acting) **Dr. Jeffrey Congdon** . . . . (907) 257-4929
E-mail: jeffrey.congdon@va.gov Fax: (907) 257-4905
VA Police Chief **Gerald Loftus** . . . . (907) 257-6950
E-mail: gerald.loftus@va.gov Fax: (907) 257-6773
Voluntary Service Chief **Jeanne Fox** . . . . (907) 257-4949
Fax: (907) 257-6908
Public Affairs Officer **Samuel Hudson** . . . . (907) 257-5460
E-mail: samuel.hudson@va.gov
Joint Venture Team Leader **(Vacant)** . . . . (907) 580-3088
Fax: (907) 580-3150
VA Strategic Planner **Scott Kelter** . . . . (907) 257-5460
E-mail: scott.kelter@va.gov
Logistics Chief **Brian Schuyler** . . . . (907) 257-7453

Idaho

Boise (ID) VA Medical Center
VA Medical Center, 500 West Fort Street, Boise, ID 83702
Tel: (208) 422-1000 Fax: (208) 422-1157 Internet: www.boise.va.gov

● Director **David P. Wood** . . . . (208) 422-1100
Education: BYU 1989 BS; Duke 1991 MHA
Associate Director **Nate Stewart** . . . . (208) 422-1303
Chief of Staff **Andrew Wilper** . . . . (208) 422-1102
Education: Harvard 2008 MS
Information Technology Chief **Scott Brown** . . . . (208) 422-1195
Librarian **Greg Whitmore** . . . . (208) 422-1306

Oregon

VA Portland (OR) Health Care System
3710 SW U.S. Veterans Hospital Road, Portland, OR 97239
Tel: (503) 220-8262 Fax: (503) 273-5319 Internet: www.portland.va.gov
Areas Covered: Tertiary referral center: ID - partial, OR, Southwest WA

● Director (Interim) **Tracye B. Davis** . . . . (503) 273-5247
Education: Trinity U BS; Washington U (MO) MHA
Deputy Director (Acting) **Karla Azcuy** . . . . (503) 721-1014
Education: Clemson BS; North Florida 2009 MHA
Deputy Director for Patient Care Services, Chief Nursing Officer
Kathleen M. Chapman FACHE . . . . (503) 220-8262 ext. 57203
Education: Illinois (Chicago) 1975 BSN, 1977 MSN
Assistant Director
Bernard G. "Bernie" Deazley . . . . (503) 220-8262 ext. 57200
Chief of Staff (Acting) **Sahana Misra** . . . . (503) 273-5005 ext. 55414
Deputy Chief of Staff (Interim) **David Kagen** . . . . (503) 273-5005
Deputy Chief Nurse Executive
Jenny Richardson . . . . (503) 220-8262 ext. 57203
E-mail: jeanette.richardson@va.gov
Facilities Management Director
John Dodier . . . . (503) 220-8262 ext. 56323
Hospital and Specialty Director
Kenneth Scalapino . . . . (503) 220-8262 ext. 55591
E-mail: kenneth.scalapino@va.gov
Human Resources Director **Karla Azcuy** . . . . . . (503) 220-8262 ext. 52161
Education: Clemson BS; North Florida 2009 MHA

VA Portland (OR) Health Care System *(continued)*

Information Management Director
Andy Covington . . . . (503) 220-8262 ext. 51992
E-mail: zandrew.covington@va.gov
Veterans Justice Outreach Specialist **Peggy Kuhn** . . . . (503) 220-8262
Veterans Justice Outreach Specialist **Adam Watkins** . . . . . (503) 220-8262

VA Roseburg (OR) Healthcare System
913 NW Garden Valley Boulevard, Roseburg, OR 97471
Tel: (541) 440-1000 Fax: (541) 440-1225 Internet: www.roseburg.va.gov

● Director (Interim)
David L. Whitmer FACHE . . . . (541) 440-1000 ext. 44208
Education: South Florida BA, MPA
Associate Director
Ryan J. Baker MBA, CDFM . . . . (541) 440-1000 ext. 44140
Education: Hawaii Pacific BA; Louisiana Tech U MA; Webster MBA
Chief of Staff **(Vacant)** . . . . (541) 440-1000 ext. 43085
Training Coordinator **Beryl McClelland** . . . . . . (541) 440-1000 ext. 44274
Information Resource Management Manager
Keleen Wright . . . . (541) 440-1000 ext. 44440
Associate Director for Patient Care Services/Nurse Executive
Barbara A. Galbraith PhD, MBA, RN . . . . . (541) 440-1000 ext. 44202

Washington

Jonathan M. Wainwright Memorial VA Medical Center
77 Wainwright Drive, Walla Walla, WA 99362
Tel: (509) 525-5200 Fax: (509) 527-3452
Internet: www.wallawalla.va.gov Internet: http://www.wallawalla.va.gov/

● Director (Acting) **Keith M. Allen** . . . . (509) 527-3450
Chief of Staff (Acting) **James C. Mason** . . . . (509) 527-3451
Education Coordinator **Billie Fitzsimmons RN** . . . . (509) 527-6120
E-mail: billie.fitzsimmons@va.gov
Information Management Coordinator
Gary Ramer . . . . (509) 525-5200 ext. 26401
E-mail: gary.ramer@va.gov
Financial Manager **William Villani** . . . . (541) 826-2111 ext. 3344
Librarian **Darlene Fleming** . . . . (509) 525-5200 ext. 22833
E-mail: darlene.fleming@va.gov
Police Chief **Jeffrey Williams** . . . . (509) 527-6135
E-mail: jeffrey.williams@va.gov Fax: (509) 526-6221

Mann-Grandstaff VA Medical Center
4815 North Assembly Street, Spokane, WA 99205
Tel: (509) 434-7000 Internet: www.spokane.va.gov

● Director **Dr. Robert J. Fischer MD, FACOG, CPE** . . . . (509) 434-7200
Executive Secretary **Michelle Delgado** . . . . (509) 434-7200
Associate Director
Richard "Rick" Richards MS, MBA, FACHE . . . . (509) 434-7202
Associate Director of Patient Care Services
Darci Raschke MS, BSN, RN . . . . (509) 434-7208
Education: Minnesota St (Mankato) BSN
Chief of Staff **Dr. Scott Nye MD, FACS** . . . . (509) 434-7201
Education: Ohio State 1994 MD
Engineering and Technology Chief **Douglas Hardman** . . . (509) 434-7400
Fax: (509) 434-7119
Information Technology Specialist
Robert W. "Rob" Fortenberry . . . . (509) 434-7000
Fax: (509) 434-7119
Human Resources Specialist **Robyn Highbarger** . . . . (509) 434-7393
E-mail: robyn.highbarger@va.gov

VA Puget Sound Health Care System
1660 South Columbian Way, Seattle, WA 98108-1597
Tel: (206) 762-1010 Tel: (800) 329-8387
Internet: www.pugetsound.va.gov

● Director **Michael C. "Mike" Tadych FACHE, LCSW** . . . . . (206) 277-1340
E-mail: mike.tadych@va.gov
Education: Wisconsin 1989 BSE; Loyola U (Chicago) 1997 MSW
Deputy Director (Acting) **Kathryn Sherrill** . . . . (206) 277-1040
Education: Cal State (Fresno) 1988 BS; San José State 1996 MSW
Associate Director **Simon Kim** . . . . (253) 582-8440
Chief of Staff **Dr. Catherine Kaminetzky MD** . . . . (206) 277-1330
E-mail: catherine.kaminetzky@va.gov

(continued on next page)

VA Puget Sound Health Care System *(continued)*

Public Affairs Officer **(Vacant)** .... (206) 764-2589
Associate Director, Nursing **(Vacant)** .... (206) 277-1040
Chief Librarian **Jason Oleston** .... (206) 762-1010
E-mail: jason.oleston2@va.gov
Police Chief **(Vacant)** .... (206) 762-1010

VISN 21 - VA Sierra Pacific Network

201 Walnut Avenue, Vallejo, CA 94592-1107
Tel: (707) 562-8350 Fax: (707) 562-8369 Internet: www.visn21.va.gov

• Network Director **John Arthur Brandecker** .... (707) 562-8350
Education: SUNY (Stony Brook) BA; St John's U (NY) MBA; Columbia 1992 MPH
Staff Assistant **Linda Pierce** .... (707) 562-8356
E-mail: linda.pierce@va.gov
Acting Deputy Network Director **Cassandra M. Law** .... (707) 562-8350
Chief Information Officer **William L. Harris** .... (707) 562-8490
E-mail: william.harris@va.gov
Chief Financial Officer **Roxanne Hargrove** .... (916) 923-4530
Chief Medical Officer **(Vacant)** .... (707) 562-8350
Network Contract Manager **Samuel Harbin** .... (916) 923-4585
Small Business Liaison **Jeanne S. Chun** .... (650) 849-0388
E-mail: jeanne.chun@va.gov

California

Northern California Health Care System (VA Northern California Health Care System)
10535 Hospital Way, Mather, CA 95655
Tel: (916) 843-7000 Fax: (916) 843-9001
Internet: www.northerncalifornia.va.gov

• Director **David Stockwell** .... (916) 843-9058
E-mail: david.stockwell@va.gov
Associate Director **(Vacant)** .... (916) 366-5337
East Bay Division Associate Director **Timothy Graham** .... (925) 372-2015
Staff Assistant to the Director **Beverley Atherton-Pierce** .... (916) 843-9046
Sacramento Valley Division Associate Director **(Vacant)** .... (916) 366-5337
Patient Care Service/Nursing Associate Director **Kathryn K. Bucher** .... (916) 366-5338
Chief of Staff **William T. Cahill MD** .... (916) 843-9045
E-mail: william.cahill2@va.gov
Associate Chief of Staff for Education **Dr. Regina Godbout MD** .... (916) 366-5451
E-mail: regina.godbout@va.gov
Audiology and Speech Pathology Chief **Janet Patterson** .... (925) 372-2643
Benefits and Data Management Service Chief **Elizabeth "Liz" Blohm** .... (925) 372-2358
E-mail: elizabeth.blohm@va.gov
Dental Service Chief **Steven Nevins DDS** .... (916) 561-7800
Engineering and Facilities Management Service Chief **Kevin Maxson** .... (916) 843-2774
Fiscal Service Chief **Krista Hudalla** .... (707) 647-8955
Human Resources Management Service Chief **Christopher Howell** .... (916) 843-7282
E-mail: christopher.howell@va.gov
Information and Technology Service Chief **Ronald Walker** .... (925) 370-4094
E-mail: ron.walker3@va.gov
Medical Service Chief **Dr. David Siegel MD** .... (916) 843-7096
Education: Wesleyan U 1969 AB
Mental Health Chief **Dr. Donald Hilty MD** .... (916) 843-9121
Education: Cincinnati MD
Neurology Service Chief **Michael Remler MD** .... (925) 372-2059
Pathology and Laboratory Medicine Service Chief **Dr. Ivan Meadows MD** .... (916) 843-7294
Pharmacy Service Chief **Julio Lopez** .... (925) 372-2161
Physical Medical and Rehabilitation Chief **Dr. Martin Hoffman MD** .... (916) 843-7331
E-mail: martin.hoffman@va.gov
Police Service Chief **Michael Kilburn** .... (916) 843-7281
Radiology Service Chief **Dr. Charles Barnett MD** .... (916) 843-7244

Northern California Health Care System *(continued)*

Research and Development Service Chief **Dr. Dawn Schwenke** .... (916) 843-2776
Social Work Service Chief **Brenda Davis** .... (916) 843-9239
E-mail: brenda.davis5@va.gov
Surgical Service Chief **Dr. Scott Alfred Hundahl MD** .... (916) 843-7324
Education: Harvard 1977 BA; Yale 1981 MD
Equal Employment Opportunity Manager **Kevin Kasnick** .... (916) 843-9204
Logistics Management Officer **John P. Hinson** .... (916) 843-9128
E-mail: john.hinson2@va.gov
Public Affairs Officer **(Vacant)** .... (916) 843-9247
Librarian **Alda Scott** .... (916) 843-7039
E-mail: alda.scott@va.gov

Palo Alto (CA) Health Care System
3801 Miranda Avenue, Palo Alto, CA 94304-1207
Tel: (650) 493-5000 Fax: (650) 852-3228 Internet: www.paloalto.va.gov

• Director **Thomas J. "Tony" Fitzgerald III** .... (650) 493-5000
Education: American InterContinental BS
Associate Director for Patient Care and Nursing Services **Gloria N. Martinez RN** .... (650) 493-5000
Education: Grossmont 1981 ASN; UC San Francisco 1987 BS, 1987 MS
Deputy Associate Director **Michelle R. Mountfort** .... (650) 493-5000
Chief of Staff **Dr. Lawrence Leung** .... (650) 493-5000
Deputy Chief of Staff **Stephen Ezeji-Okoye MD** .... (650) 493-5000
3801 Miranda Avenue, Palo Alto, CA 94304
Education: Harvard AB; Texas (Houston) MD
Public Affairs Officer **Damian McGee** .... (650) 493-5000 ext. 64888
Deputy Public Affairs Officer **Michael Hill-Jackson** .... (650) 849-1222
E-mail: michael.hill-jackson@va.gov
Librarian **(Vacant)** .... (650) 493-5000 ext. 64649
Police Service Chief **Ron Jones** .... (650) 493-5000 ext. 65891
Webmaster **Andrea Ritz** .... (650) 493-5000 ext. 68993

San Francisco (CA) VA Health Care System
4150 Clement Street, San Francisco, CA 94121-1598
Tel: (415) 221-4810 Fax: (415) 750-2185
Internet: www.sanfrancisco.va.gov
Areas Covered: Northern CA

Director **Bonnie S. Graham MBA** .... (415) 750-2041
Deputy Medical Center Director **Jia F. Li MBA** .... (415) 750-2042
Patient Care Services Associate Director **Mary Ann Nihart** .... (415) 750-2040
Hep C Clinic Director **Alexander Monto MD** .... (415) 750-2105
Parkinson's Disease and Movement Disorders Center Director **Caroline M. Tanner MD, PhD, FAAN** .... (415) 221-4810 ext. 26497
Education: UC Berkeley PhD
Chief of Prosthetic Treatment Center **Kenneth Sarver** .... (415) 221-4810 ext. 26402
Chief of Staff **Dr. Bruce Ovbiagele** .... (415) 750-2047
E-mail: rina.shah@va.gov
Chief of Ambulatory Care **Dr. Amy Noack MD** .... (415) 281-5125
Education Associate Chief of Staff **Rebecca Shunk MD** .... (415) 221-4810 ext. 24878
Associate Chief of Staff for Extended Care **Dr. Anne Fabiny MD** .... (415) 221-4810 ext. 25876
Associate Chief of Staff for Mental Health **John McQuaid PhD** .... (415) 221-4810 ext. 24106
Research and Development Associate Chief of Staff **Carl Grunfeld MD, PhD** .... (415) 750-2005
Logistics Chief **Stephen Ruggirello** .... (415) 221-4810 ext. 22134
E-mail: stephen.ruggirello@va.gov
Police Chief **Robert Baczek** .... (415) 750-2003
E-mail: robert.baczek@va.gov
Business Services Chief **Neil Gordon** .... (415) 221-4810 ext. 22015
E-mail: neil.gordon@va.gov
Dental Service Chief **Rebeka Silva DMD** .... (415) 221-4810 ext. 22784
Engineering Service Chief **Michele Millers** .... (415) 750-2009
E-mail: michelle.millers@va.gov

★ Presidential Appointment Requiring Senate Confirmation ☆ Presidential Appointment □ Schedule C Appointment ◇ Career Senior Foreign Service Appointment
● Career Senior Executive Service (SES) Appointment ○ Non-Career Senior Executive Service (SES) Appointment ■ Postal Career Executive Service

San Francisco (CA) VA Health Care System *(continued)*

Environmental Management Service Chief
Charles Lemle . . . . . (415) 221-4810 ext. 26310
E-mail: charles.lemle@va.gov
Food and Nutrition Service Chief
Karen Arnold RD . . . . . (415) 221-4810 ext. 23354
E-mail: karen.arnold@va.gov
Gastroenterology Section Chief
Dr. Kenneth R. McQuaid MD, FASGE . . . . . (415) 221-4810 ext. 23842
Education: Stanford 1977 BS; UC San Francisco 1981 MD
Health Information Management Services
Chief **Mary Engel** . . . . . (415) 221-4810 ext. 24823
Human Resources Service Chief
Jerry Mills . . . . . (415) 221-4810 ext. 22507
E-mail: jerry.mills@va.gov
Information Resources Management Chief **Ryan Chun** . . . (415) 750-2132
E-mail: ryan.chun@va.gov
Laboratory Medicine Service Chief **Mark Lu** . . . . . (415) 750-2276
Library Services Chief **Katherine Wolf** . . . . . (415) 221-4810 ext. 23302
E-mail: katherine.wolf@va.gov
Medical Service Chief
Dr. Kenneth R. McQuaid MD, FASGE . . . . . (415) 750-2035
Education: Stanford 1977 BS; UC San Francisco 1981 MD
Neurology Service Chief **Raymond Swanson MD** . . . . . (415) 750-2011
Pathology Service Chief **Sanjay Kakar MD** . . . (415) 221-4810 ext. 22619
Education: Chandigarh U 1986 BS; Christian Med 1991 MBBS; Chandigarh U 1994 MD
Fax: (415) 750-6947
Pharmacy Service Chief **Donna Dare PharmD** . . . . . (415) 750-2053
Quality Management Chief (Acting)
Deborah Hitt . . . . . (415) 221-4810 ext. 23835
Radiology Service Chief **(Vacant)** . . . . . (415) 750-2120
Social Work Service Chief **Joanne Peters** . . . . . (415) 750-2044
Surgical Service Chief **Hubert Kim MD** . . . . . (415) 750-2056
Public Affairs Officer **Matthew Coulson** . . . . . (415) 750-2275
E-mail: matthew.coulson@va.gov
Training Officer **Karen Leigh** . . . . . (415) 221-4810 ext. 22980

VA Central California Health Care System
2615 East Clinton Avenue, Fresno, CA 93703
Tel: (559) 225-6100 Fax: (559) 228-6903 Internet: www.fresno.va.gov

● Director **Stephen R. Bauman** . . . . . (559) 225-6100 ext. 5400
Executive Assistant to the Director
(Vacant) . . . . . (559) 228-6100 ext. 5990
Associate Director **Demitric Franklin** . . . . . (559) 225-6100 ext. 5337
Education: Harris-Stowe State 2004 BS; Saint Louis U 2007
Associate Director for Patient Care Services/Chief Nurse Executive
Charles V. Silveri RN, MS . . . . . (559) 225-6100 ext. 5118
E-mail: charles.silveri@va.gov
Chief of Staff **Wessel Meyer FACP** . . . . . (559) 225-6100 ext. 5337
E-mail: wessel.meyer@va.gov
Public Affairs Officer
CSM Cameron V. Porter USA . . . . . (559) 225-6100 ext. 6641
E-mail: cameron.porter@va.gov
Information Resource Management Service
Ron Mills . . . . . (559) 225-6100 ext. 6901
E-mail: ron.mills@va.gov
Chief of Medicine Service
Dr. Regina Godbout MD . . . . . (559) 225-6100 ext. 5327
Physician **Khampha Thephavong** . . . . . (559) 225-6100
Education: Cal State (Fresno) BSN; Ohio DO
Veterans Justice Outreach Specialist **Brenda Blum** . . . . . (559) 225-6100
Veterans Justice Outreach Specialist **Susan Basmajian** . . . (559) 225-6100

Hawaii

Pacific Islands Healthcare System
459 Patterson Road, Honolulu, HI 96819-1522
Tel: (808) 433-0100 Fax: (808) 433-0390 Internet: www.hawaii.va.gov

Director
Jennifer S. Gutowski MHA, FACHE, CSSGB . . . . . (808) 433-0100
Education: Tulane; Richard Stockton Col
Associate Director **Chandra Lake** . . . . . (808) 433-0103
Education: U Washington BA; City U (WA) MPA

Pacific Islands Healthcare System *(continued)*

Chief of Staff **William F. Dubbs MD** . . . . . (808) 433-0650
E-mail: william.dubbs@va.gov
Deputy Chief of Staff **Kathryn M. Ryder** . . . . . (808) 433-0100
District Counsel **Miles Miyamoto** . . . . . (808) 433-0135
E-mail: miles.miyamoto@va.gov

Nevada

VA Sierra Nevada Health Care System
975 Kirman Avenue, Reno, NV 89502-2597
Tel: (775) 786-7200 Fax: (775) 328-1447 Internet: www.reno.va.gov

Director **Lisa M. Howard** . . . . . (775) 789-6630
Executive Assistant **Arlee Fisher** . . . . . (775) 786-7200
Associate Director **Jack R. Smith** . . . . . (775) 789-6630
Education: US Coast Guard Acad BS; Stanford MS
Associate Director for Patient Care Services/Nurse
Executive **Charles O. Benninger RN, MN, MHA** . . . . . (775) 789-6620
Education: South Alabama 1981 BSN; South Carolina 1983 MN
Chief of Staff **Dr. Ivan Correa MD** . . . . . (775) 789-6610
E-mail: ivan.correa@va.gov
Education: Puerto Rico BS

VA Southern Nevada Healthcare System
6900 North Pecos Road, North Las Vegas, NV 89086
Tel: (702) 791-9000 Fax: (702) 224-6930 Internet: www.lasvegas.va.gov

● Director **Peggy W. Kearns FACHE, MS** . . . . . (702) 791-9010
E-mail: peggy.kearns2@va.gov
Education: Purdue BS; Indiana MS; Capella U MS
Associate Director **Tracy L. Skala** . . . . . (702) 791-9010
Education: Wayland Baptist BS; Troy U MS
Assistant Director **John L. Stelsel** . . . . . (702) 791-9010
Chief of Staff
Dr. Ramanujam "Ramu" Komanduri MD . . . . . (702) 791-9007
E-mail: ramanujam.komanduri@va.gov
Public Affairs Officer **Charles "Chuck" Ramey** . . . . . (702) 791-9003
E-mail: charles.ramey2@va.gov
Education: UNLV 2002 BS

Philippines

Manila Outpatient Clinic
1501 Roxas Boulevard, Pasay City, 1302, Philippines
Tel: 63 (2) 550-3888 Fax: 63 (2) 310-5957
E-mail: manlopc.inqry@vba.va.gov
Internet: www2.va.gov/directory/guide/facility.asp?ID=682

● Regional Office Director (Acting) **Mary Souza** 63 (2) 550-3888
Associate Director **Mary Souza** 63 (2) 550-3870
Chief Information Officer **Roel M. Crucillo** . . . 63 (2) 833-4566 ext. 8401
E-mail: roel.crucillo@va.gov
Clinic Manager **Vicki Randall** 63 (2) 318-8335
Chief Medical Officer, Compensation and Pension
Examination Program **Chad Carungin** 63 (2) 318-8344
E-mail: chad.carungin@va.gov
Chief Medical Officer, Outpatient Treatment Program
Dr. Eleanor Lopez MD 63 (2) 318-8348
E-mail: eleanor.lopez@va.gov
Quality Management Coordinator
Ma. Socorro B. Torrijos 63 (2) 318-8331
Fax: 63 (2) 831-4566 ext. 4500
Security Officer/Chief LFSD **(Vacant)** 63 (2) 318-8396
Support Services Division Chief **Christian Mejia** 63 (2) 550-3888
Education: Seattle BA
Veterans Service Center Manager
Dean Jason T. Arcano 63 (2) 550-3888
Education: Central Florida BA

VISN 22 - VA Desert Pacific Healthcare Network

300 Oceangate, Suite 700, Long Beach, CA 90802
Tel: (562) 826-5963 Fax: (562) 826-5987
Internet: www.desertpacific.va.gov

● Network Director (Acting) **Dr. Robert M. Smith MD** . . . . (858) 642-3201
E-mail: robert.smith@va.gov
Education: Princeton BSE; McGill (Canada) MD

(continued on next page)

DEPARTMENTS

VISN 22 - VA Desert Pacific Healthcare Network *(continued)*

Deputy Network Director **Randy Quinton** . . . . . (562) 826-5963
Network Chief Financial Officer **Janine Genovese** . . . . . (562) 826-5963
Capital Asset Manager
Sheila Nematollahi-Rad . . . . . (562) 826-8000 ext. 8047
Network Chief Information Officer (Acting)
William L. Harris . . . . . (707) 562-8490
E-mail: william.harris@va.gov
Network Chief Logistics Officer **Yolanda Brown** . . . . . (562) 826-5533
Network Chief Medical Officer **Araceli Revote** . . . . . (480) 397-2777
E-mail: araceli.revote@va.gov
Network Operations and Public Affairs Officer
(Vacant) . . . . . (562) 826-5963
Network Pharmacy Executive (Acting)
Winston "Frank" Evans . . . . . (602) 402-7938
Network Prosthetics Service Line Director
Pamela D. "Pam" Westbrooks . . . . . (818) 891-7711 ext. 39482
16111 Plummer Street, Sepulveda, CA 91343
Network Quality Management Officer **Jimmie Bates** . . . . (562) 826-5963
Mental Health Coordinator
Lucretia "Lucia" Vaughan . . . . . (520) 792-1450 ext. 1792
Small Business Liaison **Catalina Fernandez** . . . . . (915) 433-7348
E-mail: catalina.fernandez@va.gov
Small Business Liaison **Prisco "Eric" Ravelli** . . . . . (562) 766-2295
E-mail: prisco.ravelli@va.gov

Arizona

Phoenix VA Health Care System

650 East Indian School Road, Phoenix, AZ 85012-1892
Tel: (602) 277-5551 Fax: (602) 222-6489 Internet: www.phoenix.va.gov

● Director
RimaAnn O. "Rima" Nelson RN, MPH . . . . . (602) 277-5551 ext. 7891
E-mail: rima.nelson@va.gov
Deputy Director **Shawn Bransky** . . . . . (602) 277-5551
Education: Mercer 1992 BBA; Chapman 1998 MA
Associate Director of Patient Care Services
Alyshia W. Smith DNP, RN, NEA-BC . . . . . (602) 222-6461
Information Security Officer **B.J. Munoz** . . . . . (602) 277-5551 ext. 7156
E-mail: bj.munoz@va.gov
Information Security Officer **(Vacant)** . . . . . (602) 277-5551 ext. 5822
Librarian **Mark Simmons** . . . . . (602) 277-5551 ext. 7533
E-mail: mark.simmons@va.gov Fax: (602) 222-6472

Northern Arizona VA Health Care System

500 Highway 89 North, Prescott, AZ 86313
Tel: (928) 445-4860 Fax: (928) 776-6098 Internet: www.prescott.va.gov

● Health Care System Director
Barbara "Barb" Oemcke . . . . . (928) 445-4860 ext. 6009
Associate Director **Lisa Martin** . . . . . (928) 445-4860 ext. 6553
Education: U St Thomas (TX) 1988 BBA; Cal State (Bakersfield) 2004 MPA
Associate Director for Patient Care (Nurse Executive) **Mary "Pittman" Mach** . . . . . (928) 445-4860 ext. 6557
Education: St Benedict 1984 BSN; U Phoenix 2011 MSN
Chief of Staff **(Vacant)** . . . . . (928) 445-4860 ext. 6961
Hospital Police Chief **Brian Schuman** . . . . . (928) 776-6190
Fax: (928) 717-7427
Office of Information and Technologies Service Line Manager **Joseph Wilkinson** . . . . (928) 445-4860 ext. 6900
Public Affairs Officer **Mary Dillinger** . . . . . (928) 717-7587
E-mail: mary.dillinger@va.gov
Library Technician **Karen DeGroat** . . . . . (928) 776-6491

Southern Arizona VA Healthcare System

3601 South Sixth Avenue, Tucson, AZ 85723
Tel: (520) 792-1450 Fax: (520) 629-1818 Internet: www.tucson.va.gov

● Director **William J. Caron FACHE** . . . . . (520) 792-1450
E-mail: william.caron@va.gov
Education: U New England 1991 BS; Independence U 2006 MHA
Associate Director **Katie A. Landwehr MBA, FACHE** . . . . (520) 792-1450
Associate Director for Patient Care Services/Nurse Executive **Kerri Baxter Wilhoite** . . . . . (520) 792-1450
Education: Tennessee State 1997 BSN; U Phoenix 2005 MBA; Old Dominion 2014 DNP

Southern Arizona VA Healthcare System *(continued)*

Assistant Director
Steven J. "Steve" Sample MS, CHC . . . . . (520) 792-1450
Chief of Staff
Dr. Anthony M. Stazzone MD, EMBA, FACP . . . . . (520) 629-1450
Education: Arizona 1998 MD, 1993 BS, 2015 MBA
Deputy Chief of Staff **Karen L. MacKichan** . . . . . (520) 629-1450
Education: U Washington MD
Patient Education Coordinator
Sharon Hammond . . . . . (520) 792-1450 ext. 6449
E-mail: sharon.hammond@va.gov
Police Service Chief **Timothy Napier** . . . . . (520) 629-4720
Fax: (520) 629-4731
Assistant Public Affairs Officer **Luke Johnson** . . . . . (520) 629-1819
E-mail: luke.johnson6@va.gov
Webmaster **(Vacant)** . . . . . (520) 792-1450 ext. 6450

California

Loma Linda (CA) VA Medical Center

VA Loma Linda Healthcare System, 11201 Benton Street, Loma Linda, CA 92357
Tel: (800) 741-8387 Tel: (909) 825-7084 Fax: (909) 422-3106
Internet: www.lomalinda.va.gov
Areas Covered: CA (Counties of Riverside, San Bernardino)

● Medical Center Director (Interim) **Randy Quinton** . . . . . (562) 826-5963
E-mail: randy.quinton@va.gov
Associate Director of Administration
Shane M. Elliott MBA . . . . . (909) 825-7084
E-mail: shane.elliott@va.gov
Education: Loma Linda 1993 BS; U Redlands 2009 MBA
Chief of Staff (Acting) **John Tacheff** . . . . . (909) 825-7084
E-mail: john.tacheff@va.gov
Education: Chaminade BS; U Pacific DDSc
Public Affairs Officer **Wade Habshey** . . . . . (909) 583-6193
Education: Texas A&M 1973 BA
Librarian **Erica Bass** . . . . . (909) 583-6063
E-mail: erica.bass@va.gov Fax: (909) 422-3164

VA Long Beach Healthcare System

5901 East Seventh Street, Long Beach, CA 90822-5201
Tel: (562) 826-8000 Fax: (562) 826-5906
Internet: www.longbeach.va.gov

● Director **Walt C. Dannenberg FACHE** . . . . . (562) 826-5403
Education: Texas A&M 2003 BA; Houston (Clear Lake) 2005 MBA
Secretary to the Director **Betty Holden** . . . . . (562) 826-5400
Associate Director **Jean J. Gurga** . . . . . (562) 826-5401
Education: Mills BA; Tufts MOT
Associate Director, Patient Care Services/Nurse Executive **Cory Ramsey** . . . . . (562) 826-5402
Assistant Director **Dustin Thompson** . . . . . (562) 826-8000
Education: Mississippi Women BA; Mississippi 1998 MA
Chief of Staff (Acting) **Elizabeth Aubry** . . . . . (562) 826-5403
Associate Chief of Staff for Education Resources and Affiliations **William Baumann** . . . . . (562) 826-5403
Fax: (562) 826-5906
Human Resources Chief **(Vacant)** . . . . . (562) 826-5642
Fax: (562) 826-5549
Information Management Service Chief
Rodney Sagmit . . . . . (562) 826-5457
E-mail: rodney.sagmit@va.gov Fax: (562) 826-5853
Police Chief **David Wiener** . . . . . (562) 826-5532
Fax: (562) 826-5945
Voluntary Service Chief **Thomas Kleczkowski** . . . . . (562) 826-5715
Education: Maryland 1999 BA Fax: (562) 826-5721
Librarian **Marie H. Carter** . . . . . (562) 826-5465
E-mail: marie.carter@va.gov Fax: (562) 826-5447

VA San Diego Healthcare System

3350 La Jolla Village Drive, San Diego, CA 92161
Tel: (858) 552-8585 Fax: (858) 642-1161 Internet: www.sandiego.va.gov

● Director **Dr. Robert M. Smith MD** . . . . . (858) 642-3201
Education: Princeton BSE; McGill (Canada) MD
Associate Director **Cynthia E. Abair MHA** . . . . . (858) 642-3205

★ Presidential Appointment Requiring Senate Confirmation ☆ Presidential Appointment ☐ Schedule C Appointment ◇ Career Senior Foreign Service Appointment
● Career Senior Executive Service (SES) Appointment ○ Non-Career Senior Executive Service (SES) Appointment ■ Postal Career Executive Service

VA San Diego Healthcare System *(continued)*

Associate Director, Patient Care Services/Nurse Executive **Carmen Concepcion** .... (858) 642-3839
Assistant Director (Acting) **Sarah E. Guerard** .... (858) 642-3839
Chief of Staff/Medical Director
Dr. Kathleen Kim MD, MPH .... (858) 642-3241
Fax: (858) 552-7452
Chief Information Officer **Nara Um** .... (858) 552-8585
Education: KAIST (Korea) 1990 BS; Albert Einstein Medical 1993 MS; St George's U 2002 MD; Pittsburgh 2012 MS
Fax: (858) 552-7493
Librarian **(Vacant)** .... (858) 552-8585
Education Trainer **Elaine A. Muchmore MD** ... (858) 552-8585 ext. 3626
Police and Security Management Chief
Martin Sizemore .... (858) 552-8585 ext. 3222
Fax: (858) 552-7452

VA Greater Los Angeles Healthcare System
11301 Wilshire Boulevard, Los Angeles, CA 90073
Tel: (310) 478-3711 Fax: (310) 268-3494
Internet: www.losangeles.va.gov

● Director **Ann R. Brown FACHE** .... (310) 478-3711
Associate Director of Administrative Operations
(Vacant) .... (310) 478-3711
Executive Director of Clinical Care
Robert W. McKenrick .... (310) 478-3711
Education: Eastern Kentucky BS; Webster MA; Pennsylvania 1994 MA; Temple 1994 JD; Army War Col 2013 MSS
Associate Director, Patient Care Services/Nurse Executive **(Vacant)** .... (310) 268-3603
Assistant Director (Acting) **Olivia Freda** .... (310) 268-4862
Education: Converse 2007 BA; Medical U (SC) 2009 MHA
Chief of Staff
Dr. Scotte Hartronft MD, MBA, FACP, FACHE .... (310) 268-3284
Education: Southwestern Oklahoma St 1994 BS; Oklahoma 1998 MD; U Washington 2015 MBA
Information Resources Management Chief
Eugene Archey .... (818) 895-9548
E-mail: eugene.archey@va.gov
Education: Grambling State 1983 BS
Librarian **(Vacant)** .... (310) 268-3003
Quality, Performance Improvement **(Vacant)** .... (310) 268-3585
Communications and External Affairs **Erik Gutierrez** .... (310) 268-3340
Executive Office Manager **(Vacant)** .... (310) 268-3132

New Mexico

New Mexico VA Health Care System
2401 Centre Ave SE, Albuquerque, NM 87106-4180
Tel: (505) 265-1711 Fax: (505) 256-2855
Internet: www.albuquerque.va.gov

● Medical Center Director
Andrew M. Welch MHA, FACHE .... (505) 265-1711 ext. 2220
Associate Director **Sonja D. Brown** .... (505) 265-1711 ext. 2076
Education: U Phoenix BA
Associate Director for Patient Care Services
Tina Prince DNP, MBA, RN, NEA-BC .... (505) 265-1711 ext. 6040
Assistant Director **Katrina Bressler** .... (505) 265-1711 ext. 2076
E-mail: katrina.bressler@va.gov
Chief of Staff
Dr. James M. Goff, Jr. MD, FACS .... (505) 265-1711 ext. 2702
Deputy Chief of Staff **(Vacant)** .... (505) 265-1711
Information Security Officer **(Vacant)** .... (505) 767-6083
Librarian **Bette Jean Ingui** .... (505) 265-1711 ext. 2248

Raymond G. Murphy Medical Center
1501 San Pedro Drive SE, Albuquerque, NM 87108
Tel: (505) 265-1711 Fax: (505) 256-2855

Director **(Vacant)** .... (505) 265-1711
Tel: (505) 265-1711 2200

VISN 23 - VA Midwest Health Care Network
2805 Dodd Road, Eagan, MN 55121
Tel: (651) 405-5600 Internet: www.visn23.va.gov
Areas Covered: Northwest IA, MN, Northwestern NE, ND, SD, Northwestern WI, Northeastern WY

Deputy Network Director
Jason Christopher Petti MSHA .... (651) 405-5600
Education: St Thomas U BBA; Barry MSHA
Secretary **DeAnne Pavel** .... (651) 405-5600
Secretary **Cheryl Bennett** .... (651) 405-5600
Chief Business Officer **Andrew Frost** .... (651) 405-5600
Chief Financial Officer **Christopher A. Stomberg** .... (651) 405-5600
Chief Information Officer **Stan Bush** .... (651) 405-5600
Chief Medical Officer (Acting)
Dr. Jason Johanning MD .... (651) 405-5600
Education: Northwestern; Kansas MD
Director of Planning and Rural Health **Marsha Herke** .... (651) 405-5600
Network Contract Manager **Daryl Berg** .... (612) 344-2153
E-mail: daryl.berg@va.gov
Contracting Officer **Karen Cox** .... (612) 344-2145
E-mail: karen.cox@va.gov
Capital Assets Manager **Cynthia Dolittle** .... (651) 405-5633

Iowa

Iowa City (VA) Health Care System
601 Highway 6 West, Iowa City, IA 52246
Tel: (319) 338-0581 Fax: (319) 339-7171 Internet: www.iowacity.va.gov

● Director **Judith L. Johnson-Mekota FACHE** .... (319) 339-7100
Education: Coe; Iowa
Associate Director for Operations
Heath J. Streck FACHE .... (319) 338-0581 ext. 6201
Education: South Dakota 1994 BSBA; Touro U Cal 2004 MBA; Army War Col 2013 MSS
Associate Director for Patient Care Services
Tammy Neff MBA, MSN, NEA-BC, RN .... (319) 338-0581 ext. 6260
Chief of Staff **Javed H. Tunio** .... (319) 338-0581 ext. 7102
Director, Ambulatory Care Service Line
Lynda Hemann .... (319) 338-0581 ext. 5218
Director, Extended Care & Rehabilitation Service Line **Nathan Brady** .... (319) 338-0581 ext. 6080

VA Central Iowa Healthcare System (VACIHCS)
3600 30th Street, Des Moines, IA 50310
Tel: (515) 699-5999 Internet: www.centraliowa.va.gov

● Director **Gail L. Graham RHIA** .... (515) 699-5850
E-mail: gail.graham@va.gov
Associate Director of Resources (Acting)
Nicole A. Findlay .... (515) 699-5850
Associate Director for Patient Services and Nurse Executive **Amy Dawson** .... (515) 699-5850
Chief of Staff **Jerry Blow** .... (515) 699-5853
Acquisition Officer **Stacie Halverson** .... (515) 699-5803
Chief Information Officer **Dawn Sturtz** .... (515) 699-5892
Librarian **(Vacant)** .... (515) 699-5636

Minnesota

Minneapolis (MN) VA Health Care System
One Veterans Drive, Minneapolis, MN 55417
Tel: (612) 725-2000 Fax: (612) 725-2049
Internet: www.minneapolis.va.gov

Medical Center Director **Patrick J. Kelly** .... (612) 725-2101
Education: Creighton 1979 BA; North Carolina 1982 MPH
Associate Director **(Vacant)** .... (612) 467-4194
Chief Experience Officer **Martina D. Malek** .... (612) 467-3242
Chief of Staff **Kent Crossley** .... (612) 725-2000 ext. 3017
E-mail: kent.crossley@va.gov
Education: Minnesota 2000 MHCA
Associate Chief of Education **Dr. Esgi Tiryaki MD** .... (612) 725-2000
Fax: (612) 725-2046
Library Services Chief
Dorothy Pamer Sinha .... (612) 725-2000 ext. 4200
E-mail: dorothy.sinha@va.gov
Nurse Executive **Helen V. Pearlman** .... (612) 725-2101

(continued on next page)

★ Presidential Appointment Requiring Senate Confirmation ☆ Presidential Appointment □ Schedule C Appointment ◇ Career Senior Foreign Service Appointment
● Career Senior Executive Service (SES) Appointment ○ Non-Career Senior Executive Service (SES) Appointment ■ Postal Career Executive Service

DEPARTMENTS

Minneapolis (MN) VA Health Care System *(continued)*

Police Chief **Rick Encinas** .... (612) 725-2000
E-mail: rick.encinas@va.gov
Public Affairs Director **Ralph Heussner** .... (612) 725-2102
E-mail: ralph.heussner@va.gov

Saint Cloud (MN) VA Health Care Center
4801 Veterans Drive, St. Cloud, MN 56303-2099
Tel: (320) 252-1670 Fax: (320) 255-6494 Internet: www.stcloud.va.gov

● Director **Stephen D. Black** .... (320) 252-1670 ext. 6315
Associate Director **Cheryl Thieschafer** .... (320) 252-1670 ext. 6012
Associate Director for Patient Care Services/Nurse Executive **Mark Aberle** .... (320) 252-1670 ext. 7618
Education: South Dakota State 1992 BSN, 1998 MSN
Chief of Staff **Dr. Scott C. Bartley** .... (320) 252-1670 ext. 6317
Public Affairs Officer **Barry Venable** .... (320) 255-6381
E-mail: barry.venerable@va.gov
Education Service Line Director **Cathy Town** .... (320) 255-6440
E-mail: cathy.town2@va.gov Fax: (320) 255-6493
Information Management Director **Denise J. Hanson** .... (320) 252-1670 ext. 6791
E-mail: denise.hanson@va.gov Fax: (320) 255-6426
Librarian **Patricia Grelon** .... (320) 255-6342
Fax: (320) 255-6473
VA Police Chief **(Vacant)** .... (320) 255-6476
Veterans Justice Outreach Specialist **Michael Mathies** ... (320) 252-1670

Nebraska

VA Nebraska-Western Iowa Health Care System
Omaha VA Medical Center, 4101 Woolworth Avenue, Omaha, NE 68105
Tel: (402) 346-8800 Internet: www.nebraska.va.gov

● Director **B. Don Burman** .... (402) 995-3100
Associate Director **Spencer Mion** .... (615) 405-5636
Chief of Staff **David Williams** .... (402) 995-3106
Public Affairs Officer (Acting) **Teresa Forbes** .... (402) 995-4719
E-mail: teresa.forbes@va.gov Fax: (402) 995-4896
VA Police Services Chief **(Vacant)** .... (402) 489-3802 ext. 6641
Chief Financial Officer **Jay B. Helming** .... (402) 346-8800
Chief Information Officer **(Vacant)** .... (402) 346-8800
Education Coordinator **Amy Rosauer** .... (402) 489-3802 ext. 2456
Fax: (402) 486-7866
Nurse Executive and Associate Director for Patient Care **Eileen Kingston RN** .... (402) 995-3316
Data Analyst **(Vacant)** .... (402) 486-7953
Librarian **Darrel Willoughby** .... (402) 346-8800

North Dakota

Fargo VA Health Care System
2101 Elm Street, Fargo, ND 58102
Tel: (701) 232-3241 Fax: (701) 239-3705 Internet: www.fargo.va.gov

● Healthcare Center Director **Lavonne Liversage FACHE** .... (701) 239-3701
Secretary to the Director **Rhonda Cross** .... (701) 239-3701
E-mail: rhonda.cross@va.gov
Associate Director for Operations and Resources **Dale DeKrey** .... (701) 239-3700 ext. 93205
Associate Director for Patient Care/Nurse Executive **Rodney Gellner** .... (701) 239-3700 ext. 93416
Education: Jamestown Col BSN; St Mary's U (MN) MHSA
Chief of Staff **Dr. Breton Weintraub MD** ..... (701) 239-3700 ext. 3202
Medical Librarian **Ron Padot** .... (701) 232-3755

South Dakota

VA Black Hills Healthcare System
113 Comanche Road, Fort Meade, SD 57741
500 North Fifth Street, Hot Springs, SD 57747
Tel: (800) 743-1070 Tel: (605) 347-2511 (Fort Meade)
Tel: (605) 745-2000 (Hot Springs) Fax: (605) 745-2091
Internet: www.blackhills.va.gov

● Director **Sandra L. Horsman** .... (605) 720-7170
Chief of Staff **Neil Goodloe** .... (605) 720-7172

VA Black Hills Healthcare System *(continued)*

Associate Director **Carla Belle "C.B." Alexander FACHE** .... (605) 720-7170
Associate Director for Patient Care Services/Nurse Executive **MaDonna Schnider RN, MS, CPHQ** .... (605) 720-7172
Chief Information Officer **Jeanie Dodson** .... (605) 347-7232
E-mail: jeanine.dodson@va.gov Fax: (605) 347-7202
Education Chief and Designated Learning Officer **Laura Knutson** .... (605) 720-7073
Library Technician **(Vacant)** .... (605) 720-7055
Chief of Diagnostics **(Vacant)** .... (605) 720-7301
Public Affairs Officer **Teresa Forbes** .... (605) 720-7451

Sioux Falls VA Health Care System
2501 West 22nd Street, Sioux Falls, SD 57105
Mail: Sioux Falls, SD 57105
Tel: (605) 336-3230 Fax: (605) 333-6878 Internet: www.siouxfalls.va.gov

● Director **Darwin G. Goodspeed FACHE** .... (605) 333-6842
E-mail: darwin.goodspeed@va.gov
Education: Maryland 1987 BS; Webster 1992 MA; Southern New Hampshire 1995 MBA; Baylor 1997 MHA
Associate Director **Sara Ackert** .... (605) 333-6842
Education: Grand View BS; Des Moines U MHCA Fax: (605) 333-6872
Associate Director for Patient Care Services/Nurse Executive **Barbara Teal** .... (605) 333-6843
Chief of Staff **Dr. Timothy Pendergrass MD** .... (605) 333-6843
Police Chief **James Lawson** .... (605) 336-3230 ext. 6377
E-mail: james.lawson@va.gov

Office of the Deputy Under Secretary for Health for Policy and Services

Office of Patient Care Services (PCS)

810 Vermont Avenue, NW, Washington, DC 20420
Tel: (202) 461-7800 Fax: (202) 273-9274
Internet: www.patientcare.va.gov

Mental Health Services

810 Vermont Avenue, NW, Room 990, Washington, DC 20420
Internet: www.mentalhealth.va.gov

Mental Illness Research, Education Clinical Centers (MIRECC)
810 Vermont Avenue, NW, Washington, DC 20420
Internet: www.mirecc.va.gov

Capitol Mental Illness Research, Education and Clinical Center
10 North Greene Street, Baltimore, MD 21201
Tel: (410) 605-7451 Fax: (410) 605-7739

Director **Dr. Richard W. Goldberg PhD** .... (410) 637-1851
Education: Cornell BA; Maryland PhD

Desert Pacific Mental Illness Research, Education and Clinical Center
11301 Wilshire Boulevard, Los Angeles, CA 90073
Tel: (310) 268-3647 Fax: (310) 268-4056
Internet: http://www.mirecc.va.gov/visn22/

Director **Stephen R. Marder MD** .... (310) 268-3647
E-mail: marder@ucla.edu

Mid-Atlantic Mental Illness Research, Education and Clinical Center
508 Fulton Street, Durham, NC 27705-3875
Tel: (919) 416-5915 E-mail: mirecc.studies@va.gov

Director **Paul S. Crews MPH, CPHQ, FACHE** .... (919) 286-0411
Education: Southwest Texas State 2000 BHCA; Texas A&M 2002 MPH

New England Mental Illness Research, Education and Clinical Center
950 Campbell Avenue, Room 151D, West Haven, CT 06516
Tel: (203) 932-5711 ext. 4338 Internet: www.mirecc.va.gov/visn1

Director **Dr. Mehmet Sofuoglu MD** .... (203) 937-4809
E-mail: mehmet.sofuoglu@va.gov

New York/New Jersey Mental Illness Research, Education and Clinical Center
130 West Kingsbridge Road, Bronx, NY 10468
Tel: (718) 584-9000 ext. 3704 Internet: http://www.mirecc.va.gov/visn3/

Director **Dr. René S. Kahn MD** .... (718) 584-9000 ext. 5227
Education Director **(Vacant)** .... (718) 584-9000 ext. 5204
Administrative Officer **Mark H. Levinson**
VISN 3 Mental Illness Research Education and Clinical Center, Room 6A-44 .... (718) 584-9000 ext. 3698
E-mail: mark.levinson@va.gov Fax: (718) 364-3576

Northwest Mental Illness Research, Education and Clinical Center
VA Puget Sound Health Care System, 1660 South Columbian Way, Seattle, WA 98108-1597
Mail: 1034, Portland, OR 97207
Tel: (503) 220-3481 Fax: (503) 273-5390

Director **Michael Fisher** .... (503) 220-3481

Rocky Mountain Mental Illness Research, Education and Clinical Center (MIRECC)
1055 Clermont Street, Denver, CO 80220
Tel: (303) 399-5275 Fax: (303) 370-7519
Internet: www.mirecc.va.gov/visn19

Director **Lisa A. Brenner PhD, ABPP** .... (720) 723-6488
Education: Brandeis 1991 BA; Wright Inst 1995 MA, 1997 PhD
Associate Director for Clinical Services
Bridget B. Matarazzo .... (720) 723-6482
E-mail: bridget.matarazzo@va.gov
Education: Denver 2010 PsyD
Director of Training and Advanced Psychology
Jennifer Olson-Madden .... (303) 355-5811
E-mail: jennifer.olson-madden@va.gov
Tel: (720) 723-6483
Education: Denver 2007 PhD
Psychiatric Fellowship Director **Hal S. Wortzel MD** ..... (720) 723-6481
Education: Amherst 1996 BA; NYU 2001 MD
Data and Statistical Core Director **Jeri E. Forster** .... (720) 938-2708
Education: Denver 2006 PhD
Scientific Director **Robert Freedman MD** ..... (303) 399-8020 ext. 5643
Clinical Researcher **Theresa D. Hernandez PhD** .... (303) 492-8654

Sierra Pacific Mental Illness Research, Education and Clinical Center
3801 Miranda Avenue, Palo Alto, CA 94304
Tel: (650) 493-5000 Fax: (650) 852-3286

Director **Jerome Yesavage MD** .... (650) 493-5000
E-mail: yesavage@stanford.edu

South Central Mental Illness Research, Education and Clinical Center
2200 Fort Roots Drive, North Little Rock, AR 72114-1756
Tel: (501) 257-1236 Fax: (501) 257-1718
Internet: http://www.mirecc.va.gov/visn16/

Director **Mark E. Kunik MD** .... (713) 791-1414 ext. 10330
Co-Director **Michael R. Kauth** .... (713) 440-4460
Associate Director for Education
Dr. Ali Abbas Asghar-Ali MD .... (713) 791-1414 ext. 26771
Associate Director for Improving Clinical Care **Tracey L. Smith** .... (713) 791-1414 ext. 10287
Michael DeBakey Veterans Affairs Medical Center, 2002 Holcombe Boulevard, Houston, TX 77030
Associate Director for Research **Jeffrey Pyne** .... (501) 257-1083
2200 Fort Roots Drive, North Little Rock, AR 72114
Associate Director for Research Training
Michael Cucciare Building 58 .... (501) 257-1068
E-mail: michael.cucciare@va.gov
Fiscal Management Analyst/Administrative Officer
Kristin Ward .... (501) 257-1236

Stars and Stripes Mental Illness Research, Education and Clinical Center
Director **Dr. David W. "Dave" Oslin MD** .... (215) 823-5857
E-mail: Dave.Oslin@va.gov

Stars and Stripes Mental Illness Research, Education and Clinical Center *(continued)*

Associate Director **Dr. Gretchen Haas PhD** .... (412) 365-4900
7180 Highland Drive, Pittsburgh, PA 18206-1298
E-mail: gretchen.haas@va.gov
Education: Wayne State U MA, PhD
Co-Associate Director for Research - Pittsburgh
Dr. Robert A. Sweet MD .... (412) 365-4900
E-mail: sweetra@upmc.edu
Co-Associate Director for Research - Philadelphia
Henry Richard Kranzler .... (215) 823-5800
E-mail: henry.kranzler@va.gov
Director, Psychology **Dr. Steven L. Sayers PhD** .... (215) 823-5894
E-mail: steven.sayers@va.gov
Education: South Florida 1982 BA; North Carolina 1985 MA, 1990 PhD
Director, Psychiatry **Dr. John Kasckow MD, PhD** .... (412) 365-4900
E-mail: john.kasckow2@va.gov
Director, Behavioral Health Lab **Johanna Klaus PhD** .... (215) 823-5894
E-mail: johanna.klaus@va.gov
Administrative Officer- Pittsburgh **Deborah Coudriet** ... (412) 365-4900
E-mail: deborah.coudriet@va.gov

Centers of Excellence (CoE)

Center for Integrated Health (CIH)
800 Irving Avenue, Room 116C, Syracuse, NY 13210
Tel: (315) 425-4400 ext. 56546 Tel: (315) 425-6546

Executive Director
Stephen A. Maisto PhD .... (315) 425-4400 ext. 54005
Chief Operating Officer **Larry J. Lantinga PhD** .... (315) 425-3487
Director of Education and Clinical Care **Laurie Wray** .... (716) 862-8598
Administrative Officer **Brenda Chewning-Kulick** .... (315) 425-4005
E-mail: brenda.chewning-kulick@va.gov

Center of Excellence at Canandaigua
400 Fort Hill Avenue, Canandaigua, NY 14424
Tel: (585) 394-2000 Internet: www.mirecc.va.gov/suicideprevention

Executive Director and Research Director
Wilfred R. Pigeon PhD .... (585) 393-7918
E-mail: wilfred.pigeon2@va.gov
Director of Fellowship and Graduate Training
Deborah A. King .... (585) 393-7950
Epidemiology and Populations Research Core Chief
(Vacant) .... (585) 393-7565

Center of Excellence for Research on Returning War Veterans
4800 Memorial Drive, Room 151C, Waco, TX 76711
Tel: (254) 297-3586 Fax: (254) 297-5267
Internet: www.mirecc.va.gov/visn17

Director **Michael L. Russell PhD** .... (254) 297-3586
E-mail: michael.russell5@va.gov
Business and Strategic Core Leader **David Steeley** ...... (254) 297-5169
E-mail: david.steeley@va.gov
Administrative Officer **David Steeley** .... (254) 297-3666
E-mail: david.steeley@va.gov
Deputy Director for Research **Dena Davidson PhD** ...... (254) 297-5169
Behavioral Science Core Leader
Diane T. Castillo PhD .... (254) 297-5170
Education and Dissemination Core Leader
Richard Seim .... (254) 297-5155
Education: Western Michigan 2006 MA, 2011 PhD
Implementation Science Core Leader **Justin Benzer** ..... (254) 297-5155
Neuroimaging Core Leader **Steven Nelson** .... (254) 297-5155
External Advisory Panel Chair **Steven Holliday PhD** .... (210) 694-6223
Internal Advisory Panel Chair **(Vacant)** .... (254) 297-1478
Budget Analyst **John Eline** .... (254) 297-3586
E-mail: john.eline@va.gov

Center of Excellence for Stress and Mental Health
3350 La Jolla Village Drive, San Diego, CA 92161
Tel: (858) 642-3762 Internet: www.mirecc.va.gov/cesamh

Director **James B. Lohr PhD** .... (858) 642-3762
Director of Clinical Affairs **(Vacant)** .... (858) 642-3762
Director of Education **Laurie Lindamer PhD** .... (858) 642-3762

(continued on next page)

Center of Excellence for Stress and Mental Health *(continued)*

Director of Research **Dewleen Baker MD** . . . . (858) 642-3762
Administrative Officer **Heather Donovan** . . . . (858) 642-3762

Spinal Cord Injury and Disorders Strategic Healthcare Group

VA Medical Center Seattle, 1660 Columbian Way,
Mail Stop 128 NAT, Seattle, WA 98108
Fax: (206) 768-5258
Chief Consultant **Dr. Barry Goldstein MD** . . . . (206) 764-2332

Independent Agencies

Table of Contents

United States Commission on Civil Rights (USCCR)

Description: The United States Commission on Civil Rights investigates and studies discrimination based on race, color, religion, sex, age, handicap, and national origin in the areas of voting rights, education, employment, and housing.

1331 Pennsylvania Avenue, NW, Suite 1150, Washington, DC 20425
Tel: (202) 376-7700 TTY: (202) 376-8116
Tel: (202) 376-8513 (Civil Rights Complaints - DC Metropolitan Area)
Tel: (800) 552-6843 (Civil Rights Complaints - Continental US)
TTY: (800) 877-8339 (Civil Rights Complaints - Continental US)
Tel: (202) 376-8351 (Freedom of Information/Privacy Act)
Tel: (202) 376-8128 (Publications Information) Fax: (202) 376-7672
E-mail: referrals@usccr.gov (Civil Rights Complaints)
E-mail: publications@usccr.gov (Publications Information)
Internet: www.usccr.gov

THE COMMISSION

1331 Pennsylvania Avenue, NW, Suite 1150, Washington, DC 20425

Note: Four Commission members are appointed by the President, two are appointed by the President Pro Tempore of the Senate and two are appointed by the Speaker of the House of Representatives. The President designates the Chairperson and Vice Chairperson.

Commissioners may continue to serve until reappointed or replaced.

Office of the Staff Director

1331 Pennsylvania Avenue, NW, Washington, DC 20425
Tel: (202) 376-7700 Fax: (202) 376-7672

Regional Offices

Central Regional Office

400 State Avenue, Suite 908, Kansas City, KS 66101-2406
Tel: (913) 551-1400 TTY: (913) 551-1414 Fax: (913) 551-1413
Areas Covered: AL, AR, IA, KS, LA, MS, MO, NE, OK

Regional Director **(Vacant)** . . . . (913) 551-1400

Eastern Regional Office

1331 Pennsylvania Avenue, NW, Suite 1150, Washington, DC 20425
Tel: (202) 376-7533 Fax: (202) 376-7548
Areas Covered: CT, DE, DC, ME, MD, MA, NH, NJ, NY, PA, RI, VT, VA, WV

Director **Ivy L. Davis** . . . . (202) 376-7533
E-mail: idavis@usccr.gov
Deputy Director **Barbara de La Viez** . . . . (202) 376-7533
E-mail: bdelaviez@usccr.gov

Midwestern Regional Office

55 West Monroe Street, Suite 410, Chicago, IL 60603
Tel: (312) 353-8311 TTY: (312) 353-8362 Fax: (312) 353-8324
Areas Covered: IL, IN, MI, MN, OH, WI

Director **David J. Mussatt** . . . . (312) 353-8311
E-mail: dmussatt@usccr.gov

Rocky Mountain Regional Office

1961 Stout Street, Suite 13-201, Denver, CO 80294
Internet: www.usccr.gov Tel: (303) 866-1040
Tel: (800) 877-8339 (Federal Relay Service) Fax: (303) 866-1050
Areas Covered: CO, MT, NM, ND, SD, UT, WY

Director **(Vacant)** . . . . (303) 866-1040

Southern Regional Office

Atlanta Federal Center, 61 Forsyth Street, SW, Suite 16T126, Atlanta, GA 30303
Tel: (404) 562-7000 TTY: (404) 562-7004 Fax: (404) 562-7005
Areas Covered: FL, GA, KY, NC, SC, TN

Director **Jeffrey Hinton** . . . . (404) 562-7006
E-mail: jhinton@usccr.gov

Western Regional Office

300 North Los Angeles Street, Suite 2010, Los Angeles, CA 90012
Tel: (213) 894-3437 TTY: (213) 894-3435 Fax: (213) 894-0508
Areas Covered: AK, AZ, CA, HI, ID, NV, OR, TX, WA

Director **Peter Minarik PhD** . . . . (213) 894-3437
E-mail: pminarik@usccr.gov
Education: Purdue PhD

Commodity Futures Trading Commission (CFTC)

Description: The Commodity Futures Trading Commission promotes economic growth, safeguards the rights of customers, and ensures fairness and integrity in the marketplace through the regulation of futures trading.

Three Lafayette Centre, 1155 21st Street, NW,
Washington, DC 20581-0001
Tel: (202) 418-5000 Tel: (202) 418-5105 (Freedom of Information)
Tel: (202) 418-5009 (Job Information Hotline)
Tel: (202) 418-5000 (Personnel Locator)
Tel: (202) 418-5180 (Procurement Information)
Tel: (202) 418-5080 (Public Information, Publications Information)
Tel: (202) 418-5100 (Records Secretary)
Tel: (866) 366-2382 (Complaints)
Tel: (202) 418-5178 (Travel Office) Fax: (202) 418-5521
Fax: (202) 418-5543 (Freedom of Information/Records Secretary)
Internet: www.cftc.gov
Internet: www.cftc.gov/transparency (Open Government Directive)
Internet: www.cftc.gov/cftc/cftcreports.htm (Reports and Publications)
Internet: www.cftc.gov/cftc/cftcfoia.htm (Public Information)

THE COMMISSION

Three Lafayette Centre, 1155 21st Street, NW,
Washington, DC 20581-0001

Note: Commissioners may continue to serve after their specified term has expired through the next session of Congress or until reappointed or replaced.

Regional Offices

Central Region

525 West Monroe Street, Suite 1100, Chicago, IL 60661
Tel: (312) 596-0700 Fax: (312) 596-0712
Areas Covered: IL, IN, MI, OH, WI and matters related to trading on the Chicago Board of Trade or the Chicago Mercantile Exchange

Regional Administrator (Acting) **Rosemary Hollinger** ... (312) 596-0520
Associate Director of Enforcement
Rosemary Hollinger ... (312) 596-0520
Office Manager **Thomas J. Williams** ... (312) 596-0702

Division of Clearing and Risk
525 West Monroe Street, Suite 1100, Chicago, IL 60661
Tel: (312) 596-0700 Fax: (312) 596-0711

Deputy Director, Examinations Branch
Julie Mohr Room 11710 ... (312) 596-0568
E-mail: jmohr@cftc.gov Fax: (312) 596-0711
Associate Director, Examinations Branch
Thomas Koprowski Room 11602 ... (312) 596-0593
Associate Director, Examinations Branch
James Ortlieb ... (312) 596-0603
Associate Director, Examinations Branch
Kenji K. Takaki Room 11008 ... (312) 596-0522
Associate Director, Examinations Branch
Tamara Roust ... (312) 596-0636
Associate Director, Risk Surveillance Branch
Shallom Moses ... (202) 418-7644
Three Lafayette Centre, 1155 21st Street, NW,
Washington, DC 20581-0001

Division of Enforcement
525 West Monroe Street, Chicago, IL 60661
Tel: (312) 596-0551 Fax: (312) 596-0714

Deputy Regional Counsel **Scott Williamson** ... (312) 596-0560

Division of Enforcement *(continued)*

Secretary **Ted Pollard** ... (312) 596-0551

Division of Market Oversight
Compliance/Rule Enforcement Unit Branch Chief
John Reeden ... (312) 596-0650
Auditor **Walter N. Maksymec** ... (312) 596-0571
E-mail: wmaksymec@cftc.gov
Program Assistant **Sonja D. Williams** ... (312) 596-0652
Futures Trading Investigator **Edmond Carpenter** ... (312) 596-0526
Tel: (617) 223-9683
Futures Trading Counselor **(Vacant)** ... (312) 596-0583
Futures Trading Assistant **(Vacant)** ... (312) 596-0581
Futures Trading Assistant **(Vacant)** ... (312) 596-0583

Eastern Region

140 Broadway, New York, NY 10005-1101
Tel: (646) 746-9700 Fax: (646) 746-9938
Areas Covered: AL, CT, DE, DC, FL, GA, KY, ME, MD, MA, MS, NH, NJ, NY, NC, PA, RI, SC, TN, VT, VA, WV, PR, VI

Regional Administrator **Kevin Piccoli** ... (646) 746-9700
Logistics and Operations Supervisor **Henry Hansen** ... (646) 746-9700
E-mail: hhansen@cftc.gov
Information Resources Management Office Computer
Specialist **Ron Hood** ... (646) 746-9700
E-mail: rhood@cftc.gov

Division of Enforcement
Director **Manal Sultan** ... (646) 746-9700
E-mail: msultan@cftc.gov
Secretary **(Vacant)** ... (646) 746-9700
Deputy Regional Counsel **Lenel Hickson, Jr.** ... (646) 746-9700
E-mail: lhickson@cftc.gov

Division of Market Oversight
Market Surveillance Branch Director **(Vacant)** ... (646) 746-9700
Secretary **(Vacant)** ... (646) 746-9700
Futures Trading Assistant **Denise Thompson** ... (646) 746-9700
Market Compliance Branch Chief **(Vacant)** ... (646) 746-9700
Market Surveillance Group Analyst **Carrie Kennedy** ... (646) 746-9700
E-mail: ckennedy@cftc.gov
Market Surveillance Group Analyst **(Vacant)** ... (646) 746-9700

Division of Swap, Dealer, and Intermediary Oversight
Branch Chief **Gerald Nudge** ... (646) 746-9700
E-mail: gnudge@cftc.gov
Futures Trading Assistant **Jennell Francis** ... (646) 746-9700
E-mail: jfrancis@cftc.gov

Southwestern Region

4900 Main Street, Suite 500, Kansas City, MO 64112
Tel: (816) 960-7700 Fax: (816) 960-7750
Areas Covered: AK, AR, AZ, CA, CO, HI, IA, ID, KS, LA, MN, MO, MT, NE, NM, ND, NV, OK, OR, SD, TX, UT, WA, WY

Regional Administrator **Charles "Chuck" Marvine** ... (816) 960-7743
Network Manager **Joyce Kelly** ... (816) 960-7735
E-mail: jkelly@cftc.gov

Division of Swap Dealers and Intermediary Oversight
Branch Chief **Thomas J. Bloom** . . . . (816) 960-7710

Division of Enforcement
Branch Chief **Jeff Le Riche** . . . . (816) 960-7700
Branch Chief **Charles "Chuck" Marvine** . . . . (816) 960-7700

United States Consumer Product Safety Commission (CPSC)

Description: The Consumer Product Safety Commission protects the public against unreasonable risk of injury from consumer products through comparative product evaluation, development of uniform safety standards, and research and investigation into both the causes and prevention of product-related illnesses, injuries, and deaths.

4330 East West Highway, Bethesda, MD 20814-4408
Tel: (301) 504-7948 (Agenda Information) Tel: (301) 504-7923 (Commission Meeting Agendas and Freedom of Information Act) Tel: (301) 504-7912 (Compliance Information)
Tel: (301) 504-7925 (Employment Information)
Tel: (301) 504-7928 (Procurement Information)
Tel: (301) 504-7908 (Public Affairs/Media Relations)
Tel: (866) 230-6229 (Inspector General's Hotline)
Tel: (800) 638-2772 (Consumer Hotline)
TTY: (800) 638-8270 (Consumer Hotline)
Fax: (301) 504-0124 Fax: (301) 504-0025 (Alternate)
Fax: (800) 638-2772 (Freedom of Information) Internet: www.cpsc.gov
Internet: www.recalls.gov (Government Recalls)
Internet: www.saferproducts.gov

THE COMMISSION

4330 East West Highway, Bethesda, MD 20814-4408
Fax: (301) 504-0124 Fax: (301) 504-0025 (Alternate)
E-mail: info@cpsc.gov

Note: Commissioners may continue to serve for up to one year after their term has expired, until their successor has taken office.

Office of the Executive Director

4330 East West Highway, Room 720, Bethesda, MD 20814-4408
Fax: (301) 504-0121

Office of Compliance and Field Operations

4330 East West Highway, Room 610, Bethesda, MD 20814-4408
Fax: (301) 504-0359

Field Investigations Division

4330 East West Highway, Room 610, Bethesda, MD 20814-4408
Fax: (301) 504-0359

Compliance Field Investigations-East

Deputy Director **Beverly J. Kohen** .... (516) 938-5215
Fax: (866) 686-7937

Baltimore (MD) Investigator

4330 East West Highway, Bethesda, MD 20814-4408
Investigator **Randall D. Poth** .... (410) 374-4541

Buffalo (NY) Office

4330 East West Highway, Bethesda, MD 20814-4408
Investigator **Jackie Martinez** .... (718) 948-9129

Orlando (FL) Investigator

PMB #952888, Lake Mary, FL 32795
Investigator **Glenn Dunlap** .... (407) 227-6443

Pittsburgh (PA) Investigator

4330 East West Highway, Bethesda, MD 20814-4408
Investigator **Marc Bernstein** .... (724) 591-5352

Washington (DC) Office

4330 East West Highway, Bethesda, MD 20814-4408
Investigator **Shawn Cerutti** .... (301) 504-6811

Compliance Field Investigations-West

Deputy Director **Justin S. McDonough** .... (334) 521-0201
Education: Auburn 1996 BA Fax: (866) 689-7190

Los Angeles (CA) Investigators

Product Safety Investigator **Kathy Bellenfant** .... (240) 620-4194
Note: Telecommuter Fax: (775) 719-3421

Seattle (WA) Investigator

4330 East West Highway, Bethesda, MD 20814-4408
Tel: (800) 638-2772 Fax: (775) 248-5792
Supervisory Investigator **Eugene Staebell** .... (253) 631-6806
Note: Telecommuter

★ Presidential Appointment Requiring Senate Confirmation ☆ Presidential Appointment □ Schedule C Appointment ◇ Career Senior Foreign Service Appointment
● Career Senior Executive Service (SES) Appointment ○ Non-Career Senior Executive Service (SES) Appointment ■ Postal Career Executive Service

Corporation for National and Community Service (CNCS)

Description: The Corporation for National and Community Service provides opportunities for Americans of all ages and backgrounds to engage in service that addresses the nation's educational, public safety, environmental, and other human needs to achieve direct and demonstrable results and to encourage all Americans to engage in such service. In doing so, the Corporation will foster civic responsibility, strengthen the ties that bind us together as a people, and provide educational opportunities for those who make a substantial commitment to service.

INDEPENDENT AGENCIES

250 E Street, SW, Washington, DC 20525
Tel: (202) 606-5000 (Personnel Locator/Public Information)
Tel: (202) 606-6988 (Procurement Information)
Tel: (800) 942-2677 (AmeriCorps Information)
Tel: (800) 424-8867 (National Senior Service Corps)
TTY: (800) 833-3722 (AmeriCorps Information)
Internet: www.nationalservice.gov

Board of Directors

250 E Street, SW, Washington, DC 20525
Fax: (202) 606-3460

Note: Members may serve past their expiration date until a replacement is announced.

OFFICE OF THE CHIEF EXECUTIVE OFFICER

250 E Street, SW, Washington, DC 20525
Tel: (202) 606-6735 Fax: (202) 606-3460

OFFICE OF THE CHIEF OF PROGRAM OPERATIONS

AmeriCorps

250 E Street, SW, Washington, DC 20525
Fax: (202) 606-3475

AmeriCorps National Civilian Community Corps (NCCC)
250 E Street, SW, Washington, DC 20525

AmeriCorps*NCCC Atlantic Region Campus
VA Medical Center, P.O. Box 27, Perry Point, MD 21902
Tel: (410) 642-2411 ext. 6850 Tel: (800) 949-1003 ext. 6850
Fax: (410) 642-1888
Areas Covered: CT, DC, DE, MA, MD, ME, NH, NJ, NY, OH, PA, RI, VA, VT, WV

Region Director **LaQuine V. Roberson** .... (410) 642-2411 ext. 6851
Deputy Director **David Beach** .... (410) 642-2411 ext. 6848

AmeriCorps*NCCC North Central Region Campus
1004 G Avenue, Vinton, IA 52349
Tel: (319) 472-9664 Fax: (319) 472-4371

Director **Robert Levis** .... (319) 472-9664
Program Associate **Jennifer Uretsky** .... (319) 472-9664
E-mail: juretsky@cns.gov
Community Relations Specialist **Angela Farrels** .... (319) 472-9667

AmeriCorps*NCCC Pacific Region Campus
3427 Laurel Street, Sacramento, CA 95652
Tel: (916) 640-0302 Fax: (916) 640-0318
Areas Covered: AK, AZ, CA, HI, ID, NV, OR, UT, WA

Regional Director **Moira Carpenter** .... (916) 640-0301
Deputy Director **Nicole Shala** .... (916) 640-0302
Resource Manager **(Vacant)** .... (916) 640-0300

AmeriCorps*NCCC Southern Region Campus
2715 Confederate Avenue, Vicksburg, MS 39180
Tel: (601) 630-4041 Fax: (601) 638-5443
Areas Covered: AL, FL, GA, KY, LA, MS, NC, SC, TN, VA, WV

Region Director **Kathy Ricks** .... (601) 630-4041

AmeriCorps*NCCC Southwest Region Campus
3001 South Federal Boulevard, Denver, CO 80236-2711
Tel: (303) 844-7400 Fax: (303) 844-7410
Areas Covered: AR, AZ, CO, KS, MO, NM, OK, TX

Regional Director **Ken Goodson** .... (303) 844-7401

Field Liaison

250 E Street, SW, Washington, DC 20525
Fax: (202) 565-2789

Director (Acting) **Malcolm Coles** .... (202) 606-5284
Area Manager **Malcolm Coles** .... (617) 565-7001
10 Causeway Street, Room 473, Boston, MA 02222
Area Manager **Darryl James** .... (404) 965-2101
401 West Peachtree Street, NW, Suite 1600, Atlanta, GA 30038
Education: Lehman Col 1978 BSW
Area Manager **(Vacant)** .... (303) 390-2211
P.O. Box 25505, Denver, CO 80225
Area Manager **(Vacant)** .... (206) 607-2601
915 Second Avenue, Suite 3190, Seattle, WA 98174

Northeast Region

The Curtis Center, 601 Walnut Street, Suite 876E, Philadelphia, PA 19106
Fax: (215) 597-4933

State Program Offices

Connecticut
280 Trumbull Street, 21st Floor, Hartford, CT 06103-3510
Tel: (860) 240-3240 Fax: (860) 240-3238 E-mail: ct@cns.gov

State Program Director **Anne Ostberg** .... (860) 240-3240

Maine, New Hampshire, Vermont
J.C. Cleveland Federal Building, 55 Pleasant Street, Concord, NH 03301
Tel: (603) 931-3721 Fax: (603) 225-1459 E-mail: nh@cns.gov

State Program Director **Shireen Tilley** .... (603) 226-7780
E-mail: stilley@cns.gov
State Program Officer **Susan Cheeseman** .... (603) 225-1452
State Program Officer **Elizabeth "Libby" Hite** .... (603) 225-1451
State Program Officer **Eileen Smart** .... (603) 225-1456

Maryland - Delaware
George H. Fallon Federal Building, 31 Hopkins Plaza, Suite 400-B, Baltimore, MD 21201-3418
Tel: (410) 962-4443 Fax: (410) 962-3201 E-mail: md@cns.gov

State Program Director (Acting)
Elizabeth "Betsy" Southall .... (410) 962-4443
State Program Officer **Briana Lawson** .... (410) 962-4444

★ Presidential Appointment Requiring Senate Confirmation ☆ Presidential Appointment ☐ Schedule C Appointment ◇ Career Senior Foreign Service Appointment
● Career Senior Executive Service (SES) Appointment ○ Non-Career Senior Executive Service (SES) Appointment ■ Postal Career Executive Service

Massachusetts
Thomas P. O'Neill Federal Building, 10 Causeway Street,
Room 473, Boston, MA 02222-1038
Tel: (857) 317-5285 Fax: (617) 565-8607 E-mail: ma@cns.gov

State Program Director **Sherry McClintock** . . . . (857) 317-5285
E-mail: smcclintock@cns.gov
State Program Officer **(Vacant)** . . . .(857) 317-5285
State Program Officer **(Vacant)** . . . .(857) 317-5285
Area Manager **Malcolm Coles** . . . .(857) 317-5285

New Jersey
44 South Clinton Avenue, Suite 312, Trenton, NJ 08609
Tel: (609) 989-2246 Fax: (609) 989-2304 E-mail: nj@cns.gov

State Program Director **Melissa Allen** . . . . (609) 989-2246
Fax: (609) 989-2304
State Program Officer **Colleen Hummer** . . . . (609) 989-2243
E-mail: chummer@cns.gov

New York
Leo O'Brien Federal Building, Clinton Avenue and North Pearl Street,
Suite 900, Albany, NY 12207
Tel: (518) 649-8043 Fax: (518) 431-4154 E-mail: ny@cns.gov

State Program Director **Jessica Vasquez** . . . . (518) 649-8043
Education: Bryn Mawr BA; New York Law JD
State Program Officer **Kathleen Carey** . . . . (518) 649-8044
State Program Officer **Kara Holwick** . . . . (518) 649-8048
State Program Officer **Kim Judy** . . . . (518) 649-8049
State Program Officer **Karen Talbot** . . . .(518) 649-8047

Pennsylvania
Robert N. C. Nix Federal Building, 900 Market Street,
Suite 229, Philadelphia, PA 19107
Tel: (215) 964-6350 Fax: (215) 597-2807 E-mail: pa@cns.gov

State Program Director **Bernard Brown** . . . . (215) 964-6352
E-mail: bbrown@cns.gov
State Program Officer **Debra Lytle** . . . .(215) 964-6354
State Program Officer **Taryn Vanaskie** . . . . (215) 964-6353
State Program Officer **(Vacant)** . . . .(215) 597-2847

Puerto Rico-Virgin Islands
U.S. Federal Building, 150 Carlos Chardon Avenue,
Suite 662, Hato Rey, PR 00918-1737
Tel: (787) 766-5314 Fax: (787) 766-5189 E-mail: pr@cns.gov

State Program Director (Acting) **Jessica Vasquez** . . . . (787) 766-5314
Education: Bryn Mawr BA; New York Law JD
State Program Officer **Kenia Colon-Torres** . . . . (787) 766-5188
State Program Officer **Amanda Prestamo** . . . . (787) 766-4979
E-mail: aprestamo@cns.gov

Rhode Island
400 Westminster Street, Room 203, Providence, RI 02903
Tel: (401) 528-5426 Fax: (401) 528-5220 E-mail: ri@cns.gov

State Program Director **Marisa Petreccia** . . . . (401) 528-5426
E-mail: mpetreccia@cns.gov
State Program Officer **Deborah O'Gara** . . . . (401) 528-5424

North Central Region

Areas Covered: IL, IN, IA, MI, MN, NE, ND, SD, OH, WI

AmeriCorps State and National

Americorps Vista Training Coordinator
Katelyn Norton . . . . (617) 565-7015

State Program Offices

Illinois
Ralph H. Metcalfe Federal Building, 77 West Jackson Boulevard,
Suite 442, Chicago, IL 60604-3511
Tel: (312) 897-2121 Fax: (312) 353-6496 E-mail: il@cns.gov

State Program Director **James L. "John" Hosteny** . . . . . .(312) 353-3622
E-mail: jhosteny@cns.gov

Illinois *(continued)*

State Program Specialist **Sarah Monroe** . . . . (312) 353-3622
State Program Specialist **James Watts** . . . . (312) 353-3624

Indiana
46 East Ohio Street, Room 226, Indianapolis, IN 46204-4317
Tel: (317) 226-6724 Fax: (317) 226-5437 E-mail: in@cns.gov

State Program Director **Louis Lopez** . . . . (317) 226-6726
E-mail: llopez@cns.gov
State Program Specialist **Emily Porshevski** . . . . (317) 226-6722
State Program Specialist **Terry Weiner** . . . . (317) 226-6553

Iowa
Federal Building, 210 Walnut Street, Room 917,
Des Moines, IA 50309-2195
Tel: (515) 284-4816 Fax: (515) 284-6640 E-mail: ia@cns.gov

State Program Director **Vicki Hover Williamson** . . . . (515) 284-4819
E-mail: vhover@cns.gov
State Program Specialist **Jancy LaFollette** . . . . (515) 284-4817

Michigan
Federal Building, 211 West Fort Street,
Suite 1408, Detroit, MI 48226-2799
Tel: (313) 226-7848 Fax: (313) 226-2557 E-mail: mi@cns.gov

State Program Director **Cathy Sharp** . . . .(313) 226-6510
E-mail: csharp@cns.gov
Program Officer **Benjamin Holland** . . . .(313) 226-3024
Program Officer **Kevin Murphy** . . . .(313) 226-4630
Program Officer **Sheila Smith** . . . .(313) 226-7874

Minnesota
431 South Seventh Street, Room 2405, Minneapolis, MN 55415-1854
Tel: (612) 334-4083 Fax: (612) 334-4084 E-mail: mn@cns.gov

State Program Director **Samuel "Sam" Schuth** . . . . (612) 334-4081
State Program Specialist **Cara Bolderzak** . . . . (612) 334-4083
State Program Specialist **Jamie Renner** . . . . (612) 334-4083

Nebraska
Federal Building and U.S. Courthouse, 100 Centennial Mall North,
Room 274-A, Lincoln, NE 68508-3896
Tel: (402) 437-5474 Fax: (402) 437-5495 E-mail: ne@cns.gov

State Program Director (Acting)
Samuel "Sam" Schuth . . . . (612) 334-4083
E-mail: sschuth@cns.gov

North Dakota - South Dakota
657 Second Avenue North, Room 347, Fargo, ND 58102
Tel: (701) 232-0320 E-mail: nd_sd@cns.gov

State Program Director **Jill Deitz** . . . .(701) 232-0320
State Program Specialist **(Vacant)** . . . .(701) 232-0320

Ohio
51 North High Street, Suite 800, Columbus, OH 43215
Tel: (614) 493-2755 Fax: (614) 469-2125 E-mail: oh@cns.gov

State Program Director **Tina Dunphy** . . . . (614) 493-2755
E-mail: tdunphy@cns.gov
State Program Specialist **Jennifer Irwin** . . . . (614) 493-2757
State Program Specialist **(Vacant)** . . . . (614) 493-2756

Wisconsin
Henry Reuss Federal Plaza, East Tower, 310 West Wisconsin Avenue,
Room 1240, Milwaukee, WI 53203-2211
Tel: (414) 297-1065 Fax: (414) 297-1863 E-mail: wi@cns.gov

State Program Director **Sarah Brady** . . . .(414) 297-1065
E-mail: sbrady@cns.gov

Pacific Region

Areas Covered: AK, CA, HI, GU, ID, MT, NV, OR, UT, WA, WY, American Samoa

State Program Offices

California
11150 Olympic Boulevard, Suite 670, Los Angeles, CA 90064
Tel: (310) 235-7421 Fax: (310) 235-7422 E-mail: ca@cns.gov

State Program Director **Laurie Cannady** .... (310) 235-7709
Senior State Program Specialist **Gayle A. Hawkins** ...... (310) 235-7704
State Program Officer **Barbara Boehringer** .... (310) 235-7705
State Program Officer **Greg Ericksen** .... (310) 235-7711
State Program Officer **Danette Martin** .... (310) 235-7708

Northern California State Office
1301 Clay Avenue, Suite 365-S, Oakland, CA 94612
Tel: (510) 637-1750 Fax: (510) 637-1748

State Program Officer **Roy Ennis** .... (510) 637-1752
State Program Officer **Katherine Goyette** .... (510) 637-1752
State Program Officer **Gail Benton Shoemaker** .... (510) 637-1750

Hawaii, Guam, American Samoa
Prince Jonah Kuhio Kalanianaole Federal Building,
300 Ala Moana Boulevard, Room 6-213, Honolulu, HI 96850-0001
Tel: (808) 541-2832 Fax: (808) 541-3603

State Program Director **Derrick Ariyoshi** .... (808) 541-2832
E-mail: dariyoshi@cns.gov

Idaho
550 West Fort Street, Suite 395, Boise, ID 83724
Tel: (208) 334-1646 Fax: (208) 334-1647 E-mail: id@cns.gov

State Program Director **April Durrant** .... (208) 334-1646
E-mail: adurrant@cns.gov
State Program Officer **Kayla Ludwigson** .... (208) 334-1646

Montana
Capitol One Center, 208 North Montana Avenue,
Suite 206, Helena, MT 59601-3837
Tel: (406) 449-5404 Fax: (406) 449-5412 E-mail: mt@cns.gov

State Program Director **Jacqueline Girard** .... (406) 449-5404
State Program Officer **Anna Yeagle** .... (406) 449-5404

Nevada
400 South Virginia Street, Suite 548, Reno, NV 89501
Tel: (775) 784-7474 Fax: (775) 784-7476 E-mail: nv@cns.gov

State Program Director **Matt Johnson** .... (775) 686-7474
E-mail: mjohnson@cns.gov
State Program Specialist **(Vacant)** .... (775) 784-7474

Oregon
620 SW Main Street, Room 714, Portland, OR 97205
Tel: (503) 821-2162 Fax: (503) 326-3474 E-mail: or@cns.gov

State Program Director **Geoffrey Hickox** .... (503) 326-3282 ext. 2
State Program Officer **(Vacant)** .... (503) 326-3282 ext. 2
State Program Officer **(Vacant)** .... (503) 326-3282 ext. 1

Utah
125 South State Street, Room 8146, Salt Lake City, UT 84138
Tel: (801) 524-5411 Fax: (801) 524-3599 E-mail: ut@cns.gov

State Program Director **Jacob Murakami** .... (801) 524-5411 ext. 1

Washington/Alaska
Jackson Federal Building, 915 Second Avenue,
Room 3190, Seattle, WA 98174
Fax: (206) 553-4415 E-mail: wa@cns.gov

Area Manager for Pacific Cluster **Amy Dailey** .... (503) 326-3304
Alaska State Program Director **Jennifer Moore** .... (503) 326-3282 ext. 2
Washington State Program Director **Jennifer Moore** ..... (503) 326-3460
Fax: (503) 326-3474
State Program Officer **Alyssa Bosian** .... (206) 607-2606
State Program Officer **Bill Dillon** .... (206) 607-2604
State Program Officer **Cat Koehn** .... (206) 607-2606
State Program Officer **Tom Langhuag** .... (206) 607-2606

Wyoming
308 West 21st Street, Room 206, Cheyenne, WY 82001-3663
Tel: (307) 772-2385 Fax: (307) 772-2389 E-mail: wy@cns.gov

State Program Director **Amy Busch** .... (307) 772-2385
E-mail: abusch@cns.gov

Southern Region

Areas Covered: AL, FL, GA, KY, MS, NC, SC, TN, VA, WV

State Program Offices

Alabama
Medical Forum, 950 - 22nd Street North,
Suite 428, Birmingham, AL 35203
Tel: (205) 731-0030 Fax: (205) 731-0031

State Program Director (Acting) **Patti Smith** .... (205) 731-0030
E-mail: psmith@cns.gov
State Program Specialist **Patti Smith** .... (205) 731-0027
State Program Specialist **LaVera Butler** .... (205) 731-1580

Florida
3165 McCrory Place, Suite 115, Orlando, FL 32803-3750
Tel: (407) 587-2979 Fax: (407) 648-6116 E-mail: fl@cns.gov

State Program Director **Billie Louis** .... (407) 648-2979
Fax: (407) 648-6116
State Program Specialist **(Vacant)** .... (407) 587-2979
State Program Specialist **Renee Johnson** .... (407) 648-2978
State Program Specialist **Gail Killeen** .... (407) 648-2977
State Program Specialist **Billy Lewis** .... (407) 648-6495

Georgia
401 West Peachtree Street, Suite 1600, Atlanta, GA 30308
Tel: (404) 965-2102 Fax: (404) 331-2898 E-mail: ga@cns.gov

Southern Cluster Area Manager **Darryl James** .... (404) 965-2101
E-mail: djames@cns.gov
Education: Lehman Col 1978 BSW
State Program Director **Amieko Watson** .... (404) 965-6615
State Program Specialist **Robert O'Harra** .... (404) 965-2104
State Program Specialist **(Vacant)** .... (404) 965-2103
Administrative Assistant **(Vacant)** .... (404) 965-2105

Kentucky
Ramono L. Mazzoli Federal Building, 600 Martin Luther King Place,
Room 190, Louisville, KY 40202-2230
Tel: (502) 582-6384 Fax: (502) 582-6386 E-mail: ky@cns.gov

State Program Director (Acting) **Robin Corindo** .... (502) 582-6385
Fax: (502) 582-6386
State Program Specialist **(Vacant)** .... (502) 582-6384
Administrative Assistant **(Vacant)** .... (502) 582-6384

Mississippi
210 East Capitol Street, Suite 920, Jackson, MS 39201
Tel: (601) 965-5664 Fax: (601) 965-4617 E-mail: ms@cns.gov

State Program Director (Acting)
Frank DiSilvestro .... (601) 965-5664 ext. 3
State Program Specialist **Retha Harrison** .... (601) 965-4463
State Program Specialist **Michelle Newman** .... (601) 965-4463

North Carolina
Century Station Federal Building, 300 Fayetteville Street,
Room 414, Raleigh, NC 27601-1739
Tel: (984) 269-4523 Fax: (919) 856-4738 E-mail: nc@cns.gov

State Program Director **Alexandria Cooley** .... (984) 269-4523
State Program Specialist **(Vacant)** .... (919) 856-4737
State Program Specialist **(Vacant)** .... (919) 856-4507
State Program Specialist **(Vacant)** .... (919) 856-4732

INDEPENDENT AGENCIES

★ Presidential Appointment Requiring Senate Confirmation ☆ Presidential Appointment ☐ Schedule C Appointment ◇ Career Senior Foreign Service Appointment
● Career Senior Executive Service (SES) Appointment ○ Non-Career Senior Executive Service (SES) Appointment ■ Postal Career Executive Service

South Carolina
Strom Thurmond Federal Building, 1835 Assembly Street, Room 872, Columbia, SC 29201-2430
Tel: (803) 765-5771 Fax: (803) 765-5777 E-mail: sc@cns.gov

State Program Director **Frank DiSilvestro** .... (919) 856-4733
State Program Specialist **Myra Cunningham** .... (803) 765-5773

Tennessee
233 Cumberland Bend Drive, Suite 112, Nashville, TN 37228-1806
Tel: (615) 736-5561 Fax: (615) 736-7937 E-mail: tn@cns.gov

State Program Director **Robin Corindo** .... (615) 736-5563
State Program Specialist **Mark Gage** .... (615) 736-5562
State Program Specialist **Michael Lafferty** .... (615) 736-5563

Virginia
400 N. Eighth Street, Room 446, Richmond, VA 23240-1832
P.O. Box 10066, Richmond, VA 23240-1832
Tel: (804) 771-2197 Fax: (804) 771-2157 E-mail: va@cns.gov

State Program Director **Tynetta Darden-Smith** ... (804) 771-2197 ext. 23
State Program Specialist **Kelly Maddenly** .... (804) 771-2197 ext. 24
State Program Specialist **Kimberly Wiggins** ...... (804) 771-2197 ext. 26

West Virginia
One Bridge Place, 10 Hale Street, Suite 203, Charleston, WV 25301-1409
Tel: (304) 347-5246 Fax: (304) 347-5464 E-mail: wv@cns.gov

State Program Director (Acting) **Michelle Teare** ... (304) 347-5246 ext. 1
State Program Specialist **Karalisa Bradley** .... (304) 347-5246 ext. 2
State Program Specialist **Michelle Tear** .... (304) 347-5246 ext. 3

Southwest Region

2345 Grand Boulevard, Kansas City, MO 64108
Tel: (816) 426-2096 Fax: (816) 426-2082
Areas Covered: AZ, AR, CO, KS, LA, MO, NM, OK, TX

Area Manager **Michael Laverty** .... (816) 426-2096

State Program Offices

Arizona
230 North First Avenue, Suite 200, Phoenix, AZ 85003
Tel: (602) 514-7171 Fax: (602) 379-4030 E-mail: az@cns.gov

State Program Director **Kimberly Will** .... (602) 514-7171
State Program Officer **Neill Mimish** .... (602) 514-7171
State Program Officer **Jacqueline Wasik** .... (602) 514-7171

Arkansas
Federal Building, 700 West Capitol Street, Room 2506, Little Rock, AR 72201
Tel: (501) 324-5234 Fax: (501) 324-6949 E-mail: ar@cns.gov

State Program Director (Acting) **Theresa Long-Pettijohn** .... (501) 324-5235
State Program Officer **Derek Cromwell** .... (501) 324-6460

Colorado
Denver Federal Center, Building 46, West Sixth Avenue and Kipling Street, Denver, CO 80225
P.O. Box 25505, Denver, CO 80225
Fax: (303) 236-2039 E-mail: co@cns.gov

State Program Director **Dan Dunlap** .... (303) 390-2212
State Program Officer **Ventana Harding** .... (303) 390-2213
State Program Officer **Roger Palmer** .... (303) 390-2215

Kansas
2345 Grand Boulevard, Suite 650, Kansas City, MO 64108
Tel: (816) 905-3706 Fax: (816) 426-2082 E-mail: ks@cns.gov

State Program Director **Margaret "Maggie" Garvey** .... (816) 905-3706

Louisiana
707 Florida Street, Suite 316, Baton Rouge, LA 70801
Tel: (225) 389-0473 Fax: (225) 389-0510 E-mail: la@cns.gov

State Program Director **Lora Grady** .... (225) 389-0472

Louisiana *(continued)*

State Program Officer **(Vacant)** .... (225) 389-0472 ext. 22
State Program Officer **Jillian Winters** .... (225) 389-0471 ext. 21

Missouri
2345 Grand Boulevard, Suite 650, Kansas City, MO 64108
Tel: (816) 905-3706 Fax: (816) 426-2082 E-mail: mo@cns.gov

State Program Director **Margaret "Maggie" Garvey** .... (816) 905-3706
State Program Officer **Erin Balleine** .... (816) 905-3706
State Program Officer **Sarah Forgey** .... (816) 905-3706
State Program Officer **Josh Lyman** .... (816) 905-3706
State Program Officer **Kirsty Morgan** .... (816) 905-3706

New Mexico
Federal Building, 120 South Federal Place, Suite 315, Santa Fe, NM 87501-2026
Tel: (505) 988-6577 Fax: (505) 988-6661 E-mail: nm@cns.gov

State Program Director **Michael Garcia** .... (505) 988-6578
State Program Officer **(Vacant)** .... (505) 988-6579

Oklahoma
215 Dean A. McGee, Suite 324, Oklahoma City, OK 73102
Tel: (405) 231-5201 Fax: (405) 231-4329 E-mail: ok@cns.gov

State Program Director **Theresa Long-Pettijohn** .... (405) 231-5203
State Program Officer **Abby Klepper** .... (405) 231-5202

Texas
300 East Eighth Street, Room G-100, Austin, TX 78701-3220
Tel: (512) 391-2900 Fax: (512) 916-7020 E-mail: tx@cns.gov

State Program Director **Katy Dooley Baxter** .... (512) 391-2945
State Program Officer **Ben Alamprese** .... (512) 391-2944
State Program Officer **(Vacant)** .... (512) 391-2941
State Program Officer **Leslie McLain** .... (214) 880-2943
1999 Bryan, Suite 2050, Dallas, TX 75201
State Program Officer **Mary Rolle** .... (512) 391-2942

United States Environmental Protection Agency (EPA)

Description: The Environmental Protection Agency protects and enhances the environment. It aims to regulate and curb pollution in the areas of air, water, solid waste, pesticides, radiation, and toxic substances in cooperation with state and local governments through a variety of research, monitoring, standard setting and enforcement activities.

William Jefferson Clinton Federal Building,
1200 Pennsylvania Avenue, NW, Washington, DC 20460
Tel: (202) 272-0167 (Personnel Locator)
Tel: (202) 564-4310 (Procurement Information)
Tel: (202) 566-1667 (Freedom of Information/Privacy Act)
Tel: (202) 566-2476 (Inspector General's Hotline)
Tel: (800) 490-9198 (Publications Clearinghouse Hotline)
Tel: (202) 267-2675 (National Response Center for Oil and Hazardous Material Spills - DC Metropolitan Area) Tel: (800) 424-8802 (National Response Center for Oil and Hazardous Material Spills - Continental US)
Tel: (800) 296-1996 (Stratospheric Ozone Information Hotline)
Tel: (800) 424-9346 (Superfund and Resource Conservation and Recovery Act Community Right-to-Know Hotline - Continental US) Tel: (800) 832-7828 (Wetlands Information Hotline)
Internet: www.epa.gov
Internet: www.usa.gov (Official US Government Website)

OFFICE OF THE ADMINISTRATOR

William Jefferson Clinton Federal Building,
1200 Pennsylvania Avenue, NW, Washington, DC 20460
Tel: (202) 564-4700 Fax: (202) 501-1450

Regions

Region 1

5 Post Office Square, Suite 100, Boston, MA 02109-3912
Tel: (617) 918-1111 Tel: (888) 372-7341 (Information)
Tel: (888) 372-5427 (Research Library) Fax: (617) 918-1112
Internet: www.epa.gov/aboutepa/epa-region-1-new-england
Areas Covered: CT, ME, MA, NH, RI, VT

○ Regional Administrator **Alexandra Dunn** .... (617) 918-1012
E-mail: Dunn.alexandra@Epa.gov
Education: James Madison 1989 BA; Columbus Law 1994 JD
● Deputy Regional Administrator **Deborah Szaro** .... (617) 918-1011
E-mail: szaro.deb@epa.gov
Criminal Investigation Division Chief **Tyler Amon** .... (617) 918-2310
E-mail: amon.tyler@epa.gov
Public Affairs Director **Douglas S. Gutro** .... (617) 918-1021
E-mail: Gutro.doug@Epa.gov
Regional Counsel **Carl Dierker** .... (617) 918-1091
E-mail: dierker.carl@epa.gov
Strategic Planning **Sarah Levinson** .... (617) 918-1390
Civil Rights and Urban Affairs Director **Sharon Wells** ... (617) 918-1007
E-mail: wells.sharon@epa.gov

Office of Administration and Resource Management

5 Post Office Square, Boston, MA 02109-3912
Tel: (617) 918-1900

Office Director (Acting) **Arthur Johnson** .... (617) 918-8301
E-mail: Johnson.arthur@Epa.gov
Deputy Office Director **Frederick "Fred" Weeks** .... (617) 918-1855
E-mail: weeks.fred@epa.gov
Budget Planning and Coordination Manager (Comptroller) **(Vacant)** .... (617) 918-1921
Information Services Manager **(Vacant)** .... (617) 918-1951

Office of Administration and Resource Management *(continued)*

Contracts and Procurement Manager **Francis Callaghan** .... (617) 918-1055
E-mail: callaghan.francis@epa.gov
Customer Service and Facilities Manager **(Vacant)** .... (617) 918-1064
Grants Management Manager **Cheryl Scott** .... (617) 918-1174
E-mail: scott.cheryll@epa.gov
Human Resources Officer **Katherine Shanahan** .... (617) 918-1619
E-mail: shanahan.katherine@epa.gov
Library Director **(Vacant)** .... (617) 918-1990
Regional Health and Safety Officer **John Suiter** .... (617) 918-1996
E-mail: suiter.john@epa.gov

Office of Ecosystem Protection

5 Post Office Square, Boston, MA 02109-3912
Tel: (617) 918-1500

Office Director **Ken Moraff** .... (617) 918-1502
E-mail: moraff.ken@epa.gov
Deputy Office Director **Lynne Hamjian** .... (617) 918-1601
E-mail: hamjian.lynne@epa.gov
Air Programs Branch Chief **David Conroy** .... (617) 918-1661
Drinking Water Branch Chief **Jane Downing** .... (617) 918-1571
E-mail: downing.jane@epa.gov
Grants, Tribal, Community, and Municipal Assistance Branch Chief **(Vacant)** .... (617) 918-1591
Municipal and Water Permits Branch Chief **David Webster** .... (617) 918-1791
Surface Water Branch Chief (Acting) **Lynne Hamjian** .... (617) 918-1601
E-mail: hamjian.lynne@epa.gov
Water Quality Branch Chief **Ralph Abele** .... (617) 918-1629
Wetlands and Information Branch Chief **Jacqueline LeClair** .... (617) 918-1549

Office of Environmental Measurement and Evaluation

11 Technology Drive, Chelmsford, MA 01863
Tel: (617) 918-8300

Office Director (Acting) **Johanna Hunter** .... (617) 918-8601
E-mail: Hunter.johanna@Epa.gov
Deputy Office Director **Johanna Hunter** .... (617) 918-8601
E-mail: Hunter.johanna@Epa.gov
Facilities Team Leader **Scott Pellerin** .... (617) 918-8678
E-mail: pellerin.scott@epa.gov
Ecosystem Assessment Manager **Katrina Kipp** .... (617) 918-8309
E-mail: kipp.katrina@epa.gov
Investigations and Analysis Manager **Ernest Waterman** .... (617) 918-8632
E-mail: waterman.ernest@epa.gov
Education: Northeastern BS; New Hampshire MS
Quality Assurance Manager **(Vacant)** .... (617) 918-8311

Office of Environmental Stewardship

5 Post Office Square, Boston, MA 02109-3912
Tel: (617) 918-1701

● Office Director (Acting) **Karen McGuire** .... (617) 918-1711
E-mail: McGuire.karen@Epa.gov
Deputy Office Director **(Vacant)** .... (617) 918-1731
Assistance and Pollution Prevention Office **(Vacant)** ..... (617) 918-1801

(continued on next page)

★ Presidential Appointment Requiring Senate Confirmation ☆ Presidential Appointment ☐ Schedule C Appointment ◇ Career Senior Foreign Service Appointment
● Career Senior Executive Service (SES) Appointment ○ Non-Career Senior Executive Service (SES) Appointment ■ Postal Career Executive Service

Office of Environmental Stewardship *(continued)*

Legal Enforcement Office **Joanna Jerison** . . . . (617) 918-1781
E-mail: jerison.joanna@epa.gov
Technical Enforcement Office **James Chow** . . . . (617) 918-1394
E-mail: chow.james@epa.gov

Office of Site Remediation and Restoration

5 Post Office Square, Boston, MA 02109-3912
Tel: (617) 918-1200

Office Director **Bryan Olson** . . . . (617) 918-1201
E-mail: Olson.bryan@Epa.gov
Deputy Director **Sharon Hayes** . . . . (617) 918-1328
E-mail: hayes.sharon@epa.gov
Emergency Planning and Response Manager
Carol Tucker . . . . (617) 918-1221
E-mail: tucker.carol@epa.gov
Remediation and Restoration I Manager **(Vacant)** . . . . (617) 918-1365
Remediation and Restoration II Manager **(Vacant)** . . . . (617) 918-1381
Technical and Support Manager **(Vacant)** . . . . (617) 918-1401

Region 2

290 Broadway, New York, NY 10007-1866
Tel: (212) 637-3333 (Environmental Protection Agency General Information) Fax: (212) 637-3526 Internet: www.epa.gov/region02
Areas Covered: NJ, NY, PR, VI

○ Regional Administrator **Peter D. "Pete" Lopez** . . . . (202) 637-5000
E-mail: Lopez.peter@Epa.gov
Education: SUNY (Cobleskill) BA; SUNY (Albany) MPA
Executive Assistant **(Vacant)** . . . . (212) 637-5028
● Deputy Regional Administrator (Acting)
Walter E. Mugdan . . . . (212) 637-4390
E-mail: Mugdan.walter@Epa.gov
Secretary **Maureen Hickey** . . . . (212) 637-5035
E-mail: hickey.maureen@epa.gov
□ Chief of Staff **(Vacant)** . . . . (212) 637-5039
Divisional Inspector General **Paul Brezinski** . . . . (732) 906-6909
Environmental Justice Coordinator **Christine Ash** . . . . (212) 637-4006
E-mail: ash.christine@epa.gov
Secretary **Beth Soltani** . . . . (212) 637-5038
E-mail: soltani.beth@epa.gov

Office of Policy and Management (OPM)

290 Broadway, New York, NY 10007-1866
Tel: (212) 637-3556 Fax: (212) 637-5045

Director **Richard J. Manna** . . . . (212) 637-3591
E-mail: manna.richard@epa.gov
Deputy Director (Acting) **Donald Pace** . . . . (212) 637-4135
E-mail: pace.donald@epa.gov
Equal Employment Opportunity Officer
Mavis Johnson . . . . (212) 637-3339
E-mail: johnson.mavis@epa.gov
Contracts Management Branch Chief **(Vacant)** . . . . (212) 637-3380
Facilities and Administrative Management Branch
Chief **(Vacant)** . . . . (212) 637-3556
Financial Management Branch Chief (Acting)
Carlos Kercado . . . . (212) 637-4151
Grants and Contracts Management Branch Chief
(Acting) **Rudnell O'Neal** . . . . (212) 637-3421
E-mail: oneal.rudnell@epa.gov
Human Resources Branch Chief **Barbara J. Pastalove** . . . (212) 637-4102
E-mail: pastalove.barbara@epa.gov
Information Systems Branch Chief **Frank Demarco** . . . . . . (212) 637-3332
E-mail: demarco.frank@epa.gov

Office of Regional Counsel (ORC)

290 Broadway, New York, NY 10007-1866
Tel: (212) 637-3113 Fax: (212) 637-3115

Regional Counsel **Eric H. Schaaf** . . . . (212) 637-3107
E-mail: schaaf.eric@epa.gov
Deputy Regional Counsel **Paul F. Simon** . . . . (212) 637-3152
E-mail: simon.paul@epa.gov
Associate Regional Counsel for Criminal Enforcement
Patricia Hick . . . . (212) 637-3137
E-mail: hick.patricia@epa.gov

Office of Regional Counsel *(continued)*

Air Branch Chief **(Vacant)** . . . . (212) 637-3228
New Jersey Superfund Branch Chief
Deborah L. Mellott . . . . (212) 637-3147
E-mail: mellott.deborah@epa.gov
New York/Caribbean Superfund Branch Chief
Thomas Lieber . . . . (212) 637-3158
E-mail: lieber.thomas@epa.gov
Waste and Toxic Substances Branch Chief
William Kent Sawyer . . . . (212) 637-3196
E-mail: sawyer.william@epa.gov
Education: Yale 1975 BA
Water and General Law Branch Chief
Phyllis S. Feinmark . . . . (212) 637-3232
E-mail: feinmark.phyllis@epa.gov
Supervisory General Attorney **Virginia Capon** . . . . (212) 637-3163
E-mail: capon.virginia@epa.gov

New York City Response and Recovery Operations

World Trade Center Coordinator
Pasquale "Pat" Evangelista . . . . (212) 637-4447
E-mail: evangelista.pat@epa.gov

Public Affairs

290 Broadway, New York, NY 10007-1866
Tel: (212) 637-3660 Fax: (212) 637-5046

Director **Mary Mears** . . . . (212) 637-3673
E-mail: mears.mary@epa.gov
Administrative Assistant **Valencia Johnson** . . . . (212) 637-4441
E-mail: johnson.valencia@epa.gov
Deputy Director **(Vacant)** . . . . (212) 637-4972
Intergovernmental and Community Affairs Branch
Chief (Acting) **David "Dave" Kluesner** . . . . (212) 637-3653
E-mail: kluesner.david@epa.gov

Caribbean Environmental Protection Division (CEPD)

Centro Europa Building, 1492 Ponce de Leon Avenue,
Suite 417, Stop 22, Santurce, PR 00909-4127
Tel: (787) 977-5870 Fax: (787) 289-7982 Fax: (787) 729-7748

Director **Carmen Guerrero** . . . . (787) 977-5875
E-mail: guerrero.carmen@epa.gov
Deputy Director **Teresita Rodriguez** . . . . (787) 977-5864
E-mail: rodriguez.teresita@epa.gov
Multimedia Programs Branch Chief **Nancy Rodriguez** . . . (787) 977-5887
E-mail: rodriguez.nancy@epa.gov
Municipal Water Branch **Jaime Geliga** . . . . (787) 977-5840
Remedial Response Branch Chief **(Vacant)** . . . . (787) 977-5870
290 Broadway, 18th Floor, New York, NY 10007-1866
Virgin Islands Coordinator **Jim C. Casey** . . . . (340) 714-2333
The Tunick Building, Fax: (340) 714-2332
1336 Beltjen Road, Charlotte Amalie,
1st Floor, St. Thomas, VI 00802
E-mail: casey.jim@epa.gov

Clean Air and Sustainability Division (CASD)

290 Broadway, New York, NY 10007-1866
Tel: (212) 637-3725 Fax: (212) 637-3772

Director **John Filippelli** . . . . (212) 637-3736
E-mail: filippelli.john@epa.gov
Deputy Director for Planning **Ariel Iglesias-Portalatin** . . . (212) 637-3315
E-mail: iglesias.ariel@epa.gov
Administrative Assistant **Evelyn Rivera-Thomas** . . . . . . (212) 637-3737
E-mail: rivera-thomas.evelyn@epa.gov
Air Programs Branch Chief **Richard Ruvo** . . . . (212) 637-4014
E-mail: ruvo.richard@epa.gov
Radiation and Indoor Air Branch Chief **(Vacant)** . . . . (212) 637-3725
Hazardous Waste Program Branch Chief
Adolph S. Everett . . . . (212) 637-4109
E-mail: everett.adolph@epa.gov
Sustainability and Multi-Media Programs Branch Chief
Judy-Ann Mitchell . . . . (212) 637-3721
E-mail: mitchell.judy-ann@epa.gov

★ Presidential Appointment Requiring Senate Confirmation ☆ Presidential Appointment □ Schedule C Appointment ◇ Career Senior Foreign Service Appointment
● Career Senior Executive Service (SES) Appointment ○ Non-Career Senior Executive Service (SES) Appointment ■ Postal Career Executive Service

Clean Water Division (CWD)

Director **Javier Laureano** .... (212) 637-3333

Division of Enforcement and Compliance Assistance (DECA)

290 Broadway, New York, NY 10007-1866
Tel: (212) 637-4000 Fax: (212) 637-4035

Director **Dore F. LaPosta** .... (212) 637-4000
E-mail: laposta.dore@epa.gov
Deputy Director **(Vacant)** .... (212) 637-4043
Administrative Assistant **Carmen Castro** .... (212) 637-4041
E-mail: castro.carmen@epa.gov
Air Compliance Branch Chief **Robert Buettner** .... (212) 637-5031
E-mail: buettner.robert@epa.gov
Compliance Assistance and Program Support Branch Chief **Barbara McGarry** .... (212) 637-4072
E-mail: mcgarry.barbara@epa.gov
Pesticides and Toxics Substances Branch Chief **John W. Gorman** .... (732) 321-6765
2890 Woodbridge Avenue, Edison, NJ 08837-3679
E-mail: gorman.john@epa.gov
RCRA Compliance Branch Chief **Leonard Voo** .... (212) 637-1473
E-mail: voo.leonard@epa.gov
Water Compliance Branch Chief **Doughlas McKenna** .... (212) 637-4244
E-mail: mckenna.douglas@epa.gov

Emergency and Remedial Response Division (ERRD)

290 Broadway, New York, NY 10007-1866
Tel: (212) 637-4391 Fax: (212) 637-4439

Director (Acting) **John Prince** .... (212) 637-4380
E-mail: Prince.john@Epa.gov
Deputy Director **Angela Carpenter** .... (212) 637-4435
E-mail: carpenter.angela@epa.gov
Accelerated Cleanup Manager and Ombudsman **George H. Zachos** .... (732) 321-6621
Building 209, Bay A, 2890 Woodbridge Avenue, MS211, Edison, NJ 08837-3679
E-mail: zachos.george@epa.gov
Hudson River Field Office Director **Gary Klawinski** .... (518) 407-0400
421 Lower Main Street, Hudson Falls, NY 12839 Fax: (518) 747-8149
Lower River Project Director **(Vacant)** .... (212) 637-4417
Remedy Selection/Design and Construction Manager **John Prince** .... (212) 637-4380
E-mail: prince.john@epa.gov
New Jersey Remediation Branch Chief **(Vacant)** .... (212) 637-4418
New York Remediation Branch Chief **Doug Garbarini** .... (212) 637-4288
E-mail: garbarini.doug@epa.gov
Program Support Branch Chief **Courtney McEnery** .... (212) 637-4295
E-mail: mcenery.courtney@epa.gov
Removal Action Branch Chief **Joseph "Joe" Rotola** .... (732) 321-6658
Building 209, Bay A, 2890 Woodbridge Avenue, MS211, Edison, NJ 08837-3679
E-mail: rotola.joe@epa.gov
Response and Prevention Branch Chief **Eric Mosher** .... (732) 321-4368
Building 209, Bay A, 2890 Woodbridge Avenue, MS211, Edison, NJ 08837-3679
E-mail: mosher.eric@epa.gov
Special Projects Branch Chief **Michael Sivak** .... (212) 637-4310
E-mail: sivak.michael@epa.gov

Division of Environmental Science and Assessment (DESA)

Building 10, 2890 Woodbridge Avenue, MS 100, Edison, NJ 08837-3679
Tel: (732) 482-1080 Fax: (732) 321-4381

Director **Anahita Williamson** .... (732) 321-6686
Secretary **Jacqueline Lopez** .... (732) 321-6784
E-mail: lopez.jacqueline@epa.gov
Deputy Director **Kevin Kubik** .... (732) 321-6755
E-mail: kubik.kevin@epa.gov
Hazardous Waste Support Branch Chief **Jon Gabry** .... (732) 321-6650
E-mail: gabry.jon@epa.gov
Laboratory Branch Chief **John R. Bourbon** .... (732) 321-6706
E-mail: bourbon.john@epa.gov

Division of Environmental Science and Assessment *(continued)*

Monitoring and Assessment Branch Chief **John Kushwara** .... (732) 321-6686
E-mail: kushwara.john@epa.gov
Quality Assurance Manager (Acting) **Kevin Kubik** .... (732) 321-6755
E-mail: kubik.kevin@epa.gov
Regional Science Liaison **Marie Oshea** .... (212) 637-3585
290 Broadway, 26th Floor, New York, NY 10007-1866
E-mail: oshea.marie@epa.gov

Headquarters Field Components – Region II

Office of Criminal Enforcement, Forensics and Training – Criminal Investigations Division

290 Broadway, Room 1551, New York, NY 10007-1866
Tel: (212) 637-3610 Fax: (212) 637-3637

Special Agent-in-Charge **Jessica Taylor** .... (202) 564-2455

Syracuse (NY) Resident Agency Office

P.O. Box 7086, Syracuse, NY 13261
Tel: (315) 422-2603 Fax: (315) 452-1074

Resident Agent-in-Charge **(Vacant)** .... (315) 422-2603

Trenton (NJ) Resident Agency Office

402 East State Street, Trenton, NJ 08608
Tel: (732) 321-4380

Resident Agent-in-Charge **Robin Traub** .... (609) 656-2727
E-mail: traub.robin@epa.gov

Office of Research and Development - Water Resources Recovery Branch

Building 10, 2890 Woodbridge Avenue, MS 104, Edison, NJ 08837-3679
Tel: (732) 906-6989 Fax: (732) 321-6640

Environmental Engineer **(Vacant)** .... (732) 906-6989
Budget Analyst **Diana Ruffini** .... (732) 321-6678
E-mail: ruffini.diana@epa.gov

Region 3

1650 Arch Street, Room 3RA00, Philadelphia, PA 19103-2029
Tel: (215) 814-5000 Fax: (215) 814-2901
E-mail: region3ra@epamail.epa.gov
Areas Covered: DE, DC, MD, PA, VA, WV

○ Regional Administrator **Cosmo Servidio** .... (215) 814-2900
E-mail: servidio.cosmo@epa.gov
Education: Wheeling Jesuit BA
Executive Assistant **Marycate Opila** .... (215) 814-2041
E-mail: Opila.marycate@Epa.gov
● Deputy Regional Administrator **Cecil Rodrigues** .... (215) 814-2683
E-mail: rodrigues.cecil@epa.gov
Regional Counsel **Mary B. Coe** .... (215) 814-2617
E-mail: coe.mary@epa.gov
Librarian **(Vacant)** .... (215) 814-5519
Equal Employment Opportunity Manager **Cynthia Burrows** .... (215) 814-5326
E-mail: burrows.cynthia@epa.gov

Office of Enforcement, Compliance, and Environmental Justice

1650 Arch Street, Philadelphia, PA 19103-2029
Tel: (215) 814-2950

Director **Samantha Beers** .... (215) 814-2627
E-mail: beers.samantha@epa.gov

Office of Policy and Management

1650 Arch Street, Philadelphia, PA 19103-2029
Tel: (215) 814-5200

● Assistant Regional Administrator **Diana Esher** .... (215) 814-2706
E-mail: esher.diana@epa.gov
Deputy Assistant Regional Administrator (Acting) **John Krakowiak** .... (215) 814-5611
E-mail: krakowiak.john@epa.gov
Comptroller **Lisa White** .... (215) 814-2391
E-mail: White.lisa@Epa.gov

(continued on next page)

INDEPENDENT AGENCIES

★ Presidential Appointment Requiring Senate Confirmation ☆ Presidential Appointment ☐ Schedule C Appointment ◇ Career Senior Foreign Service Appointment
● Career Senior Executive Service (SES) Appointment ○ Non-Career Senior Executive Service (SES) Appointment ■ Postal Career Executive Service

Office of Policy and Management *(continued)*

Computer Services Branch Chief **Geoffrey Fala** . . . . (215) 814-5344
E-mail: fala.geoffrey@epa.gov
Contracts Branch Chief **Jim Clark** . . . . (215) 814-5198
E-mail: Clark.jim@Epa.gov
Grants and Audit Management Branch Chief
Jacqueline Guerry . . . . (215) 814-2184
E-mail: Guerry.jacqueline@Epa.gov
Facilities Management and Services Branch Chief
Joseph F. Smith . . . . (215) 814-5669
Human Resources Management Branch Chief **(Vacant)** . . . (215) 814-5240
Information Systems Branch Chief **Carol O'Tormey** . . . . . (215) 814-2677
E-mail: otormey.carol@epa.gov
Policy and Analysis Branch Chief **John Krakowiak** . . . . . (215) 814-5611
Small and Disadvantaged Business Utilization Manager
(Acting) **Cynthia Burrows** . . . . (215) 814-5326
E-mail: burrows.cynthia@epa.gov

Office of Communications and Government Relations (OCGR)
1650 Arch Street, Philadelphia, PA 19103-2029
Tel: (215) 814-5100

Director **Michael D'Andrea** . . . . (215) 814-5615
E-mail: dandrea.michael@epa.gov
Deputy Director **Terri A. White** . . . . (215) 814-5523
E-mail: white.terri@epa.gov

Chesapeake Bay Program Office
410 Severn Avenue, Suite 109, Annapolis, MD 21403
Tel: (410) 267-5700 Fax: (410) 267-5777
Internet: http://www.chesapeakebay.net

Chesapeake Bay Program Office Director (Acting)
James Edward . . . . (410) 267-5705
E-mail: edward.james@epa.gov
Deputy Director **James Edward** . . . . (410) 267-5705
E-mail: edward.james@epa.gov
Senior Advisor to the Administrator **(Vacant)** . . . . (410) 267-9836

Air Protection Division
1650 Arch Street, Philadelphia, PA 19103-2029
Tel: (215) 814-2172 Fax: (215) 814-2101

Director **Cristina Fernandez** . . . . (215) 814-2178
Deputy Director **David L. "Dave" Arnold** . . . . (215) 814-2172

Environmental Assessment and Innovation Division
1650 Arch Street, Philadelphia, PA 19103-2029
Tel: (215) 814-2700

Director (Acting) **John D. Forren** . . . . (215) 814-2705
E-mail: Forren.john@Epa.gov
Deputy Director **Walter "Walt" Wilkie** . . . . (215) 814-2150
E-mail: wilkie.walter@epa.gov

Hazardous Site Cleanup Division
1650 Arch Street, Philadelphia, PA 19103-2029
Tel: (215) 814-3000

Director **Karen Melvin** . . . . (215) 814-3275
E-mail: melvin.karen@epa.gov
Deputy Director **(Vacant)** . . . . (215) 814-3725
Associate Director of Brownfields and Outreach
(Vacant) . . . . (215) 814-3195
Associate Director of Enforcement **(Vacant)** . . . . (215) 814-2165
Associate Director of Federal Facility Remediation and
Site Assessment **(Vacant)** . . . . (215) 814-5435
Associate Director of Preparedness and Response
(Vacant) . . . . (215) 814-3241
Associate Director of Superfund Site Remediation
Linda Dietz . . . . (215) 814-3195
E-mail: dietz.linda@epa.gov
Associate Director of Technical and Administrative
Support **Bonnie Gross** . . . . (215) 814-3229
E-mail: gross.bonnie@epa.gov

Land and Chemicals Division
Director **John A. Armstead** . . . . (215) 814-3127
E-mail: Armstead.john@Epa.gov
Deputy Director **(Vacant)** . . . . (215) 814-2737
Land Enforcement Associate Director
Carol A. Amend . . . . (215) 814-5430
Materials Management Associate Director
Donna Weiss . . . . (215) 814-2198
Pennsylvania Remediation Associate Director
Paul Gotthold . . . . (215) 814-3410
Remediation Associate Director **Luis A. Pizarro** . . . . (215) 814-3444
State Programs Associate Director
Richard A. "Rick" Rogers . . . . (215) 814-5711
Toxics and Pesticides Associate Director **Harry Daw** . . . . . (215) 814-3244
E-mail: daw.harry@epa.gov
Administrative Assistant **Dionne Stokes** . . . . (215) 814-2992

Water Protection Division
1650 Arch Street, Philadelphia, PA 19103-2029
Tel: (215) 814-2300 Fax: (215) 814-2301

● Director (Acting) **Catherine McManus** . . . . (215) 814-5337
E-mail: mcmanus.catharine@epa.gov
Deputy Director **(Vacant)** . . . . (215) 814-2300
National Pollutant Discharge Elimination System
(NPDES) Permits and Enforcement Associate
Director **David McGuigan** . . . . (215) 814-2158
Drinking Water and Source Water Protection Office
Associate Director **(Vacant)** . . . . (215) 814-3367
Infrastructure and Assistance Associate Director
Lori Reynolds . . . . (215) 814-5435
Program Support Associate Director **(Vacant)** . . . . (215) 814-3145
Standards Assessment and Information Management
Associate Director **Evelyn S. MacKnight** . . . . (215) 814-5717
E-mail: macknight.evelyn@epa.gov
State and Watersheds Partnerships Associate Director
Diane McNally . . . . (215) 814-3297

Region 4
Sam Nunn Atlanta Federal Center, 61 Forsyth Street, SW,
Suite 9T25, Atlanta, GA 30303-3104
Tel: (404) 562-9900 Tel: (800) 241-1754
Tel: (404) 562-9655 (Legal Support) Tel: (404) 562-8327 (Press Office)
Tel: (404) 562-9590 (Technical Support) Fax: (404) 562-9961
Internet: www.epa.gov/region4/index.html
Areas Covered: AL, FL, GA, KY, MS, NC, SC, TN

○ Regional Administrator **Onis "Trey" Glenn III** . . . . (404) 562-8357
E-mail: Glenn.trey@Epa.gov
Education: Auburn 1994 BSCE; Alabama Birmingham 1999 MBA
● Deputy Regional Administrator **V. Anne Heard** . . . . (404) 562-8357
E-mail: heard.anne@epa.gov
Head Librarian (Acting) **Joshua Grimes** . . . . (404) 562-8190
Fax: (404) 562-8114
Assistant Librarian **(Vacant)** . . . . (404) 562-8190
Webmaster **(Vacant)** . . . . (404) 562-8031
Chief of Staff **Blake Ashbee** . . . . (404) 562-8355
E-mail: Ashbee.blake@Epa.gov
Education: Alabama BS, 2011 MBA, 2011 JD

Office of Government Relations
61 Forsyth Street SW, Atlanta, GA 30303
Tel: (404) 562-8327 Fax: (404) 562-8335

Director **Allison Wise** . . . . (404) 562-8346
E-mail: wise.allison@epa.gov

Office of Regional Counsel
61 Forsyth Street SW, Atlanta, GA 30303
Tel: (404) 562-9655 Fax: (404) 562-9663

Director (Acting) **Leif Palmer** . . . . (404) 562-9542
E-mail: Palmer.leif@Epa.gov Fax: (404) 562-9663
Deputy Regional Counsel **Nancy Tommelleo** . . . . (404) 562-9571
E-mail: tommelleo.nancy@epa.gov
Associate Director Technical Support **Scott Gordon** . . . . . (404) 562-9741
E-mail: gordon.scott@epa.gov

★ Presidential Appointment Requiring Senate Confirmation ☆ Presidential Appointment ☐ Schedule C Appointment ◇ Career Senior Foreign Service Appointment
● Career Senior Executive Service (SES) Appointment ○ Non-Career Senior Executive Service (SES) Appointment ■ Postal Career Executive Service

Office of Regional Counsel *(continued)*

Enforcement and Compliance Planning and Analysis Branch Chief **(Vacant)** .... (404) 562-9054
Office of Air/Pesticides/Toxic/Legal Support Chief **Suzanne Rubini** .... (404) 562-9674
E-mail: rubini.suzanne@epa.gov
Office of CERCLA A Legal Support Chief **David Clay** ... (404) 562-9565
E-mail: clay.david@epa.gov
Office of CERCLA B Legal Support Chief **Mary Johnson** .... (404) 562-9526
E-mail: johnson.maryc@epa.gov
Office of CERCLA C Legal Support Chief **Leif Palmer** .... (404) 562-9542
E-mail: palmer.leif@epa.gov
Office of RCRA/OPA Legal Support Chief **Susan Hansen** .... (404) 562-9700
E-mail: hansen.susan@epa.gov
Office of Water Legal Support Chief **Mita Ghosh** .... (404) 562-9568
E-mail: ghosh.mita@epa.gov

Office of External Affairs
61 Forsyth Street SW, Atlanta, GA 30303
Tel: (404) 562-8327 Fax: (404) 562-8335

Office of External Affairs Director **Larry Lincoln** .... (404) 562-8304
E-mail: lincoln.larry@epa.gov
Secretary **Queen Lovett** .... (404) 562-8319
E-mail: lovett.queen@epa.gov

Office of Policy and Management
61 Forsyth Street SW, Atlanta, GA 30303
Tel: (404) 562-8295 Fax: (404) 562-8300

Assistant Regional Administrator **BrigGen Kenneth R. LaPierre USAFR** .... (404) 562-8570
E-mail: Lapierre.kenneth@Epa.gov
Chief of Staff **(Vacant)** .... (404) 562-8158
Special Assistant **(Vacant)** .... (404) 562-8383
Deputy Assistant Regional Administrator for IAG, IT, Finance, and Facilities Management **(Vacant)** .... (404) 562-8276
Deputy Assistant Regional Administrator for Grants, Human Capital, and Enterprise Management **(Vacant)** .... (404) 562-8570
Environmental Information Services Branch Chief **Keith R. Mills** .... (404) 562-8366
E-mail: mills.keith@epa.gov
Facilities and Records Management Branch Chief **(Vacant)** .... (404) 562-9060
Grants, Finance and Cost Recovery Branch Chief **(Vacant)** .... (404) 562-9278
Human Capital Management Branch Chief **Barbara Schwartz** .... (404) 562-8182
E-mail: schwartz.barbara@epa.gov
National Environmental Policy Act (NEPA) Office Chief **Chris Militscher** .... (404) 562-9512
E-mail: militscher.chris@epa.gov
Office of Acquisition Management Section Chief **(Vacant)** .... (404) 562-8203
Office of Budget Operations and Management Chief **(Vacant)** .... (404) 562-8242
Office of Civil Rights Chief **Naima Halim-Chestnut** .... (404) 562-9220
Policy Planning and Environmental Accountability Branch Chief **Vickie Tellis** .... (404) 562-8218
E-mail: tellis.vickie@epa.gov

Gulf of Mexico Program Office
2510 14th Street, Suite 1212, Gulfport, MS 39501
Tel: (228) 679-5915 Fax: (228) 679-5921

● Director (Acting) **LaKeshia Robertson** .... (228) 679-5910
E-mail: robertson.lakeshia@epa.gov
Physical Scientist **Jeanne Allen** .... (228) 679-5892
Program Analyst **Matt Beiser** .... (228) 679-5893
Environmental Protection Specialist **Jerry Binniger** ...... (228) 679-5894
E-mail: binninger.jerry@epa.gov
Physical Scientist **Tripp Boone** .... (228) 679-5884

Gulf of Mexico Program Office *(continued)*

Environmental Engineer **John F. Bowie** .... (228) 679-5891
E-mail: bowie.john@epa.gov
Education: LSU BCE
Program Analyst **Rachel Houge** .... (228) 679-5895
Education: Texas State (San Marcos) 2000 BA; Johns Hopkins 2012 MS
Environmental Engineer **Amy Newbold** .... (228) 679-5890
E-mail: newbold.amy@epa.gov
Education: Alabama 2004 BChE; Georgia Tech 2010 MEnvE
Program Analyst **Gerry Martin** .... (228) 679-5916
Physical Scientist **Calista Mills** .... (228) 679-5879
Chief Scientist **Troy Pierce** .... (228) 679-5909
Environmental Engineer **Danny Wiegand** .... (228) 679-5897
E-mail: wiegand.danny@epa.gov
Education: Col Charleston 1993 BS; North Carolina State 1998 BS; Tulane 2007 MSPH
Executive Assistant **Beverly O'Hara** .... (228) 679-5915
E-mail: ohara.beverly@epa.gov
Community Liaison Specialist **Claudette Walker** .... (228) 860-3916
E-mail: walker.claudette@epa.gov
Education Specialist **Sharon Saucier** .... (228) 254-0548

Air, Pesticides and Toxics Management Division
61 Forsyth Street SW, Atlanta, GA 30303
Tel: (404) 562-9077 Fax: (404) 562-9066

● Director **Beverly H. Banister** .... (404) 562-9326
E-mail: banister.beverly@epa.gov
Deputy Director **Jeaneanne M. Gettle** .... (404) 562-8979
E-mail: gettle.jeaneanne@epa.gov
Deputy Director **Carol L. Kemker** .... (404) 562-8975
E-mail: kemker.carol@epa.gov
Air and EPCRA Enforcement Branch Chief **Beverly Spagg** .... (404) 562-9170
Air Planning Branch Chief **Scott Davis** .... (404) 562-9127
E-mail: davis.scottr@epa.gov
Air, Toxics and Monitoring Branch Chief **Gregg Worley** .... (404) 562-9141
E-mail: worley.gregg@epa.gov
Pesticides and Toxic Substances Branch Chief **Anthony Toney** .... (404) 562-9085
E-mail: toney.anthony@epa.gov

Resource Conservation and Recovery Act Division (RCRA)
61 Forsyth Street SW, Atlanta, GA 30303
Tel: (404) 562-8651 Fax: (404) 562-8063 Fax: (404) 562-8628

● Division Director (Acting) **Carol Monell** .... (404) 562-8719
E-mail: Monell.carol@Epa.gov
Deputy Director **(Vacant)** .... (404) 562-8569
RCRA Enforcement Compliance Branch Chief **(Vacant)** .... (404) 562-9744
RCRA Programs and Materials Management Branch Chief **(Vacant)** .... (404) 562-8527
Restoration and Underground Storage Tank Branch Chief **(Vacant)** .... (404) 562-8792

Science and Ecosystem Support Division
980 College Station Road, Athens, GA 30605
Tel: (706) 355-8500 Fax: (706) 355-8508

● Director (Acting) **Vickie Tellis** .... (404) 562-8218
E-mail: Tellis.vickie@Epa.gov
Deputy Director **Doug Mundrick** .... (706) 355-8704
E-mail: mundrick.doug@epa.gov
Analytical Support Branch Chief (Acting) **Danny France** .... (706) 355-8738
E-mail: france.danny@epa.gov
Ecological Assessment Branch Chief (Acting) **Mike Bowden** .... (706) 355-8734
E-mail: bowden.mike@epa.gov
Enforcement and Investigations Branch Chief **John Deatrick** .... (706) 355-8774
E-mail: deatrick.john@epa.gov

INDEPENDENT AGENCIES

★ Presidential Appointment Requiring Senate Confirmation ☆ Presidential Appointment ☐ Schedule C Appointment ◇ Career Senior Foreign Service Appointment
● Career Senior Executive Service (SES) Appointment ○ Non-Career Senior Executive Service (SES) Appointment ■ Postal Career Executive Service

Superfund Division
61 Forsyth Street SW, Atlanta, GA 30303
Tel: (404) 562-8583

Division Director **Franklin Hill** .... (404) 562-8599
E-mail: hill.franklin@epa.gov
Deputy Director **Randall Chaffins** .... (404) 562-8910
E-mail: chaffins.randall@epa.gov
Federal Facilities Branch Chief **(Vacant)** .... (404) 562-9742
Superfund Emergency Response and Removal Branch Chief **(Vacant)** .... (404) 562-8718
Superfund Enforcement and Information Management Branch Chief **(Vacant)** .... (404) 562-8844
Superfund Program Support Branch Chief **(Vacant)** .... (404) 562-8845
Superfund Remedial and Site Evaluation Branch Chief **Don Rigger** .... (404) 562-8744
E-mail: rigger.don@epa.gov
Superfund Remedial Branch Chief **Carol Monell** .... (404) 562-8719
E-mail: monell.carol@epa.gov

Water Protection Division
61 Forsyth Street SW, Atlanta, GA 30303
Tel: (404) 562-9345 Fax: (404) 562-9318

Director **Jeaneanne M. Gettle** .... (706) 355-8549
Special Assistant **(Vacant)** .... (404) 562-9406
Deputy Division Director **Cesar Zapata** .... (404) 562-9345
Deputy Division Director **Doug Mundrick** .... (706) 355-8704
E-mail: mundrick.doug@epa.gov
Clean Water Enforcement Branch Chief **Denisse Diaz** .... (706) 355-8554
Grants and Infrastructure Branch Chief **Thomas McGill** .... (404) 562-9243
E-mail: mcgill.thomas@epa.gov
Safe Drinking Water Branch Chief **Becky Allenbach** .... (404) 562-9687
Water Quality Planning Branch Chief **(Vacant)** .... (404) 562-9125
Watershed Coordination Section Chief **Chris Thomas** .... (404) 562-9459

Region 5

Ralph H. Metcalfe Federal Building, 77 West Jackson Boulevard, Chicago, IL 60604-3590
Tel: (312) 353-2000 Fax: (312) 353-1120 Internet: www.epa.gov/region5
Areas Covered: IL, IN, MI, MN, OH, WI

○ Regional Administrator **Cathy Stepp** .... (312) 886-3000
E-mail: stepp.cathy@epa.gov
Special Assistant to the Regional Administrator **(Vacant)** .... (312) 353-6059
● Deputy Regional Administrator (Acting) **James "Jim" Payne** .... (312) 886-3000
Congressional Relations Officer **Ronna Beckman** .... (312) 886-0689
E-mail: beckmann.ronna@epa.gov
Congressional Relations Officer **Denise Fortin** .... (312) 886-9859
E-mail: fortin.denise@epa.gov

Office of Civil Rights
Director (Acting) **Angela Brown** .... (312) 886-7156
E-mail: brown.angela@epa.gov

Office of Enforcement and Compliance Assurance
Director **Alan Walts** .... (312) 353-8894
E-mail: walts.alan@epa.gov

Indian Environmental Office
Director (Acting) **Kestutis Ambutas** .... (312) 353-1394
E-mail: ambutas.kestutis@epa.gov

Office of External Communications
Ralph Metcalfe Federal Building, 77 West Jackson Boulevard, Chicago, IL 60604-3590
Tel: (312) 353-2072 Fax: (312) 353-1155

Director **Jeff Kelley** .... (312) 353-1159
E-mail: kelley.jeff@epa.gov

Office of Regional Counsel
Ralph Metcalfe Federal Building, 77 West Jackson Boulevard, Chicago, IL 60604-3590
Tel: (312) 886-6675 Fax: (312) 886-0747

Regional Counsel **Leverett Nelson** .... (312) 886-6666
E-mail: nelson.leverett@epa.gov
Deputy Regional Counsel **Bertram C. Frey** .... (312) 886-1308
E-mail: frey.bertram@epa.gov
Education: Haverford 1969 BA; U Washington 1974 JD

Great Lakes National Program Office (GLNPO)
Ralph Metcalfe Federal Building, 77 West Jackson Boulevard, Chicago, IL 60604-3590
Tel: (312) 353-2117 Fax: (312) 886-6869

Director **Christopher "Chris" Korleski** .... (312) 353-8320
E-mail: korleski.christopher@epa.gov
Deputy Director **Wendy Carney** .... (312) 353-6553
E-mail: carney.wendy@epa.gov

Air and Radiation Division
Ralph Metcalfe Federal Building, 77 West Jackson Boulevard, Chicago, IL 60604-3590
Tel: (312) 353-2212 Fax: (312) 886-0617

Director **Ed Nam** .... (312) 353-2192
E-mail: nam.ed@epa.gov
Deputy Director (Acting) **Eileen Furey** .... (312) 886-7950
E-mail: furey.eileen@epa.gov
Air Enforcement and Compliance Assurance Branch Chief **Sara Breneman** .... (312) 353-2043
E-mail: breneman.sara@epa.gov
Air Programs Branch Chief **John Mooney** .... (312) 886-6043
Air Toxics and Assessment Branch Chief **Kathryn "Katie" Siegel** .... (312) 886-3006
E-mail: Siegel.kathryn@Epa.gov
Education: Illinois 2005 BS; Yale 2012 MBA, 2012 MEM

Criminal Investigation Division
Ralph Metcalfe Federal Building, 77 West Jackson Boulevard, Chicago, IL 60604-3590
Tel: (312) 886-9872 Fax: (312) 886-1518

Special Agent-in-Charge **Richard Conrad** .... (312) 353-6656
E-mail: conrad.richard@epa.gov

Land and Chemicals Division
Ralph Metcalfe Federal Bulding, 77 West Jackson Boulevard, Chicago, IL 60604-3590
Tel: (312) 886-7435

Director **Tinka Hyde** Ralph Metcalfe Federal Building .... (312) 886-9296
E-mail: Hyde.tinka@Epa.gov
Deputy Director **Michael Harris** .... (312) 886-0760
E-mail: harris.michael@epa.gov
Materials Management Branch Chief **Jerri-Anne Garl** .... (312) 353-1441
Program Services Branch Chief **Allen Melcer** .... (312) 886-1498
E-mail: melcer.allen@epa.gov
RCRA Branch Chief **(Vacant)** .... (312) 886-1479
Remediation and Reuse Branch Chief **Arturo "Jose" Cisneros** .... (312) 886-7447
E-mail: cisneros.arturo@epa.gov
Education: Harvard 1984 BA; Missouri 1987 MS
Chemicals Management Branch Chief **Mardi Klevs** .... (312) 353-5490

Resources Management Division
Ralph Metcalfe Federal Building, 77 West Jackson Boulevard, Chicago, IL 60604-3590
Tel: (312) 353-2024 Fax: (312) 353-4135

Assistant Regional Administrator **Cheryl Newton** .... (312) 353-6730
E-mail: newton.cheryl@epa.gov
Education: Bradley 1985 SB
Deputy Assistant Regional Administrator **Bruce Sypniewski** .... (312) 886-6189
E-mail: sypniewski.bruce@epa.gov
Central Regional Laboratory Chief **(Vacant)** .... (312) 353-9084

★ Presidential Appointment Requiring Senate Confirmation ☆ Presidential Appointment ☐ Schedule C Appointment ◇ Career Senior Foreign Service Appointment
● Career Senior Executive Service (SES) Appointment ○ Non-Career Senior Executive Service (SES) Appointment ■ Postal Career Executive Service

Resources Management Division *(continued)*

Cleveland Office Chief **Brooke Furio** . . . . (440) 250-1705
25089 Center Ridge Rd., Westlake, OH 44145
E-mail: furio.brooke@epa.gov
Acquisition and Assistance Branch Chief
William Massie . . . . (312) 886-5855
E-mail: massie.william@epa.gov
Comptroller Branch Chief **Dale Meyer** . . . . (312) 886-7561
E-mail: meyer.dale@epa.gov
Human Resources Branch Chief **Amy Sanders** . . . . (312) 353-9196
E-mail: sanders.amy@epa.gov
Information Management Branch Chief
Kenneth W. Tindall . . . . (312) 886-9895
E-mail: tindall.kenneth@epamail.epa.gov

Superfund Division

● Director (Acting) **Robert A. Kaplan** . . . . (312) 886-1499
E-mail: Kaplan.robert@Epa.gov
Deputy Director **Douglas E. "Doug" Ballotti** . . . . (312) 886-4752
E-mail: ballotti.douglas@epa.gov
Community Involvement Section Chief
Yolanda Bouchee . . . . (312) 353-3209
E-mail: bouchee.yolanda@epa.gov
CEPP Office Chief **Mick Hans** . . . . (312) 353-5050
E-mail: hans.mick@epa.gov
Emergency and Enforcement Response Branch Chief
Jason El-Zein . . . . (312) 886-6039
E-mail: el-zein.jason@epa.gov
Program Management Branch Chief **Joe Dufficy** . . . . (312) 886-1960
E-mail: dufficy.joseph@epa.gov

Water Division

Ralph Metcalfe Federal Building, 77 West Jackson Boulevard, Chicago, IL 60604-3590
Tel: (312) 353-2147 Fax: (312) 886-0957

● Director (Acting) **David Garcia** . . . . (312) 353-2147
Education: Texas (Arlington) 1986 BSCE
Associate Director **(Vacant)** . . . . (312) 886-6107
Water Quality Branch Chief **Linda Holst** . . . . (312) 886-6758
NPDES Programs Branch Chief **Kevin Pierard** . . . . (312) 886-4448
Ground Water and Drinking Water Branch Chief
Thomas Poy . . . . (312) 886-5991
State and Tribal Programs Branch Chief
Deborah "Debbie" Baltazar . . . . (312) 886-3205
E-mail: baltazar.debbie@epa.gov
Underground Injection Control Branch Chief
Stephen "Steve" Jann . . . . (312) 886-2446
E-mail: jann.stephen@epa.gov
Water Enforcement and Compliance Assurance Branch Chief **Dean Maraldo** . . . . (312) 353-2098
Wetlands and Watersheds Branch Chief
Peter Swenson . . . . (312) 886-0236
E-mail: swenson.peter@epa.gov

Region 6

1445 Ross Avenue, Suite 1200, Dallas, TX 75202-2733
Tel: (214) 665-2200 Tel: (214) 665-2118 (Environmental Protection Agency Region 6 Information Desk) Tel: (800) 887-6063 (Toll Free)
Internet: www.epa.gov/region6
Areas Covered: AR, LA, NM, OK, TX

○ Regional Administrator **Anne Idsal** . . . . (214) 665-2100
E-mail: Idsal.anne@Epa.gov
Education: Washington and Lee 2005 BA; Baylor 2010 JD
Secretary **Odessa Williams** . . . . (214) 665-2100
E-mail: williams.odessa@epa.gov
● Deputy Regional Administrator (Acting)
James McDonald . . . . (214) 665-2200
External Affairs Office Director **David W. Gray** . . . . (214) 665-2200
E-mail: gray.david@epa.gov

Office of Environmental Justice and International Affairs

Director **Arturo Blanco** . . . . (214) 665-3182
E-mail: blanco.arturo@epa.gov

Office of Environmental Justice and International Affairs *(continued)*

Deputy Director **Rhonda Smith** . . . . (214) 665-8006
E-mail: smith.rhonda@epa.gov

Office of Regional Counsel

Regional Counsel **James "Jim" Payne** . . . . (214) 665-8170
Note: On detail.
E-mail: payne.james@epa.gov
Regional Counsel (Acting) **Ben Harrison** . . . . (214) 665-2139
Note: On detail.
E-mail: harrison.ben@epa.gov
Deputy Regional Counsel (Acting) **Michael Barra** . . . . (214) 665-2143
E-mail: barra.michael@epa.gov
Deputy Regional Counsel for Enforcement
Cheryl Seager . . . . (214) 665-3114
E-mail: seager.cheryl@epa.gov
Multimedia Counseling Branch Chief
Suzanne J. Smith . . . . (214) 665-8027
E-mail: smith.suzanne@epa.gov
Pesticides and Toxics Enforcement Branch Chief
Michael Barra . . . . (214) 665-2143
E-mail: barra.michael@epa.gov
Superfund Branch Chief **Mark Peycke** . . . . (214) 665-2135
E-mail: peycke.mark@epa.gov
Water Enforcement Branch Chief **Scott P. McDonald** . . . . (214) 665-2718

Compliance Assurance and Enforcement Division

Director **John Blevins** . . . . (214) 665-2266
E-mail: blevins.john@epa.gov
Deputy Director (Acting) **Stephen A. "Steve" Gilrein** . . . (214) 665-8179
E-mail: gilrein.stephen@epa.gov
Associate Director **(Vacant)** . . . . (214) 665-7548
Air, Toxics and Inspection Coordination Branch Chief
Steve Thompson . . . . (214) 665-2769
E-mail: thompson.steve@epa.gov
Air Permitting Enforcement Section Chief
Darrin Larson . . . . (214) 665-7115
E-mail: larson.darrin@epa.gov
Toxics Enforcement Section Chief (Acting)
Margaret Osbourne . . . . (214) 665-6508
E-mail: osbourne.margaret@epa.gov
Surveillance Section Chief **Samuel "Sam" Tates** . . . . (214) 665-2243
E-mail: tates.samuel@epa.gov
Houston Surveillance Team **(Vacant)** . . . . (281) 983-2105
Hazardous Waste Enforcement Branch Chief
Mark Potts . . . . (214) 665-2723
E-mail: potts.mark@epa.gov
Compliance Enforcement Section Chief
Guy Tidmore . . . . (214) 665-3142
E-mail: tidmore.guy@epa.gov
Corrective Action and Compliance Inspection Section Chief **Troy Stuckey** . . . . (214) 665-6432
E-mail: stuckey.troy@epa.gov
Multimedia Enforcement Section Chief
Sunita Singhvi . . . . (214) 665-7290
E-mail: singhvi.sunita@epa.gov
Strategic Planning and Analyses Branch Chief
(Vacant) . . . . (214) 665-8126
Planning and Coordination Office **(Vacant)** . . . . (214) 665-6766
Water Enforcement Branch Chief **Jerry Saunders** . . . . (214) 665-6470
National Pollutant Discharge Elimination System (NPDES) Compliance Monitoring Section Chief
(Vacant) . . . . (214) 665-7521
NPDES Industrial and Municipal Section Chief
(Vacant) . . . . (214) 665-3145
Water Resources Section Chief **(Vacant)** . . . . (214) 665-8460

Criminal Investigations Division

Special Agent-in-Charge (Acting) **Daniel Pflaster** . . . . (214) 665-8488
E-mail: pflaster.dan@epa.gov

Management Division

Assistant Regional Administrator for Management (Acting) **James McDonald** . . . . (214) 665-3150
E-mail: mcdonald.james@epa.gov

(continued on next page)

★ Presidential Appointment Requiring Senate Confirmation ☆ Presidential Appointment ☐ Schedule C Appointment ◇ Career Senior Foreign Service Appointment
● Career Senior Executive Service (SES) Appointment ○ Non-Career Senior Executive Service (SES) Appointment ■ Postal Career Executive Service

Management Division *(continued)*

Deputy Director (Acting) **Troy C. Hill** . . . . (214) 665-6647
E-mail: hill.troy@epa.gov
Equal Employment Opportunity Officer
Olivia R. Balandran . . . . (214) 665-7257
E-mail: balandran.olivia-r@epa.gov
Enterprise Operations and Support Branch Chief
Verne McFarland . . . . (214) 665-6617
E-mail: mcfarland.verne@epa.gov
Environmental Services Branch Chief
David W. "Wes" McQuiddy . . . . (214) 665-6722
E-mail: mcquiddy.david@epa.gov
Human Resources Branch Chief **Ray Rodriguez** . . . . (214) 665-7477
E-mail: rodriguez.ray@epa.gov
Quality Assurance Officer **Donald Johnson** . . . . (214) 665-8343
Regional Comptroller **Regina Milbeck** . . . . (919) 541-3732
E-mail: milbeck.regina@epa.gov

Multimedia Planning and Permitting Division

Director **Wren Stenger** . . . . (214) 665-6583
E-mail: stenger.wren@epa.gov
Deputy Director **(Vacant)** . . . . (214) 665-8154
Associate Director for Air **(Vacant)** . . . . (214) 665-7548
Air Permits Section Chief **Jeffrey Robinson** . . . . (214) 665-6435
E-mail: robinson.jeffrey@epa.gov
Air Planning Section Chief **Guy Donaldson** . . . . (214) 665-7242
E-mail: donaldson.guy@epa.gov
Air Quality Analysis Section Chief **(Vacant)** . . . . (214) 665-2230
Air, State and Tribal Operations Section Chief
Mary A. Stanton . . . . (214) 665-8377
Associate Director for Pesticides, Toxics and UST
Steve Vargo . . . . (214) 665-2730
E-mail: vargo.steve@epa.gov
Air Monitoring and Grant Section Chief **(Vacant)** . . . . (214) 665-2172
Pesticides Section Chief **Craig Carroll** . . . . (214) 665-2220
E-mail: carroll.craig@epa.gov
Toxics Section Chief **Robert "Robbie" Snowbarger** . . . . (214) 665-7131
Associate Director for Resource Conservation and
Recovery Act **(Vacant)** . . . . (214) 665-8022
E-mail: spalding.susan@epa.gov
Corrective Action/Waste Minimization Section Chief
Melissa L. Smith . . . . (214) 665-7357
RCRA Permit Section Chief **Kishor Fruitwala** . . . . (214) 665-6669
RCRA Corrective Action Section Chief **Laurie King** . . . . . (214) 665-6771
Ecosystem Protection Branch/Watershed Management
Section Chief **Randall Rush** . . . . (214) 665-7107
E-mail: rush.randall@epa.gov
Strategic Planning/Information Management Section
Chief **(Vacant)** . . . . (214) 665-6750

Border Outreach Office

4050 Rio Bravo, Suite 100, El Paso, TX 79902

Director **Carlos Rincon** . . . . (214) 665-7273
E-mail: rincon.carlos@epa.gov
Regional Coordinator **(Vacant)** . . . . (214) 665-6787

Superfund Division

1445 Ross Avenue, Dallas, TX 75202-2733
Tel: (214) 665-6428 (24 hour Response and Prevention Hotline)

Director **Carl E. Edlund PE** . . . . (214) 665-8124
Education: Maryland BSME
Deputy Director **Pamela "Pam" Phillips** . . . . (214) 665-6701
Emergency Management Branch Chief
Ronnie Crossland . . . . (214) 665-2721
Planning and Prevention Team Leader
Monica C. Smith . . . . (214) 665-6780
E-mail: smith.monica@epa.gov
Oil and CERCLA Removals Section Chief
Chris Petersen . . . . (214) 665-3167
Oil Spills and Response Team Leader **Steve Mason** . . . . (214) 665-2276
Removal Site Section Leader **Susan Webster** . . . . (214) 665-6784
Remedial Branch Chief **John Meyer** . . . . (214) 665-6742
E-mail: meyer.john@epa.gov
Remedial Branch Deputy Branch Chief **(Vacant)** . . . . (214) 665-2197

Superfund Division *(continued)*

Community Involvement and Information Management
and Logistics Section Chief **(Vacant)** . . . . (214) 665-7205
Revitalization and Resources Branch Chief
Anthony "Tony" Talton . . . . (214) 665-7205
Brownfields Section Chief **Mary Kemp** . . . . (214) 665-8358
E-mail: kemp.mary@epa.gov
Community Involvement Team Leader **(Vacant)** . . . . (214) 665-8553
Contracts and Budget Section Chief **(Vacant)** . . . . (214) 665-3181
Information Management and Logistics Team Leader
Derek Ragon . . . . (214) 665-7362
E-mail: ragon.derek@epa.gov
Technical and Enforcement Branch Chief (Acting)
Ben Banipal . . . . (214) 665-7324
Deputy Associate Director, Technical and
Enforcement Branch **(Vacant)** . . . . (214) 665-6780
Enforcement Assessment Section Chief
Lydia Johnson . . . . (214) 665-8419
Risk and Site Assessment Section Chief
Christopher Villarreal . . . . (214) 665-6758
Education: Texas (San Antonio) 1989 BSCE

Water Quality Protection Division

77 West Jackson Boulevard, Chicago, IL 60604-3590
Tel: (214) 665-7101

Director **Charles Maguire** . . . . (214) 665-8138
Deputy Director **David Garcia** . . . . (214) 665-7593
Assistance Programs Branch Chief **Claudia Hosch** . . . . . . (214) 665-6464
State/Tribal Programs Section Chief **Curry Jones** . . . . . . (214) 665-6793
SRF and Projects Section Chief **Salvador Gandara** . . . . (214) 665-3194
Ecosystems Protection Branch Chief **(Vacant)** . . . . (214) 665-6653
Marine and Coastal Section Chief **Karen McCormick** . . . (214) 665-8365
Watershed Management Section Chief
Philip Crocker . . . . (214) 665-6644
Wetlands Section Chief **Maria Martinez** . . . . (214) 665-2230
NPDES Permits Associate Director **Stacey Dwyer** . . . . . . (214) 665-6729
E-mail: dwyer.stacey@epa.gov
Assessment Listing and TMDL Section Chief
Richard A. Wooster . . . . (214) 665-6473
Permits and Technical Assistance Section Chief
Brent Larsen . . . . (214) 665-7523
Permits and Oversight Section Chief **Paul Kaspar** . . . . . . (214) 665-7459
Sourcewater Protection Associate Director
James R. Brown . . . . (214) 665-3175
Drinking Water Section Chief **Blake Atkins** . . . . (214) 665-2297
Groundwater/UIC Section Chief **Philip Dellinger** . . . . . . (214) 665-8324

Region 7

11201 Renner Boulevard, Lenexa, KS 66219
Tel: (913) 551-7003
Tel: (913) 551-7999 (Criminal Investigation Division)
Tel: (314) 539-3422 (St. Louis, Criminal Investigation Division)
Internet: www.epa.gov/region07
Areas Covered: IA, KS, MO, NE

○ Regional Administrator **James B. "Jim" Gulliford** . . . . . . (913) 551-7546
Education: Iowa State 1973 BS, 1975 MS
Senior Advisor **Karen A. Flournoy** . . . . (913) 551-7882
E-mail: flournoy.karen@epa.gov
● Principal Deputy Regional Administrator
Edward H. Chu . . . . (913) 551-7003
● Deputy Regional Administrator **(Vacant)** . . . . (913) 551-7003
Executive Office Manager **Dana Peters** . . . . (913) 551-7444
Staff Coordinator **Julia Cacho** . . . . (913) 551-7071
E-mail: cacho.julia@epa.gov

Enforcement Coordination Office

11201 Renner Boulevard, Lenexa, KS 66219
Fax: (913) 551-7941

Director (Acting) **Althea Moses** . . . . (913) 551-7649
E-mail: Moses.althea@Epa.gov
Deputy Director **Althea Moses** . . . . (913) 551-7649
E-mail: moses.althea@epa.gov

★ Presidential Appointment Requiring Senate Confirmation ☆ Presidential Appointment □ Schedule C Appointment ◇ Career Senior Foreign Service Appointment
● Career Senior Executive Service (SES) Appointment ○ Non-Career Senior Executive Service (SES) Appointment ■ Postal Career Executive Service

Office of Public Affairs
11201 Renner Boulevard, Lenexa, KS 66219
Tel: (913) 551-7003 Fax: (913) 551-7066

Associate Regional Administrator for Media and Intergovernmental Relations **Curtis D. Carey PhD** ...... (913) 551-7506
E-mail: carey.curtis@epa.gov
Education: Regents BA; Oklahoma 2002 MA; Howard U PhD
Deputy Director **Angela Marie Brees** .... (913) 551-7940
E-mail: brees.angela@epa.gov

Office of Policy and Management
11201 Renner Boulevard, Lenexa, KS 66219
Tel: (913) 551-7003 Fax: (913) 551-7956

Director **Michael "Mike" Brincks** .... (913) 551-7653
E-mail: brincks.mike@epa.gov
Deputy Director **Ben A. Krehbiel** .... (913) 551-7106
E-mail: krehbiel.ben@epa.gov
Education: Troy State 1998 BS
Equal Employment Opportunity **Michael Butkovich** ..... (913) 551-7189
E-mail: butkovich.michael@epa.gov
Human Resources and Organizational Development Branch **Pat Price** .... (913) 551-7129
Resources and Financial Management Branch **Carla Koahler** .... (913) 551-7014
Safety, Infrastructure and Information Management Branch (Acting) **Eric Gibbs** .... (913) 551-7223 ext. 7192
Information Resources Management Section Chief **Raymond Booke** .... (913) 551-7120
E-mail: booke.raymond@epa.gov
Infrastructure Support Services Section Chief **(Vacant)** ... (913) 551-7144
MOVE Project Manager **Eric Gibbs** .... (913) 551-7223

Office of Regional Counsel
11201 Renner Boulevard, Lenexa, KS 66219
Tel: (800) 223-0425

Regional Counsel **David "Dave" Cozad** .... (913) 551-7587
E-mail: cozad.david@epa.gov
Deputy Regional Counsel **Leslie Humphrey** .... (913) 551-7227
E-mail: humphrey.leslie@epa.gov

Air and Waste Management Division
11201 Renner Boulevard, Lenexa, KS 66219
Tel: (913) 551-7122

Director **Rebecca "Becky" Weber** .... (913) 551-7487
E-mail: weber.rebecca@epa.gov
Deputy Director **John Smith** .... (913) 551-7845
E-mail: smith.john@epa.gov
Air Compliance and Enforcement Section Manager **Leslye Werner** .... (913) 551-7858
E-mail: werner.leslye@epa.gov
Air Permitting and Compliance Branch Manager **Mark Smith** .... (913) 551-7876
E-mail: smith.mark@epa.gov
Air Planning and Development Branch Manager **Michael "Mike" Jay** .... (913) 551-7460
E-mail: jay.michael@epa.gov
Chemical Risk Information Branch Manager **Scott Hayes** .... (913) 551-7936
E-mail: hayes.scott@epa.gov
Radiation, Asbestos, Lead and Indoor Program Branch **(Vacant)** .... (913) 551-7605
RCRA Corrective Actions and Permits Branch Manager **(Vacant)** .... (913) 551-7883
Waste Enforcement and Materials Management (WEMM) Branch Manager **(Vacant)** .... (913) 551-7446
Resource Conservation and Pollution Prevention Section (RCPP) Manager **James "Jim" Callier** .... (913) 551-7646
Storage Tanks and Oil Pollution Branch Manager **(Vacant)** .... (913) 551-7936

Environmental Services Division
Director **Cecilia Tapia** .... (913) 551-7733
E-mail: tapia.cecilia@epa.gov
Deputy Director **Joshua Tapp** .... (913) 551-7606
E-mail: tapp.joshua@epa.gov

Environmental Services Division *(continued)*

Assessment and Monitoring Branch **Michael Barn** .... (913) 551-7438
Chemical Analysis and Response Branch Chief **Michael F. Davis** .... (913) 551-5042
Analytical Services and Response Section Chief **Maggie St. Germaine** .... (913) 551-5266
Inorganic Chemistry Section Chief **(Vacant)** .... (913) 551-5097
Field Compliance Branch **Jeffrey Field** .... (913) 551-7432
Organic Chemistry Section Chief **Tabitha Atkins** .... (913) 551-5154

Superfund Division
11201 Renner Boulevard, Lenexa, KS 66219
Tel: (800) 223-0425

Director **Mary Peterson** .... (913) 551-7882
E-mail: peterson.mary@epa.gov
Deputy Director **Robert Jackson** .... (913) 551-7952
Emergency Response and Removal Branch (North) **Kenneth S. Buchholz** .... (913) 551-7473
Emergency Response and Removal Branch (South) **Scott Hayes** .... (913) 551-7670
E-mail: hayes.scott@epa.gov
Special Emphasis and Remedial Branch **Gene Gunn** ..... (913) 551-7776
E-mail: gunn.gene@epa.gov
Iowa/Nebraska Remedial **(Vacant)** .... (913) 551-7454
Missouri/Kansas Remedial Branch **(Vacant)** .... (913) 551-7548
Superfund Technical Assistance and Reuse Branch **Stanley Walker** .... (913) 551-7494
E-mail: walker.stanley@epa.gov

Water, Wetlands and Pesticides Division
11201 Renner Boulevard, Lenexa, KS 66219
Tel: (800) 223-0425

Director **Jeffery Robichaud** .... (913) 551-7146
E-mail: robichaud.jeffery@epa.gov
Deputy Director **(Vacant)** .... (913) 551-7146
Drinking Water Management Branch **Mary Tietjen-Mindrup** .... (913) 551-7431
Toxics and Pesticides Branch **Jamie Green** .... (913) 551-7139
E-mail: green.jamie@epa.gov
Waste Water and Infrastructure Management Branch **Glenn Curtis** .... (913) 551-7726
E-mail: curtis.glenn@epa.gov
Water Enforcement Branch **Diane Huffman** .... (913) 551-7544
E-mail: huffman.diane@epa.gov
Water Quality Management **(Vacant)** .... (913) 551-7821
Watershed Planning and Implementation Branch **Steve Kovac** .... (913) 551-7698

Region 8
1595 Wynkoop Street, Denver, CO 80202
Tel: (303) 312-6532 Fax: (303) 312-6882
Internet: www.epa.gov/region08
Areas Covered: CO, MT, ND, SD, UT, WY

○ Regional Administrator **Douglas H. Benevento** .... (303) 312-6532
E-mail: Benevento.douglas@Epa.gov
Education: Colorado 1988 BA; Johns Hopkins 1998 MA; Denver 2002 JD
Staff Assistant to the Regional Administrator **(Vacant)** .... (303) 312-6532
● Deputy Regional Administrator **Debra H. Thomas** ...... (303) 312-6532
E-mail: thomas.debra@epa.gov
Head Librarian **Caroline Williams** .... (303) 312-6299
E-mail: williams.caroline@epa.gov Fax: (303) 312-7061

Office of Communications and Public Involvement
1595 Wynkoop Street, Denver, CO 80202
Tel: (303) 312-6592 Fax: (303) 312-6961

Director **Andrew Mutter** .... (303) 312-6448
E-mail: mutter.andrew@epa.gov
Assistant Director **Richard Mylott** .... (303) 312-6654
E-mail: mylott.richard@epa.gov
Community Involvement (Acting) **Libby Faulk** .... (303) 312-6083
E-mail: faulk.libby@epa.gov

(continued on next page)

★ Presidential Appointment Requiring Senate Confirmation ☆ Presidential Appointment ☐ Schedule C Appointment ◇ Career Senior Foreign Service Appointment
● Career Senior Executive Service (SES) Appointment ○ Non-Career Senior Executive Service (SES) Appointment ■ Postal Career Executive Service

Office of Communications and Public Involvement *(continued)*

Congressional Relations **Rebecca Russo** .... (303) 312-6604
Congressional and Intergovernmental Liaison
Jody Ostendorf .... (303) 312-7814
Environmental Education **Wendy Dew** .... (303) 312-6605
E-mail: dew.wendy@epa.gov
Environmental Information Service Center/Library
Caroline Williams .... (303) 312-6312
E-mail: williams.caroline@epa.gov
Freedom of Information Act Officer **Alan Engels** .... (303) 312-6306
E-mail: engels.alan@epa.gov
Media Officer **Lisa McClain-Vanderpool** .... (303) 312-6077
E-mail: mcclain-vanderpool.lisa@epa.gov

INDEPENDENT AGENCIES

Office of Ecosystems Protection and Remediation

1595 Wynkoop Street, Denver, CO 80202
Tel: (303) 312-6598 Fax: (303) 312-6716

Assistant Regional Administrator **Betsy B. Smidinger** ... (303) 312-4017
E-mail: smidinger.betsy@epa.gov
Deputy Assistant Regional Administrator
Sandra Stavnes .... (303) 312-6117
E-mail: stavnes.sandra@epa.gov
Secretary **Nawodit "Noah" Gautam** .... (303) 312-7836
E-mail: gautam.nawodit@epa.gov
Program Analyst **Mandi Rodriguez** .... (303) 312-6697
Ecosystems Protection Program **Bert Garcia** .... (303) 312-6670
E-mail: garcia.bert@epa.gov
Federal On-Scene Coordinator **Joni Sandoval** .... (303) 312-6988
E-mail: sandoval.joni@epa.gov
Superfund Assessment, Emergency Response and
Preparedness Program **David Ostrander** .... (303) 312-6827
E-mail: ostrander.david@epa.gov
Superfund Remedial Response Program **Bill Murray** ..... (303) 312-6401
E-mail: murray.bill@epa.gov
Support Program **Russell LeClerc** .... (303) 312-6693
E-mail: leclerc.russell@epa.gov

Office of Enforcement, Compliance and Environmental Justice

1595 Wynkoop Street, Denver, CO 80202
Tel: (303) 312-6051 Fax: (303) 312-6409

• Assistant Regional Administrator **Kimberly Opekar** ...... (303) 312-6352
E-mail: opekar.kimberly@epa.gov
Secretary **Diane Moon** .... (303) 312-6051
E-mail: moon.diane@epa.gov
Deputy Assistant Regional Administrator **(Vacant)** .... (303) 312-6051
Legal Enforcement Program **Kenneth C. Schefski** .... (303) 312-6843
E-mail: schefski.kenneth@epa.gov
Air and Toxics Technical Enforcement Program
(Vacant) .... (303) 312-6206
Alternative Dispute Resolution Coordinator/Senior
Superfund Enforcement Specialist **Maureen O'Reilly** ... (303) 312-6402
CERCLA Response Cost Recovery **(Vacant)** .... (303) 312-6393
FIFRA/UIC/OPA Technical Enforcement Program
David Cobb .... (303) 312-6592
E-mail: cobb.david@epa.gov
NPDES Enforcement Unit **(Vacant)** .... (303) 312-6463
Policy, Information Management, and Environmental
Justice Program **Kimberly Opekar** .... (303) 312-6352
E-mail: opekar.kimberly@epa.gov
Regulatory Enforcement Unit **James Eppers** .... (303) 312-6917
E-mail: eppers.jim@epa.gov
Senior Enforcement Specialist/Civil Investigator
Mike Rudy .... (303) 312-6332
Water Technical Enforcement Program **Art Palomares** ... (303) 312-6053

Office of Partnership and Regulatory Assistance

1595 Wynkoop Street, Denver, CO 80202
Tel: (303) 312-6241 Fax: (303) 312-6064

Assistant Regional Administrator (Acting)
Darcy O'Connor .... (303) 312-6392
E-mail: oconnor.darcy@epa.gov
Deputy Assistant Regional Administrator **Bert Garcia** .... (303) 312-6670
E-mail: Garcia.bert@Epa.gov

Office of Partnership and Regulatory Assistance *(continued)*

Secretary **Debra Lucas** .... (303) 312-7028
E-mail: lucas.debra@epa.gov
Air Program **Carl Daly** .... (303) 312-6416
E-mail: daly.carl@epa.gov
Pollution Prevention Pesticides and Toxics Program
Melanie L. Wood .... (303) 312-7006
E-mail: wood.melaniel@epa.gov
State Partnerships and Sustainable Practices Program
(Acting) **Monica Morales** .... (303) 312-6936
E-mail: morales.monica@epa.gov
Resource Conservation and Recovery Program
Lauren Hammond .... (303) 312-7081
E-mail: Hammond.lauren@Epa.gov
Tribal Assistance Program **Callie Videtich** .... (303) 312-6434
E-mail: videtich.callie@epa.gov
Water Program **Bert Garcia** .... (303) 312-6670

Office of Regional Counsel

1595 Wynkoop Street, Denver, CO 80202
Tel: (303) 312-6890 Fax: (303) 312-6953

Regional Counsel **Kenneth C. Schefski** .... (303) 312-6843
E-mail: schefski.kenneth@epa.gov
Deputy Regional Counsel **Paul Logan** .... (303) 312-6854
E-mail: logan.paul@epa.gov
Deputy Regional Counsel **Elyana Sutin-McCeney** .... (303) 312-6899
E-mail: sutin.elyana@epa.gov
Secretary **Melissa Haniewicz** .... (303) 312-7059
E-mail: haniewicz.melissa@epa.gov
Regional Judicial Officer **Elyana Sutin-McCeney** .... (303) 312-6899
E-mail: sutin.elyana@epa.gov
Regional Hearing Clerk **Tina Artemis** .... (303) 312-6765
E-mail: artemis.tina@epa.gov
Employee Rights **Michael Gleason** .... (303) 312-6898
E-mail: gleason.michael@epa.gov

Office of Technical and Management Services

1595 Wynkoop Street, Denver, CO 80202
Tel: (303) 312-6300 Fax: (303) 312-6558

• Assistant Regional Administrator **Richard "Rick" Buhl** ... (303) 312-6920
E-mail: buhl.rick@epa.gov
Deputy Assistant Regional Administrator
Patrice Maureen Kortuem .... (303) 312-6150
E-mail: kortuem.patrice@epa.gov
Secretary **Melissa Haniewicz** .... (303) 312-7059
E-mail: haniewicz.melissa@epa.gov
Equal Employment Opportunity Program
Mario Merida .... (303) 312-6297
E-mail: merida.mario@epa.gov
Fiscal Management and Planning Program
Ben Bielenberg .... (303) 312-6771
E-mail: bielenberg.ben@epa.gov
Financial Management Unit **Joe Poetter** .... (303) 312-6186
E-mail: poetter.joe@epa.gov
Grants, Audits and Procurement Program **(Vacant)** .... (303) 312-6305
Human Resources Program **Mike Shanahan** .... (303) 312-6121
E-mail: shanahan.mike@epa.gov
Information Systems Program **Matt Duran** .... (303) 312-6921
E-mail: duran.matt@epa.gov
Infrastructure Program **(Vacant)** .... (303) 312-6074
Quality Assurance Program **Linda Himmelbauer** .... (303) 312-6020

Montana Operations Office

Federal Office Building, 301 South Park Avenue,
Drawer 10096, Helena, MT 59626-0096
Tel: (406) 457-5000

Director (Acting) **Debra H. Thomas** .... (303) 312-6532
E-mail: thomas.debrah@epa.gov Fax: (406) 457-5001
Secretary **Shawna Nelson** .... (406) 457-5002
E-mail: nelson.shawna@epa.gov
Superfund Unit **Carson Coate** .... (406) 457-5042
E-mail: Coate.carson@Epa.gov
Administration **Deb Clevenger** .... (406) 457-5004

★ Presidential Appointment Requiring Senate Confirmation ☆ Presidential Appointment □ Schedule C Appointment ◇ Career Senior Foreign Service Appointment
● Career Senior Executive Service (SES) Appointment ○ Non Career Senior Executive Service (SES) Appointment ■ Postal Career Executive Service

Region 9

75 Hawthorne Street, San Francisco, CA 94105-3901
Tel: (415) 947-8000 (Environmental Information Center)
TTY: (415) 744-1514 Fax: (415) 947-3588 E-mail: r9.info@epa.gov
Internet: www.epa.gov/region9
Areas Covered: AZ, CA, HI, NV, The Pacific Islands and Tribal Nations

○ Regional Administrator **Michael "Mike" Stoker** .... (415) 947-4235
E-mail: Stoker.michael@Epa.gov
Education: UC Berkeley BA; Loyola Law JD

● Deputy Regional Administrator **Deborah Jordan** .... (415) 972-3133
E-mail: jordan.deborah@epa.gov
Education: Kansas BSChE; UC Berkeley PhD

Regional Counsel **Sylvia Quast** .... (415) 947-3936
E-mail: quast.sylvia@epa.gov

Deputy Regional Counsel **(Vacant)** .... (415) 947-8705

Office of Public Affairs

75 Hawthorne Street, San Francisco, CA 94105-3920
Tel: (415) 947-8702

Director **Kelly Zito** .... (415) 947-8702
E-mail: zito.kelly@epa.gov

Associate Director (Acting) **William "Bill" Keener** .... (415) 947-3940
E-mail: keener.bill@epa.gov

Team Leader and Editor **Bonnie Barkett** .... (415) 947-4175
E-mail: barkett.bonnie@epa.gov

Air Division

75 Hawthorne Street, San Francisco, CA 94105-3920
Tel: (415) 947-8715

Director (Acting) **Elizabeth Adams** .... (415) 972-3183
E-mail: adams.eizabeth@Epa.gov

Deputy Director **Elizabeth Adams** .... (415) 972-3183
E-mail: adams.elizabeth@epa.gov

Land Division

75 Hawthorne Street, San Francisco, CA 94105-3920
Tel: (415) 947-8704

Director **Jeffrey B. Scott** .... (415) 972-3311
E-mail: scott.jeff@epa.gov

Deputy Director **Bridget Coyle** .... (415) 947-4286
E-mail: coyle.bridget@epa.gov

Tribal Liaison **Laura Ebbert** .... (415) 947-3561

Enforcement Division

75 Hawthorne Street, San Francisco, CA 94105-3920
Tel: (415) 972-3873

Director **Kathleen Johnson** .... (415) 972-4288
E-mail: johnson.kathleen@epa.gov

Environmental Management Division

75 Hawthorne Street, San Francisco, CA 94105-3920
Tel: (415) 947-8706

Assistant Regional Administrator **Kerry Drake** .... (415) 947-8706
E-mail: Drake.kerry@Epa.gov

Deputy Director **(Vacant)** .... (415) 972-3016

Superfund Division

75 Hawthorne Street, San Francisco, CA 94105-3920
Tel: (415) 947-8709

Director **Enrique Manzanilla** .... (415) 972-3843
E-mail: manzanilla.enrique@epa.gov

Deputy Director **(Vacant)** .... (415) 947-8709

Water Division

75 Hawthorne Street, San Francisco, CA 94105-3920
Tel: (415) 947-8707

Director **Tomás Torres** .... (415) 972-3275

Deputy Director **Kristin Gullatt** .... (415) 972-3432

Associate Director **Michael Montgomery** .... (415) 972-3438

Associate Director **Nancy Woo** .... (415) 972-3409

Region 10

1200 Sixth Avenue, Suite 900, Seattle, WA 98101-1128
Tel: (206) 553-1200 Tel: (800) 424-4372 (AK, ID, OR, WA)
Fax: (206) 553-0059 E-mail: epa-seattle@epa.gov
Internet: www.epa.gov/region10
Areas Covered: AK, ID, OR, WA

○ Regional Administrator **Chris Hladick** .... (206) 553-1234
Education: Eastern Illinois BS

● Deputy Regional Administrator **Michelle Pirzadeh** .... (206) 553-1272
E-mail: pirzadeh.michelle@epa.gov

Executive Assistant to the Deputy Regional Administrator **Linda Erikson** .... (206) 553-1191
E-mail: erikson.linda@epa.gov

Executive Assistant to the Deputy Regional Administrator **(Vacant)** .... (206) 553-0290

Policy Advisor **Bill Dunbar** .... (206) 553-1019
E-mail: dunbar.bill@epa.gov

Public Affairs Director **Marianne Holsman** .... (206) 553-1237
E-mail: holsman.marianne@epa.gov

Special Assistant **Kendra Tyler** .... (206) 553-0041
E-mail: tyler.kendra@epa.gov

Executive Office Manager **Matthew Magorrian** .... (206) 553-6284
E-mail: magorrian.matthew@epa.gov

Senior Tribal Policy Advisor **(Vacant)** .... (206) 553-2871

Office of Compliance and Enforcement

1200 Sixth Avenue, Suite 900, Seattle, WA 98101-1128
Tel: (202) 564-2220 Fax: (206) 553-7176

Director **Edward Kowalski** .... (206) 553-4198
E-mail: kowalski.edward@epa.gov

Associate Director **Lauris Davies** .... (206) 553-2857
E-mail: davies.lauris@epa.gov

Office of Regional Counsel

1200 Sixth Avenue, Mail Stop ORC-158, Seattle, WA 98101-1128
Tel: (206) 553-2456 Fax: (206) 553-0163

Regional Counsel **Allyn Stern** .... (206) 553-1223
E-mail: stern.allyn@epa.gov

Deputy Regional Counsel **Lisa Castanon** .... (206) 553-0464
E-mail: castanon.lisa@epamail.epa.gov

Office of Air, Waste and Toxics

1200 Sixth Avenue, Mail Stop AWT-107, Seattle, WA 98101-1128
Tel: (206) 553-1266 Fax: (206) 553-8509

Director **Janis Hastings** .... (206) 553-1582
E-mail: hastings.janis@epa.gov

Associate Director **(Vacant)** .... (206) 553-1582

Physical Scientist **Jerrold "Jay" McAlpine** .... (206) 553-0094

Office of Ecosystems, Tribal and Public Affairs

1200 Sixth Avenue, Mail Stop ETPA-086, Seattle, WA 98101-1128
Tel: (206) 553-1901 Fax: (206) 553-6984

Director **David Allnutt** .... (206) 553-2581
E-mail: allnutt.david@epamail.epa.gov

Deputy Director **Linda Anderson-Carnahan** .... (206) 553-2601
E-mail: anderson-carnahan.linda@epamail.epa.gov

Associate Director **(Vacant)** .... (206) 553-2601

Office of Environmental Assessment

1200 Sixth Avenue, Mail Stop OEA-095, Seattle, WA 98101-1128
Tel: (206) 553-2146 Fax: (206) 553-0119

Director **David Allnutt** .... (206) 553-2581
E-mail: allnut.david@epamail.gov

Associate Director **Ann Williamson** .... (206) 553-2739
E-mail: williamson.ann@epa.gov

Office of Environmental Cleanup

1200 Sixth Avenue, Mail Stop ECL-117, Seattle, WA 98101-1128
Tel: (206) 553-1090 Fax: (206) 553-0124

Director **Sheryl Bilbrey** .... (206) 553-2957
E-mail: bilbrey.sheryl@epamail.epa.gov

Associate Director **Sheila Fleming** .... (206) 553-1417
E-mail: fleming.sheila@epamail.epa.gov

INDEPENDENT AGENCIES

★ Presidential Appointment Requiring Senate Confirmation ☆ Presidential Appointment □ Schedule C Appointment ◇ Career Senior Foreign Service Appointment
● Career Senior Executive Service (SES) Appointment ○ Non-Career Senior Executive Service (SES) Appointment ■ Postal Career Executive Service

Office of Management Programs
1200 Sixth Avenue, Mail Stop OMP-147, Seattle, WA 98101-1128
Tel: (206) 553-1233 Fax: (206) 553-6647

Director **Nancy Lindsay** .... (206) 553-0275
E-mail: lindsay.nancy@epamail.epa.gov
Associate Director **Tim Hamlin** .... (206) 553-1563
E-mail: hamlin.tim@epa.gov

Office of Water and Watersheds
1200 Sixth Avenue, Mail Stop OWW-135, Seattle, WA 98101-1128
Tel: (206) 553-1643 Fax: (206) 553-0165 Fax: (206) 553-1280

Director **Daniel Opalski** .... (206) 553-1855
Associate Director **(Vacant)** .... (206) 553-1906
Senior Policy Advisor **John Palmer** .... (206) 553-6521
E-mail: palmer.john@epa.gov

Alaska Operations Office
Federal Building, 222 West Seventh Avenue, Unit 19,
Room 537, Mail Stop AOO/A, Anchorage, AK 99513-7588
Tel: (907) 271-5083 Fax: (907) 271-3424

Director **Dianne Soderlund** .... (907) 271-3425
E-mail: soderlund.dianne@epamail.epa.gov

Idaho Operations Office
1435 North Orchard Street, Mail Stop IOO, Boise, ID 83706
Tel: (208) 378-5750 Fax: (208) 378-5744

Idaho Operations Office Director
James "Jim" Werntz .... (208) 378-5743
E-mail: werntz.james@epa.gov
Management Analyst **(Vacant)** .... (208) 378-5750

Oregon Operations Office
808 SW Broadway, Portland, OR 97205
Tel: (503) 326-3250 Fax: (503) 326-3399

Director **Anthony Barber** .... (503) 326-6890
E-mail: barber.anthony@epa.gov

Washington Operations Office
300 Desmond Drive, SE, Suite 102, Mail Stop WOO, Lacey, WA 98503
Tel: (360) 753-9437 Fax: (360) 753-8080

Washington Operations Office Director
Lucy Edmondson .... (360) 753-9082
E-mail: edmondson.lucy@epamail.epa.gov

Office of Civil Rights
William Jefferson Clinton Federal Building,
1200 Pennsylvania Avenue, NW, Washington, DC 20460
Fax: (202) 501-1836 Internet: www.epa.gov/civilrights

Area Offices

Area Office of Civil Rights – Cincinnati (OH)
26 West Martin Luther King Drive, Cincinnati, OH 45268
Tel: (513) 569-7941 Fax: (513) 569-7530

Area Director **Letitia V. "Tish" Newland** .... (513) 569-7913
E-mail: newland.letitia@epa.gov

Area Office of Civil Rights – Research Triangle Park (NC)
USEPA Area Office of Civil Rights, (C639-05),
Research Triangle Park, NC 27711
Tel: (919) 541-4249 Fax: (919) 541-0847

Area Director **Norwood Dennis** .... (919) 541-4249
E-mail: dennis.norwood@epa.gov

Office of the Chief Financial Officer
1200 Pennsylvania Avenue, NW, Washington, DC 20460
Tel: (202) 564-1151 Fax: (202) 501-0771 E-mail: ocfoinfo@epa.gov

Office of E-Enterprise
Ronald Reagan Building, 1300 Pennsylvania Avenue, NW,
Washington, DC 20004
Fax: (202) 564-0164

Cincinnati Finance Center
26 West Martin Luther King Drive, Mail Stop 002, Cincinnati, OH 45268
Tel: (513) 487-2080 Fax: (513) 487-2063

Director **Molly C. Williams** .... (513) 487-2076

Las Vegas (NV) Finance Center
P.O. Box 98515, Las Vegas, NV 89193-8515
Tel: (702) 798-2485 Fax: (702) 798-2423

Director **Dany Lavergne** .... (702) 798-2483

Research Triangle Park – Financial Management Center
109 T.W. Alexander Drive, Mail Code D143-02, Durham, NC 27711
Tel: (919) 541-3500 Fax: (919) 541-3055

Director **(Vacant)** .... (919) 541-3500

Office of Inspector General
William Jefferson Clinton Federal Building,
1200 Pennsylvania Avenue, NW, Mail Code 2410T,
Washington, DC 20460
Tel: (202) 566-2391 Fax: (202) 566-0857

Regional Offices

Northeastern Resource Center
290 Broadway, Room 1520, New York, NY 10007-1865
Tel: (212) 637-3041 Fax: (212) 637-3071
Areas Covered: CT, ME, MA, NH, NJ, NY, PR, RI, VT, VI

Manager **Lauretta Joseph** .... (212) 637-3049
Management Analyst **Eleanor Burrus** .... (212) 637-3041
E-mail: burrus.eleanor@epa.gov

Investigations - Northeastern Resource Center

Boston (MA) Investigations Branch
One Congress Street, Boston, MA 02114
Tel: (617) 918-1470 Fax: (617) 918-1469

Team Leader **Jeffrey Yung** .... (617) 918-1466
E-mail: yung.jeffrey@epa.gov

Washington (DC) Branch
2733 South Crystal Drive, SUite 4710, Arlington, VA 22202
Tel: (703) 347-8747 Fax: (202) 566-0915

Special Agent-in-Charge **Thomas Muskett** .... (202) 566-0432

Eastern Resource Center
EPA, OIG, 1650 Arch Street, Mail Stop 3A100,
Philadelphia, PA 19103-2029
Tel: (215) 814-5800 Fax: (215) 814-2351

Eastern Resource Center Director **Patrick J. Milligan** .... (215) 814-2326
E-mail: milligan.patrick@epa.gov
Administrative Office Coordinator **(Vacant)** .... (215) 814-2329

Audits - Eastern Resource Center
Areas Covered: DE, DC, MD, PA, VA, WV

Research Triangle Park (NC) Audit Branch
Research Triangle Park, NC 27711
Tel: (919) 541-1028 Fax: (919) 541-2504

Director **James "Jim" Hatfield** .... (919) 541-1030
E-mail: Hatfield.jim@Epa.gov

★ Presidential Appointment Requiring Senate Confirmation ☆ Presidential Appointment ☐ Schedule C Appointment ◇ Career Senior Foreign Service Appointment
● Career Senior Executive Service (SES) Appointment ○ Non-Career Senior Executive Service (SES) Appointment ■ Postal Career Executive Service

Investigations - Eastern Resource Center

Atlanta (GA) Office
OIG Central Investigating Branch, 61 Forsyth Street, SW, 16th Floor, Atlanta, GA 30303
Tel: (404) 562-9862 Fax: (404) 562-9856

Special Agent-in-Charge **Sean Earle** .... (404) 562-9865
E-mail: Earle.sean@Epa.gov
Program Assistant **(Vacant)** .... (404) 962-9862

Research Triangle Park (NC) Branch
USEPA Mailroom, N283-01, Research Triangle Park, NC 27711
Tel: (919) 541-0517

Special Agent-in-Charge (Acting) **Jerry Polk** .... (919) 541-0517
E-mail: polk.jerry@epa.gov
Resident Agent-in-Charge **Jerry Polk** .... (919) 541-0517
E-mail: polk.jerry@epa.gov

Chicago Field Office
77 West Jackson Boulevard, 13th Floor, Mail Stop IA-13J, Chicago, IL 60604-3507
Tel: (312) 353-2503 Fax: (312) 353-4225

Director, Contracts and Assistance Agreement Audits
Janet Kasper .... (312) 886-3059
E-mail: kasper.janet@epa.gov
Secretary **(Vacant)** .... (312) 886-4033

Audits - Central Resource Center

Cincinnati (OH) Branch
26 West Martin Luther King Drive, Cincinnati, OH 45268
Tel: (513) 487-2365

Lead Auditor **Leah L. Nikaidoh** .... (513) 487-2365
E-mail: nikaidoh.leah@epa.gov

Dallas (TX) Branch
1445 Ross Avenue, Suite 1200, Dallas, TX 75202-2733
Tel: (214) 665-6620

Lead Auditor **Randy Holthaus** .... (214) 665-6620
E-mail: holthaus.randy@epa.gov

Investigations - Central Resource Center
77 West Jackson Boulevard, 13th Floor (II-13J), Chicago, IL 60604
Tel: (312) 353-2507 Fax: (312) 353-3220

Special Agent-in-Charge **(Vacant)** .... (312) 353-3219
Program Assistant **Beverly K. Lampkin** .... (312) 353-2507
E-mail: lampkin.beverly@epa.gov

Western Resource Center
75 Hawthorne Street, Mail Stop IGA-1, San Francisco, CA 94105
Tel: (415) 947-4520 Fax: (415) 947-4540
Areas Covered: AK, AZ, CA, HI, ID, NV, OR, WA

Audits - Western Resource Center

Denver (CO) Audits Branch
1595 Wynkoop Street, 4th Floor, Denver, CO 80202
Tel: (303) 312-6969

Manager **Patrick Gilbride** .... (303) 312-6969
E-mail: gilbride.patrick@epa.gov Fax: (303) 312-6063

San Francisco (CA) Audits Branch
75 Hawthorne Street, Mail Stop IGA-1, San Francisco, CA 94105-3920
Tel: (415) 947-4502 Fax: (415) 947-4540

Director **(Vacant)** .... (415) 947-4521
Secretary **(Vacant)** .... (415) 947-4521

Seattle (WA) Audits Branch
1200 Sixth Avenue, Suite 1920, Mail Stop OIG-195, Seattle, WA 98101

Manager **Madeline Mullen** .... (206) 553-4032
E-mail: mullen.madeline@epamail.epa.gov

Investigations - Western Resource Center

Denver (CO) Investigations Branch
1595 Wynkoop Street, 4th Floor, Denver, CO 80202
Tel: (303) 312-6815 Fax: (303) 312-7088

Resident Agent-in-Charge **Daniel Hawthorne** .... (303) 312-6815
E-mail: hawthorne.daniel@epa.gov

San Francisco (CA) Investigations Office
75 Hawthorne Street, 7th Floor, IGI-1, San Francisco, CA 94105-3920
Tel: (415) 947-4500 Fax: (415) 947-4511
Areas Covered: AK, AZ, CA, CO, HI, ID, MT, NV, ND, OR, SD, UT, WA, WY; American Samoa, Marianas Islands, Palau

Special Agent-in-Charge **Joseph Gonzales** .... (206) 553-2590
Special Agent **Victoria Schwarz** .... (415) 947-4503
Special Agent **Jessica Knight** .... (415) 947-4542
E-mail: knight.jessica@epa.gov
Office Manager **(Vacant)** .... (415) 972-3842

Seattle (WA) Investigations Branch
1200 Sixth Street, Suite 1920, Mail Stop OIG-195, Seattle, WA 98101-3123
Tel: (206) 553-1273 Fax: (206) 553-6225

Special Agent **Sanchai Dean** .... (206) 553-1273
E-mail: dean.sanchai@epamail.epa.gov
Special Agent **Brian Scriver** .... (206) 553-2543
E-mail: scriver.brian@epa.gov
Special Agent **(Vacant)** .... (206) 553-2590
Chemist **Bruce Woods PhD** .... (206) 553-6224

Office of Administration and Resources Management (OARM)
William Jefferson Clinton Federal Building, 1200 Pennsylvania Avenue, NW, Washington, DC 20460
Tel: (202) 564-4600

Office of Acquisition Management
William Jefferson Clinton Federal Building, 1200 Pennsylvania Avenue, NW, Mail Code 3801 R, Washington, DC 20460
Tel: (202) 564-4310 Fax: (202) 565-2473

Procurement Operations Division (Cincinnati)
26 West Martin Luther King Drive, Mail Stop NWD-001, Cincinnati, OH 45268
Fax: (513) 487-2004

Director (Acting) **Lisa M. Stultz** .... (513) 487-2015
E-mail: stultz.lisa@epa.gov
Assistant Director **Pamela Legare** .... (513) 487-2015
E-mail: legare.pamela@epa.gov
Office of Research and Development Service Center Manager **Kathleen "Kathy" Roe** .... (513) 487-2144
E-mail: roe.kathleen@epa.gov
Office of Water Service Center Manager
Lisa M. Stultz .... (513) 487-2041
E-mail: stultz.lisa@epa.gov
Specialized Service Center Manager
H. David "Dave" Hincks .... (513) 487-2146
E-mail: hincks.dave@epa.gov
Small Business Specialist **(Vacant)** .... (513) 487-2126

Procurement Operations Division (Research Triangle Park)
109 T.W. Alexander Drive, Room E105-02, Research Triangle Park, NC 27711
Fax: (919) 541-0611

Director **Rodney-Daryl Jones** Room E110D .... (919) 541-3112
E-mail: jones.rodney-daryl@epa.gov
Administrative Officer **(Vacant)** Room E110E .... (919) 541-3044
Office of Administration and Resources Management/Research Triangle Park Management Service Center Manager
Lauranne M. Vogel Room D140D .... (919) 541-2311
E-mail: vogel.lauranne@epa.gov

(continued on next page)

★ Presidential Appointment Requiring Senate Confirmation ☆ Presidential Appointment □ Schedule C Appointment ◇ Career Senior Foreign Service Appointment
● Career Senior Executive Service (SES) Appointment ○ Non-Career Senior Executive Service (SES) Appointment ■ Postal Career Executive Service

Procurement Operations Division (Research Triangle Park) *(continued)*

Office of Air and Radiation Service Center Manager **(Vacant)** Room E120D . . . . (919) 541-4364

Office of Research and Development Service Center Manager **Christopher M. Baker** Room D140I . . . . (919) 541-2501
E-mail: baker.christopher@epa.gov

Small Business Specialist **(Vacant)** Room E110C . . . . (919) 541-2249

Office of Administration and Resources Management (Cincinnati)

26 West Martin Luther King Drive, Cincinnati, OH 45268
Fax: (513) 569-7903

● Director **Richard L. "Rick" Carter** Room 243 . . . . (513) 569-7910
E-mail: carter.rick@epa.gov

Deputy Director (Acting) **Debbie Young** Room 244 . . . . (513) 569-7544
E-mail: Young.debbie@Epa.gov

Secretary **Roxanne Hubig** Room 244 . . . . (513) 569-7858
E-mail: hubig.roxanne@epa.gov

Facilities Management and Services Division Director **Terry Brothers** Room 263 . . . . (513) 569-7902
Fax: (513) 569-7545

Program Management Analyst **Almethyist Abercrombie** Room 291-B . . . . (513) 569-7751
E-mail: abercrombie.almethyist@epa.gov

Headquarters Operations Branch Chief **Lori Carter** . . . . (513) 569-7382
E-mail: Carter.lori@Epa.gov

Human Resources Management Division Director **Jerome Bonner** Room 275 . . . . (513) 569-7950
E-mail: bonner.jerome@epa.gov Fax: (513) 569-7826

Human Resources Management Division Deputy Director **(Vacant)** . . . . (513) 569-7818

Information Resources Management Division Director **Vique Caro** Room 290 . . . . (513) 569-7912
E-mail: caro.vique@epa.gov

Regional Operations Branch Chief **(Vacant)** . . . . (513) 569-7408

Employee Benefits Services Branch Chief **Sue Mairose** . . . . (513) 569-7951

Office of Administration and Resources Management (Research Triangle Park)

109 T.W. Alexander Drive, Research Triangle Park, NC 27711
Fax: (919) 541-3552

● Director **Arron Helm** . . . . (919) 541-2258
E-mail: helm.arron@epa.gov

● Deputy Director **Benjamin "BJ" Collins** Room C601D . . . . (919) 541-5515
E-mail: collins.bj@epa.gov

Chief of Staff **(Vacant)** Room C665-D . . . . (202) 564-4600

Executive Assistant **(Vacant)** Room C601B . . . . (919) 541-7516

Facility Management and Support Division Director **Shawn Lafferty** Room C611-C . . . . (919) 541-5449

Human Resources Management Division Deputy Director **Jeremy Taylor** Room C635-E . . . . (919) 541-0537
E-mail: taylor.jeremy@epa.gov Fax: (919) 541-1360

Information Services Division Director **Myra Ezell** Room C605-J . . . . (919) 541-9408
E-mail: ezell.myra@epa.gov

Human Resources Management Division Deputy Director **(Vacant)** . . . . (919) 541-2249

Facility Operations Branch Chief **Timothy McClellan** . . . . (919) 541-2963

Facility Operations Branch Chief **Greg Eades** . . . . (919) 541-3099

Support Services Branch Chief **Dustin Riego** . . . . (919) 541-1426
E-mail: dustin.riego@epa.gov

Office of Human Resources

William Jefferson Clinton Federal Building,
1200 Pennsylvania Avenue, NW, Washington, DC 20460
Tel: (202) 564-4606 Fax: (202) 564-4613

Regional Centers

Cincinnati Shared Service Center

26 West Martin Luther King Drive, Cincinnati, OH 45268
Tel: (513) 569-7700 Fax: (513) 569-7826

Human Resources Officer **Richard L. "Rick" Carter** . . . . (513) 569-7910
E-mail: carter.rick@epa.gov

Las Vegas Shared Service Center

Building A, 4220 South Maryland Parkway,
Suite 100, Las Vegas, NV 89119
Tel: (702) 798-2401 Fax: (702) 798-2416

Director **Lizabeth Engebretson** . . . . (702) 798-2432
E-mail: engebretson.lizabeth@epa.gov

Headquarters Operations Branch Chief **Darrel Collier** . . . . (702) 646-8931

Regional Operations Branch Chief **Chonette R. Taylor-Smith** . . . . (702) 798-2444

Employee Services Branch Chief **Elaine Jimenez** . . . . (702) 798-2402

Research Triangle Park Shared Service Center

Research Triangle Park, NC 27711
Tel: (919) 541-2201 Fax: (919) 541-1360

Director **Jeremy Taylor** . . . . (919) 541-0537
E-mail: taylor.jeremy@epa.gov

Deputy Director **Ryan Atkinson** . . . . (919) 541-2425
E-mail: atkinson.ryan@epa.gov

Office of Air and Radiation (OAR)

William Jefferson Clinton Federal Building,
1200 Pennsylvania Avenue, NW, Washington, DC 20460
Tel: (202) 564-7400 Fax: (202) 501-0394

Office of Radiation and Indoor Air (ORIA)

1310 L Street, NW, Washington, DC 20005
Fax: (202) 343-2395

National Analytical Radiation Environmental Laboratory

540 South Morris Avenue, Montgomery, AL 36115-2601
Fax: (334) 270-3450

Director **John G. Griggs** . . . . (334) 270-3401
E-mail: griggs.john@epa.gov

Secretary **Charlotte S. Andress** . . . . (334) 270-3402
E-mail: andress.charlotte@epa.gov

Deputy Director **Michael Clark** . . . . (334) 270-3404

Center for Environmental Analytical Laboratory Science Director **Cynthia "Cindy" White** . . . . (334) 270-7052
E-mail: white.cindy@epa.gov

Center for Environmental Monitoring Director **Samuel "Sam" Poppell** . . . . (334) 270-3414
E-mail: Poppell.sam@Epa.gov

National Center for Radiation Field Operations

Building C, 4220 South Maryland Parkway, Las Vegas, NV 89119
P.O. Box 98517, Las Vegas, NV 89193-8517
Fax: (702) 784-8201

Director **Edward Wilds** . . . . (702) 784-8220
E-mail: wilds.edward@epa.gov

Secretary **Shirley T. Campagna** . . . . (702) 784-8224

Deputy Director **Andrea M. Stafford** . . . . (702) 784-8203
E-mail: stafford.andrea@epa.gov

Center for Radiation Preparedness and Response (CRPR) Director **Jeremy Johnson** . . . . (702) 784-8334
E-mail: johnson.jeremy@epa.gov

Center for Planning and Training (CPT) Director **Ken Yale** . . . . (702) 784-8314
E-mail: Yale.kenneth@Epa.gov

Safety Director **Paul J. Weeden** . . . . (702) 798-2301

★ Presidential Appointment Requiring Senate Confirmation ☆ Presidential Appointment □ Schedule C Appointment ◇ Career Senior Foreign Service Appointment
● Career Senior Executive Service (SES) Appointment ○ Non-Career Senior Executive Service (SES) Appointment ■ Postal Career Executive Service

Office of Enforcement and Compliance Assurance (OECA)
William Jefferson Clinton Federal Building,
1200 Pennsylvania Avenue, NW, Washington, DC 20460
Tel: (202) 564-2440 Fax: (202) 501-3842

Office of Criminal Enforcement, Forensics and Training (OCEFT)
William Jefferson Clinton Federal Building,
1200 Pennsylvania Avenue, NW, Room 1215, Washington, DC 20460
Fax: (202) 501-0599

Criminal Investigation Division
William Jefferson Clinton Building, 1200 Pennsylvania Avenue, NW,
Room 1230, Washington, DC 20460
Fax: (202) 501-0540

Region I
Boston (MA) Area Office
5 Post Office Square, 15th Floor, Suite 100, CID15-2,
Boston, MA 02109-3912
Tel: (617) 918-2300 Fax: (617) 918-2301

Special Agent-in-Charge **Tyler Amon** .... (617) 918-2010
E-mail: amon.tyler@epa.gov
Assistant Special Agent-in-Charge **John Gauthier** .... (617) 918-2345
E-mail: gauthier.john@epa.gov
Administrative Specialist **Vanessa Williams** .... (617) 918-2303
E-mail: williams.vanessa@epa.gov

Region II
New York (NY) Area Office
290 Broadway, Room 1551, New York, NY 10007-1866
Tel: (212) 637-3622 Fax: (212) 637-3602

Special Agent-in-Charge **Vernesa Jones-Allen** .... (212) 637-3622
E-mail: jones-allen.vernesa@epa.gov
Assistant Special Agent-in-Charge **Tara Donn** .... (212) 637-3627
E-mail: donn.tara@epa.gov

Region III
Philadelphia (PA) Area Office
1650 Arch Street, Philadelphia, PA 19103-2029
Tel: (215) 814-2360 Fax: (215) 814-2383

Special Agent-in-Charge (Acting) **Jennifer Lynn** .... (215) 814-2362
E-mail: lynn.jennifer@epa.gov
Assistant Special Agent-in-Charge **Jennifer Lynn** .... (215) 814-2790
E-mail: lynn.jennifer@epa.gov

Region IV
Atlanta (GA) Area Office
Atlanta Federal Center, 61 Forsyth Street SW,
Suite 16T90, Atlanta, GA 30303
Tel: (404) 562-9795 Tel: (800) 241-1754 Fax: (404) 562-9800

Special Agent-in-Charge (Acting)
Andres "Andy" Castro .... (404) 562-9815
E-mail: castro.andy@epa.gov
Assistant Special Agent-in-Charge (Acting)
Chris Aiello .... (404) 562-8734
E-mail: aiello.chris@epa.gov
Assistant Special Agent-in-Charge
Andres "Andy" Castro .... (404) 562-9815
E-mail: castro.andy@epa.gov

National Computer Forensics Laboratory
701 San Marco Boulevard, Suite 7-West, Jacksonville, FL 32207
Tel: (904) 899-5220 Fax: (904) 899-5221

Assistant Special Agent in Charge **William Fortuno** ..... (904) 899-5220
E-mail: fortuno.william@epa.gov

Region V
Chicago (IL) Area Office
300 South Riverside Plaza, Suite 1970 South, Chicago, IL 60606
Mail: 77 West Jackson Boulevard, Mail Code N19R, Chicago, IL 60606
Tel: (312) 886-9872 Tel: (800) 621-8431 Fax: (312) 886-1518

Special Agent-in-Charge **(Vacant)** .... (312) 886-9874
Assistant Special Agent-in-Charge **Brad Ostendorf** ...... (440) 202-4437
E-mail: Ostendorf.brad@Epa.gov

Region VI
Dallas (TX) Area Office
1445 Ross Avenue, Suite 1200, Mail Code 6CID, Dallas, TX 75202-2733
Tel: (214) 665-6600 Tel: (800) 887-6063 Fax: (214) 665-7449

Special Agent-in-Charge **(Vacant)** .... (214) 665-6600

Region VII
Kansas City (KS) Area Office
901 North Fifth Street, Kansas City, KS 66101
Fax: (913) 551-7891 Tel: (913) 551-7999

Special Agent-in-Charge **Michael Burnett** .... (913) 551-7990
E-mail: burnett.michael@epa.gov
Resident Agent in Charge **Kenneth Jamison** .... (314) 539-3422
1222 Spruce Street, Fax: (314) 539-3423
2.102, St. Louis, MO 63103
E-mail: jamison.kenneth@epa.gov

Region VIII
Denver (CO) Area Office
1595 Wynkoop Street, 8-CID, Denver, CO 80202
Tel: (303) 312-6134 Fax: (303) 312-6517

Special Agent-in-Charge **(Vacant)** .... (303) 312-6134
Assistant Special Agent-in-Charge **(Vacant)** .... (303) 312-6134

Region IX
San Francisco (CA) Area Office
75 Hawthorne Street, 7th Floor, Mail Code CID-1,
San Francisco, CA 94105-3901
Tel: (415) 947-8713 Fax: (415) 947-4559

Special Agent-in-Charge **Jay M. Green** .... (415) 947-4560
E-mail: green.jay-m@epa.gov
Assistant Special Agent-in-Charge **Scot Adair** .... (415) 947-4549
E-mail: adair.scot@epa.gov
Administrative Specialist **Jeanette Cordero** .... (415) 947-8713
E-mail: cordero.jeanette@epa.gov

Region X
Seattle (WA) Area Office
1200 Sixth Avenue, Mail Code CID-073, Seattle, WA 98101-9797
Tel: (206) 553-8306

Special Agent-in-Charge **Jeanne Proctor PhD** .... (206) 553-2913
E-mail: proctor.jeanne@epamail.epa.gov
Administrative Specialist **Lisa Marie Nakamura** .... (206) 553-0511
E-mail: nakamura.lisamarie@epa.gov

National Enforcement Investigations Center Division
PO Box 25227, Denver Federal Center Building 25, Denver, CO 80225
Tel: (303) 462-9000

Director **Erica Canzler** .... (303) 462-9003
E-mail: canzler.erica@epa.gov
Secretary **(Vacant)** .... (303) 462-9000
Associate Director **Konrad Eric Nottingham** .... (303) 462-9101
Field Branch Chief **Rebecca Connell** .... (303) 462-9253
E-mail: Connell.rebecca@Epa.gov
Forensic Administrative Support Chief
Michael "Mike" Roach .... (303) 462-9080
E-mail: Roach.michael@Epa.gov
Laboratory Branch Chief **Francisco Cruz, Jr.** .... (303) 462-9104
E-mail: Cruz.francisco@Epa.gov

United States Equal Employment Opportunity Commission (EEOC)

Description: The Equal Employment Opportunity Commission works to eliminate discrimination based on race, color, disability, religion, sex, national origin, or age in hiring, promoting, firing, setting wages, testing, training, and all other terms and conditions of employment. The Commission oversees all compliance and enforcement activities relating to equal employment opportunity among federal employees.

131 M Street, NE, Washington, DC 20507
Tel: (202) 663-4900 (Public Information)
Tel: (202) 663-4222 (Procurement Information)
Tel: (800) 669-3362 (Publications Information)
Tel: (202) 663-4634 (Freedom of Information/Privacy Act)
Tel: (800) 849-4230 (Inspector General's Hot Line)
Tel: (800) 669-4000 (Discrimination Claims)
TTY: (800) 800-3302 (Publications Information)
TTY: (800) 669-6820 (Discrimination Claims) Internet: www.eeoc.gov
Internet: www.eeoc.gov/open (Open Government Website)
Internet: www.usa.gov (Official US Government Website)

THE COMMISSION

131 M Street, NE, Washington, DC 20507
Fax: (202) 663-4110

Note: Commissioners may continue to serve for 60 days past their term expiration.

Office of Field Programs

131 M Street, NE, Washington, DC 20507
Tel: (202) 663-4801 Fax: (202) 663-7190

District Offices

Atlanta (GA) District Office
Sam Nunn Federal Center, 100 Alabama Street, SW, Suite 4R30, Atlanta, GA 30303
Tel: (800) 669-4000 TTY: (800) 669-6820 Fax: (404) 562-6909
E-mail: atlanta@eeoc.gov

● District Director **Bernice Williams-Kimbrough** .... (404) 562-6930
E-mail: bernice.williams-kimbrough@eeoc.gov
Deputy Director **Darrell Graham** .... (404) 562-6804
Regional Attorney **Antonette Sewell** .... (404) 562-6818
E-mail: antonette.sewell@eeoc.gov
District Resources Manager **Henry A. Wesloski** .... (404) 562-6805
E-mail: henry.wesloski@eeoc.gov
Administrative Judge **(Vacant)** .... (404) 562-6807
Enforcement Manager **William Batts** .... (404) 562-6840
E-mail: william.batts@eeoc.gov
Enforcement Manager **(Vacant)** .... (404) 562-6824
Alternative Dispute Resolution Coordinator **Clinton Smith** .... (404) 562-6814
E-mail: clinton.smith@eeoc.gov
State-Local Coordinator **Joyce Dawkins** .... (404) 562-6881
Information Technology Specialist **Ronald Mifflin** .... (404) 562-6886
E-mail: ronald.mifflin@eeoc.gov
Small Business Liaison **Terrie Dandy** .... (404) 562-6811

Birmingham (AL) District Office
Ridge Park Place, 1130 South 22nd Street, Suite 2000, Birmingham, AL 35205
Tel: (205) 212-2100 TTY: (205) 212-2112 Fax: (205) 212-2105
Areas Covered: AL, MS

● District Director **Bradley A. Anderson** .... (205) 212-2089
Secretary **Jeannette Kay Lindsey** .... (205) 212-2089
E-mail: jeannette.lindsey@eeoc.gov

Birmingham (AL) District Office *(continued)*

Deputy Director **Linda J. Sales-Long** .... (205) 212-2119
E-mail: linda.sales-long@eeoc.gov
District Resources Manager **Latoya Lowe** .... (205) 212-2048
E-mail: latoya.lowe@eeoc.gov
Regional Attorney **Marsha Rucker** .... (205) 212-2046
E-mail: marsha.rucker@eeoc.gov

Charlotte (NC) District Office
129 West Trade Street, Suite 400, Charlotte, NC 28202
Tel: (704) 344-6682 TTY: (704) 344-6684 Fax: (704) 344-6734
Areas Covered: NC, SC, VA

● District Director (Acting) **Thomas Colclough** .... (704) 344-6682
Fax: (704) 344-6731
● District Director **Reuben Daniels, Jr.** .... (704) 344-6682
E-mail: reuben.daniels@eeoc.gov Fax: (704) 344-6731
Deputy Director **Thomas Colclough** .... (704) 344-6682
E-mail: thomas.colclough@eeoc.gov
District Resource Manager **Tonya Johnson** .... (704) 344-6682
E-mail: tonya.johnson@eeoc.gov
Regional Attorney **Lynette Barnes** .... (704) 344-6682
E-mail: lynette.barnes@eeoc.gov
Enforcement Manager **Michael Whitlow** .... (704) 344-6682
E-mail: michael.whitlow@eeoc.gov
Enforcement Manager **(Vacant)** .... (704) 344-6682

Chicago (IL) District Office
500 West Madison Street, Suite 2000, Chicago, IL 60661
Tel: (312) 869-8000 TTY: (312) 869-8001 Fax: (312) 869-8077
Areas Covered: The entire State of Illinois except for 16 counties in the southwest portion of the state which are covered by the St. Louis District Office.

● District Director **Julianne Bowman** .... (312) 353-2713
E-mail: julianne.bowman@eeoc.gov
Deputy Director **(Vacant)** .... (312) 353-2713
Fax: (312) 353-4041
Regional Attorney **Gregory M. Gochanour** .... (312) 353-2713
E-mail: gregory.gouchanour@eeoc.gov
Enforcement Manager **Patricia Jaramillo** .... (312) 353-0684
E-mail: patricia.jaramillo@eeoc.gov
Alternative Dispute Resolution Supervisor **Julie Bretz** .... (312) 869-8051
E-mail: julie.bretz@eeoc.gov Fax: (312) 353-6676
Information Technology Specialist **Alison Hardiman** .... (312) 869-8005
E-mail: alison.hardiman@eeoc.gov Fax: (312) 353-4041

Dallas (TX) District Office
207 South Houston Street, Third Floor, Dallas, TX 75202-4726
Tel: (800) 669-4000 TTY: (214) 253-2710 Fax: (214) 253-2720
Areas Covered: Northern TX, San Antonio, El Paso

● District Director **Belinda McCallister** .... (214) 253-2852
E-mail: belinda.mccallister@eeoc.gov
Education: Dallas Baptist BABA; Southern Methodist MA
Executive Secretary **Maria J. Soto** .... (214) 253-2852
E-mail: maria.soto@eeoc.gov
Deputy Director **(Vacant)** .... (214) 253-2856
Regional Attorney **Robert A. Canino** .... (214) 253-2750
E-mail: robert.canino@eeoc.gov

★ Presidential Appointment Requiring Senate Confirmation ☆ Presidential Appointment □ Schedule C Appointment ◇ Career Senior Foreign Service Appointment
● Career Senior Executive Service (SES) Appointment ○ Non-Career Senior Executive Service (SES) Appointment ■ Postal Career Executive Service

Dallas (TX) District Office *(continued)*

District Resource Manager **Steve Carrillo** . . . . (214) 253-2813
E-mail: steve.carrillo@eeoc.gov
Chief Administrative Judge **Dwight Lewis** . . . . (214) 253-2730
E-mail: dwight.lewis@eeoc.gov

Houston (TX) District Office

1919 Smith St/, 7th Floor, Houston, TX 77002-8049
Tel: (713) 651-4951 Fax: (713) 651-4902
Areas Covered: Central TX

● District Director **Rayford O. Irvin** . . . . (713) 651-4960
E-mail: rayford.irvin@eeoc.gov
Deputy Director **(Vacant)** . . . . (713) 651-4950
District Resources Manager **Shanita Williams** . . . . (713) 651-4979
E-mail: shanita.williams@eeoc.gov
Regional Attorney **Rudy L. Sustaita** . . . . (713) 651-4963
E-mail: rudy.sustaita@eeoc.gov
Education: Texas 1990 JD
State-Local Coordinator/Enforcement Manager
(Vacant) . . . . (713) 651-4951
Supervisory Administrative Judge **(Vacant)** . . . . (713) 651-4950

Indianapolis (IN) District Office

101 West Ohio Street, Suite 1900, Indianapolis, IN 46204-4203
Tel: (317) 226-7212 TTY: (317) 226-5162 Fax: (317) 226-7953
Areas Covered: IN, KY, OH, MI

● District Director **Michelle F. Eisele** . . . . (317) 226-7212
E-mail: michelle.eisele@eeoc.gov
Education: Indiana 1985
Secretary to the District Director **Minnia Coates** . . . . . . (317) 226-6418
E-mail: minnia.coates@eeoc.gov
Deputy Director **Randy Poynter** . . . . (317) 226-6422
E-mail: randy.poynder@eeoc.gov
Enforcement Manager **Joy Pentz** . . . . (317) 226-5372
E-mail: joy.pentz@eeoc.gov
District Resource Manager **Mark Donaldson** . . . . (317) 226-6140
E-mail: mark.donaldson@eeoc.gov
Regional Attorney **Kenneth Bird** . . . . (317) 226-7202
Supervisory Trial Attorney **Nancy Edmonds** . . . . (317) 226-7059
Program Analyst **(Vacant)** . . . . (317) 226-7469
State-Local Coordinator **(Vacant)** . . . . (317) 226-6144
Alternative Dispute Resolution Supervisory
Coordinator **Kathy Campbell** . . . . (317) 226-7212

Los Angeles (CA) District Office

Roybal Federal Building, 255 East Temple,
4th Floor, Los Angeles, CA 90012
Tel: (213) 894-1000 Tel: (877) 403-8609 (FOIA Service Center)
Fax: (213) 894-1118 E-mail: losafoia@eeoc.gov (FOIA Service Center)
Areas Covered: American Samoa, Central and Southern CA, CNMI, Guam, Hawaiian Islands, Nevada, Wake Island

● District Director **Rosa Viramontes** . . . . (213) 894-1112
E-mail: rosa.viramontes@eeoc.gov
Deputy Director **Christine Park-Gonzalez** . . . . (213) 894-1101
□ Regional Attorney **Anna Y. Park** . . . . (213) 894-1080
District Resources Manager **Thomas Profit** . . . . (213) 894-1074
E-mail: thomas.profit@eeoc.gov
Intake Supervisor **Patricia Kane** . . . . (213) 894-1090
Small Business Liaison **Ramiro Gutierrez** . . . . (213) 894-1090
E-mail: ramiro.gutierrez@eeoc.gov

Memphis (TN) District Office

1407 Union Avenue, Suite 901, Memphis, TN 38104
Tel: (901) 544-0115 TTY: (901) 544-0112 Fax: (901) 544-0111
Areas Covered: The Memphis District Office has jurisdiction over the states of Tennessee and Arkansas, with direct charge over the West Tennessee counties of Shelby, Fayette, Hardeman, Tipton, Haywood, Madison, Lauderdale, McNairy, Hardin, Chester, Henderson, Decatur, Crockett, Dyer, Gibson, Carroll, Benton, Henry, Weakley and Obion.

● District Director **Delner Franklin-Thomas** . . . . (901) 544-0151
E-mail: delner.franklin-thomas@eeoc.gov
Education: Yale BA; Columbia JD

Memphis (TN) District Office *(continued)*

Deputy Director **(Vacant)** . . . . (901) 544-0132
Regional Attorney **Faye A. Williams** . . . . (901) 544-0088
E-mail: faye.williams@eeoc.gov
Supervisory Attorney **Gerald L. Thornton** . . . . (901) 544-0140
E-mail: gerald.thornton@eeoc.gov
District Resource Manager **Edmond Sims** . . . . (901) 544-0076
E-mail: edmond.sims@eeoc.gov
Enforcement Manager **Audrey Bonner** . . . . (901) 544-0163
E-mail: audrey.bonner@eeoc.gov
Alternative Dispute Resolution Coordinator
Theodore Lamb . . . . (501) 324-5071
820 Louisiana Street, Little Rock, AR 72201 Fax: (501) 324-5991
E-mail: theodore.lamb@eeoc.gov
IT Specialist **Joan Ward** . . . . (901) 544-0089
E-mail: joan.ward@eeoc.gov

Miami (FL) District Office

Miami Tower, 100 SE Second Street, Suite 1500, Miami, FL 33131
Tel: (305) 808-1740 TTY: (305) 808-1742 Fax: (305) 808-1855

● District Director **Michael Farrell** . . . . (305) 808-1800
E-mail: michael.farrell@eeoc.gov
Deputy Director **(Vacant)** . . . . (305) 808-1745
District Resources Manager **Michael L. Bethea** . . . . (305) 808-1763
E-mail: michael.bethea@eeoc.gov
Regional Attorney **Robert Weisberg** . . . . (305) 808-1853
E-mail: robert.weisberg@eeoc.gov
State-Local Coordinator **Ina Depaz** . . . . (305) 808-1740
E-mail: ina.depaz@eeoc.gov

New York (NY) District Office

33 Whitehall Street, 5th Floor, New York, NY 10004-2112
Tel: (212) 336-3620 TTY: (212) 336-3622 Fax: (212) 336-3625
Areas Covered: The Bronx, Columbia, Dutchess, Greene, Kings, New York, Orange, Putnam, Queens, Richmond, Rockland, Suffolk, Sullivan, Ulster, Westchester counties.

● District Director **Kevin Berry** . . . . (212) 336-3742
E-mail: kevin.berry@eeoc.gov
Deputy District Director **Judy Kennan** . . . . (212) 336-3742
Fax: (212) 336-3621
Regional Attorney **Jeffrey Burstein** . . . . (212) 336-3708
E-mail: jeffrey.burstein@eeoc.gov
Chief Administrative Judge **William Macauley** . . . . (212) 336-3743
E-mail: william.macauley@eeoc.gov Fax: (212) 336-3624
Education: Notre Dame BA;
National U Ireland MA; Saint Louis U JD
Program Analyst **Michael Rojas** . . . . (212) 336-3670
E-mail: michael.rojas@eeoc.gov Fax: (212) 336-3621

Philadelphia (PA) District Office

801 Market Street, Suite 1300, Philadelphia, PA 19107-3127
Tel: (215) 440-2601 TTY: (215) 440-2610 Fax: (215) 440-2604
Areas Covered: DE, NJ, PA, WV

● District Director **Jamie R. Williamson** . . . . (215) 440-2601
E-mail: jamie.williamson@eeoc.gov
Education: Smith
Deputy Director **Deana Hutter** . . . . (215) 440-2601
District Resource Manager **Catherine Steffler** . . . . (215) 440-2626
E-mail: catherine.steffler@eeoc.gov
Regional Attorney **Debra M. Lawrence** . . . . (215) 440-2828
E-mail: debra.lawrence@eeoc.gov
Enforcement Manager **(Vacant)** . . . . (215) 440-2601
Alternative Dispute Resolution Coordinator
Stephanie Marino . . . . (215) 440-2819
E-mail: stephanie.marino@eeoc.gov
Supervisory Trial Attorney **Maria Morocco** . . . . (215) 440-2669
E-mail: maria.morocco@eeoc.gov
Federal Hearings Unit Supervisor **Francis Polito** . . . . (215) 440-2608
E-mail: francis.polito@eeoc.gov
Program Analyst **Mary M. Tiernan** . . . . (215) 440-2671
E-mail: mary.tiernan@eeoc.gov

★ Presidential Appointment Requiring Senate Confirmation ☆ Presidential Appointment □ Schedule C Appointment ◇ Career Senior Foreign Service Appointment
● Career Senior Executive Service (SES) Appointment ○ Non-Career Senior Executive Service (SES) Appointment ■ Postal Career Executive Service

Phoenix (AZ) District Office
3300 North Central Avenue, Suite 690, Phoenix, AZ 85012-2504
Tel: (602) 640-5000 TTY: (602) 640-5072 Fax: (602) 640-5071
Areas Covered: AZ, NM, UT

● District Director **Elizabeth Cadle** .... (602) 640-5041
E-mail: elizabeth.cadle@eeoc.gov
Deputy Director **(Vacant)** .... (602) 640-5041
Regional Attorney **Mary Jo O'Neill** .... (602) 640-5044
E-mail: mary.oneill@eeoc.gov
District Resources Manager **Ronald Davis** .... (602) 640-5015
E-mail: ronald.davis@eeoc.gov
Enforcement Manager **(Vacant)** .... (602) 640-5034
State-Local Coordinator **Pam Pershing** .... (602) 640-5054
Intake Officer **Patricia Miner** .... (602) 640-5036
E-mail: patricia.miner@eeoc.gov
Program Analyst **Krista L. Watson** .... (602) 640-4995
E-mail: krista.watson@eeoc.gov

San Francisco (CA) District Office
450 Golden Gate Avenue, 5th Floor West, San Francisco, CA 94102
36025, San Francisco, CA 94102-3661
Tel: (415) 522-3000 TTY: (415) 522-3152 Fax: (415) 522-3415
Areas Covered: AK, ID, MT, Northern CA, Northern NV, OR, and WA

● District Director **William R. Tamayo** .... (415) 522-3011
E-mail: william.tamayo@eeoc.gov
Deputy District Director **Michael Connolly** .... (415) 625-3000
Regional Attorney **Roberta L. Steele** .... (415) 522-3366
District Resource Manager **Lorraine Strayhorn** .... (415) 522-3016
E-mail: lorraine.strayhorn@eeoc.gov
Enforcement Manager **Deborah Randall** .... (415) 522-3107
E-mail: deborah.randall@eeoc.gov

St. Louis (MO) District Office
1222 Spruce, Room 8.100, St. Louis, MO 63103
Tel: (314) 539-7800 TTY: (314) 539-7803 Fax: (314) 539-7893
Areas Covered: KS, MO, IL (Counties of Alexander, Bond, Calhoun, Clinton, Greene, Jackson, Jersey, Macoupin, Madison, Monroe, Perry, Pulaski, Randolph, St. Clair, Union, Washington)

● District Director **James R. Neely, Jr.** .... (314) 539-7830
E-mail: james.neely@eeoc.gov
Deputy District Director **Lloyd Jack Vasquez, Jr.** .... (314) 539-7831
E-mail: lloyd.vasquez@eeoc.gov
Regional Attorney **Andrea G. Baran** .... (314) 539-7910
E-mail: andrea.baran@eeoc.gov
Enforcement Manager **Dana Engelhardt** .... (314) 539-7870
E-mail: dana.engelhardt@eeoc.gov
Secretary **(Vacant)** .... (314) 539-7832

Washington (DC) Field Office
131 M Street, NE, Suite 4NWO2F, Washington, DC 20507
Tel: (202) 419-0700 TTY: (202) 419-0702 Fax: (202) 653-6052
Fax: (202) 653-6053 Tel: (202) 419-0713 Fax: (202) 653-6054
Areas Covered: DC, MD (Counties of Montgomery, Prince George's, Charles, Calvert, and St. Mary's), VA (Counties of Arlington, Clarke, Fairfax, Fauquier, Frederick, Loudoun, Prince William, Stafford, Warren, and Independent Cities of Alexandria, Fairfax City, Falls Church, Manassas, Manassas Park, Winchester, Quantico, Dumfries, and Occoquan)

Field Director (Acting) **Mindy E. Weinstein** .... (202) 419-0713
E-mail: mindy.weinstein@eeoc.gov
Administrative Officer **Ijeri Johnson** .... (202) 419-0700
E-mail: ijeri.johnson@eeoc.gov
Regional Attorney **Debra M. Lawrence** .... (202) 419-0700

★ Presidential Appointment Requiring Senate Confirmation ☆ Presidential Appointment □ Schedule C Appointment ◇ Career Senior Foreign Service Appointment
● Career Senior Executive Service (SES) Appointment ○ Non-Career Senior Executive Service (SES) Appointment ■ Postal Career Executive Service

Export-Import Bank of the United States (EXIM)

Description: The Export-Import Bank of the United States aids in financing and facilitating U.S. exports. It provides guarantees of working capital loans for U.S. exporters, guarantees the repayment of loans or makes loans to foreign purchasers of U.S. goods and services, and provides insurance against non-payment by foreign buyers for political or commercial risk.

811 Vermont Avenue, NW, Washington, DC 20571-0002
Tel: (202) 565-3946 (Public Information, Job Vacancy Listing)
Tel: (202) 565-3248 (Freedom of Information/Privacy Act)
Tel: (202) 565-3980 (Library) Tel: (202) 565-3912 (Small Business Information and Seminar Registration) TTY: (202) 565-3377
Fax: (202) 565-3380 E-mail: info@exim.gov Internet: www.exim.gov

BOARD OF DIRECTORS

811 Vermont Avenue, NW, Washington, DC 20571-0002
Tel: (202) 565-3545 (General Information) Fax: (202) 565-3513

Note: Members may continue to serve until reappointed or replaced.

Administrative Offices

Office of Small Business

811 Vermont Avenue, NW, Washington, DC 20571-0002
Tel: (202) 565-3900 Fax: (202) 565-3931
E-mail: smallbizhelp@exim.gov

Regional Sales

811 Vermont Avenue, NW, Washington, DC 20571-0002

Vice President **Sean Luke** Room 645 .... (202) 565-3801
Education: New Col South Florida 2005 BA; Maryland 2009 MBA

Regional Export Finance Centers

Central Region

Managing Director **Michael F. "Mike" Howard** .... (312) 353-8093
233 North Michigan Avenue, Chicago, IL 60601
E-mail: michael.howard@exim.gov

Export-Import Bank of the United States (Chicago Office)

233 North Michigan Avenue, Suite 260, Chicago, IL 60601
Tel: (312) 353-8081 Fax: (312) 353-8098
Areas Covered: IA, IL, IN, KS, KY, MI, MN, MO, NE, ND, OH, SD, WI

Managing Director **Michael F. "Mike" Howard** .... (312) 353-8093
E-mail: michael.howard@exim.gov

Deputy Managing Director **Jan Blaho** .... (312) 353-8072
E-mail: jan.blaho@exim.gov

Regional Director **Mark Klein** .... (312) 375-1883
E-mail: mark.klein@exim.gov

Regional Director **(Vacant)** .... (312) 353-8071

Minneapolis Field Office

330 2nd Ave. South, Suite 410, Minneapolis, MN 55401
Tel: (612) 348-1213 Fax: (612) 348-1650

Regional Director **Denis M. Griffin** .... (612) 348-1213
E-mail: denis.griffin@exim.gov

Export-Import Bank of the United States (Houston Field Office)

Mikey Leland Federal Building, 1919 Smith Street, Suite 10087, Houston, TX 77002
Tel: (281) 721-0465 Fax: (281) 679-0156
Areas Covered: AL, AR, CO, LA, MS, NM, OK, Western TN, TX

Regional Director **Eric Miller** .... (713) 306-7969
E-mail: eric.miller@exim.gov

Eastern Region

Managing Director **Sharyn H. Koenig** .... (305) 526-7436 ext. 17
5835 Blue Lagoon Drive, Miami, FL 33126
E-mail: sharyn.koenig@exim.gov

Deputy Managing Director **Regina Gordin** .... (917) 826-5642
Areas Covered: New Jersey, Delaware, Pennsylvania, Virginia, Maryland, West Virginia, District of Columbia
290 Broadway, 13th Floor, New York, NY 10007
E-mail: regina.gordin@exim.gov

Export-Import Bank of the United States (New York City Office)

Ted Weiss Federal Building, 290 Broadway, 13th floor, New York, NY 10007
Tel: (212) 809-2650 Fax: (212) 809-2687
Areas Covered: CT, DE, MA, ME, NH, NJ, NY, PA, RI, VT

Deputy Managing Director **Regina Gordin** .... (917) 826-5642
Areas Covered: New Jersey, Delaware, Pennsylvania, Virginia, Maryland, West Virginia, District of Columbia
E-mail: regina.gordin@exim.gov

Regional Director **Richard Foy** .... (212) 809-2651
E-mail: richard.foy@exim.gov

Export-Import Bank of the United States (Miami Field Office)

5835 Blue Lagoon Drive, Suite 203, Miami, FL 33126
Tel: (305) 526-7436 Fax: (305) 526-7435
Areas Covered: FL, GA, PR, Eastern TN, VI

Managing Director **Sharyn H. Koenig** .... (305) 526-7436 ext. 17
E-mail: sharyn.koenig@exim.gov

Regional Director **Jennifer Simpson** .... (305) 526-7436 ext. 24
E-mail: jennifer.simpson@exim.gov

Regional Director **Elena Mendez** .... (305) 526-7436 ext. 19
E-mail: elena.mendez@exim.gov

Business Development Assistant
Mary Janette "Janette" Iker .... (305) 526-7436 ext. 16
E-mail: janette.iker@exim.gov

Atlanta Regional Export Finance Center

Atlanta U.S. Export Assistance Center, 75 Fifth Street NW, Suite 1060, Atlanta, GA 30308
Tel: (404) 955-2219 Fax: (404) 897-6085

Regional Director **Susan Kintanar** .... (404) 955-2219
E-mail: susan.kintanar@exim.gov

Export-Import Bank of the United States (Washington, DC Field Office)

811 Vermont Avenue, NW, Washington, DC 20571-0002

Regional Director **(Vacant)** .... (202) 565-3918

Western Region

Managing Director **Sharyn H. Koenig** .... (305) 526-7436 ext. 17
Areas Covered: CA, MT, WY, AK, HI
2302 Martin Court, Suite 315, Irvine, CA 92612
E-mail: sharyn.koenig@exim.gov

★ Presidential Appointment Requiring Senate Confirmation ☆ Presidential Appointment □ Schedule C Appointment ◇ Career Senior Foreign Service Appointment
● Career Senior Executive Service (SES) Appointment ○ Non-Career Senior Executive Service (SES) Appointment ■ Postal Career Executive Service

Export-Import Bank of the United States (Western Regional Office)
2302 Martin Court, Suite 315, Suite 315, Irvine, CA 92612
Tel: (949) 660-1341 Fax: (949) 660-9553
Areas Covered: AZ, CA, HI, ID, MT, NV, UT, WA, WY

Regional Director **Paul E. Duncan** . . . . (949) 660-0633
Areas Covered: NV, UT, Los Angeles County, CA, Orange County CA
Regional Director **Marianne Hughes** . . . . (949) 660-0603
Areas Covered: Arizona, Los Angeles County, CA; Santa Barbara County, CA; Ventura County, CA
Regional Director **Gregory Moore** . . . . (949) 224-4245

Farm Credit Administration (FCA)

Description: The Farm Credit Administration examines and regulates the operation of the banks, associations, and affiliated service organizations that comprise the Farm Credit System. It also protects the interests of the public and those who borrow from farm credit institutions or invest in farm credit securities.

1501 Farm Credit Drive, McLean, VA 22102-5090
Tel: (703) 883-4000 (Personnel Locator Directory, Procurement Information) Tel: (703) 883-4056 (General Information)
Tel: (703) 883-4020 (Freedom of Information/Privacy Act)
Tel: (703) 883-4316 (Inspector General's Hotline - DC Metropolitan Area)
Tel: (800) 437-7322 (Inspector General's Hotline - Continental US)
TTY: (703) 883-4056 Fax: (703) 734-5784 E-mail: info-line@fca.gov
Internet: www.fca.gov

OFFICE OF THE BOARD

1501 Farm Credit Drive, McLean, VA 22102-5090
Fax: (703) 734-5784

Note: Members may continue to serve until reappointed or replaced.

Office of the Chief Operating Officer

1501 Farm Credit Drive, Room 4301, McLean, VA 22102-5090
Fax: (703) 790-5241

Office of Examination

1501 Farm Credit Drive, McLean, VA 22102-5090
Fax: (703) 893-2978

Bloomington (MN) Field Office

7900 International Drive, Suite 200, Bloomington, MN 55425-2563
Tel: (952) 854-7151 Fax: (952) 854-4736

Field Director **Chester Slipek** .... (952) 251-0401
Education: Wisconsin 1977 BS, 1986 MS

Dallas (TX) Field Office

500 East John Carpenter Freeway, Suite 400, Irving, TX 75062-3957
Tel: (972) 869-0550 Fax: (972) 869-9531

Field Director **Sharon Wilhite** .... (469) 359-4107
Education: Texas Tech 1985 BBA

Denver (CO) Field Office

Prentice Plaza, 8101 E Prentice Avenue,
Suite 1200, Greenwood Village, CO 80111-2939
Tel: (303) 696-9737 Fax: (303) 696-7114

Field Director **Doug Alford** .... (720) 213-0961

McLean (VA) Field Office

1501 Farm Credit Drive, McLean, VA 22102-5090
Tel: (703) 883-4160 Fax: (703) 893-2704

Examiner Director **Samuel R. Coleman** .... (703) 893-2978

Sacramento (CA) Field Office

2180 Harvard Street, Suite 300, Sacramento, CA 95815-3323
Tel: (916) 648-1118 Fax: (916) 649-0512

Field Director **(Vacant)** .... (916) 604-3139

Federal Communications Commission (FCC)

Description: The Federal Communications Commission is charged with regulating interstate and international communications by radio, television, wire, satellite, and cable.

445 12th Street, SW, Washington, DC 20554
Tel: (888) 225-5322 (Federal Communications Commission Consumer Center) TTY: (888) 835-5322 (Federal Communications Commission Consumer Center) Tel: (202) 418-1919 (Procurement Information)
Tel: (202) 418-0500 (Press Information)
Tel: (202) 418-0210 (Freedom of Information/Privacy Act Information)
Fax: (202) 418-0232 Fax: (202) 418-0188 (General Correspondence)
Internet: www.fcc.gov Internet: www.usa.gov

OFFICES OF THE COMMISSIONERS

445 12th Street, SW, Washington, DC 20554
Fax: (202) 418-2801 Internet: www.fcc.gov/leadership

Note: Commissioners may continue to serve until reappointed or replaced.

Enforcement Bureau

445 12th Street, SW, Washington, DC 20554
Tel: (202) 418-7450 Fax: (202) 418-2810 Internet: www.fcc.gov/eb

Office of the Field Director

Field Director **Charles Cooper** .... (202) 418-7590
Field Counsel **Janet Moran** .... (202) 418-7923
Field Counsel **Matthew Gibson** .... (202) 418-1214
Education: William & Mary 2000 BA; Georgetown 2006 JD
Field Counsel **Joy Ragsdale** .... (202) 418-1697

Region One

Park Ridge Office Center, 1550 Northwest Highway, Suite 306, Park Ridge, IL 60068-1460
Tel: (215) 880-1161

Regional Director **David C. "Dave" Dombrowski** .... (215) 880-1161
E-mail: david.dombrowski@fcc.gov
Regional Counsel **(Vacant)** .... (215) 880-1161

Boston (MA) Office

One Batterymarch Park, Quincy, MA 02169-7495
Tel: (617) 786-7746 Fax: (617) 770-2408

District Director **(Vacant)** .... (617) 786-7746

Region Two

520 NE Colbern Road, Lees Summit, MO 64086
Tel: (678) 293-3194

Regional Director **Ronald D. Ramage** .... (678) 293-3194
E-mail: ronald.eamage@fcc.gov
Regional Counsel **(Vacant)** .... (678) 293-3194
Deputy Director **(Vacant)** .... (678) 293-3194

Atlanta (GA) Office

Koger Center - Gwinnett Building, 3575 Koger Boulevard, Suite 320, Duluth, GA 30096-4958
Tel: (770) 935-3370 Fax: (770) 279-4633

District Director **Douglas G. Miller** .... (770) 935-3370
E-mail: douglas.miller@fcc.gov

Dallas (TX) Office

9330 LBJ Freeway, Room 1170, Dallas, TX 75243-3429
Tel: (214) 575-6361

District Director **James D. "Jim" Wells** .... (214) 575-6361

Kansas City (MO) Office

520 NE Colbern Road, 2nd Floor, Lees Summit, MO 64086
Tel: (816) 316-1248

District Director **(Vacant)** .... (816) 316-1248

New Orleans (LA) Office

2424 Edendorne Avenue, Suite 460, Metairie, LA 70001
Tel: (504) 219-8999 Fax: (504) 834-9230

District Director **(Vacant)** .... (504) 219-8999

Tampa (FL) Office

Airport Executive Center, 2203 North Lois Avenue, Room 1215, Tampa, FL 33607-2356
Tel: (813) 348-1741 Fax: (813) 348-1581

District Director **Ralph M. Barlow** .... (888) 225-5322
E-mail: ralph.barlow@fcc.gov

Region Three

One Denver Federal Center, Building 1A, Denver, CO 80225
P.O. Box 25446, Denver, CO 80225
Tel: (562) 865-0235
Areas Covered: AK, AS, AZ, CA, CO, GU, HI, ID, Mariana and Midway Islands, MT, NV, NM, OR, Pacific Trust Territories, UT, WA, WY

Regional Director **Lark Hadley** .... (562) 865-0235
E-mail: lark.hadley@fcc.gov
Deputy Regional Director **(Vacant)** .... (562) 865-0235
Regional Counsel **(Vacant)** .... (562) 865-0235

Denver (CO) Office

215 South Wadsworth Boulevard, Suite 303, Lakewood, CO 80226-1566
Tel: (303) 231-5212 Fax: (303) 231-5200

District Director **Nikki Shears** .... (303) 231-5212
E-mail: nikki.shears@fcc.gov

Los Angeles (CA) Office

Cerritos Corporate Tower, 18000 Studebaker Road, Room 660, Cerritos, CA 90703-2692
Tel: (562) 860-7474 Fax: (562) 865-0736

District Director **(Vacant)** .... (562) 865-0235

San Diego (CA) Office

Interstate Office Park, 4542 Ruffner Street, Room 370, San Diego, CA 92111-2216
Tel: (858) 496-5111 Fax: (858) 496-5112

District Director **James T. Lyon** .... (858) 496-5111
E-mail: james.lyon@fcc.gov

San Francisco (CA) Office

5653 Stoneridge Drive, Suite 105, Pleasanton, CA 94588-8543
Tel: (925) 416-9717 Fax: (925) 924-0282

District Director **David Hartshorn** .... (925) 416-9717

Seattle (WA) Office
11410 NE 122nd Way, Suite 312, Kirkland, WA 98034-6927
Tel: (425) 820-6271 Fax: (425) 820-0126
District Director **(Vacant)** . . . . (425) 820-6271

Wireless Telecommunications Bureau (WTB)

445 - 12th Street, SW, Washington, DC 20554
Tel: (202) 418-0600 Tel: (717) 338-2868 (Auctions Hot Line)
Tel: (888) 225-5322 (Cellular, PCS, CMRS Application Status)
Fax: (202) 418-0787 E-mail: fccinfo@fcc.gov
Internet: www.fcc.gov/wireless-telecommunications

Gettysburg (PA) Office

1270 Fairfield Road, Gettysburg, PA 17325

Auctions and Spectrum Access Division
Deputy Division Chief, Analysis & Implementation
(Vacant) . . . . (717) 338-2868
Fax: (717) 338-2850

Broadband Division
Deputy Chief **Stephen C. Buenzow** . . . . (717) 338-2647
E-mail: stephen.buenzow@fcc.gov

Mobility Division
Associate Chief **(Vacant)** . . . . (717) 338-2602

Technologies, Systems, and Innovation Division
1270 Fairfield Rd, Gettysburg, PA 17325
Tel: (888) 225-5322 Fax: (717) 338-2698
Internet: http://wireless.fcc.gov/organization/smart.html

Chief **Diane Dupert** . . . . (717) 338-2658
E-mail: diane.dupert@fcc.gov
Deputy Chief **(Vacant)** . . . . (717) 338-2621
Associate Chief (Licensing Support) **Mary Deatrick** . . . . . (717) 338-2656
E-mail: mary.deatrick@fcc.gov
Associate Chief (Outreach) **Dorothy Stifflemire** . . . . (202) 418-7349
445 - 12th Street, SW, Washington, DC 20554
E-mail: dorothy.stifflemire@fcc.gov
Associate Chief (Performance Measurement)
Melvin Del Rosario . . . . (202) 418-0615
445 - 12th Street, SW, Washington, DC 20554
E-mail: melvin.delrosario@fcc.gov

★ Presidential Appointment Requiring Senate Confirmation ☆ Presidential Appointment □ Schedule C Appointment ◇ Career Senior Foreign Service Appointment
● Career Senior Executive Service (SES) Appointment ○ Non-Career Senior Executive Service (SES) Appointment ■ Postal Career Executive Service

INDEPENDENT AGENCIES

Federal Deposit Insurance Corporation (FDIC)

Description: The Federal Deposit Insurance Corporation preserves and promotes public confidence in the U.S. financial system by insuring deposits in banks and thrift institutions for at least $250,000; by identifying, monitoring, and addressing risks to the deposit insurance funds; and by limiting the effect on the economy and the financial system when a bank or thrift institution fails.

1310 Courthouse Road, Arlington, VA 22201
Tel: (877) 275-3342 (Federal Deposit Insurance Corporation Call Center)
Tel: (800) 688-3342 (Call Reports)
Tel: (800) 759-6596 (Deposit Insurance Assessment Information)
Tel: (800) 964-3342 (Office of the Inspector General Hotline)
Tel: (800) 765-3342 (Southeast Service Center-Atlanta, GA)
Tel: (800) 568-9161 (Southwest Service Center-Dallas, TX)
TTY: (800) 925-4618
E-mail: opengov@fdic.gov (Open Government Directive Email)
Internet: www.fdic.gov
Internet: www.usa.gov (Official US Government Web site)
Internet: www.fdic.gov/open (Open Government Directive Web site)

BOARD OF DIRECTORS

550 17th Street, NW, Washington, DC 20429-9990
Note: Members may continue to serve until reappointed or replaced.

Office of Inspector General

3501 Fairfax Drive, Arlington, VA 22226-3500
Tel: (800) 964-3342 (Hotline)

Regional Offices

Office of Investigations - Atlanta Region
10 Tenth Street, NE, Suite 800, Atlanta, GA 30309-3906
Tel: (678) 916-2354
Special Agent-in-Charge **Jason Moran** . . . . (678) 916-2358

Office of Investigations - Chicago Region
500 West Monroe Street, Suite 3300, Chicago, IL 60661-3697
Tel: (312) 382-7513
Special Agent-in-Charge **Joseph E. Moriarty** . . . . (312) 382-7513

Office of Investigations - Dallas Region
1601 Bryan Street, Dallas, TX 75201-4586
Tel: (972) 761-2614
Special Agent-in-Charge **Lauri L. Younger** . . . . (972) 761-2618

Office of Investigations - Kansas City Region
1100 Walnut Street, Kansas City, MO 64106
Special Agent-in-Charge **David Anderson** . . . . (816) 234-8094

Office of Investigations - New York Region
350 Fifth Avenue, New York, NY 10118
Special Agent-in-Charge **Patricia Tarasca** . . . . (917) 320-2564

Office of Investigations - San Francisco Region
25 Jessie Street at Ecker Square, San Francisco, CA 94105-2780
Special Agent-in-Charge **Wade V. Walters IV** . . . . (415) 808-8215

Office of the Ombudsman

Virginia Square, L. William Seidman Center,
3501 Fairfax Drive, Arlington, VA 22226
Tel: (202) 942-3500 (General Information) Tel: (800) 250-9286

Office of the Ombudsman - Atlanta
Regional Ombudsman **Edith A. "Edye" Fulcher** . . . . (678) 916-2184
10 Tenth Street, NE, Suite 800, Atlanta, GA 30309-3906

Office of the Ombudsman - Chicago
500 West Monroe Street, Suite 3300, Chicago, IL 60661-3697
Regional Ombudsman **Daniel Marcotte** . . . . (312) 382-6908
25 Jessie Street at Ecker Square, Suite 2300,
San Francisco, CA 94105-2780

Office of the Ombudsman - Dallas
1601 Bryan Street, Dallas, TX 75201-4586
Tel: (214) 754-0098
Regional Ombudsman **Marvin B. Payne** . . . . (972) 761-2301

Office of the Ombudsman - Kansas City
1100 Walnut Street, Suite 2100, Kansas City, MO 64106
Regional Ombudsman **Dennis "Todd" Gochenour** . . . . . . (816) 234-8532

Office of the Ombudsman - New York
20 Exchange Place, 4th Floor, New York, NY 10005
Regional Ombudsman (Acting) **Robert R. Brown** . . . . (917) 320-2699
10 Tenth Street, NE, Suite 800, Atlanta, GA 30309-3906

Office of the Ombudsman - San Francisco
25 Jessie Street at Ecker Square, SFR 1622,
San Francisco, CA 94105-2780
Regional Ombudsman **Terre E. Price** Suite 2300 . . . . (415) 808-8114
E-mail: tprice@fdic.gov

Division of Insurance and Research

550 17th Street, NW, Washington, DC 20429-9990

Regional Offices

Division of Insurance and Research - Atlanta
10 Tenth Street, NE, Suite 800, Atlanta, GA 30309-3906
Tel: (678) 916-2200
Areas Covered: AL, FL, GA, NC, SC, VA, WV
Regional Manager **Marlon Cook** . . . . (678) 916-2171

Division of Insurance and Research - Boston
15 Braintree Hill Office Park, Suite 100, Braintree, MA 02184-8701
Tel: (781) 794-5500
Areas Covered: CT, MA, ME, NH, VT
Regional Manager **Cameron Tabor** . . . . (781) 794-5676

Division of Insurance and Research - Chicago
300 South Riverside Plaza, Suite 1700, Chicago, IL 60606
Tel: (312) 382-6000
Areas Covered: IL, IN, KY, MI, OH, WI
Regional Manager **Eric Robbins** . . . . (312) 382-7545

★ Presidential Appointment Requiring Senate Confirmation ☆ Presidential Appointment ☐ Schedule C Appointment ◇ Career Senior Foreign Service Appointment
● Career Senior Executive Service (SES) Appointment ○ Non-Career Senior Executive Service (SES) Appointment ■ Postal Career Executive Service

Division of Insurance and Research - Dallas
1601 Bryan Street, Dallas, TX 75201-4586
Tel: (214) 754-0098
Areas Covered: CO, NM, OK, TX
Regional Manager **Alan C. Bush** . . . . (972) 761-2072

Division of Insurance and Research - Kansas City
1100 Walnut Street, Suite 2100, Kansas City, MO 64106
Tel: (816) 234-8000
Areas Covered: IA, KS, MN, MS, ND, NE, SD
Regional Manager **Richard D. Cofer, Jr.** . . . . (816) 234-8066

Division of Insurance and Research - Memphis
Clark Tower, 5100 Poplar Avenue, Suite 1900, Memphis, TN 38137-5900
Tel: (901) 685-1603
Areas Covered: AR, LA, MS, TN
Regional Manager **(Vacant)** . . . . (901) 821-5234

Division of Insurance and Research - New York
20 Exchange Place, Room 2024, New York, NY 10005
Tel: (917) 320-2500
Areas Covered: DC, DE, MD, NJ, NY, PA, PR, VI
Regional Manager **Robert DiChiara** . . . . (917) 320-2735

Division of Insurance and Research - San Francisco
25 Jessie Street at Ecker Square, Suite 912,
San Francisco, CA 94105-2780
Tel: (415) 546-0160
Areas Covered: AK, AZ, CA, Guam, HI, ID, MT, NV, OR, UT, WA, WY
Regional Manager **John McGee** . . . . (415) 808-7962

Division of Resolutions and Receiverships

550 17th Street, NW, Washington, DC 20429-9990

Regional Offices

Division of Resolutions and Receiverships - Dallas
1601 Bryan Street, Dallas, TX 75201-4586
Tel: (214) 754-0098
Areas Covered: CO, NM, OK, TX
Deputy Director - Receivership Operations
Randy Taylor . . . . (972) 761-8555
Deputy Director - Business Operations Support
David Cooley . . . . (972) 761-8638
Associate Director - Receivership Operations
Frank Campagna . . . . (972) 761-8025
Resolution Strategy Regional Manager
Michael D. Houston . . . . (972) 761-2223
Assistant Director - Claims Administration Operations
Janice Hearn . . . . (972) 761-8635
Assistant Director - Contract Oversight **Wes Kilmer** . . . . . (972) 761-2579
Assistant Director - Franchise Marketing **(Vacant)** . . . . (972) 761-8207
Assistant Director - Investigations **Connie Dryden** . . . . (972) 761-2201
Assistant Director - Monitoring and Risk Analysis
(Vacant) . . . . (214) 754-0098
Assistant Director - Owned Real Estate **Dan Walker** . . . . . (972) 761-2215
Manager - Internal Review **(Vacant)** . . . . (214) 754-0098

Division of Risk Management Supervision (RMS)

550 17th Street, NW, Washington, DC 20429-9990

Regional Offices

Atlanta (GA) Regional Office
10 Tenth Street, NE, Suite 800, Atlanta, GA 30309-3906
Tel: (877) 275-3342
Areas Covered: AL, FL, GA, NC, SC, VA, WV
Regional Director **Michael J. Dean** . . . . (678) 916-2224
Education: UMass (Amherst) MBA
Deputy Regional Director (Compliance) **Phyllis Patton** . . . (877) 275-3342
Deputy Regional Director (Risk Management)
John P. Henrie . . . . (678) 916-2220

Chicago (IL) Regional Office
500 West Monroe Street, Suite 3300, Chicago, IL 60661-3697
Tel: (312) 382-7500 Fax: (312) 382-6901
Areas Covered: IL, IN, KY, MI, OH, WI
Regional Director **John Conneely** . . . . (312) 382-7500
Deputy Regional Director (Risk Management)
Christopher J. Newbury . . . . (312) 382-7506
E-mail: cnewbury@fdic.gov

Dallas (TX) Regional Office
1601 Bryan Street, Dallas, TX 75201-4586
Tel: (800) 568-9161
Areas Covered: CO, NM, OK, TX
Regional Director **Kristie K. Elmquist** . . . . (972) 761-8215
E-mail: kelmquist@fdic.gov
Deputy Regional Director (Compliance) **(Vacant)** . . . . (972) 761-8001
Deputy Regional Director (Risk Management)
Serena L. Owens . . . . (972) 761-8200

Memphis (TN) Regional Office
6060 Primacy Parkway, Suite 300, Memphis, TN 38119
Tel: (800) 210-6354
Areas Covered: AR, LA, MS, TN
Regional Director **Kristie K. Elmquist** . . . . (972) 761-8215
1601 Bryan Street, Dallas, TX 75201-4586
Deputy Regional Director (Compliance) **(Vacant)** . . . . (972) 761-8001
1601 Bryan Street, Dallas, TX 75201-4586
Deputy Regional Director (Risk Management)
Serena L. Owens . . . . (972) 761-8200

Kansas City (MO) Regional Office
1100 Walnut Street, Suite 2100, Kansas City, MO 64106
Tel: (800) 209-7459
Areas Covered: IA, KS, MN, MO, NE, ND, SD
Regional Director **James D. "Jim" LaPierre** . . . . (816) 234-8141
E-mail: jlapierre@fdic.gov
Deputy Regional Director (Compliance) **(Vacant)** . . . . (816) 234-8172
Deputy Regional Director (Risk Management)
John Jilovec . . . . (816) 234-8141

New York (NY) Regional Office
20 Exchange Place, Room 6014, New York, NY 10005
Tel: (917) 320-2511
Areas Covered: DC, DE, MD, NJ, NY, PA, PR, VI
Regional Director **John F. Vogel** . . . . (917) 320-2570
Education: Keene State; Georgetown
Deputy Regional Director **Frank R. Hughes** . . . . (917) 320-2841

Boston (MA) Regional Office
15 Braintree Hill Office Park, Suite 200, Braintree, MA 02184-8701
Tel: (781) 794-5500 Fax: (781) 794-5533
Areas Covered: CT, ME, MA, NH, RI, VT
Regional Director **John F. Vogel** . . . . (917) 320-2570
Education: Keene State; Georgetown
Deputy Regional Director **Scott D. Strockoz** . . . . (917) 320-2511
E-mail: sstrockoz@fdic.gov

San Francisco (CA) Regional Office
25 Jessie Street at Ecker Square, Suite 2300,
San Francisco, CA 94105-2780
Tel: (415) 546-0160
Areas Covered: AK, AZ, CA, GU, HI, ID, MT, NV, OR, UT, WA, WY
Regional Director **Kathy L. Moe** . . . . (415) 808-8052
Education: Nebraska BS
Deputy Regional Director (Acting) **G. Chris Finnegan** . . . (415) 546-0160

INDEPENDENT AGENCIES

★ Presidential Appointment Requiring Senate Confirmation ☆ Presidential Appointment ☐ Schedule C Appointment ◇ Career Senior Foreign Service Appointment
● Career Senior Executive Service (SES) Appointment ○ Non-Career Senior Executive Service (SES) Appointment ■ Postal Career Executive Service

Legal Division
550 17th Street, NW, Washington, DC 20429-9990

Regional Offices

Legal Division - Atlanta
10 Tenth Street, NE, Suite 800, Atlanta, GA 30309-3906
Tel: (678) 916-2268

Regional Counsel **Andrea Fulton Toliver** .... (678) 916-2268
E-mail: atoliver@fdic.gov

Legal Division - Boston
15 Braintree Hill Office Park, Room 223, Braintree, MA 02184-8701
Tel: (781) 794-5615

Regional Counsel **David Alan Schecker** .... (781) 794-5615
E-mail: dschecker@fdic.gov
Education: Yale 1977 BA

Legal Division - Chicago
500 West Monroe Street, Suite 3200, Chicago, IL 60661-3697
Tel: (312) 382-6515

Regional Counsel **Timothy E. Divis** .... (312) 382-6515
Deputy Regional Counsel **Monica Tynan** .... (312) 382-6515
E-mail: mtynan@fdic.gov
Counsel **Samuel Brooks** .... (312) 382-6515

Legal Division - Dallas
1601 Bryan Street, Dallas, TX 75201-4586
Tel: (214) 754-0098

Regional Counsel **Victoria Dancy** .... (972) 761-8258
E-mail: vdancy@fdic.gov
Regional Counsel **Stephen C. Zachary** .... (972) 761-2626
E-mail: szachary@fdic.gov

Legal Division - Kansas City
1100 Walnut Street, Suite 2100, Kansas City, MO 64106
Tel: (816) 234-8000

Regional Counsel **Edward G. Lanning** .... (816) 234-8045

Legal Division - Memphis
Clark Tower, 5100 Poplar Avenue, Suite 1900, Memphis, TN 38137-5900
Tel: (901) 685-1603

Regional Counsel **Stephen C. Zachary** .... (972) 761-2626
1601 Bryan Street, Dallas, TX 75201-4586
E-mail: szachary@fdic.gov

Legal Division - San Francisco
25 Jessie Street at Ecker Square, Suite 2300,
San Francisco, CA 94105-2780
Tel: (415) 808-8177

Regional Counsel **Joseph J. Sano** .... (415) 808-8177
E-mail: jsano@fdic.gov

Deputy to the Chairman and Chief Financial Officer
550 17th Street, NW, Washington, DC 20429-9990
Tel: (202) 416-7232 (Public Information)

Division of Administration
Virginia Square, L. William Seidman Center,
3501 Fairfax Drive, Arlington, VA 22226
Tel: (202) 416-6940 (Public Information Center)

Regional Offices

Division of Administration - Atlanta
10 Tenth Street, NE, Suite 800, Atlanta, GA 30309-3906
Tel: (678) 916-2200

Regional Manager (Acting) **Michael Blaylock** .... (678) 916-2235
E-mail: mblaylock@fdic.gov

Division of Administration - Atlanta *(continued)*

Assistant Regional Manager/Chief, Corporate Services Branch **Greg Potz** .... (678) 916-2318
E-mail: gpotz@fdic.gov
Human Resources Officer **Michael Blaylock** .... (678) 916-2235

Division of Administration - Boston
15 Braintree Hill Office Park, Suite 100, Braintree, MA 02184-8701
Tel: (781) 794-5500

Regional Manager (Acting) **Karen Cieply** .... (781) 794-5759
E-mail: kcieply@fdic.gov
Assistant Regional Manager **(Vacant)** .... (781) 794-5751
Corporate Services Branch Chief **Karen Cieply** .... (781) 794-5759
Human Resources Officer, HR Branch **Dan V. Nowell** .... (917) 320-2800
350 Fifth Avenue, New York, NY 10118
E-mail: dnowell@fdic.gov

Division of Administration - Chicago
500 West Monroe Street, Suite 3200, Chicago, IL 60661-3697
Tel: (312) 382-6000

Regional Manager **Diane Fier** .... (312) 382-6871
E-mail: dfier@fdic.gov
Corporate Services Branch Chief **Diana Stefani** .... (312) 382-6886
Human Resources Officer, HR Branch **Joseph Arellano** .... (312) 382-6891
1601 Bryan Street, Dallas, TX 75201-4586

Division of Administration - Dallas
1601 Bryan Street, Dallas, TX 75201-4586
Tel: (214) 754-0098

Regional Manager **G. Mark Buck** .... (972) 761-2856
Assistant Regional Manager **Debra S. Jones** .... (972) 761-2183
Human Resources Officer, HR Branch **Carrie R. Quick** ... (972) 761-2587

Division of Administration - Kansas City
1100 Walnut Street, Suite 2100, Kansas City, MO 64106
Tel: (816) 234-8000

Regional Manager **Laura Lowry** .... (816) 234-8070
E-mail: llowry@fdic.gov
Corporate Services Branch Chief **Donald Forsyth** .... (816) 234-8081
25 Jessie Street at Ecker Square, Suite 2300,
San Francisco, CA 94105-2780
Assistant Regional Manager **(Vacant)** .... (816) 234-8070
Human Resources Officer, HR Branch **William Carey** .... (816) 234-8178

Division of Administration - New York
350 Fifth Avenue, New York, NY 10118
Tel: (917) 320-2500

Regional Manager **Avelino Rodriguez** .... (917) 320-2700

Division of Administration - San Francisco
25 Jessie Street at Ecker Square, San Francisco, CA 94105-2780
Tel: (415) 546-0160

Regional Manager **Joyce Yamasaki** .... (415) 808-8155
E-mail: jyamasaki@fdic.gov
Corporate Services Branch and Facilities Manager **Thomas "Tom" Zilka** .... (415) 808-8223
Human Resources Officer, HR Branch (Acting) **Barbara Pfaffenberger** .... (415) 808-8144

Division of Information Technology
Virginia Square, L. William Seidman Center,
3501 N. Fairfax Drive, Arlington, VA 22226
Tel: (877) 275-3342 Fax: (703) 516-5119

Regional Offices

Division of Information Technology - Atlanta
10 Tenth Street, NE, Suite 857, Atlanta, GA 30309-3906
Tel: (678) 916-2280

Client Services Section Chief **John Irizarry** .... (678) 916-5652
E-mail: jirizarry@fdic.gov

Division of Information Technology - Chicago
500 West Monroe Street, Suite 33030, Chicago, IL 60661-3697
Tel: (312) 382-6838

Client Services Section Chief **Kenneth Briscoe** . . . . (312) 382-6837
E-mail: kbriscoe@fdic.gov

Division of Information Technology - Dallas
1601 Bryan Street, PAC-09040, Dallas, TX 75201-4586
Tel: (972) 761-2457

Client Services Section Chief **Cheri M. Sims** . . . . (972) 761-2552

Division of Information Technology - Kansas City
1100 Walnut Street, Suite 2100, Kansas City, MO 64106
Tel: (816) 234-8014

Client Services Section Chief **Nicholas Patruno** . . . . (816) 234-8014
E-mail: npatruno@fdic.gov

Division of Information Technology - New York
20 Exchange Place, 4th Floor, Room 4012, New York, NY 10005
Tel: (917) 320-2660

Chief **Tricia Ensminger** . . . . (917) 320-2660
E-mail: tensminger@fdic.gov

Division of Information Technology - San Francisco
25 Jessie Street at Ecker Square, Suite 1522,
San Francisco, CA 94105-2780
Tel: (415) 808-8128

Client Services Section Chief **Earl Bears** . . . . (415) 808-8128

United States Federal Labor Relations Authority (FLRA)

Description: The Federal Labor Relations Authority oversees the federal service labor-management relations program and administers the law that protects the rights of employees of the federal government to organize, bargain collectively, and participate in policy decisions through labor organizations of their choice.

1400 K Street, NW, Washington, DC 20424-0001
Tel: (202) 218-7770 (Personnel Locator) Tel: (202) 218-7740 (Case Processing Information Duty Officer, Publications Information) Tel: (202) 218-7750 (Procurement Information)
Tel: (202) 218-7999 (Freedom of Information/Privacy Act)
Fax: (202) 482-6778 Internet: www.flra.gov
Internet: www.usa.gov (Official US Government Website)

THE AUTHORITY

1400 K Street, NW, Washington, DC 20424-0001

Note: Members may continue to serve until a successor takes office or until the close of the Congress beginning after their expiration date, whichever comes first.

Office of the General Counsel

1400 K Street, NW, Suite 200, Washington, DC 20424-0001
Tel: (202) 218-7910 Fax: (202) 482-6608 E-mail: ogcmail@flra.gov

Atlanta (GA) Regional Office

225 Peachtree Street, Suite 1950, Atlanta, GA 30323-1203
Tel: (404) 331-5300 Fax: (404) 331-5280 E-mail: aromail@flra.gov
Areas Covered: AL, FL, GA, MS, NC, SC, VI

Regional Director **Richard S. Jones** .... (404) 331-5300 ext. 5018
Education: DePauw; Toledo JD
Regional Attorney **Brent S. Hudspeth** .... (404) 331-5300 ext. 5022
Education: Mississippi BA, BS, MBA, 1989 JD
Administrative Officer **Melissa Hardy** .... (404) 331-5300 ext. 5011
E-mail: mhardy@flra.gov
Administrative Assistant **Carnell Stuckey** ...... (404) 331-5300 ext. 5030
Senior Attorney **Ayo Stone** .... (404) 331-5300 ext. 5013
Senior Attorney **Mark Halverson** .... (404) 331-5300 ext. 5015
Senior Attorney **Patricia Kush** .... (404) 331-5300 ext. 5016
Senior Attorney **Brian Locke** .... (404) 331-5300 ext. 5021
Senior Attorney **Carrie McCready** .... (404) 331-5300 ext. 5024
Senior Labor Relations Specialist
Veneka Henderson .... (404) 331-5300 ext. 5014

Chicago (IL) Regional Office

224 S. Michigan Avenue, Suite 445, Chicago, IL 60604-2505
Tel: (312) 886-3465 Fax: (312) 886-5977 E-mail: cromail@flra.gov
Areas Covered: IA, IL, IN, KY, MI, MN, MO, ND, OH, TN, WI

Regional Director **Sandra LeBold** .... (312) 886-3465 ext. 4015
E-mail: slebold@flra.gov
Education: Indiana BA; Purdue MA; DePaul JD
Administrative Officer **Inez Thomas** .... (312) 886-3465 ext. 4011
E-mail: ithomas@flra.gov
Senior Labor Relations Specialist **(Vacant)** ..... (312) 886-3465 ext. 4014

Denver (CO) Regional Office

Cesar Chavez Memorial Building, 1244 Speer Boulevard, Suite 446, Denver, CO 80204-3581
Tel: (303) 844-5224 Fax: (303) 844-2774 E-mail: deromail@flra.gov
Areas Covered: AZ, CO, KS, MT, NE, SD, UT, WY

● Regional Director
Timothy J. "Tim" Sullivan .... (303) 844-5224 ext. 1012
E-mail: tsullivan@flra.gov
Education: Oklahoma BA, 1987 JD
Administrative Officer **Emestyne Benford** ..... (303) 844-5226 ext. 1010

San Francisco (CA) Regional Office

901 Market Street, Suite 470, San Francisco, CA 94103-1791
Tel: (415) 356-5000 Fax: (415) 356-5017 E-mail: sromail@flra.gov
Areas Covered: AK, CA, HI, ID, NV, OR, WA, all land and water areas west of the continents of North and South America (except coastal islands) to longitude 90 degrees East.

● Regional Director **John Pannozzo, Jr.** .... (415) 356-5000 ext. 2021
E-mail: jpannozzo@flra.gov
Education: Ohio State 1979 BA; Georgetown 1982 MA; New England 1984 JD
Administrative Officer **Richard Armstrong** .... (415) 356-5000 ext. 2011

Washington (DC) Regional Office

1400 K Street, NW, 2nd Floor, Washington, DC 20424-0001
Tel: (202) 357-6029 Fax: (202) 482-6724 E-mail: wromail@flra.gov
Areas Covered: DC, MD, VA, WV, All land and water areas east of the continents of North and South America to longitude 90 degrees East, except the Virgin Islands, Panama, Puerto Rico and coastal islands.

Regional Director **Jessica S. Bartlett** .... (202) 357-6029 ext. 6017
E-mail: jbartlett@flra.gov
Education: Mary Washington Col BA; George Mason JD
Regional Attorney **Douglas J. Guerrin** .... (202) 357-6029 ext. 6027
E-mail: dguerrin@flra.gov

Federal Maritime Commission (FMC)

Description: The Federal Maritime Commission regulates waterborne foreign commerce, develops and administers policies and regulations that foster a fair, efficient and secure maritime transportation system, protects U.S. maritime commerce from unfair foreign trade practices and market-distorting activities, facilitates compliance with U.S. shipping statutes through oversight and outreach, and assists in resolving disputes.

800 North Capitol Street, NW, Washington, DC 20573-0001
Tel: (202) 523-5725 Tel: (202) 523-5773 (Personnel Locator)
Tel: (202) 523-5865 (Inspector General Hotline)
Tel: (202) 523-5856 (Service Contracts Inquiries) Fax: (202) 523-3782
E-mail: inquiries@fmc.gov Internet: www.fmc.gov
Internet: www.usa.gov (Official US Government Website)

THE COMMISSION

800 North Capitol Street, NW, Washington, DC 20573-0001
Note: Commissioners may continue to serve until reappointed or replaced.

Office of the Managing Director

800 North Capitol Street, NW, Washington, DC 20573-0001
Fax: (202) 523-3646

Bureau of Enforcement (BOE)

800 North Capitol Street, NW, Washington, DC 20573-0001
Tel: (202) 523-5783 Fax: (202) 523-5785
Fax: (202) 523-3725 (Alternate) E-mail: boe@fmc.gov

Headquarters Area Representative

Director of Field Investigations
Michael F. Carley Room 1078 . . . . (202) 523-5800

Houston (TX) Area Representative

650 North Sam Houston Parkway, Houston, TX 77060-5908
Tel: (281) 591-6088 Fax: (281) 591-6099
Areas Covered: Houston Gulf Coast

Area Representative **Adam Sinko** . . . . (281) 386-8211

Los Angeles (CA) Area Representative

839 South Beacon Street, San Pedro, CA 90733-0230
Mail: P.O. Box 230, San Pedro, CA 90733-0230
Tel: (310) 514-4905 Fax: (310) 514-3931
Areas Covered: Pacific - Southwest

Area Representative **(Vacant)** . . . . (310) 514-4905
Assistant Area Representative **(Vacant)** . . . . (310) 514-8618

New Orleans (LA) Area Representative

423 Canal Street, New Orleans, LA 70130
P.O. Box 700, St. Rose, LA 70087-0700
Tel: (504) 466-6380 Fax: (504) 466-6379
Areas Covered: Gulf Coast

Area Representative **(Vacant)** . . . . (504) 466-6380

New York (NY) Area Representative

Woodbridge Place, 517 Route One South,
Suite 2220, Iselin, NJ 08830
Fax: (732) 283-2498

Area Representative **Erin Tasova** . . . . (732) 283-2496
Assistant Area Representative **Matthew D. Forst** . . . . (732) 283-2497

Seattle (WA) Area Representative

The Fabulich Center, 3600 Port of Tacoma Road,
Suite 508, Tacoma, WA 98424-1044
Tel: (253) 922-7622 Fax: (253) 922-7859
Areas Covered: Pacific - Northwest

Area Representative
LCDR Shadrack L. Scheirman USCG . . . . (253) 922-7622
Assistant Area Representative **Diane Rebello** . . . . (206) 731-7319

South Florida Area Representative

P.O. Box 813609, Hollywood, FL 33081-3609
Tel: (954) 963-5362 Fax: (954) 963-5630
Areas Covered: Atlantic - Southeast

Area Representative **Andrew Margolis** . . . . (954) 963-5362
Area Representative **Eric O. Mintz** . . . . (954) 963-5284
E-mail: emintz@fmc.gov

Federal Mediation and Conciliation Service (FMCS)

Description: The Federal Mediation and Conciliation Service promotes the development of stable labor-management relationships. It assists in disputes through mediation, collective bargaining, and voluntary arbitration, and fosters constructive, joint relationships between labor and management leaders to achieve solutions to common problems.

One Independence Square, 250 E Street, SW, Washington, DC 20427
Tel: (202) 606-5460 (Personnel Locator)
Tel: (202) 606-3664 (Procurement Information)
Tel: (202) 606-8080 (Public Information)
Tel: (202) 606-5444 (Freedom of Information/Privacy Act)
Fax: (202) 606-4251 Fax: (202) 606-4216 (Human Resources)
Internet: www.fmcs.gov

OFFICE OF THE DIRECTOR

One Independence Square, 250 E Street, SW, Washington, DC 20427
Tel: (202) 606-8100 Fax: (202) 606-4251

Office of Field Operations

● Deputy Director **Gary R. Hattal** .... (202) 606-8100
301 Grant Street, Pittsburgh, PA 15219-1407
E-mail: ghattal@fmcs.gov

Regional Office (Glendale, CA)

Glendale Financial Square, 500 North Brand Boulevard, Suite 410, Glendale, CA 91203
Tel: (818) 507-9002 Fax: (818) 409-1321

Regional Director **Linda A. Gonzalez** .... (818) 409-1324
E-mail: lgonzalez@fmcs.gov
Administrative Assistant **Stephanie Tucker** .... (818) 507-9002
E-mail: stucker@fmcs.gov

Regional Office (Hinsdale, IL)

Elm Plaza, 908 North Elm Street, Suite 203, Hinsdale, IL 60521
Tel: (630) 887-4750 Fax: (630) 887-7183

Regional Director **David F. Bom** .... (630) 887-4761
E-mail: dborn@fmcs.gov
Secretary **Elda Radogno** .... (630) 887-4750
E-mail: eradogno@fmcs.gov
Secretary **Kathy Tunney** .... (630) 887-4750
E-mail: ktunney@fmcs.gov

Regional Office (Independence, OH)

6161 Oak Tree Boulevard, Suite 100, Independence, OH 44131
Fax: (216) 520-4819

Regional Director **Carolyn T. Brommer** .... (216) 520-4811
E-mail: cbrommer@fmcs.gov
Regional Administrative Specialist **Bernadette Pace** .... (216) 520-4800
E-mail: bpace@fmcs.gov
Administrative Assistant **Brenda M. Brain** .... (216) 520-4801

Regional Office (Iselin, NJ)

Woodbridge Place Building, 517 U.S. Highway One South, Suite 3020, Iselin, NJ 08830
Tel: (732) 726-3120 Fax: (732) 726-3124

Regional Director **Peter Donatello** .... (732) 726-3120
E-mail: pdonatello@fmcs.gov
Administrative Assistant **Donna Filosa** .... (732) 726-3122
E-mail: dfilosa@fmcs.gov

Regional Office (Minneapolis, MN)

Broadway Place West, 1300 Godward Street, Suite 3950, Minneapolis, MN 55413
Tel: (612) 331-6670 Fax: (612) 331-5272

Regional Director **Lane Harstad** .... (612) 331-6193
E-mail: lharstad@fmcs.gov
Secretary **Steven Geisen** .... (612) 331-6672
E-mail: sgeisen@fmcs.gov

Regional Office (Nashville, TN)

617 Potomac Place, Suite 405, Smyrna, TN 37167

Regional Director **Peter M. Cheng** .... (615) 223-6917
E-mail: pcheng@fmcs.gov Fax: (615) 223-7262
Administrative Assistant **(Vacant)** .... (407) 730-4661
3452 Lake Lynda Drive, Suite 122, Orlando, FL 32817-1472

Regional Office (Philadelphia, PA)

1601 Market Street, Suite 910, Philadelphia, PA 19103
Fax: (215) 717-7508

Regional Director **D. Scott Blake** .... (215) 717-7500
E-mail: sblake@fmcs.gov
Regional Administrative Specialist
Sharon L. Rafferty .... (215) 717-7500
E-mail: srafferty@fmcs.gov

Regional Office (Pittsburgh, PA)

One Oxford Centre, 301 Grant Street, Suite 2570, Pittsburgh, PA 15219-1407
Fax: (412) 235-7451

Regional Director **Michael Franczak** .... (216) 520-4809
E-mail: mfranczak@fmcs.gov

Regional Office (Seattle, WA)

Weston Building, 2001 Sixth Avenue, Suite 2500, Seattle, WA 98121
Tel: (206) 553-5800 Fax: (206) 553-6653

Regional Director **Beth M. Schindler** .... (206) 553-5801
E-mail: bschindler@fmcs.gov
Administrative Assistant **Cindy Arbogast** .... (206) 553-5800

Regional Office (St. Louis, MO)

12140 Woodcrest Executive Drive, Suite 325, St. Louis, MO 63141-5013
Tel: (314) 576-3977 Fax: (314) 576-2738

Regional Director **Barbara Rumph** .... (314) 205-2007

★ Presidential Appointment Requiring Senate Confirmation ☆ Presidential Appointment □ Schedule C Appointment ◇ Career Senior Foreign Service Appointment
● Career Senior Executive Service (SES) Appointment ○ Non-Career Senior Executive Service (SES) Appointment ■ Postal Career Executive Service

Federal Reserve System (FRS)

Description: The Federal Reserve System is the central bank of the United States, responsible for administering and making policy for the nation's credit and monetary affairs. The system consists of 12 Federal Reserve Banks and supporting branches and facilities situated throughout the country.

20th Street and Constitution Avenue, NW, Washington, DC 20551
Tel: (202) 452-3000 (Personnel Locator)
Tel: (202) 452-3296 (Procurement Information)
Tel: (202) 452-3204 (Public Information)
Tel: (202) 452-3245 (Publications Information)
Tel: (202) 452-3684 (Freedom of Information/Privacy Act)
Fax: (202) 452-3819 Internet: www.federalreserve.gov
Internet: www.federalreserve.gov/careers (Career Opportunities)
Internet: www.federalreserve.gov/consumers.htm (Consumer Education)
Internet: www.federalreserveeducation.org (Educational Website)
Internet: www.federalreserve.gov/rnd.htm
(Federal Reserve Economic Data)
Internet: www.federalreserve.gov/newsevents.htm (News and Events)

The Board of Governors

20th Street and Constitution Avenue, NW, Washington, DC 20551
Tel: (202) 452-3000 Fax: (202) 452-3819

FEDERAL RESERVE BANKS

Federal Reserve Bank of Atlanta (GA) (FRBGA)

1000 Peachtree Street, NE, Atlanta, GA 30309-4470
Tel: (404) 498-8500 Fax: (404) 498-8050 Internet: www.frbatlanta.org
Areas Covered: AL, FL, GA, Southern LA, Southern MS, Central and Eastern TN

Executive Office

President and Chief Executive Officer
Dr. Raphael William Bostic . . . . (404) 498-8500
Education: Harvard 1987 BA; Stanford 1995 PhD
First Vice President and Chief Operating Officer
Andre T. Anderson . . . . (404) 498-8503

District Operations and Administrative Services

1000 Peachtree Street, NE, Atlanta, GA 30309-4470
Fax: (404) 498-8572

Senior Vice President **Jeffrey "Jeff" Devine** . . . . (404) 498-8195

Auditing

Vice President and General Auditor **Joan Buchanan** . . . . (404) 498-7345
Education: Georgia Tech BS
Assistant Vice President and Assistant General Auditor
Craig Griffin . . . . (404) 498-8500
Education: Auburn BA; Samford MBA
Vice President for Auditor Development and System Audit Services **Jeff Thomas** . . . . (404) 498-8500
E-mail: jeff.thomas@atl.frb.org
Education: Auburn BA
Assistant Vice President for Auditor Development and System Audit Services **Gregory "Greg" Odum** . . . . . . (404) 498-8500
Education: North Florida BBA

Corporate Engagement

Senior Vice President **Leah Davenport** . . . . (404) 498-8512
Education: Tennessee Tech BS

Corporate Engagement *(continued)*

Assistant Vice President **Donna Fay** . . . . (404) 498-8500

Corporate Secretary

1000 Peachtree Street, NE, Atlanta, GA 30309-4470
Tel: (404) 498-8107

Corporate Secretary and Assistant to the Vice President
(Vacant) . . . . (404) 498-8504

Human Resources

Vice President **Kim Blythe** . . . . (404) 498-8500
Education: Cornell
Assistant Vice President **Pam Barton** . . . . (404) 498-8500
Assistant Vice President **Tonya Byrd-Sorrells** . . . . (404) 498-8500

Public Affairs

Vice President and Public Affairs Officer
Michael "Mike" Chriszt . . . . (404) 498-8847
E-mail: michael.chriszt@atl.frb.org
Education: Miami U (OH) BA, MA

Corporate Services Division

Senior Vice President, Chief Financial Officer and Chief Technology Officer **W. Brian Bowling** . . . . (404) 498-8512
E-mail: brian.bowling@atl.frb.org

Financial Services

Senior Vice President [Law Enforcement, Facility Management] **Leah Davenport** . . . . (404) 498-8512
Education: Tennessee Tech BS
Assistant Vice President **(Vacant)** . . . . (404) 498-8500

Research

Executive Vice President and Director of Research
David E. Altig . . . . (404) 498-8824
Education: Iowa; Brown U 1987
Senior Vice President and Associate Director of Research **Paula Tkac** . . . . (404) 498-8813
Education: Chicago 1993 PhD
Vice President **(Vacant)** . . . . (404) 498-8776
Vice President and Senior Economist **Mark Jensen** . . . . . . (404) 498-8019
Education: Weber State BSEc; Washington U (MO) MS, PhD
Vice President **Paige Wilcox** . . . . (404) 498-8782

Community and Economic Development

Vice President and Community Affairs Officer
(Vacant) . . . . (404) 498-7297
Vice President **Karen Leone de Nie** . . . . (404) 498-8500
E-mail: karen.leonedenie@atl.frb.org
Education: Wisconsin BS; Georgia Tech MS

Retail Payments Risk Forum

Senior Vice President and Director **Mary Kepler** . . . . (404) 498-8713
Education: Central Missouri BBA

Retail Payments Office

First Vice President and Retail Product Office Director
(Vacant) . . . . (404) 498-8503

(continued on next page)

★ Presidential Appointment Requiring Senate Confirmation ☆ Presidential Appointment □ Schedule C Appointment ◇ Career Senior Foreign Service Appointment
● Career Senior Executive Service (SES) Appointment ○ Non-Career Senior Executive Service (SES) Appointment ■ Postal Career Executive Service

INDEPENDENT AGENCIES

Retail Payments Office *(continued)*

Executive Vice President and Retail Product Office Manager **Cheryl Venable** . . . . . . (404) 498-8390
Education: Saint Louis U BBA, MBA
Assistant Vice President **(Vacant)** . . . . . . (404) 498-8390
Senior Vice President **Denise I. Connor MBA** . . . . . . (404) 498-8390
Education: Missouri MBA

Atlanta (GA) Branch
1000 Peachtree Street, NE, Atlanta, GA 30309-4470
Tel: (404) 498-8500

Vice President and Regional Executive **Rebecca "Becky" Gunn** . . . . . . (404) 498-8776

Birmingham (AL) Branch
524 Liberty Parkway, Birmingham, AL 35242-7531
Tel: (205) 968-6700 Fax: (205) 968-6715

Vice President and Regional Executive **Anoop Mishra** . . . (205) 968-6701

Jacksonville (FL) Branch
800 West Water Street, Jacksonville, FL 32204
Tel: (904) 632-1154

Vice President and Regional Executive **Christopher L. Oakley** . . . . . . (904) 632-1003
Education: Georgia Tech BS

Miami (FL) Branch
9100 NW 36th Street, Miami, FL 33178-2425
P.O. Box 520847, Miami, FL 33152-0847
Tel: (305) 591-2065 Fax: (305) 471-6240

Vice President and Branch Manager **Paul Graham** . . . . . . (305) 591-2065
Vice President and Regional Executive **Karen Gilmore** . . . (305) 471-6471
Education: Central Florida BA
Assistant Vice President and Branch Manager **Beverly Ferrell** . . . . . . (305) 591-2065

Nashville (TN) Branch
301 Eighth Avenue North, Nashville, TN 37203-4407
Tel: (615) 251-7100 Fax: (615) 251-7206

Vice President and Regional Executive **(Vacant)** . . . . . . (615) 251-2201
Vice President **Laurel Graefe** . . . . . . (615) 251-2201

New Orleans (LA) Branch
525 St. Charles Avenue, New Orleans, LA 70130
P.O. Box 61630, New Orleans, LA 70161-1630
Tel: (504) 593-3200 Fax: (504) 593-3213 Fax: (504) 593-3238

Vice President and Regional Executive **Adrienne Slack** . . . . . . (504) 593-3201
Assistant Vice President and Branch Manager **Richard Squires** . . . . . . (504) 593-3200

Federal Reserve Bank of Boston (MA) (FRBMA)

600 Atlantic Avenue, Boston, MA 02210
Mail: P.O. Box 55882, Boston, MA 02205
Tel: (617) 973-3000 Fax: (617) 973-5903
E-mail: bos.webmaster@bos.frb.org Internet: www.bos.frb.org
Areas Covered: CT (Excluding Fairfield County), ME, MA, NH, RI, VT

Executive Office

President and Chief Executive Officer **Eric S. Rosengren** . . . . . . (617) 973-3000
E-mail: eric.rosengren@bos.frb.org
Education: Colby 1979 BA; Wisconsin 1984 MS, 1986 PhD
First Vice President and Chief Operating Officer **Kenneth C. Montgomery** . . . . . . (617) 973-3387
E-mail: kenneth.montgomery@bos.frb.org
Education: Seton Hall; Fairleigh Dickinson MBA
Assistant Vice President and Corporate Secretary **(Vacant)** . . . . . . (617) 973-3000
Vice President and Accounting Officer **Astier Sium** . . . . . (617) 973-3000

Administrative Services
Vice President **Leah A. Maurer** . . . . . . (617) 973-3000

Auditing
Senior Vice President and General Auditor **Jon D. Colvin** . . . . . . (617) 973-5909
E-mail: jon.colvin@bos.frb.org

Human Resources and Legal Services
Senior Vice President and General Counsel **Cynthia A. Conley** . . . . . . (617) 973-3525
E-mail: cynthia.conley@bos.frb.org
Vice President and Deputy General Counsel **(Vacant)** . . . . (617) 973-3000
Vice President **John J. Kroen** . . . . . . (617) 973-3000
Vice President and Associate General Counsel **Patricia Allouise** . . . . . . (617) 973-3000
Assistant Vice President and Assistant General Counsel **Mary Bickerton** . . . . . . (617) 973-3000

Finance, Strategy and Planning, and Information Technology
Senior Vice President and Chief Financial Officer **Aparna Ramesh** . . . . . . (617) 973-5942
Education: MIT MBA
Senior Vice President and Payments Security Strategy Leader **Kenneth C. Montgomery** . . . . . . (617) 973-3387
Education: Seton Hall; Fairleigh Dickinson MBA

National Financial and Accounting Services
Executive Vice President, Financial Support Office **Robert J. Whelan** . . . . . . (617) 973-3544
Education: Bowdoin BA; Harvard MBA
Senior Vice President **(Vacant)** . . . . . . (617) 973-3544

Research Department
Executive Vice President and Director of Research **Geoffrey M. B. Tootell** . . . . . . (617) 973-3430
Education: Harvard 1983 AB, 1989 PhD

Regional and Community Outreach
Executive Vice President and Senior Policy Advisor **Jeffrey C. "Jeff" Fuhrer** . . . . . . (617) 973-3410
Education: Princeton 1979 AB; Harvard 1983 MA, 1985 PhD
Senior Vice President and Community Affairs Officer **Prabal Chakrabarti** . . . . . . (617) 973-3959
Senior Vice President and Special Advisor to the President for Community Development **Richard C. Walker III** . . . . . . (617) 973-3059
Education: Villanova
Vice President, Department Administrative Officer **Anna Steiger** . . . . . . (617) 973-3201
E-mail: anna.steiger@bos.frb.org
Education: Barnard BA; JFK School Govt MPP
Vice President **Thomas L. Lavelle** . . . . . . (617) 973-3647
E-mail: thomas.l.lavelle@bos.frb.org
Assistant Vice President, Working Cities Initiative **Tamar Kotelchuck** . . . . . . (617) 973-2982
Assistant Vice President, Community Development Outreach **Sol Carbonell** . . . . . . (617) 973-3285
E-mail: sol.carbonell@bos.frb.org
Education: Harvard MPA
Deputy Director, Business Analytics and Outreach Support **Sharon St. Louis** . . . . . . (617) 973-3262
E-mail: sharon.stlouis@bos.frb.org
Education: Virginia State BS
Deputy Director **Chris Shannon** . . . . . . (617) 973-3483
E-mail: chris.shannon@bos.frb.org
Education: Delaware BA; VCU MFA

Supervision, Regulation and Credit Department
Executive Vice President and Director of Supervision, Regulation and Credit **James T. "Jim" Nolan** . . . . . . (617) 973-3348
Education: Babson MBA

Treasury and Financial Services
Senior Vice President **James S. "Jim" Cunha** . . . . . . (617) 973-3837

★ Presidential Appointment Requiring Senate Confirmation ☆ Presidential Appointment □ Schedule C Appointment ◇ Career Senior Foreign Service Appointment
● Career Senior Executive Service (SES) Appointment ○ Non-Career Senior Executive Service (SES) Appointment ■ Postal Career Executive Service

Federal Reserve Bank of Chicago (IL) (FRBIL)

230 South LaSalle Street, Chicago, IL 60604-1413
Mail: P.O. Box 834, Chicago, IL 60690-0834
Tel: (312) 322-5322 Tel: (312) 322-5111 (Public Information)
Fax: (312) 322-5959 E-mail: information.chi@chi.frb.org
Internet: www.chicagofed.org
Areas Covered: Northern IL, IN, IA, Southern MI, Southern WI

President and Chief Executive Officer
Charles L. Evans .... (312) 322-5001
Education: Virginia 1980 BA; Carnegie Mellon 1985 MS, 1989 PhD
Executive Assistant **Karen Johnston** .... (312) 322-5003
E-mail: karen.johnston@chi.frb.org
First Vice President and Chief Operating Officer
Ellen Bromagen .... (312) 322-5004
Education: Wisconsin; DePaul
Executive Vice President, Customer Relations and Support Office **Shonda Clay** .... (312) 322-5066
Executive Vice President and Director of Research
Daniel G. Sullivan .... (312) 322-5790
E-mail: daniel.sullivan@chi.frb.org
Education: Chicago 1981 AB; Princeton 1987 PhD
Executive Vice President, Supervision and Regulation
Catharine "Cathy" Lemieux .... (312) 322-4246
Education: Texas A&M PhD
Senior Vice President and Chief Financial Officer
Margaret K. "Peg" Koenigs .... (312) 322-2367
E-mail: margaret.koenigs@chi.frb.org
Senior Vice President and Detroit Branch Manager, District Operations, Administrative Services, Law Enforcement **Robert G. Wiley** .... (312) 322-5488
Education: St Mary Col BA
Senior Vice President and Equal Employment Opportunity Officer, Central Bank Services and Finance **Valerie J. Van Meter** .... (312) 322-5888
E-mail: valerie.vanmeter@chi.frb.org
Education: Michigan; Stonier; Chicago MBA
Senior Vice President, Customer Relations and Support Office **Tracy Harrington** .... (312) 322-5322
Senior Vice President, Marketing and Sales **(Vacant)** .... (312) 322-5322
Senior Vice President, Payments Industry Outreach
Sean Rodriguez CCM .... (312) 322-5531
Education: Colorado 1983 BA; Wisconsin 1991
Senior Vice President, People, Culture and Communications **Nokihomis Willis** .... (312) 322-5322
Senior Vice President, Director of Financial Markets and Associate Director of Research **David Marshall** .... (312) 322-5102
E-mail: david.marshall@chi.frb.org
Education: Yale 1972 BA; Carnegie Mellon 1985 MS, 1988 PhD
Senior Vice President and General Counsel, Ethics [Corporate Secretary]
Katherine Hilton "Kathy" Schrepfer .... (312) 322-5322
Education: Illinois BA; Loyola U (Chicago)
Senior Vice President, Supervision and Regulation
Steven M. "Steve" Durfey .... (312) 322-6844
Education: Iowa 1986 BA
Senior Vice President, Supervision and Regulation
Pamela Rieger .... (312) 322-5322
Senior Vice President, Supervision and Regulation
Julie Williams .... (312) 322-4032
Senior Vice President and Senior Research Advisor
Spencer Krane .... (312) 322-2382
E-mail: spencer.krane@chi.frb.org
Education: Kalamazoo 1978 BA; UC Berkeley 1985 PhD
Senior Vice President, Risk Specialists Division
Grant Thornton .... (312) 322-6164
Vice President and Associate General Counsel
Eurie Sturm .... (312) 322-5422
E-mail: eurie.sturm@chi.frb.org
Vice President, Administrative Services and Operations
Matt LaRocco .... (312) 322-5382
E-mail: matt.larocco@chi.frb.org
Education: Aurora U BBA
Vice President, Budget and Financial Reporting, PACS Compliance and Financial Systems Group
Jeffery Anderson .... (312) 322-6029
E-mail: jeffery.anderson@chi.frb.org
Education: Indiana 1984 BSA; Northern Illinois 1991 MBA

Vice President, Chicago Cash **Mary H. Sherburne** .... (312) 322-5457
Education: Iowa 1986 BSA
Vice President, Finance **(Vacant)** .... (312) 322-5322
Vice President, Supervision and Regulation
Mark H. Kawa .... (312) 322-2439
E-mail: mark.h.kawa@chi.frb.org
Vice President, General Auditor **Jeffrey B. Marcus** .... (312) 322-5322
Education: Northern Illinois BS; DePaul MBA
Vice President, Information Technology
Daniel Reimann .... (312) 322-5485
E-mail: daniel.reimann@chi.frb.org
Vice President, Public Affairs **Douglas "Doug" Tillett** .... (312) 322-5201
E-mail: doug.tillett@chi.frb.org
Tel: (312) 493-8088
Communications Manager **Dan Wassmann** .... (312) 322-2374
Education: Illinois 1981 BAJ
Vice President, Regional and Foreign Group Technology **(Vacant)** .... (312) 322-5895
Vice President, Customer Relations and Support
(Vacant) .... (312) 322-8344
Economic Advisor and Senior Economist
William A. Strauss .... (312) 322-8151
Education: SUNY (Buffalo) BA; Northwestern MA
Payments Strategy Director **David A. Sapenaro** .... (314) 444-8721
Education: Missouri (Kansas City) 1985 BBA

Economic Research Department
230 South LaSalle Street, Chicago, IL 60604-1413
Mail: P.O. Box 834, Chicago, IL 60690-0834

Community Development and Policy Studies

Vice President **Alicia Williams** .... (312) 322-5910
E-mail: alicia.williams@chi.frb.org
Education: Western Illinois 1997 BB
Business Economist **Emily Engel** .... (312) 322-5322
Community Affairs Managing Director
Jeremiah P. Boyle .... (312) 322-5322
Director of Policy Studies **Michael V. Berry** .... (312) 322-5192
Economic Development and Iowa State Director
Marva Williams .... (312) 322-5322
Senior Economist **Susan Longworth** .... (312) 322-5322
Education: Michigan BA; Chicago MBA

Finance Section

Senior Vice President, Associate Director of Research and Director of Financial Markets
Anna Louise Paulson .... (312) 322-2169
Education: Carleton 1987 BA; Chicago 1991 MA, 1994 PhD
Vice President and Senior Research Advisor **Ed Nosal** .... (312) 322-6070
Education: Queen Mary (UK) 1978 BA; McMaster 1979 MEc; Queen Mary (UK) 1985 PhD
Vice President, Economic Advisor for Banking and Financial Services **Douglas D. Evanoff** .... (312) 322-5322
E-mail: douglas.evanoff@chi.frb.org
Education: Western Kentucky 1973 BSE; New Orleans 1974 MEcon; Southern Illinois 1980 PhD
Vice President, Payments Group **(Vacant)** .... (312) 322-2156

Macroeconomics Section

Vice President, Economic Advisor for Macroeconomic Policy **Jonas Fisher** .... (312) 322-8177
E-mail: jonas.fisher@chi.frb.org
Education: Toronto 1987 BS; Queen's U (Canada) 1988 MA; Northwestern 1994 PhD
Senior Economist and Research Advisor
Alejandro Justiniano .... (312) 322-5900
Education: Maryland 1996 BA; Princeton 2000 MA, 2004 PhD
Senior Economist and Research Advisor
Francois R. Velde .... (312) 322-2526
Education: Ecole Polytechnique (France) 1987 BA; Stanford 1992 PhD
Senior Economist and Research Advisor
Marcelo Veracierto .... (312) 322-5695
Education: Minnesota 1995 PhD

INDEPENDENT AGENCIES

★ Presidential Appointment Requiring Senate Confirmation ☆ Presidential Appointment ☐ Schedule C Appointment ◇ Career Senior Foreign Service Appointment
● Career Senior Executive Service (SES) Appointment ○ Non-Career Senior Executive Service (SES) Appointment ■ Postal Career Executive Service

Market Analytics Section
Vice President, Financial Markets **Robert Cox** .... (312) 322-5322

Microeconomics Section
Vice President, Director for Microeconomic Research
Daniel Aaronson .... (312) 322-5650
E-mail: dan.aaronson@chi.frb.org
Education: Washington U (MO) 1989 BA; Northwestern 1996 PhD
Director, Chicago Census Research Data Center and
Senior Economist **Bhashkar Mazumder** .... (312) 322-8166
Education: NYU BA, MEc; UC Berkeley PhD
Senior Economist and Research Advisor **Lisa Barrow** .... (312) 322-5073
Education: Carleton 1991 BA; Princeton 1999 PhD
Senior Economist and Research Advisor **Luojia Hu** ...... (312) 322-8122
Education: UC San Diego 1995 MA; Princeton 2000 PhD

Regional Analysis Section
Economic Advisor and Vice President Regional
Economics **William A. "Bill" Testa** .... (312) 322-5791
Education: Northwestern 1975; Ohio State 1981 PhD
Policy Economist **Scott A. Brave** .... (312) 322-5784
Senior Associate Economist, Detroit Branch
Martin Lavelle .... (312) 322-5322
Senior Business Economist **David Oppedahl** .... (312) 322-6122
Senior Business Economist **Paul Traub** .... (313) 964-6297
Senior Economist and Economic Advisor
Rick Mattoon .... (312) 322-2428
Senior Economist and Research Advisor
Leslie McGranahan .... (312) 322-5655
Education: Northwestern PhD

Information Systems
230 South LaSalle Street, Chicago, IL 60604-1413
Mail: P.O. Box 834, Chicago, IL 60690-0834
Information Security Officer **Daniel Reimann** .... (312) 322-5485
E-mail: daniel.reimann@chi.frb.org Fax: (312) 322-5959

Library/Knowledge Center
230 South LaSalle Street, Chicago, IL 60604-1413
Mail: P.O. Box 834, Chicago, IL 60690-0834
Tel: (312) 322-5824 Fax: (312) 322-5091
Knowledge Center Manager **Susan Chenoweth** .... (312) 322-6169
E-mail: susan.chenoweth@chi.frb.org

Real Estate and Facilities
230 South LaSalle Street, Chicago, IL 60604-1413
Mail: P.O. Box 834, Chicago, IL 60690-0834
Fax: (312) 322-5959
Assistant Vice President, District Administrative
Services **(Vacant)** .... (312) 322-5322

Detroit (MI) Branch
1600 East Warren Avenue, Detroit, MI 48207
Tel: (313) 964-6880 Fax: (313) 964-6149
Chair **(Vacant)** .... (313) 964-6880
Director **Joseph B. Anderson, Jr.**
Term Expires: December 31, 2019
Education: West Point BS; UCLA
Director **Santanu K. "Sandy" Baruah**
Term Expires: December 31, 2020
Education: Oregon BS; Willamette 1995 MBA
Director **Linda Hubbard**
Director **James M. Nicholson**
Director **Richard "Rip" Rapson**
Term Expires: December 31, 2018
Education: Pomona BA; Columbia JD
Director **(Vacant)**
Vice President, District Cash **Donna Dziak** .... (313) 964-6174
Education: Michigan State; Wayne State U MBA
Chief Information Officer and Detroit Branch Manager
Robert G. Wiley .... (313) 961-6880
E-mail: robert.wiley@chi.frb.org
Education: St Mary Col BA

Federal Reserve Bank of Cleveland (OH) (FRBOH)
Federal Reserve Bank of Cleveland, 1455 East Sixth Street,
Cleveland, OH 44114
P.O. Box 6387, Cleveland, OH 44101-1387
Tel: (216) 579-2000 Fax: (216) 579-3185 Internet: www.clevelandfed.org
Areas Covered: Eastern KY, OH, Western PA, WV (Northern Panhandle)
President and Chief Executive Officer
Loretta J. Mester .... (216) 579-2114
Education: Barnard 1980 BA; Princeton 1983 MA, 1985 PhD
Executive Secretary **(Vacant)** .... (216) 579-2111
First Vice President and Chief Operating Officer
Gregory L. Stefani .... (216) 774-2514
Education: Bowling Green State BBA, MBA
Executive Vice President and Chief Financial Officer
Susan G. Steinbrick .... (216) 579-3056
E-mail: susan.steinbrick@clev.frb.org
Education: Lake Erie BA; Case Western MBA
Executive Vice President and Chief Policy Officer,
Economic Research, Community Development
Martha Jake .... (216) 579-2044
E-mail: martha.jake@clev.frb.org
Executive Vice President and Director of Research
Ellis Tallman .... (216) 579-2014
Education: Rochester PhD, MA; Indiana AB
Group Vice President for Regional Outreach and
Analytics **Guhan Venkatu** .... (216) 579-2000
Education: Miami U (OH)
Senior Vice President and Chief of Staff
Peggy A. Velimesis .... (216) 579-2820
E-mail: peggy.velimesis@clev.frb.org Fax: (216) 579-3198
Education: Cleveland State,
Senior Vice President, External Outreach and Regional
Analytics **Mark E. Schweitzer** .... (216) 579-2000
Senior Vice President and General Counsel
William D. Fosnight .... (216) 579-2174
E-mail: william.fosnight@clev.frb.org
Senior Vice President and Research Economist
Todd E. Clark .... (216) 579-2015
E-mail: todd.clark@clev.frb.org
Education: Wabash Col 1985 AB; Michigan 1988 MA, 1992 PhD
Senior Vice President and Research Economist
Bruce Fallick .... (216) 579-2970
E-mail: bruce.fallick@clev.frb.org
Education: Pittsburgh 1983 BA; Pennsylvania 1988 PhD
Senior Vice President and Research Economist
Edward S. Knotek II .... (216) 579-2180
E-mail: edward.knotek@clev.frb.org
Education: Denison 2000 BA; Michigan 2002 MEcon, 2005 PhD
Senior Vice President, Bank Supervision and
Regulation, Credit Risk Management, Statistics and
Analysis **Stephen H. Jenkins** .... (216) 579-2905
E-mail: stephen.jenkins@clev.frb.org
Education: Bowling Green State; Pittsburgh MBA
Senior Vice President of Cash Services, Facilities, and
Law Enforcement **Mouneer Ahmad** .... (216) 579-2823
Education: Northern Illinois BSc
Senior Vice President, eGovernment Treasury Services
Susan M. Kenney .... (216) 579-2194
E-mail: susan.kenney@clev.frb.org
Education: John Carroll
Senior Vice President, Financial Services Policy
Committee **(Vacant)** .... (216) 579-2873
Senior Vice President, General Auditor **Mark Meder** ..... (216) 579-2114
E-mail: mark.meder@clev.frb.org
Education: Cleveland State BBA
Senior Vice President, Human Resources
David W. Hollis .... (216) 579-2820
Senior Vice President, Human Resources and Diversity
and Inclusion **Margie Wright-McGowan** .... (216) 579-2820
Education: Ohio BA
Senior Vice President, Public Affairs, Community
Relations, Outreach **Lisa Vidacs** .... (216) 579-3078
E-mail: lisa.vidacs@clev.frb.org
Education: Kent State BBA

★ Presidential Appointment Requiring Senate Confirmation ☆ Presidential Appointment □ Schedule C Appointment ◇ Career Senior Foreign Service Appointment
● Career Senior Executive Service (SES) Appointment ○ Non-Career Senior Executive Service (SES) Appointment ■ Postal Career Executive Service

Federal Reserve Bank of Cleveland (OH) *(continued)*

Vice President and Community Development Officer
Paul E. Kaboth (216) 579-2951
Vice President and Corporate Secretary
Cheryl L. Davis (216) 579-2110
Education: Ohio State; Harvard MBA
Vice President and Counsel **Christine Weiss** (216) 579-2000
Education: Franklin & Marshall BA; Pittsburgh JD
Vice President, Applied Microeconomics **(Vacant)** (216) 579-2000
Vice President, Cash Services **Ken Green** (216) 579-2000
Education: Baldwin-Wallace; Cleveland State MBA
Vice President, Community Relations **Kelly A. Banks** (216) 579-2392
Vice President, Credit Risk Management, Statistics and Analysis **Douglas A. Banks** (216) 579-3059
Vice President, Diversity and Inclusion **Diana Starks** (216) 579-2000
Education: Hiram BBA; Cleveland State MA
Vice President, eCommerce Strategic Initiatives
(Vacant) (216) 579-2000
Vice President for eGovernment Operations
Thomas Dockman (216) 579-2894
Education: Cleveland State BBA
Vice President, eGovernment Internet Channel Services
Timothy McFadden (216) 579-2000
Vice President, Financial Institutions and Regulations
Joseph G. Haubrich (216) 579-2802
Vice President, Information Technology Services
Evelyn Magas (216) 579-2000
Vice President, Large Banking Organization Function
Jenni Frazer (216) 579-2000
Education: Wright State BS; Dayton MBA
Vice President, Public Affairs, Corporate Communications and Engagement Department
Marilyn Wimp (216) 579-2000
E-mail: marilyn.wimp@clev.frb.org
Education: Stephens BA
Vice President, Public Affairs **Iris Cumberbatch MBA** (216) 579-3079
Education: Penn State; Queens U Charlotte MBA
Vice President, Regional Issues
Timothy "Tim" Dunne (216) 579-2024
Vice President, Risk Supervision and Policy Development **Stephen J. Ong** (216) 579-2098
Vice President, Risk Supervision, Surveillance and Analytics **Jason Tarnowski** (216) 579-2000
Fax: (216) 579-3050
Vice President, Supervision and Regulation
Nadine M. Wallman (216) 774-2553
E-mail: nadine.wallman@clev.frb.org
Assistant Vice President, Assistant Chief of Staff
Susan Black (216) 579-2000
Education: Ashland BEc; Kent State MS
Assistant Vice President, Business Services
Joan Phelan (216) 579-2000
Education: Rutgers BEc; Cleveland State MBA
Assistant Vice President, Capital Risk Planning
Jeff Hirsch (216) 579-2000
Education: Miami U (OH) BS; Case Western MBA
Assistant Vice President, Corporate Secretary
Toby Trocchio (216) 579-2000
Education: Akron BS; Ashland MBA
Assistant Vice President, eGovernment Settlement Services **Patrick Devine** (216) 579-2000
Assistant Vice President, Executive Communications
Doug Campbell (216) 579-2000
E-mail: doug.campbell@clev.frb.org
Education: North Carolina Greensboro MBA; UC Berkeley BA
Assistant Vice President, Executive Support Services
Terri Bialowas (216) 579-2000
Education: Kent State BBA; Cleveland State MBA
Assistant Vice President, Information Technology Services **Seshu Dasari** (216) 579-2000
Education: Jawaharlal Nehru Tech MA; Indian Inst Tech BA
Assistant Vice President, Large Banking Organization Supervision **Amy Berardinelli** (216) 579-2000
Education: Duquesne BSBA
Assistant Vice President, Public Affairs **John Lytell** (216) 579-2000

Federal Reserve Bank of Cleveland (OH) *(continued)*

Assistant Vice President, Research Administration
Jean Burson (216) 579-2000
Education: Oberlin BEc; Case Western MBA
Assistant Vice President, Risk Management and Innovation **Todd Berardinelli** (216) 579-2000
Assistant Vice President, Strategic Bank Services Department **Lana Zachlin** (216) 579-2000
Education: John Carroll BS; Case Western MMgmtS
Assistant Vice President, Supervision and Regulation
Mike Coldwell (216) 579-2000
Assistant Vice President, Supervision and Regulation
Jackie Dalton (216) 579-2000
Education: Cleveland State BBA; Case Western MBA
Assistant Vice President, Surveillance and Analytics
Denise Duffy (216) 579-2000

eGov Department
Tel: (216) 579-3188
Vice President for eCommerce and Strategic Initiatives
Nancy Nee (216) 579-2961
Education: National-Louis BS; DePaul MA Fax: (216) 579-3172

Real Estate and Facilities
Assistant Vice President, Facilities **Anthony Notaro** (216) 579-2807
Education: Kent State BS, BS; Cleveland State MBA

Cincinnati (OH) Branch
150 East Fourth Street, Cincinnati, OH 45202
Mail: P.O. Box 999, Cincinnati, OH 45201-0999
Tel: (800) 432-1343 Tel: (513) 721-4787 Fax: (513) 455-4582
Vice President and Senior Regional Officer
Gary Wagner (513) 455-4206
Education: West Virginia PhD, MEc; Youngstown State BEc
Vice President, Check Operations **(Vacant)** (513) 455-4200
Assistant Vice President, Supervision and Regulation
Bryan Huddleston (513) 455-4397
Education: Clarion BBA
Assistant Vice President and Central Point of Contact for Fifth Third Bancorp **Brian Dragoo** (513) 455-4397
Education: Florida International; Akron MA

Pittsburgh (PA) Branch
717 Grant Street, Pittsburgh, PA 15219
Mail: P.O. Box 867, Pittsburgh, PA 15230-0867
Tel: (412) 261-7800 Fax: (412) 261-7898
Vice President and Senior Regional Officer
Guhan Venkatu (412) 261-7800
Education: Miami U (OH)
Vice President, Protection and Business Continuity
Robert B. Schaub (412) 261-7806
Assistant Vice President, Supervision and Regulation
David Johnston (216) 579-2000

Community Advisory Council (CAC)
Federal Reserve Bank of Cleveland, 1455 East Sixth Street, Cleveland, OH 44114
Tel: (216) 579-2000
Member **Eric P. Avner** (216) 579-2000
Member **Keith Burwell** (216) 579-2000
Member **Heidi L. Gartland MHA** (216) 579-2000
Member **Presley L. Gillespie** (216) 579-2000
Member **Ernest E. Hogan** (216) 579-2000
Member **David W. James**
Member **Tawana Jones**
Member **Bryan K. Kieler** (216) 579-2000
Member **Edwin King**
Member **Breen Masciotra** (216) 579-2000
Education: Washington U (MO) BA; Pittsburgh MPA
Member **August A. Napoli, Jr.** (216) 579-2000
Member **Jillian Olinger** (216) 579-2000
Education: Wisconsin BA; Ohio State MRP, MPP
Member **James M. Stark** (216) 579-2000
Member **Stephanie Stiene** (216) 579-2000

(continued on next page)

★ Presidential Appointment Requiring Senate Confirmation ☆ Presidential Appointment ☐ Schedule C Appointment ◇ Career Senior Foreign Service Appointment
● Career Senior Executive Service (SES) Appointment ○ Non-Career Senior Executive Service (SES) Appointment ■ Postal Career Executive Service

Community Advisory Council *(continued)*

Member **Danny R. Williams** .... (216) 579-2000

Federal Reserve Bank of Dallas (TX) (FRBTX)

Federal Reserve Bank of Dallas, 2200 North Pearl Street,
Dallas, TX 75201-2272
P.O. Box 655906, Dallas, TX 75265-5906
Tel: (214) 922-6000 Tel: (800) 333-4460 Fax: (214) 922-6500
E-mail: info@dallasfed.org Internet: www.dallasfed.org
Areas Covered: Northern LA, Southern NM, TX

President and Chief Executive Officer
Dr. Robert Steven "Rob" Kaplan .... (214) 922-5001
Education: Kansas 1979 BS; Harvard 1983 MBA

Executive Vice President and Senior Advisor to the President **Joseph S. Tracy** .... (800) 333-4460
Education: Missouri 1978 BA; Chicago 1984 PhD
Executive Assistant **Dawn Williamson** .... (214) 922-5002
E-mail: dawn.williamson@dal.frb.org

First Vice President and Chief Operating Officer
Meredith N. Black .... (214) 922-5007

Senior Vice President and Chief Information Officer
Sherry M. Garvin .... (214) 922-5746
Education: Arizona State BS; Texas (Dallas) MBA

Senior Vice President and Chief Financial Officer
KaSandra Goulding .... (214) 922-5255

Senior Vice President and Principal Policy Advisor
Evan F. Koenig .... (214) 922-5156
Education: Wisconsin 1974 BEc; Harvard 1981 PhD

Senior Vice President and Chief of Staff
Harvey Mitchell III .... (214) 922-5133
Education: Chicago BS; Texas MBA

Senior Vice President, General Counsel and Corporate Secretary **Sharon A. Sweeney** .... (214) 922-5105

Senior Vice President and Director of Research
Marc Giannoni .... (800) 333-4460
Education: Geneva (Switzerland) 1990 BA, 1991 MA; Princeton 1998 MA, 2001 PhD

Senior Vice President and Senior Research Advisor
Mine K. Yücel .... (214) 922-5160
Education: Bogaziçi U (Turkey) 1975 BS, 1977 MS; Rice 1984 PhD

Senior Vice President
Thomas E. "Tommy" Alsbrooks .... (800) 333-4460

Senior Vice President **Joanna O. Kolson** .... (214) 922-5126
Tel: (214) 922-5377

Senior Vice President **Alfreda B. Norman** .... (214) 922-5377

Senior Vice President **Robert L. Triplett III** .... (214) 922-6226

Senior Vice President **(Vacant)** .... (214) 922-5377

Vice President and General Auditor
Glenda S. Balfantz .... (214) 922-6802

Vice President and Associate Director of Research
John V. Duca .... (214) 922-5154
Education: Yale BA; Princeton 1986 PhD

Vice President and OMWI Director **Dana Merritt** .... (800) 333-4460
Education: Michigan State

Vice President and Deputy General Counsel
David K. Teeples .... (800) 333-4460

Vice President and Associate Director of Research
Mark A. Wynne .... (214) 922-5159
Education: National U Ireland 1981 BA, 1982 MA; Rochester 1987 MA, 1990 PhD

Vice President for Supervision
Robert E. "Bobby" Coberly, Jr. .... (214) 922-6209

Vice President **Hazel W. Adams** .... (800) 333-4460

Vice President **Jill K. Cetina** .... (800) 333-4460

Vice President **Paul T. Elzner** .... (800) 333-4460

Vice President **Robert G. Feil** .... (800) 333-4460

Vice President **Jeffrey L. Garrett** .... (800) 333-4460

Vice President **John S. Insley, Jr.** .... (800) 333-4460
Education: Maryland; Stonier

Vice President **Katherine K. "Kathy" Johnsrud** .... (214) 922-5480
Education: Wisconsin (Stout) BS

Vice President **Richard J. "Rick" Mase, Jr.** .... (214) 922-6156

Vice President **Pia Orrenius** .... (214) 922-5747
Education: Illinois 1990 BA; UCLA 1999 PhD

Federal Reserve Bank of Dallas (TX) *(continued)*

Vice President **Vincent G. Pacheco** .... (800) 333-4460

Vice President **Shareef Shaik** .... (800) 333-4460

Assistant Vice President and Shared Support Services Officer **Amy J. McGregor** .... (214) 922-6261

Assistant Vice President **Bridget K. Aman** .... (800) 333-4460

Assistant Vice President **Alexander "Dex" Beyene** .... (800) 333-4460

Assistant Vice President **Stephan D. Booker** .... (800) 333-4460

Assistant Vice President **Matthew C. Davies** .... (800) 333-4460

Assistant Vice President **Claude H. Davis** .... (800) 333-4460

Assistant Vice President **Mario Hernandez** .... (214) 922-5399

Assistant Vice President **Mark Hillyer** .... (800) 333-4460

Assistant Vice President **James Hoard** .... (214) 922-5270
Fax: (214) 922-5268

Assistant Vice President **Michael A. "Ike" Ikner** .... (800) 333-4460
Education: Dallas Baptist BA; Texas 2004 MA

Assistant Vice President **Michael D. Johnson** .... (800) 333-4460

Assistant Vice President **Nicki G. Korb** .... (800) 333-4460

Assistant Vice President **Roy C. Lopez** .... (800) 333-4460

Assistant Vice President **Robert F. Mahalik** .... (800) 333-4460

Assistant Vice President **Daniel "Danny" Oursbourn** .... (800) 333-4460

Assistant Vice President **Marcus A. Propps** .... (800) 333-4460

Assistant Vice President **Jane L. Pyke** .... (800) 333-4460

Assistant Vice President **Allen E. Qualman** .... (800) 333-4460

Assistant Vice President **Rita Riley** .... (800) 333-4460

Assistant Vice President **Gary A. Scott** .... (800) 333-4460

Assistant Vice President **Katherine Sedgwick** .... (800) 333-4460

Assistant Vice President **Timothy "Tim" Stearns** .... (800) 333-4460

Assistant Vice President **Trisna Y. Tan** .... (800) 333-4460

Vice President and Endpoint Services Executive
Melissa D. Hunt .... (800) 333-4460
Education: Austin State 1990 BBA

Examining Officer **Jesse Barrientes** .... (800) 333-4460

Human Resources Officer **R. Greg Carpenter** .... (800) 333-4460

Economic Policy Advisor and Senior Economist
Alexander Chudik .... (214) 922-5055

Accounts, Risk and Credit Officer **Elisa J. Johnson** .... (800) 333-4460

Administrative Officer **Paige Johnson** .... (800) 333-4460

Senior Economic Policy Advisor **Karel R. Mertens** .... (214) 922-6715

Economic Policy Advisor and Senior Economist
Anil Kumar .... (800) 333-4460

Audit Officer and Assistant General Auditor
Pamela K. Mann .... (800) 333-4460

Privacy Officer **Heidi M. Mitchell** .... (800) 333-4460

Senior Economic Policy Advisor **Anthony Murphy** .... (800) 333-4460

Macrosurveillance Officer **Edward "Ed" Skelton** .... (800) 333-4460

Administrative Officer **Terri Elzner** .... (800) 333-4460

Corporate Planning Officer **Susan Frear** .... (800) 333-4460

El Paso (TX) Branch

301 East Main Street, El Paso, TX 79901-1326
Tel: (915) 521-5200 Fax: (915) 521-8284 E-mail: info@dallasfed.org
Internet: www.dallasfed.org

Senior Vice President in Charge **(Vacant)** .... (210) 978-1400

Assistant Vice President in Charge
Roberto A. Coronado .... (915) 521-5288
E-mail: roberto.coronado@dal.frb.org

Houston (TX) Branch

1801 Allen Parkway, Houston, TX 77019
P.O. Box 2578, Houston, TX 77252-2578
Tel: (713) 483-3000 Fax: (713) 483-3569 E-mail: info@dallasfed.org

Senior Vice President in Charge **Daron D. Peschel** .... (713) 483-3536
Education: Sam Houston State MBA

Vice President **Donald Bowers II** .... (713) 483-3536

Assistant Vice President **Jason K. Ritchie** .... (713) 483-3000

Assistant Vice President **Michelle D. Treviño** .... (713) 483-3000

Assistant Vice President **Paul Wheeler** .... (713) 483-3183

★ Presidential Appointment Requiring Senate Confirmation ☆ Presidential Appointment □ Schedule C Appointment ◇ Career Senior Foreign Service Appointment
● Career Senior Executive Service (SES) Appointment ○ Non-Career Senior Executive Service (SES) Appointment ■ Postal Career Executive Service

San Antonio (TX) Branch
126 East Nueva Street, San Antonio, TX 78204-1020
P.O. Box 1471, San Antonio, TX 78295-1471
Tel: (210) 978-1200 Fax: (210) 978-1407 E-mail: info@dallasfed.org
Internet: www.dallasfed.org

Senior Vice President in Charge **Blake Hastings** .... (210) 978-1400
Vice President **Tara Ford Payne** .... (800) 333-4460
Assistant Vice President **Keith R. Phillips** .... (800) 333-4460
Assistant Vice President **Lawrence B. "Larry" Schiff** .... (800) 333-4460

Federal Reserve Bank of Kansas City (MO) (FRBMO)

Federal Reserve Bank of Kansas City, 925 Grand Boulevard,
Kansas City, MO 64198-0001
Tel: (816) 881-2000 Fax: (816) 218-7434
Internet: www.kansascityfed.org
Areas Covered: CO, KS, Western MO, NE, Northern NM, OK, WY

Library/Information Center
Librarian **Ellen M. Johnson** .... (816) 881-2000
Fax: (816) 881-2807

Executive Office

President and Chief Executive Officer
Esther L. George .... (816) 881-2000
Education: Missouri Western State Col BSBA; Missouri (Kansas City) MBA
First Vice President and Chief Operating Officer
Kelly J. Dubbert .... (816) 881-2000
Senior Vice President, Regional, Public and Community Affairs Division, and Chief of Staff
Diane M. Raley .... (202) 452-3000
Federal Advisory Council Representative
Jonathan M. Kemper .... (816) 881-2000
Education: Harvard 1975 BA, 1979 MBA

Administrative Services Division
Senior Vice President **Donna J. Ward** .... (816) 881-2000
Education: Drury Col BBA; Missouri (Kansas City) MBA

Audit
Senior Vice President and General Auditor
Josias A. Aleman .... (816) 881-2000
Education: Oklahoma BBA, MBA
Senior Vice President and General Auditor **(Vacant)** ..... (816) 881-2000
Vice President **Megan Hruda** .... (816) 881-2000
E-mail: megan.hruda@kc.frb.org

Economic Research Division
Vice President and Director of Research
Luke Woodward .... (816) 881-2000
Education: Rockhurst U MBA
Assistant Vice President and Economist, Banking and Financial Markets **James Wilkinson** .... (816) 881-2000
Vice President and Economist, Macroeconomics and Monetary Policy **George A. Kahn** .... (816) 881-2000
E-mail: george.a.kahn@kc.frb.org
Education: North Carolina 1978 BA; Northwestern 1983 PhD
Vice President and Economist, Macroeconomics and Monetary Policy **Jonathan Willis** .... (816) 881-2852
Education: Grinnell 1993 BA; Boston U 1999 MA, 2001 PhD
Economist **Brent Bundick** .... (816) 881-2000
Education: William & Mary 2006 BA; Missouri (Kansas City) 2008 MS; Boston Col 2014 PhD
Commodity Specialist **David Rodziewicz** .... (816) 881-2000
Education: Colorado Mines 2016 MS; Illinois 2008 BSEc

Financial Services Department
Senior Vice President **Barbara S. Pacheco** .... (816) 881-2000

Information Technology and Financial Services Divisions
Senior Vice President **Karen A. Pennell** .... (816) 881-2000
Vice President **Kris Hogan** .... (816) 881-2000

Information Technology and Financial Services Divisions *(continued)*
Vice President **(Vacant)** .... (816) 881-2000

Legal Department
Senior Vice President **(Vacant)** .... (816) 881-2000

Supervision and Risk Management Division
Senior Vice President **Kevin L. Moore** .... (816) 881-2000
Vice President **Larry D. Bailey** .... (816) 881-2000
Education: Missouri (Kansas City) BA, MBA
Vice President **James H. Hunter** .... (816) 881-2000
Vice President **Charles S. "Chuck" Morris** .... (816) 881-2000
Vice President **Linda S. Schroeder** .... (816) 881-2000
Vice President **(Vacant)** .... (816) 881-2000

Treasury Services and Technology Support Division
Senior Vice President **Dawn B. Morhaus** .... (816) 881-2000

Denver (CO) Branch
1020 16th Street, Denver, CO 80202
Tel: (303) 572-2300 Fax: (303) 572-2491
Vice President and Branch Executive **Alison Felix** .... (303) 572-2314
E-mail: alison.felix@kc.frb.org

Denver Board
1020 16th Street, Denver, CO 80202
Chair **Richard L. Lewis** .... (816) 881-2000
Education: Air Force Acad BBA; William & Mary MBA
Director **Ashley J. Burt** .... (816) 881-2000
Director **Taryn L. Edwards**
Director **Edmond Johnson** .... (816) 881-2000
Director **Denny Marie Post** .... (816) 881-2000
Education: Trinity U BA
Director **Jeff Wallace** .... (816) 881-2000
Director **Katharine W. Winograd** .... (816) 881-2000

Oklahoma City (OK) Branch
226 Dean A. McGee Avenue, Oklahoma City, OK 73102-3463
P.O. Box 25129, Oklahoma City, OK 73125-0129
Tel: (800) 333-1030 Tel: (405) 270-8400 Fax: (405) 232-0902
Vice President and Branch Executive **Chad Wilkerson** ... (405) 270-8400
E-mail: chad.wilkerson@kc.frb.org
Education: William Jewell; Chicago

Oklahoma City Board
226 Dean A. McGee Avenue, Oklahoma City, OK 73102-3463
Chair **Clint D. Abernathy** .... (816) 881-2000
Director **Michael C. Coffman**
Director **Tina Patel** .... (816) 881-2000
Director **Susan Plumb** .... (816) 881-2000
Director **Christopher C. Turner** .... (816) 881-2000
Director **Katrina Washington** .... (816) 881-2000
Director **Dana S. Weber**

Omaha (NE) Branch
2201 Farnam Street, Omaha, NE 68102
P.O. Box 3958, Omaha, NE 68103
Tel: (402) 221-5500 Fax: (402) 221-5715
Assistant Vice President and Branch Manager
Nathan Kauffman .... (402) 221-5000
Education: Iowa State 2012 PhD

Omaha Board
2201 Farnam Street, Omaha, NE 68102
Chair **Eric L. Butler**
Education: Carnegie Mellon 1981 BS, 1986 MSIA
Director **John F. Bourne** .... (816) 881-2000
Director **Brian D. Esch** .... (816) 881-2000
Director **Annette Hamilton** .... (816) 881-2000
Director **Thomas J. Henning** .... (816) 881-2000
Director **Kimberly Russel FACHE** .... (816) 881-2000

(continued on next page)

INDEPENDENT AGENCIES

★ Presidential Appointment Requiring Senate Confirmation ☆ Presidential Appointment ☐ Schedule C Appointment ◇ Career Senior Foreign Service Appointment
● Career Senior Executive Service (SES) Appointment ○ Non-Career Senior Executive Service (SES) Appointment ■ Postal Career Executive Service

Omaha Board *(continued)*

Director **Dwayne Sieck**
Education: Northern Iowa

Federal Reserve Bank of Minneapolis (MN) (FRBMN)

Federal Reserve Bank of Minneapolis,
90 Hennepin Avenue, Minneapolis, MN 55480-0291
Mail: P.O. Box 291, Minneapolis, MN 55480-0291
Tel: (800) 553-9656 Tel: (612) 204-5000 Fax: (612) 204-5430
Internet: www.minneapolisfed.org
Areas Covered: MI (Upper Peninsula), MN, MT, ND, SD, Northern WI

President and Chief Executive Officer **Neel Tushar Kashkari** .... (800) 553-9656
Education: Illinois 1995 BS, 1998 MSME; Wharton 2002 MBA
Administrative Assistant **Barb Pierce** .... (612) 204-5443
E-mail: barb.pierce@mpls.frb.org
Special Policy Counsel to the President **Danita Ng** .... (800) 553-9656
First Vice President **Ron Feldman** .... (612) 204-5440
Education: Wisconsin BA; Syracuse MPA
Senior Vice President **Duane Carter** .... (612) 204-5585
Education: Minnesota; U St Thomas (MN) MBA
Senior Vice President **Michael Garrett** .... (612) 204-5368
Senior Vice President and Director of Research **Mark L.J. Wright** .... (612) 204-5448
Education: Chicago 2001 MA, 2001 PhD
Senior Vice President, General Counsel, and Corporate Secretary **Niel D. Willardson** .... (612) 204-5314
E-mail: niel.willardson@mpls.frb.org
Education: South Dakota State; Minnesota JD
Senior Vice President for Community Development and Outreach **(Vacant)** .... (612) 204-5000
Senior Vice President of Information Technology and Risk **Matthew D. Larson** .... (612) 204-5585
E-mail: matt.larson@mpls.frb.org
Senior Vice President for Supervision, Regulation and Credit **Christine M. Gaffney** .... (612) 204-5862
Senior Vice President and General Auditor **(Vacant)** .... (800) 553-9656
Senior Vice President and Research Director **(Vacant)** .... (800) 553-9656
Vice President **Peter Baatrup** .... (212) 204-5770
Vice President **Karin M. Bearss** .... (612) 204-5000
Vice President **Guy Berg** .... (800) 553-9656
Vice President **Sheryl L. Britsch** .... (612) 204-5000
Vice President **Michelle Brunn** .... (612) 204-7877
Vice President **Timothy Devaney** .... (212) 204-5770
Vice President **Joseph W. Fahnhorst** .... (612) 204-6174
Vice President **Terry Fitzgerald** .... (612) 204-7877
Vice President **Sharon T. Hill** .... (612) 204-5864
Vice President **Jacqueline G. King** .... (612) 204-5470
Vice President **Debra L. Knilans** .... (612) 204-5000
Vice President **Barbara J. Pfeffer** .... (612) 204-5787
Vice President **Amy Phenix** .... (612) 204-5864
Education: Macalester 1988; Minnesota MBA
Vice President **Mark A. Rauzi** .... (612) 204-5864
Vice President **Paul Rimmereid** .... (612) 204-5401
Vice President **David L. Schwietz** .... (612) 204-5000
Vice President **Richard M. Todd** .... (612) 204-5864
Vice President **Diann Townsend** .... (612) 204-5864
Vice President **James West** .... (612) 204-5787
Vice President and Assistant Corporate Secretary **Amy Kytonen** .... (612) 204-5274
Vice President and Deputy General Counsel **John E. Yanish** .... (612) 204-5015
E-mail: john.yanish@mpls.frb.org
Education: Minnesota, JD
Vice President, Public Affairs **David M. Goodwin** .... (612) 204-5274
E-mail: david.goodwin@mpls.frb.org
Vice President for Law Enforcement and Operations **Richard T. "Rick" Thornton** .... (612) 204-5787
E-mail: richard.thornton@mpls.frb.org
Education: Missouri BSBA
Senior Economist **Jonathan Heathcote** .... (612) 204-6385
Education: Oxford (UK) 1993 BA; Pennsylvania 1998 PhD

Federal Reserve Bank of Minneapolis (MN) *(continued)*

Assistant Vice President and Assistant General Counsel **LuAnne Pederson** .... (800) 553-9656
Monetary Advisor **Ellen R. McGrattan** .... (612) 204-5523
Education: Boston Col 1984 BS; Stanford 1989 PhD
Assistant Vice President **Bradley Beytien** .... (800) 553-9656
Assistant Vice President **Mesude Cingilli** .... (800) 553-9656
Assistant Vice President **Gregory Cutshall** .... (800) 553-9656
Assistant Vice President **Michael Grover** .... (800) 553-9656
Assistant Vice President **Jean Hinz** .... (800) 553-9656
Education: St Thomas U 1996
Assistant Vice President **Shane Hughley** .... (800) 553-9656
Assistant Vice President **Christopher Johnson** .... (800) 553-9656
Assistant Vice President **Mark Kafka** .... (800) 553-9656
Assistant Vice President **Anand Krishnan** .... (800) 553-9656
Assistant Vice President **Scott Larsen** .... (800) 553-9656
Assistant Vice President **Chad Lauber** .... (800) 553-9656
Assistant Vice President **Jorge Lomeli** .... (800) 553-9656
Assistant Vice President **Casey Winn Lozar** .... (800) 553-9656
Education: Dartmouth BA; Harvard 2006 MEd; Colorado (Denver) 2013 MBA
Assistant Vice President **Todd Maki** .... (800) 553-9656
Assistant Vice President **Daniel Maynard** .... (800) 553-9656
Assistant Vice President **Frederick L. Miller** .... (800) 553-9656
Assistant Vice President **Brendan Murrin** .... (800) 553-9656
Assistant Vice President **Robert "Bob" Pederson** .... (800) 553-9656
Assistant Vice President **Chris Riba** .... (800) 553-9656
Assistant Vice President **Derek Richardson** .... (800) 553-9656
Assistant Vice President **Sharon Richner** .... (800) 553-9656
Assistant Vice President **Sridevi Srivatsan** .... (800) 553-9656
Assistant Vice President **Randall "Randy" St. Aubin** .... (800) 553-9656
Assistant Vice President **Thomas Tallarini** .... (800) 553-9656
Assistant Vice President **Mark Vukelich** .... (800) 553-9656
Assistant Vice President **Chris Wangen** .... (800) 553-9656
Assistant Vice President **Aaron Zabler** .... (800) 553-9656
Assistant Vice President and Center for Indian Country Development Director **Patrice Kunesh** .... (612) 204-5815
E-mail: patrice.kunesh@mpls.frb.org
Education: Colorado 1989 JD; JFK School Govt 2010 MPA
Assistant Vice President and Information Security Officer **Jeff Peal** .... (612) 204-5864

Library/Information Center

90 Hennepin Avenue, Minneapolis, MN 55480-0291
Tel: (612) 204-5000

Research Library Manager **Jannelle Ruswick** .... (612) 204-5000
E-mail: jannelle.ruswick@mpls.frb.org

Helena (MT) Branch

100 Neill Avenue, Helena, MT 59601
Tel: (406) 447-3800 Fax: (406) 447-3808

Chair **Sarah Walsh** .... (406) 447-3800
Term Expires: December 31, 2020
Education: Carroll Col (MT) BAcc
Deputy Chair **Marsha Goetting** .... (406) 447-3800
Term Expires: December 31, 2018
Education: Kansas State BS, MS, MSE; Iowa State PhD
Branch Director **William E. Coffee** .... (406) 447-3800
Term Expires: December 31, 2020
Education: Montana State BS; Montana JD
Branch Director **Dr. Norma Nickerson** .... (406) 447-3800
Term Expires: December 31, 2019
Education: North Dakota BS; Utah MS, PhD
Branch Director **Barbara "Barb" Stiffarm** .... (406) 447-3800
Term Expires: December 31, 2018
Education: Missoula Vo-Tech; Montana BA
Branch Executive **(Vacant)** .... (406) 447-3800

★ Presidential Appointment Requiring Senate Confirmation ☆ Presidential Appointment □ Schedule C Appointment ◇ Career Senior Foreign Service Appointment
● Career Senior Executive Service (SES) Appointment ○ Non-Career Senior Executive Service (SES) Appointment ■ Postal Career Executive Service

Federal Reserve Bank of New York (NY) (FRBNY)

33 Liberty Street, New York, NY 10045
Tel: (212) 720-5000 Fax: (212) 720-5780 Internet: www.newyorkfed.org
Areas Covered: CT (Fairfield County), Northern NJ, NY, Puerto Rico, U.S. Virgin Islands.

Executive Office

President and Chief Executive Officer
Dr. John C. Williams .... (212) 720-5000
Education: UC Berkeley 1984 AB; London School Econ (UK) 1989 MSc; Stanford 1994 PhD
Senior Advisor **(Vacant)** .... (212) 720-5000
First Vice President and Chief Operating Officer
Dr. Michael Strine .... (212) 720-1830
Term Expires: February 28, 2021
E-mail: michael.strine@ny.frb.org
Education: Delaware 1986 BA; Johns Hopkins 1990 MA, 1992 PhD
Vice President **Sarah Bell** .... (212) 720-5000
Officer **Elizabeth Mahoney** .... (212) 720-5000

Office of the Chief of Staff

Vice President and Chief of Staff **Sarah Bell** .... (212) 720-5000
E-mail: sarah.bell@ny.frb.gov
Assistant Vice President and Deputy Chief of Staff for Operations **(Vacant)** .... (212) 720-5000
Deputy Chief of Staff and First-Level Officer
Luis Uranga .... (212) 720-5000
E-mail: luis.uranga@ny.frb.org
Executive Vice President and Special Advisor to the President **(Vacant)** .... (212) 720-5000
Vice President **(Vacant)** .... (212) 720-5000

Office of the Corporate Secretary

Senior Vice President and Corporate Secretary
(Vacant) .... (212) 720-5000

Equal Employment Opportunity Office

Senior Vice President and Equal Employment Opportunity Officer **(Vacant)** .... (212) 720-5000
Senior Vice President and Equal Employment Opportunity Officer **Susan E. McLaughlin CFA** .... (212) 720-5000
E-mail: susan.mclaughlin@ny.frb.org
Education: Oberlin BA; Michigan MBA, 1993 MPP

Policy and Financial Services Strategy

Senior Vice President and Director **Linda Goldberg** .... (212) 720-5000

Wholesale Product Office

Executive Vice President and Product Manager
Kenneth S. Isaacson .... (212) 720-5000
Senior Vice President **Robyn Brandow** .... (212) 720-5000
Senior Vice President **Sarina Pang** .... (212) 720-5000
Assistant Vice President **Lisa Pacheco** .... (212) 720-5000
Assistant Vice President **Gina Russo** .... (212) 720-5000
Assistant Vice President **Wendy Wong** .... (212) 720-5000
Officer **Mansour Djailani** .... (212) 720-5000

Audit Group

Executive Vice President and General Auditor
Clive W. Blackwood .... (212) 720-5000
E-mail: clive.blackwood@ny.frb.org
Education: Stern 1998 BB
Vice President **(Vacant)** .... (212) 720-5000
Assistant Vice President **Audrey Foster** .... (212) 720-5000
E-mail: audrey.foster@ny.frb.gov
Assistant Vice President **Padma Kumar** .... (212) 720-5000
E-mail: padma.kumar@ny.frb.gov
Assistant Vice President **Isaac Smith, Jr.** .... (212) 720-5000
Audit Officer **Donna M Gallo** .... (212) 720-5000

Communications and Outreach

Executive Vice President **Jack Gutt** .... (212) 720-6142
E-mail: jack.gutt@ny.frb.org
Education: Syracuse 1992 BAJ

Communications and Outreach *(continued)*

Regional and Community Outreach Senior Vice President **Kausar Hamdani** .... (212) 720-8258
E-mail: kausar.hamdani@ny.frb.org
Digital and Multimedia Communications Vice President **Dona Wong** .... (212) 720-5000
E-mail: dona.wong@ny.frb.org
Education: Yale 1985 MFA; Louisville BFA
Vice President and Head of Outreach and Education
Anand Marri .... (212) 720-7499
E-mail: anand.marri@ny.frb.org
Education: Bowdoin AB; Stanford AM; Wisconsin PhD
Assistant Vice President and Deputy Function Manager
Anika Pratt .... (212) 720-5000
Director of Community Development Finance
Adrian Franco .... (212) 720-7499
E-mail: adrian.franco@ny.frb.org
Director of Community Development
Claire Kramer PhD .... (212) 720-5371
E-mail: claire.kramer@ny.frb.org
Education: Duke PhD
Director of Community Engagement **Tony Davis** .... (212) 720-6369
E-mail: tony.davis@ny.frb.org
Director of Operations **Heather Daly** .... (212) 720-6006
Executive Assistant **Kellye Jackson** .... (212) 720-1356
Senior Outreach and Education Analyst **Chelsea Cruz** .... (212) 720-7969
Senior Outreach and Education Analyst
Scott Lieberman .... (212) 720-2629
Associate Director for Community Engagement
Maria Carmelita Recto .... (212) 720-7965
Associate Director for Community Engagement
Javier Silva .... (212) 720-2789
E-mail: javier.silva@ny.frb.org
Outreach and Education Analyst **Jessica Battisto** .... (212) 720-5498
Outreach and Education Analyst **Sanjay Sudhir** .... (212) 720-7965
Outreach and Education Associate
Marisa Casellas-Barnes .... (212) 720-7372
E-mail: marisa.casellas-barnes@ny.frb.org
Outreach and Education Associate **Jennifer Kahn** .... (212) 720-7678
E-mail: jennifer.kahn@ny.frb.org
Outreach and Education Associate **Edison Reyes** .... (212) 720-8385
E-mail: edison.reyes@ny.frb.org
Business Operations Coordinating Senior Analyst
Jesus Gonzalez .... (212) 720-7925
E-mail: jesus.gonzalez@ny.frb.org

Corporate Group

Executive Vice President, Principal Financial Officer and Head **Helen E. Mucciolo** .... (212) 720-5000
Education: Syracuse 1988 BS; Pace MBA
Assistant Vice President **Ellen Orman** .... (212) 720-5000
Officer **Albert D'Agostino** .... (212) 720-5000

Business and Finance Partners

33 Liberty Street, New York, NY 10045
Senior Vice President **Robert D. Beyer** .... (212) 720-5000
Senior Vice President **Thomas P. Reilly** .... (212) 720-5000
Vice President **Bob Beyer** .... (212) 720-5000
Vice President **Scott R. Gurba** .... (212) 720-5000
E-mail: scott.gurba@ny.frb.org
Education: Northern Arizona BA; Hofstra 1995 MBA
Assistant Vice President **Deborah From** .... (212) 720-5000

Enterprise Services and Resiliency Planning

33 Liberty Street, New York, NY 10045
Senior Vice President **Lola S. Judge** .... (212) 720-5000
E-mail: lola.judge@ny.frb.org
Senior Vice President **(Vacant)** .... (212) 720-5000
Vice President **(Vacant)** .... (212) 720-5000
Vice President **Michael East** .... (212) 720-5000
Assistant Vice President **Joseph D.J. DeMartini** .... (212) 720-5000

INDEPENDENT AGENCIES

★ Presidential Appointment Requiring Senate Confirmation ☆ Presidential Appointment ☐ Schedule C Appointment ◇ Career Senior Foreign Service Appointment
● Career Senior Executive Service (SES) Appointment ○ Non-Career Senior Executive Service (SES) Appointment ■ Postal Career Executive Service

Financial Operations, Reporting and Risk Management
33 Liberty Street, New York, NY 10045
Senior Vice President **Maria Grace C. Ambrosio** .... (212) 720-5000
Education: Pace
Senior Vice President **(Vacant)** .... (212) 720-5000
Assistant Vice President **Zachery R. Brice** .... (212) 720-5000
Assistant Vice President **Mark Slagus** .... (212) 720-5000

Procurement Value Management
33 Liberty Street, New York, NY 10045
Vice President **Maria Frangelaki** .... (212) 720-5000
Assistant Vice President **Christopher Grandich** .... (212) 720-5000
Officer **Brian Henry** .... (212) 720-5000

Emerging Markets and International Affairs Group
Executive Vice President **(Vacant)** .... (212) 720-5000
Development Studies and Foreign Research Senior Vice President **(Vacant)** .... (212) 720-5000
Financial Markets and Institutions Senior Vice President **B. Gerard Dages** .... (212) 720-5000
Education: Illinois BS; Princeton MPA
Assistant Vice President **(Vacant)** .... (212) 720-5000
Assistant Vice President **(Vacant)** .... (212) 720-5000

Financial Services Group
Executive Vice President **Richard P. Dzina** .... (212) 720-5000
Education: Princeton 1985 AB; Columbia MABA
Cash and Custody Senior Vice President **Christopher D. Armstrong** .... (212) 720-5000
Education: Virginia Tech BME
Cash and Custody Senior Vice President **David Duttenhofer** .... (212) 720-5000
E-mail: david.duttenhofer@ny.frb.org
Fedwire Securities Service Senior Vice President **Christopher Burke** .... (212) 720-5000
FSB Group Support Services Officer **William Schaefer** .... (212) 720-5000
Cash and Custody Vice President **Eileen M. Goodman** .... (212) 720-5000
E-mail: eileen.goodman@ny.frb.gov
Currency Services Vice President **Tony McGuirk** .... (212) 720-5000
Electronic Payments Vice President **Gail R. Armendinger** .... (212) 720-5000
Government-Wide Accounting Vice President **Donna J. Crouch** .... (212) 720-5000
International Treasury Services Vice President **Pat Hilt** .... (212) 720-5000
E-mail: pat.hilt@ny.frb.org
Assistant Vice President **Trupti Amin** .... (212) 720-5000
Assistant Vice President **Peggy Au** .... (212) 720-5000
Assistant Vice President **Robert Impalli** .... (212) 720-5000
Assistant Vice President **Anthony McGuirk** .... (212) 720-5000
Officer **Karen Christensen** .... (212) 720-5000
Officer **Bernadette Ksepka** .... (212) 720-5000
Officer **Elliot Shuke** .... (212) 720-5000
Officer **Kevin Young** .... (212) 720-5000

Human Resources Group
Executive Vice President **Susan Ward Mink** .... (212) 720-5000
E-mail: susan.mink@ny.frb.org
Education: Penn State 1965 BA
Senior Vice President of Compensation and Benefits **Dr. Gerald L. Stagg** .... (212) 720-5000
E-mail: gerald.stagg@ny.frb.org
Education: New Orleans BS; LSU Medical Center MD; NYU MPA
Senior Vice President **Cristina Juvier** .... (212) 720-5000
Education: UC Berkeley BA; Houston JD
Vice President and Chief Diversity Officer **Diane T. Ashley** .... (212) 720-5000
E-mail: diane.ashley@ny.frb.org
Education: Yale; Boston U; Rutgers JD
Vice President and Senior Administrative Officer, HR Operations and Support Services **Matthew S. Wagner** .... (212) 720-5000
E-mail: matthew.wagner@ny.frb.org
Education: Kansas State BS; Baker U MBA

Human Resources Group *(continued)*
Senior Vice President, Talent Management **Louis J. Scenti, Jr.** .... (212) 720-5000
E-mail: louis.scenti@ny.frb.org
Education: Rhode Island Col 1979 BA; New School 1989 MA
Vice President, Human Resources Business Partners **Christina Juvier** .... (212) 720-5000
Assistant Vice President **Lori Swan** .... (212) 720-5000
Officer **Cira Rom** .... (212) 720-5000

Legal Group
Executive Vice President and General Counsel **Michael Adam Held** .... (212) 720-5000
E-mail: michael.held@ny.frb.org
Education: Cornell 1992 BS; NYU 1995 JD
Deputy General Counsel and Bank Supervision and Markets SVP **(Vacant)** .... (212) 720-5000
Deputy General Counsel and Financial Services and Technology SVP **(Vacant)** .... (212) 720-5000
Administrative Division Assistant Vice President **Mary L. Colon** .... (212) 720-5000
Chief Compliance and Ethics Officer and Senior Vice President **Martin C. Grant** .... (212) 720-5000
Education: Princeton 1986 AB; Harvard 1989 JD
Compliance Vice President **Barry M. Schindler** .... (212) 720-5000
Corporate Secretary Office Vice President **Rona B Stein** .... (212) 720-5000
E-mail: rona.stein@ny.frb.org
Enforcement and Litigation Senior Vice President **Sean O'Malley** .... (212) 720-7943
Federal Reserve Law Enforcement and Senior Vice President **Nicholas Proto** .... (212) 720-5000
Records Management Officer **(Vacant)** .... (212) 720-5000
Senior Vice President and Special Advisor to the Executive Vice President of Legal **James P. Bergin** .... (212) 720-5000
E-mail: james.bergin@ny.frb.gov
Senior Vice President **Yoon Hi Greene** .... (212) 720-5000
Education: Fordham JD
Senior Vice President **Michael S. Nelson** .... (212) 720-5000
E-mail: michael.nelson@ny.frb.org

Markets Group
Executive Vice President **Simon M. Potter** .... (212) 720-6309
Education: Oxford (UK) 1983 BA, 1986 MPhil; Wisconsin 1990 PhD
Chief Operating Officer and Senior Vice President of Operations **John J. Clark, Jr.** .... (212) 720-5000
E-mail: john.clark@ny.frb.org
Education: Harvard BS; Yale 1983 MA, 1988 MPhil, 1988 PhD
Vice President and Chief of Staff **Alexandra Merle-Huet** .... (212) 720-5000
E-mail: alexandra.merle-huet@ny.frb.org

Business Technology
33 Liberty Street, New York, NY 10045
Senior Vice President **Michael J. Burk** .... (212) 720-5000
Education: Fordham MBA
Senior Vice President **Michael J. Recupero** .... (212) 720-5000
E-mail: michael.recupero@ny.frb.org
Education: Baruch Col 1978 BBA

Central Bank and International Account Services
33 Liberty Street, New York, NY 10045
Senior Vice President **Anne F. Baum** .... (212) 720-5000
E-mail: anne.baum@ny.frb.org
Vice President **Amelia Moncayo** .... (212) 720-5000
Education: Columbia MIA, MBA
Vice President **Annmarie Rowe-Straker** .... (212) 720-5000
Assistant Vice President **Tamara Wheeler** .... (212) 720-5000

Group Shared Services
33 Liberty Street, New York, NY 10045
Vice President **Gerald McCrink** .... (212) 720-5000
Assistant Vice President **James Egelhof** .... (212) 720-5000
E-mail: james.egelhof@ny.frb.gov
Assistant Vice President **Larissa Ezra** .... (212) 720-5000

Group Shared Services *(continued)*

Assistant Vice President **Ryan Hirschey** . . . . (212) 720-5000
Officer **Fabiola Ravazzolo** . . . . (212) 720-5000
Officer **William Riordan** . . . . (212) 720-5000
Officer **Geza Sardi** . . . . (212) 720-5000

Discount Window and Collateral Valuation
33 Liberty Street, New York, NY 10045

Monitoring and Analysis Division
33 Liberty Street, New York, NY 10045

Senior Vice President **Joshua L. Frost** . . . . (212) 720-5000
E-mail: joshua.frost@ny.frb.org
Education: NYU MBA
Senior Vice President **Lorie K. Logan** . . . . (212) 720-5000
Education: Davidson BA; Columbia MPA
Senior Vice President **Angela L. O'Connor** . . . . (212) 720-5000
Senior Vice President **Nathaniel Wuerffel** . . . . (212) 720-5000
Education: Valparaiso BA; Chicago MA
Vice President **Kathryn Chen** . . . . (212) 720-5000
Vice President **Oliver Giannotti** . . . . (212) 720-5000
Vice President **Frank M. Keane** . . . . (212) 720-5000
Vice President **Deborah L. Leonard** . . . . (212) 720-5000
Education: Duke BA
Vice President **Michael McMorrow** . . . . (212) 720-5000
Education: Notre Dame BS; SUNY Col (Buffalo) MS
Vice President **Matthew D. Raskin** . . . . (212) 720-5000
Vice President **Patricia Zobel** . . . . (212) 720-5000
Education: UC Berkeley BSMS; Columbia MSFS
Assistant Vice President **John McGowan** . . . . (212) 720-5000
Assistant Vice President **Rania C. Perry** . . . . (212) 720-5000
E-mail: rania.perry@ny.frb.gov
Assistant Vice President **Jamie Pfeifer** . . . . (212) 720-5000
Officer **Alex Cohen** . . . . (212) 720-5000
Officer **Mary Fleisch** . . . . (212) 720-5000
Officer **Luis Gonzalez** . . . . (212) 720-5000
Officer **Bruce Weiner** . . . . (212) 720-5000

Risk Group

Executive Vice President, Chief Risk Officer and Head of the Risk Group **Joshua Rosenberg** . . . . (212) 720-5000
E-mail: joshua.rosenberg@ny.frb.org
Education: Oberlin; UC San Diego PhD
Credit Risk Management Senior Vice President **Adam B. Ashcraft** . . . . (212) 720-5000
Education: Miami U (OH) 1996; MIT 2001 PhD
Credit Risk Management Vice President **Eric L. Parsons** . . . . (212) 720-5000
Education: Pace BA; Fordham MA
Credit Risk Management Vice President **Steven B. Schoen** . . . . (212) 720-5000
Education: Michigan 1987 BA; NYU MBA
Enterprise Risk Oversight **Melanie L. Heintz** . . . . (212) 720-5000
Education: SUNY (Brockport) BA
Payments Policy Senior Vice President **Lawrence M. Sweet** . . . . (212) 720-5000
Education: Rutgers BA; Columbia MA, MPhil
Payments Policy Vice President **Marsha K. Takagi** . . . . . . (212) 720-5000
E-mail: marsha.takagi@ny.frb.org
Financial Risk Oversight Vice President **Rita Csejtey** . . . . (212) 720-5000
SCRM Technology Group Support Vice President **Robert Aller** . . . . (212) 720-5000
Assistant Vice President **Nisso Bucay** . . . . (212) 720-5000
Assistant Vice President **Rachel Lu** . . . . (212) 720-5000

Supervision Group

Executive Vice President **Kevin J. Stiroh** . . . . (212) 720-5268
Education: Swarthmore BA; Harvard PhD
Chief of Staff **James R. Hennessy** . . . . (212) 720-5000
E-mail: james.hennessy@ny.frb.org
Education: St John's Col (IL) BA; Columbia MUP, JD
Chief Operating Officer **Randy Tokar** . . . . (212) 720-5000
Education: Penn State BA; Harvard MBA
Senior Vice President **Martha Cummings** . . . . (212) 720-5000

Supervision Group *(continued)*

Senior Vice President **Patricia T. Meadow** . . . . (212) 720-5000
Education: Arcadia BA; Columbia MA
Cybersecurity Team Lead **Roy D. Thetford** . . . . (212) 720-5000

Large Institution Supervision Coordinating Committee Portfolio
33 Liberty Street, New York, NY 10045

Senior Vice President and Head **Lauren A. Hargraves** . . . (212) 720-5000
Education: Columbia 1991 MBA, 1991 MAPA; Trinity Col (CT) 1985 AB
Senior Vice President **Denise B. Schmedes** . . . . (212) 720-5000
Education: Trenton State BBA; NYU MBA
Senior Vice President **Vandana Sharma** . . . . (212) 720-5000
Vice President **Steven Mirsky** . . . . (212) 720-5000
Education: Washington U (MO) BA; Columbia MBA
Vice President **Glen Reppy** . . . . (212) 720-5000
Vice President **Tricia E. Kissinger** . . . . (212) 720-5000
Vice President **Stephanie J. Chaly** . . . . (212) 720-5000
Vice President **Wendy Ng** . . . . (212) 720-5000
Education: Baruch Col BAcc
Vice President **Daniel Sullivan** . . . . (212) 720-5000
Assistant Vice President **Claudia Franco** . . . . (212) 720-5000
Assistant Vice President **Anna Ng** . . . . (212) 720-5000
Officer **Yogesh Attre** . . . . (212) 720-5000
Officer **Caren Cox** . . . . (212) 720-5000
Officer **Sarah Hewitt** . . . . (212) 720-5000
Officer **Caleb Roepe** . . . . (212) 720-5000

Large and Foreign Banking Organizations
33 Liberty Street, New York, NY 10045

Senior Vice President and Head **Brian O'Halloran** . . . . (212) 720-5000
Senior Vice President **Daniel A. Muccia** . . . . (212) 720-5000
E-mail: daniel.muccia@ny.frb.org
Education: CUNY BA
Vice President **Marilyn Arbuthnott** . . . . (212) 720-5000
Education: NYU BA
Assistant Vice President **Mari Baca** . . . . (212) 720-5000
Assistant Vice President **David Kim** . . . . (212) 720-5000
Assistant Vice President **Dennis Ryan** . . . . (212) 720-5000
Officer **Barbara Biel** . . . . (212) 720-5000
Officer **Frederick Engel** . . . . (212) 720-5000
Officer **Isabella Lo Piccolo** . . . . (212) 720-5000
Officer **Allister Silverton** . . . . (212) 720-5000

Regional, Community and Foreign Institutions
33 Liberty Street, New York, NY 10045

Senior Vice President (Interim) **Lawrence "Larry" Bonnemere** . . . . (212) 720-5000
Vice President **Eric A. Caban** . . . . (212) 720-5000
Vice President **Bettyann Griffith** . . . . (212) 720-5000
Assistant Vice President **Sukhpal Bhatti** . . . . (212) 720-5000
Assistant Vice President **Martin Lord** . . . . (212) 720-5000
Assistant Vice President **Wilma Sabado** . . . . (212) 720-5000
Officer **Heather Bynoe** . . . . (212) 720-5000
Officer **Laxmi Grabowski** . . . . (212) 720-5000
Officer **Sanjiv Mathur** . . . . (212) 720-5000

Financial Market Infrastructure
33 Liberty Street, New York, NY 10045

Senior Vice President and Head **Vic Chakrian** . . . . (201) 720-5000
Senior Vice President **(Vacant)** . . . . (201) 720-5000
Senior Vice President **Thomas Ferlazzo** . . . . (201) 720-5000
Vice President **Johanna Schwab** . . . . (201) 720-5000
Vice President **Jainaryan Sooklal** . . . . (212) 702-5000
Assistant Vice President **Steven Block** . . . . (212) 720-5000
Assistant Vice President **Amy Man** . . . . (212) 720-5000
Assistant Vice President **Sean Sullivan** . . . . (212) 720-5000
Officer **James Cheatham** . . . . (212) 720-5000
Officer **Soo Green** . . . . (212) 720-5000
Officer **Tim Moy** . . . . (212) 720-5000

INDEPENDENT AGENCIES

★ Presidential Appointment Requiring Senate Confirmation ☆ Presidential Appointment □ Schedule C Appointment ◇ Career Senior Foreign Service Appointment
● Career Senior Executive Service (SES) Appointment ○ Non-Career Senior Executive Service (SES) Appointment ■ Postal Career Executive Service

Enterprise Risk Supervision
33 Liberty Street, New York, NY 10045

Senior Vice President **Ronald J. "Ron" Cathcart** .... (212) 720-5000
Senior Vice President **James M. "Jim" Mahoney** ...... (212) 720-5000
Education: Pennsylvania BA, PhD
Senior Vice President **Wing Y. Oon** .... (212) 720-5000
Education: SUNY (Stony Brook) BS, MSOR
Vice President **Brian Hefferle** .... (212) 720-5000
Vice President **Dina Maher** .... (212) 720-5000
Vice President **Karen Schneck** .... (212) 720-5000
Education: Touro BS; NYU MS
Vice President **Ronald P. Stroz** .... (212) 720-5000
Education: Rutgers
Assistant Vice President **Louis Braunstein** .... (212) 720-5000
Assistant Vice President **Jacqueline McCormack** .... (212) 720-5000
Officer **Peter Cheris** .... (212) 720-5000
Officer **Daniel Gutierrez** .... (212) 720-5000
Officer **Patrick Roche** .... (212) 720-5000

Supervisory Policy and Strategy
33 Liberty Street, New York, NY 10045

Senior Vice President and Head **Dianne K. Dobbeck** ... (212) 720-2610
Education: Kalamazoo BA; Princeton 1997 MPA
Vice President **Charles C. Gray** .... (212) 720-2610
Education: Harvard BA, JD
Vice President **Katherine Tilghman Hill** .... (212) 720-5000
Vice President **Emily Yang** .... (212) 720-5000
Assistant Vice President **Paul Coppola** .... (212) 720-5000
Assistant Vice President **Scott Nagel** .... (212) 720-5000
Officer **Deborah Arndell** .... (212) 720-5000
Officer **Toni Dechario** .... (212) 720-5000
Officer **Min Kim** .... (212) 720-5000
Officer **Debra Saito** .... (212) 720-5000

Group Operations
33 Liberty Street, New York, NY 10045

Vice President and Head **Gary J. Kaplan** .... (212) 720-5000
Senior Vice President **Caroline Frawley** .... (212) 720-5000
Education: Iona
Senior Vice President **Joonho J. Lee** .... (201) 720-5000
Education: Connecticut; Rensselaer Poly. ; New York Law JD
Vice President and Chief Information Officer
Danny Brando .... (212) 720-5898
Assistant Vice President **Yuliya Keylin** .... (212) 720-5000
Assistant Vice President **John O'Sullivan** .... (212) 720-5000
Officer **Kenton Beerman** .... (212) 720-5000
Officer **Thomas Doheny** .... (212) 720-5000
Officer **Jeffrey Kowalak** .... (212) 720-5000
Officer **Karen Sharf** .... (212) 720-5000

Technology Group
Executive Vice President [Chief Information Officer]
Pamela C. "Pam" Dyson .... (212) 720-5000
E-mail: pamela.dyson@ny.frb.org
Education: Maryland 1984 BS
Senior Vice President **Nicolae Stanescu** .... (212) 720-5000
Vice President and Chief of Staff **Stephen Silverman** ... (212) 720-5000

Governance
33 Liberty Street, New York, NY 10045

Senior Vice President **Ming Chan** .... (212) 720-5000
Senior Vice President **Matthew D. Larson** .... (212) 720-5000
Vice President **John J. Mosquera** .... (212) 720-5000
Vice President **Paul R. Sans** .... (212) 720-5000
Assistant Vice President **John Barra** .... (212) 720-5000
E-mail: john.barra@ny.frb.gov
Assistant Vice President **Sharona Noe** .... (212) 720-5000
Assistant Vice President **Pamela W. Yip** .... (212) 720-5000
Officer **Douglas Tapper** .... (212) 720-5000
Officer **Vimal Bhut** .... (212) 720-5000

Information Security
33 Liberty Street, New York, NY 10045

Vice President **Stephen Cospolich** .... (212) 720-5000
Assistant Vice President **David Capps** .... (212) 720-5000
Assistant Vice President **Bernadette Russell** .... (212) 720-5000
Officer **Srikanth Ojili** .... (212) 720-5000

Service Management
33 Liberty Street, New York, NY 10045

Senior Vice President **Kathryn K. Smith** .... (212) 720-5000
E-mail: kathryn.smith@ny.frb.org
Education: Maine
Assistant Vice President **Susan R. Chase** .... (212) 720-5000
Assistant Vice President **Peter Schwab** .... (212) 720-5000
E-mail: peter.schwab@ny.frb.org
Officer **Terry Misquith** .... (212) 720-5000

Solution Delivery
33 Liberty Street, New York, NY 10045

Senior Vice President **Sean G. Mahon** .... (212) 720-5000
E-mail: sean.mahon@ny.frb.org
Education: Fordham BS; Maryland MS
Vice President **David Arzt** .... (212) 720-5000
Vice President **Anat Gourji** .... (212) 720-5000
E-mail: anat.gourji@ny.frb.org
Vice President **Joseph D. Leonard** .... (212) 720-5000
E-mail: joseph.leonard@ny.frb.gov
Assistant Vice President **Amy Liu** .... (212) 720-5000
Officer **Dinesh Lalwani** .... (212) 720-5000

Enterprise Architecture and Strategy
33 Liberty Street, New York, NY 10045

Senior Vice President **Jean Bolwell** .... (212) 720-5000
Senior Vice President **William T. Christie** .... (212) 720-5000
Education: St John's U (NY) 1983 BS; Marist 1989 MS
Senior Vice President **Michael Kane** .... (212) 720-5000
Education: Queens Col (NY) BA
Senior Vice President **Jeff Weinstein** .... (212) 720-5000
Vice President **Colin Wynd** .... (212) 720-5000
Education: Glasgow (Scotland) BS
Vice President **Robert Goodman** .... (212) 720-5000
Assistant Vice President **Rafael Koscialkowski** .... (212) 720-5000
Assistant Vice President **Jia Ye** .... (212) 720-5000
E-mail: jia.ye@ny.frb.org
Officer **Jonathan DeRose** .... (212) 720-5000

Client Engagement
33 Liberty Street, New York, NY 10045

Senior Vice President **Joe Rodriguez** .... (212) 720-5000
Senior Vice President **Jean Stoloff** .... (212) 720-5000
Vice President **Richard I. Barrett** .... (212) 720-5000
Vice President **Ron Zoldy** .... (212) 720-5000
Assistant Vice President **Howard Morgasen** .... (212) 720-5000
E-mail: howard.morgansen@ny.frb.gov
Officer **Robert Braccia** .... (212) 720-5000

Library/Information Center
33 Liberty Street, New York, NY 10045
Fax: (212) 720-1372

Chief Librarian **Kathleen McKiernan** .... (212) 720-8289
E-mail: kathleen.mckiernan@ny.frb.org

Federal Reserve Bank of Philadelphia (PA) (FRBPA)

Federal Reserve Bank of Philadelphia,
Ten Independence Mall, Philadelphia, PA 19106-1574
Mail: P.O. Box 66, Philadelphia, PA 19106
Tel: (215) 574-6000 Fax: (215) 574-3980 Internet: www.phil.frb.org
Areas Covered: DE, Southern NJ, Eastern PA

President and Chief Executive Officer
Dr. Patrick T. "Pat" Harker .... (215) 574-6401
E-mail: patrick.harder@phil.frb.org
Education: Pennsylvania 1981 BSE, 1981 MSE, 1983 MA, 1983 PhD

★ Presidential Appointment Requiring Senate Confirmation ☆ Presidential Appointment ☐ Schedule C Appointment ◇ Career Senior Foreign Service Appointment
● Career Senior Executive Service (SES) Appointment ○ Non-Career Senior Executive Service (SES) Appointment ■ Postal Career Executive Service

Federal Reserve Bank of Philadelphia (PA) *(continued)*

First Vice President and Chief Operating Officer
James D. Narron .... (215) 574-6462
E-mail: james.narron@phil.frb.org
Education: Rockhurst Col 1988 BS; South Carolina MBA

Senior Vice President and Lending Officer, Supervision, Regulation and Credit
William G. Spaniel .... (215) 574-6487

Senior Vice President and Chief Information Officer
Terry E. Harris .... (215) 574-3871
E-mail: terry.harris@phil.frb.org
Education: Virginia Tech

Senior Vice President and General Counsel
Jeanne Rentezelas .... (215) 574-6390
E-mail: jeanne.rentezelas@phil.frb.org

Senior Vice President, Cash and Treasury Services and Retail Payments **Arun K. Jain** .... (215) 574-6531
E-mail: arun.jain@phil.frb.org
Education: Minnesota MS, MBA

Senior Vice President and Chief Financial Officer
Donna L. Franco .... (215) 574-6547
E-mail: donna.franco@phil.frb.org

Senior Vice President of Corporate Affairs
Deborah L. Hayes .... (215) 574-6439
E-mail: deborah.hayes@phil.frb.org

Senior Vice President, General Auditor
Michelle M. Scipione .... (215) 574-6508
E-mail: michelle.scipione@phil.frb.org
Education: Temple; La Salle U MBA

Senior Vice President, Human Resources
Mary Ann Hood .... (215) 574-3413
E-mail: maryann.hood@phil.frb.org
Education: Hood; Villanova

Senior Vice President, Community Development and Regional Outreach **Theresa Y Singleton** .... (215) 574-6482
Education: Temple AB, AM, PhD Fax: (215) 574-2512

Senior Vice President **(Vacant)** .... (215) 574-3807

Senior Vice President, Chief of Staff and Corporate Secretary **Patricia A. Wilson** .... (215) 574-6425
E-mail: patricia.wilson@phil.frb.gov
Assistant Corporate Secretary
Linda "Lynn" O'Donnell .... (215) 574-6389

Vice President and Director of the Payment Cards Center **Robert M. Hunt** .... (215) 574-3806
E-mail: bob.hunt@phil.frb.org
Education: Butler 1986 BA; Pennsylvania 1996 PhD

Vice President, Public Affairs **Michelle Reardon** .... (215) 574-4197
E-mail: michelle.reardon@phil.frb.org

Vice President and Economist, Regional and Microeconomics **Leonard I. Nakamura** .... (215) 574-3804
Education: Swarthmore; Princeton, PhD

Vice President, Enterprise Risk Management
Donna Brenner .... (215) 574-6612
Education: Temple BBA, MBA

Vice President and Director of the Real-Time Data Research Center **Keith Sill** .... (215) 574-3815
Education: Virginia 1982 BS, 1987 MA, 1992 PhD

Vice President, Financial Management Services
Jennifer E. Cardy .... (215) 574-3875
Education: Bethany (WV) BS; Villanova MBA, JD

Vice President, Financial Statistics **Charles Kirkland** .... (215) 574-6605
Education: Penn State BA

Manager of Public Affairs **Bob McCarthy** .... (215) 574-6112

Media Relations Lead **Daneil Mazone** .... (215) 574-7163

Media Relations Representative **(Vacant)** .... (215) 574-6000

Information Systems

Vice President, Information Services
Patrick M. Regan .... (215) 574-6070
E-mail: pat.regan@phil.frb.org
Education: Drexel, MBA

Vice President, Information Technology Services
Gregory Fanelli .... (215) 574-6019
E-mail: gregory.fanelli@phil.frb.org
Education: Drexel BS

Information Systems *(continued)*

Vice President, Information Security and Data Privacy
Keith Morales .... (215) 574-6606
E-mail: keith.morales@phil.frb.org

Library/Information Center

Head Librarian and Library/Research Center Manager
Christine Le .... (215) 574-6543
E-mail: christine.le@phil.frb.org

Federal Reserve Bank of Richmond (VA) (FRBVA)

Federal Reserve Bank of Richmond, 701 East Byrd Street, Richmond, VA 23219
P.O. Box 27622, Richmond, VA 23261-7622
Tel: (804) 697-8000 Internet: www.richmondfed.org
Areas Covered: DC, MD, NC, SC, VA, WV (Except Northern Panhandle)

Executive Office

President and Chief Executive Officer
Thomas I. "Tom" Barkin .... (804) 697-8921
E-mail: thomas.barkin@rich.frb.org
Education: Harvard AB, MBA, JD
Assistant to the President **Cyanne Yates** .... (804) 697-8921
E-mail: cyanne.yates@rich.frb.org

First Vice President and Chief Operating Officer
Becky C. Bareford .... (804) 697-8501

Assistant Vice President [Government Affairs]
Chris Murphy .... (804) 697-8084
Education: VCU BS

Audit

Senior Vice President, General Auditor
Michael D. Stough .... (804) 697-8546

Vice President **Gregory A. Johnson** .... (804) 697-8521

Cash Services

Senior Vice President **David E. Beck** .... (410) 576-3310
Education: Richmond BS; Loyola Col (MD) 1984 MBA

Group Vice President **Terry J. Wright** .... (704) 358-2114
Education: Georgia State 1993

Vice President **Kerri Coard** .... (804) 697-8000

Assistant Vice President **Kelly J. Stewart** .... (804) 697-8000

Assistant Vice President **Megan Wlaz** .... (804) 697-8000

Check Services

Vice President **Terry J. Wright** .... (704) 358-2114
Education: Georgia State 1993

Community Affairs

Assistant Vice President **Sandra Tormoen** .... (704) 358-2101

Corporate Accounting

Senior Vice President and Chief Financial Officer
Claudia N. MacSwain .... (804) 697-8516
E-mail: claudia.macswain@rich.frb.org
Education: Longwood BS; VCU, MBA

Vice President and Principal Financial Officer
Michael L. "Mike" Wilder .... (804) 697-8731
E-mail: michael.wilder@rich.frb.org
Education: VCU MBA

Corporate Communications

Executive Vice President **Michelle H. Gluck** .... (804) 697-8706
Education: Michigan 1980 BA, 1983 JD

Group Vice President **Lisa T. Oliva** .... (804) 697-8192

Assistant Vice President **Cheryl Moore** .... (804) 697-8000
Education: Virginia BS

INDEPENDENT AGENCIES

Corporate Support Services
Senior Vice President and Chief Information Officer
(Vacant) .... (804) 697-8715
Vice President, Corporate Support Services
Bruce Grinnell .... (804) 697-5469
E-mail: bruce.grinnell@rich.frb.org
Education: Purdue MIA
Vice President, Facilities Management
Mattison W. "Matt" Harris .... (804) 697-8740
Education: Clemson
Vice President, Law Enforcement
James Tommy Nowlin .... (804) 697-8378

Currency Technology Office
Senior Vice President and Chief Technology Officer
William "Bill" Riley .... (804) 697-8000
Vice President **Niranjan Chandramowli** .... (804) 697-8000
Assistant Vice President **Jonathan P. Martin** .... (704) 358-2363

Enterprise Risk Management and Strategic Planning
Senior Vice President and Chief Financial Officer
Claudia N. MacSwain .... (804) 697-8516
E-mail: claudia.macswain@rich.frb.org
Education: Longwood BS; VCU, MBA

Health Services
Federal Reserve Bank of Richmond, 701 East Byrd Street, Richmond, VA 23219
Tel: (804) 697-8407 Tel: (804) 697-4850
Senior Vice President, Medical Director
Kevin W. Fergusson .... (804) 697-8407
E-mail: kevin.fergusson@rich.frb.org

Human Resources
Vice President and Chief Human Resources Officer
(Vacant) .... (804) 697-8000
Vice President, Human Resources and Payroll **(Vacant)** ... (804) 697-8000
Vice President **Andrew S. McAllister** .... (804) 697-8186
Education: VMI BSEE; Virginia Tech MS
Assistant Vice President **Kimberley Fuller** .... (804) 697-8000

Information Technology
Senior Vice President and Chief Information Officer
(Vacant) .... (804) 697-8715
Vice President **Constance B. "Connie" Frudden** .... (804) 697-4406

Legal and Corporate Secretary
Executive Vice President, General Counsel
Michelle H. Gluck .... (804) 697-8425
E-mail: michelle.gluck@rich.frb.org
Education: Michigan 1980 BA, 1983 JD
Deputy General Counsel **Patricia A. Lacey Nunley** ...... (804) 697-8435
Education: Miami U (OH); Richmond JD
Assistant Vice President and Assistant General Counsel
Dennis P. Smith .... (804) 697-8554
E-mail: dennis.smith@rich.frb.org
Assistant General Counsel **(Vacant)** .... (804) 697-8554
Assistant Vice President, Secretary **Page W. Marchetti** ... (804) 697-8258

National Procurement Office
Senior Vice President and Chief Financial Officer
Claudia N. MacSwain .... (804) 697-8516
Education: Longwood BS; VCU, MBA
Vice President **Howard S. Goldfine** .... (804) 697-8708
Education: SUNY (Binghamton) BA; Virginia MBA

Payments Outreach
Vice President and Senior Payments Advisor **(Vacant)** .... (804) 697-8000

Research
Senior Vice President, Research Director
John A. Weinberg .... (804) 697-8205
Education: Pennsylvania 1979 BA; Minnesota PhD

Research *(continued)*
Vice President, Monetary Policy and Macroeconomics
Alexander L. Wolman .... (804) 697-8266
Education: Carleton BA; Virginia PhD
Vice President, Financial Institutions and Payment System Analysis **Edward S. Prescott** .... (804) 697-8206

Statistics and Reserve Accounts
Senior Vice President and Chief Financial Officer
Claudia N. MacSwain .... (804) 697-8516
E-mail: claudia.macswain@rich.frb.org
Education: Longwood BS; VCU, MBA
Vice President **Hattie R. C. Barley** .... (804) 697-8464
Assistant Vice President **Karen J. Williams** .... (804) 697-8238
Assistant Vice President **(Vacant)** .... (804) 697-8464

Supervision, Regulation and Credit
Executive Vice President **Lisa A. White** .... (704) 358-2548
Vice President **Marshal S. Auron** .... (704) 358-2445
Education: American U 1979 BS; Pittsburgh 1980 MBA
Vice President **John A. Beebe** .... (704) 358-2533
Vice President **Richard B. Gilbert** .... (804) 697-2883
Vice President **(Vacant)** .... (804) 697-8000
Vice President **(Vacant)** .... (704) 358-2579

Treasury and Payment Services
Senior Vice President **David E. Beck** .... (410) 576-3310
Education: Richmond BS; Loyola Col (MD) 1984 MBA
Vice President **(Vacant)** .... (804) 697-8574

Baltimore (MD) Office
502 South Sharp Street, Baltimore, MD 21201
Mail: P.O. Box 1378, Baltimore, MD 21203
Tel: (410) 576-3300 Tel: (410) 576-3353
Senior Vice President and Baltimore Regional Executive **David E. Beck** .... (410) 576-3310
Education: Richmond BS; Loyola Col (MD) 1984 MBA

Charlotte (NC) Office
530 East Trade Street, Charlotte, NC 28202
P.O. Box 30248, Charlotte, NC 28230
Tel: (704) 358-2100 Fax: (704) 358-2300
Senior Vice President and Charlotte Regional Executive
Matthew A. Martin .... (704) 358-2101

Federal Reserve Bank of San Francisco (CA) (FRBSF)
101 Market Street, San Francisco, CA 94105
Mail: P.O. Box 7702, San Francisco, CA 94120-7702
Tel: (415) 974-2000 Tel: (800) 227-4133 Fax: (415) 974-2318
Internet: www.frbsf.org
Areas Covered: AK, AZ, CA, HI, ID, NV, OR, UT, WA
President and Chief Executive Officer
Mary C. Daly PhD .... (415) 974-3186
Education: Missouri (Kansas City) 1985 BA; Illinois 1987 MS; Syracuse 1994 PhD
Executive Assistant **Candice Mann** .... (415) 974-2000
E-mail: candice.mann@sf.frb.org Fax: (415) 974-2113
Chief Financial Officer **Philip B. Johnson** .... (415) 974-2000
Executive Vice President **Roger W. Replogle** .... (213) 683-2300
Fax: (213) 683-2499
Executive Vice President and Chief Information Officer
Gopa Kumar .... (415) 974-2000
Executive Vice President and Financial Institution Supervision and Credit Director **Tracy Basinger** .... (415) 974-2000
Education: Cal State (East Bay) BS
First Vice President and Chief Operating Officer
Mark A. Gould .... (415) 974-2000
Education: Pacific Lutheran 1991; Seattle
Group Vice President, Statistics **Darren Post** .... (415) 974-2000
Library Manager **Cynthia "Cindy" Hill** .... (415) 974-2000
E-mail: cindy.hill@sf.frb.org

★ Presidential Appointment Requiring Senate Confirmation ☆ Presidential Appointment ☐ Schedule C Appointment ◇ Career Senior Foreign Service Appointment
● Career Senior Executive Service (SES) Appointment ○ Non-Career Senior Executive Service (SES) Appointment ■ Postal Career Executive Service

Federal Reserve Bank of San Francisco (CA) *(continued)*

President and Chief Executive Officer **(Vacant)** . . . . (415) 974-2000
Senior Vice President **Deborah M. Awai** . . . . (415) 974-2000
Senior Vice President **Teuila Hanson** . . . . (415) 974-2000
Senior Vice President and General Auditor
Azher Abbasi . . . . (415) 974-2000
Senior Vice President and General Counsel
Erik Z. Revai . . . . (415) 974-2000
Senior Vice President, Communications
Adrian Rodriguez . . . . (415) 974-2000
Education: Cal Poly (Pomona) BSC
Senior Vice President and Chief Information Officer, Information and Technology Services **(Vacant)** . . . . (415) 974-2000
Vice President and Secretary of the Board **(Vacant)** . . . . . . (415) 974-2000

Economic Research
Executive Vice President and Director **Sylvain Leduc** . . . . (415) 974-3059
Education: McGill (Canada) 1991 BA, 1993 MA; Rochester 1999 PhD
Executive Vice President and Senior Policy Advisor
Glenn D. Rudebusch . . . . (415) 974-2000
Education: Northwestern 1981 BA; Pennsylvania 1986 PhD
Associate Director of Research and Group Vice President, Micro and Macro **(Vacant)** . . . . (415) 974-2000
Group Vice President, International Research
Reuven Glick . . . . (415) 974-3184
Education: Chicago 1973 BEc; Princeton 1979 MEcon
Group Vice President, Financial Markets and Institutions Research **Frederick T. Furlong** . . . . (415) 974-3205
Education: Mount St Mary's 1970 BSE; UCLA 1975 MEc, 1978 PhD
Vice President, Research Communications
Robert G. "Rob" Valletta . . . . (415) 974-3345
Education: UC Berkeley 1982 AB; Harvard 1985 AM, 1987 PhD

Los Angeles (CA) Branch
950 South Grand Avenue, Los Angeles, CA 90051
P.O. Box 2077, Los Angeles, CA 90051
Tel: (213) 683-2300 Fax: (213) 683-2499

Chairman **James A. Hughes** . . . . (213) 683-2300

Portland (OR) Branch
1500 SW First Avenue, Suite 100, Portland, OR 97201
P.O. Box 3436, Portland, OR 97208
Tel: (503) 221-5900 Fax: (503) 221-5943

Regional Executive **Lynn Jorgensen** . . . . (503) 221-5900

Salt Lake City (UT) Branch
120 South State Street, Salt Lake City, UT 84125
P.O. Box 30780, Salt Lake City, UT 84125-0780
Tel: (801) 322-7900 Fax: (801) 322-7845

Regional Executive **Robin Rockwood** . . . . (801) 322-7900

Seattle (WA) Branch
1015 Second Avenue, Seattle, WA 98124
P.O. Box 3567 - Terminal Annex, Seattle, WA 98124-3567
Tel: (425) 203-0800

Regional Executive **Darlene Wilczynski** . . . . (425) 203-0800

Federal Reserve Bank of St. Louis (MO) (FRBMO)

P.O. Box 442, St. Louis, MO 63166-0442
One Federal Reserve Bank Plaza, St. Louis, MO 63102
Tel: (314) 444-8444 Fax: (314) 444-8430 Internet: www.stlouisfed.org
Areas Covered: AR, Southern IL, Southern IN, Western KY, Eastern MO, Northern MS, Western TN

President and Chief Executive Officer
James "Jim" Bullard . . . . (314) 444-8301
E-mail: jbullard@stls.frb.org
Education: St Cloud State 1984 BS; Indiana 1990 PhD
First Vice President and Chief Operating Officer
David A. Sapenaro . . . . (314) 444-8721
Education: Missouri (Kansas City) 1985 BBA

Federal Reserve Bank of St. Louis (MO) *(continued)*

Executive Vice President for Administration and Payments **Karl W. Ashman** . . . . (314) 444-8516
E-mail: karl.ashman@stls.frb.org
Education: Grace Col 1976 BS; Washington U (MO) 1988 MBA
Executive Vice President for Treasury Relations
Kathleen O'Neill Paese . . . . (314) 444-8630
E-mail: kathy.o.paese@stls.frb.org
Education: Illinois 1987 BA
Executive Vice President and Director of Research
Christopher J. Waller MA, PhD . . . . (314) 444-6237
E-mail: cwaller@stls.frb.org Fax: (314) 444-8731
Education: Bemidji State 1981 BS; Washington State 1984 MA, 1985 PhD
Executive Vice President for Supervision, Credit and Community Development **Julie L. Stackhouse** . . . . (314) 444-8431
Education: Drake 1980 BS
Senior Vice President and Chief of Staff
Cletus C. Coughlin . . . . (414) 444-8640
Education: Iowa 1974 BBA; North Carolina 1981 PhD Fax: (314) 444-8731
Senior Vice President **Francois G. Henriquez** . . . . (314) 444-8444
Senior Vice President **Matthew W. Torbett** . . . . (314) 444-8444
Senior Vice President and General Auditor
Michael D. Renfro . . . . (314) 444-8429
Senior Vice President, General Counsel and Secretary
Roy A. Hendin . . . . (314) 444-8526
Senior Vice President for Public Affairs
Karen L. Branding . . . . (314) 444-8444
Education: Drake; Indiana; Washington U (MO) MBA
Administrative Officer **Jeffrey M. Zove** . . . . (314) 444-8902
Senior Manager **David L. Hubbard** . . . . (314) 444-8444

Little Rock (AR) Branch
111 Center Street, Suite 1000, Little Rock, AR 72201
P.O. Box 1261, Little Rock, AR 72203
Tel: (501) 324-8300 Fax: (501) 324-8201

Chair **Millie A. Ward**
Director **R. Andrew Clyde**
Education: Southern Methodist BBA; Kellogg MM
Director **Keith Glover**
Director **Vickie Judy** . . . . (314) 444-8444
Director **Jeff Lynch** . . . . (501) 324-8300
Director **Robert Martinez** . . . . (314) 444-8444
Director **Karama Neal** . . . . (314) 444-8444

Louisville (KY) Branch
101 South Fifth Street, Suite 1920, Louisville, KY 40202
P.O. Box 32710, Louisville, KY 40232
Tel: (502) 568-9200 Fax: (502) 568-9211

Senior Vice President **Nikki R. Jackson** . . . . (502) 568-9200
Education: Hampton BA; Miami JD

Memphis (TN) Branch
200 North Main Street, Memphis, TN 38103
P.O. Box 407, Memphis, TN 38101
Tel: (901) 523-7171 Fax: (901) 579-2406

Chair **Eric D. Robertson**
Director **Michael E. Cary** . . . . (314) 444-8444
Director **David T. Cochran, Jr.** . . . . (314) 444-8444
Director **J. Brice Fletcher** . . . . (314) 444-8444
Director **Julianne Goodwin** . . . . (314) 444-8444
Director **Carolyn Hardy** . . . . (314) 444-8444
Director **Michael Ugwueke** . . . . (314) 444-8444
Education: Shaw BS; Emory MPH; Medical U (SC) DHA
Media Contact **Matuschka Briggs** . . . . (314) 444-3795
Tel: (314) 296-7526

INDEPENDENT AGENCIES

★ Presidential Appointment Requiring Senate Confirmation ☆ Presidential Appointment ☐ Schedule C Appointment ◇ Career Senior Foreign Service Appointment
● Career Senior Executive Service (SES) Appointment ○ Non-Career Senior Executive Service (SES) Appointment ■ Postal Career Executive Service

Federal Trade Commission (FTC)

Description: The Federal Trade Commission protects consumers against unfair, deceptive, or fraudulent practices and promotes competition by preventing anticompetitive mergers and other like business practices in the marketplace.

600 Pennsylvania Avenue, NW, Washington, DC 20580
Tel: (877) 382-4357 (Consumer Complaints)
Tel: (202) 326-2430 (Freedom of Information/Privacy Act)
Tel: (202) 326-2222 (General Information)
Tel: (202) 326-2021 (Human Resources)
Tel: (202) 326-2395 (Library) Tel: (202) 326-2000 (Personnel Locator)
Tel: (202) 326-2339 (Procurement Information)
Tel: (202) 326-2180 (Public Affairs Office)
TTY: (202) 326-3422 (Human Resources)
TTY: (866) 653-4261 (Consumer Complaints)
TTY: (202) 326-3413 (Library) Internet: www.ftc.gov
Internet: www.consumer.gov (Consumer Page)
Internet: www.ftc.gov/open (Open Government Initiative)

THE COMMISSION

600 Pennsylvania Avenue, NW, Washington, DC 20580
Tel: (202) 326-2222 Fax: (202) 326-2396

Note: Commissioners may continue to serve until reappointed or replaced.

Regional Offices

East Central Region

1111 Superior Avenue, Suite 200, Cleveland, OH 44114-2507
Tel: (216) 263-3455 Fax: (216) 263-3426
Areas Covered: DE, DC, MD, MI, OH, PA, VA, WV

Director **Jon Miller Steiger** .... (216) 263-3442
Education: Michigan 1991; Columbia JD
Assistant Director **Larissa L. Bungo** .... (216) 263-3403
Administrative Officer **Bonnie Hessoun** .... (216) 263-3408
E-mail: bhessoun@ftc.gov

Midwest Region

55 West Monroe Street, Suite 1825, Chicago, IL 60603
Tel: (877) 382-4357 (Consumer Complaint Calls) Tel: (312) 960-5634
Fax: (312) 960-5600
Areas Covered: IL, IN, IA, KS, KY, MN, MO, NE, ND, SD, WI

Director **Todd M. Kossow** .... (312) 960-5634
Assistant Director **Jason M. Adler** .... (312) 960-5614
Administrative Officer **Michele Smith** .... (312) 960-5634
E-mail: msmith@ftc.gov

Northeast Region

One Bowling Green, Suite 318, New York, NY 10004
Tel: (212) 607-2829 Tel: (877) 382-4357 (Consumer Complaint Calls)
Fax: (212) 607-2822
Areas Covered: CT, ME, MA, NH, NJ, NY, PR, RI, VI, VT

Director **William H. Efron** .... (212) 607-2827
Education: Pennsylvania BA; Virginia JD
Assistant Director **Deborah Marrone** .... (212) 607-2802
Administrative Officer **Jolanta Marchel** .... (212) 607-2825

Northwest Region

Jackson Federal Building, 915 Second Avenue,
Room 2896, Seattle, WA 98174
Tel: (206) 220-6350 Fax: (206) 220-6366
Areas Covered: AK, ID, MT, OR, WA, WY

Director **Charles A. "Chuck" Harwood** .... (206) 220-4480
E-mail: charwood@ftc.gov
Education: Whitman 1980 BA; Willamette 1983 JD
Assistant Director **Tina Kondo** .... (206) 220-4477
E-mail: tkondo@ftc.gov
Administrative Officer **Stella A. Schuller** .... (206) 220-4478
E-mail: sschuller@ftc.gov

Southeast Region

225 Peachtree Street, NE, Suite 1500, Atlanta, GA 30303-1729
Tel: (404) 656-1390 Fax: (404) 656-1379
Areas Covered: AL, FL, GA, MS, NC, SC, TN

Director **Cindy A. Liebes** .... (404) 656-1359
Assistant Director **Anna Burns** .... (404) 656-1390
Education: Emory BA
Administrative Officer **Doris P. Walton** .... (404) 656-1363
E-mail: dwalton@ftc.gov

Southwest Region

1999 Bryan Street, Suite 2150, Dallas, TX 75201-6808
Tel: (214) 979-9350 Fax: (214) 953-3079
Areas Covered: AR, LA, NM, OK, TX

Director **Dama J. Brown** .... (214) 979-9374
Education: Eastern Michigan 1992; Wayne State U 1995 JD
Assistant Director **James E. "Jim" Elliot** .... (214) 979-9373
Education: Marist 1975 BA; Drake 1980 JD
Administrative Officer **Arlene Hughes-Carpenter** .... (214) 979-9380

Western Region

Los Angeles Office

10990 Wilshire Boulevard, Suite 400, Los Angeles, CA 90024
Tel: (310) 824-4343 Fax: (310) 824-4380
Areas Covered: AZ, Southern CA, CO, HI, NV, UT

Director **Thomas N. "Tom" Dahdouh** .... (310) 824-4320
Education: Yale; Harvard JD
Assistant Director **Dominique Alepin Johnson** .... (310) 824-4317
Education: Bowdoin 2002 BA; Columbia 2005 JD
Administrative Officer **Frank Bogardus** .... (310) 824-4319
E-mail: fbogardus@ftc.gov

San Francisco Office

901 Market Street, Suite 570, San Francisco, CA 94103
Tel: (415) 848-5100 Fax: (415) 848-5184
Areas Covered: AZ, CA, CO, HI, NV, UT

Director **Thomas N. "Tom" Dahdouh** .... (415) 848-5122
Education: Yale; Harvard JD
Secretary **Violet B. Orence** .... (415) 848-5166
E-mail: vorence@ftc.gov
Assistant Director **Kerry O'Brien** .... (415) 848-5189
Administrative Officer **Rosa Dominguez-Aldama** .... (415) 848-5172
E-mail: raldama@ftc.gov

★ Presidential Appointment Requiring Senate Confirmation ☆ Presidential Appointment □ Schedule C Appointment ◇ Career Senior Foreign Service Appointment
● Career Senior Executive Service (SES) Appointment ○ Non-Career Senior Executive Service (SES) Appointment ■ Postal Career Executive Service

United States General Services Administration (GSA)

Description: The General Services Administration provides workplaces by constructing, managing and preserving government buildings and by leasing and managing commercial real estate. GSA's acquisition solutions offer private sector professional services, equipment, supplies, telecommunications and information technology to government organizations and the military. GSA policies promote best management practices and efficient government operations.

1800 F Street, NW, Washington, DC 20405-0001
Tel: (202) 501-1231 (Public Information)
Tel: (202) 501-1235 (Publications Information)
Tel: (202) 501-1659 (Freedom of Information/Privacy Act)
Tel: (202) 501-1780 (Fraud Hotline - DC Metropolitan Area)
Tel: (800) 424-5210 (Fraud Hotline - Continental US, Alaska and Hawaii)
Tel: (888) 878-3256 (Consumer Information Center Hotline)
Tel: (800) 669-8331 (Federal Domestic Assistance Catalog Staff Hotline)
Tel: (800) 472-1313 (Surplus Real Estate Sales Hotline)
Tel: (866) 333-7472 (Surplus Personal Property Sales)
Fax: (202) 501-1489 Fax: (202) 501-0664 (Board of Contract Appeals)
Internet: www.gsa.gov
Internet: www.gsa.gov/socialmedia (Social Media Directory)
Internet: www.usa.gov (Official US Government Website)

OFFICE OF THE ADMINISTRATOR

1800 F Street, NW, Washington, DC 20405-0001
Tel: (202) 501-0800 Fax: (202) 219-1243

Regional Services

Region 1 - New England Region

Thomas P. O'Neill Federal Building, 10 Causeway Street, Room 1100, Boston, MA 02222-8512
Tel: (866) 734-1727 Fax: (617) 565-8170
Internet: https://www.gsa.gov/portal/content/104933
Areas Covered: CT, ME, MA, NH, RI, VT

○ Regional Administrator (Acting) **Glenn C. Rotondo** . . . . . (617) 565-5694
E-mail: glenn.rotondo@gsa.gov
Education: Providence 1984 BS; New England 1988 JD

□ Special Assistant **(Vacant)** . . . . . (866) 734-1727

FOIA Coordinator **Carlene Polynice** . . . . . (617) 565-6001
E-mail: carlene.polynice@gsa.gov

Public Affairs Officer **Paul Hughes** . . . . . (617) 283-6142
E-mail: paul.hughes@gsa.gov

Human Resources Manager **Bob Foley** . . . . . (617) 565-6634
E-mail: bob.foley@gsa.gov

Federal Acquisition Service

Thomas P. O'Neill, Jr. Federal Building,
10 Causeway Street, Boston, MA 02222-1076
Tel: (617) 565-5721 Tel: (617) 565-5760 (Telecommunications Teams)
Fax: (617) 565-5767

● Regional Commissioner (Acting) **Joseph "Joe" Nickerson** . . . . . (617) 565-6727
E-mail: joe.nickerson@gsa.gov

Acquisition Operations Division, Deputy Regional Commissioner **Michael Attachi** . . . . . (617) 565-6573
E-mail: michael.attachi@gsa.gov Fax: (617) 565-5767

Assisted Acquisition Services Director **(Vacant)** . . . . . (617) 565-5721

Customer Service Director **Peter Sullivan** . . . . . (617) 565-7315

Network Services Division Director **John K. Sullivan** . . . . (617) 565-5762
E-mail: john.sullivan@gsa.gov

Office of Inspector General

Thomas P. O'Neill, Jr. Federal Building,
10 Causeway Street, Boston, MA 02222-1076
Tel: (617) 565-6800 Fax: (617) 565-6817

Special Agent in Charge for Investigations **Luis A. Hernandez** . . . . . (617) 565-6800
Fax: (617) 565-6798

Office of Regional Counsel

Thomas P. O'Neill, Jr. Federal Building,
10 Causeway Street, Boston, MA 02222-1076
Tel: (617) 565-5896 Fax: (617) 565-7278

Regional Counsel **Nancy E. O'Connell** . . . . . (617) 565-5891
E-mail: nancy.oconnell@gsa.gov

Public Buildings Service

Thomas P. O'Neill, Jr. Federal Building,
10 Causeway Street, Boston, MA 02222-1076
Tel: (617) 565-5693 Fax: (617) 565-8170

● Regional Commissioner **Glenn C. Rotondo** . . . . . (617) 565-5694
E-mail: glenn.rotondo@gsa.gov
Education: Providence 1984 BS; New England 1988 JD

Client Solutions Division Director **Denis Thibodeau** . . . . . (617) 565-5777
Fax: (617) 565-8170

Congressional Services Representative **John Foley** . . . . . (617) 565-6000

Regional Emergency Coordinator **Kevin D. LaPierre** . . . . . (617) 960-0364
E-mail: kevin.lapierre@gsa.gov

Facilities Management Division Director **Walter Perez** . . . (617) 565-5820
Fax: (617) 565-7146

Lease Acquisitions Division Director **Kevin Richards** . . . . (617) 893-9473
E-mail: kevin.richards@gsa.gov

Portfolio Management Deputy Director **(Vacant)** . . . . . (617) 565-5693

Program Administration Division Director **Matthew Bailey** . . . . . (617) 565-4636
E-mail: matthew.bailey@gsa.gov

Chief Financial Officer **(Vacant)** . . . . . (617) 565-5055
Fax: (617) 565-8391

Systems Support Branch Chief **Steven Gillespie** . . . . . (617) 565-6749
E-mail: steven.gillespie@gsa.gov Fax: (617) 565-4639

Property Disposal Director **David E. Kiernan** . . . . . (617) 565-5078
Fax: (617) 565-5720

Service Center Division Director **Karen Palladino** . . . . . (617) 565-5825
Fax: (617) 565-7147

Boston Service Center Branch Chief **Michael L. Franzese** . . . . . (617) 565-7255
Fax: (617) 565-7147

North Service Center Branch Chief **Timothy Shobbrook** . . . . . (617) 565-5653
Fax: (617) 565-8170

South Service Center Branch Chief **(Vacant)** . . . . . (617) 565-5693
Fax: (617) 565-7147

Design and Construction Division

Thomas P. O'Neill, Jr. Federal Building,
10 Causeway Street, Boston, MA 02222-1076

Director **Janice Ramsey** . . . . . (617) 565-7218
Fax: (617) 565-7145

★ Presidential Appointment Requiring Senate Confirmation ☆ Presidential Appointment □ Schedule C Appointment ◇ Career Senior Foreign Service Appointment
● Career Senior Executive Service (SES) Appointment ○ Non-Career Senior Executive Service (SES) Appointment ■ Postal Career Executive Service

INDEPENDENT AGENCIES

Small Business Utilization Center
Thomas P. O'Neill, Jr. Federal Building,
10 Causeway Street, Boston, MA 02222-1076
Tel: (617) 565-8100 Fax: (617) 565-5748

Director **Jerry D. Smith** .... (617) 565-8102
E-mail: jerry.d.smith@gsa.gov

Region 2 - Northeast and Caribbean Region
One World Trade Center, Floor 55, Room 55W09,
New York, NY 10007-0089
Tel: (212) 264-4282 Internet: www.gsa.gov/region2
Areas Covered: NJ, NY, PR, VI

○ Regional Administrator **John A. Sarcone III** .... (212) 264-2600
E-mail: r2ra@gsa.gov
Education: Pace BS, JD
□ Special Assistant **(Vacant)** .... (212) 265-3305
Civil Rights Officer **Jill A. Badami** .... (212) 264-4793
Human Resources Officer **Maureen Gannon** .... (215) 446-4963
100 S Independence Mall West, Philadelphia, PA 19106
E-mail: maureen.gannon@gsa.gov
Public Affairs Officer (Acting) **Paul Hughes** .... (617) 283-6142
E-mail: paul.hughes@gsa.gov
Emergency Management Coordinator **Roy Crowe** .... (212) 264-0596
Lead Small Business Specialist **Janice Bracey** .... (212) 264-1235
E-mail: janice.bracey@gsa.gov
Freedom of Information Act Requests
Marianna Medve .... (212) 264-8338
E-mail: marianna.medve@gsa.gov

Federal Acquisition Service
One World Trade Center, New York, NY 10007-0089

● Regional Commissioner **Jeffrey "Jeff" Lau** .... (212) 264-3590
E-mail: jeffrey.lau@gsa.gov
Business Management Division Director **Tricia Sieveke**... (212) 264-1372
E-mail: tricia.sieveke@gsa.gov

Assisted Acquisition Services Division
Assisted Acquisition Service Director **Jo-Ann Lee** .... (212) 264-1885
E-mail: joann.lee@gsa.gov

Stakeholder Engagement Branch
Director **Frank Mayer** .... (212) 264-1179
Deputy Director **Christine Lincoln Naples** .... (212) 264-2698
Customer Service Director
Andrew "Andy" Kirkpatrick .... (512) 364-3298

Fleet Management Services Division
One World Trade Center, Floor 55, Room 55W09,
New York, NY 10007-0089

Director **Brian Smith** .... (212) 264-3930
E-mail: brian.smith@gsa.gov

National Administrative Acquisition Division
One World Trade Center, 285 Fulton St., New York, NY 10007

Director **(Vacant)** .... (212) 264-1885
Acquisition Policy Advisor **Theresa Ramos** .... (212) 264-2690
E-mail: theresa.ramos@gsa.gov
Administrative Services Acquisition Branch Chief
Wei Lu-Gin .... (212) 264-2693
Office Products Acquisition Branch Chief
Maria Viscione .... (212) 264-8727
201 Varick Street, New York, NY 10014
E-mail: maria.viscione@gsa.gov
Contracting Officer, Federal Strategic Sourcing
Initiative for Office Supplies – Third Generation
Wdonna Wood .... (212) 577-8623
E-mail: wdonna.woods@gsa.gov

Network Services Division
Network Services Division Director (Acting)
Theresa Ramos .... (212) 264-2690
E-mail: theresa.ramos@gsa.gov

Northeast and Caribbean Supply and Acquisition Center
One World Trade Center, 285 Fulton St.,
Floor 55, New York, NY 10007

Director **Peter J. Han** .... (212) 264-6949
E-mail: peter.han@gsa.gov

Personal Property Division
Director **Christina Shaw** .... (215) 446-5083
E-mail: christina.shaw@gsa.gov

Office of Inspector General
One World Trade Center, Floor 55, Room 55W09,
New York, NY 10007-0089
Tel: (212) 264-8620 (Audits) Tel: (212) 264-7300 (Investigations)

Regional Inspector General for Auditing
Steven D. Jurysta .... (212) 264-8620
26 Federal Plaza, JA-2, New York, NY 10278
E-mail: steven.jurysta@gsaig.gov
Regional Inspector General for Investigations **(Vacant)** ... (212) 264-7300
26 Federal Plaza, JI-2, New York, NY 10278
Assistant Regional Inspector General for
Investigations **(Vacant)** .... (212) 264-7300

Office of Regional Counsel
One World Trade Center, Floor 55, Room 55W09,
New York, NY 10007-0089
Tel: (212) 264-8306

Regional Counsel **Carol A. Latterman** .... (212) 264-8308
E-mail: carol.latterman@gsa.gov

Public Buildings Service
One World Trade Center, Floor 55, Room 55W09,
New York, NY 10007-0089
Tel: (212) 264-4282

● Regional Commissioner **(Vacant)** .... (212) 264-4282
Regional Energy Coordinator **Brian Magden** .... (212) 264-0591
E-mail: brian.magden@gsa.gov
Systems Information Technology Specialist **(Vacant)** ..... (212) 264-4140
Design and Construction Division Director
David McDonald .... (212) 264-4247
Project Management Branch C Chief **Ken Chin** .... (212) 264-0802
Project Management Branch D Chief
Robert Granato .... (212) 264-3544
Facilities Management and Services Program Division
Director **David Segermeister** .... (212) 264-4273
Emergency Management Branch Chief **Roy Crowe** ..... (212) 264-0596
Safety and Environmental Management Branch Chief
Eric Marrinan .... (212) 264-8784
E-mail: eric.marrinan@gsa.gov
Technical Program Branch Chief **(Vacant)** .... (212) 264-1254
Portfolio Management Division Director
Vincent Scalcione .... (212) 264-1547
Client Solutions Staff **Maria Guida** .... (212) 264-2236
Everything but Manhattan Service Center Director
Gary Palmer .... (315) 448-0920
Organizational Resources Division Director
Warren Hall .... (212) 264-4241
Education: Western Connecticut St BS
Acquisition Management Division Director
Maureen L. Lennon .... (212) 264-9151
E-mail: maureen.lennon@gsa.gov

Region 3 - Mid-Atlantic Region
Dow Building, 100 S Independence Mall West,
Floor 3, Philadelphia, PA 19106
Tel: (215) 446-4900 Fax: (215) 446-5136
Internet: www.gsa.gov/midatlantic and www.gsa.gov/r3

○ Regional Administrator **Joyce C. Haas** .... (215) 446-4900
E-mail: joyce.haas@gsa.gov Fax: (215) 446-5125
Education: Penn State BS
Executive Assistant **Maria Ortiz** .... (215) 446-4903
Special Assistant to the Regional Administrator
(Vacant) .... (215) 446-5077

★ Presidential Appointment Requiring Senate Confirmation ☆ Presidential Appointment □ Schedule C Appointment ◇ Career Senior Foreign Service Appointment
● Career Senior Executive Service (SES) Appointment ○ Non-Career Senior Executive Service (SES) Appointment ■ Postal Career Executive Service

Region 3 - Mid-Atlantic Region *(continued)*

Director, Human Resources Division
Maureen Gannon . . . . (215) 446-4963
E-mail: maureen.gannon@gsa.gov
Deputy Director, Human Resources Division
Joseph Malick . . . . (215) 446-4969
E-mail: joe.malick@gsa.gov
Equal Employment Opportunity Officer
Sylvia Anderson . . . . (215) 446-4967
E-mail: sylvia.anderson@gsa.gov
Public Affairs Officer (Acting) **Adam C. Rondeau** . . . . . . (470) 495-7496
E-mail: adam.rondeau@gsa.gov
Reimbursable Work Authorizations (RWAs)
Robert J. Scheible . . . . (215) 446-4920
E-mail: robert.scheible@gsa.gov
Regional Emergency Coordinator **Maryann Toniazzo** . . . . (215) 446-4911
E-mail: maryann.toniazzo@gsa.gov
Regional IT Manager **Christopher Cozzalio** . . . . (215) 446-5710

Federal Acquisition Service

● Regional Commissioner **Dena M. McLaughlin** . . . . (215) 446-4900
E-mail: dena.mclaughlin@gsa.gov
● Deputy Regional Commissioner
Joseph M. "Joe" Hvorecky . . . . (215) 446-5006
E-mail: joe.hvorecky@gsa.gov
Director, Office of Regional Acquisition Operations
John E. "Jack" Wise . . . . (215) 446-5848
E-mail: jack.wise@gsa.gov
Director, Office of Strategic Solutions **Mike Wano** . . . . . . (215) 446-5013
E-mail: mike.wano@gsa.gov
Director, Assisted Acquisition Services Division
Mark Aucello . . . . (215) 446-5802
E-mail: mark.aucello@gsa.gov Fax: (215) 814-6157
Director, Customer Accounts and Research Division
Stacy Buechele . . . . (215) 446-5002
E-mail: stacy.buechele@gsa.gov
Director, Financial Management and Oversight Division **Clyde Reeves** . . . . (215) 446-5010
Director, Fleet Management Zone 1 Division
Brian Smith . . . . (212) 264-3930
285 Fulton St., New York, NY 10007
Director, National Clients Acquisition Operations Division **(Vacant)** . . . . (215) 446-5826
Director, Network Services Division **Ray Cwenar** . . . . . . (215) 446-5811
E-mail: ray.cwenar@gsa.gov
Director, Property Management Division
Susan Labman . . . . (215) 446-5827
Director, Regional Clients Acquisition Operations Division **Robert "Bob" Vitelli** . . . . (215) 446-5826
E-mail: robert.vitelli@gsa.gov
Customer Service Director **Jaime Kern** . . . . (215) 446-4891
Fax: (215) 446-0271
Small Business Utilization Officer **Helena E. Koch** . . . . . . (215) 446-4918
E-mail: helena.koch@gsa.gov

Financial Service Center

Director **Dennis McNamara** . . . . (215) 446-4788
E-mail: dennis.mcnamara@gsa.gov

Integrated Workplace Acquisition Center (IWAC)

Crystal Plaza 4, 2200 Crystal Drive, Suite 400, Arlington, VA 22202
Tel: (703) 605-9300 Fax: (703) 605-5777

Director **Brian Knapp** . . . . (215) 446-5033
100 S Independence Mall West, Philadelphia, PA 19106
E-mail: brian.knapp@gsa.gov

Office of Inspector General

Dow Building, 100 S Independence Mall West,
Floor 3, Philadelphia, PA 19106
Tel: (215) 446-4840 Fax: (215) 446-5888

Regional Inspector General for Auditing
Thomas Tripple . . . . (215) 446-4835
E-mail: thomas.tripple@gsaig.gov

Office of Regional Counsel

● Regional Counsel (Acting) **Robert Notigan, Jr.** . . . . (215) 446-4939
E-mail: robert.notigan@gsa.gov

Public Buildings Service

Dow Building, 100 S Independence Mall West,
Floor 3, Philadelphia, PA 19106
Fax: (215) 446-6006 Fax: (215) 446-5140

● Regional Commissioner **Joanna Rosato** . . . . (215) 446-4500
E-mail: joanna.rosato@gsa.gov
Education: Temple 1985 BA
Deputy Regional Commissioner **Dorothy Baratta** . . . . (215) 446-4641
Director, North Service Center (DE/PA/NJ)
Thomas L. "Tom" Lyman . . . . (215) 446-4752
Director, South Service Center (MD/VA/WV)
John Morrell . . . . (215) 446-4614
Director, Acquisition Management **Liliana DelBonifro** . . . . (215) 446-4496
E-mail: liliana.delbonifro@gsa.gov
Director, Client Solutions **(Vacant)** . . . . (215) 446-2886
Director, Design and Construction **Albert Torjman** . . . . . . (215) 446-2844
Director, Facilities Management and Services
John Hofmann . . . . (215) 446-5764
Director, Portfolio Management **John Calhoun** . . . . (215) 446-2890
Director, Project Management **Ian Grey** . . . . (215) 446-2886
Director, Real Estate Acquisition **Dale Anderson** . . . . (215) 446-2842
E-mail: dale.anderson@gsa.gov

Region 4 - Southeast Sunbelt Region

77 Forsyth Street, Suite 600, Atlanta, GA 30303
Tel: (404) 331-3200 Fax: (404) 331-0931 Internet: www.gsa.gov/r4
Areas Covered: AL, FL, GA, KY, MS, NC, SC, TN

○ Regional Administrator **Brian Stern** . . . . (404) 331-3200
E-mail: r4administrator@gsa.gov
Education: Col Charleston BA
Public Affairs Officer **Adam C. Rondeau** . . . . (470) 495-7496
E-mail: adam.rondeau@gsa.gov
□ Senior Advisor **(Vacant)** . . . . (404) 331-3200
Regional Credit Card Coordinator **Janice Evans** . . . . (404) 331-9899
E-mail: janice.evans@gsa.gov
Regional Emergency Coordinator
Jermaine Brown Suite 650 . . . . (404) 331-5708
E-mail: jermaine.brown@gsa.gov
Congressional Support Services Lead
Regina D. Harden . . . . (404) 331-3243
Congressional Services Representative
Jenny Lynn Mooney . . . . (404) 331-4404

Human Resources Division

77 Forsyth Street, Suite 600, Atlanta, GA 30303
Tel: (404) 331-3186 Fax: (404) 331-1721

Director of Human Resources **Kathy W. Day** . . . . (404) 331-3186
E-mail: kathy.day@gsa.gov
Deputy Director of Human Resources
Gary M. Samaha . . . . (404) 331-3181
E-mail: gary.samaha@gsa.gov
Equal Employment Opportunity Officer
Kellyann D. Williams . . . . (216) 446-4906
100 S Independence Mall West, Philadelphia, PA 19106
Lead Human Resources Specialist **Matilda D. Hatchell** . . . (404) 331-5286
E-mail: matilda.hatchell@gsa.gov
Agency Telework Coordinator **Marge Higgins** . . . . (202) 501-3764
1800 F Street, NW, Washington, DC 20405-0001
E-mail: marge.higgins@gsa.gov

Office of Inspector General

401 West Peachtree Street, NW, Atlanta, GA 30308
Fax: (404) 331-5885

Regional Inspector General for Auditing
Nicholas Painter . . . . (404) 331-5520
E-mail: nicholas.painter@gsaig.gov
Auditor **(Vacant)** . . . . (404) 331-5573
Auditor **(Vacant)** . . . . (404) 331-0380
Special Agent in Charge for Investigations **(Vacant)** . . . . . . (404) 331-5126

★ Presidential Appointment Requiring Senate Confirmation ☆ Presidential Appointment □ Schedule C Appointment ◇ Career Senior Foreign Service Appointment
● Career Senior Executive Service (SES) Appointment ○ Non-Career Senior Executive Service (SES) Appointment ■ Postal Career Executive Service

Office of Regional Counsel

Regional Counsel **Liana D. Henry** .... (404) 215-6860
E-mail: liana.henry@gsa.gov

Office of Small Business Utilization (ROSBU)

77 Forsyth Street, Suite 600, Atlanta, GA 30303
Tel: (404) 331-5103 Fax: (404) 331-1721 E-mail: r4smallbiz@gsa.gov

Director **Chasity Ash** .... (404) 331-1053
E-mail: chasity.ash@gsa.gov
E-mail: r4smallbiz@gsa.gov
Small Business Development Specialist
Rebecca A. Vanover .... (404) 331-3374
E-mail: rebecca.vanover@gsa.gov

Federal Acquisition Service

401 West Peachtree Street, NW, Suite 2600, Atlanta, GA 30308
Tel: (404) 331-5114 Fax: (404) 331-0200

● Regional Commissioner **Thomas Meiron** .... (404) 331-5114
E-mail: thomas.meiron@gsa.gov
Deputy Regional Commissioner **Kelley Holcombe, Jr.** .... (404) 331-0652
E-mail: kelley.holcombe@gsa.gov Fax: (404) 331-7563
Director, Contract Management Division **(Vacant)** .... (404) 331-1605
Assistant Director, Operational Chief **(Vacant)** .... (404) 331-7198

Assisted Acquisition Services

401 West Peachtree Street, NW, Suite 2700, Atlanta, GA 30308

Director **Kelley Holcombe, Jr.** .... (404) 331-0652
E-mail: kelley.holcombe@gsa.gov

Customer Accounts and Research Division

77 Forsyth Street, Suite 600, Atlanta, GA 30303
Fax: (404) 331-7563

Director **Debbie Nicoletti** .... (478) 319-8835
Customer Service Director **Dhana Moore** .... (757) 618-5720

Fleet Zone 2

Director **William A. "Bill" Sisk** .... (404) 331-2949
Education: Citadel 1989

Office of Telecom Services

401 West Peachtree Street, NW, Suite 2700, Atlanta, GA 30308

Director **Bridget Williams** .... (404) 331-6218
E-mail: bridget.williams@gsa.gov

Personal Property Management

77 Forsyth Street, Suite 600, Atlanta, GA 30303
Tel: (404) 332-3323

Director **Karen L. Warrior** .... (404) 331-3323
E-mail: karen.warrior@gsa.gov
Reverse Auctions Division Manager **Dallas Hayes** .... (404) 215-8700

Public Buildings Service

77 Forsyth Street, Atlanta, GA 30303
Tel: (404) 331-3200 Fax: (404) 331-0200

● Regional Commissioner (Acting) **John "JD" Dennis** .... (404) 215-6881
E-mail: johnm.dennis@gsa.gov
Special Assistant to the Regional Commissioner
(Vacant) .... (404) 215-6794
Facilities Management and Services Program Division
Director **Sabina Sims** .... (404) 331-0503
Safety and Occupational Health Manager **(Vacant)** .... (404) 331-3126
Fax: (404) 331-3275

Acquisition Division

401 West Peachtree Street, NW, Suite 2513, Atlanta, GA 30308

Director **Pamela "Pam" Mitschke** .... (404) 224-2169
E-mail: pam.mitschke@gsa.gov

Budget and Financial Management Division

77 Forsyth Street, T-01, Atlanta, GA 30303

Director **Gwendolyn Gladman** .... (404) 562-1571
E-mail: gwendolyn.gladman@gsa.gov Fax: (404) 331-3801

Budget and Financial Management Division *(continued)*

Reimbursable Work Authorizations Manager
Maletha Singleton .... (404) 562-1639
E-mail: maletha.singleton@gsa.gov

Client Solutions Division

401 West Peachtree Street, NW, Suite 2300, Atlanta, GA 30308

Director **David "Dave" Hofstetter** .... (404) 562-2750

Design and Construction Division

Director **Courtney DeBord** .... (404) 331-5130

Environmental/Recycling

77 Forsyth Street, Suite 600, Atlanta, GA 30303
Fax: (404) 730-9723

Sustainability Program Manager **Jason Grimes** .... (404) 431-0122

Portfolio Management Division

Director **Victoria Corkren** .... (404) 562-0034

Property Disposal Division

77 Forsyth Street, Suite 600, Atlanta, GA 30303
Fax: (404) 331-2727

Director **Angela Risch** .... (404) 331-1652

Real Estate Acquisition Services Division

Director **(Vacant)** .... (404) 331-3200
401 West Peachtree Street, NW, Atlanta, GA 30308

Service Center Division

401 West Peachtree Street, NW, Atlanta, GA 30308
Fax: (404) 331-1105

Director **Robert L. "Rob" Miller, Jr.** .... (404) 331-3107
Education: Southern Illinois 1992 BSAv; Fax: (404) 331-2727
Troy State 2003 (ABD)

Region 5 - Great Lakes

John C. Kluczynski Federal Building, 230 South Dearborn Street, 3500, Chicago, IL 60604
Tel: (312) 353-5572 Fax: (312) 886-5595

○ Regional Administrator **Brad Hansher** .... (312) 385-4121
E-mail: brad.hansher@gsa.gov
Education: Wisconsin 2000 BA
Regional Public Affairs Officer
Catherine "Cat" Langel .... (312) 353-5663
E-mail: catherine.langel@gsa.gov
Regional Human Resources Director
Ronnie Redmond .... (312) 353-4091
E-mail: ronnie.redmond@gsa.gov
Regional Equal Employment Opportunity Officer
Kellyann D. Williams .... (215) 446-4906
Regional Emergency Coordinator
Mark McConnaughhay .... (312) 353-3487
E-mail: mark.mcconnaughhay@gsa.gov
Regional FOIA Officer **Megan Brown** .... (312) 886-4410
E-mail: megan.brown@gsa.gov
Regional Information Technology Manager
Charles "Chuck" Pierce .... (312) 353-2173
E-mail: charles.pierce@gsa.gov

Office of the Inspector General

Regional Inspector General for Audits
Adam R. Gooch .... (312) 353-0500
E-mail: adam.gooch@gsaig.gov
Special Agent in Charge for Investigations
Jeffrey "Jeff" Ryan .... (312) 353-0836
E-mail: jeffrey.ryan@gsaig.gov

Office of Regional Counsel

230 South Dearborn Street, Room 3700, Chicago, IL 60604
Tel: (312) 353-5392 Fax: (312) 353-6484

Regional Counsel **Thomas Y. "Tom" Hawkins** .... (312) 353-5423
E-mail: thomas.hawkins@gsa.gov

★ Presidential Appointment Requiring Senate Confirmation ☆ Presidential Appointment ☐ Schedule C Appointment ◇ Career Senior Foreign Service Appointment
● Career Senior Executive Service (SES) Appointment ○ Non-Career Senior Executive Service (SES) Appointment ■ Postal Career Executive Service

Federal Acquisition Service
230 South Dearborn Street, Room 3800, Chicago, IL 60604
Tel: (312) 886-8800 Fax: (312) 886-3827

● Regional Commissioner **Kim E. Brown** . . . . (312) 886-8906
E-mail: kim.brown@gsa.gov
Deputy Regional Commissioner **Anne Mesch** . . . . (312) 886-3478
E-mail: anne.mesch@gsa.gov
Executive and Financial Management Officer
Janie Burmeister . . . . (312) 886-8971
E-mail: janie.burmeister@gsa.gov
Director, Office of Regional Small Business Management **Stephanie E. Wilson-Coleman** . . . . (312) 886-8194
E-mail: stephanie.wilson-coleman@gsa.gov
Acquisition Operations Division Director
Micky Mayes . . . . (312) 886-8820
E-mail: micky.mayes@gsa.gov
Assisted Acquisition Services Director **Rodney Couick** . . . (618) 622-5801
E-mail: rodney.couick@gsa.gov
Customer Accounts and Research Director **Kurt Regep** . . . (312) 886-8870
E-mail: kurt.regep@gsa.gov
Customer Service Director **Hakeem Ali** . . . . (312) 353-5531
Fleet Management Division Director **Troy Williams** . . . . (937) 427-5635
E-mail: troy.williams@gsa.gov
Network Services Division Director **Gayle Dybel** . . . . (312) 886-3806
E-mail: gayle.dybel@gsa.gov
National Marketing and Communication Division Director **Christine "Chris" Lundstrom** . . . . (312) 886-8275
E-mail: chris.lundstrom@gsa.gov
Supplier Management, Midwest Operations Center Director (Acting) **Eric Horton** . . . . (312) 515-3282
E-mail: eric.horton@gsa.gov

Public Buildings Service
230 South Dearborn Street, Chicago, IL 60604
Tel: (312) 353-5572 Fax: (312) 353-9320

● Regional Commissioner **John Thomas Cooke** . . . . (312) 353-5572
E-mail: john.cooke@gsa.gov
Deputy Regional Commissioner
Robert A. "Bob" Nawrocki . . . . (312) 353-5301
Chief of Staff **Jennifer Enyart** . . . . (312) 353-5572
E-mail: jennifer.enyart@gsa.gov
Budget and Financial Management Division Director
Alicia Saucedo de Flores . . . . (312) 353-5046
E-mail: alicia.saucedo@gsa.gov
Design and Construction Project Programs Division Director **Robert P. Theel** . . . . (312) 353-1445
Design and Construction Project Delivery Division Director **John Caswell** . . . . (312) 353-0888
Facilities Management and Services Programs Division Director **Jeffrey "Jeff" Mornar** . . . . (217) 801-9714
Portfolio Management Division Director **Bill R. James** . . . (312) 886-1925
Real Estate Division Director **Robert "Rob" Green** . . . . (312) 353-3308
E-mail: robert.green@gsa.gov
Chicagoland Service Center Operations Division Director **William Earle** . . . . (312) 886-7112
Northern Service Center Operations Division Director
Michele A. Sharples . . . . (312) 353-0953
Southern Service Center Operations Division Director
Jesse J. Ozuna . . . . (312) 886-4493
Real Property Utilization and Disposal Chief
Richard Balsano . . . . (312) 353-0302
E-mail: richard.balsano@gsa.gov

Region 6 - Heartland
Two Pershing Square, 2300 Main Street, Kansas City, MO 64108
Tel: (816) 926-7201 Fax: (816) 926-7513
Internet: www.gsa.gov/heartland

○ Regional Administrator **Michael Copeland** . . . . (816) 926-7201
E-mail: michael.copeland@gsa.gov
□ Senior Advisor to the Regional Administrator
Judy Dungan . . . . (816) 216-3462
E-mail: judy.dungan@gsa.gov
Administrative Assistant **Diane Neal** . . . . (816) 926-7025
E-mail: diane.neal@gsa.gov

Region 6 - Heartland *(continued)*

Director, Financial and Payroll Services Division
Vicki Jones . . . . (816) 823-2886
Director, Human Resources **(Vacant)** . . . . (816) 823-2653
Director, Small Business Utilization **(Vacant)** . . . . (816) 926-7201
Director, Strategic Planning and Support Services
William Dunn . . . . (816) 926-5794
E-mail: william.dunn@gsa.gov
Chief Information Officer
Gregory T. "Greg" Gdanski . . . . (816) 823-5784
E-mail: gregory.gdanski@gsa.gov
Congressional Services Representative **Gail Allen** . . . . (816) 926-7291
Fax: (816) 246-0072
Freedom of Information Act Specialist **(Vacant)** . . . . (816) 926-5305
Public Affairs Officer **(Vacant)** . . . . (816) 823-2931
Deputy Regional Director, Office of Emergency Response and Recovery **(Vacant)** . . . . (816) 926-7201
1800 F Street, NW, Washington, DC 20405-0001
Regional EEO Officer **(Vacant)** . . . . (816) 926-7073
Fax: (816) 823-1970
Media Relations **Charles T. Cook** . . . . (816) 823-1043

Federal Acquisition Service
Two Pershing Square, 2300 Main Street, Kansas City, MO 64108
Tel: (816) 823-1700 Fax: (816) 926-5670

● Regional Commissioner **Mary Ruwwe** . . . . (816) 823-1700
E-mail: mary.ruwwe@gsa.gov
Education: Peru State BSBA, BSSecEd; Weber State MBA
Deputy Regional Commissioner **Sharon M. Henry** . . . . (816) 926-7266
1500 East Bannister Road, Room 1121, Kansas City, MO 64131-3009
E-mail: sharon.henry@gsa.gov
Education: Southwest Missouri State 1989 BS; Kansas 1999 MS
Heartland Acquisition Center Director
Teresa Florence McCarthy . . . . (816) 389-3918
E-mail: teresa.mccarthy@gsa.gov
Small Business Governmentwide Acquisition Contracts Center Director **Stephen P. "Steve" Triplett** . . . . (816) 926-7245
1500 East Bannister Road, Room 1121, Kansas City, MO 64131-3009
E-mail: steve.triplett@gsa.gov
Education: Wichita State 1983 BS, 1990 MPA
National Customer Service Center Director
Debbie Harms . . . . (816) 926-3114
Information Technology Schedule Contract Operations
Bradley "Brad" Cornell . . . . (816) 823-1281
1500 East Bannister Road, Room 1085, Kansas City, MO 64131
E-mail: bradley.cornell@gsa.gov
Customer Accounts and Research Division Director
(Vacant) . . . . (816) 823-1700
Customer Service Director **Jerry Johnson** . . . . (816) 518-6597
Customer Service Director **Russell Luttrall** . . . . (816) 926-3992
Fleet Management Services Director **(Vacant)** . . . . (816) 926-7223
1500 East Bannister Road, Room 1102, Kansas City, MO 64131-3009
Marketing Director **Thomas F. Brown** . . . . (816) 823-2009
1500 East Bannister Road, Room 1102, Kansas City, MO 64131-3009
E-mail: thomasf.brown@gsa.gov
Network Services Division Director **Darrel Davis** . . . . (816) 926-5794
1500 East Bannister Road, Room 1085, Kansas City, MO 64131-3009
E-mail: darrel.davis@gsa.gov
Area Telecommunications Manager **Tyrone M. Davis** . . . (816) 426-3021
E-mail: tyrone.davis@gsa.gov
Print Management Division Director **(Vacant)** . . . . (816) 926-5511
Supervisory Contracting Officer **(Vacant)** . . . . (816) 823-1700
1500 East Bannister Road, Kansas City, MO 64131

Office of Inspector General
Regional Inspector General for Auditing
John L. Walsh . . . . (816) 926-8615
Fax: (816) 926-5649
Special Agent In Charge **(Vacant)** . . . . (816) 926-7214
Fax: (816) 926-2464

INDEPENDENT AGENCIES

★ Presidential Appointment Requiring Senate Confirmation ☆ Presidential Appointment □ Schedule C Appointment ◇ Career Senior Foreign Service Appointment
● Career Senior Executive Service (SES) Appointment ○ Non-Career Senior Executive Service (SES) Appointment ■ Postal Career Executive Service

Office of Regional Counsel

Two Pershing Square, 2300 Main Street, Kansas City, MO 64108
Tel: (816) 926-7212 Fax: (816) 926-1347

Regional Counsel **Dennis O'Connell** .... (816) 823-5267
E-mail: dennis.oconnell@gsa.gov
Education: Kenyon 1967 AB; USC 1972 MA; Pierce Law 1978 JD

Public Buildings Service

Two Pershing Square, 2300 Main Street, Kansas City, MO 64108
Tel: (816) 926-7231 Fax: (816) 926-5751

Regional Commissioner **(Vacant)** .... (816) 823-2252
Regional Commissioner (Acting) **Kevin Rothmier** .... (816) 926-1100
1500 East Bannister Road, Kansas City, MO 64131
Deputy Regional Commissioner **Kevin Rothmier** .... (816) 926-1100
1500 East Bannister Road, Room 2161, Kansas City, MO 64131-3009
Acquisition Management Director **Courtney Springer** ... (816) 823-2276
E-mail: courtney.springer@gsa.gov
Equal Employment Office Head **Vickie Russaw** .... (816) 926-7073
Facilities Management Director **Cy Houston** .... (816) 823-2252
Portfolio Management Division Director
Barbara Jo Schmitt-Cole .... (816) 823-4492
1500 East Bannister Road, Room 7300, Kansas City, MO 64131-3009
Realty Services Division Director **Brian McDevitt** .... (816) 823-2693
1500 East Bannister Road, Room 2211, Kansas City, MO 64131-3009
Property Disposal Coordinator **Laura McGinnis** .... (816) 823-5355
1500 East Bannister Road, Kansas City, MO 64131-3009
Regional Energy Coordinator **Chris N. Cockrill** .... (816) 823-5120
E-mail: chris.cockrill@gsa.gov
Service Centers Division Director
William "Bill" McGowan .... (816) 823-1211
1500 East Bannister Road, Room 2101, Kansas City, MO 64131-3009
Media Relations Coordinator **Alison Kohler** .... (816) 216-3406

Region 7 - Greater Southwest Region

819 Taylor Street, Fort Worth, TX 76102-6124
Tel: (817) 978-2321 Fax: (817) 978-4867

○ Regional Administrator **Robert "Bobby" Babcock** ...... (817) 850-5511
E-mail: robert.babcock@gsa.gov
Education: Southern Methodist 2010 BA
□ Senior Advisor to the Regional Administrator **(Vacant)** ... (817) 978-2321
Staff Assistant **Melissa A. Carrion** .... (817) 978-1889
E-mail: melissa.carrion@gsa.gov
Director of Regional Public Affairs **Tina Jaegerman** ... (817) 978-2321
Financial Services Director **(Vacant)** .... (817) 978-3096
Accounting Program Executive **(Vacant)** .... (817) 978-3096
Fax: (817) 978-3340
Human Resources Division Director
Cheryl R. Zimmerman .... (303) 236-7153
E-mail: cheryl.zimmerman@gsa.gov
Small Business Utilization Director **Albert Garza** .... (817) 978-2828
E-mail: albert.garza@gsa.gov Fax: (817) 978-0440
Regional Emergency Coordinator **David C. Waishes** ..... (817) 978-4440
Regional Vice President, AFGE Council 236
JD Bellows .... (817) 850-8108
Congressional Services Representative **Donna Benne** .... (817) 850-8487
409 Third Street, SW, Washington, DC 20416

Federal Acquisition Service

819 Taylor Street, Fort Worth, TX 76102
Tel: (817) 574-2357 (Sales Section)
Tel: (817) 574-2354 (Utilization, Donation) Fax: (817) 978-4867
Areas Covered: AR, CO, LA, MT, NM, ND, OK, SD, TX, UT, WY

● Regional Commissioner **George R. Prochaska** .... (817) 850-8223
E-mail: george.prochaska@gsa.gov
Deputy Regional Commissioner **(Vacant)** .... (817) 850-8484
Assisted Acquisition Services Director
Bradley W. McCall .... (817) 978-0431
E-mail: brad.mccall@gsa.gov
Fleet Management Director **Gene Selzer** .... (817) 850-8196
E-mail: gene.selzer@gsa.gov
Property Management Director **Alberta Brown** .... (817) 850-8353
Supervisory Customer Service Director
Paulette Sepulvado .... (817) 850-8483

Federal Acquisition Service *(continued)*

Customer Service Director **Darren Hickman** .... (817) 850-8486
Customer Service Director **Sheila Patterson** .... (817) 574-8235
819 Taylor Street, Room 13A33, Fort Worth, TX 76102-6124
Customer Service Director **Mark King** .... (512) 916-5555
Regional Marketing Manager **Michael McDaniel** .... (817) 850-8472
Fax: (817) 574-4228
Program Analyst **(Vacant)** .... (817) 850-8487
Supply Systems Analyst **(Vacant)** .... (817) 850-8482

Office of Inspector General

819 Taylor Street, Fort Worth, TX 76102
Tel: (817) 978-2571 Tel: (817) 978-2572 Fax: (817) 978-7201

Regional Inspector General for Auditing
Paula Denman .... (817) 978-4817
E-mail: paula.denman@gsaig.gov
Special Agent-in-Charge **(Vacant)** .... (817) 978-4600
Fax: (817) 978-7014

Office of Regional Counsel

819 Taylor Street, Fort Worth, TX 76102
Tel: (817) 978-2325 Fax: (817) 978-4924

Regional Counsel (Acting) **Mark A. Duffy** .... (817) 978-9904
E-mail: mark.duffy@gsa.gov
Education: Oklahoma State 1974 BA; Oklahoma City 1977 JD
Assistant Regional Counsel **Mark A. Duffy** .... (817) 978-2325
E-mail: mark.duffy@gsa.gov
Education: Oklahoma State 1974 BA; Oklahoma City 1977 JD

Public Buildings Service

819 Taylor Street, Fort Worth, TX 76102
Fax: (817) 978-7098

● Regional Commissioner **Giancarlo Brizzi** .... (202) 501-4707
E-mail: giancarlo.brizzi@gsa.gov
Education: Virginia Tech BS, MBA
● Deputy Regional Commissioner
James "Jimmy" Ferracci .... (817) 978-2522
E-mail: james.ferracci@gsa.gov
Education: Louisiana (Monroe) BBA; LSU Hebert Law JD
Border Executive **(Vacant)** .... (817) 978-0346
Acquisition Services **Bobby J. Davis** .... (817) 978-0193
E-mail: bobby.davis@gsa.gov
Budget and Financial Management Division
Cecelia Keeley .... (817) 978-0396
E-mail: cecilia.keeley@gsa.gov
Emergency Management and Security **(Vacant)** .... (214) 781-2811
Program Manager **Kevin M. Myles** .... (817) 978-9942
E-mail: kevin.myles@gsa.gov
Education: Metro State Col Denver 1975 BA; Tulsa 1977 JD
Organizational Resources **Bethany Toppert** .... (817) 978-3042
Client Solution Division **Matthew F. Madison** .... (817) 978-3875
E-mail: matthew.madison@gsa.gov Fax: (817) 978-8644
Service Centers Division **(Vacant)** .... (817) 978-6176
Fax: (817) 978-7194
Portfolio Management **Tunisia Sadruddin** .... (817) 978-3577
E-mail: tunisia.sadruddin@gsa.gov
Design and Construction Division **Charlie Hart** .... (817) 978-4192
E-mail: charlie.hart@gsa.gov Fax: (817) 978-8644
Real Property Disposal **Melvin Freeman** .... (817) 978-3856
Fax: (817) 978-2063
Realty **Janice Trevino** .... (817) 978-4432
Regional Energy Coordinator **(Vacant)** .... (817) 978-2553
Financial Management Officer **(Vacant)** .... (817) 978-8400
PBS Payments Branch Chief **(Vacant)** .... (817) 978-8576

Arkansas/East Texas Service Center

Federal Building, 700 West Capitol, Room 3423, Little Rock, AR 72201
Tel: (501) 324-5226 Fax: (501) 324-5286

Service Center Manager **(Vacant)** .... (501) 324-5226
Little Rock (AR) Property Manager **Kriss Hinebaugh** .... (501) 324-5225

★ Presidential Appointment Requiring Senate Confirmation ☆ Presidential Appointment □ Schedule C Appointment ◇ Career Senior Foreign Service Appointment
● Career Senior Executive Service (SES) Appointment ○ Non-Career Senior Executive Service (SES) Appointment ■ Postal Career Executive Service

Border Service Center
819 Taylor Street, Room 11A30N, Fort Worth, TX 76102
Tel: (915) 534-6269 Fax: (915) 534-6051

Service Center Manager **Michael "Mike" Clardy** . . . . (817) 978-6164
El Paso Senior Property Manager **Samuel Tran** . . . . (915) 534-6269
McAllen Senior Property Manager **Lisa Langham** . . . . (956) 618-8175
Fax: (956) 618-8129

Dallas (TX) Service Center
Earle Cabell Federal Building, 1100 Commerce Street,
Suite 720, Dallas, TX 75242
Tel: (214) 767-0084 Fax: (214) 767-0095

Senior Property Manager **Paul Sherman Catalon** . . . . (214) 767-5596

Fort Worth (TX) Service Center
Federal Building, 819 Taylor Street, Room 12B04,
Fort Worth, TX 76102-6124
Tel: (817) 978-2321 Fax: (817) 978-7508

Service Center Manager **Peter F. "Chip" Pierpont, Jr.** . . . . (817) 978-3615
Program Support Manager **(Vacant)** . . . . (817) 978-6190

Louisiana Service Center
500 Poydras Street, New Orleans, LA 70130
Tel: (504) 589-6094 Fax: (504) 589-6698

Service Center Manager/OPS Manager (South East Louisiana) SE LA **Ken Livingston** . . . . (504) 589-6094 ext. 109

New Mexico Service Center
421 Gold Avenue, SW, Room 400, Albuquerque, NM 87101
Fax: (505) 248-7327

Operations Manager **Christopher D. Adams** . . . . (505) 248-7321
Supervisory Property Manager **Steven Currin** . . . . (505) 248-7360

Oklahoma Service Center
Federal Building/Courthouse, 200 NW Fourth Street,
Suite 4050, Oklahoma City, OK 73102
Tel: (405) 231-4706 Fax: (405) 231-4574

Service Center Manager **Stan McCourry** . . . . (405) 231-4978
Oklahoma City Senior Building Manager **Sheila D. Dimick** . . . . (405) 231-5622

South Central Texas Service Center
Leland Federal Building, 1919 Smith Street,
Suite 1600, Houston, TX 77002
Fax: (832) 397-8466

Service Center Manager **Johnny South** . . . . (832) 397-8475
Tel: (832) 397-8455
Austin (TX) Property Manager **Steve Rutledge** . . . . (512) 916-5016
San Antonio Operations Manager **Lynn Evans** . . . . (210) 306-2936
Fax: (210) 472-4045

Region 8 - Rocky Mountain

Building 41, Denver Federal Center, West Sixth Avenue and Kipling Street, Denver, CO 80225
Tel: (303) 236-7329 Fax: (303) 236-7280 Internet: www.gsa.gov/r8

○ Regional Administrator (Acting) **Timothy O. "Tim" Horne** . . . . (303) 236-8448
E-mail: tim.horne@gsa.gov Fax: (303) 236-7175
□ Advisor **(Vacant)** . . . . (303) 236-7329
Human Resources Division Director **Cheryl R. Zimmerman** . . . . (303) 236-7153
E-mail: cheryl.zimmerman@gsa.gov
Public Affairs Officer **Chad Hutson** . . . . (253) 561-8477
400 15th Street SW, Auburn, WA 98001
E-mail: chad.hutson@gsa.gov

Office of Regional Counsel

Regional Counsel **Leigh Ann Bunetta** . . . . (303) 236-7352
E-mail: leighann.bunetta@gsa.gov
Deputy Regional Counsel **(Vacant)** . . . . (303) 236-7329

Small Business Utilization Center
Building 41, Denver Federal Center, West Sixth Avenue and Kipling Street, Denver, CO 80225

Program Manager **Michelle Leshe** . . . . (303) 236-2099
E-mail: michelle.leshe@gsa.gov

Federal Acquisition Service
West Sixth Avenue and Kipling Street, Denver, CO 80225

● Regional Commissioner **Penny Grout** . . . . (303) 236-7411
E-mail: penny.grout@gsa.gov
Supervisory Customer Service Director **Christopher Cole** . . . . (202) 497-4983

Public Buildings Service
Building 41, Denver Federal Center, West Sixth Avenue and Kipling Street, Denver, CO 80225
Tel: (303) 236-8000 Tel: (303) 236-7245 Fax: (303) 236-1133

● Regional Commissioner **(Vacant)** . . . . (303) 236-8448
Regional Emergency Coordinator (Acting) **Timothy O. "Tim" Horne** . . . . (303) 236-8448
Regional Security Manager **J. Michael Ortega** . . . . (303) 236-0966
E-mail: j.michael.ortega@gsa.gov
Property Development Office/Build Green Contact **Mike Lowell** . . . . (303) 236-2769

Region 9 - Pacific Rim

50 United Nations Plaza, San Francisco, CA 94102
Tel: (415) 522-3001 Fax: (415) 522-3005 Internet: www.gsa.gov/r9
Areas Covered: AZ, CA, GU, HI, NV, American Samoa and Pacific Trust

○ Regional Administrator **Thomas "Tom" Scott** . . . . (415) 522-2805
E-mail: thomas.scott@gsa.gov
Education: Cal State (Long Beach) BA; USC MPA
□ Special Assistant to the Regional Administrator **(Vacant)** . . . . (415) 522-3001
● Regional Counsel **Samuel J. "Chip" Morris III** . . . . (415) 522-2622
E-mail: chip.morris@gsa.gov
Education: North Carolina 1975 BS; South Carolina 1979 JD
Director, Human Resources (Acting) **David Yun** . . . . (415) 522-2720
E-mail: david.yun@gsa.gov
Public Affairs Officer **Andra Higgs** . . . . (415) 436-8778
E-mail: andra.higgs@gsa.gov
Emergency Preparedness Coordinator **(Vacant)** . . . . (415) 522-3001
Equal Employment Opportunity Officer **Deborah Hum** . . . (415) 522-2709

Office of Inspector General
450 Golden Gate Avenue, San Francisco, CA 94102
Fax: (415) 522-2766

Regional Inspector General for Auditing **Hilda M. Garcia** . . . . (415) 522-2740
E-mail: hilda.garcia@gsaig.gov
Resident Investigations Staff-in-Charge **Theresa Quellhorst** . . . . (415) 522-3001

Office of Small Business Utilization
300 North Los Angeles Street, Room 3259, Los Angeles, CA 90012
Tel: (213) 894-3210 Fax: (213) 894-3473
Areas Covered: AZ, CA, HI, NV

Director **Pamela "Pam" Smith-Cressel** . . . . (213) 894-3210
E-mail: pam.smith-cressel@gsa.gov Fax: (213) 215-5980
Deputy Director and Regional Emergency Coordinator **Maurice "Chris" Craft** . . . . (415) 522-2613
E-mail: maurice.craft@gsa.gov Fax: (213) 215-5980
Small Business Specialist **Lori B. Falkenstrom** . . . . (510) 637-1413
E-mail: lori.falkenstrom@gsa.gov
Small Business Specialist **Anthony Caruso** . . . . (213) 894-3210
E-mail: anthony.caruso@gsa.gov

INDEPENDENT AGENCIES

★ Presidential Appointment Requiring Senate Confirmation ☆ Presidential Appointment □ Schedule C Appointment ◇ Career Senior Foreign Service Appointment
● Career Senior Executive Service (SES) Appointment ○ Non-Career Senior Executive Service (SES) Appointment ■ Postal Career Executive Service

Federal Acquisition Service

450 Golden Gate Avenue, San Francisco, CA 94102
Tel: (415) 522-2777 Fax: (415) 522-2811

● Regional Commissioner (Acting)
Leslie "Les" Yamagata . . . . (415) 522-4520
E-mail: les.yamagata@gsa.gov
Deputy Regional Commissioner
Leslie "Les" Yamagata . . . . (415) 522-4520
E-mail: les.yamagata@gsa.gov
Director, Acquisition Operations Division
Billie J. "B.J." Eldien . . . . (415) 522-2838
Director, Assisted Acquisition Service
Lawrence "Larry" Levandowski . . . . (415) 522-4520
E-mail: lawrence.levandowski@gsa.gov Fax: (415) 522-4504
Director, Customer Accounts and Research Division
William "Bill" Villarroel . . . . (415) 522-2803
E-mail: william.villarroel@gsa.gov
Director, Fleet Management Division
Christopher "Chris" Bross . . . . (415) 522-2858
E-mail: chris.bross@gsa.gov Fax: (415) 522-2866
Director, Enterprise Governmentwide Acquisition Contracts Center (GWACC) Division **Casey Kelley** . . . . (858) 537-2222
9988 Hibert Street, Fax: (858) 530-3182
Suite 310, San Diego, CA 92131
E-mail: casey.kelley@gsa.gov
Director, Network Services **Bernard "Bill" Caton** . . . . (415) 522-4536
E-mail: bernard.caton@gsa.gov
Director, Property Management Division
Drew Della Valle . . . . (415) 522-3030
Fax: (415) 522-3033
Chief, Transportation Management Branch **(Vacant)** . . . . (415) 522-2845
Fax: (415) 522-2815
Sales Director, Japan **(Vacant)** 81 (3117) 55-9252
GSA, Unit 5234, APO, AP 96328-5234 Fax: 81 (3117) 55-2970
Customer Service Director, Arizona **Florence Francis** . . . . (520) 879-5148
102 South 30th Street, Phoenix, AZ 85034
E-mail: florence.francis@gsa.gov
Customer Service Director, Coastal California and Greater Bay Area **Mark Reiss** . . . . (415) 522-2799
E-mail: mark.reiss@gsa.gov Fax: (415) 522-2812
Customer Service Director, Korea
Ronald D. "Ron" Eisley 82 (31) 6616515
51 LRS, Unit 2064, Fax: 82 (31) 6611070
GSA Mart #48, APO, AP 96205-5234
E-mail: ronald.eisley@gsa.gov
Customer Service Director, Northern California and Northern Nevada **Elizabeth K. Belenis** . . . . (530) 304-5002
Building #CA0515W, Fax: (530) 756-3892
2800 Cottage Way, Sacramento, CA 95825
E-mail: liz.belenis@gsa.gov
Customer Service Director, San Diego and Imperial County **Mark A. Carico** . . . . (858) 537-5145
750 B Street, Suite 1710, San Diego, CA 92101 Fax: (619) 557-6815
E-mail: mark.carico@gsa.gov
Customer Service Officer, Hawaii, Pacific, and Far East
(Vacant) . . . . (808) 541-1777
3375 Koapaka St. Fax: (808) 541-3406
590, Honolulu, HI 96819
Customer Service Officer, Southern California and Nevada **Charles Lee** . . . . (323) 526-7485
1055 Corporate Center Drive, Monterey Park, CA 91754
E-mail: charles.lee@gsa.gov
Special Assistant to the Regional Commissioner and Program Analyst **Ozel Kirkland** . . . . (415) 522-3477
E-mail: ozel.kirkland@gsa.gov

Public Buildings Service

50 United Nations Plaza, San Francisco, CA 94102
Tel: (415) 522-3100 Fax: (415) 522-3111
Areas Covered: AZ, CA, HI, NV, Trust Territories of the Pacific

● Regional Commissioner **Daniel R. "Dan" Brown** . . . . (253) 931-7321
E-mail: dan.brown@gsa.gov
● Deputy Regional Commissioner **Patricia Chang-Lynn** . . . . (415) 522-3072
E-mail: patricia.lynn@gsa.gov
● Deputy Regional Commissioner **Samuel Mazzola** . . . . (415) 522-3485
E-mail: samuel.mazzola@gsa.gov

Public Buildings Service *(continued)*

Chief of Staff **(Vacant)** . . . . (415) 581-1717
Director, Design and Construction Division
Maria Ciprazo . . . . (415) 522-3128
Director, Facility Management and Services Division
Chris Anne Halpin . . . . (415) 522-3663
Director, Financial Management Division
Katariina Amara Raja Tuovinen . . . . (415) 436-8724
Director, Portfolio Management Division
Matthew Jear . . . . (415) 522-3159
Fax: (415) 522-3316
Director, Real Estate Acquisition Division (Acting)
Abdee Gharavi . . . . (415) 522-3085
E-mail: abdee.gharavi@gsa.gov
Director, Real Property Utilization and Disposal Division **David Haase** . . . . (415) 522-3426
Director, Los Angeles Service Center **Lorenzo Davis** . . . . (213) 894-4984
Director, San Diego Service Center **Michael Wirtz** . . . . (619) 557-5309
333 West Broadway, San Diego, CA 92101
Director, San Francisco Service Center
Jason Cawthorne . . . . (415) 522-4476
Client Services Officer **(Vacant)** . . . . (415) 522-3347
Administrative Officer **Betta Ramos** . . . . (415) 522-2707
E-mail: betta.ramos@gsa.gov
Program Analyst **Molly Ng** . . . . (415) 522-3398

Region 10 - Northwest/Arctic Region

400 15th Street SW, Auburn, WA 98001
Tel: (253) 931-7000 Internet: www.gsa.gov/r10
Areas Covered: AK, ID, OR, WA

○ Regional Administrator **Corey E. Cooke** . . . . (253) 931-7000
E-mail: corey.cooke@gsa.gov
Education: UMass (Amherst) BA; New Hampshire JD
□ Special Assistant to the Regional Administrator
(Vacant) . . . . (253) 931-7000
Administrative Assistant **(Vacant)** . . . . (253) 931-7000
Director, Human Resources **Michael Mann** . . . . (253) 931-7322
E-mail: michael.mann@gsa.gov
Public Affairs Manager **Chad Hutson** . . . . (253) 561-8477
E-mail: chad.hutson@gsa.gov
Deputy Regional Director, Mission Assurance
Kay Lynn Smartt . . . . (253) 931-7947
E-mail: kaylynn.smartt@gsa.gov
Congressional Services Representative **Denise Boyd** . . . . (253) 931-7126
E-mail: denise.boyd@gsa.gov

Federal Acquisition Service

400 15th Street SW, Auburn, WA 98001
Fax: (253) 931-7389

● Regional Commissioner **Tiffany T. Hixson** . . . . (253) 931-7115
E-mail: tiffany.hixson@gsa.gov
Deputy Regional Commissioner **Geraldine Watson** . . . . (253) 931-7040
● Assistant Regional Commissioner for Professional Services and Human Capital **(Vacant)** . . . . (253) 931-7000
Business Operations Director **(Vacant)** . . . . (253) 931-7000
Contract Operations Director **(Vacant)** . . . . (253) 931-7000
Fleet Management Director
Christopher "Chris" Bross . . . . (415) 522-2866
50 United Nations Plaza, San Francisco, CA 94102
Network Services Division Director **John Norton** . . . . (253) 931-7519
E-mail: john.norton@gsa.gov
Program Operations Director **(Vacant)** . . . . (253) 931-7000

Office of Inspector General

Resident Investigations Staff-in-Charge **Terry Pfeifer** . . . . (253) 833-6070

Office of Regional Counsel

Regional Counsel **Elizabeth "Betsy" Kruger** . . . . (253) 931-7007
E-mail: betsy.kruger@gsa.gov Fax: (253) 931-7842

Office of Small Business Utilization

Manager **Kenyon Taylor** . . . . (253) 931-7956
E-mail: kenyon.taylor@gsa.gov

★ Presidential Appointment Requiring Senate Confirmation ☆ Presidential Appointment □ Schedule C Appointment ◇ Career Senior Foreign Service Appointment
● Career Senior Executive Service (SES) Appointment ○ Non-Career Senior Executive Service (SES) Appointment ■ Postal Career Executive Service

Public Buildings Service
400 15th Street SW, Auburn, WA 98001
Fax: (253) 931-7958

● Regional Commissioner **Chaun Benjamin** . . . . . (253) 931-7000
E-mail: chaun.benjamin@gsa.gov
Acquisition Division Director **(Vacant)** . . . . . (253) 931-7305
Executive Officer **Anne Weigle** . . . . . (253) 931-7233
Design and Construction Division Director
Todd Gillies . . . . . (253) 931-7546
Planning Division Director **Cynthia Tolentino** . . . . . (253) 931-7413
Leasing Division Director **Ann Crawley** . . . . . (206) 220-4383
E-mail: ann.crawley@gsa.gov
Facilities Management Division Director
Kimberly S. Gray . . . . . (253) 931-7401

Region 11 - National Capital Region
301 Seventh Street SW, Room 7022, Washington, DC 20407
Tel: (202) 708-9100 Fax: (202) 708-9966 Internet: www.gsa.gov/ncr
Areas Covered: Metropolitan Washington DC area

○ Regional Administrator **Scott D. Anderson** . . . . . (202) 708-9100
E-mail: scott.anderson@gsa.gov
Education: North Adams State BA; South Carolina MEd
□ Special Assistant to the Regional Administrator
Robert Sinners . . . . . (202) 431-7963
E-mail: robert.sinners@gsa.gov
Agency Liaison Division Director **(Vacant)** . . . . . (202) 205-2900
Chief People Officer **(Vacant)** . . . . . (202) 708-9100
Program Support Services Division Director
Alonzo J. Tyler . . . . . (202) 205-4940
E-mail: alonzo.tyler@gsa.gov Fax: (202) 708-4849
Equal Employment Opportunity Staff Director
(Vacant) . . . . . (202) 708-9100
Customer Service Branch Chief **(Vacant)** . . . . . (202) 708-5369
Employee and Labor Relations Branch Chief **(Vacant)** . . . . (202) 708-5314
Strategy and Policy Division Director **Melanie Lewis** . . . . (202) 708-6679
E-mail: melanie.lewis@gsa.gov
Acquisition Management Program Analyst **(Vacant)** . . . . . (202) 708-8353
Administrative, Budget and Accounting Services Team
(Vacant) . . . . . (202) 708-9100
Public Affairs Officer **(Vacant)** . . . . . (202) 690-8977
Information Technology Director
(Vacant) Room 6628 . . . . . (202) 260-0717
● Facilities Management Office Director **(Vacant)** . . . . . (202) 708-9100
Marketing Director **(Vacant)** Room 1610 . . . . . (202) 708-6280
Service Delivery Support Director **(Vacant)** . . . . . (202) 205-4895

Business Service Center
301 Seventh Street SW, Room 7022, Washington, DC 20407
Fax: (202) 205-2872

Lead Small Business Specialist **Charles Aycock** . . . . . (202) 205-0251

Federal Acquisition Service
301 Seventh Street SW, Room 7022, Washington, DC 20407
Tel: (202) 708-6100

● Regional Commissioner **Houston S. Taylor** . . . . . (703) 605-2759
E-mail: houston.taylor@gsa.gov
Executive Assistant **(Vacant)** . . . . . (202) 708-6100
Deputy Regional Commissioner **Darrick Early** . . . . . (202) 690-9420
E-mail: darrick.early@gsa.gov
Assisted Acquisition Services Division Director
Lakita Ayers . . . . . (202) 401-9420
E-mail: lakita.ayers@gsa.gov
Chief of Staff **Vivieca Pierce** . . . . . (202) 260-6379
E-mail: vivieca.pierce@gsa.gov
Customer Accounts and Research Division Director
Tonya Butler . . . . . (703) 605-9235
E-mail: tonya.butler@gsa.gov
Customer Service Director **Brian Talley** . . . . . (405) 231-4825
Personal Property Management Division Director
Denise Webster . . . . . (202) 708-7278
Property Disposal Services and Solutions Division
Deputy Director **Charles Robinson** . . . . . (202) 619-8986

Office of Inspector General
300 D Street, SW, Suite 800, Washington, DC 20024
Tel: (202) 252-0008

Supervisory Auditor **Marisa Roinestad** . . . . . (202) 273-7241
E-mail: marisa.roinestad@gsaig.gov

Office of Regional Counsel
301 Seventh Street SW, Room 7022, Washington, DC 20407
Tel: (202) 708-5155 Fax: (202) 708-4655

Regional Counsel **Paula J. DeMuth** . . . . . (202) 708-9870
Fax: (202) 708-4655
Deputy Regional Counsel **(Vacant)** . . . . . (202) 708-5155
General Attorney, Technology **Maria Bellizzi** . . . . . (202) 708-9880
E-mail: maria.bellizzi@gsa.gov
General Attorney, Property Development
Robert W. Schlattman . . . . . (202) 708-5810
E-mail: robert.schlattman@gsa.gov
General Attorney, Real Property Disposal
Stephen Schwartz . . . . . (202) 708-5905
E-mail: stephen.schwartz@gsa.gov

Public Buildings Service
301 Seventh Street SW, Room 7080, Washington, DC 20407
Tel: (202) 708-5891 Fax: (202) 708-8801

● Regional Commissioner **Darren J. Blue** . . . . . (202) 365-7675
E-mail: darren.blue@gsa.gov
Education: George Mason; Indust'l Col Armed Forces MS
Chief of Staff **(Vacant)** . . . . . (202) 708-5891
● Deputy Regional Commissioner **Thomas E. James** . . . . . (202) 708-5891
E-mail: thomas.james@gsa.gov
Regional Financial Officer
Georgia D. Davis-Leggett Room 7919 . . . . . (202) 260-2901
Tel: (202) 692-3450
Financial Management Division Director
Genevieve Gilinger . . . . . (202) 708-6196
E-mail: genevieve.gilinger@gsa.gov
Chief Greening Officer **Robin Snyder** . . . . . (202) 708-5891
Assignments Division Director **William Longhi** . . . . . (202) 690-8936
Capital Planning Division Director **Carla Knode** . . . . . (202) 708-4858
Capital Projects Division Director
(Vacant) Room 2002 . . . . . (202) 708-6550
Energy and Sustainability Division Director
Ronald Allard . . . . . (202) 260-5320
Heating Operations and Transmission Division Director
Dave Mbonu . . . . . (202) 690-9703
13th and C Streets, SW, Washington, DC 20407 Fax: (202) 692-3108
Internal Resources Division Director
Verneka Roberts Room 6651 . . . . . (202) 260-4720
Fax: (202) 708-4964
Metropolitan Service Division Director **(Vacant)** . . . . . (202) 708-5891
1099 - 14th Street, SW, Washington, DC 20005
Real Property Disposal and Utilization Division
Director **Timothy "Tim" Sheckler** Room 7709 . . . . . (202) 401-5806
Tel: (202) 205-5295
Special Services Division Director **(Vacant)** . . . . . (202) 205-2371
Triangle Service Division Director
Calvin Myint Room 7660 . . . . . (202) 708-8480
Education: Maryland 1995 BSME; Johns Hopkins 2002 MEM
White House Service Division Director
Alan Zawatsky . . . . . (202) 606-0765
Tel: (202) 606-1086
Client Solutions Office Director **(Vacant)** Room 3652 . . . . (202) 708-5891
● Office of Design and Construction Director
Shapour Ebadi Room 4606 . . . . . (202) 561-7847
E-mail: shapour.ebadi@gsa.gov
Lease Executions Division (Acting) **T.C. Hairston** . . . . . (202) 690-9490
● Leasing Office Director **(Vacant)** Room 7919 . . . . . (202) 708-5891
Office of Acquisition Director (Acting) **Kathy Geisler** . . . . (202) 708-9835
E-mail: kathleen.geisler@gsa.gov
Planning and Design Quality Office Director
Mina Wright Room 2002 . . . . . (202) 401-4522
● Portfolio Management Office Director
Ivan G. Swain Room 7909 . . . . . (202) 708-5334
E-mail: ivan.swain@gsa.gov

(continued on next page)

INDEPENDENT AGENCIES

★ Presidential Appointment Requiring Senate Confirmation ☆ Presidential Appointment □ Schedule C Appointment ◇ Career Senior Foreign Service Appointment
● Career Senior Executive Service (SES) Appointment ○ Non-Career Senior Executive Service (SES) Appointment ■ Postal Career Executive Service

Public Buildings Service *(continued)*

Procurement Management Director
Melanie Lewis Room 7107 . . . . (202) 708-6679
E-mail: melanie.lewis@gsa.gov

● Project Delivery Office Director **(Vacant)** Room 2002 . . . . (202) 708-5891

United States Merit Systems Protection Board (MSPB)

Description: The Merit Systems Protection Board hears and adjudicates appeals by federal employees involved in personnel actions, including removals, suspensions, and demotions. The board also reviews regulations issued by the Office of Personnel Management and conducts studies of the federal personnel system.

1615 M Street, NW, Washington, DC 20419
Tel: (202) 653-7200
Tel: (202) 254-4800 (General Information Message Line)
Tel: (202) 653-7200 (General Information - Merit Systems Protection Board Headquarters) Tel: (202) 653-6772 (Personnel Locator)
Tel: (202) 653-7263 (Employment and Procurement Information)
TTY: (800) 877-8339 Tel: (202) 690-1622 (Inspector General's Hotline)
Tel: (800) 424-9121 (Inspector General's Hotline)
Fax: (202) 653-7130 E-mail: mspb@mspb.gov
E-mail: opengovernment@mspb.gov (Open Government Initiative)
Internet: www.mspb.gov Internet: fedbbs.access.gpo.gov (Telnet)
Internet: www.usa.gov (Official US Government Website)

OFFICES OF THE BOARD

1615 M Street, NW, Washington, DC 20419
Tel: (202) 653-7200 Fax: (202) 653-7208

Note: Members may continue to serve until reappointed or replaced, but may not serve for longer than one additional year past the original expiration date.

Office of Regional Operations

1615 M Street, NW, Washington, DC 20419
Fax: (202) 653-8911

Atlanta (GA) Regional Office

Peachtree Summit Federal Building, 401 West Peachtree Street, NW, Suite 1050, Atlanta, GA 30308-3519
Tel: (404) 730-2751 Tel: (404) 730-2755 (Voicemail)
Fax: (404) 730-2767 E-mail: atlanta@mspb.gov
Areas Covered: AL, FL, GA, MS, SC, TN

● Regional Director/Chief Administrative Judge **Thomas J. Lanphear** .... (404) 730-2751 ext. 8011
E-mail: thomas.lanphear@mspb.gov
Administrative Judge **R. Brian Bohlen** .... (404) 730-2751 ext. 8022
Administrative Judge **Silvia de La Cruz** .... (404) 730-2751 ext. 8015
Administrative Judge **Pamela Jackson** .... (404) 730-2751 ext. 8014
Administrative Judge **Sherry Linville** .... (404) 730-2751 ext. 8029
Administrative Judge **Jeffrey S. Morris** .... (404) 730-2751 ext. 8033
Administrative Judge **Sharon J. Pomeranz** .... (404) 730-2751 ext. 8026
Administrative Judge **Greg Prophet** .... (404) 730-2751 ext. 8013
Administrative Judge **Chris Sprague** .... (404) 730-2751
Administrative Judge **Alexander Thompson** ... (404) 730-2751 ext. 8009
Administrative Judge **Richard W. Vitaris** ...... (404) 730-2751 ext. 8012
Education: Georgetown 1977 AB; Rutgers 1980 JD; George Washington 1983 MLaw

Central Regional Office

230 South Dearborn Street, Room 3100, Chicago, IL 60604-1669
Tel: (312) 353-2923 Tel: (312) 353-2924 (Voicemail)
Fax: (312) 886-4231 E-mail: chicago@mspb.gov
Areas Covered: IL, IN, IA, Kansas City (KS), KY, MI, MN, MO, OH, WI

● Chief Administrative Judge **Michele S. Schroeder** ...... (312) 353-2923
E-mail: michele.schroeder@mspb.gov
Supervisory Paralegal Specialist **Rob Nail** .... (312) 353-2923
E-mail: rob.nail@mspb.gov

Dallas (TX) Regional Office

Earle Cabell Federal Building, 1100 Commerce Street, Room 620, Dallas, TX 75242-9979
Tel: (214) 767-0555 Fax: (214) 767-0102 E-mail: dallas@mspb.gov
Areas Covered: AR, LA, OK, TX

Chief Administrative Law Judge **Laura M. Albornoz** ..... (214) 767-0555
Supervisory Paralegal Specialist **Ann R. Fluellen** .... (214) 767-0555
E-mail: ann.fluellen@mspb.gov

Denver (CO) Field Office

165 South Union Boulevard, Suite 318, Lakewood, CO 80228
Tel: (303) 969-5101 Fax: (303) 969-5109
Areas Covered: AZ, CO, KS, MT, NE, NM, ND, SD, UT, WY

Chief Administrative Judge **Stephen Mish** .... (303) 969-5101
Administrative Judge **David Brooks** .... (303) 969-5101
Administrative Judge **James A. Kasic** .... (303) 969-5101
Administrative Judge **Patricia "Pat" Miller** .... (303) 969-5101
Administrative Judge **Evan Roth** .... (303) 969-5101
Administrative Judge **Glen Williams** .... (303) 969-5101

New York (NY) Field Office

Jacob K. Javits Federal Building, 26 Federal Plaza, Room 3137A, New York, NY 10278-0022
Tel: (212) 264-9372 Fax: (212) 264-1417 E-mail: newyork@mspb.gov
Areas Covered: NJ (Counties of Bergen, Essex, Hudson, and Union), NY, PR, VI

Chief Administrative Judge **Arthur S. Joseph** .... (212) 264-9372
Administrative Judge **Nicole Decrescenzo** .... (212) 264-9372
Administrative Judge **Maureen Briody** .... (212) 264-9372
Administrative Judge **Maria Dominguez** .... (212) 264-9372
Administrative Judge **JoAnn M. Ruggiero** .... (212) 264-9372
Paralegal Specialist **Gwendolyn Gatling** .... (212) 264-9372
E-mail: gwendolyn.gatling@mspb.gov

Northeastern Regional Office

1601 Market Street, Suite 1700, Philadelphia, PA 19103
Tel: (215) 597-9960 Fax: (215) 597-3456
E-mail: philadelphia@mspb.gov
Areas Covered: CT, DE, ME, MD (except Montgomery and Prince George's counties), MA, NH, NJ (except Bergen, Essex, Hudson and Union counties), PA, RI, VT, and WV.

● Regional Director **William L. Boulden** .... (215) 597-9960
E-mail: william.boulden@mspb.gov
Administrative Judge **Elizabeth D. Milligan** .... (215) 597-9960
Administrative Judge **Michael T. Rudisill** .... (215) 597-9960
Administrative Judge **(Vacant)** .... (215) 597-9960
Administrative Judge **(Vacant)** .... (215) 597-9960
Administrative Judge **(Vacant)** .... (215) 597-9960
Supervisory Paralegal Specialist **Gwendolyn Gatling** .... (215) 597-9960
E-mail: gwendolyn.gatling@mspb.gov

★ Presidential Appointment Requiring Senate Confirmation ☆ Presidential Appointment ☐ Schedule C Appointment ◇ Career Senior Foreign Service Appointment
● Career Senior Executive Service (SES) Appointment ○ Non-Career Senior Executive Service (SES) Appointment ■ Postal Career Executive Service

Washington D.C. Regional Office

1901 S. Bell Street, Suite 950, Arlington, VA 22202
Tel: (703) 756-6250 Fax: (703) 756-7112
E-mail: washingtonregionaloffice@mspb.gov
Areas Covered: DC, MD (Counties of Montgomery and Prince Georges), NC, VA and all overseas areas not otherwise covered.

● Regional Director/Chief Administrative Judge
Jeremiah Cassidy . . . . (703) 756-6250
Administrative Officer **Marie Sumner** . . . . (703) 756-6250
E-mail: marie.sumner@mspb.gov

Western Regional Office

Ronald V. Dellums Federal Building and US Courthouse,
1301 Clay Street, Suite 1380N, Oakland, CA 94612-5217
Tel: (510) 273-7022 Fax: (510) 273-7136
E-mail: sanfrancisco@mspb.gov
Areas Covered: AK, CA, HI, ID, NV, OR, WA, and Pacific overseas.

● Chief Administrative Judge **Sara Snyder** . . . . (415) 904-6772
E-mail: sara.snyder@mspb.gov
Administrative Judge **LuNell C. Anderson** . . . . (415) 904-6772
Administrative Judge **Samantha Black** . . . . (415) 904-6772
Administrative Judge **Grace Carter** . . . . (415) 904-6772
Administrative Judge **Anthony L. Ellison, Jr.** . . . . (415) 904-6772
Administrative Judge **Andrew Flick** . . . . (415) 904-6772
Administrative Judge **Kelly Humphrey** . . . . (415) 904-6772
Administrative Judge **Franklin Kang** . . . . (415) 904-6772
Administrative Judge **Holly Parks** . . . . (415) 904-6772
Administrative Judge **Tamara Ribas** . . . . (415) 904-6772
Administrative Judge **Richard Slizeski** . . . . (415) 904-6772

Morris K. Udall and Stewart L. Udall Foundation (UDALL)

Description: The Udall Foundation works to both strengthen the appreciation and stewardship of the environment, public lands, and natural resources and strengthen Native Nations to facilitate their self-determination, governance, and human capital goals.

130 South Scott Avenue, Tucson, AZ 85701-1922 (Main Office)
Tel: (520) 901-8500 Fax: (520) 670-5530 E-mail: info@udall.gov
Internet: www.udall.gov

BOARD OF TRUSTEES

1825 K St NW, Washington, DC 20006
Tel: (520) 901-8500 Fax: (520) 670-5530

★ Chair **Eric D. Eberhard** .... (520) 901-8500
Education: Case Western 1967 BA; Cincinnati 1970 JD; George Washington 1970 LLM

★ Vice Chair **Dr. Anne J. Udall** .... (520) 901-8500
Education: New Mexico BA, MA; Arizona 1987 PhD

★ Trustee **Camilla C. Feibelman** .... (520) 901-8500
Term Expires: April 15, 2017
Education: Columbia BES; Puerto Rico MUPP

★ Trustee **James Lloyd "Jim" Huffman II**
Term Expires: October 6, 2020
Education: Montana State 1967 BA; Fletcher Law & Diplomacy 1969 MA; Chicago 1972 JD

★ Trustee **Tadd M. Johnson** .... (520) 901-8500
Term Expires: October 6, 2022
Education: U St Thomas (MN) BA; Minnesota JD

Trustee **Lisa L. Johnson-Billy** .... (520) 901-8500
Note: Designated by law
Term Expires: August 25, 2024
Education: Northeastern State BA; Oklahoma MEd

Trustee **James F. "Jim" Manning**
Note: Designated by law
Education: Northeastern BA

★ Trustee **Mark Thomas Nethery** .... (520) 901-8500

★ Trustee **D. Michael Rappoport** .... (520) 901-8500
Education: American U 1961 BA; Hawaii 1963 MA

★ Trustee **Dr. Robert Clayton "Bobby" Robbins**
Affiliation: President, The University of Arizona
Tucson, AZ 85721-0040
Tel: (520) 621-5511 Fax: (520) 621-9323
E-mail: president@email.arizona.edu
Education: Millsaps 1979 BS; Mississippi 1983 MD

★ Trustee **Charles P. "Charlie" Rose** .... (520) 901-8500
Term Expires: May 26, 2019
Education: Villanova 1979 BA; DePaul 1982 JD

Trustee (Secretary of Education or designee) **(Vacant)** .... (520) 901-8500
Note: Designated by law

Trustee (Secretary of the Interior or designee) **(Vacant)** ... (520) 901-8500
Note: Designated by law

OFFICE OF THE EXECUTIVE DIRECTOR

130 South Scott Avenue, Tucson, AZ 85701-1922
Tel: (520) 901-8500 Fax: (520) 670-5530

Executive Director [Open Government Directive Official] **Philip J. Lemanski** .... (520) 901-8560
E-mail: lemanski@udall.gov

Executive Assistant **Elizabeth Monroe** .... (520) 901-8567
E-mail: monroe@udall.gov

U.S. Institute for Environmental Conflict Resolution

130 South Scott Avenue, Tucson, AZ 85701-1922
Tel: (520) 901-8501 Fax: (520) 670-5530 E-mail: usiecr@udall.gov
Internet: www.ecr.gov

Director (Acting) **Brian Manwaring** .... (520) 901-8513
E-mail: manwaring@udall.gov

Senior Program Manager **Henrietta DeGroot** .... (520) 901-8524
E-mail: degroot@udall.gov

Senior Program Associate **Melanie Knapp** .... (520) 901-8546
E-mail: knapp@udall.gov

Washington D.C. Office

1825 K St NW, Suite 701, Washington, DC 20006
Tel: (202) 540-1040 Fax: (202) 540-1044

Director **Stephanie Kavanaugh** .... (202) 540-1041
E-mail: kavanaugh@udall.gov

Senior Program Associate **Courtney Owen** .... (202) 540-1040
E-mail: owen@udall.gov

Education Programs

Director **Jane R. Curlin** .... (520) 901-8565
E-mail: curlin@udall.gov

Internship Program Manager **(Vacant)** .... (520) 901-8561

Parks in Focus Program Manager **Bret Muter** .... (520) 901-8569

Scholarship Program Manager **Kellcee Baker** .... (520) 901-8564
E-mail: kbaker@udall.gov

Finance and Operations

130 South Scott Avenue, Tucson, AZ 85701-1922
Tel: (520) 901-8500 Fax: (520) 670-5530

Director [Open Government Directive Official, Senior Agency Official for Records Management]
Susan Vest .... (520) 901-8510
E-mail: vest@udall.gov

Contracting Officer's Representative **Elisa Baca** .... (520) 901-8538
E-mail: baca@udall.gov

Senior Financial Manager **Katherine McPherson** .... (520) 901-8516

Senior Information Technology Manager **Jerry Carter** .... (520) 901-8520
E-mail: carter@udall.gov

Application Programmer **Adam Baker** .... (520) 901-8522
E-mail: baker@udall.gov

Program Analyst **(Vacant)** .... (520) 901-8512

Financial Technician **Theresa Cocio** .... (520) 901-8502
E-mail: cocio@udall.gov

Financial Technician **Olivia Montes** .... (520) 901-8574
E-mail: montes@udall.gov

General Counsel

130 South Scott Avenue, Tucson, AZ 85701-1922
Tel: (520) 901-8500 Fax: (520) 670-5530

General Counsel [Chief FOIA Officer, Designated Agency Ethics Official (DAEO)]
Stephanie Zimmt-Mack .... (520) 901-8576
E-mail: zimmt-mack@udall.gov

INDEPENDENT AGENCIES

★ Presidential Appointment Requiring Senate Confirmation ☆ Presidential Appointment ☐ Schedule C Appointment ◇ Career Senior Foreign Service Appointment
● Career Senior Executive Service (SES) Appointment ○ Non-Career Senior Executive Service (SES) Appointment ■ Postal Career Executive Service

National Aeronautics and Space Administration (NASA)

Description: The National Aeronautics and Space Administration's mission is to pioneer the future in space exploration, scientific discovery, and aeronautics research.

Two Independence Square, 300 E Street, SW, Washington, DC 20546
Tel: (202) 358-0000 (Personnel Locator)
Tel: (202) 358-2090 (Procurement Information)
Tel: (800) 424-9183 (Inspector General's Hot Line)
TTY: (800) 535-8134 (Inspector General's Hot Line)
Internet: www.nasa.gov
Internet: www.hq.nasa.gov/office/procurement/index.html (Business Opportunities) Internet: https://www.nasa.gov/FOIA/index.html (Freedom of Information Act) Internet: www.hq.nasa.gov (Headquarters)
Internet: www.nasa.gov/news/highlights/index.html (News and Information) Internet: www.nasa.gov/open/ (Open Government Directive)

OFFICE OF THE ADMINISTRATOR

Two Independence Square, 300 E Street, SW,
Room 9F44, Washington, DC 20546
Tel: (202) 358-1010 Fax: (202) 358-2810

Office of Inspector General

Two Independence Square, 300 E Street, SW,
Suite 8V39, Washington, DC 20546
Tel: (202) 358-1220 Fax: (202) 358-2767 Internet: http://oig.nasa.gov/

Field Offices

Central Field Office
Building 265E-Investigations, Johnson Space Center,
Houston, TX 77058-3696
Fax: (281) 244-6999

Special Agent-in-Charge (Criminal Investigations)
John H. Corbett .... (281) 244-1153
Building 45, OIG - Lyndon B. Johnson Space Center,
Mail Code W-JS2, Houston, TX 77058-3696

OIG - George C. Marshall Space Flight Center
OIG - George C. Marshall Space Flight Center,
Building 4201, Huntsville, AL 35812-0001
Tel: (256) 544-9188 Fax: (256) 544-8561

Resident Agent-in-Charge **David J. Balwinski** .... (256) 544-0072
Education: Columbia Col (MO) 2004 BA

OIG - John F. Kennedy Space Center
OIG - John F. Kennedy Space Center, MS KSC/OIG-INV,
Kennedy Space Center, FL 32815-0001

Resident Agent-in-Charge (Criminal Investigations)
William K. Shores .... (321) 867-4064
Fax: (321) 867-4085

OIG - Lyndon B. Johnson Space Center
OIG - Lyndon B. Johnson Space Center, Houston, TX 77058-3696
Fax: (281) 244-6999

Resident Agent-in-Charge
Michael C. Mataya Building 265E, MC W-JS2 .... (281) 483-6016

OIG - Stennis Space Center
Building 3101, OIG - Stennis Space Center,
Room 119, Stennis Space Center, MS 39529
Stennis Space Center, P.O. Box 70, Stennis Space Center, MS 39556
Fax: (228) 688-3136

Special Agent **Marcia S. Fox** .... (228) 688-1493

Eastern Field Office
Building 1149, Langley Research Center,
Mail Stop 205, Hampton, VA 23681-2199
Fax: (757) 864-9705

Special Agent-in-Charge (Criminal Investigations)
Michael W. Sonntag .... (757) 864-8116

OIG - Goddard Space Flight Center
Goddard Space Flight Center, Code 190, Building 1,
Greenbelt, MD 20771-0001
Tel: (301) 286-6890

Resident Agent-in-Charge **Curtis W. Vaughn** .... (301) 286-7776

OIG - John H. Glenn Research Center at Lewis Field
Building 501, John H. Glenn Research Center at Lewis Field,
2100 Brookpark Rd., Mail Stop 501-9, Cleveland, OH 44135
Fax: (216) 977-7030

Resident Agent-in-Charge **Mark J. Zielinski** .... (216) 433-5414

OIG - Langley Research Center
Bldg. 1149, OIG - Langley Research Center,
Mail Stop Code 205 (Investigations),
2nd Floor, Hampton, VA 23681-2199
Fax: (757) 864-9705

Resident Agent-in-Charge **William E. Rosser** .... (757) 864-3267

Western Field Office
Glenn Anderson Federal Building, 501 West Ocean Boulevard,
Suite 5120, Long Beach, CA 90802

Special Agent-in-Charge **Keith Tate** .... (562) 951-5486

OIG - Ames Research Center
Building N204, OIG - Ames Research Center,
Mail Stop Code 207-11, Moffett Field, CA 94035-1000
Fax: (650) 604-2319

Resident Agent-in-Charge (Criminal Investigations)
Helen H. Koh .... (650) 604-3682

OIG - Jet Propulsion Laboratory
Building 180, OIG - Jet Propulsion Laboratory,
Mail Stop 180-301, 4800 Oak Grove Dr., Pasadena, CA 91109-8099
Tel: (818) 354-0160 Fax: (818) 393-4271

Special Agent **Michael Harrison** .... (818) 354-6630
E-mail: michael.harrison@jpl.nasa.gov

★ Presidential Appointment Requiring Senate Confirmation ☆ Presidential Appointment ☐ Schedule C Appointment ◇ Career Senior Foreign Service Appointment
● Career Senior Executive Service (SES) Appointment ○ Non-Career Senior Executive Service (SES) Appointment ■ Postal Career Executive Service

Ames Research Center

Building N200, Mail Stop 200-1, Moffett Field, CA 94035-1000
Tel: (650) 604-5000 Fax: (650) 604-3786 Fax: (650) 604-3992
Internet: www.nasa.gov/centers/ames/home

● Director **Dr. Eugene L. Tu** .... (650) 604-5111
E-mail: eugene.l.tu@nasa.gov
Education: UC Berkeley 1988 BSME; Stanford 1996 PhD

● Deputy Director **Carol W. Carroll** .... (650) 604-5068
E-mail: carol.w.carroll@nasa.gov

Associate Center Director - Mission Support
Deborah L. Feng .... (650) 604-0256
Education: De Anza 1983 AA; UC Berkeley 1985 BA; San José State 2004 MBA

Associate Center Director - Research and Technical
Dr. Steven F. Zornetzer .... (650) 604-2800
E-mail: steven.f.zornetzer@nasa.gov

Chief Engineer **(Vacant)** .... (650) 604-6757

Chief Scientist **Jacob Cohen** .... (650) 604-3261

Chief Technologist **Dr. Harry Partridge III** .... (650) 604-5236
E-mail: harry.partridge@nasa.gov
Education: Indiana 1979 PhD

Deputy Chief Technologist **Dr. Jill J. Bauman** .... (650) 604-0318
E-mail: jill.bauman@nasa.gov

Director of Diversity and Equal Opportunity
Dr. Barbara E. Miller .... (650) 604-0783
E-mail: barbara.e.miller@nasa.gov Fax: (650) 604-2720

FOIA Public Liaison Officer **Martha E. Terry** .... (202) 358-2339
E-mail: martha.e.terry@nasa.gov

NASA Research Park Office

Director **Janice Fried** .... (650) 604-3815
Fax: (650) 604-3786

Deputy Director **Mejghan K. Haider** .... (650) 604-4771

Office of the Chief Counsel

Building N200, Mail Stop 200-1, Moffett Field, CA 94035-1000
Fax: (650) 604-2767

● Chief Counsel **Thomas W. Berndt** .... (650) 604-2181
E-mail: thomas.w.berndt@nasa.gov Fax: (650) 604-2346

Secretary **Norma J. Caldwell** .... (650) 604-2654

Chief Patent Counsel **Robert M. Padilla** .... (650) 604-5104
E-mail: robert.m.padilla@nasa.gov

Associate Chief Counsel for Environmental, Information Access and Property Law
George P. Sloup .... (650) 604-5959
E-mail: george.p.sloup@nasa.gov

Associate Chief Counsel for Procurement and Ethics
Kevin F. Kouba .... (650) 604-1320
E-mail: kevin.f.kouba@nasa.gov

Associate Chief Counsel for Transactional and Fiscal Law **Komal Sadhwani** .... (650) 604-2809
E-mail: komal.sadhwani@nasa.gov

Attorney Advisor **Colleen J. Burt** .... (650) 604-6470
E-mail: colleen.burt@nasa.gov

Attorney Advisor **Lauren Thuy Ladwig** .... (650) 604-1707
E-mail: lauren.ladwig@nasa.gov

Attorney Advisor **Christine M. Pham** .... (650) 604-5074
E-mail: christine.m.pham@nasa.gov

Patent Attorney **John F. Schipper** .... (650) 604-5286
E-mail: john.f.schipper@nasa.gov

Paralegal Specialist **Raiza N. Singh** .... (650) 604-0887
Fax: (650) 604-2767

Legal Technician **Femy D. McGrath** .... (650) 604-5116
E-mail: femy.d.mcgrath@nasa.gov Fax: (650) 604-2346

Office of the Chief Financial Officer

Building N200, Mail Stop 200-1, Moffett Field, CA 94035-1000
Fax: (650) 604-1668

Chief Financial Officer **Paul R. Agnew** .... (650) 604-1301
Fax: (650) 604-1668

Financial Management Division

Chief **Nicolina S. Tubbs** .... (650) 604-2054
Fax: (650) 604-0638

Financial Management Division *(continued)*

Cost Accounting Branch Chief **Farzana Moreno** .... (650) 604-6071
Fax: (650) 604-6082

Financial Reporting Branch Chief
Josie D. Valdez-Long .... (650) 604-4464
Fax: (650) 604-1191

Reimbursable Management Branch Chief **(Vacant)** .... (650) 604-4959

Mission Director and Program Analysis Division
Director **Thomas C. Paine** .... (650) 604-4943
E-mail: thomas.c.paine@nasa.gov

Resources Management Division

Division Chief **Diane P. Selby** .... (650) 604-0387
E-mail: diane.p.selby@nasa.gov Fax: (650) 604-1004

Deputy Chief (Acting) **Onike E. Love** .... (650) 604-1014

Assistant Chief **Pamela Joy Sotelo** .... (650) 604-4138

Office of the Chief Information Officer

Building N200, Mail Stop 200-1, Moffett Field, CA 94035-1000
Tel: (650) 810-4222

● Chief Information Officer **(Vacant)** .... (650) 604-6875

Deputy Chief Information Officer **(Vacant)** .... (650) 604-3257

Information Security Division Chief
Ernest M. Lopez, Jr. .... (650) 604-2333
E-mail: ernest.m.lopez@nasa.gov

IT Operations Division Chief **William K. Notley** .... (650) 604-1415
E-mail: william.k.notley@nasa.gov

Aeronautics Directorate

Building N200, Mail Stop 200-1, Moffett Field, CA 94035-1000
Tel: (650) 604-5059 Fax: (650) 604-0228

Director **Huy K. Tran** .... (650) 604-4465
E-mail: huy.k.tran@nasa.gov

Deputy Director **Dr. William R. Van Dalsem** .... (650) 604-4469

Associate Director **Cheryl Mi Quinn** .... (650) 604-5793

Secretary **Suzanne Cisneros** .... (650) 604-5059

Aeromechanics Office Chief
Dr. William G. Warmbrodt .... (650) 604-5642

Systems Analysis Office Chief **Mary E. Livingston** .... (650) 604-0148
E-mail: mary.e.livingston@nasa.gov

Advanced Aircraft Project Office

Building N200, Mail Stop 200-1, Moffett Field, CA 94035-1000
Fax: (650) 604-6990

Chief **Douglas A. Wardwell** .... (650) 604-6566
E-mail: douglas.a.wardwell@nasa.gov

Aviation Systems Division

Building N200, Mail Stop 200-1, Moffett Field, CA 94035-1000
Fax: (650) 604-0752

Chief **Sandra C. Lozito** .... (650) 604-0008
E-mail: sandra.c.lozito@nasa.gov

Deputy Chief **Katharine K. Lee** .... (650) 604-5051
E-mail: katharine.lee@nasa.gov

Wind Tunnel Division

Building N200, Mail Stop 200-1, Moffett Field, CA 94035-1000
Fax: (650) 604-4357

Chief (Acting) **Francis J. Kmak** .... (650) 604-1463
E-mail: frank.j.kmak@nasa.gov

Experimental Aero-Physics Branch Chief
Dr. Rabindra D. Mehta .... (650) 604-4141
E-mail: rabindra.d.mehta@nasa.gov

Operations Branch Chief **Thomas E. Hegland** .... (650) 604-6045

Systems Branch Chief **Jon B. Bader** .... (650) 604-4005
E-mail: jon.b.bader@nasa.gov

Center Operations Directorate

Building N200, Mail Stop 200-1, Moffett Field, CA 94035-1000
Tel: (650) 604-6335 Fax: (650) 604-0031

● Director **Robin C. Aube-Warren** .... (650) 604-6335
E-mail: robin.c.aube-warren@nasa.gov
Education: Florida BA; Troy U MA

(continued on next page)

★ Presidential Appointment Requiring Senate Confirmation ☆ Presidential Appointment ☐ Schedule C Appointment ◇ Career Senior Foreign Service Appointment
● Career Senior Executive Service (SES) Appointment ○ Non-Career Senior Executive Service (SES) Appointment ■ Postal Career Executive Service

INDEPENDENT AGENCIES

Center Operations Directorate *(continued)*

Deputy Director **(Vacant)** . . . . . . (650) 604-3472

Acquisition Division

Ames Research Center, Mail Stop 241-1, Moffett Field, CA 94035-1000
Fax: (650) 604-4646

• Chief **Kelly G. Kaplan** . . . . . . (650) 604-5814
E-mail: kelly.g.kaplan@nasa.gov
Deputy Chief (Acting) **Sarah M. Pollock** . . . . . . (650) 604-3136

Environmental Management Division

Building N200, Mail Stop 200-1, Moffett Field, CA 94035-1000
Fax: (650) 604-7572

Chief **Donald M. Chuck** . . . . . . (650) 604-0237
E-mail: donald.m.chuck@nasa.gov

Facilities Engineering and Real Property Management Division

Building N200, Mail Stop 200-1, Moffett Field, CA 94035-1000
Fax: (650) 604-4984

Chief **Steve A. Frankel** . . . . . . (650) 604-4214

Logistics and Documentation Services Division

Building N200, Mail Stop 200-1, Moffett Field, CA 94035-1000
Fax: (650) 604-3796

Chief **(Vacant)** . . . . . . (650) 604-5137
Deputy Chief **(Vacant)** . . . . . . (650) 604-5828

Protective Services Office

Building N200, Mail Stop 200-1, Moffett Field, CA 94035-1000
Fax: (650) 604-2163

Chief **Phillip T. Snyder** . . . . . . (650) 604-4592
E-mail: phillip.t.snyder@nasa.gov

Engineering Directorate

Building N200, Mail Stop 200-1, Moffett Field, CA 94035-1000
Fax: (650) 604-1726

Director **Dr. David J. Korsmeyer** . . . . . . (650) 604-3114
E-mail: david.korsmeyer@nasa.gov
Deputy Director (Acting) **Chad R. Frost** . . . . . . (650) 604-4449
E-mail: chad@nasa.gov

Applied Manufacturing Division

Chief **Dean P. Giovannetti** . . . . . . (650) 604-3871
Fax: (650) 604-1417

Composites and Metals Development Technical Area Supervisor **Robert S. Kornienko** . . . . . . (650) 604-4644
E-mail: robert.s.kornienko@nasa.gov Fax: (650) 604-1417
Machining and Instrumentation Technical Area Supervisor (Acting) **Robert S. Kornienko** . . . . . . (650) 604-4644
E-mail: robert.s.kornienko@nasa.gov Fax: (650) 604-3956

Engineering Systems Division

Building N200, Mail Stop 200-1, Moffett Field, CA 94035-1000
Fax: (650) 604-3267

Chief **Craig A. Myhre** . . . . . . (650) 604-5479
E-mail: craig.a.myhre@nasa.gov
Electronic Systems, Software and Controls Technical Area Supervisor **Kuok Y. Ling** . . . . . . (650) 604-4785
E-mail: kuok.y.ling@nasa.gov Fax: (650) 604-7453
Spaceflight and Project Office Supervisor **(Vacant)** . . . . . . (650) 604-1313
Mechanical Systems and Analysis Technical Area Supervisor **William F. Caldwell** . . . . . . (650) 604-4093
E-mail: william.caldwell@nasa.gov
Systems Engineering Technical Area Supervisor **Andrew G. Demo** . . . . . . (650) 604-6124
E-mail: andrew.g.demo@nasa.gov

Mission Development Division

Chief **Charles S. Richey** . . . . . . (650) 604-0333

Exploration Technology Directorate

Building N200, Mail Stop 200-1, Moffett Field, CA 94035-1000
Tel: (650) 604-4486 Fax: (650) 604-1726

Director **Dr. Rupak Biswas** . . . . . . (650) 604-4486
E-mail: rupak.biswas@nasa.gov
Deputy Director **Dr. Aga M. Goodsell** . . . . . . (650) 604-2139
E-mail: aga.m.goodsell@nasa.gov
Associate Director (Acting) **Patti P. Powell** . . . . . . (650) 604-3059
E-mail: patti.p.powell@nasa.gov

Entry System and Technology Division

Building N200, Mail Stop 200-1, Moffett Field, CA 94035-1000
Fax: (650) 604-5244

Chief (Acting) **Dr. Dean A. Kontinos** . . . . . . (650) 604-4283
E-mail: dean.a.kontinos@nasa.gov

Human Systems Integration Division

Building N200, Mail Stop 200-1, Moffett Field, CA 94035-1000
Fax: (650) 604-3323 Internet: http://human-factors.arc.nasa.gov

Chief (Acting) **Dr. Alonso Humberto Vera** . . . . . . (650) 604-6294
Education: McGill (Canada) 1985 BS; Cornell 1991 PhD
Deputy Chief **Jeffrey W. McCandless** . . . . . . (650) 604-1162
Education: Washington U (MO) 1990 BSME; UC Berkeley 1992 MS, 1996 PhD
Assistant Chief of Human-Machine Interaction **Matthew Sharpe** . . . . . . (650) 604-4588
Assistant Chief of Human Performance **Brent R. Beutter** . . . . . . (650) 604-5150
Education: Notre Dame 1981 BA; UC Berkeley 1983 MS, 1993 PhD
Assistant Chief of Integration and Training **Jessica Lang Nowinski** . . . . . . (650) 604-5086
E-mail: jessica.l.nowinski@nasa.gov

Intelligent Systems Division

Building N200, Mail Stop 200-1, Moffett Field, CA 94035-1000
Fax: (650) 604-3594 Internet: http://ti.arc.nasa.gov

Chief (Acting) **David D. Alfano** . . . . . . (650) 604-6285
Deputy Chief (Acting) **Scott Poll** . . . . . . (650) 604-6285

NASA Advanced Supercomputing (NAS) Systems Division

Building N200, Mail Stop 200-1, Moffett Field, CA 94035-1000
Internet: www.nas.nasa.gov

Chief **Dr. Piyush Mehrotra** . . . . . . (650) 604-5126
E-mail: piyush.mehrotra@nasa.gov Fax: (650) 604-0439
Deputy Chief **(Vacant)** . . . . . . (650) 604-0171

Human Capital Directorate

• Director **(Vacant)** . . . . . . (650) 604-0267

Human Resources Division

Building N200, Mail Stop 200-1, Moffett Field, CA 94035-1000
Fax: (650) 604-3622

Chief **Marjorie Joy Murphy** . . . . . . (650) 604-3415

Partnerships Directorate

Building N200, Mail Stop 200-1, Moffett Field, CA 94035-1000
Internet: http://sbir.gsfc.nasa.gov/SBIR

Director **Gary L. Martin** . . . . . . (650) 604-2400
E-mail: gary.l.martin-1@nasa.gov
Technology Partnership Office Chief **David R. Morse** . . . . (650) 604-4724
E-mail: david.r.morse@nasa.gov

Programs and Projects Directorate

Ames Research Center, Moffett Field, CA 94035-1000
Tel: (650) 604-3306 Fax: (650) 604-1726

Director **Jay A. Bookbinder** . . . . . . (650) 604-3306
E-mail: jay.bookbinder@nasa.gov
Deputy Director (Acting) **Julie A. Mikula** . . . . . . (650) 604-6483
Project Management Division Chief **Julie A. Mikula** . . . . . (650) 604-6483
E-mail: julie.mikula@nasa.gov

★ Presidential Appointment Requiring Senate Confirmation ☆ Presidential Appointment □ Schedule C Appointment ◇ Career Senior Foreign Service Appointment
● Career Senior Executive Service (SES) Appointment ○ Non-Career Senior Executive Service (SES) Appointment ■ Postal Career Executive Service

Safety and Mission Assurance Directorate

Director **Michel "Mike" Liu** .... (650) 604-1132
E-mail: mike.liu@nasa.gov Fax: (650) 604-1316
Deputy Director **David B. King** .... (650) 604-1316
E-mail: david.b.king@nasa.gov
Occupational Safety, Health & Medical Services Chief
Stanleigh W. Phillips .... (650) 604-3530
E-mail: stanleigh.w.phillips@nasa.gov Fax: (650) 604-0680
System Safety and Mission Assurance Office Chief
Donald R. Mendoza .... (650) 604-2845
E-mail: donald.r.mendoza@nasa.gov Fax: (650) 604-6508

Science Directorate

Moffett Field, CA 94035-1000
Tel: (650) 604-5763 Fax: (650) 604-0031

Director **Michael D. Bicay** .... (650) 604-2198
E-mail: michael.d.bicay@nasa.gov
• Deputy Director **(Vacant)** .... (650) 604-0267
Associate Director for Management Operations
(Acting) **Karen E. Tambua** .... (650) 604-0457
E-mail: karen.e.tambua@nasa.gov

Earth Science Division

• Chief **(Vacant)** .... (650) 604-5076
Fax: (650) 604-3625

Space Biosciences Division

Chief **Sidney C. Sun** .... (650) 604-4835

Space Science Division and Astrobiology

Chief **Timothy J. Lee** .... (650) 604-5208
Fax: (650) 604-6779

Neil A. Armstrong Flight Research Center

P.O. Box 273, Edwards, CA 93523-0273
Tel: (661) 276-3311 Fax: (661) 276-3567
E-mail: armstrongpao@nasa.gov

• Director **David D. McBride** .... (661) 276-2851
E-mail: david.d.mcbride@nasa.gov
Education: New Mexico 1985 BSEE, 1998 MBA
• Deputy Director **Patrick C. Stoliker** .... (661) 276-2706
E-mail: patrick.c.stoliker@nasa.gov
Education: USC 1978 BS; Stanford 1979 MS
Assistant Director for Strategic Implementation
Steven G. Schmidt .... (661) 276-3324
Education: Cal State (Fresno) 1977 BSME; Syracuse MPA
• Director for Mission Support **Jack Irvin Gregory, Jr.** .... (661) 276-3141
E-mail: jack.i.gregory@nasa.gov
Education: Berry 1978 BS; Oklahoma 1994 MPA
Deputy Director for Mission Support **Brian C. Barr** .... (661) 276-2585
• Chief Counsel **David A. Samuels** .... (661) 276-3047
E-mail: david.a.samuels@nasa.gov
Chief Engineer **Bradford A. Neal** .... (661) 276-3204
E-mail: bradford.a.neal@nasa.gov
Education: Purdue 1981 BS, MS
Chief Financial Officer **(Vacant)** .... (661) 276-3604
Chief Information Officer **Sean E. McMorrow** .... (661) 276-5858
E-mail: sean.e.mcmorrow@nasa.gov
Education: Cal Poly (Pomona) BS; Golden Gate MS
Chief Scientist **Albion H. Bowers** .... (661) 276-3716
Education: Cal Poly San Luis Obispo 1982 BS, 1989 ME
Chief Technologist **David F. Voracek** .... (661) 276-2463
E-mail: david.f.voracek@nasa.gov
Education: Iowa State 1986 BS; Northrop U 1991 MSAE; USC 2008 MS
Acquisition Management Chief **James W. Eastman** .... (661) 276-2881
E-mail: james.w.eastman@nasa.gov
Education: Embry-Riddle 1990 BS; Webster 1995 MA
Advanced Planning and Partnerships Director
Tony E. Ginn .... (661) 276-3530
E-mail: tony.e.ginn@nasa.gov
Education Director **Karla S. Shy** .... (661) 276-7785
Equal Employment Opportunity Officer **Keri L. Eliason** .... (661) 276-3033
Education: U Phoenix; Cal State (Dominguez)

Neil A. Armstrong Flight Research Center *(continued)*

• Facilities Engineering and Asset Management Chief
Daniel J. Crowley .... (661) 276-3369
E-mail: daniel.j.crowley@nasa.gov
Human Resources Management **Dana L. Askins** .... (661) 276-7313
E-mail: dana.l.askins@nasa.gov Fax: (661) 276-2276
Education: Cal State (Bakersfield) 1990 BS
Safety and Mission Assurance Director
Col Glenn L. Graham USAF (Ret) .... (661) 276-3210
E-mail: glenn.l.graham@nasa.gov
Stratospheric Observatory for Infrared Astronomy
Program Manager **Eddie Zavala** .... (661) 276-2250
Education: Texas A&M 1991 BS

John H. Glenn Research Center at Lewis Field (GRC)

21000 Brookpark Road, Cleveland, OH 44135-3191
Tel: (216) 433-4000 Fax: (216) 433-8000
Internet: www.nasa.gov/centers/glenn/home

• Director **Janet L. Kavandi** .... (216) 433-3339
E-mail: janet.l.kavandi@nasa.gov
Education: Missouri Southern State Col 1980 BS; Missouri (Rolla) 1982 MS; U Washington 1990 PhD
Executive Support Assistant **Monica M. Palivoda** .... (216) 433-2933
E-mail: monica.m.palivoda@nasa.gov
Deputy Director **Marla E. Perez-Davis** .... (216) 433-6755
E-mail: marla.e.perez-davis@nasa.gov Fax: (216) 433-3437
Education: Puerto Rico BSChE; Toledo MSChE; Case Western 1991 PhD
Executive Support Assistant **Kathryn M. Roser** .... (216) 433-2374
E-mail: kathryn.m.roser@nasa.gov
• Associate Director **Janet L. Watkins** .... (216) 433-2350
E-mail: janet.l.watkins@nasa.gov Fax: (216) 433-2946
Education: Wright State; Central Michigan MPA
Executive Support Assistant **Meghan R. Ganss** .... (216) 433-2059
E-mail: meghan.r.ganss@nasa.gov
Associate Director for Strategy **(Vacant)** .... (216) 433-6551
Chief of Staff **Lori A. Manthey** .... (216) 433-9658
E-mail: lori.a.manthey@nasa.gov
Executive Support Assistant **(Vacant)** .... (216) 433-5835
Chief Engineer **Richard T. Manella** .... (216) 433-2596
Chief Knowledge Officer **Marton Forkosh** .... (216) 433-8791
Chief Scientist **(Vacant)** .... (216) 433-5881
Fax: (216) 433-3501

Aeronautics Research Office

21000 Brookpark Road, Mail Stop 3-5, Cleveland, OH 44135-3191
Fax: (216) 433-8581

Director **Rubén Del Rosario** .... (216) 433-5679
Deputy Director **Gregory J. "Greg" Follen** .... (216) 433-5193
Administrative Officer **(Vacant)** .... (216) 433-8018

Center Operations Directorate

21000 Brookpark Road, Cleveland, OH 44135-3191
Fax: (216) 433-2348

Director **Robyn N. Gordon** .... (216) 433-2175
Education: Cleveland State
Deputy Director **Seth A. Harbaugh** .... (216) 433-6332
Administrative Officer **Xynique R. Sims** .... (216) 433-2493
E-mail: xynique.r.sims@nasa.gov
Management Support Assistant **Anabel Falcon** .... (216) 433-8993
E-mail: anabel.falcon-1@nasa.gov

Office of Communications and External Relations

21000 Brookpark Road, Cleveland, OH 44135-3191
Fax: (216) 433-8143

Chief **Dovie E. Lacy** Mail Stop 3-13 .... (216) 433-5163
E-mail: dovie.e.lacy@nasa.gov
Deputy Chief **Francis T. "Frank" Jennings** .... (216) 433-2776
E-mail: francis.t.jennings@nasa.gov

★ Presidential Appointment Requiring Senate Confirmation ☆ Presidential Appointment □ Schedule C Appointment ◇ Career Senior Foreign Service Appointment
● Career Senior Executive Service (SES) Appointment ○ Non-Career Senior Executive Service (SES) Appointment ■ Postal Career Executive Service

Office of Education
21000 Brookpark Road, Cleveland, OH 44135-3191
Fax: (216) 433-3344

Chief **Robert F. LaSalvia** Mail Stop 7-4 . . . . (216) 433-8981
E-mail: robert.f.lasalvia@nasa.gov
Deputy Chief **Darlene S. Walker** MS 7-4 . . . . (216) 433-8664
E-mail: darlene.s.walker@nasa.gov

Logistics and Technical Information Division
21000 Brookpark Road, Cleveland, OH 44135-3191
Fax: (216) 433-5807

Chief **Richard M. Flaisig** . . . . (216) 433-3088
Deputy Chief **Gary L. Crawford** . . . . (216) 433-5807

Procurement Division
21000 Brookpark Road, Cleveland, OH 44135-3191
Fax: (216) 433-5489
Internet: http://www.grc.nasa.gov/WWW/Procure/home.htm

Chief **Kurt A. Straub** . . . . (216) 433-2769
E-mail: kurt.a.straub@nasa.gov
Deputy Chief **Timothy C. Pierce** . . . . (216) 433-2147
E-mail: timothy.c.pierce@nasa.gov

Office of Protective Services
21000 Brookpark Road, Cleveland, OH 44135-3191
Fax: (216) 433-6664

Chief **Christi Anne Tomaro** . . . . (216) 433-8681
E-mail: christi.a.tomaro@nasa.gov
Deputy Chief **Del R. Simonovich** . . . . (216) 433-5049
E-mail: del.r.simonovich@nasa.gov

Facilities, Test and Manufacturing Directorate
21000 Brookpark Road, Cleveland, OH 44135-3191
Fax: (216) 433-5125

• Director **Thomas W. Hartline** . . . . (216) 433-5298
E-mail: tom.hartline@nasa.gov
• Deputy Director **Susan L. Kevdzija** . . . . (216) 433-5718
E-mail: susan.l.kevdzija@nasa.gov

Aircraft Operations Office
21000 Brookpark Road, Cleveland, OH 44135-3191
Fax: (216) 433-3184

Chief **Alan J. "Al" Micklewright** . . . . (216) 433-2036
Education: Embry-Riddle BAE, MAS; Naval Postgrad
Deputy Chief **Kurt S. Blankenship** . . . . (216) 433-2024

Energy and Environmental Management Office
Chief **(Vacant)** . . . . (216) 433-3032

Planning and Integration Office
Manager **Susan L. Kevdzija** . . . . (216) 977-7547

Facilities Division
21000 Brookpark Road, Cleveland, OH 44135-3191
Fax: (216) 433-3124

Chief **(Vacant)** . . . . (216) 433-9717
Deputy Chief **Renee D. Palyo** . . . . (216) 433-6460
Education: Toledo BSCE
Engineering Management Branch Chief
Sue A. Gaudreau . . . . (216) 433-2330
Operations Management Branch Chief **(Vacant)** . . . . (216) 433-6217
Project Management Branch Chief **(Vacant)** . . . . (216) 433-6807
Systems Management Branch Chief **(Vacant)** . . . . (216) 433-2331

Testing Division
21000 Brookpark Road, Cleveland, OH 44135-3191
Tel: (216) 433-5731 Fax: (216) 433-8551

Chief **John F. Schubert** . . . . (216) 433-2605
Facility Management and Planning Office Chief
(Vacant) . . . . (216) 433-9370
Aviation Environments Technical Branch Chief
(Vacant) . . . . (216) 433-5746

Testing Division *(continued)*

Data System Branch Chief **Joseph W. Panek** . . . . (216) 433-5670
E-mail: joseph.w.panek@nasa.gov
Space Combustion and Materials Branch Chief
William P. Camperchioli . . . . (216) 433-8301
Space Power and Propulsion, Communication and
Instrumentation Branch Chief **Sandra M. Doehne** . . . . . (216) 433-8636
Wind Tunnel and Propulsion Test Branch Chief
John F. Leone . . . . (216) 433-5722
E-mail: john.f.leone@nasa.gov

Office of the Chief Counsel
21000 Brookpark Road, Cleveland, OH 44135-3191
Fax: (216) 433-6790

• Chief Counsel **Laura A. Henry JD** 500-118 . . . . (216) 433-2318
E-mail: laura.a.henry@nasa.gov

Office of the Chief Financial Officer
21000 Brookpark Road, Cleveland, OH 44135-3191
Fax: (216) 433-3940

Chief Financial Officer **Laurence A. Sivic** . . . . (216) 433-2599
Education: Bowling Green State BS

Accounting and Financial Analysis Division
Chief **Vicki L. Hagerman** . . . . (216) 433-9643

Mission Support and Integration Office
21000 Brookpark Road, Cleveland, OH 44135-3191
Fax: (216) 433-3940

Chief **Robert J. Piccus** . . . . (216) 433-5539

Office of the Chief Information Officer
21000 Brookpark Road, Cleveland, OH 44135-3191
Fax: (216) 433-5050

• Chief Information Officer **Sean M. Gallagher** . . . . (216) 433-9349
E-mail: sean.gallagher@nasa.gov
Deputy Chief Information Officer **Louise M. Moroney** . . . (216) 433-6350
E-mail: louise.m.moroney@nasa.gov
Information Technology Specialist [Section 508
Coordinator] **Jill D. Noble** . . . . (216) 433-3711
E-mail: jill.d.noble@nasa.gov

Office of Human Capital Management
21000 Brookpark Road, Cleveland, OH 44135-3191
Fax: (216) 433-8701

Chief **Lori O. Pietravoia** . . . . (216) 433-2506
E-mail: lori.o.pietravoia@nasa.gov
Deputy Chief **Thomas A. Spicer** . . . . (216) 433-2762
E-mail: thomas.a.spicer@nasa.gov

Office of Diversity and Equal Opportunity
21000 Brookpark Road, Cleveland, OH 44135-3191
Fax: (216) 433-3437

Chief **Aretha Lynn Carr** . . . . (216) 433-2463
E-mail: aretha.l.carr@nasa.gov
Management Support Assistant **Carmen I. Marrero** . . . . . . (216) 433-2378
E-mail: carmen.i.marrero@nasa.gov

Office of Technology Incubation and Innovation
21000 Brookpark Road, Cleveland, OH 44135-3191
Fax: (216) 977-7005

Director **(Vacant)** . . . . (216) 977-7429
Deputy Director **Sandra T. Reehorst** . . . . (216) 433-5384
E-mail: sandra.t.reehorst@nasa.gov

Research and Engineering Directorate (L)
21000 Brookpark Road, Cleveland, OH 44135-3191
Fax: (216) 433-8581

Director **Dr. Rickey J. Shyne** Mail Stop 3-5 . . . . (216) 433-3595
E-mail: rickey.j.shyne@nasa.gov
Education: Tennessee State BSME; Toledo MSME, PhD
Deputy Director **Dr. Ajay K. Misra** . . . . (216) 433-8193

Research and Engineering Directorate (L) *(continued)*

Associate Director **Maria Babula** .... (216) 433-5221
Executive Support Assistant **Maria F. Ernst** .... (216) 433-2977
Small Business Technical Advisor
Dr. Michael A. Meador .... (216) 433-9518
E-mail: michael.a.meador@nasa.gov

Communications and Intelligent Systems Division
21000 Brookpark Road, Cleveland, OH 44135-3191
Tel: (216) 433-3831 Fax: (216) 433-8705

Chief **Dawn C. Emerson** Mail Stop 54-1 .... (216) 433-8901
E-mail: dawn.c.emerson@nasa.gov Fax: (216) 433-6382
Education: Ohio State BSEE; Toledo MSEE
Deputy Chief **Dr. Felix A. Miranda** Mail Stop 54-1 .... (216) 433-3495
E-mail: felix.a.miranda@nasa.gov
Administrative Support **Kimberly A. Sivillo** .... (216) 433-9313
E-mail: kimberly.a.sivillo@nasa.gov
Advanced High Frequency Branch Chief **(Vacant)** .... (216) 433-6589
Architectures, Networks and Systems Integration Branch Chief **David A. Buchanan** .... (216) 433-5228
E-mail: david.a.buchanan@nasa.gov
Deputy Branch Chief
Denise S. Ponchak Mail Stop 54-8 .... (216) 433-3465
E-mail: denise.s.ponchak@nasa.gov
Information and Signal Processing Branch
Gene Fujikawa .... (216) 433-3495
E-mail: gene.fujikawa@nasa.gov
Intelligent Control and Autonomy Branch Chief
(Vacant) Mail Stop 77-1 .... (216) 433-2685
Optics and Photonics Branch Chief
Margaret L. Nazario Mail Stop 77-1 .... (216) 433-8665
Smart Sensors and Electronics Systems Branch Chief
Diana I. Centeno-Gomez Mail Stop 77-1 .... (216) 433-3259
E-mail: diana.i.centeno-gomez@nasa.gov

Materials and Structures Division
21000 Brookpark Road, Cleveland, OH 44135-3191
Fax: (216) 433-3680

Chief **James J. Zakrajsek** Mail Stop 49-1 .... (216) 433-3968
Deputy Chief **Joyce A. Dever** Mail Stop 49-1 .... (216) 433-6294
E-mail: joyce.a.dever@nasa.gov
Ceramics and Polymer Composites Branch Chief
Dr. Joseph E. Grady Mail Stop 106-5 .... (216) 433-6728
E-mail: joseph.e.grady@nasa.gov Fax: (216) 433-5544
Environmental Effects and Coatings Branch Chief
Raymond C. Robinson .... (216) 433-5590
High Temperature and Smart Alloys Branch Chief
Robert W. Carter Mail Stop 106-1 .... (216) 433-6524
Materials Chemistry and Physics Branch Chief
(Vacant) .... (216) 433-6779
Mechanical Systems Design and Integration Branch Chief **(Vacant)** .... (216) 433-3815
Mechanisms and Tribology Branch Chief
Damian R. Ludwiczak .... (216) 433-3791
Multiscale and Multiphysics Modeling Branch Chief
George L. Stefko .... (216) 433-3920
Rotating and Drive Systems Branch Chief
Robert F. Handschuh Mail Stop 23-2 .... (216) 433-3969
E-mail: robert.f.handschuh@nasa.gov Fax: (216) 433-3954
Structural Dynamics Branch Chief
Dr. Dexter Johnson Mail Stop 49-8 .... (216) 433-6046
E-mail: dexter.johnson@nasa.gov
Structural Mechanics Branch Chief **Nelson Morales** .... (216) 977-7050

Power Division
21000 Brookpark Road, Cleveland, OH 44135-3191
Fax: (216) 433-2306

● Chief **Randall B. Furnas** Mail Stop 301-3 .... (216) 433-2321
E-mail: randall.b.furnas@nasa.gov
Education: Miami U (OH) 1979 BS; Case Western 1981 MSME
Deputy Chief **Robert M. Button** Mail Stop 301-2 .... (216) 433-8010
Avionics Branch Chief **Timothy J. Ruffner** .... (216) 433-2391
Diagnostics and Electromagnetics Branch Chief
John E. Thomas .... (216) 433-2658

Power Division *(continued)*

Photovoltaic and Electrochemical Systems Branch Chief **(Vacant)** Mail Stop 302-1 .... (216) 433-2237
Power Management and Distribution Branch Chief (Acting) **Robert J. Scheidegger** .... (216) 433-8342
Thermal Energy Conversion Branch Chief
Lee S. Mason Mail Stop 301-2 .... (216) 977-7106
E-mail: lee.s.mason@nasa.gov
Education: Dayton 1987 BSME; Cleveland State 1996 MSME
Power Architecture and Analysis Branch Chief
David J. Hoffman .... (216) 433-2445

Propulsion Division
21000 Brookpark Road, Cleveland, OH 44135-3191
Fax: (216) 977-3000

Chief **Dr. George R. Schmidt PhD** Mail Stop 5-3 .... (216) 433-3944
Education: Stanford 1980 BS, 1981 MS; U Washington 1985 MS; Alabama Huntsville 1993 PhD
Deputy Chief **Dhanireddy R. Reddy** Mailstop 5-3 .... (216) 433-8133
E-mail: dhanireddy.r.reddy@nasa.gov
Acoustics Branch Chief
E. Brian "Eric" Fite Mail Stop 54-3 .... (216) 433-3892
E-mail: brian.fite@nasa.gov
Engine Combustion Branch Chief (Acting)
Paul F. Senick Mail Stop 5-10 .... (216) 977-7024
E-mail: paul.f.senick@nasa.gov Fax: (216) 433-5802
Icing Branch Chief **Mary F. Wadel** Mail Stop 11-2 .... (216) 977-7510
E-mail: mary.wadel@nasa.gov Fax: (216) 977-7469
Inlet and Nozzle Branch Chief
Mary Jo Long-Davis Mail Stop 5-12 .... (216) 433-8708
E-mail: mary.j.long-davis@nasa.gov Fax: (216) 433-5802
Propulsion Systems Analysis Branch Chief
Mary S. Reveley Mail Stop 5-11 .... (216) 433-6511
E-mail: mary.s.reveley@nasa.gov Fax: (216) 433-5802
Turbomachinery and Turboelectric Systems Branch Chief **Kenneth L. Suder** .... (216) 433-5899
E-mail: kenneth.l.suder@nasa.gov

Systems Engineering and Architecture Division
21000 Brookpark Road, Cleveland, OH 44135-3191
Tel: (216) 433-5396 Fax: (216) 433-8050

Chief **Derrick J. Cheston** .... (216) 433-3879
E-mail: derrick.j.cheston@nasa.gov
Education: North Carolina State 1984 BS; Cleveland State 1991 MSME, 2000 MBA; JFK School Govt 2007
Deputy Chief **(Vacant)** .... (216) 433-5324
Aeronautics and Ground-Based Systems Branch Chief
Dennis W. Rohn .... (216) 433-2044
E-mail: dennis.w.rohn@nasa.gov
Flight Software Branch Chief
Laura A. Maynard-Nelson .... (216) 433-8756
E-mail: laura.a.maynard-nelson@nasa.gov
Human Space Flight Systems Branch Chief
Leah M. McIntyre .... (216) 433-3804
E-mail: leah.m.mcintyre@nasa.gov
Mission Architecture and Analysis Branch Chief
Joshua E. Freeh .... (216) 433-5014
Science and Space Technology Systems Branch Chief
Lynn A. Capadona .... (216) 433-5013
E-mail: lynn.a.capadona@nasa.gov

Safety and Mission Assurance Directorate
21000 Brookpark Road, Cleveland, OH 44135-3191
Fax: (216) 433-5749

Director **Anita D. Liang** .... (216) 433-5298
Education: McGill (Canada) 1979 BEng, 1982 MEng
Deputy Director **Kathleen E. Schubert** .... (216) 433-5331
E-mail: kathleen.e.schubert@nasa.gov
Associate Director **(Vacant)** .... (216) 433-2340

Safety, Health and Environmental Division
Chief **Osvaldo Rivera** .... (216) 433-5699
E-mail: osvaldo.rivera-1@nasa.gov

INDEPENDENT AGENCIES

★ Presidential Appointment Requiring Senate Confirmation ☆ Presidential Appointment □ Schedule C Appointment ◇ Career Senior Foreign Service Appointment
● Career Senior Executive Service (SES) Appointment ○ Non-Career Senior Executive Service (SES) Appointment ■ Postal Career Executive Service

Program and Project Assurance Division
Chief **(Vacant)** .... (216) 433-4000

Space Flight Systems Directorate
21000 Brookpark Road, Cleveland, OH 44135-3191
Fax: (216) 977-7537 Internet: https://spaceflightsystems.grc.nasa.gov/

• Director **Bryan K. Smith** Mail Stop 3-6 .... (216) 433-6149
E-mail: bryan.k.smith@nasa.gov
Administrative Officer **(Vacant)** Mail Stop 3-6 .... (216) 433-9304
Deputy Director **Joel Kenneth Kearns** .... (256) 544-4081
E-mail: joel.k.kearns@nasa.gov
Education: Worcester Polytech 1983 BSME, 1985 MS
Associate Director **Scott R. Graham** .... (216) 433-7123
E-mail: scott.r.graham@nasa.gov
Executive Support Assistant **Denise Anne Kelly** .... (216) 433-3372

European Service Module Integration Office
21000 Brookpark Road, Cleveland, OH 44135-3191
Fax: (216) 433-6382
Chief **Susan M. Motil** .... (216) 433-8589
E-mail: susan.m.motil@nasa.gov
Deputy Chief **Ann P. Over** .... (216) 433-6535
E-mail: ann.p.over@nasa.gov

Exploration Systems Project Office
Chief **(Vacant)** .... (216) 433-8616
Deputy Chief **Frank Gati** .... (216) 433-2746

Space Technology Project Office
Chief **Trudy F. Kortes** .... (216) 433-3632
Deputy Chief **Michael J. Barrett** .... (216) 433-5424

Program/Project Integration Office
21000 Brookpark Road, Cleveland, OH 44135-3191
Fax: (216) 433-5100
Chief **Michael J. Zernic** .... (216) 433-5286

Radioisotope Power Systems Program Office
Program Manager **John A. Hamley** .... (216) 977-7430
E-mail: john.a.hamley@nasa.gov

Space Operations Project Office
Chief **(Vacant)** .... (216) 433-3557

Space Communications and Spectrum Management Office
Chief **Elias T. Naffah** .... (216) 433-2639

International Space Station and Human Health Projects Office
Chief **Robert R. Corban** .... (216) 433-6642
E-mail: robert.r.corban@nasa.gov

Space Science Project Office
Chief **Tibor Kremic** .... (216) 433-5003

Vehicle Technology Directorate (Army)
21000 Brookpark Road, Cleveland, OH 44135-3191
Fax: (216) 433-3720
Director (Acting) **LTC Keith S. Morgan USA** .... (216) 433-5742

Goddard Space Flight Center (GSFC)
8800 Greenbelt Road, Greenbelt, MD 20771
Tel: (301) 286-2000 Fax: (301) 286-0205
Internet: www.nasa.gov/centers/goddard/home

• Director **Christopher J. Scolese** .... (301) 286-5121
E-mail: cscolese@nasa.gov
Education: SUNY (Buffalo) 1978 BSEE; George Washington 1982 MSEE
• Deputy Director **George W. Morrow** .... (301) 286-5121
• Deputy Director for Technology and Research Investments **Christyl C. "Christy" Johnson** .... (301) 286-5177
E-mail: christyl.johnson@nasa.gov
Education: Lincoln U (CA) BS; Penn State MS

Goddard Space Flight Center *(continued)*

• Associate Director **Nancy A. Abell** .... (301) 286-5867
E-mail: nancy.a.abell@nasa.gov
Chief Financial Officer **Stephen Andrew Shinn** .... (301) 286-8096
Fax: (301) 286-1715
Chief Knowledge Officer **Dr. Edward W. Rogers** .... (301) 286-4467
E-mail: edward.w.rogers@nasa.gov
Equal Employment Opportunity Programs Office Chief **Daniel A. "Dan" Krieger** .... (301) 286-7913
E-mail: dan.krieger@nasa.gov Fax: (301) 286-0298
Public Affairs Office Chief **Mark S. Hess** .... (301) 286-6255
E-mail: mark.s.hess@nasa.gov Fax: (301) 286-1707
Librarian **Robin M. Dixon** .... (301) 286-9230
E-mail: robin.m.dixon@nasa.gov Fax: (301) 286-1755
Staffing Coordinator **Linda J. Ledman** .... (301) 286-6111
E-mail: linda.j.ledman@nasa.gov Fax: (301) 286-5588
FOIA Public Liaison Officer **Joan E. Belt** .... (301) 286-1520

Office of Human Capital Management (OHCM)
Director **(Vacant)** .... (301) 358-1998
Deputy Director **Crystal A. Gayhart** .... (301) 286-8851
E-mail: crystal.a.gayhart@nasa.gov
Recruitment and Outreach Manager and Selective Placement Coordinator **Esteban Morales** .... (301) 286-3093
E-mail: esteban.morales@nasa.gov
Human Resources Specialist **Deborah M. Baker** .... (301) 286-5392
E-mail: deborah.m.baker@nasa.gov
Human Resources Specialist **Cheryllynn M. Rosanova** .... (301) 286-4832
E-mail: cheryllynn.m.rosanova@nasa.gov
Project Support Specialist **Erica A. Moran** .... (301) 286-5025
E-mail: erica.a.moran@nasa.gov

Office of the Chief Counsel
Mail Code 140, Greenbelt, MD 20771
Tel: (301) 286-9181 Fax: (301) 286-1713
• Chief Counsel **Richard Andrew Falcon** .... (301) 286-9181
E-mail: r.a.falcon-1@nasa.gov
Deputy Chief Counsel **Laura Marie Giza** .... (301) 286-9181
E-mail: laura.m.giza@nasa.gov

Applied Engineering and Technology Directorate
AETD/Code 500, 8800 Greenbelt Road, Greenbelt, MD 20771
Tel: (301) 286-6218 Fax: (301) 286-1600
• Director **Felicia L. Jones-Selden** .... (301) 286-6218
E-mail: felicia.jones@nasa.gov
Deputy Director **Juan A. Román Velázquez** .... (301) 286-6422
E-mail: juan.a.roman@nasa.gov
Deputy Director **(Vacant)** .... (301) 286-6422
Deputy Director for Planning and Business Management **Karen E. Flynn** .... (301) 286-8776
Assistant Director for Business Development **Carl M. Stahle** .... (301) 286-6182
Assistant Director for Engineering Operations **Barry N. Green** .... (301) 286-2520
Education: Lehigh 1984
Assistant Director for Engineering Safety and Compliance Management **Dann Alfred Brown** .... (301) 286-5503
E-mail: dann.brown@nasa.gov
Chief Engineer **Steven S. Scott** .... (301) 286-2529
E-mail: steven.s.scott@nasa.gov
Chief Technologist **Michael A. Johnson** .... (301) 286-5386
Business Management Office Chief **Shanta Narayan Arur** .... (301) 286-5052
Fax: (301) 286-2605
Integrated Design Center Manager **Jennifer Medlin Bracken** .... (301) 286-5127

Electrical Engineering Division
AETD/Code 500, 8800 Greenbelt Road, Greenbelt, MD 20771
Chief **Ardeshir A. "Art" Azarbarzin** .... (301) 286-5118
Wallops Electrical Engineering Branch Head **Lissette M. Martinez** .... (757) 824-2281
Wallops Flight Facility, Wallops Island, VA 23337
E-mail: lissette.martinez-1@nasa.gov

★ Presidential Appointment Requiring Senate Confirmation ☆ Presidential Appointment ☐ Schedule C Appointment ◇ Career Senior Foreign Service Appointment
● Career Senior Executive Service (SES) Appointment ○ Non-Career Senior Executive Service (SES) Appointment ■ Postal Career Executive Service

Instrument Systems and Technology Division
AETD/Code 500, 8800 Greenbelt Road, Greenbelt, MD 20771
Internet: https://istd.gsfc.nasa.gov/
Associate Chief **Cynthia Willis Simmons** . . . . (301) 286-7531

Mechanical Systems Division
AETD/Code 500, 8800 Greenbelt Road, Greenbelt, MD 20771
Chief **(Vacant)** . . . . (301) 286-7101

Mission Engineering and Systems Analysis Division
AETD/Code 500, 8800 Greenbelt Road, Greenbelt, MD 20771
Chief **Tristram T. "Tupper" Hyde** . . . . (301) 286-8496
E-mail: tupper.hyde@nasa.gov Fax: (301) 286-1718

Software Engineering Division
AETD/Code 500, 8800 Greenbelt Road, Greenbelt, MD 20771
Chief **Jerome D. Bennett** . . . . (301) 286-8623
E-mail: jerome.d.bennett@nasa.gov Fax: (301) 286-1767
Wallops Systems Software Engineering Branch Head
Pamela L. Pittman . . . . (757) 824-1506
Mail Stop 589.W, Wallops Island, VA 23337-5099
E-mail: pamela.l.pittman@nasa.gov

Flight Projects Directorate
Code 400, Greenbelt, MD 20771
Tel: (301) 286-6306 Fax: (301) 286-1709
Director **David F. "Dave" Mitchell** . . . . (301) 286-0415
E-mail: david.f.mitchell@nasa.gov
Education: SUNY (Buffalo) BSME; George Washington MS
Secretary to the Director **(Vacant)** . . . .(301) 286-4965
Deputy Director **Thomas V. "Tom" McCarthy** . . . . (240) 684-0502
E-mail: thomas.v.mccarthy@nasa.gov
Deputy Director for Planning and Business
Management **Wanda Peters** . . . . (301) 286-5894
Project Support Specialist to the Deputy Director
for Planning and Business Management
Linda K. Wunderlick . . . . (301) 286-3484
E-mail: linda.k.wunderlick@nasa.gov
Associate Director **(Vacant)** . . . . (301) 286-5196
Associate Director for Project Formulation
John T. Van Sant . . . . (301) 286-6024
E-mail: john.t.vansant@nasa.gov
Assistant Director **James D. "Dan" Blackwood** . . . . (301) 286-9151
E-mail: dan.blackwood@nasa.gov
Assistant Director **Donna J. Swann** . . . . (301) 286-7871
E-mail: donna.j.swann@nasa.gov
Assistant Director **(Vacant)** . . . .(301) 286-7398
Administrative Officer **Lisa R. Hoffmann** . . . .(301) 286-2154
E-mail: lisa.r.hoffmann@nasa.gov

Astrophysics Projects Division
Code 400, Greenbelt, MD 20771
Internet: apd440.gsfc.nasa.gov
Associate Director and Program Manager
Mansoor Ahmed . . . . (301) 286-2201
Education: Maryland BS; George Washington MS
Deputy Program Manager **Dr. Azita Valinia** . . . . (301) 286-5155

Earth Science Projects Division
Code 400, Greenbelt, MD 20771
Internet: https://espd.gsfc.nasa.gov/
Associate Director **Jeffrey "Jeff" Gramling** . . . .(301) 286-7568

Exploration and Space Communications Project
Code 400, Greenbelt, MD 20771
Tel: (301) 286-5220 Internet: esc.gsfc.nasa.gov
Associate Director **Robert J. "Bob" Menrad** . . . . (301) 286-6527
E-mail: robert.j.menrad@nasa.gov
Deputy Program Manager, Execution
Catherine B. "Cathy" Barclay . . . . (301) 286-8626
E-mail: catherine.b.barclay@nasa.gov

Exploration and Space Communications Project *(continued)*
Deputy Program Manager, Implementation
Mark D. Brumfield . . . . (301) 286-5196
E-mail: mark.d.brumfield@nasa.gov
Associate Program Manager **(Vacant)** . . . . (301) 286-5720
Business Manager **Tracy D. Felton** . . . . (301) 286-9547
E-mail: tracy.d.felton@nasa.gov
Deputy Business Manager **Chikia Barnes** . . . .(301) 286-2056

Explorers and Heliophysics Projects Division
Code 400, Greenbelt, MD 20771
Associate Director of Flight Projects
Nicholas G. Chrissotimos . . . . (301) 286-8212
E-mail: nicholas.g.chrissotimos@nasa.gov
Deputy Program Manager for Explorers Program
Greg V. Frazier . . . .(301) 286-6619
E-mail: gregory.v.frazier@nasa.gov
Deputy Program Manager for Living With a Star and
Solar Terrestrial Probes **Michael Delmont** . . . .(301) 286-1228
E-mail: michael.delmont-1@nasa.gov

Planetary Science Projects Division
Code 400, Greenbelt, MD 20771
Associate Director (Acting) **David F. "Dave" Mitchell** . . . (301) 286-0415
Education: SUNY (Buffalo) BSME; George Washington MS

Information Technology and Communications Directorate
8800 Greenbelt Road, Greenbelt, MD 20771
Tel: (301) 286-7342
Director and Chief Information Officer
Dennis C. Vander Tuig . . . .(301) 286-5710
E-mail: dennis.c.vandertuig@nasa.gov Fax: (301) 286-4262
Deputy Director and Deputy Chief Information Officer
(Acting) **Dwaine A. Kronser** . . . .(301) 286-5700
Associate Chief Strategy and Planning Officer
Frederic Joshua Krage . . . . (301) 286-0152
E-mail: joshua.krage@nasa.gov
Chief Information Security Officer and IT Security
Manager **Frederic Joshua Krage** . . . . (301) 286-0152
E-mail: joshua.krage@nasa.gov
Chief, Regional Information Technology Services and
Solutions Division **Carl E. Johnson** . . . .(757) 824-2444
Mail Stop 708.0, Wallops Island, VA 23337-5099
E-mail: carl.e.johnson@nasa.gov

Management Operations Directorate
Code 200, Greenbelt, MD 20771
Fax: (301) 286-1706
Director **Raymond J. Rubilotta** . . . . (301) 286-8214
E-mail: raymond.j.rubilotta@nasa.gov
Deputy Director **David Alexander Reth** . . . .(301) 286-8641
E-mail: david.a.reth@nasa.gov

Facilities Management Division
Chief **(Vacant)** . . . .(301) 286-9350
Fax: (301) 286-1652
Wallops Facilities Management Branch Head
Glenn D. Lilly . . . .(757) 824-1299
Mail Stop 228.0, Wallops Island, VA 23337-5099

Information and Logistics Management Division
Chief **Marilyn C. Tolliver** . . . . (301) 286-7244
Fax: (301) 286-1774

Medical and Environmental Management Division
Chief **(Vacant)** . . . . (301) 286-4230
Wallops Environmental Office Head **Carolyn Turner** . . . . . (757) 824-1720
Mail Stop 250.W, Wallops Island, VA 23337-5099
E-mail: carolyn.turner-1@nasa.gov

Procurement Operations Division
Goddard Space Flight Center, Greenbelt, MD 20771

Chief **Michael E. "Mike" McGrath** . . . . . (301) 286-7247
E-mail: michael.e.mcgrath@nasa.gov Fax: (301) 286-0237
Procurement Manager **(Vacant)** . . . . . (757) 824-1277
Mail Stop 210.W, Wallops Island, VA 23337-5099

Security Division
Chief **Madison Paul Townley** . . . . . (301) 286-7233
E-mail: madison.townley@nasa.gov
Wallops Security Office Specialist **Jean S. Lopez** . . . . . (757) 824-2536
Mail Stop 240.W, Wallops Island, VA 23337-5099
E-mail: jean.s.lopez@nasa.gov

Safety and Mission Assurance Directorate
Code 300, Greenbelt, MD 20771
Fax: (301) 286-1667

Director **Richard D. Barney** . . . . . (301) 286-4601
Deputy Director **Eric K. Isaac** . . . . . (301) 286-6737
E-mail: eric.k.isaac@nasa.gov
Associate Director **(Vacant)** . . . . . (301) 286-2000

Quality and Reliability Division
Chief **Jeannette Plante** . . . . . (301) 614-5944

Safety Division
Chief **Bo Lewis** . . . . . (301) 286-7123

System Review Office
Chief **Gaspare Maggio** . . . . . (301) 286-4010
E-mail: gaspare.maggio@nasa.gov

Sciences and Exploration Directorate
Code 600, Greenbelt, MD 20771
Tel: (301) 286-6066 Fax: (301) 286-1772

Director **Colleen N. Hartman** . . . . . (301) 286-8824
E-mail: colleen.hartman@nasa.gov
Education: Pomona 1977 BA; USC 1982 MPA; Catholic U 1992 MS, 1996 PhD
Deputy Director **Mark Clampin** . . . . . (301) 286-4532
Deputy Director for Institutions, Programs and Business **David L. Pierce** . . . . . (202) 358-3808
E-mail: david.l.pierce@nasa.gov
Chief Scientist **Dr. James B. Garvin** . . . . . (301) 286-5154
Education: Brown U 1978; Stanford MS; Brown U MS, 1984 PhD

Astrophysics Science Division
Code 600, Greenbelt, MD 20771
Fax: (301) 286-0250

Division Director **Robert Petre** . . . . . (301) 286-3844
E-mail: robert.petre-1@nasa.gov
Deputy Director (Acting) **Joanne Elizabeth Hill-Kittle** . . . (301) 286-0572
E-mail: joanne.e.hill@nasa.gov
Assistant Director **Ryan J. Smallcomb** . . . . . (301) 286-9641
E-mail: ryan.smallcomb@nasa.gov
Education: Scranton 2000 BS
Associate Director **Amber Nicole Straughn** . . . . . (301) 286-7098
Senior Scientist for Advanced Concepts **Harley A. Thronson** . . . . . (301) 286-5155
E-mail: harley.a.thronson@nasa.gov
Administrative Officer **Esther C. Johnson** . . . . . (301) 286-4683
E-mail: esther.c.johnson@nasa.gov

Earth Sciences Division
Director **Dr. James R. Irons** . . . . . (301) 614-6657
Education: Penn State 1976 BS, 1979 MS; Maryland 1993 PhD
Deputy Director **(Vacant)** . . . . . (301) 614-6657
Associate Director for Institutional Planning and Development **Dr. Dorothy J. Zukor** . . . . . (301) 614-5635
Education: Col Notre Dame (MD) 1972 BA; Maryland 1976 MS, 1982 PhD
Associate Director for Mission Planning and Technology Development **(Vacant)** . . . . . (301) 286-1212

Earth Sciences Division *(continued)*

Assistant Director for Operations **(Vacant)** . . . . . (301) 614-5341
Assistant Director for Information Technology **Rosa C. Kao** . . . . . (301) 614-5673
E-mail: rosa.c.kao@nasa.gov
Deputy Director for Atmospheres **Steven E. Platnick** . . . . (301) 614-5636
Education: Duke 1979 BSEE; UC Berkeley 1980 MSEE; Arizona 1991 PhD
Associate Deputy Director for Atmospheres **Karen Irene Mohr** . . . . . (301) 614-6360
Education: Col Holy Cross 1986 BA; Penn State 1987 BS; Texas A&M 1995 MS; Texas 2000 PhD
Deputy Director for Hydrospheric, Biospheric, and Geophysics **Christa D. Peters-Lidard** . . . . . (301) 614-5811
Education: Virginia Tech 1991 BS; Princeton 1993 MA, 1997 PhD
Assistant Deputy Director for Hydrospheric, Biospheric, and Geophysics **Torry A. Johnson** . . . . . (301) 614-5683
Administrative Officer for Hydrospheric, Biospheric, and Geophysics **Deborah A. Brasel** . . . . . (301) 614-5671
E-mail: deborah.a.brasel@nasa.gov
Chief Technologist **Matthew J. McGill** . . . . . (301) 614-6281
E-mail: matthew.j.mcgill@nasa.gov
Airborne Science Manager **Christy Hansen** . . . . . (301) 614-7018
Applied Sciences Manager **Stephanie Schollaert Uz** . . . . (301) 286-0549

Heliophysics Science Division
Director **Dr. Holly R. Gilbert** . . . . . (301) 286-2493
Education: Colorado BA; Oslo (Norway) 2005 PhD
Deputy Director **(Vacant)** . . . . . (301) 286-2493
Associate Director for Science **C. Alex Young** . . . . . (301) 286-4441
E-mail: c.a.young@nasa.gov
Education: Florida State 1991 BS; New Hampshire 1996
Associate Director for Science Information Systems **Dr. Robert E. McGuire** . . . . . (301) 286-7794
E-mail: robert.e.mcguire@nasa.gov
Education: UC Berkeley 1970 AB, 1976 PhD
Assistant Director (Acting) **Marlo M. Maddox** . . . . . (301) 286-5202
E-mail: marlo.m.maddox@nasa.gov
Chief Technologist **Nikolaos P. Paschalidis** . . . . . (301) 286-0166
E-mail: nikolaos.paschalidis@nasa.gov
Project Support Specialist **Amy R. Shimonkevitz** . . . . . (301) 286-6418
E-mail: amy.r.shimonkevitz@nasa.gov

Solar System Exploration Division
Code 600, Greenbelt, MD 20771
Fax: (301) 614-6015

Director **Paul R. Mahaffy** . . . . . (301) 614-6379
E-mail: paul.r.mahaffy@nasa.gov
Deputy Director **Stephanie A. Getty** . . . . . (301) 614-5442
E-mail: stephanie.a.getty@nasa.gov
Education: Florida 1998 BS, 2001 PhD
Associate Director for Planning, Research and Development **Brook Lakew** . . . . . (301) 286-8442
E-mail: brook.lakew-1@nasa.gov
Associate Director for Strategic Science **Daniel P. Glavin** . . . . . (301) 614-6361
E-mail: daniel.p.glavin@nasa.gov

Wallops Flight Facility
Wallops Flight Facility, Wallops Island, VA 23337-5099
Tel: (757) 824-1000

Office of the Director
● Director **William Anthony "Bill" Wrobel** . . . . . (757) 824-1201
E-mail: william.a.wrobel@nasa.gov
Education: Ohio State 1982 BS
Section 508 Coordinator [Section 508 Coordinator] **Susan K. Semancik** . . . . . (757) 824-1655
E-mail: Susan.K.Semancik@nasa.gov

★ Presidential Appointment Requiring Senate Confirmation ☆ Presidential Appointment ☐ Schedule C Appointment ◇ Career Senior Foreign Service Appointment
● Career Senior Executive Service (SES) Appointment ○ Non-Career Senior Executive Service (SES) Appointment ■ Postal Career Executive Service

Suborbital and Special Orbital Projects Directorate
Wallops Flight Facility, Wallops Island, VA 23337
Tel: (757) 824-1201 Fax: (757) 824-2313

Director **William Anthony "Bill" Wrobel** .... (757) 824-1201
E-mail: william.a.wrobel@nasa.gov
Education: Ohio State 1982 BS
Deputy Director **(Vacant)** .... (757) 824-2555
Administrative Officer **(Vacant)** .... (757) 824-1204
Advanced Projects Office Chief **Bruce E. Underwood** .... (757) 824-1350
E-mail: bruce.e.underwood@nasa.gov Fax: (757) 824-2415
Aircraft Office Chief **Shane G. Dover** .... (757) 864-2543
E-mail: shane.g.dover@nasa.gov Fax: (757) 824-2135
Balloon Program Office Chief **Debora A. Fairbrother** .... (757) 824-1453
E-mail: debora.a.fairbrother@nasa.gov
Range and Mission Management Office Chief
Steven E. Kremer .... (757) 824-1114
E-mail: steven.kremer@nasa.gov
Resource Management Office Chief
Hope Wescott Garrison .... (757) 824-1206
E-mail: hope.w.garrison@nasa.gov
Safety Office Chief **Glen M. Liebig** .... (757) 824-1498
E-mail: glen.m.liebig@nasa.gov
Sounding Rockets Program Office Chief **(Vacant)** .... (757) 824-2202
Fax: (757) 824-2425

Jet Propulsion Laboratory (JPL)
4800 Oak Grove Drive, Pasadena, CA 91109
Tel: (818) 354-4321 Fax: (818) 393-4746
Internet: https://www.jpl.nasa.gov/

Director
Dr. Michael M. Watkins PhD Mail Stop 180-904 ...... (818) 354-5673
E-mail: michael.m.watkins@jpl.nasa.gov Fax: (818) 393-4218
Education: Texas BS, MSAE, PhD
Special Assistant to the Director **Nora Mainland** ...... (818) 354-2581
E-mail: nora.mainland@jpl.nasa.gov
Deputy Director **LtGen Larry D. James USAF (Ret)** .... (818) 354-3400
E-mail: larry.d.james@jpl.nasa.gov
Education: Air Force Acad 1978 BS; MIT 1983 MS; Air Command Col 1989; Air War Col 1993
Associate Director for Flight Projects and Mission
Success **Richard A. Cook** .... (818) 354-0811
E-mail: richard.a.cook@jpl.nasa.gov
Associate Director for Strategic Integration
David B. "Dave" Gallagher .... (818) 354-1365
E-mail: david.b.gallagher@nasa.gov
Education: Purdue 1982 BS
Chief of Staff **Gail K. Robinson** .... (818) 354-7510
E-mail: gail.k.robinson@jpl.nasa.gov

Office of Business Operations
4800 Oak Grove Drive, Pasadena, CA 91109
Tel: (818) 354-2728 Fax: (818) 354-3122

Chief Financial Officer and Director **Marc J. Goettel** .... (818) 354-5453

Office of Communications and Education
Director **W. Michael Greene** Mail Stop 186-131 .... (818) 354-1277
E-mail: michael.greene@jpl.nasa.gov Fax: (818) 393-0034
Education: Harvard; UCLA MBA
Manager, Institutional Communications **Carl Marziali** .... (818) 354-7170
E-mail: carl.g.marziali@jpl.nasa.gov

Human/Robotic Mission Systems
Manager **Garry M. Burdick** .... (818) 354-3441
E-mail: garry.m.burdick@jpl.nasa.gov

Office of Legislative Affairs
Executive Manager **(Vacant)** .... (818) 354-3409

Office of Safety and Mission Success
Director **Sammy Kayali** .... (818) 354-5624

Astronomy and Physics Directorate
Director **Leslie L. Livesay** .... (818) 354-2705
E-mail: leslie.l.livesay@nasa.gov

Earth Science and Technology Directorate
Director **Diane L. Evans** .... (818) 354-2418
E-mail: diane.l.evans@nasa.gov
Education: Occidental; U Washington PhD

Engineering and Science Directorate
Director **Janis Lea "Jan" Chodas** .... (818) 354-2705
E-mail: janis.l.chodas@jpl.nasa.gov
Education: Toronto

Human Resources Directorate
Director **Cozette M. Hart** Mail Stop 180-200 .... (818) 393-7543
E-mail: cozette.m.hart@nasa.gov Fax: (818) 393-4592

Interplanetary Network Directorate
Director **Suzanne Dodd** .... (818) 354-1128
E-mail: srdodd@jpl.nasa.gov

Mars Exploration Directorate
Director **Fuk K. Li** .... (818) 354-2849
E-mail: fuk.k.li@nasa.gov

Solar System Exploration Directorate
4800 Oak Grove Drive, Pasadena, CA 91109
Tel: (818) 354-5037 Fax: (818) 393-3335

Director **Jakob J. Van Zyl** .... (818) 393-7820
E-mail: jakob.j.vanzyl@nasa.gov

Lyndon B. Johnson Space Center (JSC)
2101 NASA Parkway, Houston, TX 77058-3696
Tel: (281) 483-0123 Tel: (281) 483-5111 (News Media Information)
Fax: (281) 483-2000

● Director **Mark S. Geyer** .... (281) 244-7441
E-mail: mark.s.geyer@nasa.gov
● Deputy Director **Vanessa Ellerbe Wyche** MC-AB ...... (281) 483-7343
E-mail: vanessa.e.wyche@nasa.gov
Education: Clemson BS, MS
Associate Director (Management)
Melanie W. Saunders MC-AC .... (281) 483-0490
E-mail: melanie.saunders-1@nasa.gov
Associate Director (Technical) **(Vacant)** .... (281) 483-5428
Chief of Staff **(Vacant)** MC-AG .... (281) 483-2823
Administrative Officer **(Vacant)** MC-AC .... (281) 483-2646
Chief Knowledge Officer **(Vacant)** .... (281) 483-4990
Chief Technologist **Dr. Douglas A. Terrier PhD** .... (281) 483-0903
E-mail: douglas.a.terrier@nasa.gov
Education: Texas MSME, PhD
Equal Opportunity and Diversity Office Director
Deborah Henshaw Urbanski MC-AJ .... (281) 483-0603
E-mail: deborah.h.urbanski@nasa.gov
Education: Texas 1983; South Texas 1992 JD
Human Resources Office Director (Acting)
Brady A. Pyle MC-AH .... (281) 483-2012
E-mail: brady.a.pyle@nasa.gov
Performance Management and Integration Director
Glenn C. Lutz .... (281) 483-9257
Strategic Opportunities and Partnership Development
Director **Yolanda Y. Marshall** .... (281) 483-2422
E-mail: yolanda.y.marshall@nasa.gov
Technology Infusion Manager **Kathryn B. Packard** ...... (281) 244-5378
E-mail: Kathryn.B.Packard@nasa.gov
Librarian **(Vacant)** MC-GP .... (281) 792-5319

Office of the Chief Counsel
Mail Code AL, Houston, TX 77058
Tel: (281) 483-3021 Fax: (281) 483-6936

● Chief Counsel (Acting) **Donna M. Shafer** .... (281) 483-4258
E-mail: donna.m.shafer@nasa.gov
Deputy Chief Counsel **Donna M. Shafer** .... (281) 483-4258
E-mail: donna.m.shafer@nasa.gov

Office of the Chief Financial Officer
Chief Financial Officer **Stephen A. Koerner** MC-LA .... (281) 483-0671

(continued on next page)

★ Presidential Appointment Requiring Senate Confirmation ☆ Presidential Appointment ☐ Schedule C Appointment ◇ Career Senior Foreign Service Appointment
● Career Senior Executive Service (SES) Appointment ○ Non-Career Senior Executive Service (SES) Appointment ■ Postal Career Executive Service

Office of the Chief Financial Officer *(continued)*

Deputy Chief Financial Officer, Resources
Sidney H. Schmidt MC-LB . . . . . (281) 483-1237
E-mail: sidney.h.schmidt@nasa.gov
Deputy Chief Financial Officer, Financial
(Vacant) MC-LF . . . . . (281) 483-4822

Commercial Space Capabilities Office (CSCO)
2101 NASA Parkway, Houston, TX 77058-3696
Manager **(Vacant)** . . . . . (281) 244-7064

EVA (Extravehicular Activities) Management Office
2101 NASA Parkway, Houston, TX 77058-3696
Tel: (281) 244-1030 Fax: (281) 244-5513
Manager **(Vacant)** MC-XA . . . . . (281) 244-0202

Office of External Relations
Director **Michael A. "Mike" Kincaid** MC-SA . . . . . (281) 483-5005
E-mail: michael.a.kincaid@nasa.gov
Education: Texas A&M BBA; Houston (Clear Lake) MBA
Education Director **Susan M. White** MC-AE . . . . . (281) 483-7011
Public Affairs Director
James A. "Jim" Rostohar AD911 . . . . . (281) 483-7486
E-mail: james.a.rostohar@nasa.gov
Office of University Research
Kamlesh P. Lulla MC-AD2 . . . . . (281) 483-5066
E-mail: kamlesh.p.lulla@nasa.gov

International Space Station (ISS) Program Office
2101 NASA Parkway, Houston, TX 77058-3696
Fax: (281) 483-2968
• Program Manager **Kirk A. Shireman** MC-OA . . . . . (281) 244-7402
E-mail: kirk.a.shireman@nasa.gov
Education: Texas A&M BAE
Deputy Manager **Daniel W. "Dan" Hartman** MC-OA . . . . (281) 244-7048
E-mail: daniel.w.hartman@nasa.gov
Chief of Staff **(Vacant)** MC-OL . . . . . (281) 244-8972
• Avionics and Software Office Manager
(Vacant) MC-OD . . . . . (281) 244-7661
Human Space Flight Programs (Russia) Director
Michael R. "Mike" Surber MC-OA . . . . . (281) 483-4626
E-mail: michael.r.surber@nasa.gov
Education: Oklahoma State 1990
NASA/ISS Representative to Houston Technology
Center **(Vacant)** MC-OI . . . . . (281) 244-7744
Mission Integration and Operations Office Manager
Kenneth O. Todd MC-OC . . . . . (281) 792-5581
Payloads Office Manager **(Vacant)** MC-OZ . . . . . (281) 244-7048
Program Integration Office Manager
Caris A. Hatfield MC-OM . . . . . (281) 244-7766
Program Planning and Control Office Manager
(Vacant) MC-OG . . . . . (281) 244-7141
Safety and Mission Assurance/Program Risk Office
Manager **Ven C. Feng** MC-OE . . . . . (281) 244-7353
E-mail: ven.c.feng@nasa.gov
Vehicle Office Manager **Dana J. Weigel** MC-OB . . . . . (281) 483-4372
Education: Texas A&M 1993 BSME

Multi-Purpose Crew Vehicle Program (Orion Program)
Manager **Mark A. Kirasich** . . . . . (281) 244-0246
E-mail: mark.a.kirasich@nasa.gov

Orbital Debris Program Office
2101 NASA Parkway, Houston, TX 77058-3696
Fax: (281) 483-5276 Internet: http://orbitaldebris.jsc.nasa.gov
Program Manager **Eugene G. Stansbery** . . . . . (281) 483-8417
E-mail: eugene.g.stansbery@nasa.gov
Chief Scientist **Jer-Chyi "J.-C." Liou** . . . . . (281) 483-5313
E-mail: jer-chyi.liou-1@nasa.gov

Procurement Office
2101 NASA Parkway, Houston, TX 77058-3696
Tel: (281) 483-0034 Internet: procurement.jsc.nasa.gov
Director **Debra L. Johnson** MC-BA . . . . . (281) 244-5245
E-mail: debra.l.johnson@nasa.gov
Deputy Director **Jose C. Garcia** MC-BA . . . . . (281) 483-4117
E-mail: jose.c.garcia@nasa.gov
Associate Director **Delene R. Sedillo** MC-BA . . . . . (281) 244-5767
E-mail: delene.r.sedillo@nasa.gov
Exploration Systems Procurement Office Manager
Eric J. Schell . . . . . (281) 244-6966
E-mail: eric.j.schell@nasa.gov
Institutional Procurement Office Manager
Lisa Rea Phillips . . . . . (281) 483-8395
E-mail: lisa.r.phillips@nasa.gov
Operations Support Office Manager
Michelle B. Isermann . . . . . (281) 483-8510
E-mail: michelle.b.isermann@nasa.gov
Projects Procurement Office Manager
Stephen H. Janney . . . . . (281) 483-3500
E-mail: stephen.h.janney@nasa.gov
Source Selection and Analysis Office Deputy Manager
Charles C. Bell . . . . . (281) 483-8479
2101 NASA Parkway, MC-BB, Houston, TX 77058-3696
E-mail: charles.c.bell@nasa.gov
Space Station Procurement Office Manager
Bradley John Niese . . . . . (281) 483-8510
E-mail: bradley.j.niese@nasa.gov

Safety and Mission Assurance Directorate
Director **Patricia Petete** MC-NA . . . . . (281) 483-8695
E-mail: patricia.petete-1@nasa.gov
Education: Oklahoma 1986 BSME
Deputy Director **Rex Walheim** MC-NA . . . . . (281) 483-4348
Associate Director **Robert C. "Bob" Doremus** . . . . . (281) 483-0680
E-mail: robert.c.doremus@nasa.gov
Associate Director for Technical
Nigel J. Packham MC-NA . . . . . (281) 483-5138
Advanced Programs and Analysis Division Chief
Jeffrey A. Williams MC-NX . . . . . (281) 483-8424
Flight Equipment and Quality Division Chief
(Vacant) MC-NT . . . . . (281) 483-3729
International Space Station Division Chief
Michael Fodroci MC-NE . . . . . (281) 483-4206
Safety and Test Operations Division Chief
David T. Loyd MC-NS . . . . . (281) 483-1935
E-mail: david.t.loyd@nasa.gov

Technology Transfer and Commercialization Office
2101 NASA Parkway, Houston, TX 77058-3696
Tel: (281) 483-3809
Manager **(Vacant)** MC-HA . . . . . (281) 244-9097
Deputy Manager **Anh Hong Huynh** . . . . . (281) 483-0888

White Sands Test Facility
12600 NASA Road, Las Cruces, NM 88012
Mail: P.O. Box 20, Las Cruces, NM 88004-0020
Tel: (575) 524-5521
Manager **Robert M. Cort** . . . . . (575) 524-5521
E-mail: robert.m.cort@nasa.gov
Deputy Manager **(Vacant)** . . . . . (575) 524-5521
Administration Office Chief
Patricia A. "Patsy" Segura . . . . . (575) 524-5131
E-mail: patricia.a.segura@nasa.gov
Environmental Office Chief **Timothy J. Davis** . . . . . (575) 524-5024
E-mail: timothy.j.davis@nasa.gov
Facility Engineering Office Chief **John J. Villegas** . . . . . (575) 524-5189
E-mail: john.j.villegas@nasa.gov
Materials and Components Laboratories Office Chief
Harold D. Beeson . . . . . (575) 524-5723
Propulsion Test Office Chief **Mary A. Burke** . . . . . (575) 524-5449
E-mail: mary.a.burke@nasa.gov
Safety and Mission Assurance Office Chief
Alton B. Luper . . . . . (575) 524-5284
E-mail: alton.b.luper@nasa.gov

★ Presidential Appointment Requiring Senate Confirmation ☆ Presidential Appointment ☐ Schedule C Appointment ◇ Career Senior Foreign Service Appointment
● Career Senior Executive Service (SES) Appointment ○ Non-Career Senior Executive Service (SES) Appointment ■ Postal Career Executive Service

White Sands Test Facility *(continued)*

Technical Services Office Chief **Miguel J. Maes** .... (575) 524-5677
Public Affairs Officer and Associate Manager
Radel L. Bunker-Farrah .... (575) 524-5733
E-mail: radel.l.bunker-farrah@nasa.gov
Information Technology Manager [Section 508 Coordinator] **James M. "Jim" Krupovage** .... (575) 524-5732
E-mail: jim.krupovage@nasa.gov
Education: New Mexico State 1992 BSME

Astromaterials Research and Exploration Science Directorate (ARES)

2101 NASA Parkway, Houston, TX 77058-3696
Internet: ares.jsc.nasa.gov

Director **Dr. Eileen K. Stansbery** .... (281) 483-5540
E-mail: eileen.k.stansbery@nasa.gov
Deputy Director **Dr. Gregory J. Byrne** .... (281) 483-0500
E-mail: gregory.j.byrne@nasa.gov
Education: Syracuse 1979 BS; Rice 1985 PhD

Center Operations Directorate

Director **Joel B. Walker** MC-JA .... (281) 483-0541
E-mail: joel.b.walker@nasa.gov
Deputy Director (Acting)
Stephen P. Campbell MC-JA .... (281) 483-3200
Facilities Engineering Division Chief **(Vacant)** MC-JC.... (281) 483-3142
Logistics Division Chief **Vincent L. Johnson** MC-JB .... (281) 483-6517
Planning and Integration Office Chief
(Vacant) MC-JA161 .... (281) 483-3157
Project Management Office Chief
Stephen P. Campbell MC-JA151 .... (281) 483-3200
Security Office Chief **Alan T. Mather** JA141 .... (281) 483-2619
E-mail: alan.t.mather@nasa.gov

Engineering Directorate

2101 NASA Parkway, Houston, TX 77058-3696
Tel: (281) 483-1206

● Director **(Vacant)** MC-EA .... (281) 483-2823
Deputy Director **(Vacant)** MC-EA .... (281) 483-3307
Commercial Spaceflight Associate Director **(Vacant)** ..... (281) 483-8695
Aeroscience and Flight Mechanics Division Chief
Steven G. Labbe MC-EG .... (281) 483-4656
E-mail: steven.g.labbe@nasa.gov
Automation, Robotics and Simulation Division Chief
(Vacant) MC-ER .... (281) 244-5561
Avionic Systems Division Chief
Christopher J. Culbert MC-EV111 .... (281) 483-8080
E-mail: christopher.j.culbert@nasa.gov
Biomedical Systems Division Chief **(Vacant)** MC-EB .... (281) 244-7081
Crew and Thermal Systems Division Chief
(Vacant) MC-EC .... (281) 483-8695
Energy Systems Division Chief **(Vacant)** MC-EP .... (281) 483-8695
Structural Engineering Division Chief
Edgar O. Castro MC-ES1 .... (281) 483-7112
E-mail: edgar.o.castro@nasa.gov

Human Health and Performance Directorate

Director and Chief Medical Officer
Catherine A. Koerner MC-SA .... (281) 483-2617
Secretary **Vanessa T. Thomas** .... (281) 483-3278
E-mail: vanessa.t.jordan@nasa.gov
Deputy Director **(Vacant)** MC-SA12 .... (281) 483-2617
Associate Director for Risk Management
Michael L. Richardson MC SM .... (281) 483-7483
E-mail: michael.l.richardson@nasa.gov
Deputy Chief Medical Officer **(Vacant)** .... (281) 483-2432
Administrative Officer **Lisa A. Navy** MC ST .... (281) 483-2466
E-mail: lisa.a.navy@nasa.gov

Flight Operations Directorate

2101 NASA Parkway, Houston, TX 77058-3696
Tel: (281) 483-4131

Director **Brian K. Kelly** MC-CA .... (281) 483-4995

Flight Operations Directorate *(continued)*

Deputy Director **Norman D. "Norm" Knight** MC-DA ... (281) 483-0671
Education: Embry-Riddle 1990 BS
Chief of Staff **Bernadette M. Hajek** MC-CA .... (281) 244-8993
E-mail: bernadette.m.hajek@nasa.gov
Aircraft Operation Division Chief **(Vacant)** MC-CC ...... (281) 792-8641
Aviation Safety Office Chief
Raymond Gerald Heineman MC-CA2 .... (281) 244-9695
E-mail: raymond.g.heineman@nasa.gov
Education: Georgia Tech 1984 BSIM, 2001 BS; Alabama Huntsville 2012 MS
Mission Integration and Schedule Management Office Chief **(Vacant)** MC-DA6 .... (281) 244-7841
Vehicle Integration Test Office Chief
(Vacant) MC-CA4 .... (281) 244-8905

Astronaut Office

Astronaut Office Chief
COL Patrick G. Forrester USA (Ret) .... (281) 483-4131

Flight Director Office

Flight Director Office Chief (Acting) **Holly E. Ridings** ... (281) 483-4805

Information Resources Directorate

2101 NASA Parkway, Houston, TX 77058-3696
Tel: (281) 483-0236

Director and Chief Information Officer
Annette M. Moore MC-GA .... (281) 483-6232
E-mail: annette.moore-1@nasa.gov
Education: Prairie View A&M

John F. Kennedy Space Center (KSC)

Kennedy Space Center, FL 32899
Tel: (321) 867-5000 Fax: (321) 867-7787

● Center Director **Robert D. Cabana** .... (321) 867-5553
E-mail: robert.d.cabana@nasa.gov
Education: Naval Acad 1971 BS
● Deputy Director **Janet E. Petro** .... (321) 867-4443
E-mail: janet.e.petro@nasa.gov
Education: West Point BS; Boston U MS
Associate Director **Kelvin M. Manning** .... (321) 867-2204
Education: Air Force Acad BS; Central Florida MS — Fax: (321) 867-8807
● Associate Director, Management **(Vacant)** .... (321) 867-5000
Senior Advisor for Institutional Management to the Associate Director **Burton R. Summerfield** .... (321) 867-4598
Education: Old Dominion 1982; Florida Tech 1996 MBA
Director, Communication and Public Engagement
Cheryl C. Hurst .... (321) 867-2415
E-mail: cheryl.c.hurst@nasa.gov
Chief, Communications **David A. Culp** .... (321) 867-1063
E-mail: david.a.culp@nasa.gov
Education: Iowa State 1989; Webster 2006 MBA

Office of the Chief Counsel

Mail Code CC, Kennedy Space Center, FL 32899
Tel: (321) 867-2550 Fax: (321) 867-1817
Internet: https://chiefcounsel.ksc.nasa.gov/

● Chief Counsel **Daniel Paul Shaver** .... (321) 867-2919
E-mail: daniel.p.shaver@nasa.gov
Education: West Point 1980 BS; Washington and Lee 1986 JD; Virginia 1993 ML
Deputy Chief Counsel **Geoffrey S. Swanson** .... (321) 867-8317
E-mail: geoffrey.s.swanson@nasa.gov
Education: Florida State 1979 BA; George Washington 1989 JD
Patent Counsel **Michelle L. "Shelley" Ford** .... (321) 867-2076
E-mail: shelley.ford-1@nasa.gov
Education: Bemidji State 1994 BS; Florida Tech 1996 MS; Barry 2009 JD
Assistant Chief Counsel **Timothy M. Bass** .... (321) 867-2645
Assistant Chief Counsel **Harry Joseph Batey** .... (321) 867-7591
Assistant Chief Counsel **Tracy Lee Belford** .... (321) 867-2603
Education: Southern Oregon State 1989 BS; Oklahoma City 1992 JD

(continued on next page)

INDEPENDENT AGENCIES

★ Presidential Appointment Requiring Senate Confirmation ☆ Presidential Appointment ☐ Schedule C Appointment ◇ Career Senior Foreign Service Appointment
● Career Senior Executive Service (SES) Appointment ○ Non-Career Senior Executive Service (SES) Appointment ■ Postal Career Executive Service

Office of the Chief Counsel *(continued)*

Assistant Chief Counsel **Thomas M. Browder** .... (321) 867-2659
Education: Hampden-Sydney 1990 BA; William & Mary 1993 JD
Assistant Chief Counsel **Miata Loretta Coleman** .... (321) 867-7214
Education: Columbia 2005 BA; Pennsylvania 2011 JD
Assistant Chief Counsel **Adhana Melissa Davis** .... (321) 867-6547
Education: Pomona 2008 BA; UCLA 2012 JD
Assistant Chief Counsel **Ellen E. Espenschied** .... (321) 867-3037
Education: Florida 2008 BS, 2011 JD
Assistant Chief Counsel **Steven G. Horn** .... (321) 867-2667
Education: Florida 1984 BS, 1987 JD
Assistant Chief Counsel
Louis Thomas "Lou" Shernisky .... (321) 867-9175
Education: Gannon 2008 BA; Virginia 2013 JD
Assistant Chief Counsel **Bradley W. Smith** .... (321) 867-2621
Education: Georgia 2003; Mississippi 2009 JD
Assistant Chief Counsel
Charles Alexander "Alex" Vinson .... (321) 867-3043
Education: Princeton 1999 AB; Florida 2004 MA; Lewis & Clark 2007 JD

Center Planning and Development Office

Kennedy Space Center, FL 32899
Internet: kscpartnerships.ksc.nasa.gov

Director **Thomas O. "Tom" Engler** .... (321) 867-2640
E-mail: tom.engler@nasa.gov
Education: Alabama Huntsville BSEE; Florida Tech MS

Chief Financial Officer

Mail Code GG, Kennedy Space Center, FL 32899
Fax: (321) 867-4969

● Chief Financial Officer **Susan P. Kroskey** .... (321) 867-3726
E-mail: susan.p.kroskey@nasa.gov Fax: (321) 867-4969
Deputy Chief Financial Officer
Sandra A. "Sandy" Massey .... (321) 867-6262
Fax: (321) 867-4969
Administrative Officer **Margarita Cunningham** .... (321) 867-5477
E-mail: margarita.cunningham-1@nasa.gov

Commercial Crew Program (CCP)

Kennedy Space Center, FL 32899

Associate Director **Tyrell J. Hawkins** .... (321) 861-3957
E-mail: tyrell.j.hawkins@nasa.gov
Education: Southern U A&M BSEE; Central Florida MS
Chief Engineer **Steven J. Sullivan** .... (321) 861-3681
Education: Auburn BS; Florida Tech MS
Integrated Performance Manager
Christopher A. Gerace .... (321) 867-8053
Education: Carnegie Mellon BS; Denver MBA; Central Florida MEM
Launch Vehicle Manager **Patrick E. "Pat" Hanan** .... (321) 867-7612
Partner Manager **Gennaro Caliendo** .... (321) 867-6489
Partner Manager **Cheryl A. McPhillips** .... (321) 867-6403
Education: South Florida 1984 BS; Florida Tech 1989 MS
Program Manager **Kathryn L. "Kathy" Lueders** .... (321) 867-0764
E-mail: kathryn.l.lueders@nasa.gov
Education: New Mexico BBA; New Mexico State BSIE, MSIE
Deputy Partner Manager **Jon N. Cowart** .... (321) 867-4815
Deputy Partner Manager **Cheryl A. Malloy** .... (321) 867-3778
Deputy Partner Manager **John M. McKinnie** .... (281) 483-0792
Johnson Space Center, Houston, TX 77058
Education: Texas A&M 1991 BSEE
Associate Program Manager **Lisa M. Colloredo** .... (321) 867-0826
Education: Dayton BSME; Florida Tech MBA
Associate Program Manager **Wayne L. Ordway** .... (281) 483-6626
Johnson Space Center, Houston, TX 77058
Education: Rensselaer Poly BS; Rice MBA
Systems Engineering and Integration Deputy Manager
Dana M. Hutcherson .... (321) 861-9105
E-mail: dana.m.hutcherson@nasa.gov

Communications Office

Kennedy Space Center, FL 32899
Tel: (321) 867-2525

Chief **David A. Culp** .... (321) 867-1063
E-mail: david.a.culp@nasa.gov
Education: Iowa State 1989; Webster 2006 MBA
News Chief **Tracy G. Young** .... (321) 867-9284
E-mail: tracy.g.young@nasa.gov
Media Accreditation **Jennifer P. Horner** .... (321) 867-6598
E-mail: jennifer.p.horner@nasa.gov

Diversity and Equal Opportunity Office

Mail Code AJ, Kennedy Space Center, FL 32899
Fax: (321) 867-1066

Manager **Milton R. "Rob" Grant** .... (321) 867-9169
E-mail: milton.r.grant@nasa.gov

Ground Systems Development and Operations Program

Mail Code LX, Kennedy Space Center, FL 32899

Program Manager **Michael J. Bolger** .... (321) 867-6400
Education: Indiana 1987 BS; Central Florida 1999 MBA
Deputy Program Manager **Jennifer C. Kunz** .... (321) 867-6411
Education: Auburn 1990 BS; Central Florida 1994 MS
Associate Program Manager **Shawn M. Quinn** .... (321) 867-4721
E-mail: shawn.m.quinn@nasa.gov
Education: Georgia Tech 1990; Central Florida 1994
Launch Director
Judith C. "Charlie" Blackwell-Thompson .... (321) 861-9347
E-mail: j.c.blackwellthompson@nasa.gov
Manager of Production Operations for the Orion Program and Offline Processing and Infrastructure Development **Scott B. Wilson** .... (321) 867-4365
Senior Technical Integration Manager
Philip J. "Phil" Weber .... (321) 867-2057
E-mail: philip.j.weber@nasa.gov
21st Century Integrated Product Team Manager
Kimberlyn B. "Kim" Carter .... (321) 867-9252
E-mail: kirk.d.lougheed@nasa.gov

Human Resources Office

Mail Code BA, Kennedy Space Center, FL 32899
Fax: (321) 867-2454

Director **Digna M. Carballosa** .... (321) 867-4747
E-mail: digna.carballosa@nasa.gov
Education: Florida International 1992 BA

Human Resources Development and Recognition Office

Chief **David M. Wilson** .... (321) 867-1859
E-mail: david.m.wilson@nasa.gov

Human Resources Operations Office

Chief **(Vacant)** .... (321) 867-3364

Workforce Planning and Information Systems Office

Kennedy Space Center, FL 32899
Fax: (321) 867-4279

Chief **Christina M. Brown** .... (321) 867-8463
E-mail: christina.m.brown@nasa.gov

Information Technology and Communications Services

Kennedy Space Center, FL 32899
Fax: (321) 867-9847

Director and Chief Information Officer
Vanessa K. Stromer .... (321) 867-7210
E-mail: vanessa.stromer-1@nasa.gov
Deputy Director and Deputy Chief Information Officer
(Vacant) .... (321) 867-7210

Launch Services Program

Mail Code VA, Kennedy Space Center, FL 32899
Fax: (321) 867-3256

Program Manager **Amanda M. Mitskevich** .... (321) 867-4789
E-mail: amanda.m.mitskevich@nasa.gov

★ Presidential Appointment Requiring Senate Confirmation ☆ Presidential Appointment □ Schedule C Appointment ◇ Career Senior Foreign Service Appointment
● Career Senior Executive Service (SES) Appointment ○ Non-Career Senior Executive Service (SES) Appointment ■ Postal Career Executive Service

Launch Services Program *(continued)*

Deputy Program Manager **(Vacant)** .... (321) 867-4173
Chief Engineer **James S. Wood** .... (321) 867-5402
Technical Integration Manager **Darren M. Bedell** .... (321) 867-3110
E-mail: darren.m.bedell@nasa.gov

Procurement Office

Mail Code OP, Kennedy Space Center, FL 32899
Fax: (321) 867-8599 Internet: http://procurement.ksc.nasa.gov/

Director **Michael S. "Mike" McCarty** .... (321) 867-9340
E-mail: michael.s.mccarty@nasa.gov
Deputy Director **Laura B. Rochester** .... (321) 861-3979
E-mail: laura.rochester-1@nasa.gov
Administrative Officer **Elizabeth Renee Minor** .... (321) 867-4046
E-mail: renee.minor-1@nasa.gov

Spaceport Integration and Services (SI)

Mail Code TA, Kennedy Space Center, FL 32899
Fax: (321) 867-9191

Director **Nancy P. Bray** .... (321) 867-7933
Education: Florida BS; Florida Tech 1992 MBA
Deputy Director **Maria Ann Collura** .... (321) 867-3257
Education: Central Florida BS

Operations Support Division

Mail Code TA, Kennedy Space Center, FL 32899
Fax: (321) 867-1458

Chief **Joseph P. Gordon, Jr.** .... (321) 867-2202
Logistics and Services Branch Chief **(Vacant)** .... (321) 867-9701
Propellants and Life Support Branch Chief
Kenneth G. Madyda .... (321) 867-2824
Fax: (321) 867-7369

Protective Services Office

Mail Code TA, Kennedy Space Center, FL 32899
Fax: (321) 867-7206

Chief **Michael D. Stephens** .... (321) 867-6075
E-mail: michael.d.stephens@nasa.gov

Engineering and Technology Directorate

Mail Code NE, Kennedy Space Center, FL 32899
Fax: (321) 867-4812

Director **Patrick A. Simpkins** .... (321) 867-7770
E-mail: patricksimpkins@bellsouth.net
Education: Florida 1983 BS; Florida Tech 1997 MS; Nova Southeastern 2005 DBA
● Deputy Director **Scott T. Colloredo** .... (321) 867-7770
Education: Tennessee 1989; Central Florida 1994 MS
● Deputy Director, Management **(Vacant)** .... (321) 867-1930
Associate Director **Pedro R. "Ronnie" Rodriguez** ...... (321) 867-6059
Chief Administrative Officer **Bonni P. McClure** .... (321) 867-2569
E-mail: bonni.p.mcclure@nasa.gov
Technical Assistant **(Vacant)** .... (321) 867-4794

Avionics Division

Chief **Arnold T. Postell** .... (321) 861-3771
E-mail: arnold.t.postell@nasa.gov
Deputy Chief **Andrew C. Bundy** .... (321) 861-3773
E-mail: andrew.c.bundy@nasa.gov

Control and Data Systems Division

Chief **Gregory R. Clements** .... (321) 867-8992
E-mail: gregory.r.clements@nasa.gov
Deputy Chief **(Vacant)** .... (321) 867-3769

Design and Development Engineering Division

Chief **(Vacant)** .... (321) 867-1460
Deputy Chief **(Vacant)** .... (321) 867-6742

Electrical Division

Mail Code NE, Kennedy Space Center, FL 32899
Fax: (321) 861-0042

Chief **(Vacant)** .... (321) 861-3692

Electrical Division *(continued)*

Deputy Chief **Steven K. Czaban** .... (321) 861-3694
E-mail: steven.k.czaban@nasa.gov

Fluids and Liquid Propulsion Division

Mail Code NE, Kennedy Space Center, FL 32899
Fax: (321) 861-3036

Chief **Henry Bursian** .... (321) 867-3870
E-mail: henry.bursian-1@nasa.gov
Deputy Chief **Robert A. Mott** .... (321) 867-0836
E-mail: robert.a.mott@nasa.gov

Management Integration Services Office

Chief **(Vacant)** .... (321) 867-4413

Material Sciences Division

Chief **Donald S. Parker** .... (321) 861-8957
Deputy Chief **Richard W. Russell** .... (321) 861-8618

Mechanical Division

Chief **Emilio A. Cruz** .... (321) 867-1204
Deputy Chief **(Vacant)** .... (321) 867-3258

Operational Systems Engineering Office

Chief **Shaun L. Green** .... (321) 861-4244
E-mail: shaun.l.green@nasa.gov

ISS (International Space Station) and Spacecraft Processing Directorate

Mail Code UB, Kennedy Space Center, FL 32899
Fax: (321) 867-6080

Director **Josephine B. Burnett** .... (321) 867-6478
E-mail: josephine.b.burnett@nasa.gov
Mission Manager **(Vacant)** .... (321) 867-6183

Administrative Office

Mail Code UB, Kennedy Space Center, FL 32899
Fax: (321) 867-6425

Chief **Tamara L. Belk** .... (321) 867-6414
E-mail: tamara.l.belk@nasa.gov

Business Office

Mail Code UB, Kennedy Space Center, FL 32899
Fax: (321) 867-0544

Chief **Robert A. Yaskovic** .... (321) 867-5295
E-mail: robert.a.yaskovic@nasa.gov

Ground Processing and Research Project Office

Senior Project Manager **(Vacant)** .... (321) 867-2399

International Space Station Research Office

Chief Scientist **Howard G. Levine** .... (321) 861-3502
E-mail: howard.g.levine@nasa.gov
Education: UMass (Amherst) BS, MS, 1982 PhD

Launch Vehicle Processing Directorate

Mail Code PH, Kennedy Space Center, FL 32899
Fax: (321) 867-3658

Director **(Vacant)** .... (321) 867-4343
Senior Launch Director **Omar Baez, Jr.** .... (321) 867-1309

Safety and Mission Assurance

Mail Code SA, Kennedy Space Center, FL 32899
Fax: (321) 867-2960

Director **(Vacant)** .... (321) 867-6448
Deputy Director **(Vacant)** .... (321) 867-2118

Business and Administrative Office

Chief **Linda D. Euell** .... (321) 867-4027
E-mail: linda.d.euell@nasa.gov Fax: (321) 867-9504
Administrative Officer **Suzanne H. Dininny** .... (321) 867-7721
E-mail: suzanne.h.dininny@nasa.gov

(continued on next page)

INDEPENDENT AGENCIES

★ Presidential Appointment Requiring Senate Confirmation ☆ Presidential Appointment ☐ Schedule C Appointment ◇ Career Senior Foreign Service Appointment
● Career Senior Executive Service (SES) Appointment ○ Non-Career Senior Executive Service (SES) Appointment ■ Postal Career Executive Service

Business and Administrative Office *(continued)*

Senior Resources Manager **Mary J. Mulligan** . . . . (321) 867-1104
E-mail: mary.j.mulligan@nasa.gov

International Space Station and Spacecraft Processing Division
Chief **(Vacant)** . . . . (321) 867-6593

Langley Research Center (LaRC)

Building 2101, Five Langley Boulevard, Hampton, VA 23681-2199
Tel: (757) 864-1000 (Operator) Fax: (757) 864-6117
Internet: https://www.nasa.gov/langley

- ● Center Director **David E. Bowles** Room 300A . . . . (757) 864-4111
  E-mail: david.e.bowles@nasa.gov
  Education: Virginia Tech 1978 BS, 1980 MS, 1990 PhD
- ● Deputy Center Director **Clayton P. Turner** Room 300C . . . (757) 864-4222
  E-mail: clayton.p.turner@nasa.gov

Associate Director **Cathy H. Mangum** . . . . (757) 864-4333
E-mail: cathy.h.mangum@nasa.gov

Mission Support

Equal Opportunity
Director **Steven W. "Steve" Gayle** . . . . (757) 864-4240
E-mail: steven.w.gayle@nasa.gov

Human Capital Management
Director **David A LeDoux** . . . . (757) 864-2954
E-mail: david.ledoux@nasa.gov

Chief Counsel
Building 2101, Five Langley Boulevard, Hampton, VA 23681-2199
Tel: (757) 864-3221 Fax: (757) 864-8298

- ● Chief Counsel (Acting) **Charles A. "Pete" Polen** . . . . (757) 864-3225
  E-mail: charles.a.polen@nasa.gov

Deputy Chief Counsel **Charles A. "Pete" Polen** . . . . (757) 864-3225
E-mail: charles.a.polen@nasa.gov
Associate Chief Counsel and BLT Lead
Michael I. Mark . . . . (757) 864-3209
E-mail: michael.i.mark@nasa.gov
Associate Chief Counsel and HRELT Lead
Kenneth H. "Ken" Goetzke, Jr. . . . . (757) 864-7390
E-mail: kenneth.goetzke@nasa.gov
Patent Counsel **Robin W. Edwards** . . . . (757) 864-3230
E-mail: robin.w.edwards@nasa.gov

Chief Financial Officer
Chief Financial Officer **Kathryn Ferrare** . . . . (757) 864-8084

Chief Information Officer
Chief Information Officer **(Vacant)** . . . . (757) 864-6627

Procurement
Langley Research Center, Hampton, VA 23681-2199
Director **Susan McClain** . . . . (757) 864-2421

Public Affairs
Building 2101, Five Langley Boulevard, Hampton, VA 23681-2199
Tel: (757) 864-6300
Director **Robert David Morris "Rob" Wyman** . . . . (757) 864-6120
E-mail: rob.wyman@nasa.gov
Education: Thomas Edison State 2002 BA; Averett Col 2012 MBA

Agency Function

NASA Engineering and Safety Center Director
Timmy R. Wilson . . . . (757) 864-2400
E-mail: timmy.r.wilson@nasa.gov
Education: Air Force Acad 1981 BS; Central Florida MS
Principal Engineer **David McGowan** . . . . (757) 864-2422

Mission

Aeronautics Research Director **George B. Finelli** . . . . (757) 864-6515
E-mail: george.b.finelli@nasa.gov
Center Operations Directorate **Loretta Kelemen** . . . . (757) 864-9580
Engineering Directorate **Dawn M. Schaible** . . . . (757) 864-7103

Mission *(continued)*

Flight Research Services Directorate **Shane G. Dover** . . . . (757) 864-7700
Research and Technology Directorate **Jill M. Marlowe** . . . (757) 864-1718
E-mail: jill.marlowe@nasa.gov
Research and Technology Directorate Deputy
Director **Kevin Rivers** . . . . (757) 864-1718
Building 1268A, Fax: (757) 864-8320
Five North Dryden Street,
Room 1106C, Mail Stop 162, Hampton, VA 23681
Science Director **David F. Young** . . . . (757) 864-1607
E-mail: david.f.young@nasa.gov
DEVELOP National Director **Michael L. Ruiz** . . . . (757) 864-3748
STARSS Contracting Officer's Representative
Shannon L. Walker . . . . (757) 864-2458
E-mail: shannon.l.walker@nasa.gov
Systems Analysis and Concepts Director
Melvin J. Ferebee . . . . (757) 864-4421
Building 1209, 1 North Dryden Street,
Room 131, Hampton, VA 23681
E-mail: melvin.j.ferebee@nasa.gov

Office of Strategic Analysis, Communications and Business Development
Director **Charles E. Cockrell** . . . . (757) 864-5576
E-mail: charles.e.cockrell@nasa.gov
Deputy Director **Harry Belvin** . . . . (757) 864-2809

Safety and Mission Assurance
Director **Grant M. Watson** . . . . (757) 864-3358
E-mail: grant.m.watson@nasa.gov

George C. Marshall Space Flight Center (MSFC)

Marshall Space Flight Center, Building 4200, Huntsville, AL 35812-0001
Tel: (256) 544-2121 (Operator) Tel: (256) 544-1382 (Public Inquiries)
Tel: (256) 544-0034 (Media Inquiries) Fax: (256) 544-7580
Internet: https://www.nasa.gov/centers/marshall/home/index.html

- ● Director **Joan Adams "Jody" Singer** . . . . (256) 544-1911
  Marshall Space Flight Center, DA01, Huntsville, AL 35812
  E-mail: jody.singer@nasa.gov
- ● Deputy Director **Paul K. McConnaughey** . . . . (256) 544-1599
  Marshall Space Flight Center, DD01, Huntsville, AL 35812
  E-mail: paul.k.mcconnaughey@nasa.gov
  Education: Oregon State 1973; Cornell 1980, 1983 PhD
- ● Associate Director **Steven C. "Steve" Miley** . . . . (256) 544-1919
  Education: Campbellsville U 1983; Southern Baptist 1986; Wright State 1992 MBA
- ● Associate Director, Technical **(Vacant)** DA01 . . . . (256) 544-1599

Office of the Chief Counsel
Huntsville, AL 35812-0001
Tel: (256) 544-0026 Fax: (256) 544-0258

- ● Chief Counsel **Audrey D. Robinson** . . . . (256) 544-0026
  Marshall Space Flight Center, LS01, Huntsville, AL 35812
  E-mail: audrey.d.robinson@nasa.gov
  Education: Florida Tech 1989; Emory 1993 JD

Deputy Chief Counsel **James R. "Jim" Frees** . . . . (256) 544-0017
Marshall Space Flight Center, LS01, Huntsville, AL 35812
E-mail: jim.frees@nasa.gov

Office of the Chief Financial Officer
Marshall Space Flight Center, Building 4200, Huntsville, AL 35812-0001
Tel: (256) 544-7345

- ● Chief Financial Officer **William R. "Bill" Hicks** . . . . (256) 544-7345
  Marshall Space Flight Center, Fax: (256) 544-3635
  RS01, Huntsville, AL 35812
  E-mail: bill.hicks@nasa.gov
  Education: Tennessee Tech 1980
- ● Deputy Chief Financial Officer **Rhega C. Gordon** . . . . (256) 544-4633
  E-mail: rhega.c.gordon@nasa.gov

INDEPENDENT AGENCIES

★ Presidential Appointment Requiring Senate Confirmation ☆ Presidential Appointment ☐ Schedule C Appointment ◇ Career Senior Foreign Service Appointment
● Career Senior Executive Service (SES) Appointment ○ Non-Career Senior Executive Service (SES) Appointment ■ Postal Career Executive Service

Office of Chief Information Officer
Marshall Space Flight Center, Building 4200, Huntsville, AL 35812-0001
Tel: (256) 544-9271

○ Director **(Vacant)** .... (256) 544-9271
Marshall Space Flight Center, IS01, Huntsville, AL 35812 Fax: (256) 544-5842

● Deputy Director **John B. McDougle** .... (256) 544-3000
E-mail: john.b.mcdougle@nasa.gov

Office of Center Operations
Marshall Space Flight Center, Building 4200, Huntsville, AL 35812-0001
Tel: (256) 544-1978 Fax: (256) 544-5893

● Director **Roy W. Malone, Jr.** .... (256) 544-0506
Marshall Space Flight Center, AS01, Huntsville, AL 35812
E-mail: roy.w.malone@nasa.gov
Education: Georgia Tech 1980 BSEE

● Deputy Director **Robert J. Devlin** .... (256) 544-5965
Marshall Space Flight Center, AS01, Huntsville, AL 35812
E-mail: robert.j.devlin@nasa.gov

Environmental Engineering and Occupational Health Office
Supervisor **Edward H. Kiessling** .... (256) 544-7421
E-mail: edward.h.kiessling@nasa.gov

Facilities Management Office
Supervisor **Timothy A. "Tim" Corn** .... (256) 544-9451
Marshall Space Flight Center, AD20, Huntsville, AL 35812
E-mail: tim.corn@nasa.gov

Logistics Services Office
Supervisor **Elbert F. "Farley" Davis** .... (256) 544-6935
Marshall Space Flight Center, AD40, Huntsville, AL 35812 Fax: (256) 544-6570

Protective Services Office
Supervisor **Michael D. Wilson** .... (256) 544-5205
E-mail: michael.wilson@msfc.nasa.gov

Resources Management and Integration Office
Supervisor **Melvin L. Scruggs** .... (256) 544-3994
E-mail: melvin.l.scruggs@nasa.gov

Office of Diversity and Equal Opportunity
Huntsville, AL 35812-0001
Tel: (256) 544-5377

● Director **Loucious Hires** .... (256) 544-6764
Marshall Space Flight Center, OS01, Huntsville, AL 35812 Fax: (256) 544-2411
E-mail: loucious.hires@nasa.gov
Education: Troy U ABA, 2003 BA

Assistant Manager **Abbie J. Johnson** .... (256) 544-0014
Marshall Space Flight Center, OS01, Huntsville, AL 35812
E-mail: abbie.j.johnson@nasa.gov

Affirmative Employment and Federal Women's Program Manager **Abbie J. Johnson** .... (256) 544-0014
Marshall Space Flight Center, OS01, Huntsville, AL 35812
E-mail: abbie.j.johnson@nasa.gov

Disability and Disabled Veterans Program Manager
Phyllis Y. Olinger .... (256) 544-0022
Marshall Space Flight Center, OS01, Huntsville, AL 35812
E-mail: phyllis.y.olinger@nasa.gov

Hispanic Program Resources Manager
Elia Saenz Rivas .... (256) 544-6658
Marshall Space Flight Center, OS01, Huntsville, AL 35812
E-mail: elia.s.ordonez@nasa.gov

Office of Human Capital
Marshall Space Flight Center, Building 4200, Huntsville, AL 35812-0001
Tel: (256) 544-7491

● Director **Marcus L. Lea** HS01 .... (256) 544-7491

Deputy Director **Larry K. Mack** .... (256) 544-2723
HS01, Marshall Space Flight Center, Huntsville, AL 35812
E-mail: larry.k.mack@nasa.gov

Office of Procurement
Marshall Space Flight Center, Huntsville, AL 35812
Tel: (256) 544-0866

● Director **Jason T. Detko** PS01 .... (256) 544-8660
E-mail: jason.t.detko@nasa.gov

Deputy Director **David A. Iosco** PS01 .... (256) 544-0387
E-mail: david.a.iosco@nasa.gov

Small Business Specialist **David E. Brock** .... (256) 544-0267
E-mail: david.e.brock@nasa.gov

Office of Strategic Analysis and Communications
Huntsville, AL 35812-0001
Tel: (256) 544-2875

● Director **Johnny F. Stephenson** CS01 .... (256) 544-9352
E-mail: johnny.f.stephenson@nasa.gov
Education: Alabama Huntsville 1986 BE

Deputy Director **Kevin M. McGhaw** CS01 .... (256) 961-1120
E-mail: kevin.mcghaw@nasa.gov

Engineering Directorate (ED01)
Marshall Space Flight Center, Huntsville, AL 35812-0001
Tel: (256) 544-7058

● Director **Carl Preston Jones** .... (256) 544-7058
Marshall Space Flight Center, ED01, Huntsville, AL 35812
E-mail: carl.p.jones@nasa.gov

● Deputy Director **Joe L. "Larry" Leopard** ED01 .... (256) 544-5716
E-mail: larry.leopard@nasa.gov

● Associate Director for Operations
Lisa A. Watson-Morgan .... (256) 544-3523
Marshall Space Flight Center, Huntsville, AL 35812
E-mail: lisa.a.watson-morgan@nasa.gov

● Associate Director for Technical Management
James E. "Jim" Turner .... (256) 544-2679
Marshall Space Flight Center, EE01, Huntsville, AL 35812
E-mail: jim.turner@nasa.gov

Advanced Concepts Office
Supervisor **Mark N. Rogers** .... (256) 544-6969

Materials and Processes Laboratory
Marshall Space Flight Center, Huntsville, AL 35812-0001
Tel: (256) 544-2725 Fax: (256) 544-5877

● Manager **Surendra N. "Suren" Singhal** .... (256) 544-4236
Marshall Space Flight Center, EM01, Huntsville, AL 35812
E-mail: suren.singhal@nasa.gov

Mission Operations Laboratory
Marshall Space Flight Center, Huntsville, AL 35812-0001
Tel: (256) 544-4638

● Supervisor (Acting) **Lewis Wooten** EO01 .... (256) 544-2272
E-mail: lewis.wooten@nasa.gov

Propulsion Systems Department
Marshall Space Flight Center, Huntsville, AL 35812-0001
Tel: (256) 544-7101

● Manager **Mary Beth E. Koelbl** ER01 .... (256) 544-7073
E-mail: mary.beth.koelbl@nasa.gov

● Deputy Manager **Robert H. Champion** .... (256) 544-0478
E-mail: robert.champion@nasa.gov

Resource Management Office
Supervisor **Tony L. Clark** .... (256) 544-2394
E-mail: tony.clark@nasa.gov

Spacecraft and Vehicle Systems Department
Marshall Space Flight Center, Huntsville, AL 35812-0001
Tel: (256) 544-1165 Fax: (256) 544-3103

● Manager **Danielle Coogan** .... (256) 544-1165
Marshall Space Flight Center, EV01, Huntsville, AL 35812

Space Systems Department
Marshall Space Flight Center, Huntsville, AL 35812-0001
Tel: (256) 544-3950

● Manager **(Vacant)** ES01 .... (256) 544-4638

(continued on next page)

INDEPENDENT AGENCIES

★ Presidential Appointment Requiring Senate Confirmation ☆ Presidential Appointment □ Schedule C Appointment ◇ Career Senior Foreign Service Appointment
● Career Senior Executive Service (SES) Appointment ○ Non Career Senior Executive Service (SES) Appointment ■ Postal Career Executive Service

Space Systems Department *(continued)*

• Deputy Manager **Tia Ferguson** .... (256) 544-0478

Test Laboratory
Marshall Space Flight Center, Huntsville, AL 35812-0001
Tel: (256) 544-7647

• Manager **Melvin Ralph Carruth** ET01 .... (256) 544-7647
E-mail: ralph.carruth@nasa.gov
Education: Central Arkansas 1975; Arkansas 1978

Office of the Chief Engineer

Flight Programs and Partnerships Office (FP01)

• Manager **(Vacant)** .... (256) 544-0612
• Deputy Manager (Acting) **Stacy M. Counts** .... (256) 544-6004
E-mail: stacy.m.counts@nasa.gov
Associate Manager **Dennon J. Clardy** .... (256) 544-1214

Discovery and New Frontiers Program Officer (FP20)
Supervisor **Allen S. Bacskay** .... (256) 544-2121

Exploration and Space Transportation Development Office (FP30)
Supervisor **(Vacant)** .... (256) 544-1857

International Space Station Office (FP10)
Manager **Annette M. Sledd** .... (256) 544-2457

Partnerships Office (FP40)
Supervisor **Stacy M. Counts** .... (256) 544-6004

Technology Demonstration Missions Office (FP50)
Manager **Larry S. Gagliano** .... (256) 544-7175

Human Exploration Development and Operations Office

• Manager **Bobby J. Watkins** .... (256) 544-2875
E-mail: bobby.j.watkins@nasa.gov
• Deputy Manager **Joseph J. Pelfrey** .... (256) 961-1857
E-mail: joseph.pelfrey@nasa.gov

Michoud Assembly Facility (SF01)

• Director **Nathaniel Sanders** SF01 .... (256) 544-0756
E-mail: nathan.r.daniher@nasa.gov
• Deputy Director **Michael H. Kynard** SF02 .... (256) 544-8314
E-mail: michael.h.kynard@nasa.gov

Safety and Mission Assurance Directorate (QD01)

Marshall Space Flight Center, Huntsville, AL 35812-0001
Tel: (256) 544-7158

• Director **Richard K. "Rick" Burt** .... (256) 544-9129
Marshall Space Flight Center, Fax: (256) 544-6570
QD01, Huntsville, AL 35812
E-mail: richard.k.burt@nasa.gov
• Deputy Director **Peter W. Allen** .... (256) 544-7909
Marshall Space Flight Center, QD01, Huntsville, AL 35812
E-mail: pete.allen@nasa.gov

Science and Technology Office (ZP01)

Marshall Space Flight Center, Huntsville, AL 35812-0001
Tel: (256) 544-5099

• Manager **Marvin W. Posey** .... (256) 544-6128
Marshall Space Flight Center, VP01, Huntsville, AL 35812
E-mail: marvin.w.posey@nasa.gov
• Deputy Manager
Dr. Raymond G. "Corky" Clinton VP01 .... (256) 544-2682
E-mail: raymond.g.clinton@nasa.gov
Education: Georgia Tech 1973, 1982 PhD

Program Planning and Control Office
Supervisor **Brent A. Harper** .... (256) 961-7003
E-mail: brent.harper@nasa.gov

Science Research Office
Supervisor **James F. "Jim" Spann** .... (256) 961-7512
E-mail: jim.spann@nasa.gov

Science and Space Technology Projects Office
Supervisor (Acting) **Judy L. C. Ballance** .... (256) 961-7488
E-mail: judy.l.ballance@nasa.gov

Technology Development and Transfer Office
Supervisor **Michael R. LaPointe** .... (256) 544-6756

Space Launch System Program Office (XP01)

• Manager **John H. Honeycutt** .... (256) 544-6971
E-mail: john.h.honeycutt@nasa.gov
• Deputy Manager **Jerry R. Cook** .... (256) 544-8257
E-mail: jerry.r.cook@nasa.gov
Education: Alabama 1984 BSME

Program Integration Office (XP02)
Supervisor **Sharon D. Cobb** .... (256) 544-7791

Boosters Office (XP10)
• Supervisor **Alex S. Priskos** .... (256) 544-4453
E-mail: alex.s.priskos@nasa.gov
Education: Utah 1982; Utah State 1984 MBA

Engines Office (XP20)
• Supervisor **Edith Bakos** .... (256) 544-2470
E-mail: edith.bakos@nasa.gov

Stages Office (XP30)
• Supervisor **Stephen C. "Steve" Doering** .... (256) 544-1978
E-mail: stevedoering@comcast.net
Education: Notre Dame 1983 BS

Spacecraft and Payload Integration Office (XP50)
Supervisor **(Vacant)** .... (256) 544-1502

Ground Operations Liaison Office (XP60)
Supervisor **Brian Matisak** .... (256) 544-4311

John C. Stennis Space Center

Stennis Space Center, MS 39529-6000
Tel: (228) 688-2211 Internet: www.nasa.gov/centers/stennis/home

• Director **Dr. Richard J. Gilbrech** .... (228) 688-2123
E-mail: richard.j.gilbrech@nasa.gov
Education: Mississippi State 1984 BAE; Caltech MS, PhD
• Deputy Director **Thomas Randy Galloway** .... (228) 688-2123
E-mail: thomas.r.galloway@nasa.gov
• Associate Director **John W. Bailey** .... (228) 688-1128
E-mail: john.w.bailey@nasa.gov
Legislative Affairs **Anne H. Peek** .... (228) 688-1413

Office of the Chief Counsel

Mail Code CA00, Stennis Space Center, MS 39529-6000
Tel: (228) 688-2165 Fax: (228) 688-3692

• Chief Counsel **Monica M. Allison-Ceruti** .... (228) 688-1588
E-mail: monica.m.ceruti@nasa.gov

Office of the Chief Financial Officer

Mail Code BA00, Stennis Space Center, MS 39529-6000
Tel: (228) 688-3471 Fax: (228) 688-3542

Chief Financial Officer **Rena L. Perwien** .... (228) 688-2348
Deputy Chief Financial Officer **(Vacant)** .... (228) 688-3471
Deputy Chief Financial Officer for Finance
Patricia H. Fairley .... (228) 688-2389
Deputy Chief Financial Officer for Resources
Deborah S. Norton .... (228) 688-1168
E-mail: deborah.s.norton@nasa.gov

Office of Communications

Mail Code IA00, Stennis Space Center, MS 39529-6000
Tel: (228) 688-1792 Fax: (228) 688-1094

Manager **Pamela G. Covington** .... (228) 688-1498
E-mail: pamela.g.covington@nasa.gov
Public Affairs Officer **Earnest P. "Paul" Foerman** ...... (228) 688-1880
E-mail: paul.foerman-1@nasa.gov

★ Presidential Appointment Requiring Senate Confirmation ☆ Presidential Appointment □ Schedule C Appointment ◇ Career Senior Foreign Service Appointment
● Career Senior Executive Service (SES) Appointment ○ Non-Career Senior Executive Service (SES) Appointment ■ Postal Career Executive Service

INDEPENDENT AGENCIES

Office of Education
Mail Code UA00, Stennis Space Center, MS 39529-6000
Manager **Kelly E. Martin-Rivers** .... (228) 688-3802

Office of Human Capital
Mail Code LA00, Stennis Space Center, MS 39529-6000
Tel: (228) 688-2336 Fax: (228) 688-2202
Manager **Dorsie Jones** .... (228) 688-2337
E-mail: dorsie.jones-1@nasa.gov
Staffing Specialist **Ashley H. Speed** .... (228) 688-1271
E-mail: ashley.h.speed@nasa.gov

Office of Procurement
Mail Code DAOO, Stennis Space Center, MS 39529-6000
Tel: (228) 688-1709 Fax: (228) 688-1141
Procurement Officer **Gerald L. Norris** .... (228) 688-1718
E-mail: gerald.l.norris@nasa.gov
Deputy Procurement Officer **Marvin L. Horne** .... (228) 688-3528
E-mail: marvin.l.horne@nasa.gov

Center Operations Directorate
Stennis Space Center, MS 39529-6000
Tel: (228) 688-2004 Fax: (228) 688-6699
Director **Keith D. Brock** .... (228) 688-1311
E-mail: keith.d.brock@nasa.gov
Deputy Director **Mary R. Byrd** .... (228) 688-2635
E-mail: mary.r.byrd@nasa.gov
Chief Information Officer **Dinna L. Cottrell** RA40 .... (228) 688-2759
E-mail: dinna.l.cottrell@nasa.gov
Operations and Maintenance Division Chief
Michael F. Killam .... (228) 688-2032
Design and Construction Project Management Division
Chief **Scott M. Olive** .... (228) 688-1161
Chief Security Officer **Lavaniel S. Ward** .... (228) 688-3592
E-mail: lavaniel.s.ward@nasa.gov
Chief Technology Officer [Section 508 Coordinator]
Christopher A. Carmichael .... (228) 688-1664
E-mail: christopher.a.carmichael@nasa.gov
Education: Mississippi State 2002 BS

Engineering and Test Directorate
Mail Code EA00, Stennis Space Center, MS 39529-6000
Tel: (228) 688-2225 Fax: (228) 688-3699
Director **Joseph R. Schuyler** .... (228) 688-1643
Deputy Director **(Vacant)** .... (228) 688-1643
Associate Director and Chief of Staff **John E. Stealey** ... (228) 688-2236
E-mail: john.e.stealey@nasa.gov
Design and Analysis Division Chief
Thomas O. Meredith .... (228) 688-3907
Systems Engineering and Integration Division Chief
Christine Q. Powell .... (228) 688-3043
E-mail: christine.q.powell@nasa.gov
Operations Division Chief **Maury A. Vander** .... (228) 688-1787
Electrical Branch Chief **Joseph W. Lacher** .... (228) 688-1066
Mechanical Branch Chief **Jeffrey W. Lott** .... (228) 688-2070
E-mail: jeffrey.w.lott@nasa.gov

Rocket Propulsion Test Program Office
Mail Code TA00, Stennis Space Center, MS 39529-6000
Tel: (228) 688-2351 Fax: (228) 688-1580
Director **Roger D. Simpson** .... (228) 688-1874
E-mail: roger.d.simpson@nasa.gov
Deputy Director **Steven A. Taylor** .... (228) 688-3180

Safety and Mission Assurance Directorate
Mail Code QA00, Stennis Space Center, MS 39529-6000
Fax: (228) 688-3701
Manager **Freddie Douglas** .... (228) 688-2236
E-mail: freddie.douglas-1@nasa.gov
Deputy Manager **Marguerite T. "Maggie" Jones** .... (228) 688-1135
E-mail: marguerite.t.jones@nasa.gov

INDEPENDENT AGENCIES

★ Presidential Appointment Requiring Senate Confirmation ☆ Presidential Appointment □ Schedule C Appointment ◇ Career Senior Foreign Service Appointment
● Career Senior Executive Service (SES) Appointment ○ Non-Career Senior Executive Service (SES) Appointment ■ Postal Career Executive Service

United States National Archives and Records Administration (NARA)

Description: The National Archives and Records Administration establishes policies and procedures for managing U.S. government records and maintains historically valuable records dating from the American Revolution. In addition, the agency manages the Presidential Libraries system; administers the National Historical Publications and Records Commission; provides policy guidance and mediation services for FOIA activities government-wide; oversees the government-wide security classification system; monitors the National Industrial Security Program; and publishes laws, regulations and Presidential and other public documents through the Federal Register.

700 Pennsylvania Avenue, NW, Washington, DC 20408-0001
Tel: (866) 272-6272 Tel: (301) 837-2000 (Archives Information)
Tel: (202) 357-5400 (Archives Information - ARCH-1)
Tel: (202) 741-6070 (Federal Register)
Tel: (301) 837-2002 (Personnel Locator)
Tel: (202) 357-5300 (Public Affairs)
Tel: (202) 357-5210 (Public Programs)
Tel: (800) 234-8861 (Publications Information)
Tel: (301) 837-3500 (NARA Inspector General's Hotline)
Tel: (800) 786-2551 (NARA Inspector General's Hotline - Continental US, Alaska and Hawaii) Tel: (202) 741-6043 (Public Laws - Recording)
Tel: (202) 357-5000 (Washington, DC Public Events Information)
Fax: (301) 837-0483 Internet: www.archives.gov
Internet: catalog.archives.gov (National Archives Catalog)
Internet: www.usa.gov (Official US Government Website)

ARCHIVIST OF THE UNITED STATES

Archives I, 700 Pennsylvania Avenue, NW, Washington, DC 20408-0001
Tel: (202) 357-5900 Fax: (202) 357-5901

Office of the Chief Operating Officer (C)

8601 Adelphi Road, Room 4200, College Park, MD 20740-6001
Tel: (301) 837-1982

Agency Services (A)

8601 Adelphi Road, Room 3600, College Park, MD 20740-6001
Fax: (301) 837-1617

● Executive for Agency Services **Jay A. Trainer** .... (301) 837-3064
E-mail: jay.trainer@nara.gov

Federal Records Centers Program (AF)

8601 Adelphi Road, College Park, MD 20740-6001
Fax: (301) 837-1617 Internet: www.archives.gov/locations

● Director **David M. Weinberg** Room 3600 .... (301) 837-3115
E-mail: david.weinberg@nara.gov

National Personnel Records Center (AFN)

1 Archives Drive, St. Louis, MO 63138
Tel: (314) 801-0800 Fax: (314) 801-9195 E-mail: mpr.center@nara.gov
Internet: www.archives.gov/st-louis

● Director **Scott A. Levins** Room 2075 .... (314) 801-0587
E-mail: scott.levins@nara.gov Fax: (314) 801-0605
Management Systems Staff Director **Jason Hardy** .... (314) 801-0597
E-mail: jason.hardy@nara.gov

Civilian Personnel Records (AFN-C)

1411 Boulder Boulevard, Room 103, Valmeyer, IL 62295
Tel: (314) 801-9249 Fax: (314) 801-9269 E-mail: cpr.center@nara.gov

Civilian Personnel Records Director
Kimberly A. Gentile .... (618) 935-3005
E-mail: kimberly.gentile@nara.gov
Civilian Operations Branch Chief **Patricia S. Resler** .... (618) 935-3010
Civilian Reference Services Branch Chief **(Vacant)** ..... (301) 837-1636

Military Personnel Records (AFN-M)

1 Archives Drive, Room 360, St. Louis, MO 63138
Tel: (314) 801-0800 Fax: (314) 801-9195 E-mail: mpr.center@nara.gov

Assistant Director for Military Personnel Records
Kevin M. Pratt .... (314) 801-0582
E-mail: kevin.pratt@nara.gov
Military Operations Branch Chief **Karen L. Mellott** .... (314) 801-0647
E-mail: karen.mellott@nara.gov
Military Records Retrieval Branch Chief
Michael A. Ledyard Room 280 .... (314) 801-9141
E-mail: michael.ledyard@nara.gov
Military Reference Core 1 (Acting)
Joseph J. Stewart .... (314) 801-0602
E-mail: Joseph.Stewart@nara.gov
Military Reference Core 2 **Sharon Box** Room 200 ...... (314) 801-2505
E-mail: sharon.box@nara.gov
Military Reference Core 3 **Gregory Sampson** .... (314) 801-0797
E-mail: gregory.sampson@nara.gov
Military Reference Core 4 **Dana M. Nelson** .... (314) 801-0512
E-mail: dana.nelson@nara.gov

Operations Branch (AFO)

Director **Leanne M. Townsend-Cerame** .... (404) 736-2825
Atlanta Federal Records Center, Fax: (404) 736-2921
5780 Jonesboro Road, Morrow, GA 30260
E-mail: leanne.townsend-cerame@nara.gov

Operations East (AFOE)

Director **Steven J. "Steve" Ourada** .... (816) 994-1702
E-mail: steven.ourada@nara.gov

Atlanta (AFOE-AT)

5780 Jonesboro Road, Morrow, GA 30260
Tel: (770) 968-2100 Fax: (770) 968-2547
E-mail: atlanta.archives@nara.gov Internet: www.archives.gov/atlanta

Records Center Operations Director **Angela R. Foster** ... (404) 736-2888
E-mail: angela.foster@nara.gov
Archival Operations Director
Robert G. "Rob" Richards .... (770) 968-2485
E-mail: rob.richards@nara.gov
Administrative Officer **Marian Jones-Smith** .... (404) 736-2826
E-mail: marian.jones-smith@nara.gov

Boston

Frederick C. Murphy Federal Center, 380 Trapelo Road, Waltham, MA 02452-6399
Tel: (781) 663-0144 Tel: (866) 406-2379 (Toll Free) Fax: (781) 663-0154
E-mail: boston.archives@nara.gov Internet: www.archives.gov/boston

Records Center Operations Director (Acting)
Jonathan Morse .... (781) 663-0136
E-mail: jonathan.morse@nara.gov
Archival Operations Director **Alfie Paul** .... (781) 663-0121
E-mail: alfie.paul@nara.gov
Administrative Officer **Donna Perkins** .... (781) 663-0122
E-mail: donna.perkins@nara.gov

Chicago (AFOE-CH)
7358 South Pulaski Road, Chicago, IL 60629-5898
Tel: (773) 948-9011 Fax: (312) 767-8860
E-mail: chicago.archives@nara.gov Internet: www.archives.gov/chicago

Records Center Operations Director (Acting)
Chloe René Reed .... (773) 948-9007
E-mail: chloe.reed@nara.gov

Archival Operations Director **Douglas A. Bicknese** ...... (773) 948-9009
E-mail: douglas.bicknese@nara.gov

Management Assistant **Mary Ann Zulevic** .... (773) 948-9005
E-mail: maryann.zulevic@nara.gov

Administrative Officer **Thomas "Tom" Kruski** .... (773) 948-9006
E-mail: thomas.kruski@nara.gov

Dayton
3150 Springboro Road, Dayton, OH 45439-1883
Tel: (937) 425-0600 Fax: (937) 425-0640
E-mail: dayton.reference@nara.gov (Reference Services)
E-mail: dayton.transfer@nara.gov (Transfer and Disposition)
Internet: www.archives.gov/frc/dayton

Director **Chloe René Reed** .... (937) 425-0661
E-mail: chloe.reed@nara.gov

Deputy Director **Charles Lintz** .... (937) 425-0602
E-mail: charles.lintz@nara.gov

Senior Records Analyst **Galen R. Wilson** .... (937) 425-0613
E-mail: galen.wilson@nara.gov
Education: Muskingum Col; Michigan

Administrative Officer **Jodi Ballard** .... (937) 425-0607
E-mail: jodi.ballard@nara.gov

Fort Worth (AFOE-FW)
1400 John Burgess Drive, Fort Worth, TX 76140
P.O. Box 6216, Fort Worth, TX 76115-0216
Tel: (817) 551-2051 Fax: (817) 551-2034
E-mail: ftworth.archives@nara.gov Internet: www.archives.gov/fort-worth

Director **Scott Beadle** .... (817) 551-2003
E-mail: scott.beadle@nara.gov

Records Management Program Director **Bill Fellers** ...... (281) 841-8519
E-mail: bill.fellers@nara.gov

Administrative Officer **Louise Riley** .... (817) 551-2004
E-mail: louise.riley@nara.gov

Kingsridge (AFOE-KR)
8801 Kingsridge Drive, Miamisburg, OH 45458
Tel: (937) 425-0690 Fax: (937) 425-0622

Director **Lloyd Mitch Mitchell** .... (937) 425-0601
E-mail: lloyd.mitchell@nara.gov

Philadelphia
14700 Townsend Road, Philadelphia, PA 19154-1096
Tel: (215) 305-2044 Fax: (215) 305-2038
E-mail: philadelphia.archives@nara.gov
Internet: www.archives.gov/philadelphia

Records Center Operations Director **Aaron T. Swann** .... (215) 305-2011
E-mail: aaron.swann@nara.gov

Field Support Officer **David Roland** .... (215) 305-2003
E-mail: david.roland@nara.gov

Pittsfield (AFOE-PF)
10 Conte Drive, Pittsfield, MA 01201-8230
Tel: (413) 236-3600 Fax: (413) 236-3609
E-mail: pittsfield.reference@nara.gov (Reference Services)
E-mail: pittsfield.transfer@nara.gov (Transfer and Disposition)
Internet: www.archives.gov/frc/pittsfield

Director **Anna M. Lankford** .... (413) 236-3606
E-mail: Anna.Lankford@nara.gov

Operations West (AFOW)

Director **Michael J. "Mike" Kretch** .... (951) 956-2015
E-mail: michael.kretch@nara.gov

Denver
17101 Huron Street, Broomfield, CO 80023-8909
Tel: (303) 604-4740 Fax: (303) 407-5707
E-mail: denver.archives@nara.gov Internet: www.archives.gov/denver

Director, Archival Operations
Nora E. "Eileen" Bolger .... (303) 604-4749
E-mail: eileen.bolger@nara.gov

Director, Records Center Operations
Samantha M. Wade Denver Federal Records Center ... (303) 604-4763
E-mail: samantha.wade@nara.gov

Administrative Officer **(Vacant)** .... (303) 407-4703

Kansas City (AFOW-KC)
8600 NE Underground Drive, Pillar 300-G, Kansas City, MO 64161
Tel: (816) 994-1700 Fax: (816) 994-1720
E-mail: kansascity.archives@nara.gov

Director (Acting) **Theresa L. Mellon** Kansas City
Federal Records Center .... (816) 994-1702
E-mail: theresa.mellon@nara.gov

Administrative Officer **Karen Cashio** .... (913) 825-5554
E-mail: karen.cashio@nara.gov

Lee's Summit (AFOW-LS)
200 Space Center Drive, Lees Summit, MO 64064-1182
Tel: (816) 268-8100 Fax: (816) 268-8160
E-mail: leesummit.reference@nara.gov

Director **Sean P. Murphy** .... (816) 268-8149
E-mail: sean.murphy@nara.gov

Lenexa (AFOW-LX)
17501 W. 98th Street, Lenexa, KS 66219
Tel: (913) 563-7600 Fax: (913) 563-7691

Director **David H. Diamond** .... (913) 563-7667
E-mail: david.diamond@nara.gov

Riverside (AFOW-RS)
23123 Cajalco Road, Perris, CA 92570-7298
Tel: (951) 956-2000 Fax: (951) 956-2079
E-mail: riverside.archives@nara.gov
Internet: https://www.archives.gov/frc/riverside

Federal Records Center Director **Jason A. Glover** .... (956) 951-2016
E-mail: jason.glover@nara.gov

Archival Operations Director **Gwen E. Granados** .... (951) 956-2040
E-mail: gwen.granados@nara.gov

Field Support Officer **David M. Piff** .... (650) 238-3463
E-mail: david.piff@nara.gov

San Bruno (AFOW-SB)
1000 Commodore Drive, San Bruno, CA 94066-2350
Tel: (650) 238-3501 Fax: (650) 238-3507
E-mail: sanbruno.archives@nara.gov
Internet: www.archives.gov/san-francisco

Director, Federal Records Center **George Morash** .... (650) 238-3528
E-mail: george.morash@nara.gov

Director, Archival Operations **Stephanie M. Bayless** .... (650) 238-3478
E-mail: stephanie.bayless@nara.gov

Director, Records Center Operations
Lawrence J. Monroe .... (650) 238-3471
E-mail: lawrence.monroe@nara.gov

Director, Records Management Program
Richard Boyden .... (650) 238-3461
E-mail: richard.boyden@nara.gov

Field Support Officer **David M. Piff** .... (650) 238-3463
E-mail: david.piff@nara.gov

Administrative Officer **(Vacant)** .... (650) 238-3501

Seattle (AFOW-SE)
6125 Sand Point Way, NE, Seattle, WA 98115-7999
Tel: (206) 336-5115 Fax: (206) 336-5112
E-mail: seattle.archives@nara.gov Internet: www.archives.gov/seattle

Records Center Operations Director **Patrick M. Weigel** ... (206) 336-5129
E-mail: patrick.weigel@nara.gov

Archival Operations Director **Susan H. "Sue" Karren** ... (206) 336-5141
E-mail: susan.karren@nara.gov

(continued on next page)

★ Presidential Appointment Requiring Senate Confirmation ☆ Presidential Appointment □ Schedule C Appointment ◇ Career Senior Foreign Service Appointment
● Career Senior Executive Service (SES) Appointment ○ Non-Career Senior Executive Service (SES) Appointment ■ Postal Career Executive Service

INDEPENDENT AGENCIES

Seattle *(continued)*

Management and Program Analyst **Kelley Yackley** . . . . (206) 336-5144
E-mail: kelley.yackley@nara.gov

Legislative Archives, Presidential Libraries, and Museum Services (L)

700 Pennsylvania Avenue, NW, Room 104, Washington, DC 20408-0001
Tel: (202) 357-7451

Office of Presidential Libraries (LP)

Herbert Hoover Presidential Library and Museum (LP-HH)
210 Parkside Drive, West Branch, IA 52358
P.O. Box 488, West Branch, IA 52358-0488
Tel: (319) 643-5301 Fax: (319) 643-6045
E-mail: hoover.library@nara.gov Internet: https://hoover.archives.gov/

Library Director **Thomas F. Schwartz** . . . . (319) 643-6029
E-mail: thomas.schwartz@nara.gov
Education: Illinois 1977 BA, 1979 MS, 2000 PhD
Curator **Marcus Eckhardt** . . . . (319) 643-6009
Audiovisual Archivist **Lynn Smith** . . . . (319) 643-6010
E-mail: lynn.smith@nara.gov
Education Specialist **Elizabeth Dinschel** . . . . (319) 643-6031
Public Affairs Specialist **Janlyn Slach** . . . . (319) 643-6033
E-mail: janlyn.slach@nara.gov

Franklin D. Roosevelt Presidential Library and Museum
4079 Albany Post Road, Hyde Park, NY 12538-1999
Tel: (845) 486-7770 Fax: (845) 486-1159
E-mail: roosevelt.library@nara.gov Internet: fdrlibrary.org

Deputy Director **William Harris** . . . . (845) 486-1977
E-mail: william.harris@nara.gov
Supervisory Curator **Herman R. Eberhardt** . . . . (845) 486-7763
Education: Yale 1985 MA, 1990 MPhil

Harry S. Truman Library and Museum (LP-HST)
500 West U.S. Highway 24, Independence, MO 64050-1798
Tel: (816) 268-8200 Fax: (816) 268-8295
E-mail: truman.library@nara.gov Internet: www.trumanlibrary.org

Library Director **Dr. Kurt Graham** . . . . (816) 268-8210
E-mail: kurt.graham@nara.gov
Education: BYU BA, MA; Brown U PhD
Deputy Director **Amy Williams** . . . . (816) 268-8229
E-mail: amy.williams@nara.gov
Supervisory Archivist **Samuel W. "Sam" Rushay** . . . . . . (816) 268-8211
E-mail: samuel.rushay@nara.gov
Facility Manager **Kevin McMurry** . . . . (816) 268-8202
Museum Curator **Clay Bauske** . . . . (816) 268-8203

Dwight D. Eisenhower Presidential Library and Museum
200 Southeast Fourth Street, Abilene, KS 67410-2900
Tel: (785) 263-6700 Fax: (785) 263-6715
E-mail: eisenhower.library@nara.gov
Internet: www.eisenhower.archives.gov

Deputy Director **Timothy D. "Tim" Rives** . . . . (785) 263-6738
E-mail: timothy.rives@nara.gov Fax: (785) 263-6715
Education: Emporia State MA;
Wichita State BGS

John Fitzgerald Kennedy Presidential Library and Museum (LP-JFK)
Columbia Point, Boston, MA 02125-3398
Tel: (617) 514-1600 Fax: (617) 514-1683
E-mail: kennedy.library@nara.gov Internet: www.jfklibrary.org

Director **Alan C. Price** . . . . (617) 514-1600
Education: Earlham 1988 AB; Harvard 1992 JD
Deputy Director **James Roth** . . . . (617) 514-1633
E-mail: james.roth@nara.gov
Director of Archives **Karen A. Abramson** . . . . (617) 514-1653
E-mail: karen.abramson@nara.gov
Facilities Manager **Norm Beland** . . . . (617) 514-1558
Museum Curator **Stacey Bredhoff** . . . . (617) 514-1682
Fax: (617) 514-1683

John Fitzgerald Kennedy Presidential Library and Museum *(continued)*

Administrative Officer **Marie Carbone** . . . . (617) 514-1541
E-mail: marie.carbone@nara.gov

Lyndon Baines Johnson Library and Museum (LP-LBJ)
2313 Red River Street, Austin, TX 78705-5702
Tel: (512) 721-0200 Fax: (512) 721-0170
E-mail: johnson.library@nara.gov Internet: www.lbjlibrary.org

Library Director **Dr. Kyle Longley PhD** . . . . (501) 244-2884
Education: Angelo State BA; Texas Tech MA; Kentucky PhD
Administrative Assistant **Suzanne R. Mirabal** . . . . (512) 721-0217
E-mail: suzanne.mirabal@nara.gov
Deputy Director **Michael MacDonald** . . . . (512) 721-0199
E-mail: michael.macdonald@nara.gov
Education Specialist **Amanda Melancon** . . . . (512) 721-0172
Education: Texas 2006 BA
Communications Director **Anne Wheeler** . . . . (512) 721-0216
E-mail: awheeler@lbjfoundation.org
Facility Manager and Information Technology Specialist **Darren E. Jernigan** . . . . (512) 721-0167
E-mail: darren.jernigan@nara.gov
Museum Curator **(Vacant)** . . . . (512) 721-0200
Supervisory Archivist **Jennifer Cuddeback** . . . . (512) 721-0181
E-mail: jennifer.cuddeback@nara.gov
Director of Public Programs **Sarah McCracken** . . . . (512) 721-0176
E-mail: sarah@lbjfoundation.org
Volunteer and Visitor Services Coordinator **Laura Eggert** . . . . (512) 721-0225
E-mail: laura.eggert@nara.gov
Senior Designer **Balmore Lazo** . . . . (512) 721-0155
E-mail: balmore@lbjlibrary.net
Administrative Officer **Shirley P. Baker** . . . . (512) 721-0185
E-mail: shirley.baker@nara.gov

Richard Nixon Presidential Library and Museum (LP-RN)
18001 Yorba Linda Boulevard, Yorba Linda, CA 62886
8601 Adelphi Road, Room 1350, College Park, MD 20740-6001
Tel: (714) 983-9120 (Yorba Linda) Tel: (301) 837-3290 (College Park)
Tel: (714) 983-9320 (Archives) Fax: (714) 983-9111 (Yorba Linda)
Fax: (301) 837-3202 (College Park) E-mail: nixon@nara.gov
Internet: www.nixonlibrary.gov

Library Director **Michael D. "Mike" Ellzey** . . . . (714) 983-9121
E-mail: michael.ellzey@nara.gov
Deputy Director **(Vacant)** . . . . (714) 983-9119
Resource Archivist and Staff Historian **Gregory "Greg" Cumming** . . . . (714) 983-9131
E-mail: gregory.cumming@nara.gov
Supervisory Museum Curator **Olivia Anastasiadis** . . . . . . (714) 983-9125
Education Specialist **Cliff B. Wallace** . . . . (714) 983-9138

Gerald R. Ford Presidential Library
1000 Beal Avenue, Ann Arbor, MI 48109-2114
Tel: (734) 205-0555 Fax: (734) 205-0571 (Library)
E-mail: ford.library@nara.gov Internet: www.fordlibrarymuseum.gov

Library Director **Elaine K. Didier** . . . . (734) 205-0566
E-mail: elaine.didier@nara.gov
Deputy Director **Joel W. Westphal** . . . . (616) 254-0385
E-mail: joel.westphal@nara.gov
Supervisory Archivist **Geir Gundersen** . . . . (734) 205-0556
E-mail: geir.gundersen@nara.gov

Gerald R. Ford Presidential Museum
303 Pearl Street, NW, Grand Rapids, MI 49504-5353
Tel: (616) 254-0400 Fax: (616) 254-0386
E-mail: ford.museum@nara.gov

Director **Elaine K. Didier** . . . . (616) 254-0398
Supervisory Curator **Donald Holloway** . . . . (616) 254-0378
Administrative Officer **Bridget Carrigan** . . . . (616) 254-0371
E-mail: bridget.carrigan@nara.gov
Program Assistant **Desiree Ruhland** . . . . (616) 254-0367
E-mail: desiree.ruhland@nara.gov

★ Presidential Appointment Requiring Senate Confirmation ☆ Presidential Appointment ☐ Schedule C Appointment ◇ Career Senior Foreign Service Appointment
● Career Senior Executive Service (SES) Appointment ○ Non-Career Senior Executive Service (SES) Appointment ■ Postal Career Executive Service

Jimmy Carter Library and Museum
441 Freedom Parkway, Atlanta, GA 30307-1498
Tel: (404) 865-7100 Fax: (404) 865-7102 E-mail: carter.library@nara.gov
Internet: www.jimmycarterlibrary.gov

Deputy Director **David Stanhope** .... (404) 865-7128
E-mail: david.stanhope@nara.gov
Museum Curator **Sylvia M. Naguib** .... (404) 865-7123
Supervisory Archivist **Aisha Johnson-Jones** .... (404) 865-7155
Education Specialist **(Vacant)**
Management and Program Analyst **(Vacant)** .... (404) 865-7119

Ronald Reagan Presidential Library and Museum (LP-RR)
40 Presidential Drive, Simi Valley, CA 93065-0699
Tel: (805) 577-4000 Tel: (800) 410-8354 Fax: (805) 577-4074
E-mail: reagan.library@nara.gov Internet: reaganlibrary.gov

Library Director **R. Duke Blackwood** .... (805) 577-4014
E-mail: duke.blackwood@nara.gov
Education: Cal Poly (Pomona) 1980 BA
Deputy Director **Michael "Mike" Duggan** .... (805) 577-4016
E-mail: mike.duggan@nara.gov
Administrative Officer **Kimberly "Kim" Killion** .... (805) 577-4020
E-mail: kimberly.killion@nara.gov
Supervisory Archivist **Ira Pemstein** .... (805) 577-4073
E-mail: ira.pemstein@nara.gov
Education Specialist **Mira Cohen** .... (805) 577-4019

George Bush Library and Museum (LP-GB)
1000 George Bush Drive, West, College Station, TX 77845
P.O. Box 14141, College Station, TX 77841-4141
Tel: (979) 691-4000 TTY: (979) 691-4091 Fax: (979) 691-4050
E-mail: info.bush@nara.gov Internet: bush41.org

Library Director **Warren L. Finch** .... (979) 691-4001
E-mail: warren.finch@nara.gov
Administrative Officer **Karen Gonzalez** .... (979) 691-4007
E-mail: karen.gonzalez@nara.gov
Deputy Director **Dr. Robert Holzweiss** .... (979) 691-4003
E-mail: robert.holzweiss@nara.gov
Supervisory Curator **Susanne "Susie" Cox** .... (979) 691-4065
Facility Operations Specialist **Robert Spacek** .... (979) 691-4005
Education Director **Dr. Shirley Hammond** .... (979) 691-4013

William Jefferson Clinton Presidential Library and Museum (LP-WJC)
1200 President Clinton Avenue, Little Rock, AR 72201
Tel: (501) 244-2877 (Archival Reference) Fax: (501) 244-2883
E-mail: clinton.library@nara.gov Internet: www.clintonlibrary.gov

Library Director **Mary T. "Terri" Garner** .... (501) 244-2884
E-mail: terri.garner@nara.gov
Education: Chatham BA; Colorado (Denver) MA
Deputy Director **Kurt Senn** .... (501) 244-2891
E-mail: kurt.senn@nara.gov
Curator **Christine Mouw** .... (501) 244-2840
E-mail: christine.mouw@nara.gov
Supervisory Archivist **Dana Simmons** .... (501) 244-2866
E-mail: dana.simmons@nara.gov
Administrative Officer **Mary Ruth Rash** .... (501) 244-2888
E-mail: maryruth.rash@nara.gov
Education Specialist **Kathleen Pate** .... (501) 244-2704
E-mail: kathleen.pate@nara.gov
Facility Manager **Edward Kamarra** .... (501) 244-2832

George W. Bush Library and Museum (LP-GWB)
2943 SMU Boulevard, Dallas, TX 75205
Tel: (214) 346-1650 Fax: (214) 346-1699
E-mail: gwbush.library@nara.gov
Internet: http://www.georgewbushlibrary.smu.edu

Library Director (Acting) **Emily Robison** .... (214) 346-1684
E-mail: emily.robison@nara.gov
Deputy Director **Emily Robison** .... (214) 346-1684
E-mail: emily.robison@nara.gov
Curator **Amy Polley** .... (214) 346-1687
E-mail: amy.polley@nara.gov
Administrative Officer **Shelly R. DiCiolli** .... (214) 346-1691
E-mail: shelly.diciolli@nara.gov

George W. Bush Library and Museum *(continued)*

Supervisory Archivist **Shannon R. Jarrett** .... (214) 346-1689
E-mail: shannon.jarrett@nara.gov
Audiovisual Archivist **Sarah E. Barca** .... (214) 346-1655
E-mail: sarah.barca@nara.gov

Barack Obama Presidential Library (LP-BHO)
2500 W. Golf Road, Hoffman Estates, IL 60169-1114
Tel: (847) 252-5700 Fax: (847) 252-5799
E-mail: obama.library@nara.gov Internet: www.obamalibrary.gov

Note: NARA has announced that for President Obama, it will administer neither a museum nor a traditional "presidential library," and will instead focus on preserving the presidential records and making them accessible in digital format to the greatest extent possible.

Director **(Vacant)** .... (847) 252-5700
Deputy Director **Brooke L. Clement** .... (847) 252-5714
E-mail: brooke.clement@nara.gov

INDEPENDENT AGENCIES

★ Presidential Appointment Requiring Senate Confirmation ☆ Presidential Appointment ☐ Schedule C Appointment ◇ Career Senior Foreign Service Appointment
● Career Senior Executive Service (SES) Appointment ○ Non-Career Senior Executive Service (SES) Appointment ■ Postal Career Executive Service

National Credit Union Administration (NCUA)

Description: The National Credit Union Administration charters and supervises federal credit unions and insures savings in federal and most state-chartered credit unions across the country through the National Credit Union Share Insurance Fund (NCUSIF), a federal fund backed by the full faith and credit of the United States government. The Administration also manages the Central Liquidity Facility, a mixed-ownership government corporation whose purpose is to supply emergency loans to member credit unions.

1775 Duke Street, Alexandria, VA 22314-3428
Tel: (703) 518-6300 (General Information)
Tel: (703) 518-6510 (Personnel Locator)
Tel: (703) 518-6410 (Procurement Information)
Tel: (703) 518-6540 (Freedom of Information/Privacy Act)
Tel: (703) 518-6340 (Publications)
Tel: (703) 518-6550 (Fraud Hotline - DC Metro Area)
Tel: (800) 827-9650 (Fraud Hotline - Toll Free)
Tel: (703) 518-6357 (Inspector General's Hotline - DC Metro Area)
Tel: (800) 778-4806 (Inspector General's Hotline - Toll Free)
Internet: www.ncua.gov
Internet: www.usa.gov (Official US Government Website)

THE BOARD

1775 Duke Street, Alexandria, VA 22314-3428
Fax: (703) 518-6319 E-mail: boardmail@ncua.gov

Note: Members may continue to serve until reappointed or replaced.

Office of the Executive Director

1775 Duke Street, Alexandria, VA 22314-3428
Tel: (703) 518-6320 Fax: (703) 518-6661 E-mail: oedmail@ncua.gov

Regional Offices

Region I - Albany (NY)

Nine Washington Square, Washington Avenue Extension, Albany, NY 12205-5576
Tel: (518) 862-7400 Fax: (518) 862-7420 E-mail: region1@ncua.gov
Areas Covered: CT, ME, MA, MI, NH, NY, RI, VT, WI

Regional Director **Lawrence J. "L.J." Blankenberger** . . . (518) 862-7400
Education: Indiana State
Associate Regional Director - Operations
Rebecca Paliwodzinski . . . . (518) 862-7400
Associate Regional Director - Programs **Joanne Black** . . . (207) 776-9841

Region II - Capital

1900 Duke Street, Suite 300, Alexandria, VA 22314-3437
Tel: (703) 519-4600 Fax: (703) 519-4620 E-mail: region2@ncua.gov
Areas Covered: DC, DE, MD, NJ, OH, PA, VA, and WV.

Regional Director **Jane A. Walters** . . . . (703) 519-4600 ext. 2001
E-mail: jwalters@ncua.gov
Education: Dayton BS; Loyola U (Chicago) MBA
Associate Regional Director - Operations
Michael "Mike" Ryan . . . . (703) 519-4600
Associate Regional Director - Programs
Wendy Angus . . . . (703) 519-4600

Region III - Atlanta (GA)

7000 Central Parkway, Suite 1600, Atlanta, GA 30328
Tel: (678) 443-3000 Fax: (678) 443-3020 E-mail: region3@ncua.gov
Areas Covered: AL, AR, FL, GA, IN, KY, LA, MS, NC, OH, PR, SC, TN, VI

Regional Director **Myra Toeppe** . . . . (678) 443-3001
E-mail: mtoeppe@ncua.gov
Education: Central Florida 1983 BSBA, 1986 MBA

Region III - Atlanta (GA) *(continued)*

Associate Regional Director - Operations
Joseph Ostrowidzki . . . . (678) 443-3003
Associate Regional Director - Programs **(Vacant)** . . . . (678) 443-3002

Region IV - Austin (TX)

4807 Spicewood Springs Road, Suite 5200, Austin, TX 78759-8490
Tel: (512) 342-5600 Fax: (512) 342-5620 E-mail: region4@ncua.gov
Areas Covered: CO, IA, IL, KS, MN, MO, MT, NE, NM, ND, OK, SD, TX, WY

Regional Director **C. Keith Morton** . . . . (512) 342-5600 ext. 4001
Education: Frostburg State U BS
Associate Regional Director - Operations
Tracy C. Bombarger . . . . (512) 342-5600 ext. 4002
Education: West Texas State BBA
Associate Regional Director - Programs
Milagro S. Avalos . . . . (512) 342-5600 ext. 4003
E-mail: mavalos@ncua.gov
Director of Supervision **Christine Bryant** . . . . . . (512) 342-5600 ext. 4004
E-mail: cbryant@ncua.gov
Deputy Director of Supervision
John H. Shook . . . . (512) 342-5600 ext. 4005
E-mail: jshook@ncua.gov
Management Services Division Director
Alisha Massey-Williams . . . . (512) 342-5600 ext. 4006
E-mail: amwilliams@ncua.gov

Region V - Tempe (AZ)

1230 West Washington Street, Suite 301, Tempe, AZ 85281
Tel: (602) 302-6000 Fax: (602) 302-6024 E-mail: region5@ncua.gov
Areas Covered: AK, AZ, CA, GU, HI, ID, NV, OR, UT, WA

Regional Director **Cherie Freed** . . . . (602) 302-6000
E-mail: cfreed@ncua.gov
Associate Regional Director for Operations
Linda Thompson . . . . (602) 302-6000
Associate Regional Director for Programs **Mike Dyer** . . . . (602) 302-6000
E-mail: mdyer@ncua.gov
Education: St Mary's U (MN); Wisconsin MBA

Asset Management and Assistance Center

4807 Spicewood Springs Road, Suite 5100, Austin, TX 78759-8490
Tel: (512) 231-7900 Fax: (512) 231-7920 E-mail: amacmail@ncua.gov

President **C. Keith Morton** . . . . (512) 231-7900 ext. 7001
Education: Frostburg State U BS
Deputy to the President **Donald Klein** . . . . (512) 231-7900 ext. 7002

National Labor Relations Board (NLRB)

Description: The National Labor Relations Board is an independent federal agency vested with the authority to safeguard employees' rights to organize and to determine whether to have unions as their collective bargaining representative. The agency also acts to prevent and remedy unfair labor practices committed by private sector employers and unions.

1015 Half Street, SE, Washington, DC 20570
Tel: (202) 273-1000 (Personnel Locator)
Tel: (202) 273-4210 (Acquisitions Management Branch)
Tel: (202) 273-1991 (Public Information)
Tel: (202) 273-3930 (Publications Information)
Tel: (202) 273-1940 (Freedom of Information/Privacy Act)
Tel: (202) 273-1960 (Inspector General's Hotline - DC Metropolitan Area)
Tel: (800) 736-2983 (Inspector General's Hotline - Continental US, Alaska, Hawaii and Puerto Rico) Fax: (202) 273-4266 Internet: www.nlrb.gov
Internet: www.nlrb.gov/open (Open Government Initiative)

OFFICES OF THE BOARD

Division of Judges

1015 Half Street, SE, Washington, DC 20570
Tel: (202) 501-8800 Fax: (202) 501-8686

New York Branch Office

26 Federal Plaza, 17th Floor, New York, NY 10278
Tel: (212) 944-2941 Fax: (212) 944-4904

Associate Chief Administrative Law Judge
Kenneth W. Chu .... (212) 944-2941
E-mail: kenneth.chu@nlrb.gov
Education: CCNY BA; Brooklyn Law JD
Office Manager **Dana Brown** .... (212) 944-2941
E-mail: dana.brown@nlrb.gov

San Francisco Branch Office

901 Market Street, Room 300, San Francisco, CA 94103
Tel: (415) 356-5255 Fax: (415) 356-5254

Associate Chief Administrative Law Judge
Gerald Etchingham .... (415) 356-5255
Education: Hastings JD
Legal Technician **Brian DiCrocco** .... (415) 356-5255
E-mail: joyce.coleman@nlrb.gov
Office Manager **Kathryn Goetz** .... (415) 356-5255

Regional Offices

Region 1 - Boston (MA)

Thomas P. O'Neill, Jr. Federal Building, 10 Causeway Street, Room 601, Boston, MA 02222-1001
Tel: (617) 565-6700 Fax: (617) 565-6725 Internet: www.nlrb.gov
Areas Covered: ME, MA, NH, RI, VT

● Regional Director **(Vacant)** .... (857) 317-7818
Assistant to the Regional Director
Elizabeth Gemperline .... (857) 317-7788
E-mail: elizabeth.gemperline@nlrb.gov
Regional Attorney **(Vacant)** .... (857) 317-7794
Deputy Regional Attorney **Scott F. Burson** .... (857) 317-7791
E-mail: scott.burson@nlrb.gov
Deputy Regional Attorney **Robert P. Redbord** .... (857) 317-7799
E-mail: robert.redbord@nlrb.gov
Compliance Officer **Dina M. Raimo** .... (959) 200-7377
Office Manager **Michelle Cassata** .... (857) 317-7793

Subregion 34 - Hartford (CT)

Abraham A. Ribicoff Federal Building, 450 Main Street, Suite 410, Hartford, CT 06103
Tel: (860) 240-3522 Fax: (860) 240-3564 Internet: www.nlrb.gov
Areas Covered: CT

Officer in Charge **Michael C. Cass** .... (959) 200-7362
E-mail: michael.cass@nlrb.gov
Education: UMass (Amherst) 1977 BA, 1980 MS
Deputy Regional Attorney **(Vacant)** .... (860) 240-3522
Supervisory Attorney **Thomas E. Quigley** .... (959) 200-7376
E-mail: thomas-quigley@nlrb.gov Fax: (860) 240-3564
Supervisory Examiner **(Vacant)** .... (860) 240-3522
Compliance Officer **Megan Millar** .... (857) 317-7816
Office Manager **Jean M. McCarrick** .... (959) 200-7371
E-mail: jean.mccarrick@nlrb.gov

Region 2 - New York (NY)

Jacob K. Javits Federal Building, 26 Federal Plaza, Room 3614, New York, NY 10278
Tel: (212) 264-0300 Fax: (212) 264-2450
Internet: www.nlrb.gov/region/new-york
Areas Covered: Manhattan, Bronx, Orange, Putnam, Rockland, and Westchester

● Regional Director **John J. Walsh, Jr.** .... (212) 776-8615
E-mail: john.walsh@nlrb.gov
Education: Northeastern 1979
Assistant to the Regional Director
Nicholas H. Lewis .... (212) 776-8625
E-mail: nicholas.lewis@nlrb.gov
Regional Attorney **Geoffrey Dunham** .... (212) 776-8619
E-mail: geoffrey.dunham@nlrb.gov
Deputy Regional Attorney **(Vacant)** .... (212) 776-8609
Compliance Officer **Rachel Kurtzleben** .... (212) 776-8640
E-mail: rachel.kurtzleben@nlrb.gov
Office Manager **Wanda Spratley** .... (212) 776-8644

Region 3 - Buffalo (NY)

Niagara Center Building, 130 South Elmwood Avenue, Suite 630, Buffalo, NY 14202-2465
Tel: (716) 551-4931 Fax: (716) 551-4972 E-mail: region3@nlrb.gov
Areas Covered: NY (except Metropolitan New York City and Long Island)

● Regional Director **Paul J. Murphy** .... (716) 398-7021
E-mail: paul.murphy@nlrb.gov
Assistant to the Regional Director (Acting)
Sandra L. Larkin .... (716) 398-7016
Regional Attorney **Linda Leslie** .... (716) 551-4931
E-mail: linda.leslie@nlrb.gov
Education: Buffalo 1995 BA, 1999 JD
Compliance Officer **(Vacant)** .... (716) 551-4931
Office Manager **Barbara Keough** .... (716) 398-7015

★ Presidential Appointment Requiring Senate Confirmation ☆ Presidential Appointment ☐ Schedule C Appointment ◇ Career Senior Foreign Service Appointment
● Career Senior Executive Service (SES) Appointment ○ Non-Career Senior Executive Service (SES) Appointment ■ Postal Career Executive Service

Region 4 - Philadelphia (PA)
615 Chestnut Street, 7th Floor, Philadelphia, PA 19106-4404
Tel: (215) 597-7601 Fax: (215) 597-7658
Areas Covered: Eastern PA, Northern DE, Southern NJ

● Regional Director **Dennis P. Walsh** .... (215) 597-7608
E-mail: dennis.walsh@nlrb.gov
Education: Hamilton 1976 BA; Cornell 1983 JD
Assistant to the Regional Director **Harold A. Maier** .... (215) 597-7610
Education: Penn State 1994 BS
Regional Attorney **Richard P. Heller** .... (215) 597-7633
E-mail: richard.heller@nlrb.gov
Education: Cornell 1977; Rutgers (Newark) 1980 JD
Deputy Regional Attorney **(Vacant)** .... (215) 597-7626
Deputy Regional Attorney **(Vacant)** .... (215) 597-7625
Compliance Officer **Shane D. Thurman** .... (215) 597-5354
E-mail: shane.thurman@nlrb.gov
Office Manager **James Kaminski** .... (215) 597-7621
E-mail: james.kaminski@nlrb.gov

Region 5 - Baltimore (MD)
Bank of America Center, Tower II, 100 Charles Street,
Sixth Floor, Baltimore, MD 21201-2700
Tel: (410) 962-2822 Fax: (410) 962-2198 E-mail: region_5@nlrb.gov
Internet: www.nlrb.gov/region/baltimore
Areas Covered: DE, DC, MD, 4 PA counties, 61 VA counties.

● Regional Director (Acting) **Nancy Wilson** .... (410) 962-2822
E-mail: nancy.wilson@nlrb.gov
Education: Rutgers
Assistant to the Regional Director
Kimberly E. Andrews .... (410) 962-3120
Regional Attorney **Sean R. Marshall** .... (410) 962-2785
E-mail: sean.marshall@nlrb.gov
Compliance Officer **Heather Keough** .... (410) 962-2864
E-mail: heather.keough@nlrb.gov
Office Manager **John Chambers** .... (410) 962-1712
E-mail: john.chambers@nlrb.gov

Region 6 - Pittsburgh (PA)
William S. Moorhead Federal Building, 1000 Liberty Avenue,
Suite 904, Pittsburgh, PA 15222-4111
Tel: (412) 395-4400 Fax: (412) 395-5986
Areas Covered: Western and Central PA and Northern WV

● Regional Director **Nancy Wilson** .... (412) 690-7123
E-mail: nancy.wilson@nlrb.gov
Education: Rutgers
Assistant to the Regional Director **Tara N. Yoest** .... (412) 690-7124
Education: Penn State 1998 BS
Regional Attorney **Suzanne C. Bernett** .... (412) 690-7102
Office Manager **Charlene Prosser** .... (412) 690-7111

Region 7 - Detroit (MI)
Patrick V. McNamara Federal Building, 477 Michigan Avenue,
Room 300, Detroit, MI 48226-2569
Tel: (313) 226-3200 Fax: (313) 226-2090
Areas Covered: MI

● Regional Director **Terry A. Morgan** .... (313) 335-8036
E-mail: terry.morgan@nlrb.gov
Education: Wisconsin BA, 1988 JD
Assistant to the Regional Director **Elizabeth Kerwin** ... (313) 335-8026
Regional Attorney **Dennis R. Boren** .... (313) 335-8046
E-mail: dennis.boren@nlrb.gov
Education: Wayne State U 1974 BA, 1977 JD
Deputy Regional Attorney **Erikson Karmol** .... (313) 335-8025
E-mail: erikson.karmol@nlrb.gov
Education: Cincinnati 1993 BA, 1994 MA; Toledo 1997 JD
Deputy Regional Attorney **Amy Roemer** .... (313) 335-8051
E-mail: amy.roemer@nlrb.gov
Education: Michigan (Dearborn) 1988 BABA; Wayne State U 1993 JD
Compliance Officer **Mark D. Baines** .... (313) 335-8042
E-mail: mark.baines@nlrb.gov
Office Manager **Karen Roock** .... (313) 335-8063
E-mail: karen.roock@nlrb.gov

Region 8 - Cleveland (OH)
A. J. Celebrezze Federal Building, 1240 East Ninth Street,
Room 1695, Cleveland, OH 44199-2086
Tel: (216) 522-3715 Tel: (866) 667-6572 Fax: (216) 522-2418
Areas Covered: Northern OH

● Regional Director **Allen Binstock** .... (216) 303-7368
E-mail: allen.binstock@nlrb.gov
Education: Case Western 1969 AB; Wisconsin 1971; Connecticut 1979 JD
Assistant to the Regional Director
Randall A. Malloy .... (216) 303-7382
Regional Attorney **Iva Y. Choe** .... (216) 303-7375
E-mail: iva.choe@nlrb.gov
Education: Columbia 1992 AB; Ohio State 1995 JD
Deputy Regional Attorney **(Vacant)** .... (216) 522-3723
Compliance Officer **Megan Sobczak** .... (216) 303-7399
Office Manager **Cynthia Clark** .... (216) 303-7376
E-mail: cindy.clark@nlrb.gov

Region 9 - Cincinnati (OH)
John Weld Peck Federal Building, 550 Main Street,
Room 3003, Cincinnati, OH 45202-3271
Tel: (513) 684-3686 Fax: (513) 684-3946
Areas Covered: Portions of OH, portions of KY, portions of WV

Regional Director **Garey E. Lindsay** .... (513) 684-3621
E-mail: garey.lindsay@nlrb.gov
Education: Wayne State U BA, JD
Assistant to the Regional Director
Matthew T. Denholm .... (513) 684-3625
Education: Akron 1977
Regional Attorney **Eric V. Oliver** .... (513) 684-3626
E-mail: eric.oliver@nlrb.gov
Education: Oberlin 1980; Case Western 1983 JD
Deputy Regional Attorney **(Vacant)** .... (513) 684-3630
Compliance Officer **Ann Marie Behrle** .... (513) 684-3733
Office Manager **Marlene Dole** .... (513) 684-3668
E-mail: marlene.dole@nlrb.gov

Region 10 - Atlanta (GA)
Harris Tower, 233 Peachtree Street, NE,
Suite 1000, Atlanta, GA 30303-1504
Tel: (404) 331-2896 Fax: (404) 331-2858 E-mail: region10@nlrb.gov
Areas Covered: Most of GA, Northern and Central AL, Northeastern TN

● Regional Director **John D. Doyle, Jr.** .... (470) 343-7484
E-mail: john.doyle@nlrb.gov
Education: Colgate 1992; Fordham 1995 JD
Assistant to the Regional Director **Terry D. Combs** ...... (470) 343-7477
Education: Miami U (OH); Cincinnati
Regional Attorney **Lisa Henderson** .... (470) 343-7483
E-mail: lisa.henderson@nlrb.gov
Deputy Regional Attorney **Gaye Nell Hymon** .... (470) 343-7488
E-mail: gaye.hymon@nlrb.gov
Education: Southern U A&M 1973 BS, 1976 JD
Compliance Officer **Morris J. Newman** .... (205) 518-7517
Ridge Park Place, 1130 22nd Street, South,
Suite 3400, Birmingham, AL 35205-2870
E-mail: morris.newman@nlrb.gov
Office Manager **Yvette Teel** .... (470) 343-7495

Subregion 11 - Winston-Salem (NC)
Republic Square, 4035 University Parkway,
Suite 200, Winston-Salem, NC 27106-3325
P.O. Box 11467, Winston-Salem, NC 27116-1467
Tel: (336) 631-5201 Fax: (336) 631-5210
Areas Covered: NC, SC

Officer in Charge **Scott C. Thompson** .... (336) 582-7143
E-mail: scott.c.thompson@nlrb.gov
Deputy Regional Attorney **Lisa Shearin** .... (336) 582-7142
E-mail: lisa.shearin@nlrb.gov
Supervisory Attorney **Shannon Meares** .... (336) 582-7137
E-mail: shannon.meares@nlrb.gov
Compliance Officer **Jenny Dunn** .... (336) 582-7134
E-mail: jenny.dunn@nlrb.gov

★ Presidential Appointment Requiring Senate Confirmation ☆ Presidential Appointment □ Schedule C Appointment ◇ Career Senior Foreign Service Appointment
● Career Senior Executive Service (SES) Appointment ○ Non-Career Senior Executive Service (SES) Appointment ■ Postal Career Executive Service

Subregion 11 - Winston-Salem (NC) *(continued)*

Office Manager **Lisa A. Davis** . . . . . (336) 582-7133
E-mail: lisa.davis@nlrb.gov

Region 12 - Tampa (FL)

201 East Kennedy Boulevard, Suite 530, Tampa, FL 33602-5824
Tel: (813) 228-2641 Fax: (813) 228-2874
Areas Covered: FL

- • Regional Director **David Cohen** . . . . . (813) 228-2646
  E-mail: david.cohen@nlrb.gov
  Education: Lafayette; Rutgers (Newark) JD
  Assistant to the Regional Director **Amy Ferrell** . . . . . (813) 228-2661

Regional Attorney **(Vacant)** . . . . . (813) 228-2345
Supervisory Attorney **Christopher Zerby** . . . . . (813) 228-2683
E-mail: christopher.zerby@nlrb.gov
Compliance Officer **(Vacant)** . . . . . (813) 228-2455
Office Manager **Macy D. Sanchez** . . . . . (813) 228-2659

Subregion 24 - San Juan (PR)

La Torre De Plaza, 525 F. D. Roosevelt Avenue,
Suite 1002, San Juan, PR 00918-1002
Tel: (787) 766-5347 Fax: (787) 766-5478
Areas Covered: PR, VI

- • Office-in-Charge **Vanessa Garcia** . . . . . (787) 771-3667
  Education: Texas 1983 BA; Inter American 1996 JD

Deputy Regional Attorney **(Vacant)** . . . . . (787) 771-3667
Compliance Officer **Sigfredo G. Nieves** . . . . . (787) 766-5377
E-mail: sigfredo.nieves@nlrb.gov
Office Manager **Lydia Quiñones** . . . . . (787) 766-5424
E-mail: lydia.quinones@nlrb.gov

Region 13 - Chicago (IL)

219 South Dearborn Street, Suite 808, Chicago, IL 60604-5208
Tel: (312) 353-7570 Fax: (312) 886-1341
Areas Covered: Northern IL, Northwestern IN

- • Regional Director **Peter Sung Ohr** . . . . . (312) 353-7574
  E-mail: peter.ohr@nlrb.gov
  Education: UC Riverside 1989 BA; Pepperdine 1994 JD; Hawaii Pacific 2000 MBA
  Assistant to the Regional Director **Daniel N. Nelson** . . . (312) 886-3036
  Education: Syracuse 1994 BA; Illinois MA

Regional Attorney **Paul Hitterman** . . . . . (312) 353-7577
E-mail: paul.hitterman@nlrb.gov
Deputy Regional Attorney **Jessica Muth** . . . . . (312) 353-7643
E-mail: jessica.muth@nlrb.gov
Deputy Regional Attorney **Richard Kelliher-Paz** . . . . . (312) 353-7629
E-mail: richard.kelliher-paz@nlrb.gov
Education: Loyola U (Chicago) 1976 BS; Chicago-Kent 1988 JD
Compliance Officer **Thomas Porter** . . . . . (312) 353-7170
E-mail: thomas.porter@nlrb.gov
Office Manager **Catherine Jones** . . . . . (312) 353-0516

Region 14 - St. Louis (MO)

1222 Spruce Street, Room 8.302, St. Louis, MO 63103-2829
Tel: (314) 539-7770 Fax: (314) 539-7794
Areas Covered: Southern IL, Eastern MO

- • Regional Director **Leonard J. "Pete" Perez** . . . . . (314) 449-7486
  E-mail: leonard.perez@nlrb.gov
  Assistant to the Regional Director **(Vacant)** . . . . . (314) 539-7770

Regional Attorney **Mary J. Tobey** . . . . . (314) 449-7491
E-mail: mary.tobey@nlrb.gov
Education: Wisconsin 1978 BA, 1981 JD
Deputy Regional Attorney **(Vacant)** . . . . . (314) 539-7770
Compliance Officer **AnnG K. Wright** . . . . . (314) 449-7493
E-mail: anng.wright@nlrb.gov
Office Manager **Gina L. Yochim** . . . . . (314) 449-7494
E-mail: gina.yochim@nlrb.gov

Subregion 17 - Overland Park (KS)

8600 Farley, Suite 100, Overland Park, KS 66212-4677
Tel: (913) 967-3000 Fax: (913) 967-3010
Areas Covered: KS, MO, NE, OK

Officer in Charge **Mary G. Taves** . . . . . (913) 275-6526
E-mail: mary.taves@nlrb.gov
Education: Wichita State 1983; Kansas
Deputy Regional Attorney **(Vacant)** . . . . . (913) 967-3003
Compliance Officer **(Vacant)** . . . . . (913) 967-3005
Assistant Office Manager **Wilma Carlson** . . . . . (913) 275-6534

Region 15 - New Orleans (LA)

600 South Maestri Place, Seventh Floor, New Orleans, LA 70130
Tel: (504) 589-6362 Fax: (504) 589-4069
Areas Covered: LA; portions of AL, FL, MS

- • Regional Director **M. Kathleen McKinney** . . . . . (504) 321-9577
  E-mail: kathleen.mckinney@nlrb.gov
  Education: Jacksonville U 1984 BA; Wake Forest 1989 JD
  Assistant to the Regional Director **Rebecca Dormon** . . . (504) 321-9489

Regional Attorney **Sandra Hightower** . . . . . (504) 321-9493
E-mail: sandra.hightower@nlrb.gov
Compliance Officer **Debra Warner** . . . . . (504) 321-9476
E-mail: debra.warner@nlrb.gov
Office Manager **Gail L. Fields** . . . . . (504) 321-9490
E-mail: gail.fields@nlrb.gov

Subregion 26 - Memphis (TN)

The Brinkley Plaza Building, 80 Monroe Avenue,
Suite 350, Memphis, TN 38103-2416
Tel: (901) 544-0018 Fax: (901) 544-0008
Areas Covered: AR, Northern MS, Western TN

Officer-in-Charge **Christopher Roy** . . . . . (901) 425-7236
E-mail: christopher.roy@nlrb.gov
Education: USC 1991 BA, 1996 JD
Regional Director Secretary **Carolyn Hobson** . . . . . (901) 425-7233
Supervisory Attorney **(Vacant)** . . . . . (901) 544-0015
Compliance Officer **(Vacant)** . . . . . (901) 544-0011
Office Manager **Geraldine "Jeri" Termon** . . . . . (901) 425-7238
E-mail: jeri.termon@nlrb.gov

Region 16 - Fort Worth (TX)

Lanham Federal Building, 819 Taylor Street,
Room 8A24, Fort Worth, TX 76102
Tel: (817) 978-2921 Fax: (817) 978-2928
Areas Covered: TX

- • Regional Director **Timothy L. Watson** . . . . . (682) 703-7228
  E-mail: timothy.watson@nlrb.gov
  Education: Oklahoma 1985, 1988 JD
  Assistant to the Regional Director **Ofelia Gonzalez** . . . . (682) 703-7224
  Education: Texas (Arlington) 1992 BBA, 1998 MBA

Regional Attorney **(Vacant)** . . . . . (682) 703-7632
Compliance Officer **Marene Steben** . . . . . (682) 703-7489
Office Manager **Kari L. Kolb** . . . . . (682) 703-7229

Region 18 - Minneapolis (MN)

212 3rd Avenue South, Suite 200, Minneapolis, MN 55401
Tel: (612) 348-1757 Fax: (612) 348-1785
Areas Covered: IA, MN, ND, SD, portions of WI

- • Regional Director **Jennifer A. Hadsall** . . . . . (952) 703-2887
  E-mail: jennifer.hadsall@nlrb.gov
  Education: Minnesota BA

Assistant to the Regional Director **(Vacant)** . . . . . (952) 703-2881
Regional Attorney **(Vacant)** . . . . . (612) 348-1768
Supervisory Attorney **Nichole L. Burgess** . . . . . (952) 703-2876
E-mail: nichole.burgess@nlrb.gov
Compliance Officer **(Vacant)** . . . . . (612) 348-1757
Office Manager **Olga Bestilny** . . . . . (952) 703-2892
E-mail: olga.bestilny@nlrb.gov

INDEPENDENT AGENCIES

★ Presidential Appointment Requiring Senate Confirmation ☆ Presidential Appointment ☐ Schedule C Appointment ◇ Career Senior Foreign Service Appointment
● Career Senior Executive Service (SES) Appointment ○ Non-Career Senior Executive Service (SES) Appointment ■ Postal Career Executive Service

INDEPENDENT AGENCIES

Subregion 30 - Milwaukee (WI)
Henry S. Reuss Federal Plaza, 310 West Wisconsin Avenue,
Suite 700W, Milwaukee, WI 53203-2211
Tel: (414) 297-3861 Fax: (414) 297-3880
Areas Covered: WI

Officer in Charge **Benjamin Mandelman** . . . . . (414) 930-7201
E-mail: benjamin.mandelman@nlrb.gov
Education: Wisconsin (Milwaukee) 1970 BA; Wisconsin 1973 JD
Deputy Regional Attorney **Percy J. Courseault III** . . . . . (414) 930-7195
E-mail: percy.courseault@nlrb.gov
Education: Rhodes 1993 BA; Wisconsin 1996 JD
Supervising Attorney **Anita O'Neil** . . . . . (414) 930-7204
Compliance Officer **Richard J. Neuman** . . . . . (414) 930-7203
Assistant Office Manager **Carla Becker** . . . . . (414) 930-7191
E-mail: carla.becker@nlrb.gov

Region 19 - Seattle (WA)
Jackson Federal Building, 915 Second Avenue,
Room 2948, Seattle, WA 98174-1078
Tel: (206) 220-6300 Fax: (206) 220-6305
Areas Covered: AK, Northern ID, Western MT, OR, WA

Regional Director **Ronald K. "Ron" Hooks** . . . . . (206) 220-6310
E-mail: ronald.hooks@nlrb.gov
Assistant to the Regional Director **James Kobe** . . . . . (206) 220-6314
Education: Stanford 1973 BA
Regional Attorney **Anne Pomerantz** . . . . . (206) 220-6311
E-mail: anne.pomerantz@nlrb.gov
Education: Washington U (MO) 1983 BA; Cardozo 1990 JD
Deputy Regional Attorney **Martin Eskenazi** . . . . . (206) 220-6289
E-mail: martin.eskenazi@nlrb.gov
Deputy Regional Attorney **Brian Sweeney** . . . . . (206) 220-6327
E-mail: brian.sweeney@nlrb.gov
Administrative Officer **Dennis Snook** . . . . . (206) 220-6317
E-mail: dennis.snook@nlrb.gov
Education: City U (WA) BS
Compliance Officer **James E. Lorang** . . . . . (206) 220-6284
E-mail: james.lorang@nlrb.gov

Region 20 - San Francisco (CA)
901 Market Street, Suite 400, San Francisco, CA 94103-1735
Tel: (415) 356-5130 Fax: (415) 356-5156
Areas Covered: Northern CA, HI

● Regional Director **Jill Coffman** . . . . . (628) 221-8852
E-mail: jill.coffman@nlrb.gov
Education: Le Moyne 1989 BSBA; Washington U (MO) 1989 JD
Assistant to the Regional Director **Daniel J. Owens** . . . . . (628) 221-8866
Regional Attorney **(Vacant)** . . . . . (628) 221-8849
Deputy Regional Attorney **(Vacant)** . . . . . (415) 356-5181
Office Manager **Elizabeth "Liz" Baker** . . . . . (628) 221-8845
E-mail: elizabeth.baker@nlrb.gov
Automation Staff Assistant **Katherine Yan** . . . . . (628) 221-8837
E-mail: katherine.yan@nlrb.gov
Compliance Officer **Karen K. Thompson** . . . . . (628) 221-8875

Region 21 - Los Angeles (CA)
312 North Spring Street, 10th Floor, Los Angeles, CA 90012
Tel: (213) 894-5254 Fax: (213) 894-2778 E-mail: nlrbregion21@nlrb.gov
Areas Covered: Southern CA

● Regional Director **William B. Cowen** . . . . . (213) 634-6506
E-mail: william.cowen@nlrb.gov
Education: Case Western 1976 BA; Cleveland-Marshall 1979 JD;
Wesley Sem 2005 MTS
Assistant to the Regional Director
Nathan M. Seidman . . . . . (213) 634-6518
Education: UCLA BA; Baltimore MS
Regional Attorney **William M. Pate, Jr.** . . . . . (213) 634-6410
E-mail: william.pate@nlrb.gov
Supervisory Attorney **Stephanie J. Cahn** . . . . . (213) 634-6501
E-mail: stephanie.cahn@nlrb.gov
Deputy Regional Attorney **Neil A. Warheit** . . . . . (213) 634-6525
E-mail: neil.warheit@nlrb.gov
Supervisory Examiner **John Hatem** . . . . . (213) 634-6510
E-mail: john.hatem@nlrb.gov

Region 21 - Los Angeles (CA) *(continued)*

Compliance Officer **Sylvia Meza** . . . . . (213) 634-6409
Office Manager **Mara Estudillo** . . . . . (213) 634-6504
E-mail: mara.estudillo@nlrb.gov

Region 22 - Newark (NJ)
Veterans Administration Building, 20 Washington Place,
5th Floor, Newark, NJ 07102-3115
Tel: (973) 645-2100 Fax: (973) 645-3852
Areas Covered: NJ

● Regional Director **David E. Leach III** . . . . . (862) 229-7031
E-mail: david.leach@nlrb.gov
Education: Cathedral Col; Brooklyn Law
Assistant Regional Director **Eric Schechter** . . . . . (862) 229-7053
Regional Attorney **Richard Fox** . . . . . (862) 229-7053
E-mail: richard.fox@nlrb.gov
Education: Franklin & Marshall BA; Washington U (MO) JD
Deputy Regional Attorney **Dorothy Foley** . . . . . (862) 229-7052
E-mail: dorothy.foley@nlrb.gov
Education: Fairleigh Dickinson BA, MA; Northeastern MA;
Cardozo 1988 JD
Deputy Regional Attorney **Julie Kaufman** . . . . . (862) 229-7028
E-mail: julie.kaufman@nlrb.gov
Compliance Officer **Rhonda Fricke** . . . . . (862) 229-7055
E-mail: rhonda.fricke@nlrb.gov
Office Manager **Gwendolyn Campbell** . . . . . (862) 229-7043
E-mail: gwendolyn.campbell@nlrb.gov

Region 25 - Indianapolis (IN)
Minton-Capehart Federal Building, 575 North Pennsylvania Street,
Room 238, Indianapolis, IN 46204
Tel: (317) 226-7430 Fax: (317) 226-5103
Areas Covered: IN, KY (Daviess and Henderson Counties)

● Regional Director **Patricia K. Nachand** . . . . . (317) 991-7624
E-mail: patricia.nachand@nlrb.gov
Education: Indianapolis 1983 BS, 1997 MBA
Assistant to the Regional Director **(Vacant)** . . . . . (317) 226-7430
Regional Attorney **Joanne C. Mages** . . . . . (317) 991-7645
E-mail: joanne.mages@nlrb.gov
Education: Indiana 1987 BSB, 1990 JD
Assistant Regional Attorney **Colleen Maples** . . . . . (317) 226-7430
Compliance Officer **Lisabeth Luther** . . . . . (317) 991-7644
E-mail: lisabeth.luther@nlrb.gov
Office Manager **Constance Trent** . . . . . (317) 991-7629
E-mail: constance.trent@nlrb.gov

Subregion 33 - Peoria (IL)
101 SW Adams Street, Fourth Floor, Peoria, IL 61602
Tel: (309) 671-7080 Fax: (309) 671-7095
Areas Covered: Northern IL

Officer-in-Charge **Nathaniel E. "Nate" Strickler** . . . . . (309) 740-2102
E-mail: nathaniel.strickler@nlrb.gov
Education: Wooster 2000 BA; Southern Illinois 2006 JD
Office Manager **Josh Hinkle** . . . . . (309) 218-1723
Attorney Librarian **(Vacant)** . . . . . (309) 671-7080

Region 27 - Denver (CO)
Byron Rogers Federal Office Building, 1961 Stout Street,
Suite 13-103, Denver, CO 80294
Tel: (303) 844-3551 Fax: (303) 844-6249
Areas Covered: CO, Southern ID, Eastern MT, UT, WY

● Regional Director **Paula Schaeffer Sawyer** . . . . . (720) 709-7199
E-mail: paula.sawyer@nlrb.gov
Education: Cornell 1977 BS; North Carolina 1980 JD
Assistant to the Regional Director **Kelly A. Selvidge** . . . (720) 709-7389
Education: UCLA BA
Regional Attorney **Leticia Peña** . . . . . (720) 598-7412
E-mail: leticia.pena@nlrb.gov
Deputy Regional Attorney **(Vacant)** . . . . . (303) 844-6629
Supervisory Field Examiner **Matthew Lomax** . . . . . (720) 598-7405
E-mail: matthew.lomax@nlrb.gov

★ Presidential Appointment Requiring Senate Confirmation ☆ Presidential Appointment □ Schedule C Appointment ◇ Career Senior Foreign Service Appointment
● Career Senior Executive Service (SES) Appointment ○ Non-Career Senior Executive Service (SES) Appointment ■ Postal Career Executive Service

Region 27 - Denver (CO) *(continued)*

Compliance Officer **Erika K. Bailey** . . . . (720) 598-7398
E-mail: erika.bailey@nlrb.gov
Office Manager **Donna L. Brown** . . . . (720) 598-7401

Region 28 - Phoenix (AZ)

2600 North Central Avenue, Suite 1400, Phoenix, AZ 85004-3099
Tel: (602) 640-2160 Fax: (602) 640-2178
Areas Covered: AZ, NM, Southern NV

● Regional Director **Cornele A. Overstreet** . . . . (602) 416-4755
E-mail: cornele.overstreet@nlrb.gov
Assistant to the Regional Director **(Vacant)** . . . . (602) 416-4753
Regional Attorney **Stephen E. "Steve" Wamser** . . . . (602) 640-2160
Deputy Regional Attorney **(Vacant)** . . . . (505) 248-5130
Compliance Officer **(Vacant)** . . . . (702) 820-7461
Office Manager **Kathleen Rourke-Osborne** . . . . (602) 336-5184
E-mail: kathleen.rourke-osborne@nlrb.gov

Region 29 - Brooklyn (NY)

Two Metro Tech Center, 100 Myrtle Avenue,
5th Floor, Brooklyn, NY 11201-4202
Tel: (718) 330-7713 Fax: (718) 330-7579
Areas Covered: Brooklyn, Nassau County, Queens, Staten Island, Suffolk County

● Regional Director **Kathy Drew King** . . . . (718) 765-6205
E-mail: kathy.king@nlrb.gov
Assistant Regional Director **Teresa Poor** . . . . (718) 765-6153
Regional Attorney **Nancy Reibstein** . . . . (718) 765-6155
E-mail: nancy.reibstein@nlrb.gov
Office Manager **Ellie Izzo** . . . . (718) 765-6201

Region 31 - Los Angeles (CA)

Olympic Plaza, 11500 West Olympic Boulevard,
Suite 600, Los Angeles, CA 90064
Tel: (310) 235-7352 Fax: (310) 235-7420
Areas Covered: Central CA

● Regional Director **Mori Rubin** . . . . (310) 307-7306
E-mail: mori.rubin@nlrb.gov
Education: UCLA 1977 BA; Boalt Hall JD
Assistant to the Regional Director **Tom Chang** . . . . (310) 307-7328
E-mail: tom.chang@nlrb.gov
Regional Attorney **Brian Gee** . . . . (310) 307-7334
E-mail: brian.gee@nlrb.gov
Education: Occidental 1987 BA; Vanderbilt 1995 JD
Deputy Regional Attorney **(Vacant)** . . . . (310) 235-7638
Compliance Supervisor **Danielle Pierce** . . . . (310) 307-7302
E-mail: danielle.pierce@nlrb.gov
Office Manager **Susan Shintaku** . . . . (310) 307-7308
E-mail: susan.shintaku@nlrb.gov

Region 32 - Oakland (CA)

Federal Building, 1301 Clay Street, Suite 300N, Oakland, CA 94612-5224
Tel: (510) 637-3300 Fax: (510) 637-3315
Areas Covered: Northern CA

● Regional Director **Valerie Hardy-Mahoney** . . . . (510) 637-3300
E-mail: valerie.hardy-mahoney@nlrb.gov
Education: Notre Dame BA; UC Berkeley JD
Assistant to the Regional Director **(Vacant)** . . . . (510) 637-3300
Regional Attorney **Christy J. Kwon** . . . . (510) 637-3300
Education: UC Berkeley BA; UCLA JD
Deputy Regional Attorney **Jeffrey Henze** . . . . (510) 637-3300
E-mail: jeffrey.henze@nlrb.gov
Compliance Officer **Paloma Loya** . . . . (510) 637-3300
E-mail: paloma.loya@nlrb.gov
Office Manager **(Vacant)** . . . . (510) 637-3300

INDEPENDENT AGENCIES

★ Presidential Appointment Requiring Senate Confirmation ☆ Presidential Appointment ☐ Schedule C Appointment ◇ Career Senior Foreign Service Appointment
● Career Senior Executive Service (SES) Appointment ○ Non-Career Senior Executive Service (SES) Appointment ■ Postal Career Executive Service

National Transportation Safety Board (NTSB)

Description: The National Transportation Safety Board is charged with investigating every civil aviation accident in the United States as well as significant railroad, highway, marine, and pipeline accidents, and with issuing safety recommendations aimed at preventing future accidents.

490 L'Enfant Plaza, SW, Washington, DC 20594
Tel: (202) 314-6000 (Personnel Locator)
Tel: (202) 314-6220 (Facilities Services and Procurement Information)
Tel: (202) 314-6100 (Public Affairs)
Tel: (202) 314-6551 (Records Management Division)
Tel: (202) 314-6540 (Freedom of Information/Privacy Act)
E-mail: pubinq@ntsb.gov Internet: www.ntsb.gov
Internet: www.ntsb.gov/publications (Publications)
Internet: www.usa.gov (Official US Government Website)

The Board

490 L'Enfant Plaza, SW, Washington, DC 20594
Note: Members may continue to serve until reappointed or replaced.

Office of Administrative Law Judges (ALJ)

490 L'Enfant Plaza, SW, Washington, DC 20594
Tel: (202) 314-6150 Fax: (202) 314-6158 (Virtual Fax)
E-mail: aljappeals@ntsb.gov

Circuit I

Areas Covered: CT, DE, DC, ID, ME, MD, MA, MI, NH, NJ, NY, OH, PA, RI, VT, WI

Administrative Law Judge **Stephen R. Woody** .... (202) 314-6150
E-mail: stephen.woody@ntsb.gov
Education: West Virginia JD

Circuit II

Areas Covered: AL, FL, GA, KY, LA, MS, NC, SC, TN, VA, WV

Administrative Law Judge **Alfonso J. Montano** .... (202) 314-6150
E-mail: alfonso.montano@ntsb.gov
Education: U San Francisco JD

Circuit III

4760 Oakland Street, Denver, CO 80239
Fax: (303) 373-3507
Areas Covered: AZ, CA, CO, ID, MT, NV, OR, UT, WA, WY

Administrative Law Judge **(Vacant)** Room 500 .... (303) 373-3511

Circuit IV

490 L'Enfant Plaza, SW, Washington, DC 20594
Tel: (202) 314-6150
Areas Covered: AR, IL, IA, KS, LA, MN, MO, NE, NM, ND, OK, SD, TX, WI

Administrative Law Judge **William R. Mullins** .... (202) 314-6150
E-mail: mullinw@ntsb.gov
Education: Panhandle State 1963 BA; Colorado 1969 JD

OFFICE OF THE MANAGING DIRECTOR (MD)

490 L'Enfant Plaza, SW, Washington, DC 20594
Tel: (202) 314-6060

Office of Aviation Safety (AS)

490 L'Enfant Plaza, SW, Washington, DC 20594
Fax: (202) 314-6309

Regional Offices

Alaska Regional Office (ANC)
222 West Seventh Avenue, Room 216 (Box 11), Anchorage, AK 99513-7504
Tel: (907) 271-5001 Fax: (907) 271-3007
Areas Covered: AK

Regional Chief **Clint Johnson** .... (907) 271-5001
Education: Alaska BA

Central Regional Office (CEN)
4760 Oakland Street, Suite 500, Denver, CO 80239
Tel: (303) 373-3500 Fax: (303) 373-3507
Areas Covered: AR, CO, IA, IL, IN, KS, LA, MI, MN, MO, OH, OK, ND, NE, NM, SD, TX, WI, WY

Regional Chief **David Bowling** .... (303) 373-3500 ext. 1
E-mail: bowlind@ntsb.gov
Deputy Regional Chief
Timothy "Tim" LeBaron .... (303) 373-3500 ext. 2
E-mail: tim.lebaron@ntsb.gov

Eastern Regional Office (ERA)
45065 Riverside Parkway, Ashburn, VA 20147
Tel: (571) 223-3930 Fax: (571) 223-3926
Areas Covered: AL, CT, DE, FL, GA, KY, ME, MA, MD, MS, NC, NH, NJ, NY, PA, RI, SC, TN, VA, VT, WV

Regional Chief **Dennis Diaz** .... (571) 223-3925
E-mail: dennis.diaz@ntsb.gov
Deputy Regional Chief **Luke Schiada** .... (571) 223-3930
E-mail: luke.schiada@ntsb.gov

Western Pacific Regional Office (WPR)
505 South 336th Street, Suite 540, Federal Way, WA 98003
Tel: (253) 874-2880 Fax: (240) 752-6343
Areas Covered: AZ, CA, HI, ID, MT, OR, NV, UT, WA

Regional Chief **Debra J. Eckrote** .... (253) 874-0621
E-mail: eckrotd@ntsb.gov
Deputy Chief **Dennis Hogenson** .... (253) 874-0622
Senior Aviation Accident Investigator
Joshua "Josh" Cawthra .... (202) 314-6651
Senior Aviation Accident Investigator **Zoë Keliher** .... (202) 314-6653
Senior Aviation Accident Investigator **Thomas Little** ..... (202) 314-6654
Senior Aviation Accident Investigator **Albert Nixon** ...... (202) 314-6655
Senior Aviation Accident Investigator **Eliott Simpson** .... (202) 314-6487
Aviation Accident Investigator **Tealeye Cornejo** .... (202) 314-6507
Aviation Accident Investigator **Samantha Link** .... (202) 314-6332
Aviation Accident Investigator **Maja Smith** .... (253) 874-7836
Aviation Accident Investigator **Stephen Stein** .... (253) 835-5383

Western Pacific Regional Office *(continued)*

Aviation Accident Investigator **Andrew Swick** . . . . (202) 314-6659
Aviation Accident Investigator **Jackie. L. Vanover** . . . . (253) 874-0641
Aerospace Engineer **Michael Huhn** . . . . (202) 314-6489
Staff Assistant **Monica Stachowiak** . . . . (253) 874-0626
E-mail: stachom@ntsb.gov

★ Presidential Appointment Requiring Senate Confirmation ☆ Presidential Appointment ☐ Schedule C Appointment ◇ Career Senior Foreign Service Appointment
● Career Senior Executive Service (SES) Appointment ○ Non-Career Senior Executive Service (SES) Appointment ■ Postal Career Executive Service

Neighborhood Reinvestment Corporation (NeighborWorks® America)

Description: The Neighborhood Reinvestment Corporation promotes reinvestment in older neighborhoods by local financial institutions working cooperatively with community members and the local government.

999 North Capitol Street NE, Suite 900, Washington, DC 20002
Tel: (202) 760-4000 (Personnel Locator)
Tel: (202) 220-2308 (Procurement Information)
Tel: (202) 220-2471 (Publications Information)
Tel: (202) 220-2415 (Freedom of Information/Privacy Act)
Fax: (202) 220-2600 Internet: www.neighborworks.org
Internet: www.usa.gov (Official US Government Website)

Board of Directors

999 North Capitol Street NE, Washington, DC 20002

OFFICE OF THE CHIEF EXECUTIVE OFFICER

999 North Capitol Street NE, Washington, DC 20002
Fax: (202) 376-2160

Office of the Chief Operating Officer

Division of Field Operations

Midwest Region
4435 Main Street, Suite 700, Kansas City, MO 64111
Tel: (816) 931-4176 Fax: (816) 714-1291
Areas Covered: IL, IN, IA, KS, MI, MN, MO, NE, ND, OH, OK, SD, WI

Regional Vice President **John Santner** . . . . (816) 714-1224
E-mail: jsantner@nw.org

Northeast Region
Areas Covered: CT, DE, ME, MA, NH, NY, NJ, PA, PR, RI, VT, VI

Regional Vice President
Joan Straussman Brandon . . . . (212) 269-6553 ext. 32
80 Pine Street, New York, NY 10005

Southern Region
One Georgia Center, 260 Peachtree Street,
Suite 1000, Atlanta, GA 30303
Tel: (404) 526-1270 Fax: (404) 526-1271
Areas Covered: AL, AR, DC, FL, GA, KY, LA, MD, MS, NC, SC, TN, VA, WV

Regional Vice President **Donald R. Phoenix** . . . . (404) 526-1290
E-mail: dphoenix@nw.org

Western Region
Areas Covered: AK, AR, CA, CO, HI, ID, MT, NV, NM, OR, TX, UT, WA, WY

Regional Vice President **Gary Wolfe** . . . . (303) 782-5191
501 South Cherry Street, Denver, CO 80246-3326
E-mail: gwolfe@nw.org

Northwest Power and Conservation Council (NPCC)

Description: The Northwest Power and Conservation Council is a four-state compact formed by Idaho, Montana, Oregon, and Washington to oversee electric power system planning as well as fish and wildlife recovery in the Columbia River Basin.

Public Affairs Division, 851 Southwest Sixth Avenue,
Suite 1100, Portland, OR 97204-1348
Tel: (503) 222-5161 Fax: (503) 820-2370 E-mail: info@nwcouncil.org
Internet: www.nwcouncil.org

COUNCIL MEMBERS

Chair **Jim Yost** Suite 1020 .... (208) 947-4080
Education: Southern Idaho 1968 AA; Boise State 1971 BAE

Vice Chair **Jennifer Anders** .... (406) 603-4013
30 W 14th Street, Room #207, Helena, MT 59601
Education: Montana JD

State Member **Ted Ferrioli** Suite 1020 .... (503) 229-5171
E-mail: tferirioli@nwcouncil.org
Education: Oregon 1973 BA

State Member **Dr. Tom Karier** .... (509) 828-1330
Term Expires: January 1, 2019 Fax: (509) 828-1329
668 N. Riverpoint Boulevard,
Suite 137, Spokane, WA 99202
Education: Illinois BS; UC Berkeley PhD

State Member **Richard Devlin** Suite 1020 .... (503) 229-5171
Education: Portland State 1976 BS; Pepperdine 1980 MA

State Member **Guy Norman** .... (360) 816-1172
Term Expires: January 1, 2019
315 W Mill Plain Boulevard, Room #202, Vancouver, WA 98660

State Member **Tim Baker** .... (406) 603-4013
30 W 14th Street, Room #207, Helena, MT 59601

State Member **Jim Yost** .... (208) 947-4080
Term Expires: January 1, 2018 Fax: (208) 908-7318
244 South Academy Ave, Eagle, ID 83616
Education: Southern Idaho 1968 AA; Boise State 1971 BAE

State Member **William B. "Bill" Booth** .... (208) 660-4127
244 South Academy Ave, Eagle, ID 83616
Education: Idaho 1974 BS; North Dakota MBA

Fish and Wildlife Committee

Committee Chair **Jennifer Anders** .... (406) 403-4013
E-mail: janders@nwcouncil.org
Education: Montana JD

Council Member **Ted Ferrioli** .... (503) 229-5171
E-mail: tferrioli@nwcouncil.org
Education: Oregon 1973 BA

Council Member **William B. "Bill" Booth** .... (208) 772-2447
Education: Idaho 1974 BS; North Dakota MBA Fax: (208) 772-9254

Council Member **Guy Norman** .... (360) 816-1172
E-mail: gnorman@nwcouncil.org

Power Committee

Committee Chair **Dr. Tom Karier** .... (509) 828-1330
E-mail: tkarier@nwcouncil.org Fax: (509) 455-7251
Education: Illinois BS; UC Berkeley PhD

Council Member **Tim Baker** .... (406) 603-4016
30 W. 14th Street, Fax: (406) 444-4339
Suite 207, Helena, MT 59601
E-mail: tbaker@nwcouncil.org

Council Member **Richard Devlin** .... (503) 229-5171
851 SW Sixth Avenue, Fax: (503) 229-5173
Suite 1020, Portland, OR 97204-1347
E-mail: rdevlin@nwcouncil.org
Education: Portland State 1976 BS; Pepperdine 1980 MA

Power Committee *(continued)*

Council Member **Jim Yost** .... (208) 334-6970
244 South Academy Ave, Eagle, ID 83616 Fax: (208) 334-2112
E-mail: jyost@nwcouncil.org
Education: Southern Idaho 1968 AA; Boise State 1971 BAE

Central Office Staff

851 Southwest Sixth Avenue, Suite 1100, Portland, OR 97204-1348
Tel: (503) 222-5161 Tel: (800) 452-5161 Fax: (503) 820-2370

Executive Division

Executive Director **Steve Crow** .... (503) 222-5161
E-mail: scrow@nwcouncil.org
Education: Oregon State BA; Oregon JD

Executive Assistant and Legal Assistant **Judi Hertz** ...... (503) 222-5161
E-mail: jhertz@nwcouncil.org
Education: BYU; Portland State

Administrative Division

Administrative Division Director **Sharon Ossmann** ..... (503) 222-5161
E-mail: sossmann@nwcouncil.org
Education: Washington State

Accountant/Financial Specialist **Michael Osborne** .... (503) 222-5161
E-mail: mosborne@nwcouncil.org

Information Systems Manager **Bud Decker** .... (503) 222-5161
E-mail: bdecker@nwcouncil.org

Information Systems Assistant **Barry Richardson** ...... (503) 222-5161
E-mail: brichardson@nwcouncil.org

Travel Coordinator/Accounting Assistant **Trina Gerlack** ... (503) 222-5161
E-mail: tgerlack@nwcouncil.org

Payroll/Accounting Assistant **Tamara Fleming** .... (503) 222-5161
E-mail: tfleming@nwcouncil.org

Production and Facilities Support **Bethany Slyter** .... (503) 222-5161

Receptionist **Deb Woolf** .... (503) 222-5161
E-mail: dwoolf@nwcouncil.org

Fish and Wildlife Division

Director **Tony Grover** .... (503) 222-5161
E-mail: tgrover@nwcouncil.org

Program Implementation Manager **Patty O'Toole** .... (503) 222-5161
E-mail: potoole@nwcouncil.org
Education: Oregon State BS

Project Implementation Manager **Mark Fritsch** .... (503) 222-5161
E-mail: mfritsch@nwcouncil.org
Education: Oregon State BS

Program Implementation and Liaison Specialist
Laura Robinson .... (503) 222-5161
E-mail: lrobinson@nwcouncil.org

Senior Program Manager **Leslie Bach** .... (503) 222-5161
E-mail: lbach@nwcouncil.org

Program Development Manager **Lynn Palensky** .... (503) 222-5161
E-mail: lpalensky@nwcouncil.org
Education: U Washington 1987 BS; Troy State MPA

Fish, Wildlife, and Ecosystem Monitoring and
Evaluation Manager **Nancy Leonard** .... (503) 222-5161
E-mail: nleonard@nwcouncil.org

Wildlife and Resident Fish Manager **(Vacant)** .... (503) 222-5161

Administrative Assistant **Kendra Coles** .... (503) 222-5161
E-mail: kcoles@nwcouncil.org

(continued on next page)

★ Presidential Appointment Requiring Senate Confirmation ☆ Presidential Appointment ☐ Schedule C Appointment ◇ Career Senior Foreign Service Appointment
● Career Senior Executive Service (SES) Appointment ○ Non-Career Senior Executive Service (SES) Appointment ■ Postal Career Executive Service

Fish and Wildlife Division *(continued)*

ISRP/ISAB (Independent Scientific Review Panel/Independent Scientific Advisory Board)
Coordinator **Erik Merrill** . . . . (503) 222-5161
E-mail: emerrill@nwcouncil.org
Education: Arizona BA; Lewis & Clark JD

Legal Division

General Counsel [Chief FOIA Officer] **John Shurts** . . . . . (503) 222-5161
E-mail: jshurts@nwcouncil.org
Education: Colorado Col BA; Lewis & Clark JD; Oregon PhD

Senior Counsel **Sandra Hirotsu** . . . . (503) 222-5161
E-mail: shirotsu@nwcouncil.org

Executive Assistant and Legal Assistant **Judi Hertz** . . . . . . (503) 222-5161
E-mail: jhertz@nwcouncil.org
Education: BYU; Portland State

Power Planning Division

Director **Ben Kujala** . . . . (503) 222-5161
E-mail: bkujala@nwcouncil.org

Regional Technical Forum Manager **Jennifer Light** . . . . . . (503) 222-5161
E-mail: jlight@nwcouncil.org

Regional Technical Forum Assistant **Garrett Herndon** . . . . (503) 222-5161
E-mail: gherndon@nwcouncil.org

Economic Analysis Manager **Massoud Jourabchi** . . . . (503) 222-5161
E-mail: mjourabchi@nwcouncil.org

System Analysis Manager **(Vacant)** . . . . (503) 222-5161

Senior Energy Analyst **Kevin Smit** . . . . (503) 222-5161
E-mail: ksmit@nwcouncil.org

Senior Economic Analyst **Steve Simmons** . . . . (503) 222-5161
E-mail: ssimmons@nwcouncil.org

Senior Energy Efficiency Analyst **Tina Jayaweera** . . . . . . (503) 222-5161
E-mail: tjayaweera@nwcouncil.org

Senior Economist **(Vacant)** . . . . (503) 222-5161

Senior Power System Analyst **John Fazio** . . . . (503) 222-5161
E-mail: jfazio@nwcouncil.org
Education: Portland BS; Oregon 1976 MS

Power System Analyst **John Ollis** . . . . (503) 222-5161
E-mail: jollis@nwcouncil.org

Power System Analyst **Dan Hua** . . . . (503) 222-5161
E-mail: dhua@nwcouncil.org

Conservation Resources Manager **Charlie Grist** . . . . (503) 222-5161
E-mail: cgrist@nwcouncil.org
Education: Wisconsin BS

Energy Policy Analyst **Gillian Charles** . . . . (503) 222-5161
E-mail: gcharles@nwcouncil.org

Project Analyst **Chad Madron** . . . . (503) 222-5161

Energy Policy Analyst **Mike Starrett** . . . . (503) 222-5161
E-mail: mstarrett@nwcouncil.org

Public Affairs Division

Director **Mark Walker** . . . . (503) 222-5161
E-mail: mwalker@nwcouncil.org Fax: (503) 820-2370
Education: Linfield BA; Willamette MBA; Oregon MA

Public Information Officer **John Harrison** . . . . (503) 222-5161
E-mail: jharrison@nwcouncil.org
Education: Washington State BA; Oregon MA

Senior Writer and Editor **Carol Winkel** . . . . (503) 222-5161
E-mail: cwinkel@nwcouncil.org
Education: Reed BA

Technical/Web Data Specialist **Eric Schrepel** . . . . (503) 820-2328
E-mail: eschrepel@nwcouncil.org
Education: Cal State (Chico) BA

United States Nuclear Regulatory Commission (NRC)

Description: The Nuclear Regulatory Commission regulates the nation's civilian use of byproduct, source, and special nuclear materials in order to protect public health and safety, promote common defense and security, and conserve the environment.

11555 Rockville Pike, Mail Stop 14D21, Rockville, MD 20852-2738
Tel: (301) 415-7000 Tel: (800) 368-5642 (Personnel Locator)
Tel: (301) 415-7314 (Procurement Information)
Tel: (202) 634-3273 (Public Documents Room)
Tel: (301) 415-8200 (Public Information)
Tel: (301) 415-7166 (Publications Information)
Tel: (301) 816-5100 (Emergency Response Hotline)
Tel: (301) 415-7169 (Freedom of Information/Privacy Act)
Tel: (800) 695-7403 (Unsafe Nuclear Facilities Reporting Hotline)
Internet: www.nrc.gov

The Commission (COMM)

One White Flint North Building, 11555 Rockville Pike,
Rockville, MD 20852-2738

OFFICE OF THE EXECUTIVE DIRECTOR FOR OPERATIONS (EDO)

One White Flint North Building, 11555 Rockville Pike,
Rockville, MD 20852-2738
Fax: (301) 415-2162 Fax: (301) 415-2700

Deputy Executive Director for Reactor and Preparedness Programs

One White Flint North Building, 11555 Rockville Pike,
Rockville, MD 20852-2738
Fax: (301) 415-2700

Regional Offices

Region I (R-I)
2100 Renaissance Boulevard, Suite 100, King of Prussia, PA 19406-2713
Tel: (610) 337-5000 Fax: (610) 337-5368 E-mail: opa@nrc.gov
Areas Covered: CT, DE, DC, ME, MD, MA, NH, NJ, NY, PA, RI, VT

● Regional Administrator **David C. Lew** . . . . (610) 337-5340
E-mail: david.lew@nrc.gov
Education: Columbia BS
● Deputy Regional Administrator **Raymond K. Lorson** . . . . (610) 337-5000
E-mail: raymond.lorson@nrc.gov
Regional Counsel **Brett Michael Klukan** . . . . (610) 337-5301
E-mail: brett.klukan@nrc.gov
Senior Public Affairs Officer **Diane Screnci** . . . . (610) 337-5330
E-mail: diane.screnci@nrc.gov
Field Public Affairs Officer **Neil A. Sheehan** . . . . (610) 337-5331
E-mail: neil.sheehan@nrc.gov
State Liaison Officer **Douglas B. Tifft** . . . . (610) 337-6918
Team Leader, Allegations/Enforcement Staff
Brice Bickett . . . . (610) 337-5312
E-mail: brice.bickett@nrc.gov

Office of Investigations
2100 Renaissance Boulevard, King of Prussia, PA 19406-2713
Tel: (610) 337-5305
Special Agent In Charge **Jeffrey A. Teator** . . . . (610) 337-5243

Nuclear Materials Safety Division (R-I/DNMS)
● Director (Acting) **Joseph L. Nick** . . . . (610) 337-5283
E-mail: joseph.nick@nrc.gov
Deputy Director **Joseph L. Nick** . . . . (610) 337-5283
E-mail: joseph.nick@nrc.gov
Decommissioning, ISFSI and Reactor Health Physics
Branch Chief **Raymond J. Powell** . . . . (610) 337-6967
E-mail: raymond.powell@nrc.gov
Commercial, Industrial, Research and Development,
and Academic Branch Chief **Arthur L. Burritt** . . . . (610) 337-5069
E-mail: arthur.burritt@nrc.gov
Medical and Licensing Assistance Branch Chief
Donna M. Janda . . . . (610) 337-5371
E-mail: donna.janda@nrc.gov

Reactor Projects Division (R-I/DRP)
● Director **(Vacant)** . . . . (610) 337-5126
● Deputy Director **David "Dave" Pelton** . . . . (610) 337-5126
E-mail: david.pelton@nrc.gov
Projects Branch 1 Chief **(Vacant)** . . . . (610) 337-6953
Projects Branch 2 Chief **Jonathan E. Greives** . . . . (610) 337-5120
E-mail: jonathan.greives@nrc.gov
Projects Branch 3 Chief **Fred Bower** . . . . (610) 337-5200
E-mail: fred.bower@nrc.gov
Projects Branch 4 Chief **Daniel L. "Dan" Schroeder** . . . . (610) 337-5262
E-mail: daniel.schroeder@nrc.gov
Projects Branch 5 Chief **Anthony Dimitriadis** . . . . (610) 337-6953
E-mail: anthony.dimitriadis@nrc.gov
Projects Branch 6 Chief **Matthew R. Young** . . . . (610) 337-5205
Technical Support and Assessment Branch Chief
Marc S. Ferdas . . . . (610) 337-5022
E-mail: marc.ferdas@nrc.gov
Education: Drexel; Rutgers

Reactor Safety Division
2100 Renaissance Boulevard, King of Prussia, PA 19406-2713
E-mail: keith.heater@nrc.gov
● Director **Jimi T. Yerokun** . . . . (610) 337-5128
E-mail: jimi.yerokun@nrc.gov
Education: Benedict 1977 BSc; Georgia Tech 1980 BME
● Deputy Director **Blake D. Welling** . . . . (610) 337-5081
E-mail: blake.welling@nrc.gov
Engineering Branch 1 Chief **Melvin Gray** . . . . (610) 337-5209
Engineering Branch 2 Chief **Glenn T. Dentel** . . . . (610) 337-5233
E-mail: glenn.dentel@nrc.gov
Operations Branch Chief **Donald Jackson** . . . . (610) 337-5306
E-mail: donald.jackson@nrc.gov
Plant Support Branch Chief **Raymond McKinley, Jr.** . . . . . (610) 337-5150
E-mail: raymond.mckinley@nrc.gov

Division of Resource Management
2100 Renaissance Boulevard, King of Prussia, PA 19406-2713
Fax: (610) 337-5180
Director **Tracy E. Walker** . . . . (610) 337-5381
E-mail: tracy.walker@nrc.gov
Deputy Director **(Vacant)** . . . . (610) 337-5079
Financial Resources Branch Chief **David Rule** . . . . (610) 337-5350
Information Resources Branch Chief **Michael B. Dean** . . . (610) 337-5079
E-mail: michael.dean@nrc.gov

(continued on next page)

★ Presidential Appointment Requiring Senate Confirmation ☆ Presidential Appointment ☐ Schedule C Appointment ◇ Career Senior Foreign Service Appointment
● Career Senior Executive Service (SES) Appointment ○ Non-Career Senior Executive Service (SES) Appointment ■ Postal Career Executive Service

Division of Resource Management *(continued)*

Human Resources Staff Chief **Colleen Todd** (610) 337-5352
E-mail: colleen.todd@nrc.gov
Administrative Assistant/Events Planning
Linda M. Larche (610) 337-5201
E-mail: linda.larche@nrc.gov

Region II (R-II)

245 Peachtree Center Avenue NE, Suite 1200, Atlanta, GA 30303-1257
Tel: (404) 997-4000 Fax: (404) 997-4900
Areas Covered: AL, FL, GA, KY, NC, PR, SC, TN, VI, VA, WV

● Regional Administrator **Catherine Haney** (404) 997-4410
E-mail: catherine.haney@nrc.gov
● Deputy Regional Administrator for Construction
Laura A. Dudes (404) 997-4472
E-mail: laura.dudes@nrc.gov
● Deputy Regional Administrator for Operations
(Vacant) (404) 997-4410
Regional Counsel **Sarah Price** (404) 997-4414
E-mail: sarah.price@nrc.gov
Enforcement Officer **Mark G. Kowal** (404) 997-4523
E-mail: mark.kowal@nrc.gov
Regional State Liaison Officer **John Pelchat** (404) 997-4739
E-mail: john.pelchat@nrc.gov
Senior Public Affairs Officer **Roger D. Hannah** (404) 997-4417
E-mail: roger.hannah@nrc.gov
Field Public Affairs Officer **Joseph "Joey" Ledford** (404) 997-4416
E-mail: joey.ledford@nrc.gov

Construction Oversight Division

● Director **William B. Jones** (404) 997-4200
E-mail: william.jones@nrc.gov
● Deputy Director **Shakur A. Walker** (404) 997-4639
E-mail: shakur.walker@nrc.gov
Education: Alabama A&M 2000 BS; Wisconsin 2015 MEng
Construction Inspection Branch I Chief
Jamie M. Heisserer (404) 997-4451
E-mail: jamie.heisserer@nrc.gov
Construction Inspection Branch II Chief
Michael E. Ernstes (404) 997-4540
E-mail: michael.ernstes@nrc.gov

Fuel Facility Inspection Division (R-II/DFFI)

● Director **Mark S. Lesser** (404) 997-4501
E-mail: mark.lesser@nrc.gov
● Deputy Director **LaDonna Suggs** (404) 997-4539
E-mail: ladonna.suggs@nrc.gov
Projects Branch 1 Chief **Omar Lopez-Santiago** (404) 997-4703
E-mail: omar.lopez@nrc.gov
Projects Branch 2 Chief **Eric Michel** (404) 997-4555
E-mail: eric.michel@nrc.gov
Safety Branch Chief **Rebecca L. Nease** (404) 997-4530
E-mail: rebecca.nease@nrc.gov

Reactor Projects Division (R-II/DRP)

245 Peachtree Center Avenue NE, Atlanta, GA 30303-1257
Tel: (404) 997-4500

● Director **Joel T. Munday** (404) 997-4500
E-mail: joel.munday@nrc.gov
● Deputy Director **Mark Franke** (404) 997-4501
E-mail: mark.franke@nrc.gov
Reactor Projects Branch I Chief **Frank Ehrhardt** (404) 997-4607
E-mail: frank.ehrhardt@nrc.gov
Reactor Projects Branch II Chief **Alan J. Blamey** (404) 997-4415
E-mail: alan.blamey@nrc.gov
Reactor Projects Branch III Chief
Randall A. "Randy" Musser (404) 997-4603
E-mail: randy.musser@nrc.gov
Reactor Projects Branch IV Chief **Steven D. Rose** (404) 997-4609
E-mail: steven.rose@nrc.gov
Reactor Projects Branch V Chief **Anthony Masters** (404) 997-4645
E-mail: anthony.masters@nrc.gov
Reactor Projects Branch VI Chief **Shane Sandal** (404) 997-4513
E-mail: shane.sandal@nrc.gov

Reactor Safety Division (R-II/DRS)

● Director **Anthony T. "Tony" Gody, Jr.** (404) 997-4201
E-mail: tony.gody@nrc.gov
Education: Florida 1986 BSEE
● Deputy Director **Mark S. Miller** (404) 997-4601
E-mail: mark.miller@nrc.gov
Engineering Branch I Chief **Marvin D. Sykes** (404) 997-4629
E-mail: marvin.sykes@nrc.gov
Engineering Branch II Chief **Scott Shaeffer** (404) 997-4530
E-mail: scott.shaeffer@nrc.gov
Engineering Branch III Chief **Brian Bonser** (404) 997-4653
E-mail: brian.bonser@nrc.gov
Operations Branch I Chief **Gerald J. "Gerry" McCoy** (404) 997-4550
E-mail: gerald.mccoy@nrc.gov
Operations Branch II Chief **Eugene F. Guthrie** (404) 997-4550
E-mail: eugene.guthrie@nrc.gov
Plant Support Branch Chief **Binoy Desai** (770) 997-4519
E-mail: binoy.desai@nrc.gov

Incident Response Center

Emergency Response Coordinator
Steven "Steve" Rudisail (404) 997-4512
E-mail: steven.rudisail@nrc.gov

Resource Management and Administration Division

● Director **Glenn Trent** (404) 997-4800
E-mail: glenn.trent@nrc.gov
● Deputy Director **(Vacant)** (404) 997-4801
Information Resources Branch Chief **Jose Diaz-Velez** (404) 997-4736
E-mail: jose.diaz@nrc.gov
Human Resources Branch Chief **Gloria Reeves** (404) 997-4843
E-mail: gloria.reeves@nrc.gov

Financial Management Branch

245 Peachtree Center Avenue NE, Atlanta, GA 30303-1257
Financial Management Branch Chief **Clinton McGill** (404) 997-4808
E-mail: clinton.mcgill@nrc.gov

Region III (R-III)

2443 Warrenville Road, Suite 210, Lisle, IL 60532-4352
Tel: (630) 829-9500 Fax: (630) 515-1078
Areas Covered: IL, IN, IA, MI, MN, MO, OH, WI

● Regional Administrator **K. Steven "Steve" West** (630) 829-9658
E-mail: steven.west@nrc.gov
Education: Maryland 1979 BS
● Deputy Regional Administrator **Darrell J. Roberts** (630) 829-9654
E-mail: darrell.roberts@nrc.gov
Regional Counsel **Jared K. Heck** (630) 829-9653
E-mail: jared.heck@nrc.gov
Enforcement and Investigation Officer
Richard A. Skokowski (630) 810-4373
E-mail: richard.skokowski@nrc.gov
Regional State Liaison Officer **Allan R. Barker** (630) 829-9660
E-mail: allan.barker@nrc.gov
Senior Public Affairs Officer **Viktoria Mitlyng** (630) 829-9663
E-mail: viktoria.mitlyng@nrc.gov
Field Public Affairs Officer **Prema S. Chandrathil** (630) 829-9663
E-mail: prema.chandrathil@nrc.gov

Nuclear Materials Safety Division (R-III/DNMS)

● Director **John B. Giessner** (630) 829-9800
E-mail: john.giessner@nrc.gov
Deputy Director (Acting) **Christine A. Lipa** (630) 829-9801
E-mail: christine.lipa@nrc.gov
State Agreement Program Officer **Darren W. Piccirillo** (630) 829-9661
E-mail: darren.piccirillo@nrc.gov
Materials Control, ISFSI and Decommissioning Branch
Chief **Michael A. Kunowski** (630) 829-9834
E-mail: michael.kunowski@nrc.gov
Materials Inspection Branch Chief **Aaron McCraw** (630) 829-9876
E-mail: aaron.mccraw@nrc.gov
Materials Licensing Branch Chief **Patricia J. Pelke** (630) 829-9834
E-mail: patricia.pelke@nrc.gov

★ Presidential Appointment Requiring Senate Confirmation ☆ Presidential Appointment ☐ Schedule C Appointment ◇ Career Senior Foreign Service Appointment
● Career Senior Executive Service (SES) Appointment ○ Non-Career Senior Executive Service (SES) Appointment ■ Postal Career Executive Service

Reactor Projects Division

- ● Director **Patrick L. Louden** .... (630) 829-9600
  E-mail: patrick.louden@nrc.gov
- ● Deputy Director **Julio F. Lara** .... (630) 829-9601
  E-mail: julio.lara@nrc.gov
- Branch I Chief **Karla K. Stoedter** .... (630) 829-9703
  E-mail: karla.stoedter@nrc.gov
- Branch II Chief **Kenneth R. Riemer** .... (630) 829-9705
  E-mail: kenneth.riemer@nrc.gov
- Branch III Chief **Eric R. Duncan** .... (630) 829-9729
  E-mail: eric.duncan@nrc.gov
- Branch IV Chief **Jamnes L. Cameron** .... (630) 829-9833
  E-mail: jamnes.cameron@nrc.gov
- Branch V Chief **Billy C. Dickson** .... (630) 829-9618
  E-mail: billy.dickson@nrc.gov
- Technical Staff Support Chief **Ann Marie J. Stone** .... (630) 829-9500
  E-mail: annmarie.stone@nrc.gov

Reactor Safety Division

- ● Director **Kenneth G. O'Brien** .... (630) 829-9700
  E-mail: kenneth.obrien@nrc.gov
- ● Deputy Director **Mohammed A. Shuaibi** .... (630) 829-9701
  E-mail: mohammed.shuaibi@nrc.gov
- Engineering Branch 1 Chief **David E. Hills** .... (630) 829-9733
  E-mail: david.hills@nrc.gov
- Engineering Branch 2 Chief (Acting) **Mark T. Jeffers** .... (630) 829-9798
  E-mail: mark.jeffers@nrc.gov
- Engineering Branch 3 Chief **Robert C. Daley** .... (630) 829-9631
  E-mail: robert.daley@nrc.gov
- Operations Branch Chief **Robert Orlikowski** .... (630) 829-9707
- Plant Support Branch Chief **Steven K. Orth** .... (630) 829-9757
  E-mail: steven.orth@nrc.gov
- Health Physics and Incident Response Branch Chief
  Hironori Peterson .... (630) 829-9757
  E-mail: hironori.peterson@nrc.gov

Resource Management and Administration Division

2443 Warrenville Road, Suite 210, Lisle, IL 60532-4352

- Director **Dina Sotiropoulos** .... (630) 829-9517
  E-mail: dina.sotiropoulos@nrc.gov
- Deputy Director **Mary Elizabeth Walsh** .... (630) 829-9517
  E-mail: mary.walsh@nrc.gov
- Financial and Human Resources Branch Chief
  Dawn M. Jonsson .... (630) 829-9516
  E-mail: dawn.jonsson@nrc.gov
- Technology and Information Resources Branch Chief
  Michael A. King .... (630) 829-9612
  E-mail: michael.king@nrc.gov

Region IV (R-IV)

1600 East Lamar Boulevard, Arlington, TX 76011-4511
Tel: (817) 860-8100 Fax: (817) 200-1122 Fax: (817) 200-1210
Areas Covered: AK, AZ, AR, CA, CO, HI, ID, KS, LA, MS, MT, NE, NV, NM, ND, OK, OR, SD, TX, UT, WA, WY, U.S. territories and possessions in the Pacific

- ● Regional Administrator **Kriss M. Kennedy** .... (817) 200-1225
  E-mail: kriss.kennedy@nrc.gov
  Education: Naval Acad 1981
- ● Deputy Regional Administrator **Scott A. Morris** .... (817) 200-1226
  E-mail: scott.morris@nrc.gov
- Regional Counsel **(Vacant)** .... (817) 860-8100
- Allegation Coordination and Enforcement Chief
  Michael "Mike" Hay .... (817) 200-1182
  E-mail: michael.hay@nrc.gov
- Response Coordination Branch Chief
  Gregory "Greg" Warnick .... (817) 200-1223
  E-mail: greg.warnick@nrc.gov
- Senior Public Affairs Officer **Victor L. Dricks** .... (817) 200-1128
  E-mail: victor.dricks@nrc.gov
- Regional State Liaison Officer **William "Bill" Maier** .... (817) 200-1267

Office of Investigations

- Special Agent In Charge **Gayle R. Walker** .... (817) 200-1115
  E-mail: gayle.walker@nrc.gov

Nuclear Materials Safety Division (R-IV/DNMS)

- ● Director **Troy W. Pruett** .... (817) 200-1248
  E-mail: Troy.Pruett@nrc.gov
- Deputy Director **Linda L. Howell** .... (817) 200-1287
  E-mail: linda.howell@nrc.gov
- Fuel Cycle and Decommission Branch Chief
  Ray L. Keller .... (817) 200-1197
- Materials Licensing and Inspection Branch Chief
  Vivian H. Campbell .... (817) 200-1455

Reactor Projects Division (R-IV/DRP)

- ● Director **Anton Vegel** .... (817) 200-1146
  E-mail: Anton.Vegel@nrc.gov
- ● Deputy Director **Ryan Lantz** .... (817) 200-1291
  E-mail: ryan.lantz@nrc.gov
- Reactor Projects Branch A Chief **Mark S. Haire** .... (817) 200-1148
  E-mail: mark.haire@nrc.gov
- Reactor Projects Branch B Chief
  Nicholas "Nick" Taylor .... (817) 200-1141
  E-mail: nick.taylor@nrc.gov
- Reactor Projects Branch C Chief **Jason W. Kozal** .... (817) 200-1144
  E-mail: jason.kozal@nrc.gov
- Reactor Projects Branch D Chief
  Geoffrey "Geoff" Miller .... (817) 200-1173
  E-mail: geoffrey.miller@nrc.gov
- Reactor Projects Branch E Chief
  Cornelius "Neil" O'Keefe .... (817) 200-1156
  E-mail: neil.okeefe@nrc.gov

Reactor Safety Division

- ● Director **Mark R. Shaffer** .... (817) 200-1146
  E-mail: Mark.Shaffer@nrc.gov
- ● Deputy Director **Jeffrey "Jeff" Clark** .... (817) 200-1180
  E-mail: jeff.clark@nrc.gov
- Engineering Branch 1 Chief
  Thomas "Tom" Farnholtz .... (817) 200-1243
  E-mail: thomas.farnholtz@nrc.gov
- Engineering Branch 2 Chief
  Gregory F. "Greg" Werner .... (817) 200-1137
  E-mail: greg.werner@nrc.gov
- Operations Branch Chief **Vincent "Vince" Gaddy** .... (817) 200-1159
  E-mail: vince.gaddy@nrc.gov
- Plant Support Branch 1 Chief **Jeremy Groom** .... (817) 200-1527
  E-mail: jeremy.groom@nrc.gov
- Plant Support Branch 2 Chief **Heather J. Gepford** .... (817) 200-1558
  E-mail: heather.gepford@nrc.gov
- Inspection Programs and Assessment Team Leader
  (Vacant) .... (817) 200-1491

Resource Management and Administration Division

- Director **B. Jerome Murphy** .... (817) 200-1108
  E-mail: jerome.murphy@nrc.gov
- Administrative Management Team Leader
  Earnestine Clay .... (817) 200-1085
  E-mail: earnestine.clay@nrc.gov
- Financial Resource Management Team Leader
  Lora Nute-Blackshear .... (817) 200-1265
  E-mail: lora.nute-blackshear@nrc.gov
- Human Resources Team Leader **Joseph Lopez** .... (817) 200-1133
  E-mail: joseph.lopez@nrc.gov
- Information Technology Team Leader **(Vacant)** .... (817) 200-1134

INDEPENDENT AGENCIES

★ Presidential Appointment Requiring Senate Confirmation ☆ Presidential Appointment □ Schedule C Appointment ◇ Career Senior Foreign Service Appointment
● Career Senior Executive Service (SES) Appointment ○ Non-Career Senior Executive Service (SES) Appointment ■ Postal Career Executive Service

United States Office of Personnel Management (OPM)

Description: The Office of Personnel Management works to implement human capital policies that assist federal agencies in meeting their strategic goals. The office connects people and their skills and talents to agencies that need specific human resources, and provides these agencies with policies and guidance that enable them to capitalize on these skills and talents.

Theodore Roosevelt Federal Building, 1900 E Street, NW,
Washington, DC 20415-0001
Tel: (202) 606-1800 (General Inquiries)
Tel: (202) 606-2200 (Procurement Information)
Tel: (202) 606-1212 (Public Information)
Tel: (202) 606-2150 (Freedom of Information/Privacy Act)
Tel: (202) 418-3300 (Inspector General's Hotline)
Tel: (888) 767-6738 (Retirement Information)
TTY: (202) 606-2532 (General Inquiries) Fax: (202) 606-2573
E-mail: open@opm.gov (Open Government Initiative)
Internet: www.opm.gov
Internet: www.opm.gov/open (Open Government Initiative)
Internet: http://usajobs.gov (USA Jobs Homepage)

OFFICE OF THE DIRECTOR

Theodore Roosevelt Federal Building, 1900 E Street, NW,
Washington, DC 20415-0001
Fax: (202) 606-2573

Human Resources Solutions (HRS)

Theodore Roosevelt Federal Building, 1900 E Street, NW,
Washington, DC 20415-0001
Tel: (202) 606-1800 Fax: (202) 606-2711

Note: The Office of Personnel Management has announced that Human Resources Solutions will be merging into the General Services Administration, with an initial merger expected by Spring 2019, and a full merger by 2020.

Center for Leadership Development

1301 Emmet Street, Charlottesville, VA 22903-4899
Tel: (434) 980-6200 Internet: www.leadership.opm.gov

Eastern Management Development Group

1900 E Street, NW, Washington, DC 20415
Tel: (202) 606-2005

Director **Sandra "Sandy" Wells** .... (202) 606-2005
E-mail: sandra.wells@opm.gov

Western Management Development Group

Cherry Creek Place III, 3151 South Vaughn Way, Aurora, CO 80014
Fax: (303) 671-1017
Internet: www.leadership.opm.gov/Locations/wmdc/index.aspx

Director **William Bonds** Room 300 .... (303) 671-1027
E-mail: william.bonds@opm.gov

Merit System Accountability and Compliance (MSAC)

Theodore Roosevelt Federal Building, 1900 E Street, NW,
Room 6484, Washington, DC 20415-0001
Tel: (202) 606-2980

Agency Compliance and Evaluation

Atlanta (GA) Oversight
Richard B. Russell Federal Building, 75 Spring Street, SW,
Room 1018, Atlanta, GA 30303
Tel: (404) 331-3451 Fax: (404) 331-3331
Areas Covered: AL, FL, GA, MS, NC, SC, TN, VA - except for areas served by Washington, DC

Manager **Vonda Kenion** .... (404) 331-3451
E-mail: vonda.kenion@opm.gov
Team Leader **Tony B. Williams** .... (404) 331-3451

Chicago (IL) Oversight
230 South Dearborn Street, Room 3060, Chicago, IL 60604
Tel: (312) 353-0387 Fax: (312) 353-8479
Areas Covered: IL, IN, IA, KS, KY, MI, MN, MO, NE, ND, OH, SD, WV, WI

Manager **Joanne M. Plasky** .... (312) 353-8001
Operations Chief **Victoria Berlanga** .... (312) 353-2309
Education: Illinois (Chicago) BA

Dallas (TX) Oversight
700 North Pearl Street, Suite 525, Dallas, TX 75201
Tel: (214) 880-4959

Manager **Bruce E. McGilvray** .... (214) 880-4987
E-mail: bruce.mcgilvray@opm.gov
Operations Supervisor **Lynn Matherly** .... (214) 880-4989
E-mail: lynn.matherly@opm.gov

Philadelphia (PA) Oversight
William J. Green Federal Building, 600 Arch Street,
Room 3400, Philadelphia, PA 19106
Tel: (215) 861-3093 Fax: (215) 861-3100
Areas Covered: CT, DE, ME, MD - except for counties served by the Washington, DC, Oversight Division, MA, NH, NJ, NY, PA, RI, VT, PR, VI

Group Manager **Paul S. Pelullo** .... (215) 861-3084
E-mail: paul.pelullo@opm.gov
Team Leader **Paul S. Pelullo** .... (215) 861-3084

San Francisco (CA) Oversight
90 Seventh Street, Room 13-300, San Francisco, CA 94103
Tel: (415) 281-7050 Fax: (415) 281-7051
Areas Covered: AK, CA, HI, ID, NV, OR, WA, Pacific Ocean Area

Manager **Robert Trefault** .... (415) 281-7050
E-mail: robert.trefault@opm.gov

★ Presidential Appointment Requiring Senate Confirmation ☆ Presidential Appointment ☐ Schedule C Appointment ◇ Career Senior Foreign Service Appointment
● Career Senior Executive Service (SES) Appointment ○ Non-Career Senior Executive Service (SES) Appointment ■ Postal Career Executive Service

Regional Services

Atlanta (GA) Services Branch
Richard B. Russell Federal Building, 75 Spring Street SW,
Suite 1000, Atlanta, GA 30303-3309
Tel: (404) 331-6285 Fax: (404) 730-9738 E-mail: atlanta@opm.gov

Manager **Jacqueline Y. Moses** . . . . (404) 331-6285
E-mail: jacqueline.moses@opm.gov

Chicago (IL) Services Branch
John C. Kluczynski Federal Building, 230 South Dearborn Street,
DPN 30-3, Chicago, IL 60604-1687
Tel: (312) 353-0387 Fax: (312) 353-6211 E-mail: chicago@opm.gov

Manager **(Vacant)** . . . . (312) 353-0387

Mid-Atlantic Services Branch
Federal Building, 200 Granby Street, Norfolk, VA 23510-1886
Tel: (757) 441-3373 Fax: (757) 441-6145 E-mail: norfolkmail@opm.gov

Manager **Teresa Kelly** . . . . (757) 441-3373
E-mail: teresa.kelly@opm.gov

Midwest Services Branch
Federal Building, 601 East 12th Street,
Room W139, Kansas City, MO 64106-2826
Tel: (816) 426-5706 E-mail: kansascity@opm.gov

Branch Manager **Jennifer Minor** . . . . (816) 426-7024
E-mail: jennifer.minor@opm.gov

Philadelphia (PA) Service Branch
William J. Green, Jr., Federal Building, 600 Arch Street,
Room 3400, Philadelphia, PA 19106-0001
Tel: (215) 861-3074 (Job Information Line) Tel: (215) 861-3035
Fax: (215) 861-3030 E-mail: philadelphia@opm.gov

Manager **Gloria Garza** . . . . (215) 861-3077
E-mail: gloria.garza@opm.gov

San Antonio (TX) Service Branch
8610 Broadway, Suite 305, San Antonio, TX 78217
Tel: (210) 805-2401 Fax: (210) 805-2407 E-mail: sasbmailbox@opm.gov

Manager **Katherine Hidalgo** . . . . (210) 805-2438
Administrative Assistant **Karen Wood** . . . . (210) 805-2412

Washington (DC) Service Branch
1900 E Street, NW, Room 2469, Washington, DC 20415
Tel: (202) 606-2575 Fax: (202) 606-1768 E-mail: washington@opm.gov

Director **(Vacant)** . . . . (202) 606-2575

INDEPENDENT AGENCIES

Peace Corps (PC)

Description: The Peace Corps is committed to promoting world peace by helping the people of interested countries meet their need for trained men and women, promoting a better understanding of Americans on the part of the peoples served, and promoting a better understanding of other peoples on the part of all Americans.

1111 20th Street, NW, Washington, DC 20526
Tel: (202) 692-1904 (Freedom of Information/Privacy Act)
Tel: (202) 692-1040 (Volunteer Recruiting Information - DC Metropolitan Area)
Tel: (855) 855-1961 (Volunteer Recruiting Information - Continental US)
E-mail: opengov@peacecorps.gov
E-mail: peacecorpsjobs@peacecorps.gov (Job Opportunities)
Internet: www.peacecorps.gov
Internet: www.usa.gov (Official US Government Website)

Note: The Peace Corps will be moving to a new headquarters at 1275 First Street, NE, Washington, DC, in January 2020.

OFFICE OF THE DIRECTOR (D)

1111 20th Street, NW, Washington, DC 20526
Tel: (202) 692-2100 Fax: (202) 692-2101

Office of Volunteer Recruitment and Selection (VRS)

1111 20th Street, NW, Washington, DC 20526
Tel: (202) 692-2408 Fax: (202) 692-1801

Office of Recruitment

Regional Recruiting Offices (RROs)

Central Region

Chicago (IL) Office
230 South Dearborn Street, Suite 2020, Chicago, IL 60604
Tel: (312) 353-4990 Fax: (312) 353-4192
E-mail: chicago@peacecorps.gov

Regional Manager **Brad Merryman** .... (312) 353-9093
E-mail: bmerryman@peacecorps.gov
Webmaster **John Clark** .... (312) 353-4990
E-mail: jclark@peacecorps.gov
Colorado Field Based Recruiter **Karyn Sweeney** .... (480) 265-6461
Colorado Field Based Recruiter **Cedar Wolf** .... (504) 541-3747
Houston Field Based Recruiter **Holly Van Groll** .... (281) 432-1155
New Orleans Field Based Recruiter **Julie Crow** .... (504) 457-9796

East Region

New York (NY) Office
201 Varick Street, Suite 1025, New York, NY 10014
Tel: (212) 352-5440 Fax: (212) 352-5441
E-mail: nyinfo@peacecorps.gov

Regional Manager (Acting) **Katrina "Kat" Bowser** ...... (212) 352-5440
Recruitment Supervisor **Katrina "Kat" Bowser** .... (212) 352-5440
Supervisory Public Affairs Specialist **(Vacant)** .... (212) 352-5440
Public Affairs Specialist **Emily Webb** .... (212) 352-5455
E-mail: ewebb@peacecorps.gov
Public Affairs Specialist **Dan Ingala** .... (212) 352-5455
E-mail: dingala@peacecorps.gov
Administrative Officer (Acting) **Kadijat Oladiran** ...... (212) 352-5462

Washington, D.C. Office
1111 20th Street, NW, Washington, DC 20526
Tel: (202) 692-1040 Fax: (202) 692-1065
E-mail: dcinfo@peacecorps.gov
Manager **(Vacant)** .... (202) 692-1040

West Region

San Francisco (CA) Office
1301 Clay Street, Suite 620N, Oakland, CA 94612
Tel: (510) 452-8444 Fax: (510) 452-8441 E-mail: sfinfo@peacecorps.gov
Regional Manager **Michael "Mike" McKay** .... (510) 452-8444
E-mail: mmckay@peacecorps.gov
Education: Southern Methodist 1987 MPA
Regional Recruitment Supervisor **Lorry Marvin** .... (510) 452-8444
Supervisory Public Affairs Specialist **David Reese** ...... (310) 356-1114
E-mail: dreese@peacecorps.gov
Regional Administrative Officer **Debra Booker** .... (214) 235-5559
E-mail: dbooker@peacecorps.gov

United States Postal Service (USPS)

Description: The mission of the United States Postal Service is to bind the country together through the personal, educational, literary, and business correspondence of the people. It shall provide prompt, reliable, and efficient service to all communities.

475 L'Enfant Plaza, SW, Washington, DC 20260-0010
Tel: (202) 268-3207 (DC Headquarters)
Tel: (202) 268-2000 (Personnel Locator)
Tel: (800) 275-8777 (Customer Service)
Tel: (800) 372-8347 (Fraud Complaint)
Tel: (202) 268-2608 (Freedom of Information/Privacy Act)
Tel: (888) 877-7644 (Inspector General)
Tel: (800) 654-8896 (Postal Crimes Hot Line)
Tel: (202) 268-5789 (Procurement Information) Tel: (202) 268-2284 (Public Information/Consumer Advocate/Customer Service) Tel: (703) 292-3655 (Publications Information)
Internet: www.usps.com Internet: www.usps.com/green (Sustainability)
Internet: http://m.usps.com/ (Mobile Website)
Internet: www.usa.gov (Official US Government Website)

BOARD OF GOVERNORS

475 L'Enfant Plaza West, SW, Washington, DC 20260-1000
Tel: (202) 268-4800 Fax: (202) 268-5472

Note: Members may continue to serve until reappointed or replaced, but not for more than one year.

Office of the Postmaster General and Chief Executive Officer

475 L'Enfant Plaza, SW, Washington, DC 20260-0010
Fax: (202) 268-4860

Chief Operating Officer

Regional Offices

Capital Metro Area
16501 Shady Grove Road, Gaithersburg, MD 20898-9998
Tel: (301) 548-1410 Fax: (301) 548-1434
Areas Covered: DC, MD, NC, Atlanta GA, SC, VA.
Vice President, Area Operations **Linda Marie Malone** . . . (301) 548-1410

Atlanta (GA) District
1605 Boggs Road, North Metro, GA 30026-9300
P.O. Box 599300, North Metro, GA 30026-9300
Tel: (770) 717-3736 Fax: (770) 717-3735
Areas Covered: ZIP Code areas: 300-306
District Manager **Samuel E. Jaudon** . . . . (770) 717-3736

Baltimore (MD) District
900 East Fayette Street, Room 309, Baltimore, MD 21233-9990
Tel: (410) 347-4314 Fax: (410) 347-4289
District Manager **Dane A. Coleman** . . . . (410) 347-4314

Capital District
900 Brentwood Road, NE, Washington, DC 20066-9998
Tel: (202) 636-2210 Fax: (202) 636-5301
District Manager **Salvatore N. Vacca** . . . . (202) 636-2210

Greater South Carolina District
2001 Dixiana Road, West Columbia, SC 29172
P.O. Box 929998, Columbia, SC 29292-9998
Tel: (803) 926-6469 Fax: (803) 926-6470
Areas Covered: ZIP Code areas: 290-296, 299
District Manager **Darryl Martin** . . . . (803) 926-6469
Confidential Secretary **Rosa Marie Pearson** . . . . (803) 926-6469
E-mail: rosa.m.pearson@usps.gov

Greensboro (NC) District
P.O. Box 27499, Greensboro, NC 27498-9900
Tel: (336) 668-1202 Fax: (336) 668-1366
Areas Covered: ZIP Code areas: 270-279, 286
District Manager **Russell D. Gardner** . . . . (336) 668-1202
Secretary **Susan N. Albright** . . . . (336) 668-1202
E-mail: susan.n.albright@usps.gov

Mid-Carolinas District
2901 Scott Futrell Drive, Charlotte, NC 28228-9980
Tel: (704) 424-4400 Fax: (704) 424-4489
Areas Covered: ZIP Code areas: 280-285, 287-289, 297
District Manager (Acting) **Angela H. Curtis** . . . . (704) 424-4400

Northern Virginia District
8409 Lee Highway, Merrifield, VA 22081-9996
Tel: (703) 698-6464 Fax: (703) 698-6500
District Manager **Jeffrey Baker** . . . . (703) 698-6464

Richmond (VA) District
1801 Brook Road, Richmond, VA 23232-9990
Tel: (804) 775-6365 Fax: (804) 775-6058
Areas Covered: Zip Code areas 224, 225, 228, 229, 230-239, 244
District Manager (Acting) **Janice Atherly** . . . . (804) 775-6365

Eastern Area
One Marquis Plaza, 5315 Campbells Run Road, Pittsburgh, PA 15277-7010
Tel: (412) 494-2510 Fax: (412) 494-2582
Areas Covered: KY, NJ, OH, PA, Southern VA, TN, WV
Vice President, Area Operations **Joshua D. Colin** . . . . (412) 494-2510

Appalachian District
1002 Lee Street East, Charleston, WV 25301
P.O. Box 59992, Charleston, WV 25350-9992
Tel: (304) 561-1200 Fax: (304) 561-1209
District Manager **LeeAnn T. Theriault** . . . . (304) 561-1200
E-mail: Leeann.T.Theriault@usps.com
Information Systems Manager **Fred Luckett** . . . . (304) 561-1200

Central PA District
1425 Crooked Hill Road, Harrisburg, PA 17107-9996
Tel: (717) 257-2100 Fax: (717) 257-2152
District Manager **Debra Gless** . . . . (717) 257-2100
Secretary **Theresa Strunk** . . . . (717) 257-2104
Finance Manager **Eric Stouffer** . . . . (717) 257-2310
Human Resources Manager **Barbara Kirchner** . . . . (717) 257-2253
HR Secretary **Patty Marshall** . . . . (717) 257-2250

(continued on next page)

★ Presidential Appointment Requiring Senate Confirmation ☆ Presidential Appointment ☐ Schedule C Appointment ◇ Career Senior Foreign Service Appointment
● Career Senior Executive Service (SES) Appointment ○ Non-Career Senior Executive Service (SES) Appointment ■ Postal Career Executive Service

Central PA District *(continued)*

Information Systems Manager **Robert Paddock** .... (717) 257-2353
Marketing Manager **(Vacant)** .... (717) 257-4804
Operations Programs Support Manager
Robert L. Varano .... (717) 257-4828
Post Office Operations Manager **Mary Tyneway** .... (610) 882-3305

Ohio Valley District
1591 Dalton Avenue, Cincinnati, OH 45234-9990
Tel: (513) 684-5794 Fax: (513) 684-5197

District Manager **Melvin J. "Sandy" Anderson** .... (513) 684-5360

Kentuckiana District
4500 Annshire Avenue, Louisville, KY 40213
P.O. Box 31000, Louisville, KY 40231
Tel: (502) 454-1814 Fax: (502) 454-1990

District Manager **David Jones** .... (502) 454-1814

Northern Ohio District
2200 Orange Avenue, Room 210, Cleveland, OH 44101
Tel: (216) 443-4573 Fax: (216) 443-4577

District Manager **Melvin J. "Sandy" Anderson** .... (216) 443-4573
E-mail: melvin.j.anderson@usps.gov
Marketing Manager **LaVonda Fondren** .... (216) 443-4416

Philadelphia (PA) District
3190 South 70th Street, Philadelphia, PA 19153
Tel: (215) 863-6063 Fax: (215) 863-5363

District Manager **(Vacant)** .... (215) 863-6063
Administrative Assistant **Terrie Bacino** .... (215) 863-6063

South Jersey District
501 Benigno Boulevard, Bellmawr, NJ 08031-9998
P.O. Box 9001, Bellmawr, NJ 08099-9998
Tel: (856) 933-4400 Fax: (856) 933-4004

District Manager **James G. Drummer** .... (856) 933-4400
E-mail: james.g.drummer@usps.gov
Information Systems Manager **James W. Fisher** .... (856) 933-4498
E-mail: james.w.fisher@usps.gov

Tennessee District
811 Royal Parkway, Nashville, TN 37229-9998
Tel: (615) 885-9252 Fax: (615) 885-9317

District Manager **Chris Alexander** .... (615) 885-9252

Western PA District
1001 California Avenue, Pittsburgh, PA 15290-9000
Tel: (412) 359-7771 Fax: (412) 321-3373

District Manager **Troy R. Seanor** .... (412) 359-7771
E-mail: troy.r.seanor@usps.gov
Secretary **Rebecca A. "Becky" Mikelonis** .... (412) 359-7771
E-mail: rebecca.a.mikelonis@usps.gov

Western New York District
1200 William Street, Buffalo, NY 14240-9990
Tel: (716) 846-2532 Fax: (716) 846-2407

District Manager (Acting) **Rose M. Spraggins** .... (716) 846-2532
E-mail: rosie.spraggins@usps.gov

Great Lakes Area
500 Fullerton Avenue, Carol Stream, IL 60199-1000
Tel: (630) 539-5556 Fax: (630) 539-7171
Areas Covered: IL, IN, MI, MO, WI

Vice President, Area Operations (Acting) **Erica Brix** ..... (630) 539-5556
Local Area Network Administrator **John L. Anderson** ... (630) 539-5558
E-mail: john.l.anderson@usps.gov Fax: (630) 539-7744

Central Illinois District
6801 West 73rd Street, Bedford Park, IL 60499-9998
Tel: (708) 563-7807 Fax: (708) 563-2013

District Manager/Lead Executive **(Vacant)** .... (708) 563-7807

Chicago (IL) District
433 West Harrison Street, 2nd Floor, Chicago, IL 60699-9998
Tel: (312) 983-8030 Fax: (312) 983-8010

District Manager **Gregory W. Johnson** .... (312) 983-8030
E-mail: gregory.w.johnson@usps.gov
Postmaster **Tangela L. Bush** .... (312) 983-8030
E-mail: tangela.l.bush@usps.gov
Senior Plant Manager **John Colao** .... (312) 983-7519
433 West Harrison Street, Fax: (312) 983-7698
7th Floor, Chicago, IL 60699-9997
Manager of Learning and Development
Jamila S. McIntosh .... (312) 983-8666
Fax: (312) 983-8680

Detroit (MI) District
1401 West Fort Street, Detroit, MI 48233-9998
Tel: (313) 226-8605 Fax: (313) 226-8001

District Manager **Lee A. Thompson** .... (313) 226-8605
E-mail: lee.a.thompson@usps.gov
Postmaster **Derron M. Bray** .... (313) 226-8611
E-mail: derron.m.bray@usps.gov
Finance Manager **Larry Dean** .... (313) 226-8614
Human Resources Manager **Petri McHerron** .... (313) 226-8616
Information Systems Manager **Madelyn Read** .... (313) 226-8596
Marketing Customer Service Support Manager
Timothy Robinson .... (313) 226-8634
Operations Programs Support Manager
Donald Dombrowski .... (313) 226-8040

Gateway District
1720 Market Street, Room 3027, St. Louis, MO 63155
Tel: (314) 436-4114 Fax: (314) 436-4565
Areas Covered: ZIP Code areas: 620-629; 630-635; 650-653

District Manager **Charles J. Miller** .... (314) 436-4114
E-mail: charles.j.miller@usps.gov
Senior Plant Manager **Charles A. Sciurba** .... (314) 436-4160
E-mail: charles.sciurba@usps.gov

Greater Indiana District
P.O. Box 9850, Indianapolis, IN 46298-9850
Tel: (317) 870-8201 Fax: (317) 870-8688

District Manager **Todd S. Hawkins** .... (317) 870-8201
E-mail: todd.s.hawkins@usps.gov

Greater Michigan District
Riverview Center Building, 678 Front Street, NW,
Grand Rapids, MI 49504
P.O. Box 999997, Grand Rapids, MI 49599
Tel: (616) 336-5300 Fax: (616) 336-5399

District Manager (Acting) **Krista A. Finazzo** .... (616) 336-5300
E-mail: krista.a.finazzo@usps.gov

Lakeland District
345 West St. Paul Avenue, Room 2267, Milwaukee, WI 53203
P.O. Box 5000, Milwaukee, WI 53201-5000
Tel: (414) 287-2240 Fax: (414) 287-2296

District Manager **Debra Woodrum** .... (414) 287-2240

Northeast Area
Six Griffin Road, North, Windsor, CT 06006-7010
Tel: (860) 285-7040 Fax: (860) 285-1253
Areas Covered: CT, MA, ME, NH, NJ, NY, PR, RI, VI, VT

Vice President, Area Operations
Edward F. "Ed" Phelan, Jr. .... (860) 285-7040

Albany (NY) District
30 Karner Road, Albany, NY 12288-9992

District Manager **Thomas F. Kelley** .... (518) 452-2201
E-mail: thomas.f.kelley@usps.gov

★ Presidential Appointment Requiring Senate Confirmation ☆ Presidential Appointment ☐ Schedule C Appointment ◇ Career Senior Foreign Service Appointment
● Career Senior Executive Service (SES) Appointment ○ Non-Career Senior Executive Service (SES) Appointment ■ Postal Career Executive Service

Boston (MA) District
25 Dorchester Avenue, Boston, MA 02205-0098
Tel: (617) 654-5302 Fax: (617) 654-5186

District Manager **Michael W. Rakes** .... (617) 654-5302
E-mail: michael.w.rakes@usps.gov

Caribbean District
585 Avenue F. D. Roosevelt, San Juan, PR 00936-9998
Tel: (787) 622-1950 Fax: (787) 622-1955

District Manager/Executive In-Charge **Lisa M. Ojeda** .... (787) 622-1800
E-mail: lisa.m.ojeda@usps.gov
Finance Manager **Juan A. Paz** .... (787) 622-1715
Human Resources Manager **Juan Delgado** .... (787) 622-1820
E-mail: juan.delgado@usps.gov
Information Systems Manager **Juan R. Lugo** .... (787) 622-1950
E-mail: juan.r.lugo@usps.gov
Marketing Manager **Martin Caballero** .... (787) 622-1790
Operations Program Support Manager **Bruce Branning** ... (787) 622-1870
Post Office Operations Manager **David R. Carvajal** ...... (787) 622-1660
Post Office Operations Manager **Jose A Marengo** .... (787) 622-1952
Postmaster **Yvonne I. Rodriguez** .... (787) 622-1920

Connecticut Valley District
141 Weston Street, Hartford, CT 06101-9996
Tel: (860) 524-6137 Fax: (860) 524-6199

District Manager **David D. Mastroianni, Jr.** .... (860) 524-6137

Long Island (NY) District
160 Duryea Road, Melville, NY 11760
P.O. Box 8800, Melville, NY 11760
Tel: (631) 391-6510 Fax: (631) 391-6576

District Manager/Lead Executive **Frank Calabrese** .... (631) 391-6510
E-mail: frank.calabrese@usps.gov

New York (NY) District
380 West 33rd Street, Room 4056, New York, NY 10199
Tel: (212) 330-3600 Fax: (212) 330-3934

District Manager **Lorraine G. Castellano** .... (212) 330-3600
E-mail: lorraine.g.castellano@usps.gov
Information Technology Director **Frank A. Iannone** ..... (212) 330-3831
341 Ninth Avenue, Fax: (212) 330-2882
Room 924A, New York, NY 10199-9472
E-mail: frank.a.iannone@usps.gov

Northern New England District
151 Forest Avenue, Portland, ME 04101
Tel: (207) 482-7109 Fax: (207) 482-7105

District Manager **John T. Godlewski, Jr.** .... (207) 482-7108
Customer Relations **Anne Cordero** .... (207) 482-7181

Northern New Jersey District
21 Kilmer Road, Edison, NJ 08899
Tel: (732) 819-3265 Fax: (732) 819-3632

District Manager **Scott Hooper** .... (732) 819-3265
Secretary **Irma I. Nieves** .... (732) 819-3265
E-mail: irma.i.nieves@usps.gov

Triboro (NY) District
1050 Forbell Street, Room 2011, Brooklyn, NY 11256
Tel: (718) 348-3990 Fax: (718) 348-3992

District Manager/Executive-in-Charge **Elvin Mercado** .... (718) 348-3991

Westchester (NY) District
1000 Westchester Avenue, White Plains, NY 10610-9800
P.O. Box 9800, White Plains, NY 10610-9800
Tel: (914) 697-7104 Fax: (914) 697-7128

District Manager **Richard Conte** .... (914) 697-7104

Pacific Area
11255 Rancho Carmel Drive, San Diego, CA 92197-0100
Tel: (858) 674-3100 Fax: (858) 674-3101
Areas Covered: CA, HI

Vice President, Area Operations (Acting)
Larry P. Muñoz .... (858) 674-3100
E-mail: larry.p.munoz@usps.gov
Delivery Programs Support Manager
Jodi Nascimento .... (858) 674-3110
Distribution Networks Manager **Robert Bryant** .... (858) 674-3110
Finance Manager and Controller **Lisa Jackson** .... (858) 674-3150
Human Resources Manager **Toni Simon** .... (858) 674-3180
In-Plant Support Manager **Shawn West** .... (858) 674-2696
Marketing Manager **Bridgett Carroll** .... (858) 674-3180
Operations Support Manager **Larry J. Belair** .... (858) 674-3110
Information Systems Manager **Ernie Pelina** .... (858) 674-3143

Bay-Valley (CA) District
1675 Seventh Street, Room 307, Oakland, CA 94615-9987
Tel: (510) 874-8222
Areas Covered: CA (Counties of Alameda, Contra Costa, Napa and Solano)

District Manager (Acting) **Jagdeep K. Grewal** .... (510) 874-8222
E-mail: jagdeep.k.grewal@usps.gov
Finance Manager **Romy de Guzman** .... (510) 874-8355
Fax: (510) 251-3230

San Jose Mail Processing and Distribution Center
1750 Lundy Avenue, San Jose, CA 95101-8000
Tel: (408) 437-6700 Fax: (408) 437-6699

Plant Manager (Acting) **Lawrence W. Engler** .... (408) 437-6700
E-mail: lawrence.w.engler@usps.gov

Honolulu (HI) District
3600 Aolele Street, Honolulu, HI 96820-3600
Tel: (808) 423-3700 Fax: (808) 423-3708

District Manager **Gregory D. "Greg" Wolny** .... (808) 423-3700
E-mail: greg.d.wolny@usps.gov

Los Angeles (CA) District
7001 South Central Avenue, Los Angeles, CA 90052-9998
Tel: (323) 586-1200 Fax: (323) 586-1248
Areas Covered: Zip Codes: 900-901

District Manager **Al Santos** .... (323) 586-1200
Postmaster **Kenneth A. "Ken" Snavely** .... (323) 586-3829
E-mail: kenneth.a.snavely@usps.gov
Finance Manager **Susan Labadie-Taylor** .... (323) 586-1700
Human Resources Manager **Linda G. Shumate** .... (323) 586-1300
E-mail: linda.g.shumate@usps.gov
Information Systems Manager **Richard Anderson** .... (323) 586-5988
Mailing Solution Manager **Darrell Morrow** .... (323) 586-4390
Marketing Manager **Beth Rubio** .... (323) 586-1475
Operations Programs Support Manager **Rick Perez** .... (323) 586-1207

Sacramento (CA) District
3775 Industrial Boulevard, West Sacramento, CA 95799-0010
Tel: (916) 373-8001 Fax: (916) 373-8704

District Manager **Jeffrey C. "Jeff" Lelevich** .... (916) 373-8001
E-mail: jeff.c.lelevich@usps.gov

San Diego (CA) District
11251 Rancho Carmel Drive, San Diego, CA 92199-9990
Tel: (858) 674-0301 Fax: (858) 674-0063

District Manager **James P. Olson** .... (858) 674-0301
Senior Plant Manager **Jeff Vibbert** .... (858) 674-0100

San Francisco (CA) District
1300 Evans Avenue, Suite 300, San Francisco, CA 94124
P.O. Box 885050, San Francisco, CA 94188-5050
Tel: (415) 550-5591 Fax: (415) 550-5327

District Manager **Noemi Luna** .... (415) 550-5591

(continued on next page)

★ Presidential Appointment Requiring Senate Confirmation ☆ Presidential Appointment ☐ Schedule C Appointment ◇ Career Senior Foreign Service Appointment
● Career Senior Executive Service (SES) Appointment ○ Non-Career Senior Executive Service (SES) Appointment ■ Postal Career Executive Service

San Francisco (CA) District *(continued)*

Information Systems Manager **Cristina B. Baldeviso** .... (415) 550-5659
P.O. Box 882350, San Francisco, CA 94188-2350
E-mail: crisitina.b.baldeviso@usps.gov

Santa Ana (CA) District
3101 West Sunflower Avenue, Santa Ana, CA 92799-9993
Tel: (714) 662-6229 Fax: (714) 557-5837

District Manager **Eduardo "Ed" Ruiz** .... (714) 662-6229
Secretary **Tricella A. Al-Mesned** .... (714) 662-6229
E-mail: tricella.a.al-mesned@usps.gov

Sierra Coastal District
28201 Franklin Parkway, Santa Clarita, CA 91383-9990
Tel: (661) 775-6500 Fax: (661) 775-7184

District Manager (Acting) **Gregory D. "Greg" Wolny** ... (661) 775-6500
E-mail: greg.d.wolny@usps.gov

Southern Area
P.O. Box 224748, Dallas, TX 75222-4748
Tel: (214) 819-8650 Fax: (214) 905-9227
Areas Covered: AL, AR, FL, LA, MS, OK, Southern GA, TX

Vice President, Area Operations **Shaun E. Mossman** .... (214) 819-8650
Secretary **Marianne Bean** .... (214) 819-8650
E-mail: marianne.bean@usps.gov
Information Systems Specialist **David Henry** .... (214) 819-7177
LAN Administrator **(Vacant)** .... (214) 819-8650

Alabama District
351 24th Street North, Birmingham, AL 35203-9997
Tel: (205) 521-0201 Fax: (205) 521-0058

District Manager **Susan E. Aronson** .... (205) 521-0201
E-mail: susan.e.aronson@usps.gov

Arkansas District
420 Natural Resources Drive, Little Rock, AR 72205-9800
Tel: (501) 228-4100 Fax: (501) 228-4105

District Manager (Acting)
Thomas O. "Tom" Billington .... (501) 228-4100
E-mail: thomas.o.billingtonIII@usps.gov

Dallas (TX) District
951 West Bethel Road, Coppell, TX 75099-9998
Tel: (972) 393-6787 Fax: (972) 393-6192

District Manager (Acting) **Scott Hooper** .... (972) 393-6787

Fort Worth (TX) District
4600 Mark IV Parkway, Fort Worth, TX 76161-9100
Tel: (817) 317-3301 Fax: (817) 317-3320

District Manager **Timothy J. Vierling** .... (817) 317-3301
E-mail: timothy.j.vierling@usps.gov
Postmaster **Kevin S. Farmer** .... (817) 317-3802
E-mail: kevin.s.farmer1@usps.gov
Finance Manager **Mary L. Staub** .... (817) 317-3501
Human Resources Manager **Donna M. Dunker** .... (817) 317-3351
E-mail: donna.m.dunker@usps.gov
Information Systems Manager/Webmaster
Kilnagar Bhaskar .... (817) 317-3527
Marketing Manager **Janice Godlewski** .... (817) 317-3609
Operations Programs Support Manager **Hope Mareno** .... (817) 317-3650

Gulf Atlantic District
P.O. Box 40005, Jacksonville, FL 32203-0005
Tel: (904) 783-7292 Fax: (904) 858-6610

District Manager **David F. Martin** .... (904) 783-7292
E-mail: david.f.martin@usps.gov
Administrative Assistant **Kevin Patrick** .... (904) 783-7292

Houston (TX) District
600 North Sam Houston Parkway West, Houston, TX 77067-9997
Tel: (713) 226-3717 Fax: (713) 226-3755

District Manager **David W. Camp** .... (713) 226-3717

Houston (TX) District *(continued)*

Executive Assistant **Jessica Fountain-Carter** .... (713) 226-3717

Louisiana District
701 Loyola Avenue, Room 11001, New Orleans, LA 70113-9800
Tel: (504) 589-1950 Fax: (504) 589-1432

District Manager **Steve Hardin** .... (504) 589-1950
Information Systems Manager **Anna Amos** .... (504) 589-1031

Mississippi District
P.O. Box 99990, Jackson, MS 39205-9990
Tel: (601) 351-7350 Fax: (601) 351-7504

District Manager **Elizabeth A. Johnson** .... (601) 351-7350
E-mail: elizabeth.a.johnson@usps.gov
Information Systems Manager **Dan Moulder** .... (601) 351-7247
Marketing Manager **Monica Minor** .... (601) 351-7360
Congressional Liaison **Lori DuBose** .... (601) 351-7102

Oklahoma District
4025 West Reno Avenue, Oklahoma City, OK 73125-9800
Tel: (405) 815-2101 Fax: (405) 815-2010
Areas Covered: OK (except the Counties of Cimarron, Harper and Texas)

District Manager **Julie A. Gosdin** .... (405) 815-2101
E-mail: julie.a.gosdin@usps.gov

Rio Grande District
One Post Office Drive, San Antonio, TX 78284-9997
Tel: (210) 368-5548 Fax: (210) 368-5511

District Manager **Steven Hernandez** .... (210) 368-5548
Marketing Relations Manager **Adrienne Marshall** .... (210) 368-5597
Finance Manager **Sharon Fernandez** .... (210) 368-5538
Health and Resources Manager **Gaye Gresham** .... (210) 368-8419
Human Resources Manager **Charisse Newberry** .... (210) 368-1776
Information Systems Manager **Jim F. Moderow** .... (210) 368-5529
E-mail: jim.f.moderow@usps.gov
Operations Programs Support Manager
Jamie Fernandez .... (210) 368-5525
Post Office Operations Manager **Ayda I. Alderete** .... (210) 368-5575

South Florida District
1900 West Oakland Park Boulevard, Fort Lauderdale, FL 33310
Tel: (954) 527-2941 Fax: (954) 450-3015
Areas Covered: Pompano Beach to the Keys

District Manager **Jeffrey Taylor** .... (954) 527-6987
Secretary **Carolina Wilson** .... (954) 527-6987

Suncoast (FL) District
3501 Bessie Coleman Boulevard, Tampa, FL 33630
Tel: (813) 354-6099 Fax: (813) 877-8656

District Manager **Eric D. Chavez** .... (813) 354-6099
E-mail: eric.d.chavez@usps.gov
Media Liaison **Enola Rice** .... (813) 354-6022
2203 North Lois Avenue, Tampa, FL 33607-7101

Western Area
1745 Stout Street, Suite 1000, Denver, CO 80299-3034
Tel: (303) 313-5100 Fax: (303) 313-5102
Areas Covered: AK, AZ, Northeastern CA, CO, ID, IA, Northwestern IL, KS, MN, Western and Southern MO, MT, NM, ND, NE, NV, OR, SD, UT, WA, Western WI, WY

Vice President, Area Operations
Gregory G. "Greg" Graves .... (303) 313-5100
Executive Administrative Assistant **Rita Rodriguez** ...... (303) 313-5101

Alaska District
3720 Barrow Street, Anchorage, AK 99599-0001
Tel: (907) 261-5418 Fax: (907) 273-5866

District Manager **Ronald Haberman** .... (907) 261-5418
E-mail: ronald.s.harberman@usps.gov
Administrative Assistant **Elvie Aquino** .... (907) 261-5418

Central Plains District
6005 Lockheed Court, Omaha, NE 68110
P.O. Box 199500, Omaha, NE 68119
Tel: (402) 930-4400 Fax: (402) 930-4434
District Manager **Rick Pivovar** . . . . (402) 930-4400
Postmaster **Keith J. Reid** . . . . (402) 930-4390

Colorado - Wyoming District
7500 East 53rd Place, Room 1131, Denver, CO 80266-9998
Tel: (303) 853-6160 Fax: (303) 853-6752
District Manager (Acting) **Kevin Romero** . . . . (303) 853-6160

Dakotas District
2801 South Kiwanis Avenue, Suite 400, Sioux Falls, SD 57105
P.O. Box 7500, Sioux Falls, SD 57117-7500
Tel: (605) 333-2601 Fax: (605) 333-2777
District Manager **Douglas Stephens, Sr.** . . . . (605) 333-2601

Hawkeye (IA) District
7900 Hickman Road, Des Moines, IA 50324-4400
Tel: (515) 251-2100 Fax: (515) 251-2050
District Manager **Shawneen Betha** . . . . (515) 251-2106
E-mail: shawneen.l.betha@usps.gov
Information Technology Manager **Dwight Porter** . . . . (515) 251-2160
Fax: (515) 251-2164

Mid-America District
300 West Pershing Road, Suite 210, Kansas City, MO 64108-9000
Fax: (816) 374-9153
District Manager **Gail Hendrix** . . . . (816) 374-9104
Postmaster (Acting) **Eddie Morgan, Jr.** . . . . (816) 374-9144
Senior Confidential Secretary **Carmen L. Mabon** . . . . (816) 374-9105
E-mail: carmen.l.mabon@usps.gov
Information Systems Manager **Bond F. Marrs** . . . . (816) 374-9462
E-mail: bond.f.marrs@usps.gov Fax: (816) 374-9666
Senior Plant Manager (Acting) **Jeffrey Drake** . . . . (816) 504-3300

Nevada - Sierra District
1001 East Sunset Road, Las Vegas, NV 89199-1000
Tel: (702) 361-9300 Fax: (702) 361-9508
District Manager (Acting) **Brenda L. Olson** . . . . (702) 361-9300

Northland (MN/WI) District
100 South First Street, Room 409, Minneapolis, MN 55401-9990
Tel: (612) 349-3500 Fax: (612) 349-6377
District Manager **Anthony C. "Tony" Williams** . . . . (612) 349-3500
E-mail: anthony.c.williams@usps.gov

Phoenix (AZ) District
4949 East Van Buren Street, Phoenix, AZ 85026-9900
Tel: (602) 225-5400 Fax: (602) 225-3286
District Manager **John J. DiPeri** . . . . (602) 225-5400
E-mail: john.j.diperi@usps.gov
Postmaster **Humberto Trujillo** . . . . (602) 225-5400
E-mail: humberto.trujillo@usps.gov
Administrative Assistant **Dawn M. Simpson** . . . . (602) 225-5400
E-mail: dawn.m.simpson@usps.gov

Portland (OR) District
715 NW Hoyt Street, Room 3029, Portland, OR 97208-3609
P.O. Box 3609, Portland, OR 97208-3609
Tel: (503) 294-2500 Fax: (503) 276-2020
District Manager **Tyrone Williams** . . . . (503) 294-2500

Salt Lake (UT) District
1760 W 2100 S, Salt Lake City, UT 84199-8800
Tel: (801) 974-2947 Fax: (801) 974-2339
District Manager **Darrell Stoke** . . . . (801) 974-2947

Seattle (WA) District
34301 Ninth Avenue South, Federal Way, WA 98003-9032
Tel: (253) 214-1703 Fax: (253) 214-1824
District Manager **Don E. Jacobus** . . . . (253) 214-1701
E-mail: don.e.jacobus@usps.gov

United States Postal Inspection Service (USPIS)
475 L'Enfant Plaza SW, Room 3100, Washington, DC 20260-2100
Tel: (877) 876-2455 Fax: (202) 268-7316
Internet: postalinspectors.uspis.gov

Boston Division
495 Summer Street, Suite 600, Boston, MA 02210-2114
Postal Inspector in Charge **Shelly A. Binkowski** . . . . (617) 556-0489

Charlotte Division
P.O. Box 3000, Charlotte, NC 28228-3000
Tel: (704) 329-9121
Postal Inspector in Charge **Thomas L. Noyes** . . . . (704) 329-9121
P.O. Box 300, Charlotte, NC 28228-3000
E-mail: tnoyes@uspis.gov

Chicago Division
433 West Harrison Street, Room 50190, Chicago, IL 60669-2201
Tel: (312) 983-7901
Postal Inspector in Charge **E.C. Woodson** . . . . (312) 983-7901

Denver Division
1745 Stout Street, Suite 900, Denver, CO 80299-3034
Tel: (303) 313-5320
Postal Inspector in Charge **Craig Goldberg** . . . . (303) 313-5320 ext. 4

Detroit Division
P.O. Box 330119, Detroit, MI 48232-6119
Tel: (313) 226-8221
Postal Inspector in Charge **Patricia A. Armstrong** . . . . (313) 226-8221

Fort Worth Division
14800 Trinity Boulevard, Suite 600, Fort Worth, TX 76155-2675
Postal Inspector in Charge **Thomas L. Noyes** . . . . (877) 876-2455
E-mail: tnoyes@uspis.gov

Houston Division
P.O. Box 1276, Fort Worth, TX 76155-2675
Tel: (713) 238-4479
Postal Inspector in Charge **Adrian Gonzalez** . . . . (713) 238-4479
E-mail: adrian.gonzalez@uspis.gov

Los Angeles Division
P.O. Box 2000, Pasadena, CA 91102-2000
Postal Inspector in Charge **Nichole Cooper** . . . . (877) 876-2455
E-mail: ncooper@uspis.gov

Miami Division
3400 Lakeside Drive, 6th Floor, Miramar, FL 33027-3242
Postal Inspector in Charge **Antonio J. Gomez** . . . . (877) 876-2455
E-mail: agomez@uspis.gov

Newark Division
P.O. Box 509, Newark, NJ 07101-0509
Tel: (973) 693-5450 Tel: (973) 693-5391
Postal Inspector in Charge **Joseph Cronin** . . . . (973) 693-5450

New York Division
P.O. Box 555, New York, NY 10116-0555
Tel: (212) 330-3900
Postal Inspector in Charge **Philip R. Bartlett** . . . . . . (212) 330-3900 ext. 4

INDEPENDENT AGENCIES

★ Presidential Appointment Requiring Senate Confirmation ☆ Presidential Appointment ☐ Schedule C Appointment ◇ Career Senior Foreign Service Appointment
● Career Senior Executive Service (SES) Appointment ○ Non-Career Senior Executive Service (SES) Appointment ■ Postal Career Executive Service

Philadelphia Division
P.O. Box 3001, Bala Cynwyd, PA 19004-3601
Tel: (877) 876-2455
Postal Inspector in Charge **Daniel Brubaker** . . . . (877) 876-2455

Pittsburgh Division
1001 California Avenue, Pittsburgh, PA 15290-9000
Postal Inspector in Charge **Tommy Coke** . . . . (877) 876-2455

Phoenix Division
P.O. Box 20666, Phoenix, AZ 85036-0666
Postal Inspector in Charge **Terry W. Donnelly** . . . . (602) 223-3270
E-mail: twdonnelly@uspis.gov

San Francisco Division
2501 Rydin Road, Floor 2S, Richmond, CA 94804-9712
Postal Inspector in Charge **Rafael Nunez** . . . . (877) 876-2455

Seattle Division
P.O. Box 400, Seattle, WA 98111-4000
Postal Inspector in Charge **Anthony Galetti** . . . . (877) 876-2455

Washington Division
10500 Little Patuxent Parkway, 2nd Floor, Columbia, MD 21044-3509
Postal Inspector in Charge **(Vacant)** . . . . (202) 268-4547

United States Railroad Retirement Board (RRB)

Description: The United States Railroad Retirement Board administers comprehensive retirement-survivor and unemployment-sickness benefit programs for the nation's railroad workers and their families under the Railroad Retirement and Railroad Unemployment Insurance Acts.

844 North Rush Street, Chicago, IL 60611-1275
Tel: (877) 772-5772 (General Information)
TTY: (312) 751-4701 (General Information)
Tel: (312) 751-4300 (Personnel Locator)
Tel: (312) 751-4943 (Equal Opportunity Office)
Tel: (312) 751-4565 (Procurement Information)
Tel: (312) 751-4777 (Public Affairs)
Tel: (312) 751-4935 (Freedom of Information Act)
Tel: (312) 751-4548 (Privacy Act) TTY: (312) 751-4701 (Operator)
Tel: (800) 772-4258 (Inspector General's Hotline)
Fax: (312) 751-4923 Internet: www.rrb.gov
Internet: www.usa.gov (Official US Government Website)

OFFICES OF THE BOARD

844 North Rush Street, Chicago, IL 60611-1275

Note: Members may continue to serve until reappointed or replaced.

Bureau of Field Service

844 North Rush Street, Ninth Floor, Chicago, IL 60611-1275
Fax: (312) 751-3360

Regional Networks

Network 1
Areas Covered: Parts of: IL, MI, WI, IN, IA, and Parts of Canada
Manager **Brandi Splitter** .... (877) 772-5772
132 South Water Street, Suite 517, Decatur, IL 62523-1077

Chicago (IL) District Office
844 North Rush Street, Room 901, Chicago, IL 60611-1275
Tel: (877) 772-5772 Fax: (312) 751-7136 E-mail: chicago@rrb.gov
District Manager **Eric Jensen** .... (877) 772-5772

Decatur (IL) District Office
132 South Water Street, Suite 517, Decatur, IL 62523-1077
Tel: (877) 772-5772 Fax: (217) 423-7872 E-mail: decatur@rrb.gov
District Manager **Brandi Splitter** .... (877) 772-5772

Joliet (IL) District Office
63 West Jefferson Street, Suite 102, Joliet, IL 60432
Tel: (877) 772-5772 Fax: (815) 740-2139 E-mail: joliet@rrb.gov
District Manager **Antoine Alexander** .... (877) 772-5772

Milwaukee (WI) District Office
Henry S. Reuss Federal Plaza, 310 West Wisconsin Avenue, Suite 1168, Milwaukee, WI 53203-2213
Tel: (877) 772-5772 Fax: (414) 297-3833 E-mail: milwaukee@rrb.gov
District Manager **Gregory Schram** .... (877) 772-5772

Network 2
Areas Covered: MA, ME, NH, RI, VT, Parts of OH, IN, MI, NY, PA, WV, KY and Canada
Manager **Mary A. Tonnemacher** .... (877) 772-5772
408 Atlantic Avenue, Room 441, Boston, MA 02110

Boston (MA) District Office
408 Atlantic Avenue, Room 441, Boston, MA 02110
Tel: (877) 772-5772 Fax: (617) 223-8551 E-mail: boston@rrb.gov
District Manager **Mary A. Tonnemacher** .... (877) 772-5772

Cincinnati (OH) District Office
525 Vine Street, Suite 1940, Cincinnati, OH 45202
Tel: (877) 772-5772 Fax: (513) 684-3182 E-mail: cincinnati@rrb.gov
District Manager **Ashley Horn** .... (877) 772-5772

Cleveland (OH) District Office
A. J. Celebrezze Federal Building, 1240 East Ninth Street, Room 907, Cleveland, OH 44199-2001
Tel: (877) 772-5772 Fax: (216) 522-2320 E-mail: cleveland@rrb.gov
District Manager **Angela Bellack** .... (877) 772-5772

Detroit (MI) District Office
Patrick V. McNamara Federal Building, 477 West Michigan Avenue, Room 1199, Detroit, MI 48226-2596
Tel: (877) 772-5772 Fax: (313) 226-4233 E-mail: detroit@rrb.gov
District Manager **Deanna Smith** .... (877) 772-5772

Pittsburgh (PA) District Office
Moorhead Federal Building, 1000 Liberty Avenue, Room 1511, Pittsburgh, PA 15222-4107
Tel: (877) 772-5772 Fax: (412) 395-4711 E-mail: pittsburgh@rrb.gov
District Manager **Danica Miller** .... (877) 772-5772

Network 3
1514 11th Avenue, Altoona, PA 16601
Areas Covered: DC, DE, MD and parts of NJ, NY, PA, VA, WV
Manager **Jason Vizanko** .... (877) 772-5772

Altoona (PA) District Office
1514 11th Avenue, Altoona, PA 16601
Tel: (877) 772-5772 Fax: (814) 946-3620 E-mail: altoona@rrb.gov
District Manager **Jason Vizanko** .... (877) 772-5772

Baltimore (MD) District Office
31 Hopkins Plaza, Suite 820, Baltimore, MD 21201-2896
Tel: (877) 772-5772 Fax: (410) 962-9835 E-mail: baltimore@rrb.gov
District Manager **Lisa Portis** .... (877) 772-5772

Harrisburg (PA) District Office
Federal Building, 228 Walnut Street, Room 576, Harrisburg, PA 17108
P.O. Box 11697, Harrisburg, PA 17108-1697
Tel: (877) 772-5772 Fax: (717) 221-3464 E-mail: harrisburg@rrb.gov
District Manager **Mary Schmidt** .... (877) 772-5772

Philadelphia (PA) District Office
NIX Federal Building, 900 Market Street, Suite 301, Philadelphia, PA 19107-4293
Tel: (877) 772-5772 Fax: (215) 597-2794 E-mail: philadelphia@rrb.gov
District Manager **Dwight Daniels** .... (877) 772-5772

★ Presidential Appointment Requiring Senate Confirmation ☆ Presidential Appointment □ Schedule C Appointment ◇ Career Senior Foreign Service Appointment
● Career Senior Executive Service (SES) Appointment ○ Non-Career Senior Executive Service (SES) Appointment ■ Postal Career Executive Service

Scranton (PA) District Office
Siniawa Plaza II, 717 Scranton Carbondale Highway,
Scranton, PA 18508-1121
Tel: (877) 772-5772 Fax: (570) 346-6042 E-mail: scranton@rrb.gov
District Manager **Christine Shay** .... (877) 772-5772

Network 4
Areas Covered: Parts of CT, NJ, NY, PA, and parts of Canada
Manager **Cathleen Quinn** .... (877) 772-5772
490 Federal Plaza, Central Islip, NY 11722-4424

Albany (NY) District Office
Leo O'Brien Federal Building, 11A Clinton Avenue,
Suite 264, Albany, NY 12207-2382
Tel: (877) 772-5772 Fax: (631) 232-5701 E-mail: albany@rrb.gov
District Manager **Starlette Stokes** .... (877) 772-5772

Buffalo (NY) District Office
186 Exchange Street, Suite 110, Buffalo, NY 14204-2085
Tel: (877) 772-5772 Fax: (716) 551-3802 E-mail: buffalo@rrb.gov
District Manager **Patricia McCulle** .... (877) 772-5772

Newark (NJ) District Office
20 Washington Place, Suite 516, Newark, NJ 07102-3127
Tel: (877) 772-5772 Fax: (973) 645-3373 E-mail: newark@rrb.gov
District Manager **Bryan Shortino** .... (877) 772-5772

New York (NY) District Office
Jacob K. Javits Federal Building, 26 Federal Plaza,
Suite 3404, New York, NY 10278-3499
Tel: (877) 772-5772 Fax: (212) 264-1687 E-mail: newyork@rrb.gov
District Manager **Angie Martinez** .... (877) 772-5772

Central Islip (NY) District Office
490 Federal Plaza, Central Islip, NY 11722-4424
Tel: (877) 772-5772 Fax: (631) 232-5701 E-mail: westbury@rrb.gov
District Manager **Cathleen Quinn** .... (877) 772-5772

Network 5
Areas Covered: Parts of IL, IN, KY, NC, OH, TN, VA, WV
Manager **Janet Scarberry** .... (877) 772-5772
640 4th Avenue, Fax: (304) 529-5546
Room 145, Huntington, WV 25721-2153

Huntington (WV) District Office
New Federal Building, 640 4th Avenue,
Room 145, Huntington, WV 25721-2153
P.O. Box 2153, Huntington, WV 25721-2153
Tel: (877) 772-5772 Fax: (304) 529-5546 E-mail: huntington@rrb.gov
District Manager **Janet Scarberry** .... (877) 772-5772

Indianapolis (IN) District Office
Birch Bayh Federal Building, 46 East Ohio Street,
Suite 413, Indianapolis, IN 46204-1946
Tel: (877) 772-5772 Fax: (317) 226-5374 E-mail: indianapolis@rrb.gov
District Manager **Robert Braitman** .... (877) 772-5772

Louisville (KY) District Office
Theatre Building, 629 South 4th Street,
Suite 301, Louisville, KY 40202-2461
Tel: (877) 772-5772 Fax: (502) 582-5518 E-mail: louisville@rrb.gov
District Manager **Gene Guihan** .... (877) 772-5772

Richmond (VA) District Office
400 North Eighth Street, Suite 470, Richmond, VA 23219-4819
Tel: (877) 772-5772 Fax: (804) 771-8481 E-mail: richmond@rrb.gov
District Manager **John Macomber** .... (877) 772-5772

Roanoke (VA) District Office
First Campbell Square, 210 First Street, SW,
Suite 110, Roanoke, VA 24011-1606
P.O. Box 270, Roanoke, VA 24002-0270
Tel: (877) 772-5772 Fax: (540) 857-2769 E-mail: roanoke@rrb.gov
District Manager **Sarah Assaid** .... (877) 772-5772

Network 6
Areas Covered: SC, and parts of FL, GA and AL, NC
Manager **Virginia Waller** .... (877) 772-5772
550 Water Street, Fax: (704) 344-6429
Suite 220, Jacksonville, FL 32202-4411

Atlanta (GA) District Office
401 West Peachtree Street, Room 1702, Atlanta, GA 30308
Tel: (877) 772-5772 Fax: (404) 331-1629 E-mail: atlanta@rrb.gov
District Manager **Robin Odum** .... (877) 772-5772

Charlotte (NC) District Office
Quorum Business Park, 7508 East Independence Boulevard,
Suite 120, Charlotte, NC 28227-9409
Tel: (877) 772-5772 Fax: (704) 344-6429 E-mail: charlotte@rrb.gov
District Manager **Antony "Tony" Haynes** .... (877) 772-5772

Jacksonville (FL) District Office
550 Water Street Building, 550 Water Street,
Suite 220, Jacksonville, FL 32202-4411
Tel: (877) 772-5772 Fax: (904) 232-2874 E-mail: jacksonville@rrb.gov
District Manager **Virginia Waller** .... (877) 772-5772

Tampa (FL) District Office
Robert Timberlake Federal Building Annex, 500 East Zack Street,
Suite 300, Tampa, FL 33602-3918
Tel: (877) 772-5772 Fax: (813) 228-2939 E-mail: tampa@rrb.gov
District Manager **Michael Condon** .... (877) 772-5772

Network 7
Areas Covered: Parts of AL, KS, GA, IL, MO, MS, TN
Manager **Ada Foster** .... (877) 772-5772
Federal Building, 601 East 12th Street, Fax: (816) 426-5334
Room G47, Kansas City, MO 64106-2818

Birmingham (AL) District Office
Medical Forum Building, 950 22nd Street North,
Room 426, Birmingham, AL 35203-1134
Tel: (877) 772-5772 Fax: (205) 731-0026 E-mail: birmingham@rrb.gov
District Manager **Yulanda Bowman** .... (877) 772-5772

Kansas City (MO) District Office
Federal Building, 601 East 12th Street,
Room G-47, Kansas City, MO 64106-2818
Tel: (877) 772-5772 Fax: (816) 426-5334 E-mail: kansascity@rrb.gov
District Manager **Ada Foster** .... (877) 772-5772

Nashville (TN) District Office
Cumberland Bend Office Center, 233 Cumberland Bend,
Suite 104, Nashville, TN 37228-1806
Tel: (877) 772-5772 Fax: (615) 736-7071 E-mail: nashville@rrb.gov
District Manager **Susan McGranahan** .... (877) 772-5772

Saint Louis (MO) District Office
Robert A. Young Federal Building, 1222 Spruce Street,
Room 7.303, St. Louis, MO 63103-2846
Tel: (877) 772-5772 Fax: (314) 539-6229 E-mail: stlouis@rrb.gov
District Manager **Jodi Huskey** .... (877) 772-5772

Network 8
Areas Covered: AR, LA, and parts of AL, FL, MS, OK, TN, TX
Manager **Carol d'Aquin** .... (877) 772-5772
500 Poydras Street, Fax: (504) 589-4899
Suite 1045, New Orleans, LA 70130

Fort Worth (TX) District Office
Lanham Federal Building, 819 Taylor Street,
Room 10G02, Fort Worth, TX 76102
P.O. Box 17420, Fort Worth, TX 76102-0420
Tel: (877) 772-5772 Fax: (817) 978-2740 E-mail: fortworth@rrb.gov
District Manager **Michelle Fields** .... (877) 772-5772

Houston (TX) District Office
Mickey Leland Federal Building, 1919 Smith Street,
Suite 8090, Houston, TX 77002-8049
Tel: (877) 772-5772 Fax: (713) 759-0349 E-mail: houston@rrb.gov
District Manager **Cheryl Donahue** .... (877) 772-5772

Little Rock (AR) District Office
1200 Cherry Brook Drive, Suite 500, Little Rock, AR 72211-4122
Tel: (877) 772-5772 Fax: (501) 225-6782 E-mail: littlerock@rrb.gov
District Manager **Claudinell Busick** .... (877) 772-5772

New Orleans (LA) District Office
500 Poydras Street, Suite 1045, New Orleans, LA 70130
Tel: (877) 772-5772 Fax: (504) 589-4899 E-mail: neworleans@rrb.gov
District Manager **Carol d'Aquin** .... (877) 772-5772

Network 9
Areas Covered: CO, NE, and parts of IA, KS, MO, NM, OK, SD, TX, WY
Manager **Joseph A. "Joe" Gray** .... (877) 772-5772
721 19th Street, Fax: (303) 844-2609
Room 177, Denver, CO 80202-2514
P.O. Box 8869, Denver, CO 80201-8869

Albuquerque (NM) District Office
421 Gold Avenue SW, Suite 304, Albuquerque, NM 87103-0334
P.O. Box 334, Albuquerque, NM 87103-0334
Tel: (877) 772-5772 Fax: (505) 346-6407 E-mail: albuquerque@rrb.gov
District Manager **Tracy Davis** .... (877) 772-5772

Denver (CO) District Office
721 19th Street, Room 177, Denver, CO 80202-2514
P.O. Box 8869, Denver, CO 80201-8869
Tel: (877) 772-5772 Fax: (303) 844-2609 E-mail: denverdistrict@rrb.gov
District Manager **Joseph A. "Joe" Gray** .... (877) 772-5772

Omaha (NE) District Office
1299 Farnam Street, Suite 200, Omaha, NE 68102
Tel: (877) 772-5772 Fax: (402) 346-6077 E-mail: omaha@rrb.gov
District Manager **Donna Baker** .... (877) 772-5772

Wichita (KS) District Office
2020 North Webb Road, Suite 104, Wichita, KS 67206-3408
Tel: (877) 772-5772 Fax: (316) 687-3572 E-mail: wichita@rrb.gov
District Manager **John Gilliand** .... (877) 772-5772

Network 10
Areas Covered: AZ, CA, HI and parts of NV
Manager **Thomas "Tom" Hamm** .... (877) 772-5772
Federal Building, 1301 Clay Street, Fax: (510) 637-2978
Suite 110S, Oakland, CA 94612-5215

Covina (CA) District Office
858 South Oak Park Road, Suite 102, Covina, CA 91724-3674
Tel: (877) 772-5772 Fax: (626) 339-8223 E-mail: covina@rrb.gov
District Manager **Robert Jimenez** .... (877) 772-5772

Mesa (AZ) District Office
1220 South Alma School Road, Suite 106, Mesa, AZ 85210
Tel: (877) 772-5772 Fax: (480) 610-5988 E-mail: mesa@rrb.gov
District Manager **Gale Bowman** .... (877) 772-5772

Oakland (CA) District Office
Federal Building, 1301 Clay Street, Suite 110S, Oakland, CA 94612-5215
Tel: (877) 772-5772 Fax: (510) 637-2978 E-mail: oakland@rrb.gov
District Manager **Thomas "Tom" Hamm** .... (877) 772-5772

Roseville (CA) District Office
910 Cirby Way, Suite 100, Roseville, CA 95661-4420
Tel: (877) 772-5772 Fax: (916) 787-6204 E-mail: roseville@rrb.gov
District Manager **Jeramie Wondercheck** .... (877) 772-5772

Network 11
Areas Covered: AK, ID, MT, OR, SD, UT, WA and parts of Canada, NV, WY
Manager **Vonna Ward** .... (877) 772-5772
125 South State Street, Fax: (801) 524-4313
Room 1205, Salt Lake City, UT 84138-1137

Bellevue (WA) District Office
Pacific Plaza, 155 - 108th Avenue, NE,
Suite 201, Bellevue, WA 98004-5901
Tel: (877) 772-5772 Fax: (425) 450-5472 E-mail: bellevue@rrb.gov
District Manager **Gregory "Greg" Pesek** .... (877) 772-5772

Billings (MT) District Office
2900 Fourth Avenue, North, Room 101, Billings, MT 59101-1266
Tel: (877) 772-5772 Fax: (406) 247-7379 E-mail: billings@rrb.gov
District Manager **Becky Harris** .... (877) 772-5772

Portland (OR) District Office
620 Southwest Main Street, Suite 112, Portland, OR 97205-3025
Tel: (877) 772-5772 Fax: (503) 326-2157 E-mail: portland@rrb.gov
District Manager **Paula Mills** .... (877) 772-5772

Salt Lake City (UT) District Office
125 South State Street, Room 1205, Salt Lake City, UT 84138-1137
Tel: (877) 772-5772 Fax: (801) 524-4313 E-mail: saltlakecity@rrb.gov
District Manager **Vonna Ward** .... (877) 772-5772

Spokane (WA) District Office
U.S. Courthouse, West 920 Riverside Avenue,
Suite 492B, Spokane, WA 99201-1008
Tel: (877) 772-5772 Fax: (509) 353-2741 E-mail: spokane@rrb.gov
District Manager **Amy Galloway** .... (877) 772-5772

Network 12
Areas Covered: MN, ND and parts of Canada, IA, MI, MO, SD, WI
Manager **Debbie Helbling** .... (877) 772-5772
657 Second Avenue, North, Fax: (701) 239-5261
Room 312, Fargo, ND 58102-4727

Des Moines (IA) District Office
Federal Building, 210 Walnut Street, Room 921,
Des Moines, IA 50309-2116
Tel: (877) 772-5772 Fax: (515) 288-1437 E-mail: desmoines@rrb.gov
District Manager **Patrick Vaughan** .... (877) 772-5772

Duluth (MN) District Office
Federal Building, 515 West First Street,
Suite 125, Duluth, MN 55802-1399
Tel: (877) 772-5772 Fax: (218) 720-5315 E-mail: duluth@rrb.gov
District Manager **Dawn Barto** .... (877) 772-5772

Fargo (ND) District Office
U.S. Post Office Building, 657 Second Avenue, North,
Room 312, Fargo, ND 58102-4727
Tel: (877) 772-5772 Fax: (701) 239-5261 E-mail: fargo@rrb.gov
District Manager **Debbie Helbling** .... (877) 772-5772

Saint Paul (MN) District Office
180 East Fifth Street, Suite 255, St. Paul, MN 55101-1764
Tel: (877) 772-5772 Fax: (651) 290-3076 E-mail: stpaul@rrb.gov
District Manager **Elizabeth Fairfax** .... (877) 772-5772

★ Presidential Appointment Requiring Senate Confirmation ☆ Presidential Appointment ☐ Schedule C Appointment ◇ Career Senior Foreign Service Appointment
● Career Senior Executive Service (SES) Appointment ○ Non-Career Senior Executive Service (SES) Appointment ■ Postal Career Executive Service

United States Securities and Exchange Commission (SEC)

Description: The United States Securities and Exchange Commission's goal is to protect investors and maintain the integrity of the securities markets. It also oversees other key participants in the securities world, including stock exchanges, broker-dealers, investment advisors, mutual funds, and public utility holding companies.

100 F Street, NE, Washington, DC 20549
Tel: (888) 732-6585 (General Information)
Tel: (800) 732-0330 (Investor Information Service)
Tel: (202) 551-6000 (Personnel/Office Locator - Automated)
Tel: (202) 551-7300 (Procurement Information)
Tel: (202) 551-4120 (Public Affairs)
Tel: (202) 551-8090 (Public Reference)
Tel: (202) 551-4040 (Publications Unit)
Tel: (202) 551-7900 (Freedom of Information/Privacy Act)
Internet: www.sec.gov
Internet: www.sec.gov/edgar.shtml (EDGAR Database)
Internet: https://www.sec.gov/smallbusiness (Small Business Information)
Internet: www.investor.gov (Investor Education)
Internet: www.usa.gov (Official US Government Website)

OFFICES OF THE COMMISSIONERS

100 F Street, NE, Room 10700, Washington, DC 20549
Fax: (202) 772-9200

Note: Commissioners may continue to serve beyond the expiration of their terms until reappointed or replaced.

Regional Offices

Atlanta (GA) Regional Office

950 East Paces Ferry Road NE, Suite 900, Atlanta, GA 30326-1232
Tel: (404) 842-7600 Fax: (404) 842-7666 E-mail: atlanta@sec.gov

Regional Director **Richard R. Best** .... (404) 842-7600
Education: SUNY (Old Westbury); Howard U JD
Senior Trial Counsel **William P. "Bill" Hicks** .... (404) 842-7622
E-mail: hicksw@sec.gov
Education: Dickinson Law 1975 BA; Brooklyn Law 1978 JD
Assistant Regional Director for Operations
Roderick Goodwin .... (404) 842-7605
E-mail: goodwinr@sec.gov
Administrative Officer **Michael Ashmore** .... (404) 842-7650
E-mail: ashmorem@sec.gov

Enforcement

950 East Paces Ferry Road NE, Suite 900, Atlanta, GA 30326-1232
Fax: (404) 842-7666

Associate Regional Director (Enforcement)
Aaron W. Lipson .... (404) 842-7675
Education: Yale 1997; Georgia 2000 JD

Examinations

950 East Paces Ferry Road NE, Suite 900, Atlanta, GA 30326-1232
Fax: (404) 842-7666

Associate Regional Director (Examinations)
Donna C. Esau .... (404) 842-7645
E-mail: esaud@sec.gov
Education: North Carolina Pembroke BS; Kennesaw State U

Boston (MA) Regional Office

33 Arch Street, 23rd Floor, Boston, MA 02110-1424
Tel: (617) 573-8900 Fax: (617) 573-4590 E-mail: boston@sec.gov

Regional Director **Paul G. Levenson** .... (617) 573-8900
Education: Harvard, JD

Boston (MA) Regional Office *(continued)*

Supervisory Regional Trial Counsel **Martin Healey** ...... (617) 573-8952
E-mail: healeym@sec.gov
Assistant Regional Director for Operations
Ragan Willis .... (617) 573-8971
E-mail: willisr@sec.gov

Enforcement

Associate Regional Director - Enforcement
John T. Dugan .... (617) 573-8936
Education: UMass (Amherst) 1988 BA; George Washington 1993 JD

Examinations

Associate Regional Director **Kevin M. Kelcourse** .... (617) 573-8944
Education: Georgetown

Chicago (IL) Regional Office (CHRO)

175 West Jackson Boulevard, Suite 900, Chicago, IL 60604
Tel: (312) 353-7390 Fax: (312) 353-7398 E-mail: chicago@sec.gov
Areas Covered: IL, IN, IA, KY, MI, MN, MO, OH, WI

Regional Director **Joel R. Levin** .... (312) 596-6055
Business Manager **Barry Isenman** .... (312) 886-8515
Supervisory Program Support Specialist
Karen A. Gniedziejko .... (312) 886-9898
E-mail: gniedziejkok@sec.gov
Information Technology Branch Chief **Mary M. Styles** ... (312) 353-1811
E-mail: stylesm@sec.gov
Senior Special Counsel **Tina Diamantopoulos-Burgis** ... (312) 353-6313

Enforcement

175 West Jackson Boulevard, Suite 900, Chicago, IL 60604
Fax: (312) 353-7398

• Senior Associate Regional Director **Robert J. Burson** .... (312) 353-7428
E-mail: bursonr@sec.gov
• Associate Regional Director **Kathryn A. Pyszka** .... (312) 353-7394
E-mail: pyszkak@sec.gov
Education: Wisconsin; Illinois JD
Senior Trial Counsel **Timothy Leiman** .... (312) 353-6884
Education: Michigan 1999 JD
Senior Trial Counsel **(Vacant)** .... (312) 353-6884

Examinations

175 West Jackson Boulevard, Suite 900, Chicago, IL 60604
Tel: (312) 353-7390 Fax: (312) 353-7398

Associate Regional Director for Broker-Dealer
Examinations **Daniel "Dan" Gregus** .... (312) 353-7423
Education: Illinois 1983 BBA, 1986 JD
Deputy Associate Regional Director for Broker-Dealer
Examinations **John Brodersen** .... (312) 886-8506
• Associate Regional Director for Investment
Advisor/Investment Company Exams
Steven J. Levine .... (312) 886-1774
E-mail: levines@sec.gov
Education: Yale 1991 JD
Deputy Associate Regional Director for
Investment Advisor/Investment Company Exams
Louis A. Gracia .... (312) 353-6888
Attorney-Adviser **Chan Grewal** .... (312) 596-6013
Attorney-Adviser **Anita Mehra** .... (312) 596-6031

★ Presidential Appointment Requiring Senate Confirmation ☆ Presidential Appointment □ Schedule C Appointment ◇ Career Senior Foreign Service Appointment
● Career Senior Executive Service (SES) Appointment ○ Non-Career Senior Executive Service (SES) Appointment ■ Postal Career Executive Service

Examinations *(continued)*

Attorney-Adviser **Susan Rudzinski** . . . . (312) 596-6009

Denver (CO) Regional Office

1961 Stout Street, Suite 1700, Denver, CO 80294-1961
Tel: (303) 844-1000 Fax: (303) 297-1730 E-mail: denver@sec.gov
Areas Covered: AR, CO, KS, NE, NM, ND, OK, SD, TX, UT, WY

● Regional Director **Kurt L. Gottschall** . . . . (303) 844-1000
E-mail: gottschallk@sec.gov
Education: Claremont McKenna 1992; Hastings 1995 JD

Assistant Regional Director, Office of Operations
Christopher Friedman . . . . (303) 844-1000

Enforcement

● Associate Regional Director **(Vacant)** . . . . (303) 844-1000

Examinations

Associate Regional Director **Thomas M. Piccone** . . . . (303) 844-1016
Education: Colorado, 1987 JD

Fort Worth (TX) Regional Office

801 Cherry Street, 19th Floor, Fort Worth, TX 76102-6882
Tel: (817) 978-3821 Fax: (817) 978-2700 E-mail: dfw@sec.gov

Regional Director **Shamoil T. Shipchandler** . . . . (817) 978-3821
Education: Middlebury 1996 BA; Cornell 2000 JD

Program Specialist **Ida Fowlds** . . . . (817) 978-6432
E-mail: fowldsi@sec.gov

Investor Assistant Specialist **Farol Parco** . . . . (817) 978-6485

Enforcement Program

801 Cherry Street, 1900, Fort Worth, TX 76102-6882

Associate Regional Director **Eric R. Werner** . . . . (817) 978-1417
Education: Occidental BA; Washington U (MO) JD

Examination Program

801 Cherry Street, Suite 1900, Fort Worth, TX 76102-6882

Associate Regional Director for Examinations
Marshall M. Gandy . . . . (817) 900-2622
Education: Sam Houston State; Southern Methodist JD

Los Angeles (CA) Regional Office

444 South Flower Street, Suite 900, Los Angeles, CA 90071
Tel: (323) 965-3998 Fax: (323) 965-3815 E-mail: losangeles@sec.gov
Areas Covered: AZ, CA, GU, HI, NV

● Regional Director **Michele Wein Layne** . . . . (323) 965-3850
E-mail: laynem@sec.gov
Education: UCLA; USC JD

Assistant Regional Director for Operations
Rabia Cebeci . . . . (323) 965-3853
E-mail: cebecir@sec.gov

Regional Trial Counsel **(Vacant)** . . . . (323) 965-3890

Administrative Officer **David E. Levinson** . . . . (323) 965-3906
E-mail: levinsond@sec.gov

Supervisory Information Technology Specialist
Bradford Rothschild . . . . (323) 965-4505
E-mail: rothschildb@sec.gov Fax: (323) 965-4528

Enforcement

Associate Regional Director **John W. Berry** . . . . (323) 965-3998
Education: Duke 1992 BS; Virginia

Associate Regional Director **Alka Patel** . . . . (323) 965-3998
Education: USC; Southwestern JD

Examinations

Associate Regional Director for Examinations
Bryan Bennett . . . . (323) 965-3861
Education: UCLA; Iowa

Miami (FL) Regional Office

801 Brickell Avenue, Suite 1800, Miami, FL 33131
Tel: (305) 982-6300 Fax: (305) 536-4146 E-mail: miami@sec.gov
Areas Covered: AL, FL, GA, LA, MS, NC, PR, SC, TN, VI

● Regional Director **Eric Bustillo** . . . . (305) 982-6300
E-mail: bustilloe@sec.gov
Education: Miami 1985 BBA, 1989 JD

Associate Regional Director (Enforcement)
Glenn S. Gordon . . . . (305) 982-6360
Education: Pennsylvania 1983 BA; Wharton 1983 BS; Cornell 1986 JD

Associate Regional Director (Examination)
John C. Mattimore . . . . (305) 982-6357

Regional Trial Counsel **Andrew O. Schiff** . . . . (305) 982-6390
E-mail: schiffa@sec.gov

Administrative Officer **L. Alexandria Ledezma** . . . . (305) 982-6343
E-mail: ledezmaa@sec.gov

Information Technology Specialist **Reinaldo Conejo** . . . . . (305) 416-6278
E-mail: conejor@sec.gov Fax: (305) 536-4158

Information Technology Specialist **Raymond Schafer** . . . . (305) 982-6333
E-mail: schaferr@sec.gov Fax: (305) 536-4158

Assistant Regional Director, Office of Operations
David A. Cardona . . . . (305) 982-6384
Education: Case Western

New York (NY) Regional Office

Brookfield Place, 200 Vesey Street, Suite 400, New York, NY 10281
Tel: (212) 336-1100 E-mail: newyork@sec.gov
Internet: https://www.sec.gov/newyork
Areas Covered: CT, DE, DC, ME, MD, MA, NH, NJ, NY, PA, RI, VT, VA, WV

Regional Director **Marc P. Berger** . . . . (212) 336-1020
Education: Cornell 1996 BA; Virginia 1999 JD

Assistant Regional Director and Chief of Regional Office Operations **Edward Fallacaro** . . . . (212) 336-5543

Administrative Officer **James H. Green** . . . . (212) 336-0957
E-mail: greenjh@sec.gov

Broker - Dealer Examinations

Assistant Regional Director **Linda A. Lettieri** . . . . (212) 336-1100

Associate Regional Director **Robert A. Sollazzo** . . . . (212) 336-1070

Enforcement

Senior Associate Regional Director **Sanjay Wadhwa** . . . . (212) 336-0181
Education: Florida Atlantic 1990 BBA; South Texas 1995 JD; NYU 1996 LLM

Associate Regional Director **Lara Shalov Mehraban** . . . . (212) 336-1100
Education: Duke 1994 BA; Michigan 1999 JD

Associate Regional Director **(Vacant)** . . . . (212) 336-0153

Investment Adviser - Investment Company Examinations

Associate Regional Director **Thomas J. Butler** . . . . (212) 336-1100
Education: Rutgers BA; Rutgers (Newark) JD

Associate Regional Director **Maurya C. Keating** . . . . (212) 336-1100
Education: Catholic U BA, MA; St John's U (NY) JD

Assistant Regional Director **George V. DeAngelis** . . . . (212) 336-0494

Assistant Regional Director **William J. Delmage** . . . . (212) 336-0495

Assistant Regional Director **Joseph P. DiMaria** . . . . (212) 336-0497

Assistant Regional Director **Anthony P. Fiduccia** . . . . (212) 336-0505

Assistant Regional Director **Raymond J. Slezak** . . . . (212) 336-0559

Philadelphia (PA) Regional Office

One Penn Center, 1617 JFK Boulevard,
Suite 520, Philadelphia, PA 19103-1844
Tel: (215) 597-3100 Fax: (215) 597-3194 E-mail: philadelphia@sec.gov

Regional Director **G. Jeffrey Boujoukos** . . . . (215) 597-3100
Education: Lehigh 1989; Temple 1992 JD

Chief of Regional Office Operations **Nancy Brown** . . . . . . (215) 597-1043

Administrator **David Butler** . . . . (215) 597-3107
E-mail: butlerda@sec.gov

Regional Trial Counsel **(Vacant)** . . . . (215) 597-0687

INDEPENDENT AGENCIES

★ Presidential Appointment Requiring Senate Confirmation ☆ Presidential Appointment ☐ Schedule C Appointment ◇ Career Senior Foreign Service Appointment
● Career Senior Executive Service (SES) Appointment ○ Non-Career Senior Executive Service (SES) Appointment ■ Postal Career Executive Service

Enforcement
1617 JFK Boulevard, Suite 520, Philadelphia, PA 19103-1844
Fax: (215) 597-2740 Fax: (215) 597-5585

Associate Regional Director - Enforcement
Kelly L. Gibson . . . . (215) 597-3100
Education: Rowan U BA; Villanova JD

Examinations
1617 JFK Boulevard, Suite 520, Philadelphia, PA 19103-1844
Fax: (215) 446-4272 (Reg I/A) Fax: (215) 446-4282 (Reg B/D)

Associate Regional Director - Regulation
Joy G. Thompson . . . . (215) 597-6135
Education: Tufts 1979 BA; Pennsylvania 1982 JD

Salt Lake City (UT) Regional Office (SLRO)
351 South West Temple Street, Room 6.100,
Salt Lake City, UT 84101-1407
Tel: (801) 524-5796 Fax: (801) 524-3558 E-mail: saltlake@sec.gov
Internet: https://www.sec.gov/saltlake

Regional Director **Daniel J. "Dan" Wadley** . . . . (801) 524-6745
Education: BYU 1997; Georgetown 2000 JD
Regional Trial Counsel **(Vacant)** . . . . (801) 524-6748

San Francisco (CA) Regional Office
44 Montgomery Street, Suite 2800, San Francisco, CA 94104
Tel: (415) 705-2500 Fax: (415) 705-2501 E-mail: sanfrancisco@sec.gov

Regional Director **Jina L. Choi** . . . . (415) 705-2500
Education: Oberlin 1991 BA; Yale JD
Associate Regional Director (Enforcement)
Erin E. Schneider . . . . (415) 705-2500
Education: UC Berkeley 1995; Hastings 2001 JD
Associate Regional Director for Examinations
Kristin A. Snyder . . . . (415) 705-2500
Education: UC Davis BA; Hastings JD
Administrative Officer **Michael Walker** . . . . (415) 705-2500
E-mail: walkermi@sec.gov

Selective Service System (SSS)

Description: The Selective Service System's mission is to provide manpower to the armed forces in an emergency and to run an Alternative Service Program for men classified as conscientious objectors during a draft. The obligation to register for the draft is imposed by the Military Selective Service Act, which establishes and governs the operations of the Selective Service System.

1515 Wilson Boulevard, Arlington, VA 22209-2425
Tel: (703) 605-4040 (Personnel Locator)
Tel: (703) 605-4038 (Procurement Information)
Tel: (703) 605-4005 (Freedom of Information/Privacy Act)
Tel: (847) 688-6888 (Data Management Center and Registration Inquiries)
Fax: (703) 688-2860 E-mail: open@sss.gov (Open Government Initiative)
Internet: www.sss.gov
Internet: www.sss.gov/open (Open Government Initiative)
Internet: www.usa.gov (Official US Government Website)

OFFICE OF THE DIRECTOR

1515 Wilson Boulevard, 5th Floor, Arlington, VA 22209-2425
Tel: (703) 605-4010 Fax: (703) 605-4006

Operations and Information Technology Directorate

1515 Wilson Boulevard, 6th Floor, Arlington, VA 22209-2425

Data Management Center
P.O. Box 4638, Palatine, IL 60094-4638

Manager **Nicole F. Harris** . . . . (847) 688-7911
E-mail: nicole.harris@sss.gov

Regional Offices

Region I

Building 3400, Suite 276, 2834 Green Bay Rd.,
North Chicago, IL 60064-9983
Tel: (847) 688-4540 Fax: (847) 688-3433
Areas Covered: CT, DC, DE, IL, IN, MA, MD, ME, MI, NH, NJ, NY, OH, PA, RI, VT, WI

Regional Director **Thomas "T.J." Kenney** . . . . (847) 688-7985
E-mail: tkenney@sss.gov
Operations Manager **Katherine Murphy** . . . . (847) 688-4540

Region II

1295 Barracks Avenue Southeast, Marietta, GA 30069-5010
Tel: (678) 655-9591 Fax: (770) 319-5631
Areas Covered: AL, AR, FL, GA, KY, LA, MS, NC, PR, SC, TN, TX, VA, VI, WV

Regional Director **Carlos M. Perez** . . . . (678) 655-9591
E-mail: cperez@sss.gov

Region III

Stapleton Building, 3401 Quebec Street,
Suite 1014, Denver, CO 80207-2323
Tel: (720) 847-4200 Fax: (720) 941-1685
Areas Covered: AK, AZ, CA, CO, GU, HI, IA, ID, KS, MN, MO, MT, NE, ND, NM, NV, OK, OR, SD, UT, WA, WY, Northern Mariana Islands

Regional Director **John J. Wilber** . . . . (720) 847-4200
E-mail: John.Wilber@sss.gov
Administrative Officer **Maryann Rangel** . . . . (720) 847-4200
E-mail: maryann.rangel@sss.gov

★ Presidential Appointment Requiring Senate Confirmation ☆ Presidential Appointment □ Schedule C Appointment ◇ Career Senior Foreign Service Appointment
● Career Senior Executive Service (SES) Appointment ○ Non-Career Senior Executive Service (SES) Appointment ■ Postal Career Executive Service

United States Small Business Administration (SBA)

Description: The United States Small Business Administration aids, counsels, assists, and protects the interests of small businesses and helps families and businesses to recover from national disasters.

409 Third Street, SW, Washington, DC 20416
Tel: (800) 827-5722 (Answer Desk)
Tel: (202) 401-8200 (Freedom of Information/Privacy Act)
Tel: (800) 767-0385 (Inspector General's Hotline)
Tel: (800) 972-2504 (Loan Information Packet)
Tel: (202) 205-6600 (Personnel Locator)
Tel: (202) 205-6460 (Procurement Assistance for Businesses)
Tel: (202) 205-6740 (Public Information - Media Inquiries Only)
Tel: (202) 205-6665 (Publications Information)
TTY: (800) 877-8339 Internet: www.sba.gov
Internet: www.usa.gov (Official US Government Website)

OFFICE OF THE ADMINISTRATOR

409 Third Street, SW, Suite 7000, Washington, DC 20416
Tel: (202) 205-6605 Fax: (202) 205-6802

Office of Disaster Assistance (ODA)

409 Third Street, SW, Suite 6050, Washington, DC 20416
Tel: (202) 205-6734 Fax: (202) 205-7728
E-mail: disastercustomerservice@sba.gov
E-mail: disaster.assistance@sba.gov

Area Offices

Customer Service Center - Buffalo (NY)
130 South Elmwood Avenue, Suite 516, Buffalo, NY 14202
Tel: (716) 843-4100 Tel: (800) 659-2955 Fax: (716) 843-4290

Center Director **Colleen M. Hiam** .... (716) 843-4100 ext. 1202
E-mail: colleen.hiam@sba.gov
Deputy Center Director **Jeffrey Zinn** .... (716) 843-4100 ext. 1203
E-mail: jeffrey.zinn@sba.gov

Field Operations Center East - Atlanta (GA)
101 Marietta Street, NW, Suite 700, Atlanta, GA 30303-2725
Tel: (404) 331-0333 Fax: (404) 331-0273
Areas Covered: AL, CT, DC, DE, FL, GA, IL, IN, KY, MA, MD, ME, MI, MN, MS, NC, NH, NJ, NY, OH, PA, RI, SC, TN, VA, VT, WI, WV; and Puerto Rico and Virgin Islands

Director **Frank Skaggs** .... (404) 331-0333 ext. 2174
E-mail: timothy.skaggs@sba.gov
Education: Morehead State 1979 BA
Deputy Director **Brenda K. Ballew** .... (404) 331-0333 ext. 2173
Education: Athens State 1972 BA
Public Affairs Director **Michael Lampton** ..... (404) 331-0333 ext. 2177
E-mail: michael.lampton@sba.gov
Education: Jackson State U 1977 BSAcc

Field Operations Center West - Sacramento (CA)
P.O. Box 419004, Sacramento, CA 95841-9004
Tel: (916) 735-1500
Areas Covered: AK, AZ, CA, GU, HI, ID, NV, OR, WA, AS, CNMI, FSM, RMI

Director **Tanya N. Garfield** .... (916) 735-1500
E-mail: tanya.garfield@sba.gov
Deputy Director **(Vacant)** .... (916) 735-1500
Field Operations Manager **Donna Gross** .... (916) 735-1500

Field Operations Center West - Sacramento (CA) *(continued)*
Public Information Supervisor **Richard Jenkins** .... (916) 735-1500

Processing and Disbursement Center - Fort Worth (TX)
14925 Kingsport Road, Fort Worth, TX 76155
Tel: (817) 868-2300 Fax: (817) 684-5616
Areas Covered: Nationwide
Center Director **Roger B. Garland** .... (817) 868-2300

Office of International Trade (OIT)

409 Third Street, SW, Suite 8500, Washington, DC 20416
Tel: (202) 205-6720 Fax: (202) 205-7272 Internet: www.sba.gov/oit

Arlington (VA) US Export Assistance Center
1501 Wilson Boulevard, Suite 1225, Arlington, VA 22209
Tel: (202) 557-4063 Fax: (202) 292-3539
Areas Covered: Delaware, the District of Columbia, Maryland, Virginia, and West Virginia
SBA Representative **William Houck** .... (202) 557-4063
E-mail: william.houck@sba.gov Fax: (202) 292-3539

Atlanta (GA) U.S. Export Assistance Center
75 Fifth Street, NW, Suite 1060, Atlanta, GA 30308
Fax: (202) 481-2966
Areas Covered: Alabama, Georgia, Kentucky, West/Central Tennessee
SBA Representative **David Leonard** .... (404) 242-6373
E-mail: david.leonard@sba.gov

Boston (MA) U.S. Export Assistance Center
JFK Building, 55 New Sudbury Street,
Suite 1826A, Boston, MA 02203
Tel: (617) 565-4301 Fax: (617) 565-4313
Areas Covered: Connecticut, Maine, Massachusetts, New Hampshire, Rhode Island and Vermont
SBA Representative **John Joyce** .... (617) 565-4305
E-mail: john.joyce@sba.gov

Charlotte (NC) U.S. Export-Assistance Center
521 East Morehead Street, Suite 435, Charlotte, NC 28202
Fax: (704) 332-2681
Areas Covered: North Carolina, South Carolina, Eastern Tennessee
SBA Representative **Daniel "Dan" Holt** .... (704) 333-4886 ext. 226
E-mail: daniel.holt@sba.gov

Chicago (IL) U.S. Export Assistance Center
233 North Michigan Avenue, Suite 260, Chicago, IL 60601
Fax: (202) 481-2281
Areas Covered: Wisconsin, Illinois, and Iowa.
SBA Representative **(Vacant)** .... (202) 205-6720

Cleveland (OH) U.S. Export Assistance Center
Howard M. Metzenbaum U.S. Courthouse, 201 Superior Avenue East, Suite 440, Cleveland, OH 44114
Tel: (216) 522-4731 Fax: (216) 522-2235
Areas Covered: Western New York, Ohio, and Western Pennsylvania
SBA Representative **Patrick K. "Pat" Hayes** . . . . (216) 522-4731
E-mail: patrick.hayes@sba.gov

Dallas (TX) U.S. Export Assistance Center
4300 Amon Carter Boulevard, Suite 114, Fort Worth, TX 76155
Tel: (202) 412-4657 Fax: (202) 741-6989
Areas Covered: Oklahoma, New Mexico, and Texas
SBA Representative **Alale Allal** . . . . (202) 412-4657
E-mail: alale.allal@sba.gov

Denver (CO) U.S. Export Assistance Center
1625 Broadway Avenue, Suite 680, Denver, CO 80202-4725
Tel: (303) 844-6622 Fax: (202) 481-0540
Internet: www.buyusa.gov/colorado
Areas Covered: Colorado, Utah, Montana, New Mexico and Wyoming
SBA Representative **Bryson Patterson** . . . . (303) 844-6622
E-mail: bryson.patterson@sba.gov

Detroit (MI) U.S. Export Assistance Center
211 West Fort Street, Suite 315, Detroit, MI 48202
Tel: (313) 226-3038 Fax: (202) 481-2666
Areas Covered: Michigan and Indiana
SBA Representative **(Vacant)** . . . . (313) 226-3038

Irvine (CA) International Trade Office
2302 Martin Court, Suite 315, Irvine, CA 92612
Fax: (202) 481-4434
Areas Covered: Nevada and Southern California.
SBA Representative **Martin Selander** . . . . (949) 660-8935
E-mail: martin.selander@sba.gov

Los Angeles (CA) U.S. Export Assistance Center
444 South Flower Street, 37th Floor, Los Angeles, CA 90071
Tel: (213) 894-8267 Fax: (202) 481-1525
Areas Covered: Southern California and Arizona.
SBA Representative **Pellson Lau** . . . . (213) 894-8267
E-mail: pellson.lau@sba.gov

Miami (FL) U.S. Export Assistance Center
5835 Blue Lagoon Drive, Suite 203, Miami, FL 33132
Fax: (202) 481-4471
Areas Covered: Florida, Puerto Rico, Virgin Islands
Regional Manager **Mary Hernandez** . . . .(305) 526-7425 ext. 21
E-mail: mary.hernandez@sba.gov

Minneapolis (MN) U.S. Export Assistance Center
330 Second Avenue South, Suite 402A, Minneapolis, MN 55401
Tel: (612) 348-1642 Fax: (202) 481-4065
Areas Covered: Minnesota, North Dakota and South Dakota
SBA Representative **Carlos Sosa** . . . .(612) 348-1642
E-mail: carlos.sosa@sba.gov

New Orleans (LA) US Export Assistance Center
423 Canal Street, Suite 419, New Orleans, LA 70130
Tel: (504) 589-6730 Fax: (202) 481-1525
Areas Covered: Arkansas, Louisiana, and Mississippi
SBA Representative **Reginald Harley** . . . . (504) 589-6730
E-mail: reginald.harley@sba.gov

New York (NY) U.S. Export Assistance Center
290 Broadway, Room 1312, New York, NY 10007
Fax: (212) 809-2687
Areas Covered: New York City (The Bronx, Brooklyn, Manhattan, Queens, Staten Island), Long Island, Westchester, Mid-Hudson and Eastern Upstate New York, and New Jersey
SBA Representative **Eduard Ekel** . . . .(212) 809-2645
E-mail: eduard.ekel@sba.gov

Philadelphia (PA) U.S. Export Assistance Center
Parkview Tower, 1150 First Avenue, Suite 1001, King of Prussia, PA 19406
Tel: (610) 382-3069 Fax: (202) 481-5216
Areas Covered: Eastern Pennsylvania
SBA Representative **Robert L. Elsas** . . . .(610) 382-3069
E-mail: robert.elsas@sba.gov
Education: SUNY (Albany) BS

San Francisco (CA) U.S. Export Assistance Center
75 Hawthorne Street, Suite 2500, San Francisco, CA 94105
Fax: (202) 292-3534
Areas Covered: Northern California, Hawaii and Guam
SBA Representative **Jeff Deiss** . . . .(415) 902-6027
E-mail: jeff.deiss@sba.gov

Seattle (WA) U.S. Export Assistance Center
Westin Building, 2001 Sixth Avenue, Suite 2610, Seattle, WA 98121
Tel: (206) 553-5615 Fax: (206) 553-7253
Areas Covered: Washington, Alaska and Northern Idaho
SBA Representative **Leland "Lee" Gibbs** . . . .(206) 553-0051
E-mail: leland.gibbs@sba.gov

St. Louis (MO) U.S. Export Assistance Center
Building 110, 4300 Goodfellow Boulevard, Suite 1100A, St. Louis, MO 63120
Tel: (314) 540-7587 Fax: (314) 260-3792
Areas Covered: Kansas, Missouri and Nebraska
SBA Representative **Larry Cresswell** . . . .(314) 540-7587
E-mail: larry.cresswell@sba.gov

Tampa (FL) U.S. Export Assistance Center
13805 58th Street North, Suite 1-200, Clearwater, FL 33760
Tel: (727) 464-7177 Fax: (202) 481-0999
Areas Covered: Northern and Central Florida
SBA Representative **Sandro Murtas** . . . . (727) 464-7177
E-mail: sandro.murtas@sba.gov

Office of the Chief Financial Officer
409 Third Street, SW, Washington, DC 20416
Tel: (202) 205-6449 Fax: (202) 205-6969
Fax: (202) 205-7274 (Alternate)
E-mail: opengov@sba.gov (Open Government Directive)
Internet: www.sba.gov/open (Open Government Website)

Denver Finance Center
721 - 19th Street, Denver, CO 80202
Mail: P.O. Box 205, Denver, CO 80201-0205
Fax: (303) 844-3464
Director **Melissa J. Atwood** . . . . (303) 844-0538
Deputy Director **(Vacant)** . . . . (303) 844-3499
Fax: (202) 481-4984

Office of Field Operations

409 Third Street, SW, 8th Floor, Suite 8400, Washington, DC 20416
Tel: (202) 205-6808 Fax: (202) 205-6832

Region I - New England

Thomas P. O'Neill, Jr. Federal Building, 10 Causeway Street,
Room 265, Boston, MA 02222-1093
Tel: (617) 565-8416 Fax: (617) 565-8420
Internet: www.sba.gov/about-offices-content/3/3070
Areas Covered: CT, MA, ME, NH, RI, VT

○ Regional Administrator **Wendell G. Davis** .... (802) 828-4422
Education: Notre Dame JD
Regional Advocate **(Vacant)** .... (617) 565-8418
Regional Communications Director **Elizabeth Moisuk** .... (617) 565-8416
E-mail: elizabeth.moisuk@sba.gov

Connecticut District Office

280 Trumbull Street, Floor 2, Hartford, CT 06103
Tel: (860) 240-4700 TTY: (800) 827-5722 Fax: (860) 240-4659
Internet: www.sba.gov/ct

District Director **Anne Hunt** .... (860) 240-4670
E-mail: anne.hunt@sba.gov
Deputy District Director **Julio C. Casiano** .... (860) 240-4896
E-mail: julio.casiano@sba.gov
District Counsel **(Vacant)** .... (860) 240-4889
Assistant District Director for Economic Development **Moraima Gutierrez** .... (860) 240-4654
E-mail: moraima.gutierrez@sba.gov
Economic Development Specialist **Lisa Powell** .... (860) 240-4892
E-mail: lisa.powell@sba.gov
Economic Development Specialist **Jessica Rivera** .... (860) 240-4638
E-mail: jessica.rivera@sba.gov
Economic Development Specialist **Tanisha Baptiste** ..... (860) 240-4671
E-mail: tanisha.baptiste@sba.gov
Lender Relations Specialist **William Tierney** .... (860) 240-4894
E-mail: william.tierney@sba.gov
Lender Relations Specialist **John Xu** .... (860) 240-4672
E-mail: john.xu@sba.gov
Veterans Affairs Officer **Frank Alvarado** .... (860) 240-4850
E-mail: frank.alvarado@sba.gov
Women's Business Ownership and Public Information Officer **(Vacant)** .... (860) 240-4700

Maine District Office

68 Sewall Street, Room 512, Augusta, ME 04330
Tel: (207) 622-8551 Fax: (207) 622-8277

District Director **Amy Bassett** .... (207) 622-8382
E-mail: amy.bassett@sba.gov
Deputy District Director and Women's Business Ownership Representative **Diane L. Sturgeon** .... (207) 622-8286
E-mail: diane.sturgeon@sba.gov
Economic Development Specialist **William S. Card** ...... (207) 622-8551
E-mail: william.card@sba.gov
Program Support Assistant and Public Information Officer **Keith Lind** .... (207) 622-8551
E-mail: keith.lind@sba.gov
Senior Area Manager - Bangor **James Pineau** .... (207) 945-2021
E-mail: james.pineau@sba.gov
Senior Area Manager - Portland **Bradley "Brad" Currie** .... (207) 248-9040
E-mail: bradley.currie@sba.gov

Massachusetts District Office

Thomas P. O'Neill, Jr. Federal Building, 10 Causeway Street,
Room 265, Boston, MA 02222-1093
Tel: (617) 565-5590 Fax: (617) 565-5598 Internet: www.sba.gov/ma

District Director **Robert H. "Bob" Nelson** .... (617) 565-5561
E-mail: rhnelson@sba.gov
Education: Hobart 1980 BA
Deputy District Director **David Polatin** .... (617) 565-5562
E-mail: david.polatin@sba.gov
Lead Business Development Specialist **Nadine Boone** ... (617) 565-8514
E-mail: nadine.boone@sba.gov

Massachusetts District Office *(continued)*

Lead Lender Relations Specialist **Ili Spahiu** .... (617) 565-5569
E-mail: ili.spahiu@sba.gov
District Counsel **Mary Laura Russell** .... (617) 565-8411
E-mail: mary.russell@sba.gov
Public Information Officer **Norman Eng** .... (617) 565-8510
E-mail: norman.eng@sba.gov

New Hampshire District Office

55 Pleasant Street, Suite 3101, Concord, NH 03301
Tel: (603) 225-1400 Fax: (603) 225-1409
Internet: www.sba.gov/localresources/district/nh

District Director **Greta Johansson** .... (603) 225-1401
E-mail: greta.johansson@sba.gov
Education: Stanford 1980 BS
Deputy District Director and Lender Relations Chief **(Vacant)** .... (603) 225-1400
District Counsel **Robert Welch** .... (603) 225-1406
E-mail: robert.welch@sba.gov
Government Contracting Officer **Rachael Roderick** ...... (603) 225-1603
E-mail: rachael.roderick@sba.gov
Veterans Affairs Officer **Miguel A. Moralez** .... (603) 225-1601
E-mail: miguel.moralez@sba.gov
Lender Relations Specialist **(Vacant)** .... (603) 225-1400
Economic Development Specialist and Public Information Officer **Hugh A. Curley** .... (603) 225-1402
E-mail: hugh.curley@sba.gov
Economic Development Specialist **Warren Haggerty** ..... (603) 225-1405
E-mail: warren.haggerty@sba.gov

Rhode Island District Office

380 Westminster Street, Suite 511, Providence, RI 02903-3246
Tel: (401) 528-4561 Fax: (401) 528-4539 Internet: www.sba.gov/ri

District Director **Mark S. Hayward** .... (401) 528-4540
E-mail: mark.hayward@sba.gov
Education: Providence BA
Deputy District Director **Joan L. Moran** .... (401) 528-4580
Public Information Officer **Ryan Brissette** .... (401) 528-4561
E-mail: ryan.brissette@sba.gov

Vermont District Office

87 State Street, Room 205, Montpelier, VT 05602
P.O. Box 605, Montpelier, VT 05601-0605
Tel: (802) 828-4422 Fax: (802) 828-4485

District Director **Darcy Carter** .... (802) 828-4422 ext. 203
E-mail: darcy.carter@sba.gov
Education: Rollins 1988 MBA
Deputy District Director **Vallerie Morse** .... (802) 828-4422 ext. 211
E-mail: vallerie.hamel@sba.gov
Economic Development Specialist and Veterans Affairs Officer **Chris Herriman** ...... (802) 828-4422 ext. 206
E-mail: chris.herriman@sba.gov
Lender Relations Specialist **Kevin Morehouse** .... (802) 828-4422 ext. 221
E-mail: kevin.morehouse@sba.gov
Lender Relations Specialist for International Trade **Susan Mazza** .... (802) 828-4422 ext. 209
Public Information Officer **Daniel "Danny" Monahan** .... (802) 828-4422 ext. 215
E-mail: daniel.monahan@sba.gov

Region II - New York

26 Federal Plaza, Room 3100, New York, NY 10278
Tel: (212) 264-1450 Fax: (212) 264-0038
Areas Covered: NJ, NY, PR, VI

□ Regional Administrator **Steve Bulger** .... (212) 264-1450
Education: SUNY (Albany) MPA
Area Resource Coordinator **Denise M. Galgano** .... (212) 264-1450
E-mail: denise.galgano@sba.gov
Regional Communications Director **(Vacant)** .... (212) 264-7750
Regional Advocate **Christine Myers** .... (212) 264-7752

★ Presidential Appointment Requiring Senate Confirmation ☆ Presidential Appointment □ Schedule C Appointment ◇ Career Senior Foreign Service Appointment
● Career Senior Executive Service (SES) Appointment ○ Non-Career Senior Executive Service (SES) Appointment ■ Postal Career Executive Service

Buffalo (NY) District Office
130 South Elmwood Avenue, Suite 540, Buffalo, NY 14202
Tel: (716) 551-4301 Fax: (716) 551-4418
Internet: www.sba.gov/localresources/district/ny/buffalo

District Director **Franklin J. Sciortino** . . . . (716) 551-4305
E-mail: franklin.sciortino@sba.gov
Education: Canisius BS
Deputy District Director and Women's Business Ownership Representative **Victoria L. Reynolds** . . . . (716) 551-5668
E-mail: victoria.reynolds@sba.gov
Education: Nazareth Rochester BSBA
District Counsel **Mollie B. Gaughan** . . . . (716) 551-4690
Economic Development Specialist **Gregory Lindberg** . . . . (716) 551-5670
E-mail: gregory.lindberg@sba.gov
Economic Development Specialist **Kelly LoTempio** . . . . (202) 481-2919
E-mail: kelly.lotempio@sba.gov
Lender Relations Specialist **Paul Hoffman** . . . . (716) 551-3242
Program Support Assistant **Tammi Bennett** . . . . (585) 263-6700 ext. 100
Business Opportunity Specialist **Jennifer Talarico** . . . . (716) 551-3240
Administrative Officer **Scot Thompson** . . . . (716) 604-0015
E-mail: scot.thompson@sba.gov

New Jersey District Office
Two Gateway Center, Suite 1002, Newark, NJ 07102-5003
Tel: (973) 645-2434 Fax: (973) 645-6265 Internet: www.sba.gov/nj

District Director **Alfred J. "Al" Titone** . . . . (973) 645-3680
E-mail: alfred.titone@sba.gov
Education: St John's U (NY) 1988 MBA
Deputy District Director **John M. Blackstock** . . . . (973) 645-3580
E-mail: john.blackstock@sba.gov
District Counsel **Diana St. Louis** . . . . (212) 264-7770
E-mail: diana.stlouis@sba.gov
District Counsel **Suzanne Ulicny** . . . . (212) 264-1482
E-mail: suzanne.ulicny@sba.gov
Education: Michigan State; Fordham LLM
Public Information Officer **Harry D. Menta** . . . . (973) 645-6064
E-mail: harry.menta@sba.gov

New York (NY) District Office
Jacob K. Javits Federal Building, 26 Federal Plaza, Room 3100, New York, NY 10278
Tel: (212) 264-4354 Fax: (212) 264-7751 Internet: www.sba.gov/ny
Areas Covered: 14 Downstate counties of New York

District Director **Beth L. Goldberg** . . . . (212) 264-1318
Education: Columbia MS; Brooklyn BS
Deputy District Director **John Mallano** . . . . (212) 264-1480
E-mail: john.mallano@sba.gov
Supervisory Economic Development Specialist **Jennifer Jackson** . . . . (212) 264-1472
Public Information Officer **Bailey Wolff** . . . . (212) 264-1489
E-mail: bailey.wolff@sba.gov Fax: (202) 481-4056

Puerto Rico and U.S. Virgin Islands District Office
273 Ponce de Leon Avenue, Suite 510, San Juan, PR 00917
Tel: (787) 766-5572 Fax: (787) 766-5309

District Director **Yvette T. Collazo** . . . . (787) 766-5002
E-mail: yvette.collazo@sba.gov
Education: Puerto Rico BS; Illinois Tech MS
Deputy District Director **Maria de los Angeles de Jesus** . . . . (787) 766-5520
E-mail: maria.dejesus@sba.gov
District Counsel **Liana Gonzalez** . . . . (787) 766-5269
Education: Puerto Rico 1989 JD
Business Opportunity Specialist **Myriam Rodriguez** . . . . (787) 766-5904
E-mail: myriam.rodriguez@sba.gov
Economic Development Specialist **Jorge W. Betancourt** . . . . (787) 766-5556
E-mail: jorge.betancourt@sba.gov
Education: Inter American 1989 BBA
Lender Relations Specialist **Samuel Maldonado** . . . . (787) 766-5220
E-mail: samuel.maldonado@sba.gov
Lender Relations Specialist **Wilma Sosa** . . . . (787) 766-5519
E-mail: wilma.sosa@sba.gov

Puerto Rico and U.S. Virgin Islands District Office *(continued)*

Public Affairs Officer **Angelique F. Adjutant** . . . . (787) 766-5570
E-mail: angelique.adjutant@sba.gov
Education: U of Sacred Heart 1991 BA
Administrative Officer **Jose Rodriguez** . . . . (787) 766-5537
E-mail: jose.l.rodriguez@sba.gov

Syracuse (NY) District Office
224 Harrison Street, Suite 506, Syracuse, NY 13202-2415
Tel: (315) 471-9393 Fax: (315) 471-9288
Internet: www.sba.gov/ny/syracuse

District Director **Bernard J. Paprocki** . . . . (315) 471-9393 ext. 235
E-mail: bernard.paprocki@sba.gov
Education: SUNY (Cortland) 1977 BA
Deputy District Director **Cathy Rae Pokines** . . . . (315) 471-9393 ext. 241
E-mail: cathy.pokines@sba.gov Fax: (315) 471-9273
Veterans Affairs Officer **Michael Stout** . . . . (315) 471-9393 ext. 226
Women's Business Ownership Representative [Information Officer] **Rachael Stanton** . . . . (315) 471-9393 ext. 244
E-mail: rachel.stanton@sba.gov

Region III - Mid-Atlantic
Parkview Tower, 1150 First Avenue, Suite 1001, King of Prussia, PA 19406
Tel: (610) 382-3092 Fax: (610) 382-1930
Areas Covered: DE, DC, MD, PA, VA, WV

□ Regional Administrator **Michelle Christian** . . . . (610) 382-3092
Education: St John's U (MN) BA; Seton Hall JD
Regional Advocate **Elmo Rinaldi** . . . . (610) 382-3093
Regional Communications Director **Christopher J. Hatch** . . . . (610) 382-3088
E-mail: christopher.hatch@sba.gov
Regional Administrative Resource Coordinator **Brenda L. Jones** . . . . (610) 382-3092
E-mail: brenda.jones@sba.gov

Baltimore (MD) District Office
City Crescent Building, 10 South Howard Street, Suite 6220, Baltimore, MD 21201-2525
Tel: (410) 962-6195 Fax: (410) 962-1805
Internet: www.sba.gov/localresources/district/md

District Director **Stephen D. Umberger** . . . . (410) 962-6195
E-mail: stephen.umberger@sba.gov
Deputy District Director **Edward Knox** . . . . (410) 244-3326
E-mail: edward.knox@sba.gov
Deputy District Director, Economic Development **Samuel Reprogel** . . . . (410) 244-3325
E-mail: samuel.reprogel@sba.gov
District Counsel **Liana Gonzalez** . . . . (202) 205-7425
E-mail: liana.gonzalez@sba.gov
Education: Puerto Rico 1989 JD
Public Information Officer **Rachel Howard** . . . . (410) 244-3337
E-mail: rachel.howard@sba.gov
Veterans Affairs Officer **Courtney McCalla** . . . . (410) 244-3330
E-mail: courtney.mccalla@sba.gov
8(a) Team Leader **Christine Kingston** . . . . (410) 244-3336
Women's Business Ownership Representative and Business Development Specialist **Tonia McCoy** . . . . (410) 244-3323
E-mail: tonia.mccoy@sba.gov

Clarksburg (WV) District Office
320 West Pike Street, Suite 330, Clarksburg, WV 26301
Tel: (304) 623-5631 Fax: (304) 623-0023 Internet: www.sba.gov/wv

District Director **Karen Friel** . . . . (304) 623-5631 ext. 223
E-mail: karen.friel@sba.gov Fax: (202) 481-2799
Deputy District Director **George Murray** . . . . (304) 623-5631 ext. 238
E-mail: george.murray@sba.gov
Business Development/Lender Relations Specialist **Richard Haney** . . . . (304) 623-5631 ext. 230
Fax: (202) 481-5158
Program Support Assistant **Barbara Carder** . . . . (304) 623-5631 ext. 225
E-mail: barbara.carder@sba.gov Fax: (202) 481-4718

(continued on next page)

INDEPENDENT AGENCIES

★ Presidential Appointment Requiring Senate Confirmation ☆ Presidential Appointment □ Schedule C Appointment ◇ Career Senior Foreign Service Appointment
● Career Senior Executive Service (SES) Appointment ○ Non-Career Senior Executive Service (SES) Appointment ■ Postal Career Executive Service

Clarksburg (WV) District Office *(continued)*

Public Information Officer **Nicole "Nikki" Bowmar** ..... (304) 623-7445
E-mail: nikki.bowmar@sba.gov Fax: (202) 292-3490

Delaware District Office
I.M. PEI Building, 1105 Market Street,
Lobby Level, Suite 1120, Wilmington, DE 19801-1239
Tel: (302) 573-6294 Fax: (302) 573-6060 Internet: www.sba.gov/de

• Director **John F. Fleming** .... (302) 573-6294 ext. 225
E-mail: john.fleming@sba.gov
Education: Widener 1992 BBA
• Deputy Director **John L. Banks** .... (302) 573-6294 ext. 223
E-mail: john.banks@sba.gov
District Counsel (Regulations, Statutes and Ethics)
Robert T. Williamson .... (610) 382-3062
1150 First Avenue, King of Prussia, PA 19406
E-mail: robert.williamson@sba.gov
Education: Georgetown 1986 AB, 1990 JD
8A Business Development/Government
Contracting Specialist **Gedell Hawkins** .... (302) 573-6294 ext. 226
E-mail: gedell.hawkins@sba.gov Fax: (302) 571-5222
Economic Development Specialist **(Vacant)** ..... (302) 573-6294 ext. 224
Economic Development Specialist
James "Jim" Provo .... (302) 573-6294 ext. 227
E-mail: james.provo@sba.gov
Lender Relations Specialist
Michael "Mike" Rossi .... (302) 573-6294 ext. 231
E-mail: michael.rossi@sba.gov
Public Information Officer **Jennifer Pilcher** ..... (302) 573-6294 ext. 222
E-mail: jennifer.pilcher@sba.gov
Women's Business Ownership
Representative/Economic Development
Specialist **Ellyn Herbert** .... (302) 573-6294 ext. 228
E-mail: ellyn.herbert@sba.gov

Philadelphia District Office
Parkview Tower, 1150 First Avenue, Suite 1001,
King of Prussia, PA 19406
Tel: (610) 382-3062 Fax: (610) 382-1928

District Director **Antonio L. "Tony" Leta** .... (610) 382-3073
Education: Syracuse BS; USC MBA Fax: (610) 382-1926
Deputy District Director **Michael T. "Mike" Kane** .... (610) 382-3071
E-mail: michael.kane@sba.gov
Public Information Officer **Robert A. Goza** .... (610) 382-3084
E-mail: robert.goza@sba.gov
Lead Economic Development Specialist
Donald Jefferson .... (610) 382-3079
E-mail: donald.jefferson@sba.gov
Supervisory Business Opportunity Specialist
Jennifer Tilden .... (610) 382-3083
E-mail: jennifer.tilden@sba.gov
Administrative Officer **Amy Logan** .... (610) 382-3075
E-mail: amy.logan@sba.gov

Pittsburgh (PA) District Office
411 Seventh Avenue, Room 1450, Pittsburgh, PA 15219-1919
Tel: (412) 395-6560 Fax: (412) 395-6562

District Director **Kelly Hunt PhD** .... (412) 395-6560 ext. 106
E-mail: kelly.hunt@sba.gov
Deputy District Director **Regina Abel** .... (412) 395-6560 ext. 119
Lead Economic Development Specialist
Angel Marsehik .... (412) 395-6560
E-mail: angel.marsehik@sba.gov
Public Affairs Specialist **Janet Heyl** .... (412) 395-6560 ext. 103
E-mail: janet.heyl@sba.gov
Veterans Affairs Officer **Jonathan Bennett** ..... (412) 395-6560 ext. 107
E-mail: jonathan.bennett@sba.gov
Women's Business Ownership Representative
Karan Waigand .... (412) 395-6560 ext. 127
E-mail: karan.waigand@sba.gov
District Office Technical Representative
Karan Waigand .... (412) 395-6560 ext. 127
E-mail: karan.waigand@sba.gov

Richmond (VA) District Office
400 Eighth Street, Suite 1150, Richmond, VA 23219-4829
Tel: (804) 771-2400 Fax: (804) 771-8018 E-mail: richmond.va@sba.gov
Internet: www.sba.gov/va

District Director **Carl B. Knoblock** .... (804) 253-9087
E-mail: carl.b.knoblock@sba.gov
Education: Ball State 1980 BS, 1985 MA
Deputy District Director **(Vacant)** .... (804) 771-2400 ext. 141
District Counsel **Dawn DiBenedetto** .... (804) 253-8902
E-mail: dawn.dibenedetto@sba.gov
Lead Business Opportunity Specialist
(Vacant) .... (804) 771-2400 ext. 116
Lead Economic Development Specialist
James A. Williams .... (804) 253-8134
E-mail: james.williams@sba.gov
Economic Development Specialist, Administrative
Officer and Local Technical Representative
Robert F. McLoone .... (804) 253-8270
E-mail: robert.mcloone@sba.gov
Economic Development Specialist and Lender
Relations Specialist **(Vacant)** .... (804) 771-2400
Lender Relations Specialist **Ford Scott** .... (804) 253-8027
E-mail: ford.scott@sba.gov
District Support **(Vacant)** .... (804) 771-2400
Economic Development Specialist and Women's
Business Representative, District International Trade
Officer **(Vacant)** .... (804) 253-8135
Economic Development Specialist, Native American
Initiatives, SCORE Liaison **Marci Posey** .... (804) 253-8906
Business Opportunity Specialist **Florine E. Duncan** ...... (804) 253-8904
Business Opportunity Specialist **Cassandra L. Zeigler** ... (804) 253-8907
Public Affairs Specialist **Monet Chapman** .... (804) 253-8133
E-mail: monet.chapman@sba.gov
Procurement Center Representative **(Vacant)** .... (804) 279-5242
Secretary **(Vacant)** .... (804) 253-8002

Washington (DC) Metropolitan Area District Office
409 Third Street, SW, Suite 2000, Washington, DC 20416
Tel: (202) 205-8800 Internet: www.sba.gov/localresources/district/dc

• District Director **Antonio D. Doss** .... (202) 205-0010
Education: Robert Morris Col (PA) BA
Deputy District Director **(Vacant)** .... (202) 205-8800
Assistant District Director for Marketing and Outreach
Jack Spirakes .... (202) 205-0536
E-mail: jack.spirakes@sba.gov Fax: (202) 481-0797
Administrative Officer **(Vacant)** .... (202) 205-8800
Public Information Officer **(Vacant)** .... (202) 205-8800
SBA Business Information Center Manager **(Vacant)** ..... (202) 205-8800

Region IV - Southeast
233 Peachtree Street, NE, Suite 200, Atlanta, GA 30303
Tel: (404) 331-4999 Fax: (404) 331-2354
Areas Covered: AL, FL, GA, KY, MS, NC, SC, TN

□ Regional Administrator **Ashley Daniel Bell** .... (601) 965-5371
E-mail: ashley.bell@sba.gov Fax: (601) 965-5335
Education: Valdosta State U BA; LSU JD
Staff Assistant **Tawana L. Farley** .... (404) 331-4943
E-mail: tawana.farley@sba.gov
Government Contracting Area Director
Carol L. Thompson 19th Floor, 1805 .... (404) 331-7587
E-mail: carol.thompson@sba.gov
Regional Communications Director **Lola Kress** .... (404) 331-2798
E-mail: lola.kress@sba.gov
Education: Colorado 2004 MPA
Regional Advocate **Bruce E. LeVell** .... (404) 331-3081

Alabama District Office
801 Tom Martin Drive, Suite 201, Birmingham, AL 35211
Tel: (205) 290-7101 Fax: (205) 290-7404 Internet: www.sba.gov/al

District Director **Thomas "Tom" Todt** .... (205) 290-7009
E-mail: thomas.todt@sba.gov
Education: Alabama BS

★ Presidential Appointment Requiring Senate Confirmation ☆ Presidential Appointment □ Schedule C Appointment ◇ Career Senior Foreign Service Appointment
● Career Senior Executive Service (SES) Appointment ○ Non-Career Senior Executive Service (SES) Appointment ■ Postal Career Executive Service

Alabama District Office *(continued)*

Deputy District Director **Lafero D. Ralph** . . . . (205) 290-7684
E-mail: lafero.ralph@sba.gov
General Attorney **Valerie A. Parente** . . . . (404) 331-0100 ext. 215
Senior Area Manager **Brent McMahan** . . . . (205) 290-7401
E-mail: brent.mcmahan@sba.gov
Lead Lender Relations Specialist **(Vacant)** . . . . (205) 290-7101
Women's Business Ownership Representative **(Vacant)** . . . (205) 290-7101

Charlotte (NC) District Office
6302 Fairview Road, Suite 300, Charlotte, NC 28210-2234
Tel: (704) 344-6563 Fax: (704) 344-6769 E-mail: charlotte.nc@sba.gov
Internet: www.sba.gov/nc

District Director **Lynn Douthett** . . . . (704) 344-6579
E-mail: lynn.douthett@sba.gov
Deputy District Director **Michael "Mike" Arriola** . . . . (704) 344-6578
Administrative Officer **Linda Bennett** . . . . (704) 344-6409
E-mail: linda.bennett@sba.gov Fax: (704) 344-6644
Veterans Affairs Officer **Erin Connell** . . . . (704) 344-6590
E-mail: erin.connell@sba.gov
Women's Business Ownership Representative
Eileen Joyce . . . . (704) 344-6787
E-mail: eileen.joyce@sba.gov

Georgia District Office
233 Peachtree Street, NE, Suite 1900, Atlanta, GA 30303
Tel: (404) 331-0121 (Service Corps of Retired Executives)
Tel: (470) 891-5576 Fax: (404) 331-0101 E-mail: georgia@sba.gov
Internet: www.sba.gov/ga

District Director **Terri L. Denison** . . . . (404) 331-0108
Fax: (202) 481-5783
Deputy District Director **Rosemarie Drake** . . . . (404) 331-0126
Fax: (202) 481-0989
Administrative Officer **Darlene Milhouse** . . . . (404) 331-0107
Fax: (202) 481-0949
Program Support Assistant **(Vacant)** . . . . (404) 331-0121
Public Information Officer **Lindsay A. Williams** . . . . (404) 331-0124
E-mail: lindsay.williams@sba.gov

Kentucky District Office
Mazzoli Federal Building, 600 Dr. Martin Luther King Place,
Room 188, Louisville, KY 40202
Tel: (502) 582-5971 Fax: (502) 582-5009

District Director **Ralph E. Ross** . . . . (502) 582-5971 ext. 222
E-mail: ralph.ross@sba.gov
Education: Iowa BA
Deputy District Director **Robert A. Coffey** . . . . . . (502) 582-5971 ext. 266
E-mail: robert.coffey@sba.gov
Administrative Officer **Diana Hurley** . . . . (502) 582-5971 ext. 241
E-mail: diana.hurley@sba.gov
Business Opportunity Specialist
Cherie Guilford . . . . (502) 582-5971 ext. 261

Mississippi District Office
Regions Plaza, 210 East Capitol Street,
Suite 900, Jackson, MS 39201-2303
Tel: (601) 965-4378 Fax: (601) 965-5629 Fax: (601) 965-4294
Internet: www.sba.gov/ms

District Director **Janita R. Stewart** . . . . (601) 965-4378 ext. 20
E-mail: janita.stewart@sba.gov
Education: Southern Mississippi BS
Deputy District Director **Gary K. Reed** . . . . (601) 965-4378
Supervisory Business Opportunity Specialist
Alice A. Doss . . . . (601) 965-4378 ext. 14
E-mail: alice.doss@sba.gov
Supervisory Lender Relations Specialist
Rhonda H. Fisher . . . . (601) 965-4378 ext. 15
E-mail: rhonda.fisher@sba.gov

Nashville (TN) District Office
Two International Plaza, Suite 500, Nashville, TN 37217
Tel: (615) 736-5881 Fax: (615) 736-7232

District Director **LaTanya Channel** . . . . (615) 736-5881
E-mail: latanya.channel@sba.gov
Deputy District Director
Christopher Shawn McKeehan . . . . (615) 736-2499
E-mail: christopher.mckeehan@sba.gov
District Counsel **Richard "Dick" Cummings** . . . . (901) 736-5092
E-mail: richard.cummings@sba.gov
District Counsel **David Higgs** . . . . (901) 736-5629
E-mail: david.higgs@sba.gov
Administrative Officer **David E. Walley** . . . . (615) 736-7766
E-mail: david.walley@sba.gov
Business Opportunity Specialist **Kena Dixon** . . . . (615) 736-7426
E-mail: kena.dixon@sba.gov
Veterans Affairs Officer **Eric W. Terrell** . . . . (901) 494-6906
E-mail: eric.terrell@sba.gov

North Florida District Office
7825 Baymeadows Way, Suite 100B, Jacksonville, FL 32256-7504
Tel: (904) 443-1900 Fax: (904) 443-1980 Internet: www.sba.gov/fl/north

District Director **Wilfredo J. Gonzalez** . . . . (904) 443-1900
E-mail: wilfredo.gonzalez@sba.gov
Education: Puerto Rico BA
Deputy Director **Gilbert Colon** . . . . (904) 443-1900
E-mail: gilbert.colon@sba.gov
Public Information Officer **Nayana Sen** . . . . (904) 443-1933
E-mail: nayana.sen@sba.gov
Veterans Representative **Natalie C. Hall** . . . . (904) 443-1902
E-mail: natalie.hall@sba.gov
Women's Business Ownership Representative
Thaddeus Hammond . . . . (904) 443-1971
Administrative Officer **Jacqueline "Jackie" Gardner** . . . . (904) 443-1967
E-mail: Jacqueline.gardner@sba.gov

South Carolina District Office
Strom Thurmond Federal Building, 1835 Assembly Street,
Suite 1425, Columbia, SC 29201
Tel: (803) 765-5377 Fax: (803) 765-5962 Internet: www.sba.gov/sc

District Director **Richard Gregg White** . . . . (803) 253-3360
E-mail: richard.white@sba.gov
Deputy District Director **(Vacant)** . . . . (803) 765-5339
Lead Business Opportunity Specialist **Michael Corp** . . . . . (803) 765-5961
E-mail: micahel.corp@sba.gov
Lender Relations Specialist **Frank Anderson** . . . . (803) 253-3018
E-mail: frank.anderson@sba.gov
Economic Development Specialist and Public
Information Officer **Martin Short** . . . . (803) 253-3753
5900 Core Drive, North Charleston, SC 29406
E-mail: martin.short@sba.gov

South Florida District Office
100 South Biscayne Boulevard, 7th Floor, Miami, FL 33131
Tel: (305) 536-5521 Fax: (305) 536-5058

● District Director **Victoria Guerrero** . . . . (305) 536-5521
E-mail: victoria.guerrero@sba.gov
Deputy District Director **Jonel Hein** . . . . (305) 536-5521
E-mail: jonel.hein@sba.gov
Senior Area Manager, Ft. Pierce
Vincent LoPresti . . . . (813) 228-2100 ext. 24
Senior Area Manager, Tampa
Hipolito "C.J." Castro . . . . (813) 228-2100 ext. 24
Assistant District Director Business Development
Division **Joshua R. Stutzman** . . . . (305) 536-5521
Assistant District Director for Marketing and
Outreach Area 1 **Althea Harris** . . . . (305) 536-5521 ext. 142
E-mail: althea.harris@sba.gov
Assistant District Director for Lending
Relations **(Vacant)** . . . . (813) 228-2100 ext. 27
Administrative Officer **Tina Davis** . . . . (305) 536-5521 ext. 117
E-mail: tina.davis@sba.gov

(continued on next page)

★ Presidential Appointment Requiring Senate Confirmation ☆ Presidential Appointment ☐ Schedule C Appointment ◇ Career Senior Foreign Service Appointment
● Career Senior Executive Service (SES) Appointment ○ Non-Career Senior Executive Service (SES) Appointment ■ Postal Career Executive Service

INDEPENDENT AGENCIES

South Florida District Office *(continued)*

Business Opportunity Specialist
Rabon "Ray" Lewis ....(305) 536-5521 ext. 137
E-mail: rabon.lewis@sba.gov
Business Opportunity Specialist **Aimee Perez** ... (305) 536-5521 ext. 131
E-mail: aimee.perez@sba.gov
Public Information Officer **Heather W. Hines** ... (305) 536-5521 ext. 104
E-mail: heather.hines@sba.gov

Region V - Great Lakes

500 West Madison Street, Suite 1150, Chicago, IL 60661
Tel: (312) 353-0357 Fax: (312) 353-3426
Areas Covered: IL, IN, MI, MN, OH, WI

□ Regional Administrator **Robert L. Scott** .... (312) 353-0357
E-mail: robert.scott@sba.gov
Education: Wright State BA; Dayton JD
Administrative Resource Coordinator
Latrice Thomas .... (312) 353-4493
E-mail: latrice.thomas@sba.gov
Regional Advocate **Leslie "Les" Davies** .... (614) 469-6860
401 North Front Street, Columbus, OH 43215
Tel: (312) 353-0357
Education: BYU BA
Regional Communications Director **Andrea Roebker** .... (312) 888-6516
Office of Government Contracting Area Director
Pamela Beavers .... (312) 353-7381
E-mail: pamela.beavers@sba.gov
Senior Counsel **Hatem H. El-Gabri** .... (312) 353-0355

Central and Southern Ohio District Office

401 North Front Street, Suite 200, Columbus, OH 43215
Tel: (614) 469-6860 Fax: (614) 469-2391
Internet: www.sba.gov/oh/columbus

District Director (Acting) **Scot Hardin** ....(614) 469-6860 ext. 261
E-mail: scot.hardin@sba.gov
Administrative Officer **Robin Wotring** ....(614) 469-6860 ext. 282
Deputy District Director **Scot Hardin** ....(614) 469-6860 ext. 261
E-mail: scot.hardin@sba.gov
District Counsel **Philip Morrison** ....(614) 469-6860 ext. 241
Senior Area Manager, Dayton **Alexander Kohls** ....(614) 633-6372
E-mail: alexander.kohls@sba.gov
Business Opportunity Specialist
Shanda Harris ....(614) 469-6860 ext. 236
E-mail: shanda.harris@sba.gov
Business Opportunity Specialist
Jill Nagy-Reynolds ....(614) 469-6860 ext. 276
Lead Economic Development Specialist
Shannon Feucht ....(614) 469-6860 ext. 244
E-mail: shannon.feucht@sba.gov
Economic Development Specialist **(Vacant)** .... (614) 469-6860
Lead Lender Relations Specialist
David Townsend ....(614) 469-6860 ext. 237
Lender Relations Specialist **(Vacant)** .... (614) 469-6860
Lender Relations/Economic Development Specialist
(Vacant) ....(614) 469-6860
Public Information Officer **Brooke Betit** ....(614) 469-6860 ext. 238
E-mail: brooke.betit@sba.gov Fax: (614) 469-2391
Veterans Affairs Officer **(Vacant)** ....(614) 469-6860

Cleveland (OH) District Office

1350 Euclid Avenue, Suite 211, Cleveland, OH 44115-1815
Tel: (216) 522-4180
Tel: (216) 522-4194 (SCORE, Counselors to America's Small Business)
TTY: (800) 750-0750 Fax: (216) 522-2038 E-mail: cleveland@sba.gov
Internet: https://www.sba.gov/oh/cleveland

District Director **Gilbert B. Goldberg** ....(216) 522-4182
E-mail: gilbert.goldberg@sba.gov
Education: Georgetown 1968 BSFS; Notre Dame MBA
Deputy District Director
James F. "Jim" Donato ....(216) 522-4180 ext. 215
E-mail: james.donato@sba.gov
District Counsel **Richard A. Lukich** .... (216) 522-4180 ext. 206
E-mail: richard.lukich@sba.gov

Cleveland (OH) District Office *(continued)*

Assistant District Director For Lender
Relations **(Vacant)** ....(216) 522-4180 ext. 218
Supervisory Business Opportunity Specialist
John L. Renner ....(216) 522-4180 ext. 211
E-mail: john.renner@sba.gov
International Trade Export Finance Manager
Patrick K. "Pat" Hayes ....(216) 522-4731
201 Superior Avenue East, Cleveland, OH 44114 Fax: (202) 481-4843
Information Technology Specialist/Webmaster
Vanessa Behrend ....(216) 522-4180 ext. 201
E-mail: vanessa.behrend@sba.gov
Education: U Phoenix BSIT
Public Information Officer **Patricia Welsh** .... (216) 522-4172
E-mail: patricia.welsh@sba.gov Fax: (216) 522-2038

Illinois District Office

Illinois District Office, 500 West Madison Street,
Suite 1250, Chicago, IL 60661
Tel: (312) 353-4528 Fax: (312) 886-5688 Internet: www.sba.gov/il

● District Director **Robert S. "Bo" Steiner** ....(312) 353-4508
E-mail: robert.steiner@sba.gov
Education: Naval Acad
District Support Assistant **Luz Rodriguez** ....(312) 353-4528
E-mail: luz.rodriguez@sba.gov
Deputy District Director **Dr. Ricardo S. "Rick" Garcia** ... (312) 353-5031
E-mail: ricardo.garcia@sba.gov
Supervisor Lender Relations Specialist
Robert Esquivel ....(312) 353-6557
E-mail: robert.esquivel@sba.gov
Supervisory Business Opportunity Specialist
Rosalyn Putman .... (312) 353-5037
E-mail: rosalyn.putman@sba.gov
Lead Economic Development Specialist
Mark Ferguson .... (312) 353-4528
E-mail: mark.ferguson@sba.gov
Education: Illinois Tech MBA
Economic Development Specialist **Carole Harris** .... (312) 353-4003
Education: Illinois BS
Public Affairs Specialist **Jessica Mayle** .... (312) 886-0409
E-mail: jessica.mayle@sba.gov
Veterans Business Development Officer
Stephen Konkle ....(312) 886-4208
Education: Illinois Tech MBA

Indiana District Office

8500 Keystone Crossing, Suite 400, Indianapolis, IN 46240
Tel: (317) 226-7272 Fax: (317) 226-7259 Internet: www.sba.gov/in

District Director **Stacey Poynter** ....(317) 226-7272
E-mail: stacey.poynter@sba.gov
Economic Development Specialist
Ronda Crouch ....(317) 226-7272 ext. 112
Lender Relations Specialist **Peter Smith** .... (317) 226-7272 ext. 119
Public Affairs Specialist **Laura Schafsnitz** ......(317) 226-7272 ext. 123
E-mail: laura.schafsnitz@sba.gov Fax: (317) 226-7259

Madison (WI) District Office

740 Regent Street, Suite 100, Madison, WI 53715-2648
Tel: (608) 441-5261 Fax: (608) 441-5500 Internet: www.sba.gov/wi

District Director **Eric M. Ness** ....(414) 297-1471
E-mail: eric.ness@sba.gov
Education: Minnesota BS; Southern Methodist MBA
Economic Development Specialist and IT Specialist
Robin Dittberner ....(608) 441-5521
E-mail: robin.dittberner@sba.gov

Michigan District Office

Patrick V. McNamara Federal Building, 477 Michigan Avenue,
Room 515, Detroit, MI 48226
Tel: (313) 226-6075 Fax: (313) 226-4769 E-mail: michigan@sba.gov

District Director **Constance Logan** ....(405) 609-8011
301 NW 6th Street, Oklahoma City, OK 73102
Education: Maryland BABA
Deputy District Director **(Vacant)** .... (313) 226-6075 ext. 279

★ Presidential Appointment Requiring Senate Confirmation ☆ Presidential Appointment □ Schedule C Appointment ◇ Career Senior Foreign Service Appointment
● Career Senior Executive Service (SES) Appointment ○ Non-Career Senior Executive Service (SES) Appointment ■ Postal Career Executive Service

Michigan District Office *(continued)*

District Counsel **Richard Pasiak** .... (313) 324-3613
E-mail: richard.pasiak@sba.gov
Lead Business Opportunity Specialist **Thomas Vargo** .... (313) 324-3617
E-mail: thomas.vargo@sba.gov
Lead Economic Development Specialist and Public Information Officer **Catherine Gase** .... (313) 324-3609
Lead Lender Relations Specialist **Allen Cook** .... (313) 324-3605
Administrative Officer **(Vacant)** .... (313) 226-6075
International Trade - Export Assistance Representative **(Vacant)** .... (313) 872-6793
Veterans Affairs Officer **(Vacant)** .... (313) 226-6075
Webmaster **June Foyt** .... (313) 324-3608
Women's Business Ownership Specialist **Thomas "Tom" McFadden** .... (313) 324-3611
E-mail: thomas.mcfadden@sba.gov
Administrative **Dyann Williams** .... (313) 324-3607
E-mail: dyann.williams@sba.gov

Milwaukee (WI) District Office

310 West Wisconsin Avenue, Suite 580W, Milwaukee, WI 53203
Tel: (414) 297-3941 Fax: (414) 297-1377 Internet: www.sba.gov/wi

District Director **Eric M. Ness** .... (414) 297-1471
E-mail: eric.ness@sba.gov
Education: Minnesota BS; Southern Methodist MBA
Deputy District Director **Frank Demarest, Jr.** .... (414) 297-1099
E-mail: frank.demarest@sba.gov
District Counsel **Bradley Trimble** .... (414) 297-4090
E-mail: bradley.trimble@sba.gov
Public Affairs Specialist **Shirah L. "Rachel" Apple** ..... (414) 297-1096
E-mail: rachel.apple@sba.gov
Lead Business Opportunity Specialist **Darryl "Shane" Mahaffy** .... (414) 297-1455
E-mail: shane.mahaffy@sba.gov
Lead Economic Development Specialist **Mary Trimmier** .... (414) 297-1093
E-mail: mary.trimmier@sba.gov

Minnesota District Office

330 Second Avenue South, Suite 430, Minneapolis, MN 55401
Tel: (612) 370-2324 Fax: (202) 481-0139 Internet: www.sba.gov/mn

District Director **Nancy Libersky** .... (612) 370-2306
Deputy District Director **Andrew Amoroso** .... (612) 370-2337
E-mail: andrew.amoroso@sba.gov
Lead Lender Relations Specialist **Melvin Boser** .... (612) 370-2335
Lender Relations Specialist **Thomas Osborne** .... (612) 370-2356
Supervisory Business Opportunity Specialist **Randall Czaia** .... (612) 370-2314
Business Opportunity Specialist **Shaun McClary** .... (612) 370-2320
Economic Development Specialist **Twila Kennedy** .... (612) 370-2312
E-mail: twila.kennedy@sba.gov
Economic Development Specialist **Charles Shortridge** ... (612) 370-2324
District Counsel **Royce Nelligan** .... (612) 370-2328
Program Support Assistant **Maribel Reigstad** .... (612) 370-2321
Administrative Officer **Patrick Saxton** .... (612) 370-2325
Public Information Officer **Sarah Swenty** .... (612) 370-2316
E-mail: sarah.swenty@sba.gov Fax: (612) 370-2303

Region VI - South Central

4300 Amon Carter Boulevard, Suite 108, Fort Worth, TX 76155
Tel: (817) 684-5581 Fax: (817) 684-5588
Internet: www.sba.gov/localresources/regionaloffices/region6
Areas Covered: AR, LA, NM, OK, TX

☐ Regional Administrator (Acting) **Dorothy A. "Dottie" Overal** .... (405) 609-8011
E-mail: dorothy.overal@sba.gov
Western Senior Area Counsel **Andrew "Drew" Baka** .... (817) 684-5509
E-mail: andrew.baka@sba.gov
Regional Advocate **Rhett Davis** .... (504) 202-6946
Louisiana Tech Park, 7177 Florida Blvd., Ste 313, Baton Rouge, LA 70806
E-mail: rhett.davis@sba.gov

Region VI - South Central *(continued)*

Regional Communications Director **Darla Booker** .... (817) 684-5535
E-mail: darla.booker@sba.gov
Government Contracting Area Director **Robert Taylor** .... (817) 684-5302
Equal Employment Opportunity Specialist **Robin Montalbo** .... (817) 684-5328
Administrative Resource Coordinator **Virginia Geary** .... (817) 684-5581
E-mail: virginia.geary@sba.gov

Albuquerque (NM) District Office

500 Gold Avenue, SW, Suite 11301, Albuquerque, NM 87102
P.O. Box 2206, Albuquerque, NM 87103
Tel: (505) 248-8225 Fax: (505) 248-8245

District Director **John M. Garcia** .... (505) 248-8238
E-mail: john.garcia@sba.gov
Deputy Director **(Vacant)** .... (505) 248-8225
Lead Business Opportunity Specialist **Mary Drobot** ...... (505) 248-8229
Business Opportunity Specialist **Joshua Baca** .... (505) 248-8236
Business Opportunity Specialist **Alice Mora** .... (505) 248-8234
E-mail: alice.mora@sba.gov
Administrative Officer **(Vacant)** .... (505) 248-8225
Lender Relations Specialist **Shelley Brown** .... (505) 248-8228
E-mail: shelley.brown@sba.gov
Lender Relations Specialist **Michael Altamirano** .... (505) 248-8243
E-mail: michael.altamirano@sba.gov
District Counsel **Marta Nesbitt** .... (505) 248-8231
E-mail: marta.nesbitt@sba.gov
Public Information Officer **(Vacant)** .... (505) 248-8225
Business Opportunity Specialist and Veterans Business Development Officer **Ivan Corrales** .... (505) 248-8227
E-mail: ivan.corrales@sba.gov

Arkansas District Office

2120 Riverfront Drive, Suite 250, Little Rock, AR 72202-1796
Tel: (501) 324-7379 Fax: (501) 324-7394 Internet: www.sba.gov/ar

District Director **Edward Haddock** .... (501) 324-7379
Deputy District Director **(Vacant)** .... (501) 324-7379 ext. 279
Lender Relations Specialist **Herb Lawrence** .... (501) 324-7379
Lender Relations Specialist **Karen Musick** .... (501) 324-7379
Assistant District Director for Minority Enterprise Development **(Vacant)** .... (501) 324-7379 ext. 227
Public Information Officer **Carol J. Silverstrom** .... (501) 324-7379 ext. 227
District Counsel **Lynley Arnett** .... (501) 324-7379 ext. 235
Women's Business Ownership Program Representative **Wanda May** .... (501) 324-7379 ext. 294
E-mail: wanda.may@sba.gov
Information Technology Specialist **Frank Fields** Suite 100 .... (501) 324-5871 ext. 285
E-mail: frank.fields@sba.gov
Information Technology Specialist **Eric J. Fuller** Suite 100 .... (501) 324-5871 ext. 268
E-mail: eric.fuller@sba.gov
Veteran-Owned Small Businesses Development Officer **Daniel Salman** .... (501) 324-7379
E-mail: daniel.salman@sba.gov

Dallas-Fort Worth (TX) District Office

4300 Amon Carter Boulevard, Suite 114, Fort Worth, TX 76155
Tel: (817) 684-5500
Tel: (817) 871-6002 (SCORE, Service Corps of Retired Executives)
Tel: (214) 860-5865 (Small Business Development Center, SBDC)
Fax: (817) 684-5516 E-mail: dfwdo.email@sba.gov
Internet: www.sba.gov/localresources/district/tx/dallas
Areas Covered: 72 counties in North, East and Central TX

District Director **Herbert Austin** .... (817) 684-5502
E-mail: herbert.austin@sba.gov
Education: NYU BS; Pace MBA
District Counsel **Andrew "Drew" Baka** .... (817) 684-5509
Deputy District Director **Elsie Collins** .... (817) 684-5530
E-mail: elsie.collins@sba.gov
Administrative Officer **Derenda Fisher** .... (817) 684-5513
E-mail: derenda.fisher@sba.gov

(continued on next page)

★ Presidential Appointment Requiring Senate Confirmation ☆ Presidential Appointment ☐ Schedule C Appointment ◇ Career Senior Foreign Service Appointment
● Career Senior Executive Service (SES) Appointment ○ Non-Career Senior Executive Service (SES) Appointment ■ Postal Career Executive Service

Dallas-Fort Worth (TX) District Office *(continued)*

Economic Development Specialist [Information Officer]
Ahmad Goree .... (817) 684-5539
E-mail: ahmad.goree@sba.gov
Supervisor Business Opportunity Specialist
Nancy Alvarez .... (817) 684-5529

El Paso (TX) District Office
211 North Florence, Suite 201, El Paso, TX 79901
Tel: (915) 834-4600 Fax: (915) 834-4689
Internet: www.sba.gov/localresources/district/tx/elpaso

District Director **Phillip C. Silva** .... (915) 834-4620
E-mail: phillip.silva@sba.gov
Business Opportunity Specialist
Ruth Suzanne "Suze" Aguirre .... (915) 834-4634
E-mail: ruth.aguirre@sba.gov

Houston (TX) District Office
8701 South Gessner Drive, Suite 1200, Houston, TX 77074-2926
Tel: (713) 773-6500
Tel: (713) 773-6500 ext. 236 (Minority Small Business Division)
Tel: (713) 773-6565 (SCORE, Service Corps of Retired Executives)
Fax: (713) 773-6550

District Director **Timothy Jeffcoat** .... (713) 773-6500 ext. 6518
E-mail: timothy.jeffcoat@sba.gov
Deputy District Director **Mark Winchester** .... (713) 773-6508
E-mail: mark.winchester@sba.gov
Lead Business Opportunity Specialist **Miguel Ruiz** .... (713) 773-6513
Lead Lender Relations Specialist
Russell F. Hughes .... (713) 773-6500 ext. 6527
E-mail: russell.hughes@sba.gov
Administrative Officer **Myung "Kim" Moss** .... (713) 773-6535
E-mail: myung.moss@sba.gov
Public Information Officer **Charles Abell** .... (713) 773-6512
E-mail: charles.abell@sba.gov Fax: (713) 773-6550

Lower Rio Grande Valley District Office
2422 East Tyler Street, Suite E, Harlingen, TX 78550-6855
Tel: (956) 427-8533 Fax: (956) 427-8537

District Director [Information Officer]
Angela R. Burton .... (956) 427-8533 ext. 231
E-mail: angela.burton@sba.gov
Deputy District Director **Thomas Hasenauer** .... (956) 427-8533 ext. 223
International Trade Representative
Reynaldo Vasquez .... (956) 427-8533 ext. 300
Veterans Business Development Officer
Reynaldo Vasquez .... (956) 427-8533 ext. 300
E-mail: reynaldo.vasquez@sba.gov
Women's Business Ownership Representative
Veronica Ortega .... (956) 427-8533 ext. 233
E-mail: veronica.ortega@sba.gov

Lubbock (TX) District Office
1205 Texas Avenue, Room 408, Lubbock, TX 79401-2693
Tel: (806) 472-7462 Fax: (806) 472-7487

District Director **Calvin Orlando Davis** .... (806) 472-7462
E-mail: calvin.davis@sba.gov
Deputy District Director **Reynald R. "Rey" Lops** .... (806) 472-7462
E-mail: reynalds.lops@sba.gov
Public Information Officer **Sandra Caldwell** .... (806) 481-4409
E-mail: sandra.caldwell@sba.gov
Lender Relations Specialist **Jennifer Oldham** .... (806) 472-7462 ext. 106
E-mail: jennifer.oldham@sba.gov
Lead Economic Development Specialist
Scotty Arnold .... (806) 472-7462 ext. 112
E-mail: scotty.arnold@sba.gov
Economic Development Specialist **(Vacant)** .... (806) 472-7462
Business Opportunity Specialist
Smiley Garcia .... (806) 472-7462 ext. 107
Administrative Officer **(Vacant)** .... (806) 472-7462

New Orleans (LA) District Office
One Canal Place, 365 Canal Street, Suite 2820, New Orleans, LA 70130
Tel: (504) 589-6685 Fax: (504) 589-2339

District Director **Michael W. Ricks** .... (504) 589-2879
E-mail: michael.ricks@sba.gov
Education: Houston
Deputy District Director **Jo Ann Lawrence** .... (504) 558-9287
E-mail: jo.lawrence3@sba.gov
Public Affairs Officer and Economic Development
District International Trade Officer **Marjorae Ball** .... (504) 589-2037
E-mail: marjorae.ball@sba.gov
Lead Lender Relations Specialist **Vallery Brumfield** .... (504) 589-2705
Fax: (202) 481-5944
Lender Relations Specialist **Ronald P. Douglass** .... (504) 589-2058
Fax: (202) 481-4955
Business Opportunity Specialist **Benita Rice** .... (504) 589-2055
Fax: (202) 741-6744
Business Opportunity Specialist **Gail Brogan** .... (504) 589-6688
Fax: (202) 481-1998
Business Opportunity Specialist **Alec Banks, Jr.** .... (504) 589-2054
Fax: (504) 589-2339
District Support Assistant
Jeremiah "Jerry" Boudreaux .... (504) 589-6685
E-mail: jerry.boudreaux@sba.gov Fax: (202) 481-2504

Oklahoma District Office
301 NW 6th Street, Suite 116, Oklahoma City, OK 73102
Tel: (405) 609-8000 Fax: (405) 609-8990

District Director **(Vacant)** .... (405) 609-8000
Deputy District Director **John D. Veal, Jr.** .... (405) 609-8020
E-mail: john.veal@sba.gov
Administrative Officer and Economic Development
Specialist **Pam Walker** .... (405) 609-8013
Economic Development Specialist **Jeffery Salzer** .... (405) 609-8021
E-mail: jeffrey.salzer@sba.gov
8a Lead Business Opportunity Specialist
Vanessa Woodfork .... (405) 609-8029
E-mail: vanessa.woodfork@sba.gov
8a Business Opportunity Specialist **L. Pat Smith** .... (405) 609-8027
8a Business Opportunity Specialist **Stephanie Farris** .... (405) 609-8010
E-mail: stephanie.farris@sba.gov
Lead Lender Relations Specialist **Sandra Ransome** .... (405) 609-8019
Lender Relations Specialist **Dustin Allen** .... (405) 609-8000
Lender Relations Specialist **Cindi Carter-Renfro** .... (405) 609-8018
Public Affairs Specialist and Veterans Business
Development Officer **Larry Weatherford** .... (405) 609-8012
E-mail: larry.weatherford@SBA.gov
Women's Business Ownership Representative
Pam Walker .... (405) 609-8013

San Antonio (TX) District Office
615 East Houston Street, Suite 298, San Antonio, TX 78205
Tel: (210) 403-5900 TTY: (210) 403-5933 Fax: (210) 403-5936
E-mail: sado.email@sba.gov
Areas Covered: 55 counties in Southern Central Texas

District Director **Anthony Ruiz** .... (210) 403-5904
E-mail: anthony.ruiz@sba.gov
Deputy District Director **Kelle S. Acock** .... (210) 403-5914
E-mail: kelle.acock@sba.gov
Administrative Officer **Ashley Morales** .... (210) 403-5903
E-mail: ashley.morales@sba.gov
Lead Business Opportunity Specialist **Theresa Scott** .... (210) 403-5929
E-mail: theresa.scott@sba.gov
Program Support Specialist **Daniel Del Rossi** .... (210) 403-5900
E-mail: daniel.delrossi@sba.gov
Business Opportunity Specialist **Sean P. Smith** .... (210) 403-5921
E-mail: sean.smith@sba.gov
Business Opportunity Specialist **Eric Spencer** .... (210) 403-5940
E-mail: eric.spencer@sba.gov
Lead Lender Relations Specialist **Cindy Solano** .... (210) 403-5917
Lender Relations Specialist [Veterans Affairs]
Lionel "Leo" Davila .... (210) 403-5917
Lender Relations Specialist **Annie M. Hudspeth** .... (210) 403-5918

San Antonio (TX) District Office *(continued)*

Public Information Officer **Nina Ramon** . . . . . (210) 403-5920
E-mail: nina.ramon@sba.gov Fax: (210) 403-5936

Region VII - Great Plains

1000 Walnut Street, Suite 530, Kansas City, MO 64106
Tel: (816) 426-4840 Fax: (816) 426-4848
Internet: www.sba.gov/about-offices-content/3/3076
Areas Covered: IA, KS, MO, NE

□ Regional Administrator
Thomas J. "Tom" Salisbury . . . . . (816) 426-4840 ext. 4841
Education: Missouri BA Fax: (314) 539-6615
Resource Coordinator and Administrative Officer
Judith James . . . . . (816) 426-4851
E-mail: judith.james@sba.gov
Regional Advocate **Adrienne Foster** Ste 500 . . . . . (816) 426-4843
Regional Communications Director **June Teasley** . . . . . (816) 426-4845
E-mail: june.teasley@sba.gov
Education: Fort Hays State BA
Designated Agency Ethics Official
Robert L. Gangwere . . . . . (816) 426-4844
Education: Missouri (Kansas City) 1981 JD

Des Moines (IA) District Office

Federal Building, 210 Walnut Street, Room 749,
Des Moines, IA 50309-2186
Tel: (515) 284-4422 Fax: (515) 284-4572

District Director **Jayne E. Armstrong** . . . . . (515) 284-4026
E-mail: jayne.armstrong@sba.gov
Education: West Virginia BS, MA
Deputy District Director **Dawnelle Conley** . . . . . (515) 284-4913
E-mail: dawnelle.conley@sba.gov
Administrative Officer **Lori Hackney** . . . . . (515) 284-4118
E-mail: lori.hackney@sba.gov
Lender Relations Specialist and Public Information
Officer **Thomas D. "Dave" Lentell** . . . . . (515) 284-4522

Cedar Rapids (IA) Branch Office

2750 1st Avenue, NE, Suite 350, Cedar Rapids, IA 52402-4831
Tel: (319) 362-6405 Fax: (319) 362-7861
Internet: www.sba.gov/localresources/district/ia/cedar

Branch Manager **(Vacant)** . . . . . (319) 362-6405
Business Opportunity Specialist **Seung "Sean" Hong** . . . (319) 362-6405
E-mail: seung.hong@sba.gov
Lender Relations Specialist **Keith McBride** . . . . (319) 362-6405 ext. 2021
Education: Western Washington 1975 BSEnvStud;
City U (WA) 1990 MBA
Veterans Affairs Officer **(Vacant)** . . . . . (319) 362-6405

Kansas City (MO) District Office

1000 Walnut Street, Suite 500, Kansas City, MO 64106
Tel: (816) 426-4900 Fax: (816) 426-4939

District Director **Jon Malcolm Richards** . . . . . (816) 426-4903 ext. 4903
E-mail: jon.richards@sba.gov
Deputy District Director **G. Dennis Larkin** . . . . . (816) 426-4914
Assistant District Director for Business Development
Danny Lobina . . . . . (816) 426-4914
Assistant District Director for Economic Development
(Vacant) . . . . . (816) 426-4910
Public Information Officer **(Vacant)** . . . . . (816) 426-4902
Veterans Affairs Officer **Don Reese** . . . . . (417) 890-8501
Business Opportunity Specialist **Kenneth Surmeier** . . . . . (816) 426-4919
E-mail: kenneth.surmeier@sba.gov
Women's Business Ownership **(Vacant)** . . . . . (816) 426-4901

Omaha (NE) District Office

10675 Bedford Avenue, Omaha, NE 68134
Tel: (402) 221-4691 Fax: (402) 221-3680 Internet: www.sba.gov/ne

District Director **Leon J. Milobar** . . . . . (402) 221-3620
E-mail: leon.milobar@sba.gov
Education: Nebraska (Omaha) 1982 MBA
Deputy District Director **Kathleen F. Piper** . . . . . (402) 221-7205

Omaha (NE) District Office *(continued)*

Women's Business Ownership Representative
Elizabeth Yearwood . . . . . (402) 221-7200
E-mail: elizabeth.yearwood@sba.gov
Veterans Affairs Officer **Elizabeth Yearwood** . . . . . (402) 221-7200
E-mail: elizabeth.yearwood@sba.gov
Public Information Officer
Melissa M. "Lisa" Tedesco . . . . . (402) 221-7211
E-mail: melissa.tedesco@sba.gov Fax: (402) 221-3680

St. Louis (MO) District Office

200 North Broadway, Suite 1500, St. Louis, MO 63102
Tel: (314) 539-6600 Fax: (314) 539-3785

District Director **Maureen Brinkley** . . . . . (314) 539-6609
E-mail: maureen.brinkley@sba.gov Fax: (202) 481-4514
Deputy District Director **(Vacant)** . . . . . (314) 539-6609
Area Manager **Suzanne Stearman** . . . . . (314) 539-6600
Economic Development Specialist **Angie Wells** . . . . . (314) 539-6613
E-mail: angie.wells@sba.gov
Business Opportunity Specialist **Gary Alexander** . . . . . (314) 539-6612
Veterans Affairs Officer **Angie Wells** . . . . . (314) 539-6613
E-mail: angie.wells@sba.gov
Women's Business Ownership
Representative [Information Officer]
Patricia "Trish" Freeland . . . . . (314) 539-6600 ext. 223
E-mail: patricial.freeland@sba.gov
Human Resources Specialist **(Vacant)** . . . . . (314) 539-6600

Wichita (KS) District Office

220 West Douglas Avenue, Suite 450, Wichita, KS 67202
Tel: (316) 269-6273 (SCORE, Service Corps of Retired Executives)
Tel: (316) 269-6616 Fax: (316) 269-6499 E-mail: wichita_do@sba.gov
Areas Covered: 77 Central and Western KS counties

District Director **Wayne Bell** . . . . . (316) 269-6566
E-mail: wayne.bell@sba.gov
Deputy District Director **Stephon Aash** . . . . . (316) 269-6273
Veterans Affairs Officer **Doug Clary** . . . . . (316) 269-6571
E-mail: doug.clary@sba.gov
Supervisory Lead Lender Relations Specialist
Doug Clary . . . . . (316) 269-6571
E-mail: doug.clary@sba.gov
Business Opportunity Specialist **Teri L. Taylor** . . . . . (316) 269-6426
E-mail: teri.taylor@sba.gov
Economic Development Specialist **Michael Aumack** . . . . . (316) 269-6275
E-mail: michael.aumack@sba.gov

Region VIII - Rocky Mountains

721 19th Street, Suite 400, Denver, CO 80202
Fax: (303) 844-0506
Areas Covered: CO, MT, ND, SD, UT, WY

□ Regional Administrator **Daniel P. "Dan" Nordberg** . . . . . (202) 205-6808
Education: Colorado State
Regional Advocate **(Vacant)** . . . . . (303) 844-0503
Regional Communications Director
Christopher J. "Chris" Chavez . . . . . (303) 844-0508
E-mail: christopher.chavez@sba.gov
Education: Colorado 1986 BB
Administrative Resource Coordinator **Carol Helm** . . . . . (303) 844-0504

Colorado District Office

721 19th Street, Suite 426, Denver, CO 80202-2517
Tel: (303) 844-2607 Fax: (303) 844-6490

District Director **Frances Padilla** . . . . . (303) 844-4293
E-mail: frances.padilla@sba.gov
Deputy District Director **Joshua Vigil** . . . . . (303) 844-2159
E-mail: joshua.vigil@sba.gov
Public Information Officer
Christopher J. "Chris" Chavez . . . . . (303) 844-0508
E-mail: christopher.chavez@sba.gov
Education: Colorado 1986 BB

INDEPENDENT AGENCIES

★ Presidential Appointment Requiring Senate Confirmation ☆ Presidential Appointment □ Schedule C Appointment ◇ Career Senior Foreign Service Appointment
● Career Senior Executive Service (SES) Appointment ○ Non-Career Senior Executive Service (SES) Appointment ■ Postal Career Executive Service

Montana District Office
Federal Office Building, 10 West 15th Street,
Suite 1100, Helena, MT 59626
Tel: (406) 441-1081 Fax: (406) 441-1090

District Director **Wayne L. Gardella CPA** .... (406) 441-1080
E-mail: wayne.gardella@sba.gov
Education: UNLV 1981 BS; Marymount U 1987 MBA
District Counsel **(Vacant)** .... (406) 441-1082
Senior Area Manager **(Vacant)** .... (406) 441-1081
222 North 32nd Street, Suite 200, Billings, MT 59101
Deputy District Director **Roger Hopkins** .... (406) 441-1083
E-mail: roger.hopkins@sba.gov
Lead Lender Relations Specialist **Lorena Carlson** .... (406) 202-3401
Lender Relations Specialist **Thomas "Tom" White** ...... (406) 441-1078
E-mail: thomas.white@sba.gov
Economic Development Specialist **John Donovan** .... (406) 441-1087
E-mail: john.donovan@sba.gov
Economic Development Specialist **(Vacant)** .... (406) 441-1089
Business Opportunity Specialist **Kelly Dixon** .... (406) 441-1085

North Dakota District Office
657 Second Avenue North, Room 218, Fargo, ND 58102
P.O. Box 3086, Fargo, ND 58108-3086
Tel: (701) 239-5131 Fax: (701) 239-5645 E-mail: north.dakota@sba.gov

District Director **Alan Haut** .... (701) 239-5131 ext. 209
E-mail: alan.haut@sba.gov
Deputy District Director **(Vacant)** .... (701) 239-5131
Senior Area Manager, Bismarck **Dale Van Eckhout** ...... (701) 250-4303
E-mail: dale.vaneckhout@sba.gov
Senior Area Manager, Grand Forks **Eric Giltner** .... (701) 746-5160
E-mail: eric.giltner@sba.gov
Government Contracting Specialist **Sherri Komrosky** .... (701) 239-5658
E-mail: sherri.komrosky@sba.gov
Economic Development Specialist **(Vacant)** ..... (701) 239-5131 ext. 208
Lender Relations Specialist
Deborah "Deb" Kantrud .... (701) 239-5131 ext. 209
E-mail: deborah.kantrud@sba.gov
Public Information Officer **Sheri Weston** .... (701) 239-5131 ext. 210
E-mail: sheri.weston@sba.gov

Utah District Office
Federal Building, 125 South State Street,
Room 2227, Salt Lake City, UT 84138-1195
Tel: (801) 524-3209 Fax: (801) 524-4160 E-mail: utahgeneral@sba.gov
Internet: www.sba.gov/localresources/district/ut

District Director **Marla Trollan** .... (801) 524-3200
E-mail: marla.trollan@sba.gov Fax: (202) 481-5631
Deputy District Director **Steve Price** .... (801) 524-3215
Fax: (202) 481-5688
Lead Business Opportunity Specialist **(Vacant)** .... (801) 524-3209
Business Opportunity Specialist **Dennis Wengert** .... (801) 524-3204
Fax: (202) 292-3694
Business Opportunity Specialist **Suzan Yoshimura** ...... (801) 524-3206
Fax: (202) 481-5726
Lender Relations Specialist **Ted Elliot** .... (801) 524-3228
E-mail: ted.elliott@sba.gov Fax: (202) 741-6703
Lender Relations Specialist **Karl Wernick** .... (801) 524-3210
E-mail: karl.wernick@sba.gov Fax: (202) 481-6335
Economic Development Specialist **Ian A. Lorenzana** ..... (801) 524-3218
E-mail: ian.lorenzana@sba.gov Fax: (202) 741-6674
Economic Development Specialist **Melinda Workman** ... (801) 524-3213
E-mail: melinda.workman@sba.gov Fax: (202) 481-4526
Program Support Assistant **Rachel Bennett** .... (801) 524-3223
Fax: (202) 481-6040
District Counsel **John Gygi** .... (801) 524-3205
Fax: (202) 481-2670
Paralegal Specialist **Sharlene Miller** .... (801) 524-3221
Fax: (202) 481-5526
Public Affairs Specialist **Siobhan Carlile** .... (801) 524-3217
E-mail: siobhan.carlile@sba.gov
Administrative Officer **Cheryl Richens** .... (801) 524-3219
E-mail: cheryl.richens@sba.gov Fax: (202) 481-0758

South Dakota District Office
2329 North Career Avenue, Suite 105, Sioux Falls, SD 57107
Tel: (605) 330-4243 Fax: (605) 330-4215 Internet: www.sba.gov/sd

District Director **John L. Brown II** .... (605) 330-4243 ext. 14
E-mail: john.l.brown@sba.gov
Deputy District Director **(Vacant)** .... (605) 330-4243
Public Affairs Specialist **Jennifer Kelly** .... (605) 330-4243 ext. 22
E-mail: jennifer.kelly@sba.gov Fax: (605) 330-4215

Wyoming District Office
Dick Cheney Building, 150 East B Street,
Room 1101, Casper, WY 82601
P.O. Box 44001, Casper, WY 82602-5013
Tel: (307) 261-6500

District Director **Amy Catherine Lea** .... (307) 247-3191
E-mail: amy.lea@sba.gov
Deputy District Director **Debra Farris** .... (307) 261-6503
E-mail: debra.farris@sba.gov
Lender Relations Specialist **Susan Rezanina** .... (307) 261-6520
E-mail: susan.rezanina@sba.gov
Administrative Officer **Marilyn Coy** .... (307) 261-6512
E-mail: marilyn.coy@sba.gov
Public Information Officer **Marilyn Coy** .... (307) 261-6512
E-mail: marilyn.coy@sba.gov

Region IX - Pacific

330 North Brand Boulevard, Suite 1270, Glendale, CA 91203
Tel: (818) 552-3437 Fax: (818) 552-3267
Areas Covered: AZ, CA, GU, HI, NV

□ Regional Administrator **Michael A Vallante** .... (818) 552-3437
Education: Providence BB
Regional Advocate **Marina DeWit** .... (602) 745-7231
2828 North Central Avenue, Ste 800, Phoenix, AZ 85004-1093
Regional Communications Director **Miryam Barajas** ..... (818) 552-3437
E-mail: miryam.barajas@sba.gov
Administrative Resource Coordinator
Maribel P. Plascencia .... (818) 552-3437

Arizona District Office
2828 North Central Avenue, Suite 800, Phoenix, AZ 85004-1093
Tel: (602) 745-7200 Fax: (602) 745-7210

District Director **Robert J. Blaney** .... (602) 745-7200
Education: SUNY (Buffalo)
Deputy Director **Shivani Dubey** .... (602) 745-7200
E-mail: shivani.dubey@sba.gov
Public Information Officer **Stephen Hart** .... (602) 745-7200
E-mail: stephen.hart@sba.gov
Veterans Affairs Officer **James Pipper** .... (602) 745-7230
E-mail: james.pipper@sba.gov
Women's Business Ownership State Representative
Delia Gomez .... (602) 745-7228

Fresno (CA) District Office
801 R Street, Suite 201, Fresno, CA 93721
Tel: (559) 487-5791 Fax: (559) 487-5636

District Director **Dawn Golik** .... (559) 487-5791 ext. 2705
E-mail: dawn.golik@sba.gov
Deputy District Director **(Vacant)** .... (559) 487-5791
Public Information Officer **Dawn Golik** .... (559) 487-5791 ext. 2705
E-mail: dawn.golik@sba.gov
Veterans Affairs Officer **Peter Estrada** .... (559) 487-5791 ext. 2703
E-mail: peter.estrada@sba.gov

Hawaii District Office
500 Ala Moana Boulevard, Suite 1-306, Honolulu, HI 96813
Mail Code: 0951, 500 Ala Moana Boulevard, Honolulu, HI 96813
Tel: (808) 541-2990 Fax: (808) 541-2976
Internet: www.sba.gov/localresources/district/hi

District Director and Women's Business
Ownership Representative **Jane A. Sawyer** .... (808) 541-2990 ext. 202
E-mail: jane.sawyer@sba.gov
Education: Colorado BA

★ Presidential Appointment Requiring Senate Confirmation ☆ Presidential Appointment □ Schedule C Appointment ◇ Career Senior Foreign Service Appointment
● Career Senior Executive Service (SES) Appointment ○ Non-Career Senior Executive Service (SES) Appointment ■ Postal Career Executive Service

Hawaii District Office *(continued)*

Deputy District Director
Thornton Mark Spain .... (808) 541-2990 ext. 209
E-mail: thornton.spain@sba.gov
Veterans Affairs Officer **Jerry M. Hirata** .... (808) 541-2990 ext. 210
E-mail: jerry.hirata@sba.gov
Lead Business Opportunity Specialist
Michael Youth .... (808) 541-2990 ext. 214
E-mail: michael.youth@sba.gov

Los Angeles (CA) District Office
330 North Brand Boulevard, Suite 1200, Glendale, CA 91203
Tel: (818) 552-3201
Tel: (818) 552-3206 (SCORE, Service Corps of Retired Executives)
Tel: (562) 938-5020 (Long Beach Community College District - Lead Center) Tel: (213) 473-1605 (Asian Pacific Islander SBP)
Tel: (661) 362-3305 (College of the Canyons) Tel: (805) 384-1801 ((Economic Development Collaborative-Ventura County))
Fax: (818) 552-3267
Areas Covered: CA (Counties of Los Angeles, Ventura and Santa Barbara)

● District Director **(Vacant)** .... (818) 552-3201
Deputy District Director **Janan T. "Ben" Raju** .... (818) 552-3201
E-mail: janan.raju@sba.gov
Assistant District Director For Lender Relations
Terri Billups .... (818) 552-3201
E-mail: terri.billups@sba.gov
Lead Business Opportunity Specialist **Stephen Ash** ..... (818) 552-3320
E-mail: stephen.ash@sba.gov
Administrative Officer **Leigh A. Kearns** .... (818) 552-3201
E-mail: leigh.kearns@sba.gov
District Counsel **Dace Pavlavskis** .... (818) 552-3307
E-mail: dace.pavlavskis@sba.gov
Public Information Officer **Michael "Mike" Blass** .... (818) 552-3222
E-mail: mike.blass@sba.gov

Nevada District Office
300 S. 44th Street, Suite 400, Las Vegas, NV 89101
Tel: (702) 388-6611
Tel: (702) 388-6104 (SCORE, Service Corps of Retired Executives)
Fax: (702) 388-6469 Internet: www.sba.gov/localresources/district/nv

District Director **Joseph Amato** .... (702) 388-6019
E-mail: joseph.amato@sba.gov
Deputy District Director **Daniel Lucero** .... (702) 388-6015
E-mail: daniel.lucero@sba.gov
District Counsel (Acting) **Dace Pavlovskis** .... (702) 388-6611
Lead Business Development Specialist and Chief of Finance **Roy Brady** .... (702) 388-6686
E-mail: roy.brady@sba.gov
Business Opportunity Specialist **Barry VanOrden** .... (702) 388-6674
E-mail: barry.vanorden@sba.gov
Economic Development Specialist **Christina Stace** ...... (702) 388-6652
E-mail: christina.stace@sba.gov
Information Technology Specialist **Steve Studards** ...... (702) 388-6654

Sacramento (CA) District Office
6501 Sylvan Road, Suite 100, Citrus Heights, CA 95610
Tel: (916) 735-1700 Fax: (916) 735-1719 E-mail: sac-needhelp@sba.gov
Internet: www.sba.gov/ca/sacr

District Director **Heather Luzzi** .... (916) 735-1709
E-mail: heather.luzzi@sba.gov
Deputy District Director **George Flores ARNG (Ret)** .... (916) 735-1700
E-mail: george.flores@sba.gov
Education: Cal State (Fresno) BA

San Diego (CA) District Office
550 West C Street, Suite 550, San Diego, CA 92101-3540
Tel: (619) 557-7250
Tel: (619) 557-7272 (SCORE, Counselors to America's Small Business)
Fax: (619) 557-5894 E-mail: sandiego@sba.gov
Internet: www.sba.gov/ca/sandiego Internet: www.sandiego.score.org (SCORE, Counselors to America's Small Business)

District Director **Ruben R. Garcia** .... (619) 727-4880
E-mail: ruben.garcia@sba.gov
Education: Texas Tech BA
Public Information Officer/Women's Business Ownership Representative/ District International Trade Representative **Cynthia Y. "Cyndi" Harris** ...... (619) 727-4884
E-mail: cynthia.harris@sba.gov
Veterans Affairs Officer **Michael Sovacool** .... (619) 727-4881
E-mail: michael.sovacool@sba.gov

San Francisco (CA) District Office
455 Market Street, Suite 600, San Francisco, CA 94105-2420
Tel: (415) 744-6820
Tel: (415) 744-6827 (SCORE, Service Corps of Retired Executives)
Fax: (415) 744-6812 Internet: www.sba.gov/ca/sf

● District Director **Julie Clowes** .... (415) 744-6820
E-mail: julie.clowes@sba.gov
Deputy District Director and Director for Asian American and Pacific Islander Outreach
Tong Qin CPA, CISA .... (415) 744-8475
E-mail: tong.qin@sba.gov
Administrative Officer **Emily Navarra-Refugio** .... (415) 744-6805
E-mail: emily.navarra@sba.gov
Public Information Officer **Marlow Schindler** .... (415) 744-6771
E-mail: marlow.schindler@sba.gov
Veterans Affairs Officer **Michael Jordan** .... (415) 744-8477
E-mail: michael.jordan@sba.gov
Women's Business Ownership Representative
Noah Brod .... (415) 744-4244

Orange County / Inland Empire District Office
5 Hutton Centre Drive, Suite 900, Santa Ana, CA 92707
Tel: (714) 550-7420 Fax: (714) 550-7409

District Director **J. Adalberto Quijada** .... (714) 560-7440
E-mail: adalberto.quijada@sba.gov
Education: Arizona BA; Northern Arizona MA
Deputy District Director **Rachel Baranick** .... (714) 560-7441
E-mail: rachel.baranick@sba.gov
Education: UCLA BS
Public Information Officer **Douglas A. Dare** .... (714) 560-7467
E-mail: douglas.dare@sba.gov

Region X - Pacific Northwest
2401 Fourth Avenue, Suite 400, Seattle, WA 98121-1128
Tel: (206) 553-5676 Fax: (206) 553-4155
Areas Covered: AK, ID, OR, WA

□ Regional Administrator **M. Jeremy Field** .... (206) 553-5676
E-mail: jeremy.field@sba.gov
Education: BYU 2003 BA; Idaho 2007 JD; Idaho State MPA
Regional Communications Director
Melanie M. Norton .... (206) 553-5231
E-mail: melanie.norton@sba.gov Fax: (206) 553-4155
Administrative Resource Coordinator **(Vacant)** .... (206) 553-5676
Regional Advocate **Apollo Fuhriman** .... (206) 553-0390

Alaska District Office
420 L Street, Suite 300, Anchorage, AK 99501
Tel: (907) 271-4022 Fax: (907) 271-4545 E-mail: alaska_do@sba.gov

District Director **(Vacant)** .... (907) 271-4022
Deputy District Director **Marichu Relativo** .... (907) 271-4844
E-mail: marichu.relativo@sba.gov
Senior Area Manager for Economic Development Division **Scott Swingle** .... (907) 271-4878
E-mail: scott.swingle@sba.gov
Lender Relations Specialist **Nelida Irvine** .... (907) 271-4027
E-mail: nelida.irvine@sba.gov

(continued on next page)

★ Presidential Appointment Requiring Senate Confirmation ☆ Presidential Appointment □ Schedule C Appointment ◇ Career Senior Foreign Service Appointment
● Career Senior Executive Service (SES) Appointment ○ Non-Career Senior Executive Service (SES) Appointment ■ Postal Career Executive Service

Alaska District Office *(continued)*

District Program Support Assistant **Yolanda Lassiter** .... (907) 271-4022
E-mail: yolanda.lassiter@sba.gov

Boise (ID) District Office
380 East Parkcenter Boulevard, Suite 330, Boise, ID 83706
Tel: (208) 334-9004 Fax: (208) 334-9353

District Director **Gary E. Eisenbraun** .... (208) 334-9004 ext. 333
E-mail: gary.eisenbraun@sba.gov
Deputy District Director **Shannon Madsen** ..... (208) 334-9004 ext. 334
Administrative Officer **Bueford Borron** .... (208) 334-9004 ext. 336
E-mail: bueford.borron@sba.gov
Women's Business Ownership Representative
Catherine "Catie" Bennett .... (208) 334-9004 ext. 327
E-mail: catherine.bennett@sba.gov
Public Information Officer
Christian Pennington .... (208) 334-9004 ext. 336
E-mail: christian.pennington@sba.gov Fax: (208) 334-9353

Portland (OR) District Office
620 SW Main Street, 313, Portland, OR 97205
Tel: (503) 326-2682 Fax: (503) 326-2808 E-mail: pdxhelp@sba.gov
Internet: www.sba.gov/OR

District Director **Martin D. Golden** .... (503) 326-5221
E-mail: martin.golden@sba.gov
Education: UC Santa Barbara BB; UC Berkeley MBA
Deputy District Director **Jennifer Baker** .... (503) 326-5122
E-mail: jennifer.baker@sba.gov Fax: (202) 481-4446
Regional Export Finance Manager
James "Jim" Newton .... (503) 326-5498
Lead Lender Relations Specialist **Larry Trujillo** .... (503) 326-5205
E-mail: larry.trujillo@sba.gov
Lender Relations Specialist **Scott Bossom** .... (503) 326-5204
E-mail: scott.bossom@sba.gov
Business Opportunity Specialist **Yuri Dyson** .... (503) 326-6692
E-mail: yuri.dyson@sba.gov
Administrative Officer **Warren Givens** .... (503) 326-5200
Economic Development Specialist **Anna Shapiro** .... (503) 326-5220
E-mail: anna.shapiro@sba.gov
District Support Assistant **Melissa Davis** .... (503) 326-2657
E-mail: melissa.davis@sba.gov
Public Affairs Specialist **Sean Wilson** .... (503) 326-2682
Social Media Specialist **Natale S. Goriel** .... (503) 326-5207
Program Support Assistant **(Vacant)** .... (503) 326-2682

Seattle (WA) District Office
2401 Fourth Avenue, Suite 450, Seattle, WA 98121-1128
Tel: (206) 553-7310 Fax: (206) 553-7099
Internet: www.sba.gov/localresources/district/wa

District Director **Kerrie T. Hurd ARNG (Ret)** .... (206) 553-7040
E-mail: kerrie.hurd@sba.gov
Deputy District Director **Mark F. Costello** .... (206) 553-7312
E-mail: mark.costello@sba.gov
District Counsel **Jayson Pang** .... (206) 553-7081
E-mail: jayson.pang@sba.gov
Women's Business Ownership District Representative
Desiree Albrecht .... (206) 553-2664
E-mail: desiree.albrecht@sba.gov
Veterans Affairs Officer **Matthew "Matt" Williams** ..... (206) 553-7315
E-mail: matthew.williams@sba.gov
Public Information Officer **Lisa White** .... (206) 553-7050
E-mail: lisa.white@sba.gov
Business Opportunity Specialist
Ranvir "Ana" Singh USAF .... (206) 553-7080

Office of Management and Administration
409 Third Street, SW, Washington, DC 20416
Tel: (202) 205-6610 Fax: (202) 205-7693

Office of Human Capital Management (OHCM)
409 Third Street, SW, Room 5300, Washington, DC 20416
Tel: (202) 205-6780 Fax: (202) 205-4604

Denver - Human Resources Operations Division (HROD)
721 19th Street, Suite 392, Denver, CO 80202
Tel: (303) 844-7800

Center Director **Denise M. Sandoval** .... (303) 844-7794
E-mail: denise.sandoval@sba.gov
Deputy Center Director **Yahida Salazar** .... (303) 844-7785
E-mail: yahida.salazar@sba.gov

★ Presidential Appointment Requiring Senate Confirmation ☆ Presidential Appointment ☐ Schedule C Appointment ◇ Career Senior Foreign Service Appointment
● Career Senior Executive Service (SES) Appointment ○ Non-Career Senior Executive Service (SES) Appointment ■ Postal Career Executive Service

Social Security Administration (SSA)

Description: The Social Security Administration provides general welfare, such as continuing income, disability coverage and medical benefits, to workers after retirement.

6401 Security Boulevard, Baltimore, MD 21235
Tel: (800) 772-1213 TTY: (800) 325-0778 (General Information)
E-mail: open.government@ssa.gov (Open Government Initiative)
Internet: www.ssa.gov
Internet: www.ssa.gov/open (Open Government Initiative)

OFFICE OF THE COMMISSIONER

Robert M. Ball Building, 6401 Security Boulevard,
Room 2607, Baltimore, MD 21235
Tel: (410) 965-3120 Fax: (410) 966-1463

Office of Operations

West High Rise Building, 6401 Security Boulevard,
Room 1204, Baltimore, MD 21235
Tel: (410) 965-3145 Fax: (410) 966-7941

Regional Offices

Boston Region

J.F.K. Federal Building, 15 New Sudbury Street,
Room 1900, Boston, MA 02203
Tel: (617) 565-2870 Fax: (617) 565-2143 Internet: www.ssa.gov/boston
Areas Covered: CT, ME, MA, NH, RI, VT

● Regional Commissioner **Linda M. Dorn** . . . . (617) 565-2870
E-mail: linda.dorn@ssa.gov
● Deputy Regional Commissioner **Anatoly A. Shnaider** . . . (617) 565-2870
E-mail: anatoly.shnaider@ssa.gov
Staff Assistant **Barbara McNeill** . . . . (617) 565-2870
E-mail: barbara.mcneill@ssa.gov
Executive Officer **Linda Tuttle** . . . . (617) 565-2870
E-mail: linda.tuttle@ssa.gov
Executive Analyst **Laura Cocozzella** . . . . (617) 565-2872
Executive Analyst **Elizabeth Hanover** . . . . (617) 565-2870

Management and Operations Support

● Assistant Regional Commissioner **(Vacant)** . . . . (617) 565-2840
Deputy Assistant Regional Commissioner **Alison Seto** . . . (617) 565-2840
Executive Analyst **Wilson Osorio** . . . . (617) 565-2840

Center for Material Resources

J.F.K. Federal Building, Room 1975, Boston, MA 02203
Center Director **Judy Bernstein** . . . . (617) 565-2861

Center for Human Resources

15 New Sudbury Street, Boston, MA 02203
Fax: (617) 565-1401
Center Director **Donna Abbott** . . . . (617) 565-1397
E-mail: donna.abbott@ssa.gov
Systems Coordinator **Jay Nunes** . . . . (617) 565-2401
E-mail: jay.nunes@ssa.gov

Office of General Counsel

J.F.K. Federal Building, 15 New Sudbury Street,
Room 1900, Boston, MA 02203
Tel: (617) 565-2380 Fax: (617) 565-4447
● Regional Chief Counsel **Michael J. Pelgro** Room 625 . . . . (617) 565-2380
E-mail: michael.pelgro@ssa.gov
Education: Boston Col AB, JD

Office of Disability Adjudication and Review

One Bowdoin Square, 10th Floor, Boston, MA 02114
Tel: (888) 870-7578 Fax: (617) 723-2985
Regional Chief Administrative Law Judge (Acting)
Aaron M. Morgan . . . . (888) 870-7578
E-mail: aaron.morgan@ssa.gov
Regional Management Officer **Carolyn Tedino** . . . . (888) 870-7578
E-mail: carolyn.tedino@ssa.gov
Regional Director of Operations **(Vacant)** . . . . (888) 870-7578
Team Leader **Mary DeCaro** . . . . (888) 870-7578
E-mail: mary.decaro@ssa.gov
Team Leader **Joanna Gillis** . . . . (888) 870-7578
Regional Supervisory Information Technology
Specialist **Edward Demaso** . . . . (888) 870-7578
E-mail: edward.demaso@ssa.gov

Boston (MA) Office

One Bowdoin Square, 4th Floor, Boston, MA 02114
Tel: (888) 870-7573 Fax: (617) 248-0978
Chief Administrative Law Judge **James Packer** . . . . (888) 870-7573
E-mail: james.packer@ssa.gov
Hearings Office Director **Lisa Cataldo** . . . . (888) 870-7573

Decision Writers Unit

One Bowdoin Square, 9th Floor, Boston, MA 02114
Group Supervisor **Eric Gross** . . . . (888) 870-7578

Program Policy and Systems Team

15 New Sudbury Street, Room 1925, Boston, MA 02203
Center Director **Carol Rozen** . . . . (617) 565-2882
Team Leader SSI **Jackie Medina** . . . . (617) 565-2882
Program Manager **Charles Schaenman** . . . . (617) 565-2882
E-mail: charles.schaenman@ssa.gov

Automation and Security Team

J.F.K. Federal Building, 15 New Sudbury Street,
Room 1925, Boston, MA 02203
Tel: (617) 565-4229 Fax: (617) 565-4814
Center Director **Roberto Medina** . . . . (617) 565-9245
E-mail: roberto.medina@ssa.gov
Deputy Center Director **Jennifer Lee** . . . . (617) 565-2866
E-mail: jennifer.lee@ssa.gov
MI Specialist **Casy Nguyen** . . . . (617) 565-2866
E-mail: casy.nguyen@ssa.gov
LAN Administrator **Melissa LaChance** . . . . (617) 565-2866
E-mail: melissa.lachance@ssa.gov
IT Specialist **Alicia Brown** . . . . (617) 565-2893
E-mail: alicia.brown@ssa.gov
IT Specialist **Gina Muscato** . . . . (617) 565-2893
E-mail: gina.muscato@ssa.gov

(continued on next page)

INDEPENDENT AGENCIES

★ Presidential Appointment Requiring Senate Confirmation ☆ Presidential Appointment ☐ Schedule C Appointment ◇ Career Senior Foreign Service Appointment
● Career Senior Executive Service (SES) Appointment ○ Non-Career Senior Executive Service (SES) Appointment ■ Postal Career Executive Service

INDEPENDENT AGENCIES

Automation and Security Team *(continued)*

IT Specialist **Glenn Romero** . . . . (617) 565-2866
E-mail: glenn.romero@ssa.gov
IT Specialist **Thomas Savlidis** . . . . (617) 565-2895
E-mail: thomas.savlidis@ssa.gov
IT Specialist **Mike Shaw** . . . . (617) 565-2866
E-mail: mike.shaw@ssa.gov

Disability Team
J.F.K. Federal Building, 15 New Sudbury Street,
Room 1925, Boston, MA 02203
Tel: (617) 565-2390 Fax: (617) 565-2402

Center Director **Frederick Gilbert** . . . . (617) 565-2390
E-mail: fred.gilbert@ssa.gov
Disability Program Administrator **Steve Delosh** . . . . (617) 565-2390
E-mail: steve.delosh@ssa.gov
Disability Program Administrator **Naomi Frankel** . . . . (617) 565-2390
E-mail: naomi.frankel@ssa.gov
Team Leader **Elizabeth "Liz" Sanfilippo** . . . . (617) 565-2390
Program Expert **Janet Feasel** . . . . (617) 565-2390
Program Expert **Erin Genova** . . . . (617) 565-2390
Program Expert **Jennifer Lyons** . . . . (617) 565-2390
Program Expert **Yadira Vega** . . . . (617) 565-2390
Social Insurance Specialist **(Vacant)** . . . . (617) 565-2390

Retirement and Survivors Insurance Issues
Social Insurance Specialist **Michael Bonner** . . . . (617) 565-2882
Social Insurance Specialist **Christopher Contreras** . . . . . . (617) 565-2882
Social Insurance Specialist **Susan Fay** . . . . (617) 565-2882
Social Insurance Specialist **Asilis Y. Mejia** . . . . (617) 565-2882
Social Insurance Specialist **Sharon Valerio** . . . . (617) 565-2882

Supplemental Security Income Issues
J.F.K. Federal Building, 15 New Sudbury Street,
Room 1925, Boston, MA 02203
Internet: www.ssa.gov/ssi

Social Insurance Specialist **Lauren Cronin-Wilkens** . . . . . (617) 565-2887
Social Insurance Specialist **John Donovan** . . . . (617) 565-2887
Social Insurance Specialist **Shannon Keady** . . . . (617) 565-2887
Social Insurance Specialist **Jonathan McInnis** . . . . (617) 565-2887
Social Insurance Specialist **Tyisha Robinson** . . . . (617) 565-2887
Social Insurance Specialist **(Vacant)** . . . . (617) 565-2887

Regional Office of Quality Review
99 High Street, Suite 400, Boston, MA 02110

Director **Michael J. Scott** . . . . (866) 716-7420 ext. 14902
E-mail: michael.scott@ssa.gov
Secretary **Marcia R. Vinocoor** . . . . (866) 716-7420
E-mail: marcia.vinocoor@ssa.gov
Systems Specialist **Thomas Manning** . . . . (866) 716-7420

Assistance and Insurance Program Quality Branch
99 High Street, Suite 400, Boston, MA 02110
Tel: (866) 755-5346 Fax: (617) 695-6620

Branch Chief **To-Quyen Vu-Goulas** . . . . (866) 755-5346
E-mail: to-quyen.vu-goulas@ssa.gov
Branch Chief **Domingo A. Taveras** . . . . (866) 755-5346
E-mail: domingo.taveras@ssa.gov
Program Leader (RSI) **Patricia "Tricia" White** . . . . (866) 755-5346
E-mail: patricia.white@ssa.gov

Disability Quality Branch
99 High Street, Suite 400, Boston, MA 02110
Tel: (866) 365-7031 Fax: (617) 695-6622

Branch Chief **Greca Benjamin** . . . . (866) 365-7031
E-mail: greca.benjamin@ssa.gov
Branch Chief **Adele Mitrano** . . . . (866) 365-7031
E-mail: adele.mitrano@ssa.gov
Branch Chief **John Noone** . . . . (866) 365-7031
E-mail: john.noone@ssa.gov
Program Leader **Peter Carr** . . . . (866) 365-7031
E-mail: peter.carr@ssa.gov
Program Leader **Leslie Hill** . . . . (866) 365-7031

Disability Quality Branch *(continued)*

Program Leader **Sal Natalie** . . . . (866) 365-7031
Program Leader **Patricia "Pat" Peckrill** . . . . (866) 365-7031
Program Leader **Christine Santosa** . . . . (866) 365-7031
E-mail: christine.santosa@ssa.gov
Program Leader **Susan Skayne** . . . . (866) 365-7031
E-mail: susan.skayne@ssa.gov
Program Leader **Joan Smith-Fiorentini** . . . . (866) 365-7031
E-mail: joan.smith-fiorentini@ssa.gov

New York Region
Jacob K. Javits Federal Building, 26 Federal Plaza,
40th Floor, Room 40-100, New York, NY 10278
Tel: (800) 772-1213 Tel: (212) 264-3915 Fax: (212) 264-6847
Internet: www.socialsecurity.gov/ny
Areas Covered: NJ, NY, PR, VI

● Regional Commissioner **Frederick M. "Fred" Maurin** . . . . (212) 264-3915
E-mail: frederick.maurin@ssa.gov
● Deputy Regional Commissioner **Bryant Wilder** . . . . (212) 264-4988
E-mail: bryant.wilder@ssa.gov
Regional Communications Director
John Shallman Room 40-120 . . . . (212) 264-2500
E-mail: ny.rpa@ssa.gov Fax: (212) 264-1444
Senior Public Affairs Specialist **Everett Lo** . . . . (212) 264-2715
Fax: (212) 264-1444
Senior Public Affairs Specialist **(Vacant)** . . . . (212) 264-7261
Jacob K. Javits Federal Building, Fax: (212) 264-1444
26 Federal Plaza,
Room 40-100, New York, NY 10278
Executive Officer **Diana Valdes** . . . . (212) 264-4007
E-mail: diana.valdes@ssa.gov
Equal Opportunity Manager **Althea Phipps** . . . . (212) 264-4513
E-mail: althea.phipps@ssa.gov
Teleservice Center Operations Manager **Garry McBean** . . . (212) 264-8482

Center for Program Support
Jacob K. Javits Federal Building, 26 Federal Plaza, New York, NY 10278

Director **Mary Groot** Room 4032D . . . . (212) 264-4004
Deputy Director and Supplemental Security
Income Operations Team Leader
Emmanuel Fernandez Room 4032D . . . . (212) 264-4005

Automation Center
Director **Greg Narowski** 40th Floor . . . . (212) 264-2463
E-mail: greg.narowski@ssa.gov
Deputy Director and RO/Field Automation Support
Team Leader **Victoria Shteyman** 40th Floor . . . . (212) 264-5983
E-mail: victoria.shteyman@ssa.gov
RO/Field Network Support Team Leader
Jie Zhang 40th Floor . . . . (212) 264-1477
E-mail: JIE.ZHANG.SAMMON@SSA.GOV

Center for Disability
Jacob K. Javits Federal Building, 26 Federal Plaza, New York, NY 10278
Tel: (212) 264-2085

Director (Acting) **Joseph Cafaro** . . . . (212) 264-7250
E-mail: joseph.cafaro@ssa.gov
Deputy Director **Melissa Brucker** Room 40-140 . . . . (212) 264-7250
E-mail: melissa.bruckner@ssa.gov
Regional Medical Advisor **(Vacant)** Room 40-140 . . . . (212) 264-4943
Program Administrator **Susan Palais** Room 40-140 . . . . . . (212) 264-7317
E-mail: susan.palais@ssa.gov
Disability Program Operations Team Leader
(Vacant) Room 40-140 . . . . (212) 264-7290
Technical Support Team Leader
Peggy Fleming Room 40-140 . . . . (212) 264-4519

Office of the General Counsel
Jacob K. Javits Federal Building, 26 Federal Plaza, New York, NY 10278
Fax: (212) 264-6372

● Regional Chief Counsel
Stephen P. Conte Room 3904 . . . . (212) 264-3650 ext. 32216
E-mail: steve.conte@ssa.gov

★ Presidential Appointment Requiring Senate Confirmation ☆ Presidential Appointment ☐ Schedule C Appointment ◇ Career Senior Foreign Service Appointment
● Career Senior Executive Service (SES) Appointment ○ Non-Career Senior Executive Service (SES) Appointment ■ Postal Career Executive Service

Disability Adjudication and Review
Regional Chief Administrative Law Judge
Aaron M. Morgan .... (212) 264-4036
E-mail: aaron.morgan@ssa.gov

Management and Operations Support
• Assistant Regional Commissioner
Raymond Egan Room 4010 .... (212) 264-2507
E-mail: raymond.egan@ssa.gov
Executive Assistant **Raquel Tevara** Room 40-10D ...... (212) 264-2509
Deputy Assistant Regional Commissioner **Jean Hall** ..... (212) 264-2507

Human Resources Center
Director **Joseph Carafo** Room 4010 .... (212) 264-2508
Deputy Director **Jonathan Addy** Room 4010 .... (212) 264-1493
E-mail: jonathan.addy@ssa.gov
Regional Training Center Team Leader **Jaclyn Lurker** .... (718) 557-3801
155-10 Jamaica Ave., P.O. Box 4300, Jamaica, NY 11432-3830
Special Training Initiatives and Career Development
Team Leader **(Vacant)** Room 4030 .... (212) 264-3725

Materiel Resources Center
Director **Stephanie Francis** .... (212) 264-4519
E-mail: stephanie.francis@ssa.gov
Field Services Team Leader **Alba Jimenez** .... (212) 264-8486
Jacob K. Javits Federal Building, 26 Federal Plaza,
40th Floor, Room 4010, New York, NY 10278
Financial Management Team Leader
Greg Naroski Room 4010 .... (212) 264-2463

Northeastern Program Service Center, Management and Budget Branch
Addabbo Federal Building, 155-10 Jamaica Avenue,
Jamaica, NY 11431-3830
P.O. Box 4300, Jamaica, NY 11432-9942
Tel: (718) 557-5012
Facilities Management Team Leader **Mike Trant** .... (718) 557-5101

Processing Center Operations
Addabbo Federal Building, 155-10 Jamaica Avenue,
Jamaica, NY 11432-3830
P.O. Box 4300, Jamaica, NY 11432-9942
• Assistant Regional Commissioner **Bernard Bowles** ...... (718) 557-5000
Deputy Assistant Regional Commissioner
Francis X. Barry .... (718) 557-5005
E-mail: francis.x.barry@ssa.gov
Executive Officer **Ruth A. Harron** .... (718) 557-5020
Operations Support Branch Director **Caren Unger** .... (718) 557-5023
E-mail: caren.unger@ssa.gov
Process Division I Manager **Timothy Cummings** .... (718) 557-3421
Process Division II Manager **Luther Godwin** .... (718) 557-3431
E-mail: luther.godwin@ssa.gov
Process Division III Manager **John D. Drummond, Jr.** ... (718) 557-3441
Process Division IV Manager **Joseph Burt** .... (718) 557-3411

Regional Program and Integrity Reviews
Director **Darryl A. Donaldson** .... (212) 264-2827
Jacob K. Javits Federal Building, 26 Federal Plaza,
39-100, New York, NY 10278
E-mail: darryl.donaldson@ssa.gov

Philadelphia Region
300 Spring Garden Street, Philadelphia, PA 19123
P.O. Box 8788, Philadelphia, PA 19101-8788
Tel: (215) 597-5157 Fax: (215) 597-2827 Internet: www.ssa.gov/phila
Areas Covered: DE, DC, MD, PA, VA, WV
• Regional Commissioner **Terry M. Stradtman** .... (215) 597-5157
E-mail: terry.stradtman@ssa.gov
• Deputy Regional Commissioner **Eric P. Kressman** .... (215) 597-5157
E-mail: eric.kressman@ssa.gov
Regional Communications Director **Daniel O'Connor** .... (215) 597-3747
E-mail: phi.rpa@ssa.gov Fax: (215) 597-1415
Executive Officer **Sandra A. Saunders** .... (215) 597-5157

Philadelphia Region *(continued)*

Executive Support and Planning Team Officer
Yamilette Lopez .... (215) 597-1084
E-mail: yamilette.lopez@ssa.gov
Civil Rights and Equal Opportunity Manager
Sharon Stallings .... (215) 597-2804
Webmaster **(Vacant)** .... (215) 597-6184
Fax: (215) 597-7271

Office of the General Counsel
300 Spring Garden Street, Philadelphia, PA 19123
Tel: (215) 597-3300 Fax: (215) 597-4662
• Regional Chief Counsel (Acting) **Nora R. Koch** .... (215) 597-4642
E-mail: nora.koch@ssa.gov

Office of Disability Adjudication and Review
300 Spring Garden Street, Philadelphia, PA 19123
Tel: (215) 597-9980 Fax: (215) 597-4183
Regional Chief Administrative Law Judge
Tamara Turner-Jones .... (215) 597-3300
Regional Management Officer **Sandra Shultis** .... (215) 597-4130

Management and Operations Support
300 Spring Garden Street, Philadelphia, PA 19123
P.O. Box 8788, Philadelphia, PA 19101-8788
Tel: (215) 597-7745
• Assistant Regional Commissioner **Van T. Roland** .... (215) 597-7745
E-mail: van.roland@ssa.gov
Deputy Assistant Regional Commissioner
Nancy Anthony .... (215) 597-7740

Center for Automation, Security and Integrity
Director **Marty Moran** .... (215) 597-7792
E-mail: marty.moran@ssa.gov Fax: (215) 597-7271
Deputy Director **Bill Zammarrelli** .... (215) 597-2315
E-mail: bill.zammarrelli@ssa.gov Fax: (215) 597-7271
Automation Design and Development Team Leader
Marylin Melendez .... (215) 597-0972
E-mail: marylin.melendez@ssa.gov
Automation Infrastructure Team Leader
William Myers .... (215) 597-1563
E-mail: william.myers@ssa.gov
Team Leader **Terri Weist** .... (215) 597-1750
E-mail: terri.weist@ssa.gov

Center for Human Resources
Director **Harry Brown** .... (215) 597-1939
E-mail: harry.brown@ssa.gov
Deputy Director **Leslie Thomas** .... (215) 597-1915
E-mail: leslie.thomas@ssa.gov
Employee and Labor Relations Team Leader (Acting)
Clare McFeeley .... (215) 597-4074
E-mail: clare.mcfeeley@ssa.gov
Pay and Benefits Team Leader **Harees McCray** .... (215) 597-2254
E-mail: harees.mccray@ssa.gov
Staffing and Classification Supervisor **David Todd** .... (215) 597-4457
E-mail: david.todd@ssa.gov

Center for Material Resources
300 Spring Garden Street, Philadelphia, PA 19123
Fax: (215) 597-0428
Director **Loretta HixenBaugh** .... (215) 597-4154
Deputy Director **Ludwig C. Haller** .... (215) 597-2537
E-mail: ludwig.haller@ssa.gov
Building Management Section Chief **Lisa Otto** .... (215) 597-1909
Field Services Team Leader **Grace Kim** .... (215) 597-1297
Resource Management and Contracting Team Leader
Carolyn Geiger .... (215) 597-9012
E-mail: carolyn.geiger@ssa.gov

Center for Disability and Programs Support
Director **Howard Hughes** .... (215) 597-2967
E-mail: howard.hughes@ssa.gov
Deputy Director **Colleen McBride** .... (215) 597-9295

(continued on next page)

★ Presidential Appointment Requiring Senate Confirmation ☆ Presidential Appointment ☐ Schedule C Appointment ◇ Career Senior Foreign Service Appointment
● Career Senior Executive Service (SES) Appointment ○ Non-Career Senior Executive Service (SES) Appointment ■ Postal Career Executive Service

Center for Disability and Programs Support *(continued)*

Disability Program Administrator **Aidan Diviny** . . . . (215) 597-1727
E-mail: aidan.diviny@ssa.gov
Disability Program Administrator **Lillian Rairigh** . . . . (215) 597-1223
E-mail: lillian.rairigh@ssa.gov
Disability Program Administrator **Roy Morgan** . . . . (215) 597-1809
Disability Program Administrator
James Wojciechowski . . . . (215) 597-1806
E-mail: james.wojciechowski@ssa.gov
Title II Team Leader **Joan Heller** . . . . (215) 597-1961
E-mail: joan.heller@ssa.gov
Title XVI Team Leader **Desha Henfield** . . . . (215) 597-8091
E-mail: desha.henfield@ssa.gov
Program Expert **(Vacant)** . . . . (215) 597-2046

INDEPENDENT AGENCIES

Processing Center Operations
300 Spring Garden Street, Philadelphia, PA 19123
Tel: (215) 597-2831 Fax: (215) 597-0857

● Assistant Regional Commissioner **(Vacant)** . . . . (215) 597-2831
Deputy Assistant Regional Commissioner
Patrick Robinson . . . . (215) 597-6064
Debt Management Section Chief
Tracy Bodison . . . . (877) 445-0839 ext. 22574
Disability Processing Branch Manager
Eugene "Gene" Shirley . . . . (215) 597-5571
E-mail: gene.shirley@ssa.gov

Operations Support Branch
300 Spring Garden Street, Philadelphia, PA 19123
Tel: (215) 597-5306 Fax: (215) 597-5200

Chief **Kim Jones** . . . . (215) 597-2840
E-mail: kim.jones@ssa.gov
Computer Operations and Mail Intake Section Manager
(Vacant) . . . . (215) 597-2037
E-mail: britt.greaves@ssa.gov
Operations Analysis Section Team Leader **(Vacant)** . . . . . . (215) 597-5158

Regional Office of Quality Performance
Branch Chief **Judy Yokshan** . . . . (215) 597-1190
Assistance and Insurance Programs
Quality Branch Director
Brenda Council . . . . (215) 597-7877 ext. 37877
Assistance and Insurance Programs Quality Program
Advisor **Fred Polohovich** . . . . (215) 597-0962
Assistance and Insurance Programs Quality
Program Advisor **(Vacant)** . . . .(215) 597-1235 ext. 31235
Columbia Satellite Office Manager
Deborah A. Thomas . . . . (410) 597-0950
Deputy Director **Peter Krumbhar** . . . . (215) 597-1188 ext. 1187

Atlanta Region
Atlanta Federal Center, 61 Forsyth Street, SW,
Suite 22T64, Atlanta, GA 30303-8907
Tel: (404) 562-5600 Fax: (404) 562-5506 Internet: www.ssa.gov/atlanta
Areas Covered: AL, FL, GA, KY, MS, NC, SC, TN

● Regional Commissioner **Rose Mary Buehler** . . . . (404) 562-5600
E-mail: rose.mary.buehler@ssa.gov
● Deputy Regional Commissioner **Diane Jamison** . . . . (404) 562-5600
E-mail: diane.jamison@ssa.gov
Executive Officer **Darrell Sheffield** . . . . (404) 562-5600
E-mail: darrell.sheffield@ssa.gov
Project Manager **Cedric Robinson** . . . . (404) 562-5600
E-mail: cedric.robinson@ssa.gov
Executive Assistant **Charmaine Gibson** . . . . (404) 562-5600
Civil Rights and Equal Opportunity Manager
Marilyn Thompson . . . . (404) 562-1393
E-mail: marilyn.thompson@ssa.gov
Public Affairs Officer **Patti Patterson** . . . . (404) 562-5500
E-mail: patti.patterson@ssa.gov
Regional Inquiries Unit Supervisor **Marie Carson** . . . . (404) 562-1176
E-mail: marie.carson@ssa.gov

Office of General Counsel
Atlanta Federal Center, 61 Forsyth Street, SW,
Suite 22T64, Atlanta, GA 30303-8907
Tel: (404) 562-1028 Fax: (404) 562-1001

● Chief Counsel **Christopher G. Harris** 20T45 . . . . (404) 562-1028
E-mail: christopher.harris@ssa.gov

Office of Inspector General
Office of Audit - Deputy Director **(Vacant)** . . . .(404) 562-5552
Office of Investigation - Special Agent-in-Charge
Margaret Moore Jackson . . . . (404) 562-5544

Hearings and Appeals
Atlanta Federal Center, 61 Forsyth Street, SW,
Suite 22T64, Atlanta, GA 30303-8907
Tel: (404) 562-5570
Regional Chief Administrative Law Judge
Sheila C. Lowther . . . .(404) 562-1182

Management and Operation Support
Atlanta Federal Center, 61 Forsyth Street, SW,
Suite 22T64, Atlanta, GA 30303-8907
Fax: (404) 562-5764

● Assistant Regional Commissioner **Howard Bowles** . . . . . . (404) 562-5760
E-mail: howard.bowles@ssa.gov
Deputy Assistant Regional Commissioner
Tamika Cleveland . . . . (404) 562-5760
Project Manager **Yolanda Coger** . . . . (404) 562-5760
E-mail: yolanda.coger@ssa.gov
Special Projects Manager **(Vacant)** . . . .(404) 562-5760
Staff Assistant **George Salyer** . . . . (404) 562-5760
E-mail: george.p.salyer@ssa.gov

Center for Automation and Security Integrity
Center Director **Nathan L. Holmes** . . . . (404) 562-1288
Deputy Center Director **(Vacant)** . . . . (404) 562-5834
Management Information and Office Automation Team
Leader **Olivia Rencher** . . . .(404) 562-1331
E-mail: olivia.rencher@ssa.gov

Center for Disability Operations and Program Support
Atlanta Federal Center, 61 Forsyth Street, SW,
Suite 22T64, Atlanta, GA 30303-8907
Tel: (404) 562-1411 Fax: (404) 562-1414

Center Director **Yelitza Sanchez-Garrido** . . . . (404) 562-1292
E-mail: yelitza.sanchez-garrido@ssa.gov

Center for Human Resources
Center Director **Billy Donner** . . . .(404) 562-1240
E-mail: billy.donner@ssa.gov
Education: Troy State 1999 BS
Labor Management Employee Relations Team Leader
Kismet Harris . . . .(404) 562-2608
E-mail: kismet.m.harris@ssa.gov
Lead Human Resources Specialist **(Vacant)** . . . . (404) 562-5752
Management Analysis Policy Team Leader **(Vacant)** . . . . . (404) 562-1241
Personnel Operations Team A Leader
LaTonya Cormier . . . . (404) 562-1208
E-mail: latonya.cormier@ssa.gov
Personnel Operations Team B Leader **Cathy Denton** . . . . . (404) 562-1276
E-mail: cathy.denton@ssa.gov
Servicing Personnel Team Leader **Rosa Smith** . . . . (205) 801-1416
E-mail: rosa.b.smith@ssa.gov
Training and Employee Development Team Leader
(Vacant) . . . .(404) 562-5751
Benefits Team Leader **Jonathan Harpe** . . . .(404) 562-1191

Center for Material Resources
Center Director **Terri Cason** . . . . (404) 562-5748
E-mail: terri.cason@ssa.gov
Acquisition and Property Management Team Leader
(Vacant) . . . .(404) 562-1432
Field Management Team Leader **Rodney Williams** . . . . . . (404) 562-5743
Field Service Team Leader **(Vacant)** . . . . (404) 562-5743

★ Presidential Appointment Requiring Senate Confirmation ☆ Presidential Appointment ☐ Schedule C Appointment ◇ Career Senior Foreign Service Appointment
● Career Senior Executive Service (SES) Appointment ○ Non-Career Senior Executive Service (SES) Appointment ■ Postal Career Executive Service

Center for Material Resources *(continued)*

Financial Management Team Leader **Sandra Milligan** . . . . (404) 562-1836
Fiscal and Building Management Team Leader
Jimmy D. Collins . . . . (205) 801-1018
1200 Reverend Abraham Woods Jr., Boulevard, Birmingham, AL 35285

Regional Office of Quality Review

Atlanta Federal Center, 61 Forsyth Street, SW,
Suite 21T50, Atlanta, GA 30303
Tel: (404) 562-5700 Fax: (404) 562-5702

Director **Gavin J. Lane** . . . . (404) 562-5676
E-mail: gavin.lane@ssa.gov
Deputy Director **(Vacant)** . . . . (404) 562-5700

Southeastern Processing Center Operations

1200 Reverend Abraham Woods Jr., Boulevard, Birmingham, AL 35285
Tel: (205) 801-2201 Fax: (205) 801-2207

• Assistant Regional Commissioner
Frankie B. Hall Birmingham Social Security Center . . . . (205) 801-2201
E-mail: frankie.b.hall@ssa.gov
Deputy Assistant Regional Commissioner **Joe Collins** . . . . (205) 801-2201
Secretary **Terri Body** . . . . (205) 801-3150
E-mail: terri.body@ssa.gov
Project Manager **(Vacant)** . . . . (205) 801-2202
Executive Officer **Carmen B. Joy** . . . . (205) 801-2204
E-mail: carmen.b.joy@ssa.gov
Staff Advisor **Joyce D. Edson** . . . . (205) 801-2237
Staff Advisor **Jerome Hill** . . . . (205) 801-2208

Operations Support Branch

1200 Reverend Abraham Woods Jr., Boulevard, Birmingham, AL 35285
Fax: (205) 801-2229

Branch Manager **Leila K. Powers** . . . . (205) 801-2232
Deputy Branch Manager **Sallie Shipley** . . . . (205) 801-2231

Process Divisions

Process Division I Operations Manager **(Vacant)** . . . . (205) 801-2311
Process Division II Operations Manager
Mattie P. Akins . . . . (205) 801-2341
Process Division III Operations Manager **Terry Kleiser** . . . . (205) 801-2351
Process Division IV Operations Manager
Wayne A. Hunter . . . . (205) 801-2352
Process Division V Operations Manager
Annie H. Cottrell . . . . (205) 801-2455
Disability Processing Branch Manager **Vernita Gillam** . . . . (205) 801-2331

Chicago Region

Harold Washington Social Security Center,
600 West Madison Street, Chicago, IL 60661-2474
P.O. Box 8280, Chicago, IL 60680-8280
Tel: (312) 575-4000 Fax: (312) 575-4016 E-mail: chi.orc@ssa.gov
Internet: www.ssa.gov/chicago
Areas Covered: IL, IN, MI, MN, OH, WI

• Regional Commissioner **Phyllis M. Smith** . . . . (312) 575-4000
E-mail: phyllis.m.smith@ssa.gov
• Deputy Regional Commissioner **Brad A. Flick** . . . . (312) 575-4000
E-mail: brad.flick@ssa.gov
Executive Officer **Aaron Conway** . . . . (312) 575-4041
Executive Assistant **Anett Rajca** . . . . (312) 575-6362
E-mail: anett.rajca@ssa.gov
Executive Assistant **Carita Timms** . . . . (312) 575-6362
E-mail: carita.timms@ssa.gov
Civil Rights and Equal Opportunity Staff Director
Mary Gavin . . . . (312) 575-6394
E-mail: mary.gavin@ssa.gov
Regional Communications Director **Doug Nguyen** . . . . (312) 575-4050
E-mail: doug.nguyen@ssa.gov
Teleservices Operations Director **Diane Ellis** . . . . (312) 575-4300

Office of the General Counsel

200 West Adams Street, Suite 3000, Chicago, IL 60606
Tel: (877) 800-7578 Fax: (312) 353-4754 E-mail: chi.ogc@ssa.gov

• Chief Counsel **Kathryn A. Caldwell** . . . . (877) 800-7578 ext. 19110
E-mail: kathryn.caldwell@ssa.gov

Office of the Inspector General

200 West Adams Street, Suite 2951, Chicago, IL 60606
Tel: (877) 800-7580 ext. 19691 Fax: (312) 353-8035
E-mail: chi.oig@ssa.gov

Special Agent-in-Charge **(Vacant)** . . . . (877) 800-7580 ext. 19691

Office of Disability Adjudication and Review (ODAR)

200 West Adams Street, Suite 2901, Chicago, IL 60606
Tel: (877) 800-7576 E-mail: emily.robinson@ssa.gov

• Regional Chief Administrative Law Judge
Sherry D. Thompson . . . . (877) 800-7576 ext. 19552
E-mail: sherry.thompson@ssa.gov
Regional Director for Operations and
Administration **Velda Cousins** . . . . (877) 800-7576 ext. 19511
E-mail: velda.cousins@ssa.gov
Regional Management Officer **(Vacant)** . . . . (877) 800-7576 ext. 19511
Regional Attorney **Emily Robinson** . . . . (877) 800-7576 ext. 19520
Regional Director of Operations
Victor Glowacki . . . . (877) 800-7576 ext. 19521
Quality Review Officer **(Vacant)** . . . . (877) 800-7576 ext. 19524

Management and Operations Support

Harold Washington Social Security Center,
600 West Madison Street, Chicago, IL 60661-2474
Tel: (312) 575-4100 Fax: (312) 575-4101 E-mail: chi.arc.mos@ssa.gov

• Assistant Regional Commissioner **Ann P. Robert** . . . . (312) 575-5043
Deputy Assistant Regional Commissioner **Anne Mills** . . . . (312) 575-5044
E-mail: anne.mills@ssa.gov
Staff Assistant **Susan Veazie** . . . . (312) 575-6005
E-mail: susan.veazie@ssa.gov

Center for Disability Policy

Harold Washington Social Security Center,
600 West Madison Street, Chicago, IL 60661-2474
Tel: (312) 575-4200 Fax: (312) 575-4221

Director **Robert Coplin** . . . . (312) 575-4200
Program Director **(Vacant)** . . . . (312) 575-4117
Regional Medical Advisor **Henry Conroe** . . . . (312) 575-6033
E-mail: henry.conroe@ssa.gov
Team Leader **Alicia Hall** . . . . (312) 575-4768

Center for Human Resources

Harold Washington Social Security Center,
600 West Madison Street, Chicago, IL 60661-2474
Tel: (312) 575-6400 Fax: (312) 575-6424

Director **Elsa Cruz** . . . . (312) 575-6360
E-mail: elsa.cruz@ssa.gov
Deputy Director **Eileen Koney** . . . . (312) 575-5955
E-mail: eileen.koney@ssa.gov
Regional Training Officer **Celine Valdespino** . . . . (312) 575-6400
Secretary **(Vacant)** . . . . (312) 575-6464
Human Resources Pay and Benefits Staff Supervisor
Almir Ovcina . . . . (312) 575-6386
E-mail: almir.ovcina@ssa.gov
Human Resources Pay and Benefits Specialist
Charlie Johnson . . . . (312) 575-5849
Labor and Employee Relations Supervisor
Rose Mosley . . . . (312) 575-4022
E-mail: rose.mosley@ssa.gov
Operations Supervisor **Beauty Jackson** . . . . (312) 575-5685
E-mail: beauty.jackson@ssa.gov

INDEPENDENT AGENCIES

★ Presidential Appointment Requiring Senate Confirmation ☆ Presidential Appointment ☐ Schedule C Appointment ◇ Career Senior Foreign Service Appointment
● Career Senior Executive Service (SES) Appointment ○ Non-Career Senior Executive Service (SES) Appointment ■ Postal Career Executive Service

Center for Materiel Resources
Harold Washington Social Security Center,
600 West Madison Street, Chicago, IL 60661-2474
Tel: (312) 575-5500 Fax: (312) 575-4101
E-mail: chi.arc.mos.cmr@ssa.gov

Director **(Vacant)** .... (312) 575-4104
Contracts and Procurement Officer
Babafemi Littlejohn .... (312) 575-4148
E-mail: babafemi.littlejohn@ssa.gov
Facilities Services Supervisor **Cynthia Walker** .... (312) 575-5500
Field Services Supervisor **Dave Dawson** .... (312) 575-4069
Field Services Team Leader **Masheba Gailey-Harris** ..... (312) 575-4060
Financial Management Supervisory Analyst
Melinda Robinson .... (312) 575-4151

Center for Retirement and Survivors Insurance and Supplemental Security Income
Director **Arturo Cardenas** .... (312) 575-4236
Deputy Director **Paul Faddersen** .... (312) 575-5982
Supplemental Security Income Team Leader (Acting)
Roberta Faison .... (312) 575-5982

Center for Security and Integrity
Harold Washington Social Security Center,
600 West Madison Street, Chicago, IL 60661-2474
Tel: (312) 575-4120 Fax: (312) 575-4121

Director **(Vacant)** .... (312) 575-4120
Security and Integrity Team Leader **Yesenia Hill** .... (312) 575-4125

Center for Systems and Automation
Harold Washington Social Security Center,
600 West Madison Street, Chicago, IL 60661-2474
Tel: (312) 575-6350 Fax: (312) 575-6251
E-mail: chi.arc.mos.csa@ssa.gov

Director **Andrew "Andy" Philipson** .... (312) 575-6255
E-mail: andrew.philipson@ssa.gov
Education: Minnesota 1983 BA
Deputy Director **Cedric Tims** .... (312) 575-6298
Program Team Leader **Kimberly Thomas** .... (312) 575-6350
Project Manager **David "Dave" Broomell** .... (651) 430-0789
Project Manager **Mary Kay Skorcz** .... (312) 575-4012
E-mail: mary.kay.skorcz@ssa.gov
Project Manager **(Vacant)** .... (312) 575-6255

Processing Center Operations
Harold Washington Social Security Center,
600 West Madison Street, Chicago, IL 60661-2474
Tel: (312) 575-4300 Fax: (312) 575-4303 E-mail: chi.arc.pco@ssa.gov

● Assistant Regional Commissioner **Rick Lenoir** .... (312) 575-4300
E-mail: rick.lenoir@ssa.gov
Education: Lewis U
Deputy Assistant Regional Commissioner **(Vacant)** ...... (312) 575-4300
Staff Assistant **Scott Howard** .... (312) 575-4300
E-mail: scott.howard@ssa.gov
Staff Assistant **Alicia Sewell** .... (312) 575-4300
E-mail: alicia.sewell@ssa.gov
Computer Operations Section Chief **Rachel Leon** .... (312) 575-5212
Debt Management Section Chief **Tameka Nathaniel** ..... (312) 575-6799
Disability Processing Branch Chief **(Vacant)** .... (312) 575-4106
Inquiry and Expediting Staff Manager
Rochelle Hambrick .... (312) 575-6057
Operations Support Branch Chief **Angelo Petros** .... (312) 575-5340
Operations Division 2 Manager **(Vacant)** .... (312) 575-5630
Operations Division 3 Manager **Patricia Duke-Smith** .... (312) 575-6600
Operations Division 1 Manager **Bernard Mull** .... (312) 575-4800
Operations Division 4 Manager **JoAnn Kravaritis** .... (312) 575-4400

Regional Office of Quality Performance
Harold Washington Social Security Center,
600 West Madison Street, Chicago, IL 60661-2474
Tel: (312) 575-4000 Fax: (312) 575-6001 E-mail: chi.roqa@ssa.gov

Director **Mary J. Byrns** .... (312) 575-6000

Regional Office of Quality Performance *(continued)*

Supervisory Information Technology Specialist
Brad Savenson .... (312) 575-4000
Management Analyst **Keisha Marks-Evans** .... (312) 575-4000

Dallas Region
1301 Young Street, Suite 500, Dallas, TX 75202
Tel: (214) 767-4207 Fax: (214) 767-4259 Internet: www.ssa.gov/dallas
Areas Covered: AR, LA, NM, OK, TX

● Regional Commissioner **Sheila Everett** .... (214) 767-4207
E-mail: sheila.everett@ssa.gov
Deputy Regional Commissioner **Robert Pagan** .... (214) 767-4207
E-mail: robert.pagan@ssa.gov
Executive Officer **Maryann Sampat-Stevens** .... (214) 767-4207
E-mail: maryann.sampat@ssa.gov
Regional Communications Director
Sarah Schultz-Lackey Suite 630 .... (214) 767-3407
E-mail: da.rpa@ssa.gov
Civil Rights and Equal Opportunity Staff Manager
Evelyn Resto Suite 520 .... (214) 767-3036
E-mail: evelyn.resto@ssa.gov
Training Team Officer **Dawn Blount-Williams** .... (214) 767-4580
Fax: (214) 767-4514

Office of the General Counsel
1301 Young Street, Dallas, TX 75202
Tel: (214) 767-3212 Fax: (214) 767-3507

● Regional Chief Counsel (Acting)
Traci B. Davis Suite A702 .... (214) 767-3212
E-mail: traci.davis@ssa.gov

Hearings and Appeals
1301 Young Street, Dallas, TX 75202
Tel: (214) 767-9401 Fax: (214) 767-9407

Regional Chief Administrative Law Judge
Joan Saunders Suite 460 .... (214) 767-9401
E-mail: joan.parks.saunders@ssa.gov
Regional Management Officer **Fay Adams** Suite 460 ..... (214) 767-9401
E-mail: fay.adams@ssa.gov

Management and Operations Support
1301 Young Street, Dallas, TX 75202
Tel: (214) 767-4331 Fax: (214) 767-8577

Assistant Regional Commissioner
Renee Ferguson Suite 550 .... (214) 767-4331
Staff Assistant **Jennifer Hannon** Suite 550 .... (214) 767-4331
E-mail: jennifer.hannon@ssa.gov

Center for Disability
1301 Young Street, Dallas, TX 75202
Tel: (214) 767-4281 Fax: (214) 767-8267 E-mail: da.dp@ssa.gov

Director **Irving Wilkerson** Suite 670 .... (214) 767-4281
E-mail: irving.wilkerson@ssa.gov
Regional Medical Advisor **Steven Bowers** .... (214) 767-8958
E-mail: steven.bowers@ssa.gov

Center for Human Resources
1301 Young Street, Dallas, TX 75202
Tel: (214) 767-4331 Fax: (214) 767-0639

Director **Vicki A. Mathews** Suite 550 .... (214) 767-4331
E-mail: vicki.a.mathews@ssa.gov

Center for Material Resources
1301 Young Street, Dallas, TX 75202
Tel: (214) 767-4331 Fax: (214) 767-8210

Director **(Vacant)** Suite 550 .... (214) 767-4331
Purchasing/Procurement Officer **(Vacant)** .... (214) 767-4331

Center for Programs and Systems
1301 Young Street, Dallas, TX 75202
Tel: (214) 767-4224 Fax: (214) 767-1348

Director **Irving Wilkerson** Suite 670 .... (214) 767-4224

★ Presidential Appointment Requiring Senate Confirmation ☆ Presidential Appointment ☐ Schedule C Appointment ◇ Career Senior Foreign Service Appointment
● Career Senior Executive Service (SES) Appointment ○ Non-Career Senior Executive Service (SES) Appointment ■ Postal Career Executive Service

Center for Programs and Systems *(continued)*

Deputy Director **Elizabeth Bass** .... (214) 767-4331
E-mail: elizabeth.bass@ssa.gov

Center for Security and Integrity
1301 Young Street, Dallas, TX 75202
Tel: (214) 767-4331 Fax: (214) 767-3103

Director **Jeffrey "Jeff" Talbert** Suite 550 .... (214) 767-4331
E-mail: jeffrey.talbert@ssa.gov

Regional Quality Assurance and Performance Assessment
1301 Young Street, Dallas, TX 75202
Tel: (214) 767-3448 Fax: (214) 767-3391

Director **Sheena Hayes** Suite 300 .... (214) 767-3164
E-mail: sheena.hayes@ssa.gov
Assistance and Insurance Programs Quality Branch
Director **Juanita Campbell** .... (214) 767-3448
E-mail: juanita.campbell@ssa.gov
Disability Quality Branch Director **Tom Johns** .... (214) 767-3417
Systems Director **Rashida Donastorg-Bess** .... (214) 767-3475
E-mail: rashida.donastorg-bess@ssa.gov

Kansas City Region
Federal Building, 601 East 12th Street,
Suite 1028, Kansas City, MO 64106
Tel: (816) 936-5700 Fax: (816) 936-5972 Internet: www.ssa.gov/kc
Areas Covered: IA, KS, MO, NE

• Regional Commissioner **Michael R. "Mike" Kramer** ..... (816) 936-5700
E-mail: mike.kramer@ssa.gov
E-mail: kc.orc@ssa.gov
• Deputy Regional Commissioner **Linda Kerr-Davis** .... (816) 936-5700
E-mail: linda.kerr-davis@ssa.gov
Deputy Assistant Regional Commissioner **(Vacant)** ...... (816) 936-5700
Regional Communications Director **Jewell Colbert** ...... (816) 936-5740
E-mail: jewell.colbert@ssa.gov Fax: (816) 936-5727
Regional Office of Quality Performance Director
Carrie A. Taber .... (816) 936-5151
E-mail: carrie.taber@ssa.gov
Civil Rights and Equal Opportunity Manager (Acting)
Tina William .... (816) 936-5720
Executive Officer **Kerry Heckman** .... (816) 936-5700
E-mail: kerry.heckman@ssa.gov

Office of Disability Adjudication and Review
2300 Main Street, Suite 600, Kansas City, MO 64108
Tel: (888) 238-7975 Fax: (816) 842-4250

Regional Chief Administrative Law Judge
Sherrianne Laba .... (888) 238-7975 ext. 18721
E-mail: sherrianne.laba@ssa.gov
Regional Management Officer
Stephen Hayes .... (888) 527-9325 ext. 21470
E-mail: stephen.hayes@ssa.gov

Office of the General Counsel
Federal Building, 601 East 12th Street, Kansas City, MO 64106

• Regional Chief Counsel (Acting) **Lisa Thomas** .... (816) 936-5750
E-mail: lisa.thomas@ssa.gov

Management and Operations Support
Federal Building, 601 East 12th Street,
Suite 1028, Kansas City, MO 64106
Tel: (816) 936-5705 Fax: (816) 936-5979

• Assistant Regional Commissioner **(Vacant)** .... (816) 936-5705
Deputy Assistant Regional Commissioner
Shara Sevart .... (816) 936-5705
E-mail: shara.sevart@ssa.gov

Processing Center Operations
Federal Building, 601 East 12th Street,
Suite 1028, Kansas City, MO 64106
Tel: (816) 936-5703 Fax: (816) 936-5973

• Assistant Regional Commissioner
Michelle Sanders-Sparks .... (816) 936-5703

Denver Region
Byron Rogers Federal Office Building,
1961 Stout Street, Denver, CO 80294
Tel: (303) 844-2388 Fax: (303) 844-6767 Internet: www.ssa.gov/denver
Areas Covered: CO, MT, ND, SD, UT, WY

• Regional Commissioner (Acting)
Mary Lisa Lewandowski .... (206) 615-2100
701 Fifth Avenue, Seattle, WA 98104
• Deputy Regional Commissioner
Wanda Colon-Mollfulleda .... (303) 844-2388
E-mail: wanda.colon-mollfulleda@ssa.gov
Executive Officer **Kate Kintz** .... (303) 844-2388
E-mail: kate.kintz@ssa.gov
Executive Assistant **Sandy Morgan** .... (303) 844-2389
E-mail: sandy.morgan@ssa.gov
Regional Communications Director **Ann Mohageri** ...... (303) 844-1888
600 West Madison Street, Fax: (303) 844-6767
Tenth Floor, Chicago, IL 60606
E-mail: ann.mohageri@ssa.gov
Civil Rights and Equal Opportunity Manager
Jacqueline Johannes .... (303) 844-7212
E-mail: jacqueline.johannes@ssa.gov Fax: (303) 844-2471

Area Office
Byron Rogers Federal Office Building,
1961 Stout Street, Denver, CO 80294
Fax: (303) 844-3935

Area Director I **Jill Mayemura** .... (303) 844-4174
Area Director II **Mark Blythe** .... (303) 844-4174

Office of General Counsel
Byron Rogers Federal Office Building,
1961 Stout Street, Denver, CO 80294
Fax: (303) 844-0770

• Regional Chief Counsel **John J. Lee** .... (303) 844-0012
E-mail: john.lee@ssa.gov

Office of Hearings and Appeals
Cesar Chavez Memorial Building, 1244 North Speer Boulevard,
Suite 600, Denver, CO 80204
Fax: (303) 844-6092

Regional Chief Administrative Law Judge
Nicholas LoBurgio .... (303) 844-6100
Regional Management Officer
Arlene Quinones .... (888) 397-9803 ext. 23003
E-mail: arlene.quinones@ssa.gov
Regional Director of Operation and
Administration **David Pinnt** .... (888) 397-9803 ext. 23017
Regional Attorney Adviser **Frank Bobbitt** .... (888) 397-9803 ext. 23013

Denver Office of Inspector General Field Division
Byron Rogers Federal Office Building,
1961 Stout Street, Denver, CO 80294
Fax: (303) 844-4173

Special Agent-in-Charge **Wilbert Craig** .... (303) 844-7189
Assistant Special Agent-in-Charge **Lina Rivera** .... (303) 844-0165

Management and Operations Support
Byron Rogers Federal Office Building,
1961 Stout Street, Denver, CO 80294
Fax: (303) 844-2183

• Assistant Regional Commissioner **Vikash Chahagan** ..... (303) 844-4069
Workload Analysis and Management Information Team
Leader **(Vacant)** .... (303) 844-7374

INDEPENDENT AGENCIES

★ Presidential Appointment Requiring Senate Confirmation ☆ Presidential Appointment □ Schedule C Appointment ◇ Career Senior Foreign Service Appointment
● Career Senior Executive Service (SES) Appointment ○ Non-Career Senior Executive Service (SES) Appointment ■ Postal Career Executive Service

Center for Automation
Byron Rogers Federal Office Building,
1961 Stout Street, Denver, CO 80294
Tel: (303) 844-5903 Fax: (303) 844-4170

Director **Fritz Layman** .... (303) 844-5903

Center for Disability
Byron Rogers Federal Office Building,
1961 Stout Street, Denver, CO 80294
Fax: (303) 844-3256

Director **Kevin Mashak** .... (303) 844-0849
E-mail: kevin.mashak@ssa.gov

Center for Material Resources

Director **Bob Boles** .... (303) 844-2238
E-mail: bob.boles@ssa.gov

Contracting Officer **Lisa Walker** .... (303) 844-7344
E-mail: lisa.walker@ssa.gov

Center for Operations Support
Byron Rogers Federal Office Building,
1961 Stout Street, Denver, CO 80294
Tel: (303) 844-5717 Fax: (303) 844-4280

Director **Kevin Mashak** .... (303) 844-0849
E-mail: kevin.mashak@ssa.gov

Center for Security and Integrity
Byron Rogers Federal Office Building,
1961 Stout Street, Denver, CO 80294
Fax: (303) 844-7007

Director **Art Cota** .... (303) 844-3278

Quality Review
Byron Rogers Federal Office Building,
1961 Stout Street, Denver, CO 80294
Fax: (303) 844-6547

Director **Cathy B. Horiuchi** .... (303) 844-3694
E-mail: cathy.horiuchi@ssa.gov

Deputy Director **(Vacant)** .... (303) 844-2601

Richmond Region

1221 Nevin Avenue, Richmond, CA 94801
P.O. Box 4201, Richmond, CA 94804
Tel: (510) 970-8430 Fax: (510) 970-8218 E-mail: sf.rpa@ssa.gov
Internet: www.socialsecurity.gov/sf
Areas Covered: AZ, CA, GU, HI, NV, American Samoa, Northern Mariana Islands

● Regional Commissioner (Acting)
Stephen J. "Steve" Breen .... (510) 970-8400
E-mail: steve.breen@ssa.gov

● Deputy Regional Commissioner
Stephen J. "Steve" Breen .... (510) 970-8400
E-mail: steve.breen@ssa.gov

Executive Officer **Yolanda Whitaker** .... (510) 970-8400

Regional Communications Director **Patricia Raymond** ... (510) 970-8430
E-mail: patricia.raymond@ssa.gov Fax: (510) 970-8218

Civil Rights and Equal Opportunity Manager
Nelson Arcilla .... (510) 970-8420
SSA Region IX, P.O. Box 4116, Richmond, CA 94804
E-mail: nelson.arcilla@ssa.gov

Office of General Counsel
333 Market Street, Suite 1500, San Francisco, CA 94105
Fax: (415) 744-0134 E-mail: sf.ogc.general@ssa.gov

● Regional Chief Counsel (Acting) **Deborah L. Stachel** .... (415) 977-8943
E-mail: deborah.stachel@ssa.gov

Management and Operations Support
1221 Nevin Avenue, Richmond, CA 94801
P.O. Box 4204, Richmond, CA 94804
E-mail: sf.mos.arc.immediate.office@ssa.gov

● Assistant Regional Commissioner **(Vacant)** .... (510) 970-8390

Center for Automation, Security and Integrity
1221 Nevin Avenue, Richmond, CA 94801
Mail: P.O. Box 4205, Richmond, CA 94804
Tel: (510) 970-8345

Director **Tuan Nguyen** .... (510) 970-8344
E-mail: tuan.nguyen@ssa.gov

Center for Disability and Program Support
P.O. Box 4207, Richmond, CA 94804
E-mail: sf.mos.disability.center@ssa.gov

Center Director **Florina Docena** .... (510) 970-8300

Center for Human Resources
P.O. Box 4115, Richmond, CA 94804
E-mail: sf.mos.hrc.director@ssa.gov

Center Director **Ana Profit** .... (510) 970-2780
E-mail: ana.proffit@ssa.gov

Center for Materiel Resources (CMR)
P.O. Box 4205, Richmond, CA 94804
E-mail: sf.mos.materiel.resources.center@ssa.gov

Center Manager **Janet Bryant** .... (510) 970-1500
E-mail: janet.bryant@ssa.gov

Center for Programs Support
P.O. Box 4206, Richmond, CA 94804
E-mail: sf.mos.programs.support.center@ssa.gov

Center Manager **(Vacant)** .... (510) 970-8444

Processing Center Operations
Western Program Service Center, 1221 Nevin Avenue, Richmond, CA 94802
P.O. Box 2346, Richmond, CA 94802
E-mail: sf.arc.pco@ssa.gov

● Assistant Regional Commissioner **Debby S. Ellis** .... (510) 970-1400
E-mail: debby.ellis@ssa.gov

Deputy Assistant Regional Commissioner
Rosa Serrano .... (510) 970-1402 ext. 1511

Regional Teleservice Operations Director
Martin White .... (510) 970-8318
P.O. Box 4208, Richmond, CA 94804
E-mail: martin.white@ssa.gov

Office of Quality Review
1301 Clay Street, Suite 900N, Oakland, CA 94612
E-mail: oqp.field.sfo.directors.office@ssa.gov

Director **(Vacant)** .... (877) 700-4841 ext. 18047

Seattle Region

701 Fifth Avenue, Suite 2900, Seattle, WA 98104
Tel: (206) 615-2100 Fax: (206) 615-2193
Areas Covered: AK, ID, OR, WA

● Regional Commissioner (Acting)
Mary Lisa Lewandowski M/S 301 .... (206) 615-2100

● Deputy Regional Commissioner **(Vacant)** M/S 301 ...... (206) 615-2100

Regional Communications Director
Ann Mohageri M/S 301 .... (206) 615-2666
E-mail: ann.mohageri@ssa.gov Fax: (206) 615-2097

Area I Director **Chris Kuhel** M/S 201 .... (206) 615-3635

Area II Director **Stephen Hughes** .... (206) 615-2762

Civil Rights and Equal Opportunity Manager
William "Bill" Shie M/S 291A .... (206) 615-2132

Office of Disability Adjudication and Review
701 Fifth Avenue, Mail Stop 904, Seattle, WA 98104
Fax: (206) 615-2247

Regional Chief Administrative Law Judge
David J. DeLaittre M/S 904 .... (206) 615-3617
E-mail: david.j.delaittre@ssa.gov
Education: U Washington JD

Regional Management Officer **Joy Jenkins** .... (206) 615-2242
E-mail: joy.jenkins@ssa.gov
Education: Duke BA; Virginia JD

★ Presidential Appointment Requiring Senate Confirmation ☆ Presidential Appointment ☐ Schedule C Appointment ◇ Career Senior Foreign Service Appointment
● Career Senior Executive Service (SES) Appointment ○ Non-Career Senior Executive Service (SES) Appointment ■ Postal Career Executive Service

Office of General Counsel
701 Fifth Avenue, Mail Stop 901, Seattle, WA 98104
Tel: (206) 615-2539 Fax: (206) 615-2531

● Chief Counsel **Reggie Horn** M/S 901 . . . . (206) 615-2539
E-mail: reggie.horn@ssa.gov Fax: (206) 615-2531

Management and Operations Support
701 Fifth Avenue, M/S 301, Seattle, WA 98104
Fax: (206) 615-2193

● Assistant Regional Commissioner **(Vacant)** . . . . (206) 615-3604

Center for Automation
701 Fifth Avenue, M/S 302B, Seattle, WA 98104
Fax: (206) 615-3612

Center Director **Carol Voelker** . . . . (206) 615-2140
E-mail: carol.voelker@ssa.gov

Center for Disability
701 Fifth Avenue, M/S 351A, Seattle, WA 98104
Fax: (206) 615-2641

Center Director **Janet Shiver** . . . . (206) 615-2199
Regional Medical Advisor **L. Jean Weaver** . . . . (206) 615-2194
Disability Program Administrator **Don Larsen** . . . . (206) 615-2651
Disability Program Administrator **Dale McGruder** . . . . (206) 615-2148

Center for Programs Support
701 Fifth Avenue, M/S 303A, Seattle, WA 98104
Fax: (206) 615-2643

Center Director **Laura F. White** . . . . (206) 615-2674

Retirement and Survivors Insurance - Supplemental Security Income Programs Branch
701 Fifth Avenue, M/S 303A, Seattle, WA 98104
Fax: (206) 615-2643

RSI Programs and Systems Team Leader **(Vacant)** . . . . (206) 615-2127
SSI Programs and Systems Team Leader **(Vacant)** . . . . (206) 615-2126

Regional Office of Quality Performance
701 Fifth Avenue, M/S 103, Seattle, WA 98104
Tel: (206) 615-2686 Fax: (206) 615-2235

Director **(Vacant)** . . . . (206) 615-2146

INDEPENDENT AGENCIES

★ Presidential Appointment Requiring Senate Confirmation ☆ Presidential Appointment ☐ Schedule C Appointment ◇ Career Senior Foreign Service Appointment
● Career Senior Executive Service (SES) Appointment ○ Non-Career Senior Executive Service (SES) Appointment ■ Postal Career Executive Service

Geographical Index

This index has three sections. The first lists all departments, independent agencies, and congressional support agencies located in the U.S., including their sub-agencies, bureaus, and offices, alphabetically by state, and by city within each state. The second lists all departments, independent agencies, and congressional support agencies located in the U.S. Territories, including their sub-agencies, bureaus, and offices, alphabetically by territory, and by city within each territory. The third lists all organizations, including embassies and consulates, located outside of the U.S. alphabetically by country, and by city within each country.

Arkansas

GEOGRAPHICAL INDEX

California

Colorado

GEOGRAPHICAL INDEX

GEOGRAPHICAL INDEX

Nebraska

Nevada

GEOGRAPHICAL INDEX

North Carolina

Rhode Island

Texas

Washington

Non-U.S.

GEOGRAPHICAL INDEX

Name Index

This index lists all individuals in the directory alphabetically by last name.

A

NAME INDEX

B

NAME INDEX

NAME INDEX

D

E

G

NAME INDEX

H

I

J

NAME INDEX

K

NAME INDEX

L

NAME INDEX

NAME INDEX

M

NAME INDEX

N

O

P

Q

R

NAME INDEX

NAME INDEX

S

NAME INDEX

T

U

NAME INDEX

W

X

Y

Z

NAME INDEX

Organization Index

This index lists all departments, independent agencies, and congressional support agencies including their sub-agencies, bureaus, and offices.

3

A

B

C

D

E

M

N

O

P

R

S

T

U

V

W